Hospital, Address, Telephone, Approval, Facility, and Physician Codes, Health Care System	Classi-fication Codes		Utilization Data					Expense (thousands) of dollars		
★ American Hospital Association (AHA) membership □ Joint Commission on Accreditation of Healthcare Organizations (JCAHO) accreditation ○ American Osteopathic Association (AOA) accreditation △ Commission on Accreditation of Rehabilitation Facilities (CARF) accreditation	Control	Service	Staffed Beds	Admissions	Census	Outpatient Visits	Births	Total	Payroll	Personnel

ANYTOWN—Universal County
★ COMMUNITY HOSPITAL, First Street and Main Avenue Zip 62835; tel 204/391–2345;
A1 2 3 4 6 9 10 **F**1 2 3 4 5 6 8 9 10 23 24 34; **P**1 2 3 4; **S** Acme HCS

		Control	Service	Staffed Beds	Admissions	Census
		23	10	346	10778	24...

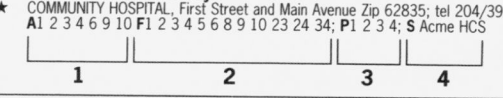

1 **2** **3** **4**

1 Approval Codes

Reported by the approving bodies specified, as of the dates noted.

1 Accreditation under the hospital program of the Joint Commission on Accreditation of Healthcare Organizations (April 2005).

2 Cancer program approved by American College of Surgeons (March 2005).

†3 Approval to participate in residency training, by the Accreditation Council for Graduate Medical Education (April 2005). As of June 30, 1975, internship (formerly code 4) was included under residency, code 3.

†5 Medical school affiliation, reported to the American Medical Association (April 2005).

6 Hospital–controlled professional nursing school, reported by National League for Nursing.

7 Accreditation by Commission on Accreditation of Rehabilitation Facilities (March 2005).

8 Member of Council of Teaching Hospitals of the Association of American Medical Colleges (February 2005).

9 Hospitals contracting or participating in a Plan, reported by the Blue Cross and Blue Shield Association (March 2005).

10 Certified for participation in the Health Insurance for the Aged (Medicare) Program by the Centers for Medicare and Medical Services (February 2005).

11 Accreditation by American Osteopathic Association (May 2005).

12 Inte... ... ...y ...erican Osteopathic Association (June 2005).

13 Residency approved by American Osteopathic Association (June 2005).

18 Critical Access Hospitals (May 2005).

19 Rural Referral Center (May 2005).

20 Sole Community Provider (May 2005).

Nonreporting indicates that the 2004 Annual Survey questionnaire for the hospital was not received prior to publication.

2 Facility Codes

Provided directly by the hospital; for definitions, see page A6.

(Numerical Order)

1 Adult Day Care program
2 Airborne infection isolation room
3 Alcoholism–drug abuse or dependency inpatient unit
4 Alcoholism–drug abuse or dependency outpatient services
5 Alzheimer Center
6 Ambulance Services
7 Arthritis treatment center
8 Assisted Living
9 Auxiliary organization
10 Bariatric/weight control services
11 Birthing room–LDR room–LDRP room
12 Breast cancer screening/mammograms
13 Burn care services
14 Cardiac intensive care services
15 Adult diagnostic/invasive catheterization
16 Pediatric diagnostic/invasive catheterization
17 Adult interventional cardiac catheterization
18 Pediatric interventional cardiac catheterization
19 Adult cardiac surgery
20 Pediatric cardiac surgery
21 Case management
22 Chaplaincy/pastoral care services
23 Chemotherapy
24 Children wellness program
25 Chiropractic services
26 Community health reporting
27 Community health status assessment
28 Community health status based service planning
29 Community outreach
30 Complementary medicine
31 Crisis Prevention
32 Dental services
33 Emergency department
34 Trauma center (certified)
35 Enabling services

36 Hospice program
37 Pain management
38 Palliative care program
39 Enrollment Assistance Services
40 Extracorporeal shock wave lithotripter (ESWL)
41 Fitness center
42 Freestanding outpatient care center
43 Gamma Knife
44 Geriatric services
45 Health facility transportation (to/from)
46 Health fair
47 Health information center
48 Health screenings
49 Hemodialysis
50 HIV–AIDS services
51 Home health services
52 Hospital–based outpatient care center services
53 Linguistic/translation services
54 Meals on wheels
55 Medical surgical intensive care services
56 Neonatal intensive care
57 Neurological services
58 Nutrition programs
59 Obstetrics services
60 Occupational health services
61 Oncology services
62 Orthopedic services
63 Outpatient surgery
64 Patient controlled analgesia (PCA)
65 Patient education center
66 Patient representative services
67 Pediatric intensive care services
68 Physical rehabilitation inpatient services
69 Physical rehabilitation outpatient services
70 Primary care department
71 Psychiatric care
72 Psychiatric–child adolescent services
73 Psychiatric consultation–liaison services
74 Psychiatric education services

75 Psychiatric emergency services
76 Psychiatric geriatric services
77 Psychiatric outpatient services
78 Psychiatric partial hospitalization services
79 Intensity-modulated radiation therapy (IMRT)
80 Shaped-beam radiation system
81 CT scanner
82 Diagnostic radioisotope facility
83 Electron beam computed tomography (EBCT)
84 Magnetic resonance imaging (MRI)
85 Multi-slice spiral computed tomography (MSCT)
86 Positron Emission Tomography (PET)
87 Single Photon Emission Computerized Tomography (SPECT)
88 Ultrasound
89 Fertility Clinic
90 Genetic Testing/Counseling
91 Retirement housing
92 Skilled nursing or other long-term care services
93 Sleep center
94 Social work services
95 Sports medicine
96 Support groups
97 Swing bed services
98 Teen outreach services
99 Bone marrow transplant
100 Heart transplant
101 Kidney transplant
102 Liver transplant
103 Lung transplant
104 Tissue transplant
105 Other transplant
106 Tobacco treatment/cessation program
107 Urgent care center
108 Volunteer services department
109 Women's health center/services
110 Wound management services

†Data from the Graduate Medical Education Database, Copyright 2003, American Medical Association, Chicago, Illinois.

Hospital, Address, Telephone, Approval, Facility, and Physician Codes, Health Care System	Classi-fication Codes		Utilization Data					Expense (thousands) of dollars		
★ American Hospital Association (AHA) membership □ Joint Commission on Accreditation of Healthcare Organizations (JCAHO) accreditation ○ American Osteopathic Association (AOA) accreditation △ Commission on Accreditation of Rehabilitation Facilities (CARF) accreditation	Control	Service	Staffed Beds	Admissions	Census	Outpatient Visits	Births	Total	Payroll	Personnel
ANYTOWN—Universal County ★ COMMUNITY HOSPITAL, First Street and Main Avenue Zip 62835; tel 204/391–2345; **A**1 2 3 4 6 9 10 **F**1 2 3 4 5 6 8 9 10 23 24 34; **P**1 2 3 4; **S** Acme HCS **John Doe, President and Chief Executive Officer** Robert Brown, Vice President Information Systems **Web address:** www.webaddress.org	23	10	346	10778	248	75953	1693	20695	9973	796

5   **6**   **7**

3 Physician Codes

Actually available within, and reported by the institution; for definitions, see page A9.

(Alphabetical/Numerical Order)

1 Closed physician–hospital organization (PHO)
2 Equity model
3 Foundation

4 Group practice without walls
5 Independent practice association (IPA)
6 Integrated salary model

7 Management service organization (MSO)
8 Open physician–hospital organization (PHO)

4 Health Care System Name

The inclusion of the letter ''S'' (1) indicates that the hospital belongs to a health care system and (2) identifies the specific system to which the hospital belongs.

5 Titles of Chief Administrators

6 Classification Codes

Control

Government, nonfederal
12 State
13 County
14 City
15 City–county
16 Hospital district or authority

Nongovernment not–for–profit
21 Church operated
23 Other

Investor–owned (for–profit)
31 Individual
32 Partnership
33 Corporation

Government, federal
41 Air Force
42 Army
43 Navy
44 Public Health Service other than 47

45 Veterans Affairs
46 Federal other than 41–45, 47–48
47 Public Health Service Indian Service
48 Department of Justice

Osteopathic
61 Church operated
63 Other not–for–profit
64 Other
71 Individual for–profit
72 Partnership for–profit
73 Corporation for–profit

Service
10 General medical and surgical
11 Hospital unit of an institution (prison hospital, college infirmary, etc.)
12 Hospital unit within an institution for the mentally retarded
13 Surgical
22 Psychiatric
33 Tuberculosis and other respiratory diseases
41 Cancer
42 Heart

44 Obstetrics and gynecology
45 Eye, ear, nose, and throat
46 Rehabilitation
47 Orthopedic
48 Chronic disease
49 Other specialty
50 Children's general
51 Children's hospital unit of an institution
52 Children's psychiatric
53 Children's tuberculosis and other respiratory diseases
55 Children's eye, ear, nose, and throat
56 Children's rehabilitation
57 Children's orthopedic
58 Children's chronic disease
59 Children's other specialty
62 Institution for mental retardation
80 Long–Term Acute Care
82 Alcoholism and other chemical dependency
90 Children's Long–Term Acute Care
91 Children's Cancer
92 Children's Heart

* When a hospital restricts its service to a specialty not defined by a specific code, it is coded 49 (59 if a children's hospital) and the specialty is indicated in parentheses following the name of the hospital.

7 Headings

Definitions are based on the American Hospital Association's Hospital Administration Terminology. In completing the survey, hospitals were requested to report data for a full year, in accord with their fiscal year, ending in 2003. Hospitals reporting for less than a 12–month period are so designated.

Utilization Data:

Beds–Number of beds regularly maintained (set up and staffed for use) for inpatients as of the close of the reporting period. Excludes newborn bassinets.

Admissions–Number of patients accepted for inpatient service during a 12–month period; does not include newborn.

Census–Average number of inpatients receiving care each day during the 12–month reporting period; does not include newborn.

Outpatient Visits–A visit by a patient who is not lodged in the hospital while receiving medical, dental, or other services. Each appearance of an outpatient in each unit constitutes one visit regardless of the number of diagnostic and/or therapeutic treatments that a patient receives.

Births–Number of infants born in the hospital and accepted for service in a newborn infant bassinet during a 12–month period; excludes stillbirths.

Expense: Expense for a 12–month period; both total expense and payroll components are shown. Payroll expenses include all salaries and wages.

Personnel: Represents personnel situations as they existed at the end of the reporting period; includes full-time equivalents of part–time personnel. Full–time equivalents were calculated on the basis that two part–time persons equal one full–time person.

AHA Guide® to the Health Care Field

2006 Edition

AHA Members $215
Nonmembers $330
AHA Item Number 010006
Telephone ORDERS 1–800–AHA–2626

Online ORDERS www.ahadata.com/products

ISSN 0094–8969
ISBN 0–87258–816–5

Contents

† List supplied by the Joint Commission on Accreditation of Healthcare Organizations

Acknowledgements and Advisements

Acknowledgements

The AHA Guide® to the Health Care Field is published annually by Health Forum LLC, an affiliate of the American Hospital Association. Contributions are made by Information Systems and Technology, Member Relations, Office of the President, Office of the Secretary, Printing Services Group and AHA Resource Center.

Health Forum LLC acknowledges the cooperation given by many professional groups and government agencies in the health care field, particularly the following: American College of Surgeons; American Medical Association; Blue Cross and Blue Shield Association; Council of Teaching Hospitals of the Association of American Medical Colleges; Joint Commission on Accreditation of Healthcare Organizations; Commission on Accreditation of Rehabilitation Facilities; American Osteopathic Association; Centers for Medicare & Medicaid Services; and various offices within the U.S. Department of Health and Human Services.

Advisements

The data published here should be used with the following advisements: The data are based on replies to an annual survey that seeks a variety of information, not all of which is published in this book. The information gathered by the survey includes specific services, but not all of each hospital's services. Therefore, the data do not reflect an exhaustive list of all services offered by all hospitals. For information on the availability of additional data and products, please contact Health Forum LLC at 800/821–2039, or visit our web site: www.ahadata.com/products.

Health Forum LLC does not assume responsibility for the accuracy of information voluntarily reported by the individual institutions surveyed. **The purpose of this publication is to provide basic data reflecting the delivery of health care in the United States and associated areas, and is not to serve as an official and all inclusive list of services offered by individual hospitals. The information reflected is based on data collected as of June 30, 2005.**

An introduction to *AHA Guide*

Welcome to the 2006 edition of *AHA Guide*. While the publication primarily focuses on hospitals it also serves as a guide to the health care field. There are 3 major sections of *AHA Guide*:

- Section A: Hospitals
- Section B: Health care systems, networks, and alliances
- Section C: Health care organizations, agencies, and other health care providers

Data for this publication is compiled using AHA membership and the AHA Annual Survey of Hospitals. This directory is the leading hospital directory and represents both AHA Member and non-member hospitals.

Start Here: the AHA Guide Code Chart

Open the front cover and *AHA Guide* begins with the *2006 AHA Guide Code Chart*. This two page insert, front and back, is specially perforated so it can be easily removed and used as a companion to *AHA Guide*. It demonstrates where to find the most important elements of each entry. Don't worry about removing this page

because this chart is repeated again on **page A4** with a full explanation.

Remember, the *Code Chart* is important to understanding the unique columnar listing of the hospitals in Section A. The columnar listing is designed to view several listings per page, locate information quickly and easily, make at-a-glance comparisons of hospitals in the state or in a particular city.

Other important information included at the beginning of *AHA Guide* is:

- The complete section by section table of contents on **page iii**
- Recognition for the source of data in the *Acknowledgements and Advisements*, **page v**
- A demonstration of our rich history and a listing of our awards included as part of *AHA Offices, Officers, Historical Data, and Awards*, **page viii**

How To Use This Book

Section A begins with *An Explanation of the Hospital Listings*, these two pages explain the Code Chart and are vital to identifying the information, symbols, and numerical codes for each hospital listing. The chart demonstrates where to find these important elements:

1) **Approval codes** refer to approvals held by the hospital; they represent information supplied by various national approving and reporting bodies. For example, code A–1 indicates accreditation under one of the programs of the Joint Commission on Accreditation of Healthcare Organizations-formal evidence that a hospital meets established standards for quality of patient care.

2) **Facility Codes** describe the types of specific services offered by each hospital.

3) **Physician codes** refer to the different types of physician arrangements in which the hospital participates.

4) **Health Care system names** reference specific health care system headquarters. The presence of the system name indicates the hospital belongs to a health care system. Absence of a system name indicates that the hospital does not belong to a health care system.

5) **Titles of Chief Administrators** including the Chief Executive Officer and where available the Chief Financial Officer, Chief Information Officer, Chief Medical Officer, Chief Operating Officer, and Chief Human Resources.

6) **Classification codes** indicate the type of organization that controls or operates the hospital

2006 AHA Guide Code Chart

Hospital, Address, Telephone, Approval, Facility, and Physician Codes, Health Care System	Classi-fication Codes		Utilization Data					Expense (thousands) of dollars		
★ American Hospital Association (AHA) membership □ Joint Commission on Accreditation of Healthcare Organizations (JCAHO) accreditation ○ American Osteopathic Association (AOA) accreditation △ Commission on Accreditation of Rehabilitation Facilities (CARF) accreditation	Control	Service	Staffed Beds	Admissions	Census	Outpatient Visits	Births	Total	Payroll	Personnel
ANYTOWN—Universal County ★ COMMUNITY HOSPITAL, First Street and Main Avenue Zip 62835; tel 204/391–2345; A1 2 3 4 6 9 10 F1 2 3 4 5 6 8 9 10 23 24 34; P1 2 3 4; S Acme HCS	23	10	346	10778	248	75953	1693	20695	9973	796
	1	**2**			**3**			**4**		

1 Approval Codes

Reported by the approving bodies specified, as of the dates noted.

1 Accreditation under the hospital program of the Joint Commission on Accreditation of Healthcare Organizations (April 2005).

2 Cancer program approved by American College of Surgeons (March 2005).

†3 Approval to participate in residency training, by the Accreditation Council for Graduate Medical Education (April 2005). As of June 30, 1975, internship (formerly code 4) was included under residency, code 3.

†5 Medical school affiliation, reported to the American Medical Association (April 2005).

6 Hospital–controlled professional nursing school, reported by National League for Nursing.

7 Accreditation by Commission on Accreditation of Rehabilitation Facilities (March 2005).

8 Member of Council of Teaching Hospitals of the Association of American Medical Colleges (February 2005).

9 Hospitals contracting or participating in a Plan, reported by the Blue Cross and Blue Shield Association (March 2005).

10 Certified for participation in the Health Insurance for the Aged (Medicare) Program by the Centers for Medicare and Medical Services (February 2005).

11 Accreditation by American Osteopathic Association (May 2005).

12 Internship approved by American Osteopathic Association (June 2005).

13 Residency approved by American Osteopathic Association (June 2005).

18 Critical Access Hospitals (May 2005).

19 Rural Referral Center (May 2005).

20 Sole Community Provider (May 2005).

Nonreporting indicates that the 2004 Annual Survey questionnaire for the hospital was not received prior to publication.

2 Facility Codes

Provided directly by the hospital; for definitions, see page A6.

(Numerical Order)

1 Adult Day Care program
2 Airborne infection isolation room
3 Alcoholism–drug abuse or dependency inpatient unit
4 Alcoholism–drug abuse or dependency outpatient services
5 Alzheimer Center
6 Ambulance Services
7 Arthritis treatment center
8 Assisted Living
9 Auxiliary organization
10 Bariatric/weight control services
11 Birthing room–LDR room–LDRP room
12 Breast cancer screening/mammograms
13 Burn care services
14 Cardiac intensive care services
15 Adult diagnostic/invasive catheterization
16 Pediatric diagnostic/invasive catheterization
17 Adult interventional cardiac catheterization
18 Pediatric interventional cardiac catheterization
19 Adult cardiac surgery
20 Pediatric cardiac surgery
21 Case management
22 Chaplaincy/pastoral care services
23 Chemotherapy
24 Children wellness program
25 Chiropractic services
26 Community health reporting
27 Community health status assessment
28 Community health status based service planning
29 Community outreach
30 Complementary medicine
31 Crisis Prevention
32 Dental services
33 Emergency department
34 Trauma center (certified)
35 Enabling services

36 Hospice program
37 Pain management
38 Palliative care program
39 Enrollment Assistance Services
40 Extracorporeal shock wave lithotripter (ESWL)
41 Fitness center
42 Freestanding outpatient care center
43 Gamma Knife
44 Geriatric services
45 Health facility transportation (to/from)
46 Health fair
47 Health information center
48 Health screenings
49 Hemodialysis
50 HIV–AIDS services
51 Home health services
52 Hospital–based outpatient care center services
53 Linguistic/translation services
54 Meals on wheels
55 Medical surgical intensive care services
56 Neonatal intensive care
57 Neurological services
58 Nutrition programs
59 Obstetrics services
60 Occupational health services
61 Oncology services
62 Orthopedic services
63 Outpatient surgery
64 Patient controlled analgesia (PCA)
65 Patient education center
66 Patient representative services
67 Pediatric intensive care services
68 Physical rehabilitation inpatient services
69 Physical rehabilitation outpatient services
70 Primary care department
71 Psychiatric care
72 Psychiatric–child and adolescent services
73 Psychiatric consultation–liaison services
74 Psychiatric education services

75 Psychiatric emergency services
76 Psychiatric geriatric services
77 Psychiatric outpatient services
78 Psychiatric partial hospitalization services
79 Intensity–modulated radiation therapy (IMRT)
80 Shaped-beam radiation system
81 CT scanner
82 Diagnostic radioisotope facility
83 Electron beam computed tomography (EBCT)
84 Magnetic resonance imaging (MRI)
85 Multi-slice spiral computed tomography (MSCT)
86 Positron Emission Tomography (PET)
87 Single Photon Emission Computerized Tomography (SPECT)
88 Ultrasound
89 Fertility Clinic
90 Genetic Testing/Counseling
91 Retirement housing
92 Skilled nursing or other long-term care services
93 Sleep center
94 Social work services
95 Sports medicine
96 Support groups
97 Swing bed services
98 Teen outreach services
99 Bone marrow transplant
100 Heart transplant
101 Kidney transplant
102 Liver transplant
103 Lung transplant
104 Tissue transplant
105 Other transplant
106 Tobacco treatment/cessation program
107 Urgent care center
108 Volunteer services department
109 Women's health center/services
110 Wound management services

†Data from the Graduate Medical Education Database, Copyright 2003, American Medical Association, Chicago, Illinois.

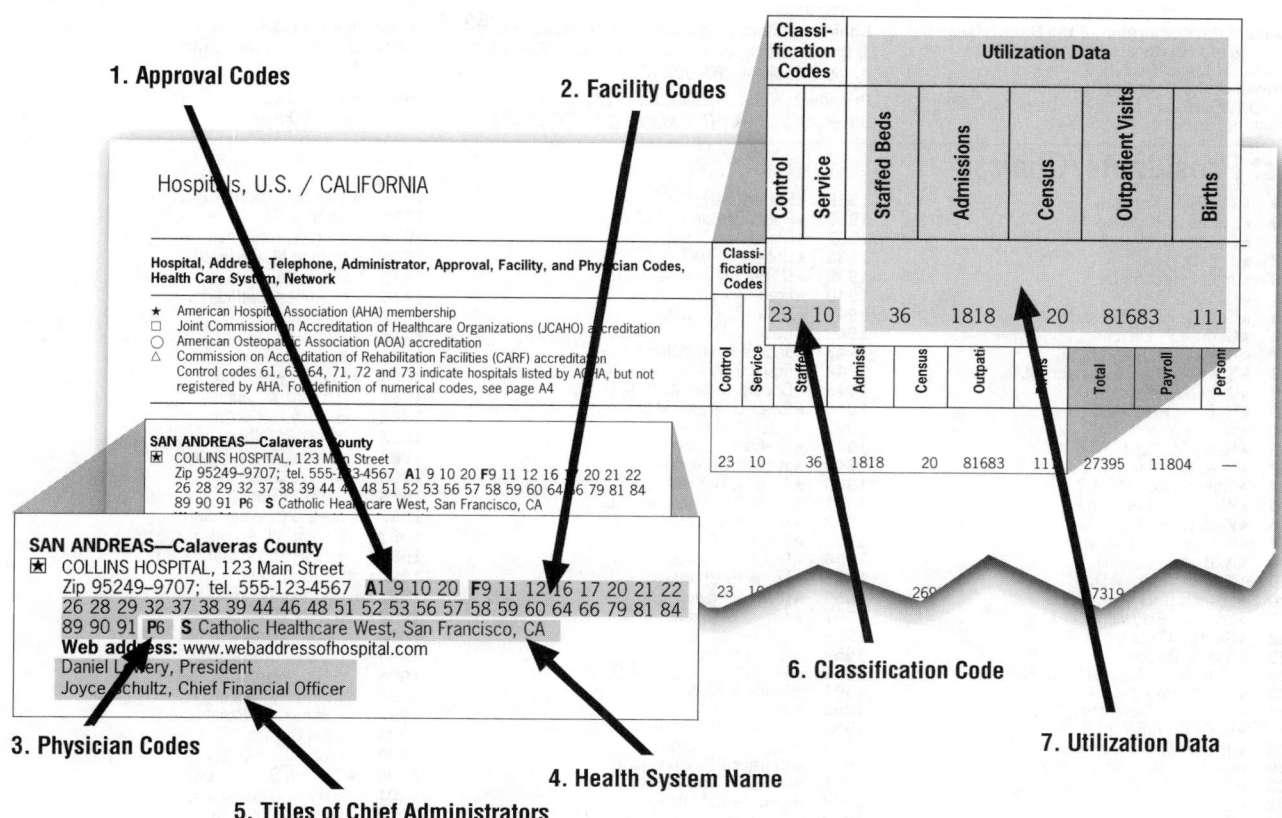

1. Approval Codes

2. Facility Codes

Hospitals, U.S. / CALIFORNIA

Hospital, Address, Telephone, Administrator, Approval, Facility, and Physician Codes,
Health Care System, Network

★ American Hospital Association (AHA) membership
☐ Joint Commission on Accreditation of Healthcare Organizations (JCAHO) accreditation
○ American Osteopathic Association (AOA) accreditation
△ Commission on Accreditation of Rehabilitation Facilities (CARF) accreditation
   Control codes 61, 63, 64, 71, 72 and 73 indicate hospitals listed by AOHA, but not
   registered by AHA. For definition of numerical codes, see page A4

SAN ANDREAS—Calaveras County
☒ COLLINS HOSPITAL, 123 Main Street
   Zip 95249–9707; tel. 555-123-4567 **A**1 9 10 20 **F**9 11 12 16 17 20 21 22
   26 28 29 32 37 38 39 44 46 48 51 52 53 56 57 58 59 60 64 66 79 81 84
   89 90 91 **P**6 **S** Catholic Healthcare West, San Francisco, CA

SAN ANDREAS—Calaveras County
☒ COLLINS HOSPITAL, 123 Main Street
   Zip 95249–9707; tel. 555-123-4567 **A**1 9 10 20 **F**9 11 12 16 17 20 21 22
   26 28 29 32 37 38 39 44 46 48 51 52 53 56 57 58 59 60 64 66 79 81 84
   89 90 91 **P**6 **S** Catholic Healthcare West, San Francisco, CA
   Web address: www.webaddressofhospital.com
   Daniel Lowery, President
   Joyce Schultz, Chief Financial Officer

3. Physician Codes

5. Titles of Chief Administrators

4. Health System Name

6. Classification Code

7. Utilization Data

Classification Codes		Utilization Data				
Control	Service	Staffed Beds	Admissions	Census	Outpatient Visits	Births
23	10	36	1818	20	81683	111

Control	Service	Staffed	Admissi	Census	Outpati	ents	Total	Payroll	Personn
23	10	36	1818	20	81683	111	27395	11804	—

and primary type of service. Code number in the
10s denote nonfederal (state and local)
government hospitals; in the 20s, nongovernment
not-for-profit hospitals; the 40s, federal
government hospitals; and in the 60s and 70s
nonregistered osteopathic hospitals.

Among **service codes**, the most common code is
10, indicating a general hospital. Other numbers
designate various special services. For example,
code 22 indicates psychiatric hospitals and codes
in the 50s indicate different types of children's
hospitals.

7) **Utilization data** like the number of admissions
   and number of births, etc. that are described here.

The *Annual Survey* definitions follow on **page A6** and
give greater detail on the facility codes and physician
codes. Please note that these are arranged alphabetically
and numerically to correspond with the code chart. **Page
A11** begins the listing of *Hospitals in the United States,
by State*.

Finding Hospitals & Health Care Professionals in Section A

There are two ways to locate hospitals in *AHA Guide*.
The first is by geographic classification. Hospitals are
arranged alphabetically by state and then by city. The
second is by using the *Hospital Index* that appears on
page A501. The Medicare Provider Number appears
next the hospital's name in the index.

There is also a *Healthcare Professionals Index* that
begins on **page A536** that lists professionals from
hospitals and health systems. Look for the side page
tabs that clearly mark each index.

AHA Membership Organizations

At the conclusion of Section A is a description of AHA
Membership categories along with a listing of various
AHA Membership organizations. Please turn to **page
A569** for a listing of these organizations.

For more information on Systems, Networks and
Alliances, please read the introduction to Section B on
page B1. Health organizations, agencies, and providers
listed in Section C are described on page C2.

AHA Offices, Officers, and Historical Data

Chicago: One North Franklin, Chicago, IL 60606–3401; tel. 312/422–3000

Washington: 325 Seventh Street, N.W., Suite 700, Washington, DC 20004; tel. 202/638–1100

Immediate Past Chairman of the Board: David L. Bernd, Sentara Healthcare, 6015 Poplar Hall Drive, Suite 300, Norfolk, VA 23502

Chairman of the Board of Trustees: George F. Lynn, AtlantiCare, 2500 English Creek Ave., Bldg. C, Egg Harbor Township, NJ 08234

Chairman–Elect of the Board of Trustees: Richard J. Umbdenstock, Providence Services, 9 East Ninth Avenue, Spokane, WA 99202

President: Richard J. Davidson, 325 Seventh Street, N.W., Suite 700, Washington, DC 20004

Senior Vice President and Secretary: Michael P. Guerin, One North Franklin, Chicago, IL 60606–3401

Treasurer: John Evans, One North Franklin, Chicago, IL 60606–3401

Past Presidents/Chairs†

1899 ★James S. Knowles	1935 ★Robert Jolly	1971 ★Jack A. L. Hahn
1900 ★James S. Knowles	1936 ★Robin C. Buerki, M.D.	1972 Stephen M. Morris
1901 ★Charles S. Howell	1937 ★Claude W. Munger, M.D.	1973 ★John W. Kauffman
1902 ★J. T. Duryea	1938 ★Robert E. Neff	1974 ★Horace M. Cardwell
1903 ★John Fehrenbatch	1939 ★G. Harvey Agnew, M.D.	1975 Wade Mountz
1904 ★Daniel D. Test	1940 ★Fred G. Carter, M.D.	1976 H. Robert Cathcart
1905 ★George H. M. Rowe, M.D.	1941 ★B. W. Black, M.D.	1977 ★John M. Stagl
1906 ★George P. Ludlam	1942 ★Basil C. MacLean, M.D.	1978 ★Samuel J. Tibbitts
1907 ★Renwick R. Ross, M.D.	1943 ★James A. Hamilton	1979 W. Daniel Barker
1908 ★Sigismund S. Goldwater, M.D.	1944 ★Frank J. Walter	1980 ★Sister Irene Kraus
1909 ★John M. Peters, M.D.	1945 ★Donald C. Smelzer, M.D.	1981 Bernard J. Lachner
1910 ★H. B. Howard, M.D.	1946 ★Peter D. Ward, M.D.	1982 Stanley R. Nelson
1911 ★W. L. Babcock, M.D.	1947 ★John H. Hayes	1983 Elbert E. Gilbertson
1912 ★Henry M. Hurd, M.D.	1948 ★Graham L. Davis	1984 Thomas R. Matherlee
1913 ★F. A. Washburn, M.D.	1949 ★Joseph G. Norby	1985 Jack A. Skarupa
1914 ★Thomas Howell, M.D.	1950 ★John N. Hatfield	1986 Scott S. Parker
1915 ★William O. Mann, M.D.	1951 ★Charles F. Wilinsky, M.D.	1987 Donald C. Wegmiller
1916 ★Winford H. Smith, M.D.	1952 ★Anthony J. J. Rourke, M.D.	1988 Eugene W. Arnett
1917 ★Robert J. Wilson, M.D.	1953 ★Edwin L. Crosby, M.D.	1989 Edward J. Connors
1918 ★A. B. Ancker, M.D.	1954 ★Ritz E. Heerman	1990 David A. Reed
1919 ★A. R. Warner, M.D.	1955 ★Frank R. Bradley	1991 C. Thomas Smith
1920 ★Joseph B. Howland, M.D.	1956 ★Ray E. Brown	1992 D. Kirk Oglesby, Jr.
1921 ★Louis B. Baldwin, M.D.	1957 ★Albert W. Snoke, M.D.	1993 Larry L. Mathis
1922 ★George O'Hanlon, M.D.	1958 ★Tol Terrell	1994 Carolyn C. Roberts
1923 ★Asa S. Bacon	1959 ★Ray Amberg	1995 Gail L. Warden
1924 ★Malcolm T. MacEachern, M.D.	1960 ★Russell A. Nelson, M.D.	1996 Gordon M. Sprenger
1925 ★E. S. Gilmore	1961 ★Frank S. Groner	1997 Reginald M. Ballantyne III
1926 ★Arthur C. Bachmeyer, M.D.	1962 ★Jack Masur, M.D.	1998 John G. King
1927 ★R. G. Brodrick, M.D.	1963 ★T. Stewart Hamilton, M.D.	1999 Fred L. Brown
1928 ★Joseph C. Doane, M.D.	1964 ★Stanley A. Ferguson	2000 ★Carolyn Boone Lewis
1929 ★Louis H. Burlingham, M.D.	1965 ★Clarence E. Wonnacott	2001 Gary A. Mecklenburg
1930 ★Christopher G. Parnall, M.D.	1966 ★Philip D. Bonnet, M.D.	2002 Sr. Mary Roch Rocklage
1931 ★Lewis A. Sexton, M.D.	1967 ★George E. Cartmill	2003 Dennis R. Barry
1932 ★Paul H. Fesler	1968 ★David B. Wilson, M.D.	2004 David L. Bernd
1933 ★George F. Stephens, M.D.	1969 ★George William Graham, M.D.	
1934 ★Nathaniel W. Faxon, M.D.	1970 ★Mark Berke	

Chief Executive Officers

1917–18 ★William H. Walsh, M.D.	1943–54 ★George Bugbee	1986–91 Carol M. McCarthy, Ph.D., J.D.
1919–24 ★Andrew Robert Warner, M.D.	1954–72 ★Edwin L. Crosby, M.D.	1991 Jack W. Owen (acting)
1925–27 ★William H. Walsh, M.D.	1972 Madison B. Brown, M.D. (acting)	1991 Richard J. Davidson (current)
1928–42 ★Bert W. Caldwell, M.D.	1972–86 J. Alexander McMahon	

Distinguished Service Award

The award recognizes significant lifetime contributions and service to health care institutions and associations.

1934 Matthew O. Foley	1961 E. M. Bluestone, M.D.	1985 J. Alexander McMahon
1939 Malcolm T. MacEachern, M.D.	1962 Mother Loretto Bernard, S.C., R.N.	1986 Sister Irene Kraus
1940 Sigismund S. Goldwater, M.D.	1963 Ray E. Brown	1987 W. Daniel Barker
1941 Frederic A. Washburn, M.D.	1964 Russell A. Nelson, M.D.	1988 Elbert E. Gilbertson
1942 Winford H. Smith, M.D.	1965 Albert W. Snoke, M.D.	1989 Donald G. Shropshire
1943 Arthur C. Bachmeyer, M.D.	1966 Frank S. Groner	1990 John W. Colloton
1944 Rt. Rev. Msgr. Maurice F. Griffin, LL.D.	1967 Rev. John J. Flanagan, S.J.	1991 Carol M. McCarthy, Ph.D., J.D.
1945 Asa S. Bacon	1968 Stanley W. Martin	1992 David H. Hitt
1946 George F. Stephens, M.D.	1969 T. Stewart Hamilton, M.D.	1993 Edward J. Connors
1947 Robin C. Buerki, M.D.	1970 Charles Patteson Cardwell, Jr.	Jack W. Owen
1948 James A. Hamilton	1971 Mark Berke	1994 George Adams
1949 Claude W. Munger, M.D.	1972 Stanley A. Ferguson	1995 Scott S. Parker
1950 Nathaniel W. Faxon, M.D.	1973 Jack A. L. Hahn	1996 John A. Russell
1951 Bert W. Caldwell, M.D.	1974 George William Graham, M.D.	1997 D. Kirk Oglesby, Jr.
1952 Fred G. Carter, M.D.	1975 George E. Cartmill	1998 Henry B. Betts, M.D.
1953 Basil C. MacLean, M.D.	1976 D. O. McClusky, Jr.	1999 Mitchell T. Rabkin, M.D.
1954 George Bugbee	1977 Boone Powell	2000 Gail L. Warden
1955 Joseph G. Norby	1978 Richard J. Stull	2001 Gordon M. Sprenger
1956 Charles F. Wilinsky, M.D.	1979 Horace M. Cardwell	2002 Carolyn Boone Lewis
1957 John H. Hayes	1980 Donald W. Cordes	2003 C. Thomas Smith
1958 John N. Hatfield	1981 Sister Mary Brigh Cassidy	2004 Michael C. Waters
1959 Edwin L. Crosby, M.D.	1982 R. Zach Thomas, Jr.	2005 John G. King
1960 Oliver G. Pratt	1983 H. Robert Cathcart	
	1984 Matthew F. McNulty, Jr., Sc.D.	

Award of Honor

Awarded to individuals, organizations, or groups to recognize an exemplary contribution to the health and well being of the people through leadership on a major health policy or social initiative.

1966	Senator Lister Hill	1993	Elliott C. Roberts, Sr.	1999	Joseph Cardinal Bernardin, Literacy
1967	Emory W. Morris, D.D.S.		William A. Spencer, M.D.		Volunteers of America
1971	Special Committee on Provision of Health	1994	Robert A. Derzon	2000	Institute for Safe Medication Practices
	Services (staff also)	1995	Russell G. Mawby, Ph.D.	2001	Dennis R. Barry
1982	Walter J. McNemey		John K. Springer	2002	Donald M. Berwick, M.D.
1989	Ruth M. Rothstein	1996	Stephen J. Hegarty	2003	Steven A. Schroeder, M.D.
1990	Joyce C. Clifford, R.N.		Mothers Against Drunk Driving (MADD)		Dan S. Wilford
1991	Haynes Rice	1997	Paul B. Batalden, M.D.	2004	Ron J. Anderson, M.D.
1992	Donald W. Dunn		Habitat for Humanity International		Johnson & Johnson
	Ira M. Lane, Jr.	1998	John E. Curley, Jr.	2005	Sr. Mary Jean Ryan
			National Civic League		

Justin Ford Kimball Innovators Award

Recognition to an individual who makes outstanding, innovative contributions in bringing together health care delivery and financing.

1958	E. A. van Steenwyk	1972	John R. Mannix	1990	James A. Vohs
1959	George A. Newbury	1973	Herman M. Somers	1993	John C. Lewin, M.D.
1960	C. Rufus Rorem, Ph.D.	1974	William H. Ford, Ph.D.	1994	Donald A. Brennan
1961	James E. Stuart	1975	Earl H. Kammer	1995	E. George Middleton, Jr.
1962	Frank Van Dyk	1976	J. Ed McConnell		Glenn R. Mitchell
1963	William S. McNary	1978	Edwin R. Werner	1997	Harvey Pettry
1964	Frank S. Groner	1979	Robert M. Cunningham, Jr.		D. David Sniff
1965	J. Douglas Colman	1981	Maurice J. Norby	1998	Montana Health Research and Education
1967	Walter J. McNemey	1982	Robert E. Rinehimer		Foundation
1968	John W. Paynter	1983	John B. Morgan, Jr.	1999	Kenneth W. Kizer, M.D.
1970	Edwin L. Crosby, M.D.	1984	Joseph F. Duplinsky	2002	David M. Lawrence, M.D.
1971	H. Charles Abbott	1985	David W. Stewart	2003	Lowell C. Kruse
		1988	Ernest W. Saward, M.D.		

Board of Trustees Award

Individuals or groups who have made substantial and noteworthy contributions to the work of the American Hospital Association.

1959	Joseph V. Friel		Helen McGuire		Stephen W. Gamble
	John H. Hayes	1979	Newton J. Jacobson		Yoshi Honkawa
1960	Duncan D. Sutphen, Jr.		Edward W. Weimer	1994	Roger M. Busfield, Jr., Ph.D.
1963	Eleanor C. Lambertsen, R.N., Ed.D.	1980	Robert B. Hunter, M.D.	1995	Stephen E. Dorn
1964	John R. Mannix		Samuel J. Tibbitts		William L. Yates
1965	Albert G. Hahn	1981	Vernon A. Knutson	1996	Leigh E. Morris
	Maurice J. Norby		John E. Sullivan		John Quigley
1966	Madison B. Brown, M.D.	1982	John Bigelow	1998	John D. Leech
	Kenneth Williamson		Robert W. O'Leary	1999	Sister Carol Keehan
1967	Alanson W. Wilcox		Jack W. Owen		C. Edward McCawley
1968	E. Dwight Barnett, M.D.	1984	Howard J. Berman		Stephen Rogness
1969	Vane M. Hoge, M.D.		O. Ray Hurst	2000	Dennis May
	Joseph H. McNinch, M.D.		James R. Neely	2001	Spencer C. Johnson
1972	David F. Drake, Ph.D.	1985	James E. Ferguson		Michael M. Mitchel
	Paul W. Earle		Cleveland Rodgers	2002	Victor L. Campbell
	Michael Lesparre	1986	Rex N. Olsen		Joseph A. Parker
	Andrew Pattullo	1987	Michael Lesparre	2003	J. Richard Gaintner, M.D.
1973	Tilden Cummings	1988	Barbara A. Donaho, R.N.		Donald A. Wilson
	Edmond J. Lanigan	1989	Walter H. MacDonald	2004	Richard L. Clarke
1974	James E. Hague		Donald R. Newkirk		Thelma Traut
	Sister Marybelle	1990	William T. Robinson	2005	Merrill Gappmayer
1975	Helen T. Yast	1992	Jack C. Bills		Leo Greenawalt
1976	Boynton P. Livingston		Anne Hall Davis		
	James Ludlam	1993	Theodore C. Eickhoff, M.D.		

Citation for Meritorious Service

1968	F. R. Knautz		Gordon McLachlan	1983	David M. Kinzer
	Sister Conrad Mary, R.N.	1977	Theodore Cooper, M.D.	1984	Donald L. Custis, M.D.
1971	Hospital Council of Southern California	1979	Norman D. Burkett	1985	John A. D. Cooper, M.D.
1972	College of Misericordia, Dallas, PA		John L. Quigley		Imperial Council of the Ancient Arabic
1973	Madison B. Brown, M.D.		William M. Whelan		Order of the Nobles of the Mystic Shrine
	Samuel J. Tibbitts	1980	Sister Grace Marie Hiltz		for North America
1975	Kenneth B. Babcock, M.D.		Leo J. Gehrig, M.D.	1986	Howard F. Cook
	Sister Mary Maurita Sengelaube	1981	Richard Davi	1987	David H. Hitt
1976	Chaiker Abbis		Pearl S. Fryar		Lucile Packard
	Susan Jenkins	1982	Jorge Brull Nater		

This citation is no longer awarded

AHA NOVA Awards

This award honors effective, collaborative programs focused on improving community health status.

1994

Health Partners of Philadelphi (PA): Albert Einstein Medical Center, Episcopal Hospital, Frankford Hospital, Medical College of Pennsylvania Hospital, St. Christopher's Hospital for Children, Temple University Hospital

1995

Bladen Community Care Network: Bladen County Hospital, Elizabethtown, NC
Building a Healthier Community: Community–Kimball Health Care System, Toms River, NJ

1996

Lincoln and Sunnyslope: John C. Lincoln Hospital and Health Center, Sunnyslope, AZ
Growing into Life Task Force: Aiken (SC) Regional Medical Centers

1997

Health Promotion Schools of Excellence Program: Alliant Health System and Kosair Children's Hospital, Louisville, KY
Health, Outreach, Prevention, and Education (HOPE): Health First Holmes Regional Medical Center, Melbourne, FL

1998

Partners for a Healthier Community: Evergreen Community Health Care, Group Health Cooperative of Puget Sound, Overlake Hospital Medical Center, Providence Health System/Medalia HealthCare, Seattle, WA
Glenwood–Lyndale Community Clinic: Hennepin County Medical Center, Minneapolis, MN

1999

Making a Case for Community Health: Middletown (OH) Regional Hospital
The Family Resource Center: Mount Carmel Medical Center, Pittsburgh, KS

2000

Community Healthcare Network: Columbus (GA) Regional Healthcare System
Pasadena County Asthma Project: Huntington Memorial Hospital, Pasadena, CA

2001

J.C. Lewis Health Center: Memorial Health and St. Joseph's Candler Health System, Savannah, GA
Project C.A.R.E.: Mercy Medical Center, Canton, OH

2002

Chester Community Connections: Crozer–Keystone Health System, Springfield, PA
The Hope Street Family Center: California Hospital Medical Center, Los Angeles, CA
Mobile Health Outreach Ministry: St. Vincent's Health System, Jacksonville, FL

2003

C.O.A.C.H. for Kids: Cedars–Sinai Medical Center, Los Angeles, CA
Community Action Network: Trinity Regional Medical Center, Fort Dodge, IA

2004

Better Beginnings: Brockton Hospital, Brockton, MA
Buffalo County Community Health Partners: Good Samaritan Health Systems, Kearney, NE

Decker Family Development Center: Children's Hospital Medical Center of Akron (OH)
Denver (CO) School–Based Clinics: The Children's Hospital
Basic Health Plan: Dominican Network; Mount Carmel Hospital, Colville, WA; St. Joseph's

Injury Prevention Program: Harlem Hospital Center, New York City, NY
The Community Ministries & Outreach Program: Reaching Out to Our Vickery/Meadow

People Caring for People: Beatrice (NE) Community Hospital and Health Center
Injury Prevention Center of the Greater Dayton (OH) Area: The Children's Medical Center, Good

Healthy Community Initiative: Roper Care Alliance, Charleston, SC
Obstetrical Care and Prenatal Counseling Program: St. Alexius Medical Center, Bismarck, ND
HIV/AIDS Neighborhood Service Program: Yale–New Haven Hospital, New Haven, CT

Greater Dallas (TX) Injury Prevention Center: Parkland Health & Hospital System, Children's Medical Center of Dallas, Baylor Health Care System, Methodist Hospitals of Dallas, and Presbyterian Healthcare System
Network of Trust: Phoebe Putney Memorial Hospital, Albany, GA

The Health Neighborhood Project: St. Patrick Hospital, Missoula, MT
Kids for Health: Washington Regional Medical Center, Fayetteville, AR

Ashe County Health Council "Health Carolinias Task Force": Ashe Memorial Hospital, Jefferson, NC
Caritas–Connection Project: St. Mary's Hospital, Passaic, NJ

TeenHealthFX.com: Atlantic Health System, Florham Park, NJ

Vista ElderCARE: Vista Health, Waukegan, IL

Operation Access: Kaiser Foundation Hospitals, Oakland; Sutter Health, Sacramento; San Francisco General Hospital, San Francisco; St. Rose Hospital, Hayward; and Santa Rosa Memorial Hospital, Santa Rosa, CA

Hearts N' Health: Glendale Adventist Medical Center, Glendale, CA
Saint Joseph Health Center: Saint Joseph Regional Medical Center, South Bend, IN

Quad City Health Initiative: Genesis Health System, Davenport, IA and Trinity Regional Health System, Rock Island, IL
Quality of Life in the Truckee Meadows: Washoe Health System, Reno, NV

Hospital, Chewelah, WA; and Holy Family Hospital, Spokane, WA
HealthLink: Lakes Region General Hospital, Laconia, NH

Neighborhood: Presbyterian Healthcare System, Dallas, TX
"CHOICES": Shriners Hospitals for Crippled Children, Tampa, FL

Samaritan Hospital and Health Center, Grandview Hospital, Kettering Memorial Hospital, Miami Valley Hospital, and St. Elizabeth Medical Center
Family Road: Hutzel Hospital, Detroit, MI

The Lauderdale Court: A Community Partnership: St. Joseph Hospital and Health Centers, Memphis, TN

Children's Village: Yakima Memorial Hospital, Yakima, WA

Correctional Health Care Program: Baystate Health System, Springfield, MA

Western Village Enterprise School: INTEGRIS Health, Oklahoma City, OK

Wilmington Health Access for Teens: New Hanover Health Network, Wilmington, NC

St. Mary Medical Center Bensalem Ministries: St. Mary Medical Center, Langhorne, PA

Solano Coalition for Better Health, Inc.: NorthBay Healthcare Group, Fairfield, CA; Sutter Solano Medical Center, Vallejo, CA; and Kaiser Permanente, Martinez, CA

2005
Children's Health Connection: McKay-Dee Hospital Center, Ogden, UT
Palmetto Health's Vision Health Initiative: Palmetto Health, Columbia, SC

Project Dulce, Whittier Institute for Diabetes: Scripps Health, San Diego, CA
Toledo/Lucas County CareNet: Mercy Health Partners, ProMedica Health System, and Medical

University of Ohio, all of Toledo, OH and St. Luke's Hospital, Maumee, OH
Volunteer Health Advisor (VHA) Program: Cambridge Health Alliance, Cambridge, MA

The Carolyn Boone Lewis Living the Vision Award

Organizations and individuals living AHA's vision of a society of healthy communities where all individuals reach their highest potential for health.

1998	Memorial Healthcare System, Hollywood, FL	**2001**	Salina Regional Health Center, Salina, KS	**2005**	Fairbanks Memorial Hospital, Fairbanks, AK
	Baptist Health System, Montgomery, AL	**2002**	Health Improvement Collaborative of Greater Cincinnati, Cincinnati, OH		
1999	Robert A. DeVries, Battle Creek, MI	**2003**	Franklin Memorial Hospital, Farmington, ME		
	Memorial Health System, South Bend, IN				
2000	Rockingham Memorial Hospital, Harrisonburg, VA	**2004**	Jamaica Hospital Medical Center, Jamaica, New York		

Circle of Life Award: Celebrating Innovation in End–of–Life Care

This award celebrates innovation in palliative and end-of-life care.

2000
Improving Care through the End of Life, Franciscan Health System, Gig Harbor, WA

The Hospice of The Florida Suncoast, Largo, FL

Louisiana State Penitentiary Hospice Program, Angola, LA

2001
Department of Pain Medicine and Palliative Care, Beth Israel Medical Center, New York, NY

Palliative CareCenter & Hospice of the North Shore, Evanston , IL

St. Joseph's Manor, Trumbull, CT

2002
Children's Program of San Diego Hospice and Children's Hospital and Health Center of San Diego, San Diego, CA

Hospice of the Bluegrass, Lexington, KY
Project Safe Conduct, Hospice of the Western Reserve and Ireland Cancer Center, Cleveland, OH

Special Circle of Life Award Population–based Palliative Care Research Network (PoPCRN), Denver, CO

2003
Hospice & Palliative CareCenter, Winston–Salem, NC

Providence Health System, Portland, OR

University of California Davis Health System, Sacramento, CA

2004
Hope Hospice and Palliative Care, Fort Myers, FL

St. Mary's Healthcare System for Children, Bayside, NY

University of Texas M.D. Anderson Cancer Center Palliative Care, Houston, TX

2005
High Point Regional Health System, High Point, NC

Palliative and End-of-life Care Program, Hoag Memorial Hospital Presbyterian, Newport Beach, CA

Thomas Palliative Care Unit, VCU Massey Cancer Center, Richmond, VA

The American Hospital Association McKesson Quest for Quality Prize

Honoring Leadership and Innovation in Patient Care Quality, Safety, and Commitment

2002
Missouri Baptist Medical Center, St. Louis, MO

Finalist: Fairview Hospital, Greater, Barrington, MA

Finalist: Minnesota Children's Hospital and Clinics, Minneapolis, MN

2003
Abington Memorial Hospital, Abington, PA

Finalist: Beaumont Hospitals, Royal Oak, MI

Finalist: University of Wisconsin Hospital and Clinics, Madison, WI

2004
Sentara Norfolk General Hospital, Norfolk, VA

Finalist: The Johns Hopkins Hospital, Baltimore, MD

Finalist: Mary Lanning Memorial Hospital, Hastings, NE

2005
North Mississippi Medical Center, Tupelo, MS

Finalist: El Camino Hospital, Mountain View, CA

Finalist: NewYork-Presbyterian Hospital, New York, NY

Foster G. McGaw Prize

Honors health delivery organizations that have demonstrated exceptional commitment to community service.

1986	Lutheran Medical Center, Brooklyn, NY	**1993**	The Cambridge Hospital, Cambridge, MA	**2001**	Memorial Hospital of South Bend, South Bend, IN
1987	Copley Hospital, Morrisville, VT	**1994**	Parkland Memorial Hospital, Dallas, TX		
	Mount Sinai Hospital, Hartford, CT	**1995**	Our Lady of Lourdes Medical Center, Camden, NJ	**2002**	John C. Lincoln Health Network, Phoenix, AZ
1988	MetroHealth System, Cleveland, OH	**1996**	St. Mary's Hospital, Rochester, NY		
1989	Greater Southeast Healthcare System, Washington, DC	**1997**	Bladen County Hospital Rural Health Network, Elizabethtown, NC	**2003**	Phoebe Putney Memorial Hospital, Albany, GA
1990	Mount Zion Medical Center of The University of California-San Francisco, San Francisco, CA	**1998**	Allina Health System, Minneapolis, MN	**2004**	Henry Ford Health System, Detroit, MI
		1999	LAC+USC Healthcare Network, Los Angeles, CA		
1991	Franklin Regional Hospital, Franklin, NH	**2000**	Kaweah Delta Health Care District, Visalia, CA		
1992	Mount Sinai Hospital Medical Center of Chicago, Chicago, IL				

An institution may be listed by the American Hospital Association as a hospital if it is accredited as a hospital by the Joint Commission on Accreditation of Healthcare Organizations or is certified as a provider of acute services under Title 18 of the Social Security Act. Membership in the American Hospital Association is not a prerequisite.

In lieu of the preceding accreditation or certification, an institution licensed as a hospital by the appropriate state agency may be registered by AHA as a hospital by meeting the following alternative requirements:

Function: The primary function of the institution is to provide patient services, diagnostic and therapeutic, for particular or general medical conditions.

1. The institution shall maintain at least six inpatient beds, which shall be continuously available for the care of patients who are nonrelated and who stay on the average in excess of 24 hours per admission.
2. The institution shall be constructed, equipped, and maintained to ensure the health and safety of patients and to provide uncrowded, sanitary facilities for the treatment of patients.

3. There shall be an identifiable governing authority legally and morally responsible for the conduct of the hospital.
4. There shall be a chief executive to whom the governing authority delegates the continuous responsibility for the operation of the hospital in accordance with established policy.
5. There shall be an organized medical staff of fully licensed physicians* that may include other licensed individuals permitted by law and by the hospital to provide patient care services independently in the hospital. The medical staff shall be accountable to the governing authority for maintaining proper standards of medical care, and it shall be governed by bylaws adopted by said staff and approved by the governing authority.
6. Each patient shall be admitted on the authority of a member of the medical staff who has been granted the privilege to admit patients to inpatient services in accordance with state law and criteria for standards of medical care established by the individual medical staff. Each patient's general medical condition is the responsibility of a qualified physician member of the medical staff. When nonphysician members of

the medical staff are granted privileges to admit patients, provision is made for prompt medical evaluation of these patients by a qualified physician. Any graduate of a foreign medical school who is permitted to assume responsibilities for patient care shall possess a valid license to practice medicine, or shall be certified by the Educational Commission for Foreign Medical Graduates, or shall have qualified for and have successfully completed an academic year of supervised clinical training under the direction of a medical school approved by the Liaison Committee onGAT Medical Education.
7. Registered nurse supervision and other nursing services are continuous.
8. A current and complete+ medical record shall be maintained by the institution for each patient and shall be available for reference.
9. Pharmacy service shall be maintained in the institution and shall be supervised by a registered pharmacist.
10. The institution shall provide patients with food service that meets their nutritional and therapeutic requirements; special diets shall also be available.

---

* Physician–Term used to describe an individual with an M.D. or D.O. degree who is fully licensed to practice medicine in all its phases.

‡ The completed records in general shall contain at least the following: the patient's identifying data and consent forms, medical history, record of physical examination, physicians' progress notes, operative notes, nurses' notes, routine x–ray and laboratory reports, doctors' orders, and final diagnosis.

Types of Hospitals

In addition to meeting these 10 general requirements, hospitals are listed as one of four types of hospitals: general, special, rehabilitation and chronic disease, or psychiatric. The following definitions of function by type of hospital and special requirements are:

General

The primary function of the institution is to provide patient services, diagnostic and therapeutic, for a variety of medical conditions. A general hospital also shall provide:

- diagnostic x–ray services with facilities and staff for a variety of procedures
- clinical laboratory service with facilities and staff for a variety of procedures and with anatomical pathology services regularly and conveniently available
- operating room service with facilities and staff.

Special

The primary function of the institution is to provide diagnostic and treatment services for patients who have specified medical conditions, both surgical and nonsurgical. A special hospital also shall provide:

- such diagnostic and treatment services as may be determined by the Executive Committee of the Board of Trustees of the American Hospital Association to

be appropriate for the specified medical conditions for which medical services are provided shall be maintained in the institution with suitable facilities and staff. If such conditions do not normally require diagnostic x–ray service, laboratory service, or operating room service, and if any such services are therefore not maintained in the institution, there shall be written arrangements to make them available to patients requiring them.
- clinical laboratory services capable of providing tissue diagnosis when offering pregancy termination services.

Rehabilitation and Chronic Disease

The primary function of the institution is to provide diagnostic and treatment services to handicapped or disabled individuals requiring restorative and adjustive services. A rehabilitation and chronic disease hospital also shall provide:

- arrangements for diagnostic x–ray services, as required, on a regular and conveniently available basis
- arrangements for clinical laboratory service, as required on a regular and conveniently available basis
- arrangements for operating room service, as required, on a regular and conveniently available basis
- a physical therapy service with suitable facilities and staff in the institution
- an occupational therapy service with suitable facilities and staff in the institution

- arrangements for psychological and social work services on a regular and conveniently available basis
- arrangements for educational and vocational services on a regular and conveniently available basis
- written arrangements with a general hospital for the transfer of patients who require medical, obstetrical, or surgical services not available in the institution.

Psychiatric

The primary function of the institution is to provide diagnostic and treatment services for patients who have psychiatric–related illnesses. A psychiatric hospital also shall provide:

- arrangements for clinical laboratory service, as required, on a regular and conveniently available basis
- arrangements for diagnostic x–ray services, as required on a regular and conveniently available basis
- psychiatric, psychological, and social work service with facilities and staff in the institution
- arrangements for electroencephalograph services, as required, on a regular and conveniently available basis.
- written arrangements with a general hospital for the transfer of patients who require medical, obstetrical, or surgical services not available in the institution.

The American Hospital Association may, at the sole discretion of the Executive Committee of the Board of Trustees, grant, deny, or withdraw the listing of an institution.

* Physician–Term used to describe an individual with an M.D. or D.O. degree who is fully licensed to practice medicine in all its phases.

‡ The completed records in general shall contain at least the following: the patient's identifying data and consent forms, medical history, record of physical examination, physicians' progress notes, operative notes, nurses' notes, routine x–ray and laboratory reports, doctors' orders, and final diagnosis.

Explanation of Hospital Listings

Hospital, Address, Telephone, Approval, Facility, and Physician Codes, Health Care System	Classi-fication Codes		Utilization Data					Expense (thousands) of dollars		
★ American Hospital Association (AHA) membership □ Joint Commission on Accreditation of Healthcare Organizations (JCAHO) accreditation ○ American Osteopathic Association (AOA) accreditation △ Commission on Accreditation of Rehabilitation Facilities (CARF) accreditation	Control	Service	Staffed Beds	Admissions	Census	Outpatient Visits	Births	Total	Payroll	Personnel

ANYTOWN—Universal County

★ COMMUNITY HOSPITAL, First Street and Main Avenue Zip 62835; tel 204/391–2345; **A**1 2 3 4 6 9 10 **F**1 2 3 4 5 6 8 9 10 23 24 34; **P**1 2 3 4; **S** Acme HCS	23	10	346	10778	248	75953	1693	20695	9973	796

1 **A**1 2 3 4 6 9 10   **2** **F**1 2 3 4 5 6 8 9 10 23 24 34   **3** **P**1 2 3 4   **4** **S** Acme HCS

1 Approval Codes

Reported by the approving bodies specified, as of the dates noted.

1 Accreditation under the hospital program of the Joint Commission on Accreditation of Healthcare Organizations (April 2005).

2 Cancer program approved by American College of Surgeons (March 2005).

†3 Approval to participate in residency training, by the Accreditation Council for Graduate Medical Education (April 2005). As of June 30, 1975, internship (formerly code 4) was included under residency, code 3.

†5 Medical school affiliation, reported to the American Medical Association (April 2005).

6 Hospital–controlled professional nursing school, reported by National League for Nursing.

7 Accreditation by Commission on Accreditation of Rehabilitation Facilities (March 2005).

8 Member of Council of Teaching Hospitals of the Association of American Medical Colleges (February 2005).

9 Hospitals contracting or participating in a Plan, reported by the Blue Cross and Blue Shield Association (March 2005).

10 Certified for participation in the Health Insurance for the Aged (Medicare) Program by the Centers for Medicare and Medical Services (February 2005).

11 Accreditation by American Osteopathic Association (May 2005).

12 Internship approved by American Osteopathic Association (June 2005).

13 Residency approved by American Osteopathic Association (June 2005).

18 Critical Access Hospitals (May 2005).

19 Rural Referral Center (May 2005).

20 Sole Community Provider (May 2005).

Nonreporting indicates that the 2004 Annual Survey questionnaire for the hospital was not received prior to publication.

2 Facility Codes

Provided directly by the hospital; for definitions, see page A6.

(Numerical Order)

1 Adult Day Care program
2 Airborne infection isolation room
3 Alcoholism–drug abuse or dependency inpatient unit
4 Alcoholism–drug abuse or dependency outpatient services
5 Alzheimer Center
6 Ambulance Services
7 Arthritis treatment center
8 Assisted Living
9 Auxiliary organization
10 Bariatric/weight control services
11 Birthing room–LDR room–LDRP room
12 Breast cancer screening/mammograms
13 Burn care services
14 Cardiac intensive care services
15 Adult diagnostic/invasive catheterization
16 Pediatric diagnostic/invasive catheterization
17 Adult interventional cardiac catheterization
18 Pediatric interventional cardiac catheterization
19 Adult cardiac surgery
20 Pediatric cardiac surgery
21 Case management
22 Chaplaincy/pastoral care services
23 Chemotherapy
24 Children wellness program
25 Chiropractic services
26 Community health reporting
27 Community health status assessment
28 Community health status based service planning
29 Community outreach
30 Complementary medicine
31 Crisis Prevention
32 Dental services
33 Emergency department
34 Trauma center (certified)
35 Enabling services

36 Hospice program
37 Pain management
38 Palliative care program
39 Enrollment Assistance Services
40 Extracorporeal shock wave lithotripter (ESWL)
41 Fitness center
42 Freestanding outpatient care center
43 Gamma Knife
44 Geriatric services
45 Health facility transportation (to/from)
46 Health fair
47 Health information center
48 Health screenings
49 Hemodialysis
50 HIV–AIDS services
51 Home health services
52 Hospital–based outpatient care center services
53 Linguistic/translation services
54 Meals on wheels
55 Medical surgical intensive care services
56 Neonatal intensive care
57 Neurological services
58 Nutrition programs
59 Obstetrics services
60 Occupational health services
61 Oncology services
62 Orthopedic services
63 Outpatient surgery
64 Patient controlled analgesia (PCA)
65 Patient education center
66 Patient representative services
67 Pediatric intensive care services
68 Physical rehabilitation inpatient services
69 Physical rehabilitation outpatient services
70 Primary care department
71 Psychiatric care
72 Psychiatric–child adolescent services
73 Psychiatric consultation–liaison services
74 Psychiatric education services

75 Psychiatric emergency services
76 Psychiatric geriatric services
77 Psychiatric outpatient services
78 Psychiatric partial hospitalization services
79 Intensity-modulated radiation therapy (IMRT)
80 Shaped-beam radiation system
81 CT scanner
82 Diagnostic radioisotope facility
83 Electron beam computed tomography (EBCT)
84 Magnetic resonance imaging (MRI)
85 Multi-slice spiral computed tomography (MSCT)
86 Positron Emission Tomography (PET)
87 Single Photon Emission Computerized Tomography (SPECT)
88 Ultrasound
89 Fertility Clinic
90 Genetic Testing/Counseling
91 Retirement housing
92 Skilled nursing or other long-term care services
93 Sleep center
94 Social work services
95 Sports medicine
96 Support groups
97 Swing bed services
98 Teen outreach services
99 Bone marrow transplant
100 Heart transplant
101 Kidney transplant
102 Liver transplant
103 Lung transplant
104 Tissue transplant
105 Other transplant
106 Tobacco treatment/cessation program
107 Urgent care center
108 Volunteer services department
109 Women's health center/services
110 Wound management services

†Data from the Graduate Medical Education Database, Copyright 2003, American Medical Association, Chicago, Illinois.

Hospital, Address, Telephone, Approval, Facility, and Physician Codes, Health Care System	Classification Codes		Utilization Data					Expense (thousands) of dollars		
★ American Hospital Association (AHA) membership ☐ Joint Commission on Accreditation of Healthcare Organizations (JCAHO) accreditation ○ American Osteopathic Association (AOA) accreditation △ Commission on Accreditation of Rehabilitation Facilities (CARF) accreditation	Control	Service	Staffed Beds	Admissions	Census	Outpatient Visits	Births	Total	Payroll	Personnel
ANYTOWN—Universal County ★ COMMUNITY HOSPITAL, First Street and Main Avenue Zip 62835; tel 204/391–2345; A1 2 3 4 6 9 10 F1 2 3 4 5 6 8 9 10 23 24 34; P1 2 3 4; S Acme HCS **John Doe, President and Chief Executive Officer** Robert Brown, Vice President Information Systems **Web address:** www.webaddress.org	23	10	346	10778	248	75953	1693	20695	9973	796

| 5 | 6 | 7 |

3 Physician Codes

Actually available within, and reported by the institution; for definitions, see page A10.

(Alphabetical/Numerical Order)

1 Closed physician–hospital organization (PHO)	**4** Group practice without walls	**7** Management service organization (MSO)
2 Equity model	**5** Independent practice association (IPA)	**8** Open physician–hospital organization (PHO)
3 Foundation	**6** Integrated salary model	

4 Health Care System Name

The inclusion of the letter ''S'' (1) indicates that the hospital belongs to a health care system and (2) identifies the specific system to which the hospital belongs.

5 Titles of Chief Administrators

6 Classification Codes

Control

Government, nonfederal
12 State
13 County
14 City
15 City–county
16 Hospital district or authority

Nongovernment not–for–profit
21 Church operated
23 Other

Investor–owned (for–profit)
31 Individual
32 Partnership
33 Corporation

Government, federal
41 Air Force
42 Army
43 Navy
44 Public Health Service other than 47

45 Veterans Affairs
46 Federal other than 41–45, 47–48
47 Public Health Service Indian Service
48 Department of Justice

Osteopathic
61 Church operated
63 Other not–for–profit
64 Other
71 Individual for–profit
72 Partnership for–profit
73 Corporation for–profit

Service
10 General medical and surgical
11 Hospital unit of an institution (prison hospital, college infirmary, etc.)
12 Hospital unit within an institution for the mentally retarded
13 Surgical
22 Psychiatric
33 Tuberculosis and other respiratory diseases
41 Cancer
42 Heart

44 Obstetrics and gynecology
45 Eye, ear, nose, and throat
46 Rehabilitation
47 Orthopedic
48 Chronic disease
49 Other specialty
50 Children's general
51 Children's hospital unit of an institution
52 Children's psychiatric
53 Children's tuberculosis and other respiratory diseases
55 Children's eye, ear, nose, and throat
56 Children's rehabilitation
57 Children's orthopedic
58 Children's chronic disease
59 Children's other specialty
62 Institution for mental retardation
80 Long–Term Acute Care
82 Alcoholism and other chemical dependency
90 Children's Long–Term Acute Care
91 Children's Cancer
92 Children's Heart

* When a hospital restricts its service to a specialty not defined by a specific code, it is coded 49 (59 if a children's hospital) and the specialty is indicated in parentheses following the name of the hospital.

7 Headings

Definitions are based on the American Hospital Association's Hospital Administration Terminology. In completing the survey, hospitals were requested to report data for a full year, in accord with their fiscal year, ending in 2004. Hospitals reporting for less than a 12–month period are so designated.

Utilization Data:

Beds–Number of beds regularly maintained (set up and staffed for use) for inpatients as of the close of the reporting period. Excludes newborn bassinets.

Admissions–Number of patients accepted for inpatient service during a 12–month period; does not include newborn.

Census–Average number of inpatients receiving care each day during the 12–month reporting period; does not include newborn.

Outpatient Visits–A visit by a patient who is not lodged in the hospital while receiving medical, dental, or other services. Each appearance of an outpatient in each unit constitutes one visit regardless of the number of diagnostic and/or therapeutic treatments that a patient receives.

Births–Number of infants born in the hospital and accepted for service in a newborn infant bassinet during a 12–month period; excludes stillbirths.

Expense: Expense for a 12–month period; both total expense and payroll components are shown. Payroll expenses include all salaries and wages.

Personnel: Represents personnel situations as they existed at the end of the reporting period; includes full-time equivalents of part–time personnel. Full-time equivalents were calculated on the basis that two part–time persons equal one full–time person.

Annual Survey

Each year, an annual survey of hospitals is conducted by the American Hospital Association through its Health Forum affiliate.

The facilities and services found below are provided by the hospital. For data products reflecting the services provided by a hospital through its health care system, or network or through a formal arrangement with another provider contact Health Forum at 800/821–2039, or visit www.healthforum.com.

The AHA Guide to the Health Care Field does not include all data collected from the 2004 Annual Survey. Requests for purchasing other Annual Survey data should be directed to Health Forum LLC, an affiliate of the American Hospital Association, One North Franklin, Chicago, IL 60606–3401, 800/821–2039.

Definitions of Facility Codes

1. **Adult day care program.** Program providing supervision, medical and psychological care, and social activities for older adults who live at home or in another family setting, but cannot be alone or prefer to be with others during the day. May include intake assessment, health monitoring, occupational therapy, personal care, noon meal, and transportation services.

2. **Airborne infection isolation room.** A single–occupancy room for patient care where environmental factors are controlled in an effort to minimize the transmission of those infectious agents, usually spread person to person by droplet nuclei associated with coughing and inhalation. Such rooms typically have specific ventilation requirements for controlled ventilation, air pressure and filtration.

3. **Alcoholism–drug abuse or dependency inpatient unit.** Provides, diagnosis and therapeutic services to patients with alcoholism or other drug dependencies. Includes care for inpatient/residential treatment for patients whose course of treatment involves more intensive care than provided in an outpatient setting or where patient requires supervised withdrawal.

4. **Alcoholism–drug abuse or dependency outpatient unit.** Organized hospital services that provide medical care and/or rehabilitative treatment services to outpatients for whom the primary diagnosis is alcoholism or other chemical dependency.

5. **Alzheimer Center.** Facility that offers care to persons with Alzheimer's disease and their families through an integrated program of clinical services, research, and education.

6. **Ambulance Services.** Provision of ambulance services to the ill and injured who require medical attention on a scheduled or unscheduled basis.

7. **Arthritis treatment center.** Specifically equipped and staffed center for the diagnosis and treatment of arthritis and other joint disorders.

8. **Assisted Living.** A special combination of housing, supportive services, personalized assistance and health care designed to respond to the individual needs of those who need help in activities of daily living and instrumental activities of daily living. Supportive services are available, 24 hours a day, to meet scheduled and unscheduled needs, in a way that promotes maximum independence and dignity for each resident and encourages the involvement of a resident's family, neighbor and friends.

9. **Auxiliary organization.** A volunteer community organization formed to assist the hospital in carrying out its purpose and to serve as a link between the institution and the community.

10. **Bariatric/weight control services.** Bariatrics is the medical practice of weight reduction.

11. **Birthing room–LDR room–LDRP room.** A single room–type of maternity care with a more homelike setting for families than the traditional three–room unit (labor/delivery/recovery) with a separate postpartum area. A birthing room combines labor and delivery in one room. An LDR room accommodates three stages in the birthing process— labor, delivery, and recovery. An LDRP room accommodates all four stages of the birth process—labor, delivery, recovery and postpartum.

12. **Breast cancer screening/mammograms.** Mammography screening–the use of breast x–ray to detect unsuspected breast cancer in asymptomatic women. Diagnostic mammography–the x–ray imaging of breast tissue in symptomatic women who are considered to have a substantial likelihood of having breast cancer already.

13. **Burn care services.** Provides care to severely burned patients. Severely burned patients are those with any of the following: 1. Second–degree burns of more than 25% total body surface area for adults or 20% total body surface area for children; 2. Third–degree burns of more than 10% total body surface area; 3. Any severe burns of the hands, face, eyes, ears or feet or; 4. All inhalation injuries, electrical burns, complicated burn injuries involving fractures and other major traumas, and all other poor risk factors.

14. **Cardiac intensive care services.** Provides patient care of a more specialized nature than the usual medical and surgical care, on the basis of physicians' orders and approved nursing care plans. The unit is staffed with specially trained nursing personnel and contains monitoring and specialized support or treatment equipment for patients who, because of heart seizure, open–heart surgery, or other life–threatening conditions, require intensified, comprehensive observation and care. May include myocardial infarction, pulmonary care, and heart transplant units.

15. **Adult diagnostic/invasive catheterization.** (also called coronary angiography or coronary arteriography) is used to assist in diagnosing complex heart conditions. Cardiac angiography involves the insertion of a tiny catheter into the artery in the groin then carefully threading the catheter up into the aorta where the coronary arteries originate. Once the catheter is in place, a dye is injected which allows the cardiologist to see the size, shape, and distribution of the coronary arteries. These images are used to diagnose heart disease and to

determine, among other things, whether or not surgery is indicated.

16. **Pediatric diagnostic/invasive catheterization.**

17. **Adult interventional cardiac catheterization.** Non surgical procedure that utilizes the same basic principles as diagnostic catheterization and then uses advanced techniques to improve the heart's function. It can be a less-invasive alternative to heart surgery.

18. **Pediatric interventional cardiac catheterization.**

19. **Adult cardiac surgery.** Includes minimally invasive procedures that include surgery done with only a small incision or no incision at all, such as through a laparoscope or an endoscope and more invasive major surgical procedures that include open chest and open heart surgery.

20. **Pediatric cardiac surgery.**

21. **Case management.** A system of assessment, treatment planning, referral and follow-up that ensures the provision of comprehensive and continuous services and the coordination of payment and reimbursement for care.

22. **Chaplaincy/pastoral care services.** A service ministering religious activities and providing pastoral counseling to patients, their families, and staff of a health care organization.

23. **Chemotherapy.** An organized program for the treatment of cancer by the use of drugs or chemicals.

24. **Children wellness program.** A program that encourages improved health status and a healthful lifestyle of children through health education, exercise, nutrition and health promotion.

25. **Chiropractic services.** An organized clinical service including spinal manipulation or adjustment and related diagnostic and therapeutic services.

26. **Community health reporting.** Does your hospital either by itself or in conjunction with others disseminate reports to the community on the quality and costs of health care services?

27. **Community health status assessment.** Does your hospital work with other providers, public agencies, or community representatives to conduct a health status assessment of the community?

28. **Community health status based service planning.** Does your hospital use health status indicators (such as rates of health problems or surveys of self-reported health) for defined populations to design new services or modify existing services?

29. **Community outreach.** A program that systematically interacts with the community to identify those in need of services, alerting persons and their families to the availability of services, locating needed services, and enabling persons to enter the service delivery system.

30. **Complementary medicine.** Organized hospital services or formal arrangements to providers that provide care or treatment not based solely on traditional western allopathic medical teachings as instructed in most U.S. medical schools. Includes any of the following; acupuncture, chiropractic, homeopathy, osteopathy, diet and lifestyle changes, herbal medicine, massage therapy, etc.

31. **Crisis Prevention** Services provided in order to promote physical and mental well being and the early identification of disease and ill health prior to the onset and recognition of symptoms so as to permit early treatment.

32. **Dental services.** An organized dental service, not necessarily involving special facilities, that provides dental or oral services to inpatients or outpatients.

33. **Emergency department.** Hospital facilities for the provision of unscheduled outpatient services to patients whose conditions require immediate care. Must be staffed 24 hours a day.

34. **Trauma center (certified).** A facility certified to provide emergency and specialized intensive care to critically ill and injured patients.

35. **Enabling services.** A program that is designed to help the patient access health care services by offering any of the following linguistic services, transportation services, and/or referrals to local social services agencies.

36. **Hospice program.** A program providing palliative care, chiefly medical relief of pain and supportive services, addressing the emotional, social, financial, and legal needs of terminally ill patients and their families. Care can be provided in a variety of settings, both inpatient and at home.

37. **Pain management.** A hospital wide formalized program that includes staff education for the management of chronic and acute pain based on guidelines and protocols like those developed by the agency for Health Care Policy Research, etc.

38. **Palliative care program.** An organized program providing specialized medical care, drugs or therapies for the management of acute or chronic pain and/or the control of symptoms administered by specially trained physicians and other clinicians; and supportive care services, such as counseling on advanced directives, spiritual care, and social services, to patients with advanced disease and their families.

39. **Enrollment assistance services.** A program that provides enrollment assistance for patients who are potentially eligible for public health insurance programs such as Medicaid, State Children's Health Insurance, or local/state indigent care programs. The specific services offered could include explanation of benefits, assist applicants in completing the application and locating all relevant documents, conduct eligibilty interviews, and/or forward applications and documentation to state/local social service or health agency.

40. **Extracorporeal shock wave lithotripter (ESWL).** A medical device used for treating stones in the kidney or ureter. The device disintegrates kidney stones noninvasively through the transmission of acoustic shock waves directed at the stones.

41. **Fitness Center.** Provides exercise, testing, or evaluation programs and fitness activities to the community and hospital employees.

42. **Freestanding outpatient care center.** A facility owned and operated by the hospital, but physically separate from the hospital, that provides various medical treatments on an outpatient basis only. In addition to treating minor illnesses or injuries, the center will stabilize seriously ill or injured patients before transporting them to a hospital. Laboratory and radiology services are usually available.

43. **Gamma Knife** A non-invasive and bloodless procedure which uses a technological device that delivers

concentrated gamma radiation to target points selected in the brain and is used for treatment on patients with brain tumors and other brain disorders.

44. **Geriatric services.** The branch of medicine dealing with the physiology of aging and the diagnosis and treatment of disease affecting the aged. Services could include: Adult day care program; Alzheimer's diagnostic–assessment services; Comprehensive geriatric assessment; Emergency response system; Geriatric acute care unit; and/or Geriatric clinics.

45. **Health facility transportation (to/from).** A long–term care support service designed to assist the mobility of the elderly. Some programs offer improved financial access by offering reduced rates and barrier–free buses or vans with ramps and lifts to assist the elderly or handicapped; others offer subsidies for public transport systems or operate mini–bus services exclusively for use by senior citizens.

46. **Health fair.** Community health education events that focus on the prevention of disease and promotion of health through such activities as audiovisual exhibits and free diagnostic services.

47. **Health information center.** Education which is directed at increasing the information of individuals and populations. It is intended to increase the ability to make informed personal, family and community health decisions by providing consumers with informed choices about health matters with the objective of improving health status.

48. **Health screenings.** A preliminary procedure, such as a test or examination to detect the most characteristic sign or signs of a disorder that may require further investigation.

49. **Hemodialysis.** Provision of equipment and personnel for the treatment of renal insufficiency on an inpatient or outpatient basis.

50. **HIV–AIDS services.** Services may include one or more of the following: HIV–AIDS unit (special unit or team designated and equipped specifically for diagnosis, treatment, continuing care planning, and counseling services for HIV–AIDS patients and their families.) General inpatient care for HIV–AIDS (inpatient diagnosis and treatment for human immunodeficiency virus and acquired immunodeficiency syndrome patients, but dedicated unit is not available.) Specialized outpatient program for HIV–AIDS (special outpatient program providing diagnostic, treatment, continuing care planning, and counseling for HIV–AIDS patients and their families.)

51. **Home health services.** Service providing nursing, therapy, and health–related homemaker or social services in the patient's home.

52. **Hospital–based outpatient care center services.** Organized hospital health care services offered by appointment on an ambulatory basis. Services may include outpatient surgery, examination, diagnosis, and treatment of a variety of medical conditions on a nonemergency basis, and laboratory and other diagnostic testing as ordered by staff or outside physician referral.

53. **Linguistic/translation services.** Services provided by the hospital designed to make health care more accessible to non–English speaking patients and their physicians.

54. **Meals on wheels.** A hospital sponsored program which delivers meals to people, usually the elderly, who are unable to prepare their own meals. Low cost, nutritional meals are delivered to individuals' homes on a regular basis.

55. **Medical surgical intensive care services.** Provides patient care of a more intensive nature than the usual medical and surgical care, on the basis of physicians' orders and approved nursing care plans. These units are staffed with specially trained nursing personnel and contain monitoring and specialized support equipment of patients who, because of shock, trauma, or other life–threatening conditions, require intensified, comprehensive observation and care. Includes mixed intensive care units.

56. **Neonatal intensive care.** A unit that must be separate from the newborn nursery providing intensive care to all sick infants including those with the very lowest birth weights (less that 1500 grams). NICU has potential for providing mechanical ventilation, neonatal surgery, and special care for the sickest infants born in the hospital or transferred from another institution. A full–time neonatologist serves as director of the NICU.

57. **Neurological services.** Services provided by the hospital dealing with the operative and nonoperative management of disorders of the central, peripheral, and autonomic nervous system.

58. **Nutrition programs.** Those services within a health care facility which are designed to provide inexpensive, nutritionally sound meals to patients.

59. **Obstetrics services.** Levels should be designated: (1) unit provides services for uncomplicated maternity and newborn cases; (2) unit provides services for uncomplicated cases, the majority of complicated problems, and special neonatal services; and (3) unit provides services for all serious illnesses and abnormalities and is supervised by a full–time maternal/fetal specialist.

60. **Occupational health services.** Includes services designed to protect the safety of employees from hazards in the work environment.

61. **Oncology services.** An organized program for the treatment of cancer by the use of drugs or chemicals.

62. **Orthopedic services.** Services provided for the prevention or correction of injuries or disorders of the skeletal system and associated muscles, joints, and ligaments.

63. **Outpatient surgery.** Scheduled surgical services provided to patients who do not remain in the hospital overnight. The surgery may be performed in operating suites also used for inpatient surgery, specially designated surgical suites for outpatient surgery, or procedure rooms within an outpatient care facility.

64. **Patient controlled analgesia (PCA).** Patient-controlled Analgesia (PCA) is intravenously administered pain medicine under the patient's control. The patient has a button on the end of a cord than can be pushed at will, whenever more pain medicine is desired. This button will only deliver more pain medicine at pre-determined intervals, as programmed by the doctor's order.

65. **Patient education center.** Written goals and objectives for the patient and/or family related to therapeutic regimens, medical procedures, and self care.

66. **Patient representative services.** Organized hospital services providing personnel through whom patients and staff can seek solutions to institutional problems affecting the

delivery of high–quality care and services.

67. Pediatric intensive care services. Provides care to pediatric patients that is of a more intensive nature than that usually provided to pediatric patients. The unit is staffed with specially trained personnel and contains monitoring and specialized support equipment for treatment of patients who, because of shock, trauma, or other life–threatening conditions, require intensified, comprehensive observation and care.

68. Physical rehabilitation inpaiton services. Provides care encompassing a comprehensive array of restoration services for the disabled and all support services necessary to help patients attain their maximum functional capacity.

69. Physical rehabilitation outpatient services. Outpatient program providing medical, health–related, therapy, social, and/or vocational services to help disabled persons attain or retain their maximum functional capacity.

70. Primary care department. A unit or clinic within the hospital that provides primary care services (e.g. general pediatric care, general internal medicine, family practice and gynecology) through hospital–salaried medical and or nursing staff, focusing on evaluating and diagnosing medical problems and providing medical treatment on an outpatient basis.

71. Psychiatric care. Provides acute or long–term care to emotionally disturbed patients, including patients admitted for diagnosis and those admitted for treatment of psychiatric problems, on the basis of physicians' orders and approved nursing care plans. Long–term care may include intensive supervision to the chronically mentally ill, mentally disordered, or other mentally incompetent persons.

72. Psychiatric–child adolescent services. Provides care to emotionally disturbed children and adolescents, including those admitted for diagnosis and those admitted for treatment.

73. Psychiatric consultation–liaison services. Provides organized psychiatric consultation/liaison services to nonpsychiatric hospital staff and/or department on psychological aspects of medical care that may be generic or specific to individual patients.

74. Psychiatric education services. Provides psychiatric educational services to community agencies and workers such as schools, police, courts, public health nurses, welfare agencies, clergy and so forth. The purpose is to expand the mental health knowledge and competence of personnel not working in the mental health field and to promote good mental health through improved understanding, attitudes, and behavioral patterns.

75. Psychiatric emergency services. Services or facilities available on a 24–hour basis to provide immediate unscheduled outpatient care, diagnosis, evaluation, crisis intervention, and assistance to persons suffering acute emotional or mental distress.

76. Psychiatric geriatric services. Provides care to emotionally disturbed elderly patients, including those admitted for diagnosis and those admitted for treatment.

77. Psychiatric outpatient services. Provides medical care, including diagnosis and treatment of psychiatric outpatients.

78. Psychiatric partial hospitalization services. Organized hospital services of intensive day/evening outpatient services of three hours or more duration, distinguished from other outpatient visits of one hour.

79. Intensity–Modulated Radiation Therapy (IMRT). A type of three–dimensional radiation therapy, which improves the targeting of treatment delivery in a way that is likely to decrease damage to normal tissues and allows varying intensities diagnosis of genetic diseases in newborns, children, and adults; the identification of future health risks; the prediction of drug responses; and the assessment of risks to future children.

80. Shaped beam radiation system. A precise, non-invasive treatment that involves targeting beams of radiation that mirror the exact size and shape of a tumor at a specific area of a tumor to shrink or destroy cancerous cells. This procedure delivers a therapeutic dose of radiation that conforms precisely to the shape of the tumor, thus minimizing the risk to nearby tissues.

81. CT scanner. Computed tomographic scanner for head and whole body scans.

82. Diagnostic radioisotope facility. The use of radioactive isotopes (Radiopharmaceutical) as tracers or indicators to detect an abnormal condition or disease.

83. Electron Beam Computed Tomography (EBCT). A high tech computed tomography scan used to detect coronary artery disease by measuring coronary calcifications. This imaging procedure uses electron beams which are magnetically steered to produce a visual of the coronary artery and the images are produced faster than conventional CT scans.

84. Magnetic resonance imaging (MRI). The use of a uniform magnetic field and radio frequencies to study tissue and structure of the body. This procedure enables the visualization of biochemical activity of the cell in vivo without the use of ionizing radiation, radioisotopic substances, or high–frequency sound.

85. Multi-slice Spiral Computed Tomography (MSCT). A specialized computed tomography procedure that provides three-dimensional processing and allows narrower and multiple slices with increased spatial resolution and faster scanning times as compared to a regular computed tomography scan.

86. Positron emission tomography scanner (PET). is a nuclear medicine imaging technology which uses radioactive (positron emitting) isotopes created in a cyclotron or generator and computers to produce composite pictures of the brain and heart at work. PET scanning produces sectional images depicting metabolic activity or blood flow rather than anatomy.

87. Single photon emission computerized tomography (SPECT). is a nuclear medicine imaging technology that combines existing technology of gamma camera imaging with computed tomographic imaging technology to provide a more precise and clear image.

88. Ultrasound. The use of acoustic waves above the range of 20,000 cycles per second to visualize internal body structures.

89. Fertility Clinic. A specialized program set in an infertility center that provides counseling and education as well as advanced reproductive techniques such as: injectable therapy, reproductive surgeries, treatment for endometriosis, male factor infertility, tubal reversals, in vitro fertilization (IVF), donor eggs, and other such services to help patients achieve successful pregnancies.

90. **Genetic Testing/Counseling** A service equipped with adequate laboratory facilities and directed by a qualified physician to advise parents and prospective parents on potential problems in cases of genetic defects. A genetic test is the analysis of human DNA, RNA, chromosomes, proteins, and certain metabolites in order to detect heritable disease-related genotypes, mutations, phenotypes, or karyotypes for clinical purposes. Genetic tests can have diverse purposes, including the diagnosis of genetic diseases in newborns, children, and adults; the identification of future health risks; the prediction of drug responses; and the assessment of risks to future children.

91. **Retirement housing.** A facility which provides social activities to senior citizens, usually retired persons, who do not require health care but some short–term skilled nursing care may be provided. A retirement center may furnish housing and may also have acute hospital and long–term care facilities, or it may arrange for acute and long term care through affiliated institutions.

92. **Skilled nursing or other long–term care services.** Provides non–acute medical and skilled nursing care services, therapy, and social services under the supervision of a licensed registered nurse on a 24–hour basis.

93. **Sleep Center.** Specially equipped and staffed center for the diagnosis and treatment of sleep disorders.

94. **Social work services.** Services may include one or more of the following: Organized social work services (services that are properly directed and sufficiently staffed by qualified individuals who provide assistance and counseling to patients and their families in dealing with social, emotional, and environmental problems associated with illness or disability, often in the context of financial or discharge planning coordination.) Outpatient social work services (social work services provided in ambulatory care areas.) Emergency department social work services (social work services provided to emergency department patients by social workers dedicated to the emergency department or on call.)

95. **Sports medicine.** Provision of diagnostic screening and assessment and clinical and rehabilitation services for the prevention and treatment of sports–related injuries.

96. **Support groups.** A hospital sponsored program which allows a group of individuals with the same or similar problems who meet periodically to share experiences, problems, and solutions, in order to support each other.

97. **Swing bed services.** A hospital bed that can be used to provide either acute or long–term care depending on community or patients needs. To be eligible a hospital must have a Medicare provider agreement in place, have fewer than 100 beds, be located in a rural area, not have a 24 hour nursing service waiver in effect, have not been terminated from the program in the prior two years, and meet various service conditions.

98. **Teen outreach services.** A program focusing on the teenager which encourages an improved health status and a healthful lifestyle including physical, emotional, mental, social, spiritual and economic health through education, exercise, nutrition and health promotion.

99.–105. **Transplant services.** The branch of medicine that transfers an organ or tissue from one person to another or from one body part to another to replace a diseased structure or to restore function or to change appearance. Services could include: Bone marrow transplant program (**99. Bone marrow**); heart (**100. Heart**), kidney (**101. Kidney**), liver (**102. Liver**) lung (**103. Lung**), tissue (**104. Tissue Transplant**). Please include heart/lung or other multi- transplant surgeries in other (**105. Other**).

106. **Tobacco Treatment/Cessation Program.** Organized hospital services with the purpose of ending tobacco–use habits of patients addicted to tobacco/nicotine.

107. **Urgent care center.** A facility that provides care and treatment for problems that are not life–threatening but require attention over the short term. These units function like emergency rooms but are separate from hospitals with which they may have backup affiliation arrangements.

108. **Volunteer services department.** An organized hospital department responsible for coordinating the services of volunteers working within the institution.

109. **Women's health center/services.** An area set aside for coordinated education and treatment services specifically for and promoted by women as provided by this special unit. Services may or may not include obstetrics but include a range of services other than OB.

110. **Wound management services.** Services for patients with chronic wounds and non–healing wounds often resulting from diabetes, poor circulation, improper seating and immunocompromising conditions. The goals are to progress chronic wounds through stages of healing, reduce and eliminate infections, increase physical function to minimize complications from current wounds and prevent future chronic wounds. Wound management services are provided on an inpatient or outpatient basis, depending on the intensity of service needed.

Definitions of Physician Codes

1. **Closed physician–hospital organization (PHO).** A PHO that restricts physician membership to those practitioners who meet criteria for cost effectiveness and/or high quality.

2. **Equity model.** Allows established practitioners to become shareholders in a professional corporation in exchange for tangible and intangible assets of their existing practices.

3. **Foundation.** A corporation, organized either as a hospital affiliate or subsidiary, which purchases both the tangible and intangible assets of one or more medical group practices. Physicians remain in a separate corporate entity but sign a professional services agreement with the foundation.

4. **Group practice without walls.** Hospital sponsors the formation of, or provides capital to physicians to establish, a 'quasi' group to share administrative expenses while remaining independent practitioners.

5. **Independent practice association (IPA).** An IPA is a legal entity that hold managed care contracts. The IPA then contracts with physicians, usually in solo practice, to provide care either on a fee–for–services or capitated basis. The purpose of an IPA is to assist solo physicians in obtaining managed care contracts.

6. **Integrated salary model.** Physicians are salaried by the hospital or another entity of a health system to provide medical services for primary care and specialty care.

7. **Management services organization (MSO).** A corporation, owned by the hospital or a physician/hospital joint venture, that provides management services to one or more medical group practices. The MSO purchases the tangible assets of the practices and leases them back as part of a full–service management agreement, under which the MSO employs all non–physician staff and provides all supplies/administrative systems for a fee.

8. **Open physician–hospital organization (PHO).** A joint venture between the hospital and all members of the medical staff who wish to participate. The PHO can act as a unified agent in managed care contracting, own a managed care plan, own and operate ambulatory care centers or ancillary services projects, or provide administrative services to physician members.

Hospitals in the United States, by State

ALABAMA

Hospital, Address, Telephone, Approval, Facility, and Physician Codes, Health Care System	Classi-fication Codes		Utilization Data					Expense (thousands) of dollars		
	Control	Service	Staffed Beds	Admissions	Census	Outpatient Visits	Births	Total	Payroll	Personnel

★ American Hospital Association (AHA) membership
□ Joint Commission on Accreditation of Healthcare Organizations (JCAHO) accreditation
○ American Osteopathic Association (AOA) accreditation
△ Commission on Accreditation of Rehabilitation Facilities (CARF) accreditation

ALABASTER—Shelby County

✠ **SHELBY BAPTIST MEDICAL CENTER**, 1000 First Street North, Zip 35007–0488; tel. 205/620–8100, (Nonreporting) **A**1 2 3 5 9 10 **S** Baptist Health System, Birmingham, AL
Primary Contact: Charles C. Colvert, President
CMO: Darrel Weaver, M.D., Vice President Medical Staff Affairs
CIO: David Sellers, Director Information Services
CHR: Cindy Nicholson, Director Human Resources
Web address: www.baptistmedical.org
23 10 187 — — — — — — —

ALEXANDER CITY—Tallapoosa County

✠ ○ **RUSSELL MEDICAL CENTER**, 3316 Highway 280, Zip 35010–3369, Mailing Address: P.O. Box 939, Zip 35011–0939; tel. 256/329–7100 **A**1 9 10 11 12 **F**2 9 11 12 15 17 21 22 23 27 28 29 30 33 34 36 38 41 45 46 48 49 52 54 55 56 58 59 60 61 62 63 64 66 69 79 80 81 82 84 86 87 88 93 94 95 96 107 108 109
Primary Contact: Frank W. Harris, President and Chief Executive Officer
CFO: Richard M. Lucas, Chief Financial Officer
CIO: Joseph George, Director Information Services
CHR: Mary Shockley, Director Human Resources
Web address: www.russellmedcenter.com
23 10 59 4329 38 81580 480 48941 17203 569

ANDALUSIA—Covington County

✠ **ANDALUSIA REGIONAL HOSPITAL**, 849 South Three Notch Street, Zip 36420–5325, Mailing Address: P.O. Box 760, Zip 36420–0760; tel. 334/222–8466 **A**1 9 10 **F**11 12 21 22 23 27 28 29 33 34 39 49 52 53 54 55 59 62 63 64 66 68 69 70 81 82 84 88 94 95 108 110 **S** LifePoint Hospitals, Inc., Brentwood, TN
Primary Contact: Michael A. Callahan, Chief Executive Officer
CFO: Shirley M. Smith, Chief Financial Officer
CIO: Betty Blair, Director Information Systems
Web address: www.andalusiaregionalhospital.com
33 10 99 4674 46 36513 410 — — 228

ANNISTON—Calhoun County

LONG TERM HOSPITAL OF ANNISTON, 400 East 10th Street, 4th Floor, Zip 36207; tel. 256/741–6141, (Nonreporting) **A**10
Primary Contact: Adam Wright, Interim Administrator
33 80 34 — — — — — — —

✠ **NORTHEAST ALABAMA REGIONAL MEDICAL CENTER**, 400 East Tenth Street, Zip 36207–4716, Mailing Address: P.O. Box 2208, Zip 36202–2208; tel. 256/235–5121 **A**1 2 9 10 **F**2 9 10 11 12 14 15 17 19 21 22 23 26 27 28 29 30 33 34 39 42 46 47 48 49 50 51 52 53 55 57 58 59 60 61 62 63 65 66 69 71 73 74 75 76 77 78 81 82 84 85 86 88 93 94 95 96 108 109 110
Primary Contact: Allen P. Fletcher, President and Chief Executive Officer
CFO: James E. Riddle, Vice President Finance
CMO: Robert H. Hurlbutt, IV, M.D., Chief Medical Staff
CIO: Fred Wilson, Director Management Information Services
CHR: Michael S. Simms, Sr, Vice President Human Resources
Web address: www.rmccares.org
16 10 235 16579 196 118634 1612 118642 46610 1299

□ **STRINGFELLOW MEMORIAL HOSPITAL**, 301 East 18th Street, Zip 36207–0038, Mailing Address: P.O. Box 38, Zip 36207–0038; tel. 256/235–8900 **A**1 9 10 **F**17 21 23 26 27 28 33 40 46 49 52 54 55 58 63 66 81 82 84 88 96 108 110 **S** Health Management Associates, Naples, FL
Primary Contact: David Orcutt, Chief Executive Officer
Web address: www.stringfellowhealth.com
33 10 125 5784 63 42470 0 38721 14498 —

ASHLAND—Clay County

★ **CLAY COUNTY HOSPITAL**, 83825 Highway 9, Zip 36251, Mailing Address: P.O. Box 1270, Zip 36251–1270; tel. 256/354–2131, (Nonreporting) **A**9 10
Primary Contact: Linda U. Jordan, Administrator
CFO: Kerry W. Tomlin, Associate Administrator
13 10 46 — — — — — — —

ATHENS—Limestone County

✠ **ATHENS–LIMESTONE HOSPITAL**, 700 West Market Street, Zip 35611–2457, Mailing Address: P.O. Box 999, Zip 35612–0999; tel. 256/233–9292 **A**1 9 10 **F**2 6 9 11 12 21 27 28 29 33 35 38 39 40 41 44 45 46 47 48 49 51 52 53 55 56 58 59 63 64 65 66 69 81 82 84 88 93 94 95 96 98 106 107 108 109
Primary Contact: Philip E. Dotson, Chief Executive Officer
COO: Cary J. Payne, Chief Operating Officer
CFO: Gary Tate, Chief Financial Officer
CMO: Belinda Maples, M.D., Chief of Staff
CIO: Kim Hoback, Supervisor Information Systems
CHR: Rachel Frey, Director Human Resources
Web address: www.athenslimestonehospital.com
16 10 101 4054 39 111381 400 41611 17717 548

AL

Hospital, Address, Telephone, Approval, Facility, and Physician Codes, Health Care System	Classi-fication Codes		Utilization Data					Expense (thousands) of dollars		
★ American Hospital Association (AHA) membership ☐ Joint Commission on Accreditation of Healthcare Organizations (JCAHO) accreditation ◯ American Osteopathic Association (AOA) accreditation △ Commission on Accreditation of Rehabilitation Facilities (CARF) accreditation	Control	Service	Staffed Beds	Admissions	Census	Outpatient Visits	Births	Total	Payroll	Personnel

ATMORE—Escambia County

☐ **ATMORE COMMUNITY HOSPITAL**, 401 Medical Park Drive, Zip 36502–3091; tel. 251/368–2500, (Nonreporting) **A**1 3 5 9 10 **S** Baptist Health Care Corporation, Pensacola, FL
Primary Contact: Robert E. Gowing, Administrator

| | 23 | 10 | 51 | — | — | — | — | — | — | — |

BAY MINETTE—Baldwin County

NORTH BALDWIN INFIRMARY, 1815 Hand Avenue, Zip 36507–4110, Mailing Address: P.O. Box 1409, Zip 36507–1409; tel. 251/937–5521, (Nonreporting) **A**9 10 **S** Gulf Health Hospitals, Mobile, AL
Primary Contact: John S. Eads, Administrator
Web address: www.mobileinfirmary.org

| | 23 | 10 | 130 | — | — | — | — | — | — | — |

BESSEMER—Jefferson County

⊠ **UAB MEDICAL WEST**, 995 Ninth Avenue S.W., Zip 35022–4527, Mailing Address: P.O. Box 847, Zip 35021–0847; tel. 205/481–7000 **A**1 2 9 10 **F**2 9 11 12 14 15 21 22 23 26 27 28 33 34 36 45 46 48 55 57 58 59 60 61 62 63 64 65 68 69 71 73 74 75 76 81 82 84 88 92 94 96 108 109 **P**6 **S** UAB Health System, Birmingham, AL
Primary Contact: Timothy J. Thornton, Chief Executive Officer
Web address: www.health.uab.edu

| | 23 | 10 | 226 | 8604 | 136 | 81889 | 528 | 85712 | 32097 | 953 |

BIRMINGHAM—Jefferson County

⊠ **BAPTIST MONTCLAIR**, (Formerly Montclair Baptist Medical Center), 800 Montclair Road, Zip 35213–1984; tel. 205/592–1000, (Total facility includes 26 beds in nursing home–type unit) **A**1 2 3 5 9 10 **F**2 3 9 10 11 12 14 15 17 19 21 22 23 26 27 28 29 33 34 37 40 44 46 47 48 50 52 55 56 57 59 61 62 63 64 65 66 68 69 71 72 73 74 75 76 77 79 80 81 82 84 85 86 87 88 92 94 95 96 106 108 109 110 **S** Baptist Health System, Birmingham, AL
Primary Contact: Michael Cowling, President
CFO: Paul Graham, Chief Financial Officer
CMO: Becky Byrd, M.D., Vice President Medical Affairs
CIO: Richard Shirey, Chief Information Officer
CHR: Ginger Azbik, Director Human Resources
Web address: www.bhsala.com

| | 21 | 10 | 350 | 19245 | 255 | 262568 | 894 | 207882 | 56720 | 1702 |

⊠ **BAPTIST PRINCETON**, (Formerly Princeton Baptist Medical Center), 701 Princeton Avenue S.W., Zip 35211–1305; tel. 205/783–3000 **A**1 2 3 5 9 10 **F**2 10 11 12 14 15 17 19 21 22 23 26 27 28 29 33 34 37 40 44 45 46 48 49 52 55 56 57 58 59 60 61 62 63 64 66 69 71 76 79 80 81 82 83 84 85 86 87 88 91 92 93 94 96 106 108 110 **S** Baptist Health System, Birmingham, AL
Primary Contact: Charlie Faulkner, President
COO: Betsy Postlethwait, Chief Operating Officer and Chief Financial Officer
CFO: Greg Johnston, Chief Financial Officer
Web address: www.bhsala.com

| | 21 | 10 | 299 | 13666 | 216 | 45972 | 585 | 152812 | 58897 | 1305 |

⊠ **BROOKWOOD MEDICAL CENTER**, 2010 Brookwood Medical Center Drive, Zip 35209–6875; tel. 205/877–1000 **A**1 2 5 9 10 **F**2 3 7 9 10 11 12 14 15 17 19 21 22 23 26 27 28 29 31 33 34 35 37 38 44 46 47 48 49 52 53 55 56 57 58 59 61 62 63 65 66 68 69 71 73 74 75 76 81 82 83 84 85 86 87 88 89 90 92 93 94 96 106 108 109 **S** TENET Healthcare Corporation, Dallas, TX
Primary Contact: Garry L. Gause, Chief Executive Officer
CFO: Doug Carter, Chief Financial Officer
CIO: Manuel Price, Director Information Systems
Web address: www.brookwood–medical.com

| | 33 | 10 | 568 | 27969 | 395 | 120956 | 3947 | 247197 | 86040 | 2235 |

☐ **CALLAHAN EYE FOUNDATION HOSPITAL**, 1720 University Boulevard, Zip 35233–1816; tel. 205/325–8100 **A**1 3 5 9 10 **F**27 28 29 33 46 47 48 52 60 63 65 94 **S** UAB Health System, Birmingham, AL
Primary Contact: Raymond Butler, President
Web address: www.health.uab.edu/eyes

| | 23 | 45 | 20 | 556 | 3 | 18483 | 0 | 21576 | 6254 | 158 |

⊠ **CARRAWAY METHODIST MEDICAL CENTER**, 1600 Carraway Boulevard, Zip 35234–1990; tel. 205/502–6000 **A**1 3 5 8 9 10 **F**2 3 10 12 14 15 17 19 21 22 26 27 29 31 33 34 36 37 39 40 41 42 44 46 47 48 49 50 52 53 55 57 58 61 62 63 66 68 69 70 71 73 74 75 76 81 82 84 88 93 94 95 96 107 108 109 110 **P**3
Primary Contact: Thomas H. Litz, FACHE, Chief Executive Officer
COO: Richard E. Salerno, Senior Vice President and Chief Operating Officer
CFO: Peggy Allen, Chief Financial Officer
CMO: Stephen Hamburger, Senior Vice President, Academic Affairs and Medical Staff Affairs
CIO: Tim Townes, Director, Information Systems
CHR: Samantha D. Crawford, Director, Human Resources
Web address: www.carraway.org

| | 23 | 10 | 288 | 10358 | 143 | 120642 | 0 | 117659 | 38658 | 879 |

⊠ **COOPER GREEN HOSPITAL**, 1515 Sixth Avenue South, Zip 35233–1688; tel. 205/930–3200 **A**1 3 5 9 10 **F**2 11 12 21 22 23 27 29 33 34 37 38 39 42 46 48 50 52 53 55 58 59 60 61 62 63 64 65 69 70 81 82 88 92 94 108 109 **P**5
Primary Contact: Sandral Hullett, M.D., Chief Executive Officer and Medical Director
CFO: Bomar Harrison, Interim Chief Financial Officer
CMO: Nass Cannon, M.D., Chief of Staff
CIO: Harriett Lewis, Interim Chief Information Officer
CHR: Huberta Mayfield Howe, Director Human Resources

| | 13 | 10 | 141 | 5293 | 50 | 158690 | 748 | 76854 | 25158 | 522 |

Many Facility Codes have changed. Please refer to the AHA Guide Code Chart. © 2005 AHA Guide

Hospital, Address, Telephone, Approval, Facility, and Physician Codes, Health Care System	Classi-fication Codes		Utilization Data					Expense (thousands) of dollars		
	Control	Service	Staffed Beds	Admissions	Census	Outpatient Visits	Births	Total	Payroll	Personnel

★ American Hospital Association (AHA) membership
□ Joint Commission on Accreditation of Healthcare Organizations (JCAHO) accreditation
○ American Osteopathic Association (AOA) accreditation
△ Commission on Accreditation of Rehabilitation Facilities (CARF) accreditation

Hospital	Control	Service	Staffed Beds	Admissions	Census	Outpatient Visits	Births	Total	Payroll	Personnel
✠ **HEALTHSOUTH LAKESHORE REHABILITATION HOSPITAL**, 3800 Ridgeway Drive, Zip 35209–5599; tel. 205/868–2000 **A**1 10 **F**2 26 27 28 45 48 52 66 68 69 94 96 **P**8 **S** HEALTHSOUTH Corporation, Birmingham, AL Primary Contact: Terry Brown, Administrator and Chief Executive Officer CFO: Tammy Young, Controller CMO: Paula Stewart, M.D., Medical Director CHR: John Estis, Human Resources Director Web address: www.healthsouth.com	33	46	100	1943	83	15144	0	—	—	275
✠ **HEALTHSOUTH MEDICAL CENTER**, 1201 11th Avenue South, Zip 35205–5299; tel. 205/930–7000 **A**1 3 9 10 **F**2 12 15 21 23 33 37 43 52 55 57 58 61 62 63 64 81 82 84 85 87 88 93 94 95 96 110 **S** HEALTHSOUTH Corporation, Birmingham, AL Primary Contact: Don Lilly, Interim Administrator CFO: Jan DiCesare, Chief Financial Officer CHR: Alan Sconiers, Director Human Resources Web address: www.healthsouth.com	33	10	153	6188	69	62003	0	92371	32211	877
□ **HILL CREST BEHAVIORAL HEALTH SERVICES**, 6869 Fifth Avenue South, Zip 35212–1866; tel. 205/833–9000 **A**1 10 **F**4 21 22 27 28 29 65 71 72 77 94 96 **S** Psychiatric Solutions, Franklin, TN Primary Contact: Steve McCabe, Chief Executive Officer Web address: www.psysolutions.com	33	22	76	2103	58	15462	0	13826	8318	268
□ **LONG TERM CARE HOSPITAL**, 50 Medical Park East Drive, 8th Floor, Zip 35235; tel. 205/808–5100, (Nonreporting) **A**1 10 Primary Contact: Dale Jones, Administrator	33	49	23	—						
✠ **MEDICAL CENTER EAST**, 50 Medical Park East Drive, Zip 35235–9987; tel. 205/838–3000 **A**1 2 3 5 9 10 **F**2 7 9 10 11 12 14 15 17 19 21 22 23 26 27 28 29 33 34 35 36 37 39 40 42 44 45 46 47 48 50 51 52 55 57 58 59 60 61 62 63 64 65 66 68 69 70 79 80 81 82 84 86 87 88 91 93 94 95 96 106 108 109 110 **P**6 8 **S** Eastern Health System, Inc., Birmingham, AL Primary Contact: George McGowan, FACHE, Chief Executive Officer CFO: Bryan E. Karson, Acting Vice President Finance and Chief Financial Officer CIO: William Terrell, Vice President Web address: www.ehs.org	23	10	269	14948	182	115644	1127	127897	48658	1910
□ **SELECT SPECIALTY HOSPITAL–BIRMINGHAM**, 800 Montclair Road, Zip 35213; tel. 205/599–4600, (Nonreporting) **A**1 10 Primary Contact: Jim Baird, Chief Executive Officer	33	80	38	—						
✠ **ST. VINCENT'S HOSPITAL**, 810 St. Vincent's Drive, Zip 35205–1695, Mailing Address: P.O. Box 12407, Zip 35202–2407; tel. 205/939–7000 **A**1 2 3 5 9 10 **F**2 3 9 11 12 13 14 15 17 19 21 22 23 27 28 29 30 33 35 37 39 41 46 47 48 49 52 53 55 56 57 58 59 60 61 62 63 64 65 66 67 68 69 70 71 79 81 82 84 86 88 92 93 94 108 109 **P**5 **S** Ascension Health, Saint Louis, MO Primary Contact: Curtis James, President and Chief Executive Officer COO: Michael L. McEachern, Chief Operating Officer and Senior Vice President CFO: Ann Purdy, Senior Vice President and Chief Financial Officer CMO: William A. Leitner, M.D., Vice President Medical Affairs CIO: Timothy Stettheimer, Vice President and Chief Information Officer CHR: Major Joel Windham, Vice President Human Resources Web address: www.stv.org	21	10	274	19350	218	154395	3338	182038	66705	1943
✠ **THE CHILDREN'S HOSPITAL OF ALABAMA**, 1600 Seventh Avenue South, Zip 35233–1785; tel. 205/939–9100 **A**1 3 5 9 10 **F**6 9 10 13 21 22 23 24 26 27 28 29 32 33 34 37 39 42 45 46 47 48 49 50 52 53 56 57 58 60 61 62 63 64 65 66 67 69 70 71 72 73 74 75 77 81 82 84 87 88 93 94 95 96 98 99 107 108 **P**1 Primary Contact: Jim Dearth, M.D., Chief Executive Officer COO: Tom Shufflebarger, Chief Operating Officer CFO: Mike Burgess, Chief Financial Officer CMO: Crayton A. Fargason, M.D., Medical Director CIO: Mike McDewitt, Chief Information Officer CHR: Doug Dean, Chief Human Resources Officer Web address: www.chsys.org	23	50	248	13478	193	602303	0	288346	125954	2688
✠ **UNIVERSITY OF ALABAMA HOSPITAL**, 619 South 19th Street, Zip 35233–6505; tel. 205/934–4011, (Total facility includes 25 beds in nursing home–type unit) **A**1 2 3 5 8 9 10 **F**2 3 4 6 7 9 10 11 12 13 14 15 16 17 18 19 20 21 22 23 26 27 28 29 31 32 33 34 35 36 37 38 44 45 46 48 49 50 51 52 53 55 56 57 58 59 60 61 62 63 65 66 67 68 69 70 71 72 73 74 75 76 77 78 79 81 82 84 85 87 88 92 93 94 95 96 98 99 100 101 102 103 104 106 107 108 109 110 **P**3 **S** UAB Health System, Birmingham, AL Primary Contact: David E. Hoidal, Chief Executive Officer CFO: Stephen A. Pickett, Chief Financial Officer CMO: Scott Buchalter, M.D., Chief of Staff CIO: Joan Hicks, Interim Chief Information Officer Web address: www.health.uab.edu	12	10	867	41357	717	310187	3029	644152	242106	5917
✠ **VETERANS AFFAIRS MEDICAL CENTER**, 700 South 19th Street, Zip 35233–1927; tel. 205/933–8101, (Nonreporting) **A**1 2 3 5 8 **S** Department of Veterans Affairs, Washington, DC Primary Contact: Y. C. Parris, Director CFO: Mary S. Mitchell, Chief Resource Management Services CIO: Thad Phillips, Chief Information Officer Web address: www.va.gov/sta/guide/home.asp	45	10	134	—	—	—	—	—	—	—

Hospital, Address, Telephone, Approval, Facility, and Physician Codes, Health Care System	Classi-fication Codes		Utilization Data					Expense (thousands) of dollars		
★ American Hospital Association (AHA) membership □ Joint Commission on Accreditation of Healthcare Organizations (JCAHO) accreditation ○ American Osteopathic Association (AOA) accreditation △ Commission on Accreditation of Rehabilitation Facilities (CARF) accreditation	Control	Service	Staffed Beds	Admissions	Census	Outpatient Visits	Births	Total	Payroll	Personnel
BOAZ—Marshall County ⊠ **MARSHALL MEDICAL CENTER SOUTH**, U.S. Highway 431 North, Zip 35957–0999, Mailing Address: P.O. Box 758, Zip 35957–0758; tel. 256/593–8310, (Nonreporting) **A**1 9 10 **S** Marshall County Health Care Authority, Guntersville, AL Primary Contact: John D. Anderson, Administrator CFO: Kathy Nelson, Chief Financial Officer Web address: www.mmcs.org	13	10	102	—	—	—	—	—	—	—
BREWTON—Escambia County □ **D. W. MCMILLAN MEMORIAL HOSPITAL**, 1301 Belleville Avenue, Zip 36426–1306, Mailing Address: P.O. Box 908, Zip 36427–0908; tel. 251/867–8061, (Nonreporting) **A**1 9 10 Primary Contact: Phillip L. Parker, Administrator Web address: www.bhcpns.org	23	10	67	—	—	—	—	—	—	—
CAMDEN—Wilcox County **J. PAUL JONES HOSPITAL**, 317 McWilliams Avenue, Zip 36726–1610; tel. 334/682–4131 **A**9 10 20 **F**27 33 51 52 69 81 88 97 Primary Contact: Elizabeth M. Kennedy, Administrator	15	10	32	368	3	13899	1	2924	1355	52
CARROLLTON—Pickens County **PICKENS COUNTY MEDICAL CENTER**, 241 Robert K. Wilson Drive, Zip 35447–9802, Mailing Address: P.O. Box 478, Zip 35447–0478; tel. 205/367–8111, (Nonreporting) **A**9 10 20 Primary Contact: Wayne McElroy, Administrator	13	10	52	—	—	—	—	—	—	—
CENTRE—Cherokee County ⊠ **BAPTIST CHEROKEE**, (Formerly Cherokee Baptist Medical Center), 400 Northwood Drive, Zip 35960–1023; tel. 256/927–5531 **A**1 9 10 **F**2 9 12 21 22 24 26 27 28 29 33 34 36 38 46 48 51 52 55 63 66 69 81 82 88 92 94 95 97 108 **S** Baptist Health System, Birmingham, AL Primary Contact: J. Peter Selman, Chief Executive Officer COO: Iris Tillery, Vice President Patient Services CFO: Beverly Haymon, Chief Financial Officer CHR: Diane McMichan, Director of Human Resources Web address: www.bhsala.com/cherokee/index.asp	21	10	45	1317	13	22049	0	9590	3462	102
CENTREVILLE—Bibb County **BIBB MEDICAL CENTER**, 208 Pierson Avenue, Zip 35042–1199; tel. 205/926–4881, (Total facility includes 125 beds in nursing home–type unit) **A**9 10 **F**2 9 12 21 23 27 28 29 32 33 39 45 46 48 51 52 60 61 62 63 69 81 88 91 92 94 97 107 108 **P**6 Primary Contact: Terry J. Smith, Administrator	13	10	160	852	109	20382	0	7522	4323	96
CHATOM—Washington County ★ **WASHINGTON COUNTY HOSPITAL AND NURSING HOME**, (Formerly Washington County Infirmary and Nursing Home), 14600 St. Stephens Avenue, Zip 36518–9998, Mailing Address: P.O. Box 1299, Zip 36518–1299; tel. 251/847–2223 **A**9 10 18 **F**12 21 22 27 33 46 48 52 65 81 88 95 97 **P**6 Primary Contact: Douglas Tanner, Administrator CFO: Alyson Overstreet, Chief Financial Officer CMO: Nino Kurtsikidze, Chief of Staff CHR: Kerry Goff, Director of Operations and Personnel Services Web address: www.wchnh.org	13	10	19	559	5	19833	0	3366	1927	98
CLANTON—Chilton County ⊠ **CHILTON MEDICAL CENTER**, 1010 Lay Dam Road, Zip 35045–2306; tel. 205/755–2500 **A**1 9 10 **F**9 21 22 27 28 33 46 47 48 51 52 63 69 81 82 88 94 97 **S** Sunlink Healthcare, Atlanta, GA Primary Contact: Terry Frech, Chief Executive Officer Web address: www.sunlinkealth.com/chilton.html	33	10	60	762	8	41909	0	8530	3396	141
CULLMAN—Cullman County ⊠ **CULLMAN REGIONAL MEDICAL CENTER**, 1912 Alabama Highway 157, Zip 35055, Mailing Address: P.O. Box 1108, Zip 35056–1108; tel. 256/737–2000 **A**1 2 9 10 **F**2 6 9 10 11 12 15 21 22 26 27 28 29 33 36 37 40 41 46 47 48 49 51 55 57 58 59 60 61 62 63 64 65 66 69 73 79 81 82 84 87 88 93 94 95 96 98 108 109 110 Primary Contact: Barry S. Cochran, FACHE, President CFO: Kim Shrewsbury, Vice President Finance CMO: Bill Smith, M.D., Chief of Staff CHR: Jim Miller, Assistant Vice President Human Resources Web address: www.baptistmedical.org/cullman/	23	10	115	8466	80	126442	880	77649	29843	1001
□ **WOODLAND MEDICAL CENTER**, 1910 Cherokee Avenue S.W., Zip 35055–5502; tel. 256/739–3500 **A**1 9 10 **F**9 10 11 12 21 23 27 28 33 34 37 39 43 44 46 48 51 52 55 57 58 59 61 62 63 64 65 66 71 72 73 74 75 76 77 81 82 88 93 94 95 96 97 106 108 109 110 **P**6 **S** Community Health Systems, Inc., Brentwood, TN Primary Contact: David W. Fuller, Chief Executive Officer Web address: www.woodlandmedicalcenter.com	33	10	70	3143	32	27162	103	22879	8609	259
DADEVILLE—Tallapoosa County **LAKE MARTIN COMMUNITY HOSPITAL**, 201 Mariarden Road, Zip 36853–6251, Mailing Address: P.O. Box 629, Zip 36853–0629; tel. 256/825–7821 **A**9 10 **F**6 9 21 22 29 33 36 45 46 51 52 63 81 88 108 Primary Contact: Michael D. Bruce, Administrator	32	10	20	1642	11	4739	0	7900	2737	112

Hospital, Address, Telephone, Approval, Facility, and Physician Codes, Health Care System	Classi-fication Codes		Utilization Data					Expense (thousands) of dollars		
★ American Hospital Association (AHA) membership □ Joint Commission on Accreditation of Healthcare Organizations (JCAHO) accreditation ○ American Osteopathic Association (AOA) accreditation △ Commission on Accreditation of Rehabilitation Facilities (CARF) accreditation	Control	Service	Staffed Beds	Admissions	Census	Outpatient Visits	Births	Total	Payroll	Personnel

DAPHNE—Baldwin County

★ **MERCY MEDICAL**, 101 Villa Drive, Zip 36526–4653, Mailing Address: P.O. Box 1090, Zip 36526–1090; tel. 251/621–4200, (Total facility includes 137 beds in nursing home–type unit) **A**1 10 **F**5 8 9 10 21 22 26 27 28 29 36 37 38 44 45 51 52 54 58 68 69 91 92 94 96 108 110 **S** Catholic Health East, Newtown Square, PA Primary Contact: Mary Kay Polys, President and Chief Executive Officer CFO: Val Daniels, Vice President and Chief Financial Officer CMO: Alfred B. Chance, Jr, M.D., Chief Medical Director CIO: Andrew Wilhelm, Director Information Technology Services CHR: Harry Bishop, Director Human Resources Web address: www.mercymedical.com	21	46	162	1854	127	93194	0	40193	19106	567

DECATUR—Morgan County

★ **DECATUR GENERAL HOSPITAL**, 1201 Seventh Street S.E., Zip 35601–3303, Mailing Address: P.O. Box 2239, Zip 35609–2239; tel. 256/341–2000, (Includes DECATUR GENERAL HOSPITAL–WEST, 2205 Beltline Road S.W., Zip 35601–3687, Mailing Address: P.O. Box 2240, Zip 35609–2240; tel. 256/306–4000) **A**1 2 9 10 **F**2 9 10 11 12 14 15 17 19 21 23 27 28 33 41 44 46 47 48 49 53 55 56 58 59 60 61 63 64 65 66 69 71 72 73 74 75 76 77 81 82 84 85 87 88 93 94 96 106 108 109 110 **P**6 Primary Contact: James W. Hahn, Administrator CFO: David Cashio, Chief Financial Officer CMO: Randy Buckner, M.D., President of Medical Staff CIO: Mark Megehee, Vice President and Chief Information Officer CHR: Dean A. Griffin, Vice President Human Resources Web address: www.decaturgeneral.org	16	10	244	11843	136	199146	1613	80430	39503	1054
□ **NORTH ALABAMA REGIONAL HOSPITAL**, 4218 Highway 31 South, Zip 35603–5039; tel. 256/560–2200 **A**1 10 **F**26 27 28 71 74 94 108 **P**6 Primary Contact: Charles Cutts, Director	12	22	81	604	81	0	0	9765	5813	165
□ **PARKWAY MEDICAL CENTER**, 1874 Beltline Road S.W., Zip 35601–5509, Mailing Address: P.O. Box 2211, Zip 35609–2211; tel. 256/350–2211, (Nonreporting) **A**1 9 10 **S** Community Health Systems, Inc., Brentwood, TN Primary Contact: Tom R. McDougal, Jr, Chief Executive Officer	33	10	120	—	—	—	—	—	—	—

DEMOPOLIS—Marengo County

□ **BRYAN W. WHITFIELD MEMORIAL HOSPITAL**, 105 U.S. Highway 80 East, Zip 36732–3616, Mailing Address: P.O. Box 890, Zip 36732–0890; tel. 334/289–4000 **A**1 9 10 20 **F**1 2 6 9 10 11 12 21 22 23 24 26 27 28 29 33 39 41 46 47 48 51 52 53 55 58 59 61 62 63 64 65 69 70 81 82 84 87 88 94 95 96 97 98 108 110 Primary Contact: Michael D. Marshall, Administrator and Chief Executive Officer Web address: www.tombigbeehealth.com	16	10	99	3904	37	33795	322	—	—	285

DOTHAN—Houston County

★ **FLOWERS HOSPITAL**, 4370 West Main Street, Zip 36305–4000, Mailing Address: P.O. Box 6907, Zip 36302–6907; tel. 334/793–5000 **A**1 2 9 10 **F**2 6 10 11 12 14 15 17 19 21 23 26 28 29 33 34 37 39 40 44 46 47 48 49 50 52 55 57 58 59 60 61 62 63 64 65 66 69 70 79 81 82 84 85 87 88 93 94 96 98 106 108 109 110 **P**6 **S** Triad Hospitals, Inc., Plano, TX Primary Contact: Keith Granger, President and Chief Executive Officer CFO: Talana Bell, Chief Financial Officer Web address: www.flowershospital.com	33	10	235	13259	159	159447	1093	133339	45900	1176
★ **HEALTHSOUTH REHABILITATION HOSPITAL**, 1736 East Main Street, Zip 36301, Mailing Address: P.O. Box 6708, Zip 36302–6708; tel. 334/712–6333, (Nonreporting) **A**1 10 **S** HEALTHSOUTH Corporation, Birmingham, AL Primary Contact: Margaret Futch, Chief Operating Officer and Administrator COO: Margaret Futch, Chief Operating Officer and Administrator CFO: Dennis Farmer, Controller CMO: Edwin Morriss, III, Medical Director CHR: Jill Pittman, Regional Human Resources Director Web address: www.healthsouth.com	33	46	34	—	—	—	—	—	—	—
□ **LAUREL OAKS BEHAVIORAL CENTER**, 700 East Cottonwood Road, Zip 36301; tel. 334/794–7373 **A**1 10 **F**28 71 72 **S** Psychiatric Solutions, Franklin, TN Primary Contact: Robert Turner, M.D., Chief Executive Officer Web address: www.psysolutions.com	33	22	24	490	21	0	0	16832	5107	201
□ **LONG TERM HOSPITAL OF DOTHAN**, 1108 Ross Clark Circle, 4th Floor, Zip 36302; tel. 334/699–4300, (Nonreporting) **A**1 10 Primary Contact: Kaye Burke, Administrator	33	80	30	—	—	—	—	—	—	—
★ **SOUTHEAST ALABAMA MEDICAL CENTER**, 1108 Ross Clark Circle, Zip 36301–3024, Mailing Address: P.O. Box 6987, Zip 36302–6987; tel. 334/793–8111 **A**1 2 9 10 **F**11 12 14 15 17 19 21 22 23 28 29 33 34 37 40 45 46 47 48 49 51 52 53 55 57 58 59 60 61 62 63 65 66 69 71 74 77 78 79 81 82 84 86 87 88 93 94 96 108 109 **P**6 Primary Contact: Ronald S. Owen, Chief Executive Officer COO: Charles C. Brannen, Senior Vice President and Chief Operating Officer CFO: Derek Miller, Senior Vice President and Chief Financial Officer CMO: Wayne Hannah, M.D., JD, Vice President Medical Affairs CHR: Jim Treglown, Vice President Human Resources Web address: www.samc.org	16	10	337	20976	254	207184	1443	181133	79582	2020

Hospital, Address, Telephone, Approval, Facility, and Physician Codes, Health Care System	Classi-fication Codes		Utilization Data					Expense (thousands) of dollars		
★ American Hospital Association (AHA) membership □ Joint Commission on Accreditation of Healthcare Organizations (JCAHO) accreditation ○ American Osteopathic Association (AOA) accreditation △ Commission on Accreditation of Rehabilitation Facilities (CARF) accreditation	Control	Service	Staffed Beds	Admissions	Census	Outpatient Visits	Births	Total	Payroll	Personnel

ELBA—Coffee County

★ **ELBA GENERAL HOSPITAL**, 987 Drayton Street, Zip 36323–1494; tel. 334/897–2257, (Total facility includes 111 beds in nursing home–type unit) (Nonreporting) **A**9 10
Primary Contact: Ellen C. Briley, Administrator and Chief Executive Officer
CFO: Nicki Jinright, Chief Financial Officer
CMO: Lance K. Dyess, M.D., Chief Medical Officer
CHR: Judi Qualls, Director Human Resources

| | 16 | 10 | 131 | — | — | — | — | — | — | — |

ENTERPRISE—Coffee County

⊠ **MEDICAL CENTER ENTERPRISE**, 400 North Edwards Street, Zip 36330; tel. 334/347–0584 **A**1 9 10 **F**2 11 12 21 28 33 60 62 63 64 69 81 82 84 88 94 95 **S** Triad Hospitals, Inc., Plano, TX
Primary Contact: Jeffrey M. Brannon, Chief Executive Officer
CFO: Greg McGilvray, Chief Financial Officer
Web address: www.mcehospital.com

| | 33 | 10 | 117 | 5469 | 50 | 52990 | 851 | — | — | 348 |

EUFAULA—Barbour County

□ **LAKEVIEW COMMUNITY HOSPITAL**, 820 West Washington Street, Zip 36027–1899; tel. 334/687–5761, (Nonreporting) **A**1 9 10 20
Primary Contact: Steven Honeycutt, Chief Executive Officer
Web address: www.lakeviewcommunityhospital.com

| | 33 | 10 | 74 | — | — | — | — | — | — | — |

EUTAW—Greene County

GREENE COUNTY HOSPITAL, 509 Wilson Avenue, Zip 35462–1099; tel. 205/372–3388, (Nonreporting) **A**9 10
Primary Contact: Robert J. Coker, Jr, Administrator

| | 13 | 10 | 20 | — | — | — | — | — | — | — |

EVERGREEN—Conecuh County

EVERGREEN MEDICAL CENTER, 101 Crestview Avenue, Zip 36401–0706, Mailing Address: P.O. Box 706, Zip 36401–0706; tel. 251/578–2480 **A**9 10 **F**9 12 21 22 27 28 29 33 46 48 51 63 66 69 71 81 88 94 97 **S** Gilliard Health Services, Montgomery, AL
Primary Contact: L. E. Peace, III, Administrator
Web address: www.evergreenmedical.org

| | 33 | 10 | 42 | 3385 | 27 | 15471 | 0 | 12320 | 5460 | 169 |

FAIRHOPE—Baldwin County

⊠ **THOMAS HOSPITAL**, 750 Morphy Avenue, Zip 36532–1812, Mailing Address: P.O. Drawer 929, Zip 36533–0929; tel. 251/928–2375 **A**1 5 9 10 **F**2 4 9 11 12 14 15 17 19 21 22 23 26 27 28 29 31 33 41 42 46 47 48 49 51 52 53 55 57 58 59 60 61 62 63 65 66 69 73 74 75 77 78 79 81 82 84 85 88 93 94 96 109 110
Primary Contact: G. Owen Bailey, President and Chief Executive Officer
COO: Douglas Garner, Vice President
CFO: Philip L. Cusa, Senior Vice President and Chief Financial Officer
CMO: Michael McBrearty, M.D., Vice President Medical Affairs
Web address: www.thomashospital.com

| | 16 | 10 | 129 | 8753 | 93 | 82272 | 956 | 78506 | 33645 | 935 |

FAYETTE—Fayette County

□ **FAYETTE MEDICAL CENTER**, 1653 Temple Avenue North, Zip 35555–1314, Mailing Address: P.O. Drawer 710, Zip 35555–0710; tel. 205/932–5966, (Total facility includes 122 beds in nursing home–type unit) **A**1 9 10 **F**2 6 9 12 21 23 27 28 33 36 47 51 52 55 61 63 81 84 88 92 94 97 108 **S** DCH Health System, Tuscaloosa, AL
Primary Contact: Harold Reed, Administrator
Web address: www.dchsystem.com

| | 13 | 10 | 183 | 1906 | 140 | 43161 | 0 | 19500 | 10556 | 357 |

FLORALA—Covington County

FLORALA MEMORIAL HOSPITAL, 515 East Fifth Avenue, Zip 36442–0189, Mailing Address: P.O. Box 189, Zip 36442–0189; tel. 334/858–3287 **A**9 10 **F**33 81 88
Primary Contact: Blair W. Henson, Administrator

| | 33 | 10 | 23 | 672 | 4 | — | 0 | — | — | 40 |

FLORENCE—Lauderdale County

⊠ **ELIZA COFFEE MEMORIAL HOSPITAL**, 205 Marengo Street, Zip 35630–6033, Mailing Address: P.O. Box 818, Zip 35631–0818; tel. 256/768–9191 **A**1 9 10 **F**2 11 12 14 15 17 19 21 23 27 33 40 46 49 53 55 57 58 59 61 62 63 64 66 69 71 81 82 87 88 93 94 96 106 108 **S** Coffee Health Group, Florence, AL
Primary Contact: Carl W. Bailey, Administrator
CFO: Jody Pigg, Chief Financial Officer
Web address: www.chgroup.org

| | 16 | 10 | 322 | 15606 | 210 | 81621 | 961 | 117544 | 39334 | 1150 |

FOLEY—Baldwin County

□ **SOUTH BALDWIN REGIONAL MEDICAL CENTER**, 1613 North McKenzie Street, Zip 36535–2299; tel. 251/949–3400 **A**1 5 9 10 **F**9 11 12 15 21 33 37 46 48 51 55 58 59 60 62 63 66 69 81 82 84 88 94 96 108 109 **S** Community Health Systems, Inc., Brentwood, TN
Primary Contact: Stephen Pennington, Chief Executive Officer
Web address: www.southbaldwinrmc.com

| | 33 | 10 | 82 | 5808 | 63 | 67654 | 463 | — | — | 486 |

FORT PAYNE—DeKalb County

⊠ **BAPTIST DEKALB MEDICAL CENTER**, (Formerly DeKalb Baptist Medical Center), 200 Medical Center Drive, Zip 35968–3415, Mailing Address: P.O. Box 680778, Zip 35968–1608; tel. 256/845–3150 **A**1 9 10 20 **F**2 9 10 11 12 15 17 19 21 22 26 27 28 29 32 33 34 37 41 46 48 51 52 55 58 59 60 62 63 66 69 81 82 88 94 108 109 **S** Baptist Health System, Birmingham, AL
Primary Contact: J. Peter Selman, Chief Executive Officer
CFO: Beverly Haymon, Vice President Finance
CMO: Robert Raymond, M.D., President Medical Staff
CHR: Diane McMichen, Director Human Resources
Web address: www.bhsala.com

| | 21 | 10 | 103 | 4887 | 40 | 74511 | 862 | 36316 | 12082 | 324 |

Many Facility Codes have changed. Please refer to the AHA Guide Code Chart.

© 2005 AHA Guide

Hospital, Address, Telephone, Approval, Facility, and Physician Codes, Health Care System	Classi-fication Codes		Utilization Data					Expense (thousands) of dollars		
★ American Hospital Association (AHA) membership □ Joint Commission on Accreditation of Healthcare Organizations (JCAHO) accreditation ○ American Osteopathic Association (AOA) accreditation △ Commission on Accreditation of Rehabilitation Facilities (CARF) accreditation	Control	Service	Staffed Beds	Admissions	Census	Outpatient Visits	Births	Total	Payroll	Personnel

FORT RUCKER—Coffee County

★ **LYSTER U. S. ARMY COMMUNITY HOSPITAL**, U.S. Army Aeromedical Center, Zip 36362–5333; tel. 334/255–7361, (Nonreporting) **A**9 **S** Department of the Army, Office of the Surgeon General, Falls Church, VA
Primary Contact: Colonel Suzan Denny, Commanding Officer
CMO: Colonel Steven Swann, Deputy Commander for Clinical Services
CIO: Captain Eric McClung, Chief Information Management Division
Web address: www.rucker.amedd.army.mil

| | 42 | 10 | 37 | — | — | — | — | — | — | — |

GADSDEN—Etowah County

⊞ **GADSDEN REGIONAL MEDICAL CENTER**, 1007 Goodyear Avenue, Zip 35903–1195; tel. 256/494–4000 **A**1 2 9 10 **F**9 11 12 14 15 17 19 21 22 23 24 26 28 33 34 36 40 44 46 47 48 49 51 52 53 55 57 59 60 61 62 63 64 69 70 71 75 76 79 80 81 82 84 85 88 93 94 96 108 109 **P**6 7 **S** Triad Hospitals, Inc., Plano, TX
Primary Contact: Douglas P. DeGraaf, Chief Executive Officer
COO: Tom Moore, Chief Operating Officer
CFO: Joseph F. Kerr, Chief Financial Officer
CMO: James R. Phillips, M.D., Chief of Staff
CIO: Glenn Phillips, Director Information Systems
CHR: Gale H. Sanders, Director
Web address: www.gadsdenregional.com

| | 33 | 10 | 259 | 13286 | 188 | 97640 | 1294 | 112589 | 38430 | 1043 |

⊞ **HEALTHSOUTH REHABILITATION OF GADSDEN**, 801 Goodyear Avenue, Zip 35903; tel. 256/439–5000, (Nonreporting) **A**1 10 **S** HEALTHSOUTH Corporation, Birmingham, AL
Primary Contact: Michael W. Thompson, Administrator

| | 33 | 46 | 40 | — | — | — | — | — | — | — |

□ **MOUNTAIN VIEW HOSPITAL**, 3001 Scenic Highway, Zip 35901–9956, Mailing Address: P.O. Box 8406, Zip 35902–8406; tel. 256/546–9265 **A**1 10 **F**1 26 27 28 42 52 71 72 75 77 78 92 **P**6
Primary Contact: John A. Romano, Chief Executive Officer
Web address: www.mtnviewhospital.com

| | 33 | 22 | 68 | 1288 | 39 | 22043 | 0 | 9675 | 5777 | 216 |

□ **RIVERVIEW REGIONAL MEDICAL CENTER**, 600 South Third Street, Zip 35901–5399, Mailing Address: P.O. Box 268, Zip 35999–0268; tel. 256/543–5200, (Nonreporting) **A**1 9 10 **S** Health Management Associates, Naples, FL
Primary Contact: J. Matthew Hayes, Executive Director
Web address: www.riverviewregional.com

| | 33 | 10 | 281 | — | — | — | — | — | — | — |

GENEVA—Geneva County

⊞ **WIREGRASS MEDICAL CENTER**, 1200 West Maple Avenue, Zip 36340–1694; tel. 334/684–3655, (Total facility includes 96 beds in nursing home–type unit) **A**1 9 10 **F**9 12 21 28 33 46 52 55 63 69 81 88 92 94
Primary Contact: Al W. Allred, Chief Executive Officer
COO: Greg Dykes, Chief Operating Officer
CFO: Tina Segers, Accounting Officer
CIO: Tom Garske, Director Information Systems
Web address: www.alaweb.com/~tgarske

| | 16 | 10 | 161 | 2202 | 116 | 25399 | 0 | 16634 | 8308 | 245 |

GEORGIANA—Butler County

GEORGIANA HOSPITAL, 515 Miranda Street, Zip 36033, Mailing Address: P.O. Box 548, Zip 36033–0548; tel. 334/376–2205 **A**9 10 **F**33 51 52 81 88 94
Primary Contact: Harry Cole, Jr, Administrator

| | 32 | 10 | 28 | 1046 | 7 | — | 0 | — | — | — |

GREENSBORO—Hale County

HALE COUNTY HOSPITAL, 508 Green Street, Zip 36744–0017, Mailing Address: P.O. Box 17, Zip 36744–0017; tel. 334/624–3024, (Nonreporting) **A**9 10
Primary Contact: Richard M. McGill, Administrator

| | 13 | 10 | 39 | — | — | — | — | — | — | — |

GREENVILLE—Butler County

□ **L. V. STABLER MEMORIAL HOSPITAL**, 29 L. V. Stabler Drive, Zip 36037–3800; tel. 334/382–2671, (Nonreporting) **A**1 9 10 **S** Community Health Systems, Inc., Brentwood, TN
Primary Contact: Daniel L. Perryman, Chief Executive Officer
Web address: www.lvstabler.com

| | 33 | 10 | 72 | — | — | — | — | — | — | — |

GROVE HILL—Clarke County

★ **GROVE HILL MEMORIAL HOSPITAL**, 295 South Jackson Street, Zip 36451–0935, Mailing Address: P.O. Box 935, Zip 36451–0935; tel. 251/275–3191 **A**9 10 **F**26 27 28 59 71 76 92
Primary Contact: Hybart D. Sewell, Administrator
CFO: Elaine Averett, Chief Financial Officer
CMO: Ralph D. Neal, Jr., M.D., Chief Medical Staff
CIO: Judy Payne, Health Information Officer

| | 14 | 10 | 41 | 1569 | 14 | 20353 | 117 | — | — | 128 |

GUNTERSVILLE—Marshall County

⊞ **MARSHALL MEDICAL CENTER NORTH**, 8000 Alabama Highway 69, Zip 35976; tel. 256/753–8000 **A**1 9 10 **F**6 9 11 12 21 26 27 28 29 30 33 34 40 41 46 48 51 55 57 58 59 60 62 63 66 69 71 73 74 75 76 81 82 84 87 88 94 95 108 **S** Marshall County Health Care Authority, Guntersville, AL
Primary Contact: Cheryl M. Hays, FACHE, Administrator
COO: Cheryl M. Hays, FACHE, Administrator
CFO: Kathy Nelson, Chief Financial Officer
CIO: Billy Herrin, Information Technology Director
CHR: Jeff Stone, Director Human Resources
Web address: www.mmcenters.com

| | 16 | 10 | 90 | 4997 | 59 | 180487 | 474 | 46580 | 15292 | — |

Hospital, Address, Telephone, Approval, Facility, and Physician Codes, Health Care System	Classi-fication Codes		Utilization Data					Expense (thousands) of dollars		
★ American Hospital Association (AHA) membership □ Joint Commission on Accreditation of Healthcare Organizations (JCAHO) accreditation ○ American Osteopathic Association (AOA) accreditation △ Commission on Accreditation of Rehabilitation Facilities (CARF) accreditation	Control	Service	Staffed Beds	Admissions	Census	Outpatient Visits	Births	Total	Payroll	Personnel
HALEYVILLE—Winston County										
⊠ **LAKELAND COMMUNITY HOSPITAL**, Highway 195 East, Zip 35565–9536, Mailing Address: P.O. Box 780, Zip 35565–0780; tel. 205/486–5213 **A**1 9 10 20 **F**2 12 21 26 28 33 37 46 51 55 58 63 64 65 69 78 81 82 88 93 94 95 97 **S** LifePoint Hospitals, Inc., Brentwood, TN Primary Contact: Wes Sigler, Administrator Web address: www.lifepointhospitals.com	33	10	42	2279	20	11339	—	10865	5266	136
HAMILTON—Marion County										
⊠ **NORTH MISSISSIPPI MEDICAL CENTER–HAMILTON**, 1256 Military Street South, Zip 35570–5001; tel. 205/921–6200, (Total facility includes 79 beds in nursing home–type unit) **A**1 9 10 **F**2 9 12 21 22 26 27 28 29 33 41 46 47 48 51 52 60 63 65 66 69 81 82 84 88 92 94 95 96 97 106 108 **S** North Mississippi Health Services, Inc., Tupelo, MS Primary Contact: Donald J. Jones, Administrator Web address: www.nmhs.net	23	10	111	1599	86	15728	0	16002	6866	217
HARTSELLE—Morgan County										
□ **HARTSELLE MEDICAL CENTER**, 201 Pine Street N.W., Zip 35640–2309, Mailing Address: P.O. Box 969, Zip 35640–0969; tel. 256/773–6511 **A**1 9 10 **F**2 12 21 22 26 27 28 29 33 44 46 55 58 60 62 63 69 71 76 81 84 88 108 **S** Community Health Systems, Inc., Brentwood, TN Primary Contact: David R. Jones, Chief Executive Officer Web address: www.hartsellemedicalcenter.com	33	10	119	1948	24	16875	0	14605	5663	150
HUNTSVILLE—Madison County										
⊠ **CRESTWOOD MEDICAL CENTER**, One Hospital Drive, Zip 35801–3403; tel. 256/882–3100 **A**1 9 10 11 12 15 17 21 22 23 33 36 37 40 44 46 47 48 49 52 53 55 57 58 59 61 62 63 64 65 66 69 70 71 73 74 75 76 77 81 82 84 85 88 93 94 95 96 106 108 109 **S** Triad Hospitals, Inc., Plano, TX Primary Contact: Bradley E. Jones, Chief Executive Officer COO: Pamela Hudson, M.D., Chief Operating Officer CFO: Donald E. Hagan, Chief Financial Officer CIO: Arthur Kirshner, Director Information System Web address: www.crestwoodmedcenter.com	33	10	120	7736	87	58936	552	89636	31488	734
⊠ **HEALTHSOUTH REHABILITATION HOSPITAL OF NORTH ALABAMA**, 107 Governors Drive S.W., Zip 35801–4329; tel. 256/535–2300, (Nonreporting) **A**1 10 **S** HEALTHSOUTH Corporation, Birmingham, AL Primary Contact: Douglas H. Beverly, CHE, Administrator Web address: www.healthsouth.com	33	46	50	—	—	—	—	—		
□ **HUNTSVILLE HOSPITAL**, 101 Sivley Road, Zip 35801–4470; tel. 256/265–1000, (Includes HUNTSVILLE HOSPITAL FOR WOMEN AND CHILDREN, 911 Big Cove Road S.E., Zip 35801–3784) **A**1 2 3 5 9 10 **F**4 6 10 11 12 14 15 16 17 18 19 20 21 22 23 26 27 28 29 31 32 33 34 37 40 41 42 43 44 46 49 52 55 56 57 59 61 62 63 67 68 69 71 72 73 74 75 76 77 78 79 81 82 83 84 85 86 87 88 93 95 107 108 109 110 Primary Contact: L. Joe Austin, Chief Executive Officer Web address: www.huntsvillehospital.org	16	10	715	40822	548	526509	3974	—	—	4137
JACKSON—Clarke County										
JACKSON MEDICAL CENTER, 220 Hospital Drive, Zip 36545–2459, Mailing Address: P.O. Box 428, Zip 36545–0428; tel. 251/246–9021, (Nonreporting) **A**9 10 **S** Gilliard Health Services, Montgomery, AL Primary Contact: Teresa F. Grimes, Administrator Web address: www.jacksonmedicalcenter.com	33	10	26	—	—	—	—	—		
JACKSONVILLE—Calhoun County										
⊠ **JACKSONVILLE MEDICAL CENTER**, 1701 Pelham Road South, Zip 36265–3399, Mailing Address: P.O. Box 999, Zip 36265–0999; tel. 256/435–4970 **A**1 9 10 **F**2 11 12 21 22 26 28 29 33 46 48 53 54 55 58 59 63 66 69 81 84 93 108 109 **S** Triad Hospitals, Inc., Plano, TX Primary Contact: Roger Collins, Chief Executive Officer COO: Jean Ann McMurray, R.N., Chief Nursing Officer CFO: Robbin Curlee, Chief Financial Officer CMO: Russell Ulrich, D.O., Chief of Staff CIO: Richard Maust, Chief Information Officer CHR: Amy Martin, Human Resources Director Web address: www.jmcfirst.com	33	10	56	1918	16	—	—	19497	6984	—
JASPER—Walker County										
⊠ **WALKER BAPTIST MEDICAL CENTER**, 3400 Highway 78 East, Zip 35501–8956, Mailing Address: P.O. Box 3547, Zip 35502–3547; tel. 205/387–4000 **A**1 9 10 20 **F**9 10 11 12 15 21 27 28 29 33 34 46 47 48 51 52 55 58 59 60 63 65 66 69 70 71 73 74 76 77 78 81 82 84 86 88 92 93 94 108 **S** Baptist Health System, Birmingham, AL Primary Contact: Joel W. Tate, FACHE, President CFO: Lee Stephens, Vice President Finance CIO: Kenny Horton, Director Information Systems CHR: Pat Morrow, Director Human Resources Web address: www.bhsala.com	23	10	195	9401	93	236920	646	65132	21949	570
LUVERNE—Crenshaw County										
CRENSHAW COMMUNITY HOSPITAL, 101 Hospital Circle, Zip 36049–7317; tel. 334/335–3374 **A**9 10 **F**2 3 9 11 12 21 22 31 33 41 45 49 52 59 62 63 69 70 71 73 74 75 76 81 88 107 110 Primary Contact: Allen J. Gamble, Administrator	33	10	65	1601	12	10207	163	—	—	169

Many Facility Codes have changed. Please refer to the AHA Guide Code Chart.

© 2005 AHA Guide

Hospital, Address, Telephone, Approval, Facility, and Physician Codes, Health Care System	Classi-fication Codes		Utilization Data					Expense (thousands) of dollars		
★ American Hospital Association (AHA) membership □ Joint Commission on Accreditation of Healthcare Organizations (JCAHO) accreditation ○ American Osteopathic Association (AOA) accreditation △ Commission on Accreditation of Rehabilitation Facilities (CARF) accreditation	Control	Service	Staffed Beds	Admissions	Census	Outpatient Visits	Births	Total	Payroll	Personnel

MADISON—Madison County

BRADFORD HEALTH SERVICES AT HUNTSVILLE, 1600 Browns Ferry Road, Zip 35758–9769, Mailing Address: P.O. Box 176, Zip 35758–0176; tel. 256/461–7272, (Nonreporting) **S** Bradford Health Services, Birmingham, AL
Primary Contact: Bob Hinds, Executive Director
Web address: www.bradfordhealth.com
— Control 33, Service 82, Staffed Beds 84

MOBILE—Mobile County

□ △ **MOBILE INFIRMARY MEDICAL CENTER**, 5 Mobile Infirmary Drive North, Zip 36607–3513, Mailing Address: P.O. Box 2144, Zip 36652–2144; tel. 251/435–2400, (Includes ROTARY REHABILITATION HOSPITAL), (Nonreporting) **A**1 2 3 5 7 9 10 **S** Gulf Health Hospitals, Mobile, AL
Primary Contact: E. Chandler Bramlett, Jr, President and Chief Executive Officer
Web address: www.mobileinfirmary.org
— Control 23, Service 10, Staffed Beds 704

★ **PROVIDENCE HOSPITAL**, 6801 Airport Boulevard, Zip 36608–3785, Mailing Address: P.O. Box 850429, Zip 36685–0429; tel. 251/633–1000 **A**1 2 9 10 **F**9 11 12 14 15 19 21 22 24 27 28 29 30 31 33 35 37 39 40 41 42 46 48 49 50 52 53 55 57 58 59 60 62 63 65 66 69 75 81 82 84 85 88 93 94 95 96 106 108 110 **P**5 6 7 **S** Ascension Health, Saint Louis, MO
Primary Contact: Clark P. Christianson, President and Chief Executive Officer
COO: Cheryl Y. Ward, Executive Vice President and Chief Operating Officer
CFO: Vince N. Formica, Senior Vice President Finance and Chief Financial Officer
CMO: William M. Lightfoot, M.D., Vice President Medical Services
CIO: Cynthia Hyde, Director Information Systems
CHR: David G. Powell, Vice President Human Resources
Web address: www.providencehospital.org
ROTARY REHABILITATION HOSPITAL See Mobile Infirmary Medical Center
Control 21, Service 10, Staffed Beds 349, Admissions 16625, Census 214, Outpatient Visits 112230, Births 1364, Total 161420, Payroll 56930, Personnel 1610

□ **SPRINGHILL MEMORIAL HOSPITAL**, 3719 Dauphin Street, Zip 36608–1798, Mailing Address: P.O. Box 8246, Zip 36608–8246; tel. 251/344–9630 **A**1 2 5 9 10 12 13 **F**9 11 12 14 15 17 19 21 23 33 37 40 46 47 55 57 58 59 60 61 62 63 64 65 66 67 69 81 84 87 88 93 94 96 108 109 110
Primary Contact: Bill A. Mason, President and Chief Executive Officer
Web address: www.springhillmemorial.com
Control 33, Service 10, Staffed Beds 206, Admissions 13027, Census 168, Outpatient Visits 118171, Births 1201, Total 112629, Payroll 40479, Personnel 1261

★ **UNIVERSITY OF SOUTH ALABAMA KNOLLWOOD PARK HOSPITAL**, 5600 Girby Road, Zip 36693–3398; tel. 251/660–5120 **A**1 3 5 9 10 **F**9 12 21 23 33 37 49 52 53 55 57 61 62 63 66 81 84 86 88 93 94 95 108 109 **S** University of South Alabama Hospitals, Mobile, AL
Primary Contact: Thomas J. Gibson, Administrator
CFO: William B. Bush, Assistant Administrator Finance
CHR: Janice Rehm, Human Resources Manager
Web address: www.southalabama.edu/usakph/index.html
Control 12, Service 10, Staffed Beds 88, Admissions 3310, Census 72, Outpatient Visits 48221, Births 0, Total 46831, Payroll 21026, Personnel 533

★ **UNIVERSITY OF SOUTH ALABAMA MEDICAL CENTER**, 2451 Fillingim Street, Zip 36617–2293; tel. 251/471–7000 **A**1 2 3 5 8 9 10 **F**6 9 10 13 15 19 21 33 34 45 49 50 52 53 55 57 61 62 63 66 81 82 84 88 94 101 108 110 **S** University of South Alabama Hospitals, Mobile, AL
Primary Contact: Beth Anderson, Administrator
COO: Elizabeth Ramsey, Chief Operating Officer
CFO: William B. Bush, Assistant Administrator Finance
CIO: Susan Ankersen, Manager Information Services
Web address: www.usahospitals.org
Control 12, Service 10, Staffed Beds 112, Admissions 5898, Census 101, Outpatient Visits 55856, Births 0, Total 98160, Payroll 51679, Personnel 1119

★ **USA CHILDREN'S AND WOMEN'S HOSPITAL**, 1700 Center Street, Zip 36604–3301; tel. 251/415–1000 **A**1 3 5 10 **F**6 9 11 12 21 23 33 45 52 53 56 57 58 59 61 62 63 66 67 69 81 88 89 90 94 108 109 **S** University of South Alabama Hospitals, Mobile, AL
Primary Contact: Becky DeVillier, Administrator
CFO: William B. Bush, Assistant Administrator Finance
CMO: Richard Teplick, M.D., Chief of Staff
CIO: Susan Ankersen, Manager Information Services
CHR: Pamela Henderson, Assistant Vice President
Web address: www.southalabama.edu/usacwh
Control 12, Service 44, Staffed Beds 185, Admissions 7366, Census 150, Outpatient Visits 64306, Births 2612, Total 77197, Payroll 33918, Personnel 815

MONROEVILLE—Monroe County

★ **MONROE COUNTY HOSPITAL**, 1901 South Alabama Avenue, Zip 36460, Mailing Address: P.O. Box 886, Zip 36461–0886; tel. 251/575–3111 **A**1 9 10 20 **F**2 9 12 21 22 23 27 28 29 33 46 48 51 55 58 59 61 62 63 66 69 81 82 84 88 94 95 96 108 109 110 **P**3 **S** Quorum Health Resources, Plano, TX
Primary Contact: Chris Johns, Chief Executive Officer
CFO: Nellie Chunn, Chief Financial Officer
CMO: Burt Baroughs, Chief of Staff
CHR: Tara Nowlins, Director of Human Resources
Web address: www.mchcare.com
Control 13, Service 10, Staffed Beds 62, Admissions 3050, Census 28, Outpatient Visits 49822, Births 266, Total 16365, Payroll 9117, Personnel 273

MONTGOMERY—Montgomery County

★ **BAPTIST MEDICAL CENTER EAST**, 400 Taylor Road, Zip 36117–3512, Mailing Address: P.O. Box 241267, Zip 36124–1267; tel. 334/277–8330, (Nonreporting) **A**1 9 10 **S** Baptist Health, Montgomery, AL
Primary Contact: Mindy Burdick, Administrator
COO: Robin Barca, Senior Vice President and Chief Operating Officer
CFO: Guy J. LaPrad, Interim Chief Financial Officer
CIO: Jim Chesney, Chief Information Officer
CHR: Kay Foss, System Director Human Resources
Web address: www.baptistfirst.org
— Control 23, Service 10, Staffed Beds 138

Hospital, Address, Telephone, Approval, Facility, and Physician Codes, Health Care System	Classi- fication Codes		Utilization Data					Expense (thousands) of dollars		
★ American Hospital Association (AHA) membership □ Joint Commission on Accreditation of Healthcare Organizations (JCAHO) accreditation ○ American Osteopathic Association (AOA) accreditation △ Commission on Accreditation of Rehabilitation Facilities (CARF) accreditation	Control	Service	Staffed Beds	Admissions	Census	Outpatient Visits	Births	Total	Payroll	Personnel
✠ **BAPTIST MEDICAL CENTER SOUTH**, 2105 East South Boulevard, Zip 36116–2498, Mailing Address: Box 11010, Zip 36111–0010; tel. 334/288–2100 **A**1 3 5 9 10 **F**4 9 11 12 14 15 21 24 29 33 36 37 40 41 42 44 46 47 48 51 52 55 56 59 60 61 62 63 65 66 69 70 71 74 75 77 78 81 82 84 88 89 91 94 95 107 108 109 **S** Baptist Health, Montgomery, AL Primary Contact: Lynne Parker, Administrator COO: Robin Barca, Senior Vice President and Chief Operating Officer CFO: Joe Denton, Chief Financial Officer CIO: Jim Chesney, Chief Information Officer CHR: Kay Foss, System Director Human Resources Web address: www.baptistfirst.org	23	10	342	20436	244	—	—	—	—	1528
✠ **CENTRAL ALABAMA VETERANS HEALTH CARE SYSTEM**, 215 Perry Hill Road, Zip 36109–3798; tel. 334/272–4670, (Includes MONTGOMERY DIVISION; TUSKEGEE DIVISION, 2400 Hospital Road, Tuskegee, Zip 36083–5001; tel. 334/727–0550), (Total facility includes 160 beds in nursing home–type unit) **A**1 3 5 **F**4 10 12 21 22 27 28 29 30 31 32 35 36 37 38 39 42 44 45 46 47 48 50 51 52 54 55 57 58 60 61 62 63 65 66 68 69 70 71 73 74 76 77 81 82 88 92 93 94 96 106 107 108 109 110 **S** Department of Veterans Affairs, Washington, DC Primary Contact: N. Rao Chava, M.D., Director CFO: Brenda Schmitz, Financial Manager CMO: N Rao Chava, M.D., Chief of Staff CIO: William Greer, Acting Chief Information Officer CHR: Linda King, Chief Human Resources Management Service Web address: www.va.gov/sta/guide/home.asp	45	10	270	3062	60	303754	0	—	—	1473
□ **GREIL MEMORIAL PSYCHIATRIC HOSPITAL**, 2140 Upper Wetumpka Road, Zip 36107; tel. 334/262–0363, (Nonreporting) **A**1 10 Primary Contact: Susan Chambers, Administrator	33	22	25	—	—	—	—	—	—	—
✠ **HEALTHSOUTH REHABILITATION HOSPITAL OF MONTGOMERY**, 4465 Narrow Lane Road, Zip 36116–2900; tel. 334/284–7700 **A**1 10 **F**7 21 27 28 42 44 45 46 48 52 58 60 65 68 69 94 95 96 108 110 **P**5 **S** HEALTHSOUTH Corporation, Birmingham, AL Primary Contact: Linda Wade, Administrator CFO: Heath Watson, Controller CMO: Jeffrey Eng, M.D., Medical Director CIO: Diane Davis, Business Office Manager CHR: Keri Curtis, Director Human Resources Web address: www.healthsouth.com	33	46	80	1500	68	7589	0	14341	7805	229
✠ **JACKSON HOSPITAL AND CLINIC**, 1725 Pine Street, Zip 36106–1117; tel. 334/293–8000, (Nonreporting) **A**1 2 9 10 Primary Contact: Donald G. Henderson, President and Chief Executive Officer CFO: Edward C. Scholl, Assistant Administrator Finance CIO: Richard E. Caldwell, Chief Information Officer CHR: Peggy Benson, Assistant Administrator Human Resources Web address: www.jackson.org	23	10	281	—	—	—	—	—	—	—
✠ **LONG TERM HOSPITAL OF MONTGOMERY**, (Formerly Long Term Care Hospital at Jackson), 1725 Pine Street, 5 North, Zip 36106–1109, Mailing Address: P.O. Box 11649, Zip 36111–1649; tel. 334/240–0532, (Nonreporting) **A**1 10 Primary Contact: Lewis A. Ransdell, Administrator Web address: www.nolandhealth.com	23	80	36	—	—	—	—	—	—	—
MONTGOMERY DIVISION See Central Alabama Veterans Health Care System										
MOULTON—Lawrence County										
✠ **LAWRENCE MEDICAL CENTER**, (Formerly Lawrence Baptist Medical Center), 202 Hospital Street, Zip 35650, Mailing Address: P.O. Box 39, Zip 35650–0039; tel. 256/974–2200 **A**1 9 10 **F**2 11 22 27 33 51 55 63 69 81 82 87 88 **P**6 Primary Contact: Barry L. Keel, Administrator CFO: Danny Crowe, Chief Financial Officer CIO: Jeremy Duncan, Director of Information Systems	16	10	37	1754	27	—	0	—	—	151
MOUNT VERNON—Mobile County										
□ **SEARCY HOSPITAL**, Mailing Address: P.O. Box 1090, Zip 36560–1090; tel. 251/829–9411 **A**1 10 **F**26 66 71 74 76 94 Primary Contact: Beatrice J. McLean, Facility Director	12	22	261	502	261	—	0	—	—	524
MUSCLE SHOALS—Colbert County										
✠ **SHOALS HOSPITAL**, 201 Avalon Avenue, Zip 35661–2805, Mailing Address: P.O. Box 3359, Zip 35662–3359; tel. 256/386–1600 **A**1 9 10 **F**2 12 15 21 27 28 33 37 40 46 53 55 58 60 61 62 63 64 66 68 81 82 84 85 86 87 88 93 94 108 **S** Coffee Health Group, Florence, AL Primary Contact: Jody Pigg, Interim Administrator Web address: www.chgroup.org	14	10	100	3006	39	26973	0	27408	9934	269
NORTHPORT—Tuscaloosa County										
□ **NORTHPORT MEDICAL CENTER**, (Formerly Northport Hospital–DCH), 2700 Hospital Drive, Zip 35476–1079, Mailing Address: P.O. Box 1079, Zip 35476–1079; tel. 205/333–4500 **A**1 9 10 **F**2 9 11 12 21 22 26 27 28 29 33 37 46 47 48 50 52 53 55 56 57 58 59 62 63 65 66 68 69 71 73 74 75 76 77 81 82 84 85 88 94 95 96 106 108 109 110 **P**7 8 **S** DCH Health System, Tuscaloosa, AL Primary Contact: Charles L. Stewart, Administrator Web address: www.dchsystem.com	16	10	196	9304	152	99149	1399	66264	31371	687

Many Facility Codes have changed. Please refer to the AHA Guide Code Chart.

© 2005 AHA Guide

Hospital, Address, Telephone, Approval, Facility, and Physician Codes, Health Care System	Classi-fication Codes		Utilization Data					Expense (thousands) of dollars		
★ American Hospital Association (AHA) membership □ Joint Commission on Accreditation of Healthcare Organizations (JCAHO) accreditation ○ American Osteopathic Association (AOA) accreditation △ Commission on Accreditation of Rehabilitation Facilities (CARF) accreditation	Control	Service	Staffed Beds	Admissions	Census	Outpatient Visits	Births	Total	Payroll	Personnel

ONEONTA—Blount County

| ✠ **MEDICAL CENTER BLOUNT**, (Formerly Blount Memorial Hospital), 150 Gilbreath, Zip 35121–2534, Mailing Address: P.O. Box 1000, Zip 35121–1000; tel. 205/274–3000 **A**1 9 10 **F**9 12 27 28 33 46 51 52 55 58 60 61 62 63 81 88 94 108 109 **S** Eastern Health System, Inc., Birmingham, AL
Primary Contact: Jacki W. Phillips, CHE, Chief Executive Officer
Web address: www.medicalcenterblount.com | 23 | 10 | 40 | 1713 | 20 | 24372 | 0 | 17516 | 6136 | 172 |

OPELIKA—Lee County

| ✠ **EAST ALABAMA MEDICAL CENTER**, 2000 Pepperell Parkway, Zip 36802–3201; tel. 334/749–3411, (Total facility includes 38 beds in nursing home–type unit) (Nonreporting) **A**1 2 9 10 19
Primary Contact: Terry W. Andrus, President
CFO: Sam Price, Vice President Finance
CIO: Tommy Chittom, Assistant Vice President Information Services
Web address: www.eamc.org | 16 | 10 | 284 | — | — | — | — | — | — | — |

OPP—Covington County

| ★ **MIZELL MEMORIAL HOSPITAL**, 702 Main Street, Zip 36467–1626, Mailing Address: P.O. Box 1010, Zip 36467–1010; tel. 334/493–3541 **A**9 10 **F**9 11 12 14 21 22 27 28 29 33 37 41 46 48 50 51 59 62 63 66 69 81 82 84 85 87 88 93 94 95 97 106 108 109 110
Primary Contact: Allen Foster, Chief Executive Officer
CFO: Jana Wyatt, Chief Financial Officer
CMO: Wheeler Gunnels, M.D., Medical Director
CIO: Elizabeth Cook, Chief Information Officer
Web address: www.mizellmh.com | 23 | 10 | 57 | 2731 | 29 | 25262 | 132 | 10495 | 5862 | 245 |

OZARK—Dale County

| **DALE MEDICAL CENTER**, 100 Hospital Avenue, Zip 36360–2080; tel. 334/774–2601 **A**9 10 **F**9 11 12 15 21 26 27 28 33 41 42 46 47 48 51 52 55 58 59 60 63 65 71 76 81 82 84 87 88 107 109
Primary Contact: Vernon Johnson, Administrator
Web address: www.dalemedical.org | 13 | 10 | 69 | 2957 | 31 | 45276 | 85 | 22829 | 11958 | 335 |

PELL CITY—St. Clair County

| ★ **ST. CLAIR REGIONAL HOSPITAL**, 2805 Doctor John Haynes Drive, Zip 35125–1499; tel. 205/338–3301 **A**9 10 **F**2 9 12 21 23 27 28 33 39 45 46 47 48 51 52 53 57 60 61 62 63 65 66 69 81 84 85 88 94 106 108 110 **S** Eastern Health System, Inc., Birmingham, AL
Primary Contact: Terrell Vick, Chief Executive Officer
CIO: Susan Evans, Director Health Information Services
Web address: www.stclairregional.com | 23 | 10 | 40 | 1642 | 18 | — | 0 | — | — | 233 |

PHENIX CITY—Russell County

| ✠ **REGIONAL REHABILITATION HOSPITAL**, 3715 Highway 280, Zip 36869; tel. 334/732–2200 **A**1 10 **F**26 27 28 68 **P**5 **S** HEALTHSOUTH Corporation, Birmingham, AL
Primary Contact: Jill Jordan, Administrator
CFO: Bobby Edmondson, Accounting Supervisor
CMO: Debra Schilling, M.D., Medical Director
CIO: Penelope Russell, Director of Health Information Services
CHR: Debra Blanks, Human Resources Manager
Web address: www.healthsouth.com | 33 | 46 | 38 | 723 | 30 | 3243 | 0 | 7014 | 4042 | 133 |

PRATTVILLE—Autauga County

| ✠ **PRATTVILLE BAPTIST HOSPITAL**, 124 South Memorial Drive, Zip 36067–3619, Mailing Address: P.O. Box 681630, Zip 36067–1638; tel. 334/365–0651, (Nonreporting) **A**1 9 10 **S** Baptist Health, Montgomery, AL
Primary Contact: Ginger Irsik, Administrator
CIO: B Blaine Brown, General Counsel
Web address: www.baptistfirst.org | 23 | 10 | 47 | — | — | — | — | — | — | — |

RED BAY—Franklin County

| **RED BAY HOSPITAL**, 211 Hospital Road, Zip 35582–0490, Mailing Address: P.O. Box 490, Zip 35582–0490; tel. 256/356–9532 **A**9 10 20 **F**12 27 28 33 41 46 48 51 52 63 69 81 88 95 97 106 108
Primary Contact: Mike Holway, Administrator
Web address: www.helenkeller.com | 16 | 10 | 25 | 864 | 11 | — | 0 | — | — | 121 |

ROANOKE—Randolph County

| **RANDOLPH MEDICAL CENTER**, 59928 Highway 22, Zip 36274–2410, Mailing Address: P.O. Box 670, Zip 36274–0670; tel. 334/863–4111, (Nonreporting) **A**9 10 **S** Gilliard Health Services, Montgomery, AL
Primary Contact: John L. Robertson, Chief Executive Officer
Web address: www.randolphmedicalcenter.com | 13 | 10 | 40 | — | — | — | — | — | — | — |

RUSSELLVILLE—Franklin County

| ✠ **RUSSELLVILLE HOSPITAL**, (Formerly Russellville Medical Center), 15155 Highway 43, Zip 35653–1975, Mailing Address: P.O. Box 1089, Zip 35653–1089; tel. 256/332–1611, (Nonreporting) **A**1 9 10 **S** LifePoint Hospitals, Inc., Brentwood, TN
Primary Contact: Christine R. Stewart, Administrator
Web address: www.chgroup.org | 33 | 10 | 100 | — | — | — | — | — | — | — |

SCOTTSBORO—Jackson County

| □ **JACKSON COUNTY HOSPITAL**, 380 Woods Cove Road, Zip 35768–2428, Mailing Address: P.O. Box 1050, Zip 35768–1050; tel. 256/259–4444, (Nonreporting) **A**1 9 10 20
Primary Contact: Thomas O. Lackey, Chief Executive Officer | 13 | 10 | 85 | — | — | — | — | — | — | — |

Hospital, Address, Telephone, Approval, Facility, and Physician Codes, Health Care System	Classi-fication Codes		Utilization Data					Expense (thousands) of dollars		
★ American Hospital Association (AHA) membership □ Joint Commission on Accreditation of Healthcare Organizations (JCAHO) accreditation ○ American Osteopathic Association (AOA) accreditation △ Commission on Accreditation of Rehabilitation Facilities (CARF) accreditation	Control	Service	Staffed Beds	Admissions	Census	Outpatient Visits	Births	Total	Payroll	Personnel

SELMA—Dallas County

⊠ **VAUGHAN REGIONAL MEDICAL CENTER**, 1015 Medical Center Parkway, Zip 36701–6352; tel. 334/418–4100 **A**1 3 5 9 10 19 **F**12 15 17 21 22 33 41 46 48 49 55 59 60 62 63 69 81 82 84 88 93 94 **S** LifePoint Hospitals, Inc., Brentwood, TN
Primary Contact: Stephen Mahan, Chief Executive Officer
CFO: Don Ikner, Chief Financial Officer
Web address: www.uabsfm.org/vaughan.html

| 33 | 10 | 149 | 9339 | 97 | 38457 | 955 | 49221 | 19745 | 493 |

SHEFFIELD—Colbert County

⊠ **HELEN KELLER HOSPITAL**, 1300 South Montgomery Avenue, Zip 35660–6334, Mailing Address: P.O. Box 610, Zip 35660–0610; tel. 256/386–4196 **A**1 9 10 **F**6 9 11 12 14 21 24 29 33 37 40 41 45 46 48 49 52 55 57 58 59 60 61 62 63 66 69 81 82 84 85 86 87 88 94 95 96 106 108
Primary Contact: William H. Anderson, President
CFO: Morris S. Strickland, Chief Financial Officer
CIO: Larry Walker, Chief Information Officer
Web address: www.helenkeller.com

| 16 | 10 | 92 | 4984 | 46 | — | — | — | — | — |

SYLACAUGA—Talladega County

⊠ **COOSA VALLEY MEDICAL CENTER**, 315 West Hickory Street, Zip 35150–2996; tel. 256/249–5000, (Nonreporting) **A**1 9 10
Primary Contact: Glenn C. Sisk, President
CFO: Pam Townsend, Vice President Finance
CIO: Sandra Murchison, Director Medical Records
CHR: Christy Knowles, Director Human Resources
Web address: www.cvhealth.net

| 23 | 10 | 101 | — | — | — | — | — | — | — |

TALLADEGA—Talladega County

⊠ **CITIZENS BAPTIST MEDICAL CENTER**, (Formerly Baptist Citizens), 604 Stone Avenue, Zip 35160–2217, Mailing Address: P.O. Box 978, Zip 35161–0978; tel. 256/362–8111 **A**1 9 10 **F**9 10 11 12 21 22 26 27 28 29 33 41 46 48 49 51 52 57 58 60 61 62 63 65 69 70 81 84 88 96 106 108 **P**7 **S** Baptist Health System, Birmingham, AL
Primary Contact: Steven Gautney, President
CFO: Patrick Jarvis, Vice President Finance
Web address: www.bhsala.com

| 23 | 10 | 106 | 3773 | 34 | 126340 | 375 | 26911 | 9924 | 260 |

TALLASSEE—Elmore County

★ **COMMUNITY HOSPITAL**, 805 Friendship Road, Zip 36078–1234; tel. 334/283–6541, (Nonreporting) **A**9 10
Primary Contact: Jennie R. Rhinehart, Administrator and Chief Executive Officer

| 23 | 10 | 69 | — | — | — | — | — | — | — |

THOMASVILLE—Clarke County

★ **SOUTHWEST ALABAMA MEDICAL CENTER**, (Formerly Thomasville Infirmary), 33700 Highway 43, Zip 36784–3351; tel. 334/636–4431 **A**9 10 **F**9 12 21 27 33 34 46 48 51 52 63 66 69 81 88 94 97 106 108 **S** Resurgence Health Group, Sugar Hill, GA
Primary Contact: Kevin Bierschenk, Chief Executive Officer
CFO: Kevin Bierschenk, Chief Executive Officer
Web address: www.resurgencehealthgroup.com

| 23 | 10 | 27 | 1261 | 12 | — | 0 | — | — | 118 |

TROY—Pike County

□ **TROY REGIONAL MEDICAL CENTER**, 1330 Highway 231 South, Zip 36081–1224; tel. 334/670–5000, (Nonreporting) **A**1 9 10
Primary Contact: Benton L. Busbee, Chief Executive Officer

| 33 | 10 | 78 | — | — | — | — | — | — | — |

TUSCALOOSA—Tuscaloosa County

□ **BRYCE HOSPITAL**, 200 University Boulevard, Zip 35401–1294; tel. 205/759–0799 **A**1 5 10 **F**2 9 21 22 26 27 28 31 32 37 45 47 48 53 57 58 65 71 72 73 74 92 94 96 106 108 110 **P**5
Primary Contact: David Bennett, Director

| 12 | 22 | 310 | 1810 | 1 | 0 | 0 | 43228 | 23315 | 672 |

□ **DCH REGIONAL MEDICAL CENTER**, 809 University Boulevard East, Zip 35401–9961; tel. 205/759–7111 **A**1 3 5 9 10 **F**2 9 11 12 14 15 17 19 21 22 23 26 28 29 31 33 34 37 39 40 46 48 50 51 52 53 55 56 57 58 59 60 61 62 63 65 66 67 79 81 82 84 85 87 88 93 94 96 108 109 110 **P**7 **S** DCH Health System, Tuscaloosa, AL
Primary Contact: William H. Cassels, Administrator
Web address: www.dchsystem.com

| 23 | 10 | 414 | 26140 | 357 | 381571 | 1318 | 220887 | 107596 | 2596 |

LONG TERM HOSPITAL OF TUSCALOOSA, 809 University Boulevard E, 4th Floor, Zip 35401; tel. 205/759–7241, (Nonreporting) **A**10
Primary Contact: James L. Ashbaugh, Chief Executive Officer

| 33 | 80 | 27 | — | — | — | — | — | — | — |

□ **MARY S HARPER GERIATRIC PSYCHIATRIC CENTER**, 200 University Boulevard, Zip 35401; tel. 205/590–0900, (Nonreporting) **A**1 10
Primary Contact: Beverly Bell–Shambley, Ph.D., Facility Director

| 33 | 49 | 96 | — | — | — | — | — | — | — |

□ **TAYLOR HARDIN SECURE MEDICAL FACILITY**, 1301 Jack Warner Parkway, Zip 35404; tel. 205/556–7060, (Nonreporting) **A**1 10
Primary Contact: James F. Reddoch, Jr, Director

| 33 | 22 | 114 | — | — | — | — | — | — | — |

⊠ **VETERANS AFFAIRS MEDICAL CENTER**, 3701 Loop Road, Zip 35404–5015; tel. 205/554–2000, (Total facility includes 178 beds in nursing home–type unit) **A**1 **F**2 4 21 22 28 32 37 38 44 52 57 58 60 66 70 71 76 77 78 81 85 88 92 94 106 108 109 **S** Department of Veterans Affairs, Washington, DC
Primary Contact: W. Kenneth Ruyle, Director
CFO: Dwain Winstead, Director Financial Management
Web address: www.va.gov/sta/guide/home.asp

| 45 | 22 | 324 | 1117 | 85 | 155817 | 0 | 85910 | 50483 | 705 |

Many Facility Codes have changed. Please refer to the AHA Guide Code Chart. © 2005 AHA Guide

Hospital, Address, Telephone, Approval, Facility, and Physician Codes, Health Care System	Classi-fication Codes		Utilization Data					Expense (thousands) of dollars		
★ American Hospital Association (AHA) membership □ Joint Commission on Accreditation of Healthcare Organizations (JCAHO) accreditation ○ American Osteopathic Association (AOA) accreditation △ Commission on Accreditation of Rehabilitation Facilities (CARF) accreditation	Control	Service	Staffed Beds	Admissions	Census	Outpatient Visits	Births	Total	Payroll	Personnel

TUSKEGEE—Macon County
TUSKEGEE DIVISION See Central Alabama Veterans Health Care System, Montgomery

UNION SPRINGS—Bullock County

BULLOCK COUNTY HOSPITAL, 102 West Conecuh Avenue, Zip 36089–1303; tel. 334/738–2140 **A**9 10 20 **F**2 12 21 22 24 29 33 37 39 46 51 52 60 69 74 75 76 81 88 94 Primary Contact: Daniel Hall, Administrator	33	10	41	1761	16	—	0	—	—	—

VALLEY—Chambers County

□ ○ **LANIER HEALTH SERVICES**, 4800 48th Street, Zip 36854–3666; tel. 334/756–1400, (Total facility includes 103 beds in nursing home–type unit) **A**1 9 10 11 12 **F**2 9 11 12 15 21 22 26 33 40 46 48 51 52 53 55 57 59 61 62 63 64 65 66 69 73 75 81 82 84 88 92 94 96 97 106 108 109 Primary Contact: Robert J. Humphrey, Chief Executive Officer and Administrator Web address: www.lanierhospital.com	23	10	192	3784	137	50319	468	29174	14393	460

WEDOWEE—Randolph County

★ **WEDOWEE HOSPITAL**, 209 North Main Street, Zip 36278–5138, Mailing Address: P.O. Box 307, Zip 36278–0307; tel. 256/357–2111, (Nonreporting) **A**9 10 Primary Contact: Farrell Turner, Interim Administrator	16	10	23	—	—	—	—	—	—	—

WETUMPKA—Elmore County

ELMORE COMMUNITY HOSPITAL, 500 Hospital Drive, Zip 36092–1625, Mailing Address: P.O. Box 130, Zip 36092–0130; tel. 334/567–4311, (Nonreporting) **A**9 10 Primary Contact: Gordon Faulk, Administrator	32	10	40	—	—	—	—	—	—	—

WINFIELD—Marion County

⊠ **NORTHWEST MEDICAL CENTER**, 1530 U.S. Highway 43, Zip 35594–5056; tel. 205/487–7000 **A**1 9 10 **F**6 11 12 21 26 27 28 29 33 41 46 47 48 51 52 55 58 59 60 62 63 65 66 68 69 70 71 76 81 82 84 86 88 93 94 95 109 110 **P**6 **S** LifePoint Hospitals, Inc., Brentwood, TN Primary Contact: Barry L. Keel, Chief Executive Officer CFO: Chuck Spann, Chief Financial Officer Web address: www.northwestmedcenter.com	33	10	66	2812	26	71713	394	28202	10423	315

YORK—Sumter County

HILL HOSPITAL OF SUMTER COUNTY, 751 Derby Drive, Zip 36925; tel. 205/392–5263 **A**9 10 **F**22 33 46 48 51 88 97 Primary Contact: Kathy Jordan, Administrator	15	10	33	771	17	—	—	—	—	—

AK

ALASKA

Hospital, Address, Telephone, Approval, Facility, and Physician Codes, Health Care System	Classi-fication Codes		Utilization Data					Expense (thousands) of dollars		
★ American Hospital Association (AHA) membership □ Joint Commission on Accreditation of Healthcare Organizations (JCAHO) accreditation ○ American Osteopathic Association (AOA) accreditation △ Commission on Accreditation of Rehabilitation Facilities (CARF) accreditation	Control	Service	Staffed Beds	Admissions	Census	Outpatient Visits	Births	Total	Payroll	Personnel

ANCHORAGE—2nd Judicial Division

⊞ **ALASKA NATIVE MEDICAL CENTER**, 4315 Diplomacy Drive, Zip 99508;
tel. 907/563–2662 **A**1 3 5 10 **F**1 2 4 6 8 9 10 11 12 21 23 24 25 26 27 28
29 30 31 32 33 34 37 39 42 44 45 46 47 48 50 51 52 53 55 57 58 59 60
61 62 63 64 65 66 69 70 73 75 77 81 82 84 85 88 90 94 96 97 98 105
106 107 108 109 110 **P**6 **S** U. S. Indian Health Service, Rockville, MD
Primary Contact: Dee Hutchison, R.N., Administrator
CMO: Edward Gilkey, M.D., Chief Physician Executive
CIO: Thomas East, Ph.D., Chief Information Officer
Web address: www.anmc.org
| 23 | 10 | 150 | 5713 | 89 | 352633 | 1299 | — | — | 1277 |

□ **ALASKA PSYCHIATRIC INSTITUTE**, 2900 Providence Drive, Zip 99508–4677;
tel. 907/269–7100, (Nonreporting) **A**1 10
Primary Contact: Ronald M. Adler, Chief Executive Officer
Web address: www.hss.state.ak.us/dbh/API/
| 12 | 22 | 74 | | | | | | | |

⊞ △ **ALASKA REGIONAL HOSPITAL**, 2801 Debarr Road, Zip 99508–2997,
Mailing Address: P.O. Box 143889, Zip 99514–3889; tel. 907/264–1754 **A**1 7 9
10 **F**2 6 9 10 11 12 14 15 17 19 21 22 23 24 27 28 29 32 33 37 38 40 41
45 46 47 48 49 52 53 55 56 57 58 59 60 61 62 63 64 65 66 68 69 81 82
84 85 87 88 92 93 94 96 108 109 **P**5 8 **S** HCA, Nashville, TN
Primary Contact: Edward H. Lamb, FACHE, President and Chief Executive Officer
CFO: Dan Houghton, Chief Financial Officer
CMO: Norman Wilder, M.D., Vice President Medical Affairs
CIO: Kjerstin Lastufka, Director Marketing and Public Relations
CHR: Terry McCarty, Human Resources Director
Web address: www.alaskaregional.com
| 33 | 11 | 178 | 4839 | 62 | 79348 | 742 | 115689 | 34319 | 576 |

⊞ **NORTH STAR BEHAVIORAL HEALTH SYSTEM**, 2530 DeBarr Road,
Zip 99508–2948; tel. 907/258–7575, (Includes NORTH STAR BEHAVIORAL
HEALTH SYSTEM, 1650 South Bragaw, Zip 99508–3467; tel. 907/258–7575;
James Shill, Chief Executive Officer), (Nonreporting) **A**1 9 10 **S** Universal Health
Services, Inc., King of Prussia, PA
Primary Contact: James Shill, Chief Executive Officer and Managing Director
CFO: Michele Fissori, Chief Financial Officer
CMO: Daniel Mardones, M.D., Medical Director
CIO: Jess Johnson, Director Information Services
CHR: Patrick Higgins, Director Human Resources
Web address: www.northstarbehavioral.com
| 32 | 22 | 117 | | | | | | | |

⊞ **PROVIDENCE ALASKA MEDICAL CENTER**, 3200 Providence Drive,
Zip 99508–4615, Mailing Address: P.O. Box 196604, Zip 99519–6604;
tel. 907/562–2211, (Nonreporting) **A**1 2 3 5 9 10 **S** Providence Health System,
Seattle, WA
Primary Contact: E. Al Parrish, Vice President and Chief Executive Officer
COO: Vince Huntington, Administrator and Chief Operating Officer
CFO: Robert M. Dvorak, Interim Chief Financial Officer
CMO: Ron Davis, M.D., Chief Medical Officer
CIO: Stephanie Morton, Chief Information Officer
CHR: Russell Grange, Chief Human Resources Officer
Web address: www.providence.org/alaska/pamc/default.htm
| 21 | 10 | 345 | — | — | — | — | — | — | — |

BARROW—4th Judicial Division

⊞ **SAMUEL SIMMONDS MEMORIAL HOSPITAL**, 1296 Agvik Street, Zip 99723,
Mailing Address: P.O. Box 29, Zip 99723; tel. 907/852–4611, (Nonreporting) **A**1
10 **S** U. S. Indian Health Service, Rockville, MD
Primary Contact: Michael S. Herring, Administrator
| 47 | 10 | 14 | — | — | — | — | — | — | — |

BETHEL—1st Judicial Division

⊞ **YUKON–KUSKOKWIM DELTA REGIONAL HOSPITAL**, Mailing Address: P.O.
Box 528, Zip 99559–3000; tel. 907/543–6300, (Nonreporting) **A**1 10 **S** U. S.
Indian Health Service, Rockville, MD
Primary Contact: Jack Crow, Vice President Health Services
CFO: Craig Ambrosiani, Vice President of Finance
Web address: www.ykhc.org
| 47 | 10 | 54 | — | — | — | — | — | — | — |

CORDOVA—2nd Judicial Division

CORDOVA COMMUNITY MEDICAL CENTER, 602 Chase Avenue, Zip 99574,
Mailing Address: P.O. Box 160, Zip 99574; tel. 907/424–8000, (Total facility
includes 10 beds in nursing home–type unit) (Nonreporting) **A**9 10 18 20
Primary Contact: Dean Otey, Interim Administrator and Chief Executive Officer
Web address: www.cityofcordova.net
| 14 | 10 | 23 | — | — | — | — | — | — | — |

Many Facility Codes have changed. Please refer to the AHA Guide Code Chart.

Hospital, Address, Telephone, Approval, Facility, and Physician Codes, Health Care System	Classi-fication Codes		Utilization Data					Expense (thousands) of dollars		
★ American Hospital Association (AHA) membership □ Joint Commission on Accreditation of Healthcare Organizations (JCAHO) accreditation ○ American Osteopathic Association (AOA) accreditation △ Commission on Accreditation of Rehabilitation Facilities (CARF) accreditation	Control	Service	Staffed Beds	Admissions	Census	Outpatient Visits	Births	Total	Payroll	Personnel

DILLINGHAM—1st Judicial Division

☒ **BRISTOL BAY AREA HEALTH CORPORATION**, 6000 Kanakanak Road, Zip 99576; Mailing Address: P.O. Box 130, Zip 99576; tel. 907/842–5201, (Nonreporting) **A**1 9 10 18 **S** U. S. Indian Health Service, Rockville, MD
Primary Contact: Darrel C. Richardson, Executive Vice President and Chief Operations Officer
COO: Darrel C. Richardson, Executive Vice President and Chief Operations Officer
CFO: Tom Berner, Vice President and Chief Financial Officer
CMO: Arnold Loera, M.D., Vice President and Medical Director
CIO: Bill Pearch, Chief Information Officer
CHR: Victor Sifsof, Human Resources Director
Web address: www.bbahc.org
— Classification: 23 10 — Staffed Beds: 14

	Control	Service	Staffed Beds	Admissions	Census	Outpatient Visits	Births	Total	Payroll	Personnel
BRISTOL BAY AREA HEALTH CORPORATION	23	10	14	—	—	—	—	—	—	—
U. S. AIR FORCE REGIONAL HOSPITAL	41	10	64	—	—	—	—	—	—	—
FAIRBANKS MEMORIAL HOSPITAL	23	10	162	—	—	—	—	—	—	—
BASSETT ARMY COMMUNITY HOSPITAL	42	10	32	2059	11	145471	588	—	—	—
SOUTH PENINSULA HOSPITAL	16	10	49	1396	30	—	102	—	—	—
BARTLETT REGIONAL HOSPITAL	15	10	72	—	—	—	—	—	—	—
KETCHIKAN GENERAL HOSPITAL	21	10	64	1469	31	46055	—	—	—	—
PROVIDENCE KODIAK ISLAND MEDICAL CENTER	23	10	25	—	—	—	—	—	—	—

ELMENDORF AFB—2nd Judicial Division

☒ **U. S. AIR FORCE REGIONAL HOSPITAL**, 5955 Zeamer Avenue, Zip 99506–3700; tel. 907/560–6260, (Nonreporting) **A**1 **S** Department of the Air Force, Washington, DC
Primary Contact: Colonel Deborah Kretzchmer, Commander
COO: Colonel Stan Stancil, Deputy Commander
CFO: Captain Christopher Marcus, Resource Management Flight Commander
CIO: Major Lynn Johnson, Medical Information Systems Flight Commander
Web address: www.elmendorf.af.mil/units/3mdg

FAIRBANKS—1st Judicial Division

☒ **FAIRBANKS MEMORIAL HOSPITAL**, 1650 Cowles Street, Zip 99701–5998; tel. 907/452–8181, (Total facility includes 90 beds in nursing–type unit) (Nonreporting) **A**1 2 9 10 19 20 **S** Banner Health, Phoenix, AZ
Primary Contact: Michael K. Powers, FACHE, Chief Executive Officer
CFO: Robert Gould, Associate Administrator and Chief Financial Officer
CIO: Leigh Thurston, System Director, Information Technology
CHR: Jim Lynch, Director People Resources
Web address: www.bannerhealth.com

FORT WAINWRIGHT—1st Judicial Division

☒ **BASSETT ARMY COMMUNITY HOSPITAL**, 1060 Gaffney Road, Box 7400, Zip 99703–7400; tel. 907/353–5172 **A**1 **F**4 6 11 12 21 22 24 27 28 29 32 33 39 42 44 47 48 52 53 58 59 60 62 63 64 65 66 69 70 72 73 74 75 76 77 81 88 89 94 96 106 107 109 110 **P**6 **S** Department of the Army, Office of the Surgeon General, Falls Church, VA
Primary Contact: Colonel Koji Nishimura, Commander
CIO: Bob Shankle, Chief Information Management
Web address: www.alaska.amedd.army.mil

HOMER—3rd Judicial Division

★ **SOUTH PENINSULA HOSPITAL**, 4300 Bartlett Street, Zip 99603–7000; tel. 907/235–8101, (Total facility includes 25 beds in nursing home–type unit) **A**9 10 20 **F**2 9 11 12 21 22 23 29 33 44 47 51 52 55 58 59 60 62 63 64 69 81 84 88 92 94 97
Primary Contact: Charles C. Franz, CHE, Chief Executive Officer
CFO: Brenda Parnell, Chief Financial Officer
CMO: Charles Burgess, M.D., Chief of Staff
CIO: Steve Pyfer, Manager Information Systems
CHR: Cindy Brinkerhoff, Human Resources Director
Web address: www.sphosp.com

JUNEAU—3rd Judicial Division

☒ **BARTLETT REGIONAL HOSPITAL**, 3260 Hospital Drive, Zip 99801–7808; tel. 907/586–2611, (Nonreporting) **A**1 9 10 20 **S** Quorum Health Resources, Plano, TX
Primary Contact: Robert F. Valliant, Chief Executive Officer
CFO: Garth Hamblin, Chief Financial Officer
Web address: www.bartletthospital.org

KETCHIKAN—3rd Judicial Division

☒ **KETCHIKAN GENERAL HOSPITAL**, 3100 Tongass Avenue, Zip 99901–5746; tel. 907/225–5171, (Total facility includes 29 beds in nursing home–type unit) **A**1 2 9 10 20 **F**2 9 11 12 21 22 23 26 27 28 29 33 36 42 44 46 47 51 52 58 59 60 62 63 69 70 71 73 75 77 81 82 84 85 88 92 94 95 96 97 98 106 108 **S** PeaceHealth, Bellevue, WA
Primary Contact: Patrick J. Branco, Chief Executive Officer
CFO: Ken Tonjes, Assistant Administrator Finance
CMO: Alan Wolf, M.D., Chief of Staff
CIO: Tim Walker, Manager Information Services
CHR: Joan Nugent, Assistant Administrator Human Resources
Web address: www.peacehealth.org

KODIAK—2nd Judicial Division

☒ **PROVIDENCE KODIAK ISLAND MEDICAL CENTER**, 1915 East Rezanof Drive, Zip 99615–6602; tel. 907/486–3281, (Total facility includes 19 beds in nursing home–type unit) (Nonreporting) **A**1 9 10 18 20 **S** Providence Health System, Seattle, WA
Primary Contact: Donald J. Rush, Chief Executive Officer
CFO: Timothy Hocum, Chief Financial Officer
CMO: Steve Smith, M.D., Chief Medical Staff
CIO: Fritz Ferrante, Information Services Manager
CHR: Brian Beck, Human Resources Director
Web address: www.providence.org

Hospital, Address, Telephone, Approval, Facility, and Physician Codes, Health Care System	Classi-fication Codes		Utilization Data					Expense (thousands) of dollars		
★ American Hospital Association (AHA) membership □ Joint Commission on Accreditation of Healthcare Organizations (JCAHO) accreditation ○ American Osteopathic Association (AOA) accreditation △ Commission on Accreditation of Rehabilitation Facilities (CARF) accreditation	Control	Service	Staffed Beds	Admissions	Census	Outpatient Visits	Births	Total	Payroll	Personnel

KOTZEBUE—2nd Judicial Division

| ⊞ **MANIILAQ HEALTH CENTER**, Zip 99752–0043; tel. 907/442–3321, (Nonreporting) **A**1 10 18 **S** U. S. Indian Health Service, Rockville, MD
Primary Contact: Hugh R. Hallgren, Administrator
CFO: Manny De La Cruz, Controller
CMO: James M. Orms, M.D., Medical Director
CIO: Eugene Smith, Chief Information Officer
Web address: www.maniilaq.org | 47 | 10 | 17 | — | — | — | — | — | — | |

NOME—2nd Judicial Division

| ⊞ **NORTON SOUND REGIONAL HOSPITAL**, Bering Straits, Zip 99762, Mailing Address: P.O. Box 966, Zip 99762–0966; tel. 907/443–3311, (Total facility includes 15 beds in nursing home–type unit) (Nonreporting) **A**1 9 10 18 20 **S** U. S. Indian Health Service, Rockville, MD
Primary Contact: Angela Gorn, Vice President
COO: Helen Pootoogooluk, Chief Operating Officer
CFO: Amy Miller, Chief Financial Officer
CMO: David Head, M.D., Chief Medical Staff
CIO: Phil Wheelehan, Information Systems Manager
CHR: Sylvia Rasko, Director Human Resources
Web address: www.nortonsoundhealth.org | 23 | 10 | 34 | — | — | — | — | — | — | |

PALMER—2nd Judicial Division

| ⊞ **VALLEY HOSPITAL**, 515 East Dahlia Street, Zip 99645–6489, Mailing Address: P.O. Box 1687, Zip 99645–1687; tel. 907/746–8600, (Nonreporting) **A**1 9 10 20 **S** Triad Hospitals, Inc., Plano, TX
Primary Contact: Norman F. Stephens, Chief Executive Officer
COO: Lynn Wagoner, Chief Operating Officer
CFO: John Abreu, Chief Financial Officer
CMO: Mark Clyde, M.D., Chief of Staff
CIO: Dan Schurnann, Director Information Systems
CHR: Patricia Crofford, Vice President Employee Services
Web address: www.valley–hosp.com | 33 | 10 | 36 | — | — | — | — | — | — | |

PETERSBURG—3rd Judicial Division

| ★ **PETERSBURG MEDICAL CENTER**, 103 Fram Street, Zip 99833, Mailing Address: Box 589, Zip 99833–0589; tel. 907/772–4291, (Total facility includes 15 beds in nursing home–type unit) **A**9 10 18 **F**11 12 16 23 24 26 27 28 29 33 44 46 48 51 52 59 63 69 81 88 92 95 97 **P**4
Primary Contact: John F. Bringhurst, Administrator
CFO: Jan Baird, Chief Financial Officer
CHR: Cynthia Newman, Human Resources Manager
Web address: www.petersburgmedicalcenter.org | 14 | 80 | 27 | 184 | 17 | 15093 | 18 | — | — | 80 |

SEWARD—2nd Judicial Division

| ★ **PROVIDENCE SEWARD MEDICAL CENTER**, 417 First Avenue, Zip 99664, Mailing Address: P.O. Box 365, Zip 99664–0365; tel. 907/224–5205, (Nonreporting) **A**9 10 18 **S** Providence Health System, Seattle, WA
Primary Contact: Kathy Kloster, Administrator
CMO: Jennet Hermiston, Medical Director
Web address: www.providence.org | 21 | 10 | 6 | — | — | — | — | — | — | |

SITKA—3rd Judicial Division

| ⊞ **SEARHC MT. EDGECUMBE HOSPITAL**, 222 Tongass Drive, Zip 99835–9416; tel. 907/966–2411 **A**1 9 10 **F**2 11 12 21 22 23 26 27 28 30 32 33 39 45 46 48 52 53 55 58 59 60 63 64 69 70 71 72 73 75 76 77 85 88 94 96 98 106 110 **P**6 **S** U. S. Indian Health Service, Rockville, MD
Primary Contact: Frank Sutton, Vice President Hospital Services
CFO: Barbara Searls, Chief Financial Officer
CIO: Bob Cita, Director Information Services
CHR: William Perket, Human Resources Director
Web address: www.searhc.org | 23 | 10 | 49 | 1503 | 24 | 42466 | 83 | — | — | 321 |
| ★ **SITKA COMMUNITY HOSPITAL**, 209 Moller Avenue, Zip 99835–7145; tel. 907/747–3241, (Total facility includes 15 beds in nursing home–type unit) (Nonreporting) **A**9 10 18
Primary Contact: Lee Bennett, Interim Administrator
CFO: Mark D. Nellis, Chief Financial Officer
Web address: www.sitkahospital.org | 14 | 10 | 27 | — | — | — | — | — | — | |

SOLDOTNA—3rd Judicial Division

| ⊞ **CENTRAL PENINSULA GENERAL HOSPITAL**, 250 Hospital Place, Zip 99669–6999; tel. 907/714–4404 **A**1 9 10 20 **F**2 4 9 11 12 21 23 26 27 28 29 31 33 34 35 37 39 44 46 48 50 52 53 55 58 59 61 63 66 69 75 78 81 82 84 85 88 92 93 94 95 97 106 108 109 **P**5
Primary Contact: David D. Gilbreath, President and Chief Executive Officer
COO: Lee J. Jackson, Vice President of Nursing Services
CMO: Curt Buchholz, Chief of Staff
CIO: Bryan Downs, Director, Information Services
CHR: Debi Honer, Vice President Human Resources
Web address: www.cpgh.org | 23 | 10 | 41 | 2157 | 19 | 55229 | 363 | 40164 | 19369 | 332 |

Many Facility Codes have changed. Please refer to the AHA Guide Code Chart.

© 2005 AHA Guide

Hospital, Address, Telephone, Approval, Facility, and Physician Codes, Health Care System	Classi-fication Codes		Utilization Data					Expense (thousands) of dollars		
★ American Hospital Association (AHA) membership □ Joint Commission on Accreditation of Healthcare Organizations (JCAHO) accreditation ○ American Osteopathic Association (AOA) accreditation △ Commission on Accreditation of Rehabilitation Facilities (CARF) accreditation	Control	Service	Staffed Beds	Admissions	Census	Outpatient Visits	Births	Total	Payroll	Personnel

VALDEZ—3rd Judicial Division

★ **PROVIDENCE VALDEZ MEDICAL CENTER**, (Formerly Valdez Community Hospital), 911 Meals Avenue, Zip 99686–0550, Mailing Address: P.O. Box 550, Zip 99686–0550; tel. 907/835–2249 **A**9 10 18 **F**4 6 9 11 21 26 27 28 29 31 33 39 46 48 58 59 63 69 73 75 77 78 81 88 94 96 97 98 106 **P**4
Primary Contact: Kanute Rarey, Administrator
CFO: Lindsie King, Finance Manager
CMO: John Cullen, M.D., Chief of Staff and Long Term Care Medical Director
CHR: Maureen Radotich, Director Human Resources
Web address: www.providence.org/alaska

| | 14 | 10 | 10 | 140 | 3 | 7848 | 27 | 5312 | 1867 | 48 |

WRANGELL—3rd Judicial Division

★ **WRANGELL MEDICAL CENTER**, First Avenue and Bennett Street, Zip 99929, Mailing Address: P.O. Box 1081, Zip 99929; tel. 907/874–7000, (Total facility includes 14 beds in nursing home–type unit) **A**9 10 18 20 **F**12 14 23 33 46 51 52 59 61 63 88 92 97 **P**4
Primary Contact: Brian D. Gilbert, Chief Executive Officer
CFO: Olinda White, Chief Financial Officer
Web address: www.wrangellmedicalcenter.com

| | 14 | 10 | 22 | 181 | 10 | 15308 | 10 | 5608 | 2908 | 42 |

ARIZONA

AZ

Hospital, Address, Telephone, Approval, Facility, and Physician Codes, Health Care System	Classi-fication Codes		Utilization Data					Expense (thousands) of dollars		
★ American Hospital Association (AHA) membership ☐ Joint Commission on Accreditation of Healthcare Organizations (JCAHO) accreditation ○ American Osteopathic Association (AOA) accreditation △ Commission on Accreditation of Rehabilitation Facilities (CARF) accreditation	Control	Service	Staffed Beds	Admissions	Census	Outpatient Visits	Births	Total	Payroll	Personnel

BENSON—Cochise County

BENSON HOSPITAL, 450 South Ocotillo Street, Zip 85602, Mailing Address: P.O. Box 2290, Zip 85602; tel. 520/586–2261, (Nonreporting) **A**9 10 18
Primary Contact: Ronald A. McKinnon, Chief Executive Officer
Web address: www.bensonhospital.org
| 16 | 10 | 22 | — | — | — | — | — | — | — |

BISBEE—Cochise County

☐ **COPPER QUEEN COMMUNITY HOSPITAL**, 101 Cole Avenue, Zip 85603–1399; tel. 520/432–5383 **A**1 9 10 20 **F**9 12 21 22 26 28 29 33 51 52 60 63 69 75 81 88 97 108 110 **P**6
Primary Contact: James J. Dickson, Administrator and Chief Executive Officer
Web address: www.cqch.org
| 23 | 10 | 13 | 410 | 3 | 6892 | 0 | — | — | 112 |

BULLHEAD CITY—Mohave County

☐ **WESTERN ARIZONA REGIONAL MEDICAL CENTER**, 2735 Silver Creek Road, Zip 86442–8303; tel. 928/763–2273 **A**1 9 10 **F**4 9 11 12 14 17 21 29 33 36 46 48 51 58 59 60 63 77 81 82 84 87 88 94 96 **S** Community Health Systems, Inc., Brentwood, TN
Primary Contact: Kenneth W. Randall, Chief Executive Officer
Web address: www.warmc.com
| 33 | 10 | 115 | 7223 | 77 | 59741 | 628 | — | — | 541 |

CASA GRANDE—Pinal County

⊠ **CASA GRANDE REGIONAL MEDICAL CENTER**, 1800 East Florence Boulevard, Zip 85222–5399; tel. 520/381–6300, (Total facility includes 128 beds in nursing home–type unit) (Nonreporting) **A**1 9 10
Primary Contact: J. Marty Dernier, President and Chief Executive Officer
CFO: John F. Dempsey, Chief Financial Officer
CIO: Jim Begin, Director Information Systems
CHR: Charlene Wilson, Vice President Human Resources
Web address: www.casagrandehospital.com
| 23 | 10 | 244 | | | | | | | |

CHANDLER—Maricopa County

ARIZONA ORTHOPEDIC SURGICAL HOSPITAL, 2905 West Warner Road, Zip 85224; tel. 480/603–9000, (Nonreporting) **A**9 10 **S** United Surgical Partners International, Addison, TX
Primary Contact: Robert Conoway, Chief Executive Officer
| 33 | 13 | 16 | | | | | | | |

⊠ **CHANDLER REGIONAL HOSPITAL**, 475 South Dobson Road, Zip 85224–4230; tel. 480/963–4561, (Nonreporting) **A**1 9 10 **S** Catholic Healthcare West, San Francisco, CA
Primary Contact: David G. Covert, President and Chief Administrative Officer
COO: Marguerite Smith, R.N., Vice President and Chief Nursing Officer
CFO: Mark Kem, Vice President Finance
CMO: Terry J. Happel, M.D., Medical Director, Medical Staff Affairs
CHR: Jo Beth Crawford, Vice President Human Resources
Web address: www.chandlerregional.com
| 21 | 10 | 147 | | | | | | | |

CHINLE—Apache County

⊠ **CHINLE COMPREHENSIVE HEALTH CARE FACILITY**, Highway 191, Zip 86503, Mailing Address: P.O. Drawer PH, Zip 86503; tel. 928/674–7011 **A**1 10 **F**2 4 12 21 30 32 33 41 42 48 50 52 53 55 58 59 60 63 64 66 69 70 72 73 75 77 81 88 92 94 109 110 **S** U. S. Indian Health Service, Rockville, MD
Primary Contact: Ronald Tso, Chief Executive Officer
CMO: Kevin Rand, M.D., Clinical Director
| 47 | 10 | 52 | 2693 | 21 | 150682 | 595 | — | — | 101 |

COTTONWOOD—Yavapai County

⊠ **VERDE VALLEY MEDICAL CENTER**, 269 South Candy Lane, Zip 86326–4170; tel. 928/634–2251, (Nonreporting) **A**1 9 10 20 **S** Northern Arizona Healthcare, Flagstaff, AZ
Primary Contact: James J. Sinek, President and Senior Executive Officer
CFO: James Puffenberger, Executive Vice President and Chief Financial Officer
Web address: www.nahealth.com
| 23 | 10 | 99 | — | — | — | — | — | — | — |

DOUGLAS—Cochise County

SOUTHEAST ARIZONA MEDICAL CENTER, 2174 Oak Avenue, Zip 85607–9801; tel. 520/364–7931 **A**9 10 18 **F**12 33 45 69 81 84 88 97
Primary Contact: Michael J. Carter, Chief Executive Officer
| 23 | 10 | 20 | 531 | 4 | 10294 | 0 | — | — | 103 |

FLAGSTAFF—Coconino County

⊠ **FLAGSTAFF MEDICAL CENTER**, 1200 North Beaver Street, Zip 86001–3198; tel. 928/779–3366 **A**1 9 10 19 20 **F**2 4 6 9 11 12 15 17 19 21 22 23 24 26 27 28 29 30 33 34 37 38 39 40 41 45 46 47 48 49 50 52 53 55 56 57 58 59 60 61 62 63 64 65 66 67 68 69 71 72 73 74 75 76 77 78 79 81 82 84 85 86 87 88 92 94 95 96 106 107 108 109 110 **S** Northern Arizona Healthcare, Flagstaff, AZ
Primary Contact: James Puffenberger, Interim Chief Executive Officer
COO: Stephen G. Carlson, President
CFO: Gregory Kuzma, Vice President and Chief Financial Officer
CMO: Charles Swetnam, M.D., Vice President Medical Affairs
CIO: David Paschall, Vice President and Chief Information Officer
CHR: Bruce Blankenship, Vice President Human Resources
Web address: www.flagstaffmedicalcenter.com
| 23 | 10 | 267 | 11789 | 156 | 77518 | 1557 | 210159 | 72982 | 2116 |

Many Facility Codes have changed. Please refer to the AHA Guide Code Chart.   © 2005 AHA Guide

	Classi-fication Codes		Utilization Data					Expense (thousands) of dollars		
Hospital, Address, Telephone, Approval, Facility, and Physician Codes, Health Care System	Control	Service	Staffed Beds	Admissions	Census	Outpatient Visits	Births	Total	Payroll	Personnel

★ American Hospital Association (AHA) membership
□ Joint Commission on Accreditation of Healthcare Organizations (JCAHO) accreditation
○ American Osteopathic Association (AOA) accreditation
△ Commission on Accreditation of Rehabilitation Facilities (CARF) accreditation

AZ

FORT DEFIANCE—Apache County

✠ **FORT DEFIANCE INDIAN HEALTH SERVICE HOSPITAL**, Mailing Address: P.O. Box 649, Zip 86504–0649; tel. 928/729–5741, (Nonreporting) **A**1 10 **S** U. S. Indian Health Service, Rockville, MD
Primary Contact: Franklin R. Freeland, Ed.D., Chief Executive Officer

47	10	39	—	—	—	—	—	—	—

GANADO—Apache County

SAGE MEMORIAL HOSPITAL, Highway 264, Zip 86505, Mailing Address: P.O. Box 457, Zip 86505–0457; tel. 928/755–4500, (Nonreporting) **A**9 10 18 20
Primary Contact: Taylor McKenzie, M.D., Chief Executive Officer
Web address: www.navajosage.org

23	33	25	—	—	—	—	—	—	—

GLENDALE—Maricopa County

□ **ARROWHEAD COMMUNITY HOSPITAL AND MEDICAL CENTER**, 18701 North 67th Avenue, Zip 85308–5722; tel. 623/561–1000, (Nonreporting) **A**1 9 10 **S** Vanguard Health System, Nashville, TN
Primary Contact: Jonathan W. Bartlett, Chief Executive Officer
Web address: www.baptisthealth.com

33	10	115							

✠ **BANNER THUNDERBIRD MEDICAL CENTER**, 5555 West Thunderbird Road, Zip 85306–4696; tel. 602/865–5555, (Includes BANNER BEHAVIORAL HEALTH CENTER–THUNDERBIRD CAMPUS) **A**1 9 10 **F**2 4 11 12 15 17 19 21 22 23 26 27 28 29 30 31 33 37 45 47 49 52 53 55 56 57 58 59 60 61 62 63 64 65 66 69 71 73 74 75 76 77 78 79 80 81 82 84 85 87 88 92 93 94 96 97 108 109 110 **P**4 **S** Banner Health, Phoenix, AZ
Primary Contact: Colleen Hallberg, Chief Executive Officer
COO: Kathy Scott, Associate Administrator and Chief Nursing Officer
CFO: Richard Miller, Administrator Finance
CMO: Ted Laughlin, M.D., Medical Director
CHR: Laura Witt, Administrator Human Resources
Web address: www.bannerhealth.com

23	10	369	29883	322	96855	4959	245296	99526	2155

✠ **HEALTHSOUTH VALLEY OF THE SUN REHABILITATION HOSPITAL**, 13460 North 67th Avenue, Zip 85304–1042; tel. 623/878–8800 **A**1 10 **F**21 27 45 57 58 65 66 68 69 73 88 96 110 **S** HEALTHSOUTH Corporation, Birmingham, AL
Primary Contact: Beth Bacher, Administrator
Web address: www.healthsouth.com

33	46	60	1243	33	0	0	14188	6441	158

✠ **U. S. AIR FORCE HOSPITAL LUKE**, Luke AFB, 7219 North Litchfield Road, Zip 85309–1525; tel. 623/856–7502, (Nonreporting) **A**1 **S** Department of the Air Force, Washington, DC
Primary Contact: Colonel Schuyler K. Geller, Commander
COO: Colonel Jerrold Flyer, Deputy Commander
CFO: Major Brad Weast, Chief Business Operations
CMO: Colonel Richard Williams, Chief, Medical Staff
CIO: Major Randell Smithson, Chief, Systems
Web address: www.luke.af.mil/56mg/

41	10	23	—	—	—	—	—	—	—

GLOBE—Gila County

★ **COBRE VALLEY COMMUNITY HOSPITAL**, 5880 South Hospital Drive, Zip 85501–9454; tel. 928/425–3261 **A**9 10 20 **F**2 9 11 12 21 22 23 26 27 28 29 33 34 39 40 44 46 47 48 52 53 55 57 58 59 61 62 63 66 69 81 82 84 85 87 88 94 97 106 108 **S** Brim Healthcare, Inc., Brentwood, TN
Primary Contact: James H. Gingerich, Chief Executive Officer
CFO: Neal Jensen, Chief Financial Officer
CMO: McLaren Ruesch, M.D., Chief of Staff
CIO: Sharon Bennett, Information Systems Manager
CHR: Rita Murphy, Human Resources Manager
Web address: www.cvchospital.com

23	10	43	1603	17	53224	335	—	—	209

GOODYEAR—Maricopa County

□ **WEST VALLEY HOSPITAL**, 13677 West McDowell Road, Zip 85338; tel. 623/882–1500 **A**1 9 10 **F**2 9 11 12 15 21 29 33 34 39 46 48 53 55 58 59 62 63 64 69 81 88 92 94 108
Primary Contact: Tom Resendez, Chief Executive Officer
Web address: www.wvhospital.com

33	10	74	4148	32	37630	840	—	—	310

KEAMS CANYON—Navajo County

✠ **HOPI HEALTH CARE CENTER**, Mailing Address: P.O. Box 4000, Polacca, Zip 86042; tel. 928/737–6000 **A**1 10 18 **F**2 11 21 24 29 30 32 33 37 39 41 44 46 47 48 52 53 58 60 66 69 81 88 89 94 107 108 110 **S** U. S. Indian Health Service, Rockville, MD
Primary Contact: Daryl Melvin, Chief Executive Officer
CFO: Thelma Tewahaftewa, Finance Officer
CMO: Darren Vicenti, M.D., Clinical Director
CIO: Adrian Tom, Management Information Systems Supervisor
CHR: Karen Lee, Human Resources Director

47	10	6	491	2	70250	61	—	—	265

KINGMAN—Mohave County

✠ **KINGMAN REGIONAL MEDICAL CENTER**, 3269 Stockton Hill Road, Zip 86401–3691; tel. 928/757–2101 **A**1 9 10 12 13 20 **F**2 9 11 12 21 22 23 26 29 33 34 36 37 41 46 47 48 49 51 52 55 58 59 60 61 62 63 64 65 66 68 69 70 80 81 82 84 85 87 88 93 94 96 106 108 **P**6
Primary Contact: Brian Turney, Chief Executive Officer
COO: Lawrence E. Lewis, Chief Operating Officer and Chief Financial Officer
CFO: Lawrence E. Lewis, Chief Operating Officer and Chief Financial Officer
CIO: Shawn Burgess, Director Information Systems
CHR: Heather Crowl, Executive Director Human Resources
Web address: www.azkrmc.com

23	10	133	8170	89	137096	614	89588	33462	869

Hospital, Address, Telephone, Approval, Facility, and Physician Codes, Health Care System	Classi-fication Codes		Utilization Data					Expense (thousands) of dollars		
★ American Hospital Association (AHA) membership □ Joint Commission on Accreditation of Healthcare Organizations (JCAHO) accreditation ○ American Osteopathic Association (AOA) accreditation △ Commission on Accreditation of Rehabilitation Facilities (CARF) accreditation	Control	Service	Staffed Beds	Admissions	Census	Outpatient Visits	Births	Total	Payroll	Personnel

LAKE HAVASU CITY—Mohave County

▣ **HAVASU REGIONAL MEDICAL CENTER**, 101 Civic Center Lane, Zip 86403–5683; tel. 928/855–8185, (Nonreporting) **A**1 9 10 20 **S** LifePoint Hospitals, Inc., Brentwood, TN
Primary Contact: Dorothy Sawyer, Chief Executive Officer
CFO: Craig M. Wagner, Chief Financial Officer
CIO: Bill Udovich, Information Systems Director
CHR: Sheena Benson, Director Human Resources
Web address: www.havasuregional.com

	33	10	138	—	—	—	—	—	—	—

MESA—Maricopa County

□ **ARIZONA SPINE AND JOINT HOSPITAL**, 4620 East Baseline Road, Zip 85206; tel. 480/832–4770, (Nonreporting) **A**1 10 **S** National Surgical Hospitals, Chicago, IL
Primary Contact: Lloyd Scarrow, Chief Executive Officer

	33	47	22	—	—	—	—	—	—	—

▣ **BANNER BAYWOOD HEART HOSPITAL**, 6750 East Baywood Avenue, Zip 85206; tel. 480/854–5000 **A**1 9 10 **F**2 14 15 17 19 21 22 26 27 28 30 41 48 49 53 58 63 69 85 87 88 92 94 96 106 108 **P**3 8 **S** Banner Health, Phoenix, AZ
Primary Contact: Kathy Bollinger, Chief Executive Officer
Web address: www.bannerhealth.com

	23	42	111	6468	65	27211	0	82483	23964	459

▣ **BANNER BAYWOOD MEDICAL CENTER**, 6644 Baywood Avenue, Zip 85206–1797; tel. 480/981–2000 **A**1 9 10 **F**2 9 11 12 21 22 23 26 27 28 30 33 37 40 42 44 46 47 48 49 50 52 53 55 57 58 59 60 61 62 63 64 65 66 69 73 75 77 81 82 84 85 88 92 93 94 96 106 108 109 110 **P**8 **S** Banner Health, Phoenix, AZ
Primary Contact: Don A. Evans, FACHE, Chief Executive Officer
COO: Mindy Richardson, Associate Administrator
CFO: Karen Scremin, Chief Financial Officer
CMO: Larry Spratling, M.D., Chief Medical Officer
CIO: Michael S. Warden, Director, Human Resources
CHR: Brian Peterson, Telecommunications Officer
Web address: www.bannerhealth.com

	23	10	242	18243	204	216514	2282	163047	70344	1451

▣ **BANNER DESERT MEDICAL CENTER**, 1400 South Dobson Road, Zip 85202–9879; tel. 480/512–3000, (Includes SAMARITAN BEHAVIORAL HEALTH CENTER–DESERT SAMARITAN MEDICAL CENTER, 2225 West Southern Avenue, Zip 85202; tel. 602/464–4000) **A**1 9 10 **F**2 4 9 11 12 14 15 17 19 21 22 23 24 26 27 28 29 31 33 35 37 38 40 45 46 48 49 50 52 53 55 56 57 58 59 60 61 62 63 64 65 66 67 69 71 72 73 74 75 77 78 79 80 81 82 83 84 85 86 87 88 92 93 94 96 107 108 109 110 **S** Banner Health, Phoenix, AZ
Primary Contact: Bruce E. Pearson, Chief Executive Officer
CFO: Lori Linder, Chief Financial Officer
CMO: Mary Lou Erwin, M.D., Medical Staff Administrator
CIO: Dennis Webb, Director Information Technology
CHR: Janet Oxford, Chief Human Resources Officer
Web address: www.bannerhealth.com

	23	10	611	36757	499	116000	8248	326138	141249	3221

▣ **BANNER MESA MEDICAL CENTER**, 1010 North Country Club Drive, Zip 85201–3299; tel. 480/834–1211 **A**1 9 10 **F**1 2 9 10 11 12 21 22 23 26 28 30 33 37 40 44 46 47 48 49 50 52 53 55 57 58 59 60 61 62 63 65 66 68 69 71 72 73 74 75 76 77 78 81 82 84 85 88 92 94 106 108 109 110 **P**8 **S** Banner Health, Phoenix, AZ
Primary Contact: Rebecca C. Kuhn, Chief Executive Officer
COO: Pamela Nenaber, Chief Operating Officer
CFO: Kirk Kearl, Chief Financial Officer
CMO: Leslie Paulus, M.D., Medical Director
CHR: Robin Houston, Director
Web address: www.bannerhealth.com

	23	10	201	11379	136	101885	1924	113462	44193	877

□ **MESA GENERAL HOSPITAL MEDICAL CENTER**, 515 North Mesa Drive, Zip 85201–5989; tel. 480/969–9111, (Total facility includes 13 beds in nursing home–type unit) (Nonreporting) **A**1 9 10 12 13 **S** IASIS Healthcare, Franklin, TN
Primary Contact: C. Mark Gregson, Chief Executive Officer
Web address: www.mesageneralhospital.com
SAMARITAN BEHAVIORAL HEALTH CENTER–DESERT SAMARITAN MEDICAL CENTER See Banner Desert Medical Center

	33	10	143	—	—	—	—	—	—	—

□ **SELECT SPECIALTY HOSPITAL–MESA**, 1010 North Country Club Drive, 7th Floor, Zip 85201; tel. 480/461–2706, (Nonreporting) **A**1 9 10
Primary Contact: James Camp, Chief Operating Officer

	33	49	32	—	—	—	—	—	—	—

NOGALES—Santa Cruz County

▣ **CARONDELET HOLY CROSS HOSPITAL**, 1171 West Target Range Road, Zip 85621–2496; tel. 520/285–3000, (Total facility includes 49 beds in nursing home–type unit) **A**1 9 10 20 **F**9 11 21 22 24 26 27 28 29 33 36 38 39 40 44 46 48 49 52 53 55 58 59 60 63 65 66 69 75 81 84 88 92 94 96 97 98 108 **S** Ascension Health, Saint Louis, MO
Primary Contact: Richard Polheber, Senior Vice President and Chief Executive Officer
CFO: Tom Pepping, Senior Vice President and Chief Financial Officer
CMO: Maria Pina, Chief of Staff
CIO: John Braswell, Vice President and Chief Information Officer
Web address: www.carondelet.org

	21	10	79	1980	58	35961	767	16764	7559	178

Hospital, Address, Telephone, Approval, Facility, and Physician Codes, Health Care System	Classi-fication Codes		Utilization Data					Expense (thousands) of dollars		
★ American Hospital Association (AHA) membership □ Joint Commission on Accreditation of Healthcare Organizations (JCAHO) accreditation ○ American Osteopathic Association (AOA) accreditation △ Commission on Accreditation of Rehabilitation Facilities (CARF) accreditation	Control	Service	Staffed Beds	Admissions	Census	Outpatient Visits	Births	Total	Payroll	Personnel

ORO VALLEY—Pima County

★ **NORTHWEST MEDICAL CENTER, ORO VALLEY**, 1551 East Tangerine Road, Zip 85737; tel. 520/901–3500, (Nonreporting) **A**9 **S** Triad Hospitals, Inc., Plano, TX
Primary Contact: Paul Kappelman, Chief Executive Officer
Web address: www.nmcorovalley.com

| 33 | 10 | 96 | — | — | — | — | — | — | — |

PAGE—Coconino County

⊞ **PAGE HOSPITAL**, 501 North Navajo Drive, Zip 86040, Mailing Address: P.O. Box 1447, Zip 86040–1447; tel. 928/645–2424 **A**1 9 10 18 **F**2 9 11 12 21 22 23 27 28 29 30 32 33 34 46 47 48 52 53 58 59 60 62 63 64 65 66 69 81 84 88 94 97 106 108 110 **S** Banner Health, Phoenix, AZ
Primary Contact: Sandy Haryasz, R.N., Chief Executive Officer
Web address: www.bannerhealth.com

| 23 | 10 | 25 | 687 | 3 | 23539 | 192 | 10902 | 5437 | 116 |

PARKER—La Paz County

○ **LA PAZ REGIONAL HOSPITAL**, 1200 Mohave Road, Zip 85344–6349; tel. 928/669–9201 **A**9 10 11 20 **F**2 9 12 21 22 26 27 33 42 46 47 48 52 55 57 62 63 64 66 69 81 88 93 94 108
Primary Contact: M. Victoria Clark, Chief Executive Officer
Web address: www.lapazhospital.org

| 23 | 10 | 39 | 1346 | 11 | 19414 | 0 | 11580 | 5468 | 153 |

⊞ **U. S. PUBLIC HEALTH SERVICE INDIAN HOSPITAL**, Mailing Address: Route 1, Box 12, Zip 85344; tel. 928/669–2137, (Nonreporting) **A**1 10 18 **S** U. S. Indian Health Service, Rockville, MD
Primary Contact: Robert O'Rielly, Deputy Chief Executive Officer
CFO: Robert O'Rielly, Deputy Chief Executive Officer
CMO: Clare Helminiak, Clinical Director
CIO: Carol Otter, Chief Information Officer

| 44 | 10 | 20 | — | — | — | — | — | — | — |

PAYSON—Gila County

□ **PAYSON REGIONAL MEDICAL CENTER**, 807 South Ponderosa Street, Zip 85541–5599; tel. 928/474–3222, (Nonreporting) **A**1 9 10 20 **S** Community Health Systems, Inc., Brentwood, TN
Primary Contact: R. Chris Wolf, Chief Executive Officer
Web address: www.paysonhospital.com

| 33 | 10 | 34 | — | — | — | — | — | — | — |

PHOENIX—Maricopa County

□ **ARIZONA HEART HOSPITAL**, 1930 East Thomas Road, Zip 85016; tel. 602/532–1000, (Nonreporting) **A**1 9 10 **S** MedCath, Inc., Charlotte, NC
Primary Contact: Kenneth Howell, President and Chief Executive Officer
Web address: www.azheart.com

| 32 | 42 | 59 | — | — | — | — | — | — | — |

□ **ARIZONA STATE HOSPITAL**, 2500 East Van Buren Street, Zip 85008–6079; tel. 602/244–1331 **A**1 10 **F**4 21 22 32 39 45 47 53 58 65 66 71 72 73 74 89 94 96 108
Primary Contact: John C. Cooper, Chief Executive Officer
Web address: www.hs.state.az.us

| 12 | 22 | 338 | 356 | 290 | — | 0 | — | — | 715 |

⊞ **BANNER ESTRELLA MEDICAL**, 9201 West Thomas Road, Zip 85037–3332, Mailing Address: P.O. Box 120, Zip 85001–0120; tel. 623/327–4000, (Nonreporting) **A**1 9 **S** Banner Health, Phoenix, AZ
Primary Contact: Constance Harmsen, R.N., Chief Executive Officer
Web address: www.bannerhealth.org

| 23 | 10 | 172 | — | — | — | — | — | — | — |

⊞ **BANNER GOOD SAMARITAN MEDICAL CENTER**, 1111 East McDowell Road, Zip 85006–2666, Mailing Address: P.O. Box 2989, Zip 85062–2989; tel. 602/239–2000 **A**1 2 3 5 8 9 10 **F**2 10 11 12 14 15 17 19 21 22 23 26 27 28 29 33 34 37 38 49 52 53 55 57 58 59 60 61 62 65 68 69 71 73 75 76 77 78 79 81 82 84 86 87 88 89 92 93 94 99 100 101 102 103 104 108 109 110 **S** Banner Health, Phoenix, AZ
Primary Contact: Paul Mullings, FACHE, Chief Executive Officer
CFO: Kathy Kotin, Chief Financial Officer
CMO: Paul Stander, M.D., Physician Director
CIO: Michael S. Warden, Senior Vice President Information Technology
CHR: Sandra Herr, Administrator Human Resources
Web address: www.bannerhealth.com

| 23 | 10 | 577 | 35031 | 462 | 190414 | 6754 | 452356 | 161814 | 3233 |

⊞ **CARL T. HAYDEN VETERANS AFFAIRS MEDICAL CENTER**, 650 East Indian School Road, Zip 85012–1892; tel. 602/277–5551, (Total facility includes 104 beds in nursing home–type unit) (Nonreporting) **A**1 2 3 5 **S** Department of Veterans Affairs, Washington, DC
Primary Contact: John R. Fears, Director
COO: John R. Fears, Director
CFO: Richard A. Pasquale, Administrator Resources and Financial Management Services
CMO: Eugene Ross, M.D., Chief of Staff
CHR: Rafael Martinez, Human Resources Officer
Web address: www.phoenix.med.va.gov

| 45 | 10 | 188 | — | — | — | — | — | — | — |

AZ

AZ

Hospital, Address, Telephone, Approval, Facility, and Physician Codes, Health Care System	Classi-fication Codes		Utilization Data					Expense (thousands) of dollars		
★ American Hospital Association (AHA) membership □ Joint Commission on Accreditation of Healthcare Organizations (JCAHO) accreditation ○ American Osteopathic Association (AOA) accreditation △ Commission on Accreditation of Rehabilitation Facilities (CARF) accreditation	Control	Service	Staffed Beds	Admissions	Census	Outpatient Visits	Births	Total	Payroll	Personnel

	Control	Service	Staffed Beds	Admissions	Census	Outpatient Visits	Births	Total	Payroll	Personnel
★ **JOHN C. LINCOLN HOSPITAL – NORTH MOUNTAIN**, 250 East Dunlap Avenue, Zip 85020–2446; tel. 602/943–2381 **A**9 10 12 **F**2 9 11 12 14 15 17 19 21 22 23 26 27 28 29 33 34 39 41 46 49 52 53 54 55 57 58 59 60 61 62 63 64 68 81 82 84 85 87 88 93 94 96 106 108 110 **P**8 **S** John C. Lincoln Health Network, Phoenix, AZ Primary Contact: Rhonda Forsyth, Executive Vice President and Chief Executive Officer COO: Rhonda Forsyth, Executive Vice President and Chief Executive Officer CFO: David Lamparter, Chief Financial Officer CMO: Nelson Faux, M.D., Chief of Staff CIO: Robert Israel, Network Administrator Information Systems CHR: Dale Spartz, Vice President Human Resources Web address: www.jcl.com	23	10	262	16155	149	75183	1799	150432	58476	1680
★ ○ **JOHN C. LINCOLN HOSPITAL–DEER VALLEY**, 19829 North 27th Avenue, Zip 85027–4002; tel. 623/879–6100 **A**9 10 11 13 **F**2 9 12 14 15 17 19 21 22 23 26 27 28 29 33 39 46 48 49 52 53 55 57 58 60 61 62 63 64 68 81 82 84 85 87 88 94 96 108 110 **P**8 **S** John C. Lincoln Health Network, Phoenix, AZ Primary Contact: Tim Tracy, Executive Vice President and Chief Executive Officer CFO: David Lamparter, Chief Financial Officer CIO: Robert Israel, Network Administrator Information Systems CHR: Dale Spartz, Vice President Human Resources Web address: www.jcl.com	23	10	143	8977	97	65691	0	96467	38693	851
□ **KINDRED HOSPITAL – PHOENIX**, 40 East Indianola Avenue, Zip 85012–2059; tel. 602/280–7000, (Nonreporting) **A**1 10 **S** Kindred Healthcare, Louisville, KY Primary Contact: Steve Smith, Chief Executive Officer Web address: www.kindredhealthcare.com	33	10	58	—	—	—	—	—	—	—
LOS NINOS HOSPITAL, 2303 East Thomas, Zip 85016; tel. 602/954–7311 **A**9 10 **F**2 45 52 69 94 Primary Contact: William Timmons, Chief Executive Officer	33	80	15	285	10	3205	—	—	—	27
□ **MARICOPA INTEGRATED HEALTH SYSTEM**, 2601 East Roosevelt Street, Zip 85008–4956; tel. 602/344–5011, (Nonreporting) **A**1 2 3 5 8 9 10 12 Primary Contact: Ted Shaw, Interim Chief Executive Officer Web address: www.maricopa.gov/medcenter/mmc.html	13	10	482	—	—	—	—	—	—	—
□ **MARYVALE HOSPITAL MEDICAL CENTER**, 5102 West Campbell Avenue, Zip 85031–1799; tel. 623/848–5000, (Nonreporting) **A**1 2 9 10 12 **S** Vanguard Health System, Nashville, TN Primary Contact: Gregory Padilla, Chief Executive Officer Web address: www.maryvalehospital.com	33	10	175	—	—	—	—	—	—	—
⊠ **MAYO CLINIC HOSPITAL**, 5777 East Mayo Boulevard, Zip 85054–4502; tel. 480/515–6296, (Total facility includes 9 beds in nursing home–type unit) **A**1 3 5 10 **F**2 10 12 15 17 19 21 22 23 28 33 37 38 40 49 52 53 55 57 58 60 61 62 63 64 66 68 69 79 81 82 84 85 88 92 93 94 96 99 101 102 106 107 108 110 **P**6 **S** Mayo Foundation, Rochester, MN Primary Contact: Thomas C. Bour, Administrator Web address: www.mayoclinic.org	23	10	202	12278	151	30269	0	184033	51793	1740
□ **PARADISE VALLEY HOSPITAL**, 3929 East Bell Road, Zip 85032–2196; tel. 602/923–5000 **A**1 9 10 **F**2 10 11 12 15 17 21 22 23 27 28 29 33 37 41 42 45 46 48 53 55 57 58 59 60 61 62 63 64 69 70 71 73 76 78 81 84 85 88 94 96 108 109 110 **S** Vanguard Health System, Nashville, TN Primary Contact: John L. Harrington, Jr, FACHE, President and Chief Executive Officer Web address: www.paradisevalleyhospital.com	33	10	126	8576	74	78758	1744	76531	32348	503
□ **PHOENIX BAPTIST HOSPITAL**, 2000 West Bethany Home Road, Zip 85015–2110; tel. 602/249–0212 **A**1 3 5 9 10 **F**2 11 12 14 15 17 19 21 22 26 28 29 33 39 48 52 55 57 58 59 62 63 64 69 81 82 84 88 94 106 108 109 110 **S** Vanguard Health System, Nashville, TN Primary Contact: Dennis M. Knox, Chief Executive Officer Web address: www.baptisthealth.com	33	10	201	9786	93	72027	2144	102099	34393	940
⊠ **PHOENIX CHILDREN'S HOSPITAL**, 1919 East Thomas Road, Zip 85016; tel. 602/546–1000 **A**1 3 5 9 10 **F**4 9 16 18 20 21 22 23 24 28 29 31 33 34 39 42 44 45 46 47 48 49 50 52 53 54 56 57 58 61 62 63 65 66 67 69 70 71 72 73 74 75 77 81 82 84 85 88 90 93 94 95 96 98 99 101 107 108 Primary Contact: Robert L. Meyer, M.D., President and Chief Executive Officer CFO: Larry J. Smith, Chief Financial Officer CMO: Paul Stillwell, M.D., Physician in Chief CIO: Laura Busko, Interim Chief Information Officer CHR: Thomas Diederich, Vice President Human Resources Web address: www.phoenixchildrens.com	23	50	285	11518	208	121637	0	192102	88981	1668
⊠ **PHOENIX MEMORIAL HOSPITAL**, 1201 South Seventh Avenue, Zip 85007–3995; tel. 602/258–5111 **A**1 2 9 10 **F**2 11 12 14 15 17 19 21 22 33 55 59 61 63 69 81 82 84 88 109 **S** Vanguard Health System, Nashville, TN Primary Contact: Sonja Hagel, Vice President Operations and Chief Executive Officer COO: Victoria King, Chief Nursing Officer CFO: Roger Faculak, Chief Financial Officer CMO: Michael Kralik, M.D., Chief of Staff CHR: Thomas Hauer, Director Human Resources Web address: www.phxmemorialhospital.com	33	10	159	2779	30	—	—	—	—	305

Many Facility Codes have changed. Please refer to the AHA Guide Code Chart.

Hospital, Address, Telephone, Approval, Facility, and Physician Codes, Health Care System	Classi-fication Codes		Utilization Data					Expense (thousands) of dollars		
★ American Hospital Association (AHA) membership □ Joint Commission on Accreditation of Healthcare Organizations (JCAHO) accreditation ○ American Osteopathic Association (AOA) accreditation △ Commission on Accreditation of Rehabilitation Facilities (CARF) accreditation	Control	Service	Staffed Beds	Admissions	Census	Outpatient Visits	Births	Total	Payroll	Personnel
PROMISE SPECIALTY HOSPITAL OF PHOENIX, 1800 East Van Buren Street, 2nd Floor, Zip 85006; tel. 602/251–8525, (Nonreporting) **A**9 10 **S** Promise Healthcare, Lafayette, LA Primary Contact: Brian Holt, Chief Executive Officer Web address: www.promise–phoenix.com	33	80	36	—	—	—	—	—	—	—
✖ △ **ST. JOSEPH'S HOSPITAL AND MEDICAL CENTER**, 350 West Thomas Road, Zip 85013–4496, Mailing Address: P.O. Box 2071, Zip 85001–2071; tel. 602/406–3000 **A**1 2 3 5 7 8 9 10 **F**1 2 5 8 9 11 12 14 15 16 17 18 19 20 21 22 23 24 27 29 31 32 33 34 35 36 37 38 39 40 42 43 44 45 46 47 48 49 50 52 53 55 56 57 58 59 60 61 62 63 64 65 66 67 68 69 70 72 73 75 79 81 82 84 85 86 87 88 90 92 94 95 96 97 98 106 108 109 110 **P**4 5 6 **S** Catholic Healthcare West, San Francisco, CA Primary Contact: Linda A. Hunt, President COO: Patricia White, R.N., MS, Chief Operating Officer CFO: Dennis Laraway, Chief Financial Officer CMO: Robert Pryor, M.D., Chief Medical Officer CIO: Chip Venable, Chief Information Officer CHR: Maureen Sterbach, Vice President Human Resources Web address: www.ichosestjoes.com	21	10	536	31703	415	353553	5968	481817	185514	4542
□ **ST. LUKE'S BEHAVIORAL HEALTH CENTER**, 1800 East Van Buren, Zip 85006–3742; tel. 602/251–8546, (Nonreporting) **A**1 9 10 **S** IASIS Healthcare, Franklin, TN Primary Contact: Paul M. Jenson, Chief Executive Officer Web address: www.iasishealthcare.com	33	22	85	—	—	—	—	—	—	—
✖ **ST. LUKE'S MEDICAL CENTER**, 1800 East Van Buren Street, Zip 85006–3742; tel. 602/251–8100, (Nonreporting) **A**1 9 10 **S** IASIS Healthcare, Franklin, TN Primary Contact: Paul M. Jenson, Chief Executive Officer CFO: Daniel D. Powell, Chief Financial Officer CMO: Dolores Marshall, Chief Nursing Officer CIO: Marlena Cantelope, Director Management Information Systems CHR: Robert Bodine, Director Human Resources Web address: www.iasishealthcare.com	33	10	225	—	—	—	—	—	—	—
□ **SURGICAL SPECIALTY HOSPITAL OF ARIZONA**, (Formerly Arizona Surgical Hospital), 6501 North 19th Avenue, Zip 85015; tel. 602/795–6020 **A**1 9 10 **F**10 21 28 37 63 64 81 110 Primary Contact: Beverly Carpenter, Chief Executive Officer	32	13	27	119	1	931	0	5846	1646	43
✖ **U. S. PUBLIC HEALTH SERVICE PHOENIX INDIAN MEDICAL CENTER**, 4212 North 16th Street, Zip 85016–5389; tel. 602/263–1200 **A**1 9 10 **F**2 4 9 10 11 12 21 22 23 24 26 27 28 29 30 31 32 33 35 37 38 39 41 42 44 46 47 48 50 52 53 55 57 59 61 62 63 65 66 70 72 73 74 75 76 77 81 85 88 89 93 94 96 97 106 108 109 110 **P**4 5 **S** U. S. Indian Health Service, Rockville, MD Primary Contact: John Meeth, M.D., Acting Chief Executive Officer COO: Rinda Hathcoat, Associate Director Fiscal and Administrative Services CFO: Geraldine Harney, Chief Financial Officer CMO: Dave Civic, Associate Director Clinical Services CIO: Vina Montour, Director, Information Technology CHR: Geraldine Fox, Chief Human Resources Web address: www.ihs.gov	47	10	84	4293	51	—	—	101117	49700	1056
PRESCOTT—Yavapai County										
✖ **NORTHERN ARIZONA VA HEALTH CARE SYSTEM**, 500 Highway 89 North, Zip 86313–5000; tel. 928/445–4860, (Total facility includes 85 beds in nursing home–type unit) (Nonreporting) **A**1 9 **S** Department of Veterans Affairs, Washington, DC Primary Contact: Deborah A. Thompson, Director CFO: Michael Kuchyak, Resource Manager CMO: Michael A. Spooner, Chief of Staff CIO: David McAllister, Ph.D., Chief Information Officer Web address: www.va.gov/sta/guide/home.asp	45	10	236	—	—	—	—	—	—	—
✖ **YAVAPAI REGIONAL MEDICAL CENTER**, 1003 Willow Creek Road, Zip 86301–1668; tel. 928/445–2700 **A**1 9 10 20 **F**11 12 15 21 22 26 27 28 29 33 36 37 38 41 42 45 46 47 49 51 52 53 55 57 58 59 60 61 62 63 64 65 66 69 81 84 88 94 95 96 106 108 110 **P**5 Primary Contact: Timothy Barnett, Chief Executive Officer COO: Kevin Keighron, Chief Operating Officer CFO: Doug Bristol, Chief Financial Officer CIO: David Woodcock, Director Information Systems Web address: www.yrmc.org	16	10	125	9438	92	107450	1126	107656	49720	957
SACATON—Pinal County										
✖ **HUHUKAM MEMORIAL HOSPITAL**, Seed Farm and Skill Center Road, Zip 85247–0038, Mailing Address: P.O. Box 38, Zip 85247–0038; tel. 602/528–1200 **A**1 9 10 18 **F**2 4 21 24 26 27 28 30 31 32 33 34 39 41 47 48 52 53 58 62 65 66 69 70 77 88 89 92 94 96 108 109 110 **S** U. S. Indian Health Service, Rockville, MD Primary Contact: Loren Ellery, M.P.H., Chief Executive Officer COO: Karen Shammas, Chief Operating Officer CFO: Corrine Wilson, Chief Financial Officer CMO: Noel Habib, M.D., Chief Medical Officer CHR: Michael Freeman, Human Resources Director Web address: www.grhc.org	23	10	10	548	6	115968	0	—	—	430

Hospital, Address, Telephone, Approval, Facility, and Physician Codes, Health Care System	Classi-fication Codes		Utilization Data						Expense (thousands) of dollars		
★ American Hospital Association (AHA) membership □ Joint Commission on Accreditation of Healthcare Organizations (JCAHO) accreditation ○ American Osteopathic Association (AOA) accreditation △ Commission on Accreditation of Rehabilitation Facilities (CARF) accreditation	Control	Service	Staffed Beds	Admissions	Census	Outpatient Visits	Births	Total	Payroll	Personnel

SAFFORD—Graham County

⊠ **MT. GRAHAM REGIONAL MEDICAL CENTER**, 1600 20th Avenue, Zip 85546–4097; tel. 928/348–4000 **A**1 9 10 20 **F**2 9 11 12 21 23 27 28 29 33 36 37 38 39 41 46 47 48 51 52 55 58 59 62 63 64 65 66 69 81 84 87 88 93 94 96 97 98 106 108 110 Primary Contact: Patrick O'Brien, Chief Executive Officer COO: Roland Knox, Vice President and Chief Operating Officer CFO: Lori Meyer, Vice President and Chief Financial Officer CIO: Roland Knox, Vice President and Chief Operating Officer CHR: Sandy Frazier, Vice President Human Resources and Medical Staff Services Web address: www.mtgraham.org	16	10	55	2397	23	61435	472	31362	12382	300

SAN CARLOS—Gila County

⊠ **U. S. PUBLIC HEALTH SERVICE INDIAN HOSPITAL**, Mailing Address: P.O. Box 208, Zip 85550–0208; tel. 928/475–2371, (Nonreporting) **A**1 10 **S** U. S. Indian Health Service, Rockville, MD Primary Contact: Nella J. Ben, Chief Executive Officer COO: Nella J. Ben, Chief Executive Officer CFO: Shirley M. Boni, Administrative Officer CMO: Karen Health, M.D., Clinical Director CIO: Shirley M. Boni, Administrative Officer CHR: Shirley M. Boni, Administrative Officer	47	10	8	—	—	—	—	—	—	—

SCOTTSDALE—Maricopa County

⊠ **BANNER BEHAVIORAL HEALTH HOSPITAL**, 7575 East Earll Drive, Zip 85251–6915; tel. 480/941–7500 **A**1 9 10 **F**3 4 21 22 26 27 28 29 31 33 44 45 47 52 53 58 65 66 71 72 73 74 75 76 77 78 94 96 108 **P**5 **S** Banner Health, Phoenix, AZ Primary Contact: Patricia A. Little–Upah, Chief Executive Officer COO: Thomas Williams, Clinical Administrator CFO: Melonie Bonnett, Financial Analyst CMO: James Clark, M.D., Medical Director CIO: Melonie Bonnett, Financial Analyst CHR: Joe Abdai, Chief Human Resources Web address: www.bannerhealth.com	23	22	100	2914	63	7201	0	13657	7945	190
⊠ **HEALTHSOUTH SCOTTSDALE REHABILITATION HOSPITAL**, 9630 East Shea Boulevard, Zip 85260; tel. 480/551–5400 **A**1 10 **F**21 27 28 52 60 68 69 108 **S** HEALTHSOUTH Corporation, Birmingham, AL Primary Contact: Richard Schulz, Administrator Web address: www.healthsouth.com	33	46	46	1044	42	—	0	—	—	183
⊠ **SCOTTSDALE HEALTHCARE–OSBORN**, 7400 East Osborn Road, Zip 85251–6403; tel. 480/882–4000 **A**1 2 3 5 9 10 **F**2 9 10 11 15 16 17 18 19 21 22 23 24 27 28 29 30 31 33 34 37 38 40 42 43 44 45 46 47 48 49 50 51 52 53 57 58 59 60 61 63 64 66 68 69 70 81 82 84 85 87 88 89 94 96 98 106 108 109 110 **P**6 **S** Scottsdale Healthcare, Scottsdale, AZ Primary Contact: Gary E. Baker, Vice President CFO: Randy B. Luster, Senior Vice President and Chief Financial Officer CMO: James Burke, M.D., Senior Vice President and Chief Medical Officer CIO: James R. Cramer, Vice President and Chief Information Officer Web address: www.shc.org	23	10	300	17481	204	73591	1764	226037	87194	2198
⊠ **SCOTTSDALE HEALTHCARE–SHEA**, 9003 East Shea Boulevard, Zip 85260–6771; tel. 480/323–3000 **A**1 2 9 10 **F**2 9 10 11 12 14 15 17 19 21 22 23 24 25 26 27 28 29 30 32 33 37 38 39 40 41 42 43 44 46 47 48 49 50 51 52 53 55 56 57 58 59 60 61 62 63 64 65 66 68 69 79 81 82 84 86 87 88 89 90 93 94 95 96 98 106 107 108 109 110 **P**6 **S** Scottsdale Healthcare, Scottsdale, AZ Primary Contact: Peggy Reiley, Senior Vice President and Chief Clinical Officer COO: Jeffrey K. Norman, Chief Operating Officer CFO: Randy B. Luster, Senior Vice President and Chief Financial Officer CMO: James Burke, M.D., Senior Vice President and Chief Medical Officer CIO: James R. Cramer, Vice President and Chief Information Officer CHR: Carol Henderson, Vice President Human Resources Web address: www.shc.org	23	10	343	22924	231	110225	4287	250252	90972	1679

SELLS—Pima County

⊠ **U. S. PUBLIC HEALTH SERVICE INDIAN HOSPITAL**, Mailing Address: P.O. Box 548, Zip 85634–0548; tel. 520/383–7251, (Nonreporting) **A**1 10 **S** U. S. Indian Health Service, Rockville, MD Primary Contact: Darrell Rumley, Service Unit Director CFO: Nadine K. Kauley, Chief Financial Officer CIO: Jason Lockwood, Information Systems Manager	47	10	34	—	—	—	—	—	—	—

SHOW LOW—Navajo County

★ **NAVAPACHE REGIONAL MEDICAL CENTER**, 2200 Show Low Lake Road, Zip 85901–7800; tel. 928/537–4375 **A**9 10 20 **F**2 3 9 11 12 14 21 22 23 26 27 28 29 30 31 33 34 37 39 40 41 42 46 47 48 51 52 53 55 56 57 58 59 60 61 62 63 64 65 66 67 68 70 71 80 81 82 84 85 87 88 92 94 106 108 **S** Brim Healthcare, Inc., Brentwood, TN Primary Contact: Leigh Cox, Chief Executive Officer CFO: Brian Hoefle, Chief Financial Officer CMO: David Van Buren, M.D., Chief of Staff CIO: Kent McQuillan, Chief Information Officer CHR: Correen Bales, Director Human Resources Web address: www.nrmc.org	23	10	66	5140	41	62094	935	55622	21484	534

Many Facility Codes have changed. Please refer to the AHA Guide Code Chart. © 2005 AHA Guide

Hospital, Address, Telephone, Approval, Facility, and Physician Codes, Health Care System	Classification Codes		Utilization Data					Expense (thousands) of dollars		
★ American Hospital Association (AHA) membership □ Joint Commission on Accreditation of Healthcare Organizations (JCAHO) accreditation ○ American Osteopathic Association (AOA) accreditation △ Commission on Accreditation of Rehabilitation Facilities (CARF) accreditation	Control	Service	Staffed Beds	Admissions	Census	Outpatient Visits	Births	Total	Payroll	Personnel

SIERRA VISTA—Cochise County

☒ **SIERRA VISTA REGIONAL HEALTH CENTER**, 300 El Camino Real, Zip 85635–2899; tel. 520/458–4641 **A**1 9 10 20 **F**2 9 11 12 16 21 22 33 36 37 39 42 53 55 59 60 63 64 69 81 84 87 88 94 96 106 108 110
Primary Contact: Margaret Hepburn, President and Chief Executive Officer
COO: Linda Wojtowicz, Vice President Patient Care Services and Chief Operating Officer
CFO: Bruce J. Norton, Vice President Finance and Chief Financial Officer
CIO: Ed Dindal, Information Services Manager
CHR: Marie Wurth, Vice President Human Resources and Public Relations Officer
Web address: www.svrhc.org

| | 23 | 10 | 77 | 5558 | 45 | 86886 | 1460 | 56125 | 26262 | 656 |

SPRINGERVILLE—Apache County

WHITE MOUNTAIN REGIONAL MEDICAL CENTER, 118 South Mountain Avenue, Zip 85938–5104; tel. 928/333–4368 **A**9 10 20 **F**2 29 33 46 48 52 58 60 63 69 81 88 108
Primary Contact: Ann Coleman–Hall, Chief Executive Officer
Web address: www.wmrmc.com

| | 23 | 10 | 12 | 532 | 3 | 67351 | 0 | — | — | 105 |

SUN CITY—Maricopa County

☒ **WALTER O. BOSWELL MEMORIAL HOSPITAL**, 10401 West Thunderbird Boulevard, Zip 85351–3092, Mailing Address: P.O. Box 1690, Zip 85372–1690; tel. 623/977–7211 **A**1 2 9 10 **F**2 9 12 14 17 19 21 22 23 26 27 28 33 37 42 44 47 49 52 54 55 57 58 60 61 62 63 66 68 69 77 78 81 82 84 85 87 88 94 107 108 **P**1 8 **S** Sun Health Corporation, Sun City, AZ
Primary Contact: Thomas C. Dickson, Chief Executive Officer
CFO: William Sellner, Vice President and Chief Financial Officer
CIO: David Runt, Vice President Information Services and Chief Information Officer
CHR: Frank Cummins, Vice President Human Resources
Web address: www.sunhealth.org

| | 23 | 10 | 324 | 20891 | 270 | 100315 | 0 | 122616 | 54928 | 1883 |

SUN CITY WEST—Maricopa County

☒ **DEL E. WEBB MEMORIAL HOSPITAL**, 14502 West Meeker Boulevard, Zip 85375–5299, Mailing Address: P.O. Box 5169, Sun City, Zip 85375–5169; tel. 623/214–4000, (Total facility includes 27 beds in nursing home–type unit) **A**1 9 10 **F**2 4 9 11 12 15 17 21 22 23 27 28 29 33 34 37 38 44 49 52 55 57 58 59 60 61 62 63 64 65 66 68 69 71 73 74 75 76 77 78 81 82 84 85 87 88 92 94 106 107 108 109 **P**1 8 **S** Sun Health Corporation, Sun City, AZ
Primary Contact: Jo Adkins, Chief Executive Officer
CFO: William Sellner, Vice President and Chief Financial Officer
CIO: David Runt, Chief Information Officer
Web address: www.sunhealth.org

| | 23 | 10 | 334 | 15260 | 198 | 120230 | 1869 | 122681 | 54927 | 1143 |

TEMPE—Maricopa County

□ **TEMPE ST. LUKE'S HOSPITAL**, 1500 South Mill Avenue, Zip 85281–6699; tel. 480/784–5510, (Nonreporting) **A**1 9 10 12 13 **S** IASIS Healthcare, Franklin, TN
Primary Contact: Jeff R. Egbert, Chief Executive Officer
Web address: www.tempestlukehospital.com

| | 33 | 10 | 110 | — | — | — | — | — | — | — |

TUBA CITY—Coconino County

☒ **TUBA CITY INDIAN MEDICAL CENTER**, 167 Main Street, Zip 86045–0611, Mailing Address: P.O. Box 600, Zip 86045–0600; tel. 928/283–2501, (Nonreporting) **A**1 5 10 **S** U. S. Indian Health Service, Rockville, MD
Primary Contact: Scott Deasy, M.D., Acting Chief Executive Officer
CFO: James Hopkins, Finance Officer
Web address: www.tcrhcc.org

| | 47 | 10 | 69 | | | | | | | |

TUCSON—Pima County

☒ **CARONDELET ST. JOSEPH'S HOSPITAL–TUCSON**, 350 North Wilmot Road, Zip 85711–2678; tel. 520/296–3211 **A**1 9 10 **F**2 4 9 11 12 14 15 17 21 22 26 27 28 31 33 35 36 37 38 39 46 47 48 50 52 53 54 55 57 58 59 60 61 62 63 66 68 69 71 73 74 75 76 77 78 81 82 84 88 94 95 96 97 108 109 110 **S** Ascension Health, Saint Louis, MO
Primary Contact: Wesley E. Colvin, Chief Executive Officer
CFO: Tom Pepping, Chief Financial Officer
CMO: Jose M. Santiago, M.D., Senior Vice President and Chief Medical Officer
CIO: John Braswell, Chief Information Officer
CHR: Linda Werbylo, Vice President Human Resources
Web address: www.carondelet.org

| | 21 | 10 | 287 | 16269 | 202 | 147014 | 2438 | 144246 | 61804 | 1163 |

☒ **CARONDELET ST. MARY'S HOSPITAL–TUCSON**, 1601 West St. Mary's Road, Zip 85745–2682; tel. 520/872–3000 **A**1 9 10 **F**2 4 9 12 13 14 15 17 21 22 26 27 28 31 33 35 36 37 38 39 40 46 47 48 49 50 52 53 55 57 60 61 62 63 66 68 69 71 73 74 75 76 77 78 81 82 84 86 88 94 96 97 108 110 **S** Ascension Health, Saint Louis, MO
Primary Contact: Gregory R. Angle, Chief Executive Officer
CFO: Tom Pepping, Chief Financial Officer
CMO: Jose M. Santiago, M.D., Senior Vice President and Chief Medical Officer
CIO: John Braswell, Chief Information Officer
CHR: Linda Werbylo, Vice President Human Resources
Web address: www.carondelet.org

| | 21 | 10 | 402 | 16851 | 228 | 132027 | 0 | 157496 | 65848 | 1210 |

□ **CORNERSTONE HOSPITAL OF SOUTHEAST ARIZONA**, 7220 East Rosewood Drive, Zip 85710; tel. 520/546–4595 **A**1 9 10 **F**2 21 28 32 33 58 66 94 110 **S** Cornerstone Healthcare Group, Austin, TX
Primary Contact: Louise Cassidy, Chief Executive Officer
Web address: www.cornerstonehealthcaregroup.com

| | 33 | 10 | 34 | 402 | 27 | 0 | 0 | — | — | 88 |

AZ

Hospital, Address, Telephone, Approval, Facility, and Physician Codes, Health Care System	Classi-fication Codes		Utilization Data					Expense (thousands) of dollars		
★ American Hospital Association (AHA) membership ☐ Joint Commission on Accreditation of Healthcare Organizations (JCAHO) accreditation ◯ American Osteopathic Association (AOA) accreditation △ Commission on Accreditation of Rehabilitation Facilities (CARF) accreditation	Control	Service	Staffed Beds	Admissions	Census	Outpatient Visits	Births	Total	Payroll	Personnel
⊠ **EL DORADO HOSPITAL**, 1400 North Wilmot Road, Zip 85712–4498, Mailing Address: P.O. Box 13070, Zip 85732–3070; tel. 520/886–6361 **A**1 9 10 **F**2 9 14 15 17 21 22 23 26 27 28 33 37 39 45 46 47 48 53 54 55 57 58 60 62 63 64 68 69 71 73 74 76 82 88 94 108 110 **P**4 **S** TMC HealthCare, Tucson, AZ Primary Contact: Rhonda Dean, Chief Executive Officer Web address: www.eldoradohospital.com	33	10	90	5974	76	27933	0	58908	19264	457
⊠ **HEALTHSOUTH REHABILITATION HOSPITAL OF SOUTHERN ARIZONA**, 1921 West Hospital Drive, Zip 85704–7806; tel. 520/742–2800, (Nonreporting) **A**1 10 **S** HEALTHSOUTH Corporation, Birmingham, AL Primary Contact: Elena Roman, Administrator Web address: www.healthsouth.com	33	46	60	—	—	—	—	—	—	—
⊠ **HEALTHSOUTH REHABILITATION INSTITUTE OF TUCSON**, 2650 North Wyatt Drive, Zip 85712–6108; tel. 520/325–1300, (Nonreporting) **A**1 10 **S** HEALTHSOUTH Corporation, Birmingham, AL Primary Contact: Kelly Silverschlag, Administrator COO: Dave Tupper, Chief Operating Officer CFO: Mary Donovan, Controller CMO: Jon Larson, Medical Director CIO: Mary Donovan, Controller CHR: Risa Noble, Director Human Resources Web address: www.healthsouth.com	33	46	80	—	—	—	—	—	—	—
☐ **KINDRED HOSPITAL – TUCSON**, 355 North Wilmot Road, Zip 85711–2635; tel. 520/584–4500 **A**1 10 **F**2 21 22 26 27 28 37 38 58 60 65 66 94 110 **P**6 **S** Kindred Healthcare, Louisville, KY Primary Contact: Alex Wilcox, R.N., Chief Executive Officer Web address: www.kindredhealthcare.com	33	80	51	354	26	0	0	12756	6688	138
⊠ **NORTHWEST MEDICAL CENTER**, 6200 North La Cholla Boulevard, Zip 85741–3599; tel. 520/742–9000 **A**1 9 10 **F**2 6 10 11 12 14 15 17 19 21 22 23 26 28 29 33 37 42 44 45 46 47 48 52 54 55 57 58 59 60 61 62 63 64 65 66 68 69 82 88 92 94 96 98 106 107 108 109 110 **S** Triad Hospitals, Inc., Plano, TX Primary Contact: W. Jefferson Comer, Sr, FACHE, Chief Executive Officer CFO: Ronald Patrick, Chief Financial Officer Web address: www.northwestmedicalcenter.com	33	10	250	20829	220	245212	2706	197526	70551	1619
PALO VERDE MENTAL HEALTH SERVICES See Tucson Medical Center										
SIERRA TUCSON, 39580 South Lago Del Oro Parkway, Zip 85739–9637; tel. 520/624–4000, (Nonreporting) Primary Contact: David E. Anderson, Ph.D., Chief Executive Officer Web address: www.sierratucson.com	33	82	77	—	—	—	—	—	—	—
⊠ △ **SOUTHERN ARIZONA VETERANS AFFAIRS HEALTH CARE SYSTEM**, 3601 South 6th Avenue, Zip 85723–0002; tel. 520/792–1450 **A**1 3 5 7 8 **F**2 3 4 9 12 15 17 19 21 22 23 28 29 31 32 33 36 37 38 39 42 44 45 46 47 48 49 50 51 52 53 55 57 58 60 61 62 63 64 65 66 69 70 71 73 74 75 76 77 78 81 82 84 85 86 88 92 93 94 96 106 107 108 109 110 **P**1 **S** Department of Veterans Affairs, Washington, DC Primary Contact: Jonathan H. Gardner, Chief Executive Officer COO: Debra Hirschman, Chief Operating Officer, Patient Support Services CFO: Larry Korn, Financial Manager CMO: Jayendra H. Shah, M.D., Chief Medical Officer CIO: Donald Meehan, Chief Information Officer Web address: www.va.gov/sta/guide/home.asp	45	10	279	6596	135	476387	0	206885	112714	1593
☐ **TUCSON HEART HOSPITAL**, 4888 North Stone Avenue, Zip 85704; tel. 520/696–2328 **A**1 10 **F**2 14 15 21 22 26 28 33 42 48 63 64 66 81 82 85 88 106 108 110 **P**5 **S** MedCath, Inc., Charlotte, NC Primary Contact: Gary Toche, President Web address: www.tucsonhearthospital.com	33	42	60	3582	29	14666	0	46552	14886	300
⊠ **TUCSON MEDICAL CENTER**, 5301 East Grant Road, Zip 85712–2874; tel. 520/327–5461, (Includes PALO VERDE MENTAL HEALTH SERVICES, 2695 North Craycroft, Zip 85712–2244; tel. 520/324–4340) **A**1 3 5 9 10 **F**2 4 9 11 12 14 15 17 19 21 23 24 26 27 28 29 31 32 33 34 35 36 37 38 39 44 45 46 47 48 49 52 53 54 55 56 57 58 59 60 61 62 63 64 66 67 69 71 72 73 74 75 76 77 78 81 84 85 87 88 93 94 95 96 104 106 108 109 110 **S** TMC HealthCare, Tucson, AZ Primary Contact: Frank D. Alvarez, President and Chief Executive Officer COO: Judy F. Rich, Senior Vice President and Chief Operations Officer CFO: Nestorio Tanpiengco, Senior Vice President and Chief Financial Officer CMO: Richard P. Rodriguez, M.D., Senior Vice President and Chief Medical Officer CIO: Frank R. Marini, Director Information Services CHR: Gloria Smith, Vice President Human Resources Web address: www.tmcaz.com	23	10	533	32861	358	215220	5890	290962	111719	2559
⊠ **UNIVERSITY MEDICAL CENTER**, 1501 North Campbell Avenue, Zip 85724–5128; tel. 520/694–6148 **A**1 3 5 8 9 10 **F**2 5 7 9 11 12 14 15 16 17 18 19 20 21 22 23 26 27 28 29 30 32 33 34 35 37 38 39 40 41 42 43 44 46 47 48 50 51 52 53 55 56 57 58 59 60 61 62 63 64 65 66 67 69 70 71 72 73 74 75 76 77 79 80 81 82 83 84 85 87 88 89 90 92 93 94 95 96 99 100 101 102 103 104 105 106 107 108 109 110 **P**4 6 Primary Contact: Gregory A. Pivirotto, President and Chief Executive Officer CFO: Kevin J. Burns, Chief Financial Officer CIO: Sam Miller, Chief Information Officer CHR: Bob Black, Vice President Web address: www.umcaz.edu	23	10	304	19463	257	421038	2640	326592	138255	2867

Hospital, Address, Telephone, Approval, Facility, and Physician Codes, Health Care System	Classi-fication Codes		Utilization Data					Expense (thousands) of dollars		
★ American Hospital Association (AHA) membership ☐ Joint Commission on Accreditation of Healthcare Organizations (JCAHO) accreditation ◯ American Osteopathic Association (AOA) accreditation △ Commission on Accreditation of Rehabilitation Facilities (CARF) accreditation	Control	Service	Staffed Beds	Admissions	Census	Outpatient Visits	Births	Total	Payroll	Personnel

☐ **UNIVERSITY PHYSICIANS HEALTHCARE HOSPITAL AT KINO CAMPUS**, (Formerly Kino Community Hospital), 2800 East Ajo Way, Zip 85713–6289; tel. 520/294–4471, (Total facility includes 20 beds in nursing home–type unit) (Nonreporting) **A**1 3 5 9 10 Primary Contact: Norm Botsford, Chief Executive Officer Web address: www.uph.org	13	10	114	—	—	—	—	—	—	—
WHITERIVER—Navajo County										
☒ **U. S. PUBLIC HEALTH SERVICE INDIAN HOSPITAL–WHITERIVER**, State Route 73, Box 860, Zip 85941–0860; tel. 928/338–4911, (Nonreporting) **A**1 10 18 **S** U. S. Indian Health Service, Rockville, MD Primary Contact: Dean Seyler, Chief Executive Officer CFO: Desdemona Leslie, Finance Officer CIO: Russell Barker, Chief Information Officer Web address: www.ihs.gov	47	10	15	—	—	—	—	—	—	—
WICKENBURG—Maricopa County										
★ **WICKENBURG REGIONAL MEDICAL CENTER**, 520 Rose Lane, Zip 85390–1447; tel. 928/684–5421 **A**10 18 **F**9 21 33 37 41 42 44 46 55 58 60 63 65 68 69 81 82 88 94 96 107 Primary Contact: Dale A. Decker, Administrator CFO: Ron Smith, Chief Financial Officer Web address: www.wickenburgregional.com	23	10	6	217	2	16687	—	—	—	79
WILLCOX—Cochise County										
★ **NORTHERN COCHISE COMMUNITY HOSPITAL**, 901 West Rex Allen Drive, Zip 85643–1009; tel. 520/384–3541, (Total facility includes 24 beds in nursing home–type unit) **A**9 10 18 20 **F**9 12 21 27 33 34 46 52 63 69 70 81 92 94 96 97 **P**6 Primary Contact: Chris Cronberg, Chief Executive Officer CFO: Gary Pea, Chief Financial Officer CIO: Ellen Clark, Community Relations Officer Web address: www.ncch.net	23	10	48	368	33	17265	0	8555	4626	121
WINSLOW—Navajo County										
★ **WINSLOW MEMORIAL HOSPITAL**, 1501 Williamson Avenue, Zip 86047–2797; tel. 928/289–4691 **A**9 10 18 20 **F**2 11 33 46 48 59 63 68 69 81 88 94 96 Primary Contact: Jeffrey J. Hamblen, Administrator CFO: Lee H. Holter, Chief Financial Officer CMO: Perry Mitchell, M.D., Chief of Staff CHR: Cheryl Peterson, Director Human Resources	23	10	25	1159	7	7238	214	—	—	—
YUMA—Imperial County U. S. PUBLIC HEALTH SERVICE INDIAN HOSPITAL See Winterhaven, CA										
☒ **YUMA REGIONAL MEDICAL CENTER**, 2400 South Avenue A, Zip 85364–7170; tel. 928/344–2000 **A**1 9 10 19 20 **F**2 9 11 12 15 17 19 21 22 24 27 28 29 32 33 35 38 42 46 48 49 51 52 53 55 56 57 58 59 60 62 63 64 66 81 82 84 85 86 87 88 93 94 96 107 108 109 110 Primary Contact: Robert T. Olsen, FACHE, President and Chief Executive Officer CFO: Pat Walz, Chief Financial Officer CMO: Stewart Hamilton, M.D., Vice President Medical Affairs CIO: Gene Shaw, Chief Information Officer CHR: Sharon Gardner, Vice President Human Resources Web address: www.yumaregional.org	23	10	277	17748	179	148841	3466	170471	72321	1753
☒ **YUMA REHABILITATION HOSPITAL**, 901 West 24th Street, Zip 85364; tel. 928/726–5000, (Nonreporting) **A**1 10 **S** HEALTHSOUTH Corporation, Birmingham, AL Primary Contact: Dennis R. Shelby, Chief Executive Officer CFO: Ronald Wild, Controller	33	46	41	—	—	—	—	—	—	—

AZ

ARKANSAS

Hospital, Address, Telephone, Approval, Facility, and Physician Codes, Health Care System ★ American Hospital Association (AHA) membership □ Joint Commission on Accreditation of Healthcare Organizations (JCAHO) accreditation ○ American Osteopathic Association (AOA) accreditation △ Commission on Accreditation of Rehabilitation Facilities (CARF) accreditation	Classi- fication Codes		Utilization Data					Expense (thousands) of dollars		
	Control	Service	Staffed Beds	Admissions	Census	Outpatient Visits	Births	Total	Payroll	Personnel
ARKADELPHIA—Clark County										
⊞ **BAPTIST HEALTH MEDICAL CENTER–ARKADELPHIA**, 3050 Twin Rivers Drive, Zip 71923–4299; tel. 870/245–2622 **A**1 9 10 18 20 **F**2 6 9 11 12 21 27 28 33 34 36 48 50 51 54 55 59 63 69 81 82 84 88 94 97 108 **S** Baptist Health, Little Rock, AR Primary Contact: Dan Gathright, Senior Vice President and Administrator Web address: www.baptist–health.org	23	10	25	1537	15	21528	198	15207	6961	204
ASHDOWN—Little River County										
★ **LITTLE RIVER MEMORIAL HOSPITAL**, 451 West Locke Street, Zip 71822–3398; tel. 870/898–5011 **A**9 10 18 **F**2 12 21 23 27 29 33 34 46 48 51 52 69 81 85 88 97 110 Primary Contact: David Deaton, Administrator and Chief Executive Officer CFO: Barbra Crow, Chief Financial Officer	13	10	25	608	9	8982	0	5848	3351	91
BARLING—Sebastian County										
VISTA HEALTH OF FORT SMITH, 10301 Mayo Drive, Zip 72923; tel. 479/494–5700 **A**10 **F**27 28 66 71 72 73 74 75 77 94 **P**6 Primary Contact: Patrick Kelly, Chief Executive Officer Web address: www.vistahealthservices.com	33	22	57	1005	41	3173	0	7002	4296	118
BATESVILLE—Independence County										
⊞ △ **WHITE RIVER MEDICAL CENTER**, 1710 Harrison Street, Zip 72501–2197, Mailing Address: P.O. Box 2197, Zip 72503–2197; tel. 870/793–1200, (Total facility includes 14 beds in nursing home–type unit) **A**1 7 9 10 19 20 **F**2 9 10 11 12 14 15 17 21 22 23 26 27 28 29 32 33 34 37 39 40 41 46 48 49 50 51 52 55 58 59 60 61 62 63 64 66 68 69 71 72 74 76 77 80 81 82 84 86 88 92 93 94 95 96 106 107 108 109 110 **P**8 Primary Contact: Gary Bebow, Administrator and Chief Executive Officer COO: Tammy Gavin, Assistant Administrator and Chief Operating Officer CFO: Mike Weeks, Chief Financial Officer CIO: Shirley Davis, Director Information Services CHR: Charlie Wright, Assistant Administrator Human Resources Web address: www.wrmc.com	23	10	174	8188	113	110942	481	81591	30373	891
BENTON—Saline County										
□ **RIVENDELL BEHAVIORAL HEALTH SERVICES**, 100 Rivendell Drive, Zip 72015–9100; tel. 501/316–1255 **A**1 9 10 **F**21 26 31 42 48 52 58 71 72 73 74 75 77 78 94 96 98 **P**5 **S** Universal Health Services, Inc., King of Prussia, PA Primary Contact: Scott Williams, Administrator Web address: www.ccskids.com	33	52	77	1115	72	13312	0	7530	—	169
⊞ △ **SALINE MEMORIAL HOSPITAL**, 1 Medical Park Drive, Zip 72015–3354; tel. 501/776–6000, (Total facility includes 5 beds in nursing home–type unit) **A**1 7 9 10 **F**2 6 9 11 12 15 21 22 23 26 27 28 29 32 33 36 46 48 51 52 55 58 59 60 62 63 64 66 68 69 71 81 82 84 88 92 93 94 106 108 **P**8 **S** Quorum Health Resources, Plano, TX Primary Contact: James Richardson, FACHE, Chief Executive Officer CFO: Carla Robertson, Chief Financial Officer CMO: Bill Thomas, M.D., Vice President Medical Affairs and Chief Information Officer CIO: Bill Thomas, M.D., Vice President Medical Affairs and Chief Information Officer CHR: Pat Pope, Vice President Human Resources Web address: www.scmc.com	23	10	106	5912	79	55805	621	52734	23376	705
BENTONVILLE—Benton County										
★ **NORTHWEST MEDICAL CENTER OF BENTON COUNTY**, 3000 Medical Center Parkway, Zip 72712; tel. 479/553–1000 **A**9 10 **F**2 9 11 12 15 17 19 21 22 27 28 33 37 40 42 44 46 47 48 52 53 55 57 58 59 60 61 62 63 66 69 70 81 82 84 88 94 96 107 108 109 110 **P**5 7 8 **S** Triad Hospitals, Inc., Plano, TX Primary Contact: Gary N. Looper, Chief Executive Officer CFO: Mary Millington, Chief Financial Officer CMO: Ronny Phipps, M.D., Chief of Staff CIO: Shannon Williams, Chief Information Officer CHR: Kim Swieter, Vice President Human Resources Web address: www.northwesthealth.com	33	10	73	4675	46	57618	512	41100	16069	401
BERRYVILLE—Carroll County										
⊞ **ST. JOHN'S HOSPITAL–BERRYVILLE**, 214 Carter Street, Zip 72616–4303; tel. 870/423–3355 **A**1 9 10 **F**2 9 11 12 21 22 23 26 27 28 29 33 35 36 41 46 47 48 50 51 52 53 55 58 59 60 61 62 63 64 65 66 69 70 81 82 85 88 92 93 94 95 96 97 106 108 109 110 **P**6 8 **S** Sisters of Mercy Health System, Chesterfield, MO Primary Contact: David Dennis, President CFO: Sharon Ash, Vice President Finance CHR: Taya James, Director Web address: www.stjohnsberryville.com	23	10	45	1833	17	20330	187	14726	7505	215

Many Facility Codes have changed. Please refer to the AHA Guide Code Chart.

Hospital, Address, Telephone, Approval, Facility, and Physician Codes, Health Care System	Classification Codes		Utilization Data					Expense (thousands) of dollars		
	Control	Service	Staffed Beds	Admissions	Census	Outpatient Visits	Births	Total	Payroll	Personnel

★ American Hospital Association (AHA) membership
☐ Joint Commission on Accreditation of Healthcare Organizations (JCAHO) accreditation
○ American Osteopathic Association (AOA) accreditation
△ Commission on Accreditation of Rehabilitation Facilities (CARF) accreditation

AR

BLYTHEVILLE—Mississippi County

⊠ **GREAT RIVER MEDICAL CENTER**, (Formerly Baptist Memorial Hospital–Blytheville), 1520 North Division Street, Zip 72315–1448, Mailing Address: P.O. Box 108, Zip 72316–0108; tel. 870/838–7300 **A**1 9 10 19 **F**2 6 9 11 12 21 23 26 27 28 33 36 41 46 48 51 52 55 59 61 62 63 69 71 76 81 82 84 88 93 108 109 **S** Ameris Health Systems, Nashville, TN
Primary Contact: Ian W. Watson, Chief Executive Officer
COO: Larry Burton, Chief Operating Officer
CFO: Alan Lovelace, Chief Financial Officer
CMO: David Dye, M.D., Chief of Staff
CIO: Ben Bizzle, Information Systems Manager
Web address: www.greatrivermc.com
Control 33, Service 10, Staffed Beds 111, Admissions 222, Census 25, Outpatient Visits 2568, Births 50, Total 1523, Payroll 640, Personnel 278

BOONEVILLE—Logan County

★ **BOONEVILLE COMMUNITY HOSPITAL**, 880 West Main Street, Zip 72927–3420, Mailing Address: P.O. Box 290, Zip 72927–0290; tel. 479/675–2800 **A**9 10 18 20 **F**2 9 21 22 33 46 48 51 52 63 70 81 97 108 **P**6
Primary Contact: Gary L. DelForge, Chief Executive Officer
CMO: William Daniel, M.D., Chief of Staff
CHR: Doris Whitaker, Human Resources Director
Web address: www.boonevillehospital.com
Control 23, Service 10, Staffed Beds 25, Admissions 807, Census 6, Outpatient Visits 7567, Births 0, Total 5583, Payroll 2548, Personnel 84

CALICO ROCK—Izard County

COMMUNITY MEDICAL CENTER OF IZARD COUNTY, 103 Grasse Street, Zip 72519, Mailing Address: P.O. Box 438, Zip 72519–0438; tel. 870/297–3726 **A**9 10 18 **F**2 9 12 21 22 23 26 27 28 29 33 36 46 48 51 52 53 58 60 61 62 63 69 70 81 84 88 92 94 96 97 108 **P**5
Primary Contact: A. Meryl Grasse, M.D., Chief Executive Officer
Control 23, Service 10, Staffed Beds 25, Admissions 680, Census 8, Outpatient Visits 3074, Births 1, Total 6053, Payroll 2841, Personnel 100

CAMDEN—Ouachita County

⊠ **OUACHITA MEDICAL CENTER**, 638 California Street, Zip 71701–4699, Mailing Address: P.O. Box 797, Zip 71701–0797; tel. 870/836–1000 **A**1 9 10 20 **F**1 3 4 6 9 11 12 21 23 26 27 33 34 36 40 45 46 48 51 52 54 55 58 59 60 61 63 69 71 76 81 84 88 93 94 97 106 108 **P**8
Primary Contact: David Cicero, President
CFO: Robert Anders, Chief Financial Officer
CHR: Mary Bridges, Director Human Resources
Web address: www.ouachitamedcenter.com
Control 23, Service 10, Staffed Beds 98, Admissions 3427, Census 37, Outpatient Visits 28515, Births 297, Total 28743, Payroll 12830, Personnel 506

CLARKSVILLE—Johnson County

★ **JOHNSON REGIONAL MEDICAL CENTER**, 1100 East Poplar Street, Zip 72830–4419, Mailing Address: P.O. Box 738, Zip 72830–0738; tel. 479/754–5454 **A**9 10 **F**2 6 9 11 12 14 21 26 27 28 32 33 46 48 51 52 55 58 59 60 63 68 69 71 76 81 82 84 85 88 94 96 97 106 109 110
Primary Contact: Larry Morse, Chief Executive Officer and Administrator
CFO: Edward Anderson, Chief Financial Officer
CIO: Deb Bjorgum, Data Processing Manager
CHR: Maribel Baker, Human Resource Director
Web address: www.jrmc.com
Control 23, Service 10, Staffed Beds 80, Admissions 2981, Census 36, Outpatient Visits 41364, Births 387, Total 22192, Payroll —, Personnel 275

CLINTON—Van Buren County

★ **OZARK HEALTH MEDICAL CENTER**, Highway 65 South, Zip 72031–9045, Mailing Address: P.O. Box 206, Zip 72031–0206; tel. 501/745–7000, (Total facility includes 132 beds in nursing home–type unit) **A**9 10 18 **F**2 9 12 21 26 27 28 29 33 44 46 48 51 52 53 60 63 65 69 81 84 85 88 92 93 94 96 97 108
Primary Contact: Herbert K. Reamey, III, Chief Executive Officer and Administrator
COO: Herbert K. Reamey, Chief Executive Officer
CFO: John Zeiler, Chief Financial Officer
CMO: Harry Starns, M.D., Chief Medical Staff
CHR: Lisa Swofford, Human Resource Director and Administrative Assistant
Web address: www.myozarkhealth.com
Control 23, Service 10, Staffed Beds 157, Admissions 908, Census 123, Outpatient Visits 17023, Births 3, Total 11690, Payroll 5536, Personnel 281

CONWAY—Faulkner County

⊠ **CONWAY REGIONAL MEDICAL CENTER**, 2302 College Avenue, Zip 72032–6297; tel. 501/329–3831 **A**1 2 9 10 **F**2 3 9 10 11 12 13 14 15 17 19 21 22 23 26 27 28 29 33 38 39 40 41 44 46 48 49 51 52 55 56 58 59 60 61 62 63 64 66 67 68 69 71 76 81 82 84 88 92 94 95 96 106 108 109 110 **P**8
Primary Contact: John N. Robbins, President and Chief Executive Officer
COO: James M. Lambert, Chief Operating Officer
CFO: Steven P. Rose, Chief Financial Officer
CMO: Bart Throneberry, M.D., Chief of Staff
CIO: Bob Hambuchen, Director Information Systems
CHR: John Dodd, Corporate Director Human Resources
Web address: www.conwayregional.org
Control 23, Service 10, Staffed Beds 149, Admissions 7146, Census 74, Outpatient Visits 107051, Births 1595, Total 84922, Payroll 35147, Personnel 880

CROSSETT—Ashley County

★ **ASHLEY COUNTY MEDICAL CENTER**, 1015 Unity Road, Zip 71635–2930, Mailing Address: P.O. Box 400, Zip 71635–0400; tel. 870/364–4111 **A**9 10 18 20 **F**2 9 11 12 22 23 26 27 28 29 33 39 41 46 48 51 52 55 58 59 60 61 62 63 64 69 71 76 81 82 84 87 88 93 94 96 97
Primary Contact: Russ D. Sword, Administrator
CFO: Shannon Clark, Chief Financial Officer
CIO: Dan Austin, Data Processing Manager
CHR: Shirley White, Director Human Resources
Web address: www.acmconline.org
Control 23, Service 10, Staffed Beds 36, Admissions 1375, Census 13, Outpatient Visits 43356, Births 118, Total 14299, Payroll 6648, Personnel 185

Hospital, Address, Telephone, Approval, Facility, and Physician Codes, Health Care System	Classi-fication Codes		Utilization Data					Expense (thousands) of dollars		
★ American Hospital Association (AHA) membership □ Joint Commission on Accreditation of Healthcare Organizations (JCAHO) accreditation ○ American Osteopathic Association (AOA) accreditation △ Commission on Accreditation of Rehabilitation Facilities (CARF) accreditation	Control	Service	Staffed Beds	Admissions	Census	Outpatient Visits	Births	Total	Payroll	Personnel

DANVILLE—Yell County

★ **CHAMBERS MEMORIAL HOSPITAL**, Highway 10 at Detroit, Zip 72833, Mailing Address: P.O. Box 639, Zip 72833–0639; tel. 479/495–2241 **A**9 10 20 **F**2 9 11 21 27 28 29 33 46 51 63 81 88 92 94 97 **P**5
Primary Contact: Scott Peek, Chief Executive Officer
CFO: Scott Peek, Chief Executive Officer and Chief Financial Officer
CMO: William A. Isely, M.D., Chief of Staff
CIO: Amber Bottoms, Director Medical Records
CHR: Stacey Lane, Executive Assistant Human Resources
Web address: www.chambershospital.com
| | 23 | 10 | 37 | 2054 | 21 | 23100 | 82 | 11696 | 5121 | 168 |

DARDANELLE—Yell County

DARDANELLE HOSPITAL, 200 North Third Street, Zip 72834–3802, Mailing Address: P.O. Box 578, Zip 72834–0578; tel. 479/229–4677 **A**9 10 18 **F**9 12 21 27 33 46 48 52 53 58 63 69 81 92 97 **P**5 6
Primary Contact: Sondra Wear, Administrator
| | 13 | 10 | 25 | 297 | 3 | 10087 | 0 | 3663 | 1921 | 73 |

DE QUEEN—Sevier County

★ **DE QUEEN REGIONAL MEDICAL CENTER**, 1306 Collin Raye Drive, Zip 71832–2198; tel. 870/584–4111 **A**9 10 18 20 **F**2 9 11 12 21 22 27 33 46 48 52 53 59 60 63 69 81 82 85 88 97 106 **S** Promise Healthcare, Lafayette, LA
Primary Contact: Amy Vines, Chief Executive Officer
COO: Teresa Hodges, Assistant Administrator
CFO: Lorie Tudor, Chief Financial Officer
Web address: www.dequeenmedicalcenter.com
| | 23 | 10 | 44 | 1486 | 12 | 35376 | 292 | 9229 | 3895 | 113 |

DE WITT—Arkansas County

★ **DEWITT HOSPITAL**, Highway 1 and Madison Street, Zip 72042–9481, Mailing Address: P.O. Box 32, Zip 72042–0032; tel. 870/946–3571, (Total facility includes 60 beds in nursing home–type unit) **A**9 10 18 **F**2 6 9 21 28 33 51 52 69 81 88 92 97 106 **P**5 8
Primary Contact: Darren Caldwell, Chief Executive Officer
CMO: Stan Burleson, M.D., Chief Medical Staff
CIO: Christy McFerrin, Chief Information Officer
| | 23 | 10 | 85 | 541 | 54 | 7698 | 0 | 6948 | 3376 | 149 |

DUMAS—Desha County

★ **DELTA MEMORIAL HOSPITAL**, 300 East Pickens Street, Zip 71639–2710, Mailing Address: P.O. Box 887, Zip 71639–0887; tel. 870/382–4303 **A**9 10 20 **F**2 9 12 14 21 27 28 29 33 37 44 46 48 51 52 59 60 63 65 66 69 71 76 81 82 88 94 96 106 108 109 110 **P**6 8 **S** Quorum Health Resources, Plano, TX
Primary Contact: Mark Deal, Chief Executive Officer
CFO: Jon Sorensen, Director Business Services
CMO: Steve Oboma Asemota, Chief of Staff
CIO: Paula Smith, Chief Information Officer
CHR: Doris Fortenberry, Human Resources Coordinator
Web address: www.deltafasthealth.com
| | 23 | 10 | 50 | 720 | 5 | 12283 | 104 | 8135 | 3142 | 106 |

EL DORADO—Union County

✶ **MEDICAL CENTER OF SOUTH ARKANSAS**, 700 West Grove Street, Zip 71730–4416, Mailing Address: P.O. Box 1998, Zip 71731–1998; tel. 870/864–3200 **A**1 9 10 19 20 **F**2 9 11 12 15 21 23 26 27 28 29 33 37 44 46 47 48 51 52 55 56 57 58 59 60 61 62 63 64 65 68 70 75 80 81 82 84 87 88 92 94 96 108 109 **P**7 8 **S** Triad Hospitals, Inc., Plano, TX
Primary Contact: Luther J. Lewis, FACHE, Chief Executive Officer
COO: Charles H. Long, Chief Operating Officer
CFO: Frank Canova, Jr, Chief Financial Officer
CHR: Judi Wilson, Director Human Resources
Web address: www.themedcenter.net
| | 32 | 10 | 140 | 5750 | 88 | 63879 | 672 | 52624 | 22947 | 662 |

EUREKA SPRINGS—Carroll County

★ **EUREKA SPRINGS HOSPITAL**, 24 Norris Street, Zip 72632–3541; tel. 479/253–7400 **A**9 10 18 **F**2 9 12 21 22 26 27 28 29 33 35 36 39 46 48 51 52 53 58 60 63 65 66 68 69 81 88 92 94 95 96 97 108 110 **P**5
Primary Contact: David Wheeler, Administrator
Web address: www.eurekaspringshospital.com
| | 14 | 10 | 15 | 352 | 6 | 3818 | 0 | 4771 | 2223 | 79 |

FAYETTEVILLE—Washington County

✶ **HEALTHSOUTH REHABILITATION HOSPITAL**, 153 East Monte Painter Drive, Zip 72703–4002; tel. 479/444–2200 **A**1 9 10 **F**2 21 27 29 30 37 44 46 48 52 60 65 68 69 94 95 96 109 **S** HEALTHSOUTH Corporation, Birmingham, AL
Primary Contact: Jeffrey Huff, Administrator
CFO: Jeffrey Huff, Controller
Web address: www.healthsouth.com
| | 32 | 46 | 60 | 1191 | 43 | 38182 | 0 | 13521 | 6956 | 178 |

★ **REGENCY HOSPITAL OF NORTHWEST ARKANSAS**, 1125 North College, Zip 72703; tel. 479/713–7000 **A**10 **F**2 21 53 58 60 64 65 66 94 110 **P**8 **S** Regency Hospital Company, Alpharetta, GA
Primary Contact: Michael A. McLean, Chief Executive Officer
Web address: www.regencyhospital.com
| | 33 | 80 | 25 | 188 | 14 | 0 | 0 | 5440 | 2407 | 50 |

Many Facility Codes have changed. Please refer to the AHA Guide Code Chart.
© 2005 AHA Guide

Hospital, Address, Telephone, Approval, Facility, and Physician Codes, Health Care System	Classification Codes		Utilization Data					Expense (thousands) of dollars		
★ American Hospital Association (AHA) membership □ Joint Commission on Accreditation of Healthcare Organizations (JCAHO) accreditation ○ American Osteopathic Association (AOA) accreditation △ Commission on Accreditation of Rehabilitation Facilities (CARF) accreditation	Control	Service	Staffed Beds	Admissions	Census	Outpatient Visits	Births	Total	Payroll	Personnel
☒ **VETERANS AFFAIRS MEDICAL CENTER**, 1100 North College Avenue, Zip 72703–6995; tel. 479/443–4301 **A**1 **F**2 4 15 21 22 23 26 27 28 29 30 31 32 35 36 37 38 39 42 44 45 46 48 50 51 52 53 55 57 58 61 62 63 64 65 66 69 70 71 73 74 75 76 77 78 81 88 92 94 96 97 106 107 108 109 **S** Department of Veterans Affairs, Washington, DC Primary Contact: Michael R. Winn, Director COO: Doris B. Cassidy, Associate Director CFO: James Hurst, Chief Fiscal Service CMO: Bonnie Baker, M.D., Chief Medical Services CIO: Dale Nelson, Chief Information Officer Web address: www.va.gov/sta/guide/home.asp	45	10	53	3554	53	314464	0	121369	54553	859
□ **VISTA HEALTH**, 4253 North Crossover Road, Zip 72703–4596; tel. 479/521–5731 **A**1 9 10 **F**27 28 66 71 72 73 74 75 77 94 **P**6 Primary Contact: Patrick Kelly, Chief Executive Officer Web address: www.vistahealthservices.com	33	22	62	889	46	9349	0	10474	5284	160
☒ **WASHINGTON REGIONAL MEDICAL CENTER**, 3215 North Hills Boulevard, Zip 72703–1994; tel. 479/713–1000 **A**1 2 9 10 **F**2 8 9 10 11 14 15 17 19 21 22 23 24 26 27 28 29 33 34 36 37 38 39 40 41 42 44 45 46 47 48 49 50 51 52 53 55 56 57 58 59 60 61 62 63 64 65 66 68 69 70 71 73 76 81 84 85 88 91 92 93 94 95 96 105 106 107 108 109 110 **P**8 Primary Contact: William L. Bradley, President and Chief Executive Officer CFO: Dan Eckels, Chief Financial Officer CMO: David Ratcliff, M.D., Chief Medical Affairs CIO: Becky Magee, Chief Information Officer CHR: Steve Percival, Director Human Resources Web address: www.wregional.com	23	10	290	13885	160	145724	1859	139640	51753	1384
FORDYCE—Dallas County										
★ **DALLAS COUNTY MEDICAL CENTER**, 201 Clifton Street, Zip 71742–3099; tel. 870/352–6300 **A**9 10 18 **F**21 26 27 28 33 38 63 81 88 92 97 106 **P**3 5 Primary Contact: Craig A. Ortego, Administrator and Chief Executive Officer CFO: Billie Lavnius, Business Finance Director CMO: Hugh A. Nutt, M.D., Chief of Staff CIO: Melissa Mooney, Information Systems Director and Data Processor CHR: Regina Cortez, Administrative Assistant and Human Resource Director	13	10	25	454	5	11996	2	6048	2501	72
FORREST CITY—St. Francis County										
☒ **BAPTIST MEMORIAL HOSPITAL–FORREST CITY**, 1601 Newcastle Road, Zip 72335, Mailing Address: P.O. Box 667, Zip 72336–0667; tel. 870/261–0000 **A**1 9 10 20 **F**2 6 9 11 12 21 22 28 33 36 44 46 48 51 59 62 63 66 71 74 81 88 94 106 108 109 **S** Baptist Memorial Health Care Corporation, Memphis, TN Primary Contact: Jerry Pope, Administrator and Chief Executive Officer CFO: Tracy Pollock, Controller CMO: Henein Iskander, M.D., Chief of Staff CIO: Thomas Hughes, Director Information Systems Web address: www.bmhcc.org	23	10	70	1946	20	39647	705	20156	7736	202
FORT SMITH—Sebastian County										
★ **ADVANCE CARE HOSPITAL OF FORT SMITH**, 7301 Rogers Avenue, 4th Floor, Zip 72917; tel. 479/314–4900 **A**10 **F**2 21 22 37 38 58 94 110 **S** Dubuis Health System, Houston, TX Primary Contact: Amy Riley, Administrator Web address: www.dubuis.org	21	80	25	177	12	0	0	4578	1834	91
☒ **HEALTHSOUTH REHABILITATION HOSPITAL OF FORT SMITH**, 1401 South J Street, Zip 72901–5155; tel. 479/785–3300 **A**1 9 10 **F**2 21 27 28 29 30 37 44 46 47 48 52 58 60 65 66 68 69 93 96 110 **S** HEALTHSOUTH Corporation, Birmingham, AL Primary Contact: Juli Stec, Chief Executive Officer CFO: Kathy McRay, Chief Financial Officer Web address: www.healthsouth.com	33	46	80	1445	47	20545	0	11266	5750	164
□ **SELECT SPECIALTY HOSPITAL – FORT SMITH**, 1131 South I Street, Zip 72917; tel. 479/441–3960 **A**1 10 **F**2 21 22 26 27 28 29 32 53 57 58 60 61 62 66 94 110 Primary Contact: Mary Jackson, Chief Executive Officer Web address: www.selectmedicalcorp.com	33	10	34	421	29	0	0	10730	4006	86
☒ **SPARKS REGIONAL MEDICAL CENTER**, 1311 South I Street, Zip 72901–4995, Mailing Address: P.O. Box 17006, Zip 72917–7006; tel. 479/441–4000 **A**1 2 9 10 **F**9 10 11 14 15 17 19 21 22 26 28 29 33 34 39 41 42 44 45 46 47 48 49 50 51 52 54 55 56 57 58 59 61 62 63 65 69 71 75 76 81 82 84 86 87 88 92 94 95 96 106 108 110 **P**1 3 Primary Contact: John A. Guest, Chief Executive Officer COO: Wesley Oswald, Chief Operating Officer CFO: Dan Hamman, Chief Financial Officer CHR: Robert Nicodemus, Vice President Human Resources Web address: www.sparks.org	23	10	275	15396	203	103785	1196	141166	53412	1654

AR

Hospital, Address, Telephone, Approval, Facility, and Physician Codes, Health Care System	Classification Codes		Utilization Data					Expense (thousands) of dollars		
	Control	Service	Staffed Beds	Admissions	Census	Outpatient Visits	Births	Total	Payroll	Personnel

Approval / accreditation key:
- ★ American Hospital Association (AHA) membership
- □ Joint Commission on Accreditation of Healthcare Organizations (JCAHO) accreditation
- ○ American Osteopathic Association (AOA) accreditation
- △ Commission on Accreditation of Rehabilitation Facilities (CARF) accreditation

⊠ △ ST. EDWARD MERCY MEDICAL CENTER, 7301 Rogers Avenue, Zip 72903–4189, Mailing Address: P.O. Box 17000, Zip 72917–7000; tel. 479/314–6000 **A**1 2 7 9 10 **F**2 4 9 10 11 12 15 17 19 21 22 23 26 27 28 29 33 35 36 37 38 40 41 42 46 48 49 51 53 55 56 57 58 59 60 61 62 63 64 65 66 68 69 79 81 84 85 88 92 93 94 106 108 109 **S** Sisters of Mercy Health System, Chesterfield, MO
Primary Contact: Jerry L. Stevenson, Chief Executive Officer
COO: Doug Gautier, Chief Operating Officer
CFO: James Newman, Vice President and Chief Financial Officer
CMO: Larry W. Pearce, M.D., Vice President Medical Affairs
CHR: Ron Summerhill, Vice President Human Resources
Web address: www.stedwardmercy.com

Control 21, Service 10, Staffed Beds 370, Admissions 15980, Census 239, Outpatient Visits 125596, Births 2153, Total 153590, Payroll 58097, Personnel 1718

GRAVETTE—Benton County

GRAVETTE MEDICAL CENTER HOSPITAL, 1101 Jackson Street S.W., Zip 72736–0450, Mailing Address: P.O. Box 450, Zip 72736–0450; tel. 479/787–5291, (Nonreporting) **A**9 10
Primary Contact: Mary Ross, Administrator
Web address: www.gravettehospital.org

Control 23, Service 10, Staffed Beds 61, Admissions —, Census —, Outpatient Visits —, Births —, Total —, Payroll —, Personnel —

HARRISON—Boone County

⊠ NORTH ARKANSAS REGIONAL MEDICAL CENTER, 620 North Willow Street, Zip 72601–2994; tel. 870/365–2000 **A**1 9 10 19 20 **F**2 6 9 11 12 14 15 21 23 26 27 28 29 32 33 36 39 40 46 48 49 51 53 55 59 60 61 62 63 64 65 66 69 80 81 82 84 86 87 88 92 93 94 96 108 109 **P**8
Primary Contact: Timothy E. Hill, President and Chief Executive Officer
CFO: Debbie Henry, Vice President Financial Services
CIO: Kent Kimes, Director Information Systems
CHR: Linda Dickey Melton, Vice President Human Resources
Web address: www.narmc.com

Control 23, Service 10, Staffed Beds 125, Admissions 5662, Census 59, Outpatient Visits 83442, Births 583, Total 48143, Payroll 22588, Personnel 665

HEBER SPRINGS—Cleburne County

⊠ BAPTIST HEALTH MEDICAL CENTER–HEBER SPRINGS, 2319 Highway 110 West, Zip 72543–3442; tel. 501/206–3000 **A**1 9 10 18 **F**2 9 12 21 22 29 33 46 47 48 51 52 53 57 60 62 63 69 75 81 85 88 93 96 97 106 108 **S** Baptist Health, Little Rock, AR
Primary Contact: Edward L. Lacy, Vice President and Administrator
Web address: www.baptist-health.com

Control 23, Service 10, Staffed Beds 18, Admissions 717, Census 7, Outpatient Visits 26933, Births 0, Total 13435, Payroll 5883, Personnel 157

HELENA—Phillips County

□ HELENA REGIONAL MEDICAL CENTER, 1801 Martin Luther King Drive, Zip 72342, Mailing Address: P.O. Box 788, Zip 72342–0788; tel. 870/338–5800 **A**1 5 9 10 20 **F**2 6 9 11 12 21 28 29 33 47 48 49 51 52 55 58 59 63 65 66 68 69 70 81 82 84 88 94 96 97 107 108 109 **S** Community Health Systems, Inc., Brentwood, TN
Primary Contact: Tom Kinnebrew, Chief Executive Officer
Web address: www.helenaregionalmedicalcenter.com

Control 33, Service 10, Staffed Beds 100, Admissions 3409, Census 35, Outpatient Visits 17737, Births 343, Total 19534, Payroll 8892, Personnel 230

HOPE—Hempstead County

⊠ MEDICAL PARK HOSPITAL, 2001 South Main Street, Zip 71801–8194; tel. 870/777–2323 **A**1 9 10 20 **F**2 9 11 12 21 26 28 33 37 39 46 48 52 53 55 58 59 62 63 64 66 69 71 76 81 82 84 88 93 94 97 108 109 **P**7 **S** Triad Hospitals, Inc., Plano, TX
Primary Contact: Jimmy Leopard, Chief Executive Officer
COO: Faye Hughes, Chief Nursing Officer and Chief Operating Officer
CFO: Jack Wilcox, Chief Financial Officer
Web address: www.mphhope.com

Control 33, Service 10, Staffed Beds 79, Admissions 3080, Census 35, Outpatient Visits 30785, Births 360, Total 25259, Payroll 8955, Personnel 264

HOT SPRINGS—Garland County

⊠ △ NATIONAL PARK MEDICAL CENTER, 1910 Malvern Avenue, Zip 71901–7799; tel. 501/321–1000 **A**1 7 9 10 19 **F**2 6 9 11 12 15 17 19 21 22 23 28 29 33 44 45 46 47 48 51 52 55 57 58 59 61 62 63 64 66 68 69 81 82 84 88 92 94 96 106 107 108 109 110 **P**1 **S** Triad Hospitals, Inc., Plano, TX
Primary Contact: Jerry D. Mabry, Chief Executive Officer
CFO: Robbie Pettey, Chief Financial Officer
CIO: Thomas Elmore, Information System Director
CHR: Sandra Culliver, Director, Human Resources
Web address: www.nationalparkmedical.com

Control 33, Service 10, Staffed Beds 181, Admissions 5786, Census 100, Outpatient Visits 68899, Births 684, Total 60240, Payroll 23648, Personnel 863

HOT SPRINGS NATIONAL—Cherokee County

△ HOT SPRINGS REHABILITATION CENTER, 105 Reserve Avenue, Zip 71902, Mailing Address: Post Office Box 1358, Zip 71902; tel. 501/624–4411, (Nonreporting) **A**7 9 10
Primary Contact: Howard J. Rutenberg, Administrator
Web address: www.hotsprings.dina.org/health/hsrc.html

Control 12, Service 46, Staffed Beds 26, Admissions —, Census —, Outpatient Visits —, Births —, Total —, Payroll —, Personnel —

HOT SPRINGS NATIONAL PARK—Garland County

⊠ ADVANCE CARE HOSPITAL, 300 Werner Street, 3rd Floor East, Zip 71913; tel. 501/609–4300 **A**1 10 **F**2 21 22 53 60 62 64 66 92 94 106 110 **P**5 **S** Dubuis Health System, Houston, TX
Primary Contact: Keith Rogers, Administrator
CFO: Paul Veillon, CPA, Chief Financial Officer
CIO: David Hammon, Director Information Services
CHR: Deborah Farrer, Human Resources Manager
Web address: www.dubuis.org

Control 21, Service 80, Staffed Beds 27, Admissions 309, Census 22, Outpatient Visits 0, Births 0, Total 7386, Payroll 2992, Personnel 71

Many Facility Codes have changed. Please refer to the AHA Guide Code Chart. © 2005 AHA Guide

Hospital, Address, Telephone, Approval, Facility, and Physician Codes, Health Care System	Classi-fication Codes		Utilization Data						Expense (thousands) of dollars		
★ American Hospital Association (AHA) membership □ Joint Commission on Accreditation of Healthcare Organizations (JCAHO) accreditation ○ American Osteopathic Association (AOA) accreditation △ Commission on Accreditation of Rehabilitation Facilities (CARF) accreditation	Control	Service	Staffed Beds	Admissions	Census	Outpatient Visits	Births		Total	Payroll	Personnel
HEALTHPARK HOSPITAL, 1600 Higdon Ferry Road, Zip 71913, Mailing Address: P.O. Box 71903, Zip 71913; tel. 501/520–2000 **A**10 **F**2 12 21 23 28 33 37 46 48 52 53 57 60 61 62 63 64 69 81 84 85 88 93 94 95 108 109 110 Primary Contact: Jason A. Spring, Chief Executive Officer and Administrator Web address: www.healthparkhospital.com	33	10	20	1589	11	2220	0		16671	4333	157
⊞ △ **LEVI HOSPITAL**, 300 Prospect Avenue, Zip 71901–4097; tel. 501/624–1281 **A**1 7 9 10 **F**1 7 26 27 28 33 36 44 45 46 47 48 51 52 53 69 71 75 76 77 94 95 96 108 Primary Contact: Patrick G. McCabe, Jr, President and Chief Executive Officer CFO: Charles Oswalt, Vice President and Chief Financial Officer CMO: P Ross Bandy, M.D., Chief Medical Officer and Chief of Staff Web address: www.levihospital.com	23	22	15	335	9	16089	0		8849	5147	136
⊞ **ST. JOSEPH'S MERCY HEALTH CENTER**, 300 Werner Street, Zip 71913–9937, Mailing Address: P.O. Box 29001, Zip 71913–9001; tel. 501/622–1000 **A**1 2 9 10 19 **F**2 6 9 11 12 14 15 17 19 21 22 23 26 27 28 29 33 36 37 38 39 44 45 46 47 48 51 52 53 54 55 57 58 59 60 61 62 63 64 65 66 68 69 71 76 79 81 82 85 88 92 93 94 96 106 107 108 109 110 **P**2 7 **S** Sisters of Mercy Health System, Chesterfield, MO Primary Contact: Randall J. Fale, FACHE, President and Chief Executive Officer COO: Randy Fortner, Chief Operating Officer CFO: Larry D. Alford, Chief Financial Officer CMO: Mark Larey, D.O., Vice President Medical Affairs CIO: Judy Preuitt, Director Information Systems CHR: Ray Pelton, Vice President Human Resources Web address: www.saintjosephs.com	21	10	261	13052	207	383803	890		149746	67374	1589
JACKSONVILLE—Pulaski County											
⊞ △ **REBSAMEN MEDICAL CENTER**, 1400 West Braden Street, Zip 72076–3788; tel. 501/985–7000 **A**1 7 9 10 **F**2 9 11 12 14 17 21 28 29 31 33 39 40 43 44 46 51 52 53 55 57 58 59 60 61 62 63 65 68 70 71 76 81 82 84 85 87 88 93 94 95 96 98 106 108 109 110 **P**1 **S** Quorum Health Resources, Plano, TX Primary Contact: Kurt Meyer, Chief Executive Officer CFO: Daniel Smith, Chief Financial Officer Web address: www.rebsamenmedicalcenter.com	23	10	87	3790	56	64973	384		40251	17418	388
JOHNSON—Washington County											
★ **WILLOW CREEK WOMEN'S HOSPITAL**, 4301 Greathouse Springs Road, Zip 72741–0544, Mailing Address: P.O. Box 544, Zip 72741–0544; tel. 479/684–3000 **A**9 10 **F**2 9 11 12 27 33 46 53 58 59 63 88 109 **S** Triad Hospitals, Inc., Plano, TX Primary Contact: Gary N. Looper, Chief Executive Officer CFO: Mary Millington, Chief Financial Officer CHR: Kim Sweiter, Vice President Web address: www.northwesthealth.com	33	44	30	2304	13	11574	1935		14238	4180	118
JONESBORO—Craighead County											
⊞ **HEALTHSOUTH REHABILITATION HOSPITAL OF JONESBORO**, 1201 Fleming Avenue, Zip 72401–4311, Mailing Address: P.O. Box 1680, Zip 72403–1680; tel. 870/932–0440 **A**1 9 10 **F**21 27 28 42 45 46 48 52 68 69 94 95 96 **S** HEALTHSOUTH Corporation, Birmingham, AL Primary Contact: Donna Bloodworth, Administrator CFO: Diane Berry, Controller CMO: Terence Braden, III, D.O., Medical Director CHR: Tammy Barley, Manager Human Resources Web address: www.healthsouth.com	33	46	67	1340	52	19907	0		7932	6161	191
⊞ **NEA MEDICAL CENTER**, (Formerly Methodist Hospital of Jonesboro), 3024 Stadium Boulevard, Zip 72401–7493; tel. 870/972–7000 **A**1 9 10 **F**2 9 10 11 12 14 15 17 19 21 22 23 26 28 29 32 33 39 44 46 47 48 49 50 52 53 55 57 58 59 60 61 62 63 65 66 69 73 81 82 84 87 88 94 95 96 108 109 110 **P**8 **S** Triad Hospitals, Inc., Plano, TX Primary Contact: William C. Lievense, Chief Executive Officer CFO: Max Owens, Chief Financial Officer CHR: Kevin Thielemier, Director Human Resources Web address: www.neamedicalcenter.com	32	10	104	4581	51	29358	463		42214	14250	409
□ **ST. BERNARD'S BEHAVIORAL HEALTH**, 2712 East Johnson Avenue, Zip 72401–1874; tel. 870/932–2800 **A**1 9 10 **F**4 21 22 26 27 28 29 31 37 44 45 58 65 71 72 73 74 75 76 77 92 94 96 **P**1 Primary Contact: Lee A. Simpson, Jr, Administrator	21	22	60	1572	42	4129	0		7686	3588	99
⊞ **ST. BERNARDS MEDICAL CENTER**, 225 East Jackson Avenue, Zip 72401; tel. 870/972–4100, (Total facility includes 27 beds in nursing home–type unit) **A**1 2 9 10 19 **F**1 2 9 11 12 14 15 17 19 21 22 23 24 26 27 28 29 33 36 37 38 39 40 41 42 44 45 46 47 48 49 50 51 52 53 54 55 57 58 59 60 61 63 65 69 79 81 82 84 86 88 92 93 94 95 96 106 108 109 110 **P**2 6 Primary Contact: Chris Barber, Administrator CFO: Harry Hutchison, Vice President Fiscal Services CMO: David Pyle, Vice President Medical Affairs CHR: Pat Overman, Vice President Human Resources Web address: www.sbrmc.com	21	10	305	18410	229	178642	1519		166216	53073	1500

AR

Hospital, Address, Telephone, Approval, Facility, and Physician Codes, Health Care System	Classi-fication Codes		Utilization Data					Expense (thousands) of dollars		
★ American Hospital Association (AHA) membership ☐ Joint Commission on Accreditation of Healthcare Organizations (JCAHO) accreditation ○ American Osteopathic Association (AOA) accreditation △ Commission on Accreditation of Rehabilitation Facilities (CARF) accreditation	Control	Service	Staffed Beds	Admissions	Census	Outpatient Visits	Births	Total	Payroll	Personnel
SURGICAL HOSPITAL OF JONESBORO, 909 Enterprise Drive, Zip 72401; tel. 870/336–1100 **A**10 **F**2 21 33 37 52 57 58 62 63 64 81 84 93 94 Primary Contact: Nate Miller, Chief Executive Officer Web address: www.tshj.com	32	13	12	616	3	9217	0	4489	2909	54
LAKE VILLAGE—Chicot County										
★ **CHICOT MEMORIAL HOSPITAL**, 2729 Highway 65 and 82 South, Zip 71653; tel. 870/265–5351 **A**9 10 **F**2 12 14 21 26 29 33 34 42 46 51 52 53 55 58 59 62 63 66 69 81 88 94 96 **P**5 **S** Quorum Health Resources, Plano, TX Primary Contact: Robert R. Reddish, Administrator and Chief Executive Officer COO: Toma G. Hardin, R.N., Chief Nursing Officer CMO: Charles Hicks, M.D., Chief of Staff CIO: Becky P. Rossini, Information Systems Manager CHR: Nancy Dill, Human Resources Director	13	10	35	1850	18	25132	138	6738	5079	169
LITTLE ROCK—Pulaski County										
⊞ **ARKANSAS CHILDREN'S HOSPITAL**, 800 Marshall Street, Zip 72202–3591; tel. 501/364–1100 **A**1 3 5 8 9 10 **F**2 6 7 9 10 13 14 16 18 20 21 22 23 24 29 31 32 33 34 37 38 39 41 45 46 48 49 50 52 53 55 56 57 58 60 61 62 63 64 65 66 67 68 69 70 73 75 81 82 84 85 87 88 90 93 94 95 96 99 100 101 106 108 **P**1 Primary Contact: Jonathan R. Bates, M.D., President and Chief Executive Officer COO: Scott Gordon, Executive Vice President and Chief Operating Officer CFO: Gena Wingfield, Chief Financial Officer CMO: Bonnie Taylor, M.D., Senior Vice President and Medical Director CIO: Darrell Leonhardt, Senior Vice President Information Systems CHR: Andrea Trosclair, Vice President Human Resources Web address: www.archildrens.org	23	50	259	11848	209	260132	0	282020	131865	2605
☐ **ARKANSAS HEART HOSPITAL**, 1701 South Shackleford Road, Zip 72211–4335; tel. 501/219–7000 **A**1 5 9 10 **F**2 9 14 15 17 19 21 29 33 34 37 38 46 47 48 55 58 63 65 75 81 84 85 88 94 109 110 **P**8 **S** MedCath, Inc., Charlotte, NC Primary Contact: Charles Mitchener, Jr, President Web address: www.arheart.com	33	10	84	5805	61	8471	0	64782	18529	435
☐ **ARKANSAS STATE HOSPITAL**, 4313 West Markham Street, Zip 72205–4096; tel. 501/686–9000 **A**1 3 5 9 10 **F**9 21 22 26 28 39 45 58 60 65 66 70 71 72 73 74 94 96 106 108 **P**6 Primary Contact: Glenn R. Sago, Administrator Web address: www.state.ar.us/dhs/dmhs	12	22	202	999	189	0	0	26954	14776	446
⊞ △ **BAPTIST HEALTH MEDICAL CENTER–LITTLE ROCK**, 9601 Interstate 630, Exit 7, Zip 72205–7299; tel. 501/202–2000 **A**1 3 5 6 7 9 10 **F**2 3 4 6 9 10 11 12 14 15 17 19 21 22 23 24 26 27 28 29 30 31 33 35 37 39 42 44 45 46 47 48 49 50 51 52 53 55 56 57 58 59 60 61 62 63 64 65 66 69 71 72 73 74 75 76 77 81 82 83 84 85 86 87 88 92 93 94 95 96 98 100 101 106 107 108 109 110 **S** Baptist Health, Little Rock, AR Primary Contact: Steven Douglas Weeks, Senior Vice President and Administrator CFO: Allen F. Smith, Senior Vice President Financial Services CMO: Philip L. Mizell, M.D., Vice President Clinical Affairs CIO: David House, Vice President and Chief Information Officer CHR: Anthony Kendall, Vice President Human Resources Web address: www.baptist–health.org	23	10	692	30282	494	315393	2589	345573	130054	2922
⊞ △ **BAPTIST HEALTH REHABILITATION INSTITUTE**, 9601 Interstate 630, Exit 7, Zip 72205–7249; tel. 501/202–7000 **A**1 3 5 7 9 10 **F**9 21 22 26 27 28 29 39 41 45 52 58 62 66 68 69 92 94 96 108 **S** Baptist Health, Little Rock, AR Primary Contact: Greg Crain, Vice President CFO: Allen F. Smith, Senior Vice President Financial Services CIO: David House, Vice President and Chief Information Officer Web address: www.baptist–health.com	23	46	100	2405	75	133503	0	28443	14221	275
⊞ △ **CENTRAL ARKANSAS VETERANS HEALTHCARE SYSTEM**, (Formerly Central Arkansas Veterans Affairs Healthcare System), 4300 West Seventh Street, Zip 72205–5484; tel. 501/257–1000, (Includes NORTH LITTLE ROCK DIVISION, North Little Rock), (Total facility includes 152 beds in nursing home–type unit) **A**1 2 3 5 7 8 **F**1 2 4 5 12 14 15 17 21 22 23 27 28 29 31 32 33 37 38 39 41 42 44 45 46 47 48 49 50 51 52 53 55 57 58 60 61 62 63 65 66 68 69 70 71 73 74 75 76 77 78 81 82 84 85 87 88 90 92 93 94 96 97 106 107 108 109 110 **P**6 **S** Department of Veterans Affairs, Washington, DC Primary Contact: Nicholas P. Lang, M.D., Interim Director CFO: Debby Felton, Chief Financial Officer CMO: Nicholas P. Lang, M.D., Chief of Staff CIO: Tony Stephens, Chief Information Officer CHR: Daniel Peterson, Chief Human Resource Management Service Web address: www.va.gov/sta/guide/home.asp	45	10	551	10558	468	547870	0	315704	133917	2992
☐ **PINNACLE POINTE HOSPITAL**, 11501 Financial Center Parkway, Zip 72211–3715; tel. 501/223–3322 **A**1 9 10 **F**21 71 72 73 74 75 77 94 96 **S** Psychiatric Solutions, Franklin, TN Primary Contact: Lucinda DeBruce, Chief Executive Officer Web address: www.bhcpinnaclepoint.com	33	22	102	1356	75	—	0	13456	6775	182
☐ **SELECT SPECIALTY HOSPITAL–LITTLE ROCK**, 2 St. Vincent Circle, 6th Floor, Zip 72204; tel. 501/661–4198 **A**1 10 **F**2 13 21 22 26 27 28 50 57 58 66 70 71 92 94 110 **P**8 **S** Select Medical Corporation, Mechanicsburg, PA Primary Contact: Maureen Henneken, Chief Executive Officer Web address: www.selectmedicalcorp.com	33	80	43	293	21	0	0	9847	4254	110

AR

Hospital, Address, Telephone, Approval, Facility, and Physician Codes, Health Care System	Classi-fication Codes		Utilization Data					Expense (thousands) of dollars		
★ American Hospital Association (AHA) membership ☐ Joint Commission on Accreditation of Healthcare Organizations (JCAHO) accreditation ○ American Osteopathic Association (AOA) accreditation △ Commission on Accreditation of Rehabilitation Facilities (CARF) accreditation	Control	Service	Staffed Beds	Admissions	Census	Outpatient Visits	Births	Total	Payroll	Personnel

AR

Hospital	Control	Service	Staffed Beds	Admissions	Census	Outpatient Visits	Births	Total	Payroll	Personnel
☐ **SEMPERCARE HOSPITAL OF LITTLE ROCK**, 9601 Interstate 630, Exit 7, 10th Floor, Zip 72205; tel. 501/202–1070 **A**1 9 10 **F**2 21 26 60 94 110 Primary Contact: Phillip D. Hurley, Chief Executive Officer Web address: www.selectmedicalcorp.com	31	80	37	314	26	0	0	9434	4306	100
☐ **SOUTHWEST REGIONAL MEDICAL CENTER**, 11401 Interstate 30, Zip 72209–7056; tel. 501/455–7100 **A**1 9 10 **F**2 9 10 12 14 15 21 22 26 27 28 29 32 33 34 37 39 40 44 46 48 52 53 55 58 60 62 63 64 65 66 69 71 73 76 81 82 84 85 87 88 94 104 106 108 **S** Health Management Associates, Naples, FL Primary Contact: Nancy C. Fodi, R.N., Chief Executive Officer Web address: www.hma–corp.com	33	10	125	2162	39	27256	0	26940	9963	222
⊠ **ST. VINCENT INFIRMARY MEDICAL CENTER**, Two St. Vincent Circle, Zip 72205–5499; tel. 501/552–3000, (Includes ST. VINCENT DOCTORS HOSPITAL, 6101 West Capitol, Zip 72205–5331; tel. 501/552–6000; Angie Cabantac, R.N., Administrator), (Total facility includes 31 beds in nursing home–type unit) **A**1 3 5 9 10 **F**2 9 10 11 12 14 15 17 19 21 22 23 27 28 29 33 34 35 37 38 39 40 41 42 43 44 45 46 47 48 49 50 51 52 53 55 56 57 58 59 60 61 62 63 64 65 66 68 69 70 71 76 81 82 83 84 85 86 87 88 92 93 94 96 106 108 109 110 **P**8 **S** Catholic Health Initiatives, Denver, CO Primary Contact: Stephen L. Mansfield, President and Chief Executive Officer COO: Ken Haynes, Senior Vice President and Chief Operating Officer CFO: Pam Stoyanoff, Senior Vice President and Chief Financial Officer CMO: David Hall, M.D., Senior Vice Presdient and Chief Medical Affairs CIO: Tommye Billing, Vice President and Chief Information Officer CHR: LeRoy Walker, Vice President Human Resources Web address: www.stvincenthealth.com	21	10	542	21516	325	172799	2284	214700	82472	2139
⊠ **UAMS MEDICAL CENTER**, 4301 West Markham Street, Zip 72205–7102; tel. 501/686–7000 **A**1 3 5 8 9 10 12 13 **F**9 11 12 14 15 17 19 21 22 23 27 28 33 37 38 39 41 43 44 46 48 50 52 53 55 56 57 58 59 60 61 62 63 64 65 66 69 70 73 75 81 82 84 85 86 87 88 89 94 96 99 100 101 104 105 108 109 **P**6 Primary Contact: Richard Pierson, Executive Director CFO: Daniel J. Riley, Chief Financial Officer CMO: Charles W. Smith, M.D., Medical Director CIO: Kari Cassel, Director Clinical Information Systems CHR: Hosea Long, Director Human Resources Web address: www.uams.edu/medcenter	12	10	310	14324	266	315801	2171	273461	107961	2525

MAGNOLIA—Columbia County

Hospital	Control	Service	Staffed Beds	Admissions	Census	Outpatient Visits	Births	Total	Payroll	Personnel
⊠ **MAGNOLIA HOSPITAL**, 101 Hospital Drive, Zip 71753–2416, Mailing Address: P.O. Box 629, Zip 71753–0629; tel. 870/235–3000 **A**1 9 10 20 **F**9 11 12 14 21 23 33 51 52 53 58 59 63 64 65 69 70 81 82 85 88 93 94 96 97 108 **S** Christus Health, Irving, TX Primary Contact: Terry L. Amstutz, CHE, Chief Executive Officer CFO: Hoye A. Bowman, Chief Financial Officer Web address: www.magnoliahospital.org	14	10	62	2081	21	23637	207	16072	7251	231

MALVERN—Hot Spring County

Hospital	Control	Service	Staffed Beds	Admissions	Census	Outpatient Visits	Births	Total	Payroll	Personnel
★ **H.S.C. MEDICAL CENTER**, 1001 Schneider Drive, Zip 72104–4828; tel. 501/337–4911 **A**9 10 **F**9 12 14 21 22 27 28 29 33 36 46 47 48 51 52 55 58 60 63 66 68 70 71 73 74 75 76 81 82 84 88 93 94 96 108 Primary Contact: Phillip K. Gilmore, Chief Executive Officer CFO: Sheila Williams, Chief Financial Officer Web address: www.hscmc.org	23	10	81	3358	46	28478	0	22000	10538	362

MAUMELLE—Pulaski County

Hospital	Control	Service	Staffed Beds	Admissions	Census	Outpatient Visits	Births	Total	Payroll	Personnel
☐ **METHODIST BEHAVIORAL HOSPITAL OF ARKANSAS**, 1601 Murphy Drive, Zip 72113, Mailing Address: P.O. Box 13340, Zip 72113; tel. 501/803–3388 **A**1 9 10 **F**26 27 28 52 71 72 77 **P**1 Primary Contact: T. David Beall, Chief Executive Officer Web address: www.umch.org	23	22	60	611	54	2277	0	6227	4898	130

MCGEHEE—Desha County

Hospital	Control	Service	Staffed Beds	Admissions	Census	Outpatient Visits	Births	Total	Payroll	Personnel
MCGEHEE–DESHA COUNTY HOSPITAL, 900 South Third, Zip 71654–0351, Mailing Address: P.O. Box 351, Zip 71654–0351; tel. 870/222–5600 **A**9 10 18 **F**2 9 21 26 27 28 33 34 46 47 48 51 52 53 63 65 81 88 96 97 106 Primary Contact: John E. Heard, Chief Executive Officer Web address: www.menamedicaql.com	15	10	25	700	6	13577	0	5732	2684	98

MENA—Polk County

Hospital	Control	Service	Staffed Beds	Admissions	Census	Outpatient Visits	Births	Total	Payroll	Personnel
★ **MENA MEDICAL CENTER**, 311 North Morrow Street, Zip 71953–2516; tel. 479/394–6100 **A**9 10 20 **F**9 11 12 21 23 24 26 27 28 29 33 36 38 39 42 44 46 47 48 51 52 55 58 59 60 61 62 63 65 66 68 69 70 71 73 74 75 76 77 81 82 84 87 88 92 93 94 97 107 108 109 **P**8 **S** Quorum Health Resources, Plano, TX Primary Contact: Vince DiFranco, Chief Executive Officer CFO: Charles Powell, Chief Financial Officer CHR: Jonathan Voelkel, Director Human Resources Web address: www.menamedical.com	14	10	58	2076	28	60065	312	18890	8314	239

Hospital, Address, Telephone, Approval, Facility, and Physician Codes, Health Care System	Classi-fication Codes		Utilization Data					Expense (thousands) of dollars		
★ American Hospital Association (AHA) membership □ Joint Commission on Accreditation of Healthcare Organizations (JCAHO) accreditation ○ American Osteopathic Association (AOA) accreditation △ Commission on Accreditation of Rehabilitation Facilities (CARF) accreditation	Control	Service	Staffed Beds	Admissions	Census	Outpatient Visits	Births	Total	Payroll	Personnel

MONTICELLO—Drew County

★ **DREW MEMORIAL HOSPITAL**, 778 Scogin Drive, Zip 71655–5728; tel. 870/367–2411 **A**9 10 **F**2 9 11 12 21 22 26 27 28 29 33 46 47 48 51 52 53 54 55 58 59 63 65 66 81 82 83 84 85 88 97 108 **P**8
Primary Contact: Richard L. Goddard, Chief Executive Officer
CFO: Shanna Knowles, Chief Financial Officer
CMO: Sylvia Simon, Chief of Staff
CIO: Rusty Bryant, Information Technology Director
CHR: Rick Donham, Human Resources Director
Web address: www.drewmemorial.org

| 13 | 10 | 58 | 2197 | 21 | 12132 | 253 | 16000 | 6340 | 279 |

MORRILTON—Conway County

★ **ST. ANTHONY'S HEALTHCARE CENTER**, 4 Hospital Drive, Zip 72110–4510; tel. 501/977–2300 **A**9 10 18 **F**1 2 9 11 12 14 21 22 28 29 33 36 44 45 51 59 60 63 64 66 69 71 76 81 84 88 93 94 96 97
Primary Contact: Jonathan S. Davis, Chief Executive Officer and Administrator
CFO: Herbert Crum, Jr, Chief Financial Officer
CIO: Jeanie Voss, Manager Information Systems
CHR: Tammy Smith, Director Human Resourceds
Web address: www.stvincenthealth.com

| 21 | 10 | 35 | 1133 | 12 | 19272 | 51 | 14272 | 6621 | 241 |

MOUNTAIN HOME—Baxter County

★ △ **BAXTER REGIONAL MEDICAL CENTER**, 624 Hospital Drive, Zip 72653–2954; tel. 870/508–1000 **A**7 9 10 19 20 **F**6 9 10 11 12 14 15 17 19 21 22 23 27 28 33 36 37 38 41 46 48 51 52 55 59 60 61 62 63 64 65 66 68 69 71 76 77 81 82 88 93 94 96 106 108 109 110 **P**6 8
Primary Contact: Stephen M. Erixon, Chief Executive Officer
COO: Robert L. Marshall, Jr, Chief Operating Officer
CFO: Ivan Holleman, Chief Financial Officer
Web address: www.baxterregional.org

| 23 | 10 | 266 | 11922 | 153 | 90736 | 759 | 109653 | 43693 | 1127 |

MOUNTAIN VIEW—Stone County

★ **STONE COUNTY MEDICAL CENTER**, 2106 East Main Street, Zip 72560, Mailing Address: P.O. Box 510, Zip 72560–0510; tel. 870/269–4361 **A**9 10 18 **F**9 12 21 27 28 33 35 39 46 48 52 60 62 63 69 72 73 75 76 77 81 83 88 92 94 95 97 108 **P**1
Primary Contact: Karen Craft, Administrator
CFO: Mike Weeks, Chief Financial Officer
CIO: Ken Poole, Information Systems Coordinator
CHR: Charlie Wright, Assistant Administrator Human Resources
Web address: www.wrmc.com

| 23 | 10 | 25 | 964 | 9 | 30520 | 0 | 7534 | 3719 | 105 |

MURFREESBORO—Pike County

PIKE COUNTY MEMORIAL HOSPITAL, 315 East 13th Street, Zip 71958–9541; tel. 870/285–3182 **A**9 10 **F**2 14 27 33 36 51 52 69 88 92 97 **P**5
Primary Contact: Rosemary Fritts, Administrator

| 13 | 10 | 32 | 675 | 6 | 6941 | 0 | 2028 | 891 | 49 |

NASHVILLE—Howard County

★ **HOWARD MEMORIAL HOSPITAL**, 800 West Leslie Street, Zip 71852–0381, Mailing Address: P.O. Box 381, Zip 71852–0381; tel. 870/845–4400 **A**9 10 18 **F**2 9 12 21 29 32 33 46 48 51 52 55 58 60 63 65 69 81 88 97 110 **P**8
S Quorum Health Resources, Plano, TX
Primary Contact: Brian E. Bickel, President and Chief Executive Officer
CFO: Marilyn Hockaday, Chief Financial Officer
CMO: Hasmukh Patel, M.D., Chief of Staff
CIO: Becky Porter, Information Management Director
CHR: Gayla Lacefield, Human Resources Director

| 23 | 10 | 25 | 892 | 9 | 39835 | 0 | 9204 | 4004 | 129 |

NEWPORT—Jackson County

□ **HARRIS HOSPITAL**, 1205 McLain Street, Zip 72112–3533; tel. 870/523–8911 **A**1 9 10 **F**2 11 12 14 21 22 26 27 28 29 31 33 39 44 46 48 51 52 55 58 59 60 61 62 63 64 66 69 73 75 76 81 84 85 88 94 97 106 108 109 **P**6
S Community Health Systems, Inc., Brentwood, TN
Primary Contact: George F. Naylor, III, FACHE, Chief Executive Officer
Web address: www.harrishospital.com

| 33 | 10 | 83 | 3616 | 40 | 21421 | 590 | 19590 | 8682 | 217 |

NEWPORT HOSPITAL AND CLINIC, 2000 McLain Street, Zip 72112–3697; tel. 870/523–6721 **A**9 10 **F**2 9 12 14 15 21 23 28 33 46 48 51 52 55 57 58 59 61 62 63 69 81 82 84 85 88 94 95 97 108
Primary Contact: Eugene Zuber, Administrator
Web address: www.newporthospitalandclinic.com

| 33 | 10 | 86 | 2358 | 25 | 28538 | 71 | 15396 | 6330 | 206 |

NORTH LITTLE ROCK—Pulaski County

⊠ △ **BAPTIST HEALTH MEDICAL CENTER – NORTH LITTLE ROCK**, 3333 Springhill Drive, Zip 72117–2922; tel. 501/202–3000 **A**1 7 9 10 **F**2 9 11 12 14 15 17 19 21 22 23 24 26 27 28 29 30 31 33 34 37 39 41 42 43 44 45 46 47 48 49 52 53 55 57 58 59 60 61 62 63 64 65 66 68 69 70 81 82 84 88 92 93 94 96 106 107 108 109 **S** Baptist Health, Little Rock, AR
Primary Contact: Harrison M. Dean, Senior Vice President and Administrator
CFO: Allen F. Smith, Senior Vice President Financial Services
CIO: David House, Vice President and Chief Information Officer
Web address: www.baptist-health.org

| 23 | 10 | 210 | 11537 | 137 | 91858 | 1435 | 124561 | 46651 | 1003 |

□ **BRIDGEWAY**, 21 Bridgeway Road, Zip 72113–9516; tel. 501/771–1500 **A**1 9 10 **F**3 26 27 28 71 72 78 **P**5 **S** Universal Health Services, Inc., King of Prussia, PA
Primary Contact: Joel Klein, Chief Executive Officer and Managing Director
Web address: www.thebridgeway.com
NORTH LITTLE ROCK DIVISION See Central Arkansas Veterans Healthcare System, Little Rock

| 33 | 22 | 98 | 3009 | 74 | 6361 | 0 | 12808 | 6566 | 137 |

Many Facility Codes have changed. Please refer to the AHA Guide Code Chart.

© 2005 AHA Guide

Hospital, Address, Telephone, Approval, Facility, and Physician Codes, Health Care System	Classi-fication Codes		Utilization Data					Expense (thousands) of dollars		
★ American Hospital Association (AHA) membership □ Joint Commission on Accreditation of Healthcare Organizations (JCAHO) accreditation ○ American Osteopathic Association (AOA) accreditation △ Commission on Accreditation of Rehabilitation Facilities (CARF) accreditation	Control	Service	Staffed Beds	Admissions	Census	Outpatient Visits	Births	Total	Payroll	Personnel

OSCEOLA—Mississippi County

⊠ SOUTH MISSISSIPPI COUNTY REGIONAL MEDICAL CENTER, (Formerly Baptist Memorial Hospital–Osceola), 611 West Lee Avenue, Zip 72370–3001, Mailing Address: P.O. Box 607, Zip 72370–0607; tel. 870/563–7000 **A**1 9 10 18 **F**2 6 9 12 21 33 63 64 69 81 88 92 97 **P**5 **S** Ameris Health Systems, Nashville, TN
Primary Contact: Andrea Conley, Chief Executive Officer
CFO: Alan Lovelace, Chief Financial Officer
CMO: Stephen E. Pirtle, M.D., Chief of Staff

| 21 | 10 | 25 | 1074 | 8 | 16812 | 0 | — | — | 107 |

OZARK—Franklin County

★ MERCY HOSPITAL–TURNER MEMORIAL, 801 West River Street, Zip 72949–3000; tel. 479/667–4138 **A**9 10 18 **F**2 23 26 27 28 29 33 46 47 48 52 63 64 81 88 97 108 **S** Sisters of Mercy Health System, Chesterfield, MO
Primary Contact: Jim L. Maddox, Administrator
COO: Jim L. Maddox, Administrator
CFO: James Newman, Vice President and Chief Financial Officer
CMO: Jason Richey, M.D., Chief Medical Officer
CIO: Tiana Bolduc, Chief Information Officer
CHR: Ron Summerhill, Chief Human Resources
Web address: www.gravettehospital.org

| 21 | 10 | 25 | 683 | 7 | 8679 | 0 | 4818 | 1954 | 70 |

PARAGOULD—Greene County

⊠ △ ARKANSAS METHODIST MEDICAL CENTER, 900 West Kingshighway, Zip 72450–5942, Mailing Address: P.O. Box 339, Zip 72451–0339; tel. 870/239–7000 **A**1 7 9 10 **F**2 6 9 11 12 15 17 19 21 23 26 27 28 29 33 34 37 39 41 46 47 48 51 52 55 58 59 61 62 63 64 65 66 68 69 81 84 88 94 96 97 106 108 109 110 **P**1
Primary Contact: Ronald K. Rooney, President
COO: Barry L. Davis, Vice President Operations
CFO: Bryan Jackson, Vice President Finance
CMO: William Bulkley, M.D., Chief of Staff
CIO: Claude Greer, Director Information Technology
CHR: Dennis Cooper, Director Human Resources
Web address: www.arkansasmethodist.org

| 23 | 10 | 129 | 5719 | 73 | 103385 | 555 | 46565 | 17798 | 570 |

PARIS—Logan County

★ NORTH LOGAN MERCY HOSPITAL, 500 East Academy, Zip 72855–4099; tel. 479/963–6101 **A**9 10 18 **F**2 23 26 27 28 29 33 46 48 52 63 64 81 88 97 **S** Sisters of Mercy Health System, Chesterfield, MO
Primary Contact: Jim L. Maddox, Administrator
Web address: www.stedwardmercy.com

| 21 | 10 | 16 | 307 | 4 | 6893 | 0 | 3643 | 1784 | 44 |

PIGGOTT—Clay County

★ PIGGOTT COMMUNITY HOSPITAL, 1206 Gordon Duckworth Drive, Zip 72454–1911; tel. 870/598–3881 **A**9 10 **F**2 6 9 12 21 22 27 33 45 46 48 51 52 63 69 81 84 88 93 94 96 97 108
Primary Contact: James L. Magee, Executive Director
CFO: Linda Ort, Chief Financial Officer
Web address: www.piggottcommunityhospital.com

| 14 | 10 | 35 | 968 | 12 | 128729 | 0 | 10164 | 5528 | 187 |

PINE BLUFF—Jefferson County

⊠ △ JEFFERSON REGIONAL MEDICAL CENTER, 1600 West 40th Avenue, Zip 71603–7089; tel. 870/541–7100 **A**1 2 6 7 9 10 13 20 **F**2 11 12 14 15 17 19 21 22 26 27 28 29 33 34 40 41 42 44 45 46 47 48 49 50 51 52 55 56 57 58 59 60 61 62 63 64 65 66 68 69 70 71 73 74 75 76 78 81 82 84 87 88 92 94 95 96 106 107 108 109 **P**7
Primary Contact: Robert P. Atkinson, President and Chief Executive Officer
COO: Walter E. Johnson, Jr, Senior Vice President Operations
CFO: Nathan VanGenderen, Assistant Vice President Finance
CMO: Robert Gullett, M.D., Medical Director
CIO: Marshall Veerkamp, Chief Information Officer
CHR: Daryl Scott, Human Resources Director
Web address: www.jrmc.org

| 23 | 10 | 373 | 13543 | 193 | 150971 | 1303 | 135631 | 53010 | 1341 |

□ SELECT SPECIALTY HOSPITAL–PINE BLUFF, (Formerly SemperCare Hospital of Pine Bluff), 1515 West 42nd Avenue, 3rd Floor, S.E., Zip 71603; tel. 870/541–8700 **A**1 9 10 **F**21 28 94 109 110
Primary Contact: Larry Marr, Chief Executive Officer
Web address: www.selectmedicalcorp.com

| 33 | 80 | 23 | 231 | 11 | 0 | 0 | 6206 | 3154 | 69 |

POCAHONTAS—Randolph County

□ RANDOLPH COUNTY MEDICAL CENTER, 2801 Medical Center Drive, Zip 72455–9497; tel. 870/892–6000 **A**1 9 10 **F**2 9 12 21 27 28 33 46 48 51 55 62 63 69 71 76 81 84 88 94 97 108 **S** Associated Healthcare Systems, Inc., Brentwood, TN
Primary Contact: Terry G. Whittington, Chief Executive Officer

| 33 | 10 | 45 | 1218 | 17 | 18950 | 1 | 13218 | 4405 | 130 |

ROGERS—Benton County

⊠ ST. MARY–ROGERS MEMORIAL HOSPITAL, 1200 West Walnut Street, Zip 72756–3599; tel. 479/636–0200 **A**1 2 9 10 **F**1 9 11 12 15 17 19 21 22 26 27 28 33 36 46 48 51 52 55 58 59 60 62 63 65 69 81 82 84 87 88 93 94 96 108 109 110 **P**6 **S** Sisters of Mercy Health System, Chesterfield, MO
Primary Contact: Susan Barrett, President and Chief Executive Officer
COO: Edward Mirzabegian, Executive Vice President and Chief Operating Officer
CFO: Kenneth C. Robinson, Senior Vice President and Chief Financial Officer
CMO: Randall Black, Chief of Staff
CIO: Raymon Nance, Director Information Systems
CHR: Rick Barclay, Vice President Human Resources
Web address: www.mercyhealthnwa.smhs.com

| 21 | 10 | 133 | 7395 | 60 | 110932 | 1174 | 69351 | 29921 | 934 |

Hospital, Address, Telephone, Approval, Facility, and Physician Codes, Health Care System	Classi-fication Codes		Utilization Data					Expense (thousands) of dollars		
★ American Hospital Association (AHA) membership □ Joint Commission on Accreditation of Healthcare Organizations (JCAHO) accreditation ○ American Osteopathic Association (AOA) accreditation △ Commission on Accreditation of Rehabilitation Facilities (CARF) accreditation	Control	Service	Staffed Beds	Admissions	Census	Outpatient Visits	Births	Total	Payroll	Personnel

RUSSELLVILLE—Pope County

⊠ △ **SAINT MARY'S REGIONAL MEDICAL CENTER**, 1808 West Main Street, Zip 72801–2724; tel. 479/968–2841, (Total facility includes 15 beds in nursing home–type unit) **A**1 7 9 10 19 **F**2 9 10 11 12 15 21 23 26 27 28 29 33 37 40 41 42 44 46 47 48 51 52 53 55 57 59 61 62 63 64 65 66 68 69 78 81 82 84 88 92 93 94 95 96 106 108 109 110 **P**8 **S** Triad Hospitals, Inc., Plano, TX
Primary Contact: Mike McCoy, Chief Executive Officer
COO: Bill Brown, Chief Operating Officer
CFO: Wendell VanEs, Chief Financial Officer
CMO: V Anthony Harden, M.D., Chief of Staff
CHR: Connie Gragg, Director Human Resources
Web address: www.saintmarysregional.com — 33 10 154 6259 80 70038 994 45078 18443 498

SALEM—Fulton County

FULTON COUNTY HOSPITAL, 679 North Main Street, Zip 72576–9122, Mailing Address: P.O. Box 517, Zip 72576–0517; tel. 870/895–2691 **A**9 10 18 20 **F**6 33 51 52 63 69 81 88 97
Primary Contact: Franklin E. Wise, Administrator — 13 10 40 707 8 16496 0 3967 2324 110

SEARCY—White County

⊠ △ **CENTRAL ARKANSAS HOSPITAL**, 1200 South Main Street, Zip 72143–7397; tel. 501/278–3100 **A**1 7 9 10 19 **F**2 9 10 11 15 17 19 21 22 26 27 28 29 31 33 36 39 40 44 46 47 48 49 51 52 53 55 57 58 59 60 61 62 63 64 65 66 68 70 71 72 73 74 75 76 77 81 82 83 84 87 88 93 94 96 108 110 **P**8 **S** Triad Hospitals, Inc., Plano, TX
Primary Contact: Ben Frank, Chief Executive Officer
CFO: John Everett, Chief Financial Officer
CMO: Glen Blue, M.D., Chief of Staff
CIO: James Croker, Director Information Services
CHR: Jack Russell, Director Human Resources
Web address: www.centralarkhospital.com — 33 10 145 4903 69 19521 357 45416 15016 366

★ **WHITE COUNTY MEDICAL CENTER**, 3214 East Race, Zip 72143–4847; tel. 501/268–6121 **A**2 9 10 **F**2 9 11 14 15 17 19 21 22 23 26 27 28 29 32 33 40 42 43 46 47 48 50 51 52 53 55 57 58 59 60 61 62 63 65 66 68 69 73 75 81 82 84 85 88 91 93 94 95 96 98 106 108 109 110 **P**6
Primary Contact: Raymond W. Montgomery, II, President and Chief Executive Officer
CFO: Stuart Hill, Vice President and Treasurer
CMO: Michael Justus, M.D., Chief of Staff
CIO: Kevin Hoofman, Director Management Information
CHR: Pam Williams, Human Resources Director
Web address: www.wcmc.org — 23 10 173 9338 103 63619 758 96917 45092 961

SHERWOOD—Pulaski County

★ **ST. VINCENT MEDICAL CENTER–NORTH**, 2215 Wildwood Avenue, Zip 72120; tel. 501/552–7100 **A**9 10 **F**2 9 12 15 21 22 23 27 28 29 33 37 39 40 42 45 46 48 52 53 55 57 61 62 63 64 75 81 82 84 85 87 88 92 94 108 **S** Catholic Health Initiatives, Denver, CO
Primary Contact: Randall R. Cason, Administrator and Chief Executive Officer
COO: Ken Haynes, Senior Vice President and Chief Operating Officer
CFO: Pam Stoyanoff, Senior Vice President and Chief Financial Officer
CMO: David Hall, M.D., Senior Vice Presdient and Chief Medical Affairs
CIO: Tommye Billing, Vice President and Chief Information Officer
CHR: LeRoy Walker, Vice President Human Resources
Web address: www.stvincenthealth.com — 21 10 35 2031 25 37384 84 25163 7903 201

⊠ **ST. VINCENT REHABILITATION HOSPITAL**, 2201 Wildwood Avenue, Zip 72120–5074, Mailing Address: P.O. Box 6930, Zip 72124–6930; tel. 501/834–1800 **A**1 9 10 **F**2 9 21 28 29 37 45 46 48 52 58 60 68 69 93 96 108 110 **S** Catholic Health Initiatives, Denver, CO
Primary Contact: Robert Shane Everett, Administrator
CFO: Pat Robinson, Accounting Manager
CMO: Sean Foley, M.D., Medical Director
CHR: Connie Kelley, Human Resources Manager
Web address: www.healthsouth.com — 32 46 60 1023 34 11497 0 11403 5198 121

SILOAM SPRINGS—Benton County

⊠ **SILOAM SPRINGS MEMORIAL HOSPITAL**, 205 East Jefferson Street, Zip 72761–3697; tel. 479/524–4141, (Nonreporting) **A**1 9 10
Primary Contact: Penny McClain, Chief Executive Officer
CFO: James E. Little, Chief Financial Officer
CMO: Angela Fangmeier, M.D., Chief of Staff
CHR: Sheri Karsh, Director Human Resources
Web address: www.ssmh.us — 14 10 65 — — — — — — —

SPRINGDALE—Washington County

⊠ **NORTHWEST MEDICAL CENTER OF WASHINGTON COUNTY**, 609 West Maple Avenue, Zip 72764; tel. 479/751–5711 **A**1 9 10 **F**2 9 12 14 15 17 19 21 22 23 25 28 29 33 37 44 46 47 48 51 52 53 55 56 57 58 60 61 62 63 64 65 66 68 69 70 81 82 84 85 87 88 93 94 95 96 104 107 108 110 **P**7 **S** Triad Hospitals, Inc., Plano, TX
Primary Contact: Gary N. Looper, Chief Executive Officer
CFO: Shawn Barnett, Chief Financial Officer
CMO: David Cannon, Chief of Staff
CIO: Shannon Williams, Chief Information Officer
CHR: Kim Swieter, Vice President Human Resources
Web address: www.northwesthealth.com — 33 10 180 8312 119 45863 0 135802 46631 932

Many Facility Codes have changed. Please refer to the AHA Guide Code Chart. © 2005 AHA Guide

Hospital, Address, Telephone, Approval, Facility, and Physician Codes, Health Care System	Classi- fication Codes		Utilization Data					Expense (thousands) of dollars		
★ American Hospital Association (AHA) membership ☐ Joint Commission on Accreditation of Healthcare Organizations (JCAHO) accreditation ○ American Osteopathic Association (AOA) accreditation △ Commission on Accreditation of Rehabilitation Facilities (CARF) accreditation	Control	Service	Staffed Beds	Admissions	Census	Outpatient Visits	Births	Total	Payroll	Personnel
★ **REGENCY HOSPITAL OF SPRINGDALE**, 609 West Maple Avenue, 6th Floor, Zip 72764; tel. 479/757–2600, (Nonreporting) **S** Regency Hospital Company, Alpharetta, GA Web address: www.regencyhospital.com	33	80	15	—	—	—	—	—	—	—
STUTTGART—Arkansas County										
★ **STUTTGART REGIONAL MEDICAL CENTER**, North Buerkle Road, Zip 72160–3420, Mailing Address: P.O. Box 1905, Zip 72160–1905; tel. 870/673–3511 **A**9 10 20 **F**6 9 10 11 21 22 27 28 29 32 33 45 46 48 52 53 55 58 63 65 66 69 70 81 88 93 97 108 110 **P**5 Primary Contact: John C. Neal, Chief Executive Officer COO: Lynn Shock, Controller CFO: Bryan Nichols, Chief Financial Officer CMO: Raymond Coker, Chief of Staff CIO: Warren Horton, Information and Technology Support Services Officer CHR: Sheila Sims, Human Resources Director Web address: www.stuttgart-medical.org	23	10	37	2642	23	24815	218	22959	9478	302
TEXARKANA—Miller County										
☐ **LIVING HOPE TEXARKANA**, 801 Arkansas Boulevard, Zip 71854; tel. 870/774–4673 **A**1 9 10 **F**4 21 22 27 28 33 44 45 48 52 58 66 71 72 73 74 75 76 77 94 96 **P**5 Primary Contact: Kimbro Stephens, President and Chief Executive Officer	33	22	62	1273	40	23053	0	7874	3985	128
VAN BUREN—Crawford County										
⊞ **CRAWFORD MEMORIAL HOSPITAL**, East Main and South 20th Streets, Zip 72956–5715, Mailing Address: P.O. Box 409, Zip 72957–0409; tel. 479/474–3401 **A**1 9 10 **F**2 9 11 12 21 22 32 33 34 39 44 46 47 48 52 53 55 57 58 59 61 62 63 64 66 69 81 82 84 85 88 94 95 96 106 107 108 110 **P**6 **S** Health Management Associates, Naples, FL Primary Contact: Kevin Clement, Chief Executive Officer CFO: Andrew Davis, Chief Financial Officer Web address: www.crawfordmemorial.com	33	10	103	2625	27	20571	108	25980	9404	223
WALDRON—Scott County										
★ **MERCY HOSPITAL OF SCOTT COUNTY**, 895 West 6th Street, Zip 72958–7001; tel. 479/637–4135 **A**9 10 18 **F**2 23 26 27 28 29 33 46 48 52 63 64 81 88 97 **S** Sisters of Mercy Health System, Chesterfield, MO Primary Contact: Jim L. Maddox, Administrator CFO: James Newman, Senior Vice President and Chief Financial Officer Web address: www.stedwardmercy.com	21	10	24	829	6	14175	0	4063	2112	52
WALNUT RIDGE—Lawrence County										
★ **LAWRENCE MEMORIAL HOSPITAL**, 1309 West Main, Zip 72476–1430, Mailing Address: P.O. Box 839, Zip 72476–0839; tel. 870/886–1200, (Includes LAWRENCE HALL NURSING HOME), (Total facility includes 189 beds in nursing home–type unit) **A**9 10 18 **F**2 9 12 21 22 26 27 28 29 33 34 39 46 48 52 54 58 63 66 69 81 84 87 88 92 93 94 96 97 108 Primary Contact: Leah Osbahr, President CFO: Sandy Sullins, Chief Financial Officer CMO: Paul Vellozo, M.D., Chief Medical Officer and Chief of Staff CHR: Sherri Brown, Director Human Resources Web address: www.lawrencehealth.net	13	10	214	1228	182	27393	0	16731	7904	324
WARREN—Bradley County										
★ **BRADLEY COUNTY MEDICAL CENTER**, 404 South Bradley Street, Zip 71671–3493; tel. 870/226–3731 **A**9 10 **F**9 11 12 14 28 33 44 48 51 52 59 63 65 76 81 88 94 **P**4 Primary Contact: Harry H. Stevens, President and Chief Executive Officer CFO: Harold Mitchell, Chief Financial Officer CMO: James W. Marsh, Chief of Staff CHR: Debra Marshall, Human Resources Director Web address: www.geocities.com/bcmc71671	23	10	49	1743	17	9767	213	12803	6017	197
WEST MEMPHIS—Crittenden County										
☐ △ **CRITTENDEN MEMORIAL HOSPITAL**, 200 Tyler Avenue, Zip 72301–4223, Mailing Address: P.O. Box 2248, Zip 72303–2248; tel. 870/735–1500 **A**1 7 9 10 **F**2 9 11 12 21 23 26 27 28 29 33 34 36 46 48 51 52 55 58 59 61 62 63 65 66 68 69 81 82 84 88 94 96 106 108 **P**5 Primary Contact: Ross Hooper, Chief Executive Officer Web address: www.crittendenmemorial.org	23	10	121	3741	45	42836	721	42057	18972	497
WYNNE—Cross County										
★ **CROSSRIDGE COMMUNITY HOSPITAL**, 310 South Falls Boulevard, Zip 72396–3013, Mailing Address: P.O. Box 590, Zip 72396–0590; tel. 870/238–3300 **A**9 10 18 **F**2 9 12 27 28 29 33 46 48 51 52 54 63 69 81 94 96 97 Primary Contact: Gary R. Sparks, Administrator COO: Bryan Mattes, Associate Administrator CFO: Janice Morris, Accountant CIO: Gail Copeland, Director Management Information Systems CHR: Bertha Ragle, Director Personnel Web address: www.crosscountychamber.com/wynne/crossridge_hospital.htm	21	10	15	633	7	18058	0	9994	3596	107

CALIFORNIA

Hospital, Address, Telephone, Approval, Facility, and Physician Codes, Health Care System	Classi-fication Codes		Utilization Data					Expense (thousands) of dollars		
★ American Hospital Association (AHA) membership □ Joint Commission on Accreditation of Healthcare Organizations (JCAHO) accreditation ○ American Osteopathic Association (AOA) accreditation △ Commission on Accreditation of Rehabilitation Facilities (CARF) accreditation	Control	Service	Staffed Beds	Admissions	Census	Outpatient Visits	Births	Total	Payroll	Personnel

ALAMEDA—Alameda County

☒ **ALAMEDA HOSPITAL**, 2070 Clinton Avenue, Zip 94501–4397; tel. 510/522–3700, (Total facility includes 35 beds in nursing home–type unit) **A**1 9 10 **F**2 9 12 14 21 26 27 28 29 30 31 32 33 34 35 37 39 41 46 47 48 49 52 53 55 58 60 62 63 64 65 66 69 81 82 85 87 88 92 94 106 108 110
Primary Contact: Stuart A. Jed, Chief Executive Officer
CFO: Gary K. Wiggins, Chief Financial Officer
CMO: Eric Otani, M.D., President Medical Staff
CIO: Mark Moran, Director Information Systems
CHR: Tony Corica, Director Human Resources
Web address: www.alamedahospital.org
| 16 | 10 | 101 | 3107 | 61 | 49307 | 0 | 46388 | 27410 | 372 |

ALHAMBRA—Los Angeles County

□ △ **ALHAMBRA HOSPITAL MEDICAL CENTER**, 100 South Raymond Avenue, Zip 91801–3199, Mailing Address: P.O. Box 510, Zip 91802–0510; tel. 626/570–1606, (Total facility includes 26 beds in nursing home–type unit) **A**1 2 7 9 10 **F**68 **S** AHMC, Inc, Alhambra, CA
Primary Contact: Iris Lai, Acting Chief Executive Officer
Web address: www.alhambrahospital.com
| 32 | 10 | 144 | 4369 | 110 | 18509 | 0 | 50358 | — | — |

ALTURAS—Modoc County

MODOC MEDICAL CENTER, 228 McDowell Street, Zip 96101–3915; tel. 530/233–5131, (Total facility includes 71 beds in nursing home–type unit) **A**9 10 20 **F**6 9 11 12 33 46 52 63 69 70 87 88 92 93 97 108
Primary Contact: Teresa Jacques, Chief Executive Officer
Web address: www.modocmedicalcenter.org
| 13 | 10 | 87 | 247 | 52 | 28949 | — | 7947 | | |

ANAHEIM—Orange County

□ **ANAHEIM GENERAL HOSPITAL**, 3350 West Ball Road, Zip 92804–3799; tel. 714/827–6700, (Total facility includes 21 beds in nursing home–type unit) (Nonreporting) **A**1 9 10 **S** Pacific Health Corporation, Tustin, CA
Primary Contact: Josh Luke, Chief Executive Officer
Web address: www.anaheimgeneral.com
| 31 | 10 | 143 | — | — | — | — | — | — | — |

☒ **ANAHEIM MEMORIAL MEDICAL CENTER**, 1111 West La Palma Avenue, Zip 92801–2881; tel. 714/774–1450 **A**1 2 9 10 **F**2 9 11 12 14 15 17 19 21 22 23 26 27 28 29 31 33 35 37 38 39 42 44 45 46 47 48 52 53 55 56 57 58 59 60 61 62 63 64 65 66 69 81 82 84 88 92 94 95 96 106 108 109 110 **P**5 7 **S** Memorial Health Services, Long Beach, CA
Primary Contact: Melinda D. Beswick, Chief Executive Officer
COO: Liz Dunne, Chief Operating Officer
CFO: Steve McNamara, Chief Financial Officer
CIO: John Stewart, Director Information Systems
CHR: Kim Wright, Executive Director Human Resources
Web address: www.memorialcare.org
| 23 | 10 | 217 | 13345 | 151 | 103314 | 2136 | 139164 | 48014 | 977 |

☒ **KAISER FOUNDATION HOSPITAL – ORANGE COUNTY**, 441 North Lakeview Avenue, Zip 92807–3089; tel. 714/279–4100 **A**1 2 3 5 10 **F**2 11 12 14 15 17 21 23 26 27 28 33 35 39 42 45 48 50 51 52 53 55 56 57 58 59 60 61 62 63 64 66 73 81 82 84 85 87 88 92 94 108 110 **S** Kaiser Foundation Hospitals, Oakland, CA
Primary Contact: Julie K. Miller–Phipps, Senior Vice President and Service Area Manager
COO: Gregory A. Adams, Chief Operating Officer
CMO: Edward Ellison, M.D., Area Associate Medical Director
CIO: Donald Carren, Information Technology Leader
CHR: Jean Melnikoff, Human Resources Leader
Web address: www.kaiserpermanente.org
| 23 | 10 | 167 | 12391 | 126 | 142156 | 3229 | — | — | 1084 |

□ **WEST ANAHEIM MEDICAL CENTER**, 3033 West Orange Avenue, Zip 92804–3184; tel. 714/827–3000, (Nonreporting) **A**1 5 9 10 **S** Vanguard Health System, Nashville, TN
Primary Contact: David K. Culberson, Chief Executive Officer
Web address: www.westanaheimmedctr.com
| 32 | 10 | 219 | — | — | — | — | — | — | — |

☒ **WESTERN MEDICAL CENTER ANAHEIM**, 1025 South Anaheim Boulevard, Zip 92805–5806; tel. 714/533–6220 **A**1 9 10 **F**55 56 59 71
Primary Contact: Patrick W. Rafferty, Chief Executive Officer
COO: Margie Harrier, Chief Operating Officer
CFO: Karen Kretz, Chief Financial Officer
CMO: Jayanti Patel, M.D., Chief Medical Officer
CIO: Nova Stewart, Chief Information Officer
CHR: Kathryn Van Dyk, Director
Web address: www.westernmedanaheim.com
| 33 | 10 | 181 | 7555 | 116 | 49025 | 2898 | 64878 | 32094 | 565 |

ANTIOCH—Contra Costa County

☒ **SUTTER DELTA MEDICAL CENTER**, 3901 Lone Tree Way, Zip 94509–6200; tel. 925/779–7200, (Nonreporting) **A**1 9 10 **S** Sutter Health, Sacramento, CA
Primary Contact: Linda Horn, Chief Executive Officer
CFO: Becky Levy, Chief Financial Officer
CMO: Sanjay Ray, M.D., Chief of Staff
CIO: Brenda Buccellato, Information Technology Manager
CHR: Sandra Speer, Administrative Director Human Resources
Web address: www.sutterdelta.org
| 23 | 10 | 111 | — | — | — | — | — | — | — |

Many Facility Codes have changed. Please refer to the AHA Guide Code Chart.   © 2005 AHA Guide

Hospital, Address, Telephone, Approval, Facility, and Physician Codes, Health Care System	Classi-fication Codes		Utilization Data					Expense (thousands) of dollars		
★ American Hospital Association (AHA) membership □ Joint Commission on Accreditation of Healthcare Organizations (JCAHO) accreditation ○ American Osteopathic Association (AOA) accreditation △ Commission on Accreditation of Rehabilitation Facilities (CARF) accreditation	Control	Service	Staffed Beds	Admissions	Census	Outpatient Visits	Births	Total	Payroll	Personnel

APPLE VALLEY—San Bernardino County

☒ **ST. MARY MEDICAL CENTER**, 18300 Highway 18, Zip 92307–2255, Mailing Address: P.O. Box 7025, Zip 92307–0725; tel. 760/242–2311 **A**1 2 9 10 **F**9 11 12 15 16 17 18 19 20 21 22 24 26 27 28 29 33 37 46 47 48 49 53 55 56 59 60 61 62 63 66 69 81 82 84 88 92 94 96 98 106 108 109 110 **P**5 **S** St. Joseph Health System, Orange, CA
Primary Contact: George Perez, President and Chief Executive Officer
CFO: James McManus, Chief Financial Officer
CIO: Dale Lepper, Director Information Services

| | 21 | 10 | 186 | 11423 | 133 | 68158 | 1829 | 119379 | 40455 | 1187 |

ARCADIA—Los Angeles County

☒ **METHODIST HOSPITAL OF SOUTHERN CALIFORNIA**, 300 West Huntington Drive, Zip 91007–3473, Mailing Address: P.O. Box 60016, Zip 91066–6016; tel. 626/445–4441 **A**1 2 9 10 **F**9 11 12 14 15 17 19 21 22 26 27 28 29 31 33 41 46 47 48 49 52 53 54 55 56 57 58 59 60 61 62 63 64 65 66 68 69 79 80 81 82 84 86 88 90 94 95 96 108 109 110
Primary Contact: Dennis M. Lee, President and Chief Executive Officer
CFO: Kay Berglund, Vice President Finance and Chief Financial Officer
CIO: Albert Hicks, Director
CHR: Jill Underwood, Vice President Human Resources
Web address: www.methodisthospital.org

| | 23 | 10 | 346 | 16358 | 219 | 71921 | 2152 | 158706 | — | 1741 |

ARCATA—Humboldt County

MAD RIVER COMMUNITY HOSPITAL, 3800 Janes Road, Zip 95521–4788, Mailing Address: P.O. Box 1115, Zip 95521–1115; tel. 707/822–3621, (Nonreporting) **A**9 10
Primary Contact: Douglas A. Shaw, Administrator

| | 33 | 10 | 68 | — | | | | | | |

ARROYO GRANDE—San Luis Obispo County

☒ **ARROYO GRANDE COMMUNITY HOSPITAL**, 345 South Halcyon Road, Zip 93420–3899; tel. 805/489–4261 **A**1 9 10 **F**12 40 44 46 50 51 52 55 60 61 63 69 81 82 84 88 94 107 **S** Catholic Healthcare West, San Francisco, CA
Primary Contact: Rick Castro, President and Chief Executive Officer
CIO: Cyndi Lang, Director Information Services
CHR: Ami Chauarria, Director Human Resources
Web address: www.agfh.org

| | 23 | 10 | 65 | 3320 | 35 | — | 0 | — | — | — |

ATASCADERO—San Luis Obispo County

□ **ATASCADERO STATE HOSPITAL**, 10333 El Camino Real, Zip 93422–7001, Mailing Address: P.O. Box 7001, Zip 93423–7001; tel. 805/468–2000 **A**1 **F**2 22 26 32 37 46 47 48 50 53 58 65 68 76 94 96 106 107 108 **P**6
Primary Contact: Melvin Hunter, Executive Director
Web address: www.dmh.ca.gov/statehospitals/atascadero

| | 12 | 22 | 1191 | 1020 | 1191 | 0 | 0 | 168384 | 99719 | 2059 |

AUBURN—Placer County

☒ **SUTTER AUBURN FAITH HOSPITAL**, 11815 Education Street, Zip 95602–2410; tel. 530/888–4500 **A**1 9 10 **F**9 10 11 12 14 15 21 22 23 26 27 28 29 33 36 37 38 41 46 47 48 49 51 52 55 58 59 60 61 63 66 68 69 70 81 88 94 96 106 108 109 **P**3 5 **S** Sutter Health, Sacramento, CA
Primary Contact: Mitchell J. Hanna, Chief Administrative Officer
CFO: Richard SooHoo, Administrative Director Finance
CMO: John Mesic, M.D., Chief Medical Officer
Web address: www.sutterhealth.org

| | 23 | 10 | 82 | 3272 | 51 | 91583 | 476 | 71611 | 25830 | 425 |

AVALON—Los Angeles County

CATALINA ISLAND MEDICAL CENTER, 100 Falls Canyon Road, Zip 90704, Mailing Address: Box 1563, Zip 90704–1563; tel. 310/510–0700, (Total facility includes 4 beds in nursing home–type unit) **A**9 10 18 **F**2 9 28 29 33 39 46 48 51 52 58 69 70 81 88 92 94 97 106 108 **P**6
Primary Contact: William M. Greene, FACHE, Chief Executive Officer

| | 23 | 10 | 12 | 92 | 6 | 11807 | 0 | 3543 | 1757 | 25 |

BAKERSFIELD—Kern County

BAKERSFIELD HEART HOSPITAL, 3001 Sillect Avenue, Zip 93308–6337; tel. 661/316–6000 **A**10 **F**2 14 15 17 19 21 22 27 28 33 45 63 81 82 87 88 94 108 **S** MedCath, Inc., Charlotte, NC
Primary Contact: Randall H. Rolfe, President
Web address: www.bakersfieldhearthospital.com

| | 23 | 10 | 47 | 3868 | 42 | 7897 | 0 | 47310 | — | — |

☒ **BAKERSFIELD MEMORIAL HOSPITAL**, 420 34th Street, Zip 93301–2237, Mailing Address: P.O. Box 1888, Zip 93303–1888; tel. 661/327–1792, (Includes MEMORIAL CENTER, 5201 White Lane, Zip 93309; tel. 805/398–1800), (Total facility includes 24 beds in nursing home–type unit) **A**1 9 10 **F**2 3 4 9 11 12 14 21 22 27 28 33 39 53 55 56 57 59 61 62 63 65 69 71 72 73 74 77 78 81 82 83 84 85 88 92 94 108 109 **S** Catholic Healthcare West, San Francisco, CA
Primary Contact: Jon Van Boening, President
COO: Bruce Peters, Vice President and Chief Operating Officer
CFO: Kevin Walters, Chief Financial Officer
CMO: Robert Marshall, M.D., Vice President Medical Affairs
Web address: www.chw.edu

| | 21 | 10 | 339 | 15102 | 203 | 70568 | 2457 | — | — | — |

□ **GOOD SAMARITAN HOSPITAL**, 901 Olive Drive, Zip 93308–4144, Mailing Address: P.O. Box 85002, Zip 93380–5002; tel. 661/399–4461, (Nonreporting) **A**1 9 10
Primary Contact: David A. Huff, President

| | 33 | 10 | 29 | — | | | | | | |

Hospital, Address, Telephone, Approval, Facility, and Physician Codes, Health Care System	Classi-fication Codes		Utilization Data					Expense (thousands) of dollars		
★ American Hospital Association (AHA) membership □ Joint Commission on Accreditation of Healthcare Organizations (JCAHO) accreditation ○ American Osteopathic Association (AOA) accreditation △ Commission on Accreditation of Rehabilitation Facilities (CARF) accreditation	Control	Service	Staffed Beds	Admissions	Census	Outpatient Visits	Births	Total	Payroll	Personnel

	Control	Service	Staffed Beds	Admissions	Census	Outpatient Visits	Births	Total	Payroll	Personnel
⊠ **HEALTHSOUTH BAKERSFIELD REHABILITATION HOSPITAL**, 5001 Commerce Drive, Zip 93309–0689; tel. 661/323–5500 **A**1 9 10 **F**2 21 22 26 27 28 29 37 53 60 68 69 94 95 96 106 110 **P**5 **S** HEALTHSOUTH Corporation, Birmingham, AL Primary Contact: Ann Feaver, Administrator CFO: Robert Mosesian, Assistant Controller CMO: Chris Yoon, M.D., Medical Director Web address: www.healthsouth.com	33	46	60	1022	35	17588	0	12707	—	—
□ **KERN MEDICAL CENTER**, 1830 Flower Street, Zip 93305–4186; tel. 661/326–2000, (Nonreporting) **A**1 2 3 5 8 9 10 12 Primary Contact: Peter K. Bryan, Chief Executive Officer Web address: www.kernmedicalcenter.com	13	10	180	—	—	—	—	—	—	—
MEMORIAL CENTER See Bakersfield Memorial Hospital										
⊠ **MERCY HOSPITAL**, 2215 Truxtun Avenue, Zip 93301–3698, Mailing Address: P.O. Box 119, Zip 93302–0119; tel. 661/632–5000, (Includes MERCY SOUTHWEST HOSPITAL, 400 Old River Road, Zip 93311; tel. 661/663–6000), (Total facility includes 50 beds in nursing home–type unit) **A**1 2 9 10 **F**9 10 11 12 21 22 27 28 29 33 37 38 46 48 49 51 52 55 56 57 58 59 60 61 62 63 65 66 69 79 80 81 82 84 87 88 92 94 107 108 **S** Catholic Healthcare West, San Francisco, CA Primary Contact: Russell V. Judd, President CFO: Rodney Winegarner, Chief Financial Officer CMO: Mitesh Patel, M.D., Chief Medical Officer CIO: Wendy Valdez, Chief Information Officer CHR: William R. Moore, Vice President Human Resources Web address: www.chw.edu	21	10	261	12585	187	130411	3002	135660	63120	1010
⊠ **SAN JOAQUIN COMMUNITY HOSPITAL**, 2615 Eye Street, Zip 93301–2006, Mailing Address: P.O. Box 2615, Zip 93303–2615; tel. 661/395–3000 **A**1 9 10 **F**2 9 10 11 14 15 17 19 21 22 26 27 28 29 33 38 46 48 51 55 57 58 59 62 63 64 65 68 81 82 84 88 92 94 96 108 110 **S** Adventist Health, Roseville, CA Primary Contact: Robert J. Beehler, President and Chief Executive Officer COO: Ellen Tryon, Chief Operating Officer CMO: Kerry Oliver, M.D., Chief Medical Officer CIO: Adrienne McReynolds, Chief Information Officer CHR: Debbie Hankins, Director Human Resources Web address: www.sanjoaquinhospital.org	21	10	166	9098	139	53746	1815	107178	44530	948
BALDWIN PARK—Los Angeles County										
⊠ **KAISER FOUNDATION HOSPITAL–BALDWIN PARK**, 1011 Baldwin Park Boulevard, Zip 91706–5806; tel. 626/851–1011 **A**1 10 **F**2 11 12 21 22 23 26 27 28 29 33 34 37 39 44 46 47 48 50 52 53 55 56 57 58 59 60 61 62 63 64 65 66 69 70 81 84 88 92 94 106 107 108 109 110 **P**6 **S** Kaiser Foundation Hospitals, Oakland, CA Primary Contact: Gerald A. McCall, Senior Vice President and Administrator Web address: www.kp.org	23	10	207	15941	116	73664	3080	—	—	847
BANNING—Riverside County										
⊠ **SAN GORGONIO MEMORIAL HOSPITAL**, 600 North Highland Springs Avenue, Zip 92220–3046; tel. 909/845–1121, (Total facility includes 16 beds in nursing home–type unit) **A**1 9 10 **F**2 9 11 12 21 22 26 27 28 29 33 36 37 38 46 48 55 58 59 63 66 77 81 88 92 107 108 109 **S** Brim Healthcare, Inc., Brentwood, TN Primary Contact: Donald N. Larkin, Chief Executive Officer COO: Michelle Sayer, Chief Operating Officer CFO: Jonathan Goh, Chief Financial Officer CHR: Katy Weston, Chief Human Resources Web address: www.sgmh.org	16	10	70	3893	49	29779	0	—	—	—
BARSTOW—San Bernardino County										
□ **BARSTOW COMMUNITY HOSPITAL**, 555 South Seventh Street, Zip 92311–3086; tel. 760/256–1761 **A**1 9 10 **F**2 9 11 12 14 21 46 48 58 59 63 65 81 82 85 88 **S** Community Health Systems, Inc., Brentwood, TN Primary Contact: Randall Hempling, Chief Executive Officer Web address: www.barstowhospital.com	33	10	24	2679	23	32360	—	15690	—	—
BELLFLOWER—Los Angeles County										
□ **BELLFLOWER MEDICAL CENTER**, 9542 East Artesia Boulevard, Zip 90706–6511; tel. 562/925–8355 **A**1 9 10 **F**10 12 21 22 23 29 33 44 48 49 50 51 53 57 58 60 62 63 64 66 69 74 75 81 82 88 94 96 108 109 110 **S** Pacific Health Corporation, Tustin, CA Primary Contact: James Linhares, Chief Executive Officer	33	10	113	5066	74	20967	1042	—	—	427
⊠ **KAISER FOUNDATION HOSPITAL–BELLFLOWER**, 9400 East Rosecrans Avenue, Zip 90706–2246; tel. 562/461–3000 **A**1 3 5 10 **F**2 4 11 12 21 22 23 24 26 27 28 29 31 33 37 40 44 46 47 48 49 50 51 52 55 56 59 62 63 64 65 66 72 73 74 75 76 81 82 84 87 88 90 92 93 94 96 107 108 109 110 **S** Kaiser Foundation Hospitals, Oakland, CA Primary Contact: Gerald A. McCall, Senior Vice President and Administrator Web address: www.kaiserpermanente.org	23	10	307	33625	162	88612	3321	—	—	—
BERKELEY—Alameda County										
⊠ △ **ALTA BATES SUMMIT MEDICAL CENTER**, 2450 Ashby Avenue, Zip 94705–2067; tel. 510/204–4444, (Includes ALTA BATES MEDICAL CENTER–HERRICK CAMPUS, 2001 Dwight Way, Zip 94704; tel. 510/204–4444), (Total facility includes 59 beds in nursing home–type unit) (Nonreporting) **A**1 2 7 9 10 **S** Sutter Health, Sacramento, CA Primary Contact: Warren J. Kirk, Chief Executive Officer Web address: www.altabates.com	23	10	509	—	—	—	—	—	—	—

Many Facility Codes have changed. Please refer to the AHA Guide Code Chart. © 2005 AHA Guide

Hospital, Address, Telephone, Approval, Facility, and Physician Codes, Health Care System	Classi-fication Codes		Utilization Data					Expense (thousands) of dollars		
★ American Hospital Association (AHA) membership □ Joint Commission on Accreditation of Healthcare Organizations (JCAHO) accreditation ○ American Osteopathic Association (AOA) accreditation △ Commission on Accreditation of Rehabilitation Facilities (CARF) accreditation	Control	Service	Staffed Beds	Admissions	Census	Outpatient Visits	Births	Total	Payroll	Personnel

BIG BEAR LAKE—San Bernardino County

★ **BEAR VALLEY COMMUNITY HOSPITAL**, 41870 Garstin Road, Zip 92315, Mailing Address: P.O. Box 1649, Zip 92315–1649; tel. 909/866–6501, (Total facility includes 21 beds in nursing home–type unit) **A**9 10 20 **F**2 9 21 22 26 33 54 63 81 85 88 92 94
Primary Contact: Mary Norman, Administrator and Chief Executive Officer
COO: Ann Haggard, R.N., Chief Operating Officer
CMO: Mike Norman, D.O., Chief Medical Staff
Web address: www.bvchd.com

| 16 | 10 | 24 | 417 | 22 | 31683 | 0 | 11569 | — | — |

BISHOP—Inyo County

⊞ **NORTHERN INYO HOSPITAL**, 150 Pioneer Lane, Zip 93514–2599; tel. 760/873–5811 **A**1 9 10 20 **F**2 9 11 12 23 27 28 33 36 52 53 55 59 62 63 69 81 84 88 94
Primary Contact: John Halfen, Administrator, Chief Executive Officer and Chief Financial Officer
CFO: John Halfen, Chief Executive Officer and Chief Financial Officer
CMO: Michael Dillon, M.D., Chief of Staff
CIO: Adam Taylor, Manager Information Technology
CHR: Gayla Blua, Human Resources Director
Web address: www.nih.org

| 16 | 10 | 30 | 1047 | 9 | 53666 | 190 | 29717 | 11666 | 281 |

BLYTHE—Riverside County

⊞ **PALO VERDE HOSPITAL**, 250 North First Street, Zip 92225–1702; tel. 760/922–4115, (Nonreporting) **A**1 9 10 20 **S** LifePoint Hospitals, Inc., Brentwood, TN
Primary Contact: Dale R. Mulder, Chief Executive Officer
CFO: Norma Hudson, Chief Financial Officer

| 33 | 10 | 35 | — | — | — | — | — | — | — |

BRAWLEY—Imperial County

□ **PIONEERS MEMORIAL HEALTHCARE DISTRICT**, 207 West Legion Road, Zip 92227–7780; tel. 760/351–3333 **A**1 9 10 **F**2 9 11 12 21 27 29 30 33 34 39 46 47 48 49 55 56 58 59 60 62 63 65 66 69 81 82 84 87 88 94 96 108 109 **S** Brim Healthcare, Inc., Brentwood, TN
Primary Contact: Richard L. Mendoza, Chief Executive Officer
Web address: www.pmhd.org

| 16 | 10 | 105 | 5902 | 56 | 92095 | 1482 | 51327 | 19286 | 437 |

BREA—Orange County

□ **KINDRED HOSPITAL–BREA**, 875 North Brea Boulevard, Zip 92821–2606; tel. 714/529–6842, (Nonreporting) **A**1 10 **S** Kindred Healthcare, Louisville, KY
Primary Contact: Kathleen Smith, Chief Executive Officer
Web address: www.kindredhealthcare.com

| 33 | 10 | 48 | — | — | — | — | — | — | — |

BURBANK—Los Angeles County

⊞ **PROVIDENCE SAINT JOSEPH MEDICAL CENTER**, 501 South Buena Vista Street, Zip 91505–4866; tel. 818/843–5111, (Total facility includes 93 beds in nursing home–type unit) **A**1 2 9 10 **F**9 10 11 12 14 15 16 17 19 21 22 23 24 26 27 28 29 33 35 36 37 38 39 40 41 42 44 45 46 47 48 51 52 53 55 56 57 58 59 60 61 62 63 65 66 68 69 79 81 82 84 85 86 87 88 92 94 96 98 107 108 109 110 **P**5 **S** Providence Health System, Seattle, WA
Primary Contact: Arnold R. Schaffer, Chief Executive Officer
CFO: Mitchell T. Thomas, Chief Financial Officer
CMO: Myron Berdischewsky, M.D., Chief Medical Officer
CIO: Patty Mayberry, Director Applications System and Support
CHR: Wayne Cassard, Service Area Director Human Resources
Web address: www.providence.org

| 21 | 10 | 427 | 18139 | 243 | 248923 | 2306 | 260434 | 107724 | 1827 |

BURLINGAME—San Mateo County

⊞ **MILLS–PENINSULA HEALTH SERVICES**, 1783 El Camino Real, Zip 94010–3282; tel. 650/696–5400, (Includes MILLS HOSPITAL, 100 South San Mateo Drive, San Mateo, Zip 94401; PENINSULA HOSPITAL), (Nonreporting) **A**1 2 9 10 **S** Sutter Health, Sacramento, CA
Primary Contact: Robert W. Merwin, Chief Executive Officer
COO: Jeff Gerard, Chief Operating Officer
CFO: Iftikhar Hussain, Chief Financial Officer
CMO: Michael K. Wood, M.D., Chief of Staff
Web address: www.mills–pensinsula.org

| 23 | 10 | 398 | — | — | — | — | — | — | — |

CAMARILLO—Ventura County

⊞ **ST. JOHN'S PLEASANT VALLEY HOSPITAL**, 2309 Antonio Avenue, Zip 93010–1414; tel. 805/389–5800, (Total facility includes 92 beds in nursing home–type unit) **A**1 9 10 **F**2 9 11 12 21 22 23 26 27 28 29 33 37 38 46 47 48 55 59 60 63 64 65 66 69 81 85 87 88 92 94 108 109 110 **S** Catholic Healthcare West, San Francisco, CA
Primary Contact: T. Michael Murray, President
COO: Maureen A. Malone, Chief Operating Officer
CFO: Ed Matthews, Chief Financial Officer
Web address: www.catholichealthcarewest.org

| 23 | 10 | 163 | 4351 | 112 | 47170 | 533 | 60914 | 31392 | 391 |

Hospital, Address, Telephone, Approval, Facility, and Physician Codes, Health Care System	Classification Codes		Utilization Data					Expense (thousands) of dollars		
★ American Hospital Association (AHA) membership □ Joint Commission on Accreditation of Healthcare Organizations (JCAHO) accreditation ○ American Osteopathic Association (AOA) accreditation △ Commission on Accreditation of Rehabilitation Facilities (CARF) accreditation	Control	Service	Staffed Beds	Admissions	Census	Outpatient Visits	Births	Total	Payroll	Personnel

CA

CAMP PENDLETON—San Diego County

✠ **NAVAL HOSPITAL**, Mailing Address: Box 555191, Zip 92055–5191; tel. 760/725–1304 **A**1 3 5 **F**6 11 12 21 22 24 25 29 32 33 39 41 42 44 46 47 48 50 52 53 55 57 58 59 60 63 65 66 69 70 81 84 85 88 89 92 94 95 96 108 109 **S** Bureau of Medicine and Surgery, Department of the Navy, Washington, DC Primary Contact: Captain Richard Jeffries, Commanding Officer CFO: Lieutenant Colonel S Loberg, Director Resource Support Services CMO: Colonel R Meade, M.D., Executive Director Primary Care CIO: Colin Archibald, Chief Information Officer CHR: Lieutenant M Edusada, Head Staff Administration Web address: www.enhcp.com	43	10	83	3730	25	—	—	—	—	1763

CANOGA PARK—Los Angeles County, See Los Angeles

CARMICHAEL—Sacramento County

✠ **MERCY SAN JUAN MEDICAL CENTER**, 6501 Coyle Avenue, Zip 95608–0306, Mailing Address: P.O. Box 479, Zip 95608–0479; tel. 916/537–5000, (Includes MERCY SAN JUAN HOSPITAL) **A**1 9 10 **F**2 9 10 11 12 14 15 17 19 21 22 23 27 28 29 33 34 36 37 38 48 51 52 53 55 56 57 58 59 60 61 62 63 64 69 81 82 84 88 92 93 94 96 106 107 108 109 110 **S** Catholic Healthcare West, San Francisco, CA Primary Contact: Michael J. Uboldi, R.N., President Web address: www.mercysanjuan.org	21	10	260	15834	202	194816	2985	227103	104127	1339

CEDARVILLE—Modoc County

SURPRISE VALLEY HEALTHCARE DISTRICT, Main and Washington Streets, Zip 96104, Mailing Address: P.O. Box 246, Zip 96104–0246; tel. 530/279–6111, (Total facility includes 22 beds in nursing home–type unit) **A**9 10 18 **F**6 9 24 26 27 28 33 44 45 46 48 52 54 58 63 88 92 97 108 **P**6 Primary Contact: Dannette E. DePaul, Administrator	16	10	26	54	22	404	0	—	—	—

CERRITOS—Los Angeles County

□ **COLLEGE HOSPITAL**, 10802 College Place, Zip 90703–1579; tel. 562/924–9581 **A**1 10 **F**27 71 72 73 74 75 76 78 **P**8 **S** College Health Enterprises, Santa Fe Springs, CA Primary Contact: Stephen Witt, Chief Executive Officer Web address: www.collegehospitals.com	33	22	125	6027	120	44650	0	28665	—	—

CHESTER—Plumas County

★ **SENECA HEALTHCARE DISTRICT**, 130 Brentwood Drive, Zip 96020–0737, Mailing Address: P.O. Box 737, Zip 96020–0737; tel. 530/258–2151, (Total facility includes 16 beds in nursing home–type unit) **A**9 10 20 **F**6 9 12 26 29 33 34 36 46 48 50 52 53 62 63 69 81 88 92 96 108 **P**5 Primary Contact: Warren Benincosa, Chief Executive Officer COO: Warren Benincosa, Chief Executive Officer CMO: Thomas Archie, M.D., Chief of Staff CIO: Steve Hamilton, Chief Information Officer CHR: Doreen Ayres, Human Resources Director Web address: www.senecahospital.org	16	10	26	398	18	34165	0	10638	4157	114

CHICO—Butte County

✠ **ENLOE MEDICAL CENTER**, 1531 Esplanade, Zip 95926–3310; tel. 530/332–7300, (Includes ENLOE MEDICAL CENTER–COHASSET, 560 Cohasset Road, Zip 95926; tel. 530/332–7300; Dan Neumeister, Chief Operations Officer) **A**1 2 9 10 **F**2 4 6 9 10 11 14 21 22 24 26 28 29 33 34 36 45 46 48 51 52 54 55 56 57 58 59 60 61 62 63 65 69 75 81 82 87 88 93 94 96 107 108 109 110 Primary Contact: Philip R. Wolfe, President and Chief Executive Officer COO: Daniel P. Neumeister, CHE, Chief Operations Officer CFO: Christine Sarrico, Chief Financial Officer CMO: Daniel Thomas, M.D., Chief of Staff CIO: James Preece, Chief Information Officer CHR: Carol Linscheid, Vice President Human Resources Web address: www.enloe.org	23	10	283	14240	195	279920	—	202150	—	—

CHINO—San Bernardino County

CANYON RIDGE HOSPITAL, 5353 G Street, Zip 91710–5250; tel. 909/590–3700 **A**10 **F**1 4 28 71 72 73 74 75 76 77 78 Primary Contact: Jeff McDonald, Chief Executive Officer	33	22	59	3381	44	2586	0	8275	—	—
○ **CHINO VALLEY MEDICAL CENTER**, 5451 Walnut Avenue, Zip 91710–2672; tel. 909/464–8600 **A**10 11 12 13 **F**11 12 21 22 33 55 59 63 81 84 88 108 **P**5 Web address: www.cvmc.com	33	10	126	46	1	31	0	—	—	480

CHOWCHILLA—Madera County

CHOWCHILLA DISTRICT MEMORIAL HOSPITAL, 1104 Ventura Avenue, Zip 93610–2298; tel. 559/665–3781, (Total facility includes 23 beds in nursing home–type unit) (Nonreporting) **A**9 10 Primary Contact: Cathy Flores, R.N., Administrator and Controller	16	10	24	—	—	—	—	—	—	—

CHULA VISTA—San Diego County

BAYVIEW HOSPITAL AND MENTAL HEALTH SYSTEM, 330 Moss Street, Zip 91911–2005; tel. 619/426–6310, (Nonreporting) Primary Contact: Rudra Sabaratnam, M.D., Chief Executive Officer Web address: www.bayviewhospital.com	33	22	64	—	—	—	—	—	—	—

Many Facility Codes have changed. Please refer to the AHA Guide Code Chart. © 2005 AHA Guide

Hospital, Address, Telephone, Approval, Facility, and Physician Codes, Health Care System	Classi-fication Codes		Utilization Data					Expense (thousands) of dollars		
★ American Hospital Association (AHA) membership □ Joint Commission on Accreditation of Healthcare Organizations (JCAHO) accreditation ○ American Osteopathic Association (AOA) accreditation △ Commission on Accreditation of Rehabilitation Facilities (CARF) accreditation	Control	Service	Staffed Beds	Admissions	Census	Outpatient Visits	Births	Total	Payroll	Personnel
⊞ **SHARP CHULA VISTA MEDICAL CENTER**, 751 Medical Center Court, Zip 91911–6617, Mailing Address: P.O. Box 1297, Zip 91912–1297; tel. 619/482–5800, (Total facility includes 100 beds in nursing home–type unit) **A**1 2 9 10 **F**9 10 11 12 15 17 19 21 22 23 26 27 28 29 33 36 37 40 42 45 46 47 48 49 52 55 56 58 59 60 61 62 63 65 66 69 79 80 81 82 83 84 85 86 87 88 92 94 100 108 109 110 **S** Sharp Healthcare, San Diego, CA Primary Contact: Christopher L. Boyd, Chief Executive Officer CMO: Francisco Anguiano, M.D., Chief of Staff CHR: Zoe Gardner, Manager Human Resources Web address: www.sharp.com	23	10	326	12769	256	70025	2826	156932	66425	1269
CLEARLAKE—Lake County ⊞ **REDBUD COMMUNITY HOSPITAL**, 15630 18th Avenue, Zip 95422–9339, Mailing Address: P.O. Box 6720, Zip 95422–6720; tel. 707/994–6486, (Nonreporting) **A**1 9 10 18 20 **S** Adventist Health, Roseville, CA Primary Contact: Kendall R. Fults, President and Chief Executive Officer CFO: Buck McDonald, Chief Financial Officer Web address: www.adventisthealth.org	23	10	32	—	—	—	—	—	—	—
CLOVIS—Fresno County **COMMUNITY MEDICAL CENTER–CLOVIS**, 2755 Herndon Avenue, Zip 93611–6800; tel. 559/324–4000 **A**10 **F**2 10 11 12 15 17 21 22 23 33 55 59 63 64 69 81 84 85 88 92 94 **S** Community Medical Centers, Fresno, CA Primary Contact: Lori Ruffner, Chief Executive Officer Web address: www.communitymedical.org	23	10	110	9393	79	50552	—	86137	—	—
COALINGA—Fresno County **COALINGA REGIONAL MEDICAL CENTER**, 1191 Phelps Avenue, Zip 93210–9609; tel. 559/935–6400, (Total facility includes 54 beds in nursing home–type unit) **A**9 10 20 **F**33 46 55 63 81 84 88 92 Primary Contact: Sharon Spurgeon, Interim Chief Executive Officer Web address: www.crmc2k.com	16	10	78	635	39	14519	2		—	106
COLTON—San Bernardino County ○ **ARROWHEAD REGIONAL MEDICAL CENTER**, 400 North Pepper Avenue, Zip 92324–1819; tel. 909/580–1000 **A**2 3 5 10 11 12 13 **F**2 11 12 13 15 17 19 21 22 23 26 27 28 29 30 33 34 35 37 39 44 46 47 51 52 53 55 56 57 58 59 60 61 62 63 65 66 69 70 71 72 73 74 75 81 82 84 85 87 88 89 90 92 94 96 101 106 107 108 109 110 **P**5 Primary Contact: June Griffith–Collison, Chief Executive Officer Web address: www.arrowheadmedcenter.org	13	10	327	21408	301	332662	3087	434816	109661	2357
COLUSA—Colusa County □ **COLUSA REGIONAL MEDICAL CENTER**, 199 East Webster Street, Zip 95932–2954, Mailing Address: P.O. Box 331, Zip 95932–0331; tel. 530/458–5821, (Total facility includes 6 beds in nursing home–type unit) **A**1 9 10 20 **F**2 9 10 11 21 22 23 27 29 33 38 42 46 51 52 53 55 59 60 62 63 69 81 88 92 93 94 97 108 Primary Contact: Dale A. Kirby, Chief Executive Officer	23	10	48	997	11	—	208	—	—	122
CONCORD—Contra Costa County ⊞ **MOUNT DIABLO MEDICAL CENTER**, 2540 East Street, Zip 94520; tel. 925/682–8200 **A**1 2 9 10 **F**2 9 10 12 14 15 17 19 21 22 23 26 27 28 33 37 40 44 46 47 48 52 55 57 58 61 62 63 64 65 66 69 70 79 80 81 82 85 87 88 90 94 96 108 110 **P**3 5 **S** John Muir/Mount Diablo Health System, Walnut Creek, CA Primary Contact: Thomas M. Harlan, President and Chief Administrative Officer CFO: Jerome Klusky, Chief Financial Officer Web address: www.jmmdhs.com/index.php/jmmdhs_mdmc.html	23	10	188	9517	133	195985	7	211561	84196	966
⊞ **MT. DIABLO MEDICAL PAVILION**, 2740 Grant Street, Zip 94520; tel. 925/674–4100 **A**1 9 10 **F**3 4 26 27 28 71 72 73 74 75 76 77 78 94 Primary Contact: Elizabeth Stallings, Chief Operating Officer CFO: Jerry Klusky, Chief Financial Officer CMO: O B. Towery, M.D., Chief of Staff CIO: Eric Saff, Chief Information Officer CHR: Alice Villanueva, Vice President Human Resources Web address: www.johnmuirmtdiablo.com	23	22	72	2617	49	9933	0	18501	9099	185
CORCORAN—Kings County ★ **CORCORAN DISTRICT HOSPITAL**, 1310 Hanna Avenue, Zip 93212–2395, Mailing Address: P.O. Box 758, Zip 93212–0758; tel. 559/992–5051, (Total facility includes 8 beds in nursing home–type unit) **A**9 10 **F**21 25 27 28 29 30 33 39 46 48 52 53 63 66 70 81 84 88 92 94 97 108 Primary Contact: Evan J. Rayner, Chief Executive Officer CFO: Debbie Bach, Chief Financial Officer CMO: Juan Medina, M.D., Chief of Staff CHR: Cheryl Burruss, Human Resources Director Web address: www.cdhosp.com	16	10	32	614	10	29909	1	7365	2566	123
CORONA—Riverside County □ **CORONA REGIONAL MEDICAL CENTER**, 800 South Main Street, Zip 92882–3420; tel. 951/737–4343, (Includes CORONA REGIONAL MEDICAL CENTER–REHABILITATION, 730 Magnolia Avenue, Zip 92879; tel. 951/736–7200) **A**1 2 9 10 **F**3 11 12 13 14 21 22 23 24 26 27 28 29 33 36 37 45 46 47 48 51 52 55 56 58 59 60 61 63 65 66 67 68 69 71 77 78 81 84 86 88 92 94 96 108 109 **S** Universal Health Services, Inc., King of Prussia, PA Primary Contact: John A. Calderone, Ph.D., Chief Executive Officer Web address: www.coronaregional.com	33	10	228	9220	164	99973	1920	78966	45053	863

Many Facility Codes have changed. Please refer to the AHA Guide Code Chart.

Hospital, Address, Telephone, Approval, Facility, and Physician Codes, Health Care System	Classi-fication Codes		Utilization Data					Expense (thousands) of dollars		
★ American Hospital Association (AHA) membership □ Joint Commission on Accreditation of Healthcare Organizations (JCAHO) accreditation ○ American Osteopathic Association (AOA) accreditation △ Commission on Accreditation of Rehabilitation Facilities (CARF) accreditation	Control	Service	Staffed Beds	Admissions	Census	Outpatient Visits	Births	Total	Payroll	Personnel

CORONADO—San Diego County

⊞ **SHARP CORONADO HOSPITAL AND HEALTH CENTER**, 250 Prospect Place, Zip 92118–1943; tel. 619/522–3600, (Total facility includes 140 beds in nursing home–type unit) **A**1 9 10 **F**1 9 12 21 23 29 30 33 36 41 46 48 52 54 55 57 58 60 61 62 63 64 65 66 69 81 88 92 94 96 106 108 109 110 **S** Sharp Healthcare, San Diego, CA
Primary Contact: Marcia K. Hall, Chief Executive Officer
COO: Susan Olsen–Nakada, Chief Operating Officer and Chief Nursing Officer
CFO: Tony Guerra, Chief Financial Officer
Web address: www.sharp.com
| 23 | 10 | 204 | 2269 | 136 | 45078 | — | — | | |

COSTA MESA—Orange County

□ **COLLEGE HOSPITAL COSTA MESA**, 301 Victoria Street, Zip 92627–7131; tel. 949/642–2734 **A**1 9 10 **F**1 10 21 45 71 78 94 96 106 **S** College Health Enterprises, Santa Fe Springs, CA
Primary Contact: Wayne M. Lingenfelter, Ed.D., Chief Executive Officer
Web address: www.collegehospitals.com
| 33 | 22 | 84 | 4874 | 83 | 12798 | — | 28929 | | |

COVINA—Los Angeles County

□ **AURORA BEHAVIORAL HEALTHCARE–CHARTER OAK**, 1161 East Covina Boulevard, Zip 91724–1599; tel. 626/966–1632 **A**1 10 **F**1 21 29 31 71 72 73 74 75 76 77 78 94 96
Primary Contact: Todd A. Smith, Chief Executive Officer
Web address: www.aurorabehavioral.com
| 33 | 22 | 69 | 4097 | 68 | 13021 | — | 11768 | | |

CITRUS VALLEY MEDICAL CENTER–INTER–COMMUNITY CAMPUS, 210 West San Bernardino Road, Zip 91723–1901, Mailing Address: P.O. Box 6108, Zip 91722–5108; tel. 626/331–7331, (Nonreporting) **A**2 9 10 **S** Citrus Valley Health Partners, Covina, CA
Primary Contact: James T. Yoshioka, President and Chief Executive Officer
Web address: www.cvhp.org
| 23 | 10 | 252 | — | — | — | — | — | | |

CRESCENT CITY—Del Norte County

⊞ **SUTTER COAST HOSPITAL**, 800 East Washington Boulevard, Zip 95531–8359; tel. 707/464–8511 **A**1 9 10 20 **F**9 11 12 21 22 27 29 33 36 45 46 51 53 55 58 59 63 69 81 82 84 88 96 107 108 **S** Sutter Health, Sacramento, CA
Primary Contact: John E. Menaugh, Chief Executive Officer
CFO: Judi Swartout, Chief Financial Officer
Web address: www.sutterhealth.org
| 23 | 10 | 59 | 3217 | 33 | — | — | — | — | 346 |

CULVER CITY—Los Angeles County

⊞ **BROTMAN MEDICAL CENTER**, 3828 Delmas Terrace, Zip 90232–6806, Mailing Address: P.O. Box 2459, Zip 90231–2459; tel. 310/836–7000 **A**1 9 10 **F**2 3 4 10 14 15 17 19 21 23 27 28 29 33 37 39 42 45 46 47 48 49 52 53 55 57 58 60 61 62 63 66 68 69 71 73 74 75 77 78 81 82 85 88 93 94 96 108 110 **P**5 **S** TENET Healthcare Corporation, Dallas, TX
Primary Contact: Maurine Cate, Chief Executive Officer
COO: Kay Deol, Chief Operating Officer
CMO: Jordan Goodstein, M.D., Chief of Staff
CIO: Terry Moede, Chief Information Officer
CHR: Norma Braun, Director Human Resources
Web address: www.brotmanmedicalcenter.com
| 33 | 10 | 250 | 9244 | 215 | 33811 | 0 | 109660 | 49066 | 795 |

DALY CITY—San Mateo County

⊞ **SETON MEDICAL CENTER**, 1900 Sullivan Avenue, Zip 94015–2229; tel. 650/992–4000 **A**1 2 3 5 9 10 **F**2 9 11 12 14 15 17 19 21 22 23 26 27 28 29 32 33 34 41 42 45 46 47 48 49 51 52 53 56 57 58 59 60 61 62 63 64 65 66 69 78 81 82 84 85 87 88 92 96 106 108 110 **S** Daughters of Charity Health System, Los Altos Hills, CA
Primary Contact: Bernadette M. Smith, President and Chief Executive Officer
CFO: J Marc Golan, Chief Financial Officer
CMO: Stephen Conrad, M.D., President Medical Staff
CIO: Richard Hutsell, Vice President, Chief Information Officer
CHR: Linde Cheema, Director Human Resources
Web address: www.setonmedicalcenter.org
| 21 | 10 | 263 | 9572 | 221 | 242490 | 650 | 208131 | 93379 | 1247 |

DAVIS—Yolo County

⊞ **SUTTER DAVIS HOSPITAL**, 2000 Sutter Place, Zip 95616–6201, Mailing Address: P.O. Box 1617, Zip 95617–1617; tel. 530/756–6440, (Nonreporting) **A**1 9 10 **S** Sutter Health, Sacramento, CA
Primary Contact: Janet Wagner, R.N., Chief Administrative Officer
CFO: Robert Pascuzzi, Controller
Web address: www.sutterhealth.org
| 23 | 10 | 48 | — | — | — | — | — | | |

DEER PARK—Napa County

ST. HELENA HOSPITAL See Saint Helena

DELANO—Kern County

□ **DELANO REGIONAL MEDICAL CENTER**, 1401 Garces Highway, Zip 93215–3690, Mailing Address: P.O. Box 460, Zip 93216–0460; tel. 661/725–4800, (Nonreporting) **A**1 9 10
Primary Contact: Allan G. Komarek, Ph.D., Executive Director
Web address: www.drmc.com
| 23 | 10 | 89 | — | — | — | — | — | — | — |

DOWNEY—Los Angeles County

□ **DOWNEY REGIONAL MEDICAL CENTER**, 11500 Brookshire Avenue, Zip 90241–4917; tel. 562/904–5000 **A**1 9 10 12 13 **F**2 6 9 10 11 12 14 15 16 17 18 19 21 22 23 29 30 33 46 48 49 51 52 53 55 56 57 59 61 62 63 66 69 81 82 84 86 87 88 90 108
Primary Contact: Allen R. Korneff, President and Chief Executive Officer
Web address: www.drmci.org
| 23 | 10 | 193 | 11959 | 125 | 118103 | — | 124081 | — | — |

Many Facility Codes have changed. Please refer to the AHA Guide Code Chart.   © 2005 AHA Guide

Hospital, Address, Telephone, Approval, Facility, and Physician Codes, Health Care System	Classi-fication Codes		Utilization Data					Expense (thousands) of dollars		
★ American Hospital Association (AHA) membership □ Joint Commission on Accreditation of Healthcare Organizations (JCAHO) accreditation ○ American Osteopathic Association (AOA) accreditation △ Commission on Accreditation of Rehabilitation Facilities (CARF) accreditation	Control	Service	Staffed Beds	Admissions	Census	Outpatient Visits	Births	Total	Payroll	Personnel

□ △ **RANCHO LOS AMIGOS NATIONAL REHABILITATION CENTER**, 7601
East Imperial Highway, Zip 90242–3496; tel. 562/401–7022 **A**1 3 5 7 10 **F**1 2
5 9 21 22 32 44 52 53 55 58 60 63 66 68 69 81 82 84 88 94 108 **S** Los
Angeles County–Department of Health Services, Los Angeles, CA
Primary Contact: Valerie Orange, Chief Executive Officer
Web address: www.rancho.org
| | | | | | | | | | |
| 13 | 46 | 167 | 2267 | 145 | 35709 | — | 150777 | — | — |

DUARTE—Los Angeles County
⊠ **CITY OF HOPE NATIONAL MEDICAL CENTER**, 1500 East Duarte Road,
Zip 91010–3012; tel. 626/359–8111 **A**1 2 3 5 9 10 **F**2 9 12 21 22 23 26 27
28 29 35 37 38 39 46 47 48 52 53 55 57 58 60 61 63 64 65 66 67 68 69
73 79 80 81 82 84 86 87 88 94 96 99 105 108 109 **P**5
Primary Contact: Michael A. Friedman, M.D., Chief Executive Officer
COO: Anne McCune, Chief Operating Officer
CFO: Terry W. Blackwood, Senior Vice President and Chief Financial Officer
CMO: James Miser, M.D., Chief Executive Officer
CIO: Michael Sauk, Chief Information Officer
CHR: Chris Roederer, Chief Corporate Services
Web address: www.cityofhope.org
| 23 | 41 | 153 | 4523 | 123 | 108736 | 0 | 266702 | 100517 | 1823 |

EL CENTRO—Imperial County
⊠ **EL CENTRO REGIONAL MEDICAL CENTER**, 1415 Ross Avenue,
Zip 92243–4398; tel. 760/339–7100 **A**1 9 10 **F**2 9 11 12 21 22 25 28 29 33
34 37 40 42 45 46 48 49 52 53 55 57 58 59 60 62 63 65 66 69 70 81 82
84 85 88 94 96 108 109 110 **P**5
Primary Contact: David R. Green, Administrator and Chief Executive Officer
CFO: Kathleen Farmer, Assistant Administrator Finance and Chief Financial Officer
CIO: David Buchanan, Director Information Systems
CHR: Victor Ramirez, Chief Human Resources
Web address: www.ecrmc.org
| 14 | 10 | 165 | 6866 | 78 | 123676 | 1267 | 65814 | 26195 | 695 |

EL MONTE—Los Angeles County
⊠ **GREATER EL MONTE COMMUNITY HOSPITAL**, 1701 Santa Anita Avenue,
Zip 91733–3411; tel. 626/579–7777 **A**1 9 10 **F**2 11 12 14 21 22 27 28 29
32 33 39 45 46 47 48 52 53 55 58 59 62 63 64 65 66 69 81 82 84 87 88
92 94 108 109 **P**5 **S** AHMC, Inc, Alhambra, CA
Primary Contact: Philip A. Cohen, Chief Executive Officer
COO: Carolyn Catton, R.N., Chief Operating Officer
CFO: Harold Way, Chief Financial Officer
CIO: Paul Daly, Director Information Systems
CHR: Margaret Small, Director Human Resources
Web address: www.greaterelmonte.com
| 32 | 10 | 117 | 4305 | 73 | 21464 | 1093 | 31492 | 20432 | 234 |

ELDRIDGE—Sonoma County
SONOMA DEVELOPMENTAL CENTER, 15000 Arnold Drive, Zip 95431;
tel. 707/938–6000 **A**10 **F**1 6 9 21 22 29 31 32 35 36 37 38 41 44 45 46 48
57 58 60 62 63 66 69 70 73 74 75 76 81 88 92 94 96 108 110
Primary Contact: Loretta Vlaardingerbroek, Executive Director
Web address: www.dds.ca.gov/sonoma/sonoma.cfm
| 12 | 62 | 805 | 43 | 792 | 0 | 0 | 154284 | — | — |

ENCINITAS—San Diego County
⊠ △ **SCRIPPS MEMORIAL HOSPITAL–ENCINITAS**, 354 Santa Fe Drive,
Zip 92024–5182, Mailing Address: P.O. Box 230817, Zip 92023–0817;
tel. 760/753–6501 **A**1 2 7 9 10 **F**2 11 12 15 17 21 22 23 26 27 28 29 33 37
38 40 46 53 55 57 58 59 60 61 62 63 64 65 66 68 69 75 81 84 88 94 108
109 110 **S** Scripps Health, San Diego, CA
Primary Contact: Carl J. Etter, Chief Executive
CFO: Linda Honaker, Director Financial Services
CIO: Jean Balgrosky, Vice President and Chief Information Officer
Web address: www.scrippshealth.org/scripps_locations_1458.asp
| 23 | 10 | 109 | 7107 | 108 | 57230 | 1606 | 95588 | 38498 | 617 |

ENCINO—Los Angeles County, See Los Angeles

ESCONDIDO—San Diego County
⊠ **PALOMAR MEDICAL CENTER**, 555 East Valley Parkway, Zip 92025–3084;
tel. 760/739–3000, (Total facility includes 96 beds in nursing home–type unit) **A**1
9 10 **F**2 9 11 14 15 16 18 19 20 21 22 23 27 28 33 34 52 53 55 56 57 58
59 60 61 62 63 64 65 67 68 69 70 71 75 77 78 79 80 81 82 84 88 92 93
94 95 96 106 108 109 **P**7 **S** Palomar Pomerado Health, San Diego, CA
Primary Contact: Gerald E. Bracht, Chief Administrative Officer
COO: Gerald E. Bracht, Chief Administrative Officer
CFO: Robert Hemker, Chief Financial Officer
CIO: Elizabeth Renfree, Chief Information Officer
CHR: Marcelo Rivera, M.D., Chairman
Web address: www.pph.org
| 16 | 10 | 315 | 21377 | 315 | 182507 | — | 219919 | — | — |

EUREKA—Humboldt County
⊠ △ **ST. JOSEPH HOSPITAL**, 2700 Dolbeer Street, Zip 95501–4799;
tel. 707/445–8121, (Includes GENERAL HOSPITAL, 2200 Harrison Avenue,
Zip 95501–3299; tel. 707/445–5111) **A**1 2 7 9 10 **F**2 9 11 12 14 15 16 17
21 22 26 27 28 29 33 37 48 52 53 55 56 58 59 61 62 63 64 65 68 79 81
82 84 86 88 93 94 107 108 **P**5 **S** St. Joseph Health System, Orange, CA
Primary Contact: Michael L. Purvis, President and Chief Executive Officer
COO: Mary Anne McCrea, Vice President and Chief Operating Officer
CFO: Galen Gorman, Chief Financial Officer
CMO: Ken Stiver, M.D., Vice President Medical Affairs
CIO: Larry Raizen, Area Director Information Systems
CHR: Bob Sampson, Vice President Human Resources
Web address: www.stjosepheureka.org
| 21 | 10 | 159 | 7186 | 82 | 163805 | 642 | 111140 | 34019 | 830 |

CA

Hospital, Address, Telephone, Approval, Facility, and Physician Codes, Health Care System	Classi-fication Codes		Utilization Data					Expense (thousands) of dollars		
★ American Hospital Association (AHA) membership □ Joint Commission on Accreditation of Healthcare Organizations (JCAHO) accreditation ○ American Osteopathic Association (AOA) accreditation △ Commission on Accreditation of Rehabilitation Facilities (CARF) accreditation	Control	Service	Staffed Beds	Admissions	Census	Outpatient Visits	Births	Total	Payroll	Personnel

FAIRFIELD—Solano County

✣ **NORTHBAY MEDICAL CENTER**, 1200 B. Gale Wilson Boulevard, Zip 94533–3587; tel. 707/429–3600 **A**1 2 9 10 **F**2 9 11 15 21 22 23 24 27 28 30 33 37 39 42 48 52 55 56 58 59 60 61 62 63 64 66 69 70 81 82 85 87 88 92 94 96 108 **S** NorthBay Healthcare System, Fairfield, CA Primary Contact: Deborah Sugiyama, President CFO: Arthur E. DeNio, Chief Financial Officer CIO: Paul Alcala, Vice President and Chief Information Officer Web address: www.northbay.org	23	10	113	5628	70	100284	1573	132507	49458	558

FALL RIVER MILLS—Shasta County

MAYERS MEMORIAL HOSPITAL DISTRICT, 43563 Highway 299 East, Zip 96028–0459, Mailing Address: P.O. Box 459, Zip 96028–0459; tel. 530/336–5511, (Total facility includes 99 beds in nursing home–type unit) **A**9 10 18 20 **F**4 5 6 11 27 36 46 52 55 59 63 71 81 88 92 97 **P**5 Primary Contact: Jerald Fikes, Administrator and Chief Executive Officer Web address: www.mayersmemorial.com	16	10	121	682	88	20692	78	14880	5656	177

FALLBROOK—San Diego County

□ **FALLBROOK HOSPITAL**, 624 East Elder Street, Zip 92028–3099; tel. 760/728–1191, (Total facility includes 93 beds in nursing home–type unit) (Nonreporting) **A**1 9 10 20 **S** Community Health Systems, Inc., Brentwood, TN Primary Contact: Larry W. Payton, Chief Executive Officer	16	10	179	—	—	—	—	—	—	—

FOLSOM—Sacramento County

□ **KINDRED HOSPITAL–SACRAMENTO**, 223 Fargo Way, Zip 95630–2961; tel. 916/351–9151 **A**1 9 10 **F**21 49 55 81 94 110 **S** Kindred Healthcare, Louisville, KY Primary Contact: Meredith Taylor, Chief Executive Officer Web address: www.kindredhealthcare.com	33	10	34	265	27	0	—	12263		
✣ **MERCY HOSPITAL OF FOLSOM**, 1650 Creekside Drive, Zip 95630–3405; tel. 916/983–7400 **A**1 9 10 **F**2 9 11 12 14 21 22 26 27 28 29 30 33 37 38 40 46 47 48 52 55 57 59 60 61 62 63 64 65 69 81 82 87 88 92 94 96 108 109 **P**5 **S** Catholic Healthcare West, San Francisco, CA Primary Contact: Donald C. Hudson, President CFO: Robin Rogness, Chief Financial Officer CHR: Amy Mantell, Director Human Resources Web address: www.mercyfolsom.org	21	10	85	4196	39	36722	1183	42260	26229	295

FONTANA—San Bernardino County

✣ **KAISER FOUNDATION HOSPITAL**, 9961 Sierra Avenue, Zip 92335–6720; tel. 909/427–5000 **A**1 3 5 10 **F**2 3 4 11 12 14 15 17 21 22 23 26 27 28 29 33 35 36 38 39 46 49 51 52 53 55 56 57 58 59 60 61 62 63 64 65 66 68 75 81 82 84 85 87 88 92 94 96 108 110 **S** Kaiser Foundation Hospitals, Oakland, CA Primary Contact: Terry A. Belmont, Senior Vice President and Administrator CIO: Lori C. Drozd, Director Public Affairs Web address: www.kaiserpermanente.org	23	10	393	27105	269	84869	3950	—	—	3834

FORT BRAGG—Mendocino County

□ **MENDOCINO COAST DISTRICT HOSPITAL**, 700 River Drive, Zip 95437–5495; tel. 707/961–1234 **A**1 9 10 20 **F**2 6 9 11 12 21 22 23 26 27 28 33 36 46 48 51 52 53 55 58 59 60 61 62 63 64 69 81 82 84 85 87 88 94 96 97 108 109 110 Primary Contact: Bryan M. Ballard, Chief Executive Officer Web address: www.mcdh.org	16	10	52	1906	26	67363	178	30615	10289	220

FORT IRWIN—San Bernardino County

✣ **WEED ARMY COMMUNITY HOSPITAL**, Mailing Address: P.O. Box 105109, Zip 92310–5109; tel. 760/380–3108 **A**1 **F**2 6 11 12 21 22 24 26 27 28 29 31 32 33 39 42 45 46 47 48 50 52 58 59 60 62 63 64 65 66 69 70 73 74 75 77 81 88 94 96 106 107 108 109 **P**1 **S** Department of the Army, Office of the Surgeon General, Falls Church, VA Primary Contact: Colonel Ronald Eskew, Commander Web address: www.irwin.amedd.army.mil	42	10	19	674	4	82650	360	—	—	386

FORTUNA—Humboldt County

✣ **REDWOOD MEMORIAL HOSPITAL**, 3300 Renner Drive, Zip 95540–3198; tel. 707/725–3361, (Nonreporting) **A**1 2 9 10 **S** St. Joseph Health System, Orange, CA Primary Contact: Michael L. Purvis, President and Chief Executive Officer COO: Robert C. Brannigan, VicePresident, Chief Operating Officer and Chief Nursing Officer	21	10	46	—	—	—	—	—	—	—

FOUNTAIN VALLEY—Orange County

✣ **FOUNTAIN VALLEY REGIONAL HOSPITAL AND MEDICAL CENTER**, 17100 Euclid Street, Zip 92708–4043; tel. 714/966–7200 **A**1 2 5 9 10 **F**2 9 10 11 12 14 15 17 19 21 22 23 26 27 28 29 33 39 42 45 46 47 48 52 53 55 56 57 58 59 61 62 63 64 66 67 69 81 84 85 87 88 94 96 107 108 109 110 **S** TENET Healthcare Corporation, Dallas, TX Primary Contact: Tim Smith, Chief Executive Officer COO: Kathy Dowling, Vice President Operations CFO: Pam Alderson, Chief Financial Officer CMO: Jin–Jou Lu, M.D., Chief of Staff CIO: Bill Mathiasen, Director Information Systems CHR: Glenda Giles–Luick, Director Human Resources Web address: www.fountainvalleyhospital.com	33	10	360	17602	245	108693	3657	205010	87996	1479

Many Facility Codes have changed. Please refer to the AHA Guide Code Chart. © 2005 AHA Guide

Hospital, Address, Telephone, Approval, Facility, and Physician Codes, Health Care System	Classi-fication Codes		Utilization Data					Expense (thousands) of dollars		
★ American Hospital Association (AHA) membership □ Joint Commission on Accreditation of Healthcare Organizations (JCAHO) accreditation ○ American Osteopathic Association (AOA) accreditation △ Commission on Accreditation of Rehabilitation Facilities (CARF) accreditation	Control	Service	Staffed Beds	Admissions	Census	Outpatient Visits	Births	Total	Payroll	Personnel

	Control	Service	Staffed Beds	Admissions	Census	Outpatient Visits	Births	Total	Payroll	Personnel
□ **ORANGE COAST MEMORIAL MEDICAL CENTER**, 9920 Talbert Avenue, Zip 92708–5153; tel. 714/378-7000 **A**1 9 10 **F**2 9 10 11 12 15 21 22 23 26 27 28 29 30 31 33 35 37 38 39 40 42 44 45 46 47 48 52 53 55 56 57 58 59 60 61 62 63 64 65 66 69 81 82 84 85 87 88 92 94 95 96 106 108 109 110 **P**5 **S** Memorial Health Services, Long Beach, CA Primary Contact: Marcia Manker, Chief Executive Officer Web address: www.memorialcare.org	23	10	172	9643	99	52614	1291	99459	39775	812
FREMONT—Alameda County										
□ **FREMONT HOSPITAL**, 39001 Sundale Drive, Zip 94538–2005; tel. 510/796-1100 **A**1 9 10 **F**4 21 71 72 75 77 78 **S** Psychiatric Solutions, Franklin, TN Primary Contact: Terry Bridges, Chief Executive Officer Web address: www.fremonthospital.com	33	22	78	3502	67	3468	0	14113	—	—
⊠ **WASHINGTON TOWNSHIP HEALTH CARE DISTRICT**, 2000 Mowry Avenue, Zip 94538–1746; tel. 510/797-1111 **A**1 2 9 10 **F**2 6 11 12 14 15 17 19 21 22 23 27 28 29 31 33 39 46 47 48 49 52 53 55 57 58 59 60 61 62 63 64 65 66 69 75 79 80 81 82 88 93 94 95 96 108 110 **P**5 7 Primary Contact: Nancy D. Farber, Chief Executive Officer COO: Edward J. Fayen, Chief of Operations and Support CFO: Catherine Souza, Chief Financial Officer CMO: Ranjana Sharma, M.D., Chief of Staff CIO: Lee Herrmann, Chief Information Officer CHR: Kathy Hunt, Chief of Human Resources Web address: www.whhs.com	16	10	311	15631	185	148698	2900	222036	101974	1219
FRENCH CAMP—San Joaquin County										
□ △ **SAN JOAQUIN GENERAL HOSPITAL**, 500 West Hospital Road, Zip 95231, Mailing Address: P.O. Box 1499, Zip 95213; tel. 209/468-6600 **A**1 3 5 7 9 10 **F**2 9 11 12 14 15 21 23 24 26 27 28 29 32 33 37 39 42 44 45 46 47 48 49 50 52 55 56 58 59 60 61 62 63 64 65 66 68 69 70 81 82 87 88 92 93 94 95 96 107 108 **P**5 6 Primary Contact: Kenneth B. Cohen, Chief Executive Officer Web address: www.sjgeneralhospital.com	13	10	179	9217	130	264289	2400	157558	58576	1356
FRESNO—Fresno County										
COMMUNITY BEHAVIORAL HEALTH CENTER, 7171 North Cedar Avenue, Zip 93720–3311; tel. 559/449-8000 **A**10 **F**21 22 53 71 73 75 **S** Community Medical Centers, Fresno, CA Primary Contact: Anne Peterson, Director	33	22	670	32553	471	485715	0	427215	—	—
□ **COMMUNITY MEDICAL CENTER–FRESNO**, 2823 Fresno Street, Zip 93721–1324, Mailing Address: P.O. Box 1232, Zip 93715–1232; tel. 559/459-6000, (Total facility includes 272 beds in nursing home–type unit) **A**1 2 9 10 **F**2 5 10 11 12 13 14 15 17 19 21 22 23 24 26 27 28 29 31 32 33 34 35 37 38 39 40 41 42 43 44 46 47 48 49 50 51 52 53 55 56 58 59 60 61 62 63 64 65 66 68 69 70 71 73 74 75 76 77 78 79 80 81 82 83 84 85 87 88 89 90 92 94 95 96 98 106 107 108 109 110 **S** Community Medical Centers, Fresno, CA Primary Contact: Lori Ruffner, Chief Executive Officer Web address: www.communitymedical.org	23	10	1004	41038	791	553079	10605	547071	229145	4987
FRESNO HEART HOSPITAL, 15 East Audubon Drive, Zip 93720; tel. 559/433-8000, (Nonreporting) **A**10 Primary Contact: Carolyn Webster, R.N., Interim Chief Executive Officer	33	42	60	—	—	—	—	—	—	—
FRESNO SURGERY CENTER–THE HOSPITAL FOR SURGERY, 6125 North Fresno Street, Zip 93710–5207; tel. 559/431-8000 **A**9 10 **F**2 10 26 27 48 52 57 62 63 64 82 88 Primary Contact: Toni Angle, Administrator Web address: www.fresnosurgerycenter.com	32	10	20	1764	10	3714	0	22876	—	—
⊠ **KAISER FOUNDATION HOSPITAL**, 7300 North Fresno Street, Zip 93720–2941; tel. 559/448-4040, (Nonreporting) **A**1 10 **S** Kaiser Foundation Hospitals, Oakland, CA Primary Contact: Corwin Harper, Vice President and Administrator CFO: Richard Alves, Chief Financial Officer CMO: Varouj Altebarmakian, M.D., Physician in Chief CIO: Brad Bain, Information Systems Leader Web address: www.kaiserpermanente.org	23	10	121	—	—	—	—	—	—	—
⊠ **SAINT AGNES MEDICAL CENTER**, 1303 East Herndon Avenue, Zip 93720–3309; tel. 559/450-3000 **A**1 2 9 10 **F**1 2 9 10 11 12 14 15 17 19 21 22 23 26 27 28 29 30 31 33 35 36 37 39 40 44 46 47 48 50 51 52 55 57 58 59 60 61 62 63 64 65 66 69 75 79 81 82 84 85 87 88 93 94 95 96 108 109 110 **S** Trinity Health, Novi, MI Primary Contact: Mathew Abraham, President and Chief Executive Officer CMO: Patrick Marabella, M.D., Chief Medical Officer CIO: Robert Foos, Senior Vice President and Chief Information Officer Web address: www.samc.com	21	10	330	23181	282	293418	2663	299004	130676	2334
□ **SAN JOAQUIN VALLEY REHABILITATION HOSPITAL**, 7173 North Sharon Avenue, Zip 93720–3329; tel. 559/436-3600 **A**1 9 10 **F**41 42 52 68 69 96 **S** VIBRA Healthcare, Mechanicsburg, PA Primary Contact: Edward C. Palacios, R.N., Chief Executive Officer Web address: www.sjvrehab.com	33	46	38	1063	38	31025	0	14262	—	—

CA

Hospital, Address, Telephone, Approval, Facility, and Physician Codes, Health Care System	Classi-fication Codes		Utilization Data					Expense (thousands) of dollars		
★ American Hospital Association (AHA) membership □ Joint Commission on Accreditation of Healthcare Organizations (JCAHO) accreditation ○ American Osteopathic Association (AOA) accreditation △ Commission on Accreditation of Rehabilitation Facilities (CARF) accreditation	Control	Service	Staffed Beds	Admissions	Census	Outpatient Visits	Births	Total	Payroll	Personnel

	Control	Service	Staffed Beds	Admissions	Census	Outpatient Visits	Births	Total	Payroll	Personnel
UNIVERSITY MEDICAL CENTER, 445 South Cedar Avenue, Zip 93702–2998; tel. 559/459–4000, (Nonreporting) **A**3 5 8 9 **S** Community Medical Centers, Fresno, CA Primary Contact: Bruce Kinder, R.N., Chief Operating Officer Web address: www.communitymedical.org	13	10	334	—	—	—	—	—	—	—
✶ **VETERANS AFFAIRS MEDICAL CENTER**, 2615 East Clinton Avenue, Zip 93703–2223; tel. 559/225–6100, (Total facility includes 60 beds in nursing home–type unit) (Nonreporting) **A**1 2 3 5 8 **S** Department of Veterans Affairs, Washington, DC Primary Contact: Alan S. Perry, Director CFO: Kathy Yeager–Lowry, Chief, Business Administration CMO: Malcolm Anderson, M.D., Acting Chief of Staff Web address: www.fresno.med.va.gov	45	10	125	—	—	—	—	—	—	—
FULLERTON—Orange County										
✶ △ **ST. JUDE MEDICAL CENTER**, 101 East Valencia Mesa Drive, Zip 92835–3809; tel. 714/992–3000, (Total facility includes 37 beds in nursing home–type unit) (Nonreporting) **A**1 2 5 7 9 10 **S** St. Joseph Health System, Orange, CA Primary Contact: Robert J. Fraschetti, President and Chief Executive Officer COO: Doreen Dann, R.N., Executive Vice President and Chief Operating Officer CFO: Lee Penrose, Vice President Fiscal Services and Chief Financial Officer CMO: Mark Song, M.D., Chief of Staff CIO: DruAnn Copping, Director Public Affairs Web address: www.stjudemedicalcenter.org	21	10	293	—	—	—	—	—	—	—
GARBERVILLE—Humboldt County										
JEROLD PHELPS COMMUNITY HOSPITAL, 733 Cedar Street, Zip 95542–3201; tel. 707/923–3921, (Total facility includes 8 beds in nursing home–type unit) **A**9 10 18 **F**12 26 27 28 33 47 48 52 92 98 Primary Contact: Debbie Scaife, R.N., MSN, Administrator and Director of Nursing Web address: www.shchd.org	16	10	16	102	9	—	0	3306	—	60
GARDEN GROVE—Orange County										
✶ **GARDEN GROVE HOSPITAL AND MEDICAL CENTER**, 12601 Garden Grove Boulevard, Zip 92843–1908; tel. 714/537–5160 **A**1 9 10 **F**2 9 11 12 21 22 23 24 26 27 28 29 33 37 39 40 44 45 46 48 50 51 52 53 55 56 59 60 61 63 66 69 81 82 84 87 88 94 108 110 **S** TENET Healthcare Corporation, Dallas, TX Primary Contact: Maxine T. Cooper, Chief Executive Officer COO: Karen Gulbenkian, Chief Operating Officer CMO: Peter Wang, M.D., Chief of Staff CIO: Eileen Nicodemus, Director Information Systems CHR: Linda Lyons, Director Human Resources Web address: www.gardengrovehospital.com	33	10	79	7463	73	69907	—	—	—	469
GARDENA—Los Angeles County										
□ **COMMUNITY HOSPITAL OF GARDENA**, 1246 West 155th Street, Zip 90247–4011; tel. 310/323–5330, (Total facility includes 20 beds in nursing home–type unit) (Nonreporting) **A**1 10 Primary Contact: Raymond N. Smith, Chief Executive Officer Web address: www.gardenahospital.com	33	10	58	—	—	—	—	—	—	—
□ **MEMORIAL HOSPITAL OF GARDENA**, 1145 West Redondo Beach Boulevard, Zip 90247–3528; tel. 310/532–4200, (Total facility includes 69 beds in nursing home–type unit) (Nonreporting) **A**1 9 10 **S** HealthPlus, Houston, TX Primary Contact: Steve Popkin, Chief Executive Officer	33	10	107	—	—	—	—	—	—	—
GILROY—Santa Clara County										
✶ **ST. LOUISE REGIONAL HOSPITAL**, 9400 No Name Uno, Zip 95020–3528; tel. 408/848–2000 **A**1 9 10 **F**11 12 14 21 22 23 26 27 28 29 33 43 48 52 53 54 55 63 81 82 84 88 92 94 108 **S** Daughters of Charity Health System, Los Altos Hills, CA Primary Contact: Theodore P. Fox, President and Chief Operating Officer CFO: Robert Issai, Chief Financial Officer CIO: Dick Hutsell, Vice President Information Technology Services CHR: Steve Sharrer, Vice President Human Resources Web address: www.dochs.org	23	10	93	3696	43	54350	694	53592	22525	296
GLENDALE—Los Angeles County										
✶ **GLENDALE ADVENTIST MEDICAL CENTER**, 1509 Wilson Terrace, Zip 91206–4098; tel. 818/409–8000 **A**1 2 3 5 9 10 **F**4 11 12 14 21 22 23 27 28 29 33 37 39 40 41 46 48 49 51 55 56 57 59 60 61 62 63 66 68 69 71 73 74 75 76 77 78 79 81 82 84 85 87 88 92 93 94 95 96 106 108 109 110 **P**5 **S** Adventist Health, Roseville, CA Primary Contact: Scott Reiner, President and Chief Executive Officer CFO: Kelly Turner, Senior Vice President Finance Web address: www.glendaleadventist.com	21	10	394	16730	294	221962	—	193972	—	—
✶ **GLENDALE MEMORIAL HOSPITAL AND HEALTH CENTER**, 1420 South Central Avenue, Zip 91204–2594; tel. 818/502–1900, (Nonreporting) **A**1 9 10 **S** Catholic Healthcare West, San Francisco, CA Primary Contact: Catherine M. Pelley, President COO: Kim Strange, Senior Vice President and Chief Operating Officer CFO: C Patrick Lash, Chief Financial Officer CMO: Milton Louie, M.D., Chief of Staff CIO: Robert Drewniak, Senior Vice President Clinical Resources CHR: Deborah Wilson, Senior Vice President Human Resources and Organizational Development Web address: www.glendalememorial.com	23	10	334	—	—	—	—	—	—	—

Many Facility Codes have changed. Please refer to the AHA Guide Code Chart. © 2005 AHA Guide

Hospital, Address, Telephone, Approval, Facility, and Physician Codes, Health Care System	Classi-fication Codes		Utilization Data					Expense (thousands) of dollars		
★ American Hospital Association (AHA) membership □ Joint Commission on Accreditation of Healthcare Organizations (JCAHO) accreditation ○ American Osteopathic Association (AOA) accreditation △ Commission on Accreditation of Rehabilitation Facilities (CARF) accreditation	Control	Service	Staffed Beds	Admissions	Census	Outpatient Visits	Births	Total	Payroll	Personnel

	Control	Service	Staffed Beds	Admissions	Census	Outpatient Visits	Births	Total	Payroll	Personnel
□ **VERDUGO HILLS HOSPITAL**, 1812 Verdugo Boulevard, Zip 91208–1409; tel. 818/790–7100, (Total facility includes 42 beds in nursing home–type unit) **A**1 9 10 **F**11 12 13 14 21 24 26 27 28 33 41 44 46 47 48 51 53 55 56 59 63 65 67 68 69 71 76 77 78 81 82 84 87 88 92 94 96 108 110 **P**5 6 Primary Contact: Leonard LaBella, President and Chief Executive Officer Web address: www.verdugohillshospital.org	23	10	145	6298	114	82695	940	66362	27697	463
GLENDORA—Los Angeles County										
□ **EAST VALLEY HOSPITAL MEDICAL CENTER**, 150 West Route 66, Zip 91740–6207; tel. 626/852–5000 **A**1 9 10 **F**4 11 14 21 22 33 44 46 55 59 63 71 73 75 76 77 78 81 88 94 108 109 **P**5 Primary Contact: C. Joseph Chang, President and Chief Executive Officer Web address: www.eastvalleyhospital.org	31	10	80	3265	51	—	—	—	—	225
⊞ **FOOTHILL PRESBYTERIAN HOSPITAL–MORRIS L. JOHNSTON MEMORIAL**, 250 South Grand Avenue, Zip 91741–4218; tel. 626/963–8411 **A**1 9 10 **F**2 9 11 12 14 21 22 23 26 27 28 29 33 37 44 46 47 48 52 53 55 57 58 59 60 61 62 63 64 65 66 81 82 88 94 96 108 **P**5 8 **S** Citrus Valley Health Partners, Covina, CA Primary Contact: Larry S. Fetters, Administrator COO: Elvia Foulke, Executive Vice President and Chief Operating Officer CFO: Lois Conyers, Senior Vice President and Chief Financial Officer CMO: John DiMare, M.D., Medical Director CIO: David McCobb, Chief Information Officer CHR: Lisa Foust, Senior Vice President Human Resources Web address: www.cvhp.org	23	10	106	5807	59	75801	777	45146	17312	708
GRANADA HILLS—Los Angeles County, See Los Angeles										
GRASS VALLEY—Nevada County										
⊞ **SIERRA NEVADA MEMORIAL HOSPITAL**, 155 Glasson Way, Zip 95945–5723, Mailing Address: P.O. Box 1029, Zip 95945–1029; tel. 530/274–6000, (Total facility includes 14 beds in nursing home–type unit) **A**1 2 9 10 19 **F**2 6 9 11 12 21 22 23 26 27 28 33 37 38 39 40 46 51 52 53 55 58 59 60 61 62 63 65 79 80 81 82 84 86 87 88 94 96 106 107 **P**5 **S** Catholic Healthcare West, San Francisco, CA Primary Contact: C. Thomas Collier, President and Chief Executive Officer CFO: Tom Morrissey, Chief Financial Officer Web address: www.snmh.org	23	10	75	7238	75	170130	450	84592	37697	635
GREENBRAE—Marin County										
⊞ **MARIN GENERAL HOSPITAL**, 250 Bon Air Road, Zip 94904–1784, Mailing Address: P.O. Box 8010, San Rafael, Zip 94912–8010; tel. 415/925–7000 **A**1 2 9 10 **F**1 11 12 14 15 16 17 18 19 21 22 23 26 27 28 29 30 31 33 34 40 47 48 50 52 53 55 56 57 58 59 60 61 62 63 64 65 66 69 70 71 73 76 77 78 79 82 84 88 94 96 108 **P**5 **S** Sutter Health, Sacramento, CA Primary Contact: David Bradley, Chief Executive Officer COO: Richard S. Liszewski, CHE, Chief Operating Officer CFO: Stephen Walter, Chief Financial Officer CMO: Robert MacInnes, M.D., Medical Director CIO: Terry Mann, Director Management Information Services Web address: www.maringeneral.sutterhealth.org	23	10	235	11072	119	135264	1792	226761	66401	945
GREENVILLE—Plumas County										
INDIAN VALLEY HEALTH CARE DISTRICT, 184 Hot Springs Road, Zip 95947–9747; tel. 530/284–7191, (Total facility includes 17 beds in nursing home–type unit) (Nonreporting) **A**9 10 20 Primary Contact: Larry S. Pressley, Administrator	16	10	26	—	—	—	—	—	—	—
GRIDLEY—Butte County										
BIGGS–GRIDLEY MEMORIAL HOSPITAL, 240 Spruce Street, Zip 95948–2216, Mailing Address: P.O. Box 97, Zip 95948–0097; tel. 530/846–5671, (Total facility includes 21 beds in nursing home–type unit) **A**9 10 18 **F**9 12 21 26 27 28 33 34 44 51 52 53 55 60 62 63 69 81 84 88 92 94 97 108 **P**5 Primary Contact: Thomas P. Hayes, Chief Executive Officer Web address: www.dmh.ca.gov/statehospitals/atascadero	23	10	41	717	29	—	0	—	—	130
HANFORD—Kings County										
⊞ **CENTRAL VALLEY GENERAL HOSPITAL**, 1025 North Douty Street, Zip 93230–3722, Mailing Address: P.O. Box 480, Zip 93232–0480; tel. 559/583–2100 **A**1 9 10 **F**2 9 11 12 21 26 27 28 29 32 33 40 42 46 48 49 52 58 59 60 63 69 81 84 88 95 108 109 **P**3 5 **S** Adventist Health, Roseville, CA Primary Contact: Douglas L. Lafferty, Administrator Web address: www.hanfordhealth.com	33	10	26	3566	25	152078	—	36348	—	—
⊞ **HANFORD COMMUNITY MEDICAL CENTER**, 450 Greenfield Avenue, Zip 93230–3513, Mailing Address: P.O. Box 240, Zip 93232–0240; tel. 559/582–9000 **A**1 9 10 **F**2 9 12 21 22 23 26 27 28 33 36 46 47 48 49 51 52 53 55 57 58 60 61 62 63 65 66 68 69 81 82 84 88 94 95 96 106 107 108 110 **P**3 5 **S** Adventist Health, Roseville, CA Primary Contact: Richard L. Rawson, President and Chief Executive Officer COO: Douglas L. Lafferty, President and Chief Executive Officer CFO: Kirby McKague, Chief Financial Officer CMO: Chuck Craft, M.D., Chief of Staff CIO: Michael Aubry, Director Information Systems CHR: Darla Phelps, Director Human Resources Web address: www.hanfordhealth.com	21	10	50	4033	48	145721	0	64256	—	—
HARBOR CITY—Los Angeles County, See Los Angeles										

CA

Hospital, Address, Telephone, Approval, Facility, and Physician Codes, Health Care System	Classi-fication Codes		Utilization Data					Expense (thousands) of dollars		
★ American Hospital Association (AHA) membership ☐ Joint Commission on Accreditation of Healthcare Organizations (JCAHO) accreditation ○ American Osteopathic Association (AOA) accreditation △ Commission on Accreditation of Rehabilitation Facilities (CARF) accreditation	Control	Service	Staffed Beds	Admissions	Census	Outpatient Visits	Births	Total	Payroll	Personnel

HAWAIIAN GARDENS—Los Angeles County

☐ **TRI–CITY REGIONAL MEDICAL CENTER**, 21530 South Pioneer Boulevard, Zip 90716; tel. 562/860–0401 **A**1 10 **F**10 14 21 23 29 33 37 45 46 52 55 60 63 69 81 84 85 88 94
Primary Contact: Arthur J. Gerrick, President and Chief Executive Officer
Web address: www.tri–cityrmc.org
| 23 | 10 | 125 | 2527 | 30 | 12546 | — | 30516 | — | — |

HAWTHORNE—Los Angeles County

HAWTHORNE HOSPITAL See Los Angeles Metropolitan Medical Center, Los Angeles

HAYWARD—Alameda County

⊠ **KAISER FOUNDATION HOSPITAL**, 27400 Hesperian Boulevard, Zip 94545–4235; tel. 510/784–4000, (Nonreporting) **A**1 10 **S** Kaiser Foundation Hospitals, Oakland, CA
Primary Contact: Kim Pardini–Keily, Chief Operating Officer
Web address: www.kaiserpermanente.org
| 23 | 10 | 208 | — | — | — | — | — | — | — |

☐ **ST. ROSE HOSPITAL**, 27200 Calaroga Avenue, Zip 94545–4383; tel. 510/264–4000, (Total facility includes 22 beds in nursing home–type unit) **A**1 2 9 10 **F**9 11 12 15 17 21 22 23 24 27 28 29 32 33 37 38 46 48 52 53 55 59 60 61 62 63 64 68 69 81 84 87 88 92 94 96 97 98 108 **P**5
Primary Contact: Michael P. Mahoney, President and Chief Executive Officer
Web address: www.strosehospital.org
| 21 | 10 | 148 | 7446 | 101 | 112441 | 1352 | 93431 | 43163 | 681 |

HEALDSBURG—Sonoma County

HEALDSBURG DISTRICT HOSPITAL, 1375 University Avenue, Zip 95448–3382; tel. 707/431–6500, (Total facility includes 9 beds in nursing home–type unit) **A**9 10 **F**9 21 22 29 33 36 39 44 47 48 55 58 59 60 62 63 64 69 81 88 92 97 108
Primary Contact: Dale E. Iversen, Chief Executive Officer
Web address: www.nschd.org
| 16 | 10 | 19 | 734 | 13 | 36838 | — | 17076 | — | — |

HEMET—Riverside County

⊠ **HEMET VALLEY MEDICAL CENTER**, 1117 East Devonshire Avenue, Zip 92543–3083; tel. 909/652–2811, (Total facility includes 113 beds in nursing home–type unit) (Nonreporting) **A**1 9 10 **S** Valley Health System, Hemet, CA
Primary Contact: Lynda Wills, Interim Administrator
CFO: Michael Garko, Chief Financial Officer
CHR: George Leisher, Chief Human Resources Officer
Web address: www.valleyhealthsystem.com
| 16 | 10 | 356 | — | — | — | — | — | — | — |

HOLLISTER—San Benito County

⊠ **HAZEL HAWKINS MEMORIAL HOSPITAL**, 911 Sunset Drive, Zip 95023–5695; tel. 831/637–5711, (Includes HAZEL HAWKINS CONVALESCENT HOSPITAL–SOUTHSIDE, 3110 Southside Road, Zip 95023; tel. 408/637–5711), (Total facility includes 93 beds in nursing home–type unit) (Nonreporting) **A**1 9 10 **S** Brim Healthcare, Inc., Brentwood, TN
Primary Contact: Ken Underwood, Chief Executive Officer
CFO: Mark Robinson, Associate Administrator and Chief Financial Officer
CIO: Julio Gil, Manager Information Services
Web address: www.hazelhawkins.com
| 16 | 10 | 113 | — | — | — | — | — | — | — |

HOLLYWOOD—Los Angeles County, See Los Angeles

HUNTINGTON BEACH—Orange County

☐ **HUNTINGTON BEACH HOSPITAL**, 17772 Beach Boulevard, Zip 92647–6819; tel. 714/842–1473, (Total facility includes 14 beds in nursing home–type unit) (Nonreporting) **A**1 9 10 **S** Vanguard Health System, Nashville, TN
Primary Contact: Mary Botticella, Chief Executive Officer
Web address: www.hbhospital.com
| 32 | 10 | 102 | — | — | — | — | — | — | — |

HUNTINGTON PARK—Los Angeles County

⊠ **COMMUNITY AND MISSION HOSPITALS OF HUNTINGTON PARK**, 2623 East Slauson Avenue, Zip 90255–2900; tel. 323/583–1931, (Includes MISSION HOSPITAL OF HUNTINGTON PARK, 3111 East Florence Avenue, Zip 90255; tel. 213/582–8261), (Nonreporting) **A**1 9 10 **S** TENET Healthcare Corporation, Dallas, TX
Primary Contact: Barbara Schneider, R.N., Chief Executive Officer
CFO: Nick Lymberopoulos, Chief Financial Officer
Web address: www.communityhosp.com
| 33 | 10 | 157 | — | — | — | — | — | — | — |

INDIO—Riverside County

⊠ **JOHN F. KENNEDY MEMORIAL HOSPITAL**, 47–111 Monroe Street, Zip 92201; tel. 760/347–6191 **A**1 9 10 **F**2 7 9 11 12 15 17 21 22 24 27 28 29 33 42 46 47 48 52 55 57 59 60 62 63 64 66 81 82 84 85 88 94 95 108 109 110 **S** TENET Healthcare Corporation, Dallas, TX
Primary Contact: John J. Ferrelli, Chief Executive Officer
COO: Brian Thomas, Chief Operating Officer
CFO: Scott Leckey, Chief Financial Officer
Web address: www.jfkmemorialhosp.com
| 33 | 10 | 145 | 8845 | 76 | 62662 | 3110 | 67774 | 31052 | 550 |

Many Facility Codes have changed. Please refer to the AHA Guide Code Chart.

Hospital, Address, Telephone, Approval, Facility, and Physician Codes, Health Care System	Classi-fication Codes		Utilization Data					Expense (thousands) of dollars		
★ American Hospital Association (AHA) membership ☐ Joint Commission on Accreditation of Healthcare Organizations (JCAHO) accreditation ○ American Osteopathic Association (AOA) accreditation △ Commission on Accreditation of Rehabilitation Facilities (CARF) accreditation	Control	Service	Staffed Beds	Admissions	Census	Outpatient Visits	Births	Total	Payroll	Personnel

INGLEWOOD—Los Angeles County

✠ △ **CENTINELA FREEMAN REGIONAL MEDICAL CENTER, CENTINELA CAMPUS**, (Formerly Centinela Hospital Medical Center), 555 East Hardy Street, Zip 90301–4011, Mailing Address: P.O. Box 720, Zip 90307–0720; tel. 310/673–4660 **A**1 2 7 9 10 **F**2 9 12 14 15 17 19 21 22 27 28 33 37 52 53 55 56 58 59 60 62 63 68 69 70 71 76 81 82 84 88 92 94 108 **P**5 **S** Centinela Freeman HealthSystem, Inglewood, CA
Primary Contact: Michael A. Rembis, FACHE, Chief Executive Officer
CMO: Etie Moghissi, M.D., Chief Medical Staf
CIO: Vicky Morgan, Director Information Services
CHR: Margaret Morgan, Director Human Resources
Web address: www.centinelafreeman.com

	33	10	333	14648	223	123559	2328	164424	101255	1546

✠ △ **CENTINELA FREEMAN REGIONAL MEDICAL CENTER, MEMORIAL CAMPUS**, (Formerly Daniel Freeman Memorial Hospital), 333 North Prairie Avenue, Zip 90301–4514; tel. 310/674–7050 **A**1 5 7 9 10 **F**9 11 12 14 15 17 19 21 29 33 37 39 41 44 45 46 47 49 52 55 56 58 59 60 61 63 66 68 69 81 82 84 88 92 94 100 107 108 **S** Centinela Freeman HealthSystem, Inglewood, CA
Primary Contact: Harris Koenig, Chief Executive Officer
COO: Nancy Lee, Chief Operating Officer
CFO: Cheryl Matias, Chief Financial Officer
CIO: Dennis Ladnier, Manager, Information Systems

	31	10	221	10559	177	55033	1710	115014	47311	—

IRVINE—Orange County

✠ **IRVINE REGIONAL HOSPITAL AND MEDICAL CENTER**, 16200 Sand Canyon Avenue, Zip 92618–3714; tel. 949/753–2000 **A**1 9 10 **F**2 9 11 12 15 17 19 21 22 23 26 27 28 29 32 33 37 39 44 46 47 48 52 55 56 57 58 59 60 61 62 63 64 65 66 69 73 81 82 84 87 88 94 108 109 110 **P**5 **S** TENET Healthcare Corporation, Dallas, TX
Primary Contact: Dan F. Ausman, Chief Executive Officer
COO: Steve Sisto, Chief Operating Officer
CFO: Matthew Keating, Chief Financial Officer
CIO: Dan Galindo, Director Information Systems
CHR: Sharon McKay, Director Human Resources
Web address: www.irvineregionalhospital.com

	33	10	176	9336	82	21176	2069	74843	35331	419

JACKSON—Amador County

✠ **SUTTER AMADOR HOSPITAL**, 200 Mission Boulevard, Zip 95642–2132; tel. 209/223–7500, (Total facility includes 24 beds in nursing home–type unit) **A**1 9 10 **F**9 27 33 40 43 46 52 55 58 59 62 63 65 66 69 81 84 88 92 94 96 109 **S** Sutter Health, Sacramento, CA
Primary Contact: Anne Platt, Chief Executive Officer
CFO: Siri Nelson, Chief Financial Officer
CMO: Thomas Bowhay, M.D., Chief of Staff
CIO: Tony Jackson, Information Technology Director
CHR: Barbara Wells, Human Resources Director
Web address: www.sutteramador.com

	23	10	66	2423	42	33005	145	44436	16512	311

JOSHUA TREE—San Bernardino County

✠ **HI–DESERT MEDICAL CENTER**, 6601 White Feather Road, Zip 92252–6601; tel. 760/366–3711, (Total facility includes 106 beds in nursing home–type unit) **A**1 9 10 20 **F**9 11 12 21 22 26 27 28 29 33 36 39 42 45 46 48 51 53 55 58 59 60 62 63 66 69 77 81 84 85 88 92 93 94 96 97 108 109 **S** Brim Healthcare, Inc., Brentwood, TN
Primary Contact: David B. Selman, Chief Executive Officer
COO: David B. Selman, Chief Executive Officer
CFO: Thomas J. Duda, Chief Financial Officer
CMO: Ayad Gharghoury, M.D., Chief Medical Staff
CIO: Dan McClure, Director Information Services
CHR: Cindy Schmall, Vice President Human Resources
Web address: www.hdmc.org

	16	10	140	3184	138	70802	260	42093	15985	410

KING CITY—Monterey County

☐ **GEORGE L. MEE MEMORIAL HOSPITAL**, 300 Canal Street, Zip 93930–3431; tel. 831/385–6000, (Total facility includes 16 beds in nursing home–type unit) (Nonreporting) **A**1 9 10 20
Primary Contact: Walter G. Beck, Chief Executive Officer

	23	10	42	—	—	—	—	—	—	—

KINGSBURG—Fresno County

KINGSBURG MEDICAL CENTER, 1200 Smith Street, Zip 93631–2216; tel. 559/897–5841, (Total facility includes 20 beds in nursing home–type unit) (Nonreporting) **A**9 10
Primary Contact: Doug Skubitz, Administrator

	16	10	35	—	—	—	—	—	—	—

LA JOLLA—San Diego County

✠ **SCRIPPS GREEN HOSPITAL**, 10666 North Torrey Pines Road, Zip 92037–1093; tel. 858/455–9100 **A**1 2 5 8 9 10 **F**2 3 9 10 12 14 15 17 19 21 22 23 26 27 28 36 40 41 42 52 55 56 58 59 60 61 62 63 64 66 68 69 71 79 80 81 82 84 87 88 89 92 94 96 99 101 102 104 105 108 **P**3 **S** Scripps Health, San Diego, CA
Primary Contact: Robin Brown, Chief Executive Officer
CFO: Chris Fritz, Chief Financial Officer
CMO: Brent Eastman, M.D., Chief Medical Officer
CIO: Jean Balgrosky, Senior Vice President and Chief Information Officer
CHR: Vic Buzachero, Vice President Human Resources
Web address: www.scrippshealth.org

	23	10	153	10064	100	126850	0	—	—	944

Hospital, Address, Telephone, Approval, Facility, and Physician Codes, Health Care System	Classi-fication Codes		Utilization Data					Expense (thousands) of dollars		
	Control	Service	Staffed Beds	Admissions	Census	Outpatient Visits	Births	Total	Payroll	Personnel

★ American Hospital Association (AHA) membership
□ Joint Commission on Accreditation of Healthcare Organizations (JCAHO) accreditation
○ American Osteopathic Association (AOA) accreditation
△ Commission on Accreditation of Rehabilitation Facilities (CARF) accreditation

CA

☒ **SCRIPPS MEMORIAL HOSPITAL–LA JOLLA**, 9888 Genesee Avenue, Zip 92037–1200, Mailing Address: P.O. Box 28, Zip 92038–0028; tel. 858/626–4123 **A**1 2 3 5 9 10 **F**3 4 10 11 12 14 15 17 19 21 22 23 26 27 28 29 31 33 34 37 38 39 40 41 42 43 44 46 47 48 49 50 53 55 57 59 60 61 62 63 64 65 66 69 72 73 74 75 76 77 79 80 81 82 84 85 87 88 89 92 93 94 95 96 97 98 107 108 109 **P**3 **S** Scripps Health, San Diego, CA
Primary Contact: Gary G. Fybel, Chief Executive Officer
CFO: Lisa Thakur, Chief Financial Executive
CIO: Jean Balgrosky, Vice President and Chief Information Officecr
CHR: Vic Buzachero, Vice President Human Resources
Web address: www.scrippshealth.org
12 | 10 | 278 | 18832 | 271 | 108708 | 3815 | 285724 | 106410 | 1840

LA MESA—San Diego County
☒ △ **SHARP GROSSMONT HOSPITAL**, 5555 Grossmont Center Drive, Zip 91942–3019, Mailing Address: P.O. Box 158, Zip 91944–0158; tel. 619/740–6000 **A**1 2 7 9 10 **F**2 9 11 12 15 17 19 21 22 23 26 27 28 29 31 33 36 37 38 40 44 45 46 47 48 49 52 53 55 56 57 58 59 60 61 62 63 64 65 66 68 69 71 73 74 75 76 79 81 82 84 85 86 87 88 92 93 94 96 98 108 109 110 **S** Sharp Healthcare, San Diego, CA
Primary Contact: Michele T. Tarbet, R.N., Chief Executive Officer
CFO: Kari Cornicelli, Chief Financial Officer
CMO: Michael Long, M.D., Executive Medical Staff
CIO: William T. Spooner, Senior Vice President and Chief Information Officer
CHR: Ruth Shannon, Director Human Resources
Web address: www.sharp.com
23 | 10 | 457 | 23009 | 305 | 316777 | 3426 | 309251 | 129852 | 2467

LA MIRADA—Los Angeles County
□ **KINDRED HOSPITAL – LA MIRADA**, 14900 East Imperial Highway, Zip 90638; tel. 562/944–1900, (Nonreporting) **A**1
Primary Contact: Robert D. Blair, Chief Executive Officer
33 | 80 | 10 | — | — | — | — | — | — | —

LA PALMA—Orange County
☒ △ **LA PALMA INTERCOMMUNITY HOSPITAL**, 7901 Walker Street, Zip 90623–1722, Mailing Address: P.O. Box 5850, Buena Park, Zip 90622–5850; tel. 714/670–7400 **A**1 7 9 10 **F**2 4 9 11 12 14 15 21 23 29 32 33 45 46 47 48 55 60 62 63 64 68 69 71 74 75 77 78 81 82 84 85 88 94 96 106 108 109 110 **S** Vanguard Health System, Nashville, TN
Primary Contact: Patricia L. Wolfram, R.N., Chief Executive Officer
CMO: Mahendra Patel, M.D., Chief of Staff
CIO: Debbie Horgan, Director
CHR: Tim Howard, Regional Director Human Resources
Web address: www.lapalmaintercommunityhospital.com
23 | 10 | 141 | 4972 | 63 | — | — | — | — | —

LAGUNA BEACH—Orange County
☒ **SOUTH COAST MEDICAL CENTER**, 31872 Coast Highway, Zip 92651–6775; tel. 949/499–1311 **A**1 9 10 **F**2 4 9 10 11 12 21 22 23 26 27 28 29 33 37 39 45 46 47 48 51 52 53 54 55 57 58 59 60 61 62 63 66 69 71 73 74 75 76 77 78 81 82 84 88 94 95 96 108 109 110 **P**7 **S** Adventist Health, Roseville, CA
Primary Contact: Gary G. Irish, President and Chief Executive Officer
COO: Karolyn Scheneman, Vice President Patient Care Services and Chief Nursing Officer
CFO: Scott Perryman, Vice President and Chief Financial Officer
CMO: William Anderson, M.D., Chief of Staff
CIO: Mindra Fielding, Director Information System Services
CHR: Donald Balli, Human Resources Director
Web address: www.southcoastmedcenter.com
21 | 10 | 208 | 5197 | 81 | 29314 | 520 | 65070 | 28145 | 606

LAGUNA HILLS—Orange County
□ **SADDLEBACK MEMORIAL MEDICAL CENTER**, 24451 Health Center Drive, Zip 92653–3689; tel. 949/837–4500 **A**1 2 5 9 10 **F**2 9 11 12 15 17 19 21 22 23 26 27 28 29 31 33 35 36 39 41 44 45 46 47 48 51 52 53 54 55 56 57 58 59 60 61 62 63 64 65 68 69 73 79 80 81 82 85 87 88 92 94 96 104 105 107 108 109 110 **P**5 7 **S** Memorial Health Services, Long Beach, CA
Primary Contact: Steve Geidt, Chief Executive Officer
Web address: www.memorialcare.org
23 | 10 | 252 | 15618 | 172 | 287253 | 3314 | 196506 | 85601 | 2067

LAKE ARROWHEAD—San Bernardino County
☒ **MOUNTAINS COMMUNITY HOSPITAL**, 29101 Hospital Road, Zip 92352, Mailing Address: P.O. Box 70, Zip 92352–0070; tel. 909/336–3651, (Total facility includes 18 beds in nursing home–type unit) **A**1 9 10 18 **F**9 11 12 21 22 24 26 27 28 29 31 33 39 44 46 52 54 59 63 66 69 81 88 92 94 97 107
Primary Contact: James R. Hoss, Executive Director
CFO: Ronald E. Luke, Chief Financial Officer
CMO: Edward M. Pallette, M.D., Acting Chief of Staff
CIO: Sherri Sanders, Manager Information Systems
CHR: Julie Atwood, Director Human Resources
Web address: www.mchcares.com
16 | 10 | 35 | 567 | 22 | 17483 | 98 | 11304 | 5143 | 127

LAKE ISABELLA—Kern County
★ **KERN VALLEY HEALTHCARE DISTRICT**, 6412 Laurel Avenue, Zip 93240–1628, Mailing Address: P.O. Box 1628, Zip 93240–1628; tel. 760/379–2681, (Total facility includes 74 beds in nursing home–type unit) **A**9 10 18 20 **F**9 21 22 24 29 33 46 48 52 55 63 68 69 81 92 97 98
Primary Contact: Pamela Ott, R.N., Chief Executive Officer
CFO: Barbara Figueroa, Controller
CMO: Gary A. Finstad, M.D., Chief of Staff
CIO: Dena Griffith, Information Systems Manager
Web address: www.kvhd.org
16 | 10 | 101 | 1300 | 79 | 29135 | — | 20413 | — | —

Many Facility Codes have changed. Please refer to the AHA Guide Code Chart.   © 2005 AHA Guide

Hospital, Address, Telephone, Approval, Facility, and Physician Codes, Health Care System	Classi-fication Codes		Utilization Data					Expense (thousands) of dollars		
★ American Hospital Association (AHA) membership □ Joint Commission on Accreditation of Healthcare Organizations (JCAHO) accreditation ○ American Osteopathic Association (AOA) accreditation △ Commission on Accreditation of Rehabilitation Facilities (CARF) accreditation	Control	Service	Staffed Beds	Admissions	Census	Outpatient Visits	Births	Total	Payroll	Personnel

LAKEPORT—Lake County

✠ **SUTTER LAKESIDE HOSPITAL**, 5176 Hill Road East, Zip 95453–6300; tel. 707/262–5001 **A**1 9 10 20 **F**9 11 12 15 21 22 24 26 27 28 29 33 37 41 42 45 46 50 51 55 58 59 60 62 63 66 69 81 83 84 86 88 94 95 97 106 107 108 109 110 **S** Sutter Health, Sacramento, CA Primary Contact: Kelly Mather, Chief Executive Officer COO: Tracy Gleason, Assistant Administrator CFO: Avery Schlesenberg, Chief Financial Officer CMO: Diane Pege, M.D., Medical Director CIO: Jack Buell, Chief Information Officer CHR: Steve Morales, Chief Human Resources Officer Web address: www.sutterlake.org	23	10	53	2514	26	147778	338	57796	21490	333

LAKEWOOD—Los Angeles County

✠ **LAKEWOOD REGIONAL MEDICAL CENTER**, 3700 East South Street, Zip 90712–1498, Mailing Address: P.O. Box 6070, Zip 90714–6070; tel. 562/531–2550 **A**1 9 10 **F**2 9 11 12 14 15 17 19 21 22 26 27 28 29 31 33 35 39 42 45 46 47 48 52 53 55 57 58 59 60 63 66 68 69 81 82 84 88 94 96 108 109 **S** TENET Healthcare Corporation, Dallas, TX Primary Contact: Michael Hunn, Chief Executive Officer COO: Steve Sisto, Chief Operating Officer CFO: Steven Payne, Chief Financial Officer CMO: Ronald Kaufman, M.D., Chief Medical Officer CIO: Eleanor Laneaux, Director Information Systems CHR: Mary Okuhara, Director Human Resources Web address: www.lakewoodregional.com	33	10	161	8251	102	63606	194	89706	39619	535

LANCASTER—Los Angeles County

✠ **ANTELOPE VALLEY HOSPITAL**, 1600 West Avenue J, Zip 93534–2894; tel. 661/949–5000 **A**1 9 10 **F**2 11 12 14 15 17 19 21 22 23 27 28 29 33 37 51 52 53 56 58 59 60 61 62 63 65 69 71 75 81 82 83 84 85 86 87 88 89 92 94 97 106 108 109 **P**7 Primary Contact: Leslie H. Wong, Chief Executive Officer CFO: Leon Choiniere, Vice President CMO: Doddanna Krishna, M.D., Chief of Staff CIO: Humberto Quintana, Chief Information Officer CHR: John Sullivan, Vice President Human Resources Web address: www.avhospital.org	16	10	332	22344	252	107762	—	158799	—	—
□ **LANCASTER COMMUNITY HOSPITAL**, 43830 North Tenth Street West, Zip 93534–4895; tel. 661/948–4781 **A**1 9 10 **F**2 9 14 21 23 26 27 28 33 40 48 52 55 57 58 60 61 62 63 68 81 82 84 88 92 96 107 108 110 **S** Universal Health Services, Inc., King of Prussia, PA Primary Contact: Robert J. Trautman, Chief Executive Officer Web address: www.lancastercommunityhospital.net	33	10	117	5853	72	30160	0	51907	—	—

LEMOORE—Kings County

✠ **NAVAL HOSPITAL**, 937 Franklin Avenue, Zip 93246–5004; tel. 559/998–4201, (Nonreporting) **A**1 **S** Bureau of Medicine and Surgery, Department of the Navy, Washington, DC Primary Contact: Captain Sandra DeGroot, Commanding Officer COO: Captain Colin Chinn, Executive Officer Web address: www.lemoore.med.navy.mil	43	10	16	—	—	—	—	—	—	—

LIVERMORE—Alameda County

VALLEY MEMORIAL See ValleyCare Medical Center, Pleasanton
VETERANS AFFAIRS PALO ALTO HEALTH CARE SYSTEM, LIVERMORE DIVISION See Veterans Affairs Palo Alto Health Care System, Palo Alto

LODI—San Joaquin County

✠ **LODI MEMORIAL HOSPITAL**, 975 South Fairmont Avenue, Zip 95240–5179, Mailing Address: P.O. Box 3004, Zip 95241–1908; tel. 209/334–3411, (Includes LODI MEMORIAL HOSPITAL WEST, 800 South Lower Sacramento Road, Zip 95242; tel. 209/333–0211) **A**1 9 10 **F**1 2 9 11 15 21 24 26 27 28 29 33 37 39 41 44 46 47 48 49 51 52 53 55 58 59 60 62 63 65 66 68 69 70 81 82 88 92 94 95 96 107 108 109 110 **P**1 5 Primary Contact: Joseph P. Harrington, Chief Executive Officer COO: Deborah Aspling, Vice President and Chief Operating Officer CFO: Ron Kreutner, Chief Financial Officer CHR: Mark Wallace, Director Human Resources Web address: www.lodihealth.org	23	10	170	7587	118	209979	1317	70015	46414	892

LOMA LINDA—San Bernardino County

✠ △ **JERRY L. PETTIS MEMORIAL VETERANS MEDICAL CENTER**, 11201 Benton Street, Zip 92357; tel. 909/825–7084, (Total facility includes 108 beds in nursing home–type unit) (Nonreporting) **A**1 3 5 7 8 **S** Department of Veterans Affairs, Washington, DC Primary Contact: Dean R. Stordahl, Director CFO: William Lysaght, Chief Financial Officer CMO: Dwight Evans, M.D., Chief of Staff CIO: Shane Elliott, Chief Information Technology Service CHR: Eugene Wylie, Chief Human Resources Officer Web address: www.va.gov/sta/guide/home.asp	45	10	205	—	—	—	—	—	—	—

Hospital, Address, Telephone, Approval, Facility, and Physician Codes, Health Care System	Classi-fication Codes		Utilization Data					Expense (thousands) of dollars		
★ American Hospital Association (AHA) membership □ Joint Commission on Accreditation of Healthcare Organizations (JCAHO) accreditation ○ American Osteopathic Association (AOA) accreditation △ Commission on Accreditation of Rehabilitation Facilities (CARF) accreditation	Control	Service	Staffed Beds	Admissions	Census	Outpatient Visits	Births	Total	Payroll	Personnel

CA

☒ △ **LOMA LINDA UNIVERSITY MEDICAL CENTER**, 11234 Anderson Street, Zip 92354–2870, Mailing Address: P.O. Box 2000, Zip 92354–0200; tel. 909/558–4000, (Includes LOMA LINDA UNIVERSITY COMMUNITY MEDICAL CENTER, 25333 Barton Road, Zip 92354–3053; tel. 909/558–6000) **A**1 2 3 5 7 8 9 10 **F**1 2 6 11 12 14 15 16 17 18 19 20 21 22 23 24 26 27 28 29 33 34 37 38 40 42 46 47 48 49 51 52 53 55 56 57 58 59 60 61 62 63 66 67 68 69 80 81 82 84 85 86 87 88 93 94 96 98 99 100 101 102 104 105 107 108 109 110 **P**3 **S** Loma Linda University Adventist Health Sciences Center, Loma Linda, CA
Primary Contact: Ruthita J. Fike, Chief Executive Officer
COO: Ruthita J. Fike, Chief Executive Officer
CFO: Steve Mohr, Senior Vice President Finance and Chief Financial Officer
CMO: Daniel Giang, M.D., Vice President for Medical Administration
CIO: Richard Hergert, Chief Information Officer
CHR: Lizette Norton, Executive Director Human Resources Management
Web address: www.llumc.edu
`23 10 701 30361 518 526969 2536 659228 274397 5412`

LOMPOC—Santa Barbara County
☒ **LOMPOC HEALTHCARE DISTRICT**, 508 East Hickory Street, Zip 93436–7337, Mailing Address: P.O. Box 1058, Zip 93438–1058; tel. 805/737–3300, (Total facility includes 110 beds in nursing home–type unit) **A**1 9 10 **F**12 21 26 27 28 29 33 34 46 55 59 62 63 65 69 81 82 84 85 88 92 94 106 108
Primary Contact: James J. Raggio, Administrator and Chief Executive Officer
CMO: John Sawyer, M.D., Chief of Staff
CIO: Jim White, Chief Information Officer
CHR: Sandi Stinson, Director Human Resources
Web address: www.lompochospital.org
`16 10 170 2737 126 60288 524 33070 13798 381`

LONE PINE—Inyo County
SOUTHERN INYO HEALTHCARE DISTRICT, 501 East Locust Street, Zip 93545–1009, Mailing Address: P.O. Box 1009, Zip 93545–1009; tel. 760/876–5501, (Total facility includes 33 beds in nursing home–type unit) **A**9 10 18 20 **F**9 21 22 24 26 27 28 29 30 33 36 38 39 42 44 45 46 47 48 52 53 60 69 70 81 88 92 94 96 97 98 106 107 108 109 110 **P**8
Primary Contact: Richard Gering, Interim Chief Executive Officer
Web address: www.sihd.org
`16 10 37 125 32 14997 0 4600 2320 73`

LONG BEACH—Los Angeles County
☒ **COMMUNITY HOSPITAL OF LONG BEACH**, 1720 Termino Avenue, Zip 90804–2180; tel. 562/498–1000, (Nonreporting) **A**1 10
Primary Contact: Raymond M. Jankowski, President and Chief Executive Officer
COO: Diane DeWalsche, R.N., Chief Operating Officer
CFO: Robert Schirripa, Administrative Director Finance
CMO: Andrew Manos, D.O., Chief Medical Staff
CIO: Rafael Gamboa, Information Systems Manager
CHR: Tom Miller, Administrative Director Human Resources
Web address: www.chlb.org
`23 10 107 — — — — — — —`

□ **LONG BEACH MEMORIAL MEDICAL CENTER**, 2801 Atlantic Avenue, Zip 90806–1737, Mailing Address: P.O. Box 1428, Zip 90801–1428; tel. 562/933–2000 **A**1 2 3 5 8 9 10 13 **F**2 7 9 11 12 14 15 17 19 21 22 23 26 27 28 29 30 31 32 33 34 35 36 37 38 39 40 41 43 44 45 46 47 48 50 51 52 53 55 57 58 60 61 62 63 64 65 66 68 69 70 73 74 79 80 81 82 83 85 88 89 90 92 93 94 95 96 104 105 106 107 108 109 110 **P**4 5 7 **S** Memorial Health Services, Long Beach, CA
Primary Contact: Byron F. Schweigert, Chief Executive Officer
Web address: www.memorialcare.org
`23 10 462 24648 352 168525 — 311250 138464 3419`

□ **MILLER CHILDREN'S HOSPITAL**, 2801 Atlantic Avenue, Zip 90806; tel. 562/933–2000 **A**1 9 10 **F**2 9 16 18 20 21 22 23 24 26 27 28 29 30 31 32 33 34 35 36 37 38 39 41 43 45 46 47 48 50 51 52 53 56 57 58 59 60 61 62 63 64 65 66 67 69 70 72 73 74 79 80 81 82 83 85 88 92 93 94 95 96 98 104 105 107 108 110 **P**4 5 7 **S** Memorial Health Services, Long Beach, CA
Primary Contact: Melvin Marks, M.D., Administrator
Web address: www.memorialcare.org
`23 50 281 16018 209 70814 5682 206941 89239 2998`

□ **PACIFIC HOSPITAL OF LONG BEACH**, 2776 Pacific Avenue, Zip 90806–2699, Mailing Address: P.O. Box 1268, Zip 90801; tel. 562/595–1911, (Total facility includes 27 beds in nursing home–type unit) (Nonreporting) **A**1 10 12 13
Primary Contact: Michael D. Drobot, Chairman and Chief Executive Officer
Web address: www.phlb.org
`23 10 171 — — — — — — —`

REDGATE MEMORIAL HOSPITAL, 1775 Chestnut Avenue, Zip 90813–1674; tel. 562/599–8444, (Nonreporting)
Primary Contact: Lawrence Gentile, President and Chief Executive Officer
`23 82 63 — — — — — — —`

☒ **ST. MARY MEDICAL CENTER**, 1050 Linden Avenue, Zip 90801–3393, Mailing Address: P.O. Box 887, Zip 90813–0887; tel. 562/491–9000, (Total facility includes 32 beds in nursing home–type unit) **A**1 2 3 5 9 10 **F**2 9 11 12 14 21 22 23 24 27 28 29 32 33 34 36 37 38 39 40 44 45 46 47 48 49 50 51 52 53 55 56 57 58 59 60 61 62 63 66 67 68 69 71 76 81 82 84 88 91 92 94 95 96 98 107 108 109 **S** Catholic Healthcare West, San Francisco, CA
Primary Contact: Christopher DiCicco, Chief Executive Officer
COO: Joel Yuhas, Chief Operating Officer
CFO: Adolfo Chavez, Chief Financial Officer
CMO: Thomas Gates, M.D., Chief of Staff
CIO: Earle Johnson, Site Manager
CHR: Christine Carson, Director Human Resources
Web address: www.sc.chw.edu
`21 10 236 11732 214 165166 — 142212 — —`

Many Facility Codes have changed. Please refer to the AHA Guide Code Chart. © 2005 AHA Guide

Hospital, Address, Telephone, Approval, Facility, and Physician Codes, Health Care System	Classi-fication Codes		Utilization Data					Expense (thousands) of dollars		
	Control	Service	Staffed Beds	Admissions	Census	Outpatient Visits	Births	Total	Payroll	Personnel

★ American Hospital Association (AHA) membership
□ Joint Commission on Accreditation of Healthcare Organizations (JCAHO) accreditation
○ American Osteopathic Association (AOA) accreditation
△ Commission on Accreditation of Rehabilitation Facilities (CARF) accreditation

	Control	Service	Staffed Beds	Admissions	Census	Outpatient Visits	Births	Total	Payroll	Personnel
★ △ **VETERANS AFFAIRS LONG BEACH HEALTHCARE SYSTEM**, 5901 East Seventh Street, Zip 90822–5201; tel. 562/826–8000, (Total facility includes 95 beds in nursing home–type unit) **A**1 2 3 5 7 8 **F**1 2 4 7 9 12 21 22 23 26 27 28 29 31 32 33 35 36 37 38 39 40 41 42 44 45 46 47 48 49 50 51 52 53 55 57 58 60 61 62 63 64 65 66 68 69 70 71 73 74 75 76 77 79 80 81 82 84 85 87 88 90 92 93 94 95 96 106 107 108 109 110 **P**6 **S** Department of Veterans Affairs, Washington, DC Primary Contact: Ronald Norby, Director COO: Ada Neale, Associate Director CFO: Charles H. Feistman, Chief Resources Health Care Group CMO: Sandor Szabo, M.D., Ph.D., Chief of Staff CIO: Michael Mitchell, Chief Information Management CHR: Mary Beth McCartan, Human Resources Manager Web address: www.long–beach.va.gov	45	10	327	5516	142	427154	0	—	—	1881
LOS ALAMITOS—Orange County										
★ **LOS ALAMITOS MEDICAL CENTER**, 3751 Katella Avenue, Zip 90720–3164; tel. 562/598–1311 **A**1 2 9 10 **F**9 11 12 14 21 33 49 54 55 58 59 60 61 69 76 81 82 84 88 94 108 **S** TENET Healthcare Corporation, Dallas, TX Primary Contact: Michele Finney, Chief Executive Officer COO: Mark Korth, Chief Operating Officer CFO: Dave Vickers, Chief Financial Officer CMO: Prakash Narain, M.D., Chief of Staff CIO: Sally Andrada, Chief Information Officer CHR: Angie Driscoll, Director Human Resources Web address: www.losalamitosmedctr.com	33	10	167	8800	116	—	—	—	—	—
LOS ANGELES—Los Angeles County **(Mailing Addresses - Canoga Park, Encino, Granada Hills, Harbor City, Hollywood, Mission Hills, North Hollywood, Northridge, Panorama City, San Pedro, Sepulveda, Sherman Oaks, Sun Valley, Sylmar, Tarzana, Van Nuys, West Hills, West Los Angeles, Woodland Hills)**										
★ **BARLOW RESPIRATORY HOSPITAL**, 2000 Stadium Way, Zip 90026–2696; tel. 213/250–4200 **A**1 3 5 9 10 **F**2 21 27 28 29 46 52 55 60 66 69 94 96 108 **P**8 Primary Contact: Margaret W. Crane, Chief Executive Officer COO: Terry Sepulveda, Chief Operating Officer CFO: Ted Sirotta, Chief Financial Officer and Chief Information Officer CIO: Ted Sirotta, Chief Financial Officer and Chief Information Officer Web address: www.barlow2000.org	23	33	75	542	48	352	0	25785	10610	216
★ **CALIFORNIA HOSPITAL MEDICAL CENTER**, 1401 South Grand Avenue, Zip 90015–3010; tel. 213/748–2411 **A**1 2 3 5 9 10 **F**2 9 11 12 14 21 22 23 24 27 28 29 31 33 37 38 39 42 45 46 47 48 50 52 53 55 56 57 58 59 60 61 62 63 64 65 66 70 88 90 92 94 96 98 107 108 109 110 **S** Catholic Healthcare West, San Francisco, CA Primary Contact: Mark A. Meyers, President COO: Helen Lidholm, Chief Operting Officer CFO: David Yeager, Chief Financial Officer CMO: Alan R. Weiss, M.D., Chief of Staff CIO: Michael Kenealy, Director Information Technology CHR: David Milovich, Senior Vice President Human Resources Web address: www.chmcla.org	23	10	316	13499	190	158644	4630	158580	73694	1395
★ △ **CEDARS–SINAI MEDICAL CENTER**, 8700 Beverly Boulevard, Zip 90048–1865, Mailing Address: Box 48750, Zip 90048–0750; tel. 310/423–5000 **A**1 2 3 5 7 8 9 10 **F**2 4 9 10 11 12 14 21 22 23 24 25 26 27 28 29 30 31 32 33 34 36 37 38 39 40 41 42 44 46 47 48 49 50 52 53 54 55 56 57 58 59 61 62 63 64 65 66 67 68 69 70 71 72 73 74 75 76 77 78 79 80 81 82 83 84 85 86 87 88 89 90 94 96 97 99 100 101 102 103 104 108 109 110 **P**3 5 8 Primary Contact: Thomas M. Priselac, President and Chief Executive Officer COO: Mark R. Gavens, Chief Operating Officer and Senior Vice President Clinical Care Services CFO: Edward Prunchunas, Senior Vice President and Chief Financial Officer CMO: Michael Langberg, M.D., Senior Vice President Medical Affairs and Chief Medical Officer CIO: Steve Reeves, Interim Chief Information Officer CHR: Jeanne Flores, Senior Vice President Human Resources and Organizational Development Web address: www.cedars–sinai.edu	23	10	875	46416	779	316373	7202	1200078	481638	7343
□ **CHILDRENS HOSPITAL LOS ANGELES**, 4650 Sunset Boulevard, Zip 90027–6062, Mailing Address: P.O. Box 54700, Zip 90054–0700; tel. 323/660–2450 **A**1 2 3 5 9 10 **F**2 4 7 9 10 16 18 20 21 22 23 24 26 27 28 29 31 32 33 34 35 37 38 39 42 45 46 47 48 49 50 52 53 56 57 58 60 61 62 63 64 65 66 67 68 69 70 72 73 74 75 77 79 80 81 82 84 85 88 90 93 94 95 96 98 99 100 101 102 103 104 105 108 110 **P**7 Primary Contact: Walter W. Noce, Jr, President and Chief Executive Officer Web address: www.chla.org	23	50	286	10806	230	294094	0	409963	177839	3193
□ **CITY OF ANGELS MEDICAL CENTER**, 1711 West Temple Street, Zip 90026; tel. 213/989–6100, (Nonreporting) **A**1 10 Primary Contact: Rudra Sabaratnam, M.D., President and Chief Executive Officer	33	10	180	—	—	—	—	—	—	—

Hospital, Address, Telephone, Approval, Facility, and Physician Codes, Health Care System	Classi-fication Codes		Utilization Data					Expense (thousands) of dollars		
★ American Hospital Association (AHA) membership □ Joint Commission on Accreditation of Healthcare Organizations (JCAHO) accreditation ○ American Osteopathic Association (AOA) accreditation △ Commission on Accreditation of Rehabilitation Facilities (CARF) accreditation	Control	Service	Staffed Beds	Admissions	Census	Outpatient Visits	Births	Total	Payroll	Personnel
□ **EAST LOS ANGELES DOCTORS HOSPITAL**, 4060 East Whittier Boulevard, Zip 90023–2526; tel. 323/268–5514, (Total facility includes 25 beds in nursing home–type unit) **A**1 10 **F**11 14 21 29 33 45 52 53 60 63 69 81 88 92 94 **S** HealthPlus, Houston, TX Primary Contact: Araceli Lonergan, Administrator and Chief Executive Officer	33	10	127	3678	73	19892	—	31975	—	—
⊠ **ENCINO–TARZANA REGIONAL MEDICAL CENTER ENCINO CAMPUS**, 16237 Ventura Boulevard, Encino, Zip 91436–2201; tel. 818/995–5000 **A**1 9 10 **F**11 12 14 15 16 17 18 19 21 22 23 27 29 33 37 40 44 46 52 55 56 58 59 61 65 66 67 76 81 88 92 94 96 108 109 110 **P**5 7 **S** TENET Healthcare Corporation, Dallas, TX Primary Contact: Dale Surowitz, Chief Executive Officer COO: Don Kreitz, Chief Operating Officer CFO: Nick Lymberopoulos, Chief Financial Officer CMO: Glenn Irani, M.D., Medical Chief of Staff CIO: Chris Livanos, Chief Information Officer CHR: Jo Lewis, Director Human Resources Web address: www.encino–tarzana.com	33	10	232	4480	141	32384	0	—	—	—
⊠ **ENCINO–TARZANA REGIONAL MEDICAL CENTER TARZANA CAMPUS**, 18321 Clark Street, Tarzana, Zip 91356–3521; tel. 818/881–0800 **A**1 9 10 **F**2 14 26 27 52 55 56 58 59 60 61 63 67 68 71 92 **P**5 **S** TENET Healthcare Corporation, Dallas, TX Primary Contact: Dale Surowitz, Chief Executive Officer CFO: Nick Lymberopoulos, Chief Financial Officer CMO: Glenn Irani, M.D., Medical Chief of Staff CIO: Chris Livanos, Chief Information Officer CHR: Jo Lewis, Director Human Resources Web address: www.encino–tarzana.com	33	10	286	13763	185	52780	3226	144374	—	—
□ **GATEWAYS HOSPITAL AND MENTAL HEALTH CENTER**, 1891 Effie Street, Zip 90026–1711; tel. 323/644–2000 **A**1 10 **F**21 27 60 71 72 77 94 Primary Contact: Mara Pelsman, Chief Executive Officer Web address: www.gatewayshospital.org GENERAL HOSPITAL See LAC/University of Southern California Medical Center	23	22	31	631	31	53472	0	14637	8010	248
□ △ **GOOD SAMARITAN HOSPITAL**, 1225 Wilshire Boulevard, Zip 90017–1901; tel. 213/977–2121 **A**1 2 3 5 7 9 10 **F**2 6 7 9 11 12 14 15 17 19 21 22 23 26 27 28 29 30 31 32 33 37 38 39 40 41 42 43 44 45 46 47 48 49 50 51 52 53 55 56 57 58 59 60 61 62 63 64 65 66 68 69 70 75 79 80 81 82 84 85 86 87 88 89 91 92 94 95 96 107 108 109 110 **P**5 Primary Contact: Andrew B. Leeka, President and Chief Executive Officer Web address: www.goodsam.org	23	10	408	16373	247	82739	3278	209588	71197	1386
□ **HOLLYWOOD COMMUNITY HOSPITAL**, 6245 De Longpre Avenue, Zip 90028–9001; tel. 323/462–2271, (Includes HOLLYWOOD COMMUNITY HOSPITAL OF VAN NUYS, 14433 Emelita Street, Zip 91401; tel. 818/787–1511), (Nonreporting) **A**1 10 **S** Alta Healthcare System, Bellflower, CA Primary Contact: Casey Fatch, Chief Executive Officer	33	10	45	—	—	—	—	—	—	—
⊠ **HOLLYWOOD PRESBYTERIAN MEDICAL CENTER**, 1300 North Vermont Avenue, Zip 90027–0069; tel. 323/913–4800 **A**1 2 9 10 **F**2 7 9 10 11 12 14 15 21 22 23 27 28 29 33 36 37 38 39 40 45 46 48 50 52 53 55 56 57 58 59 61 62 63 64 66 68 69 79 81 82 84 87 88 92 94 96 107 108 110 Primary Contact: Albert L. Greene, Chief Executive Officer CFO: Abby Maldonado, Chief Financial Officer Web address: www.qahpmc.com	33	10	274	15497	273	80952	—	136416	—	—
⊠ **KAISER FOUNDATION HOSPITAL**, 4867 Sunset Boulevard, Zip 90027–5969; tel. 323/783–4011, (Includes KAISER FOUNDATION MENTAL HEALTH CENTER, 765 West College Street, Zip 90012; tel. 213/580–7200) **A**1 2 3 5 10 **F**2 11 12 14 15 16 17 18 19 20 21 22 23 26 27 28 29 30 31 33 36 37 38 39 43 49 51 52 53 55 56 57 58 59 61 62 63 64 65 66 67 71 75 78 79 80 82 92 96 107 108 109 110 **P**6 **S** Kaiser Foundation Hospitals, Oakland, CA Primary Contact: Barry A. Wolfman, Senior Vice President and Area Manager COO: Rodney Hanners, Director Operations CFO: Alice H. Issai, Business Strategy and Finance Leader CMO: Thomas Godfrey, M.D., Medical Director CIO: Raymond Lowe, Information Technology Leader CHR: Regina O'Leary, Human Resources Leader Web address: www.kaiserpermanente.org	23	10	475	40168	283	67552	2241	—	—	2947
⊠ **KAISER FOUNDATION HOSPITAL**, 25825 South Vermont Avenue, Harbor City, Zip 90710–3599; tel. 310/325–5111, (Nonreporting) **A**1 10 **S** Kaiser Foundation Hospitals, Oakland, CA Primary Contact: Gerald A. McCall, Senior Vice President and Administrator Web address: www.kaiserpermanente.org	23	10	193	—	—	—	—	—	—	—
⊠ **KAISER FOUNDATION HOSPITAL**, 13652 Cantara Street, Panorama City, Zip 91402–5497; tel. 818/375–2000 **A**1 5 10 **F**2 11 12 21 22 23 26 27 28 29 31 33 36 37 38 44 45 47 48 50 51 52 53 55 56 57 58 59 60 61 62 63 64 65 66 69 70 73 75 76 81 82 84 85 88 90 94 95 96 98 104 106 107 108 110 **P**6 **S** Kaiser Foundation Hospitals, Oakland, CA Primary Contact: Jane Finley, Interim Service Area Manager COO: Jane Finley, Interim Service Area Manager CFO: Dennis Benton, Business Strategy and Finance Leader CMO: Virginia Ambrosini, M.D., Area Medical Director CIO: Laura Gallardo, Interim Public Affairs Leader CHR: Carole Erken, Human Resources Leader Web address: www.kaiserpermanente.org	23	10	205	19506	104	43216	1601	—	—	983

CA

Many Facility Codes have changed. Please refer to the AHA Guide Code Chart. © 2005 AHA Guide

Hospital, Address, Telephone, Approval, Facility, and Physician Codes, Health Care System	Classification Codes		Utilization Data					Expense (thousands) of dollars		
★ American Hospital Association (AHA) membership □ Joint Commission on Accreditation of Healthcare Organizations (JCAHO) accreditation ○ American Osteopathic Association (AOA) accreditation △ Commission on Accreditation of Rehabilitation Facilities (CARF) accreditation	Control	Service	Staffed Beds	Admissions	Census	Outpatient Visits	Births	Total	Payroll	Personnel
⊠ **KAISER FOUNDATION HOSPITAL**, 5601 DeSoto Avenue, Woodland Hills, Zip 91365–6701; tel. 818/719–3800 **A**1 3 5 10 **F**2 11 12 14 21 22 23 24 26 27 28 33 36 37 40 45 46 49 50 52 53 55 56 57 58 59 60 61 62 63 64 65 66 73 75 76 81 82 84 86 88 90 93 94 104 107 108 110 **P**6 **S** Kaiser Foundation Hospitals, Oakland, CA Primary Contact: Jane Finley, Interim Service Area Manager COO: Jane Finley, Interim Service Area Manager CFO: Dennis Benton, Business Strategy and Finance Leader CMO: Shirley Suda, M.D., Associate Area Medical Director CIO: Linda Quon, Public Affairs Leader Web address: www.kaiserpermanente.org	23	10	218	16300	133	39529	1737	—	—	1119
⊠ **KAISER FOUNDATION HOSPITAL–WEST LOS ANGELES**, 6041 Cadillac Avenue, Zip 90034–1702; tel. 323/857–2201 **A**1 2 3 5 10 **F**2 4 11 12 21 22 23 24 26 27 28 29 33 37 42 44 48 50 51 52 55 57 58 59 60 61 62 63 64 65 66 67 69 70 72 73 74 75 76 77 78 81 82 84 87 88 90 92 94 98 106 107 108 109 110 **P**6 **S** Kaiser Foundation Hospitals, Oakland, CA Primary Contact: Gloria Blackburn, Director Operations and Chief Nursing Executive COO: Gloria Blackburn, Director Operations CFO: Alice H. Issai, Business Strategy and Finance Leader CMO: Fred Alexander, M.D., Medical Director CIO: Gregory M. Sincock, Information Technology Leader Web address: www.kaiserpermanente.org KAISER FOUNDATION MENTAL HEALTH CENTER See Kaiser Foundation Hospital	23	10	166	10857	117	872065	1428	—	—	2091
□ **KINDRED HOSPITAL–LOS ANGELES**, 5525 West Slauson Avenue, Zip 90056–1067; tel. 310/642–0325 **A**1 10 **F**2 21 23 26 44 94 110 **P**8 **S** Kindred Healthcare, Louisville, KY Primary Contact: Adam Darvish, M.P.H., Chief Executive Officer Web address: www.kindredhealthcare.com	33	10	81	537	73	0	0	—	—	—
LAC–KING–DREW MEDICAL CENTER, 12021 South Wilmington Avenue, Zip 90059–3019; tel. 310/668–4321 **A**2 3 5 10 **F**2 12 14 15 16 21 22 23 24 27 28 32 33 34 42 44 47 48 49 50 52 53 55 56 57 59 60 61 62 63 64 67 69 71 73 75 81 82 84 85 88 94 107 108 **P**6 **S** Los Angeles County–Department of Health Services, Los Angeles, CA Primary Contact: Hank Wells, Interim Chief Executive Officer Web address: www.ladhs.org/mlk	13	10	206	11310	203	210465	673	335764	145382	2461
□ **LAC–OLIVE VIEW–UCLA MEDICAL CENTER**, 14445 Olive View Drive, Sylmar, Zip 91342–1495; tel. 818/364–1555, (Nonreporting) **A**1 5 10 **S** Los Angeles County–Department of Health Services, Los Angeles, CA Primary Contact: Melinda Anderson, Chief Executive Officer Web address: www.ladhs.org	13	10	226	—	—	—	—	—	—	—
□ **LAC/UNIVERSITY OF SOUTHERN CALIFORNIA MEDICAL CENTER**, 1200 North State Street, Zip 90033–1029; tel. 323/226–2622, (Includes GENERAL HOSPITAL, 1200 North State Street, Zip 90033; WOMEN'S AND CHILDREN'S HOSPITAL, 1240 North Mission Road, Zip 90033) **A**1 2 3 5 8 10 **F**2 6 7 9 10 11 12 13 14 15 16 17 19 20 22 23 24 27 28 29 32 33 34 35 39 42 46 47 48 49 50 52 53 55 56 57 58 59 60 61 62 63 64 65 66 67 69 70 71 72 73 74 75 77 78 79 81 82 84 88 89 93 94 96 97 107 108 110 **P**6 **S** Los Angeles County–Department of Health Services, Los Angeles, CA Primary Contact: Pete Delgado, Chief Executive Officer Web address: www.lacusc.org	13	10	737	37922	700	751634	1424	1179173	326978	6482
□ **LOS ANGELES COMMUNITY HOSPITAL**, 4081 East Olympic Boulevard, Zip 90023–3330; tel. 323/267–0477, (Includes LOS ANGELES COMMUNITY HOSPITAL OF NORWALK, 13222 Bloomfield Avenue, Zip 90650; tel. 562/863–4763), (Total facility includes 30 beds in nursing home–type unit) (Nonreporting) **A**1 9 10 **S** Alta Healthcare System, Bellflower, CA Primary Contact: David Topper, Chief Executive Officer	33	10	180	—	—	—	—	—	—	—
LOS ANGELES COUNTY CENTRAL JAIL HOSPITAL, 441 Bauchet Street, Zip 90012–2994; tel. 213/473–6100, (Nonreporting) Primary Contact: Tom Flaherty, Assistant Administrator	13	11	190	—	—	—	—	—	—	—
□ **LOS ANGELES METROPOLITAN MEDICAL CENTER**, 2231 South Western Avenue, Zip 90018–1302; tel. 323/730–7342, (Includes HAWTHORNE HOSPITAL, 13300 South Hawthorne Boulevard, Zip 90250; tel. 310/679–3321) **A**1 10 **F**2 10 11 14 21 26 27 28 29 45 55 59 64 71 74 76 77 78 81 88 94 **S** Pacific Health Corporation, Tustin, CA Primary Contact: John V. Fenton, Chief Executive Officer MISSION COMMUNITY HOSPITAL–PANORAMA CITY CAMPUS See Mission Community Hospital–San Fernando Campus, San Fernando	32	10	213	7141	121	—	—	—	—	—
□ **MOTION PICTURE AND TELEVISION FUND HOSPITAL AND RESIDENTIAL SERVICES**, 23388 Mulholland Drive, Woodland Hills, Zip 91364–2733; tel. 818/876–1888 **A**1 10 **F**5 8 9 14 21 22 29 38 42 44 48 52 55 64 69 70 81 85 88 91 92 94 96 97 108 Primary Contact: David Tillman, President and Chief Executive Officer Web address: www.mptvfund.org	23	10	303	1374	300	124153	—	80345	—	—

CA

Hospital, Address, Telephone, Approval, Facility, and Physician Codes, Health Care System	Classi-fication Codes		Utilization Data					Expense (thousands) of dollars		
★ American Hospital Association (AHA) membership ☐ Joint Commission on Accreditation of Healthcare Organizations (JCAHO) accreditation ○ American Osteopathic Association (AOA) accreditation △ Commission on Accreditation of Rehabilitation Facilities (CARF) accreditation	Control	Service	Staffed Beds	Admissions	Census	Outpatient Visits	Births	Total	Payroll	Personnel
⊠ △ **NORTHRIDGE HOSPITAL MEDICAL CENTER–ROSCOE BOULEVARD CAMPUS**, 18300 Roscoe Boulevard, Northridge, Zip 91328–4167; tel. 818/885–8500 **A**1 2 3 5 7 9 10 **F**1 2 4 9 11 12 14 15 17 19 21 22 23 26 27 28 29 31 33 34 36 37 38 41 44 46 47 48 49 50 52 53 55 56 57 58 59 60 61 62 63 64 65 67 68 69 70 71 72 73 74 75 76 77 78 79 81 82 84 85 87 88 93 94 96 98 107 108 109 110 **S** Catholic Healthcare West, San Francisco, CA Primary Contact: Michael L. Wall, President CFO: Saliba Salo, Senior Vice President Finance and Chief Financial Officer Web address: www.nmhc–roscoe.org	23	10	370	16179	244	109781	2512	207071	82908	1734
⊠ **OLYMPIA MEDICAL CENTER**, (Formerly Midway Hospital Medical Center), 5900 West Olympic Boulevard, Zip 90036; tel. 310/657–5900, (Total facility includes 21 beds in nursing home–type unit) (Nonreporting) **A**1 9 10 Primary Contact: Lee Suyenaga, Acting Chief Executive Officer CFO: Steve Maekawa, Chief Financial Officer CMO: Robert Sacks, M.D., Chief of Staff CIO: Patrick Wiseman, Director Information Systems CHR: Lisa Valenzuela, Director Human Resources Web address: www.olympiamedicalcenter.com	33	10	225	—	—	—	—	—	—	—
☐ **ORTHOPAEDIC HOSPITAL**, 2400 South Flower Street, Zip 90007–2697, Mailing Address: Box 60132, Terminal Annex, Zip 90060; tel. 213/742–1000, (Nonreporting) **A**1 2 3 5 9 10 Primary Contact: James V. Luck, Jr, M.D., Chief Executive Officer and Medical Director Web address: www.orthohospital.org	23	47	73							
☐ △ **PACIFIC ALLIANCE MEDICAL CENTER**, 531 West College Street, Zip 90012–2315; tel. 213/624–8411, (Nonreporting) **A**1 7 9 10 Primary Contact: John R. Edwards, Administrator and Chief Executive Officer Web address: www.pamc.net	32	10	138							
☐ **PACIFICA HOSPITAL OF THE VALLEY**, 9449 San Fernando Road, Sun Valley, Zip 91352–1421; tel. 818/767–3310 **A**1 9 10 **F**2 21 23 26 28 29 33 37 46 55 59 62 63 69 71 75 81 84 88 92 94 Primary Contact: S. K. Durairaj, M.D., Chief Executive Officer Web address: www.pacificahospital.com	33	10	231	5710	163	17192	1099	61668	31387	519
☐ **PROMISE HOSPITAL OF EAST LOS ANGELES**, 443 South Soto Street, Zip 90033–4398; tel. 323/261–1181, (Nonreporting) **A**1 10 Primary Contact: Richard McCarthy, Chief Executive Officer	33	10	36	—						
⊠ △ **SAN PEDRO PENINSULA HOSPITAL**, 1300 West Seventh Street, San Pedro, Zip 90732–3505; tel. 310/514–5233, (Total facility includes 328 beds in nursing home–type unit) **A**1 2 7 9 10 **F**3 4 9 21 22 26 27 28 29 33 37 45 46 47 48 55 58 59 60 61 62 63 64 65 66 68 69 70 71 72 76 77 81 82 84 87 88 92 94 96 97 108 **P**5 7 **S** Providence Health System, Seattle, WA Primary Contact: Nancy Carlson, Administrator CFO: Karl Carrier, Chief Financial Officer Web address: www.lcmhs.org	23	10	521	8101	322	54505	766	103572	47095	904
☐ **SAN VICENTE HOSPITAL**, 6000 San Vicente Boulevard, Zip 90036–4404; tel. 323/937–2504 **A**1 10 **F**21 26 28 39 52 88 94 107 **P**8 Primary Contact: R. Wayne Ives, Administrator	33	11	17	174	1	4331	0	3837	—	—
☐ **SHERMAN OAKS HOSPITAL AND HEALTH CENTER**, 4929 Van Nuys Boulevard, Sherman Oaks, Zip 91403–1702; tel. 818/981–7111 **A**1 9 10 **F**12 13 14 21 23 26 27 28 29 31 33 37 38 44 46 48 50 52 55 58 60 61 62 63 64 69 71 76 77 78 81 82 87 88 92 94 95 96 108 110 **P**7 Primary Contact: David Levinsohn, President and Chief Executive Officer Web address: www.shermanoakshospital.com	23	10	153	5097	79	63365	0	64988	—	437
☐ **SHRINERS HOSPITALS FOR CHILDREN, LOS ANGELES**, 3160 Geneva Street, Zip 90020–1199; tel. 213/388–3151, (Nonreporting) **A**1 3 5 **S** Shriners Hospitals for Children, Tampa, FL Primary Contact: Frank LaBonte, FACHE, Administrator Web address: www.shrinehg.org	23	57	60	—						
⊠ **ST. VINCENT MEDICAL CENTER**, 2131 West Third Street, Zip 90057–7992, Mailing Address: P.O. Box 57992, Zip 90057–7992; tel. 213/484–7111, (Total facility includes 27 beds in nursing home–type unit) **A**1 2 3 5 9 10 **F**2 9 12 14 21 22 23 26 27 28 29 30 32 35 40 41 45 46 48 49 52 53 54 55 57 58 60 61 62 63 65 66 68 69 79 81 82 84 88 92 94 95 96 106 107 108 **P**5 **S** Daughters of Charity Health System, Los Altos Hills, CA Primary Contact: Gustavo A. Valdespino, Chief Executive Officer COO: Jerry Clute, Senior Vice President and Chief Operating Officer CMO: Donald Tschirhart, M.D., Chief of Staff CHR: Susan Smith–Burrows, Senior Vice President Human Resources Web address: www.stvincentmedicalcenter.com	21	10	314	9891	150	64581	0	174129	—	—
☐ **TEMPLE COMMUNITY HOSPITAL**, 235 North Hoover Street, Zip 90004–3672; tel. 213/382–7252, (Total facility includes 11 beds in nursing home–type unit) **A**1 10 **F**2 14 23 27 29 46 52 55 57 58 61 62 63 64 70 73 81 88 92 94 Primary Contact: Herbert G. Needman, Administrator and Chief Executive Officer Web address: www.templecommunityhospital.com	33	10	141	3426	76	3195	0		—	276

Many Facility Codes have changed. Please refer to the AHA Guide Code Chart. © 2005 AHA Guide

CA

Hospital, Address, Telephone, Approval, Facility, and Physician Codes, Health Care System	Classi-fication Codes		Utilization Data					Expense (thousands) of dollars		
	Control	Service	Staffed Beds	Admissions	Census	Outpatient Visits	Births	Total	Payroll	Personnel

★ American Hospital Association (AHA) membership
☐ Joint Commission on Accreditation of Healthcare Organizations (JCAHO) accreditation
○ American Osteopathic Association (AOA) accreditation
△ Commission on Accreditation of Rehabilitation Facilities (CARF) accreditation

UNIVERSITY OF CALIFORNIA LOS ANGELES MEDICAL CENTER, 10833 Le Conte Avenue, Zip 90095–3075; tel. 310/825–9111 **A**1 3 5 8 9 10 **F**2 6 9 10 11 12 14 15 16 17 18 19 20 21 22 23 27 28 29 33 34 40 42 45 46 47 48 50 51 52 53 55 56 57 58 59 60 61 62 63 64 65 66 67 68 69 70 75 79 80 81 82 83 84 85 86 87 88 94 95 96 99 100 101 102 103 105 108 109 110 **P**6 **S** University of California–Systemwide Administration, Oakland, CA
Primary Contact: David L. Callender, M.D., Director
COO: Jay D. Kasey, Interim Chief Operating Officer
CFO: Paul Staton, Chief Financial Officer
CMO: J Thomas Rosenthal, M.D., Chief Medical Officer
CIO: Michael McCoy, M.D., Chief Information Officer
CHR: Mark Speare, Senior Asociate Director Human Resourcdes
Web address: www.healthcare.ucla.edu
Classification: 12 10 | Staffed Beds 592 | Admissions 26626 | Census 471 | Outpatient Visits 780919 | Births 1829 | Total 743127 | Payroll 304695 | Personnel 5434

UNIVERSITY OF CALIFORNIA LOS ANGELES NEUROPSYCHIATRIC HOSPITAL, 760 Westwood Plaza, Zip 90095–8353; tel. 310/825–0511, (Nonreporting) **A**1 3 5 10 **S** University of California–Systemwide Administration, Oakland, CA
Primary Contact: Fawzy I. Fawzy, M.D., Chief Executive Officer
CMO: David Feinberg, M.D., Medical Director
CHR: Cindy Cohen, Director Human Resources
Web address: www.npi.ucla.edu
Classification: 12 22 | Staffed Beds 70 | — — — — — — —

UNIVERSITY OF SOUTHERN CALIFORNIA–NORRIS COMPREHENSIVE CANCER CENTER AND HOSPITAL, 1441 Eastlake Avenue, Zip 90033–3804; tel. 323/865–3000 **A**1 2 3 5 9 10 **F**2 12 21 22 23 29 37 38 43 48 50 52 53 55 58 60 61 63 64 65 66 69 73 79 80 81 82 85 87 88 94 96 99 108 110 **P**1 **S** TENET Healthcare Corporation, Dallas, TX
Primary Contact: Ted Schreck, Chief Executive Officer
CMO: Alexandra Levine, Medical Director
CIO: David Wueste, Director Information Services
Web address: www.uscnorris.com
Classification: 33 41 | Staffed Beds 60 | Admissions 2636 | Census 45 | Outpatient Visits 72773 | Births 0 | Total 96576 | Payroll 37369 | Personnel 388

USC UNIVERSITY HOSPITAL, (Quaternary Tertiary Med/Surg), 1500 San Pablo Street, Zip 90033–4587; tel. 323/442–8500 **A**1 3 5 8 9 10 **F**2 7 9 10 15 17 19 21 22 28 37 40 42 43 44 46 52 53 55 57 58 60 62 63 64 66 71 73 74 76 78 80 81 82 83 84 85 87 88 92 94 95 96 100 101 102 103 108 **S** TENET Healthcare Corporation, Dallas, TX
Primary Contact: Ted Schreck, Chief Executive Officer
COO: Debbie Walsh, Chief Operating Officer
CFO: Joseph M. Nowicki, Chief Financial Officer
CMO: David Thordarson, M.D., Chief of Staff
CIO: George Murillo, Director Information Services
CHR: Elaine Garnett, Director Human Resources
Web address: www.uscuh.com
Classification: 33 49 | Staffed Beds 269 | Admissions 8441 | Census 182 | Outpatient Visits 49587 | Births 0 | Total 106465 | Payroll 81706 | Personnel 1290

VALLEY PRESBYTERIAN HOSPITAL, 15107 Vanowen Street, Van Nuys, Zip 91405–4598; tel. 818/782–6600 **A**1 9 10 **F**11 12 14 21 22 23 26 27 28 29 33 37 38 41 42 44 45 46 47 48 52 53 55 56 57 58 59 61 62 63 65 66 67 68 81 82 88 94 96 108 109
Primary Contact: Robert C. Bills, President
Web address: www.valleypres.org
Classification: 23 10 | Staffed Beds 290 | Admissions 11960 | Census 155 | Outpatient Visits 101583 | — | Total 107114 | — —

△ **VETERANS AFFAIRS GREATER LOS ANGELES HEALTHCARE SYSTEM**, 11301 Wilshire Boulevard, Zip 90073–1003; tel. 310/478–3711, (Total facility includes 277 beds in nursing home–type unit) **A**1 2 5 7 8 **F**1 2 4 10 12 14 15 17 19 21 22 23 25 29 30 32 33 36 37 38 39 41 42 44 47 48 49 50 51 52 55 57 58 60 61 62 63 64 65 66 68 69 70 71 73 74 75 76 77 78 92 **S** Department of Veterans Affairs, Washington, DC
Primary Contact: Charles M. Dorman, Acting Director
CFO: Ann Marie Wilk, Chief Financial Officer
CIO: Karl Syndulko, Ph.D., Director Information Management
Web address: www.va.gov/sta/guide/home.asp
Classification: 45 10 | Staffed Beds 589 | Admissions 8119 | Census 589 | Outpatient Visits 944765 | Births 0 | Total 506902 | Payroll 302288 | —

WEST HILLS HOSPITAL AND MEDICAL CENTER, 7300 Medical Center Drive, Canoga Park, Zip 91307–1902; tel. 818/676–4000 **A**1 9 10 **F**2 9 10 11 12 15 17 19 21 23 26 27 29 33 36 40 41 42 44 46 47 48 49 52 53 56 58 59 60 61 62 63 64 65 66 69 78 81 82 83 84 86 87 88 94 96 107 108 109 **P**5 **S** HCA, Nashville, TN
Primary Contact: Beverly Gilmore, President and Chief Executive Officer
CFO: Tony Lopez, Chief Financial Officer
CMO: Michael B. Levey, M.D., Chief Medical Staff
CIO: Tony Lopez, Chief Financial Officer
Web address: www.westhillshospital.com
Classification: 33 10 | Staffed Beds 120 | Admissions 8066 | Census 113 | Outpatient Visits 77927 | — | Total 101096 | — —

△ **WHITE MEMORIAL MEDICAL CENTER**, 1720 Cesar E Chavez Avenue, Zip 90033–2481; tel. 323/268–5000 **A**1 2 3 5 7 9 10 **F**2 11 12 14 15 16 17 18 19 20 21 22 23 27 28 29 33 35 44 45 46 47 48 50 52 55 56 58 59 60 61 62 63 65 66 67 68 69 71 75 81 82 84 87 88 92 94 96 98 106 108 109 110 **P**5 **S** Adventist Health, Roseville, CA
Primary Contact: Beth D. Zachary, President and Chief Executive Officer
CFO: John Raffoul, Vice President Finance
CMO: Rosalio J. Lopez, M.D., Vice President of Medical Affairs
CIO: Mark Amey, Chief Information Officer
Web address: www.whitememorial.com
Classification: 21 10 | Staffed Beds 369 | Admissions 17134 | Census 265 | Outpatient Visits 144439 | Births 3562 | Total 195061 | Payroll 81341 | Personnel 1617

WOMEN'S AND CHILDREN'S HOSPITAL See LAC/University of Southern California Medical Center

Hospital, Address, Telephone, Approval, Facility, and Physician Codes, Health Care System	Classi-fication Codes		Utilization Data					Expense (thousands) of dollars		
	Control	Service	Staffed Beds	Admissions	Census	Outpatient Visits	Births	Total	Payroll	Personnel

★ American Hospital Association (AHA) membership
☐ Joint Commission on Accreditation of Healthcare Organizations (JCAHO) accreditation
◯ American Osteopathic Association (AOA) accreditation
△ Commission on Accreditation of Rehabilitation Facilities (CARF) accreditation

LOS BANOS—Merced County

MEMORIAL HOSPITAL LOS BANOS See Memorial Hospitals Association, Modesto

LOS GATOS—Santa Clara County

✸ △ COMMUNITY HOSPITAL OF LOS GATOS, 815 Pollard Road, Zip 95032–1438; tel. 408/378–6131 A1 7 9 10 F2 9 11 12 14 21 22 23 26 27 28 33 37 38 40 41 44 46 47 48 51 53 55 56 57 58 59 60 61 62 63 65 66 68 69 81 82 84 85 88 92 93 94 95 96 108 109 P5 S TENET Healthcare Corporation, Dallas, TX Primary Contact: Gary Honts, Chief Executive Officer Web address: www.communityhospitallg.com	33	10	77	5645	77	58947	—	101502	—	—

LOYALTON—Sierra County

SIERRA VALLEY DISTRICT HOSPITAL, 700 Third Street, Zip 96118–0178, Mailing Address: P.O. Box 178, Zip 96118–0178; tel. 530/993–1225, (Total facility includes 34 beds in nursing home–type unit) (Nonreporting) A9 10 20 Primary Contact: Vic Biswell, Administrator	16	10	34	—	—	—	—	—	—	—

LYNWOOD—Los Angeles County

✸ ST. FRANCIS MEDICAL CENTER, 3630 East Imperial Highway, Zip 90262–2636; tel. 310/900–8900, (Total facility includes 30 beds in nursing home–type unit) A1 9 10 F2 11 12 15 17 19 21 22 23 24 26 27 28 29 33 34 37 39 45 46 47 48 49 50 52 53 55 56 57 58 59 60 61 62 63 64 65 66 69 71 73 75 77 78 79 81 82 84 86 88 92 94 107 108 109 110 P5 S Daughters of Charity Health System, Los Altos Hills, CA Primary Contact: Gerald T. Kozai, President COO: Gerald L. Russell, Senior Vice President and Chief Operating Officer CFO: Jesse Guevara, Senior Vice President and Chief Financial Officer CHR: Laura Kato, Vice President Human Resources Web address: www.dochs.org	21	10	353	19410	269	227003	5982	199413	79039	1487

MADERA—Madera County

☐ △ CHILDREN'S HOSPITAL CENTRAL CALIFORNIA, 9300 Valley Children's Place, Zip 93638–8762; tel. 559/353–3000 A1 7 9 10 F2 7 9 16 18 20 21 22 23 24 26 27 28 29 30 31 32 33 34 35 37 39 42 43 45 46 47 48 49 50 51 52 53 56 57 58 60 61 62 63 64 65 66 67 68 69 70 72 77 81 82 84 88 90 93 94 95 96 108 110 Primary Contact: William F. Haug, FACHE, President and Chief Executive Officer Web address: www.childrenscentralcal.org	23	50	255	12440	190	153890	0	249431	98482	1953
☐ MADERA COMMUNITY HOSPITAL, 1250 East Almond Avenue, Zip 93637–5696, Mailing Address: P.O. Box 1328, Zip 93639–1328; tel. 559/675–5501 A1 9 10 19 F2 9 10 11 12 21 23 27 28 33 37 38 39 42 48 51 52 53 55 58 59 60 61 62 63 64 66 69 81 82 84 88 94 107 108 P5 Primary Contact: Robert C. Kelley, President and Chief Executive Officer Web address: www.maderahospital.org	23	10	106	6933	79	89457	1580	51626	23576	664

MAMMOTH LAKES—Mono County

MAMMOTH HOSPITAL, 85 Sierra Park Road, Zip 93546–0660, Mailing Address: P.O. Box 660, Zip 93546–0660; tel. 760/934–3311, (Nonreporting) A9 10 18 Primary Contact: Gary Myers, Chief Executive Officer Web address: www.mammothhospital.com	23	10	15	—	—	—	—	—	—	—

MANTECA—San Joaquin County

✸ DOCTORS HOSPITAL OF MANTECA, 1205 East North Street, Zip 95336–4900; tel. 209/823–3111 A1 9 10 F2 9 11 12 21 26 27 29 33 39 40 52 58 59 63 65 66 75 81 82 84 85 88 94 108 S TENET Healthcare Corporation, Dallas, TX Primary Contact: Katherine Medeiros, Chief Executive Officer COO: Carmen Silva, Chief Operating Officer and Chief Nursing Officer CFO: Greg Berry, Chief Financial Officer CHR: Michele Bava, Director Human Resources Web address: www.doctorsmanteca.com	33	10	73	3751	41	63343	675	44970	19935	340
✸ ST. DOMINIC'S HOSPITAL, 1777 West Yosemite Avenue, Zip 95337–5187; tel. 209/825–3500, (Total facility includes 50 beds in nursing home–type unit) A1 10 F2 9 11 12 21 22 23 26 27 28 29 33 37 38 46 48 52 53 55 59 60 62 63 69 81 82 88 94 96 108 S Kaiser Foundation Hospitals, Oakland, CA Primary Contact: Margaret Hepburn, President CFO: Karen Biggins, Chief Financial Officer CMO: Andrew Jaramillo, M.D., Chief of Staff CIO: Jeff Mazikowski, Information Technology Site Manager CHR: Diane Formby–Renger, Human Resources Manager Web address: www.stdominicscares.org	21	10	65	1874	47	48145	—	26274		

MARINA DEL REY—Los Angeles County

✸ CENTINELA FREEMAN REGIONAL MEDICAL CENTER, MARINA CAMPUS, (Formerly Daniel Freeman Marina Hospital), 4650 Lincoln Boulevard, Zip 90292–6360; tel. 310/823–8911 A1 9 10 F2 7 9 21 22 23 26 27 28 29 33 46 48 52 55 57 58 60 62 63 64 66 71 81 84 88 92 94 108 S Centinela Freeman HealthSystem, Inglewood, CA Primary Contact: Michael A. Rembis, FACHE, Chief Executive Officer COO: Phyllis Buchart, Chief Operating Officer CFO: Stephen A. Hargett, Senior Vice President and Chief Financial Officer Web address: www.centinelafreeman.com	33	10	90	2669	38	21757	0	20965	14525	227

Many Facility Codes have changed. Please refer to the AHA Guide Code Chart. © 2005 AHA Guide

Hospital, Address, Telephone, Approval, Facility, and Physician Codes, Health Care System	Classi-fication Codes		Utilization Data					Expense (thousands) of dollars		
★ American Hospital Association (AHA) membership □ Joint Commission on Accreditation of Healthcare Organizations (JCAHO) accreditation ○ American Osteopathic Association (AOA) accreditation △ Commission on Accreditation of Rehabilitation Facilities (CARF) accreditation	Control	Service	Staffed Beds	Admissions	Census	Outpatient Visits	Births	Total	Payroll	Personnel

MARIPOSA—Mariposa County

JOHN C. FREMONT HEALTHCARE DISTRICT, 5189 Hospital Road, Zip 95338–9524, Mailing Address: P.O. Box 216, Zip 95338–0216; tel. 209/966–3631, (Total facility includes 16 beds in nursing home–type unit) **A**9 10 18 **F**11 21 22 23 24 29 33 39 46 48 50 51 58 60 61 62 63 70 72 81 84 88 92 94 96 97 107 108 109 110
Primary Contact: Elnora George, Administrator, Chief Executive Officer and Chief Financial Officer
Web address: www.jcfremonthospital.org

| 16 | 10 | 34 | 297 | 28 | 31825 | — | 12058 | — | — |

MARTINEZ—Contra Costa County

□ **CONTRA COSTA REGIONAL MEDICAL CENTER**, 2500 Alhambra Avenue, Zip 94553–3156; tel. 925/370–5000 **A**1 2 3 5 10 **F**2 9 11 12 22 23 26 27 28 30 32 33 39 44 45 48 50 52 53 55 57 59 60 61 62 63 64 65 66 69 71 73 75 76 81 82 84 88 94 96 108 109 **P**6
Primary Contact: Jeff Smith, M.D., Executive Director
Web address: www.co.contra–costa.ca.us
KAISER FOUNDATION HOSPITAL See Kaiser Foundation Hospital, Walnut Creek

| 13 | 10 | 126 | 9761 | 126 | 402862 | 1930 | 301621 | 124459 | 1837 |

MARYSVILLE—Yuba County

RIDEOUT MEMORIAL HOSPITAL, 726 Fourth Street, Zip 95901–5600, Mailing Address: P.O. Box 2128, Zip 95901–2128; tel. 530/749–4300 **A**9 10 **F**9 14 15 17 19 21 22 23 26 27 28 33 36 48 49 50 51 52 53 55 56 59 60 61 63 69 81 84 88 92 93 94 108 110 **P**5 **S** Fremont–Rideout Health Group, Yuba City, CA
Primary Contact: Thomas P. Hayes, Chief Executive Officer
Web address: www.frhg.org

| 23 | 10 | 281 | 11104 | 131 | 63821 | — | 132765 | 49647 | 1185 |

MENLO PARK—San Mateo County

□ **MENLO PARK SURGICAL HOSPITAL**, 570 Willow Road, Zip 94025–2617; tel. 650/324–8500 **A**1 5 9 10 **F**2 27 28 47 52 53 63 **S** Kindred Healthcare, Louisville, KY
Primary Contact: Sean P. McCarthy, Chief Executive Officer
Web address: www.kindredhealthcare.com

| 33 | 10 | 16 | 417 | 2 | 1412 | 0 | — | — | — |

MERCED—Merced County

☒ **MERCY MEDICAL CENTER MERCED–COMMUNITY CAMPUS**, 301 East 13th Street, Zip 95340–6211; tel. 209/385–7000, (Total facility includes 24 beds in nursing home–type unit) **A**1 3 5 9 10 **F**11 12 15 16 21 22 23 24 26 27 28 29 30 31 33 38 39 40 42 46 47 48 49 51 52 53 55 58 59 60 63 66 69 70 81 82 84 88 92 94 95 96 98 106 108 109 **P**5 **S** Catholic Healthcare West, San Francisco, CA
Primary Contact: David S. Dunham, President
COO: Deborah Kolhede, Vice President Operations
CFO: Doreen Hartmann, Vice President and Chief Financial Officer
CMO: Lynn Cooman, M.D., Vice President Medical Affairs
CIO: Keith Whalen, Administrative Director and Chief Information Officer
CHR: Joe Lombardi, Vice President Human Resources
Web address: www.sutterhealth.org

| 21 | 10 | 174 | 8603 | 93 | 113797 | 2575 | 80808 | 33560 | 759 |

☒ **MERCY MEDICAL CENTER MERCED–DOMINICAN CAMPUS**, 2740 M Street, Zip 95340–2880; tel. 209/384–6444 **A**1 9 10 19 **F**21 22 23 26 27 28 29 42 46 47 48 49 51 52 55 58 60 61 63 65 66 69 81 88 92 93 94 96 106 108 **P**5 **S** Catholic Healthcare West, San Francisco, CA
Primary Contact: David S. Dunham, President
COO: Deborah Kolhede, Vice President Operations
CFO: Doreen Hartmann, Vice President and Chief Financial Officer
CMO: Lynn Cooman, M.D., Vice President Medical Affairs
CIO: Keith Whalen, Administrative Director and Chief Information Officer
Web address: www.mercymercedcares.org

| 21 | 10 | 115 | 1536 | 26 | 59857 | 0 | 41614 | 18464 | 118 |

MISSION HILLS—Los Angeles County, See Los Angeles

MISSION VIEJO—Orange County

□ **CHILDREN'S HOSPITAL AT MISSION**, 27700 Medical Center Road, Zip 92691–6426; tel. 949/364–1400 **A**1 10 **F**2 26 27 28 30 32 39 56 57 62 63 64 67
Primary Contact: Kimberly C. Cripe, President and Chief Executive Officer
Web address: www.choc.org

| 23 | 50 | 48 | 2000 | 22 | 24140 | 0 | 27869 | 4675 | 73 |

☒ △ **MISSION HOSPITAL**, 27700 Medical Center Road, Zip 92691–6426; tel. 949/364–1400 **A**1 2 7 9 10 **F**2 9 10 11 12 14 15 17 19 21 22 23 24 26 27 28 29 33 34 35 36 37 38 39 40 41 45 46 47 48 49 51 52 55 57 58 59 60 61 62 63 65 66 68 69 70 81 82 84 85 87 88 92 94 95 96 98 106 108 109 110 **P**5 **S** St. Joseph Health System, Orange, CA
Primary Contact: Peter F. Bastone, President and Chief Executive Officer
COO: Markie Cowley, Executive Vice President and Chief Operating Officer
CFO: Kenneth McFarland, Chief Financial Officr and Vice President Finance
CIO: Loretta Mann, Director Information Services
CHR: Shirley Barnes, Senior Vice President Human Resources
Web address: www.mission4health.com

| 21 | 10 | 272 | 16092 | 199 | 102401 | 2929 | 219169 | 74152 | 1368 |

Hospital, Address, Telephone, Approval, Facility, and Physician Codes, Health Care System	Classi-fication Codes		Utilization Data					Expense (thousands) of dollars		
★ American Hospital Association (AHA) membership □ Joint Commission on Accreditation of Healthcare Organizations (JCAHO) accreditation ○ American Osteopathic Association (AOA) accreditation △ Commission on Accreditation of Rehabilitation Facilities (CARF) accreditation	Control	Service	Staffed Beds	Admissions	Census	Outpatient Visits	Births	Total	Payroll	Personnel

MODESTO—Stanislaus County

☒ **DOCTORS MEDICAL CENTER**, 1441 Florida Avenue, Zip 95350–4418, Mailing Address: P.O. Box 4138, Zip 95352–4138; tel. 209/578–1211 **A**1 2 3 5 9 10 **F**11 14 15 17 19 21 22 27 28 29 33 34 39 40 44 46 48 49 52 53 55 56 57 58 59 60 61 62 63 64 65 66 81 82 84 85 88 93 94 **P**5 **S** TENET Healthcare Corporation, Dallas, TX
Primary Contact: Katherine Medeiros, Interim Chief Executive Officer
COO: Wanda Holderman, Chief Operating Officer
CFO: Mike King, Chief Financial Officer
CIO: Debbie Fuller, Director Health Information Systems and Chief Information Officer
CHR: Michele West, Director Human Resources
Web address: www.dmc–modesto.com

	33	10	398	19334	276	111336	4567	251692	110925	1731

☒ **MEMORIAL HOSPITALS ASSOCIATION**, Mailing Address: P.O. Box 942, Zip 95353–0942; tel. 209/526–4500, (Includes MEMORIAL HOSPITAL LOS BANOS, 520 West I Street, Los Banos, Zip 93635; tel. 209/826–0591; MEMORIAL MEDICAL CENTER, 1700 Coffee Road, Zip 95355) **A**1 2 9 10 **F**6 9 10 11 12 15 16 17 18 19 20 21 22 23 26 27 28 29 32 33 34 46 47 48 49 51 52 55 56 58 59 60 61 62 63 69 81 82 84 88 94 108 **S** Sutter Health, Sacramento, CA
Primary Contact: David P. Benn, Chief Executive Officer
COO: Steve Mitchell, Chief Operating Officer
CFO: Joe Hirt, Chief Financial Officer
CIO: Jennifer Sierras, Chief Information Officer
CHR: Susan Donker, Vice President Human Resources
Web address: www.memorialmedicalcenter.org

	23	10	313	17785	248	106488	1803	303332	104661	2212

STANISLAUS SURGICAL HOSPITAL, 1421 Oakdale Road, Zip 95355–3359; tel. 209/572–2700, (Nonreporting) **A**5 9 10
Primary Contact: Michael Lipomi, Chief Executive Officer

	31	10	23	—	—	—	—	—	—	—

MONTCLAIR—San Bernardino County

□ **DOCTORS HOSPITAL MEDICAL CENTER OF MONTCLAIR**, 5000 San Bernardino Street, Zip 91763–2326; tel. 909/625–5411, (Nonreporting) **A**1 10 12 13 **S** AHMC, Inc, Alhambra, CA
Primary Contact: David Chu, Chief Executive Officer
Web address: www.dhmcm.com

	33	10	102	—	—	—	—	—	—	—

MONTEBELLO—Los Angeles County

□ **BEVERLY HOSPITAL**, 309 West Beverly Boulevard, Zip 90640–4308; tel. 323/726–1222 **A**1 2 9 10 **F**2 9 11 12 14 21 22 27 28 29 33 39 40 45 46 47 48 51 52 53 55 56 57 58 59 60 61 62 63 65 66 69 81 82 84 88 94 96 97 98 107 108 109 **P**8
Primary Contact: Gary V. Kiff, President and Chief Executive Officer
Web address: www.beverly.org

	23	10	127	10287	127	67128	—	85829		

MONTEREY—Monterey County

☒ **COMMUNITY HOSPITAL OF THE MONTEREY PENINSULA**, 23625 Holman Highway, Zip 93940–5902, Mailing Address: Box 'HH', Zip 93942–1085; tel. 831/624–5311, (Total facility includes 28 beds in nursing home–type unit) **A**1 2 9 10 **F**3 4 9 10 11 12 13 14 22 23 26 27 28 29 33 36 37 40 42 46 48 49 50 51 52 53 55 56 58 59 60 61 63 64 65 66 67 68 69 71 72 73 74 75 76 77 78 79 80 81 82 84 85 86 87 88 92 93 94 96 98 106 108 110 **P**7
Primary Contact: Steven J. Packer, M.D., Chief Executive Officer
CFO: Laura Zehm, Vice President and Chief Financial Officer
CIO: Tom McNamara, Director Information Technology
CHR: Joanne Webster, Director Human Resources
Web address: www.chomp.org

	23	10	201	13133	168	290847	1227	267837	99099	1624

MONTEREY PARK—Los Angeles County

☒ **GARFIELD MEDICAL CENTER**, 525 North Garfield Avenue, Zip 91754–1205; tel. 626/573–2222 **A**1 9 10 **F**2 9 11 12 14 15 17 19 21 23 27 28 29 33 37 39 40 45 46 48 49 52 53 55 56 57 58 59 62 63 64 66 68 69 82 88 94 106 108 109 110 **P**5 **S** AHMC, Inc, Alhambra, CA
Primary Contact: Philip A. Cohen, Chief Executive Officer
COO: James W. Maki, Chief Operating Officer
CFO: Harold Way, Chief Financial Officer
CMO: Dennis Chan, M.D., Chief of Staff
CIO: Paul Daly, Director Information Systems
CHR: Jeanette Auth, Human Resources Director
Web address: www.garfieldmedicalcenter.com

	32	10	208	11823	193	55210	3818	121255	63968	1143

☒ **MONTEREY PARK HOSPITAL**, 900 South Atlantic Boulevard, Zip 91754–4780; tel. 626/570–9000 **A**1 2 9 10 **F**2 11 12 21 23 27 28 29 33 37 38 39 44 45 46 47 48 49 52 53 55 57 58 59 60 62 63 64 65 66 69 70 73 75 76 81 82 84 88 92 94 108 109 110 **S** AHMC, Inc, Alhambra, CA
Primary Contact: Philip A. Cohen, Chief Executive Officer
COO: Ericka Smith, Chief Operating Officer
CMO: H Schubert Palmer, M.D., Chief of Staff
CIO: Paul Daly, Director Information Systems
CHR: Jeanette Auth, Human Resources Director
Web address: www.montereyparkhosp.com

	32	10	101	7112	72	23760	1704	43191	18668	448

CA

Many Facility Codes have changed. Please refer to the AHA Guide Code Chart. © 2005 AHA Guide

Hospital, Address, Telephone, Approval, Facility, and Physician Codes, Health Care System	Classi-fication Codes		Utilization Data					Expense (thousands) of dollars		
	Control	Service	Staffed Beds	Admissions	Census	Outpatient Visits	Births	Total	Payroll	Personnel

MORENO VALLEY—Riverside County

★ **MORENO VALLEY COMMUNITY HOSPITAL**, 27300 Iris Avenue, Zip 92555–4800; tel. 951/243–0811 **A**1 9 10 **F**9 11 12 21 26 27 33 55 59 62 63 71 81 84 88 94 **P**5 **S** Valley Health System, Hemet, CA
Primary Contact: Corey A. Seale, Administrator
Web address: www.valleyhealthsystem.com

| 16 | 10 | 101 | 5647 | 58 | 30478 | — | 29287 | — | — |

★ **RIVERSIDE COUNTY REGIONAL MEDICAL CENTER**, 26520 Cactus Avenue, Zip 92555–3911; tel. 951/486–4000 **A**1 3 5 10 12 13 **F**2 3 9 11 12 13 14 21 22 23 24 26 27 28 31 32 33 34 35 39 44 45 47 48 50 52 53 55 56 57 58 59 60 61 62 63 64 65 66 67 68 69 70 71 72 73 74 75 76 81 82 83 84 85 87 88 89 90 92 94 96 106 108 109 110 **P**6 8
Primary Contact: Douglas D. Bagley, Chief Executive Officer
COO: Ellie Bennett, Chief Operating Officer
CFO: David Spitler, Chief Financial Officer
CIO: Ed Papp, Chief Information Officer
Web address: www.rcrmc.org

| 13 | 10 | 359 | 20587 | 247 | 203579 | 2401 | 239082 | 85105 | 1720 |

MOSS BEACH—San Mateo County

★ **SETON MEDICAL CENTER COASTSIDE**, 600 Marine Boulevard, Zip 94038–9641; tel. 650/563–7100, (Total facility includes 116 beds in nursing home–type unit) (Nonreporting) **A**1 9 10 **S** Daughters of Charity Health System, Los Altos Hills, CA
Primary Contact: Bernadette M. Smith, President and Chief Executive Officer
Web address: www.setonmedicalcenter.com/coastside

| 21 | 48 | 121 | — | — | — | — | — | — | — |

MOUNT SHASTA—Siskiyou County

★ **MERCY MEDICAL CENTER MOUNT SHASTA**, 914 Pine Street, Zip 96067–2143; tel. 530/926–6111, (Total facility includes 47 beds in nursing home–type unit) **A**1 9 10 20 **F**2 9 11 12 21 22 23 27 28 29 32 33 34 36 37 38 41 44 45 46 48 50 51 52 53 55 58 59 60 61 62 63 69 79 81 84 88 92 93 94 95 96 97 106 108 110 **S** Catholic Healthcare West, San Francisco, CA
Primary Contact: Chuck Gersdorf, President
CMO: Jack Saunders, Chief of Staff
CHR: Gary Blevins, Director Human Resources
Web address: www.mercy.org

| 23 | 10 | 80 | 1597 | 57 | 33674 | 125 | 35688 | 15418 | 303 |

MOUNTAIN VIEW—Santa Clara County

★ **EL CAMINO HOSPITAL**, 2500 Grant Road, Zip 94040–4378, Mailing Address: P.O. Box 7025, Zip 94039–7025; tel. 650/940–7000, (Total facility includes 60 beds in nursing home–type unit) **A**1 9 10 **F**2 9 10 11 12 14 15 17 19 21 22 23 27 28 29 31 33 37 41 42 45 46 47 48 49 52 53 55 56 57 58 59 60 61 62 63 65 66 69 71 75 76 77 78 79 80 81 82 84 85 87 88 90 94 96 97 106 108 109
Primary Contact: Lee Domanico, Chief Executive Officer
CIO: Major Mark Zielazinski, Chief Information Officer
Web address: www.elcaminohospital.org

| 16 | 10 | 379 | 16750 | 225 | 471223 | 4421 | 241569 | 118916 | 1206 |

MURRIETA—Riverside County

☐ **RANCHO SPRINGS MEDICAL CENTER**, 25500 Medical Center Drive, Zip 92562–5965; tel. 951/696–6000, (Nonreporting) **A**1 9 10 **S** Universal Health Services, Inc., King of Prussia, PA
Primary Contact: Linda Bradley, Chief Executive Officer
Web address: www.ivrmc–rsmc.com

| 33 | 10 | 51 | — | — | — | — | — | — | — |

NAPA—Napa County

☐ **NAPA STATE HOSPITAL**, 2100 Napa–Vallejo Highway, Zip 94558–6293; tel. 707/253–5000 **A**1 10 **F**22 44 50 60 65 71 76 92 94 108 **P**6
Primary Contact: Dave Graziani, Executive Director

| 12 | 22 | 1138 | 449 | 1132 | 0 | 0 | 197612 | — | — |

★ **QUEEN OF THE VALLEY HOSPITAL**, 1000 Trancas Street, Zip 94558–2906, Mailing Address: P.O. Box 2340, Zip 94558–2340; tel. 707/252–4411, (Total facility includes 24 beds in nursing home–type unit) **A**1 2 9 10 **F**2 3 9 10 11 12 13 14 15 17 19 21 22 23 26 27 28 29 31 33 34 35 37 39 40 44 45 46 47 48 49 50 52 53 55 56 58 59 60 61 63 64 65 66 67 68 69 70 71 79 80 81 82 83 84 85 86 87 88 92 94 96 107 108 109 110 **S** St. Joseph Health System, Orange, CA
Primary Contact: Dennis Sisto, President and Chief Executive Officer
COO: Jane Willemsen, Executive Vice President and Chief Operating Officer
CFO: John Clark, Vice President and Chief Financial Officer
CMO: Vincent Morgese, M.D., Vice President Medical Affairs
CIO: Rhonda Fitzgerald, Vice President Patient Care Services
CHR: Ronald Scott, Vice President Human Resources
Web address: www.thequeen.org

| 21 | 10 | 179 | 7994 | 123 | 215613 | 929 | 152769 | 58117 | 1015 |

NATIONAL CITY—San Diego County

★ △ **PARADISE VALLEY HOSPITAL**, 2400 East Fourth Street, Zip 91950–2099; tel. 619/470–4321, (Nonreporting) **A**1 7 9 10 **S** Adventist Health, Roseville, CA
Primary Contact: Alan Soderblom, President and Chief Executive Officer
CFO: Gary R. Foll, Vice President Finance and Chief Financial Officer
Web address: www.adventisthealth.org

| 21 | 10 | 207 | — | — | — | — | — | — | — |

NEEDLES—San Bernardino County

★ **COLORADO RIVER MEDICAL CENTER**, 1401 Bailey Avenue, Zip 92363–3103; tel. 760/326–4531 **A**1 9 10 20 **F**2 9 12 11 22 27 33 45 46 52 55 57 58 59 60 62 63 68 69 81 82 94 96 106 **S** LifePoint Hospitals, Inc., Brentwood, TN
Primary Contact: John Pruitt, Chief Executive Officer
CFO: Greg Schultz, Chief Financial Officer
CMO: Brad Barth, M.D., Chief of Staff

| 33 | 10 | 49 | 2250 | 23 | 27822 | — | 17642 | — | — |

Hospital, Address, Telephone, Approval, Facility, and Physician Codes, Health Care System	Classi-fication Codes		Utilization Data					Expense (thousands) of dollars		
	Control	Service	Staffed Beds	Admissions	Census	Outpatient Visits	Births	Total	Payroll	Personnel

★ American Hospital Association (AHA) membership
☐ Joint Commission on Accreditation of Healthcare Organizations (JCAHO) accreditation
○ American Osteopathic Association (AOA) accreditation
△ Commission on Accreditation of Rehabilitation Facilities (CARF) accreditation

NEWPORT BEACH—Orange County

⊠ **HOAG MEMORIAL HOSPITAL PRESBYTERIAN**, One Hoag Drive, Zip 92663–4120, Mailing Address: P.O. Box 6100, Zip 92658–6100; tel. 949/764–4624 **A**1 2 9 10 **F**2 3 4 9 10 11 12 14 15 16 17 18 19 20 21 22 23 26 27 28 29 30 33 37 38 40 42 43 45 46 47 48 49 52 53 55 56 57 58 59 60 61 62 63 64 65 66 79 81 82 84 85 87 88 93 94 96 108 109 110 **P**5 7
Primary Contact: Michael D. Stephens, President and Chief Executive Officer
CFO: Jennifer C. Mitzner, Vice President Finance and Chief Financial Officer
CIO: Mary Kay Payne, Vice President and Chief Information Officer
CHR: Sherri Hollingsworth, Vice President Human Resources
Web address: www.hoaghospital.org
... 23 10 | 353 | 24841 | 288 | 282183 | 4716 | 435048 | 152695 | 3297

NORTH HOLLYWOOD—Los Angeles County, See Los Angeles

NORTHRIDGE—Los Angeles County, See Los Angeles

NORWALK—Los Angeles County

⊠ ○ **COAST PLAZA DOCTORS HOSPITAL**, 13100 Studebaker Road, Zip 90650–2531; tel. 562/868–3751 **A**1 10 11 **F**2 10 12 14 21 26 28 33 45 46 49 52 55 58 62 63 64 66 69 78 81 84 85 86 88 92 94 108 110
Primary Contact: Craig B. Garner, Chief Executive Officer
COO: Harvey Garner, Chief Operating Officer
CFO: Mihi Lee, Chief Financial Officer
CMO: Galal S. Gough, M.D., Chief of Staff
CHR: Matthew Kempiak, Human Resources Director
Web address: www.coastplazahospital.com
... 32 10 | 123 | 4313 | 45 | 29108 | 0 | 55327 | 17491 | —

LOS ANGELES COMMUNITY HOSPITAL OF NORWALK See Los Angeles Community Hospital, Los Angeles

☐ **METROPOLITAN STATE HOSPITAL**, 11401 Bloomfield Avenue, Zip 90650; tel. 562/863–7011, (Total facility includes 400 beds in nursing home–type unit) (Nonreporting) **A**1 10
Primary Contact: William G. Silva, Executive Director
Web address: www.dmh.cahwnet.gov/statehospitals/metro
... 12 22 | 1041 | — | — | — | — | — | — | —

NOVATO—Marin County

⊠ **NOVATO COMMUNITY HOSPITAL**, 180 Rowland Way, Zip 94945–5009, Mailing Address: P.O. Box 1108, Zip 94948–1108; tel. 415/209–1300 **A**1 9 10 **F**2 12 21 22 23 26 27 28 33 40 42 44 45 47 48 55 57 58 60 61 62 63 65 66 81 84 86 88 94 108 **P**5 **S** Sutter Health, Sacramento, CA
Primary Contact: Anne L. Hosfeld, Chief Administrative Officer
CFO: Stephen Walter, Chief Financial Officer
CMO: Timothy Murphy, M.D., Chief of Staff
CIO: Kathryn Graham, Director Communications and Community Relations
CHR: Diana G. Johnson, Acting Chief Human Resources Officer
Web address: www.novatocommunity.sutterhealth.org
... 23 10 | 47 | 2059 | 25 | 74615 | 0 | 50060 | 14579 | 221

OAKDALE—Stanislaus County

⊠ **OAK VALLEY DISTRICT HOSPITAL**, 350 South Oak Street, Zip 95361–3519; tel. 209/847–3011, (Total facility includes 115 beds in nursing home–type unit) **A**1 9 10 **F**9 11 12 21 26 27 28 29 32 33 38 44 46 47 55 59 62 63 66 81 82 92 94 **P**5 **S** Catholic Healthcare West, San Francisco, CA
Primary Contact: John P. Friel, Chief Executive Officer
CFO: Wayne Mills, Chief Financial Officer
CMO: Andres Arellano, M.D., Chief of Staff
CIO: David Rodrigues, Information Systems Manager
CHR: Kim Bukhari, Human Resources Manager
Web address: www.oakvalleycares.org
... 16 10 | 150 | 2428 | 128 | 82969 | 329 | — | — | 409

OAKLAND—Alameda County

☐ **ALAMEDA COUNTY MEDICAL CENTER–HIGHLAND CAMPUS**, 1411 East 31st Street, Zip 94602–1018; tel. 510/437–4800, (Total facility includes 109 beds in nursing home–type unit) **A**1 3 5 10 **F**2 4 11 12 21 22 26 27 28 29 31 32 33 34 39 42 44 45 46 47 48 50 52 53 55 56 57 58 59 60 61 63 65 66 68 69 70 71 73 74 75 77 78 81 82 84 88 92 94 96 107 108 109 110 **P**4 6 **S** Alameda Medical Center, San Leandro, CA
Primary Contact: Kenneth B. Cohen, Chief Executive Officer
Web address: www.acmedctr.org
... 16 10 | 420 | 14363 | 310 | 174713 | — | 308697 | — | —

⊠ **ALTA BATES SUMMIT MEDICAL CENTER – SUMMIT CAMPUS**, 350 Hawthorne Avenue, Zip 94609–3100; tel. 510/655–4000, (Total facility includes 46 beds in nursing home–type unit) (Nonreporting) **A**1 2 9 10 **S** Sutter Health, Sacramento, CA
Primary Contact: Warren J. Kirk, President and Chief Executive Officer
CFO: Robert Petrina, Chief Financial Officer
CMO: John Gentile, M.D., Vice President Medical Affairs
CHR: Mark Beiting, Vice President Human Resources
Web address: www.altabatessummit.com
... 23 10 | 877 | — | — | — | — | — | — | —

☐ **CHILDREN'S HOSPITAL AND RESEARCH CENTER AT OAKLAND**, 747 52nd Street, Zip 94609–1859; tel. 510/428–3000 **A**1 3 5 9 10 **F**2 9 16 18 20 21 22 23 24 25 26 27 28 29 30 31 33 34 37 38 39 42 45 46 47 48 50 52 53 56 57 58 60 61 62 63 65 66 67 68 69 70 72 73 74 75 77 81 82 84 88 90 93 94 95 96 98 99 108 110 **P**5 8
Primary Contact: Frank Tiedemann, President and Chief Executive Officer
Web address: www.chodfoundation.org
... 23 50 | 170 | 8898 | 130 | 190856 | 0 | 269446 | 114563 | 1425

Many Facility Codes have changed. Please refer to the AHA Guide Code Chart.

CA

Hospital, Address, Telephone, Approval, Facility, and Physician Codes, Health Care System	Classi- fication Codes		Utilization Data					Expense (thousands) of dollars		
	Control	Service	Staffed Beds	Admissions	Census	Outpatient Visits	Births	Total	Payroll	Personnel

★ American Hospital Association (AHA) membership
□ Joint Commission on Accreditation of Healthcare Organizations (JCAHO) accreditation
○ American Osteopathic Association (AOA) accreditation
△ Commission on Accreditation of Rehabilitation Facilities (CARF) accreditation

	Control	Service	Staffed Beds	Admissions	Census	Outpatient Visits	Births	Total	Payroll	Personnel
⊠ **KAISER FOUNDATION HOSPITAL**, 280 West MacArthur Boulevard, Zip 94611–5693; tel. 510/752–1000, (Nonreporting) **A**1 3 5 10 **S** Kaiser Foundation Hospitals, Oakland, CA Primary Contact: Bettie L. Coles, R.N., Senior Vice President and Administrator CIO: Johnny Law, Information Technology Leader Web address: www.kaiserpermanente.org	23	10	341	—	—	—	—	—	—	—
OCEANSIDE—San Diego County										
⊠ **TRI–CITY MEDICAL CENTER**, 4002 Vista Way, Zip 92056–4506; tel. 760/724–8411 **A**1 2 5 9 10 **F**2 6 9 11 12 14 15 17 19 21 22 23 24 27 28 29 33 36 37 38 39 41 42 45 46 47 48 51 52 53 55 56 57 58 60 61 62 63 64 65 66 68 69 71 73 75 77 78 81 83 84 85 86 88 92 94 96 98 106 107 108 109 110 Primary Contact: Arthur A. Gonzalez, Dr.PH, FACHE, President and Chief Executive Officer CFO: Robert D. Wardwell, Vice President and Chief Financial Officer CIO: Tom Stafford, Director Information Systems Web address: www.tricitymed.org	16	10	397	16701	202	217140	3263	202795	86445	1676
OJAI—Ventura County										
□ **OJAI VALLEY COMMUNITY HOSPITAL**, 1306 Maricopa Highway, Zip 93023–3163; tel. 805/646–1401, (Total facility includes 66 beds in nursing home–type unit) **A**1 9 10 **F**2 11 14 21 33 38 46 52 62 63 64 69 81 88 92 97 108 Primary Contact: Victoria A. Alexander, Chief Executive Officer Web address: www.ojaihospital.org	23	10	76	1243	64	27909	—	18046	—	—
ONTARIO—San Bernardino County										
□ **KINDRED HOSPITAL–ONTARIO**, 550 North Monterey Avenue, Zip 91764–3399; tel. 909/391–0333, (Nonreporting) **A**1 10 **S** Kindred Healthcare, Louisville, KY Primary Contact: Scott Floden, Chief Executive Officer Web address: www.kindredhealthcare.com	33	10	91	—	—	—	—	—	—	—
ORANGE—Orange County										
⊠ **CHAPMAN MEDICAL CENTER**, 2601 East Chapman Avenue, Zip 92869–3206; tel. 714/633–0011 **A**1 9 10 **F**3 4 9 10 21 29 33 44 46 47 51 55 57 58 60 61 62 63 64 69 70 71 73 76 81 82 88 92 93 95 Primary Contact: Doug Norris, Chief Executive Officer CFO: Jason McLaughlin, Chief Financial Officer CMO: Norman Harris, M.D., Chief of Staff CHR: Gretchen Lindeman, Director Human Resources Web address: www.chapmanmedicalcenter.com	33	10	71	2513	71	31008	—	38439	—	—
□ **CHILDREN'S HOSPITAL OF ORANGE COUNTY**, 455 South Main Street, Zip 92868–3874, Mailing Address: P.O. Box 5700, Zip 92863–5700; tel. 714/997–3000 **A**1 2 3 5 9 10 **F**16 18 20 21 22 23 24 26 27 28 29 45 46 47 48 50 52 53 56 57 58 60 61 62 63 64 65 66 67 69 70 79 81 84 90 93 94 96 98 99 108 **P**4 5 Primary Contact: Kimberly C. Cripe, President and Chief Executive Officer Web address: www.choc.org	23	50	202	10406	136	172581	0	252742	62773	1434
□ **HEALTHBRIDGE CHILDRENS REHABILITATION HOSPITAL**, 393 South Tustin Street, Zip 92868; tel. 714/289–2400, (Nonreporting) **A**1 10 Primary Contact: Ronelo Mysburgh, Administrator	33	46	6	—	—	—	—	—	—	—
⊠ **ST. JOSEPH HOSPITAL**, 1100 West Stewart Drive, Zip 92668–3891, Mailing Address: P.O. Box 5600, Zip 92613–5600; tel. 714/633–9111 **A**1 2 5 9 10 **F**2 9 10 11 12 14 15 16 17 18 19 20 21 22 23 26 27 28 29 30 32 33 35 37 38 39 40 41 42 46 47 48 49 51 52 53 54 55 57 58 59 60 61 62 63 64 65 66 69 71 73 75 77 78 79 80 81 82 84 85 86 87 88 93 94 95 96 99 101 108 109 110 **P**3 5 **S** St. Joseph Health System, Orange, CA Primary Contact: Larry K. Ainsworth, President and Chief Executive Officer COO: Robert A. Minkin, CHE, Executive Vice President and Chief Operating Officer CFO: Alan Garrett, Vice President and Chief Financial Officer CMO: Douglas Halcrow, Vice President Medical Affairs CIO: Alan Garrett, Vice President and Chief Financial Officer Web address: www.sjo.stjoe.org	23	10	366	21667	237	236304	4553	357949	118553	2345
⊠ **UNIVERSITY OF CALIFORNIA, IRVINE MEDICAL CENTER**, 101 The City Drive, Zip 92868–3298; tel. 714/456–6011 **A**1 2 3 5 8 9 10 **F**2 9 11 12 13 14 15 16 17 18 19 20 21 22 23 24 26 27 28 29 30 32 33 34 35 37 38 39 42 44 45 46 47 48 49 50 52 53 55 56 57 58 59 60 61 62 63 64 65 66 67 68 69 70 71 72 73 75 76 77 79 80 81 82 84 85 86 88 90 93 94 96 99 101 102 105 106 107 108 109 110 **P**6 **S** University of California–Systemwide Administration, Oakland, CA Primary Contact: Ralph Cygan, M.D., Chief Executive Officer COO: Maureen Zehntner, R.N., Chief Operating Officer CFO: Ron King, Chief Financial Officer CMO: Eugene Spiritus, M.D., Chief Medical Officer CIO: Joy Grosser, Chief Information Officer CHR: Patricia Thatcher, Executive Director Human Resources and Customer Services Web address: www.ucihealth.com	12	10	383	17738	286	594751	1105	354333	155901	3045

Hospital, Address, Telephone, Approval, Facility, and Physician Codes, Health Care System	Classi-fication Codes		Utilization Data					Expense (thousands) of dollars		
★ American Hospital Association (AHA) membership □ Joint Commission on Accreditation of Healthcare Organizations (JCAHO) accreditation ○ American Osteopathic Association (AOA) accreditation △ Commission on Accreditation of Rehabilitation Facilities (CARF) accreditation	Control	Service	Staffed Beds	Admissions	Census	Outpatient Visits	Births	Total	Payroll	Personnel

OROVILLE—Butte County

OROVILLE HOSPITAL, 2767 Olive Highway, Zip 95966–6118; tel. 530/533–8500, (Total facility includes 20 beds in nursing home–type unit) **A**9 10 **F**2 9 12 21 22 23 24 26 27 29 31 32 33 34 36 37 38 39 40 41 42 44 47 48 49 51 52 53 55 57 58 59 60 61 62 63 65 66 69 70 81 82 84 85 87 88 89 90 92 93 94 96 107 108 109 110
Primary Contact: Robert J. Wentz, President and Chief Executive Officer
Web address: www.orovillehospital.com

| 23 | 10 | 120 | 8239 | 93 | 288256 | 629 | 82217 | 31341 | 871 |

OXNARD—Ventura County

⊠ △ **ST. JOHN'S REGIONAL MEDICAL CENTER**, 1600 North Rose Avenue, Zip 93030–3723; tel. 805/988–2500 **A**1 7 9 10 **F**2 9 10 11 12 14 15 17 19 21 22 23 26 27 28 29 33 37 38 46 47 48 55 56 59 60 63 64 65 66 68 69 71 81 85 87 88 94 108 109 **S** Catholic Healthcare West, San Francisco, CA
Primary Contact: T. Michael Murray, President
COO: Maureen A. Malone, Chief Operating Officer
CMO: Eugene Fussell, Vice President Medical Affairs and Clinical Operations
CIO: James Kloosterman, Information Technology Site Manager – Perot Systems
CHR: John Bibi, Director Human Resources
Web address: www.chw.edu

| 23 | 10 | 218 | 12412 | 180 | 87815 | 2259 | 171890 | 70305 | 1145 |

PALM SPRINGS—Riverside County

⊠ **DESERT REGIONAL MEDICAL CENTER**, 1150 North Indian Canyon Drive, Zip 92262–4872, Mailing Address: P.O. Box 2739, Zip 92263–2739; tel. 760/323–6511, (Total facility includes 30 beds in nursing home–type unit) **A**1 2 9 10 **F**2 7 9 10 11 14 15 17 19 20 21 22 23 26 27 28 29 30 31 33 34 35 36 37 38 39 41 44 45 46 47 48 50 51 52 53 54 55 56 57 58 59 60 61 62 63 64 65 66 68 69 70 71 73 75 77 78 81 82 84 88 92 94 96 98 106 108 109 110 **P**5 **S** TENET Healthcare Corporation, Dallas, TX
Primary Contact: Barry Dykes, President and Chief Executive Officer
Web address: www.desertmedctr.com

| 33 | 10 | 325 | 18308 | 275 | 192015 | 3309 | 184892 | 106188 | 1565 |

PALO ALTO—Santa Clara County

⊠ **LUCILE SALTER PACKARD CHILDREN'S HOSPITAL AT STANFORD**, 725 Welch Road, Zip 94304–1601; tel. 650/497–8000 **A**1 3 5 9 10 **F**2 9 10 11 14 16 18 19 21 22 23 24 30 33 34 37 38 39 43 45 46 47 48 49 52 53 56 57 58 59 60 61 62 63 65 66 67 70 72 73 77 79 81 84 85 88 90 93 94 96 98 99 100 101 102 108 **S** Stanford Health Care, Palo Alto, CA
Primary Contact: Christopher G. Dawes, President and Chief Executive Officer
COO: Susan Flanagan, Chief Operating Officer
CFO: Keith Gundy, Chief Financial Officer
CMO: Kenneth Cox, Chief Medical Officer
CIO: Cynthia Haines, Vice President Strategic Planning and Business Development
CHR: Cindy Johnson, Vice President Human Resources
Web address: www.lpch.org

| 23 | 50 | 248 | 12950 | 217 | 143226 | — | 414649 | — | — |

⊠ **STANFORD HOSPITAL AND CLINICS**, 300 Pasteur Drive, Zip 94304–2299; tel. 650/723–4000 **A**1 3 5 8 9 10 **F**2 9 10 12 14 15 16 17 18 19 20 21 22 23 26 27 28 29 30 31 32 33 34 35 37 38 39 42 43 45 46 47 48 49 50 52 53 55 57 58 60 61 62 63 64 65 66 68 69 70 71 72 73 74 75 76 77 79 80 81 82 84 85 86 87 88 89 93 94 95 96 99 100 101 102 103 104 105 106 107 108 109 110 **P**7 **S** Stanford Health Care, Palo Alto, CA
Primary Contact: Martha H. Marsh, President and Chief Executive Officer
CFO: Kenneth J. Sharigian, Chief Financial Officer
CIO: Carolyn Byerly, Chief Information Officer
Web address: www.stanfordhospital.com/

| 23 | 10 | 439 | 21250 | 346 | 694882 | 0 | 986418 | 281681 | 4955 |

⊠ △ **VETERANS AFFAIRS PALO ALTO HEALTH CARE SYSTEM**, 3801 Miranda Avenue, Zip 94304–1207; tel. 650/493–5000, (Includes PALO ALTO DIVISION, 3801 Miranda Avenue, tel. 650/493–5000; VETERANS AFFAIRS PALO ALTO HEALTH CARE SYSTEM, LIVERMORE DIVISION, 4951 Arroyo Road, Livermore, Zip 94550; tel. 510/447–2560), (Total facility includes 554 beds in nursing home–type unit) **A**1 2 3 5 7 8 **F**1 2 3 4 5 8 9 10 15 17 19 21 22 23 26 27 28 29 30 31 32 33 34 35 36 37 38 39 40 41 42 44 45 46 47 48 49 50 51 52 55 57 58 60 61 62 63 64 65 66 68 69 70 71 73 74 75 76 77 78 81 82 84 85 86 87 88 92 93 94 96 106 107 108 109 110 **P**6 **S** Department of Veterans Affairs, Washington, DC
Primary Contact: Elizabeth Joyce Freeman, Director
COO: John Sisty, Associate Director
CFO: Mel Niese, Chief, Fiscal Service
CMO: Javaid Sheikh, M.D., Chief of Staff
CIO: Peg Grahm, Chief Information Officer
CHR: Arlene Sambrano, Chief Human Resources Management Services
Web address: www.va.gov/sta/guide/home.asp

| 45 | 10 | 913 | 10288 | 776 | 692227 | 0 | 470297 | 217218 | 3075 |

PANORAMA CITY—Los Angeles County, See Los Angeles

PARADISE—Butte County

⊠ **FEATHER RIVER HOSPITAL**, 5974 Pentz Road, Zip 95969–5509; tel. 530/877–9361, (Total facility includes 21 beds in nursing home–type unit) **A**1 9 10 **F**2 9 11 12 21 22 23 27 29 32 33 36 37 39 42 46 48 51 52 53 54 55 57 58 59 60 61 62 63 69 79 81 83 84 87 92 93 94 106 108 110 **S** Adventist Health, Roseville, CA
Primary Contact: A. Wayne Ferch, President and Chief Executive Officer
CFO: Dan Gordon, Chief Financial Officer
CHR: Don Williams, Director Human Resources
Web address: www.frhosp.org

| 21 | 10 | 80 | 4648 | 64 | — | — | — | — | 743 |

Many Facility Codes have changed. Please refer to the AHA Guide Code Chart. © 2005 AHA Guide

Hospital, Address, Telephone, Approval, Facility, and Physician Codes, Health Care System	Classi-fication Codes		Utilization Data					Expense (thousands) of dollars		
★ American Hospital Association (AHA) membership □ Joint Commission on Accreditation of Healthcare Organizations (JCAHO) accreditation ○ American Osteopathic Association (AOA) accreditation △ Commission on Accreditation of Rehabilitation Facilities (CARF) accreditation	Control	Service	Staffed Beds	Admissions	Census	Outpatient Visits	Births	Total	Payroll	Personnel

PARAMOUNT—Los Angeles County

★ **PROMISE HOSPITAL OF EAST LOS ANGELES, SUBURBAN MEDICAL CENTER CAMPUS**, (Formerly Suburban Medical Center), 16453 South Colorado Avenue, Zip 90723–5000; tel. 562/531–3110, (Total facility includes 34 beds in nursing home–type unit) (Nonreporting) **A**9 10 **S** Promise Healthcare, Lafayette, LA
Primary Contact: Richard McCarthy, Chief Executive Officer
COO: Steve Cornejo, Chief Operating Officer
CFO: Ray Rivas, Chief Financial Officer
CMO: Liberation Deleon, M.D., Chief of Staff
CHR: Mary Okuhara, Director Human Resources
Web address: www.promiseeastla.com

	Control	Service	Staffed Beds	Admissions	Census	Outpatient Visits	Births	Total	Payroll	Personnel
Promise Hospital of East Los Angeles	33	10	182	—	—	—	—	—	—	—

PASADENA—Los Angeles County

✶ **HUNTINGTON MEMORIAL HOSPITAL**, 100 West California Boulevard, Zip 91105–3097, Mailing Address: P.O. Box 7013, Zip 91109–7013; tel. 626/397–5000 **A**1 2 3 5 8 9 10 **F**2 9 10 11 12 14 15 17 19 21 22 23 27 28 29 33 34 35 37 40 44 47 48 49 50 52 53 55 56 57 58 59 60 61 62 63 65 67 68 69 71 73 74 75 76 79 80 81 82 84 85 86 87 88 93 94 96 108 110 **P**3
Primary Contact: Stephen A. Ralph, President and Chief Executive Officer
COO: William J. Murin, Senior Vice President Operations
CFO: James S. Noble, Vice President Finance and Chief Financial Officer
CMO: Vance Polich, M.D., Vice President Medical Affairs and Chief Medical Officer
CIO: Tim Kirk, Chief Information Officer
CHR: Debra Ortega, Vice President Human Resources
Web address: www.huntingtonhospital.com

	Control	Service	Staffed Beds	Admissions	Census	Outpatient Visits	Births	Total	Payroll	Personnel
Huntington Memorial Hospital	23	10	522	25225	377	230216	3402	315405	132081	2410

IMPACT DRUG AND ALCOHOL TREATMENT CENTER, 1680 North Fair Oaks Avenue, Zip 91103–1642; tel. 323/681–2575, (Nonreporting)
Primary Contact: James M. Stillwell, Director

	Control	Service	Staffed Beds	Admissions	Census	Outpatient Visits	Births	Total	Payroll	Personnel
Impact Drug and Alcohol Treatment Center	23	82	130	—	—	—	—	—	—	—

□ **LAS ENCINAS HOSPITAL**, 2900 East Del Mar Boulevard, Zip 91107–4399; tel. 626/795–9901, (Nonreporting) **A**1 10
Primary Contact: James Wilcox, Chief Executive Officer
Web address: www.lasencinashospital.com

	Control	Service	Staffed Beds	Admissions	Census	Outpatient Visits	Births	Total	Payroll	Personnel
Las Encinas Hospital	33	22	138	—	—	—	—	—	—	—

PATTON—San Bernardino County

□ **PATTON STATE HOSPITAL**, 3102 East Highland Avenue, Zip 92369; tel. 909/425–7000 **A**1 **F**2 21 22 32 41 45 46 48 50 57 58 60 65 66 71 73 74 76 94 96 106 108
Primary Contact: William L. Summers, Executive Director
Web address: www.dmh.cahwnet.gov/statehospitals/patton

	Control	Service	Staffed Beds	Admissions	Census	Outpatient Visits	Births	Total	Payroll	Personnel
Patton State Hospital	12	22	1414	1414	1335	0	0	—	—	2019

PETALUMA—Sonoma County

✶ **PETALUMA VALLEY HOSPITAL**, 400 North McDowell Boulevard, Zip 94954–2369; tel. 707/778–1111, (Total facility includes 20 beds in nursing home–type unit) **A**1 2 9 10 **F**2 9 11 12 21 22 26 27 28 29 31 33 35 36 37 39 40 43 44 46 47 49 50 52 53 54 55 58 59 60 61 62 63 65 66 69 70 73 75 77 78 79 81 84 87 88 92 94 108 110 **P**5 8 **S** St. Joseph Health System, Orange, CA
Primary Contact: George Perez, President and Chief Executive Officer
COO: Michael Glasberg, Chief Operating Officer
CFO: Donald Miller, Chief Financial Officer
CMO: Gary Greensweig, D.O., Chief Medical Officer
CIO: Patrick Wylie, Director Information Systems
CHR: Carol Aaron, Senior Vice President Human Resources
Web address: www.stjosephhealth.org/petalumavalley

	Control	Service	Staffed Beds	Admissions	Census	Outpatient Visits	Births	Total	Payroll	Personnel
Petaluma Valley Hospital	23	10	69	3822	41	78564	515	51763	22704	352

PLACENTIA—Orange County

✶ **PLACENTIA LINDA HOSPITAL**, 1301 Rose Drive, Zip 92870–3899; tel. 714/993–2000 **A**1 9 10 **F**2 9 11 12 14 21 22 23 26 27 28 33 36 45 46 47 48 49 55 57 58 59 60 61 62 63 64 65 66 69 70 81 82 84 87 88 92 94 95 96 106 108 **P**5 **S** TENET Healthcare Corporation, Dallas, TX
Primary Contact: Kent G. Clayton, President and Chief Executive Officer
COO: Pat Swaller, R.N., Chief Operating Officer and Chief Nursing Officer
CFO: Kristi Liberatore, Chief Financial Officer
CMO: Paul Jordan, M.D., Chief of Staff
CIO: Judy Murdock, Director of Information Systems
CHR: Diane McCluskey, Human Resources Director
Web address: www.placentialinda.com

	Control	Service	Staffed Beds	Admissions	Census	Outpatient Visits	Births	Total	Payroll	Personnel
Placentia Linda Hospital	33	10	114	3929	33	30338	814	37532	16823	333

PLACERVILLE—El Dorado County

✶ **MARSHALL HOSPITAL**, 1100 Marshall Way, Zip 95667–6599; tel. 530/622–1441, (Total facility includes 14 beds in nursing home–type unit) **A**1 9 10 **F**2 9 14 21 22 26 27 28 29 33 37 38 40 42 47 48 51 52 53 55 58 59 60 61 62 63 65 66 70 81 82 84 86 88 92 94 107 108 110
Primary Contact: James Whipple, Administrator
Web address: www.marshallhospital.org

	Control	Service	Staffed Beds	Admissions	Census	Outpatient Visits	Births	Total	Payroll	Personnel
Marshall Hospital	23	10	105	5956	71	130708	612	98953	40754	781

Hospital, Address, Telephone, Approval, Facility, and Physician Codes, Health Care System	Classi-fication Codes		Utilization Data					Expense (thousands) of dollars		
★ American Hospital Association (AHA) membership □ Joint Commission on Accreditation of Healthcare Organizations (JCAHO) accreditation ○ American Osteopathic Association (AOA) accreditation △ Commission on Accreditation of Rehabilitation Facilities (CARF) accreditation	Control	Service	Staffed Beds	Admissions	Census	Outpatient Visits	Births	Total	Payroll	Personnel

PLEASANTON—Alameda County

⊠ **VALLEYCARE MEDICAL CENTER**, 5555 West Las Positas Boulevard, Zip 94588–4000; tel. 925/847–3000, (Includes VALLEY MEMORIAL, 1111 East Stanley Boulevard, Livermore, Zip 94550–4115; tel. 925/447–7000), (Total facility includes 20 beds in nursing home–type unit) **A**1 2 9 10 **F**2 7 9 10 11 12 15 17 21 23 24 26 27 28 29 33 37 39 41 44 46 47 48 49 52 54 55 56 57 58 59 60 61 62 63 65 66 68 69 71 76 81 82 84 85 86 88 92 94 95 96 97 106 107 108 **P**5
Primary Contact: Marcy L. Feit, President and Chief Executive Officer
CFO: Ken Jensen, Chief Financial Officer
CMO: Raman Nambisan, M.D., Chief of Staff
CIO: Bob Woods, Chief Information Officer
CHR: Ron Bickert, Director Human Resources
Web address: www.valleycare.com
| | 23 | 10 | 177 | 7804 | 114 | 175245 | 1266 | 159508 | 69728 | 977 |

POMONA—Los Angeles County

⊠ △ **CASA COLINA HOSPITAL FOR REHABILITATIVE MEDICINE**, 255 East Bonita Avenue, Zip 91767–1933, Mailing Address: P.O. Box 6001, Zip 91769–6001; tel. 909/593–7521, (Total facility includes 26 beds in nursing home–type unit) (Nonreporting) **A**1 7 10
Primary Contact: Felice Loverso, Ph.D., President and Chief Executive Officer
Web address: www.casacolina.org
| | 23 | 46 | 64 | — | — | — | — | — | — | — |

LANTERMAN DEVELOPMENTAL CENTER, 3530 Pomona Boulevard, Zip 91768–3238, Mailing Address: P.O. Box 100, Zip 91769–0100; tel. 909/444–7200, (Total facility includes 196 beds in nursing home–type unit) (Nonreporting) **A**10
Primary Contact: Alan H. Medeiros, Executive Director
| | 12 | 12 | 718 | — | — | — | — | — | — | — |

⊠ **POMONA VALLEY HOSPITAL MEDICAL CENTER**, 1798 North Garey Avenue, Zip 91767–2918; tel. 909/865–9500 **A**1 2 5 9 10 **F**2 9 11 12 14 15 17 19 21 22 23 24 26 27 28 29 33 37 39 40 41 42 46 47 48 49 50 52 53 54 55 56 57 58 59 60 61 62 63 64 65 66 69 70 79 80 81 82 83 84 85 86 87 88 90 92 93 94 95 96 106 107 108 109 110 **P**5
Primary Contact: Richard E. Yochum, President and Chief Executive Officer
COO: Kurt Weinmeister, Chief Operating Officer and Executive Vice President
CFO: Michael Nelson, Executive Vice President and Chief Executive Officer
CIO: Kent Hoyos, Director of Information
Web address: www.pvhmc.org
| | 23 | 10 | 436 | 20848 | 280 | 444182 | 6695 | 247514 | 131191 | 2261 |

PORTERVILLE—Tulare County

PORTERVILLE DEVELOPMENTAL CENTER, 26501 Avenue 140, Zip 93257–9430, Mailing Address: Box 2000, Zip 93258–2000; tel. 559/782–2222 **A**10 **F**2 10 12 21 22 27 28 32 37 38 39 41 42 44 46 47 48 50 52 53 57 58 62 63 65 66 70 72 73 74 75 76 77 92 94 96 97 106 108 110
Primary Contact: John Sawyer, Executive Director
| | 12 | 62 | 805 | 96 | 761 | 0 | 0 | 141865 | — | — |

□ **SIERRA VIEW DISTRICT HOSPITAL**, 465 West Putnam Avenue, Zip 93257–3320; tel. 559/784–1110, (Total facility includes 29 beds in nursing home–type unit) **A**1 9 10 **F**2 11 12 21 22 23 27 29 32 33 34 40 48 49 55 58 59 60 61 62 63 64 66 69 73 81 82 84 85 88 92 94 96 106 108 109
Primary Contact: Kelly C. Morgan, President and Chief Executive Officer
Web address: www.sierra–view.com
| | 16 | 10 | 132 | 7798 | 107 | 145406 | 1935 | 78151 | 27861 | 674 |

PORTOLA—Plumas County

★ **EASTERN PLUMAS DISTRICT HOSPITAL**, 500 First Avenue, Zip 96122–9406; tel. 530/832–6500, (Total facility includes 66 beds in nursing home–type unit) **A**9 10 18 **F**6 9 12 26 27 28 32 33 42 46 48 51 52 60 62 63 64 81 85 88 92 97 **P**6
Primary Contact: Charles R. Guenther, Chief Executive Officer
CFO: Jeri Nelson, Chief Financial Officer
CHR: Cathy Conant, Chief Human Resources and Personnel
Web address: www.ephc.org
| | 16 | 10 | 76 | 617 | 51 | 26407 | 0 | 16151 | 6762 | 168 |

POWAY—San Diego County

⊠ **POMERADO HOSPITAL**, 15615 Pomerado Road, Zip 92064–2460; tel. 858/485–6511, (Total facility includes 129 beds in nursing home–type unit) **A**1 2 9 10 **F**2 3 9 10 11 12 13 14 21 22 27 28 29 33 50 51 52 54 55 56 57 59 60 61 62 63 65 67 71 75 76 77 78 88 92 93 94 96 108 109 **P**7
S Palomar Pomerado Health, San Diego, CA
Primary Contact: James T. Flinn, Chief Administrative Officer
COO: James T. Flinn, Chief Administrative Officer
CFO: Robert Hemker, Chief Financial Officer
CMO: Alan Conrad, M.D., Chief of Staff
CIO: Elizabeth Renfree, Director Information Systems
CHR: Gil Taylor, Chief Human Resources Officer
Web address: www.pphs.org
| | 16 | 10 | 188 | 7373 | 187 | 86010 | — | 83654 | — | — |

QUINCY—Plumas County

□ **PLUMAS DISTRICT HOSPITAL**, 1065 Bucks Lake Road, Zip 95971–9599; tel. 530/283–2121 **A**1 9 10 20 **F**5 9 11 12 24 32 33 41 46 50 57 59 62 63 81 88 92 106
Primary Contact: Richard D. Hathaway, Chief Executive Officer
Web address: www.pdh.org
| | 16 | 10 | 26 | 586 | 4 | 49145 | — | 16006 | — | — |

Hospital, Address, Telephone, Approval, Facility, and Physician Codes, Health Care System	Classi-fication Codes		Utilization Data					Expense (thousands) of dollars		
★ American Hospital Association (AHA) membership □ Joint Commission on Accreditation of Healthcare Organizations (JCAHO) accreditation ○ American Osteopathic Association (AOA) accreditation △ Commission on Accreditation of Rehabilitation Facilities (CARF) accreditation	Control	Service	Staffed Beds	Admissions	Census	Outpatient Visits	Births	Total	Payroll	Personnel

RANCHO MIRAGE—Riverside County

☒ **EISENHOWER MEMORIAL HOSPITAL AND BETTY FORD CENTER AT EISENHOWER**, 39000 Bob Hope Drive, Zip 92270–3221; tel. 760/340–3911 **A**1 2 5 9 10 **F**1 7 9 12 14 15 17 19 21 22 23 27 28 29 30 33 39 40 41 42 44 46 47 48 49 52 53 55 57 58 59 60 61 62 63 65 66 69 79 80 81 82 84 85 88 93 94 95 96 108 109 **P**7
Primary Contact: G. Aubrey Serfling, President and Chief Executive Officer
COO: Craig A. Owens, Senior Vice President and Chief Operating Officer
CFO: Thomas J. Tokheim, Vice President and Chief Financial Officer
CMO: Alan Williamson, M.D., Chief Medical Officer
CIO: David Perez, Chief Information Officer
CHR: Liz Guignier, Vice President Human Resources
Web address: www.emc.org

	23	10	253	16340	198	442262	287	259540	83038	1870

RED BLUFF—Tehama County

☒ **ST. ELIZABETH COMMUNITY HOSPITAL**, 2550 Sister Mary Columba Drive, Zip 96080–4397; tel. 530/529–8000 **A**1 9 10 20 **F**2 6 9 11 12 21 22 24 26 27 28 29 33 36 37 38 40 42 45 46 51 52 53 55 58 59 60 62 63 69 81 82 84 87 88 94 96 97 107 108 110 **S** Catholic Healthcare West, San Francisco, CA
Primary Contact: Jon W. Halfhide, President
CFO: Tim Panks, Chief Financial Officer
CIO: Henry Niessink, Senior Manager Information Technology Systems Perot
Web address: www.mercy.org

	21	10	64	3806	31	93006	634	51106	20349	371

REDDING—Shasta County

☒ **MERCY MEDICAL CENTER REDDING**, 2175 Rosaline Avenue, Zip 96001–2509, Mailing Address: P.O. Box 496009, Zip 96049–6009; tel. 530/225–6000 **A**1 2 3 5 9 10 **F**1 2 6 9 11 12 14 15 17 19 21 22 23 27 28 29 33 34 36 37 38 41 42 45 47 48 50 51 52 54 55 56 58 59 60 61 62 63 64 69 70 79 80 81 82 84 85 87 88 94 96 107 108 109 **P**5 **S** Catholic Healthcare West, San Francisco, CA
Primary Contact: Richard J. Barnett, President
CFO: Tim Panks, Regional Vice President Finance and Chief Financial Officer
CMO: James DeSoto, M.D., Vice President Medical Affairs
CIO: Henry Niessink, Regional Director Information Technology Services
CHR: Alan Gugin, Director Human Resources
Web address: www.mercy.org

	21	10	250	12934	154	36788	1982	185125	71511	1502

NORTHERN CALIFORNIA REHABILITATION HOSPITAL, 2801 Eureka Way, Zip 96001; tel. 530/246–9000, (Nonreporting) **A**9 10
Primary Contact: Chris Jones, Administrator

	33	46	24	—	—	—	—	—	—	—

PATIENT'S HOSPITAL OF REDDING, 1900 Eureka Way, Zip 96001; tel. 330/225–8700, (Nonreporting) **A**10
Primary Contact: Jacky Gregore, Chief Executive Officer

	33	13	10	—	—	—	—	—	—	—

☒ **SHASTA REGIONAL MEDICAL CENTER**, 1100 Butte Street, Zip 96001–0853, Mailing Address: Box 496072, Zip 96049–6072; tel. 530/244–5454, (Nonreporting) **A**1 2 9 10 **S** Hospital Partners of America, Charlotte, NC
Primary Contact: Thomas A. Salerno, Chief Executive Officer
CFO: Richard Phillips, Chief Financial Officer
Web address: www.reddingmedicalcenter.com

	33	10	238	—	—	—	—	—	—	—

REDLANDS—San Bernardino County

□ **LOMA LINDA UNIVERSITY BEHAVIORAL MEDICINE CENTER**, 1710 Barton Road, Zip 92373–5304; tel. 909/558–9200 **A**1 5 10 **F**3 4 21 22 44 71 72 73 74 75 76 77 78 96 **S** Loma Linda University Adventist Health Sciences Center, Loma Linda, CA
Primary Contact: Ruthita J. Fike, President
Web address: www.llu.edu

	21	22	89	4497	76	20051	—	18089	—	—

☒ **REDLANDS COMMUNITY HOSPITAL**, 350 Terracina Boulevard, Zip 92373–4897, Mailing Address: P.O. Box 3391, Zip 92373–3391; tel. 909/335–5500, (Total facility includes 31 beds in nursing home–type unit) (Nonreporting) **A**1 9 10
Primary Contact: James R. Holmes, President and Chief Executive Officer
Web address: www.redlandshospital.org

	23	10	172	—	—	—	—	—	—	—

REDWOOD CITY—San Mateo County

☒ **KAISER FOUNDATION HOSPITAL**, 1150 Veterans Boulevard, Zip 94063–2037; tel. 650/299–2000 **A**1 3 5 10 **F**2 9 11 12 21 22 24 33 35 36 37 38 39 42 44 47 48 50 51 52 53 55 57 58 59 60 62 63 64 65 66 69 70 73 76 77 81 84 88 92 94 96 106 107 108 109 110 **S** Kaiser Foundation Hospitals, Oakland, CA
Primary Contact: Linda Jensen, Senior Vice President and Area Manager
CFO: Doug Reynolds, Chief Financial Officer
CIO: Angel Shew, Area Technology Director
Web address: www.kaiserpermanente.org

	23	10	168	8049	89	0	0	—	—	—

☒ **SEQUOIA HOSPITAL**, 170 Alameda De Las Pulgas, Zip 94062–2799; tel. 650/369–5811, (Total facility includes 44 beds in nursing home–type unit) **A**1 9 10 **F**9 10 11 12 15 17 19 21 22 23 27 28 29 33 37 38 39 41 46 47 48 49 52 53 55 57 58 59 60 61 62 63 65 66 69 71 79 80 81 82 84 85 87 88 92 93 94 96 106 108 109 110 **S** Catholic Healthcare West, San Francisco, CA
Primary Contact: Glenna L. Vaskelis, President and Administrator
COO: Kathy Romano, Chief Operating Officer
CFO: Gratia Barton, Chief Financial Officer
CMO: Sandy Margolis, M.D., President Professional Staff
CIO: David Furst, Information Officer
CHR: Sharon Henderson, Director Human Resources
Web address: www.sequoiahospital.org

	23	10	205	8768	121	126029	1276	158004	60271	758

Hospital, Address, Telephone, Approval, Facility, and Physician Codes, Health Care System	Classi-fication Codes		Utilization Data					Expense (thousands) of dollars		
★ American Hospital Association (AHA) membership □ Joint Commission on Accreditation of Healthcare Organizations (JCAHO) accreditation ○ American Osteopathic Association (AOA) accreditation △ Commission on Accreditation of Rehabilitation Facilities (CARF) accreditation	Control	Service	Staffed Beds	Admissions	Census	Outpatient Visits	Births	Total	Payroll	Personnel

REEDLEY—Fresno County

☒ **SIERRA–KINGS DISTRICT HOSPITAL**, 372 West Cypress Avenue, Zip 93654–2199; tel. 559/638–8155 **A**1 9 10 **F**3 9 11 12 13 14 21 24 28 29 33 41 46 52 55 56 58 59 63 67 68 69 70 71 81 85 88 92 97 106
Primary Contact: Melvyn Patashnick, Chief Executive Officer
CFO: Barbara Jennings, Chief Financial Officer
CIO: Celeese Kai, Director Foundation and Communications
CHR: Janice Gray, Director Human Resources
Web address: www.skdh.org

| 16 | 10 | 32 | 2361 | 14 | 102287 | 1422 | 21666 | 9255 | — |

RIDGECREST—Kern County

☒ **RIDGECREST REGIONAL HOSPITAL**, 1081 North China Lake Boulevard, Zip 93555–3198; tel. 760/446–3551 **A**1 9 10 20 **F**2 9 11 12 14 21 22 27 28 29 46 51 54 55 59 62 63 66 69 81 84 88 94 108
Primary Contact: David A. Mechtenberg, Chief Executive Officer
CFO: Robert Miller, Chief Financial Officer
CMO: William Ferguson, M.D., Chief of Staff
CIO: Scott Bue, Health Information Systems Manager
CHR: Angie Girardot, Director Human Resources
Web address: www.rrh.org

| 23 | 10 | 80 | 2700 | 27 | 44591 | 441 | 33188 | 13501 | 315 |

RIVERSIDE—Riverside County

☒ **KAISER FOUNDATION HOSPITAL–RIVERSIDE**, 10800 Magnolia Avenue, Zip 92505–3000; tel. 909/353–4600 **A**1 2 3 5 10 **F**2 11 12 14 21 22 23 26 27 28 33 50 51 53 55 59 60 61 62 63 64 66 69 70 75 81 82 84 85 86 87 88 94 108 109 110 **S** Kaiser Foundation Hospitals, Oakland, CA
Primary Contact: Terry A. Belmont, Senior Vice President and Administrator
Web address: www.kaiserpermanente.org

| 23 | 10 | 215 | 17747 | 139 | 41668 | 3157 | — | — | 1517 |

□ **PARKVIEW COMMUNITY HOSPITAL MEDICAL CENTER**, 3865 Jackson Street, Zip 92503–3998; tel. 951/688–2211 **A**1 10 **F**2 10 11 12 14 21 22 27 28 29 33 35 39 46 47 48 49 52 53 55 56 59 62 63 65 66 69 81 82 84 85 88 94 108
Primary Contact: Douglas Drumwright, Chief Executive Officer
Web address: www.pchmc.org

| 23 | 10 | 153 | 7631 | 89 | 97618 | 1667 | 73444 | 29708 | 737 |

☒ **RIVERSIDE COMMUNITY HOSPITAL**, 4445 Magnolia Avenue, Zip 92501–4199; Mailing Address: P.O. Box 1669, Zip 92502–1669; tel. 951/788–3000 **A**1 9 10 **F**2 9 11 12 14 15 17 19 21 22 23 26 27 28 33 34 38 39 48 53 54 55 56 59 61 62 63 64 65 69 79 80 81 82 85 87 88 94 96 101 105 108 109 **P**5 **S** HCA, Nashville, TN
Primary Contact: Jaime A. Wesolowski, President and Chief Executive Officer
COO: Gregory A. Seiler, Chief Operating Officer
CFO: Daniel Perritt, Senior Vice President and Chief Financial Officer
CIO: Ann Matich, Vice President Marketing
CHR: Paul Woerz, Vice President Human Resources
Web address: www.riversidecommunityhospital.com

| 32 | 10 | 338 | 17025 | 225 | 105489 | 3300 | 187235 | 74143 | 1005 |

ROSEMEAD—Los Angeles County

□ **ALHAMBRA HOSPITAL**, 4619 North Rosemead Boulevard, Zip 91770–1478; Mailing Address: P.O. Box 369, Zip 91770–0369; tel. 626/286–1191 **A**1 10 **F**71 72 77 78 **S** Psychiatric Solutions, Franklin, TN
Primary Contact: Peggy Minnick, R.N., Chief Executive Officer
Web address: www.ardenthealth.com

| 33 | 22 | 85 | 3146 | 59 | — | 0 | — | — | — |

ROSEVILLE—Placer County

☒ **SUTTER ROSEVILLE MEDICAL CENTER**, One Medical Plaza, Zip 95661–3037; tel. 916/781–1000, (Nonreporting) **A**1 2 9 10 **S** Sutter Health, Sacramento, CA
Primary Contact: Patrick R. Brady, Chief Executive Officer
CIO: Janelle Dickey, Director Information Systems
Web address: www.sutterroseville.org

| 23 | 10 | 172 | — | — | — | — | — | — | — |

SACRAMENTO—Sacramento County

□ **HERITAGE OAKS HOSPITAL**, 4250 Auburn Boulevard, Zip 95841–4164; tel. 916/489–3336 **A**1 10 **F**27 71 72 76 78 **P**4 **S** Psychiatric Solutions, Franklin, TN
Primary Contact: Nancy Faulkner, Chief Executive Officer
Web address: www.bhcheritageoaks.com

| 33 | 22 | 76 | 2765 | 65 | 7053 | 0 | 12339 | — | — |

☒ **KAISER FOUNDATION HOSPITAL**, 2025 Morse Avenue, Zip 95825–2115; tel. 916/973–5000, (Nonreporting) **A**1 3 5 10 **S** Kaiser Foundation Hospitals, Oakland, CA
Primary Contact: Beverly Werntz, Chief Operating Officer
CFO: Jim Eldridge, Business, Strategy and Finance Leader
CIO: Kathleen McKenna, Public Affairs Leader
Web address: www.kp.org

| 23 | 10 | 463 | — | — | — | — | — | — | — |

☒ **KAISER FOUNDATION HOSPITAL**, 6600 Bruceville Road, Zip 95823–4671; tel. 916/688–2430 **A**1 3 10 **F**11 12 14 21 22 23 26 28 29 30 33 36 37 38 47 49 50 51 52 53 55 57 58 59 60 61 62 63 64 65 66 69 70 73 77 81 82 84 87 88 89 90 92 93 94 96 106 107 108 109 110 **S** Kaiser Foundation Hospitals, Oakland, CA
Primary Contact: Max Villalobos, Chief Operating Officer
CFO: Jim Eldridge, Business, Strategy and Financial Leader
CIO: Kathleen McKenna, Public Affairs Leader
Web address: www.kp.org

| 23 | 10 | 162 | 12283 | 121 | 61055 | 3512 | — | — | 1143 |

Many Facility Codes have changed. Please refer to the AHA Guide Code Chart.   © 2005 AHA Guide

CA

Hospital, Address, Telephone, Approval, Facility, and Physician Codes, Health Care System	Classi-fication Codes		Utilization Data					Expense (thousands) of dollars		
★ American Hospital Association (AHA) membership □ Joint Commission on Accreditation of Healthcare Organizations (JCAHO) accreditation ○ American Osteopathic Association (AOA) accreditation △ Commission on Accreditation of Rehabilitation Facilities (CARF) accreditation	Control	Service	Staffed Beds	Admissions	Census	Outpatient Visits	Births	Total	Payroll	Personnel
⊠ **MERCY GENERAL HOSPITAL**, 4001 J Street, Zip 95819–3600; tel. 916/453–4545, (Total facility includes 38 beds in nursing home–type unit) **A**1 2 3 5 9 10 **F**9 11 12 14 15 17 19 21 22 23 26 27 28 29 33 37 38 39 41 42 44 46 47 48 52 55 57 58 59 60 61 62 63 64 65 66 68 69 81 82 83 84 85 86 88 92 94 106 108 **P**3 **S** Catholic Healthcare West, San Francisco, CA Primary Contact: Denny W. Powell, President CFO: Ronald Kroll, Chief Financial Officer CMO: Dan Ferguson, M.D., Chief Medical Officer CHR: Lynda Gregory, Human Resources Director Web address: www.mercygeneral.org	21	10	329	17175	215	96339	—	264304	—	—
⊠ **METHODIST HOSPITAL OF SACRAMENTO**, 7500 Hospital Drive, Zip 95823–5477; tel. 916/423–3000, (Total facility includes 171 beds in nursing home–type unit) **A**1 9 10 **F**9 14 21 22 26 27 28 29 32 33 37 40 41 44 45 48 49 50 52 55 56 59 60 62 63 65 66 69 70 81 82 84 86 87 88 92 94 95 107 108 **S** Catholic Healthcare West, San Francisco, CA Primary Contact: Timothy M. Moran, President CFO: Bonnie Jenkins, Chief Financial Officer CHR: Christopher Joyce, Director Human Resources Web address: www.mercyhospitals.org	23	10	333	7742	215	64545	910	106280	53401	611
□ **SHRINERS HOSPITALS FOR CHILDREN, NORTHERN CALIFORNIA**, 2425 Stockton Boulevard, Zip 95817–2215; tel. 916/453–2000 **A**1 3 5 **F**2 7 9 13 21 29 46 47 52 58 65 68 69 72 73 88 94 95 96 108 110 **S** Shriners Hospitals for Children, Tampa, FL Primary Contact: Margaret Bryan, Administrator Web address: www.shrinershq.org	23	50	70	1230	23	17834	0	32673	—	—
SIERRA VISTA HOSPITAL, 8001 Bruceville Road, Zip 95823–2329; tel. 916/423–2000, (Nonreporting) **A**10 **S** Psychiatric Solutions, Franklin, TN Primary Contact: Nancy Purtell, Chief Executive Officer Web address: www.bhcsierravista.com	33	22	72	—	—	—	—	—	—	—
★ **SUTTER CENTER FOR PSYCHIATRY**, 7700 Folsom Boulevard, Zip 95826–2608; tel. 916/386–3000 **A**10 **F**21 26 27 28 71 72 73 74 76 77 78 92 **S** Sutter Health, Sacramento, CA Primary Contact: Diane Gail Stewart, Chief Administrative Officer COO: Diane Gail Stewart, Chief Administrative Officer CFO: Marcus Armstrong, Director Finance CMO: Richard Bowdle, M.D., Medical Director Service Line CIO: John Hummel, Vice President and Chief Information Officer CHR: Kent Bradbury, Human Resources Coordinator Web address: www.sutterhealth.org	23	22	69	2337	50	15904	0	18346	8755	183
⊠ **SUTTER MEDICAL CENTER, SACRAMENTO**, 5151 F Street, Zip 95819–3295; tel. 916/454–3333, (Includes SUTTER GENERAL HOSPITAL, 2801 L Street, Zip 95816; tel. 916/454–2222; SUTTER MEMORIAL HOSPITAL), (Total facility includes 176 beds in nursing home–type unit) **A**1 2 3 5 9 10 **F**2 9 11 12 14 15 16 17 19 20 21 22 23 26 27 28 29 33 38 39 43 44 47 48 49 50 52 53 55 56 57 58 59 60 61 62 63 64 65 66 67 69 71 72 73 77 78 81 88 90 92 93 94 96 99 100 101 103 104 106 108 110 **P**3 5 **S** Sutter Health, Sacramento, CA Primary Contact: Thomas C. Gagen, Chief Executive Officer CFO: Katherine Green, Chief Financial Officer CIO: Janelle Dickey, Information Technology Director CHR: Laurie Rose, Director Human Resources Web address: www.sutterhealth.org	23	10	742	30315	543	182359	5295	588881	195836	4079
⊠ **UNIVERSITY OF CALIFORNIA, DAVIS MEDICAL CENTER**, 2315 Stockton Boulevard, Zip 95817–2282; tel. 916/734–2011 **A**1 2 3 5 8 9 10 **F**2 7 9 10 11 12 13 14 15 16 17 18 19 20 21 22 23 24 26 27 28 29 31 32 33 34 35 36 37 38 39 40 41 42 43 44 45 46 47 48 49 50 51 52 53 55 56 57 58 59 60 61 62 63 64 65 66 67 68 69 70 79 80 81 82 84 85 86 87 88 89 90 93 94 95 96 98 99 101 102 104 105 106 107 108 109 110 **P**6 **S** University of California–Systemwide Administration, Oakland, CA Primary Contact: Robert E. Chason, Chief Executive Officer CFO: William McGowan, Chief Financial Officer CMO: Allan Siefkin, M.D., Chief Medical Officer CIO: Guy Koppel, Chief Information Officer CHR: Gloria Alvarado, Associate Director Human Resources Web address: www.ucdmc.ucdavis.edu	12	10	526	26747	400	846795	2408	711573	326796	5827
SAINT HELENA—Napa County										
⊠ **ST. HELENA HOSPITAL**, 10 Woodland Road, Zip 94574; tel. 707/963–3611, (Total facility includes 23 beds in nursing home–type unit) **A**1 10 **F**2 3 4 10 11 12 15 17 19 21 22 23 26 27 28 29 31 33 35 37 38 39 41 42 46 47 48 49 51 52 53 55 57 58 59 60 61 62 63 64 65 66 69 70 71 72 73 74 75 76 77 78 81 82 85 88 92 93 94 95 96 106 108 109 **S** Adventist Health, Roseville, CA Primary Contact: JoAline Olson, R.N., President and Chief Executive Officer CFO: Edward A. McDonald, Chief Financial Officer CHR: Mark Fowler, Executive Director Human Resources Web address: www.sthelenahospital.org	21	10	242	7016	125	69780	337	102491	45559	777

CA

Hospital, Address, Telephone, Approval, Facility, and Physician Codes, Health Care System	Classi-fication Codes		Utilization Data					Expense (thousands) of dollars		
★ American Hospital Association (AHA) membership □ Joint Commission on Accreditation of Healthcare Organizations (JCAHO) accreditation ○ American Osteopathic Association (AOA) accreditation △ Commission on Accreditation of Rehabilitation Facilities (CARF) accreditation	Control	Service	Staffed Beds	Admissions	Census	Outpatient Visits	Births	Total	Payroll	Personnel

SALINAS—Monterey County

☒ **NATIVIDAD MEDICAL CENTER**, 1441 Constitution Boulevard, Zip 93906–3100, Mailing Address: P.O. Box 81611, Zip 93912–1611; tel. 831/755–4111, (Total facility includes 40 beds in nursing home–type unit) (Nonreporting) **A**1 3 5 9 10
Primary Contact: Lionel K. Chadwick, Chief Executive Officer
CFO: Tim Nguyen, Chief Financial Officer
CMO: Peter Leeson, M.D., Chief Medical Officer
CHR: Janine Bouyea, Human Resources Director
Web address: www.natividad.com

| | 13 | 10 | 163 | — | — | — | — | — | — | |

☒ **SALINAS VALLEY MEMORIAL HEALTHCARE SYSTEM**, 450 East Romie Lane, Zip 93901–4098; tel. 831/757–4333 **A**1 2 9 10 **F**2 9 11 14 15 17 19 21 22 23 26 27 28 29 33 41 42 46 47 48 49 54 55 56 57 58 59 60 61 62 63 64 65 66 69 70 81 82 83 84 85 86 87 88 93 94 96 97 98 106 108 109 110
Primary Contact: Samuel W. Downing, President and Chief Executive Officer
COO: Bev Ranzenberger, Senior Vice President Operations
CFO: John Fletcher, Senior Vice President Finance
CMO: David Perrott, M.D., Vice President and Medical Director
Web address: www.svmh.com

| | 16 | 10 | 249 | 12654 | 157 | 87161 | 1770 | 235805 | 107244 | 1411 |

SAN ANDREAS—Calaveras County

☒ **MARK TWAIN ST. JOSEPH'S HOSPITAL**, 768 Mountain Ranch Road, Zip 95249–9707; tel. 209/754–3521 **A**1 9 10 20 **F**2 9 11 12 21 22 23 26 27 28 29 33 38 40 42 46 48 52 53 55 59 60 62 63 69 81 82 84 88 92 94 97 107 108 **P**5 **S** Catholic Healthcare West, San Francisco, CA
Primary Contact: Michael P. Lawson, President
CFO: John Deakyne, Chief Financial Officer
CMO: Peter Gierke, M.D., Chief of Staff
Web address: www.marktwainhospital.com

| | 23 | 10 | 30 | 1722 | 18 | 81905 | 128 | 32075 | 14246 | 247 |

SAN BERNARDINO—San Bernardino County

☒ **COMMMUNITY HOSPITAL OF SAN BERNARDINO**, 1805 Medical Center Drive, Zip 92411–1214; tel. 909/887–6333, (Total facility includes 99 beds in nursing home–type unit) (Nonreporting) **A**1 9 10 **S** Catholic Healthcare West, San Francisco, CA
Primary Contact: Bruce G. Satzger, President
Web address: www.communityhospitalsb.org

| | 23 | 10 | 374 | — | — | — | — | — | — | |

□ △ **ROBERT H. BALLARD REHABILITATION HOSPITAL**, 1760 West 16th Street, Zip 92411; tel. 909/473–1200, (Nonreporting) **A**1 5 7 10
Primary Contact: Robert Herrick, Chief Executive Officer

| | 33 | 46 | 60 | — | — | — | — | — | — | |

☒ **ST. BERNARDINE MEDICAL CENTER**, 2101 North Waterman Avenue, Zip 92404–4836; tel. 909/883–8711, (Nonreporting) **A**1 2 9 10 **S** Catholic Healthcare West, San Francisco, CA
Primary Contact: Steven R. Barron, President
COO: Jack Ivie, Executive Vice President and Chief Operating Officer
CFO: Darryl VandenBosch, Senior Vice President and Chief Financial Officer
CMO: C John Udeh, M.D., Chief of Staff
CIO: Terry Ficklin, Director Information Systems
CHR: Dee Webb, Vice President Human Resources
Web address: www.stbernardinemedicalcenter.com

| | 21 | 10 | 280 | — | — | — | — | — | — | |

SAN CLEMENTE—Orange County

□ **SADDLEBACK MEMORIAL MEDICAL CENTER – SAN CLEMENTE CAMPUS**, (Formerly San Clemente Hospital and Medical Center), 654 Camino De Los Mares, Zip 92673–2827; tel. 949/496–1122 **A**1 9 10 **F**2 21 26 28 33 48 52 53 55 60 62 63 64 65 66 68 69 81 84 85 88 94 108 109 110 **S** Memorial Health Services, Long Beach, CA
Primary Contact: Diana Hendel, PharmD, Administrator
Web address: www.sanclementehospital.com

| | 32 | 10 | 73 | 2900 | 33 | — | 0 | — | — | 292 |

SAN DIEGO—San Diego County

☒ **ALVARADO HOSPITAL MEDICAL CENTER**, 6655 Alvarado Road, Zip 92120–5208; tel. 619/287–3270, (Includes SAN DIEGO REHABILITATION INSTITUTE, 6645 Alvarado Road, Zip 92120; tel. 619/286–3270) **A**1 2 9 10 **F**2 6 9 10 12 14 21 22 23 26 27 28 29 33 37 39 41 45 46 47 48 49 51 52 53 55 57 58 60 61 62 63 65 66 68 69 81 82 84 85 88 92 94 96 108 109 110 **P**8 **S** TENET Healthcare Corporation, Dallas, TX
Primary Contact: Mark R. Palmer, Chief Executive Officer
COO: Darlene Wetton, Chief Operating Officer
CFO: Augustine Lopez, Chief Financial Officer
CIO: Rogelio Tapnio, Director Health Information Services
CHR: Floss Manning, Director Human Resources
Web address: www.alvaradohospital.com

| | 33 | 10 | 151 | 8251 | 150 | 72481 | — | 119773 | | |

□ **AURORA BEHAVIORAL HEALTHCARE/SAN DIEGO**, 11878 Avenue of Industry, Zip 92128–3423; tel. 858/487–3200 **A**1 10 **F**3 4 21 27 29 31 44 46 47 48 52 71 72 73 74 75 76 77 78 94 96 **P**8
Primary Contact: James S. Plummer, Chief Executive Officer
Web address: www.aurorabehavioral.com

| | 33 | 22 | 80 | 2628 | 60 | 10228 | 0 | — | — | 145 |

□ **CHILDREN'S HOSPITAL AND HEALTH CENTER**, 3020 Children's Way, Zip 92123–4282; tel. 858/576–1700, (Total facility includes 58 beds in nursing home–type unit) **A**1 3 5 9 10 **F**2 6 8 9 10 16 18 20 21 22 23 24 27 28 29 30 31 32 33 34 37 39 42 45 46 47 48 49 51 52 53 56 57 58 60 61 62 63 66 67 68 69 72 73 74 75 77 81 82 88 90 92 93 94 95 96 97 98 99 101 102 106 107 108 **P**5 7
Primary Contact: Blair L. Sadler, President and Chief Executive Officer
Web address: www.chsd.org

| | 23 | 59 | 306 | 12869 | 219 | 259207 | 0 | 302410 | 110796 | 2511 |

Many Facility Codes have changed. Please refer to the AHA Guide Code Chart. © 2005 AHA Guide

Hospital, Address, Telephone, Approval, Facility, and Physician Codes, Health Care System	Classi-fication Codes		Utilization Data					Expense (thousands) of dollars		
	Control	Service	Staffed Beds	Admissions	Census	Outpatient Visits	Births	Total	Payroll	Personnel

★ American Hospital Association (AHA) membership
☐ Joint Commission on Accreditation of Healthcare Organizations (JCAHO) accreditation
○ American Osteopathic Association (AOA) accreditation
△ Commission on Accreditation of Rehabilitation Facilities (CARF) accreditation

	Control	Service	Staffed Beds	Admissions	Census	Outpatient Visits	Births	Total	Payroll	Personnel
☐ **CONTINENTAL REHABILITATION HOSPITAL**, 555 Washington Street, Zip 92103; tel. 619/260–8300, (Nonreporting) **A**1 10 Primary Contact: Greg Davis, Chief Executive Officer	33	46	88	—		—	—	—	—	—
⊠ **KAISER FOUNDATION HOSPITAL**, 4647 Zion Avenue, Zip 92120–2507; tel. 619/528–5000 **A**1 2 3 5 10 **F**2 11 12 21 22 23 26 27 28 33 36 37 38 39 44 49 50 53 55 56 57 58 59 61 62 63 64 65 66 72 73 75 76 81 82 84 85 86 88 90 92 94 108 110 **P**3 **S** Kaiser Foundation Hospitals, Oakland, CA Primary Contact: Arthur Flippin, M.D., Administrator CFO: Lorna Curtis, Assistant Administrator Finance Web address: www.kaiserpermanente.org	23	10	392	25479	269	112123	3996	—	—	694
☐ **KINDRED HOSPITAL–SAN DIEGO**, 1940 El Cajon Boulevard, Zip 92104–1096; tel. 619/543–4500 **A**1 10 **F**21 22 60 94 **S** Kindred Healthcare, Louisville, KY Primary Contact: Susan Bailey, Chief Executive Officer Web address: www.kindredsandiego.com	33	80	70	382	35	248	—	14804	—	—
⊠ **NAVAL MEDICAL CENTER**, 34800 Bob Wilson Drive, Zip 92134–5000; tel. 619/532–6400 **A**1 2 3 5 **F**2 4 10 11 12 14 15 16 17 18 19 20 21 22 23 24 25 26 27 28 30 31 32 33 37 39 40 41 42 43 46 47 48 49 50 53 55 56 57 58 59 60 61 62 63 65 66 67 69 70 71 77 78 81 82 84 85 86 88 89 90 92 93 94 95 96 106 107 108 110 **S** Bureau of Medicine and Surgery, Department of the Navy, Washington, DC Primary Contact: Rear Admiral John M. Mateczun, MC, USN, Commander CMO: Captain John Thiringer, Chief Medical Officer CIO: Commander Mary La Croix, MSC, USN, Director Informatics Web address: www.nmcsd.med.navy.mil	43	10	272	16819	158	1361924	3738	—	—	6319
☐ **SAN DIEGO COUNTY PSYCHIATRIC HOSPITAL**, 3853 Rosecrans Street, Zip 92110–3115, Mailing Address: P.O. Box 85524, Zip 92138–5524; tel. 619/692–8211, (Total facility includes 322 beds in nursing home–type unit) (Nonreporting) **A**1 10 Primary Contact: Karen C. Hogan, Administrator and Chief Executive Officer	13	22	357	—		—	—	—	—	—
★ **SAN DIEGO HOSPICE & PALLIATIVE CARE**, (HOSPICE), 4311 Third Avenue, Zip 92103–7499; tel. 619/688–1600 **A**10 **F**26 27 28 29 30 36 37 94 108 109 Primary Contact: Janet E. Cetti, President and Chief Executive Officer CFO: Kathleen Jones, Vice President Finance and Chief Financial Officer CMO: Laurel Herbst, Vice President, Medical Affairs CIO: Barbara Radice, Vice President and Chief Information Officer Web address: www.sdhospice.org	23	49	24	655	21	0	0	5975	—	—
⊠ **SCRIPPS MERCY HOSPITAL**, 4077 Fifth Avenue, Zip 92103–2105; tel. 619/294–8111, (Includes SCRIPPS MEMORIAL HOSPITAL CHULA VISTA, 435 H Street, Chula Vista, Zip 91912–6617, Mailing Address: P.O. Box 1537, Zip 91910–1537; tel. 619/691–7000; Thomas A. Gammiere, Chief Executive Officer), **A**1 2 3 5 9 10 **F**1 2 7 9 10 11 14 15 17 19 21 22 23 24 26 27 28 29 30 31 32 33 34 35 37 38 39 40 42 44 45 46 47 48 49 50 52 53 55 56 57 58 59 60 61 62 63 64 65 66 68 70 71 73 74 75 76 77 78 81 82 84 85 87 88 93 94 95 96 98 104 106 107 108 110 **S** Scripps Health, San Diego, CA Primary Contact: Thomas A. Gammiere, Chief Executive COO: Leanne M. Hunstock, R.N., Chief Operating Officer CFO: Edward Turk, Chief Financial Officer CMO: Davis Cracroft, M.D., Medical Director CIO: Jean Balgrosky, Vice President and Chief Information Officer CHR: Kathy Frederick, Senior Director Human Resources Web address: www.scrippshealth.org	23	10	700	30788	397	168094	4426	—	—	—
☐ **SHARP MARY BIRCH HOSPITAL FOR WOMEN**, 3003 Health Center Drive, Zip 92123; tel. 858/541–3400, (Nonreporting) **A**1 10 Primary Contact: Mary Henrikson, Chief Operating Officer	23	49	166	—		—	—	—	—	—
⊠ △ **SHARP MEMORIAL HOSPITAL**, 7901 Frost Street, Zip 92123–2701; tel. 858/939–3400, (Includes SHARP MESA VISTA HOSPITAL, 7850 Vista Hill Avenue, Zip 92123–2717; tel. 858/694–8300; Karenlee Robinson, Chief Operating Officer) **A**1 2 7 9 10 **F**2 3 4 9 10 11 12 14 15 17 19 21 22 23 26 27 28 29 33 34 37 42 44 45 46 47 48 51 52 55 56 57 58 59 60 61 62 63 64 65 66 68 69 71 72 73 74 75 76 77 78 79 81 82 83 85 88 89 92 93 94 95 96 99 100 101 105 108 109 110 **P**8 **S** Sharp Healthcare, San Diego, CA Primary Contact: Daniel Gross, Chief Executive Officer COO: David Tew, Chief Operating Officer CFO: Kevin Thompson, Chief Financial Officer CIO: William T. Spooner, Senior Vice President and Chief Information Officer CHR: Diane Delaney, Vice President Web address: www.sharp.com	23	10	731	34876	553	353815	7680	419790	188032	2972
☐ **UNIVERSITY COMMUNITY HOSPITAL**, 5550 University Avenue, Zip 92105–2307, Mailing Address: P.O. Box 5587, Zip 92105–5507; tel. 619/582–3516 **A**1 10 **F**1 5 21 29 32 47 55 71 74 75 76 81 88 94 108 Primary Contact: Roy Rodriguez, Chief Executive Officer	32	22	72	4007	71	13884	—	30635	—	—

CA

Hospital, Address, Telephone, Approval, Facility, and Physician Codes, Health Care System	Classi-fication Codes		Utilization Data					Expense (thousands) of dollars		
★ American Hospital Association (AHA) membership □ Joint Commission on Accreditation of Healthcare Organizations (JCAHO) accreditation ○ American Osteopathic Association (AOA) accreditation △ Commission on Accreditation of Rehabilitation Facilities (CARF) accreditation	Control	Service	Staffed Beds	Admissions	Census	Outpatient Visits	Births	Total	Payroll	Personnel

UNIVERSITY OF CALIFORNIA SAN DIEGO MEDICAL CENTER, 200 West
Arbor Drive, Zip 92103–8970; tel. 619/543–6222 **A**1 2 3 5 8 9 10 **F**2 7 9 11
12 13 14 15 17 19 21 22 23 27 33 34 37 38 39 44 46 47 48 49 50 52 53
55 56 57 58 59 60 61 62 63 64 65 66 69 70 71 72 75 76 80 81 85 87 88
90 93 94 95 96 99 100 101 102 103 104 105 107 108 109 110 **P**1
S University of California–Systemwide Administration, Oakland, CA
Primary Contact: Richard Liekweg, Director
COO: Scott Hofferber, Chief Operating Officer
CFO: Robert Hogan, Chief Financial Officer
CMO: Thomas V. McAfee, M.D., Physician–in–Chief
CIO: Ed Babakanian, Chief Information Officer
CHR: Ann Skinner, Director Human Resources
Web address: www.health.ucsd.edu

| 12 | 10 | 485 | 21702 | 342 | 555354 | 2707 | 439132 | 166158 | 3741 |

VETERANS AFFAIRS SAN DIEGO HEALTHCARE SYSTEM, 3350 LaJolla
Village Drive, Zip 92161–0002; tel. 858/552–8585, (Total facility includes 40
beds in nursing home–type unit) **A**1 2 3 5 7 8 **F**1 2 3 4 7 8 9 10 12 15 17 19
21 22 23 25 26 27 28 29 30 31 32 35 36 37 38 39 41 42 44 45 46 47 48
49 50 51 52 53 55 57 58 60 61 62 63 64 65 66 69 70 71 73 74 75 76 77
78 81 82 84 85 86 87 88 90 92 93 94 96 99 100 101 102 103 104 105 106
107 108 109 110 **P**6 **S** Department of Veterans Affairs, Washington, DC
Primary Contact: Gary J. Rossio, Director
CFO: Barbara Angius, Chief Financial Officer
CMO: Jacqueline G. Parthemore, M.D., Chief of Staff
CIO: Debra Dyer, Chief Information Officer
CHR: Stephanie Wright, Director Human Resources Management
Web address: www.va.gov/sta/guide/home.asp

| 45 | 10 | 238 | 6313 | 145 | 476938 | — | 291619 | 113463 | 2176 |

SAN DIMAS—Los Angeles County

SAN DIMAS COMMUNITY HOSPITAL, 1350 West Covina Boulevard,
Zip 91773–3219; tel. 909/599–6811 **A**1 9 10 **F**11 12 14 21 22 28 33 46 48
55 59 62 63 69 81 84 88 92 94 108 **S** TENET Healthcare Corporation,
Dallas, TX
Primary Contact: Dan Bowers, Chief Executive Officer
COO: David Batista, Chief Operating Officer
CFO: Frederick J. Drewette, Chief Financial Officer
CMO: Steven Davis, D.O., Chief Medical Staff
CHR: Vahan Demlakian, Human Resources Director
Web address: www.sandimashospital.com

| 33 | 10 | 93 | 3999 | 72 | 17293 | 749 | — | | 255 |

SAN FERNANDO—Los Angeles County

MISSION COMMUNITY HOSPITAL–SAN FERNANDO CAMPUS, 700
Chatsworth Drive, Zip 91346; tel. 818/787–2222, (Includes MISSION
COMMUNITY HOSPITAL–PANORAMA CITY CAMPUS, 14850 Roscoe Boulevard,
Panorama City, Zip 91402–4618; tel. 818/787–2222) **A**10 **F**2 3 9 12 21 22 27
28 29 31 33 45 46 48 55 62 63 66 69 70 71 73 74 75 76 77 78 79 81 82
83 84 85 88 94 96 108 110 **P**5
Primary Contact: William W. Daniel, Chief Executive Officer
Web address: www.mchonline.org

| 23 | 10 | 145 | 6347 | 99 | 33965 | 0 | 40965 | 18642 | 334 |

PROVIDENCE HOLY CROSS MEDICAL CENTER, 15031 Rinaldi Street,
Zip 91346–9600; tel. 818/365–8051, (Total facility includes 48 beds in nursing
home–type unit) **A**1 2 9 10 **F**2 9 11 12 14 15 17 19 21 22 23 24 26 27 28 29
33 34 35 36 37 38 39 41 42 44 47 48 52 53 55 57 58 59 60 61 62 63 65
66 68 69 81 82 84 85 87 88 92 94 96 98 108 109 **P**5 **S** Providence Health
System, Seattle, WA
Primary Contact: Kerry Carmody, Administrator
CFO: Mitch Thomas, Chief Financial Officer
CMO: Myron Berdischewsky, M.D., Regional Chief Medical Officer
CIO: Dan Robins, Regional Director Information System
CHR: Wayne Cassard, Service Area Director Human Resources
Web address: www.providence.org/losangeles/facilities/providence_holy_cross/

| 21 | 10 | 254 | 13881 | 177 | 103081 | 2386 | 163162 | 67196 | 1211 |

SAN FRANCISCO—San Francisco County

CALIFORNIA PACIFIC MEDICAL CENTER, 2333 Buchanan Street,
Zip 94115–1925, Mailing Address: P.O. Box 7999, Zip 94120–7999;
tel. 415/563–4321, (Includes CALIFORNIA PACIFIC MEDICAL CENTER–DAVIES
CAMPUS, Castro and Duboce Streets, Zip 94114; tel. 415/565–6000) **A**1 2 3 5
7 8 9 10 **F**1 5 10 11 12 14 15 16 17 18 19 20 21 22 23 24 26 27 28 29 30
33 36 37 38 40 44 47 48 49 50 51 53 55 56 57 59 60 61 63 64 65 66 67
68 69 70 71 75 76 77 79 81 84 85 87 88 90 92 94 96 100 101 102 108
109 **S** Sutter Health, Sacramento, CA
Primary Contact: Martin Brotman, M.D., President and Chief Executive Officer
CFO: Michael P. Holdsworth, Vice President Finance and Chief Financial Officer
CMO: Morris Flaum, M.D., Vice President Medical Affairs
CIO: Jerry Padavano, Chief Information Officer
CHR: Linda Isaacs, Vice President Human Resources
Web address: www.cpmc.org

| 23 | 10 | 783 | 30600 | 504 | 1345559 | — | 653701 | — | — |

CHINESE HOSPITAL, 845 Jackson Street, Zip 94133–4899;
tel. 415/982–2400 **A**1 9 10 **F**2 9 12 21 22 23 26 27 28 29 33 39 46 47 48
49 52 55 58 60 61 62 63 65 66 70 81 82 87 88 92 94 96 106 108 109 **P**5
Primary Contact: Brenda Yee, R.N., MSN, Chief Executive Officer
CFO: Thomas Bolger, Chief Financial Officer
CMO: Joseph Woo, M.D., Chief of Staff
CIO: Helen Lee, Manager Information Systems
CHR: Karen Chow, Director Human Resources
Web address: www.chinesehospital–sf.org

| 23 | 10 | 54 | 2190 | 30 | 58109 | 0 | 49649 | 14066 | 234 |

Many Facility Codes have changed. Please refer to the AHA Guide Code Chart.   © 2005 AHA Guide

Hospital, Address, Telephone, Approval, Facility, and Physician Codes, Health Care System	Classi-fication Codes		Utilization Data					Expense (thousands) of dollars		
★ American Hospital Association (AHA) membership □ Joint Commission on Accreditation of Healthcare Organizations (JCAHO) accreditation ○ American Osteopathic Association (AOA) accreditation △ Commission on Accreditation of Rehabilitation Facilities (CARF) accreditation	Control	Service	Staffed Beds	Admissions	Census	Outpatient Visits	Births	Total	Payroll	Personnel

KAISER FOUNDATION HOSPITAL, 2200 O'Farrell Street, Zip 94115–3358; tel. 415/833–2000 **A**1 3 5 10 **F**9 14 15 16 17 18 19 20 21 22 26 27 28 29 33 35 36 37 38 46 47 48 49 50 51 52 53 55 56 57 58 59 60 61 62 63 65 66 73 75 81 82 84 88 92 94 96 101 108 110 **S** Kaiser Foundation Hospitals, Oakland, CA
Primary Contact: R. Michael Alexander, Senior Vice President and Area Manager
COO: Linda Groah, Chief Operating Officer
CFO: Jim Phillips, Business Strategy and Finance Leader
CMO: Bruce Blumberg, M.D., Physician in Chief
CIO: Beverly Seyfert, Information Technology Leader
CHR: Michael H. Sweet, Human Resources Business Partner
Web address: www.kaiserpermanente.org
— Control 23, Service 10, Staffed Beds 247, Admissions 13052, Census 178, Outpatient Visits —, Births 2437, Total —, Payroll —, Personnel —

★ **LAGUNA HONDA HOSPITAL AND REHABILITATION CENTER**, (Skilled–Nursing Facility), 375 Laguna Honda Boulevard, Zip 94116–1499; tel. 415/664–1580 **A**10 **F**1 2 5 26 27 28 32 36 37 38 44 47 48 49 50 53 58 60 66 68 71 76 92 94 96 106 108 110
Primary Contact: John Kanaley, Chief Executive Officer
COO: Robert Christmas, Chief Operating Officer
CFO: Nancy Arata, Chief Financial Officer
CIO: Pat Skala, Chief Information Officer
— Control 15, Service 49, Staffed Beds 1070, Admissions 1298, Census 1034, Outpatient Visits 21109, Births 0, Total 152429, Payroll —, Personnel —

△ **SAINT FRANCIS MEMORIAL HOSPITAL**, 900 Hyde Street, Zip 94109–4899, Mailing Address: Box 7726, Zip 94120–7726; tel. 415/353–6000 **A**1 2 7 9 10 **F**2 9 12 13 14 21 22 23 29 33 37 38 39 42 45 46 47 49 52 53 55 57 58 60 61 62 63 64 65 66 68 69 71 73 75 77 78 79 81 82 84 85 86 88 92 94 95 96 107 108 109 110 **S** Catholic Healthcare West, San Francisco, CA
Primary Contact: Cheryl A. Fama, President and Chief Executive Officer
CFO: Alan Fox, Chief Financial Officer
CHR: Richard Mead, Senior Director Human Resources
Web address: www.chw.edu
— Control 23, Service 10, Staffed Beds 210, Admissions 6827, Census 118, Outpatient Visits 104929, Births —, Total 110443, Payroll —, Personnel —

SAN FRANCISCO GENERAL HOSPITAL MEDICAL CENTER, 1001 Potrero Avenue, Zip 94110–3594; tel. 415/206–8000 **A**1 2 3 5 8 10 **F**1 2 11 12 14 21 22 24 28 29 30 31 32 33 34 35 37 39 46 47 48 49 50 52 53 55 56 57 58 59 60 61 62 63 65 66 69 70 71 72 73 75 78 81 82 84 88 92 93 94 95 96 106 107 108 109 110 **P**8
Primary Contact: Gene Marie O'Connell, Executive Administrator
CFO: Gregg Sass, Chief Financial Officer
CIO: Robert Brody, M.D., Chief Information Officer
CHR: Rod Auyang, Director Human Resources
Web address: www.dph.sf.ca.us/chn/SFGH/sfghmenu.htm
— Control 15, Service 10, Staffed Beds 496, Admissions 17340, Census 391, Outpatient Visits 521214, Births —, Total 422668, Payroll —, Personnel —

ST. LUKE'S HOSPITAL, 3555 Cesar Chavez Street, Zip 94110–4490; tel. 415/647–8600 **A**1 5 9 10 12 **F**2 9 10 11 12 14 15 19 21 22 23 26 27 28 29 30 33 37 38 46 48 55 59 60 61 62 63 64 69 71 77 78 81 84 88 92 94 96 108 109 **S** Sutter Health, Sacramento, CA
Primary Contact: John G. Williams, President and Chief Executive Officer
CFO: Jim Strong, Chief Financial Officer
CMO: Ernesto Puletti, M.D., Chief Medical Staff
CHR: Phil Gardner, Director Human Resources
Web address: www.stlukes–sf.org
— Control 23, Service 10, Staffed Beds 220, Admissions 5111, Census 143, Outpatient Visits 86288, Births 1053, Total 119617, Payroll 42776, Personnel 1033

ST. MARY'S MEDICAL CENTER, 450 Stanyan Street, Zip 94117–1079; tel. 415/668–1000, (Total facility includes 32 beds in nursing home–type unit) **A**1 3 5 8 9 10 **F**1 2 3 9 10 12 13 14 15 17 19 21 22 23 26 27 28 29 33 36 37 38 41 42 44 45 46 47 48 49 50 52 53 55 56 57 58 60 61 62 63 66 67 68 69 71 72 73 74 75 76 77 78 81 82 84 88 92 94 95 96 98 108 109 **S** Catholic Healthcare West, San Francisco, CA
Primary Contact: Kenneth R. Steele, President
CFO: Dennis Morris, Vice President and Chief Financial Officer
CMO: Ken Mills, Chief Medical Staff
CHR: Maynard Jenkins, Director Human Resources
Web address: www.stmarysmedicalcenter.com
— Control 23, Service 10, Staffed Beds 232, Admissions 7426, Census 134, Outpatient Visits 81858, Births 0, Total 145522, Payroll 65879, Personnel 922

UCSF MEDICAL CENTER, 500 Parnassus Avenue, Zip 94143–0296, Mailing Address: 505 Parnassus Avenue, Box 0296, Zip 94143–0296; tel. 415/476–1000 **A**1 2 3 5 8 9 10 **F**2 7 9 10 11 12 14 15 16 17 18 19 20 21 22 23 24 26 27 28 29 30 33 34 35 40 41 42 43 44 45 46 47 48 49 50 51 52 53 55 56 57 58 59 60 61 62 63 64 65 66 67 69 70 79 80 81 82 84 85 86 87 88 89 90 93 94 95 96 98 99 100 101 102 103 104 105 106 107 108 109 **S** University of California–Systemwide Administration, Oakland, CA
Primary Contact: Mark R. Laret, Chief Executive Officer
COO: Tomi S. Ryba, Chief Operating Officer
CFO: Ken M. Jones, Chief Financial Officer
CMO: Ernest Ring, M.D., Chief Medical Officer
CIO: Larry Lotenero, Chief Information Officer
CHR: David Odato, Executive Director Human Resources
Web address: www.ucsfhealth.org
— Control 23, Service 10, Staffed Beds 574, Admissions 27052, Census 443, Outpatient Visits 679060, Births 1827, Total 955917, Payroll 358787, Personnel 5433

CA

Hospital, Address, Telephone, Approval, Facility, and Physician Codes, Health Care System	Classification Codes		Utilization Data					Expense (thousands) of dollars		
★ American Hospital Association (AHA) membership ☐ Joint Commission on Accreditation of Healthcare Organizations (JCAHO) accreditation ○ American Osteopathic Association (AOA) accreditation △ Commission on Accreditation of Rehabilitation Facilities (CARF) accreditation	Control	Service	Staffed Beds	Admissions	Census	Outpatient Visits	Births	Total	Payroll	Personnel

⊠ VETERANS AFFAIRS MEDICAL CENTER, 4150 Clement Street, Zip 94121–1598; tel. 415/221–4810, (Total facility includes 112 beds in nursing home–type unit) (Nonreporting) **A**1 2 3 5 **S** Department of Veterans Affairs, Washington, DC
Primary Contact: Sheila M. Cullen, Director
CFO: Del Lewis, Chief Fiscal Services
CIO: Roy Chaney, Chief Information Management Service
CHR: Marie Boland, Chief Human Resource Management Service
Web address: www.va.gov/sta/guide/home.asp

	45	10	244	—	—	—	—	—	—	—

SAN GABRIEL—Los Angeles County

⊠ SAN GABRIEL VALLEY MEDICAL CENTER, 438 West Las Tunas Drive, Zip 91776–1216, Mailing Address: P.O. Box 1507, Zip 91778–1507; tel. 626/289–5454, (Total facility includes 41 beds in nursing home–type unit) **A**1 9 10 **F**11 12 15 17 21 22 23 27 28 29 33 37 38 39 45 46 48 49 52 53 55 56 57 58 59 60 61 62 63 64 66 69 71 81 82 85 87 88 92 93 94 96 98 108 109 110 **P**5 **S** Catholic Healthcare West, San Francisco, CA
Primary Contact: Makoto Nakayama, President
CFO: Paula LaMar, Chief Financial Officer
CMO: Hubert Chow, M.D., Chief of Staff
CIO: Frank Vargas, Director Information Management Systems
Web address: www.sgvmc.org

	21	10	190	9969	145	46584	2042	111165	44581	674

SAN JOSE—Santa Clara County

⊠ GOOD SAMARITAN HOSPITAL, 2425 Samaritan Drive, Zip 95124–3997, Mailing Address: P.O. Box 240002, Zip 95154–2402; tel. 408/559–2011, (Total facility includes 19 beds in nursing home–type unit) **A**1 2 9 10 **F**4 9 10 11 12 14 15 17 19 21 22 23 29 32 33 46 48 55 56 57 59 60 61 63 64 69 71 75 77 78 79 81 82 84 88 92 94 108 **S** HCA, Nashville, TN
Primary Contact: William K. Piche, Chief Executive Officer
COO: Brian Knecht, Chief Operating Officer
CFO: Darrel Neuenschwander, Chief Financial Officer
CMO: William Lewis, M.D., Chief of Staff
CIO: Maggie Ratliff, Director Information Services
CHR: Daniel Camp, Vice President Human Resources
Web address: www.goodsamsanjose.com

	33	10	269	17358	210	135083	3168	233107	101534	1072

⊠ KAISER FOUNDATION HOSPITAL – SANTA TERESA, 250 Hospital Parkway, Zip 95119–1199; tel. 408/972–7000 **A**1 10 **F**2 4 11 12 14 15 17 21 23 26 27 28 30 33 36 37 38 46 47 48 49 50 51 52 53 55 57 58 59 60 61 62 63 64 65 66 69 70 72 73 74 75 76 77 81 82 84 87 88 89 90 94 95 96 98 99 104 106 107 108 109 110 **S** Kaiser Foundation Hospitals, Oakland, CA
Primary Contact: Terry L. Austen, Senior Vice President and Area Manager
COO: Terry L. Austen, Director Operations
CFO: Flora Asuncion, Area Finance Officer
CMO: Raj Bhandari, M.D., Physician–in–Chief
CIO: Sue Becker, Area Technology Director
CHR: Carl Kettler, Human Resources Business Partner
Web address: www.kaiserpermanete.org

	23	10	228	17008	152	1053461	2482	—	—	1872

⊠ O'CONNOR HOSPITAL, 2105 Forest Avenue, Zip 95128–1471; tel. 408/947–2500, (Total facility includes 22 beds in nursing home–type unit) **A**1 2 9 10 **F**2 11 12 14 15 17 19 21 22 23 24 26 27 28 29 33 39 41 44 46 47 48 49 51 52 53 54 55 56 57 58 59 60 61 62 63 64 65 66 69 70 71 73 74 76 82 84 85 88 92 94 95 96 108 109 110 **S** Daughters of Charity Health System, Los Altos Hills, CA
Primary Contact: Robert H. Curry, President and Chief Executive Officer
CFO: Robert Issai, Executive Vice President and Chief Financial Officer
CMO: Constance Bowie, M.D., Chief Medical Staff
CIO: Richard Hutsell, Vice President and Chief Information Officer
Web address: www.oconnorhospital.org

	21	10	225	13015	163	136521	—	181224	—	952

⊠ REGIONAL MEDICAL CENTER OF SAN JOSE, 225 North Jackson Avenue, Zip 95116–1691; tel. 408/729–2801 **A**1 9 10 **F**2 11 12 14 15 21 22 23 27 28 29 33 37 39 44 46 48 49 53 55 56 57 59 60 61 62 63 64 66 69 79 81 82 84 85 86 87 88 94 97 107 108 **S** HCA, Nashville, TN
Primary Contact: William L. Gilbert, Chief Executive Officer
CFO: David P. Delaney, Chief Financial Officer
CIO: Shirley Joyal, Director Information Systems
CHR: Dennis Mills, Director Human Resources
Web address: www.regionalmedicalsanjose.com

	32	10	204	9939	123	91041	2215	148128	63817	915

☐ SANTA CLARA VALLEY MEDICAL CENTER, 751 South Bascom Avenue, Zip 95128–2604; tel. 408/885–5000 **A**1 3 5 8 9 10 **F**1 2 5 9 10 11 12 13 14 15 17 19 21 22 23 26 27 28 29 30 33 34 35 37 39 42 44 47 48 49 50 52 53 55 56 57 59 60 61 62 63 64 65 66 67 68 69 70 71 73 74 75 76 78 79 81 82 83 84 85 87 88 90 94 95 96 97 107 108 110 **P**6
Primary Contact: Susan G. Murphy, Director
Web address: www.scvmed.org

	13	10	510	23466	334	719857	5017	610011	316161	5892

SAN LEANDRO—Alameda County

ALAMEDA COUNTY MEDICAL CENTER–FAIRMONT CAMPUS, 15400 Foothill Boulevard, Zip 94578–1009; tel. 510/437–4800, (Total facility includes 113 beds in nursing home–type unit) (Nonreporting) **S** Alameda Medical Center, San Leandro, CA
Primary Contact: Claude D. Watts, Jr, Chief Executive Officer
Web address: www.acmedctr.org

	13	10	399	—	—	—	—	—	—	—

Hospital, Address, Telephone, Approval, Facility, and Physician Codes, Health Care System	Classi-fication Codes		Utilization Data					Expense (thousands) of dollars		
★ American Hospital Association (AHA) membership □ Joint Commission on Accreditation of Healthcare Organizations (JCAHO) accreditation ○ American Osteopathic Association (AOA) accreditation △ Commission on Accreditation of Rehabilitation Facilities (CARF) accreditation	Control	Service	Staffed Beds	Admissions	Census	Outpatient Visits	Births	Total	Payroll	Personnel
□ **KINDRED HOSPITAL–SAN FRANCISCO BAY AREA**, 2800 Benedict Drive, Zip 94577–6840; tel. 510/357-8300, (Nonreporting) **A**1 10 **S** Kindred Healthcare, Louisville, KY Primary Contact: Jim Linhares, Chief Executive Officer Web address: www.kindredhospitalsfba.com	33	10	80	—	—	—	—	—	—	—
✠ **SAN LEANDRO HOSPITAL**, 13855 East 14th Street, Zip 94578–2600; tel. 510/357-6500, (Includes EDEN MEDICAL CENTER, 20103 Lake Chabot Road, Castro Valley, Zip 94546–5341; tel. 510/537-1234; George Bischalaney, President and Chief Executive Officer) **A**1 2 9 10 **F**2 9 11 12 14 21 22 23 27 28 29 31 33 34 35 39 44 45 46 47 48 49 52 53 55 57 58 59 60 61 62 63 64 66 68 69 71 73 74 75 76 78 81 82 83 84 88 91 92 94 96 106 108 109 110 Primary Contact: Ronnie Bayduza, Administrator CFO: Kathleen Cain, Chief Financial Officer CIO: B J. Martin, Director Information Services CHR: Phyllis Weiss, Director Human Resources Web address: www.sanleandrohospital.org	33	10	428	17294	236	156651	—	184245	—	—
SAN LUIS OBISPO—San Luis Obispo County										
CALIFORNIA MENS COLONY HOSPITAL, Highway 1, Zip 93409–8101, Mailing Address: P.O. Box 8101, Zip 93409–8101; tel. 805/547-7913, (Nonreporting) Primary Contact: Galen Kirn, Administrator	12	11	39	—	—	—	—	—	—	—
✠ **FRENCH HOSPITAL MEDICAL CENTER**, 1911 Johnson Avenue, Zip 93401–4131; tel. 805/543-5353, (Nonreporting) **A**1 9 10 **S** Catholic Healthcare West, San Francisco, CA Primary Contact: Alan Iftiniuk, President CFO: Susan Andersen, Chief Financial Officer CMO: Mark Soll, M.D., Chief of Staff CIO: Cyndi Lang, Director Information Services CHR: Susan Winsell, Director Human Resources Web address: www.agfh.org	33	10	112	—	—	—	—	—	—	—
✠ **SIERRA VISTA REGIONAL MEDICAL CENTER**, 1010 Murray Street, Zip 93405–8800, Mailing Address: P.O. Box 1367, Zip 93406–1367; tel. 805/546-7600 **A**1 9 10 19 **F**9 12 14 15 17 19 21 23 26 27 28 29 32 33 44 55 56 58 59 60 61 62 63 64 81 88 94 109 **S** TENET Healthcare Corporation, Dallas, TX Primary Contact: Candace L. Markwith, Chief Executive Officer COO: Joseph DeSchryver, Chief Operating Officer CFO: Richard Phillips, Chief Financial Officer CIO: Robert Leonard, Director Information Services Web address: www.sierravistaregional.com	33	10	160	6538	83	102465	1171	—	—	654
SAN MATEO—San Mateo County										
MILLS HOSPITAL See Mills–Peninsula Health Services, Burlingame										
□ **SAN MATEO MEDICAL CENTER**, 222 West 39th Avenue, Zip 94403–4398; tel. 650/573-2222 **A**1 5 10 **F**2 12 21 22 23 26 27 28 29 31 32 33 38 39 44 45 46 50 52 53 55 57 58 60 61 62 63 64 69 70 71 73 75 81 84 88 92 94 96 108 110 **P**6 8 Primary Contact: Nancy Steiger, Chief Executive Officer Web address: www.sanmateomedicalcenter.org	13	10	367	3507	283	239684	0	156635	68909	1141
SAN PABLO—Contra Costa County										
✠ **DOCTORS MEDICAL CENTER–SAN PABLO CAMPUS**, 2000 Vale Road, Zip 94806–3808; tel. 510/970-5000 **A**1 2 9 10 **F**2 3 9 12 13 15 17 19 21 22 26 28 29 33 39 41 46 47 48 52 55 56 58 59 60 61 62 63 66 69 79 81 82 88 93 94 95 108 109 110 **P**5 Primary Contact: Irwin C. Hansen, Chief Executive Officer CFO: Dev Mahadevan, Chief Financial Officer CMO: Mark Kogan, M.D., President, Medical Staff CIO: Vickie Lampert, Director Information Systems and Data Center Web address: www.drsmedicalcenter.com	16	10	247	3152	97	37019	296	53405	28113	645
SAN PEDRO—Los Angeles County, See Los Angeles										
SAN RAFAEL—Marin County										
✠ **KAISER FOUNDATION HOSPITAL**, 99 Montecillo Road, Zip 94903–3308; tel. 415/444-2000 **A**1 10 **F**9 21 22 26 27 28 33 34 35 46 47 50 51 52 53 55 58 60 61 62 63 65 66 81 82 84 88 92 94 96 108 110 **S** Kaiser Foundation Hospitals, Oakland, CA Primary Contact: Jill Magri, Senior Vice President and Administrator Web address: www.kaiserpermanente.org	23	10	110	6003	70	9063	0	—	—	—
□ **KENTFIELD REHABILITATION HOSPITAL**, 1125 Sir Francis Drake Boulevard, Zip 94904–1455; tel. 415/456-9680 **A**1 9 10 **F**21 22 28 45 52 60 69 88 110 **S** VIBRA Healthcare, Mechanicsburg, PA Primary Contact: Ann Gors, Chief Executive Officer Web address: www.nbhd.org	33	80	57	518	39	0	0	—	—	195
SAN RAMON—Contra Costa County										
✠ **SAN RAMON REGIONAL MEDICAL CENTER**, 6001 Norris Canyon Road, Zip 94583–5400; tel. 925/275-9200 **A**1 9 10 **F**2 11 12 14 15 17 19 21 23 28 29 30 31 33 37 42 46 47 48 52 55 56 57 58 59 60 61 62 63 64 66 69 81 82 85 88 94 96 108 109 110 **S** TENET Healthcare Corporation, Dallas, TX Primary Contact: Gary Sloan, Chief Executive Officer COO: Susan C. Micheletti, Chief Operating Officer CFO: Beenu Chadha, Chief Financial Officer CMO: Carl Critz, M.D., Chief of Staff CIO: Jay Juarez, Director Information Systems Web address: www.sanramonmedctr.com	33	10	123	5227	59	72638	850	93064	44398	558

Hospital, Address, Telephone, Approval, Facility, and Physician Codes, Health Care System	Classi-fication Codes		Utilization Data					Expense (thousands) of dollars		
★ American Hospital Association (AHA) membership □ Joint Commission on Accreditation of Healthcare Organizations (JCAHO) accreditation ○ American Osteopathic Association (AOA) accreditation △ Commission on Accreditation of Rehabilitation Facilities (CARF) accreditation	Control	Service	Staffed Beds	Admissions	Census	Outpatient Visits	Births	Total	Payroll	Personnel

SANGER—Fresno County

SANGER GENERAL HOSPITAL, 2558 Jensen Avenue, Zip 93657–2296; tel. 559/875–6571, (Nonreporting) **A**9 10
Primary Contact: Royce C. Scales, Chief Executive Officer

| | 32 | 10 | 39 | — | — | — | — | — | — | |

SANTA ANA—Orange County

✠ **COASTAL COMMUNITIES HOSPITAL**, 2701 South Bristol Street, Zip 92704–6201; tel. 714/754–5454 **A**1 9 10 **F**6 11 12 21 27 28 29 33 35 39 40 44 45 46 47 48 49 50 52 53 55 58 59 60 62 63 65 66 69 71 74 75 76 77 78 81 82 84 86 87 88 92 94 96 97 108 109 110
Primary Contact: John M. Chubb, Chief Executive Officer
CFO: Jason McLaughlin, Chief Financial Officer
CHR: Geoff Migala, Director Human Resources
Web address: www.coastalcommhospital.com

| | 33 | 10 | 178 | 5784 | 112 | 32593 | 2777 | 56389 | 35313 | 549 |

SPECIALTY HOSPITAL OF SANTA ANA, 1901 North College Avenue, Zip 92706–2334; tel. 714/564–7800, (Nonreporting)
Primary Contact: Vu Le, M.D., Chief Executive Officer
Web address: www.specialtyhealthcare.com

| | 33 | 10 | 54 | | | | | | | |

✠ **WESTERN MEDICAL CENTER–SANTA ANA**, 1001 North Tustin Avenue, Zip 92705–3577; tel. 714/835–3555 **A**1 3 5 9 10 **F**2 9 11 13 14 15 17 19 21 22 23 29 33 34 37 39 41 46 48 49 50 53 55 56 57 58 59 61 62 63 67 71 76 81 85 88 94 96 101 104 106 108
Primary Contact: Daniel Brothman, Chief Executive Officer
CFO: Kathy Hammack, Chief Financial Officer
CMO: Robert Steedman, M.D., Chief of Staff
CIO: Nova Stewart, Chief Information Officer
CHR: Gwen Chambers, Director Human Resources
Web address: www.westernmedicalcenter.com

| | 33 | 10 | 280 | 13321 | 160 | 65226 | — | 130127 | — | — |

SANTA BARBARA—Santa Barbara County

✠ **GOLETA VALLEY COTTAGE HOSPITAL**, 351 South Patterson Avenue, Zip 93111–2496, Mailing Address: Box 6306, Zip 93160–6306; tel. 805/967–3411, (Total facility includes 55 beds in nursing home–type unit) (Nonreporting) **A**1 9 10 **S** Cottage Health System, Santa Barbara, CA
Primary Contact: Diane Wisby, Administrator
Web address: www.sbch.org

| | 23 | 10 | 109 | — | — | — | — | — | — | |

★ △ **REHABILITATION INSTITUTE AT SANTA BARBARA**, 2415 De la Vina Street, Zip 93105–3819; tel. 805/687–7444 **A**7 9 10 **F**21 28 29 35 41 45 60 62 65 68 69 72 73 77 96 108 110
Primary Contact: Melinda Staveley, President and Chief Executive Officer
CFO: Scott Silic, Vice President Operations and Chief Financial Officer
CMO: Cheryl Ellis, M.D., Vice President Medical Services and Medical Director
CHR: Karen Aldridge, Director Human Resources
Web address: www.rehabsb.org

| | 23 | 46 | 24 | 748 | 23 | 9113 | 0 | 16431 | — | — |

✠ **SANTA BARBARA COTTAGE HOSPITAL**, Pueblo at Bath Streets, Zip 93105–4390, Mailing Address: P.O. Box 689, Zip 93102–0689; tel. 805/682–7111 **A**1 2 3 5 9 10 **F**2 3 4 9 11 12 14 21 22 23 27 28 29 33 34 37 41 42 46 47 48 49 53 55 56 57 58 59 61 62 63 65 66 67 69 71 73 75 76 77 81 84 85 88 94 96 106 108 110 **S** Cottage Health System, Santa Barbara, CA
Primary Contact: Ronald C. Werft, President and Chief Executive Officer
COO: Steven A. Fellows, Executive Vice President and Chief Operating Officer
CFO: Joan Bricher, Senior Vice President Finance
CMO: Robert E. Reid, M.D., Direct of Medical Affairs
CIO: Alberto Kywi, Chief Information Officer
Web address: www.cottagehealthsystem.org

| | 23 | 10 | 307 | 18554 | 214 | 132340 | 2519 | 240034 | 91834 | 1907 |

SANTA CLARA—Santa Clara County

✠ **KAISER FOUNDATION HOSPITAL**, 900 Kiely Boulevard, Zip 95051–5329; tel. 408/236–6400 **A**1 3 5 10 **F**2 4 11 12 21 23 24 26 27 28 29 30 31 33 36 37 38 39 42 44 46 47 48 49 50 51 53 55 56 57 58 59 60 61 62 63 64 65 66 67 69 70 72 73 74 75 76 77 78 79 80 81 82 84 86 87 88 89 90 92 94 95 96 106 107 108 109 110 **P**6 **S** Kaiser Foundation Hospitals, Oakland, CA
Primary Contact: Charles S. Koch, Chief Operating Officer
Web address: www.kaiserpermanente.org

| | 23 | 10 | 265 | 20412 | 184 | — | 3276 | — | — | 1995 |

SANTA CRUZ—Santa Cruz County

✠ **DOMINICAN HOSPITAL**, 1555 Soquel Drive, Zip 95065–1794; tel. 831/462–7700, (Total facility includes 37 beds in nursing home–type unit) **A**1 9 10 **F**2 3 9 11 13 14 15 17 19 21 22 23 26 27 28 29 31 33 37 38 39 40 48 51 52 53 55 56 57 58 59 60 61 62 63 64 65 66 67 68 69 71 75 78 81 82 84 85 88 92 94 95 108 110 **S** Catholic Healthcare West, San Francisco, CA
Primary Contact: Sister Julie Hyer, President
COO: Roger Hite, Chief Operating Officer
CFO: Rick Harron, Chief Financial Officer
CMO: Nanette Mickiewicz, M.D., Chief Medical Officer
CIO: Lee Vanderpool, Vice President
CHR: Vicki Miranda, Director Human Resources
Web address: www.dominicanhospital.org

| | 21 | 10 | 282 | 13596 | 186 | 147456 | 1096 | 183427 | 87958 | 1199 |

Many Facility Codes have changed. Please refer to the AHA Guide Code Chart.

Hospital, Address, Telephone, Approval, Facility, and Physician Codes, Health Care System	Classi-fication Codes		Utilization Data					Expense (thousands) of dollars		
	Control	Service	Staffed Beds	Admissions	Census	Outpatient Visits	Births	Total	Payroll	Personnel

★ American Hospital Association (AHA) membership
□ Joint Commission on Accreditation of Healthcare Organizations (JCAHO) accreditation
○ American Osteopathic Association (AOA) accreditation
△ Commission on Accreditation of Rehabilitation Facilities (CARF) accreditation

SUTTER MATERNITY AND SURGERY CENTER OF SANTA CRUZ, 2900
Chanticleer Avenue, Zip 95065–1816; tel. 831/477–2200 **A**1 9 10 **F**2 11 21 22
26 27 28 29 40 46 48 59 63 64 108 **P**3 **S** Sutter Health, Sacramento, CA
Primary Contact: Richard Nichols, Administrator
COO: Katherine Manuel, Vice President Foundation Affairs and Chief Operating Officer
CFO: Glen Groves, Chief Financial Officer
CMO: Dean Walker, M.D., Chief of Staff
CHR: Al Nocella, Vice President Human Resources
Web address: www.suttermatsurg.org
23 44 28 1921 13 5458 — 24361 — —

SANTA MARIA—Santa Barbara County
MARIAN MEDICAL CENTER, 1400 East Church Street, Zip 93454–5906,
Mailing Address: P.O. Box 1238, Zip 93456–1238; tel. 805/739–3000, (Total
facility includes 95 beds in nursing home–type unit) **A**1 2 9 10 **F**2 9 11 12 14 21
22 23 26 27 28 29 32 33 34 35 36 37 38 39 40 41 42 44 45 46 47 48 49
50 51 52 53 58 59 61 62 63 65 66 69 70 73 75 81 82 84 85 86 88 92 94
95 96 97 106 107 108 109 110 **S** Catholic Healthcare West, San Francisco, CA
Primary Contact: Charles J. Cova, President
Web address: www.marianmedicalcenter.org
21 10 242 11587 198 254443 — 113193 — —

SANTA MONICA—Los Angeles County
SAINT JOHN'S HEALTH CENTER, 1328 Twenty Second Street,
Zip 90404–2091; tel. 310/829–5511 **A**1 2 9 10 **F**2 12 14 21 22 23 26 27 29
31 33 46 47 48 49 51 52 53 55 56 57 58 59 60 61 62 63 65 69 72 77 79
81 82 84 86 87 88 94 96 106 108 109 **P**5 **S** Sisters of Charity of Leavenworth
Health System, Lenexa, KS
Primary Contact: Lou Lazatin, Interim President
CMO: Charles Pietrafesa, M.D., Executive Medical Director
CHR: David Blake, Ph.D., JD, Vice President
Web address: www.stjohns.org
21 10 195 12958 173 193032 — 189658 — —

SANTA MONICA–UCLA MEDICAL CENTER, 1250 16th Street, Zip 90404;
tel. 310/319–4000 **A**1 2 3 5 9 10 **F**2 9 10 11 12 15 17 19 21 22 23 27 28
29 33 37 38 44 46 48 52 53 55 56 57 58 59 61 62 63 64 66 75 81 82 83
84 85 86 87 88 93 94 108 109 **P**6 **S** University of California–Systemwide
Administration, Oakland, CA
Primary Contact: John Stone, Interim Director
COO: Brenda Kuhn, R.N., Ph.D., Chief Operating Officer
CFO: Sergio L. Melgar, Chief Financial Officer
CIO: Michael McCoy, M.D., Senior Associate Director, Chief Information Officer
Web address: www.healthcare.ucla.edu
12 10 221 9713 140 98210 1860 129449 59793 983

SANTA ROSA—Sonoma County
KAISER FOUNDATION HOSPITAL, 401 Bicentennial Way, Zip 95403–2192;
tel. 707/571–4000 **A**1 10 **F**9 11 21 23 26 27 28 29 33 35 50 51 52 53 55
56 57 58 59 60 61 62 63 65 66 75 81 82 84 88 92 94 96 108 110 **S** Kaiser
Foundation Hospitals, Oakland, CA
Primary Contact: Susan Janvrin, R.N., Senior Vice President and Administrator
Web address: www.ca.kaiserpermanente.org
23 10 117 9179 85 — 1789 — — 716

SANTA ROSA MEMORIAL HOSPITAL, 1165 Montgomery Drive,
Zip 95405–4897, Mailing Address: P.O. Box 522, Zip 95402–0522;
tel. 707/546–3210 **A**1 2 9 10 **F**9 11 12 15 16 17 19 21 22 23 24 26 27 28
29 32 33 34 36 37 38 42 44 45 46 48 49 52 53 55 56 57 58 59 60 61 62
63 65 69 70 71 75 76 77 78 81 82 84 85 87 88 92 95 96 101 107 108 110
S St. Joseph Health System, Orange, CA
Primary Contact: George Perez, President and Chief Executive Officer
COO: Michael Glasberg, Chief Operating Officer
CFO: Donald Miller, Chief Financial Officer
CMO: Gary Greensweig, D.O., Chief Medical Officer
CIO: Patrick Wylie, Director Information Systems
CHR: Carol Aaron, Senior Vice President Human Resources
Web address: www.stjosephhealth.org
23 10 325 14350 225 184591 1319 226066 90932 1510

SUTTER MEDICAL CENTER OF SANTA ROSA, 3325 Chanate Road,
Zip 95404–1707; tel. 707/576–4000, (Includes SUTTER WARRACK HOSPITAL,
2449 Summerfield Road, Zip 95405–7815; tel. 707/576–4200) (Total facility
includes 10 beds in nursing home–type unit) **A**1 3 5 9 10 **F**2 9 10 11 12 14 15
17 19 21 22 23 26 27 28 29 30 32 33 38 40 42 46 49 50 53 55 56 59 62
63 64 69 70 71 81 82 84 85 88 92 94 96 108 109 110 **P**3 5 **S** Sutter Health,
Sacramento, CA
Primary Contact: Michael J. Cohill, Chief Executive Officer
COO: F Dana Ellerbe, Assistant Administrator
CFO: Avery Schlesenberg, Chief Financial Officer
CMO: Robert R. Wright, M.D., Chief of Staff
CHR: Susan Vachon, Administrative Director Human Resources
Web address: www.sutterhealth.org
23 10 181 8602 118 119710 1965 147621 51433 706

SEBASTOPOL—Sonoma County
PALM DRIVE HOSPITAL, 501 Petaluma Avenue, Zip 95472–4281;
tel. 707/823–8511 **A**9 10 **F**2 9 12 21 29 30 33 36 37 46 48 52 55 62 63 64
69 81 88 97
Primary Contact: Shawndra Nimtz, Chief Executive Officer
Web address: www.palmdrivehospital.com
23 10 17 1142 12 27656 — 18673 — —

Hospital, Address, Telephone, Approval, Facility, and Physician Codes, Health Care System	Classi-fication Codes		Utilization Data					Expense (thousands) of dollars		
★ American Hospital Association (AHA) membership □ Joint Commission on Accreditation of Healthcare Organizations (JCAHO) accreditation ○ American Osteopathic Association (AOA) accreditation △ Commission on Accreditation of Rehabilitation Facilities (CARF) accreditation	Control	Service	Staffed Beds	Admissions	Census	Outpatient Visits	Births	Total	Payroll	Personnel

SELMA—Fresno County

⊠ **SELMA COMMUNITY HOSPITAL**, 1141 Rose Avenue, Zip 93662–3241; tel. 559/891–1000, (Total facility includes 8 beds in nursing home–type unit) **A**1 3 5 9 10 **F**9 11 12 21 22 26 27 28 29 33 37 46 52 58 59 62 63 65 81 84 92 98 **S** Adventist Health, Roseville, CA
Primary Contact: Richard L. Rawson, President and Chief Executive Officer
COO: Richard L. Rawson, President
Web address: www.adventisthealth.org

| | 23 | 10 | 24 | 2759 | 22 | 135870 | — | 29412 | — | — |

SEPULVEDA—Los Angeles County, See Los Angeles
SHERMAN OAKS—Los Angeles County, See Los Angeles
SIMI VALLEY—Ventura County

⊠ **SIMI VALLEY HOSPITAL AND HEALTH CARE SERVICES**, 2975 North Sycamore Drive, Zip 93065–1201; tel. 805/955–6000, (Includes SIMI VALLEY HOSPITAL AND HEALTH CARE SERVICES–SOUTH CAMPUS, 1850 Heywood Street, Zip 93065; tel. 805/955–7000), (Total facility includes 44 beds in nursing home–type unit) **A**1 2 9 10 **F**2 11 12 21 22 26 27 28 33 35 39 42 46 48 51 52 55 58 59 60 63 65 66 68 71 75 81 82 84 85 87 88 92 106 108 110 **S** Adventist Health, Roseville, CA
Primary Contact: Margaret R. Peterson, Ph.D., President and Chief Executive Officer
CFO: Larry W. Pugh, Vice President Finance
CMO: Jonathan Kurohara, M.D., Chief of Staff
CIO: Orville Beach, Director Information Systems
CHR: Wesley Schmidt, Director Human Resources
Web address: www.simivalleyhospital.com

| | 21 | 10 | 191 | 7607 | 107 | 108920 | — | 76822 | | |

SOLVANG—Santa Barbara County

⊠ **SANTA YNEZ VALLEY COTTAGE HOSPITAL**, 700 Alamo Pintado Road, Zip 93463–2295; tel. 805/688–6431 **A**1 9 10 20 **F**2 3 9 12 13 14 33 45 46 52 55 56 63 64 67 68 71 81 88 92 97 **S** Cottage Health System, Santa Barbara, CA
Primary Contact: Wende Cappetta, Administrator
Web address: www.cottagehealthsystem.org

| | 23 | 10 | 6 | 298 | 2 | 29124 | 0 | 7509 | 3527 | 53 |

SONOMA—Sonoma County

□ **SONOMA VALLEY HOSPITAL**, 347 Andrieux Street, Zip 95476–6811, Mailing Address: P.O. Box 600, Zip 95476–0600; tel. 707/935–5000 **A**1 9 10 **F**11 21 22 26 27 28 29 33 36 40 41 46 48 51 52 53 55 58 59 60 62 63 69 81 82 84 88 92 94 96 106 108 110
Primary Contact: Robert P. Kowal, President and Chief Executive Officer
Web address: www.svh.com

| | 16 | 10 | 49 | 1996 | 32 | 74860 | — | 33678 | | |

SONORA—Tuolumne County

⊠ **SONORA REGIONAL MEDICAL CENTER**, 1000 Greenley Road, Zip 95370–4819; tel. 209/532–5000, (Total facility includes 64 beds in nursing home–type unit) **A**1 9 10 **F**2 9 11 12 14 15 21 22 27 28 29 30 33 37 42 44 45 46 47 48 51 52 55 58 59 60 61 63 64 65 66 69 70 81 82 84 85 88 92 94 95 96 97 107 108 **S** Adventist Health, Roseville, CA
Primary Contact: Lary Davis, President and Chief Executive Officer
CFO: David Larsen, Vice President Finance
CMO: Danny Anderson, M.D., Chief of Staff
CIO: Gail Witzlsteiner, Marketing Director
CHR: Donn Swartz, Director Human Resources
Web address: www.sonorahospital.org

| | 21 | 10 | 147 | 3824 | 99 | 229314 | 513 | 91493 | 33490 | 694 |

□ **TUOLUMNE GENERAL HOSPITAL**, 101 Hospital Road, Zip 95370–5297; tel. 209/533–7100, (Total facility includes 42 beds in nursing home–type unit) **A**1 9 10 **F**1 9 12 21 27 28 29 32 33 39 41 42 44 46 48 50 52 55 58 60 61 62 63 65 66 67 68 69 70 71 75 77 81 85 88 92 94 96 97 108 110 **P**6
Primary Contact: Barry M. Woerman, Administrator
Web address: www.tghospital.com

| | 13 | 10 | 79 | 1773 | 66 | 111876 | 0 | 26292 | 11356 | 266 |

SOUTH LAKE TAHOE—El Dorado County

⊠ **BARTON MEMORIAL HOSPITAL**, 2170 South Avenue, Zip 96150–7008, Mailing Address: P.O. Box 9578, Zip 96158–9578; tel. 530/541–3420 **A**1 9 10 20 **F**2 9 11 12 21 22 29 33 36 37 46 47 49 52 53 55 57 58 59 60 62 63 64 65 69 81 84 85 88 92 93 94 95 97 106 107 108 110
Primary Contact: William G. Gordon, Chief Executive Officer
CFO: Richard P. Derby, Chief Financial Officer
CMO: M Kelly Shanahan, M.D., Chief of Staff
CIO: Rob Quadri, Management Information Systems Director
CHR: LeAnne Kankel, Director Human Resources
Web address: www.bartonhealth.org

| | 23 | 10 | 114 | 3811 | 81 | 124468 | — | 77569 | | |

SOUTH SAN FRANCISCO—San Mateo County

⊠ **KAISER FOUNDATION HOSPITAL**, 1200 El Camino Real, Zip 94080–3299; tel. 650/742–2000 **A**1 10 **F**9 21 22 26 27 28 33 35 36 44 46 50 51 52 53 55 58 60 61 62 63 66 81 82 88 92 94 96 108 110 **S** Kaiser Foundation Hospitals, Oakland, CA
Primary Contact: Linda Jensen, Senior Vice President and Administrator
Web address: www.kaiserpermanente.org

| | 23 | 10 | 105 | 6319 | 75 | — | 0 | — | — | — |

STOCKTON—San Joaquin County

□ **DAMERON HOSPITAL**, 525 West Acacia Street, Zip 95203–2484; tel. 209/944–5550, (Nonreporting) **A**1 9 10
Primary Contact: Christopher Arismendi, M.D., Chief Executive Officer
Web address: www.dameronhospital.com

| | 23 | 10 | 188 | — | — | — | — | — | | |

Many Facility Codes have changed. Please refer to the AHA Guide Code Chart.

© 2005 AHA Guide

Hospital, Address, Telephone, Approval, Facility, and Physician Codes, Health Care System	Classi-fication Codes		Utilization Data					Expense (thousands) of dollars		
★ American Hospital Association (AHA) membership ☐ Joint Commission on Accreditation of Healthcare Organizations (JCAHO) accreditation ○ American Osteopathic Association (AOA) accreditation △ Commission on Accreditation of Rehabilitation Facilities (CARF) accreditation	Control	Service	Staffed Beds	Admissions	Census	Outpatient Visits	Births	Total	Payroll	Personnel
⊠ **ST. JOSEPH'S BEHAVIORAL HEALTH CENTER**, 2510 North California Street, Zip 95204–5502; tel. 209/461–2000 **A**1 10 **F**3 4 5 21 24 26 27 28 39 44 48 53 71 72 73 74 75 76 77 78 92 94 96 **S** Catholic Healthcare West, San Francisco, CA Primary Contact: James Sondecker, President CFO: Wayne Silveria, Chief Financial Officer CMO: Michael Smith, M.D., Medical Director Web address: www.stjosephscanhelp.org	21	22	35	1563	32	6767	0	7299	3786	88
⊠ **ST. JOSEPH'S MEDICAL CENTER**, 1800 North California Street, Zip 95204–6019, Mailing Address: P.O. Box 213008, Zip 95213–3008; tel. 209/943–2000, (Total facility includes 27 beds in nursing home–type unit) **A**1 2 9 10 **F**2 11 14 15 17 19 21 22 23 26 27 28 29 33 37 38 41 47 49 51 52 55 56 57 58 59 60 61 63 64 66 69 79 81 82 87 88 92 94 96 107 110 **P**5 **S** Catholic Healthcare West, San Francisco, CA Primary Contact: Donald J. Wiley, President CFO: Wayne Silveria, Chief Financial Officer CMO: Sandon Saffier, M.D., Vice President CHR: Debbie Murillo, Vice President Human Resources Web address: www.stjosephsCARES.org	21	10	294	14307	233	505125	2043	218108	96964	1905
SUN CITY—Riverside County										
⊠ **MENIFEE VALLEY MEDICAL CENTER**, 28400 McCall Boulevard, Zip 92585–9537; tel. 951/679–8888 **A**1 9 10 **F**9 12 14 21 27 28 29 33 44 45 46 47 48 50 52 55 58 59 61 63 65 81 84 88 94 108 **S** Valley Health System, Hemet, CA Primary Contact: Kim Eastman, R.N., Administrator CFO: Michael Garko, Chief Financial Officer CIO: Weldon Clark, Chief Information Officer	16	10	84	5139	60	31040	—	22549		—
SUN VALLEY—Los Angeles County, See Los Angeles										
SUSANVILLE—Lassen County										
⊠ **BANNER LASSEN MEDICAL CENTER**, 1800 Spring Ridge Drive, Zip 96130–4809; tel. 530/252–2000 **A**1 9 10 20 **F**2 9 11 12 21 23 26 27 28 29 33 36 39 44 46 48 51 52 53 55 58 59 60 61 62 63 64 66 81 84 88 93 94 97 108 110 **S** Banner Health, Phoenix, AZ Primary Contact: David S. Anderson, FACHE, Chief Executive Officer CFO: Raoul Miranda, Chief Financial Officer Web address: www.bannerhealth.com	23	10	38	1192	12	46850	266	20801	9487	166
SYLMAR—Los Angeles County, See Los Angeles										
TARZANA—Los Angeles County, See Los Angeles										
TEHACHAPI—Kern County										
★ **TEHACHAPI VALLEY HEALTHCARE DISTRICT**, 115 West E Street, Zip 93561, Mailing Address: P.O. Box 1900, Zip 93581–1900; tel. 661/823–3000, (Nonreporting) **A**9 10 18 Primary Contact: Raymond T. Hino, Chief Executive Officer CFO: Brian J. Doe, Jr, Chief Financial Officer CIO: Ed Gordon, Director Information Services CHR: Debbie Thebeau, Human Resources Director Web address: www.tvhd.org	16	10	24	—	—	—	—	—	—	—
TEMPLETON—San Luis Obispo County										
⊠ **TWIN CITIES COMMUNITY HOSPITAL**, 1100 Las Tablas Road, Zip 93465–9704; tel. 805/434–3500 **A**1 9 10 **F**2 11 21 22 23 27 28 29 33 46 47 48 52 55 57 58 59 60 61 62 63 81 82 85 88 94 96 107 108 **P**5 **S** TENET Healthcare Corporation, Dallas, TX Primary Contact: Richard D. Lyons, Chief Executive Officer COO: Suellen Smith, Chief Operating Officer CFO: Paul Posmoga, Chief Financial Officer CMO: Terry Ann Murphy, Chief Nursing Officer CIO: David Pollock, Director Information Systems CHR: Eloise Rendon, Human Resources Director Web address: www.twincitieshospital.com	33	10	60	5024	59	58405	—	48671	—	—
THOUSAND OAKS—Los Angeles County										
⊠ **LOS ROBLES HOSPITAL AND MEDICAL CENTER**, (Formerly Los Robles Regional Medical Center), 215 West Janss Road, Zip 91360–1847; tel. 805/497–2727, (Total facility includes 42 beds in nursing home–type unit) **A**1 2 9 10 **F**2 9 10 11 14 15 17 19 21 22 23 27 28 29 32 33 34 42 44 45 46 48 50 52 54 55 56 57 58 59 60 61 62 63 64 66 68 69 71 74 75 76 81 82 88 92 94 96 97 98 106 108 109 **S** HCA, Nashville, TN Primary Contact: Jim Sherman, President and Chief Exeuctive Officer COO: Bernard Klein, M.D., Chief Operating Officer and Medical Director CFO: Debra J. Herwaldt, Chief Financial Officer CMO: Bernard Klein, M.D., Chief Operating Officer and Medical Director CHR: Dayle Dalton, Vice President Human Resources Web address: www.losrobleshospital.com	33	10	265	13241	192	93576	1992	169180	66320	1108
TORRANCE—Los Angeles County										
☐ **DEL AMO HOSPITAL**, 23700 Camino Del Sol, Zip 90505–5000; tel. 310/530–1151, (Nonreporting) **A**1 10 **S** Universal Health Services, Inc., King of Prussia, PA Primary Contact: Lisa K. Montes, Chief Executive Officer Web address: www.delamohospital.com	33	22	70	—	—	—	—	—	—	—

Hospital, Address, Telephone, Approval, Facility, and Physician Codes, Health Care System	Classi-fication Codes		Utilization Data					Expense (thousands) of dollars		
★ American Hospital Association (AHA) membership □ Joint Commission on Accreditation of Healthcare Organizations (JCAHO) accreditation ○ American Osteopathic Association (AOA) accreditation △ Commission on Accreditation of Rehabilitation Facilities (CARF) accreditation	Control	Service	Staffed Beds	Admissions	Census	Outpatient Visits	Births	Total	Payroll	Personnel
□ **LAC–HARBOR–UNIVERSITY OF CALIFORNIA AT LOS ANGELES MEDICAL CENTER**, 1000 West Carson Street, Zip 90502–2004; tel. 310/222–2345 **A**1 2 3 5 10 **F**2 9 10 11 12 14 15 16 17 18 19 20 21 22 23 26 27 28 29 31 33 34 35 37 39 42 44 45 47 48 49 50 52 53 55 56 57 58 59 60 61 62 63 64 66 67 69 70 71 73 75 81 82 85 88 89 90 93 94 95 96 98 101 107 108 109 110 **P**3 6 **S** Los Angeles County–Department of Health Services, Los Angeles, CA Primary Contact: Tecla A. Mickoseff, Chief Executive Officer Web address: www.humc.edu	13	10	325	21550	321	361998	934	519387	163576	2748
⊠ **PROVIDENCE–LITTLE COMPANY OF MARY SERVICE AREA**, 4101 Torrance Boulevard, Zip 90503–4698; tel. 310/540–7676, (Total facility includes 110 beds in nursing home–type unit) **A**1 2 9 10 **F**9 11 14 15 17 19 21 22 26 27 28 29 33 37 45 46 47 48 51 52 54 55 56 57 58 59 60 61 62 63 64 65 66 69 70 81 82 84 86 87 88 92 94 96 97 107 108 109 110 **P**5 **S** Providence Health System, Seattle, WA Primary Contact: Blair Contratto, Chief Executive Officer CFO: Karl Carrier, Vice President Corporate Finance CIO: Brad Osborne, Chief Information Officer Web address: www.lcmweb.org	23	10	360	17591	252	246637	2782	198915	75192	1488
⊠ **TORRANCE MEMORIAL MEDICAL CENTER**, 3330 Lomita Boulevard, Zip 90505–5002; tel. 310/325–9110 **A**1 2 9 10 **F**2 4 9 10 11 12 13 14 15 17 19 21 22 23 26 27 28 29 31 33 36 37 38 39 40 42 45 46 47 48 49 50 51 52 55 56 57 58 59 60 61 62 63 64 65 66 69 70 79 80 81 82 83 84 85 86 87 88 92 93 94 96 107 108 109 110 Primary Contact: George W. Graham, President and Chief Executive Officer COO: Craig Leach, Executive Vice President and Chief Operating Officer CFO: Douglas Klebe, Chief Financial Officer CMO: John McNamara, M.D., Chief of Staff CHR: Lois Michael, Vice President Human Resources Web address: www.torrancememorial.org	23	10	355	22900	269	237740	3906	262907	117601	2114
TRACY—San Joaquin County										
⊠ **SUTTER TRACY COMMUNITY HOSPITAL**, 1420 North Tracy Boulevard, Zip 95376–3497; tel. 209/835–1500 **A**1 9 10 **F**9 12 21 22 23 26 27 28 30 33 37 46 47 48 50 52 53 55 58 59 60 61 62 63 64 69 81 82 84 88 94 95 96 106 108 109 110 **S** Sutter Health, Sacramento, CA Primary Contact: Gary D. Rapaport, Chief Executive Officer COO: Fred Ford, Assistant Administrator CFO: Eric Dalton, Chief Financial Officer CIO: Karen Mudd, Director Marketing and Public Affairs CHR: Vanessa Dega, Human Resources Manager Web address: www.suttertracy.org	23	10	79	3915	43	77533	760	61103	23495	392
TRAVIS AFB—Solano County										
⊠ **DAVID GRANT MEDICAL CENTER**, 101 Bodin Circle, Zip 94535–1800; tel. 707/423–7300, (Nonreporting) **A**1 3 5 **S** Department of the Air Force, Washington, DC Primary Contact: Colonel George Johnson, Administrator	41	10	172	—	—	—	—	—	—	—
TRUCKEE—Nevada County										
○ **TAHOE FOREST HOSPITAL DISTRICT**, 10121 Pine Avenue, Zip 96161–4856, Mailing Address: P.O. Box 759, Zip 96160–0759; tel. 530/587–6011, (Total facility includes 39 beds in nursing home–type unit) **A**9 10 11 20 **F**2 9 11 12 21 22 27 28 29 33 36 46 47 48 51 55 59 60 62 63 64 66 69 81 88 92 93 94 96 97 106 108 Primary Contact: Robert A. Schapper, Chief Executive Officer Web address: www.tfhd.com	16	10	76	1946	49	68974	444	57405	20794	403
TULARE—Tulare County										
⊠ **TULARE LOCAL HEALTH CARE DISTRICT**, 869 Cherry Street, Zip 93274–2207; tel. 559/688–0821 **A**1 9 10 **F**2 6 9 11 12 21 22 23 24 27 28 29 33 40 44 46 48 51 53 57 58 59 61 62 63 65 66 69 81 82 84 87 88 93 94 96 106 107 108 Primary Contact: Robert M. Montion, Chief Executive Officer COO: Denise Perry, Chief Operating Officer CFO: Lucy Reimche, Chief Financial Officer CMO: Douglas Malcolm, M.D., Chief Medical Staff CIO: Lucy Reimche, Chief Financial Officer CHR: Brooke Brown, Human Resources Coordinator Web address: www.tdhs.org	16	10	100	5645	61	100452	—	47619	—	—
TURLOCK—Stanislaus County										
⊠ **EMANUEL MEDICAL CENTER**, 825 Delbon Avenue, Zip 95382–2016, Mailing Address: P.O. Box 819005, Zip 95381–9005; tel. 209/667–4200, (Total facility includes 145 beds in nursing home–type unit) **A**1 9 10 **F**8 9 11 12 14 21 22 29 32 33 36 37 40 42 44 45 46 47 48 49 51 52 53 54 55 58 59 60 61 62 63 69 81 82 84 88 92 94 96 107 108 109 110 **P**1 5 Primary Contact: John R. Sigsbury, President and Chief Executive Officer COO: Michael T. Iltis, Vice President Professional Services CFO: Margaret Lera, Chief Financial Officer CHR: Terry Gray, Vice President Human Resources Web address: www.emanuelmed.org	21	10	270	12019	240	90047	2398	109939	50719	1079

Many Facility Codes have changed. Please refer to the AHA Guide Code Chart.   © 2005 AHA Guide

Hospital, Address, Telephone, Approval, Facility, and Physician Codes, Health Care System	Classi-fication Codes		Utilization Data					Expense (thousands) of dollars		
★ American Hospital Association (AHA) membership □ Joint Commission on Accreditation of Healthcare Organizations (JCAHO) accreditation ○ American Osteopathic Association (AOA) accreditation △ Commission on Accreditation of Rehabilitation Facilities (CARF) accreditation	Control	Service	Staffed Beds	Admissions	Census	Outpatient Visits	Births	Total	Payroll	Personnel

TUSTIN—Orange County

☒ **HEALTHSOUTH TUSTIN REHABILITATION HOSPITAL**, 14851 Yorba Street, Zip 92780–2925; tel. 714/832–9200, (Nonreporting) **A**1 9 10 **S** HEALTHSOUTH Corporation, Birmingham, AL
Primary Contact: Scott Rifkin, Administrator
CFO: Susan Wilson, Controller
CMO: Wilfredo Escober, M.D., President of Staff
CHR: Tobi Williams, Manager Human Resources
Web address: www.healthsouth.com

| | 33 | 46 | 48 | — | — | — | — | — | — | — |

□ **TUSTIN HOSPITAL AND MEDICAL CENTER**, 14662 Newport Avenue, Zip 92680–6064; tel. 714/838–9600, (Total facility includes 42 beds in nursing home–type unit) (Nonreporting) **A**1 9 10 **S** Pacific Health Corporation, Tustin, CA
Primary Contact: R. Michael Hartman, Chief Executive Officer
Web address: www.tustinhospital.com

| | 33 | 10 | 64 | — | — | — | — | — | — | — |

TWENTYNINE PALMS—San Bernardino County

☒ **NAVAL HOSPITAL**, Mailing Address: Box 788250, MCAGCC, Zip 92278–8250; tel. 760/830–2190, (Nonreporting) **A**1 **S** Bureau of Medicine and Surgery, Department of the Navy, Washington, DC
Primary Contact: Captain Robert Engelhart, Commanding Officer
CFO: Lieutenant Kristin Kobi, Comptroller
Web address: www.nhtp.med.navy.mil/nhtp

| | 43 | 10 | 29 | — | — | — | — | — | — | — |

UKIAH—Mendocino County

☒ **UKIAH VALLEY MEDICAL CENTER**, 275 Hospital Drive, Zip 95482–4531; tel. 707/462–3111, (Includes UKIAH VALLEY MEDICAL CENTER–HOSPITAL DRIVE) **A**1 9 10 **F**9 11 12 21 22 23 26 27 28 29 33 39 40 46 48 53 55 56 58 59 60 61 62 63 66 69 81 82 84 87 88 94 108 109 **S** Adventist Health, Roseville, CA
Primary Contact: Mark LaRose, President and Chief Executive Officer
CFO: Cheryl Curry, Vice President Finance
Web address: www.adventisthealth.org

| | 21 | 10 | 56 | 3864 | 33 | 67148 | — | 46524 | — | — |

UPLAND—San Bernardino County

☒ **SAN ANTONIO COMMUNITY HOSPITAL**, 999 San Bernardino Road, Zip 91786–4920, Mailing Address: Box 5001, Zip 91785–5001; tel. 909/985–2811 **A**1 2 9 10 **F**2 9 11 12 14 15 17 19 21 23 26 28 29 31 32 33 37 38 39 42 46 48 49 50 52 54 55 56 57 58 59 60 61 62 63 65 66 69 81 82 84 85 87 88 89 94 96 107 108 110
Primary Contact: Steven C. Moreau, President and Chief Executive Officer
CFO: Roger Parsons, Senior Vice President Finance
CMO: Nabil Koudsi, M.D., President Medical Staff
CIO: Perry Strength, Director Information Services
CHR: Lynn Kelly, Vice President Human Resources
Web address: www.sach.org

| | 23 | 10 | 283 | 14468 | 163 | 201584 | 2272 | 199321 | 88880 | 1528 |

VACAVILLE—Solano County

CALIFORNIA MEDICAL FACILITY, 1600 California Drive, Zip 95696–2000; tel. 707/448–6841, (Nonreporting)
Primary Contact: Brenda Green, R.N., Correctional Health Services Administrator II

| | 12 | 11 | 215 | — | — | — | — | — | — | — |

★ **NORTHBAY VACAVALLEY HOSPITAL**, 1000 Nut Tree Road, Zip 95687–4100; tel. 707/446–4000 **A**9 10 **F**2 9 21 22 27 28 33 39 52 55 58 60 62 63 64 66 69 70 81 82 87 88 94 96 108 110 **S** NorthBay Healthcare System, Fairfield, CA
Primary Contact: Deborah Sugiyama, President
CFO: Arthur E. DeNio, Chief Financial Officer
CIO: Paul Alcala, Vice President and Chief Information Officer
Web address: www.northbay.org

| | 23 | 10 | 49 | 2460 | 34 | 60150 | 2 | 56511 | 19186 | 202 |

VALENCIA—Los Angeles County

□ **HENRY MAYO NEWHALL MEMORIAL HOSPITAL**, 23845 McBean Parkway, Zip 91355–2083; tel. 661/253–8000 **A**1 2 9 10 **F**2 4 6 9 12 14 21 22 23 26 27 28 29 33 34 36 38 42 46 47 48 49 51 52 53 55 57 59 60 61 62 63 65 66 68 69 71 73 75 77 81 82 84 87 88 92 94 96 106 107 108 109 110 **P**5
Primary Contact: Roger E. Seaver, President and Chief Executive Officer
Web address: www.henrymayo.com

| | 23 | 10 | 217 | 10905 | 148 | 67734 | 1290 | 99311 | 36772 | 834 |

VALLEJO—Solano County

☒ △ **KAISER FOUNDATION HOSPITAL AND REHABILITATION CENTER**, 975 Sereno Drive, Zip 94589–2441; tel. 707/651–1000 **A**1 7 10 **F**4 11 12 14 21 22 23 26 27 28 29 33 36 37 38 46 47 48 49 50 51 52 53 55 56 57 58 59 60 61 62 63 65 68 69 70 77 81 82 84 88 93 94 106 107 108 109 110 **S** Kaiser Foundation Hospitals, Oakland, CA
Primary Contact: Deborah D. Romer, Senior Vice President and Area Manager
COO: Mariann White, Chief Operating Officer
CFO: Pamela Booher, Area Finance Officer
CMO: Steve Stricker, Physician–in–Chief
CIO: Brad Pfeifer, Area Technology Director
CHR: Mike McClure, Human Resources Director
Web address: www.kaiserpermanente.org

| | 23 | 10 | 270 | 17895 | 231 | — | 2252 | — | — | 381 |

☒ **ST HELENA HOSPITAL–CENTER FOR BEHAVIORAL HEALTH**, (Formerly California Specialty Hospital), 525 Oregon Street, Zip 94590–3201; tel. 707/648–2200 **A**1 10 **F**1 26 27 28 71 72 77 78 94 **S** Adventist Health, Roseville, CA
Primary Contact: JoAline Olson, R.N., President and Chief Executive Officer
CFO: Edward A. McDonald, Chief Financial Officer
Web address: www.sthelenahospital.org/Hospital/HS_California/Cal_child.html

| | 21 | 22 | 61 | 2228 | 49 | 2084 | 0 | 12634 | — | — |

Hospital, Address, Telephone, Approval, Facility, and Physician Codes, Health Care System	Classi-fication Codes		Utilization Data					Expense (thousands) of dollars		
★ American Hospital Association (AHA) membership □ Joint Commission on Accreditation of Healthcare Organizations (JCAHO) accreditation ○ American Osteopathic Association (AOA) accreditation △ Commission on Accreditation of Rehabilitation Facilities (CARF) accreditation	Control	Service	Staffed Beds	Admissions	Census	Outpatient Visits	Births	Total	Payroll	Personnel

⊠ **SUTTER SOLANO MEDICAL CENTER**, 300 Hospital Drive, Zip 94589–2517, Mailing Address: P.O. Box 3189, Zip 94589–3189; tel. 707/554–4444, (Total facility includes 9 beds in nursing home–type unit) **A**1 9 10 12 **F**9 11 12 22 23 33 37 48 49 53 55 59 61 62 63 81 82 84 85 88 92 94 96 108 **S** Sutter Health, Sacramento, CA Primary Contact: Theresa Glubka, Chief Executive Officer CFO: Benny Stafford, Interim Finance Director CHR: Peter Eggleton, Human Resources Director Web address: www.suttersolano.org	23	10	111	5797	66	80038	—	77147	—	—
VAN NUYS—Los Angeles County, See Los Angeles										
VENTURA—Ventura County										
□ **AURORA VISTA DEL MAR HOSPITAL**, 801 Seneca Street, Zip 93001–1411; tel. 805/653–6434 **A**1 10 **F**28 71 72 73 74 75 77 78 **P**5 Primary Contact: Mayla Krebsbach, Chief Executive Officer Web address: www.aurorabehavioral.com	33	22	87	2830	60	2466	0	12466	6190	152
⊠ **COMMUNITY MEMORIAL HOSPITAL OF SAN BUENAVENTURA**, 147 North Brent Street, Zip 93003–2854; tel. 805/652–5011 **A**1 9 10 **F**2 9 10 11 12 14 15 17 19 21 23 27 33 40 41 46 48 49 53 55 56 59 60 61 62 63 64 69 81 82 84 85 86 87 88 94 96 Primary Contact: Gary Wilde, Chief Executive Officer COO: Ken Strople, Senior Vice President Operations CFO: David Glyer, Director Financial Services CMO: Peter Gaal, M.D., Medical Director CIO: Nick Pappas, Manager Information Systems CHR: Jon Crozier, Director Web address: www.cmhhospital.org	23	10	240	14662	158	132987	3401	163571	59728	1305
□ **VENTURA COUNTY MEDICAL CENTER**, 3291 Loma Vista Road, Zip 93003–3099; tel. 805/652–6000 **A**1 5 9 10 **F**2 12 14 23 27 28 33 34 42 50 52 55 56 58 59 60 61 62 63 66 69 71 75 76 77 81 87 88 90 94 107 108 109 **P**5 Primary Contact: Pierre Durand, Administrator Web address: www.vchca.org	13	10	144	10713	134	596964	—	146404	—	—
VICTORVILLE—Riverside County										
VICTOR VALLEY COMMUNITY HOSPITAL See Wildomar										
VISALIA—Tulare County										
⊠ △ **KAWEAH DELTA HEALTH CARE DISTRICT**, 400 West Mineral King Boulevard, Zip 93291–6263; tel. 559/624–2000, (Includes COMMUNITY HEALTH CENTER, 1633 South Court Street, Zip 93277, Mailing Address: Box 911, Zip 93277; tel. 209/824–2221), (Total facility includes 70 beds in nursing home–type unit) **A**1 2 7 9 10 **F**2 4 11 12 15 17 19 21 22 23 26 27 28 29 33 36 37 38 39 40 41 42 44 46 47 48 49 51 52 53 55 57 58 59 60 61 62 63 64 65 66 68 69 70 71 72 73 74 75 76 77 81 82 84 85 86 88 92 93 94 95 96 98 106 107 108 109 110 Primary Contact: Lindsay K. Mann, Chief Executive Officer CFO: Gary Herbst, Senior Vice President and Chief Financial Officer CIO: Dave Gravender, Vice President and Chief Information Officer CHR: Jean Haskell, Vice President Human Resources Web address: www.kaweahdelta.org	16	10	490	20947	366	369511	4003	270987	113523	2643
WALNUT CREEK—Contra Costa County										
⊠ **JOHN MUIR MEDICAL CENTER**, 1601 Ygnacio Valley Road, Zip 94598–3194; tel. 925/939–3000 **A**1 10 **F**2 9 11 12 14 15 17 19 21 22 23 26 27 28 29 32 33 34 35 38 39 44 46 47 48 49 51 52 53 55 56 57 58 59 61 62 63 64 65 66 68 69 73 75 80 81 82 84 85 87 88 90 92 94 96 106 108 109 110 **P**3 5 **S** John Muir/Mount Diablo Health System, Walnut Creek, CA Primary Contact: Kenneth L. Meehan, President and Chief Administrative Officer Web address: www.jmmdhs.com/index.php/jmmdhs_jmmc.html	23	10	380	16624	247	198794	3032	384340	147382	1582
⊠ **KAISER FOUNDATION HOSPITAL**, 1425 South Main Street, Zip 94596–5300; tel. 925/295–4000, (Includes KAISER FOUNDATION HOSPITAL, 200 Muir Road, Martinez, Zip 94553–4696; tel. 510/372–1000) **A**1 5 10 **F**2 4 10 11 12 21 22 23 24 26 27 28 29 33 36 37 38 39 42 46 47 48 49 50 51 55 56 58 59 61 62 63 64 65 66 70 73 77 81 84 85 86 88 89 93 94 106 107 108 109 110 **S** Kaiser Foundation Hospitals, Oakland, CA Primary Contact: Sandi Small, Senior Vice President and Administrator COO: Christine Robisch, Chief Operating Officer CFO: Yakesun Wing, Business Strategy and Finance Leader CMO: Don Palmer, Chief of Staff CIO: Jim Greendale, Information Technology Leader CHR: Raymond Konieczek, Human Resource Business Partner Web address: www.kaiserpermanente.org	23	10	288	18453	240	112731	4037	—	—	996
WATSONVILLE—Santa Cruz County										
□ **WATSONVILLE COMMUNITY HOSPITAL**, 75 Nielson Street, Zip 95076–2468; tel. 831/724–4741, (Nonreporting) **A**1 9 10 **S** Community Health Systems, Inc., Brentwood, TN Primary Contact: Kaylor E. Shemberger, FACHE, Chief Executive Officer Web address: www.watsonvillehospital.com	33	10	64	—	—	—	—	—	—	—
WEAVERVILLE—Trinity County										
TRINITY HOSPITAL, 410 North Taylor Street, Zip 96093, Mailing Address: P.O. Box 1229, Zip 96093–1229; tel. 530/623–5541, (Total facility includes 26 beds in nursing home–type unit) (Nonreporting) **A**9 10 18 20 Primary Contact: Lawrence J. McDonough, Interim Administrator	13	10	51	—	—	—	—	—	—	—

Many Facility Codes have changed. Please refer to the AHA Guide Code Chart.   © 2005 AHA Guide

Hospital, Address, Telephone, Approval, Facility, and Physician Codes, Health Care System	Classification Codes		Utilization Data					Expense (thousands) of dollars		
★ American Hospital Association (AHA) membership □ Joint Commission on Accreditation of Healthcare Organizations (JCAHO) accreditation ○ American Osteopathic Association (AOA) accreditation △ Commission on Accreditation of Rehabilitation Facilities (CARF) accreditation	Control	Service	Staffed Beds	Admissions	Census	Outpatient Visits	Births	Total	Payroll	Personnel

WEST COVINA—Los Angeles County

□ **CITRUS VALLEY MEDICAL CENTER–QUEEN OF THE VALLEY CAMPUS**, 1115 South Sunset Avenue, Zip 91790–3940, Mailing Address: P.O. Box 1980, Zip 91793–1980; tel. 626/962–4011, (Nonreporting) **A**1 9 10 **S** Citrus Valley Health Partners, Covina, CA
Primary Contact: James T. Yoshioka, President and Chief Executive Officer
Web address: www.cvhp.org

| | 23 | 10 | 263 | — | — | — | — | — | — | — |

□ **DOCTORS HOSPITAL OF WEST COVINA**, 725 South Orange Avenue, Zip 91790–2614; tel. 626/338–8481, (Total facility includes 24 beds in nursing home–type unit) **A**1 9 10 **F**32 55 62 63 64 77 78 92 94 110 **P**5
Primary Contact: Gerald H. Wallman, Administrator

| | 33 | 10 | 51 | 359 | 25 | — | 0 | 9736 | — | — |

SPECIALTY HOSPITAL, 845 North Lark Ellen Avenue, Zip 91791–1069; tel. 626/339–5451, (Nonreporting) **A**9
Primary Contact: Nenda Estudillo, Administrator

| | 32 | 10 | 76 | — | — | — | — | — | — | — |

WEST HILLS—Los Angeles County, See Los Angeles
WEST LOS ANGELES—Los Angeles County, See Los Angeles
WESTMINSTER—Orange County

□ **KINDRED HOSPITAL–WESTMINSTER**, 200 Hospital Circle, Zip 92683–3910; tel. 714/893–4541, (Nonreporting) **A**1 10 **S** Kindred Healthcare, Louisville, KY
Primary Contact: Virgis Narbutas, Chief Executive Officer
Web address: www.kindredhealthcare.com

| | 33 | 10 | 99 | — | — | — | — | — | — | — |

WHITTIER—Los Angeles County

□ **PRESBYTERIAN INTERCOMMUNITY HOSPITAL**, 12401 Washington Boulevard, Zip 90602–1099; tel. 562/698–0811 **A**1 2 3 5 9 10 **F**3 9 10 11 12 15 16 17 18 19 21 22 23 24 25 27 28 29 32 33 37 38 39 40 41 42 44 45 46 47 48 50 52 53 55 56 57 58 59 60 61 62 63 64 65 66 68 69 70 71 74 76 77 78 79 80 81 82 84 85 87 88 90 92 94 96 98 106 108 109 110
Primary Contact: James R. West, CHE, President and Chief Executive Officer
Web address: www.whittierpres.com

| | 23 | 10 | 234 | 17505 | 217 | 249453 | 3548 | 196370 | 86023 | 2312 |

⊠ **WHITTIER HOSPITAL MEDICAL CENTER**, 9080 Colima Road, Zip 90605–1600; tel. 562/945–3561, (Total facility includes 22 beds in nursing home–type unit) **A**1 9 10 **F**11 21 23 29 30 33 45 46 48 52 53 54 55 59 62 63 64 65 66 69 81 82 88 92 94 108 109 **P**5 **S** AHMC, Inc, Alhambra, CA
Primary Contact: Howard Ternes, Chief Executive Officer
CFO: Mary Anne Monje, Chief Financial Officer
CIO: Jay Geldhof, Director Information Systems
CHR: Jocelyn Herrera, Director Human Resources
Web address: www.whittierhospital.com

| | 32 | 10 | 171 | 8442 | 102 | 60014 | 2155 | 69887 | 34759 | 631 |

WILDOMAR—Riverside County

○ **DESERT VALLEY HOSPITAL**, 16850 Bear Valley Road, Zip 92395–5794; tel. 760/241–8000 **A**10 11 12 **F**2 9 11 15 21 22 27 28 33 39 45 46 52 55 58 59 60 61 62 63 65 66 69 81 82 84 86 88 93 94 107 108 110 **P**6
Primary Contact: Lex Reddy, President and Chief Executive Officer
Web address: www.dvmc.com

| | 33 | 10 | 83 | 5584 | 53 | 33134 | 410 | 47479 | 18771 | 429 |

INLAND VALLEY MEDICAL CENTER, 36485 Inland Valley Drive, Zip 92595–9700; tel. 951/677–1111, (Nonreporting) **A**9 **S** Universal Health Services, Inc., King of Prussia, PA
Primary Contact: Linda Bradley, Chief Executive Officer
Web address: www.ivrmc–rsmc.com

| | 33 | 10 | 80 | — | — | — | — | — | — | — |

□ **VICTOR VALLEY COMMUNITY HOSPITAL**, 15248 11th Street, Zip 92395; tel. 760/245–8691, (Nonreporting) **A**1 9 10
Primary Contact: Larry Knetzer, Chief Executive Officer

| | 23 | 10 | 115 | — | — | — | — | — | — | — |

WILLITS—Mendocino County

⊠ **FRANK R. HOWARD MEMORIAL HOSPITAL**, One Madrone Street, Zip 95490–4225; tel. 707/459–6801 **A**1 9 10 18 **F**9 12 21 22 27 28 29 33 36 46 51 55 58 60 63 65 69 81 84 88 94 97 108 **S** Adventist Health, Roseville, CA
Primary Contact: Kevin R. Erich, President and Chief Executive Officer
CFO: Carlton Jacobson, Vice President Finance
Web address: www.howardhospital.com

| | 21 | 10 | 25 | 1047 | 10 | 24943 | 10 | 21141 | 9617 | 181 |

WILLOWS—Glenn County

GLENN MEDICAL CENTER, 1133 West Sycamore Street, Zip 95988–2745; tel. 530/934–1800 **A**9 10 18 **F**6 24 25 27 28 29 30 33 53 58 60 63 66 68 69 70 81 84 88 93 97 107 109
Primary Contact: Woody J. Laughnan, Jr, Administrator

| | 23 | 10 | 10 | 181 | 1 | 30967 | 0 | 3070 | 2661 | 86 |

WINTERHAVEN—Imperial County

⊠ **U. S. PUBLIC HEALTH SERVICE INDIAN HOSPITAL**, 1 Indian Hill Road, Zip 92283–1368, Mailing Address: P.O. Box 1368, Yuma, AZ, Zip 85366–1368; tel. 760/572–0217, (Nonreporting) **A**1 10 18 **S** U. S. Indian Health Service, Rockville, MD
Primary Contact: Hortense Miguel, R.N., Service Unit Director

| | 47 | 10 | 15 | — | — | — | — | — | — | — |

WOODLAND—Yolo County

⊠ **WOODLAND HEALTHCARE**, (Formerly Woodland Memorial Hospital), 1325 Cottonwood Street, Zip 95695–5199; tel. 530/662–3961, (Nonreporting) **A**1 9 10 **S** Catholic Healthcare West, San Francisco, CA
Primary Contact: H. Kevin Vaziri, President
Web address: www.chw.edu

| | 23 | 10 | 111 | — | — | — | — | — | — | — |

WOODLAND HILLS—Los Angeles County, See Los Angeles

Hospital, Address, Telephone, Approval, Facility, and Physician Codes, Health Care System	Classi-fication Codes		Utilization Data					Expense (thousands) of dollars		
★ American Hospital Association (AHA) membership □ Joint Commission on Accreditation of Healthcare Organizations (JCAHO) accreditation ○ American Osteopathic Association (AOA) accreditation △ Commission on Accreditation of Rehabilitation Facilities (CARF) accreditation	Control	Service	Staffed Beds	Admissions	Census	Outpatient Visits	Births	Total	Payroll	Personnel

YOUNTVILLE—Napa County

VETERANS HOME OF CALIFORNIA, 100 California Drive, Zip 94599–1411; tel. 707/944–4500, (Nonreporting) **A**10
Primary Contact: Marcella M. McCormack, Administrator

| 12 | 11 | 431 | — | — | — | — | — | — | — |

YREKA—Siskiyou County

□ **FAIRCHILD MEDICAL CENTER**, 444 Bruce Street, Zip 96097–3450; tel. 530/842–4121 **A**1 9 10 18 20 **F**9 11 12 27 28 29 33 34 46 59 63 69 82 84 85 87 88 93
Primary Contact: Dwayne Jones, Chief Executive Officer
Web address: www.fairchildmed.org

| 23 | 10 | 30 | 1863 | 13 | 59365 | 216 | 26928 | 11001 | 255 |

YUBA CITY—Sutter County

□ **FREMONT MEDICAL CENTER**, 970 Plumas Street, Zip 95991–4087; tel. 530/751–4000 **A**1 10 **F**9 11 12 21 22 26 27 28 55 56 59 60 63 69 81 84 88 92 94 108 109 **P**5 **S** Fremont–Rideout Health Group, Yuba City, CA
Primary Contact: Thomas P. Hayes, Chief Executive Officer
Web address: www.frhg.org

| 23 | 10 | 90 | 2249 | 62 | 2131 | 767 | 17876 | 7322 | 460 |

Many Facility Codes have changed. Please refer to the AHA Guide Code Chart. © 2005 AHA Guide

COLORADO

Hospital, Address, Telephone, Approval, Facility, and Physician Codes, Health Care System	Classi-fication Codes		Utilization Data					Expense (thousands) of dollars		

★ American Hospital Association (AHA) membership
□ Joint Commission on Accreditation of Healthcare Organizations (JCAHO) accreditation
○ American Osteopathic Association (AOA) accreditation
△ Commission on Accreditation of Rehabilitation Facilities (CARF) accreditation

	Control	Service	Staffed Beds	Admissions	Census	Outpatient Visits	Births	Total	Payroll	Personnel

ALAMOSA—Alamosa County

☒ **SAN LUIS VALLEY REGIONAL MEDICAL CENTER**, 106 Blanca Avenue, Zip 81101–2393; tel. 719/589–2511 **A**1 9 10 **F**6 9 11 22 23 27 28 29 33 34 49 55 58 59 60 62 63 65 69 81 84 85 88 93 94 96
Primary Contact: Russell Johnson, Chief Executive Officer
COO: Henry Garvin, Chief Operating Officer
CFO: David Freshour, Chief Financial Officer
CHR: Leonard Snow, Chief Quality Officer
Web address: www.slvrmc.org
| 23 | 10 | 57 | 2748 | 19 | — | — | — | — | — |

ASPEN—Pitkin County

□ **ASPEN VALLEY HOSPITAL DISTRICT**, 401 Castle Creek Road, Zip 81611–1159; tel. 970/925–1120, (Nonreporting) **A**1 10 18
Primary Contact: David R. Ressler, Chief Executive Officer
Web address: www.avhaspen.org
| 16 | 10 | 25 | — | — | — | — | — | — | — |

AURORA—Adams County

☒ **MEDICAL CENTER OF AURORA**, 1501 South Potomac Street, Zip 80012–5499; tel. 303/695–2600, (Includes COLUMBIA REGIONAL MEDICAL CENTER–SOUTH CAMPUS, Zip 80012; MEDICAL CENTER OF AURORA NORTH, 700 Potomac Street, Zip 80011–6792; tel. 303/363–7200) **A**1 2 9 10 **F**2 4 9 11 12 19 21 22 23 26 28 29 33 34 35 37 38 39 42 44 46 47 48 52 53 55 56 57 58 59 60 61 62 63 64 65 66 71 73 75 76 81 82 84 85 87 88 93 94 96 108 109 110 **S** HCA, Nashville, TN
Primary Contact: Sylvia Young, President and Chief Executive Officer
Web address: www.auroramed.com
| 32 | 10 | 314 | 17057 | 195 | 81893 | 2888 | — | — | 1253 |

□ **SCCI HOSPITAL – AURORA**, 700 Potomac Street, Zip 80012; tel. 720/857–8333, (Nonreporting) **A**1 9 10
Primary Contact: Steve Ramsey, Chief Executive Officer
| 33 | 80 | 29 | — | — | — | — | — | — | — |

☒ △ **SPALDING REHABILITATION HOSPITAL**, 900 Potomac Street, Zip 80011–6716; tel. 303/367–1166, (Nonreporting) **A**1 3 5 7 10 13 **S** HCA, Nashville, TN
Primary Contact: Cynthia Kruetz, President and Chief Executive Officer
COO: Marianne Dexter, R.N., Chief Operating Officer
CFO: Joyce Webber, Chief Financial Officer
Web address: www.spaldingrehab.com
| 32 | 46 | 122 | — | — | — | — | — | — | — |

BOULDER—Boulder County

☒ △ **BOULDER COMMUNITY HOSPITAL**, 1100 Balsam Avenue, Zip 80304–3496, Mailing Address: P.O. Box 9019, Zip 80301–9019; tel. 303/440–2273 **A**1 2 7 9 10 **F**2 4 7 9 11 12 14 15 17 19 21 22 23 26 27 28 30 31 33 34 35 36 37 38 39 40 41 42 44 47 48 49 50 51 52 53 55 56 57 58 59 60 61 62 63 64 65 66 68 69 70 71 72 73 74 75 76 77 78 79 80 81 82 84 85 86 87 88 93 94 95 96 98 107 108 109 110
Primary Contact: David P. Gehant, President and Chief Executive Officer
CFO: Joe McDonald, Vice President Finance
Web address: www.bch.org
| 23 | 10 | 212 | 11485 | 147 | 548036 | 1947 | 240150 | 106962 | 2060 |

BRIGHTON—Adams County

☒ **PLATTE VALLEY MEDICAL CENTER**, 1850 Egbert Street, Zip 80601–2404; tel. 303/659–1531 **A**1 9 10 **F**2 6 11 12 21 22 23 25 26 28 29 33 34 36 37 41 45 46 47 48 52 53 55 57 58 59 60 61 62 63 65 66 69 70 81 82 84 88 90 94 108 109 **P**5
Primary Contact: John R. Hicks, President and Chief Executive Officer
CFO: Harold Dupper, Chief Financial Officer
CMO: John Simon, M.D., Chief of Staff
CIO: Mark Albright, Director Information Services
Web address: www.pvmc.org
| 23 | 10 | 52 | 2903 | 20 | 46328 | 1088 | 40706 | 16764 | 307 |

BRUSH—Morgan County

★ **EAST MORGAN COUNTY HOSPITAL**, 2400 West Edison Street, Zip 80723–1640; tel. 970/842–6200 **A**9 10 18 **F**2 9 12 21 22 23 26 27 28 29 30 33 34 41 44 45 46 48 52 53 58 60 61 62 63 66 69 70 73 77 81 82 84 88 93 94 95 96 97 106 107 108 109 110 **P**6 **S** Banner Health, Phoenix, AZ
Primary Contact: Larry E. Leaming, Chief Executive Officer
CFO: Linda Thorpe, Finance Manager
Web address: www.emchbrush.com
| 23 | 10 | 15 | 338 | 4 | 55161 | 0 | 9878 | 4825 | 107 |

BURLINGTON—Kit Carson County

★ **KIT CARSON COUNTY MEMORIAL HOSPITAL**, 286 16th Street, Zip 80807–1697; tel. 719/346–5311 **A**9 10 18 **F**2 11 12 21 22 23 26 27 28 33 34 36 37 38 39 41 42 47 48 51 52 53 58 59 60 63 65 66 69 70 81 88 92 94 95 97 **P**6
Primary Contact: James Jordan, Chief Executive Officer
COO: Regina Korsvold, R.N., Chief Operating Officer
CFO: Mona Masters, Chief Financial Officer
CMO: Wayne Hoppe, M.D., Chief Medical Officer
CIO: Arlan Tanner, Chief Information Officer
Web address: www.kccmh.org
| 16 | 10 | 22 | 602 | 6 | 33578 | 90 | 8017 | 4017 | 114 |

Hospital, Address, Telephone, Approval, Facility, and Physician Codes, Health Care System	Classi-fication Codes		Utilization Data					Expense (thousands) of dollars		
★ American Hospital Association (AHA) membership □ Joint Commission on Accreditation of Healthcare Organizations (JCAHO) accreditation ○ American Osteopathic Association (AOA) accreditation △ Commission on Accreditation of Rehabilitation Facilities (CARF) accreditation	Control	Service	Staffed Beds	Admissions	Census	Outpatient Visits	Births	Total	Payroll	Personnel

CANON CITY—Fremont County

⊠ **ST. THOMAS MORE HOSPITAL**, 1338 Phay Avenue, Zip 81212–2221; tel. 719/269–2000, (Total facility includes 15 beds in nursing home–type unit) (Nonreporting) **A**1 9 10 20 **S** Catholic Health Initiatives, Denver, CO
Primary Contact: C. Ray Honaker, President and Chief Executive Officer
CFO: Sheri Trahern, Chief Financial Officer
CMO: Gary McKinney, Chief of Staff
CHR: Stan Miller, Vice President Human Resources
Web address: www.centura.org

| | 21 | 10 | 55 | — | — | — | — | — | — | — |

CHEYENNE WELLS—Cheyenne County

★ **KEEFE MEMORIAL HOSPITAL**, 602 North 6th Street West, Zip 80810, Mailing Address: P.O. Box 578, Zip 80810–0578; tel. 719/767–5661 **A**9 10 20 **F**2 9 12 21 22 23 26 27 28 29 30 32 33 34 37 39 46 47 48 51 52 53 61 62 63 65 66 69 70 81 85 88 97 106 109 110 **P**6
Primary Contact: Curtis Hawkinson, Chief Executive Officer
CMO: Saeid Ashmadpour, M.D., Chief of Staff
CHR: Kara Talbert, Director Human Resources
Web address: www.keefememorialhospital.org

| | 13 | 10 | 12 | 105 | 1 | 3704 | 0 | 3366 | 1780 | 55 |

COLORADO SPRINGS—El Paso County

□ **CEDAR SPRINGS HOSPITAL**, 2135 Southgate Road, Zip 80906–2693; tel. 719/633–4114 **A**1 10 **F**3 4 21 52 58 60 71 72 73 74 75 76 77 94 **S** Psychiatric Solutions, Franklin, TN
Primary Contact: Robert E. Marshall, Chief Executive Officer
Web address: www.psysolutions.com

| | 33 | 22 | 110 | 1493 | 69 | 4429 | 0 | — | — | 145 |

⊠ **HEALTHSOUTH REHABILITATION HOSPITAL OF COLORADO SPRINGS**, 325 Parkside Drive, Zip 80910; tel. 719/630–8000 **A**1 10 **F**2 21 22 52 58 68 69 93 94 **S** HEALTHSOUTH Corporation, Birmingham, AL
Primary Contact: Ellen DeAustin, Administrator

| | 33 | 46 | 56 | 915 | 36 | 7267 | 0 | — | — | 111 |

⊠ △ **MEMORIAL HOSPITAL**, 1400 East Boulder Street, Zip 80909–5599, Mailing Address: P.O. Box 1326, Zip 80901–1326; tel. 719/365–5000 **A**1 2 7 9 10 **F**2 9 11 12 14 15 16 17 18 19 22 23 27 28 29 30 33 34 35 36 37 38 42 44 46 47 48 49 52 53 55 56 57 58 59 60 61 62 63 64 65 66 67 68 69 79 81 82 83 84 85 86 87 88 90 93 94 96 99 106 107 108 110 **P**1
Primary Contact: Richard Eitel, Chief Executive Officer
COO: Cherie Gorby, R.N., MSN, Chief Operating Officer
CFO: Gary Flansburg, Chief Financial Officer
CMO: John Slack, M.D., Chief Medical Officer
CIO: Thomas Kerwin, Administrator Information Systems and Chief Information Officer
CHR: Ron Burnside, Chief Human Resources Officer
Web address: www.memorialhospital.com

| | 14 | 10 | 392 | 25552 | 330 | 395270 | 2873 | 285519 | 145208 | 3301 |

⊠ △ **PENROSE–ST. FRANCIS HEALTH SERVICES**, 2215 North Cascade Avenue, Zip 80907–6799, Mailing Address: P.O. Box 7021, Zip 80933–7021; tel. 719/776–5000, (Includes PENROSE COMMUNITY HOSPITAL, 3205 North Academy Boulevard, Zip 80917; tel. 719/776–5000; PENROSE HOSPITAL; ST FRANCIS HEALTH CENTER, 825 East Pikes Peak Avenue, Zip 80903; tel. 719/776–5000) **A**1 2 7 9 10 **F**2 4 9 10 11 12 15 17 19 21 22 23 26 27 28 29 30 31 32 33 34 35 37 38 39 41 42 44 46 47 48 50 51 52 53 55 56 58 59 60 61 62 63 64 65 66 68 69 70 71 72 73 74 75 76 77 79 80 81 82 85 87 88 89 90 92 93 94 95 96 106 107 108 109 110 **P**5 **S** Catholic Health Initiatives, Denver, CO
Primary Contact: Rick O'Connell, President and Chief Executive Officer
COO: Andrea C. Coleman, Chief Operating Officer
CFO: Michael A. Scialdone, Chief Financial Officer
CMO: Jeffrey C. Oram–Smith, M.D., Chief Medical Officer
CIO: Tanya Bell, Public Information Officer
CHR: James Humphrey, Director, Human Resource and Educational Resources
Web address: www.penrosestfrancis.org

| | 21 | 10 | 392 | 23547 | 261 | 226936 | 3014 | 246588 | 93356 | 2221 |

□ **SELECT SPECIALTY HOSPITAL OF COLORADO SPRINGS**, (Formerly Sempercare Hospital of Colorado Springs), 825 Pikes Peak Avenue, Zip 80903; tel. 719/667–1009 **A**1 9 10 **F**2 13 21 33 37 57 62 64 68 94 110
Primary Contact: Donna Berty, Chief Executive Officer

| | 33 | 80 | 30 | 294 | 20 | 0 | 0 | — | — | 68 |

CORTEZ—Montezuma County

⊠ **SOUTHWEST MEMORIAL HOSPITAL**, 1311 North Mildred Road, Zip 81321–2299; tel. 970/565–6666 **A**1 8 9 10 20 **F**2 6 9 11 21 26 27 28 33 51 53 55 58 59 60 62 63 66 69 81 82 84 88 94 96 **P**8 **S** Quorum Health Resources, Plano, TX
Primary Contact: Charles E. Bill, CHE, Chief Executive Officer
COO: Robert A. Lindberg, Chief Clinical Officer
CFO: Daniel L. Jessup, Chief Financial Officer
CMO: Dianna Fury, Chief Medical Officer
CIO: Stephen Day, Director Management Information Systems
CHR: Sharon Williams, Human Resources Director
Web address: www.swhealth.org

| | 23 | 10 | 61 | 1979 | 17 | 36319 | 190 | 25119 | 11054 | 264 |

Many Facility Codes have changed. Please refer to the AHA Guide Code Chart.

Hospital, Address, Telephone, Approval, Facility, and Physician Codes, Health Care System	Classi-fication Codes		Utilization Data					Expense (thousands) of dollars		
★ American Hospital Association (AHA) membership □ Joint Commission on Accreditation of Healthcare Organizations (JCAHO) accreditation ○ American Osteopathic Association (AOA) accreditation △ Commission on Accreditation of Rehabilitation Facilities (CARF) accreditation	Control	Service	Staffed Beds	Admissions	Census	Outpatient Visits	Births	Total	Payroll	Personnel

CRAIG—Moffat County

☒ **MEMORIAL HOSPITAL**, 785 Russell Street, Zip 81625–9906; tel. 970/824–9411, (Nonreporting) **A**1 9 10 18 **S** Quorum Health Resources, Plano, TX
Primary Contact: M. Randell Phelps, Chief Executive Officer
CFO: Roger White, Chief Financial Officer
CMO: Michael Crane, M.D., Chief of Staff
CHR: Alice Rigney, Human Resource Director
Web address: www.thememorialhospital.com
| 13 | 10 | 25 | — | — | — | — | — | — | — |

DEL NORTE—Rio Grande County

★ **RIO GRANDE HOSPITAL**, 1280 Grande Avenue, Zip 81132; tel. 719/657–2510, (Nonreporting) **A**9 10 18
Primary Contact: Norman Haug, M.D., Administrator
CFO: Greg Porter, Chief Financial Officer
| 33 | 10 | 6 | | | | | | | |

DELTA—Delta County

☒ **DELTA COUNTY MEMORIAL HOSPITAL**, 1501 East 3rd Street, Zip 81416–2297, Mailing Address: P.O. Box 10100, Zip 81416–5003; tel. 970/874–7681 **A**1 9 10 **F**11 12 23 33 34 36 46 48 51 52 53 55 58 59 60 61 62 63 64 66 69 81 82 84 85 88 93 96 108 110 **P**1 5
Primary Contact: Tom Mingen, Chief Executive Officer
COO: Sharon Saunders, Chief Clinical Officer
CFO: Bev Carlson, Chief Financial Officer
CMO: Kay Lovesink, Chief Medical Staff
CIO: Mitch Van Scoy, Manager
CHR: Sandy Myers, Human Resource Director
Web address: www.deltahospital.org
| 16 | 10 | 48 | 2652 | 24 | 58975 | 276 | 27066 | 12798 | 305 |

DENVER—Denver, Adams and Arapahoe Counties

☒ **CHILDREN'S HOSPITAL**, 1056 East 19th Avenue, Zip 80218–1088; tel. 303/861–8888 **A**1 3 5 8 10 **F**2 14 16 18 20 21 22 23 24 26 27 28 29 30 31 32 33 34 36 37 38 39 42 47 48 49 50 52 53 56 57 58 60 61 62 63 64 65 66 67 68 69 70 71 72 73 74 75 77 78 81 82 84 88 90 93 94 95 96 98 99 100 101 102 104 107 108 110
Primary Contact: Dori J. Biester, Ph.D., R.N., President and Chief Executive Officer
COO: Mike Farrell, Executive Vice President, Chief Operating Officer
CFO: Len Dryer, Chief Financial Officer
CIO: James Turnbull, Vice President and Chief Information Officer
Web address: www.thechildrenshospital.org
| 23 | 50 | 250 | 10447 | 181 | 341207 | 0 | 323189 | 137338 | 2324 |

COLORADO ACUTE SPECIALTY CARE HOSPITAL, 1601 North Lowell Boulevard, Zip 80204–1545; tel. 303/899–5166, (Nonreporting) **A**10 **S** LifeCare Management Services, Plano, TX
Primary Contact: William Fox, Interim Chief Executive Officer
Web address: www.lifecare–hospitals.com
| 23 | 80 | 24 | — | — | — | — | — | — | — |

□ **COLORADO MENTAL HEALTH INSTITUTE AT FORT LOGAN**, 3520 West Oxford Avenue, Zip 80236–3197; tel. 303/761–0220, (Nonreporting) **A**1 10
Primary Contact: Elizabeth M. Stillman, Acting Director
| 12 | 22 | 297 | — | — | — | — | — | — | — |

□ **DENVER HEALTH MEDICAL CENTER**, 777 Bannock Street, Zip 80204–4507; tel. 303/436–6000 **A**1 3 5 9 10 **F**2 3 4 6 7 9 11 12 15 17 19 21 22 23 24 26 27 28 29 31 32 33 34 35 37 38 39 41 42 44 45 46 47 48 50 52 53 55 56 57 58 59 60 61 62 63 64 65 66 67 68 69 70 71 72 73 75 76 77 81 82 84 85 87 88 89 90 93 94 95 96 98 106 107 108 109 110 **P**6
Primary Contact: Patricia A. Gabow, M.D., Chief Executive Officer and Medical Director
Web address: www.denverhealth.org
| 16 | 10 | 330 | 18187 | 240 | 438845 | 3654 | 398354 | 211127 | 4068 |

☒ **EXEMPLA SAINT JOSEPH HOSPITAL**, 1835 Franklin Street, Zip 80218–1191; tel. 303/837–7111 **A**1 2 3 5 9 10 **F**2 10 11 12 14 15 17 19 21 22 23 26 27 28 29 30 32 33 34 36 40 48 49 50 52 53 55 56 57 58 59 60 61 62 63 65 66 69 70 75 79 81 82 84 85 87 88 92 108 109 **P**6 **S** Exempla Healthcare, Inc., Denver, CO
Web address: www.exempla.org
| 23 | 10 | 436 | 24263 | 267 | 114706 | 5140 | 274700 | 132668 | 2114 |

□ **KINDRED HOSPITAL–DENVER**, 1920 High Street, Zip 80218–1213; tel. 303/320–5871, (Nonreporting) **A**1 9 10 **S** Kindred Healthcare, Louisville, KY
Primary Contact: April Myers, Chief Executive Officer
Web address: www.kindredhealthcare.com
| 33 | 10 | 55 | — | — | — | — | — | — | — |

☒ **NATIONAL JEWISH MEDICAL AND RESEARCH CENTER**, (allergy, asthma, immunologic d), 1400 Jackson Street, Zip 80206–2762; tel. 303/388–4461 **A**1 3 5 9 10 **F**2 9 21 22 26 29 39 41 45 48 52 53 58 60 65 66 69 72 73 77 81 82 85 87 88 93 94 96 106 107 108 **P**6
Primary Contact: Lynn M. Taussig, M.D., President and Chief Executive Officer
COO: J Verne Singleton, Chief Administrative Officer
CFO: Christine Forkner, Chief Financial Officer
CIO: Jim Harbin, Director Information Systems
CHR: Susan Roll, Chief of Human Resources
Web address: www.nationaljewish.org
| 23 | 49 | 60 | 164 | 2 | 34424 | 0 | 107546 | 56960 | 1092 |

CO

Hospital, Address, Telephone, Approval, Facility, and Physician Codes, Health Care System	Classi-fication Codes		Utilization Data					Expense (thousands) of dollars		
	Control	Service	Staffed Beds	Admissions	Census	Outpatient Visits	Births	Total	Payroll	Personnel

★ American Hospital Association (AHA) membership
□ Joint Commission on Accreditation of Healthcare Organizations (JCAHO) accreditation
○ American Osteopathic Association (AOA) accreditation
△ Commission on Accreditation of Rehabilitation Facilities (CARF) accreditation

CO

Hospital	Control	Service	Staffed Beds	Admissions	Census	Outpatient Visits	Births	Total	Payroll	Personnel
⊠ **PORTER ADVENTIST HOSPITAL**, 2525 South Downing Street, Zip 80210–5876; tel. 303/778–1955 **A**1 2 9 10 **F**9 11 12 14 15 17 19 21 22 23 26 27 28 29 30 33 34 37 41 49 52 55 56 57 58 59 60 61 62 63 65 66 68 69 70 71 73 74 75 76 77 78 79 81 82 84 85 86 87 88 92 93 95 97 99 101 102 108 110 **P**5 **S** Adventist Health System Sunbelt Health Care Corporation, Winter Park, FL Primary Contact: James W. Boyle, Chief Executive Officer COO: Sharon Pappas, Chief Operating Officer CFO: Terry Forde, Chief Financial Officer Web address: www.centura.org	21	10	239	19672	237	80331	1623	125772	62498	1143
⊠ △ **PRESBYTERIAN–ST. LUKE'S MEDICAL CENTER**, 1719 East 19th Avenue, Zip 80218–1281; tel. 303/839–6000, (Includes PRESBYTERIAN–DENVER HOSPITAL, 1719 East 19th Avenue, Zip 80218–1124; tel. 303/839–6000) **A**1 2 3 5 7 9 10 **F**2 4 12 14 15 16 17 18 19 20 21 22 29 33 36 45 46 47 48 50 55 56 57 58 59 60 61 63 65 67 69 79 81 82 88 92 95 96 99 100 101 107 108 109 110 **S** HCA, Nashville, TN Primary Contact: Madeleine Roberson, President and Chief Executive Officer COO: Hugh C. Tappan, Chief Operating Officer CFO: David McClung, Chief Financial Officer CIO: Ron Rubin, Director Information Services CHR: Nora Anderson, Director, Human Resources Web address: www.pslmc.com	33	10	400	12892	213	87320	1806	—	—	—
⊠ △ **ROSE MEDICAL CENTER**, 4567 East Ninth Avenue, Zip 80220–3941; tel. 303/320–2121 **A**1 2 3 5 7 9 10 **F**2 7 9 10 11 12 14 15 17 19 21 22 23 24 26 27 28 29 33 35 37 39 41 42 46 47 48 49 50 52 53 55 56 57 58 59 60 61 62 63 64 65 66 68 69 70 81 82 84 85 86 87 88 89 90 93 94 95 106 108 109 110 **P**6 8 **S** HCA, Nashville, TN Primary Contact: Kenneth H. Feiler, President and Chief Executive Officer CFO: Jack Connelly, Chief Financial Officer CIO: Maureen Murphy, Director Information Systems Web address: www.rosebabies.com	33	10	246	15568	163	152173	4256	168527	64465	1007
□ **SELECT SPECIALTY HOSPITAL**, 1719 East 19th Avenue, 5th Floor, Zip 80218; tel. 303/563–3700, (Nonreporting) **A**1 9 10 Primary Contact: Lynn Dawson, Chief Executive Officer	33	49	65	—	—	—	—	—	—	—
⊠ **ST. ANTHONY CENTRAL HOSPITAL**, 4231 West 16th Avenue, Zip 80204–4098; tel. 303/629–3511 **A**1 2 3 5 9 10 **F**2 6 9 10 11 12 14 15 17 19 21 22 23 26 27 28 29 30 33 34 41 44 46 48 52 53 55 56 57 58 59 60 61 62 63 64 66 68 69 70 71 75 76 77 79 80 81 82 83 85 87 88 92 93 94 96 97 98 106 108 109 **S** Catholic Health Initiatives, Denver, CO Primary Contact: George A. Zara, Chief Executive Officer CMO: Pete Vellman, M.D., Chief Medical Officer CIO: Elaine Callas, Chief Information Officer CHR: Gary Jones, Vice President Human Resources Web address: www.stanthonyhosp.org	21	10	319	16167	217	69686	1481	201589	73709	1215
⊠ **UNIVERSITY OF COLORADO HOSPITAL**, 4200 East Ninth Avenue, Zip 80262–0001; tel. 303/372–0000 **A**1 2 3 5 8 9 10 **F**2 4 7 10 11 12 13 15 17 19 21 22 23 25 26 27 28 29 30 31 32 33 34 37 38 39 41 42 43 44 46 47 48 49 50 52 53 55 56 57 58 59 60 61 62 63 64 65 66 68 69 70 71 72 75 77 79 80 81 82 83 84 85 86 87 88 89 90 93 94 95 96 100 101 102 103 104 105 106 108 109 110 **P**3 Primary Contact: Dennis C. Brimhall, President and Chief Executive Officer Web address: www.uch.edu	16	10	399	16045	240	513531	2498	473569	168170	3107
⊠ △ **VETERANS AFFAIRS EASTERN COLORADO HEALTH CARE SYSTEM**, 1055 Clermont Street, Zip 80220–3877; tel. 303/399–8020, (Total facility includes 100 beds in nursing home–type unit) **A**1 2 3 5 7 8 9 **F**2 4 10 12 15 17 19 21 22 23 25 26 27 28 32 33 36 37 38 41 42 43 44 45 46 48 49 50 51 52 53 55 57 58 60 61 62 63 64 66 68 69 70 71 73 77 81 84 88 92 93 94 96 106 108 110 **S** Department of Veterans Affairs, Washington, DC Primary Contact: Ed Thorsland, Jr, Director COO: Ralph T. Gigliotti, Associate Director CFO: Eliott R. Vanderstek, Chief, Fiscal Service CMO: Leigh Anderson, M.D., Chief of Staff CIO: Don Huckaby, Chief, Information Management Service Web address: www.va.gov/sta/guide/home.asp	45	10	228	4978	109	481769	0	246917	102721	1557
DURANGO—La Plata County										
ANIMAS SURGICAL HOSPITAL, 575 Rivergate Lane, Zip 81301; tel. 970/247–3537, (Nonreporting) **A**9 10 Primary Contact: Brett Gosney, Chief Executive Officer	33	13	12	—	—	—	—	—	—	—
⊠ **MERCY MEDICAL CENTER**, 375 East Park Avenue, Zip 81301–5089; tel. 970/247–4311 **A**1 2 9 10 20 **F**2 9 11 12 14 15 21 22 23 27 29 30 33 34 36 38 39 41 42 48 50 51 52 53 55 56 57 58 59 60 61 62 63 68 69 73 75 81 83 84 88 93 94 95 96 97 108 109 110 **P**6 **S** Catholic Health Initiatives, Denver, CO Primary Contact: Kirk Dignum, Ph.D., President and Chief Executive Officer COO: Brad Cochennet, Chief Operating Officer CMO: John A K Boyd, M.D., Executive Director Mission and Chief Medical Officer CIO: Neil Stock, Executive Director Information Services CHR: Cathy Roberts, Human Resource Director Web address: www.mercydurango.org	21	10	75	4046	37	144953	776	66492	27504	534

Many Facility Codes have changed. Please refer to the AHA Guide Code Chart.

Hospital, Address, Telephone, Approval, Facility, and Physician Codes, Health Care System	Classi-fication Codes		Utilization Data					Expense (thousands) of dollars		
★ American Hospital Association (AHA) membership □ Joint Commission on Accreditation of Healthcare Organizations (JCAHO) accreditation ○ American Osteopathic Association (AOA) accreditation △ Commission on Accreditation of Rehabilitation Facilities (CARF) accreditation	Control	Service	Staffed Beds	Admissions	Census	Outpatient Visits	Births	Total	Payroll	Personnel

EADS—Kiowa County

★ **WEISBROD MEMORIAL COUNTY HOSPITAL**, 1208 Luther Street, Zip 81036, Mailing Address: P.O. Box 817, Zip 81036–0817; tel. 719/438–5401, (Total facility includes 34 beds in nursing home–type unit) (Nonreporting) **A**9 10 18
Primary Contact: Warren Yule, Administrator and Chief Executive Officer
CFO: Anna Randel, Business Office Manager
CMO: John Hadley, M.D., Chief of Staff
CHR: Shannon Dixon, Human Resources Executive Secretary
Web address: www.weisbrod.org
| | 16 | 10 | 42 | — | — | — | — | — | — | — |

ENGLEWOOD—Arapahoe County

⊞ **CRAIG HOSPITAL**, 3425 South Clarkson Street, Zip 80113–2899; tel. 303/789–8000 **A**1 10 **F**21 22 26 27 28 29 30 35 39 41 42 47 52 53 57 58 60 63 65 66 68 69 94 96 108 110
Primary Contact: Dennis O'Malley, President
CFO: Ron Branish, Vice President Finance
CMO: Daniel P. Lammertse, M.D., Medical Director
Web address: www.craighospital.org
| | 23 | 46 | 78 | 414 | 69 | 6100 | 0 | 46159 | 21496 | 516 |

⊞ **SWEDISH MEDICAL CENTER**, 501 East Hampden Avenue, Zip 80110–0101; tel. 303/788–5000 **A**1 2 3 5 9 10 **F**2 6 9 10 11 12 14 15 17 19 21 22 23 26 27 28 29 32 33 34 37 38 39 40 41 42 43 46 47 48 49 52 55 56 57 58 59 61 62 63 64 65 66 67 68 69 79 80 81 82 83 84 85 86 87 88 93 94 96 106 108 109 110 **P**8 **S** HCA, Nashville, TN
Primary Contact: Mary M. White, President and Chief Executive Officer
COO: William Wagnon, Chief Operating Officer
CFO: Kathy Ashenfelter, Chief Financial Officer
CMO: Bruce Bairch, M.D., President Medical Staff
CIO: Chad Landry, Information Systems Director
CHR: Maria Isquierdo, Director, Human Resources
Web address: www.swedishhospital.com
| | 32 | 10 | 333 | 21823 | 229 | 101229 | 2647 | — | — | 1579 |

ESTES PARK—Larimer County

★ **ESTES PARK MEDICAL CENTER**, 555 Prospect Avenue, Zip 80517–2740, Mailing Address: P.O. Box 2740, Zip 80517–2740; tel. 970/586–2317, (Total facility includes 60 beds in nursing home–type unit) **A**9 10 18 **F**2 6 11 12 22 23 26 33 36 44 45 46 51 52 58 59 60 61 62 63 65 66 68 69 70 81 84 87 88 91 92 94 96 97 108 110 **P**7
Primary Contact: Douglas Faus, Chief Executive Officer
COO: Roxann Hause, Administrator Ancillary and Support Services
CFO: Timothy B. Bishop, Administrator Financial Services
CMO: Mark Hansen, M.D., Chief of Staff
CHR: Tim Coakley, Human Resources Director
Web address: www.epmedcenter.com
| | 16 | 10 | 76 | 693 | 43 | 33017 | 90 | 18578 | 8335 | 204 |

FORT CARSON—El Paso County

⊞ **EVANS U. S. ARMY COMMUNITY HOSPITAL**, 7500 Cochrane Circle, Zip 80913–5101; tel. 719/526–7200, (Nonreporting) **A**1 2 9 **S** Department of the Army, Office of the Surgeon General, Falls Church, VA
Primary Contact: Colonel Brian C. Lein, Commander
CIO: Jeff Hoffa, Chief Information Management Division
Web address: www.evans.amedd.army.mil
| | 42 | 10 | 78 | — | — | — | — | — | — | — |

FORT COLLINS—Larimer County

⊞ **POUDRE VALLEY HOSPITAL**, 1024 South Lemay Avenue, Zip 80524–3998; tel. 970/495–7000, (Includes MOUNTAIN CREST HOSPITAL, 4601 Corbett Drive, Zip 80525; tel. 970/270–4800) **A**1 2 9 10 **F**4 6 9 11 12 14 15 16 17 18 19 20 21 22 23 24 26 27 28 29 31 33 34 37 38 41 42 48 49 50 52 54 55 57 59 60 61 62 63 65 66 69 70 71 72 73 74 75 76 77 78 81 82 84 87 88 93 94 96 106 107 108 109 110 **P**1
Primary Contact: Margo A. Karsten, Chief Executive Officer and President
COO: Kevin Unger, Vice President Operations
CFO: Stephanie Doughty, Chief Financial Officer
CMO: Chris Staszak, M.D., Chief of Staff
CIO: Russ Branzell, Chief Information Officer
Web address: www.pvhs.org
| | 23 | 10 | 266 | 16899 | 186 | 386272 | 2572 | 254161 | 108561 | 2159 |

FORT MORGAN—Morgan County

⊞ **COLORADO PLAINS MEDICAL CENTER**, 1000 Lincoln Street, Zip 80701–3298; tel. 970/867–3391 **A**1 9 10 20 **F**9 11 12 21 22 23 26 27 28 29 33 34 39 44 46 47 48 50 51 52 53 55 58 59 62 63 64 65 66 68 69 70 81 82 84 88 94 97 106 108 109 110 **S** LifePoint Hospitals, Inc., Brentwood, TN
Primary Contact: Michael A. Anaya, Sr, FACHE, Chief Executive Officer
CFO: Janet Montel, Chief Financial Officer
| | 33 | 10 | 50 | 1983 | 17 | 29056 | 342 | 20561 | 8537 | 226 |

FRUITA—Mesa County

★ **FAMILY HEALTH WEST**, 228 North Cherry Street, Zip 81521–2101, Mailing Address: P.O. Box 130, Zip 81521–0130; tel. 970/858–9871, (Total facility includes 120 beds in nursing home–type unit) **A**9 10 18 **F**2 5 8 21 29 33 36 37 38 44 45 48 62 66 68 69 70 92 94 95 96 97 107 110
Primary Contact: Dennis E. Ficklin, Chief Executive Officer
| | 23 | 10 | 126 | 272 | 109 | 6278 | 0 | — | — | 162 |

CO

Hospital, Address, Telephone, Approval, Facility, and Physician Codes, Health Care System	Classi-fication Codes		Utilization Data					Expense (thousands) of dollars		
	Control	Service	Staffed Beds	Admissions	Census	Outpatient Visits	Births	Total	Payroll	Personnel

★ American Hospital Association (AHA) membership
☐ Joint Commission on Accreditation of Healthcare Organizations (JCAHO) accreditation
◯ American Osteopathic Association (AOA) accreditation
△ Commission on Accreditation of Rehabilitation Facilities (CARF) accreditation

CO

GLENWOOD SPRINGS—Garfield County

⊠ **VALLEY VIEW HOSPITAL**, 1906 Blake Avenue, Zip 81601–4259, Mailing Address: P.O. Box 1970, Zip 81602–1970; tel. 970/945–6535 **A**1 9 10 20 **F**2 3 9 10 11 12 21 22 23 27 28 29 30 33 34 35 36 37 38 39 40 42 44 46 47 48 52 53 54 55 57 58 59 60 61 62 63 64 65 66 68 69 70 81 82 84 85 87 88 89 93 94 95 96 106 108 **P**6 **S** Quorum Health Resources, Plano, TX
Primary Contact: Gary L. Brewer, Chief Executive Officer
CFO: Larry L. Dupper, Chief Financial Officer
CMO: Jeffrey Fegan, M.D., Chief of Staff
CIO: Ron Hines, Information Technology Director
CHR: Elizabeth Hanckel, Human Resources Director
Web address: www.vvh.org
| | 23 | 10 | 71 | 2876 | 32 | 92979 | 651 | 57907 | 23799 | 492 |

GRAND JUNCTION—Mesa County

⊠ ◯ △ **COMMUNITY HOSPITAL**, 2021 North 12th Street, Zip 81501–2999; tel. 970/242–0920 **A**1 7 9 10 11 **F**22 26 27 28 33 46 47 48 51 52 55 58 60 62 63 65 66 69 81 82 84 88 93 94 95 96 106 108 109 **P**4 8
Primary Contact: Mark J. Francis, President and Chief Executive Officer
CMO: AnnMarie Kjosa, R.N., MSN, Vice President & Chief Nursing Officer
CIO: Mike Kansgen, Director Information Services
CHR: Charles Rafowicz, Vice President
Web address: www.gjhosp.org
| | 23 | 10 | 40 | 1765 | 18 | 130697 | 0 | 30223 | 13357 | 333 |

⊠ **ST. MARY'S HOSPITAL AND MEDICAL CENTER**, 2635 North 7th Street, Zip 81501–8204, Mailing Address: P.O. Box 1628, Zip 81502–1628; tel. 970/244–2273 **A**1 2 9 10 19 20 **F**2 3 4 9 11 12 14 15 17 19 21 22 23 26 27 28 29 33 34 37 39 40 41 42 46 48 49 50 52 53 54 55 56 57 58 59 60 61 62 63 65 66 68 69 70 71 72 73 74 75 76 79 80 81 82 84 85 86 87 88 93 94 95 96 106 108 109 110 **S** Sisters of Charity of Leavenworth Health System, Lenexa, KS
Primary Contact: Robert W. Ladenburger, President and Chief Executive Officer
CFO: Forest Binder, Vice President Finance
CMO: John C. Beeson, M.D., Vice President Medical Affairs
CHR: Terry Weinburger, Vice President Human Resources
Web address: www.stmarygj.com
| | 21 | 10 | 300 | 13898 | 165 | 353108 | 2012 | 192238 | 81988 | — |

⊠ **VETERANS AFFAIRS MEDICAL CENTER**, 2121 North Avenue, Zip 81501–6499; tel. 970/242–0731, (Total facility includes 30 beds in nursing home–type unit) **A**1 9 **F**2 4 9 10 21 22 23 26 27 28 29 30 31 32 36 37 38 39 40 42 44 46 47 48 50 51 52 55 57 58 60 61 62 63 64 65 66 69 70 71 73 74 75 76 77 78 81 84 85 88 92 94 96 106 107 108 109 110 **P**6 **S** Department of Veterans Affairs, Washington, DC
Primary Contact: William R. Berryman, M.D., Acting Director
COO: Patricia A. Hitt, Associate Director
CFO: Judith A. Simon, Chief Resources Management Services
CIO: Craig Frerichs, Chief Information Technology Service
CHR: William Chester, Manager Human Resources
Web address: www.va.gov/sta/guide/home.asp
| | 45 | 10 | 53 | 1595 | 48 | 84504 | 0 | 47712 | 18810 | 325 |

GREELEY—Weld County

⊠ **NORTH COLORADO MEDICAL CENTER**, 1801 16th Street, Zip 80631–5199; tel. 970/352–4121 **A**1 2 9 10 **F**2 3 4 9 10 11 12 13 14 15 17 19 21 22 23 24 26 27 28 29 30 32 33 34 37 39 41 42 44 45 46 47 48 50 51 52 53 55 57 58 59 60 61 62 63 64 65 66 67 68 69 70 71 72 73 74 75 76 77 78 81 82 84 85 87 88 92 93 94 95 96 106 107 108 109 110 **P**7 8 **S** Banner Health, Phoenix, AZ
Primary Contact: Gene L. O'Hara, Chief Executive Officer
CFO: Bill Munson, Chief Financial Officer
CMO: Donald Mellman, M.D., Chief Medical Officer
CIO: Paul Hobson–Panico, Chief Information Officer
Web address: www.ncmcgreeley.com
| | 23 | 10 | 276 | 15519 | 175 | 217550 | 2364 | 235926 | 93360 | 1850 |

GUNNISON—Gunnison County

★ **GUNNISON VALLEY HOSPITAL**, 711 North Taylor Street, Zip 81230–2296; tel. 970/641–1456 **A**9 10 18 20 **F**2 6 9 11 12 22 23 26 27 28 29 32 33 34 44 46 48 51 52 53 55 59 60 61 62 63 64 69 81 84 85 88 96 97 106 108 109
Primary Contact: Judy L. Spinella, R.N., President and Chief Executive Officer
CFO: Tim Cashman, Chief Financial Officer
CMO: Jay Wolkov, M.D., Chief of Staff
CIO: Trevor Smith, Chief Management Information Services
Web address: www.gvh–colorado.org
| | 13 | 10 | 24 | 603 | 4 | 39633 | 140 | 13594 | 5566 | 121 |

HAXTUN—Phillips County

★ **HAXTUN HOSPITAL DISTRICT**, (Critical Access), 235 West Fletcher Street, Zip 80731–0308; tel. 970/774–6123 **A**9 10 18 **F**6 9 26 27 33 34 46 64 92 97 **P**8
Primary Contact: Aaron Wood, Chief Executive Officer
COO: Lona Salyards, Director, Health Information Management
CFO: Sandra Lambrecht, Chief Financial Officer
CMO: Lila Statz, M.D., Chief of Staff
Web address: www.haxtunhealth.org
| | 16 | 49 | 42 | 181 | 3 | 5445 | 11 | 2547 | 1202 | 44 |

Many Facility Codes have changed. Please refer to the AHA Guide Code Chart.   © 2005 AHA Guide

Hospital, Address, Telephone, Approval, Facility, and Physician Codes, Health Care System	Classification Codes		Utilization Data					Expense (thousands) of dollars		
★ American Hospital Association (AHA) membership □ Joint Commission on Accreditation of Healthcare Organizations (JCAHO) accreditation ○ American Osteopathic Association (AOA) accreditation △ Commission on Accreditation of Rehabilitation Facilities (CARF) accreditation	Control	Service	Staffed Beds	Admissions	Census	Outpatient Visits	Births	Total	Payroll	Personnel

HOLYOKE—Phillips County

★ **MELISSA MEMORIAL HOSPITAL**, 505 South Baxter Avenue, Zip 80734–1496; tel. 970/854–2241 **A**9 10 18 **F**6 11 23 27 28 33 34 39 41 46 52 59 63 70 81 92 97 **P**4
Primary Contact: Arlene Harms, Administrator
CFO: Shelly Larson, Chief Financial Officer
CHR: Sharon Greenman, Human Resources Director
Web address: www.melissamemorial.org

| | 16 | 10 | 15 | 380 | 4 | 23332 | 32 | 5130 | 2997 | 72 |

HUGO—Lincoln County

★ **LINCOLN COMMUNITY HOSPITAL AND NURSING HOME**, 111 6th Street, Zip 80821–0248, Mailing Address: P.O. Box 248, Zip 80821–0248; tel. 719/743–2421, (Total facility includes 35 beds in nursing home–type unit) **A**9 10 18 **F**6 11 33 34 36 51 60 63 69 81 84 88 92 94 97
Primary Contact: Herman Schreivogel, Chief Executive Officer
CFO: Herman Schreivogel, Administrator and Chief Executive Officer
CMO: John E. Fox, M.D., Chief of Staff

| | 13 | 10 | 50 | 294 | 26 | 10172 | 1 | 4715 | 3299 | 97 |

JULESBURG—Sedgwick County

SEDGWICK COUNTY HEALTH CENTER, 900 Cedar Street, Zip 80737–1199; tel. 970/474–3323, (Total facility includes 52 beds in nursing home–type unit) **A**9 10 18 **F**8 11 12 26 27 28 33 34 41 46 48 52 59 63 81 88 92 96 97 **P**6
Primary Contact: David Garnas, Chief Executive Officer

| | 13 | 10 | 64 | 273 | 49 | 11657 | 22 | 6254 | 2646 | 92 |

KREMMLING—Grand County

★ **KREMMLING MEMORIAL HOSPITAL**, 214 South Fourth Street, Zip 80459, Mailing Address: P.O. Box 399, Zip 80459–0399; tel. 970/724–3442 **A**9 10 18 20 **F**21 27 29 30 33 34 41 46 48 52 58 63 66 69 70 81 88 92 108 **P**6
Primary Contact: Deborah Pellini, Administrator and Chief Executive Officer
CFO: Jerri Pollman, Finance Director
CMO: Paul Cump, D.O., Medical Director

| | 16 | 10 | 19 | 111 | 8 | 1367 | 0 | 6848 | 3688 | 83 |

LA JARA—Conejos County

★ **CONEJOS COUNTY HOSPITAL**, 19021 U.S. Highway 285, Zip 81140–0639, Mailing Address: P.O. Box 639, Zip 81140–0639; tel. 719/274–5121 **A**9 10 18 **F**9 11 12 21 24 26 27 28 29 33 34 37 38 42 44 46 47 48 51 52 58 59 60 61 65 66 69 70 88 92 94 95 96 108 109 **P**5 6
Primary Contact: Richard M. Ash, Chief Executive Officer
COO: Richard M. Ash, Chief Executive Officer
CFO: Pat Cooper, Comptroller
CMO: Vaughn Jackson, M.D., Chief of Staff
CHR: Teri Jo Rogers, Human Resources Assistant
Web address: www.cchoo.org

| | 16 | 10 | 47 | 531 | 34 | 19537 | — | 7733 | 3978 | 96 |

LA JUNTA—Otero County

⊞ **ARKANSAS VALLEY REGIONAL MEDICAL CENTER**, 1100 Carson Avenue, Zip 81050–2799; tel. 719/383–6000, (Total facility includes 110 beds in nursing home–type unit) **A**1 9 10 20 **F**2 9 11 12 21 23 26 27 28 29 33 34 39 46 47 48 51 52 53 55 58 59 60 61 62 63 64 65 66 69 70 81 85 88 92 93 94 96 98 106 107 109 110 **P**6 **S** Quorum Health Resources, Plano, TX
Primary Contact: Lynn Crowell, Chief Executive Officer
CFO: Robert Henshaw, Chief Financial Officer
CMO: M Lee Schmucken, M.D., Chief of Staff
CIO: Rocky Ackelson, Director Information Services
CHR: Janet Davidson, Director of Human Resources
Web address: www.avrmc.org

| | 23 | 10 | 176 | 2338 | 120 | 65709 | 368 | 31868 | 13901 | 409 |

LAFAYETTE—Boulder County

★ **EXEMPLA GOOD SAMARITAN MEDICAL CENTER**, 2600 Campus Drive, Suite C., Zip 80026; tel. 303/689–4000, (Nonreporting) **A**10 **S** Exempla Healthcare, Inc., Denver, CO
Primary Contact: David Hamm, President and Chief Executive Officer
Web address: www.exempla.org

| | 23 | 10 | 143 | — | — | — | — | — | — | — |

LAMAR—Prowers County

⊞ **PROWERS MEDICAL CENTER**, 401 Kendall Drive, Zip 81052–3993; tel. 719/336–4343 **A**1 9 10 18 20 **F**2 9 11 12 21 23 26 27 28 29 33 34 37 46 47 48 51 52 55 58 59 60 61 62 63 66 69 70 81 88 92 94 95 97 108 109 110 **P**5 **S** Quorum Health Resources, Plano, TX
Primary Contact: Greg D. Gerard, Administrator and Chief Executive Officer
CMO: Edward J. Smith, M.D., Chief of Staff
CIO: Vince Yoder, Information Technology Manager
CHR: Karen Bryant, Chief Officer Support Services
Web address: www.lpmc.org

| | 16 | 10 | 25 | 1599 | 13 | — | 221 | — | — | 210 |

LEADVILLE—Lake County

ST. VINCENT GENERAL HOSPITAL DISTRICT, 822 West 4th Street, Zip 80461–3897; tel. 719/486–0230, (Nonreporting) **A**9 10 18 20
Primary Contact: Larry E. Leaming, Chief Executive Officer
Web address: www.svghd.org

| | 16 | 10 | 25 | — | — | — | — | — | — | — |

LITTLETON—Arapahoe County

⊞ **LITTLETON ADVENTIST HOSPITAL**, 7700 South Broadway Street, Zip 80122–2628; tel. 303/730–8900, (Nonreporting) **A**1 9 10 **S** Adventist Health System Sunbelt Health Care Corporation, Winter Park, FL
Primary Contact: David Crane, Chief Executive Officer
COO: Dennis Hansen, Vice President Operations
CFO: Dan Janicak, Chief Financial Officer
CMO: Tom Fawell, Chief Medical Officer
CHR: Deb Canales, Senior Vice President Human Resources
Web address: www.centura.org

| | 21 | 10 | 134 | — | — | — | — | — | — | — |

Hospital, Address, Telephone, Approval, Facility, and Physician Codes, Health Care System	Classi-fication Codes		Utilization Data					Expense (thousands) of dollars		
★ American Hospital Association (AHA) membership □ Joint Commission on Accreditation of Healthcare Organizations (JCAHO) accreditation ○ American Osteopathic Association (AOA) accreditation △ Commission on Accreditation of Rehabilitation Facilities (CARF) accreditation	Control	Service	Staffed Beds	Admissions	Census	Outpatient Visits	Births	Total	Payroll	Personnel

LONE TREE—Douglas County

⊠ **SKY RIDGE MEDICAL CENTER**, 10101 Ridge Gate Parkway, Zip 80124; tel. 720/225–1000 **A**1 9 10 **F**2 9 10 11 12 15 17 21 22 23 26 27 28 29 30 32 33 34 44 46 47 48 50 52 55 56 57 58 59 60 61 62 63 64 65 66 69 70 79 80 81 82 84 85 87 88 94 95 106 108 109 110 **P**5 **S** HCA, Nashville, TN
Primary Contact: Maureen Tarrant, Chief Executive Officer
COO: Susan Hicks, Chief Operating Officer
CFO: Craig Sammons, Chief Financial Officer
CMO: Stephen Heinz, M.D., President, Medicl Staff
CIO: Gene Hubbard, Director, Information Technology and Systems
CHR: Carol Haun, Director Human Resources
Web address: www.skyridgemedcenter.com

	33	10	106	7320	65	54336	1990	—	—	450

LONGMONT—Boulder County

⊠ **LONGMONT UNITED HOSPITAL**, 1950 West Mountain View Avenue, Zip 80501–3162, Mailing Address: P.O. Box 1659, Zip 80502–1659; tel. 303/651–5111, (Total facility includes 15 beds in nursing home–type unit) **A**1 2 9 10 **F**1 2 9 11 12 15 17 19 21 22 23 26 27 28 29 30 32 33 35 37 38 39 41 42 44 45 46 47 48 50 51 52 53 55 57 58 59 61 62 63 64 65 66 69 71 73 74 75 76 78 79 80 81 82 84 85 87 88 90 92 93 94 95 96 106 108 110 **P**6
Primary Contact: Mitchell C. Carson, President and Chief Executive Officer
CFO: Neil W. Bertrand, Chief Financial Officer
CMO: Sam Smith, M.D., Chief of Staff
CIO: John Peterson, Director Information Systems
CHR: Warren Laughlin, Director of Human Resources
Web address: www.luhcares.org

	23	10	162	9625	104	255304	1524	107874	48643	945

LOUISVILLE—Boulder County

⊠ **AVISTA ADVENTIST HOSPITAL**, 100 Health Park Drive, Zip 80027–9583; tel. 303/673–1000 **A**1 9 10 **F**11 12 15 17 19 21 22 23 26 27 28 29 30 31 33 34 42 47 48 49 52 56 58 59 60 61 63 65 66 69 70 84 88 95 97 108 110 **P**1 **S** Adventist Health System Sunbelt Health Care Corporation, Winter Park, FL
Primary Contact: John Sackett, Chief Executive Officer
COO: David A. Smith, Vice President and Chief Operating Officer
CFO: Terry Forde, Vice President and Chief Financial Officer
Web address: www.avistahosp.org

	21	10	85	10097	84	53513	2393	40696	22798	388

□ **CENTENNIAL PEAKS HOSPITAL**, 2255 South 88th Street, Zip 80027–9716; tel. 303/673–9990 **A**1 10 **F**3 4 21 26 27 28 29 31 45 58 63 66 71 72 73 74 75 76 77 78 94 96 **P**5
Primary Contact: Mick Kirby, President and Chief Executive Officer
Web address: www.centennialpeaks.org

	23	22	72	1969	41	7022	0	8081	4063	107

LOVELAND—Larimer County

⊠ **MCKEE MEDICAL CENTER**, 2000 Boise Avenue, Zip 80538–4281, Mailing Address: P.O. Box 830, Zip 80539–0830; tel. 970/669–4640 **A**1 2 9 10 **F**1 2 9 10 11 12 15 17 21 22 23 26 27 28 29 30 31 33 34 37 39 42 44 46 47 48 49 50 51 52 53 55 57 58 59 60 61 62 63 64 65 66 69 70 77 79 80 81 82 84 85 88 92 93 94 95 96 97 98 106 107 108 109 110 **P**1 7 **S** Banner Health, Phoenix, AZ
Primary Contact: Richard O. Sutton, Chief Executive Officer
CFO: Mary McCabe, Chief Financial Officer
CMO: Bert Honea, M.D., Medical Director
CIO: Steve Rains, Director Information Services
Web address: www.mckeeloveland.com

	23	10	109	6053	63	—	895	86707	—	754

MEEKER—Rio Blanco County

★ **PIONEERS HOSPITAL OF RIO BLANCO COUNTY**, 345 Cleveland Street, Zip 81641–3238; tel. 970/878–5047, (Includes WALBRIDGE MEMORIAL CONVALESCENT WING), (Total facility includes 31 beds in nursing home–type unit) **A**9 10 20 **F**12 21 24 26 29 33 34 41 44 45 48 51 52 54 58 60 62 63 65 66 69 70 81 88 92 94 95 97 106 108 109 110 **P**6 **S** Quorum Health Resources, Plano, TX
Primary Contact: Robert W. Omer, FACHE, Chief Executive Officer
CFO: Keri Jensen, Chief Financial Officer
CMO: Victor Mihal, M.D., Chief of Staff
CHR: Twyla Jensen, Director Human Resources
Web address: www.pioneershospital.com

	13	10	48	296	32	24292	1	7668	3542	104

MONTROSE—Montrose County

⊠ **MONTROSE MEMORIAL HOSPITAL**, 800 South Third Street, Zip 81401–4291; tel. 970/249–2211 **A**1 9 10 20 **F**2 4 9 11 12 14 15 17 19 21 22 23 27 28 29 31 33 34 40 42 46 47 52 55 57 58 59 61 62 63 64 66 67 68 69 70 73 77 81 82 84 88 93 94 95 96 98 106 108 **P**5 8 **S** Quorum Health Resources, Plano, TX
Primary Contact: Kenneth E. S. Platou, Chief Executive Officer
COO: Mary E. Snyder, Associate Administrator
CFO: Connie Prewitt, Chief Financial Officer
CIO: Bill McClelland, Director Information Systems
CHR: Tom Sams, Assistant Administrator Human Resources
Web address: www.montrosehospital.com

	13	10	51	2943	29	83743	493	45030	17583	432

Many Facility Codes have changed. Please refer to the AHA Guide Code Chart. © 2005 AHA Guide

CO

Hospital, Address, Telephone, Approval, Facility, and Physician Codes, Health Care System	Classi-fication Codes		Utilization Data					Expense (thousands) of dollars		
★ American Hospital Association (AHA) membership □ Joint Commission on Accreditation of Healthcare Organizations (JCAHO) accreditation ○ American Osteopathic Association (AOA) accreditation △ Commission on Accreditation of Rehabilitation Facilities (CARF) accreditation	Control	Service	Staffed Beds	Admissions	Census	Outpatient Visits	Births	Total	Payroll	Personnel

PARKER—Douglas County

□ **PARKER ADVENTIST HOSPITAL**, 9395 Crown Crest Boulevard, Zip 80138; tel. 303/269–6000, (Nonreporting) **A**1 9 10 **S** Adventist Health System Sunbelt Health Care Corporation, Winter Park, FL
Primary Contact: Ken Bacon, President

| | 33 | 49 | 10 | — | — | — | — | — | — | — |

PUEBLO—Pueblo County

□ **COLORADO MENTAL HEALTH INSTITUTE AT PUEBLO**, 1600 West 24th Street, Zip 81003–1499; tel. 719/546–4000, (Nonreporting) **A**1 3 5 9 10
Primary Contact: Steve Schoenmakers, Superintendent

| | 12 | 22 | 514 | — | — | — | — | — | — | — |

✖ △ **PARKVIEW MEDICAL CENTER**, 400 West 16th Street, Zip 81003–2781; tel. 719/584–4000 **A**1 7 9 10 **F**1 2 3 4 9 11 12 15 17 19 21 22 23 26 27 28 29 31 33 34 37 38 39 43 44 46 51 52 55 57 58 59 61 62 63 64 66 68 69 71 72 73 74 75 76 77 78 81 82 84 86 87 88 92 93 94 96 106 108 109 110 **P**8 **S** Quorum Health Resources, Plano, TX
Primary Contact: C. W. Smith, President and Chief Executive Officer
COO: Mike Baxter, Chief Operating Officer
CFO: William Patterson, Chief Financial Officer
CMO: Robert Alsever, M.D., Vice President Medical Affairs
CHR: Dorothy Gill, Vice President Human Resources
Web address: www.parkviewmc.org

| | 23 | 10 | 287 | 13833 | 191 | 132313 | 1478 | 143303 | 66758 | 1517 |

✖ **ST. MARY–CORWIN MEDICAL CENTER**, 1008 Minnequa Avenue, Zip 81004–3798; tel. 719/560–4000 **A**1 2 9 10 12 **F**9 11 12 21 22 27 28 29 32 33 34 37 40 41 47 48 55 57 58 59 60 61 62 63 65 66 68 70 71 73 74 75 78 81 82 84 86 87 88 92 93 94 96 97 106 108 110 **S** Catholic Health Initiatives, Denver, CO
Primary Contact: Thomas E. Anderson, Administrator
Web address: www.centura.org

| | 21 | 10 | 254 | 9052 | 120 | — | — | — | — | — |

RANGELY—Rio Blanco County

★ **RANGELY DISTRICT HOSPITAL**, 511 South White Avenue, Zip 81648–2104; tel. 970/675–5011 **A**9 10 18 **F**6 8 12 27 33 34 46 48 51 54 58 69 88 93
Primary Contact: Michael E. Boyles, Chief Executive Officer
CFO: Sue Broughton, CPA, Vice President and Chief Financial Officer
Web address: www.rangelyhospital.com

| | 16 | 10 | 25 | 63 | 6 | 15914 | — | 5138 | 2378 | 77 |

RIFLE—Garfield County

★ **GRAND RIVER HOSPITAL DISTRICT**, 501 Airport Road, Zip 81650–2970, Mailing Address: P.O. Box 912, Zip 81650–0912; tel. 970/625–1510, (Total facility includes 57 beds in nursing home–type unit) **A**10 18 20 **F**2 9 12 21 22 30 33 34 39 40 41 42 48 52 53 54 55 58 60 62 63 64 66 69 70 81 84 88 92 93 94 95 96 97 108 **P**6
Primary Contact: Michael J. Raymond, Chief Executive Officer
CMO: Deborah Brown, M.D., Chief of Staff
CHR: Michael Weerts, Director
Web address: www.grhd.org

| | 16 | 10 | 71 | 581 | 57 | 30854 | 0 | 14697 | 6320 | 204 |

SALIDA—Chaffee County

★ **HEART OF THE ROCKIES REGIONAL MEDICAL CENTER**, 448 East First Street, Zip 81201–0429, Mailing Address: P.O. Box 429, Zip 81201–0429; tel. 719/539–6661, (Nonreporting) **A**9 10 18 20
Primary Contact: Nathan C. Olson, Chief Executive Officer
CFO: Lesley Fagerberg, Vice President of Fiscal Services
CHR: Barbara Abel, Vice President of Human Resources
Web address: www.hrrmc.com

| | 16 | 10 | 25 | — | — | — | — | — | — | — |

SPRINGFIELD—Baca County

★ **SOUTHEAST COLORADO HOSPITAL AND LONG TERM CARE**, 373 East Tenth Avenue, Zip 81073–1699; tel. 719/523–4501, (Total facility includes 56 beds in nursing home–type unit) **A**9 10 18 **F**6 9 12 25 26 29 33 42 45 46 51 52 63 69 81 84 88 92 94 109 **P**6
Primary Contact: Gary Steinbach, Administrator
COO: Gary Steinbach, Chief Executive Officer
CFO: James L. Forrest, Jr, Controller
CMO: Judit Marton, M.D., Chief of Staff
CHR: Virginia Basham, Human Resources Director

| | 16 | 10 | 81 | 431 | 57 | 29847 | 0 | — | — | 157 |

STEAMBOAT SPRINGS—Routt County

✖ **YAMPA VALLEY MEDICAL CENTER**, 1024 Central Park Drive, Zip 80487–5010; tel. 970/879–1322, (Total facility includes 59 beds in nursing home–type unit) **A**1 9 10 20 **F**2 6 9 11 12 21 22 23 28 29 30 33 34 37 40 41 45 46 47 48 52 55 58 59 60 62 63 64 65 66 69 81 84 85 88 92 93 94 95 96 97 106 108 109
Primary Contact: Karl B. Gills, Chief Executive Officer
CFO: Frank May, Chief Financial Officer
CIO: Laura Kaster, Chief Information Officer
CHR: Michael Turner, Director Human Resources
Web address: www.yvmc.org

| | 23 | 10 | 88 | 1498 | 69 | 37402 | 369 | 41995 | 16090 | 446 |

STERLING—Logan County

✖ **STERLING REGIONAL MEDCENTER**, 615 Fairhurst Street, Zip 80751–0500; tel. 970/522–0122 **A**1 9 10 20 **F**9 11 12 21 22 23 24 26 28 29 33 34 37 40 41 44 45 46 47 48 49 50 52 53 54 55 58 59 60 61 62 63 65 66 69 70 81 82 84 85 88 92 93 94 95 96 97 106 109 110 **P**6 **S** Banner Health, Phoenix, AZ
Primary Contact: Michael J. Gillen, Chief Executive Officer
CFO: Pamela Stieb, Finance Coordinator
Web address: www.bannerhealth.com

| | 23 | 10 | 36 | 1786 | 16 | 103017 | 316 | 34293 | 12792 | 271 |

CO

Hospital, Address, Telephone, Approval, Facility, and Physician Codes, Health Care System	Classi-fication Codes		Utilization Data					Expense (thousands) of dollars		
★ American Hospital Association (AHA) membership □ Joint Commission on Accreditation of Healthcare Organizations (JCAHO) accreditation ○ American Osteopathic Association (AOA) accreditation △ Commission on Accreditation of Rehabilitation Facilities (CARF) accreditation	Control	Service	Staffed Beds	Admissions	Census	Outpatient Visits	Births	Total	Payroll	Personnel

THORNTON—Adams County

☒ **NORTH SUBURBAN MEDICAL CENTER**, 9191 Grant Street, Zip 80229–4341; tel. 303/451–7800 **A**1 9 10 **F**12 15 17 21 22 23 27 28 33 34 37 38 46 48 52 55 56 57 58 59 62 63 66 68 81 84 88 93 94 108 109 110 **S** HCA, Nashville, TN
Primary Contact: Todd Steward, President and Chief Executive Officer
COO: Kathy D. Moore, Chief Operating Officer
CFO: Douglas Zehner, Chief Financial Officer
CIO: Kim Miller, Director Information Services
CHR: Linda Pruiett, Vice President Human Resources
Web address: www.northsuburban.com

| | 33 | 10 | 140 | 7780 | 71 | 80711 | 1902 | 74064 | 31927 | 514 |

□ **NORTH VALLEY REHABILITATION HOSPITAL**, 8451 Pearl Street, Zip 80229–4804; tel. 303/288–3000, (Nonreporting) **A**1 5 9 10 **S** VIBRA Healthcare, Mechanicsburg, PA
Primary Contact: Walter Sackett, Chief Executive Officer
Web address: www.mediplexhospital.com

| | 33 | 46 | 117 | — | — | — | — | — | — | — |

TRINIDAD—Las Animas County

☒ **MT. SAN RAFAEL HOSPITAL**, 410 Benedicta Avenue, Zip 81082–2093; tel. 719/846–9213 **A**1 9 10 18 20 **F**2 9 12 26 27 28 33 34 46 48 58 60 63 81 82 84 88 93 94 97
Primary Contact: Carolyn E. Riley, Chief Executive Officer
CFO: Jason Peret, Chief Financial Officer
CMO: Charles Yeagle, M.D., Chief Medical Officer
CHR: Lori Corsentino, Director Human Resources
Web address: www.msrhc.org

| | 23 | 10 | 25 | 1007 | 10 | 42230 | 132 | 12422 | 4422 | 123 |

USAF ACADEMY—El Paso County

☒ **U. S. AIR FORCE ACADEMY HOSPITAL**, 4102 Pinion Drive, Zip 80840–4000; tel. 719/333–5102 **A**1 9 **F**2 9 10 12 21 22 24 25 26 27 28 29 31 32 33 35 39 42 46 47 48 52 53 55 57 58 60 62 63 65 66 69 70 72 73 75 77 81 82 84 85 87 88 92 94 95 98 106 108 109 110 **P**6 **S** Department of the Air Force, Washington, DC
Primary Contact: Colonel Peter T. Walsh, Commander
COO: Colonel Carl M. Alley, USAF, MSC, Administrator
CFO: Major Richard Terry, Financial Manager
CIO: Captain James Hughes, Information Systems Flight Commander
Web address: www.usafa.af.mil

| | 41 | 10 | 24 | 706 | 5 | 201972 | 0 | — | — | 974 |

VAIL—Eagle County

☒ **VAIL VALLEY MEDICAL CENTER**, 181 West Meadow Drive, Zip 81657–5059; tel. 970/476–2451 **A**1 9 10 20 **F**2 9 11 12 22 23 27 28 33 34 36 37 40 42 46 48 51 52 53 55 58 59 60 61 62 63 64 65 66 69 79 80 81 82 84 85 87 88 93 94 95 96 107 108 109 110 **P**5
Primary Contact: Thomas J. Zellers, President and Chief Executive Officer
COO: Thomas Kyllo, Executive Vice President
CFO: Shaun J. Scanlon, Senior Vice President Finance and Chief Financial Officer
CMO: John Woodland, M.D., Medical Director
CIO: Dave Pluta, Chief Information Officer
CHR: David Blackwell, Vice President of Human Resources
Web address: www.vvmc.com

| | 23 | 10 | 58 | 2471 | 20 | — | 647 | 79517 | 26366 | 691 |

WALSENBURG—Huerfano County

★ **SPANISH PEAKS REGIONAL HEALTH CENTER**, 23500 U.S. Highway 160, Zip 81089–9524; tel. 719/738–5100, (Nonreporting) **A**9 10 18 20
Primary Contact: Steven J. Perkins, President and Chief Executive Officer
CFO: Richard L. Corradino, Chief Finance Officer
CHR: L Anthony Marostica, Human Resources Director
Web address: www.sprhc.org

| | 16 | 10 | 25 | — | — | — | — | — | — | — |

WESTMINSTER—Jefferson County

CLEO WALLACE CENTERS HOSPITAL, 8405 Church Ranch Boulevard, Zip 80021–3918; tel. 303/466–7391, (Nonreporting) **A**10
Primary Contact: Michael J. Montgomery, President and Chief Executive Officer
Web address: www.devereux.org

| | 23 | 52 | 61 | — | — | — | — | — | — | — |

★ **ST. ANTHONY NORTH HOSPITAL**, 2551 West 84th Avenue, Zip 80031; tel. 303/426–2151 **A**9 10 **F**9 10 11 12 15 17 21 22 23 27 28 29 33 34 46 49 53 55 56 57 58 59 60 61 62 63 64 66 69 70 75 81 82 85 87 88 94 108 109 **S** Catholic Health Initiatives, Denver, CO
Primary Contact: James F. Dover, FACHE, Administrator
CMO: Jodi Chambers, M.D., Chief Medical Officer
Web address: www.centura.org

| | 21 | 10 | 132 | 7005 | 76 | 69531 | 609 | 73880 | 28165 | 380 |

WHEAT RIDGE—Jefferson County

☒ **EXEMPLA LUTHERAN MEDICAL CENTER**, 8300 West 38th Avenue, Zip 80033–6005; tel. 303/425–4500, (Includes EXEMPLA WEST PINES, 3400 Lutheran Parkway, Zip 80033; tel. 303/467–4000), (Total facility includes 120 beds in nursing home–type unit) **A**1 2 9 10 **F**3 4 8 9 11 12 14 15 17 19 21 22 23 27 28 29 30 33 34 36 37 38 39 44 48 49 52 53 55 56 57 58 59 60 61 62 63 64 65 66 69 71 72 73 74 75 76 77 78 79 80 81 82 84 87 88 91 92 93 94 96 106 108 109 110 **P**6 7 **S** Exempla Healthcare, Inc., Denver, CO
Primary Contact: Robert H. Malte, President and Chief Executive Officer
COO: M Colleen Whalen, Chief Operating Officer
CFO: Brad Ludford, Vice President Finance
CMO: David Munch, M.D., Vice President and Chief Clinical and Quality Officer
CIO: George Welton, Vice President Information Services
CHR: Scott Day, Vice President Human Resources
Web address: www.exempla.org

| | 23 | 10 | 494 | 22483 | 365 | 170005 | 2654 | 228231 | 117020 | 2057 |

Many Facility Codes have changed. Please refer to the AHA Guide Code Chart. © 2005 AHA Guide

CO

Hospital, Address, Telephone, Approval, Facility, and Physician Codes, Health Care System	Classi-fication Codes		Utilization Data					Expense (thousands) of dollars		
★ American Hospital Association (AHA) membership □ Joint Commission on Accreditation of Healthcare Organizations (JCAHO) accreditation ○ American Osteopathic Association (AOA) accreditation △ Commission on Accreditation of Rehabilitation Facilities (CARF) accreditation	Control	Service	Staffed Beds	Admissions	Census	Outpatient Visits	Births	Total	Payroll	Personnel

WRAY—Yuma County

★ **WRAY COMMUNITY DISTRICT HOSPITAL**, 1017 West 7th Street, Zip 80758–1420; tel. 970/332–4811 **A**9 10 18 **F**2 11 12 21 23 27 29 33 34 37 39 46 48 52 53 58 59 61 62 63 64 81 88 92 97 108 110 **P**4
Primary Contact: Edward Finley, Administrator
CFO: Rod Larsen, Chief Financial Officer
CMO: Robert Loyd, M.D., Chief of Staff

| | 16 | 10 | 15 | 344 | 3 | 25260 | 99 | 7460 | 2605 | 72 |

YUMA—Yuma County

★ **YUMA DISTRICT HOSPITAL**, 910 South Main Street, Zip 80759–3098; tel. 970/848–5405 **A**9 10 18 **F**9 11 12 22 23 26 27 28 29 30 33 34 35 37 39 41 45 46 47 48 51 52 53 57 58 59 60 61 62 63 66 69 70 75 81 88 97 110 **P**6
Primary Contact: Lyndia Loppe, Interim Administrator
COO: Lyndia Loppe, Vice President Administrative Services and Chief Operating Officer
CFO: Cathy Wolff, Vice President of Financial Services and Chief Financial Officer
CMO: Martin Smart, M.D., Chief of Medical Staff
CIO: Mick Brant, Vice President of Information Systems
CHR: Gini Adams, Director of Human Resources
Web address: www.yumahospital.org

| | 16 | 10 | 11 | 409 | 3 | 45822 | 29 | 10475 | 5122 | 117 |

CO

CONNECTICUT

Hospital, Address, Telephone, Approval, Facility, and Physician Codes, Health Care System	Classi-fication Codes		Utilization Data					Expense (thousands) of dollars		
Approval codes: ★ American Hospital Association (AHA) membership □ Joint Commission on Accreditation of Healthcare Organizations (JCAHO) accreditation ○ American Osteopathic Association (AOA) accreditation △ Commission on Accreditation of Rehabilitation Facilities (CARF) accreditation	Control	Service	Staffed Beds	Admissions	Census	Outpatient Visits	Births	Total	Payroll	Personnel

BETHLEHEM—Litchfield County

WELLSPRING FOUNDATION, 21 Arch Bridge Road, Zip 06751–0370, Mailing Address: P.O. Box 370, Zip 06751–0370; tel. 203/266–7235, (Nonreporting)
Primary Contact: Richard E. Beauvais, Ph.D., Chief Executive Officer
Web address: www.wellspring.org
— 23 22 36 — — — — — — —

BRANFORD—New Haven County

□ **THE CONNECTICUT HOSPICE**, 100 Double Beach Road, Zip 06405–4096; tel. 203/481–6231, (Nonreporting) **A**1 10
Primary Contact: Rosemary Johnson Hurzeler, President and Chief Executive Officer
Web address: www.hospice.com
— 23 49 52 — — — — — — —

BRIDGEPORT—Fairfield County

✠ **BRIDGEPORT HOSPITAL**, 267 Grant Street, Zip 06610–0120, Mailing Address: P.O. Box 5000, Zip 06610–5000; tel. 203/384–3000 **A**1 2 3 5 6 8 9 10 **F**1 2 9 10 11 12 13 15 17 19 21 22 23 24 26 27 28 29 31 33 34 35 36 37 38 39 40 44 46 47 48 49 50 52 53 55 56 57 58 59 60 61 62 63 64 65 66 67 68 69 70 71 72 73 74 75 76 77 78 79 80 81 82 84 85 86 87 88 93 94 95 96 98 106 107 108 109 110 **P**8 **S** Yale New Haven Health System, New Haven, CT
Primary Contact: Robert J. Trefry, President and Chief Executive Officer
COO: Carolyn Salsgiver, Senior Vice President Planning and Marketing
CFO: Patrick McCabe, Senior Vice President Finance and Chief Financial Officer
CMO: Bruce M. McDonald, M.D., Senior Vice President Medical Affairs
CIO: Mark Tepping, Chief Information Officer
CHR: Joseph Janell, Senior Vice President Human Resources
Web address: www.bridgeporthospital.org
— 23 10 383 17891 279 158648 2529 259358 100446 1881

SOUTHWEST CONNECTICUT MENTAL HEALTH SYSTEM, 97 Middle Street, Zip 06604; tel. 203/551–7400, (Nonreporting) **A**10 **S** Connecticut Department of Mental Health and Addiction Services, Hartford, CT
Primary Contact: James M. Pisciotta, Chief Executive Officer
— 12 22 62 — — — — — — —

✠ **ST. VINCENT'S MEDICAL CENTER**, 2800 Main Street, Zip 06606–4292; tel. 203/576–6000, (Includes HALL–BROOKE HOSPITAL, A DIVISION OF HALL–BROOKE BEHAVIORAL HEALTH SERVICES, 47 Long Lots Road, Westport, Zip 06880–3800; tel. 203/221–8802; Stephen P. Fahey, President and Chief Executive Officer) **A**1 2 3 5 9 10 12 **F**9 10 11 12 14 15 17 18 19 21 22 23 27 28 29 33 34 37 38 41 44 46 47 48 49 50 52 55 57 58 59 60 61 62 63 64 65 66 68 69 70 71 72 73 74 75 76 77 79 81 82 84 85 86 88 93 94 95 96 106 107 108 109 **S** Ascension Health, Saint Louis, MO
Primary Contact: Susan L. Davis, R.N., Ed.D., President and Chief Executive Officer
CFO: John M. Ahle, Corporate Senior Vice President and Chief Financial Officer
CIO: Gary Weiner, Chief Information Officer
CHR: Pamela Tarulli, Corporatae Vice President Human Resources
Web address: www.stvincents.org
— 21 10 320 17721 258 114565 1398 225571 94603 —

BRISTOL—Hartford County

✠ **BRISTOL HOSPITAL**, Brewster Road, Zip 06011; tel. 860/585–3000, (Nonreporting) **A**1 2 5 9 10
Primary Contact: Thomas D. Kennedy, III, President and Chief Executive Officer
CFO: Kelvin Kreho, Vice President Finance
CMO: Daniel J. Scoppetta, M.D., Chief of Staff
Web address: www.bristolhospital.org
— 23 10 101 8368 101 178005 819 103382 46137 912

DANBURY—Fairfield County

✠ **DANBURY HOSPITAL**, 24 Hospital Avenue, Zip 06810–6099; tel. 203/797–7000 **A**1 2 3 5 8 9 10 **F**2 4 7 10 11 12 14 15 17 19 21 22 23 24 25 26 27 28 29 30 31 32 33 34 35 37 38 39 40 41 42 43 44 46 47 48 49 50 51 52 53 55 56 57 58 59 60 61 62 63 64 65 66 68 69 70 71 72 73 74 75 76 77 78 79 80 81 82 83 84 85 86 87 88 90 93 94 95 96 98 106 107 108 109 110 **P**8
Primary Contact: Frank J. Kelly, President and Chief Executive Officer
CFO: Art Tedesco, Chief Financial Officer
CMO: Matthew Miller, M.D., Vice President Medical Affairs
CIO: Peter Courtway, Chief Information Officer
CHR: Phyllis Zappala, Vice President Human Resources
Web address: www.danburyhospital.org
— 23 10 304 17344 201 229750 2362 299674 128085 2064

DERBY—New Haven County

✠ **GRIFFIN HOSPITAL**, 130 Division Street, Zip 06418–1326; tel. 203/735–7421 **A**1 2 9 10 12 **F**2 4 11 12 21 22 23 26 27 28 29 30 31 33 36 37 38 39 41 44 46 47 48 49 50 52 53 55 57 58 59 60 61 62 63 64 65 66 69 70 71 72 73 74 75 76 77 78 81 82 84 85 86 87 88 93 94 96 98 106 107 108 109 110
Primary Contact: Patrick Charmel, President and Chief Executive Officer
CFO: James J. Moylan, Vice President Finance
CMO: Kenneth V. Schwartz, M.D., Medical Director
CIO: George Tomas, Director Information Services
Web address: www.griffinhealth.org
— 23 10 111 6663 84 160427 709 86407 40646 778

Many Facility Codes have changed. Please refer to the AHA Guide Code Chart.   © 2005 AHA Guide

Hospital, Address, Telephone, Approval, Facility, and Physician Codes, Health Care System	Classification Codes		Utilization Data					Expense (thousands) of dollars		
	Control	Service	Staffed Beds	Admissions	Census	Outpatient Visits	Births	Total	Payroll	Personnel

★ American Hospital Association (AHA) membership
☐ Joint Commission on Accreditation of Healthcare Organizations (JCAHO) accreditation
○ American Osteopathic Association (AOA) accreditation
△ Commission on Accreditation of Rehabilitation Facilities (CARF) accreditation

FARMINGTON—Hartford County

⊠ UNIVERSITY OF CONNECTICUT HEALTH CENTER, JOHN DEMPSEY HOSPITAL, 263 Farmington Avenue, Zip 06030–0001; tel. 860/679–2000 **A**1 2 3 5 8 9 10 12 **F**4 6 7 9 10 11 12 15 17 19 21 22 23 26 27 28 29 30 31 32 33 40 44 45 48 49 50 52 53 55 56 57 58 59 60 61 62 63 65 66 69 71 73 74 75 76 77 78 79 81 82 84 85 86 87 88 89 90 93 94 95 96 108 109 **P**6
Primary Contact: Steven Strongwater, M.D., Associate Dean Clinical Affairs and Hospital Director
CFO: Daniel Upton, Chief Financial Officer
CMO: Richard Simon, M.D., Chief of Staff
CIO: Sandra Armstrong, Vice Chancellor Information Technology
CHR: Joan Mazzone, Associate Vice President
Web address: www.uconnhealth.org

| | 12 | 10 | 155 | 8788 | 155 | 225881 | 613 | 177906 | 67856 | 2790 |

GREENWICH—Fairfield County

⊠ GREENWICH HOSPITAL, 5 Perryridge Road, Zip 06830–4697; tel. 203/863–3000 **A**1 2 3 5 8 9 10 **F**3 4 9 10 11 12 14 15 16 17 18 19 20 21 22 23 24 26 27 28 29 30 31 32 33 34 36 37 38 40 41 44 46 47 48 49 50 51 52 53 55 56 57 58 59 60 61 62 63 64 65 66 69 70 72 73 74 75 76 77 79 81 82 84 85 86 87 88 90 92 93 94 95 96 98 106 108 109 110 **S** Yale New Haven Health System, New Haven, CT
Primary Contact: Frank A. Corvino, President and Chief Executive Officer
COO: Quinton J. Friesen, Executive Vice President and Chief Operating Officer
CFO: Eugene Colucci, Vice President Finance
CMO: A Michael Marino, M.D., Senior Vice President Medical Administration
CIO: James Weeks, Chief Information Officer
Web address: www.greenhosp.org

| | 23 | 10 | 175 | 9139 | 109 | 402691 | 2243 | 202773 | 93425 | 1573 |

HARTFORD—Hartford County

⊠ CONNECTICUT CHILDREN'S MEDICAL CENTER, 282 Washington Street, Zip 06106–3322; tel. 860/545–9000 **A**1 3 5 9 10 **F**2 9 16 18 20 22 23 24 28 29 32 33 39 47 50 53 56 57 58 61 62 63 64 65 67 69 81 84 88 94 95 96 108
Primary Contact: Larry M. Gold, President and Chief Executive Officer
CFO: Gerald J. Boisvert, Vice President and Chief Financial Officer
CMO: Paul Dworkin, M.D., Physician–in–Chief
CIO: Richard Johnson, Director Information Services
Web address: www.ccmckids.org

| | 23 | 50 | 114 | 5536 | 84 | 106129 | — | 114948 | 48472 | 1304 |

⊠ △ HARTFORD HOSPITAL, 80 Seymour Street, Zip 06102–5037, Mailing Address: P.O. Box 5037, Zip 06102–5037; tel. 860/545–5000, (Includes INSTITUTE OF LIVING, 400 Washington Street, Zip 06106–3392; tel. 860/545–7000) **A**1 2 3 5 7 8 9 10 **F**1 2 3 4 8 9 10 11 12 14 15 17 19 21 22 23 26 27 28 29 30 31 32 33 34 36 37 38 40 41 42 44 46 47 48 49 50 52 53 54 55 57 58 59 60 61 62 63 64 65 66 68 69 70 71 72 73 74 75 76 77 78 79 80 81 82 84 85 86 87 88 89 90 91 92 93 94 95 96 99 100 101 102 103 104 105 106 108 109 110 **P**5 6 8
Primary Contact: John J. Meehan, President and Chief Executive Officer
COO: Kevin R. Hannifan, Executive Vice President and Chief Operating Officer
CFO: John Biancamano, Vice President Finance
CMO: Alfred Herzog, M.D., Vice President, Medical Affairs
CIO: Stephan O'Neill, Vice President Information Services
CHR: Richard McAloon, Vice President, Human Resources
Web address: www.harthosp.org

| | 23 | 10 | 573 | 33397 | 572 | 205802 | 4062 | 521343 | 275139 | 4914 |

⊠ SAINT FRANCIS HOSPITAL AND MEDICAL CENTER, 114 Woodland Street, Zip 06105–1299; tel. 860/714–7440 **A**1 2 3 5 8 9 10 **F**2 9 10 11 12 14 15 17 19 21 22 23 24 26 27 28 29 30 32 33 34 36 37 38 39 41 42 44 46 47 48 50 51 52 53 55 56 57 58 59 60 61 62 63 64 65 66 69 70 71 72 73 74 75 76 77 78 79 80 81 82 84 87 88 89 93 94 95 96 98 106 107 108 109 110 **P**8 **S** Saint Francis Care, Inc., Hartford, CT
Primary Contact: Christopher M. Dadlez, President and Chief Executive Officer
COO: Amit Mody, M.D., Executive Vice President and Chief Operating Officer
CFO: Steven Rosenberg, Senior Vice President and Chief Financial Officer
CMO: Rolf W. Knoll, M.D., Senior Vice President Medical Affairs
CIO: Catherine Szenczy, Chief Information Officer and Senior Vice President Information Systems
CHR: Beth Frechette, Vice President Human Resources
Web address: www.saintfranciscare.com

| | 21 | 10 | 515 | 29145 | 410 | 324645 | — | — | — | — |

☐ THE REHABILITATION HOSPITAL OF CONNECTICUT, 490 Blue Hills Avenue, Zip 06112; tel. 860/714–3500, (Nonreporting) **A**1 10 **S** Saint Francis Care, Inc., Hartford, CT
Primary Contact: Christopher M. Dadlez, President and Chief Executive Officer

| | 33 | 46 | 38 | — | — | — | — | — | — | — |

MANCHESTER—Hartford County

⊠ MANCHESTER MEMORIAL HOSPITAL, 71 Haynes Street, Zip 06040–4188; tel. 860/646–1222 **A**1 2 9 10 **F**2 4 9 11 12 21 22 24 26 27 29 31 33 35 39 44 46 47 48 52 54 55 57 58 59 60 62 63 65 66 69 71 72 73 74 75 76 77 78 81 82 84 87 88 92 93 94 95 96 98 106 107 108 110 **P**5 6 8 **S** Eastern Connecticut Health Network, Manchester, CT
Primary Contact: Peter J. Karl, President and Chief Executive Officer
CFO: Kevin G. Murphy, Senior Vice President Finance and Chief Financial Officer
CMO: Joel R. Reich, M.D., Senior Vice President Medical Affairs
CIO: Charles Covin, Chief Information Officer
Web address: www.echn.org

| | 23 | 10 | 145 | 7788 | 105 | 264360 | 1022 | 129352 | 60214 | 1009 |

CT

Hospital, Address, Telephone, Approval, Facility, and Physician Codes, Health Care System	Classi-fication Codes		Utilization Data					Expense (thousands) of dollars		
★ American Hospital Association (AHA) membership □ Joint Commission on Accreditation of Healthcare Organizations (JCAHO) accreditation ○ American Osteopathic Association (AOA) accreditation △ Commission on Accreditation of Rehabilitation Facilities (CARF) accreditation	Control	Service	Staffed Beds	Admissions	Census	Outpatient Visits	Births	Total	Payroll	Personnel

MANSFIELD CENTER—Tolland County

□ **NATCHAUG HOSPITAL**, 189 Storrs Road, Zip 06250–1638; tel. 860/456–1311 **A**1 10 **F**3 4 28 71 72 77 78 **P**1
Primary Contact: Stephen W. Larcen, Ph.D., President and Chief Executive Officer
Web address: www.natchaug.org
| 23 | 22 | 54 | 1638 | 47 | — | 0 | — | — | — |

MERIDEN—New Haven County

✠ **MIDSTATE MEDICAL CENTER**, 435 Lewis Avenue, Zip 06451–2101; tel. 203/694–8200, (Includes EAST CAMPUS, 883 Paddock Avenue, Zip 06450–7094) **A**1 2 9 10 **F**2 9 10 11 12 15 21 22 23 26 27 28 29 30 31 33 36 37 39 40 42 44 46 47 48 50 51 52 53 55 57 58 59 61 62 63 64 65 66 71 75 79 80 81 82 84 85 86 87 88 94 95 96 107 108 109 110 **P**5
Primary Contact: Lucille A. Janatka, President and Chief Executive Officer
COO: Jeffrey A. Flaks, Executive Vice President and Chief Operating Officer
CFO: Ralph W. Becker, Chief Financial Officer
CMO: Gary F. Tansino, M.D., Chief of Staff
CIO: Jennifer Comerford, Information Services Manager
CHR: Ken Cesca, Director Human Resources
Web address: www.midstatemedical.org
| 23 | 10 | 124 | 7939 | 106 | 150164 | 1064 | 124162 | 46424 | 876 |

MIDDLETOWN—Middlesex County

□ **CONNECTICUT VALLEY HOSPITAL**, Eastern Drive, Zip 06457–3947, Mailing Address: P.O. Box 351, Zip 06457–0351; tel. 860/262–5000, (Includes WHITING FORENSIC DIVISION OF CONNECTICUT VALLEY HOSPITAL, O'Brien Drive, Zip 06457, Mailing Address: Box 70, Zip 06457–3942; tel. 203/344–2541), (Nonreporting) **A**1 5 10 **S** Connecticut Department of Mental Health and Addiction Services, Hartford, CT
Primary Contact: Garrell S. Mullaney, Chief Executive Officer
| 12 | 22 | 548 | — | — | — | — | — | — | — |

✠ **MIDDLESEX HOSPITAL**, 28 Crescent Street, Zip 06457–3650; tel. 860/344–6000 **A**1 2 3 5 9 10 **F**2 4 10 11 12 14 15 17 19 21 22 23 26 28 29 30 31 33 36 37 38 39 42 46 48 49 50 51 52 55 57 58 59 60 61 62 63 64 65 66 69 70 71 72 73 74 75 76 77 78 79 81 82 84 85 86 87 88 93 94 95 96 98 106 108 109 110 **P**8
Primary Contact: Robert Gerard Kiely, President and Chief Executive Officer
CFO: Vincent Capece, Vice President Finance and Treasurer
CMO: Deborah A. Whitehead, M.D., President, Medical Staff
CIO: Ludwig Johnson, Vice President Information Technology
CHR: Thomas F. Murray, Vice President Human Resources
Web address: www.middlesexhealth.org
| 23 | 10 | 168 | 11202 | 134 | 1071000 | 1240 | 199140 | 99879 | 1491 |

□ **RIVERVIEW HOSPITAL FOR CHILDREN AND YOUTH**, (Formerly Riverview Hospital for Children), 915 River Road, Zip 06457–2792, Mailing Address: P.O. Box 2792, Zip 06457–2792; tel. 860/704–4000, (Nonreporting) **A**1
Primary Contact: Robert Plant, Ph.D., Superintendent
| 12 | 52 | 102 | — | — | — | — | — | — | — |

WHITING FORENSIC DIVISION OF CONNECTICUT VALLEY HOSPITAL See Connecticut Valley Hospital

MILFORD—New Haven County

✠ △ **MILFORD HOSPITAL**, 300 Seaside Avenue, Zip 06460–4603; tel. 203/876–4000 **A**1 7 9 10 **F**9 11 12 17 21 22 23 24 26 27 28 29 33 37 46 48 52 53 54 55 57 58 59 61 62 63 64 66 75 81 82 84 85 86 87 88 94 96 98 106 107 108 109
Primary Contact: Paul E. Moss, President
CFO: Joseph Pelaccia, Vice President Finance
Web address: www.milfordhospital.org
| 23 | 10 | 87 | 4548 | 58 | 76423 | 521 | 63663 | 29234 | 586 |

NEW BRITAIN—Hartford County

✠ △ **HOSPITAL FOR SPECIAL CARE**, 2150 Corbin Avenue, Zip 06053–2263; tel. 860/827–4758 **A**1 5 7 10 **F**2 9 21 22 26 27 28 32 37 41 44 52 53 57 58 60 68 69 73 94 95 96 108 **P**6
Primary Contact: David Crandall, FACHE, President and Chief Executive Officer
COO: Mary Ann Camelleri, Senior Vice President, Chief Operating Officer and General Counsel
CFO: Laurie A. Whelan, Vice President Finance and Chief Financial Officer
CMO: Mervet Elkair, M.D., Chief of Medicine
CIO: Stan Jankowski, Corporate Manager Information Technology
Web address: www.hfsc.org
| 23 | 46 | 199 | 600 | 187 | 19414 | 0 | 71263 | 38315 | 666 |

✠ **NEW BRITAIN GENERAL HOSPITAL**, 100 Grand Street, Zip 06052–2017, Mailing Address: P.O. Box 100, Zip 06050–0100; tel. 860/224–5011 **A**1 2 3 5 8 9 10 **F**2 3 4 9 10 11 12 14 15 17 21 22 23 26 27 28 29 31 33 34 35 36 37 38 39 40 41 42 45 46 47 48 49 50 51 52 53 55 56 57 58 59 60 61 62 63 64 65 66 69 70 71 72 73 74 75 76 77 78 79 80 81 82 84 85 86 87 88 89 92 93 94 95 96 106 107 108 109 **P**5
Primary Contact: Laurence A. Tanner, President and Chief Executive Officer
COO: Clarence J. Silvia, Senior Vice President and Chief Operating Officer
CFO: David R. Newton, Senior Vice President Finance and Chief Financial Officer
CMO: Steven D. Hanks, M.D., Senior Vice President Medical Affairs and Chief Medical Officer
CIO: James A. Wesley, Chief Information Officer
CHR: Elizabeth A. Lynch, Vice President Human Resources
Web address: www.nbgh.org
| 23 | 10 | 255 | 14915 | 175 | 298096 | 1942 | 211674 | 98648 | 1695 |

Hospital, Address, Telephone, Approval, Facility, and Physician Codes, Health Care System	Classi-fication Codes		Utilization Data					Expense (thousands) of dollars		
★ American Hospital Association (AHA) membership □ Joint Commission on Accreditation of Healthcare Organizations (JCAHO) accreditation ○ American Osteopathic Association (AOA) accreditation △ Commission on Accreditation of Rehabilitation Facilities (CARF) accreditation	Control	Service	Staffed Beds	Admissions	Census	Outpatient Visits	Births	Total	Payroll	Personnel

NEW CANAAN—Fairfield County

□ **SILVER HILL HOSPITAL**, 208 Valley Road, Zip 06840–3899; tel. 203/966–3561, (Nonreporting) **A**1 10
Primary Contact: Sigurd H. Ackerman, M.D., President and Chief Executive Officer
Web address: www.silverhillhospital.org
23	22	64	—	—	—	—	—	—	—

NEW HAVEN—New Haven County

□ **CONNECTICUT MENTAL HEALTH CENTER**, 34 Park Street, Zip 06519–1187, Mailing Address: P.O. Box 1842, Zip 06508–1842; tel. 203/974–7144, (Nonreporting) **A**1 3 5 9 10 **S** Connecticut Department of Mental Health and Addiction Services, Hartford, CT
Primary Contact: Selby Jacobs, M.D., Chief Executive Officer
Web address: www.dmhas.state.ct.us/lmha.htm
12	22	29	—	—	—	—	—	—	—

☒ **HOSPITAL OF SAINT RAPHAEL**, 1450 Chapel Street, Zip 06511–1450; tel. 203/789–3000 **A**1 2 3 5 8 9 10 **F**2 4 9 10 11 12 14 15 17 19 21 22 23 24 26 27 28 29 30 31 32 33 34 35 37 38 39 42 44 46 47 48 49 50 52 53 55 57 58 59 60 61 62 63 64 65 66 68 69 70 71 72 73 74 75 76 77 78 79 80 81 82 84 85 86 87 88 89 92 93 94 96 98 106 107 108 109 110 **P**5 8
Primary Contact: David W. Benfer, FACHE, President and Chief Executive Officer
CMO: Charles Riordan, M.D., Vice President Medical Affairs
CIO: Gary Davidson, Vice President and Chief Information Officer
Web address: www.srhs.org
21	10	439	24274	383	274023	1085	359808	157768	2333

☒ **YALE–NEW HAVEN HOSPITAL**, 20 York Street, Zip 06510–3202; tel. 203/688–4242, (Includes YALE–NEW HAVEN CHILDREN'S HOSPITAL, 1 Park Street, Zip 06504–8901; tel. 203/688–4242; YALE–NEW HAVEN PSYCHIATRIC HOSPITAL, 184 Liberty Street, Zip 06519–1625; tel. 203/688–9704; Paul Haeberle, Executive Director) **A**1 2 3 5 8 9 10 **F**2 4 5 9 10 11 12 14 15 16 17 18 19 20 21 22 23 24 26 27 28 29 30 31 32 33 34 35 37 38 39 40 43 44 45 46 47 48 50 52 53 55 56 57 58 59 60 61 62 63 64 65 66 67 69 70 71 72 73 74 75 76 77 78 79 81 82 84 85 86 87 88 89 90 93 94 95 96 98 99 100 101 102 103 104 105 106 107 108 109 110 **P**5 **S** Yale New Haven Health System, New Haven, CT
Primary Contact: Joseph A. Zaccagnino, President and Chief Executive Officer
COO: Marna P. Borgstrom, Executive Vice President and Chief Operating Officer
CFO: James Staten, Senior Vice President Finance
CMO: Peter N. Herbert, M.D., Senior Vice President Medical Affairs and Chief of Staff
CIO: Mark Andersen, Senior Vice President, Information Systems and Chief Information Officer
CHR: Edward J. Dowling, Senior Vice President Human Resources
Web address: www.ynhh.org
23	10	830	42188	603	265960	4761	688460	304788	5906

NEW LONDON—New London County

☒ △ **LAWRENCE & MEMORIAL HOSPITAL**, 365 Montauk Avenue, Zip 06320–4769; tel. 860/442–0711 **A**1 2 7 9 10 **F**2 9 11 12 14 15 17 21 22 23 24 26 27 28 29 30 31 32 33 35 36 37 38 39 40 41 42 44 46 47 48 49 50 52 53 55 56 57 58 59 60 61 62 63 64 65 66 68 69 71 72 73 74 75 76 77 78 79 81 82 84 86 87 88 93 94 95 96 98 106 107 108 109 110 **P**6
Primary Contact: William T. Christopher, President and Chief Executive Officer
COO: Cynthia B. Kane, Executive Vice President and Chief Operating Officer
CFO: Elwin Bresette, Vice President and Chief Financial Officer
CIO: Randy Scarpati, Chief Information Officer
CHR: Joan Bennett, Vice President, Human Resources
Web address: www.lmhospital.org
23	10	249	13064	172	162895	1804	199105	102535	1722

NEW MILFORD—Litchfield County

☒ **NEW MILFORD HOSPITAL**, 21 Elm Street, Zip 06776–2993; tel. 860/355–2611 **A**1 9 10 **F**2 11 12 14 15 21 22 23 26 27 28 29 31 32 33 36 37 38 40 46 50 53 55 57 58 59 60 61 62 63 64 75 77 79 80 81 82 84 85 86 87 88 90 93 94 95 96 108 109
Primary Contact: Richard E. Pugh, President and Chief Executive Officer
CFO: Joseph Hart, Controller and Chief Financial Officer
CMO: Thomas Koobatian, M.D., President Medical Staff
CIO: Stephen Veillette, Director Management Information Systems
CHR: Robert Sommer, Vice President Human Resources
Web address: www.newmilfordhospital.org
23	10	62	3006	37	93548	333	64672	28480	577

NEWINGTON—Hartford County

□ **CEDARCREST HOSPITAL**, 525 Russell Road, Zip 06111–1595; tel. 860/666–4613, (Nonreporting) **A**1 10 **S** Connecticut Department of Mental Health and Addiction Services, Hartford, CT
Primary Contact: Susan Graham, R.N., MSN, Chief Executive Officer
12	22	135	—	—	—	—	—	—	—

NORWALK—Fairfield County

☒ △ **NORWALK HOSPITAL**, 34 Maple Street, Zip 06850–3894; tel. 203/852–2000 **A**1 2 3 5 7 8 9 10 **F**2 3 4 6 10 11 12 14 15 17 21 22 23 26 27 28 29 32 33 34 36 37 39 40 46 47 48 53 54 55 56 57 58 59 60 61 62 63 64 66 68 69 71 73 75 77 80 81 82 84 85 86 87 88 90 93 94 96 106 107 108 109 110 **P**5 7
Primary Contact: Geoffrey F. Cole, President and Chief Executive Officer
COO: Paul E. Nurick, Senior Vice President & Chief Operating Officer
CFO: Thomas Breen, Vice President Finance
CMO: Stephen P. Michaelson, M.D., Chief of Staff
CIO: Christian Randon, Chief Information Officer and Vice President Information Technology
CHR: Michael Dimenstein, Vice President Human Resources
Web address: www.norwalkhosp.org
23	10	237	14148	212	140402	1462	227636	99159	1720

Hospital, Address, Telephone, Approval, Facility, and Physician Codes, Health Care System	Classi-fication Codes		Utilization Data					Expense (thousands) of dollars		
★ American Hospital Association (AHA) membership □ Joint Commission on Accreditation of Healthcare Organizations (JCAHO) accreditation ○ American Osteopathic Association (AOA) accreditation △ Commission on Accreditation of Rehabilitation Facilities (CARF) accreditation	Control	Service	Staffed Beds	Admissions	Census	Outpatient Visits	Births	Total	Payroll	Personnel

NORWICH—New London County

⊠ **THE WILLIAM W. BACKUS HOSPITAL**, 326 Washington Street, Zip 06360–2733; tel. 860/889–8331 **A**1 2 9 10 **F**2 7 9 11 12 15 21 22 23 27 28 29 30 33 34 36 37 40 42 46 47 48 50 51 52 55 57 58 59 60 61 62 63 64 65 66 69 70 71 73 74 75 76 77 78 81 82 84 85 86 87 88 92 94 96 98 106 107 108 109 110
Primary Contact: Thomas P. Pipicelli, President and Chief Executive Officer
COO: Mark A. Santamaria, Vice President and Chief Operating Officer
CFO: Daniel E. Lohr, Senior Vice President and Chief Financial Officer
CMO: W Gordon Van Nes, M.D., Medical Director
CIO: Edward L. Fisher, Chief Information Officer
Web address: www.backushospital.org
(23 10 | 179 | 10847 | 136 | 326087 | 1079 | 169828 | 73023 | 1290)

PUTNAM—Windham County

⊠ **DAY KIMBALL HOSPITAL**, 320 Pomfret Street, Zip 06260–0901, Mailing Address: P.O. Box 6001, Zip 06260–6001; tel. 860/928–6541 **A**1 9 10 19 20 **F**2 9 11 12 22 26 27 28 29 33 36 37 38 44 46 47 50 55 58 59 60 61 62 63 64 65 66 69 71 72 73 74 75 76 77 81 84 85 86 87 88 93 94 96 106 107 108 109
Primary Contact: Ann Errichetti, M.D., President and Chief Executive Officer
CFO: Crista Durand, Senior Vice President Finance and Chief Financial Officer
CMO: Douglas White, Director of Medical Affairs
CIO: Carl Gentry, Chief Information Officer and Vice President Management Information Systems
CHR: Tom Denton, Vice President Human Resources
Web address: www.daykimball.org
(23 10 | 68 | 6462 | 58 | 307187 | 621 | 79590 | 36110 | 512)

ROCKY HILL—Hartford County

VETERANS HOME AND HOSPITAL, 287 West Street, Zip 06067–3501; tel. 860/529–2571, (Nonreporting) **A**10
Primary Contact: Margaret Concannon, Acting Administrator
Web address: www.state.ct.us/ctva/
(12 48 | 215 | — | — | — | — | — | — | —)

SHARON—Litchfield County

□ **SHARON HOSPITAL**, 50 Hospital Hill Road, Zip 06069–0789, Mailing Address: P.O. Box 789, Zip 06069–0789; tel. 860/364–4141, (Nonreporting) **A**1 2 9 10 **S** Essent Healthcare, Nashville, TN
Primary Contact: Daniel R. Kelly, Chief Executive Officer
Web address: www.sharonhospital.com
(33 10 | 78 | — | — | — | — | — | — | —)

SOMERS—Tolland County

CONNECTICUT DEPARTMENT OF CORRECTION'S HOSPITAL, 100 Bilton Road, Zip 06071, Mailing Address: P.O. Box 100, Zip 06071–0100; tel. 860/749–8391, (Nonreporting)
Primary Contact: Edward A. Blanchette, M.D., Director
(12 11 | 29 | — | — | — | — | — | — | —)

SOUTHINGTON—Hartford County

⊠ **BRADLEY MEMORIAL HOSPITAL AND HEALTH CENTER**, 81 Meriden Avenue, Zip 06489–3297; tel. 860/276–5000 **A**1 9 10 **F**9 12 14 21 23 27 29 33 36 40 46 47 48 52 53 55 57 58 60 61 62 63 65 69 73 74 75 76 81 82 84 87 88 94 96 106 108 109 110
Primary Contact: Clarence J. Silvia, President and Chief Executive Officer
CFO: Brian Rogoz, Vice President Finance and Chief Financial Officer
CIO: Petra Knowles, Chief Information Officr
Web address: www.bradleymemorial.org
(23 10 | 46 | 2308 | 29 | 73987 | 0 | 35297 | 17671 | 225)

STAFFORD SPRINGS—Tolland County

⊠ **JOHNSON MEMORIAL HOSPITAL**, 201 Chestnut Hill Road, Zip 06076–0860, Mailing Address: P.O. Box 860, Zip 06076–0860; tel. 860/684–4251 **A**1 9 10 **F**2 4 9 11 12 21 23 26 27 28 29 31 33 36 37 38 40 42 44 46 47 48 49 50 52 53 55 57 58 59 61 62 63 64 65 66 69 70 71 72 73 74 75 76 77 78 81 82 83 84 85 86 87 88 92 93 94 95 96 98 107 108 109 **P**5
Primary Contact: Alfred A. Lerz, President and Chief Executive Officer
CFO: Richard F. Werkowski, Chief Financial Officer
CMO: Herbert J. Dimeola, M.D., Vice President Medical Affairs
CIO: Paul Russell, Director Information Services
CHR: M Clark Kearney, Vice President Human Resources
Web address: www.johnsonhealthnetwork.com
(23 10 | 89 | 3461 | 51 | 88052 | 159 | 48142 | 22970 | 410)

STAMFORD—Fairfield County

⊠ **STAMFORD HEALTH SYSTEM**, 30 Shelburne Road, Zip 06902, Mailing Address: P.O. Box 9317, Zip 06904–9317; tel. 203/325–7000 **A**1 2 3 5 8 9 10 **F**2 4 11 12 15 21 22 23 28 29 30 33 34 37 39 40 41 42 44 46 47 48 50 52 53 55 56 57 58 59 60 61 62 63 65 66 68 69 70 71 73 74 75 76 77 81 82 84 85 87 88 89 90 92 93 94 95 96 99 104 106 107 108 109 110
Primary Contact: Brian G. Grissler, President and Chief Executive Officer
CFO: Richard L. Jones, Jr, CPA, Senior Vice President Finance and Chief Financial Officer
CMO: John Rodis, M.D., Senior Vice President Medical Services and Chief Clinical Officer
CIO: Keith Ryan, Vice President Information Systems and Chief Information Officer
CHR: Darryl McCormick, Senior Vice President Human Resources
Web address: www.stamhealth.org
(23 10 | 296 | 14510 | 193 | 235061 | 2721 | 239929 | 96185 | 1631)

CT

Many Facility Codes have changed. Please refer to the AHA Guide Code Chart.

Hospital, Address, Telephone, Approval, Facility, and Physician Codes, Health Care System	Classi-fication Codes		Utilization Data					Expense (thousands) of dollars		
	Control	Service	Staffed Beds	Admissions	Census	Outpatient Visits	Births	Total	Payroll	Personnel

★ American Hospital Association (AHA) membership
□ Joint Commission on Accreditation of Healthcare Organizations (JCAHO) accreditation
○ American Osteopathic Association (AOA) accreditation
△ Commission on Accreditation of Rehabilitation Facilities (CARF) accreditation

TORRINGTON—Litchfield County

✠ **THE CHARLOTTE HUNGERFORD HOSPITAL**, 540 Litchfield Street, Zip 06790–0988, Mailing Address: P.O. Box 988, Zip 06790–0988; tel. 860/496–6666 **A**1 2 9 10 **F**2 4 9 11 12 14 21 22 23 24 27 28 29 30 31 33 34 36 37 39 40 41 42 46 47 48 50 52 53 55 57 58 59 61 62 63 64 65 66 71 72 73 74 75 76 77 78 79 81 82 84 86 87 88 93 94 96 106 107 108 109 110
Primary Contact: Daniel J. McIntyre, President and Chief Executive Officer
CFO: Gary J. DePaul, Vice President Finance and Treasurer
CMO: Mark Prete, M.D., Vice President Medical Affairs
CIO: Jonathan Trask, Director Management Information Services
CHR: R James Elliott, Vice President Human Resources
Web address: www.charlottesweb.hungerford.org

Control 23, Service 10, Staffed Beds 109, Admissions 5111, Census 59, Outpatient Visits 210179, Births 517, Total 80274, Payroll 37556, Personnel 686

VERNON ROCKVILLE—Hartford County

✠ **ROCKVILLE GENERAL HOSPITAL**, 31 Union Street, Zip 06066–3160; tel. 860/872–0501 **A**1 9 10 **F**2 9 11 12 15 21 22 26 27 29 33 35 39 44 46 47 48 49 50 52 54 55 57 58 59 62 63 64 65 66 69 81 82 84 88 92 94 95 96 106 107 108 **P**5 6 8 **S** Eastern Connecticut Health Network, Manchester, CT
Primary Contact: Peter J. Karl, President and Chief Executive Officer
CFO: Kevin G. Murphy, Senior Vice President Finance and Chief Financial Officer
CMO: Joel R. Reich, M.D., Senior Vice President Medical Affairs
CIO: Charles Covin, Chief Information Officer
CHR: Mary Kohanski, Senior Vice President Human Resources
Web address: www.echn.org

Control 23, Service 10, Staffed Beds 57, Admissions 3647, Census 41, Outpatient Visits 134402, Births 498, Total 57740, Payroll 28763, Personnel 467

WALLINGFORD—New Haven County

□ △ **GAYLORD HOSPITAL**, Gaylord Farm Road, Zip 06492–7048, Mailing Address: P.O. Box 400, Zip 06492–0400; tel. 203/284–2800 **A**1 5 7 10 **F**10 22 29 37 38 42 45 52 58 60 66 68 69 93 94 96 108 110
Primary Contact: James J. Cullen, President and Chief Executive Officer
Web address: www.gaylord.org

Control 23, Service 80, Staffed Beds 99, Admissions 1125, Census 86, Outpatient Visits 64032, Births 0, Total 46284, Payroll 25934, Personnel 501

✠ **MASONIC HEALTHCARE CENTER**, 22 Masonic Avenue, Zip 06492–3048, Mailing Address: P.O. Box 70, Zip 06492–7002; tel. 203/679–5900, (Total facility includes 382 beds in nursing home–type unit) (Nonreporting) **A**1 5 10
Primary Contact: Arthur E. Santilli, President
COO: Stephen B. McPherson, Chief Financial Officer
CFO: Stephen B. McPherson, Chief Financial Officer
CMO: Ronald Schwartz, M.D., Medical Director
CIO: James Albert, Director Information Services
Web address: www.masonicare.org

Control 23, Service 49, Staffed Beds 507, Admissions —, Census —, Outpatient Visits —, Births —, Total —, Payroll —, Personnel —

WATERBURY—New Haven County

✠ **SAINT MARY'S HOSPITAL**, 56 Franklin Street, Zip 06706–1281; tel. 203/709–6000 **A**1 2 3 5 9 10 **F**2 9 10 11 12 14 17 21 22 23 25 26 27 28 30 32 33 34 36 37 38 39 40 42 46 47 48 52 55 56 59 60 61 62 63 64 66 69 71 73 75 77 78 81 82 85 88 93 94 96 106 108 **P**6
Primary Contact: Robert P. Ritz, President and Chief Executive Officer
CMO: Michael Matzkin, D.D.S., Chief of Staff
CIO: Charles Podesta, Vice President and Chief Information Officer
CHR: Philip B. Johnson, Vice President, Human Resources
Web address: www.stmh.org

Control 21, Service 10, Staffed Beds 197, Admissions 11377, Census 144, Outpatient Visits 207323, Births 1020, Total 137979, Payroll 61560, Personnel 1352

✠ **WATERBURY HOSPITAL**, 64 Robbins Street, Zip 06708–2600; tel. 203/573–6000 **A**1 2 3 5 9 10 **F**2 4 7 11 12 15 17 21 22 26 27 28 29 31 32 33 34 37 40 41 46 47 48 50 52 53 55 56 57 58 59 60 62 63 64 65 66 69 70 71 72 73 74 75 76 77 78 81 82 84 85 87 88 93 94 95 96 105 108 109 110 **P**7
Primary Contact: John H. Tobin, President and Chief Executive Officer
CFO: Colleen M. Scott, Vice President Finance
CIO: James Olson, Chief Information Officer
Web address: www.waterburyhospital.org

Control 23, Service 10, Staffed Beds 264, Admissions 13617, Census 176, Outpatient Visits 232688, Births 1496, Total 179400, Payroll 89785, Personnel 1529

WEST HARTFORD—Hartford County

✠ **HEBREW HEALTH CARE**, (Comprehensive Geriatric Health), 1 Abrahms Boulevard, Zip 06117–1525; tel. 860/523–3800, (Total facility includes 289 beds in nursing home–type unit) **A**1 5 10 **F**1 5 8 9 21 22 25 31 32 37 38 42 44 45 51 52 54 58 60 61 69 76 91 92 94 96 108 **P**6
Primary Contact: Bonnie B. Gauthier, President and Chief Executive Officer
COO: Kristen Kinney, Administrative Operations Manager and Patient Advocate
CFO: David Houle, Senior Vice President and Chief Financial Officer
CMO: Henry Schneiderman, M.D., Vice President Medical Services and Physician in Chief
CHR: Kathy Schroder, Director, Administrative Services and Human Resources
Web address: www.hebrewhealthcare.org

Control 23, Service 49, Staffed Beds 334, Admissions 926, Census 321, Outpatient Visits 360, Births 0, Total 32403, Payroll 21797, Personnel 488

WEST HAVEN—New Haven County

✠ **VETERANS AFFAIRS CONNECTICUT HEALTHCARE SYSTEM–NEW HAVEN DIVISION**, 950 Campbell Avenue, Zip 06516–2770; tel. 203/932–5711, (Includes WEST HAVEN DIVISION), (Total facility includes 40 beds in nursing home–type unit) (Nonreporting) **A**1 2 3 5 8 9 **S** Department of Veterans Affairs, Washington, DC
Primary Contact: Roger L. Johnson, Director
CFO: Karen Meffert, Chief Financial Officer
CIO: Joseph Erdos, M.D., Chief Information Officer
Web address: www.va.gov/sta/guide/home.asp

Control 45, Service 10, Staffed Beds 200, Admissions —, Census —, Outpatient Visits —, Births —, Total —, Payroll —, Personnel —

CT

Hospital, Address, Telephone, Approval, Facility, and Physician Codes, Health Care System	Classi-fication Codes		Utilization Data					Expense (thousands) of dollars		
★ American Hospital Association (AHA) membership □ Joint Commission on Accreditation of Healthcare Organizations (JCAHO) accreditation ○ American Osteopathic Association (AOA) accreditation △ Commission on Accreditation of Rehabilitation Facilities (CARF) accreditation	Control	Service	Staffed Beds	Admissions	Census	Outpatient Visits	Births	Total	Payroll	Personnel

WESTPORT—Fairfield County
  HALL–BROOKE HOSPITAL, A DIVISION OF HALL–BROOKE BEHAVIORAL HEALTH
  SERVICES See St. Vincent's Medical Center, Bridgeport

WILLIMANTIC—Windham County

✶ **WINDHAM COMMUNITY MEMORIAL HOSPITAL**, 112 Mansfield Avenue, Zip 06226–2040; tel. 860/456–9116 **A**1 9 10 19 **F**2 9 11 12 14 21 23 28 29 33 37 39 46 47 48 54 55 57 58 59 62 63 64 65 66 69 81 82 84 87 88 93 94 95 96 106 107 108 109 **P**8 Primary Contact: Richard A. Brvenik, FACHE, President and Chief Executive Officer CFO: James Papadakos, Vice President Finance and Chief Financial Officer CMO: Herbert Ridyard, M.D., Chief of Staff CIO: Kevin Tupper, Director Information Technology CHR: Marty Levine, Vice President Human Resources Web address: www.windhamhospital.org	23	10	79	4686	55	106547	467	66187	29737	449

CT

DELAWARE

Hospital, Address, Telephone, Approval, Facility, and Physician Codes, Health Care System	Classi-fication Codes		Utilization Data					Expense (thousands) of dollars		
★ American Hospital Association (AHA) membership □ Joint Commission on Accreditation of Healthcare Organizations (JCAHO) accreditation ○ American Osteopathic Association (AOA) accreditation △ Commission on Accreditation of Rehabilitation Facilities (CARF) accreditation	Control	Service	Staffed Beds	Admissions	Census	Outpatient Visits	Births	Total	Payroll	Personnel

DOVER—Kent County

✠ △ **BAYHEALTH MEDICAL CENTER**, 640 South State Street, Zip 19901–3597; tel. 302/674–4700, (Includes BAYHEALTH MEDICAL CENTER AT KENT GENERAL, 640 South State Street; BAYHEALTH MEDICAL CENTER, MILFORD MEMORIAL HOSPITAL, 21 West Clarke Avenue, Milford, Zip 19963–1840; tel. 302/430–5738) **A**1 2 7 9 10 **F**2 9 11 12 15 17 21 22 23 24 26 27 28 29 31 33 34 35 37 38 39 40 41 42 46 47 48 49 50 51 52 53 55 56 57 58 59 60 61 62 63 64 65 66 67 68 69 71 72 73 74 75 76 77 78 79 80 81 82 84 85 86 87 88 93 94 95 96 98 106 107 108 109 **P**6 8

Primary Contact: Dennis E. Klima, President and Chief Executive Officer
COO: Terry Murphy, Executive Vice President and Chief Operating Officer
CFO: Earl P. Tanis, Senior Vice President Financial Operations
CMO: William Rosenfeld, M.D., Senior Vice President Clinical Integration
CIO: Terry Feinour, Senior Vice President and Corporate Services
CHR: Jon McDowell, Vice President
Web address: www.bayhealth.org
(Row data: 23 | 10 | 352 | 17600 | 269 | 401369 | 2141 | 231295 | 97639 | 2256)

★ **U. S. AIR FORCE HOSPITAL DOVER**, 300 Tuskegee Boulevard, Zip 19902–7307; tel. 302/677–2525, (Nonreporting) **S** Department of the Air Force, Washington, DC
Primary Contact: Colonel Genanne Hansen–Bayless, Administrator
CFO: Captain Richard Cornell, Commander Resource Management
(Row data: 41 | 10 | 16 | — | | | | | |)

LEWES—Sussex County

✠ **BEEBE MEDICAL CENTER**, 424 Savannah Road, Zip 19958–0226; tel. 302/645–3300, (Total facility includes 89 beds in nursing home–type unit) **A**1 2 6 9 10 19 **F**1 9 11 12 15 17 21 22 23 24 26 27 28 29 30 31 33 34 39 40 41 42 44 45 46 47 48 49 50 51 52 53 55 58 59 61 62 63 64 66 69 70 73 75 79 80 81 82 83 84 85 86 87 88 92 93 94 96 108 109 110 **P**6
Primary Contact: Jeffrey M. Fried, FACHE, President and Chief Executive Officer
COO: Richard Schaffner, Executive Vice President
CFO: James W. Bartle, Vice President Finance
CMO: Srihari Peri, M.D., President, Medical Dental Staff
CIO: Barbara P. Vugrinec, Vice President Information Systems
CHR: Catherine Halen, Vice President Human Resources
Web address: www.beebemed.org
(Row data: 23 | 10 | 208 | 8354 | 177 | 329952 | 879 | 135020 | 54274 | 1294)

MILFORD—Sussex County

BAYHEALTH MEDICAL CENTER, MILFORD MEMORIAL HOSPITAL See Bayhealth Medical Center, Dover

NEW CASTLE—New Castle County

□ **DELAWARE PSYCHIATRIC CENTER**, 1901 North Dupont Highway, Zip 19720–1199; tel. 302/255–2700, (Total facility includes 39 beds in nursing home–type unit) **A**1 10 **F**21 22 32 44 53 58 66 70 71 75 76 94 96 108 **P**6
Primary Contact: Martha Boston, Ph.D., Director
Web address: www.dhss.delaware.gov
(Row data: 12 | 22 | 281 | 402 | 255 | 0 | 0 | 40205 | 20693 | 466)

□ **MEADOW WOOD BEHAVIORAL HEALTH SYSTEM**, 575 South Dupont Highway, Zip 19720–4600; tel. 302/328–3330, (Nonreporting) **A**1 10
Primary Contact: Patricia Wright, Administrator
(Row data: 33 | 52 | 50 | — | — | — | — | — | — | —)

NEWARK—New Castle County

CHRISTIANA HOSPITAL See Christiana Care Health System, Wilmington

□ **ROCKFORD CENTER**, 100 Rockford Drive, Zip 19713–2121; tel. 302/996–5480 **A**1 10 **F**27 28 71 72 75 76 78 **P**6 8 **S** Universal Health Services, Inc., King of Prussia, PA
Primary Contact: John F. McKenna, Chief Executive Officer
Web address: www.rockfordcenter.com
(Row data: 33 | 22 | 74 | 3189 | 67 | 11381 | 0 | 12398 | 6908 | 152)

SEAFORD—Sussex County

✠ **NANTICOKE MEMORIAL HOSPITAL**, 801 Middleford Road, Zip 19973–3698; tel. 302/629–6611, (Total facility includes 120 beds in nursing home–type unit) (Nonreporting) **A**1 2 9 10
Primary Contact: Daniel J. Werner, President and Chief Executive Officer
CFO: J Douglas Connell, Chief Financial Officer
CMO: Anthony M. Policastro, M.D., Senior Vice President Medical Affairs
CHR: Justin Lofurno, Director Human Resources
Web address: www.nanticoke.org
(Row data: 23 | 10 | 229 | — | — | — | — | — | — | —)

WILMINGTON—New Castle County

✠ △ **ALFRED I. DUPONT HOSPITAL FOR CHILDREN**, (Formerly duPont Hospital for Children), 1600 Rockland Road, Zip 19803–3616, Mailing Address: Box 269, Zip 19899–0269; tel. 302/651–4000 **A**1 3 5 7 9 10 **F**2 6 7 9 10 13 14 15 16 18 20 21 22 23 24 26 27 32 33 34 35 37 39 42 46 48 49 50 52 53 56 57 58 60 61 62 63 64 66 67 68 73 74 75 77 81 84 85 87 88 90 93 94 95 96 99 100 101 102 104 108 **P**6
Primary Contact: Thomas P. Ferry, Administrator and Chief Executive Officer
COO: Paul D. Kempinski, Chief Operating Officer
CFO: William N. Britton, Associate Administrator for Finance
CMO: Roy Proujansky, M.D., Medical Director
CIO: Ann Altoe, Senior Information Systems Director and Security Officer
Web address: www.nemours.org
(Row data: 23 | 50 | 172 | 9113 | 116 | 411922 | 0 | 173861 | 64663 | 1786)

Hospital, Address, Telephone, Approval, Facility, and Physician Codes, Health Care System	Classi-fication Codes		Utilization Data					Expense (thousands) of dollars		
	Control	Service	Staffed Beds	Admissions	Census	Outpatient Visits	Births	Total	Payroll	Personnel

★ American Hospital Association (AHA) membership
□ Joint Commission on Accreditation of Healthcare Organizations (JCAHO) accreditation
○ American Osteopathic Association (AOA) accreditation
△ Commission on Accreditation of Rehabilitation Facilities (CARF) accreditation

☒ **CHRISTIANA CARE HEALTH SYSTEM**, 501 West 14th Street, Zip 19801; tel. 302/428–2570, (Includes CHRISTIANA HOSPITAL, 4755 Ogletown–Stanton Road, Newark, Zip 19718; tel. 302/428–2570; WILMINGTON HOSPITAL, 501 West 14th Street, Mailing Address: Box 1668, Zip 19899; tel. 302/733–1000), (Total facility includes 101 beds in nursing home–type unit) **A**1 2 3 5 8 9 10 12 13 **F**1 2 5 9 10 11 12 14 15 17 19 21 22 23 24 26 27 28 29 30 31 32 33 34 35 37 38 39 41 42 44 46 47 48 49 50 51 52 53 55 56 57 58 59 60 61 62 63 64 65 66 67 68 69 70 71 72 73 74 75 76 77 78 79 80 81 82 84 85 86 87 88 90 92 93 94 95 96 98 99 106 108 109 **P**6 **S** Christiana Care Health System, Wilmington, DE Primary Contact: Robert J. Laskowski, M.D., President and Chief Executive Officer COO: Gary W. Ferguson, Executive Vice President and Chief Operating Officer CFO: Buddy Elmore, Senior Vice President Finance and Managed Care, and Chief Financial Officer CMO: Keith R. Doram, M.D., Chief Medical Officer CIO: Steve Hess, Chief Information Officer CHR: Benjamin T. Shaw, Senior Vice President Human Resources Web address: www.christianacare.org	23	10	865	52518	863	665036	7241	814430	384234	7616
□ **SELECT SPECIALTY HOSPITAL WILMINGTON**, 7 Clayton Street, 5th Floor, Zip 19801; tel. 302/421–4545, (Nonreporting) **A**1 10 Primary Contact: Carol Chrisman, Chief Executive Officer	33	49	35	—	—	—	—	—	—	—
☒ **ST. FRANCIS HOSPITAL**, Seventh and Clayton Streets, Zip 19805–0500, Mailing Address: P.O. Box 2500, Zip 19805–0500; tel. 302/421–4100, (Total facility includes 16 beds in nursing home–type unit) (Nonreporting) **A**1 2 3 5 9 10 12 **S** Catholic Health East, Newtown Square, PA Primary Contact: Richard A. Long, President and Chief Executive Officer CFO: Bernard P. Citerone, Chief Financial Officer CMO: Kim Carpenter, M.D., Vice President Medical Management CIO: Paul W. Rowe, Director Information Technology Web address: www.stfrancishealthcare.org	23	10	129	—	—	—	—	—	—	—
☒ **VETERANS AFFAIRS MEDICAL CENTER**, 1601 Kirkwood Highway, Zip 19805–4989; tel. 302/994–2511, (Total facility includes 60 beds in nursing home–type unit) **A**1 2 3 5 8 9 **F**2 4 7 9 21 22 23 26 27 28 29 30 31 32 33 35 37 38 39 40 41 42 44 45 46 47 48 49 50 51 52 53 55 57 58 60 61 62 63 64 65 66 69 70 73 74 76 77 81 82 85 87 88 92 94 96 106 107 108 109 110 **P**6 **S** Department of Veterans Affairs, Washington, DC Primary Contact: Richard S. Citron, Director CFO: Lori Barbanel, Resource Management Center Leader CMO: Morris D. Kerstein, M.D., Chief of Staff CIO: Thomas Tierney, Chief Information Officer Web address: www.va.gov/sta/guide/home.asp	45	10	118	2356	97	220740	0	95568	46860	641

WILMINGTON HOSPITAL See Christiana Care Health System

DE

Many Facility Codes have changed. Please refer to the AHA Guide Code Chart. © 2005 AHA Guide

DISTRICT OF COLUMBIA

Hospital, Address, Telephone, Approval, Facility, and Physician Codes, Health Care System	Classi-fication Codes		Utilization Data					Expense (thousands) of dollars		
★ American Hospital Association (AHA) membership □ Joint Commission on Accreditation of Healthcare Organizations (JCAHO) accreditation ○ American Osteopathic Association (AOA) accreditation △ Commission on Accreditation of Rehabilitation Facilities (CARF) accreditation	Control	Service	Staffed Beds	Admissions	Census	Outpatient Visits	Births	Total	Payroll	Personnel

WASHINGTON—District of Columbia County

⊠ **CHILDREN'S NATIONAL MEDICAL CENTER**, 111 Michigan Avenue N.W., Zip 20010–2970; tel. 202/884–5000 **A**1 3 5 8 9 10 **F**1 2 6 7 15 16 17 18 19 20 21 22 23 24 26 27 28 29 32 33 34 35 37 38 39 42 45 46 47 48 49 50 52 53 56 57 58 60 61 62 63 64 65 66 67 69 70 71 72 73 74 75 77 78 81 82 84 85 87 88 90 93 94 95 96 98 99 100 101 105 107 108 110 **P**6 Primary Contact: Edwin K. Zechman, Jr, President and Chief Executive Officer CFO: Gary Manion, Chief Financial Officer CMO: Peter Holbrook, M.D., Chief Medical Officer CIO: Kelly R. Styles, Chief Information Officer Web address: www.dcchildrens.com	23	50	188	11127	175	345448	0	302218	143475	—
⊠ △ · **GEORGE WASHINGTON UNIVERSITY HOSPITAL**, 900 23rd Street N.W., Zip 20037–2377; tel. 202/715–4000, (Nonreporting) **A**1 2 3 5 7 8 9 10 **S** Universal Health Services, Inc., King of Prussia, PA Primary Contact: Richard B. Becker, M.D., Chief Executive Officer COO: Trent Crable, Chief Operating Officer CFO: Richard Davis, Chief Financial Officer CMO: Michael Berrigan, M.D., Interim Medical Director CIO: Gretchen Tegethoff, Vice President Information Resources CHR: Karen Frazier, Director Web address: www.gwhospital.com	32	10	326	—	—	—	—	—	—	—
□ **GREATER SOUTHEAST COMMUNITY HOSPITAL**, 1310 Southern Avenue S.E., Zip 20032–4699; tel. 202/574–6000, (Nonreporting) **A**1 2 3 5 10 Primary Contact: Joan Phillips, Administrator Web address: www.greatersoutheast.org	33	10	303	—	—	—	—	—	—	—
□ **HADLEY MEMORIAL HOSPITAL**, 4601 Martin Luther King Jr. Avenue S.W., Zip 20032–1199; tel. 202/574–5700, (Total facility includes 39 beds in nursing home–type unit) (Nonreporting) **A**1 10 Primary Contact: Janine Finck–Boyle, Administrator	33	10	109							
⊠ △ **HOSPITAL FOR SICK CHILDREN**, 1731 Bunker Hill Road N.E., Zip 20017–3096; tel. 202/832–4400 **A**1 5 7 9 **F**13 21 27 28 29 32 38 45 47 52 53 58 65 66 68 69 70 94 108 110 **P**6 Primary Contact: Deborah T. Zients, Chief Operating Officer COO: Deborah T. Zients, Chief Operating Officer CFO: Nancy J. Southers, Vice President and Chief Information Officer CMO: Robert A L Blake, M.D., Chief Medical Officer CIO: Nancy J. Southers, Vice President and Chief Information Officer CHR: Lynne Hostetter, Director Human Resources Web address: www.hfscsite.org	23	56	101	339	52	16780	0	29282	12160	285
⊠ **HOWARD UNIVERSITY HOSPITAL**, 2041 Georgia Avenue N.W., Zip 20060–0002; tel. 202/865–6100, (Total facility includes 28 beds in nursing home–type unit) **A**1 2 3 5 8 9 10 **F**2 3 6 9 11 12 14 15 17 19 21 22 23 26 27 28 29 32 33 34 36 37 39 41 44 46 47 48 49 50 51 52 53 55 56 57 58 59 60 61 62 63 64 65 66 68 69 70 71 72 73 75 76 77 81 82 84 85 87 88 92 93 94 95 96 101 106 107 108 109 **P**5 Primary Contact: Sherman P. McCoy, Executive Director and Chief Executive Officer COO: Debra D. Carey, Associate Executive Director and Chief Operating Officer CFO: Joel Celestin, Assistant Executive Director and Chief Financial Officer CIO: Dennis Hermonstyne, Interim Director Management Information Systems Web address: www.huhosp.org	23	10	282	12652	212	105022	663	243565	100714	2345
MEDLINK HOSPITAL AND NURSING CENTER AT CAPITOL HILL, 700 Constitution Avenue N.E., Zip 20002–6058; tel. 202/546–5700, (Total facility includes 117 beds in nursing home–type unit) **A**10 **F**39 49 58 60 64 92 94 110 Primary Contact: Peter Shin, DPM, President and Chairman of the Board Web address: www.medlink–dc.com	33	80	177	880	164	0	0	33902	18631	358
⊠ **MEDSTAR–GEORGETOWN MEDICAL CENTER**, 3800 Reservoir Road N.W., Zip 20007–2197; tel. 202/444–3000 **A**1 2 3 5 8 9 10 **F**2 4 7 10 11 12 14 15 17 20 21 22 23 24 26 27 28 29 30 31 33 35 37 38 40 42 43 44 46 47 48 49 50 52 53 55 56 57 58 59 60 61 62 63 64 65 66 67 69 70 71 73 74 75 76 77 78 79 81 82 84 85 86 87 88 90 93 94 95 96 98 99 101 102 103 104 105 106 108 109 110 **P**6 **S** MedStar Health, Columbia, MD Primary Contact: Joy Drass, M.D., President COO: Joyce E. Johnson, R.N., Senior Vice President Operations CFO: Peter L. Munger, Chief Financial Officer CMO: Sam Wiesel, M.D., Senior Vice President and Chief Medical Officer CIO: Alton Brantley, M.D., Ph.D., Senior Vice President and Chief Information Officer Web address: www.georgetownuniversityhospital.org	23	10	367	14959	262	154166	1771	460497	214209	3399

DC

Hospital, Address, Telephone, Approval, Facility, and Physician Codes, Health Care System	Classi-fication Codes		Utilization Data					Expense (thousands) of dollars		
★ American Hospital Association (AHA) membership □ Joint Commission on Accreditation of Healthcare Organizations (JCAHO) accreditation ○ American Osteopathic Association (AOA) accreditation △ Commission on Accreditation of Rehabilitation Facilities (CARF) accreditation	Control	Service	Staffed Beds	Admissions	Census	Outpatient Visits	Births	Total	Payroll	Personnel
✠ △ **NATIONAL REHABILITATION HOSPITAL**, 102 Irving Street N.W., Zip 20010–2949; tel. 202/877–1000 **A**1 3 5 7 9 10 **F**2 7 21 22 27 29 30 31 37 42 45 52 53 57 58 62 65 66 68 69 88 89 93 94 95 96 108 109 110 **P**6 **S** MedStar Health, Columbia, MD Primary Contact: Edward A. Eckenhoff, President and Chief Executive Officer CFO: Dennis Werner, Chief Financial Officer CMO: Edward B. Healton, M.D., Senior Vice President and Medical Director Web address: www.nrhrehab.org	23	46	137	2041	99	148374	0	61454	33522	855
✠ **PROVIDENCE HOSPITAL**, 1150 Varnum Street N.E., Zip 20017–2180; tel. 202/269–7000, (Total facility includes 250 beds in nursing home–type unit) **A**1 2 3 5 9 10 **F**2 3 4 5 10 11 12 13 14 17 21 22 23 26 27 28 29 31 33 35 37 38 39 41 42 44 45 46 47 48 50 54 55 56 58 59 60 61 62 63 65 67 68 69 70 71 73 74 75 76 77 78 81 84 85 88 89 92 93 94 95 96 98 106 107 108 109 110 **P**6 **S** Ascension Health, Saint Louis, MO Primary Contact: Julius D. Spears, Jr, President and Chief Executive Officer CFO: David G. Sparks, Senior Vice President Finance CMO: Robert Simmons, M.D., Vice President Medical Affairs CIO: Paul W. Smith, Vice President General Services CHR: LaVerne Street, Associate Vice President Web address: www.provhosp.org	21	10	522	13699	442	158815	2000	187028	91491	2075
□ **PSYCHIATRIC INSTITUTE OF WASHINGTON**, 4228 Wisconsin Avenue N.W., Zip 20016–2138; tel. 202/885–5600, (Nonreporting) **A**1 3 5 10 Primary Contact: Kenneth F. Courage, Chief Executive Officer and Chairman of the Board Web address: www.psychinstitute.com	33	22	104	—	—	—	—	—	—	—
✠ **SIBLEY MEMORIAL HOSPITAL**, 5255 Loughboro Road N.W., Zip 20016–2695; tel. 202/537–4000, (Total facility includes 32 beds in nursing home–type unit) (Nonreporting) **A**1 2 3 5 9 10 Primary Contact: Robert L. Sloan, President and Chief Executive Officer COO: Jerry L. Price, Executive Vice President and Chief Operating Officer CFO: Stephen C. McDonnell, Senior Vice President and Chief Financial Officer CMO: Robert M. Ludewig, M.D., Vice President Medical Affairs CIO: Lorraine Fordham, Chief Information Officer CHR: Queenie Plater, Vice President Human Resources Web address: www.sibley.org	23	10	273	—	—	—	—	—	—	—
★ **ST. ELIZABETHS HOSPITAL**, 2700 Martin Luther King Jr. Avenue S.E., Zip 20032–2698; tel. 202/562–4000, (Nonreporting) **A**10 Primary Contact: Joy Holland, Chief Executive Officer CFO: Gerald Tolliver, Associate Director Finance and Administration CMO: Rizwan Malik, Acting Associate Director Medical Affairs	14	22	817	—	—	—	—	—	—	—
✠ △ **VETERANS AFFAIRS MEDICAL CENTER**, 50 Irving Street N.W., Zip 20422–0002; tel. 202/745–8100, (Nonreporting) **A**1 3 5 7 8 9 **S** Department of Veterans Affairs, Washington, DC Primary Contact: Sanford M. Garfunkel, Director CFO: Frank Filosa, Fiscal Manager CIO: Amanda Graves, Chief Information Systems Web address: www.va.gov/sta/guide/home.asp	45	10	291	—	—	—	—	—	—	—
✠ **WALTER REED ARMY MEDICAL CENTER**, 6900 Georgia Avenue N.W., Zip 20307–5001; tel. 202/782–6395 **A**1 2 3 5 **F**2 4 6 7 10 12 14 15 16 17 18 19 20 21 22 23 24 25 26 27 28 29 31 32 33 35 37 39 40 41 43 44 45 46 47 48 49 52 53 55 57 58 60 61 62 63 64 65 66 67 69 70 71 72 73 74 75 76 77 78 79 81 82 83 84 85 86 87 88 89 90 92 93 94 95 96 101 102 105 106 108 109 110 **S** Department of the Army, Office of the Surgeon General, Falls Church, VA Primary Contact: Colonel James K. Gilman, Commander COO: Lieutenant Colonel Michael Amarol, Chief, Directorate of Medical Administration CFO: Lieutenant Colonel Reginald A. Miller, Director Resource Management CMO: Colonel Thomas Fitzpatrick, Chief Medical Staff CIO: Lieutenant Colonel Paul Lavan, Chief Information Management Division Web address: www.wramc.amedd.army.mil	42	10	261	10296	183	785927	0	301657	81507	4890
✠ **WASHINGTON HOSPITAL CENTER**, 110 Irving Street N.W., Zip 20010–2975; tel. 202/877–7000 **A**1 2 3 5 8 9 10 **F**2 4 6 9 10 11 12 13 14 26 27 28 29 31 32 33 34 35 37 38 39 43 44 45 46 47 48 49 50 52 53 55 56 57 58 59 60 61 62 63 65 66 69 70 71 73 74 75 76 77 78 79 81 82 84 85 86 87 88 89 90 94 95 96 98 100 101 107 108 109 110 **P**1 6 **S** MedStar Health, Columbia, MD Primary Contact: James F. Caldas, President CFO: Leisa Russell, Senior Vice President Finance and Chief Financial Officer CMO: Janis M. Orlowski, M.D., Senior Vice President Medical Affairs and Chief Medical Officer CIO: John D. Dayhoff, Interim Chief Information Officer CHR: Christina Younger, Vice President Human Resources Web address: www.whcenter.org	23	10	786	42397	620	341184	4397	737618	348178	4884

DC

FLORIDA

Hospital, Address, Telephone, Approval, Facility, and Physician Codes, Health Care System	Classi-fication Codes		Utilization Data					Expense (thousands) of dollars		
★ American Hospital Association (AHA) membership □ Joint Commission on Accreditation of Healthcare Organizations (JCAHO) accreditation ○ American Osteopathic Association (AOA) accreditation △ Commission on Accreditation of Rehabilitation Facilities (CARF) accreditation	Control	Service	Staffed Beds	Admissions	Census	Outpatient Visits	Births	Total	Payroll	Personnel

ALTAMONTE SPRINGS—Seminole County

   FLORIDA HOSPITAL–ALTAMONTE See Florida Hospital, Orlando

APALACHICOLA—Franklin County

⊠ **GEORGE E. WEEMS MEMORIAL HOSPITAL**, 135 Avenue G., Zip 32320–1613, Mailing Address: P.O. Box 580, Zip 32329–0580; tel. 850/653–8853, (Nonreporting) **A**9 10 18 **S** DasSee Community Health System, Quincy, FL Primary Contact: Michael C. Lake, Chief Executive Officer	32	10	25	—	—	—	—	—	—	—

APOPKA—Orange County

   FLORIDA HOSPITAL–APOPKA See Florida Hospital, Orlando

ARCADIA—De Soto County

⊠ **DESOTO MEMORIAL HOSPITAL**, 900 North Robert Avenue, Zip 34266–8765, Mailing Address: P.O. Box 2180, Zip 34265–2180; tel. 863/494–3535 **A**1 5 9 10 20 **F**2 9 11 21 27 28 29 33 44 46 48 51 52 55 58 59 60 62 63 69 70 81 82 84 88 94 96 97 107 **P**6 Primary Contact: James R. Chromik, President CFO: Nancy L. Frisby, CPA, Senior Vice President and Chief Financial Officer CMO: Ana Hernandez, M.D., Chief of Staff CHR: Lois Hilton, Director Human Resources Web address: www.dmh.org	23	10	49	2624	21	41775	653	23469	10603	392

ATLANTIS—Palm Beach County

⊠ **J. F. K. MEDICAL CENTER**, 5301 South Congress Avenue, Zip 33462–1197; tel. 561/965–7300, (Nonreporting) **A**1 2 9 10 **S** HCA, Nashville, TN Primary Contact: Gina Melby, Chief Executive Officer COO: Robbin M. Moore, Chief Operating Officer CFO: Terence VanArkel, Chief Financial Officer CIO: Jane Stewart, Director Information Services Web address: www.jfkmc.com	32	10	387	—	—	—	—	—	—	—

AVENTURA—Dade County

⊠ **AVENTURA HOSPITAL AND MEDICAL CENTER**, 20900 Biscayne Boulevard, Zip 33180–1407; tel. 305/682–7000 **A**1 9 10 **F**2 6 9 12 14 15 17 19 21 22 23 28 29 31 32 33 35 39 42 46 47 48 51 52 55 57 58 60 61 62 63 64 65 66 69 71 73 74 75 76 77 81 82 83 84 85 86 87 88 90 93 94 96 108 109 110 **S** HCA, Nashville, TN Primary Contact: Davide M. Carbone, Chief Executive Officer COO: Richard S. Kennedy, Chief Operating Officer CFO: Lester Eljaiek, Chief Financial Officer CHR: Maria Naranjo, Director Human Resources Web address: www.aventurahospital.com	33	10	407	14614	208	63877	0	119322	42727	792

BARTOW—Polk County

⊠ **BARTOW REGIONAL MEDICAL CENTER**, (Formerly Bartow Memorial Hospital), 2200 Osprey Boulevard, Zip 33830–3308, Mailing Address: P.O. Box 1050, Zip 33830–1050; tel. 863/533–8111 **A**1 9 10 **F**9 11 12 15 21 22 27 29 33 48 55 57 58 59 62 63 64 65 69 82 84 85 88 108 **S** Health Management Associates, Naples, FL Primary Contact: Justin Davis, Chief Executive Officer CFO: Alan Behr, Chief Financial Officer Web address: www.lifepointhospitals.com	33	10	56	3513	36	47805	575	24508	10718	260

BAY PINES—Pinellas County

⊠ △ **VETERANS AFFAIRS MEDICAL CENTER**, 10000 Bay Pines Boulevard, Zip 33744, Mailing Address: P.O. Box 5005, Zip 33744–5005; tel. 727/398–6661, (Total facility includes 150 beds in nursing home–type unit) **A**1 2 3 5 7 **F**2 3 4 12 15 17 21 22 23 28 29 30 31 32 33 36 37 38 44 45 46 47 48 49 50 51 52 53 55 57 58 60 61 62 63 64 65 66 68 69 70 71 73 74 75 76 77 78 81 82 84 88 92 94 96 106 107 108 109 110 **S** Department of Veterans Affairs, Washington, DC Primary Contact: Wallace M. Hopkins, FACHE, Director COO: Kaye Green, CHE, Asociate Director CFO: Jeanine Ergle, Chief Financial Officer CMO: George F. Van Buskirk, M.D., Chief of Staff CIO: John Williams, Chief Information Resources Management Service CHR: Christine Garrett, Chief Human Resources Management Service Web address: www.va.gov/sta/guide/home.asp	45	10	469	8866	325	765983	0	346500	176042	2534

BELLE GLADE—Palm Beach County

⊠ **GLADES GENERAL HOSPITAL**, 1201 South Main Street, Zip 33430–4911; tel. 561/996–6571 **A**1 10 **F**2 21 22 26 27 28 29 33 48 50 57 58 59 62 63 66 68 70 81 82 88 93 94 95 96 108 109 Primary Contact: Dan Aranda, Chief Executive Officer CFO: Carlene Williams, Chief Financial Officer CIO: Adam Levenson, Information Systems Manager Web address: www.gladesgeneralhospital.com	33	10	73	4320	41	—	—	—	—	245

Hospital, Address, Telephone, Approval, Facility, and Physician Codes, Health Care System	Classi-fication Codes		Utilization Data					Expense (thousands) of dollars		
	Control	Service	Staffed Beds	Admissions	Census	Outpatient Visits	Births	Total	Payroll	Personnel

★ American Hospital Association (AHA) membership
☐ Joint Commission on Accreditation of Healthcare Organizations (JCAHO) accreditation
◯ American Osteopathic Association (AOA) accreditation
△ Commission on Accreditation of Rehabilitation Facilities (CARF) accreditation

BLOUNTSTOWN—Calhoun County

CALHOUN–LIBERTY HOSPITAL, 20370 N.E. Burns Avenue, Zip 32424–1097, Mailing Address: P.O. Box 419, Zip 32424–0419; tel. 850/674–5411, (Nonreporting) **A**9 10 18 **S** DasSee Community Health System, Quincy, FL
Primary Contact: Ben Burnham, Administrator

	23	10	25	—	—	—	—	—	—	—

BOCA RATON—Palm Beach County

✠ **BOCA RATON COMMUNITY HOSPITAL**, 800 Meadows Road, Zip 33486–2368; tel. 561/955–7100 **A**1 2 10 **F**2 9 10 11 12 21 22 23 26 27 28 29 30 33 35 37 39 40 41 42 44 46 47 48 49 50 51 52 53 55 56 57 58 59 60 61 62 63 65 66 69 72 73 75 76 79 81 82 84 85 86 87 88 94 96 107 108 109 110 **P**8
Primary Contact: J. Gary Strack, President and Chief Executive Officer
COO: Dianne Aleman, Senior Vice President and Chief Operating Officer
CFO: Kenneth Meinke, Vice President and Chief Financial Officer
CMO: Richard A. Greenwald, M.D., Vice President Medical Affairs
CIO: Robin Hildwein, Chief Information Officer
CHR: Rose Amberson, Vice President Human Resources
Web address: www.brch.com

	23	10	380	21294	272	249914	1690	220392	87171	1828

✠ **WEST BOCA MEDICAL CENTER**, 21644 State Road 7, Zip 33428–1899; tel. 561/488–8000 **A**1 9 10 **F**2 9 11 12 21 23 29 33 35 39 42 45 46 47 48 52 55 56 59 60 62 63 66 67 69 81 82 84 85 88 94 108 **S** TENET Healthcare Corporation, Dallas, TX
Primary Contact: Walt Mickens, Chief Executive Officer
CFO: Cynthia McCauley, Chief Financial Officer
Web address: www.westbocamedctr.com

	33	10	185	11251	130	61431	2376	—	—	752

BONIFAY—Holmes County

☐ **DOCTORS MEMORIAL HOSPITAL**, 401 East Byrd Avenue, Zip 32425–3007, Mailing Address: P.O. Box 188, Zip 32425–0188; tel. 850/547–1120 **A**1 9 10 18 **F**9 14 21 26 27 28 30 33 46 53 60 63 68 69 81 88 92 97
Primary Contact: Robert E. Winkler, Chief Executive Officer
Web address: www.panhandleareahealth.net

	23	10	25	1047	10	13983	0	5908	2882	91

BOYNTON BEACH—Palm Beach County

✠ **BETHESDA MEMORIAL HOSPITAL**, 2815 South Seacrest Boulevard, Zip 33435–7995; tel. 561/737–7733 **A**1 2 9 10 **F**9 10 11 14 15 21 23 27 28 29 33 44 45 49 50 52 55 56 57 58 59 60 61 62 63 65 66 67 69 79 82 84 86 87 88 93 94 95 96 108 110
Primary Contact: Robert B. Hill, President and Chief Executive Officer
COO: Robert B. Hill, President and Chief Executive Officer
CFO: Robert B. Taylor, Jr, Vice President Finance and Chief Financial Officer
CMO: Albert Biehl, M.D., Vice President Medical Affairs
CIO: Tracey Legenos, Vice President, Information Systems
CHR: Regina Crafa, Vice President Human Resources
Web address: www.bethesdahealthcare.com

	23	10	362	19392	251	182235	2959	167803	63954	1909

BRADENTON—Manatee County

✠ △ **BLAKE MEDICAL CENTER**, 2020 59th Street West, Zip 34209–4669; tel. 941/792–6611 **A**1 2 7 9 10 **F**9 12 14 15 17 19 21 22 23 26 27 28 29 33 36 46 48 52 55 57 58 61 62 63 64 65 66 69 75 81 82 85 87 88 93 94 96 108 109 **S** HCA, Nashville, TN
Primary Contact: Daniel J. Friedrich, III, Chief Executive Officer
COO: Daniel J. Friedrich, III, President and Chief Executive Officer
CFO: Priscilla Parrish, Chief Financial Officer
CMO: Lawrence Lieberman, M.D., Medical Director
CHR: Cass Palmer, Vice President Human Resources
Web address: www.blakemedicalcenter.com

	33	10	298	13314	187	89869	344	108586	43328	920

LAKEWOOD RANCH MEDICAL CENTER, 8330 Lakewood Ranch Boulevard, Zip 34202; tel. 941/782–2100, (Nonreporting) **A**9 10 **S** Universal Health Services, Inc., King of Prussia, PA
Primary Contact: Lynn M. Mergen, Interim Chief Executive Officer and Managing Director

	33	80	120	—	—	—	—	—	—	—

MANATEE GLEN HOSPITAL, 2020 26th Avenue East, Zip 34208, Mailing Address: P.O. Box 9478, Zip 34208; tel. 941/741–3117, (Nonreporting) **A**10
Primary Contact: Mary Ruiz, Chief Executive Officer

	33	49	27	—	—	—	—	—	—	—

☐ **MANATEE MEMORIAL HOSPITAL**, 206 Second Street East, Zip 34208–1000; tel. 941/746–5111, (Total facility includes 10 beds in nursing home–type unit) (Nonreporting) **A**1 2 5 9 10 **S** Universal Health Services, Inc., King of Prussia, PA
Primary Contact: Brian T. Flynn, Chief Executive Officer
Web address: www.manateememorial.com

	33	10	512							

BRANDON—Hillsborough County

✠ **BRANDON REGIONAL HOSPITAL**, 119 Oakfield Drive, Zip 33511–5799; tel. 813/681–5551 **A**1 5 9 10 **F**2 9 11 12 14 15 17 19 21 23 26 27 28 33 37 38 40 46 49 52 53 55 56 57 58 59 60 61 62 63 64 67 69 81 82 84 85 87 88 96 107 108 109 **S** HCA, Nashville, TN
Primary Contact: Michael M. Fencel, Chief Executive Officer
COO: Hal Muetzel, Chief Operating Oficer
CFO: Michael T. Terrell, Chief Financial Officer
CMO: John Butterick, M.D., Medical Advisor
CIO: Scott Morrison, Director of Information Systems
CHR: Karen Casteel, Director Human Resources
Web address: www.brandonhospital.com

	33	10	327	18830	234	116440	3777	152265	67847	1103

FL

Many Facility Codes have changed. Please refer to the AHA Guide Code Chart.   © 2005 AHA Guide

Hospital, Address, Telephone, Approval, Facility, and Physician Codes, Health Care System	Classi-fication Codes		Utilization Data					Expense (thousands) of dollars		
★ American Hospital Association (AHA) membership □ Joint Commission on Accreditation of Healthcare Organizations (JCAHO) accreditation ○ American Osteopathic Association (AOA) accreditation △ Commission on Accreditation of Rehabilitation Facilities (CARF) accreditation	Control	Service	Staffed Beds	Admissions	Census	Outpatient Visits	Births	Total	Payroll	Personnel

BROOKSVILLE—Hernando County

□ **BROOKSVILLE REGIONAL HOSPITAL**, 55 Ponce De Leon Boulevard, Zip 34601, Mailing Address: P.O. Box 37, Zip 34605–0037; tel. 352/796–5111 **A**1 9 10 **F**2 9 12 21 27 28 33 49 55 58 60 61 62 63 65 66 81 82 84 88 108 **S** Health Management Associates, Naples, FL Primary Contact: Thomas D. Barb, Executive Director Web address: www.hernandohealthcare.com	33	10	91	4101	57	—	0			
★ **HEALTHSOUTH REHABILITATION HOSPITAL OF SPRING HILL**, 12440 Cortez Boulevard, Zip 34613–2628; tel. 352/592–4250, (Nonreporting) **A**10 **S** HEALTHSOUTH Corporation, Birmingham, AL Primary Contact: Mario A. Mudano, Administrator CFO: Debbie Punzirudu, Controller CMO: Christine Weot, M.D., Medical Director CHR: Linda Campo, Regional Director of Human Resources Web address: www.healthsouth.com	33	46	60	—	—	—	—	—	—	—
⊠ **OAK HILL HOSPITAL**, 11375 Cortez Boulevard, Zip 34613, Mailing Address: P.O. Box 5300, Spring Hill, Zip 34611–5300; tel. 352/596–6632 **A**1 2 10 **F**2 9 12 15 21 22 23 27 28 29 32 33 37 39 40 44 46 48 49 52 54 55 57 58 60 61 62 63 64 65 69 81 82 83 84 85 88 93 94 95 96 107 108 109 110 **S** HCA, Nashville, TN Primary Contact: Mickey Smith, Chief Executive Officer COO: Sonia I. Gonzalez, R.N., Chief Operating Officer CFO: Robert Grace, Chief Financial Officer CMO: David Deam, M.D., Chief of Staff CIO: Kurt Hornung, Chief Information Officer CHR: Doug Goodman, Director Human Resources Web address: www.oakhillhospital.com	33	10	204	11529	148	43207	0	76102	30194	604
SPRING HILL REGIONAL HOSPITAL, 10461 Quality Drive, Zip 34609–9634; tel. 352/688–8200 **A**9 10 **F**11 12 21 22 23 27 28 33 49 55 56 58 59 60 61 62 63 65 81 82 84 88 **S** Health Management Associates, Naples, FL Primary Contact: James R. Beatty, Executive Director Web address: www.hernandohealthcare.com	33	10	85	6737	69	—	—	—	—	—
□ **SPRINGBROOK HOSPITAL**, 7007 Grove Road, Zip 34609–8610; tel. 352/596–4306, (Nonreporting) **A**1 10 Primary Contact: James E. O'Shea, Administrator	23	22	50	—	—	—	—	—	—	—

CAPE CORAL—Lee County

CAPE CORAL HOSPITAL, 636 Del Prado Boulevard, Zip 33990–2695; tel. 239/574–2323 **A**9 10 **F**14 55 59 75 81 Primary Contact: James R. Nathan, Chief Executive Officer Web address: www.leememorial.org	23	10	156	13091	152	—	—	—	—	—

CELEBRATION—Osceola County

FLORIDA HOSPITAL CELEBRATION HEALTH See Florida Hospital, Orlando

CHATTAHOOCHEE—Gadsden County

FLORIDA STATE HOSPITAL, U.S. Highway 90 East, Zip 32324–1000, Mailing Address: P.O. Box 1000, Zip 32324–1000; tel. 850/663–7536, (Nonreporting) **A**10 Primary Contact: Diane R. James, Administrator	12	22	987	—	—	—	—	—	—	—

CHIPLEY—Washington County

⊠ **NORTHWEST FLORIDA COMMUNITY HOSPITAL**, 1360 Brickyard Road, Zip 32428–6303, Mailing Address: P.O. Box 889, Zip 32428–0889; tel. 850/638–1610, (Total facility includes 34 beds in nursing home–type unit) **A**1 9 10 18 **F**1 2 9 12 21 22 26 27 28 29 33 39 42 44 46 47 48 51 52 58 60 63 65 66 69 70 76 81 88 92 94 97 106 108 Primary Contact: Patrick A. Schlenker, President COO: Gregg Moreau, Chief Operating Officer and Chief Financial Officer CFO: Gregg Moreau, Chief Operating Officer and Chief Financial Officer CMO: James A. Clemmon, M.D., Chief of Staff CHR: Mark Brock, Human Resources Manager Web address: www.nfch.org	13	10	59	369	39	13525	0	7465	3101	99

CLEARWATER—Pinellas County

⊠ **MORTON PLANT HOSPITAL**, 300 Pinellas Street, Zip 33756–3825, Mailing Address: P.O. Box 210, Zip 34657–0210; tel. 727/462–7000 **A**1 2 3 5 8 9 10 **F**2 9 10 11 12 14 15 17 19 21 22 23 26 27 28 29 33 35 37 38 39 41 42 44 45 46 47 48 49 50 52 53 55 56 57 58 59 60 61 62 63 64 65 69 70 71 72 75 76 77 79 80 81 84 85 86 87 88 91 92 93 94 95 96 106 107 108 109 110 **P**6 7 **S** Morton Plant Mease Health Care, Dunedin, FL Primary Contact: Philip K. Beauchamp, FACHE, President and Chief Executive Officer CFO: David J. O'Neil, Vice President and Chief Financial Officer CMO: Roger Ray, M.D., Chief Medical Officer Web address: www.mortonplant.com	23	10	524	31928	352	69902	3343	277972	92059	1856
□ **WINDMOOR HEALTHCARE OF CLEARWATER**, 11300 U.S. 19 North, Zip 33764; tel. 727/541–2646, (Nonreporting) **A**1 10 Primary Contact: C. William Brett, Ph.D., President and Owner Web address: www.windmoor–healthcare.com	33	22	100	—	—	—	—	—	—	—

CLERMONT—Lake County

□ **SOUTH LAKE HOSPITAL**, 1099 Citrus Tower Boulevard, Zip 34711–2787; tel. 352/394–4071 **A**1 9 10 **F**2 9 11 12 15 21 22 23 27 28 29 33 37 41 46 47 48 51 52 53 55 57 58 59 61 62 63 64 65 66 69 81 84 85 88 92 95 96 106 108 109 **S** Orlando Regional Healthcare, Orlando, FL Primary Contact: Leslie Longacre, Executive Director and Chief Executive Officer Web address: www.southlakehospital.com	16	10	80	4814	61	33053	242	59250	24083	647

FL

Hospital, Address, Telephone, Approval, Facility, and Physician Codes, Health Care System	Classi-fication Codes		Utilization Data					Expense (thousands) of dollars		
★ American Hospital Association (AHA) membership □ Joint Commission on Accreditation of Healthcare Organizations (JCAHO) accreditation ○ American Osteopathic Association (AOA) accreditation △ Commission on Accreditation of Rehabilitation Facilities (CARF) accreditation	Control	Service	Staffed Beds	Admissions	Census	Outpatient Visits	Births	Total	Payroll	Personnel

CLEWISTON—Hendry County

⊞ **HENDRY REGIONAL MEDICAL CENTER**, 500 West Sugarland Highway, Zip 33440–3094; tel. 863/983–9121 **A**1 9 10 18 **F**9 12 21 22 23 26 27 28 29 33 39 48 51 52 53 55 58 60 63 69 81 82 85 88 108 **P**6 **S** Quorum Health Resources, Plano, TX
Primary Contact: Craig R. Cudworth, Chief Executive Officer
CFO: Nick Braccino, Chief Financial Officer
CMO: James Forbes, Chief Medical Director
CIO: Steven Hess, Director of Information Systems
CHR: Rodney Larson, Human Resource Director
Web address: www.hendryregional.org — 13 10 25 995 11 41118 0 16182 7083 159

COCOA BEACH—Brevard County

⊞ **CAPE CANAVERAL HOSPITAL/HEALTH FIRST**, 701 West Cocoa Beach Causeway, Zip 32931–5595, Mailing Address: P.O. Box 320069, Zip 32932–0069; tel. 321/799–7111 **A**1 2 9 10 **F**2 9 11 12 15 21 22 23 26 27 28 29 33 37 38 40 42 44 45 46 47 48 49 51 52 53 55 57 58 59 61 62 63 64 65 69 73 81 82 84 86 88 94 96 106 108 109 110 **S** First Health, Inc., Rockledge, FL
Primary Contact: Roy Wright, FACHE, President and Chief Executive Officer
CFO: Robert Galloway, Senior Vice President Finance and Chief Financial Officer
CMO: Rodney Moore, M.D., Vice President Medical Affairs
CIO: Rich Rogers, Vice President Information Technology and Chief Information Officer
CHR: Robert Suttles, Vice President Human Resources
Web address: www.health–first.org — 23 10 150 6737 78 176713 705 97265 44083 748

CORAL GABLES—Dade County

⊞ **CORAL GABLES HOSPITAL**, 3100 Douglas Road, Zip 33134–6990; tel. 305/445–8461 **A**1 9 10 **F**2 12 21 27 29 33 37 44 46 47 48 52 55 57 60 61 62 63 66 69 81 84 88 94 96 108 **S** TENET Healthcare Corporation, Dallas, TX
Primary Contact: Jay S. Miranda, Chief Executive Officer
COO: Caridad Nieves, Chief Nursing Officer and Chief Operating Officer
CFO: Maggie Gill, Chief Financial Officer
Web address: www.coralgableshospital.com — 33 10 188 7839 111 — 0 — — —

⊞ **DOCTORS HOSPITAL**, 5000 University Drive, Zip 33146–2094; tel. 305/666–2111, (Nonreporting) **A**1 3 5 9 10 **S** Baptist Health South Florida, Coral Gables, FL
Primary Contact: Lincoln S. Mendez, Chief Executive Officer
CFO: Manlia Garner, Chief Financial Officer
Web address: www.baptisthealth.net — 33 10 281 — — — — — — —

KINDRED HOSPITAL–SOUTH FLORIDA/CORAL GABLES, 5190 S.W. Eighth Street, Zip 33134–2495; tel. 305/445–1364, (Nonreporting) **S** Kindred Healthcare, Louisville, KY
Primary Contact: Charles Doten, Chief Executive Officer
Web address: www.kindredhealthcare.com — 33 49 53 — — — — — — —

CORAL SPRINGS—Broward County

⊞ **CORAL SPRINGS MEDICAL CENTER**, 3000 Coral Hills Drive, Zip 33065; tel. 954/344–3000 **A**1 9 10 **F**2 9 10 11 12 14 21 23 24 26 27 28 29 33 35 36 37 38 39 40 41 46 47 48 49 52 53 55 56 57 58 59 60 61 62 63 64 65 66 67 69 70 75 81 82 84 85 87 88 93 94 95 96 98 106 108 109 110 **P**8 **S** North Broward Hospital District, Fort Lauderdale, FL
Primary Contact: Deborah Mulvihill, Chief Executive Officer
COO: Chantal Leconte, Chief Operating Officer
CFO: Gary Kemske, Chief Financial Officer
CMO: Mark Shachner, M.D., Chief of Staff
CHR: Gina Dotson, Director of Human Resources
Web address: www.nbhd.org — 16 10 200 12380 131 126120 2392 104857 45250 809

CRESTVIEW—Okaloosa County

□ **NORTH OKALOOSA MEDICAL CENTER**, 151 Redstone Avenue S.E., Zip 32539–6026; tel. 850/689–8100, (Nonreporting) **A**1 9 10 **S** Community Health Systems, Inc., Brentwood, TN
Primary Contact: Doug Sills, Chief Executive Officer
Web address: www.nomc.net — 33 10 110 — — — — — — —

CRYSTAL RIVER—Citrus County

□ **SEVEN RIVERS REGIONAL MEDICAL CENTER**, (Formerly Seven Rivers Community Hospital), 6201 North Suncoast Boulevard, Zip 34428–6712; tel. 352/795–6560, (Nonreporting) **A**1 9 10 19 **S** Health Management Associates, Naples, FL
Primary Contact: Joyce Brancato, Chief Executive Officer
Web address: www.srrmc.com — 33 10 128 — — — — — — —

DADE CITY—Pasco County

□ **PASCO REGIONAL MEDICAL CENTER**, 13100 Fort King Road, Zip 33525–5294; tel. 352/521–1100, (Nonreporting) **A**1 9 10 **S** Health Management Associates, Naples, FL
Primary Contact: Michael J. Arno, Chief Executive Officer
Web address: www.pascoregionalmc.com — 33 10 120 — — — — — — —

FL

Hospital, Address, Telephone, Approval, Facility, and Physician Codes, Health Care System	Classi- fication Codes		Utilization Data					Expense (thousands) of dollars		
★ American Hospital Association (AHA) membership □ Joint Commission on Accreditation of Healthcare Organizations (JCAHO) accreditation ○ American Osteopathic Association (AOA) accreditation △ Commission on Accreditation of Rehabilitation Facilities (CARF) accreditation	Control	Service	Staffed Beds	Admissions	Census	Outpatient Visits	Births	Total	Payroll	Personnel

DAVENPORT—Polk County

□ **HEART OF FLORIDA REGIONAL MEDICAL CENTER**, 40100 Highway 27, Zip 33837–5902, Mailing Address: P.O. Box 67, Haines City, Zip 33844–0067; tel. 863/419–2259 **A**1 9 10 **F**2 9 10 11 12 15 21 22 26 27 28 29 33 37 39 40 46 47 48 49 52 53 55 58 59 62 63 64 65 66 69 73 81 82 84 85 87 88 94 95 96 108 109 110 **S** Health Management Associates, Naples, FL Primary Contact: Ann Barnhart, Chief Executive Officer Web address: www.heartofflorida.com	33	10	142	9865	103	44930	768	—	—	778

DAYTONA BEACH—Volusia County

✠ **HALIFAX FISH COMMUNITY HEALTH**, 303 North Clyde Morris Boulevard, Zip 32114–2700; tel. 386/254–4000, (Includes HALIFAX BEHAVIORAL SERVICES, 841 Jimmy Ann Drive, Zip 32117–4599; tel. 904/274–5333; HALIFAX MEDICAL CENTER, 303 North Clyde Morris Boulevard, Zip 32114; tel. 386/254–4000) **A**1 2 3 5 9 10 **F**2 9 10 11 12 14 15 17 19 21 22 23 26 27 28 29 33 34 37 39 40 41 42 43 44 46 47 48 49 50 52 53 55 56 57 58 59 60 61 62 63 64 65 66 67 69 71 72 73 74 75 76 77 78 79 80 81 82 83 84 85 86 87 88 89 92 94 95 96 106 107 108 109 110 **P**5 Primary Contact: Jeff Feasel, Chief Executive Officer CFO: Harry Reese, Chief Financial Officer CMO: Frank Herrero, M.D., Director Medical Affairs and Medical Staff CIO: Lori Delone, Chief Technology Officer CHR: Albert Alexander, Chief Human Resources Officer Web address: www.hfch.org	16	10	551	28816	410	309718	1867	332575	143428	3782

DE LAND—Union County

✠ **FLORIDA HOSPITAL – DELAND**, 701 West Plymouth Avenue, Zip 32720; tel. 386/734–3320 **A**1 9 10 **F**2 3 4 9 11 12 15 21 22 23 26 27 28 29 33 37 40 41 46 47 48 49 53 55 57 58 59 61 62 63 64 65 66 69 71 72 75 76 81 84 85 86 88 93 94 96 106 108 109 110 **S** Adventist Health System Sunbelt Health Care Corporation, Winter Park, FL Primary Contact: Rob Fulbright, Administrator CFO: Lawrence E. Schalk, Chief Financial Officer CMO: Brent Schlapper, M.D., Chief of Staff CIO: Mike Freeland, Regional Director CHR: Sharon Campbell, Director Human Resources Web address: www.fhdeland.org	23	10	156	7979	95	111937	977	78111	28671	599

DEFUNIAK SPRINGS—Walton County

HEALTHMARK REGIONAL MEDICAL CENTER, 4413 U.S. Highway 331 South, Zip 32435; tel. 850/951–4500 **A**9 10 **F**2 9 21 33 34 51 52 55 63 65 66 81 88 108 Primary Contact: James H. Thompson, Ph.D., Owner and Chief Executive Officer Web address: www.healthmarkregional.com	33	10	50	1841	20	23793	0	12137	5092	171

DELRAY BEACH—Palm Beach County

✠ **DELRAY MEDICAL CENTER**, 5352 Linton Boulevard, Zip 33484–6580; tel. 561/498–4440, (Includes FAIR OAKS PAVILION, 5440 Linton Boulevard, Zip 33484–6578; tel. 561/495–1000) **A**1 9 10 **F**2 3 9 10 12 14 15 17 19 21 22 23 27 28 29 33 34 36 38 39 42 44 45 46 48 52 53 55 57 58 61 62 63 64 66 71 73 74 75 76 81 82 85 87 88 93 94 96 108 109 110 **P**8 **S** TENET Healthcare Corporation, Dallas, TX Primary Contact: Mitchell S. Feldman, Chief Executive Officer COO: Matt Heywod, Chief Operating Officer CFO: Ralph Decerbo, Chief Financial Officer CIO: Cathy Christiansen, Director Information Systems CHR: Veronica Leque, Director, Human Resources Web address: www.delraymedicalctr.com	33	10	372	19754	286	76244	0	—	—	976
□ △ **PINECREST REHABILITATION HOSPITAL**, 5360 Linton Boulevard, Zip 33484–6538; tel. 561/495–0400, (Nonreporting) **A**1 7 10 **S** TENET Healthcare Corporation, Dallas, TX Primary Contact: Mitchell S. Feldman, Chief Executive Officer Web address: www.pinecrestrehab.com	33	46	90	—	—	—	—	—	—	—

DESTIN—Okaloosa County

✠ **SACRED HEART HOSPITAL ON THE EMERALD COAST**, 7800 Highway 98 West, Zip 32550; tel. 850/278–3000 **A**1 9 10 **F**2 12 15 17 19 21 22 26 27 28 29 30 33 35 40 41 42 46 47 48 52 53 55 58 61 62 63 64 65 66 69 70 81 82 83 84 85 88 94 106 108 110 **P**7 **S** Ascension Health, Saint Louis, MO Primary Contact: Roger L. Hall, Chief Executive Officer Web address: www.sacredheartemerald.org	23	10	50	2349	24	36724	0	31158	11527	308

DUNEDIN—Pinellas County

□ **MEASE HOSPITAL DUNEDIN**, 601 Main Street, Zip 34698–5891, Mailing Address: P.O. Box 760, Zip 34697–0760; tel. 727/733–1111, (Total facility includes 20 beds in nursing home–type unit) (Nonreporting) **A**1 9 10 **S** Morton Plant Mease Health Care, Dunedin, FL Primary Contact: James A. Pfeiffer, President and Chief Executive Officer Web address: www.measehospitals.com	23	10	258	—	—	—	—	—	—	—

EGLIN AFB—Okaloosa County

✠ **U. S. AIR FORCE REGIONAL HOSPITAL**, 307 Boatner Road, Suite 114, Zip 32542–1282; tel. 850/883–8221 **A**1 3 5 **F**3 6 10 11 12 21 22 23 25 26 27 28 29 30 31 32 33 37 39 41 46 47 48 50 52 53 55 57 58 59 60 61 62 63 65 66 69 70 77 81 88 92 94 95 96 106 108 109 110 **P**4 **S** Department of the Air Force, Washington, DC Primary Contact: Lieutenant Colonel Gary S. Forthman, MSC, USAF, Commander	41	10	51	4186	28	264030	933	57087	6159	1240

FL

Hospital, Address, Telephone, Approval, Facility, and Physician Codes, Health Care System	Classi-fication Codes		Utilization Data					Expense (thousands) of dollars		
★ American Hospital Association (AHA) membership □ Joint Commission on Accreditation of Healthcare Organizations (JCAHO) accreditation ○ American Osteopathic Association (AOA) accreditation △ Commission on Accreditation of Rehabilitation Facilities (CARF) accreditation	Control	Service	Staffed Beds	Admissions	Census	Outpatient Visits	Births	Total	Payroll	Personnel

ENGLEWOOD—Sarasota County

✠ **ENGLEWOOD COMMUNITY HOSPITAL**, 700 Medical Boulevard, Zip 34223–3978; tel. 941/475–6571, (Nonreporting) **A**1 9 10 **S** HCA, Nashville, TN Primary Contact: Robert C. Meade, Chief Executive Officer CFO: Charles Schwaner, III, Chief Financial Officer Web address: www.englewoodcommunityhospital.com	33	10	100	—	—	—	—	—	—	—

FERNANDINA BEACH—Nassau County

✠ **BAPTIST MEDICAL CENTER NASSAU**, 1250 South 18th Street, Zip 32034–3098; tel. 904/321–3500 **A**1 9 10 **F**2 9 11 12 21 22 28 29 33 37 55 59 63 68 69 81 82 84 85 88 93 108 **S** Baptist Health, Jacksonville, FL Primary Contact: Jim L. Mayo, Administrator CFO: Lynie Spencer, Director Finance CHR: Jason Fouraker, Director of Human Resources Web address: www.e-baptisthealth.com	23	10	32	2536	27	51997	436	24393	12451	259

FORT LAUDERDALE—Broward County

□ **ATLANTIC SHORES HOSPITAL**, 4545 North Federal Highway, Zip 33308–5274; tel. 954/771–2711, (Nonreporting) **A**1 10 Primary Contact: Jeffrey Byrd, Administrator Web address: www.atlanticshoreshospital.com	31	22	86	—	—	—	—	—	—	—
✠ **BROWARD GENERAL MEDICAL CENTER**, 1600 South Andrews Avenue, Zip 33316–2510; tel. 954/355–4400 **A**1 2 3 5 9 10 12 13 **F**2 9 11 12 14 15 17 19 21 22 23 26 27 28 29 31 33 34 36 37 38 39 41 43 44 45 46 47 48 50 52 55 56 57 58 59 60 61 62 63 64 65 66 67 69 71 73 74 75 76 80 81 82 84 85 87 88 90 92 93 94 96 98 102 106 108 109 **P**6 8 **S** North Broward Hospital District, Fort Lauderdale, FL Primary Contact: Joseph F. Scott, Chief Executive Officer COO: Gail Gillenwaters, Chief Operating Officer CFO: Matthew Moore, Interim Chief Financial Officer CMO: Richard Callari, M.D., Chief of Staff CIO: Joe Wagner, Vice President and Chief Information Officer CHR: Wilhelmina Mack, Vice President and Chief Human Resources Officer Web address: www.nbhd.org	16	10	567	23928	398	197235	3604	281920	121166	2381
✠ **FLORIDA MEDICAL CENTER**, 5000 West Oakland Park Boulevard, Zip 33313–1585; tel. 954/735–6000, (Nonreporting) **A**1 10 **S** TENET Healthcare Corporation, Dallas, TX Primary Contact: Aurelio Fernandez, Chief Executive Officer Web address: www.floridamedicalctr.com	32	10	459	—	—	—	—	—	—	—
□ **FORT LAUDERDALE HOSPITAL**, 1601 East Las Olas Boulevard, Zip 33301–2393; tel. 954/463–4321, (Nonreporting) **A**1 10 **S** Psychiatric Solutions, Franklin, TN Primary Contact: Tim Kenna, Administrator	33	22	100	—	—	—	—	—	—	—
✠ △ **HEALTHSOUTH SUNRISE REHABILITATION HOSPITAL**, 4399 Nob Hill Road, Zip 33351–5899; tel. 954/749–0300, (Nonreporting) **A**1 7 10 **S** HEALTHSOUTH Corporation, Birmingham, AL Primary Contact: Kevin R. Conn, Administrator CFO: Walter D. Whitchurch, Controller CMO: Scott Tannenbaum, M.D., Medical Director CIO: Angela Crippen, Director of Health Information Services CHR: Barbara Dunkiel, Human Resources Director Web address: www.healthsouth.com	33	46	116	—	—	—	—	—	—	—
✠ **HOLY CROSS HOSPITAL**, 4725 North Federal Highway, Zip 33308–4668, Mailing Address: P.O. Box 23460, Zip 33307–3460; tel. 954/771–8000 **A**1 2 9 10 **F**2 9 10 11 12 13 14 15 17 19 21 22 23 27 29 30 33 37 38 39 41 44 45 46 47 48 50 51 52 53 55 56 57 58 59 60 61 62 63 64 65 66 67 68 69 70 79 81 82 84 85 88 92 93 94 95 96 98 106 107 108 109 **S** Catholic Health East, Newtown Square, PA Primary Contact: John C. Johnson, Chief Executive Officer COO: Jim Boote, Executive Vice President and Chief Operating Officer CFO: Linda Wilford, Chief Financial Officer CIO: Doris Crain, Vice President Information Services CHR: Clayton Fitzhugh, Vice President of Human Resources Web address: www.holy-cross.com	21	10	450	16899	260	138374	1337	237880	95427	—
✠ **IMPERIAL POINT MEDICAL CENTER**, 6401 North Federal Highway, Zip 33308–1495; tel. 954/776–8500 **A**1 9 10 **F**2 9 12 17 21 23 26 27 28 30 33 36 38 41 46 50 52 55 62 63 64 69 71 75 76 81 84 87 88 94 95 106 108 110 **P**6 **S** North Broward Hospital District, Fort Lauderdale, FL Primary Contact: Dorothy J. Mancini, R.N., Chief Executive Officer CFO: Robert Bugg, Chief Financial Officer CMO: Geosges Boutin, M.D., Chief Medical Officer Web address: www.nbhd.org	16	10	180	7330	119	91967	0	78187	32292	657
□ **KINDRED HOSPITAL–FORT LAUDERDALE**, 1516 East Las Olas Boulevard, Zip 33301–2399; tel. 954/764–8900, (Nonreporting) **A**1 10 **S** Kindred Healthcare, Louisville, KY Primary Contact: Clifford J. Bauer, Chief Executive Officer Web address: www.kindredhealthcare.com	33	49	64	—	—	—	—	—	—	—

FL

Many Facility Codes have changed. Please refer to the AHA Guide Code Chart. © 2005 AHA Guide

Hospital, Address, Telephone, Approval, Facility, and Physician Codes, Health Care System	Classification Codes		Utilization Data					Expense (thousands) of dollars		
	Control	Service	Staffed Beds	Admissions	Census	Outpatient Visits	Births	Total	Payroll	Personnel

★ American Hospital Association (AHA) membership
□ Joint Commission on Accreditation of Healthcare Organizations (JCAHO) accreditation
○ American Osteopathic Association (AOA) accreditation
△ Commission on Accreditation of Rehabilitation Facilities (CARF) accreditation

✦ **NORTH RIDGE MEDICAL CENTER**, 5757 North Dixie Highway, Zip 33334–4182, Mailing Address: P.O. Box 23160, Zip 33307; tel. 954/776–6000, (Total facility includes 12 beds in nursing home–type unit) (Nonreporting) **A**1 9 10 **S** TENET Healthcare Corporation, Dallas, TX Primary Contact: Jeffrey A. Feeney, Interim Chief Executive Officer CFO: Peter Mercer, Chief Financial Officer CIO: Kevin Lynch, Director Information Systems CHR: Pamela Johnson–Brown, Human Resources Director Web address: www.northridgemedical.com	33	10	391	—	—	—	—	—	—	—

FORT MYERS—Lee County

✦ ○ **GULF COAST HOSPITAL**, 13681 Doctors Way, Zip 33912–4309; tel. 239/768–5000 **A**1 9 10 11 **F**2 9 11 12 21 22 24 26 27 28 29 30 33 35 37 39 44 45 46 47 48 50 52 53 55 58 59 60 63 64 65 66 69 81 82 85 88 93 94 96 106 108 109 **P**8 **S** HCA, Nashville, TN Primary Contact: Mark F. Weber, FACHE, President and Chief Executive Officer CFO: Robert F. Carrel, Chief Financial Officer CMO: David Reardon, M.D., President Medical Staff Web address: www.gulfcoasthospital.com	33	10	107	4044	43	30210	1496	29243	12179	217
✦ △ **LEE MEMORIAL HEALTH SYSTEM**, 2776 Cleveland Avenue, Zip 33901–5855, Mailing Address: P.O. Box 2218, Zip 33902–2218; tel. 239/332–1111, (Total facility includes 112 beds in nursing home–type unit) **A**1 2 7 9 10 **F**2 5 9 10 11 12 14 15 17 19 21 22 23 24 26 28 30 31 33 34 37 38 39 41 42 53 55 56 57 59 62 63 66 67 68 69 70 81 82 83 84 85 86 87 88 92 93 94 107 108 109 110 **P**1 Primary Contact: James R. Nathan, Chief Executive Officer CFO: John K. Wiest, Chief Financial and Insitutional Service Officer CMO: Chuck Krivenko, M.D., Chief Medical Officer Clinical and Quality Services CIO: Mike J. Smith, Chief Information Officer CHR: Jon C. Cecil, Chief Human Resource Officer Web address: www.leememorial.org	16	10	971	43757	678	331748	4634	517449	251724	5023
✦ **SOUTHWEST FLORIDA REGIONAL MEDICAL CENTER**, 2727 Winkler Avenue, Zip 33901–9396; tel. 239/939–1147 **A**1 2 9 10 **F**2 9 10 14 15 17 19 21 22 23 26 27 28 29 33 35 37 38 39 44 45 46 47 48 49 50 53 55 57 58 61 62 63 64 65 66 69 70 79 80 81 82 84 85 88 93 94 95 96 101 106 108 109 110 **P**8 **S** HCA, Nashville, TN Primary Contact: Mark F. Weber, FACHE, President and Chief Executive Officer COO: Bud Wethington, Chief Operating Officer CFO: Robert F. Carrel, Chief Financial Officer CMO: Douglas Savage, M.D., President Medical Staff CIO: Keith Brooks, Director Information and Technology Services CHR: Peggy Hanover, Vice President Human Resources Web address: www.swfrmc.com	33	10	279	14015	176	33557	0	129611	47131	758

FORT PIERCE—St. Lucie County

✦ **LAWNWOOD REGIONAL MEDICAL CENTER**, 1700 South 23rd Street, Zip 34950–0188; tel. 772/461–4000, (Includes LAWNWOOD PAVILION, 1860 North Lawnwood Circle, Zip 34950; tel. 361/466–1500) **A**1 9 10 **F**2 3 9 11 12 13 14 15 17 19 21 22 23 27 28 33 37 43 46 48 50 52 53 55 56 57 58 59 60 61 62 63 67 68 69 70 71 73 74 75 76 77 81 82 84 85 88 92 94 96 108 109 110 **S** HCA, Nashville, TN Primary Contact: Thomas R. Pentz, President and Chief Executive Officer COO: Brian P. Baumgardner, Chief Executive Officer CFO: Robert Dunwoody, Chief Financial Officer CIO: Eric Castle, Director Information Services CHR: Pam Burchell, Director of Human Resources Web address: www.lawnwoodmed.com	33	10	345	13539	217	71436	1034	139135	53356	954

FORT WALTON BEACH—Okaloosa County

✦ △ **FORT WALTON BEACH MEDICAL CENTER**, 1000 Mar–Walt Drive, Zip 32547–6795; tel. 850/862–1111 **A**1 7 9 10 **F**2 9 10 11 12 14 15 17 19 21 22 23 26 27 28 29 32 33 40 41 42 46 47 48 49 52 53 55 57 58 59 60 61 62 63 64 65 66 68 70 71 73 74 75 76 77 81 82 84 85 86 87 88 94 96 106 108 109 110 **S** HCA, Nashville, TN Primary Contact: Wayne Campbell, Chief Executive Officer CFO: Vincent N. Wyatt, Chief Financial Officer Web address: www.fwbmedicalcenter.com	33	10	247	12240	246	115484	1531	—	—	784

GAINESVILLE—Alachua County

✦ **MALCOM RANDALL VETERANS AFFAIRS MEDICAL CENTER**, 1601 S.W. Archer Road, Zip 32608–1197; tel. 352/376–1611, (Total facility includes 264 beds in nursing home–type unit) **A**1 3 5 8 **F**1 2 3 4 9 14 15 17 19 21 22 23 26 27 28 31 32 33 35 36 37 38 39 42 44 45 46 47 48 49 50 51 52 55 57 58 60 61 62 63 64 65 66 69 70 71 73 74 75 76 77 78 79 80 81 82 83 84 85 86 87 88 92 93 94 96 106 107 108 109 110 **P**6 **S** Department of Veterans Affairs, Washington, DC Primary Contact: Frederick L. Malphurs, Director COO: Thomas Sutton, Associate Director CFO: Jim Taylor, Chief Business Office CMO: Brad Bender, M.D., Chief of Staff CIO: Deborah Michel–Ogborn, Chief Information Resource Management CHR: Michelle Manderino, Chief Human Resources Web address: www.va.gov/visn8/nfsg	45	10	589	10793	371	1096534	0	492168	191957	3319

FL

Hospital, Address, Telephone, Approval, Facility, and Physician Codes, Health Care System	Classification Codes		Utilization Data					Expense (thousands) of dollars		
	Control	Service	Staffed Beds	Admissions	Census	Outpatient Visits	Births	Total	Payroll	Personnel

★ American Hospital Association (AHA) membership
□ Joint Commission on Accreditation of Healthcare Organizations (JCAHO) accreditation
○ American Osteopathic Association (AOA) accreditation
△ Commission on Accreditation of Rehabilitation Facilities (CARF) accreditation

Hospital	Control	Service	Staffed Beds	Admissions	Census	Outpatient Visits	Births	Total	Payroll	Personnel
⊠ **NORTH FLORIDA REGIONAL MEDICAL CENTER**, 6500 Newberry Road, Zip 32605–4392, Mailing Address: P.O. Box 147006, Zip 32614–7006; tel. 352/333–4000, (Total facility includes 24 beds in nursing home–type unit) (Nonreporting) **A**1 2 9 10 **S** HCA, Nashville, TN Primary Contact: James R. Thomas, Chief Executive Officer COO: John Quinlivan, Vice President and Chief Operating Officer CFO: David L. Dye, Chief Financial Officer CIO: Debbie Bush, Director Information Services CHR: William Coorpender, Assistant Vice President Human Resources Web address: www.nfrmc.com	33	10	267	—	—	—	—	—	—	—
⊠ **SHANDS AT AGH**, 801 S.W. Second Avenue, Zip 32601–6289; tel. 352/372–4321, (Total facility includes 30 beds in nursing home–type unit) (Nonreporting) **A**1 3 5 9 **S** Shands HealthCare, Gainesville, FL Primary Contact: Charles K. Van Sluyter, Interim Administrator COO: Jodi J. Mansfield, Executive Vice President and Chief Operating Officer CFO: Elizabeth Matthews, Director Finance CIO: William L. Montgomery, Senior Vice President and Chief Information Officer CHR: Janet L. Christie, Vice President Human Resources Web address: www.shands.org/hospitals/agh	23	10	269	—	—	—	—	—	—	—
⊠ **SHANDS AT THE UNIVERSITY OF FLORIDA**, 1600 S.W. Archer Road, Zip 32610–0326, Mailing Address: P.O. Box 100326, Zip 32610–0326; tel. 352/265–0111 **A**1 2 3 5 8 9 10 **F**2 6 9 10 11 12 13 14 15 16 17 18 19 20 21 22 23 26 27 28 29 30 31 33 35 37 39 40 42 44 45 46 47 48 49 50 51 52 53 55 56 57 58 59 60 61 62 63 64 65 66 67 69 70 71 73 74 75 76 79 81 82 84 85 86 87 88 89 90 92 94 95 96 99 100 101 102 103 104 108 109 110 **P**8 **S** Shands HealthCare, Gainesville, FL Primary Contact: Timothy J. Goldfarb, Chief Executive Officer COO: Jodi J. Mansfield, Executive Vice President and Chief Operating Officer CFO: William J. Robinson, Senior Vice President and Treasurer CIO: Joan Hovhanesian, Vice President and Chief Information Officer CHR: Janet L. Christie, Senior Vice President Human Resources Web address: www.shands.org	23	10	602	27389	487	497114	2251	525839	189517	3529
★ △ **SHANDS REHAB HOSPITAL**, 4101 N.W. 89th Boulevard, Zip 32606–3813; tel. 352/265–5491, (Nonreporting) **A**7 **S** Shands HealthCare, Gainesville, FL Primary Contact: Marina T. Cecchini, Administrator CFO: William J. Robinson, Senior Vice President and Chief Financial Officer Web address: www.shands.org	23	46	35	—	—	—	—	—	—	—
GRACEVILLE—Jackson County										
★ **CAMPBELLTON GRACEVILLE HOSPITAL**, 5429 College Drive, Zip 32440–1897; tel. 850/263–4431 **A**9 10 18 **F**9 21 27 28 33 48 81 88 92 97 Primary Contact: Jimmy Rigsby, Chief Executive Officer CFO: Tom Meadows, Consulting Controller CMO: Jack Sanders, M.D., Chief Medical Officer CHR: Judy Austin, Human Resources Director	16	10	15	366	3	—	0	—	—	—
GREEN COVE SPRINGS—Clay County										
□ **KINDRED HOSPITAL NORTH FLORIDA**, 801 Oak Street, Zip 32043–4317; tel. 904/284–9230 **A**1 10 **F**2 21 22 37 49 55 57 58 60 61 62 63 66 88 94 110 **S** Kindred Healthcare, Louisville, KY Primary Contact: Tim Simpson, Chief Executive Officer Web address: www.khnorthflorida.com	33	10	60	453	54	—	0	—	—	245
GULF BREEZE—Santa Rosa County										
□ **GULF BREEZE HOSPITAL**, 1110 Gulf Breeze Parkway, Zip 32561, Mailing Address: P.O. Box 159, Zip 32562–0159; tel. 850/934–2000 **A**1 9 10 **F**2 9 12 21 22 23 26 27 28 30 33 35 37 39 42 44 45 46 48 52 53 55 58 61 62 63 64 65 69 79 80 81 82 84 85 88 89 92 94 95 96 108 109 **S** Baptist Health Care Corporation, Pensacola, FL Primary Contact: Robert Harriman, Administrator Web address: www.e–baptisthealthcare.org	23	10	60	2808	33	90712	0	35331	13369	346
THE FRIARY OF BAPTIST HEALTH CENTER, 4400 Hickory Shores Boulevard, Zip 32561–9113; tel. 850/932–9375, (Nonreporting) **S** Baptist Health Care Corporation, Pensacola, FL Primary Contact: Leo J. Donnelly, Executive Director	23	82	30	—	—	—	—	—	—	—
HIALEAH—Dade County										
⊠ **HIALEAH HOSPITAL**, 651 East 25th Street, Zip 33013–3878; tel. 305/693–6100, (Nonreporting) **A**1 9 10 **S** TENET Healthcare Corporation, Dallas, TX Primary Contact: Ana J. Mederos, Chief Executive Officer CFO: Aurelio Gonzalez, Chief Financial Officer Web address: www.hialeahhosp.com	33	10	220	—	—	—	—	—	—	—
□ **PALM SPRINGS GENERAL HOSPITAL**, 1475 West 49th Street, Zip 33012–3275, Mailing Address: Box 2804, Zip 33012–2804; tel. 305/558–2500, (Nonreporting) **A**1 9 10	33	10	190	—	—	—	—	—	—	—

Many Facility Codes have changed. Please refer to the AHA Guide Code Chart.

FL

Hospital, Address, Telephone, Approval, Facility, and Physician Codes, Health Care System	Classi-fication Codes		Utilization Data					Expense (thousands) of dollars		
★ American Hospital Association (AHA) membership □ Joint Commission on Accreditation of Healthcare Organizations (JCAHO) accreditation ○ American Osteopathic Association (AOA) accreditation △ Commission on Accreditation of Rehabilitation Facilities (CARF) accreditation	Control	Service	Staffed Beds	Admissions	Census	Outpatient Visits	Births	Total	Payroll	Personnel

PALMETTO GENERAL HOSPITAL, 2001 West 68th Street, Zip 33016–1898; tel. 305/823–5000 **A**1 9 10 12 13 **F**2 3 10 11 12 14 15 21 22 23 29 33 36 37 40 42 44 45 46 47 48 49 53 54 56 57 58 59 60 61 62 63 64 66 68 69 71 73 75 76 77 78 79 81 82 84 86 88 93 94 95 96 108 109 110 **S** TENET Healthcare Corporation, Dallas, TX
Primary Contact: Ralph A. Aleman, Chief Executive Officer
COO: Alex Contreras–Soto, Chief Operating Officer
CFO: Oscar Vicente, Chief Financial Officer
CMO: Albert Tano, M.D., Chief of Staff
Web address: www.palmettogeneral.com

| | 33 | 10 | 360 | 17889 | 242 | 143776 | 2940 | — | — | — |

HOLLYWOOD—Broward County

△ **HOLLYWOOD MEDICAL CENTER**, 3600 Washington Street, Zip 33021–8216; tel. 954/966–4500, (Nonreporting) **A**1 7 9 10 **S** TENET Healthcare Corporation, Dallas, TX
Primary Contact: Larry Melby, Chief Executive Officer
CFO: Anne Bauer, Chief Financial Officer
Web address: www.hollywoodmedicalctr.com

| | 33 | 10 | 324 | | | | | | | |

HOLLYWOOD PAVILION, 1201 North 37th Avenue, Zip 33021–5498; tel. 954/962–1355 **A**1 10 **F**3 71 73 74 76 77
Primary Contact: Karen Kallen–Zury, Chief Executive Officer

| | 33 | 22 | 46 | 650 | 29 | | | — | — | 69 |

△ **MEMORIAL REGIONAL HOSPITAL**, 3501 Johnson Street, Zip 33021–5421; tel. 954/987–2000, (Includes JOE DIMAGGIO CHILDREN'S HOSPITAL) **A**1 2 3 5 7 9 10 **F**1 2 3 4 9 10 11 12 14 15 16 17 18 19 20 21 22 23 24 26 27 28 31 32 33 34 35 37 39 40 41 42 44 45 46 47 48 49 50 51 52 53 55 56 57 58 59 60 61 62 63 64 65 66 67 68 69 70 71 72 73 74 75 76 77 78 79 80 81 82 84 85 87 88 90 92 94 95 96 106 108 109 110 **S** Memorial Healthcare System, Hollywood, FL
Primary Contact: J. E. Piriz, Administrator
COO: Deborah Tedder, Chief Operating Officer
CFO: David Smith, Chief Financial Officer
CIO: Forest Blanton, Administrator Management Systems
Web address: www.mhs.net

| | 16 | 10 | 684 | 35230 | 536 | 324660 | 3946 | 468840 | 194835 | 2880 |

SOUTH FLORIDA STATE HOSPITAL, 800 East Cypress Drive, Zip 33025–4543; tel. 954/392–3000, (Nonreporting) **A**1 10
Primary Contact: Sal A. Barbera, FACHE, Administrator
Web address: www.sfsh.org

| | 12 | 22 | 355 | — | — | — | — | — | — | — |

HOMESTEAD—Dade County

HOMESTEAD HOSPITAL, 160 N.W. 13th Street, Zip 33030–4299; tel. 786/243–8000 **A**1 9 10 **F**2 9 11 12 21 22 23 26 27 28 29 33 36 37 38 39 41 42 46 47 48 49 52 53 55 58 59 60 62 63 64 66 69 81 82 84 85 88 93 94 96 106 107 108 109 110 **S** Baptist Health South Florida, Coral Gables, FL
Primary Contact: Bo Boulenger, Chief Executive Officer
COO: Bill Duquette, Vice President Operations
CFO: Erik Long, Controller
CMO: Jorge Mejia, M.D., Chief of Staff
CIO: Mimi Taylor, Corporate Vice President Information Technology
Web address: www.baptisthealth.net

| | 23 | 10 | 116 | 7206 | 85 | 64346 | 1204 | 80602 | 30350 | 570 |

HUDSON—Pasco County

REGIONAL MEDICAL CENTER–BAYONET POINT, 14000 Fivay Road, Zip 34667–7199; tel. 727/863–2411 **A**1 9 10 **F**2 6 10 12 14 15 17 19 21 22 23 27 28 33 37 44 46 47 48 49 50 52 53 55 57 58 60 61 62 63 64 65 66 81 82 84 85 88 92 93 94 95 96 108 110 **S** HCA, Nashville, TN
Primary Contact: David R. Williams, Chief Executive Officer
COO: Robert B. Conroy, Jr, Chief Operating Officer
CFO: Patrick Long, Chief Financial Officer
CMO: Marshall DeSantis, M.D., Chief of Staff
CIO: Stephen Goldstein, Director Information Systems
CHR: Andrea Pinion, Vice President
Web address: www.rmchealth.com

| | 33 | 10 | 243 | 14090 | 190 | 34719 | 0 | — | — | 1248 |

INVERNESS—Citrus County

CITRUS MEMORIAL HOSPITAL, 502 West Highland Boulevard, Zip 34452–4754; tel. 352/726–1551 **A**1 9 10 19 **F**2 9 11 12 14 15 17 19 21 22 23 26 27 28 29 33 35 39 42 46 51 52 53 54 55 58 59 61 62 63 64 69 70 81 82 87 88 94 96 107 108 **P**6
Primary Contact: Ryan D. Beaty, President and Chief Executive Officer
COO: Jerrald Deloach, Chief Operating Officer
CFO: Emery Hensley, Chief Financial Officer
CIO: William Richel, Director Information System
CHR: Lee Glotzback, Director of Human Resources
Web address: www.citrusmh.com

| | 23 | 10 | 171 | 10610 | 124 | 145494 | 565 | 96920 | 33906 | 930 |

FL

Hospital, Address, Telephone, Approval, Facility, and Physician Codes, Health Care System	Classi-fication Codes		Utilization Data					Expense (thousands) of dollars		
★ American Hospital Association (AHA) membership □ Joint Commission on Accreditation of Healthcare Organizations (JCAHO) accreditation ○ American Osteopathic Association (AOA) accreditation △ Commission on Accreditation of Rehabilitation Facilities (CARF) accreditation	Control	Service	Staffed Beds	Admissions	Census	Outpatient Visits	Births	Total	Payroll	Personnel

JACKSONVILLE—Duval County

☒ **BAPTIST MEDICAL CENTER**, 800 Prudential Drive, Zip 32207–8203; tel. 904/202–2000 **A**1 2 3 5 9 10 **F**2 4 9 11 12 14 15 16 17 18 19 20 21 22 23 26 27 28 29 30 31 32 33 37 39 41 42 44 47 49 51 52 55 56 57 58 59 61 62 63 64 65 66 67 69 71 72 73 74 75 76 77 78 79 81 82 84 85 87 88 90 93 94 95 96 97 98 99 106 108 109 110 **P**6 **S** Baptist Health, Jacksonville, FL
Primary Contact: Joseph Mitrick, Administrator
COO: John F. Wilbanks, Chief Operating Officer
CFO: Mike Lukaszewski, Chief Financial Officer
CMO: Keith Stein, M.D., Senior Vice President Medical Affairs
CIO: Roland Garcia, Chief Information Officer
CHR: Beth Mehaffey, Administrative Director Human Resources
Web address: www.e-baptisthealth.com
`23 10 547 27383 390 366429 2330 365587 136345 3828`

☒ △ **BROOKS REHABILITATION HOSPITAL**, 3599 University Boulevard South, Zip 32216–4211, Mailing Address: P.O. Box 16406, Zip 32245–6406; tel. 904/858–7200, (Nonreporting) **A**1 7 10
Primary Contact: Charles A. Schauer, Ph.D., President and Chief Executive Officer
COO: Douglas Baer, President and Chief Operating Officer
CFO: Becky Chaudoin, Director Finance
CMO: Deborah G. Stewart, M.D., Chief Medical Officer and Medical Director
CIO: Karen Green, Chief Information Officer
CHR: Elizabeth Figura, Vice President, Human Resources
Web address: www.brookshealth.org
`23 46 127 — — — — — — —`

☒ **MEMORIAL HOSPITAL OF JACKSONVILLE**, 3625 University Boulevard South, Zip 32216–4240, Mailing Address: P.O. Box 16325, Zip 32216–6325; tel. 904/399–6111, (Nonreporting) **A**1 2 9 10 **S** HCA, Nashville, TN
Primary Contact: H. Rex Etheredge, President and Chief Executive Officer
Web address: www.memorialhospitaljax.com
`33 10 353 — — — — — — —`

☒ **NAVAL HOSPITAL**, 2080 Child Street, Zip 32214–5000; tel. 904/542–7300, (Nonreporting) **A**1 3 5 **S** Bureau of Medicine and Surgery, Department of the Navy, Washington, DC
Primary Contact: Captain John Sentell, Commanding Officer
COO: Captain Elaine Wagner, M.D., Executive Officer
CFO: Lieutenant Commander Dave Breier, Comptroller
CMO: Captain Malcolm Horry, Director Medical Services
CIO: Lieutenant Commander Mike Haytaian, Head Director, Information Resources Management Department
Web address: www.199.208.118.223/
`43 10 60 — — — — — — —`

☒ **SHANDS JACKSONVILLE MEDICAL CENTER**, 655 West Eighth Street, Zip 32209–6595; tel. 904/244–0411 **A**1 2 3 5 8 9 10 **F**2 6 9 11 12 14 15 17 19 21 22 23 26 27 28 29 31 32 33 34 39 42 46 48 49 50 51 52 55 56 57 58 59 60 61 62 63 64 65 66 67 69 70 71 72 73 74 75 78 79 81 82 83 84 85 86 87 88 92 93 94 95 96 97 101 108 109 110 **S** Shands HealthCare, Gainesville, FL
Primary Contact: James R. Burkhart, FACHE, President and Administrator
COO: James R. Burkhart, FACHE, President and Chief Executive Officer
CFO: Bill Ryan, Chief Financial Officer
CMO: David Vukich, M.D., Senior Vice President and Chief Medical Officer
CIO: Bill Ryan, Chief Financial Officer
Web address: www.shandsjacksonville.org
`23 10 508 24119 375 376231 3071 399777 138541 3241`

☒ **SPECIALTY HOSPITAL JACKSONVILLE**, 4901 Richard Street, Zip 32207–7328; tel. 904/737–3120 **A**1 9 10 **F**2 21 22 37 49 58 62 64 66 73 88 94 110
Primary Contact: W. Raymond C. Ford, Chief Executive Officer
COO: W Raymond C Ford, Chief Executive Officer
CFO: Jim Ayersman, Chief Financial Officer
CMO: Wendell H. Williams, Jr, M.D., Medical Director
CIO: Liz Rhodes, Director Information Services
CHR: Lisa Ayala, R.N., Human Resources Manager
Web address: www.specialtyhospitaljax.com
`33 80 61 720 60 0 0 25620 11037 158`

☒ **ST. LUKE'S HOSPITAL**, 4201 Belfort Road, Zip 32216–5898; tel. 904/296–3700 **A**1 2 3 5 8 9 10 **F**2 10 11 15 17 19 21 22 23 26 27 28 30 33 37 40 46 48 49 55 56 58 59 60 61 62 63 64 66 69 81 82 84 85 87 88 94 96 99 100 101 102 103 104 105 108 110 **S** Mayo Foundation, Rochester, MN
Primary Contact: Hilary G. Mathews, Administrator
CFO: Mary Hoffman, Chief Financial Officer
CMO: Paul Rebenack, M.D., President Medical Staff
CIO: Cheryl Croft, Chairman, Information Services
CHR: Michael Estes, Chair, Human Resources
Web address: www.mayoclinic.org
`23 10 289 16841 222 45298 1414 274542 73446 1474`

FL

Many Facility Codes have changed. Please refer to the AHA Guide Code Chart.   © 2005 AHA Guide

Hospital, Address, Telephone, Approval, Facility, and Physician Codes, Health Care System	Classi-fication Codes		Utilization Data					Expense (thousands) of dollars		
★ American Hospital Association (AHA) membership □ Joint Commission on Accreditation of Healthcare Organizations (JCAHO) accreditation ○ American Osteopathic Association (AOA) accreditation △ Commission on Accreditation of Rehabilitation Facilities (CARF) accreditation	Control	Service	Staffed Beds	Admissions	Census	Outpatient Visits	Births	Total	Payroll	Personnel
✸ **ST. VINCENT'S MEDICAL CENTER**, 1800 Barrs Street, Zip 32204–2982, Mailing Address: P.O. Box 2982, Zip 32203–2982; tel. 904/308–7300 **A**1 2 3 5 9 10 **F**2 9 11 12 14 15 17 19 21 22 23 26 27 28 29 31 32 33 34 35 36 37 38 39 40 41 44 46 47 48 49 50 52 53 55 57 58 59 60 61 62 63 64 65 66 69 75 79 80 81 82 84 85 86 87 88 90 92 93 94 95 96 98 105 106 108 109 110 **P**6 **S** Ascension Health, Saint Louis, MO Primary Contact: Margaret Mortensen, Interim Executive Vice President and Chief Operating Officer COO: Margaret Mortensen, Interim Executive Vice President and Chief Executive Officer CFO: James M. Corrigan, Chief Financial Officer CIO: Warren L. Chandler, Senior Vice President and Chief Information Officer CHR: Jan Lipsky, Vice President Organizational Effectiveness Web address: www.jaxhealth.com	21	10	528	26579	369	100101	2374	292305	113471	2993
□ **TEN BROECK HOSPITAL JACKSONVILLE**, 6300 Beach Boulevard, Zip 32216–2782; tel. 904/724–9202, (Nonreporting) **A**1 10 **S** United Medical Corporation, Windermere, FL Primary Contact: Paul Andrews, Chief Executive Officer Web address: www.tenbroeck.com	33	22	99	—	—	—	—	—	—	—
JACKSONVILLE BEACH—Duval County										
✸ **BAPTIST MEDICAL CENTER–BEACHES**, 1350 13th Avenue South, Zip 32250–3205; tel. 904/247–2900 **A**1 9 10 **F**2 9 11 12 21 22 23 26 27 28 30 33 34 37 39 46 48 52 55 57 58 59 60 61 62 63 64 65 69 81 82 84 87 88 93 94 108 110 **S** Baptist Health, Jacksonville, FL Primary Contact: Mark Slyter, Administrator CFO: Joni Smith, Director of Finance CMO: Keith Stein, M.D., Chief Medical Officer CIO: Roland Garcia, Senior Vice President and Chief Information Officer CHR: Cindy Sechrist, Director Human Resources Web address: www.e–baptisthealth.com	23	10	98	6941	83	87218	781	62594	26528	587
JASPER—Hamilton County										
TRINITY COMMUNITY HOSPITAL, 506 N.W. Fourth Street, Zip 32052–6603; tel. 386/792–7200, (Nonreporting) **A**9 10 Primary Contact: Mary Feraudo, Chief Executive Officer	33	10	42	—	—	—	—	—	—	—
JAY—Santa Rosa County										
★ **JAY HOSPITAL**, 14114 South Alabama Street, Zip 32565–1070; tel. 850/675–8000 **A**9 10 **F**12 21 22 26 27 28 29 33 35 39 45 46 48 50 52 60 62 63 64 69 81 84 85 88 92 94 97 108 **S** Baptist Health Care Corporation, Pensacola, FL Primary Contact: Michael T. Hutchins, Administrator CFO: Keith Strickling, Chief Accountant CMO: Marian Stewart, M.D., Chief of Staff CHR: Sandra Copple, Human Resources Manager Web address: www.e–baptisthealthcare.org	23	10	55	1434	22	26395	0	9474	4178	125
JUPITER—Palm Beach County										
✸ **JUPITER MEDICAL CENTER**, 1210 South Old Dixie Highway, Zip 33458–7299; tel. 561/747–2234, (Total facility includes 120 beds in nursing home–type unit) **A**1 2 10 **F**9 10 11 12 14 21 22 23 24 26 27 28 29 30 33 35 37 38 40 41 45 46 47 48 51 52 54 57 58 59 60 61 62 63 64 65 66 69 79 80 81 82 84 85 87 88 90 92 93 94 96 106 109 110 **P**6 7 **S** Brim Healthcare, Inc., Brentwood, TN Primary Contact: R. Michael Barry, Chief Executive Officer COO: Terri Wentz, Chief Operating Officer CFO: Gary R. Wright, Chief Financial Officer CIO: Mike Fehr, Director Information System CHR: James Harper, Chief Human Resources Officer Web address: www.jupitermed.com	23	10	276	9975	225	120875	1011	133517	49441	1118
KEY WEST—Monroe County										
□ **LOWER KEYS MEDICAL CENTER**, 5900 College Road, Zip 33040–4396, Mailing Address: P.O. Box 9107, Zip 33041–9107; tel. 305/294–5531, (Includes DE POO HOSPITAL, 1200 Kennedy Drive, Zip 33041; tel. 305/294–4692; FLORIDA KEYS MEMORIAL HOSPITAL) **A**1 9 10 20 **F**2 3 4 6 9 11 12 14 21 23 24 29 33 36 37 39 45 46 48 49 50 52 53 56 58 59 60 61 62 63 65 69 70 71 73 74 75 76 77 78 81 84 88 94 95 96 108 110 **S** Health Management Associates, Naples, FL Primary Contact: Nicki Will, Ph.D., President and Chief Executive Officer Web address: www.lkmc.com	33	10	115	4716	52	—	—	—	—	—
KISSIMMEE—Osceola County										
FLORIDA HOSPITAL KISSIMMEE See Florida Hospital, Orlando										
✸ **OSCEOLA REGIONAL MEDICAL CENTER**, 700 West Oak Street, Zip 34741–4996; tel. 407/846–2266 **A**1 9 10 **F**2 9 11 12 14 15 17 19 21 22 23 26 27 28 29 31 33 35 37 39 42 44 46 47 48 50 52 53 55 56 57 58 59 60 61 62 63 64 65 66 69 70 81 82 84 85 87 88 94 95 96 106 108 109 110 **S** HCA, Nashville, TN Primary Contact: E. Tim Cook, Chief Executive Officer COO: Randy Gross, Director Fiscal Services CHR: Sylvia Lollis, Director Human Resources Web address: www.osceolaregional.com	33	10	231	11565	143	95434	2573	125824	45640	843

FL

Hospital, Address, Telephone, Approval, Facility, and Physician Codes, Health Care System	Classi-fication Codes		Utilization Data					Expense (thousands) of dollars		
★ American Hospital Association (AHA) membership □ Joint Commission on Accreditation of Healthcare Organizations (JCAHO) accreditation ○ American Osteopathic Association (AOA) accreditation △ Commission on Accreditation of Rehabilitation Facilities (CARF) accreditation	Control	Service	Staffed Beds	Admissions	Census	Outpatient Visits	Births	Total	Payroll	Personnel

LAKE BUTLER—Union County

LAKE BUTLER HOSPITAL HAND SURGERY CENTER, 850 East Main Street, Zip 32054–1335, Mailing Address: P.O. Box 748, Zip 32054–0748; tel. 386/496–2323, (Nonreporting) **A**9 10 18
Primary Contact: Pamela Howard, Administrator
Web address: www.lakebutlerhospital.com

| | 33 | 10 | 25 | — | — | — | | — | — | |

NORTH FLORIDA RECEPTION CENTER HOSPITAL, (Formerly Reception and Medical Center Hospital), State Road 231 South, Zip 32054, Mailing Address: P.O. Box 628, Zip 32054–0628; tel. 386/496–6000 **F**2 21 22 23 31 32 33 45 47 48 50 52 53 58 61 65 66 70 71 73 74 75 76 77 78 92 94 96 106 110
Primary Contact: Brent Merson, Administrator

| | 12 | 11 | 153 | 2084 | 91 | 146130 | 0 | — | — | 239 |

LAKE CITY—Columbia County

✚ **LAKE CITY MEDICAL CENTER**, 340 N.W. Commerce Drive, Zip 32055–3718; tel. 386/719–9000 **A**1 9 10 **F**2 9 12 21 22 26 27 28 29 33 40 41 44 46 48 52 53 55 58 60 62 63 65 66 69 81 82 84 88 93 94 108 **S** HCA, Nashville, TN
Primary Contact: Garry L. Karsner, Chief Executive Officer
CFO: Jennifer B. Adams, Chief Financial Officer
CMO: Ernest de Leon, M.D., Chief of Medicine
CIO: Taylor Dickerson, Chief Information Officer
CHR: Scott Parton, Director Human Resources
Web address: www.lakecitymedical.com

| | 33 | 10 | 67 | 3665 | 45 | — | 0 | — | — | 266 |

✚ **SHANDS AT LAKE SHORE**, 368 N.E. Franklin Street, Zip 32055–3047; tel. 386/754–8000 **A**1 9 10 **F**2 9 11 12 21 23 26 27 28 29 33 39 46 47 48 51 52 55 58 59 60 61 62 63 64 66 69 70 81 84 85 88 92 94 96 106 108 109 110 **P**5 **S** Shands HealthCare, Gainesville, FL
Primary Contact: Neil Whipkey, Administrator
CMO: Waseem Khan, M.D., President Medical Staff
CHR: Janice Jackson, Director Human Resources
Web address: www.shands.org

| | 23 | 10 | 87 | 6021 | 63 | 78578 | 649 | 31065 | 15065 | 333 |

★ **VETERANS AFFAIRS MEDICAL CENTER**, 619 South Marion Avenue, Zip 32025–5898; tel. 386/755–3016, (Total facility includes 180 beds in nursing home–type unit) (Nonreporting) **S** Department of Veterans Affairs, Washington, DC
Primary Contact: Frederick L. Malphurs, Director
CIO: James Hudson, Assistant Chief IRM
Web address: www.va.gov/sta/guide/home.asp

| | 45 | 10 | 360 | — | | | | | | |

LAKE WALES—Polk County

□ **LAKE WALES MEDICAL CENTERS**, 410 South 11th Street, Zip 33853–4256; tel. 863/676–1433, (Total facility includes 80 beds in nursing home–type unit) **A**1 9 10 **F**2 12 21 22 33 37 46 48 54 55 57 58 62 63 64 81 82 88 92 106 108 **S** Community Health Systems, Inc., Brentwood, TN
Primary Contact: Carol Negoshian, Administrator
Web address: www.winterhavenhospital.org/fac/lwmc/

| | 33 | 10 | 154 | 4872 | 113 | 37013 | 0 | 34026 | 13549 | |

LAKELAND—Polk County

✚ **LAKELAND REGIONAL MEDICAL CENTER**, 1324 Lakeland Hills Boulevard, Zip 33805–4543, Mailing Address: P.O. Box 95448, Zip 33804–5448; tel. 863/687–1100 **A**1 2 5 9 10 **F**2 3 4 5 9 11 14 15 17 19 21 22 23 26 28 29 31 33 34 35 37 43 44 45 46 47 48 49 50 52 53 55 56 57 58 59 60 61 62 63 64 65 67 69 71 72 73 74 75 76 77 78 81 82 83 84 85 88 90 94 96 98 106 107 108 109 110 **P**6
Primary Contact: Jack T. Stephens, Jr, President and Chief Executive Officer
CFO: Paul A. Powers, Vice President
CMO: Edwin Sammer, M.D., Vice President and Chief Medical Officer
Web address: www.lrmc.com

| | 23 | 10 | 735 | 35035 | 470 | 158061 | 2592 | 368557 | 148459 | 3620 |

LANTANA—Palm Beach County

A. G. HOLLEY STATE HOSPITAL, 1199 West Lantana Road, Zip 33462–1514, Mailing Address: P.O. Box 3084, Zip 33465–3084; tel. 561/540–3783, (Nonreporting) **A**10
Primary Contact: David Ashkin, M.D., Medical Executive Director

| | 12 | 33 | 50 | — | — | — | — | — | — | |

LARGO—Pinellas County

✚ △ **HEALTHSOUTH REHABILITATION HOSPITAL**, 901 North Clearwater–Largo Road, Zip 33770–4126; tel. 727/586–2999, (Nonreporting) **A**1 7 10 **S** HEALTHSOUTH Corporation, Birmingham, AL
Primary Contact: Elaine D. Ebaugh, Administrator
CFO: Judith Johnson, Controller
CMO: Richard A. Liles, M.D., Medical Director
Web address: www.healthsouth.com

| | 33 | 46 | 60 | — | — | — | — | — | — | |

✚ **LARGO MEDICAL CENTER**, 201 14th Street S.W., Zip 33770–3133, Mailing Address: P.O. Box 2905, Zip 33779–2905; tel. 727/588–5200, (Total facility includes 13 beds in nursing home–type unit) (Nonreporting) **A**1 2 5 9 10 **S** HCA, Nashville, TN
Primary Contact: Thomas L. Herron, FACHE, President and Chief Executive Officer
COO: Lawrence W. Kaufman, Administrator and Chief Operating Officer
CFO: Robert E. Billings, Chief Financial Officer
CIO: Silvia Padro, Director Information Services
CHR: Debra Dennis, Human Resources Director
Web address: www.largomedical.com

| | 33 | 10 | 243 | — | — | — | — | — | — | |

Many Facility Codes have changed. Please refer to the AHA Guide Code Chart.   © 2005 AHA Guide

Hospital, Address, Telephone, Approval, Facility, and Physician Codes, Health Care System	Classi-fication Codes		Utilization Data					Expense (thousands) of dollars		
★ American Hospital Association (AHA) membership □ Joint Commission on Accreditation of Healthcare Organizations (JCAHO) accreditation ○ American Osteopathic Association (AOA) accreditation △ Commission on Accreditation of Rehabilitation Facilities (CARF) accreditation	Control	Service	Staffed Beds	Admissions	Census	Outpatient Visits	Births	Total	Payroll	Personnel

Hospital	Control	Service	Staffed Beds	Admissions	Census	Outpatient Visits	Births	Total	Payroll	Personnel
□ ○ **SUN COAST HOSPITAL**, 2025 Indian Rocks Road, Zip 33774–1096, Mailing Address: P.O. Box 2025, Zip 33779–2025; tel. 727/581–9474, (Total facility includes 14 beds in nursing home–type unit) (Nonreporting) **A**1 9 10 11 12 13 **S** University Community Health, Tampa, FL Primary Contact: Larry J. Archbell, Chief Executive Officer Web address: www.suncoasthealthcare.com	23	10	300	—	—	—	—	—	—	—
LAUDERDALE LAKES—Broward County										
△ **ST. ANTHONY'S REHABILITATION HOSPITAL**, 3485 N.W. 30th Street, Zip 33311; tel. 954/739–6233, (Nonreporting) **A**7 10 Primary Contact: Joe Catania, Chief Executive Officer	33	46	26	—	—	—	—	—	—	—
LEESBURG—Lake County										
⊞ △ **LEESBURG REGIONAL MEDICAL CENTER**, 600 East Dixie Avenue, Zip 34748–5999; tel. 352/323–5762, (Total facility includes 120 beds in nursing home–type unit) **A**1 2 7 9 10 19 **F**9 10 11 12 14 15 17 21 22 23 26 27 28 33 37 40 41 42 44 46 47 48 49 51 52 55 57 58 59 60 61 62 63 66 68 69 81 82 84 86 88 92 93 94 96 107 108 109 Primary Contact: Louis H. Bremer, Jr, Interim Chief Executive Officer COO: Douglas L. Rahn, Chief Operating Officer CFO: Dale E. Hocking, Chief Financial Officer CMO: Jeffrey D. Robinson, M.D., President Medical Staff CIO: Nancy Vester, Vice President Information Technology CHR: Darlene Stone, Vice President Human Resources Web address: www.Leesburgregional.org	23	10	429	17256	284	103042	1289	174696	64762	1461
LEHIGH ACRES—Lee County										
□ **LEHIGH REGIONAL MEDICAL CENTER**, 1500 Lee Boulevard, Zip 33936–4897; tel. 239/369–2101 **A**1 9 10 **F**2 9 12 21 22 26 27 28 29 33 39 44 46 48 52 54 55 57 58 60 62 63 66 69 70 81 82 84 87 88 93 96 108 109 110 **S** Health Management Associates, Naples, FL Primary Contact: Dan Buckner, Chief Executive Officer Web address: www.lehighregional.com	33	10	88	3051	29	—	—	—	—	—
LIVE OAK—Suwannee County										
⊞ **SHANDS AT LIVE OAK**, 1100 S.W. 11th Street, Zip 32060–3608; tel. 386/362–1413, (Nonreporting) **A**1 9 10 18 **S** Shands HealthCare, Gainesville, FL Primary Contact: Rhonda Sherrod, Administrator Web address: www.shands.org	23	10	15	—	—	—	—	—	—	—
LONGWOOD—Seminole County										
ORLANDO REGIONAL SOUTH SEMINOLE HOSPITAL, 555 West State Road 434, Zip 32750–4999; tel. 407/767–1200, (Nonreporting) **S** Orlando Regional Healthcare, Orlando, FL Primary Contact: Stephen M. Glazier, Executive Director	32	10	206	—	—	—	—	—	—	—
LOXAHATCHEE—Palm Beach County										
⊞ **PALMS WEST HOSPITAL**, 13001 Southern Boulevard, Zip 33470–1150; tel. 561/798–3300, (Nonreporting) **A**1 9 10 12 13 **S** HCA, Nashville, TN Primary Contact: Heather J. Rohan, Chief Executive Officer CFO: Robert Preato, Chief Financial Officer Web address: www.palmswesthospital.com	33	10	140	—	—	—	—	—	—	—
MACCLENNY—Baker County										
ED FRASER MEMORIAL HOSPITAL AND BAKER COMMUNITY HEALTH CENTER, 159 North Third Street, Zip 32063–0484, Mailing Address: P.O. Box 484, Zip 32063–0484; tel. 904/259–3151, (Total facility includes 62 beds in nursing home–type unit) (Nonreporting) **A**9 10 Primary Contact: Dennis R. Markos, Chief Executive Officer	23	10	68	—	—	—	—	—	—	—
MACDILL AFB—Hillsborough County										
⊞ **U. S. AIR FORCE HOSPITAL**, 8415 Bayshore Boulevard, Zip 33621–1607; tel. 813/827–9521, (Nonreporting) **A**1 **S** Department of the Air Force, Washington, DC Primary Contact: Colonel Charles W. Mackett, Commander CMO: Howard Riker, M.D., Chief Medical Staff CIO: Captain Thomas Stewart, Medical Information Services Flight Commander	41	10	12	—	—	—	—	—	—	—
MADISON—Madison County										
MADISON COUNTY MEMORIAL HOSPITAL, 201 East Marion Street, Zip 32340–2561; tel. 850/973–2271 **A**9 10 20 **F**12 21 22 29 33 42 46 48 51 52 53 60 63 64 65 66 69 70 81 88 93 94 96 97 108 **P**5 Primary Contact: Bob Pugh, Interim Chief Executive Officer	23	10	31	950	13	23504	0	8498	4254	136
MARATHON—Monroe County										
□ **FISHERMEN'S HOSPITAL**, 3301 Overseas Highway, Zip 33050–0068; tel. 305/743–5533 **A**1 9 10 20 **F**2 9 12 21 27 29 33 37 45 47 55 57 58 60 62 63 64 65 66 69 81 82 88 93 94 95 108 **S** Health Management Associates, Naples, FL Primary Contact: Michael Kissner, Chief Executive Officer Web address: www.fishermenshospital.com	33	10	58	1542	17	14716	0	21240	7513	178

FL

Hospital, Address, Telephone, Approval, Facility, and Physician Codes, Health Care System	Classi-fication Codes		Utilization Data					Expense (thousands) of dollars		
★ American Hospital Association (AHA) membership □ Joint Commission on Accreditation of Healthcare Organizations (JCAHO) accreditation ○ American Osteopathic Association (AOA) accreditation △ Commission on Accreditation of Rehabilitation Facilities (CARF) accreditation	Control	Service	Staffed Beds	Admissions	Census	Outpatient Visits	Births	Total	Payroll	Personnel

MARGATE—Broward County

✠ **NORTHWEST MEDICAL CENTER**, 2801 North State Road 7, Zip 33063; tel. 954/978–4000 **A**1 9 10 **F**2 9 10 11 12 15 21 22 23 26 27 28 29 30 33 36 37 38 39 40 41 44 46 47 48 49 50 52 53 55 57 58 59 60 61 62 63 64 65 66 67 69 81 82 84 85 88 89 90 93 94 95 96 106 108 109 110 **S** HCA, Nashville, TN Primary Contact: MaryLynn Swartz, Chief Executive Officer COO: Michael Bass, Chief Operating Officer CFO: C Lynn Dick, Chief Financial Officer CMO: Steven Foster, Chief of Staff CIO: Bob Wyszkowski, Director of Information Systems CHR: Scott Mazo, Vice President Human Resources Web address: www.northwestmed.com	33	10	175	12799	139	71076	1888	91094	39501	862

MARIANNA—Jackson County

✠ **JACKSON HOSPITAL**, 4250 Hospital Drive, Zip 32446–1939, Mailing Address: P.O. Box 1608, Zip 32447–1608; tel. 850/526–2200 **A**1 9 10 **F**2 9 11 12 21 22 27 28 29 33 39 40 41 48 55 58 59 62 63 65 66 81 82 84 85 88 94 95 96 97 108 **P**5 **S** Quorum Health Resources, Plano, TX Primary Contact: David L. Hample, Chief Executive Officer CFO: Kevin Rovito, Interim Chief Financial Officer CMO: George Sanchez, M.D., Chief Medical Officer CHR: Brooke Donaldson, Assistant Administrator, Human Resources Web address: www.jacksonhosp.com	16	10	86	2942	37	—	456	31876	14054	388

MELBOURNE—Brevard County

□ **CIRCLES OF CARE**, 400 East Sheridan Road, Zip 32901–3184; tel. 321/722–5200, (Nonreporting) **A**1 9 10 Primary Contact: James B. Whitaker, President Web address: www.circlesofcare.org	23	22	134	—	—	—	—	—	—	—
DEVEREUX HOSPITAL AND CHILDREN'S CENTER OF FLORIDA, 8000 Devereux Drive, Zip 32940–7907; tel. 321/242–9100 **F**26 28 71 72 94 **S** Devereux, Villanova, PA Primary Contact: Patty Hurst, Administrator Web address: www.devereux.org	23	52	100	86	95	0	0	13932	7401	—
✠ △ **HEALTHSOUTH SEA PINES REHABILITATION HOSPITAL**, 101 East Florida Avenue, Zip 32901–9966; tel. 321/984–4600, (Nonreporting) **A**1 7 10 **S** HEALTHSOUTH Corporation, Birmingham, AL Primary Contact: Denise B. McGrath, Administrator CFO: Dana Edwards, Controller CMO: Stuart P. Miller, M.D., Medical Director CHR: Donna Anderson, Director of Human Resources Web address: www.healthsouth.com	33	46	90	—	—	—	—	—	—	—
✠ **HOLMES REGIONAL MEDICAL CENTER**, 1350 South Hickory Street, Zip 32901–3276; tel. 321/434–7000 **A**1 2 10 **F**2 9 10 11 12 14 21 22 27 28 30 33 34 37 38 49 50 52 53 55 56 57 58 59 61 62 63 65 66 81 82 84 87 88 94 96 106 108 110 **S** First Health, Inc., Rockledge, FL Primary Contact: Christopher S. Kennedy, President and Chief Executive Officer COO: Kent L. Brown, Chief Operating Officer CFO: Robert Galloway, Senior Vice President Finance and Chief Financial Officer CMO: Chris Finton, M.D., Senior Vice President Medical Staff Services CIO: Rich Rogers, Vice President Information Technology CHR: Robert Suttles, Vice President Human Resources Web address: www.health–first.org	23	10	504	28837	401	—	—	—	—	—
□ **WUESTHOFF MEDICAL CENTER – MELBOURNE**, 250 North Wickham Road, Zip 32935; tel. 321/752–1200 **A**1 9 10 **F**2 9 11 12 15 21 26 27 28 29 33 40 46 48 49 52 53 55 57 58 59 60 62 63 64 66 69 75 81 82 84 85 87 88 92 94 95 96 106 107 108 109 110 **S** Wuesthoff Health System, Rockledge, FL Primary Contact: Donald McKenna, Administrator Web address: www.wuesthoff.org	23	10	115	5124	47	—	—	—	—	417

MIAMI—Dade County

✠ △ **BAPTIST HOSPITAL OF MIAMI**, 8900 North Kendall Drive, Zip 33176–2197; tel. 786/596–1960 **A**1 2 7 9 10 **F**7 9 10 11 12 14 15 17 19 21 22 23 26 27 28 29 33 36 37 39 40 41 42 44 45 46 47 48 49 50 51 52 53 55 56 57 58 59 60 61 62 63 64 65 66 67 68 69 75 78 79 80 81 82 84 85 86 87 88 93 94 95 96 107 108 109 110 **S** Baptist Health South Florida, Coral Gables, FL Primary Contact: Lee S. Huntley, Chief Executive Officer CFO: Ralph E. Lawson, Executive Vice President and Chief Financial Officer CMO: Mark J. Hauser, M.D., Chief Medical Officer CIO: Mimi Taylor, Corporate Vice President CHR: Carl Gustafson, Vice President Web address: www.baptisthealth.net	23	10	541	33774	496	251178	4122	508123	177139	3306
✠ **BASCOM PALMER EYE INSTITUTE–ANNE BATES LEACH EYE HOSPITAL**, 900 N.W. 17th Street, Zip 33136–1199, Mailing Address: Box 016880, Zip 33101–6880; tel. 305/326–6000 **A**1 3 5 9 10 **F**26 33 42 46 48 52 53 57 58 60 62 63 64 65 66 84 88 92 95 104 108 **P**6 Primary Contact: Michael B. Gittelman, Administrator COO: Michael B. Gittelman, Administrator CFO: Harry Rohrer, Chief Financial Officer CMO: Carmen Puliafito, M.D., Chairman of the Department of Ophthalmology CIO: Elizabeth Rockowitz, Director Business Information Management Systems CHR: Paul Hudgins, Associate Vice President Human Resources Web address: www.bascompalmer.org	23	45	20	181	2	196688	0	50198	19685	—

Many Facility Codes have changed. Please refer to the AHA Guide Code Chart. © 2005 AHA Guide

FL

Hospital, Address, Telephone, Approval, Facility, and Physician Codes, Health Care System	Classi-fication Codes		Utilization Data					Expense (thousands) of dollars		
★ American Hospital Association (AHA) membership □ Joint Commission on Accreditation of Healthcare Organizations (JCAHO) accreditation ○ American Osteopathic Association (AOA) accreditation △ Commission on Accreditation of Rehabilitation Facilities (CARF) accreditation	Control	Service	Staffed Beds	Admissions	Census	Outpatient Visits	Births	Total	Payroll	Personnel

	Control	Service	Staffed Beds	Admissions	Census	Outpatient Visits	Births	Total	Payroll	Personnel
✠ **CEDARS MEDICAL CENTER**, 1400 N.W. 12th Avenue, Zip 33136–1003; tel. 305/325–5511, (Total facility includes 25 beds in nursing home–type unit) (Nonreporting) **A**1 2 3 5 9 10 **S** HCA, Nashville, TN Primary Contact: Michael G. Joseph, Administrator COO: Lee Chaykin, Chief Operating Officer CFO: Elizabeth Izquierdo, Chief Financial Officer CMO: Dagoberto Garces Milanes, M.D., Chief and President of the Medical Staff CIO: Ken Zelnik, Director Information Web address: www.cedarsmedicalcenter.com	32	10	515	—	—	—	—	—	—	—
✠ △ **HEALTHSOUTH REHABILITATION HOSPITAL**, 20601 Old Cutler Road, Zip 33189–2400; tel. 305/251–3800, (Nonreporting) **A**1 7 10 **S** HEALTHSOUTH Corporation, Birmingham, AL Primary Contact: Jacqueline Arocho, Administrator CFO: Charles Findo, Chief Financial Officer Web address: www.healthsouth.com	33	46	60	—	—	—	—	—	—	—
✠ △ **JACKSON MEMORIAL HOSPITAL**, 1611 N.W. 12th Avenue, Zip 33136–1094; tel. 305/585–6754, (Includes HIGHLAND PARK HOSPITAL, 1695 N.W. Ninth Avenue, Zip 33136; tel. 305/355–8234; Stuart Podolnick, Administrator), (Total facility includes 320 beds in nursing home–type unit) **A**1 2 3 5 7 8 9 10 **F**2 3 4 9 10 12 13 14 15 16 17 18 19 20 21 22 23 24 26 27 28 29 30 31 32 33 34 35 37 38 39 40 43 44 45 46 47 48 49 50 52 53 55 56 57 58 59 60 61 62 63 64 65 66 67 68 69 70 71 72 73 74 75 76 77 78 80 81 82 84 85 86 87 88 89 90 92 94 95 96 98 99 100 101 102 103 104 105 106 107 108 109 110 **S** Jackson Health System, Miami, FL Primary Contact: Marvin O'Quinn, President and Chief Executive Officer COO: Steven M. Klein, Executive Vice President and Chief Operating Officer CFO: Frank Barrett, Executive Vice President Corporate Affairs and Chief Financial Officer CMO: Gerard A. Kaiser, M.D., Senior Vice President CIO: James Sandy Phillips, Vice President and Chief Information Officer CHR: Trummell Valdera, Senior Vice President and Chief Human Resources Officer Web address: www.um–jmh.org/JHS/Jackson.html	13	10	1764	61806	1489	617421	6044	1261576	597032	10188
★ **JACKSON SOUTH COMMUNITY HOSPITAL**, 9333 S.W. 152nd Street, Zip 33157–1780; tel. 305/251–2500, (Nonreporting) **A**9 10 **S** Jackson Health System, Miami, FL Primary Contact: Leigh Massengill, Chief Administrative Officer COO: Robert Owers, Associate Administrator Web address: www.um–jmh.org/JHS/JSCH/Jaxsouth.html	33	10	233	—	—	—	—	—	—	—
✠ **KENDALL REGIONAL MEDICAL CENTER**, 11750 Bird Road, Zip 33175–3530; tel. 305/223–3000, (Nonreporting) **A**1 9 10 **S** HCA, Nashville, TN Primary Contact: Victor Maya, Chief Executive Officer COO: Georgina Diaz, Chief Operating Officer CFO: Mauricio Sirvent, Chief Financial Officer CMO: Hugo Garcia, M.D., Chief of Staff CIO: Carlos Bitar, Assistant Administrator CHR: Lazara Marchante, Director Human Resources Web address: www.kendallmed.com	32	10	322	—	—	—	—	—	—	—
□ △ **MEADOWBROOK REHABILITATION HOSPITAL OF WEST GABLES**, 2525 S.W. 75th Avenue, Zip 33155; tel. 305/260–1816, (Nonreporting) **A**1 7 10 Primary Contact: Charlotte Raymor, Chief Executive Officer	33	46	60	—	—	—	—	—	—	—
✠ △ **MERCY HOSPITAL**, 3663 South Miami Avenue, Zip 33133–4237; tel. 305/854–4400, (Nonreporting) **A**1 2 7 9 10 **S** Catholic Health East, Newtown Square, PA Primary Contact: John E. Matuska, President and Chief Executive Officer CFO: Jerry Mashburn, Senior Vice President and Chief Financial Officer CMO: Manuel P. Anton, III, M.D., Senior Vice President and Medical Director CIO: Fernando Martinez, Chief Information Officer CHR: Eduard Rundle, Vice President Human Resources Web address: www.mercymiami.com	21	10	339	—	—	—	—	—	—	—
□ **MIAMI CHILDREN'S HOSPITAL**, 3100 S.W. 62nd Avenue, Zip 33155–3009; tel. 305/666–6511 **A**1 3 5 9 10 12 13 **F**2 6 7 14 16 18 20 21 22 23 24 26 27 28 29 31 32 33 34 37 38 39 41 42 46 47 48 49 50 52 53 55 56 57 58 60 61 62 63 64 65 66 67 69 70 71 72 73 74 75 77 78 81 82 84 87 88 90 93 94 96 99 107 108 **P**1 6 Primary Contact: Thomas M. Rozek, President and Chief Executive Officer Web address: www.mch.com	23	50	252	13210	187	261620	0	289177	129016	2465
MIAMI HEART INSTITUTE AND MEDICAL CENTER See Mount Sinai Medical Center, Miami Beach										
✠ **MIAMI JEWISH HOME AND HOSPITAL FOR AGED**, 5200 N.E. Second Avenue, Zip 33137–2706; tel. 305/751–8626, (Total facility includes 462 beds in nursing home–type unit) **A**1 3 5 10 **F**2 37 42 44 45 52 57 58 60 62 69 70 76 91 92 94 96 108 110 **P**6 Primary Contact: Fred Stock, Chief Operating Officer and Executive Director of Nursing Home COO: Fred Stock, Chief Operating Officer and Executive Director of Nursing Home CFO: Lourdes Boue, Chief Financial Officer CMO: Michael Silverman, M.D., Medical Director CIO: David Wolff, Director Information Technology CHR: Larry McDonald, Director Human Resources Web address: www.mjhha.org	23	10	494	1410	451	—	0	—	—	365

FL

Hospital, Address, Telephone, Approval, Facility, and Physician Codes, Health Care System	Classi-fication Codes		Utilization Data					Expense (thousands) of dollars		
	Control	Service	Staffed Beds	Admissions	Census	Outpatient Visits	Births	Total	Payroll	Personnel

★ American Hospital Association (AHA) membership
□ Joint Commission on Accreditation of Healthcare Organizations (JCAHO) accreditation
○ American Osteopathic Association (AOA) accreditation
△ Commission on Accreditation of Rehabilitation Facilities (CARF) accreditation

	Control	Service	Staffed Beds	Admissions	Census	Outpatient Visits	Births	Total	Payroll	Personnel
✠ **NORTH SHORE MEDICAL CENTER**, 1100 N.W. 95th Street, Zip 33150–2098; tel. 305/835–6000 **A**1 2 9 10 **F**11 12 14 21 25 33 34 36 46 48 49 50 52 55 56 59 60 61 63 65 66 69 70 71 75 76 81 82 84 88 94 96 108 109 **S** TENET Healthcare Corporation, Dallas, TX Primary Contact: Edward D. Banos, Chief Executive Officer COO: Manny Linares, Chief Operating Officer CFO: Jennifer Pittman, Chief Financial Officer CMO: Andrew Nullman, Chief of Staff CIO: Luis Estrada, Director of Multifacility Information Systems Web address: www.northshoremedical.com	33	10	185	11365	181	—	—	—	—	—
□ **PAN AMERICAN HOSPITAL**, 5959 N.W. Seventh Street, Zip 33126–3198; tel. 305/264–1000 **A**1 9 10 **F**1 23 33 37 46 48 51 52 55 60 63 64 66 81 82 88 94 96 108 Primary Contact: Roberto Tejidor, Chief Executive Officer Web address: www.pahnet.org	23	10	146	8430	130	41355	0	64198	28741	717
□ **SELECT SPECIALTY HOSPITAL OF MIAMI**, 955 N.W. 3rd Street, Zip 33128; tel. 305/416–5700, (Nonreporting) **A**1 10 Primary Contact: Dionisio Bencomo, Chief Executive Officer	33	49	40	—	—	—	—	—	—	—
SISTER EMMANUEL HOSPITAL FOR CONTINUING CARE, 3663 South Miami Avenue, 4th Floor, Zip 33133; tel. 305/285–2939, (Nonreporting) **A**10 Primary Contact: Shed Boren, Administrator	33	49	29	—	—	—	—	—	—	—
✠ **SOUTH MIAMI HOSPITAL**, 6200 S.W. 73rd Street, Zip 33143–9990; tel. 786/662–4000 **A**1 2 9 10 **F**2 3 4 9 10 11 12 14 15 17 19 21 22 23 26 27 28 29 30 32 33 35 37 38 39 40 41 45 46 47 48 49 50 51 52 53 55 56 57 58 59 60 61 62 63 64 65 66 68 69 79 80 81 82 83 84 85 88 89 93 94 96 106 108 109 110 **P**6 7 **S** Baptist Health South Florida, Coral Gables, FL Primary Contact: D. Wayne Brackin, Chief Executive Officer CFO: Michael Durr, Controller CMO: George Tershakovec, M.D., President Medical Staff CHR: Mercedes del Rey, Director Human Resources Web address: www.baptisthealth.net	23	10	336	21485	235	—	3930	269863	100577	—
✠ **UNIVERSITY OF MIAMI HOSPITAL AND CLINICS**, 1475 N.W. 12th Avenue, Zip 33136–1002; tel. 305/243–1000 **A**1 2 3 5 9 10 **F**9 10 12 21 22 23 26 27 28 29 30 31 35 37 42 45 46 47 48 52 53 57 58 60 61 62 63 64 65 66 70 73 77 79 80 81 82 85 86 87 88 92 94 95 108 109 110 **P**6 Primary Contact: David L. Stansberry, Administrator CFO: Harry Rohrer, Chief Financial Officer CMO: W Jarrad Goodwin, M.D., Director CIO: Liz Rockowitz, Director Information System CHR: Paul Hudgins, Associate Vice President Human Resources Web address: www.sylvester.org	23	10	40	1336	24	181638	0	120841	36169	678
✠ △ **VETERANS AFFAIRS MEDICAL CENTER**, 1201 N.W. 16th Street, Zip 33125–1624; tel. 305/575–7000, (Total facility includes 120 beds in nursing home–type unit) **A**1 3 5 7 8 **F**1 2 4 7 12 14 15 17 19 21 22 23 26 27 28 29 30 31 32 33 35 36 37 38 39 42 44 45 46 47 48 49 50 51 52 53 55 57 58 60 61 62 63 64 65 66 68 69 70 71 73 75 76 77 78 79 80 81 82 84 85 87 88 92 93 94 96 106 108 109 110 **P**6 **S** Department of Veterans Affairs, Washington, DC Primary Contact: Stephen M. Lucas, FACHE, Director CFO: Manuel Saleta, Service Chief CIO: Susan Ward, Public Affairs Officer Web address: www.va.gov/miami	45	10	347	6535	269	542111	0	285014	169370	2402
○ **WESTCHESTER GENERAL HOSPITAL**, 2500 S.W. 75th Avenue, Zip 33155–9947; tel. 305/264–5252, (Includes SOUTHERN WINDS HOSPITAL, 4225 West 20th Street, Hialeah, Zip 33012–5835; tel. 305/558–9700; Gilda Baldwin, Chief Executive Officer) **A**9 10 11 12 13 **F**12 21 26 27 33 44 55 60 63 71 73 75 76 81 88 94 Primary Contact: Gilda Baldwin, Chief Executive Officer Web address: www.westchesterhospital.com	33	10	172	5938	143	24105	0	50462	26117	550
MIAMI BEACH—Dade County										
□ △ **MOUNT SINAI MEDICAL CENTER**, 4300 Alton Road, Zip 33140–2800; tel. 305/674–2121, (Includes MIAMI HEART INSTITUTE AND MEDICAL CENTER, 4701 North Meridian Avenue, Miami, Zip 33140–2910; tel. 305/674–3114; Steven D. Sonenreich, Chief Executive Officer) **A**1 2 3 5 7 8 9 10 12 13 **F**5 10 11 12 15 17 19 21 23 26 27 28 33 40 41 45 46 47 48 49 50 52 53 55 56 57 58 59 60 61 62 63 65 66 68 69 70 71 73 74 75 76 79 80 81 82 83 84 85 86 87 88 93 94 95 96 107 108 109 110 Primary Contact: Steven D. Sonenreich, President and Chief Executive Officer Web address: www.msmc.com	23	10	685	25564	428	186789	1684	356026	129995	2602
SOUTH SHORE HOSPITAL AND MEDICAL CENTER, 630 Alton Road, Zip 33139–5502; tel. 305/672–2100, (Nonreporting) **A**9 10 Primary Contact: William Zubkoff, Ph.D., Chief Executive Officer	23	10	155	—	—	—	—	—	—	—
MILTON—Santa Rosa County										
□ **SANTA ROSA MEDICAL CENTER**, 1450 Berryhill Road, Zip 32570–4028, Mailing Address: P.O. Box 648, Zip 32572–0648; tel. 850/626–7762, (Total facility includes 10 beds in nursing home–type unit) (Nonreporting) **A**1 9 10 **S** Health Management Associates, Naples, FL Primary Contact: M. P. Gandy, Jr, Chief Executive Officer	33	10	77	—	—	—	—	—	—	—

FL

Many Facility Codes have changed. Please refer to the AHA Guide Code Chart.
© 2005 AHA Guide

Hospital, Address, Telephone, Approval, Facility, and Physician Codes, Health Care System	Classi-fication Codes		Utilization Data					Expense (thousands) of dollars		
★ American Hospital Association (AHA) membership □ Joint Commission on Accreditation of Healthcare Organizations (JCAHO) accreditation ○ American Osteopathic Association (AOA) accreditation △ Commission on Accreditation of Rehabilitation Facilities (CARF) accreditation	Control	Service	Staffed Beds	Admissions	Census	Outpatient Visits	Births	Total	Payroll	Personnel

MIRAMAR—Broward County

★ **MEMORIAL HOSPITAL MIRAMAR**, 1901 S.W. 172nd Avenue, Zip 33029; tel. 954/538–5000, (Nonreporting) **A**10 **S** Memorial Healthcare System, Hollywood, FL
Primary Contact: C. Kennon Hetlage, Administrator

	23	10	100	—	—	—	—	—	—	—

NAPLES—Collier County

⊞ **CLEVELAND CLINIC HOSPITAL–NAPLES**, 6101 Pine Ridge Road, Zip 34119; tel. 239/348–4468, (Nonreporting) **A**1 9 10 **S** Cleveland Clinic Health System, Cleveland, OH
Primary Contact: Geoffrey D. Moebius, Administrator
Web address: www.clevelandclinic.org/florida/naples/hospital/

	23	10	70	—	—	—	—	⊞	—	—

⊞ △ **NAPLES COMMUNITY HOSPITAL**, 350 Seventh Street North, Zip 34102–4746, Mailing Address: P.O. Box 413029, Zip 34101–3029; tel. 239/436–5000 **A**1 2 7 9 10 **F**2 6 9 11 14 15 17 19 21 22 23 26 27 28 33 37 39 41 42 44 45 46 47 48 52 53 55 56 57 58 59 60 61 62 63 64 65 66 68 71 73 75 79 81 82 84 85 88 93 94 95 96 106 107 108 109 110 **P**8
Primary Contact: Edward A. Morton, Chief Executive Officer
COO: Allen Weiss, President
CFO: James A. Warnken, Executive Vice President and Chief Financial Officer
CMO: Perry Gotsis, M.D., Executive Vice President and Medical Director
CIO: Susan Wolff, Chief Information Officer
CHR: Brian Settle, Vice President Human Resources
Web address: www.nchmd.org

	23	10	548	32680	407	124078	3818	323519	129497	3003

WILLOUGH HEALTHCARE SYSTEM, 9001 Tamiami Trail East, Zip 34113–3316; tel. 239/775–4500, (Nonreporting) **A**10
Primary Contact: James E. O'Shea, Administrator

	33	22	80	—	—	—	—	—	—	—

NEW PORT RICHEY—Pasco County

⊞ **COMMUNITY HOSPITAL**, 5637 Marine Parkway, Zip 34652–4331, Mailing Address: P.O. Box 996, Zip 34656–0996; tel. 727/848–1733, (Nonreporting) **A**1 5 9 10 **S** HCA, Nashville, TN
Primary Contact: Kathryn Gillette, Chief Executive Officer
CFO: Glenn Romig, Chief Financial Officer
CIO: Kirk Hendrick, Director
CHR: Jay Kuhns, Director Human Resources
Web address: www.communityhospitalnpr.com

	33	10	414	—	—	—	—	—	—	—

⊞ △ **MORTON PLANT NORTH BAY HOSPITAL**, 6600 Madison Street, Zip 34652–1900; tel. 727/842–8468, (Nonreporting) **A**1 7 9 10 **S** Morton Plant Mease Health Care, Dunedin, FL
Primary Contact: William M. Jennings, Administrator and Chief Operating Officer
CFO: Linda Wolfe, Finance Manager

	23	10	122	—	—	—	—	—	—	—

NEW SMYRNA BEACH—Volusia County

⊞ **BERT FISH MEDICAL CENTER**, 401 Palmetto Street, Zip 32168–7399; tel. 386/424–5000 **A**1 10 **F**2 9 10 12 15 21 22 23 26 27 28 29 30 33 35 37 39 44 46 48 49 50 51 52 55 58 60 61 62 63 64 65 66 69 73 81 82 84 85 87 88 92 94 96 102 106 108 109 110
Primary Contact: Robert B. Williams, Chief Executive Officer
COO: Carole H. Patterson, R.N., Chief Nursing Officer
CFO: Tim Drury, Chief Financial Officer
CIO: Rosemarie Goodrich, Director, Information Services
CHR: Carol Shields, Director Human Resources
Web address: www.bertfish.com

	16	10	116	5076	61	156851	0	62950	21559	575

NICEVILLE—Okaloosa County

⊞ **TWIN CITIES HOSPITAL**, 2190 Highway 85 North, Zip 32578–1045; tel. 850/678–4131, (Nonreporting) **A**1 9 10 **S** HCA, Nashville, TN
Primary Contact: David Whalen, Chief Executive Officer
CFO: Mark Day, Chief Financial Officer
CHR: Joan Hudson, Director Human Resources
Web address: www.tchealthcare.com

	33	10	65	—	—	—	—	⊞	—	—

NORTH MIAMI—Dade County

□ △ **ST. CATHERINE'S REHABILITATION HOSPITAL**, 1050 N.E. 125th Street, Zip 33161–5881; tel. 305/357–1735, (Nonreporting) **A**1 7 10
Primary Contact: Ginger Irving, Administrator
Web address: www.catholichealthservices.org

	21	46	272	—	—	—	—	□	—	—

NORTH MIAMI BEACH—Dade County

⊞ **PARKWAY REGIONAL MEDICAL CENTER**, 160 N.W. 170th Street, Zip 33169–5576; tel. 305/651–1100 **A**1 9 10 13 **F**2 6 11 12 14 15 17 21 22 28 29 33 35 36 37 39 40 45 46 48 49 52 53 55 56 57 58 59 60 61 62 63 64 65 66 68 69 70 71 72 81 82 84 85 88 93 94 96 107 108 110 **S** TENET Healthcare Corporation, Dallas, TX
Primary Contact: John E. Walker, FACHE, Chief Executive Officer
COO: Walt Mickens, Chief Operating Officer
CMO: Scott English, M.D., Chief Medical Officer
CIO: Greggory Sanders, Information Systems Director
Web address: www.parkwayregionalmedctr.com

	33	10	347	14126	205	74196	1908	102873	41022	935

FL

Hospital, Address, Telephone, Approval, Facility, and Physician Codes, Health Care System	Classi-fication Codes		Utilization Data					Expense (thousands) of dollars		
★ American Hospital Association (AHA) membership □ Joint Commission on Accreditation of Healthcare Organizations (JCAHO) accreditation ○ American Osteopathic Association (AOA) accreditation △ Commission on Accreditation of Rehabilitation Facilities (CARF) accreditation	Control	Service	Staffed Beds	Admissions	Census	Outpatient Visits	Births	Total	Payroll	Personnel

OCALA—Marion County

⊞ **MUNROE REGIONAL MEDICAL CENTER**, 131 S.W. 15th Street,
Zip 34474–4059, Mailing Address: P.O. Box 6000, Zip 34478–6000;
tel. 352/351–7200 **A**1 5 9 10 **F**9 10 11 12 14 17 19 21 22 23 24 26 27 28
29 33 40 41 44 46 47 48 49 50 51 52 53 55 57 58 59 60 62 63 64 65 66
69 70 81 82 88 93 94 95 107 108 109 **P**8
Primary Contact: Dyer T. Michell, President
COO: Paul Clark, President and Chief Executive Officer
CFO: Richard Mutarelli, Chief Financial Officer
CIO: Carl Candullo, Chief Information Officer
CHR: Katherine Miller, Vice President Human Resources
Web address: www.munroeregional.com

| | 23 | 10 | 408 | 22472 | 277 | 132912 | 2006 | 206656 | 91811 | 2073 |

⊞ **OCALA REGIONAL MEDICAL CENTER**, 1431 S.W. First Avenue,
Zip 34474–4058, Mailing Address: P.O. Box 2200, Zip 34478–2200;
tel. 352/401–1000, (Nonreporting) **A**1 2 9 10 **S** HCA, Nashville, TN
Primary Contact: James B. Wood, President and Chief Executive Officer
CFO: Jeffrey D. Baiocco, Chief Financial Officer
CIO: Taylor Dickerson, Director Information Services
CHR: Wayne Nielsen, Director Human Resources
Web address: www.ocalaregional.com

| | 33 | 10 | 270 | — | — | — | — | — | — | — |

OCOEE—Orange County

⊞ **HEALTH CENTRAL**, 10000 West Colonial Drive, Zip 34761–3499;
tel. 407/296–1000, (Total facility includes 228 beds in nursing home–type unit)
A1 9 10 **F**2 6 9 11 12 14 15 21 22 23 26 27 28 39 37 40 41 42 45 46
48 49 50 52 55 57 58 59 60 61 62 63 64 65 66 73 75 81 82 84 85 87 88
92 93 94 96 106 107 108 109 110 **P**6 8
Primary Contact: Richard M. Irwin, Jr, President and Chief Executive Officer
CFO: Alan L. Crowell, Senior Vice President and Chief Financial Officer
CMO: Shahid Usmani, M.D., Chief of Staff
CIO: Robert B. Williams
CHR: John Sullivan, Vice President Human Resources
Web address: www.health–central.org

| | 16 | 10 | 399 | 11021 | 327 | 117636 | 1369 | 108535 | 51568 | 1190 |

OKEECHOBEE—Okeechobee County

⊞ **RAULERSON HOSPITAL**, 1796 Highway 441 North, Zip 34972–1918, Mailing
Address: P.O. Box 1307, Zip 34973–1307; tel. 863/763–2151, (Nonreporting)
A1 9 10 20 **S** HCA, Nashville, TN
Primary Contact: Robert H. Lee, President
CFO: Ricardo Pavon, Chief Financial Officer
CIO: Doug Schneider, Director Information Systems
CHR: Janis Stevens, Director Human Resources
Web address: www.raulersonhospital.com

| | 33 | 10 | 101 | — | — | — | — | — | — | — |

ORANGE CITY—Volusia County

⊞ **FLORIDA HOSPITAL FISH MEMORIAL**, 1055 Saxon Boulevard,
Zip 32763–8468; tel. 386/917–5000 **A**1 9 10 **F**2 9 12 15 21 22 23 27 28 29
33 37 46 48 51 52 53 55 57 58 61 62 63 64 66 69 79 81 82 84 85 86 87
88 94 96 107 108 109 110 **P**8 **S** Adventist Health System Sunbelt Health Care
Corporation, Winter Park, FL
Primary Contact: Joe Johnson, President and Chief Executive Officer
CFO: Lawrence E. Schalk, Senior Vice President and Chief Financial Officer
CMO: Paul T. Smith, M.D., Chief of Staff
CIO: Trish Stebbins, Director of Management Information Systems
CHR: Bonne Barrows, Director
Web address: www.fhfishmemorial.org

| | 21 | 10 | 139 | 8241 | 110 | 118027 | 0 | 84277 | 30616 | 794 |

ORANGE PARK—Clay County

⊞ **ORANGE PARK MEDICAL CENTER**, 2001 Kingsley Avenue, Zip 32073–5156;
tel. 904/276–8500 **A**1 9 10 **F**2 9 11 12 15 17 21 22 23 26 27 28 29 33 37
42 44 47 48 49 52 53 55 56 57 58 59 60 61 62 63 64 65 66 68 69 71 73
74 75 76 77 81 82 84 85 86 88 94 96 107 108 109 110 **S** HCA, Nashville, TN
Primary Contact: Robert M. Krieger, Chief Executive Officer
COO: Marsha A. Easley, Chief Operating Officer
CFO: Debra Noyes, Chief Financial Officer
CMO: Michel Dagher, M.D., Chief Medical Officer
CIO: Mike Whiddon, Director Information Systems
CHR: Paula Shields, Director Human Resources
Web address: www.opmedical.com

| | 33 | 10 | 230 | 13290 | 170 | 116830 | 1860 | 104058 | 40785 | 728 |

FL

Many Facility Codes have changed. Please refer to the AHA Guide Code Chart. © 2005 AHA Guide

Hospital, Address, Telephone, Approval, Facility, and Physician Codes, Health Care System	Classi-fication Codes		Utilization Data					Expense (thousands) of dollars		
★ American Hospital Association (AHA) membership □ Joint Commission on Accreditation of Healthcare Organizations (JCAHO) accreditation ○ American Osteopathic Association (AOA) accreditation △ Commission on Accreditation of Rehabilitation Facilities (CARF) accreditation	Control	Service	Staffed Beds	Admissions	Census	Outpatient Visits	Births	Total	Payroll	Personnel

ORLANDO—Orange County

★ ○ △ **FLORIDA HOSPITAL**, 601 East Rollins Street, Zip 32803–1489; tel. 407/303–6611, (Includes FLORIDA HOSPITAL CELEBRATION HEALTH, 400 Clebration Place, Celebration, Zip 34747; tel. 407/303–4000; David P. Banks, Administrator; FLORIDA HOSPITAL EAST ORLANDO, 7727 Lake Underhill Drive, Zip 32822; tel. 407/277–8110; Ed Noseworthy, Administrator; FLORIDA HOSPITAL KISSIMMEE, 2450 North Orange Blossom Trai, Kissimmee, Zip 34741; tel. 407/846–4343; William Haupt, Administrator; FLORIDA HOSPITAL–ALTAMONTE, 601 East Altamonte Drive, Altamonte Springs, Zip 32701; tel. 407/830–4321; FLORIDA HOSPITAL–APOPKA, 201 North Park Avenue, Apopka, Zip 32703; tel. 407/889–2566; Verbalee Neilsen Swanson, Administrator; WINTER PARK MEMORIAL HOSPITAL, 200 North Lakemont Avenue, Winter Park, Zip 32792–3273; tel. 407/646–7000; Kenneth Bradley, Administrator) **A**1 2 3 5 7 9 10 11 **F**2 6 7 9 10 11 12 14 15 16 17 19 21 22 23 24 25 26 27 28 29 30 31 32 33 35 37 38 39 40 41 42 43 44 46 47 48 49 50 51 52 53 55 56 57 58 59 60 61 62 63 64 65 66 67 68 69 70 71 72 73 74 75 76 77 79 80 81 82 84 85 86 87 88 92 93 94 95 96 98 99 101 104 106 107 108 109 110 **P**1 **S** Adventist Health System Sunbelt Health Care Corporation, Winter Park, FL
Primary Contact: Donald L. Jernigan, Ph.D., President
CFO: J Brian Paradis, Chief Financial Officer
CMO: Monica Reed, M.D., Senior Medical Officer
CHR: Richard M. Tibbits, Chief People Officer
Web address: www.flhosp.org | 23 | 10 | 1758 | 103633 | 1354 | 798362 | 8470 | 1303178 | 523226 | 12642 |

★ △ **ORLANDO REGIONAL MEDICAL CENTER**, 1414 Kuhl Avenue, Zip 32806–2093; tel. 407/841–5111, (Includes ARNOLD PALMER HOSPITAL FOR CHILDREN AND WOMEN; M. D. ANDERSON CANCER CENTER ; ORLANDO REGIONAL–LUCERNE, 818 Main Lane, Zip 32801–3727; tel. 407/649–6111; Dilys Jagger, Executive Director) **A**1 2 3 5 7 8 9 10 **F**2 3 4 6 11 12 13 14 15 16 17 18 19 20 21 23 24 26 28 31 33 34 37 38 39 40 41 43 44 46 47 48 49 50 51 52 53 55 56 57 58 59 60 61 62 63 64 65 66 67 68 69 71 72 73 74 75 76 77 78 79 80 81 84 85 86 87 88 90 92 93 94 95 96 98 107 108 109 110 **S** Orlando Regional Healthcare, Orlando, FL
Primary Contact: Sherrie Sitarik, Executive Vice President
CFO: Paul Goldstein, Vice President Finance and Chief Financial Officer
CMO: Timothy Bullard, M.D., Chief of Staff
CIO: Rick Schooler, Vice President and Chief Information Officer
CHR: Nancy Dinon, Chief Human Resources
Web address: www.orhs.org | 23 | 10 | 1354 | 76228 | 1012 | 789882 | 12397 | — | — | 10171 |

□ **SELECT SPECIALTY HOSPITAL OF ORLANDO**, 791 East Rollins Street, Zip 32803; tel. 407/303–1766, (Nonreporting) **A**1 10
Primary Contact: Rose O'Neil, Chief Executive Officer | 33 | 49 | 35 | — | — | — | — | — | — | — |

ORMOND BEACH—Volusia County

★ △ **FLORIDA HOSPITAL–ORMOND MEMORIAL**, 875 Sterthaus Avenue, Zip 32174–5197; tel. 386/676–6000, (Includes FLORIDA HOSPITAL–OCEANSIDE, 264 South Atlantic Avenue, Zip 32176–8192; tel. 386/672–4161; Daryl Tol, Administrator and Chief Operating Officer) **A**1 2 7 9 10 12 **F**9 11 12 14 15 17 19 21 22 23 26 27 28 29 33 37 40 41 42 44 46 47 48 49 50 52 55 57 58 59 60 61 62 63 65 66 68 69 70 79 80 81 82 84 86 88 94 95 96 106 107 108 109 110 **P**7 **S** Adventist Health System Sunbelt Health Care Corporation, Winter Park, FL
Primary Contact: Michael V. Gentry, President
COO: Daryl Tol, Chief Operating Officer
CFO: Debora Thomas, Chief Financial Officer
CHR: Jeff Jones, Director Human Resources
Web address: www.memorial–health.com | 21 | 10 | 324 | 13032 | 180 | 108531 | 1090 | 138905 | 42359 | 1024 |

PALATKA—Putnam County

★ **PUTNAM COMMUNITY MEDICAL CENTER**, Highway 20 West, Zip 32177–8118, Mailing Address: P.O. Box 778, Zip 32178–0778; tel. 386/328–5711, (Total facility includes 10 beds in nursing home–type unit) **A**1 9 10 19 20 **F**2 9 11 15 21 22 26 27 28 29 33 37 38 39 45 46 47 48 49 52 53 55 57 58 59 60 61 62 63 64 65 66 69 70 81 82 84 85 87 88 92 93 96 108 **S** LifePoint Hospitals, Inc., Brentwood, TN
Primary Contact: Bruce A. Baldwin, Chief Executive Officer
CFO: James McGonnell, Chief Financial Officer
Web address: www.pcmcfl.com | 33 | 10 | 141 | 6927 | 91 | 80803 | 548 | — | — | 413 |

PALM BEACH GARDENS—Palm Beach County

★ **PALM BEACH GARDENS MEDICAL CENTER**, 3360 Burns Road, Zip 33410–4304; tel. 561/622–1411 **A**1 9 10 **F**2 9 11 12 14 21 28 33 35 37 44 48 49 52 54 55 56 57 58 59 62 63 65 66 69 73 81 82 84 87 88 94 96 109 **S** TENET Healthcare Corporation, Dallas, TX
Primary Contact: Mary Jo Gregory, Chief Executive Officer
CFO: Judi Stimson–Rusin, Chief Financial Officer
CIO: Kevin Smith, Director Information Systems
Web address: www.pbgmc.com | 33 | 10 | 204 | 11366 | 138 | — | — | — | — | — |

FL

Hospital, Address, Telephone, Approval, Facility, and Physician Codes, Health Care System	Classi-fication Codes		Utilization Data					Expense (thousands) of dollars		
★ American Hospital Association (AHA) membership □ Joint Commission on Accreditation of Healthcare Organizations (JCAHO) accreditation ○ American Osteopathic Association (AOA) accreditation △ Commission on Accreditation of Rehabilitation Facilities (CARF) accreditation	Control	Service	Staffed Beds	Admissions	Census	Outpatient Visits	Births	Total	Payroll	Personnel

PALM COAST—Flagler County

☒ **FLORIDA HOSPITAL–FLAGLER**, 60 Memorial Medical Parkway, Zip 32164; tel. 386/586–2000 **A**1 9 10 19 **F**9 12 15 21 22 23 26 27 28 29 33 36 37 41 42 44 46 47 48 50 51 52 55 58 60 61 62 63 65 66 69 70 79 80 81 82 84 88 94 95 96 106 107 108 109 110 **S** Adventist Health System Sunbelt Health Care Corporation, Winter Park, FL
Primary Contact: Daryl Tol, Administrator
CFO: Debbie Thomas, Vice President and Chief Financial Officer
Web address: www.fhmd.com
| | 21 | 10 | 81 | 5163 | 55 | 59944 | 0 | 54268 | 17961 | 426 |

PANAMA CITY—Bay County

☒ **BAY MEDICAL CENTER**, 615 North Bonita Avenue, Zip 32401–3600, Mailing Address: P.O. Box 59515, Zip 32402–2515; tel. 850/769–1511 **A**1 2 9 10 **F**2 6 9 11 12 14 15 17 19 21 22 23 26 27 28 29 33 37 41 42 45 46 48 49 50 52 53 55 57 58 59 60 61 62 63 66 69 71 72 73 74 75 77 78 81 82 84 85 87 88 93 94 95 96 98 107 108 109 110
Primary Contact: Steven M. Johnson, President and Chief Executive Officer
COO: Mary J. Montgomery, Chief Operating Officer
CFO: Daniel R. Morgan, Chief Financial Officer
CMO: Gregory Morrow, President Medical Staff
CIO: Tom Bialorvcki, Chief Information Officer
CHR: Donna Vincent, Vice President Corporate Services
Web address: www.baymedical.org
| | 16 | 10 | 364 | 17933 | 232 | 170789 | 762 | 176661 | 67727 | 1606 |

☒ **GULF COAST MEDICAL CENTER**, 449 West 23rd Street, Zip 32405–4593, Mailing Address: P.O. Box 15309, Zip 32406–5309; tel. 850/769–8341 **A**1 2 9 10 **F**2 10 11 12 15 21 22 23 26 27 28 32 33 40 42 44 46 47 48 49 52 53 55 57 58 59 60 61 62 63 64 65 66 69 81 82 83 84 85 86 87 88 94 95 96 106 107 108 109 110 **P**5 **S** HCA, Nashville, TN
Primary Contact: Todd Gallati, Chief Executive Officer
COO: Mark Robinson, Chief Operating Officer
CFO: Wesley Fountain, Chief Financial Officer
CHR: Wanda Salley, Administrative Director Human Resources
Web address: www.egulfcoastmedical.com
| | 33 | 10 | 176 | 10534 | 115 | 119744 | 2098 | 82671 | 29417 | 585 |

☒ △ **HEALTHSOUTH EMERALD COAST REHABILITATION HOSPITAL**, 1847 Florida Avenue, Zip 32405–4640; tel. 850/914–8600 **A**1 7 10 **F**21 28 35 37 39 46 53 58 60 65 68 69 93 94 95 96 110 **S** HEALTHSOUTH Corporation, Birmingham, AL
Primary Contact: Tony N. Bennett, Administrator
CFO: Angela Whitehurst, Finance Manager
CMO: Michael Hennigan, M.D., Medical Director
Web address: www.healthsouth.com
| | 33 | 46 | 65 | 1361 | 54 | 19073 | 0 | 13101 | 6795 | 217 |

SELECT SPECIALTY HOSPITAL OF PANAMA CITY, 615 North Bonita Avenue, 3rd Floor, Zip 32401; tel. 850/767–3180, (Nonreporting) **A**10
Primary Contact: Phyllis Johnson, Chief Executive Officer
| | 33 | 49 | 30 | — | — | — | — | — | — | — |

PEMBROKE PINES—Broward County

☒ **MEMORIAL HOSPITAL PEMBROKE**, 7800 Sheridan Street, Zip 33024–2536; tel. 954/962–9650 **A**1 9 10 **F**2 5 9 12 14 21 22 26 27 28 33 36 37 38 39 40 44 45 46 48 49 52 53 55 57 58 60 61 62 63 64 65 66 69 81 82 88 92 93 94 107 108 110 **P**5 **S** Memorial Healthcare System, Hollywood, FL
Primary Contact: Martha Garcia, Administrator
CFO: Joseph Stuczynski, Assistant Administrator Finance and Support
CMO: Stanley Marks, M.D., Chief Medical Officer
CIO: Robert Reiss, Chief Information Officer
CHR: Margie Vargas, Director Human Resources
Web address: www.mhs–net.com
| | 16 | 10 | 149 | 6687 | 78 | 131878 | 0 | 79368 | 36992 | 616 |

☒ **MEMORIAL HOSPITAL WEST**, 703 North Flamingo Road, Zip 33028–1014; tel. 954/436–5000 **A**1 9 10 **F**2 11 12 14 15 17 21 22 23 26 27 28 33 37 41 44 46 47 48 49 50 52 53 55 56 57 58 59 61 62 63 64 66 69 79 81 82 84 87 88 92 94 95 96 108 109 110 **S** Memorial Healthcare System, Hollywood, FL
Primary Contact: Zeff Ross, Administrator
COO: Sue E. Bradford, R.N., Chief Operating Officer
CFO: Walter Bussell, Chief Financial Officer
CMO: Miguel Venereo, M.D., Director Medical Staff
CIO: Robert Reese, Chief Information Officer
CHR: Christopher Perry, Director Human Resources
Web address: www.mhs.net
| | 16 | 10 | 237 | 21399 | 237 | 259359 | 5403 | 190313 | 81687 | 1672 |

PENSACOLA—Escambia County

☒ **BAPTIST HOSPITAL**, 1000 West Moreno, Zip 32501–2393, Mailing Address: P.O. Box 17500, Zip 32522–7500; tel. 850/469–2313, (Total facility includes 57 beds in nursing home–type unit) **A**1 2 9 10 **F**2 6 9 10 11 12 14 15 17 19 21 22 23 26 27 28 29 30 31 33 34 35 36 37 38 39 40 42 44 46 47 48 49 50 51 52 53 55 57 58 59 60 61 62 63 64 65 66 69 71 72 73 74 75 76 77 78 79 80 81 82 84 85 86 87 88 89 92 93 94 98 106 107 108 109 110 **S** Baptist Health Care Corporation, Pensacola, FL
Primary Contact: Robert Murphy, R.N., JD, Administrator
CFO: Joseph Felkner, Chief Financial Officer and Senior Vice President Finance
CMO: Craig Miller, M.D., Senior Vice President Medical Affairs
CHR: Celeste Norris, Vice President Human Resources
Web address: www.ebaptisthealthcare.org
| | 23 | 10 | 492 | 15711 | 241 | 346052 | 1031 | 181083 | 69256 | 1674 |

FL

Hospital, Address, Telephone, Approval, Facility, and Physician Codes, Health Care System	Classi-fication Codes		Utilization Data					Expense (thousands) of dollars		
★ American Hospital Association (AHA) membership □ Joint Commission on Accreditation of Healthcare Organizations (JCAHO) accreditation ○ American Osteopathic Association (AOA) accreditation △ Commission on Accreditation of Rehabilitation Facilities (CARF) accreditation	Control	Service	Staffed Beds	Admissions	Census	Outpatient Visits	Births	Total	Payroll	Personnel

✠ **NAVAL HOSPITAL**, 6000 West Highway 98, Zip 32512–0003; tel. 850/505–6413, (Nonreporting) **A**1 3 5 **S** Bureau of Medicine and Surgery, Department of the Navy, Washington, DC Primary Contact: Captain Matthew L. Nathan, Commanding Officer Web address: www.psa10.med.navy.mil REHABILITATION INSTITUTE OF WEST FLORIDA See West Florida Hospital	43	10	63	—	—	—	—	—	—	—
✠ **SACRED HEART HOSPITAL OF PENSACOLA**, (Formerly Sacred Heart Health System), 5151 North Ninth Avenue, Zip 32504–8795, Mailing Address: P.O. Box 2700, Zip 32513–2700; tel. 850/416–7000 **A**1 2 3 5 9 10 **F**2 6 9 11 12 14 15 17 19 21 22 23 24 26 27 28 29 32 33 34 35 37 38 39 40 41 42 44 46 47 48 51 52 55 56 57 58 59 60 61 62 63 64 65 66 67 69 70 79 80 81 82 84 86 87 88 94 96 106 107 108 109 110 **P**7 **S** Ascension Health, Saint Louis, MO Primary Contact: William R. McLaughlin, President CFO: Robert P. Granger, Senior Vice President and Chief Financial Officer CMO: Paul T. Baroco, Senior Vice President, Medical Affairs CIO: Bill Winter, Director Information Technology CHR: Sue Byrd, Vice President Human Resources Web address: www.sacred–heart.org	21	10	449	24872	345	304822	3560	242232	83195	2374
✠ △ **WEST FLORIDA HOSPITAL**, 8383 North Davis Highway, Zip 32514–6088; tel. 850/494–4000, (Includes REHABILITATION INSTITUTE OF WEST FLORIDA, tel. 850/494–6000; THE PAVILION, tel. 904/494–5000) **A**1 7 9 10 **F**2 5 7 11 12 14 15 17 19 21 22 23 26 27 28 29 33 34 36 37 38 39 40 41 42 44 45 46 47 48 49 52 53 55 57 58 59 60 61 62 63 64 65 68 69 70 71 73 74 75 76 81 82 83 84 85 87 88 93 94 95 96 106 108 109 110 **P**6 **S** HCA, Nashville, TN Primary Contact: Dennis A. Taylor, Chief Executive Officer COO: Robert Peterson, Chief Operating Officer CFO: Randy Butler, Chief Financial Officer CMO: Louis Perillo, M.D., Senior Vice President Medical Affairs CIO: Jeff Amerson, Director Information System CHR: Karen Oliver, Vice President Human Resources Web address: www.westfloridahospital.com	33	10	339	10885	176	179788	471	156387	49168	1209
PERRY—Taylor County										
DOCTOR'S MEMORIAL HOSPITAL, 333 North Byron Butler Parkway, Zip 32347–2104; tel. 850/584–0800, (Nonreporting) **A**9 10 20 Primary Contact: John T. Ray, Chief Executive Officer Web address: www.doctorsmemorial.com	23	10	48	—	—	—	—	—	—	—
PLANT CITY—Hillsborough County										
✠ **SOUTH FLORIDA BAPTIST HOSPITAL**, 301 North Alexander Street, Zip 33563–9058, Mailing Address: Drawer H, Zip 33564–9058; tel. 813/757–1200, (Nonreporting) **A**1 9 10 **S** Catholic Health East, Newtown Square, PA Primary Contact: William G. Ulbricht, Chief Operating Officer COO: William G. Ulbricht, Chief Operating Officer CFO: Cathy Yoder, Chief Financial Officer CMO: Mark Vaaler, M.D., Chief Medical Officer CHR: Juanita Radford, Team Resource Coordinator Web address: www.sjbhealth.org	23	10	147	—	—	—	—	—	—	—
PLANTATION—Broward County										
✠ **PLANTATION GENERAL HOSPITAL**, 401 N.W. 42nd Avenue, Zip 33317–2882; tel. 954/587–5010, (Nonreporting) **A**1 9 10 **S** HCA, Nashville, TN Primary Contact: Anthony M. Degina, Jr, Chief Executive Officer COO: Barbara Simmons, R.N., Chief Operating Officer CFO: David Hughes, Chief Financial Officer CIO: MaryEllen Lee, Director Management Information Systems CHR: Ben Bittner, Director Human Resources Web address: www.plantationgeneral.com	33	10	264	—	—	—	—	—	—	—
✠ **WESTSIDE REGIONAL MEDICAL CENTER**, 8201 West Broward Boulevard, Zip 33324–9937; tel. 954/473–6600 **A**1 9 10 **F**2 9 12 14 15 17 19 21 22 23 27 28 29 32 33 37 44 45 46 47 48 49 50 52 53 55 57 58 61 62 63 64 65 66 69 81 82 84 85 87 88 93 94 96 106 108 **S** HCA, Nashville, TN Primary Contact: Earl H. Denning, Chief Executive Officer COO: Scott A. Cihak, Chief Operating Officer CFO: Michael Houston, Chief Financial Officer CMO: Joel Shulman, M.D., Chief of Staff CIO: Trish Campbell, Director Management Information Systems CHR: Amy Paces, Director Human Resources Web address: www.westsideregional.com	33	10	224	15253	178	80590	0	126353	—	696
POMPANO BEACH—Broward County										
CORAL SPRINGS MEDICAL CENTER See Coral Springs										

FL

Hospital, Address, Telephone, Approval, Facility, and Physician Codes, Health Care System	Classi-fication Codes		Utilization Data					Expense (thousands) of dollars		
★ American Hospital Association (AHA) membership □ Joint Commission on Accreditation of Healthcare Organizations (JCAHO) accreditation ○ American Osteopathic Association (AOA) accreditation △ Commission on Accreditation of Rehabilitation Facilities (CARF) accreditation	Control	Service	Staffed Beds	Admissions	Census	Outpatient Visits	Births	Total	Payroll	Personnel

⊠ △ **NORTH BROWARD MEDICAL CENTER**, 201 Sample Road, Zip 33064–3502; tel. 954/941–8300 **A**1 2 7 9 10 **F**2 5 9 10 12 14 21 23 26 27 28 29 30 33 34 36 37 38 39 40 41 44 46 48 49 50 52 53 55 57 58 60 61 62 63 65 66 68 69 81 82 84 86 87 88 93 94 96 106 108 **S** North Broward Hospital District, Fort Lauderdale, FL Primary Contact: Pauline Grant, Chief Executive Officer COO: Kevin Fusco, Chief Operating Officer CFO: Louis Fung Sang, Chief Financial Officer CMO: Gary S. Lehr, M.D., Chief of Staff CIO: Joe Wagner, Vice President Chief Information Officer CHR: Grace King, Regional Director Web address: www.nbhd.org	16	10	337	15289	212	151939	0	153068	61941	1192
PORT CHARLOTTE—Charlotte County										
⊠ △ **FAWCETT MEMORIAL HOSPITAL**, 21298 Olean Boulevard, Zip 33952–6765, Mailing Address: P.O. Box 494960, Punta Gorda, Zip 33949–4960; tel. 941/629–1181, (Nonreporting) **A**1 7 9 10 **S** HCA, Nashville, TN Primary Contact: Thomas J. Rice, President and Chief Executive Officer COO: R Trent Lind, Associate Administrator CFO: James P. Burns, Vice President and Chief Financial Officer CHR: Patricia Tobin, Administrative Director, Human Resources Web address: www.fawcetthospital.com	33	10	200	—	—	—	—	—	—	—
⊠ **PEACE RIVER REGIONAL MEDICAL CENTER**, (Formerly Peace River Regional Medical Center), 2500 Harbor Boulevard, Zip 33952–5396; tel. 941/766–4122, (Total facility includes 124 beds in nursing home–type unit) (Nonreporting) **A**1 5 9 10 **S** Health Management Associates, Naples, FL Primary Contact: David McCormack, Chief Executive Officer CIO: Ted Bailey, Vice President Information Systems Web address: www.bssjconnections.com	21	10	314	—	—	—	—	—	—	—
PORT SAINT JOE—Gulf County										
GULF PINES HOSPITAL, 102 20th Street, Zip 32456–2356, Mailing Address: P.O. Box 70, Zip 32456–0070; tel. 850/227–1121, (Nonreporting) **A**9 10 Primary Contact: Hubert Steeley, Administrator	33	10	30	—	—	—	—	—	—	—
PORT ST. LUCIE—St. Lucie County										
□ **SAVANNAS HOSPITAL**, 2550 S.E. Walton Road, Zip 34952–7197; tel. 772/335–0400 **A**1 10 **F**3 71 72 73 74 75 76 78 **S** Liberty Management Group, Inc., Ramsey, NJ Primary Contact: Maria Nixon, Executive Director	33	22	75	2329	44	—	0	—	—	—
⊠ **ST. LUCIE MEDICAL CENTER**, 1800 S.E. Tiffany Avenue, Zip 34952–7580; tel. 772/335–4000 **A**1 2 9 10 **F**2 12 16 21 22 23 28 29 33 40 41 46 48 53 55 56 57 58 59 60 61 62 63 64 69 73 81 82 84 85 88 92 93 95 96 108 110 **S** HCA, Nashville, TN Primary Contact: Gary Cantrell, President and Chief Executive Officer CFO: Steve Barnhill, Chief Financial Officer Web address: www.stluciemed.com	33	10	194	11342	140	62375	915	91574	33480	555
PUNTA GORDA—Charlotte County										
□ **CHARLOTTE REGIONAL MEDICAL CENTER**, 809 East Marion Avenue, Zip 33950–3898, Mailing Address: P.O. Box 51–1328, Zip 33951–1328; tel. 941/639–3131 **A**1 9 10 **F**2 3 4 9 12 14 15 17 19 21 22 26 28 29 31 32 33 39 41 44 45 46 47 48 49 51 52 53 55 57 58 60 61 62 63 65 66 69 70 71 73 74 75 76 78 81 82 84 85 86 88 92 93 94 95 96 108 110 **S** Health Management Associates, Naples, FL Primary Contact: Joshua S. Putter, Chief Executive Officer Web address: www.charlotteregional.com	33	10	208	9025	128	54514	0	—	—	864
QUINCY—Gadsden County										
GADSDEN COMMUNITY HOSPITAL, 23186 Blue Star Highway, Zip 32351–2857, Mailing Address: P.O. Box 1979, Zip 32353–1979; tel. 850/875–1100, (Nonreporting) **A**10 18 **S** DasSee Community Health System, Quincy, FL Primary Contact: Alma Jones, Administrator	33	10	25	—	—	—	—	—	—	—
ROCKLEDGE—Brevard County										
□ **WUESTHOFF MEDICAL CENTER – ROCKLEDGE**, 110 Longwood Avenue, Zip 32955–2887, Mailing Address: P.O. Box 565002, Mail Stop 1, Zip 32956–5002; tel. 321/636–2211 **A**1 2 9 10 **F**2 9 11 12 14 15 17 19 21 22 23 26 27 28 32 33 37 40 42 44 46 47 48 49 50 52 53 55 56 57 58 59 60 61 62 63 64 65 66 69 71 73 74 75 76 81 82 84 85 87 88 92 93 94 95 96 106 107 108 109 **P**2 7 **S** Wuesthoff Health System, Rockledge, FL Primary Contact: Emil P. Miller, President and Chief Executive Officer Web address: www.wuesthoff.org	23	10	359	13493	170	—	—	—	—	1158
SAFETY HARBOR—Pinellas County										
MEASE COUNTRYSIDE HOSPITAL, 3231 McMullen–Booth Road, Zip 34695–1098, Mailing Address: P.O. 1098, Zip 34695–1098; tel. 727/725–6111, (Nonreporting) **A**9 10 **S** Morton Plant Mease Health Care, Dunedin, FL Primary Contact: James A. Pfeiffer, President and Chief Executive Officer Web address: www.measehospitals.com	23	10	100	—	—	—	—	—	—	—

Many Facility Codes have changed. Please refer to the AHA Guide Code Chart.

© 2005 AHA Guide

Hospital, Address, Telephone, Approval, Facility, and Physician Codes, Health Care System	Classi-fication Codes		Utilization Data					Expense (thousands) of dollars		
	Control	Service	Staffed Beds	Admissions	Census	Outpatient Visits	Births	Total	Payroll	Personnel

★ American Hospital Association (AHA) membership
□ Joint Commission on Accreditation of Healthcare Organizations (JCAHO) accreditation
○ American Osteopathic Association (AOA) accreditation
△ Commission on Accreditation of Rehabilitation Facilities (CARF) accreditation

SAINT AUGUSTINE—St. Johns County

□ **FLAGLER HOSPITAL**, 400 Health Park Boulevard, Zip 32086–5779;
tel. 904/829–5155 **A**1 2 9 10 **F**2 9 11 12 14 15 17 19 21 22 23 27 28 33 37 39 40 42 46 51 52 55 57 58 59 60 61 62 63 64 66 69 70 71 76 81 82 84 85 87 88 92 93 94 108 109
Primary Contact: Joseph S. Gordy, President
Web address: www.flaglerhospital.com

| | 23 | 10 | 300 | 14650 | 197 | 140917 | 1037 | 130986 | 51216 | 1248 |

SAINT CLOUD—Lowndes County

ST. CLOUD HOSPITAL, 2906 17th Street, Zip 34769–6099;
tel. 407/892–2135, (Nonreporting) **S** Orlando Regional Healthcare, Orlando, FL
Primary Contact: Mark Aanonson, Executive Director

| | 23 | 10 | 68 | — | — | — | — | — | — | — |

SAINT PETERSBURG—Pinellas County

□ **ALL CHILDREN'S HOSPITAL**, 801 Sixth Street South, Zip 33701–4899;
tel. 727/898–7451 **A**1 3 5 8 9 10 **F**2 9 10 14 15 16 17 18 19 20 21 22 23 24 26 27 28 29 30 32 33 34 35 37 38 39 41 42 48 49 50 51 52 53 56 57 58 60 61 62 63 64 65 66 67 69 70 72 73 77 81 82 84 85 87 88 90 93 94 95 96 98 99 100 101 107 108 110
Primary Contact: Gary Carnes, President and Chief Executive Officer
Web address: www.allkids.org

| | 23 | 50 | 216 | 9330 | 163 | 235488 | 0 | 213951 | 92671 | 2048 |

✠ △ **BAYFRONT MEDICAL CENTER**, 701 Sixth Street South, Zip 33701–4891;
tel. 727/823–1234, (Total facility includes 16 beds in nursing home–type unit) **A**1 2 3 5 7 9 10 **F**2 9 11 12 14 15 17 19 21 22 23 24 27 28 29 30 31 33 34 37 38 39 40 41 42 43 44 46 47 48 49 50 51 52 53 55 56 57 58 59 60 61 62 63 65 66 68 69 70 79 81 82 84 85 86 87 88 92 93 94 95 96 98 106 107 108 109 110 **P**6
Primary Contact: Sue G. Brody, President and Chief Executive Officer
COO: Eric Feder, Chief Operating Officer
CFO: Bob Thornton, Chief Financial Officer
CMO: Karen Williams, M.D., Chief of Staff
CIO: John McLendon, Chief Information Officer
CHR: Deborah Menendez, Director Human Resources
Web address: www.bayfront.org

| | 23 | 10 | 400 | 17274 | 255 | 173992 | 2746 | 241118 | 83598 | 2104 |

✠ **EDWARD WHITE HOSPITAL**, 2323 Ninth Avenue North, Zip 33713–6898,
Mailing Address: P.O. Box 12018, Zip 33733–2018; tel. 727/323–1111 **A**1 9 10 **F**2 12 21 23 26 29 33 41 46 48 52 53 55 57 60 62 63 66 69 81 82 84 85 87 88 93 94 95 96 108 110 **S** HCA, Nashville, TN
Primary Contact: Roland Metivier, Chief Executive Officer
CFO: Andrew Smith, Chief Financial Officer
CIO: Luz Meyer, Director Information Services
Web address: www.edwardwhitehospital.com

| | 33 | 10 | 113 | 3482 | 59 | 40207 | 0 | 36924 | 14035 | 327 |

KINDRED HOSPITAL–ST. PETERSBURG, 3030 Sixth Street South,
Zip 33705–3720; tel. 727/894–8719, (Nonreporting) **S** Kindred Healthcare, Louisville, KY
Primary Contact: Pamela M. Riter, R.N., Chief Executive Officer
Web address: www.kindredstpete.com

| | 33 | 10 | 112 | — | — | — | — | — | — | — |

✠ ○ **NORTHSIDE HOSPITAL AND HEART INSTITUTE**, 6000 49th Street North,
Zip 33709–2145; tel. 727/521–4411, (Nonreporting) **A**1 9 10 11 12 13 **S** HCA, Nashville, TN
Primary Contact: Ward Boston, III, Chief Executive Officer
COO: Betsy Bomar, Chief Operating Officer
CFO: Shalin Shah, Chief Financial Officer
CIO: Steve McDonald, Director, Information Systems
CHR: Maggie Miklos, Director Human Resources
Web address: www.northsidehospital.com

| | 23 | 10 | 288 | — | — | — | — | — | — | — |

□ **PALMS OF PASADENA HOSPITAL**, 1501 Pasadena Avenue South,
Zip 33707–3798; tel. 727/381–1000, (Total facility includes 13 beds in nursing home–type unit) (Nonreporting) **A**1 2 9 10 **S** IASIS Healthcare, Franklin, TN
Primary Contact: Steven J. Greene, Chief Executive Officer
Web address: www.palmspasadena.com

| | 33 | 10 | 307 | — | — | — | — | — | — | — |

✠ **ST. ANTHONY'S HOSPITAL**, 1200 Seventh Avenue North, Zip 33705–1388,
Mailing Address: P.O. Box 12588, Zip 33733–2588; tel. 727/825–1100, (Total facility includes 30 beds in nursing home–type unit) (Nonreporting) **A**1 2 9 10 **S** Catholic Health East, Newtown Square, PA
Primary Contact: Ford Kyes, President
Web address: www.stanthonys.org

| | 23 | 10 | 370 | — | — | — | — | — | — | — |

✠ **ST. PETERSBURG GENERAL HOSPITAL**, 6500 38th Avenue North,
Zip 33710–1629; tel. 727/384–1414 **A**1 9 10 **F**9 11 15 19 21 26 27 28 37 44 46 48 55 57 58 59 61 62 63 68 69 81 82 86 88 94 95 96 107 108 110 **S** HCA, Nashville, TN
Primary Contact: Richard H. Satcher, President and Chief Executive Officer
CFO: Timothy J. Cerullo, Chief Financial Officer
CHR: Sandra Edwards, Director Human Resources
Web address: www.stpetegeneral.com

| | 33 | 10 | 219 | 8364 | 105 | 55450 | 1534 | 77960 | 26676 | 530 |

FL

Hospital, Address, Telephone, Approval, Facility, and Physician Codes, Health Care System	Classi-fication Codes		Utilization Data					Expense (thousands) of dollars		
★ American Hospital Association (AHA) membership □ Joint Commission on Accreditation of Healthcare Organizations (JCAHO) accreditation ○ American Osteopathic Association (AOA) accreditation △ Commission on Accreditation of Rehabilitation Facilities (CARF) accreditation	Control	Service	Staffed Beds	Admissions	Census	Outpatient Visits	Births	Total	Payroll	Personnel

SANFORD—Seminole County

⊠ **CENTRAL FLORIDA REGIONAL HOSPITAL**, 1401 West Seminole Boulevard, Zip 32771–6764; tel. 407/321–4500, (Total facility includes 18 beds in nursing home–type unit) **A**1 9 10 **F**2 9 11 12 14 15 17 19 21 22 23 26 27 28 33 34 37 40 41 46 48 52 53 55 57 58 59 60 61 62 63 64 65 66 69 81 82 84 85 86 87 88 92 93 94 96 106 108 109 110 **S** HCA, Nashville, TN
Primary Contact: Rodney R. Smith, Chief Executive Officer
COO: Bland Eng, Chief Operating Officer
CFO: Ashley F. Johnson, Chief Financial Officer
CIO: Nancy Ryerson, Director Information Systems
CHR: Karla Langlotz, Director, Human Resources
Web address: www.centralfloridaregional.com

| | 33 | 10 | 226 | 9627 | 131 | 72532 | 1043 | — | — | 609 |

SARASOTA—Sarasota County

⊠ **DOCTORS HOSPITAL OF SARASOTA**, 5731 Bee Ridge Road, Zip 34233–5056; tel. 941/342–1100, (Nonreporting) **A**1 5 9 10 **S** HCA, Nashville, TN
Primary Contact: Robert C. Meade, Chief Executive Officer
CFO: Gary Searls, Chief Financial Officer
CHR: Bob Ehlers, Director Human Resources
Web address: www.doctorsofsarasota.com

| | 33 | 10 | 168 | — | — | — | — | — | — | — |

⊠ △ **HEALTHSOUTH REHABILITATION HOSPITAL OF SARASOTA**, 3251 Proctor Road, Zip 34231–8538; tel. 941/921–8600, (Nonreporting) **A**1 7 10 **S** HEALTHSOUTH Corporation, Birmingham, AL
Primary Contact: Margaret Holloway, Administrator
CFO: Sally Bailey, Chief Financial Officer
CMO: Alexander De Jesus, M.D., Medical Director
Web address: www.healthsouth.com

| | 33 | 46 | 76 | — | — | — | — | — | — | — |

⊠ △ **SARASOTA MEMORIAL HOSPITAL**, 1700 South Tamiami Trail, Zip 34239–3555; tel. 941/917–9000 **A**1 2 5 7 9 10 **F**2 4 5 6 9 10 11 12 14 15 17 19 21 22 23 26 27 28 29 33 35 37 38 39 40 42 44 46 47 48 49 51 52 53 55 56 57 58 59 60 61 62 63 64 65 66 68 69 70 71 72 73 74 75 76 77 78 81 82 84 85 86 87 88 92 93 94 95 96 107 108 109 110 **P**4 8
Primary Contact: Gwen MacKenzie, R.N., Chief Executive Officer
CFO: Michael F. Rolph, Chief Financial Officer
CMO: Bruce Fleegler, M.D., Chief Medical Officer
CIO: Denis Baker, Chief Information Officer
CHR: Laurie Bennett, Director Human Resources
Web address: www.smh.com

| | 16 | 10 | 601 | 29910 | 385 | 291348 | 3534 | 303578 | 137052 | 3320 |

SEBASTIAN—Indian River County

□ **SEBASTIAN RIVER MEDICAL CENTER**, 13695 North U.S. Highway 1, Zip 32958–3230, Mailing Address: Box 780838, Zip 32978–0838; tel. 772/589–3186 **A**1 9 10 **F**2 9 12 15 21 23 27 28 29 31 33 36 37 38 44 45 46 48 51 52 55 57 58 60 61 62 63 64 65 66 69 81 82 84 86 88 93 94 96 106 108 110 **P**5 **S** Health Management Associates, Naples, FL
Primary Contact: Kathy A. Burke, Chief Executive Officer
Web address: www.srmcenter.com

| | 33 | 10 | 129 | 4543 | 60 | 21000 | 0 | 37763 | — | 431 |

SEBRING—Highlands County

⊠ **FLORIDA HOSPITAL HEARTLAND MEDICAL CENTER**, 4200 Sun'n Lake Boulevard, Zip 33872–1986, Mailing Address: P.O. Box 9400, Zip 33871–9400; tel. 863/314–4466 **A**1 9 10 19 **F**9 11 12 15 17 21 22 26 27 28 29 33 35 37 39 40 41 46 47 48 51 52 55 58 59 62 63 65 66 71 72 73 74 76 77 81 82 84 86 87 88 92 93 94 96 97 98 108 109 110 **P**1 7 **S** Adventist Health System Sunbelt Health Care Corporation, Winter Park, FL
Primary Contact: John R. Harding, President and Chief Executive Officer
CFO: Todd Goodman, Vice President and Chief Financial Officer
CHR: Douglas Harcombe, Director Human Resources
Web address: www.flhosp–heartland.org

| | 21 | 10 | 186 | 10525 | 145 | 131116 | 962 | 100254 | 39517 | 965 |

□ **HIGHLANDS REGIONAL MEDICAL CENTER**, 3600 South Highlands Avenue, Zip 33870–5495, Mailing Address: Drawer 2066, Zip 33871–2066; tel. 863/471–5800 **A**1 9 10 19 **F**9 10 14 21 33 37 39 40 48 49 52 55 58 60 61 63 65 69 82 84 86 87 88 93 94 95 108 **S** Health Management Associates, Naples, FL
Primary Contact: Linda Harrison, Chief Executive Officer
Web address: www.highlandsregional.com

| | 33 | 10 | 64 | 5263 | 63 | — | — | — | — | — |

SOUTH MIAMI—Dade County

□ **LARKIN COMMUNITY HOSPITAL**, 7031 S.W. 62nd Avenue, Zip 33143–4781; tel. 305/284–7500, (Nonreporting) **A**1 9 10
Primary Contact: Jack J. Michel, M.D., President and Chief Executive Officer
Web address: www.larkinhopsital.com

| | 33 | 10 | 122 | — | — | — | — | — | — | — |

STARKE—Bradford County

⊠ **SHANDS AT STARKE**, 922 East Call Street, Zip 32091–3699; tel. 904/368–2300, (Nonreporting) **A**1 9 10 18 **S** Shands HealthCare, Gainesville, FL
Primary Contact: Jeannie Baker, Administrator
Web address: www.shands.org

| | 23 | 10 | 25 | — | — | — | — | — | — | — |

Many Facility Codes have changed. Please refer to the AHA Guide Code Chart. © 2005 AHA Guide

FL

Hospital, Address, Telephone, Approval, Facility, and Physician Codes, Health Care System	Classi-fication Codes		Utilization Data					Expense (thousands) of dollars		
★ American Hospital Association (AHA) membership □ Joint Commission on Accreditation of Healthcare Organizations (JCAHO) accreditation ○ American Osteopathic Association (AOA) accreditation △ Commission on Accreditation of Rehabilitation Facilities (CARF) accreditation	Control	Service	Staffed Beds	Admissions	Census	Outpatient Visits	Births	Total	Payroll	Personnel

STUART—Martin County

☒ **MARTIN MEMORIAL HEALTH SYSTEMS**, 300 S.E. Hospital Drive, Zip 34994, Mailing Address: P.O. Box 9010, Zip 34995–9010; tel. 772/287–5200, (Includes MARTIN MEMORIAL HOSPITAL SOUTH, 2100 S.E. Salerno Road, Zip 34997; tel. 772/223–2300) **A**1 2 9 10 **F**2 3 9 10 11 12 13 14 17 21 22 23 24 26 27 28 29 30 33 37 38 39 41 44 50 52 53 55 56 57 58 59 60 61 62 63 64 65 66 67 68 69 71 75 79 81 82 85 87 88 90 92 93 94 96 108 109 **P**6
Primary Contact: Richmond M. Harman, President and Chief Executive Officer
CFO: Mark Cocorullo, Senior Vice President and Chief Financial Officer
CMO: Howard M. Robbins, M.D., Chief Medical Officer
CIO: Bill Bollig, Chief Information Officer
CHR: Amy Barry, Vice President Human Resources
Web address: www.mmhs.com
Classification: 23 10; Staffed Beds 308; Admissions 16461; Census 208; Outpatient Visits 71480; Births 1762; Total 192687; Payroll 81998; Personnel 1674

SUN CITY CENTER—Hillsborough County

☒ **SOUTH BAY HOSPITAL**, 4016 State Road 674, Zip 33573–5298; tel. 813/634–3301 **A**1 9 10 **F**2 6 9 12 21 27 28 29 33 37 38 39 40 42 44 46 47 48 49 52 54 55 57 58 60 61 62 63 65 66 69 75 81 82 84 87 88 94 95 96 108 109 **S** HCA, Nashville, TN
Primary Contact: Stephen A. Rector, Chief Executive Officer
COO: Alex Chang, Chief Operating Officer
CFO: Martha Bakos, Chief Financial Officer
CIO: Ronald Proulx, Director Public Relations and Marketing
CHR: Patrick Kerrwood, Director Human Resources
Web address: www.southbayhospital.com
Classification: 33 10; Staffed Beds 122; Admissions 6353; Census 93; Outpatient Visits 48729; Births 0; Total —; Payroll —; Personnel —

TALLAHASSEE—Leon County

☒ **CAPITAL REGIONAL MEDICAL CENTER**, 2626 Capital Medical Boulevard, Zip 32308–4499; tel. 850/325–5000 **A**1 9 10 **F**2 9 10 11 12 14 15 17 19 21 22 23 26 27 28 29 33 34 37 44 46 48 49 52 55 57 58 59 61 62 63 64 69 81 82 88 94 108 109 110 **S** HCA, Nashville, TN
Primary Contact: Sharon L. Roush, Chief Executive Officer
COO: Richard Huth, Chief Operating Officer
CMO: William Yahr, M.D., Director Medical Affairs
CIO: Robert A. Steed, Director Information Systems
CHR: Melody Miller, Director Human Resources
Web address: www.capitalregionalmedicalcenter.com
Classification: 33 10; Staffed Beds 198; Admissions 8935; Census 113; Outpatient Visits 69801; Births 1008; Total —; Payroll —; Personnel 697

☒ **HEALTHSOUTH REHABILITATION HOSPITAL OF TALLAHASSEE**, 1675 Riggins Road, Zip 32308–5315; tel. 850/656–4800, (Nonreporting) **A**1 10 **S** HEALTHSOUTH Corporation, Birmingham, AL
Primary Contact: Lynn Streetman, Administrator
CFO: Charles Findo, Controller
Web address: www.healthsouth.com
Classification: 33 46; Staffed Beds 70; all data —

☒ **TALLAHASSEE MEMORIAL HEALTHCARE**, 1300 Miccosukee Road, Zip 32308–5093; tel. 850/431–1155, (Total facility includes 42 beds in nursing home–type unit) **A**1 2 3 5 9 10 **F**1 2 4 5 9 11 12 14 15 16 17 18 19 20 21 23 26 27 28 29 33 37 38 40 41 44 45 46 47 48 49 50 51 52 53 55 56 57 58 59 60 61 62 63 64 65 66 67 69 70 71 72 73 74 75 77 79 80 81 82 84 85 87 88 89 90 92 94 95 96 108 109 **P**6
Primary Contact: G. Mark O'Bryant, Chief Executive Officer
COO: Evan S. Dillard, Chief Operating Officer and Vice President
CFO: William A. Giudice, Chief Financial Officer and Vice President
CMO: John P. Mahoney, M.D., Chief Medical Officer
CIO: Mary Bland, Chief Information Officer and Vice President
CHR: Steve Adriaanse, Chief Human Resources Officer and Vice President
Web address: www.tmh.org
Classification: 23 10; Staffed Beds 545; Admissions 25140; Census 346; Outpatient Visits 259374; Births 3803; Total 287214; Payroll 126691; Personnel 2721

TAMARAC—Broward County

☒ **UNIVERSITY HOSPITAL AND MEDICAL CENTER**, 7201 North University Drive, Zip 33321–2996; tel. 954/721–2200, (Includes UNIVERSITY PAVILION, 7425 North University Drive, Zip 33328; tel. 305/722–9933) **A**1 9 10 **F**2 4 9 10 12 14 15 19 21 26 28 33 46 47 52 53 55 57 58 60 61 62 63 66 69 71 72 75 76 78 81 82 84 88 96 108 110 **S** HCA, Nashville, TN
Primary Contact: James A. Cruickshank, Chief Executive Officer
COO: Joseph Melchione, Chief Operating Officer
CFO: Alisa Bert, Chief Financial Officer
CMO: Alfred Kalman, M.D., Chief of Staff
CIO: Tom Scharff, Director Information Services
CHR: Robert Diano, Director Human Resources
Web address: www.uhmchealth.com
Classification: 33 10; Staffed Beds 271; Admissions 10460; Census 148; Outpatient Visits 51621; Births 0; Total 73324; Payroll 29907; Personnel 727

FL

Hospital, Address, Telephone, Approval, Facility, and Physician Codes, Health Care System	Classi-fication Codes		Utilization Data					Expense (thousands) of dollars		
★ American Hospital Association (AHA) membership □ Joint Commission on Accreditation of Healthcare Organizations (JCAHO) accreditation ○ American Osteopathic Association (AOA) accreditation △ Commission on Accreditation of Rehabilitation Facilities (CARF) accreditation	Control	Service	Staffed Beds	Admissions	Census	Outpatient Visits	Births	Total	Payroll	Personnel

TAMPA—Hillsborough County

⊠ **H. LEE MOFFITT CANCER CENTER AND RESEARCH INSTITUTE**, 12902 Magnolia Drive, Zip 33612–9497; tel. 813/972–4673 **A**1 2 3 5 8 9 10 **F**2 12 21 22 23 26 27 28 29 30 32 35 36 37 38 39 43 44 45 46 47 48 49 51 52 53 55 57 58 60 61 62 63 64 65 66 69 73 76 77 79 80 81 82 84 85 86 87 88 90 94 96 98 99 104 106 108 109 110 **P**1 Primary Contact: William S. Dalton, M.D., Ph.D., Chief Executive Officer and Director COO: Nicolas Porter, Associate Center Director for Administration CFO: John A. Kolosky, Executive Vice President Planning, Finance and Chief Financial Officer CMO: W Michael Alberts, M.D., Associate Center Director Clinical Affairs/Chief Medical Officer CIO: Edward Martinez, Vice President Information Technology and Chief Information Officer CHR: Lon Estes, Vice President Human Resources Web address: www.moffitt.usf.edu	23	41	137	6208	99	195636	0	223659	73919	2142
⊠ △ **JAMES A. HALEY VETERANS HOSPITAL**, 13000 Bruce B. Downs Boulevard, Zip 33612–4798; tel. 813/972–2000, (Total facility includes 228 beds in nursing home–type unit) (Nonreporting) **A**1 3 5 7 8 **S** Department of Veterans Affairs, Washington, DC Primary Contact: Forest Farley, Director COO: Steven W. Young, Associate Director CFO: James Skidmore, Financial Manager CMO: Thomas Bowen, M.D., Chief of Staff CIO: Jose Seymour, Chief Information Resource Management CHR: Victoria Rosas, Chief Human Resources Web address: www.va.gov/visn8/tampa	45	10	321	—	—	—	—	—	—	—
□ **KINDRED HOSPITAL – CENTRAL TAMPA**, 4801 North Howard Avenue, Zip 33603–1484; tel. 813/874–7575, (Nonreporting) **A**1 5 10 **S** Kindred Healthcare, Louisville, KY Primary Contact: Danny R. Edwards, Chief Executive Officer Web address: www.kindredhealthcare.com	33	49	73	—	—	—	—	—	—	—
□ **KINDRED HOSPITAL BAY AREA –TAMPA**, 4555 South Manhattan Avenue, Zip 33611–2397; tel. 813/839–6341, (Nonreporting) **A**1 5 10 **S** Kindred Healthcare, Louisville, KY Primary Contact: Sally Hoffmann, Chief Executive Officer Web address: www.kindredhealthcare.com	33	49	73	—	—	—	—	—	—	—
□ **MEMORIAL HOSPITAL OF TAMPA**, 2901 Swann Avenue, Zip 33609–4057; tel. 813/873–6400 **A**1 5 9 10 **F**2 12 21 23 27 28 33 34 42 48 50 52 53 55 63 69 71 75 81 82 84 88 108 **S** IASIS Healthcare, Franklin, TN Primary Contact: John J. Mainieri, Chief Executive Officer Web address: www.memorialhospitaltampa.com	33	10	149	6213	91	—	0	—	—	—
□ **SHRINERS HOSPITALS FOR CHILDREN, TAMPA**, 12502 North Pine Drive, Zip 33612–9499; tel. 813/972–2250 **A**1 3 5 **F**22 26 27 29 45 48 52 53 60 62 63 65 69 87 88 94 108 110 **S** Shriners Hospitals for Children, Tampa, FL Primary Contact: Alice Reed Lanford, R.N., Administrator Web address: www.shrinershq.org	23	57	60	1139	15	9585	0	—	—	259
⊠ **ST. JOSEPH'S HOSPITAL**, 3001 West Martin Luther King Jr. Boulevard, Zip 33607–6387, Mailing Address: P.O. Box 4227, Zip 33677–4227; tel. 813/870–4000, (Includes ST. JOSEPH'S HOSPITAL, ST. JOSEPH'S WOMEN'S HOSPITAL – TAMPA, 3030 West Dr. Martin L. King Boulevard, Zip 33607–6394; tel. 813/879–4730), (Nonreporting) **A**1 2 5 9 10 **S** Catholic Health East, Newtown Square, PA Primary Contact: Isaac Mallah, President and Chief Executive Officer CFO: Cathy Yoder, Chief Financial Officer CMO: Mark Vaaler, M.D., Chief Medical Officer CIO: Rick Perry, Vice President Information Services CHR: Pat Teeuwen, Director Human Resources Web address: www.sjbhealth.org	21	10	883	—	—	—	—	—	—	—
⊠ △ **TAMPA GENERAL HOSPITAL**, 2 Columbia Drive, Zip 33606–3508, Mailing Address: P.O. Box 1289, Zip 33601–1289; tel. 813/844–7000, (Total facility includes 31 beds in nursing home–type unit) **A**1 5 7 8 9 10 **F**2 9 10 11 12 13 14 15 17 19 21 22 23 26 27 28 29 30 32 33 34 37 40 41 42 44 46 48 49 52 55 56 57 58 59 61 62 63 66 67 68 69 70 71 73 75 81 82 86 88 92 93 94 95 96 100 101 102 103 105 108 109 110 Primary Contact: Ronald A. Hytoff, President and Chief Executive Officer CFO: Steve Short, Executive Vice President Finance and Administration CMO: Joseph Thomas Danzi, M.D., Senior Vice President and Chief Medical Officer CIO: Ginger Oliver, Vice President Information Systems CHR: Steven Durbin, Vice President Human Resources Web address: www.tgh.org	23	10	877	30121	573	236973	4473	538669	193877	4288
□ **TOWN AND COUNTRY HOSPITAL**, 6001 Webb Road, Zip 33615–3291; tel. 813/888–7060 **A**1 9 10 **F**2 3 4 9 10 12 21 22 23 28 29 32 33 37 39 40 46 48 52 53 55 57 58 60 61 62 63 69 73 81 82 84 85 88 92 96 108 **S** IASIS Healthcare, Franklin, TN Primary Contact: James P. Seward, Jr, Chief Executive Officer Web address: www.townandcountryhospital.com	33	10	127	5423	61	—	0	—	—	—

FL

Many Facility Codes have changed. Please refer to the AHA Guide Code Chart. © 2005 AHA Guide

Hospital, Address, Telephone, Approval, Facility, and Physician Codes, Health Care System	Classification Codes		Utilization Data					Expense (thousands) of dollars		
★ American Hospital Association (AHA) membership □ Joint Commission on Accreditation of Healthcare Organizations (JCAHO) accreditation ○ American Osteopathic Association (AOA) accreditation △ Commission on Accreditation of Rehabilitation Facilities (CARF) accreditation	Control	Service	Staffed Beds	Admissions	Census	Outpatient Visits	Births	Total	Payroll	Personnel

□ **UNIVERSITY COMMUNITY HOSPITAL**, 3100 East Fletcher Avenue, Zip 33613–4688; tel. 813/971–6000 **A**1 2 5 9 10 **F**2 9 10 11 12 14 15 17 19 21 22 23 24 26 27 28 29 30 32 33 35 37 39 41 42 44 45 46 47 48 50 51 52 53 55 56 57 58 59 60 61 62 63 65 66 67 68 69 70 79 81 82 84 85 87 88 89 90 93 94 95 96 98 107 108 109 110 **P**6 **S** University Community Health, Tampa, FL Primary Contact: Calvin Glidewell, Chief Executive Officer Web address: www.uch.org	23	10	360	22005	304	136541	3150	242847	103970	1876
UNIVERSITY COMMUNITY HOSPITAL–CARROLLWOOD, 7171 North Dale Mabry Highway, Zip 33614–2699; tel. 813/932–2222 **A**9 10 13 **F**2 9 21 22 26 27 28 29 33 35 37 39 41 44 45 46 47 48 50 51 52 55 57 58 60 62 63 64 65 66 69 70 81 82 84 85 88 94 96 106 108 110 **S** University Community Health, Tampa, FL Primary Contact: Donald D. Evans, Chief Executive Officer Web address: www.uch.org	23	10	90	4883	61	61160	0	52221	22760	315
TARPON SPRINGS—Pinellas County										
□ **HELEN ELLIS MEMORIAL HOSPITAL**, 1395 South Pinellas Avenue, Zip 34689–3721, Mailing Address: P.O. Box 1487, Zip 34688–1487; tel. 727/942–5000 **A**1 5 9 10 **F**2 9 11 12 14 21 22 23 26 27 28 29 32 33 39 40 42 47 48 51 52 53 55 57 58 59 60 61 62 63 65 66 69 81 82 84 85 88 92 93 94 96 106 108 109 110 **S** University Community Health, Tampa, FL Primary Contact: Steven MacLauchlan, Chief Executive Officer Web address: www.helenellis.com	23	10	168	6509	80	—	—	—	—	—
TAVARES—Lake County										
★ **FLORIDA HOSPITAL WATERMAN**, 1000 Waterman Way, Zip 32778–5266; tel. 352/253–3333 **A**1 2 9 10 19 **F**2 9 11 12 15 21 22 29 33 38 41 45 46 48 51 52 55 57 58 59 61 62 63 64 69 79 80 81 82 84 85 88 93 94 96 106 107 108 109 110 **S** Adventist Health System Sunbelt Health Care Corporation, Winter Park, FL Primary Contact: Kenneth R. Mattison, President and Chief Executive Officer COO: Carrie Fish, Vice President and Chief Operating Officer CFO: Ronald K. Benfield, Chief Financial Officer and Vice President CMO: Phillip Dascher, Chief of Staff CIO: Mike Freeland, Regional Manager CHR: Madge Springer, Director of Human Resources Web address: www.fhwat.org	23	10	204	10606	129	129435	857	123594	45971	—
TAVERNIER—Monroe County										
★ **MARINERS HOSPITAL**, 91500 Overseas Highway, Zip 33070–2547; tel. 305/434–1582 **A**1 9 10 20 **F**2 9 12 21 27 28 29 33 41 46 47 48 52 55 57 58 63 64 65 66 69 81 82 84 85 87 88 93 94 96 106 108 109 110 **P**1 **S** Baptist Health South Florida, Coral Gables, FL Primary Contact: Robert H. Luse, Chief Executive Officer CFO: Erik Long, Controller CIO: Mimi Taylor, Vice President Information Technology CHR: John Fernandez, Director, Human Resources Web address: www.baptisthealth.net	23	10	42	1231	15	25311	0	29757	9739	184
TEQUESTA—Martin County										
SANDYPINES, 11301 S.E. Tequesta Terrace, Zip 33469–8146; tel. 561/744–0211 **F**71 72 96 **S** Health Management Associates, Naples, FL Primary Contact: John W. Thompson, Ph.D., Chief Executive Officer	32	52	78	181	70	—	—	—	—	129
THE VILLAGES—Sumter County										
★ **THE VILLAGES REGIONAL HOSPITAL**, 1451 El Camino Real, Zip 32159; tel. 352/751–8000 **A**1 9 10 **F**2 9 21 22 23 26 29 33 39 46 47 48 49 52 53 55 57 58 61 62 63 64 69 73 81 82 88 92 94 96 Primary Contact: Timothy P. Menton, Chief Executive Officer CFO: Dale E. Hocking, Chief Financial Officer CIO: Nancy Vester, Vice President Information Technology CHR: Darlene Stone, Vice President Human Resources Web address: www.tvrmc.org	23	10	60	5755	55	31108	0	39424	15445	378
TITUSVILLE—Brevard County										
★ **PARRISH MEDICAL CENTER**, 951 North Washington Avenue, Zip 32796–2194; tel. 321/268–6111 **A**1 2 9 10 **F**2 9 11 12 15 17 21 22 26 27 28 29 33 37 38 40 41 46 47 48 49 51 55 57 58 59 61 62 63 65 66 69 81 84 86 87 88 93 94 95 96 106 107 108 109 110 **P**7 Primary Contact: George Mikitarian, Jr, Chief Executive Officer CFO: Timothy K. Skeldon, Senior Vice President and Chief Financial Officer CIO: Chris Biderman, Director Information Systems CHR: Roberta Chaildin, Manager Human Resources Web address: www.parrishmed.com	16	10	210	7907	95	121614	694	110322	37209	803
VENICE—Sarasota County										
★ **VENICE REGIONAL MEDICAL CENTER**, (Formerly Bon Secours–Venice Hospital), 540 The Rialto, Zip 34285–2900; tel. 941/485–7711 **A**1 2 9 10 **F**2 8 9 12 21 22 26 27 28 29 32 33 42 44 48 50 51 52 57 58 60 61 62 63 65 69 70 81 82 84 87 88 94 106 107 108 109 110 **S** Health Management Associates, Naples, FL Primary Contact: Melody Trimble, Chief Executive Officer COO: Kathy Connerton, Chief Operating Officer CFO: Steve Maxwell, Chief Financial Officer CMO: John Kontor, M.D., Chief Medical Officer CIO: Ted Baily, Vice President Information Systems CHR: Ann Roggero, Director Human Resources	23	10	128	8193	103	—	—	—	—	—

FL

Hospital, Address, Telephone, Approval, Facility, and Physician Codes, Health Care System	Classi-fication Codes		Utilization Data					Expense (thousands) of dollars		
★ American Hospital Association (AHA) membership ☐ Joint Commission on Accreditation of Healthcare Organizations (JCAHO) accreditation ◯ American Osteopathic Association (AOA) accreditation △ Commission on Accreditation of Rehabilitation Facilities (CARF) accreditation	Control	Service	Staffed Beds	Admissions	Census	Outpatient Visits	Births	Total	Payroll	Personnel

VERO BEACH—Indian River County

☒ △ **HEALTHSOUTH TREASURE COAST REHABILITATION HOSPITAL**, 1600 37th Street, Zip 32960–6549; tel. 772/778–2100, (Nonreporting) **A**1 7 10 **S** HEALTHSOUTH Corporation, Birmingham, AL
Primary Contact: Jason N. Roeback, Administrator
COO: Jason N. Roeback, Administrator
CFO: Kevin Hardy, Chief Financial Officer
Web address: www.healthsouth.com

| | 33 | 46 | 90 | — | — | — | — | — | — | — |

☒ **INDIAN RIVER MEMORIAL HOSPITAL**, 1000 36th Street, Zip 32960–6592; tel. 772/567–4311, (Total facility includes 20 beds in nursing home–type unit) **A**1 2 9 10 **F**2 4 6 9 10 11 12 14 15 21 22 23 26 27 28 29 33 35 37 39 40 43 45 46 47 48 49 50 52 55 57 58 59 60 61 62 63 64 65 66 69 70 71 72 73 74 75 76 77 79 80 81 82 83 84 85 87 88 92 93 94 95 96 106 107 108 109 110 **P**6 8
Primary Contact: Jeffrey L. Susi, President and Chief Executive Officer
COO: W Carl Martin, Senior Vice President and Chief Operating Officer
CFO: Greg Gardner, Senior Vice President and Chief Financial Officer
CMO: Dudley Teel, M.D., Vice President Medical Management
CHR: Robert Zomok, Director, Human Resources
Web address: www.irmh.com

| | 23 | 10 | 335 | 12491 | 186 | 95776 | 1153 | 123281 | 49461 | 1122 |

WAUCHULA—Hardee County

☐ **FLORIDA HOSPITAL WAUCHULA**, 533 West Carlton Street, Zip 33873; tel. 863/773–3101, (Nonreporting) **A**1 9 10 18 **S** Adventist Health System Sunbelt Health Care Corporation, Winter Park, FL
Primary Contact: David Ottati, Administrator
Web address: www.flhosp–heartland.org/Facilities/Wauchula.htm

| | 23 | 10 | 25 | — | — | — | — | — | — | — |

WEST PALM BEACH—Palm Beach County

☒ ◯ **COLUMBIA HOSPITAL**, 2201 45th Street, Zip 33407–2069; tel. 561/842–6141, (Nonreporting) **A**1 9 10 11 12 13 **S** HCA, Nashville, TN
Primary Contact: Valerie A. Jackson, Chief Executive Officer
COO: Eric Goldman, Chief Operating Officer
CFO: Ananda Rampat, Chief Financial Office
CMO: David Stern, M.D., Chief of Staff
CIO: Martha Stinson, Director
CHR: Donna Boyle, Director
Web address: www.columbiahospital.com

| | 33 | 10 | 250 | — | — | — | — | — | — | — |

☒ **GOOD SAMARITAN MEDICAL CENTER**, Flagler Drive at Palm Beach Lakes Boulevard, Zip 33401–3499; tel. 561/655–5511, (Nonreporting) **A**1 2 9 10 **S** TENET Healthcare Corporation, Dallas, TX
Primary Contact: Paul D. Echelard, Chief Executive Officer
COO: Mary T. Bazzicalupo, Chief Operating Officer
CFO: Oscar J. Fernandez, Chief Financial Officer
CIO: Candace Helms, Director Information Services
CHR: Nancy Bentley, Director Human Resources

| | 23 | 10 | 341 | | | | | | | |

HOSPICE OF PALM BEACH COUNTY, 5300 East Avenue, Zip 33407–2352; tel. 561/848–5200, (Nonreporting)
Primary Contact: David Fielding, Chief Executive Officer
Web address: www.hpbc.com

| | 23 | 49 | 24 | — | — | — | — | — | — | — |

OAKWOOD CENTER OF THE PALM BEACHES, INC., 1041 45th Street, Zip 33407–2494; tel. 561/383–8000, (Nonreporting) **A**10
Primary Contact: Linda De Piano, Ph.D., Chief Executive Officer and Executive Director
Web address: www.oakwoodcenter.org

| | 23 | 22 | 44 | | | | | | | |

☒ △ **ST. MARY'S MEDICAL CENTER**, 901 45th Street, Zip 33407–2495, Mailing Address: P.O. Box 24620, Zip 33416–4620; tel. 561/844–6300, (Nonreporting) **A**1 7 9 10 **S** TENET Healthcare Corporation, Dallas, TX
Primary Contact: Paul A. Walker, Chief Executive Officer
COO: Jeff Rosenberg, Chief Operating Officer
CFO: Joel Dalva, Chief Financial Officer
CIO: Rich Avato, Director
CHR: Sandy Wyant, Director Human Resources
Web address: www.stmarysmc.com

| | 21 | 10 | 460 | — | — | — | — | — | — | — |

☒ **VETERANS AFFAIRS MEDICAL CENTER**, 7305 North Military Trail, Zip 33410–6400; tel. 561/422–8262, (Total facility includes 98 beds in nursing home–type unit) **A**1 **F**1 2 4 7 9 10 12 21 22 23 26 27 28 29 30 31 32 33 34 35 37 38 39 41 42 44 45 46 47 48 49 50 51 52 53 55 57 58 60 61 62 63 65 66 69 70 71 73 75 76 77 81 82 84 86 87 88 92 94 96 106 107 108 109 110 **S** Department of Veterans Affairs, Washington, DC
Primary Contact: Edward H. Seiler, Director
CFO: Randall Sommer, Chief Business Office
CIO: Karen Gabaldon, Chief Management Information Systems
Web address: www.va.gov/sta/guide/home.asp

| | 45 | 10 | 186 | 5863 | 114 | 527404 | 0 | 129935 | 90497 | 1751 |

☐ ◯ **WELLINGTON REGIONAL MEDICAL CENTER**, 10101 Forest Hill Boulevard, Zip 33414–6199; tel. 561/798–8500, (Nonreporting) **A**1 2 9 10 11 12 13 **S** Universal Health Services, Inc., King of Prussia, PA
Primary Contact: Kevin DiLallo, Chief Executive Officer
Web address: www.wellingtonregional.com

| | 33 | 10 | 108 | — | — | — | — | — | — | — |

FL

Hospital, Address, Telephone, Approval, Facility, and Physician Codes, Health Care System	Classi-fication Codes		Utilization Data					Expense (thousands) of dollars		
★ American Hospital Association (AHA) membership □ Joint Commission on Accreditation of Healthcare Organizations (JCAHO) accreditation ○ American Osteopathic Association (AOA) accreditation △ Commission on Accreditation of Rehabilitation Facilities (CARF) accreditation	Control	Service	Staffed Beds	Admissions	Census	Outpatient Visits	Births	Total	Payroll	Personnel

WESTON—Broward County

☒ **CLEVELAND CLINIC HOSPITAL**, 3100 Weston Road, Zip 33331–3602; tel. 954/689–5000 **A**1 9 10 **F**2 10 21 22 33 37 46 49 55 57 58 59 60 61 63 69 81 82 84 86 88 108 **S** TENET Healthcare Corporation, Dallas, TX
COO: Chantal Leconte, Chief Operating Officer
CFO: Dave Pettit, Chief Financial Officer
CMO: Steven D. Wexner, M.D., Chief of Staff
CIO: Donna Evelyn, Director Information Technology
Web address: www.clevelandclinic.org/florida

| | 32 | 10 | 150 | 8660 | 92 | 102740 | 0 | 92193 | 32863 | 766 |

WILLISTON—Levy County

NATURE COAST REGIONAL HOSPITAL, 125 S.W. Seventh Street, Zip 32696–2403; tel. 352/528–2801 **A**9 10 **F**2 9 21 26 27 33 46 48 52 81 88 92 97 108 109 110 **P**6
Primary Contact: Alan Bird, Administrator

| | 33 | 10 | 40 | 1356 | 11 | 10632 | 0 | 6816 | 2353 | 88 |

WINTER HAVEN—Polk County

☒ △ **WINTER HAVEN HOSPITAL**, 200 Avenue F. N.E., Zip 33881–4193; tel. 863/293–1121 **A**1 7 9 10 **F**2 9 10 11 12 14 15 21 22 23 27 28 30 33 37 38 46 47 48 53 55 56 57 58 59 60 61 62 63 64 65 66 68 69 70 71 73 74 75 76 77 78 79 80 81 82 84 85 87 88 89 94 96 106 107 108 109 110 **P**6
Primary Contact: Lance W. Anastasio, President
CFO: David MacDougall, Vice President Finance
CMO: Charles C. Inman, M.D., Medical Staff President
CIO: Pat Mongoven, Director Information Systems
Web address: www.winterhavenhospital.org

| | 23 | 10 | 364 | 16777 | 233 | 281402 | 2081 | 181738 | 87811 | 2296 |

ZEPHYRHILLS—Pasco County

☒ **EAST PASCO MEDICAL CENTER**, 7050 Gall Boulevard, Zip 33541–1399; tel. 813/788–0411 **A**1 5 9 10 **F**2 9 11 12 15 21 22 26 27 28 29 33 40 41 47 48 52 55 59 60 63 66 69 70 71 76 81 84 85 86 87 88 93 94 96 106 108 110 **S** Adventist Health System Sunbelt Health Care Corporation, Winter Park, FL
Primary Contact: Scott M. Pittman, President and Chief Executive Officer
COO: Robert Ruchti, Vice President and Chief of Operations
CFO: Donald E. Welch, Chief Financial Officer
CMO: Joseph W. Nystrom, M.D., Chief of Staff
CIO: Kelley Sasser, Director Information Systems
CHR: Sylvia Seals–Brown, Vice President Human Resources
Web address: www.epmc.org

| | 21 | 10 | 154 | 8555 | 98 | 63566 | 587 | 840520 | 27204 | 649 |

FL

GEORGIA

Hospital, Address, Telephone, Approval, Facility, and Physician Codes, Health Care System	Classi-fication Codes		Utilization Data					Expense (thousands) of dollars		
★ American Hospital Association (AHA) membership □ Joint Commission on Accreditation of Healthcare Organizations (JCAHO) accreditation ○ American Osteopathic Association (AOA) accreditation △ Commission on Accreditation of Rehabilitation Facilities (CARF) accreditation	Control	Service	Staffed Beds	Admissions	Census	Outpatient Visits	Births	Total	Payroll	Personnel

ADEL—Cook County

□ **MEMORIAL HOSPITAL OF ADEL**, 706 North Parrish Avenue, Zip 31620–0677, Mailing Address: 705 North Parrish Avenue, Zip 31620–0677; tel. 229/896–8000, (Total facility includes 95 beds in nursing home–type unit) **A**1 9 10 **F**9 11 12 21 27 33 44 46 48 51 55 59 63 65 66 69 70 81 82 84 88 92 94 97 108 **S** Sunlink Healthcare, Atlanta, GA
Primary Contact: William Hawley, Chief Executive Officer
Web address: www.sunlinkhealth.com/memorial.html

| 33 | 10 | 155 | 1833 | 108 | 15558 | 173 | 15024 | 6818 | 154 |

ALBANY—Dougherty County

✠ **PALMYRA MEDICAL CENTERS**, 2000 Palmyra Road, Zip 31702–1908, Mailing Address: P.O. Box 1908, Zip 31702–1908; tel. 229/434–2000 **A**1 9 10 **F**2 10 14 21 26 27 28 33 34 37 40 44 46 52 55 57 58 60 62 63 68 69 81 84 88 94 95 96 108 110 **P**5 **S** HCA, Nashville, TN
Primary Contact: Bud Wethington, Chief Executive Officer
COO: Dennis Durham, Chief Operating Officer
Web address: www.palmyramedicalcenters.com

| 33 | 10 | 174 | 3429 | 63 | 46117 | 0 | 45833 | 19507 | 387 |

✠ **PHOEBE PUTNEY MEMORIAL HOSPITAL**, 417 Third Avenue, Zip 31701–1828, Mailing Address: P.O. Box 1828, Zip 31703–1828; tel. 229/883–1800, (Total facility includes 7 beds in nursing home–type unit) **A**1 2 3 5 9 10 **F**2 4 6 9 11 12 14 15 17 19 21 22 23 27 28 29 33 35 36 37 38 39 40 42 45 46 47 48 49 51 52 53 55 56 57 58 59 60 61 62 63 64 65 66 68 69 70 71 73 74 75 76 77 78 79 80 81 82 84 85 87 88 92 93 94 95 96 98 99 106 107 108 109 110 **P**1 6 7 **S** Phoebe Putney Health Systems, Albany, GA
Primary Contact: Joel Wernick, President and Chief Executive Officer
COO: Jim Hobson, Chief Operating Officer
CFO: Kerry Londewilk, Senior Vice President and Chief Financial Officer
CIO: Larry Brown, Assistant Vice President Information Systems
Web address: www.phoebeputney.com

| 23 | 10 | 439 | 21070 | 308 | 621264 | 2844 | 329473 | 107033 | — |

ALMA—Bacon County

✠ **BACON COUNTY HOSPITAL AND HEALTH SYSTEM**, 302 South Wayne Street, Zip 31510–2997, Mailing Address: P.O. Drawer 1987, Zip 31510–1987; tel. 912/632–8961, (Total facility includes 88 beds in nursing home–type unit) **A**1 9 10 18 **F**9 11 12 21 22 26 27 28 29 33 34 36 37 38 41 46 48 52 53 59 60 62 63 68 69 81 88 92 94 97 106 108 **P**5
Primary Contact: Cindy R. Turner, Interim Chief Executive Officer
COO: Cindy R. Turner, Chief Financial Officer and Chief Operating Officer
CFO: Cindy R. Turner, Chief Financial Officer
CMO: Lou Ellen Hutcheson, M.D., Chief of Staff
CHR: Jackie Lewis, Human Resources Director
Web address: www.baconcountyhospital.com

| 23 | 10 | 113 | 2096 | 60 | 18738 | 67 | 15882 | 5884 | 252 |

AMERICUS—Sumter County

✠ △ **SUMTER REGIONAL HOSPITAL**, 100 Wheatley Drive, Zip 31709–3799; tel. 229/924–6011, (Total facility includes 100 beds in nursing home–type unit) **A**1 7 9 10 **F**2 6 9 11 12 14 15 21 22 23 26 27 28 29 30 33 34 36 38 39 40 44 45 46 47 48 50 53 57 58 59 60 61 62 63 64 65 66 68 69 70 71 74 75 76 81 82 84 85 88 92 93 94 95 96 108 109 110 **P**3 6 8
Primary Contact: David H. Seagraves, President and Chief Executive Officer
COO: Stephen J. Machen, Senior Vice President and Chief Operations Officer
CFO: Troy Hammett, Vice President Finance and Chief Financial Officer
CMO: Gatewood Dudley, M.D., Vice President of Medical Staff Services
Web address: www.sumterregional.org/

| 15 | 10 | 232 | 4278 | 122 | 58410 | 802 | 33584 | 21680 | 726 |

ARLINGTON—Calhoun County

CALHOUN MEMORIAL HOSPITAL, 209 Academy and Carswell Streets, Zip 31713, Mailing Address: Drawer R, Zip 31713; tel. 229/725–4272, (Nonreporting) **A**10 18
Primary Contact: Peggy Pierce, Administrator

| 16 | 10 | 25 | — | — | — | — | — | — | — |

ATHENS—Clarke County

✠ **ATHENS REGIONAL MEDICAL CENTER**, 1199 Prince Avenue, Zip 30606–2793; tel. 706/475–7000 **A**1 2 9 10 **F**6 9 11 12 14 15 17 19 21 22 23 26 27 28 29 30 33 40 42 44 46 48 49 51 52 53 55 56 57 59 60 61 62 63 64 65 66 69 71 76 78 81 82 84 86 88 93 94 95 96 106 107 108 109 110
Primary Contact: John A. Drew, President and Chief Executive Officer
COO: Gary L. Phelps, Senior Vice President and Chief Operating Officer
CFO: W Larry Webb, Senior Vice President and Chief Financial Officer
CMO: Cecil Hudson, M.D., Chief Medical Officer
CIO: Tim Penning, Chief Information Officer
CHR: Kevin Thigpen, Vice President Human Resources
Web address: www.armc.org

| 23 | 10 | 315 | 19339 | 235 | 238562 | 2518 | 205137 | 100686 | 2374 |

GA

Hospital, Address, Telephone, Approval, Facility, and Physician Codes, Health Care System	Classi-fication Codes		Utilization Data					Expense (thousands) of dollars		
★ American Hospital Association (AHA) membership □ Joint Commission on Accreditation of Healthcare Organizations (JCAHO) accreditation ○ American Osteopathic Association (AOA) accreditation △ Commission on Accreditation of Rehabilitation Facilities (CARF) accreditation	Control	Service	Staffed Beds	Admissions	Census	Outpatient Visits	Births	Total	Payroll	Personnel
⊠ **ST. MARY'S HEALTH CARE SYSTEM**, 1230 Baxter Street, Zip 30606–3791; tel. 706/389–3000, (Total facility includes 120 beds in nursing home–type unit) (Nonreporting) **A**1 9 10 **S** Catholic Health East, Newtown Square, PA Primary Contact: Thomas E. Fitz, Jr, FACHE, President and Chief Executive Officer CFO: Theresa Vintyard, Chief Financial Officer CIO: Kerry Vaughn, Director Information Services CHR: Jeff English, Vice President Human Resources Web address: www.stmarysathens.com	23	10	302	—	—	—	—	—	—	—
ATLANTA—Fulton and De Kalb Counties County										
□ **ANCHOR HOSPITAL**, 5454 Yorktowne Drive, Zip 30349–5305; tel. 770/991–6044 **A**1 9 10 **F**3 4 26 71 72 74 76 77 78 92 94 **S** Universal Health Services, Inc., King of Prussia, PA Primary Contact: Trey Carter, Chief Executive Officer Web address: www.anchorhospital.com	33	82	92	3634	76	10770	0	9325	5241	169
⊠ **ATLANTA MEDICAL CENTER**, 303 Parkway Drive N.E., Zip 30312–1212; tel. 404/265–4000 **A**1 2 3 5 8 9 10 **F**6 9 10 11 12 14 15 17 19 21 22 23 26 27 29 31 33 34 35 36 37 39 40 41 42 44 45 46 47 48 49 50 52 53 55 56 57 58 59 60 61 62 63 64 65 66 68 69 70 71 73 74 75 76 77 79 81 82 84 85 86 87 88 89 90 93 94 95 96 108 109 110 **P**8 **S** TENET Healthcare Corporation, Dallas, TX Primary Contact: William T. Moore, Chief Executive Officer COO: Kem Mullins, Chief Operating Officer CFO: William J. Masterton, Chief Financial Officer CMO: Steven Saltzman, M.D., Senior Vice President and Medical Director CIO: Maryland McCarty, Director Information Systems CHR: Troy Bond, Chief Human Resources Officer Web address: www.atlantamedcenter.com	33	10	408	13418	223	78220	2871	195599	73597	1456
□ △ **CHILDREN'S HEALTHCARE OF ATLANTA**, (Pediatric medical/surgical), 1600 Tullie Circle, N.E., Zip 30329–2303; tel. 404/325–6000, (Includes CHILDREN'S HEALTHCARE OF ATLANTA AT EGLESTON, 1600 Tullie Circle, Zip 30329; tel. 404/325–6000; CHILDREN'S HEALTHCARE OF ATLANTA AT SCOTTISH RITE, 1001 Johnson Ferry Road N.E., Zip 30342–1600; tel. 404/256–5252) **A**1 3 5 7 8 10 **F**2 6 10 14 16 18 20 21 22 23 24 27 28 29 32 33 34 37 42 45 46 47 48 49 50 52 53 56 57 58 60 61 62 63 64 65 66 67 68 69 70 73 81 84 87 88 93 94 95 96 97 99 100 101 102 103 104 107 108 **P**8 Primary Contact: James E. Tally, Ph.D., President and Chief Executive Officer Web address: www.choa.org	23	59	412	21461	319	458630	0	549868	284852	4870
⊠ **EMORY CRAWFORD LONG HOSPITAL**, 550 Peachtree Street N.E., Zip 30308; tel. 404/686–4411 **A**1 2 3 5 8 9 10 **F**2 9 10 11 12 14 15 16 17 18 19 20 21 22 29 33 35 37 39 40 42 46 47 48 49 50 52 53 55 56 57 58 59 61 62 63 64 65 66 69 73 80 81 82 84 85 86 87 88 89 92 94 96 98 106 108 109 110 **S** Emory Healthcare, Atlanta, GA Primary Contact: John T. Fox, Chief Executive Officer COO: Albert K. Blackwelder, FACHE, Chief Operating Officer CFO: Mark Aycock, Chief Financial Officer CMO: William A. Bornstein, M.D., Ph.D., Chief Quality and Medical Officer CIO: Debra Cantrell, Chief Information Officer CHR: Margaret A. Bloomquist, Chief Human Resources Web address: www.emoryhealthcare.org	23	10	419	21275	305	109364	3061	327755	103457	2185
⊠ **EMORY DUNWOODY MEDICAL CENTER**, 4575 North Shallowford Road, Zip 30338–6499; tel. 770/454–2000 **A**1 9 10 **F**2 9 10 11 12 14 15 21 22 27 28 29 33 34 37 46 48 53 55 56 57 59 60 62 63 64 65 66 69 70 73 81 82 84 88 94 96 108 **S** HCA, Nashville, TN Primary Contact: Thomas D. Gilbert, President and Chief Executive Officer CFO: JoAnn Manning, Chief Financial Officer CIO: Avary Bales, Director Information Systems CHR: Monica M. Fleece, Director Human Resources Web address: www.emorydunwoody.com	33	10	118	3863	36	24450	902	—	—	296
⊠ △ **EMORY UNIVERSITY HOSPITAL**, 1364 Clifton Road N.E., Zip 30322–1102; tel. 404/712–2000 **A**1 2 3 5 7 8 9 10 **F**2 4 9 10 12 14 15 17 19 21 22 23 29 33 37 38 39 46 48 50 53 55 57 58 60 61 62 63 64 65 66 68 69 71 73 74 75 78 81 82 84 85 86 87 88 92 93 94 96 99 100 101 102 103 104 105 106 108 109 **S** Emory Healthcare, Atlanta, GA Primary Contact: John T. Fox, Chief Executive Officer COO: Robert J. Bachman, Chief Operating Officer CFO: James T. Hatcher, Chief Financial Officer CMO: Robert B. Smith, III, M.D., Medical Director CIO: Dedra Cantrell, Chief Information Officer CHR: Margaret A. Bloomquist, Assistant Administrator Human Resources Web address: www.emory.org	23	10	508	22672	390	84898	0	422950	148011	2867

GA

Hospital, Address, Telephone, Approval, Facility, and Physician Codes, Health Care System	Classi-fication Codes		Utilization Data					Expense (thousands) of dollars		
★ American Hospital Association (AHA) membership □ Joint Commission on Accreditation of Healthcare Organizations (JCAHO) accreditation ○ American Osteopathic Association (AOA) accreditation △ Commission on Accreditation of Rehabilitation Facilities (CARF) accreditation	Control	Service	Staffed Beds	Admissions	Census	Outpatient Visits	Births	Total	Payroll	Personnel
⊠ **GRADY MEMORIAL HOSPITAL**, 80 Jesse Hill Jr. Drive S.E., Zip 30303, Mailing Address: P.O. Box 26189, Zip 30303–3801; tel. 404/616–4307, (Total facility includes 260 beds in nursing home–type unit) **A**1 3 5 8 9 10 **F**2 4 6 11 12 13 14 15 17 19 21 22 23 26 27 28 29 32 33 34 35 36 37 38 39 40 42 43 44 45 46 47 48 49 50 52 53 55 56 57 58 59 60 61 62 63 64 65 66 67 69 70 71 72 73 74 75 76 77 78 81 82 83 84 85 86 87 88 89 90 92 93 94 96 98 99 100 101 102 103 104 105 106 107 108 109 110 **P**6 Primary Contact: Andrew Agwunobi, M.D., President and Chief Executive Officer COO: John D. Henry, Sr, FACHE, Chief Operating Officer CFO: Teresa Finch, Chief Financial Officer CMO: Curtis Lewis, M.D., Chief of Staff CIO: Michael Payne, Chief Informaton Officer CHR: Michael Black, Vice President Human Resources Web address: www.gradyhealthsystem.org	16	10	1004	27564	733	866924	3928	620531	231404	5243
HILLSIDE HOSPITAL, 690 Courtney Drive N.E., Zip 30306–0206, Mailing Address: P.O. Box 8247, Zip 31106–0247; tel. 404/875–4551 **F**21 26 28 29 65 66 71 72 74 92 96 108 **P**5 Primary Contact: Teresa Stoker, Chief Executive Officer Web address: www.hside.org	23	52	74	65	68	0	0	10474	5914	198
□ **KINDRED HOSPITAL–ATLANTA**, 705 Juniper Street N.E., Zip 30365–2500; tel. 404/873–2871, (Nonreporting) **A**1 9 10 **S** Kindred Healthcare, Louisville, KY Primary Contact: Craig Hoover, Chief Executive Officer Web address: www.kindredhealthcare.com	32	49	70	—	—	—	—	—	—	—
⊠ **NORTHSIDE HOSPITAL**, 1000 Johnson Ferry Road N.E., Zip 30342–1611; tel. 404/851–8000 **A**1 2 9 10 **F**4 9 10 11 12 14 15 21 22 23 26 27 28 29 33 35 37 39 40 42 46 47 48 49 52 53 55 56 57 58 59 60 61 62 63 64 65 66 69 70 73 77 78 79 80 81 82 84 85 86 87 88 93 94 96 99 106 108 109 **P**6 Primary Contact: Robert Quattrocchi, President and Chief Executive Officer CFO: Debbie Mitcham, Chief Financial Officer CIO: Tina Wakim, Vice President, Operations CHR: Dwight Hill, Vice President Human Resources Web address: www.northside.com	23	10	487	35844	415	300251	17990	525526	200714	—
□ **PEACHFORD BEHAVIORAL HEALTH SYSTEM**, 2151 Peachford Road, Zip 30338–6599; tel. 770/455–3200, (Nonreporting) **A**1 10 **S** Universal Health Services, Inc., King of Prussia, PA Primary Contact: Matthew Crouch, Chief Executive Officer Web address: www.peachfordhospital.com	33	22	224	—	—	—	—	—	—	—
⊠ △ **PIEDMONT HOSPITAL**, 1968 Peachtree Road N.W., Zip 30309–1231; tel. 404/605–5000, (Total facility includes 9 beds in nursing home–type unit) **A**1 2 3 5 7 9 10 **F**2 9 11 12 14 15 17 19 21 22 23 26 27 28 29 33 36 37 38 39 40 41 42 43 44 45 46 47 48 49 52 53 55 56 57 58 59 60 61 62 63 64 65 66 68 69 79 80 81 82 84 85 86 87 88 92 93 94 95 96 101 106 107 108 109 110 **P**1 3 **S** Piedmont Healthcare, Atlanta, GA Primary Contact: Robert W. Maynard, President and Chief Executive Officer CFO: Gregory A. Hurst, Executive Vice President and Chief Financial Officer CMO: Steve Taylor, M.D., Executive Vice President and Chief Medical Officer CIO: John Hilliard, Vice President Information Systems CHR: Joseph W. Herzberg, Vice President Human Resources Web address: www.piedmonthospital.org	23	10	441	27517	354	239928	4038	—	—	3251
⊠ **SAINT JOSEPH'S HOSPITAL OF ATLANTA**, 5665 Peachtree Dunwoody Road N.E., Zip 30342–1764; tel. 404/851–7001 **A**1 2 9 10 **F**2 9 10 12 14 15 17 19 21 22 23 26 27 28 29 33 35 36 37 38 39 41 43 46 47 48 49 50 52 53 55 57 58 60 61 62 63 64 65 66 69 79 80 81 82 84 85 86 87 88 94 96 100 108 110 **P**8 **S** Catholic Health East, Newtown Square, PA Primary Contact: Bonnie Phipps, President and Chief Executive Officer CFO: Michael Gardenier, Chief Financial Officer CMO: Eugene Davidson, Chief of Staff CHR: Alan Bradford, Vice President Human Resources Web address: www.stjosephsatlanta.org	23	10	346	23389	295	165883	0	294521	104600	1676
□ **SELECT SPECIALTY HOSPITAL–ATLANTA**, 550 Peachtree Street N.E., Zip 30327; tel. 404/350–4623, (Nonreporting) **A**1 10 Primary Contact: Phil Greenhill, Chief Executive Officer	33	49	30	—	—	—	—	—	—	—
□ △ **SHEPHERD CENTER**, 2020 Peachtree Road N.W., Zip 30309–1465; tel. 404/352–2020, (Nonreporting) **A**1 7 9 10 Primary Contact: Gary R. Ulicny, Ph.D., President and Chief Executive Officer Web address: www.shepherd.org	23	10	100	—	—	—	—	—	—	—
⊠ △ **SOUTH FULTON MEDICAL CENTER**, 1170 Cleveland Avenue, Zip 30344–3665; tel. 404/305–3500 **A**1 2 5 7 9 10 **F**1 10 11 12 14 15 17 19 21 23 33 37 44 46 47 48 49 52 53 55 56 57 58 59 61 62 63 65 68 69 79 80 81 82 84 88 92 94 108 109 **S** TENET Healthcare Corporation, Dallas, TX Primary Contact: Christopher Hummer, Chief Executive Officer COO: Roland Cruickshank, Chief Operating Officer Web address: www.southfultonmedicalcenter.com	33	10	260	9004	155	71281	1423	90573	34022	779

GA

Many Facility Codes have changed. Please refer to the AHA Guide Code Chart.

© 2005 AHA Guide

Hospital, Address, Telephone, Approval, Facility, and Physician Codes, Health Care System	Classi-fication Codes		Utilization Data					Expense (thousands) of dollars		
★ American Hospital Association (AHA) membership □ Joint Commission on Accreditation of Healthcare Organizations (JCAHO) accreditation ○ American Osteopathic Association (AOA) accreditation △ Commission on Accreditation of Rehabilitation Facilities (CARF) accreditation	Control	Service	Staffed Beds	Admissions	Census	Outpatient Visits	Births	Total	Payroll	Personnel

✸ **WESLEY WOODS CENTER OF EMORY UNIVERSITY**, (Multi–Discip Geri Hospital), 1821 Clifton Road N.E., Zip 30329–5102; tel. 404/728–6200, (Total facility includes 210 beds in nursing home–type unit) **A**1 3 5 9 10 **F**1 2 5 9 21 22 26 27 28 29 31 32 35 37 39 42 44 45 47 48 52 53 57 58 60 64 65 66 68 69 70 71 73 74 76 77 78 81 88 92 93 94 96 108 110 **S** Emory Healthcare, Atlanta, GA Primary Contact: John T. Fox, Chief Executive Officer COO: Peter A. Basler, Chief Operating Officer CFO: James T. Hatcher, Chief Financial Officer CMO: Joseph Auslander, Chief Medical Officer CIO: Dedra Cantrell, Chief Information Officer CHR: Margaret A. Bloomquist, Associate Administrator Web address: www.emory.org	23	49	304	2848	261	34496	0	48486	24980	592
AUGUSTA—Richmond County										
✸ **DOCTORS HOSPITAL**, 3651 Wheeler Road, Zip 30909–6426; tel. 706/651–3232 **A**1 9 10 **F**2 9 11 12 13 15 17 21 22 24 26 27 28 29 32 33 37 38 39 42 44 46 47 48 49 50 52 53 55 57 58 59 60 61 62 63 65 66 68 69 79 80 81 82 84 85 88 93 94 95 96 106 108 109 110 **P**5 8 **S** HCA, Nashville, TN Primary Contact: C. Shayne George, President and Chief Executive Officer CFO: Kelly Penton, Chief Financial Officer CMO: Howard A. Cohen, M.D., Medical Staff President CIO: Paul Patterson, Director Information Technology and Services Web address: www.doctors–hospital.net	33	10	255	10730	153	110327	1264	125915	51193	869
EAST CENTRAL REGIONAL HOSPITAL, (Formerly Georgia Regional Hospital at Augusta), 3405 Mike Padgett Highway, Zip 30906–3897; tel. 706/792–7000, (Includes EAST CENTRAL REGIONAL HOSPITAL, 100 Myrtle Boulevard, Gracewood, Zip 30812–1299; tel. 706/790–2011), (Total facility includes 100 beds in nursing home–type unit) (Nonreporting) **A**3 5 10 Primary Contact: Gail C. Jackson, M.D., Chief Executive Officer Web address: www.augustareg.dhr.state.ga.us	12	22	778	—	—	—	—	—	—	—
✸ **MEDICAL COLLEGE OF GEORGIA HOSPITAL AND CLINICS**, 1120 15th Street, Zip 30912–5000; tel. 706/721–0211 **A**1 2 3 5 8 9 10 12 **F**1 2 5 9 10 11 12 14 15 16 17 18 19 20 21 22 23 24 26 27 28 29 30 31 32 33 34 35 37 38 39 40 42 43 44 45 46 47 48 49 50 52 53 55 56 57 58 59 60 61 62 63 64 65 66 67 69 70 71 72 73 74 75 76 77 79 80 81 82 84 85 86 87 88 90 93 94 95 96 98 99 101 104 105 106 108 109 110 **P**3 7 Primary Contact: Donald F. Snell, President and Chief Executive Officer COO: Patricia Sodomka, FACHE, Executive Vice President/Chief Operating Officer CFO: Thomas Kelly, Jr, Senior Vice President and Chief Financial Officer CMO: Ralph Caruana, M.D., Senior Vice President and Chief Medical Officer CIO: Harold Scott, Chief Information Officer CHR: William G. Hayes, IV, Vice President Human Resources Web address: www.mcghealth.org	23	10	466	20577	322	465235	1640	333504	127716	3631
□ **SELECT SPECIALTY HOSPITAL**, 3651 Wheeler Road, 4th Floor, Zip 30909; tel. 706/651–3520, (Nonreporting) **A**1 10 Primary Contact: Brian Davis, Chief Executive Officer	33	49	34	—	—	—	—	—	—	—
SELECT SPECIALTY HOSPITAL OF AUGUSTA, 1350 Walton Way, 7th Floor, Zip 30901; tel. 706/774–7101, (Nonreporting) **A**10 Primary Contact: Brian Davis, Chief Executive Officer	33	49	30	—	—	—	—	—	—	—
✸ **ST. JOSEPH HOSPITAL**, 2260 Wrightsboro Road, Zip 30904–4726; tel. 706/481–7000, (Nonreporting) **A**1 5 9 10 **S** Ascension Health, Saint Louis, MO Primary Contact: Andrew A. Lasser, Dr.PH, President and Chief Executive Officer CFO: Raymond Owings, Chief Financial Officer CMO: Theresa Christie, Chief of Staff CIO: Charlotte Choate, Director Information Systems Web address: www.stjosephhospital.org	21	10	142	—	—	—	—	—	—	—
✸ **UNIVERSITY HEALTH CARE SYSTEM**, 1350 Walton Way, Zip 30901–2629; tel. 706/722–9011 **A**1 2 3 5 9 10 **F**2 10 11 12 14 15 17 19 21 22 23 24 26 27 28 29 31 33 34 35 37 38 39 41 42 44 46 47 48 49 50 51 52 53 55 56 57 58 59 60 61 62 63 64 65 66 69 70 73 81 82 84 85 86 87 88 92 93 94 95 96 98 106 107 108 109 110 **P**8 Primary Contact: J. Larry Read, President and Chief Executive Officer COO: Jason H. Moore, Chief Operating Officer CFO: Robert M. Taylor, Chief Financial Officer CMO: William L. Farr, M.D., Chief Medical Officer CIO: William Colbert, Chief Information Officer CHR: Richard J. Roche, Vice President for Human Resources Web address: www.universityhealth.org	23	10	499	20732	303	275633	2867	313208	121510	2451
✸ △ **VETERANS AFFAIRS MEDICAL CENTER**, 1 Freedom Way, Zip 30904–6285; tel. 706/733–0188, (Total facility includes 132 beds in nursing home–type unit) (Nonreporting) **A**1 2 3 5 7 8 9 **S** Department of Veterans Affairs, Washington, DC Primary Contact: James F. Trusley, III, Director COO: Ralph R. Angelo, Associate Director for Operations CFO: Walter Hitch, Chief Fiscal CMO: Thomas Kiernan, M.D., Chief of Staff CIO: Susan Lloyd, Chief Health Information Management and Revenue Administration CHR: Julie Choate, Chief Human Resources Web address: www.va.gov/sta/guide/home.asp	45	10	305	—	—	—	—	—	—	—

GA

Hospital, Address, Telephone, Approval, Facility, and Physician Codes, Health Care System	Classi-fication Codes		Utilization Data					Expense (thousands) of dollars		
★ American Hospital Association (AHA) membership □ Joint Commission on Accreditation of Healthcare Organizations (JCAHO) accreditation ○ American Osteopathic Association (AOA) accreditation △ Commission on Accreditation of Rehabilitation Facilities (CARF) accreditation	Control	Service	Staffed Beds	Admissions	Census	Outpatient Visits	Births	Total	Payroll	Personnel

	Control	Service	Staffed Beds	Admissions	Census	Outpatient Visits	Births	Total	Payroll	Personnel
□ △ **WALTON REHABILITATION HOSPITAL**, 1355 Independence Drive, Zip 30901–1037; tel. 706/724–7746 **A**1 7 9 10 **F**7 8 22 26 27 28 29 41 42 45 47 49 52 57 60 65 68 69 94 96 110 **P**1 Primary Contact: Dennis B. Skelley, President and Chief Executive Officer Web address: www.wrh.org	23	46	58	1078	38	82693	0	19759	8622	228
AUSTELL—Cobb County										
✠ △ **WELLSTAR COBB HOSPITAL**, 3950 Austell Road, Zip 30106–1121; tel. 770/732–4000 **A**1 7 10 **F**2 3 9 10 11 12 14 15 21 22 23 26 27 28 29 31 33 35 36 37 38 39 42 46 47 48 49 50 51 52 53 55 56 57 58 59 60 61 62 63 64 65 66 68 69 71 73 74 75 76 81 82 84 85 87 88 92 94 96 104 108 109 110 **P**1 6 **S** WellStar Health System, Marietta, GA Primary Contact: Randy Cook, Vice President and Administrator COO: Paul Johnson, Executive Vice President Operations CFO: Marsha Burke, Senior Vice President and Chief Financial Officer CMO: Larry Haldeman, M.D., Executive Vice President and Chief Medical Officer CIO: Leigh Cox, Chief Information Officer CHR: Mary Louise Tavernaro, Director Human Resources Web address: www.wellstar.org	23	10	342	22423	269	209145	4705	—	—	2038
BAINBRIDGE—Decatur County										
✠ **MEMORIAL HOSPITAL AND MANOR**, 1500 East Shotwell Street, Zip 39819–4256; tel. 229/246–3500, (Total facility includes 107 beds in nursing home–type unit) (Nonreporting) **A**1 9 10 Primary Contact: James G. Peak, Chief Executive Officer COO: Lee Harris, Assistant Administrator Support Services CFO: Billy Walker, Chief Financial Officer CIO: Nelda Moore, Data Processing Director CHR: Cathy Willis, Director Human Resources Web address: www.mh–m.org	16	10	221	—	—	—	—	—	—	—
BAXLEY—Appling County										
✠ **APPLING HEALTHCARE SYSTEM**, 163 East Tollison Street, Zip 31513–2898; tel. 912/367–9841, (Total facility includes 101 beds in nursing home–type unit) (Nonreporting) **A**1 9 10 Primary Contact: Dale Spell, Chief Executive Officer COO: Dale Spell, Chief Operating Officer CFO: Greg Jones, Chief Financial Officer CIO: Brian Snow, Information Systems Manager Web address: www.appling–hospital.org	23	10	140	—	—	—	—	—	—	—
BLAIRSVILLE—Union County										
✠ **UNION GENERAL HOSPITAL**, 214 Hospital Drive, Zip 30512–6538; tel. 706/745–2111, (Total facility includes 150 beds in nursing home–type unit) **A**1 9 10 20 **F**2 6 9 11 12 21 22 23 26 27 28 32 33 46 48 55 59 61 62 63 64 69 81 82 84 88 92 94 97 Primary Contact: Rebecca T. Dyer, Administrator COO: Mike Gowder, Assistant Administrator CFO: Tim Henry, Chief Financial Officer CMO: Andre Schaeffer, M.D., Chief of Staff CHR: Kathy Hood, Administrative Assistant Web address: www.uniongeneralhospital.com	16	10	195	1790	170	56456	205	23762	10659	348
BLAKELY—Early County										
✠ **EARLY MEMORIAL HOSPITAL**, 11740 Columbia Street, Zip 39823–9604; tel. 229/723–4241, (Total facility includes 127 beds in nursing home–type unit) **A**1 9 10 18 **F**2 6 11 12 21 22 26 27 28 29 33 35 39 44 45 46 47 48 52 53 58 59 60 63 65 66 69 70 73 81 88 92 94 96 97 106 108 109 110 **P**6 8 **S** Archbold Medical Center, Thomasville, GA Primary Contact: Robin Rau, Administrator CFO: William H. Sellers, Senior Vice President Web address: www.archbold.org	23	10	152	556	133	14935	34	12049	6185	187
BLUE RIDGE—Fannin County										
□ **FANNIN REGIONAL HOSPITAL**, 2855 Old Highway 5, Zip 30513–6248; tel. 706/632–3711 **A**1 9 10 **F**2 9 11 12 21 22 26 27 28 29 32 33 39 46 48 52 53 55 58 59 60 62 63 64 65 66 69 81 82 84 85 88 92 94 96 97 98 106 108 109 **P**6 **S** Community Health Systems, Inc., Brentwood, TN Primary Contact: Michael H. Huff, Interim Chief Executive Officer Web address: www.fanninregionalhospital.com	33	10	34	2903	25	28334	419	17402	8049	183
BREMEN—Haralson County										
✠ **HIGGINS GENERAL HOSPITAL**, 200 Allen Memorial Drive, Zip 30110–2012, Mailing Address: P.O. Box 655, Zip 30110–0655; tel. 770/537–5851, (Nonreporting) **A**1 9 10 18 Primary Contact: Robbie Smith, Administrator Web address: www.tanner.org	23	10	25	—	—	—	—	—	—	—

GA

Many Facility Codes have changed. Please refer to the AHA Guide Code Chart.

© 2005 AHA Guide

Hospital, Address, Telephone, Approval, Facility, and Physician Codes, Health Care System	Classi-fication Codes		Utilization Data					Expense (thousands) of dollars		
	Control	Service	Staffed Beds	Admissions	Census	Outpatient Visits	Births	Total	Payroll	Personnel

★ American Hospital Association (AHA) membership
☐ Joint Commission on Accreditation of Healthcare Organizations (JCAHO) accreditation
◯ American Osteopathic Association (AOA) accreditation
△ Commission on Accreditation of Rehabilitation Facilities (CARF) accreditation

BRUNSWICK—Glynn County

★ **SOUTHEAST GEORGIA HEALTH SYSTEM BRUNSWICK CAMPUS**, 2415 Parkwood Drive, Zip 31520–4252, Mailing Address: P.O. Box 1518, Zip 31521–1518; tel. 912/466–7000, (Total facility includes 16 beds in nursing home–type unit) **A**1 2 9 10 19 20 **F**2 9 10 11 12 14 15 17 21 22 23 24 26 27 28 29 31 33 35 37 38 39 40 42 43 44 46 47 48 50 53 55 57 58 59 60 61 62 63 64 65 66 68 69 70 71 73 74 75 76 79 80 81 82 84 85 86 88 92 93 94 95 96 106 107 108 109 110 **P**6 8 **S** Southeast Georgia Health System, Brunswick, GA
Primary Contact: Gary R. Colberg, CHE, President and Chief Executive Officer
CFO: Michael D. Scherneck, Vice President and Chief Financial Officer
CMO: T Wayne Rentz, M.D., Chief of Staff
CIO: Chuck Bumgardner, Director Information Systems
CHR: Rachel West, Vice President Human Resources
Web address: www.sghs.org
| 16 | 10 | 247 | 10646 | 157 | 123738 | 1355 | 126848 | 48981 | 1149 |

CAIRO—Grady County

★ **GRADY GENERAL HOSPITAL**, 1155 Fifth Street S.E., Zip 39828–0360, Mailing Address: P.O. Box 360, Zip 39828–0360; tel. 229/377–1150 **A**1 10 **F**9 11 12 21 26 27 28 29 33 39 46 47 48 52 53 55 58 59 60 62 63 65 66 69 75 81 88 93 97 **P**6 8 **S** Archbold Medical Center, Thomasville, GA
Primary Contact: Kenneth D. Rhudy, Administrator
CFO: Bill Sellers, Chief Financial Officer
CIO: William Zimmermann, Chief Information Officer
Web address: www.archbold.org
| 23 | 10 | 48 | 3151 | 25 | 36911 | 306 | 20314 | 7207 | 173 |

CALHOUN—Gordon County

★ **GORDON HOSPITAL**, 1035 Red Bud Road, Zip 30701–2082, Mailing Address: P.O. Box 12938, Zip 30703–7013; tel. 706/629–2895 **A**1 9 10 **F**2 6 9 11 12 21 22 23 26 27 28 29 33 37 46 48 51 52 55 58 59 60 61 62 63 64 69 76 77 78 81 82 84 85 88 93 106 107 108 109 **P**1 6 **S** Adventist Health System Sunbelt Health Care Corporation, Winter Park, FL
Primary Contact: Carlene Jamerson, President and Chief Executive Officer
CFO: Ed Klein, Chief Financial Officer
CMO: David Brannon, M.D., Chief of Staff
Web address: www.gordonhospital.com
| 21 | 10 | 65 | 3886 | 39 | 47854 | 704 | 42904 | 19562 | 445 |

CAMILLA—Mitchell County

★ **MITCHELL COUNTY HOSPITAL**, 90 Stephens Street, Zip 31730, Mailing Address: P.O. Box 639, Zip 31730–0639; tel. 229/336–5284, (Total facility includes 156 beds in nursing home–type unit) **A**1 9 10 18 **F**11 12 26 27 28 33 36 46 48 53 58 59 60 63 65 66 81 84 88 92 94 97 **P**6 8 **S** Archbold Medical Center, Thomasville, GA
Primary Contact: J. Randall Phillips, CHE, Administrator
COO: Perry Mustian, Chief Operating Officer
CFO: J William Sellers, Jr, Senior Vice President and Chief Financial Officer
CMO: Melvin Hartsfield, M.D., Vice President Medical Affairs
CIO: William Zimmermann, Chief Information Officer
CHR: Vickie County, Coordinator Human Resources
Web address: www.archbold.org/mitchellcountyhospital
| 13 | 10 | 181 | 926 | 171 | 18779 | 155 | 18758 | 9228 | 165 |

CANTON—Cherokee County

★ **NORTHSIDE HOSPITAL – CHEROKEE**, 201 Hospital Road, Zip 30114–2408, Mailing Address: P.O. Box 906, Zip 30114–0906; tel. 770/720–5100, (Nonreporting) **A**1 9 10
Primary Contact: William M. Hayes, Chief Executive Officer
CFO: Steve Greene, Chief Financial Officer
Web address: www.northside.com
| 23 | 10 | 85 | — | — | — | — | — | — | — |

CARROLLTON—Carroll County

★ **TANNER MEDICAL CENTER**, 705 Dixie Street, Zip 30117–3818; tel. 770/836–9666, (Total facility includes 20 beds in nursing home–type unit) (Nonreporting) **A**1 9 10
Primary Contact: Loy M. Howard, Chief Executive Officer
COO: Richard L. McConahy, Chief Operating Officer
CFO: Lee Sherseth, Chief Financial Officer
CHR: Vivian Barr, Director Human Resources
Web address: www.tanner.org/
| 23 | 10 | 176 | — | — | — | — | — | — | — |

CARTERSVILLE—Bartow County

★ **EMORY CARTERSVILLE MEDICAL CENTER**, 960 Joe Frank Harris Parkway, Zip 30120–2129, Mailing Address: P.O. Box 200008, Zip 30120–9001; tel. 770/382–1530, (Nonreporting) **A**1 9 10 **S** HCA, Nashville, TN
Primary Contact: Keith Sandlin, Chief Executive Officer
Web address: www.cartersvillemedical.com
| 33 | 10 | 80 | — | — | — | — | — | — | — |

CEDARTOWN—Polk County

★ **POLK MEDICAL CENTER**, 424 North Main Street, Zip 30125–2698; tel. 770/748–2500 **A**1 9 10 18 **F**2 12 21 26 27 28 33 36 39 48 52 53 58 60 63 69 81 82 88 93 94 97 98 108 110 **S** HCA, Nashville, TN
Primary Contact: Steve C. Hoelscher, Chief Executive Officer
CFO: Tim Prestridge, Chief Financial Officer
CHR: Jeanna Smith, Administrative Assistant and Human Resources Officer
Web address: www.polkmedicalcenter.com
| 33 | 10 | 22 | 473 | 5 | 35299 | 0 | 9948 | 4456 | 108 |

GA

Hospital, Address, Telephone, Approval, Facility, and Physician Codes, Health Care System	Classi-fication Codes		Utilization Data					Expense (thousands) of dollars		
★ American Hospital Association (AHA) membership □ Joint Commission on Accreditation of Healthcare Organizations (JCAHO) accreditation ○ American Osteopathic Association (AOA) accreditation △ Commission on Accreditation of Rehabilitation Facilities (CARF) accreditation	Control	Service	Staffed Beds	Admissions	Census	Outpatient Visits	Births	Total	Payroll	Personnel

CHATSWORTH—Murray County

□ **MURRAY MEDICAL CENTER**, 707 Old Ellijay Road, Zip 30705–2060, Mailing Address: P.O. Box 1406, Zip 30705–1406; tel. 706/695–4564 **A**1 9 10 **F**9 12 21 27 28 33 46 48 55 60 63 66 70 79 81 88 93 108
Primary Contact: James Hazel, M.D., Chief Executive Officer
Web address: www.hamiltonhealth.com/hhcs/
| 23 | 10 | 33 | 1208 | 12 | 32478 | 0 | 15452 | 7543 | 158 |

CLAXTON—Evans County

⊠ **EVANS MEMORIAL HOSPITAL**, 200 North River Street, Zip 30417–1659, Mailing Address: P.O. Box 518, Zip 30417–0518; tel. 912/739–5000, (Total facility includes 160 beds in nursing home–type unit) **A**1 9 10 **F**2 6 9 11 12 21 26 33 41 46 48 58 62 63 69 81 82 84 87 88 92 93 94 97 106
Primary Contact: Ronald M. Gilliard, FACHE, Chief Executive Officer
CFO: Martha Tatum, Chief Financial Officer
CMO: Randy Hawkins, M.D., Chief of Staff
CHR: Gina Waters, Director Human Resources
| 23 | 10 | 195 | 1405 | 154 | 38367 | 262 | 22632 | 10817 | 436 |

CLAYTON—Rabun County

★ **RABUN COUNTY HOSPITAL**, 196 Ridgecrest Circle, Zip 30525–4111; tel. 706/782–4233 **A**9 10 18 **F**2 9 12 21 22 26 27 28 29 33 46 47 48 52 53 58 60 63 65 81 88 97 108 **P**5
Primary Contact: Bill Allen, Chief Executive Officer
Web address: www.rabunhospital.com
| 16 | 10 | 25 | 768 | 9 | 17470 | 0 | 8210 | 3675 | 91 |

COCHRAN—Bleckley County

□ **BLECKLEY MEMORIAL HOSPITAL**, 408 Peacock Street, Zip 31014–1559, Mailing Address: P.O. Box 536, Zip 31014–0536; tel. 478/934–6211, (Nonreporting) **A**1 9 10 18 **S** Memorial Health Services, Adel, GA
Primary Contact: Cary Martin, Administrator
| 16 | 10 | 25 | — | — | — | — | — | — | — |

COLQUITT—Miller County

★ **MILLER COUNTY HOSPITAL**, 209 North Cuthbert Street, Zip 39837, Mailing Address: P.O. Box 7, Zip 39837; tel. 229/758–3385, (Total facility includes 97 beds in nursing home–type unit) **A**9 10 18 **F**11 12 21 22 26 27 33 46 48 59 60 63 66 69 77 81 84 88 92 93 94 97 108 110
Primary Contact: Harley Smith, Chief Executive Officer
CFO: Lesli Evans, Chief Financial Officer
CMO: David McCann, M.D., Chief of Staff
CIO: Keith Lovering, Information Technician
CHR: Starling Bussey, Director Human Resources
Web address: www.millercountyhospital.com
| 16 | 10 | 135 | 902 | 99 | 15510 | 46 | 17960 | 8196 | 258 |

COLUMBUS—Muscogee County

BRADLEY CENTER OF ST. FRANCIS See St. Francis Hospital, Inc.

COLUMBUS SPECIALTY HOSPITAL, 710 Center Street, 9th Floor, Zip 31901; tel. 706/321–6712, (Nonreporting) **A**9 10
Primary Contact: Greg Thomsen, Chief Executive Officer
| 23 | 80 | 30 | — | — | — | — | — | — | — |

⊠ **DOCTORS HOSPITAL OF COLUMBUS**, 616 19th Street, Zip 31901–1528, Mailing Address: P.O. Box 2188, Zip 31902–2188; tel. 706/494–4262 **A**1 2 10 **F**2 9 10 11 12 15 17 21 23 26 27 28 29 33 34 37 39 45 46 47 48 50 52 53 55 57 58 59 61 62 63 66 70 81 82 85 88 93 94 96 108 109 **S** HCA, Nashville, TN
Primary Contact: Hugh D. Wilson, Chief Executive Officer
CFO: Bill Saller, Chief Financial Officer
CMO: Thomas L. Theus, M.D., Chief of Medicine
CIO: David Cornelius, Director Information Services
CHR: Louise Truitt, Director of Human Resources
Web address: www.doctorshospital.net
| 33 | 10 | 171 | 6312 | 82 | 62767 | 1162 | 59880 | 25713 | 617 |

⊠ **HUGHSTON ORTHOPEDIC HOSPITAL**, (Formerly Hughston Sports Medicine Hospital), 100 Frist Court, Zip 31908–7188, Mailing Address: P.O. Box 7188, Zip 31908–7188; tel. 706/576–2101 **A**1 3 5 10 **F**2 21 22 27 28 29 48 52 53 55 60 62 63 65 66 68 69 81 82 84 88 94 95 **S** HCA, Nashville, TN
Primary Contact: Donald R. Avery, FACHE, President and Chief Executive Officer
Web address: www.hughstonsports.com
| 33 | 47 | 100 | 3966 | 43 | 5168 | 0 | 46470 | 12260 | 254 |

⊠ **ST. FRANCIS HOSPITAL, INC.**, 2122 Manchester Expressway, Zip 31904–6878, Mailing Address: P.O. Box 7000, Zip 31908–7000; tel. 706/596–4000, (Includes BRADLEY CENTER OF ST. FRANCIS, 2000 16th Avenue, Zip 31906–0308; tel. 706/320–3700) **A**1 9 10 **F**1 2 9 12 14 15 17 19 21 22 23 28 29 30 31 33 35 37 39 41 42 44 46 47 48 49 52 53 55 58 60 61 62 63 64 65 69 73 75 81 82 84 85 88 92 93 96 106 107 108 109 110 **P**6
Primary Contact: James V. Giordano, Interim President and Chief Executive Officer
CFO: Robert C. Kelly, Senior Vice President Finance and Chief Financial Officer
CMO: H Belk Brooks, M.D., Chief of Staff
CIO: Scott Rattray, Vice President and Chief Information Officer
CHR: Mike Meeks, Vice President Human Resources
Web address: www.sfhga.com
| 23 | 10 | 217 | 9297 | 130 | 86699 | 0 | 116061 | 46176 | 1161 |

GA

Hospital, Address, Telephone, Approval, Facility, and Physician Codes, Health Care System	Classi-fication Codes		Utilization Data					Expense (thousands) of dollars		
★ American Hospital Association (AHA) membership □ Joint Commission on Accreditation of Healthcare Organizations (JCAHO) accreditation ○ American Osteopathic Association (AOA) accreditation △ Commission on Accreditation of Rehabilitation Facilities (CARF) accreditation	Control	Service	Staffed Beds	Admissions	Census	Outpatient Visits	Births	Total	Payroll	Personnel
✦ **THE MEDICAL CENTER**, 710 Center Street, Zip 31901–1527, Mailing Address: P.O. Box 951, Zip 31902–0951; tel. 706/571–1000, (Total facility includes 128 beds in nursing home–type unit) **A**1 2 3 5 9 10 12 **F**4 9 11 12 15 21 22 23 27 28 29 33 35 37 39 44 46 47 48 49 50 52 53 55 56 58 59 60 61 62 63 65 66 67 69 70 71 73 74 75 77 79 80 81 82 84 85 87 88 92 93 94 96 98 106 107 108 109 110 **P**6 8 **S** Columbus Regional Healthcare System, Columbus, GA Primary Contact: Lance B. Duke, FACHE, President and Chief Executive Officer CFO: Roland Thacker, Senior Vice President and Chief Financial Officer CMO: Andrew P. Morley, Jr, M.D., Senior Vice President and Chief Medical Officer CIO: Joe Wood, Vice President and Chief Information Officer CHR: Wayne Joiner, Vice President Human Resources Web address: www.columbusregional.com	23	10	537	15248	321	184412	2841	199193	79193	2032
□ **WEST CENTRAL GEORGIA REGIONAL HOSPITAL**, 3000 Schatulga Road, Zip 31995–3117, Mailing Address: P.O. Box 12435, Zip 31995–2435; tel. 706/568–5000, (Total facility includes 40 beds in nursing home–type unit) **A**1 9 10 **F**22 26 27 28 32 37 41 47 58 60 65 66 71 72 74 75 92 94 96 98 106 108 **P**6 Primary Contact: James L. Dodd, Ph.D., Superintendent Web address: www.wcgrh.org	12	22	205	2282	173	522	0	24326	14419	457
COMMERCE—Jackson County										
✦ **BJC MEDICAL CENTER**, 70 Medical Center Drive, Zip 30529–9989; tel. 706/335–1000, (Total facility includes 167 beds in nursing home–type unit) (Nonreporting) **A**1 9 10 Primary Contact: James Yarborough, Chief Executive Officer CFO: Ralph D. Williams, Chief Financial Officer CMO: Peter Markov, M.D., Chief of Staff CIO: Gary Fortner, Systems Support Manager CHR: Marilyn Anglin, Director of Human Resources Web address: www.bjcmc.org	16	10	233	—	—	—	—	—	—	—
CONYERS—Rockdale County										
✦ **ROCKDALE MEDICAL CENTER**, (Formerly Rockdale Hospital and Health System), 1412 Milstead Avenue N.E., Zip 30012; tel. 770/918–3000 **A**1 2 9 10 **F**2 9 10 11 12 14 15 21 22 23 27 28 29 33 37 42 46 47 48 51 52 53 55 56 57 58 59 60 61 62 63 64 65 66 69 81 82 84 87 88 94 95 96 98 106 107 108 109 110 **P**1 Primary Contact: David Huber, Chief Executive Officer CFO: Anne H. Finlon, Chief Financial Officer CMO: Frank Patton, Chief of Staff CIO: Jennifer Croly, Vice President Technology Web address: www.rockdalehospital.org	23	10	115	7778	95	131206	1882	83125	38796	745
CORDELE—Crisp County										
✦ **CRISP REGIONAL HOSPITAL**, 902 North Seventh Street, Zip 31015–5007; tel. 229/276–3100, (Total facility includes 143 beds in nursing home–type unit) **A**1 9 10 20 **F**8 9 11 12 22 23 24 29 33 36 37 40 42 44 45 46 47 48 49 51 52 55 58 59 60 61 63 65 66 69 70 81 82 83 84 85 87 91 92 93 94 96 106 108 110 Primary Contact: D. Wayne Martin, President and Chief Executive Officer CFO: Charlotte Vestal, Chief Financial Officer CIO: Mark Dose, Director Marketing Web address: www.crispregional.org	13	10	208	4955	166	95819	415	—	—	887
COVINGTON—Newton County										
✦ **NEWTON MEDICAL CENTER**, 5126 Hospital Drive, Zip 30014–2567; tel. 770/786–7053 **A**1 9 10 **F**6 9 11 12 15 21 23 27 28 29 33 37 41 46 47 48 51 52 53 55 57 58 59 62 63 64 65 66 69 70 73 81 82 83 84 85 87 88 93 94 96 106 108 109 110 **P**6 8 Primary Contact: James F. Weadick, Administrator and Chief Executive Officer CFO: Troy Brooks, Assistant Administrator Fiscal Services CMO: Clinton Holladay, M.D., Chief of Staff CIO: Sheila Higgins, Interim Director CHR: Greg Richardson, Director Human Resources Web address: www.ngh.org/	23	10	90	5695	55	171991	784	48657	23812	583
CUMMING—Forsyth County										
★ **NORTHSIDE HOSPITAL FORSYTH**, 1200 Baptist Medical Center Drive, Zip 30041–7659; tel. 770/844–3200, (Nonreporting) **A**9 10 Primary Contact: Lynn Jackson, Administrator CFO: Mitch Logan, Director Finance Web address: www.northside.com	23	10	41	—	—	—	—	—	—	—
CUTHBERT—Randolph County										
★ **SOUTHWEST GEORGIA REGIONAL MEDICAL CENTER**, 109 Randolph Street, Zip 39840–1338; tel. 229/732–2181, (Total facility includes 80 beds in nursing home–type unit) **A**9 10 18 **F**12 27 28 33 52 60 63 69 76 81 88 92 97 108 **P**8 Primary Contact: Robert F. Letson, Chief Executive Officer CFO: Todd Cox, Chief Financial Officer	16	10	105	372	81	19274	0	9294	4083	310
DAHLONEGA—Lumpkin County										
□ **CHESTATEE REGIONAL HOSPITAL**, 227 Mountain Drive, Zip 30533–1606; tel. 706/864–6136, (Nonreporting) **A**1 9 10 **S** Sunlink Healthcare, Atlanta, GA Primary Contact: Rob Followell, Chief Executive Officer Web address: www.chestateeregionalhospital.com	33	10	49	—	—	—	—	—	—	—

GA

Hospital, Address, Telephone, Approval, Facility, and Physician Codes, Health Care System	Classi-fication Codes		Utilization Data					Expense (thousands) of dollars		
★ American Hospital Association (AHA) membership □ Joint Commission on Accreditation of Healthcare Organizations (JCAHO) accreditation ○ American Osteopathic Association (AOA) accreditation △ Commission on Accreditation of Rehabilitation Facilities (CARF) accreditation	Control	Service	Staffed Beds	Admissions	Census	Outpatient Visits	Births	Total	Payroll	Personnel

DALLAS—Paulding County

☒ **WELLSTAR PAULDING HOSPITAL**, 600 West Memorial Drive, Zip 30132–1335; tel. 770/445–4411, (Total facility includes 182 beds in nursing home–type unit) **A**1 9 10 **F**2 9 10 12 21 22 26 27 28 29 31 33 35 39 46 48 50 52 53 55 57 58 60 62 63 64 65 66 69 75 81 82 85 87 88 92 94 96 108 110 **P**1 6 **S** WellStar Health System, Marietta, GA
Primary Contact: John Law, Site Administrator
CFO: Marsha Burke, Senior Vice President Financial Services
CMO: Larry Halderman, M.D., Executive Vice President and Chief Medical Officer
Web address: www.wellstar.org
| 23 | 10 | 216 | 1934 | 179 | 46998 | 0 | — | — | 386 |

DALTON—Whitfield County

☒ **HAMILTON MEDICAL CENTER**, 1200 Memorial Drive, Zip 30720–2529, Mailing Address: P.O. Box 1168, Zip 30722–1168; tel. 706/272–6000 **A**1 2 9 10 19 **F**1 3 4 10 11 12 15 21 22 23 24 27 28 29 31 33 34 35 36 37 39 40 41 42 46 48 50 51 52 53 55 57 58 59 60 61 62 63 64 65 69 71 72 73 74 75 76 77 78 81 82 84 88 92 93 94 95 96 106 108 109 110 **P**8
Primary Contact: John S. Bowling, President and Chief Executive Officer
COO: Karen J. Wisdom, Chief Operating Officer and Senior Vice President
CFO: Gary L. Howard, Chief Financial Officer
CIO: John M. Forrester, Director
CHR: Steven Pound, Vice President
Web address: www.hamiltonhealth.com
| 23 | 10 | 256 | 10661 | 118 | 202729 | 2384 | — | — | 1102 |

DECATUR—De Kalb County

DECATUR HOSPITAL See Dekalb Medical Center at Decatur

☒ △ **DEKALB MEDICAL CENTER**, 2701 North Decatur Road, Zip 30033–5995; tel. 404/501–1000, (Nonreporting) **A**1 2 7 9 10 **S** DeKalb Medical Center, Decatur, GA
Primary Contact: Eric P. Norwood, President and Chief Executive Officer
COO: John Shelton, Chief Operating Officer
CFO: Susan G. Sciullo, Chief Financial Officer
CMO: Duane Barclay, M.D., Vice President Physician Support Services
CIO: Cynthia Davis, Chief Information Officer
CHR: Tom Crawford, Vice President Human Resources
Web address: www.dekalbmedicalcenter.org
| 23 | 10 | 389 | — | — | — | — | — | — | — |

□ **DEKALB MEDICAL CENTER AT DECATUR**, (Formerly Decatur Hospital), 450 North Candler Street, Zip 30030–2671; tel. 404/501–6700, (Nonreporting) **A**1 9 10 **S** DeKalb Medical Center, Decatur, GA
Primary Contact: Skip Wright, Vice President and Administrator
Web address: www.dekalbmedicalcenter.org
| 23 | 10 | 84 | — | — | — | — | — | — | — |

□ **GEORGIA REGIONAL HOSPITAL AT ATLANTA**, 3073 Panthersville Road, Zip 30034–3828; tel. 404/243–2100, (Total facility includes 110 beds in nursing home–type unit) **A**1 3 5 9 10 **F**9 21 22 32 35 47 53 66 70 71 72 75 76 92 94 106 **P**6
Primary Contact: Ronald C. Hogan, Chief Executive Officer
Web address: www.atlantareg.dhr.state.ga.us
| 12 | 22 | 352 | 3739 | 298 | 2951 | 0 | 43024 | 27521 | 794 |

☒ **VETERANS AFFAIRS MEDICAL CENTER**, 1670 Clairmont Road, Zip 30033–4004; tel. 404/321–6111, (Total facility includes 120 beds in nursing home–type unit) **A**1 2 3 5 8 **F**1 2 3 4 7 10 12 14 15 21 22 25 28 29 30 31 32 33 36 37 38 39 42 44 45 47 48 49 50 51 52 53 55 57 58 60 61 62 63 65 66 69 70 71 73 74 75 76 77 78 79 81 82 84 86 87 88 93 94 95 96 106 107 108 109 110 **S** Department of Veterans Affairs, Washington, DC
Primary Contact: Thomas A. Cappello, Director
CFO: Joseph Albanese, Chief Financial Officer
CMO: David Bower, M.D., Chief of Staff
CIO: Linda Feaselman, Chief Information Officer
Web address: www.va.gov/sta/guide/home.asp
| 45 | 10 | 173 | 4114 | 146 | | | | | |

DEMOREST—Habersham County

☒ **HABERSHAM COUNTY MEDICAL CENTER**, 541 Historic Highway 441, Zip 30535–3118, Mailing Address: P.O. Box 37, Zip 30535–0037; tel. 706/754–2161, (Total facility includes 106 beds in nursing home–type unit) **A**1 9 10 **F**2 3 6 8 9 11 12 13 14 21 22 27 28 29 31 33 35 36 37 41 42 45 46 47 48 51 52 53 55 56 58 59 60 62 63 65 66 67 68 69 71 81 82 84 86 88 92 93 94 95 96 106 108 109 **P**7 **S** Quorum Health Resources, Plano, TX
Primary Contact: C. Richard Dwozan, Chief Executive Officer
CFO: James Peterson, Chief Financial Officer
CMO: David Beaty, M.D., Chief of Staff
CIO: Roger Ivester, Information Systems Manager
CHR: Janet Chapman, Vice President Human Resources
Web address: www.hcmcmed.org
| 16 | 10 | 159 | 2355 | 125 | 73529 | 498 | 35975 | 15133 | 487 |

DONALSONVILLE—Seminole County

□ **DONALSONVILLE HOSPITAL**, 102 Hospital Circle, Zip 39845–1199; tel. 229/524–5217, (Total facility includes 75 beds in nursing home–type unit) (Nonreporting) **A**1 10
Primary Contact: Charles H. Orrick, Administrator
| 23 | 10 | 140 | — | — | — | — | — | — | — |

Hospital, Address, Telephone, Approval, Facility, and Physician Codes, Health Care System	Classi-fication Codes		Utilization Data					Expense (thousands) of dollars		
★ American Hospital Association (AHA) membership □ Joint Commission on Accreditation of Healthcare Organizations (JCAHO) accreditation ○ American Osteopathic Association (AOA) accreditation △ Commission on Accreditation of Rehabilitation Facilities (CARF) accreditation	Control	Service	Staffed Beds	Admissions	Census	Outpatient Visits	Births	Total	Payroll	Personnel

DOUGLAS—Coffee County

☒ **COFFEE REGIONAL MEDICAL CENTER**, 1101 Ocilla Road, Zip 31533–3617, Mailing Address: P.O. Box 1287, Zip 31534–1287; tel. 912/384–1900 **A**1 9 10 20 **F**2 6 9 11 12 21 22 23 24 26 27 28 29 31 33 36 37 42 44 45 46 47 48 50 51 53 55 58 59 61 62 63 64 65 66 69 70 81 82 84 85 88 94 95 96 106 107 108 109 **P**8
Primary Contact: George L. Heck, III, President and Chief Executive Officer
CFO: Donald C. Lewis, Jr, Vice President and Chief Financial Officer
CMO: C J. Reddy, M.D., Medical Staff President
CIO: George L. Heck, III, President and Chief Executive Officer
CHR: Stewart King, Vice President Human Resources
Web address: www.coffeeregional.org
| 23 | 10 | 88 | 5813 | 54 | 37881 | 685 | 57603 | 24487 | 595 |

DOUGLASVILLE—Douglas County

INNER HARBOUR HOSPITALS, 4685 Dorsett Shoals Road, Zip 30135–4999; tel. 770/942–2391 **A**9 **F**4 42 66 71 72 73 74 77 78 94 96 108 **P**6
Primary Contact: Emily Acker, Administrator
Web address: www.innerharbour.org
| 23 | 52 | 225 | 407 | 214 | 4578 | 0 | 25575 | 15841 | 489 |

☒ **WELLSTAR DOUGLAS HOSPITAL**, 8954 Hospital Drive, Zip 30134–2282; tel. 770/949–1500 **A**1 9 10 **F**2 9 11 12 21 22 26 27 28 29 31 33 35 39 46 47 48 49 50 52 53 55 57 58 59 60 62 63 64 65 66 69 75 81 82 84 85 87 88 92 94 96 108 109 110 **P**1 6 **S** WellStar Health System, Marietta, GA
Primary Contact: Michael Poore, Vice President and Administrator
COO: Paul Johnson, Executive Vice President Operations
CFO: Marsha Burke, Senior Vice President and Chief Financial Officer
CMO: Larry Halderman, M.D., Executive Vice President and Chief Medical Officer
CIO: Leigh Cox, Chief Information Officer
Web address: www.wellstar.org
| 23 | 10 | 71 | 5083 | 58 | 94232 | 423 | — | — | 483 |

DUBLIN—Laurens County

☒ **CARL VINSON VETERANS AFFAIRS MEDICAL CENTER**, 1826 Veterans Boulevard, Zip 31021–3620; tel. 478/272–1210, (Total facility includes 161 beds in nursing home–type unit) (Nonreporting) **A**1 **S** Department of Veterans Affairs, Washington, DC
Primary Contact: Richard W. Fry, Director
COO: Kelly O. Duke, Associate Director
CFO: Marcy Chambless, Business Office Service Line Manager
CMO: Eva Martin, M.D., Chief of Staff
CIO: Sandra Clem, Manager Information Management Service Line
CHR: Teresa L. Lindsey, Human Resources Supervisor
Web address: www.va.gov/sta/guide/home.asp
| 45 | 10 | 339 | — | — | — | — | — | — | — |

☒ **FAIRVIEW PARK HOSPITAL**, 200 Industrial Boulevard, Zip 31021–2997, Mailing Address: P.O. Box 1408, Zip 31040–1408; tel. 478/275–2000 **A**1 9 10 **F**2 9 11 12 14 15 21 23 26 27 28 29 33 34 37 41 44 46 48 52 55 57 58 59 60 61 62 63 64 65 68 69 81 82 84 85 87 88 93 94 95 96 106 108 109 110 **S** HCA, Nashville, TN
Primary Contact: James E. Raynor, Chief Executive Officer
COO: Brad Griffin, Associate Administrator
CFO: Ted Short, Chief Financial Officer
CMO: Jeri Miller, M.D., President Medical Staff
CIO: Marsha Morris, Manager Information Services
CHR: Jeff Bruton, Director, Human Resources
Web address: www.fairviewparkhospital.com
| 33 | 10 | 190 | 7646 | 82 | 79208 | 1150 | 61197 | 22832 | 619 |

DULUTH—Gwinnett County

JOAN GLANCY MEMORIAL HOSPITAL See Gwinnett Hospital System, Lawrenceville

EAST POINT—Fulton County

★ **REGENCY HOSPITAL OF SOUTH ATLANTA**, 1170 Cleveland Avenue, 4th Floor, Zip 30344; tel. 404/466–6250, (Nonreporting) **A**10 **S** Regency Hospital Company, Alpharetta, GA
Primary Contact: Carolyn S. Gray, Chief Executive Officer
| 33 | 80 | 25 | — | — | — | — | — | — | — |

EASTMAN—Dodge County

□ **DODGE COUNTY HOSPITAL**, 901 Griffin Avenue, Zip 31023–2223, Mailing Address: P.O. Box 4309, Zip 31023–4309; tel. 478/374–4000 **A**1 9 10 **F**2 6 9 12 22 23 26 27 28 29 33 41 46 48 52 54 55 58 59 60 63 65 66 69 71 76 81 84 88 94 96 97 108 110
Primary Contact: Kenneth Stegner, Interim Chief Executive Officer
Web address: www.dodgecountyhospital.com
| 16 | 10 | 87 | 3036 | 34 | 46998 | 194 | 23562 | 11223 | 331 |

EATONTON—Putnam County

□ **PUTNAM GENERAL HOSPITAL**, 101 Lake Oconee Parkway, Zip 31024–4330, Mailing Address: Box 4330, Zip 31024–4330; tel. 706/485–2711 **A**1 9 10 18 **F**9 12 21 26 27 28 33 46 52 55 58 63 65 69 81 88 92 97 107
Primary Contact: Darrell M. Oglesby, Administrator
Web address: www.putnamgeneral.com
| 16 | 10 | 25 | 961 | 8 | 21103 | 0 | 11238 | 4671 | 120 |

ELBERTON—Elbert County

☒ **ELBERT MEMORIAL HOSPITAL**, 4 Medical Drive, Zip 30635–1897; tel. 706/283–3151, (Nonreporting) **A**1 9 10 **S** Quorum Health Resources, Plano, TX
Primary Contact: Mark LeNeave, Chief Executive Officer
CFO: Larry Magers, Chief Financial Officer
Web address: www.elbertmemorialhospital.net
| 16 | 10 | 52 | — | — | — | — | — | — | — |

GA

Hospital, Address, Telephone, Approval, Facility, and Physician Codes, Health Care System	Classi-fication Codes		Utilization Data					Expense (thousands) of dollars		
★ American Hospital Association (AHA) membership □ Joint Commission on Accreditation of Healthcare Organizations (JCAHO) accreditation ○ American Osteopathic Association (AOA) accreditation △ Commission on Accreditation of Rehabilitation Facilities (CARF) accreditation	Control	Service	Staffed Beds	Admissions	Census	Outpatient Visits	Births	Total	Payroll	Personnel

ELLIJAY—Gilmer County

□ **NORTH GEORGIA MEDICAL CENTER**, 1362 South Main Street, Zip 30540–0346, Mailing Address: P.O. Box 2239, Zip 30540–0346; tel. 706/276–4741, (Total facility includes 100 beds in nursing home–type unit) (Nonreporting) **A**1 9 10 **S** Sunlink Healthcare, Atlanta, GA
Primary Contact: Jeffrey Dunn, Chief Executive Officer
Control 33, Service 10, Staffed Beds 150

FAYETTEVILLE—Fayette County

□ **PIEDMONT FAYETTE HOSPITAL**, (Formerly Fayette Community Hospital), 1255 Highway 54 West, Zip 30214; tel. 770/719–7000, (Nonreporting) **A**1 10 **S** Piedmont Healthcare, Atlanta, GA
Primary Contact: W. Darrell Cutts, President and Chief Executive Officer
Control 33, Service 10, Staffed Beds 100

FITZGERALD—Ben Hill County

□ **DORMINY MEDICAL CENTER**, Perry House Road, Zip 31750, Mailing Address: P.O. Box 1447, Zip 31750–1447; tel. 229/424–7100 **A**1 9 10 **F**2 9 11 12 21 22 26 28 29 33 36 38 39 46 47 48 52 53 55 58 59 60 63 66 68 69 81 84 88 93 94 97 110
Primary Contact: Bruce Shepard, Administrator
Web address: www.dorminymedical.org
Control 16, Service 10, Staffed Beds 67, Admissions 2167, Census 24, Outpatient Visits 11033, Births 175, Total 17979, Payroll 8116, Personnel 233

FOLKSTON—Charlton County

CHARLTON MEMORIAL HOSPITAL, 1203 North Third Street, Zip 31537–1303, Mailing Address: P.O. Box 188, Zip 31537–0188; tel. 912/496–2531 **A**9 10 18 **F**6 27 32 33 34 46 63 81 88 97
Primary Contact: Sue Spivey, Administrator
Control 16, Service 10, Staffed Beds 25, Admissions 368, Census 3, Outpatient Visits 7378, Births 0, Total 6993, Payroll 3123, Personnel 137

FORSYTH—Monroe County

□ **MONROE COUNTY HOSPITAL**, 88 Martin Luther King Jr. Drive, Zip 31029–1682, Mailing Address: P.O. Box 1068, Zip 31029–1068; tel. 478/994–2521 **A**1 9 10 18 **F**2 9 26 27 29 33 34 58 63 84 85 88 96 97 108 **P**1 2
Primary Contact: Oliver J. Booker, Chief Executive Officer
Web address: www.monroehospital.com
Control 16, Service 10, Staffed Beds 25, Admissions 727, Census 7, Outpatient Visits 18470, Births 0, Total 7887, Payroll 3993, Personnel 101

FORT BENNING—Muscogee County

⊠ **MARTIN ARMY COMMUNITY HOSPITAL**, 7950 Martin Loop, Zip 31905–6100, Mailing Address: P.O. Box 56100, Building 9200, Zip 31905–6100; tel. 706/544–2516, (Nonreporting) **A**1 2 3 5 **S** Department of the Army, Office of the Surgeon General, Falls Church, VA
Primary Contact: Colonel Margaret Rivera, Commander
CIO: Major Shawn Faherty, Chief Information Management Division
Web address: www.martin.amedd.army.mil
Control 42, Service 10, Staffed Beds 62

FORT GORDON—Richmond County

⊠ **DWIGHT DAVID EISENHOWER ARMY MEDICAL CENTER**, Hospital Drive, Building 300, Zip 30905–5650; tel. 706/787–5811 **A**1 2 3 5 **F**2 4 6 9 12 15 17 19 21 22 23 24 25 26 27 28 29 31 32 33 35 39 44 45 46 47 48 49 53 55 57 58 60 61 62 63 64 65 66 69 70 71 73 74 75 77 81 82 84 88 92 93 94 95 96 106 107 108 109 110 **S** Department of the Army, Office of the Surgeon General, Falls Church, VA
Primary Contact: Colonel Donald M. Bradshaw, Commander
COO: Lieutenant Colonel Brian Canfield, Deputy Chief for Administration
CMO: Colonel John Wesley, Deputy Chief for Clinical Services
CIO: Major Robert Curee, Chief Information Management
CHR: Elizabeth Shelt, Civilian Personnel Officer
Web address: www.ddeamc.amedd.army.mil
Control 42, Service 10, Staffed Beds 111, Admissions 4828, Census 59, Outpatient Visits 421903, Births 0, Personnel 2014

FORT OGLETHORPE—Catoosa County

⊠ **HUTCHESON MEDICAL CENTER**, 100 Gross Crescent Circle, Zip 30742–3669; tel. 706/858–2000, (Total facility includes 109 beds in nursing home–type unit) **A**1 9 10 **F**2 6 9 11 12 14 15 21 22 23 26 27 28 29 33 35 36 37 39 40 46 47 48 49 51 52 53 55 56 59 60 61 62 63 65 66 69 81 82 84 87 88 92 94 95 96 106 107 108 109
Primary Contact: David M. Snyder, Interim President and Chief Executive Officer
COO: Kurt Schley, Chief Operating Officer
CFO: David Cranford, Chief Financial Officer
CMO: Daniel Heithold, M.D., Chief of Staff
CIO: Don Williams, Director Information Systems
CHR: Kim Sexton, Director of Human Resources
Web address: www.hutcheson.org
Control 16, Service 10, Staffed Beds 294, Admissions 7436, Census 220, Outpatient Visits 194565, Births 891, Total 90629, Payroll 42582, Personnel 1183

FORT VALLEY—Peach County

⊠ **PEACH REGIONAL MEDICAL CENTER**, 601 Blue Bird Boulevard, Zip 31030–4599; tel. 478/825–8691 **A**1 9 10 18 **F**3 9 12 13 14 21 27 28 29 33 39 44 46 47 48 55 56 58 62 63 64 65 66 67 68 70 71 81 92 94 96 97 108 **P**1 6
Primary Contact: Nancy Peed, Administrator and Chief Executive Officer
CFO: Lisa Urbistondo, Chief Financial Officer
CMO: Crystal Brown, M.D., Medical Director
Web address: www.peachregional.org
Control 16, Service 10, Staffed Beds 25, Admissions 491, Census 4, Outpatient Visits 25127, Births 0, Total 4871, Payroll 4215, Personnel 124

Hospital, Address, Telephone, Approval, Facility, and Physician Codes, Health Care System	Classi-fication Codes		Utilization Data					Expense (thousands) of dollars		
★ American Hospital Association (AHA) membership □ Joint Commission on Accreditation of Healthcare Organizations (JCAHO) accreditation ○ American Osteopathic Association (AOA) accreditation △ Commission on Accreditation of Rehabilitation Facilities (CARF) accreditation	Control	Service	Staffed Beds	Admissions	Census	Outpatient Visits	Births	Total	Payroll	Personnel

GAINESVILLE—Hall County

✖ △ **NORTHEAST GEORGIA MEDICAL CENTER**, 743 Spring Street N.E., Zip 30501–3899; tel. 770/535–3553, (Total facility includes 285 beds in nursing home–type unit) (Nonreporting) **A**1 2 7 9 10 19 Primary Contact: Jim Gardner, President and Chief Executive Officer COO: Carol H. Burrell, Executive Vice President and Chief Operating Officer CFO: Tony Herdener, Vice President Systems and Finance CMO: David Westfall, M.D., Vice President Medical Affairs CIO: Mark Jennings, Director Information Systems Web address: www.nghs.com	23	10	418	—	—	—	—	—	—	—

GLENWOOD—Wheeler County

✖ **WHEELER COUNTY HOSPITAL**, 111 Third Street, Zip 30428–2301, Mailing Address: P.O. Box 398, Zip 30428–0398; tel. 912/523–5113, (Total facility includes 48 beds in nursing home–type unit) **A**1 9 10 18 **F**2 26 27 28 29 30 33 44 46 48 53 63 69 70 81 82 88 92 93 94 97 **P**6 **S** Accord Health Care Corporation, Clearwater, FL Primary Contact: Brenda Josey, Administrator CFO: Lynan Fowler, Director Patient Financial Services	33	10	73	645	8	11203	0	7453	4211	129

GREENSBORO—Greene County

□ **MINNIE G. BOSWELL MEMORIAL HOSPITAL**, 1201 Siloam Highway, Zip 30642–2811; tel. 706/453–7331, (Total facility includes 29 beds in nursing home–type unit) (Nonreporting) **A**1 9 10 18 Primary Contact: Floyd D. Bounds, Chief Executive Officer	16	10	54	—	—	—	—	—	—	—

GRIFFIN—Spalding County

✖ **SPALDING REGIONAL MEDICAL CENTER**, 601 South Eighth Street, Zip 30224–4294, Mailing Address: P.O. Drawer V, Zip 30224–1168; tel. 770/228–2721 **A**1 2 9 10 **F**2 6 9 11 12 21 23 26 27 28 29 33 45 46 48 51 52 57 58 59 60 61 62 63 65 68 69 81 82 84 88 92 93 94 96 106 107 108 109 110 **P**8 **S** TENET Healthcare Corporation, Dallas, TX Primary Contact: John A. Quinn, Chief Executive Officer COO: Rebekah Logan, Chief Operating Officer CFO: Lisa Napier–Evans, Chief Financial Officer CIO: Steven E. Brown, Director Information Systems CHR: Amanda Moore, Director Human Resources Web address: www.spaldingregional.com	33	10	160	7987	98	92234	1041	69862	31140	570

HARTWELL—Hart County

✖ **HART COUNTY HOSPITAL**, Gibson and Cade Streets, Zip 30643–0280, Mailing Address: P.O. Box 280, Zip 30643–0280; tel. 706/856–6100, (Nonreporting) **A**1 9 10 **S** Ty Cobb Healthcare System, Inc., Royston, GA Primary Contact: Jerry R. Wise, Administrator and Vice President Web address: www.tycobbhealthcare.org	23	10	174	—	—	—	—	—	—	—

HAWKINSVILLE—Pulaski County

□ **TAYLOR REGIONAL HOSPITAL**, Macon Highway, Zip 31036, Mailing Address: P.O. Box 1297, Zip 31036–1297; tel. 478/783–0200, (Nonreporting) **A**1 9 10 Primary Contact: Dan S. Maddock, President Web address: www.taylorregional.org	23	10	55	—	—	—	—	—	—	—

HAZLEHURST—Jeff Davis County

□ **JEFF DAVIS HOSPITAL**, 1215 South Tallahassee Street, Zip 31539–2921, Mailing Address: P.O. Box 1200, Zip 31539–1200; tel. 912/375–7781 **A**1 9 10 18 **F**2 12 21 26 27 28 32 33 36 46 48 52 53 55 63 64 75 81 85 88 93 94 Primary Contact: Rich McClements, Administrator	23	10	25	864	8	20572	38	6993	7147	111

HIAWASSEE—Towns County

CHATUGE REGIONAL HOSPITAL AND NURSING HOME, 110 Main Street, Zip 30546–2212, Mailing Address: P.O. Box 509, Zip 30546–0509; tel. 706/896–2222, (Nonreporting) **A**9 10 18 Primary Contact: Lewis Kelley, Administrator	13	10	25	—	—	—	—	—	—	—

HINESVILLE—Liberty County

□ **LIBERTY REGIONAL MEDICAL CENTER**, 462 East G. Parkway, Zip 31313, Mailing Address: P.O. Box 919, Zip 31313; tel. 912/369–9438, (Total facility includes 66 beds in nursing home–type unit) **A**1 9 10 18 20 **F**6 9 11 12 21 26 27 28 32 33 45 46 47 48 52 59 60 63 66 69 81 88 92 108 Primary Contact: H. Scott Kroell, Jr, Chief Executive Officer Web address: www.libertyregional.org	16	10	91	2229	82	45818	427	25572	11671	390
✖ **WINN ARMY COMMUNITY HOSPITAL**, 1061 Harmon Avenue, Zip 31314–5611; tel. 912/435–6965, (Nonreporting) **A**1 3 5 **S** Department of the Army, Office of the Surgeon General, Falls Church, VA Primary Contact: Colonel Scott Goodrich, Commander	42	44	79	—	—	—	—	—	—	—

HOMERVILLE—Clinch County

★ **CLINCH MEMORIAL HOSPITAL**, 282 Carswell Street, Zip 31634–1507, Mailing Address: P.O. Box 516, Zip 31634–0516; tel. 912/487–5211 **A**9 10 18 **F**2 6 12 27 28 32 33 48 52 60 69 70 81 84 88 93 94 97 **P**5 Primary Contact: Bill Forbes, Administrator CFO: Sandra Hughes, Chief Financial Officer CMO: Kuldeep Singh, M.D., Chief of Staff CIO: Shelly Studebaker, Management Information Systems Director Web address: www.sgmc.org/healthsystem/clinchmemorial.htm	13	10	25	305	3	14325	0	6362	2665	100

GA

Hospital, Address, Telephone, Approval, Facility, and Physician Codes, Health Care System	Classi-fication Codes		Utilization Data					Expense (thousands) of dollars		
★ American Hospital Association (AHA) membership □ Joint Commission on Accreditation of Healthcare Organizations (JCAHO) accreditation ○ American Osteopathic Association (AOA) accreditation △ Commission on Accreditation of Rehabilitation Facilities (CARF) accreditation	Control	Service	Staffed Beds	Admissions	Census	Outpatient Visits	Births	Total	Payroll	Personnel

JACKSON—Butts County

★ **SYLVAN GROVE HOSPITAL**, 1050 McDonough Road, Zip 30233–1599; tel. 770/775–7861 **A**9 10 18 **F**12 21 27 28 29 33 39 46 47 48 52 53 58 60 66 69 70 81 88 97 110 **S** TENET Healthcare Corporation, Dallas, TX
Primary Contact: John A. Quinn, Chief Executive Officer
COO: Edward J. Whitehouse, Chief Operating Officer
CFO: Lisa Napier–Evans, Chief Financial Officer
CIO: Steve Brown, Information Officer
Web address: www.sylvangrovehospital.com

| 33 | 10 | 21 | 496 | 9 | 19187 | 0 | 6792 | 3650 | 57 |

JASPER—Pickens County

⊠ **PIEDMONT MOUNTAINSIDE HOSPITAL**, 1266 Highway 515 South, Zip 30143; tel. 706/692–2441 **A**1 9 10 **F**2 9 11 12 21 27 33 34 42 48 52 55 57 58 59 60 62 63 64 81 84 88 94 97 **P**8 **S** Piedmont Healthcare, Atlanta, GA
Primary Contact: Ed Lovern, President and Chief Executive Officer
CFO: Sheryl Klink, Chief Financial Officer
CMO: Rosemarie Spillane, Chief of Medical Staff
Web address: www.piedmontmountainsidehospital.org

| 16 | 10 | 40 | 1762 | 18 | 44257 | 202 | 18967 | 7583 | 184 |

JESUP—Wayne County

⊠ **WAYNE MEMORIAL HOSPITAL**, 865 South First Street, Zip 31598–0210, Mailing Address: P.O. Box 410, Zip 31598–0410; tel. 912/427–6811 **A**1 9 10 20 **F**2 9 11 12 21 22 27 28 29 32 33 34 39 40 44 46 48 50 53 55 58 59 60 62 63 65 66 69 81 84 85 88 95 108 109 110 **P**5 **S** Quorum Health Resources, Plano, TX
Primary Contact: Charles R. Morgan, Chief Executive Officer
CFO: George King, Controller
CMO: Jose De La Cruz, M.D., Chief of Staff
CIO: Deborah Six, Data Processing Coordinator
CHR: Mary Gunther, Director Human Resources
Web address: www.wmhweb.com

| 13 | 10 | 84 | 3425 | 38 | 45812 | 431 | 30762 | 13514 | 348 |

KENNESAW—Cobb County

DEVEREUX GEORGIA TREATMENT NETWORK, (IRTC), 1291 Stanley Road N.W., Zip 30152–4359, Mailing Address: P.O. Box 1688, Zip 30156–8688; tel. 770/422–2135 **F**27 28 72 **P**1 **S** Devereux, Villanova, PA
Primary Contact: Mario Bolivar, Executive Director
Web address: www.devereuxga.org

| 23 | 59 | 187 | 116 | 144 | 0 | 0 | — | — | 291 |

LA GRANGE—Troup County

⊠ **WEST GEORGIA HEALTH SYSTEM**, 1514 Vernon Road, Zip 30240–4199; tel. 706/882–1411, (Total facility includes 266 beds in nursing home–type unit) **A**1 2 9 10 19 **F**1 2 9 11 12 15 21 22 23 26 27 28 29 32 33 34 35 36 37 38 39 40 41 42 44 46 47 48 49 51 52 53 55 56 57 58 59 60 61 62 63 64 65 69 70 75 76 81 82 85 87 88 92 93 94 96 106 107 108 110
Primary Contact: Gerald N. Fulks, President and Chief Executive Officer
COO: Charis Acree, Senior Vice President
CFO: Paul R. Perrotti, CPA, Chief Financial Officer
CIO: Paul R. Perrotti, CPA, Chief Financial Officer
Web address: www.wghs.org

| 23 | 10 | 448 | 9684 | 374 | 87037 | 1023 | 105325 | 46199 | 1333 |

LAKELAND—Lanier County

⊠ **LOUIS SMITH MEMORIAL HOSPITAL**, 852 West Thigpen Avenue, Zip 31635–1099; tel. 229/482–3110, (Total facility includes 62 beds in nursing home–type unit) **A**1 9 10 18 **F**6 33 52 60 63 66 69 70 81 84 85 88 92 93 94 97 **P**5
Primary Contact: Neil W. Ginty, Administrator
CFO: Teena Buchanan, CPA, Chief Financial Officer
CMO: Bruce Herrington, Chief Medical Officer
CIO: Lucile Mann, Chief Information Officer
CHR: Vicki Dinkins, Human Resources Director
Web address: www.sgmc.org

| 23 | 10 | 87 | 905 | 68 | 10149 | 0 | 9269 | 4605 | 81 |

LAWRENCEVILLE—Gwinnett County

⊠ **GWINNETT HOSPITAL SYSTEM**, Mailing Address: P.O. Box 348, Zip 30246–0348; tel. 678/442–4321, (Includes GWINNETT MEDICAL CENTER, 1000 Medical Center Boulevard, Zip 30245; JOAN GLANCY MEMORIAL HOSPITAL, McClure Bridge Road, Duluth, Zip 30136; tel. 770/497–4800), (Total facility includes 89 beds in nursing home–type unit) (Nonreporting) **A**1 2 9 10
Primary Contact: Franklin M. Rinker, President and Chief Executive Officer
CFO: Thomas Y. McBride, III, Vice President and Chief Financial Officer
CMO: Miles H. Mason, III, M.D., President, Medical Staff
CIO: Ed Brown, Chief Information Officer
CHR: Steve Nadeau, Vice President Human Resources
Web address: www.promina.org

| 23 | 10 | 503 | — | — | — | — | — | — | — |

LOUISVILLE—Jefferson County

□ **JEFFERSON HOSPITAL**, 1067 Peachtree Street, Zip 30434–1599; tel. 478/625–7000, (Nonreporting) **A**1 9 10 20
Primary Contact: Rita Culvern, Administrator

| 16 | 10 | 37 | — | — | — | — | — | — | — |

Many Facility Codes have changed. Please refer to the AHA Guide Code Chart. © 2005 AHA Guide

GA

Hospital, Address, Telephone, Approval, Facility, and Physician Codes, Health Care System	Classi-fication Codes		Utilization Data					Expense (thousands) of dollars		
★ American Hospital Association (AHA) membership □ Joint Commission on Accreditation of Healthcare Organizations (JCAHO) accreditation ○ American Osteopathic Association (AOA) accreditation △ Commission on Accreditation of Rehabilitation Facilities (CARF) accreditation	Control	Service	Staffed Beds	Admissions	Census	Outpatient Visits	Births	Total	Payroll	Personnel

MACON—Bibb County

COLISEUM MEDICAL CENTERS, 350 Hospital Drive, Zip 31217–3871; tel. 478/765–7000 **A**1 2 9 10 **F**2 11 12 14 15 17 19 21 22 23 27 28 29 33 40 42 44 45 46 47 48 49 52 55 56 57 58 59 60 61 62 63 64 65 66 68 69 81 82 84 88 90 94 96 108 109 110 **S** HCA, Nashville, TN
Primary Contact: Allen Golson, Chief Executive Officer
COO: David A. Portwood, Chief Operating Officer
CFO: Roger Simmons, Chief Financial Officer
CIO: Joan Morstad, Director Information Systems
Web address: www.coliseumhealthsystem.com
| 33 | 10 | 214 | 7756 | 113 | 78417 | 1061 | — | — | 739 |

COLISEUM PSYCHIATRIC CENTER, 340 Hospital Drive, Zip 31217–8002; tel. 478/741–1355 **A**1 9 10 **F**3 4 5 21 22 27 28 29 31 33 44 48 58 71 73 74 75 76 77 78 94 96 **S** HCA, Nashville, TN
Primary Contact: Mark Nichols, FACHE, Chief Executive Officer
CFO: Roger Simmons, Chief Financial Officer
Web address: www.hcahealthcare.com
| 33 | 22 | 32 | 1125 | 25 | 1928 | 0 | — | — | 77 |

HEALTHSOUTH CENTRAL GEORGIA REHABILITATION HOSPITAL, 3351 Northside Drive, Zip 31210–2591; tel. 478/471–3500 **A**1 9 10 **F**2 9 21 22 26 27 28 29 37 42 44 45 46 47 48 52 57 58 60 61 62 65 66 68 69 93 94 95 96 108 109 110 **P**5 **S** HEALTHSOUTH Corporation, Birmingham, AL
Primary Contact: Elbert T. McQueen, Administrator
CFO: Beverly Owens, Controller
Web address: www.healthsouth.com
| 33 | 46 | 58 | 1078 | 47 | 17112 | 0 | 13241 | 6709 | — |

MACON NORTHSIDE HOSPITAL, 400 Charter Boulevard, Zip 31210–4853, Mailing Address: P.O. Box 4627, Zip 31208–4627; tel. 478/757–8200 **A**1 9 10 **F**2 12 21 22 23 26 27 28 33 35 37 39 46 47 48 49 52 55 57 58 62 63 64 66 69 81 84 85 87 88 93 94 108 **P**7 **S** HCA, Nashville, TN
Primary Contact: Bud Costello, Administrator and Chief Executive Officer
CFO: Will Hursey, Controller
CHR: Pat Luttrell, Director Human Resources
Web address: www.coliseumhealthsystem.com
| 33 | 10 | 103 | 2346 | 32 | 30405 | 0 | 34010 | 12252 | 239 |

MEDICAL CENTER OF CENTRAL GEORGIA, 777 Hemlock Street, Zip 31201–2155, Mailing Address: P.O. Box 6000, Zip 31208–6000; tel. 478/633–1000 **A**1 2 3 5 8 9 10 **F**4 6 9 10 11 12 14 15 17 19 21 22 23 26 27 28 29 30 32 33 34 36 38 39 41 42 44 45 46 47 48 49 50 51 52 53 55 56 57 58 59 60 61 62 63 65 66 67 68 69 70 71 73 74 75 76 77 81 82 84 86 88 94 96 106 107 108 109 110 **P**1
Primary Contact: A. Donald Faulk, FACHE, President
COO: Mike Gilstrap, Chief Operating Officer
CFO: Rhonda Perry, Chief Financial Officer
CMO: Louis Goolsby, M.D., Senior Vice President Medical Affairs
CIO: Madison Mock, Vice President Information Services
Web address: www.mccg.org
| 16 | 10 | 567 | 29562 | 433 | 435795 | 3276 | 491898 | 197195 | 4104 |

★ **REGENCY HOSPITAL OF CENTRAL GEORGIA**, 700 Spring Street, Zip 31201; tel. 478/633–8260 **A**10 **F**2 21 22 27 28 49 50 58 62 68 92 94 110 **P**5 **S** Regency Hospital Company, Alpharetta, GA
Primary Contact: Richard W. Graham, Chief Executive Officer
| 23 | 80 | 34 | 172 | 3 | 0 | 0 | 700 | 328 | — |

MADISON—Morgan County

MORGAN MEMORIAL HOSPITAL, Mailing Address: P.O. Box 860, Zip 30650–0860; tel. 706/342–1667, (Total facility includes 21 beds in nursing home–type unit) (Nonreporting) **A**9 10 18
Primary Contact: Chris Bonham, Chief Executive Officer
| 16 | 10 | 46 | — | — | — | — | — | — | — |

MARIETTA—Cobb County

△ **WELLSTAR KENNESTONE HOSPITAL**, 677 Church Street, Zip 30060–1148; tel. 770/793–5000 **A**1 2 7 9 10 **F**2 8 9 10 11 12 14 15 21 22 23 24 26 27 28 29 31 33 35 37 38 39 41 42 46 47 48 49 50 52 53 55 56 57 58 59 60 61 62 63 64 65 66 68 69 73 75 79 80 81 82 84 85 86 87 88 92 94 96 98 104 108 109 110 **P**1 6 **S** WellStar Health System, Marietta, GA
Primary Contact: Linda A. Clark, Senior Vice President and Administrator
COO: Paul Johnson, Executive Vice President Operations
CFO: Marsha Burke, Senior Vice President and Chief Financial Officer
CMO: Larry Haldeman, M.D., Executive Vice President and Chief Medical Officer
CIO: Leigh Cox, Chief Information Officer
CHR: David Anderson, Vice President Human Resources
Web address: www.wellstar.org
| 23 | 10 | 487 | 33599 | 409 | 320362 | 6220 | — | — | 3263 |

WELLSTAR WINDY HILL HOSPITAL, 2540 Windy Hill Road, Zip 30067–8632; tel. 770/644–1000 **A**1 2 10 **F**4 9 12 21 22 26 27 28 29 31 35 39 40 46 48 49 50 52 53 58 60 62 63 64 65 66 69 74 77 78 81 82 84 85 87 88 92 93 94 96 108 110 **P**1 6 **S** WellStar Health System, Marietta, GA
Primary Contact: Lou Little, Vice President and Administrator
COO: Paul Johnson, Executive Vice President Operations
CFO: Marsha Burke, Senior Vice President and Chief Financial Officer
CMO: Larry Haldeman, M.D., Executive Vice President and Chief Medical Officer
CIO: Leigh Cox, Chief Information Officer
CHR: Mary Louise Tavernaro, Director Human Resources
Web address: www.wellstar.org
| 23 | 80 | 29 | 265 | 26 | 25885 | 0 | — | — | 248 |

GA

Hospital, Address, Telephone, Approval, Facility, and Physician Codes, Health Care System	Classi-fication Codes		Utilization Data					Expense (thousands) of dollars		
★ American Hospital Association (AHA) membership □ Joint Commission on Accreditation of Healthcare Organizations (JCAHO) accreditation ○ American Osteopathic Association (AOA) accreditation △ Commission on Accreditation of Rehabilitation Facilities (CARF) accreditation	Control	Service	Staffed Beds	Admissions	Census	Outpatient Visits	Births	Total	Payroll	Personnel

MCRAE—Telfair County

□ **TAYLOR–TELFAIR REGIONAL HOSPITAL**, U.S. 341 South, Zip 31055, Mailing Address: P.O. Box 150, Zip 31055–0150; tel. 229/868–5621, (Nonreporting) **A**1 9 10 18 **S** Memorial Health Services, Adel, GA
Primary Contact: Joan Hartley, Chief Executive Officer

	23	10	25	—	—	—	—	—	—	—

METTER—Candler County

□ **CANDLER COUNTY HOSPITAL**, 400 Cedar Road, Zip 30439–1448, Mailing Address: P.O. Box 597, Zip 30439–0597; tel. 912/685–5741, (Nonreporting) **A**1 9 10 18
Primary Contact: Michael Alexander, President and Chief Executive Officer
Web address: www.candlercountyhospital.com

	16	10	25	—	—	—	—	—	—	—

MILLEDGEVILLE—Baldwin County

□ **CENTRAL STATE HOSPITAL**, 620 Broad Street, Zip 31062–0001; tel. 478/445–4128, (Total facility includes 745 beds in nursing home–type unit) (Nonreporting) **A**1 9 10
Primary Contact: Marvin Bailey, Chief Executive Officer
Web address: www.centralstatehospital.org

	12	22	1125	—	—	—	—	—	—	—

⊠ **OCONEE REGIONAL MEDICAL CENTER**, 821 North Cobb Street, Zip 31061–2351, Mailing Address: P.O. Box 690, Zip 31061–0690; tel. 478/454–3500 **A**1 9 10 19 **F**4 9 11 12 21 23 26 27 28 29 33 36 40 41 46 48 55 58 59 61 63 64 65 66 69 72 73 74 76 77 80 81 82 84 86 88 92 93 94 96 98 107 108 109
Primary Contact: Brian L. Riddle, President and Chief Executive Officer
CFO: John Cornell, Chief Operating Officer
Web address: www.oconeeregional.com

	16	10	109	4718	56	94209	720	66490	—	636

MILLEN—Jenkins County

★ **JENKINS COUNTY HOSPITAL**, 931 East Winthrope Avenue, Zip 30442–1839; tel. 478/982–4221, (Nonreporting) **A**9 10 18
Primary Contact: Pete Mills, Chief Executive Officer

	16	10	25	—	—	—	—	—	—	—

MONROE—Walton County

□ **WALTON REGIONAL MEDICAL CENTER**, 330 Alcovy Street, Zip 30655–2140, Mailing Address: P.O. Box 1346, Zip 30655–1346; tel. 770/267–8461, (Total facility includes 58 beds in nursing home–type unit) (Nonreporting) **A**1 9 10 **S** Health Management Associates, Naples, FL
Primary Contact: Alan E. George, Chief Executive Officer
Web address: www.waltonregional.org

	33	10	115	—	—	—	—	—	—	—

MONTEZUMA—Macon County

□ **FLINT RIVER COMMUNITY HOSPITAL**, 509 Sumter Street, Zip 31063–0770, Mailing Address: P.O. Box 770, Zip 31063–0770; tel. 478/472–3100, (Nonreporting) **A**1 9 10 **S** Resurgence Health Group, Sugar Hill, GA
Primary Contact: Curt L. Roberts, Chief Executive Officer
Web address: www.resurgencehealthgroup.com

	33	10	49	—	—	—	—	—	—	—

MONTICELLO—Jasper County

★ **JASPER MEMORIAL HOSPITAL**, 898 College Street, Zip 31064–1298; tel. 706/468–6411 **A**9 10 18 **F**21 27 28 33 69 81 88 92 97 **P**6
Primary Contact: David J. Owens, Chief Executive Officer
CFO: Laura Hammonds, Controller
Web address: www.jaspermemorialhospital.org

	16	10	67	317	2	6127	0	6906	3202	34

MOULTRIE—Colquitt County

⊠ **COLQUITT REGIONAL MEDICAL CENTER**, 3131 South Main Street, Zip 31768–6701, Mailing Address: P.O. Box 40, Zip 31776–0040; tel. 229/985–3420 **A**1 9 10 20 **F**1 2 6 9 11 12 14 15 21 22 23 24 26 27 28 29 32 33 36 37 44 45 46 48 49 50 51 53 55 57 58 59 60 61 62 63 64 65 66 69 70 77 78 81 82 84 85 88 93 94 95 96 106 107 108 109 110 **P**5
Primary Contact: James R. Lowry, FACHE, Chief Executive Officer
COO: Madis Spires, Vice President of Patient Services
CFO: W Larry Sims, Chief Financial Officer and Vice President Financial Services
CMO: D W. Adcock, M.D., Medical Director
CIO: Mitch Hiers, Director Information Services
Web address: www.colquittregional.com

	16	10	73	4222	45	107026	670	55813	21878	658

TURNING POINT HOSPITAL, 3015 East By–Pass, Zip 31768–6705, Mailing Address: P.O. Box 1177, Zip 31776–1177; tel. 229/985–4815 **A**9 10 **F**3 4 45 58 66 77 78 94 106 **P**6 **S** Universal Health Services, Inc., King of Prussia, PA
Primary Contact: Ben Marion, Chief Executive Officer
Web address: www.turningpointcare.com

	33	82	59	995	11	15379	0	5768	2692	72

NASHVILLE—Berrien County

□ **BERRIEN COUNTY HOSPITAL**, 1221 East McPherson Street, Zip 31639–2326, Mailing Address: P.O. Box 665, Zip 31639–0665; tel. 229/543–7100, (Total facility includes 108 beds in nursing home–type unit) **A**1 9 10 **F**12 21 27 28 33 36 46 48 51 52 55 63 69 77 82 88 92 97 **S** Associated Healthcare Systems, Inc., Brentwood, TN
Primary Contact: Rick Langosch, Interim Chief Executive Officer
Web address: www.berriencountyhospital.com

	33	10	171	905	102	11619	0	12176	6516	201

GA

Many Facility Codes have changed. Please refer to the AHA Guide Code Chart. © 2005 AHA Guide

Hospital, Address, Telephone, Approval, Facility, and Physician Codes, Health Care System	Classi- fication Codes		Utilization Data					Expense (thousands) of dollars		
★ American Hospital Association (AHA) membership □ Joint Commission on Accreditation of Healthcare Organizations (JCAHO) accreditation ○ American Osteopathic Association (AOA) accreditation △ Commission on Accreditation of Rehabilitation Facilities (CARF) accreditation	Control	Service	Staffed Beds	Admissions	Census	Outpatient Visits	Births	Total	Payroll	Personnel

NEWNAN—Coweta County

☒ **NEWNAN HOSPITAL EAST**, 80 Jackson Street, Zip 30263–1941, Mailing Address: P.O. Box 997, Zip 30264–0997; tel. 770/253–2330, (Includes EMORY PEACHTREE REGIONAL HOSPITAL, 60 Hospital Road, Zip 30263–1210; tel. 770/253–1912; NEWNAN HOSPITAL, 80 Jackson Street, Mailing Address: Box 997, Zip 30264–0997; tel. 770/253–2330; Glenn M. Flake, Executive Director), (Total facility includes 143 beds in nursing home–type unit) **A**1 9 10 **F**9 12 14 15 17 21 27 28 33 37 40 41 46 48 55 58 59 60 61 62 63 66 69 81 82 84 86 88 92 93 94 108 109 110
Primary Contact: Glenn M. Flake, Executive Director
CFO: Alexis Klamke, Chief Financial Officer
CIO: Henry Scott, Management Information Systems Director
Web address: www.newnanhospital.com
| 23 | 10 | 271 | 5788 | 207 | 96816 | 801 | 88196 | 36452 | 803 |

OCILLA—Irwin County

☒ **IRWIN COUNTY HOSPITAL**, 710 North Irwin Avenue, Zip 31774–1098; tel. 229/468–3800 **A**1 9 10 **F**2 11 12 26 27 33 39 40 52 58 59 63 81 87 88 92 93 94
Primary Contact: Sue Spivey, Administrator
CFO: Tami Gray, Chief Financial Officer
CMO: Ashfaq Saiyed, M.D., Medical Director
CHR: Becky Edwards, Human Resource Manager
Web address: www.irwincntyhospital.com
| 16 | 10 | 34 | 1612 | 13 | 11075 | 431 | 11525 | 4659 | — |

PERRY—Houston County

☒ **PERRY HOSPITAL**, 1120 Morningside Drive, Zip 31069–2906; tel. 478/987–3600 **A**1 9 10 **F**2 6 9 10 12 21 22 24 27 28 29 32 33 35 37 39 44 45 46 47 48 50 52 53 55 58 62 63 64 65 66 73 81 84 85 88 93 94 95 96 97 98 106 108 109 110 **P**1 7
Primary Contact: Lora Davis, Administrator
CFO: Frank R. Powell, Chief Financial Officer
CMO: Tony Alford, D.O., Executive Director of Medical Affairs
CHR: Marilu Crosby, Director of Human Resources
Web address: www.hhc.org
| 16 | 10 | 45 | 1826 | 22 | 33430 | 0 | 20454 | 8837 | 181 |

QUITMAN—Brooks County

☒ **BROOKS COUNTY HOSPITAL**, 903 North Court Street, Zip 31643–1315, Mailing Address: P.O. Box 5000, Zip 31643–5000; tel. 229/263–4171 **A**1 9 10 18 **F**21 22 26 27 28 29 33 46 65 66 69 70 81 84 88 97 106 110 **P**6 8 **S** Archbold Medical Center, Thomasville, GA
Primary Contact: LaDon Toole, Administrator
COO: LaDon Toole, Administrator
CFO: LaDon Toole, Administrator
CMO: Payvand Tiurchy, Chief of Staff
Web address: www.archbold.org/BrooksCountyHospital
| 13 | 10 | 35 | 1414 | 19 | 16035 | 0 | 7596 | 3959 | 104 |

REIDSVILLE—Tattnall County

TATTNALL COMMUNITY HOSPITAL, 247 South Main Street, Zip 30453; tel. 912/557–1000 **A**9 10 18 **F**2 6 9 12 21 27 33 39 52 53 58 63 66 69 81 88 94 96 97 106 108 110 **P**6 **S** Resurgence Health Group, Sugar Hill, GA
Primary Contact: Karen O'Neal, Chief Executive Officer
Web address: www.resurgencehealthgroup.com
| 33 | 10 | 25 | 427 | 3 | 13788 | 0 | 5009 | 2694 | 79 |

RICHLAND—Stewart County

★ **STEWART–WEBSTER HOSPITAL**, 300 Alston Street, Zip 31825–1406, Mailing Address: P.O. Box 190, Zip 31825–0190; tel. 229/887–3366 **A**9 10 18 **F**2 26 28 33 46 48 52 60 63 69 81 88 93 94 97 **P**5 6 **S** Accord Health Care Corporation, Clearwater, FL
Primary Contact: Stephen H. Noble, President
CFO: Randy Stigleman, Chief Financial Officer
| 33 | 10 | 25 | 541 | 6 | 7451 | 1 | 5171 | 2210 | 66 |

RIVERDALE—Clayton County

★ **SOUTHERN CRESCENT HOSPITAL FOR SPECIALTY CARE**, 11 Upper Riverdale Road S.W., 6th Floor, Zip 30274; tel. 770/897–7603, (Nonreporting) **A**10 **S** Dubuis Health System, Houston, TX
Primary Contact: Janice Harrison, Administrator
| 23 | 80 | 30 | — | — | — | — | — | — | — |

☒ **SOUTHERN REGIONAL MEDICAL CENTER**, 11 Upper Riverdale Road S.W., Zip 30274–2600; tel. 770/991–8000 **A**1 2 9 10 **F**2 3 4 9 11 12 15 21 22 23 26 27 28 29 31 33 35 37 38 39 40 44 46 47 48 49 50 51 52 55 56 57 58 59 60 61 62 63 64 65 66 69 71 72 73 74 75 76 77 78 81 82 84 85 87 88 93 94 96 98 106 108 109 110 **P**1
Primary Contact: Edward J. Bonn, President and Chief Executive Officer
COO: Mary Kay Kiesling, Senior Vice President Operations and Chief Operating Officer
CFO: Ray R. Dziesinski, Senior Vice President Fiscal Services and Chief Financial Officer
CMO: Steven Muller, M.D., Senior Vice President Medical Affairs
CIO: Terry Wilk, Vice President Information Technology and Chief Information Officer
CHR: John Hursh, Vice President Human Resources
Web address: www.southernregional.org
| 23 | 10 | 336 | 19591 | 245 | 163141 | 5051 | 201829 | 95217 | 2042 |

GA

Hospital, Address, Telephone, Approval, Facility, and Physician Codes, Health Care System	Classi-fication Codes		Utilization Data					Expense (thousands) of dollars		
★ American Hospital Association (AHA) membership □ Joint Commission on Accreditation of Healthcare Organizations (JCAHO) accreditation ○ American Osteopathic Association (AOA) accreditation △ Commission on Accreditation of Rehabilitation Facilities (CARF) accreditation	Control	Service	Staffed Beds	Admissions	Census	Outpatient Visits	Births	Total	Payroll	Personnel

ROME—Floyd County

★ △ **FLOYD MEDICAL CENTER**, 304 Turner McCall Boulevard,
Zip 30165–2734, Mailing Address: P.O. Box 233, Zip 30162–0233;
tel. 706/802–2000 **A**1 2 3 5 7 9 10 19 **F**2 3 4 5 6 7 9 10 11 12 14 15 21 22
23 24 26 27 28 29 30 31 32 33 34 35 36 37 38 39 40 41 42 44 45 46 47
48 51 52 53 55 56 57 58 59 60 61 62 63 64 65 66 68 69 70 71 73 74 75
76 77 78 81 82 84 87 88 89 90 93 94 95 96 98 106 107 108 109 110
Primary Contact: Kurt Stuenkel, FACHE, President and Chief Executive Officer
COO: Sonny Rigas, Senior Vice President
CFO: Rick Sheerin, Vice President Fiscal Services
CMO: Dee B. Russell, M.D., Chief Executive Officer
CIO: Sonny Rigas, Senior Vice President
Web address: www.floydmed.org
| 23 | 10 | 304 | 10845 | 160 | 198014 | 2394 | 164093 | 76186 | 1757 |

□ **NORTHWEST GEORGIA REGIONAL HOSPITAL**, 1305 Redmond Circle,
Zip 30165–1393; tel. 706/295–6011, (Nonreporting) **A**1 9 10
Primary Contact: Karl H. Schwarzkopf, Regional Hospital Administrator
| 12 | 22 | 297 | — | — | — | — | — | — | — |

★ **REDMOND REGIONAL MEDICAL CENTER**, 501 Redmond Road,
Zip 30165–7001, Mailing Address: Box 107001, Zip 30164–7001;
tel. 706/291–0291, (Nonreporting) **A**1 2 9 10 19 **S** HCA, Nashville, TN
Primary Contact: Brenda M. Waltz, FACHE, Chief Executive Officer
COO: Shawn G. Strash, Chief Operating Officer
CFO: Danny Smith, Chief Financial Officer
CMO: Al Diaz, M.D., Medical Director
CIO: Brad Treglown, Director Information Systems
CHR: Patsy Adams, Director Human Resources
Web address: www.redmondregional.com
| 33 | 10 | 191 | — | — | — | — | — | — | — |

SPECIALTY HOSPITAL, 304 Turner McCall Boulevard, Zip 30162;
tel. 706/802–4100, (Nonreporting) **A**9 10
Primary Contact: Mark Fall, Chief Executive Officer
| 33 | 49 | 20 | — | — | — | — | — | — | — |

ROSWELL—Fulton County

★ △ **NORTH FULTON REGIONAL HOSPITAL**, 3000 Hospital Boulevard,
Zip 30076–3899; tel. 770/751–2500, (Nonreporting) **A**1 7 9 10 **S** TENET
Healthcare Corporation, Dallas, TX
Primary Contact: John F. Holland, Chief Executive Officer
CFO: Jon Zilkow, Chief Financial Officer
CHR: Susan Brown, Chief Human Resources Officer
Web address: www.northfultonregional.com
| 33 | 10 | 167 | — | — | — | — | — | — | — |

ROYSTON—Franklin County

□ **COBB MEMORIAL HOSPITAL**, 521 Franklin Springs Street, Zip 30662–3909,
Mailing Address: P.O. Box 589, Zip 30662–0589; tel. 706/245–5071, (Includes
BROWN MEMORIAL CONVALESCENT CENTER, COBB HEALTH CARE CENTER AND
THE GABLES), (Total facility includes 260 beds in nursing home–type unit)
(Nonreporting) **A**1 9 10 **S** Ty Cobb Healthcare System, Inc., Royston, GA
Primary Contact: John M. Herron, Administrator
Web address: www.tycobbhealthcare.org
| 23 | 10 | 331 | — | — | — | — | — | — | — |

SAINT MARYS—Camden County

★ **SOUTHEAST GEORGIA HEALTH SYSTEM CAMDEN CAMPUS**, 2000 Dan
Proctor Drive, Zip 31558–3810; tel. 912/576–6200 **A**1 9 10 20 **F**2 9 11 12 21
22 24 26 27 28 29 33 35 38 39 45 46 47 48 52 53 55 58 59 60 62 63 64
65 66 68 69 70 73 81 82 85 88 93 94 96 106 108 109 **P**6 8 **S** Southeast
Georgia Health System, Brunswick, GA
Primary Contact: Howard W. Sepp, Jr, Administrator
CFO: Michael D. Scherneck, Vice President Finance
Web address: www.sghs.org
| 16 | 10 | 40 | 1940 | 15 | 46932 | 740 | 22953 | 9174 | 207 |

SAINT SIMONS ISLAND—Glynn County

FOCUS BY–THE–SEA, 2927 Demere Road, Zip 31522–1620;
tel. 912/638–1999, (Nonreporting) **A**9 10
Primary Contact: Mark Apodaca, Vice President Operations
Web address: www.focushealthcare.com
| 33 | 22 | 85 | — | — | — | — | — | — | — |

SANDERSVILLE—Washington County

□ **WASHINGTON COUNTY REGIONAL MEDICAL CENTER**, 610 Sparta Road,
Zip 31082–1362, Mailing Address: P.O. Box 636, Zip 31082–0636;
tel. 478/240–2000, (Total facility includes 60 beds in nursing home–type unit) **A**1
9 10 20 **F**2 6 9 11 12 21 22 23 24 27 28 29 30 33 34 37 41 46 52 55 58
59 60 61 62 63 65 69 81 82 84 85 88 92 93 94 95 97 106 108 110 **P**6
Primary Contact: H. Thomas Brown, Chief Executive Officer
Web address: www.wcrmc.org
| 16 | 10 | 116 | 2070 | 87 | 35861 | 226 | 23941 | 11126 | 377 |

SAVANNAH—Chatham County

COASTAL HARBOR TREATMENT CENTER, 1150 Cornell Avenue,
Zip 31406–2797; tel. 912/354–3911, (Nonreporting) **A**9 10 **S** Universal Health
Services, Inc., King of Prussia, PA
Primary Contact: Ray Heckerman, Chief Executive Officer
Web address: www.coastalharbor.com
| 33 | 12 | 112 | — | — | — | — | — | — | — |

□ **GEORGIA REGIONAL HOSPITAL AT SAVANNAH**, 1915 Eisenhower Drive,
Zip 31406–5098; tel. 912/356–2011, (Nonreporting) **A**1 9 10
Primary Contact: Frank J. Drummond, M.D., Chief Executive Officer
| 12 | 22 | 167 | — | — | — | — | — | — | — |

GA

Hospital, Address, Telephone, Approval, Facility, and Physician Codes, Health Care System	Classi-fication Codes		Utilization Data					Expense (thousands) of dollars		
	Control	Service	Staffed Beds	Admissions	Census	Outpatient Visits	Births	Total	Payroll	Personnel

★ American Hospital Association (AHA) membership
□ Joint Commission on Accreditation of Healthcare Organizations (JCAHO) accreditation
○ American Osteopathic Association (AOA) accreditation
△ Commission on Accreditation of Rehabilitation Facilities (CARF) accreditation

✸ △ MEMORIAL HEALTH, 4700 Waters Avenue, Zip 31404–6283, Mailing Address: P.O. Box 23089, Zip 31403–3089; tel. 912/350–8000 **A**1 2 3 5 7 8 9 10 **F**2 4 9 10 11 12 14 15 17 19 21 22 23 24 27 28 29 30 32 33 34 35 37 38 39 41 42 44 45 46 47 48 49 50 52 53 55 56 57 58 59 61 62 63 65 67 68 69 70 71 73 74 75 76 77 78 79 81 82 84 85 86 87 88 89 90 93 94 95 96 106 108 109 110
Primary Contact: Robert A. Colvin, President and Chief Executive Officer
CFO: Suzanne Heck, Vice President and Interim Chief Financial Officer
CMO: Ramon V. Mequiar, Senior Vice President and Chief Medical Officer
CIO: Steve Stanic, Chief Information Officer
CHR: Cassandra L. Johnson, Vice President Human Resources
Web address: www.memorialhealth.com

| | 16 | 10 | 476 | 27496 | 426 | 274148 | 2945 | 371889 | 154308 | 3317 |

□ SELECT SPECIALTY HOSPITAL OF SAVANNAH, 5353 Reynolds Street, 4 South, Zip 31405; tel. 912/819–7972, (Nonreporting) **A**1 10
Primary Contact: John Heffner, Chief Executive Officer

| | 33 | 49 | 40 | — | — | — | — | — | — | — |

✸ △ ST. JOSEPH'S/CANDLER, CANDLER HOSPITAL, 5353 Reynolds Street, Zip 31405–6013; tel. 912/819–6000, (Total facility includes 11 beds in nursing home–type unit) **A**1 7 9 10 **F**1 2 9 11 12 15 17 21 22 23 24 26 27 28 29 30 31 32 33 34 35 37 38 39 40 41 44 45 46 47 48 49 50 51 52 53 55 57 58 59 60 61 62 63 64 65 66 68 69 70 81 82 84 85 87 88 92 93 94 95 96 98 106 108 109 110 **P**6
Primary Contact: Paul P. Hinchey, President and Chief Executive Officer
COO: Paul P. Hinchey, President and Chief Executive Officer
CFO: Gregory J. Schaack, Vice President and Chief Financial Officer
CMO: James Jackson, M.D., Vice President Medical Affairs
CIO: John Adkins, Vice President and Chief Information Officer
Web address: www.sjchs.org

| | 21 | 10 | 284 | 10083 | 204 | 165862 | 2384 | 154130 | 72524 | 1521 |

□ △ ST. JOSEPH'S/CANDLER, ST. JOSEPH'S HOSPITAL, 11705 Mercy Boulevard, Zip 31419–1791; tel. 912/925–4100, (Total facility includes 11 beds in nursing home–type unit) **A**1 2 7 9 10 **F**2 12 14 15 17 21 22 23 24 26 27 28 29 30 31 32 33 34 35 37 38 39 40 44 46 47 48 49 51 52 53 55 57 58 60 61 62 63 64 65 66 68 69 81 82 84 85 87 88 92 93 94 95 96 106 108 110
Primary Contact: Paul P. Hinchey, President and Chief Executive Officer
Web address: www.sjchs.org

| | 21 | 10 | 223 | 10045 | 166 | 87856 | 0 | 135518 | 57474 | 1138 |

SMYRNA—Cobb County

✸ EMORY–ADVENTIST HOSPITAL, 3949 South Cobb Drive S.E., Zip 30080–6300; tel. 770/434–0710, (Total facility includes 12 beds in nursing home–type unit) **A**1 9 10 **F**2 9 10 12 21 22 28 32 33 37 39 46 47 48 52 55 57 58 62 63 64 65 66 69 70 81 82 84 88 92 94 106 108 110 **S** Adventist Health System Sunbelt Health Care Corporation, Winter Park, FL
Primary Contact: Dennis Kiley, President
CFO: Carol Hazen, Vice President Finance
CHR: Sheila Kimball, Director of Human Resources
Web address: www.ahss.org

| | 21 | 10 | 69 | 2141 | 27 | 52653 | 0 | 31360 | 13038 | 314 |

✸ RIDGEVIEW INSTITUTE, 3995 South Cobb Drive S.E., Zip 30080–6397; tel. 770/434–4567 **A**1 9 10 **F**3 4 26 27 28 58 66 71 72 74 76 77 78 94 96 109
Primary Contact: Robert M. Fink, Chief Executive Officer
COO: Paul Hackman, Chief Operating Officer
CFO: Lynn Wilson, Chief Financial Officer
CMO: James Vargo, M.D., Medical Director
CIO: Lynn Leger, Director Information Systems
Web address: www.ridgeviewinstitute.com

| | 23 | 22 | 96 | 3805 | 63 | 40624 | 0 | 23462 | 11621 | 221 |

SNELLVILLE—Gwinnett County

✸ EMORY EASTSIDE MEDICAL CENTER, 1700 Medical Way, Zip 30078–2195, Mailing Address: P.O. Box 587, Zip 30078–0587; tel. 770/979–0200 **A**1 2 9 10 **F**2 9 11 12 15 21 22 23 26 27 28 32 33 37 39 44 45 46 47 48 52 55 56 57 58 59 60 62 63 65 66 69 71 74 76 81 82 84 85 87 88 93 94 96 107 108 109 110 **S** HCA, Nashville, TN
Primary Contact: Les Beard, Chief Executive Officer
COO: Richard Tumlin, Chief Operating Officer
CFO: Greg Caples, Chief Financial Officer
CIO: James Keith, Director Information Systems
CHR: Scott Lowe, Director of Human Resources
Web address: www.emoryeastside.com

| | 33 | 10 | 171 | 9102 | 122 | 116777 | 2210 | 85400 | 38319 | 907 |

SPRINGFIELD—Effingham County

✸ EFFINGHAM HOSPITAL, 459 Highway 119 South, Zip 31329–3021, Mailing Address: P.O. Box 386, Zip 31329–0386; tel. 912/754–6451, (Total facility includes 105 beds in nursing home–type unit) **A**1 9 10 18 **F**9 12 21 26 27 28 29 33 39 42 44 45 48 52 63 65 66 70 92 94 97 107 108
Primary Contact: Don E. Tomberlin, Chief Executive Officer
CFO: Ed Brown, Chief Financial Officer
CHR: Vicky B. Edwards, Director Human Resources
Web address: www.effinghamhospital.com

| | 16 | 10 | 130 | 275 | 107 | 28734 | 0 | 13192 | 6608 | 206 |

STATESBORO—Bulloch County

□ EAST GEORGIA REGIONAL MEDICAL CENTER, 1499 Fair Road, Zip 30458–5105, Mailing Address: P.O. Box 1048, Zip 30459–1048; tel. 912/486–1000, (Nonreporting) **A**1 9 10 19 **S** Health Management Associates, Naples, FL
Primary Contact: Robert F. Bigley, Executive Director
Web address: www.egrmc.com

| | 33 | 10 | 114 | — | — | — | — | — | — | — |

GA

Hospital, Address, Telephone, Approval, Facility, and Physician Codes, Health Care System	Classi-fication Codes		Utilization Data					Expense (thousands) of dollars		
	Control	Service	Staffed Beds	Admissions	Census	Outpatient Visits	Births	Total	Payroll	Personnel

★ American Hospital Association (AHA) membership
□ Joint Commission on Accreditation of Healthcare Organizations (JCAHO) accreditation
○ American Osteopathic Association (AOA) accreditation
△ Commission on Accreditation of Rehabilitation Facilities (CARF) accreditation

WILLINGWAY HOSPITAL, 311 Jones Mill Road, Zip 30458–4765; tel. 912/764–6236, (Nonreporting) **A**9 Primary Contact: Jimmy Mooney, Chief Executive Officer Web address: www.willingway.com	33	82	40	—	—	—	—	—	—	—
STOCKBRIDGE—Henry County										
⊠ HENRY MEDICAL CENTER, 1133 Eagle's Landing Parkway, Zip 30281–5099; tel. 770/389–2200, (Total facility includes 74 beds in nursing home–type unit) **A**1 2 9 10 **F**2 9 11 12 14 21 22 23 26 27 28 29 33 37 39 42 46 47 48 50 52 57 58 59 60 61 62 63 64 65 69 73 81 82 87 88 92 94 96 106 107 108 109 110 Primary Contact: G. Sam Ahern, President and Chief Executive Officer COO: Leon F. Echols, III, Executive Vice President and Chief Operating Officer CFO: Claude Carruth, Vice President and Chief Financial Officer CMO: Hitesh Chokshi, M.D., Chief of Staff CIO: Natalie Wilkerson, Director Information Technology Services CHR: Maribeth Ledford, Director Human Resources Web address: www.henrymedical.com	16	10	196	9815	187	110961	2022	95898	38624	1006
SWAINSBORO—Emanuel County										
□ EMANUEL MEDICAL HOSPITAL, 117 Kite Road, Zip 30401–3231, Mailing Address: P.O. Box 879, Zip 30401–0879; tel. 478/237–9911, (Total facility includes 49 beds in nursing home–type unit) **A**1 9 10 20 **F**2 6 11 12 21 22 26 29 33 34 35 39 45 46 48 52 55 58 59 62 63 66 75 77 78 81 82 88 92 94 96 97 106 108 **P**6 Primary Contact: Bob Via, Chief Executive Officer Web address: www.emanuelmedical.org	16	10	91	2451	71	31299	173	25927	11365	395
SYLVANIA—Screven County										
★ SCREVEN COUNTY HOSPITAL, 215 Mims Road, Zip 30467–2097; tel. 912/564–7426 **A**9 10 18 **F**2 9 12 21 26 27 28 29 33 39 46 48 52 58 62 63 69 70 81 88 94 97 108 Primary Contact: George H. St. George, Chief Executive Officer CFO: Marsha Carroll, Director Financial Services	16	10	25	640	7	15973	0	5878	2826	78
SYLVESTER—Worth County										
⊠ PHOEBE WORTH MEDICAL CENTER, 807 South Isabella Street, Zip 31791–0545, Mailing Address: P.O. Box 545, Zip 31791–0545; tel. 229/776–6961 **A**1 9 10 18 **F**2 6 9 12 21 27 28 29 33 45 46 59 63 66 69 81 88 92 93 94 97 **S** Phoebe Putney Health Systems, Albany, GA Primary Contact: Keith J. Petersen, Chief Executive Officer COO: Keith J. Petersen, Chief Executive Officer CFO: Todd Cox, Interim Chief Financial Officer CMO: Natu M. Patel, M.D., Chief of Staff CHR: Kim Littleton, Director Web address: www.ppmh.org	23	10	25	695	11	19239	44	10529	5099	202
THOMASTON—Upson County										
⊠ UPSON REGIONAL MEDICAL CENTER, 801 West Gordon Street, Zip 30286–2831, Mailing Address: P.O. Box 1059, Zip 30286–1059; tel. 706/647–8111 **A**1 9 10 19 20 **F**2 6 9 11 12 21 22 26 27 28 29 32 33 46 48 52 55 58 59 60 61 62 63 65 66 69 81 82 84 86 88 93 94 95 96 97 106 107 108 110 **P**5 **S** Brim Healthcare, Inc., Brentwood, TN Primary Contact: Gene B. Wright, Interim Chief Executive Officer CFO: John Williams, Chief Financial Officer CIO: Paul Patterson, Director Information Technology and Services CHR: Claudia Jackson, Director Human Resources Web address: www.urmc.org	23	10	115	4893	50	101774	600	51990	22160	560
THOMASVILLE—Thomas County										
⊠ JOHN D. ARCHBOLD MEMORIAL HOSPITAL, Gordon Avenue at Mimosa Drive, Zip 31792–6113, Mailing Address: P.O. Box 1018, Zip 31799–1018; tel. 229/228–2000, (Total facility includes 64 beds in nursing home–type unit) **A**1 2 9 10 19 **F**2 3 4 9 11 12 14 15 21 22 23 26 27 28 29 30 31 33 34 39 40 42 43 44 45 46 47 48 49 50 52 53 55 57 58 59 60 61 62 63 65 66 68 69 71 72 73 74 75 76 77 78 79 81 82 84 85 86 87 88 92 93 94 95 96 98 106 107 108 109 110 **P**8 **S** Archbold Medical Center, Thomasville, GA Primary Contact: James L. Story, Jr, M.D., President COO: J Perry Mustian, Executive Senior Vice President and Chief Operating Officer CFO: J William Sellers, Jr, Senior Vice President and Chief Financial Officer CMO: Melvin Hartsfield, M.D., Vice President Medical Affairs CIO: William Zimmermann, Vice President Information Services CHR: Zach Wheeler, Vice President Human Resources Web address: www.archbold.org	23	10	328	9506	208	207264	819	—	—	1487
□ SOUTHWESTERN STATE HOSPITAL, Pine Tree Boulevard, Zip 31792, Mailing Address: P.O. Box 1378, Zip 31799–1378; tel. 229/227–2833, (Total facility includes 20 beds in nursing home–type unit) (Nonreporting) **A**1 9 10 Primary Contact: Beverly Bajerski, Regional Administrator	12	22	236	—	—	—	—	—	—	—
THOMSON—McDuffie County										
⊠ MCDUFFIE REGIONAL MEDICAL CENTER, 521 Hill Street S.W., Zip 30824–2199; tel. 706/595–1411 **A**1 9 10 **F**2 6 9 12 14 21 22 26 28 29 33 37 41 46 47 48 52 53 55 58 60 62 63 64 65 66 75 81 88 94 96 106 108 110 **S** Quorum Health Resources, Plano, TX Primary Contact: Douglas C. Keir, Chief Executive Officer CFO: Pat Parris, Chief Financial Officer CIO: Lisa Tucker, Chief Information Officer Web address: www.mrmc.org	16	10	35	1467	16	30575	2	17282	6895	232

Many Facility Codes have changed. Please refer to the AHA Guide Code Chart. © 2005 AHA Guide

GA

Hospital, Address, Telephone, Approval, Facility, and Physician Codes, Health Care System	Classi-fication Codes		Utilization Data					Expense (thousands) of dollars		
★ American Hospital Association (AHA) membership □ Joint Commission on Accreditation of Healthcare Organizations (JCAHO) accreditation ○ American Osteopathic Association (AOA) accreditation △ Commission on Accreditation of Rehabilitation Facilities (CARF) accreditation	Control	Service	Staffed Beds	Admissions	Census	Outpatient Visits	Births	Total	Payroll	Personnel

TIFTON—Tift County

☒ **TIFT REGIONAL MEDICAL CENTER**, 901 East 18th Street, Zip 31794–3648, Mailing Address: Drawer 747, Zip 31793–0747; tel. 229/382–7120, (Total facility includes 15 beds in nursing home–type unit) **A**1 2 9 10 19 **F**2 9 11 12 15 21 23 26 27 28 29 33 36 45 46 48 49 52 53 55 57 58 59 60 61 62 63 64 65 66 68 69 79 80 81 82 84 85 88 92 93 94 96 107 108 109 110
Primary Contact: William T. Richardson, President and Chief Executive Officer
CFO: Dennis L. Crum, Chief Financial Officer and Vice President
CMO: Raymond Moreno, M.D., Vice President Medical Affairs
CHR: Ellen Eaton, Director Human Resources
Web address: www.tiftregional.com
| 16 | 10 | 191 | 8869 | 99 | 107311 | 1212 | 109755 | 37281 | 1058 |

TOCCOA—Stephens County

☒ **STEPHENS COUNTY HOSPITAL**, 2003 Falls Road, Zip 30577–9700; tel. 706/282–4200, (Total facility includes 82 beds in nursing home–type unit) **A**1 9 10 **F**2 6 8 9 11 12 22 26 27 28 29 33 37 40 46 47 48 49 52 53 55 58 59 60 62 63 64 65 69 81 84 88 91 92 93 94 105 108 110
Primary Contact: Edward C. Gambrell, Jr, Administrator
CFO: Jeff Laird, Controller
CHR: Diane Hardeman, Personnel Director
Web address: www.stephenscountyhospital.com
| 16 | 10 | 178 | 3548 | 105 | 40129 | 501 | 36631 | 17296 | 490 |

TUCKER—De Kalb County

☒ **NORTHLAKE MEDICAL CENTER**, 1455 Montreal Road, Zip 30084–8100; tel. 770/270–3000, (Nonreporting) **A**1 9 10 **S** HCA, Nashville, TN
Primary Contact: Daniel W. Jackson, Chief Executive Officer
CFO: William Dohn, Chief Financial Officer
CMO: Eric A. Deal, D.O., Chief of Staff
CIO: Michael Gibson, Director Information Systems
Web address: www.northlakemedical.com
| 33 | 10 | 116 | — | — | — | — | — | — | — |

VALDOSTA—Lowndes County

☒ **SMITH NORTHVIEW HOSPITAL**, 4280 North Valdosta Road, Zip 31602, Mailing Address: P.O. Box 10010, Zip 31604; tel. 229/671–2000 **A**1 9 10 **F**2 9 11 12 21 22 27 32 33 37 44 46 48 52 57 58 59 62 63 65 81 82 88 93 94 108 **S** Ameris Health Systems, Nashville, TN
Primary Contact: Robert Bauer, Chief Executive Officer
CFO: Shamb Purohit, Chief Financial Officer
CMO: Thomas Getman, M.D., Chief of Staff
CHR: Brenda Pridgen, Director Personnel
Web address: www.smithhospital.com
| 32 | 10 | 29 | 2265 | 22 | 25548 | 297 | 23310 | 7406 | 255 |

☒ △ **SOUTH GEORGIA MEDICAL CENTER**, 2501 North Patterson Street, Zip 31602–1735, Mailing Address: P.O. Box 1727, Zip 31603–1727; tel. 229/333–1000, (Includes GREENLEAF CENTER, 2209 Pineview Drive, Zip 31602–7316; tel. 229/247–4357; Michael Lane, Administrator and Chief Executive Officer) **A**1 2 7 9 10 19 **F**3 4 6 9 11 12 13 14 15 17 19 21 22 23 24 26 27 28 29 30 31 32 33 37 38 39 40 42 44 45 46 47 48 49 50 52 55 56 57 58 59 60 61 62 63 64 65 66 67 68 69 70 71 72 73 74 75 76 77 78 80 81 82 84 86 87 88 92 93 94 95 96 97 106 107 108 109 110 **P**5
Primary Contact: James McGahee, Administrator and Chief Executive Officer
COO: Randy Sauls, Chief Operating Officer
CFO: Greg Hembree, Chief Financial Officer
CIO: William Okuma, Director, Management Systems
Web address: www.sgmc.org
| 16 | 10 | 335 | 15291 | 202 | 166893 | 1813 | 170044 | 66337 | 1757 |

VIDALIA—Toombs County

□ **MEADOWS REGIONAL MEDICAL CENTER**, 1703 Meadows Lane, Zip 30474–8915, Mailing Address: P.O. Box 1048, Zip 30475–1048; tel. 912/537–8921, (Total facility includes 35 beds in nursing home–type unit) **A**1 9 10 **F**6 9 11 12 21 22 26 27 28 29 33 40 41 42 46 48 50 52 53 55 58 59 60 62 63 69 81 82 84 85 86 87 88 92 93 94 95 108
Primary Contact: Alan Kent, Chief Executive Officer
Web address: www.meadowsregional.org
| 23 | 10 | 89 | 4576 | 63 | 45055 | 479 | 42042 | 18570 | 504 |

VILLA RICA—Carroll County

☒ **TANNER MEDICAL CENTER–VILLA RICA**, 601 Dallas Road, Zip 30180–1202, Mailing Address: P.O. Box 638, Zip 30180–0638; tel. 770/456–3100, (Nonreporting) **A**1 9 10
Primary Contact: Larry N. Steed, Administrator
CFO: Lee Sherseth, Chief Financial Officer
Web address: www.tanner.org
| 23 | 10 | 39 | — | — | — | — | — | — | — |

WARM SPRINGS—Meriwether County

□ **ROOSEVELT WARM SPRINGS INSTITUTE FOR REHABILITATION**, Highway 27, Zip 31830, Mailing Address: P.O. Box 1000, Zip 31830–1000; tel. 706/655–5000, (Nonreporting) **A**1 9 10
Primary Contact: Frank C. Ruzycki, Executive Director
Web address: www.rooseveltrehab.org
| 12 | 80 | 64 | — | — | — | — | — | — | — |

☒ **WARM SPRINGS MEDICAL CENTER**, (Formerly Baptist Meriwether Hospital), 5995 Spring Street, Zip 31830–2149, Mailing Address: P.O. Box 8, Zip 31830–0008; tel. 706/655–3331 **A**1 9 10 18 **F**2 11 12 21 22 29 33 46 52 53 58 60 63 64 69 81 85 88 92 94 97 **S** Quorum Health Resources, Plano, TX
Primary Contact: Jon L. Dixon, Chief Executive Officer
CFO: Phillip Fonts, Chief Financial Officer
CIO: Milo Varnadoe, Director of Systems
CHR: Charlene Winslett, Director of Human Resources
| 21 | 10 | 25 | 634 | 6 | — | 48 | 10442 | 6497 | 122 |

GA

Hospital, Address, Telephone, Approval, Facility, and Physician Codes, Health Care System	Classi-fication Codes		Utilization Data					Expense (thousands) of dollars		
★ American Hospital Association (AHA) membership □ Joint Commission on Accreditation of Healthcare Organizations (JCAHO) accreditation ○ American Osteopathic Association (AOA) accreditation △ Commission on Accreditation of Rehabilitation Facilities (CARF) accreditation	Control	Service	Staffed Beds	Admissions	Census	Outpatient Visits	Births	Total	Payroll	Personnel

WARNER ROBINS—Houston County

☒ **HOUSTON MEDICAL CENTER**, 1601 Watson Boulevard, Zip 31093–3431, Mailing Address: P.O. Box 2886, Zip 31099–2886; tel. 478/922–4281 **A**1 9 10 **F**9 11 12 21 22 23 26 27 28 31 32 33 37 44 46 50 52 55 57 58 59 60 61 62 63 64 65 66 69 71 73 74 75 76 77 81 82 84 85 87 88 93 94 95 96 107 108 109 110
Primary Contact: Arthur P. Christie, Administrator
CFO: Frank R. Powell, Chief Financial Officer
CMO: Tony Alford, D.O., Executive Director of Medical Affairs
CIO: Beth Benefield, Executive Director of Hospital Information Systems
CHR: Marilu Crosby, Director of Human Resources
Web address: www.hhc.org

	13	10	186	10125	112	180070	1744	99055	39760	1012

WASHINGTON—Wilkes County

☒ **WILLS MEMORIAL HOSPITAL**, 120 Gordon Street, Zip 30673–1602, Mailing Address: P.O. Box 370, Zip 30673–0370; tel. 706/678–2151 **A**1 9 10 18 **F**2 9 11 12 26 27 28 29 32 33 46 48 55 58 59 62 63 64 69 81 88 97 108
Primary Contact: T. Marvin Goldman, Chief Executive Officer
CFO: Cliff Cooper, Chief Financial Officer
CHR: Anna Norman, Director Human Resources
Web address: www.willsmemorialhospital.com

	16	10	25	1266	16	17261	30	9618	4765	155

WAYCROSS—Ware County

☒ **SATILLA REGIONAL MEDICAL CENTER**, 410 Darling Avenue, Zip 31501–5246, Mailing Address: P.O. Box 139, Zip 31502–0139; tel. 912/283–3030 **A**1 9 10 19 20 **F**2 10 11 12 14 15 21 26 27 28 33 34 37 40 46 48 49 55 59 60 61 63 64 66 68 69 81 82 84 85 86 88 93 94 96 108 109 **P**8
Primary Contact: Robert M. Trimm, President and Chief Executive Officer
COO: Windell Smith, Chief Operating Officer
CFO: Katrina Wheeler, Chief Financial Officer
CMO: Larry Duane, M.D., Medical Staff Director
CIO: Michael Gogola, Chief Information Officer
CHR: John K. Pharr, Jr, Director Human Resources
Web address: www.satilla.org

	23	10	181	7788	88	114028	737	88528	32434	872

WAYNESBORO—Burke County

□ **BURKE MEDICAL CENTER**, 351 Liberty Street, Zip 30830–9686; tel. 706/554–4435, (Nonreporting) **A**1 9 10
Primary Contact: Jennifer A. Royal, Administrator
Web address: www.burkemedical.net

	16	10	40	—	—	—	—	—	—	—

WILDWOOD—Dade County

WILDWOOD LIFESTYLE CENTER AND HOSPITAL, Lifestyle Lane, Zip 30757–4128, Mailing Address: P.O. Box 129, Zip 30757–0129; tel. 706/820–1493
Primary Contact: Larry E. Clements, Administrator
Web address: www.taquet.org/wildwood

	23	10	13	109	4	—	—	—	—	—

WINDER—Barrow County

□ **BARROW COMMUNITY HOSPITAL**, 316 North Broad Street, Zip 30680–2150, Mailing Address: P.O. Box 768, Zip 30680–0768; tel. 770/867–3400 **A**1 9 10 **F**2 9 11 12 21 22 26 27 28 33 39 46 53 55 58 59 60 62 63 64 69 81 82 88 93 94 96 106 108 110 **S** Ty Cobb Healthcare System, Inc., Royston, GA
Primary Contact: Jim Litchford, Administrator
Web address: www.barrowcommunityhospital.com

	23	10	56	1355	12	48161	296	10716	7939	228

GA

Many Facility Codes have changed. Please refer to the AHA Guide Code Chart. © 2005 AHA Guide

HAWAII

Hospital, Address, Telephone, Approval, Facility, and Physician Codes, Health Care System	Classi-fication Codes		Utilization Data					Expense (thousands) of dollars		
★ American Hospital Association (AHA) membership ☐ Joint Commission on Accreditation of Healthcare Organizations (JCAHO) accreditation ○ American Osteopathic Association (AOA) accreditation △ Commission on Accreditation of Rehabilitation Facilities (CARF) accreditation	Control	Service	Staffed Beds	Admissions	Census	Outpatient Visits	Births	Total	Payroll	Personnel

AIEA—Honolulu County

☒ **KAPIOLANI MEDICAL CENTER AT PALI MOMI**, 98–1079 Moanalua Road, Zip 96701–4713; tel. 808/486–6000, (Nonreporting) **A**1 2 5 9 10 **S** Hawaii Pacific Health, Honolulu, HI
Primary Contact: Ray Vara, Chief Executive Officer
CMO: Mark Grief, M.D., Chief of Staff
Web address: www.kapiolani.org

| | 23 | 10 | 100 | — | — | — | — | — | — | — |

EWA BEACH—Honolulu County

☒ **KAHI MOHALA BEHAVIORAL HEALTH**, 91–2301 Old Fort Weaver Road, Zip 96706–3602; tel. 808/671–8511 **A**1 9 10 **F**4 21 27 28 71 72 73 74 77 78 **P**6 **S** Sutter Health, Sacramento, CA
Primary Contact: Mark R. Mitchell, Ph.D., Chief Executive Officer
CFO: Leonard Licina, Chief Financial Officer
CMO: Celia M. Ona, M.D., Medical Director
CHR: Christina Enoka, Director Human Resources
Web address: www.kahi.org

| | 23 | 22 | 88 | 721 | 61 | 0 | 0 | 15145 | 8045 | 178 |

☒ **ST. FRANCIS MEDICAL CENTER—WEST**, 91–2141 Fort Weaver Road, Zip 96706–1993; tel. 808/678–7000 **A**1 5 9 10 **F**2 12 22 26 27 28 29 33 46 48 55 58 60 63 65 69 70 81 82 88 92 94 96 108 **P**8 **S** Sisters of Saint Francis, Syracuse, NY
Primary Contact: Sister Beatrice Tom, Chief Executive Officer
COO: Malcolm J. Tom, Chief Operations Officer
CFO: Terry L. Long, Chief Financial Officer
CIO: Jerry Correa, Vice President Information Services
CHR: Jessica Sphar, Director Human Resources
Web address: www.sfhs-hi.org

| | 21 | 10 | 102 | 4212 | 77 | 33224 | 0 | 52007 | 18955 | 519 |

HILO—Hawaii County

☒ **HILO MEDICAL CENTER**, 1190 Waianuenue Avenue, Zip 96720–2095; tel. 808/974–4700, (Total facility includes 134 beds in nursing home–type unit) **A**1 5 9 10 20 **F**2 11 14 21 22 23 26 27 28 32 33 37 48 50 51 55 58 59 60 61 63 69 71 73 74 75 76 78 81 82 84 85 88 92 94 108 110 **P**5 **S** Hawaii Health Systems Corporation, Honolulu, HI
Primary Contact: Ronald J. Schurra, Chief Executive Officer
CFO: Julie Rukstad, Chief Financial Officer
CMO: Nancy Lundblad, M.D., Medical Director
CIO: Summer Taylor, Director Information Systems
CHR: Charles Bolden, Human Resources Director
Web address: www.hmc.hhsc.org

| | 12 | 10 | 275 | 8286 | 224 | 55004 | 1075 | 77729 | 34160 | 814 |

HONOKAA—Hawaii County

★ **HALE HO'OLA HAMAKUA**, 45–547 Plumeria Street, Zip 96727–6902; tel. 808/775–7211, (Total facility includes 48 beds in nursing home–type unit) **A**5 9 10 20 **F**9 27 28 29 35 44 53 58 82 92 94 96 97 108 **S** Hawaii Health Systems Corporation, Honolulu, HI
Primary Contact: Romel Dela Cruz, Administrator
CFO: Felisa Rosario, Accountant
Web address: www.hhsc.org

| | 12 | 10 | 50 | 82 | 47 | 590 | 0 | 4852 | 3307 | 82 |

HONOLULU—Honolulu County

☒ **KAISER PERMANENTE MEDICAL CENTER**, 3288 Moanalua Road, Zip 96819–1469; tel. 808/432–0000, (Total facility includes 28 beds in nursing home–type unit) **A**1 2 3 5 10 **F**2 11 12 14 15 16 17 19 20 21 22 23 24 26 27 28 30 31 33 35 37 38 39 44 48 49 50 51 52 53 55 56 57 58 59 60 61 62 63 64 66 67 81 82 84 85 87 88 92 94 96 98 108 109 110 **P**3 **S** Kaiser Foundation Hospitals, Oakland, CA
Primary Contact: Susan R. Murray, Administrator
COO: Patricia Rodriguez, Chief Operating Officer
CFO: Jeffrey Wright, Chief Financial Officer
CIO: Brian Yoshii, Chief Information Officer
Web address: www.kaiserhawaii.com

| | 23 | 10 | 270 | 11562 | 196 | 62197 | 1946 | — | — | 1504 |

☐ **KAPIOLANI MEDICAL CENTER FOR WOMEN & CHILDREN**, 1319 Punahou Street, Zip 96826–1032; tel. 808/983–6000, (Nonreporting) **A**1 3 5 9 10 **S** Hawaii Pacific Health, Honolulu, HI
Primary Contact: Ray Vara, Chief Executive Officer
Web address: www.kapiolani.org

| | 23 | 44 | 225 | — | — | — | — | — | — | — |

☒ **KUAKINI MEDICAL CENTER**, 347 North Kuakini Street, Zip 96817–2381; tel. 808/536–2236 **A**1 2 3 5 9 10 **F**2 9 12 14 15 17 19 21 23 26 27 28 29 30 33 37 38 46 47 48 49 53 55 57 58 60 61 62 63 64 65 66 69 79 81 82 84 85 87 88 92 93 94 95 96 108 109 110 **P**8
Primary Contact: Gary K. Kajiwara, President and Chief Executive Officer
CFO: Quin Ogawa, Vice President and Chief Financial Officer
CMO: Nobuyuki Miki, M.D., Vice President Medical Affairs
Web address: www.kuakini.org

| | 23 | 10 | 109 | 5901 | 109 | 62931 | 0 | 106301 | 49066 | 1046 |

HI

Hospital, Address, Telephone, Approval, Facility, and Physician Codes, Health Care System	Classi-fication Codes		Utilization Data					Expense (thousands) of dollars		
★ American Hospital Association (AHA) membership □ Joint Commission on Accreditation of Healthcare Organizations (JCAHO) accreditation ○ American Osteopathic Association (AOA) accreditation △ Commission on Accreditation of Rehabilitation Facilities (CARF) accreditation	Control	Service	Staffed Beds	Admissions	Census	Outpatient Visits	Births	Total	Payroll	Personnel

	Control	Service	Staffed Beds	Admissions	Census	Outpatient Visits	Births	Total	Payroll	Personnel
★ **LEAHI HOSPITAL**, (SNF/ICF; Acute TB Inpatient), 3675 Kilauea Avenue, Zip 96816–2398; tel. 808/733–8000, (Total facility includes 179 beds in nursing home–type unit) **A**9 10 **F**1 28 60 92 94 97 **S** Hawaii Health Systems Corporation, Honolulu, HI Primary Contact: Vincent H. S. Lee, FACHE, Administrator CFO: Nathan Yim, Chief Financial Officer CMO: Clifford Chang, M.D., Medical Director CHR: Glenn Sakumoto, Regional Director Human Resources Web address: www.hhsc.org	12	49	192	208	179	0	0	—	—	285
⊠ **QUEEN'S MEDICAL CENTER**, 1301 Punchbowl Street, Zip 96813–2499; tel. 808/538–9011, (Total facility includes 26 beds in nursing home–type unit) **A**1 2 3 5 8 9 10 **F**2 4 9 10 11 12 14 15 16 17 18 19 21 22 23 26 27 28 29 31 32 33 34 35 36 37 38 39 40 43 44 46 47 48 49 50 52 53 55 57 58 59 60 61 62 63 64 65 66 69 70 71 72 73 74 75 76 77 78 79 80 81 82 84 85 86 87 88 90 92 93 94 96 99 106 107 108 109 **P**6 **S** Queen's Health Systems, Honolulu, HI Primary Contact: Arthur A. Ushijima, President and Chief Executive Officer COO: Daniel E. Jessop, Executive Vice President and Chief Operating Officer CFO: Rix Maurer, III, Vice President Finance and Chief Financial Officer CMO: Richard Friedman, M.D., Vice President Medical Affairs CIO: Ken Kudla, ice President Information Technology and Chief Information Officer CHR: Bert Kido, Vice President Human Resources Web address: www.queens.org	23	10	456	20104	363	218139	1893	387942	157534	2879
⊠ **REHABILITATION HOSPITAL OF THE PACIFIC**, 226 North Kuakini Street, Zip 96817–9881; tel. 808/531–3511 **A**1 9 10 **F**2 9 21 26 27 28 37 42 45 52 53 57 58 60 62 68 69 94 95 96 108 110 Primary Contact: Stuart Ho, President and Chief Executive Officer CFO: Pauline Osbourne, Senior Vice President and Chief Financial Officer CMO: Thomas Au, M.D., Senior Vice President Clinical Operations and Medical Director CIO: Dave Orme, Chief Information Officer CHR: Faye Miyamoto, Vice President Human Resources Web address: www.rehabhospital.org	23	46	80	1992	80	64919	0	35890	18712	356
□ **SHRINERS HOSPITALS FOR CHILDREN, HONOLULU**, 1310 Punahou Street, Zip 96826–1099; tel. 808/941–4466 **A**1 3 5 **F**2 21 45 52 62 63 66 69 88 94 96 108 **S** Shriners Hospitals for Children, Tampa, FL Primary Contact: Thomas R. Schneider, Administrator Web address: www.shrinershq.org	23	59	40	532	11	—	—	—	—	150
□ **ST. FRANCIS MEDICAL CENTER**, 2230 Liliha Street, Zip 96817–9979, Mailing Address: P.O. Box 30100, Zip 96820–0100; tel. 808/547–6011, (Total facility includes 52 beds in nursing home–type unit) **A**1 2 3 5 9 10 **F**2 12 15 17 19 22 23 26 27 28 29 33 34 37 40 43 46 48 49 52 55 57 58 60 61 63 65 66 69 70 81 82 84 88 92 94 96 99 100 101 102 105 108 **P**8 **S** Sisters of Saint Francis, Syracuse, NY Primary Contact: Sister Beatrice Tom, Chief Executive Officer Web address: www.stfrancishawaii.org	21	10	240	5017	143	199931	0	134986	46091	940
□ **STRAUB CLINIC & HOSPITAL**, 888 South King Street, Zip 96813–3083; tel. 808/522–4000 **A**1 2 3 5 9 10 **F**2 7 10 12 13 14 15 16 17 18 19 21 22 23 26 27 28 33 37 42 44 46 47 48 52 53 55 57 58 60 61 62 63 64 65 66 69 70 77 81 82 84 85 88 93 94 95 96 106 108 110 **P**6 **S** Hawaii Pacific Health, Honolulu, HI Primary Contact: Ray Vara, Chief Executive Officer Web address: www.straubhealth.com	23	10	143	6110	96	632919	0	219331	91825	1431
⊠ **TRIPLER ARMY MEDICAL CENTER**, 1 Jarret White Road, Zip 96859–5000; tel. 808/433–6661, (Nonreporting) **A**1 2 3 5 **S** Department of the Army, Office of the Surgeon General, Falls Church, VA Primary Contact: Major General Gale Pollock, Commander COO: Colonel Frederick J. Gargiulo, Administrator CFO: Lieutenant Colonel David Petray, Chief Resource Management CMO: Captain Kevin G. Berry, Deputy Commander for Clinical Services CIO: Lieutenant Colonel Ralph A. Franco, Chief Information Management Division CHR: Colonel Paul W. Wingo, Troop Commander Web address: www.tamc.amedd.army.mil	42	10	209	—	—	—	—	—	—	—
KAHUKU—Honolulu County										
KAHUKU HOSPITAL, 56–117 Pualalea Street, Zip 96731–2052; tel. 808/293–9221, (Total facility includes 10 beds in nursing home–type unit) **A**9 10 18 **F**2 11 12 22 25 29 32 33 39 46 52 53 54 59 63 69 88 92 94 97 108 Primary Contact: R. Don Olden, Chief Executive Officer	23	10	23	465	11	6894	124	—	—	85
KAILUA—Honolulu County										
⊠ **CASTLE MEDICAL CENTER**, 640 Ulukahiki Street, Zip 96734–4498; tel. 808/263–5500, (Total facility includes 10 beds in nursing home–type unit) (Nonreporting) **A**1 9 10 **S** Adventist Health, Roseville, CA Primary Contact: Kevin Roberts, President and Chief Executive Officer COO: A John Monge, Vice President Operations CFO: Dale Northrop, Vice President Finance CMO: David Randell, M.D., Chief of Staff CIO: Robert Wells, Chief Information Officer CHR: Adele Hoe, Director Human Resources Web address: www.castlemed.com	21	10	157	—	—	—	—	—	—	—

HI

Many Facility Codes have changed. Please refer to the AHA Guide Code Chart.

Hospital, Address, Telephone, Approval, Facility, and Physician Codes, Health Care System	Classi-fication Codes		Utilization Data					Expense (thousands) of dollars		
★ American Hospital Association (AHA) membership ☐ Joint Commission on Accreditation of Healthcare Organizations (JCAHO) accreditation ◯ American Osteopathic Association (AOA) accreditation △ Commission on Accreditation of Rehabilitation Facilities (CARF) accreditation	Control	Service	Staffed Beds	Admissions	Census	Outpatient Visits	Births	Total	Payroll	Personnel

KAMUELA—Hawaii County

☒ **NORTH HAWAII COMMUNITY HOSPITAL**, 67–1125 Mamalahoa Highway, Zip 96743; tel. 808/885–4444, (Nonreporting) **A**1 5 9 10 **S** Adventist Health, Roseville, CA
Primary Contact: Stan B. Berry, FACHE, Chief Executive Officer
CFO: Lexi M. Fields, Vice President, Finance
CMO: John Dawson, M.D., Chief of Staff
CIO: Victor Gouge, Information Systems Leader
CHR: Delsa Bentelmann, Human Resources Leader
Web address: www.northhawaiicommunityhospital.org

| 23 | 10 | 35 | — | — | — | — | — | — | — |

KANEOHE—Honolulu County

☐ **HAWAII STATE HOSPITAL**, 45–710 Keaahala Road, Zip 96744–3597; tel. 808/236–8237 **A**1 3 5 **F**26 27 28 44 45 47 50 66 71 73 74 76 94 96
Primary Contact: Paul A. Guggenheim, Administrator
Web address: www.hshweb.health.state.hi.us

| 12 | 22 | 178 | 184 | 170 | 0 | 0 | 49786 | 25751 | 551 |

KAPAA—Kauai County

★ **SAMUEL MAHELONA MEMORIAL HOSPITAL**, 4800 Kawaihau Road, Zip 96746–1998; tel. 808/822–4961, (Total facility includes 70 beds in nursing home–type unit) **A**9 10 **F**2 9 12 21 29 32 44 45 58 60 69 71 92 94 97 108 **S** Hawaii Health Systems Corporation, Honolulu, HI
Primary Contact: Orianna A. Skomoroch, Regional Chief Executive Officer
CFO: Michael Perel, Regional Chief Financial Officer
CMO: Gerald Tomory, M.D., Regional Medical Director
CIO: Sandra McMaster, Regional Chief Information Officer
Web address: www.mahelona.org

| 12 | 22 | 81 | 210 | 71 | — | 0 | — | — | 127 |

KAUNAKAKAI—Maui County

☒ **MOLOKAI GENERAL HOSPITAL**, (CAH), Mailing Address: P.O. Box 408, Zip 96748–0408; tel. 808/553–5331, (Total facility includes 4 beds in nursing home–type unit) **A**1 9 10 18 **F**11 12 21 27 28 29 36 37 38 39 48 52 53 54 58 59 60 66 69 81 88 92 94 97 107 109 110 **S** Queen's Health Systems, Honolulu, HI
Primary Contact: Janice Kalanihuia, Administrator
CFO: Jerry Clemente, Controller
CMO: N Emmett Aluli, M.D., Medical Executive Director
CIO: Randy Lite, Chief Information Officer
CHR: Chrisey Paleka, Human Resources Coordinator
Web address: www.queens.org

| 23 | 49 | 30 | 182 | 8 | 19642 | 29 | 6973 | 2974 | 72 |

KEALAKEKUA—Hawaii County

☒ **KONA COMMUNITY HOSPITAL**, 79–1019 Haukapila Street, Zip 96750–7920; tel. 808/322–4430, (Total facility includes 34 beds in nursing home–type unit) **A**1 5 9 10 20 **F**2 9 11 21 22 23 27 28 33 37 39 40 53 55 58 59 60 61 62 63 66 69 71 72 75 81 82 84 85 88 92 94 110 **P**8 **S** Hawaii Health Systems Corporation, Honolulu, HI
Primary Contact: Ira F. Walton, III, FACHE, Chief Executive Officer
COO: Glenn Sparks, Assistant Administrator
CFO: Ira F. Walton, III, FACHE, Chief Executive Officer
CMO: Roy Nagle, M.D., Medical Director
CIO: Ed Heaukulani, Information Technology Manager
CHR: Sharon Toriano, Chief Human Resources
Web address: www.kch.hhsc.org

| 23 | 10 | 88 | 3634 | 66 | 20527 | 491 | 42171 | 18032 | 361 |

KOHALA—Hawaii County

★ **KOHALA HOSPITAL**, 54–383 Hospital Road, Zip 96755, Mailing Address: P.O. Box 10, Kapaau, Zip 96755–0010; tel. 808/889–6211, (Total facility includes 22 beds in nursing home–type unit) (Nonreporting) **A**9 10 18 **S** Hawaii Health Systems Corporation, Honolulu, HI
Primary Contact: Ira F. Walton, III, FACHE, Chief Executive Officer
CFO: Eugene Amar, Jr, Chief Financial Officer
CMO: Silvia Sonnenschein, Chief of Staff
Web address: www.koh.hhsc.org

| 12 | 10 | 26 | — | — | — | — | — | — | — |

KULA—Maui County

★ **KULA HOSPITAL**, 204 Kula Highway, Zip 96790–9499; tel. 808/878–1221, (Nonreporting) **A**9 10 **S** Hawaii Health Systems Corporation, Honolulu, HI
Primary Contact: John Schaumburg, Administrator
CFO: Lloyd Kawabata, Chief Financial Officer
CMO: Chad Meyer, M.D., Medical Director
Web address: www.hhsc.org

| 12 | 10 | 115 | — | — | — | — | — | — | — |

LANAI CITY—Maui County

★ **LANAI COMMUNITY HOSPITAL**, 628 Seventh Street, Zip 96763–0650, Mailing Address: P.O. Box 630650, Zip 96763–0650; tel. 808/565–6411, (Total facility includes 10 beds in nursing home–type unit) **A**9 10 18 **F**2 9 26 27 28 33 92 94 97 **S** Hawaii Health Systems Corporation, Honolulu, HI
Primary Contact: Mary Catiel, Acting Administrator
Web address: www.lch.hhsc.org

| 16 | 80 | 14 | 41 | 10 | 1096 | 0 | 2460 | 1548 | 29 |

LIHUE—Kauai County

☒ **WILCOX MEMORIAL HOSPITAL**, 3420 Kuhio Highway, Zip 96766–1099; tel. 808/245–1100 **A**1 5 9 10 20 **F**1 2 9 11 12 21 22 26 27 28 33 34 37 38 42 48 49 50 52 53 55 58 59 60 62 63 64 65 69 81 82 84 88 92 94 106 108 **S** Hawaii Pacific Health, Honolulu, HI
Primary Contact: Lee Evslin, M.D., President and Chief Executive Officer
COO: Paula Dias, Vice President and Chief Operating Officer
CIO: Stevan Yee, Director Information Systems
Web address: www.wilcoxhealth.org

| 23 | 10 | 181 | 5016 | 142 | 68387 | 648 | 60908 | 26371 | 466 |

HI

Hospital, Address, Telephone, Approval, Facility, and Physician Codes, Health Care System	Classi-fication Codes		Utilization Data					Expense (thousands) of dollars		
★ American Hospital Association (AHA) membership □ Joint Commission on Accreditation of Healthcare Organizations (JCAHO) accreditation ○ American Osteopathic Association (AOA) accreditation △ Commission on Accreditation of Rehabilitation Facilities (CARF) accreditation	Control	Service	Staffed Beds	Admissions	Census	Outpatient Visits	Births	Total	Payroll	Personnel

PAHALA—Hawaii County

★ **KAU HOSPITAL**, 1 Kamani Street, Zip 96777, Mailing Address: P.O. Box 40, Zip 96777–0040; tel. 808/928–8331, (Total facility includes 16 beds in nursing home–type unit) (Nonreporting) **A**9 10 18 **S** Hawaii Health Systems Corporation, Honolulu, HI
Primary Contact: Merilyn Harris, Administrator
CFO: Russell Morinaga, Accountant
CMO: Carol Wilder, M.D., Medical Director
Web address: www.hhsc.org

| | 12 | 10 | 21 | — | — | — | — | — | — | — |

WAHIAWA—Honolulu County

✠ **WAHIAWA GENERAL HOSPITAL**, 128 Lehua Street, Zip 96786–2099; tel. 808/621–8411, (Total facility includes 103 beds in nursing home–type unit) **A**1 3 5 9 10 **F**11 21 23 27 33 51 53 58 59 61 63 64 65 66 76 81 85 88 92 94 96 106 108
Primary Contact: John D. Julius, Chief Executive Officer
CFO: Alan Ulrich, Chief Financial Officer
CMO: Leo Pascua, M.D., Chief of Staff
CIO: Paul Matsushima, Information Systems Director
CHR: Richard Aea, Human Resources Director
Web address: www.wahiawageneral.org

| | 23 | 10 | 162 | 2234 | 131 | 29721 | 254 | 29277 | 12307 | 503 |

WAILUKU—Maui County

✠ **MAUI MEMORIAL MEDICAL CENTER**, 221 Mahalani Street, Zip 96793–2581; tel. 808/244–9056 **A**1 2 3 5 9 10 20 **F**2 9 11 12 14 15 21 22 23 26 27 29 30 31 33 34 35 36 37 46 49 52 53 57 59 60 61 62 63 64 65 69 71 75 78 81 82 83 84 85 88 92 94 96 108 110 **S** Hawaii Health Systems Corporation, Honolulu, HI
Primary Contact: Wesley Lo, Chief Executive Officer
CIO: Dana Mendoza, Chief Information Officer
Web address: www.mmmc.hhsc.org

| | 12 | 10 | 193 | 11025 | 154 | 39877 | 1649 | 108728 | 57523 | 932 |

WAIMEA—Kauai County

✠ **KAUAI VETERANS MEMORIAL HOSPITAL**, Waimea Canyon Road, Zip 96796, Mailing Address: P.O. Box 337, Zip 96796–0337; tel. 808/338–9431, (Total facility includes 20 beds in nursing home–type unit) (Nonreporting) **A**1 9 10 18 **S** Hawaii Health Systems Corporation, Honolulu, HI
Primary Contact: Orianna A. Skomoroch, Regional Chief Executive Officer
CFO: Michael Perel, Regional Chief Financial Officer
CMO: Gerald Tomory, M.D., Regional Medical Director
CIO: Sandra McMaster, Regional Chief Information Officer
CHR: S Lani Aranio, Regional Human Resources Director
Web address: www.kvmh.hhsc.org

| | 12 | 10 | 45 | — | — | — | — | — | — | — |

HI

Many Facility Codes have changed. Please refer to the AHA Guide Code Chart.

IDAHO

Hospital, Address, Telephone, Approval, Facility, and Physician Codes, Health Care System	Classi-fication Codes		Utilization Data					Expense (thousands) of dollars		
★ American Hospital Association (AHA) membership □ Joint Commission on Accreditation of Healthcare Organizations (JCAHO) accreditation ○ American Osteopathic Association (AOA) accreditation △ Commission on Accreditation of Rehabilitation Facilities (CARF) accreditation	Control	Service	Staffed Beds	Admissions	Census	Outpatient Visits	Births	Total	Payroll	Personnel

AMERICAN FALLS—Power County

★ **HARMS MEMORIAL HOSPITAL DISTRICT**, 510 Roosevelt Road, Zip 83211–0420, Mailing Address: P.O. Box 420, Zip 83211–0420; tel. 208/226–3200, (Total facility includes 31 beds in nursing home–type unit) (Nonreporting) **A**9 10 18
Primary Contact: Bob Brummond, Administrator
CFO: Sandi Lehman, Chief Financial Officer
CMO: Bret Timmons, Chief Medical Staff
CIO: Mindy Earl, Administrator, Health Information Systems
CHR: Norma Hartley, Director Human Resources
Web address: www.harmsmemorial.org

| | 16 | 49 | 41 | — | — | — | — | — | — | — |

ARCO—Butte County

LOST RIVERS DISTRICT HOSPITAL, 551 Highland Drive, Zip 83213–9771, Mailing Address: P.O. Box 145, Zip 83213–0145; tel. 208/527–8206, (Total facility includes 29 beds in nursing home–type unit) (Nonreporting) **A**9 10 18 20
Primary Contact: Kim Dahlman, Administrator
Web address: www.lostriverhospital.com

| | 16 | 10 | 43 | — | — | — | — | — | — | — |

BLACKFOOT—Bingham County

⊠ **BINGHAM MEMORIAL HOSPITAL**, 98 Poplar Street, Zip 83221–1799; tel. 208/785–4100, (Total facility includes 75 beds in nursing home–type unit) **A**1 9 10 18 **F**1 2 11 12 14 21 26 27 28 29 32 33 34 39 44 46 47 48 53 55 58 59 62 63 64 65 66 69 81 84 88 92 93 94 95 96 97 98 106 108 109 110 **P**8
Primary Contact: Louis D. Kraml, CHE, Chief Executive Officer
COO: Dan Cochran, Chief Operating Officer
CFO: Charlie Button, Chief Financial Officer
CIO: Justin Hansen, Information Systems Director
Web address: www.binghammemorial.org

| | 13 | 10 | 100 | 1899 | 71 | 26339 | 414 | 21834 | 8639 | 279 |

□ **STATE HOSPITAL SOUTH**, 700 East Alice Street, Zip 83221–0400, Mailing Address: Box 400, Zip 83221–0400; tel. 208/785–1200, (Total facility includes 29 beds in nursing home–type unit) (Nonreporting) **A**1 10
Primary Contact: Ray Laible, Administrator

| | 12 | 22 | 165 | — | — | — | — | — | — | — |

BOISE—Ada County

⊠ **HEALTHSOUTH TREASURE VALLEY HOSPITAL**, 8800 West Emerald Street, Zip 83704; tel. 208/373–5000, (Nonreporting) **A**1 10 **S** HEALTHSOUTH Corporation, Birmingham, AL
Primary Contact: Michael L. Long, Administrator
CMO: Jeffrey Hessing, M.D., Medical Director
CHR: Kathleen Phelps, Director Human Resources

| | 33 | 10 | 9 | — | — | — | — | — | — | — |

★ △ **IDAHO ELKS REHABILITATION HOSPITAL**, 600 North Robbins Road, Zip 83702–4597, Mailing Address: P.O. Box 1100, Zip 83701–1100; tel. 208/489–4444, (Total facility includes 12 beds in nursing home–type unit) **A**7 9 10 **F**9 21 22 28 41 42 45 48 58 60 68 69 92 94 95 96 108 110
Primary Contact: Joseph P. Caroselli, Administrator
CFO: Ed Rees, Chief Financial Officer
CMO: Robert Friedman, M.D., Medical Director
CIO: Dan Zillner, Information Systems Director
CHR: Jim Atkins, Employee Services Director
Web address: www.idahoelksrehab.org

| | 23 | 46 | 71 | 1446 | 48 | 16521 | 0 | 20732 | 10897 | 305 |

□ **INTERMOUNTAIN HOSPITAL**, 303 North Allumbaugh Street, Zip 83704–9266; tel. 208/377–8400 **A**1 10 **F**3 26 27 28 71 72 74 75 76 77 78 94 106 **S** Psychiatric Solutions, Franklin, TN
Primary Contact: Richard Failla, Chief Executive Officer
Web address: www.bhcintermountain.com

| | 33 | 22 | 125 | 2705 | 100 | 9489 | 0 | 15374 | 8112 | 205 |

⊠ △ **SAINT ALPHONSUS REGIONAL MEDICAL CENTER**, 1055 North Curtis Road, Zip 83706–1370; tel. 208/367–2121 **A**1 2 3 5 7 9 10 **F**2 4 6 9 10 11 12 14 15 17 19 21 22 23 24 25 26 27 28 29 30 31 32 33 34 35 37 38 39 42 44 46 47 48 49 50 51 52 53 55 56 57 58 59 60 61 62 63 64 65 66 68 69 70 71 72 73 74 75 76 77 79 80 81 82 85 88 92 93 94 95 96 98 105 106 107 108 109 110 **P**1 6 7 **S** Trinity Health, Novi, MI
Primary Contact: Sandra B. Bruce, President and Chief Executive Officer
COO: Janelle Reilly, Chief Operating Officer
CFO: Kenneth Fry, Chief Financial Officer
CMO: J Robert Polk, M.D., Vice President Physician and Clinical Care Services
CIO: Leslie Kelly Hall, Vice President Information Technology
CHR: Derek Carissimi, Vice President Human Resources and Support Services
Web address: www.saintalphonsus.org

| | 21 | 10 | 392 | 17300 | 222 | 224487 | 1010 | 274276 | 117079 | 2486 |

ID

Hospital, Address, Telephone, Approval, Facility, and Physician Codes, Health Care System	Classi-fication Codes		Utilization Data					Expense (thousands) of dollars		
	Control	Service	Staffed Beds	Admissions	Census	Outpatient Visits	Births	Total	Payroll	Personnel

★ American Hospital Association (AHA) membership
□ Joint Commission on Accreditation of Healthcare Organizations (JCAHO) accreditation
○ American Osteopathic Association (AOA) accreditation
△ Commission on Accreditation of Rehabilitation Facilities (CARF) accreditation

Hospital	Control	Service	Staffed Beds	Admissions	Census	Outpatient Visits	Births	Total	Payroll	Personnel
⊠ **ST. LUKE'S REGIONAL MEDICAL CENTER**, 190 East Bannock Street, Zip 83712–6298; tel. 208/381–2222 **A**1 2 3 5 9 10 **F**6 9 10 11 12 14 15 16 17 18 19 20 21 22 23 24 28 29 30 33 36 37 38 39 42 44 46 47 48 50 51 52 53 55 56 57 58 59 60 61 62 63 65 66 67 68 79 80 81 82 83 84 85 86 87 88 93 94 95 96 98 99 108 109 **P**2 5 6 Primary Contact: Edwin E. Dahlberg, President and Chief Executive Officer COO: Gary Fletcher, Executive Vice President CFO: Chuck Pomeroy, Vice President Finance CMO: Gary Krouth, M.D., Vice President Professional Relations CIO: Sheryl Bell, Director Information Technology CHR: Wayne Freiders, Vice President Human Resources Web address: www.slrmc.org	23	10	482	24737	253	468305	6023	426462	175820	3837
⊠ **VETERANS AFFAIRS MEDICAL CENTER**, 500 West Fort Street, Zip 83702–4598; tel. 208/422–1000, (Total facility includes 40 beds in nursing home–type unit) (Nonreporting) **A**1 3 5 8 9 **S** Department of Veterans Affairs, Washington, DC Primary Contact: Wayne C. Tippets, Director CFO: Ron Blanton, Chief Fiscal Services Web address: www.va.gov/sta/guide/home.asp	45	10	176	—	—	—	—	—	—	—
BONNERS FERRY—Boundary County										
★ **BOUNDARY COMMUNITY HOSPITAL**, 6640 Kaniksu Street, Zip 83805–7532; tel. 208/267–3141, (Includes BOUNDARY COUNTY NURSING HOME), (Total facility includes 46 beds in nursing home–type unit) **A**9 10 18 **F**2 9 12 29 33 39 44 46 58 60 63 64 66 69 81 92 94 97 106 110 **P**4 5 Primary Contact: Craig A. Johnson, Chief Executive Officer and Chief Financial Officer CFO: Craig A. Johnson, Chief Executive Officer and Chief Financial Officer Web address: www.boundaryhospital.org	13	10	60	331	39	19726	0	7727	4257	150
BURLEY—Cassia County										
⊠ **CASSIA REGIONAL MEDICAL CENTER**, 1501 Hiland Avenue, Zip 83318–2648; tel. 208/678–4444 **A**1 9 10 18 20 **F**2 6 9 11 12 21 23 24 26 27 28 29 31 33 35 36 37 38 39 41 45 46 48 51 52 53 55 58 59 60 61 62 63 64 66 69 81 82 84 85 88 93 94 95 96 97 98 106 108 109 110 **P**6 7 **S** Intermountain Health Care, Inc., Salt Lake City, UT Primary Contact: Ken Harman, Administrator CFO: Brian Hickenlooper, Assistant Administrator Finance and Chief Financial Officer CMO: Brent R. Payne, M.D., Medical Director CIO: Carie Call, Chief Computer Support CHR: Keri Perrigot, Assistant Administrator Human Resources Web address: www.ihc.com	23	10	25	2163	17	61771	642	21948	8498	231
CALDWELL—Canyon County										
⊠ **WEST VALLEY MEDICAL CENTER**, 1717 Arlington, Zip 83605–4864; tel. 208/459–4641, (Nonreporting) **A**1 9 10 19 **S** HCA, Nashville, TN Primary Contact: Mark B. Adams, Chief Executive Officer COO: Deanna Martin, MSN, Chief Nursing Officer and Chief Operating Officer CFO: Judd Taylor, Chief Financial Officer CIO: Lance Christiansen, Chief Information Officer CHR: Terry Peoples, Director Human Resources Web address: www.westvalleymedctr.com	33	10	122	—	—	—	—	—	—	—
CASCADE—Valley County										
★ **CASCADE MEDICAL CENTER**, 402 Old State Highway, Zip 83611, Mailing Address: P.O. Box 1330, Zip 83611–1330; tel. 208/382–4242, (Nonreporting) **A**9 10 18 **S** Trinity Health, Novi, MI Primary Contact: Kay Garcia, Administrator CMO: Douglas Hill, M.D., Medical Director	12	10	10	—	—	—	—	—	—	—
COEUR D'ALENE—Kootenai County										
⊠ **KOOTENAI MEDICAL CENTER**, 2003 Lincoln Way, Zip 83814–2677; tel. 208/666–2000, (Includes NORTH IDAHO BEHAVIORAL HEALTH, DIVISION OF KOOTENAI MEDICAL CENTER, 2301 North Ironwood Place, Zip 83814–2650; tel. 208/765–4800) **A**1 2 9 10 19 **F**1 2 3 4 9 10 11 12 14 15 17 19 21 22 23 26 27 28 29 32 33 34 37 38 40 41 45 47 48 49 52 53 55 57 58 59 60 61 62 63 65 66 68 69 71 72 73 74 75 76 77 78 79 85 86 88 90 93 94 96 98 106 108 Primary Contact: Joseph E. Morris, Chief Executive Officer CFO: Tom Legel, Vice President and Chief Financial Officer CIO: Tom Legel, Vice President and Chief Financial Officer Web address: www.kmc.org	16	10	246	11113	136	139080	1511	134704	57743	1272
COTTONWOOD—Idaho County										
★ **ST. MARY'S HOSPITAL**, Lewiston and North Streets, Zip 83522–9750, Mailing Address: P.O. Box 137, Zip 83522–0137; tel. 208/962–3251, (Total facility includes 10 beds in nursing home–type unit) **A**9 10 18 **F**9 11 12 21 22 24 29 33 37 38 39 48 51 52 58 63 81 88 92 95 96 97 108 **S** Benedictine Health System, Duluth, MN Primary Contact: Casey Meza, Chief Executive Officer Web address: www.stmaryshospital.net	21	10	28	1038	18	—	—	—	—	167

ID

Many Facility Codes have changed. Please refer to the AHA Guide Code Chart. © 2005 AHA Guide

Hospital, Address, Telephone, Approval, Facility, and Physician Codes, Health Care System	Classi-fication Codes		Utilization Data					Expense (thousands) of dollars		
	Control	Service	Staffed Beds	Admissions	Census	Outpatient Visits	Births	Total	Payroll	Personnel

★ American Hospital Association (AHA) membership
□ Joint Commission on Accreditation of Healthcare Organizations (JCAHO) accreditation
◯ American Osteopathic Association (AOA) accreditation
△ Commission on Accreditation of Rehabilitation Facilities (CARF) accreditation

DRIGGS—Teton County

★ **TETON VALLEY HOSPITAL AND SURGICENTER**, 120 East Howard Street, Zip 83422–5112; tel. 208/354–2383 **A**9 10 18 **F**2 6 9 11 12 21 22 23 26 27 28 29 30 31 33 36 37 38 39 44 46 47 48 51 52 53 54 58 59 60 62 63 64 65 66 69 70 75 81 84 88 94 95 96 97 98 106 108 110
Primary Contact: Susan Kunz, Chief Executive Officer
CHR: Carla Romero–Erlanson, Director Human Resources
Web address: www.tetonvalleyhospital.com

| | 13 | 10 | 13 | 462 | 3 | 12731 | 68 | 7150 | 3261 | 83 |

EMMETT—Gem County

★ **WALTER KNOX MEMORIAL HOSPITAL**, 1202 East Locust Street, Zip 83617–2715; tel. 208/365–3561 **A**9 10 18 **F**2 9 11 21 23 29 33 37 46 47 48 51 52 59 63 66 81 85 88 97
Primary Contact: Max Long, Chief Executive Officer
CFO: Larry Droppers, Chief Financial Officer
CHR: Michael Cornell, Employee and Community Relations Director
Web address: www.wkmh.org

| | 13 | 10 | 16 | 488 | 3 | 16100 | 49 | 6553 | 2728 | 66 |

GOODING—Gooding County

★ **GOODING COUNTY MEMORIAL HOSPITAL**, 1120 Montana Street, Zip 83330–1858; tel. 208/934–4433 **A**9 10 18 **F**2 9 12 27 28 33 45 46 52 53 58 69 81 88 92 97 107
Primary Contact: Roland D. Gee, Interim Chief Executive Officer
CFO: Philip Quigley, Chief Financial Officer
CMO: Keith Davis, M.D., Chief of Staff

| | 16 | 10 | 14 | 564 | 4 | 21234 | 0 | — | — | 79 |

GRANGEVILLE—Idaho County

★ **SYRINGA GENERAL HOSPITAL**, 607 West Main Street, Zip 83530–1396; tel. 208/983–1700 **A**9 10 18 **F**6 9 11 12 14 22 29 33 36 46 51 52 55 58 59 60 63 65 69 81 88 96 97
Primary Contact: Jess Hawley, Administrator
COO: Jess Hawley, Administrator
CFO: Betty A. Watson, Chief Financial Officer
Web address: www.syringageneralhospital.org

| | 16 | 10 | 15 | 585 | 3 | — | 54 | 6197 | 2878 | 78 |

IDAHO FALLS—Bonneville County

⊠ **EASTERN IDAHO REGIONAL MEDICAL CENTER**, 3100 Channing Way, Zip 83404–7533, Mailing Address: P.O. Box 2077, Zip 83403–2077; tel. 208/529–6111, (Total facility includes 16 beds in nursing home–type unit) **A**1 2 9 10 19 20 **F**2 6 9 11 12 15 16 17 18 19 21 22 23 26 27 28 29 30 32 33 34 35 37 39 40 41 46 47 48 52 53 55 56 57 58 59 60 61 62 63 65 66 68 69 71 72 73 75 79 80 81 82 84 86 87 88 92 93 94 95 96 106 108 109 110 **P**5 **S** HCA, Nashville, TN
Primary Contact: Douglas Crabtree, Chief Executive Officer
COO: Thomas W. Thompson, Chief Operating Officer
CFO: Derek Lythgoe, Chief Financial Officer
CMO: Eric Baird, M.D., Medical Staff President
CIO: Joe Vilbig, Director Information Systems
CHR: Betty Simons, Director, Human Resources
Web address: www.eirmc.com

| | 33 | 10 | 291 | 12010 | 176 | 175151 | 1183 | 128351 | 49914 | 1132 |

★ **IDAHO FALLS RECOVERY CENTER**, 1957 East 17th Street, Zip 83404–6429; tel. 208/529–5285, (Nonreporting) **A**9 10
Primary Contact: Bob Spiel, Chief Executive Officer
Web address: www.ifrecoverycenter.com

| | 23 | 10 | 10 | — | — | — | — | — | — | — |

MOUNTAIN VIEW HOSPITAL, 2325 Coronado Street, Zip 83404; tel. 208/557–2700, (Nonreporting) **A**9 10
Primary Contact: Dennis Tolman, Chief Executive Officer

| | 33 | 49 | 20 | — | — | — | — | — | — | — |

JEROME—Jerome County

★ **ST. BENEDICTS FAMILY MEDICAL CENTER**, 709 North Lincoln Street, Zip 83338–1851, Mailing Address: P.O. Box 586, Zip 83338–0586; tel. 208/324–4301, (Total facility includes 40 beds in nursing home–type unit) (Nonreporting) **A**9 10 18 **S** Trinity Health, Novi, MI
Primary Contact: Ken Belke, Interim Administrator
CFO: Frank Clark, Chief Financial Officer
CMO: Elizabeth Sugden, M.D., Director Medical Staff Affairs

| | 23 | 10 | 65 | — | — | — | — | — | — | — |

KELLOGG—Shoshone County

★ **SHOSHONE MEDICAL CENTER**, 25 Jacobs Gulch, Zip 83837–2096; tel. 208/784–1221, (Nonreporting) **A**9 10 18 **S** Quorum Health Resources, Plano, TX
Primary Contact: Gary Moore, Chief Executive Officer
CFO: Jerry Brantz, Chief Financial Officer
CMO: Fred Haller, M.D., Chief of Staff
CHR: Joanna Radford, Chief Human Resources Officer
Web address: www.shomed.org

| | 16 | 10 | 25 | — | — | — | — | — | — | — |

KETCHUM—Blaine County

★ **ST. LUKE'S WOOD RIVER MEDICAL CENTER**, 100 Hospital Way, Zip 83340, Mailing Address: P.O. Box 100, Zip 83340; tel. 208/727–8800 **A**9 10 18 20 **F**2 9 11 12 21 22 23 26 28 29 33 34 37 41 46 47 48 52 53 55 58 59 62 63 64 65 81 82 84 88 93 94 97 98 108 109
Primary Contact: Bruce C. Jensen, Chief Executive Officer
COO: Paula Smith, Chief Operating Officer
CFO: Carl Hollingsworth, Chief Financial Officer
CHR: Stacey Williamson, Director of Human Resources
Web address: www.slrmc.org

| | 23 | 10 | 25 | 1363 | 9 | 25406 | 280 | 24709 | 11480 | 202 |

ID

Hospital, Address, Telephone, Approval, Facility, and Physician Codes, Health Care System	Classi-fication Codes		Utilization Data					Expense (thousands) of dollars		
	Control	Service	Staffed Beds	Admissions	Census	Outpatient Visits	Births	Total	Payroll	Personnel

★ American Hospital Association (AHA) membership
□ Joint Commission on Accreditation of Healthcare Organizations (JCAHO) accreditation
○ American Osteopathic Association (AOA) accreditation
△ Commission on Accreditation of Rehabilitation Facilities (CARF) accreditation

LEWISTON—Nez Perce County

⊞ **ST. JOSEPH REGIONAL MEDICAL CENTER**, 415 Sixth Street, Zip 83501–0816; tel. 208/743–2511, (Total facility includes 16 beds in nursing home–type unit) **A**1 2 9 10 19 **F**2 9 11 12 15 22 23 26 27 28 29 31 32 33 34 36 37 39 40 43 44 45 46 47 48 50 51 52 53 54 55 57 58 59 60 61 62 63 65 66 69 71 73 74 75 76 77 80 81 82 84 85 86 87 88 92 93 94 95 96 104 106 107 108 109 **S** Ascension Health, Saint Louis, MO
Primary Contact: Howard A. Hayes, President and Chief Executive Officer
CFO: Douglas C. Johnson, Associate Administrator and Chief Financial Officer
CMO: Kent Anderson, M.D., Chief of Staff
CIO: Tom Pfliger, Assistant Administrator
CHR: Brenda Forge, Director of Human Resources
Web address: www.sjrmc.org

| | 21 | 10 | 156 | 6912 | 89 | 91513 | 796 | 81346 | 35540 | 673 |

MALAD CITY—Oneida County

ONEIDA COUNTY HOSPITAL, 150 North 200 West, Zip 83252–0126, Mailing Address: Box 126, Zip 83252–0126; tel. 208/766–2231, (Total facility includes 41 beds in nursing home–type unit) **A**9 10 18 **F**1 2 8 9 11 21 26 28 29 30 33 37 38 39 44 45 46 47 48 51 53 54 58 62 63 64 65 66 69 81 92 94 95 96 97 98 108 109 110
Primary Contact: Todd Winder, Administrator and Chief Executive Officer
Web address: www.oneidahospital.com

| | 13 | 10 | 52 | 269 | 32 | 4629 | 9 | 2883 | 2088 | 88 |

MCCALL—Valley County

★ **MCCALL MEMORIAL HOSPITAL**, 1000 State Street, Zip 83638–3704; tel. 208/634–2221 **A**9 10 18 **F**2 9 11 12 22 23 24 26 27 28 29 30 31 32 33 35 37 39 46 47 48 52 55 59 63 64 65 66 70 81 88 94 96 97 98 104 106 108 109 110 **P**6
Primary Contact: Karen J. Kellie, President and Administrator
CFO: Joni Stright, Senior Vice President
Web address: www.mccallhosp.org

| | 16 | 10 | 15 | 576 | 4 | 19577 | 89 | 10345 | 3585 | 90 |

MONTPELIER—Bear Lake County

★ **BEAR LAKE MEMORIAL HOSPITAL**, 164 South Fifth Street, Zip 83254–1597; tel. 208/847–1630, (Total facility includes 37 beds in nursing home–type unit) **A**9 10 18 **F**1 8 9 11 21 26 27 28 33 39 41 44 45 46 47 48 51 55 58 63 65 66 69 72 77 81 88 92 94 97 108 **P**5 6
Primary Contact: Rod Jacobson, Administrator
Web address: www.blmhospital.com

| | 13 | 10 | 82 | 480 | 31 | 20421 | 67 | 9833 | 4880 | 150 |

MOSCOW—Latah County

⊞ **GRITMAN MEDICAL CENTER**, 700 South Main Street, Zip 83843–3047; tel. 208/882–4511 **A**1 9 10 18 **F**1 2 9 11 12 21 22 27 28 29 30 33 36 37 38 40 42 44 45 46 51 52 55 58 59 60 61 62 63 64 65 66 69 81 82 84 88 93 94 95 96 106 108 109 110 **P**5 **S** Quorum Health Resources, Plano, TX
Primary Contact: Jeffrey W. Martin, Chief Executive Officer
CFO: Kara Besst, Chief Financial Officer
CMO: Robert Ting, M.D., Chief Medical Staff
CIO: Kane Francetich, Chief Information Officer
CHR: Dennis Cockrell, Director Human Resources
Web address: www.gritman.org

| | 23 | 10 | 25 | 1945 | 17 | 60351 | 394 | 27067 | 11717 | 301 |

MOUNTAIN HOME—Elmore County

★ **ELMORE MEDICAL CENTER**, 895 North Sixth East Street, Zip 83647–2207, Mailing Address: P.O. Box 1270, Zip 83647–1270; tel. 208/587–8401, (Total facility includes 51 beds in nursing home–type unit) **A**9 10 18 **F**2 9 11 12 27 29 33 46 52 58 59 63 81 84 88 92 94 97 108
Primary Contact: Gregory L. Maurer, Administrator
COO: Betty Van Gheluwe, Chief Operating Officer
CFO: Tricia Senger, Chief Financial Officer
Web address: www.elmoremedicalcenter.org

| | 16 | 10 | 72 | 799 | 34 | 46419 | 133 | 12613 | 5136 | — |

NAMPA—Canyon County

⊞ △ **MERCY MEDICAL CENTER**, 1512 12th Avenue Road, Zip 83686–6008; tel. 208/467–1171 **A**1 7 9 10 19 **F**9 11 12 21 22 26 27 28 33 36 39 42 45 47 51 52 53 54 55 58 59 60 61 62 63 69 81 82 88 94 **P**8 **S** Catholic Health Initiatives, Denver, CO
Primary Contact: Joseph Messmer, President and Chief Executive Officer
CFO: B Lannie Checketts, Vice President Finance
CIO: Jason Ewing, Director Information Technology
CHR: Audra Pratt, Vice President Human Resources
Web address: www.mercynampa.org

| | 21 | 10 | 104 | 6101 | 51 | 134188 | 1206 | 58195 | 24890 | 581 |

OROFINO—Clearwater County

★ **CLEARWATER VALLEY HOSPITAL AND CLINICS**, 301 Cedar, Zip 83544–9029; tel. 208/476–4555 **A**9 10 18 20 **F**9 11 12 21 22 24 29 33 37 38 39 48 51 52 58 63 81 88 95 96 97 108 **S** Benedictine Health System, Duluth, MN
Primary Contact: Casey Meza, Chief Executive Officer
Web address: www.clearwatervalleyhospital.com

| | 21 | 10 | 23 | 813 | 7 | — | — | — | — | 167 |

STATE HOSPITAL NORTH, 300 Hospital Drive, Zip 83544–9034; tel. 208/476–4511 **F**26 28 58 71 73 94 96 **P**6
Primary Contact: A. Jay Kessinger, Administrative Director

| | 12 | 22 | 50 | 228 | 44 | 177 | 0 | 5776 | 3297 | 92 |

Many Facility Codes have changed. Please refer to the AHA Guide Code Chart.

© 2005 AHA Guide

Hospital, Address, Telephone, Approval, Facility, and Physician Codes, Health Care System	Classi-fication Codes		Utilization Data					Expense (thousands) of dollars		
★ American Hospital Association (AHA) membership ☐ Joint Commission on Accreditation of Healthcare Organizations (JCAHO) accreditation ○ American Osteopathic Association (AOA) accreditation △ Commission on Accreditation of Rehabilitation Facilities (CARF) accreditation	Control	Service	Staffed Beds	Admissions	Census	Outpatient Visits	Births	Total	Payroll	Personnel

POCATELLO—Bannock County

✚ **PORTNEUF MEDICAL CENTER**, 651 Memorial Drive, Zip 83201–4004; tel. 208/239–1000, (Total facility includes 86 beds in nursing home–type unit) **A**1 2 3 5 9 10 19 **F**2 9 11 12 14 21 23 26 27 28 29 32 33 34 35 37 38 39 40 42 44 46 47 48 49 50 51 52 53 55 56 57 58 59 60 61 62 63 64 65 66 67 68 69 70 71 73 74 75 76 77 79 80 81 82 84 85 88 92 93 94 95 96 99 100 101 102 103 104 105 107 108 109 110 **P**8
Primary Contact: Patrick M. Hermanson, FACHE, President and Chief Executive Officer
COO: Callen Northam, Executive Vice President and Chief Operating Officer
CFO: John Wilker, Vice President and Chief Financial Officer
CIO: Karl Endo, Director Information Services
CHR: Dale Mapes, Vice President Human Resources and Support Services
Web address: www.portmed.org

| | 13 | 10 | 274 | 8604 | 160 | 210699 | 1711 | 117615 | 46790 | 929 |

POST FALLS—Kootenai County

NORTHWEST SPECIALTY HOSPITAL, 1593 East Polston, Zip 83854; tel. 208/262–2300, (Nonreporting) **A**9 10 **S** National Surgical Hospitals, Chicago, IL
Primary Contact: Nick Genna, Chief Executive Officer

| | 33 | 49 | 12 | — | — | — | — | — | — | — |

PRESTON—Franklin County

★ **FRANKLIN COUNTY MEDICAL CENTER**, 44 North First East Street, Zip 83263–1399; tel. 208/852–0137, (Total facility includes 45 beds in nursing home–type unit) **A**9 10 18 **F**1 2 9 11 23 29 33 36 37 46 51 53 58 59 62 63 69 81 85 88 92 94 97 108 **P**1
Primary Contact: Michael G. Andrus, Administrator and Chief Executive Officer
CFO: Paul Smart, CPA, Chief Financial Officer
Web address: www.fcmc.org

| | 13 | 10 | 65 | 546 | 40 | 13221 | 125 | 8459 | 4517 | 154 |

REXBURG—Madison County

★ **MADISON MEMORIAL HOSPITAL**, 450 East Main Street, Zip 83440–2048, Mailing Address: P.O. Box 310, Zip 83440–0310; tel. 208/356–3691 **A**9 10 **F**2 9 11 12 14 21 22 23 25 29 32 33 37 41 46 47 48 52 53 55 58 59 60 61 62 63 64 65 66 69 81 82 84 88 94 95 96 106 108 **P**1 5
Primary Contact: Keith M. Steiner, Chief Executive Officer
COO: Brad Howell, Chief Operating Officer
CFO: Calvin Carey, Assistant Administrator and Chief Financial Officer
CMO: Michael Packer, M.D., Chief Medical Staff
Web address: www.madisonhospital.org

| | 13 | 10 | 49 | 3837 | 24 | 39754 | 1343 | 28529 | 11318 | 319 |

RUPERT—Minidoka County

★ **MINIDOKA MEMORIAL HOSPITAL AND EXTENDED CARE FACILITY**, 1224 Eighth Street, Zip 83350–1599; tel. 208/436–0481, (Total facility includes 50 beds in nursing home–type unit) **A**9 10 18 **F**2 3 6 9 11 12 13 14 21 22 23 26 27 28 29 33 36 37 38 39 44 45 46 48 51 52 53 55 56 58 59 60 61 62 63 65 66 67 68 70 71 81 82 84 88 92 94 96 97 108 109 **P**1 5
Primary Contact: Carl Hanson, Administrator
COO: Joel Rogers, Chief Operating Officer
CFO: Larry Lee, Chief Financial Officer
CMO: Greg Boettcher, D.O., Chief of Staff
CHR: Tammy Hanks, Director Human Resources
Web address: www.minidokamemorial.com

| | 13 | 10 | 79 | 834 | 46 | 13219 | 97 | 11572 | 5213 | 125 |

SAINT MARIES—Benewah County

★ **BENEWAH COMMUNITY HOSPITAL**, 229 South Seventh Street, Zip 83861–1894; tel. 208/245–5551 **A**9 10 18 **F**9 11 12 21 22 23 26 27 28 33 36 37 38 46 48 52 58 59 60 61 62 63 69 70 81 84 88 94 95 97 108 **P**4 6 **S** Quorum Health Resources, Plano, TX
Primary Contact: Erik Fox, Chief Executive Officer
CFO: Michael Anderson, Chief Financial Officer
CMO: J R. Katovich, Jr, Chief of Staff

| | 13 | 10 | 20 | 438 | 3 | 20118 | 70 | 12112 | 4707 | 119 |

SALMON—Lemhi County

★ **STEELE MEMORIAL HOSPITAL**, 707 Van Dreff, Zip 83467–4109, Mailing Address: P.O. Box 700, Zip 83467–0700; tel. 208/756–4291 **A**9 10 18 **F**9 11 12 21 26 29 33 46 48 52 59 60 63 68 69 70 77 81 84 85 88 97 **P**6 **S** Quorum Health Resources, Plano, TX
Primary Contact: Victoria A. Alexander, Chief Executive Officer
CFO: Brian Nall, Chief Financial Officer
CMO: Samuel Gardner, M.D., Chief of Staff
CIO: Abner King, Information Systems Director
CHR: Debbie Kerns, Human Resources Director
Web address: www.steelemh.org

| | 13 | 10 | 18 | 306 | 2 | 28306 | 15 | 7417 | 3507 | 112 |

SANDPOINT—Bonner County

✚ **BONNER GENERAL HOSPITAL**, 520 North Third Avenue, Zip 83864–0877, Mailing Address: Box 1448, Zip 83864–0877; tel. 208/263–1441 **A**1 9 10 20 **F**2 9 11 12 14 21 29 33 36 48 50 51 52 53 58 59 60 62 63 64 65 66 69 75 81 84 85 88 94 95 108 **P**8
Primary Contact: Sheryl Rickard, Chief Executive Officer
CFO: Norilina Harvel, Chief Financial Officer
CIO: Bob Hess, Chief Information Officer
CHR: Pam Taylor, Human Resource Director
Web address: www.bonnergen.org

| | 23 | 10 | 41 | 2319 | 16 | 42051 | 360 | 27946 | 13018 | 310 |

ID

Hospital, Address, Telephone, Approval, Facility, and Physician Codes, Health Care System	Classi-fication Codes		Utilization Data					Expense (thousands) of dollars		
★ American Hospital Association (AHA) membership □ Joint Commission on Accreditation of Healthcare Organizations (JCAHO) accreditation ○ American Osteopathic Association (AOA) accreditation △ Commission on Accreditation of Rehabilitation Facilities (CARF) accreditation	Control	Service	Staffed Beds	Admissions	Census	Outpatient Visits	Births	Total	Payroll	Personnel

SODA SPRINGS—Caribou County

★ **CARIBOU MEMORIAL HOSPITAL AND LIVING CENTER**, 300 South Third West Street, Zip 83276–1598; tel. 208/547–3341, (Total facility includes 37 beds in nursing home–type unit) (Nonreporting) **A**9 10 18
Primary Contact: John L. Hoopes, Chief Executive Officer
CFO: Leota Carver, Finance Manager
Web address: www.cariboumemorial.org

| 13 | 10 | 62 | — | — | — | — | — | — | |

TWIN FALLS—Twin Falls County

⊠ **MAGIC VALLEY REGIONAL MEDICAL CENTER**, 650 Addison Avenue West, Zip 83301–5444, Mailing Address: P.O. Box 409, Zip 83303–0409; tel. 208/737–2000, (Total facility includes 20 beds in nursing home–type unit) **A**1 2 9 10 19 **F**2 6 7 9 11 12 15 17 21 22 23 26 27 28 29 31 33 36 39 40 46 48 51 52 53 55 56 57 58 59 60 62 63 64 65 66 69 70 71 72 73 74 75 76 77 81 82 84 85 88 92 93 94 96 108 109 110 **P**7
Primary Contact: John Kee, Chief Executive Officer
COO: Kent Loosle, Chief Operating Officer
CFO: John Groesbeck, Chief Financial Officer
CIO: R'Nee Mullen, Chief Information Officer
Web address: www.mvrmc.org

| 13 | 10 | 204 | 8695 | 90 | 246509 | 1469 | 107660 | 43608 | 993 |

WEISER—Washington County

★ **WEISER MEMORIAL HOSPITAL**, 645 East Fifth Street, Zip 83672–2202; tel. 208/549–0370 **A**9 10 18 **F**9 11 22 27 28 29 33 46 47 48 51 52 59 62 63 64 81 88 94 96 97 98 106 108 **S** Trinity Health, Novi, MI
Primary Contact: Anne Oglevie, Administrator
CFO: Kymberlee S. Overacker, Chief Financial Officer
Web address: www.weisermemorialhospital.org

| 16 | 10 | 18 | 341 | 2 | 16965 | 77 | 5860 | 2399 | 75 |

ID

ILLINOIS

Hospital, Address, Telephone, Approval, Facility, and Physician Codes, Health Care System	Classi-fication Codes		Utilization Data					Expense (thousands) of dollars		
★ American Hospital Association (AHA) membership □ Joint Commission on Accreditation of Healthcare Organizations (JCAHO) accreditation ○ American Osteopathic Association (AOA) accreditation △ Commission on Accreditation of Rehabilitation Facilities (CARF) accreditation	Control	Service	Staffed Beds	Admissions	Census	Outpatient Visits	Births	Total	Payroll	Personnel

ALEDO—Mercer County

★ **MERCER COUNTY HOSPITAL**, 409 N.W. Ninth Avenue, Zip 61231–1296; tel. 309/582–5301, (Total facility includes 14 beds in nursing home–type unit) **A**9 10 18 **F**9 12 27 28 29 33 36 37 46 48 51 52 54 55 58 63 69 70 81 88 92 94 95 96 97 108 **P**6
Primary Contact: Timothy Putnam, Administrator and Chief Executive Officer
COO: Myron Higgins, Director Operations
CFO: Dee Pitts, Interim Chief Financial Officer
Web address: www.mercercountyhosp.org
| 13 | 10 | 39 | 406 | 18 | 18278 | 0 | 7699 | 3526 | 129 |

ALTON—Madison County

★ **ALTON MEMORIAL HOSPITAL**, One Memorial Drive, Zip 62002–6722; tel. 618/463–7311, (Total facility includes 62 beds in nursing home–type unit) **A**1 2 9 10 **F**2 4 5 6 9 11 12 15 21 22 23 27 28 29 32 33 37 46 48 49 52 53 55 57 58 59 60 61 62 63 64 69 76 79 81 84 85 86 87 88 92 93 94 95 96 106 108 110 **S** BJC HealthCare, Saint Louis, MO
Primary Contact: Ronald B. McMullen, President
CMO: Leo Green, Vice President, Medical Affairs
CIO: David Weiss, Vice President Information System
Web address: www.altonmemorialhospital.org
| 23 | 10 | 217 | 5660 | 131 | 101395 | 551 | 74807 | 28777 | 722 |

□ **ALTON MENTAL HEALTH CENTER**, 4500 College Avenue, Zip 62002–5099; tel. 618/474–3800, (Nonreporting) **A**1 10
Primary Contact: Kay Greenwood, R.N., MS, Administrator
| 12 | 22 | 165 | — | — | — | — | — | — | — |

★ △ **SAINT ANTHONY'S HEALTH CENTER**, 1 Saint Anthony's Way, Zip 62002–4579, Mailing Address: P.O. Box 340, Zip 62002–0340; tel. 618/465–2571, (Includes SAINT CLARE'S HOSPITAL, 915 East Fifth Street, Zip 62002–6434; tel. 618/463–5151), (Total facility includes 38 beds in nursing home–type unit) **A**1 2 7 9 10 **F**1 2 5 8 9 11 12 15 17 21 22 23 24 26 27 28 29 30 31 32 33 36 37 38 39 40 42 44 46 47 48 49 50 51 52 53 54 55 57 58 59 60 61 62 63 64 65 68 69 70 71 73 74 75 76 77 78 81 82 84 85 86 87 88 92 93 94 95 96 106 107 108 109 110 **P**3 8
Primary Contact: William E. Kessler, FACHE, President
COO: Mark J. Jaeger, CHE, Executive Vice President and Chief Operating Officer
CFO: Mike Nelson, Executive Vice President and Chief Financial Officer
CMO: Steven Zenker, M.D., Medical Director
CIO: Noncy J. Dooling, Vice President
CHR: Bruce Tisdale, Vice President Human Resources
Web address: www.sahc.org
| 23 | 10 | 229 | 6803 | 97 | 136673 | 828 | 83392 | 32899 | 794 |

ANNA—Union County

□ **CHOATE MENTAL HEALTH CENTER**, 1000 North Main Street, Zip 62906–1699; tel. 618/833–5161 **A**1 5 10 **F**21 22 26 27 28 65 71 72 73 74 75 76 94
Primary Contact: Sarah H. Andrew, Ph.D., Administrator
| 12 | 22 | 79 | 690 | 73 | 0 | 0 | — | — | 190 |

□ **UNION COUNTY HOSPITAL DISTRICT**, 517 North Main Street, Zip 62906–1696; tel. 618/833–4511, (Total facility includes 22 beds in nursing home–type unit) **A**1 9 10 18 **F**2 9 12 21 22 27 28 29 33 46 48 51 52 53 58 60 63 66 69 70 81 85 88 92 94 97 108 **P**6
Primary Contact: James R. Farris, CHE, Chief Executive Officer
Web address: www.uchd.org
| 16 | 10 | 47 | 873 | 28 | 31327 | 0 | 10590 | 5051 | 151 |

ARLINGTON HEIGHTS—Cook County

★ **NORTHWEST COMMUNITY HEALTHCARE**, 800 West Central Road, Zip 60005–2392; tel. 847/618–1000 **A**1 2 9 10 **F**1 2 4 11 12 14 15 17 19 21 22 23 24 26 27 28 29 30 31 33 34 35 38 39 42 44 45 46 47 48 49 50 51 52 53 55 57 58 59 60 61 62 63 64 65 66 69 71 72 73 74 75 76 77 78 79 80 81 82 84 85 86 87 88 93 94 95 96 106 107 108 109 110 **P**5 8
Primary Contact: Bruce K. Crowther, President and Chief Executive Officer
COO: Kathy Reno, Executive Vice President and Chief Operating Officer, Clinical Services
CFO: Michael B. Zenn, Executive Vice President and Chief Operating Officer, Corporate Services
CMO: Leighton B. Smith, M.D., Vice President Medical Affairs
CIO: George Morris, Vice President Information Technology and Chief Information Officer
CHR: Mark Lusson, Vice President Human Resources
Web address: www.nch.org
| 23 | 10 | 412 | 25408 | 266 | 433182 | 3001 | 299525 | 134641 | 2524 |

AURORA—Du Page and Kane Counties County

★ **PROVENA MERCY CENTER**, 1325 North Highland Avenue, Zip 60506–1449; tel. 630/859–2222 **A**1 2 9 10 **F**2 3 4 10 11 12 13 15 17 19 21 22 26 27 28 29 33 34 37 44 45 47 48 50 53 54 55 58 59 60 61 62 63 65 66 67 68 69 70 71 72 73 74 75 76 77 78 81 84 88 91 92 93 94 96 107 108 109 **P**5 **S** Provena Health, Mokena, IL
Primary Contact: Timothy P. Selz, President and Chief Executive Officer
CFO: Eric Krueger, Chief Financial Officer
Web address: www.provenamercy.com
| 23 | 10 | 254 | 11974 | 121 | 218288 | 1809 | 111832 | 41760 | 896 |

Hospital, Address, Telephone, Approval, Facility, and Physician Codes, Health Care System	Classi-fication Codes		Utilization Data					Expense (thousands) of dollars		
★ American Hospital Association (AHA) membership □ Joint Commission on Accreditation of Healthcare Organizations (JCAHO) accreditation ○ American Osteopathic Association (AOA) accreditation △ Commission on Accreditation of Rehabilitation Facilities (CARF) accreditation	Control	Service	Staffed Beds	Admissions	Census	Outpatient Visits	Births	Total	Payroll	Personnel

⊠ △ **RUSH–COPLEY MEDICAL CENTER**, 2000 Ogden Avenue, Zip 60504–4206; tel. 630/978–6200 **A**1 2 3 5 7 9 10 **F**2 7 11 12 14 15 17 19 21 22 23 24 25 26 27 28 29 30 31 33 34 35 37 38 39 41 42 44 45 46 47 48 49 51 52 53 55 56 57 58 59 60 61 62 63 64 65 66 68 69 70 79 81 82 84 85 86 87 88 89 90 92 94 95 96 106 108 109 110 **P**6 **S** Rush University Medical Center, Chicago, IL Primary Contact: Barry C. Finn, President and Chief Executive Officer CFO: Macario Salazar, Vice President and Chief Financial Officer CIO: Beckie Coovert, Director Information Systems CHR: Darla Mullner, Director Human Resources Web address: www.rushcopley.com	23	10	148	10687	101	143679	2742	129657	48032	1019
BARRINGTON—Lake County										
⊠ **ADVOCATE GOOD SHEPHERD HOSPITAL**, 450 West Highway 22, Zip 60010–1901; tel. 847/381–9600 **A**1 2 9 10 **F**9 10 11 12 21 22 23 27 28 30 33 34 37 38 45 46 47 48 52 53 55 58 59 60 61 62 63 66 69 71 72 73 74 75 76 77 78 79 80 81 82 85 87 88 93 94 96 106 108 109 **P**8 **S** Advocate Health Care, Oak Brook, IL Primary Contact: Karen A. Lambert, President COO: Doug Ryder, Vice President Operations CFO: George Teufel, Vice President Finance CMO: Barry Rosen, M.D., Vice President Medical Management CIO: Wolfgang Anderle, Chief Information Officer CHR: Christine Kass, Vice President Human Resources Web address: www.advocatehealth.com	21	10	142	11728	114	144143	1892	142614	53009	917
BELLEVILLE—St. Clair County										
★ ○ **MEMORIAL HOSPITAL**, 4500 Memorial Drive, Zip 62226–5399; tel. 618/233–7750, (Total facility includes 108 beds in nursing home–type unit) **A**9 10 11 **F**2 9 11 12 15 17 19 21 22 23 27 28 32 33 35 37 40 41 42 46 48 49 50 51 52 55 57 58 59 60 62 63 64 65 66 69 73 75 78 81 82 84 85 87 88 92 93 94 95 96 106 108 109 110 **P**8 Primary Contact: Harry R. Maier, President COO: Mark J. Turner, Chief Operating Officer CFO: Joe Lanius, Vice President Finance CMO: William Sutherland, M.D., Medical Director CIO: David Dawdy, Director Information Systems CHR: Ed French, Vice President Web address: www.memhosp.com	23	10	343	15519	260	271383	1436	158451	72964	1861
⊠ △ **ST. ELIZABETH'S HOSPITAL**, 211 South Third Street, Zip 62220–1998; tel. 618/234–2120 **A**1 2 3 5 7 9 10 **F**2 3 4 9 11 12 15 17 19 21 22 23 24 26 27 28 29 32 33 37 39 41 42 44 46 48 49 50 51 52 53 55 56 57 58 59 60 61 62 63 64 65 66 68 69 70 71 73 74 75 76 77 78 79 81 82 84 85 86 87 88 93 94 95 96 98 106 107 108 109 110 **P**8 **S** Hospital Sisters Health System, Springfield, IL Primary Contact: Timothy F. Brady, FACHE, Administrator COO: William Casperson, M.D., Medical Director CFO: Walter J. Yokobosky, Jr, Assistant Administrator Finance CHR: Bob Miller, Administrative Director Human Resources Web address: www.steliz.org	21	10	278	14010	189	157457	1186	137028	51594	1305
BELVIDERE—Boone County										
□ **NORTHWEST SUBURBAN COMMUNITY HOSPITAL**, 1625 South State Street, Zip 61008–5900, Mailing Address: P.O. Box 400, Zip 61008–0400; tel. 815/547–5441, (Nonreporting) **A**1 9 10 Primary Contact: Robert O. Zinnen, Jr, President and Chief Executive Officer	23	10	69	—						
BENTON—Franklin County										
⊠ **FRANKLIN HOSPITAL**, 201 Bailey Lane, Zip 62812–1999; tel. 618/439–3161 **A**1 9 10 18 **F**9 12 21 22 26 27 33 44 46 58 62 63 81 88 93 94 96 97 107 108 **S** Alliant Management Services, Louisville, KY Primary Contact: Hervey E. Davis, Chief Executive Officer CFO: Rex P. Budde, Senior Vice President and Chief Financial Officer CIO: Frank Sears, Vice President Information Services Web address: www.sih.net	16	10	25	918	13	18038	0	9616	3951	129
BERWYN—Cook County										
⊠ **MACNEAL HOSPITAL**, 3249 South Oak Park Avenue, Zip 60402–0715; tel. 708/783–9100, (Total facility includes 40 beds in nursing home–type unit) (Nonreporting) **A**1 2 3 5 8 9 10 12 13 **S** Vanguard Health System, Nashville, TN Primary Contact: Brooks Turkel, Chief Executive Officer COO: Nelson Lazo, Chief Operating Officer CFO: Brad Mucek, Vice President and Chief Financial Officer CMO: Gary Wainer, Medical Director CIO: Michael Devore, Chief Information Officer Web address: www.macneal.com	33	10	320	—	—	—	—	—	—	—

IL

Many Facility Codes have changed. Please refer to the AHA Guide Code Chart. © 2005 AHA Guide

Hospital, Address, Telephone, Approval, Facility, and Physician Codes, Health Care System	Classi-fication Codes		Utilization Data					Expense (thousands) of dollars		
★ American Hospital Association (AHA) membership □ Joint Commission on Accreditation of Healthcare Organizations (JCAHO) accreditation ○ American Osteopathic Association (AOA) accreditation △ Commission on Accreditation of Rehabilitation Facilities (CARF) accreditation	Control	Service	Staffed Beds	Admissions	Census	Outpatient Visits	Births	Total	Payroll	Personnel

BLOOMINGTON—McLean County

✠ **OSF ST. JOSEPH MEDICAL CENTER**, 2200 East Washington Street, Zip 61701–4323; tel. 309/662–3311, (Total facility includes 12 beds in nursing home–type unit) **A**1 2 9 10 **F**2 9 11 12 15 17 19 21 22 23 26 27 28 33 34 42 46 47 48 49 50 52 53 55 57 58 59 60 61 62 63 64 65 66 69 70 82 84 85 86 87 88 92 94 95 96 106 107 108 109 110 **P**6 **S** OSF Healthcare System, Peoria, IL
Primary Contact: Kenneth J. Natzke, Administrator
COO: Larry Wills, Senior Assistant Administrator and Chief Operating Officer
CFO: John Zell, Chief Financial Officer
CMO: Paul E. Pedersen, M.D., Medical Director
CHR: George Huonker, Assistant Administrator Human Resources
Web address: www.osfhealthcare.org

| | 21 | 10 | 157 | 6223 | 65 | 254353 | 888 | 90553 | 35163 | 770 |

BLUE ISLAND—Cook County

✠ **ST. FRANCIS HOSPITAL & HEALTH CENTER**, 12935 South Gregory Street, Zip 60406–2470; tel. 708/597–2000 **A**1 9 10 **F**2 9 10 11 12 15 17 19 21 22 23 26 27 28 29 32 33 37 39 41 46 47 48 49 50 52 53 55 57 58 59 60 61 62 63 64 65 69 73 81 82 85 87 88 93 94 96 106 108 109 110 **S** SSM Health Care, Saint Louis, MO
Primary Contact: Colleen Kannaday, President
COO: David Cemate, Executive Vice President and Chief Operating Officer
CFO: David Nelson, Vice President Finance and Chief Financial Officer
CMO: Joan Boomsma, M.D., Vice President Medical Affairs
CHR: Cheryl Champoux, Vice President Human Resource Management and Development
Web address: www.stfrancisblueisland.com

| | 21 | 10 | 260 | 13371 | 160 | 94479 | 1039 | 149146 | 58648 | 1103 |

BREESE—Clinton County

✠ **ST. JOSEPH'S HOSPITAL**, 9515 Holy Cross Lane, Zip 62230–0099; tel. 618/526–4511 **A**1 9 10 **F**2 9 11 12 22 23 24 26 27 28 29 33 34 46 48 52 53 55 58 59 63 64 69 81 82 88 93 94 95 96 106 108 **S** Hospital Sisters Health System, Springfield, IL
Primary Contact: Jacolyn M. Schlautman, Executive Vice President and Administrator
COO: Jacolyn M. Schlautman, Executive Vice President and Administrator
CFO: Dennis G. Herzig, Director Finance
CMO: Penny Gozia, M.D., President Medical Staff
CIO: Dennis G. Herzig, Chief Financial Officer
CHR: Kathryn Mines, Director Human Resources
Web address: www.stjoebreese.com

| | 21 | 10 | 60 | 2181 | 19 | 70180 | 420 | 24649 | 10701 | 284 |

CANTON—Fulton County

✠ **GRAHAM HOSPITAL**, 210 West Walnut Street, Zip 61520–2497; tel. 309/647–5240, (Total facility includes 54 beds in nursing home–type unit) **A**1 6 9 10 20 **F**2 9 11 12 21 22 26 27 28 29 33 36 40 41 42 44 45 46 48 51 52 53 55 59 60 63 64 66 69 81 82 88 92 93 94 96 106 108 **P**3
Primary Contact: D. Ray Slaubaugh, President
CFO: Jim Stratton, Vice President Finance
CHR: Chris Duvendack, Vice President Human Resources
Web address: www.grahamhospital.org

| | 23 | 10 | 124 | 3144 | 72 | 145920 | 259 | 47767 | 18496 | 599 |

CARBONDALE—Jackson County

□ **MEMORIAL HOSPITAL OF CARBONDALE**, 405 West Jackson Street, Zip 62901–1467, Mailing Address: P.O. Box 10000, Zip 62902–9000; tel. 618/549–0721 **A**1 2 3 5 9 10 12 13 19 **F**2 9 11 12 15 17 19 21 22 23 26 27 28 29 33 39 46 48 49 52 53 55 56 57 58 59 61 62 63 64 65 66 79 81 82 84 85 86 87 88 94 95 96 106 107 108 109 **P**6 **S** Southern Illinois Hospital Services, Carbondale, IL
Primary Contact: George Maroney, Senior Vice President and Administrator
Web address: www.sih.net

| | 23 | 10 | 142 | 9001 | 91 | 96766 | 1947 | 112660 | 34945 | 869 |

CARLINVILLE—Macoupin County

✠ **CARLINVILLE AREA HOSPITAL**, 1001 East Morgan Street, Zip 62626–1499; tel. 217/854–3141, (Nonreporting) **A**1 9 10 **S** Brim Healthcare, Inc., Brentwood, TN
Primary Contact: Steven Hannah, Interim President and Chief Executive Officer
CFO: Barry Liss, Vice President and Chief Financial Officer
CMO: G L. Laws, M.D., Medical Staff President
CIO: Tom Sidener, Director Information Systems
CHR: Brian Tieman, Director Human Resources
Web address: www.cahcare.com

| | 23 | 10 | 33 | — | — | — | — | — | — | — |

CARMI—White County

WHITE COUNTY MEDICAL CENTER, 400 Plum Street, Zip 62821–1799; tel. 618/382–4171, (Total facility includes 70 beds in nursing home–type unit) **A**10 18 **F**2 9 12 21 27 28 33 53 63 69 81 84 88 92 93 94 97 108 **P**5
Primary Contact: James R. Cheek, Administrator
Web address: www.wcmchealth.com

| | 33 | 10 | 98 | 583 | 62 | 29842 | 0 | 9539 | 3860 | 145 |

CARROLLTON—Greene County

THOMAS H. BOYD MEMORIAL HOSPITAL, 800 School Street, Zip 62016–1498; tel. 217/942–6946, (Includes REISCH MEMORIAL NURSING HOME), (Total facility includes 40 beds in nursing home–type unit) (Nonreporting) **A**9 10 18
Primary Contact: Deborah Campbell, Administrator

| | 23 | 10 | 65 | — | — | — | — | — | — | — |

IL

Hospital, Address, Telephone, Approval, Facility, and Physician Codes, Health Care System	Classi-fication Codes		Utilization Data					Expense (thousands) of dollars		
★ American Hospital Association (AHA) membership □ Joint Commission on Accreditation of Healthcare Organizations (JCAHO) accreditation ○ American Osteopathic Association (AOA) accreditation △ Commission on Accreditation of Rehabilitation Facilities (CARF) accreditation	Control	Service	Staffed Beds	Admissions	Census	Outpatient Visits	Births	Total	Payroll	Personnel

CARTHAGE—Hancock County

⊠ **MEMORIAL HOSPITAL**, 402 South Adams Street, Zip 62321–1600, Mailing Address: P.O. Box 160, Zip 62321–0160; tel. 217/357–3131, (Nonreporting) **A**1 9 10 18 **S** Quorum Health Resources, Plano, TX
Primary Contact: Ada Bair, Chief Executive Officer
CFO: Ryan Larsen, Chief Financial Officer
CIO: Syndi Horn, Director Information Systems
CHR: Ann Dunham, Director Human Resources
Web address: www.mhtlc.com

| | 23 | 10 | 15 | — | — | — | — | — | — | — |

CENTRALIA—Marion County

⊠ **ST. MARY'S HOSPITAL**, 400 North Pleasant Avenue, Zip 62801–3091; tel. 618/436–8000 **A**1 2 9 10 19 **F**4 9 11 12 15 21 22 23 26 27 28 29 31 32 33 35 37 38 39 44 46 47 48 50 52 53 55 57 58 59 60 61 62 63 64 65 69 71 73 74 75 76 77 78 80 81 82 84 85 87 88 93 94 95 96 106 108 109 110 **P**8 **S** SSM Health Care, Saint Louis, MO
Primary Contact: Bruce Merrell, President
CFO: Kay Tinsley, Vice President Finance
CIO: Mark Clark, Director Information Systems
Web address: www.smgsi.com

| | 21 | 10 | 125 | 7016 | 80 | 146209 | 499 | 75616 | 29774 | 822 |

CHAMPAIGN—Champaign County

□ **THE PAVILION**, 809 West Church Street, Zip 61820–3399; tel. 217/373–1700, (Nonreporting) **A**1 10 **S** Universal Health Services, Inc., King of Prussia, PA
Primary Contact: Joseph Sheehy, Chief Executive Officer
Web address: www.info@pavilionhospital.com

| | 33 | 22 | 46 | — | — | — | — | — | — | — |

CHESTER—Randolph County

□ **CHESTER MENTAL HEALTH CENTER**, Chester Road, Zip 62233–0031, Mailing Address: Box 31, Zip 62233–0031; tel. 618/826–4571 **A**1 3 5 **F**21 22 32 65 71 94
Primary Contact: Brian E. Thomas, Aministrator

| | 12 | 22 | 281 | 221 | 281 | 0 | 0 | 32860 | 24483 | 520 |

□ **MEMORIAL HOSPITAL**, 1900 State Street, Zip 62233–0609, Mailing Address: P.O. Box 609, Zip 62233–0609; tel. 618/826–4581 **A**1 9 10 18 **F**2 4 9 11 12 21 23 26 33 46 48 52 54 55 57 59 61 62 63 64 69 81 82 88 93 94 96 97 106 108
Primary Contact: Eric Freeburg, Administrator
Web address: www.mhchester.com

| | 16 | 10 | 35 | 1282 | 14 | 41113 | 57 | 15877 | 6675 | 225 |

CHICAGO—Cook County

⊠ **ADVOCATE BETHANY HOSPITAL**, 3435 West Van Buren Street, Zip 60624–3399; tel. 773/265–7700 **A**1 9 10 **F**2 9 11 12 21 22 23 24 27 29 33 37 38 39 42 44 46 48 49 50 55 58 59 60 61 63 69 71 81 82 85 88 94 108 110 **P**8 **S** Advocate Health Care, Oak Brook, IL
Primary Contact: Lena Dobbs–Johnson, President
CFO: Jim Gambarota, Vice President Finance
CMO: Glenn Bynum, M.D., Vice Persident Medical Management
CIO: Linda Peterson, Director Information Systems
CHR: Jason Spigner, Vice President Human Resources
Web address: www.advocatehealth.com

| | 23 | 10 | 136 | 6618 | 79 | 33745 | 637 | 54620 | 22590 | 390 |

⊠ **ADVOCATE ILLINOIS MASONIC MEDICAL CENTER**, 836 West Wellington Avenue, Zip 60657–5193; tel. 773/975–1600 **A**1 2 3 5 9 10 12 13 **F**2 4 11 12 14 15 17 19 21 22 23 24 25 26 27 28 29 30 31 32 33 34 35 36 37 38 39 42 44 45 46 47 48 49 50 51 52 53 56 57 58 59 60 61 62 63 64 65 66 67 68 69 70 71 72 73 74 75 76 77 78 79 80 81 82 84 85 87 88 89 90 94 96 98 106 108 109 **P**6 8 **S** Advocate Health Care, Oak Brook, IL
Primary Contact: Susan Nordstrom Lopez, President
CFO: Jack Gilbert, Vice President Finance
CMO: William Werner, Vice President Medical Management
CIO: Kevin Trovini, Manager, Information Systems
CHR: Marc Senesac, Vice President Human Resources
Web address: www.advocatehealth.com

| | 23 | 10 | 346 | 17940 | 241 | 161988 | 3294 | 258367 | 103216 | 2237 |

⊠ **ADVOCATE TRINITY HOSPITAL**, 2320 East 93rd Street, Zip 60617–9984; tel. 773/967–2000 **A**1 9 10 **F**9 11 12 17 21 22 27 28 29 33 39 46 49 52 53 55 59 60 63 65 66 81 82 87 88 94 96 108 110 **P**8 **S** Advocate Health Care, Oak Brook, IL
Primary Contact: John N. Schwartz, President
CFO: Maureen Morrison, Vice President Financial Services
CMO: Michael Davenport, Vice President Medical Management
Web address: www.advocatehealth.com/trinity

| | 21 | 10 | 158 | 10085 | 117 | 78586 | 1677 | 102941 | 38203 | 727 |

BERNARD MITCHELL HOSPITAL See University of Chicago Hospitals

□ **CHICAGO LAKESHORE HOSPITAL**, 4840 North Marine Drive, Zip 60640–4296; tel. 773/878–9700 **A**1 3 5 9 10 **F**27 28 71 72 73 75 77 78
Primary Contact: C. Alan Eaks, Chief Executive Officer
Web address: www.chicagolakeshorehospital.com

| | 33 | 22 | 108 | 3022 | 78 | 7198 | 0 | 14470 | 6625 | 157 |

CHICAGO LYING–IN HOSPITAL See University of Chicago Hospitals

□ **CHICAGO–READ MENTAL HEALTH CENTER**, 4200 North Oak Park Avenue, Zip 60634–1457; tel. 773/794–4000, (Nonreporting) **A**1 10
Primary Contact: Thomas Simpatico, M.D., Facility Director and Network System Manager

| | 12 | 22 | 200 | — | — | — | — | — | — | — |

IL

Many Facility Codes have changed. Please refer to the AHA Guide Code Chart. © 2005 AHA Guide

Hospital, Address, Telephone, Approval, Facility, and Physician Codes, Health Care System	Classi-fication Codes		Utilization Data					Expense (thousands) of dollars		
★ American Hospital Association (AHA) membership □ Joint Commission on Accreditation of Healthcare Organizations (JCAHO) accreditation ○ American Osteopathic Association (AOA) accreditation △ Commission on Accreditation of Rehabilitation Facilities (CARF) accreditation	Control	Service	Staffed Beds	Admissions	Census	Outpatient Visits	Births	Total	Payroll	Personnel
★ **CHILDREN'S MEMORIAL HOSPITAL**, 2300 Children's Plaza, Zip 60614–3394; tel. 773/880–4000 **A**1 2 3 5 8 9 10 **F**2 6 7 9 16 18 20 21 22 23 24 27 28 29 31 32 33 34 37 39 42 45 46 47 48 49 50 51 52 53 56 57 58 61 62 63 64 65 66 67 69 70 71 72 73 74 75 77 78 81 82 84 85 87 88 90 93 94 95 96 98 99 100 101 105 107 108 **P**5 Primary Contact: Patrick M. Magoon, President and Chief Executive Officer COO: Gordon B. Bass, Chief Operating Officer CFO: Paula Noble, Chief Financial Officer and Treasurer CMO: Edward S. Ogata, M.D., Chief Medical Officer CIO: Stan Krok, Chief Information Officer CHR: Barbara Bowman, Chief Human Resource Officer Web address: www.childrensmemorial.org	23	50	231	9089	167	330171	0	347766	144180	3076
□ **HARTGROVE HOSPITAL**, 520 North Ridgeway Avenue, Zip 60624–1299; tel. 773/722–3113, (Nonreporting) **A**1 10 **S** Universal Health Services, Inc., King of Prussia, PA Primary Contact: Steven Airhart, Chief Executive Officer Web address: www.uhsinc.com	33	22	128	—	—	—	—	—	—	—
□ **HOLY CROSS HOSPITAL**, 2701 West 68th Street, Zip 60629–1882; tel. 773/884–9000 **A**1 9 10 **F**2 11 12 14 21 22 23 27 28 29 33 37 42 48 49 52 53 55 57 58 59 60 61 62 63 66 68 69 70 81 82 85 88 94 95 108 109 **P**8 Primary Contact: Brian J. Lemon, President and Chief Executive Officer Web address: www.holycrosshospital.org	23	10	244	10958	154	148033	847	—	—	909
□ **JACKSON PARK HOSPITAL AND MEDICAL CENTER**, 7531 Stony Island Avenue, Zip 60649–3993; tel. 773/947–7500 **A**1 2 9 10 **F**2 3 12 21 22 23 26 27 28 29 31 32 33 37 38 39 44 46 47 48 49 50 55 57 58 59 60 61 62 63 64 66 69 70 71 73 75 76 77 78 81 82 88 94 110 **P**6 Primary Contact: Merritt J. Hasbrouck, President Web address: www.jacksonparkhospital.com	23	10	212	8980	199	51872	285	62480	27491	595
★ △ **JESSE BROWN VETERANS AFFAIRS CHICAGO HEALTH CARE SYSTEM**, 820 South Damen, Zip 60612–3776; tel. 312/569–8387, (Includes VETERANS AFFAIRS CHICAGO HEALTH CARE SYSTEM, 333 East Huron Street, Zip 60611–3004; tel. 312/640–2100) **A**1 3 5 7 8 **F**2 4 7 9 10 12 14 15 17 21 22 23 26 27 28 29 30 31 32 33 35 37 39 41 42 44 45 46 47 48 49 50 51 52 53 55 57 58 60 61 62 63 64 65 66 68 69 70 71 73 74 75 76 77 78 81 82 84 85 88 92 94 96 106 107 108 109 110 **P**6 **S** Department of Veterans Affairs, Washington, DC Primary Contact: Stan Johnson, Acting Director Web address: www.va.gov/sta/guide/home.asp	45	10	205	7725	137	531000	0	261559	128490	1840
★ **JOHN H. STROGER JR. HOSPITAL OF COOK COUNTY**, 1835 West Harrison Street, Zip 60612–3785; tel. 312/864–6000 **A**1 2 3 5 8 9 10 12 13 **F**13 14 55 56 59 67 **P**6 **S** Cook County Bureau of Health Services, Chicago, IL Primary Contact: Johnny C. Brown, Chief Operating Officer CMO: Bradley Langer, M.D., Interim Medical Director CIO: Dan Howard, Chief Information Officer CHR: Birdge Givens, Associate Administrator and Director Human Resources Web address: www.ccbhs.org	13	10	460	23037	353	873984	1278	475643	354605	4752
JOHNSTON R. BOWMAN HEALTH CENTER See Rush University Medical Center										
KINDRED CHICAGO CENTRAL HOSPITAL, 4058 West Melrose Street, Zip 60641–4797; tel. 773/736–7000, (Nonreporting) **A**10 **S** Kindred Healthcare, Louisville, KY Primary Contact: Larry Foster, Chief Executive Officer Web address: www.kindredhealthcare.com	33	48	76	—	—	—	—	—	—	—
KINDRED HOSPITAL–CHICAGO NORTH, 2544 West Montrose Avenue, Zip 60618–1589; tel. 773/267–2622, (Nonreporting) **S** Kindred Healthcare, Louisville, KY Primary Contact: Jack Nathan Shapiro, Chief Executive Officer Web address: www.kindredhealthcare.com	33	49	164	—	—	—	—	—	—	—
★ **LA RABIDA CHILDREN'S HOSPITAL**, East 65th Street at Lake Michigan, Zip 60649–1395; tel. 773/363–6700 **A**1 9 10 **F**2 7 10 11 21 22 24 29 33 37 39 45 46 48 52 53 58 62 65 66 69 70 72 77 94 96 107 108 **P**6 Primary Contact: Paula Kienberger Jaudes, M.D., President and Chief Executive Officer CFO: James Stolt, Vice President Administration and Chief Financial Officer CMO: Barry Rich, M.D., Chief Medical Staff CIO: Timothy Diamond, Chief Information Officer CHR: Nancy Ramski, Director Human Resources Web address: www.larabida.org	23	58	49	1007	32	35544	0	34468	17063	431
★ **LINCOLN PARK HOSPITAL**, 550 Webster Avenue, Zip 60614–9980; tel. 773/883–2000 **A**1 10 **F**15 17 19 21 22 26 28 44 52 55 61 62 63 65 68 69 70 71 73 74 75 76 77 81 84 85 88 92 94 95 **S** Merit Health Systems, Louisville, KY Primary Contact: Gregory A. Cierlik, President and Chief Executive Officer COO: Bridget Hayes, Chief Operating Officer CFO: Truman Esmond, Jr, Chief Financial Officer CMO: William Markey, M.D., Medical Staff President Web address: www.lincolnparkhospital.com	33	10	155	5430	83	23360	605	53817	21365	420

IL

Hospital, Address, Telephone, Approval, Facility, and Physician Codes, Health Care System	Classi-fication Codes		Utilization Data					Expense (thousands) of dollars		
★ American Hospital Association (AHA) membership □ Joint Commission on Accreditation of Healthcare Organizations (JCAHO) accreditation ○ American Osteopathic Association (AOA) accreditation △ Commission on Accreditation of Rehabilitation Facilities (CARF) accreditation	Control	Service	Staffed Beds	Admissions	Census	Outpatient Visits	Births	Total	Payroll	Personnel
□ **LORETTO HOSPITAL**, 645 South Central Avenue, Zip 60644–9987; tel. 773/626–4300 **A**1 10 **F**2 3 4 12 21 22 23 27 28 29 31 33 37 44 45 46 48 50 52 55 60 62 63 64 66 69 70 71 75 76 77 81 87 88 94 96 110 Primary Contact: Steve C. Drucker, President and Chief Executive Officer Web address: www.lorettohospital.org	23	10	172	6900	125	30724	0	44539	23035	426
⊠ **LOUIS A. WEISS MEMORIAL HOSPITAL**, 4646 North Marine Drive, Zip 60640–1501; tel. 773/878–8700 **A**1 2 3 5 9 10 **F**2 9 11 12 15 17 19 21 22 23 26 27 28 29 31 33 35 36 37 40 42 44 46 48 49 50 52 53 55 57 58 59 60 61 62 63 64 66 68 69 70 76 81 82 84 85 86 88 94 96 108 109 110 **P**5 6 **S** Vanguard Health System, Nashville, TN Primary Contact: Tracy A. Rogers, Chief Executive Officer COO: Frank L. Molinaro, Chief Operating Officer CFO: Richard Jones, Chief Financial Officer CMO: Michael Ruchim, M.D., Vice President Academic and Medical Affairs CIO: Michael Devore, Chief Information Officer CHR: Keoni Nader, Director Human Resources Web address: www.weisshospital.com	32	10	192	8753	118	110674	918	106803	41937	783
⊠ **MERCY HOSPITAL AND MEDICAL CENTER**, 2525 South Michigan Avenue, Zip 60616–2477; tel. 312/567–2000 **A**1 2 3 5 9 10 **F**2 3 4 9 11 12 14 15 16 17 19 21 22 23 25 27 28 29 30 31 32 33 37 39 41 42 45 46 47 48 52 53 55 56 57 58 59 60 61 62 63 64 65 66 68 69 70 71 72 73 74 75 76 77 78 79 80 81 82 84 85 86 88 90 93 94 96 97 106 108 109 110 **P**5 7 Primary Contact: Sister Sheila Lyne, President and Chief Executive Officer COO: Richard Cerceo, Executive Vice President and Chief Operating Officer CFO: Thomas J. Garvey, Chief Financial Officer CMO: Warren Furey, M.D., Chairman, Department of Medicine CIO: Thomas J. Garvey, Chief Financial Officer CHR: Nancy L. Hill–Davis, Chief Human Resources Officer Web address: www.mercychicago.org	21	10	304	12538	151	188599	2197	144528	69892	1290
□ **METHODIST HOSPITAL OF CHICAGO**, 5025 North Paulina Street, Zip 60640–2797; tel. 773/271–9040, (Total facility includes 17 beds in nursing home–type unit) (Nonreporting) **A**1 10 Primary Contact: Steven H. Friedman, Ph.D., Executive Vice President Web address: www.bethanymethodist.org	23	10	189	—	—	—	—	—	—	—
□ △ **MICHAEL REESE HOSPITAL AND MEDICAL CENTER**, 2929 South Ellis Avenue, Zip 60616–3376; tel. 312/791–2000 **A**1 2 3 5 7 9 10 **F**2 9 10 11 12 14 21 22 27 28 29 30 33 34 39 40 42 44 45 46 48 50 52 53 55 56 57 58 59 60 61 62 63 64 65 66 67 68 69 70 71 72 73 75 76 81 82 84 88 94 97 108 109 110 **P**5 Primary Contact: Kathy E. Neely, Chief Operating Officer Web address: www.michaelreesehospital.com	33	10	316	11342	168	78125	984	109499	49645	914
⊠ **MOUNT SINAI HOSPITAL MEDICAL CENTER OF CHICAGO**, California Avenue and 15th Street, Zip 60608–1610; tel. 773/542–2000 **A**1 2 3 5 8 9 10 12 13 **F**2 9 11 12 15 17 19 21 22 23 26 27 28 29 32 33 34 35 36 37 38 39 44 46 48 49 50 51 52 53 55 56 57 58 59 60 61 62 63 64 65 67 70 71 73 74 75 76 77 79 80 81 82 84 88 93 94 106 108 110 **S** Sinai Health System, Chicago, IL Primary Contact: Larry E. Volkmar, President COO: Carl Josehart, Chief Operating Officer CFO: Charles Weis, Chief Financial Officer CMO: Robert Parker, M.D., Chief Medical Officer CIO: Peter Ingram, Vice President and Chief Information Officer Web address: www.sinai.org	23	10	312	16122	196	311099	3490	197684	83251	1277
⊠ **NORTHWESTERN MEMORIAL HOSPITAL**, 251 East Huron Street, Zip 60611–2908; tel. 312/926–2000, (Includes NORMAN AND IDA STONE INSTITUTE OF PSYCHIATRY, 320 East Huron Street, Zip 60611; PRENTICE WOMEN'S HOSPITAL, 333 East Superior Street, Zip 60611) **A**1 2 3 5 8 9 10 **F**2 3 4 5 7 9 10 11 12 14 15 17 19 21 22 23 25 26 27 28 29 30 31 32 33 34 35 36 37 38 40 41 42 43 44 45 46 47 48 49 50 51 52 53 55 56 57 58 59 60 61 62 63 64 65 66 69 70 71 72 73 74 75 76 77 78 79 81 82 84 85 86 87 88 89 90 93 94 95 96 97 98 99 101 102 104 105 106 108 109 110 **P**5 6 Primary Contact: Dean M. Harrison, President and Chief Executive Officer CFO: Pete McCanna, Senior Vice President CMO: Charles M. Watts, M.D., Senior Vice President Medical Affairs CIO: Tim Zoph, Vice President Information Services CHR: Dean Manheimer, Senior Vice President, Human Resources Web address: www.nmh.org	23	10	744	42777	609	378870	9994	833960	317253	5678
□ **NORWEGIAN–AMERICAN HOSPITAL**, Mailing Address: 1044 North Francisco Avenue, Zip 60622–2794; tel. 773/292–8200, (Nonreporting) **A**1 9 10 Primary Contact: Michael J. O'Grady, Jr, President and Chief Executive Officer Web address: www.n–ahs.org	23	10	230	—	—	—	—	—	—	—
□ **OUR LADY OF THE RESURRECTION MEDICAL CENTER**, 5645 West Addison Street, Zip 60634–4455; tel. 773/282–7000, (Total facility includes 66 beds in nursing home–type unit) (Nonreporting) **A**1 3 5 9 10 12 **S** Resurrection Health Care Corporation, Chicago, IL Primary Contact: Ivette Estrada, Executive Vice President and Chief Executive Officer Web address: www.reshealthcare.org PRENTICE WOMEN'S HOSPITAL See Northwestern Memorial Hospital	21	10	265	—	—	—	—	—	—	—

Many Facility Codes have changed. Please refer to the AHA Guide Code Chart.   © 2005 AHA Guide

Hospital, Address, Telephone, Approval, Facility, and Physician Codes, Health Care System	Classi-fication Codes		Utilization Data					Expense (thousands) of dollars		
★ American Hospital Association (AHA) membership □ Joint Commission on Accreditation of Healthcare Organizations (JCAHO) accreditation ○ American Osteopathic Association (AOA) accreditation △ Commission on Accreditation of Rehabilitation Facilities (CARF) accreditation	Control	Service	Staffed Beds	Admissions	Census	Outpatient Visits	Births	Total	Payroll	Personnel
✸ **PROVIDENT HOSPITAL OF COOK COUNTY**, 500 East 51st Street, Zip 60615–2494; tel. 312/572-2000 **A**1 3 5 10 **F**2 11 12 22 23 26 27 28 29 31 33 39 46 47 48 49 50 52 53 55 56 58 59 60 61 62 63 64 65 66 69 70 81 82 88 92 94 96 106 107 108 109 **P**6 **S** Cook County Bureau of Health Services, Chicago, IL Primary Contact: Michele T. Thompson, Interim Chief Operating Officer COO: Michele T. Thompson, Interim Chief Operating Officer CFO: Barbara Patterson, Chief Financial Officer CMO: Aaron Hamb, M.D., Chief Medical Officer CIO: Donna Hart, Chief Information Officer Web address: www.ccbhs.org/pages/ProvidentHospitalofCookCounty.htm	13	10	119	6779	78	140680	609	109781	59451	772
✸ △ **REHABILITATION INSTITUTE OF CHICAGO**, 345 East Superior Street, Zip 60611–4496; tel. 312/238-1000 **A**1 3 5 7 8 9 10 **F**7 21 22 25 27 28 29 30 37 41 42 44 45 47 48 52 53 60 65 68 69 94 95 96 98 108 109 110 **P**6 Primary Contact: Wayne M. Lerner, DPH, President and Chief Executive Officer COO: Susan Cerletty, Executive Vice President CFO: Greg Ward, Vice President and Chief Financial Officer CMO: Elliot J. Roth, M.D., Senior Vice President and Medical Director CIO: Tim McKula, Vice President Information Systems and Chief Information Officer Web address: www.ric.org	23	46	155	2514	127	—	0	—	—	—
✸ △ **RESURRECTION MEDICAL CENTER**, 7435 West Talcott Avenue, Zip 60631–3746; tel. 773/774-8000 **A**1 2 3 5 7 9 10 12 **F**2 7 9 11 12 14 15 17 19 21 22 23 27 28 29 30 32 33 36 37 38 39 41 44 45 46 47 48 49 52 55 57 58 59 60 61 62 63 64 65 66 68 69 70 79 80 81 82 84 85 86 87 88 90 92 94 95 96 106 108 109 **P**5 7 **S** Resurrection Health Care Corporation, Chicago, IL Primary Contact: Sister Donna Marie Wolowicki, Executive Vice President and Chief Executive Officer CFO: Thomas Capobianco, Executive Vice President Finance CMO: William Davison, M.D., President Medical Staff CIO: George Chessum, Senior Vice President Information Systems and Chief Information Officer CHR: James P. Hill, Executive Vice President, Administrative Services Web address: www.reshealthcare.org	21	10	398	19327	307	211529	1217	242335	94769	2239
★ **ROSELAND COMMUNITY HOSPITAL**, 45 West 111th Street, Zip 60628–4294; tel. 773/995-3000 **A**9 10 **F**3 4 9 12 22 24 28 29 33 42 44 45 46 48 50 52 55 58 59 61 62 63 66 69 70 81 82 88 94 96 98 107 **P**8 Primary Contact: Donald C. Sibery, President and Chief Executive Officer COO: Anthony Tedeschi, M.D., Chief Operating Officer CFO: Maurice Washington, Director Controls and Accountability CMO: Rogelio Cave, M.D., Medical Director CHR: Brenda Mitchell, Director Human Resources Web address: www.roselandhospital.org	23	10	110	5545	63	38331	500	36922	17474	309
✸ △ **RUSH UNIVERSITY MEDICAL CENTER**, 1653 West Congress Parkway, Zip 60612–3833; tel. 312/942-5000, (Includes JOHNSTON R. BOWMAN HEALTH CENTER, 700 South Paulina, Zip 60612; tel. 312/942-7000), (Total facility includes 18 beds in nursing home–type unit) **A**1 2 3 5 7 8 9 10 **F**2 4 5 7 9 10 11 12 14 15 16 17 18 19 20 21 22 23 24 29 30 31 32 33 34 35 36 37 38 39 40 41 44 46 47 48 49 50 51 52 53 55 56 57 58 59 60 61 62 63 64 65 66 67 68 69 70 71 72 73 74 75 76 77 78 79 80 81 82 83 84 85 86 87 88 89 90 91 92 93 94 95 96 98 99 100 101 102 104 105 106 108 109 110 **P**8 **S** Rush University Medical Center, Chicago, IL Primary Contact: Larry J. Goodman, M.D., President and Chief Executive Officer COO: Peter W. Butler, Executive Vice President and Chief Operating Officer CFO: David M A Jensen, Chief Financial Officer and Treasurer CMO: Gunnar B J Andersson, M.D., Ph.D., Senior Vice President Medical Affairs CIO: John Brill, M.D., Acting Chief Information Officer Web address: www.rush.edu	23	10	679	29757	486	354144	2040	571750	221615	6834
□ **SACRED HEART HOSPITAL**, 3240 West Franklin Boulevard, Zip 60624–1599; tel. 773/722-3020, (Nonreporting) **A**1 10 Primary Contact: Edward Novak, President and Chief Executive Officer	33	10	96	—	—	—	—	—	—	—
✸ **SAINT ANTHONY HOSPITAL**, 2875 West 19th Street, Zip 60623–3596; tel. 773/484-1000 **A**1 9 10 **F**2 11 12 21 22 23 24 28 29 33 39 45 46 48 52 53 55 57 59 61 62 63 66 69 70 71 77 78 81 82 88 94 108 **P**4 8 **S** Ascension Health, Saint Louis, MO Primary Contact: Kathleen K. DeVine, Chief Executive Officer COO: Gwenn A. Rausch, Chief Operating Officer CFO: Todd A. Conklin, Vice President and Chief Financial Officer CMO: Rolando Lara, M.D., Medical Director CIO: Ray Gonzales, Manager Information Systems CHR: Margaret Loisel, Vice President Web address: www.cath-health.org	21	10	151	7571	93	121428	2143	66509	34586	589

IL

Hospital, Address, Telephone, Approval, Facility, and Physician Codes, Health Care System	Classi-fication Codes		Utilization Data					Expense (thousands) of dollars		
★ American Hospital Association (AHA) membership □ Joint Commission on Accreditation of Healthcare Organizations (JCAHO) accreditation ○ American Osteopathic Association (AOA) accreditation △ Commission on Accreditation of Rehabilitation Facilities (CARF) accreditation	Control	Service	Staffed Beds	Admissions	Census	Outpatient Visits	Births	Total	Payroll	Personnel

⊠ **SAINT JOSEPH HOSPITAL**, 2900 North Lake Shore Drive, Zip 60657–6274; tel. 773/665–3000, (Total facility includes 26 beds in nursing home–type unit) **A**1 2 3 5 9 10 **F**2 7 9 11 12 14 15 17 19 21 22 23 24 27 28 29 33 36 37 38 39 42 44 45 46 47 48 50 51 52 53 55 56 57 58 59 60 61 62 63 64 66 68 69 70 71 73 74 75 76 77 79 80 81 82 84 87 88 92 93 94 95 96 106 108 109 110 **P**6 8 **S** Resurrection Health Care Corporation, Chicago, IL Primary Contact: Ronald E. Struxness, Chief Executive Officer CFO: Donna Pareti, Controller CMO: Andrew Gorchynsky, M.D., President Medical Staff CIO: George Chessum, Senior Vice President Information Systems and Chief Information Officer CHR: Denise Brown, Vice President Human Resources Web address: www.reshealth.org	21	10	345	14891	229	126089	1938	168560	63941	1482
□ ○ **SAINT'S MARY & ELIZABETH MEDICAL CENTER, CLAREMONT AVENUE**, (Formerly Saint Elizabeth Hospital), 1431 North Claremont Avenue, Zip 60622–1791; tel. 773/278–2000, (Total facility includes 25 beds in nursing home–type unit) **A**1 2 9 10 **F**2 3 4 11 12 15 21 22 23 26 27 28 33 37 40 46 47 48 49 51 52 53 54 55 57 58 59 60 61 62 63 64 65 66 69 70 71 75 77 78 81 88 92 93 94 108 **P**8 **S** Resurrection Health Care Corporation, Chicago, IL Primary Contact: Margaret McDermott, Chief Executive Officer Web address: www.reshealthcare.org	21	10	252	13375	188	93916	1110	88448	38096	843
⊠ **SAINT'S MARY & ELIZABETH MEDICAL CENTER, DIVISION STREET**, (Formerly St. Mary of Nazareth Hospital Center), 2233 West Division Street, Zip 60622–3086; tel. 312/770–2000 **A**1 2 9 10 **F**2 9 11 12 14 15 17 19 21 22 23 27 29 31 33 39 45 46 48 49 50 52 55 57 58 59 60 61 62 63 64 66 68 69 71 75 76 81 82 84 85 87 88 92 94 96 107 108 **P**8 **S** Resurrection Health Care Corporation, Chicago, IL Primary Contact: Margaret McDermott, Chief Executive Officer CFO: Kenneth A. Kautzer, Senior Vice President Finance and Treasurer CIO: Steven Smith, Chief Information Officer Web address: www.stmaryofnazareth.org	23	10	305	14882	225	120678	1312	122579	50999	1080
⊠ △ **SCHWAB REHABILITATION HOSPITAL**, (Formerly Schwab Rehabilitation Hospital and Care Network), 1401 South California Boulevard, Zip 60608–1612; tel. 773/522–2010 **A**1 7 8 9 10 **F**7 21 22 29 37 44 45 52 53 57 58 60 62 65 66 68 69 92 94 95 96 98 108 110 **P**6 **S** Sinai Health System, Chicago, IL Primary Contact: Larry E. Volkmar, President COO: Carl Josehart, Senior Vice President and Chief Operating Officer CFO: Charles Weis, Chief Financial Officer Web address: www.schwabrehab.org	23	46	104	1748	77	103356	0	29046	15062	424
⊠ **SHRINERS HOSPITALS FOR CHILDREN–CHICAGO**, 2211 North Oak Park Avenue, Zip 60707–3361; tel. 773/622–5400 **A**1 3 5 **F**2 7 21 24 27 28 29 39 45 52 53 57 58 60 62 64 65 67 68 69 88 94 95 96 98 108 110 **P**6 **S** Shriners Hospitals for Children, Tampa, FL Primary Contact: Shana Jones, Ph.D., Administrator CFO: Philip Magid, Director Fiscal Services CMO: Peter F. Sturm, M.D., Chief of Staff CIO: Kathie Tonkovic, Director Health Information Management CHR: James E. Pawlowicz, Director Human Resources Web address: www.shrinershq.org	23	57	60	1553	18	15098	0	—	—	266
⊠ **SOUTH SHORE HOSPITAL**, 8012 South Crandon Avenue, Zip 60617–1199; tel. 773/768–0810, (Nonreporting) **A**1 10 Primary Contact: Jesus M. Ong, President CFO: Timothy Caveney, Chief Financial Officer CMO: Surinder K. Parmar, M.D., President, Medical Staff CIO: Jim Ritchie, Director Management Information Systems CHR: Joseph Perez, Director Human Resources Web address: www.southshorehospital.com	23	10	125							
□ **ST. BERNARD HOSPITAL AND HEALTH CARE CENTER**, 326 West 64th Street, Zip 60621–3146; tel. 773/962–3900, (Nonreporting) **A**1 10 Primary Contact: Sister Elizabeth Van Straten, President and Chief Executive Officer Web address: www.stbernardhospital.com	21	10	194	—	—	—	—	—	—	—
⊠ **SWEDISH COVENANT HOSPITAL**, 5145 North California Avenue, Zip 60625–3688; tel. 773/878–8200, (Total facility includes 46 beds in nursing home–type unit) **A**1 2 3 5 9 10 12 13 **F**2 10 11 12 15 17 19 21 22 23 24 26 27 28 30 31 32 33 34 35 37 38 39 44 46 52 53 55 57 58 59 60 61 62 63 64 65 66 68 69 70 71 73 74 75 76 77 78 81 82 84 85 87 88 92 93 94 95 96 98 106 108 110 **P**1 5 7 Primary Contact: Mark Newton, President and Chief Executive Officer COO: Karen Teitelbaum, Senior Vice President Operations and Chief Business Development Officer CFO: Gary M. Krugel, Senior Vice President Operations and Chief Financial Officer CIO: Karen Sheehan, Information Systems Director CHR: Anthony Guaccio, Senior Vice President Operations and Chief Human Resource Officer Web address: www.schosp.org	21	10	324	15713	252	212959	2237	182864	83903	1791

Many Facility Codes have changed. Please refer to the AHA Guide Code Chart. © 2005 AHA Guide

Hospital, Address, Telephone, Approval, Facility, and Physician Codes, Health Care System	Classi-fication Codes		Utilization Data					Expense (thousands) of dollars		
★ American Hospital Association (AHA) membership □ Joint Commission on Accreditation of Healthcare Organizations (JCAHO) accreditation ○ American Osteopathic Association (AOA) accreditation △ Commission on Accreditation of Rehabilitation Facilities (CARF) accreditation	Control	Service	Staffed Beds	Admissions	Census	Outpatient Visits	Births	Total	Payroll	Personnel
□ **THE NEUROLOGIC AND ORTHOPEDIC INSTITUTE OF CHICAGO**, 4501 North Winchester Avenue, Zip 60640; tel. 773/250–0000, (Nonreporting) **A**1 10 Primary Contact: Tom Hodson, Acting Chief Executive Officer THE UNIVERSITY OF CHICAGO COMER CHILDREN'S HOSPITAL See University of Chicago Hospitals	33	47	90	—	—	—	—	—	—	—
○ **THOREK HOSPITAL AND MEDICAL CENTER**, 850 West Irving Park Road, Zip 60613–3099; tel. 773/525–6780, (Nonreporting) **A**9 10 11 Primary Contact: Frank A. Solare, President and Chief Executive Officer Web address: www.thorek.org	23	10	137	—	—	—	—	—	—	—
▣ **UNIVERSITY OF CHICAGO HOSPITALS**, 5841 South Maryland Avenue, Zip 60637–1470; tel. 773/702–1000, (Includes BERNARD MITCHELL HOSPITAL; CHICAGO LYING–IN HOSPITAL; THE UNIVERSITY OF CHICAGO COMER CHILDREN'S HOSPITAL) **A**1 2 3 5 8 9 10 **F**2 3 4 5 6 7 9 10 11 12 13 14 15 16 17 18 19 20 21 22 23 24 26 27 28 29 30 31 32 33 34 35 36 38 39 40 41 42 43 44 45 46 47 48 49 50 51 52 53 55 56 57 58 59 60 61 62 63 64 65 66 67 69 70 71 72 73 75 76 77 79 80 81 82 84 85 86 87 88 89 90 92 93 94 95 96 98 99 100 101 102 104 105 106 107 108 109 110 **P**1 Primary Contact: Michael C. Riordan, President and Chief Executive Officer COO: Kenneth P. Kates, Executive Vice President and Chief Operating Officer Web address: www.uchospitals.edu	23	10	585	26293	461	664152	3021	657677	291370	6353
▣ △ **UNIVERSITY OF ILLINOIS MEDICAL CENTER AT CHICAGO**, 1740 West Taylor Street, Zip 60612–7236; tel. 312/996–7000 **A**1 2 3 5 7 8 9 10 **F**2 7 10 11 12 14 15 16 17 18 19 20 21 22 23 26 27 28 29 31 32 33 34 37 39 42 44 46 47 48 49 50 52 53 55 56 57 58 59 60 61 62 63 64 65 66 67 68 69 70 71 72 73 74 75 76 77 78 79 80 81 82 83 84 85 86 87 88 89 90 93 94 95 96 98 99 100 101 102 103 104 105 106 107 108 109 110 **P**4 Primary Contact: John J. DeNardo, Executive Director COO: Bernadette Biskup, Interim Chief Operating Officer CFO: Hugh Rose, Chief Financial Officer CMO: William Chamberlin, Chief Medical Officer CIO: Bernadette Biskup, Interim Chief Operating Officer Web address: www.uillinoismedcenter.org	12	10	443	18009	311	477538	2608	423952	191600	3557
CLINTON—Dewitt County										
★ **DR. JOHN WARNER HOSPITAL**, 422 West White Street, Zip 61727–2199; tel. 217/935–9571 **A**9 10 18 **F**6 9 10 12 27 28 33 52 55 58 63 64 70 81 94 96 97 106 108 **P**6 Primary Contact: Patricia Luker, Chief Executive Officer and Administrator CFO: Donna Wisner, Chief Financial Officer CMO: Jennifer Powell, President Medical Staff CIO: Chris Johnson, Information Services Manager CHR: Belinda Rittenhouse, Director Human Resources Web address: www.djwhospital.org	14	10	25	606	6	18115	0	11430	4801	146
DANVILLE—Vermilion County										
▣ **PROVENA UNITED SAMARITANS MEDICAL CENTER**, 812 North Logan, Zip 61832–3788; tel. 217/443–5000, (Includes UNITED SAMARITANS MEDICAL CENTER, 600 Sager Avenue, Zip 61832; tel. 217/442–6300) **A**1 2 9 10 19 **F**2 4 11 12 15 21 22 23 26 27 28 29 33 39 46 48 49 52 53 55 57 58 59 60 61 62 63 64 66 69 75 77 78 81 82 84 85 87 88 94 96 98 108 109 110 **S** Provena Health, Mokena, IL Primary Contact: Mark S. Wiener, President and Chief Executive Officer CFO: Cheryl A. Harmon, Vice President Finance Web address: www.provenausmc.org	23	10	170	8897	99	197328	777	82264	27961	891
▣ **VETERANS AFFAIRS ILLIANA HEALTH CARE SYSTEM**, 1900 East Main Street, Zip 61832–5198; tel. 217/554–3000, (Total facility includes 241 beds in nursing home–type unit) (Nonreporting) **A**1 3 5 **S** Department of Veterans Affairs, Washington, DC Primary Contact: Cathi Spivey–Paul, Acting Director CFO: Romeo Zamberletti, Chief Fiscal Service CMO: Sarita Prabhudesai, M.D., Chief of Staff CIO: Deron Jones, Acting Chief Information Resource Management CHR: Michael L. Palmier, Chief Human Resources and Staff Development Web address: www.va.gov/sta/guide/home.asp	45	10	370	—	—	—	—	—	—	—
DE KALB—De Kalb County										
▣ **KISHWAUKEE COMMUNITY HOSPITAL**, 626 Bethany Road, Zip 60115–4939, Mailing Address: P.O. Box 707, Zip 60115–0707; tel. 815/756–1521 **A**1 2 9 10 **F**2 9 10 11 12 26 27 28 29 33 45 46 48 53 55 57 58 59 60 61 62 63 65 66 69 71 81 85 87 88 93 94 95 96 97 108 **P**8 **S** Kishwaukee Health System, De Kalb, IL Primary Contact: Brad Copple, Administrator CFO: Loren Foelske, Vice President Finance CIO: Richard Shurson, Information Systems Director CHR: Mark Thate, Director Human Resources Web address: www.kishhospital.org	23	10	102	5066	48	116976	768	67069	26373	619

IL

Hospital, Address, Telephone, Approval, Facility, and Physician Codes, Health Care System	Classi-fication Codes		Utilization Data					Expense (thousands) of dollars		
★ American Hospital Association (AHA) membership □ Joint Commission on Accreditation of Healthcare Organizations (JCAHO) accreditation ○ American Osteopathic Association (AOA) accreditation △ Commission on Accreditation of Rehabilitation Facilities (CARF) accreditation	Control	Service	Staffed Beds	Admissions	Census	Outpatient Visits	Births	Total	Payroll	Personnel

DECATUR—Macon County

⊠ **DECATUR MEMORIAL HOSPITAL**, 2300 North Edward Street, Zip 62526–4192; tel. 217/876–8121, (Total facility includes 54 beds in nursing home–type unit) **A**1 2 3 5 9 10 12 13 **F**2 9 10 11 12 14 15 17 19 21 22 23 26 27 28 33 36 37 40 41 42 44 45 46 47 48 49 50 51 52 54 55 57 58 59 60 61 62 63 65 66 69 79 80 81 82 84 85 86 87 88 92 93 94 95 96 97 107 108 109 110 **P**1
Primary Contact: Kenneth L. Smithmier, President and Chief Executive Officer
COO: Timothy D. Stone, Jr, Executive Vice President and Chief Operating Officer
CFO: Gary Peacock, Senior Vice President and Chief Financial Officer
CIO: Jim Edwards, Director Information Systems
CHR: Mark Gates, Director Human Resources
Web address: www.dmhcares.org
| | 23 | 10 | 343 | 13636 | 182 | 309725 | 1022 | 207678 | 84900 | 2206 |

⊠ **ST. MARY'S HOSPITAL**, 1800 East Lake Shore Drive, Zip 62521–3883; tel. 217/464–2966, (Total facility includes 50 beds in nursing home–type unit) **A**1 3 5 9 10 **F**1 2 4 9 11 12 15 17 21 22 23 26 27 28 29 33 37 38 39 42 44 46 47 48 52 55 57 58 59 60 61 62 63 64 65 66 69 71 72 73 74 75 76 77 78 81 82 84 85 87 88 92 93 94 96 108 110 **P**7 **S** Hospital Sisters Health System, Springfield, IL
Primary Contact: Anthony D. Pfitzer, Executive Vice President and Administrator
CFO: George Brisson, Chief Financial Officer
Web address: www.stmarys–hospital.com
| | 21 | 10 | 224 | 7225 | 118 | 107093 | 595 | 78165 | 30834 | 887 |

DES PLAINES—Cook County

○ **HOLY FAMILY MEDICAL CENTER**, 100 North River Road, Zip 60016–1255; tel. 847/297–1800 **A**2 5 9 10 11 **F**2 3 11 12 15 17 21 22 23 26 27 28 29 33 34 37 39 45 48 49 52 55 57 58 59 60 61 62 63 64 66 67 69 81 82 84 88 92 93 94 96 105 108 109 110 **P**1 **S** Resurrection Health Care Corporation, Chicago, IL
Primary Contact: Sister Donna Marie Wolowicki, Executive Vice President and Chief Executive Officer
Web address: www.reshealth.org
| | 21 | 10 | 165 | 7185 | 79 | 88017 | 934 | 80344 | 29185 | 579 |

DIXON—Lee County

★ **KATHERINE SHAW BETHEA HOSPITAL**, 403 East First Street, Zip 61021–3187; tel. 815/288–5531, (Total facility includes 15 beds in nursing home–type unit) **A**9 10 **F**1 4 9 11 12 21 22 23 24 25 26 27 28 29 30 31 33 34 35 36 37 38 39 40 41 42 44 46 47 48 51 52 53 54 55 57 58 59 60 61 62 63 64 65 66 69 70 71 72 73 74 75 76 77 78 81 82 84 85 87 88 92 93 94 95 96 98 106 107 108 109 110 **P**6
Primary Contact: Darryl L. Vandervort, President and Chief Executive Officer
CFO: Vernon Farrell, Vice President Finance
CIO: Timothy W. Broos, Vice President Support Services
CHR: Julie Mann, Director Human Resources
Web address: www.ksbhospital.com
| | 23 | 10 | 99 | 5381 | 49 | 141768 | 335 | 68176 | 34995 | 685 |

DOWNERS GROVE—Du Page County

⊠ **ADVOCATE GOOD SAMARITAN HOSPITAL**, 3815 Highland Avenue, Zip 60515–1590; tel. 630/275–5900, (Nonreporting) **A**1 2 9 10 **S** Advocate Health Care, Oak Brook, IL
Primary Contact: David S. Fox, President
CFO: Peter Bury, Vice President Finance
CMO: Michael McKenna, M.D., Vice President Medical Management
CIO: Pete Caboor, Manager Information Systems
CHR: Sandra Norton, Vice President Human Resources
Web address: www.advocatehealth.com
| | 21 | 10 | 278 | — | — | — | — | — | — | — |

DU QUOIN—Perry County

⊠ **MARSHALL BROWNING HOSPITAL**, 900 North Washington Street, Zip 62832–1230, Mailing Address: P.O. Box 192, Zip 62832–0192; tel. 618/542–2146 **A**1 9 10 18 **F**9 12 21 27 28 29 33 46 48 54 63 69 81 88 91 97
Primary Contact: William J. Huff, Chief Executive Officer
CFO: Brice Harsy, Chief Financial Officer
CHR: Sarah Dickey, Personnel Manager
Web address: www.marshallbrowninghospital.com
| | 23 | 10 | 27 | 967 | 11 | 23944 | 0 | 10655 | 4536 | 127 |

EAST ST. LOUIS—St. Clair County

⊠ **KENNETH HALL REGIONAL HOSPITAL**, 129 North Eighth Street, Zip 62201–2999; tel. 618/274–1900 **A**1 9 10 **F**3 12 21 22 24 26 27 28 29 31 33 34 45 46 47 48 51 52 53 55 58 60 62 63 64 65 69 71 73 74 75 77 78 81 82 84 85 87 88 94 96 107 108
Primary Contact: Michael T. McManus, Chief Operating Officer
COO: Michael T. McManus, Chief Operating Officer
CFO: Ben Weber, Chief Financial Officer
CMO: Samuel Nwaobasi, M.D., President Medical Staff
CIO: Marlin Isaiah, Director Management Information Services
CHR: Kate Schwadron, Director Human Resources
| | 23 | 10 | 115 | 3066 | 43 | 47765 | 0 | 33077 | 14948 | 409 |

□ **TOUCHETTE REGIONAL HOSPITAL**, 5900 Bond Avenue, Zip 62207–2397; tel. 618/332–3060, (Nonreporting) **A**1 9 10
Primary Contact: Robert Klutts, Chief Executive Officer
Web address: www.touchette.org
| | 23 | 10 | 105 | — | — | — | — | — | — | — |

Many Facility Codes have changed. Please refer to the AHA Guide Code Chart.   © 2005 AHA Guide

Hospital, Address, Telephone, Approval, Facility, and Physician Codes, Health Care System	Classi-fication Codes		Utilization Data					Expense (thousands) of dollars		
★ American Hospital Association (AHA) membership □ Joint Commission on Accreditation of Healthcare Organizations (JCAHO) accreditation ○ American Osteopathic Association (AOA) accreditation △ Commission on Accreditation of Rehabilitation Facilities (CARF) accreditation	Control	Service	Staffed Beds	Admissions	Census	Outpatient Visits	Births	Total	Payroll	Personnel

EFFINGHAM—Effingham County

⊠ **ST. ANTHONY'S MEMORIAL HOSPITAL**, 503 North Maple Street, Zip 62401–2099; tel. 217/342–2121, (Total facility includes 13 beds in nursing home–type unit) **A**1 2 9 10 19 **F**9 11 12 22 26 27 28 33 46 48 51 52 53 55 59 62 63 64 69 79 81 82 85 87 88 92 94 96 108 110 **S** Hospital Sisters Health System, Springfield, IL
Primary Contact: Daniel J. Woods, Executive Vice President and Administrator
COO: Robert W. Esker, Assistant Administrator
CFO: Dave Storm, Director Business Support
Web address: www.stanthonyshospital.org
| 21 | 10 | 146 | 7447 | 82 | 166026 | 711 | 64357 | 24102 | 603 |

ELDORADO—Saline County

★ **FERRELL HOSPITAL**, 1201 Pine Street, Zip 62930–1634; tel. 618/273–3361 **A**9 10 18 **F**9 12 21 23 27 28 29 33 46 48 63 64 81 82 88 **S** Alliant Management Services, Louisville, KY
Primary Contact: William Hartley, FACHE, President and Chief Executive Officer
CFO: James Fraser, Chief Financial Officer
CHR: Beth Anderton, Director Human Resources
Web address: www.sih.net
| 23 | 10 | 25 | 1251 | 13 | 26888 | 0 | 9601 | 4447 | 132 |

ELGIN—Kane County

□ **ELGIN MENTAL HEALTH CENTER**, 750 South State Street, Zip 60123–7692; tel. 847/742–1040, (Nonreporting) **A**1 3 5 10
Primary Contact: Bruce E. Bonecutter, Ph.D., Executive Director
| 12 | 22 | 500 | — | — | — | — | — | — | — |

⊠ △ **PROVENA SAINT JOSEPH HOSPITAL**, 77 North Airlite Street, Zip 60123–4912; tel. 847/695–3200 **A**1 2 7 9 10 **F**4 9 10 11 12 14 15 17 19 21 22 23 27 28 29 30 31 33 34 36 38 41 42 44 45 46 47 48 49 50 51 52 53 54 55 57 58 59 60 61 62 63 64 66 69 70 71 72 73 74 75 76 77 78 79 80 81 82 84 85 86 88 93 94 96 98 106 108 109 110 **P**5 **S** Provena Health, Mokena, IL
Primary Contact: William A. Brown, CHE, President and Chief Executive Officer
COO: Darryl L. Duncan, Chief Operating Officer
CFO: Odin Berg, Vice President Finance and Chief Financial Officer
CMO: Charles Cavallo, M.D., Vice President Medical Affairs
CIO: Trevor O'Malley, Site Manager
CHR: Diane Hargreaves, Vice President Human Resources
Web address: www.provenahealth.com
| 23 | 10 | 174 | 8328 | 119 | 182707 | 914 | 106825 | 41433 | 808 |

⊠ **SHERMAN HOSPITAL**, 934 Center Street, Zip 60120–2198; tel. 847/742–9800 **A**1 2 9 10 **F**2 9 11 12 14 15 17 19 21 22 23 24 26 27 28 29 33 34 35 37 42 44 45 46 47 48 49 50 52 53 54 55 56 57 58 59 60 61 62 63 64 65 66 69 70 81 82 84 85 87 88 92 93 94 96 98 107 108 109 110 **P**1 5 7
Primary Contact: Richard B. Floyd, President and Chief Executive Officer
COO: Timothy Wadman, Executive Vice President and Chief Operating Officer
CFO: John Dennison, Vice President and Chief Financial Officer
CIO: Barbara Mills, Chief Information Officer
Web address: www.shermanhealthsystems.com
| 23 | 10 | 274 | 14364 | 160 | 146634 | 2527 | 182055 | 75716 | 1565 |

ELK GROVE VILLAGE—Cook County

⊠ **ALEXIAN BROTHERS MEDICAL CENTER**, 800 Biesterfield Road, Zip 60007–3397; tel. 847/437–5500, (Nonreporting) **A**1 2 5 9 10 **S** Alexian Brothers Health System, Arlington Heights, IL
Primary Contact: Roger Johnson, President and Chief Executive Officer
Web address: www.alexian.org
| 21 | 10 | 348 | — | — | — | — | — | — | — |

ELMHURST—Du Page County

⊠ **ELMHURST MEMORIAL HOSPITAL**, 200 Berteau Avenue, Zip 60126–2989; tel. 630/833–1400, (Total facility includes 38 beds in nursing home–type unit) **A**1 2 9 10 **F**4 11 12 15 17 19 21 22 23 26 27 28 29 33 34 36 37 38 41 42 44 46 47 48 49 50 51 52 53 55 57 58 59 60 61 62 63 65 66 69 70 71 72 73 74 75 76 77 78 79 80 81 82 84 86 87 88 92 93 94 95 96 108 109 110 **P**1 8
Primary Contact: Leo F. Fronza, Jr, President and Chief Executive Officer
CFO: James F. Doyle, Senior Vice President Finance
CMO: Fred M. Jacobs, JD, M.D., President Medical Staff
CIO: Frank Scafidi, Vice President Information Systems and Chief Information Officer
CHR: Jayson B. Strode, Vice President Human Resources
Web address: www.emhc.org
| 23 | 10 | 348 | 18975 | 245 | 347184 | 1966 | 231113 | 107456 | 2263 |

EUREKA—Woodford County

□ **EUREKA COMMUNITY HOSPITAL**, 101 South Major Street, Zip 61530, Mailing Address: P.O. Box 203, Zip 61530; tel. 309/467–2371, (Nonreporting) **A**1 9 10 18
| 21 | 10 | 25 | — | — | — | — | — | — | — |

IL

Hospital, Address, Telephone, Approval, Facility, and Physician Codes, Health Care System	Classi-fication Codes		Utilization Data					Expense (thousands) of dollars		
★ American Hospital Association (AHA) membership □ Joint Commission on Accreditation of Healthcare Organizations (JCAHO) accreditation ○ American Osteopathic Association (AOA) accreditation △ Commission on Accreditation of Rehabilitation Facilities (CARF) accreditation	Control	Service	Staffed Beds	Admissions	Census	Outpatient Visits	Births	Total	Payroll	Personnel

EVANSTON—Cook County

☒ **EVANSTON NORTHWESTERN HEALTHCARE**, 1301 Central Street, Zip 60201–1613; tel. 847/570–2000, (Includes EVANSTON HOSPITAL, 2650 Ridge Avenue, Zip 60201–1797; tel. 847/570–2000; GLENBROOK HOSPITAL, 2100 Pfingsten Road, Glenview, Zip 60025; tel. 847/657–5800; HIGHLAND PARK HOSPITAL, 718 Glenview Avenue, Highland Park, Zip 60035–2497; tel. 847/432–8000), (Total facility includes 54 beds in nursing home–type unit) **A**1 2 3 5 8 9 10 **F**1 2 3 4 5 7 9 10 11 12 14 15 17 19 21 22 23 24 26 27 28 29 30 31 32 33 34 35 36 37 38 39 41 42 43 44 46 47 48 49 50 51 52 53 55 56 57 58 59 60 61 62 63 64 65 66 67 68 69 70 71 72 73 74 75 76 77 78 79 80 81 82 83 84 85 86 87 88 89 90 92 93 94 95 96 97 98 99 106 107 108 109 110
Primary Contact: Mark R. Neaman, President and Chief Executive Officer
COO: Jeffrey H. Hillebrand, Chief Operating Officer
CFO: Thomas Hodges, Executive Vice President Finance and Treasurer
CIO: Thomas Smith, Chief Information Officer
Web address: www.enh.org
`23 10 645 35973 519 1837418 5184 727799 268438 5709`

□ **SAINT FRANCIS HOSPITAL**, 355 Ridge Avenue, Zip 60202–3399; tel. 847/316–4000 **A**1 2 3 5 9 10 **F**2 7 9 10 11 12 14 15 17 19 21 22 23 26 28 29 33 34 35 46 48 50 52 53 54 55 57 58 59 60 61 62 63 64 69 70 79 80 81 82 84 85 87 88 93 94 96 108 **P**5 8 **S** Resurrection Health Care Corporation, Chicago, IL
Primary Contact: Sherlyn Hailstone, Chief Executive Officer
Web address: www.reshealth.org
`21 10 236 10961 142 130634 1012 132120 47469 1083`

EVERGREEN PARK—Cook County

□ **LITTLE COMPANY OF MARY HOSPITAL AND HEALTH CARE CENTERS**, 2800 West 95th Street, Zip 60805–2795; tel. 708/422–6200 **A**1 2 5 9 10 **F**1 2 4 10 11 12 14 15 21 22 23 24 27 29 30 33 36 37 44 46 47 48 49 51 52 53 55 56 57 58 59 60 61 62 63 64 65 67 69 71 73 74 76 77 78 81 88 93 94 96 108 110 **P**3 8 **S** American Province of Little Company of Mary Sisters, Evergreen Park, IL
Primary Contact: Dennis A. Reilly, President and Chief Executive Officer
Web address: www.lcmh.org
`23 10 294 15682 210 207062 — 155485 71047 —`

FAIRFIELD—Wayne County

☒ **FAIRFIELD MEMORIAL HOSPITAL**, 303 N.W. 11th Street, Zip 62837–1203; tel. 618/842–2611, (Total facility includes 104 beds in nursing home–type unit) **A**1 9 10 18 **F**2 9 11 12 22 23 26 27 28 33 37 44 51 52 54 55 58 59 61 63 66 69 81 82 84 88 92 94 96 106 108 **S** Alliant Management Services, Louisville, KY
Primary Contact: Katherine Bunting, Chief Nurse Executive
COO: Stephen Dawkins, Chief Operating Officer
CFO: Michael J. Brown, Chief Financial Officer
CMO: Patrick Molt, M.D., President Medical Staff
Web address: www.fairfieldmemorial.org
`23 10 163 1279 118 31271 200 17743 7780 293`

FLORA—Clay County

☒ **CLAY COUNTY HOSPITAL**, 911 Stacy Burk Drive, Zip 62839–1823, Mailing Address: P.O. Box 280, Zip 62839–0280; tel. 618/662–2131 **A**1 9 10 **F**2 6 9 21 22 27 28 29 33 46 54 58 60 63 69 70 77 81 88 96 97 108 **S** BJC HealthCare, Saint Louis, MO
Primary Contact: Susan G. Batchelor, President
CFO: Mike Stoverink, Chief Financial Officer
CMO: Ashok Kumar, M.D., Chief of Staff
CHR: Jill VanHyning, Director Human Resources and Marketing
Web address: www.bjc.org
`13 10 24 1391 14 19404 0 13100 4649 120`

FOREST PARK—Cook County

☒ **RIVEREDGE HOSPITAL**, 8311 West Roosevelt Road, Zip 60130–2500; tel. 708/771–7000, (Nonreporting) **A**1 5 9 10 **S** Psychiatric Solutions, Franklin, TN
Primary Contact: Stephen J. Quigley, Chief Executive Officer
CFO: Jack Barzilai, Chief Financial Officer
CMO: David Bawden, Executive Medical Director
CIO: Tim Tacker, Director Information System
CHR: Ron Bryson, Director Human Resources
Web address: www.psysolutions.com
`33 22 210 — — — — — — —`

FREEPORT—Stephenson County

☒ **FHN MEMORIAL HOSPITAL**, 1045 West Stephenson Street, Zip 61032–4899; tel. 815/599–6000, (Total facility includes 43 beds in nursing home–type unit) **A**1 2 9 10 19 **F**2 9 10 11 12 14 15 21 22 23 24 26 27 28 31 33 34 36 37 38 40 43 46 47 48 50 51 52 53 54 57 58 59 60 61 62 63 64 65 66 69 70 72 73 74 75 76 77 79 81 82 83 84 85 86 88 92 93 94 95 96 106 107 108 110 **P**6 7 8
Primary Contact: Dennis L. Hamilton, Chief Executive Officer
CFO: Michael Clark, Vice President Finance
CMO: Robert D. Geller, M.D., Vice President Medical Affairs
CIO: Phil Wasson, Chief Information Officer
CHR: Len Carter, Vice President Human Resources
Web address: www.fhn.org
`23 10 189 5832 94 172879 561 77139 25186 535`

IL

Many Facility Codes have changed. Please refer to the AHA Guide Code Chart. © 2005 AHA Guide

Hospital, Address, Telephone, Approval, Facility, and Physician Codes, Health Care System	Classi-fication Codes		Utilization Data					Expense (thousands) of dollars		
	Control	Service	Staffed Beds	Admissions	Census	Outpatient Visits	Births	Total	Payroll	Personnel

★ American Hospital Association (AHA) membership
□ Joint Commission on Accreditation of Healthcare Organizations (JCAHO) accreditation
○ American Osteopathic Association (AOA) accreditation
△ Commission on Accreditation of Rehabilitation Facilities (CARF) accreditation

GALENA—Jo Daviess County

★ **GALENA–STAUSS HOSPITAL AND HEALTHCARE CENTER**, 215 Summit Street, Zip 61036–1697; tel. 815/777–1340, (Total facility includes 57 beds in nursing home–type unit) **A**9 10 18 **F**1 8 9 12 27 28 33 41 47 53 63 88 92 94 95 97 **P**7
Primary Contact: Jeff Hill, Chief Executive Officer
CFO: Tracy Kiley, Chief Financial Officer
CIO: Patricia Allvin, Information Specialist
CHR: Melissa Kaiser, Human Resources Director
Web address: www.galenahealth.org

	16	10	82	153	56	18726	0	7166	3502	150

GALESBURG—Knox County

□ **GALESBURG COTTAGE HOSPITAL**, 695 North Kellogg Street, Zip 61401–2885; tel. 309/343–8131, (Total facility includes 31 beds in nursing home–type unit) (Nonreporting) **A**1 10 19 **S** Community Health Systems, Inc., Brentwood, TN
Primary Contact: Steven D. Patonai, Chief Executive Officer
Web address: www.cottagehospital.com

	23	10	150	—	—	—	—	—	—	—

⊠ **OSF ST. MARY MEDICAL CENTER**, 3333 North Seminary Street, Zip 61401–1299; tel. 309/344–3161 **A**1 9 10 19 **F**2 9 11 12 14 15 21 22 23 26 27 28 29 30 33 34 37 38 39 41 46 48 52 55 58 59 60 61 62 63 64 65 69 70 81 82 88 93 94 95 96 106 108 109 110 **P**6 **S** OSF Healthcare System, Peoria, IL
Primary Contact: Richard S. Kowalski, Administrator and Chief Executive Officer
CFO: Curt Lipe, Chief Financial Officer
CMO: Brij B. Jamnadas, M.D., Medical Staff President
CIO: Tori Kennedy, Business Entity Management Information Systems Manager
CHR: Roxanna Crosser, Senior Assistant Administrator Staff Services
Web address: www.osfhealthcare.org

	21	10	99	5311	58	127694	375	52593	22891	365

GENESEO—Henry County

⊠ **HAMMOND–HENRY HOSPITAL**, 600 North College Avenue, Zip 61254–1099; tel. 309/944–4625, (Total facility includes 52 beds in nursing home–type unit) **A**1 9 10 18 **F**9 11 12 14 21 26 27 28 29 33 34 37 39 47 48 51 52 55 58 59 60 62 63 66 67 69 81 88 92 94 95 96 97 108 **S** Brim Healthcare, Inc., Brentwood, TN
Primary Contact: Bradley Solberg, FACHE, Chief Executive Officer
CFO: Bill Murdock, Vice President Fiscal Services
CIO: Heather Henry, Information Systems Manager
CHR: Margaret Chavez, Manager Human Resources
Web address: www.hammondhenry.com

	16	10	74	1083	51	41429	93	17340	7307	227

GENEVA—Kane County

⊠ **DELNOR–COMMUNITY HOSPITAL**, 300 Randall Road, Zip 60134–4200; tel. 630/208–3000 **A**1 2 9 10 **F**2 8 9 10 11 12 15 16 17 21 22 23 24 26 27 28 29 30 32 33 34 35 37 41 45 46 47 48 51 52 53 55 57 58 59 60 61 62 63 64 65 66 69 75 77 79 81 82 84 85 86 87 88 90 93 94 95 96 106 108 109 110
Primary Contact: Craig A. Livermore, President and Chief Executive Officer
Web address: www.delnor.com

	23	10	118	9238	96	174028	1529	124523	52455	1364

GIBSON CITY—Ford County

⊠ **GIBSON AREA HOSPITAL AND HEALTH SERVICES**, 1120 North Melvin Street, Zip 60936, Mailing Address: P.O. Box 429, Zip 60936–0429; tel. 217/784–4251, (Includes GIBSON COMMUNITY HOSPITAL NURSING HOME), (Total facility includes 42 beds in nursing home–type unit) **A**1 9 10 18 **F**6 9 11 12 23 26 27 28 29 33 34 36 41 44 46 48 51 52 53 54 55 58 59 62 63 69 81 82 84 85 87 88 92 95 96 97 108 109 110 **P**1 7 **S** Quorum Health Resources, Plano, TX
Primary Contact: Gary L. Petersen, Chief Executive Officer
CFO: Rob Schmitt, Chief Financial Officer
CHR: Ty Royal, Director Human Resources
Web address: www.gibsonhospital.org

	23	10	80	948	48	52525	120	23170	9651	283

GLENDALE HEIGHTS—Du Page County

⊠ **ADVENTIST GLENOAKS HOSPITAL**, (Formerly GlenOaks Hospital), 701 Winthrop Avenue, Zip 60139–1403; tel. 630/545–8000 **A**1 9 10 **F**2 9 11 12 14 15 21 22 23 24 26 27 28 29 31 33 34 37 46 48 50 52 53 55 56 57 58 59 61 62 63 64 65 66 69 70 71 72 73 74 75 76 77 78 81 82 87 88 93 94 95 96 98 108 109 110 **P**8 **S** Adventist Health System Sunbelt Health Care Corporation, Winter Park, FL
Primary Contact: Brinsley B. Lewis, Chief Executive Officer
COO: Scott Rowley, Executive Director for Operations
CFO: Karsten Randolph, Chief Financial Officer
CMO: Joseph Lagattuta, Assistant Director of Medical Affairs
CIO: Russell Soliman, Regional Director Information Services
CHR: Norman L. McBride, Regional Director Human Resources
Web address: www.keepingyouwell.com

	21	10	149	4602	72	35389	358	45932	20767	433

GLENVIEW—Cook County

GLENBROOK HOSPITAL See Evanston Northwestern Healthcare, Evanston

GREAT LAKES—Lake County

⊠ **NAVAL HOSPITAL**, 3001A Sixth Street, Zip 60088–5230; tel. 847/688–4560, (Nonreporting) **A**1 2 3 5 **S** Bureau of Medicine and Surgery, Department of the Navy, Washington, DC
Primary Contact: Captain Michael Anderson, Commanding Officer
Web address: www.greatlakes.med.navy.mil

	43	10	47	—	—	—	—	—	—	—

IL

Hospital, Address, Telephone, Approval, Facility, and Physician Codes, Health Care System	Classi-fication Codes		Utilization Data					Expense (thousands) of dollars		
★ American Hospital Association (AHA) membership ☐ Joint Commission on Accreditation of Healthcare Organizations (JCAHO) accreditation ◯ American Osteopathic Association (AOA) accreditation △ Commission on Accreditation of Rehabilitation Facilities (CARF) accreditation	Control	Service	Staffed Beds	Admissions	Census	Outpatient Visits	Births	Total	Payroll	Personnel

GREENVILLE—Bond County

☒ **GREENVILLE REGIONAL HOSPITAL**, (Formerly Edward A. Utlaut Memorial Hospital), 200 Health Care Drive, Zip 62246–1156; tel. 618/664–1230, (Includes FAIR OAKS), (Total facility includes 108 beds in nursing home–type unit) **A**1 9 10 **F**1 6 9 11 12 21 23 27 28 33 39 44 46 48 52 53 58 59 60 61 62 63 65 66 69 71 72 73 77 81 84 88 91 93 94 95 96 97 106 108
Primary Contact: James M. Hayes, President and Chief Executive Officer
CFO: Jerald Graber, Senior Manager Finance
Web address: www.greenvilleregionalhospital.com
`23 10 150 1940 114 38298 152 23115 9131 288`

HARRISBURG—Saline County

☒ **HARRISBURG MEDICAL CENTER**, 100 Hospital Drive, Zip 62946, Mailing Address: P.O. Box 428, Zip 62946–0428; tel. 618/253–7671 **A**1 9 10 **F**2 9 12 21 22 23 27 28 33 48 51 52 61 63 64 69 71 73 76 77 78 81 88 108
Primary Contact: Claude Chatterton, Administrator and Chief Executive Officer
CHR: Rodney Smith, Director Human Resources and Development
Web address: www.harrisburgmedicalcenter.com
`23 10 71 2853 40 41673 0 24631 12432 405`

HARVARD—McHenry County

☒ **MERCY HARVARD HOSPITAL**, 901 Grant Street, Zip 60033–1898, Mailing Address: P.O. Box 850, Zip 60033–0850; tel. 815/943–5431, (Total facility includes 26 beds in nursing home–type unit) **A**1 9 10 18 **F**10 12 21 22 26 27 28 29 33 34 41 45 46 48 54 55 57 58 60 62 63 64 69 81 82 88 92 93 94 96 **P**6
Primary Contact: Sue Ripsch, Chief Operating Officer
CFO: John Cook, Chief Financial Officer
Web address: www.harvardhospital.org
`23 10 46 835 32 17540 0 16162 7163 134`

HARVEY—Cook County

☒ △ **INGALLS MEMORIAL HOSPITAL**, One Ingalls Drive, Zip 60426–3591; tel. 708/333–2300 **A**1 2 7 9 10 **F**2 3 4 9 10 11 12 14 15 17 19 21 22 23 26 27 28 29 31 32 33 34 36 37 38 39 40 41 42 44 46 47 48 50 51 52 53 55 57 58 59 60 61 62 63 64 65 66 68 69 70 71 75 76 77 79 80 81 82 83 84 85 86 87 88 90 93 94 95 96 106 107 108 109 110 **P**8
Primary Contact: Kurt E. Johnson, President and Chief Executive Officer
COO: Mary Vidaurri, Ph.D., Senior Vice President and Chief Operating Officer
CFO: Vincent Pryor, Chief Financial Officer
CHR: Chris Hargreaves, Director Human Resources
Web address: www.ingalls.org
`23 10 407 19308 275 264905 1502 196901 91283 1895`

HAVANA—Mason County

☒ **MASON DISTRICT HOSPITAL**, 615 North Promenade Street, Zip 62644–0530, Mailing Address: P.O. Box 530, Zip 62644–0530; tel. 309/543–4431 **A**1 9 10 18 **F**2 6 9 12 21 22 26 27 28 29 33 35 39 45 46 47 48 51 52 54 55 58 60 63 64 65 69 70 81 82 84 85 87 88 94 97 106 107 108 **P**6
Primary Contact: Harry Wolin, Administrator and Chief Executive Officer
CFO: Robert J. Stolba, Chief Financial Officer
Web address: www.masondistricthospital.org
`16 10 25 511 4 22946 0 13311 6763 183`

HAZEL CREST—Cook County

☒ **ADVOCATE SOUTH SUBURBAN HOSPITAL**, 17800 South Kedzie Avenue, Zip 60429–0989; tel. 708/213–3000, (Total facility includes 46 beds in nursing home–type unit) **A**1 2 9 10 **F**2 9 11 12 15 16 17 18 21 22 26 27 28 29 30 33 37 39 45 46 48 52 53 55 58 59 60 61 63 64 69 81 82 84 86 87 88 92 93 94 108 109 **P**8 **S** Advocate Health Care, Oak Brook, IL
Primary Contact: Patricia A. Martin, President
CFO: Brian Kelly, Vice President Finance
CMO: Ajay Parikh, M.D., Medical Staff President
CIO: Beth Turek, Manager Information Systems
CHR: Aletha Ross, Vice President Human Resources
Web address: www.advocatehealth.com/ssub/
`23 10 245 13485 182 105907 1265 129435 51911 984`

HERRIN—Williamson County

☐ **HERRIN HOSPITAL**, 201 South 14th Street, Zip 62948–3631; tel. 618/942–2171 **A**1 9 10 **F**2 9 12 21 22 26 27 28 29 33 42 44 45 46 47 48 52 55 57 58 60 61 62 63 64 65 68 69 73 81 82 85 87 88 94 95 96 106 108 109 **S** Southern Illinois Hospital Services, Carbondale, IL
Primary Contact: Becky Ashton, Administrator
Web address: www.sih.net
`23 10 89 4302 69 68784 0 47365 17197 453`

HIGHLAND—Madison County

☒ **ST. JOSEPH'S HOSPITAL**, 1515 Main Street, Zip 62249–1656; tel. 618/654–7421, (Total facility includes 30 beds in nursing home–type unit) **A**1 9 10 18 **F**12 21 22 26 29 33 34 36 37 38 44 45 46 48 52 53 54 55 58 60 62 63 69 81 82 85 88 92 93 94 96 97 108 **S** Hospital Sisters Health System, Springfield, IL
Primary Contact: Claudio Fort, Executive Vice President and Administrator
CFO: James Johnson, Chief Financial Officer
CMO: A Greg Miranda, President Medical Staff
CHR: Michael Wagoner, Director Human Resources
Web address: www.stjosephs–highland.org
`21 10 55 1156 32 41397 0 17740 7223 193`

HIGHLAND PARK—Lake County

HIGHLAND PARK HOSPITAL See Evanston Northwestern Healthcare, Evanston

Many Facility Codes have changed. Please refer to the AHA Guide Code Chart. © 2005 AHA Guide

IL

Hospital, Address, Telephone, Approval, Facility, and Physician Codes, Health Care System	Classi-fication Codes		Utilization Data					Expense (thousands) of dollars		
	Control	Service	Staffed Beds	Admissions	Census	Outpatient Visits	Births	Total	Payroll	Personnel

★ American Hospital Association (AHA) membership
□ Joint Commission on Accreditation of Healthcare Organizations (JCAHO) accreditation
○ American Osteopathic Association (AOA) accreditation
△ Commission on Accreditation of Rehabilitation Facilities (CARF) accreditation

HILLSBORO—Montgomery County

⊠ **HILLSBORO AREA HOSPITAL**, 1200 East Tremont Street, Zip 62049–1900; tel. 217/532–6111, (Total facility includes 40 beds in nursing home–type unit) **A**1 9 10 18 **F**2 8 9 12 21 22 24 26 27 28 29 33 34 41 46 48 51 52 58 60 62 63 64 66 69 70 81 85 91 92 94 95 97 106 108 110 **P**6 **S** Brim Healthcare, Inc., Brentwood, TN
Primary Contact: Rex H. Brown, Chief Executive Officer
CFO: Terri L. Carroll, Vice President Financial Services
CHR: Sharon Clark, Director Human Resources
Web address: www.hillsboroareahospital.org

| 23 | 10 | 66 | 1260 | 35 | 29550 | 0 | 13466 | 5568 | 177 |

HINES—Cook County

□ **JOHN J. MADDEN MENTAL HEALTH CENTER**, 1200 South First Avenue, Zip 60141; tel. 708/338–7202, (Nonreporting) **A**1 10
Primary Contact: Ugo Formigoni, Metro–West Network Manager

| 12 | 22 | 165 | — | — | — | — | — | — | — |

⊠ △ **VETERANS AFFAIRS EDWARD HINES, JR. HOSPITAL**, Fifth Avenue and Roosevelt Road, Zip 60141–5000, Mailing Address: P.O. Box 5000, Zip 60141–5000; tel. 708/202–8387, (Total facility includes 199 beds in nursing home–type unit) **A**1 2 3 5 7 8 **F**1 2 3 4 5 6 7 8 9 12 14 15 17 19 21 22 23 27 28 29 30 31 32 33 35 36 37 38 39 41 42 43 44 45 46 47 48 49 50 51 52 53 55 57 58 60 61 62 63 64 65 66 68 69 70 71 73 74 75 76 77 78 79 80 81 82 83 84 85 87 88 89 90 92 93 94 96 106 107 108 109 110 **S** Department of Veterans Affairs, Washington, DC
Primary Contact: Jack G. Hetrick, Director
COO: Jack G. Hetrick, Associate Director
CFO: Raleigh Beard, Chief Fiscal Services
CMO: Barbara Temeck, M.D., Chief of Staff
CIO: Gordon Brown, Chief Information Resources Management
Web address: www.va.gov/sta/guide/home.asp

| 45 | 10 | 484 | 7379 | 196 | 511696 | 0 | 328607 | 158419 | 2632 |

HINSDALE—Du Page County

⊠ △ **HINSDALE HOSPITAL**, 120 North Oak Street, Zip 60521–3890; tel. 630/856–9000 **A**1 2 3 5 7 9 10 **F**2 4 9 10 11 12 14 15 17 19 21 22 23 26 27 28 29 31 33 34 35 36 37 42 43 44 46 47 48 50 51 52 53 55 56 57 58 59 61 62 63 64 65 66 67 68 69 70 71 72 74 75 76 77 78 79 80 81 82 84 85 87 88 89 90 93 94 95 96 99 104 105 106 108 109 110 **P**8 **S** Adventist Health System Sunbelt Health Care Corporation, Winter Park, FL
Primary Contact: Todd S. Werner, Chief Executive Officer
COO: Alan Schneider, Vice President Operations
CFO: Steve Chen, Chief Financial Officer
CMO: Robert Zeck, M.D., Regional Vice President and Chief Medical Officer
CIO: Russell Soliman, Regional Director Information Services
CHR: Norman L. McBride, Regional Director Human Resources
Web address: www.keepingyouwell.com

| 21 | 10 | 333 | 16868 | 199 | 247989 | 2760 | 228836 | 85902 | 2162 |

□ **R M L SPECIALTY HOSPITAL**, 5601 South County Line Road, Zip 60521–8900; tel. 630/286–4000 **A**1 9 10 **F**2 21 33 41 76 81 82 88 94 96 110 **P**6
Primary Contact: James R. Prister, President and Chief Executive Officer
Web address: www.rmlspecialtyhospital.org

| 23 | 10 | 90 | 617 | 61 | 24 | 0 | 30256 | 15874 | 312 |

HOFFMAN ESTATES—Cook County

□ **ALEXIAN BROTHERS BEHAVIORAL HEALTH HOSPITAL**, 1650 Moon Lake Boulevard, Zip 60194–5000; tel. 847/882–1600, (Nonreporting) **A**1 9 10 **S** Alexian Brothers Health System, Arlington Heights, IL
Primary Contact: Mark A. Frey, President and Chief Executive Officer
Web address: www.abbhh.net

| 21 | 22 | 94 | — | — | — | — | — | — | — |

⊠ **ST. ALEXIUS MEDICAL CENTER**, 1555 Barrington Road, Zip 60194–1018; tel. 847/843–2000 **A**1 2 9 10 **F**2 9 10 11 12 14 15 17 21 22 23 24 26 27 28 29 32 33 34 36 37 46 47 48 52 55 57 58 59 60 61 62 63 64 65 66 67 69 70 75 81 82 84 85 88 90 92 94 96 106 107 108 109 110 **S** Alexian Brothers Health System, Arlington Heights, IL
Primary Contact: Edward M. Goldberg, President and Chief Executive Officer
CFO: Robin Chopp, Vice President and Chief Financial Officer
CIO: James Christie, Chief Information Officer
CHR: Linda Baker, Director Human Resources
Web address: www.stalexius.org

| 21 | 10 | 211 | 13456 | 144 | 153296 | 2758 | 160173 | 68480 | 1047 |

HOOPESTON—Vermilion County

⊠ **HOOPESTON COMMUNITY MEMORIAL HOSPITAL**, 701 East Orange Street, Zip 60942–1871; tel. 217/283–5531, (Total facility includes 75 beds in nursing home–type unit) (Nonreporting) **A**1 9 10 18
Primary Contact: Michael L. Brown, Chief Executive Officer
CFO: Terry Paligo, Chief Financial Officer
Web address: www.hoopestonhospital.org

| 23 | 10 | 100 | — | — | — | — | — | — | — |

HOPEDALE—Tazewell County

HOPEDALE MEDICAL COMPLEX, 107 Tremont Street, Zip 61747; tel. 309/449–3321, (Total facility includes 52 beds in nursing home–type unit) (Nonreporting) **A**9 10 18
Primary Contact: Alfred N. Rossi, M.D., Chief Executive Officer
Web address: www.hopedalemedicalcomplex.com

| 23 | 10 | 77 | — | — | — | — | — | — | — |

IL

Hospital, Address, Telephone, Approval, Facility, and Physician Codes, Health Care System	Classi-fication Codes		Utilization Data					Expense (thousands) of dollars		
★ American Hospital Association (AHA) membership □ Joint Commission on Accreditation of Healthcare Organizations (JCAHO) accreditation ○ American Osteopathic Association (AOA) accreditation △ Commission on Accreditation of Rehabilitation Facilities (CARF) accreditation	Control	Service	Staffed Beds	Admissions	Census	Outpatient Visits	Births	Total	Payroll	Personnel

JACKSONVILLE—Morgan County

☒ **PASSAVANT AREA HOSPITAL**, 1600 West Walnut Street, Zip 62650–1136; tel. 217/245–9541, (Total facility includes 15 beds in nursing home–type unit) **A**1 2 9 10 19 20 **F**2 9 10 11 12 14 21 22 27 28 29 33 34 37 40 46 47 48 52 53 54 55 58 59 60 62 63 64 65 66 68 69 70 72 73 75 77 81 82 83 84 87 88 92 93 94 95 96 107 108 110
Primary Contact: Chester A. Wynn, President and Chief Executive Officer
COO: Nancy Spangenberg, Vice President and Chief Operating Officer
CFO: John Bury, Vice President and Chief Financial Officer
CMO: Richard Fox, M.D., Medical Staff President
CIO: Marc Steinberg, Vice President Community Relations and Physician Recruitment
CHR: Rick Mogler, Director Human Resources
Web address: www.passavanthospital.com
| 23 | 10 | 112 | 4368 | 53 | 81770 | 455 | 56023 | 22870 | 636 |

JERSEYVILLE—Jersey County

☒ **JERSEY COMMUNITY HOSPITAL**, 400 Maple Summit Road, Zip 62052–2028, Mailing Address: P.O. Box 426, Zip 62052–0426; tel. 618/498–6402 **A**1 9 10 **F**6 9 11 12 21 27 28 33 41 45 46 48 52 54 55 58 59 60 61 63 66 69 81 82 88 93 94 95 96 97 108 109 110
Primary Contact: Lawrence P. Bear, Administrator
COO: Lawrence P. Bear, Administrator
CFO: David Kennett, Chief Financial Officer
CIO: Bob Bray, Chief Information Officer
Web address: www.jch.org
| 16 | 10 | 67 | 2214 | 18 | 41767 | 157 | 21190 | 8515 | 260 |

JOLIET—Will County

☒ △ **PROVENA SAINT JOSEPH MEDICAL CENTER**, 333 North Madison Street, Zip 60435–6595; tel. 815/725–7133 **A**1 2 3 5 7 9 10 **F**2 4 6 9 10 11 12 14 15 16 17 18 19 20 21 22 23 24 26 27 28 29 30 31 32 33 34 35 37 38 39 41 42 44 45 46 47 48 49 50 52 53 55 56 57 58 59 60 61 62 63 65 66 67 68 69 70 71 72 73 74 75 76 77 78 79 80 81 82 83 84 85 86 87 88 92 93 94 95 96 98 106 108 109 110 **P**8 **S** Provena Health, Mokena, IL
Primary Contact: Jeffrey Brickman, President and Chief Executive Officer
COO: Michael O. Ugwueke, Vice President Operations
CFO: Linda J. Charley, Chief Financial Officer
CMO: Lon McPherson, M.D., Vice President Medical Affairs
CHR: John Omel, Interim Vice President Human Resources
Web address: www.provenasaintjoe.org
| 21 | 10 | 454 | 24304 | 292 | 409894 | 1768 | 226622 | 89290 | 1851 |

☒ △ **SILVER CROSS HOSPITAL**, 1200 Maple Road, Zip 60432–1497; tel. 815/740–1100 **A**1 2 7 9 10 **F**4 6 9 10 11 12 15 21 22 23 24 26 27 28 29 31 33 34 35 41 46 47 48 49 51 52 53 54 55 58 59 60 61 62 63 64 66 68 69 71 73 74 75 76 77 78 81 82 84 85 87 88 93 94 95 96 98 106 108 110 **P**1 5
Primary Contact: Paul Pawlak, President and Chief Executive Officer
COO: Greg Repetti, Executive Vice President Operations
CFO: William R. Brownlow, Senior Vice President Finance
CMO: Rafael Castro, M.D., Chief of Staff
CIO: Donald Bansemer, Vice President Information Systems
CHR: Mark Jepson, Associate Vice President
Web address: www.silvercross.org
| 23 | 10 | 231 | 15009 | 157 | 166608 | 1874 | 137676 | 52788 | 1001 |

KANKAKEE—Kankakee County

☒ **PROVENA ST. MARY'S HOSPITAL**, 500 West Court Street, Zip 60901–3661; tel. 815/937–2490, (Total facility includes 8 beds in nursing home–type unit) **A**1 2 9 10 **F**2 4 6 9 10 11 12 15 17 21 22 23 24 26 27 28 29 30 31 32 33 34 37 38 39 40 41 44 45 46 47 48 49 50 52 53 55 57 58 59 60 61 62 63 64 65 66 69 70 71 72 73 74 75 76 77 78 80 81 82 84 85 86 88 92 93 94 95 96 106 107 108 109 110 **P**7 **S** Provena Health, Mokena, IL
Primary Contact: George N. Miller, Jr, President and Chief Executive Officer
CFO: Charles M. Wilhelm, Vice President Financial Services and Chief Financial Officer
Web address: www.provena-stmarys.com
| 21 | 10 | 160 | 8691 | 104 | 211988 | 498 | 99074 | 34481 | 836 |

☒ △ **RIVERSIDE MEDICAL CENTER**, 350 North Wall Street, Zip 60901–0749; tel. 815/933–1671 **A**1 2 7 9 10 **F**1 2 3 4 5 6 7 8 9 10 11 12 14 15 17 19 21 22 23 24 26 27 28 29 30 31 32 33 34 35 36 37 38 39 40 41 42 44 45 46 47 48 49 50 51 52 53 54 55 57 58 59 60 61 62 63 64 65 66 68 69 70 71 72 73 74 75 76 77 78 79 80 81 82 84 85 86 87 88 89 90 91 92 93 94 95 96 98 106 107 108 109 110 **P**6 8
Primary Contact: Dennis C. Millirons, President and Chief Executive Officer
COO: Phillip Kambic, Senior Vice President and Chief Operating Officer
CFO: Bill Douglas, Chief Financial Officer
CMO: John Jurica, M.D., Vice President Medical Affairs
CIO: Jeffrey Pollock, Vice President Information Services and Chief Information Officer
CHR: Brent Mallek, Vice President Human Resources
Web address: www.riversidehealthcare.org
| 23 | 10 | 256 | 12191 | 169 | 277587 | 1053 | 160242 | 61410 | 1338 |

Many Facility Codes have changed. Please refer to the AHA Guide Code Chart. © 2005 AHA Guide

Hospital, Address, Telephone, Approval, Facility, and Physician Codes, Health Care System	Classi-fication Codes		Utilization Data					Expense (thousands) of dollars		
★ American Hospital Association (AHA) membership □ Joint Commission on Accreditation of Healthcare Organizations (JCAHO) accreditation ○ American Osteopathic Association (AOA) accreditation △ Commission on Accreditation of Rehabilitation Facilities (CARF) accreditation	Control	Service	Staffed Beds	Admissions	Census	Outpatient Visits	Births	Total	Payroll	Personnel

KEWANEE—Henry County

★ **KEWANEE HOSPITAL**, 719 Elliott Street, Zip 61443–2711, Mailing Address: P.O. Box 747, Zip 61443–0747; tel. 309/853–3361 **A**1 9 10 18 **F**9 11 12 14 21 23 24 26 27 28 29 31 33 36 37 39 41 43 46 47 48 51 52 58 59 60 61 63 64 66 69 81 82 88 93 94 95 96 97 108 109 110 **P**6
Primary Contact: Margaret Gustafson, Chief Executive Officer
COO: Lynn Fulton, Chief Operating Officer
CFO: John Riley, Chief Financial Officer
CIO: Rob Coombes, Network Administrator
CHR: Renee Salisbury, Executive Director Human Resources
Web address: www.kewaneehospital.com
 — 23 10 25 1817 18 44015 145 28191 13212 378

LA GRANGE—Cook County

★ **ADVENTIST LA GRANGE MEMORIAL HOSPITAL**, (Formerly La Grange Memorial Hospital), 5101 South Willow Spring Road, Zip 60525–2680; tel. 708/352–1200 **A**1 2 3 5 9 10 **F**2 7 10 11 12 14 15 17 19 21 22 23 24 26 27 28 29 32 33 34 35 37 44 46 47 48 50 52 53 55 57 58 59 61 62 63 64 65 66 69 70 73 79 80 81 82 84 85 87 88 93 94 95 96 108 109 110 **P**8
S Adventist Health System Sunbelt Health Care Corporation, Winter Park, FL
Primary Contact: Timothy W. Cook, Chief Executive Officer
COO: Edward Gervain, Chief Operating Officer
CFO: Paul Ziegele, Chief Financial Officer
CMO: Robert Zeck, M.D., Regional Vice President and Chief Medical Officer
CIO: Russ Solimon, Chief Information Officer
Web address: www.keepingyouwell.com/facilities/LaGrange.asp
 — 21 10 178 8965 108 135886 715 121822 46310 874

LAKE FOREST—Lake County

★ **LAKE FOREST HOSPITAL**, 660 North Westmoreland Road, Zip 60045–1696; tel. 847/234–5600, (Total facility includes 76 beds in nursing home–type unit) **A**1 2 9 10 **F**1 2 7 9 10 11 12 21 22 23 24 27 28 29 30 32 33 34 35 37 39 41 42 44 46 47 48 51 52 55 57 58 59 60 61 62 63 64 65 66 69 70 73 75 76 79 80 81 82 84 85 86 88 89 92 93 94 95 96 106 107 108 109 **P**8
Primary Contact: William G. Ries, President
CFO: James F. Wuellner, Vice President and Chief Financial Officer
Web address: www.lakeforesthospital.com
 — 23 10 205 7937 152 298681 2003 164742 73393 1228

LAWRENCEVILLE—Lawrence County

★ **LAWRENCE COUNTY MEMORIAL HOSPITAL**, 2200 West State Street, Zip 62439–1853; tel. 618/943–1000 **A**9 10 18 **F**2 6 9 12 14 22 27 33 45 55 58 63 69 71 76 81 94 96 97 108
Primary Contact: Sylvia Pulleyblank, Chief Executive Officer
CFO: Ed Cooper, Chief Financial Officer
CHR: Kim Kendall, Director Human Resources
 — 13 10 54 1026 13 25891 0 9024 3358 132

LIBERTYVILLE—Lake County

★ **CONDELL MEDICAL CENTER**, 801 South Milwaukee Avenue on Condell Drive, Zip 60048–3199; tel. 847/362–2900 **A**1 2 9 10 **F**1 2 9 10 11 12 14 15 17 19 21 22 23 24 25 26 27 28 29 33 34 36 37 41 42 44 45 46 47 48 49 50 51 52 53 55 56 57 58 59 60 61 62 63 64 65 66 67 69 79 80 81 82 84 85 86 87 88 93 94 95 96 107 108 109 110 **P**1 5
Primary Contact: Eugene Pritchard, President
COO: Eugene Pritchard, President
CFO: Van A. Hanover, Executive Vice President
CHR: Gwenn Leschke, Vice President Human Resources
Web address: www.condell.org
 — 23 10 215 16232 186 387809 2412 224517 92157 1696

LINCOLN—Logan County

★ **ABRAHAM LINCOLN MEMORIAL HOSPITAL**, 315 8th Street, Zip 62656–2698; tel. 217/732–2161 **A**1 5 9 10 18 **F**11 12 27 28 29 33 37 45 46 48 52 55 58 59 60 61 63 66 69 81 82 84 88 93 94 96 97 107 108 **P**5 **S** Memorial Health System, Springfield, IL
Primary Contact: Forrest G. Hester, President and Chief Executive Officer
COO: Kathleen Vipond, Assistant Administrator and Director
CFO: Andrew Costic, Regional Chief Financial Officer
CMO: Amir John Wahab, M.D., Medical Staff President
CHR: Holley Tygrett, Director Human Resources
Web address: www.almh.org
 — 23 10 25 1443 13 49222 255 20200 8896 245

LITCHFIELD—Montgomery County

★ **ST. FRANCIS HOSPITAL**, 1215 Franciscan Drive, Zip 62056–1799, Mailing Address: P.O. Box 1215, Zip 62056–1215; tel. 217/324–2191, (Total facility includes 35 beds in nursing home–type unit) **A**1 9 10 **F**9 10 11 12 21 22 26 33 35 36 37 38 39 44 46 47 48 51 52 53 55 57 58 59 60 61 62 63 64 65 66 69 81 84 87 88 92 93 94 95 96 106 108 110 **S** Hospital Sisters Health System, Springfield, IL
Primary Contact: Michael Sipkoski, Executive Vice President and Administrator
CFO: Diane Lindsay, Chief Financial Officer
Web address: www.stfrancis–litchfield.org
 — 21 10 85 2690 39 54416 366 28394 12086 328

IL

Hospital, Address, Telephone, Approval, Facility, and Physician Codes, Health Care System	Classi-fication Codes		Utilization Data					Expense (thousands) of dollars		
	Control	Service	Staffed Beds	Admissions	Census	Outpatient Visits	Births	Total	Payroll	Personnel

★ American Hospital Association (AHA) membership
□ Joint Commission on Accreditation of Healthcare Organizations (JCAHO) accreditation
○ American Osteopathic Association (AOA) accreditation
△ Commission on Accreditation of Rehabilitation Facilities (CARF) accreditation

MACOMB—McDonough County

⊠ **MCDONOUGH DISTRICT HOSPITAL**, 525 East Grant Street, Zip 61455–3318; tel. 309/833–4101, (Total facility includes 16 beds in nursing home–type unit) **A**1 2 9 10 20 **F**1 2 4 6 9 11 12 21 22 23 26 27 28 29 33 35 36 37 41 44 46 47 48 51 52 55 58 59 60 61 62 63 64 65 66 69 75 77 81 82 88 92 93 94 95 96 106 108 109 **P**8
Primary Contact: Stephen R. Hopper, President and Chief Executive Officer
COO: Lori Moon, Vice President of Clinical Operations
CFO: Craig Sheagren, Senior Vice President
CMO: Jerome Anderson, M.D., President Medical Staff
CIO: Harlan T. Baker, Director Information Systems
CHR: Sue Dexter, Administrative Director Human Resources
Web address: www.mdh.org

| | 16 | 10 | 91 | 4001 | 43 | 56320 | 342 | 38429 | 19045 | 460 |

MARION—Williamson County

□ **HEARTLAND REGIONAL MEDICAL CENTER**, 3333 West DeYoung, Zip 62959; tel. 618/998–7000, (Nonreporting) **A**1 9 10 **S** Community Health Systems, Inc., Brentwood, TN
Primary Contact: Timothy E. Schmidt, Chief Executive Officer
Web address: www.heartlandregional.com

| | 33 | 10 | 84 | — | | — | | — | — | — |

⊠ **VETERANS AFFAIRS MEDICAL CENTER**, 2401 West Main Street, Zip 62959–1194; tel. 618/997–5311, (Total facility includes 60 beds in nursing home–type unit) **A**1 **F**2 4 10 15 21 22 23 28 29 32 33 35 36 37 39 42 44 46 47 48 50 53 55 57 58 60 61 62 63 64 65 66 69 70 73 75 76 77 81 82 88 92 93 94 96 106 107 108 109 110 **S** Department of Veterans Affairs, Washington, DC
Primary Contact: Robert D. Morrel, Director
CFO: Wayne Morris, Chief Financial Officer
CMO: Joseph Herman, M.D., Chief of Staff
CIO: Thomas J. Ziglinski, Director Information Systems
CHR: Tonya Floyd, Manager Human Resources
Web address: www.va.gov/sta/guide/home.asp

| | 45 | 10 | 115 | 2867 | 93 | 353039 | 0 | 93728 | 55616 | 912 |

MARYVILLE—Madison County

⊠ **ANDERSON HOSPITAL**, 6800 State Route 162, Zip 62062–8500; tel. 618/288–5711 **A**1 9 10 **F**2 9 11 12 21 22 24 26 27 28 29 33 34 37 44 46 47 48 51 52 54 55 57 58 59 61 62 63 64 65 66 69 81 82 84 85 87 88 90 92 93 94 95 96 106 108 109
Primary Contact: Keith Allen Page, President and Chief Executive Officer
CFO: Michael Marshall, Vice President Finance and Chief Financial Officer
CMO: K Max Eakin, M.D., President Medical Staff
CIO: Michael Ward, Information Services Director
CHR: Neil Godar, Administrative Director Personnel
Web address: www.andersonhospital.org

| | 23 | 10 | 139 | 6255 | 64 | 116619 | 1521 | 71369 | 29780 | 742 |

MATTOON—Coles County

⊠ **SARAH BUSH LINCOLN HEALTH CENTER**, 1000 Health Center Drive, Zip 61938–0372, Mailing Address: P.O. Box 372, Zip 61938–0372; tel. 217/258–2525, (Total facility includes 13 beds in nursing home–type unit) **A**1 2 9 10 20 **F**1 2 9 11 12 15 21 22 23 26 27 28 29 30 33 34 35 36 37 39 44 46 47 48 50 51 52 53 54 55 57 58 59 60 61 62 63 64 65 66 69 70 71 73 74 75 76 77 78 81 82 84 85 87 88 92 93 94 95 96 106 108 109 110 **P**6
Primary Contact: Gary L. Barnett, President and Chief Executive Officer
COO: James M. Pierce, Vice President Operations
CFO: Dennis Pluard, Chief Financial Officer
CMO: Aldo Ruffolo, M.D., President Medical Staff
CIO: Mike DeLuca, Vice President Information Systems
CHR: Eric Benson, Vice President Human Resources
Web address: www.sarahbush.org

| | 23 | 10 | 132 | 8316 | 79 | 351454 | 896 | 113296 | 57520 | 1207 |

MAYWOOD—Cook County

□ **LOYOLA UNIVERSITY MEDICAL CENTER**, 2160 South First Avenue, Zip 60153–5585; tel. 708/216–9000 **A**1 2 3 5 8 9 10 **F**2 4 5 6 7 9 10 11 12 13 14 15 16 17 18 19 20 21 22 23 24 26 27 28 29 30 31 32 33 34 35 36 37 38 39 40 41 42 43 44 46 47 48 49 50 51 52 53 55 56 57 58 59 60 61 62 63 64 65 66 67 68 69 70 72 73 74 75 76 77 79 80 81 82 84 85 86 87 88 90 93 94 95 96 98 99 100 101 102 103 104 105 106 108 109 110 **P**3
Primary Contact: Anthony L. Barbato, M.D., President and Chief Executive Officer
Web address: www.lumc.edu

| | 23 | 10 | 505 | 26474 | 372 | 905955 | 1564 | 601764 | 257926 | 5070 |

MCHENRY—McHenry County

★ △ **CENTEGRA NORTHERN ILLINOIS MEDICAL CENTER**, 4201 Medical Center Drive, Zip 60050–9506; tel. 815/344–5000, (Nonreporting) **A**2 7 9 10 **S** Centegra Health System, Woodstock, IL
Primary Contact: Michael S. Eesley, President and Chief Executive Officer
CFO: Greg Pagliuzza, Senior Vice President and Chief Financial Officer
CIO: Barbara O'Donnell, Director Information Systems
CHR: Barbara Jo Johnson, Senior Vice President Human Resources
Web address: www.centegra.org

| | 23 | 10 | 168 | — | | — | | — | — | — |

MCLEANSBORO—Hamilton County

HAMILTON MEMORIAL HOSPITAL DISTRICT, 611 South Marshall Avenue, Zip 62859–0429; tel. 618/643–2361, (Total facility includes 60 beds in nursing home–type unit) **A**9 10 18 **F**9 21 27 33 34 46 51 52 63 69 81 82 88 92 94 97
Primary Contact: Randall W. Dauby, Chief Executive Officer
Web address: www.mcleansboro.com

| | 16 | 10 | 85 | 885 | 65 | 22528 | 0 | 8514 | 4302 | 174 |

Many Facility Codes have changed. Please refer to the AHA Guide Code Chart.

© 2005 AHA Guide

IL

Hospital, Address, Telephone, Approval, Facility, and Physician Codes, Health Care System	Classi-fication Codes		Utilization Data					Expense (thousands) of dollars		
★ American Hospital Association (AHA) membership □ Joint Commission on Accreditation of Healthcare Organizations (JCAHO) accreditation ○ American Osteopathic Association (AOA) accreditation △ Commission on Accreditation of Rehabilitation Facilities (CARF) accreditation	Control	Service	Staffed Beds	Admissions	Census	Outpatient Visits	Births	Total	Payroll	Personnel

MELROSE PARK—Cook County

☒ **GOTTLIEB MEMORIAL HOSPITAL**, 701 West North Avenue, Zip 60160–1692; tel. 708/681–3200, (Total facility includes 34 beds in nursing home–type unit) **A**1 9 10 **F**1 2 7 8 9 11 12 15 17 19 21 22 23 26 27 28 29 31 33 34 35 36 37 38 39 44 45 46 47 48 50 51 52 53 55 56 57 58 59 60 61 62 63 64 65 66 69 81 82 84 85 87 88 92 93 94 95 96 108 109 110 **P**8
Primary Contact: John Morgan, President
CFO: Andrew Knauf, Vice President Finance
CMO: Raul Villasuso, M.D., Medical Staff President
CIO: Maurita Adler, Director Information Services
CHR: Brett Wakefield, Vice President Human Resources
Web address: www.gottliebhospital.org

| | 23 | 10 | 251 | 8504 | 126 | 156409 | 644 | 109993 | 49030 | 1023 |

○ △ **WESTLAKE HOSPITAL**, 1225 Lake Street, Zip 60160–4000; tel. 708/681–3000 **A**3 5 7 9 10 11 12 **F**2 9 10 11 12 14 15 17 19 21 22 23 26 27 28 29 33 37 39 41 42 44 46 47 48 49 52 53 55 57 58 59 60 62 63 64 65 66 68 69 70 71 73 74 75 76 81 86 88 93 94 96 98 108 109 110 **P**5 6 **S** Resurrection Health Care Corporation, Chicago, IL
Primary Contact: Patricia Shehorn, Chief Executive Officer
Web address: www.reshealth.org

| | 21 | 10 | 180 | 8489 | 115 | 22648 | 1360 | 88241 | 33276 | 797 |

MENDOTA—La Salle County

☒ **MENDOTA COMMUNITY HOSPITAL**, 1315 Memorial Drive, Zip 61342–1496; tel. 815/539–7461 **A**1 9 10 18 **F**2 9 12 21 23 26 27 28 29 33 48 51 52 54 55 58 60 63 64 65 66 69 81 85 93 94 96 97 108
Primary Contact: Susan Urso, Administrator
CFO: Larry Peach, Assistant Administrator and Chief Financial Officer
CHR: Lynn E. Klein, Director Human Resources
Web address: www.mendotahospital.org

| | 23 | 10 | 25 | 1183 | 14 | 44135 | 0 | 19398 | 8869 | 196 |

METROPOLIS—Massac County

☒ **MASSAC MEMORIAL HOSPITAL**, 28 Chick Street, Zip 62960, Mailing Address: P.O. Box 850, Zip 62960–0850; tel. 618/524–2176 **A**1 9 10 18 **F**2 6 9 21 28 33 46 48 55 60 63 69 81 82 88 97
Primary Contact: Jeffrey L. Durham, Chief Executive Officer
CFO: Chelle Keplinger, Chief Financial Officer
CHR: Donna Block, Director Human Resources
Web address: www.massacmemorialhospital.com

| | 16 | 10 | 25 | 840 | 9 | 21858 | 0 | 11946 | 4962 | 153 |

MOLINE—Rock Island County

TRINITY MEDICAL CENTER–EAST See Trinity Medical Center–West, Rock Island

MONMOUTH—Warren County

COMMUNITY MEDICAL CENTER AT WESTERN ILLINOIS, 1000 West Harlem Avenue, Zip 61462–1099; tel. 309/734–3141, (Total facility includes 45 beds in nursing home–type unit) **A**9 10 18 **F**9 12 21 22 24 26 27 28 29 30 33 37 39 44 46 47 48 51 52 58 60 62 63 65 66 69 70 81 82 85 87 88 92 94 95 96 97 106 107 108 109 110 **P**6
Primary Contact: Donald G. Brown, Chief Executive Officer
Web address: www.cmchospital.com

| | 23 | 10 | 68 | 894 | 48 | 50212 | 0 | 16510 | 7631 | 222 |

MONTICELLO—Piatt County

☒ **JOHN AND MARY KIRBY HOSPITAL**, 1111 North State Street, Zip 61856–1116; tel. 217/762–2115, (Nonreporting) **A**1 9 10 18
Primary Contact: Steve Tenhouse, Chief Executive Officer
CMO: James E. Manint, M.D., President, Medical Stafff
CIO: Rocky Winterbottom, Chief Information Officer
Web address: www.kirbyhospital.org

| | 23 | 10 | 16 | — | — | — | — | — | — | — |

MORRIS—Grundy County

☒ **MORRIS HOSPITAL & HEALTHCARE CENTERS**, (Formerly Morris Hospital), 150 West High Street, Zip 60450–1497; tel. 815/942–2932 **A**1 2 9 10 **F**2 9 11 12 15 21 23 26 27 28 33 34 39 42 45 46 47 48 52 54 55 57 58 59 60 61 62 63 65 69 75 79 81 82 84 87 88 94 96 97 106 108 110
Primary Contact: Clifford L. Corbett, President and Chief Executive Officer
COO: Brian Jepson, Chief Operating Officer
CFO: Tom Meyer, Vice President Finance
Web address: www.morrishospital.org

| | 23 | 10 | 83 | 4757 | 43 | 112420 | 543 | 65699 | 28784 | 540 |

MORRISON—Whiteside County

★ **MORRISON COMMUNITY HOSPITAL**, 303 North Jackson Street, Zip 61270–3042; tel. 815/772–4003, (Total facility includes 38 beds in nursing home–type unit) **A**9 10 18 **F**1 6 12 22 33 46 48 52 63 69 81 88 92 94 97 107 **S** Trinity Health, Novi, MI
Primary Contact: Terry L. Amstutz, CHE, Administrator
CFO: Amy Kophamer, Chief Financial Officer
CMO: Charles Buckley, M.D., Chief of Staff
CIO: Amy Kophamer, Chief Financial Officer
CHR: Pam Pfister, Director Human Resources

| | 16 | 10 | 63 | 286 | 40 | 11899 | 0 | 5237 | 2523 | 96 |

MOUNT CARMEL—Wabash County

☒ **WABASH GENERAL HOSPITAL DISTRICT**, 1418 College Drive, Zip 62863–2638; tel. 618/262–8621, (Nonreporting) **A**1 9 10 18 **S** Alliant Management Services, Louisville, KY
Primary Contact: Jay Purvis, Administrator
CFO: Steve McGill, Chief Financial Officer
Web address: www.wabashgeneral.com

| | 16 | 10 | 25 | — | — | — | — | — | — | — |

Hospital, Address, Telephone, Approval, Facility, and Physician Codes, Health Care System	Classi-fication Codes		Utilization Data					Expense (thousands) of dollars		
★ American Hospital Association (AHA) membership □ Joint Commission on Accreditation of Healthcare Organizations (JCAHO) accreditation ○ American Osteopathic Association (AOA) accreditation △ Commission on Accreditation of Rehabilitation Facilities (CARF) accreditation	Control	Service	Staffed Beds	Admissions	Census	Outpatient Visits	Births	Total	Payroll	Personnel

MOUNT VERNON—Jefferson County

□ **CROSSROADS COMMUNITY HOSPITAL**, 8 Doctors Park Road, Zip 62864–6224; tel. 618/244–5500 **A**1 9 10 **F**2 9 12 21 22 24 28 29 33 37 39 40 41 46 48 51 52 55 58 60 62 63 64 69 81 82 84 88 93 94 96 97 106 108 110 **P**7 **S** Community Health Systems, Inc., Brentwood, TN
Primary Contact: Gregory F. Sims, Chief Executive Officer
Web address: www.crossroadscommunityhospital.com

| | 33 | 10 | 41 | 1711 | 17 | 29177 | 0 | 18664 | 8065 | 178 |

⊠ **GOOD SAMARITAN REGIONAL HEALTH CENTER**, 605 North 12th Street, Zip 62864–2899; tel. 618/242–4600 **A**1 2 9 10 19 **F**9 11 12 15 16 17 18 19 20 21 22 26 27 28 29 31 32 33 35 36 37 38 39 42 46 47 48 50 51 52 53 55 57 58 59 60 61 62 63 65 66 68 69 81 82 84 87 88 93 94 96 106 108 109 110 **P**8 **S** SSM Health Care, Saint Louis, MO
Primary Contact: Leo F. Childers, Jr, FACHE, President
COO: Wayne Grote, Vice President Administrative Services
CFO: Kay Tinsley, Vice President Fiscal Services
CMO: Daniel Hoffman, M.D., Administrative Medical Director
CIO: Mark Clark, Director Networks
CHR: Jana Mayfield, Vice President Human Resources
Web address: www.smgsi.com

| | 21 | 10 | 149 | 7296 | 90 | 100161 | 682 | 88928 | 32815 | 977 |

MURPHYSBORO—Jackson County

★ **ST. JOSEPH MEMORIAL HOSPITAL**, 2 South Hospital Drive, Zip 62966–3333; tel. 618/684–3156 **A**9 10 18 **F**2 9 12 21 22 26 27 28 29 33 36 44 46 47 48 52 58 60 61 62 63 65 81 85 88 93 94 96 97 106 108 109 **S** Southern Illinois Hospital Services, Carbondale, IL
Primary Contact: Stephen Pautler, FACHE, Administrator
CFO: Rex P. Budde, Senior Vice President and Chief Financial Officer
CMO: Mattie Chamnes, M.D., Medical Staff President
CIO: Frank Sears, Vice President Information Services
Web address: www.sih.net

| | 23 | 10 | 25 | 1570 | 17 | 23890 | 0 | 18079 | 7676 | 191 |

NAPERVILLE—Du Page County

⊠ **EDWARD HOSPITAL**, 801 South Washington Street, Zip 60540–7499; tel. 630/527–3000 **A**1 2 9 10 **F**2 10 11 12 14 15 17 19 21 22 23 24 26 27 28 29 31 33 34 42 46 47 48 50 51 52 53 55 56 57 58 59 60 61 62 63 64 65 66 69 70 75 79 80 81 83 84 85 86 88 93 94 95 96 106 107 108 109 110 **P**7 8
Primary Contact: Pamela Meyer Davis, President and Chief Executive Officer
COO: Trish Anen, Vice President, Operations
CFO: William Devoney, Senior Vice President and Chief Financial Officer
CMO: Alan Kaplan, M.D., Vice President and Chief Medical Officer
CIO: Gary Mielak, Chief Technology Officer
CHR: Maggie Shontz, Vice President Human Resources
Web address: www.edward.org

| | 23 | 10 | 236 | 19653 | 215 | 414605 | 4098 | 290147 | 104581 | 2058 |

⊠ **LINDEN OAKS HOSPITAL AT EDWARD**, 852 West Street, Zip 60540–6400; tel. 630/305–5500 **A**1 9 10 **F**4 21 22 26 27 28 29 31 44 52 53 58 66 71 72 73 74 76 77 78 94 96 98
Primary Contact: Mary Lou Mastro, Chief Executive Officer
CFO: Gina Sharp, Controller
CMO: Barry Rabin, M.D., Medical Director
CIO: Hugh Siddiqui, System Specialist
CHR: Maggie Shontz, Vice President Human Resources
Web address: www.edward.org

| | 31 | 22 | 110 | 2367 | 43 | 21735 | 0 | 18075 | 9880 | 222 |

NASHVILLE—Washington County

⊠ **WASHINGTON COUNTY HOSPITAL**, 705 South Grand Avenue, Zip 62263–1534; tel. 618/327–8236, (Total facility includes 33 beds in nursing home–type unit) (Nonreporting) **A**1 9 10 18
Primary Contact: Nancy M. Newby, Ph.D., President and Chief Executive Officer
CIO: Kim Larkin, Chief Information Officer

| | 16 | 10 | 58 | — | — | — | — | — | — | — |

NORMAL—McLean County

⊠ **BROMENN HEALTHCARE SYSTEM**, Virginia and Franklin Streets, Zip 61761, Mailing Address: P.O. Box 2850, Bloomington, Zip 61702–2850; tel. 309/454–1400, (Includes BROMENN REGIONAL MEDICAL CENTER, tel. 309/454–1400) **A**1 2 9 10 12 13 **F**1 2 3 9 11 12 14 15 17 19 21 22 23 24 26 27 28 29 31 32 33 34 35 36 39 41 44 45 46 47 48 51 52 53 55 57 58 59 60 61 62 63 64 65 66 68 69 71 73 74 75 76 78 81 82 83 84 85 87 88 92 94 95 96 97 98 106 108 109 **P**6 7 8
Primary Contact: Roger S. Hunt, Chief Executive Officer
CFO: Penny Cermak, Vice President and Chief Financial Officer
CMO: Gary Hagens, Vice President Medical Affairs
CIO: Kathleen Davis, Vice President and Chief Information Officer
CHR: Alex Horvath, Vice President Human Resources
Web address: www.bromenn.org

| | 21 | 10 | 233 | 9772 | 112 | 207147 | 1536 | 128291 | 49906 | 1473 |

IL

Many Facility Codes have changed. Please refer to the AHA Guide Code Chart. © 2005 AHA Guide

Hospital, Address, Telephone, Approval, Facility, and Physician Codes, Health Care System	Classi-fication Codes		Utilization Data					Expense (thousands) of dollars		
★ American Hospital Association (AHA) membership □ Joint Commission on Accreditation of Healthcare Organizations (JCAHO) accreditation ○ American Osteopathic Association (AOA) accreditation △ Commission on Accreditation of Rehabilitation Facilities (CARF) accreditation	Control	Service	Staffed Beds	Admissions	Census	Outpatient Visits	Births	Total	Payroll	Personnel

NORTH CHICAGO—Lake County

☒ **VETERANS AFFAIRS MEDICAL CENTER**, 3001 Green Bay Road, Zip 60064–3049; tel. 847/688–1900, (Total facility includes 204 beds in nursing home–type unit) **A**1 3 5 8 **F**1 2 3 4 5 9 12 21 22 26 27 28 29 31 32 33 36 37 38 39 41 42 45 46 47 48 50 51 52 53 55 57 58 60 62 63 65 66 68 69 70 71 73 74 75 76 77 78 81 82 84 87 88 92 94 96 106 107 108 109 110 **P**6 **S** Department of Veterans Affairs, Washington, DC
Primary Contact: Patrick L. Sullivan, Director
COO: Marianne Semrad, Associate Director for Administrative Services
CFO: Dave Barton, Leader Business Office
CIO: Bradford P. Nystrom, Chief Informatics Program
Web address: www.va.gov/sta/guide/home.asp
| | 45 | 10 | 520 | 3957 | 416 | 211933 | 0 | 127006 | 70605 | 1142 |

NORTHLAKE—Cook County

□ **KINDRED HOSPITAL–CHICAGO NORTHLAKE**, 365 East North Avenue, Zip 60164–2628; tel. 708/345–8100, (Nonreporting) **A**1 10 **S** Kindred Healthcare, Louisville, KY
Primary Contact: Michele Dionne, Chief Executive Officer
Web address: www.kindredhealthcare.com
| | 33 | 10 | 86 | — | — | — | — | — | — | — |

OAK FOREST—Cook County

☒ △ **OAK FOREST HOSPITAL OF COOK COUNTY**, 15900 South Cicero Avenue, Zip 60452–4006; tel. 708/687–7200, (Total facility includes 340 beds in nursing home–type unit) **A**1 3 5 7 10 **F**2 21 22 23 30 32 33 35 37 38 44 45 50 52 53 54 55 57 60 61 62 63 66 68 69 70 73 81 82 85 88 92 94 96 107 108 110 **P**6 **S** Cook County Bureau of Health Services, Chicago, IL
Primary Contact: Sylvia Edwards, Acting Chief Operating Officer
CFO: Walena Valencia, Chief Financial Officer
CMO: Joseph R. Durham, M.D., Medical Director
CIO: Jet Boulware, Director Information and Technology Services
CHR: Lori Jordan, Director Human Resources Services
Web address: www.cookcountygov.com
| | 13 | 10 | 450 | 3881 | 395 | 83264 | 0 | 169665 | 83521 | 1487 |

OAK LAWN—Cook County

☒ △ **ADVOCATE CHRIST MEDICAL CENTER**, 4440 West 95th Street, Zip 60453–2699; tel. 708/684–8000, (Includes ADVOCATE HOPE CHILDREN'S HOSPITAL) **A**1 2 3 5 7 8 9 10 12 **F**2 9 11 12 14 15 16 17 18 19 20 21 22 23 24 26 27 28 29 31 32 33 34 37 39 42 45 46 47 48 49 52 53 54 55 56 57 58 59 60 61 62 63 64 65 66 67 68 69 70 71 72 73 76 77 78 79 80 81 82 83 84 85 87 88 89 90 93 94 95 96 106 108 109 110 **P**8 **S** Advocate Health Care, Oak Brook, IL
Primary Contact: Jonathan R. Bruss, Interim President
CFO: Robert Pekofske, Vice President Finance
CMO: Robert Stein, M.D., Vice President, Medical Management
CIO: Brian Banbury, Information Technology Site Manager
Web address: www.advocatehealth.com/christ
| | 21 | 10 | 649 | 38517 | 564 | 334670 | 3827 | 540817 | 208899 | 3810 |

OAK PARK—Cook County

☒ △ **RUSH OAK PARK HOSPITAL**, 520 South Maple Avenue, Zip 60304–1097; tel. 708/383–9300, (Total facility includes 47 beds in nursing home–type unit) **A**1 2 5 7 9 10 **F**1 2 12 15 19 21 22 23 27 28 29 33 36 37 38 39 44 45 46 47 48 49 52 53 55 57 58 60 61 62 63 64 65 66 68 69 70 81 82 84 85 87 88 92 94 108 110 **P**5 8 **S** Wheaton Franciscan Services, Inc., Wheaton, IL
Primary Contact: Bruce M. Elegant, President and Chief Executive Officer
CFO: Deborah Wilberding, Controller
CMO: Michael R. Silver, M.D., Vice President Medical Affairs
CIO: Sharaz Khan, Director
Web address: www.oakparkhospital.org
| | 21 | 10 | 176 | 4402 | 71 | 93881 | 0 | 69308 | 34379 | 708 |

□ **WEST SUBURBAN MEDICAL CENTER**, (Formerly West Suburban Hospital Medical Center), 3 Erie Court, Zip 60302–2599; tel. 708/383–6200, (Total facility includes 50 beds in nursing home–type unit) (Nonreporting) **A**1 2 3 5 9 10 12 13 **S** Resurrection Health Care Corporation, Chicago, IL
Primary Contact: Jay E. Kreuzer, FACHE, President and Chief Executive Officer
Web address: www.westsub.com
| | 23 | 10 | 246 | — | — | — | — | — | — | — |

OLNEY—Richland County

☒ **RICHLAND MEMORIAL HOSPITAL**, 800 East Locust Street, Zip 62450–2553; tel. 618/395–2131, (Total facility includes 20 beds in nursing home–type unit) **A**1 2 9 10 **F**6 9 11 12 21 23 26 27 28 32 33 36 45 46 47 48 50 51 52 53 54 55 58 59 60 61 62 63 69 70 71 73 75 77 78 81 82 84 88 92 94 95 96 97 106 108
Primary Contact: Harvey H. Pettry, FACHE, President and Chief Executive Officer
CFO: Nicholas LaFace, Executive Director Fiscal and Support Services
CIO: Dan Krager, Information Systems Manager
CHR: Cathy Snyder, Director Human Resources
Web address: www.richlandmemorial.com
| | 23 | 10 | 112 | 3329 | 56 | 70538 | 317 | 26764 | 12405 | 379 |

IL

Hospital, Address, Telephone, Approval, Facility, and Physician Codes, Health Care System	Classi-fication Codes		Utilization Data					Expense (thousands) of dollars		
★ American Hospital Association (AHA) membership □ Joint Commission on Accreditation of Healthcare Organizations (JCAHO) accreditation ○ American Osteopathic Association (AOA) accreditation △ Commission on Accreditation of Rehabilitation Facilities (CARF) accreditation	Control	Service	Staffed Beds	Admissions	Census	Outpatient Visits	Births	Total	Payroll	Personnel

OLYMPIA FIELDS—Cook County

○ **ST. JAMES HOSPITALS AND HEALTH CENTERS**, 20201 South Crawford Avenue, Zip 60461–1080; tel. 708/747–4000, (Includes ST. JAMES HOSPITAL AND HEALTH CENTERS – CHICAGO HEIGHTS CAMPUS, 1423 Chicago Road, Chicago Heights, Zip 60411–3483; tel. 708/756–1000; Peter J. Murphy, President and Chief Executive Officer; ST. JAMES HOSPITALS AND HEALTH CENTERS – OLYMPIA FIELDS CAMPUS, 20201 South Crawford Avenue, tel. 708/747–4000; Peter J. Murphy, President and Chief Executive Officer), (Nonreporting) **A**2 9 10 11 12 13 **S** Sisters of St. Francis Health Services, Inc., Mishawaka, IN
Primary Contact: Peter J. Murphy, President and Chief Executive Officer
Web address: www.stjameshhc.org
— 23 10 494 — — — — — — — —

OTTAWA—La Salle County

⊞ **COMMUNITY HOSPITAL OF OTTAWA**, 1100 East Norris Drive, Zip 61350–1687; tel. 815/433–3100 **A**1 9 10 19 **F**1 2 9 11 12 22 23 27 29 30 31 33 36 37 38 40 41 44 45 46 47 48 51 53 54 55 57 58 59 60 62 63 65 66 69 71 72 73 74 75 76 77 78 81 82 88 94 95 96 106 108 110 **P**8
Primary Contact: Robert A. Chaffin, President and Chief Executive Officer
CMO: Eric T. Ortinau, M.D., Medical Staff President
CIO: John Maynard, Information Systems Director
CHR: Robert Gibson, Senior Director Operating Services
Web address: www.chottawa.org
23 10 113 4355 40 162577 344 47111 20837 489

PALOS HEIGHTS—Cook County

⊞ **PALOS COMMUNITY HOSPITAL**, 12251 South 80th Avenue, Zip 60463–0930; tel. 708/923–4000 **A**1 2 9 10 **F**2 3 4 11 12 14 21 22 23 24 28 29 30 31 33 36 42 44 46 48 50 51 52 54 55 57 58 59 61 62 63 64 66 69 71 72 73 75 76 77 78 81 82 87 88 94 96 106 107 108 110
Primary Contact: Sister Margaret Wright, President
CFO: Andrew Stefo, Senior Vice President and Chief Financial Officer
CIO: Peggy Carroll, Chief Information Officer
Web address: www.paloshospital.org
23 10 357 21361 242 427906 2012 248821 123491 2086

PANA—Christian County

⊞ **PANA COMMUNITY HOSPITAL**, 101 East Ninth Street, Zip 62557–1785; tel. 217/562–2131 **A**1 9 10 18 **F**9 12 22 23 26 27 28 29 33 36 47 48 50 51 54 55 58 61 63 65 66 69 81 94 95 97 110
Primary Contact: Roland R. Carlson, Chief Executive Officer
CFO: Trina Casner, Chief Financial Officer
Web address: www.panahospital.com
23 10 25 717 6 29739 0 10237 4355 114

PARIS—Edgar County

⊞ **PARIS COMMUNITY HOSPITAL**, 721 East Court Street, Zip 61944–2420; tel. 217/465–4141 **A**1 9 10 18 **F**2 12 21 22 23 27 29 33 37 46 48 52 54 57 58 60 61 63 64 68 69 81 82 88 92 94 95 96 97 106 108 110 **P**6 **S** Alliant Management Services, Louisville, KY
Primary Contact: John D. Fajt, FACHE, President and Chief Executive Officer
CFO: Terry Brinkley, Vice President Finance
CIO: Gary Taylor, Manager Information Services
CHR: Ollie Smith, Vice President Human Resources
Web address: www.pariscommunityhospital.com
23 10 25 693 14 80128 0 18962 9111 176

PARK RIDGE—Cook County

⊞ △ **ADVOCATE LUTHERAN GENERAL HOSPITAL**, 1775 Dempster Street, Zip 60068–1174; tel. 847/723–2210 **A**1 2 3 5 7 8 9 10 **F**1 2 3 4 5 9 10 11 12 14 15 16 17 18 19 20 21 22 23 24 25 26 27 28 29 30 31 32 33 34 35 36 37 38 39 40 41 42 44 45 46 47 48 49 50 52 53 54 55 56 57 58 59 60 61 62 63 64 65 66 67 68 69 70 71 72 73 74 75 76 77 78 79 80 81 82 84 85 86 87 88 90 93 94 95 96 98 99 106 107 108 109 110 **P**6 7 8 **S** Advocate Health Care, Oak Brook, IL
Primary Contact: Bruce C. Campbell, President
COO: Julie W. Schaffner, R.N., Chief Operating Officer and Chief Nurse Executive
CFO: Susan Nibbe, Vice President Finance
CMO: James McCoy, M.D., Chief Medical Officer
CHR: Penny Pilarczyk, Vice President, Human Resources
Web address: www.advocatehealth.com
23 10 569 29804 409 302214 4028 440280 173231 3796

PEKIN—Tazewell County

⊞ **PEKIN HOSPITAL**, 600 South 13th Street, Zip 61554–5098; tel. 309/347–1151, (Total facility includes 27 beds in nursing home–type unit) **A**1 9 10 **F**2 9 11 12 15 21 22 23 26 27 28 29 33 41 46 47 48 51 53 55 57 58 59 62 63 64 65 66 73 75 81 82 85 88 92 94 96 106 107 108 109 110 **P**1 3 **S** Quorum Health Resources, Plano, TX
Primary Contact: Douglas Wilson, Chief Executive Officer
CFO: Stephen Schmidt, CPA, Chief Financial Officer
CIO: Joe Berry, Chief Information Officer
Web address: www.pekinhospital.org
23 10 107 4396 49 99312 388 49156 20261 541

Many Facility Codes have changed. Please refer to the AHA Guide Code Chart. © 2005 AHA Guide

Hospital, Address, Telephone, Approval, Facility, and Physician Codes, Health Care System	Classi-fication Codes		Utilization Data					Expense (thousands) of dollars		
	Control	Service	Staffed Beds	Admissions	Census	Outpatient Visits	Births	Total	Payroll	Personnel

★ American Hospital Association (AHA) membership
□ Joint Commission on Accreditation of Healthcare Organizations (JCAHO) accreditation
○ American Osteopathic Association (AOA) accreditation
△ Commission on Accreditation of Rehabilitation Facilities (CARF) accreditation

PEORIA—Peoria County

⊠ △ **METHODIST MEDICAL CENTER OF ILLINOIS**, 221 N.E. Glen Oak Avenue, Zip 61636–4310; tel. 309/672–5522, (Total facility includes 24 beds in nursing home–type unit) **A**1 2 3 5 6 7 10 **F**2 9 10 11 12 14 15 17 19 21 22 23 24 28 29 31 33 34 35 36 37 38 39 41 42 44 45 46 47 48 49 51 52 53 55 57 58 59 60 61 62 63 64 65 66 68 69 71 72 73 74 75 76 77 78 79 81 82 84 85 86 87 88 92 93 94 96 98 99 106 107 108 109 110 **P**8
Primary Contact: W. Michael Bryant, President and Chief Executive Officer
COO: Debbie Simon, Senior Vice President Operations and Chief Nursing Officer
CFO: Calvin R. MacKay, Chief Financial Officer
CMO: Fred Hosler, M.D., Senior Vice President for Medical Affairs
CHR: Dallis Howard, Senior Vice President Human Resources
Web address: www.mmci.org | 23 | 10 | 312 | 16266 | 240 | 418536 | 1779 | 251382 | 99509 | 2152 |

⊠ △ **OSF SAINT FRANCIS MEDICAL CENTER**, 530 N.E. Glen Oak Avenue, Zip 61637–0001; tel. 309/655–2000, (Nonreporting) **A**1 2 3 5 7 8 9 10 **S** OSF Healthcare System, Peoria, IL
Primary Contact: Keith E. Steffen, Administrator and Chief Executive Officer
COO: Susan C. Wozniak, R.N., Chief Operating Officer
CFO: Ken Harbaugh, Chief Financial Officer
CMO: Tim C. Miller, M.D., Director Medical Affairs
CHR: Lynn Gillespie, Assistant Administrator
Web address: www.osfsaintfrancis.org | 21 | 10 | 523 | — | — | — | — | — | — | — |

□ **PROCTOR HOSPITAL**, 5409 North Knoxville Avenue, Zip 61614–5094; tel. 309/691–1000, (Total facility includes 20 beds in nursing home–type unit) **A**1 9 10 **F**2 3 4 9 11 12 15 17 19 21 26 27 28 33 41 46 47 48 51 52 54 55 57 58 59 62 63 64 65 66 69 81 82 84 87 88 92 93 94 106 108 110
Primary Contact: Norman H. LaConte, President and Chief Executive Officer
Web address: www.proctor.org | 23 | 10 | 163 | 7121 | 102 | 168320 | 586 | 77442 | 29305 | 873 |

PERU—La Salle County

⊠ **ILLINOIS VALLEY COMMUNITY HOSPITAL**, 925 West Street, Zip 61354–2757; tel. 815/223–3300 **A**1 9 10 **F**2 9 11 12 21 22 23 26 27 28 31 33 37 40 44 45 46 47 48 52 53 54 55 56 57 58 59 60 61 62 63 64 65 66 69 71 72 73 74 75 76 81 82 84 88 93 94 95 96 97 106 108 109 110 **P**8
Primary Contact: Steven A. Hayes, Administrator
CMO: Robert Wojcik, M.D., Chief of Staff and Medical Staff President
CIO: Jeff Wilson, Data Processing Manager
CHR: John Moss, Assistant Administrator Human Resources
Web address: www.ivch.org | 23 | 10 | 92 | 4706 | 50 | 125115 | 573 | 44862 | 17974 | 504 |

PINCKNEYVILLE—Perry County

★ **PINCKNEYVILLE COMMUNITY HOSPITAL**, 101 North Walnut Street, Zip 62274–1099; tel. 618/357–2187, (Total facility includes 50 beds in nursing home–type unit) **A**9 10 18 **F**12 21 22 23 27 28 33 36 39 41 46 51 61 63 69 70 81 82 88 92 94 97 110 **P**6
Primary Contact: Thomas J. Hudgins, FACHE, Administrator and Chief Executive Officer
CFO: Kara Jo Carson, Chief Financial Officer
CIO: Kara Jo Carson, Chief Financial Officer | 16 | 10 | 75 | 1181 | 56 | 50929 | 0 | 16413 | 7491 | 236 |

PITTSFIELD—Pike County

★ ○ **ILLINI COMMUNITY HOSPITAL**, 640 West Washington Street, Zip 62363–1397; tel. 217/285–2113 **A**9 10 11 12 18 **F**2 12 14 22 26 27 28 33 37 41 44 46 47 48 52 53 54 55 58 60 62 63 64 65 66 69 81 88 94 97 104 108
Primary Contact: Connie L. Schroeder, Chief Executive Officer
CFO: Sandra Purcell, Administrator Director Finance
CMO: James Grote, M.D., Medical Staff President
Web address: www.illinihospital.org | 23 | 10 | 25 | 883 | 10 | 6355 | 0 | 11548 | 4949 | 131 |

PONTIAC—Livingston County

⊠ **OSF SAINT JAMES – JOHN W. ALBRECHT MEDICAL CENTER**, 2500 West Reynolds, Zip 61764–2194; tel. 815/842–2828 **A**1 9 10 20 **F**2 9 11 12 21 22 24 26 27 28 29 30 33 37 39 44 46 47 48 52 53 54 55 58 59 60 62 63 64 65 66 69 70 81 84 85 86 87 88 94 95 96 97 106 108 109 **P**7 **S** OSF Healthcare System, Peoria, IL
Primary Contact: David T. Ochs, Administrator
CFO: Paula Corrigan, Assistant Administrator Information and Financial Services
CMO: William H. Marshall, M.D., Corporate Director Medical Services
Web address: www.osfsaintjames.org | 21 | 10 | 42 | 1995 | 21 | 75862 | 292 | 32065 | 12970 | 322 |

PRINCETON—Bureau County

PERRY MEMORIAL HOSPITAL, 530 Park Avenue East, Zip 61356–2598; tel. 815/875–2811, (Total facility includes 10 beds in nursing home–type unit) **A**9 10 18 **F**2 9 11 12 21 22 23 26 27 28 29 30 33 34 37 39 44 46 47 48 52 53 54 55 58 59 60 61 62 63 64 65 66 69 81 82 84 85 88 92 93 94 95 96 97 106 108 109 110 **P**8
Primary Contact: Robert G. Senneff, CHE, President and Chief Executive Officer
Web address: www.perry–memorial.org | 14 | 10 | 59 | 1933 | 20 | 54392 | 155 | 23582 | 11078 | 272 |

IL

Hospital, Address, Telephone, Approval, Facility, and Physician Codes, Health Care System	Classi-fication Codes		Utilization Data					Expense (thousands) of dollars		
★ American Hospital Association (AHA) membership □ Joint Commission on Accreditation of Healthcare Organizations (JCAHO) accreditation ○ American Osteopathic Association (AOA) accreditation △ Commission on Accreditation of Rehabilitation Facilities (CARF) accreditation	Control	Service	Staffed Beds	Admissions	Census	Outpatient Visits	Births	Total	Payroll	Personnel

QUINCY—Adams County

★ △ **BLESSING HOSPITAL**, Broadway at 11th Street, Zip 62305–7005, Mailing Address: P.O. Box 7005, Zip 62305–7005; tel. 217/223–1200, (Includes BLESSING HOSPITAL, Broadway & 14th Street), (Total facility includes 20 beds in nursing home–type unit) **A**1 2 3 5 7 9 10 12 13 19 20 **F**2 4 9 11 12 14 15 17 19 21 22 23 24 26 27 28 29 33 34 35 36 37 39 41 44 46 47 48 49 50 51 52 53 55 57 58 59 60 61 62 63 64 65 66 68 69 71 72 73 74 75 76 77 78 79 80 81 82 84 85 86 87 88 92 93 94 95 96 106 108 109 110 **P**8
Primary Contact: Maureen A. Kahn, President and Chief Executive Officer
CFO: Patrick M. Gerveler, Vice President Finance and Chief Financial Officer
CIO: Ed Tharp, Administrative Director Information Systems
CHR: Zigrida Brown, Vice President Human Resources
Web address: www.blessinghospital.org
| 23 | 10 | 319 | 13304 | 196 | 242716 | 1129 | 149408 | 64777 | 1759 |

RED BUD—Randolph County

□ **RED BUD REGIONAL HOSPITAL**, 325 Spring Street, Zip 62278–1194; tel. 618/282–3831, (Total facility includes 155 beds in nursing home–type unit) (Nonreporting) **A**1 9 10 **S** Community Health Systems, Inc., Brentwood, TN
Primary Contact: Robert J. Moore, FACHE, Chief Executive Officer
Web address: www.redbudhospital.com
| 21 | 10 | 190 | — | — | — | — | — | — | — |

ROBINSON—Crawford County

★ **CRAWFORD MEMORIAL HOSPITAL**, 1000 North Allen Street, Zip 62454–1167; tel. 618/546–1234, (Total facility includes 39 beds in nursing home–type unit) **A**1 9 10 18 **F**2 9 11 12 21 22 23 27 28 33 41 48 51 59 60 61 62 63 64 69 81 88 92 94 97 108 **P**6 **S** Quorum Health Resources, Plano, TX
Primary Contact: Randy Simmons, Chief Executive Officer
CFO: Richard Carlson, Chief Financial Officer
CIO: Debbie Smith, Medical Records and Information Systems Director
Web address: www.crawfordmh.com
| 16 | 10 | 64 | 1454 | 47 | 31149 | 143 | 19637 | 8661 | 244 |

ROCHELLE—Ogle County

★ **ROCHELLE COMMUNITY HOSPITAL**, 900 North Second Street, Zip 61068–0330; tel. 815/562–2181 **A**1 9 10 18 **F**2 12 21 22 23 26 27 28 29 30 33 37 41 46 47 48 51 52 55 60 61 62 63 64 65 66 69 70 81 82 84 88 93 94 96 97 106 107 108 **P**6
Primary Contact: Gregg Olson, Chief Executive Officer
CFO: Tim Eckert, Vice President Finance and Chief Operations Officer
CMO: Pitamber Persaud, M.D., Chief Medical Staff
CIO: Scott Stewart, Director Management Information Systems
CHR: Robert Johns, Director Human Resources
Web address: www.rcha.net
| 23 | 10 | 54 | 947 | 9 | 45068 | 0 | 16674 | 6594 | 183 |

ROCK ISLAND—Rock Island County

★ △ **TRINITY MEDICAL CENTER–WEST**, 2701 17th Street, Zip 61201–5393; tel. 309/779–5000, (Includes TRINITY MEDICAL CENTER–EAST, 500 John Deere Road, Moline, Zip 61265; tel. 309/779–5000), (Total facility includes 29 beds in nursing home–type unit) **A**1 2 7 10 **F**2 4 9 10 11 12 15 17 19 20 21 22 23 26 27 28 29 30 31 33 34 37 42 44 45 46 48 49 50 52 53 55 57 58 59 61 62 63 64 65 66 68 69 70 71 72 73 74 75 76 77 78 79 80 81 82 84 85 88 89 90 92 93 94 96 98 106 108 109 **P**6 **S** Iowa Health System, Des Moines, IA
Primary Contact: William B. Leaver, President and Chief Executive Officer
CFO: Kevin Vermeer, Chief Financial Officer
CMO: Mark Valliere, M.D., Vice President Medical Affairs and Chief Medical Officer
Web address: www.trinityqc.com
| 23 | 10 | 327 | 18940 | 226 | 212525 | 1438 | 180771 | 73185 | 1636 |

ROCKFORD—Winnebago County

□ **H. DOUGLAS SINGER MENTAL HEALTH AND DEVELOPMENTAL CENTER**, 4402 North Main Street, Zip 61103–1278; tel. 815/987–7096, (Nonreporting) **A**1 10
Primary Contact: Gail Tennant, Director
| 12 | 22 | 162 | — | — | — | — | — | — | — |

★ **OSF SAINT ANTHONY MEDICAL CENTER**, 5666 East State Street, Zip 61108–2472; tel. 815/226–2000 **A**1 2 5 9 10 **F**2 9 11 12 13 14 15 17 19 21 22 23 26 27 28 29 33 34 35 37 38 39 41 46 47 48 52 53 55 57 58 59 60 61 62 63 64 65 66 69 79 81 82 84 87 88 93 94 95 96 106 108 109 110 **P**6 **S** OSF Healthcare System, Peoria, IL
Primary Contact: David A. Schertz, Administrator
CFO: Karen Krug, Chief Financial Officer
CMO: Robert White, M.D., Assistant Administrator Medical Affairs
CIO: Mary Madden, Director Information Services
CHR: Karen C. Brown, Assistant Director for Strategic Human Resources
Web address: www.osfhealthcare.org
| 21 | 10 | 238 | 12457 | 155 | 178218 | 870 | 194518 | 78973 | 1606 |

★ **ROCKFORD MEMORIAL HOSPITAL**, 2400 North Rockton Avenue, Zip 61103–3692; tel. 815/971–5000 **A**1 2 5 10 13 **F**2 3 4 9 10 11 14 15 16 17 18 19 21 22 23 24 26 27 28 29 31 32 33 34 35 36 37 38 39 41 43 46 47 48 49 50 52 53 55 56 57 58 59 60 61 62 63 64 65 66 67 69 70 71 72 73 74 75 76 77 78 79 80 81 82 84 85 87 88 90 93 94 96 106 108 109 110 **P**6
Primary Contact: Gary E. Kaatz, President and Chief Executive Officer
COO: Earl J. Tamar, Chief Operating Officer
CFO: Sue Petru, Vice President Finance and Chief Financial Officer
CMO: Milton G. Schmitt, Jr, M.D., Chief Medical Officer
CIO: Dennis P. L'Heureux, Chief Information Officer
CHR: Dan Parod, Vice President Human Resources
Web address: www.rhsnet.org
| 23 | 10 | 317 | 14928 | 209 | 291315 | 1988 | 256227 | 114538 | 2097 |

IL

Hospital, Address, Telephone, Approval, Facility, and Physician Codes, Health Care System	Classi-fication Codes		Utilization Data					Expense (thousands) of dollars		
★ American Hospital Association (AHA) membership □ Joint Commission on Accreditation of Healthcare Organizations (JCAHO) accreditation ○ American Osteopathic Association (AOA) accreditation △ Commission on Accreditation of Rehabilitation Facilities (CARF) accreditation	Control	Service	Staffed Beds	Admissions	Census	Outpatient Visits	Births	Total	Payroll	Personnel
⊞ SWEDISHAMERICAN HOSPITAL, 1401 East State Street, Zip 61104–2315; tel. 815/968–4400 A1 2 3 5 9 10 F2 11 12 14 15 17 19 21 22 23 24 26 27 28 29 30 31 32 33 34 35 37 38 39 44 46 47 48 50 52 53 54 55 56 57 58 59 61 62 63 64 65 66 69 71 72 73 74 75 76 78 80 81 82 84 85 86 87 88 92 93 94 96 106 108 109 110 P6 7 Primary Contact: Richard Walsh, President COO: Richard Walsh, President CFO: Don Haring, Vice President Finance and Treasurer CMO: Kathleen Kelly, M.D., Chief Medical Officer and Chief Quality Officer CIO: Don Jepsen, Director Information Systems CHR: Tom Koelbl, Vice President Human Resources Web address: www.swedishamerican.org	23	10	264	14958	180	183239	2032	180103	71283	1607
⊞ △ VAN MATRE HEALTHSOUTH REHABILITATION HOSPITAL, 950 South Mulford Road, Zip 61108; tel. 815/381–8500 A1 7 10 F7 21 26 27 28 53 62 65 68 69 94 96 110 S HEALTHSOUTH Corporation, Birmingham, AL Primary Contact: Daniel B. Woloszyn, Administrator Web address: www.healthsouth.com	32	46	40	1016	35	8168	0	9894	5058	105
ROSICLARE—Hardin County										
★ HARDIN COUNTY GENERAL HOSPITAL, Ferrell Road, Zip 62982; tel. 618/285–6634 A9 10 18 20 F2 12 27 28 33 46 52 60 63 69 81 82 84 88 93 94 97 Primary Contact: Roby D. Williams, Administrator CFO: Janie E. Parker, Director Fiscal Services CMO: M N. Sunga, M.D., Chief of Staff CHR: Joyce Shelby, Personnel Manager	23	10	25	671	6	19341	0	5218	2405	99
RUSHVILLE—Schuyler County										
★ SARAH D. CULBERTSON MEMORIAL HOSPITAL, 238 South Congress Street, Zip 62681–1472; tel. 217/322–4321, (Total facility includes 30 beds in nursing home–type unit) A9 10 18 20 F9 12 26 28 33 48 54 61 63 81 85 88 91 92 97 Primary Contact: D. David Sniff, Administrator CFO: Jerry Bartlett, Chief Financial Officer CMO: Marshall Robert, M.D., Medical Staff President Web address: www.cmhospital.com	16	10	55	779	29	21284	105	11481	4663	148
SALEM—Marion County										
⊞ SALEM TOWNSHIP HOSPITAL, 1201 Ricker Drive, Zip 62881–6250; tel. 618/548–3194 A1 9 10 18 F2 9 12 21 26 27 28 33 46 48 51 52 55 63 64 81 82 85 88 93 96 97 Primary Contact: Richelle Rennegarbe, Ph.D., President COO: Stephanie Hilton–Siebert, Chief Operating Officer CFO: Teresa Fuhrhop, Chief Financial Officer CIO: Sheri Schultz, Director Health Information CHR: Diane Boswell, Director Human Resources and Marketing Web address: www.salemtownhosp.org	15	10	31	1013	13	38668	0	13363	4978	175
SANDWICH—De Kalb County										
⊞ VALLEY WEST COMMUNITY HOSPITAL, 11 East Pleasant Avenue, Zip 60548–0901; tel. 815/786–8484 A1 9 10 18 F2 9 10 11 12 21 22 23 26 27 28 29 33 36 37 46 48 52 53 54 55 58 59 60 61 62 63 65 66 69 70 81 84 87 88 106 108 109 S Kishwaukee Health System, De Kalb, IL Primary Contact: Brad Copple, Administrator COO: Michael Muzzillo, Assistant Administrator CFO: Loren Foelske, Vice President Finance CMO: James Hawkins, M.D., D.O., Chief of Staff CHR: Mark Thate, Director Human Resources Web address: www.vwch.org	23	10	25	1408	10	24261	147	20914	5814	158
SCOTT AFB—St. Clair County										
⊞ SCOTT MEDICAL CENTER, 310 West Losey Street, Zip 62225–5252; tel. 618/256–7000 A1 3 5 F2 6 12 21 22 25 26 28 32 33 37 41 42 46 47 48 52 53 55 57 58 60 62 63 65 66 69 70 75 77 81 84 88 94 95 108 S Department of the Air Force, Washington, DC Primary Contact: Colonel Steven H. Regner, Administrator COO: Colonel Steven H. Regner, Administrator CFO: Captain Carmia Sykes, Resource Management Flight Commander CMO: Colonel James H. Heriot, Chief Medical Staff CIO: Karen Dial, Chief Systems Officer Web address: www.satx.disa.mil/mtf375/	41	10	25	1560	9	191118	0	—	—	498
SHELBYVILLE—Shelby County										
⊞ SHELBY MEMORIAL HOSPITAL, 200 South Cedar Street, Zip 62565–1899; tel. 217/774–3961, (Total facility includes 15 beds in nursing home–type unit) A1 9 10 F2 12 26 27 28 33 51 61 63 69 81 82 84 87 88 92 97 P5 Primary Contact: John Bennett, President and Chief Executive Officer CFO: Marilyn Sears, Chief Financial Officer CMO: Jack M. Levine, M.D., President Medical Staff CHR: Amy Koehler, Director Human Resources	23	10	45	1790	28	27579	0	13108	4803	166

IL

Hospital, Address, Telephone, Approval, Facility, and Physician Codes, Health Care System	Classi-fication Codes		Utilization Data						Expense (thousands) of dollars		
★ American Hospital Association (AHA) membership □ Joint Commission on Accreditation of Healthcare Organizations (JCAHO) accreditation ○ American Osteopathic Association (AOA) accreditation △ Commission on Accreditation of Rehabilitation Facilities (CARF) accreditation	Control	Service	Staffed Beds	Admissions	Census	Outpatient Visits	Births	Total	Payroll	Personnel

SILVIS—Rock Island County

☒ **GENESIS MEDICAL CENTER, ILLINI CAMPUS**, (Formerly Illini Hospital), 801 Illini Drive, Zip 61282–1893; tel. 309/792–9363 **A**1 9 10 **F**2 6 8 9 11 12 15 16 17 18 21 22 23 24 26 27 28 29 33 34 35 37 39 40 41 42 44 45 46 48 49 52 53 55 57 58 59 61 62 63 65 66 69 70 81 82 85 87 88 91 92 93 94 95 96 97 98 107 108 109 110 **S** Genesis Health System, Davenport, IA
Primary Contact: Charles E. Bruhn, Chief Executive Officer
CFO: Harold C. Holder, Vice President Financial Services
CMO: Sameena Ahmed, M.D., Medical Staff President
CIO: Robert Frieden, Vice President Information Systems
Web address: www.genesishealth.com
— Control 23, Service 10, Staffed Beds 110, Admissions 5194, Census 47, Outpatient Visits 84694, Births 842, Total 54630, Payroll 19358, Personnel 462

SKOKIE—Cook County

☒ **RUSH NORTH SHORE MEDICAL CENTER**, 9600 Gross Point Road, Zip 60076–1257; tel. 847/677–9600 **A**1 2 3 5 9 10 **F**2 11 12 15 17 19 21 22 23 26 27 28 29 31 32 33 34 35 37 39 44 46 47 48 52 53 54 55 57 58 59 60 61 62 63 64 65 66 69 71 73 74 75 76 79 80 82 85 87 88 89 90 94 95 96 108 109 110 **P**1 **S** Rush University Medical Center, Chicago, IL
Primary Contact: James T. Frankenbach, President and Chief Executive Officer
COO: Anthony Di Lorenzo, Vice President Operations
CFO: Jeffrey Rooney, Vice President Finance
CMO: Steven Sholl, President Medical Staff
CIO: Barbara O'Connell, Director Information Systems
CHR: Richard J. Casey, Assistant Vice President Operations
Web address: www.rnsmc.org
— Control 23, Service 10, Staffed Beds 239, Admissions 10237, Census 147, Outpatient Visits 80776, Births 493, Total 137129, Payroll 60305, Personnel 1190

SPARTA—Randolph County

☒ **SPARTA COMMUNITY HOSPITAL**, 818 East Broadway Street, Zip 62286–0297, Mailing Address: P.O. Box 297, Zip 62286–0297; tel. 618/443–2177 **A**1 9 10 **F**2 9 11 12 22 26 27 29 33 37 41 45 48 51 53 59 60 63 69 81 88 94 97 108 **P**5
Primary Contact: Joann Emge, Chief Executive Officer
COO: Joann Emge, Chief Executive Officer
CFO: Steve Bricker, Chief Financial Officer
CMO: Shawn Beckemeyer, M.D., Chief Medical Staff
CIO: Susan Gutjahr, Reimbursement Specialist
CHR: Debbie Pickering, Executive Assistant Human Resources
Web address: www.spartahospital.com
— Control 16, Service 10, Staffed Beds 39, Admissions 1126, Census 10, Outpatient Visits 37395, Births 179, Total 16721, Payroll 8779, Personnel 237

SPRING VALLEY—Bureau County

ST. MARGARET'S HOSPITAL, 600 East First Street, Zip 61362–2034; tel. 815/664–5311, (Total facility includes 33 beds in nursing home–type unit) (Nonreporting) **A**9 10 **S** Sisters of Mary of the Presentation Health System, Fargo, ND
Primary Contact: Tim Muntz, President and Chief Executive Officer
Web address: www.st-margarets.com
— Control 21, Service 10, Staffed Beds 93, Admissions —, Census —, Outpatient Visits —, Births —, Total —, Payroll —, Personnel —

SPRINGFIELD—Sangamon County

□ **ANDREW MCFARLAND MENTAL HEALTH CENTER**, 901 Southwind Road, Zip 62703–5195; tel. 217/786–6994 **A**1 5 10 **F**27 28 71 **P**5
Primary Contact: Karen Thurmand, Administrator
— Control 12, Service 22, Staffed Beds 122, Admissions 851, Census 103, Outpatient Visits 0, Births 0, Total 20293, Payroll 11481, Personnel 204

☒ △ **MEMORIAL MEDICAL CENTER**, 701 North First Street, Zip 62781–0001; tel. 217/788–3000 **A**1 2 3 5 7 8 9 10 **F**2 9 10 11 12 13 14 15 17 19 21 22 23 26 27 28 29 30 33 34 35 36 37 38 39 40 42 46 47 48 49 50 52 53 54 55 57 58 59 60 61 62 63 64 65 66 68 69 70 71 72 73 74 75 76 78 79 81 82 84 85 86 87 88 93 94 95 96 101 104 105 106 107 108 109 110 **P**3 5 7 **S** Memorial Health System, Springfield, IL
Primary Contact: Robert T. Clarke, President and Chief Executive Officer
COO: Edgar J. Curtis, R.N., Executive Vice President and Chief Operating Officer
CFO: Robert W. Kay, Senior Vice President and Chief Financial Officer
CMO: Robert Vautrain, M.D., Medical Director
CIO: Kerra Guffey, Senior Vice President and Chief Information Officer
CHR: Shirley Kirk, Vice President Human Resources
Web address: www.memorialmedical.com
— Control 23, Service 10, Staffed Beds 443, Admissions 22248, Census 316, Outpatient Visits 408374, Births 1680, Total 321124, Payroll 111021, Personnel 2327

☒ **ST. JOHN'S HOSPITAL**, 800 East Carpenter Street, Zip 62769–0002; tel. 217/544–6464, (Total facility includes 28 beds in nursing home–type unit) **A**1 2 3 5 8 9 10 **F**1 9 11 12 14 15 16 17 18 19 20 21 22 23 27 28 29 30 33 34 35 36 37 38 39 40 43 44 46 47 48 49 50 51 52 53 55 56 57 58 59 60 61 62 63 64 65 66 67 69 71 73 74 75 76 77 78 79 81 82 84 85 86 88 92 93 94 95 96 106 108 109 110 **P**7 **S** Hospital Sisters Health System, Springfield, IL
Primary Contact: Richard J. Carlson, Executive Vice President and Administrator
COO: John Short, Associate Administrator and Chief Operating Officer
CFO: Hugh Collins, Assistant Administrator Finance
CMO: Ronald Deering, M.D., Medical Director
CHR: Joe Bretz, Director Human Resources
Web address: www.st-johns.org
— Control 21, Service 10, Staffed Beds 539, Admissions 22089, Census 299, Outpatient Visits 201959, Births 2055, Total 319049, Payroll 118411, Personnel 2708

STAUNTON—Macoupin County

★ **COMMUNITY MEMORIAL HOSPITAL**, 400 Caldwell Street, Zip 62088–1499; tel. 618/635–2200 **A**9 10 18 **F**2 9 12 21 23 33 44 47 51 52 54 58 61 62 63 64 69 70 81 94 96 97 108 110 **S** Quorum Health Resources, Plano, TX
Primary Contact: Patrick B. Heise, Chief Executive Officer
CFO: Donald Brunnworth, Chief Financial Officer
CMO: Manish Mathur, M.D., President Medical Staff
CIO: Cheryl Horner, Data Processing Supervisor
CHR: Susie Campbell, Director Human Resources
Web address: www.stauntonhospital.org
— Control 23, Service 10, Staffed Beds 25, Admissions 700, Census 8, Outpatient Visits 22737, Births 0, Total 10983, Payroll 4596, Personnel 139

Many Facility Codes have changed. Please refer to the AHA Guide Code Chart.

© 2005 AHA Guide

Hospital, Address, Telephone, Approval, Facility, and Physician Codes, Health Care System	Classi-fication Codes		Utilization Data					Expense (thousands) of dollars		
★ American Hospital Association (AHA) membership □ Joint Commission on Accreditation of Healthcare Organizations (JCAHO) accreditation ○ American Osteopathic Association (AOA) accreditation △ Commission on Accreditation of Rehabilitation Facilities (CARF) accreditation	Control	Service	Staffed Beds	Admissions	Census	Outpatient Visits	Births	Total	Payroll	Personnel

STERLING—Whiteside County

✠ **CGH MEDICAL CENTER**, 100 East LeFevre Road, Zip 61081–1279; tel. 815/625–0400 **A**1 2 9 10 19 **F**2 6 9 11 12 15 17 21 22 27 28 29 30 33 45 46 47 48 51 55 58 59 61 63 66 69 70 81 82 84 85 87 88 93 94 96 97 106 108 **P**1 6 Primary Contact: Edward Andersen, President and Chief Executive Officer CFO: Joe Chamberlain, Chief Financial Officer CMO: Joseph Neiween, Medical Director CIO: Raymond Sharp, Vice President and Chief Information Officer CHR: Tom McCawley, Manager Human Resources Web address: www.cghmc.com	14	10	125	5412	51	95304	647	66201	28267	705

STREAMWOOD—Cook County

□ **STREAMWOOD BEHAVIORAL HEALTH CENTER**, 1400 East Irving Park Road, Zip 60107–3203; tel. 630/837–9000 **A**1 10 **F**4 21 26 27 28 29 52 71 72 73 74 77 78 94 98 **S** Psychiatric Solutions, Franklin, TN Primary Contact: Jeff Bergren, Regional Chief Executive Officer Web address: www.streamwoodhospital.com	33	52	238	2150	191	11823	0	39032	21738	515

STREATOR—La Salle County

✠ **ST. MARY'S HOSPITAL**, 111 Spring Street, Zip 61364–3399; tel. 815/673–2311, (Total facility includes 30 beds in nursing home–type unit) **A**1 9 10 **F**1 2 9 11 12 21 22 23 26 27 28 29 30 33 36 37 38 39 44 45 46 48 51 52 55 58 59 60 61 62 63 65 66 68 69 81 82 87 88 92 94 95 96 106 108 110 **P**8 **S** Hospital Sisters Health System, Springfield, IL Primary Contact: Mark S. O'Halla, Executive Vice President and Administrator CFO: Karen S. Clark, Chief Financial Officer CHR: David Smith, Director Support Services Web address: www.stmaryshospital.org	21	10	109	3778	59	51007	234	37482	15942	401

SYCAMORE—De Kalb County

□ **KINDRED HOSPITAL–SYCAMORE**, 225 Edward Street, Zip 60178–2197; tel. 815/895–2144 **A**1 10 **F**27 33 55 64 **S** Kindred Healthcare, Louisville, KY Primary Contact: Cindy Smith, Chief Executive Officer Web address: www.kindredhealthcare.com	33	80	69	477	39	0	0	15313	6074	163

TAYLORVILLE—Christian County

✠ **ST. VINCENT MEMORIAL HOSPITAL**, 201 East Pleasant Street, Zip 62568–1597; tel. 217/824–3331, (Total facility includes 50 beds in nursing home–type unit) **A**1 9 10 18 **F**2 9 11 12 21 22 24 26 27 28 29 30 31 33 36 37 39 44 46 47 48 51 52 54 55 58 59 60 61 63 65 66 69 70 81 87 88 92 93 94 96 97 106 108 109 110 **S** Memorial Health System, Springfield, IL Primary Contact: Daniel J. Raab, President and Chief Executive Officer CFO: Sue Hill, Director Finance CHR: Todd Ray, Director Human Resources Web address: www.svmh.org	21	10	75	2452	58	62945	173	24934	12319	341

TINLEY PARK—Cook County

□ **TINLEY PARK MENTAL HEALTH CENTER**, 7400 West 183rd Street, Zip 60477–3695; tel. 708/614–4000, (Nonreporting) **A**1 5 10 Primary Contact: Brenda Hampton, Network Manager	12	22	150	—	—	—	—	—	—	—

URBANA—Champaign County

✠ △ **CARLE FOUNDATION HOSPITAL**, 611 West Park Street, Zip 61801–2595; tel. 217/383–3311, (Total facility includes 231 beds in nursing home–type unit) **A**1 2 3 5 7 9 10 12 13 **F**2 4 5 6 8 9 10 11 12 14 15 17 19 21 22 23 26 27 28 29 30 33 34 36 37 38 40 42 44 45 46 47 48 49 50 51 52 53 55 56 57 58 59 60 61 62 63 64 65 66 68 69 70 81 84 88 91 92 93 94 95 96 106 107 108 109 110 **P**5 Primary Contact: James Leonard, M.D., President and Chief Executive Officer COO: John T. Snyder, Executive Vice President CFO: Robert Tonkinson, Vice President Finance CMO: Napoleon Knight, M.D., Vice President Medical Affairs CHR: Phillip Kubow, Vice President Human Resources Web address: www.carle.com	23	10	426	15495	338	92416	2144	199018	75654	1964
✠ △ **PROVENA COVENANT MEDICAL CENTER**, 1400 West Park Street, Zip 61801–2396; tel. 217/337–2000 **A**1 2 3 5 7 9 10 **F**2 6 7 8 11 12 15 17 19 21 22 23 27 28 29 31 33 36 38 39 44 46 48 50 52 55 56 57 58 59 61 62 63 64 65 66 68 69 71 73 74 75 76 79 80 82 88 94 96 108 109 110 **S** Provena Health, Mokena, IL Primary Contact: Mark S. Wiener, Regional President and Chief Executive Officer COO: Patricia A. Schulte, Chief Operations and Chief Nursing Executive CFO: Cheryl A. Harmon, Chief Financial Officer CMO: Bernard B. Gawne, M.D., Chief Medical Officer CIO: Jonathan L. Manis, System Vice President Information Services and Chief Information Officer CHR: Janet S. Payne, Vice President Human Resources Web address: www.provenacovenant.org	21	10	120	10045	108	106963	1064	116544	38586	884

VANDALIA—Fayette County

✠ **FAYETTE COUNTY HOSPITAL**, 650 West Taylor Street, Zip 62471–1296; tel. 618/283–1231, (Total facility includes 104 beds in nursing home–type unit) **A**1 9 10 18 **F**2 6 9 12 21 22 23 27 28 29 33 46 48 51 54 55 60 63 69 81 82 84 86 88 92 93 94 96 97 108 **P**5 **S** Alliant Management Services, Louisville, KY Primary Contact: Dennis L. Hutchison, Chief Executive Officer CFO: Ted Anderson, Chief Financial Officer Web address: www.bjc.org	16	10	145	1503	106	—	0	16533	7417	245

IL

Hospital, Address, Telephone, Approval, Facility, and Physician Codes, Health Care System	Classi-fication Codes		Utilization Data					Expense (thousands) of dollars		
★ American Hospital Association (AHA) membership □ Joint Commission on Accreditation of Healthcare Organizations (JCAHO) accreditation ○ American Osteopathic Association (AOA) accreditation △ Commission on Accreditation of Rehabilitation Facilities (CARF) accreditation	Control	Service	Staffed Beds	Admissions	Census	Outpatient Visits	Births	Total	Payroll	Personnel

WATSEKA—Iroquois County

□ **IROQUOIS MEMORIAL HOSPITAL AND RESIDENT HOME**, 200 Fairman Avenue, Zip 60970–1644; tel. 815/432–5841, (Total facility includes 46 beds in nursing home–type unit) (Nonreporting) **A**1 9 10 20
Primary Contact: Rex D. Conger, President and Chief Executive Officer
Web address: www.iroquoismemorial.com

| | 23 | 10 | 112 | — | — | — | — | — | — | — |

WAUKEGAN—Lake County

✣ △ **VISTA HEALTH–PROVENA SAINT THERESE MEDICAL CENTER**, 2615 Washington Street, Zip 60085–4988; tel. 847/249–3900 **A**1 7 9 10 **F**2 10 21 22 23 26 27 28 29 31 32 33 34 35 36 37 39 42 46 47 48 50 52 53 55 57 58 59 60 61 62 63 64 68 69 71 72 73 74 75 77 78 81 82 85 88 94 96 108 110 **P**5
Primary Contact: Timothy J. Harrington, President and Chief Executive Officer
CFO: James P. McNichols, Vice President Finance and Chief Financial Officer
CIO: Janna S. Peters, Vice President and Chief Information Officer
Web address: www.vistahealth.com

| | 23 | 10 | 91 | 5413 | 75 | 97698 | 0 | 61259 | 27181 | 585 |

✣ **VISTA HEALTH–VICTORY MEMORIAL HOSPITAL**, 1324 North Sheridan Road, Zip 60085–2181; tel. 847/360–4000 **A**1 2 9 10 **F**2 11 12 15 17 21 22 23 26 27 28 29 32 33 35 37 39 42 46 47 48 50 52 53 55 57 58 59 61 62 63 64 81 82 85 88 93 94 96 106 108 110 **P**5 6
Primary Contact: Barbara J. Martin, R.N., Interim President and Chief Executive Officer
CFO: Jim McNichols, Chief Financial Officer
CIO: Janna S. Peters, Vice President and Chief Information Officer
CHR: Harvey Lightbody, Vice President Human Resources
Web address: www.vistahealth.com

| | 23 | 10 | 146 | 9448 | 89 | 82220 | 2210 | 78034 | 32921 | 766 |

WHEATON—Du Page County

✣ △ **MARIANJOY REHABILITATION HOSPITAL**, 26 West 171 Roosevelt Road, Zip 60187–0795, Mailing Address: P.O. Box 795, Zip 60189–0795; tel. 630/462–4000 **A**1 3 5 7 8 9 10 **F**9 21 22 26 27 28 29 30 44 45 46 47 48 52 58 65 66 68 69 96 108 **P**6 **S** Wheaton Franciscan Services, Inc., Wheaton, IL
Primary Contact: Kathleen C. Yosko, President and Chief Executive Officer
COO: Karen Ortmann, Senior Vice President Patient Care and Operations
CFO: Michael Hedderman, Senior Vice President Finance and Chief Financial Officer
CMO: Noel Rao, M.D., Medical Director
CIO: Pat Orrison, Director Information Services
CHR: Gretchen Van Natta, Vice President Human Resources
Web address: www.marianjoy.org

| | 21 | 46 | 116 | 2311 | 99 | 32262 | 0 | 50270 | 26081 | 519 |

WINFIELD—Du Page County

✣ **CENTRAL DUPAGE HOSPITAL**, 25 North Winfield Road, Zip 60190; tel. 630/933–1600, (Includes BEHAVIORAL HEALTH CENTER, 27 West 350 High Lake Road, tel. 630/653–4000) **A**1 2 9 10 **F**2 3 4 9 10 11 12 14 15 17 19 21 22 23 26 27 28 33 34 37 39 42 46 48 49 52 53 55 56 57 58 59 61 62 63 65 66 67 69 71 72 73 74 75 76 77 78 81 82 84 85 86 87 88 90 92 93 94 96 106 107 108 109 110
Primary Contact: Luke McGuinness, President
CFO: Paul Piro, Senior Vice President and Chief Financial Officer
CIO: David Printz, Vice President and Chief Information Officer
Web address: www.cdh.org

| | 23 | 10 | 327 | 19953 | 234 | 351072 | 3277 | 325925 | 119166 | — |

WOODSTOCK—McHenry County

✣ **CENTEGRA MEMORIAL MEDICAL CENTER**, 3701 Doty Road, Zip 60098–3797, Mailing Address: P.O. Box 1990, Zip 60098–1990; tel. 815/338–2500, (Total facility includes 30 beds in nursing home–type unit) (Nonreporting) **A**1 2 9 10 **S** Centegra Health System, Woodstock, IL
Primary Contact: Michael S. Eesley, President and Chief Executive Officer
CFO: Greg Pagliuzza, Senior Vice President and Chief Financial Officer
CIO: Barbara O'Connell, Director Information Systems
CHR: Barbara Jo Johnson, Senior Vice President Human Resources
Web address: www.centegra.org

| | 23 | 10 | 140 | — | — | — | — | — | — | — |

ZION—Lake County

□ **MIDWESTERN REGIONAL MEDICAL CENTER**, 2520 Elisha Avenue, Zip 60099–2587; tel. 847/872–4561 **A**1 2 10 **F**12 21 22 23 29 30 33 36 37 38 45 46 47 48 50 52 53 55 58 60 61 63 64 65 66 69 70 75 79 80 81 82 84 85 86 87 88 94 96 99 106 107 108 110 **S** Cancer Treatment Centers of America, Arlington Heights, IL
Primary Contact: Roger C. Cary, President and Chief Executive Officer
Web address: www.cancercenter.com

| | 33 | 41 | 73 | 1977 | 30 | 39440 | 0 | 102714 | 23565 | 449 |

Many Facility Codes have changed. Please refer to the AHA Guide Code Chart. © 2005 AHA Guide

INDIANA

Hospital, Address, Telephone, Approval, Facility, and Physician Codes, Health Care System	Classi-fication Codes		Utilization Data					Expense (thousands) of dollars		
★ American Hospital Association (AHA) membership □ Joint Commission on Accreditation of Healthcare Organizations (JCAHO) accreditation ○ American Osteopathic Association (AOA) accreditation △ Commission on Accreditation of Rehabilitation Facilities (CARF) accreditation	Control	Service	Staffed Beds	Admissions	Census	Outpatient Visits	Births	Total	Payroll	Personnel

ANDERSON—Madison County

COMMUNITY HOSPITAL OF ANDERSON AND MADISON COUNTY See Community Health Network, Indianapolis

✶ **SAINT JOHN'S HEALTH SYSTEM**, 2015 Jackson Street, Zip 46016–4339; tel. 765/649–2511, (Total facility includes 20 beds in nursing home–type unit) **A**1 2 9 10 **F**2 3 4 9 11 12 15 21 22 23 24 26 27 28 29 31 32 33 35 36 37 38 39 40 42 46 47 48 50 51 52 53 55 57 58 59 60 61 62 63 64 65 66 68 69 71 72 73 74 75 76 77 78 79 80 81 82 84 85 86 87 88 92 93 94 96 98 106 107 108 109 110 **P**7 **S** Ascension Health, Saint Louis, MO | 21 | 10 | 206 | 8375 | 142 | 396561 | 465 | 125269 | 55667 | 1186
Primary Contact: Kyle De Fur, FACHE, President
CFO: Donald L. Apple, Chief Financial Officer
CMO: Gary Brazel, M.D., Vice President Physician and Clinical Services
CIO: Roger Strange, Chief Information Officer
CHR: Glenn Fields, Vice President, Human Resources
Web address: www.stjohnshealthsystem.org

ANGOLA—Steuben County

★ **CAMERON MEMORIAL COMMUNITY HOSPITAL**, 416 East Maumee Street, Zip 46703–2015; tel. 260/665–2141 **A**9 10 18 **F**2 4 8 9 11 12 22 26 27 28 36 51 55 59 63 69 81 84 85 88 94 97 106 107 108 | 23 | 10 | 25 | 1230 | 9 | 112234 | 308 | 26669 | 10898 | 315
Primary Contact: Dennis L. Knapp, President and Chief Executive Officer
Web address: www.cameronhosp.com

AUBURN—De Kalb County

★ **DEKALB MEMORIAL HOSPITAL**, 1316 East Seventh Street, Zip 46706–2515, Mailing Address: P.O. Box 542, Zip 46706–0542; tel. 260/925–4600 **A**9 10 **F**2 6 9 11 12 21 26 27 28 29 33 36 37 38 41 46 47 48 51 52 55 58 59 60 62 63 64 65 66 69 70 81 82 84 86 87 88 94 96 106 108 **P**6 8 | 23 | 10 | 45 | 2009 | 15 | 88566 | 430 | 31860 | 14237 | 339
Primary Contact: Jack M. Corey, President
CFO: Craig Polkow, Chief Financial Officer
CMO: James Buchanan, M.D., Chief Medical Officer
CIO: Ed Hobbs, Director Information Services
CHR: Deb Arend Sinclair, Human Resource Director
Web address: www.dekalbmemorial.com

AVON—Marion County

★ **CLARIAN WEST MEDICAL CENTER**, 1111 North Ronald Reagan Parkway, Zip 46123; tel. 317/217–3000, (Nonreporting) **A**10 **S** Clarian Health Partners, Indianapolis, IN | 33 | 10 | 76 | — | — | — | — | — | — | —
Primary Contact: Alfonso W. Gatmaitan, Chief Executive Officer

BATESVILLE—Ripley County

✶ **MARGARET MARY COMMUNITY HOSPITAL**, 321 Mitchell Avenue, Zip 47006–0226, Mailing Address: P.O. Box 226, Zip 47006–0226; tel. 812/934–6624, (Total facility includes 34 beds in nursing home–type unit) **A**1 9 10 **F**2 11 12 23 26 27 28 29 32 33 36 44 46 48 51 52 54 55 58 59 61 63 69 81 82 84 85 87 88 92 93 94 95 96 106 108 | 23 | 10 | 79 | 1825 | 46 | 117907 | 449 | 34209 | 15651 | 361
Primary Contact: James L. Amos, President
CFO: Brian Daeger, Vice President Financial Services
CMO: Kimberly Kick, M.D., Chief of Staff
CHR: Tate Shepard, Vice President, Human Resources
Web address: www.mmch.org

BEDFORD—Lawrence County

✶ **BEDFORD REGIONAL MEDICAL CENTER**, 2900 West 16th Street, Zip 47421–3583; tel. 812/275–1200 **A**1 2 9 10 **F**2 6 9 11 12 21 22 23 26 27 28 29 30 32 33 35 37 38 39 46 47 48 51 52 53 55 57 58 59 60 61 62 63 64 65 66 69 70 73 75 77 81 82 85 87 88 93 94 95 96 97 98 106 107 108 109 110 **P**6 **S** Clarian Health Partners, Indianapolis, IN | 23 | 10 | 49 | 1987 | 21 | 189880 | 116 | 35930 | 17255 | 421
Primary Contact: Bradford W. Dykes, President and Chief Executive Officer
CFO: Charles L. Shetler, CPA, Chief Financial Officer
CIO: Becky Johnson, Director Management Information Systems
CHR: Cindy Smale, Director Human Resources
Web address: www.brmchealthcare.com

✶ **DUNN MEMORIAL HOSPITAL**, 1600 23rd Street, Zip 47421–4704; tel. 812/275–3331 **A**1 9 10 **F**2 6 9 11 12 15 17 21 26 28 29 30 33 37 39 41 44 46 47 48 49 51 52 55 58 59 60 62 63 64 65 66 69 71 73 74 75 76 81 82 84 85 87 88 94 96 106 107 108 109 110 | 13 | 10 | 105 | 2506 | 26 | 65472 | 231 | 33582 | 15107 | 421
Primary Contact: Michael W. Cooper, Chief Executive Officer
CFO: Colin McCulloch, Chief Financial Officer
CMO: Deborah Craton, M.D., Chief Medical Staff
CIO: Debra Bruner, Director Quality, Accreditation, and Information Technology
CHR: Nancy Havill, Director Employee Services
Web address: www.dunnmemorial.org

BEECH GROVE—Marion County

□ **SELECT SPECIALTY HOSPITAL OF BEECH GROVE**, 1600 Albany Street, Suite 200, Zip 46107; tel. 317/783–8913, (Nonreporting) **A**1 10 | 33 | 49 | 32 | — | — | — | — | — | — | —

Hospital, Address, Telephone, Approval, Facility, and Physician Codes, Health Care System	Classi-fication Codes		Utilization Data					Expense (thousands) of dollars		
★ American Hospital Association (AHA) membership □ Joint Commission on Accreditation of Healthcare Organizations (JCAHO) accreditation ○ American Osteopathic Association (AOA) accreditation △ Commission on Accreditation of Rehabilitation Facilities (CARF) accreditation	Control	Service	Staffed Beds	Admissions	Census	Outpatient Visits	Births	Total	Payroll	Personnel

○ **ST. FRANCIS HOSPITAL AND HEALTH CENTERS – NORTH CAMPUS**, 1600 Albany Street, Zip 46107–1593; tel. 317/787–3311, (Includes ST. FRANCIS HOSPITAL AND HEALTH CENTERS – SOUTH CAMPUS, 8111 South Emerson Avenue, Indianapolis, Zip 46217), (Total facility includes 35 beds in nursing home–type unit) **A**2 3 5 9 10 11 **F**2 4 9 10 11 12 14 15 17 19 21 22 23 24 26 27 28 29 30 31 32 33 36 37 38 39 40 42 44 46 47 48 49 50 51 52 53 55 56 57 58 59 60 61 62 63 64 65 66 68 69 70 71 72 73 75 76 77 78 79 81 82 83 85 87 89 92 94 95 96 97 99 100 107 108 109 110 **P**7 8 **S** Sisters of St. Francis Health Services, Inc., Mishawaka, IN
Primary Contact: Robert J. Brody, President and Chief Executive Officer
Web address: www.stfrancishospitals.org

| | 21 | 10 | 463 | 19788 | 290 | 106183 | 2523 | 356315 | 137117 | — |

BLOOMINGTON—Monroe County

⊠ **BLOOMINGTON HOSPITAL**, 601 West Second Street, Zip 47403–2317, Mailing Address: P.O. Box 1149, Zip 47402–1149; tel. 812/336–6821, (Total facility includes 485 beds in nursing home–type unit) (Nonreporting) **A**1 9 10
Primary Contact: Mark E. Moore, President and Chief Executive Officer
COO: Larry Bailey, Vice President and Chief Operating Officer
CFO: Jim Myers, Chief Financial Officer
CIO: Mark W. McMath, Chief Information Officer
CHR: Steven Deckard, Vice President Human Resources
Web address: www.bhhs.org

| | 23 | 10 | 840 | — | — | — | — | — | — | — |

MEADOWS HOSPITAL, 3600 North Prow Road, Zip 47404; tel. 812/331–8000, (Nonreporting) **A**10 **S** Psychiatric Solutions, Franklin, TN
Primary Contact: Leann Moren Hutchinson, Chief Executive Officer

| | 33 | 22 | 78 | — | — | — | — | — | — | — |

SELECT SPECIALTY HOSPITAL OF BLOOMINGTON, 601 West Second Street, 4th Floor, Zip 47402; tel. 812/353–2000, (Nonreporting) **A**10
Primary Contact: Gloria Skinner, Chief Executive Officer

| | 33 | 49 | 30 | — | — | — | — | — | — | — |

BLUFFTON—Wells County

⊠ **BLUFFTON REGIONAL MEDICAL CENTER**, 303 South Main Street, Zip 46714–2529; tel. 260/824–3210, (Total facility includes 13 beds in nursing home–type unit) **A**1 2 9 10 **F**2 4 7 11 12 14 21 22 23 26 27 28 29 32 33 35 37 42 44 46 48 51 52 53 55 58 59 60 61 62 63 65 66 69 70 81 84 88 92 93 94 96 108 **P**8 **S** Triad Hospitals, Inc., Plano, TX
Primary Contact: Thomas A. Clark, Chief Executive Officer
COO: Vicki Hanselman, Chief Operating Officer
CFO: Doug BeMent, Chief Financial Officer
CMO: Carol Butler, M.D., President Medical Staff
CIO: Vicki Hanselman, Chief Operating Officer
Web address: www.blufftonregional.com

| | 33 | 10 | 79 | 3071 | 36 | 49226 | 297 | 38991 | 14130 | 330 |

BOONVILLE—Warrick County

⊠ **ST. MARY'S WARRICK HOSPITAL**, 1116 Millis Avenue, Zip 47601–0629, Mailing Address: Box 629, Zip 47601–0629; tel. 812/897–4800 **A**1 9 10 18 **F**2 6 9 12 21 22 26 27 28 29 33 39 41 44 46 48 50 52 60 62 63 69 70 71 76 81 85 88 92 94 97 106 108 **S** Ascension Health, Saint Louis, MO
Primary Contact: Mark Dooley, Executive Vice President and Administrator
Web address: www.stmarys.org

| | 23 | 10 | 40 | 1145 | 13 | 21268 | 0 | 13914 | 6794 | 173 |

BRAZIL—Clay County

⊠ **ST. VINCENT CLAY HOSPITAL**, 1206 East National Avenue, Zip 47834–2797; tel. 812/442–2500 **A**1 9 10 18 **F**9 12 21 22 26 27 28 29 33 39 46 48 53 57 58 60 62 63 64 66 69 81 82 84 88 94 95 96 97 106 108 **P**5 **S** Ascension Health, Saint Louis, MO
Primary Contact: Jerry Laue, Administrator
CMO: Charles French, M.D., Medical Director
CHR: Jennifer French, Director of Organizational Quality
Web address: www.stvincent.org

| | 21 | 10 | 25 | 1052 | 12 | 38771 | 0 | 13278 | 4895 | 124 |

BREMEN—Marshall County

★ **COMMUNITY HOSPITAL OF BREMEN**, 411 South Whitlock Street, Zip 46506–1626, Mailing Address: P.O. Box 8, Zip 46506–0008; tel. 574/546–2211 **A**9 10 18 **F**2 9 12 21 27 28 29 33 36 37 44 46 48 52 53 58 59 60 63 69 70 81 84 85 88 92 93 94 96 97 106 108 **P**1
Primary Contact: Scott R. Graybill, President and Chief Executive Officer
CFO: Deborah Kipfer, Chief Financial Officer
CMO: Jason Marker, M.D., President Medical Staff
CHR: Patricia Board, Vice President Human Resources
Web address: www.bremenhospital.com

| | 23 | 10 | 24 | 330 | 4 | 44851 | 37 | 7523 | 3645 | 98 |

CARMEL—Hamilton County

⊠ **ST. ELIZABETH ANN SETON HOSPITAL OF CARMEL**, (Formerly St. Elizabeth Ann Seton Hospital of Central Indiana), 13500 North Meridian Street, Zip 46032, Mailing Address: P.O. Box 1906, Zip 46082–1906; tel. 317/582–8500, (Nonreporting) **A**1 9 10 **S** Ascension Health, Saint Louis, MO
Primary Contact: Peter H. Alexander, Administrator
COO: Troy T. Reiff, Corporte Director Operations
CFO: David M. Girten, Corporate Director Financial Services
CHR: Terry A. Wignall, Director of Human Resources
Web address: www.stvincent.org

| | 23 | 80 | 36 | — | — | — | — | — | — | — |

Many Facility Codes have changed. Please refer to the AHA Guide Code Chart.

© 2005 AHA Guide

Hospital, Address, Telephone, Approval, Facility, and Physician Codes, Health Care System	Classi-fication Codes		Utilization Data					Expense (thousands) of dollars		
	Control	Service	Staffed Beds	Admissions	Census	Outpatient Visits	Births	Total	Payroll	Personnel

★ American Hospital Association (AHA) membership
□ Joint Commission on Accreditation of Healthcare Organizations (JCAHO) accreditation
○ American Osteopathic Association (AOA) accreditation
△ Commission on Accreditation of Rehabilitation Facilities (CARF) accreditation

CHARLESTOWN—Clark County

⊠ **MEDICAL CENTER OF SOUTHERN INDIANA**, 2200 Market Street, Zip 47111–0069, Mailing Address: P.O. Box 69, Zip 47111–0069; tel. 812/256–3301, (Nonreporting) **A**1 9 10 **S** LifePoint Hospitals, Inc., Brentwood, TN
Primary Contact: David R. Sirk, Chief Executive Officer
CFO: Christina Patterson, Chief Financial Officer
CIO: Kevin McLaughlin, Chief Information Officer
CHR: Mike Rembold, Director Human Resources
Web address: www.mcsi–charlestown.com

	23	10	77	—	—	—	—	—	—	—

CLINTON—Vermillion County

○ **WEST CENTRAL COMMUNITY HOSPITAL**, 801 South Main Street, Zip 47842–0349; tel. 765/832–2451 **A**9 10 11 18 **F**11 12 21 26 27 28 33 41 42 46 52 55 58 59 60 61 62 63 66 69 70 81 88 94 97 108 **P**6
Primary Contact: Terri L. Hill, Administrator
Web address: www.uhhg.org/wcch/index.html

	23	10	35	1372	10	51762	109	16232	6774	161

COLUMBIA CITY—Whitley County

□ **PARKVIEW WHITLEY HOSPITAL**, 353 North Oak Street, Zip 46725–1623; tel. 260/248–9000, (Total facility includes 81 beds in nursing home–type unit) **A**1 9 10 **F**2 6 11 12 21 26 27 28 29 31 33 39 41 42 46 48 52 54 55 58 59 63 64 69 81 82 84 87 88 91 92 93 106 108 110 **P**6 **S** Parkview Health, Fort Wayne, IN
Primary Contact: Bridget Johnson, Interim Chief Operating Officer
Web address: www.parkview.com

	23	10	118	1807	90	43714	282	29266	13573	341

COLUMBUS—Bartholomew County

⊠ **COLUMBUS REGIONAL HOSPITAL**, 2400 East 17th Street, Zip 47201–5360; tel. 812/379–4441 **A**1 2 9 10 19 **F**2 6 9 10 11 12 14 15 17 19 21 22 23 26 27 28 29 30 32 33 37 39 40 41 45 46 47 48 51 52 53 55 57 58 59 60 61 62 63 64 65 66 68 69 71 73 74 75 76 79 81 82 84 85 86 87 88 93 94 95 96 106 107 108 109 110 **P**8
Primary Contact: Douglas J. Leonard, Chief Executive Officer
CFO: Marlene Weatherwax, Vice President and Chief Financial Officer
CMO: Thomas Sonderman, M.D., Vice President and Chief Medical Officer
CIO: Tim Tarnowski, Chief Information Officer
Web address: www.crh.org

	13	10	235	10086	125	179265	1417	151848	59568	1434

CONNERSVILLE—Fayette County

★ ○ **FAYETTE MEMORIAL HOSPITAL**, 1941 Virginia Avenue, Zip 47331–9990; tel. 765/825–5131, (Nonreporting) **A**9 10 11 12
Primary Contact: David R. Brandon, Chief Executive Officer
COO: Steve Wohlford, Chief Operating Officer
CFO: Bill Remmich, Chief Financial Officer
CMO: Rick Robertson, M.D., Chief of Staff
CIO: Roy Cupp, Director Management Information Systems
Web address: www.fayettememorial.org

	23	10	111	—	—	—	—	—	—	—

CORYDON—Harrison County

⊠ **HARRISON COUNTY HOSPITAL**, 245 Atwood Street, Zip 47112–1774; tel. 812/738–4251 **A**1 9 10 **F**6 11 12 21 23 26 27 28 29 33 45 48 51 52 53 55 58 59 60 61 63 65 66 69 81 82 84 87 88 93 94 95 96 106 107 108 110 **P**7
Primary Contact: Steven L. Taylor, Chief Executive Officer
CFO: Jeff Davis, Chief Financial Officer
CIO: Chuck Wiley, Information Systems Manager
CHR: Angie Phelps Sells, Human Resource Manager
Web address: www.hchin.org

	13	10	47	1723	18	41247	175	21894	11747	287

CRAWFORDSVILLE—Montgomery County

○ **ST. CLARE MEDICAL CENTER**, 1710 Lafayette Road, Zip 47933–1099; tel. 765/362–2800, (Total facility includes 17 beds in nursing home–type unit) **A**9 10 11 **F**2 9 11 12 21 22 23 26 27 28 33 44 46 47 48 52 53 55 58 59 60 61 62 63 69 70 71 74 76 77 81 82 84 88 92 94 95 96 108 109 110 **P**6 **S** Sisters of St. Francis Health Services, Inc., Mishawaka, IN
Primary Contact: Jeffrey C. Zeh, Executive Director
Web address: www.stclaremedical.org

	21	10	86	2773	43	57918	279	37046	14866	438

CROWN POINT—Lake County

ST. ANTHONY MEDICAL CENTER, 1201 South Main Street, Zip 46307–8483; tel. 219/738–2100 **A**2 9 10 12 **F**2 9 11 12 14 15 16 17 19 21 22 28 29 30 33 38 39 40 41 42 46 47 48 52 53 57 58 59 60 61 62 63 65 68 69 70 79 80 81 82 84 85 86 87 88 93 94 95 96 98 106 108 109 110 **P**7 8 **S** Sisters of St. Francis Health Services, Inc., Mishawaka, IN
Primary Contact: Seth Warren, President
Web address: www.stanthonymedicalcenter.com

	21	10	267	8635	105	138553	953	123388	48483	889

DANVILLE—Hendricks County

⊠ **HENDRICKS REGIONAL HEALTH**, 1000 East Main Street, Zip 46122–0409, Mailing Address: P.O. Box 409, Zip 46122–0409; tel. 317/745–4451 **A**1 9 10 **F**2 3 9 11 12 21 22 26 27 28 29 32 33 37 38 41 42 44 46 47 48 50 52 54 55 57 58 59 60 61 62 63 64 65 66 69 70 71 73 74 75 76 79 80 81 82 84 85 88 93 94 95 96 106 107 108 109 110 **P**1 6 7
Primary Contact: Dennis W. Dawes, FACHE, President
CFO: John Komenda, Vice President Finance
CMO: John Sparzo, M.D., Vice President Medical Affairs
CIO: Lowell Nicodemus, Director Information Systems
CHR: Gary Lenard, Director Human Resources
Web address: www.hendrickshospital.org

	13	10	141	6365	70	283134	969	111227	50493	1081

IN

Hospital, Address, Telephone, Approval, Facility, and Physician Codes, Health Care System	Classi-fication Codes		Utilization Data					Expense (thousands) of dollars		
★ American Hospital Association (AHA) membership □ Joint Commission on Accreditation of Healthcare Organizations (JCAHO) accreditation ○ American Osteopathic Association (AOA) accreditation △ Commission on Accreditation of Rehabilitation Facilities (CARF) accreditation	Control	Service	Staffed Beds	Admissions	Census	Outpatient Visits	Births	Total	Payroll	Personnel

DECATUR—Adams County

⊠ **ADAMS MEMORIAL HOSPITAL**, (Formerly Adams County Memorial Hospital), 1100 Mercer Avenue, Zip 46733–2311, Mailing Address: P.O. Box 151, Zip 46733–0151; tel. 260/724–2145 **A**1 9 10 **F**1 4 6 11 12 21 23 24 26 27 28 29 33 36 37 38 44 45 46 48 51 55 57 59 60 61 62 63 64 65 66 69 70 71 73 74 75 76 77 78 81 82 84 88 92 94 106 107 108 109 110
Primary Contact: Marvin L. Baird, Executive Director
CFO: William G. Seck, Chief Financial Officer
Web address: www.adamshospital.com

| | 13 | 10 | 87 | 2111 | 41 | 64828 | 203 | 30978 | 13400 | 352 |

DYER—Lake County

SAINT MARGARET MERCY HEALTHCARE CENTERS–SOUTH CAMPUS See Saint Margaret Mercy Healthcare Centers, Hammond

EAST CHICAGO—Lake County

★ **REGENCY HOSPITAL OF NORTHWEST INDIANA**, 4321 Fir Street, 4th Floor, Zip 46312; tel. 219/392–7790, (Nonreporting) **A**10 **S** Regency Hospital Company, Alpharetta, GA
Primary Contact: Patrick Ryan, Chief Executive Officer

| | 33 | 80 | 25 | — | — | — | — | — | — | — |

□ △ **ST. CATHERINE HOSPITAL**, 4321 Fir Street, Zip 46312–3097; tel. 219/392–7000, (Total facility includes 19 beds in nursing home–type unit) **A**1 7 9 10 **F**2 11 12 15 17 19 21 22 23 27 28 29 33 34 37 39 41 42 46 48 49 50 51 52 53 55 58 59 60 61 62 63 64 65 66 69 71 72 73 74 75 76 77 81 82 84 88 92 93 94 96 106 108 109 110 **P**8 **S** Community Healthcare System, Hammond, IN
Primary Contact: JoAnn Birdzell, President and Chief Executive Officer
Web address: www.stcatherinehospital.org

| | 23 | 10 | 200 | 9086 | 138 | 112029 | 732 | 106671 | 40961 | 908 |

ELKHART—Elkhart County

★ ○ △ **ELKHART GENERAL HOSPITAL**, 600 East Boulevard, Zip 46514–2499, Mailing Address: P.O. Box 1329, Zip 46515–1329; tel. 574/294–2621, (Total facility includes 40 beds in nursing home–type unit) **A**2 7 9 10 11 **F**1 2 4 9 10 11 12 14 15 17 19 21 22 23 26 27 28 29 33 36 37 39 40 46 47 48 49 50 51 52 53 54 56 57 58 59 60 61 62 63 64 65 66 68 69 71 72 73 75 77 78 79 80 81 82 84 85 86 88 92 93 94 96 106 107 108 109 **P**8
Primary Contact: Gregory W. Lintjer, President
CFO: Kevin Higdon, Vice President Finance
CMO: Leinard Kibiloski, M.D., Chief of Staff
CIO: Wade Patrick, Director Information Systems
CHR: Kurt A. Meyer, Vice President, Human Resources
Web address: www.egh.org

| | 23 | 10 | 305 | 13714 | 187 | 416709 | 1670 | 217864 | 79024 | 1805 |

ELWOOD—Madison County

⊠ **ST. VINCENT MERCY HOSPITAL**, 1331 South A Street, Zip 46036–1942; tel. 765/552–4600 **A**1 9 10 18 **F**2 9 12 21 22 23 27 28 29 33 34 35 37 39 45 46 47 48 52 53 55 57 58 60 61 62 63 65 66 69 70 72 77 81 82 84 85 88 92 93 94 96 97 98 106 108 110 **P**6 **S** Ascension Health, Saint Louis, MO
Primary Contact: Deborah Y. Rasper, FACHE, Administrator
COO: Ann C. Yates, R.N., Director Patient Care and Clinical Services
CFO: Lora A. Webber, Director Financial Services
CHR: Barbara Whitenack, Manager, Human Resources
Web address: www.stvincent.org

| | 21 | 10 | 25 | 1114 | 12 | 46630 | 0 | 22462 | 10296 | 245 |

EVANSVILLE—Vanderburgh County

⊠ **DEACONESS CROSS POINTE CENTER**, 7200 East Indiana Street, Zip 47715; tel. 812/476–7200, (Nonreporting) **A**1 10 **S** Deaconess Health System, Evansville, IN
Primary Contact: David W. Morris, Chief Executive Officer
Web address: www.deaconess.com

| | 23 | 22 | 60 | — | — | — | — | — | — | — |

⊠ **DEACONESS HOSPITAL**, 600 Mary Street, Zip 47747–0001; tel. 812/450–5000, (Total facility includes 48 beds in nursing home–type unit) **A**1 2 3 5 9 10 **F**2 9 10 14 15 17 19 21 22 23 26 27 28 29 30 33 34 35 36 37 39 41 44 45 46 47 48 49 50 51 52 53 54 55 57 58 60 61 63 66 67 69 70 71 72 73 74 75 76 77 78 81 82 84 86 87 88 92 93 94 96 106 107 108 110 **P**8 **S** Deaconess Health System, Evansville, IN
Primary Contact: Linda E. White, President and Chief Executive Officer
COO: Shawn W. McCoy, Vice President Operations
CFO: Richard M. Stivers, Senior Vice President Health System Services
CMO: James Porter, M.D., Vice President Medical Affairs
CIO: Michael Neeley, Chief Informaiton Officer
CHR: Larry Pile, Director Human Resources
Web address: www.deaconess.com

| | 23 | 10 | 348 | 16738 | 265 | 263294 | 0 | 259550 | 107411 | 2334 |

□ **EVANSVILLE STATE HOSPITAL**, 3400 Lincoln Avenue, Zip 47714–0146; tel. 812/469–6800 **A**1 **F**71 76 94 **P**6
Primary Contact: Robert M. Spear, Superintendent

| | 12 | 22 | 168 | 58 | 18 | 0 | 0 | 25796 | 12637 | 437 |

⊠ **HEALTHSOUTH DEACONESS REHABILITATION HOSPITAL**, (Formerly HEALTHSOUTH Tri–State Rehabilitation Hospital), 4100 Covert Avenue, Zip 47714–5567, Mailing Address: P.O. Box 5349, Zip 47716–5349; tel. 812/476–9983 **A**1 10 **F**21 26 27 28 37 45 52 53 58 62 66 68 69 96 110 **P**5 **S** HEALTHSOUTH Corporation, Birmingham, AL
Primary Contact: Barbara Butler, Administrator
CFO: Diane Riley, Controller
CMO: Ashok Dhingra, Executive Medical Director
CHR: Sue Nolte, Director of Human Resources
Web address: www.healthsouth.com

| | 33 | 46 | 80 | 1298 | 58 | 7629 | 0 | 12684 | 6978 | 164 |

Hospital, Address, Telephone, Approval, Facility, and Physician Codes, Health Care System	Classi-fication Codes		Utilization Data					Expense (thousands) of dollars		
★ American Hospital Association (AHA) membership □ Joint Commission on Accreditation of Healthcare Organizations (JCAHO) accreditation ○ American Osteopathic Association (AOA) accreditation △ Commission on Accreditation of Rehabilitation Facilities (CARF) accreditation	Control	Service	Staffed Beds	Admissions	Census	Outpatient Visits	Births	Total	Payroll	Personnel
□ **SELECT SPECIALTY HOSPITAL OF EVANSVILLE**, 600 Mary Street, Suite 3325, Zip 47747; tel. 812/450–5270, (Nonreporting) **A**1 10 Primary Contact: Tracy Conroy, Chief Executive Officer	33	49	35	—	—	—	—	—	—	—
⊠ **ST. ELIZABETH ANN SETON SPECIALTY CARE HOSPITAL**, 3700 Washington Avenue, Zip 47750; tel. 812/485–7540 **A**1 9 10 **F**2 21 22 26 27 49 53 64 66 81 84 88 94 110 **S** Ascension Health, Saint Louis, MO Primary Contact: Carol Godsey, Chief Executive Officer CFO: Jared Florence, Financial Coordinator CHR: Jerri DuBord, Human Resources Manager Web address: www.stmarys.org	21	80	31	233	15	0	0	5933	3135	82
⊠ △ **ST. MARY'S MEDICAL CENTER OF EVANSVILLE**, 3700 Washington Avenue, Zip 47750–0002; tel. 812/485–4000, (Total facility includes 87 beds in nursing home–type unit) **A**1 2 3 5 7 9 10 **F**2 9 10 11 12 14 15 16 17 19 20 21 22 23 24 26 27 28 29 30 32 33 37 38 39 41 42 44 46 47 48 49 50 52 53 55 56 57 58 59 60 61 62 63 64 65 66 67 68 69 70 71 73 76 81 82 84 85 86 88 90 93 94 95 96 106 107 108 109 110 **P**6 **S** Ascension Health, Saint Louis, MO Primary Contact: Timothy A. Flesch, President and Chief Executive Officer COO: Stephen V. Kern, Chief Operating Officer CFO: Kim Richardson, Chief Financial Officer CMO: Kevin Neese, Chief Financial Officer CIO: Dennis DeMasie, Chief Information Officer CHR: Claudia Richardt, Chairman Web address: www.stmarys.org	21	10	459	17801	296	311280	2182	249696	102350	2295
FORT WAYNE—Allen County										
⊠ **DUPONT HOSPITAL**, 2520 East Dupont Road, Zip 46825; tel. 260/416–3000, (Nonreporting) **A**1 9 10 **S** Triad Hospitals, Inc., Plano, TX Primary Contact: Michael H. Schatzlein, M.D., Chief Executive Officer COO: Karen Springer, R.N., MS, Chief Operting Officer and Chief Nursing Officer CFO: Todd Lupton, Chief Financial Officer CMO: Brian Lee, M.D., Medical Staff President CIO: Sid Tuesley, Chief Information Officer CHR: Stacy Junk, Human Resources Team Specialist Web address: www.theduponthospital.com	32	10	86	—	—	—	—	—	—	—
⊠ **LUTHERAN HOSPITAL OF INDIANA**, 7950 West Jefferson Boulevard, Zip 46804–1677; tel. 260/435–7001 **A**1 3 5 9 10 **F**2 4 6 10 11 12 14 15 16 17 18 19 20 21 22 23 24 26 27 28 29 32 33 36 40 44 45 46 47 48 49 50 52 53 54 55 56 57 58 59 60 61 62 63 64 65 66 67 69 70 71 76 81 82 84 85 86 87 88 92 93 94 96 100 105 106 107 108 109 110 **P**5 **S** Triad Hospitals, Inc., Plano, TX Primary Contact: Thomas D. Miller, Chief Executive Officer COO: Joseph M. Dorko, Vice President Operations CFO: Stephen Carroll, Senior Vice President and Chief Financial Officer CMO: Michael Musgrave, M.D., Chief Medical Officer CIO: Sid Tuesley, Chief Information Officer CHR: Bruce Hamilton, Vice President Human Resources Web address: www.lutheran–hosp.com	33	10	366	18743	272	202773	1714	257976	82693	1898
⊠ △ **PARKVIEW HOSPITAL**, 2200 Randallia Drive, Zip 46805–4699; tel. 260/373–4000, (Includes ORTHOPAEDIC HOSPITAL AT PARKVIEW NORTH, 11119 Parkview Plaza Drive, Zip 46845; tel. 260/672–5000; PARKVIEW NORTH HOSPITAL, 11115 Parkview Plaza Drive, Zip 46845; tel. 260/672–4000) **A**1 3 5 7 9 10 **F**2 3 4 6 9 11 12 14 15 17 19 21 22 23 24 26 27 28 29 33 34 35 36 37 38 39 41 42 46 47 48 49 50 51 52 53 55 56 57 58 59 61 62 63 64 65 66 67 68 69 71 72 73 74 75 76 77 78 79 81 82 83 84 85 87 88 90 92 93 94 96 106 108 109 110 **P**6 **S** Parkview Health, Fort Wayne, IN Primary Contact: Duane L. Erwin, President COO: Dale R. Wilcox, Executive Vice President and Chief Operating Officer CFO: Robert Carlisle, Senior Vice President and Chief Financial Officer CMO: Seetha Atluri, M.D., President Medical Staff CIO: Patricia Thompson, Senior Vice President and Chief Information Officer CHR: Candy Knowles, Senior Vice President Human Resources Web address: www.parkview.com	23	10	654	24762	374	261593	2699	366146	154251	2934
⊠ △ **REHABILITATION HOSPITAL OF FORT WAYNE**, 7970 West Jefferson Boulevard, Zip 46804–4140; tel. 260/435–6100 **A**1 7 10 **F**21 22 68 69 92 94 96 108 **P**5 **S** Triad Hospitals, Inc., Plano, TX Primary Contact: Darlene Degener, Chief Operating Officer COO: Darlene Degener, Chief Operating Officer CFO: Stephen Carroll, Senior Vice President and Chief Financial Officer CMO: William Hedrick, Chief Medical Officer CHR: Deborah Giardina, Chief Human Resource Officer Web address: www.rehabhospital.com	33	46	36	716	25	6101	0	7738	4288	76
□ **SELECT SPECIALTY HOSPITAL**, 700 Broadway, 7th Floor, Zip 46802; tel. 260/425–3810 **A**1 10 **F**2 10 21 39 58 60 64 94 110 **P**8 Primary Contact: Kirk M. Ray, Chief Executive Officer Web address: www.selectmedicalcorp.com	33	80	27	223	20	0	0	10256	3861	94

IN

Hospital, Address, Telephone, Approval, Facility, and Physician Codes, Health Care System	Classi-fication Codes		Utilization Data					Expense (thousands) of dollars		
★ American Hospital Association (AHA) membership □ Joint Commission on Accreditation of Healthcare Organizations (JCAHO) accreditation ○ American Osteopathic Association (AOA) accreditation △ Commission on Accreditation of Rehabilitation Facilities (CARF) accreditation	Control	Service	Staffed Beds	Admissions	Census	Outpatient Visits	Births	Total	Payroll	Personnel

⊠ **ST. JOSEPH HOSPITAL**, 700 Broadway, Zip 46802–1493; tel. 260/425–3000, (Total facility includes 21 beds in nursing home–type unit) **A**1 3 5 9 10 **F**2 3 4 10 11 12 13 14 15 17 19 21 22 23 26 27 28 29 32 33 35 37 38 39 42 44 46 48 49 51 52 53 54 55 56 59 60 62 63 64 65 66 68 69 70 71 73 74 75 76 77 78 81 82 85 88 92 93 94 104 108 110 **P**6 8 **S** Triad Hospitals, Inc., Plano, TX Primary Contact: Jerry Beasley, Chief Executive Officer COO: David LeMonte, Chief Operating Officer CFO: Tom Fox, Chief Financial Officer CIO: Sid Tuesley, Chief Information Officer CHR: Charlee Hakes, Director Human Resources Web address: www.stjoehospital.com	33	10	211	6226	98	95200	538	83502	31590	696
⊠ **VETERANS AFFAIRS NORTHERN INDIANA HEALTH CARE SYSTEM**, 2121 Lake Avenue, Zip 46805–5347; tel. 260/460–1310, (Includes VETERANS AFFAIRS NORTHERN INDIANA HEALTH CARE SYSTEM–MARION CAMPUS, 1700 East 38th Street, Marion, Zip 46953–4589; tel. 765/674–3321), (Total facility includes 180 beds in nursing home–type unit) (Nonreporting) **A**1 **S** Department of Veterans Affairs, Washington, DC Primary Contact: Robert H. Beller, Acting Director COO: Robert H. Beller, Associate Director and Chief Operating Officer CIO: David Troyer, Manager Information Resources Management Web address: www.va.gov/sta/guide/home.asp	45	10	423	—	—	—	—	—	—	—
FRANKFORT—Clinton County										
⊠ **ST. VINCENT FRANKFORT HOSPITAL**, 1300 South Jackson Street, Zip 46041–3394, Mailing Address: P.O. Box 669, Zip 46041–0669; tel. 765/656–3000 **A**1 9 10 18 **F**2 9 11 12 21 22 23 25 26 28 29 33 39 46 52 53 58 59 60 61 62 63 64 69 70 77 81 84 88 94 96 97 106 **P**6 **S** Ascension Health, Saint Louis, MO Primary Contact: Thomas Crawford, Chief Executive Officer CFO: Steve Davis, Chief Financial Officer CMO: John Crane, M.D., Chief of Staff CHR: Krista Wright, Director of Human Resources Web address: www.stvincent.org	21	10	25	1812	11	38638	263	20662	10319	188
FRANKLIN—Johnson County										
★ ○ **JOHNSON MEMORIAL HOSPITAL**, 1125 West Jefferson Street, Zip 46131–2140, Mailing Address: P.O. Box 549, Zip 46131–0549; tel. 317/736–3300, (Total facility includes 55 beds in nursing home–type unit) **A**9 10 11 **F**1 6 10 11 12 15 16 21 22 23 26 27 28 29 30 33 35 39 42 46 48 51 52 53 55 58 59 60 61 62 63 64 66 68 69 79 81 82 84 86 87 88 92 93 94 95 96 98 106 107 108 109 **P**1 6 Primary Contact: Gregg A. Bechtold, President and Chief Executive Officer COO: Thomas F. Barry, Jr, Vice President CFO: Larry Heydon, Chief Financial Officer CMO: John G. Norris, M.D., Chief of Staff CIO: Al Godsoe, Director Information Systems CHR: Judy Ware, Director Human Resources Web address: www.johnsonmemorial.org	13	10	153	4117	85	138128	690	61633	26610	632
GARY—Lake County										
⊠ △ **METHODIST HOSPITALS**, 600 Grant Street, Zip 46402–6099; tel. 219/886–4000, (Includes NORTHLAKE CAMPUS, 600 Grant Street, Zip 46402; SOUTHLAKE CAMPUS, 8701 Broadway, Merrillville, Zip 46410; tel. 219/738–5500) **A**1 2 3 5 7 9 10 **F**2 3 4 9 10 11 12 15 17 19 21 22 23 24 27 28 29 31 33 34 36 37 40 42 43 46 47 48 50 51 52 55 56 57 58 59 60 61 62 63 64 65 66 68 69 70 71 72 73 74 75 76 77 78 79 81 82 84 86 87 88 90 92 93 94 96 97 108 109 110 **P**6 Primary Contact: James A. Berg, President CFO: John Diehl, Vice President CMO: David Ross, M.D., Chief Medical Officer CIO: David Parry, Chief Information Officer Web address: www.methodisthospitals.org	23	10	712	23061	366	234170	1770	295636	119360	2503
GOSHEN—Elkhart County										
⊠ **GOSHEN GENERAL HOSPITAL**, 200 High Park Avenue, Zip 46526–4899, Mailing Address: P.O. Box 139, Zip 46527–0139; tel. 574/533–2141 **A**1 9 10 **F**2 9 10 11 12 15 17 21 22 23 24 26 27 28 29 30 33 35 36 37 38 39 40 42 44 46 47 48 51 52 53 55 58 59 61 62 63 64 65 66 69 79 80 81 82 84 85 87 88 92 93 94 96 106 108 109 110 **P**1 6 7 **S** Clarian Health Partners, Indianapolis, IN Primary Contact: James O. Dague, President and Chief Executive Officer COO: Sheryl Lewis–Blake, Executive Vice President and Chief Operating Officer CFO: Randal Christophel, Executive Vice President and Chief Financial Officer CMO: James VanCuren, M.D., Vice President Medical Affairs CHR: Kristi Higgins, Vice President for Human Resources, Legal and Compliance Services Web address: www.goshenhealth.com	23	10	116	5598	60	120583	1477	93887	38731	1050
OAKLAWN PSYCHIATRIC CENTER, 330 Lakeview Drive, Zip 46528–9365, Mailing Address: P.O. Box 809, Zip 46527–0809; tel. 574/533–1234 **A**10 **F**21 22 26 27 28 29 31 45 71 72 73 74 75 76 77 78 94 108 **P**6 Primary Contact: Harold C. Loewen, President Web address: www.oaklawn.org	23	22	34	1096	21	273631	0	25453	13274	408

IN

Many Facility Codes have changed. Please refer to the AHA Guide Code Chart. © 2005 AHA Guide

Hospital, Address, Telephone, Approval, Facility, and Physician Codes, Health Care System	Classi-fication Codes		Utilization Data					Expense (thousands) of dollars		
★ American Hospital Association (AHA) membership □ Joint Commission on Accreditation of Healthcare Organizations (JCAHO) accreditation ○ American Osteopathic Association (AOA) accreditation △ Commission on Accreditation of Rehabilitation Facilities (CARF) accreditation	Control	Service	Staffed Beds	Admissions	Census	Outpatient Visits	Births	Total	Payroll	Personnel

GREENCASTLE—Putnam County

★ ○ **PUTNAM COUNTY HOSPITAL**, 1542 Bloomington Street, Zip 46135–2297; tel. 765/653–5121 **A**2 9 10 11 **F**2 9 10 11 12 21 22 23 27 28 29 32 33 36 39 41 44 46 48 52 55 58 59 60 61 62 63 64 65 66 69 70 75 81 82 84 85 88 94 95 96 97 106 109 110 **P**6
Primary Contact: Dennis Weatherford, Chief Executive Officer
CFO: Kevin Fowler, Director Finance
| 13 | 10 | 55 | 1982 | 19 | 56859 | 225 | 27277 | 11539 | 294 |

GREENFIELD—Hancock County

★ ○ **HANCOCK MEMORIAL HOSPITAL AND HEALTH SERVICES**, 801 North State Street, Zip 46140–1270, Mailing Address: P.O. Box 827, Zip 46140–0827; tel. 317/462–5544, (Total facility includes 20 beds in nursing home–type unit) **A**9 10 11 **F**2 9 11 12 14 15 21 22 23 24 26 27 28 29 30 31 33 35 36 37 38 39 41 42 44 46 47 48 50 51 52 53 54 55 57 58 59 60 61 62 63 64 65 66 68 69 71 75 76 81 82 84 85 87 88 92 93 94 95 96 98 106 107 108 109 110 **P**8
Primary Contact: Robert C. Keen, Ph.D., FACHE, President and Chief Executive Officer
CFO: Rick Edwards, Vice President Finance and Business Services
CMO: Robin Helmuth, President Medical Staff
CIO: Jon Miller, Team leader Accounting and Information Services
CHR: Dave Holmes, Vice President Support Services
Web address: www.hmhhs.org
| 13 | 10 | 100 | 3946 | 58 | 149760 | 557 | 65274 | 28816 | 692 |

GREENSBURG—Decatur County

⊠ **DECATUR COUNTY MEMORIAL HOSPITAL**, 720 North Lincoln Street, Zip 47240–1398; tel. 812/663–4331 **A**1 9 10 **F**1 2 6 9 11 12 23 24 26 27 28 33 39 42 45 46 47 48 51 52 53 54 55 58 59 60 61 62 63 64 65 66 69 70 81 82 84 85 86 87 88 93 94 95 96 97 106 108 109 **P**6
Primary Contact: David V. Trexler, President
CFO: Michael R. Ruckel, Vice President Finance
Web address: www.dcmh.net
| 13 | 10 | 71 | 1929 | 30 | 51091 | 229 | 30040 | 14302 | 327 |

GREENWOOD—Johnson County

□ **KINDRED HOSPITAL INDIANAPOLIS SOUTH**, 898 East Main Street, Zip 46143–1400; tel. 317/888–8155, (Nonreporting) **A**1 10 **S** Kindred Healthcare, Louisville, KY
Primary Contact: Mona Euler, Chief Executive Officer
Web address: www.kindredhealthcare.com
| 33 | 49 | 36 | — | — | — | — | — | — | — |

□ **VALLE VISTA HEALTH SYSTEM**, 898 East Main Street, Zip 46143–1400; tel. 317/887–1348 **A**1 9 10 **F**4 26 27 28 71 72 73 74 75 76 77 78 **S** Psychiatric Solutions, Franklin, TN
Primary Contact: David Bell, Chief Executive Officer
Web address: www.vallevistahospital.com
| 33 | 22 | 88 | 1500 | 64 | — | 0 | 10242 | 5356 | 196 |

HAMMOND—Lake County

○ △ **SAINT MARGARET MERCY HEALTHCARE CENTERS**, 5454 Hohman Avenue, Zip 46320–1999; tel. 219/933–2074, (Includes SAINT MARGARET MERCY HEALTHCARE CENTERS–NORTH CAMPUS, 5454 Hohman Avenue, Zip 46320; tel. 219/932–2300; SAINT MARGARET MERCY HEALTHCARE CENTERS–SOUTH CAMPUS, 24 Joliet Street, Dyer, Zip 46311–1799; tel. 219/865–2141; Thomas J. Gryzbek, President), (Total facility includes 67 beds in nursing home–type unit) (Nonreporting) **A**2 7 9 10 11 12 **S** Sisters of St. Francis Health Services, Inc., Mishawaka, IN
Primary Contact: Thomas J. Gryzbek, President
Web address: www.smmhc.com
| 21 | 10 | 624 | — | — | — | — | — | — | — |

□ **SELECT SPECIALTY HOSPITAL OF NORTHWEST INDIANA**, 5454 Hohman Avenue, 5th Floor, Zip 46320; tel. 219/937–9900, (Nonreporting) **A**1 10
Primary Contact: Eddie Dyer, Chief Executive Officer
| 33 | 49 | 70 | — | — | — | — | — | — | — |

HARTFORD CITY—Blackford County

⊠ **BLACKFORD COMMUNITY HOSPITAL**, 410 Pilgrim Boulevard, Zip 47348–1897; tel. 765/348–0300 **A**1 9 10 18 **F**2 6 9 12 21 29 33 35 39 46 48 53 62 63 64 65 69 81 88 94 96 97 **P**1 6 **S** Cardinal Health System, Muncie, IN
Primary Contact: Steven J. West, Chief Executive Officer
CFO: Walter Soptelean, Chief Financial Officer
CHR: John Crosbie, Director Support Services
| 23 | 10 | 25 | 515 | 6 | 12896 | 0 | 10661 | 4495 | 128 |

HOBART—Lake County

□ △ **ST. MARY MEDICAL CENTER**, 1500 South Lake Park Avenue, Zip 46342–6699; tel. 219/942–0551 **A**1 7 9 10 **F**2 9 11 12 15 17 19 21 22 23 26 27 28 29 33 35 37 40 46 48 49 51 52 55 58 59 60 61 62 63 64 66 69 70 80 81 82 84 88 92 94 96 106 108 110 **P**6 8 **S** Community Healthcare System, Hammond, IN
Primary Contact: Milton Triana, Administrator
Web address: www.stmary–hobart.com
| 23 | 10 | 176 | 8309 | 117 | 93163 | 426 | 97291 | 35564 | 647 |

HUNTINGBURG—Dubois County

□ **ST. JOSEPH'S HOSPITAL**, 1900 Medical Arts Drive, Zip 47542–9521; tel. 812/683–2121, (Nonreporting) **A**1 9 10 18 **S** Brim Healthcare, Inc., Brentwood, TN
Primary Contact: Jonathan Brenn, Chief Executive Officer
Web address: www.stjh.info
| 23 | 10 | 25 | — | — | — | — | — | — | — |

IN

Hospital, Address, Telephone, Approval, Facility, and Physician Codes, Health Care System	Classi-fication Codes		Utilization Data					Expense (thousands) of dollars		
★ American Hospital Association (AHA) membership □ Joint Commission on Accreditation of Healthcare Organizations (JCAHO) accreditation ○ American Osteopathic Association (AOA) accreditation △ Commission on Accreditation of Rehabilitation Facilities (CARF) accreditation	Control	Service	Staffed Beds	Admissions	Census	Outpatient Visits	Births	Total	Payroll	Personnel

HUNTINGTON—Huntington County

☒ **PARKVIEW HUNTINGTON HOSPITAL**, 2001 Stults Road, Zip 46750–3696;
tel. 260/356–3000 **A**1 9 10 **F**2 6 11 12 21 22 23 24 26 27 28 29 30 31 32
33 35 41 44 46 47 48 52 53 54 55 58 59 60 61 62 63 64 65 66 69 70 81
82 84 88 94 95 96 98 106 108 110 **S** Parkview Health, Fort Wayne, IN
Primary Contact: Darlene Garrett, Chief Operating Officer
CFO: Tim Lessing, Chief Financial Officer
CIO: Pat Thompson, Chief Information Officer
Web address: www.parkview.com

| | 23 | 10 | 36 | 2124 | 16 | 41493 | 326 | 28620 | 11577 | 272 |

INDIANAPOLIS—Marion County

☒ **CLARIAN HEALTH PARTNERS**, I-65 at 21st Street, Zip 46202–5250, Mailing
Address: P.O. Box 1367, Zip 46206–1367; tel. 317/962–2000, (Includes
INDIANA UNIVERSITY MEDICAL CENTER, 550 North University Boulevard,
Zip 46202–5262; tel. 317/274–5000; Samuel L. Odle, President and Chief
Executive Officer; METHODIST HOSPITAL OF INDIANA, 1701 North Senate
Boulevard, Zip 46202, Mailing Address: 1701 North Senate Boulevard,
Zip 46202; tel. 317/962–2000; Samuel L. Odle, President and Chief Executive
Officer; RILEY HOSPITAL FOR CHILDREN, 702 Barnhill Drive, Zip 46202–5225) **A**1
2 3 5 8 9 10 **F**4 6 7 9 11 12 13 14 15 16 17 18 19 20 21 22 23 24 26 27
28 29 30 31 32 33 34 36 37 38 40 41 42 43 44 46 47 48 49 50 51 52 53
54 55 56 57 58 59 60 61 62 63 64 65 66 67 69 70 71 72 73 74 75 76 77
78 79 80 81 82 83 84 85 86 87 88 89 92 93 94 95 96 98 99 100 101 102
103 104 106 107 108 109 110 **P**6 7 **S** Clarian Health Partners, Indianapolis, IN
Primary Contact: Daniel F. Evans, Jr, President and Chief Executive Officer
CFO: Marvin G. Pember, Executive Vice President and Chief Financial Officer
CMO: Richard Graffis, M.D., Executive Vice President Medical Operations
CIO: Richard F. Johnson, Senior Vice President and Chief Information Officer
CHR: Steve Wantz, Senior Vice President, Human Resources
Web address: www.clarian.org

| | 23 | 10 | 1357 | 56600 | 985 | 901155 | 5176 | 1390296 | 515622 | 10140 |

□ △ **COMMUNITY HEALTH NETWORK**, 1500 North Ritter Avenue,
Zip 46219–3095; tel. 317/355–1411, (Includes COMMUNITY HOSPITAL EAST,
1500 North Ritter Avenue, tel. 317/355–1411; COMMUNITY HOSPITAL NORTH,
7150 Clearvista Drive, Zip 46256; tel. 317/849–6262; COMMUNITY HOSPITAL
OF ANDERSON AND MADISON COUNTY, 1515 North Madison Avenue, Anderson,
Zip 46011–3453; tel. 765/642–8011; COMMUNITY HOSPITAL SOUTH, 1402
East County Line Road South, Zip 46227; tel. 317/887–7000), (Nonreporting) **A**1
2 3 5 7 9 10
Primary Contact: William E. Corley, President
Web address: www.ecommunity.com

| | 23 | 10 | 787 | — | | | | | | |

FAIRBANKS, 8102 Clearvista Parkway, Zip 46256–4698; tel. 317/849–8222
A10 **F**3 4 27 28 73 94 96 108 **P**8
Primary Contact: Helene M. Cross, President and Chief Executive Officer
Web address: www.fairbankscd.org

| | 23 | 82 | 70 | 3445 | 59 | 12419 | 0 | 10385 | 5358 | 158 |

□ **INDIANA HEART HOSPITAL**, 8075 North Shadeland Avenue, Zip 46256;
tel. 317/621–8000, (Nonreporting) **A**1 9 10
Primary Contact: David Veillette, Chief Executive Officer
Web address: www.hearthospital.com

| | 23 | 42 | 56 | — | — | — | — | — | — | — |

INDIANA UNIVERSITY MEDICAL CENTER See Clarian Health Partners

□ **KINDRED HOSPITAL–INDIANAPOLIS**, 1700 West 10th Street,
Zip 46222–3802; tel. 317/636–4400, (Nonreporting) **A**1 10 **S** Kindred
Healthcare, Louisville, KY
Primary Contact: John Pierson, Chief Executive Officer
Web address: www.kindredhealthcare.com

| | 33 | 10 | 59 | — | | | | | | |

□ **LARUE D. CARTER MEMORIAL HOSPITAL**, 2601 Cold Spring Road,
Zip 46222–2273; tel. 317/941–4000 **A**1 3 5 10 **F**22 26 28 58 71 72 74
94 **P**6
Primary Contact: Alan D. Schmetzer, M.D., Superintendent

| | 12 | 22 | 159 | 195 | 159 | 0 | 0 | 45070 | 15451 | 488 |

METHODIST HOSPITAL OF INDIANA See Clarian Health Partners

□ △ **REHABILITATION HOSPITAL OF INDIANA**, 4141 Shore Drive,
Zip 46254–2607; tel. 317/329–2000, (Nonreporting) **A**1 7 10
Primary Contact: Dennis Armington, Chief Executive Officer
Web address: www.rhin.org

| | 23 | 46 | 80 | — | | | | | | |

☒ △ **RICHARD L. ROUDEBUSH VETERANS AFFAIRS MEDICAL CENTER**,
1481 West Tenth Street, Zip 46202–2884; tel. 317/554–0000 **A**1 2 3 5 7 8 **F**1
2 4 7 9 14 15 17 19 21 22 23 26 27 28 29 31 32 33 37 38 39 41 44 45 46
47 48 49 50 51 52 55 57 58 60 61 62 63 64 65 66 68 69 70 71 73 74 75
76 77 78 79 81 82 84 85 87 88 92 94 96 106 107 108 109 110 **P**6
S Department of Veterans Affairs, Washington, DC
Primary Contact: Susan P. Bowers, Director
COO: Thomas Mattice, Associate Director
CFO: Paul Pessagno, Chief Financial Officer
CMO: Ken Klotz, M.D., Chief of Staff
CIO: John P. Burke, Chief Information Officer
CHR: Annie Herbert, Chief Human Resources Management Services
Web address: www.va.gov/sta/guide/home.asp

| | 45 | 10 | 150 | 6682 | 119 | 399090 | 0 | 211804 | 77718 | — |

RILEY HOSPITAL FOR CHILDREN See Clarian Health Partners

Many Facility Codes have changed. Please refer to the AHA Guide Code Chart.   © 2005 AHA Guide

Hospital, Address, Telephone, Approval, Facility, and Physician Codes, Health Care System	Classi-fication Codes		Utilization Data					Expense (thousands) of dollars		
★ American Hospital Association (AHA) membership □ Joint Commission on Accreditation of Healthcare Organizations (JCAHO) accreditation ○ American Osteopathic Association (AOA) accreditation △ Commission on Accreditation of Rehabilitation Facilities (CARF) accreditation	Control	Service	Staffed Beds	Admissions	Census	Outpatient Visits	Births	Total	Payroll	Personnel

	Control	Service	Staffed Beds	Admissions	Census	Outpatient Visits	Births	Total	Payroll	Personnel
□ **SELECT SPECIALTY HOSPITAL OF INDIANAPOLIS**, 1901 North Senate Boulevard, Zip 46202; tel. 317/931–1676, (Nonreporting) **A**1 10 Primary Contact: Joyce Fogler, Chief Executive Officer	33	49	54	—	—	—	—	—	—	—
ST. ELIZABETH ANN SETON HOSPITAL OF INDIANAPOLIS, 2001 West 86th Street, 7th Floor, Zip 46207; tel. 317/338–5767, (Nonreporting) **A**9 10 Primary Contact: Peter H. Alexander, Administrator	21	80	29	—	—	—	—	—	—	—
ST. FRANCIS HOSPITAL AND HEALTH CENTERS – SOUTH CAMPUS See St. Francis Hospital and Health Centers – North Campus, Beech Grove										
⊠ △ **ST. VINCENT HOSPITALS AND HEALTH SERVICES**, 2001 West 86th Street, Zip 46260–1991, Mailing Address: P.O. Box 40970, Zip 46240–0970; tel. 317/338–2345, (Includes ST. VINCENT STRESS CENTER, 8401 Harcourt Road, Zip 46260, Mailing Address: P.O. Box 80160, Zip 46280; tel. 317/338–4600; Sheila Mishler, Chief Executive Officer) **A**1 2 3 5 7 8 9 10 **F**2 4 7 9 10 11 12 14 15 16 17 18 19 20 21 22 23 24 26 27 28 29 31 32 33 34 35 36 37 38 39 40 42 44 45 46 47 48 50 51 52 53 55 56 57 59 60 61 62 63 64 65 66 67 69 70 71 72 73 74 75 76 77 78 79 80 81 82 84 85 86 87 88 92 93 94 95 96 98 99 100 106 107 108 109 110 **P**6 8 **S** Ascension Health, Saint Louis, MO Primary Contact: Patricia A. Maryland, Dr.PH, President CFO: Terry Hamilton, Executive Director Finance CMO: Michael Wieman, M.D., Senior Vice President and Chief Medical Officer CIO: Greg Jones, Interim Chief Information Officer CHR: Marty Du Rall, Executive Director Human Resources Web address: www.stvincent.org	21	10	889	39811	566	647994	7062	648367	264900	5463
⊠ **ST. VINCENT WOMEN'S HOSPITAL**, 8111 Township Line Road, Zip 46260–8043; tel. 317/415–8111, (Nonreporting) **A**1 9 10 **S** Ascension Health, Saint Louis, MO Primary Contact: Mary Lane Jackson, Administrator CIO: Ken Meyer, Head Information Systems Web address: www.stvincent.org	33	44	102	—	—	—	—	—	—	—
THE HEART CENTER OF INDIANA, 10580 North Meridian Street, Zip 46290; tel. 317/583–5000 **A**9 10 **F**2 14 15 17 19 21 26 27 28 29 33 48 55 58 63 64 81 84 85 88 94 106 108 **P**2 Primary Contact: John Stewart, Interim Chief Executive Officer Web address: www.theheartcenter.com	33	42	60	4997	46	5515	0	74286	17653	304
○ **WESTVIEW HOSPITAL**, 3630 Guion Road, Zip 46222–1699; tel. 317/924–6661, (Total facility includes 18 beds in nursing home–type unit) (Nonreporting) **A**9 10 11 12 13 Primary Contact: Jerry L. Porter, Chief Executive Officer Web address: www.westviewhospital.org	23	10	67	—	—	—	—	—	—	—
□ **WISHARD HEALTH SERVICES**, 1001 West 10th Street, Zip 46202–2879; tel. 317/630–7033, (Total facility includes 240 beds in nursing home–type unit) (Nonreporting) **A**1 3 5 8 9 10 Primary Contact: Lisa E. Harris, M.D., Chief Executive Officer and Medical Director Web address: www.wishard.edu	15	10	492	—	—	—	—	—	—	—
JASPER—Dubois County										
⊠ **MEMORIAL HOSPITAL AND HEALTH CARE CENTER**, 800 West Ninth Street, Zip 47546–2516; tel. 812/482–2345, (Total facility includes 24 beds in nursing home–type unit) **A**1 2 9 10 19 **F**1 2 3 6 9 11 12 13 14 15 17 21 22 23 27 28 29 31 33 37 38 40 42 44 45 46 48 51 52 53 55 56 57 58 59 60 61 62 63 64 65 66 67 68 69 70 71 73 74 75 76 77 81 82 84 87 88 92 94 95 96 106 107 108 109 110 **P**6 **S** American Province of Little Company of Mary Sisters, Evergreen Park, IL Primary Contact: Raymond W. Snowden, President and Chief Executive Officer CFO: E Kyle Bennett, Executive Vice President CMO: Robert Maitlen, M.D., Medical Staff President CIO: Todd Mehringer, Director Information Systems CHR: Diane Denk, Director Human Resources Web address: www.mhhcc.org	21	10	124	6054	74	126110	810	70377	34797	779
JEFFERSONVILLE—Clark County										
⊠ **CLARK MEMORIAL HOSPITAL**, 1220 Missouri Avenue, Zip 47130–3743, Mailing Address: P.O. Box 69, Zip 47131–0069; tel. 812/282–6631, (Total facility includes 22 beds in nursing home–type unit) **A**1 2 5 9 10 **F**2 4 9 11 12 14 15 17 21 22 23 24 26 27 28 29 31 33 34 37 41 42 44 46 47 48 51 52 55 57 58 59 60 61 62 63 65 66 70 73 74 75 76 77 78 81 82 84 85 88 92 93 94 96 106 107 108 109 110 **P**6 **S** Jewish Hospital HealthCare Services, Louisville, KY Primary Contact: Martin Padgett, President and Chief Executive Officer CMO: Saleem Seyal, M.D., President Medical Staff CIO: Larry Reverman, Director Information Systems CHR: Fred Horlander, Vice President Web address: www.clarkmemorial.org	13	10	241	11097	142	126896	1590	109719	48732	1228
□ **WELLSTONE REGIONAL HOSPITAL**, 2700 Vissing Park Road, Zip 47130; tel. 812/284–8000, (Nonreporting) **A**1 10 Primary Contact: Patrick T. Hammer, President and Chief Executive Officer	33	22	100	—	—	—	—	—	—	—

IN

Hospital, Address, Telephone, Approval, Facility, and Physician Codes, Health Care System	Classification Codes		Utilization Data					Expense (thousands) of dollars		
★ American Hospital Association (AHA) membership □ Joint Commission on Accreditation of Healthcare Organizations (JCAHO) accreditation ○ American Osteopathic Association (AOA) accreditation △ Commission on Accreditation of Rehabilitation Facilities (CARF) accreditation	Control	Service	Staffed Beds	Admissions	Census	Outpatient Visits	Births	Total	Payroll	Personnel

KENDALLVILLE—Noble County

✉ **PARKVIEW NOBLE HOSPITAL**, 401 Sawyer Road, Zip 46755–2293, Mailing Address: P.O. Box 728, Zip 46755–0728; tel. 260/347–8700 **A**1 9 10 **F**2 6 9 11 12 21 22 23 26 27 28 29 30 33 39 46 48 52 55 57 58 59 62 63 64 66 69 70 81 82 84 85 87 88 93 94 96 108 110 **P**6 **S** Parkview Health, Fort Wayne, IN Primary Contact: David C. Hunter, Chief Operating Officer COO: David C. Hunter, Chief Operating Officer CFO: Tim Lessing, Chief Financial Officer CMO: Abdali Jan, M.D., Chief of Staff CIO: Patricia Thompson, Chief Information Officer CHR: Bob Pruitt, Director Human Resources Web address: www.parkview.com	23	10	30	1534	13	53997	235	27372	10912	248

KNOX—Starke County

✉ **STARKE MEMORIAL HOSPITAL**, 102 East Culver Road, Zip 46534–2299, Mailing Address: P.O. Box 339, Zip 46534–2299; tel. 574/772–6231, (Nonreporting) **A**1 10 **S** LifePoint Hospitals, Inc., Brentwood, TN Primary Contact: Ron Tyrer, Interim Chief Executive Officer CMO: Teresa Alexander, M.D., President Medical Staff	33	10	35	—	—	—	—	—	—	—

KOKOMO—Howard County

✉ **HOWARD REGIONAL HEALTH SYSTEM**, 3500 South Lafountain Street, Zip 46904–9011, Mailing Address: P.O. Box 9011, Zip 46904–9011; tel. 765/453–0702 **A**1 2 9 10 **F**2 4 6 9 11 12 15 17 21 22 23 24 26 27 28 29 33 34 39 41 42 48 51 55 56 57 58 59 61 63 68 69 71 72 74 75 77 78 80 81 82 85 86 88 92 93 94 98 106 108 109 **P**3 8 Primary Contact: James P. Alender, President and Chief Executive Officer COO: Theodore Brown, Chief Operating Officer CFO: Thom Cook, Chief Financial Officer CIO: Sharon Miller, Chief Information Officer CHR: Michael L. Williams, Vice President Human Resources Web address: www.howardregional.org	13	10	180	7109	100	296092	780	117946	48141	1251
□ **HOWARD REGIONAL HEALTH SYSTEM WEST CAMPUS SPECIALTY HOSPITAL**, 829 North Dixon Road, Zip 46901–7709; tel. 765/452–6700, (Nonreporting) **A**1 9 10 Primary Contact: Michelle L. Russell, Vice and Administrator	33	46	54	—	—	—	—	—	—	—
ST ELIZABETH ANN SETON HOSPITAL OF KOKOMO, 1907 West Sycamore Street, 4th Floor, Zip 46901; tel. 765/236–8900, (Nonreporting) **A**9 10 Primary Contact: Peter H. Alexander, Administrator	21	80	30	—	—	—	—	—	—	—
✉ **ST. JOSEPH HOSPITAL**, 1907 West Sycamore Street, Zip 46901–4197, Mailing Address: P.O. Box 9010, Zip 46904–9010; tel. 765/452–5611 **A**1 9 10 **F**2 3 4 6 11 12 15 21 22 23 26 27 28 29 30 33 35 37 39 45 46 47 48 52 53 54 55 57 58 59 60 61 62 63 64 66 68 69 70 71 72 73 74 75 76 77 78 80 81 82 84 86 87 88 93 94 95 96 98 106 107 108 109 110 **P**6 7 **S** Ascension Health, Saint Louis, MO Primary Contact: Darcy K. Burthay, R.N., Interim President and Chief Nursing Officer CFO: Dennis Ressler, Chief Financial Officer CMO: John Ayers, M.D., Vice President Medical Affairs CIO: Brian Peters, Director Information Systems CHR: Cindy Babb, Director Human Resources Web address: www.stjosephhospital.net	21	10	136	5418	69	139810	757	74379	32213	576

LA PORTE—La Porte County

✉ △ **LA PORTE REGIONAL HEALTH SYSTEM**, 1007 Lincolnway, Zip 46350–3201, Mailing Address: P.O. Box 250, Zip 46352–0250; tel. 219/326–1234, (Total facility includes 55 beds in nursing home–type unit) **A**1 2 7 9 10 19 **F**2 4 9 11 12 14 15 17 19 21 22 23 24 26 27 28 29 30 31 32 33 35 36 37 38 39 40 41 42 44 45 46 47 48 49 50 51 52 53 54 55 57 58 59 60 61 62 63 64 65 66 68 69 70 71 72 73 74 75 76 77 78 80 81 82 84 85 86 87 88 92 93 94 95 96 106 107 108 109 110 **S** Clarian Health Partners, Indianapolis, IN Primary Contact: Michael E. Haley, President and Chief Executive Officer CFO: Mark Rafalski, Vice President Finance and Chief Financial Officer CMO: Linda L. Satkoski, R.N., Vice President Physician Relations and Patient Care Services CIO: Robert Gerick, Vice President Strategic Operations CHR: Connie Ford, Vice President Human Resources Web address: www.laportehealth.org	23	10	227	6374	116	94927	744	101414	43631	1037

LAFAYETTE—Tippecanoe County

○ **GREATER LAFAYETTE HEALTH SERVICES**, 2400 South Street, Zip 47904–3027; tel. 765/447–6811, (Includes LAFAYETTE HOME HOSPITAL, Terrance E. Wilson, President and Chief Executive Officer; ST. ELIZABETH MEDICAL CENTER, 1501 Hartford Street, Zip 47904–2126, Mailing Address: 1501 Hartford Street, Zip 47904–2126; tel. 765/423–6011; Terrance E. Wilson, President and Chief Executive Officer), (Total facility includes 44 beds in nursing home–type unit) **A**2 6 9 10 11 **F**6 9 11 12 14 15 17 19 21 22 23 26 27 28 29 33 36 38 40 43 44 45 47 48 49 50 51 52 54 55 56 57 58 59 60 61 62 63 65 66 68 69 77 78 81 82 84 86 88 92 93 94 96 107 108 109 110 **P**6 **S** Sisters of St. Francis Health Services, Inc., Mishawaka, IN Primary Contact: Terrance E. Wilson, President and Chief Executive Officer Web address: www.glhsi.org	21	10	440	18281	244	279605	2973	236214	92429	2214

IN

Hospital, Address, Telephone, Approval, Facility, and Physician Codes, Health Care System	Classi-fication Codes		Utilization Data					Expense (thousands) of dollars		
★ American Hospital Association (AHA) membership □ Joint Commission on Accreditation of Healthcare Organizations (JCAHO) accreditation ○ American Osteopathic Association (AOA) accreditation △ Commission on Accreditation of Rehabilitation Facilities (CARF) accreditation	Control	Service	Staffed Beds	Admissions	Census	Outpatient Visits	Births	Total	Payroll	Personnel

LAGRANGE—LaGrange County

□ **PARKVIEW LAGRANGE HOSPITAL**, (Formerly LaGrange Community Hospital), 207 North Townline Road, Zip 46761–1325; tel. 260/463–2143 **A**1 9 10 18 **F**2 6 11 12 21 26 27 28 33 46 48 52 55 58 59 60 61 62 63 64 65 66 68 69 81 85 88 93 94 97 110 **P**5 8 **S** Parkview Health, Fort Wayne, IN
Primary Contact: Debra Close, Interim Chief Executive Officer
Web address: www.lagrangech.com

| | 33 | 10 | 50 | 1087 | 15 | 21723 | 246 | 15160 | 6678 | 206 |

LAWRENCEBURG—Dearborn County

★ ○ **DEARBORN COUNTY HOSPITAL**, 600 Wilson Creek Road, Zip 47025–1199; tel. 812/537–1010, (Total facility includes 12 beds in nursing home–type unit) **A**9 10 11 **F**2 9 11 12 15 22 23 26 27 28 29 33 35 36 38 39 46 47 48 51 52 55 58 59 60 61 62 63 64 65 66 69 81 82 84 85 86 87 88 92 94 95 96 108 110 **P**6
Primary Contact: Peter V. Resnick, Executive Director
CFO: Philip A. Meyer, Director Finance
CHR: Pat Sutton, Director Human Resources
Web address: www.dch.org

| | 13 | 10 | 87 | 4734 | 57 | 132226 | 591 | 56621 | 25129 | 618 |

LEBANON—Boone County

☒ **WITHAM MEMORIAL HOSPITAL**, 2605 North Lebanon Street, Zip 46052, Mailing Address: P.O. Box 1200, Zip 46052–3005; tel. 765/485–8000 **A**1 9 10 **F**2 6 11 12 17 21 22 27 28 33 36 42 44 46 48 52 53 54 55 58 59 60 63 64 65 66 69 70 71 76 81 82 84 85 87 88 93 94 96 106 107 108 109 **P**1
Primary Contact: Raymond V. Ingham, Ph.D., President and Chief Executive Officer
CFO: George Pogas, Vice President and Chief Financial Officer
Web address: www.witham.org

| | 13 | 10 | 48 | 2417 | 25 | 81904 | 249 | 42717 | 17026 | 386 |

LINTON—Greene County

☒ **GREENE COUNTY GENERAL HOSPITAL**, Rural Route 1, Box 1000, Zip 47441–9457; tel. 812/847–2281 **A**1 9 10 18 **F**2 9 11 12 14 22 23 26 27 28 33 46 48 51 52 57 59 61 63 64 69 81 82 85 88 92 94 97 106
Primary Contact: Jonas S. Uland, Executive Director
COO: Jonas S. Uland, Executive Director
CFO: Timothy Norris, Chief Financial Officer
CMO: Owen A. Batterton, M.D., Chief of Staff
CIO: Timothy Norris, Chief Financial Officer
Web address: www.greenecountyhospital.com

| | 13 | 10 | 25 | 1352 | 13 | 368592 | 120 | 17994 | 7791 | 212 |

LOGANSPORT—Cass County

□ **LOGANSPORT STATE HOSPITAL**, 1098 South State Road 25, Zip 46947–9699; tel. 574/737–3633 **A**1 **F**2 21 26 27 28 32 45 58 71 74 76 94 106 108
Primary Contact: Jeffrey H. Smith, Ph.D., Superintendent
Web address: www.lshonline.org

| | 12 | 22 | 370 | 188 | 351 | 1801 | 0 | 80655 | 26251 | 722 |

☒ **MEMORIAL HOSPITAL**, 1101 Michigan Avenue, Zip 46947–7013, Mailing Address: P.O. Box 7013, Zip 46947–7013; tel. 574/753–7541, (Total facility includes 21 beds in nursing home–type unit) **A**1 9 10 **F**2 6 9 11 12 21 22 26 27 28 29 33 40 46 47 48 52 53 54 55 58 59 60 61 62 63 64 65 66 69 70 81 82 84 87 88 92 93 94 96 106 108 **P**8
Primary Contact: Brian T. Shockney, President and Chief Executive Officer
COO: Alan W. Biggs, Chief Financial and Operating Officer
CFO: Alan W. Biggs, Chief Financial and Operating Officer
CMO: Charles Montgomery, M.D., Medical Director
CIO: Beth Jump, Chief Information Officer
CHR: Lynda Musselman, Vice President Human Resources
Web address: www.mhlogan.org

| | 13 | 10 | 104 | 2832 | 33 | 74735 | 566 | 39816 | 17968 | 484 |

MADISON—Jefferson County

★ ○ **KING'S DAUGHTERS' HOSPITAL AND HEALTH SERVICES**, One King's Daughters' Drive, Zip 47250–3357, Mailing Address: P.O. Box 447, Zip 47250–0447; tel. 812/265–5211, (Total facility includes 27 beds in nursing home–type unit) **A**2 9 10 11 19 **F**2 6 9 11 12 14 21 22 23 26 27 28 29 33 36 37 44 46 48 51 52 53 58 59 60 61 62 63 64 65 66 69 80 81 82 84 85 88 92 94 95 96 106 108 109 110 **P**6
Primary Contact: Roger J. Allman, Chief Executive Officer
CFO: Steve Meacham, Vice President Finance
CMO: Mark Totten, M.D., President Medical Staff
CIO: Linda Darnell, Director Management Information Systems
CHR: Debbie Temple, Director Human Resources
Web address: www.kingsdaughtershospital.org

| | 23 | 10 | 112 | 4566 | 61 | 155231 | 398 | 80202 | 42215 | 888 |

□ **MADISON STATE HOSPITAL**, 711 Green Road, Zip 47250–2199; tel. 812/265–2611, (Nonreporting) **A**1 10
Primary Contact: Nikki C. Morrell, Superintendent
Web address: www.in.gov/fssa/msh

| | 12 | 22 | 160 | — | — | — | — | — | — | — |

MARION—Grant County

★ ○ **MARION GENERAL HOSPITAL**, 441 North Wabash Avenue, Zip 46952–2690; tel. 765/662–1441, (Total facility includes 21 beds in nursing home–type unit) **A**9 10 11 12 19 **F**2 6 9 11 12 14 15 21 22 23 26 27 28 29 33 37 38 39 46 47 48 52 53 54 55 57 58 59 60 61 62 63 64 65 66 69 70 80 81 82 83 84 85 87 88 92 93 94 96 106 107 108 109 110 **P**6
Primary Contact: David L. Callecod, FACHE, President and Chief Executive Officer
CFO: Paul Usher, Vice President Finance and Chief Financial Officer
CMO: Paul D. Wolfe, M.D., Chief of Staff
CHR: Sarah Nickell, Administrative Director Human Resources
Web address: www.mgh.net

| | 23 | 10 | 201 | 7241 | 71 | 163384 | 775 | 101966 | 40781 | 1050 |

IN

Hospital, Address, Telephone, Approval, Facility, and Physician Codes, Health Care System	Classi-fication Codes		Utilization Data					Expense (thousands) of dollars		
	Control	Service	Staffed Beds	Admissions	Census	Outpatient Visits	Births	Total	Payroll	Personnel

★ American Hospital Association (AHA) membership
☐ Joint Commission on Accreditation of Healthcare Organizations (JCAHO) accreditation
◯ American Osteopathic Association (AOA) accreditation
△ Commission on Accreditation of Rehabilitation Facilities (CARF) accreditation

VETERANS AFFAIRS NORTHERN INDIANA HEALTH CARE SYSTEM–MARION CAMPUS See Veterans Affairs Northern Indiana Health Care System, Fort Wayne

MARTINSVILLE—Morgan County

✸ **MORGAN HOSPITAL AND MEDICAL CENTER**, 2209 John R. Wooden Drive, Zip 46151–1840, Mailing Address: P.O. Box 1717, Zip 46151–1717; tel. 765/342–8441, (Nonreporting) **A**1 9 10

| | 13 | 10 | 86 | — | — | — | — | — | — | — |

Primary Contact: Thomas W. Laux, President and Chief Executive Officer
CFO: Roger S. Boruff, Vice President Fiscal Services
CMO: Paul Broderick, D.O., Chief of Staff
CIO: Roger S. Boruff, Vice President Fiscal Services
CHR: Charlene Hall, Vice President, Human Resources and Guest Support Services
Web address: www.morganhospital.org

MERRILLVILLE—Lake County
SOUTHLAKE CAMPUS See Methodist Hospitals, Gary

MICHIGAN CITY—La Porte County

◯ **SAINT ANTHONY MEMORIAL HEALTH CENTERS**, 301 West Homer Street, Zip 46360–4358; tel. 219/879–8511, (Nonreporting) **A**2 9 10 11 19 **S** Sisters of St. Francis Health Services, Inc., Mishawaka, IN

| | 21 | 10 | 224 | — | — | — | — | — | — | — |

Primary Contact: Bruce E. Rampage, President and Chief Executive Officer
Web address: www.sahhc.org

MISHAWAKA—St. Joseph County

✸ **SAINT JOSEPH REGIONAL MEDICAL CENTER–MISHAWAKA CAMPUS**, 215 West Fourth Street, Zip 46544–1999; tel. 574/259–2431, (Nonreporting) **A**1 9 10 13 **S** Trinity Health, Novi, MI

| | 21 | 10 | 95 | — | — | — | — | — | — | — |

Primary Contact: Lori Price, President
CFO: Deanna J. Coleman, Senior Vice President Finance and Chief Financial Officer
Web address: www.sjmed.com

MONTICELLO—White County

WHITE COUNTY MEMORIAL HOSPITAL, 1101 O'Connor Boulevard, Zip 47960–1698; tel. 574/583–7111 **A**9 10 12 18 **F**2 9 11 12 21 22 23 26 27 28 29 30 33 46 47 48 51 52 54 55 57 58 59 60 61 62 63 64 65 66 69 70 81 82 84 85 88 93 94 95 96 97 98 106 108

| | 13 | 10 | 25 | 1491 | 16 | 27768 | 118 | 18152 | 6775 | 231 |

Primary Contact: Paul Cardwell, Chief Executive Officer
Web address: www.whitecmh.org

MOORESVILLE—Morgan County

◯ **ST. FRANCIS HOSPITAL–MOORESVILLE**, 1201 Hadley Road N.W., Zip 46158–1789; tel. 317/831–1160, (Nonreporting) **A**9 10 11 **S** Sisters of St. Francis Health Services, Inc., Mishawaka, IN

| | 21 | 10 | 54 | — | — | — | — | — | — | — |

Primary Contact: D. Keith Jewell, President and Executive Officer

MUNCIE—Delaware County

✸ △ **BALL MEMORIAL HOSPITAL**, 2401 University Avenue, Zip 47303–3499; tel. 765/747–3111, (Total facility includes 48 beds in nursing home–type unit) **A**1 2 3 5 7 8 9 10 **F**2 9 11 12 14 15 17 19 21 22 23 24 26 27 28 29 32 33 34 35 36 37 38 39 40 42 43 46 47 48 49 50 52 53 54 55 56 57 58 59 60 61 62 63 64 65 66 68 69 70 71 73 74 75 76 79 80 81 82 83 84 85 86 88 89 90 92 93 94 95 96 106 108 109 110 **P**6 8 **S** Cardinal Health System, Muncie, IN

| | 23 | 10 | 393 | 18667 | 271 | 344491 | 1699 | 231692 | 81116 | 2014 |

Primary Contact: Brent L. Batman, President
CFO: Robert E. Gildersleeve, Executive Vice President and Chief Financial Officer
CMO: Thomas K. Gardiner, M.D., Executive Vice President Clinical Development
CIO: Tom Powers, Vice President Information Systems
CHR: Terry Allen, Vice President, Human Resources
Web address: www.cardinalhealthsystem.org

MUNSTER—Lake County

☐ △ **COMMUNITY HOSPITAL**, 901 MacArthur Boulevard, Zip 46321–2959; tel. 219/836–1600 **A**1 2 7 9 10 **F**2 11 12 14 15 17 19 21 23 27 28 29 33 37 41 42 48 51 52 55 56 57 58 59 61 62 63 64 65 68 69 79 80 81 82 84 85 87 88 92 93 94 96 106 108 109 110 **P**8 **S** Community Healthcare System, Hammond, IN

| | 23 | 10 | 362 | 20712 | 297 | 245605 | 2301 | 241670 | 105123 | 1905 |

Primary Contact: John Gorski, Interim Administrator
Web address: www.comhs.org

★ **ILLIANA SURGERY AND MEDICAL CENTER**, 701 Superior Avenue, Zip 46321–4029; tel. 219/924–1300, (Nonreporting) **A**10

| | 31 | 10 | 8 | — | — | — | — | — | — | — |

Primary Contact: Vijay D. Gupta, M.D., President and Chief Executive Officer
CFO: Harold E. Collins, JD, Chief Financial Officer
CMO: Vijay D. Gupta, M.D., President and Chief Executive Officer
CIO: Steven Krause, Manager Information Technology

NEW ALBANY—Floyd County

✸ **FLOYD MEMORIAL HOSPITAL AND HEALTH SERVICES**, 1850 State Street, Zip 47150–4997; tel. 812/949–5500 **A**1 2 9 10 **F**9 11 12 14 15 17 21 22 23 26 27 28 29 33 34 37 39 44 46 47 48 51 52 55 57 58 59 60 61 62 63 64 65 66 73 81 82 84 88 92 93 94 95 96 106 107 108 109 110

| | 13 | 10 | 198 | 10051 | 114 | 284609 | 853 | 119265 | 50270 | 1182 |

Primary Contact: Bryant R. Hanson, President and Chief Executive Officer
COO: Jerri Quillman, Senior Vice President and Chief Operating Officer
CFO: Ralph Mercuri, Vice President Finance and Chief Financial Officer
CMO: Joseph A. Bruckman, M.D., Medical Director
CIO: Jack McCloskey, Director Information Systems
CHR: Mike Ford, Director, Human Resources
Web address: www.floydmemorial.org

Many Facility Codes have changed. Please refer to the AHA Guide Code Chart. © 2005 AHA Guide

Hospital, Address, Telephone, Approval, Facility, and Physician Codes, Health Care System	Classi-fication Codes		Utilization Data					Expense (thousands) of dollars		
★ American Hospital Association (AHA) membership □ Joint Commission on Accreditation of Healthcare Organizations (JCAHO) accreditation ○ American Osteopathic Association (AOA) accreditation △ Commission on Accreditation of Rehabilitation Facilities (CARF) accreditation	Control	Service	Staffed Beds	Admissions	Census	Outpatient Visits	Births	Total	Payroll	Personnel
⊞ △ **SOUTHERN INDIANA REHABILITATION HOSPITAL**, 3104 Blackiston Boulevard, Zip 47150–9579; tel. 812/941–8300 **A**1 7 10 **F**21 22 26 27 28 29 45 46 47 57 58 60 62 65 66 68 94 95 96 106 108 **S** Jewish Hospital HealthCare Services, Louisville, KY Primary Contact: Randy L. Napier, President and Chief Executive Officer CFO: Stephen Scannell, Chief Financial Officer CMO: John C. Shaw, M.D., Medical Director Web address: www.sirh.org	23	46	60	977	36	22709	0	13776	6878	167
NEW CASTLE—Henry County										
★ ○ **HENRY COUNTY MEMORIAL HOSPITAL**, 1000 North 16th Street, Zip 47362–4319, Mailing Address: P.O. Box 490, Zip 47362–0490; tel. 765/521–0890 **A**9 10 11 **F**2 8 9 11 12 22 29 33 36 37 39 40 41 46 48 51 52 53 55 57 58 59 60 62 63 69 70 81 84 87 88 93 94 95 96 106 107 108 109 110 **P**1 4 Primary Contact: Blake A. Dye, President and Chief Executive Officer CFO: Paul Janssen, Chief Financial Officer/Senior Vice President CMO: Daniel House, M.D., Chief of Staff CIO: Mike Spencer, Chief Information Officer CHR: Jeff Neuman, Human Resources Director Web address: www.hcmhcares.org	13	10	107	3774	39	123575	460	47679	21676	628
NEWBURGH—Warrick County										
⊞ **THE WOMEN'S HOSPITAL**, 4199 Gateway Boulevard, Zip 47630; tel. 812/842–4200 **A**1 9 10 **F**2 9 11 21 22 26 27 28 29 37 41 46 48 53 56 58 59 63 65 66 88 89 90 94 96 106 109 **S** Deaconess Health System, Evansville, IN Primary Contact: Christina M. Ryan, Chief Executive Officer CFO: Martha McClain, Controller CIO: Liz Adams, Informatics Manager CHR: Mary Thompson, Manager, Human Resources Web address: www.deaconess.com	32	44	78	3833	40	7604	2555	28198	10255	297
NOBLESVILLE—Hamilton County										
⊞ △ **RIVERVIEW HOSPITAL**, 395 Westfield Road, Zip 46060–1425, Mailing Address: P.O. Box 220, Zip 46061–0220; tel. 317/773–0760, (Nonreporting) **A**1 7 9 10 Primary Contact: Patricia K. Fox, President and Chief Executive Officer CFO: James Porter, Vice President and Chief Financial Officer CMO: John Paris, M.D., Chief Medical Officer CIO: Randy Cox, Chief Information Officer Web address: www.riverview.org	13	10	144	—	—	—	—	—	—	—
NORTH VERNON—Jennings County										
⊞ **ST. VINCENT JENNINGS HOSPITAL**, 301 Henry Street, Zip 47265–1097; tel. 812/352–4200 **A**1 9 10 18 **F**2 12 21 22 24 26 27 28 29 30 33 35 39 46 48 53 57 60 62 63 68 69 70 81 84 88 92 94 96 97 106 107 108 **P**4 **S** Ascension Health, Saint Louis, MO Primary Contact: Joseph E. Roche, Administrator CFO: John Lines, Chief Financial Officer CMO: Hassan Zammam, M.D., President Medical Staff CHR: Kathryn Johnson, Manager Human Resources Web address: www.stvincent.org	23	10	25	565	6	50740	2	18657	8116	—
PAOLI—Orange County										
□ **BLOOMINGTON HOSPITAL OF ORANGE COUNTY**, 642 West Hospital Road, Zip 47454–0499, Mailing Address: P.O. Box 499, Zip 47454–0499; tel. 812/723–2811 **A**1 9 10 18 **F**2 6 11 12 21 22 27 28 29 33 38 45 46 48 53 58 59 60 61 62 63 64 69 81 84 88 93 96 97 106 108 110 Primary Contact: L. Gene Perry, Chief Executive Officer Web address: www.bhoc.org	23	10	24	785	6	37175	144	14434	7280	213
PERU—Miami County										
⊞ **DUKES MEMORIAL HOSPITAL**, 275 West 12th Street, Zip 46970–1698; tel. 765/472–8000, (Total facility includes 22 beds in nursing home–type unit) **A**1 9 10 18 **F**2 6 9 11 12 21 22 23 26 28 33 34 37 40 41 44 45 46 48 52 53 54 58 60 61 62 63 65 68 69 81 85 88 92 93 94 97 106 108 109 **P**6 **S** Triad Hospitals, Inc., Plano, TX Primary Contact: Michael J. Funk, President and Chief Executive Officer COO: Sue Milas, Chief Operating Officer and Chief Nursing Officer CFO: Pam Cavacini, Chief Financial Officer CIO: Nancy York, Director Information Services CHR: Marilyn Richard, Director, Human Resources Web address: www.dukeshospital.org	33	10	27	2388	27	54421	299	22028	10046	345
PLYMOUTH—Marshall County										
□ **MICHIANA BEHAVIORAL HEALTH CENTER**, 1800 North Oak Road, Zip 46563–3492; tel. 574/936–3784, (Nonreporting) **A**1 10 **S** Horizon Health Corporation, Lewisville, TX Primary Contact: Bryan W. Lett, Chief Executive Officer Web address: www.michianabhc.com	33	22	76	—	—	—	—	—	—	—

IN

Hospital, Address, Telephone, Approval, Facility, and Physician Codes, Health Care System	Classi-fication Codes		Utilization Data					Expense (thousands) of dollars		
	Control	Service	Staffed Beds	Admissions	Census	Outpatient Visits	Births	Total	Payroll	Personnel

★ American Hospital Association (AHA) membership
□ Joint Commission on Accreditation of Healthcare Organizations (JCAHO) accreditation
○ American Osteopathic Association (AOA) accreditation
△ Commission on Accreditation of Rehabilitation Facilities (CARF) accreditation

⊠ **SAINT JOSEPH REGIONAL MEDICAL CENTER–PLYMOUTH CAMPUS**, 1915 Lake Avenue, Zip 46563–9905, Mailing Address: P.O. Box 670, Zip 46563–9905; tel. 574/936–3181 **A**1 9 10 **F**2 9 11 12 21 22 23 26 27 28 29 33 37 39 45 46 47 48 52 53 55 57 58 59 60 61 62 63 64 65 66 69 79 81 82 85 88 90 92 94 95 96 106 108 109 110 **S** Trinity Health, Novi, MI Primary Contact: Lori Price, President COO: Lori Price, President CFO: Terry Heck, Vice President Finance and Chief Financial Officer CMO: Thomas F. Lavelle, Chief Medical Officer CIO: Gary L. Miller, Regional Information Systems Director CHR: Aaron Austin, Vice President Human Resources Web address: www.sjmed.com	21	10	45	2482	23	67989	419	33416	11914	229
PORTLAND—Jay County										
□ **JAY COUNTY HOSPITAL**, 500 West Votaw Street, Zip 47371–1322; tel. 260/726–7131, (Nonreporting) **A**1 9 10 18 **S** Cardinal Health System, Muncie, IN Primary Contact: Joe Johnston, Chief Executive Officer Web address: www.jaycountyhospital.com	13	10	25	—	—	—	—	—	—	—
PRINCETON—Gibson County										
⊠ **GIBSON GENERAL HOSPITAL**, 1808 Sherman Drive, Zip 47670–1043; tel. 812/385–3401, (Total facility includes 45 beds in nursing home–type unit) **A**1 9 10 18 **F**2 4 9 11 12 21 22 26 27 28 29 31 32 33 34 42 44 46 47 48 51 52 53 55 58 59 60 61 62 63 69 70 72 73 74 75 76 77 81 84 85 88 92 94 95 96 97 108 109 110 **P**7 **S** Alliant Management Services, Louisville, KY Primary Contact: Michael J. Budnick, FACHE, Chief Executive Officer Web address: www.gibsongeneral.com	23	10	70	1135	54	35583	143	19467	9392	271
RENSSELAER—Jasper County										
★ **JASPER COUNTY HOSPITAL**, 1104 East Grace Street, Zip 47978–3296; tel. 219/866–5141 **A**9 10 18 20 **F**2 9 11 12 21 22 23 27 29 33 34 36 39 40 41 42 46 47 48 51 52 53 54 55 58 59 60 61 62 63 64 69 75 81 82 84 85 87 88 92 93 94 95 96 97 106 107 108 110 **P**5 6 Primary Contact: Timothy M. Schreeg, President and Chief Executive Officer CFO: Jeffrey D. Webb, CPA, Controller CIO: Kirby Reed, Information Systems Director Web address: www.jchh.com	13	10	66	1570	31	79800	147	24819	12305	363
RICHMOND—Wayne County										
⊠ **REID HOSPITAL AND HEALTH CARE SERVICES**, 1401 Chester Boulevard, Zip 47374–1986; tel. 765/983–3000 **A**1 2 9 10 19 **F**2 4 9 11 12 14 15 17 19 21 22 23 26 27 28 29 32 33 34 35 36 37 39 40 44 46 47 48 49 52 53 55 57 58 59 60 61 62 63 64 65 66 68 69 71 73 74 75 76 77 81 82 84 86 87 88 93 94 95 96 106 108 109 110 **P**7 8 Primary Contact: Barry S. MacDowell, President CFO: Craig Kinyon, Vice President Finance and Chief Financial Officer CIO: Eric Synnestvedt, Director Information Services Web address: www.reidhosp.com	23	10	233	12105	159	128469	791	141621	56218	1243
□ **RICHMOND STATE HOSPITAL**, 498 N.W. 18th Street, Zip 47374–2898; tel. 765/966–0511 **A**1 10 **F**3 4 21 22 26 28 32 53 71 72 74 **P**6 Primary Contact: Jeffrey Butler, Superintendent Web address: www.richmondstatehospital.org	12	22	312	490	279	0	0	34095	19253	599
ROCHESTER—Fulton County										
⊠ **WOODLAWN HOSPITAL**, 1400 East Ninth Street, Zip 46975–8937; tel. 574/223–3141 **A**1 9 10 18 **F**2 6 9 11 12 21 22 23 33 36 44 46 51 52 54 55 58 59 60 61 62 63 66 69 70 81 82 84 88 93 94 96 97 108 **P**6 Primary Contact: James M. O'Keefe, President and Chief Executive Officer CFO: John L. Alley, Director Finance Web address: www.woodlawnhospital.com	13	10	35	1171	11	26761	195	23783	10743	259
RUSHVILLE—Rush County										
★ **RUSH MEMORIAL HOSPITAL**, 1300 North Main Street, Zip 46173–1198, Mailing Address: P.O. Box 608, Zip 46173–0608; tel. 765/932–4111 **A**9 10 18 **F**6 9 12 21 23 27 28 29 33 39 40 46 48 51 52 58 60 61 62 63 64 69 70 81 82 84 88 93 94 95 96 97 106 108 109 110 **P**6 Primary Contact: Brad Smith, Chief Executive Officer CFO: Karen Meyers, Chief Financial Officer CMO: Douglas Morrell, M.D., Chief Medical Officer and Chief of Staff CIO: Jim Boyer, Management Information Systems Manager CHR: Pam Renne Kamp, Human Resources Director Web address: www.rushmemorial.com	13	10	25	657	9	30659	0	13997	6332	162
SALEM—Washington County										
⊠ **WASHINGTON COUNTY MEMORIAL HOSPITAL**, 911 North Shelby Street, Zip 47167–1694; tel. 812/883–5881, (Nonreporting) **A**1 9 10 18 **S** Jewish Hospital HealthCare Services, Louisville, KY Primary Contact: Beth Sharer, R.N., Interim Chief Executive Officer CFO: Kim Scifres, Director Financial and Support Services CIO: Cale Kearschner, Manager Information Systems CHR: Betsey Johnson, Director Human Resources	13	10	15	—	—	—	—	—	—	—

IN

Many Facility Codes have changed. Please refer to the AHA Guide Code Chart.   © 2005 AHA Guide

Hospital, Address, Telephone, Approval, Facility, and Physician Codes, Health Care System	Classi-fication Codes		Utilization Data					Expense (thousands) of dollars		
	Control	Service	Staffed Beds	Admissions	Census	Outpatient Visits	Births	Total	Payroll	Personnel

★ American Hospital Association (AHA) membership
☐ Joint Commission on Accreditation of Healthcare Organizations (JCAHO) accreditation
◯ American Osteopathic Association (AOA) accreditation
△ Commission on Accreditation of Rehabilitation Facilities (CARF) accreditation

SCOTTSBURG—Scott County

✸ **SCOTT MEMORIAL HOSPITAL**, 1415 North Gardner Street, Zip 47170–0430, Mailing Address: Box 430, Zip 47170–0430; tel. 812/752–8500 **A**1 9 10 **F**2 9 11 12 21 22 26 27 28 29 33 46 47 48 52 53 55 57 59 60 62 63 64 65 70 81 82 85 88 93 96 106 108 109 **P**6 **S** Jewish Hospital HealthCare Services, Louisville, KY
Primary Contact: Clifford D. Nay, Executive Director
CFO: Angela Doan, Chief Financial Officer
Web address: www.scottmemorial.com

| 13 | 10 | 56 | 1567 | 15 | 44549 | 103 | 16514 | 7095 | 179 |

SEYMOUR—Jackson County

✸ **SCHNECK MEDICAL CENTER**, 411 West Tipton Street, Zip 47274–5000, Mailing Address: P.O. Box 2349, Zip 47274–2349; tel. 812/522–2349 **A**1 2 9 10 **F**2 9 11 12 21 23 26 27 28 29 30 33 36 37 38 39 40 46 48 51 52 54 55 58 59 60 61 62 63 64 65 66 69 81 84 87 88 93 94 95 96 97 106 108 109 110 **P**8
Primary Contact: Gary A. Meyer, President and Chief Executive Officer
CFO: Warren Forgey, Vice President Fiscal Services
CHR: William Lewis, Vice President Human Resources
Web address: www.schneckmed.org

| 13 | 10 | 108 | 3722 | 38 | 111934 | 581 | 55261 | 24487 | 571 |

SHELBYVILLE—Shelby County

★ ◯ **MAJOR HOSPITAL**, 150 West Washington Street, Zip 46176–1236; tel. 317/392–3211 **A**9 10 11 **F**2 6 9 11 12 21 22 23 26 27 28 29 33 37 39 44 45 46 47 48 51 52 53 54 55 57 58 59 60 61 62 63 64 65 66 69 70 75 81 82 84 85 88 94 95 106 108 109 110 **P**5 6 7
Primary Contact: Anthony B. Lennen, President and Chief Executive Officer
CFO: Robin Nichols, Vice President and Chief Financial Officer
CIO: John M. Horner, Vice President and Chief Information Officer
CHR: Jeff Williams, Director of Human Resources and Business Development
Web address: www.majorhospital.org

| 15 | 10 | 68 | 2931 | 29 | 102012 | 385 | 45248 | 19300 | 394 |

SOUTH BEND—St. Joseph County

MADISON CENTER AND HOSPITAL, 403 East Madison, Zip 46617; tel. 574/234–0061 **A**10 **F**3 5 21 27 29 31 39 42 44 45 48 58 71 72 73 74 75 76 77 78 94 96 98 **P**6
Primary Contact: Jack Roberts, Chief Executive Officer
Web address: www.madison.org

| 23 | 22 | 91 | 2509 | 65 | 306 | 0 | 9242 | 4619 | — |

✸ △ **MEMORIAL HOSPITAL OF SOUTH BEND**, 615 North Michigan Street, Zip 46601–9986; tel. 574/647–9041 **A**1 2 3 5 7 9 10 **F**6 7 9 10 11 12 14 15 17 19 21 22 23 24 26 27 28 29 31 33 34 37 39 41 44 45 46 47 49 50 52 53 55 56 57 58 59 60 61 62 63 64 65 66 67 68 69 79 81 82 86 87 88 92 93 94 95 96 98 106 108 109 **P**8
Primary Contact: Philip A. Newbold, President and Chief Executive Officer
CFO: Jeff Costello, Chief Financial Officer
CIO: Cathy Cooper–Weidner, Vice President Information Systems
CHR: Steven Leonard, Vice President, Human Resources
Web address: www.qualityoflife.org

| 23 | 10 | 348 | 17810 | 235 | 140779 | 3215 | 256674 | 101114 | 2095 |

☐ **OUR LADY OF PEACE HOSPITAL**, 801 East LaSalle Avenue, Zip 46617; tel. 574/237–7457 **A**1 10 **F**2 21 27 28 64
Primary Contact: Christine T. Voorde, Chief Executive Officer
Web address: www.sjmed.com/scripts/explore/southbend/southbend_ourladypeace.asp

| 23 | 80 | 32 | 327 | 24 | 0 | 0 | 8887 | 3346 | 59 |

RIVERSIDE HOSPITAL, 533 North Niles Avenue, Zip 46617; tel. 574/283–1104 **A**10 **F**3 27 73 75 94 **P**6
Primary Contact: Jack Roberts, Chief Executive Officer
Web address: www.madison.org

| 23 | 22 | 16 | 486 | 14 | 0 | 0 | 1771 | 705 | — |

✸ △ **SAINT JOSEPH REGIONAL MEDICAL CENTER**, 801 East LaSalle, Zip 46617–2800; tel. 574/237–7111, (Nonreporting) **A**1 2 3 5 7 9 10 **S** Trinity Health, Novi, MI
Primary Contact: Gary L. Perecko, President
CFO: Terry Heck, Vice President Finance and Chief Financial Officer
CMO: Thomas F. Lavelle, Chief Medical Officer
CIO: Gary L. Miller, Regional Information Systems Director
CHR: Aaron Austin, Vice President Human Resources
Web address: www.sjmed.com

| 21 | 10 | 286 | — | — | — | — | — | — | — |

SULLIVAN—Sullivan County

✸ **SULLIVAN COUNTY COMMUNITY HOSPITAL**, 2200 North Section Street, Zip 47882, Mailing Address: P.O. Box 10, Zip 47882–0010; tel. 812/268–4311 **A**1 9 10 18 **F**2 11 12 21 24 27 29 32 33 35 41 44 46 47 48 50 51 54 55 58 59 60 61 62 63 65 66 69 70 81 84 94 95 97 108 109 110 **P**8 **S** Quorum Health Resources, Plano, TX
Primary Contact: Patricia Holden, Chief Executive Officer
CFO: Alan J. Montella, Assistant Administrator Finance
CMO: Gene Bourgasser, M.D., Chief of Staff
CHR: Regina Stearns, Human Resource Director
Web address: www.schosp.com

| 13 | 10 | 37 | 1673 | 16 | 47340 | 110 | 15209 | 6459 | 236 |

IN

Hospital, Address, Telephone, Approval, Facility, and Physician Codes, Health Care System	Classi-fication Codes		Utilization Data					Expense (thousands) of dollars		
★ American Hospital Association (AHA) membership □ Joint Commission on Accreditation of Healthcare Organizations (JCAHO) accreditation ○ American Osteopathic Association (AOA) accreditation △ Commission on Accreditation of Rehabilitation Facilities (CARF) accreditation	Control	Service	Staffed Beds	Admissions	Census	Outpatient Visits	Births	Total	Payroll	Personnel

TELL CITY—Perry County

★ **PERRY COUNTY MEMORIAL HOSPITAL**, 1 Hospital Road, Zip 47586–0362; tel. 812/547–7011 **A**9 10 12 18 **F**2 6 9 11 12 21 22 23 26 27 28 29 31 33 36 39 44 46 47 48 51 52 53 55 58 59 60 61 62 63 65 66 69 75 81 82 84 85 87 88 93 94 96 97 106 108 109 **S** Alliant Management Services, Louisville, KY
Primary Contact: Joseph A. Stuber, Chief Executive Officer
COO: Becky Elder, Assistant Administrator Clinical Services
CFO: Doug Lewis, Chief Financial Officer
Web address: www.pchospital.org
13	10	25	1285	14	55890	94	18503	6689	222

TERRE HAUTE—Vigo County

HAMILTON CENTER, 620 Eighth Avenue, Zip 47804–0323; tel. 812/231–8323, (Nonreporting) **A**10
Primary Contact: Galen Goode, Chief Executive Officer
Web address: www.hamiltoncenter.org
23	22	16	—	—	—	—	—	—	—

⊞ **HEALTHSOUTH HOSPITAL OF TERRE HAUTE**, (Formerly HEALTHSOUTH Rehabilitation Hospital of Terre Haute), 501 East St. Anthony Drive, Zip 47802–9135; tel. 812/235–5656 **A**1 10 **F**7 21 22 28 30 37 44 45 46 47 48 49 52 60 65 66 69 94 96 106 110 **S** HEALTHSOUTH Corporation, Birmingham, AL
Primary Contact: Myra Wetzel, Administrator
CFO: Timothy Lambert, Controller
CMO: Gary Corby, M.D., Medical Director
CHR: George Henley, Human Resources Director
Web address: www.healthsouth.com
32	80	58	601	39	7768	0	13203	6278	149

⊞ **TERRE HAUTE REGIONAL HOSPITAL**, 3901 South Seventh Street, Zip 47802–4299; tel. 812/232–0021 **A**1 9 10 **F**2 11 12 15 16 17 18 19 21 23 26 27 28 32 33 39 40 41 46 47 48 53 54 55 57 58 59 60 61 62 63 64 65 66 69 71 73 75 76 79 81 82 84 85 87 88 93 94 96 108 109 **P**8 **S** HCA, Nashville, TN
Primary Contact: E. Kenneth Hutchenrider, Chief Executive Officer
COO: Scott Teffeteller, Chief Operating Officer
CFO: David A. Summers, Chief Financial Officer
CMO: Ruben Gonzales, M.D., President Medical Staff
CHR: Lisa Pepperworth, Director Human Resources
Web address: www.regionalhospital.com
32	10	207	7764	101	73133	783	85365	30192	806

★ △ **UNION HOSPITAL**, 1606 North Seventh Street, Zip 47804–2780; tel. 812/238–7000 **A**2 3 5 7 9 10 11 **F**2 7 11 12 14 15 17 19 21 22 26 27 28 29 30 32 33 37 38 40 41 42 46 47 48 49 50 52 53 55 56 57 58 59 60 61 62 63 65 66 68 69 70 79 81 82 84 85 88 94 95 96 108 109 110 **P**6 7
Primary Contact: David R. Doerr, Chief Executive Officer
COO: Steven B. Reed, Senior Vice President and Chief Operating Officer
CFO: Wayne Hutson, Chief Financial Officer
CMO: Ronald Leach, M.D., Medical Director
CIO: Kim Pfrank, Vice President Information Systems
CHR: Michael Chumley, Vice President Human Resources
Web address: www.uhhg.org
23	10	269	13443	178	319217	1416	201875	73401	1630

TIPTON—Tipton County

⊞ **TIPTON COUNTY MEMORIAL HOSPITAL**, 1000 South Main Street, Zip 46072–9799; tel. 765/675–8500, (Total facility includes 50 beds in nursing home–type unit) **A**1 2 9 10 18 **F**2 8 9 11 12 21 22 23 26 29 33 41 44 46 48 51 52 54 55 57 58 59 60 61 62 63 65 66 69 70 75 77 81 84 87 88 92 93 94 95 96 97 106 108 **P**7 8 **S** Clarian Health Partners, Indianapolis, IN
Primary Contact: Michael Harlowe, President and Chief Executive Officer
CFO: Vern J. Schmaltz, Vice President Finance
Web address: www.tiptonhospital.org
13	10	75	1559	67	48333	100	30503	12796	320

VALPARAISO—Porter County

⊞ **PORTER–VALPARAISO HOSPITAL CAMPUS**, 814 La Porte Avenue, Zip 46383–5898; tel. 219/465–4600 **A**1 9 10 **F**2 6 9 11 12 14 15 17 19 21 22 23 26 28 29 33 37 39 42 46 47 48 52 55 56 57 58 59 61 62 63 64 65 66 70 79 81 82 83 84 85 86 88 92 93 94 95 96 106 107 108 109
Primary Contact: Ronald C. Winger, Chief Executive Officer
COO: Chris Rael, Vice President Operations
CMO: Ramireddy K. Tummutu, M.D., Chief Medical Officer
CIO: Dennis L. Marschke, Chief Information Officer
CHR: Bill Cummins, Vice President System Resources
Web address: www.porterhealth.org
13	10	276	11641	149	214058	1552	174789	76517	1567

VINCENNES—Knox County

⊞ △ **GOOD SAMARITAN HOSPITAL**, 520 South Seventh Street, Zip 47591–1098; tel. 812/882–5220 **A**1 2 7 9 10 19 **F**2 4 9 11 12 14 15 17 19 21 22 23 24 26 27 29 30 31 32 33 34 36 40 41 46 47 48 49 53 55 57 58 59 60 61 62 63 64 65 66 68 69 71 72 73 74 75 76 77 78 81 82 84 85 86 87 88 93 94 96 106 107 108 109 110
Primary Contact: Matthew D. Bailey, President and Chief Executive Officer
COO: Gerald E. Waldroup, Senior Vice President
CFO: Robert McLin, Vice President Finance
CMO: Charles C. Hedde, M.D., Vice President Medical Affairs
CIO: Charles Christian, Director Information Systems
CHR: Dean Wagoner, Director
Web address: www.gshvin.org
13	10	232	8488	103	368710	615	121204	51239	1427

IN

Hospital, Address, Telephone, Approval, Facility, and Physician Codes, Health Care System	Classi-fication Codes		Utilization Data					Expense (thousands) of dollars		
★ American Hospital Association (AHA) membership □ Joint Commission on Accreditation of Healthcare Organizations (JCAHO) accreditation ○ American Osteopathic Association (AOA) accreditation △ Commission on Accreditation of Rehabilitation Facilities (CARF) accreditation	Control	Service	Staffed Beds	Admissions	Census	Outpatient Visits	Births	Total	Payroll	Personnel

WABASH—Wabash County

★ **WABASH COUNTY HOSPITAL**, 710 North East Street, Zip 46992–1924, Mailing Address: P.O. Box 548, Zip 46992–0548; tel. 260/563–3131, (Total facility includes 25 beds in nursing home–type unit) **A**1 2 9 10 18 **F**2 9 12 21 22 23 24 26 28 29 33 36 37 38 41 46 47 48 51 52 53 54 55 57 58 60 61 62 63 64 65 66 69 70 81 82 84 85 88 92 94 95 96 97 106 108 109 110 **P**6 **S** Alliant Management Services, Louisville, KY
Primary Contact: Jeffrey L. Buckley, President and Chief Executive Officer
COO: Jeffrey L. Buckley, President and Chief Executive Officer
CFO: Kent Giles, Director Finance
CMO: Alex Fishberg, M.D., Chief Medical Officer
CHR: Kim Shininger, Director of Human Resources
Web address: www.wchospital.com

| | | 13 | 10 | 50 | 1029 | 25 | 50209 | 45 | 26538 | 10984 | 264 |

WARSAW—Kosciusko County

★ **KOSCIUSKO COMMUNITY HOSPITAL**, 2101 East Dubois Drive, Zip 46580–3288; tel. 574/267–3200 **A**1 9 10 19 **F**10 11 12 21 22 26 27 28 33 37 40 41 46 48 52 55 58 59 61 63 69 81 84 86 87 88 93 94 95 107 108 109 **P**6 **S** Triad Hospitals, Inc., Plano, TX
Primary Contact: Michael L. Mullins, Chief Executive Officer
COO: Joan Darr, Chief Operating Officer
CFO: Steve Miller, Chief Financial Officer
CMO: Michael Williams, M.D., Medical Director
CIO: Judy Slone, Division Director
Web address: www.kch.com

| | | 33 | 10 | 72 | 3401 | 31 | 63956 | 784 | 43553 | 18502 | 684 |

WASHINGTON—Daviess County

★ **DAVIESS COMMUNITY HOSPITAL**, 1314 East Walnut Street, Zip 47501–2198, Mailing Address: P.O. Box 760, Zip 47501–0760; tel. 812/254–2760 **A**1 9 10 **F**2 9 11 12 14 21 22 23 24 27 28 29 33 36 44 45 46 47 48 51 52 54 55 58 59 60 61 62 63 65 66 68 69 70 71 77 78 81 84 87 88 94 96 97 106 108 109 110 **P**8 **S** Quorum Health Resources, Plano, TX
Primary Contact: Robert J. Heckert, Jr, Chief Executive Officer
COO: Don Kelso, Vice President Professional Services
CFO: Brad Hardcastle, Chief Financial Officer
CMO: James Spiller, M.D., Chief of Staff
CHR: Denise Brashear, Director Human Resources
Web address: www.dchosp.org

| | | 13 | 10 | 70 | 2850 | 33 | 125756 | 384 | 38875 | 16623 | 370 |

WEST LAFAYETTE—Tippecanoe County

WABASH VALLEY HOSPITAL, 2900 North River Road, Zip 47906–3766; tel. 765/463–2555, (Nonreporting) **A**10
Primary Contact: Rick Crawley, Administrator and Chief Executive Officer
Web address: www.wvhmhc.org

| | | 23 | 22 | 70 | — | — | — | — | — | — | — |

WILLIAMSPORT—Warren County

★ **ST. VINCENT WILLIAMSPORT HOSPITAL**, 412 North Monroe Street, Zip 47993–0215; tel. 765/762–4000, (Nonreporting) **A**1 9 10 18 **S** Ascension Health, Saint Louis, MO
Primary Contact: Jane Craigin, Chief Executive Officer
CFO: Janet Merritt, Chief Financial Officer
Web address: www.stvincent.org

| | | 23 | 10 | 16 | — | — | — | — | — | — | — |

WINAMAC—Pulaski County

★ **PULASKI MEMORIAL HOSPITAL**, 616 East 13th Street, Zip 46996–1117, Mailing Address: P.O. Box 279, Zip 46996–0279; tel. 574/946–2100 **A**1 9 10 18 **F**6 9 11 12 21 22 23 27 28 29 32 33 34 36 37 46 47 48 51 52 55 58 59 60 61 62 63 64 65 66 69 81 85 88 93 94 95 96 97 106 108 109
Primary Contact: Richard H. Mynark, Chief Executive Officer
CFO: Ronald A. Rusk, Chief Financial Officer
CMO: Clint Kauffman, M.D., Medical Staff President
CIO: Kevin Trusty, Information Technology Director and Materials Manager
CHR: Amy A. Bean, Human Resources Director
Web address: www.pulaskimemorial.com

| | | 13 | 10 | 25 | 743 | 7 | 48623 | 68 | 16994 | 7523 | 208 |

WINCHESTER—Randolph County

★ **ST. VINCENT RANDOLPH HOSPITAL**, 473 Greenville Avenue, Zip 47394–2235, Mailing Address: P.O. Box 407, Zip 47394–0407; tel. 765/584–0004 **A**1 9 10 18 **F**2 9 11 12 21 22 23 24 27 28 29 33 36 38 39 40 44 45 46 47 48 49 52 53 58 59 60 61 62 63 65 66 69 70 81 84 85 88 93 94 95 96 97 98 106 108 109 **P**7 **S** Ascension Health, Saint Louis, MO
Primary Contact: Wayne G. Deschambeau, Chief Executive Officer
CFO: Jon McMillan, Controller
CMO: Daniel Wegg, M.D., Medical Director
CHR: Holly Clemens, Director Human Resources
Web address: www.stvincent.org

| | | 23 | 10 | 25 | 997 | 8 | 42365 | 174 | 22706 | 10291 | 233 |

IN

IOWA

Hospital, Address, Telephone, Approval, Facility, and Physician Codes, Health Care System	Classi-fication Codes		Utilization Data					Expense (thousands) of dollars		
★ American Hospital Association (AHA) membership □ Joint Commission on Accreditation of Healthcare Organizations (JCAHO) accreditation ○ American Osteopathic Association (AOA) accreditation △ Commission on Accreditation of Rehabilitation Facilities (CARF) accreditation	Control	Service	Staffed Beds	Admissions	Census	Outpatient Visits	Births	Total	Payroll	Personnel

ALBIA—Monroe County

MONROE COUNTY HOSPITAL, 6580 165th Street, Zip 52531–8793; tel. 641/932–2134 **A**9 10 18 **F**6 9 12 21 23 29 33 36 46 48 52 63 81 106 **P**5
Primary Contact: Gregory A. Paris, Chief Executive Officer
Web address: www.mchalbia.com

| | 13 | 10 | 25 | 452 | 14 | 25012 | 0 | 8533 | 3516 | 123 |

ALGONA—Kossuth County

★ **KOSSUTH REGIONAL HEALTH CENTER**, 1515 South Phillips Street, Zip 50511–3649; tel. 515/295–2451 **A**9 10 18 **F**9 11 12 14 21 22 23 24 27 28 29 33 34 36 37 38 39 44 46 47 48 51 52 53 54 55 58 59 60 61 63 65 66 68 69 70 81 85 88 92 93 94 95 96 97 108 109 **P**8 **S** Trinity Health, Novi, MI
Primary Contact: Scott Curtis, Administrator
CFO: Dan Myers, Controller
CMO: Manasi Nadkarni, M.D., Chief of Staff
CIO: Nancy Erickson, Administrator Information Systems
Web address: www.krhc.com

| | 13 | 10 | 22 | 678 | 8 | 24689 | 80 | 13257 | 4940 | 143 |

AMES—Story County

⊠ **MARY GREELEY MEDICAL CENTER**, 1111 Duff Avenue, Zip 50010–5745; tel. 515/239–2011, (Total facility includes 11 beds in nursing home–type unit) **A**1 2 9 10 19 **F**2 6 9 10 11 12 14 15 21 22 23 26 27 28 29 30 31 33 34 36 37 39 41 44 46 47 48 49 50 51 52 53 54 55 56 57 58 59 60 61 62 63 65 68 69 71 72 73 74 75 76 77 78 80 81 82 84 85 87 88 89 92 93 94 95 96 106 108 110
Primary Contact: Kimberly A. Russel, President and Chief Executive Officer
CFO: Brian Dieter, Vice President and Chief Financial Officer
CIO: JaNelle Anderson, Director
CHR: Toni Shropshire, Vice President
Web address: www.mgmc.org

| | 14 | 10 | 198 | 9279 | 105 | 123940 | 1223 | 94079 | 42115 | 962 |

ANAMOSA—Jones County

★ **JONES REGIONAL MEDICAL CENTER**, 104 Broadway Place, Zip 52205–1100; tel. 319/462–6131 **A**9 10 18 **F**1 6 9 12 21 24 26 27 28 29 31 32 33 34 37 38 39 44 46 47 48 51 52 53 58 63 64 66 70 81 84 88 92 94 96 97 98 106 108 **P**4 **S** Iowa Health System, Des Moines, IA
Primary Contact: Sean Williams, Chief Executive Officer
CFO: Rachel Von Behren, Director Financial Services
Web address: www.jonesregional.org

| | 23 | 10 | 25 | 585 | 9 | 37881 | 0 | 6780 | 2101 | 65 |

ATLANTIC—Cass County

★ **CASS COUNTY MEMORIAL HOSPITAL**, 1501 East Tenth Street, Zip 50022–1997; tel. 712/243–3250 **A**9 10 20 **F**1 9 11 12 21 26 27 28 33 36 37 46 48 51 52 54 55 58 59 61 63 69 71 72 74 75 76 77 78 81 82 84 88 94 96 97 106 110 **P**8
Primary Contact: Patricia Markham, Administrator
CFO: Michael Collins, Assistant Administrator and Chief Financial Officere
CMO: Angie Weppler, M.D., Chief of Staff
CHR: Donald D. Johnson, Assistant Administrator Human Resources
Web address: www.casshealth.org

| | 13 | 10 | 49 | 1726 | 24 | 39711 | 143 | 20872 | 10089 | 299 |

AUDUBON—Audubon County

AUDUBON COUNTY MEMORIAL HOSPITAL, 515 Pacific Street, Zip 50025–1052; tel. 712/563–2611 **A**9 10 18 **F**2 9 11 12 23 27 33 34 41 48 52 59 61 62 63 69 88 92 106
Primary Contact: Thomas G. Smith, Chief Executive Officer
Web address: www.acmhhosp.org

| | 13 | 10 | 25 | 416 | 4 | 16482 | 20 | 6568 | 2431 | 65 |

BELMOND—Wright County

★ **BELMOND MEDICAL CENTER**, 403 First Street S.E., Zip 50421–1201; tel. 641/444–3223 **A**9 10 18 **F**6 9 12 26 27 28 33 41 46 47 48 52 54 58 60 63 64 69 70 81 84 88 93 97 106 108 110 **P**8 **S** Trinity Health, Novi, MI
Primary Contact: Suzan Brunes, Administrator and Director of Nursing
COO: Suzan Brunes, Administrator and Director of Nursing
CFO: Peggy Boehmer, Chief Financial Officer
CMO: Albert J. Kollasch, Chief Medical Staff
CHR: Lindsay Britson, Director Human Resources
Web address: www.belmondmedicalcenter.com

| | 14 | 10 | 22 | 222 | 2 | 12593 | 0 | 5073 | 1685 | 55 |

BETTENDORF—Scott County

⊠ ○ **TRINITY AT TERRACE PARK**, 4500 Utica Ridge Road, Zip 52722–1626; tel. 563/742–5000 **A**1 9 10 11 12 13 **F**9 10 11 12 21 22 26 27 28 33 44 46 47 48 52 55 58 59 60 62 63 64 65 66 69 70 80 81 82 84 88 92 93 94 96 108 109 110 **P**1 **S** Iowa Health System, Des Moines, IA
Primary Contact: William B. Leaver, President and Chief Executive Officer
COO: Jeffery Stolze, Chief Operating Officer
CMO: Mark Valliere, M.D., Vice President Medical Affairs and Chief Medical Officer
Web address: www.trinityqc.com

| | 23 | 10 | 93 | 1821 | 17 | 22123 | 137 | 34577 | 10150 | 174 |

Many Facility Codes have changed. Please refer to the AHA Guide Code Chart. © 2005 AHA Guide

Hospital, Address, Telephone, Approval, Facility, and Physician Codes, Health Care System	Classi-fication Codes		Utilization Data					Expense (thousands) of dollars		
★ American Hospital Association (AHA) membership □ Joint Commission on Accreditation of Healthcare Organizations (JCAHO) accreditation ○ American Osteopathic Association (AOA) accreditation △ Commission on Accreditation of Rehabilitation Facilities (CARF) accreditation	Control	Service	Staffed Beds	Admissions	Census	Outpatient Visits	Births	Total	Payroll	Personnel

BLOOMFIELD—Davis County

★ **DAVIS COUNTY HOSPITAL**, 507 North Madison Street, Zip 52537–1271; tel. 641/664–2145, (Total facility includes 32 beds in nursing home–type unit) **A**9 10 18 **F**6 9 11 12 24 26 27 28 33 36 46 48 50 51 52 54 55 58 59 61 62 63 65 69 70 81 84 88 92 97 108 **P**6
Primary Contact: John E. Monnahan, Chief Executive Officer
CFO: Jerri Christman, Chief Financial Officer
CIO: Deb Barker, Communications and Information Specialist
CHR: Lois Westercamp, Manager Human Resources
Web address: www.daviscountyhospital.org

| | 13 | 10 | 57 | 705 | 39 | 15341 | 51 | 11059 | 4709 | 172 |

BOONE—Boone County

⊞ **BOONE COUNTY HOSPITAL**, 1015 Union Street, Zip 50036–4821; tel. 515/432–3140 **A**1 9 10 **F**1 6 9 10 11 12 22 23 26 27 28 29 33 34 39 41 46 48 51 52 54 55 58 59 60 61 63 65 69 81 84 88 96 97 108 109 110 **P**6
S Quorum Health Resources, Plano, TX
Primary Contact: Joseph S. Smith, Chief Executive Officer
CFO: David Mellett, Chief Financial Officer
CMO: Brian Mehlhaus, M.D., Chief of Staff
Web address: www.boonehospital.com

| | 13 | 10 | 48 | 1927 | 25 | 53000 | 109 | 25639 | 10687 | 293 |

BRITT—Hancock County

★ **HANCOCK COUNTY MEMORIAL HOSPITAL**, 532 First Street N.W., Zip 50423; tel. 641/843–5000 **A**9 10 18 **F**1 9 12 21 23 26 27 28 29 30 33 34 36 41 44 48 52 54 58 60 61 63 64 69 70 81 85 93 94 96 97 108 **P**1 **S** Trinity Health, Novi, MI
Primary Contact: Toni Ebeling, Administrator
CFO: Julie Damm, Chief Financial Officer
CMO: Robert Hedges, M.D., Chief Medical Staff
CIO: Julie Damm, Chief Financial Officer
CHR: Denise Jakoubeck, Director Human Resources
Web address: www.hancockmemhospital.com

| | 13 | 10 | 25 | 487 | 6 | 14238 | 0 | 8097 | 2785 | 84 |

CARROLL—Carroll County

★ **ST. ANTHONY REGIONAL HOSPITAL**, 311 South Clark Street, Zip 51401–3038, Mailing Address: P.O. Box 628, Zip 51401–0628; tel. 712/792–3581, (Total facility includes 79 beds in nursing home–type unit) **A**9 10 **F**1 9 10 11 12 21 22 23 26 27 28 29 32 33 34 36 37 38 40 44 46 47 48 49 50 51 52 53 54 55 57 58 59 60 61 62 63 65 66 69 70 71 72 73 74 75 76 77 78 81 82 84 87 88 91 92 93 94 95 96 97 98 108 109 **P**6
Primary Contact: Gary P. Riedmann, President and Chief Executive Officer
Web address: www.stanthonyhospital.org

| | 21 | 10 | 142 | 2218 | 104 | 87772 | 322 | 32672 | 14725 | 394 |

CEDAR FALLS—Black Hawk County

⊞ **SARTORI MEMORIAL HOSPITAL**, 515 College Street, Zip 50613–2500; tel. 319/268–3000, (Total facility includes 16 beds in nursing home–type unit) **A**1 9 10 **F**2 6 9 10 12 21 22 29 32 33 35 41 45 46 48 52 55 58 60 63 69 70 71 76 79 81 88 92 94 95 96 108 **P**1 6 **S** Wheaton Franciscan Services, Inc., Wheaton, IL
Primary Contact: Sherri Greenwood, Administrator
COO: David Olejniczak, Chief Operating Officer
CFO: Shelli Panicucci, Chief Financial Officer
CMO: Steven Cardamone, D.O., Chief Medical Officer
CIO: Todd Richardson, Regional Vice President Information Services
Web address: www.covhealth.com

| | 21 | 10 | 67 | 1995 | 26 | 39775 | 0 | 24343 | 9609 | 226 |

CEDAR RAPIDS—Linn County

⊞ **MERCY MEDICAL CENTER**, 701 Tenth Street S.E., Zip 52403–1292; tel. 319/398–6011, (Total facility includes 80 beds in nursing home–type unit) **A**1 3 5 9 10 **F**2 3 4 6 9 10 11 12 15 17 21 22 23 24 26 27 28 29 31 33 34 35 36 37 38 39 41 44 45 46 47 48 49 50 51 52 53 55 56 57 58 59 60 61 62 63 64 65 66 67 69 71 72 73 74 75 76 77 78 79 80 81 82 84 85 86 87 88 92 93 94 95 96 99 106 108 109 110 **P**7 8
Primary Contact: A. James Tinker, President and Chief Executive Officer
COO: Timothy Charles, Executive Vice President and Chief Operating Officer
CFO: Philip Peterson, Senior Vice President Finance
CMO: Curt Reynolds, M.D., Senior Vice President Medical Affairs
CIO: Jeff Cash, Vice President and Chief Information Officer
CHR: Kathy Krusie, Vice President Human Resources
Web address: www.mercycare.org

| | 21 | 10 | 430 | 11282 | 194 | 266314 | 1012 | 148598 | 62876 | 1581 |

⊞ △ **ST. LUKE'S HOSPITAL**, 1026 A Avenue N.E., Zip 52402–3026, Mailing Address: P.O. Box 3026, Zip 52406–3026; tel. 319/369–7211, (Total facility includes 23 beds in nursing home–type unit) **A**1 3 5 7 9 10 **F**1 2 4 6 9 10 11 12 14 15 16 17 18 19 20 21 22 23 26 27 28 29 32 33 34 36 37 39 40 41 42 44 45 46 47 48 49 50 51 53 55 56 57 58 59 60 61 62 63 64 65 66 67 68 69 70 71 72 73 74 75 76 77 78 81 82 84 85 86 87 88 92 93 94 95 96 98 106 108 109 110 **P**8 **S** Iowa Health System, Des Moines, IA
Primary Contact: Theodore E. Townsend, President and Chief Executive Officer
COO: John C. Sheehan, Executive Vice President and Chief Operating Officer
CFO: Jerry L. Worden, Vice President and Chief Financial Officer
CMO: James LaMorgese, M.D., Vice President and Chief Medical Officer
CHR: Sue Slattery, Director Human Resources
Web address: www.crstlukes.com

| | 23 | 10 | 375 | 15012 | 213 | 334116 | 2500 | 187227 | 74144 | 1896 |

IA

Hospital, Address, Telephone, Approval, Facility, and Physician Codes, Health Care System	Classi-fication Codes		Utilization Data					Expense (thousands) of dollars		
★ American Hospital Association (AHA) membership □ Joint Commission on Accreditation of Healthcare Organizations (JCAHO) accreditation ○ American Osteopathic Association (AOA) accreditation △ Commission on Accreditation of Rehabilitation Facilities (CARF) accreditation	Control	Service	Staffed Beds	Admissions	Census	Outpatient Visits	Births	Total	Payroll	Personnel

CENTERVILLE—Appanoose County

★ **MERCY MEDICAL CENTER–CENTERVILLE**, 1 St. Joseph's Drive,
Zip 52544–8055; tel. 641/437–4111, (Total facility includes 20 beds in nursing home–type unit) **A**9 10 **F**6 11 12 23 26 27 28 33 36 37 40 41 47 48 51 55 58 59 60 63 69 81 84 88 92 94 96 **P**2 7 **S** Catholic Health Initiatives, Denver, CO
Primary Contact: Clinton J. Christianson, Chief Executive Officer
CFO: Stuart McDanel, Vice President and Chief Financial Officer
CIO: Ann Young, Vice President
CHR: Tonya Clawson, Manager Human Resources
Web address: www.mercycenterville.org

	21	10	51	1408	40	62433	128	16597	7471	219

CHARITON—Lucas County

★ **LUCAS COUNTY HEALTH CENTER**, 1200 North Seventh Street,
Zip 50049–1258; tel. 641/774–3000 **A**9 10 18 **F**1 2 4 6 9 11 12 21 23 26 27 28 31 33 34 35 39 45 48 52 53 55 58 59 63 65 66 68 69 72 73 74 75 81 85 87 88 92 94 96 97 108
Primary Contact: Dan Minkoff, Chief Executive Officer
CFO: Margaret Coons, Controller
CMO: Glenn Vogelsang, M.D., Chief Medical Staff
CIO: Richard Eikelboom, Network Manager
CHR: Lana Kuball, Administrative Services Director
Web address: www.lchcia.com

	13	10	25	747	7	22725	83	10421	4713	157

CHARLES CITY—Floyd County

FLOYD COUNTY MEMORIAL HOSPITAL, 800 Eleventh Street,
Zip 50616–3499; tel. 641/228–6830 **A**9 10 18 **F**2 9 11 12 14 21 23 26 27 29 33 46 47 48 51 52 54 55 58 59 60 62 63 64 69 70 81 85 88 94 95 96 97 108 110 **S** Mayo Foundation, Rochester, MN
Primary Contact: Bill D. Faust, Administrator

	13	10	25	1217	13	52843	70	14389	5920	166

CHEROKEE—Cherokee County

★ **CHEROKEE REGIONAL MEDICAL CENTER**, (Formerly Sioux Valley Memorial Hospital), 300 Sioux Valley Drive, Zip 51012–1205; tel. 712/225–5101 **A**9 10 18 **F**6 9 10 11 12 14 21 26 27 28 29 33 34 36 41 44 46 47 48 51 52 53 54 58 59 60 61 63 65 66 69 70 81 88 91 92 93 94 95 96 97 106 108 110 **P**6
Primary Contact: John M. Comstock, Chief Executive Officer
CFO: Joan Bierman, Controller
Web address: www.cherokeermc.org

	23	10	25	1108	12	36791	103	13014	5678	196

□ **MENTAL HEALTH INSTITUTE**, 1251 West Cedar Loop, Zip 51012–1599; tel. 712/225–2594 **A**1 9 10 **F**1 2 21 22 23 26 27 28 45 52 53 58 65 71 72 73 74 75 77 78 94 **P**6
Primary Contact: Tom Deiker, Ph.D., Superintendent
Web address: www.dhs.state.ia.us

	12	22	60	647	46	339	0	15509	9019	208

CLARINDA—Page County

★ **CLARINDA REGIONAL HEALTH CENTER**, 823 South 17th Street, Zip 51632, Mailing Address: P.O. Box 217, Zip 51632–0217; tel. 712/542–2176 **A**9 10 18 **F**2 6 9 12 21 23 27 33 34 39 41 45 46 48 51 52 54 55 58 59 60 61 63 65 69 70 81 84 88 94 95 96 97 107 **P**6
Primary Contact: Keith E. Heuser, Chief Executive Officer
COO: Deborah Herzberg, Chief Operating Officer
CFO: Alan Palo, Chief Financial Officer
CIO: Ed Blach, Director Information Systems
CHR: Deborah Herzberg, Chief Operating Officer
Web address: www.clarindahealth.com

	14	10	25	668	8	35859	42	11617	5412	171

MENTAL HEALTH INSTITUTE, Mailing Address: P.O. Box 338, Zip 51632–0338; tel. 712/542–2161, (Total facility includes 35 beds in nursing home–type unit) **A**10 **F**3 13 14 22 26 32 55 56 60 67 71 74 92 94 108 **P**6
Primary Contact: Mark Lund, Superintendent

	12	22	55	264	48	0	0	7398	5035	86

CLARION—Wright County

★ **WRIGHT MEDICAL CENTER**, 1316 South Main Street, Zip 50525–2019; tel. 515/532–2811 **A**9 10 18 **F**9 11 12 21 23 26 29 33 34 36 37 41 44 46 48 52 53 54 58 59 60 62 63 66 69 70 81 85 88 91 93 96 97 106 108 **P**6
Primary Contact: Steven J. Simonin, Chief Executive Officer
CFO: Amy McDaniel, Controller
CMO: Jon Ahrendsen, M.D., Chief of Staff
Web address: www.wrightmed.com

	14	10	25	642	14	53503	112	14535	6369	154

CLINTON—Clinton County

⊞ **MERCY MEDICAL CENTER–CLINTON**, 1410 North Fourth Street,
Zip 52732–2999; tel. 563/244–5555, (Includes MERCY SERVICES FOR AGING, 600 14th Avenue North, Zip 52732; tel. 563/244–3888), (Total facility includes 203 beds in nursing home–type unit) **A**1 9 10 19 **F**2 9 11 12 14 15 17 21 22 23 27 28 29 30 31 33 35 36 37 38 39 41 44 46 47 48 49 50 51 52 53 55 58 59 60 61 62 63 66 69 71 72 73 74 75 76 78 79 81 82 84 85 88 92 93 94 96 108 **P**1 **S** Trinity Health, Novi, MI
Primary Contact: Donna M. Oliver, Chief Executive Officer
CFO: Paul Mangin, Vice President Finance
Web address: www.mercyclinton.com

	21	10	349	6964	249	57605	511	67506	29942	777

IA

Hospital, Address, Telephone, Approval, Facility, and Physician Codes, Health Care System	Classi-fication Codes		Utilization Data					Expense (thousands) of dollars		
★ American Hospital Association (AHA) membership □ Joint Commission on Accreditation of Healthcare Organizations (JCAHO) accreditation ○ American Osteopathic Association (AOA) accreditation △ Commission on Accreditation of Rehabilitation Facilities (CARF) accreditation	Control	Service	Staffed Beds	Admissions	Census	Outpatient Visits	Births	Total	Payroll	Personnel

CORNING—Adams County

★ **ALEGENT HEALTH MERCY HOSPITAL**, 603 Rosary Drive, Zip 50841–1685, Mailing Address: P.O. Box 368, Zip 50841–0368; tel. 641/322–3121 **A**9 10 18 **F**2 9 11 12 23 26 27 28 33 34 37 41 44 46 47 48 51 52 54 57 58 59 61 62 63 70 81 88 92 94 97 108 110 **S** Alegent Health, Omaha, NE
Primary Contact: James C. Ruppert, Regional Administrator
CMO: Stephen Gruba, M.D., Medical Staff President
CHR: Sandra Lammers, Human Resources and Finance Coordinator
Web address: www.alegent.com
| | 21 | 10 | 22 | 460 | 6 | 26460 | 41 | 8727 | 3558 | 126 |

CORYDON—Wayne County

★ **WAYNE COUNTY HOSPITAL**, 417 South East Street, Zip 50060–1860, Mailing Address: P.O. Box 305, Zip 50060–0305; tel. 641/872–2260 **A**9 10 18 **F**6 9 11 12 22 27 28 29 30 33 44 45 46 47 48 49 52 54 55 58 59 60 63 66 69 70 81 85 88 91 92 94 95 96 97 108 **P**6
Primary Contact: Brian Burnside, Administrator
COO: Joyce McDanel, Chief Operating Officer
CFO: Mark Raven, Chief Financial Officer
Web address: www.waynecountyhospital.org
| | 13 | 10 | 28 | 664 | 11 | 27475 | 53 | 9228 | 3976 | 126 |

COUNCIL BLUFFS—Pottawattamie County

✶ **ALEGENT HEALTH MERCY HOSPITAL**, 800 Mercy Drive, Zip 51503–3128, Mailing Address: P.O. Box 1C, Zip 51502–3001; tel. 712/328–5000 **A**1 9 10 **F**2 3 4 9 10 11 12 21 22 23 24 26 27 28 29 31 32 33 34 35 36 37 38 39 44 45 46 47 48 50 51 52 53 55 57 58 59 60 61 62 63 64 65 66 69 71 72 73 74 75 76 77 78 81 82 84 85 87 88 92 93 94 95 96 98 107 108 109 110 **P**6 8 **S** Alegent Health, Omaha, NE
Primary Contact: Marie E. Knedler, R.N., Vice President and Chief Operating Officer
Web address: www.alegent.com/mercy
| | 21 | 10 | 181 | 6784 | 76 | 67565 | 537 | 62924 | 25000 | 548 |

✶ **JENNIE EDMUNDSON MEMORIAL HOSPITAL**, 933 East Pierce Street, Zip 51503–4652, Mailing Address: P.O. Box 2C, Zip 51502–3002; tel. 712/396–6000 **A**1 2 5 9 10 **F**2 4 9 11 12 15 17 21 22 23 27 28 29 32 33 34 37 45 46 47 48 50 53 55 57 58 59 61 62 63 64 65 66 69 71 72 73 74 75 76 77 78 80 81 82 84 85 87 88 93 94 95 96 106 107 108 109 110 **P**8 **S** Nebraska Methodist Health System, Inc., Omaha, NE
Primary Contact: David M. Holcomb, President and Chief Executive Officer
COO: Steven P. Baumert, Senior Vice President Operations
CMO: Michael A. Romano, M.D., Vice President Medical Affairs
CIO: Dennis Weeks, Director Information Services
CHR: Martha Zubke, Vice President Human Resources
Web address: www.bestcare.org
| | 23 | 10 | 118 | 6766 | 87 | 99586 | 579 | 79476 | 35279 | 698 |

CRESCO—Howard County

★ **REGIONAL HEALTH SERVICES OF HOWARD COUNTY**, 235 Eighth Avenue West, Zip 52136–1098; tel. 563/547–2101 **A**9 10 18 **F**6 9 11 12 21 23 27 33 34 35 36 46 48 51 52 58 59 60 63 64 65 66 69 81 92 94 96 97 108 **P**8 **S** Trinity Health, Novi, MI
Primary Contact: Elizabeth A. Doty, Chief Executive Officer
CFO: Brenda Moser, Chief Financial Officer
CMO: Dennis Colby, M.D., Chief of Staff
CHR: Connie Kuennen, Director Human Resources
Web address: www.rhshc.com
| | 13 | 10 | 25 | 298 | 4 | 20332 | 55 | 8927 | 4009 | 86 |

CRESTON—Union County

★ **GREATER COMMUNITY HOSPITAL**, 1700 West Townline, Zip 50801–1099; tel. 641/782–7091 **A**9 10 18 20 **F**6 9 11 12 21 22 23 26 27 28 29 31 33 36 37 38 41 44 46 47 48 51 52 54 55 58 59 60 61 62 63 66 69 71 76 81 88 91 93 94 96 97 106 108 **S** Iowa Health System, Des Moines, IA
Primary Contact: Monte Neitzel, Administrator and Chief Executive Officer
CFO: Dave Brokaw, Chief Financial Officer
CMO: John Hoyt, M.D., Chief Medical Officer
CIO: Karla Winn, Chief Information Officer
CHR: Lisa Hanson, Human Resources Officer
Web address: www.greaterch.com
| | 13 | 10 | 34 | 1648 | 18 | 26893 | 176 | 18825 | 8174 | 227 |

DAVENPORT—Scott County

✶ △ **GENESIS MEDICAL CENTER, DAVENPORT**, 1227 East Rusholme Street, Zip 52803–2498; tel. 563/421–1000, (Includes GENESIS MEDICAL CENTER–EAST CAMPUS; GENESIS MEDICAL CENTER–WEST CAMPUS, 1401 West Central Park, Zip 52804–1769; tel. 563/421–1000) **A**1 2 3 5 7 9 10 **F**2 3 4 7 9 10 11 12 15 17 19 21 22 23 26 27 28 29 30 31 33 34 35 37 39 42 43 44 47 48 49 50 52 55 56 57 58 59 60 61 62 63 64 65 66 68 69 70 71 72 73 74 75 76 77 78 80 81 82 84 85 86 87 88 92 93 94 95 96 106 107 108 109 110 **P**6 **S** Genesis Health System, Davenport, IA
Primary Contact: Leo A. Bressanelli, FACHE, Chief Executive Officer
CFO: Mark Kleinschmidt, Vice President Finance and Chief Financial Officer
CMO: Frank Claudy, M.D., Vice Persident Medical Staff Affairs
CIO: Robert Frieden, Vice President Information Systems
Web address: www.genesishealth.com
| | 23 | 10 | 427 | 19915 | 288 | 190476 | 2571 | 263783 | 90041 | 1962 |

IA

Hospital, Address, Telephone, Approval, Facility, and Physician Codes, Health Care System	Classi-fication Codes		Utilization Data					Expense (thousands) of dollars		
★ American Hospital Association (AHA) membership □ Joint Commission on Accreditation of Healthcare Organizations (JCAHO) accreditation ○ American Osteopathic Association (AOA) accreditation △ Commission on Accreditation of Rehabilitation Facilities (CARF) accreditation	Control	Service	Staffed Beds	Admissions	Census	Outpatient Visits	Births	Total	Payroll	Personnel

DE WITT—Clinton County

⊠ GENESIS MEDICAL CENTER, DEWITT, (Formerly DeWitt Community Hospital), 1118 11th Street, Zip 52742–1296; tel. 563/659–4200, (Total facility includes 77 beds in nursing home–type unit) **A**1 9 10 18 **F**6 12 21 26 27 28 29 33 34 48 52 54 58 63 66 81 88 92 93 94 97 **S** Genesis Health System, Davenport, IA
Primary Contact: Jeffrey M. Cooper, President and Chief Executive Officer
CFO: Bob Amos, Director Fiscal Services
CMO: Peter Laureijs, M.D., Medical Staff President
CHR: Deb Schuh, Director Human Resources
Web address: www.genesishealth.com

| | 23 | 10 | 90 | 372 | 75 | 29297 | 0 | 10674 | 3856 | 104 |

DECORAH—Winneshiek County

⊠ WINNESHIEK MEDICAL CENTER, (Formerly Winneshiek County Memorial Hospital), 901 Montgomery Street, Zip 52101–2325; tel. 563/382–2911 **A**1 9 10 18 **F**6 9 11 12 14 21 23 26 27 28 29 33 36 46 48 50 51 52 54 55 58 59 60 63 65 69 81 82 84 88 94 95 97 108
Primary Contact: Allan Atkinson, Chief Administrative Officer
COO: Mark Henke, Chief Operating Officer
CFO: Timothy Wren, Chief Financial Officer
CMO: David Heine, M.D., Chief Medical Officer
Web address: www.winmedical.org

| | 13 | 10 | 75 | 1402 | 13 | 49464 | 278 | 18678 | 7716 | 231 |

DENISON—Crawford County

★ CRAWFORD COUNTY MEMORIAL HOSPITAL, 2020 First Avenue South, Zip 51442–2299; tel. 712/263–5021 **A**9 10 18 **F**3 6 9 11 12 13 14 26 28 29 32 33 44 45 46 47 48 50 52 55 56 58 59 60 61 63 67 68 69 70 71 81 82 88 92 94 95 96 97 **P**6
Primary Contact: Edwin A. Gast, Chief Executive Officer and Administrator
CFO: Larry Brown, Chief Financial Officer
CHR: Fred Dietze, Director Human Resources and Community Relations
Web address: www.ccmhia.com

| | 13 | 10 | 28 | 757 | 6 | 29433 | 125 | 12531 | 6135 | 141 |

DES MOINES—Polk County

⊠ BROADLAWNS MEDICAL CENTER, 1801 Hickman Road, Zip 50314–1597; tel. 515/282–2200 **A**1 3 5 9 10 **F**1 2 4 9 11 12 21 22 23 24 26 27 28 29 31 32 33 34 35 37 39 45 48 52 53 55 57 58 59 60 62 63 64 66 69 70 71 72 73 74 75 77 78 81 82 85 88 94 96 106 107 108 109 **P**6
Primary Contact: Susan L. Hunsaker, CHE, President and Chief Executive Officer
COO: Francie Jahn, Senior Vice President Clinical Services
CFO: Al White, Senior Vice President Business Services
CMO: Donald Jensen, M.D., Chief Medical Officer
CIO: Heath Bell, VicePresident and Chief Information Officer
CHR: Tom Fauquier, Senior Vice President Support Services
Web address: www.broadlawns.org
DES MOINES DIVISION See Veterans Affairs Central Iowa Health Care System

| | 13 | 10 | 89 | 4224 | 48 | 168205 | 351 | 73943 | 35677 | 778 |

⊠ IOWA LUTHERAN HOSPITAL, 700 East University Avenue, Zip 50316–2392; tel. 515/263–5612, (Total facility includes 16 beds in nursing home–type unit) **A**1 3 5 9 10 **F**2 3 4 9 10 11 12 15 17 19 21 22 23 26 27 28 29 31 33 34 39 41 44 46 47 48 49 50 52 53 55 57 58 59 61 62 63 64 65 66 69 70 71 72 73 74 75 76 77 78 81 82 84 85 87 88 92 93 94 96 98 106 107 108 109 110 **P**6 **S** Iowa Health System, Des Moines, IA
Primary Contact: Eric T. Crowell, President and Chief Executive Officer
COO: David A. Stark, Chief Operating Officer and Chief Development Officer
CFO: Joe Crofits, Chief Financial Officer
CMO: Mark Purtle, M.D., Vice President Medical Affairs
Web address: www.ihsdesmoines.org

| | 23 | 10 | 217 | 10120 | 149 | 72308 | 1139 | 101075 | 46155 | 970 |

⊠ △ IOWA METHODIST MEDICAL CENTER, 1200 Pleasant Street, Zip 50309–9976; tel. 515/241–6212, (Includes POWELL CONVALESCENT CENTER; RAYMOND BLANK MEMORIAL HOSPITAL FOR CHILDREN; YOUNKER MEMORIAL REHABILITATION CENTER) **A**1 2 7 9 10 **F**2 9 10 11 12 14 15 17 19 21 22 23 24 26 27 28 29 32 33 34 39 41 42 44 46 47 48 49 50 52 53 55 56 57 58 59 60 61 62 63 64 65 66 67 68 69 70 73 79 80 81 82 84 85 86 87 88 89 90 92 93 94 95 96 98 101 106 108 109 110 **P**6 **S** Iowa Health System, Des Moines, IA
Primary Contact: Eric T. Crowell, President and Chief Executive Officer
COO: David A. Stark, Executive Vice President and Chief Operating Officer
CFO: Joseph Corfits, Senior Vice President Finance
CMO: Mark Purtle, M.D., Vice President Medical Affairs
CIO: Jim Moormann, Chief Information Officer
CHR: Sue Allyn, Vice President Human Resources
Web address: www.ihsdesmoines.org

| | 23 | 10 | 461 | 21445 | 316 | 234256 | 3628 | 319476 | 133913 | 3120 |

Many Facility Codes have changed. Please refer to the AHA Guide Code Chart. © 2005 AHA Guide

Hospital, Address, Telephone, Approval, Facility, and Physician Codes, Health Care System	Classi-fication Codes		Utilization Data					Expense (thousands) of dollars		
★ American Hospital Association (AHA) membership □ Joint Commission on Accreditation of Healthcare Organizations (JCAHO) accreditation ○ American Osteopathic Association (AOA) accreditation △ Commission on Accreditation of Rehabilitation Facilities (CARF) accreditation	Control	Service	Staffed Beds	Admissions	Census	Outpatient Visits	Births	Total	Payroll	Personnel

✪ △ **MERCY MEDICAL CENTER–DES MOINES**, 1111 6th Avenue, Zip 50314–2611; tel. 515/247–3121, (Includes MERCY CAPITOL, 603 East 12th Street, Zip 50309–5515; tel. 515/643–1000; David H. Vellinga, President and Chief Executive Officer; MERCY FRANKLIN CENTER, 1818 48th Street, Zip 50310; tel. 515/271–6000), (Total facility includes 35 beds in nursing home–type unit) **A**1 2 3 5 7 9 10 12 13 **F**1 2 4 5 6 7 8 9 11 12 14 15 16 17 18 19 20 21 22 23 24 26 27 28 29 30 31 32 33 34 35 36 37 38 39 41 42 44 46 47 48 49 50 51 52 53 55 56 57 58 59 60 61 62 63 64 65 66 67 69 70 71 72 73 74 75 76 77 78 79 80 81 82 83 84 85 86 87 88 91 92 93 94 95 96 98 101 105 106 107 108 109 110 **P**6 **S** Catholic Health Initiatives, Denver, CO Primary Contact: David H. Vellinga, President and Chief Executive Officer CFO: Steven F. Kukla, Senior Vice President and Chief Financial Officer CIO: Cristina Thomas, Vice President and Chief Information Officer CHR: Robyn Wilkinson, Vice President Human Resources Web address: www.mercydesmoines.org	21	10	561	29802	411	874444	3491	384660	158310	4749
✪ **VETERANS AFFAIRS CENTRAL IOWA HEALTH CARE SYSTEM**, 3600 30th Street, Zip 50310–5774; tel. 515/699–5999, (Includes DES MOINES DIVISION, 3600 30th Street; KNOXVILLE DIVISION, 1515 West Pleasant, Knoxville, Zip 50138–3399; tel. 515/842–3101), (Total facility includes 226 beds in nursing home–type unit) **A**1 2 3 5 **F**1 2 3 4 6 9 12 15 17 21 22 23 25 27 28 29 30 31 32 33 35 36 37 38 39 44 45 46 47 48 50 51 52 53 55 57 58 60 61 62 63 64 65 66 68 69 70 71 73 74 75 76 77 78 81 82 84 87 88 92 93 94 96 106 107 108 109 110 **S** Department of Veterans Affairs, Washington, DC Primary Contact: Donald C. Cooper, Director COO: Paul Backelman, Associate Director CFO: David Edge, Fiscal Officer CMO: Russell Glynn, M.D., Chief of Staff CIO: James Presley, Chief Information Resources CHR: Floyd Kuehnhoff, Human Resources Officer Web address: www.va.gov/sta/guide/home.asp	45	10	327	2883	205	274582	0	152371	81732	1138
DUBUQUE—Dubuque County										
✪ △ **FINLEY HOSPITAL**, 350 North Grandview Avenue, Zip 52001–6392; tel. 563/582–1881, (Total facility includes 10 beds in nursing home–type unit) **A**1 2 7 9 10 **F**9 10 11 12 21 22 23 24 26 27 28 29 32 33 34 35 37 39 41 44 45 46 47 48 49 50 51 52 54 55 56 57 58 59 60 61 62 63 64 65 66 68 69 70 71 76 79 80 81 82 84 85 86 87 88 89 92 94 95 96 106 107 108 109 110 **P**1 5 **S** Iowa Health System, Des Moines, IA Primary Contact: John E. Knox, President and Chief Executive Officer Web address: www.finleyhospital.org	23	10	124	4883	63	93250	610	64818	27050	710
✪ △ **MERCY MEDICAL CENTER–DUBUQUE**, 250 Mercy Drive, Zip 52001–7360; tel. 563/589–8000, (Includes MERCY MEDICAL CENTER–DYERSVILLE, 1111 Third Street S.W., Dyersville, Zip 52040; tel. 319/875–7101), (Total facility includes 40 beds in nursing home–type unit) **A**1 7 9 10 **F**2 3 4 9 11 12 15 17 19 21 22 23 24 27 28 29 30 31 32 33 34 35 39 40 41 44 45 46 47 48 50 51 52 53 55 56 57 58 59 60 61 62 63 64 65 66 68 69 70 71 72 73 74 75 76 77 81 82 84 85 86 88 92 93 94 95 96 98 106 107 108 109 110 **P**8 **S** Trinity Health, Novi, MI Primary Contact: Russell M. Knight, President and Chief Executive Officer CFO: Gary Guetzko, Vice President Finance CIO: Matt Trimmer, Director Information Services Web address: www.mercydubuque.com	21	10	320	10555	167	43421	972	110120	43188	1171
DYERSVILLE—Dubuque County										
MERCY MEDICAL CENTER–DYERSVILLE See Mercy Medical Center–Dubuque, Dubuque										
ELKADER—Clayton County										
★ **CENTRAL COMMUNITY HOSPITAL**, 901 Davidson Street N.W., Zip 52043–9015; tel. 563/245–7000 **A**9 10 18 **F**6 9 12 14 27 28 29 33 34 41 44 45 46 47 48 52 53 55 58 63 64 65 75 81 85 92 94 96 97 98 **S** Trinity Health, Novi, MI Primary Contact: Frances Zichal, Chief Executive Officer CFO: Lisa Manson, Chief Financial Officer	23	10	15	224	4	8812	0	3556	1238	55
EMMETSBURG—Palo Alto County										
★ **PALO ALTO COUNTY HEALTH SYSTEM**, 3201 First Street, Zip 50536; tel. 712/852–5500, (Total facility includes 22 beds in nursing home–type unit) **A**9 10 18 **F**6 9 11 12 21 23 26 27 28 29 33 36 45 46 47 48 51 52 54 55 58 59 60 62 63 64 65 66 69 81 88 91 92 94 96 97 106 108 **P**6 **S** Trinity Health, Novi, MI Primary Contact: Thomas J. Lee, Chief Executive Officer CFO: Renay Hauswirth, Chief Financial Officer CMO: Jennifer Boevers, Medical Staff President CIO: Deb Davis, Director Support Services Web address: www.pachs.com	13	10	47	789	27	20845	89	13665	5140	143
ESTHERVILLE—Emmet County										
★ **AVERA HOLY FAMILY HOSPITAL**, 826 North Eighth Street, Zip 51334–1598; tel. 712/362–2631 **A**9 10 18 **F**2 9 11 12 21 22 23 27 29 33 36 48 51 52 54 55 58 59 60 61 62 63 64 65 66 69 70 81 85 88 91 94 97 108 **P**4 **S** Avera Health, Yankton, SD Primary Contact: William Bumgarner, Chief Executive Officer Web address: www.avera-holyfamily.org	21	10	25	1116	10	31281	68	11306	4505	142

IA

Hospital, Address, Telephone, Approval, Facility, and Physician Codes, Health Care System	Classification Codes		Utilization Data					Expense (thousands) of dollars		
★ American Hospital Association (AHA) membership □ Joint Commission on Accreditation of Healthcare Organizations (JCAHO) accreditation ○ American Osteopathic Association (AOA) accreditation △ Commission on Accreditation of Rehabilitation Facilities (CARF) accreditation	Control	Service	Staffed Beds	Admissions	Census	Outpatient Visits	Births	Total	Payroll	Personnel

FAIRFIELD—Jefferson County

★ **JEFFERSON COUNTY HOSPITAL**, 400 Highland Avenue, Zip 52556–3713, Mailing Address: P.O. Box 588, Zip 52556–0588; tel. 641/472–4111, (Total facility includes 36 beds in nursing home–type unit) **A**9 10 18 **F**9 12 22 23 26 27 28 29 30 33 34 45 46 48 53 55 58 60 61 62 63 69 75 81 88 92 96 97 106
Primary Contact: Ralph Paulding, President and Chief Executive Officer
CFO: Gene Irwin, Chief Financial Officer
Web address: www.jchospital.org

| | 13 | 10 | 67 | 1128 | 47 | 24004 | 0 | 14116 | 5967 | 185 |

FORT DODGE—Webster County

✠ **TRINITY REGIONAL MEDICAL CENTER**, 802 Kenyon Road, Zip 50501–5795; tel. 515/573–3101 **A**1 9 10 19 **F**2 4 6 9 10 11 12 15 17 19 21 22 23 26 27 28 29 30 33 34 36 37 39 40 46 47 48 49 51 52 53 55 58 59 60 61 62 63 65 66 69 71 72 73 74 75 76 77 78 81 82 84 85 87 88 93 94 95 96 106 108 110 **S** Iowa Health System, Des Moines, IA
Primary Contact: Tom Tibbitts, President
CFO: Brian Wegener, Chief Financial Officer
Web address: www.trmc.org

| | 23 | 10 | 154 | 7272 | 77 | 144028 | 645 | 86268 | 32427 | 804 |

FORT MADISON—Lee County

✠ **FORT MADISON COMMUNITY HOSPITAL**, 5445 Avenue O, Zip 52627–0174, Mailing Address: P.O. Box 174, Zip 52627–0174; tel. 319/372–6530 **A**1 9 10 **F**2 9 11 12 21 23 26 27 28 33 34 37 39 40 41 45 46 47 48 51 52 55 57 58 59 60 61 62 63 65 66 68 69 70 77 81 84 87 88 92 93 94 95 96 97 107 108 109 110 **P**6 **S** Quorum Health Resources, Plano, TX
Primary Contact: C. James Platt, Chief Executive Officer
CHR: Jody Schulte, Director Employee Relations
Web address: www.fmchosp.com

| | 23 | 10 | 50 | 2834 | 29 | 51018 | 181 | 31057 | 13749 | 332 |

GLENWOOD—Mills County

GLENWOOD RESOURCE CENTER, 711 South Vine, Zip 51534–1927; tel. 712/527–4811 **F**27 28 32 54 94 108 **P**6
Primary Contact: Tom Hoogestraat, Superintendent

| | 12 | 62 | 397 | 39 | 386 | 0 | 0 | 54775 | 34295 | 861 |

GREENFIELD—Adair County

ADAIR COUNTY MEMORIAL HOSPITAL, 609 S.E. Kent Street, Zip 50849–9454; tel. 641/743–2123 **A**9 10 18 **F**6 9 12 21 23 26 27 28 29 30 33 34 46 48 51 52 54 55 58 60 61 62 63 69 70 81 82 84 88 93 94 97 108 **P**6
Primary Contact: Myrna Erb–Gundel, Administrator
Web address: www.adaircountyhealthsystem.org

| | 13 | 10 | 22 | 379 | 4 | 10244 | 0 | 6566 | 2572 | 95 |

GRINNELL—Poweshiek County

★ **GRINNELL REGIONAL MEDICAL CENTER**, 210 Fourth Avenue, Zip 50112–1833; tel. 641/236–7511 **A**9 10 **F**1 2 9 10 11 12 21 22 23 24 26 27 28 29 30 31 32 33 34 35 36 37 38 39 41 42 44 45 46 47 48 50 51 52 54 55 57 58 59 60 61 62 63 64 65 66 69 70 72 73 74 75 76 77 81 82 84 85 88 94 95 96 97 98 106 108 109 110 **P**7
Primary Contact: Todd C. Linden, President and Chief Executive Officer
COO: Suzanne Cooner, Vice President Operations
CFO: Todd Nelson, Vice President Finance
CMO: David C. Cranston, M.D., Vice President Medical Staff Affairs
Web address: www.grinnellregional.org

| | 23 | 10 | 51 | 3051 | 29 | 51061 | 187 | 42186 | 18790 | 449 |

GRUNDY CENTER—Grundy County

★ **GRUNDY COUNTY MEMORIAL HOSPITAL**, 201 East J Avenue, Zip 50638–2096; tel. 319/824–5421, (Total facility includes 55 beds in nursing home–type unit) **A**9 10 18 **F**9 12 21 26 27 28 29 33 34 36 46 47 48 61 63 65 66 69 70 81 82 88 92 94 96 97 108 **S** Iowa Health System, Des Moines, IA
Primary Contact: Pamela K. Delagardelle, Chief Executive Officer
CFO: Lisa Zinkula, Chief Financial Officer
Web address: www.grundyhospital.com

| | 13 | 10 | 80 | 342 | 58 | 20337 | 0 | 5510 | 2697 | 92 |

GUTHRIE CENTER—Guthrie County

★ **GUTHRIE COUNTY HOSPITAL**, 710 North 12th Street, Zip 50115–1544; tel. 641/332–2201 **A**9 10 18 **F**9 12 21 23 27 29 30 33 34 41 45 46 48 52 54 58 61 62 63 64 69 81 88 92 94 97 **P**5 **S** Iowa Health System, Des Moines, IA
Primary Contact: Gerald D. Neal, Chief Executive Officer
COO: Danielle Navarro, R.N., Chief Nursing Officer
Web address: www.gcho.org

| | 13 | 10 | 25 | 424 | 5 | 23444 | 0 | 6053 | 2777 | 94 |

GUTTENBERG—Clayton County

★ **GUTTENBERG MUNICIPAL HOSPITAL**, Second and Main Street, Zip 52052–0550, Mailing Address: P.O. Box 550, Zip 52052–0550; tel. 563/252–1121 **A**9 10 18 **F**6 9 11 12 26 27 28 29 33 34 39 41 46 48 52 53 55 59 63 64 69 75 81 88 92 94 96 97 110 **P**5 **S** Iowa Health System, Des Moines, IA
Primary Contact: Kimberley Gau, Chief Executive Officer
CMO: Michele Sadler, D.O., Chief Medical Staff
CHR: Heidi Smith, Administrative Director
Web address: www.guttenberghospital.org

| | 14 | 10 | 25 | 588 | 6 | 17391 | 35 | 5537 | 2290 | 80 |

HAMBURG—Fremont County

GRAPE COMMUNITY HOSPITAL, 2959 U.S. Highway 275, Zip 51640–5067; tel. 712/382–1515 **A**9 10 18 **F**9 12 23 26 27 28 33 34 37 41 46 48 51 52 54 58 60 61 62 63 65 69 81 84 88 92 94 97 108 110
Primary Contact: James L. Clough, Administrator and Chief Executive Officer
Web address: www.grapehospital.com

| | 23 | 10 | 25 | 462 | 16 | 31713 | 0 | 7574 | 3696 | 115 |

IA

Many Facility Codes have changed. Please refer to the AHA Guide Code Chart.

Hospital, Address, Telephone, Approval, Facility, and Physician Codes, Health Care System	Classi-fication Codes		Utilization Data					Expense (thousands) of dollars		
★ American Hospital Association (AHA) membership □ Joint Commission on Accreditation of Healthcare Organizations (JCAHO) accreditation ○ American Osteopathic Association (AOA) accreditation △ Commission on Accreditation of Rehabilitation Facilities (CARF) accreditation	Control	Service	Staffed Beds	Admissions	Census	Outpatient Visits	Births	Total	Payroll	Personnel

HAMPTON—Franklin County

★ **FRANKLIN GENERAL HOSPITAL**, 1720 Central Avenue East, Zip 50441–1859; tel. 641/456–5000, (Total facility includes 52 beds in nursing home–type unit) **A**9 10 18 **F**6 8 9 12 21 22 23 24 26 27 28 32 33 45 46 48 52 53 58 60 63 65 69 70 73 81 84 85 88 91 92 94 96 97 108 **P**6 8 **S** Trinity Health, Novi, MI
Primary Contact: Ronald D. Baker, Chief Executive Officer
CFO: Michelle Craighton, Finance Manager
Web address: www.franklingeneral.com

	13	10	77	384	51	14173	0	9737	4709	124

HARLAN—Shelby County

★ **SHELBY COUNTY MYRTUE MEMORIAL HOSPITAL**, 1213 Garfield Avenue, Zip 51537–2057; tel. 712/755–5161 **A**9 10 20 **F**9 10 11 12 21 23 24 26 27 28 29 31 33 36 37 41 46 48 51 52 54 58 59 60 61 62 63 64 69 75 77 81 82 84 88 93 95 96 97 106 108 109 110 **P**6 8
Primary Contact: Robert Mason, Interim Administrator
CFO: Barry Jacobsen, Chief Financial Officer
CMO: Don Klitgaard, M.D., Chief of Staff
CIO: Frank Espanto, Jr, Chief Information Officer
Web address: www.shelbycoheatlh.com

	13	10	40	1681	17	31942	84	13629	5611	213

HAWARDEN—Sioux County

★ **HAWARDEN COMMUNITY HOSPITAL**, 1111 11th Street, Zip 51023–1999; tel. 712/551–3100 **A**9 10 18 **F**9 12 21 23 27 33 34 41 44 46 48 53 58 60 61 63 69 81 82 84 88 92 97 110 **P**7 **S** Trinity Health, Novi, MI
Primary Contact: Brian Monsma, Chief Executive Officer
CFO: Robert Jaminet, Director Fiscal Services

	14	10	18	206	2	19029	0	3522	1344	46

HUMBOLDT—Humboldt County

★ **HUMBOLDT COUNTY MEMORIAL HOSPITAL**, 1000 North 15th Street, Zip 50548–1008; tel. 515/332–4200, (Total facility includes 28 beds in nursing home–type unit) **A**9 10 18 **F**6 9 12 14 21 23 26 27 28 33 34 36 37 38 39 40 45 48 51 54 58 60 61 62 63 66 69 81 83 84 86 88 91 92 94 97 **S** Iowa Health System, Des Moines, IA
Primary Contact: Charles Kelch, Administrator
CFO: Betty Etherington, Chief Financial Officer
Web address: www.humboldthealth.org

	13	10	49	538	33	47556	0	8938	4174	132

IDA GROVE—Ida County

★ **HORN MEMORIAL HOSPITAL**, 701 East Second Street, Zip 51445–1699; tel. 712/364–3311 **A**9 10 18 20 **F**9 11 12 23 26 27 28 29 33 34 36 37 38 46 47 48 51 52 54 59 60 61 62 63 64 69 70 77 81 84 85 88 92 93 94 96 97 98 106 108 **P**2
Primary Contact: Dan Ellis, Administrator
CFO: Gary Teut, Assistant Administrator
Web address: www.hornmemorialhospital.org

	23	10	25	888	12	28178	82	8264	3581	93

INDEPENDENCE—Buchanan County

★ **BUCHANAN COUNTY HEALTH CENTER**, 1600 First Street East, Zip 50644–3155; tel. 319/334–6071, (Total facility includes 59 beds in nursing home–type unit) **A**9 10 18 **F**6 9 11 12 21 25 26 27 28 29 30 32 33 34 37 41 44 45 46 47 48 49 50 51 52 55 58 59 60 62 63 65 66 69 81 82 88 91 92 94 95 96 97 106 108 110
Primary Contact: Robert J. Richard, Administrator
CFO: Ronald Timpe, Associate Administrator
Web address: www.bchealth.info

	13	10	84	674	50	45902	29	11087	5329	167

□ **MENTAL HEALTH INSTITUTE**, 2277 Iowa Avenue, Zip 50644–9106, Mailing Address: P.O. Box 111, Zip 50644–0111; tel. 319/334–2583 **A**1 9 10 **F**22 26 27 28 32 45 71 72 74 75 94 108 **P**6
Primary Contact: Bhasker J. Dave, M.D., Superintendent
Web address: www.dhs.state.ia.us

	12	22	95	360	92	20	0	19232	11940	285

IOWA CITY—Johnson County

⊠ **MERCY HOSPITAL**, 500 East Market Street, Zip 52245–2689; tel. 319/339–0300, (Total facility includes 16 beds in nursing home–type unit) **A**1 2 9 10 **F**2 9 11 12 15 17 19 21 22 23 26 27 28 29 32 33 34 35 39 40 43 44 46 47 48 51 52 55 56 58 59 60 61 62 63 64 65 66 70 71 81 82 83 84 85 87 88 92 94 96 106 107 108 110 **P**1
Primary Contact: Ronald R. Reed, President and Chief Executive Officer
COO: Catherine H. Abrams, R.N., MS, Vice President Nursing
CFO: Michael G. Heinrich, Vice President Finance
CMO: Peter D. Wallace, M.D., Vice President Medical Staff Affairs
CIO: Paul Foelsch, Chief Information Officer
CHR: Mary McMurray, Director Human Resources
Web address: www.mercyiowacity.org

	21	10	240	7953	108	300571	1273	109540	45908	968

IA

Hospital, Address, Telephone, Approval, Facility, and Physician Codes, Health Care System	Classification Codes		Utilization Data					Expense (thousands) of dollars		
★ American Hospital Association (AHA) membership □ Joint Commission on Accreditation of Healthcare Organizations (JCAHO) accreditation ○ American Osteopathic Association (AOA) accreditation △ Commission on Accreditation of Rehabilitation Facilities (CARF) accreditation	Control	Service	Staffed Beds	Admissions	Census	Outpatient Visits	Births	Total	Payroll	Personnel
⊠ **UNIVERSITY OF IOWA HOSPITALS AND CLINICS**, 200 Hawkins Drive, Zip 52242–1009; tel. 319/356–1616, (Includes CHEMICAL DEPENDENCY CENTER, tel. 319/384–8765; STATE PSYCHIATRIC HOSPITAL, tel. 319/356–4658; UNIVERSITY HOSPITAL SCHOOL, tel. 319/353–6456) **A**1 2 3 5 8 9 10 **F**2 3 4 5 6 7 9 10 11 12 13 14 15 16 17 18 19 20 21 22 23 24 26 27 28 29 30 31 32 33 34 35 36 37 38 39 40 42 43 44 45 46 47 48 49 50 51 52 53 55 56 57 58 59 60 61 62 63 64 65 66 67 68 69 70 71 72 73 74 75 76 77 78 79 81 82 84 85 86 87 88 89 90 93 94 95 96 99 100 101 102 103 104 105 106 107 108 109 110 **P**1 7 Primary Contact: Donna Katen–Bahensky, Director and Chief Executive Officer COO: Ann Madden Rice, Associate Director and Chief Operating Officer CFO: Anthony C. Defurio, Associate Director and Chief Financial Officer CIO: Lee Carmen, Director Health Care Information Systems CHR: Diana Leventry, Director Human Resources Web address: www.uihealthcare.com	12	10	646	25384	481	864010	1545	630667	254112	5782
⊠ **VETERANS AFFAIRS MEDICAL CENTER**, 601 Highway 6 West, Zip 52246–2208; tel. 319/338–0581 **A**1 3 5 8 **F**2 4 14 15 17 21 22 23 26 27 28 29 32 33 35 36 37 38 42 44 45 46 48 49 50 52 53 55 57 58 60 61 62 63 65 66 69 70 71 73 76 77 81 82 84 87 88 92 93 94 96 101 106 107 108 109 110 **S** Department of Veterans Affairs, Washington, DC Primary Contact: Gary L. Wilkinson, Director CFO: Daniel Kellerman, Chief Operating Officer CIO: Antonio Razavi, Chief Information Officer Web address: www.va.gov/sta/guide/home.asp	45	10	93	3265	56	272256	0	137124	73635	1151
IOWA FALLS—Hardin County										
⊠ **ELLSWORTH MUNICIPAL HOSPITAL**, 110 Rocksylvania Avenue, Zip 50126–2400; tel. 641/648–4631 **A**1 9 10 **F**4 9 11 12 21 22 29 30 33 34 41 45 46 47 48 52 55 58 59 60 63 64 65 66 69 71 72 73 74 75 77 78 81 88 93 94 95 96 97 106 108 **S** Trinity Health, Novi, MI Primary Contact: John O'Brien, Administrator CFO: Betty Riley, Chief Financial Officer CMO: David Van Gorp, M.D., Physician CIO: John Gabriel, Director CHR: Cheri Geitz, Human Resources Director Web address: www.emhia.com	14	10	40	1767	19	34648	103	11123	5488	191
JEFFERSON—Greene County										
★ **GREENE COUNTY MEDICAL CENTER**, 1000 West Lincolnway, Zip 50129–1697; tel. 515/386–2114, (Total facility includes 76 beds in nursing home–type unit) **A**9 10 18 **F**2 9 11 12 21 26 27 28 29 30 33 36 37 44 48 51 52 53 58 59 60 61 62 63 69 81 88 91 92 93 94 95 96 97 106 **P**5 6 **S** Iowa Health System, Des Moines, IA Primary Contact: Karen L. Bossard, Administrator and Chief Executive Officer CFO: William Steussy, Chief Financial Officer CMO: Steven Karber, M.D., Medical Director CIO: Kevin Kibby, Manager Information Systems Web address: www.gcmchealth.com	13	10	101	711	71	24413	69	13703	7085	212
KEOKUK—Lee County										
⊠ **KEOKUK AREA HOSPITAL**, 1600 Morgan Street, Zip 52632–3456; tel. 319/524–7150 **A**1 9 10 **F**2 11 12 14 26 27 28 29 33 34 46 47 48 51 52 53 59 62 63 65 66 68 69 71 73 74 75 81 82 85 87 88 93 95 96 97 108 **P**6 Primary Contact: Allan Zastrow, FACHE, Chief Executive Officer CFO: Walter Winkler, Chief Financial Officer CMO: William Fulcher, M.D., Chief of Staff CIO: Linda Shaffner, Chief Information Officer CHR: Vicky Kobjohn, Director Human Resources Web address: www.keokukhealthsystems.org	23	10	105	3281	36	45741	222	28216	12818	403
KEOSAUQUA—Van Buren County										
★ **VAN BUREN COUNTY HOSPITAL**, 340 Franklin, Zip 52565; tel. 319/293–3171 **A**9 10 18 **F**2 6 8 9 11 12 21 23 26 27 28 29 33 34 39 46 47 48 51 52 55 58 59 60 61 62 63 64 65 66 69 70 75 81 85 86 88 94 96 97 106 108 109 110 **P**6 Primary Contact: Lisa Schnedler, Administrator CFO: Helen Holland, Chief Financial Officer CIO: Julie Ludwig, Data Coordinator Web address: www.netins.net/showcase/forhealth/	13	10	25	904	15	14125	38	9556	3951	175
KNOXVILLE—Marion County										
★ **KNOXVILLE AREA COMMUNITY HOSPITAL AND CLINIC**, 1002 South Lincoln Street, Zip 50138–3155; tel. 641/842–2151 **A**9 10 18 **F**2 9 11 21 26 27 28 33 36 46 48 52 53 55 58 59 60 62 63 64 65 69 70 75 81 82 84 87 88 93 94 96 97 106 108 **S** Quorum Health Resources, Plano, TX Primary Contact: Ann M. Helwig, Chief Executive Officer COO: Ann M. Helwig, Chief Executive Officer CFO: Michael Creary, Chief Financial Officer CMO: Michael Van Natta, D.O., President Medical Staff CHR: Brenda Maddison, Human Resources Director Web address: www.kach.org KNOXVILLE DIVISION See Veterans Affairs Central Iowa Health Care System, Des Moines	23	10	25	753	10	16175	57	9533	3587	120

IA

Hospital, Address, Telephone, Approval, Facility, and Physician Codes, Health Care System	Classification Codes		Utilization Data					Expense (thousands) of dollars		
	Control	Service	Staffed Beds	Admissions	Census	Outpatient Visits	Births	Total	Payroll	Personnel

★ American Hospital Association (AHA) membership
□ Joint Commission on Accreditation of Healthcare Organizations (JCAHO) accreditation
○ American Osteopathic Association (AOA) accreditation
△ Commission on Accreditation of Rehabilitation Facilities (CARF) accreditation

LAKE CITY—Calhoun County

★ **STEWART MEMORIAL COMMUNITY HOSPITAL**, 1301 West Main, Zip 51449–1585; tel. 712/464–3171 **A**9 10 18 **F**6 9 10 11 12 21 22 23 26 33 34 36 47 48 51 52 54 55 58 59 60 63 65 69 81 88 94 97 109 **P**5 6
Primary Contact: Kris Baumgart, Chief Executive Officer
CFO: Jim Henkenius, Chief Financial Officer
Web address: www.stewartmemorial.org

| | 23 | 10 | 25 | 963 | 11 | 38125 | 100 | 17682 | 7199 | 188 |

LE MARS—Plymouth County

★ **FLOYD VALLEY HOSPITAL/AVERA HEALTH**, 714 Lincoln Street N.E., Zip 51031–0010, Mailing Address: P.O. Box 10, Zip 51031–0010; tel. 712/546–7871 **A**9 10 18 **F**2 8 9 11 12 14 21 22 23 24 27 28 29 33 34 41 46 47 48 51 52 54 55 59 61 63 64 65 66 81 85 88 92 96 97 106 108 110 **P**5 **S** Avera Health, Yankton, SD
Primary Contact: Michael T. Donlin, Administrator
CFO: Daryl Friedenbach, Director Fiscal Services
CMO: Sheila Holcomb, M.D., Medical Staff President
CHR: Mary Helen Nitzschke, Director Human Resources
Web address: www.floydvalleyhospital.org

| | 14 | 10 | 44 | 1531 | 13 | 43065 | 122 | 15564 | 5850 | 162 |

LEON—Decatur County

★ **DECATUR COUNTY HOSPITAL**, 1405 N.W. Church Street, Zip 50144–1299; tel. 641/446–4871 **A**9 10 18 **F**6 12 21 23 29 30 33 46 48 51 52 58 59 63 70 72 73 77 81 84 88 92 94 97 106
Primary Contact: Darrell E. Vondrak, Chief Executive Officer
CFO: Paula Pickens, Chief Financial Officer
Web address: www.decaturcountyhospital.org

| | 13 | 10 | 25 | 410 | 5 | 26755 | 37 | 7813 | 2994 | 106 |

MANCHESTER—Delaware County

★ **REGIONAL MEDICAL CENTER**, (Formerly Regional Medical Center of Northeast Iowa and Delaware County), 709 West Main Street, Zip 52057–0359, Mailing Address: P.O. Box 359, Zip 52057–0359; tel. 563/927–3232 **A**9 10 18 **F**2 6 9 11 12 21 26 27 28 29 30 31 33 34 35 36 38 39 41 46 47 48 50 51 52 53 55 58 59 60 63 65 66 69 72 73 74 75 76 77 81 82 84 85 88 92 94 95 96 97 108 109 110
Primary Contact: Lon D. Butikofer, R.N., Ph.D., Chief Executive Officer
CFO: Danette Kramer, Vice President Finance and Chief Financial Officer
CIO: Julie Bente, Vice President Human and Facility Resources
CHR: Julie Bente, Vice President Human and Facility Resources
Web address: www.regmedctr.org

| | 13 | 10 | 25 | 709 | 7 | 81416 | 147 | 15126 | 6454 | 187 |

MANNING—Carroll County

MANNING REGIONAL HEALTHCARE CENTER, 410 Main Street, Zip 51455–1093; tel. 712/655–2072, (Total facility includes 58 beds in nursing home–type unit) **A**9 10 18 **F**2 4 9 11 12 23 26 29 30 31 33 34 39 44 46 47 48 50 51 52 58 59 60 61 62 63 64 69 81 82 88 92 94 96 97 108 **P**5
Primary Contact: Jeanne Goche, Chief Executive Officer and Administrator
Web address: www.mrhcia.com

| | 23 | 10 | 73 | 271 | 53 | 6780 | 24 | 7145 | 3290 | 127 |

MAQUOKETA—Jackson County

⊠ **JACKSON COUNTY PUBLIC HOSPITAL**, 700 West Grove Street, Zip 52060–0910; tel. 563/652–2474, (Total facility includes 18 beds in nursing home–type unit) **A**1 9 10 18 **F**2 6 9 11 12 22 23 26 27 28 29 33 34 41 46 48 49 51 52 54 55 58 59 63 64 65 66 69 81 92 94 95 97 108 **S** Iowa Health System, Des Moines, IA
Primary Contact: Curt Coleman, CHE, Chief Executive Officer
CHR: Mindi Nelson, Director Human Resources

| | 13 | 10 | 43 | 678 | 25 | 21735 | 63 | 11608 | 5217 | 154 |

MARENGO—Iowa County

★ **MARENGO MEMORIAL HOSPITAL**, 300 West May Street, Zip 52301–1261, Mailing Address: P.O. Box 228, Zip 52301–0228; tel. 319/642–5543 **A**9 10 18 **F**6 9 21 26 27 28 29 33 34 35 39 46 48 52 54 58 60 62 64 66 69 81 94 96 97 108 **P**6
Primary Contact: Genice Maroc, Chief Executive Officer
CFO: Dawn Mumby, Chief Financial Officer
CMO: Sylvia Chang, M.D., Chief Medical Staff
CHR: Donna Watts, Director Staff and Community Relations
Web address: www.marengohospital.org

| | 14 | 10 | 25 | 115 | 15 | 6076 | 1 | 5660 | 3206 | 90 |

MARSHALLTOWN—Marshall County

⊠ **MARSHALLTOWN MEDICAL AND SURGICAL CENTER**, 3 South Fourth Avenue, Zip 50158–2998; tel. 641/754–5151, (Total facility includes 26 beds in nursing home–type unit) **A**1 9 10 19 20 **F**2 6 9 11 12 21 23 26 27 28 29 30 33 34 35 39 41 42 46 48 51 52 53 55 57 58 59 60 61 62 63 64 65 66 69 70 81 82 85 87 88 92 93 94 95 96 108 109 110 **P**6 7
Primary Contact: Robert Cooper, Chief Executive Officer
COO: LaRae Schelling, Vice President Operations and Chief Nursing Officer
CFO: Robert Downey, Vice President Finance
CMO: Gary Peasley, M.D., Medical Staff President
CIO: Robert Downey, Vice President Finance
CHR: Colleen Springer, Director Human Resources
Web address: www.everydaychampions.org

| | 23 | 10 | 105 | 3834 | 43 | 210304 | 642 | 44205 | 20433 | 505 |

IA

Hospital, Address, Telephone, Approval, Facility, and Physician Codes, Health Care System	Classi-fication Codes		Utilization Data					Expense (thousands) of dollars		
	Control	Service	Staffed Beds	Admissions	Census	Outpatient Visits	Births	Total	Payroll	Personnel

★ American Hospital Association (AHA) membership
□ Joint Commission on Accreditation of Healthcare Organizations (JCAHO) accreditation
○ American Osteopathic Association (AOA) accreditation
△ Commission on Accreditation of Rehabilitation Facilities (CARF) accreditation

MASON CITY—Cerro Gordo County

⊞ **MERCY MEDICAL CENTER – NORTH IOWA**, 1000 Fourth Street S.W., Zip 50401–2800; tel. 641/422–7000 **A**1 2 3 5 9 10 12 19 20 **F**2 9 10 11 12 14 15 17 19 21 22 23 24 26 27 28 29 30 31 32 33 34 35 36 37 38 39 41 43 44 45 46 47 48 49 50 51 52 53 55 56 57 58 59 60 61 62 63 64 65 66 68 69 70 71 72 73 74 75 76 77 78 79 80 81 82 84 85 87 88 91 92 93 94 95 96 98 107 108 109 110 **P**1 6 **S** Trinity Health, Novi, MI
Primary Contact: James G. FitzPatrick, President and Chief Executive Officer
CFO: Rod G. Schlader, Chief Financial Officer
CIO: Randy Haskins, Director Information Systems
CHR: Diane Fischels, Vice President Organizational Development
Web address: www.mercynorthiowa.com
| | 21 | 10 | 238 | 10845 | 137 | 603336 | 1062 | 228549 | 102551 | 2178 |

MISSOURI VALLEY—Harrison County

★ **ALEGENT HEALTH COMMUNITY MEMORIAL HOSPITAL**, 631 North Eighth Street, Zip 51555–1199; tel. 712/642–2784 **A**9 10 18 **F**9 12 22 23 26 27 28 29 33 34 42 48 49 52 53 58 60 61 62 63 69 72 73 75 77 81 85 88 94 96 97 108 **P**8 **S** Alegent Health, Omaha, NE
Primary Contact: Robert R. Sellers, Regional Health Administrator
CFO: Donald Reid, Operations Director, Support Service and Finance Lead
CMO: Charles B. Johnston, M.D., Chief of Staff
CIO: Stephanie Myers, Business Office Lead
CHR: Julie Brown, Human Resources Assistant
Web address: www.alegent.org
| | 23 | 10 | 25 | 600 | 5 | 19755 | 0 | 12434 | 4404 | 142 |

MOUNT AYR—Ringgold County

RINGGOLD COUNTY HOSPITAL, 211 Shellway Drive, Zip 50854–1299; tel. 641/464–3226 **A**9 10 20 **F**6 9 12 23 28 33 34 46 47 48 49 63 69 81 88 97 **P**6
Primary Contact: Gordon W. Winkler, Administrator
| | 13 | 10 | 23 | 416 | 7 | 17316 | 0 | 8950 | 4293 | 109 |

MOUNT PLEASANT—Henry County

★ **HENRY COUNTY HEALTH CENTER**, 407 South White Street, Zip 52641–2299; tel. 319/385–3141, (Total facility includes 49 beds in nursing home–type unit) **A**9 10 18 **F**6 9 11 12 21 23 24 26 27 28 29 33 34 37 39 44 45 46 47 48 52 53 55 58 59 60 61 62 63 65 69 70 75 81 82 85 88 92 93 94 95 96 97 106 107 108 110 **P**8
Primary Contact: Daniel F. Sheehan, Chief Executive Officer
COO: Tony Warren, Vice President Development
CMO: James Widmer, M.D., Chief of Staff
CIO: Bill Grimm, Director Support Services
CHR: Jim Carson, Human Resources Manager
Web address: www.hchc.org
| | 13 | 10 | 74 | 1398 | 60 | 55205 | 144 | 21091 | 8975 | 267 |

MENTAL HEALTH INSTITUTE, 1200 East Washington Street, Zip 52641–1898; tel. 319/385–7231 **A**9 10 **F**3 4 26 71 94 **P**5
Primary Contact: Russell E. Rogerson, Superintendent
Web address: www.dhs.state.ia.us/institutions/mtpleasantmhi.asp
| | 12 | 82 | 59 | 603 | 54 | 156 | 0 | 6458 | 4484 | 81 |

MUSCATINE—Muscatine County

⊞ **UNITY HOSPITAL**, 1518 Mulberry Avenue, Zip 52761–3499; tel. 563/264–9100, (Total facility includes 8 beds in nursing home–type unit) **A**1 9 10 20 **F**2 9 11 12 23 27 28 33 34 37 38 39 44 48 50 52 53 54 55 58 59 62 63 64 65 66 69 81 82 85 87 88 92 94 97 110
Primary Contact: Karmon T. Bjella, Chief Executive Officer
CFO: Thomas A. Huber, Vice President Finance
CMO: Matthew Sojka, M.D., Chief of Staff
CIO: Mark Reynolds, Director Information Technology
CHR: Delores Stecher, Director Human Resources
Web address: www.unityiowa.org
| | 23 | 10 | 66 | 2150 | 25 | 93814 | 303 | 28096 | 10603 | 293 |

NEVADA—Story County

★ **STORY COUNTY MEDICAL CENTER**, 630 Sixth Street, Zip 50201–2266; tel. 515/382–2111, (Total facility includes 76 beds in nursing home–type unit) **A**9 10 18 **F**6 9 21 23 24 27 29 30 33 34 39 41 45 46 48 52 53 54 58 60 61 62 63 69 70 92 94 95 96 97 106 107 108 109 110 **P**6
Primary Contact: Todd Willert, Administrator
CFO: Maggie Hamilton–Beyer, Interim Chief Financial Officer
Web address: www.scmcnevada.org
| | 13 | 10 | 94 | 273 | 75 | 22107 | 0 | 11151 | 5201 | 141 |

NEW HAMPTON—Chickasaw County

★ **MERCY MEDICAL CENTER–NEW HAMPTON**, 308 North Maple Avenue, Zip 50659–1142; tel. 641/394–4121, (Total facility includes 35 beds in nursing home–type unit) **A**9 10 18 **F**9 11 12 21 22 23 26 27 29 30 33 34 44 46 48 52 57 58 59 60 62 63 64 69 81 85 95 96 97 106 108 110 **P**5 **S** Trinity Health, Novi, MI
Primary Contact: Carolyn Martin–Shaw, Chief Executive Officer
CFO: Jennifer Rapenske, Manager Financial Services
CMO: Joseph Peraud, M.D., President Medical Staff
CIO: Janetta Taylor, Director Information Systems
CHR: Lisa Heller, Manager Human Resources and Payroll
Web address: www.mercynewhampton.com
| | 21 | 10 | 53 | 552 | 38 | 17410 | 53 | 8932 | 3714 | 96 |

IA

Many Facility Codes have changed. Please refer to the AHA Guide Code Chart. © 2005 AHA Guide

Hospital, Address, Telephone, Approval, Facility, and Physician Codes, Health Care System	Classification Codes		Utilization Data					Expense (thousands) of dollars		
	Control	Service	Staffed Beds	Admissions	Census	Outpatient Visits	Births	Total	Payroll	Personnel

★ American Hospital Association (AHA) membership
☐ Joint Commission on Accreditation of Healthcare Organizations (JCAHO) accreditation
◯ American Osteopathic Association (AOA) accreditation
△ Commission on Accreditation of Rehabilitation Facilities (CARF) accreditation

NEWTON—Jasper County

★ **SKIFF MEDICAL CENTER**, 204 North Fourth Avenue East, Zip 50208–3100, Mailing Address: P.O. Box 1006, Zip 50208–1006; tel. 641/792–1273 **A**9 10 **F**2 3 8 9 11 12 13 14 21 22 23 24 27 29 30 33 34 35 36 38 46 48 49 51 52 54 55 56 58 59 60 61 63 64 67 68 69 71 75 81 82 84 87 88 92 93 94 95 96 97 108 109 **P**6
Primary Contact: Eric L. Lothe, President and Chief Executive Officer
CFO: Cheryl Ritter, Vice President and Chief Financial Officer
CMO: Tammara Chance, D.O., Medical Director
CHR: Gena Garber, Director Human Resources
Web address: www.skiffmed.com

| | 14 | 10 | 52 | 2292 | 24 | 73802 | 238 | 27847 | 13706 | 295 |

OAKDALE—Johnson County

IOWA MEDICAL AND CLASSIFICATION CENTER, Highway 965, Zip 52319, Mailing Address: IMCC, Box A, Zip 52319; tel. 319/626–2391, (Nonreporting)
Primary Contact: Lowell Brandt, Warden

| | 12 | 22 | 23 | — | — | — | — | — | — | — |

OELWEIN—Fayette County

★ **MERCY HOSPITAL OF FRANCISCAN SISTERS**, 201 Eighth Avenue S.E., Zip 50662–2447; tel. 319/283–6000, (Total facility includes 39 beds in nursing home–type unit) **A**9 10 18 **F**3 6 9 11 12 13 14 21 22 27 29 33 44 46 47 48 54 55 56 58 59 63 65 66 67 68 70 71 81 84 88 92 94 95 96 97 108 **P**1 6 **S** Wheaton Franciscan Services, Inc., Wheaton, IL
Primary Contact: Richard Schrupp, President and Chief Executive Officer
CFO: Timothy Huber, Manager Financial Support
CMO: Stephen Cardamone, M.D., Senior Vice President and Chief Medical Officer
CIO: Penny Goodyear, R.N., Vice President Applications
Web address: www.covhealth.com

| | 21 | 10 | 64 | 786 | 43 | 23898 | 11 | 11174 | 4726 | 116 |

ONAWA—Monona County

★ **BURGESS HEALTH CENTER**, 1600 Diamond Street, Zip 51040–1548; tel. 712/423–2311 **A**9 10 18 20 **F**6 9 11 12 21 23 26 27 28 29 33 36 37 38 41 46 48 51 52 58 59 60 61 62 63 69 70 77 81 82 84 88 94 95 97 108 109 **P**6
Primary Contact: Francis Tramp, President
CFO: Les Graeff, Chief Financial Officer
CMO: John Garred, Sr, M.D., Chief Medical Officer
CIO: Sue Burtch, Director of Management Information Systems
CHR: Jean Pekarek, Director Human Resources
Web address: www.burgesshc.org

| | 23 | 10 | 38 | 1365 | 16 | 51432 | 72 | 15943 | 6720 | 179 |

ORANGE CITY—Sioux County

★ **ORANGE CITY HEALTH SYSTEM**, 400 Central Avenue N.W., Zip 51041–1398; tel. 712/737–4984, (Total facility includes 83 beds in nursing home–type unit) **A**9 10 18 **F**6 8 9 11 12 21 23 26 27 28 29 33 36 37 47 48 51 52 53 54 55 58 59 60 62 63 65 66 69 70 81 88 91 92 94 95 96 97 108 110 **P**6 **S** Sioux Valley Hospitals and Health System, Sioux Falls, SD
Primary Contact: Martin W. Guthmiller, Administrator and Chief Executive Officer
COO: Daniel P. McCarty, Chief Operating Officer
CFO: Dina Baas, Director Financial Services
Web address: www.ochealthsystem.org

| | 14 | 10 | 108 | 1307 | 87 | 63896 | 188 | 21861 | 10965 | 331 |

OSAGE—Mitchell County

★ **MITCHELL COUNTY REGIONAL HEALTH CENTER**, 616 North Eighth Street, Zip 50461–1498; tel. 641/732–6000 **A**9 10 18 **F**6 9 11 12 14 26 27 28 33 34 46 48 52 58 59 63 64 69 85 87 94 96 97 108 **P**8 **S** Trinity Health, Novi, MI
Primary Contact: Sylvia Getman, Chief Executive Officer
COO: Kay Gabriel, R.N., Assistant Administrator and Chief Nursing Officer
CFO: Edward E. Riley, Chief Financial Officer
Web address: www.osagehospital.com

| | 13 | 10 | 25 | 639 | 6 | 59140 | 52 | 11744 | 3405 | 111 |

OSCEOLA—Clarke County

★ **CLARKE COUNTY HOSPITAL**, 800 South Fillmore Street, Zip 50213–1619; tel. 641/342–2184, (Total facility includes 30 beds in nursing home–type unit) **A**9 10 18 **F**1 3 9 12 13 14 21 23 27 28 29 33 34 40 41 46 52 53 55 56 58 61 63 67 68 69 71 81 84 85 87 88 92 94 97 108 **P**5 **S** Iowa Health System, Des Moines, IA
Primary Contact: Brian Evans, Interim Chief Executive Officer
COO: Michael Thilges, Chief Operating Officer and Chief Financial Officer
CFO: Michael Thilges, Chief Operating Officer and Chief Financial Officer
CMO: Wilson Rigler, M.D., Chief of Staff
CIO: Nathan Pieken, Chief Information Officer
CHR: Kate Emanuel, Human Resources Director
Web address: www.clarkehosp.org

| | 13 | 10 | 55 | 569 | 28 | 17138 | 0 | 10247 | 3729 | 122 |

OSKALOOSA—Mahaska County

⊠ **MAHASKA HEALTH PARTNERSHIP**, (Formerly Mahaska County Hospital), 1229 C Avenue East, Zip 52577–4298; tel. 641/672–3100 **A**1 9 10 **F**4 6 9 11 12 21 22 23 27 28 29 30 33 34 36 37 39 42 44 46 48 51 52 53 54 55 58 59 60 61 62 63 64 65 66 69 70 71 72 73 74 75 76 77 81 84 88 93 94 95 96 97 98 106 108 109 110 **P**6 7
Primary Contact: Jay Christensen, Administrator
CFO: Joseph W. Hohenberger, Chief Financial Officer
CMO: Paul Riggs, M.D., President
CHR: Glenda Paulson, Human Resources Director
Web address: www.mahaskahospital.com

| | 13 | 10 | 49 | 1408 | 20 | 90111 | 245 | 22920 | 10948 | 258 |

IA

Hospital, Address, Telephone, Approval, Facility, and Physician Codes, Health Care System	Classi-fication Codes		Utilization Data					Expense (thousands) of dollars		
★ American Hospital Association (AHA) membership □ Joint Commission on Accreditation of Healthcare Organizations (JCAHO) accreditation ○ American Osteopathic Association (AOA) accreditation △ Commission on Accreditation of Rehabilitation Facilities (CARF) accreditation	Control	Service	Staffed Beds	Admissions	Census	Outpatient Visits	Births	Total	Payroll	Personnel

OTTUMWA—Wapello County

⊠ **OTTUMWA REGIONAL HEALTH CENTER**, 1001 Pennsylvania Avenue, Zip 52501–2186; tel. 641/684–2300 **A**1 2 9 10 19 **F**2 3 4 6 9 11 12 21 22 26 27 28 29 33 34 37 38 40 42 44 46 47 48 49 51 52 53 54 55 56 58 59 60 61 62 63 64 65 66 68 69 71 72 73 74 75 76 77 78 82 84 87 88 93 94 95 96 98 106 108 109 110 **P**6
Primary Contact: Lynn W. Olson, President and Chief Executive Officer
CFO: David Recupero, Vice President and Chief Financial Officer
CHR: JoEllen Randall, Vice President Human Resources
Web address: www.orhc.com

| 23 | 10 | 83 | 5808 | 70 | 148800 | 825 | 66160 | 29420 | 844 |

PELLA—Marion County

⊠ **PELLA REGIONAL HEALTH CENTER**, 404 Jefferson Street, Zip 50219–1257; tel. 641/628–3150, (Total facility includes 128 beds in nursing home–type unit) **A**1 9 10 18 **F**1 2 5 9 11 12 21 22 23 26 27 28 33 34 36 40 44 47 48 49 51 52 55 58 59 60 61 62 63 64 65 66 69 70 76 81 82 84 85 87 88 91 92 93 94 95 96 97 107 108 110 **P**5 6
Primary Contact: Robert D. Kroese, Chief Executive Officer
COO: Robert D. Kroese, Chief Executive Officer
CFO: Ron Wauters, Chief Financial Officer
CIO: Jeff Caracci, Information Systems Manager
CHR: Jennifer Savage, Chief Human Resources
Web address: www.pellahealth.org

| 23 | 10 | 153 | 2128 | 126 | 100995 | 330 | 30765 | 14205 | 613 |

PERRY—Dallas County

★ **DALLAS COUNTY HOSPITAL**, 610 10th Street, Zip 50220–2221; tel. 515/465–3547 **A**9 10 18 **F**2 8 9 12 21 23 27 28 29 30 33 34 36 44 46 48 52 53 58 60 61 62 63 69 75 81 85 88 91 92 93 96 97 106 108 **S** Iowa Health System, Des Moines, IA
Primary Contact: Laurie A. Conner, Chief Executive Officer
COO: Donna J. Vandehaar, R.N., Chief Clinical Director
CFO: Sandra Christensen, Chief Financial Officer
CMO: Eric Ash, M.D., Chief of Staff
CHR: Sherry Smith, Director Human Resources
Web address: www.dallascohospital.org

| 13 | 10 | 25 | 350 | 7 | 25597 | 0 | 8635 | 3260 | 99 |

POCAHONTAS—Pocahontas County

★ **POCAHONTAS COMMUNITY HOSPITAL**, 606 N.W. Seventh, Zip 50574–1099; tel. 712/335–3501 **A**9 10 18 **F**6 9 12 14 21 23 28 29 33 34 36 48 51 52 55 58 60 61 62 63 68 69 81 88 92 94 96 97 106 108 **P**6 **S** Iowa Health System, Des Moines, IA
Primary Contact: James D. Roetman, President and Chief Executive Officer
CFO: Lynn Raveling, Chief Financial Officer
Web address: www.pchiowa.com

| 14 | 10 | 20 | 323 | 4 | 23299 | 0 | 5106 | 1982 | 64 |

PRIMGHAR—Obrien County

★ **BAUM HARMON MERCY HOSPITAL**, 255 North Welch Avenue, Zip 51245–1034, Mailing Address: P.O. Box 528, Zip 51245–0528; tel. 712/957–2300 **A**9 10 18 **F**3 9 12 13 14 21 22 23 27 28 29 33 41 46 48 52 55 56 58 60 61 63 67 68 71 75 88 92 96 97 **P**8 **S** Trinity Health, Novi, MI
Primary Contact: Robert Monical, Chief Executive Officer and Administrator
CFO: Sue E. McCauley, Director Finance
CMO: Daniel Richter, M.D., Chief of Staff
Web address: www.baumharmon.org

| 21 | 10 | 13 | 147 | 2 | 24690 | 0 | 5290 | 2665 | 69 |

RED OAK—Montgomery County

★ **MONTGOMERY COUNTY MEMORIAL HOSPITAL**, 2301 Eastern Avenue, Zip 51566–1300, Mailing Address: P.O. Box 498, Zip 51566–0498; tel. 712/623–7000 **A**9 10 18 20 **F**9 11 12 21 23 27 29 33 35 36 37 39 41 46 47 48 51 52 53 54 55 58 59 60 61 63 64 65 66 69 81 84 87 88 93 94 97 106 108 109 110 **P**6
Primary Contact: Allen E. Pohren, Administrator
CFO: Rick Leinen, Chief Financial Officer
CMO: William Butz, M.D., Chief of Staff
CIO: Ron Kloewer, Chief Information Officer
Web address: www.mcmh.org

| 13 | 10 | 40 | 1673 | 20 | 41123 | 97 | 17259 | 8119 | 227 |

ROCK RAPIDS—Lyon County

★ **MERRILL PIONEER COMMUNITY HOSPITAL**, 801 South Greene Street, Zip 51246–1998; tel. 712/472–2591 **A**9 10 18 **F**9 11 23 27 33 41 46 48 59 60 63 70 88 97 **P**6 **S** Sioux Valley Hospitals and Health System, Sioux Falls, SD
Primary Contact: Gordon Smith, Administrator and Chief Executive Officer
CFO: Stanley Knobloch, Finance Director
CMO: David Springer, M.D., Medical Staff President
Web address: www.merrillpioneer.org

| 23 | 10 | 16 | 314 | 3 | 8719 | 29 | 5407 | 2676 | 76 |

ROCK VALLEY—Sioux County

★ **HEGG MEMORIAL HEALTH CENTER/AVERA HEALTH**, 1202 21st Avenue, Zip 51247–1497; tel. 712/476–8000, (Total facility includes 95 beds in nursing home–type unit) **A**9 10 18 **F**8 9 11 12 21 23 26 27 29 33 34 41 46 48 51 52 55 58 59 60 63 69 75 81 88 91 92 94 95 97 108 **P**5 **S** Avera Health, Yankton, SD
Primary Contact: Glenn Zevenbergen, Chief Executive Officer
CFO: Kari Hoogendoorn, Chief Financial Officer
CMO: Roy Slice, M.D., Chief Medical Officer
Web address: www.heggmemorialhealthcenter.org

| 23 | 10 | 120 | 456 | 90 | 24264 | 71 | 8082 | 4168 | 173 |

IA

Many Facility Codes have changed. Please refer to the AHA Guide Code Chart. © 2005 AHA Guide

Hospital, Address, Telephone, Approval, Facility, and Physician Codes, Health Care System	Classification Codes		Utilization Data					Expense (thousands) of dollars		
★ American Hospital Association (AHA) membership □ Joint Commission on Accreditation of Healthcare Organizations (JCAHO) accreditation ○ American Osteopathic Association (AOA) accreditation △ Commission on Accreditation of Rehabilitation Facilities (CARF) accreditation	Control	Service	Staffed Beds	Admissions	Census	Outpatient Visits	Births	Total	Payroll	Personnel

SAC CITY—Sac County

★ **LORING HOSPITAL**, 211 Highland Avenue, Zip 50583–0217; tel. 712/662–7105, (Total facility includes 19 beds in nursing home–type unit) **A**9 10 18 **F**2 7 9 11 12 21 22 23 24 26 27 28 29 33 34 36 38 44 46 47 48 51 52 53 57 58 59 60 61 62 63 65 66 69 75 77 81 88 91 92 94 95 96 97 108 110 **S** Iowa Health System, Des Moines, IA Primary Contact: Michael S. Ketcham, President and Chief Executive Officer CFO: Angie Fischer, Chief Financial Officer CIO: Kathy Veit, Director Health Information Services Web address: www.loringhospital.org	23	10	44	970	24	17753	27	7467	3603	116

SHELDON—Obrien County

★ **NORTHWEST IOWA HEALTH CENTER**, 118 North Seventh Avenue, Zip 51201–1235, Mailing Address: P.O. Box 250, Zip 51201–0250; tel. 712/324–5041, (Total facility includes 70 beds in nursing home–type unit) **A**9 10 **F**5 9 11 12 21 23 26 27 28 29 33 36 37 38 39 41 44 46 48 51 52 53 54 57 58 60 61 62 63 65 66 69 81 88 92 93 94 95 96 97 110 **P**5 6 **S** Sioux Valley Hospitals and Health System, Sioux Falls, SD Primary Contact: Charles R. Miller, Chief Executive Officer CFO: Mark Brown, Assistant Administrator and Chief Financial Officer CIO: Scott Moffitt, Information Systems Director CHR: Dianne Wolthwzen, Human Resources Director Web address: www.nwiowahealthcenter.org	23	10	95	900	75	30084	104	15024	7380	216

SHENANDOAH—Page County

★ **SHENANDOAH MEDICAL CENTER**, 300 Pershing Avenue, Zip 51601–2397; tel. 712/246–1230, (Total facility includes 53 beds in nursing home–type unit) **A**9 10 18 **F**2 8 9 11 12 23 26 27 28 30 33 34 36 41 44 46 47 48 51 52 53 54 55 58 59 60 61 62 63 64 69 71 76 77 81 82 84 85 87 88 92 93 94 96 97 108 109 **P**6 Primary Contact: Charles L. Millburg, CHE, Chief Executive Officer CFO: Sandra Franks, Chief Financial Officer Web address: www.shenandoahmedcenter.com	23	10	88	990	59	96308	81	14326	6856	206

SIBLEY—Osceola County

★ **OSCEOLA COMMUNITY HOSPITAL**, Ninth Avenue North, Zip 51249–0258, Mailing Address: P.O. Box 258, Zip 51249–0258; tel. 712/754–2574 **A**9 10 18 **F**2 8 9 11 12 14 21 23 26 27 28 29 33 34 41 44 46 47 48 50 51 52 55 58 59 60 61 63 64 65 66 69 70 81 85 88 92 94 95 96 97 106 108 109 **P**5 **S** Avera Health, Yankton, SD Primary Contact: Janet Dykstra, Administrator CFO: Jerri Palsrok, Business Office Manager CMO: W E. Hicks, M.D., Chief Medical Staff CIO: Sherry McElroy, Health Information Management Director Web address: www.osceolacommunityhospital.org	23	10	25	432	6	19524	44	6560	2580	91

SIGOURNEY—Keokuk County

★ **KEOKUK COUNTY HEALTH CENTER**, 1312 South Stuart Street, Zip 52591–0286; tel. 641/622–2720 **A**9 10 18 **F**6 9 21 22 26 27 28 29 33 34 36 37 38 39 44 46 48 52 58 60 66 69 94 97 98 106 **P**5 6 Primary Contact: Patrick Peters, Chief Executive Officer CFO: Matt Ives, Chief Financial Officer CMO: John Buckingham, M.D., Chief Medical Staff CIO: Matt Ives, Chief Financial Officer CHR: Larry Driscoll, Director Human Resources Web address: www.kchc.net	13	10	25	102	8	4826	0	3872	1910	59

SIOUX CENTER—Sioux County

★ **SIOUX CENTER COMMUNITY HOSPITAL AND HEALTH CENTER/AVERA HEALTH**, 605 South Main Avenue, Zip 51250–1398; tel. 712/722–1271, (Total facility includes 69 beds in nursing home–type unit) **A**9 10 18 **F**1 2 8 9 11 12 14 21 22 23 26 27 28 29 30 33 36 37 38 46 48 51 52 53 58 59 60 62 63 65 69 70 81 82 85 88 91 92 94 95 96 97 106 108 109 110 **P**6 **S** Avera Health, Yankton, SD Primary Contact: Michael Seda, Chief Executive Officer CFO: Nancy Carlson, Director Finance Web address: www.schospital.org	23	10	90	745	73	42984	185	16382	6939	279

SIOUX CITY—Woodbury County

⊞ △ **MERCY MEDICAL CENTER–SIOUX CITY**, 801 Fifth Street, Zip 51101–1326, Mailing Address: P.O. Box 3168, Zip 51102–3168; tel. 712/279–2010, (Includes MERCY BEHAVIORAL HEALTH CENTER, 4301 Sergeant Road, Zip 51106; tel. 712/279–2446) **A**1 2 3 5 7 9 10 **F**2 4 9 10 11 12 14 15 17 19 21 22 24 26 27 28 29 30 31 33 34 37 38 39 43 44 46 47 48 50 52 53 54 55 57 58 59 60 61 62 63 65 66 68 69 70 71 72 73 74 75 76 77 78 81 82 84 85 87 88 92 93 94 96 107 108 110 **P**6 7 8 **S** Trinity Health, Novi, MI Primary Contact: Peter E. Makowski, President and Chief Executive Officer CFO: Ron Roberson, Chief Financial Officer CMO: Larry W. Sellers, M.D., Chief Medical Officer CIO: Steve Larson, Director Information Systems CHR: Julie Anfinson, Director Human Resources Web address: www.mercysiouxcity.com	21	10	272	12423	174	336566	644	170867	77244	1667

IA

Hospital, Address, Telephone, Approval, Facility, and Physician Codes, Health Care System	Classi- fication Codes		Utilization Data					Expense (thousands) of dollars		
★ American Hospital Association (AHA) membership □ Joint Commission on Accreditation of Healthcare Organizations (JCAHO) accreditation ○ American Osteopathic Association (AOA) accreditation △ Commission on Accreditation of Rehabilitation Facilities (CARF) accreditation	Control	Service	Staffed Beds	Admissions	Census	Outpatient Visits	Births	Total	Payroll	Personnel
⊠ **ST. LUKE'S REGIONAL MEDICAL CENTER**, 2720 Stone Park Boulevard, Zip 51104–2000; tel. 712/279–3500 **A**1 3 5 9 10 **F**9 11 12 13 15 17 21 22 24 26 27 28 29 32 33 36 38 39 40 42 46 47 48 49 51 55 56 57 58 59 60 61 62 63 65 67 69 71 75 78 81 82 84 85 88 93 94 95 96 105 106 107 108 109 110 **S** Iowa Health System, Des Moines, IA Primary Contact: Peter W. Thoreen, President and Chief Executive Officer CFO: Mark Johnson, Vice President and Chief Financial Officer CMO: Ralph M. Stanifer, M.D., Vice President Medical Affairs and Chief Medical Officer CIO: Mark Johnson, Vice President and Chief Financial Officer CHR: Gary Johnson, Director Human Resources Web address: www.stlukes.org	23	10	158	8777	102	90687	1985	107296	36835	1095
SPENCER—Clay County										
★ **SPENCER HOSPITAL**, 1200 First Avenue East, Zip 51301–4321; tel. 712/264–6111 **A**9 10 **F**6 9 11 12 21 22 23 26 27 28 29 33 34 36 37 38 39 41 44 45 46 47 48 49 51 52 54 55 58 59 60 61 63 65 66 69 71 72 73 74 75 76 77 78 79 81 82 84 87 88 93 94 95 96 97 106 108 110 **P**5 Primary Contact: Douglas Doorn, Chief Executive Officer CFO: Lois Morris, Chief Financial Officer CIO: Lynn Scharn, Director Information Systems Web address: www.spencerhospital.org	14	10	85	2998	35	32099	265	37199	15231	418
SPIRIT LAKE—Dickinson County										
LAKES REGIONAL HEALTHCARE, Highway 71 South, Zip 51360–6810, Mailing Address: P.O. Box AB, Zip 51360–6810; tel. 712/336–1230 **A**9 10 **F**6 9 11 12 23 27 28 29 33 36 45 46 48 51 54 55 58 59 60 61 62 63 81 84 85 88 94 95 96 97 108 110 Primary Contact: Richard C. Kielman, President and Chief Executive Officer Web address: www.lakeshealth.org	13	10	49	1735	17	31284	192	18960	7398	223
STORM LAKE—Buena Vista County										
⊠ **BUENA VISTA REGIONAL MEDICAL CENTER**, 1525 West Fifth Street, Zip 50588–0309, Mailing Address: P.O. Box 309, Zip 50588–0309; tel. 712/732–4030 **A**1 9 10 **F**2 4 6 9 11 12 14 21 22 23 26 27 28 33 36 37 38 41 48 51 53 54 57 58 59 60 61 62 63 64 65 66 69 71 76 81 82 84 85 86 87 88 93 94 95 96 97 98 106 108 109 110 **S** Iowa Health System, Des Moines, IA Primary Contact: Todd Hudspeth, Chief Executive Officer CFO: Mike Dewerff, Chief Financial Officer CMO: David Crippin, M.D., Chief Medical Staff CIO: Stan Spack, Director Information Technology CHR: Carrie Turnquist, Director Human Resources Web address: www.bvrmc.org	13	10	42	1854	25	31144	271	22073	10505	358
SUMNER—Bremer County										
★ **COMMUNITY MEMORIAL HOSPITAL**, 909 West First Street, Zip 50674–1203, Mailing Address: P.O. Box 148, Zip 50674–0148; tel. 563/578–3275 **A**9 10 18 **F**9 12 21 22 27 28 33 46 47 48 52 63 64 65 70 81 92 93 95 97 110 **P**5 6 **S** Iowa Health System, Des Moines, IA Primary Contact: Mary Wells, Administrator CFO: Sara Trainor, Chief Financial Officer CMO: Monica Burgett, D.O., Chief Medical Staff CHR: Robin Elliott, Personnel Officer	23	10	25	246	4	10682	0	5586	2493	71
VINTON—Benton County										
★ **VIRGINIA GAY HOSPITAL**, 502 North Ninth Avenue, Zip 52349–2299; tel. 319/472–6200, (Total facility includes 58 beds in nursing home–type unit) **A**9 10 18 20 **F**21 22 27 28 33 34 45 48 51 52 58 60 63 64 69 70 81 85 91 92 93 94 95 97 106 **P**6 Primary Contact: Michael J. Riege, Chief Executive Officer CFO: Julia Meadows, Chief Financial Officer CMO: Brian Meeker, D.O., Medical Staff President CHR: Kim Frank, Chief Human Resources Officer Web address: www.vghinc.com	23	10	83	342	56	84721	0	11963	4711	163
WASHINGTON—Washington County										
★ **WASHINGTON COUNTY HOSPITAL**, 400 East Polk Street, Zip 52353, Mailing Address: P.O. Box 909, Zip 52353–0909; tel. 319/653–5481, (Total facility includes 43 beds in nursing home–type unit) **A**9 10 18 **F**2 11 12 21 22 26 27 33 34 37 46 48 52 53 54 55 57 58 59 60 62 63 65 69 81 85 92 94 96 97 108 109 Primary Contact: Donald E. Patterson, Chief Executive Officer CFO: Greg Seubert, Chief Financial Officer CIO: Jennifer Durst, Director Information Services CHR: Tracy Ousey, Director Human Resources Web address: www.wchc.org	13	10	68	1860	55	24886	91	14213	6242	181
WATERLOO—Black Hawk County										
⊠ **ALLEN MEMORIAL HOSPITAL**, 1825 Logan Avenue, Zip 50703–1916; tel. 319/235–3941, (Total facility includes 30 beds in nursing home–type unit) **A**1 3 5 9 10 **F**2 4 9 11 12 14 15 17 19 21 22 23 26 27 28 29 30 32 33 34 37 40 41 42 44 45 46 47 48 51 52 53 55 56 57 58 59 60 61 62 63 64 65 66 67 69 70 71 73 74 75 76 77 78 81 82 84 85 86 87 88 89 92 93 94 96 98 106 108 109 110 **P**6 8 **S** Iowa Health System, Des Moines, IA Primary Contact: Richard A. Seidler, FACHE, Chief Executive Officer COO: Sara Poling, Senior Vice President and Chief Operating Officer CMO: Jeff Crandall, M.D., Chief Medical Officer Web address: www.allenhospital.org	23	10	222	10357	135	270581	911	134758	53354	1205

IA

Hospital, Address, Telephone, Approval, Facility, and Physician Codes, Health Care System	Classi- fication Codes		Utilization Data					Expense (thousands) of dollars		
★ American Hospital Association (AHA) membership ☐ Joint Commission on Accreditation of Healthcare Organizations (JCAHO) accreditation ○ American Osteopathic Association (AOA) accreditation △ Commission on Accreditation of Rehabilitation Facilities (CARF) accreditation	Control	Service	Staffed Beds	Admissions	Census	Outpatient Visits	Births	Total	Payroll	Personnel
✠ △ **COVENANT MEDICAL CENTER**, 3421 West Ninth Street, Zip 50702–5499; tel. 319/272–8000, (Includes KIMBALL–RIDGE CENTER, 2101 Kimball Avenue, Zip 50702), (Total facility includes 44 beds in nursing home–type unit) **A**1 2 3 5 7 9 10 **F**2 3 4 6 9 11 12 15 21 22 23 25 27 28 29 30 31 32 33 34 35 37 38 41 45 46 47 48 49 50 51 52 53 55 56 57 58 59 60 61 62 63 65 68 69 70 71 72 73 74 75 77 78 81 82 84 85 87 88 92 93 94 95 96 98 106 107 108 109 110 **P**1 6 **S** Wheaton Franciscan Services, Inc., Wheaton, IL Primary Contact: Jack Dusenbery, President and Chief Executive Officer CFO: Michele Panicucci, Senior Vice President and Chief Financial Officer CMO: Stephen Cardamone, M.D., Vice President Medical Affairs Web address: www.covhealth.com	21	10	281	11857	161	708561	1610	194932	93832	2123
WAUKON—Allamakee County **VETERANS MEMORIAL HOSPITAL**, 40 First Street S.E., Zip 52172–2099; tel. 563/568–3411 **A**9 10 18 **F**6 9 11 12 23 26 27 28 29 33 36 41 46 47 48 51 52 58 59 61 62 63 81 95 96 97 98 107 108 Primary Contact: Michael D. Myers, Administrator Web address: www.vmhospital.com	14	10	25	680	6	41192	92	7913	3488	165
WAVERLY—Bremer County ✠ **WAVERLY HEALTH CENTER**, 312 Ninth Street S.W., Zip 50677–2999; tel. 319/352–4120 **A**1 9 10 18 **F**6 9 11 12 26 27 28 29 33 34 41 46 48 51 52 53 58 59 60 63 64 65 69 81 84 88 94 96 97 98 106 108 109 **P**6 Primary Contact: Michael D. Trachta, Chief Executive Officer COO: Mary M. Conway, Director Nursing and Clinical Services CFO: Lisa Bennett, CPA, Director Financial Services CHR: Karen Buls, Director Human Resources Web address: www.waverlyhealthcenter.org	14	10	25	1005	9	33645	99	17902	7641	206
WEBSTER CITY—Hamilton County ✠ **HAMILTON HOSPITAL**, 800 Ohio Street, Zip 50595–2824, Mailing Address: P.O. Box 430, Zip 50595–0430; tel. 515/832–9400 **A**1 9 10 18 **F**2 6 9 11 12 14 21 23 27 28 29 30 31 33 34 35 36 37 48 52 58 59 60 63 64 65 66 69 81 88 93 94 96 97 108 Primary Contact: Palmer Schneider, Chief Executive Officer COO: Susan Wright, Chief Operating Officer CFO: Alice Heinrichs, CPA, Chief Financial Officer CMO: Lisa Moffle, M.D., Chief of Staff Web address: www.hamiltonhospital.com	13	10	25	1588	16	15649	157	12860	6166	172
WEST BURLINGTON—Des Moines County ✠ **GREAT RIVER MEDICAL CENTER**, 1221 South Gear Avenue, Zip 52655–1681; tel. 319/768–1000, (Total facility includes 165 beds in nursing home–type unit) **A**1 9 10 19 **F**2 4 9 11 12 15 21 22 24 26 27 28 29 30 31 33 34 38 39 40 41 45 46 47 48 49 51 52 53 54 55 58 59 60 61 62 63 64 65 66 68 69 71 72 73 74 75 76 77 81 82 84 85 86 87 88 92 93 94 95 96 108 109 110 **P**5 6 Primary Contact: Mark D. Richardson, President and Chief Executive Officer CFO: Todd J. Sladky, Chief Financial Officer CMO: Reddy Reganti, M.D., Chief of Staff CIO: Gary Davis, Director Information Systems CHR: Ron Halligan, Vice President Human Resources Web address: www.greatrivermedical.org	23	10	378	8630	242	213000	735	100661	43564	1086
WEST UNION—Fayette County ★ **PALMER LUTHERAN HEALTH CENTER**, 112 Jefferson Street, Zip 52175–1022; tel. 563/422–3811 **A**9 10 18 **F**2 9 11 12 21 23 28 29 33 36 37 44 46 48 50 51 52 53 55 59 60 61 62 63 65 69 81 84 85 88 92 94 95 96 97 106 107 108 110 Primary Contact: Debrah Chensvold, President and Chief Executive Officer CFO: Joni Gisleson, Financial Director CMO: Ronald Myrom, M.D., Chief of Staff CIO: Kurt Chicken, Director Support Services CHR: Cheryl Meyer, Director Human Resources	23	10	25	623	7	45921	111	11278	5056	140
WINTERSET—Madison County **MADISON COUNTY HEALTH CARE SYSTEM**, 300 Hutchings Street, Zip 50273–2199; tel. 515/462–2373 **A**9 10 18 **F**3 4 12 23 29 33 34 36 46 48 51 55 60 61 63 69 70 72 73 74 75 76 77 81 84 85 88 92 93 94 95 96 97 98 106 108 **P**6 Primary Contact: Marcia Harris, Chief Executive Officer Web address: www.madisonhealth.com	13	10	25	800	10	54414	0	12510	5592	149
WOODWARD—Boone County **WOODWARD RESOURCE CENTER**, Zip 50276–9999; tel. 515/438–2600, (Nonreporting) Primary Contact: Michael J. Davis, Ph.D., Superintendent	12	62	285	—	—	—	—	—	—	—

IA

KANSAS

Hospital, Address, Telephone, Approval, Facility, and Physician Codes, Health Care System	Classi-fication Codes		Utilization Data					Expense (thousands) of dollars		
★ American Hospital Association (AHA) membership □ Joint Commission on Accreditation of Healthcare Organizations (JCAHO) accreditation ○ American Osteopathic Association (AOA) accreditation △ Commission on Accreditation of Rehabilitation Facilities (CARF) accreditation	Control	Service	Staffed Beds	Admissions	Census	Outpatient Visits	Births	Total	Payroll	Personnel

ABILENE—Dickinson County

★ **MEMORIAL HOSPITAL**, 511 N.E. Tenth Street, Zip 67410; tel. 785/263–2100, (Total facility includes 60 beds in nursing home–type unit) **A**9 10 **F**2 6 11 12 21 22 23 27 33 36 41 45 46 48 51 52 54 58 59 60 61 63 64 69 71 76 81 82 84 88 92 93 94 95 96 97 106 108 110
Primary Contact: Mark A. Miller, Chief Executive Officer
COO: Robert Brazil, Chief Operating Officer
CFO: Elgin Glanzer, Chief Financial Officer
CMO: Brian Holmes, M.D., Chairman
Web address: www.mhsks.org

16	10	109	1300	76	19917	67	12556	6327	233

ANTHONY—Harper County

★ **HOSPITAL DISTRICT NUMBER SIX OF HARPER COUNTY**, 1101 East Spring Street, Zip 67003–2122; tel. 620/842–5111 **A**9 10 18 **F**9 27 33 41 46 61 63 69 70 81 88 92 97 **P**6
Primary Contact: J. Bryant Anderson, Administrator and Chief Executive Officer

16	10	25	245	17	14424	0	4396	2287	63

ARKANSAS CITY—Cowley County

★ **SOUTH CENTRAL KANSAS REGIONAL MEDICAL CENTER**, 216 West Birch Avenue, Zip 67005–1598, Mailing Address: P.O. Box 1107, Zip 67005–1107; tel. 620/442–2500 **A**9 10 **F**9 11 12 21 22 27 28 29 32 33 47 48 51 52 53 54 55 58 59 60 63 66 69 70 81 82 83 84 88 94 97 108 **P**8
Primary Contact: Joe Jirinec, Chief Executive Officer
CFO: Pam Jackson, CPA, Chief Financial Officer
CMO: Paul A. Klaassen, M.D., Chief Medical Staff
CHR: Kaylyn Schamel, Director Human Resources
Web address: www.sckrmc.com

14	10	40	1167	13	61250	149	10248	4753	153

ASHLAND—Clark County

★ **ASHLAND HEALTH CENTER**, 709 Oak Street, Zip 67831–0188, Mailing Address: P.O. Box 188, Zip 67831–0188; tel. 620/635–2241, (Total facility includes 35 beds in nursing home–type unit) **A**9 10 18 **F**1 22 33 41 45 47 48 51 52 53 64 66 69 92 97 **P**6 **S** Great Plains Health Alliance, Inc., Phillipsburg, KS
Primary Contact: Daryl Marshall, Administrator
CFO: Debbie Filson, Office Manager
Web address: www.phn.org

16	10	47	132	30	10401	0	3571	1500	57

ATCHISON—Atchison County

★ ○ **ATCHISON HOSPITAL**, 1301 North Second Street, Zip 66002–1297; tel. 913/367–2131, (Total facility includes 31 beds in nursing home–type unit) **A**9 10 11 20 **F**2 6 9 11 12 21 22 26 27 28 33 36 44 46 48 51 52 53 55 59 60 62 63 64 66 69 70 71 81 82 88 92 93 94 95 96 97 108 109 **P**6
Primary Contact: John L. Jacobson, President and Chief Executive Officer
CFO: Lorne J. Archer, Vice President finance and Chief Financial Officer
CMO: Michael Jones, M.D., Chief of Staff
CIO: John Nunn, Manager Information Systems
CHR: Shari Boos, Director Human Resources
Web address: www.atchisonhospital.org

23	10	67	1734	41	36682	211	22180	11356	257

ATWOOD—Rawlins County

★ **RAWLINS COUNTY HEALTH CENTER**, 707 Grant Street, Zip 67730–4700, Mailing Address: P.O. Box 47, Zip 67730–4700; tel. 785/626–3211 **A**9 10 18 **F**22 26 27 28 33 44 52 58 61 63 64 69 87 91 92 97 108 110 **P**6 **S** Great Plains Health Alliance, Inc., Phillipsburg, KS
Primary Contact: Robert Garrison, Administrator and Chief Executive Officer
COO: Robert Garrison, Administrator and Chief Executive Officer
Web address: www.gpha.com

13	10	24	232	3	19865	0	3775	1827	50

BELLEVILLE—Republic County

★ **REPUBLIC COUNTY HOSPITAL**, 2420 G Street, Zip 66935–2400; tel. 785/527–2254, (Total facility includes 38 beds in nursing home–type unit) **A**9 10 18 **F**2 11 12 21 22 23 26 27 29 32 33 40 44 46 52 53 58 60 61 62 63 65 66 69 81 82 88 91 92 94 95 97 **S** Great Plains Health Alliance, Inc., Phillipsburg, KS
Primary Contact: Blaine K. Miller, Administrator
Web address: www.republiccountyhospital.org

23	10	63	1154	50	9738	52	8836	4139	137

BELOIT—Mitchell County

★ **MITCHELL COUNTY HOSPITAL**, 400 West Eighth, Zip 67420–1605, Mailing Address: P.O. Box 399, Zip 67420–0399; tel. 785/738–2266, (Total facility includes 40 beds in nursing home–type unit) **A**9 10 18 20 **F**9 11 12 21 22 29 33 36 37 39 44 51 52 53 54 60 63 65 69 71 76 81 88 92 94 96 97
Primary Contact: John M. Osse, Administrator
CFO: Eldon Koepke, Chief Financial Officer
CIO: Mark Marihugh, Information Technology Director
CHR: Phyllis Oetting, Director Human Resources
Web address: www.gpha.com

23	10	99	1890	60	16894	78	16809	7174	235

Many Facility Codes have changed. Please refer to the AHA Guide Code Chart.   © 2005 AHA Guide

Hospital, Address, Telephone, Approval, Facility, and Physician Codes, Health Care System	Classi-fication Codes		Utilization Data					Expense (thousands) of dollars		
★ American Hospital Association (AHA) membership □ Joint Commission on Accreditation of Healthcare Organizations (JCAHO) accreditation ○ American Osteopathic Association (AOA) accreditation △ Commission on Accreditation of Rehabilitation Facilities (CARF) accreditation	Control	Service	Staffed Beds	Admissions	Census	Outpatient Visits	Births	Total	Payroll	Personnel
BURLINGTON—Coffey County ★ **COFFEY COUNTY HOSPITAL**, 801 North Fourth Street, Zip 66839–0189, Mailing Address: P.O. Box 189, Zip 66839–0189; tel. 620/364–2121, (Total facility includes 42 beds in nursing home–type unit) **A**9 10 20 **F**2 6 8 9 11 12 14 23 27 33 42 46 48 51 52 55 58 59 60 61 62 63 64 66 81 84 88 91 92 94 97 108 **P**6 Primary Contact: Dennis L. George, Chief Executive Officer Web address: www.coffeyhealth.org	13	10	78	1306	44	17279	94	17643	7628	244
CALDWELL—Sumner County ★ **SUMNER COUNTY HOSPITAL DISTRICT ONE**, 601 South Osage Street, Zip 67022–1654; tel. 620/845–6492 **A**9 10 18 **F**6 22 33 46 51 63 69 81 84 88 92 93 97 108 **P**5 Primary Contact: Virgil Watson, Administrator CFO: Paul Bowerman, CPA, Chief Financial Officer CMO: Jim Blunk, D.O., Chief Medical Officer Web address: www.schd1.com	16	10	25	177	10	7094	0	3243	1527	51
CEDAR VALE—Chautauqua County **CEDAR VALE COMMUNITY HOSPITAL**, 501 Cedar Street, Zip 67024–0398, Mailing Address: P.O. Box 398, Zip 67024–0398; tel. 620/758–2266 **A**9 10 18 **F**2 6 27 33 45 52 69 92 97 **P**5 Primary Contact: Audrey Padgett, Administrator Web address: www.gpha.com	23	10	25	228	15	6343	0	1540	1265	42
CHANUTE—Neosho County ★ **NEOSHO MEMORIAL REGIONAL MEDICAL CENTER**, 629 South Plummer, Zip 66720–0426, Mailing Address: P.O. Box 426, Zip 66720–0426; tel. 620/431–4000 **A**9 10 **F**2 6 9 11 12 21 22 26 27 33 35 36 41 45 46 51 52 55 59 60 62 63 69 81 84 88 93 94 97 108 **P**8 **S** Quorum Health Resources, Plano, TX Primary Contact: Murray L. Brown, Chief Executive Officer Web address: www.nmrmc.com	13	10	59	2038	18	22279	325	18707	7898	229
CLAY CENTER—Clay County ★ **CLAY COUNTY MEDICAL CENTER**, 617 Liberty Street, Zip 67432–0512, Mailing Address: P.O. Box 512, Zip 67432–0512; tel. 785/632–2144 **A**9 10 18 20 **F**11 12 22 23 27 28 33 36 37 38 39 40 41 48 52 53 55 57 58 59 61 62 63 64 65 66 67 69 81 82 84 88 92 93 94 96 97 106 110 Primary Contact: Ronald Bender, Chief Executive Officer CFO: Jim Brinkman, Chief Financial Officer CIO: Jim Seley, Chief Information Officer CHR: Cindy Rush, Human Resources Director Web address: www.ccmcks.org	13	10	25	1073	13	35588	60	10395	4625	155
COFFEYVILLE—Montgomery County ⊞ **COFFEYVILLE REGIONAL MEDICAL CENTER**, 1400 West Fourth, Zip 67337–0856; tel. 620/251–1200, (Total facility includes 24 beds in nursing home–type unit) **A**1 2 9 10 **F**2 3 9 11 12 13 14 21 22 26 27 33 44 46 48 51 55 56 58 59 60 61 62 63 67 68 69 71 72 76 81 82 88 92 94 106 109 **P**8 **S** Quorum Health Resources, Plano, TX Primary Contact: Gerald J. Marquette, Jr, Chief Executive Officer COO: Gerald J. Marquette, Jr, Chief Executive Officer CFO: John C. Hester, Chief Financial Officer CIO: Doug Stacy, Chief Information Officer CHR: Arneda Shelton, Director Human Resources, Community Relations and Education Web address: www.crmcinc.com	23	10	105	4087	55	40046	224	27526	11825	361
COLBY—Thomas County **CITIZENS MEDICAL CENTER**, 100 East College Drive, Zip 67701–3799; tel. 785/462–7511, (Total facility includes 68 beds in nursing home–type unit) **A**9 10 18 20 **F**2 5 8 9 11 12 22 23 26 33 47 52 57 58 59 60 61 62 63 65 66 69 70 81 82 84 88 92 93 94 97 108 110 **P**6 Primary Contact: Janice McCart, Chief Executive Officer Web address: www.nwkshealthcare.com	23	10	93	1079	72	9629	71	14229	6113	203
COLDWATER—Comanche County ★ **COMANCHE COUNTY HOSPITAL**, 202 South Frisco Street, Zip 67029, Mailing Address: HC 65, Box 8A, Zip 67029; tel. 620/582–2144 **A**9 10 18 **F**9 23 27 33 41 48 50 51 53 58 60 61 69 75 92 97 **P**6 **S** Great Plains Health Alliance, Inc., Phillipsburg, KS Primary Contact: Nancy Zimmerman, R.N., Administrator CMO: Chandini Sharma, M.D., Chief of Staff CIO: LaNell Wagnon, Medical Records Director Web address: www.gpha.com	13	10	14	205	3	11104	0	2603	1409	41
COLUMBUS—Cherokee County ★ **ST. JOHN'S MAUDE NORTON MEMORIAL HOSPITAL**, 220 North Pennsylvania Street, Zip 66725–1110; tel. 620/429–2545 **A**9 10 18 **F**9 27 28 32 33 46 48 60 69 88 92 97 **S** Catholic Health Initiatives, Denver, CO Primary Contact: Cindy Neely, Administrator CMO: Darcy Selenke, M.D., Chief of Staff	21	10	18	166	3	10214	0	2421	1057	42
CONCORDIA—Cloud County **CLOUD COUNTY HEALTH CENTER**, 1100 Highland Drive, Zip 66901–3923; tel. 785/243–1234 **A**9 10 18 **F**9 11 12 23 27 29 33 37 40 44 46 48 52 57 58 59 60 62 63 64 65 66 69 70 75 81 82 84 88 94 95 96 97 108 110 **P**6 Primary Contact: Roy E. White, Chief Executive Officer Web address: www.cchc.com	23	10	25	967	10	19621	26	10317	5281	146

KS

Hospital, Address, Telephone, Approval, Facility, and Physician Codes, Health Care System	Classification Codes		Utilization Data					Expense (thousands) of dollars		
★ American Hospital Association (AHA) membership □ Joint Commission on Accreditation of Healthcare Organizations (JCAHO) accreditation ○ American Osteopathic Association (AOA) accreditation △ Commission on Accreditation of Rehabilitation Facilities (CARF) accreditation	Control	Service	Staffed Beds	Admissions	Census	Outpatient Visits	Births	Total	Payroll	Personnel

COUNCIL GROVE—Morris County

MORRIS COUNTY HOSPITAL, 600 North Washington Street, Zip 66846–0275, Mailing Address: P.O. Box 275, Zip 66846–0275; tel. 620/767–6811 **A**9 10 20 **F**6 9 11 12 23 26 27 28 29 33 48 52 55 59 60 63 66 69 81 94 96 97 108 110 Primary Contact: James H. Reagan, Jr, Ph.D., Chief Executive Officer Web address: www.mrcohosp.com	13	10	28	576	7	14234	60	4982	2099	78

DIGHTON—Lane County

★ **LANE COUNTY HOSPITAL**, 235 West Vine, Zip 67839–0969, Mailing Address: P.O. Box 969, Zip 67839–0969; tel. 620/397–5321, (Total facility includes 21 beds in nursing home–type unit) **A**9 10 18 **F**1 22 33 44 46 64 69 70 92 95 97 **P**6 **S** Great Plains Health Alliance, Inc., Phillipsburg, KS Primary Contact: Donna McGowan, Administrator CFO: Marilyn James, Chief Financial Officer CMO: Paul Chinburg, M.D., Medical Director Web address: www.gpha.com	13	10	31	217	18	10509	0	3247	1559	48

DODGE CITY—Ford County

⊞ **WESTERN PLAINS MEDICAL COMPLEX**, 3001 Avenue A, Zip 67801–6508, Mailing Address: P.O. Box 1478, Zip 67801–1478; tel. 620/225–8400, (Total facility includes 9 beds in nursing home–type unit) **A**1 9 10 20 **F**2 9 11 12 14 21 22 26 27 28 29 31 32 33 34 40 48 53 55 57 58 59 60 62 63 64 65 66 67 68 69 81 82 84 87 88 92 93 94 95 108 109 110 **S** LifePoint Hospitals, Inc., Brentwood, TN Primary Contact: Steven G. Daniel, President and Chief Executive Officer CFO: Terry Stofferson, Chief Financial Officer CMO: R C. Trotter, M.D., Chief Medical Staff CIO: Shawna Culver, Head Information Systems CHR: Ronald White, Director Human Resources Web address: www.westernplainsmc.com	33	10	99	3745	35	19020	701	28933	10059	242

EL DORADO—Butler County

⊞ **SUSAN B. ALLEN MEMORIAL HOSPITAL**, 720 West Central Avenue, Zip 67042–2112; tel. 316/321–3300 **A**1 9 10 **F**2 9 11 12 22 33 48 49 51 54 55 59 63 64 71 76 81 84 85 88 92 94 97 108 110 Primary Contact: Jim Wilson, President and Chief Executive Officer COO: David Shaw, Vice President and Chief Operating Officer CFO: Gayle Arnett, Vice President and Chief Financial Officer CIO: Mark Rooker, Director Information Systems CHR: Gay Kimble, Director Human Resources Web address: www.sbamh.com	23	10	82	2628	34	75841	250	31743	14078	333

ELKHART—Morton County

★ **MORTON COUNTY HEALTH SYSTEM**, 445 Hilltop Street, Zip 67950–0937, Mailing Address: P.O. Box 937, Zip 67950–0937; tel. 620/697–2141, (Total facility includes 80 beds in nursing home–type unit) **A**9 10 20 **F**9 12 21 27 33 42 44 45 46 47 48 52 53 55 58 60 63 65 66 69 70 72 73 74 75 76 77 81 84 88 92 93 94 95 96 97 108 109 110 **P**5 6 Primary Contact: Leonard Hernandez, Chief Executive Officer CFO: Jeff Weaver, Chief Financial Officer CHR: Sonja May, Director Human Resources Web address: www.mchswecare.com	13	10	120	1264	65	22222	1	13026	7275	189

ELLINWOOD—Barton County

★ **ELLINWOOD DISTRICT HOSPITAL**, 605 North Main Street, Zip 67526–1440; tel. 620/564–2548 **A**9 10 18 **F**9 33 52 54 92 97 **P**6 **S** Great Plains Health Alliance, Inc., Phillipsburg, KS Primary Contact: David Haneke, Administrator CFO: Richard Hushka, Chief Financial Officer CMO: David Ryan, D.O., Cheif Medical Staff Web address: www.gpha.com	23	10	25	216	12	12225	0	3141	1405	51

ELLSWORTH—Ellsworth County

★ **ELLSWORTH COUNTY MEDICAL CENTER**, 1604 Aylward Street, Zip 67439–0087, Mailing Address: P.O. Box 87, Zip 67439–0087; tel. 785/472–3111 **A**9 10 18 **F**9 33 46 60 65 66 69 81 88 92 94 97 108 Primary Contact: Roger W. Pearson, Administrator Web address: www.ewmed.com	13	10	20	597	5	12634	0	9301	4532	121

EMPORIA—Lyon County

EMPORIA SURGICAL HOSPITAL, 1602 West 15th Street, Zip 66801; tel. 620/342–8822 **A**10 **F**2 26 27 28 63 64 Primary Contact: Joseph Conroy, Administrator	32	13	4	92	1	—	0	—	—	24
★ **NEWMAN REGIONAL HEALTH**, 1201 West 12th Avenue, Zip 66801–2597; tel. 620/343–6800 **A**9 10 12 20 **F**2 4 9 11 15 21 22 23 27 28 32 33 36 37 38 40 41 46 48 50 51 52 53 55 59 60 61 62 63 64 65 66 68 69 75 81 82 84 85 87 88 93 94 96 97 108 110 **S** Quorum Health Resources, Plano, TX Primary Contact: Terry R. Lambert, CHE, Chief Executive Officer CFO: Holly French, Interim Chief Financial Officer CMO: Chester Stone, M.D., Chief of Staff CIO: Dan McBride, Information Systems and Security Officer CHR: Kathy Orear, Director Human Resources Web address: www.newmanrh.org	13	10	122	4270	51	35807	531	39609	16354	435

KS

Many Facility Codes have changed. Please refer to the AHA Guide Code Chart.   © 2005 AHA Guide

Hospital, Address, Telephone, Approval, Facility, and Physician Codes, Health Care System	Classification Codes		Utilization Data					Expense (thousands) of dollars		
★ American Hospital Association (AHA) membership ☐ Joint Commission on Accreditation of Healthcare Organizations (JCAHO) accreditation ○ American Osteopathic Association (AOA) accreditation △ Commission on Accreditation of Rehabilitation Facilities (CARF) accreditation	Control	Service	Staffed Beds	Admissions	Census	Outpatient Visits	Births	Total	Payroll	Personnel

EUREKA—Greenwood County

★ **GREENWOOD COUNTY HOSPITAL**, 100 West 16th Street, Zip 67045–1064; tel. 620/583–7451 **A**9 10 18 **F**2 9 12 33 36 46 51 60 63 69 81 88 94 97 108 **P**5 Primary Contact: Bruce K. Birchell, Administrator and Chief Executive Officer CFO: Janel Palmer, Chief Financial Officer CIO: Tito Ojeda, Quality Assurance and Information Systems Director	15	10	25	813	8	5209	0	8527	3689	114

FORT SCOTT—Bourbon County

⊞ △ **MERCY HEALTH SYSTEM OF KANSAS**, 401 Woodland Hills Boulevard, Zip 66701–8797; tel. 620/223–2200 **A**1 7 9 10 **F**2 6 9 11 12 21 22 24 26 27 28 29 30 33 34 36 37 41 45 46 47 48 51 55 56 58 59 60 62 63 68 69 70 81 82 84 87 88 94 95 96 97 108 110 **P**6 **S** Sisters of Mercy Health System, Chesterfield, MO Primary Contact: Jon Swope, President and Chief Executive Officer COO: Reta Baker, Chief Operating Officer CFO: Terri Del Chiaro, Chief Financial Officer CIO: Margie Singmaster, Chief Information Officer and Vice President Support Services CHR: Gloria Bennett, Corporate Director Human Resources Web address: www.mhsk.smhs.com	21	10	94	3597	40	84237	291	29821	15741	419

FREDONIA—Wilson County

★ **FREDONIA REGIONAL HOSPITAL**, 1527 Madison Street, Zip 66736–1751, Mailing Address: P.O. Box 579, Zip 66736–0579; tel. 620/378–2121 **A**9 10 18 **F**6 9 12 22 26 27 33 51 63 64 69 71 76 88 91 92 97 **S** Great Plains Health Alliance, Inc., Phillipsburg, KS Primary Contact: Terry Deschaine, Chief Executive Officer CFO: Clarissa Suiter, Chief Financial Officer CHR: Debbie Marr, Director Human Resources Web address: www.gpha.com	14	10	51	1114	17	16573	0	7761	2776	94

GARDEN CITY—Finney County

⊞ **ST. CATHERINE HOSPITAL**, 401 East Spuce Street, Zip 67846–5679; tel. 620/272–2561 **A**1 5 9 10 20 **F**10 11 12 21 22 23 26 27 28 29 33 36 37 38 46 48 51 52 53 55 56 58 59 60 61 62 63 64 66 69 71 73 75 80 81 82 84 85 88 90 93 94 96 104 106 108 110 **P**5 6 **S** Catholic Health Initiatives, Denver, CO Primary Contact: Scott J. Taylor, President and Chief Executive Officer CFO: John Yox, Chief Financial Officer CIO: Victor Hawkins, Executive Director Marketing Web address: www.stcath–hosp.org	21	10	101	4322	52	38711	958	54997	21295	509

GARDNER—Johnson County

MEADOWBROOK REHABILITATION HOSPITAL, 427 West Main Street, Zip 66030–1183; tel. 913/856–8747, (Total facility includes 45 beds in nursing home–type unit) **A**10 **F**21 27 28 31 36 37 41 42 44 45 46 47 48 50 52 57 58 60 62 65 66 68 69 74 76 92 94 95 96 108 110 **P**5 Primary Contact: Sharon L. Bingham, Administrator Web address: www.meadowbrookrehab.com	33	46	74	441	64	71	0	5468	3586	118

GARNETT—Anderson County

ANDERSON COUNTY HOSPITAL, 421 South Maple, Zip 66032–1334, Mailing Address: P.O. Box 309, Zip 66032–0309; tel. 785/448–3131, (Total facility includes 32 beds in nursing home–type unit) **A**9 10 18 **F**6 9 12 26 27 28 33 46 48 51 52 63 69 70 81 82 92 94 97 **P**6 **S** Saint Luke's Health System, Kansas City, MO Primary Contact: Dennis A. Hachenberg, CHE, Chief Executive Officer Web address: www.saint–lukes.org	23	10	47	332	30	29544	0	8621	4385	134

GIRARD—Crawford County

★ **HOSPITAL DISTRICT NUMBER 1 OF CRAWFORD COUNTY**, 302 North Hospital Drive, Zip 66743–2000; tel. 620/724–8291 **A**9 10 **F**9 11 12 27 28 29 33 45 46 48 51 52 55 58 59 60 63 69 70 81 82 92 96 97 108 109 110 Primary Contact: Dennis E. Nehls, Administrator and Chief Executive Officer CFO: R Martin Williams, Chief Financial Officer CIO: Pat Holt, Chief Information Officer CHR: Mary Ann Holloway, Manager Human Resources Web address: www.hd1cc.com	16	10	38	1143	13	16543	107	10835	5091	150

GOODLAND—Sherman County

GOODLAND REGIONAL MEDICAL CENTER, 220 West Second Street, Zip 67735–1602; tel. 785/890–3625 **A**9 10 18 20 **F**4 6 9 11 12 22 23 26 27 28 33 34 46 48 52 53 54 58 59 63 66 68 69 70 77 81 82 88 92 94 97 108 Primary Contact: Jay P. Jolly, Chief Executive Officer	13	10	25	942	13	32369	62	10038	4689	158

GREAT BEND—Barton County

⊞ **CENTRAL KANSAS MEDICAL CENTER**, 3515 Broadway Street, Zip 67530–3633; tel. 620/792–2511 **A**1 9 10 19 20 **F**2 11 12 21 22 23 26 27 28 30 33 34 35 36 37 38 39 51 52 54 55 58 59 60 61 62 63 64 65 68 69 70 79 80 81 82 84 85 87 88 94 95 96 97 108 110 **S** Catholic Health Initiatives, Denver, CO Primary Contact: Chris Thomas, CHE, President and Chief Executive Officer CFO: Jesse Saucedo, Vice President and Chief Financial Officer CMO: Perry N. Schuetz, M.D., Chief Medical Staff CIO: Mark Hanson, Director Information Systems CHR: Shelly Gompf, Vice President Human Resources Web address: www.ckmc.org	21	10	61	2919	36	86453	410	35932	15474	414

KS

Hospital, Address, Telephone, Approval, Facility, and Physician Codes, Health Care System	Classi-fication Codes		Utilization Data					Expense (thousands) of dollars		
★ American Hospital Association (AHA) membership □ Joint Commission on Accreditation of Healthcare Organizations (JCAHO) accreditation ○ American Osteopathic Association (AOA) accreditation △ Commission on Accreditation of Rehabilitation Facilities (CARF) accreditation	Control	Service	Staffed Beds	Admissions	Census	Outpatient Visits	Births	Total	Payroll	Personnel

SURGICAL AND DIAGNOSTIC CENTER OF GREAT BEND, 514 Cleveland Street, Zip 67530; tel. 620/792–8833 **A**10 **F**37 63 Primary Contact: Pamela Chambers, Chief Executive Officer	31	10	4	3654	1	3475	0	3553	973	36
GREENSBURG—Kiowa County										
★ **KIOWA COUNTY MEMORIAL HOSPITAL**, 501 South Walnut Street, Zip 67054–1951, Mailing Address: P.O. Box 616, Zip 67054–0616; tel. 620/723–3341 **A**9 10 18 **F**2 6 9 22 27 33 41 46 48 52 53 54 58 69 71 76 81 92 97 **P**6 **S** Great Plains Health Alliance, Inc., Phillipsburg, KS Primary Contact: Mary Colclazier, Administrator CFO: Ron Tucker, Chief Financial Officer CMO: Nizar Kibar, M.D., Chief Medical Staff CIO: Jeremy Hoover, Chief Information Officer Web address: www.gpha.com	13	10	25	584	16	15402	0	4983	2439	86
HANOVER—Washington County										
★ **WASHINGTON COUNTY HOSPITAL DISTRICT 1**, 205 South Hanover, Zip 66945–0038, Mailing Address: P.O. Box 38, Zip 66945–0038; tel. 785/337–2214, (Total facility includes 20 beds in nursing home–type unit) **A**9 10 18 **F**6 33 36 51 54 63 69 88 92 97 **P**5 Primary Contact: Roger D. Warren, M.D., Administrator	16	10	34	364	27	1118	11	2981	1528	57
HARPER—Harper County										
★ **HOSPITAL DISTRICT NUMBER FIVE OF HARPER COUNTY**, 1204 Maple, Zip 67058–1438; tel. 620/896–7324 **A**9 10 18 **F**2 8 10 21 22 24 26 27 28 29 33 34 38 39 41 46 48 51 52 54 58 60 63 66 69 70 81 84 88 91 93 94 97 108 **P**5 Primary Contact: Kim Cinelli, Administrator and Chief Executive Officer CFO: Sandra Owen, Director Fiscal and Accounting CMO: Ralph Bellar, M.D., Chief of Staff CIO: Cindi Beadman, Director Medical Records CHR: Vicki Longbine, Director Human Resources Web address: www.harperhosp.com	16	10	25	484	23	5330	1	4766	2454	102
HAYS—Ellis County										
⊞ **HAYS MEDICAL CENTER**, 2220 Canterbury Drive, Zip 67601–2342, Mailing Address: P.O. Box 8100, Zip 67601–8100; tel. 785/623–5000 **A**1 2 9 10 19 20 **F**2 9 11 12 14 15 17 19 21 22 23 24 26 27 28 29 31 33 36 37 38 40 41 44 45 46 47 48 51 52 53 54 55 56 58 59 60 61 63 65 68 69 70 72 73 74 75 77 79 81 82 84 85 86 87 88 93 94 95 96 108 109 110 **P**4 Primary Contact: John H. Jeter, M.D., President and Chief Executive Officer COO: Bryce Young, Chief Operating Officer CFO: Bill Overbey, Chief Financial Officer and Chief Information Officer CMO: Bob Cox, M.D., Medical Director CIO: Bill Overbey, Chief Financial Officer and Chief Information Officer CHR: Bruce Whittington, Vice President Human Resources Web address: www.haysmed.com	23	10	158	6357	84	245974	712	107786	45934	964
HERINGTON—Dickinson County										
HERINGTON MUNICIPAL HOSPITAL, 100 East Helen Street, Zip 67449–1606; tel. 785/258–2207 **A**9 10 18 **F**2 12 26 27 33 60 63 64 69 81 82 97 110 Primary Contact: Mary Steiner, Administrator	14	10	25	464	5	16571	11	2717	1749	92
HIAWATHA—Brown County										
HIAWATHA COMMUNITY HOSPITAL, 300 Utah Street, Zip 66434–2314; tel. 785/742–2131 **A**9 10 18 **F**11 12 27 28 33 51 54 55 59 62 63 81 86 94 97 108 **P**6 Primary Contact: John Moore, Administrator Web address: www.hiawathacommunityhospital.org	23	10	25	1044	11	28289	101	12007	4534	203
HILL CITY—Graham County										
★ **GRAHAM COUNTY HOSPITAL**, 304 West Prout Street, Zip 67642–1435, Mailing Address: P.O. Box 339, Zip 67642–0339; tel. 785/421–2121 **A**9 10 18 **F**1 9 12 26 27 28 33 36 41 46 51 52 54 58 63 69 81 84 88 97 **P**6 Primary Contact: Fred J. Meis, Administrator and Chief Executive Officer CFO: Julie Williams, Chief Financial Officer CHR: Milissa Metcalf, Human Resources Director Web address: www.grahamcountyhospital.org	13	10	25	717	8	27616	0	5381	2605	85
HILLSBORO—Marion County										
★ **HILLSBORO COMMUNITY MEDICAL CENTER**, 701 South Main Street, Zip 67063–1595; tel. 620/947–3114, (Total facility includes 61 beds in nursing home–type unit) **A**9 10 18 **F**1 5 11 21 22 27 28 29 33 44 46 47 48 52 58 59 60 63 65 69 81 91 92 94 96 97 108 **P**5 Primary Contact: Michael J. Ryan, Chief Executive Officer CFO: Marion Regier, Chief Financial Officer CIO: Marsha Setzkorn–Meyer, Public Relations and Marketing Director CHR: Wendy McCarty, Director Human Resources Web address: www.hcmcks.org	23	10	75	425	55	8695	8	5137	2655	107
HOISINGTON—Barton County										
CLARA BARTON HOSPITAL, 250 West Ninth Street, Zip 67544–1706; tel. 620/653–2114 **A**9 10 18 **F**2 3 11 12 13 14 21 27 33 40 52 54 55 56 59 60 63 66 67 68 69 70 71 81 82 84 88 92 97 **P**3 Primary Contact: Christopher Stipe, Administrator and Chief Executive Officer Web address: www.claraburtonhospital.org	23	10	25	569	8	35088	3	10883	4388	141

Many Facility Codes have changed. Please refer to the AHA Guide Code Chart. © 2005 AHA Guide

Hospital, Address, Telephone, Approval, Facility, and Physician Codes, Health Care System	Classi-fication Codes		Utilization Data					Expense (thousands) of dollars		
★ American Hospital Association (AHA) membership ☐ Joint Commission on Accreditation of Healthcare Organizations (JCAHO) accreditation ○ American Osteopathic Association (AOA) accreditation △ Commission on Accreditation of Rehabilitation Facilities (CARF) accreditation	Control	Service	Staffed Beds	Admissions	Census	Outpatient Visits	Births	Total	Payroll	Personnel

HOLTON—Jackson County

★ **HOLTON COMMUNITY HOSPITAL**, 1110 Columbine Drive, Zip 66436–1545; tel. 785/364–2116 **A**9 10 18 **F**2 26 27 33 36 51 52 60 63 69 81 84 88 97 108
Primary Contact: James W. Fairchild, Chief Executive Officer
COO: Kathi Noe, R.N., Chief Operating Officer
CFO: Marlene Kranz, Chief Financial Officer
CMO: Roy Hall, Chief of Staff
CHR: Gretchen Snavely, Director Human Resources

| | 23 | 10 | 12 | 483 | 6 | 85391 | 32 | 9457 | 4675 | 123 |

HORTON—Brown County

NORTHEAST KANSAS CENTER FOR HEALTH AND WELLNESS, 240 West 18th Street, Zip 66439–1245; tel. 785/486–2642 **A**9 10 18 **F**6 9 12 21 27 28 29 33 45 51 52 63 92 97 **P**6
Primary Contact: Dale A. White, Chief Executive Officer

| | 23 | 10 | 25 | 354 | 5 | 1741 | 0 | 6122 | 2720 | 84 |

HOXIE—Sheridan County

★ **SHERIDAN COUNTY HEALTH COMPLEX**, 826 18th Street, Zip 67740–0167, Mailing Address: P.O. Box 167, Zip 67740–0167; tel. 785/675–3281, (Total facility includes 42 beds in nursing home–type unit) **A**9 10 18 20 **F**8 33 51 52 63 68 69 70 92 97 107 **P**5
Primary Contact: Paul Hammeke, Chief Executive Officer
CFO: Rochelle Kennedy, Chief Financial Officer
CMO: Celestine Ofoma, M.D., Chief of Staff

| | 13 | 10 | 60 | 232 | 41 | 6708 | 0 | 4615 | 2377 | 106 |

HUGOTON—Stevens County

STEVENS COUNTY HOSPITAL, 1006 South Jackson Street, Zip 67951–2842, Mailing Address: P.O. Box 10, Zip 67951–0010; tel. 620/544–8511 **A**9 10 18 **F**2 9 12 21 26 33 44 45 46 47 48 51 53 58 63 68 69 70 81 88 92 94 97 109 110
Primary Contact: Linda Stalcup, Chief Executive Officer
Web address: www.healthcarefor the heartland.org

| | 13 | 10 | 17 | 335 | 3 | 12936 | 0 | 7391 | 3740 | 90 |

HUTCHINSON—Reno County

★ **HUTCHINSON HOSPITAL CORPORATION**, 1701 East 23rd Avenue, Zip 67502–1191; tel. 620/665–2000, (Total facility includes 13 beds in nursing home–type unit) **A**9 10 19 20 **F**2 6 9 11 15 17 19 21 22 23 27 28 33 39 40 49 52 53 55 57 58 59 60 61 62 63 64 68 69 71 75 76 79 80 81 82 84 88 92 93 94 108 110
Primary Contact: Gene E. Schmidt, President
CFO: Gary Witham, Vice President Finance
CIO: Bob Lies, Director Information Systems
CHR: Loretta Fletchall, Director Human Resources
Web address: www.hutchinsonhospital.com

| | 23 | 10 | 154 | 9280 | 125 | 95282 | 823 | 87439 | 34166 | 859 |

INDEPENDENCE—Montgomery County

⊞ **MERCY HEALTH SYSTEM OF KANSAS**, 800 West Myrtle Street, Zip 67301–9980, Mailing Address: P.O. Box 388, Zip 67301–0388; tel. 620/331–2200 **A**1 9 10 **F**2 9 11 12 21 22 24 26 27 28 29 31 33 34 37 41 45 46 48 51 55 59 60 62 63 69 70 81 82 83 84 87 93 94 96 97 108 **P**6
Primary Contact: Jon Swope, President and Chief Executive Officer
COO: Reta Baker, Vice President Operations
CMO: William E. Wilkins, Jr, M.D., Chief Medical Officer
CIO: Margie Singmaster, Chief Information Officer and Vice President Support Services
CHR: Gloria Bennett, Corporate Director Human Resources
Web address: www.mercykansas.com

| | 21 | 10 | 40 | 1933 | 20 | 56193 | 280 | 18853 | 8448 | 238 |

IOLA—Allen County

⊞ **ALLEN COUNTY HOSPITAL**, 101 South First Street, Zip 66749–3505, Mailing Address: P.O. Box 540, Zip 66749–0540; tel. 620/365–1000 **A**1 9 10 18 **F**9 11 12 21 22 23 26 27 28 29 33 36 37 38 41 46 48 51 52 53 55 58 59 60 61 62 63 66 81 82 84 85 88 94 96 97 108 **S** HCA, Nashville, TN
Primary Contact: Michael C. Carter, Interim Chief Executive Officer
CFO: Larry Peterson, Chief Financial Officer
CMO: John Atkins, M.D., Chief Medical Officer
CHR: Paula Sell, Director Human Resources
Web address: www.allencountyhospital.com

| | 33 | 10 | 25 | 1415 | 15 | 19750 | 75 | 13409 | 5947 | 106 |

JETMORE—Hodgeman County

★ **HODGEMAN COUNTY HEALTH CENTER**, 809 Bramley Street, Zip 67854–9320, Mailing Address: P.O. Box 310, Zip 67854–0310; tel. 620/357–8361, (Total facility includes 16 beds in nursing home–type unit) **A**9 10 18 20 **F**46 63 81 91 92 94 97 **P**4
Primary Contact: Phillip W. Lowe, Chief Executive Officer
Web address: www.hchconline.org

| | 13 | 10 | 32 | 226 | 24 | 4532 | 0 | 4188 | 1842 | 72 |

JOHNSON—Stanton County

STANTON COUNTY HEALTH CARE FACILITY, 404 North Chestnut Street, Zip 67855–0779, Mailing Address: P.O. Box 779, Zip 67855–0779; tel. 620/492–6250, (Total facility includes 25 beds in nursing home–type unit) **A**9 10 18 **F**2 26 27 28 33 39 45 46 47 48 53 57 59 65 66 69 70 92 94 96 97 108 **P**6
Primary Contact: Shae Veach, Administrator
Web address: www.phn.org

| | 13 | 10 | 43 | 203 | 25 | 4979 | 53 | 2586 | 1157 | 68 |

KS

Hospital, Address, Telephone, Approval, Facility, and Physician Codes, Health Care System	Classi- fication Codes		Utilization Data					Expense (thousands) of dollars		
★ American Hospital Association (AHA) membership □ Joint Commission on Accreditation of Healthcare Organizations (JCAHO) accreditation ○ American Osteopathic Association (AOA) accreditation △ Commission on Accreditation of Rehabilitation Facilities (CARF) accreditation	Control	Service	Staffed Beds	Admissions	Census	Outpatient Visits	Births	Total	Payroll	Personnel

JUNCTION CITY—Geary County

⊠ **GEARY COMMUNITY HOSPITAL**, 1102 St. Mary's Road, Zip 66441–4196, Mailing Address: P.O. Box 490, Zip 66441–0490; tel. 785/238–4131 **A**1 3 5 9 10 **F**2 9 10 11 12 21 22 27 28 29 33 44 50 51 52 53 55 58 59 60 62 63 65 66 67 68 70 71 76 81 84 88 93 94 96 97 106 109 110
Primary Contact: David K. Bradley, CHE, Chief Executive Officer
CFO: Melvin D. Robinson, Chief Financial Officer
Web address: www.gchks.org

	13	10	69	2121	24	162100	240	29050	13986	384

⊠ **IRWIN ARMY COMMUNITY HOSPITAL**, 600 Caisson Hill Road, Zip 66442–5037; tel. 785/239–7555 **A**1 2 **F**3 4 6 11 12 21 22 24 27 31 32 33 34 46 48 53 55 58 59 60 62 63 64 65 66 69 70 71 73 74 75 77 81 82 84 86 87 88 92 94 106 108 110 **S** Department of the Army, Office of the Surgeon General, Falls Church, VA
Primary Contact: Colonel Marilyn Brooks, Commander
CFO: Janice Mailen, Chief Resource Management Division
CMO: Colonel Bobbilynn Lee, M.D., Chief Medical Officer
CIO: May Garlick, Chief Information Officer
CHR: Dianna Kallenberger, Chief Manpower Branch
Web address: www.iach.amedd.army.mil

	42	10	27	1677	9	215148	557	—	—	632

KANSAS CITY—Wyandotte County

⊠ **PROVIDENCE MEDICAL CENTER**, 8929 Parallel Parkway, Zip 66112–1636; tel. 913/596–4000 **A**1 2 5 9 10 **F**2 9 11 12 14 15 17 19 21 22 23 26 27 28 29 33 35 37 38 44 46 47 48 50 51 52 53 55 57 58 59 60 61 62 63 64 65 69 79 80 81 82 84 87 88 93 94 95 96 106 108 109 110 **P**6 **S** Sisters of Charity of Leavenworth Health System, Lenexa, KS
Primary Contact: James T. Paquette, President and Chief Executive Officer
CFO: Juanita Roy, Vice President Finance
CIO: Robert Boysen, Vice President Information Systems
CHR: Carolyn Bowmer, Vice President Human Resources
Web address: www.providence–health.org

	21	10	257	11141	154	91236	1443	126093	53646	1223

□ **RAINBOW MENTAL HEALTH FACILITY**, 2205 West 36th Avenue, Zip 66103–2107; tel. 913/384–4706 **A**1 10 **F**9 21 26 28 35 39 53 58 65 66 71 72 73 74 75 76 94 96 108 **P**6
Primary Contact: Rosalind Underdahl, Director

	12	22	50	715	41	0	0	7514	4194	115

⊠ △ **UNIVERSITY OF KANSAS HOSPITAL**, 3901 Rainbow Boulevard, Zip 66160–7200; tel. 913/588–5000 **A**1 2 3 5 7 8 9 10 **F**2 5 7 9 10 11 12 13 14 15 17 19 21 22 23 24 26 27 28 29 30 31 32 33 34 35 37 38 39 40 41 42 44 46 47 48 49 50 52 53 55 56 57 58 59 60 61 62 63 64 65 66 67 68 69 70 71 72 73 74 75 76 77 78 79 80 81 82 84 85 86 87 88 89 93 94 95 96 99 101 102 104 105 106 107 108 109 110 **P**6
Primary Contact: Irene M. Cumming, Chief Executive Officer
COO: Bob Page, Senior Vice President and Chief Operating Officer
CFO: Scott Glasrud, Senior Vice President and Chief Financial Officer
CMO: H William Barkman, M.D., Chief of Staff
CIO: Bill Mumford, Corporate Director Information Systems
CHR: Dwight Kasperbauer, Vice President Human Resources
Web address: www.kumc.edu

	16	10	475	17803	290	231508	1404	377725	156532	2991

KINGMAN—Kingman County

★ **NINNESCAH VALLEY HEALTH SYSTEM**, 750 Avenue D West, Zip 67068–0376, Mailing Address: P.O. Box 376, Zip 67068–0376; tel. 620/532–3147 **A**9 10 20 **F**2 9 11 12 14 21 22 23 26 27 28 29 33 44 46 47 48 51 52 54 55 58 59 60 61 63 65 66 68 69 70 81 85 92 94 96 97 108 110
Primary Contact: Gary L. Tiller, Chief Executive Officer
CIO: Helio DeCastro, Director Information Systems
Web address: www.nvhsinc.com

	23	10	34	804	12	25141	12	8405	3830	119

KINSLEY—Edwards County

EDWARDS COUNTY HOSPITAL AND HEALTHCARE CENTER, 620 West Eighth Street, Zip 67547–2329, Mailing Address: P.O. Box 99, Zip 67547–0099; tel. 620/659–3621 **A**9 10 18 **F**2 6 9 22 26 27 28 33 41 53 62 81 92 97 110 **P**6 **S** Great Plains Health Alliance, Inc., Phillipsburg, KS
Primary Contact: Shaun Keef, Administrator

	13	10	12	146	5	13054	0	3193	1230	47

KIOWA—Barber County

★ **KIOWA DISTRICT HOSPITAL AND MANOR**, 810 Drumm Street, Zip 67070–1626; tel. 620/825–4131, (Total facility includes 40 beds in nursing home–type unit) **A**9 10 18 **F**21 26 27 28 33 52 53 63 64 69 70 88 92 94 97 **P**6
Primary Contact: Bryan Stacey, Chief Executive Officer
CFO: Julie Myers, Chief Financial Officer
CMO: Paul Wilhelm, Chief of Staff
CHR: Tara Girty, Director Human Resources

	16	10	64	161	37	4490	1	3668	1954	70

LA CROSSE—Rush County

★ **RUSH COUNTY MEMORIAL HOSPITAL**, 801 Locust Street, Zip 67548–9673, Mailing Address: P.O. Box 520, Zip 67548–0520; tel. 785/222–2545, (Total facility includes 26 beds in nursing home–type unit) **A**9 10 18 **F**2 27 33 41 63 70 92 **P**5
Primary Contact: Teresa L. Deuel, Administrator and Chief Executive Officer
CFO: Carol Larkin, Chief Financial Officer

	13	10	46	289	29	15345	0	2884	1351	60

Many Facility Codes have changed. Please refer to the AHA Guide Code Chart. © 2005 AHA Guide

Hospital, Address, Telephone, Approval, Facility, and Physician Codes, Health Care System	Classification Codes		Utilization Data					Expense (thousands) of dollars		
	Control	Service	Staffed Beds	Admissions	Census	Outpatient Visits	Births	Total	Payroll	Personnel

★ American Hospital Association (AHA) membership
□ Joint Commission on Accreditation of Healthcare Organizations (JCAHO) accreditation
○ American Osteopathic Association (AOA) accreditation
△ Commission on Accreditation of Rehabilitation Facilities (CARF) accreditation

LAKIN—Kearny County

KEARNY COUNTY HOSPITAL, 500 Thorpe Street, Zip 67860; tel. 620/355–7111, (Total facility includes 65 beds in nursing home–type unit) **A**9 10 18 **F**1 2 5 8 11 24 26 27 28 29 30 33 35 39 44 45 46 47 48 51 52 53 58 59 62 63 64 65 66 69 70 88 91 92 95 96 97 **P**6
Primary Contact: Sandra A. Cameron, Chief Executive Officer
Web address: www.kearnycountyhospital.com

| 13 | 10 | 90 | 234 | 59 | 13975 | 76 | 8029 | 4360 | 139 |

LARNED—Pawnee County

□ **LARNED STATE HOSPITAL**, Mailing Address: Rural Route 3, P.O. Box 89, Zip 67550–9365; tel. 620/285–2131 **A**1 10 **F**21 22 26 28 41 46 47 48 58 65 66 71 72 75 76 88 94 96 106 108 **P**6
Primary Contact: Mark E. Schutter, Ph.D., Superintendent
Web address: www.larnedstatehospital.org

| 12 | 22 | 368 | 1251 | 342 | 0 | 0 | 36032 | 21687 | 806 |

★ **ST. JOSEPH MEMORIAL HOSPITAL**, 923 Carroll Avenue, Zip 67550; tel. 620/285–3161, (Total facility includes 30 beds in nursing home–type unit) **A**9 10 18 **F**1 6 9 12 21 22 33 36 44 46 58 60 63 68 69 88 92 94 97 110 **P**6 **S** Catholic Health Initiatives, Denver, CO
Primary Contact: Danielle Johnson, Administrator
CFO: Jesse Saucedo, Vice President and Chief Financial Officer
CMO: David Sanger, M.D., Chief Medical Officer
CIO: Mark Hanson, Director Information Systems
CHR: Shelly Gompf, Vice President Human Resources
Web address: www.ckmc.org

| 21 | 10 | 55 | 271 | 30 | 21497 | 0 | 6945 | 3009 | 77 |

LAWRENCE—Douglas County

⊠ △ **LAWRENCE MEMORIAL HOSPITAL**, 325 Maine Street, Zip 66044–1389; tel. 785/749–6100, (Total facility includes 12 beds in nursing home–type unit) **A**1 5 7 9 10 20 **F**2 9 11 12 15 21 22 23 26 27 28 30 33 35 37 38 40 42 46 47 48 50 52 53 54 55 57 58 59 60 61 62 63 64 65 66 68 69 71 73 81 82 84 85 86 88 92 93 94 96 106 108 109 110 **P**6
Primary Contact: Eugene W. Meyer, President and Chief Executive Officer
CFO: Simon Scholtz, Vice President and Chief Financial Officer
CMO: Lee Reussner, M.D., Chief of Staff
CIO: Tom Pagano, Chief Information Officer
CHR: Deborah Thompson, Vice President Human Resources
Web address: www.lmh.org

| 14 | 10 | 141 | 6877 | 75 | 170310 | 1129 | 92635 | 40949 | 820 |

LEAVENWORTH—Leavenworth County

□ **CUSHING MEMORIAL HOSPITAL**, 711 Marshall Street, Zip 66048–3235; tel. 913/684–1100, (Total facility includes 16 beds in nursing home–type unit) **A**1 9 10 **F**9 10 12 19 21 22 26 27 28 33 36 37 38 39 46 51 55 57 58 59 60 62 63 66 69 71 76 81 82 88 92 93 94 106 108 110 **S** Saint Luke's Health System, Kansas City, MO
Primary Contact: Bob S. Edwards, Jr, Chief Executive Officer
Web address: www.cushinghospital.org
DWIGHT D. EISENHOWER VETERANS AFFAIRS MEDICAL CENTER See Veterans Affairs Eastern Kansas Health Care System, Topeka

| 23 | 10 | 74 | 2598 | 34 | 118968 | 145 | 24582 | 11632 | 295 |

⊠ **SAINT JOHN HOSPITAL**, 3500 South Fourth Street, Zip 66048–5043; tel. 913/680–6000 **A**1 9 10 **F**2 9 11 12 21 22 26 27 28 29 32 33 35 37 38 42 44 46 47 48 50 51 52 55 57 59 60 61 62 63 64 69 71 76 81 87 88 94 96 97 106 108 109 **S** Sisters of Charity of Leavenworth Health System, Lenexa, KS
Primary Contact: Greg Madsen, Vice President and Administrator
Web address: www.providence–health.org/sjh

| 21 | 10 | 56 | 2402 | 32 | 41228 | 268 | 25279 | 12537 | 264 |

LEAWOOD—Johnson County

□ **DOCTOR'S HOSPITAL**, 4901 College Boulevard, Zip 66211; tel. 913/529–1801, (Nonreporting) **A**1
Primary Contact: Phil Harness, Chief Executive Officer

| 33 | 49 | 10 | — | — | — | — | — | — | — |

LEOTI—Wichita County

★ **WICHITA COUNTY HEALTH CENTER**, 211 East Earl Street, Zip 67861–0968, Mailing Address: Rural Route 2, Box 38, Zip 67861–0968; tel. 620/375–2233, (Includes WICHITA COUNTY HOSPITAL LONG TERM CARE), (Total facility includes 22 beds in nursing home–type unit) **A**9 10 18 **F**1 2 9 11 21 29 30 33 44 46 59 65 66 69 70 92 94 96 97 **P**6
Primary Contact: Victoria J. Hahn, Administrator and Chief Executive Officer
CFO: Janice Campas, Chief Financial Officer
Web address: www.phn.org

| 13 | 10 | 35 | 192 | 23 | 13902 | 11 | 4342 | 2082 | 80 |

LIBERAL—Seward County

⊠ **SOUTHWEST MEDICAL CENTER**, 315 West 15th Street, Zip 67901–1340, Mailing Address: Box 1340, Zip 67905–1340; tel. 620/624–1651, (Total facility includes 18 beds in nursing home–type unit) **A**1 9 10 20 **F**9 11 12 21 33 40 53 55 59 63 71 76 77 81 82 84 92 93 94
Primary Contact: Anthony A. Daigle, Administrator
CFO: DeLany Fawkes, Vice President and Chief Financial Officer
Web address: www.swmedcenter.com

| 13 | 10 | 89 | 3633 | 42 | 37070 | 814 | 35607 | 14333 | 363 |

LINCOLN—Lincoln County

LINCOLN COUNTY HOSPITAL, 624 North Second Street, Zip 67455–1738, Mailing Address: P.O. Box 406, Zip 67455–0406; tel. 785/524–4403 **A**9 10 18 **F**33 54 60 81 88 93 97 **P**6
Primary Contact: Greg R. McNeil, Chief Executive Officer

| 13 | 10 | 14 | 363 | 4 | 1448 | 0 | 4158 | 2149 | 64 |

KS

Hospital, Address, Telephone, Approval, Facility, and Physician Codes, Health Care System	Classi-fication Codes		Utilization Data					Expense (thousands) of dollars		
★ American Hospital Association (AHA) membership □ Joint Commission on Accreditation of Healthcare Organizations (JCAHO) accreditation ○ American Osteopathic Association (AOA) accreditation △ Commission on Accreditation of Rehabilitation Facilities (CARF) accreditation	Control	Service	Staffed Beds	Admissions	Census	Outpatient Visits	Births	Total	Payroll	Personnel

LINDSBORG—McPherson County

★ **LINDSBORG COMMUNITY HOSPITAL**, 605 West Lincoln Street, Zip 67456–2328; tel. 785/227–3308 **A**9 10 18 **F**12 21 27 33 41 48 51 54 58 63 69 81 88 92 94 97 **P**6
Primary Contact: Greg Lundstrom, Administrator and Chief Executive Officer
CFO: Laraine Gengler, Chief Financial Officer
CMO: Craig Nickel, M.D., Chief of Staff
CHR: Tricia Hawk, Director Development and Human Resources
Web address: www.lindsborghospital.org

| | 23 | 10 | 24 | 525 | 6 | 20369 | 0 | 4473 | 2145 | 61 |

LYONS—Rice County

★ **RICE COUNTY HOSPITAL DISTRICT NUMBER ONE**, 619 South Clark Street, Zip 67554–0828, Mailing Address: P.O. Box 828, Zip 67554–0828; tel. 620/257–5173 **A**9 10 18 **F**8 9 11 22 26 27 28 29 33 44 46 53 58 59 63 81 91 97
Primary Contact: Robert L. Mullen, Chief Executive Officer
Web address: www.rch–lyons.com

| | 16 | 10 | 25 | 540 | 6 | 12293 | 64 | 6650 | 2930 | 106 |

MANHATTAN—Riley County

MANHATTAN SURGICAL CENTER, 1829 College Avenue, Zip 66502; tel. 785/776–5100 **A**10 **F**63 94
Primary Contact: Scott Chapman, Administrator
Web address: www.manhattansurgical.com

| | 33 | 13 | 7 | 353 | 1 | 4568 | 0 | — | — | 44 |

★ ○ **MERCY REGIONAL HEALTH CENTER**, 1823 College Avenue, Zip 66502, Mailing Address: P.O. Box 1289, Zip 66505–1289; tel. 785/776–3322, (Includes MEMORIAL HOSPITAL, 1105 Sunset Avenue, tel. 785/776–3300; SAINT MARY HOSPITAL) **A**5 9 10 11 **F**2 9 11 12 14 15 21 22 23 26 27 28 29 33 35 37 41 45 46 47 48 53 54 55 58 59 60 61 62 63 64 65 66 68 69 71 73 74 75 77 81 82 84 88 93 94 95 96 97 108 109 110 **S** Via Christi Health System, Wichita, KS
Primary Contact: Richard L. Allen, President and Chief Executive Officer
COO: James Murguia, Chief Operating Officer and Chief Financial Officer
CFO: James Murguia, Chief Operating Officer and Chief Financial Officer
CMO: Joseph Philipp, M.D., Chief Medical Officer
CIO: Andy Gagnon, Director Information Systems
Web address: www.mercyregional.org

| | 23 | 10 | 121 | 5709 | 67 | 100489 | 818 | 61741 | 24162 | 683 |

MANKATO—Jewell County

JEWELL COUNTY HOSPITAL, 100 Crestvue Avenue, Zip 66956–2407, Mailing Address: P.O. Box 327, Zip 66956–0327; tel. 785/378–3137, (Total facility includes 12 beds in nursing home–type unit) **A**9 10 18 **F**1 9 21 24 26 27 28 29 33 42 47 69 92 94
Primary Contact: Deanna Freeman, Administrator

| | 13 | 10 | 49 | 97 | 33 | 997 | 0 | 3122 | 1780 | 70 |

MARION—Marion County

★ **ST. LUKE HOSPITAL AND LIVING CENTER**, 535 South Freeborn, Zip 66861–1299; tel. 620/382–2179, (Total facility includes 32 beds in nursing home–type unit) **A**9 10 18 **F**9 12 21 22 27 29 33 37 46 51 52 58 60 63 64 69 81 82 92 97 106 108 110 **S** Quorum Health Resources, Plano, TX
Primary Contact: Thomas C. Smith, III, Chief Executive Officer
CFO: Kevin Cronkleton, Chief Financial Officer
CMO: Kim Hall, M.D., Chief Medical Officer
CIO: Jeff Methuen, Information Technology Manager
CHR: Sharon Zogelman, Human Resources Director

| | 23 | 10 | 54 | 308 | 31 | 5566 | 7 | 4318 | 2135 | 97 |

MARYSVILLE—Marshall County

★ **COMMUNITY MEMORIAL HEALTHCARE**, 708 North 18th Street, Zip 66508–1338; tel. 785/562–2311 **A**9 10 18 **F**2 9 11 21 22 23 26 33 41 46 51 52 53 54 59 60 61 62 63 66 69 70 81 82 93 94 96 97 106 **P**6
Primary Contact: David Bailey, Chief Executive Officer
CFO: Therese Landoll, Chief Financial Officer
Web address: www.cmhcare.org

| | 23 | 10 | 25 | 955 | 11 | 24261 | 84 | 10232 | 4157 | 126 |

MCPHERSON—McPherson County

★ **MEMORIAL HOSPITAL**, 1000 Hospital Drive, Zip 67460–2321; tel. 620/241–2250 **A**9 10 **F**2 6 9 11 12 26 27 28 33 37 41 46 52 54 55 58 59 60 61 63 66 81 88 97 108
Primary Contact: Rex D. Walk, President and Chief Executive Officer
COO: Terri Gehring, Vice President Operations
CHR: Jill Wenger, Vice President Human Resources
Web address: www.mcphersonmemorial.org

| | 23 | 10 | 41 | 1543 | 17 | 118212 | 170 | 20690 | 9317 | 246 |

MEADE—Meade County

★ **MEADE DISTRICT HOSPITAL**, 510 East Carthage Street, Zip 67864–0820, Mailing Address: P.O. Box 820, Zip 67864–0820; tel. 620/873–2141 **A**9 10 18 **F**2 12 21 27 28 32 33 41 46 47 48 51 63 64 69 81 82 88 92 94 97
Primary Contact: Michael P. Thomas, Administrator
CFO: Lori Smith, Chief Financial Officer
CIO: Leighton Miller, Chief Information Officer
Web address: www.meadehospital.com

| | 16 | 10 | 20 | 359 | 3 | 7783 | 0 | 5915 | 2698 | 88 |

MEDICINE LODGE—Barber County

★ **MEDICINE LODGE MEMORIAL HOSPITAL**, 710 North Walnut Street, Zip 67104–1019, Mailing Address: P.O. Drawer C, Zip 67104; tel. 620/886–3771 **A**9 10 18 **F**6 9 27 28 33 35 41 44 52 63 69 81 88 92 97 110 **P**6 **S** Great Plains Health Alliance, Inc., Phillipsburg, KS
Primary Contact: Kevin A. White, Administrator

| | 16 | 10 | 25 | 487 | 17 | 22668 | 0 | 6404 | 3402 | 101 |

Many Facility Codes have changed. Please refer to the AHA Guide Code Chart.
© 2005 AHA Guide

Hospital, Address, Telephone, Approval, Facility, and Physician Codes, Health Care System	Classi-fication Codes		Utilization Data					Expense (thousands) of dollars		
★ American Hospital Association (AHA) membership □ Joint Commission on Accreditation of Healthcare Organizations (JCAHO) accreditation ○ American Osteopathic Association (AOA) accreditation △ Commission on Accreditation of Rehabilitation Facilities (CARF) accreditation	Control	Service	Staffed Beds	Admissions	Census	Outpatient Visits	Births	Total	Payroll	Personnel

MINNEAPOLIS—Ottawa County

★ **OTTAWA COUNTY HEALTH CENTER**, 215 East Eighth, Zip 67467–1999, Mailing Address: P.O. Box 290, Zip 67467–0290; tel. 785/392–2122, (Total facility includes 27 beds in nursing home–type unit) **A**9 10 18 **F**8 22 26 27 28 29 32 33 41 44 45 51 52 54 64 65 69 81 88 92 93 94 97 **S** Great Plains Health Alliance, Inc., Phillipsburg, KS
Primary Contact: Joy Johnson, R.N., Administrator
CFO: Linda Galgerud, Chief Financial Officer
CIO: Linda Wright, Director Information
Web address: www.gpha.com

| 23 | 10 | 52 | 471 | 43 | 5581 | 0 | 4545 | 2382 | 82 |

MINNEOLA—Clark County

★ **MINNEOLA DISTRICT HOSPITAL**, 212 Main Street, Zip 67865–0127, Mailing Address: P.O. Box 127, Zip 67865–0127; tel. 620/885–4264, (Total facility includes 36 beds in nursing home–type unit) **A**9 10 18 **F**1 11 21 26 33 44 46 52 63 69 75 91 92 94 97 110 **P**6 **S** Great Plains Health Alliance, Inc., Phillipsburg, KS
Primary Contact: Donald J. Kessen, Administrator and Chief Executive Officer
CFO: Debi Johnson, Chief Financial Officer
CMO: Todd Stephens, M.D., Chief of Staff
CHR: Vena Harris, Director Human Resources
Web address: www.gpha.com

| 16 | 10 | 54 | 557 | 37 | 24058 | 28 | 6845 | 3736 | 115 |

MOUNDRIDGE—McPherson County

★ **MERCY HOSPITAL**, 218 East Pack Street, Zip 67107–0180, Mailing Address: P.O. Box 180, Zip 67107–0180; tel. 620/345–6391 **A**9 10 **F**11 27 33 44 59 63 97
Primary Contact: Doyle K. Johnson, Administrator

| 21 | 10 | 21 | 494 | 5 | 7329 | 42 | 2220 | 1081 | 41 |

NEODESHA—Wilson County

★ **WILSON COUNTY HOSPITAL**, 205 Mill Street, Zip 66757–1817, Mailing Address: P.O. Box 360, Zip 66757–0360; tel. 620/325–2611 **A**9 10 18 **F**9 21 22 29 33 41 45 46 63 64 69 81 92 97 110
Primary Contact: Deanna Pittman, Administrator
CFO: John Gutschenritter, Chief Financial Officer
CIO: Julie Quanstrom, Information Systems Director and Reimbursement Specialist
CHR: Susie Olson, Director Human Resources
Web address: www.wilsoncountyhospital.org

| 13 | 10 | 25 | 357 | 5 | 5665 | 1 | 6016 | 3129 | 108 |

NESS CITY—Ness County

★ **NESS COUNTY HOSPITAL**, 312 Custer Street, Zip 67560–1654; tel. 785/798–2291, (Total facility includes 46 beds in nursing home–type unit) **A**9 10 18 **F**6 33 51 63 91 92 97 **P**6
Primary Contact: Richard Q. Bergling, Administrator and Chief Executive Officer
CMO: Mikhail Imseis, M.D., Chief of Staff
CIO: Vicki Howe, Chief Information Officer
CHR: Susie Schlegel, Human Resources Director

| 16 | 10 | 66 | 347 | 42 | 6175 | 0 | 5482 | 2578 | 108 |

NEWTON—Harvey County

★ ○ **NEWTON MEDICAL CENTER**, Mailing Address: P.O. Box 308, Zip 67114–0308; tel. 316/283–2700 **A**9 10 11 **F**2 11 12 21 22 27 28 33 39 40 46 48 52 55 58 59 60 63 64 65 68 69 81 82 84 88 94 108 109
Primary Contact: Steven G. Kelly, President and Chief Executive Officer
COO: J Michael Keller, Vice President Operations
CFO: Paul Lavender, Vice President Finance
Web address: www.newtonmedicalcenter.com

| 23 | 10 | 79 | 3675 | 41 | 55096 | 440 | 33849 | 14616 | 430 |

□ **PRAIRIE VIEW**, 1901 East First Street, Zip 67114–0467, Mailing Address: P.O. Box 467, Zip 67114–0467; tel. 316/284–6400, (Nonreporting) **A**1 9 10
Primary Contact: Jessie Kaye, Chief Executive Officer
Web address: www.prairieview.org

| 23 | 22 | 38 | — | — | — | — | — | — | — |

NORTON—Norton County

★ **NORTON COUNTY HOSPITAL**, 102 East Holme, Zip 67654–0250, Mailing Address: P.O. Box 250, Zip 67654–0250; tel. 785/877–3351 **A**9 10 18 20 **F**2 11 12 22 23 26 27 28 33 37 44 54 59 61 62 63 68 69 81 88 92 94 97
Primary Contact: Richard Miller, Administrator and Chief Executive Officer
CFO: Brian Carlton, Chief Financial Officer
CHR: Shannan Farber, Director Human Resources
Web address: www.ntcohosp.com

| 13 | 10 | 25 | 343 | 3 | 20995 | 23 | 6103 | 3224 | 100 |

OAKLEY—Logan County

LOGAN COUNTY HOSPITAL, 211 Cherry Street, Zip 67748–1201; tel. 785/672–3211, (Total facility includes 35 beds in nursing home–type unit) **A**9 10 18 **F**2 8 22 33 37 45 52 54 60 63 69 81 91 92 94 97 110 **P**5
Primary Contact: Kyle Hahn, Administrator

| 13 | 10 | 60 | 267 | 39 | 13335 | 0 | 6223 | 3059 | 86 |

OBERLIN—Decatur County

★ **DECATUR COUNTY HOSPITAL AND CEDAR LIVING CENTER**, 810 West Columbia Street, Zip 67749–2450, Mailing Address: P.O. Box 268, Zip 67749–0268; tel. 785/475–2208, (Total facility includes 36 beds in nursing home–type unit) **A**9 10 18 20 **F**2 11 12 26 27 28 33 36 38 44 46 50 51 52 54 58 59 61 63 65 69 79 81 85 87 88 92 93 94 97 **P**5
Primary Contact: Lynn Doeden, Chief Executive Officer
CFO: Dave Nichols, Finance Manager
CMO: Richard May, M.D., Chairman Medical Staff
Web address: www.decaturhealthsystems.org

| 23 | 10 | 60 | 423 | 38 | 5078 | 16 | 4881 | 2463 | 94 |

KS

Hospital, Address, Telephone, Approval, Facility, and Physician Codes, Health Care System	Classi-fication Codes		Utilization Data					Expense (thousands) of dollars		
★ American Hospital Association (AHA) membership □ Joint Commission on Accreditation of Healthcare Organizations (JCAHO) accreditation ○ American Osteopathic Association (AOA) accreditation △ Commission on Accreditation of Rehabilitation Facilities (CARF) accreditation	Control	Service	Staffed Beds	Admissions	Census	Outpatient Visits	Births	Total	Payroll	Personnel

OLATHE—Johnson County

□ **OLATHE MEDICAL CENTER**, 20333 West 151st Street, Zip 66061–5350; tel. 913/791–4200 **A**1 2 9 10 **F**2 9 10 11 12 15 17 19 21 22 23 26 27 28 29 32 33 36 37 42 46 48 51 52 53 55 57 58 59 60 61 62 63 64 65 66 69 81 82 84 85 88 89 90 93 94 95 96 106 107 108 109 110 **P**8
Primary Contact: Frank H. Devocelle, President and Chief Executive Officer
Web address: www.omci.com

| 23 | 10 | 228 | 11343 | 117 | 169846 | 1407 | — | — | 1023 |

ONAGA—Pottawatomie County

★ **COMMUNITY HOSPITAL ONAGA**, 120 West Eighth Street, Zip 66521–0120; tel. 785/889–4272, (Total facility includes 82 beds in nursing home–type unit) **A**9 10 18 20 **F**1 2 4 8 9 10 11 12 14 21 23 24 26 27 28 29 30 33 34 37 38 39 41 44 45 46 47 48 50 51 52 55 57 58 59 60 61 62 63 65 66 69 70 72 73 74 75 76 77 81 84 85 88 91 92 94 95 96 97 98 106 107 108 109 110 **P**6
Primary Contact: Joseph T. Engelken, Chief Executive Officer
COO: Marcia S. Walsh, M.P.H., Chief Operating Officer
CFO: Becky Meyer, CPA, Chief Financial Officer
CMO: Tom Walsh, M.D., Chief of Staff
CIO: Mary Matzke, Chief Information Officer
CHR: Edana Correll, Manager Human Resources
Web address: www.chcs–ks.org

| 23 | 10 | 176 | 1319 | 150 | 76378 | 69 | 16620 | 8907 | 273 |

OSAWATOMIE—Miami County

□ **OSAWATOMIE STATE HOSPITAL**, 500 State Hospital Drive, Zip 66064–0500, Mailing Address: P.O. Box 500, Zip 66064–0500; tel. 913/755–7000 **A**1 10 **F**22 58 65 66 71 94 108 **P**6
Primary Contact: Greg Valentine, Superintendent
Web address: www.srskansas.org

| 12 | 22 | 176 | 1570 | 152 | 0 | 0 | 20992 | 12378 | 398 |

OSBORNE—Osborne County

★ **OSBORNE COUNTY MEMORIAL HOSPITAL**, 424 West New Hampshire Street, Zip 67473–0070, Mailing Address: P.O. Box 70, Zip 67473–0070; tel. 785/346–2121 **A**9 10 18 20 **F**9 11 32 33 52 54 61 63 81 92 97 **P**6
S Great Plains Health Alliance, Inc., Phillipsburg, KS
Primary Contact: Kiley Floyd, Administrator
CFO: Linda Murphy, Chief Financial Officer
CMO: Barbara Brown, D.O., Chief of Staff
CIO: Kathy Carlson, Vice President Patient Care and Support Services
Web address: www.ocmh.org

| 13 | 10 | 25 | 386 | 6 | 11562 | 12 | 3443 | 1610 | 59 |

OSWEGO—Labette County

★ **OSWEGO MEDICAL CENTER**, 800 Barker Drive, Zip 67356–9033; tel. 620/795–2921 **A**9 10 18 **F**27 33 46 52 60 69 81 88 92 94 97 **P**8
Primary Contact: LaMont Cook, Administrator
CMO: Stanley W. Haag, M.D., Medical Director
CHR: Paula Adler, Human Resources Director

| 33 | 10 | 12 | 141 | 3 | 2194 | 0 | 2082 | 989 | 27 |

OTTAWA—Franklin County

✚ **RANSOM MEMORIAL HOSPITAL**, 1301 South Main Street, Zip 66067–3598, Mailing Address: P.O. Box 643, Zip 66067–0643; tel. 785/229–8200 **A**1 9 10 **F**2 9 11 12 23 26 27 28 29 33 37 41 44 46 48 51 52 55 58 59 60 62 63 64 65 69 81 82 87 88 93 94 95 96 97 98 106 108 109 110 **P**8
Primary Contact: Larry A. Felix, CHE, Administrator
CFO: Dean Ohmart, Chief Financial Officer
CIO: Bill Ladd, Director Information Systems
Web address: www.ransom.org

| 13 | 10 | 47 | 1650 | 15 | 83613 | 153 | 18772 | 10004 | 236 |

OVERLAND PARK—Johnson County

CHILDREN'S MERCY SOUTH, 5808 West 110th Street, Zip 66211; tel. 913/696–8000 **A**9 10 **F**2 7 21 22 24 27 28 35 37 38 39 48 51 52 53 58 60 62 63 64 66 69 72 73 77 81 84 85 87 88 94 96 98 108 110 **P**6 8
Primary Contact: Randall L. O'Donnell, Ph.D., President and Chief Executive Officer
Web address: www.childrens–mercy.org

| 23 | 50 | 25 | 1592 | 10 | 63854 | 0 | 23787 | 17334 | 273 |

□ **HEARTLAND SPINE & SPECIALTY HOSPITAL**, 10720 Nall Avenue, Zip 66211; tel. 913/754–5000, (Nonreporting) **A**1 10
Primary Contact: Troy E. Clark, Chief Executive Officer
Web address: www.hssh.org

| 31 | 47 | 19 | — | — | — | — | — | — | — |

✚ **MENORAH MEDICAL CENTER**, 5721 West 119th Street, Zip 66209–3722; tel. 913/498–6000 **A**1 2 9 10 **F**2 9 11 12 15 17 19 21 22 26 27 28 29 31 33 37 46 47 48 49 52 53 55 56 57 58 59 60 61 62 63 65 66 69 70 75 81 82 84 85 86 88 92 94 95 96 108 109 **P**5 **S** HCA, Nashville, TN
Primary Contact: Steven D. Wilkinson, President and Chief Executive Officer
CFO: Deborah Gafford, Chief Financial Officer
Web address: www.menorahmedicalcenter.com

| 33 | 10 | 158 | 6895 | 81 | 52216 | 1539 | 109900 | 34377 | 563 |

✚ **OVERLAND PARK REGIONAL MEDICAL CENTER**, 10500 Quivira Road, Zip 66215–2306, Mailing Address: P.O. Box 15959, Zip 66215–5959; tel. 913/541–5000 **A**1 9 10 **F**2 11 12 15 17 19 21 22 23 26 27 28 29 33 34 37 38 44 45 46 47 48 49 50 52 53 55 56 57 58 59 60 61 62 63 64 65 66 69 81 82 83 84 85 88 89 92 93 94 106 108 109 **P**5 **S** HCA, Nashville, TN
Primary Contact: Kevin J. Hicks, Chief Executive Officer
COO: Jacqueline DeSouza, Chief Operating Officer
CFO: Shari Collier, Chief Financial Officer
CHR: Connie Miller, Director Human Resources
Web address: www.oprmc.com

| 33 | 10 | 256 | 9436 | 131 | 53674 | 2395 | 95960 | 39197 | 687 |

Many Facility Codes have changed. Please refer to the AHA Guide Code Chart. © 2005 AHA Guide

Hospital, Address, Telephone, Approval, Facility, and Physician Codes, Health Care System	Classification Codes		Utilization Data					Expense (thousands) of dollars		
	Control	Service	Staffed Beds	Admissions	Census	Outpatient Visits	Births	Total	Payroll	Personnel

★ American Hospital Association (AHA) membership
□ Joint Commission on Accreditation of Healthcare Organizations (JCAHO) accreditation
○ American Osteopathic Association (AOA) accreditation
△ Commission on Accreditation of Rehabilitation Facilities (CARF) accreditation

Hospital	Control	Service	Staffed Beds	Admissions	Census	Outpatient Visits	Births	Total	Payroll	Personnel
⊠ **SAINT LUKE'S SOUTH HOSPITAL**, 12300 Metcalf Avenue, Zip 66213; tel. 913/317–7000 **A**1 9 10 **F**2 11 12 15 17 21 22 26 27 28 33 35 37 44 46 47 48 49 52 53 55 57 58 59 60 62 63 64 68 69 81 82 84 85 88 92 93 94 95 96 108 110 **S** Saint Luke's Health System, Kansas City, MO Primary Contact: Julie Quirin, Chief Executive Officer CFO: Amy Nachtigal, Chief Financial Officer CMO: Doug Anderson, M.D., President Medical Staff CIO: John Wade, Chief Information Officer CHR: Donna Kunz, Manager Human Resources Web address: www.saint–lukes.org	21	10	93	5255	52	61948	1415	65167	22521	446
□ **SELECT SPECIALTY HOSPITAL – KANSAS CITY**, 10550 Quivira Road, Zip 66215; tel. 913/541–5886 **A**1 9 10 **F**2 21 27 28 37 38 64 94 110 **P**8 **S** Select Medical Corporation, Mechanicsburg, PA Primary Contact: Aundria Watkins, Administrator Web address: www.selectmedicalcorp.com	33	80	34	263	28	0	0	12268	4463	85
□ **SPECIALTY HOSPITAL OF MID-AMERICA**, 6509 West 103rd Street, Zip 66212–1728; tel. 913/649–3701 **A**1 9 10 **F**21 36 37 44 **S** Integrated Health Services, Sparks Glencoe, MD Primary Contact: Jerry Lindenbaum, Administrator Web address: www.thicare.com/SpecHospOfMidAmerica/	33	90	37	300	22	0	0	4650	3517	111
PAOLA—Miami County										
□ **MIAMI COUNTY MEDICAL CENTER**, 2100 Baptiste Drive, Zip 66071–0365, Mailing Address: P.O. Box 365, Zip 66071–0365; tel. 913/294–2327 **A**1 9 10 **F**2 9 12 22 28 33 37 48 50 52 53 58 60 61 62 63 66 69 70 75 81 82 84 88 94 95 108 110 **P**8 Primary Contact: Gerald Wiesner, Administrator Web address: www.ohsi.com	23	10	20	996	9	29449	0	—	—	137
PARSONS—Labette County										
★ **LABETTE COUNTY MEDICAL CENTER**, 1902 South U.S. Highway 59, Zip 67357–7404, Mailing Address: P.O. Box 956, Zip 67357–0956; tel. 620/421–4880 **A**9 10 19 20 **F**2 6 9 11 12 21 22 23 27 28 29 33 46 48 51 52 54 55 58 59 60 61 62 63 65 68 69 81 84 88 93 94 95 96 97 108 Primary Contact: William K. Mahoney, Chief Executive Officer COO: Derek Vance, Vice President Business Development and Operations CFO: Thomas Macaronas, Chief Financial Officer CHR: Christina Cartwright, Director Human Resources Web address: www.lcmc.com	13	10	70	2495	23	55311	238	36506	13394	395
PARSONS STATE HOSPITAL AND TRAINING CENTER, 2601 Gabriel Avenue, Zip 67357–0738, Mailing Address: P.O. Box 738, Zip 67357–0738; tel. 620/421–6550 **F**29 32 94 108 Primary Contact: Jerry Rea, Interim Superintendent Web address: www.pshtc.org	12	62	193	10	188	0	0	22068	13492	461
PHILLIPSBURG—Phillips County										
★ **PHILLIPS COUNTY HOSPITAL**, 1150 State Street, Zip 67661–1799, Mailing Address: P.O. Box 607, Zip 67661–0607; tel. 785/543–5226, (Total facility includes 33 beds in nursing home–type unit) **A**9 10 18 **F**1 2 9 11 12 22 23 27 32 33 52 53 61 63 66 69 81 92 94 97 108 110 **S** Great Plains Health Alliance, Inc., Phillipsburg, KS Primary Contact: Raymond Williams, III, Interim Chief Executive Officer Web address: www.phillipshospital.org	23	10	58	570	35	25390	2	8297	4150	127
PITTSBURG—Crawford County										
⊠ **MT. CARMEL REGIONAL MEDICAL CENTER**, 1102 East Centennial Drive, Zip 66762–6643; tel. 620/231–6100 **A**1 2 9 10 19 20 **F**2 9 11 12 15 17 22 23 26 27 28 29 33 37 38 40 41 45 46 48 51 52 54 55 58 59 60 61 62 63 64 68 69 71 75 77 79 81 82 84 85 86 87 88 92 93 94 95 96 106 108 109 110 **P**8 **S** Via Christi Health System, Wichita, KS Primary Contact: John Daniel Lingor, President and Chief Executive Officer CFO: Mel Goin, Chief Financial Officer CMO: Donald Holsinger, M.D., Chief Medical Officer CIO: Drew Talbott, Director Information Systems CHR: Connie McCune, Vice President Human Resources Web address: www.mtcarmel.org	21	10	141	5207	73	87039	386	62234	29365	624
PLAINVILLE—Rooks County										
★ **ROOKS COUNTY HEALTH CENTER**, 304 South Colorado Avenue, Zip 67663–0389; tel. 785/434–4553 **A**9 10 18 **F**2 9 33 45 46 48 63 69 81 85 91 97 108 Primary Contact: J. Ben Quinton, Administrator and Chief Executive Officer CFO: Julie Price, Chief Financial Officer Web address: www.rookscountyhealthcenter.com	16	10	19	448	5	5024	7	6577	2626	89
PRATT—Pratt County										
★ **PRATT REGIONAL MEDICAL CENTER**, 200 Commodore Street, Zip 67124–2903; tel. 620/672–7451, (Total facility includes 47 beds in nursing home–type unit) **A**9 10 20 **F**2 9 11 12 22 27 28 33 41 42 44 46 47 48 50 51 52 54 55 58 59 60 62 63 64 65 66 69 81 82 85 87 88 92 93 94 95 96 97 108 **P**6 Primary Contact: Susan M. Page, President and Chief Executive Officer CFO: Gordon Stofer, Vice President Fiscal Services CIO: Amy Cox, Director Health Information Services CHR: Ken Brown, Vice President Human Services Web address: www.prmc.org	23	10	85	1931	65	115623	215	29410	14891	318

KS

Hospital, Address, Telephone, Approval, Facility, and Physician Codes, Health Care System	Classi-fication Codes		Utilization Data					Expense (thousands) of dollars		
★ American Hospital Association (AHA) membership □ Joint Commission on Accreditation of Healthcare Organizations (JCAHO) accreditation ○ American Osteopathic Association (AOA) accreditation △ Commission on Accreditation of Rehabilitation Facilities (CARF) accreditation	Control	Service	Staffed Beds	Admissions	Census	Outpatient Visits	Births	Total	Payroll	Personnel

QUINTER—Gove County

GOVE COUNTY MEDICAL CENTER, 520 West Fifth Street, Zip 67752–0129, Mailing Address: P.O. Box 129, Zip 67752–0129; tel. 785/754–3341, (Total facility includes 55 beds in nursing home–type unit) **A**9 10 18 **F**9 11 23 27 33 45 46 51 63 69 81 92 94 97
Primary Contact: Paul Davis, Administrator

| 13 | 10 | 76 | 913 | 55 | 9640 | 58 | 8335 | 4020 | 151 |

RANSOM—Ness County

★ **GRISELL MEMORIAL HOSPITAL DISTRICT ONE**, 210 South Vermont Avenue, Zip 67572; tel. 785/731–2231, (Total facility includes 34 beds in nursing home–type unit) **A**9 10 18 **F**2 33 44 54 64 69 70 92 97 **P**6 **S** Great Plains Health Alliance, Inc., Phillipsburg, KS
Primary Contact: Kristine Ochs, R.N., Administrator
CMO: Allen McLain, M.D., Chief of Staff
Web address: www.gpha.com

| 16 | 10 | 46 | 83 | 31 | 9664 | 0 | 3520 | 1893 | 73 |

RUSSELL—Russell County

★ **RUSSELL REGIONAL HOSPITAL**, 200 South Main Street, Zip 67665–2997; tel. 785/483–3131, (Total facility includes 23 beds in nursing home–type unit) **A**9 10 18 20 **F**2 6 9 11 12 21 22 24 26 27 28 30 33 38 39 44 46 47 48 52 53 54 60 63 65 66 69 73 81 84 85 88 92 94 97 107 108 109 **P**4 5 6
Primary Contact: Roger Knak, R.N., Administrator and Chief Executive Officer
CFO: Duane Fields, Controller
CMO: Earl Merkel, M.D., Chief of Staff
CIO: Scott Glassman, Information Systems Director
CHR: Sharon Collins, Human Resources Director
Web address: www.russellhospital.org

| 23 | 10 | 58 | 596 | 27 | 16649 | 16 | 9998 | 5372 | 153 |

SABETHA—Nemaha County

★ **SABETHA COMMUNITY HOSPITAL**, 14th and Oregon Streets, Zip 66534–0229, Mailing Address: P.O. Box 229, Zip 66534–0229; tel. 785/284–2121 **A**9 10 18 **F**2 9 11 12 27 28 29 33 44 46 48 51 52 58 60 61 62 63 65 69 81 85 88 92 94 97 110 **P**6 **S** Great Plains Health Alliance, Inc., Phillipsburg, KS
Primary Contact: Rita K. Buurman, Chief Executive Officer
CFO: Lori Lackey, Chief Financial Officer
CIO: Sheli White, Director Health Information
Web address: www.sabethahospital.com

| 23 | 10 | 25 | 554 | 7 | 36589 | 42 | 7454 | 3339 | 82 |

SAINT FRANCIS—Cheyenne County

★ **CHEYENNE COUNTY HOSPITAL**, 210 West First Street, Zip 67756–0547, Mailing Address: P.O. Box 547, Zip 67756–0547; tel. 785/332–2104 **A**9 10 18 **F**2 9 11 23 27 28 33 46 48 61 63 64 69 70 81 92 97 **P**6 **S** Great Plains Health Alliance, Inc., Phillipsburg, KS
Primary Contact: Leslie Lacy, Administrator
CHR: Sandi Murray, Director Human Resources
Web address: www.cheyennecountyhospital.com

| 23 | 10 | 16 | 295 | 3 | 9193 | 0 | 4381 | 1960 | 66 |

SALINA—Saline County

★ ○ **SALINA REGIONAL HEALTH CENTER**, 400 South Santa Fe Avenue, Zip 67401–4198, Mailing Address: P.O. Box 5080, Zip 67401–5080; tel. 785/452–7000, (Includes SALINA REGIONAL HEALTH CENTER– PENN CAMPUS, 139 North Penn Street, Zip 67401; SALINA REGIONAL HEALTH CENTER–SANTA FE CAMPUS) **A**2 9 10 11 12 19 20 **F**2 9 11 12 14 15 17 19 21 22 23 26 27 28 29 32 33 35 36 37 38 39 40 41 45 46 47 48 50 51 52 53 54 55 56 57 58 59 61 62 63 64 65 66 68 69 71 72 73 74 75 76 77 78 79 80 81 82 84 85 86 87 88 93 94 95 96 106 108 109 110 **P**8
Primary Contact: Randy Peterson, President and Chief Executive Officer
COO: Morris H. Seligman, M.D., Senior Vice President and Chief Operating Officer and Chief Medical Officer
CFO: Stan Mitchell, Vice President Finance
CMO: Morris H. Seligman, M.D., Senior Vice President and Chief Operating Officer and Chief Medical Officer
CIO: Larry Barnes, Vice President Information Technology
CHR: David Moody, Vice President Human Resources
Web address: www.srhc.com

| 23 | 10 | 227 | 9248 | 106 | 155067 | 1126 | 99940 | 42663 | 991 |

SALINA SURGICAL HOSPITAL, 401 South Sante Fe, Zip 67401–2697; tel. 785/827–0610 **A**9 10 **F**21 22 27 52 57 63 64 88
Primary Contact: Jim Sergeant, Administrator

| 32 | 13 | 8 | 522 | 3 | 7479 | 0 | 9615 | 2917 | 69 |

SATANTA—Haskell County

★ **SATANTA DISTRICT HOSPITAL**, 401 South Cheyenne Street, Zip 67870–0159, Mailing Address: P.O. Box 159, Zip 67870–0159; tel. 620/649–2761, (Total facility includes 44 beds in nursing home–type unit) **A**9 10 18 **F**2 9 27 33 37 52 53 58 63 66 69 77 81 88 92 94 97 **P**4 **S** Great Plains Health Alliance, Inc., Phillipsburg, KS
Primary Contact: Curt Colson, Administrator
CFO: Carlene Linnebur, Chief Financial Officer
CMO: Juvenal Jabel, M.D., Chief Medical Officer
CHR: Tammy Oxford, Manager Human Resources
Web address: www.satanta.org

| 16 | 10 | 57 | 192 | 42 | 15690 | 0 | 8211 | 3481 | 115 |

SCOTT CITY—Scott County

★ **SCOTT COUNTY HOSPITAL**, 310 East Third Street, Zip 67871–1203; tel. 620/872–5811 **A**9 10 18 20 **F**6 9 11 12 21 22 23 26 29 33 39 46 48 51 52 53 54 57 58 59 61 62 63 64 69 81 88 92 94 96 97 **P**6
Primary Contact: Greg Unruh, Chief Executive Officer
CFO: Alan W. Streeter, Chief Financial Officer
Web address: www.phn.org

| 23 | 10 | 25 | 781 | 9 | 30705 | 60 | 7893 | 4479 | 138 |

KS

Many Facility Codes have changed. Please refer to the AHA Guide Code Chart. © 2005 AHA Guide

Hospital, Address, Telephone, Approval, Facility, and Physician Codes, Health Care System	Classification Codes		Utilization Data					Expense (thousands) of dollars		
★ American Hospital Association (AHA) membership □ Joint Commission on Accreditation of Healthcare Organizations (JCAHO) accreditation ○ American Osteopathic Association (AOA) accreditation △ Commission on Accreditation of Rehabilitation Facilities (CARF) accreditation	Control	Service	Staffed Beds	Admissions	Census	Outpatient Visits	Births	Total	Payroll	Personnel

SEDAN—Chautauqua County

SEDAN CITY HOSPITAL, 300 North Street, Zip 67361–0427, Mailing Address: P.O. Box C, Zip 67361–0427; tel. 620/725–3115 **A**9 10 18 **F**21 26 27 28 33 41 69 92 94 97
Primary Contact: Ron Dunkle, Administrator

| 14 | 10 | 40 | 233 | 3 | 6176 | 0 | 1244 | 1090 | 34 |

SENECA—Nemaha County

★ **NEMAHA VALLEY COMMUNITY HOSPITAL**, 1600 Community Drive, Zip 66538–9739; tel. 785/336–6181 **A**9 10 18 **F**9 10 11 12 23 27 28 33 38 44 46 48 51 52 58 59 60 62 63 64 69 81 84 85 88 93 94 96 97 **P**6
Primary Contact: Stan Regehr, Chief Executive Officer
CFO: Dorothea Mauck, Chief Financial Officer

| 23 | 10 | 30 | 455 | 5 | 16883 | 34 | 8090 | 3854 | 104 |

SHAWNEE MISSION—Johnson County

DOCTORS SPECIALTY HOSPITAL, 4901 College Boulevard, Zip 66211; tel. 913/529–1801 **A**10 **F**10 14 26 27 28 37 49 52 55 57 58 60 61 62 63 64 69 70 73 81 84 88 96 109 110 **P**8
Primary Contact: Douglas C. Palzer, Administrator
Web address: www.dshospital.net

| 32 | 10 | 10 | 459 | 3 | 4341 | 0 | 11433 | 2928 | 44 |

KANSAS CITY ORTHOPAEDIC INSTITUTE, 3651 College Boulevard, Zip 66211; tel. 913/319–7586 **A**10 **F**21 26 62 63 64 66 80 84
Primary Contact: Paul Kernes, Administrator
Web address: www.kcoi.com

| 32 | 13 | 9 | 455 | 4 | 3511 | 0 | — | — | 73 |

⊠ **MID–AMERICA REHABILITATION HOSPITAL**, 5701 West 110th Street, Zip 66211–2503; tel. 913/491–2400 **A**1 10 **F**21 26 27 28 42 45 46 48 52 61 65 66 68 69 73 88 94 95 96 110 **S** HEALTHSOUTH Corporation, Birmingham, AL
Primary Contact: Kristen De Hart, Administrator
COO: Stephanie Dutton, Chief Operating Officer
CFO: Richard Lane, Chief Financial Officer
Web address: www.selectmedicalcorp.com

| 33 | 46 | 80 | 1279 | 52 | 31856 | 0 | 14384 | 7108 | 205 |

⊠ **SHAWNEE MISSION MEDICAL CENTER**, 9100 West 74th Street, Zip 66204–4004, Mailing Address: Box 2923, Zip 66201–1323; tel. 913/676–2000 **A**1 2 5 9 10 **F**2 3 4 10 11 12 15 17 19 21 22 23 24 26 27 28 29 30 33 37 38 41 42 44 46 47 48 49 50 51 52 55 56 57 58 59 60 61 62 63 64 65 66 69 71 73 74 75 77 78 81 82 84 85 88 89 90 93 94 95 96 106 107 108 109 **P**6 **S** Adventist Health System Sunbelt Health Care Corporation, Winter Park, FL
Primary Contact: Samuel H. Turner, Sr, Chief Executive Officer
COO: Robin Harrold, Senior Vice President and Chief Operating Officer
CFO: James Hinrichs, Vice President and Chief Financial Officer
CMO: Andrew Schwartz, Medical Staff President
CIO: Dan McMillen, Director
CHR: Brad Hoffman, Administrative Director
Web address: www.shawneemission.org

| 21 | 10 | 304 | 19196 | 201 | 376229 | 3608 | 233740 | 89492 | 1976 |

SMITH CENTER—Smith County

★ **SMITH COUNTY MEMORIAL HOSPITAL**, 614 South Main Street, Zip 66967–0349, Mailing Address: P.O. Box 349, Zip 66967–0349; tel. 785/282–6845, (Total facility includes 28 beds in nursing home–type unit) **A**9 10 20 **F**1 11 12 27 33 52 53 54 63 69 81 88 92 97 **P**6 **S** Great Plains Health Alliance, Inc., Phillipsburg, KS
Primary Contact: Carolyn K. Hess, R.N., Administrator
CFO: James Wahlmeier, Chief Financial Officer
CHR: Jody Maxwell, Business Office Manager
Web address: www.gpha.com

| 23 | 10 | 54 | 558 | 33 | 28412 | 33 | 6074 | 3202 | 113 |

STAFFORD—Stafford County

★ **STAFFORD DISTRICT HOSPITAL**, 502 South Buckeye Street, Zip 67578–2035, Mailing Address: P.O. Box 190, Zip 67578–0190; tel. 620/234–5221 **A**9 10 18 **F**9 21 29 33 46 48 51 52 63 66 92 94 97 108 **P**5
Primary Contact: Vernon Minnis, Administrator and Chief Executive Officer
CFO: Janell Goodno, Chief Financial Officer

| 16 | 10 | 25 | 123 | 1 | 24662 | 0 | 2386 | 1198 | 39 |

SYRACUSE—Hamilton County

HAMILTON COUNTY HOSPITAL, East Avenue G and Huser Street, Zip 67878–0948, Mailing Address: P.O. Box 948, Zip 67878–0948; tel. 620/384–7461, (Total facility includes 48 beds in nursing home–type unit) **A**9 10 18 **F**8 26 27 33 44 46 63 69 70 91 92 94 96 97 108
Primary Contact: Edwin E. Hurysz, Administrator
Web address: www.phn.org

| 13 | 10 | 73 | 128 | 48 | 3816 | 0 | 4418 | 2238 | 90 |

TOPEKA—Shawnee County

COLMERY–O'NEIL VETERANS AFFAIRS MEDICAL CENTER See Veterans Affairs Eastern Kansas Health Care System

KANSAS NEUROLOGICAL INSTITUTE, 3107 West 21st Street, Zip 66604–3298; tel. 785/296–5301 **F**32 92 **P**6
Primary Contact: Ray Dalton, Superintendent
Web address: www.srskansas.org/kni/

| 12 | 62 | 173 | 1 | 172 | 0 | 0 | 24666 | 15838 | 546 |

⊠ **KANSAS REHABILITATION HOSPITAL**, 1504 S.W. Eighth Avenue, Zip 66606–1632; tel. 785/235–6600 **A**1 9 10 **F**2 21 26 41 42 45 52 62 66 68 69 94 95 96 108 **S** HEALTHSOUTH Corporation, Birmingham, AL
Primary Contact: Paul Livingston, Administrator
CFO: Linda Sherman, Chief Financial Officer
CMO: Ariel Tan, M.D., Chief of Medical Staff
CHR: Stephanie Burdett, Coordinator Human Resources
Web address: www.kansasrehab.com

| 33 | 46 | 69 | 941 | 38 | 15528 | 0 | 9934 | 5501 | 151 |

KS

Hospital, Address, Telephone, Approval, Facility, and Physician Codes, Health Care System	Classi-fication Codes		Utilization Data					Expense (thousands) of dollars		
★ American Hospital Association (AHA) membership □ Joint Commission on Accreditation of Healthcare Organizations (JCAHO) accreditation ○ American Osteopathic Association (AOA) accreditation △ Commission on Accreditation of Rehabilitation Facilities (CARF) accreditation	Control	Service	Staffed Beds	Admissions	Census	Outpatient Visits	Births	Total	Payroll	Personnel

□ **SELECT SPECIALTY HOSPITAL – TOPEKA**, 1700 S.W. Seventh Street, Suite 840, Zip 66606–1660; tel. 785/295–5551 **A**1 10 **F**2 21 27 28 64 66 94 110 **P**8 **S** Select Medical Corporation, Mechanicsburg, PA Primary Contact: Mark Davis, Chief Executive Officer Web address: www.selectmedicalcorp.com	33	80	34	249	19	0	0	7844	3090	69
★ △ **ST. FRANCIS HEALTH CENTER**, 1700 West Seventh Street, Zip 66606–1690; tel. 785/295–8000 **A**1 2 3 5 7 9 10 **F**2 4 9 11 12 15 17 19 21 22 23 27 28 29 32 33 37 38 39 40 41 46 48 50 51 52 53 55 57 58 59 60 61 62 63 64 65 66 68 69 70 75 79 80 81 82 84 85 86 87 88 93 94 96 98 106 108 110 **P**8 **S** Sisters of Charity of Leavenworth Health System, Lenexa, KS Primary Contact: Sister Loretto Marie Colwell, President and Chief Executive Officer COO: Michael A. Dorsey, Chief Operating Officer CFO: Mike Kongs, Vice President Finance and Information Services CMO: Emil Kleinholz, Jr, M.D., Vice President Medical Management CIO: Jeff Hall, Director Information Services CHR: Jeanne Hippe, Director Web address: www.stfrancistopeka.org	21	10	274	10462	140	316141	930	152831	67227	1440
★ **STORMONT–VAIL HEALTHCARE**, 1500 S.W. Tenth Avenue, Zip 66604–1301; tel. 785/354–6000 **A**1 3 5 9 10 **F**2 9 10 11 12 14 15 16 17 19 21 22 23 26 27 28 29 33 40 41 44 45 46 47 48 49 50 52 53 54 55 56 57 58 59 61 62 63 64 65 66 69 70 71 72 74 75 76 77 78 80 81 82 84 85 88 93 94 95 96 106 108 109 110 **P**6 Primary Contact: Maynard F. Oliverius, President and Chief Executive Officer COO: David L. Knocke, CHE, Senior Vice President and Chief Operating Officer CFO: Vernon Long, Vice President and Chief Financial Officer CMO: Kent Palmberg, M.D., Senior Vice President and Chief Medical Officer CIO: Janet Stanek, Chief Information Officer CHR: Bernard Becker, Vice President and Chief Human Resources Officer Web address: www.stormontvail.org	23	10	318	14549	168	91022	2107	251284	124432	2585
★ **VETERANS AFFAIRS EASTERN KANSAS HEALTH CARE SYSTEM**, 2200 Gage Boulevard, Zip 66622–0002; tel. 785/350–3111, (Includes COLMERY–O'NEIL VETERANS AFFAIRS MEDICAL CENTER; DWIGHT D. EISENHOWER VETERANS AFFAIRS MEDICAL CENTER, 4101 South Fourth Street Trafficway, Leavenworth, Zip 66048–5055; tel. 913/682–2000), (Total facility includes 174 beds in nursing home–type unit) **A**1 3 **F**2 4 7 9 21 22 23 26 28 29 30 31 32 33 34 35 37 38 39 41 42 44 45 46 47 48 50 52 55 57 58 60 61 62 63 64 65 66 68 69 70 71 73 74 75 76 77 78 81 82 83 85 87 88 93 94 96 97 106 107 108 109 110 **S** Department of Veterans Affairs, Washington, DC Primary Contact: Robert M. Malone, Jr, Director COO: Craig Howard, Chief Operating Officer CMO: Donald L. Courtney, M.D., Acting Chief of Staff CIO: Joni Davin, Director Information–Business Management Service Line Web address: www.va.gov/sta/guide/home.asp	45	10	597	5200	155	325168	0	142382	103577	1589
TRIBUNE—Greeley County										
★ **GREELEY COUNTY HEALTH SERVICES**, 506 Third Street, Zip 67879–0338, Mailing Address: P.O. Box 338, Zip 67879–0338; tel. 620/376–4221, (Total facility includes 32 beds in nursing home–type unit) **A**9 10 18 20 **F**1 2 8 11 27 28 33 51 54 58 63 64 66 69 81 92 94 95 96 97 **P**6 **S** Great Plains Health Alliance, Inc., Phillipsburg, KS Primary Contact: Todd Burch, Administrator and Chief Executive Officer CFO: Jeremy Clingenpeel, Business Office Manager CMO: Robert Moser, M.D., Chief Medical Staff Web address: www.phn.org	23	10	50	539	29	18770	46	6898	3459	101
ULYSSES—Grant County										
★ **BOB WILSON MEMORIAL GRANT COUNTY HOSPITAL**, 415 North Main Street, Zip 67880–2133; tel. 620/356–1266 **A**9 10 **F**9 11 12 21 22 27 29 31 33 46 51 52 55 58 63 65 69 81 84 88 94 95 97 98 108 109 **P**6 Primary Contact: Robert B. Ohlen, Chief Executive Officer CFO: Jackie Day, Chief Financial Officer CIO: Jackie Day, Chief Financial Officer CHR: Mari Honstead, Human Resources Manager Web address: www.bobwilsonmemorial.org	13	10	44	1015	9	10896	132	9833	4843	96
WAKEENEY—Trego County										
★ **TREGO COUNTY–LEMKE MEMORIAL HOSPITAL**, 320 North 13th Street, Zip 67672–2099; tel. 785/743–2182, (Total facility includes 37 beds in nursing home–type unit) **A**9 10 18 **F**9 12 27 28 33 45 46 51 63 65 69 81 88 92 94 97 110 **S** Great Plains Health Alliance, Inc., Phillipsburg, KS Primary Contact: Daniel R. Bartz, Administrator CFO: Stacey Malsam, Chief Financial Officer CIO: Jolene Schuster, Director Information Technology Web address: www.gpha.com	13	10	62	1014	48	9544	0	7285	3244	112
WAMEGO—Pottawatomie County										
★ **WAMEGO CITY HOSPITAL**, 711 Genn Drive, Zip 66547–1179; tel. 785/456–2295 **A**9 10 18 **F**2 6 9 12 21 24 27 28 33 45 48 52 58 60 63 69 76 81 84 88 94 96 97 109 Primary Contact: Mark Aldridge, Chief Executive Officer CFO: Pam Allen, Chief Financial Officer Web address: www.wamegocityhospital.com	23	10	18	425	3	19263	0	7149	3582	98

Many Facility Codes have changed. Please refer to the AHA Guide Code Chart.   © 2005 AHA Guide

Hospital, Address, Telephone, Approval, Facility, and Physician Codes, Health Care System	Classi-fication Codes		Utilization Data					Expense (thousands) of dollars		
★ American Hospital Association (AHA) membership □ Joint Commission on Accreditation of Healthcare Organizations (JCAHO) accreditation ○ American Osteopathic Association (AOA) accreditation △ Commission on Accreditation of Rehabilitation Facilities (CARF) accreditation	Control	Service	Staffed Beds	Admissions	Census	Outpatient Visits	Births	Total	Payroll	Personnel

WASHINGTON—Washington County

WASHINGTON COUNTY HOSPITAL, 304 East Third Street, Zip 66968–2033; tel. 785/325–2211 **A**9 10 18 **F**1 2 9 11 12 21 23 26 27 29 33 41 46 52 55 59 63 64 69 92 94 97 110 **P**5 Primary Contact: Everett Lutjemeier, Administrator Web address: www.washingtoncountyhospital.com	13	10	25	229	6	3917	10	2482	1105	36

WELLINGTON—Sumner County

★ **SUMNER REGIONAL MEDICAL CENTER**, 1323 North A Street, Zip 67152–4350; tel. 620/326–7451, (Total facility includes 13 beds in nursing home–type unit) **A**9 10 **F**9 11 12 22 23 26 33 34 46 48 52 54 59 60 61 62 63 69 71 76 81 84 88 92 93 108 **P**8 Primary Contact: Robert H. Bean, Ph.D., President and Chief Executive Officer CFO: Stephan Wilson, CPA, Chief Financial Officer CIO: Kathie Henton, Information Management Manager CHR: Allen Keller, Director Human Resources Web address: www.srmcks.org	14	10	61	1511	18	27549	129	10545	4279	128

WICHITA—Sedgwick County

GALICHIA HEART HOSPITAL, 2610 North Woodlawn, Zip 67220; tel. 316/858–2610 **A**10 **F**2 15 17 19 21 22 26 27 28 52 55 58 62 63 64 Primary Contact: Tom Nester, Chief Executive Officer Web address: www.ghhospital.com	32	42	72	3316	29	5445	0	—	—	197
KANSAS HEART HOSPITAL, 3601 North Webb Road, Zip 67226; tel. 316/630–5000 **A**10 **F**2 14 15 17 19 22 41 52 63 65 82 88 94 **P**7 Primary Contact: Thomas L. Ashcom, M.D., Ph.D., Chief Executive Officer Web address: www.kansasheart.com	33	42	54	2620	32	5588	0	—	—	183
KANSAS SPINE HOSPITAL, 3333 North Webb Road, Zip 67226; tel. 316/462–5338 **A**10 **F**2 21 26 28 60 63 64 81 84 85 Primary Contact: Eustaquio Abay, M.D., Chief Executive Officer	33	13	22	1212	9	3490	0	—	—	70
KANSAS SURGERY AND RECOVERY CENTER, (Surgery & Recovery), 2770 North Webb Road, Zip 67226–8112; tel. 316/634–0090 **A**9 10 **F**40 52 53 63 64 66 81 84 85 88 92 **S** Via Christi Health System, Wichita, KS Primary Contact: Ely Bartal, M.D., Administrator and Chief Executive Officer Web address: www.ksrc.org	32	49	24	1418	11	5020	0	18436	4478	106
⊠ **ROBERT J. DOLE VETERANS AFFAIRS MEDICAL CENTER**, (Formerly Robert J. Dole Veterans Affairs Medical and Regional Office), 5500 East Kellogg, Zip 67218; tel. 316/685–2221, (Total facility includes 40 beds in nursing home–type unit) **A**1 3 5 **F**2 3 4 15 21 22 23 28 29 31 32 33 36 37 38 39 42 44 45 47 48 49 50 52 53 57 58 60 61 62 63 64 66 69 70 71 73 74 75 76 77 79 80 81 82 83 87 88 92 93 94 96 106 107 108 109 110 **P**6 **S** Department of Veterans Affairs, Washington, DC Primary Contact: Thomas J. Sanders, CHE, Director CMO: Kent Murray, M.D., Chief of Staff Web address: www.va.gov/sta/guide/home.asp	45	10	71	2264	70	207758	0	82540	32655	667
□ **SELECT SPECIALTY HOSPITAL OF WICHITA**, 3243 East Murdock, Suite 103, Zip 67208; tel. 316/688–3900 **A**1 10 **F**2 10 21 28 37 38 39 44 50 57 58 61 62 64 65 66 94 110 Primary Contact: David Cross, Chief Executive Officer Web address: www.selectmedicalcorp.com	33	80	65	605	41	0	0	17222	6354	171
⊠ **VIA CHRISTI REGIONAL MEDICAL CENTER**, 929 North St. Francis Street, Zip 67214–3882; tel. 316/268–5000, (Includes ST. FRANCIS CAMPUS; ST. JOSEPH CAMPUS, 3600 East Harry Street, Zip 67218–3713; tel. 316/685–1111) **A**1 2 3 5 9 10 12 13 **F**2 4 9 10 11 12 13 14 15 16 17 19 21 22 23 24 26 27 28 29 31 33 34 35 36 37 38 39 40 42 44 46 47 48 49 50 51 52 53 55 56 57 58 59 60 61 62 63 64 65 66 67 69 70 71 72 73 74 75 76 77 78 79 80 81 82 84 85 86 87 88 94 95 96 98 99 100 101 105 106 107 108 109 110 **P**5 7 **S** Via Christi Health System, Wichita, KS Primary Contact: Larry P. Schumacher, R.N., President and Chief Executive Officer COO: Kenneth Tomlon, Chief Operating Officer CFO: Mike Wenger, Chief Financial Officer CMO: Brent Rody, M.D., Vice President Medical Affairs CIO: Diana Hilburn, Vice President Information Management Services CHR: Jill Beckman, Vice President Human Resources Web address: www.via-christi.org	21	10	811	40506	535	317818	3563	406718	168432	3704
△ **VIA CHRISTI REHABILITATION CENTER**, 1151 North Rock Road, Zip 67206–1262; tel. 316/634–3400 **A**7 9 10 **F**21 22 26 27 28 29 39 44 45 46 48 52 53 57 58 59 60 62 65 68 69 73 92 93 94 95 96 108 110 **S** Via Christi Health System, Wichita, KS Primary Contact: Laurie Labarca, Chief Operating Officer Web address: www.via-christi.org	21	46	60	937	33	62316	0	21074	9843	262
○ **VIA CHRISTI RIVERSIDE MEDICAL CENTER**, 2622 West Central Avenue, Zip 67203–4902; tel. 316/946–5000 **A**9 10 11 12 13 **F**2 9 12 21 22 23 26 27 28 33 34 39 51 52 53 55 60 61 62 63 69 81 82 84 88 92 93 108 110 **P**6 **S** Via Christi Health System, Wichita, KS Primary Contact: John Coslett, Administrator Web address: www.via-christiriverside.org	21	10	88	1889	21	27017	0	37947	15452	129

KS

Hospital, Address, Telephone, Approval, Facility, and Physician Codes, Health Care System	Classification Codes		Utilization Data					Expense (thousands) of dollars		
★ American Hospital Association (AHA) membership □ Joint Commission on Accreditation of Healthcare Organizations (JCAHO) accreditation ○ American Osteopathic Association (AOA) accreditation △ Commission on Accreditation of Rehabilitation Facilities (CARF) accreditation	Control	Service	Staffed Beds	Admissions	Census	Outpatient Visits	Births	Total	Payroll	Personnel

	Control	Service	Staffed Beds	Admissions	Census	Outpatient Visits	Births	Total	Payroll	Personnel
⊠ **WESLEY MEDICAL CENTER**, 550 North Hillside, Zip 67214–4976; tel. 316/962–2000 **A**1 3 5 9 10 **F**2 6 9 11 12 14 15 17 19 21 22 23 27 28 29 32 33 34 35 37 39 40 43 44 45 46 47 48 49 52 53 55 56 57 59 60 61 62 63 65 66 67 69 70 71 75 76 79 81 82 84 87 88 93 94 95 96 106 108 109 110 **S** HCA, Nashville, TN Primary Contact: David S. Nevill, President and Chief Executive Officer COO: G B. Serrill, Chief Operating Officer CFO: David Busatti, Chief Financial Officer CMO: Francie H. Ekengren, M.D., Chief Medical Officer CIO: Joyce McBride, Director Information System CHR: Don Morris, Vice President Human Resources Web address: www.wesleymc.com	33	10	503	26489	338	243302	5478	303835	97599	2160
⊠ **WESLEY REHABILITATION HOSPITAL**, 8338 West 13th Street North, Zip 67212–2984; tel. 316/729–9999 **A**1 9 10 **F**2 21 28 29 30 45 48 52 68 69 93 96 109 110 **S** HEALTHSOUTH Corporation, Birmingham, AL Primary Contact: Pamela Stanberry, Administrator CFO: Bob Peck, Accounting Supervisor CMO: Pastor Causin, M.D., Medical Director CIO: Debbie Patterson, Director Health Information Management CHR: Jackie Stanton, Coordinator Human Resources Web address: www.healthsouth.com	33	46	65	982	39	14077	0	12433	5178	110
□ **WICHITA SPECIALTY HOSPITAL**, 8080 East Pawnee Street, Zip 67207–5475; tel. 316/682–0004 **A**1 10 **F**21 45 49 58 60 68 **S** Integrated Health Services, Sparks Glencoe, MD Primary Contact: James D. Pethis, Chief Executive Officer Web address: www.thicare.com/WichitaSpecialty/default.aspx	33	80	26	245	20	1	0	555	—	75
WINCHESTER—Jefferson County **JEFFERSON COUNTY MEMORIAL HOSPITAL**, 408 Delaware Street, Zip 66097–4003, Mailing Address: Rural Route 1, Box 1, Zip 66097–0001; tel. 913/774–4340, (Total facility includes 50 beds in nursing home–type unit) **A**9 10 18 **F**8 27 28 33 36 44 54 58 92 97 **P**1 Primary Contact: Joye H. Huston, Chief Executive Officer Web address: www.jcmhospital.org	23	10	75	59	46	2781	0	3362	2001	73
WINFIELD—Cowley County ★ **WILLIAM NEWTON HOSPITAL**, 1300 East Fifth Street, Zip 67156–2407; tel. 620/221–2300, (Total facility includes 14 beds in nursing home–type unit) **A**9 10 **F**2 9 11 12 24 27 28 29 31 32 33 35 37 40 46 48 51 52 53 55 57 58 59 60 61 62 63 64 65 66 75 79 80 81 82 84 85 88 92 93 94 95 96 106 108 Primary Contact: Richard H. Vaught, Administrator CMO: Bruce Wells, M.D., Chief of Staff CIO: Randy Mayo, Director Information Technology CHR: Cathy McClurg, Director Human Resources Web address: www.wnmh.org	14	10	39	1467	15	52556	203	11764	9142	239

KS

KENTUCKY

Hospital, Address, Telephone, Approval, Facility, and Physician Codes, Health Care System	Classi- fication Codes		Utilization Data					Expense (thousands) of dollars		
	Control	Service	Staffed Beds	Admissions	Census	Outpatient Visits	Births	Total	Payroll	Personnel

★   American Hospital Association (AHA) membership
□   Joint Commission on Accreditation of Healthcare Organizations (JCAHO) accreditation
○   American Osteopathic Association (AOA) accreditation
△   Commission on Accreditation of Rehabilitation Facilities (CARF) accreditation

ALBANY—Clinton County

CLINTON COUNTY HOSPITAL, 723 Burkesville Road, Zip 42602–1654; tel. 606/387–6421, (Nonreporting) **A**9 10
Primary Contact: Randel Flowers, Ph.D., Administrator
Web address: www.clintoncountyhospital.com

| | 23 | 10 | 42 | — | — | — | — | — | — | — |

ASHLAND—Boyd County

⊠ △ **KING'S DAUGHTERS MEDICAL CENTER**, 2201 Lexington Avenue, Zip 41101–2874, Mailing Address: P.O. Box 151, Zip 41105–0151; tel. 606/327–4000, (Total facility includes 168 beds in nursing home–type unit) **A**1 2 7 9 10 **F**2 4 9 10 11 12 14 15 17 19 21 22 23 26 27 28 29 31 33 34 37 40 42 46 47 48 49 50 51 52 53 55 56 57 58 59 60 61 62 63 64 65 66 68 69 70 71 73 74 75 76 81 82 84 85 86 87 88 89 92 93 94 95 96 98 106 107 108 109 110 **P**8
Primary Contact: Fred L. Jackson, Chief Executive Officer
COO: Bob Lucas, Vice President Operations
CFO: Paul L. McDowell, Vice President Finance and Chief Financial Officer
CMO: Phil Fioret, M.D., Vice President Medical Affairs
CIO: David Oliver, Director Information Systems
CHR: Larry Higgins, Vice President of Human Resources
Web address: www.kdmc.com

| | 23 | 10 | 547 | 23096 | 425 | 322818 | 1465 | 269730 | 97538 | 2128 |

⊠ **OUR LADY OF BELLEFONTE HOSPITAL**, St. Christopher Drive, Zip 41101–7071, Mailing Address: P.O. Box 789, Zip 41105–0789; tel. 606/833–3333, (Nonreporting) **A**1 2 9 10 12 13 **S** Bon Secours Health System, Inc., Marriottsville, MD
Primary Contact: Mark M. Gordon, Chief Executive Officer
CFO: Walter J. Yokobosky, Jr, Chief Financial Officer
CMO: David Bush, M.D., Vice Presisdent Medical Affairs
CIO: James Meister, Director of Information Systems
CHR: Timothy Holbrook, Vice President Human Resources
Web address: www.olbh.com

| | 21 | 10 | 214 | — | — | — | — | — | — | — |

BARBOURVILLE—Knox County

□ **KNOX COUNTY HOSPITAL**, One Hospital Drive, Zip 40906–1317, Mailing Address: P.O. Box 160, Zip 40906–0160; tel. 606/546–4175, (Total facility includes 16 beds in nursing home–type unit) (Nonreporting) **A**1 9 10
Primary Contact: Connie Hensley, Acting Chief Operating Officer
Web address: www.barbourville.com

| | 13 | 10 | 58 | — | — | — | — | — | — | — |

BARDSTOWN—Nelson County

⊠ **FLAGET MEMORIAL HOSPITAL**, 4305 New Shepherdsville Road, Zip 40004; tel. 502/350–5000, (Total facility includes 12 beds in nursing home–type unit) **A**1 9 10 **F**2 11 21 22 23 27 29 33 36 37 46 47 48 53 55 58 59 60 61 63 66 69 73 81 84 88 92 93 94 96 106 107 108 109 **S** Catholic Health Initiatives, Denver, CO
Primary Contact: Bruce A. Klockars, President and Chief Executive Officer
CFO: John Bradford, Chief Financial Officer
CHR: Deborah Cowles, Vice President Human Resources
Web address: www.flaget.com

| | 23 | 10 | 52 | 2745 | 29 | 76246 | 168 | 29918 | 12733 | 289 |

BENTON—Marshall County

⊠ **MARSHALL COUNTY HOSPITAL**, 503 George McClain Drive, Zip 42025–1399, Mailing Address: P.O. Box 630, Zip 42025–0630; tel. 270/527–4800, (Total facility includes 34 beds in nursing home–type unit) **A**1 9 10 **F**6 9 12 27 28 33 40 46 48 51 55 60 61 63 68 69 81 82 88 92 96 97 **P**6 **S** Quorum Health Resources, Plano, TX
Primary Contact: Kathy Long, Chief Executive Officer
CFO: Janice Kelley, Chief Financial Officer
CMO: Robert Beale, Chief of Staff
CHR: Dana Harvey, Director Human Resources and Public Relations
Web address: www.marshallcountyhospital.org

| | 13 | 10 | 80 | 1050 | 48 | 22203 | 0 | 11207 | 5734 | 214 |

BEREA—Madison County

⊠ **BEREA HOSPITAL**, 305 Estill Street, Zip 40403–1909; tel. 859/986–3151, (Total facility includes 102 beds in nursing home–type unit) (Nonreporting) **A**1 5 9 10 **S** Catholic Health Initiatives, Denver, CO
Primary Contact: Angela Carman, President and Chief Executive Officer
CFO: Della Deerfield, Vice President Finance
CMO: Clifford Kerby, M.D., Chief of Medical Staff
CIO: Katie Heckman, Community Relations Director
CHR: Renee Bullock, Vice President for Human Resources
Web address: www.bereahospital.com

| | 23 | 10 | 150 | — | — | — | — | — | — | — |

BOWLING GREEN—Warren County

COMMONWEALTH REGIONAL SPECIALTY HOSPITAL, 250 Park Drive, 5th Floor, Zip 42101, Mailing Address: P.O. Box 90010, Zip 42101; tel. 270/796–6200, (Nonreporting) **A**10
Primary Contact: Carrel Sumner, Chief Executive Officer

| | 33 | 49 | 28 | — | — | — | — | — | — | — |

KY

	Classi-fication Codes		Utilization Data						Expense (thousands) of dollars		
Hospital, Address, Telephone, Approval, Facility, and Physician Codes, Health Care System	Control	Service	Staffed Beds	Admissions	Census	Outpatient Visits	Births		Total	Payroll	Personnel
★ American Hospital Association (AHA) membership □ Joint Commission on Accreditation of Healthcare Organizations (JCAHO) accreditation ○ American Osteopathic Association (AOA) accreditation △ Commission on Accreditation of Rehabilitation Facilities (CARF) accreditation											

⊠ **GREENVIEW REGIONAL HOSPITAL**, 1801 Ashley Circle, Zip 42104–3384, Mailing Address: P.O. Box 90024, Zip 42102–9024; tel. 270/793–1000 **A**1 9 10 19 **F**2 9 11 12 14 15 17 21 23 26 27 28 29 32 33 34 37 40 46 47 48 49 52 53 55 57 58 59 60 61 62 63 65 66 69 81 82 84 85 88 93 94 95 96 97 106 108 109 110 **S** HCA, Nashville, TN Primary Contact: Mark A. Marsh, Chief Executive Officer COO: Tom Ozburn, Chief Operating Officer CFO: Michael A. Mitchell, Chief Financial Officer CMO: Mark Jesson, M.D., Chief of Staff CHR: Judy Fulkerson, Director Human Resources Web address: www.greenviewhospital.com	33	10	211	5340	70	44107	530	—	—	480
□ **RIVENDELL BEHAVIORAL HEALTH**, 1035 Porter Pike, Zip 42103; tel. 270/843–1199, (Nonreporting) **A**1 10 **S** Universal Health Services, Inc., King of Prussia, PA Primary Contact: Janice Richardson, Chief Executive Officer Web address: www.rivendellbehavioral.com	33	49	72	—	—	—	—	—	—	—
□ △ **SOUTHERN KENTUCKY REHABILITATION HOSPITAL**, 1300 Campbell Lane, Zip 42104–4162; tel. 270/782–6900 **A**1 7 10 **F**21 26 27 58 62 68 94 96 **S** VIBRA Healthcare, Mechanicsburg, PA Primary Contact: Joanna Thomas, Chief Executive Officer Web address: www.mediplex-bowlinggreen.com	33	46	60	1337	53	0	0	17589	6339	207
⊠ **THE MEDICAL CENTER AT BOWLING GREEN**, 250 Park Street, Zip 42101–1795, Mailing Address: P.O. Box 90010, Zip 42102–9010; tel. 270/745–1000, (Includes MEDICAL CENTER AT SCOTTSVILLE, 456 Burnley Road, Scottsville, Zip 42164–6355; tel. 270/622–2800; Wade Stone, Vice President), (Total facility includes 110 beds in nursing home–type unit) **A**1 9 10 19 **F**2 11 12 14 15 17 19 21 22 23 24 26 27 28 29 32 33 38 39 40 44 46 47 48 49 51 52 53 55 57 58 59 61 62 63 64 65 66 71 73 76 77 78 81 82 84 85 86 88 92 93 94 96 106 108 109 110 Primary Contact: Connie Smith, Chief Executive Officer CFO: Ron Sowell, Executive Vice President CIO: Matt Ebaugh, Chief Information Officer Web address: www.themedicalcenter.org	23	10	487	15013	299	123097	1666	157116	55337	1690
BURKESVILLE—Cumberland County										
★ **CUMBERLAND COUNTY HOSPITAL**, Highway 90 West, Zip 42717–0280, Mailing Address: P.O. Box 280, Zip 42717–0280; tel. 270/864–2511 **A**9 10 18 **F**2 6 9 12 21 29 31 33 44 46 52 69 76 81 85 88 94 97 108 **P**6 **S** Quorum Health Resources, Plano, TX Primary Contact: Edward J. Sanford, Chief Executive Officer CFO: Ken Kimsal, Chief Financial Officer Web address: www.cchospital.org	23	10	25	1322	15	25093	0	7361	3315	111
CADIZ—Trigg County										
★ **TRIGG COUNTY HOSPITAL**, 254 Main Street, Zip 42211–9153, Mailing Address: P.O. Box 312, Zip 42211–0312; tel. 270/522–3215 **A**9 10 18 **F**2 6 9 12 27 28 33 39 45 48 51 58 60 63 66 69 70 81 88 92 94 97 Primary Contact: Lisa Powers, Chief Executive Officer CFO: Kim Huntsman, Accounting Manager CHR: Audra Hodges, Human Resources Coordinator Web address: www.trigghospital.org	13	10	25	524	14	26081	0	7047	2680	123
CAMPBELLSVILLE—Taylor County										
⊠ **TAYLOR REGIONAL HOSPITAL**, 1700 Old Lebanon Road, Zip 42718–9600; tel. 270/465–3561 **A**1 2 9 10 **F**2 9 10 11 12 14 15 21 22 23 26 27 29 30 32 33 34 36 38 39 40 45 46 47 48 49 51 52 53 54 55 58 59 60 61 62 63 64 65 66 68 69 73 81 82 83 85 87 88 94 96 106 108 109 110 **S** Jewish Hospital HealthCare Services, Louisville, KY Primary Contact: Jane Wheatley, Chief Executive Officer CFO: David Massengale, Chief Financial Officer CIO: Pam Williams, Director Information Management Systems CHR: Andrea Settle, Director Human Resources Web address: www.tchosp.org	16	10	90	3824	47	64183	272	37554	13288	441
CARLISLE—Nicholas County										
⊠ **NICHOLAS COUNTY HOSPITAL**, 2323 Concrete Road, Zip 40311–9721, Mailing Address: P.O. Box 232, Zip 40311–0232; tel. 859/289–7181, (Includes JOHNSON–MATHERS NURSING HOME), (Total facility includes 104 beds in nursing home–type unit) (Nonreporting) **A**1 9 10 18 Primary Contact: Doris Ecton, Administrator and Chief Executive Officer CFO: Trish Stone, Controller CMO: Stephen Besson, M.D., Chief of Medical Staff CHR: Wendy Price, Manager Human Resources Web address: www.johnsonmathers.org	23	10	122	—	—	—	—	—	—	—
CARROLLTON—Carroll County										
★ **CARROLL COUNTY HOSPITAL**, 309 11th Street, Zip 41008–1400; tel. 502/732–4321, (Nonreporting) **A**9 10 18 **S** Associated Healthcare Systems, Inc., Brentwood, TN Primary Contact: Kim Dees, Chief Executive Officer CFO: Joe McCullum, Financial Manager CIO: Marilynn Black, Chief Information Officer Web address: www.nortonhealthcare.com	13	10	25	—	—	—	—	—	—	—

Many Facility Codes have changed. Please refer to the AHA Guide Code Chart. © 2005 AHA Guide

Hospital, Address, Telephone, Approval, Facility, and Physician Codes, Health Care System	Classi-fication Codes		Utilization Data					Expense (thousands) of dollars		
★ American Hospital Association (AHA) membership □ Joint Commission on Accreditation of Healthcare Organizations (JCAHO) accreditation ○ American Osteopathic Association (AOA) accreditation △ Commission on Accreditation of Rehabilitation Facilities (CARF) accreditation	Control	Service	Staffed Beds	Admissions	Census	Outpatient Visits	Births	Total	Payroll	Personnel

COLUMBIA—Adair County

□ **WESTLAKE REGIONAL HOSPITAL**, 901 Westlake Drive, Zip 42728–1149,
Mailing Address: P.O. Box 1269, Zip 42728–1269; tel. 270/384–4753 **A**1 9 10
18 **F**12 27 28 33 44 60 63 66 69 77 81 88 94 97
Primary Contact: Rex A. Tungate, Administrator
Web address: www.westlake–healthcare.org
| 16 | 10 | 25 | 1621 | 20 | 21713 | 0 | 17491 | 8011 | 392 |

CORBIN—Whitley County

☒ **BAPTIST REGIONAL MEDICAL CENTER**, 1 Trillium Way, Zip 40701–8420;
tel. 606/528–1212 **A**1 9 10 **F**2 3 4 9 11 12 14 15 21 22 27 28 29 31 33 34
41 46 48 49 52 53 55 59 62 63 65 68 69 71 72 73 74 75 76 77 78 81 82
84 85 86 87 88 94 96 106 108 109 110 **S** Baptist Healthcare System,
Louisville, KY
Primary Contact: John S. Henson, President
CFO: John Burgett, Team Leader
CIO: Alan Chelf, Chief Information Officer
CHR: Tim Perry, Coordinator Human Resources
Web address: www.baptistregional.com
| 23 | 10 | 240 | 9649 | 139 | 85556 | 764 | 79716 | 32969 | 959 |

OAK TREE HOSPITAL, One Trillium Way, Lower Level, Zip 40701;
tel. 606/523–5150, (Nonreporting) **A**10
Primary Contact: Alan Coppock, Administrator
| 33 | 49 | 25 | — | — | — | — | — | — | — |

COVINGTON—Kenton County

HEALTHSOUTH NORTHERN KENTUCKY REHABILITATION HOSPITAL See
Edgewood

NORTHKEY COMMUNITY CARE, (Formerly Children's Psychiatric Hospital), 502
Farrell Drive, Zip 41011–3799, Mailing Address: P.O. Box 2680,
Zip 41012–2680; tel. 859/578–3200, (Nonreporting) **A**10
Primary Contact: Edward G. Muntel, Ph.D., President and Chief Executive Officer
Web address: www.northkey.org
| 23 | 52 | 24 | — | — | — | — | — | — | — |

☒ **ST. ELIZABETH MEDICAL CENTER–SOUTH**, 1 Medical Village Drive,
Zip 41017–3403; tel. 859/344–2000, (Includes ST. ELIZABETH MEDICAL
CENTER–NORTH, 401 East 20th Street, Zip 41014–1585; tel. 859/292–4000),
(Total facility includes 19 beds in nursing home–type unit) **A**1 2 3 5 9 10 **F**2 4 9
10 11 12 14 15 17 19 21 22 23 26 27 28 29 30 31 33 34 36 37 38 39 42
45 46 48 49 51 52 53 55 56 57 58 59 60 61 62 63 64 71 74 75 76 77 78
79 80 81 82 85 88 90 92 93 94 95 96 106 108 109 110 **P**6
Primary Contact: Joseph W. Gross, President and Chief Executive Officer
CFO: Garren Colvin, Senior Vice President and Chief Financial Officer
Web address: www.stelizabeth.com
| 21 | 10 | 456 | 25805 | 307 | 451122 | 3192 | 344286 | 152380 | 2873 |

CYNTHIANA—Harrison County

☒ **HARRISON MEMORIAL HOSPITAL**, 1210 KY Highway 36E, Zip 41031–7498;
tel. 859/234–2300 **A**1 9 10 **F**2 9 11 12 21 22 23 26 27 28 29 30 32 33 35
39 41 46 47 48 50 52 53 54 55 57 58 59 60 61 62 63 64 65 66 70 81 82
87 88 94 95 96 97 106 108 109 110 **P**8
Primary Contact: Darwin E. Root, Chief Executive Officer
COO: Sheila Currans, Chief Operating Officer
CFO: Charles Duffy, Chief Financial Officer
CIO: Martha Sullivan, Director Information Services
CHR: Janice Ogden, Director Human Resource Management
Web address: www.harrisonmemhosp.com
| 23 | 10 | 49 | 1894 | 20 | 47851 | 195 | 21027 | 8038 | 254 |

DANVILLE—Boyle County

☒ **EPHRAIM MCDOWELL REGIONAL MEDICAL CENTER**, 217 South Third Street,
Zip 40422–9983; tel. 859/239–1000, (Nonreporting) **A**1 5 9 10 19
Primary Contact: Barry Michael, President
CFO: John Ansorge, Chief Financial Officer
CIO: Allen Levi, Director Information Services
CHR: Carl Metz, Director Human Resources Office
Web address: www.emrmc.org
| 23 | 10 | 177 | — | — | — | — | — | — | — |

EDGEWOOD—Kenton County

☒ **HEALTHSOUTH NORTHERN KENTUCKY REHABILITATION HOSPITAL**, 201
Medical Village Drive, Zip 41017–3407; tel. 859/341–2044, (Nonreporting) **A**1
10 **S** HEALTHSOUTH Corporation, Birmingham, AL
Primary Contact: Brenda Gosney, Administrator
CFO: Lisa McGue, Accounting Manager
CMO: Neal Moser, M.D., Medical Director
CHR: Diane Goldschmidt, Manager Human Resources
Web address: www.healthsouth.com
| 33 | 46 | 40 | — | — | — | — | — | — | — |

ELIZABETHTOWN—Hardin County

☒ **HARDIN MEMORIAL HOSPITAL**, 913 North Dixie Avenue, Zip 42701;
tel. 270/737–1212, (Total facility includes 15 beds in nursing home–type unit) **A**1
2 9 10 19 20 **F**9 11 12 14 15 17 19 21 22 23 24 26 27 28 29 32 33 35 37
39 40 46 47 48 51 52 53 55 57 58 59 60 61 62 63 64 65 66 69 71 75 79
81 82 84 85 87 88 89 92 93 94 95 96 98 106 107 108 109 110 **S** Baptist
Healthcare System, Louisville, KY
Primary Contact: David L. Gray, President
CFO: Elmer Cummings, Vice President Financial Services
CIO: Mark Brookman, Director Information Systems
CHR: Tony Welch, Vice President Human Resources
Web address: www.hmh.net
| 13 | 10 | 268 | 12311 | 174 | 267039 | 1515 | 133161 | 56287 | 1299 |

	Classification Codes		Utilization Data					Expense (thousands) of dollars		
Hospital, Address, Telephone, Approval, Facility, and Physician Codes, Health Care System	Control	Service	Staffed Beds	Admissions	Census	Outpatient Visits	Births	Total	Payroll	Personnel

★ American Hospital Association (AHA) membership
□ Joint Commission on Accreditation of Healthcare Organizations (JCAHO) accreditation
○ American Osteopathic Association (AOA) accreditation
△ Commission on Accreditation of Rehabilitation Facilities (CARF) accreditation

Hospital	Control	Service	Staffed Beds	Admissions	Census	Outpatient Visits	Births	Total	Payroll	Personnel
⊠ **HEALTHSOUTH REHABILITATION HOSPITAL OF CENTRAL KENTUCKY**, (Formerly Lakeview Rehabilitation Hospital), 134 Heartland Drive, Zip 42701–2778; tel. 270/769–3100 **A**1 9 10 **F**2 21 27 28 44 46 47 48 52 58 60 62 68 69 94 95 96 108 110 **P**8 **S** HEALTHSOUTH Corporation, Birmingham, AL Primary Contact: Eileen Nelson, Administrator CFO: James Hutcherson, Accounting Supervisor CMO: Vickie Lowe, M.D., Medical Director CHR: Janet Morris, Coordinator Human Resources Web address: www.healthsouth.com	33	46	40	715	31	5739	0	7804	4163	121
FLEMINGSBURG—Fleming County										
⊠ **FLEMING COUNTY HOSPITAL**, 920 Elizaville Avenue, Zip 41041, Mailing Address: P.O. Box 388, Zip 41041–0388; tel. 606/849–5000, (Nonreporting) **A**1 9 10 **S** Quorum Health Resources, Plano, TX Primary Contact: Harrell L. Connelly, Interim Chief Executive Officer CFO: Ron Harrington, Chief Financial Officer CMO: Samuel Gehring, M.D., Chief of Staff CIO: Barbara Mercer, Information Systems Director CHR: Marsha Mitchell, Director Human Resources Web address: www.flemingcountyhospital.org	16	10	32	—	—	—	—	—	—	—
FLORENCE—Boone County										
□ **GATEWAY REHABILITATION HOSPITAL**, 5940 Merchant Street, Zip 41042; tel. 859/426–2400, (Nonreporting) **A**1 9 10 Primary Contact: Jim Burcham, Chief Executive Officer Web address: www.gatewaylouisville.com	33	46	40	—	—	—	—	—	—	—
★ **ST. LUKE HOSPITAL WEST**, 7380 Turfway Road, Zip 41042–1337; tel. 859/962–5200, (Total facility includes 16 beds in nursing home–type unit) **A**9 10 **F**2 4 9 10 11 12 14 15 21 22 23 24 26 27 28 29 30 32 33 35 37 39 41 44 46 47 48 49 50 52 53 55 57 58 59 60 61 62 63 64 65 66 69 70 71 73 74 76 77 78 81 82 85 86 87 88 89 92 93 94 95 96 106 107 108 109 110 **S** Health Alliance of Greater Cincinnati, Cincinnati, OH Primary Contact: Nancy Kremer, Senior Vice President COO: Nancy Kremer, Senior Vice President CFO: Jim Sommerkamp, Director Financial Services CMO: Gary Schmitt, M.D., Medical Staff President CIO: Alex Rodriguez, Vice President Information Systems Technology CHR: Jack Talbot, Director Human Resources Web address: www.health–alliance.com	23	10	177	8870	110	135005	956	74907	30196	635
FORT CAMPBELL—Christian County										
⊠ **COLONEL FLORENCE A. BLANCHFIELD ARMY COMMUNITY HOSPITAL**, 650 Joel Drive, Zip 42223–5349; tel. 270/798–8040, (Nonreporting) **A**1 2 5 9 **S** Department of the Army, Office of the Surgeon General, Falls Church, VA Primary Contact: Colonel Patricia A. H. Saulsbery, Commander Web address: www.198.250.216.210/	42	10	107	—	—	—	—	—	—	—
FORT KNOX—Hardin County										
⊠ **IRELAND ARMY COMMUNITY HOSPITAL**, 851 Ireland Avenue, Zip 40121–5520; tel. 502/624–0467, (Nonreporting) **A**1 9 **S** Department of the Army, Office of the Surgeon General, Falls Church, VA Primary Contact: Colonel Carol Pierce, Commander	42	10	76	—	—	—	—	—	—	—
FORT THOMAS—Campbell County										
□ **CARDINAL HILL SPECIALTY HOSPITAL**, 85 North Grand Avenue, Zip 41075; tel. 859/572–3880 **A**1 10 **F**2 21 22 26 27 28 32 37 38 39 50 57 58 61 62 64 65 66 73 94 110 **S** Cardinal Hill Healthcare System, Lexington, KY Primary Contact: Janice Bauer, Administrator Web address: www.cardinalhill.org/ltach.html	23	80	20	60	7	0	0	2509	1268	39
⊠ **ST. LUKE HOSPITAL EAST**, 85 North Grand Avenue, Zip 41075–1796; tel. 859/572–3100, (Total facility includes 26 beds in nursing home–type unit) **A**1 2 9 10 **F**2 3 4 9 10 11 12 14 15 21 22 23 24 26 27 28 29 30 32 33 35 37 39 41 44 46 47 48 49 50 52 53 55 57 58 59 60 61 62 63 64 65 66 69 70 73 81 82 85 86 87 88 92 93 94 95 96 106 107 108 109 110 **S** Health Alliance of Greater Cincinnati, Cincinnati, OH Primary Contact: Nancy Kremer, Senior Vice President COO: Nancy Kremer, Senior Vice President CFO: James Sommerkamp, Director Finance CMO: Nannette Bernales, M.D., Medical Staff President CIO: Alex Rodriguez, Vice President Information Systems Technology CHR: Jack Talbot, Director Human Resources Web address: www.health–alliance.com	23	10	222	8686	121	99374	830	75676	31188	723
FRANKFORT—Franklin County										
⊠ **FRANKFORT REGIONAL MEDICAL CENTER**, 299 King's Daughters Drive, Zip 40601–4186; tel. 502/875–5240 **A**1 9 10 19 **F**2 9 11 12 14 15 21 22 33 37 39 46 47 52 55 57 58 59 60 61 62 63 65 66 68 69 81 82 87 88 93 94 95 96 97 108 109 110 **S** HCA, Nashville, TN Primary Contact: Michael A. Mayo, FACHE, Chief Executive Officer CFO: Richard Patterson, Chief Financial Officer CIO: Bill Knapke, Director Information Technology and Systems CHR: Bev Young, Director Human Resources Web address: www.frankfortregional.com	33	10	146	4777	50	71131	833	48681	20230	504

Many Facility Codes have changed. Please refer to the AHA Guide Code Chart.   © 2005 AHA Guide

Hospital, Address, Telephone, Approval, Facility, and Physician Codes, Health Care System	Classi-fication Codes		Utilization Data						Expense (thousands) of dollars		
★ American Hospital Association (AHA) membership □ Joint Commission on Accreditation of Healthcare Organizations (JCAHO) accreditation ○ American Osteopathic Association (AOA) accreditation △ Commission on Accreditation of Rehabilitation Facilities (CARF) accreditation	Control	Service	Staffed Beds	Admissions	Census	Outpatient Visits	Births	Total	Payroll	Personnel

FRANKLIN—Simpson County

THE MEDICAL CENTER AT FRANKLIN, 1100 Brookhaven Road, Zip 42134–2746; tel. 270/598–4800 **A**9 10 18 **F**12 21 22 24 26 27 29 33 46 47 48 58 63 66 69 81 84 88 94 97 106 108 **P**8
Primary Contact: Clara M. Sumner, Chief Executive Officer
Web address: www.themedicalcenterfranklin.org

| | 23 | 10 | 25 | 1006 | 12 | 24473 | 0 | — | — | 77 |

FULTON—Fulton County

□ **PARKWAY REGIONAL HOSPITAL**, 2000 Holiday Lane, Zip 42041–8468; tel. 270/472–2522, (Nonreporting) **A**1 9 10 **S** Community Health Systems, Inc., Brentwood, TN
Primary Contact: Michael Patterson, Chief Executive Officer

| | 33 | 10 | 70 | — | — | — | — | — | — | — |

GEORGETOWN—Scott County

⊠ **GEORGETOWN COMMUNITY HOSPITAL**, 1140 Lexington Road, Zip 40324–9362; tel. 502/868–1100 **A**1 5 9 10 **F**2 10 11 12 21 22 27 28 29 33 34 39 40 46 48 53 54 55 58 59 60 62 63 69 81 84 94 95 96 97 108 109 **S** LifePoint Hospitals, Inc., Brentwood, TN
Primary Contact: Michael Clark, Chief Executive Officer
COO: Carrie H. Johnson, Chief Nursing Officer
CFO: George Wiley, Chief Financial Officer
CMO: Kelly Burgess, Medical Staff President
Web address: www.georgetowncommunityhospital.com

| | 33 | 10 | 60 | 2133 | 19 | 69873 | 494 | 23853 | 9694 | 220 |

GLASGOW—Barren County

⊠ **T. J. SAMSON COMMUNITY HOSPITAL**, 1301 North Race Street, Zip 42141–3483; tel. 270/651–4444, (Total facility includes 16 beds in nursing home–type unit) (Nonreporting) **A**1 3 5 9 10 19
Primary Contact: Dwayne Moss, Chief Executive Officer
COO: Larry Morgan, Controller
CFO: Roy Spencer, Chief Financial Officer
CMO: Jeff Wilson, Chief of Staff
CIO: Debbie Caudel, Director Information System
CHR: LaDonna Rogers, Director Human Resources
Web address: www.tjsamson.org

| | 23 | 10 | 196 | — | — | — | — | — | — | — |

GREENSBURG—Green County

★ **JANE TODD CRAWFORD HOSPITAL**, 202–206 Milby Street, Zip 42743–1100, Mailing Address: P.O. Box 220, Zip 42743–0220; tel. 270/932–4211, (Total facility includes 20 beds in nursing home–type unit) **A**9 10 **F**3 9 12 21 33 37 39 46 58 62 63 69 70 71 72 76 81 88 92 97 **P**6
Primary Contact: Jack Grimsley, Interim Chief Executive Officer
CMO: James G. Bland, M.D., Chief of Staff

| | 13 | 10 | 64 | 1402 | 35 | 23445 | 0 | 8356 | 5022 | 154 |

GREENVILLE—Muhlenberg County

⊠ **MUHLENBERG COMMUNITY HOSPITAL**, 440 Hopkinsville Street, Zip 42345–1172, Mailing Address: P.O. Box 387, Zip 42345–0387; tel. 270/338–8000, (Total facility includes 45 beds in nursing home–type unit) **A**1 9 10 **F**2 6 9 11 12 21 27 28 29 33 46 51 55 59 60 63 65 69 70 81 84 87 88 92 93 94 95 106 108 **S** Alliant Management Services, Louisville, KY
Primary Contact: Lloyd Ford, Chief Executive Officer
CMO: Kristy G. Wells, M.D., President Medical Staff
CIO: Christie Walker, Director Health Information Management
CHR: Lisa R. Hope, Director, Human Resources
Web address: www.mchky.org

| | 23 | 10 | 135 | 3467 | 69 | 56467 | 221 | 30862 | 13364 | 454 |

HARDINSBURG—Breckinridge County

⊠ **BRECKINRIDGE MEMORIAL HOSPITAL**, 1011 Old Highway 60, Zip 40143–2597; tel. 270/756–7000, (Total facility includes 18 beds in nursing home–type unit) **A**1 9 10 18 **F**2 9 12 21 22 27 28 29 33 36 37 41 44 46 47 48 51 52 53 58 60 62 63 66 69 73 81 88 92 94 96 97 98 106 108 **S** Alliant Management Services, Louisville, KY
Primary Contact: George Walz, CHE, President and Chief Executive Officer
CFO: David R. Hayes, Vice President and Chief Financial Officer
CIO: Virginia D. Vanderhoef, Chief Information Officer
CHR: Clara Cordelia Hall, Chief Human Resources Officer
Web address: www.breckhealth.org

| | 23 | 10 | 43 | 998 | 28 | 37830 | 0 | 10878 | 4397 | 158 |

HARLAN—Harlan County

⊠ **HARLAN ARH HOSPITAL**, 81 Ball Park Road, Zip 40831–1792; tel. 606/573–8201, (Total facility includes 20 beds in nursing home–type unit) **A**1 9 10 **F**2 9 11 12 21 22 26 27 28 29 33 37 39 42 46 47 48 51 52 55 58 59 60 63 64 65 66 68 69 70 71 75 81 82 85 87 88 92 93 94 96 108 109 **P**6 **S** Appalachian Regional Healthcare, Lexington, KY
Primary Contact: Michael G. Layfield, Community Chief Executive Officer
CFO: Pam Sutherland, Chief Financial Officer
CMO: Richard Stoltzfus, M.D., Chief of Staff
CHR: Sabra Howard, Manager Human Resources
Web address: www.arh.org

| | 23 | 10 | 150 | 5382 | 72 | 65484 | 225 | 45025 | 17425 | 519 |

HARRODSBURG—Mercer County

★ **THE JAMES B. HAGGIN MEMORIAL HOSPITAL**, 464 Linden Avenue, Zip 40330–1862; tel. 859/734–5441, (Total facility includes 34 beds in nursing home–type unit) **A**5 9 10 18 **F**9 12 14 24 26 27 28 29 33 46 47 48 51 52 55 58 63 81 88 92 94 96 97 98 108 **S** Alliant Management Services, Louisville, KY
Primary Contact: Earl James Motzer, Ph.D., FACHE, Chief Executive Officer
CFO: Tony Patterson, Chief Financial Officer

| | 23 | 10 | 59 | 847 | 38 | 36424 | 0 | 13301 | 5618 | 191 |

Hospital, Address, Telephone, Approval, Facility, and Physician Codes, Health Care System	Classi-fication Codes		Utilization Data					Expense (thousands) of dollars		
	Control	Service	Staffed Beds	Admissions	Census	Outpatient Visits	Births	Total	Payroll	Personnel

★ American Hospital Association (AHA) membership
□ Joint Commission on Accreditation of Healthcare Organizations (JCAHO) accreditation
○ American Osteopathic Association (AOA) accreditation
△ Commission on Accreditation of Rehabilitation Facilities (CARF) accreditation

HARTFORD—Ohio County

⊠ **OHIO COUNTY HOSPITAL**, 1211 Main Street, Zip 42347–1619; tel. 270/298–7411 **A**1 9 10 18 20 **F**2 9 12 14 21 22 23 26 27 28 29 30 31 32 33 34 36 37 38 41 42 46 47 48 52 55 57 58 60 61 62 63 65 69 70 81 84 88 94 95 96 97 106 108 **P**8 **S** Quorum Health Resources, Plano, TX
Primary Contact: Blaine Pieper, Chief Executive Officer
Web address: www.ohiocountyhospital.com

| | 23 | 10 | 25 | 1350 | 12 | 27645 | 0 | 15067 | 6207 | 190 |

HAZARD—Perry County

⊠ **HAZARD ARH REGIONAL MEDICAL CENTER**, 100 Medical Center Drive, Zip 41701–1000; tel. 606/439–6600 **A**1 2 3 5 9 10 19 **F**2 9 11 12 14 15 17 19 21 22 23 26 27 28 29 33 34 37 39 42 46 47 48 51 52 55 57 58 59 60 61 62 63 64 65 66 68 69 70 71 75 81 82 85 87 88 93 94 96 108 109 110 **P**6 **S** Appalachian Regional Healthcare, Lexington, KY
Primary Contact: Wayne B. Griffith, FACHE, Regional Chief Executive Officer
COO: Trena F. Hall, Community Chief Executive Officer
CFO: Hal Clark, Interim Chief Financial Officer
CMO: J D. Miller, M.D., Chief Medical Officer
CIO: Jeff Brady, Director Information Systems
CHR: Sonya Bergman, Chief Human Resources Officer
Web address: www.arh.org

| | 23 | 10 | 308 | 13823 | 203 | 107261 | 481 | 93249 | 31709 | 942 |

HENDERSON—Henderson County

□ △ **METHODIST HOSPITAL**, 1305 North Elm Street, Zip 42420–2775, Mailing Address: P.O. Box 48, Zip 42420–0048; tel. 270/827–7700 **A**1 7 9 10 12 13 **F**2 4 6 9 11 12 15 21 22 23 24 26 27 28 29 31 32 33 40 41 43 46 47 48 51 53 55 58 59 60 61 62 63 65 66 68 69 70 71 72 75 77 79 81 82 84 85 86 87 88 93 94 95 96 98 106 108 109 110 **P**8
Primary Contact: Bruce D. Begley, Executive Director
Web address: www.methodisthospital.net

| | 21 | 10 | 209 | 7786 | 91 | 197727 | 750 | 86098 | 38178 | 1121 |

HOPKINSVILLE—Christian County

□ **CUMBERLAND HALL HOSPITAL**, 210 West 17th Street, Zip 42240–1999; tel. 270/886–1919, (Total facility includes 16 beds in nursing home–type unit) **A**1 10 **F**3 4 27 28 71
Primary Contact: Alan G. Chapman, Chief Executive Officer
Web address: www.absfirst.com

| | 33 | 22 | 52 | 1164 | 46 | 325 | 0 | 6751 | 3229 | 138 |

⊠ **JENNIE STUART MEDICAL CENTER**, 320 West 18th Street, Zip 42241–2400, Mailing Address: P.O. Box 2400, Zip 42241–2400; tel. 270/887–0100 **A**1 2 9 10 **F**9 11 12 14 15 21 27 28 29 33 34 37 46 48 51 52 55 56 57 58 59 60 61 62 63 65 69 81 82 84 86 87 88 93 94 95 106 107 108 110 **S** Quorum Health Resources, Plano, TX
Primary Contact: Lewis T. Peeples, Chief Executive Officer
CFO: Samuel L. Brown, Vice President Financial Services
CIO: Ken Robertson, Director Information Systems
CHR: Austin Moss, Vice President Human Resources
Web address: www.jsmc.org

| | 23 | 10 | 139 | 6021 | 76 | 87243 | 728 | 69579 | 24613 | 633 |

□ **WESTERN STATE HOSPITAL**, Russellville Road, Zip 42240–3017, Mailing Address: P.O. Box 2200, Zip 42241–2200; tel. 270/889–6025, (Nonreporting) **A**1 10
Primary Contact: Stephen P. Wiggins, Director

| | 12 | 22 | 222 | — | — | — | — | — | — | — |

HORSE CAVE—Hart County

★ **CAVERNA MEMORIAL HOSPITAL**, 1501 South Dixie Street, Zip 42749–1477; tel. 270/786–2191 **A**9 10 18 **F**2 12 27 28 33 46 48 52 55 63 81 84 88 92 97 **S** Alliant Management Services, Louisville, KY
Primary Contact: Alan B. Alexander, Chief Executive Officer
CFO: Debra Riggs, Chief Financial Officer

| | 23 | 10 | 25 | 644 | 8 | 18001 | 0 | 6778 | 2364 | 111 |

HYDEN—Leslie County

MARY BRECKINRIDGE HOSPITAL, 130 Kate Ireland Drive, Zip 41749–0000; tel. 606/672–2901, (Nonreporting) **A**9 10 18 20
Primary Contact: Mallie S. Noble, Administrator
Web address: www.frontiernursing.org

| | 23 | 10 | 25 | — | — | — | — | — | — | — |

IRVINE—Estill County

★ **MARCUM AND WALLACE MEMORIAL HOSPITAL**, 60 Mercy Court, Zip 40336–1331; tel. 606/723–2115 **A**9 10 18 **F**12 27 28 33 46 48 52 60 63 66 69 70 81 88 97 **P**6 **S** Catholic Healthcare Partners, Cincinnati, OH
Primary Contact: Susan Starling, President and Chief Executive Officer
CFO: Danena Thacker, Controller
CMO: James Foster, M.D., Medical Director
CIO: Elizabeth Henry, Mission and Quality Coordinator

| | 21 | 10 | 25 | 847 | 6 | 36027 | 0 | 7786 | 3396 | 115 |

JACKSON—Breathitt County

□ **KENTUCKY RIVER MEDICAL CENTER**, 540 Jett Drive, Zip 41339–9620; tel. 606/666–6000, (Nonreporting) **A**1 9 10 20 **S** Community Health Systems, Inc., Brentwood, TN
Primary Contact: O. David Bevins, Chief Executive Officer
Web address: www.kentuckyrivermc.com

| | 33 | 10 | 54 | — | — | — | — | — | — | — |

JENKINS—Letcher County

□ **JENKINS COMMUNITY HOSPITAL**, Main Street, Zip 41537–9614, Mailing Address: P.O. Box 472, Zip 41537–0472; tel. 606/832–2171, (Nonreporting) **A**1 9 10
Primary Contact: Sherrie Newcomb, Administrator

| | 31 | 10 | 60 | — | — | — | — | — | — | — |

Many Facility Codes have changed. Please refer to the AHA Guide Code Chart.

© 2005 AHA Guide

Hospital, Address, Telephone, Approval, Facility, and Physician Codes, Health Care System	Classi-fication Codes		Utilization Data					Expense (thousands) of dollars		
★ American Hospital Association (AHA) membership □ Joint Commission on Accreditation of Healthcare Organizations (JCAHO) accreditation ○ American Osteopathic Association (AOA) accreditation △ Commission on Accreditation of Rehabilitation Facilities (CARF) accreditation	Control	Service	Staffed Beds	Admissions	Census	Outpatient Visits	Births	Total	Payroll	Personnel

LA GRANGE—Oldham County

✚ **BAPTIST HOSPITAL NORTHEAST**, 1025 New Moody Lane, Zip 40031–0559; tel. 502/222–5388, (Total facility includes 18 beds in nursing home–type unit) **A**1 9 10 **F**2 9 11 12 21 22 26 27 28 29 30 33 34 37 39 44 46 47 48 52 53 55 57 58 59 60 62 63 64 65 66 69 81 82 84 88 92 94 95 96 97 106 108 109 **S** Baptist Healthcare System, Louisville, KY
Primary Contact: Dennis B. Johnson, Administrator
CFO: Susanne Haynes, Executive Director Finance
CMO: Madonna Ringswald, Medical Staff President
CIO: Al Barea, Chief Information Officer and Vice President
CHR: Jean Harden, Executive Director of Human Resources
Web address: www.baptistnortheast.com

| | 23 | 10 | 82 | 3342 | 50 | 39824 | 328 | 31826 | 14928 | 257 |

LEBANON—Marion County

✚ **SPRING VIEW HOSPITAL**, 320 Loretto Road, Zip 40033–0320; tel. 270/692–3161 **A**1 9 10 **F**2 9 11 12 21 22 24 29 33 39 46 47 48 52 53 55 57 58 59 60 62 63 65 66 81 82 85 88 92 94 96 97 106 108 109 **P**3 6 **S** LifePoint Hospitals, Inc., Brentwood, TN
Primary Contact: Barry A. Papania, Chief Executive Officer
CFO: Denise Thomas, Chief Financial Officer
CIO: Douglas Bland, Manager Information Services
CHR: Ann Dabney, Manager, Human Resources
Web address: www.springviewhospital.com

| | 33 | 10 | 60 | 1983 | 19 | 48223 | 432 | 19827 | 8939 | 226 |

LEITCHFIELD—Grayson County

✚ **TWIN LAKES REGIONAL MEDICAL CENTER**, 910 Wallace Avenue, Zip 42754–1499; tel. 270/259–9400 **A**1 9 10 **F**2 9 11 12 21 22 23 28 33 41 51 53 55 59 61 62 63 64 65 66 69 81 88 94 96 97 106 108 110 **P**6 **S** Alliant Management Services, Louisville, KY
Primary Contact: Stephen L. Meredith, Chief Executive Officer
CFO: Scott Arndell, Chief Financial Officer
CMO: Gregory Skaggs, M.D., President Medical Staff
CIO: Dolores Hagan, Director Information Systems
CHR: Deneace Clemons, Director Human Resources
Web address: www.tlrmc.com

| | 23 | 10 | 75 | 2585 | 30 | 53528 | 331 | 23141 | 9528 | 291 |

LEXINGTON—Fayette County

★ △ **CARDINAL HILL REHABILITATION HOSPITAL**, 2050 Versailles Road, Zip 40504–1499; tel. 859/254–5701 **A**3 5 7 9 10 **F**1 2 7 9 21 22 24 26 27 28 29 30 31 35 39 41 44 45 46 47 48 51 52 53 57 58 60 62 65 66 68 69 94 95 96 98 108 110 **S** Cardinal Hill Healthcare System, Lexington, KY
Primary Contact: Kerry G. Gillihan, FACHE, President and Chief Executive Officer
COO: Beth Monarch, Executive Vice President and Chief Operating Officer
CFO: Timothy Wilson, Vice President for Finance and Chief Financial Officer
CMO: William Lester, M.D., Vice President of Medical Affairs
CIO: Robert Korten, Manager
CHR: Laban Miller, Ph.D., Vice President Human Resources
Web address: www.cardinalhill.org

| | 23 | 46 | 108 | 2206 | 87 | 57190 | 0 | 35539 | 20108 | 517 |

✚ **CENTRAL BAPTIST HOSPITAL**, 1740 Nicholasville Road, Zip 40503–1499; tel. 859/260–6100 **A**1 2 9 10 **F**3 9 11 12 13 14 15 17 19 21 22 23 27 28 29 30 33 35 36 37 38 41 46 47 48 49 51 52 53 55 56 57 58 59 60 61 62 63 64 65 66 67 68 69 71 79 81 82 84 85 86 87 88 89 90 92 94 95 96 106 108 109 110 **P**6 **S** Baptist Healthcare System, Louisville, KY
Primary Contact: William G. Sisson, President
CFO: Bobbie L. Prather, Chief Financial Officer
CMO: Preston Nunelley, M.D., Chief Medical Officer
CIO: Tom Carrico, Chief Information Officer
CHR: Philip L. Kubow, Vice President Human Resources
Web address: www.centralbap.com

| | 23 | 10 | 348 | 19236 | 247 | 154317 | 3970 | 246708 | 89226 | 1935 |

CONTINUING CARE HOSPITAL, 150 North Eagle Creek Drive, 5th Floor, Zip 40515; tel. 859/268–4800, (Nonreporting) **A**10
Primary Contact: Eric Gilliam, Administrator

| | 33 | 80 | 23 | — | — | — | — | — | — | — |

□ **EASTERN STATE HOSPITAL**, 627 West Fourth Street, Zip 40508–1294; tel. 859/246–7000 **A**1 3 5 10 **F**2 21 22 26 27 28 32 37 38 44 45 46 53 58 60 71 74 75 76 77 94 106 108 **P**6
Primary Contact: Joseph A. Toy, President and Chief Executive Officer
Web address: www.bluegrass.org

| | 12 | 22 | 197 | 2230 | 145 | 0 | 0 | 30483 | 14501 | 415 |

FEDERAL MEDICAL CENTER, 3301 Leestown Road, Zip 40511–8799; tel. 859/255–6812, (Nonreporting)
Primary Contact: George E. Snyder, Warden

| | 48 | 11 | 22 | — | — | — | — | — | — | — |

□ **RIDGE BEHAVIORAL HEALTH SYSTEM**, 3050 Rio Dosa Drive, Zip 40509–9990; tel. 859/269–2325, (Nonreporting) **A**1 3 5 9 10 **S** Universal Health Services, Inc., King of Prussia, PA
Primary Contact: Nina W. Eisner, Chief Executive Officer and Managing Director
Web address: www.ridgebhs.com

| | 33 | 22 | 110 | — | — | — | — | — | — | — |

✚ **SAINT JOSEPH HOSPITAL**, One St. Joseph Drive, Zip 40504–3754; tel. 859/278–3436 **A**1 2 3 5 9 10 **F**2 9 12 14 15 17 19 21 22 23 24 26 27 28 29 30 33 37 38 39 42 44 46 48 50 51 52 53 54 55 57 58 60 61 62 63 64 65 66 69 75 81 82 84 87 88 93 94 96 106 108 110 **P**3 **S** Catholic Health Initiatives, Denver, CO
Primary Contact: Eugene A. Woods, President and Chief Executive Officer
CFO: Gary J. Ermers, Vice President Finance and Chief Financial Officer
CHR: Rick Tolson, Vice President Human Resources
Web address: www.sjhlex.org

| | 21 | 10 | 344 | 18739 | 251 | 113071 | 0 | 237426 | 84649 | 2176 |

Hospital, Address, Telephone, Approval, Facility, and Physician Codes, Health Care System	Classi-fication Codes		Utilization Data					Expense (thousands) of dollars		
★ American Hospital Association (AHA) membership □ Joint Commission on Accreditation of Healthcare Organizations (JCAHO) accreditation ○ American Osteopathic Association (AOA) accreditation △ Commission on Accreditation of Rehabilitation Facilities (CARF) accreditation	Control	Service	Staffed Beds	Admissions	Census	Outpatient Visits	Births	Total	Payroll	Personnel

⊞ **SAINT JOSEPH HOSPITAL EAST**, 150 North Eagle Creek Drive, Zip 40509–1807; tel. 859/268–4800 **A**1 5 9 10 **F**2 9 10 11 12 15 17 21 22 24 26 27 28 33 39 42 44 46 48 50 52 53 55 56 57 58 59 60 61 62 63 64 65 66 69 75 81 82 88 93 94 96 106 108 109 **S** Catholic Health Initiatives, Denver, CO Primary Contact: Eugene A. Woods, President and Chief Executive Officer CFO: Chris Moore, Controller Web address: www.sjhlex.org	21	10	116	5886	62	68468	1434	59783	24848	603
⊞ **SAMARITAN HOSPITAL**, 310 South Limestone Street, Zip 40508–3008; tel. 859/226–7000 **A**1 3 5 9 10 **F**2 10 12 15 21 22 23 26 27 28 33 53 55 57 58 62 63 64 71 72 73 74 75 81 82 85 88 92 93 94 108 110 **S** Associated Healthcare Systems, Inc., Brentwood, TN Primary Contact: Frank Beirne, Chief Executive Officer CFO: Tony G. Sudduth, CPA, Chief Financial Officer CIO: Tony G. Sudduth, CPA, Chief Financial Officer CHR: Pat Imerman, Director Human Resources Web address: www.samaritanhospital.com	33	10	271	5083	53	82700	0	60988	20097	507
SELECT SPECIALTY HOSPITAL OF LEXINGTON, 310 South Limeston Street, 3rd Floor, Zip 40509; tel. 859/226–7178, (Nonreporting) **A**9 10 Primary Contact: Charles R. Daugherty, Chief Executive Officer	33	49	41	—	—	—	—	—	—	—
□ **SHRINERS HOSPITALS FOR CHILDREN–LEXINGTON**, 1900 Richmond Road, Zip 40502–1298; tel. 859/266–2101, (Nonreporting) **A**1 3 5 **S** Shriners Hospitals for Children, Tampa, FL Primary Contact: Tony Lewgood, Administrator Web address: www.shrinershq.com	23	57	50	—	—	—	—	—	—	—
⊞ **UNIVERSITY OF KENTUCKY HOSPITAL**, 800 Rose Street, N100, Zip 40536–0293; tel. 859/323–5000 **A**1 2 3 5 8 9 10 **F**2 4 5 9 10 11 12 13 14 15 16 17 18 19 20 21 22 23 24 26 27 28 29 30 31 32 33 34 39 43 44 46 47 48 49 50 52 55 56 57 58 59 60 61 62 63 65 66 67 69 70 71 72 73 74 75 76 77 78 79 80 81 82 84 85 87 88 89 90 94 95 96 98 99 100 101 102 103 104 105 106 108 109 110 **P**1 Primary Contact: Murray B. Clark, Jr, Associate Vice President Operations CFO: Sergio L. Melgar, Chief Financial Officer CMO: Richard Lofgren, Chief Medical Officer CIO: Zed Day, Chief Information Officer CHR: Kim Wilson, Director Human Resources Web address: www.ukhealthcare.uky.edu	12	10	406	19677	308	411898	1867	318406	112151	2436
⊞ **VETERANS AFFAIRS MEDICAL CENTER–LEXINGTON**, 2250 Leestown Pike, Zip 40511–1093; tel. 859/233–4511, (Total facility includes 61 beds in nursing home–type unit) (Nonreporting) **A**1 3 5 8 **S** Department of Veterans Affairs, Washington, DC Primary Contact: Forest Farley, Director CFO: Gale Beaman, Chief Fiscal Service CIO: James Critchley, Chief Information Management Web address: www.va.gov/sta/guide/home.asp	45	10	168	—	—	—	—	—	—	—
LIBERTY—Casey County										
□ **CASEY COUNTY HOSPITAL**, 187 Wolford Avenue, Zip 42539; tel. 606/787–6275 **A**1 9 10 18 **F**27 28 33 46 66 69 77 81 85 94 97 Primary Contact: Rex A. Tungate, Administrator	16	10	24	507	5	9058	0	4397	1906	90
LONDON—Laurel County										
⊞ **MARYMOUNT MEDICAL CENTER**, 310 East Ninth Street, Zip 40741–1299; tel. 606/878–6520 **A**1 9 10 13 19 **F**9 11 12 15 17 19 21 22 27 28 29 32 33 36 37 38 39 46 48 49 51 55 57 58 59 60 62 63 65 66 81 82 84 88 94 96 97 108 **S** Catholic Health Initiatives, Denver, CO Primary Contact: Virginia B. Dempsey, Chief Executive Officer CFO: Robert Brock, Chief Financial Officer CMO: William Pratt, M.D., President Medical Staff CHR: Richard Huck, Vice President of Human Resources Web address: www.marymount.com	21	10	87	6516	62	122852	698	60807	27019	548
LOUISA—Lawrence County										
□ **THREE RIVERS MEDICAL CENTER**, Highway 644, Zip 41230–9632, Mailing Address: P.O. Box 769, Zip 41230–0769; tel. 606/638–9451, (Nonreporting) **A**1 9 10 **S** Community Health Systems, Inc., Brentwood, TN Primary Contact: Greg Kiser, Chief Executive Officer Web address: www.threeriversmedicalcenter.com	33	10	90	—	—	—	—	—	—	—
LOUISVILLE—Jefferson County										
⊞ △ **BAPTIST HOSPITAL EAST**, 4000 Kresge Way, Zip 40207–4676; tel. 502/897–8100 **A**1 2 5 7 9 10 **F**2 4 9 11 12 14 15 17 19 21 22 23 26 27 28 29 30 31 33 35 37 38 39 40 41 42 44 46 47 48 51 52 53 55 56 57 58 59 61 62 63 64 65 66 68 69 71 72 73 74 75 76 77 78 79 81 82 85 88 93 94 96 98 106 108 109 110 **S** Baptist Healthcare System, Louisville, KY Primary Contact: Susan Stout Tamme, President CFO: Steve Warren, Vice President Finance CMO: Thomas Dedman, M.D., Medical Director CIO: Al Barea, Vice President Information Services CHR: Anthony Bohn, Vice President Human Resources Web address: www.baptisteast.com	23	10	407	25127	330	172698	3066	269983	114982	2314

Hospital, Address, Telephone, Approval, Facility, and Physician Codes, Health Care System	Classi-fication Codes		Utilization Data						Expense (thousands) of dollars		
★ American Hospital Association (AHA) membership □ Joint Commission on Accreditation of Healthcare Organizations (JCAHO) accreditation ○ American Osteopathic Association (AOA) accreditation △ Commission on Accreditation of Rehabilitation Facilities (CARF) accreditation	Control	Service	Staffed Beds	Admissions	Census	Outpatient Visits	Births	Total	Payroll	Personnel
⊞ **CARITAS MEDICAL CENTER**, 1850 Bluegrass Avenue, Zip 40215–1199; tel. 502/361–6000, (Total facility includes 33 beds in nursing home–type unit) **A**1 9 10 **F**3 4 6 9 10 12 14 21 22 23 27 28 29 30 31 33 37 44 45 46 48 49 50 51 52 54 55 57 58 60 61 62 63 66 69 70 71 72 73 74 75 76 77 78 81 82 84 88 92 93 94 95 96 98 106 108 **P**7 **S** Catholic Health Initiatives, Denver, CO Primary Contact: Robert M. Lovell, Interim President and Chief Executive Officer COO: Thomas Gessel, Chief Operating Officer CFO: John Katsianis, Chief Financial Officer CMO: Lawrence Goldberg, M.D., Chief Medical Officer CIO: Thomas Wittman, Director Information Systems CHR: Julie McGregor, Director of Human Resources Web address: www.caritas.org	21	10	473	14973	345	162497	0	171214	80102	1816
⊞ **CARITAS PEACE CENTER**, 2020 Newburg Road, Zip 40205–1879; tel. 502/451–3330, (Nonreporting) **A**1 9 **S** Catholic Health Initiatives, Denver, CO Primary Contact: Robert M. Lovell, Interim President and Chief Executive Officer CFO: John Katsianis, Chief Financial Officer CMO: Gerald Moore, M.D., Medical Director Web address: www.caritas.org	23	22	206	—	—	—	—	—	—	—
□ **CENTRAL STATE HOSPITAL**, 10510 LaGrange Road, Zip 40223–1228; tel. 502/253–7000, (Nonreporting) **A**1 5 10 Primary Contact: Patricia Brodie, Chief Executive Officer	12	22	123	—	—	—	—	—	—	—
★ △ **FRAZIER REHAB INSTITUTE**, 220 Abraham Flexner Way, Zip 40202–1887; tel. 502/582–7400 **A**3 7 **F**21 22 26 27 28 29 37 38 39 42 44 46 47 48 52 53 57 58 60 61 62 64 65 66 68 69 73 79 92 94 95 96 108 **S** Jewish Hospital HealthCare Services, Louisville, KY Primary Contact: Joanne Berryman, Senior Vice President CFO: Steve Scannell, Assistant Vice President Financial Services CMO: David R. Watkins, M.D., Chief of Staff CIO: David C. Pecoraro, Vice President and Chief Information Officer CHR: Lisa Burris, Manager Human Resources Web address: www.frazierrehab.org	23	46	135	2064	77	91496	0	36660	21439	393
□ **GATEWAY REHABILITATION HOSPITAL**, 315 East Broadway, Zip 40202; tel. 502/315–8300, (Nonreporting) **A**1 9 10 Primary Contact: James Parobek, Chief Executive Officer Web address: www.gatewaylouisville.com	33	46	40	—	—	—	—	—	—	—
⊞ **JEWISH HOSPITAL**, 217 East Chestnut Street, Zip 40202–1886, Mailing Address: One Audubon Plaza Drive #100, Zip 40217; tel. 502/587–4011 **A**1 2 3 5 8 9 10 **F**2 9 12 14 15 17 19 21 22 23 26 27 28 29 32 33 34 36 37 38 39 41 42 44 46 47 48 49 50 51 52 53 55 57 58 60 61 62 63 64 65 66 69 70 73 79 81 82 83 84 85 86 87 88 92 93 94 95 96 100 101 102 103 104 105 106 107 108 109 **S** Jewish Hospital HealthCare Services, Louisville, KY Primary Contact: Timothy L. Jarm, President COO: Aaron R. Hazzard, Vice President and Chief Operating Officer CFO: Alan L. Broude, Senior Vice President and Chief Financial Officer CMO: David R. Watkins, M.D., Chief of Staff CIO: David C. Pecoraro, Vice President and Chief Information Officer Web address: www.jewishhospital.org	23	10	442	21695	344	182507	0	396499	134892	2812
□ **KINDRED HOSPITAL–LOUISVILLE**, 1313 St. Anthony Place, Zip 40204–1765; tel. 502/587–7001, (Total facility includes 37 beds in nursing home–type unit) **A**1 5 9 10 **F**2 12 21 22 41 48 52 55 58 60 61 63 64 79 81 84 88 92 94 110 **S** Kindred Healthcare, Louisville, KY Primary Contact: Brian L. Pugh, Interim Chief Executive Officer Web address: www.kindredhealthcare.com	32	10	170	587	76	14097	0	—	—	—
KOSAIR CHILDREN'S HOSPITAL See Norton Hospital										
⊞ **NORTON AUDUBON HOSPITAL**, One Audubon Plaza Drive, Zip 40217–1397, Mailing Address: P.O. Box 17550, Zip 40217–0550; tel. 502/636–7111, (Total facility includes 32 beds in nursing home–type unit) **A**1 2 5 9 **F**2 7 9 12 14 15 17 19 21 22 23 26 27 28 29 31 33 37 39 44 46 47 48 52 55 57 58 61 62 63 64 65 66 69 70 81 82 84 88 92 93 94 106 108 109 **S** Norton Healthcare, Louisville, KY Primary Contact: Thomas D. Kmetz, President COO: Russ Cox, Executive Vice President CFO: Michael W. Gough, Chief Financial Officer CMO: Daniel W. Varga, M.D., Chief Medical Officer CIO: Marilynn Black, Vice President Systems Integration CHR: Doug Howell, Senior Vice President Organization and Performance Web address: www.nortonhealthcare.org	23	10	276	13650	210	135728	0	163147	60361	1307

Hospital, Address, Telephone, Approval, Facility, and Physician Codes, Health Care System	Classi-fication Codes		Utilization Data					Expense (thousands) of dollars		
	Control	Service	Staffed Beds	Admissions	Census	Outpatient Visits	Births	Total	Payroll	Personnel

★ American Hospital Association (AHA) membership
□ Joint Commission on Accreditation of Healthcare Organizations (JCAHO) accreditation
○ American Osteopathic Association (AOA) accreditation
△ Commission on Accreditation of Rehabilitation Facilities (CARF) accreditation

✷ **NORTON HOSPITAL**, 200 East Chestnut Street, Zip 40202–1800, Mailing Address: P.O. Box 35070, Zip 40232–5070; tel. 502/629–8000, (Includes KOSAIR CHILDREN'S HOSPITAL, 231 East Chestnut Street, Zip 40202, Mailing Address: 231 East Chestnut Street, Zip 40202; tel. 502/629–6000; Douglas J. Eighmey, Administrator; NORTON HEALTHCARE PAVILION, 315 East Broadway, Zip 40202–1703; tel. 502/629–2000), (Total facility includes 17 beds in nursing home–type unit) **A**1 2 3 5 9 10 **F**2 9 10 11 12 13 14 15 16 17 18 19 20 21 22 23 24 26 27 28 29 31 32 33 34 37 38 39 40 41 44 45 46 47 48 52 53 55 56 57 58 59 61 62 63 64 65 66 67 69 71 72 73 74 75 76 77 81 82 84 85 87 88 89 90 92 93 94 96 99 100 101 102 103 104 105 108 109 110 **S** Norton Healthcare, Louisville, KY Primary Contact: Kevin S. Wardell, Chief Administrative Officer COO: Allyn Simmons, Associate Vice President of Operations CFO: Carl Amorose, Associate Vice President, Finance CMO: Daniel W. Varga, M.D., Senior Vice President and Chief Medical Officer CIO: Marilynn Black, Chief Information Officer CHR: Doug Howell, Senior Vice President Organization and Performance Web address: www.nortonhealthcare.org	23	10	677	26890	418	210546	2747	414614	143828	3306
✷ **NORTON SOUTHWEST HOSPITAL**, 9820 Third Street Road, Zip 40272–9984; tel. 502/933–8100, (Total facility includes 23 beds in nursing home–type unit) **A**1 9 10 **F**2 9 12 15 21 22 23 26 27 28 29 33 35 37 44 45 46 47 48 52 55 58 61 63 64 65 66 70 81 82 84 88 92 94 96 108 109 110 **S** Norton Healthcare, Louisville, KY Primary Contact: Teresa Parker, Administrator CFO: Steve Ross, Financial Director CMO: Daniel W. Varga, M.D., Senior Vice President and Chief Medical Officer CIO: Marilynn Black, Vice President Systems Integration CHR: Doug Howell, Senior Vice President Organization and Performance Web address: www.nortonhealthcare.org	23	10	126	3686	51	53577	0	42166	17955	382
✷ **NORTON SUBURBAN HOSPITAL**, 4001 Dutchmans Lane, Zip 40207–4799; tel. 502/893–1000 **A**1 9 10 **F**2 9 10 11 12 15 17 21 22 23 26 27 28 29 30 31 33 35 37 39 40 44 45 46 47 48 52 55 56 57 58 59 61 62 63 64 65 66 69 79 80 81 82 84 88 92 94 95 96 108 109 110 **S** Norton Healthcare, Louisville, KY Primary Contact: John D. Harryman, President and Administrator CFO: Mark Kircher, Associate Vice President, Hospital Finance CMO: Daniel W. Varga, M.D., Senior Vice President and Chief Medical Officer CIO: Marilynn Black, Vice President Systems Integration CHR: Doug Howell, Senior Vice President Organization and Performance Web address: www.nortonhealthcare.com	23	10	311	15021	195	143102	5056	142925	51935	1280
□ **TEN BROECK HOSPITAL**, 8521 Old LaGrange Road, Zip 40242–3800; tel. 502/426–6380, (Nonreporting) **A**1 9 10 **S** United Medical Corporation, Windermere, FL Primary Contact: John Hollinsworth, Executive Director Web address: www.tenbroeck.com	33	22	94	—	—	—	—	—	—	—
✷ **UNIVERSITY OF LOUISVILLE HOSPITAL**, 530 South Jackson Street, Zip 40202–3611; tel. 502/562–3000 **A**1 2 3 5 8 9 10 **F**2 11 12 13 14 15 17 19 20 21 22 23 26 27 28 29 32 33 34 44 46 47 48 50 52 53 55 56 57 58 59 60 61 62 63 64 65 66 69 71 73 75 76 79 80 81 82 84 85 86 87 88 93 94 96 99 106 107 108 **P**4 Primary Contact: James H. Taylor, President and Chief Executive Officer CFO: Robert P. Barbier, Chief Financial Officer CMO: Mark P. Pfeifer, M.D., Chief of Staff CIO: Troy May, Chief Information Officer CHR: Gary Bensing, Vice President Web address: www.ulh.org	23	10	291	13791	241	180502	1957	271792	91498	2142
✷ **VETERANS AFFAIRS MEDICAL CENTER–LOUISVILLE**, 800 Zorn Avenue, Zip 40206–1499; tel. 502/895–3401, (Nonreporting) **A**1 2 3 5 8 **S** Department of Veterans Affairs, Washington, DC Primary Contact: Timothy P. Shea, FACHE, Director COO: Wanda Mims, Associate Director CFO: Barbara Roberts, Chief Financial Officer CMO: Marylee Rothschild, M.D., Chief of Staff CIO: Augustine Bittner, Chief Information Officer CHR: George Neureither, Chief Human Resources Management Service Web address: www.va.gov/603louisville	45	10	110	—	—	—	—	—	—	—

MADISONVILLE—Hopkins County

✷ **REGIONAL MEDICAL CENTER OF HOPKINS COUNTY**, 900 Hospital Drive, Zip 42431–1694; tel. 270/825–5100 **A**1 2 3 5 9 10 19 20 **F**2 3 9 11 12 13 15 17 19 21 22 23 27 29 32 33 35 36 39 40 41 48 49 51 52 53 55 56 57 58 59 60 61 62 63 64 65 66 67 68 69 71 79 81 82 84 86 87 88 92 93 94 95 96 97 106 108 110 **P**6 Primary Contact: Ron Peterson, President CFO: David Cauble, Chief Financial Officer CMO: Mark Browne, M.D., Vice President Medical Affairs CIO: Terry Jackson, Director Information System CHR: David Lang, Vice President Human Resources Web address: www.troverfoundation.org	23	10	271	10267	123	—	970	83093	36293	1397

Many Facility Codes have changed. Please refer to the AHA Guide Code Chart.

© 2005 AHA Guide

Hospital, Address, Telephone, Approval, Facility, and Physician Codes, Health Care System	Classi-fication Codes		Utilization Data					Expense (thousands) of dollars		
★ American Hospital Association (AHA) membership □ Joint Commission on Accreditation of Healthcare Organizations (JCAHO) accreditation ○ American Osteopathic Association (AOA) accreditation △ Commission on Accreditation of Rehabilitation Facilities (CARF) accreditation	Control	Service	Staffed Beds	Admissions	Census	Outpatient Visits	Births	Total	Payroll	Personnel

MANCHESTER—Clay County

⊠ **MEMORIAL HOSPITAL**, 210 Marie Langdon Drive, Zip 40962–9156; tel. 606/598–5104 **A**1 9 10 20 **F**11 12 21 22 27 29 33 41 46 48 51 55 58 59 60 63 69 81 82 88 **S** Adventist Health System Sunbelt Health Care Corporation, Winter Park, FL
Primary Contact: Dennis Meyers, President and Chief Executive Officer
COO: Helen Wilson, Chief Operating Officer
CFO: Richard Boggess, Chief Financial Officer
Web address: www.manchestermemorial.com
| | 21 | 10 | 63 | 3563 | 37 | 90314 | 266 | 28984 | 12365 | 424 |

MARION—Crittenden County

⊠ **CRITTENDEN COUNTY HOSPITAL**, Highway 60 South, Zip 42064–6201, Mailing Address: P.O. Box 386, Zip 42064–0386; tel. 270/965–5281, (Total facility includes 180 beds in nursing home–type unit) **A**1 9 10 **F**2 6 9 11 12 21 22 26 27 28 29 33 44 46 48 51 58 59 60 63 65 69 70 81 82 88 92 94 97 108 110 **P**8 **S** Quorum Health Resources, Plano, TX
Primary Contact: Claudia Ann Eisenmann, Chief Executive Officer
CIO: Reese Baker, Chief Information Technology
CHR: Jan Gregory, Vice President Human Resources
Web address: www.crittenden–health.org
| | 23 | 10 | 228 | 2340 | 154 | 31813 | 117 | 21578 | 10379 | 374 |

MARTIN—Floyd County

⊠ **OUR LADY OF THE WAY HOSPITAL**, 11203 Main Street, Zip 41649–0910; tel. 606/285–5181 **A**1 9 10 18 **F**2 12 21 22 27 28 29 33 39 46 48 58 63 70 81 88 94 97 98 106 108 **P**6 **S** Catholic Health Initiatives, Denver, CO
Primary Contact: Kathy Stumbo, Chief Executive Officer
CFO: Robert Brock, Chief Financial Officer
CMO: Terry Wright, M.D., President Medical Staff
CIO: Chris Dye, Information Systems Director
Web address: www.olwh.org
| | 21 | 10 | 25 | 989 | 11 | 56708 | 0 | 15078 | 7716 | 164 |

MAYFIELD—Graves County

⊠ **JACKSON PURCHASE MEDICAL CENTER**, 1099 Medical Center Circle, Zip 42066–1179; tel. 270/251–4100 **A**1 9 10 19 **F**2 9 11 15 21 23 33 34 57 58 59 60 62 63 64 66 69 70 81 84 88 93 95 96 97 108 109 110 **P**7 **S** LifePoint Hospitals, Inc., Brentwood, TN
Primary Contact: Mary Jo Lewis, Chief Executive Officer
CFO: Dirk Morgan, Chief Financial Officer
Web address: www.jacksonpurchase.com
| | 33 | 10 | 107 | 4744 | 51 | 69119 | 409 | 47108 | 12106 | 328 |

MAYSVILLE—Mason County

⊠ **MEADOWVIEW REGIONAL MEDICAL CENTER**, 989 Medical Park Drive, Zip 41056–8750; tel. 606/759–5311 **A**1 9 10 **F**2 3 11 12 13 14 15 17 21 22 23 26 27 28 29 30 31 33 37 44 46 47 48 52 55 56 58 59 61 62 63 64 65 66 67 68 69 70 71 81 88 92 93 94 95 97 106 108 109 **S** LifePoint Hospitals, Inc., Brentwood, TN
Primary Contact: David E. Loving, Chief Executive Officer
CFO: Pamela Chesher, Chief Financial Officer
CIO: Lori Moore, Director Information Services
CHR: Deborah J. Williams, R.N., Chief Nursing Officer
Web address: www.meadowviewregional.com
| | 33 | 10 | 101 | 3629 | 31 | 50405 | 457 | 23760 | 9443 | 241 |

MCDOWELL—Floyd County

⊠ **MCDOWELL ARH HOSPITAL**, Route 122, Zip 41647, Mailing Address: P.O. Box 247, Zip 41647–0247; tel. 606/377–3400, (Total facility includes 10 beds in nursing home–type unit) **A**1 9 10 20 **F**2 9 12 21 22 26 27 28 29 33 37 39 46 47 48 51 52 55 58 60 63 65 66 68 69 70 81 85 88 92 94 97 108 **P**6 **S** Appalachian Regional Healthcare, Lexington, KY
Primary Contact: Russel Barker, Chief Executive Officer
CFO: Chris Ellington, Chief Financial Officer
CMO: Mary A. Hall, Chief of Medical Staff
CIO: Jeff Brady, Director Information Systems
CHR: Richard Zborowski, Executive Director Human Resources
Web address: www.arh.org
| | 23 | 10 | 46 | 1879 | 20 | 37253 | 0 | 15013 | 5566 | 166 |

MIDDLESBORO—Bell County

⊠ **MIDDLESBORO APPALACHIAN REGIONAL HOSPITAL**, 3600 West Cumberland Avenue, Zip 40965–2614, Mailing Address: P.O. Box 340, Zip 40965–0340; tel. 606/242–1300 **A**1 9 10 **F**2 9 11 12 14 15 21 22 26 27 28 29 32 33 39 46 47 48 51 52 55 58 59 60 62 63 64 65 66 68 69 70 81 82 85 88 94 97 108 109 110 **P**6 **S** Appalachian Regional Healthcare, Lexington, KY
Primary Contact: J. Gene Faile, Community Chief Executive Officer
CFO: Tommy Patey, Chief Financial Officer
CMO: Gautami Dholakia, M.D., Chief of Staff
CIO: Jan Sourni, Health Information Officer
CHR: Edie Kelley, Human Resource Representative
Web address: www.arh.org/middlesboro
| | 23 | 10 | 96 | 3999 | 41 | 65131 | 189 | 27004 | 10906 | 325 |

MONTICELLO—Wayne County

□ **WAYNE COUNTY HOSPITAL**, 166 Hospital Street, Zip 42633–2416; tel. 606/348–9343 **A**1 9 10 18 **F**2 9 22 24 27 48 52 58 63 64 81 82 88 97 108
Primary Contact: Patricia Brinson, Administrator
Web address: www.waynecohospital.net
| | 23 | 10 | 30 | 850 | 7 | 35924 | 0 | 10397 | 4201 | 139 |

Hospital, Address, Telephone, Approval, Facility, and Physician Codes, Health Care System	Classi-fication Codes		Utilization Data					Expense (thousands) of dollars		
	Control	Service	Staffed Beds	Admissions	Census	Outpatient Visits	Births	Total	Payroll	Personnel

★ American Hospital Association (AHA) membership
☐ Joint Commission on Accreditation of Healthcare Organizations (JCAHO) accreditation
◯ American Osteopathic Association (AOA) accreditation
△ Commission on Accreditation of Rehabilitation Facilities (CARF) accreditation

MOREHEAD—Rowan County

✠ **ST. CLAIRE REGIONAL MEDICAL CENTER**, 222 Medical Circle, Zip 40351–1180; tel. 606/783–6500, (Total facility includes 10 beds in nursing home–type unit) **A**1 2 3 5 9 10 19 **F**2 4 9 11 12 15 21 22 23 26 27 28 29 31 32 33 34 36 37 38 39 40 42 44 46 47 48 49 50 51 52 53 55 57 58 59 60 61 62 63 64 65 66 68 69 70 71 72 73 74 75 76 77 81 82 84 87 88 92 93 94 96 106 108 109 **P**6
Primary Contact: Mark J. Neff, President and Chief Executive Officer
CFO: Sonny Jones, Vice President Finance
CMO: Kim Williams, Vice President Medical Affairs
CIO: Randy McCleese, Chief Information Services
CHR: Travis Bailey, Vice President
Web address: www.st–claire.com

| | 21 | 10 | 133 | 5552 | 64 | 302398 | 512 | 75234 | 36226 | 924 |

MORGANFIELD—Union County

✠ **METHODIST HOSPITAL UNION COUNTY**, 4604 Highway 60 West, Zip 42437–9570; tel. 270/389–5000, (Total facility includes 16 beds in nursing home–type unit) **A**1 9 10 18 **F**2 6 9 12 21 22 27 28 33 46 52 58 60 63 64 69 81 88 92 94 97 108
Primary Contact: Patrick Donahue, Administrator
Web address: www.methodisthospitaluc.net

| | 21 | 10 | 41 | 820 | 22 | 20964 | 0 | 9331 | 3827 | 129 |

MOUNT STERLING—Montgomery County

✠ **GATEWAY REGIONAL HEALTH SYSTEM**, 50 Sterling Avenue, Zip 40353–1158, Mailing Address: P.O. Box 7, Zip 40353–0007; tel. 859/497–6000 **A**1 9 10 **F**2 11 12 14 21 23 27 28 29 33 46 48 52 55 57 58 59 61 62 63 65 66 69 81 82 85 88 94 96 97 106 109 **P**5
Primary Contact: Patrick A. Romano, Jr, Chief Executive Officer
CFO: Janelle Pugh, Vice President Finance
CMO: Rezkalla Butros, M.D., Medical Staff President
CIO: Jeff Ryder, Director Information Systems
CHR: Cindy Clark, Director Human Resources
Web address: www.marychiles.org

| | 23 | 10 | 63 | 1872 | 22 | 35714 | 433 | 22662 | 9013 | 260 |

MOUNT VERNON—Rockcastle County

✠ **ROCKCASTLE HOSPITAL AND RESPIRATORY CARE CENTER**, 145 Newcomb Avenue, Zip 40456–2733, Mailing Address: P.O. Box 1310, Zip 40456–1310; tel. 606/256–2195, (Total facility includes 60 beds in nursing home–type unit) **A**1 9 10 **F**2 12 23 26 27 28 33 41 48 51 52 58 63 69 81 84 88 92 94 97 106 **P**8
Primary Contact: Stephen A. Estes, Chief Executive Officer
CFO: Charles Black, IV, Chief Financial Officer
CMO: Michael Hamilton, M.D., Chief Medical Officer
CIO: Maleigha Amyx, Chief Information Officer
CHR: Carmen Poynter, Director Human Resources
Web address: www.rockcastlehospital.org

| | 23 | 10 | 86 | 1446 | 75 | 29662 | 0 | 21908 | 10902 | 369 |

MURRAY—Calloway County

✠ **MURRAY–CALLOWAY COUNTY HOSPITAL**, 803 Poplar Street, Zip 42071–2432; tel. 270/762–1100, (Total facility includes 218 beds in nursing home–type unit) **A**1 9 10 19 **F**1 2 6 9 11 12 14 15 21 22 23 26 27 28 29 33 36 41 46 47 48 51 52 53 57 58 59 60 61 62 63 64 66 69 81 82 84 85 86 87 88 92 93 94 95 96 106 108 109 110
Primary Contact: Jon C. O'Shaughnessy, Chief Executive Officer
CFO: Brad Bloemer, Vice President Finance
CMO: Richard Crouch, M.D., Chief Medical Officer
CIO: Andy Adams, Director of Information Systems
CHR: Keith Travis, Vice President Human Resources
Web address: www.murrayhospital.org

| | 15 | 10 | 323 | 5826 | 272 | 102686 | 616 | 81185 | 25080 | — |

OWENSBORO—Daviess County

✠ △ **OWENSBORO MEDICAL HEALTH SYSTEM**, 811 East Parrish Avenue, Zip 42303, Mailing Address: P.O. Box 20007, Zip 42304–0007; tel. 270/688–2000, (Includes HEALTHPARK, 1006 Ford Avenue, Zip 42301; tel. 502/688–5433), (Total facility includes 30 beds in nursing home–type unit) **A**1 2 5 7 9 10 **F**2 4 11 12 14 15 17 19 21 22 23 24 26 27 28 29 33 37 38 40 41 42 44 46 47 48 50 51 52 55 57 59 60 61 62 63 64 65 66 68 69 71 73 74 75 76 77 78 79 80 81 82 84 85 86 87 88 92 93 94 95 96 106 107 108 109 **P**1
Primary Contact: Jeffrey B. Barber, Dr.PH, President and Chief Executive Officer
COO: Vicki Stogsdill, Chief Operating Officer
CFO: John Countzler, Senior Vice President Finance and Chief Financial Officer
CIO: Gordon Rohweder, Chief Information Officer
CHR: Mia Suter, Senior Vice President Organizational Development
Web address: www.omhs.org

| | 23 | 10 | 345 | 18560 | 231 | 286526 | 1926 | 184855 | 72587 | 1688 |

RIVERVALLEY BEHAVIORAL HEALTH HOSPITAL, 1000 Industrial Drive, Zip 42301–8715; tel. 270/689–6500 **A**9 10 **F**21 27 31 45 71 72 73 74 75 77 78 94 96 108 **P**6
Primary Contact: Gayle DiCesare, President and Chief Executive Officer
Web address: www.rvbh.com

| | 23 | 52 | 56 | 586 | 34 | 12110 | 0 | 7430 | 3486 | 123 |

Many Facility Codes have changed. Please refer to the AHA Guide Code Chart.

© 2005 AHA Guide

Hospital, Address, Telephone, Approval, Facility, and Physician Codes, Health Care System	Classi-fication Codes		Utilization Data					Expense (thousands) of dollars		
	Control	Service	Staffed Beds	Admissions	Census	Outpatient Visits	Births	Total	Payroll	Personnel

★ American Hospital Association (AHA) membership
□ Joint Commission on Accreditation of Healthcare Organizations (JCAHO) accreditation
○ American Osteopathic Association (AOA) accreditation
△ Commission on Accreditation of Rehabilitation Facilities (CARF) accreditation

OWENTON—Owen County

★ **NEW HORIZONS HEALTH SYSTEMS, INC.**, 330 Roland Avenue, Zip 40359–1502; tel. 502/484–3663, (Total facility includes 20 beds in nursing home–type unit) (Nonreporting) **A**9 10 18
Primary Contact: Bernard Poe, Administrator
CMO: Douglas Smalara, M.D., Medical Director
CHR: Jackie Webster, Director Human Resources
Web address: www.newhorizonsmedicalcenter.com
— 23 10 45 — — — — — — —

PADUCAH—McCracken County

⊠ △ **LOURDES HOSPITAL**, 1530 Lone Oak Road, Zip 42003–7900, Mailing Address: P.O. Box 7100, Zip 42002–7100; tel. 270/444–2444, (Total facility includes 20 beds in nursing home–type unit) **A**1 7 9 10 19 **F**2 8 9 10 11 12 14 15 19 21 22 23 26 27 28 29 30 33 34 35 36 37 38 39 40 44 45 46 47 48 50 51 53 55 57 58 59 60 61 62 63 65 66 68 69 71 73 74 75 76 77 78 81 82 85 86 87 88 91 92 93 94 96 106 107 108 109 110 **S** Catholic Healthcare Partners, Cincinnati, OH
Primary Contact: William G. Wheeler, M.D., President and Chief Executive Officer
COO: Gary Wood, Vice President of Facilities and Chief Information Officer
CFO: Thomas M. Hales, Vice President Finance
CIO: Gary Wood, Vice President of Facilities and Chief Information Officer
Web address: www.lourdes–pad.org
21 10 289 10466 167 — — — — —

⊠ **WESTERN BAPTIST HOSPITAL**, 2501 Kentucky Avenue, Zip 42003–3200; tel. 270/575–2100, (Total facility includes 24 beds in nursing home–type unit) **A**1 2 9 10 19 **F**2 9 11 12 14 15 17 19 21 22 23 24 27 28 29 33 37 39 41 42 45 46 47 48 51 52 53 55 57 58 59 60 61 62 63 64 65 66 69 70 75 79 80 81 82 84 85 88 92 93 94 95 96 106 107 108 109 **P**8 **S** Baptist Healthcare System, Louisville, KY
Primary Contact: Larry O. Barton, President
CFO: Jim Carmain, Vice President Financial and Information Services
CHR: Dick Thomas, Executive Director Human Resources
Web address: www.westernbaptist.com
21 10 288 13465 185 144384 988 166379 59378 1424

PAINTSVILLE—Johnson County

□ **PAUL B. HALL REGIONAL MEDICAL CENTER**, 625 James S Trimble Boulevard, Zip 41240–0000; tel. 606/789–3511, (Nonreporting) **A**1 9 10 12 13 **S** Health Management Associates, Naples, FL
Primary Contact: Deborah L. Trimble, Chief Executive Officer
Web address: www.pbhrmc.com
33 10 72 — — — — — — —

PARIS—Bourbon County

⊠ **BOURBON COMMUNITY HOSPITAL**, 9 Linville Drive, Zip 40361–2196; tel. 859/987–3600, (Nonreporting) **A**1 9 10 **S** LifePoint Hospitals, Inc., Brentwood, TN
Primary Contact: Clay Holderman, Chief Executive Officer
COO: Karrie Brazaski, Chief Nursing Officer
CFO: Fred Wilson, Chief Financial Officer
CHR: Beth Weaver, Human Resources Director
Web address: www.bourbonhospital.com
33 10 58 — — — — — — —

PIKEVILLE—Pike County

□ **PIKEVILLE MEDICAL CENTER**, 911 Bypass Road, Zip 41501–1595; tel. 606/218–3500 **A**1 2 9 10 12 13 20 **F**6 9 11 12 15 17 19 21 22 23 24 27 28 29 32 33 37 39 40 41 45 46 47 48 49 50 51 52 53 54 55 56 57 58 59 60 61 62 63 64 65 66 68 69 70 79 80 81 82 84 85 86 87 88 93 94 96 106 107 108 109 110
Primary Contact: Joann Anderson, Chief Executive Officer
Web address: www.pikevillehospital.org
23 10 226 8823 135 148423 865 144042 45530 1225

PINEVILLE—Bell County

⊠ **PINEVILLE COMMUNITY HOSPITAL ASSOCIATION**, 850 Riverview Avenue, Zip 40977–0850; tel. 606/337–3051, (Total facility includes 30 beds in nursing home–type unit) **A**1 9 10 **F**2 11 12 21 22 28 33 34 46 48 51 52 55 58 59 63 64 66 81 82 85 88 92 106 108
Primary Contact: J. Milton Brooks, III, Administrator
CFO: Colan Kelly, Chief Financial Officer
CMO: Shawn Fugate, Chief Medical Officer
CIO: David Hall, Chief Information Officer
CHR: Greg Nunnelley, Director Human Resources
23 10 150 4247 78 47242 215 26335 10967 318

PRESTONSBURG—Floyd County

⊠ **HIGHLANDS REGIONAL MEDICAL CENTER**, 5000 Kentucky Route 321, Zip 41653–1273, Mailing Address: P.O. Box 668, Zip 41653–0668; tel. 606/886–8511 **A**1 2 5 9 10 12 13 19 **F**2 7 9 11 12 15 22 28 33 34 40 41 42 46 48 51 55 58 59 60 61 62 63 65 69 71 73 74 76 77 78 81 82 84 88 92 94 108
Primary Contact: Harold C. Warman, Jr, President and Chief Executive Officer
COO: Chris Hoffman, Chief Operating Officer
CFO: Jack Blackwell, Chief Financial Officer
CIO: J D. Jackson, Chief Information Officer
CHR: Susan Ellis, R.N., Vice President of Human Resources
Web address: www.hrmc.org
23 10 139 6651 80 80161 773 49608 15510 447

Hospital, Address, Telephone, Approval, Facility, and Physician Codes, Health Care System	Classi-fication Codes		Utilization Data					Expense (thousands) of dollars		
★ American Hospital Association (AHA) membership □ Joint Commission on Accreditation of Healthcare Organizations (JCAHO) accreditation ○ American Osteopathic Association (AOA) accreditation △ Commission on Accreditation of Rehabilitation Facilities (CARF) accreditation	Control	Service	Staffed Beds	Admissions	Census	Outpatient Visits	Births	Total	Payroll	Personnel

PRINCETON—Caldwell County

☒ **CALDWELL COUNTY HOSPITAL**, 101 Hospital Drive, Zip 42445–0410; tel. 270/365–0300 **A**1 9 10 18 **F**9 12 21 26 27 28 29 33 46 48 51 55 60 63 64 81 82 87 88 93 97 106 108 **S** Quorum Health Resources, Plano, TX
Primary Contact: Charles D. Lovell, Jr, President and Chief Executive Officer
CFO: Shane Whittington, Chief Financial Officer
Web address: www.caldwellhosp.org

| | 23 | 10 | 48 | 1140 | 10 | 21459 | 0 | 11569 | 4268 | 152 |

RADCLIFF—Hardin County

□ **LINCOLN TRAIL BEHAVIORAL HEALTH SYSTEM**, 3909 South Wilson Road, Zip 40160–9714, Mailing Address: P.O. Box 369, Zip 40159–0369; tel. 270/351–9444, (Nonreporting) **A**1 10
Primary Contact: Charles L. Webb, Jr, Administrator
Web address: www.lincolnbehavioral.com

| | 33 | 22 | 67 | — | | | | | | |

RICHMOND—Madison County

☒ **PATTIE A. CLAY REGIONAL MEDICAL CENTER**, 801 Eastern Bypass, Zip 40475–2405, Mailing Address: P.O. Box 1600, Zip 40476–2603; tel. 859/623–3131 **A**1 9 10 19 **F**2 9 11 12 15 21 22 27 28 29 33 40 44 46 48 52 53 57 58 59 60 62 63 66 69 81 82 83 84 86 87 88 93 94 96 97 106 107 108 109
Primary Contact: Robert J. Hudson, Chief Executive Officer and President
CMO: John Gillespie, M.D., Chief of Staff
CIO: Robert J. Hudson, Vice President Fiscal Services
CHR: Joy Benedict, Director Human Resources
Web address: www.pattieaclay.org

| | 23 | 10 | 69 | 3708 | 41 | 84741 | 825 | 47187 | 20424 | 506 |

RUSSELL SPRINGS—Russell County

☒ **RUSSELL COUNTY HOSPITAL**, 153 Dowell Road, Zip 42642–4236, Mailing Address: P.O. Box 1610, Zip 42642–1610; tel. 270/866–4141, (Nonreporting) **A**1 9 10
Primary Contact: Patricia Ekdahl, R.N., President and Chief Executive Officer
CFO: Steve Cummins, Chief Financial Officer
CIO: Steve Cummins, Chief Financial Officer
Web address: www.russellcohospital.org

| | 13 | 10 | 45 | — | — | — | — | — | — | — |

RUSSELLVILLE—Logan County

☒ **LOGAN MEMORIAL HOSPITAL**, 1625 South Nashville Road, Zip 42276–8834, Mailing Address: P.O. Box 10, Zip 42276–0010; tel. 270/726–4011 **A**1 9 10 **F**2 9 11 12 14 21 27 28 29 33 44 46 48 52 53 58 59 60 64 65 66 69 81 82 84 87 88 93 94 95 96 97 106 108 109 **P**5 6 **S** LifePoint Hospitals, Inc., Brentwood, TN
Primary Contact: Greg Moore, Chief Executive Officer
COO: Stephen Peters, Chief Nursing Officer and Chief Operating Officer
CFO: Katrina Kie, Chief Financial Officer
CMO: James Dodson, Chief Medical Staff
CIO: Kim Richardson, Information Systems Director
CHR: Lisa Harkleroad, Director Human Resources
Web address: www.loganmemorial.com

| | 33 | 10 | 92 | 2315 | 25 | 43963 | 177 | 15527 | 6575 | 235 |

SALEM—Livingston County

★ **LIVINGSTON HOSPITAL AND HEALTHCARE SERVICES**, 131 Hospital Drive, Zip 42078–8043; tel. 270/988–2299 **A**9 10 18 **F**2 12 21 22 27 28 29 33 39 46 48 51 52 55 58 63 66 81 88 92 94 97 108 109
Primary Contact: Yvonne Maddux, Chief Executive Officer
CMO: Ghassan Yazigi, M.D., Medical Staff President
CIO: Shannan Landreth, Chief Information Technology
Web address: www.lhhs.org

| | 23 | 10 | 25 | 849 | 8 | 9505 | 0 | 8140 | 3540 | 127 |

SCOTTSVILLE—Allen County

MEDICAL CENTER AT SCOTTSVILLE See The Medical Center at Bowling Green, Bowling Green

SHELBYVILLE—Shelby County

☒ **JEWISH HOSPITAL–SHELBYVILLE**, 727 Hospital Drive, Zip 40065–1699; tel. 502/647–4000, (Total facility includes 6 beds in nursing home–type unit) **A**1 9 10 **F**2 11 12 19 21 22 23 26 27 28 33 37 44 46 48 52 53 55 57 58 59 60 61 62 63 69 81 82 84 88 92 108 109 110 **P**6 **S** Jewish Hospital HealthCare Services, Louisville, KY
Primary Contact: Michael L. Collins, President and Chief Executive Officer
CMO: Christopher Theuer, Chief Medical Officer
CIO: Becki Boles, Director of Health and Information Services
CHR: Cindy Stewart Rattray, Human Resources Director
Web address: www.jhhs.org

| | 23 | 10 | 70 | 2818 | 37 | 43005 | 341 | 34760 | 15296 | 326 |

SOMERSET—Pulaski County

☒ **LAKE CUMBERLAND REGIONAL HOSPITAL**, 305 Langdon Street, Zip 42501–2750, Mailing Address: P.O. Box 620, Zip 42502–2750; tel. 606/679–7441, (Total facility includes 12 beds in nursing home–type unit) (Nonreporting) **A**1 9 10 19 20 **S** LifePoint Hospitals, Inc., Brentwood, TN
Primary Contact: Jeffrey G. Seraphine, Chief Executive Officer
CFO: Jonathan Wall, Chief Financial Officer
Web address: www.lcrh.ky

| | 33 | 10 | 227 | — | — | — | — | — | — | — |

Many Facility Codes have changed. Please refer to the AHA Guide Code Chart.   © 2005 AHA Guide

Hospital, Address, Telephone, Approval, Facility, and Physician Codes, Health Care System	Classi-fication Codes		Utilization Data					Expense (thousands) of dollars		
★ American Hospital Association (AHA) membership □ Joint Commission on Accreditation of Healthcare Organizations (JCAHO) accreditation ○ American Osteopathic Association (AOA) accreditation △ Commission on Accreditation of Rehabilitation Facilities (CARF) accreditation	Control	Service	Staffed Beds	Admissions	Census	Outpatient Visits	Births	Total	Payroll	Personnel

SOUTH WILLIAMSON—Pike County

✠ **WILLIAMSON ARH HOSPITAL**, 260 Hospital Drive, Zip 41503–4072; tel. 606/237–1710, (Total facility includes 50 beds in nursing home–type unit) **A**1 9 10 19 **F**2 9 11 12 21 22 26 27 28 29 33 34 37 39 46 47 48 51 52 55 57 58 59 60 62 63 64 65 66 68 69 70 81 82 87 88 92 94 96 98 108 109 **P**6 **S** Appalachian Regional Healthcare, Lexington, KY
Primary Contact: Wesley Dangerfield, Community Chief Executive Officer
CFO: Chris Ellington, Chief Financial Officer
CMO: J D. Miller, M.D., Vice President Medical Affairs
CIO: Jeff Brady, Chief Information Officer
Web address: www.arh.org
| 23 | 10 | 163 | 4664 | 91 | 48224 | 202 | 36051 | 13832 | 409 |

STANFORD—Lincoln County

FORT LOGAN HOSPITAL, 124 Portman Avenue, Zip 40484–1200; tel. 606/365–2187, (Total facility includes 30 beds in nursing home–type unit) **A**9 10 18 **F**2 9 11 12 21 22 26 27 28 29 33 38 44 46 48 58 59 60 63 66 69 70 81 88 92 94 97 108 110 **P**5
Primary Contact: Mike Jackson, President and Chief Executive Officer
Web address: www.fortloganhospital.org
| 23 | 10 | 55 | 1084 | 37 | 22004 | 168 | 9572 | 4894 | 134 |

TOMPKINSVILLE—Monroe County

✠ **MONROE COUNTY MEDICAL CENTER**, 529 Capp Harlan Road, Zip 42167–1840; tel. 270/487–9231 **A**1 9 10 **F**1 2 6 12 21 26 27 28 33 46 51 64 69 81 88 96 **P**8 **S** Quorum Health Resources, Plano, TX
Primary Contact: Vicky McFall, Chief Executive Officer
CFO: Rickie F. Brown, Chief Financial Officer
CMO: Vicky McFall, Chief Clinical Officer
Web address: www.mcmccares.com
| 23 | 10 | 49 | 2505 | 27 | 29749 | 0 | 13066 | 6228 | 218 |

VERSAILLES—Woodford County

★ **BLUEGRASS COMMUNITY HOSPITAL**, 360 Amsden Avenue, Zip 40383–1286; tel. 859/873–3111 **A**9 10 18 **F**9 12 21 22 27 33 40 46 48 52 53 55 58 60 62 63 64 65 66 69 81 84 88 93 94 95 96 97 108 110 **S** LifePoint Hospitals, Inc., Brentwood, TN
Primary Contact: Kathy Scott, Administrator
| 33 | 10 | 25 | 502 | 5 | 24809 | 2 | 10422 | 3919 | 75 |

WEST LIBERTY—Morgan County

✠ **MORGAN COUNTY APPALACHIAN REGIONAL HOSPITAL**, 476 Liberty Road, Zip 41472–2049, Mailing Address: P.O. Box 579, Zip 41472–0579; tel. 606/743–3186, (Total facility includes 25 beds in nursing home–type unit) **A**1 9 10 18 **F**9 12 21 26 27 28 29 33 36 37 42 46 47 48 51 52 58 65 66 68 69 70 81 85 88 92 93 94 96 97 108 **P**6 **S** Appalachian Regional Healthcare, Lexington, KY
Primary Contact: Susan Roman, Community Chief Executive Officer
CFO: Chris Ellington, Chief Financial Officer and Vice President for Fiscal Affairs
CMO: J D. Miller, M.D., Vice President Medical Affairs
CIO: Jeff Brady, Director Information Systems
CHR: Rhonda Gevedon, Human Resources Representative
Web address: www.arh.org/morgan
| 23 | 10 | 40 | 871 | 29 | 32990 | 0 | 12272 | 4783 | 125 |

WHITESBURG—Letcher County

✠ **WHITESBURG APPALACHIAN REGIONAL HOSPITAL**, 240 Hospital Road, Zip 41858–1254; tel. 606/633–3600 **A**1 9 10 **F**2 9 11 12 21 22 26 27 28 29 33 34 37 39 46 47 48 51 52 55 58 59 60 63 64 65 66 68 69 70 81 82 85 87 88 92 93 94 97 108 109 **P**6 **S** Appalachian Regional Healthcare, Lexington, KY
Primary Contact: Donald Fields, Community Chief Executive Officer
CFO: Chris Ellington, Vice President for Fiscal Affairs
CMO: Matthew Gooch, M.D., Chief of Staff
CIO: Jeff Brody, Chief Information Officer
Web address: www.arh.org/whitesburg
| 23 | 10 | 82 | 4759 | 47 | 55988 | 503 | 31708 | 10607 | 301 |

WILLIAMSTOWN—Grant County

★ **ST. ELIZABETH MEDICAL CENTER–GRANT COUNTY**, 238 Barnes Road, Zip 41097–9460; tel. 859/824–8240 **A**9 10 18 **F**9 12 21 22 26 27 28 29 30 31 33 35 36 37 38 39 41 44 46 47 48 52 53 58 65 69 81 86 87 88 94 96 106 108 110
Primary Contact: Chris Carle, Administrator
Web address: www.stelizabeth.com
| 21 | 10 | 15 | 626 | 5 | 40922 | 0 | — | — | — |

WINCHESTER—Clark County

✠ **CLARK REGIONAL MEDICAL CENTER**, 1107 West Lexington Avenue, Zip 40391–1138, Mailing Address: P.O. Box 630, Zip 40392–0630; tel. 859/745–3500, (Nonreporting) **A**1 5 9 10
Primary Contact: Robert D. Fraraccio, Chief Executive Officer
CFO: Carol Allen, Chief Financial Officer
CMO: Mark Pascuzzi, President of the Medical Staff
CHR: Barry Lindeman, Director of Human Resources
Web address: www.clarkhospital.org
| 13 | 10 | 112 | — | — | — | — | — | — | — |

LA

LOUISIANA

Hospital, Address, Telephone, Approval, Facility, and Physician Codes, Health Care System	Classification Codes		Utilization Data					Expense (thousands) of dollars		
	Control	Service	Staffed Beds	Admissions	Census	Outpatient Visits	Births	Total	Payroll	Personnel

★ American Hospital Association (AHA) membership
□ Joint Commission on Accreditation of Healthcare Organizations (JCAHO) accreditation
○ American Osteopathic Association (AOA) accreditation
△ Commission on Accreditation of Rehabilitation Facilities (CARF) accreditation

ABBEVILLE—Vermilion Parish

☒ **ABBEVILLE GENERAL HOSPITAL**, 118 North Hospital Drive, Zip 70510–4077, Mailing Address: P.O. Box 580, Zip 70511–0580; tel. 337/893–5466 **A**1 9 10 **F**9 11 12 22 26 27 28 33 37 39 48 49 52 55 58 59 62 63 66 70 71 76 78 81 82 85 88 92 94 97 108 **P**6
Primary Contact: Ray A. Landry, Chief Executive Officer
CFO: Troy Hair, Chief Financial Officer
CIO: Pete LeBlanc, Information Systems Director
Web address: www.abbgen.net
— 16 10 60 2578 38 42726 152 13700 11293 287

□ **VERMILION REHABILITATION HOSPITAL**, 118 North Hospital Drive, Zip 70510; tel. 337/898–8800 **A**1 10 **F**26 45 53 58 60 62 65 66 68 94 110 **P**6
Primary Contact: Randy Guidry, Administrator
Web address: www.gulfstateshs.com
— 33 46 14 185 7 0 0 — — 87

ALEXANDRIA—Rapides Parish

☒ **CHRISTUS ST. FRANCES CABRINI HOSPITAL**, 3330 Masonic Drive, Zip 71301–3899; tel. 318/487–1122 **A**1 2 9 10 **F**9 11 12 15 17 19 21 22 23 24 26 27 28 29 33 34 36 37 39 40 41 45 46 48 49 52 53 55 56 57 58 59 61 62 63 64 66 68 69 79 80 81 82 84 86 88 93 94 95 96 107 108 109 110 **S** Christus Health, Irving, TX
Primary Contact: Stephen F. Wright, President and Chief Executive Officer
COO: Bruce Tassin, Chief Operating Officer
CFO: Scott Merryman, Chief Financial Officer
CMO: Jonathan Weisul, M.D., Vice President Medical Affairs & Chief Medical Officer
CIO: Ron Dekeyzer, Chief Information Officer and Vice President Planning
CHR: Gary Lacaze, Director Human Resources
Web address: www.christushealth.org/sfcabrini
— 21 10 258 19793 258 262720 1094 139731 51307 1341

□ **CROSSROADS REGIONAL HOSPITAL**, 110 John Eskew Drive, Zip 71303; tel. 318/445–5111, (Nonreporting) **A**1 10
Primary Contact: Michael E. Geissler, Chief Executive Officer
Web address: www.crossroadshospital.com
— 33 22 70 — — — — — — —

☒ **DUBUIS HOSPITAL OF ALEXANDRIA**, 3330 Masonic Drive, 4th Floor, Zip 71301; tel. 318/448–6505, (Nonreporting) **A**1 10 **S** Dubuis Health System, Houston, TX
Primary Contact: Ray Owens, Administrator and Chief Executive Officer
— 21 80 33 — — — — — — —

☒ **HEALTHSOUTH REHABILITATION HOSPITAL OF ALEXANDRIA**, 104 North Third Street, Zip 71301–8581; tel. 318/449–1370, (Nonreporting) **A**1 10 **S** HEALTHSOUTH Corporation, Birmingham, AL
Primary Contact: Kemp Wright, Administrator
CFO: Bobby Bouillion, Chief Financial Officer
CMO: Vasudeva Dhulipala, M.D., Medical Director
CHR: Suzie Wagner, Human Resource Director
Web address: www.healthsouth.com
— 32 46 47 — — — — — — —

☒ **HEALTHSOUTH RIVERSIDE HOSPITAL OF ALEXANDRIA**, 211 Fourth Street, 5th Floor, Zip 71301; tel. 318/449–8381, (Nonreporting) **A**1 10 **S** HEALTHSOUTH Corporation, Birmingham, AL
Primary Contact: Bryan Day, Administrator
— 33 46 28 — — — — — — —

☒ **RAPIDES REGIONAL MEDICAL CENTER**, 211 Fourth Street, Zip 71301–8421, Mailing Address: Box 30101, 211 Fourth Street, Zip 71306–0146; tel. 318/473–3000 **A**1 2 3 5 10 **F**2 9 11 12 14 15 17 19 21 22 23 24 26 27 28 29 30 31 33 34 35 36 37 38 39 40 42 46 47 48 49 50 52 53 55 56 57 58 59 60 61 62 63 64 65 66 67 69 70 80 81 82 84 85 87 88 89 90 93 94 95 96 97 106 107 108 109 110 **P**1 **S** HCA, Nashville, TN
Primary Contact: A. C. Buchanan, President and Chief Executive Officer
COO: Cheryl Wilson, Chief Operating Officer
CFO: Johnny Crawford, Chief Financial Officer
CMO: Francis Brian, M.D., Senior Vice President Medical Affairs
CHR: Allen Crain, Director Human Resources
Web address: www.rapidesregional.com
— 32 10 323 16829 211 136768 2073 154457 55015 1423

☒ **VETERANS AFFAIRS MEDICAL CENTER**, 2495 Shreveport Highway, 71 North, Zip 71306–6002, Mailing Address: P.O. Box 69004, Zip 71306–9004; tel. 318/473–0010, (Total facility includes 154 beds in nursing home–type unit) (Nonreporting) **A**1 2 3 5 **S** Department of Veterans Affairs, Washington, DC
Primary Contact: Barbara C. Watkins, Director
CFO: Denise Morton, Chief Financial Officer
CMO: Hollis Reed, M.D., Chief of Staff
CIO: Stefan Test, Chief, Information Resource Management Services
Web address: www.va.gov/sta/guide/home.asp
— 45 10 292 — — — — — — —

AMITE—Tangipahoa Parish

★ **HOOD MEMORIAL HOSPITAL**, 301 West Walnut Street, Zip 70422–2098; tel. 504/748–9485 **A**9 10 18 **F**2 28 33 42 52 81 88 97
Primary Contact: A. D. Richardson, Administrator
— 16 10 25 645 5 18720 0 5562 3245 84

Many Facility Codes have changed. Please refer to the AHA Guide Code Chart.
© 2005 AHA Guide

Hospital, Address, Telephone, Approval, Facility, and Physician Codes, Health Care System	Classi-fication Codes		Utilization Data					Expense (thousands) of dollars		
★ American Hospital Association (AHA) membership □ Joint Commission on Accreditation of Healthcare Organizations (JCAHO) accreditation ○ American Osteopathic Association (AOA) accreditation △ Commission on Accreditation of Rehabilitation Facilities (CARF) accreditation	Control	Service	Staffed Beds	Admissions	Census	Outpatient Visits	Births	Total	Payroll	Personnel

BASTROP—Morehouse Parish

BASTROP REHABILITATION HOSPITAL, 323 West Walnut Street, Zip 71220, Mailing Address: P.O. Box 1531, Zip 71221–1531; tel. 318/556–1191 **A**10 **F**21 45 46 47 48 53 58 62 65 68 94 110 Primary Contact: Walter O. Bigby, Administrator and Owner	33	46	15	222	6	—	—	—	—	36
★ **MOREHOUSE GENERAL HOSPITAL**, 323 West Walnut Street, Zip 71220–4521, Mailing Address: P.O. Box 1060, Zip 71221–1060; tel. 318/283–3600 **A**9 10 **F**1 2 9 11 12 21 23 27 29 32 33 34 44 45 46 51 55 58 59 60 61 62 63 65 69 71 76 77 78 81 82 84 88 94 97 110 **P**5 7 8 Primary Contact: William W. Bing, Administrator COO: William W. Bing, Administrator CFO: Brad McCormick, Chief Financial Officer CMO: Timothy Spires, M.D., Chief Medical Staff CIO: David Berry, Information Systems Director CHR: Peggy Stringer, Assistant Administrator Human Resources Web address: www.mghospital.com	16	10	60	2891	32	56405	391	25328	14494	363

BATON ROUGE—East Baton Rouge Parish

⊞ **BATON ROUGE GENERAL MEDICAL CENTER**, 3600 Florida Street, Zip 70806–3889, Mailing Address: P.O. Box 2511, Zip 70821–2511; tel. 225/387–7000, (Includes BATON ROUGE GENERAL MEDICAL CENTER–BLUEBONNET, 8585 Picardy Avenue, Zip 70809–3679, Mailing Address: P.O. Box 84330, Zip 70884–4330; tel. 225/763–4500) **A**1 2 3 5 6 8 9 10 **F**9 11 12 13 14 15 17 19 21 22 23 26 27 29 31 33 37 39 41 42 44 45 46 47 48 49 50 52 53 55 56 57 58 59 60 61 62 63 65 66 67 68 69 70 71 74 75 76 79 81 82 84 86 87 88 92 93 94 95 106 108 109 110 **P**6 Primary Contact: William R. Holman, CHE, President and Chief Executive Officer CFO: Dionne Viator, Senior Vice President and Chief Financial Officer CMO: Floyd Roberts, M.D., Chief Medical Officer CIO: David Hastings, Chief Informatio Officer CHR: Paul Douglas, Vice President, Human Resources Web address: www.generalhealth.org	23	10	429	20691	310	142912	1076	216314	79363	2090
BENTON REHABILITATION HOSPITAL, 4660 Convention Street, Zip 70806; tel. 225/336–1000, (Nonreporting) **A**10 Primary Contact: Shawanza L. Alston, Administrator	23	46	15	—	—	—	—	—	—	—
CYPRESS PSYCHIATRIC HOSPITAL, 4363 Convention Street, Suite A., Zip 70806; tel. 225/336–8940 **A**10 **F**66 71 73 75 76 94 Primary Contact: Kenneth O'Rourke, Administrator	33	46	30	67	1	—	—	—	—	30
□ **CYPRESS REHABILITATION HOSPITAL**, 4363 Convention Street, Zip 70806; tel. 225/383–6134, (Nonreporting) **A**1 10 Primary Contact: Lyndon Darenbourg, Administrator	33	46	30	—	—	—	—	—	—	—
⊞ **EARL K. LONG MEDICAL CENTER**, 5825 Airline Highway, Zip 70805–2498; tel. 225/358–1000, (Nonreporting) **A**1 3 5 9 10 **S** LSU Health Sciences Center, Baton Rouge, LA Primary Contact: Clay Dunaway, Administrator CFO: Sue Tolbert, Chief Financial Officer CIO: Kevin Bolds, Director Information Technology Web address: www.lsuhsc.edu	12	10	144	—	—	—	—	—	—	—
⊞ **HEALTHSOUTH REHABILITATION HOSPITAL OF BATON ROUGE**, 8595 United Plaza Boulevard, Zip 70809–2251; tel. 225/927–0567, (Nonreporting) **A**1 10 **S** HEALTHSOUTH Corporation, Birmingham, AL Primary Contact: Kenneth E. Alexander, Administrator CFO: Andrea Smart, Controller CMO: Gerrald Dynes, M.D., Medical Director CHR: Gayle Courtney, Director Human Resources Web address: www.healthsouth.com	33	46	80	—	—	—	—	—	—	—
NEURO MEDICAL CENTER HOSPITAL, 10105 Park Row Circle, Zip 70810; tel. 225/763–9900, (Nonreporting) **A**9 10 Primary Contact: Kirk Long, Chief Executive Officer	33	49	23	—	—	—	—	—	—	—
⊞ △ **OUR LADY OF THE LAKE REGIONAL MEDICAL CENTER**, 5000 Hennessy Boulevard, Zip 70808–4350; tel. 225/765–6565 **A**1 2 7 9 10 **F**1 2 3 4 9 12 14 15 16 17 18 19 21 22 23 24 26 27 28 29 30 31 32 33 37 38 41 42 44 45 46 47 48 50 52 53 55 57 58 60 61 62 63 64 65 66 67 68 69 70 71 72 73 74 75 76 77 78 79 81 82 84 85 87 88 91 92 93 94 95 96 99 106 108 109 110 **P**2 6 **S** Franciscan Missionaries of Our Lady Health System, Inc., Baton Rouge, LA Primary Contact: Robert C. Davidge, Chief Executive Officer COO: Kirk G. Wilson, President and Chief Operating Officer CFO: Robert Ramsey, Chief Financial Officer CMO: Ronald A. Radzikowski, M.D., Chief Medical Officer CIO: Gary Jump, Vice President Information and Materials Systems CHR: Terry Bowman, Vice President Human Resources Web address: www.olormc.com	21	10	626	31991	473	262310	0	341748	138219	3602
SAGE REHABILITATION INSTITUTE, 8225 Summa Avenue, Zip 70809, Mailing Address: P.O. Box 82681, Zip 70884; tel. 225/819–0703, (Nonreporting) **A**10 Primary Contact: Nicola Gearing, Chief Executive Officer Web address: www.aboutseniorhealthcare.com	31	46	22	—	—	—	—	—	—	—

Hospital, Address, Telephone, Approval, Facility, and Physician Codes, Health Care System	Classi-fication Codes		Utilization Data					Expense (thousands) of dollars		
★ American Hospital Association (AHA) membership □ Joint Commission on Accreditation of Healthcare Organizations (JCAHO) accreditation ○ American Osteopathic Association (AOA) accreditation △ Commission on Accreditation of Rehabilitation Facilities (CARF) accreditation	Control	Service	Staffed Beds	Admissions	Census	Outpatient Visits	Births	Total	Payroll	Personnel
□ **SELECT SPECIALTY HOSPITAL OF BATON ROUGE**, (Formerly SemperCare Hospital of Baton Rouge), 5000 Hennessy Boulevard, 3rd Floor S., Zip 70808; tel. 225/765–5822, (Nonreporting) **A**1 10 Primary Contact: Kerry McLane, Chief Executive Officer	33	80	32	—	—	—	—	—	—	—
□ **SUMMIT HOSPITAL**, 17000 Medical Center Drive, Zip 70816–3224; tel. 225/752–2470, (Nonreporting) **A**1 9 10 **S** Ardent Health Services, Nashville, TN Primary Contact: Robert F. Jernigan, Jr, Chief Executive Officer Web address: www.ahssummithospital.com	33	10	94	—	—	—	—	—	—	—
□ **SURGICAL SPECIALTY CENTRE**, 8080 Bluebonnet Boulevard, Zip 70810; tel. 225/408–8080, (Nonreporting) **A**1 10 Primary Contact: Celeste M. Wiggins, Chief Executive Officer	33	49	14	—	—	—	—	—	—	—
VISTA SURGICAL HOSPITAL OF BATON ROUGE, 9032 Perkins Road, Zip 70810; tel. 225/819–4100, (Nonreporting) **A**10 **S** Dynacq Healthcare, Inc., Houston, TX Primary Contact: Gary Guidry, Chief Executive Officer	33	49	39	—	—	—	—	—	—	—
⊠ **WOMAN'S HOSPITAL**, 9050 Airline Highway, Zip 70815–4192, Mailing Address: P.O. Box 95009, Zip 70895–5009; tel. 225/927–1300 **A**1 2 9 10 **F**2 9 11 12 21 23 24 26 27 28 29 30 31 39 41 42 46 47 48 51 52 53 55 56 58 59 60 61 63 64 65 66 69 81 82 88 89 90 94 96 98 106 108 109 **P**3 6 Primary Contact: Teri G. Fontenot, CHE, President and Chief Executive Officer CFO: Julia Lively, Vice President Finance CMO: Kenneth Brown, M.D., Medical Director CIO: Paul Kirk, Director CHR: Stan Shelton, Vice President Web address: www.womans.org	23	44	211	13044	142	138416	8003	139844	74944	1449
BERNICE—Union Parish										
TRI–WARD GENERAL HOSPITAL, 409 First Street, Zip 71222–0697, Mailing Address: P.O. Box 697, Zip 71222–0697; tel. 318/285–9066, (Nonreporting) **A**9 10 Primary Contact: Charolette Thompson, Chief Executive Officer and Chief Financial Officer	16	10	11	—	—	—	—	—	—	—
BOGALUSA—Washington Parish										
⊠ **BOGALUSA MEDICAL CENTER**, 433 Plaza Street, Zip 70427–3793; tel. 985/732–1722, (Includes BOGALUSA COMMUNITY MEDICAL CENTER, 433 Plaza Street, tel. 504/732–7122; WASHINGTON–ST. TAMMANY REGIONAL MEDICAL CENTER, 400 Memphis Street, Zip 70427–0040, Mailing Address: P.O. Box 40, Zip 70429–0040; tel. 985/735–1322) **A**1 9 10 **F**2 12 21 24 29 33 39 42 44 47 50 52 58 63 64 65 66 69 70 81 82 88 94 106 **S** LSU Health Sciences Center, Baton Rouge, LA Primary Contact: LeVern S. Meades, Administrator CFO: Bryan Lahaye, Chief Financial Officer CMO: Lee Roy Joyner, M.D., Medical Director CIO: Betina Owens, Chief Information Officer CHR: Bet Pounds, Human Resources Director	23	10	66	2630	46	—	—	—	—	455
BOSSIER CITY—Bossier Parish										
CHRISTUS SCHUMPERT BOSSIER See Christus Schumpert Health System, Shreveport										
□ **CORNERSTONE HOSPITAL OF BOSSIER CITY**, 4900 Medical Drive, Zip 71112–4596; tel. 318/747–9500, (Nonreporting) **A**1 10 **S** Cornerstone Healthcare Group, Austin, TX Primary Contact: Jack Cook, Chief Executive Officer and Administrator	33	22	54	—	—	—	—	—	—	—
△ **WILLIS–KNIGHTON BOSSIER HEALTH CENTER**, (Formerly WK Bossier Health Center), 2400 Hospital Drive, Zip 71111; tel. 318/212–7000, (Nonreporting) **A**7 9 10 **S** Willis–Knighton Health System, Shreveport, LA Primary Contact: Donald R. Hebert, FACHE, Administrator	23	46	115	—	—	—	—	—	—	—
BREAUX BRIDGE—St. Martin Parish										
ST. MARTIN HOSPITAL, 210 Champagne Boulevard, Zip 70517–3852, Mailing Address: P.O. Box 357, Zip 70517–0357; tel. 337/332–2178, (Nonreporting) **A**10 18 Primary Contact: Burton Dupuis, Chief Executive Officer	16	10	25	—	—	—	—	—	—	—
BUNKIE—Avoyelles Parish										
★ **BUNKIE GENERAL HOSPITAL**, 427 Evergreen Highway, Zip 71322–3901, Mailing Address: P.O. Box 380, Zip 71322–0380; tel. 318/346–6681 **A**9 10 18 **F**9 21 26 27 28 29 33 39 41 42 45 46 47 48 52 58 63 65 70 71 73 74 75 76 81 84 88 94 97 Primary Contact: Donald L. Kannady, Chief Executive Officer CFO: Priscilla Latta, Chief Financial Officer CMO: Carl Jory, M.D., Chief of Staff CHR: Lonnie Dufour, Human Resource Manager Web address: www.bunkiegeneral.com	16	10	25	543	6	9229	0	—	—	93
CAMERON—Cameron Parish										
SOUTH CAMERON MEMORIAL HOSPITAL, 5360 West Creole Highway, Zip 70631–5127; tel. 337/542–4111, (Nonreporting) **A**9 10 20 **S** Promise Healthcare, Lafayette, LA Primary Contact: David Byrns, Chief Executive Officer	16	10	33	—	—	—	—	—	—	—

Many Facility Codes have changed. Please refer to the AHA Guide Code Chart.

© 2005 AHA Guide

Hospital, Address, Telephone, Approval, Facility, and Physician Codes, Health Care System	Classi-fication Codes		Utilization Data					Expense (thousands) of dollars		
★ American Hospital Association (AHA) membership □ Joint Commission on Accreditation of Healthcare Organizations (JCAHO) accreditation ○ American Osteopathic Association (AOA) accreditation △ Commission on Accreditation of Rehabilitation Facilities (CARF) accreditation	Control	Service	Staffed Beds	Admissions	Census	Outpatient Visits	Births	Total	Payroll	Personnel

CHALMETTE—St. Bernard Parish

□ **CHALMETTE MEDICAL CENTER**, 9001 Patricia Street, Zip 70043–1769; tel. 504/620–6000, (Includes VIRTUE STREET MEDICAL PAVILION, 801 Virtue Street, Zip 70043), (Nonreporting) **A**1 9 10 **S** Universal Health Services, Inc., King of Prussia, PA
Primary Contact: Jon Sewell, Chief Executive Officer
Web address: www.chalmettemedical.com
| | | 33 | 10 | 194 | — | — | — | — | — | — | — |

CHURCH POINT—Acadia Parish

ACADIA–ST. LANDRY HOSPITAL, 810 South Broadway Street, Zip 70525–4497; tel. 337/684–5435, (Total facility includes 15 beds in nursing home–type unit) (Nonreporting) **A**9 10 18
Primary Contact: F. Peter Savoy, III, Chief Executive Officer
Web address: www.aslh.org
| | 23 | 10 | 48 | — | — | — | — | — | — | — |

CLINTON—East Feliciana Parish

□ **CLINTON REHABILITATION HOSPITAL**, 9725 Grace Lane, Zip 70722; tel. 225/683–1600, (Nonreporting) **A**1 10
Primary Contact: Wayne Dodge, Administrator
| | 33 | 10 | 16 | — | — | — | — | — | — | — |

COLUMBIA—Caldwell Parish

CALDWELL MEMORIAL HOSPITAL, 411 Main Street, Zip 71418, Mailing Address: P.O. Box 899, Zip 71418–0899; tel. 318/649–6111, (Nonreporting) **A**9 10
Primary Contact: Faye Long, Administrator
| | 33 | 10 | 25 | — | — | — | — | — | — | — |

CITIZENS MEDICAL CENTER, 7939 U.S. Highway 165, Zip 71418–1079, Mailing Address: P.O. Box 1079, Zip 71418–1079; tel. 318/649–6106, (Nonreporting) **A**9 10
Primary Contact: Steve Barbo, R.N., Administrator
| | 16 | 10 | 40 | — | — | — | — | — | — | — |

COUSHATTA—Red River Parish

⊞ **CHRISTUS COUSHATTA HEALTH CARE CENTER**, 1635 Marvel Street, Zip 71019–9022, Mailing Address: P.O. Box 589, Zip 71019–0589; tel. 318/932–2000 **A**1 9 10 18 20 **F**21 22 29 32 33 39 42 46 48 52 58 63 66 69 77 81 84 88 92 94 97 108 **S** Christus Health, Irving, TX
Primary Contact: Karen Mixon, Interim Administrator
CFO: Sandra Harlan, Chief Financial Officer
CMO: Wyche Coleman, Jr, M.D., Chief Medical Officer
CIO: Bruce Honea, Director Information Services
CHR: Donnette Craig, Director of Human Resources
Web address: www.christushealth.org
| | 23 | 10 | 25 | 1374 | 25 | 37213 | 0 | — | — | 112 |

COMMUNITY REHABILITATION HOSPITAL OF COUSHATTA, 1110 Ringgold Avenue, Suite B., Zip 71019; tel. 318/932–1770 **A**10 **F**2 21 45 46 58 68 69 94 110
Primary Contact: Allison Cooper, Administrator
| | 33 | 46 | 12 | 246 | 8 | 617 | 0 | — | — | 37 |

COVINGTON—St. Tammany Parish

□ **GULF STATE LONG TERM ACUTE CARE OF COVINGTON**, 20050 Crestwood Boulevard, Zip 70433; tel. 985/874–7525, (Nonreporting) **A**1 10
| | 33 | 49 | 58 | — | — | — | — | — | — | — |

⊞ **LAKEVIEW REGIONAL MEDICAL CENTER**, 95 East Fairway Drive, Zip 70433–7507; tel. 985/867–3800, (Total facility includes 12 beds in nursing home–type unit) **A**1 9 10 **F**9 10 11 12 15 17 19 21 26 27 28 29 32 33 45 46 47 48 52 53 55 58 59 60 61 63 69 71 75 76 81 82 84 85 87 88 92 94 96 108 109 **S** HCA, Nashville, TN
Primary Contact: Max Lauderdale, Chief Executive Officer
CFO: Tim Breslin, Chief Financial Officer
CMO: George Barnes, M.D., Medical Director
CIO: Debra Willie, Director Medical Records
CHR: Lyle Theriot, Director Human Resources
Web address: www.lakeviewregional.com
| | 33 | 10 | 178 | 7094 | 96 | 59972 | 1004 | 67352 | 25329 | 478 |

⊞ **REGENCY HOSPITAL OF COVINGTON**, 195 Highland Park Entrance, Zip 70433; tel. 985/867–3977 **A**1 10 **F**2 21 23 29 37 49 94 110 **S** Regency Hospital Company, Alpharetta, GA
Primary Contact: Laurence J. Frayne, Chief Executive Officer
| | 33 | 80 | 24 | 125 | 9 | — | — | — | — | 74 |

⊞ **ST. TAMMANY PARISH HOSPITAL**, 1202 South Tyler Street, Zip 70433–2394; tel. 985/898–4000 **A**1 2 9 10 **F**2 9 10 11 12 14 21 22 23 24 26 27 28 29 33 36 37 39 40 41 42 46 47 48 51 52 54 55 56 58 59 61 63 65 66 68 69 73 75 81 82 84 85 88 92 93 94 96 106 108
Primary Contact: Patti M. Ellish, R.N., President and Chief Executive Officer
COO: Sharon A. Toups, Senior Vice President and Chief Operating Officer
CFO: David L. Mabe, Senior Vice President and Chief Financial Officer
CMO: Robert Capitelli, M.D., Senior Vice President and Chief Medical Officer
CIO: Frankie Barrios, Department Head Information Systems
CHR: Judy Gracia, Vice President Human Resources
Web address: www.stph.org
| | 16 | 10 | 203 | 11341 | 149 | 133980 | 1451 | — | — | 1322 |

CROWLEY—Acadia Parish

ACADIA REHABILITATION HOSPITAL, 1305 Crowley Rayne Highway, Zip 70526, Mailing Address: P.O. Box 648, Zip 70527–0648; tel. 337/785–2111, (Nonreporting) **A**10
Primary Contact: April Bearb, Administrator
| | 33 | 46 | 10 | — | — | — | — | — | — | — |

★ **AMERICAN LEGION HOSPITAL**, 1305 Crowley Rayne Highway, Zip 70526; tel. 337/783–3222, (Nonreporting) **A**9 10
Primary Contact: Terry W. Osborne, CPA, Chief Executive Officer
CFO: Charmaine Vidrine, CPA, Chief Financial Officer
CMO: Joshua P. Mammen, M.D., Chief of Staff
Web address: www.alh.org
| | 23 | 10 | 178 | — | — | — | — | — | — | — |

Hospital, Address, Telephone, Approval, Facility, and Physician Codes, Health Care System	Classi-fication Codes		Utilization Data					Expense (thousands) of dollars		
★ American Hospital Association (AHA) membership □ Joint Commission on Accreditation of Healthcare Organizations (JCAHO) accreditation ○ American Osteopathic Association (AOA) accreditation △ Commission on Accreditation of Rehabilitation Facilities (CARF) accreditation	Control	Service	Staffed Beds	Admissions	Census	Outpatient Visits	Births	Total	Payroll	Personnel
CROWLEY REHABILITATION HOSPITAL, 713 North Avenue L., Zip 70526; tel. 337/783–2859 **A**10 **F**68 Primary Contact: Gil Pinac, Chief Executive Officer	32	46	15	71	8	0	0	1402	—	37
CUT OFF—Lafourche Parish										
✠ **LADY OF THE SEA GENERAL HOSPITAL**, 200 West 134th Place, Zip 70345–4145; tel. 985/632–6401 **A**1 9 10 20 **F**2 21 23 26 28 29 33 36 37 38 40 42 44 46 47 48 49 50 51 52 57 58 60 61 63 64 65 66 69 70 71 74 75 76 81 84 88 93 94 96 97 108 **P**6 **S** Brim Healthcare, Inc., Brentwood, TN Primary Contact: Raymond L. Ford, FACHE, Chief Executive Officer CFO: Jeff Morrow, Chief Operating Officer Web address: www.losgh.com	13	10	49	1542	19	74553	0	19342	7612	240
DE RIDDER—Beauregard Parish										
✠ **BEAUREGARD MEMORIAL HOSPITAL**, 600 South Pine Street, Zip 70634–4998, Mailing Address: P.O. Box 730, Zip 70634–0730; tel. 337/462–7100 **A**1 9 10 **F**2 9 11 12 14 15 21 22 23 29 33 39 41 46 51 52 55 58 59 61 62 63 64 69 81 85 88 92 94 97 108 **P**5 Primary Contact: Theodore J. Badger, Jr, CHE, Chief Executive Officer CFO: Darrell L. Kingham, CPA, Vice President Finance CMO: Tom Dobbins, M.D., President Medical Staff CIO: Meg Jackson, Director Biomedical Management Information Systems CHR: Mary Jones, Director Human Resources Web address: www.beauregard.org	16	10	60	3198	31	38858	394	25174	11137	313
DELHI—Richland Parish										
RICHLAND PARISH HOSPITAL, 407 Cincinnati Street, Zip 71232–3009; tel. 318/878–5171 **A**9 10 **F**2 12 21 23 27 28 33 39 45 46 48 52 60 63 65 69 71 75 76 77 81 88 94 97 106 109 110 Primary Contact: Michael W. Carroll, Administrator Web address: www.delhihospital.com	16	10	34	1042	9	—	0	—	—	181
DENHAM SPRINGS—Livingston Parish										
□ **GULF STATES LTAC OF DENHAM SPRINGS**, (Formerly Dixon Medical Center), 8375 Florida Boulevard, Zip 70726; tel. 225/665–2664, (Nonreporting) **A**1 10 Primary Contact: J. Clifton Quinn, Administrator	33	49	117							
DEQUINCY—Calcasieu Parish										
DEQUINCY MEMORIAL HOSPITAL, 110 West Fourth Street, Zip 70633–3508, Mailing Address: P.O. Box 1166, Zip 70633–1166; tel. 337/786–1200 **A**9 10 18 **F**21 46 63 81 97 108 **S** Promise Healthcare, Lafayette, LA Primary Contact: Barbara Hollingsworth, Administrator and Chief Executive Officer Web address: www.dequincyhospital.com	14	10	19	815	7	—	—	—	—	
DONALDSONVILLE—Ascension Parish										
✠ **PREVOST MEMORIAL HOSPITAL**, (CAH), 301 Memorial Drive, Zip 70346–4376; tel. 225/473–7931 **A**1 9 10 18 **F**9 12 21 33 46 48 88 93 94 97 108 **P**4 Primary Contact: Vincent A. Cataldo, Administrator CFO: Jane Arboneaux, Chief Financial Officer CMO: C K. Angelo, M.D., Chief Medical Staff CIO: Bobbie Sternfels, Medical Records Supervisor CHR: Linda Cataldo, Human Resources Secretary	16	49	25	220	2	10401	0	4108	1513	59
EUNICE—St. Landry Parish										
✠ **EUNICE COMMUNITY MEDICAL CENTER**, 400 Moosa Boulevard, Zip 70535–3628; tel. 337/457–5244, (Nonreporting) **A**1 9 10 **S** LifePoint Hospitals, Inc., Brentwood, TN Primary Contact: Charlotte Dupre, Chief Executive Officer CFO: Robert Jackson, Chief Financial Officer CMO: Robert K. Guillory, Jr, M.D., Chief Medical Staff Web address: www.eunicemedical.com	33	10	52	—	—	—	—	—	—	
FARMERVILLE—Union Parish										
UNION GENERAL HOSPITAL, 901 James Avenue, Zip 71241–0398, Mailing Address: P.O. Box 398, Zip 71241–0398; tel. 318/368–9751, (Nonreporting) **A**9 10 18 Primary Contact: Evalyn Ormond, Administrator Web address: www.uniongeneralhospital.com	23	10	25							
FERRIDAY—Concordia Parish										
□ **PROMISE SPECIALTY HOSPITAL OF FERRIDAY**, 6818–A Highway 84, Zip 71334–5101; tel. 318/757–7575, (Nonreporting) **A**1 10 **S** Promise Healthcare, Lafayette, LA Primary Contact: Lee Huckaby, Chief Executive Officer Web address: www.camelothealthcare.net	33	49	40	—	—	—	—	—	—	
RIVERLAND MEDICAL CENTER, 1700 North E 'E' Wallace Boulevard, Zip 71334–0111, Mailing Address: P.O. Box 111, Zip 71334–0111; tel. 318/757–6551 **A**9 10 18 **F**9 11 12 21 22 26 27 28 29 33 46 47 48 52 55 59 63 81 88 97 108 **P**5 Primary Contact: Vernon R. Stevens, Jr, Administrator	21	10	25	1857	17	11757	319	—	—	197

Many Facility Codes have changed. Please refer to the AHA Guide Code Chart.

© 2005 AHA Guide

Hospital, Address, Telephone, Approval, Facility, and Physician Codes, Health Care System	Classi-fication Codes		Utilization Data					Expense (thousands) of dollars		
★ American Hospital Association (AHA) membership □ Joint Commission on Accreditation of Healthcare Organizations (JCAHO) accreditation ○ American Osteopathic Association (AOA) accreditation △ Commission on Accreditation of Rehabilitation Facilities (CARF) accreditation	Control	Service	Staffed Beds	Admissions	Census	Outpatient Visits	Births	Total	Payroll	Personnel

FORT POLK—Vernon Parish

✠ **BAYNE–JONES ARMY COMMUNITY HOSPITAL**, 1585 Third Street, Zip 71459–5110; tel. 337/531–3928 **A**1 **F**2 4 6 9 10 11 12 21 22 24 27 28 29 31 32 33 34 35 37 39 41 45 46 47 48 50 52 53 58 59 60 62 63 64 65 66 69 70 72 73 74 75 77 81 88 92 94 95 96 98 106 108 109 110 **P**5 **S** Department of the Army, Office of the Surgeon General, Falls Church, VA
Primary Contact: Colonel Steven Swann, Deputy Commander for Clinical Services
COO: Colonel Steven Hale, Deputy Commander for Administration
CFO: Major Karl Devlin, Chief, Resource Management Division
CIO: Captain Daniel Bridon, Chief Information Management Division
CHR: Major Karl Devlin, Chief, Resource Management Division
Web address: www.polk.amedd.army.mil
— 42 10 33 1082 8 267379 486 — — 758

FRANKLIN—St. Mary Parish

✠ **FRANKLIN FOUNDATION HOSPITAL**, 1501 Hospital Avenue, Zip 70538–3724, Mailing Address: P.O. Box 577, Zip 70538–0577; tel. 337/828–0760 **A**1 9 10 18 **F**9 11 12 14 21 33 55 59 62 63 69 81 84 88 92 94 96 97 108 **S** Quorum Health Resources, Plano, TX
Primary Contact: J. Calvin Green, Chief Executive Officer
CFO: Gary Marti, Chief Financial Officer
CMO: Moses Kitakule, M.D., Chief of Staff
CIO: Thomas Stirling, Chief Information Officer
CHR: David Williamson, Director Human Resources
Web address: www.franklinfoundation.org
— 16 10 25 990 10 — — — — 132

FRANKLINTON—Washington Parish

✠ **RIVERSIDE MEDICAL CENTER**, 1900 Main Street, Zip 70438–3688; tel. 985/839–4431 **A**1 9 10 18 **F**2 9 12 21 23 26 27 28 33 44 46 48 52 55 58 60 61 62 63 64 69 70 81 82 85 88 94 96 97 108
Primary Contact: Conrad G. Flowers, Chief Executive Officer
CFO: Patricia A. Mizell, Chief Financial Officer
CMO: Kyle Magee, M.D., Chief of Staff
CIO: Herman Ingram, Director
— 16 10 25 1322 13 23235 0 14532 6033 142

GONZALES—Ascension Parish

□ **ASCENSION HOSPITAL**, (Formerly Ascension Hospital and Behavioral Health Services), 615 East Worthey Road, Zip 70737–4240; tel. 225/621–1248 **A**1 10 **F**2 27 28 44 55 58 71 76 94 110
Primary Contact: Michael J. Nolan, Chief Executive Officer
Web address: www.ascensionhospital.org
— 16 80 32 410 27 0 0 9502 4135 121

✠ **ST. ELIZABETH HOSPITAL**, 1125 West Highway 30, Zip 70737; tel. 225/647–5000 **A**1 9 10 **F**2 9 12 21 22 28 33 46 52 53 55 62 63 64 66 71 75 76 81 82 84 85 88 93 94 97 108 **S** Franciscan Missionaries of Our Lady Health System, Inc., Baton Rouge, LA
Primary Contact: Dee LeJeune, Chief Executive Officer
CFO: Sue Knight, Controller
CMO: Craig Vitrano, M.D., Assistant Vice President Patient Care Services
CIO: Charlotte Crummey, Director Information Services
CHR: Janice Adams, Director Human Resources
Web address: www.steh.com
— 21 10 83 2983 39 49281 0 25821 10852 292

GREENSBURG—St. Helena Parish

ST. HELENA PARISH HOSPITAL, Highway 43 North, Zip 70441, Mailing Address: P.O. Box 337, Zip 70441–0337; tel. 225/222–6111, (Nonreporting) **A**9 10 18
Primary Contact: Alcus Trahan, Administrator and Chief Executive Officer
— 23 10 25 — — — — — — —

GRETNA—Jefferson Parish

HEALTHWEST REHABILITATION HOSPITAL, 3201 Wall Boulevard, Suite B., Zip 70056; tel. 504/433–5551, (Nonreporting) **A**10
Primary Contact: Vicki Cressionnie, Executive Director
— 31 46 15 — — — — — — —

✠ **MEADOWCREST HOSPITAL**, 2500 Belle Chase Highway, Zip 70056–7196; tel. 504/392–3131 **A**1 9 10 **F**2 9 11 12 14 15 17 19 21 22 23 28 33 34 40 41 52 53 55 56 57 59 60 61 62 63 64 65 66 68 69 81 82 84 86 87 88 92 94 106 108 109 110 **S** TENET Healthcare Corporation, Dallas, TX
Primary Contact: Phillip E. Sowa, Chief Executive Officer
COO: Michael Beaver, Chief Operating Officer
CFO: Christopher W. Daniel, Chief Financial Officer
CIO: Stephen Coffman, Chief Information Officer
CHR: Juanita Haas, Human Resources Director
Web address: www.meadowcresthosp.com
— 33 10 221 8353 121 63508 1758 73522 33412 593

HAMMOND—Tangipahoa Parish

HAMMOND REHABILITATION HOSPITAL, 15719 Belle Drive, Zip 70403; tel. 985/902–8148, (Nonreporting) **A**10
Primary Contact: James McEwen, Administrator
— 33 46 20 — — — — — — —

✠ △ **NORTH OAKS MEDICAL CENTER**, 15790 Paul Vega, M. D. Drive, Zip 70403–1436, Mailing Address: P.O. Box 2668, Zip 70404–2668; tel. 985/345–2700 **A**1 7 9 10 19 **F**2 11 12 14 15 17 19 21 22 26 27 28 33 36 37 38 39 44 45 46 48 51 55 56 57 58 59 60 61 62 63 64 65 66 69 71 75 76 77 81 82 84 85 87 88 92 93 94 95 96 107 108 109 110 **P**6
Primary Contact: James E. Cathey, Jr, Chief Executive Officer
COO: Brian D. Hannah, Chief Operating Officer
CFO: Shirley Hsing, Chief Financial Officer
CMO: James Nelson, M.D., Chief Medical Officer
CIO: Bach Nguyen, Information Systems Director
CHR: Carolyn Adema, Human Resources Officer
Web address: www.northoaks.org
— 16 10 199 13055 199 183035 1441 133536 73024 1908

Hospital, Address, Telephone, Approval, Facility, and Physician Codes, Health Care System	Classi-fication Codes		Utilization Data					Expense (thousands) of dollars		
	Control	Service	Staffed Beds	Admissions	Census	Outpatient Visits	Births	Total	Payroll	Personnel

★ American Hospital Association (AHA) membership
□ Joint Commission on Accreditation of Healthcare Organizations (JCAHO) accreditation
○ American Osteopathic Association (AOA) accreditation
△ Commission on Accreditation of Rehabilitation Facilities (CARF) accreditation

□ **NORTH OAKS REHABILITATION HOSPITAL**, 1900 South Morrison Boulevard, Zip 70403; tel. 504/230–5700 **A**1 10 **F**21 27 28 44 45 46 49 58 60 65 66 68 94 96 108 **P**6 Primary Contact: Sybil Paulson, R.N., Administrator Web address: www.northoaks.org	16	46	27	622	19	0	0	10129	2395	46

HOMER—Claiborne Parish

HOMER MEMORIAL HOSPITAL, 620 East College Street, Zip 71040–3202; tel. 318/927–2024 **A**9 10 **F**2 11 12 21 22 26 27 28 29 33 37 44 45 46 48 51 52 55 58 59 63 65 66 71 74 76 81 88 92 94 96 97 110 **P**5 Primary Contact: Douglas P. Efferson, Administrator Web address: www.homerhospital.com	23	10	60	2349	33	18447	30	13154	5532	193

HOUMA—Terrebonne Parish

✠ **LEONARD J. CHABERT MEDICAL CENTER**, 1978 Industrial Boulevard, Zip 70363–7094; tel. 985/873–2200, (Nonreporting) **A**1 9 10 **S** LSU Health Sciences Center, Baton Rouge, LA Primary Contact: Daniel M. Trahan, Administrator CFO: Elizabeth Callais, Chief Fiscal Officer CMO: Michael Garcia, M.D., Medical Director CIO: Susan Arceneaux, R.N., Information Technology Coordinator CHR: Steve Curry, Human Resources Director	12	10	83	—	—	—	—	—	—	—
PHYSICIANS SURGICAL SPECIALTY HOSPITAL, 218 Corporate Drive, Zip 70360–2764; tel. 985/853–1390, (Nonreporting) **A**9 10 Primary Contact: Connie Martin, Administrator	33	49	10	—	—	—	—	—	—	—
✠ △ **TERREBONNE GENERAL MEDICAL CENTER**, 8166 Main Street, Zip 70360–3498, Mailing Address: P.O. Box 6037, Zip 70361–6037; tel. 985/873–4141, (Total facility includes 16 beds in nursing home–type unit) **A**1 7 9 10 **F**3 4 11 12 14 15 17 19 21 23 27 28 29 33 35 39 43 44 47 48 52 55 56 58 59 60 61 62 63 64 65 66 68 69 71 72 73 74 75 76 77 81 82 84 87 88 92 93 94 96 98 106 108 109 110 **P**6 Primary Contact: Phyllis Peoples, MSN, R.N., President and Chief Executive Officer CFO: Diane Yeates, Senior Vice President Financial Services CMO: Peter Fail, M.D., Chief of Staff CHR: John Ford, Director of Human Resources Web address: www.tgmc.com	16	10	327	13819	176	107780	1793	145081	58211	1387

INDEPENDENCE—Tagipahoa Parish

✠ **LALLIE KEMP MEDICAL CENTER**, 52579 Highway 51 South, Zip 70443–2231; tel. 985/878–9421 **A**1 9 10 **F**2 12 21 24 26 27 28 30 33 34 46 47 48 50 52 53 55 58 60 61 63 65 66 70 81 88 94 106 108 109 110 **P**6 **S** LSU Health Sciences Center, Baton Rouge, LA Primary Contact: LeVern S. Meades, Administrator COO: Sherre P. Hookfin, Associate Administrator CFO: Mike Hathorn, Chief Financial Officer CMO: Terry R. Jones, M.D., Medical Director CIO: Charles Tate, Information Technology Director CHR: Kevin Brady, Director Human Resources Web address: www.lak.lsuhsc.edu	12	10	28	1382	17	108575	0	27298	14678	396

JACKSON—East Feliciana Parish

□ **EASTERN LOUISIANA MENTAL HEALTH SYSTEM**, 4502 Highway 951, Zip 70748–5842, Mailing Address: P.O. Box 498, Zip 70748–0498; tel. 225/634–0100, (Nonreporting) **A**1 10 **S** Louisiana State Hospitals, New Orleans, LA Primary Contact: Herbert Erwin, Chief Executive Officer	12	22	605	—	—	—	—	—	—	—
VILLA FELICIANA MEDICAL COMPLEX, 5002 Highway 10, Zip 70748–3627, Mailing Address: P.O. Box 438, Zip 70748–0438; tel. 225/634–4000 **A**10 **F**2 6 32 76 92 94 Primary Contact: James E. Bradham, Administrator	12	80	225	83	182	—	0	—	—	345

JENA—La Salle Parish

★ **LASALLE GENERAL HOSPITAL**, 187 Ninth Street, Zip 71342–2780, Mailing Address: P.O. Box 2780, Zip 71342–2780; tel. 318/992–9200 **A**9 10 **F**6 9 12 21 26 33 41 46 48 51 52 63 69 81 82 88 94 97 **P**5 6 Primary Contact: Mary B. Moffett, CPA, Administrator CFO: Allyson Fannin, CPA, Chief Financial Officer CMO: M Moosa, M.D., Chief of Staff Web address: www.lasallegeneralhospital.com	16	10	60	2068	35	21323	0	14432	6960	228

JENNINGS—Jefferson Davis Parish

□ **JENNINGS AMERICAN LEGION HOSPITAL**, 1634 Elton Road, Zip 70546–3614; tel. 337/616–7000 **A**1 9 10 **F**2 9 11 12 14 21 33 39 44 46 48 49 52 53 55 58 59 65 66 70 81 82 84 88 92 94 97 108 Primary Contact: Terry J. Terrebonne, Chief Executive Officer Web address: www.jalh.com	23	10	60	4229	41	—	0	—	—	299

JONESBORO—Jackson Parish

JACKSON PARISH HOSPITAL, 165 Beech Springs Road, Zip 71251–2059; tel. 318/259–4435, (Nonreporting) **A**9 10 18 Primary Contact: L. J. Pecot, Administrator Web address: www.jacksonparishhospital.com	16	10	25	—	—	—	—	—	—	—

KAPLAN—Vermilion Parish

ABROM KAPLAN MEMORIAL HOSPITAL, 1310 West Seventh Street, Zip 70548–2998; tel. 337/643–8300 **A**9 10 **F**26 27 33 48 63 71 76 81 92 97 108 Primary Contact: Lyman Trahan, Chief Executive Officer	16	10	15	686	8	29763	0	—	—	115

Hospital, Address, Telephone, Approval, Facility, and Physician Codes, Health Care System	Classi-fication Codes		Utilization Data					Expense (thousands) of dollars		
	Control	Service	Staffed Beds	Admissions	Census	Outpatient Visits	Births	Total	Payroll	Personnel

★ American Hospital Association (AHA) membership
□ Joint Commission on Accreditation of Healthcare Organizations (JCAHO) accreditation
○ American Osteopathic Association (AOA) accreditation
△ Commission on Accreditation of Rehabilitation Facilities (CARF) accreditation

Hospital	Control	Service	Staffed Beds	Admissions	Census	Outpatient Visits	Births	Total	Payroll	Personnel
KAPLAN REHABILITATION HOSPITAL, 1310 West 7th Street, Zip 70548, Mailing Address: P.O. Box 219, Zip 70548; tel. 337/643–6009 **A**10 **F**21 44 68 94 110 Primary Contact: Mark Cullen, Chief Executive Officer	33	46	20	117	5	0	0	—	—	45

KENNER—Jefferson Parish

Hospital	Control	Service	Staffed Beds	Admissions	Census	Outpatient Visits	Births	Total	Payroll	Personnel
⊞ **KENNER REGIONAL MEDICAL CENTER**, 180 West Esplanade Avenue, Zip 70065–6001; tel. 504/468–8600 **A**1 3 5 9 10 **F**2 9 11 12 21 23 26 27 28 33 41 44 45 47 48 52 55 57 58 59 60 61 62 63 65 71 73 74 76 78 81 82 84 85 88 94 95 106 108 110 **S** TENET Healthcare Corporation, Dallas, TX Primary Contact: Paolo Zambito, Interim Chief Executive Officer COO: Paolo Zambito, Chief Operating Officer CFO: Mark Eckert, Chief Financial Officer Web address: www.kennerregional.com	33	10	104	4812	86	54748	568	55631	24181	524
□ **LIFECARE HOSPITALS–KENNER CAMPUS**, 180 West Esplanade Avenue, Zip 70065; tel. 504/461–0710, (Nonreporting) **A**1 10 **S** LifeCare Management Services, Plano, TX Primary Contact: Tim Burke, Chief Executive Officer	33	49	28	—	—	—	—	—	—	—

KENTWOOD—Tangipahoa Parish

Hospital	Control	Service	Staffed Beds	Admissions	Census	Outpatient Visits	Births	Total	Payroll	Personnel
SOUTHEAST REGIONAL MEDICAL CENTER, 719 Avenue G., Zip 70444–2601; tel. 985/229–9193, (Nonreporting) **A**10 Primary Contact: Lionel Murphy, Chief Executive Officer	33	49	14	—	—	—	—	—	—	—

KINDER—Allen Parish

Hospital	Control	Service	Staffed Beds	Admissions	Census	Outpatient Visits	Births	Total	Payroll	Personnel
★ **ALLEN PARISH HOSPITAL**, 108 North Sixth Avenue, Zip 70648–3519, Mailing Address: P.O. Box 1670, Zip 70648–1670; tel. 337/738–2527 **A**9 10 **F**3 21 28 71 81 88 92 93 97 Primary Contact: Scott Barrilleaux, Chief Executive Officer and Administrator	16	22	49	367	4	6114	0	—	—	115

LA PLACE—St. John the Baptist Parish

Hospital	Control	Service	Staffed Beds	Admissions	Census	Outpatient Visits	Births	Total	Payroll	Personnel
LA PLACE REHABILITATION HOSPITAL, 508 West 5th Street, Zip 70068; tel. 985/653–8447 **A**10 **F**21 35 37 45 46 49 66 68 94 **P**5 Primary Contact: Peter Jolet, Administrator Web address: www.gulfstateshs.com	33	46	22	230	11	—	0	—	—	30
⊞ **RIVER PARISHES HOSPITAL**, 500 Rue de Sante, Zip 70068–5420; tel. 985/652–7000 **A**1 9 10 **F**9 11 12 21 22 29 33 37 46 48 49 55 57 58 59 60 61 63 69 81 82 84 88 93 94 95 108 109 110 **S** LifePoint Hospitals, Inc., Brentwood, TN Primary Contact: Scott Boudreaux, Chief Executive Officer CFO: Stephen East, Controller CIO: Wayne Philebar, Chief Information Officer CHR: Kat Trepagnier, Human Resource Director Web address: www.riverparisheshospital.com	33	10	60	2677	27	43282	361	—	—	280

LACOMBE—St. Tammany Parish

Hospital	Control	Service	Staffed Beds	Admissions	Census	Outpatient Visits	Births	Total	Payroll	Personnel
□ **LOUISIANA HEART HOSPITAL**, 64030 Highway 434, Zip 70445; tel. 985/690–7500 **A**1 10 **F**14 15 16 17 18 19 20 21 22 23 26 33 34 37 39 46 47 48 49 55 57 58 61 62 63 65 66 73 81 82 84 88 96 106 109 **S** MedCath, Inc., Charlotte, NC Primary Contact: Larry D. Walker, President and Chief Executive Officer Web address: www.louisianahearthospital.com	33	10	58	1956	15	—	0	36027	10589	—

LAFAYETTE—Lafayette Parish

Hospital	Control	Service	Staffed Beds	Admissions	Census	Outpatient Visits	Births	Total	Payroll	Personnel
COMMUNITY REHABILITATION HOSPITAL OF LAFAYETTE, 811 Martin Luther King Jr. Drive, Zip 70501; tel. 337/234–4031, (Nonreporting) **A**10 Primary Contact: John E. Jumonville, III, Administrator	33	10	36	—	—	—	—	—	—	—
□ **HEART HOSPITAL OF LAFAYETTE**, 1105 Kaliste Saloom, Zip 70508; tel. 337/521–1000 **A**1 9 10 **F**2 14 15 17 19 21 22 26 27 28 33 48 58 63 64 65 81 82 85 88 **P**2 **S** MedCath, Inc., Charlotte, NC Primary Contact: Phil Young, President Web address: www.hearthospitaloflafayette.com	33	42	24	580	8	1580	0	16217	4812	150
⊞ **LAFAYETTE GENERAL MEDICAL CENTER**, 1214 Coolidge Avenue, Zip 70503–2696, Mailing Address: P.O. Box 52009 OCS, Zip 70505–2009; tel. 337/289–7991 **A**1 2 9 10 **F**2 9 10 11 12 14 15 16 17 18 19 20 21 22 23 24 28 29 33 34 37 38 39 40 41 42 44 45 46 48 49 51 52 55 56 57 58 59 60 61 62 63 64 66 67 68 69 70 71 75 76 79 81 82 84 85 87 88 92 94 96 106 107 108 109 110 **P**8 Primary Contact: James G. Thaw, President and Chief Executive Officer COO: Donna Landry, Chief Operating Officer CFO: Roger Mattke, Chief Financial Officer CMO: Maurice Sullivan, M.D., Medical Director CIO: Anne D. Pyle, Chief Information Officer CHR: Diane Broussard, Director Human Resources Web address: www.lafayettegeneral.org	23	10	297	14359	191	160885	1558	147969	56580	1512
□ **LAFAYETTE SURGICAL SPECIALTY HOSPITAL**, 1101 Kaliste Saloom Road, Zip 70508, Mailing Address: P.O. Box 52812, Zip 70505; tel. 337/769–4100, (Nonreporting) **A**1 10 Primary Contact: Thomas W. Cooper, Chief Executive Officer	33	49	20	—	—	—	—	—	—	—
LOUISIANA EXTENDED CARE HOSPITAL OF LAFAYETTE, 2707 Kaliste Saloom Road, Zip 70508; tel. 337/984–8878, (Nonreporting) **A**10 Primary Contact: Stuart Archer, Administrator	13	46	10	—	—	—	—	—	—	—

Hospital, Address, Telephone, Approval, Facility, and Physician Codes, Health Care System	Classi-fication Codes		Utilization Data					Expense (thousands) of dollars		
★ American Hospital Association (AHA) membership □ Joint Commission on Accreditation of Healthcare Organizations (JCAHO) accreditation ○ American Osteopathic Association (AOA) accreditation △ Commission on Accreditation of Rehabilitation Facilities (CARF) accreditation	Control	Service	Staffed Beds	Admissions	Census	Outpatient Visits	Births	Total	Payroll	Personnel
□ **MEADOWBROOK REHABILITATION HOSPITAL OF LAFAYETTE**, 204 Energy Parkway, Zip 70508; tel. 337/232–1905, (Nonreporting) **A1** 10 Primary Contact: Nick Zaunbrecher, CPA, Chief Operating Officer	33	10	50	—	—	—	—	—	—	—
⊞ **OUR LADY OF LOURDES REGIONAL MEDICAL CENTER**, 611 St. Landry Street, Zip 70506–4627, Mailing Address: P.O. Box 4027, Zip 70502–4027; tel. 337/289–2000, (Total facility includes 26 beds in nursing home–type unit) **A1** 2 9 10 **F2** 7 9 12 15 17 19 21 22 23 24 26 27 28 29 33 34 37 38 39 40 41 42 45 46 48 49 52 53 55 57 58 60 61 62 63 64 66 68 69 81 82 84 85 87 88 92 93 94 95 96 106 107 108 109 110 **P8 S** Franciscan Missionaries of Our Lady Health System, Inc., Baton Rouge, LA Primary Contact: Robert Peebles, President and Chief Executive Officer COO: Barbara Feske, Administrator Management and Support CFO: Jeff Limbocker, Chief Financial Officer CIO: Nona Mire, Director Information Systems CHR: Kevin Domingue, Director, Human Resources Web address: www.lourdes.net	21	10	264	11404	175	113678	1	170144	59305	1309
PARK PLACE SURGERY CENTER, 901 Wilson Street, Zip 70503; tel. 337/237–8119, (Nonreporting) **A**10 Primary Contact: Brandon Moore, CHE, Administrator and Chief Executive Officer	33	49	10	—	—	—	—	—	—	—
REHABILITATION HOSPITAL OF ACADIANA, 310 Youngsville Highway, Zip 70508; tel. 337/839–9880 **A**10 **F**21 45 52 53 58 65 69 70 88 94 107 110 Primary Contact: James H. Morgan, Chief Executive Officer	31	10	27	292	20	—	0	—	—	98
⊞ **SOUTHWEST MEDICAL CENTER**, 2810 Ambassador Caffery Parkway, Zip 70506–5900; tel. 337/981–2949 **A**1 9 10 **F**2 10 12 14 15 17 19 21 22 23 27 28 29 33 37 38 46 48 52 55 57 58 62 63 64 65 66 68 69 81 82 84 85 88 94 107 108 110 **S** HCA, Nashville, TN Primary Contact: Stephen K. Jones, Jr, FACHE, Chief Executive Officer COO: Alan Fabian, Chief Operating Officer CFO: Penny Hutson, Chief Financial Officer Web address: www.southwestmc.com	33	10	135	4594	68	64301	1	52419	15917	363
ST. LUKE'S REHABILITATION HOSPITAL, 2500 East Simcoe, Zip 70501; tel. 337/233–2864, (Nonreporting) **A**10 Primary Contact: David L. Vaughn, Administrator	33	46	21	—	—	—	—	—	—	—
⊞ **UNIVERSITY MEDICAL CENTER**, 2390 West Congress Street, Zip 70506–4298, Mailing Address: P.O. Box 69300, Zip 70596–9300; tel. 337/261–6001, (Nonreporting) **A**1 2 3 5 9 10 **S** LSU Health Sciences Center, Baton Rouge, LA Primary Contact: Lawrence T. Dorsey, Administrator and Chief Executive Officer CFO: Karen Gardiner, Director Fiscal Services CMO: James Falterman, Jr, M.D., Medical Director CIO: J Barry Daigle, Manager Information Systems CHR: Jennifer Simms, Director of Human Resources	12	10	124	—	—	—	—	—	—	—
★ **VERMILION HOSPITAL**, (Formerly Vermilion Hospital for Psychiatric and Addictive Medicine), 2520 North University Avenue, Zip 70507–5306; tel. 337/234–5614 **A**10 **F**1 4 71 76 77 78 Primary Contact: Russell Kahn, Administrator CIO: Errol Labat, Chief Information Officer Web address: www.vermilionhospital.com	33	22	52	1394	34	—	—	—	—	146
⊞ **WOMEN'S AND CHILDREN'S HOSPITAL**, 4600 Ambassador Caffery Parkway, Zip 70508–6923, Mailing Address: P.O. Box 88030, Zip 70598–8030; tel. 337/521–9100 **A**1 9 10 **F**2 11 12 21 22 23 26 27 28 29 32 33 39 46 48 53 56 57 58 59 60 63 65 66 67 69 81 85 88 89 90 94 96 108 109 **S** HCA, Nashville, TN Primary Contact: Kathy J. Bobbs, Chief Executive Officer COO: Andre duPlessis, Chief Operating Officer CFO: James Miller, Chief Financial Officer CIO: Jeff Johnson, Information Systems Director CHR: Ariel Campos, Director Human Resources Web address: www.womens–childrens.com	33	44	157	6402	71	47136	3024	40508	18565	480
LAKE CHARLES—Calcasieu Parish										
⊞ △ **CHRISTUS ST. PATRICK HOSPITAL OF LAKE CHARLES**, 524 South Ryan Street, Zip 70601–5799, Mailing Address: P.O. Box 3401, Zip 70602–3401; tel. 337/436–2511 **A**1 2 7 9 10 **F**2 4 9 10 12 14 15 17 19 21 22 23 24 26 27 28 29 31 33 35 38 41 44 45 46 47 48 50 51 52 53 55 57 58 61 62 63 64 65 66 68 69 71 73 74 75 76 77 78 80 81 87 88 92 94 96 98 108 109 110 **P8 S** Christus Health, Irving, TX Primary Contact: Ellen M. Jones, President and Chief Executive Officer COO: Bill Hecht, Chief Operating Officer CMO: Darrell Dixon, M.D., Vice President Medical Affairs CIO: Allen Abshire, Director Information Services CHR: Lana Lake, Assistant Administrator Human Resources Web address: www.sphchristushealth.org	21	10	290	9699	143	151503	0	104647	35640	779
⊞ **DUBUIS HOSPITAL OF LAKE CHARLES**, 524 South Ryan, 5th Floor, Zip 70601–5725; tel. 337/491–7752, (Nonreporting) **A**1 10 **S** Dubuis Health System, Houston, TX Primary Contact: Michael M. Fuselier, FACHE, Administrator CMO: Ron Lewis, M.D., Medical Director	21	80	20	—	—	—	—	—	—	—

Hospital, Address, Telephone, Approval, Facility, and Physician Codes, Health Care System	Classi-fication Codes		Utilization Data					Expense (thousands) of dollars		
★ American Hospital Association (AHA) membership □ Joint Commission on Accreditation of Healthcare Organizations (JCAHO) accreditation ○ American Osteopathic Association (AOA) accreditation △ Commission on Accreditation of Rehabilitation Facilities (CARF) accreditation	Control	Service	Staffed Beds	Admissions	Census	Outpatient Visits	Births	Total	Payroll	Personnel
EXTENDED CARE OF SOUTHWEST LOUIASIANA, 2837 Ernest Street, Building B., Zip 70601; tel. 337/436–6111 **A**10 **F**2 21 22 27 28 55 73 94 96 110 Primary Contact: Mark D. Severns, Chief Executive Officer Web address: www.lcmh.com/extcare.htm	23	10	25	213	18	0	0	—	—	—
✠ **LAKE CHARLES MEMORIAL HOSPITAL**, 1701 Oak Park Boulevard, Zip 70601–8911, Mailing Address: P.O. Drawer M, Zip 70602; tel. 337/494–3000 **A**1 2 3 5 9 10 12 **F**2 3 9 12 14 15 21 27 28 33 36 37 40 41 44 45 46 48 51 55 56 58 59 60 63 65 66 67 68 69 71 72 75 76 81 82 84 87 88 89 92 94 95 96 108 109 **P**1 7 Primary Contact: Elton L. Williams, Jr, CPA, FACHE, President COO: David Usher, Vice President of Operations CFO: Charles P. Whitson, CPA, Vice President Finance CMO: Paul Comeaux, M.D., Medical Staff Director CIO: Belinda Sommers, Chief Information Officer CHR: Betty Mitchell, Director of Human Resources Web address: www.lcmh.com	23	10	337	11874	163	99027	1243	—	—	1407
★ **WALTER OLIN MOSS REGIONAL MEDICAL CENTER**, 1000 Walters Street, Zip 70605–4647; tel. 337/475–8100 **A**5 9 10 **F**2 9 12 21 23 26 28 32 33 34 39 46 48 50 52 53 55 63 64 65 66 70 71 73 75 81 88 94 108 109 **P**4 **S** LSU Health Sciences Center, Baton Rouge, LA Primary Contact: Patrick C. Robinson, M.D., Administrator CFO: Cheryl Savoy, Administrative Manager and Fiscal Officer CIO: Steve Demourelle, Chief Information Officer CHR: Joetta Brown, Director Human Resources	12	10	32	1459	25	81874	0	28242	12789	—
✠ **WOMEN AND CHILDREN'S HOSPITAL**, 4200 Nelson Road, Zip 70605–4118; tel. 337/474–6370 **A**1 9 10 **F**9 10 11 12 21 28 29 32 33 37 46 47 48 55 56 59 60 63 65 66 81 82 88 89 94 96 108 109 **S** Triad Hospitals, Inc., Plano, TX Primary Contact: William L. Willis, Chief Executive Officer CFO: Gary Troutman, CPA, Vice President Finance CMO: Floyd Guidry, M.D., Medical Director CIO: Tracy Leger, Information Systems Director CHR: Kasey Cormier, Director Human Resources Web address: www.women–childrens.com	33	10	114	3726	26	45762	1699	29156	11234	307
LAKE PROVIDENCE—East Carroll Parish **EAST CARROLL PARISH HOSPITAL**, 336 North Hood Street, Zip 71254–2194; tel. 318/559–2441, (Nonreporting) **A**9 10 Primary Contact: Ladonna Englerth, Administrator	16	49	11	—	—	—	—	—	—	—
LEESVILLE—Vernon Parish □ **BYRD REGIONAL HOSPITAL**, 1020 Fertitta Boulevard, Zip 71446–4697; tel. 337/239–9041 **A**1 9 10 **F**2 11 15 21 27 28 33 34 46 47 48 55 57 58 59 61 62 63 65 66 81 82 85 88 93 94 97 108 109 **P**5 7 **S** Community Health Systems, Inc., Brentwood, TN Primary Contact: Roger C. LeDoux, Chief Executive Officer Web address: www.byrdregional.com	33	10	60	3733	34	30287	275	26891	10692	259
□ **LEESVILLE REHABILITATION HOSPITAL**, 900 South Sixth Street, Zip 71446; tel. 337/392–8118 **A**1 10 **F**7 21 27 45 68 88 92 94 110 **P**6 Primary Contact: Jack Causey, Administrator	32	46	16	291	13	0	0	2935	963	43
LULING—St. Charles Parish **LULING REHABILITATION HOSPITAL**, 1125 Paul Maillard Road, Zip 70070, Mailing Address: P.O. Box 243, Zip 70070–0243; tel. 985/331–2281, (Nonreporting) **A**10 Primary Contact: Juanita Bates, Administrator	13	46	16	—	—	—	—	—	—	—
□ **ST. CHARLES PARISH HOSPITAL**, 1057 Paul Maillard Road, Zip 70070–0087, Mailing Address: P.O. Box 87, Zip 70070–0087; tel. 985/785–6242 **A**1 9 10 **F**2 6 9 12 21 23 26 27 29 33 41 44 46 47 48 49 52 55 57 58 60 61 62 63 65 69 71 73 74 75 76 81 84 88 94 95 96 108 110 Primary Contact: Fred Martinez, Jr, Chief Executive Officer Web address: www.stch.net	16	10	56	1902	31	26761	0	23910	9964	306
LUTCHER—St. James Parish ✠ **ST. JAMES PARISH HOSPITAL**, 2471 Louisiana Avenue, Zip 70071; tel. 225/869–5512 **A**1 9 10 18 **F**12 21 27 28 33 46 48 54 58 63 66 81 88 92 97 Primary Contact: Joan Z. Murray, R.N., Administrator and Chief Executive Officer CFO: Tracy L. George, Chief Financial Officer CIO: Kim Scharwath, Director Medical Records CHR: Lisa Faucheux, Director Human Resources Web address: www.stjamesparishhospital.com	16	10	16	257	2	17304	0	7500	3168	103
ST. JAMES PSYCHIATRIC HOSPITAL, 2471 Louisiana Avenue, Zip 70071; tel. 225/869–3344 **A**10 **F**21 22 44 71 76 94 **P**5 Primary Contact: Candy Lewis, Administrator	33	22	10	301	8	0	0	—	—	—
MAMOU—Evangeline Parish ✠ **SAVOY MEDICAL CENTER**, 801 Poinciana Avenue, Zip 70554–2298; tel. 337/468–5261 **A**1 9 10 **F**2 11 12 15 21 24 33 34 36 39 44 46 47 48 51 52 55 59 61 62 63 65 66 68 69 71 74 76 81 82 84 88 92 94 108 109 110 **S** HCA, Nashville, TN Primary Contact: Gerald A. Fornoff, Chief Executive Officer CFO: David Hanna, Chief Financial Officer CIO: Daniel Lahaye, Manager CHR: Annette Beaubouef, Human Resources Officer Web address: www.savoymedicalcenter.com	33	10	180	5282	67	—	431	—	—	575

Hospital, Address, Telephone, Approval, Facility, and Physician Codes, Health Care System	Classi-fication Codes		Utilization Data					Expense (thousands) of dollars		
★ American Hospital Association (AHA) membership □ Joint Commission on Accreditation of Healthcare Organizations (JCAHO) accreditation ○ American Osteopathic Association (AOA) accreditation △ Commission on Accreditation of Rehabilitation Facilities (CARF) accreditation	Control	Service	Staffed Beds	Admissions	Census	Outpatient Visits	Births	Total	Payroll	Personnel

MANDEVILLE—St. Tammany Parish

□ **SOUTHEAST LOUISIANA HOSPITAL**, 23515 Highway 190, Zip 70448–5612, Mailing Address: P.O. Box 3850, Zip 70470–3850; tel. 985/626–6300 **A**1 10 **F**21 22 26 28 32 58 60 71 72 73 74 78 94 108 **P**6 **S** Louisiana State Hospitals, New Orleans, LA
Primary Contact: Michael E. Teague, Chief Executive Officer
Web address: www.dhh.state.la.us/OMH/inpatient–serv/seast–la–hosp.htm

| 12 | 22 | 162 | 270 | 135 | 0 | 0 | — | — | 533 |

MANSFIELD—De Soto Parish

★ **DE SOTO REGIONAL HEALTH SYSTEM**, 207 Jefferson Street, Zip 71052–2603, Mailing Address: P.O. Box 1636, Zip 71052–2603; tel. 318/871–3100 **A**9 10 20 **F**2 9 12 23 27 28 33 34 41 46 52 61 63 69 70 71 76 81 84 88 93 97 **P**6 **S** Brim Healthcare, Inc., Brentwood, TN
Primary Contact: John Scott Stafford, Chief Executive Officer
CFO: Sandra Anderson, Chief Financial Officer
CMO: Leigh Dillard, Chief of Staff
CHR: Becky Smith, Director Human Resources
Web address: www.desotoregional.com

| 23 | 10 | 57 | 1653 | 21 | 27082 | 0 | 15318 | 5743 | — |

MANY—Sabine Parish

□ **SABINE MEDICAL CENTER**, 240 Highland Drive, Zip 71449–3718; tel. 318/256–5691 **A**1 9 10 20 **F**12 21 26 27 28 29 32 33 34 39 46 48 52 63 69 81 84 88 92 94 97 **S** Associated Healthcare Systems, Inc., Brentwood, TN
Primary Contact: Patrick W. Gandy, Chief Executive Officer

| 33 | 10 | 44 | 1231 | 13 | 13780 | 0 | 7948 | 3574 | 87 |

MARION—Union Parish

EDGEWOOD HOSPITAL, 160 McVicker Street, Zip 71260; tel. 318/292–2740, (Nonreporting) **A**10
Primary Contact: Jennifer Qayyum, Administrator

| 33 | 49 | 10 | — | — | — | — | — | — | — |

MARKSVILLE—Avoyelles Parish

⊠ **AVOYELLES HOSPITAL**, 4231 Highway 1192, Zip 71351, Mailing Address: P.O. Box 249, Zip 71351–0249; tel. 318/253–8611 **A**1 9 10 **F**2 9 12 21 27 33 46 52 55 60 63 69 71 76 78 81 88 92 94 108 **P**7 **S** HCA, Nashville, TN
Primary Contact: David M. Mitchel, Chief Executive Officer
CFO: Craig A. Roy, Chief Financial Officer
CHR: Kenneth Gremillion, Director Human Resources
Web address: www.avoyelleshospital.com

| 32 | 10 | 47 | 1652 | 19 | 35876 | 0 | — | — | 194 |

MARRERO—Jefferson Parish

ADVANCE CARE HOSPITAL, 1111 Medical Center Boulevard, Zip 70072; tel. 504/349–2476, (Nonreporting) **A**10
Primary Contact: Stephanie Wells, Chief Executive Officer

| 33 | 80 | 56 | — | — | — | — | — | — | — |

⊠ △ **WEST JEFFERSON MEDICAL CENTER**, 1101 Medical Center Boulevard, Zip 70072–3191; tel. 504/347–5511 **A**1 2 7 9 10 **F**1 2 4 5 6 9 10 11 12 14 15 16 17 18 19 20 21 23 26 27 28 29 32 33 36 37 39 41 45 46 47 48 49 51 53 55 56 57 59 60 61 62 63 64 65 66 67 68 69 71 74 78 79 81 82 84 85 87 88 92 93 94 95 96 108 109 110
Primary Contact: A. Gary Muller, FACHE, President and Chief Executive Officer
COO: Erie J. Hebert, Jr, FACHE, Senior Vice President
CFO: Mark J. McGinnis, Senior Vice President
CMO: Alfred E. Abaunza, M.D., Chief Medical Officer
CIO: David Graser, Chief Information Officer
CHR: Francine Miguel, Director of Human Resources
Web address: www.wjmc.org

| 16 | 10 | 317 | 15614 | 228 | 138583 | 1245 | 157977 | 75041 | 1842 |

METAIRIE—Jefferson Parish

⊠ △ **EAST JEFFERSON GENERAL HOSPITAL**, 4200 Houma Boulevard, Zip 70011–2996; tel. 504/454–4000, (Includes DOCTORS HOSPITAL OF JEFFERSON, 4320 Houma Boulevard, Zip 70006–2973; tel. 504/849–4000) **A**1 2 7 9 10 **F**1 2 5 6 9 11 12 14 15 17 19 21 22 23 28 29 30 33 34 37 41 44 45 46 47 48 49 52 53 55 56 57 58 59 60 61 62 63 66 68 69 71 74 75 76 77 79 80 81 82 84 85 86 87 88 92 93 94 96 108 109 110 **P**8
Primary Contact: Mark Peters, M.D., President and Chief Executive Officer
COO: Janice Kishner, Chief Operating Officer and Nurse Executive
CFO: Bruce Naremore, Chief Financial Officer
Web address: www.eastjeffhospital.com

| 16 | 10 | 439 | 18950 | 317 | 218183 | 1984 | 252608 | 108233 | 2551 |

⊠ **LAKESIDE HOSPITAL**, 4700 I–10 Service Road, Zip 70001–1269; tel. 504/780–8282 **A**1 9 10 **F**2 11 12 21 22 27 28 37 39 52 53 55 56 57 58 59 60 62 63 64 65 66 69 70 81 88 89 94 95 107 108 109 **S** HCA, Nashville, TN
Primary Contact: Shirley A. Stewart, CHE, Chief Executive Officer
CFO: Annette Strait, Chief Financial Officer
CHR: Lisa Talbot, Human Resource Manager
Web address: www.lakesidehospital.com

| 33 | 10 | 75 | 2629 | 45 | 17663 | 1716 | 25662 | 10820 | 239 |

□ **SELECT SPECIALTY HOSPITAL–JEFFERSON PARISH**, 4200 Houma Boulevard, Zip 70006; tel. 504/780–3020, (Nonreporting) **A**1 10 **S** Select Medical Corporation, Mechanicsburg, PA
Primary Contact: Meg McNally, Chief Executive Officer
Web address: www.selectmedicalcorp.com

| 33 | 80 | 32 | — | — | — | — | — | — | — |

MINDEN—Webster Parish

BERNICE COMMUNITY REHABILITATION HOSPITAL – MINDEN, 108 Meadowbrook Drive, Zip 71055; tel. 318/377–5555, (Nonreporting) **A**10
Primary Contact: Kathy M. Rowland, Administrator

| 23 | 10 | 28 | | | | | | | |

Many Facility Codes have changed. Please refer to the AHA Guide Code Chart.   © 2005 AHA Guide

Hospital, Address, Telephone, Approval, Facility, and Physician Codes, Health Care System	Classi-fication Codes		Utilization Data					Expense (thousands) of dollars		
★ American Hospital Association (AHA) membership □ Joint Commission on Accreditation of Healthcare Organizations (JCAHO) accreditation ○ American Osteopathic Association (AOA) accreditation △ Commission on Accreditation of Rehabilitation Facilities (CARF) accreditation	Control	Service	Staffed Beds	Admissions	Census	Outpatient Visits	Births	Total	Payroll	Personnel

✚ **MINDEN MEDICAL CENTER**, 1 Medical Plaza, Zip 71055–3330, Mailing Address: P.O. Box 5003, Zip 71058–5003; tel. 318/377–2321 **A**1 9 10 **F**9 11 12 15 17 21 22 27 28 33 44 46 47 48 51 52 55 58 59 60 61 62 63 66 68 69 71 76 81 84 88 93 94 108 109 **S** LifePoint Hospitals, Inc., Brentwood, TN
Primary Contact: George E. French, III, CHE, Chief Executive Officer
CFO: Patty Doles, Chief Financial Officer
CMO: J Robert Kemmerly, M.D., Medical Director
CIO: Renae Simmons, Director Information Systems
CHR: Mary Winget, Human Resource Director
Web address: www.mindenmedicalcenter.com
| 33 | 10 | 159 | 5226 | 57 | 43530 | 730 | 27151 | 13674 | 393 |

MONROE—Ouachita Parish

□ **E. A. CONWAY MEDICAL CENTER**, 4864 Jackson Street, Zip 71202–6497, Mailing Address: P.O. Box 1881, Zip 71210–8005; tel. 318/330–7000 **A**1 3 5 9 10 **F**2 9 12 21 22 23 24 29 33 34 39 46 48 50 52 55 56 57 58 59 61 62 63 66 69 70 71 75 81 82 84 87 88 94 106 108
Primary Contact: H. Aryon McGuire, Administrator
Web address: www.conway.lsuhsc.edu
| 12 | 10 | 153 | 7320 | 115 | 156907 | 1074 | — | — | — |

✚ **MONROE SURGICAL HOSPITAL**, 2408 Broadmoor Boulevard, Zip 71201, Mailing Address: P.O. Box 4887, Zip 71211–4887; tel. 318/410–0002, (Nonreporting) **A**1 9 10
Primary Contact: Alan Daugherty, Administrator
| 33 | 10 | 10 | — | — | — | — | — | — | — |

✚ **NORTH MONROE MEDICAL CENTER**, 3421 Medical Park Drive, Zip 71203–2399; tel. 318/388–1946, (Nonreporting) **A**1 9 10 **S** HCA, Nashville, TN
Primary Contact: Betty P. Scriber, FACHE, Chief Executive Officer
COO: Mark Bethell, Chief Operating Officer
CFO: Brian McCauley, Chief Financial Officer
Web address: www.northmonroe.net
| 33 | 10 | 239 | — | — | — | — | — | — | — |

★ **P & S SURGICAL HOSPITAL**, 312 Grammont Street, Suite 101, Zip 71201; tel. 318/388–4040 **A**10 **F**2 24 26 27 28 29 37 40 46 53 63 64 95 **P**8
Primary Contact: Linda Holyfield, Chief Executive Officer and Administrator
COO: Terri Hicks, Chief Operating Officer and Chief Financial Officer
CMO: Terry Tugwell, M.D., Chief of Staff
CIO: Joseph Vicknair, Chief Information Officer
CHR: Lori Crotwell, Human Resources Manager
Web address: www.pssurgery.com
| 32 | 13 | 10 | 500 | 3 | 8273 | 0 | 13388 | 3582 | 115 |

★ **PREMIER REHABILITATION HOSPITAL**, 4310 South Grand Street, Zip 71202; tel. 318/812–1000 **A**10 **F**2 4 21 39 42 46 47 48 52 53 58 60 65 66 68 69 71 77 94 110
Primary Contact: James A. Joubert, Chief Executive Officer
COO: Denise S. Dugas, Administrator
CFO: Scott Markstrom, Chief Financial Officer
CIO: Marilyn North, Health Information Management Coordinator
| 33 | 46 | 20 | 366 | 10 | — | — | — | — | 43 |

✚ **ST. FRANCIS MEDICAL CENTER**, 309 Jackson Street, Zip 71201–7407, Mailing Address: P.O. Box 1901, Zip 71210–1901; tel. 318/327–4000 **A**1 2 9 10 **F**1 2 9 10 11 12 14 15 16 17 18 19 21 22 23 26 27 28 29 31 32 33 35 42 44 46 48 49 50 52 54 55 56 57 58 59 60 61 62 63 64 67 68 69 71 76 78 81 84 86 88 92 93 94 96 108 109 110 **P**8 **S** Franciscan Missionaries of Our Lady Health System, Inc., Baton Rouge, LA
Primary Contact: K. Scott Wester, FACHE, President and Chief Executive Officer
COO: Christine T. Kipp, Vice President Patient Care Services
CFO: Ronald E. Hogan, Senior Vice President and Chief Financial Officer
CMO: Henry H. Macler, M.D., Vice President Medical Affairs
CIO: Thomas H. Hammond, Chief Information Officer
CHR: Debbie S. Horstmann, Director Human Resources
Web address: www.stfran.com
| 21 | 10 | 316 | 12687 | 185 | 79306 | 1446 | 153388 | 50915 | 1425 |

✚ △ **ST. FRANCIS SPECIALTY HOSPITAL**, 309 Jackson Street, Zip 71210, Mailing Address: P.O. Box 1532, Zip 71210–1532; tel. 318/327–4000 **A**1 7 10 **F**2 21 23 27 28 38 44 46 53 58 60 68 81 94 106 **P**8
Primary Contact: George W. Hightower, CHE, President and Chief Executive Officer
Web address: www.specialtyhospital.com
| 23 | 80 | 50 | 429 | 32 | 0 | 0 | 16220 | 4970 | 127 |

ST. PATRICK'S PSYCHIATRIC HOSPITAL, 309 Jackson Street, Zip 71201, Mailing Address: P.O. Box 1901, Zip 71201–1901; tel. 318/327–4686 **A**10 **F**71 77 **S** Franciscan Missionaries of Our Lady Health System, Inc., Baton Rouge, LA
Primary Contact: Cindy J. Rogers, FACHE, Chief Executive Officer
Web address: www.stpatrickshospital.net
| 21 | 22 | 28 | 492 | 10 | 5356 | 0 | 4037 | 1361 | 37 |

MORGAN CITY—St. Mary Parish

LOUISIANA REHABILITATION HOSPITAL OF MORGAN CITY, 1125 Marguerite Street, 5th Floor, Zip 70380; tel. 985/380–4536, (Nonreporting) **A**10
Primary Contact: Robbie Senette, R.N., Administrator
| 33 | 46 | 10 | — | — | — | — | — | — | — |

✚ **TECHE REGIONAL MEDICAL CENTER**, 1125 Marguerite Street, Zip 70380–1855, Mailing Address: P.O. Box 2308, Zip 70381–2308; tel. 985/384–2200 **A**1 9 10 **F**2 9 11 12 15 17 21 22 23 24 33 37 38 44 46 47 48 51 52 53 57 58 60 61 62 63 69 70 75 76 81 82 84 85 88 109 110 **S** LifePoint Hospitals, Inc., Brentwood, TN
Primary Contact: Michael J. Landry, Chief Executive Officer
CFO: Forrest Whichard, Chief Financial Officer
CMO: Sharon Bass, M.D., Chief of Staff
CIO: Cheryl Lipari, Manager Information Systems
CHR: Tim Hebert, Director Human Resources
Web address: www.techeregional.com
| 16 | 10 | 50 | 3464 | 36 | 46169 | 322 | — | — | 278 |

LA

Hospital, Address, Telephone, Approval, Facility, and Physician Codes, Health Care System	Classi-fication Codes		Utilization Data					Expense (thousands) of dollars		
★ American Hospital Association (AHA) membership □ Joint Commission on Accreditation of Healthcare Organizations (JCAHO) accreditation ○ American Osteopathic Association (AOA) accreditation △ Commission on Accreditation of Rehabilitation Facilities (CARF) accreditation	Control	Service	Staffed Beds	Admissions	Census	Outpatient Visits	Births	Total	Payroll	Personnel

NAPOLEONVILLE—Assumption Parish

★ **ASSUMPTION COMMUNITY HOSPITAL**, (Critical Access Hospital), 135 Highway 402, Zip 70390; tel. 985/369–3600 **A**9 10 18 **F**2 12 27 33 46 52 88 **S** Franciscan Missionaries of Our Lady Health System, Inc., Baton Rouge, LA
Primary Contact: Wayne M. Arboneaux, Administrator
Web address: www.ololrmc.com

| | 23 | 49 | 6 | 170 | 1 | 20468 | 0 | 4046 | 1721 | 33 |

NATCHITOCHES—Natchitoches Parish

LOUISIANA EXTENDED CARE HOSPITAL OF NATCHITOCHES, (Formerly Genesis Specialty Hospital), 501 Keyser Avenue, Zip 71457; tel. 318/354–2044 **A**10 **F**2 21 37 44 57 58 61 62 65 66 76 94 110
Primary Contact: Russel Bienvenu, Administrator
Web address: www.genesisspecialty.com

| | 33 | 10 | 21 | 222 | 16 | 0 | 0 | — | — | 48 |

⊠ **NATCHITOCHES PARISH HOSPITAL**, 501 Keyser Avenue, Zip 71457–6036, Mailing Address: P.O. Box 2009, Zip 71457–2009; tel. 318/214–4200, (Total facility includes 112 beds in nursing home–type unit) **A**1 9 10 20 **F**2 6 9 11 12 21 26 27 28 29 33 36 44 45 46 48 52 54 58 59 60 62 63 64 66 69 71 76 81 82 84 85 88 92 94 95 97 108 110 **P**4 5 **S** Christus Health, Irving, TX
Primary Contact: Mark E. Marley, CHE, Administrator
CFO: Gerard Hebert, Chief Financial Officer
Web address: www.natchitochesparishhospital.org

| | 16 | 10 | 190 | 4171 | 146 | 34188 | 609 | 29222 | 11995 | 351 |

NEW IBERIA—Iberia Parish

⊠ **DAUTERIVE HOSPITAL**, 600 North Lewis Street, Zip 70560–2043; tel. 337/365–7311 **A**1 10 **F**10 11 12 15 17 21 23 28 33 40 46 47 48 49 52 55 58 59 60 61 63 65 66 68 69 71 76 81 82 84 85 88 94 95 108 **S** HCA, Nashville, TN
Primary Contact: Kyle J. Viator, Chief Executive Officer
CFO: Michael Mayeux, Chief Financial Officer
CMO: Mike Alvarez, M.D., Chief Medical Officer
CIO: Terry Stewart, Director Information Systems
CHR: Suzanne Minor, Director of Human Resources
Web address: www.dauterivehospital.com

| | 33 | 10 | 103 | 4468 | 57 | 29100 | 469 | 46606 | 15045 | |

⊠ **IBERIA MEDICAL CENTER**, 2315 East Main Street, Zip 70560–4031, Mailing Address: P.O. Box 13338, Zip 70562–3338; tel. 337/364–0441 **A**1 9 10 **F**2 9 10 11 12 15 17 21 22 23 24 29 33 39 42 46 47 48 51 52 53 55 57 59 61 62 63 64 65 66 69 70 81 85 88 94 96 107 108 109 110 **S** Brim Healthcare, Inc., Brentwood, TN
Primary Contact: James H. Youree, FACHE, Chief Executive Officer
COO: Shane P. Myers, R.N., Chief Operating Officer
CFO: Wally Piekarczyk, Chief Financial Officer
CIO: Ross Leleux, Chief Information Officer
CHR: Lori Zachry, Director Human Resources
Web address: www.iberiamedicalcenter.com

| | 16 | 10 | 63 | 4447 | 46 | 129791 | 480 | 33665 | 15305 | 423 |

NEW ORLEANS—Orleans Parish

□ **BYWATER HOSPITAL**, 3419 St. Claude Avenue, Zip 70117–6198; tel. 504/948–8200, (Nonreporting) **A**1 9 10 **S** United Medical Corporation, Windermere, FL
Primary Contact: John McGee, Chief Executive Officer
CHARITY CAMPUS See Medical Center of Louisiana at New Orleans

| | 33 | 10 | 136 | — | — | — | — | — | — | — |

□ △ **CHILDREN'S HOSPITAL**, 200 Henry Clay Avenue, Zip 70118–5799; tel. 504/899–9511 **A**1 2 3 5 7 9 10 **F**2 7 9 13 14 16 18 20 21 22 23 24 28 29 30 32 33 37 38 39 42 46 47 48 49 50 52 56 57 58 61 62 63 64 65 66 67 68 69 70 73 77 81 82 84 88 93 94 95 96 99 101 102 107 108 110 **P**4 8
Primary Contact: Steve Worley, President and Chief Executive Officer
Web address: www.chnola.org

| | 23 | 50 | 175 | 7916 | 120 | 339891 | 0 | — | — | 1483 |

COMMUNITY CARE HOSPITAL, 1421 General Taylor Street, Zip 70115; tel. 504/899–2500, (Nonreporting) **A**10
Primary Contact: Paul B. Kavanaugh, President and Chief Executive Officer
DEPAUL/TULANE BEHAVIORAL HEALTH CENTER See Tulane University Hospital and Clinic

| | 12 | 22 | 36 | — | — | — | — | — | — | — |

□ **GENESIS SPECIALTY HOSPITAL – NEW ORLEANS**, 301 North Jefferson Davis Parkway, Zip 70119; tel. 504/486–5841 **A**1 10 **F**21 23 38 44 53 57 58 60 61 62 65 94 110
Primary Contact: Frederick H. Nelson, Chief Executive Officer
Web address: www.genesisspecialty.com

| | 33 | 80 | 38 | 300 | 20 | — | — | — | — | 64 |

★ **HEALTHSOUTH SPECIALTY HOSPITAL OF NEW ORLEANS**, 5620 Read Boulevard, 6th Floor N., Zip 70127; tel. 504/240–4260, (Nonreporting) **A**10 **S** HEALTHSOUTH Corporation, Birmingham, AL
Primary Contact: Susan R. Davis, Administrator

| | 33 | 46 | 28 | — | — | — | — | — | — | — |

□ **KINDRED HOSPITAL – NEW ORLEANS**, 3601 Coliseum Street, Zip 70115–3606; tel. 504/899–1555 **A**1 10 **F**2 21 44 49 52 55 58 60 66 69 71 74 75 76 77 78 88 94 96 110 **S** Kindred Healthcare, Louisville, KY
Primary Contact: Jan Turk, Chief Executive Officer
Web address: www.kindredhealthcare.com

| | 12 | 10 | 94 | 880 | 63 | — | — | — | — | — |

□ **LIFECARE HOSPITALS OF NEW ORLEANS–BAPTIST CAMPUS**, 2700 Napoleon Avenue, Zip 70115; tel. 504/896–5524, (Nonreporting) **A**1 10 **S** LifeCare Management Services, Plano, TX
Primary Contact: Tim Burke, Chief Executive Officer

| | 33 | 80 | 130 | — | — | — | — | — | — | — |

Many Facility Codes have changed. Please refer to the AHA Guide Code Chart.

Hospital, Address, Telephone, Approval, Facility, and Physician Codes, Health Care System	Classi-fication Codes		Utilization Data					Expense (thousands) of dollars		
★ American Hospital Association (AHA) membership □ Joint Commission on Accreditation of Healthcare Organizations (JCAHO) accreditation ○ American Osteopathic Association (AOA) accreditation △ Commission on Accreditation of Rehabilitation Facilities (CARF) accreditation	Control	Service	Staffed Beds	Admissions	Census	Outpatient Visits	Births	Total	Payroll	Personnel
⊠ **MEDICAL CENTER OF LOUISIANA AT NEW ORLEANS**, 2021 Perdido Street, Zip 70112–1396; tel. 504/903–3000, (Includes CHARITY CAMPUS, 1532 Tulane Avenue, Zip 70140; tel. 504/903–0125; UNIVERSITY CAMPUS) **A**1 2 3 5 8 9 10 **F**2 3 4 9 11 12 15 19 21 22 23 27 28 29 31 32 33 34 35 37 38 39 40 42 44 46 47 48 49 50 52 53 55 56 57 58 59 60 61 62 63 64 65 66 67 68 69 70 71 73 74 75 76 81 82 84 85 88 90 93 94 96 106 108 109 110 **P**1 **S** LSU Health Sciences Center, Baton Rouge, LA Primary Contact: Dwayne Thomas, M.D., Chief Executive Officer COO: Adler Voltaire, Chief Administrative Officer CFO: Ed Burke, Chief Financial Officer CMO: Cathi E. Fontenot, M.D., Medical Director CIO: Mitch Perlin, Chief Information Officer CHR: Ronald Broadus, Assistant Administrator Human Resources Web address: www.mclno.org	12	10	449	23523	389	461302	2553	451308	160814	3237
⊠ △ **MEMORIAL MEDICAL CENTER**, (Includes LINDY BOGGS MEDICAL CENTER, 301 North Jefferson Davis Parkway, Zip 70119–5397; tel. 504/483–5000; George J. Saucier, Chief Executive Officer; MEMORIAL MEDICAL CENTER–BAPTIST CAMPUS, 2700 Napoleon Avenue, Zip 70115–6996; tel. 504/899–9311), (Nonreporting) **A**1 2 3 5 7 8 9 10 **S** TENET Healthcare Corporation, Dallas, TX Primary Contact: L. Rene' Goux, Chief Executive Officer COO: Edward Gray, Chief Operating Officer CFO: Wayne Thompson, Chief Financial Officer CIO: Glenn Turner, Director, Information Systems Web address: www.memmedctr.com	33	10	603	—	—	—	—	—	—	—
□ **METHODIST HOSPITAL**, 5620 Read Boulevard, Zip 70127–3154; tel. 504/244–5100, (Includes LAKELAND MEDICAL CENTER, 6000 Bullard Avenue, Zip 70128–2898; tel. 504/241–6335) **A**1 9 10 **F**10 15 17 19 21 22 23 28 29 33 34 40 46 47 48 49 53 56 57 58 59 60 62 63 66 68 69 71 76 78 81 84 88 89 92 93 94 108 109 110 **P**4 **S** Universal Health Services, Inc., King of Prussia, PA Web address: www.methodisthospitalnola.org	33	10	295	10593	173	93798	1488	137239	55089	1119
□ **NEW ORLEANS ADOLESCENT HOSPITAL**, 210 State Street, Zip 70118–5797; tel. 504/897–3400, (Nonreporting) **A**1 10 **S** Louisiana State Hospitals, New Orleans, LA Primary Contact: Shelby Price, Chief Executive Officer	12	52	30	—	—	—	—	—	—	—
NEW ORLEANS EAST REHABILITATION HOSPITAL, 14500 Hayne Boulevard, Zip 70128; tel. 504/248–2797, (Nonreporting) **A**10 Primary Contact: Bruce Walker, Chief Executive Officer	33	46	12	—	—	—	—	—	—	—
OASIS LONG TERM CARE ACUTE HOSPITAL, 1601 Perdido Street, 10th Floor, Zip 70112; tel. 504/585–2956, (Nonreporting) **A**10 Primary Contact: Joslyn Blackburn, Administrator	33	46	15	—	—	—	—	—	—	—
⊠ **OCHSNER CLINIC FOUNDATION**, 1514 Jefferson Highway, Zip 70121–2484; tel. 504/842–3000, (Total facility includes 25 beds in nursing home–type unit) **A**1 2 3 5 8 9 10 **F**2 4 7 9 10 11 12 14 15 16 17 18 19 20 21 22 23 24 26 28 29 31 33 34 35 37 39 41 44 45 46 47 48 49 50 51 52 53 55 56 57 58 59 60 61 62 63 64 65 66 67 68 69 70 71 72 73 74 75 76 77 78 79 80 81 82 84 85 87 88 89 90 92 93 94 95 96 100 101 102 104 105 106 107 108 109 110 Primary Contact: Patrick J. Quinlan, M.D., Chief Executive Officer COO: Warner L. Thomas, President and Chief Operating Officer CFO: Scott J. Posecai, Executive Vice President and Chief Financial Officer CMO: Patrick J. Quinlan, M.D., Chief Executive Officer CIO: Lynn Witherspoon, Vice President and Chief Information Officer CHR: Joan Mollohan, Vice President Human Resources Web address: www.ochsner.org	23	10	460	22328	334	1603723	867	370069	156306	3084
RIVER OAKS CHILD AND ADOLESCENT HOSPITAL, 1525 River Oaks Road West, Zip 70123; tel. 504/734–1740, (Nonreporting) **A**10 Primary Contact: Jennifer Nolan, Chief Executive Officer	33	22	26	—	—	—	—	—	—	—
□ **RIVER OAKS HOSPITAL**, 1525 River Oaks Road West, Zip 70123–2199; tel. 504/734–1740 **A**1 10 **F**3 4 34 42 71 72 73 74 75 76 77 78 94 **S** Universal Health Services, Inc., King of Prussia, PA Primary Contact: Jennifer Nolan, Chief Executive Officer Web address: www.riveroakshospital.com	33	22	126	3561	84	—	0	—	—	232
□ **SPECIALTY HOSPITAL OF NEW ORLEANS**, 1401 Foucher Street, Zip 70115; tel. 504/897–8942 **A**1 10 **F**2 21 49 51 64 66 81 84 88 93 94 110 **S** Promise Healthcare, Lafayette, LA Primary Contact: Irving B. Sawyers, Jr, Chief Executive Officer	23	10	27	230	18	—	—	—	—	66
⊠ **ST. CHARLES SPECIALTY HOSPITAL**, (Formerly St. Charles General Hospital), 3700 St. Charles Avenue, Zip 70115–4680; tel. 504/899–7441, (Nonreporting) **A**1 9 10 Primary Contact: Sean S. Fowler, Chief Executive Officer CFO: Blaise Bondi, Chief Financial Officer Web address: www.stcharleshospital.com	33	10	154	—	—	—	—	—	—	—
ST. JOHN'S SPECIALTY HOSPITAL, (Formerly St. John's Rehabilitation Hospital), 405 Folse Road, Zip 70123, Mailing Address: P.O. Box 84360, Baton Rouge, Zip 70884–4360; tel. 504/738–3339 **A**10 **F**21 49 52 60 68 69 94 Primary Contact: Robert S. Rotolo, Chief Executive Officer and Administrator	33	46	24	320	18	—	—	—	—	—

Hospital, Address, Telephone, Approval, Facility, and Physician Codes, Health Care System	Classification Codes		Utilization Data					Expense (thousands) of dollars		
★ American Hospital Association (AHA) membership □ Joint Commission on Accreditation of Healthcare Organizations (JCAHO) accreditation ○ American Osteopathic Association (AOA) accreditation △ Commission on Accreditation of Rehabilitation Facilities (CARF) accreditation	Control	Service	Staffed Beds	Admissions	Census	Outpatient Visits	Births	Total	Payroll	Personnel
⊞ △ **TOURO INFIRMARY**, 1401 Foucher Street, Zip 70115–3593; tel. 504/897–7011, (Total facility includes 120 beds in nursing home–type unit) **A**1 2 3 5 7 8 9 10 **F**1 2 5 8 9 10 11 12 14 15 17 19 21 22 23 28 29 30 31 32 33 34 35 37 38 39 40 41 42 43 44 45 46 47 48 49 50 51 52 53 55 56 57 58 59 60 61 62 63 64 65 66 68 69 70 71 73 74 75 76 77 78 79 80 81 82 83 84 85 86 87 88 90 91 92 93 94 95 96 99 106 107 108 109 110 **P**8 Primary Contact: Leslie D. Hirsch, President and Chief Executive Officer CFO: Robert A. Ficken, Vice President Finance CIO: Peter Dougherty, Director Information Services CHR: Lois Woodall, Director Human Resources Web address: www.touro.com	23	10	465	11992	352	369467	1749	176770	80221	1821
TOURO REHABILITATION CENTER, 1401 Foucher Street, Zip 70115; tel. 504/897–8560, (Nonreporting) **A**10 Primary Contact: Gary M. Stein, CHE, Chief Executive Officer	33	46	63	—	—	—	—	—	—	—
⊞ **TULANE UNIVERSITY HOSPITAL AND CLINIC**, 1415 Tulane Avenue, Zip 70112–2605; tel. 504/988–5263, (Includes DEPAUL/TULANE BEHAVIORAL HEALTH CENTER, 1040 Calhoun Street, Zip 70118–5999; tel. 504/899–8282; Susan Andrews, Executive Director Behavioral Health Center), (Nonreporting) **A**1 2 3 5 8 9 10 **S** HCA, Nashville, TN Primary Contact: James T. Montgomery, CHE, President and Chief Executive Officer CFO: Robert Hatcher, Chief Financial Officer CMO: Jeanne James, M.D., Chief Medical Officer CIO: Sue Rachuig, Director Information Services Web address: www.tuhc.com	32	10	353	—	—	—	—	—	—	—
UNITED MEDICAL REHABILITATION HOSPITAL, 5650 Read Boulevard, 4th Floor, Zip 70127; tel. 504/242–4246, (Nonreporting) **A**10 Primary Contact: John B. Day, Administrator	33	46	10	—	—	—	—	—	—	—
UNIVERSITY CAMPUS See Medical Center of Louisiana at New Orleans										
⊞ **VETERANS AFFAIRS MEDICAL CENTER**, 1601 Perdido Street, Zip 70112–1262; tel. 504/568–0811, (Total facility includes 60 beds in nursing home–type unit) **A**1 2 3 5 8 **F**1 2 3 4 9 12 14 15 17 19 21 22 23 29 31 32 33 34 36 37 38 39 42 44 45 46 47 48 49 50 51 52 53 55 57 58 60 61 62 63 64 65 66 69 70 71 73 74 75 76 77 78 81 84 85 87 88 92 93 95 96 106 107 108 109 110 **P**6 **S** Department of Veterans Affairs, Washington, DC Primary Contact: John D. Church, Jr, FACHE, Director CFO: Michael W. Fisher, Chief Financial Officer CMO: Paul S. Rosenfeld, M.D., Chief of Staff CHR: William Insley, Chief Human Resources Management Web address: www.va.gov/new–orleans	45	10	206	5040	95	516216	0	223649	95280	1793
NEW ROADS—Pointe Coupee Parish										
★ **POINTE COUPEE GENERAL HOSPITAL**, 2202 False River Drive, Zip 70760–2698; tel. 225/638–6331 **A**9 10 18 20 **F**9 21 27 28 29 33 63 81 82 84 88 93 Primary Contact: Larry J. Ayres, Administrator and Chief Executive Officer CFO: Chad Olinde, Assistant Administrator and Chief Financial Officer CMO: Paul Rachal, M.D., Chief of Staff CHR: Lisa Patterson, Director Human Resources	16	10	25	1215	9	22488	0	—	—	151
OAK GROVE—West Carroll Parish										
WEST CARROLL MEMORIAL HOSPITAL, 706 Ross Street, Zip 71263; tel. 318/428–3237, (Nonreporting) **A**9 10 Primary Contact: R. Randall Morris, Administrator	23	10	21	—	—	—	—	—	—	—
OAKDALE—Allen Parish										
⊞ **OAKDALE COMMUNITY HOSPITAL**, 130 North Hospital Drive, Zip 71463, Mailing Address: P.O. Box 629, Zip 71463–0629; tel. 318/335–3700 **A**1 9 10 **F**21 33 34 41 46 47 55 63 69 81 82 88 94 108 **S** HCA, Nashville, TN Primary Contact: H. J. Gaspard, Chief Executive Officer CFO: Todd LaCaze, Chief Financial Officer CMO: Aaron Lirette, M.D., Chief of Staff CIO: Melissa Welch, Health Information Management Director CHR: Dana McDaniel, Director of Human Resources Web address: www.oakdalecommunityhospital.com	32	10	59	1817	19	—	0	—	—	157
OLLA—La Salle Parish										
HARDTNER MEDICAL CENTER, 1102 North Pine Road, Zip 71465; tel. 318/495–3131 **A**9 10 18 **F**6 21 22 26 28 33 44 46 52 53 63 68 69 71 76 81 88 92 94 97 **P**6 Primary Contact: Paul G. Mathews, Administrator Web address: www.hardtnermedical.com	16	10	35	588	9	8514	0	6238	2800	115
OPELOUSAS—St. Landry Parish										
⊞ **DOCTOR'S HOSPITAL OF OPELOUSAS**, 3983 I–49 South Service Road, Zip 70570–8975; tel. 337/948–2100, (Nonreporting) **A**1 9 10 **S** LifePoint Hospitals, Inc., Brentwood, TN Primary Contact: Mark W. Caton, Chief Executive Officer CFO: Stephen Downs, Chief Financial Officer CIO: Jamie D. Miller Web address: www.doctorshospital.com	33	10	145	—	—	—	—	—	—	—

Many Facility Codes have changed. Please refer to the AHA Guide Code Chart.

Hospital, Address, Telephone, Approval, Facility, and Physician Codes, Health Care System	Classi-fication Codes		Utilization Data					Expense (thousands) of dollars		
★ American Hospital Association (AHA) membership □ Joint Commission on Accreditation of Healthcare Organizations (JCAHO) accreditation ○ American Osteopathic Association (AOA) accreditation △ Commission on Accreditation of Rehabilitation Facilities (CARF) accreditation	Control	Service	Staffed Beds	Admissions	Census	Outpatient Visits	Births	Total	Payroll	Personnel

⊠ **OPELOUSAS GENERAL HEALTH SYSTEM**, 539 East Prudhomme Street, Zip 70570, Mailing Address: P.O. Box 1389, Zip 70571–1389; tel. 337/948–3011 **A**1 2 9 10 19 **F**10 11 12 17 21 22 29 33 46 50 55 59 63 65 66 69 78 79 81 82 84 86 87 88 93 94 108 109 **S** Quorum Health Resources, Plano, TX Primary Contact: William F. Barrow, II, Chief Executive Officer CFO: James P. Barbuat, Vice President Financial Services CMO: John Kempf, M.D., Chief of Staff CIO: Jared Lormand, Vice President Information Technology CHR: Suzanne Kidder, Director Human Resources Web address: www.opelousasgeneral.com	16	10	154	7250	92	78217	789	—	—	651
ST. LANDRY EXTENDED CARE HOSPITAL, 539 East Prudhomme Lane, Zip 70570; tel. 337/948–5184 **A**10 **F**2 21 27 29 39 44 45 46 47 49 53 57 58 60 62 64 65 66 92 94 108 110 **P**5 Primary Contact: Roddy Hebert, Administrator Web address: www.lhcgroup.com	33	10	23	212	15	0	0	—	—	47
PINEVILLE—Rapides Parish										
□ **CENTRAL LOUISIANA STATE HOSPITAL**, 242 West Shamrock Avenue, Zip 71361–5031, Mailing Address: P.O. Box 5031, Zip 71360–5031; tel. 318/484–6200 **A**1 10 **F**32 45 48 58 71 72 94 108 **S** Louisiana State Hospitals, New Orleans, LA Primary Contact: Thomas L. Davis, Chief Executive Officer Web address: www.dhh.state.us.la/omh/inpatient–serv/clsh.htm	12	22	180	87	146	0	0	22510	12080	368
⊠ **HUEY P. LONG MEDICAL CENTER**, 352 Hospital Boulevard, Zip 71360, Mailing Address: P.O. Box 5352, Zip 71361–5352; tel. 318/448–0811 **A**1 3 5 9 10 **F**9 11 12 21 22 23 24 26 27 28 29 31 33 34 38 39 42 46 48 50 52 55 58 59 60 61 62 63 65 66 70 71 75 81 88 94 96 106 **P**6 **S** LSU Health Sciences Center, Baton Rouge, LA Primary Contact: James E. Morgan, Administrator CFO: Nita Chambers, Chief Financial Officer CMO: David Barnard, M.D., Medical Director CIO: Mickey Roberts, Information Systems Director CHR: Marsha Crittle, Human Resource Director Web address: www.lsuhsc.edu/hcsd/hpl	12	10	60	3186	42	101100	298	48883	17725	544
PLAQUEMINE—Iberville Parish										
⊠ **RIVER WEST MEDICAL CENTER**, 59355 River West Drive, Zip 70764–0737, Mailing Address: P.O. Box 737, Zip 70764–0737; tel. 225/687–9222, (Nonreporting) **A**1 9 10 **S** Community Health Systems, Inc., Brentwood, TN Primary Contact: Scott Smith, Chief Executive Officer CFO: Terri Logsdon, Chief Financial Officer CMO: Micheal DiLeo, Chief of Staff CIO: Doug Arbour, Assistant Administrator CHR: Shelly Stafford, Director Human Resources Web address: www.riverwestmc.com	33	10	75	—	—	—	—	—	—	—
RACELAND—Lafourche Parish										
□ **ST. ANNE GENERAL HOSPITAL**, 4608 Highway 1, Zip 70394–2623; tel. 985/537–6841 **A**1 9 10 **F**2 9 12 15 21 28 33 39 51 55 59 63 71 75 76 81 82 88 94 97 Primary Contact: Milton D. Bourgeois, Jr, Chief Executive Officer Web address: www.stannegeneral.com	16	10	45	1394	12	34043	234	22214	9666	463
RAYVILLE—Richland Parish										
★ **RICHARDSON MEDICAL CENTER**, 254 Highway 3048 at Christian Drive, Zip 71269–0388, Mailing Address: P.O. Box 388, Zip 71269–0388; tel. 318/728–4181, (Nonreporting) **A**9 10 Primary Contact: William E. Klamfoth, Administrator CFO: Lisa Krause, Chief Financial Officer CMO: Dan LaFleur, M.D., Chief of Staff CHR: Cathy Cooper, Director Human Resources Web address: www.richardsonmedicalcenter.org	16	10	49	—	—	—	—	—	—	—
RICHLAND PARISH REHABILITATION HOSPITAL, 307 Hayes Street, Zip 71269; tel. 318/728–4410 **A**10 **F**21 42 68 69 110 Primary Contact: John M. Jones, Administrator	33	46	16	279	10	—	—	—	—	35
ROSEPINE—Vernon Parish										
TRI PARISH REHABILITATION HOSPITAL, 8088 Hawks Road, Zip 70659; tel. 337/462–8880, (Nonreporting) **A**10 Primary Contact: Craig Ball, President and Chief Executive Officer	33	46	33	—	—	—	—	—	—	—
RUSTON—Lincoln Parish										
GREEN CLINIC SURGICAL HOSPITAL, 1118 Farmerville Street, Zip 71270, (Nonreporting) **A**10	33	49	13	—	—	—	—	—	—	—
⊠ **HEALTHSOUTH NORTH LOUISIANA REHABILITATION HOSPITAL**, 1401 Ezell Street, Zip 71270–7221; tel. 318/251–5354, (Nonreporting) **A**1 10 **S** HEALTHSOUTH Corporation, Birmingham, AL Primary Contact: Mark J. Rice, Administrator Web address: www.healthsouth.com	33	46	90	—	—	—	—	—	—	—

LA

Hospital, Address, Telephone, Approval, Facility, and Physician Codes, Health Care System	Classi-fication Codes		Utilization Data					Expense (thousands) of dollars		
	Control	Service	Staffed Beds	Admissions	Census	Outpatient Visits	Births	Total	Payroll	Personnel
☒ **LINCOLN GENERAL HOSPITAL**, 401 East Vaughn Avenue, Zip 71270–5950, Mailing Address: P.O. Drawer 1368, Zip 71273–1368; tel. 318/254–2100, (Total facility includes 12 beds in nursing home–type unit) **A**1 9 10 19 **F**2 9 11 12 14 21 24 29 33 40 46 48 49 51 52 55 57 58 59 60 62 63 66 68 69 81 82 84 88 92 94 109 Primary Contact: Thomas J. Stone, Chief Executive Officer COO: David Caston, Assistant Vice President Administrative Services CFO: Jim Allbritton, Chief Financial Officer CMO: Tommy Smith, M.D., President Medical Staff CIO: Harry Brawley, Information Services Director CHR: Sue Campbell, Vice President Human Resources Web address: www.lincolnhealth.com	23	10	124	5964	73	—	—	—	—	—
SAINT FRANCISVILLE—West Feliciana Parish										
☒ **WEST FELICIANA PARISH HOSPITAL**, 5266 Commerce Street, Zip 70775–0368, Mailing Address: P.O. Box 368, Zip 70775–0368; tel. 225/635–3811 **A**1 9 10 18 **F**6 21 27 28 33 46 81 92 94 97 Primary Contact: Mark Chustz, Administrator CFO: Linda Harvey, Chief Financial Officer Web address: www.wfph.org	16	10	22	272	2	11723	0	7292	3194	—
SHREVEPORT—Caddo Parish										
☐ **BRENTWOOD BEHAVIORAL HEALTH COMPANY**, 1006 Highland Avenue, Zip 71101–4103; tel. 318/618–7500 **A**1 10 **F**4 21 29 31 42 44 45 71 73 74 75 76 77 78 94 **S** Psychiatric Solutions, Franklin, TN Primary Contact: J. Paul Smith, Chief Executive Officer	33	22	150	3330	83	—	—	—	—	221
☒ **CHRISTUS SCHUMPERT HEALTH SYSTEM**, (Formerly Christus Schumpert Medical Center), One St. Mary Place, Zip 71101–4399; tel. 318/681–4500, (Includes CHRISTUS SCHUMPERT BOSSIER, 2105 Airline Drive, Bossier City, Zip 71111–3190; tel. 318/741–6000; CHRISTUS SCHUMPERT HEALTH SYSTEM, Mailing Address: P.O. Box 21976, Zip 71120–1976; tel. 318/681–4500; CHRISTUS SCHUMPERT HIGHLAND, 1453 East Bert Kouns Industrial Loop, Zip 71105–6050; tel. 318/798–4300) **A**1 2 3 5 9 10 **F**1 2 6 9 10 11 12 14 15 17 19 21 22 23 24 27 28 29 30 32 33 34 36 37 38 41 42 44 45 46 47 48 49 51 52 55 56 57 58 59 60 61 62 63 64 66 67 68 69 70 71 73 74 75 76 79 81 82 84 85 86 87 88 92 93 94 95 96 98 106 107 108 109 110 **P**6 **S** Christus Health, Irving, TX Primary Contact: Charles J. Paine, M.D., President and Chief Executive Officer COO: Linda Neu Ollis, Vice President CFO: Wayne Thompson, Chief Financial Officer CMO: Charles J. Paine, M.D., Chief Medical Officer Web address: www.christussantarosa.org	21	10	745	18269	261	193739	1054	231687	84091	1552
☐ **DOCTORS' HOSPITAL OF SHREVEPORT**, 1130 Louisiana Avenue, Zip 71101–3998, Mailing Address: P.O. Box 1526, Zip 71165–1526; tel. 318/227–1211 **A**1 9 10 **F**2 3 4 10 12 21 33 45 52 55 58 60 68 69 70 81 82 84 88 94 95 96 109 110 **P**6 Primary Contact: David B. LeBlanc, Interim Chief Executive Officer Web address: www.doctorshospitalshreveport.com	32	10	101	2379	45	68640	1	35284	15492	396
☒ **DUBUIS HOSPITAL OF SHREVEPORT**, One St. Mary Place, 6th Floor, Zip 71101; tel. 318/221–3802 **A**1 2 10 **F**21 **S** Dubuis Health System, Houston, TX Primary Contact: Kay B. Allen, R.N., Administrator Web address: www.dubuis.org	21	80	36	401	29	0	0	10023	4070	89
☐ **LIFECARE HOSPITALS OF SHREVEPORT**, 9320 Linwood Avenue, Zip 71106–7003; tel. 318/688–8504, (Nonreporting) **A**1 9 10 **S** LifeCare Management Services, Plano, TX Primary Contact: Douglas Parker, Chief Executive Officer Web address: www.lifecare–hospitals.com	33	80	130	—	—	—	—	—	—	—
☐ **LSU MEDICAL CENTER–UNIVERSITY HOSPITAL**, 1501 Kings Highway, Zip 71130–4299, Mailing Address: P.O. Box 33932, Zip 71130–3932; tel. 318/675–5000 **A**1 2 3 5 9 10 **F**2 7 10 11 12 13 14 15 16 17 18 19 20 21 22 23 24 29 30 33 34 37 38 39 42 43 44 46 47 48 49 51 55 56 57 58 59 60 61 62 63 64 65 66 67 69 70 71 72 73 74 75 76 77 78 81 82 83 84 85 86 87 88 90 93 94 99 100 101 102 103 104 105 106 107 108 109 110 Primary Contact: Joseph M. Miciotto, Administrator Web address: www.lsumc.edu	12	10	423	20482	371	444806	1736	—	—	—
☒ **OVERTON BROOKS VETERANS AFFAIRS MEDICAL CENTER**, 510 East Stoner Avenue, Zip 71101–4295; tel. 318/221–8411 **A**1 2 3 5 8 **F**1 2 4 6 9 12 21 22 23 26 27 28 29 32 33 37 38 39 41 45 46 47 48 49 50 51 52 55 57 58 60 61 62 63 65 66 69 70 71 73 74 75 76 77 78 81 82 84 88 92 93 94 96 97 106 107 108 109 110 **P**6 **S** Department of Veterans Affairs, Washington, DC Primary Contact: George M. Moore, Jr, Director CFO: Randy Farris, Chief Fiscal Service CMO: Lloyd Phillips, M.D., Chief of Staff CIO: Mike Vesta, Chief Information Resource Management Service CHR: Carolyn Gray, Chief Human Resources Management Web address: www.va.gov/sta/guide/home.asp	45	10	112	5917	94	330898	0	—	—	—

Many Facility Codes have changed. Please refer to the AHA Guide Code Chart. © 2005 AHA Guide

Hospital, Address, Telephone, Approval, Facility, and Physician Codes, Health Care System	Classi-fication Codes		Utilization Data					Expense (thousands) of dollars		
★ American Hospital Association (AHA) membership □ Joint Commission on Accreditation of Healthcare Organizations (JCAHO) accreditation ○ American Osteopathic Association (AOA) accreditation △ Commission on Accreditation of Rehabilitation Facilities (CARF) accreditation	Control	Service	Staffed Beds	Admissions	Census	Outpatient Visits	Births	Total	Payroll	Personnel

□ **PROMISE SPECIALTY HOSPITAL OF SHREVEPORT**, 1800 Irving Place, Zip 71101–4608; tel. 318/425–4096 **A**1 10 **F**21 22 27 37 44 45 49 58 60 69 71 76 77 81 88 94 110 **P**8 **S** Promise Healthcare, Lafayette, LA Primary Contact: Michael O. Choo, Chief Executive Officer Web address: www.promise–shreveport.com	33	80	137	1128	79	9410	0	25987	11783	344
SHREVEPORT REHABILITATION HOSPITAL, 2140 Midway Street, Zip 71108; tel. 318/631–2345, (Nonreporting) **A**10 Primary Contact: Jerry Thomas, Administrator	33	46	45	—	—	—	—	—	—	—
□ **SHRINERS HOSPITALS FOR CHILDREN, SHREVEPORT**, 3100 Samford Avenue, Zip 71103–4289; tel. 318/222–5704, (Nonreporting) **A**1 3 5 **S** Shriners Hospitals for Children, Tampa, FL Primary Contact: Garry K. Green, Administrator Web address: www.shriners.com	23	59	45							
✶ △ **WILLIS–KNIGHTON MEDICAL CENTER**, 2600 Greenwood Road, Zip 71103–2600, Mailing Address: P.O. Box 32600, Zip 71130–2600; tel. 318/212–4600 **A**1 3 5 7 8 9 10 **F**2 3 4 6 9 10 11 12 14 15 17 19 21 22 23 24 27 28 29 31 33 35 36 37 38 39 40 41 42 43 44 45 46 47 48 49 50 51 52 53 55 56 57 58 59 60 61 62 63 64 65 66 67 68 69 71 72 73 74 75 76 77 78 80 81 82 84 85 87 88 89 90 92 94 95 96 97 98 100 101 102 103 106 107 108 109 110 **P**6 7 8 **S** Willis–Knighton Health System, Shreveport, LA Primary Contact: Ira L. Moss, Vice President and Administrator COO: Gary Lex Whatley, Senior Vice President and Chief Operating Officer CFO: Robert Huie, Executive Vice President and Chief Financial Officer CIO: Charles Laster, Director Information Management CHR: Jaf Fielder, Director Human Resources Web address: www.wkhs.com	23	10	719	37654	494	130586	3776	—	—	3705
SLIDELL—St. Tammany Parish										
DOCTORS HOSPITAL OF SLIDELL, 989 Robert Boulevard, Zip 70458; tel. 985/690–8200 **A**10 **F**2 12 63 64 66 81 88 108 Primary Contact: Peter Hertzak, M.D., Administrator	33	10	10	92	2	—	—	—	—	39
✶ **NORTHSHORE REGIONAL MEDICAL CENTER**, 100 Medical Center Drive, Zip 70461–8572; tel. 985/646–5025 **A**1 9 10 **F**2 9 11 12 14 15 21 22 29 33 34 37 40 41 44 45 48 52 53 55 56 57 58 59 60 61 62 63 65 66 67 68 73 81 82 84 87 88 93 94 95 96 106 108 109 110 **S** TENET Healthcare Corporation, Dallas, TX Primary Contact: Michael O'Bryan, M.D., Chief Executive Officer CFO: Randy Humphrey, Chief Financial Officer Web address: www.northshoremedctr.com	33	10	165	7669	102	—	—	—	—	606
✶ △ **SLIDELL MEMORIAL HOSPITAL AND MEDICAL CENTER**, 1001 Gause Boulevard, Zip 70458–2987; tel. 985/643–2200, (Nonreporting) **A**1 2 7 9 10 Primary Contact: Robert L. Hawley, Jr, Chief Executive Officer CFO: Carolyn Greene, Chief Financial Officer CIO: Harvey Ganong, Chief Information Officer Web address: www.smhplus.org	16	10	173	—	—	—	—	—	—	—
SPRINGHILL—Webster Parish										
□ **SPRINGHILL MEDICAL CENTER**, 2001 Doctors Drive, Zip 71075–4526, Mailing Address: P.O. Box 920, Zip 71075–0920; tel. 318/539–1000 **A**1 9 10 **F**2 12 21 23 26 27 28 33 46 48 55 61 62 63 69 71 76 81 84 88 94 97 108 **P**6 Primary Contact: Todd Blanchard, Chief Executive Officer Web address: www.sprhill.net/smc	23	10	60	1496	17	—	—	—	—	178
STERLINGTON—Ouachita Parish										
STERLINGTON REHABILITATION HOSPITAL, 111 Highway 2, Zip 71280, Mailing Address: P.O. Box 627, Zip 71280–0627; tel. 318/665–9950 **A**10 **F**4 29 44 45 60 68 69 73 74 76 77 93 94 Primary Contact: Cathy Perot, Administrator	33	46	29	250	7	2000	0	—	—	—
SULPHUR—Calcasieu Parish										
□ **CORNERSTONE HOSPITAL OF SOUTHWEST LOUISIANA**, 703 Cypress Street, Zip 70663; tel. 337/527–1102, (Nonreporting) **A**1 10 **S** Cornerstone Healthcare Group, Austin, TX Primary Contact: Wade K. Lester, Chief Executive Officer	32	80	30	—	—	—	—	—	—	—
✶ **WEST CALCASIEU CAMERON HOSPITAL**, 701 Cypress Street, Zip 70663–5000, Mailing Address: P.O. Box 2509, Zip 70664–2509; tel. 337/527–4240 **A**1 9 10 **F**2 6 9 11 12 15 17 19 21 22 24 27 28 29 31 32 33 34 38 39 41 46 47 48 51 52 55 58 59 60 62 63 65 66 69 81 82 84 87 88 94 95 106 108 109 110 Primary Contact: Timothy Broussard, CHE, Chief Executive Officer COO: Theresa Woods, MSN, R.N., Chief Operating Officer CFO: Tammy Broussard, Controller CIO: Melinda Sanner, Director of Information Systems CHR: Christi Kingsley, Director Human Resources Web address: www.wcch.com	16	10	74	5440	36	—	—	—	—	—
TALLULAH—Madison Parish										
MADISON PARISH HOSPITAL, 900 Johnson Street, Zip 71282–4537, Mailing Address: P.O. Box 1559, Zip 71284–1559; tel. 318/574–2374 **A**9 10 18 20 **F**33 39 49 50 52 55 71 81 **P**5 Primary Contact: Wendell Alford, Administrator	16	10	25	1103	12	—	0	—	—	116

Hospital, Address, Telephone, Approval, Facility, and Physician Codes, Health Care System	Classi-fication Codes		Utilization Data					Expense (thousands) of dollars		
★ American Hospital Association (AHA) membership □ Joint Commission on Accreditation of Healthcare Organizations (JCAHO) accreditation ○ American Osteopathic Association (AOA) accreditation △ Commission on Accreditation of Rehabilitation Facilities (CARF) accreditation	Control	Service	Staffed Beds	Admissions	Census	Outpatient Visits	Births	Total	Payroll	Personnel

THIBODAUX—Lafourche Parish

☒ △ **THIBODAUX REGIONAL MEDICAL CENTER**, 602 North Acadia Road, Zip 70301–4847, Mailing Address: P.O. Box 1118, Zip 70302–1118; tel. 985/447–5500 **A**1 2 7 9 10 **F**9 11 12 15 17 19 21 22 23 26 27 28 44 46 47 48 51 55 57 58 59 60 61 62 63 64 65 66 68 69 78 79 81 82 84 86 88 92 93 94 95 96 108 109 **S** Quorum Health Resources, Plano, TX
Primary Contact: Greg K. Stock, Chief Executive Officer
CFO: Steve C. Gaubert, Chief Financial Officer
CIO: Terry Evans, Chief Information Officer
CHR: Mickie Rousseau, Director Human Resources
Web address: www.thibodaux.com
| | 16 | 10 | 140 | 7462 | 84 | 104993 | 668 | 68806 | 25888 | 655 |

VILLE PLATTE—Evangeline Parish

☒ **VILLE PLATTE MEDICAL CENTER**, 800 East Main Street, Zip 70586–4618, Mailing Address: P.O. Box 349, Zip 70586–0349; tel. 337/363–5684 **A**1 9 10 **F**11 12 18 21 23 33 41 55 59 60 61 62 63 81 84 85 88 93 97 **S** LifePoint Hospitals, Inc., Brentwood, TN
Primary Contact: Steven Downs, Chief Executive Officer and Administrator
CFO: Donald E. McDaniel, III, Chief Financial Officer
CMO: Nick Cantu, Chief of Stafff
CIO: Courtney Bieber, Director Information Systems
CHR: Rita Aucoin, Director Human Resources
Web address: www.vpmc.com
| | 23 | 10 | 81 | 3139 | 38 | 26509 | 106 | 21458 | 8253 | 265 |

VIVIAN—Caddo Parish

NORTH CADDO MEDICAL CENTER, 1000 South Spruce Street, Zip 71082–3232, Mailing Address: P.O. Box 792, Zip 71082–0792; tel. 318/375–3235 **A**9 10 18 **F**2 9 11 21 22 25 26 27 28 29 30 33 37 39 41 45 46 47 48 52 53 58 59 62 63 66 68 70 81 88 92 93 94 97 107 108 109 110 **P**5
Primary Contact: Steve Bowman, Interim Administrator
| | 16 | 10 | 25 | 876 | 8 | — | — | — | — | 112 |

WEST MONROE—Ouachita Parish

□ **CORNERSTONE HOSPITAL–WEST MONROE**, 6198 Cypress Street, Zip 71291–9010; tel. 318/396–5600 **A**1 10 **F**45 66 94 **S** Cornerstone Healthcare Group, Austin, TX
Primary Contact: Chris Simpson, Chief Executive Officer
| | 33 | 10 | 40 | 381 | 24 | 0 | 0 | — | — | 77 |

☒ **GLENWOOD REGIONAL MEDICAL CENTER**, 503 McMillan Road, Zip 71291–5327, Mailing Address: P.O. Box 35805, Zip 71294–5805; tel. 318/329–4200 **A**1 9 10 **F**2 9 11 12 14 15 17 19 21 22 23 24 27 28 29 33 39 41 42 46 47 48 54 55 57 58 59 60 61 62 63 64 65 66 67 68 69 71 74 75 81 82 84 85 87 88 92 93 94 95 108 109 110
Primary Contact: Charles F. Scott, President and Chief Executive Officer
CFO: Ken Fisher, Interim Chief Financial Officer
CMO: Darline Smith, R.N., Chief Nursing Officer
CIO: Ronnie Maxwell, Director Information Systems
CHR: Jan Walker, Vice President Human Resources
Web address: www.grmc.com
| | 16 | 10 | 257 | 10368 | 153 | 93706 | 610 | 106264 | 39512 | 1063 |

LOUISIANA EXTENDED CARE HOSPITAL WEST MONROE, 593 McMillan Road, 3rd Floor, Zip 71291; tel. 318/329–4300, (Nonreporting) **A**10
Primary Contact: Theresa Marsala, Administrator
| | 33 | 80 | 18 | — | — | — | — | — | — | — |

□ **OUACHITA SURGICAL HOSPITAL**, 1275 Glenwood Drive, Zip 71291; tel. 318/322–1339, (Nonreporting) **A**1 10
Primary Contact: W. Benjamin Patterson, Administrator
| | 33 | 49 | 10 | — | — | — | — | — | — | — |

WINNFIELD—Winn Parish

★ **HEALTHSOUTH SPECIALTY HOSPITAL OF WINNFIELD**, 915 First Street, Zip 71483; tel. 318/648–0212, (Nonreporting) **A**10 **S** HEALTHSOUTH Corporation, Birmingham, AL
Primary Contact: Mark J. Rice, Administrator
| | 33 | 80 | 20 | — | — | — | — | — | — | — |

☒ **WINN PARISH MEDICAL CENTER**, 301 West Boundary Street, Zip 71483–3427, Mailing Address: P.O. Box 152, Zip 71483–0152; tel. 318/648–3000 **A**1 9 10 **F**2 12 21 27 28 29 32 37 46 48 49 52 55 58 60 63 64 65 66 69 75 81 82 84 88 92 94 95 97 110 **P**8 **S** HCA, Nashville, TN
Primary Contact: Bobby Jordan, Chief Executive Officer
CFO: Jennifer Tarver, Chief Financial Officer
CMO: Bobby Ensminger, M.D., Chief of Staff
CHR: Kimberly Ingles, Director Human Resources
Web address: www.winnparishmedical.com
| | 33 | 10 | 60 | 1836 | 24 | 13785 | 0 | 12783 | 5768 | 160 |

WINNSBORO—Franklin Parish

★ **FRANKLIN MEDICAL CENTER**, 2106 Loop Road, Zip 71295–3398, Mailing Address: P.O. Box 1300, Zip 71295–1300; tel. 318/435–9411 **A**9 10 **F**9 21 26 27 28 29 33 34 45 46 55 63 66 71 75 76 81 82 88 94 96 97 108 **P**5
Primary Contact: Paula H. Walker, R.N., Chief Executive Officer
CFO: Harold F. Naff, Chief Financial Officer
CMO: Thomas Colvin, M.D., Chief Medical Staff
CIO: Dwaine Boothe, Chief Engineer
CHR: Rita Brown, Personnel Director
Web address: www.fmc–cares.com
| | 16 | 10 | 57 | 1897 | 19 | 10581 | 3 | 13815 | 5597 | 204 |

Many Facility Codes have changed. Please refer to the AHA Guide Code Chart. © 2005 AHA Guide

LA

Hospital, Address, Telephone, Approval, Facility, and Physician Codes, Health Care System	Classi-fication Codes		Utilization Data					Expense (thousands) of dollars		
★ American Hospital Association (AHA) membership □ Joint Commission on Accreditation of Healthcare Organizations (JCAHO) accreditation ○ American Osteopathic Association (AOA) accreditation △ Commission on Accreditation of Rehabilitation Facilities (CARF) accreditation	Control	Service	Staffed Beds	Admissions	Census	Outpatient Visits	Births	Total	Payroll	Personnel

ZACHARY—East Baton Rouge Parish

⊠ **LANE MEMORIAL HOSPITAL**, 6300 Main Street, Zip 70791–9990; tel. 225/658–4000, (Total facility includes 50 beds in nursing home–type unit) **A**1 9 10 **F**2 9 10 11 12 21 29 32 33 44 46 47 48 51 52 55 58 59 60 62 63 64 66 68 69 81 82 87 88 92 93 94 108 110 **P**6
Primary Contact: Randall M. Olson, Chief Executive Officer
CFO: Michael Zimmerman, Chief Financial Officer
CMO: Kent Rhodes, M.D., Chief Medical Staff
CHR: David Beck, Chief Administrative Officer and Director Human Resources
Web address: www.lanehospital.org

	Control	Service	Staffed Beds	Admissions	Census	Outpatient Visits	Births	Total	Payroll	Personnel
LANE MEMORIAL HOSPITAL	16	10	167	4659	110	30926	71	36694	17029	492

MAINE

Hospital, Address, Telephone, Approval, Facility, and Physician Codes, Health Care System	Classi-fication Codes		Utilization Data					Expense (thousands) of dollars		
★ American Hospital Association (AHA) membership □ Joint Commission on Accreditation of Healthcare Organizations (JCAHO) accreditation ○ American Osteopathic Association (AOA) accreditation △ Commission on Accreditation of Rehabilitation Facilities (CARF) accreditation	Control	Service	Staffed Beds	Admissions	Census	Outpatient Visits	Births	Total	Payroll	Personnel

AUGUSTA—Kennebec County

MAINEGENERAL MEDICAL CENTER–AUGUSTA CAMPUS See MaineGeneral Medical Center–Waterville Campus, Waterville

□ **RIVERVIEW PSYCHIATRIC CENTER**, (Formerly Augusta Mental Health Institute), 250 Arsenal Street, Zip 04330, Mailing Address: P.O. Box 724, Zip 04330–0724; tel. 207/287–7200, (Nonreporting) **A**1 9 10 Primary Contact: David S. Proffitt, Superintendent Web address: www.state.me.us/bds/amh/index.html	12	22	102	—	—	—	—	—	—	—

BANGOR—Penobscot County

⊠ **ACADIA HOSPITAL**, 268 Stillwater Avenue, Zip 04401–3945, Mailing Address: P.O. Box 422, Zip 04402–0422; tel. 207/973–6100 **A**1 10 **F**3 4 21 22 26 27 28 29 39 48 52 57 58 60 66 71 72 73 74 75 76 77 78 92 94 96 98 108 **P**6 **S** Eastern Maine Healthcare, Bangor, ME Primary Contact: Dorothy E. Hill, Chief Executive Officer and Chief Nursing Officer COO: Lynn M. Madden, Vice President & Chief Operating Officer CFO: Marie Suitter, Chief Financial Officer CMO: Paul W. Tisher, Vice President and Chief Medical Officer CIO: Jeanne Paradis, Director Information Systems CHR: Sally Baughman, Director Human Resources Web address: www.acadiahospital.org	23	22	91	2507	91	75864	0	35487	20460	405
□ **BANGOR MENTAL HEALTH INSTITUTE**, 656 State Street, Zip 04402–0926, Mailing Address: P.O. Box 926, Zip 04402–0926; tel. 207/941–4000 **A**1 10 **F**32 52 71 77 **P**6 Primary Contact: Mary Louise McEwen, Superintendent Web address: www.state.me.us/bds/bmhi/bangormhi/index.htm	12	22	74	214	59	6967	0	24588	13601	333
⊠ **EASTERN MAINE MEDICAL CENTER**, 489 State Street, Zip 04401–6674, Mailing Address: P.O. Box 404, Zip 04402–0404; tel. 207/973–7000, (Includes ROSS SKILLED NURSING FACILITY) **A**1 2 3 5 9 10 12 13 **F**2 9 10 11 12 14 15 17 19 21 22 23 26 27 28 29 30 33 34 35 36 37 38 39 40 41 42 44 46 47 49 50 52 53 55 56 57 58 59 60 61 62 63 64 65 66 67 68 69 70 75 79 80 81 82 85 86 88 90 92 93 94 95 96 106 107 108 109 110 **P**6 **S** Eastern Maine Healthcare, Bangor, ME Primary Contact: Deborah Carey Johnson, R.N., President and Chief Executive Officer CFO: Daniel B. Coffey, Senior Vice President and Chief Financial Officer CIO: Catherine Bruno, Chief Information Officer Web address: www.emh.org	23	10	329	17610	250	378721	1658	349948	139875	2573
⊠ **ST. JOSEPH HOSPITAL**, 360 Broadway, Zip 04401–3897, Mailing Address: P.O. Box 403, Zip 04402–0403; tel. 207/262–1000 **A**1 9 10 **F**9 12 14 15 21 22 23 27 28 29 33 36 37 38 44 46 48 51 58 61 62 63 65 66 81 82 88 93 94 96 106 108 109 110 Primary Contact: Sister Mary Norberta Malinowski, President CFO: Matthew Flynn, Vice President and Chief Financial Officer CMO: James Sears, M.D., Chief of Staff CIO: Ron Crall, Chief Information Officer CHR: TinaMarie Bowlin–Norris, Assistant Vice President Human Resources Web address: www.sjhhealth.com	21	10	84	5432	53	115738	0	71126	26090	619

BAR HARBOR—Hancock County

★ **MOUNT DESERT ISLAND HOSPITAL**, 10 Wayman Lane, Zip 04609–0008, Mailing Address: P.O. Box 8, Zip 04609–0008; tel. 207/288–5081 **A**9 10 18 **F**2 4 5 8 9 11 12 21 23 26 27 28 29 33 42 44 47 48 52 55 57 58 59 60 61 62 63 64 66 69 70 72 73 77 81 82 85 88 91 92 94 95 96 97 106 109 **P**6 7 Primary Contact: Arthur J. Blank, President and Chief Executive Officer CFO: Wendy Fielding, Vice President Finance and Support Services CMO: Mary Dudzik, M.D., President Medical Staff CIO: Tim Zeiher, Director Information Services CHR: Chris Owen, Director Web address: www.mdihospital.org	23	10	25	1363	11	52693	67	29987	13899	279

BELFAST—Waldo County

WALDO COUNTY GENERAL HOSPITAL, 118 Northport Avenue, Zip 04915–6072, Mailing Address: P.O. Box 287, Zip 04915–0287; tel. 207/338–2500 **A**9 10 20 **F**14 23 26 27 33 36 46 48 49 51 52 55 57 58 59 61 63 69 70 81 82 84 85 86 88 93 94 96 108 Primary Contact: Mark A. Biscone, Executive Director Web address: www.wchi.com	23	10	45	2059	23	60383	211	34250	15842	401

Many Facility Codes have changed. Please refer to the AHA Guide Code Chart. © 2005 AHA Guide

Hospital, Address, Telephone, Approval, Facility, and Physician Codes, Health Care System	Classi-fication Codes		Utilization Data					Expense (thousands) of dollars		
★ American Hospital Association (AHA) membership □ Joint Commission on Accreditation of Healthcare Organizations (JCAHO) accreditation ○ American Osteopathic Association (AOA) accreditation △ Commission on Accreditation of Rehabilitation Facilities (CARF) accreditation	Control	Service	Staffed Beds	Admissions	Census	Outpatient Visits	Births	Total	Payroll	Personnel

BIDDEFORD—York County

⊞ **SOUTHERN MAINE MEDICAL CENTER**, One Medical Center Drive, Zip 04005–9496, Mailing Address: P.O. Box 626, Zip 04005–0626; tel. 207/283–7000 **A**1 2 9 10 12 13 **F**2 4 9 10 11 12 15 17 21 22 23 24 26 27 28 29 30 31 33 35 36 37 38 39 40 42 44 46 47 48 51 52 55 57 58 59 60 61 62 63 64 65 66 69 71 73 74 76 77 78 81 82 84 87 88 94 96 106 107 108 109 110 **P**5 8 Primary Contact: Edward J. McGeachey, President and Chief Executive Officer CFO: Christopher Robinson, Chief Financial Officer CMO: Terrance J. Sheehan, M.D., Chief Medical Officer CIO: Michael McLaughlin, Director Information Systems CHR: Lorraine Bouchard, Director Human Resources Web address: www.smmc.org	23	10	130	5716	81	187325	597	87173	42620	922

BLUE HILL—Hancock County

★ **BLUE HILL MEMORIAL HOSPITAL**, 57 Water Street, Zip 04614–0823, Mailing Address: P.O. Box 823, Zip 04614–0823; tel. 207/374–3400 **A**9 10 18 **F**8 9 11 12 21 23 26 27 28 29 33 36 39 46 47 48 51 52 55 58 59 60 61 63 65 69 70 81 85 88 91 92 94 96 97 106 108 109 **P**6 Primary Contact: Timothy Garrity, Chief Executive Officer CFO: Jeff Provenzano, Chief Financial Officer CMO: Thomas Bugbee, M.D., Chief of Staff CHR: Judy Pendleton, Manager Human Resources Web address: www.bhmh.org	23	10	25	868	9	100060	166	22315	11844	250

BOOTHBAY HARBOR—Lincoln County

★ **ST. ANDREWS HOSPITAL AND HEALTHCARE CENTER**, 6 St. Andrews Lane, Zip 04538–1732, Mailing Address: P.O. Box 417, Zip 04538–0417; tel. 207/633–2121, (Total facility includes 50 beds in nursing home–type unit) **A**9 10 18 **F**1 2 5 8 9 12 21 22 23 26 28 29 32 33 34 37 38 42 44 45 47 48 51 52 54 58 60 61 62 63 64 69 70 81 88 91 92 94 95 96 106 108 110 **P**8 Primary Contact: Margaret G. Pinkham, President and Chief Executive Officer CFO: Wayne Printy, Vice President CMO: John J. Kazalski, M.D., President Medical Staff CIO: Brooks Betts, Director Information Systems CHR: Susan Ray, Vice President Human Resources Web address: www.standrewshealthcare.org	23	10	71	594	54	39455	0	14587	6914	140

BRIDGTON—Cumberland County

⊞ **BRIDGTON HOSPITAL**, 10 Hospital Drive, Zip 04009; tel. 207/647–6000 **A**1 9 10 18 **F**2 9 11 12 21 22 23 26 27 28 29 33 42 46 48 55 58 59 61 62 63 64 69 81 82 85 88 94 95 96 97 108 109 110 **P**1 6 Primary Contact: John M. Carlson, President and Chief Executive Officer CMO: Ramesh Gaindh, M.D., President Medical Staff CHR: Katy Sperl, Human Resources Director Web address: www.bridgtonhospital.com	23	10	21	1333	11	57066	127	21769	9414	174

BRUNSWICK—Cumberland County

⊞ **MID COAST HOSPITAL**, 123 Medical Center Drive, Zip 04011; tel. 207/729–0181 **A**1 9 10 **F**2 4 9 11 12 15 21 22 26 27 28 29 30 33 37 38 40 41 42 46 47 48 50 52 55 57 58 59 60 61 62 63 64 65 66 69 70 71 76 78 81 84 87 88 92 93 94 96 98 106 108 109 110 **P**6 Primary Contact: Herbert Paris, President CFO: Robert N. McCue, Vice President Finance CMO: Scott Mills, M.D., Director Medical Staff Affairs CIO: Gale S. Toy, Manager Information Systems CHR: George Hunter, Vice President Administration and Human Resources Web address: www.midcoasthealth.com	23	10	74	4587	53	188000	576	66170	27611	591
⊞ **PARKVIEW ADVENTIST MEDICAL CENTER**, 329 Maine Street, Zip 04011–3398; tel. 207/373–2000 **A**1 9 10 **F**9 11 12 21 22 23 27 28 29 30 31 33 39 44 47 48 50 52 53 55 58 59 60 61 62 63 64 65 66 69 70 81 82 84 88 93 94 96 106 108 109 **P**7 8 Primary Contact: Theodore M. Lewis, President and Chief Executive Officer CFO: Wing Choi, Vice President Finance and Chief Financial Officer CMO: Larry Losey, M.D., President Medical Staff CIO: Bill McQuaid, Director Information Systems CHR: Robin White, Director Human Resources Web address: www.parkviewamc.org	21	10	55	2052	23	78561	306	31360	12771	307

CALAIS—Washington County

★ **CALAIS REGIONAL HOSPITAL**, 22 Hospital Lane, Zip 04619–1398; tel. 207/454–7521 **A**9 10 18 **F**2 9 11 12 21 23 24 26 27 28 29 33 37 38 46 48 51 53 55 58 59 60 61 62 63 64 65 69 81 82 84 85 87 88 94 96 97 106 108 109 110 **P**7 8 **S** Quorum Health Resources, Plano, TX Primary Contact: Ray H. Davis, Jr, Chief Executive Officer CFO: P Bernard McAdam, Chief Financial Officer CMO: David Feiner, M.D., Chief of Staff CIO: Dee Dee Travis, Director Community Relations CHR: Kristi K. Saunders, Director and Compliance Officer Web address: www.calaishospital.com	23	10	25	1123	11	19775	104	16996	7705	207

ME

Hospital, Address, Telephone, Approval, Facility, and Physician Codes, Health Care System	Classi-fication Codes		Utilization Data					Expense (thousands) of dollars		
★ American Hospital Association (AHA) membership □ Joint Commission on Accreditation of Healthcare Organizations (JCAHO) accreditation ○ American Osteopathic Association (AOA) accreditation △ Commission on Accreditation of Rehabilitation Facilities (CARF) accreditation	Control	Service	Staffed Beds	Admissions	Census	Outpatient Visits	Births	Total	Payroll	Personnel

CARIBOU—Aroostook County

⊞ **CARY MEDICAL CENTER**, 163 Van Buren Road, Suite 1, Zip 04736–2599; tel. 207/498–3111, (Total facility includes 9 beds in nursing home–type unit) **A**1 9 10 **F**2 9 11 12 21 23 24 26 27 28 29 30 31 33 34 35 37 38 40 41 42 44 46 47 48 50 52 53 55 58 59 60 61 62 63 64 65 66 68 69 70 79 81 82 84 87 88 89 92 93 94 95 96 106 107 108 109 110 **S** Quorum Health Resources, Plano, TX
Primary Contact: Kris Doody–Chabre, Chief Executive Officer
COO: Shawn Anderson, Chief Operating Officer
CFO: Galen Dickinson, Chief Financial Officer
CMO: Beth Collamore, M.D., President Medical Staff
CIO: Dave Silsbee, Chief Information Officer
CHR: Paula Parent, Director Human Resources
Web address: www.carymedicalcenter.org

	14	10	49	1785	31	87139	158	36346	13823	338

DAMARISCOTTA—Lincoln County

★ **MILES MEMORIAL HOSPITAL**, 35 Miles Street, Zip 04543–9767; tel. 207/563–1234 **A**9 10 20 **F**2 11 12 21 22 26 27 28 29 33 34 36 38 51 55 58 59 60 62 63 66 69 81 88 92 93 94 106 108 110 **P**3
Primary Contact: Judith Tarr, Chief Executive Officer
CFO: Wayne Printy, Vice President Finance
CMO: Jennifer Smith, M.D., Chief of Staff
CIO: Wayne Printy, Vice President Finance
CHR: Lisa McIlwain, Vice President Human Resources
Web address: www.mileshealthcare.org

	23	10	35	1661	20	100420	200	28669	11067	—

DOVER–FOXCROFT—Piscataquis County

★ **MAYO REGIONAL HOSPITAL**, 897 West Main Street, Zip 04426–1099; tel. 207/564–8401 **A**9 10 18 20 **F**2 4 6 9 11 12 21 22 23 24 26 27 28 29 31 33 39 46 48 55 58 59 60 61 62 63 65 66 69 70 72 73 74 75 76 77 78 81 82 84 87 88 94 98 106 108 109 110 **P**6
Primary Contact: Ralph Gabarro, Chief Executive Officer
CFO: Dennis Allen, Chief Financial Officer
CMO: Thomas Murray, M.D., President Medical Staff
CIO: Jeff Hastings, Information Technology Manager
CHR: Ken Proctor, Director Human Resources
Web address: www.mayohospital.com

	16	10	46	1345	12	—	181	25003	12293	246

ELLSWORTH—Hancock County

⊞ **MAINE COAST MEMORIAL HOSPITAL**, 50 Union Street, Zip 04605–1599; tel. 207/664–5311 **A**1 9 10 **F**2 11 12 21 23 26 27 28 29 33 42 44 46 47 48 50 52 53 55 58 59 60 61 62 63 65 66 69 81 82 84 87 88 94 95 96 97 106 107 108 109 **P**8
Primary Contact: Douglas T. Jones, Chief Executive Officer
CFO: Kevin Sedgwick, Chief Financial Officer
CIO: Julie Hagle, Director Information Systems
CHR: Lois Macias, Vice President Ancillary Services
Web address: www.mainehospital.org

	23	10	48	2755	26	119329	234	49612	24602	455

FARMINGTON—Franklin County

⊞ **FRANKLIN MEMORIAL HOSPITAL**, 111 Franklin Health Commons, Zip 04938–9990; tel. 207/778–6031 **A**1 9 10 20 **F**2 6 9 11 12 21 22 23 24 26 27 28 29 30 33 39 40 42 44 46 47 48 50 52 55 58 59 60 61 62 63 64 65 66 69 70 75 81 87 88 92 94 95 96 97 106 107 108 109 110 **P**6 8
Primary Contact: Richard A. Batt, President and Chief Executive Officer
COO: Jerry Cayer, Vice President and Chief Operating Officer
CFO: Eric Martinsen, Vice President Finance
CMO: Roderick Prior, M.D., Medical Director and Chief Information Officer
CIO: Roderick Prior, M.D., Medical Director and Chief Information Officer
CHR: Tom Hagerstrom, Director Human Resources
Web address: www.fchn.org

	23	10	56	2534	24	128114	304	47457	22163	537

FORT FAIRFIELD—Aroostook County

COMMUNITY GENERAL HEALTH CENTER See Aroostook Medical Center, Presque Isle

FORT KENT—Aroostook County

⊞ **NORTHERN MAINE MEDICAL CENTER**, 194 East Main Street, Zip 04743–1497; tel. 207/834–3155, (Total facility includes 45 beds in nursing home–type unit) **A**1 9 10 20 **F**11 12 21 26 27 28 33 42 46 48 51 52 54 55 58 59 60 61 62 63 65 66 69 71 72 73 74 75 76 77 81 82 84 87 88 92 94 95 96 106 109 **P**6
Primary Contact: Martin B. Bernstein, Chief Executive Officer
COO: Peter Sirois, Associate Administrator
CFO: Roger Lagasse, Chief Financial Officer
CMO: Asif Ansari, M.D., Chief Medical Staff
CIO: Tony Chasse, Computer Systems Coordinator
CHR: Robin Damboise, Director Human Resources
Web address: www.nmmc.org

	23	10	81	2153	66	33760	81	35759	18680	462

Many Facility Codes have changed. Please refer to the AHA Guide Code Chart. © 2005 AHA Guide

Hospital, Address, Telephone, Approval, Facility, and Physician Codes, Health Care System	Classification Codes		Utilization Data					Expense (thousands) of dollars		
★ American Hospital Association (AHA) membership □ Joint Commission on Accreditation of Healthcare Organizations (JCAHO) accreditation ○ American Osteopathic Association (AOA) accreditation △ Commission on Accreditation of Rehabilitation Facilities (CARF) accreditation	Control	Service	Staffed Beds	Admissions	Census	Outpatient Visits	Births	Total	Payroll	Personnel

GREENVILLE—Piscataquis County

★ **CHARLES A. DEAN MEMORIAL HOSPITAL AND NURSING HOME**, Pritham Avenue, Zip 04441–1395, Mailing Address: P.O. Box 1129, Zip 04441–1129; tel. 207/695–5200, (Total facility includes 24 beds in nursing home–type unit) **A**9 10 18 **F**6 9 21 22 26 27 28 29 33 41 48 52 60 62 63 66 69 70 92 94 97 **S** Eastern Maine Healthcare, Bangor, ME
Primary Contact: Geno Murray, President and Chief Executive Officer
CMO: Brian Griffin, M.D., Chief of Staff
CHR: Nancy Pelletier, Director Human Resources
Web address: www.cadean.org
| 23 | 10 | 36 | 209 | 24 | 27913 | 0 | 7425 | 3860 | — |

HOULTON—Aroostook County

★ **HOULTON REGIONAL HOSPITAL**, 20 Hartford Street, Zip 04730–9998; tel. 207/532–9471, (Total facility includes 26 beds in nursing home–type unit) **A**9 10 18 20 **F**2 3 9 11 13 14 21 26 27 28 33 34 37 40 41 44 46 47 48 55 56 57 58 59 60 61 62 63 65 66 67 68 69 70 71 81 82 88 92 93 94 96 106 108 109 **P**8
Primary Contact: Thomas J. Moakler, Chief Executive Officer
CFO: Cindy Morin, Chief Financial Officer
Web address: www.houlton.net/hrh
| 23 | 10 | 51 | 1854 | 38 | 83654 | 165 | 29465 | 13203 | 292 |

LEWISTON—Androscoggin County

⊞ **CENTRAL MAINE MEDICAL CENTER**, 300 Main Street, Zip 04240–0305; tel. 207/795–0111 **A**1 2 3 5 9 10 12 **F**2 9 10 11 12 14 15 17 19 21 22 23 24 26 27 28 29 30 33 34 35 37 38 39 40 41 46 48 49 52 53 55 57 58 59 60 61 62 63 64 65 66 68 69 70 75 79 81 82 85 87 88 89 90 92 93 94 96 106 107 108 109 110 **P**5 6 8
Primary Contact: Peter E. Chalke, President and Chief Executive Officer
COO: Laird P. Covey, Exec Vice President and Chief Operating Officer
CFO: Charles T. Orne, Executive Vice President Finance and Chief Financial Officer
CIO: Jonathan Lyon, Chief Information Officer
Web address: www.cmmc.org
| 23 | 10 | 189 | 8613 | 117 | 243604 | 735 | 173699 | 74593 | 1481 |

⊞ **ST. MARY'S REGIONAL MEDICAL CENTER**, 330 Sabattus Street, Zip 04240, Mailing Address: P.O. Box 291, Zip 04243–0291; tel. 207/777–8100 **A**1 2 9 10 **F**2 3 4 6 9 11 12 14 15 21 22 23 24 26 27 28 29 32 33 35 36 37 38 39 40 46 47 48 49 50 52 53 55 57 58 59 60 61 62 63 64 65 66 69 71 72 73 74 75 76 77 78 81 82 84 86 87 88 92 93 94 96 98 106 108 109 110 **P**6 **S** Covenant Health Systems, Inc., Lexington, MA
Primary Contact: James E. Cassidy, President and Chief Executive Officer
COO: Lee T. Myles, Chief Operating Officer
CFO: Carolyn Kasabian, Chief Financial Officer
CMO: Peter Watko, Vice President Medical Affairs and Quality
CHR: Kevin Healey, Vice President Human Resources
Web address: www.stmarysmaine.com
| 23 | 10 | 171 | 6496 | 102 | 154933 | 631 | 96945 | 29683 | 638 |

LINCOLN—Penobscot County

★ **PENOBSCOT VALLEY HOSPITAL**, 7 Transalpine Road, Zip 04457–0368, Mailing Address: P.O. Box 368, Zip 04457–0368; tel. 207/794–3321 **A**9 10 18 **F**2 6 9 11 12 14 21 22 23 26 28 33 44 45 46 48 53 55 58 59 60 62 63 64 66 68 69 75 81 82 94 97 106 108 **S** Quorum Health Resources, Plano, TX
Primary Contact: Ronald D. Victory, Chief Executive Officer
Web address: www.pvhhealthcare.org
| 23 | 10 | 25 | 1157 | 14 | 38178 | 96 | 14956 | 6184 | 128 |

MACHIAS—Washington County

⊞ **DOWN EAST COMMUNITY HOSPITAL**, Upper Court Street, Zip 04654, Mailing Address: Rural Route 1, Box 11, Zip 04654–9702; tel. 207/255–3356 **A**1 9 10 20 **F**11 21 23 27 28 29 33 34 58 59 62 63 64 69 81 82 88 93 94 96 108 109 **P**6 **S** Quorum Health Resources, Plano, TX
Primary Contact: Wayne Dodwell, Chief Executive Officer
CFO: Lynnette Haskell, Chief Financial Officer
CIO: Lynnette Haskell, Chief Financial Officer
CHR: Mary Jo Gripp, Human Resources Director
Web address: www.dech.org
| 23 | 10 | 34 | 1108 | 10 | 32485 | 103 | 21222 | 8957 | 193 |

MARS HILL—Aroostook County

AROOSTOOK HEALTH CENTER See Aroostook Medical Center, Presque Isle

MILLINOCKET—Penobscot County

★ **MILLINOCKET REGIONAL HOSPITAL**, 200 Somerset Street, Zip 04462–1298; tel. 207/723–5161 **A**9 10 18 20 **F**2 9 12 21 22 23 26 27 28 29 33 34 37 38 39 40 41 44 46 47 48 52 53 55 62 63 64 65 66 69 70 81 82 92 94 95 97 106 109 **P**6 **S** Quorum Health Resources, Plano, TX
Primary Contact: Marie E. Vienneau, R.N., Chief Executive Officer
CFO: Nancy Glidden, Chief Financial Officer
CMO: Daniel Herbert, M.D., Medical Administrative Officer
CIO: Joe Grant, Information Systems Manager
CHR: Lisa Arsenault, Human Resources Director
Web address: www.mrhme.org
| 23 | 10 | 25 | 923 | 11 | 26705 | 0 | 17553 | 8261 | 189 |

NORWAY—Oxford County

⊞ **STEPHENS MEMORIAL HOSPITAL**, 181 Main Street, Zip 04268–1297; tel. 207/743–5933 **A**1 2 9 10 **F**2 4 6 9 11 12 14 21 22 23 26 27 28 29 33 34 38 47 48 52 53 55 58 59 61 62 63 64 65 69 81 82 84 85 92 94 96 97 106 108 110 **P**8
Primary Contact: Timothy A. Churchill, President
Web address: www.wmhcc.com
| 23 | 10 | 50 | 2151 | 22 | 135871 | 238 | 28990 | 13052 | 318 |

Hospital, Address, Telephone, Approval, Facility, and Physician Codes, Health Care System	Classi-fication Codes		Utilization Data					Expense (thousands) of dollars		
★ American Hospital Association (AHA) membership ☐ Joint Commission on Accreditation of Healthcare Organizations (JCAHO) accreditation ○ American Osteopathic Association (AOA) accreditation △ Commission on Accreditation of Rehabilitation Facilities (CARF) accreditation	Control	Service	Staffed Beds	Admissions	Census	Outpatient Visits	Births	Total	Payroll	Personnel

PITTSFIELD—Somerset County

⊞ **SEBASTICOOK VALLEY HOSPITAL**, 99 Grove Street, Zip 04967–1199;
tel. 207/487–5141 **A**1 9 10 **F**6 12 21 26 27 28 32 33 37 39 46 48 51 52 53
55 58 60 61 62 63 66 69 81 82 88 93 94 96 106 108 109 110 **P**6 **S** Eastern
Maine Healthcare, Bangor, ME
Primary Contact: John C. May, Chief Executive Officer
CFO: Randall Clark, Vice President Finance
CMO: Thomas Moskalewicz, M.D., Chief of Staff
Web address: www.sebasticookhospital.org

23	10	25	1110	11	57495	0	16756	7440	205

PORTLAND—Cumberland County

⊞ **MAINE MEDICAL CENTER**, 22 Bramhall Street, Zip 04102–3175;
tel. 207/871–0111, (Includes MAINE MEDICAL CENTER, BRIGHTON CAMPUS,
335 Brighton Avenue, Zip 04102–9735; tel. 207/879–8000) **A**1 2 3 5 8 9 10
F2 4 9 10 11 12 13 14 15 16 17 18 19 20 21 22 23 24 25 26 27 28 29 30
31 32 33 34 37 38 39 40 42 44 45 46 47 48 49 50 52 53 55 56 57 58 59
60 61 62 63 64 65 66 69 70 71 72 73 74 75 76 77 78 79 81 82 84 85 87
88 90 93 94 95 96 98 99 101 102 105 106 107 108 109 110 **P**4 6 8
Primary Contact: Vincent S. Conti, President and Chief Executive Officer
CFO: John E. Heye, Chief Financial Officer
Web address: www.mmc.org

23	10	557	28191	421	255190	2350	469161	200820	5088

⊞ **MERCY HOSPITAL OF PORTLAND**, 144 State Street, Zip 04101–3795;
tel. 207/879–3000 **A**1 9 10 12 **F**3 4 9 11 12 15 21 22 23 26 27 28 29 30 33
37 40 42 44 45 46 47 48 50 52 53 55 57 58 59 60 61 62 63 69 70 73 75
77 78 81 82 84 85 87 88 94 96 106 107 108 109 110 **P**6 **S** Catholic Health
East, Newtown Square, PA
Primary Contact: Eileen F. Skinner, President and Chief Executive Officer
COO: Timothy Prince, Vice President Planning and Ancillary Services
CFO: Michael Hachey, Chief Financial Officer
CMO: David T. Bachman, Vice President of Medical Affairs
CIO: Jonathan Roderick, Chief Information Officer
CHR: Robert Nutter, Vice President Human Resources and Support Services
Web address: www.mercyhospital.com

21	10	168	9021	103	246902	1183	119921	55050	1111

⊞ **NEW ENGLAND REHABILITATION HOSPITAL OF PORTLAND**, 335 Brighton
Avenue, Zip 04102–9735; tel. 207/775–4000, (Nonreporting) **A**1 10
S HEALTHSOUTH Corporation, Birmingham, AL
Primary Contact: Amy Morse, Administrator
CFO: Jeanine Chesley, Controller
CMO: Elissa Charbonneau, D.O., Medical Director
CHR: Leigh Baade, Director Human Resources
Web address: www.healthsouth.com

33	46	76	—	—	—	—	—	—	—

SPRING HARBOR HOSPITAL See Westbrook

PRESQUE ISLE—Aroostook County

⊞ **AROOSTOOK MEDICAL CENTER**, 140 Academy Street, Zip 04769–3171,
Mailing Address: P.O. Box 151, Zip 04769–0151; tel. 207/768–4000, (Includes
AROOSTOOK HEALTH CENTER, 15 Highland Avenue, Mars Hill, Zip 04758;
tel. 207/768–4900; ARTHUR R. GOULD MEMORIAL HOSPITAL; COMMUNITY
GENERAL HEALTH CENTER, 3 Green Street, Fort Fairfield, Zip 04742;
tel. 207/768–4700), (Total facility includes 72 beds in nursing home–type unit)
A1 9 10 **F**2 4 6 10 11 12 15 21 22 23 24 26 27 28 29 30 33 34 37 38 39
42 44 45 46 47 48 49 50 52 53 55 57 58 59 60 61 62 63 64 65 66 68 69
70 71 72 73 74 75 76 77 78 81 82 88 89 90 92 93 94 95 96 106 108 109
110 **P**6 **S** Eastern Maine Healthcare, Bangor, ME
Primary Contact: David A. Peterson, President and Chief Executive Officer
COO: John J. Ginty, Jr, Senior Vice President, Patient Services
CFO: C Bruce Sandstrom, Senior Vice President Finance
CMO: Jay Reynolds, M.D., Vice President Medical Affairs
CIO: Catherine Bruno, Chief Information Officer
CHR: Thomas Umphrey, Senior Vice President
Web address: www.tamc.org

23	10	147	2999	87	96628	273	69733	34507	867

ROCKPORT—Knox County

⊞ **PENOBSCOT BAY MEDICAL CENTER**, 6 Glen Cove Drive, Zip 04856–4241;
tel. 207/596–8000, (Total facility includes 84 beds in nursing home–type unit)
(Nonreporting) **A**1 2 9 10 20
Primary Contact: Roy A. Hitchings, Jr, FACHE, President and Chief Executive
Officer
COO: Steve Mansfield, Vice President Support Services
CFO: Elmer Doucette, Vice President Fiscal Services
CMO: Dana L. Goldsmith, M.D., Vice President Medical Affairs
CIO: Dennis Puls, Information Systems Director
CHR: Thomas A. Bosica, Jr, Vice President Human Resources
Web address: www.nehealth.org

23	10	171	—	—	—	—	—	—	—

RUMFORD—Oxford County

★ **RUMFORD HOSPITAL**, 420 Franklin Street, Zip 04276–2145;
tel. 207/369–1000 **A**9 10 18 20 **F**9 11 12 21 23 26 27 28 29 33 39 40 46
48 52 55 58 59 60 61 62 63 64 69 81 82 87 88 92 94 96 97 108 **P**6 8
Primary Contact: John H. Welsh, Chief Executive Officer
Web address: www.rumfordhospital.org

23	10	25	1205	12	45912	99	22762	10182	161

Hospital, Address, Telephone, Approval, Facility, and Physician Codes, Health Care System	Classi-fication Codes		Utilization Data					Expense (thousands) of dollars		
★ American Hospital Association (AHA) membership □ Joint Commission on Accreditation of Healthcare Organizations (JCAHO) accreditation ○ American Osteopathic Association (AOA) accreditation △ Commission on Accreditation of Rehabilitation Facilities (CARF) accreditation	Control	Service	Staffed Beds	Admissions	Census	Outpatient Visits	Births	Total	Payroll	Personnel

SANFORD—York County

⊠ **HENRIETTA D. GOODALL HOSPITAL**, 25 June Street, Zip 04073–2645; tel. 207/324–4310, (Total facility includes 112 beds in nursing home–type unit) (Nonreporting) **A**1 2 9 10
Primary Contact: Darlene Stromstad, Chief Executive Officer
Web address: www.goodallhosp.org

| | 23 | 10 | 161 | — | — | — | — | — | — | — |

SKOWHEGAN—Somerset County

⊠ **REDINGTON–FAIRVIEW GENERAL HOSPITAL**, Fairview Avenue, Zip 04976, Mailing Address: P.O. Box 468, Zip 04976–0468; tel. 207/474–5121 **A**1 2 9 10 **F**2 6 9 11 12 14 21 22 23 26 27 28 29 33 37 39 40 41 44 46 48 53 55 57 58 59 60 61 62 63 64 67 69 70 72 73 77 81 82 85 87 88 94 95 96 98 106 108 109 **P**6
Primary Contact: Richard Willett, Chief Executive Officer
CFO: Dana Kempton, Associate Director and Chief Financial Officer
CMO: Roger Renfrew, Medical Director
CHR: Deborah Buckingham, R.N., Director Human Resources
Web address: www.rfgh.net

| | 23 | 10 | 65 | 2480 | 25 | 76102 | 202 | 35762 | 15988 | 374 |

TOGUS—Kennebec County

⊠ **VETERANS AFFAIRS MEDICAL CENTER**, 1 VA Center, Zip 04330; tel. 207/623–8411, (Total facility includes 100 beds in nursing home–type unit) **A**1 2 **F**1 2 4 15 21 22 23 25 26 27 28 32 36 37 38 42 44 45 46 48 49 50 51 52 53 55 57 58 60 61 62 63 64 66 69 70 71 73 75 76 77 78 81 88 92 93 94 96 106 107 108 109 110 **P**6 **S** Department of Veterans Affairs, Washington, DC
Primary Contact: John H. Sims, Jr, Director
CFO: Daniel Howard, Chief Financial Officer
CMO: Timothy J. Richardson, M.D., Chief of Staff
CIO: Richard McNaughton, Chief Information Management Service
CHR: David Rankin, Chief Human Resources Management Services
Web address: www.visn1.med.va.gov/togus/

| | 45 | 10 | 167 | 1953 | 115 | 297200 | 0 | 156037 | 68111 | 937 |

WATERVILLE—Kennebec County

★ ○ **INLAND HOSPITAL**, 200 Kennedy Memorial Drive, Zip 04901–4595; tel. 207/861–3000 **A**9 10 11 **F**11 12 21 22 27 29 31 33 37 39 46 48 51 53 55 58 59 62 63 69 70 81 82 84 87 88 93 96 106 108 110 **S** Eastern Maine Healthcare, Bangor, ME
Primary Contact: Sally Conary, President and Chief Executive Officer
COO: Sally Conary, President and Chief Executive Officer
CFO: David Trunnell, Chief Financial Officer
CMO: Catherine M. Kimball, D.O., Chief of Staff
CIO: Kevin Dieterich, Manager Information Services
CHR: Daniel Booth, Vice President Human Resources and Facilities
Web address: www.inlandhospital.org

| | 23 | 10 | 48 | 2093 | 20 | — | 397 | 30313 | 14367 | 408 |

⊠ **MAINEGENERAL MEDICAL CENTER–WATERVILLE CAMPUS**, 149 North Street, Zip 04901–4974; tel. 207/872–1000, (Includes MAINEGENERAL MEDICAL CENTER–AUGUSTA CAMPUS, 6 East Chestnut Street, Augusta, Zip 04330–9988; tel. 207/626–1000) **A**1 2 5 9 10 19 **F**2 3 4 9 10 11 12 15 19 21 22 23 26 27 28 29 33 34 37 38 39 40 48 49 50 51 52 53 55 57 58 59 60 61 62 63 64 65 66 68 69 70 71 72 73 75 76 77 78 80 81 82 84 85 86 87 88 92 93 94 95 96 97 106 107 108 110 **P**8
Primary Contact: Scott B. Bullock, President
COO: Chuck Hays, Chief Operating Officer
CFO: Anthony Marple, Executive Vice President and Treasurer
CMO: Stephen Sears, M.D., Chief Medical Officer
CIO: Kash Basavappa, Senior Vice President and Chief Information Officer
CHR: Rebecca Lamey, Vice President Human Resources
Web address: www.mainegeneral.org

| | 23 | 10 | 247 | 14287 | 180 | 396795 | 1040 | 203814 | 85656 | 1946 |

WESTBROOK—Cumberland County

⊠ **SPRING HARBOR HOSPITAL**, 123 Andover Road, Zip 04092–3850; tel. 207/761–2200 **A**1 10 **F**3 4 27 28 42 52 71 72 74 75 76 77 78 94 96 106 108
Primary Contact: Dennis P. King, Chief Executive Officer
COO: Richard Hanley, Chief Operating Officer
CFO: Gregory Bowers, Chief Financial Officer
CMO: Girard Robinson, M.D., Chief Medical Officer
CIO: Bonnie Thibault, Chief Information Officer
Web address: www.springharbor.org

| | 23 | 22 | 100 | 2901 | 78 | 3396 | 0 | 25297 | 14832 | 319 |

YORK—York County

★ **YORK HOSPITAL**, 15 Hospital Drive, Zip 03909–1099; tel. 207/363–4321, (Total facility includes 13 beds in nursing home–type unit) **A**9 10 **F**4 9 11 12 15 17 21 22 23 24 27 28 29 30 33 36 41 45 48 50 51 52 54 55 58 59 61 63 66 69 81 82 84 87 88 92 93 94 96 97 98 106 107 108 110 **P**8
Primary Contact: Jud Knox, President
COO: Stephen Pelletier, Leader, Guest Services
CFO: Robin LaBonte, Leader Financial Care
CMO: Brian Collins, D.O., Medical Staff President
CIO: Robin LaBonte, Leader Financial Care
Web address: www.yorkhospital.com

| | 23 | 10 | 79 | 3967 | 47 | 126507 | 434 | 77033 | 33686 | 581 |

MARYLAND

Hospital, Address, Telephone, Approval, Facility, and Physician Codes, Health Care System	Classi-fication Codes		Utilization Data					Expense (thousands) of dollars		
★ American Hospital Association (AHA) membership □ Joint Commission on Accreditation of Healthcare Organizations (JCAHO) accreditation ○ American Osteopathic Association (AOA) accreditation △ Commission on Accreditation of Rehabilitation Facilities (CARF) accreditation	Control	Service	Staffed Beds	Admissions	Census	Outpatient Visits	Births	Total	Payroll	Personnel

ANDREWS AFB—Prince George's County

☒ **MALCOLM GROW MEDICAL CENTER**, 1050 West Perimeter, Zip 20762–6600, Mailing Address: 1050 West Perimeter, Suite A1–19, Zip 20762–6600; tel. 240/857–3001 **A**1 2 3 5 9 **F**2 4 11 12 21 22 23 25 26 27 29 30 31 32 33 41 42 46 48 52 53 55 57 58 59 60 61 62 63 64 65 66 70 72 73 74 75 76 77 81 84 88 106 108 109 110 **P**1 **S** Department of the Air Force, Washington, DC
Primary Contact: Brigadier General William Germann, Commanding Officer
CFO: Major Charles J. McCloud, Director, Medical Resource Management Flight
CMO: Colonel Robert Williamson, Chief Medical Staff
CIO: Major Charles Groh, Flight Commander, Medical Information Management
Web address: www.mgmc.af.mil

| | 41 | 10 | 68 | 3764 | 28 | 320311 | 655 | — | — | 1383 |

ANNAPOLIS—Anne Arundel County

☒ **ANNE ARUNDEL MEDICAL CENTER**, 2001 Medical Parkway, Zip 21401–3019; tel. 443/481–1000 **A**1 2 9 10 **F**2 3 4 9 11 12 15 17 21 22 23 26 27 28 29 30 31 33 37 39 40 42 44 46 47 48 52 55 56 57 58 59 60 61 62 63 64 65 66 69 70 73 75 79 80 81 82 84 85 86 88 93 94 96 97 106 108 109 110 **P**6
Primary Contact: Martin L. Doordan, President
COO: Linda Holmgren, Chief Operating Officer
CFO: William L. Hughes, Chief Financial Officer and Vice President of Business Development
CMO: Joseph Moser, M.D., Vice President Medical Staff Affairs
CIO: Daniel Moffatt, Chief Information Officer
CHR: Joyce Phillip, Vice President and Human Resources
Web address: www.aahs.org

| | 23 | 10 | 308 | 22730 | 215 | 345659 | 5156 | 241624 | 99933 | 1962 |

BALTIMORE—Baltimore City County

☒ **BON SECOURS BALTIMORE HEALTH SYSTEM**, 2000 West Baltimore Street, Zip 21223–1597; tel. 410/362–3000 **A**1 9 10 **F**2 9 12 15 21 22 23 26 27 28 29 33 37 38 39 42 45 46 48 49 50 52 55 57 61 62 63 65 66 69 71 72 73 74 75 77 78 81 82 84 88 94 96 107 108 109 110 **S** Bon Secours Health System, Inc., Marriottsville, MD
Primary Contact: Percy Allen, II, FACHE, Chief Executive Officer
COO: Vivian Jones, Senior Vice President Operations
CFO: George A. Blair, Jr, Chief Financial Officer
CIO: Nancy Stokes, Director
CHR: Gloria Clarke, Vice President Human Resources
Web address: www.bonsecours.org

| | 23 | 10 | 148 | 7655 | 101 | 120549 | 0 | 89983 | 39673 | 853 |

☒ **FRANKLIN SQUARE HOSPITAL CENTER**, 9000 Franklin Square Drive, Zip 21237–2998; tel. 443/777–7000 **A**1 2 3 5 8 9 10 **F**2 4 8 9 10 11 12 14 15 17 21 22 23 24 26 27 28 29 30 31 32 33 35 37 38 39 40 44 46 47 48 49 50 52 53 55 56 57 58 59 60 61 62 63 64 65 66 69 70 71 72 73 74 75 76 77 78 81 82 85 87 88 89 90 92 93 94 95 96 97 98 106 108 109 110 **P**6 **S** MedStar Health, Columbia, MD
Primary Contact: Carl J. Schindelar, President
COO: Eric Conley, Senior Vice President and Chief Operating Officer
CFO: Robert P. Lally, Jr, Vice President Finance
CMO: Tony Sclama, M.D., Vice President Medical Affairs
CHR: Karen Robertson–Keck, Assistant Vice President Human Resources
Web address: www.franklinsquare.org

| | 23 | 10 | 358 | 23315 | 247 | 180949 | 2555 | 250886 | 115935 | 2301 |

☒ △ **GOOD SAMARITAN HOSPITAL OF MARYLAND**, 5601 Loch Raven Boulevard, Zip 21239–2995; tel. 410/532–8000, (Total facility includes 27 beds in nursing home–type unit) **A**1 2 3 5 7 9 10 **F**2 7 9 12 14 15 17 19 21 22 24 26 27 28 29 30 31 33 35 36 37 38 39 40 41 44 45 46 47 48 49 50 52 55 57 58 60 61 62 63 64 65 66 68 69 70 75 81 82 84 85 87 88 92 93 94 95 96 106 107 108 110 **P**6 **S** MedStar Health, Columbia, MD
Primary Contact: Lawrence M. Beck, President
CFO: Deanna Stout, Vice President Financial Services
Web address: www.goodsam-md.org

| | 23 | 10 | 244 | 16187 | 221 | 122046 | 0 | 190025 | 81856 | 1740 |

☒ **GREATER BALTIMORE MEDICAL CENTER**, 6701 North Charles Street, Zip 21204–6892; tel. 443/849–2000, (Total facility includes 23 beds in nursing home–type unit) **A**1 2 3 5 8 9 10 **F**2 9 10 11 12 14 15 21 22 23 24 26 27 28 29 32 33 35 36 37 38 39 40 42 44 46 47 48 49 50 51 52 53 55 58 59 60 61 62 63 64 65 66 69 70 72 73 74 75 76 79 80 81 82 84 85 86 87 88 89 90 92 93 94 96 97 98 106 107 108 109 110 **P**4
Primary Contact: Laurence M. Merlis, President and Chief Executive Officer
COO: Vincent D. Joseph, Executive Vice President and Chief Operating Officer
CFO: Eric L. Melchior, Executive Vice President and Chief Financial Officer
CMO: Rodney W. Williams, M.D., JD, Executive Vice President and Chief Medical Officer
CIO: Tressa Springmann, Chief Information Officer
CHR: Frank M. Smith, Vice President Human Resources and Organizational Development
Web address: www.gbmc.org

| | 23 | 10 | 253 | 22435 | 234 | 155392 | 4688 | 322901 | 149460 | 2323 |

Many Facility Codes have changed. Please refer to the AHA Guide Code Chart.

Hospital, Address, Telephone, Approval, Facility, and Physician Codes, Health Care System	Classi-fication Codes		Utilization Data					Expense (thousands) of dollars		
★ American Hospital Association (AHA) membership □ Joint Commission on Accreditation of Healthcare Organizations (JCAHO) accreditation ○ American Osteopathic Association (AOA) accreditation △ Commission on Accreditation of Rehabilitation Facilities (CARF) accreditation	Control	Service	Staffed Beds	Admissions	Census	Outpatient Visits	Births	Total	Payroll	Personnel

MD

✱ **HARBOR HOSPITAL CENTER**, 3001 South Hanover Street, Zip 21225–1290; tel. 410/350–3200 **A**1 2 3 5 9 10 **F**1 2 7 9 11 12 21 22 23 24 26 27 28 29 33 35 37 39 40 41 42 44 46 47 48 52 53 55 57 58 59 60 61 62 63 64 65 66 69 70 73 79 81 82 84 85 86 87 88 90 93 94 95 96 97 106 107 108 109 110 **P**6 **S** MedStar Health, Columbia, MD Primary Contact: Joseph M. Oddis, President and Chief Executive Officer Web address: www.harborhospital.org	23	10	145	11625	125	56715	1714	124804	55782	1185
✱ △ **JAMES LAWRENCE KERNAN HOSPITAL**, 2200 Kernan Drive, Zip 21207–6697; tel. 410/448–2500 **A**1 3 5 7 9 10 **F**1 7 9 21 26 27 29 30 32 41 42 46 47 48 52 53 55 57 58 62 63 64 66 68 69 73 88 92 93 94 95 96 108 110 **P**6 7 **S** University of Maryland Medical System, Baltimore, MD Primary Contact: James E. Ross, FACHE, Chief Executive Officer CFO: Paul Nicholson, Director Financial Services CMO: James P G. Flynn, M.D., Vice President Medical Affairs CIO: Allen Tracey, Manager Information Systems Web address: www.umm.edu	23	46	131	2997	103	88355	0	70488	28272	556
✱ △ **JOHNS HOPKINS BAYVIEW MEDICAL CENTER**, 4940 Eastern Avenue, Zip 21224–2780; tel. 410/550–0100, (Total facility includes 242 beds in nursing home–type unit) **A**1 3 5 7 8 9 10 **F**1 2 3 4 5 8 10 11 12 13 14 15 17 21 22 23 24 26 27 28 29 31 33 34 35 37 39 41 44 46 47 48 49 50 52 53 55 56 57 58 59 60 61 62 63 64 65 66 68 69 70 71 72 73 74 75 76 77 78 81 84 85 86 87 88 89 90 92 93 94 95 96 98 104 106 108 109 110 **S** Johns Hopkins Health System, Baltimore, MD Primary Contact: Gregory F. Schaffer, President CFO: L Kenneth Grabill, II, Vice President Finance CMO: Richard G. Bennett, M.D., Senior Vice President Medical Affairs CIO: P Susan Davis, Director Communications and Public Affairs CHR: Craig Brodian, Vice President Human Resources Web address: www.jhbmc.jhu.edu	23	10	586	22512	478	365429	1321	349063	129848	2980
✱ △ **JOHNS HOPKINS HOSPITAL**, 600 North Wolfe Street, Zip 21287–2182; tel. 410/955–5000 **A**1 2 3 5 7 8 9 10 **F**2 4 5 6 7 9 11 12 14 15 16 17 18 19 20 21 22 23 24 26 27 28 29 30 31 32 33 34 35 37 38 39 42 43 44 45 46 47 48 49 50 52 53 55 56 57 58 59 60 61 62 63 64 65 66 67 68 69 70 71 72 73 74 75 76 77 78 79 80 81 82 84 85 86 87 88 89 90 92 93 94 95 96 98 99 100 101 102 103 104 105 106 108 109 110 **S** Johns Hopkins Health System, Baltimore, MD Primary Contact: Ronald R. Peterson, President CFO: Ronald J. Werthman, Vice President Finance, Chief Financial Officer and Treasurer CMO: Beryl Rosenstein, M.D., Vice President Medical Affairs CIO: Stephanie L. Reel, Vice President Information Services CHR: Pamela Paulk, Vice President Human Resources Web address: www.hopkinsmedicine.org	23	10	909	44730	721	305192	1948	1005190	337605	7634
✱ △ **KENNEDY KRIEGER INSTITUTE**, (Special Pediatric), 707 North Broadway, Zip 21205–1890; tel. 443/923–9200 **A**1 5 7 9 10 **F**2 11 21 22 26 27 28 29 30 35 39 47 52 53 57 58 62 65 66 68 69 72 73 74 77 90 94 96 108 **P**6 Primary Contact: Gary W. Goldstein, M.D., President and Chief Executive Officer COO: James M. Anders, Jr, Administrator and Chief Operating Officer CFO: Michael J. Neuman, Vice President Finance CMO: Michael V. Johnston, M.D., Chief Medical Officer and Senior Vice President Medical Programs CIO: Kenneth Davis, Assistant Vice President Information Systems CHR: Michael Loughran, Vice President Human Resources Web address: www.kennedykrieger.org	23	59	70	385	39	89747	0	62701	33340	1832
✱ △ **LEVINDALE HEBREW GERIATRIC CENTER AND HOSPITAL**, 2434 West Belvedere Avenue, Zip 21215–5299; tel. 410/466–8700, (Total facility includes 323 beds in nursing home–type unit) **A**1 2 7 9 10 **F**1 5 9 22 29 32 36 37 38 44 45 54 76 77 78 92 94 108 110 **P**6 **S** LifeBridge Health, Baltimore, MD Primary Contact: Ronald Rothstein, President and Chief Operating Officer CFO: Raul Lujan, Vice President Finance CMO: Susan M. Levy, M.D., Vice President Medical Affairs CIO: Karen Barker, Vice President and Chief Information Officer Web address: www.sinai–balt.com	23	48	443	1344	408	0	0	66238	27097	—
✱ △ **MARYLAND GENERAL HOSPITAL**, 827 Linden Avenue, Zip 21201–4681; tel. 410/225–8000 **A**1 2 3 5 7 9 10 **F**4 7 9 11 12 14 15 17 21 22 23 24 26 27 28 29 31 33 34 35 37 39 44 45 46 47 48 49 50 52 53 55 57 58 59 60 61 62 63 64 65 66 68 69 70 71 72 73 74 75 76 77 81 82 84 85 87 88 92 93 94 98 106 107 108 109 **P**8 **S** University of Maryland Medical System, Baltimore, MD Primary Contact: Colene Daniel, President and Chief Executive Officer CFO: Leslie J. Carter, Senior Vice President Finance Web address: www.marylandgeneral.org	23	10	242	11372	165	95701	1128	139646	61740	1284

Hospital, Address, Telephone, Approval, Facility, and Physician Codes, Health Care System	Classification Codes		Utilization Data					Expense (thousands) of dollars		
★ American Hospital Association (AHA) membership □ Joint Commission on Accreditation of Healthcare Organizations (JCAHO) accreditation ○ American Osteopathic Association (AOA) accreditation △ Commission on Accreditation of Rehabilitation Facilities (CARF) accreditation	Control	Service	Staffed Beds	Admissions	Census	Outpatient Visits	Births	Total	Payroll	Personnel

☒ **MERCY MEDICAL CENTER**, 301 St. Paul Place, Zip 21202–2165; tel. 410/332–9000 **A**1 2 3 5 8 9 10 **F**3 9 12 14 15 17 21 22 23 26 27 28 29 32 33 46 47 48 52 55 56 57 58 59 60 61 62 63 65 66 69 73 75 80 81 82 84 85 86 87 88 90 92 93 94 96 107 108 109 110 **P**6 Primary Contact: Thomas R. Mullen, President and Chief Executive Officer COO: Amy E. Freeman, Executive Vice President CFO: John E. Topper, Senior Vice President and Chief Financial Officer CMO: Scott A. Spier, M.D., Senior Vice President Medical Affairs CIO: James C. Stalder, Senior Vice President and Chief Information Officer CHR: Jessie Reed, Senior Vice President Human Resources Web address: www.mercymed.com	21	10	275	17428	195	132703	2520	222977	85533	1889
☒ △ **MT. WASHINGTON PEDIATRIC HOSPITAL**, 1708 West Rogers Avenue, Zip 21209–4537; tel. 410/578–8600 **A**1 5 7 9 10 **F**13 27 28 42 52 53 58 62 66 68 69 71 72 77 78 92 93 94 96 108 110 **P**6 **S** University of Maryland Medical System, Baltimore, MD Primary Contact: Sheldon J. Stein, President and Chief Executive Officer COO: Sheldon J. Stein, President and Chief Executive Officer CFO: Al Pietsch, CPA, Director Finance CMO: Richard Katz, M.D., Senior Vice President Medical Affairs CIO: Tim Brady, Director Information Systems Web address: www.mwph.org	23	50	70	837	56	26996	0	31648	17894	381
□ **SHEPPARD AND ENOCH PRATT HOSPITAL**, 6501 North Charles Street, Zip 21285, Mailing Address: P.O. Box 6815, Zip 21285–6815; tel. 410/938–3000, (Includes TAYLOR MANOR HOSPITAL, 4100 College Avenue, Ellicott City, Zip 21043–5506, Mailing Address: P.O. Box 396, Zip 21041–0396; tel. 410/465–3322) **A**1 3 5 9 10 **F**8 9 22 26 27 28 29 44 45 46 48 58 66 71 72 73 74 76 77 78 94 96 108 **P**4 Primary Contact: Steven S. Sharfstein, M.D., President and Chief Executive Officer Web address: www.sheppardpratt.org	23	22	223	5938	173	20458	0	103185	55953	1689
☒ △ **SINAI HOSPITAL OF BALTIMORE**, 2401 West Belvedere Avenue, Zip 21215–5271; tel. 410/601–9000 **A**1 2 3 5 7 8 9 10 **F**2 4 7 9 10 11 12 14 15 17 19 21 22 23 24 26 27 28 29 30 31 32 33 34 35 37 38 39 45 46 47 48 49 50 52 53 55 56 57 58 59 60 61 62 63 64 65 66 67 68 69 70 71 72 73 74 75 76 77 78 79 81 82 84 85 87 88 89 90 92 93 94 96 106 107 108 109 **P**2 6 **S** LifeBridge Health, Baltimore, MD Primary Contact: Neil M. Meltzer, President and Chief Operating Officer COO: Neil M. Meltzer, President and Chief Operating Officer CFO: Charles Orlando, Senior Vice President and Chief Financial Officer CIO: Karen Barker, Vice President and Chief Information Officer CHR: Taylor Foss, Vice President Human Resources Web address: www.lifebridgehealth.org	23	10	423	24524	331	129722	2223	389771	169549	2621
□ **SPRING GROVE HOSPITAL CENTER**, 60 Wade Avenue, Zip 21228–4689; tel. 410/402–6000 **A**1 3 5 9 10 **F**8 9 26 32 46 60 71 72 74 76 94 96 108 Primary Contact: David S. Helsel, M.D., Superintendent Web address: www.springgrove.com	12	22	446	855	324	0	0	52921	26680	900
☒ **ST. AGNES HEALTHCARE**, 900 Caton Avenue, Zip 21229–5299; tel. 410/368–6000 **A**1 2 3 5 9 10 **F**2 9 10 11 12 14 15 17 21 22 23 24 26 27 28 29 33 35 36 37 38 39 40 41 42 44 46 47 48 49 50 51 52 53 55 56 57 58 59 60 61 62 63 64 65 66 67 69 70 79 80 81 82 84 85 86 87 88 90 93 94 95 96 98 106 107 108 109 110 **P**6 **S** Ascension Health, Saint Louis, MO Primary Contact: Kenneth H. Bancroft, President and Chief Executive Officer COO: William T. Bradel, Executive Director and Chief Operating Officer CFO: Rhonda Anderson, Chief Financial Officer CMO: Adrian Long, Executive Vice President and Chief Medical Officer CIO: William Greskovich, Chief Information Officer CHR: Thomas C. Conley, Vice President, Human Resources Web address: www.stagnes.org	21	10	327	20755	231	273383	1757	256414	118031	2449
☒ △ **UNION MEMORIAL HOSPITAL**, 201 East University Parkway, Zip 21218–2895; tel. 410/554–2000, (Nonreporting) **A**1 2 3 5 7 9 10 **S** MedStar Health, Columbia, MD Primary Contact: Harrison J. Rider, III, President COO: Bradley Chambers, Senior Vice President CFO: Joseph B. Smith, Vice President Finance CMO: Stuart Bell, M.D., Vice President Medical Affairs CHR: Pamela Ashby, Associate Vice President, Human Resources Web address: www.unionmemorial.org	23	10	327	—	—	—	—	—	—	—
☒ **UNIVERSITY OF MARYLAND MEDICAL CENTER**, 22 South Greene Street, Zip 21201–1595; tel. 410/328–8667 **A**1 2 3 5 8 9 10 **F**2 4 5 6 7 9 10 11 12 14 15 16 17 18 19 20 21 22 23 24 26 27 28 29 30 31 32 33 34 35 36 37 38 39 40 42 43 44 45 46 47 48 49 50 52 53 55 56 57 58 59 60 61 62 63 64 65 66 67 69 70 71 72 73 74 75 76 77 78 79 80 81 82 83 84 85 86 87 88 89 90 92 93 94 95 96 98 99 100 101 102 103 104 105 106 107 108 109 110 **P**6 **S** University of Maryland Medical System, Baltimore, MD Primary Contact: Jeffrey A. Rivest, President and Chief Executive Officer CFO: Henry J. Franey, Senior Vice President Finance and Chief Financial Officer CMO: Frank M. Calia, M.D., Acting Chief Medical Officer CIO: Michael N. Minear, Senior Vice President Information Technology CHR: R Keith Allen, Senior Vice President Human Resources Web address: www.umm.edu	23	10	607	29404	495	227459	1411	712788	248053	5973

Many Facility Codes have changed. Please refer to the AHA Guide Code Chart. © 2005 AHA Guide

Hospital, Address, Telephone, Approval, Facility, and Physician Codes, Health Care System	Classi-fication Codes		Utilization Data					Expense (thousands) of dollars		
★ American Hospital Association (AHA) membership □ Joint Commission on Accreditation of Healthcare Organizations (JCAHO) accreditation ○ American Osteopathic Association (AOA) accreditation △ Commission on Accreditation of Rehabilitation Facilities (CARF) accreditation	Control	Service	Staffed Beds	Admissions	Census	Outpatient Visits	Births	Total	Payroll	Personnel

⊠ △ **UNIVERSITY SPECIALTY HOSPITAL**, 601 South Charles Street, Zip 21230–3898; tel. 410/547–8500 **A**1 7 9 10 **F**26 27 28 58 92 93 94 110 **S** University of Maryland Medical System, Baltimore, MD Primary Contact: James L. Warner, Vice President Operations COO: James L. Warner, Vice President Operations CFO: Hank Franey, Chief Financial Officer CMO: James P G. Flynn, M.D., Vice President Medical Affairs CIO: Angie Tyler, Network Technician CHR: Chuck Schevitz, Manager Human Resources Web address: www.umm.edu/ush/	23	48	135	944	135	14641	0	42096	13516	247
⊠ △ **VETERANS AFFAIRS MARYLAND HEALTH CARE SYSTEM–BALTIMORE DIVISION**, 10 North Greene Street, Zip 21201–1524; tel. 410/605–7001, (Includes VETERANS AFFAIRS MARYLAND HEALTH CARE SYSTEM–PERRY POINT DIVISION, Circle Drive, Perry Point, Zip 21902; tel. 410/642–2411; Dennis H. Smith, Director), (Total facility includes 200 beds in nursing home–type unit) **A**1 2 3 5 7 8 9 **F**2 3 4 5 6 9 10 12 14 15 17 19 21 22 23 28 29 30 31 32 33 34 35 36 37 38 39 40 41 42 43 44 45 46 47 48 51 52 53 55 57 58 60 61 62 63 64 65 66 68 69 70 71 73 74 75 76 77 78 81 82 83 84 85 86 87 88 92 93 94 96 97 106 107 108 109 110 **P**6 **S** Department of Veterans Affairs, Washington, DC Primary Contact: Dennis H. Smith, Director COO: Guy B. Richardson, Associate Director Finance CFO: Major Tom Scheffler, Chief Fiscal Officer CMO: Muhamed Al–Ibrahim, M.D., Executive Chief of Staff CIO: Sharon Zielinski, Chief Information Resource Officer Web address: www.va.gov/sta/guide/home.asp	45	10	754	9179	494	594321	0	344940	146299	2800
BEL AIR—Harford County										
⊠ **UPPER CHESAPEAKE MEDICAL CENTER**, 500 Upper Chesapeake Drive, Zip 21014–4324; tel. 443/643–1000 **A**1 9 10 **F**9 10 11 12 21 22 27 28 29 30 33 37 38 40 42 46 47 48 49 52 55 57 59 61 62 63 65 66 69 75 81 82 84 87 88 94 96 106 108 109 110 **S** Upper Chesapeake Health System, Bel Air, MD Primary Contact: Lyle Ernest Sheldon, FACHE, President and Chief Executive Officer COO: Kenneth Kozel, Senior Vice President and Chief Operating Officer CFO: Joseph Hoffman, III, Senior Vice President and Chief Financial Officer CMO: Peggy Vaughan, M.D., Senior Vice President Medical Affairs CIO: Rick Casteel, Vice President Management Information Systems and Chief Information Officer CHR: Toni Shivery, Vice President Human Resources Web address: www.uchs.org	23	10	152	11979	105	101380	1303	104901	42036	982
BERLIN—Worcester County										
⊠ **ATLANTIC GENERAL HOSPITAL**, 9733 Healthway Drive, Zip 21811–1155; tel. 410/641–1100, (Nonreporting) **A**1 9 10 Primary Contact: Barry G. Beeman, President and Chief Executive Officer CFO: Cheryl Nottingham, Chief Financial Officer CHR: Jim Brannon, Vice President, Human Resources Web address: www.atlanticgeneral.org	23	10	62	—	—	—	—	—	—	—
BETHESDA—Montgomery County										
⊠ **NATIONAL NAVAL MEDICAL CENTER**, 8901 Wisconsin Avenue, Zip 20889–5600; tel. 301/295–5800, (Nonreporting) **A**1 2 3 5 9 **S** Bureau of Medicine and Surgery, Department of the Navy, Washington, DC Primary Contact: Rear Admiral Donald C. Arthur, MC, USN, Commander CFO: Commander Kenneth Ocker, MSC, USN, Director Resource Management CIO: Lieutenant Colonel Edward Metcalf, MSC, USN, Associate Director Information, Technology and Communications Web address: www.nnmc.med.navy.mil	43	10	240	—	—	—	—	—	—	—
⊠ **SUBURBAN HOSPITAL HEALTHCARE SYSTEM**, 8600 Old Georgetown Road, Zip 20814–1497; tel. 301/896–3100 **A**1 2 3 5 9 10 **F**2 3 4 9 10 12 14 15 17 21 22 23 24 26 27 28 29 31 33 34 35 37 39 40 42 44 46 47 48 49 52 53 55 57 58 60 61 62 63 64 66 69 71 73 74 75 76 77 78 81 82 84 85 86 87 88 89 90 92 93 94 96 98 106 107 108 109 110 **P**4 Primary Contact: Brian A. Gragnolati, President and Chief Executive Officer COO: Gene A. Corapi, Senior Vice President Operations CFO: Gary G. Terrinoni, Treasurer and Senior Vice President Finance CMO: Eugene R. Passamani, M.D., Senior Vice President Medical Affairs CIO: Ronna Borenstein–Levy, Director Marketing and Communications CHR: Dennis Parnell, Senior Vice President Human Resources Web address: www.suburbanhospital.org	23	10	220	13288	165	103075	0	155763	69751	1241

MD

Hospital, Address, Telephone, Approval, Facility, and Physician Codes, Health Care System	Classi-fication Codes		Utilization Data					Expense (thousands) of dollars		
	Control	Service	Staffed Beds	Admissions	Census	Outpatient Visits	Births	Total	Payroll	Personnel

★ American Hospital Association (AHA) membership
□ Joint Commission on Accreditation of Healthcare Organizations (JCAHO) accreditation
○ American Osteopathic Association (AOA) accreditation
△ Commission on Accreditation of Rehabilitation Facilities (CARF) accreditation

⊠ **WARREN G. MAGNUSON CLINICAL CENTER, NATIONAL INSTITUTES OF HEALTH**, (Biomedical Research), 9000 Rockville Pike, Zip 20892–1504; tel. 301/496–4114 **A**1 3 5 8 **F**2 3 4 12 15 16 17 18 22 23 29 32 37 38 41 44 45 47 49 50 52 53 55 58 60 61 63 64 66 69 71 72 73 74 76 77 78 81 82 83 84 86 87 88 94 96 99 101 105 108 **S** U. S. Indian Health Service, Rockville, MD Primary Contact: John I. Gallin, M.D., Director COO: Maureen Gormley, Chief Operating Officer CFO: Lisa Lacasse, Chief Financial Officer CMO: David K. Henderson, M.D., Deputy Director Clinical Care CIO: Stephen Rosenfeld, Chief Information Officer and Director Clinical Research Information Systems CHR: Barbara Lang Web address: www.cc.nih.gov	44	49	265	6944	158	108078	0	339698	135512	1923

CAMBRIDGE—Dorchester County

★ **DORCHESTER GENERAL HOSPITAL**, 300 Byrn Street, Zip 21613–1908; tel. 410/228–5511 **A**9 10 **F**2 9 12 21 22 23 26 27 28 32 33 37 46 48 52 55 57 58 60 61 62 63 64 66 69 71 72 73 75 76 81 82 87 88 94 96 **S** Shore Health System, Easton, MD Primary Contact: Joseph P. Ross, President and Chief Executive Officer COO: Gerard M. Walsh, Senior Vice President and Chief Operating Officer CFO: Deidra S. Bell, Senior Vice President and Chief Financial Officer CMO: Richard Staiman, M.D., JD, Vice President Medical Affairs CIO: Jack Price, Director Web address: www.shorehealth.org	23	10	64	3929	42	94542	0	31755	14881	268
□ **EASTERN SHORE HOSPITAL CENTER**, 5262 Woods Road, Zip 21613, Mailing Address: P.O. Box 800, Zip 21613–0800; tel. 410/221–2525 **A**1 10 **F**9 26 27 28 65 66 71 73 74 76 94 108 **P**7 Primary Contact: Mary Kay Noren, Superintendent	12	22	80	138	75	0	0	15025	9367	200

CHESTERTOWN—Kent County

★ **CHESTER RIVER HOSPITAL CENTER**, 100 Brown Street, Zip 21620–1499; tel. 410/778–3300 **A**9 10 **F**2 9 11 12 14 15 21 22 23 26 27 28 29 33 37 48 50 52 55 58 59 61 62 63 64 65 66 70 75 81 84 87 88 92 96 108 109 110 Primary Contact: William R. Kirk, Jr, President and Chief Executive Officer COO: Robin E. Klinefelter, Vice President Support and Administrative Services CFO: Brian Bowman, Vice President CHR: Beverly Churchill, Vice President Human Resources Web address: www.chesterriverhealth.org	23	10	50	3565	41	62768	272	39691	15920	362
UPPER SHORE COMMUNITY MENTAL HEALTH CENTER, Scheeler Road, Zip 21620–1031, Mailing Address: P.O. Box 229, Zip 21620–0229; tel. 410/778–6800 **A**9 10 **F**9 26 27 28 37 71 73 74 75 94 96 106 108 Primary Contact: Mary Kay Noren, Chief Executive Officer	12	22	40	223	39	0	0	7245	4337	91

CHEVERLY—Prince George's County

□ **GLADYS SPELLMAN SPECIALTY HOSPITAL AND NURSING CENTER**, 2900 Mercy Lane, Zip 20785–1157; tel. 301/618–2010, (Nonreporting) **A**1 Primary Contact: Stewart R. Seitz, Chief Executive Officer Web address: www.dimensionshealth.org	33	48	30	—	—	—	—	—	—	—
⊠ **PRINCE GEORGE'S HOSPITAL CENTER**, 3001 Hospital Drive, Zip 20785–1189; tel. 301/618–2000, (Total facility includes 110 beds in nursing home–type unit) **A**1 3 5 9 10 **F**2 3 9 11 12 14 15 17 19 21 22 23 26 27 28 29 31 33 34 39 46 47 48 49 50 52 53 55 56 57 58 59 60 61 62 63 64 65 66 69 70 71 73 74 75 78 81 82 85 87 88 90 92 94 96 98 106 107 108 109 110 **P**6 **S** Dimensions Healthcare System, Cheverly, MD Primary Contact: G. T. Dunlop Ecker, President and Chief Executive Officer COO: Shirley H. Morgan, R.N., Vice President and Chief Nursing Officer CFO: Al Mansfield, Chief Financial Officer CMO: David Goldman, Vice President Medical Affairs and Education CIO: John Gehrke, Vice President CHR: Frank Venuto, Vice President, Human Resources Web address: www.princegeorgeshospital.org	23	10	403	15951	304	104068	3011	205428	93222	1599

CLINTON—Prince George's County

⊠ **SOUTHERN MARYLAND HOSPITAL CENTER**, 7503 Surratts Road, Zip 20735–3397; tel. 301/868–8000, (Total facility includes 24 beds in nursing home–type unit) **A**1 2 9 10 **F**2 11 14 15 17 21 22 23 26 27 28 29 33 37 46 47 48 52 53 55 57 58 59 60 61 62 63 64 66 69 71 72 74 75 76 78 81 82 85 86 87 88 92 93 94 96 106 108 110 **P**6 Primary Contact: Francis P. Chiaramonte, M.D., President CFO: Charles R. Stewart, Vice President Business, Finance and Corporate Compliance CMO: Scott A. Kelso, M.D., Vice President Medical Affairs CIO: Lou Mavromatis, Director Data Processing CHR: Keith Feeney, Director Human Resources Web address: www.princegeorgescountywebsite.com/southernmaryland.htm	33	10	300	15938	191	79753	1518	139668	52177	1372

Many Facility Codes have changed. Please refer to the AHA Guide Code Chart. © 2005 AHA Guide

Hospital, Address, Telephone, Approval, Facility, and Physician Codes, Health Care System	Classi-fication Codes		Utilization Data					Expense (thousands) of dollars		
★ American Hospital Association (AHA) membership ☐ Joint Commission on Accreditation of Healthcare Organizations (JCAHO) accreditation ○ American Osteopathic Association (AOA) accreditation △ Commission on Accreditation of Rehabilitation Facilities (CARF) accreditation	Control	Service	Staffed Beds	Admissions	Census	Outpatient Visits	Births	Total	Payroll	Personnel

COLUMBIA—Howard County

★ **HOWARD COUNTY GENERAL HOSPITAL**, 5755 Cedar Lane, Zip 21044–2999; tel. 410/740–7890 **A**1 2 5 9 10 **F**2 9 11 12 15 17 21 22 23 24 26 27 28 29 33 37 39 44 46 47 48 52 55 56 57 58 59 61 62 63 64 65 69 71 72 73 75 81 82 84 85 88 93 94 96 106 108 109 110 **S** Johns Hopkins Health System, Baltimore, MD
Primary Contact: Victor A. Broccolino, President and Chief Executive Officer
CFO: Carl Humphreys, Senior Vice President Finance
CIO: Rick Edwards, Director Information Systems
Web address: www.hcgh.org
| 23 | 10 | 204 | 14091 | 163 | 114148 | 3532 | 137529 | 53811 | 1347

CRISFIELD—Somerset County

☐ **MCCREADY HEALTH SERVICES FOUNDATION**, 201 Hall Highway, Zip 21817–1299; tel. 410/968–1200, (Total facility includes 69 beds in nursing home–type unit) **A**1 9 10 **F**9 12 22 24 26 27 28 29 30 31 33 37 41 42 44 45 46 47 48 51 52 53 58 60 62 63 65 69 71 73 74 76 81 82 84 88 92 94 95 97 106 108 **P**5 6
Primary Contact: Charles F. Pinkerman, Chief Executive Officer
Web address: www.mccreadyfoundation.org
| 23 | 10 | 101 | 834 | 78 | 28971 | 0 | 14327 | 5732 | 239

CUMBERLAND—Allegany County

★ △ **MEMORIAL HOSPITAL AND MEDICAL CENTER OF CUMBERLAND**, 600 Memorial Avenue, Zip 21502–3797; tel. 301/723–4000 **A**1 2 7 9 10 **F**2 9 11 12 15 21 22 26 27 28 29 31 33 34 35 36 37 38 39 42 44 46 47 48 49 51 52 54 55 58 59 60 61 62 63 64 65 66 68 69 73 75 81 82 85 87 88 92 93 94 96 106 107 108 109 110 **P**6 **S** Ascension Health, Saint Louis, MO
Primary Contact: Thomas C. Dowdell, Executive Director and Senior Vice President
CFO: Kimberly S. Repac, Senior Vice President and Chief Financial Officer
CMO: James M. Raver, M.D., Senior Vice President Medical Affairs
CIO: Stephen J. Conrad, Director Information Systems
CHR: Mark J. Sullivan, Vice President Human Resources
Web address: www.wmhs.com
| 23 | 10 | 160 | 8469 | 103 | 189186 | 1006 | 85013 | 37863 | 971

★ **SACRED HEART HOSPITAL**, 900 Seton Drive, Zip 21502–1874; tel. 301/723–4200, (Total facility includes 88 beds in nursing home–type unit) **A**1 2 9 10 **F**1 2 9 12 14 15 17 19 21 22 23 26 27 28 29 31 33 35 37 38 39 40 42 44 46 47 48 49 52 54 55 58 60 61 63 64 65 66 71 73 75 76 77 80 81 82 84 85 86 87 88 92 94 96 106 107 108 **P**6 **S** Ascension Health, Saint Louis, MO
Primary Contact: Francis A. Pommett, Jr, Executive Director and Senior Vice President
CFO: Kimberly S. Repac, Senior Vice President and Chief Financial Officer
CMO: James M. Raver, M.D., Senior Vice President Medical Affairs
CIO: Steve Conrad, Director Information Services
CHR: Mark J. Sullivan, Vice President Human Resources
Web address: www.wmhs.com
| 23 | 10 | 243 | 8844 | 208 | 110989 | 0 | 105717 | 41398 | 862

☐ **THOMAS B. FINAN CENTER**, 10102 Country Club Road S.E., Zip 21502–8339, Mailing Address: P.O. Box 1722, Zip 21501–1722; tel. 301/777–2240, (Nonreporting) **A**1 9 10
Primary Contact: Archie T. Wallace, Chief Executive Officer
Web address: www.dhmh.state.md.us
| 12 | 22 | 80 | — | — | — | — | — | — | —

EAST NEW MARKET—Dorchester County

WARWICK MANOR BEHAVIORAL HEALTH, 3680 Warwick Road, Zip 21631–1420; tel. 410/943–8108, (Nonreporting) **A**9
Primary Contact: Marie McBee, Chief Executive Officer
| 33 | 82 | 42 | — | — | — | — | — | — | —

EASTON—Talbot County

★ **MEMORIAL HOSPITAL AT EASTON MARYLAND**, 219 South Washington Street, Zip 21601–2996; tel. 410/822–1000, (Total facility includes 18 beds in nursing home–type unit) **A**1 2 9 10 **F**2 9 11 12 21 22 23 26 27 28 29 32 33 37 38 46 47 48 49 51 52 55 57 58 59 61 62 63 64 65 66 69 73 75 79 80 81 82 84 87 88 92 93 94 96 107 109 **P**3 8 **S** Shore Health System, Easton, MD
Primary Contact: Joseph P. Ross, President and Chief Executive Officer
COO: Gerard M. Walsh, Senior Vice President and Chief Operating Officer
CFO: Deidra S. Bell, Senior Vice President and Chief Financial Officer
CMO: Paul Reinhold, M.D., Chief Medical Staff
CIO: Jack Price, Director
Web address: www.shorehealth.org
| 23 | 10 | 111 | 9362 | 111 | 292431 | 1044 | 102827 | 43250 | 1078

ELKTON—Cecil County

★ **UNION HOSPITAL**, 106 Bow Street, Zip 21921–5596; tel. 410/398–4000 **A**1 2 9 10 **F**1 2 9 11 12 21 22 23 26 27 28 29 33 35 39 40 42 46 47 48 50 52 54 55 57 58 59 60 61 62 63 65 70 71 75 77 78 81 82 84 85 87 88 93 94 95 96 108 109 **P**5 6 7
Primary Contact: Kenneth S. Lewis, M.D., JD, President and Chief Executive Officer
COO: Thomas Sweeney, Senior Vice President and Chief Clinical Operations Officer
CFO: Stephen Neff, Chief Financial Officer
CMO: Jose Ma, M.D., Vice President Medical Affairs
CIO: Mary Jane Kamps, Chief Information Officer
CHR: Peter Gloggner, Vice President Human Resources
Web address: www.uhcc.com
| 23 | 10 | 122 | 8935 | 83 | 135001 | 586 | 76144 | 30428 | 737

MD

MD

Hospital, Address, Telephone, Approval, Facility, and Physician Codes, Health Care System	Classi-fication Codes		Utilization Data					Expense (thousands) of dollars		
★ American Hospital Association (AHA) membership □ Joint Commission on Accreditation of Healthcare Organizations (JCAHO) accreditation ○ American Osteopathic Association (AOA) accreditation △ Commission on Accreditation of Rehabilitation Facilities (CARF) accreditation	Control	Service	Staffed Beds	Admissions	Census	Outpatient Visits	Births	Total	Payroll	Personnel

EMMITSBURG—Frederick County

MOUNTAIN MANOR TREATMENT CENTER, Route 15, Zip 21727, Mailing Address: Box 136, Zip 21727; tel. 301/447–2361, (Nonreporting) Primary Contact: William J. Roby, Executive Vice President

	33	82	140	—	—	—	—	—	—	—

FORT WASHINGTON—Prince George's County

⊠ **FORT WASHINGTON MEDICAL CENTER**, (Formerly Fort Washington Hospital), 11711 Livingston Road, Zip 20744–5164; tel. 301/292–7000 **A**1 9 10 **F**2 12 21 26 27 28 29 33 46 48 52 55 60 62 63 66 81 82 88 94 Primary Contact: Paul E. Porter, Chief Executive Officer COO: Donald C. Brown, Director Corporate Operations CFO: Joseph B. Tucker, Chief Financial Officer CMO: Christopher R. Smith, M.D., President Medical Staff

	23	10	37	2971	29	44779	0	27981	12317	277

FREDERICK—Frederick County

⊠ **FREDERICK MEMORIAL HOSPITAL**, 400 West Seventh Street, Zip 21701–4593; tel. 301/698–3300, (Total facility includes 15 beds in nursing home–type unit) **A**1 2 9 10 **F**2 6 9 11 12 15 21 22 23 24 26 27 28 29 30 31 32 33 35 36 37 38 39 40 41 42 45 46 47 48 49 50 51 52 53 55 57 58 59 60 61 62 63 64 65 66 69 70 71 73 74 75 76 77 78 79 80 81 82 84 85 86 88 92 93 94 95 96 106 107 108 109 110 **P**6 7 Primary Contact: Thomas A. Kleinhanzl, President and Chief Executive Officer CFO: William H. Pugh, Senior Vice President and Chief Financial Officer CIO: Marc Delacroix, Vice President Information Services CHR: William Rotella, Vice President for Human Resources Web address: www.fmh.org

	23	10	200	15354	186	384039	2151	196737	89923	1694

GLEN BURNIE—Anne Arundel County

⊠ **BALTIMORE WASHINGTON MEDICAL CENTER**, (Formerly North Arundel Hospital), 301 Hospital Drive, Zip 21061–5899; tel. 410/787–4000 **A**1 2 9 10 **F**2 9 12 14 15 17 21 22 23 27 28 29 32 33 44 45 46 47 48 49 51 52 53 55 57 58 60 61 62 63 64 65 69 71 73 75 76 77 78 79 80 81 84 85 86 88 90 92 93 94 95 96 108 110 **P**6 **S** University of Maryland Medical System, Baltimore, MD Primary Contact: James R. Walker, FACHE, President and Chief Executive Officer COO: Karen Olscamp, Chief Operating Officer CFO: Al Pietsch, CPA, Vice President Finance CMO: Lawrence Linda, M.D., Senior Vice President and Chief Medical Officer CIO: David Peterson, Chief Information Officer CHR: Patricia Loughlin, Director, Human Resources Web address: www.northarundel.org

	23	10	253	17577	202	125671	26	177370	83751	1952

HAGERSTOWN—Washington County

□ **BROOK LANE HEALTH SERVICES**, 13218 Brook Lane Drive, Zip 21742–1945, Mailing Address: P.O. Box 1945, Zip 21742–1945; tel. 301/733–0330 **A**1 9 10 **F**4 22 26 27 28 44 71 72 73 74 76 77 78 94 108 **P**4 6 Primary Contact: R. Lynn Rushing, Chief Executive Officer Web address: www.brooklane.org

	23	22	42	1088	23	25507	0	12478	7914	242

⊠ △ **WASHINGTON COUNTY HEALTH SYSTEM**, 251 East Antietam Street, Zip 21740–5771; tel. 301/790–8000, (Total facility includes 47 beds in nursing home–type unit) **A**1 2 7 9 10 **F**2 4 6 9 11 12 14 15 21 22 23 26 27 28 29 31 33 34 35 37 41 42 44 45 46 47 48 49 50 51 52 53 55 58 59 60 61 62 63 64 65 66 68 69 70 71 72 73 74 75 76 77 78 81 82 84 85 87 88 89 92 94 95 96 106 107 108 109 110 **P**6 8 Primary Contact: James P. Hamill, President and Chief Executive Officer CFO: Raymond A. Grahe, Vice President Finance CMO: Robert L. Brooks, M.D., Vice President Medical Affairs CIO: Carey O. Leverett, Vice President for Information Services Web address: www.wchsys.org

	23	10	340	15937	202	222452	1917	169460	78363	1690

□ **WESTERN MARYLAND CENTER**, 1500 Pennsylvania Avenue, Zip 21742–3194; tel. 301/791–4400, (Total facility includes 60 beds in nursing home–type unit) (Nonreporting) **A**1 10 Primary Contact: Cynthia Miller Pellegrino, Director and Chief Executive Officer

	12	48	120	—	—	—	—	—	—	—

HAVRE DE GRACE—Harford County

★ **HARFORD MEMORIAL HOSPITAL**, 501 South Union Avenue, Zip 21078–3493; tel. 443/843–5000, (Total facility includes 17 beds in nursing home–type unit) **A**9 10 **F**10 12 21 22 27 28 29 30 33 38 40 46 48 49 52 55 57 60 61 62 63 66 69 71 75 81 82 84 88 92 93 94 96 108 **S** Upper Chesapeake Health System, Bel Air, MD Primary Contact: Lyle Ernest Sheldon, FACHE, President and Chief Executive Officer COO: Kenneth Kozel, Senior Vice President and Chief Operating Officer CFO: Joseph Hoffman, III, Senior Vice President and Chief Financial Officer CMO: Peggy Vaughan, M.D., Senior Vice President Medical Affairs CIO: Rick Casteel, Vice President Management Information Systems and Chief Information Officer CHR: Toni Shivery, Vice President Human Resources Web address: www.uchs.org

	23	10	102	6053	79	74751	0	53901	26269	607

JESSUP—Anne Arundel County

□ **CLIFTON T. PERKINS HOSPITAL CENTER**, 8450 Dorsey Run Road, Zip 20794–9414; tel. 410/724–3000, (Nonreporting) **A**1 3 5 Primary Contact: Archie T. Wallace, Chief Executive Officer Web address: www.dhmh.state.md.us/perkins/

	12	22	215	—	—	—	—	—	—	—

Many Facility Codes have changed. Please refer to the AHA Guide Code Chart. © 2005 AHA Guide

Hospital, Address, Telephone, Approval, Facility, and Physician Codes, Health Care System	Classi-fication Codes		Utilization Data					Expense (thousands) of dollars		
★ American Hospital Association (AHA) membership ☐ Joint Commission on Accreditation of Healthcare Organizations (JCAHO) accreditation ○ American Osteopathic Association (AOA) accreditation △ Commission on Accreditation of Rehabilitation Facilities (CARF) accreditation	Control	Service	Staffed Beds	Admissions	Census	Outpatient Visits	Births	Total	Payroll	Personnel

LA PLATA—Charles County

✶ **CIVISTA HEALTH**, 701 East Charles Street, Zip 20646–1070, Mailing Address: P.O. Box 1070, Zip 20646–1070; tel. 301/609–4000 **A**1 2 9 10 **F**11 12 21 22 26 27 28 29 33 37 39 42 46 47 48 49 52 55 57 59 60 62 63 66 69 70 81 82 85 87 88 94 96 106 108 109 110
Primary Contact: Christine M. Stefanides, R.N., CHE, President and Chief Executive Officer
CFO: Gregory Wiegel, Vice President Finance and Chief Financial Officer
CMO: Seetaramayya Nagula, M.D., Chief of Staff
CIO: Carolyn Core, Vice President Corporate Services
Web address: www.civista.org

| | 23 | 10 | 105 | 7602 | 83 | 40362 | 1074 | 64538 | 26166 | 496 |

LANHAM—Prince George's County

✶ **DOCTORS COMMUNITY HOSPITAL**, 8118 Good Luck Road, Zip 20706–3596; tel. 301/552–8118 **A**1 9 10 **F**2 9 12 14 15 17 21 22 23 26 28 29 33 34 37 46 47 48 49 52 55 57 58 60 61 62 63 64 65 69 81 82 84 87 88 92 93 94 96 107 108 109 110
Primary Contact: Philip B. Down, President and Chief Executive Officer
COO: Thomas J. Crowley, Jr, Executive Vice President
CFO: Dennis P. Scanlon, Vice President Finance
CMO: Gabriel Jaffe, M.D., Vice President Medical Affairs
CIO: Alan Johnson, Director Information Systems
CHR: Charlene Lundgren, Vice President
Web address: www.dchweb.org

| | 23 | 10 | 176 | 11705 | 135 | 87192 | 0 | 110666 | 47336 | 912 |

LAUREL—Prince George's County

✶ △ **LAUREL REGIONAL HOSPITAL**, 7300 Van Dusen Road, Zip 20707–9266; tel. 301/725–4300 **A**1 5 7 9 10 **F**2 9 11 12 14 21 23 29 33 41 46 48 49 53 54 55 57 59 60 61 62 63 64 66 68 69 71 73 75 78 81 82 87 88 94 96 106 108 **S** Dimensions Healthcare System, Cheverly, MD
Primary Contact: Douglas Shepherd, FACHE, President and Chief Executive Officer
CIO: John Gherke, Chief Information Officer
CHR: Frank Venuto, Vice President Human Resources
Web address: www.laurelregionalhospital.org

| | 23 | 10 | 115 | 7274 | 98 | 46180 | 696 | 70144 | 34676 | 529 |

LEONARDTOWN—St. Marys County

✶ **ST. MARY'S HOSPITAL**, 25500 Point Lookout Road, Zip 20650–9999, Mailing Address: P.O. Box 527, Zip 20650–0527; tel. 301/475–6001 **A**1 2 9 10 **F**2 9 11 12 21 23 24 26 27 28 29 30 31 32 33 35 36 37 38 39 46 47 48 52 53 55 57 58 59 60 61 62 63 65 66 69 71 72 73 74 75 76 77 78 81 82 84 85 87 88 93 94 96 106 107 108 109
Primary Contact: Christine R. Wray, President and Chief Executive Officer
COO: Kurt Barwis, Senior Vice President and Chief Operating Officer
CFO: Paul M. Barber, Jr, Vice President for Finance
CIO: Donald Sirk, Director Information Systems
Web address: www.smhwecare.com

| | 23 | 10 | 113 | 6997 | 59 | 117692 | 980 | 65049 | 29166 | 663 |

OAKLAND—Garrett County

✶ **GARRETT COUNTY MEMORIAL HOSPITAL**, 251 North Fourth Street, Zip 21550–1398; tel. 301/533–4000, (Total facility includes 10 beds in nursing home–type unit) **A**1 9 10 **F**2 9 11 12 21 22 23 24 26 27 28 29 31 33 34 37 44 46 47 48 55 58 59 61 62 63 64 66 75 81 82 84 87 88 92 94 108 109 **P**8
Primary Contact: Donald P. Battista, President and Chief Executive Officer
CFO: Gregory J. Was, CPA, Vice President Finance
CIO: Sandy Swanson, Director of Information System
CHR: Denise R. Liston, Vice President of Clinical Services
Web address: www.gcmh.com

| | 23 | 10 | 56 | 2961 | 31 | 66475 | 273 | 28086 | 10798 | 295 |

OLNEY—Montgomery County

✶ **MONTGOMERY GENERAL HOSPITAL**, 18101 Prince Philip Drive, Zip 20832–1512; tel. 301/774–8882 **A**1 2 9 10 **F**2 4 9 11 15 21 22 23 26 27 28 29 31 33 37 38 39 40 44 45 46 47 48 51 55 57 58 59 60 61 62 63 64 69 71 72 75 76 77 78 81 82 87 88 93 94 96 98 106 108
Primary Contact: Peter W. Monge, President and Chief Executive Officer
CFO: John F. Hogarty, Chief Financial Officer
CMO: Roger Leonard, M.D., Vice President Medical Affairs
CHR: Kevin Mell, Vice President, Human Resources
Web address: www.montgomerygeneral.com

| | 23 | 10 | 147 | 8904 | 109 | 54137 | 915 | 87200 | 38475 | 771 |

PRINCE FREDERICK—Calvert County

✶ **CALVERT MEMORIAL HOSPITAL**, 100 Hospital Road, Zip 20678–9675; tel. 410/535–4000, (Total facility includes 18 beds in nursing home–type unit) **A**1 2 9 10 **F**2 9 11 12 21 22 23 24 25 26 27 28 29 30 31 33 37 38 39 41 42 46 47 48 51 52 53 55 57 58 59 60 61 62 63 64 65 66 69 71 72 73 75 78 81 84 85 88 92 93 94 95 96 98 106 107 108 109 110
Primary Contact: James J. Xinis, President and Chief Executive Officer
CFO: Kirk Blandford, Vice President Finance
CMO: Robert Schlager, M.D., Chief of Staff
CIO: Ed Grogan, Vice President
CHR: Carrie Forrest, Vice President Human Resources
Web address: www.calverthospital.com

| | 23 | 10 | 118 | 7820 | 84 | 108794 | 869 | 72336 | 34432 | 627 |

MD

MD

Hospital, Address, Telephone, Approval, Facility, and Physician Codes, Health Care System	Classi-fication Codes		Utilization Data					Expense (thousands) of dollars		
★ American Hospital Association (AHA) membership □ Joint Commission on Accreditation of Healthcare Organizations (JCAHO) accreditation ○ American Osteopathic Association (AOA) accreditation △ Commission on Accreditation of Rehabilitation Facilities (CARF) accreditation	Control	Service	Staffed Beds	Admissions	Census	Outpatient Visits	Births	Total	Payroll	Personnel

RANDALLSTOWN—Baltimore County

☒ △ **NORTHWEST HOSPITAL CENTER**, 5401 Old Court Road,
Zip 21133–5185; tel. 410/521–2200, (Total facility includes 24 beds in nursing
home–type unit) **A**1 2 7 9 10 **F**2 9 12 21 22 23 28 29 33 36 37 40 44 46 48
49 52 55 58 61 62 63 64 66 69 71 73 75 81 82 84 85 87 88 92 93 94 95
96 108 109 110 **S** LifeBridge Health, Baltimore, MD
Primary Contact: Erik G. Wexler, President and Chief Operating Officer
CFO: David Krajewski, Vice President Finance
CMO: Ronald L. Ginsberg, Vice President Medical Affairs
CIO: Karen Barker, Vice President and Chief Information Officer
CHR: Barbara Atkins, Director Human Resources
Web address: www.lifebridgehealth.org
| | | | | | | | | | |
| 23 | 10 | 198 | 13030 | 165 | 86149 | 0 | 122863 | 52130 | 1151 |

ROCKVILLE—Montgomery County

☒ △ **ADVENTIST REHABILITATION HOSPITAL OF MARYLAND**, 9909 Medical
Center Drive, Zip 20850; tel. 240/864–6000 **A**1 7 9 10 **F**2 21 22 28 29 30 41
52 53 68 69 92 94 96 108 **P**6 **S** Adventist HealthCare, Rockville, MD
Primary Contact: Doris B. Reinhart, Vice President and Administrator
COO: Doris B. Reinhart, Vice President and Administrator
CFO: Curtis J. Hansen, Senior Financial Officer
CMO: Terrence P. Sheehan, M.D., Medical Director
CHR: Angela C. Baker, Manager Human Resources
Web address: www.adventisthealthcare.com
| 21 | 46 | 77 | 1274 | 39 | 18878 | 0 | 16990 | 7766 | 185 |

☒ **POTOMAC RIDGE BEHAVIORAL HEALTH SYSTEM**, 14901 Broschart Road,
Zip 20850–3395; tel. 301/251–4500 **A**1 9 10 **F**4 21 22 27 28 29 31 39 71
73 74 76 77 78 94 96 98 **P**8 **S** Adventist HealthCare, Rockville, MD
Primary Contact: Craig S. Juengling, President
COO: Pat Petralia, Vice President and Chief Operating Officer
CFO: Warren Knight, Chief Financial Officer
CMO: Leonard Goldstein, M.D., President Medical Staff
CIO: Edna Bruehl, Vice President and Chief Information Officer
CHR: Marcel Wright, Director
Web address: www.potomacridge.com
| 21 | 22 | 85 | 2619 | 64 | 5892 | 0 | 26821 | 16164 | 420 |

☒ **SHADY GROVE ADVENTIST HOSPITAL**, 9901 Medical Center Drive,
Zip 20850–3395; tel. 301/279–6000 **A**1 2 9 10 **F**2 9 10 11 12 15 17 21 22
23 26 27 28 33 35 37 38 39 49 52 53 55 56 57 58 59 60 61 62 63 64 65
66 67 81 82 84 85 86 87 88 92 94 96 106 108 109 110 **P**8 **S** Adventist
HealthCare, Rockville, MD
Primary Contact: Deborah A. Yancer, R.N., President
COO: Michael Franklin, Vice President Operations
CFO: Will de la Pena, Vice President and Chief Financial Officer
CMO: Carol Plotsky, M.D., President Medical and Affiliate Staff
CIO: Edna Bruehl, Vice President and Chief Information Officer
CHR: Tom Keefe, Director Human Resources
Web address: www.adventisthealthcare.com
| 21 | 10 | 265 | 19760 | 234 | 127726 | 4672 | 202207 | 79404 | 1590 |

SALISBURY—Wicomico County

□ **DEER'S HEAD HOSPITAL CENTER**, 351 Deer's Head Hospital Road, Zip 21801,
Mailing Address: P.O. Box 2018, Zip 21802–2018; tel. 410/543–4000, (Total
facility includes 80 beds in nursing home–type unit) **A**1 10 **F**2 9 21 22 26 27 28
35 37 38 39 44 46 47 48 49 50 53 58 60 64 65 66 68 69 92 94 96 108
110 **P**6
Primary Contact: Sandra K. Smith, Director and Chief Executive Officer
Web address: www.deershead.org
| 12 | 80 | 101 | 207 | 81 | 19108 | 0 | 29115 | 12951 | 258 |

☒ △ **HEALTHSOUTH CHESAPEAKE REHABILITATION HOSPITAL**, 220
Tilghman Road, Zip 21804–1921; tel. 410/546–4600, (Nonreporting) **A**1 7 9 10
S HEALTHSOUTH Corporation, Birmingham, AL
Primary Contact: Gary Crowley, Administrator
CFO: Karen Rounsley, Accounting Manager
CHR: Belinda Thompson, Human Resources Coordinator
Web address: www.healthsouth.com
| 33 | 46 | 42 | — | — | — | — | — | — | — |

☒ **PENINSULA REGIONAL HEALTH SYSTEM**, 100 East Carroll Street,
Zip 21801–5422; tel. 410/546–6400, (Total facility includes 30 beds in nursing
home–type unit) **A**1 2 9 10 **F**2 9 10 11 12 14 15 17 19 21 22 23 26 27 28 29
33 34 37 40 42 45 46 48 49 50 51 52 53 55 57 58 59 60 61 62 63 64 69
70 71 73 75 79 81 82 84 86 87 88 90 92 93 94 96 107 108 109 **P**5 6 8
Primary Contact: R. Alan Newberry, President and Chief Executive Officer
COO: Peggy Naleppa, Executive Vice President and Chief Operating Officer
CFO: Donald E. Durham, Vice President Finance and Chief Financial Officer
CMO: Charles B. Silvia, M.D., President Medical Staff
CIO: Raymond Adkins, Chief Information Officer
CHR: Kevin Caracciola, Vice President, Human Resources
Web address: www.peninsula.org
| 23 | 10 | 352 | 20386 | 264 | 437632 | 1998 | 233276 | 91096 | 2158 |

Many Facility Codes have changed. Please refer to the AHA Guide Code Chart. © 2005 AHA Guide

MD

Hospital, Address, Telephone, Approval, Facility, and Physician Codes, Health Care System	Classi-fication Codes		Utilization Data					Expense (thousands) of dollars		
★ American Hospital Association (AHA) membership □ Joint Commission on Accreditation of Healthcare Organizations (JCAHO) accreditation ○ American Osteopathic Association (AOA) accreditation △ Commission on Accreditation of Rehabilitation Facilities (CARF) accreditation	Control	Service	Staffed Beds	Admissions	Census	Outpatient Visits	Births	Total	Payroll	Personnel

SILVER SPRING—Montgomery County

☒ **HOLY CROSS HOSPITAL**, 1500 Forest Glen Road, Zip 20910–1487; tel. 301/754–7000, (Total facility includes 20 beds in nursing home–type unit) **A**1 2 3 5 8 9 10 **F**1 2 9 10 11 12 14 15 17 21 22 23 26 27 28 29 33 36 37 38 39 42 44 46 47 48 49 51 52 53 55 56 57 58 59 60 61 62 63 64 65 66 69 70 73 81 82 84 85 88 90 92 93 94 96 106 107 108 109 110 **S** Trinity Health, Novi, MI
Primary Contact: Kevin J. Sexton, President and Chief Executive Officer
CFO: Gary Vogan, Chief Financial Officer
CMO: Blair Eig, M.D., Senior Vice President Medical Affairs
CIO: Manuel Ocasio, Vice President Information Systems
CHR: Fernando Fleites, Vice President Human Resources
Web address: www.holycrosshealth.org

| | 21 | 10 | 406 | 25138 | 303 | 121814 | 7634 | 239579 | 115417 | 1967 |

SAINT LUKE INSTITUTE, 8901 New Hampshire Avenue, Zip 20903–3611; tel. 301/445–7970, (Nonreporting)
Primary Contact: Father Stephen J. Rossetti, Ph.D., President and Chief Executive Officer

| | 23 | 22 | 24 | — | — | — | — | — | — | — |

SYKESVILLE—Carroll County

□ **SPRINGFIELD HOSPITAL CENTER**, 6655 Sykesville Road, Zip 21784–7966; tel. 410/795–2100 **A**1 9 10 **F**8 9 26 28 29 35 41 44 46 53 58 60 65 66 71 74 76 94 96 106 108 **P**6
Primary Contact: Paula A. Langmead, Chief Executive Officer
Web address: www.dhmh.state.md.us/springfield

| | 12 | 22 | 332 | 642 | 268 | 0 | 0 | — | — | 901 |

TAKOMA PARK—Montgomery County

☒ △ **WASHINGTON ADVENTIST HOSPITAL**, 7600 Carroll Avenue, Zip 20912–6392; tel. 301/891–7600 **A**1 7 9 10 **F**2 4 10 11 12 14 15 17 19 21 22 23 26 27 28 33 49 52 53 55 57 59 60 61 62 63 64 65 66 69 71 72 73 74 75 76 77 78 79 80 81 82 84 85 87 88 90 92 93 94 96 106 108 110 **P**5 **S** Adventist HealthCare, Rockville, MD
Primary Contact: Jere D. Stocks, President
Web address: www.adventisthealthcare.com

| | 21 | 10 | 291 | 17410 | 216 | 79904 | 1963 | 201112 | 73801 | 1386 |

TOWSON—Baltimore County

☒ **ST. JOSEPH MEDICAL CENTER**, 7601 Osler Drive, Zip 21204–7582; tel. 410/337–1000, (Total facility includes 32 beds in nursing home–type unit) **A**1 2 9 10 **F**2 9 10 11 14 15 16 17 18 19 20 21 22 23 26 27 28 29 30 33 37 44 46 47 48 49 50 52 53 55 56 57 58 59 60 61 62 63 64 65 66 69 70 71 72 73 74 75 76 77 78 81 82 87 88 90 92 93 94 95 96 98 106 107 108 109 110 **P**6 **S** Catholic Health Initiatives, Denver, CO
Primary Contact: John Kerr Tolmie, President and Chief Executive Officer
COO: Sylvia Moore, Executive Vice President and Chief Operating Officer
CFO: Michelle Mahan, Executive Vice President Finance and Administration
CMO: Richard Boehler, Vice President Medical Affairs
CIO: David Hynson, Director Information Systems
CHR: Deborah Patrick, Vice President Human Resources
Web address: www.sjmcmd.org

| | 21 | 10 | 359 | 22306 | 267 | 193893 | 2386 | 257968 | 94582 | 1655 |

WESTMINSTER—Carroll County

☒ **CARROLL HOSPITAL CENTER**, 200 Memorial Avenue, Zip 21157–5799; tel. 410/848–3000 **A**1 9 10 **F**2 4 9 11 12 15 21 22 23 24 26 27 28 29 30 31 33 35 36 37 38 39 40 44 46 47 48 51 52 55 58 59 61 62 63 64 65 66 69 71 72 73 74 75 76 78 81 82 88 93 94 96 106 108 109 110 **P**8
Primary Contact: John M. Sernulka, President and Chief Executive Officer
COO: John M. Sernulka, President and Chief Executive Officer
CFO: Kevin Kelbly, Senior Vice President Finance and Corporate Fiscal Affairs
CHR: Linda Hutsell, Assistant Vice President of Human Resources
Web address: www.carrollhospitalcenter.org

| | 23 | 10 | 192 | 13674 | 137 | 257752 | 1371 | 132503 | 55098 | 1105 |

MASSACHUSETTS

Hospital, Address, Telephone, Approval, Facility, and Physician Codes, Health Care System	Classi-fication Codes		Utilization Data					Expense (thousands) of dollars		
★ American Hospital Association (AHA) membership □ Joint Commission on Accreditation of Healthcare Organizations (JCAHO) accreditation ○ American Osteopathic Association (AOA) accreditation △ Commission on Accreditation of Rehabilitation Facilities (CARF) accreditation	Control	Service	Staffed Beds	Admissions	Census	Outpatient Visits	Births	Total	Payroll	Personnel

AMHERST—Hampshire County

UNIVERSITY HEALTH SERVICES, University of Massachusetts, Box 34310, Zip 01003–4310; tel. 413/577–5000, (Nonreporting) **A**10
Primary Contact: Bernette A. Melby, Executive Director
| | 12 | 11 | 6 | — | — | — | — | — | — | — |

ANDOVER—Essex County

ISHAM HEALTH CENTER, 180 Main Street, Zip 01810–4161; tel. 978/749–4455 **F**4 42 45 47 48 58 62 65 66 70 72 77 93 95 106 107 110 **P**4 5
Primary Contact: Nneka Anaebonam, Administrator
Web address: www.andover.edu
| | 23 | 11 | 14 | 400 | 2 | — | 0 | | | |

ATHOL—Worcester County

□ **ATHOL MEMORIAL HOSPITAL**, 2033 Main Street, Zip 01331–3598; tel. 978/249–3511 **A**1 9 10 **F**12 21 27 28 29 30 33 45 46 48 50 58 60 61 62 63 69 81 84 88 93 94 96 108 **P**5
Primary Contact: Donna M. Ditch, R.N., MS, President, Chief Executive Officer and Chief Nursing Officer
Web address: www.atholhospital.org
| | 23 | 10 | 13 | 1124 | 11 | 47092 | 0 | 16078 | 7352 | 186 |

ATTLEBORO—Bristol County

□ **ARBOUR–FULLER HOSPITAL**, 200 May Street, Zip 02703–5515; tel. 508/761–8500, (Nonreporting) **A**1 10 **S** Universal Health Services, Inc., King of Prussia, PA
Primary Contact: Gary M. Gilberti, Regional Vice President
Web address: www.arbourhealth.com
| | 33 | 22 | 46 | | | | | | | |

⊠ **STURDY MEMORIAL HOSPITAL**, 211 Park Street, Zip 02703–3137, Mailing Address: P.O. Box 2963, Zip 02703–2963; tel. 508/222–5200 **A**1 2 5 9 10 **F**2 11 12 15 21 22 23 24 26 27 28 29 30 32 33 35 39 42 44 46 47 48 50 52 55 57 58 59 60 61 62 63 64 65 66 69 70 81 82 84 85 87 88 93 94 96 98 107 108 109 110 **P**6
Primary Contact: Linda Shyavitz, President and Chief Executive Officer
CFO: Joseph Casey, Chief Financial Officer
CMO: Daniel Pietro, M.D., Medical Director
CIO: Lisa McCluskie, Director Marketing and Planning
Web address: www.sturdymemorial.org
| | 23 | 10 | 126 | 6095 | 79 | 214221 | 1055 | 103266 | 56455 | 1004 |

AYER—Middlesex County

□ **NASHOBA VALLEY MEDICAL CENTER**, 200 Groton Road, Zip 01432–3300; tel. 978/784–9000 **A**1 9 10 **F**1 9 12 14 21 24 27 28 29 33 42 44 46 47 48 50 52 58 60 61 63 65 66 69 70 81 82 84 88 94 96 108 109 **S** Essent Healthcare, Nashville, TN
Primary Contact: Andrei Soran, Chief Executive Officer
Web address: www.nashoba.caregroup.org
| | 23 | 10 | 41 | 2613 | 27 | 111331 | 0 | | | |

BEDFORD—Middlesex County

⊠ **EDITH NOURSE ROGERS MEMORIAL VETERANS HOSPITAL**, 200 Springs Road, Zip 01730–1198; tel. 781/687–2000, (Total facility includes 306 beds in nursing home–type unit) (Nonreporting) **A**1 3 5 **S** Department of Veterans Affairs, Washington, DC
Primary Contact: William A. Conte, Director
CFO: Warren Berger, Chief Fiscal Service
CIO: Joseph Calabresi, Chief Information Service
Web address: www.va.gov/sta/guide/home.asp
| | 45 | 22 | 453 | — | — | — | — | — | — | — |

BELMONT—Middlesex County

⊠ **MCLEAN HOSPITAL**, 115 Mill Street, Zip 02478–9106; tel. 617/855–2000 **A**1 3 5 10 **F**1 2 3 4 5 9 35 39 44 45 46 47 52 53 57 58 60 65 71 72 73 74 75 76 77 78 84 92 93 94 96 106 108 **P**6 **S** Partners HealthCare System, Inc., Boston, MA
Primary Contact: Bruce M. Cohen, M.D., Ph.D., President and Psychiatrist–in–Chief
COO: Michele L. Gougeon, Executive Vice President and Chief Operating Officer
CFO: David A. Lagasse, Senior Vice President Fiscal Affairs
CIO: Marc DiFabbio, Director Information System
CHR: Lisa Pratt, Director Human Resources
Web address: www.mclean.harvard.edu
| | 23 | 22 | 169 | 5078 | 146 | 262083 | 0 | 118451 | 46506 | 865 |

BEVERLY—Essex County

⊠ **BEVERLY HOSPITAL**, 85 Herrick Street, Zip 01915–1777; tel. 978/922–3000, (Includes ADDISON GILBERT HOSPITAL, 298 Washington Street, Gloucester, Zip 01930–4887; tel. 978/283–4000) **A**1 2 3 5 10 **F**2 4 9 10 11 12 15 21 22 23 27 28 29 33 36 38 39 40 42 44 46 47 48 52 53 55 57 58 59 61 62 63 64 65 66 69 70 71 75 76 77 78 81 82 85 88 92 93 94 95 96 106 108 109 **P**1 6
Primary Contact: Stephen R. Laverty, President and Chief Executive Officer
COO: Philip M. Cormier, Chief Operating Officer and Executive Vice President
CFO: John O. Wilhelm, Jr, Executive Vice President and Chief Financial Officer
CMO: Peter H. Short, M.D., Senior Vice President Medical Affairs
CIO: Michael Hicks, Director Information Systems
CHR: Althea C. Lyons, Vice President Human Resources
Web address: www.nhshealth.org
| | 23 | 10 | 315 | 16748 | 219 | 426019 | 2298 | 207858 | 106656 | 1684 |

Many Facility Codes have changed. Please refer to the AHA Guide Code Chart. © 2005 AHA Guide

Hospital, Address, Telephone, Approval, Facility, and Physician Codes, Health Care System	Classi-fication Codes		Utilization Data					Expense (thousands) of dollars		
★ American Hospital Association (AHA) membership □ Joint Commission on Accreditation of Healthcare Organizations (JCAHO) accreditation ○ American Osteopathic Association (AOA) accreditation △ Commission on Accreditation of Rehabilitation Facilities (CARF) accreditation	Control	Service	Staffed Beds	Admissions	Census	Outpatient Visits	Births	Total	Payroll	Personnel

BOSTON—Suffolk County

ARBOUR HOSPITAL, 49 Robinwood Avenue, Zip 02130–2156, Mailing Address: P.O. Box 9, Zip 02130; tel. 617/522–4400 **A**10 **F**71 72 73 74 75 76 77 78 **S** Universal Health Services, Inc., King of Prussia, PA
Primary Contact: Roy A. Ettlinger, Chief Executive Officer, Managing Director and Regional Vice President
Web address: www.arbourhealth.com
— 23 22 | 118 | 3246 | 103 | 10305 | 0 | — | — | —

☒ **BETH ISRAEL DEACONESS MEDICAL CENTER**, 330 Brookline Avenue, Zip 02215–5491; tel. 617/667–7000, (Includes BETH ISRAEL DEACONESS HOSPITAL–NEEDHAM CAMPUS, 148 Chestnut Street, Needham, Zip 02492; tel. 781/453–3000; Jeffrey H. Liebman, President and Chief Executive Officer) **A**1 2 3 5 8 9 10 **F**2 5 7 9 10 11 12 14 15 17 19 21 22 23 26 27 28 29 30 31 33 34 35 36 37 38 39 40 41 42 44 45 46 47 48 50 52 53 55 56 57 58 59 60 61 62 63 64 65 66 69 70 71 73 74 75 76 77 79 80 81 82 83 84 85 86 87 88 94 95 96 98 99 101 102 105 108 109 110 **P**4 5 7
Primary Contact: Paul F. Levy, Chief Executive Officer
COO: Michael Epstein, M.D., Chief Operating Officer
CFO: Mitchell Creem, Senior Vice President Finance and Chief Financial Officer
CIO: John Halamka, M.D., Chief Information Officer
Web address: www.bidmc.harvard.edu
23 10 | 534 | 34428 | 462 | 380901 | 5198 | 864944 | 344241 | 5972

☒ △ **BOSTON MEDICAL CENTER**, One Boston Medical Center Place, Zip 02118–2393; tel. 617/638–8000, (Total facility includes 19 beds in nursing home–type unit) **A**1 2 3 5 7 8 9 10 **F**1 2 4 7 10 11 12 14 21 22 23 24 26 27 28 29 31 32 33 34 35 37 38 39 44 45 46 47 48 50 52 53 55 56 57 58 59 60 61 62 63 65 66 67 68 69 70 72 73 74 75 76 77 79 81 82 84 88 89 92 93 94 95 96 98 99 100 101 102 103 104 106 107 108 109 110 **P**7
Primary Contact: Elaine S. Ullian, President and Chief Executive Officer
CFO: Ronald E. Bartlett, Chief Financial Officer
CMO: John Chessare, M.D., Chief Medical Officer
CIO: Meg Aranow, Chief Information Officer
CHR: Patricia Webb, Vice President Human Resources
Web address: www.bmc.org
23 10 | 537 | 26096 | 403 | 877770 | 2137 | 701571 | 272967 | 4519

☒ **BRIGHAM AND WOMEN'S HOSPITAL**, 75 Francis Street, Zip 02115–6195; tel. 617/732–5500 **A**1 2 3 5 8 9 10 **F**2 4 5 7 9 10 11 12 13 14 15 17 19 21 22 23 24 26 27 28 29 30 31 32 33 34 35 37 38 39 40 42 44 45 46 47 48 49 50 52 53 55 56 57 58 59 60 61 62 63 64 65 66 69 70 72 73 74 75 76 77 79 80 81 82 84 85 86 87 88 89 90 92 93 94 95 96 98 99 100 101 103 104 105 106 107 108 109 110 **P**6 **S** Partners HealthCare System, Inc., Boston, MA
Primary Contact: Gary L. Gottlieb, M.D., Chief Executive Officer
CFO: Roger Deshaies, Chief Financial Officer
CMO: Anthony Whittemore, Chief Medical Officer
CIO: Sue Schade, Chief Information Officer
Web address: www.brighamandwomens.org
23 10 | 735 | 43100 | 626 | 652607 | 8904 | 1318115 | 420659 | 9638

☒ **CHILDREN'S HOSPITAL BOSTON**, 300 Longwood Avenue, Zip 02115–5737; tel. 617/355–6000 **A**1 3 5 8 9 10 **F**14 21 24 29 30 31 32 33 34 37 42 45 48 50 51 56 58 60 61 63 65 66 67 69 70 71 72 73 74 75 77 81 82 84 86 87 88 94 95 96 98 108
Primary Contact: James Mandell, M.D., President and Chief Executive Officer
COO: Sandra Fenwick, Chief Operating Officer
CFO: David Kirshner, Senior Vice President and Chief Financial Officer
CIO: Daniel Nigrin, M.D., Interim Vice President Information Services and Chief Information Officer
Web address: www.childrenshospital.org/
23 50 | 321 | 16830 | 252 | 318874 | 0 | — | — | —

☒ **DANA–FARBER CANCER INSTITUTE**, 44 Binney Street, Zip 02115–6084; tel. 617/632–3000 **A**1 3 5 8 9 10 **F**2 9 12 21 22 23 26 27 28 29 30 36 37 38 45 46 47 48 50 52 53 58 60 61 65 66 69 73 74 81 82 86 87 88 94 95 96 106 108 109 **P**6
Primary Contact: Edward J. Benz, Jr, M.D., President and Chief Executive Officer
COO: James B. Conway, Chief Operations Officer
CFO: Dorothy E. Puhy, Executive Vice President and Chief Financial Officer
CIO: Jeffrey R. Kessler, Vice President Information Services
CHR: Emily Barclay, Vice President Human Resources
Web address: www.dana–farber.org
23 10 | 27 | 955 | 20 | 159815 | 0 | — | — | —

☒ **FAULKNER HOSPITAL**, Mailing Address: 1153 Centre Street, Zip 02130–3400; tel. 617/983–7000 **A**1 2 3 5 8 9 10 **F**1 2 3 4 9 10 12 15 21 22 23 25 26 27 28 29 30 31 33 36 37 39 40 42 44 46 47 48 49 50 52 53 55 57 58 60 61 62 63 64 65 66 69 70 71 73 74 75 76 77 78 81 82 84 85 88 92 93 94 95 96 108 **P**5 **S** Partners HealthCare System, Inc., Boston, MA
Primary Contact: David J. Trull, President
CFO: Michael E. Conklin, Jr, Senior Vice President Finance
CMO: Stephen C. Wright, M.D., Chief Medical Officer
CIO: Jim Anzeveno, Chief Information Officer
Web address: www.faulknerhospital.org
23 10 | 124 | 8271 | 106 | 194060 | 0 | 109875 | 50454 | 1014

MA

Hospital, Address, Telephone, Approval, Facility, and Physician Codes, Health Care System	Classi-fication Codes		Utilization Data					Expense (thousands) of dollars		
★ American Hospital Association (AHA) membership □ Joint Commission on Accreditation of Healthcare Organizations (JCAHO) accreditation ○ American Osteopathic Association (AOA) accreditation △ Commission on Accreditation of Rehabilitation Facilities (CARF) accreditation	Control	Service	Staffed Beds	Admissions	Census	Outpatient Visits	Births	Total	Payroll	Personnel
⊠ **FRANCISCAN HOSPITAL FOR CHILDREN AND REHABILITATION CENTER**, (Formerly Franciscan Children's Hospital and Rehabilitation Center), Mailing Address: 30 Warren Street, Zip 02135–3680; tel. 617/254–3800 **A**1 5 10 **F**1 2 21 22 27 28 29 32 47 48 51 52 53 57 58 63 65 68 69 70 71 72 77 78 79 88 90 94 108 109 **P**6 Primary Contact: Paul J. Dellarocco, President and Chief Executive Officer COO: Donna Pohscilli, Chief Operating Officer CFO: Michael Cofone, Chief Financial Officer Web address: www.fchrc.org	23	56	60	509	49	26391	0	37819	22666	431
△ **HEBREW REHABILITATION CENTER FOR AGED**, Mailing Address: 1200 Centre Street, Zip 02131–1097; tel. 617/325–8000, (Total facility includes 21 beds in nursing home–type unit) (Nonreporting) **A**7 10 Primary Contact: Len Fishman, President and Chief Executive Officer Web address: www.hebrewrehab.org	23	49	721	—	—	—	—	—	—	—
⊠ **JEWISH MEMORIAL HOSPITAL AND REHABILITATION CENTER**, 59 Townsend Street, Zip 02119–9918; tel. 617/442–8760 **A**1 3 5 10 **F**1 21 22 46 49 53 57 58 60 64 66 68 69 71 73 76 94 110 **P**6 Primary Contact: Kimberly A. Smith, President and Chief Executive Officer CFO: Angelo J. Tartaglione, Chief Financial Officer CMO: R Nicholas Nace, M.D., Chief Medical Officer CHR: Daniel Carton, Vice President Human Resources Web address: www.jmhrc.com	23	80	109	720	87	0	0	27977	16016	213
□ **KINDRED HOSPITAL–BOSTON**, 1515 Commonwealth Avenue, Zip 02135–3696; tel. 617/254–1100 **A**1 10 **F**21 22 29 47 88 94 109 **S** Kindred Healthcare, Louisville, KY Primary Contact: Deborah Plummer, Chief Executive Officer Web address: www.kindredhealthcare.com	33	10	36	383	30	0	0	—	—	—
□ △ **MASSACHUSETTS EYE AND EAR INFIRMARY**, 243 Charles Street, Zip 02114–3096; tel. 617/523–7900 **A**1 3 5 7 9 10 **F**2 9 21 23 26 27 28 29 30 33 34 35 37 44 45 46 47 48 52 53 58 60 61 63 64 65 66 69 81 84 85 88 90 92 94 96 105 107 108 **P**8 Primary Contact: F. Curtis Smith, President Web address: www.meei.harvard.edu	23	45	45	1232	13	270652	0	120896	35453	1277
⊠ **MASSACHUSETTS GENERAL HOSPITAL**, 55 Fruit Street, Zip 02114–2696; tel. 617/726–2000 **A**1 3 5 8 9 10 **F**2 4 5 6 7 9 10 11 12 13 14 15 16 17 18 19 20 21 22 23 24 26 27 28 29 30 31 32 33 34 35 36 37 38 39 40 41 42 44 45 46 47 48 49 50 51 52 53 55 56 57 58 59 60 61 62 63 64 65 66 67 69 70 71 72 73 74 75 76 77 78 79 80 81 82 84 85 86 87 88 89 90 93 94 95 96 98 99 100 101 102 103 104 105 106 107 108 109 110 **P**6 **S** Partners HealthCare System, Inc., Boston, MA Primary Contact: Peter L. Slavin, M.D., President CMO: Britain Nicholson, M.D., Chief Medical Officer CIO: James W. Noga, Chief Information Officer CHR: Jeff Davis, Senior Vice President Human Resources Web address: www.partners.org	23	10	898	45497	808	832729	3827	1670451	542247	15213
⊠ **NEW ENGLAND BAPTIST HOSPITAL**, 125 Parker Hill Avenue, Zip 02120–3297; tel. 617/754–5800, (Total facility includes 20 beds in nursing home–type unit) **A**1 3 5 9 10 **F**2 9 12 15 21 22 23 26 27 28 29 35 39 40 42 45 46 47 48 49 52 53 55 58 60 61 62 63 64 65 66 69 70 73 81 82 84 85 86 87 88 92 94 95 96 108 109 **P**8 Primary Contact: Joseph D. Dionisio, President and Chief Executive Officer Web address: www.nebh.org	23	47	98	7638	94	124364	0	135751	49561	817
□ **SHRINERS HOSPITALS FOR CHILDREN, SHRINERS BURNS HOSPITAL–BOSTON**, (Pediatric Burns), 51 Blossom Street, Zip 02114–2699; tel. 617/722–3000 **A**1 3 5 **F**20 22 28 29 45 46 52 58 60 63 64 65 66 69 72 77 94 96 104 108 110 **S** Shriners Hospitals for Children, Tampa, FL Primary Contact: Janet L. Mulligan, R.N., MS, Administrator Web address: www.shrinershq.org	23	59	30	1010	13	5248	0	—	—	256
⊠ △ **SPAULDING REHABILITATION HOSPITAL**, 125 Nashua Street, Zip 02114–1198; tel. 617/573–7000 **A**1 3 5 7 10 **F**2 6 21 22 28 29 30 32 35 37 39 44 45 48 49 52 53 57 58 60 61 64 66 69 70 73 77 92 93 94 95 96 108 110 **P**6 **S** Partners HealthCare System, Inc., Boston, MA Primary Contact: Judith C. Waterston, President COO: Kathleen M. Murphy, Chief Operating Officer CFO: Charles Champagne, Chief Financial Officer CMO: Joel Stein, M.D., Chief Medical Officer CIO: John Campbell, Director Management Information Systems CHR: Oswald Mondejar, Vice President Human Resources Web address: www.spauldingrehab.org	23	46	296	3310	246	116183	0	103871	54915	1155
□ △ **TUFTS–NEW ENGLAND MEDICAL CENTER**, 750 Washington Street, Zip 02111–1845; tel. 617/636–5000, (Nonreporting) **A**1 2 3 5 7 8 10 Primary Contact: Ellen Zane, Chief Executive Officer Web address: www.nemc.org	23	10	374	—	—	—	—	—	—	—

MA

Many Facility Codes have changed. Please refer to the AHA Guide Code Chart. © 2005 AHA Guide

MA

Hospital, Address, Telephone, Approval, Facility, and Physician Codes, Health Care System	Classi-fication Codes		Utilization Data					Expense (thousands) of dollars		
★ American Hospital Association (AHA) membership □ Joint Commission on Accreditation of Healthcare Organizations (JCAHO) accreditation ○ American Osteopathic Association (AOA) accreditation △ Commission on Accreditation of Rehabilitation Facilities (CARF) accreditation	Control	Service	Staffed Beds	Admissions	Census	Outpatient Visits	Births	Total	Payroll	Personnel
★□ △ **VETERANS AFFAIRS BOSTON HEALTHCARE SYSTEM**, 1400 VFW Parkway, Zip 02132; tel. 617/232–9500, (Total facility includes 160 beds in nursing home–type unit) **A**1 2 3 5 7 8 **F**1 3 4 12 14 15 17 19 21 22 23 26 27 28 29 30 32 33 36 37 38 42 44 46 48 49 50 51 55 57 58 60 61 62 63 66 68 69 70 71 73 75 76 77 78 81 84 86 88 92 93 94 96 106 107 108 109 110 **S** Department of Veterans Affairs, Washington, DC Primary Contact: Michael M. Lawson, Director COO: Susan A. MacKenzie, Ph.D., Associate Director CFO: Joseph R. Costa, Chief Financial Officer CMO: Brian Hoffman, M.D., Chief Medical Services CIO: David M. Goodman, Ph.D., Chief Information Officer CHR: William Warfield, Acting Chief Human Resources Management Web address: www.va.gov/sta/guide/home.asp VETERANS AFFAIRS MEDICAL CENTER See, Washington	45	10	531	10731	524	559581	0	—	—	3199
BRAINTREE—Norfolk County										
★□ **HEALTHSOUTH BRAINTREE REHABILITATION HOSPITAL**, 250 Pond Street, Zip 02185–9020; tel. 781/348–2078 **A**1 10 **F**7 21 29 48 52 57 58 60 61 62 68 69 88 94 95 108 110 **P**5 **S** HEALTHSOUTH Corporation, Birmingham, AL Primary Contact: Randy Doherty, Administrator CFO: Andrew Rando, Senior Controller CMO: John Stevenson, M.D., Medical Director CIO: Don Andrade, Area Director Information Technology CHR: Bonnie Olson, Director Human Resources Web address: www.healthsouth.com	33	46	117	2638	117	197510	0	54974	29170	423
□ **NORTHEAST SPECIALTY HOSPITAL**, 2001 Washington Street, Zip 02184–8664; tel. 781/848–2600, (Nonreporting) **A**1 10 Primary Contact: Judyth McTiernan, Chief Executive Officer Web address: www.commonwealthcommunity.com	13	48	110	—	—	—	—	—	—	—
BRIDGEWATER—Plymouth County										
BRIDGEWATER STATE HOSPITAL, 20 Administration Road, Zip 02324–3201; tel. 508/279–4521, (Nonreporting) Primary Contact: Kenneth W. Nelson, Superintendent	12	22	350	—	—	—	—	—	—	—
BRIGHTON—Suffolk County										
★□ **CARITAS ST. ELIZABETH'S MEDICAL CENTER**, 736 Cambridge Street, Zip 02135–2997; tel. 617/789–3000, (Total facility includes 21 beds in nursing home–type unit) **A**1 2 3 5 8 9 10 **F**1 3 4 9 10 11 12 14 15 17 19 21 22 23 26 27 28 29 31 33 35 37 38 39 40 41 42 44 45 46 47 48 49 52 53 54 55 56 57 58 59 60 61 62 63 64 65 66 69 70 71 73 74 75 76 77 78 81 82 85 87 88 90 92 93 94 95 96 106 108 109 110 **P**5 **S** Caritas Christi Health Care, Boston, MA Primary Contact: Robert M. Haddad, M.D., President CFO: Joseph Iannoni, Chief Financial Officer CIO: Lynn Bowen, Vice President Information Services CHR: Nanette Smith, Vice President Human Resources Web address: www.semc.org	21	10	247	16088	238	109165	1386	304416	108183	1958
BROCKTON—Plymouth County										
★□ **BROCKTON HOSPITAL**, 680 Centre Street, Zip 02302–3395; tel. 508/941–7000, (Total facility includes 26 beds in nursing home–type unit) **A**1 2 3 5 6 9 10 **F**11 12 14 15 17 21 22 23 24 26 27 28 29 31 33 37 38 39 40 42 44 45 46 47 48 49 50 52 53 55 58 59 61 62 63 64 66 69 70 71 73 74 75 76 77 78 80 81 82 84 85 86 87 88 92 94 95 96 106 107 108 109 110 **P**6 8 Primary Contact: Norman B. Goodman, President and Chief Executive Officer CFO: Michael Connors, Vice President and Chief Financial Officer Web address: www.brocktonhospital.com	23	10	250	14092	166	240391	1266	142004	84772	1288
★ **BROCKTON VETERANS AFFAIRS MEDICAL CENTER**, 940 Belmont Street, Zip 02401–5596; tel. 508/583–4500 **A**3 5 8 **F**1 3 4 12 14 15 17 19 21 22 23 26 27 28 29 30 32 33 36 37 38 42 44 46 48 49 50 51 55 57 58 60 61 62 63 66 68 69 70 71 73 75 76 77 78 81 84 86 88 92 93 94 96 106 107 108 109 110 **S** Department of Veterans Affairs, Washington, DC Primary Contact: Michael E. Lawson, Director CFO: Joe Costa, Acting Chief Fiscal Officer Web address: www.va.gov/sta/guide/home.asp	45	10	531	10731	524	559581	0	—	—	3199
★□ **CARITAS GOOD SAMARITAN MEDICAL CENTER**, 235 North Pearl Street, Zip 02401–1794; tel. 508/427–3000, (Includes GOOD SAMARITAN MEDICAL CENTER – CUSHING CAMPUS) **A**1 2 3 5 9 10 **F**2 3 4 11 12 14 21 22 23 26 27 28 29 33 37 39 42 44 48 49 52 55 58 59 60 61 63 66 69 71 76 81 82 84 86 87 88 96 106 107 108 109 **P**4 5 6 **S** Caritas Christi Health Care, Boston, MA Primary Contact: John J. Holiver, President CFO: Allen A. Krause, Chief Financial Officer CIO: Daniel O'Neil, Vice President Information Technology CHR: William Kirkwood, Ph.D., Vice President Human Resources Web address: www.caritasgoodsam.org	23	10	231	14799	168	119925	997	—	—	—
BROOKLINE—Norfolk County										
□ **ARBOUR H. R. I. HOSPITAL**, 227 Babcock Street, Zip 02146–6799; tel. 617/731–3200, (Nonreporting) **A**1 10 **S** Universal Health Services, Inc., King of Prussia, PA Primary Contact: Marcia Hoch, Interim Chief Executive Officer Web address: www.arbourhealth.com	33	22	68	—	—	—	—	—	—	—

Hospital, Address, Telephone, Approval, Facility, and Physician Codes, Health Care System	Classi-fication Codes		Utilization Data					Expense (thousands) of dollars		
★ American Hospital Association (AHA) membership □ Joint Commission on Accreditation of Healthcare Organizations (JCAHO) accreditation ○ American Osteopathic Association (AOA) accreditation △ Commission on Accreditation of Rehabilitation Facilities (CARF) accreditation	Control	Service	Staffed Beds	Admissions	Census	Outpatient Visits	Births	Total	Payroll	Personnel

□ **BOURNEWOOD HEALTH SYSTEM**, 300 South Street, Zip 02467–3694; tel. 617/469–0300 **A**1 5 10 **F**3 4 71 72 77 78 94 **P**1 Primary Contact: Nasir A. Khan, M.D., Chief Executive Officer Web address: www.bournewood.com	33	22	81	3478	74	128	0	15756	9246	174

BURLINGTON—Middlesex County

⌘ **LAHEY CLINIC HOSPITAL**, 41 Mall Road, Zip 01805–0001; tel. 781/744–5100 **A**1 2 3 5 8 9 10 **F**2 4 7 10 12 14 15 17 19 21 22 23 24 26 27 28 29 30 31 32 33 34 35 36 37 38 39 40 42 43 44 45 46 47 48 49 50 52 53 55 57 58 60 61 62 63 64 65 66 69 70 72 73 74 75 76 77 79 80 81 82 84 85 87 88 89 90 92 93 94 95 96 98 99 101 102 105 106 107 108 109 110 **P**6 Primary Contact: David M. Barrett, M.D., Chief Executive Officer COO: Sanford R. Kurtz, M.D., Chief Operating Officer CFO: Timothy O'Connor, Chief Financial Officer CMO: Sanford R. Kurtz, M.D., Chief Operating Officer and Chief Medical Officer CIO: Nelson R. Gagnon, Chief Information Officer CHR: Joan M. Robbio, Senior Vice President Human Resources Web address: www.lahey.org	23	10	267	19139	243	741849	0	423247	171641	4207

CAMBRIDGE—Middlesex County

⌘ **CAMBRIDGE HEALTH ALLIANCE**, 1493 Cambridge Street, Zip 02139–1099; tel. 617/665–1000, (Includes CAMBRIDGE HOSPITAL, 1493 Cambridge Street; SOMERVILLE HOSPITAL, 230 Highland Avenue, Somerville, Zip 02143; tel. 617/666–4400; WHIDDEN MEMORIAL HOSPITAL, 103 Garland Street, Everett, Zip 02149–5095; tel. 617/389–6270) **A**1 2 3 5 9 10 **F**3 4 9 11 12 13 14 21 22 23 24 25 26 27 28 29 30 31 32 33 34 35 39 42 44 45 46 47 48 50 52 53 55 56 57 58 59 60 61 62 63 65 66 67 68 69 70 71 72 73 74 75 76 77 78 81 82 84 88 89 90 92 93 94 95 96 97 98 106 107 108 109 **P**6 Primary Contact: Dennis D. Keefe, Chief Executive Officer COO: Bruce Solomon, Chief Operating Officer CFO: Gordon Boudrow, Chief Financial Officer CIO: Judith K. Klickstein, Chief Information Officer CHR: Arthur Battle, Senior Vice President Human Resources Web address: www.challiance.org	16	10	307	17304	272	574096	1175	367993	202161	2750
□ **M. I. T. MEDICAL DEPARTMENT**, 77 Massachusetts Avenue, Zip 02139–4307; tel. 617/253–4481, (Nonreporting) **A**1 Primary Contact: Arnold N. Weinberg, M.D., Director	23	11	18	—	—	—	—	—	—	—
⌘ **MOUNT AUBURN HOSPITAL**, 330 Mount Auburn Street, Zip 02138–5597; tel. 617/492–3500 **A**1 2 3 5 8 9 10 **F**2 4 9 11 12 14 15 17 19 21 22 23 26 27 28 29 33 39 40 44 46 47 48 49 50 51 52 53 55 57 58 59 60 61 62 63 65 66 69 70 71 73 74 75 76 77 79 80 81 82 84 85 87 88 89 90 93 94 95 96 106 107 108 109 **P**5 6 7 Primary Contact: Jeanette G. Clough, President and Chief Executive Officer COO: Nicholas T. Dileso, R.N., Chief Operating Officer CFO: Peter Semenza, Vice President Financial Operations CMO: Lawrence Mambrino, President Medical Staff CIO: Bob Todd, Director Information Systems Web address: www.mtauburn.caregroup.org	23	10	197	12598	150	207566	1824	187157	85106	1829
□ **STILLMAN INFIRMARY, HARVARD UNIVERSITY HEALTH SERVICES**, 75 Mount Auburn Street, Zip 02138–4960; tel. 617/495–2010 **A**1 10 **F**4 11 21 24 26 27 28 29 30 32 33 39 44 46 47 48 50 52 53 57 58 60 61 62 63 66 69 70 72 73 74 75 76 77 88 94 95 96 98 106 107 109 110 **P**1 Primary Contact: David S. Rosenthal, M.D., Director Web address: www.uhs.harvard.edu	23	11	10	47	1	182129	0	—	—	—
□ △ **YOUVILLE HOSPITAL AND REHABILITATION CENTER**, 1575 Cambridge Street, Zip 02138–4398; tel. 617/876–4344 **A**1 5 7 10 **F**2 8 21 22 23 37 44 49 52 57 58 60 61 62 64 68 76 77 88 94 108 110 **S** Covenant Health Systems, Inc., Lexington, MA Primary Contact: Daniel P. Leahey, President and Chief Executive Officer Web address: www.youville.org	21	46	130	1920	124	3000	0	—	—	—

CANTON—Norfolk County

⌘ **MASSACHUSETTS HOSPITAL SCHOOL**, 3 Randolph Street, Zip 02021–2397; tel. 781/828–2440 **A**1 5 10 **F**21 27 32 42 45 60 61 62 66 70 88 94 108 **P**1 **S** Massschusetts Department of Public Health, Boston, MA Primary Contact: Mederic D. McLaughlin, Chief Executive Officer COO: Philip E. Dould, Chief Operating Officer CFO: Sharon Porter, Chief Financial Officer CMO: Carlton Akins, M.D., Medical Director CIO: Steve Cash, Director Information Systems CHR: Gene Rivers, Manager Employment Services Web address: www.state.ma.us/dph/hosp/mhs.htm	12	58	88	123	83	0	0	13321	9720	234

CHELSEA—Suffolk County

★ **LAWRENCE F. QUIGLEY MEMORIAL HOSPITAL**, 91 Crest Avenue, Zip 02150–2199; tel. 617/884–5660, (Total facility includes 109 beds in nursing home–type unit) (Nonreporting) **A**10 Primary Contact: Michael Resca, Commandant CIO: Thomas Rosa, Director Human Resources	12	49	156	—	—	—	—	—	—	—

Many Facility Codes have changed. Please refer to the AHA Guide Code Chart. © 2005 AHA Guide

Hospital, Address, Telephone, Approval, Facility, and Physician Codes, Health Care System	Classi-fication Codes		Utilization Data					Expense (thousands) of dollars		
★ American Hospital Association (AHA) membership □ Joint Commission on Accreditation of Healthcare Organizations (JCAHO) accreditation ○ American Osteopathic Association (AOA) accreditation △ Commission on Accreditation of Rehabilitation Facilities (CARF) accreditation	Control	Service	Staffed Beds	Admissions	Census	Outpatient Visits	Births	Total	Payroll	Personnel

CLINTON—Worcester County

★ **CLINTON HOSPITAL**, 201 Highland Street, Zip 01510–1096; tel. 978/368–3000 **A**1 5 9 10 **F**12 21 23 27 28 29 33 48 52 58 62 63 69 71 76 81 82 88 94 108 **S** UMass Memorial Health Care, Inc., Worcester, MA
Primary Contact: Sheila Daly, Chief Executive Officer
CFO: William Bryant, Controller
CHR: Martha Chiarchiaro, Vice President Human Resources
Web address: www.umassmemorial.org/ummhc/hospitals/clinton
| 23 | 10 | 41 | 1391 | 28 | 13863 | 0 | — | — | — |

CONCORD—Middlesex County

★ **EMERSON HOSPITAL**, 133 Old Road to Nine Acre Corner, Zip 01742–9120; tel. 978/369–1400, (Total facility includes 20 beds in nursing home–type unit) **A**1 2 5 9 10 **F**2 4 6 9 11 12 14 21 22 26 27 28 33 34 36 39 40 44 47 48 49 51 53 54 55 56 58 59 61 62 63 65 66 69 71 72 73 74 75 76 77 78 81 82 84 85 88 92 93 94 95 96 98 106 107 108 109 **P**1 5
Primary Contact: Christine C. Schuster, President and Chief Executive Officer
CFO: Dana P. Diggins, Senior Vice President and Chief Financial Officer
CIO: Pamela Muccilli, Vice President and Chief Information Officer
CHR: Ellen Nelson, Director Human Resources
Web address: www.emersonhospital.org
| 23 | 10 | 194 | 9921 | 100 | 392119 | 1249 | 119022 | 60742 | 1034 |

DORCHESTER—Suffolk County

★ **CARITAS CARNEY HOSPITAL**, 2100 Dorchester Avenue, Zip 02124–5666; tel. 617/296–4000, (Total facility includes 27 beds in nursing home–type unit) **A**1 2 3 5 9 10 **F**2 4 12 14 15 17 19 21 22 26 27 28 29 33 37 41 46 47 48 50 52 53 55 57 58 60 61 62 63 64 65 66 69 70 71 72 73 74 75 77 78 81 85 86 87 88 92 93 94 96 98 108 109 **P**5 **S** Caritas Christi Health Care, Boston, MA
Primary Contact: Joyce A. Murphy, President
COO: Cornelius P. Bulman, Jr, Senior Vice President and Chief Operating Officer
CFO: Miles Coverdale, Chief Financial Officer
CHR: Dan Michaud, Vice President Human Resources
Web address: www.carneyhospital.org
| 21 | 10 | 186 | 8376 | 137 | 91407 | 0 | 103901 | 53442 | 950 |

EAST SANDWICH—Barnstable County

□ △ **REHABILITATION HOSPITAL OF THE CAPE AND ISLANDS**, 311 Service Road, Zip 02537; tel. 508/833–4000 **A**1 7 10 **F**2 21 22 28 29 30 31 37 39 42 48 49 52 53 57 58 62 64 65 66 68 69 96 106 108 109
Primary Contact: Carol Sim, President and Chief Executive Officer
Web address: www.rhci.org
| 23 | 46 | 60 | 1544 | 51 | 59117 | 0 | — | — | 1 |

EVERETT—Middlesex County

WHIDDEN MEMORIAL HOSPITAL See Cambridge Health Alliance, Cambridge

FALL RIVER—Bristol County

CHARLTON MEMORIAL HOSPITAL See Southcoast Hospitals Group

DR. J. CORRIGAN MENTAL HEALTH CENTER, 49 Hillside Street, Zip 02720–5266; tel. 508/235–7200, (Nonreporting) **A**10 **S** Massachusetts Department of Mental Health, Boston, MA
Primary Contact: Daniel K. Amigone, Director
| 12 | 22 | 16 | — | — | — | — | — | — | — |

★ **SAINT ANNE'S HOSPITAL**, 795 Middle Street, Zip 02721–1798; tel. 508/674–5741, (Total facility includes 10 beds in nursing home–type unit) **A**1 2 5 9 10 **F**2 4 9 10 12 15 16 17 18 21 22 23 26 27 28 29 30 33 37 39 46 48 50 51 52 53 55 58 60 61 62 63 64 65 66 69 75 77 79 80 81 82 85 87 88 92 93 94 96 106 108 109 110 **P**5 **S** Caritas Christi Health Care, Boston, MA
Primary Contact: Michael W. Metzler, President
CFO: Allen A. Krause, Vice President Finance and Chief Financial Officer
CIO: Dan O'Neil, Director Management Information Systems
CHR: Sarah Jackson, Director
Web address: www.saintanneshospital.org
| 21 | 10 | 106 | 6359 | 106 | 158751 | 0 | 104793 | 43270 | 891 |

★ **SOUTHCOAST HOSPITALS GROUP**, 363 Highland Avenue, Zip 02720–3703; tel. 508/679–3131, (Includes CHARLTON MEMORIAL HOSPITAL, 363 Highland Avenue, Zip 02720–3794; tel. 508/679–3131; ST. LUKE'S HOSPITAL OF NEW BEDFORD, 101 Page Street, New Bedford, Zip 02740, Mailing Address: P.O. Box H–3000, Zip 02741–3000; tel. 508/997–1515; TOBEY HOSPITAL, 43 High Street, Wareham, Zip 02571; tel. 508/295–0880) **A**1 2 9 10 **F**2 9 10 11 12 14 15 17 19 21 22 23 27 28 29 30 31 33 35 36 37 38 39 42 44 46 47 48 49 51 52 53 55 57 58 59 60 61 62 63 64 65 66 68 69 71 73 75 76 78 81 82 84 85 87 88 93 94 95 96 98 108 109 110 **P**6
Primary Contact: Ronald B. Goodspeed, M.D., M.P.H., Chief Executive Officer
COO: Linda Bodenmann, Chief Operating Officer
CFO: William Grigg, Chief Financial Officer
CIO: Richard Smith, Vice President Information Systems
CHR: David DeJesus, Vice President Human Resources
Web address: www.southcoast.org
| 23 | 10 | 797 | 36646 | 562 | 788525 | 3652 | 422566 | 207405 | 3899 |

FALMOUTH—Barnstable County

★ **FALMOUTH HOSPITAL**, 100 Ter Heun Drive, Zip 02540–2599; tel. 508/548–5300 **A**1 2 5 9 10 **F**8 9 11 12 15 21 22 26 27 28 29 30 33 37 40 42 44 45 46 47 48 49 50 52 55 58 59 60 61 63 64 65 66 69 73 81 82 84 86 88 92 93 94 95 96 106 107 108 109 110 **P**5 6 7 **S** Cape Cod Healthcare, Inc., Hyannis, MA
Primary Contact: Susan M. Wing, Chief Operating Officer
CFO: Stephen J. Guimond, Senior Vice President and Chief Financial Officer
CMO: Richard Adams, M.D., Vice President Medical Affairs
CIO: John E. Kilroy, Vice President and Chief Information Officer
Web address: www.capecodhealth.org
| 23 | 10 | 95 | 5886 | 65 | 176405 | 616 | 101001 | 40365 | 572 |

MA

Hospital, Address, Telephone, Approval, Facility, and Physician Codes, Health Care System	Classification Codes		Utilization Data					Expense (thousands) of dollars		
★ American Hospital Association (AHA) membership □ Joint Commission on Accreditation of Healthcare Organizations (JCAHO) accreditation ○ American Osteopathic Association (AOA) accreditation △ Commission on Accreditation of Rehabilitation Facilities (CARF) accreditation	Control	Service	Staffed Beds	Admissions	Census	Outpatient Visits	Births	Total	Payroll	Personnel

FRAMINGHAM—Middlesex County

⊞ **METROWEST MEDICAL CENTER**, 115 Lincoln Street, Zip 01702–6342; tel. 508/383–1000, (Includes FRAMINGHAM UNION HOSPITAL, 115 Lincoln Street, Zip 01702; tel. 508/383–1000; LEONARD MORSE HOSPITAL, 67 Union Street, Natick, Zip 01760; tel. 508/650–7000) **A**1 2 3 5 9 10 **F**2 4 11 12 14 17 21 22 23 24 27 28 29 30 33 35 36 37 39 41 42 44 45 46 47 48 50 51 52 53 55 57 58 59 60 61 62 63 64 65 66 69 70 71 72 73 74 75 76 77 78 81 82 85 87 88 92 93 94 95 96 98 106 107 108 109 110 **S** Vanguard Health System, Nashville, TN Primary Contact: Patrick F. Mutch, Chief Executive Officer COO: Ed Moore, Chief Operating Officer CFO: William Sullivan, Chief Financial Officer CMO: Michael Gottlieb, M.D., Chief Medical Officer CIO: Michael Hebert, Director Management Information Systems CHR: John Donlin, Vice President Human Resources Web address: www.mwmc.com	33	10	372	16166	217	343011	2027	—	—	1682

GARDNER—Worcester County

⊞ **HEYWOOD HOSPITAL**, 242 Green Street, Zip 01440–1373; tel. 978/632–3420, (Total facility includes 19 beds in nursing home–type unit) **A**1 5 9 10 **F**2 7 9 11 12 21 23 27 28 29 33 37 38 39 46 48 52 53 55 57 58 59 60 61 62 63 64 66 69 70 71 73 76 78 81 82 85 87 88 92 93 94 96 108 109 110 **P**8 Primary Contact: Daniel P. Moen, President and Chief Executive Officer CFO: Kimberly Webb, Acting Vice President CHR: Wilmont Davis, Vice President Human Resources Web address: www.heywood.org	23	10	129	4984	80	191640	587	60420	28648	643

GLOUCESTER—Essex County

ADDISON GILBERT HOSPITAL See Beverly Hospital, Beverly

GREAT BARRINGTON—Berkshire County

⊞ **FAIRVIEW HOSPITAL**, 29 Lewis Avenue, Zip 01230–1713; tel. 413/528–0790 **A**1 9 10 18 **F**2 11 12 21 26 27 28 32 33 35 37 39 52 53 55 59 62 63 64 66 69 70 81 88 92 94 95 96 97 106 108 **P**6 **S** Berkshire Health Systems, Inc., Pittsfield, MA Primary Contact: Eugene A. Dellea, President COO: Doreen M. Sylvia–Hutchinson, Vice President Operations and Chief Nurse Executive CFO: Michael E. Cullen, Vice President Finance CMO: Brian Burke, M.D., Chief Medical Officer CIO: Charles Podesta, Chief Information Officer CHR: Bertha Holcomb, Director Human Resources Web address: www.berkshirehealthsystems.com	23	10	25	1100	12	12729	167	22753	9610	163

GREENFIELD—Franklin County

⊞ **FRANKLIN MEDICAL CENTER**, 164 High Street, Zip 01301–2613; tel. 413/773–0211 **A**1 2 9 10 **F**2 9 10 11 12 21 22 23 26 27 28 33 37 39 40 44 47 48 52 53 55 57 58 59 60 61 62 63 64 65 66 69 71 72 76 77 78 81 82 84 87 88 93 94 96 108 109 110 **S** Baystate Health System, Inc., Springfield, MA Primary Contact: Michael D. Skinner, President COO: Karen O. Moore, R.N., MS, Vice President CFO: Greg Brink, Director Finance CMO: Jeffrey Blomstedt, M.D., Director Medical Affairs CHR: John Brady, Director Human Resources Web address: www.baystatehealth.com	23	10	95	4701	57	159992	426	66589	29662	499

HAVERHILL—Essex County

BALDPATE HOSPITAL, 83 Baldpate Road, Zip 01833–2399; tel. 978/352–2131, (Nonreporting) **A**10 Primary Contact: Lucille M. Batal, Administrator	33	22	59	—						
□ **MERRIMACK VALLEY HOSPITAL**, 140 Lincoln Avenue, Zip 01830–6798; tel. 978/374–2000, (Total facility includes 16 beds in nursing home–type unit) **A**1 10 **F**2 12 14 21 22 23 27 28 29 33 35 37 39 40 46 47 48 52 53 55 58 60 63 65 66 69 71 76 81 82 84 87 88 92 93 94 96 108 **P**5 **S** Essent Healthcare, Nashville, TN Web address: www.merrimackvalleyhospital.com	33	10	109	4748	70	73663	0	47923	22718	336
⊞ △ **WHITTIER REHABILITATION HOSPITAL**, 76 Summer Street, Zip 01830–5896; tel. 978/372–8000 **A**1 7 10 **F**21 27 28 44 51 57 58 62 68 69 94 95 108 **P**5 Primary Contact: Alfred J. Arcidi, M.D., Senior Vice President Web address: www.whittierhealth.com	31	46	60	1262	45	12363	0	—	—	

HOLYOKE—Hampden County

⊞ **HOLYOKE MEDICAL CENTER**, 575 Beech Street, Zip 01040–2296; tel. 413/534–2500, (Total facility includes 21 beds in nursing home–type unit) **A**1 2 5 9 10 **F**2 4 7 9 11 12 14 21 23 26 27 28 29 31 33 35 39 40 45 46 47 48 49 52 53 55 57 58 59 60 61 62 63 64 65 66 69 71 73 74 75 77 78 79 81 82 84 85 87 88 92 93 94 96 106 108 109 110 **P**8 Primary Contact: Hank J. Porten, President and Chief Executive Officer CFO: Antonio Correia, Chief Financial Officer CMO: Karen Ferroni, M.D., Medical Director CIO: Thomas Drapeau, Information Systems Manager Web address: www.holyokehealth.com	23	10	202	7313	112	228502	597	87809	40811	842

Many Facility Codes have changed. Please refer to the AHA Guide Code Chart. © 2005 AHA Guide

Hospital, Address, Telephone, Approval, Facility, and Physician Codes, Health Care System	Classi-fication Codes		Utilization Data					Expense (thousands) of dollars		
★ American Hospital Association (AHA) membership □ Joint Commission on Accreditation of Healthcare Organizations (JCAHO) accreditation ○ American Osteopathic Association (AOA) accreditation △ Commission on Accreditation of Rehabilitation Facilities (CARF) accreditation	Control	Service	Staffed Beds	Admissions	Census	Outpatient Visits	Births	Total	Payroll	Personnel

SOLDIERS' HOME IN HOLYOKE, 110 Cherry Street, Zip 01040–7002; tel. 413/532–9475, (Total facility includes 287 beds in nursing home–type unit) **A**1 10 **F**22 26 32 36 37 46 52 63 92 94 96 108 **P**5
Primary Contact: Paul A. Morin, Superintendent
COO: Stephen Morneau, Director Operations
CFO: Scott Zacharie, Director Finance
CMO: John McHugh, M.D., Medical Director
CIO: Robert Morissette, Management Information Systems Coordinator
Web address: www.mass.gov/hly

| | 12 | 80 | 287 | 170 | 249 | 10024 | 0 | 26310 | 12256 | 314 |

HYANNIS—Barnstable County

CAPE COD HOSPITAL, 27 Park Street, Zip 02601–5203; tel. 508/771–1800 **A**1 2 9 10 20 **F**1 2 4 9 11 12 14 15 17 19 21 22 23 26 27 28 29 30 33 34 35 37 39 40 46 47 48 49 50 52 53 55 57 58 59 60 61 62 63 64 65 66 69 70 71 72 73 75 76 77 78 79 80 81 82 84 85 88 90 94 95 96 106 108 **P**5 6 **S** Cape Cod Healthcare, Inc., Hyannis, MA
Primary Contact: Margaret Hanson, Chief Administrative Officer
COO: Patricia Nadle, R.N., Chief Operating Officer and Chief Nursing Officer
CFO: Stephen J. Guimond, Senior Vice President and Chief Financial Officer
CMO: Herbert Mathewson, M.D., Chief Medical Officer
CIO: John E. Kilroy, Vice President and Chief Information Officer
Web address: www.capecodhealth.org

| | 23 | 10 | 223 | 16389 | 189 | 404217 | 979 | 293416 | 104770 | 1651 |

JAMAICA PLAIN—Suffolk County

LEMUEL SHATTUCK HOSPITAL, 170 Morton Street, Jamaica Plain, Zip 02130–3787; tel. 617/522–8110 **A**1 3 5 10 **F**2 4 5 12 21 22 23 26 27 28 29 32 35 36 37 38 39 42 44 45 46 47 48 49 50 52 53 55 57 58 60 61 62 63 65 66 68 69 70 71 73 74 75 76 77 78 81 82 84 94 96 97 106 108 110 **P**6 **S** Massschusetts Department of Public Health, Boston, MA
Primary Contact: Paul Romary, Chief Executive Officer
CFO: Mike Donovan, Chief Financial Officer
CMO: Joseph Cohen, M.D., Director Medical Services
CIO: Kathleen Noonan, Vice President Information
CHR: Greg Guba, Director Human Resources
Web address: www.shattuckhospital.org

| | 12 | 10 | 255 | 1657 | 247 | 42578 | 0 | 66934 | 36083 | 669 |

LAWRENCE—Essex County

LAWRENCE GENERAL HOSPITAL, 1 General Street, Zip 01842–0389, Mailing Address: P.O. Box 189, Zip 01842–0389; tel. 978/683–4000 **A**1 2 3 5 9 10 **F**9 11 12 14 15 22 23 27 28 29 33 34 37 40 46 47 48 49 50 52 53 55 56 58 59 60 61 63 64 65 66 81 82 84 85 86 87 88 94 106 107 108 109 110 **P**2 5
Primary Contact: Joseph S. McManus, President and Chief Executive Officer
Web address: www.lawrencegeneral.org

| | 23 | 10 | 175 | 9809 | 121 | 192691 | 1753 | 119217 | 61865 | 1029 |

LEEDS—Hampshire County

VETERANS AFFAIRS MEDICAL CENTER, 421 North Main Street, Zip 01053–9764; tel. 413/584–4040, (Total facility includes 65 beds in nursing home–type unit) **A**1 **F**2 4 9 12 21 22 26 28 31 32 37 38 39 42 44 45 48 50 52 57 58 62 66 69 70 71 73 74 75 76 77 78 81 88 92 94 96 106 108 109 110 **P**6 **S** Department of Veterans Affairs, Washington, DC
Primary Contact: Bruce A. Gordon, Director
COO: Alan Tyler, Associate Director
CFO: Marcia Balonis, Comptroller
CMO: William E. Bouttelle, M.D., Chief of Staff and Service Line Manager Mental Health
CIO: James Como, Chief Information Officer
Web address: www.va.gov/sta/guide/home.asp

| | 45 | 22 | 181 | 1164 | 115 | 150686 | 0 | 68710 | 38690 | 585 |

LEOMINSTER—Worcester County

HEALTH ALLIANCE HOSPITALS, 60 Hospital Road, Zip 01453–8004; tel. 978/466–2000 **A**1 5 9 10 **F**2 9 11 12 21 22 23 27 28 29 33 52 53 55 58 59 60 61 62 63 64 68 69 71 75 77 78 81 82 85 87 88 95 96 107 108 **P**8 **S** UMass Memorial Health Care, Inc., Worcester, MA
Primary Contact: Patrick L. Muldoon, President and Chief Executive Officer
CFO: Michael Cofone, Chief Financial Officer
CIO: Richard Monhk, Chief Information Officer
Web address: www.healthalliance.com

| | 23 | 10 | 103 | 7527 | 89 | 211857 | 1129 | 99909 | 47162 | 964 |

LOWELL—Middlesex County

LOWELL GENERAL HOSPITAL, 295 Varnum Avenue, Zip 01854–2195; tel. 978/937–6000, (Total facility includes 21 beds in nursing home–type unit) **A**1 2 9 10 **F**2 9 11 12 15 17 21 22 23 24 26 27 28 29 30 31 33 35 36 37 38 39 42 44 46 47 48 50 51 52 53 55 57 58 59 60 61 62 63 64 65 66 69 70 80 81 82 87 88 92 93 94 95 96 98 106 107 108 109 **P**8
Primary Contact: Normand E. Deschene, President and Chief Executive Officer
COO: Jody White, Executive Vice President and Chief Operating Officer
CFO: Richard Jeffcote, Chief Financial Officer
Web address: www.lowellgeneral.org

| | 23 | 10 | 189 | 10819 | 114 | 201159 | 1894 | 118289 | 52209 | 1064 |

△ **SAINTS MEMORIAL MEDICAL CENTER**, One Hospital Drive, Zip 01852–1389; tel. 978/458–1411 **A**1 2 5 7 9 10 **F**2 10 11 12 15 17 21 22 23 27 28 29 33 37 38 39 46 47 48 49 50 52 53 54 55 57 58 60 61 62 63 64 65 66 69 70 72 80 81 82 84 85 86 87 88 90 93 94 96 98 106 108 109 110 **P**5
Primary Contact: Thomas Clark, President and Chief Executive Officer
Web address: www.saints–memorial.org

| | 23 | 10 | 174 | 6945 | 84 | 307245 | 692 | 105109 | 48398 | 1043 |

MA

Hospital, Address, Telephone, Approval, Facility, and Physician Codes, Health Care System	Classi-fication Codes		Utilization Data					Expense (thousands) of dollars		
	Control	Service	Staffed Beds	Admissions	Census	Outpatient Visits	Births	Total	Payroll	Personnel

★ American Hospital Association (AHA) membership
☐ Joint Commission on Accreditation of Healthcare Organizations (JCAHO) accreditation
○ American Osteopathic Association (AOA) accreditation
△ Commission on Accreditation of Rehabilitation Facilities (CARF) accreditation

LUDLOW—Hampden County

⊠ **HEALTHSOUTH REHABILITATION HOSPITAL OF WESTERN MASSACHUSETTS**, 14 Chestnut Place, Zip 01056–3460; tel. 413/589–7581, (Nonreporting) **A**1 10 **S** HEALTHSOUTH Corporation, Birmingham, AL
Primary Contact: R. David Richer, Administrator
CFO: Victoria Healy, Controller
CMO: Adnan Dahdul, M.D., Medical Director
CHR: Mary Mazza, Director Human Resources
Web address: www.healthsouth.com
`33 46 40 — — — — — — —`

MALDEN—Middlesex County
HALLMARK HEALTH SYSTEM See Melrose

MARLBOROUGH—Middlesex County

⊠ **UMASS MEMORIAL–MARLBOROUGH HOSPITAL**, 157 Union Street, Zip 01752–1297; tel. 508/481–5000 **A**1 5 9 10 **F**4 9 12 21 22 23 26 27 28 29 30 33 35 37 39 42 46 47 48 49 52 53 55 60 61 63 65 66 69 70 71 73 74 75 77 78 81 82 84 85 87 88 93 94 95 96 98 106 107 108 109 **P**6
S UMass Memorial Health Care, Inc., Worcester, MA
Primary Contact: John Polanowicz, President and Chief Executive Officer
COO: Candra Szymanski, Vice President for Patient Care and Hospital Operations and Chief Nursing Officer
CFO: Robert Crosby, Chief Financial Officer
CIO: Diane Ridley, Senior Systems Analyst
CHR: Thomas Cady, Vice President Human Resources
Web address: www.marlboroughhospital.org
`23 10 67 3482 46 76415 0 44659 19813 400`

MEDFORD—Middlesex County
LAWRENCE MEMORIAL HOSPITAL OF MEDFORD See Hallmark Health System, Melrose

MELROSE—Middlesex County

⊠ **HALLMARK HEALTH SYSTEM**, 585 Lebanon Street, Zip 02176; tel. 781/979–3000, (Includes LAWRENCE MEMORIAL HOSPITAL OF MEDFORD, 170 Governors Avenue, Medford, Zip 02155–1643; tel. 781/306–6000; MELROSE–WAKEFIELD HOSPITAL, 585 Lebanon Street) **A**1 2 9 10 **F**2 4 9 10 11 12 15 17 21 22 23 24 26 27 28 29 33 36 37 38 39 40 42 44 45 46 47 48 50 52 55 57 58 59 60 61 62 63 64 65 66 69 70 71 73 75 76 77 78 81 82 87 88 92 94 95 96 106 107 108 109 **P**4 5 7
Primary Contact: Michael V. Sack, President and Chief Executive Officer
COO: Christine Candio, Executive Vice President
CFO: James A. Nania, Executive Vice President and Chief Financial Officer
CMO: Mike H. Summerer, M.D., Chief Medical Officer
CIO: Julie Corwin, Director Public Affairs and Marketing
CHR: Richard Kenny, Vice President Human Resources
Web address: www.hallmarkhealth.org
`23 10 349 16208 236 586426 1547 210749 101237 2152`

METHUEN—Essex County

⊠ **CARITAS HOLY FAMILY HOSPITAL AND MEDICAL CENTER**, 70 East Street, Zip 01844–4597; tel. 978/687–0151, (Total facility includes 15 beds in nursing home–type unit) **A**1 2 5 9 10 **F**2 4 9 11 12 14 15 21 22 23 26 27 29 31 32 33 34 35 37 39 40 44 46 47 48 49 50 52 53 55 57 58 59 60 61 62 63 64 65 66 69 70 71 73 74 75 76 80 81 82 85 87 88 90 92 93 94 95 96 98 106 107 108 109 110 **P**5 6 7 **S** Caritas Christi Health Care, Boston, MA
Primary Contact: Peter J. Holden, President and Chief Executive Officer
COO: Martha M. McDrury, R.N., Senior Vice President and Chief Operating Officer
CFO: Allen A. Krause, Chief Financial Officer
CMO: Dorairaju Thavaseelan, M.D., Vice President Medical Affairs
CIO: Dan O'Neil, Director Management Information Systems
CHR: Sabrina M. Granville, Vice President Human Resources
Web address: www.holyfamilyhosp.org
`21 10 256 11747 164 193732 1315 125169 58111 1229`

MILFORD—Worcester County

⊠ **MILFORD REGIONAL MEDICAL CENTER**, (Formerly Milford–Whitinsville Regional Hospital), 14 Prospect Street, Zip 01757–3090; tel. 508/473–1190, (Includes WHITINSVILLE MEDICAL CENTER, 18 Granite Street, Whitinsville, Zip 01588; tel. 508/234–6311) **A**1 2 5 9 10 **F**2 9 11 12 21 23 24 26 27 28 29 33 37 39 40 46 47 48 51 52 53 55 57 58 59 60 61 62 63 65 66 69 81 82 85 87 88 89 94 96 98 106 108 109 110 **P**5 6
Primary Contact: Francis M. Saba, President and Chief Executive Officer
CFO: Edward Kelly, Vice President Finance
CMO: William Muller, M.D., Vice President Medical Affairs
CIO: Larry Fraize, Director Management Information Systems
CHR: Linda Greasom, Vice President Human Resources
Web address: www.milfordregional.org
`23 10 116 7767 85 356975 891 104819 50986 1142`

MILTON—Norfolk County

☐ **MILTON HOSPITAL**, 92 Highland Street, Zip 02186–3807; tel. 617/696–4600, (Total facility includes 20 beds in nursing home–type unit) **A**1 5 9 10 **F**9 12 21 22 23 26 27 28 33 37 46 48 52 53 55 57 60 61 62 63 64 65 66 69 81 82 84 88 92 94 95 96 97 106 108 **P**6
Primary Contact: Joseph V. Morrissey, President
Web address: www.miltonhospital.org
`23 10 92 4200 70 93010 0 50028 23481 472`

Hospital, Address, Telephone, Approval, Facility, and Physician Codes, Health Care System	Classi-fication Codes		Utilization Data					Expense (thousands) of dollars		
★ American Hospital Association (AHA) membership □ Joint Commission on Accreditation of Healthcare Organizations (JCAHO) accreditation ○ American Osteopathic Association (AOA) accreditation △ Commission on Accreditation of Rehabilitation Facilities (CARF) accreditation	Control	Service	Staffed Beds	Admissions	Census	Outpatient Visits	Births	Total	Payroll	Personnel

NANTUCKET—Nantucket County

✠ **NANTUCKET COTTAGE HOSPITAL**, 57 Prospect Street, Zip 02554–2799; tel. 508/825–8100 **A**1 9 10 18 20 **F**9 11 12 23 26 27 28 29 33 36 37 46 48 49 51 52 53 54 55 58 59 60 63 69 73 75 81 84 88 94 96 **P**5
Primary Contact: Lucille C. Giddings, R.N., CHE, President and Chief Executive Officer
CFO: John R. Fitzgerald, Interim Chief Financial Officer
CMO: Timothy J. Lepore, FACS, M.D., Medical Director
CIO: Terry Hughes, Management Information Systems Coordinator
Web address: www.nantuckethospital.org

	23	10	15	752	6	48723	96	20265	7380	171

NATICK—Middlesex County

LEONARD MORSE HOSPITAL See MetroWest Medical Center, Framingham

NEEDHAM—Norfolk County

BETH ISRAEL DEACONESS HOSPITAL–NEEDHAM CAMPUS See Beth Israel Deaconess Medical Center, Boston

NEW BEDFORD—Bristol County

□ **NEW BEDFORD REHABILITATION HOSPITAL**, 4499 Acushnet Avenue, Zip 02745; tel. 508/995–6900, (Nonreporting) **A**1 **S** VIBRA Healthcare, Mechanicsburg, PA
Primary Contact: Edward B. Leary, Chief Executive Officer
ST. LUKE'S HOSPITAL OF NEW BEDFORD See Southcoast Hospitals Group, Fall River

	33	46	90	—	—	—	—	—	—	—

NEWBURYPORT—Essex County

✠ **ANNA JAQUES HOSPITAL**, 25 Highland Avenue, Zip 01950–3894; tel. 978/463–1000 **A**1 9 10 **F**2 11 12 21 23 24 27 28 29 31 33 34 46 47 48 52 53 55 57 59 60 61 62 63 64 65 66 69 70 71 75 78 81 82 87 88 92 93 94 95 96 108 110 **P**5 8
Primary Contact: Susan Green, Interim President and Chief Executive Officer
CFO: Susan Green, Vice President Finance
CMO: Leslie Sebbas, M.D., Medical Director
CIO: Robert Buchanan, M.D., Chief Information Officer
CHR: Stephen Salvo, Vice President Human Resources
Web address: www.ajh.org

	23	10	147	7164	100	197699	773	72718	33900	577

NEWTON LOWER FALLS—Middlesex County

✠ **NEWTON–WELLESLEY HOSPITAL**, 2014 Washington Street, Zip 02462–1699; tel. 617/243–6000 **A**1 2 3 5 9 10 **F**2 9 10 11 12 21 22 23 24 25 26 27 28 29 30 31 33 34 35 37 39 41 42 44 45 46 47 48 49 52 53 55 57 58 59 60 61 62 63 64 66 69 71 73 74 75 81 85 87 88 89 90 92 93 94 95 96 106 107 108 109 110 **P**1 **S** Partners HealthCare System, Inc., Boston, MA
Primary Contact: Michael Jellinek, M.D., President
COO: Patrick Jordan, Senior Vice President for Administration
CFO: Daniel Gross, Senior Vice President Finance and Chief Financial Officer
CIO: Monica Anderson, Director Information Systems
Web address: www.nwh.org

	23	10	226	13346	91	428721	2939	206799	105418	1730

NORTH ADAMS—Berkshire County

✠ **NORTH ADAMS REGIONAL HOSPITAL**, 71 Hospital Avenue, Zip 01247–2584; tel. 413/663–3701 **A**1 2 9 10 **F**11 12 21 27 28 33 52 55 58 59 63 65 69 71 75 76 77 78 81 82 85 88 92 108 **P**6
Primary Contact: Bruce Nash, M.D., President
CFO: John DeKoff, Interim Vice President Fiscal Services
CMO: Stephen St Clair, M.D., President
CIO: Dave Delano, Director Information Technology
CHR: Jeff Stevens, Vice President Human Resources
Web address: www.nbhealth.org

	23	10	56	3184	42	137907	293	46922	20525	403

NORTHAMPTON—Hampshire County

✠ **COOLEY DICKINSON HOSPITAL**, 30 Locust Street, Zip 01060–2093, Mailing Address: P.O. Box 5001, Zip 01061–5001; tel. 413/582–2000 **A**1 2 9 10 **F**2 4 9 11 12 21 22 23 26 27 28 29 30 31 32 33 34 37 39 42 44 46 47 48 50 52 55 58 59 61 62 63 65 66 69 71 72 73 74 75 76 77 78 79 81 82 84 85 87 88 93 94 95 96 98 106 108 109 110 **P**8
Primary Contact: Craig N. Melin, President and Chief Executive Officer
CFO: Edith S. Peter, Chief Financial Officer and Vice President Finance
CMO: Glenn Focht, M.D., Vice President Medical Affairs
CIO: Elise Ames, Director Information Services
CHR: Cheryl Villani, Vice President Human Resources
Web address: www.cooley-dickinson.org

	23	10	125	7676	93	161273	898	105253	54210	1053

NORWOOD—Norfolk County

✠ **CARITAS NORWOOD HOSPITAL**, 800 Washington Street, Zip 02062–3487; tel. 781/769–4000, (Total facility includes 24 beds in nursing home–type unit) **A**1 2 5 9 10 **F**3 4 9 11 12 14 21 26 27 28 29 33 37 40 45 58 59 61 63 69 71 76 77 78 81 82 84 87 92 94 107 108 **S** Caritas Christi Health Care, Boston, MA
Primary Contact: Richard Cunningham, President
CFO: Robert Guyon, Chief Financial Officer and Vice President of Finance
Web address: www.caritasnorwood.org

	21	10	200	13472	200	119925	587	—	—	—

MA

Hospital, Address, Telephone, Approval, Facility, and Physician Codes, Health Care System	Classi-fication Codes		Utilization Data					Expense (thousands) of dollars		
★ American Hospital Association (AHA) membership □ Joint Commission on Accreditation of Healthcare Organizations (JCAHO) accreditation ○ American Osteopathic Association (AOA) accreditation △ Commission on Accreditation of Rehabilitation Facilities (CARF) accreditation	Control	Service	Staffed Beds	Admissions	Census	Outpatient Visits	Births	Total	Payroll	Personnel

OAK BLUFFS—Dukes County

⊞ MARTHA'S VINEYARD HOSPITAL, One Hospital Road, Zip 02557, Mailing Address: P.O. Box 1477, Zip 02557–1477; tel. 508/693–0410 **A**1 9 10 18 **F**2 4 8 11 12 21 29 31 32 33 44 48 50 52 54 55 57 58 59 60 61 62 63 69 70 72 75 76 81 88 91 94 96 97 107 108 109
Primary Contact: Timothy J. Walsh, Chief Executive Officer
CFO: Ron Bryant, Chief Financial Officer
CMO: Michael Goldfein, M.D., Chief Medical Staff
Web address: www.marthasvineyardhospital.org

| 23 | 10 | 25 | 1055 | 13 | 33586 | 0 | — | — | — |

PALMER—Hampden County

⊞ WING MEMORIAL HOSPITAL AND MEDICAL CENTERS, 40 Wright Street, Zip 01069–1138; tel. 413/283–7651 **A**1 5 9 10 **F**2 4 9 12 21 22 23 25 26 28 29 30 33 36 37 39 42 44 46 47 48 50 51 52 55 57 58 60 61 62 63 64 69 70 71 72 73 74 75 76 77 78 81 82 85 87 88 93 94 95 96 108 109 110 **P**6 **S** UMass Memorial Health Care, Inc., Worcester, MA
Primary Contact: Charles E. Cavagnaro, M.D., President and Chief Executive Officer
CFO: George C. Leonard, Vice President and Treasurer
CMO: David L. Maguire, M.D., Vice President Medical Affairs
CIO: Kathleen Williams–Scruton, Director of Information Systems
CHR: Gail Terranova, Director Human Resources
Web address: www.winghealth.org

| 23 | 10 | 39 | 2778 | 33 | 222440 | 0 | 48566 | 25257 | 457 |

PEABODY—Essex County

□ KINDRED HOSPITAL BOSTON NORTH SHORE, 15 King Street, Zip 01960–4268; tel. 978/531–2900 **A**1 10 **F**37 39 49 55 58 76 88 94 108 **S** Kindred Healthcare, Louisville, KY
Primary Contact: Andrew Escamilla, Chief Executive Officer
Web address: www.kindredbns.com

| 33 | 10 | 50 | 487 | 42 | 0 | 0 | — | — | — |

PEMBROKE—Plymouth County

PEMBROKE HOSPITAL, 199 Oak Street, Zip 02359–1953; tel. 781/826–8161, (Nonreporting) **S** Universal Health Services, Inc., King of Prussia, PA
Primary Contact: Paul Zani, Chief Executive Officer

| 32 | 22 | 80 | | | | | | | |

PITTSFIELD—Berkshire County

⊞ BERKSHIRE MEDICAL CENTER, 725 North Street, Zip 01201–4124; tel. 413/447–2000, (Includes HILLCREST HOSPITAL, 165 Tor Court, Zip 01201–3099, Mailing Address: Box 1155, Zip 01202–1155; tel. 413/443–4761) **A**1 2 3 5 8 9 10 12 13 **F**3 4 9 11 12 14 15 21 22 23 24 26 27 28 29 31 32 33 34 35 39 40 41 42 44 46 47 48 49 50 51 52 53 55 57 58 59 60 61 62 63 65 66 68 69 71 72 73 74 75 76 77 78 79 81 82 84 85 88 90 93 94 95 96 98 106 107 108 109 110 **P**6 **S** Berkshire Health Systems, Inc., Pittsfield, MA
Primary Contact: Helen Downey, Chief Operating Officer
COO: Helen Downey, Chief Operating Officer
CFO: Michael E. Cullen, Vice President Fiscal Services
CMO: Robert Cella, M.D., Vice President Medical Affairs
CHR: Arthur Milano, Vice President Human Resources
Web address: www.berkshirehealthsystems.com

| 23 | 10 | 280 | 12127 | 188 | 179539 | 799 | 199148 | 95540 | 1840 |

PLYMOUTH—Plymouth County

⊞ JORDAN HOSPITAL, 275 Sandwich Street, Zip 02360–2196; tel. 508/746–2001 **A**1 2 9 10 **F**2 11 12 14 21 22 23 26 27 28 29 30 33 37 40 45 46 47 48 50 52 53 55 57 58 59 60 61 62 63 64 65 66 69 73 75 79 80 81 82 84 85 87 88 94 95 96 98 106 107 108 109 110 **P**6
Primary Contact: Alan D. Knight, President and Chief Executive Officer
CIO: Sheryl Crowley, Chief Information Officer
CHR: Russell Averna, Vice President Clinical and Support Services
Web address: www.jordanhospital.org

| 23 | 10 | 139 | 8492 | 100 | 345874 | 611 | 118402 | 52561 | 804 |

QUINCY—Norfolk County

⊞ QUINCY MEDICAL CENTER, 114 Whitwell Street, Zip 02169–1899; tel. 617/773–6100, (Total facility includes 38 beds in nursing home–type unit) **A**1 2 5 9 10 **F**2 9 12 21 22 23 26 27 28 29 33 44 48 50 52 53 55 57 58 60 61 62 63 64 65 66 69 71 73 74 76 77 78 81 82 85 88 92 94 96 107 108 110
Primary Contact: Gary Gibbons, M.D., Interim President and Chief Executive Officer
CFO: Mark Gronberg, Chief Financial Officer
CMO: Tom Barber, M.D., Chief Medical Officer
CIO: Robert Borr, Chief Information Officer
CHR: David Ryan, Vice President Human Resources
Web address: www.quincymc.org

| 23 | 10 | 163 | 8001 | 138 | 79149 | 0 | 92748 | 43314 | 684 |

Hospital, Address, Telephone, Approval, Facility, and Physician Codes, Health Care System	Classi-fication Codes		Utilization Data					Expense (thousands) of dollars		
★ American Hospital Association (AHA) membership □ Joint Commission on Accreditation of Healthcare Organizations (JCAHO) accreditation ○ American Osteopathic Association (AOA) accreditation △ Commission on Accreditation of Rehabilitation Facilities (CARF) accreditation	Control	Service	Staffed Beds	Admissions	Census	Outpatient Visits	Births	Total	Payroll	Personnel

SALEM—Essex County

✠ **NORTH SHORE MEDICAL CENTER**, 81 Highland Avenue, Zip 01970–2768; tel. 978/741–1200, (Includes NORTH SHORE CHILDREN'S HOSPITAL, 57 Highland Avenue, Zip 01970–6508; tel. 978/745–2100; SALEM HOSPITAL, 81 Highland Avenue, Zip 01970; tel. 978/741–1200; UNION HOSPITAL, 500 Lynnfield Street, Lynn, Zip 01904–1487; tel. 781/581–9200) **A**1 2 3 5 9 10 **F**4 10 11 12 14 15 17 19 21 22 23 24 26 27 28 29 30 31 33 34 36 37 39 40 45 46 47 48 50 52 53 55 57 58 59 60 61 62 63 64 65 66 69 71 72 73 74 75 76 77 78 79 80 81 82 84 85 86 87 88 89 90 93 94 95 96 108 109 110 **P**6 8 **S** Partners HealthCare System, Inc., Boston, MA Primary Contact: Robert G. Norton, President and Chief Executive Officer COO: Louis J. Woolf, Senior Vice President and Chief Executive Officer CFO: Roger D. Wiseman, Senior Vice President and Chief Financial Officer CMO: Mitchell S. Rein, M.D., Chief Medical Officer CIO: Mark Hulse, Vice President Information Services CHR: Arthur Bowes, Senior Vice President Human Resources Web address: www.nsmc.partners.org	23	10	417	21063	278	216906	1834	318315	154894	—
✠ △ **SHAUGHNESSY–KAPLAN REHABILITATION HOSPITAL**, Dove Avenue, Zip 01970–2999; tel. 978/745–9000, (Total facility includes 40 beds in nursing home–type unit) **A**1 7 10 **F**21 22 28 36 37 38 44 46 48 49 53 57 60 62 64 66 69 92 94 95 96 108 109 110 **P**6 **S** Partners HealthCare System, Inc., Boston, MA Primary Contact: Anthony Sciola, President CFO: Shawn Smith, Fiscal Director CMO: Maurice Greenbaum, M.D., Medical Director CIO: Christoper Maccarini, Manager Information Services CHR: Hugh Burke, Director Human Resources Web address: www.shaughnessy–kaplan.org	23	80	160	2382	127	52138	0	35480	17577	325

SOMERVILLE—Middlesex County

SOMERVILLE HOSPITAL See Cambridge Health Alliance, Cambridge

SOUTH WEYMOUTH—Norfolk County

✠ **SOUTH SHORE HOSPITAL**, 55 Fogg Road, Zip 02190–2455; tel. 781/340–8000 **A**1 2 9 10 **F**6 9 11 12 14 15 17 21 22 23 24 26 27 28 29 33 36 37 38 39 40 42 45 46 47 48 49 51 52 53 55 56 57 58 59 61 62 63 64 65 66 69 81 82 84 85 86 87 88 93 94 95 96 98 106 107 108 109 110 **P**8 Primary Contact: Richard Aubut, President and Chief Executive Officer COO: Joseph Cahill, Executive Vice President and Chief Operating Officer CIO: Del Dixon, Chief Information Officer CHR: Robert Wheeler, Vice President Human Resources Web address: www.sshosp.org	23	10	303	19596	201	501932	4230	258620	123627	2447

SOUTHBRIDGE—Worcester County

✠ **HARRINGTON MEMORIAL HOSPITAL**, 100 South Street, Zip 01550–4045; tel. 508/765–9771 **A**1 5 9 10 **F**2 4 9 11 12 14 19 23 26 27 28 29 31 33 34 36 37 43 44 46 47 48 51 52 53 55 57 58 59 60 61 62 63 64 65 66 69 70 71 72 73 74 75 76 77 78 81 84 88 93 94 96 108 **P**1 Primary Contact: Richard M. Mangion, President and Chief Executive Officer CFO: Jean Lefebvre, Vice President Fiscal Services CMO: C Scott Koenig, M.D., Director Medical Staff CIO: Mark Forsman, Director Management Information Systems CHR: Charlene Richard, Director Human Resources Web address: www.harringtonhospital.org	23	10	113	2947	40	183297	440	52169	29279	484

SPRINGFIELD—Hampden County

✠ **BAYSTATE MEDICAL CENTER**, 759 Chestnut Street, Zip 01199–0001; tel. 413/794–0000 **A**1 2 3 5 8 9 10 12 **F**2 4 9 10 11 12 14 15 17 19 21 22 23 24 25 26 27 28 29 30 31 33 34 37 39 41 42 43 44 45 46 47 48 50 52 53 55 56 57 58 59 60 61 62 63 64 65 66 67 69 70 71 72 73 74 76 77 78 79 81 82 84 85 88 89 90 93 94 95 96 99 101 104 107 108 109 110 **P**5 6 8 **S** Baystate Health System, Inc., Springfield, MA Primary Contact: Mark R. Tolosky, President and Chief Executive Officer COO: Trish Hannon, Senior Vice President and Chief Operating Officer CFO: Keith C McLean Shinaman, Senior Vice President Finance CMO: Loring S. Flint, Jr, M.D., Senior Vice President Medical Affairs CIO: Mark Gorrell, Vice President Information Services CHR: Elizabeth B. Simpson, Senior Vice President Human Resources Web address: www.baystatehealth.com	23	10	594	32516	459	765453	4298	584036	226306	4655
✠ **MERCY MEDICAL CENTER**, 271 Carew Street, Zip 01104–2398, Mailing Address: P.O. Box 9012, Zip 01102–9012; tel. 413/748–9000 **A**1 2 9 10 **F**3 4 9 10 11 12 15 17 21 22 23 29 33 37 39 40 45 46 48 52 53 55 57 59 60 61 63 64 68 69 71 72 75 76 77 78 79 81 82 84 87 88 93 94 96 106 107 108 109 110 **P**6 **S** Catholic Health East, Newtown Square, PA Primary Contact: Vincent J. McCorkle, President and Chief Executive Officer COO: James Fanale, M.D., Chief Operating Officer CFO: Robert DeVey, Senior Vice President and Chief Financial Officer CMO: James Fanale, M.D., Chief Operating Officer CIO: Michael Malerba, Chief Information Officer CHR: Leonard F. Pansa, Vice President Human Resources Web address: www.mercycares.com	23	10	327	15168	256	486505	1391	164232	74145	1176

MA

Hospital, Address, Telephone, Approval, Facility, and Physician Codes, Health Care System	Classi-fication Codes		Utilization Data					Expense (thousands) of dollars		
	Control	Service	Staffed Beds	Admissions	Census	Outpatient Visits	Births	Total	Payroll	Personnel
☐ **PARK VIEW SPECIALTY HOSPITAL**, 1400 State Street, Zip 01109–2589; tel. 413/787–6700, (Total facility includes 172 beds in nursing home–type unit) (Nonreporting) **A**1 10 Primary Contact: Andrew Calkins, Chief Executive Officer	33	49	284	—	—	—	—	—	—	—
☐ **SHRINERS HOSPITALS FOR CHILDREN, SPRINGFIELD**, 516 Carew Street, Zip 01104–2396; tel. 413/787–2000 **A**1 3 5 **F**3 13 14 24 29 55 56 67 68 71 92 **P**6 **S** Shriners Hospitals for Children, Tampa, FL Primary Contact: Mark L. Niederpruem, Administrator Web address: www.shrinerhq.org	23	57	40	852	10	19302	0	—	—	191
STOCKBRIDGE—Berkshire County										
⊠ **AUSTEN RIGGS CENTER**, 25 Main Street, Zip 01262–0962, Mailing Address: P.O. Box 962, Zip 01262–0962; tel. 413/298–5511 **A**1 **F**27 29 71 78 **P**5 Primary Contact: Edward R. Shapiro, M.D., Medical Director and Chief Executive Officer COO: Edward R. Shapiro, M.D., Medical Director and Chief Executive Officer CFO: Chauncey Collins, Director Operations CMO: Edward R. Shapiro, M.D., Medical Director and Chief Executive Officer CHR: Lisa Belair, Director Human Resources Web address: www.austenriggs.org	23	22	58	64	44	7457	0	11941	6309	111
STOUGHTON—Norfolk County										
⊠ △ **NEW ENGLAND SINAI HOSPITAL AND REHABILITATION CENTER**, 150 York Street, Zip 02072–1881; tel. 781/344–0600 **A**1 3 5 7 10 **F**1 5 7 9 21 22 28 29 37 38 39 44 47 48 50 52 57 58 61 62 64 65 68 69 73 94 95 96 108 110 Primary Contact: Lester P. Schindel, President and Chief Executive Officer CFO: Richard E. Johnson, Vice President Fiscal Services CMO: Lawrence S. Hotes, M.D., Physician–in–Chief CIO: Francine Sousa, Director Management Information Service CHR: David Tedesco, Vice President Human Resources Web address: www.newenglandsinai.org	23	46	212	1830	154	40204	0	51363	28701	564
TAUNTON—Bristol County										
⊠ **MORTON HOSPITAL AND MEDICAL CENTER**, 88 Washington Street, Zip 02780–2499; tel. 508/828–7000, (Total facility includes 21 beds in nursing home–type unit) **A**1 2 9 10 **F**2 4 9 11 12 21 22 23 27 28 29 33 34 37 39 46 47 48 50 51 52 53 55 57 58 59 60 61 62 63 64 66 69 71 72 76 77 81 82 84 87 88 92 93 94 95 96 107 108 109 **P**6 8 Primary Contact: Thomas C. Porter, President COO: Maureen A. Bryant, Executive Vice President CFO: Lawrence E. Seck, Senior Vice President Web address: www.mortonhospital.org	23	10	152	6810	96	74137	533	90033	45412	756
☐ **TAUNTON STATE HOSPITAL**, 60 Hodges Avenue Extension, Zip 02780–3034, Mailing Address: P.O. Box 4007, Zip 02780–4007; tel. 508/977–3000 **A**1 10 **F**71 72 73 74 75 76 77 78 **S** Massachusetts Department of Mental Health, Boston, MA Primary Contact: Roberta H. Guez, Administrator and Chief Operating Officer	12	22	187	249	180	0	0	—	—	—
TEWKSBURY—Middlesex County										
☐ **TEWKSBURY HOSPITAL**, 365 East Street, Zip 01876–1998; tel. 978/851–7321 **A**1 10 **F**1 2 21 22 27 28 32 36 37 38 39 44 45 48 50 53 57 58 60 64 65 66 69 70 71 73 76 94 96 106 108 110 **P**6 **S** Massschusetts Department of Public Health, Boston, MA Primary Contact: William J. White, Interim Chief Executive Officer Web address: www.state.ma.us/dph/hosp/th.htm	12	48	540	372	367	0	0	54960	41470	765
WARE—Hampshire County										
⊠ **MARY LANE HOSPITAL**, 85 South Street, Zip 01082–1697; tel. 413/967–6211 **A**1 9 10 **F**1 2 9 11 12 21 22 23 26 27 28 29 31 33 35 36 37 39 44 46 47 48 51 52 53 55 58 59 60 61 62 63 64 65 66 69 70 81 84 88 92 93 94 95 96 98 107 108 109 **S** Baystate Health System, Inc., Springfield, MA Primary Contact: Christine Shirtcliff, Executive Vice President CFO: Curtis Davis, Manager Finance CMO: Richard Gerstein, M.D., Director Medical Staff CHR: Donna Arsenault, Manager Human Resources Web address: www.baystatehealth.com	23	10	31	1363	13	72383	138	22317	10768	204
WAREHAM—Plymouth County										
TOBEY HOSPITAL See Southcoast Hospitals Group, Fall River										
WEBSTER—Worcester County										
⊠ **HUBBARD REGIONAL HOSPITAL**, 340 Thompson Road, Zip 01570–0608; tel. 508/943–2600 **A**1 5 9 10 **F**2 6 8 9 12 21 27 29 33 37 46 48 55 58 63 69 70 73 75 81 82 88 92 94 108 **P**3 Primary Contact: Chris Rich, Administrator and Chief Executive Officer CFO: William R. Falkowski, Chief Financial Officer CHR: Lisa Mason, Human Resources Director Web address: www.hubbardhealth.com	23	10	43	1532	24	263439	0	—	—	265
WELLESLEY—Norfolk County										
SIMPSON INFIRMARY, WELLESLEY COLLEGE, 106 Central Street, Zip 02481–8203; tel. 781/283–2810, (Nonreporting) Primary Contact: Vanessa M. Britto, M.D., MSC, Director Health Service	23	11	11	—	—	—	—	—	—	—

★ American Hospital Association (AHA) membership
☐ Joint Commission on Accreditation of Healthcare Organizations (JCAHO) accreditation
○ American Osteopathic Association (AOA) accreditation
△ Commission on Accreditation of Rehabilitation Facilities (CARF) accreditation

Many Facility Codes have changed. Please refer to the AHA Guide Code Chart.
© 2005 AHA Guide

Hospital, Address, Telephone, Approval, Facility, and Physician Codes, Health Care System	Classi-fication Codes		Utilization Data					Expense (thousands) of dollars		
★ American Hospital Association (AHA) membership □ Joint Commission on Accreditation of Healthcare Organizations (JCAHO) accreditation ○ American Osteopathic Association (AOA) accreditation △ Commission on Accreditation of Rehabilitation Facilities (CARF) accreditation	Control	Service	Staffed Beds	Admissions	Census	Outpatient Visits	Births	Total	Payroll	Personnel

WESTBOROUGH—Worcester County

□ **WESTBOROUGH STATE HOSPITAL**, Lyman Street, Zip 01581–0288, Mailing Address: P.O. Box 288, Zip 01581–0288; tel. 508/616–2100, (Nonreporting) **A**1 3 5 10 **S** Massachusetts Department of Mental Health, Boston, MA
Primary Contact: Theodore E. Kirousis, Area Director

| | 12 | 22 | 220 | — | | — | | — | — | — |

□ △ **WHITTIER REHABILITATION HOSPITAL**, 150 Flanders Road, Zip 01581; tel. 508/871–2000, (Nonreporting) **A**1 7 10
Primary Contact: Alfred J. Arcidi, M.D., Senior Vice President

| | 33 | 46 | 74 | — | | — | | — | — | — |

WESTFIELD—Hampden County

⊞ **NOBLE HOSPITAL**, 115 West Silver Street, Zip 01086–1634; tel. 413/568–2811 **A**1 2 5 9 10 **F**2 12 21 22 23 26 27 28 29 30 33 46 47 48 53 55 58 60 61 62 63 64 65 66 68 69 70 71 73 74 76 78 79 80 81 82 85 87 88 94 95 96 108 109
Primary Contact: George J. Koller, President and Chief Executive Officer
CFO: Robert Blondin, Vice President Finance
CMO: Francis D. Horrigan, M.D., Medical Director
CIO: Cliff Porter, Director Information Services
CHR: Jeff Whorton, Director Human Resources
Web address: www.noblehealth.org

| | 23 | 10 | 97 | 3728 | 61 | 101767 | 0 | 42553 | 20825 | 398 |

□ **WESTERN MASSACHUSETTS HOSPITAL**, 91 East Mountain Road, Zip 01085; tel. 413/562–4131 **A**1 10 **F**5 21 27 28 32 37 38 60 76 108 **S** Massschusetts Department of Public Health, Boston, MA
Primary Contact: Blake M. Molleur, Executive Director
Web address: www.mass.gov/dph/hosp/wmh.htm

| | 12 | 10 | 80 | 136 | 72 | 1950 | 0 | — | — | — |

WESTWOOD—Norfolk County

WESTWOOD LODGE HOSPITAL, 45 Clapboardtree Street, Zip 02090–2930; tel. 781/762–7764, (Nonreporting) **A**10 **S** Universal Health Services, Inc., King of Prussia, PA
Primary Contact: Robert W. Spiegel, Chief Executive Officer
Web address: www.westwoodpembroke.com

| | 23 | 22 | 65 | — | | — | | — | — | — |

WHITINSVILLE—Worcester County

WHITINSVILLE MEDICAL CENTER See Milford Regional Medical Center, Milford

WINCHESTER—Middlesex County

⊞ **WINCHESTER HOSPITAL**, 41 Highland Avenue, Zip 01890–1496; tel. 781/729–9000 **A**1 2 5 9 10 **F**10 11 12 21 22 23 24 25 26 27 28 29 30 31 33 37 39 40 42 44 46 47 48 51 52 53 55 56 57 58 59 60 61 62 63 64 65 66 69 81 82 84 87 88 93 94 96 107 108 109 110 **P**2 5 6 7
Primary Contact: Dale M. Lodge, President and Chief Executive Officer
CFO: Kevin Smith, Vice President Finance and Administrative Services
CMO: Thomas Mulvaney, M.D., Vice President Medical Affairs
Web address: www.winchesterhospital.org

| | 23 | 10 | 177 | 11894 | 125 | 420926 | 2119 | 176030 | 84885 | 1665 |

WOBURN—Middlesex County

⊞ △ **HEALTHSOUTH NEW ENGLAND REHABILITATION HOSPITAL**, Two Rehabilitation Way, Zip 01801–6098; tel. 781/935–5050 **A**1 5 7 10 **F**21 22 23 24 26 28 29 37 38 39 42 44 46 47 48 52 57 58 61 62 65 66 68 69 73 76 94 95 96 106 108 109 110 **S** HEALTHSOUTH Corporation, Birmingham, AL
Primary Contact: Eileen Gibbons, Administrator
CFO: Lester Felege, Controller
Web address: www.healthsouth.com

| | 33 | 46 | 210 | 2971 | 167 | 148622 | 0 | 53496 | 28251 | 597 |

WORCESTER—Worcester County

ADCARE HOSPITAL OF WORCESTER, 107 Lincoln Street, Zip 01605–2499; tel. 508/799–9000, (Nonreporting) **A**10
Primary Contact: David W. Hillis, President and Chief Executive Officer
Web address: www.adcare.com

| | 23 | 82 | 114 | — | — | — | — | — | — | — |

⊞ **FAIRLAWN REHABILITATION HOSPITAL**, 189 May Street, Zip 01602–4399; tel. 508/791–6351 **A**1 5 10 **F**21 22 26 27 28 29 37 44 46 48 52 57 58 60 62 66 68 69 94 95 96 108 **P**8 **S** HEALTHSOUTH Corporation, Birmingham, AL
Primary Contact: Peter M. Mantegazza, Chief Executive Officer
CFO: John Flaherty, Controller
CMO: Peter Bagley, M.D., Medical Director
Web address: www.healthsouth.com

| | 33 | 46 | 110 | 1975 | 94 | — | 0 | — | — | 310 |

⊞ **SAINT VINCENT HOSPITAL AT WORCESTER MEDICAL CENTER**, 20 Worcester Center Boulevard, Zip 01608–1320; tel. 508/363–5000 **A**1 2 3 5 8 9 10 12 **F**11 12 14 21 23 26 27 28 31 33 37 39 42 48 49 52 53 54 55 56 57 58 59 60 61 62 63 65 66 69 70 71 73 74 75 81 82 84 88 93 94 108 109 **P**6
Primary Contact: C. Barry Dykes, Chief Executive Officer
COO: Kevin R. Burchill, Chief Operating Officer
CFO: Stephen Gilmore, Chief Financial Officer
CMO: Harvey Kowaloff, Chief Medical Officer
CIO: Patricia Chassey, Director Information Services
CHR: Martin Oscadal, Vice President Human Resources
Web address: www.stvincenthospital.com

| | 33 | 10 | 366 | 21204 | 236 | 272198 | 1864 | — | — | — |

MA

MA

Hospital, Address, Telephone, Approval, Facility, and Physician Codes, Health Care System	Classi-fication Codes		Utilization Data					Expense (thousands) of dollars		
★ American Hospital Association (AHA) membership □ Joint Commission on Accreditation of Healthcare Organizations (JCAHO) accreditation ○ American Osteopathic Association (AOA) accreditation △ Commission on Accreditation of Rehabilitation Facilities (CARF) accreditation	Control	Service	Staffed Beds	Admissions	Census	Outpatient Visits	Births	Total	Payroll	Personnel
⊠ **UMASS MEMORIAL MEDICAL CENTER**, 119 Belmont Street, Zip 01605–2982; tel. 508/334–1000, (Includes HAHNEMANN CAMPUS, 281 Lincoln Street, Zip 01605; tel. 508/334–1000; MEMORIAL CAMPUS, 119 Belmont Street, Zip 01605; tel. 508/334–1000; UNIVERSITY CAMPUS, 55 Lake Avenue North, Zip 01655–0002; tel. 508/334–1000) **A**1 2 3 5 8 9 10 12 13 **F**2 3 5 6 7 10 11 12 13 14 15 16 17 18 19 20 21 22 23 29 30 33 34 36 37 38 41 42 44 45 46 47 48 49 50 51 52 53 55 56 57 58 59 60 61 62 63 64 65 66 67 68 69 70 71 72 73 74 75 76 77 78 79 80 81 82 84 86 88 89 90 92 93 94 95 96 98 99 101 105 106 107 108 109 110 **P**6 **S** UMass Memorial Health Care, Inc., Worcester, MA Primary Contact: Walter Ettinger, M.D., President CFO: Todd Keating, Chief Financial Officer CMO: Stephen Tosi, M.D., Chief Medical Officer CIO: Pamela Arora, Chief Information Officer CHR: Jeanne Bedar, Interim Vice President Human Resources Web address: www.umassmemorial.org	23	10	726	39707	533	912976	4486	731979	326940	4681
□ **WORCESTER STATE HOSPITAL**, 305 Belmont Street, Zip 01604–1695; tel. 508/368–3300, (Nonreporting) **A**1 3 5 10 **S** Massachusetts Department of Mental Health, Boston, MA Primary Contact: Anthony Riccitelli, Chief Operating Officer	12	22	176	—	—	—	—	—	—	—

Many Facility Codes have changed. Please refer to the AHA Guide Code Chart.

MICHIGAN

Hospital, Address, Telephone, Approval, Facility, and Physician Codes, Health Care System	Classi-fication Codes		Utilization Data					Expense (thousands) of dollars		
★ American Hospital Association (AHA) membership □ Joint Commission on Accreditation of Healthcare Organizations (JCAHO) accreditation ○ American Osteopathic Association (AOA) accreditation △ Commission on Accreditation of Rehabilitation Facilities (CARF) accreditation	Control	Service	Staffed Beds	Admissions	Census	Outpatient Visits	Births	Total	Payroll	Personnel

ADRIAN—Lenawee County

★ **LENAWEE HEALTH ALLIANCE – BIXBY CAMPUS**, 818 Riverside Avenue, Zip 49221–1496; tel. 517/265–0900 **A**1 2 9 10 **F**2 4 8 9 11 12 21 22 23 26 27 28 29 31 33 37 46 47 52 53 55 57 58 59 60 61 62 63 64 66 69 70 77 79 80 81 82 85 87 88 89 92 93 94 95 96 106 107 108 109 110 **P**6 7 8 **S** ProMedica Health System, Toledo, OH
Primary Contact: Randall D. Oostra, FACHE, President
COO: Gregory Corbett, Senior Vice President
CFO: James F. Wheeler, Vice President Finance
CMO: Gregory Fuller, D.O., Vice President Medical Affairs
CIO: Paul Muneio, Vice President Support Services
CHR: Dennis Wright, Vice President Human Resources
Web address: www.promedica.org

| | 23 | 10 | 66 | 3731 | 35 | 150243 | 672 | 52217 | 17149 | 459 |

ALLEGAN—Allegan County

★ **ALLEGAN GENERAL HOSPITAL**, 555 Linn Street, Zip 49010–1594; tel. 269/673–8424 **A**1 9 10 **F**2 6 11 12 14 21 22 23 27 28 30 33 34 51 52 55 56 58 59 60 61 62 63 65 71 75 76 77 81 82 94 106 108 **S** Quorum Health Resources, Plano, TX
Primary Contact: Gerald J. Barbini, President and Chief Executive Officer
CFO: W Allan Gearig, Vice President Finance
CMO: Ann Henelt, D.O., Chief of Staff
CIO: Larry Boekeloo, Chief Information Officer
Web address: www.aghosp.org

| | 23 | 10 | 63 | 1707 | 18 | 74851 | 162 | 30729 | 12729 | 285 |

ALMA—Gratiot County

□ △ **GRATIOT MEDICAL CENTER**, (Formerly Gratiot Community Hospital), 300 East Warwick Drive, Zip 48801–1096; tel. 989/463–1101 **A**1 7 9 10 19 **F**2 9 10 11 12 15 22 23 26 27 28 32 33 36 37 44 46 48 49 50 51 52 53 55 58 59 60 61 62 63 64 65 66 68 69 71 73 74 75 76 78 81 82 84 85 87 88 93 94 96 107 108 **P**6
Primary Contact: Thomas D. DeFauw, President and Chief Executive Officer
Web address: www.gratiothealth.com

| | 23 | 10 | 127 | 6273 | 82 | 221329 | 621 | 82500 | 37146 | 898 |

ALPENA—Alpena County

★ **ALPENA REGIONAL MEDICAL CENTER**, (Formerly Alpena General Hospital), 1501 West Chisholm Street, Zip 49707–1498; tel. 989/356–7390 **A**1 2 9 10 19 20 **F**2 3 4 9 11 12 15 21 23 26 27 28 29 33 34 35 37 39 47 48 51 52 55 58 59 60 61 62 63 64 65 66 68 69 70 71 72 73 74 75 76 77 81 82 84 85 87 88 93 94 95 96 106 108 109 110 **P**6
Primary Contact: John A. McVeety, Chief Executive Officer
CFO: Damone Sorensen, CPA, Chief Financial Officer
CHR: Diane Shields, Chief Human Resources Officer
Web address: www.agh.org

| | 13 | 10 | 130 | 5251 | 64 | 162993 | 412 | 79240 | 35077 | 722 |

ANN ARBOR—Washtenaw County

ST. JOSEPH MERCY HOSPITAL See Saint Joseph Mercy Health System, Ypsilanti

★ **UNIVERSITY OF MICHIGAN HOSPITALS AND HEALTH CENTERS**, 1500 East Medical Center Drive, Zip 48109; tel. 734/936–4000 **A**1 2 3 5 8 9 10 **F**2 4 5 6 7 9 10 11 12 13 14 15 16 17 18 19 20 21 22 23 24 26 27 28 29 30 31 32 33 34 35 37 38 39 40 41 42 43 44 46 47 48 49 50 51 52 53 54 55 56 57 58 59 60 61 62 63 64 65 66 67 68 69 70 71 72 73 74 75 76 77 79 80 81 82 84 85 86 87 88 89 90 93 94 95 96 98 99 100 101 102 103 104 105 106 107 108 109 110
Primary Contact: Larry Warren, Director and Chief Executive Officer
COO: Tony Denton, Chief Operating Officer
CFO: Doug Strong, Chief Financial Officer
CMO: Darrell Campbell, M.D., Chief of Clinical Affairs
CIO: Jocelyn DeWitt, Chief Information Officer
CHR: Deborah Childs, Chief Human Resources Officer
Web address: www.med.umich.edu

| | 23 | 10 | 785 | 42345 | 653 | 1575900 | 3899 | 1116576 | 457822 | 9752 |

★ **VETERANS AFFAIRS ANN ARBOR HEALTHCARE SYSTEM**, 2215 Fuller Road, Zip 48105–2399; tel. 734/769–7100, (Total facility includes 45 beds in nursing home–type unit) **A**1 2 3 5 8 9 **F**2 4 15 17 19 21 22 23 26 27 28 29 32 33 36 37 38 39 42 44 45 46 47 48 49 50 51 53 55 57 58 60 61 62 63 64 65 66 69 70 71 73 74 75 76 77 78 80 81 82 84 85 88 92 94 96 106 107 108 109 110 **S** Department of Veterans Affairs, Washington, DC
Primary Contact: James W. Roseborough, CHE, Director
COO: Paul D. Scheel, Associate Director for Operations
CFO: Karen Ruedel, Chief Resource Officer
CMO: Eric Young, Chief of Staff
CIO: Shannon Rhodes, Chief Information Officer
Web address: www.va.gov/sta/guide/home.asp

| | 45 | 10 | 140 | 4732 | 80 | 252586 | 0 | 136034 | 78560 | 1458 |

AUBURN HILLS—Oakland County

□ **HAVENWYCK HOSPITAL**, 1525 University Drive, Zip 48326–2675; tel. 248/373–9200 **A**1 9 10 **F**71 72 75 78 **P**8 **S** Psychiatric Solutions, Franklin, TN
Primary Contact: Robert A. Kercorian, Chief Executive Officer
Web address: www.havenwyckhospital.com

| | 33 | 22 | 152 | 3854 | 79 | 5417 | 0 | 18035 | 8233 | 230 |

Hospital, Address, Telephone, Approval, Facility, and Physician Codes, Health Care System	Classi-fication Codes		Utilization Data					Expense (thousands) of dollars		
★ American Hospital Association (AHA) membership □ Joint Commission on Accreditation of Healthcare Organizations (JCAHO) accreditation ○ American Osteopathic Association (AOA) accreditation △ Commission on Accreditation of Rehabilitation Facilities (CARF) accreditation	Control	Service	Staffed Beds	Admissions	Census	Outpatient Visits	Births	Total	Payroll	Personnel

BAD AXE—Huron County

★ **HURON MEDICAL CENTER**, 1100 South Van Dyke Road, Zip 48413–9799; tel. 989/269–8933 **A**9 10 **F**9 12 21 26 27 28 29 33 41 45 46 47 48 49 52 55 58 59 60 61 63 65 66 69 81 82 84 88 93 94 96 107 108 110 **P**7
Primary Contact: Kenneth F. Wilhelm, President and Chief Executive Officer
COO: Fred Meyer, Chief Operating Officer
CFO: Chris Fulks, Interim Chief Financial Officer
CMO: William Corsini, M.D., Chief of Staff
CHR: Nancy Bouck, Director Human Resources
Web address: www.huronmedicalcenter.org

| 23 | 10 | 64 | 1794 | 16 | 54885 | 297 | 24378 | 9990 | 240 |

BATTLE CREEK—Calhoun County

⊞ **BATTLE CREEK HEALTH SYSTEM**, tel. 269/966–8000, (Includes COMMUNITY SITE, 183 West Street, Zip 49017; FIELDSTONE CENTER, 165 North Washington Avenue, Zip 49017; MAIN CAMPUS, 300 North Avenue, Zip 49017), (Total facility includes 141 beds in nursing home–type unit) **A**1 2 9 10 **F**8 10 11 12 21 22 23 26 27 28 29 33 34 37 45 49 52 53 55 57 58 59 60 61 62 63 65 66 69 70 71 73 74 75 76 77 79 80 81 82 84 85 86 88 92 93 94 95 96 97 106 107 108 109 110 **P**8 **S** Trinity Health, Novi, MI
Primary Contact: Patrick R. Garrett, President and Chief Executive Officer
COO: Gene K. Miyamoto, Chief Operating Officer
CFO: Kenneth Barth, Vice President Finance
CMO: Jeffrey Mitchell, M.D., Vice President Medical Affairs
CIO: Jim Keller, Information Systems Site Director
CHR: Cathy Edwards, Director Human Resources
Web address: www.bchealth.com

| 21 | 10 | 393 | 11567 | 126 | — | — | — | — | 1121 |

□ **SELECT SPECIALTY HOSPITAL–BATTLE CREEK**, 300 North Avenue, 6th Floor, Zip 49016; tel. 269/565–8900, (Nonreporting) **A**1 10
Primary Contact: Dave Gehringer, Chief Executive Officer

| 33 | 80 | 32 | — | — | — | — | — | — | — |

⊞ **SOUTHWEST REGIONAL REHABILITATION CENTER**, 183 West Street, Zip 49017–3424; tel. 269/965–3206 **A**1 9 10 **F**21 27 28 29 44 45 48 52 68 69 94 96
Primary Contact: Diane D. Giannunzio, President and Chief Executive Officer
COO: Diane D. Giannunzio, President and Chief Executive Officer
CMO: Mehmet Yilmaz, M.D., Medical Director
CHR: Karol A. Jenney, Director Business Operations
Web address: www.sw–rehab.org

| 23 | 46 | 30 | 608 | 13 | 9276 | — | 7353 | 3659 | 100 |

⊞ **VETERANS AFFAIRS MEDICAL CENTER**, 5500 Armstrong Road, Zip 49015; tel. 269/966–5600, (Total facility includes 135 beds in nursing home–type unit) (Nonreporting) **A**1 9 **S** Department of Veterans Affairs, Washington, DC
Primary Contact: Alice L. Wood, Director
COO: Gregory R. Harris, Acting Associate Director
CFO: Mike Rupert, Chief Fiscal Services
CMO: Alan M. Sooho, M.D., Chief of Staff
CIO: Rhys Foulkes, Chief Information Management Service
CHR: Palma Simkins, Chief Human Resources Management Services
Web address: www.va.gov/sta/guide/home.asp

| 45 | 22 | 368 | — | — | — | — | — | — | — |

BAY CITY—Bay County

⊞ △ **BAY REGIONAL MEDICAL CENTER**, 1900 Columbus Avenue, Zip 48708–6880; tel. 989/894–3000, (Includes BAY REGIONAL MEDICAL CENTER–WEST CAMPUS, 3250 East Midland Road, Zip 48706; tel. 517/667–6750) **A**1 2 7 9 10 12 13 **F**2 6 9 10 11 12 14 15 17 19 21 22 23 26 27 28 29 31 33 37 39 40 46 48 52 53 55 57 58 59 61 62 63 64 65 66 68 69 70 81 82 84 86 87 88 93 94 96 108 110 **S** McLaren Health Care Corporation, Flint, MI
Primary Contact: Robert N. Wright, President and Chief Executive Officer
CFO: Brian Kay, Chief Financial Officer
CMO: John Way, M.D., Vice President Corporate Medical Affairs
CIO: Dennis Wilson, Customer Service Representative
CHR: Joseph Lyons, Vice President Human Resources
Web address: www.baymed.org

| 23 | 10 | 313 | 15358 | 195 | 315434 | 977 | 167063 | 68712 | 1501 |

BAY SPECIAL CARE HOSPITAL, Mailing Address: 3250 East Midland Road, Suite 1, Zip 48706–2835; tel. 989/667–6802 **A**10 **F**2 21 22 23 26 27 62 66 110
Primary Contact: Cheryl A. Burzynski, President
Web address: www.baymed.org

| 23 | 80 | 26 | 312 | 23 | 0 | 0 | 6057 | 2840 | 83 |

BERRIEN CENTER—Berrien County

LAKELAND SPECIALTY HOSPITAL, BERRIEN CENTER See Lakeland Hospital–St. Joseph, Saint Joseph

BIG RAPIDS—Mecosta County

⊞ △ **MECOSTA COUNTY MEDICAL CENTER**, (Formerly Mecosta County General Hospital), 605 Oak Street, Zip 49307–2099; tel. 231/796–8691 **A**1 7 9 10 **F**2 9 11 12 14 27 28 33 34 37 48 51 52 54 58 59 60 62 63 64 65 66 68 69 81 82 84 88 93 94 96 106 108 **P**1 **S** Quorum Health Resources, Plano, TX
Primary Contact: Thomas E. Daugherty, Administrator
CFO: Duane Shafer, Chief Financial Officer
Web address: www.mcmcbr.com

| 13 | 10 | 64 | 2671 | 23 | 115735 | 660 | 30450 | 12719 | 332 |

Hospital, Address, Telephone, Approval, Facility, and Physician Codes, Health Care System	Classification Codes		Utilization Data					Expense (thousands) of dollars		
★ American Hospital Association (AHA) membership □ Joint Commission on Accreditation of Healthcare Organizations (JCAHO) accreditation ○ American Osteopathic Association (AOA) accreditation △ Commission on Accreditation of Rehabilitation Facilities (CARF) accreditation	Control	Service	Staffed Beds	Admissions	Census	Outpatient Visits	Births	Total	Payroll	Personnel

BRIGHTON—Livingston County

★ **BRIGHTON HOSPITAL**, 12851 East Grand River Avenue, Zip 48116–8596; tel. 810/227–1211 **A**10 **F**3 4 21 27 29 46 52 58 60 66 92 96 98 106 108 **P**6 **S** Ascension Health, Saint Louis, MO
Primary Contact: Denise Bertin–Epp, Chief Executive Officer
COO: Denise Bertin–Epp, Chief Executive Officer
CFO: Mark Miller, Chief Financial Officer
CMO: Michael Brooks, M.D., Medical Director
Web address: www.brightonhospital.org

| | 33 | 82 | 92 | 3758 | 69 | — | 0 | — | — | — |

CADILLAC—Wexford County

⊞ **MERCY HOSPITAL CADILLAC**, 400 Hobart Street, Zip 49601–9596; tel. 231/876–7200 **A**1 9 10 20 **F**2 3 9 11 12 13 14 21 22 26 27 28 29 32 33 35 37 39 48 52 53 55 56 58 59 60 61 62 63 64 66 67 68 69 70 71 81 82 85 87 88 92 93 94 96 108 109 **P**8 **S** Trinity Health, Novi, MI
Primary Contact: John L. MacLeod, Chief Executive Officer
CFO: Dan Hogan, Vice President Finance
CIO: Randi Oehlers, Management Information Systems Site Director
CHR: Peter Lane, Director Human Resources
Web address: www.munsonhealthcare.org

| | 21 | 10 | 79 | 4115 | 35 | 76984 | 435 | 45436 | 17804 | 464 |

CARO—Tuscola County

□ **CARO CENTER**, 2000 Chambers Road, Zip 48723–9296; tel. 989/673–3191, (Nonreporting) **A**1 9 10
Primary Contact: Rose Laskowski, R.N., Hospital Director

| | 12 | 22 | 193 | — | — | — | — | — | — | — |

★ **CARO COMMUNITY HOSPITAL**, 401 North Hooper Street, Zip 48723–1476, Mailing Address: P.O. Box 435, Zip 48723–0435; tel. 989/673–3141, (Nonreporting) **A**9 10
Primary Contact: William P. Miller, President and Chief Executive Officer

| | 23 | 10 | 18 | — | — | — | — | — | — | — |

CARSON CITY—Montcalm County

★ ○ **CARSON CITY HOSPITAL**, 406 East Elm Street, Zip 48811–0879, Mailing Address: P.O. Box 879, Zip 48811–0879; tel. 989/584–3131 **A**9 10 11 19 **F**9 11 12 22 23 26 27 28 29 33 46 48 51 55 59 60 61 62 63 69 70 71 73 74 75 77 81 88 94 96 108 109 **P**8
Primary Contact: Bruce L. Traverse, President
COO: Bill Fife, Vice President Operations
CFO: Duane Miller, Vice President Finance
CMO: Lawrence Brown, D.O., Medical Director
CIO: Richard Terry, Chief Information Officer
CHR: Georgette Russell, Director Human Resources
Web address: www.carsoncityhospital.com

| | 23 | 10 | 63 | 2173 | 21 | 61174 | 332 | 29221 | 14661 | 505 |

CASS CITY—Tuscola County

⊞ **HILLS AND DALES GENERAL HOSPITAL**, 4675 Hill Street, Zip 48726–1099; tel. 989/872–2121 **A**1 9 10 18 **F**2 9 12 21 22 23 24 26 27 28 29 33 41 42 44 46 47 48 50 51 52 58 60 62 63 65 66 69 70 81 82 87 88 93 94 95 96 107 108 109 **P**4
Primary Contact: Dee McKrow, Chief Executive Officer
COO: Jean Anthony, Chief Operating Officer
CFO: David J. Oehring, Chief Financial Officer
CMO: Sohail M. Jilani, M.D., Chief of Staff
CIO: Greg Hanby, Director Ancillary Services
CHR: Tom Bardwell, Director Human Resources
Web address: www.hillsanddales.com

| | 23 | 10 | 25 | 699 | 5 | 62135 | 0 | 14538 | 7615 | 186 |

CHARLEVOIX—Charlevoix County

⊞ **CHARLEVOIX AREA HOSPITAL**, 14700 Lake Shore Drive, Zip 49720–1931; tel. 231/547–4024 **A**1 9 10 18 20 **F**9 11 12 26 27 28 33 46 48 55 59 60 61 62 63 69 81 82 88 93 94 95 97 106 107 108
Primary Contact: William Jackson, President
CFO: Tabitha Rudolph, Vice President Financial Services
CIO: David Priest, Information Systems Director
Web address: www.cah.org

| | 23 | 10 | 33 | 1389 | 14 | 27790 | 206 | 24489 | 11031 | 250 |

CHARLOTTE—Eaton County

⊞ **HAYES–GREEN–BEACH MEMORIAL HOSPITAL**, 321 East Harris Street, Zip 48813–1697; tel. 517/543–1050 **A**1 9 10 **F**2 6 9 11 12 21 22 27 33 37 41 45 46 51 52 53 54 58 59 60 62 63 64 69 70 81 85 87 88 93 94 108 110 **P**6 **S** Quorum Health Resources, Plano, TX
Primary Contact: Matthew Rush, President and Chief Executive Officer
CFO: Kim Capps, Chief Financial Officer
CMO: Robert Leeser, M.D., Director Medical Affairs
CIO: Kim Capps, Chief Financial Officer
CHR: Gail Nunamalaer, Vice President Human Resources
Web address: www.hgbhealth.com

| | 23 | 10 | 32 | 1408 | 12 | 147718 | 224 | 28277 | 13886 | 344 |

CHEBOYGAN—Cheboygan County

⊞ **CHEBOYGAN MEMORIAL HOSPITAL**, 748 South Main Street, Zip 49721–2299, Mailing Address: P.O. Box 419, Zip 49721–0419; tel. 231/627–5601, (Total facility includes 50 beds in nursing home–type unit) **A**1 9 10 20 **F**9 11 12 21 22 26 27 28 29 33 36 41 42 44 47 48 51 52 53 55 58 59 60 62 63 64 69 81 82 85 87 88 92 96 106 107 108 109 **P**6
Primary Contact: Michael J. Mihora, President and Chief Executive Officer
CFO: James Davidson, Chief Financial Officer
CMO: Timothy Burandt, D.O., Chief of Staff
CIO: Nancy Barr, Manager/Information Systems
CHR: Beth Walter, Human Resources Director
Web address: www.cheboyganhospital.org

| | 23 | 10 | 92 | 2215 | 71 | 107400 | 247 | 38682 | 18769 | 447 |

Hospital, Address, Telephone, Approval, Facility, and Physician Codes, Health Care System	Classi- fication Codes		Utilization Data					Expense (thousands) of dollars		
★ American Hospital Association (AHA) membership □ Joint Commission on Accreditation of Healthcare Organizations (JCAHO) accreditation ○ American Osteopathic Association (AOA) accreditation △ Commission on Accreditation of Rehabilitation Facilities (CARF) accreditation	Control	Service	Staffed Beds	Admissions	Census	Outpatient Visits	Births	Total	Payroll	Personnel

CHELSEA—Washtenaw County

□ **CHELSEA COMMUNITY HOSPITAL**, 775 South Main Street, Zip 48118–1399; tel. 734/475–1311 **A**1 3 5 9 10 **F**4 8 9 12 22 26 27 28 29 30 33 41 42 44 47 48 51 52 53 55 58 60 62 63 65 66 68 69 70 71 72 73 74 76 77 78 81 82 84 88 91 93 94 95 96 97 106 108 109
Primary Contact: Kathleen S. Griffiths, President and Chief Executive Officer
Web address: www.cch.org

| 23 | 10 | 99 | 3885 | 65 | 173756 | 0 | 67882 | 32389 | 712 |

CLARE—Clare County

⊠ **MIDMICHIGAN MEDICAL CENTER–CLARE**, 703 North McEwan Street, Zip 48617–1409; tel. 989/802–5000 **A**1 9 10 **F**2 11 12 22 23 26 27 28 33 41 48 52 57 58 59 60 63 69 81 82 87 88 92 96 107 108 **S** MidMichigan Health, Midland, MI
Primary Contact: Lawrence F. Barco, President
CFO: Ray Stover, Vice President and Chief Financial Officer
CHR: Penny Parsons, Vice President
Web address: www.midmichigan.org

| 23 | 10 | 64 | 2994 | 28 | 111952 | 256 | 30609 | 12331 | 284 |

CLINTON TOWNSHIP—Macomb County

⊠ **ST. JOSEPH'S MERCY OF MACOMB**, (Includes ST. JOSEPH'S MERCY HOSPITAL–EAST, 215 North Avenue, Mount Clemens, Zip 48043; tel. 810/466–9300; ST. JOSEPH'S MERCY HOSPITAL–WEST, 15855 19 Mile Road, Zip 48038; tel. 810/263–2300; ST. JOSEPH'S MERCY–NORTH, 80650 North Van Dyke, Romeo, Zip 48065; tel. 810/798–3551) **A**1 9 10 12 13 **F**2 4 9 10 11 12 15 17 19 21 22 23 24 26 27 28 29 30 31 33 35 37 38 39 40 42 45 46 47 48 51 52 53 55 57 58 59 60 61 62 63 64 65 66 68 69 70 71 72 73 74 75 76 77 78 79 81 82 88 94 96 98 106 107 108 109 110 **P**6 8 **S** Trinity Health, Novi, MI
Primary Contact: Barbara Rossmann, President and Chief Executive Officer
COO: Gary Beaulac, Chief Operating Officer
CFO: Steve Hathaway, Vice President Finance and Chief Financial Officer
CMO: Hoda El–Asmar, M.D., Chief Medical Officer
CIO: Robert Jones, Director, Trinity Information Systems
CHR: Joel Gibson, Vice President Human Resources
Web address: www.stjoe–macomb.com

| 21 | 10 | 389 | 17695 | 272 | 2215473 | 1592 | 205466 | 98311 | 1826 |

COLDWATER—Branch County

⊠ **COMMUNITY HEALTH CENTER OF BRANCH COUNTY**, 274 East Chicago Street, Zip 49036–2088; tel. 517/279–5400 **A**1 9 10 12 13 19 **F**2 4 9 10 11 12 22 23 26 27 28 33 34 36 37 46 47 48 50 51 55 57 58 59 60 61 62 63 64 65 66 69 70 71 73 74 75 76 77 78 81 82 85 87 88 93 94 96 106 107 108 110 **P**6 8
Primary Contact: Randy DeGroot, Chief Executive Officer
CFO: Richard Trufant, Chief Financial Officer
CMO: Ronald Gibson, M.D., Chief of Staff
CIO: Sheila Preston, Information Systems Director
CHR: Amy Jensen, Director Human Resources
Web address: www.chcbc.com

| 13 | 10 | 96 | 3749 | 42 | 112054 | 407 | 51008 | 21448 | 485 |

COMMERCE TOWNSHIP—Oakland County

⊠ **HURON VALLEY–SINAI HOSPITAL**, 1 William Carls Drive, Zip 48382–2201; tel. 248/937–3300 **A**1 3 5 9 10 12 13 **F**2 5 9 10 11 12 15 21 22 23 26 27 28 29 33 35 37 40 44 46 47 48 49 50 52 53 55 57 58 59 60 61 62 63 64 65 66 69 73 79 80 81 82 84 85 86 88 92 94 95 96 106 107 108 109 110 **P**8 **S** Detroit Medical Center, Detroit, MI
Primary Contact: Robert J. Yellan, President
COO: Connie Franko, Chief Operating Officer and Chief Nursing Executive
CFO: William Lantzy, Vice President of Finance
CHR: Jean Outler, Director Human Resources
Web address: www.hvsh.org

| 23 | 10 | 153 | 8959 | 105 | 85379 | 1930 | 124590 | 42619 | 918 |

DEARBORN—Wayne County

⊠ **OAKWOOD HOSPITAL AND MEDICAL CENTER–DEARBORN**, 18101 Oakwood Boulevard, Zip 48124–4093, Mailing Address: P.O. Box 2500, Zip 48123–2500; tel. 313/593–7000 **A**1 2 3 5 8 9 10 **F**2 9 11 12 14 15 17 19 21 22 23 24 26 27 28 29 30 31 32 33 34 35 36 37 38 39 44 46 47 48 49 50 51 52 53 55 56 57 58 59 60 61 62 63 64 65 66 69 70 79 80 81 82 84 85 87 88 89 90 92 94 95 96 98 99 106 108 109 110 **P**8 **S** Oakwood Healthcare, Inc., Dearborn, MI
Primary Contact: Mel Pyne, Division President
COO: J Joseph Diederich, Executive Vice President and Chief Operating Officer
CFO: Douglas D. Welday, Executive Vice President and Chief Financial Officer
CMO: Malcolm S. Henoch, M.D., Chief Medical Officer
CIO: Paula Smith, Leader Information Services and Chief Information Officer
CHR: John Furman, Executive Vice President Human Resources
Web address: www.oakwood.org

| 23 | 10 | 619 | 33217 | 434 | 184940 | 5005 | 359159 | 169817 | 3461 |

DECKERVILLE—Sanilac County

★ **DECKERVILLE COMMUNITY HOSPITAL**, 3559 Pine Street, Zip 48427–0126, Mailing Address: P.O. Box 126, Zip 48427–0126; tel. 810/376–2835 **A**9 10 18 **F**2 9 12 21 23 24 26 27 28 29 33 35 39 44 46 47 48 52 58 60 63 66 69 70 75 77 81 88 94 95 96 106 107 109 **P**5 6
Primary Contact: Edward L. Gamache, Administrator
CFO: Caren Puvalowski, Business Manager
CMO: Levi Guerrero, M.D., Chief of Staff
CIO: David West, Supervisor Information Technology
Web address: www.deckervillehosp.org

| 23 | 10 | 15 | 164 | 1 | 9949 | 0 | 4694 | 2319 | 79 |

Many Facility Codes have changed. Please refer to the AHA Guide Code Chart. © 2005 AHA Guide

MI

Hospital, Address, Telephone, Approval, Facility, and Physician Codes, Health Care System	Classi-fication Codes		Utilization Data					Expense (thousands) of dollars		
★ American Hospital Association (AHA) membership □ Joint Commission on Accreditation of Healthcare Organizations (JCAHO) accreditation ○ American Osteopathic Association (AOA) accreditation △ Commission on Accreditation of Rehabilitation Facilities (CARF) accreditation	Control	Service	Staffed Beds	Admissions	Census	Outpatient Visits	Births	Total	Payroll	Personnel

DETROIT—Wayne County

⊠ △ **CHILDREN'S HOSPITAL OF MICHIGAN**, 3901 Beaubien Street, Zip 48201–9985; tel. 313/966–5110 **A**1 3 5 7 8 9 10 **F**2 9 13 16 17 18 19 20 21 22 23 26 27 28 29 31 32 33 34 36 37 38 39 42 45 46 47 48 49 50 51 52 53 56 57 58 60 61 62 63 64 65 66 67 68 69 70 72 73 74 75 77 79 81 82 84 85 86 87 88 90 93 94 96 98 99 100 101 108 **S** Detroit Medical Center, Detroit, MI Primary Contact: Larry Fleischmann, M.D., President COO: Herman B. Gray, M.D., Chief Operating Officer CFO: Jackie Hill, Manager Finance CMO: Michael Epstein, M.D., Chief of Staff CIO: Lori Mouton, Director Public Relations and Marketing CHR: Jean Outler, Director Human Resources Web address: www.chmkids.org	23	50	228	13455	162	262515	0	256985	81533	1707
⊠ **DETROIT RECEIVING HOSPITAL AND UNIVERSITY HEALTH CENTER**, 4201 St. Antoine Boulevard, Zip 48201–2194; tel. 313/745–3603 **A**1 3 5 8 9 10 **F**2 13 14 21 22 26 27 28 31 33 34 37 38 39 52 55 57 58 60 62 63 64 66 69 70 71 73 75 76 77 81 85 88 94 95 96 104 107 108 110 **S** Detroit Medical Center, Detroit, MI Primary Contact: Iris Taylor, Ph.D., President CFO: Kathleen Ralston, Vice President and Chief Financial Officer CMO: Fernando Diaz, M.D., Ph.D., Senior Vice President and Chief Medical Officer CIO: Michael LeRoy, Chief Information Officer Web address: www.dmc.org	23	10	217	13865	187	144358	0	209782	66929	1523
⊠ **HARPER UNIVERSITY HOSPITAL**, 3990 John R., Zip 48201–9027; tel. 313/745–8040, (Includes HUTZEL HOSPITAL, 4707 St. Antoine Boulevard, Zip 48201–0154; tel. 313/745–6211) **A**1 2 3 5 8 9 10 **F**2 4 9 10 11 12 15 17 19 21 22 23 26 27 28 29 30 32 33 35 36 37 38 39 40 42 43 45 46 47 48 49 50 52 53 55 56 57 58 59 60 61 62 63 65 66 70 71 72 73 79 80 81 82 83 84 85 87 88 89 90 93 94 96 99 100 101 102 103 104 106 107 108 110 **S** Detroit Medical Center, Detroit, MI Primary Contact: Brooks Bock, M.D., President COO: Benjamin R. Carter, Executive Vice President and Chief Operating Officer CFO: Christopher Palazzolo, Executive Vice President and Chief Financial Officer CMO: Thomas Malone, M.D., Executive Vice President and Chief Medical Officer CIO: Michael LeRoy, Executive Vice President and Chief Information Officer CHR: Deloris Hunt, Corporate Vice President Human Resources Web address: www.harperhospital.org	23	10	601	27623	393	256498	5177	631061	158460	3281
⊠ **HENRY FORD HOSPITAL**, 2799 West Grand Boulevard, Zip 48202–2689; tel. 313/916–2600 **A**1 2 3 5 8 9 10 **F**2 7 10 11 12 14 15 17 19 21 22 23 24 26 27 28 29 32 33 34 35 36 37 38 39 40 44 46 47 48 49 50 52 53 55 56 57 58 59 60 61 62 63 64 65 66 69 70 73 74 75 79 80 81 82 84 85 86 87 88 90 92 93 94 95 96 98 99 100 101 102 103 104 105 106 107 108 109 110 **P**6 **S** Henry Ford Health System, Detroit, MI Primary Contact: Anthony A. Armada, President and Chief Executive Officer COO: William Schramm, Vice President Operations CFO: Joseph Schmitt, III, Vice President Finance and Chief Financial Officer CMO: Mark A. Kelley, M.D., Executive Vice President and Chief Medical Officer CIO: Arther Gross, Interim Chief Information Officer CHR: Ronald Waetzman, Senior Vice President and Chief Human Resources Web address: www.henryfordhealth.org	23	10	673	37043	568	699334	2144	629942	250633	5942
⊠ △ **JOHN D. DINGELL VETERANS AFFAIRS MEDICAL CENTER**, 4646 John R Street, Zip 48201–1932; tel. 313/576–1000, (Total facility includes 84 beds in nursing home–type unit) **A**1 2 3 5 7 8 9 **F**2 3 4 7 8 9 10 14 15 17 21 22 23 26 27 28 29 30 31 32 33 35 36 37 38 39 44 45 46 47 48 49 50 51 52 53 55 57 58 60 61 62 63 64 65 66 69 70 71 73 74 75 76 77 78 80 81 82 84 87 88 89 92 93 94 96 106 107 108 109 110 **P**6 **S** Department of Veterans Affairs, Washington, DC Primary Contact: Michael K. Wheeler, Director COO: Leslie Wiggins, Associate Director CFO: Patricia Kelly, Chief Fiscal Section CMO: Mark S. Edelstein, Assistant Chief of Staff for Medicine CIO: Robert C. Johnson, Chief Business Practices CHR: Thomas J. Paunovich, Chief Human Resources Officer Web address: www.va.gov/sta/guide/home.asp	45	10	217	4165	159	326438	0	184713	94010	1485
⊠ △ **REHABILITATION INSTITUTE OF MICHIGAN**, 261 Mack Boulevard, Zip 48201–2495; tel. 313/745–1203 **A**1 3 5 7 9 10 **F**22 26 27 28 29 31 41 42 44 45 51 52 53 65 66 68 69 92 94 95 96 108 109 **P**6 **S** Detroit Medical Center, Detroit, MI Primary Contact: Terry Reiley, President COO: Mildred Matlock, Ph.D., Chief Operating Officer CMO: Antoine Geffrard, M.D., Chief of Staff Web address: www.rimrehab.org	23	46	94	1527	57	130685	0	54741	27387	578
□ **SCCI HOSPITAL OF DETROIT**, 4777 East Outer Drive, Zip 48234; tel. 313/369–5800 **A**1 10 **F**2 21 60 64 94 110 Primary Contact: Kim Knight, Chief Executive Officer Web address: www.sccihospitals.com	33	80	53	429	30	0	0	12269	4500	107

MI

Hospital, Address, Telephone, Approval, Facility, and Physician Codes, Health Care System	Classi-fication Codes		Utilization Data					Expense (thousands) of dollars		
★ American Hospital Association (AHA) membership □ Joint Commission on Accreditation of Healthcare Organizations (JCAHO) accreditation ○ American Osteopathic Association (AOA) accreditation △ Commission on Accreditation of Rehabilitation Facilities (CARF) accreditation	Control	Service	Staffed Beds	Admissions	Census	Outpatient Visits	Births	Total	Payroll	Personnel

□ **SELECT SPECIALTY HOSPITAL–NORTHWEST DETROIT**, 6071 West Outer Drive, Zip 48235; tel. 313/966–6740, (Nonreporting) **A**1 10 Primary Contact: Jeffrey Lemon, Chief Executive Officer	33	49	36	—	—	—	—	—	—	—
✯ △ **SINAI–GRACE HOSPITAL**, 6071 West Outer Drive, Zip 48235–2679; tel. 313/966–3300 **A**1 3 5 7 8 9 10 **F**2 4 6 9 10 11 12 14 15 17 19 21 22 23 27 28 29 31 32 33 36 41 42 44 46 47 48 49 50 52 53 55 56 57 58 59 60 61 62 63 64 65 66 68 69 70 71 73 75 76 77 80 81 82 83 84 85 86 87 88 93 94 95 96 98 106 107 108 109 110 **S** Detroit Medical Center, Detroit, MI Primary Contact: Conrad L. Mallett, Jr, President COO: Vernell Williams, Vice President Operations CFO: Richard Harning, Vice President Finance and Treasurer CMO: Melvin L. Hollowell, M.D., Vice President Medical Affairs Web address: www.sinaigrace.org	23	10	404	21028	316	226328	—	325758	101531	2190
✯ ○ △ **ST. JOHN DETROIT RIVERVIEW HOSPITAL – NORTHEAST CAMPUS**, 7733 East Jefferson Avenue, Zip 48214–2598; tel. 313/499–4000 **A**1 7 9 10 11 13 **F**2 4 9 11 12 21 22 26 27 28 29 31 33 35 36 37 38 44 45 46 47 48 49 50 52 53 55 56 57 58 59 60 61 62 63 64 65 66 68 69 70 71 73 74 75 81 84 85 88 92 93 94 96 106 108 109 110 **P**8 **S** Ascension Health, Saint Louis, MO Primary Contact: Anthony E. Munroe, President and Chief Executive Officer COO: Mark Johnson, Vice President Operations CFO: Kathy Herron, Interim Chief Financial Officer CMO: W Anthony Greer, M.D., Vice President Medical Affairs Web address: www.stjohn.org/detroitriverview	21	10	262	12603	196	92806	1072	127872	67721	1301
✯ **ST. JOHN HOSPITAL AND MEDICAL CENTER**, 22101 Moross Road, Zip 48236–2172; tel. 313/343–4000 **A**1 2 3 5 8 9 10 12 13 **F**2 9 10 11 12 14 15 17 19 21 22 26 27 28 29 30 31 33 35 36 37 38 39 40 42 45 46 47 48 49 50 52 53 55 56 57 58 59 60 61 62 63 64 65 66 67 69 70 71 73 74 75 76 79 80 81 82 84 85 87 88 92 93 94 95 96 101 105 107 108 109 110 **P**8 **S** Ascension Health, Saint Louis, MO Primary Contact: Mark R. Taylor, President CFO: Tomasine Marx, Vice President Finance CMO: Noel Lawson, M.D., Vice President Medical Affairs CIO: Claudia Allen, Chief Information Officer CHR: Debbie Condino, Vice President Customer Service Web address: www.stjohn.org	21	10	607	33096	479	261255	3930	456267	213179	3902
UNITED COMMUNITY HOSPITAL, 2401 20th Street, Zip 48216; tel. 313/964–1133, (Nonreporting) **A**10 Primary Contact: Robin M. Barclay, President	23	10	86	—	—	—	—	—	—	—
DOWAGIAC—Cass County										
✯ **BORGESS–LEE MEMORIAL HOSPITAL**, (Critical Access Hospital), 420 West High Street, Zip 49047–1907; tel. 269/782–8681 **A**1 9 10 18 **F**9 12 21 22 23 26 27 28 29 31 33 35 39 42 46 47 48 52 53 55 58 60 61 63 64 65 66 69 70 81 88 94 95 96 106 107 108 110 **P**1 **S** Ascension Health, Saint Louis, MO Primary Contact: William Daam, Chief Operating Officer COO: William Daam, Chief Operating Officer CFO: Ken Holst, Chief Financial Officer CMO: Mohammad Taqi, Chief of Staff CIO: Bill Schuur, Director of Material Management CHR: Pete Krueger, Director Human Resources Web address: www.borgess.com	21	49	15	1178	10	83340	0	19528	9797	223
EAST CHINA—St. Clair County										
✯ **ST. JOHN RIVER DISTRICT HOSPITAL**, 4100 River Road, Zip 48054–2909; tel. 810/329–7111 **A**1 9 10 **F**9 11 12 21 23 27 28 29 30 33 37 38 40 44 46 48 55 58 59 60 61 62 63 65 66 69 70 73 75 81 88 93 94 96 107 108 109 **P**8 **S** Ascension Health, Saint Louis, MO Primary Contact: Frank W. Poma, President CFO: Philip Wild, Controller CMO: H Lee Bacheldor, D.O., Medical Director CIO: Linda Osterland, Director Information Services Web address: www.stjohn.org	21	10	68	2709	27	76028	410	31195	17019	322
EATON RAPIDS—Eaton County										
✯ **EATON RAPIDS MEDICAL CENTER**, 1500 South Main Street, Zip 48827–0130, Mailing Address: P.O. Box 130, Zip 48827–0130; tel. 517/663–2671 **A**1 9 10 **F**2 9 12 21 22 26 27 28 29 30 33 37 46 47 48 52 53 54 58 60 63 65 66 81 84 85 88 94 95 96 97 107 108 **P**5 Primary Contact: Jack L. Denton, President and Chief Executive Officer CFO: Tim Johnson, Chief Financial Officer CMO: Ashok K. Gupta, M.D., Chief of Staff CHR: James F. Harns, Director Human Resources Web address: www.eatonrapidscare.org	23	10	20	629	6	21379	0	14301	5340	135
ESCANABA—Delta County										
✯ **OSF ST. FRANCIS HOSPITAL**, 3401 Ludington Street, Zip 49829–1377; tel. 906/786–3311 **A**1 9 10 20 **F**2 9 11 12 22 26 27 28 29 33 36 37 38 44 46 47 48 49 51 52 53 55 57 58 59 60 61 62 63 64 65 66 69 70 81 82 84 85 88 93 94 95 96 97 106 107 108 109 110 **P**4 **S** OSF Healthcare System, Peoria, IL Primary Contact: Peter G. Jennings, Chief Executive Officer CFO: Jim Wayne, Chief Financial Officer CIO: Mark Irving, Manager Management Information Systems Web address: www.osfstfrancis.org	21	10	64	3368	35	95199	306	—	—	—

Many Facility Codes have changed. Please refer to the AHA Guide Code Chart.

© 2005 AHA Guide

Hospital, Address, Telephone, Approval, Facility, and Physician Codes, Health Care System	Classification Codes		Utilization Data					Expense (thousands) of dollars		
★ American Hospital Association (AHA) membership □ Joint Commission on Accreditation of Healthcare Organizations (JCAHO) accreditation ○ American Osteopathic Association (AOA) accreditation △ Commission on Accreditation of Rehabilitation Facilities (CARF) accreditation	Control	Service	Staffed Beds	Admissions	Census	Outpatient Visits	Births	Total	Payroll	Personnel

FARMINGTON HILLS—Oakland County

★ ○ **BOTSFORD GENERAL HOSPITAL**, 28050 Grand River Avenue, Zip 48336–5933; tel. 248/471–8000 **A**9 10 11 12 13 **F**2 9 11 12 14 15 21 22 23 24 26 27 29 30 31 33 34 35 37 38 39 41 42 44 46 47 48 49 50 52 53 55 57 58 59 60 61 62 63 64 65 66 68 69 70 71 73 74 75 76 81 82 85 87 88 89 92 93 94 95 96 98 106 107 108 110 **P**5 6
Primary Contact: Paul E. LaCasse, D.O., President and Chief Executive Officer
CFO: David Marcellino, Vice President Finance and Chief Financial Officer
CMO: Daniel Bonbrisco, D.O., Vice President and Chief Medical Officer
CIO: John Czahor, Chief Information Officer
CHR: Barbara Palmer, Director Corporate Human Resources
Web address: www.botsfordsystem.org
`23 | 10 | 310 | 15801 | 214 | 373000 | 991 | 216081 | 106121 | 1983`

FERNDALE—Oakland County

★ **HENRY FORD KINGSWOOD HOSPITAL**, 10300 West Eight Mile Road, Zip 48220–2198; tel. 248/398–3200, (Nonreporting) **A**9 10 **S** Henry Ford Health System, Detroit, MI
Primary Contact: Marilyn Grazio, Clinical Administrator
COO: Rick Young, Chief Operating Officer
`23 | 22 | 64 | — | — | — | — | — | — | —`

FLINT—Genesee County

⊞ △ **HURLEY MEDICAL CENTER**, One Hurley Plaza, Zip 48503–5993; tel. 810/257–9000 **A**1 2 3 5 7 8 9 10 **F**2 4 9 10 11 12 13 14 15 16 17 18 21 22 24 26 27 28 29 31 33 34 39 41 42 44 45 46 48 49 50 52 55 56 57 58 59 60 61 62 63 64 65 66 67 68 69 70 71 72 73 74 75 76 77 78 79 81 82 88 89 90 93 94 95 96 98 101 104 106 107 108 109 110 **P**7 8
Primary Contact: Andrea Price, Interim President and Chief Executive Officer
COO: Andrea Price, Executive Vice President and Operating Officer
CFO: Daniel Coffield, Executive Vice President and Chief Financial Officer
CIO: Gary Townsend, Chief Information Officer
Web address: www.hurleymc.com
`14 | 10 | 467 | 22837 | 335 | 463109 | 2952 | 284095 | 122217 | —`

⊞ △ **MCLAREN REGIONAL MEDICAL CENTER**, 401 South Ballenger Highway, Zip 48532–3685; tel. 810/342–2000, (Total facility includes 23 beds in nursing home–type unit) **A**1 2 3 5 7 8 9 10 **F**2 4 9 10 11 12 14 15 17 19 21 22 23 24 26 27 28 29 30 31 32 33 34 35 37 39 41 42 44 46 47 48 49 50 52 53 55 57 58 59 60 61 62 63 64 65 66 68 69 70 71 72 73 74 75 76 77 78 79 80 81 82 85 87 88 89 90 92 93 94 95 96 104 106 107 108 109 **P**6 7
S McLaren Health Care Corporation, Flint, MI
Primary Contact: Donald C. Kooy, President and Chief Executive Officer
COO: David Senchak, Vice President Ancillary and Support Services
CFO: Rick Wyles, Chief Financial Officer
CMO: Edwin H. Gullekson, M.D., Vice President Medical Affairs
CIO: Joan Maten, Vice President Nursing Services
CHR: Timothy Srock, Vice President Human Resources
Web address: www.mclaren.org
`23 | 10 | 378 | 19305 | 264 | 405357 | 679 | 238571 | 101249 | 1982`

□ **SELECT SPECIALTY HOSPITAL–FLINT**, One Hurley Plaza, 11th Floor, Zip 48503; tel. 810/237–6793, (Nonreporting) **A**1 10
Primary Contact: Grant Asay, Chief Executive Officer
`33 | 80 | 32 | — | — | — | — | — | — | —`

FRANKFORT—Benzie County

★ **PAUL OLIVER MEMORIAL HOSPITAL**, 224 Park Avenue, Zip 49635–9658; tel. 231/352–2200, (Total facility includes 40 beds in nursing home–type unit) **A**9 10 18 **F**9 12 22 27 28 29 33 39 46 48 52 60 63 65 69 81 88 92 94 96 97 108 **S** Munson Healthcare, Traverse City, MI
Primary Contact: James D. Austin, FACHE, Administrator
CFO: Mark Hepler, Chief Financial Officer
CMO: Gerard Mahoney, M.D., Chief of Staff
CHR: Julie Banktson, Human Resources Manager
Web address: www.munsonhealthcare.org
`23 | 10 | 48 | 171 | 41 | 28882 | 0 | 9559 | 3597 | 104`

FREMONT—Newaygo County

⊞ **GERBER MEMORIAL HEALTH SERVICES**, 212 South Sullivan Street, Zip 49412–1596; tel. 231/924–3300 **A**1 9 10 **F**3 9 11 12 13 14 22 26 27 28 29 30 31 33 34 37 41 44 48 51 52 55 56 58 59 60 61 62 63 65 66 67 68 69 71 73 74 75 76 77 81 82 84 85 87 88 92 93 94 95 96 97 108 109
Primary Contact: Ned B. Hughes, Jr, President
COO: Gary Allore, Vice President Financial Services
CFO: Gary Allore, Vice President Financial Services
CMO: Lynn Nevin, M.D., Chief of Staff
CIO: Pete Mulford, Director Information Systems
CHR: Ted Britton, Director Human Resources
Web address: www.gerberhospital.org
`23 | 10 | 83 | 3275 | 32 | 90272 | 477 | 41263 | 18964 | 445`

GARDEN CITY—Wayne County

★ ○ **GARDEN CITY HOSPITAL**, 6245 North Inkster Road, Zip 48135–4001; tel. 734/421–3300 **A**9 10 11 12 13 **F**2 3 9 11 12 14 15 21 23 26 27 28 29 30 33 34 35 39 45 46 47 51 52 53 55 57 58 59 60 61 62 63 66 68 69 70 81 84 88 93 94 95 96 108 110 **P**5 6 8
Primary Contact: Gary R. Ley, President and Chief Executive Officer
CFO: Robert Giddings, Chief Financial Officer
CMO: David Connett, M.D., Chief Medical Officer
CIO: Bill Moncrief, Director of Information Systems
CHR: Mitchell Nimmoor, Vice President Human Resources
Web address: www.gchosp.org
`23 | 10 | 270 | 10610 | 150 | 100515 | 837 | 113065 | 48936 | 1015`

MI

Hospital, Address, Telephone, Approval, Facility, and Physician Codes, Health Care System	Classification Codes		Utilization Data					Expense (thousands) of dollars		
★ American Hospital Association (AHA) membership ☐ Joint Commission on Accreditation of Healthcare Organizations (JCAHO) accreditation ○ American Osteopathic Association (AOA) accreditation △ Commission on Accreditation of Rehabilitation Facilities (CARF) accreditation	Control	Service	Staffed Beds	Admissions	Census	Outpatient Visits	Births	Total	Payroll	Personnel

GAYLORD—Otsego County

☒ **OTSEGO MEMORIAL HOSPITAL**, 825 North Center Street, Zip 49735–1560; tel. 989/731–2100, (Includes MCREYNOLDS HALL), (Total facility includes 34 beds in nursing home–type unit) **A**1 9 10 20 **F**2 9 11 12 21 23 24 26 27 28 30 33 34 39 42 46 47 48 49 52 55 58 59 60 61 62 63 64 65 66 68 69 70 81 82 85 87 88 92 93 94 96 98 106 107 108 109 110 **P**6 7
Primary Contact: Thomas R. Lemon, Chief Executive Officer
CIO: Timothy Hella, Director Information Management
CHR: Terra Deming, Director Human Resources
Web address: www.gaylordhospital.org

| | 23 | 10 | 87 | 2069 | 45 | 92115 | 291 | 45085 | 19631 | 469 |

GLADWIN—Gladwin County

☒ **MIDMICHIGAN MEDICAL CENTER–GLADWIN**, 515 South Quarter Street, Zip 48624–1918; tel. 989/426–9286, (Nonreporting) **A**1 9 10 **S** MidMichigan Health, Midland, MI
Primary Contact: Mark E. Bush, Executive Vice President
Web address: www.midmichigan.org

| | 33 | 10 | 42 | — | — | — | — | — | — | — |

GRAND BLANC—Genesee County

☒ ○ △ **GENESYS REGIONAL MEDICAL CENTER**, One Genesys Parkway, Zip 48439–8066; tel. 810/606–5000 **A**1 2 3 5 7 9 10 11 12 13 **F**2 9 10 11 12 14 15 17 19 21 22 23 26 27 28 29 30 33 34 35 37 39 40 42 44 46 47 48 49 50 52 53 55 57 58 59 60 61 62 63 64 65 66 68 69 70 81 82 83 85 86 87 88 92 93 94 96 106 108 109 **P**1 4 6 7 **S** Ascension Health, Saint Louis, MO
Primary Contact: Norma R. Hagenow, R.N., President and Chief Executive Officer
COO: Allen D. Tucker, Jr, Senior Executive Vice President and Chief Operating Officer
CFO: John Keuten, Senior Vice President and Chief Financial Officer
CMO: Barry Solomon, M.D., Senior Vice President Clinical Affairs
CIO: David Holland, Vice President and Chief Information Officer
CHR: Cathy Heiman, Senior Vice President Human Resources
Web address: www.genesys.org

| | 21 | 10 | 389 | 25178 | 302 | 987590 | 3107 | 322500 | 139967 | 2804 |

GRAND HAVEN—Ottawa County

☒ **NORTH OTTAWA COMMUNITY HOSPITAL**, 1309 Sheldon Road, Zip 49417–2488; tel. 616/842–3600 **A**1 9 10 **F**2 6 9 11 12 21 22 26 27 28 29 33 37 46 48 53 55 58 59 62 63 69 81 84 85 88 92 93 94 95 96 106 108 109 110
Primary Contact: Michael E. Payne, President
CIO: Ron Latta, Director Information Technology
CHR: Carla Wallis, Director Human Resources
Web address: www.noch.org

| | 23 | 10 | 45 | 2192 | 20 | 131778 | 494 | 41741 | 16603 | 382 |

GRAND RAPIDS—Kent County

☐ **FOREST VIEW PSYCHIATRIC HOSPITAL**, (Formerly Forest View Hospital), 1055 Medical Park Drive S.E., Zip 49546–3671; tel. 616/942–9610, (Nonreporting) **A**1 9 10 **S** Universal Health Services, Inc., King of Prussia, PA
Primary Contact: Wayne T. Miller, Chief Executive Officer
Web address: www.forestview.com

| | 33 | 22 | 62 | — | — | — | — | — | — | — |

☒ △ **MARY FREE BED REHABILITATION HOSPITAL**, (Formerly Mary Free Bed Hospital and Rehabilitation Center), 235 Wealthy Street S.E., Zip 49503–5299; tel. 616/242–0400 **A**1 7 9 10 **F**22 26 27 28 37 42 45 52 53 58 60 65 68 69 73 77 94 95 96 108
Primary Contact: William H. Blessing, President
CFO: Randall DeNeff, Vice President Finance
CMO: John Butzer, M.D., Medical Director
CHR: Anne Dierker, Vice President Human Resources
Web address: www.mfbrc.com

| | 23 | 46 | 80 | 1330 | 46 | 46801 | 0 | 22617 | 16573 | 513 |

○ △ **METROPOLITAN HOSPITAL**, 1919 Boston Street S.E., Zip 49506–4199, Mailing Address: P.O. Box 158, Zip 49501–0158; tel. 616/252–7200 **A**7 9 10 11 12 13 **F**2 10 11 12 15 21 22 26 27 28 29 30 33 35 37 39 40 42 46 48 52 53 55 57 58 59 60 62 63 65 68 69 70 81 82 84 85 88 93 94 96 106 108 110 **P**6 7 8
Primary Contact: Michael D. Faas, President and Chief Executive Officer
Web address: www.metrohealth.net

| | 23 | 10 | 198 | 8504 | 114 | 282756 | 1634 | 152545 | 59625 | 1293 |

☒ **PINE REST CHRISTIAN MENTAL HEALTH SERVICES**, 300 68th Street S.E., Zip 49501–0165, Mailing Address: P.O. Box 165, Zip 49501–0165; tel. 616/455–5000 **A**1 5 9 10 **F**4 5 6 21 22 27 28 29 31 44 47 48 51 53 58 65 71 72 73 74 75 76 77 78 92 94 96 108 **P**6
Primary Contact: Daniel L. Holwerda, President and Chief Executive Officer
CFO: Paul H. Karsten, Vice President Finance and Chief Financial Officer
CMO: Wayne L. Creelman, M.D., Executive Vice President and Chief Medical Officer
CIO: Bruce Eckert, Director Information Systems
Web address: www.pinerest.org

| | 23 | 22 | 150 | 4692 | 120 | 173128 | 0 | 50850 | — | 676 |

Many Facility Codes have changed. Please refer to the AHA Guide Code Chart. © 2005 AHA Guide

Hospital, Address, Telephone, Approval, Facility, and Physician Codes, Health Care System	Classi-fication Codes		Utilization Data					Expense (thousands) of dollars		
★ American Hospital Association (AHA) membership □ Joint Commission on Accreditation of Healthcare Organizations (JCAHO) accreditation ○ American Osteopathic Association (AOA) accreditation △ Commission on Accreditation of Rehabilitation Facilities (CARF) accreditation	Control	Service	Staffed Beds	Admissions	Census	Outpatient Visits	Births	Total	Payroll	Personnel

Hospital	Control	Service	Staffed Beds	Admissions	Census	Outpatient Visits	Births	Total	Payroll	Personnel
⊞ **SAINT MARY'S HEALTH CARE**, (Formerly Saint Mary's Mercy Medical Center), 200 Jefferson Avenue S.E., Zip 49503–4598; tel. 616/752–6090 **A**1 2 3 5 9 10 **F**11 12 14 15 17 21 22 23 26 27 28 29 30 33 34 35 37 38 39 41 42 44 46 47 48 49 50 52 53 55 56 57 58 59 61 62 63 65 66 70 71 73 75 79 81 82 84 87 88 92 93 94 95 96 101 106 107 108 109 110 **P**7 **S** Trinity Health, Novi, MI Primary Contact: Philip H. McCorkle, Jr, President and Chief Executive Officer COO: Jim Miller, Chief Operating Officer CFO: Steve Pirog, Vice President Finance CMO: David Baumgartner, M.D., Vice President Medical Affairs CIO: Debra Rockey, Site Director Information Services CHR: Thomas Karel, Director Human Resources Web address: www.smhealthcare.org	21	10	324	16502	231	442798	2442	244922	83672	2005
⊞ △ **SPECTRUM HEALTH**, 1840 Wealthy Street S.E., Zip 49506–2921; tel. 616/774–7444, (Includes SPECTRUM HEALTH – BLODGETT CAMPUS; SPECTRUM HEALTH – BUTTERWORTH CAMPUS, 100 Michigan Street N.E., Zip 49503–2551; tel. 616/391–1774) **A**1 2 5 7 8 9 10 **F**2 6 7 9 10 11 12 13 14 15 16 17 18 19 20 21 22 23 24 26 27 28 29 32 33 34 40 41 42 44 45 46 47 48 49 51 52 53 55 56 57 58 59 60 61 62 63 64 65 66 67 69 70 81 82 83 84 85 87 88 90 92 93 94 95 96 98 99 106 107 108 109 110 **P**6 8 **S** Spectrum Health, Grand Rapids, MI Primary Contact: Matthew Van Vranken, President CFO: Joseph J. Fifer, Senior Vice President Corporate Services and Chief Financial Officer CMO: Peter Lundeen, M.D., Vice President Medical Affairs CIO: Patrick O'Hare, Corporate Chief Information Officer CHR: Tanja Oquendo, Vice President Human Resources Web address: www.spectrum–health.org	23	10	912	51838	647	145486	8019	713458	302987	7353
⊞ △ **SPECTRUM HEALTH–KENT COMMUNITY CAMPUS**, 750 Fuller Avenue N.E., Zip 49503–1995; tel. 616/486–3000, (Total facility includes 307 beds in nursing home–type unit) **A**1 7 9 10 **F**2 3 4 21 26 27 37 39 42 44 46 47 52 65 69 92 94 108 **S** Spectrum Health, Grand Rapids, MI Primary Contact: Stephanie Hearn, Administrator CFO: Brian Pangle, Vice President Finance CMO: Carole Montgomery, M.D., Medical Director CIO: Frank Thomas, Director Informatio Systems CHR: Floyd Wilson, Jr, Chief Human Resources Officer Web address: www.kentcommunity.spectrum–health.org	23	80	373	2225	271	3737	0	35230	13228	363

GRAYLING—Crawford County

Hospital	Control	Service	Staffed Beds	Admissions	Census	Outpatient Visits	Births	Total	Payroll	Personnel
⊞ **MERCY HOSPITAL GRAYLING**, 1100 East Michigan Avenue, Zip 49738–1398; tel. 989/348–5461, (Total facility includes 40 beds in nursing home–type unit) **A**1 9 10 20 **F**2 9 11 12 21 22 24 26 27 28 29 30 31 33 35 37 39 42 45 47 48 52 55 58 59 60 62 63 64 65 66 69 70 72 73 74 75 77 81 82 88 92 94 95 96 107 108 109 110 **P**6 8 **S** Trinity Health, Novi, MI Primary Contact: Stephanie J. Riemer–Matuzak, Chief Executive Officer CFO: Dan Hogan, Vice President Finance CMO: Douglas Slater, M.D., Vice President Medical Affairs CHR: Kirsten Korth–White, Chief Human Resources Officer Web address: www.mercygrayling.munsonhealthcare.org	21	10	89	3705	67	60595	292	41054	17957	341

GREENVILLE—Montcalm County

Hospital	Control	Service	Staffed Beds	Admissions	Census	Outpatient Visits	Births	Total	Payroll	Personnel
⊞ **SPECTRUM HEALTH–UNITED MEMORIAL**, 615 South Bower Street, Zip 48838–2628; tel. 616/754–4691, (Includes SPECTRUM HEALTH – KELSEY CAMPUS, 418 Washington Avenue, Lakeview, Zip 48850; tel. 989/352–7211; Paul Bonis, Chief Executive Officer), (Total facility includes 40 beds in nursing home–type unit) (Nonreporting) **A**1 9 10 **S** Spectrum Health, Grand Rapids, MI Primary Contact: Paul Bonis, Chief Executive Officer COO: Priscillia Mahar, ChiefOperating Officer CFO: Mary Anne Jones, Chief Financial Officer CMO: Bennett Walstatler, M.D., President CIO: David Dutmers, Team Leader Information and Technology Management CHR: Vicki Jensen, Chief Human Resources Officer Web address: www.umha.org	23	10	65	—	—	—	—	—	—	—

GROSSE POINTE—Wayne County

Hospital	Control	Service	Staffed Beds	Admissions	Census	Outpatient Visits	Births	Total	Payroll	Personnel
⊞ **BON SECOURS HOSPITAL**, 468 Cadieux Road, Zip 48230–1592; tel. 313/343–1000 **A**1 3 5 9 10 **F**1 2 9 11 12 15 21 22 26 27 28 29 30 31 33 35 37 39 40 41 42 44 45 46 47 48 50 51 52 53 54 55 57 58 59 60 61 62 63 65 66 69 70 73 74 75 76 77 81 82 84 87 88 94 95 96 107 108 109 110 **P**6 7 **S** Bon Secours Health System, Inc., Marriottsville, MD Primary Contact: Jeffrey A. Collins, Interim Chief Executive Officer COO: Jeffrey A. Collins, Chief Operating Officer CFO: Pitt R. Calkin, Interim Chief Financial Officer CMO: Randolph Gordon, M.D., Interim Vice President Medical Affairs CIO: Tim Chaus, Chief Information Officer CHR: Aline Lafferty, Vice President Human Resources Web address: www.bschealth.com	21	10	221	12510	174	233883	1102	179742	77556	1126

MI

Hospital, Address, Telephone, Approval, Facility, and Physician Codes, Health Care System	Classification Codes		Utilization Data					Expense (thousands) of dollars		
★ American Hospital Association (AHA) membership □ Joint Commission on Accreditation of Healthcare Organizations (JCAHO) accreditation ○ American Osteopathic Association (AOA) accreditation △ Commission on Accreditation of Rehabilitation Facilities (CARF) accreditation	Control	Service	Staffed Beds	Admissions	Census	Outpatient Visits	Births	Total	Payroll	Personnel

GROSSE POINTE FARMS—Wayne County

⊠ **COTTAGE HOSPITAL**, 159 Kercheval Avenue, Zip 48236–3692; tel. 313/640–1000 **A**1 9 10 **F**2 4 7 12 21 22 23 25 26 27 28 29 30 31 33 37 40 46 47 48 53 57 58 60 61 62 63 65 66 68 69 70 71 72 73 74 75 76 77 78 81 84 88 93 94 95 96 107 108 109 110 **S** Bon Secours Health System, Inc., Marriottsville, MD Primary Contact: Richard Van Lith, Chief Executive Officer COO: Jeffrey A. Collins, Chief Operating Officer CFO: David Zilli, Chief Financial Officer Web address: www.bonsecourscottage.org	21	10	54	2063	47	22446	0	38054	18339	382

HANCOCK—Houghton County

⊠ **PORTAGE HEALTH SYSTEM**, 500 Campus Drive, Zip 49930–1569; tel. 906/483–1000, (Total facility includes 30 beds in nursing home–type unit) **A**1 9 10 **F**1 2 9 11 12 21 22 23 26 27 28 29 33 36 37 38 39 41 42 44 45 46 47 48 51 52 53 54 55 58 59 60 61 62 63 64 65 66 68 69 70 81 84 87 88 92 94 95 96 97 106 107 108 109 110 **P**6 Primary Contact: James Bogan, President and Chief Executive Officer CFO: Brian Donahue, Chief Financial Officer CMO: Kirk Lufkin, M.D., Medical Director CHR: Karin Van Dyke, Director Human Resources Web address: www.portagehealth.org	23	10	66	1870	51	70091	381	43107	20121	429

HARBOR BEACH—Huron County

★ **HARBOR BEACH COMMUNITY HOSPITAL**, 210 South First Street, Zip 48441–1236; tel. 989/479–3201, (Total facility includes 40 beds in nursing home–type unit) **A**9 10 18 **F**1 2 9 12 21 26 27 28 29 33 44 46 48 52 58 63 65 69 81 88 92 94 96 97 108 109 **P**3 Primary Contact: Steve Barnett, Chief Executive Officer CFO: Jill Wehner, Vice President Financial Services CMO: Jamie Tan, M.D., Chief of Staff CIO: Tami Nickrand, Chief Information Officer CHR: Gretchen Morgan, Human Resources Director Web address: www.hbch.org	23	10	65	153	40	13171	0	8989	3979	92

HARRISON TOWNSHIP—Macomb County

★ △ **ST. JOHN NORTH SHORES HOSPITAL**, 26755 Ballard Road, Zip 48045–2458; tel. 586/465–5501 **A**7 9 10 **F**2 12 21 22 26 27 28 29 32 33 36 37 41 45 46 48 52 53 54 57 58 60 63 68 69 81 88 92 94 95 96 108 **S** Ascension Health, Saint Louis, MO Primary Contact: David Sessions, Administrator CFO: Jeffrey Ewald, Director Finance CMO: Anthony Southall, M.D., Chief of Staff Web address: www.stjohn.org	21	10	55	1385	37	25616	0	21657	11484	259

HASTINGS—Barry County

□ **PENNOCK HOSPITAL**, 1009 West Green Street, Zip 49058–1790; tel. 269/945–3451 **A**1 9 10 **F**2 9 11 12 21 22 24 26 27 28 29 32 33 34 37 41 44 46 47 48 51 52 53 55 57 58 59 60 61 62 63 64 65 66 69 70 75 81 82 87 88 91 93 94 95 96 97 106 107 108 110 **P**8 Primary Contact: Harry Doele, Chief Executive Officer Web address: www.pennockhealth.com	23	10	88	3340	37	176190	390	41882	18708	515

HILLSDALE—Hillsdale County

⊠ ○ **HILLSDALE COMMUNITY HEALTH CENTER**, 168 South Howell Street, Zip 49242–2081; tel. 517/437–4451, (Total facility includes 21 beds in nursing home–type unit) (Nonreporting) **A**1 9 10 11 Primary Contact: Charles A. Bianchi, President and Chief Executive Officer CFO: Valerie Fetters, Chief Financial Officer CMO: Dan McCance, D.O., Chief of Staff CHR: Janet Marsh, Director Web address: www.hchc.com	23	10	73	—	—	—	—	—	—	—

HOLLAND—Ottawa County

⊠ △ **HOLLAND HOSPITAL**, (Formerly Holland Community Hospital), 602 Michigan Avenue, Zip 49423–4999; tel. 616/392–5141 **A**1 7 9 10 **F**2 4 11 12 15 17 21 22 24 26 27 28 29 33 34 37 47 48 51 52 53 54 55 57 58 59 62 63 65 66 69 71 72 75 76 77 78 81 84 85 88 93 94 96 106 107 108 109 110 **P**8 Primary Contact: Dale Sowders, President and Chief Executive Officer CFO: Terry L. Steele, Vice President Finance and Chief Financial Officer CMO: Bob Bates, M.D., Chief Medical Officer CHR: Chuck Kohlruss, Vice President Human Resources and Operations Support Web address: www.hoho.org	23	10	178	7425	84	330000	1735	96798	46012	1160

HOWELL—Livingston County

⊠ **SAINT JOSEPH MERCY LIVINGSTON HOSPITAL**, 620 Byron Road, Zip 48843–1093; tel. 517/545–6000 **A**1 9 10 **F**2 4 9 11 12 21 22 23 29 32 33 36 37 42 48 51 52 55 57 58 59 60 61 62 63 66 69 70 73 77 81 84 88 94 95 96 98 106 107 108 109 110 **S** Trinity Health, Novi, MI Primary Contact: Patricia Claffey, Executive Director COO: Douglas A. Edema, M.D., Vice President and Chief Operating Officer CFO: Charles Hoffman, Vice President Financial Services and Chief Financial Officer CMO: Charles Kelly, D.O., Chief of Staff CIO: David Koch, Director, Information Systems Web address: www.sjmh.com/who/mcphersn.shtml	21	10	50	3531	33	—	—	—	—	—

Many Facility Codes have changed. Please refer to the AHA Guide Code Chart. © 2005 AHA Guide

Hospital, Address, Telephone, Approval, Facility, and Physician Codes, Health Care System	Classi-fication Codes		Utilization Data					Expense (thousands) of dollars		
	Control	Service	Staffed Beds	Admissions	Census	Outpatient Visits	Births	Total	Payroll	Personnel

★ American Hospital Association (AHA) membership
☐ Joint Commission on Accreditation of Healthcare Organizations (JCAHO) accreditation
○ American Osteopathic Association (AOA) accreditation
△ Commission on Accreditation of Rehabilitation Facilities (CARF) accreditation

IONIA—Ionia County

⊠ **IONIA COUNTY MEMORIAL HOSPITAL**, 479 Lafayette Street, Zip 48846–1834, Mailing Address: Box 1001, Zip 48846–1899; tel. 616/527–4200 **A**1 9 10 **F**2 9 11 12 14 23 26 27 28 29 33 35 46 47 48 51 52 53 55 58 59 60 61 62 63 64 65 66 69 70 81 82 85 87 88 94 95 107 108 109 **P**6
Primary Contact: Evonne G. Ulmer, JD, Chief Executive Officer
CFO: Margaret Hybarger, Vice President Finance
CIO: George Rutherford, Vice President Planning, Ancillary and Support Services
Web address: www.ioniahospital.org

	23	10	56	843	9	82334	137	17883	15677	223

IRON MOUNTAIN—Dickinson County

⊠ **DICKINSON COUNTY HEALTHCARE SYSTEM**, 1721 South Stephenson Avenue, Zip 49801–3637; tel. 906/774–1313 **A**1 9 10 20 **F**2 10 11 12 14 21 22 23 26 27 28 29 33 34 40 44 46 47 48 49 51 52 53 55 58 59 60 61 62 63 64 65 66 69 70 80 81 82 84 85 87 88 92 93 94 95 96 97 106 107 108 110
Primary Contact: John Schon, Administrator and Chief Executive Officer
COO: Jeff Gussert, Director Operations
CFO: John Lee, Director Finance
CMO: Ray Cameron, M.D., Ph.D., Chief of Staff
CIO: Dean Decremer, Chief Information Officer
Web address: www.dchs.org

	13	10	96	4267	46	148967	567	60967	28160	574

⊠ **VETERANS AFFAIRS MEDICAL CENTER**, 325 East H Street, Zip 49801–4792; tel. 906/774–3300, (Total facility includes 40 beds in nursing home–type unit) **A**1 9 **F**4 21 22 23 25 26 27 28 32 38 44 50 52 55 58 61 63 65 66 69 70 77 81 82 88 92 93 94 106 108 109 110 **S** Department of Veterans Affairs, Washington, DC
Primary Contact: Janice M. Boss, CHE, Director
Web address: www.va.gov/sta/guide/home.asp

	45	10	57	1118	43	118527	0	—	—	388

IRON RIVER—Iron County

⊠ **IRON COUNTY COMMUNITY HOSPITAL**, 1400 West Ice Lake Road, Zip 49935–9594; tel. 906/265–6121 **A**1 9 10 18 20 **F**9 12 14 21 23 24 27 28 29 33 34 41 44 46 47 48 49 51 52 55 58 60 61 63 65 66 69 70 81 84 88 92 94 95 96 97 106 107 108 109 110
Primary Contact: Glenn Dobson, Interim Chief Executive Officer
CFO: Glenn Dobson, Chief Financial Officer
Web address: www.icch.org

	23	10	25	1207	11	55232	0	18322	7184	176

IRONWOOD—Gogebic County

⊠ **GRAND VIEW HOSPITAL**, N10561 Grand View Lane, Zip 49938–9622; tel. 906/932–2525 **A**1 9 10 20 **F**2 9 11 12 21 22 23 26 27 28 29 33 35 36 37 39 43 46 48 51 52 53 55 58 59 60 63 64 66 81 82 84 88 89 94 96 97 106 108 **P**6
Primary Contact: David Hartberg, Chief Executive Officer
COO: Robb Kimmes, Director of Human Resources and Operations
CFO: Charmaine Chiantello, Chief Financial Officer
CMO: James Hubbard, M.D., Chief Medical Staff
CIO: Ron Eyer, Chief Management Information Services
Web address: www.gvhs.org

	23	10	54	1425	13	54575	136	21431	8402	182

ISHPEMING—Marquette County

⊠ **BELL HOSPITAL**, 101 South Fourth Street, Zip 49849–2151; tel. 906/486–4431 **A**1 9 10 18 20 **F**4 8 9 11 12 14 26 27 28 29 33 46 48 58 59 60 62 63 66 69 81 82 88 93 95 97 107 108
Primary Contact: Jerome Morasko, President and Chief Executive Officer
COO: Scott Tuma, Chief Operating Officer and Director Human Resources
CFO: Greg Perttula, Chief Financial Officer
CMO: Terry Hayrynen, D.O., Chief of Staff
CIO: Richard Rossway, Director Community Relations
CHR: Scott Tuma, Chief Operating Officer and Director Human Resources
Web address: www.bellmemorial.org

	23	10	18	1504	14	59797	245	20832	10251	241

JACKSON—Jackson County

★ **DOCTORS HOSPITAL**, 110 North Elm Avenue, Zip 49202–3595; tel. 517/787–1440, (Nonreporting) **A**9 10 **S** Ascension Health, Saint Louis, MO
Primary Contact: Victoria Webster, President and Chief Executive Officer
CFO: Alan H. Yeates, Vice President Fiscal Services
CMO: Greg Fuller, M.D., Chief Of Staff
CIO: Ron Standley, Director Information Systems

	23	10	65	—	—	—	—	—	—	—

☐ **DUANE L. WATERS HOSPITAL**, 3857 Cooper Street, Zip 49201–7521; tel. 517/780–5600, (Nonreporting) **A**1
Primary Contact: Gerald De Voss, Acting Administrator

	12	11	86	—	—	—	—	—	—	—

⊠ **FOOTE HEALTH SYSTEM**, 205 North East Avenue, Zip 49201–1789; tel. 517/788–4800 **A**1 9 10 **F**2 3 4 7 9 11 12 14 15 17 21 22 23 26 27 28 29 31 33 36 37 40 41 42 44 46 47 48 50 51 52 53 54 55 57 58 59 60 61 62 63 64 66 69 71 72 73 74 75 76 77 78 81 82 84 85 86 87 88 92 93 94 95 96 98 106 108 109 110
Primary Contact: Georgia R. Fojtasek, President and Chief Executive Officer
COO: Karen Brant, Senior Vice President and Chief Operating Officer
CFO: Jeanne Hettinger, Chief Financial Officer
CIO: Richard Warren, Vice President Health Information Systems
CHR: Jan Blair, Vice President Human Resources
Web address: www.foote.com

	23	10	411	17517	222	351373	1973	226743	99045	2619

MI

Hospital, Address, Telephone, Approval, Facility, and Physician Codes, Health Care System	Classi-fication Codes		Utilization Data					Expense (thousands) of dollars		
★ American Hospital Association (AHA) membership □ Joint Commission on Accreditation of Healthcare Organizations (JCAHO) accreditation ○ American Osteopathic Association (AOA) accreditation △ Commission on Accreditation of Rehabilitation Facilities (CARF) accreditation	Control	Service	Staffed Beds	Admissions	Census	Outpatient Visits	Births	Total	Payroll	Personnel

KALAMAZOO—Kalamazoo County

☒ △ **BORGESS MEDICAL CENTER**, 1521 Gull Road, Zip 49048–1666; tel. 269/226–4800, (Includes BORGESS–PIPP HOSPITAL, Plainwell) **A**1 3 5 7 9 10 **F**2 6 7 9 10 11 12 14 15 17 19 21 22 23 24 26 27 28 29 30 31 32 33 34 35 36 37 38 39 41 42 44 46 47 48 49 50 51 52 53 55 57 58 59 60 61 62 63 64 65 66 68 69 70 71 72 73 74 75 76 77 78 81 82 85 87 88 93 94 95 96 106 107 108 109 110 **P**3 6 8 **S** Ascension Health, Saint Louis, MO Primary Contact: Paul A. Spaude, FACHE, President and Chief Executive Officer COO: Linda Albery, Vice President and Chief Operating Officer CFO: Richard Felbinger, Interim Chief Financial Officer CMO: Sanford Tolchin, M.D., Chief Medical Officer CIO: David Thompson, Chief Information Officer CHR: Laura Lentenbrink, Vice President Human Resources Web address: www.borgess.com	21	10	381	20072	268	389240	1646	310498	124107	2258
☒ **BRONSON METHODIST HOSPITAL**, 601 John Street, Zip 49007–5345; tel. 269/341–6000 **A**1 3 5 8 9 10 **F**2 9 10 11 12 13 14 15 17 19 21 22 23 24 26 27 28 29 30 32 33 34 37 39 40 42 44 45 46 47 48 50 51 52 53 55 56 57 58 59 60 61 62 63 64 65 66 67 68 69 70 75 81 82 84 85 87 88 90 93 94 95 96 97 98 106 107 108 109 110 **P**6 7 **S** Bronson Healthcare Group, Inc., Kalamazoo, MI Primary Contact: Frank J. Sardone, President and Chief Executive Officer COO: Kenneth L. Taft, Executive Vice President and Chief Operating Officer CFO: Mary Meitz, Vice President Finance CMO: Scott Larson, M.D., Vice President Medical Affairs and Chief Medical Officer CHR: Susan M. Ulshate, Senior Vice President Human Resources Web address: www.bronsonhealth.com	23	10	307	20481	256	453585	3294	333403	141476	3304
□ **KALAMAZOO PSYCHIATRIC HOSPITAL**, 1312 Oakland Drive, Zip 49008–1205; tel. 269/337–3000 **A**1 9 10 **F**2 26 27 28 32 37 39 41 44 45 47 58 60 65 66 70 71 73 74 75 76 94 96 106 108 **P**6 Primary Contact: James Coleman, Director	12	22	210	488	178	0	0	32532	17749	463
□ **SELECT SPECIALTY HOSPITAL OF KALAMAZOO**, 601 John Street, Zip 49007; tel. 269/836–1300, (Nonreporting) **A**1 10 Primary Contact: Robert C. Desotelle, Chief Executive Officer	33	49	25	—	—	—	—	—	—	—

KALKASKA—Kalkaska County

★ **KALKASKA MEMORIAL HEALTH CENTER**, 419 South Coral Street, Zip 49646–9438; tel. 231/258–7500, (Total facility includes 88 beds in nursing home–type unit) **A**9 10 18 **F**1 6 12 26 27 28 29 33 45 46 48 52 69 70 81 88 92 94 96 107 108 109 110 **S** Munson Healthcare, Traverse City, MI Primary Contact: James D. Austin, FACHE, Administrator CMO: Albert Brown, M.D., Chief of Staff Web address: www.munsonhealthcare.org	16	10	96	185	85	35637	0	14865	6735	188

L'ANSE—Baraga County

□ **BARAGA COUNTY MEMORIAL HOSPITAL**, 770 North Main Street, Zip 49946–1195; tel. 906/524–3300, (Total facility includes 28 beds in nursing home–type unit) **A**1 9 10 18 **F**2 12 23 27 28 33 36 37 38 48 51 52 61 62 63 69 81 82 85 87 88 92 94 96 97 106 **P**6 Primary Contact: John P. Tembreull, Administrator Web address: www.bcmh.org	13	10	52	638	33	28468	0	10372	7316	157

LAKEVIEW—Montcalm County

SPECTRUM HEALTH – KELSEY CAMPUS See Spectrum Health–United Memorial, Greenville

LANSING—Ingham County

☒ △ **INGHAM REGIONAL MEDICAL CENTER**, 401 West Greenlawn Avenue, Zip 48910–2819; tel. 517/334–2121, (Includes INGHAM REGIONAL MEDICAL CENTER, GREENLAWN CAMPUS; INGHAM REGIONAL MEDICAL CENTER, PENNSYLVANIA CAMPUS, 2727 South Pennsylvania Avenue, Zip 48910; tel. 517/372–8220) **A**1 2 3 5 7 8 9 10 11 12 13 **F**8 9 10 11 12 14 15 16 17 18 19 20 21 22 26 27 28 29 31 32 33 36 37 38 39 40 42 44 46 47 48 49 50 52 55 57 58 59 60 61 62 63 65 66 69 70 71 73 74 75 76 77 81 82 85 87 88 93 94 95 96 106 107 108 109 110 **P**1 **S** McLaren Health Care Corporation, Flint, MI Primary Contact: Dennis M. Litos, President and Chief Executive Officer CFO: Paula Reichle, Vice President Finance and Chief Financial Officer CMO: Geoffrey Linz, M.D., Chief Medical Officer CIO: Sally Bender, Director Information Services Web address: www.irmc.org	23	10	356	18869	237	474919	1951	251969	103732	1808
☒ ○ △ **SPARROW HEALTH SYSTEM**, 1215 East Michigan Avenue, Zip 48912–1811, Mailing Address: P.O. Box 30480, Zip 48909–7980; tel. 517/364–1000 **A**1 2 3 5 7 9 10 11 12 13 **F**1 2 3 4 6 9 10 11 12 13 14 15 17 19 21 22 24 26 27 28 29 30 31 32 33 34 35 36 37 38 39 40 41 42 44 45 46 47 48 49 50 51 52 53 54 55 56 57 58 59 60 61 62 63 64 65 66 67 68 69 70 71 72 73 74 75 76 77 78 79 81 82 84 85 87 88 89 90 92 93 94 95 96 98 106 107 108 109 110 **P**1 6 Primary Contact: Dennis A. Swan, President and Chief Executive Officer CFO: A James Budzinski, Vice President Finance and Chief Financial Officer CMO: Larry Rawsthorne, M.D., Vice President Medical Affairs CIO: Ronald Swenson, M.D., Chief Medical Information Officer CHR: Chris Marin, Vice President Human Resources Web address: www.sparrow.org	23	10	531	27828	379	620847	3797	444873	212544	4375

Many Facility Codes have changed. Please refer to the AHA Guide Code Chart.

© 2005 AHA Guide

Hospital, Address, Telephone, Approval, Facility, and Physician Codes, Health Care System	Classification Codes		Utilization Data					Expense (thousands) of dollars		
★ American Hospital Association (AHA) membership □ Joint Commission on Accreditation of Healthcare Organizations (JCAHO) accreditation ○ American Osteopathic Association (AOA) accreditation △ Commission on Accreditation of Rehabilitation Facilities (CARF) accreditation	Control	Service	Staffed Beds	Admissions	Census	Outpatient Visits	Births	Total	Payroll	Personnel

SPARROW SPECIALTY HOSPITAL, 1210 West Saginaw Street, Zip 48915; tel. 517/364–6800, (Nonreporting) **A**10
Primary Contact: Don Romain, Chief Executive Officer

| | 33 | 49 | 36 | — | — | — | — | — | — | — |

LAPEER—Lapeer County

□ **LAPEER REGIONAL MEDICAL CENTER**, (Formerly Lapeer Regional Hospital), 1375 North Main Street, Zip 48446–1376; tel. 810/667–5500, (Total facility includes 19 beds in nursing home–type unit) **A**1 9 10 **F**2 3 4 9 11 14 15 17 21 22 23 26 27 28 29 31 33 34 35 37 39 40 44 46 47 48 50 52 55 59 60 61 62 63 65 66 68 69 71 73 74 75 77 81 82 84 85 88 92 93 94 95 96 108 **S** McLaren Health Care Corporation, Flint, MI
Primary Contact: Barton Buxton, Chief Executive Officer
Web address: www.lapeerhospital.org

| | 23 | 10 | 145 | 6336 | 84 | 76716 | 850 | 60033 | 26428 | — |

LAURIUM—Houghton County

⊞ **KEWEENAW MEMORIAL MEDICAL CENTER**, 205 Osceola Street, Zip 49913–2199; tel. 906/337–6500 **A**1 9 10 18 **F**2 8 9 11 12 14 21 22 23 28 29 33 41 44 46 48 50 55 59 62 63 66 69 81 82 88 89 93 94 95 96 97 108 109 **P**6
Primary Contact: Charles Nelson, Chief Executive Officer
CFO: Michael Hagwell, Chief Financial Officer
CMO: Timothy Nelson, M.D., Chief of Staff
CHR: Phyllis Clevenger, Manager Human Resources
Web address: www.kmmc.org

| | 23 | 10 | 25 | 1475 | 19 | 36287 | 74 | 24308 | — | 324 |

LINCOLN PARK—Wayne County

KINDRED HOSPITAL–DETROIT, 26400 West Outer Drive, Zip 48146; tel. 313/386–2000, (Nonreporting) **A**10
Primary Contact: Shellye Yaklin, Chief Executive Officer

| | 33 | 49 | 218 | — | — | — | — | — | — | — |

LIVONIA—Wayne County

⊞ **ST. MARY MERCY HOSPITAL**, 36475 West Five Mile Road, Zip 48154–1988; tel. 734/655–4800 **A**1 2 9 10 **F**2 3 4 7 9 10 11 12 15 21 22 23 26 27 28 29 30 31 33 34 35 36 37 38 39 40 44 45 46 48 49 52 53 55 57 58 59 60 61 62 63 64 65 69 71 72 73 74 75 76 77 81 84 85 86 87 88 93 94 96 106 107 108 109 110 **P**6 **S** Trinity Health, Novi, MI
Primary Contact: David A. Spivey, President and Chief Executive Officer
CFO: Michael Gusho, Vice President and Chief Financial Officer
CMO: Asit Gokli, M.D., Vice President Medical Affairs
CIO: Julie Moran, Director Information Services
CHR: Kenneth Anttzak, Vice President
Web address: www.stmarymercy.org

| | 21 | 10 | 247 | 13241 | 159 | 151554 | 1293 | 132667 | 58427 | 1056 |

LUDINGTON—Mason County

MEMORIAL MEDICAL CENTER OF WEST MICHIGAN, One Atkinson Drive, Zip 49431–1999; tel. 231/843–2591 **A**9 10 20 **F**6 9 11 12 15 23 26 27 28 29 33 37 48 51 53 55 57 58 59 60 61 62 63 64 69 70 71 73 75 76 81 82 84 87 88 93 94 96 108 109 110 **P**8
Primary Contact: Robert C. Marquardt, FACHE, President and Chief Executive Officer
Web address: www.mmcwm.com

| | 23 | 10 | 85 | 3348 | 41 | 83896 | 396 | 41769 | 17266 | 387 |

MADISON HEIGHTS—Oakland County

MICHIGAN ORTHOPAEDIC SPECIALTY HOSPITAL, 30671 Stephenson Highway, Zip 48071–1678; tel. 248/733–2200 **A**10 **F**2 21 22 27 28 29 33 37 39 46 47 48 52 53 55 58 62 63 65 66 69 71 72 81 88 94 95 110 **S** Detroit Medical Center, Detroit, MI
Primary Contact: Frank P. Iacobell, President
Web address: www.michiganorthopaedic.org

| | 23 | 47 | 64 | 2074 | 29 | 4748 | 0 | 24822 | 8650 | 168 |

★ ○ **ST. JOHN OAKLAND HOSPITAL**, 27351 Dequindre, Zip 48071–3499; tel. 248/967–7000 **A**9 10 11 12 13 **F**2 10 12 15 21 22 23 24 26 27 28 29 30 31 33 35 36 37 38 40 41 44 45 46 47 48 49 50 52 53 55 57 58 60 61 62 63 64 65 66 69 70 71 73 74 75 77 78 81 82 83 84 85 87 88 92 93 94 96 106 107 108 109 110 **P**4 5 6 8 **S** Ascension Health, Saint Louis, MO
Primary Contact: Robert Deputat, President
COO: Christine Fornal, Chief Nursing Executive
CFO: Jennifer Fennell, Chief Financial Officer
CMO: Gary Berg, D.O., Vice President Medical Affairs
Web address: www.stjohn.org

| | 21 | 10 | 164 | 7594 | 111 | 79916 | 0 | 81294 | 40064 | 850 |

MANISTEE—Manistee County

★ **WEST SHORE MEDICAL CENTER**, 1465 East Parkdale Avenue, Zip 49660–9785; tel. 231/398–1000 **A**9 10 20 **F**6 9 11 12 14 21 22 26 28 32 33 34 41 42 46 48 52 53 58 59 60 62 63 64 69 81 87 88 94 96 106 108 109
Primary Contact: Burton O. Parks, III, President
CFO: Donn J. Lemmer, Vice President Finance
CIO: Louise Haik, Information Services Manager
CHR: Steve Solomon, Director Human Resources
Web address: www.westshoremedcenter.org

| | 13 | 10 | 54 | 1754 | 19 | 69031 | 160 | 30928 | 12427 | 325 |

MI

Hospital, Address, Telephone, Approval, Facility, and Physician Codes, Health Care System	Classi-fication Codes		Utilization Data					Expense (thousands) of dollars		
★ American Hospital Association (AHA) membership □ Joint Commission on Accreditation of Healthcare Organizations (JCAHO) accreditation ○ American Osteopathic Association (AOA) accreditation △ Commission on Accreditation of Rehabilitation Facilities (CARF) accreditation	Control	Service	Staffed Beds	Admissions	Census	Outpatient Visits	Births	Total	Payroll	Personnel

MANISTIQUE—Schoolcraft County

★ **SCHOOLCRAFT MEMORIAL HOSPITAL**, 500 Main Street, Zip 49854–0000; tel. 906/341–3200 **A**9 10 18 **F**2 8 9 12 21 22 23 24 26 27 28 29 30 32 33 35 36 37 38 39 41 44 45 46 47 48 51 52 58 60 61 62 63 64 65 66 69 70 78 81 82 84 85 87 88 92 93 94 96 97 106 107 108 109 **P**6
Primary Contact: Frederick J. Makowski, Chief Executive Officer
COO: Joy Strand, Chief Operating Officer
CFO: Tanya Edwards, Chief Financial Officer
CMO: Douglas LaBelle, M.D., Chief of Staff
CIO: Sherry Arnold, Risk Management
CHR: Gina Lindquist, Director Human Resources
Web address: www.uphcn.org/uphcn/smh.html
— 13 10 25 499 4 36633 0 16723 8700 184

MARLETTE—Sanilac County

⊠ △ **MARLETTE COMMUNITY HOSPITAL**, 2770 Main Street, Zip 48453–0307, Mailing Address: P.O. Box 307, Zip 48453–0307; tel. 989/635–4000, (Total facility includes 43 beds in nursing home–type unit) **A**1 7 9 10 **F**2 6 8 9 12 21 24 26 27 28 29 31 33 36 37 38 39 42 44 45 46 47 48 52 53 58 60 62 63 64 65 66 68 69 70 81 82 84 86 88 91 92 93 94 95 96 98 106 108 **P**6
S Quorum Health Resources, Plano, TX
Primary Contact: David S. McEwen, Chief Executive Officer
CFO: Daniel Babcock, Chief Financial Officer
CIO: Daniel Babcock, Chief Financial Officer
CHR: Diane Black, Human Resources Director
Web address: www.marlettecommunityhospital.com
— 23 10 91 1217 57 41823 0 16190 12571 336

MARQUETTE—Marquette County

⊠ △ **MARQUETTE GENERAL HEALTH SYSTEM**, 580 West College Avenue, Zip 49855–2794; tel. 906/228–9440 **A**1 2 3 5 7 9 10 13 19 20 **F**2 3 4 6 8 9 11 12 14 15 17 19 21 22 23 24 27 28 29 31 32 33 37 38 40 42 44 45 46 47 48 49 51 52 53 55 56 57 58 59 60 61 62 63 64 65 66 68 69 70 71 72 73 74 75 76 77 79 80 81 82 84 85 86 87 88 89 93 94 95 96 98 106 107 108 109 110 **P**6
Primary Contact: William Nemacheck, Chief Executive Officer
CFO: Mike Beckstrom, Chief Financial Officer
CIO: Jim Sundberg, Director Information Systems
Web address: www.mgh.org
— 23 10 290 12077 164 381367 744 233702 100437 2121

MARSHALL—Calhoun County

⊠ **OAKLAWN HOSPITAL**, 200 North Madison Street, Zip 49068–1199; tel. 269/781–4271 **A**1 9 10 **F**2 9 11 12 21 23 26 27 28 29 31 33 41 46 47 48 51 52 55 57 58 59 60 61 62 63 65 66 69 70 71 73 74 75 76 77 78 81 82 84 85 86 87 88 93 94 95 96 108
Primary Contact: Rob Covert, President and Chief Executive Officer
CFO: Colleen Koppenhaver, Chief Financial Officer
CIO: Natalie Spivak, Director Information Services
Web address: www.oaklawnhospital.org
— 23 10 74 3470 34 146901 621 53462 24509 604

MIDLAND—Midland County

⊠ **MIDMICHIGAN MEDICAL CENTER–MIDLAND**, 4005 Orchard Drive, Zip 48670–0001; tel. 989/839–3000, (Nonreporting) **A**1 2 3 5 9 10 12 13 20
S MidMichigan Health, Midland, MI
Primary Contact: Richard M. Reynolds, President
CFO: Gregory H. Rogers, Senior Vice President and Treasurer
CIO: C Harlan Goodrich, Vice President & Chief Information Officer
Web address: www.midmichigan.org
— 23 10 250 — — — — — — —

MONROE—Monroe County

⊠ **MERCY MEMORIAL HOSPITAL SYSTEM**, 718 North Macomb Street, Zip 48162–2930; tel. 734/240–8400 **A**1 9 10 **F**2 9 11 12 21 22 26 27 28 29 31 33 34 35 36 38 39 44 46 47 48 50 51 52 53 54 55 57 58 59 60 62 63 65 66 69 71 73 74 75 76 77 81 82 84 87 88 93 94 95 96 106 107 108 109 110
Primary Contact: Daniel L. Wakeman, President and Chief Executive Officer
CFO: Mark Rossman, Vice President Finance and Chief Financial Officer
CMO: Medhat Ashamalla, M.D., Vice President Medical Affairs
CIO: William Stefl, Chief Information Officer
CHR: Dennis Pogarch, Vice President Human Resources
Web address: www.mercymemorial.org
— 23 10 177 9601 105 182785 895 105475 46509 1283

MOUNT CLEMENS—Macomb County

★ ○ **MOUNT CLEMENS GENERAL HOSPITAL**, 1000 Harrington Boulevard, Zip 48043–2992; tel. 586/493–8000 **A**9 10 11 12 13 **F**2 6 9 10 11 12 14 15 17 19 21 22 23 26 27 28 29 30 31 33 35 37 39 40 42 44 46 47 48 50 51 52 55 57 58 59 60 61 62 63 64 65 66 69 70 79 80 81 82 85 87 88 93 94 95 96 104 106 107 108 109 110 **P**8
Primary Contact: Robert Milewski, President and Chief Executive Officer
COO: Mark Vipperman, Executive Vice President and Chief Operating Officer
CFO: Joseph Scallen, Jr, Senior Vice President Finance and Chief Financial Officer
CMO: Michael W. Tawney, M.D., Senior Vice President Medical Affairs
CHR: David Klinger, Vice President Human Resources
Web address: www.mcgh.org
— 23 10 288 15943 180 317355 1739 245969 101965 1662

Many Facility Codes have changed. Please refer to the AHA Guide Code Chart.

MI

Hospital, Address, Telephone, Approval, Facility, and Physician Codes, Health Care System	Classi-fication Codes		Utilization Data					Expense (thousands) of dollars		
	Control	Service	Staffed Beds	Admissions	Census	Outpatient Visits	Births	Total	Payroll	Personnel

★ American Hospital Association (AHA) membership
□ Joint Commission on Accreditation of Healthcare Organizations (JCAHO) accreditation
○ American Osteopathic Association (AOA) accreditation
△ Commission on Accreditation of Rehabilitation Facilities (CARF) accreditation

□ **SELECT SPECIALTY HOSPITAL–MOUNT CLEMENS**, 215 North Avenue, Zip 48043; tel. 586/307–9000, (Nonreporting) **A**1 10
Primary Contact: Linda Steiger, Administrator
ST. JOSEPH'S MERCY HOSPITAL–EAST See St. Joseph's Mercy of Macomb, Clinton Township
| | 33 | 80 | 32 | — | — | — | — | — | — | — |

MOUNT PLEASANT—Isabella County
⊠ ○ **CENTRAL MICHIGAN COMMUNITY HOSPITAL**, 1221 South Drive, Zip 48858–3234; tel. 989/772–6700 **A**1 9 10 11 19 **F**2 9 10 11 12 21 22 23 24 25 26 27 28 29 30 32 33 38 39 41 42 44 46 47 48 50 51 52 53 55 57 58 59 60 61 62 63 64 65 66 69 70 75 81 82 85 87 88 93 94 95 96 107 108 109 110 **P**1
Primary Contact: Roger Kerr, President and Chief Executive Officer
COO: Gregg Beeg, Vice President Finance and Operations
CFO: Gregg Beeg, Vice President Finance and Operations
CMO: Christian Allan, M.D., Chief Medical Officer
CIO: Gil Lalo, Interim Chief Executive Officer Informtion Services
Web address: www.cmch.org
| | 23 | 10 | 62 | 3537 | 30 | 150159 | 522 | 54480 | 22853 | 547 |

MUNISING—Alger County
MUNISING MEMORIAL HOSPITAL, 1500 Sand Point Road, Zip 49862–1406; tel. 906/387–4110, (Nonreporting) **A**9 10 18
Primary Contact: Carl J. Velte, Chief Executive Officer
| | 23 | 10 | 25 | — | — | — | — | — | — | — |

MUSKEGON—Muskegon County
□ **HACKLEY HEALTH**, 1700 Clinton Street, Zip 49443–3302, Mailing Address: P.O. Box 3302, Zip 49443–3302; tel. 231/726–3511 **A**1 2 9 10 **F**2 10 11 12 21 22 23 26 27 29 32 33 37 39 41 43 45 46 47 48 50 52 53 55 57 58 59 60 61 62 63 65 69 70 71 75 76 77 78 79 81 82 84 85 88 93 94 95 96 108 109 110 **P**6 **S** Hackley Health System, Muskegon, MI
Primary Contact: Gordon A. Mudler, President and Chief Executive Officer
Web address: www.hackley.org
| | 23 | 10 | 181 | 9359 | 105 | 241040 | 976 | 138273 | 57717 | 1183 |

□ **LIFECARE HOSPITALS OF WEST MICHIGAN**, 1700 Oak Avenue, 3rd Floor, Zip 49442; tel. 231/777–6202 **A**1 10 **F**21 26 28 57 58 94 110 **S** LifeCare Management Services, Plano, TX
Primary Contact: Jevne Conover, Administrator
Web address: www.lifecare–hospital.com
| | 33 | 10 | 20 | 217 | 15 | 0 | 0 | 6942 | — | — |

⊠ ○ **MERCY GENERAL HEALTH PARTNERS**, 1500 East Sherman Boulevard, Zip 49443–1849; tel. 231/739–9341, (Includes MERCY GENERAL HEALTH PARTNERS–MERCY CAMPUS; MERCY GENERAL HEALTH PARTNERS–MUSKEGON GENERAL CAMPUS, 1700 Oak Avenue, Zip 49442–2407; tel. 616/773–3311) **A**1 2 9 10 11 12 13 **F**2 9 10 11 12 14 15 17 19 21 22 23 24 26 27 28 29 30 33 35 37 39 41 42 44 46 47 48 50 52 53 57 58 59 60 61 62 63 64 65 66 68 69 70 81 82 84 86 87 88 93 94 95 96 106 107 108 109 110 **P**6 8 **S** Trinity Health, Novi, MI
Primary Contact: Roger Spoelman, President and Chief Executive Officer
COO: Greg Loomis, Chief Operation Officer
CFO: Gary Allore, Chief Financial Officer
CMO: Remington Sprague, M.D., Chief Medical Officer
CIO: Kelly Kurburski, Director Public Relations and Marketing
Web address: www.mghp.com
| | 23 | 10 | 201 | 11245 | 135 | — | — | 179050 | 76691 | 1481 |

□ **SELECT SPECIALTY HOSPITAL OF WESTERN MICHIGAN**, 1700 Clinton Street, Suite S2, Zip 49442; tel. 231/728–5800, (Nonreporting) **A**1 10
Primary Contact: Torrey Husmann, Chief Executive Officer
| | 33 | 80 | 32 | — | — | — | — | — | — | — |

NEW BALTIMORE—Macomb County
□ **HARBOR OAKS HOSPITAL**, 35031 23 Mile Road, Zip 48047–2097; tel. 586/725–5777, (Nonreporting) **A**1 9 10 **S** Pioneer Behavioral Health, Peabody, MA
Primary Contact: Patrick Moallemian, Chief Executive Officer
Web address: www.harboroaks.com
| | 33 | 22 | 64 | — | — | — | — | — | — | — |

NEWBERRY—Luce County
⊠ **HELEN NEWBERRY JOY HOSPITAL**, 502 West Harrie Street, Zip 49868–0070; tel. 906/293–9200, (Includes HELEN NEWBERRY JOY HOSPITAL ANNEX), (Total facility includes 48 beds in nursing home–type unit) **A**1 9 10 18 **F**12 21 22 23 24 26 27 28 29 30 31 33 35 36 37 38 41 42 45 46 47 48 52 58 61 63 64 65 66 68 69 70 81 82 87 88 92 94 95 96 97 98 106 107 110 **P**6
Primary Contact: Wayne P. Hellerstedt, Chief Executive Officer
CFO: Scott Pillion, Chief Financial Officer
CMO: Richard Armstrong, M.D., Chief of Staff
CIO: Steve Kinkaid, Director Information Systems
CHR: Roger Bergh, Director Human Resources
Web address: www.hnjh.org
| | 13 | 10 | 73 | 629 | 51 | 43034 | 0 | 20909 | 9383 | 239 |

NILES—Berrien County
LAKELAND HOSPITAL–NILES See Lakeland Hospital–St. Joseph, Saint Joseph

NORTHPORT—Leelanau County
★ **LEELANAU MEMORIAL HEALTH CENTER**, 215 South High Street, Zip 49670–9755, Mailing Address: P.O. Box 217, Zip 49670–0217; tel. 231/386–0000, (Total facility includes 72 beds in nursing home–type unit) (Nonreporting) **A**9 10 18 **S** Munson Healthcare, Traverse City, MI
Primary Contact: Kathrine Garthe, Administrator
CFO: Timothy Fritz, Director Accounting and Taxation
CIO: Christopher J. Podges, Chief Information Officer
CHR: Dorene Bell, Human Resources Coordinator
Web address: www.munsonhealthcare.org
| | 23 | 80 | 95 | — | — | — | — | — | — | — |

Hospital, Address, Telephone, Approval, Facility, and Physician Codes, Health Care System	Classi-fication Codes		Utilization Data					Expense (thousands) of dollars		
★ American Hospital Association (AHA) membership □ Joint Commission on Accreditation of Healthcare Organizations (JCAHO) accreditation ○ American Osteopathic Association (AOA) accreditation △ Commission on Accreditation of Rehabilitation Facilities (CARF) accreditation	Control	Service	Staffed Beds	Admissions	Census	Outpatient Visits	Births	Total	Payroll	Personnel

NORTHVILLE—Wayne County

□ **HAWTHORN CENTER**, 18471 Haggerty Road, Zip 48167–9575; tel. 248/735–6771, (Nonreporting) **A**1 3 5 9
Primary Contact: Shobhana Joshi, M.D., Facility Director

| | 12 | 52 | 118 | — | — | — | — | — | — | — |

ONTONAGON—Ontonagon County

⊠ **ONTONAGON MEMORIAL HOSPITAL**, 601 Seventh Street, Zip 49953–1496; tel. 906/884–4134, (Total facility includes 46 beds in nursing home–type unit) (Nonreporting) **A**1 9 10 18
Primary Contact: Fred Nelson, Administrator
COO: Michael R. Drew, Assistant Administrator and Director of Pharmacy
CFO: Chuck Bulinski, Chief Financial Officer
CMO: Eric Maki, M.D., Director Medical Staff
CIO: Pam Karttunen, Administrative Assistant
CHR: Gina Linna, Administrative Assistant
Web address: www.omh.org

| | 14 | 10 | 71 | — | — | — | — | — | — | — |

OWOSSO—Shiawassee County

⊠ **MEMORIAL HEALTHCARE**, 826 West King Street, Zip 48867–2198; tel. 989/723–5211, (Total facility includes 16 beds in nursing home–type unit) **A**1 2 9 10 **F**1 9 10 11 12 21 22 23 26 27 28 29 31 33 36 37 38 39 40 46 47 48 51 52 54 55 57 58 59 60 61 62 63 64 65 66 68 69 70 71 73 74 75 76 81 82 84 85 88 92 93 94 95 96 107 108 109 110 **P**1 6
Primary Contact: Cheryl Peterson, President and Chief Executive Officer
CFO: Michael Grisdela, Vice President Administration and Chief Financial Officer
CIO: Tom Ogg, Vice President Information, Support Services and Chief Information Officer
CHR: Geoffrey Washburn, Vice President Human Resources
Web address: www.memorialhealthcare.org

| | 23 | 10 | 131 | 5597 | 72 | 264014 | 610 | 66002 | 31584 | 1081 |

PAW PAW—Van Buren County

⊠ **LAKEVIEW COMMUNITY HOSPITAL**, 408 Hazen Street, Zip 49079–0209, Mailing Address: P.O. Box 209, Zip 49079–0209; tel. 269/657–3141, (Total facility includes 120 beds in nursing home–type unit) **A**1 9 10 **F**2 9 12 11 22 26 27 28 29 32 33 37 44 48 51 52 53 55 57 58 59 60 62 63 64 65 66 69 71 73 74 75 76 81 88 92 94 96 107 108 109 110 **P**6 **S** Quorum Health Resources, Plano, TX
Primary Contact: Rick Ament, President and Chief Executive Officer
COO: Sally Berglin, Vice President Patient Care Services
CMO: Ravinder P. Mediratta, M.D., Chief of Staff
CHR: Jeff Johnson, Vice President Human Resources and Community Services
Web address: www.lakeviewcares.com

| | 16 | 10 | 174 | 1597 | 138 | 78275 | 0 | 38165 | 18548 | 423 |

PETOSKEY—Emmet County

□ **NORTHERN MICHIGAN REGIONAL HEALTH SYSTEM**, 416 Connable Avenue, Zip 49770–2297; tel. 231/487–4000 **A**1 2 9 10 19 20 **F**1 2 9 11 12 21 22 23 24 26 27 28 29 33 35 36 38 39 40 44 46 47 48 49 51 52 55 56 57 58 59 60 61 62 63 65 66 68 69 71 72 73 74 75 79 81 82 84 85 86 88 93 94 95 96 106 108 110 **P**6
Primary Contact: Thomas C. Mroczkowski, President and Chief Executive Officer
Web address: www.northernhealth.org

| | 23 | 10 | 192 | 9251 | 123 | — | — | — | — | — |

PIGEON—Huron County

⊠ **SCHEURER HOSPITAL**, 170 North Caseville Road, Zip 48755–9704; tel. 989/453–3223, (Total facility includes 19 beds in nursing home–type unit) **A**1 9 10 18 **F**2 6 8 9 12 22 23 27 28 30 33 35 41 44 45 46 48 52 53 54 58 61 62 63 64 65 66 69 70 81 82 87 88 91 92 94 95 96 97 108 **P**6
Primary Contact: Dwight Gascho, President and Chief Executive Officer
CFO: Terry Lutz, Chief Financial Officer
CMO: Paul Scaddan, M.D., Chief of Staff
CIO: Suzanne LeMaire, Health Information Management Services Manager
CHR: Greg Foy, Human Resources System Leader
Web address: www.scheurer.org

| | 23 | 10 | 44 | 700 | 24 | 45115 | 1 | 22566 | 10748 | 258 |

PLAINWELL—Allegan County

BORGESS–PIPP HOSPITAL See Borgess Medical Center, Kalamazoo

PONTIAC—Oakland County

□ **NORTH OAKLAND MEDICAL CENTERS**, 461 West Huron Street, Zip 48341–1651; tel. 248/857–7200 **A**1 3 5 9 10 **F**2 9 10 11 12 14 15 21 22 23 26 27 28 29 30 31 32 33 35 39 42 44 45 46 47 48 49 50 52 53 55 56 57 58 59 60 61 62 63 64 65 66 68 69 70 71 73 74 75 76 77 81 82 84 87 88 89 93 94 96 98 107 108 109 **P**8
Primary Contact: Robert L. Davis, President and Chief Executive Officer
Web address: www.nomc.org

| | 23 | 10 | 188 | 8479 | 119 | 134360 | 1448 | 117041 | 56143 | 1065 |

○ **POH MEDICAL CENTER**, 50 North Perry Street, Zip 48342–2253; tel. 248/338–5000, (Total facility includes 120 beds in nursing home–type unit) (Nonreporting) **A**9 10 11 12 13
Primary Contact: Patrick Lamberti, Chief Executive Officer
Web address: www.pohmedical.org

| | 23 | 10 | 262 | — | — | — | — | — | — | — |

□ **SELECT SPECIALTY HOSPITAL–PONTIAC**, 44405 Woodward Avenue, 8th Floor, Zip 48341; tel. 248/452–5206, (Nonreporting) **A**1 10
Primary Contact: Peggy Kingston, Chief Executive Officer and Administrator

| | 33 | 80 | 32 | — | — | — | — | — | — | — |

Many Facility Codes have changed. Please refer to the AHA Guide Code Chart.   © 2005 AHA Guide

Hospital, Address, Telephone, Approval, Facility, and Physician Codes, Health Care System	Classi-fication Codes		Utilization Data					Expense (thousands) of dollars		
★ American Hospital Association (AHA) membership □ Joint Commission on Accreditation of Healthcare Organizations (JCAHO) accreditation ○ American Osteopathic Association (AOA) accreditation △ Commission on Accreditation of Rehabilitation Facilities (CARF) accreditation	Control	Service	Staffed Beds	Admissions	Census	Outpatient Visits	Births	Total	Payroll	Personnel
⊠ **ST. JOSEPH MERCY OAKLAND**, 44405 Woodward Avenue, Zip 48341–2985; tel. 248/858–3000 **A**1 2 3 5 9 10 13 **F**2 3 4 9 10 11 12 13 14 15 17 19 21 22 23 24 26 27 28 29 31 33 35 37 38 39 40 42 44 46 47 48 49 52 53 55 56 57 58 59 60 61 62 63 64 65 66 67 68 69 70 71 72 73 74 75 76 77 78 81 82 84 85 86 88 89 90 92 93 94 95 96 106 107 108 109 **S** Trinity Health, Novi, MI Primary Contact: Jack Weiner, President and Chief Executive Officer COO: Barbara Hertzler, Chief Operating Officer CFO: Cynthia Roush, Vice President Finance and Chief Financial Officer CMO: Donald Bignotti, M.D., Vice President Medical Affairs CIO: Robert Jones, Director Management Information Systems CHR: Deanna Kinney–Smith, Director Employee and Labor Relations Web address: www.stjoesoakland.com	21	10	478	19358	239	416556	2318	274316	110417	2174
PORT HURON—St. Clair County										
⊠ **MERCY HOSPITAL**, 2601 Electric Avenue, Zip 48060–6518; tel. 810/985–1500 **A**1 2 9 10 **F**2 9 12 15 21 22 23 26 27 28 29 33 34 37 38 39 42 46 48 50 52 55 57 58 60 61 62 63 64 65 66 68 69 80 81 82 86 87 88 94 95 96 108 109 110 **P**6 8 **S** Trinity Health, Novi, MI Primary Contact: Peter Karadjoff, President and Chief Executive Officer COO: Dannette Hayman, Chief Operating Officer CFO: Tom Goldenbogen, Chief Financial Officer CIO: Cathy Geiger, Director Information Services Web address: www.mercyporthuron.com	21	10	119	4772	63	151787	0	70833	27879	649
⊠ **PORT HURON HOSPITAL**, 1221 Pine Grove Avenue, Zip 48061–5011; tel. 810/987–5000 **A**1 2 9 10 **F**1 2 4 9 10 11 12 14 15 17 19 21 22 23 24 26 27 28 29 30 32 33 34 35 37 38 39 42 44 46 47 48 50 52 53 55 56 57 58 59 61 62 63 64 65 66 69 70 71 72 73 74 75 76 77 78 81 82 85 88 93 94 95 96 98 107 108 109 110 **P**6 8 **S** Blue Water Health Services Corporation, Port Huron, MI Primary Contact: Brian M. Connolly, President and Chief Executive Officer CFO: James B. Bridge, Vice President Finance CMO: Daniel Angeli, D.O., Vice President Medical Affairs CIO: Mary Beth Mikols, Interim Director Information Systems CHR: Dennis Hoover, Vice President Human Resources Web address: www.porthuronhosp.org	23	10	186	10587	124	250380	1588	113989	47941	1105
REED CITY—Osceola County										
⊠ **SPECTRUM HEALTH–REED CITY CAMPUS**, 300 North Patterson Road, Zip 49677–0075, Mailing Address: P.O. Box 75, Zip 49677–0075; tel. 231/832–3271, (Total facility includes 54 beds in nursing home–type unit) **A**1 9 10 18 **F**2 12 14 15 21 22 23 26 27 28 33 39 41 44 46 48 58 60 61 62 63 69 70 80 81 82 84 85 87 88 92 93 94 95 108 **P**6 **S** Spectrum Health, Grand Rapids, MI Primary Contact: Thomas D. Kaufman, President and Chief Executive Officer COO: Linda Rubin, Chief Operating Officer CFO: Thomas Knoerl, Chief Financial Officer CMO: Mark Marzolf, M.D., Chief of Staff CHR: Erika Duncan, Chief Human Resources Officer Web address: www.spectrum–health.org	23	10	82	1640	64	76071	—	28922	12934	320
ROCHESTER—Oakland County										
□ △ **CRITTENTON HOSPITAL MEDICAL CENTER**, 1101 West University Drive, Zip 48307–1831; tel. 248/652–5000 **A**1 2 7 9 10 **F**2 9 10 11 12 14 15 17 19 21 22 23 24 26 27 28 29 30 32 33 35 36 37 38 39 41 45 46 47 48 49 51 52 53 57 58 59 60 61 62 63 65 66 68 69 70 71 73 74 75 79 81 82 84 93 94 95 96 98 106 107 108 109 110 **P**5 Primary Contact: Lynn C. Orfgen, President and Chief Executive Officer Web address: www.crittenton.com	23	10	226	10027	130	182347	1223	142850	55129	1082
ROGERS CITY—Presque Isle County										
□ △ **ROGERS CITY REHABILITATION HOSPITAL**, 555 North Bradley Highway, Zip 49779–1599; tel. 989/734–7545, (Nonreporting) **A**1 7 9 10 Primary Contact: Nancy Dextrom, Executive Director Web address: www.rogerscityrehab.com	33	46	18	—	—	—	—	—	—	—
ROMEO—Macomb County										
ST. JOSEPH'S MERCY–NORTH See St. Joseph's Mercy of Macomb, Clinton Township										
ROYAL OAK—Oakland County										
⊠ **WILLIAM BEAUMONT HOSPITAL–ROYAL OAK**, 3601 West Thirteen Mile Road, Zip 48073–6769; tel. 248/551–5000 **A**1 2 3 5 8 9 10 **F**2 9 10 12 14 15 17 19 21 22 23 26 27 28 29 30 31 33 34 35 36 37 38 39 40 42 44 46 47 48 49 50 52 53 55 56 57 58 59 60 61 62 63 64 65 66 67 68 69 70 71 72 73 74 75 76 78 79 80 81 82 83 84 85 86 87 88 89 90 92 93 94 95 96 101 106 108 109 110 **P**6 8 **S** William Beaumont Hospitals, Royal Oak, MI Primary Contact: John D. Labriola, Senior Vice President and Hospital Director COO: John R. Graham, Vice President of Operations CFO: Richard P. Swaine, Vice President CMO: Leslie Rocher, M.D., Vice President Clinical Affairs and Chairman Internal Medicine CIO: Paul Peabody, Vice President and Chief Information Officer CHR: Jay Holden, Director Human Resources Web address: www.beaumonthospitals.com	23	10	1061	57970	823	1056987	6586	921521	381615	9141

MI

Hospital, Address, Telephone, Approval, Facility, and Physician Codes, Health Care System	Classification Codes		Utilization Data					Expense (thousands) of dollars		
	Control	Service	Staffed Beds	Admissions	Census	Outpatient Visits	Births	Total	Payroll	Personnel

★ American Hospital Association (AHA) membership
□ Joint Commission on Accreditation of Healthcare Organizations (JCAHO) accreditation
○ American Osteopathic Association (AOA) accreditation
△ Commission on Accreditation of Rehabilitation Facilities (CARF) accreditation

SAGINAW—Saginaw County

⊞ **ALEDA E. LUTZ VETERANS AFFAIRS MEDICAL CENTER**, 1500 Weiss Street, Zip 48602–5298; tel. 989/497–2500, (Total facility includes 81 beds in nursing home–type unit) **A**1 9 **F**2 4 9 12 14 21 22 23 26 27 28 29 30 31 32 33 35 36 37 38 39 41 42 44 45 46 47 48 50 52 53 55 57 58 60 63 64 65 66 69 70 73 74 75 76 77 81 82 88 92 94 95 96 97 99 100 101 102 103 104 105 106 107 108 109 110 **P**6 **S** Department of Veterans Affairs, Washington, DC Primary Contact: Gabriel Perez, Chief Executive Officer and Medical Director CFO: Angela Morris, Fiscal Officer CIO: Bev Doyle, Chief Information Resource Management CHR: Shelly Pullen, Chief Human Resources Management Service Web address: www.va.gov/sta/guide/home.asp	45	10	114	1510	81	147712	0	46641	—	612
○ △ **COVENANT MEDICAL CENTER**, 1447 North Harrison, Zip 48602–4785; tel. 989/583–0000, (Includes COVENANT MEDICAL CENTER–COOPER, 700 Cooper Avenue, Zip 48602–5399; tel. 517/583–0000; COVENANT MEDICAL CENTER–HARRISON, 1447 North Harrison Street, tel. 517/583–0000), (Total facility includes 20 beds in nursing home–type unit) **A**7 9 10 11 **F**2 9 11 12 14 15 17 19 21 22 23 26 27 28 29 30 33 34 36 37 38 39 42 45 46 48 49 50 51 52 55 56 57 58 59 60 61 62 63 65 66 67 68 69 70 81 82 84 87 88 92 93 94 95 96 106 107 108 109 110 **P**7 8 Primary Contact: Spencer Maidlow, President and Chief Executive Officer Web address: www.covenanthealthcare.com	23	10	521	27115	347	512979	3566	333575	138667	3730
□ △ **HEALTHSOURCE SAGINAW**, (Long Term Care, Rehab, Psychia), 3340 Hospital Road, Zip 48603–9623, Mailing Address: P.O. Box 6280, Zip 48608–6280; tel. 989/790–7700, (Total facility includes 213 beds in nursing home–type unit) **A**1 3 7 9 10 **F**3 4 9 37 44 45 50 52 58 60 65 66 68 69 71 72 73 74 75 76 77 92 94 96 108 110 Primary Contact: Lester Heyboer, Jr, President and Chief Executive Officer	23	49	319	2654	231	1874	0	26675	12520	401
⊞ **SAINT MARY'S MEDICAL CENTER**, 800 South Washington Avenue, Zip 48601–2594; tel. 989/776–8000 **A**1 2 3 5 9 10 **F**1 9 12 13 14 15 17 19 21 22 23 26 27 28 29 30 33 35 37 39 40 42 45 46 47 48 52 53 55 57 58 60 61 62 63 64 65 66 69 70 73 75 79 80 81 82 84 85 86 87 88 93 94 96 107 108 109 110 **P**6 8 **S** Ascension Health, Saint Louis, MO Primary Contact: Fleury Yelvington, President and Chief Executive Officer COO: Craig Carmichael, Vice President Operations CFO: Gary W. Chawk, Chief Financial Officer CIO: Karen Hollingsworth, Chief Information Officer CHR: Jerry Chiplock, Vice President Human Resources Web address: www.saintmarys–saginaw.org	21	10	268	13423	194	299257	0	203336	75647	1610
□ **SELECT SPECIALTY HOSPITAL–SAGINAW**, 1447 North Harrison Avenue, Zip 48602; tel. 989/583–4850, (Nonreporting) **A**1 10 Primary Contact: Jon Cohee, Chief Executive Officer	33	80	32	—	—	—	—	—	—	—

SAINT IGNACE—Mackinac County

★ **MACKINAC STRAITS HOSPITAL AND HEALTH CENTER**, 220 Burdette Street, Zip 49781–1792; tel. 906/643–8585, (Total facility includes 91 beds in nursing home–type unit) **A**9 10 18 **F**9 12 23 24 26 27 28 33 42 45 49 52 60 61 65 69 70 81 88 92 94 96 97 109 **P**6 Primary Contact: Rodney M. Nelson, President and Chief Executive Officer CFO: Jason Anderson, Chief Financial Officer CIO: Kurt Eggebrecht, Information Systems Supervisor CHR: Karen Cheeseman, Director Human Resources Web address: www.mshosp.org	16	10	106	228	97	21306	0	16099	7715	163

SAINT JOHNS—Clinton County

⊞ **CLINTON MEMORIAL HOSPITAL**, 805 South Oakland Street, Zip 48879–0260; tel. 989/224–6881 **A**1 9 10 **F**9 11 12 26 27 28 29 33 41 48 54 58 59 60 61 62 63 64 69 81 82 84 87 88 93 94 95 97 108 **P**6 Primary Contact: Edward Bruun, Chief Executive Officer CFO: Janice Stitt, Vice President and Chief Financial Officer CMO: Paul David Minnick, D.O., Chief Medical Staff CIO: Jami Thering, Manager Information Systems CHR: Lori Bernstein, Manager Human Resources Web address: www.clintonmemorial.org	23	10	28	760	8	48129	57	22612	7239	177

SAINT JOSEPH—Berrien County

□ **LAKELAND HOSPITAL–ST. JOSEPH**, 1234 Napier Avenue, Zip 49085–2112; tel. 269/983–8300, (Includes LAKELAND HOSPITAL–NILES, 31 North St. Joseph Avenue, Niles, Zip 49120–2287; tel. 269/683–5510; LAKELAND SPECIALTY HOSPITAL, BERRIEN CENTER, 6418 Dean's Hill Road, Berrien Center, Zip 49102–9704; tel. 269/471–7761), (Total facility includes 221 beds in nursing home–type unit) **A**1 2 9 10 **F**2 5 9 10 11 12 15 17 19 21 22 23 24 26 27 28 29 33 36 39 41 42 44 46 47 48 49 50 51 52 53 55 57 58 59 60 61 62 63 64 65 68 69 71 75 78 79 81 82 84 85 86 87 88 92 93 94 95 96 98 108 109 110 **P**1 Primary Contact: Joseph A. Wasserman, President and Chief Executive Officer Web address: www.lakelandhealth.org	23	10	577	15749	342	305938	1836	135793	92098	2216

Many Facility Codes have changed. Please refer to the AHA Guide Code Chart.   © 2005 AHA Guide

Hospital, Address, Telephone, Approval, Facility, and Physician Codes, Health Care System	Classi-fication Codes		Utilization Data					Expense (thousands) of dollars		
★ American Hospital Association (AHA) membership □ Joint Commission on Accreditation of Healthcare Organizations (JCAHO) accreditation ○ American Osteopathic Association (AOA) accreditation △ Commission on Accreditation of Rehabilitation Facilities (CARF) accreditation	Control	Service	Staffed Beds	Admissions	Census	Outpatient Visits	Births	Total	Payroll	Personnel

SALINE—Washtenaw County

⊞ **SAINT JOSEPH MERCY SALINE HOSPITAL**, 400 West Russell Street, Zip 48176–1101; tel. 734/429–1500 **A**1 9 10 **F**9 12 21 22 26 27 28 29 33 34 35 36 39 45 46 47 48 52 53 57 58 59 60 61 62 63 65 66 69 70 73 74 75 76 77 78 81 84 88 92 94 95 96 97 98 106 107 108 109 110 **S** Trinity Health, Novi, MI
Primary Contact: Stacey Breedveld, Executive Director
CFO: Barbara Fielder, Unit Financial Director
Web address: www.sjmh.com

| 21 | 10 | 28 | 1306 | 13 | 38637 | 0 | 26389 | 9458 | — |

SANDUSKY—Sanilac County

★ **MCKENZIE MEMORIAL HOSPITAL**, 120 Delaware Street, Zip 48471–1087; tel. 810/648–3770 **A**9 10 18 **F**4 6 12 21 22 23 27 28 33 42 44 46 52 59 62 63 65 66 69 75 81 82 87 88 94 97 108 **P**6
Primary Contact: Diane D. Torres, R.N., Administrator
CFO: Ron Srebinski, Chief Financial Officer
Web address: www.greatlakes.net/~mckenzie

| 23 | 10 | 25 | 720 | 7 | — | — | — | — | — |

SAULT STE. MARIE—Chippewa County

⊞ **WAR MEMORIAL HOSPITAL**, 500 Osborn Boulevard, Zip 49783–4467; tel. 906/635–4460, (Total facility includes 51 beds in nursing home–type unit) (Nonreporting) **A**1 9 10 20
Primary Contact: W. David Rencher, President and Chief Executive Officer
CFO: Kevin Kalchik, Chief Financial Officer
CMO: Satish Chawla, M.D., Vice President Medical Affairs
CIO: Steve Pietrangelo, Director Information Services
CHR: Jen Prpich, Director Human Resources
Web address: www.warmemorialhospital.org

| 23 | 10 | 133 | | | | | | | |

SHELBY—Oceana County

□ **HACKLEY LAKESHORE HOSPITAL**, 72 South State Street, Zip 49455–1299; tel. 231/861–2156 **A**1 9 10 18 **F**2 9 11 12 21 26 27 28 29 33 34 37 46 47 48 50 52 53 57 58 59 62 63 70 75 81 84 88 93 96 108 **P**4 **S** Hackley Health System, Muskegon, MI
Primary Contact: Jay Bryan, Chief Executive Officer

| 23 | 10 | 24 | 829 | 6 | 29235 | 137 | 7963 | 3185 | 81 |

SHERIDAN—Montcalm County

○ **SHERIDAN COMMUNITY HOSPITAL**, 301 North Main Street, Zip 48884–9220, Mailing Address: P.O. Box 279, Zip 48884–0279; tel. 989/291–3261 **A**9 10 11 18 **F**27 30 33 46 48 52 60 61 62 63 81 88 93 94 97 106 107 108 **P**1
Primary Contact: Robert J. Bultema, Chief Executive Officer
Web address: www.sheridanhospital.com

| 23 | 10 | 18 | 584 | 4 | — | 0 | — | — | — |

SOUTH HAVEN—Van Buren County

⊞ **SOUTH HAVEN COMMUNITY HOSPITAL**, 955 South Bailey Avenue, Zip 49090–9797; tel. 269/637–5271 **A**1 9 10 **F**2 9 11 12 21 22 23 24 26 28 29 30 33 41 46 48 51 52 53 55 58 59 60 61 62 63 64 66 69 70 81 82 87 88 89 90 93 94 96 107 108 109 110
Primary Contact: Craig J. Marks, President and Chief Executive Officer
COO: Joanne Urbanski, Chief Operating Officer
CFO: Tom Degen, Vice President Administrative Services
CIO: John Kirshman, Chief Information Officer
CHR: E. D. Johnson, Vice President Employee Development
Web address: www.shch.org

| 16 | 10 | 33 | 1214 | 9 | 105329 | 302 | 22665 | 10051 | 262 |

SOUTHFIELD—Oakland County

○ **OAKLAND REGIONAL HOSPITAL**, 22401 Foster Winter Drive, Zip 48075–3708; tel. 248/569–1500, (Total facility includes 20 beds in nursing home–type unit) (Nonreporting) **A**9 10 11
Primary Contact: Patrick J. Sperti, Chief Executive Officer
Web address: www.greatlakesrehab.com

| 33 | 46 | 46 | — | — | — | — | — | — | — |

⊞ **PROVIDENCE HOSPITAL AND MEDICAL CENTER**, 16001 West Nine Mile Road, Zip 48075–4854, Mailing Address: Box 2043, Zip 48037–2043; tel. 248/424–3000 **A**1 2 3 5 8 9 10 12 13 **F**2 4 7 9 11 12 14 15 17 19 21 22 23 26 27 28 29 30 33 35 36 37 38 39 40 42 44 46 47 48 49 50 52 53 55 56 57 58 59 60 61 62 63 64 65 66 68 69 70 71 72 73 74 75 76 77 78 79 80 81 82 84 85 87 88 92 93 94 95 96 106 108 109 110 **P**1 6 **S** Ascension Health, Saint Louis, MO
Primary Contact: Robert F. Casalou, President
CFO: William R. Crowe, Chief Financial Officer
CMO: Jeffrey Zaks, M.D., Vice President Medical Affairs
CHR: Therese Bologna, Director Human Resources
Web address: www.providence-stjohnhealth.org

| 21 | 10 | 384 | 25610 | 338 | 560049 | 3730 | 445550 | 192390 | 3729 |

⊞ **STRAITH HOSPITAL FOR SPECIAL SURGERY**, 23901 Lahser Road, Zip 48034–3296; tel. 248/357–3360 **A**1 9 10 **F**21 26 63 68 94 105 **P**5
Primary Contact: Gregory R. Hoose, Chief Executive Officer
CFO: H Roger Jones, Chief Financial Officer

| 23 | 10 | 29 | 1023 | 13 | 5349 | 0 | 12029 | 5396 | 138 |

STANDISH—Arenac County

★ **SAINT MARY'S STANDISH COMMUNITY HOSPITAL**, 805 West Cedar Street, Zip 48658–9526; tel. 989/846–4521, (Total facility includes 43 beds in nursing home–type unit) **A**9 10 18 **F**9 12 14 21 22 26 27 28 29 33 44 46 48 58 60 63 65 66 69 81 87 88 92 94 96 97 108 **S** Ascension Health, Saint Louis, MO
Primary Contact: Jeff L. Probus, Administrator and Chief Executive Officer
CFO: Tony Doud, Controller
CIO: Frank Kendall, Director Information Systems
Web address: www.saintmarys–standish.org

| 23 | 10 | 68 | 1513 | 52 | 39712 | 0 | 16490 | 8442 | 211 |

Many Facility Codes have changed. Please refer to the AHA Guide Code Chart.

MI

Hospital, Address, Telephone, Approval, Facility, and Physician Codes, Health Care System	Classi- fication Codes		Utilization Data					Expense (thousands) of dollars		
★ American Hospital Association (AHA) membership □ Joint Commission on Accreditation of Healthcare Organizations (JCAHO) accreditation ○ American Osteopathic Association (AOA) accreditation △ Commission on Accreditation of Rehabilitation Facilities (CARF) accreditation	Control	Service	Staffed Beds	Admissions	Census	Outpatient Visits	Births	Total	Payroll	Personnel

STURGIS—St. Joseph County

⊠ **STURGIS HOSPITAL**, 916 Myrtle, Zip 49091–2001; tel. 269/651–7824 **A**1 9 10 **F**9 11 12 21 22 23 26 28 29 31 33 36 39 46 48 51 52 53 55 57 58 59 60 61 62 63 66 69 70 75 81 82 85 87 88 93 94 95 96 106 107 108 109 110 **P**6 **S** Quorum Health Resources, Plano, TX
Primary Contact: Robert J. LaBarge, Chief Executive Officer
CFO: Connie Downs, Chief Financial Officer
CMO: Yazdi Amaria, M.D., Medical Staff President
CIO: Rita Denison, Information Systems Manager
CHR: Mary Kay Schultz, Director Human Resources
Web address: www.sturgishospital.com

| | 14 | 10 | 49 | 2365 | 20 | 105673 | 357 | 37372 | 14758 | 327 |

TAWAS CITY—Iosco County

⊠ **ST. JOSEPH HEALTH SYSTEM**, 200 Hemlock Street, Zip 48763–9360, Mailing Address: P.O. Box 659, Zip 48764–0659; tel. 989/362–3411 **A**1 9 10 20 **F**9 11 12 14 21 22 23 26 27 28 29 33 36 37 38 39 42 45 46 47 48 51 52 53 55 58 59 60 61 62 63 65 66 69 70 81 88 93 94 95 96 97 98 106 107 108 109 110 **P**6 **S** Ascension Health, Saint Louis, MO
Primary Contact: Patrick Murtha, President and Chief Executive Officer
COO: Martha Hang, R.N., Vice President Patient Care Services
CFO: Linda Stancill, Vice President and Chief Financial Officer
CMO: Fay E. Seppala, M.D., Chief Medical Officer
CIO: David Wanner, Director Information Systems
CHR: Georgette Alexander, Director Human Resources
Web address: www.sjhsys.org

| | 21 | 10 | 49 | 2757 | 20 | — | — | — | — | — |

TAYLOR—Wayne County

⊠ **OAKWOOD HERITAGE HOSPITAL**, 10000 Telegraph Road, Zip 48180–3349; tel. 313/295–5000 **A**1 9 10 **F**2 9 12 21 22 26 27 28 31 32 33 35 36 37 38 39 44 46 48 49 50 52 53 55 57 58 61 62 63 64 65 66 68 69 71 75 76 77 78 81 82 84 87 88 92 93 94 96 108 110 **P**8 **S** Oakwood Healthcare, Inc., Dearborn, MI
Primary Contact: Richard Hillbom, Division President
COO: J Joseph Diederich, Executive Vice President and Chief Operating Officer
CFO: Jackie Porter, Controller
CMO: Malcolm S. Henoch, M.D., Chief Medical Officer
CIO: Paula Smith, Leader Information Services and Chief Information Officer
CHR: Sherry Huffman, Director Human Resources
Web address: www.oakwood.org

| | 23 | 10 | 233 | 9485 | 173 | 51847 | 0 | 76389 | 38999 | 831 |

TECUMSEH—Lenawee County

⊠ **LENAWEE HEALTH ALLIANCE–HERRICK CAMPUS**, 500 East Pottawatamie Street, Zip 49286–2097; tel. 517/424–3000, (Total facility includes 25 beds in nursing home–type unit) **A**1 9 10 **F**2 4 8 9 11 12 21 22 26 27 28 29 31 33 41 46 47 48 51 52 53 55 57 58 59 60 62 63 64 66 68 69 70 71 72 73 74 75 76 77 81 82 87 88 89 92 94 95 96 107 108 109 110 **P**6 7 8 **S** ProMedica Health System, Toledo, OH
Primary Contact: Randall D. Oostra, FACHE, President
COO: Gregory Corbett, Senior Vice President
CFO: James F. Wheeler, Vice President Finance
CMO: Gordon Guild, D.O., Vice President Medical Affairs
CIO: Paul Muneio, Administrative Director, Information Resources
CHR: Dennis Wright, Vice President Human Resources
Web address: www.promedica.org

| | 23 | 10 | 95 | 2450 | 45 | 50904 | 173 | 27093 | 9834 | 232 |

THREE RIVERS—St. Joseph County

⊠ △ **THREE RIVERS HEALTH**, 701 South Health Parkway, Zip 49093–9362; tel. 269/278–1145 **A**1 7 9 10 **F**2 9 11 12 21 23 24 26 27 28 29 33 36 37 41 48 51 52 53 55 58 59 60 61 62 63 64 65 66 68 69 70 73 81 82 84 88 93 94 96 97 106 107 109 **P**6 8 **S** Quorum Health Resources, Plano, TX
Primary Contact: Matthew Chambers, Chief Executive Officer
CFO: Steve Andrews, Chief Financial Officer
CIO: Dave Parks
Web address: www.trah.org

| | 16 | 10 | 60 | 2103 | 20 | 122746 | 308 | 37698 | 14827 | 447 |

TRAVERSE CITY—Grand Traverse County

⊠ △ **MUNSON MEDICAL CENTER**, 1105 Sixth Street, Zip 49684–2386; tel. 231/935–5000 **A**1 2 3 5 7 9 10 12 13 19 20 **F**2 4 5 9 10 11 12 14 15 17 19 21 22 23 24 26 27 28 29 30 31 33 35 36 37 38 39 40 41 42 44 45 46 47 48 49 50 51 52 53 55 56 57 58 59 60 61 62 63 64 65 66 68 69 70 71 73 74 75 76 77 78 79 81 82 84 85 87 88 92 93 94 95 96 98 104 105 107 108 109 110 **P**6 **S** Munson Healthcare, Traverse City, MI
Primary Contact: Edwin Ness, President and Chief Executive Officer
CFO: Edward B. Carlson, Vice President and Chief Financial Officer
CMO: David S. McGreaham, Vice President Medical Affairs
CIO: Christopher J. Podges, Chief Information Officer
CHR: Sue Peters, Vice President Human Resources
Web address: www.munsonhealthcare.org

| | 23 | 10 | 368 | 19526 | 264 | 413807 | 2028 | 277979 | 120392 | 2975 |

Many Facility Codes have changed. Please refer to the AHA Guide Code Chart. © 2005 AHA Guide

MI

Hospital, Address, Telephone, Approval, Facility, and Physician Codes, Health Care System	Classification Codes		Utilization Data					Expense (thousands) of dollars		
★ American Hospital Association (AHA) membership □ Joint Commission on Accreditation of Healthcare Organizations (JCAHO) accreditation ○ American Osteopathic Association (AOA) accreditation △ Commission on Accreditation of Rehabilitation Facilities (CARF) accreditation	Control	Service	Staffed Beds	Admissions	Census	Outpatient Visits	Births	Total	Payroll	Personnel

TRENTON—Wayne County

☒ ○ **OAKWOOD SOUTHSHORE MEDICAL CENTER**, 5450 Fort Street, Zip 48183–4625; tel. 734/671–3800 **A**1 9 10 11 12 13 **F**2 9 11 12 14 15 21 22 23 26 27 28 29 32 33 36 37 38 39 44 46 47 48 49 50 52 53 55 57 58 59 61 62 63 64 65 66 69 81 82 84 88 92 94 108 110 **P**8 **S** Oakwood Healthcare, Inc., Dearborn, MI
Primary Contact: Edith M. Hughes, Division President
COO: J Joseph Diederich, Executive Vice President and Chief Operating Officer
CFO: Patricia Vannoy, Controller
CMO: Iqbal Nasir, M.D., Chief of Staff
CIO: Paula Smith, Vice President Information Services and Chief Information Officer
CHR: Juliet Hafford, Director Human Resources
Web address: www.oakwood.org

| | 23 | 10 | 148 | 7104 | 76 | 59092 | 593 | 62601 | 32278 | 635 |

TROY—Oakland County

☒ **WILLIAM BEAUMONT HOSPITAL–TROY**, 44201 Dequindre Road, Zip 48085; tel. 248/964–5000 **A**1 2 9 10 **F**2 9 10 11 12 14 15 17 19 21 22 23 26 27 28 29 30 31 33 34 35 36 37 38 39 42 44 46 47 48 49 50 52 53 55 57 58 59 60 61 62 63 64 65 66 69 70 73 75 79 80 81 82 83 84 85 87 88 92 93 94 95 96 106 108 109 **P**6 8 **S** William Beaumont Hospitals, Royal Oak, MI
Primary Contact: Eugene F. Michalski, Senior Vice President and Director
COO: Eugene F. Michalski, Senior Vice President and Director
CFO: Nickolas A. Vitale, Chief Financial Officer
CMO: Richard Herbert, D.O., Senior Vice President and Medical Director
CIO: Marie Baloga, Public Relations Director
CHR: Lucy Vail, Director Human Resources
Web address: www.beaumonthospitals.com
WILLIAM BEAUMONT HOSPITAL–TROY See

| | 23 | 10 | 254 | 20915 | 224 | 476347 | 2928 | 275597 | 117042 | 2599 |

VICKSBURG—Kalamazoo County

☒ △ **BRONSON VICKSBURG HOSPITAL**, 13326 North Boulevard, Zip 49097–1099; tel. 269/649–2321 **A**1 7 9 10 **F**12 21 26 27 28 29 33 35 39 46 48 52 53 60 62 63 64 65 68 69 94 107 108 **S** Bronson Healthcare Group, Inc., Kalamazoo, MI
Primary Contact: Frank J. Sardone, President
COO: Kenneth L. Taft, Executive Vice President and Chief Operating Officer
CFO: Mary Meitz, Vice President Finance
CMO: Scott Larson, M.D., Vice President Medical Affairs and Chief Medical Officer
CIO: Mac McClurkan, Vice President Information Technology
CHR: Susan Ulshafer, Vice President Human Resources
Web address: www.bronsonhealth.com

| | 23 | 46 | 21 | 395 | 10 | 36664 | 0 | 10946 | 5905 | 92 |

WARREN—Macomb County

★ ○ △ **HENRY FORD BI-COUNTY HOSPITAL**, 13355 East Ten Mile Road, Zip 48089–2065; tel. 586/759–7300 **A**7 9 10 11 12 13 **F**2 10 12 15 21 22 23 26 27 28 29 30 33 36 41 45 46 47 48 50 52 54 55 57 58 60 61 62 63 64 65 66 68 69 81 82 84 87 88 89 93 94 95 96 106 108 109 110 **P**1 **S** Henry Ford Health System, Detroit, MI
Primary Contact: Gary W. Popiel, Chief Executive Officer
CFO: Kenneth Lipan, Vice President Finance
CMO: Carl Pesta, M.D., Medical Director
Web address: www.bicountyhospital.org

| | 23 | 10 | 170 | 7598 | 111 | 120495 | 244 | 93583 | 39684 | 773 |

□ **SOUTHEAST MICHIGAN SURGICAL HOSPITAL**, 21230 Dequindre, Zip 48091–2287; tel. 586/427–1000 **A**1 9 10 **F**62 63 64 110 **S** National Surgical Hospitals, Chicago, IL
Primary Contact: Brian J. Peltz, Chief Executive Office
Web address: www.nshinc.com

| | 31 | 13 | 13 | 25 | 1 | 1565 | 0 | 8428 | 3427 | 84 |

☒ **ST. JOHN MACOMB HOSPITAL**, 11800 East Twelve Mile Road, Zip 48093–3494; tel. 586/573–5000 **A**1 2 9 10 **F**2 9 11 12 15 17 19 21 22 23 26 27 28 29 30 31 32 33 35 36 37 38 39 45 46 47 48 49 51 52 53 55 57 58 59 60 61 62 63 64 65 66 68 69 70 71 73 74 75 76 77 78 79 80 81 82 84 87 88 92 94 95 96 97 106 107 108 110 **P**8 **S** Ascension Health, Saint Louis, MO
Primary Contact: Joseph M. Tasse, President
COO: Joseph M. Tasse, President
CFO: Randolph H. Kummler, Vice President Finance
CMO: Roberto Barretto, M.D., Vice President of Medical Affairs
CIO: Mary Kay LaChance, Director Information Systems
CHR: Sue Gronbach, Director
Web address: www.stjohn.org

| | 21 | 10 | 349 | 18016 | 272 | 235076 | 1202 | 181044 | 91860 | 1851 |

WATERVLIET—Berrien County

☒ △ **COMMUNITY HOSPITAL**, 400 Medical Park Drive, Zip 49098–9225; tel. 269/463–3111 **A**1 7 9 10 **F**2 9 11 12 21 22 23 27 28 29 31 33 37 39 42 46 47 48 53 55 59 60 61 62 63 64 65 66 68 69 81 85 88 94 96 106 107 108 109 **P**8 **S** Quorum Health Resources, Plano, TX
Primary Contact: Fritz Fahrenbacher, Interim President and Chief Executive Officer
CFO: Arlene Leitz, Chief Financial Officer
CIO: Bill Roberts, Information Systems Director
Web address: www.communityhospitalwatervliet.com

| | 23 | 10 | 56 | 2085 | 23 | 49666 | 135 | 24191 | 10716 | 271 |

MI

Hospital, Address, Telephone, Approval, Facility, and Physician Codes, Health Care System	Classi-fication Codes		Utilization Data					Expense (thousands) of dollars		
	Control	Service	Staffed Beds	Admissions	Census	Outpatient Visits	Births	Total	Payroll	Personnel

★ American Hospital Association (AHA) membership
□ Joint Commission on Accreditation of Healthcare Organizations (JCAHO) accreditation
○ American Osteopathic Association (AOA) accreditation
△ Commission on Accreditation of Rehabilitation Facilities (CARF) accreditation

WAYNE—Wayne County

⊠ **OAKWOOD ANNAPOLIS HOSPITAL**, 33155 Annapolis Road, Zip 48184–2493; tel. 734/467–4000 **A**1 9 10 **F**2 9 11 12 15 21 22 23 24 26 27 28 29 31 32 33 35 36 37 38 39 44 45 46 48 49 50 52 53 55 57 58 59 61 62 63 64 65 66 69 81 82 84 85 87 88 92 94 96 108 109 110 **P**8 **S** Oakwood Healthcare, Inc., Dearborn, MI
Primary Contact: Thomas Kochis, Division President
Web address: www.oakwood.org

| 23 | 10 | 196 | 10267 | 116 | 71077 | 933 | 81904 | 40745 | 769 |

WEST BRANCH—Ogemaw County

⊠ **WEST BRANCH REGIONAL MEDICAL CENTER**, 2463 South M–30, Zip 48661–1199; tel. 989/345–3660 **A**1 9 10 20 **F**9 11 12 14 15 23 27 28 33 36 37 38 46 48 52 58 59 60 61 62 63 69 81 84 87 88 94 106
Primary Contact: Douglas E. Pattullo, Chief Executive Officer
COO: Edward A. Napierala, Chief Operating Officer
CFO: Robert McGrail, Chief Financial Officer
CMO: Michael Beasley, M.D., President Medical Staff
CIO: Cindy Miller, Driector Health Information Management
CHR: Janet Norton, Human Resources Manager
Web address: www.wbrmc.com

| 14 | 10 | 88 | 3065 | 39 | 79648 | 318 | 34690 | 11788 | 344 |

WESTLAND—Wayne County

□ **WALTER P. REUTHER PSYCHIATRIC HOSPITAL**, 30901 Palmer Road, Zip 48186–5389; tel. 734/367–8400 **A**1 9 10 **F**26 27 28 44 58 60 65 66 71 73 74 76 94 106 108 **P**5
Primary Contact: Norma C. Josef, M.D., Director

| 12 | 22 | 244 | 248 | 236 | 0 | 0 | 35857 | 19454 | 419 |

WYANDOTTE—Wayne County

⊠ ○ △ **HENRY FORD WYANDOTTE HOSPITAL**, 2333 Biddle Avenue, Zip 48192–4693; tel. 734/246–6000 **A**1 7 9 10 11 12 13 **F**1 2 4 9 11 12 14 15 21 22 23 27 28 29 31 33 36 37 38 39 41 44 46 47 48 49 51 52 53 55 58 59 60 61 62 63 64 65 66 68 69 71 73 74 75 76 77 81 84 85 87 88 92 93 94 96 97 108 110 **P**6 **S** Henry Ford Health System, Detroit, MI
Primary Contact: James J. Sexton, President and Chief Executive Officer
COO: Robert C. Smythe, Chief Operating Officer
CFO: Annette Phillips, Vice President and Chief Financial Officer
CMO: E C. Bush, M.D., Medical Staff President
CIO: Arthur K. Gross, FACHE, Executive Vice President and Chief Information Officer
CHR: Thomas Ostrander, Vice President Human Resources
Web address: www.henryfordhealth.org

| 23 | 10 | 336 | 17996 | 264 | 233549 | 1562 | 183588 | 85753 | 1813 |

□ **SELECT SPECIALTY HOSPITAL–WYANDOTTE**, 2333 Biddle Avenue, 7th Floor, Zip 48192; tel. 734/324–3571, (Nonreporting) **A**1 10
Primary Contact: Joseph R. Gordon, Chief Executive Officer

| 33 | 80 | 32 | — | — | — | — | — | — | — |

YPSILANTI—Washtenaw County

□ **FOREST HEALTH MEDICAL CENTER**, 135 South Prospect Street, Zip 48198–7914; tel. 734/547–4700, (Nonreporting) **A**1 10
Primary Contact: Robert A. Brown, President

| 16 | 10 | 24 | — | — | — | — | — | — | — |

★ **SAINT JOSEPH MERCY HEALTH SYSTEM**, 5301 East Huron River Drive, Zip 48197, Mailing Address: P.O. Box 995, Ann Arbor, Zip 48106–0995; tel. 734/712–3456, (Includes ST. JOSEPH MERCY HOSPITAL, Ann Arbor) **A**2 8 9 10 **F**1 2 4 7 9 10 11 12 14 15 17 19 21 22 23 24 25 26 27 29 30 31 32 33 34 35 36 37 38 39 40 41 42 43 44 45 46 47 48 49 50 51 52 53 55 56 57 58 59 60 61 62 63 64 65 66 68 69 70 71 72 73 74 75 76 77 78 79 80 81 82 83 84 85 86 87 88 89 90 91 93 94 95 96 97 98 106 107 108 109 110 **P**1 5 **S** Trinity Health, Novi, MI
Primary Contact: Garry C. Faja, President and Chief Executive Officer
COO: Julie MacDonald, R.N., Senior Vice President Patient Care Services and Chief Operating Officer
CFO: Charles Hoffman, Chief Financial Officer
CMO: Rolland Mambourg, M.D., Vice President Physician Services
CIO: Joan Hurray, Regional Director Information Services
CHR: Kathleen Rhine, Vice President Human Resources and Organizational Development
Web address: www.sjmh.com

| 21 | 10 | 631 | 36167 | 457 | 1343695 | 4541 | 589176 | 250204 | — |

□ **SELECT SPECIALTY HOSPITAL–ANN ARBOR**, 5301 East Huron River Drive, 6th Floor, Zip 48197; tel. 734/712–0103, (Nonreporting) **A**1 10
Primary Contact: Grant Asay, Chief Executive Officer

| 33 | 80 | 32 | — | — | — | — | — | — | — |

ZEELAND—Ottawa County

⊠ **ZEELAND COMMUNITY HOSPITAL**, 100 South Pine Street, Zip 49464–1619; tel. 616/772–4644 **A**1 9 10 **F**9 11 12 14 21 22 24 26 27 28 29 33 34 46 47 48 53 54 58 59 62 63 65 66 69 81 82 88 94 96 106 108 109 110 **P**4 8
Primary Contact: Henry A. Veenstra, President
COO: Henry A. Veenstra, President
CFO: George Smart, Vice President of Finance and System Services
CMO: Dale Terpstra, D.O., Medical Director
CIO: Gil Lalo, Information Systems Manager
CHR: Rick Crelly, Vice President Employee Services
Web address: www.zch.org

| 23 | 10 | 57 | 2170 | 21 | 61217 | 503 | 31899 | 16317 | 356 |

Many Facility Codes have changed. Please refer to the AHA Guide Code Chart. © 2005 AHA Guide

MINNESOTA

Hospital, Address, Telephone, Approval, Facility, and Physician Codes, Health Care System	Classi-fication Codes		Utilization Data					Expense (thousands) of dollars		
★ American Hospital Association (AHA) membership ☐ Joint Commission on Accreditation of Healthcare Organizations (JCAHO) accreditation ◯ American Osteopathic Association (AOA) accreditation △ Commission on Accreditation of Rehabilitation Facilities (CARF) accreditation	Control	Service	Staffed Beds	Admissions	Census	Outpatient Visits	Births	Total	Payroll	Personnel

ADA—Norman County

★ **BRIDGES MEDICAL SERVICES**, 201 9th Street West, Zip 56510–1243; tel. 218/784–5000, (Nonreporting) **A**9 10 18 **S** Benedictine Health System, Duluth, MN
Primary Contact: Steve Spaeth, Interim Chief Executive Officer
CMO: Mike Diamandi, M.D., Chief of Staff
CHR: Ann Reading, Human Resource Director
| | 14 | 10 | 14 | — | — | — | — | — | — | — |

AITKIN—Aitkin County

★ **RIVERWOOD HEALTHCARE CENTER**, 200 Bunker Hill Drive, Zip 56431–1844; tel. 218/927–2121, (Total facility includes 48 beds in nursing home–type unit) **A**9 10 18 **F**1 9 11 12 23 24 26 27 28 29 33 34 44 46 48 52 55 59 60 61 62 63 66 69 81 88 92 93 94 95 96 97 106 107 108 110 **P**6
Primary Contact: Michael Hagen, Chief Executive Officer
CFO: Kent Olson, Assistant Administrator and Chief Financial Officer
CMO: Mark Heggem, M.D., Medical Director
CHR: Teresa Jacobson, Director Human Resources
Web address: www.riverwoodhealthcare.com
| | 23 | 10 | 72 | 1302 | 60 | 79412 | 65 | 30382 | 13317 | 251 |

ALBANY—Stearns County

★ **ALBANY AREA HOSPITAL AND MEDICAL CENTER**, 300 Third Avenue, Zip 56307–9363; tel. 320/845–2121 **A**9 10 18 **F**11 12 22 27 28 29 33 36 39 48 51 52 59 60 63 69 81 94 97 108 **P**6 **S** Catholic Health Initiatives, Denver, CO
Primary Contact: Benjamin Koppelman, Administrator
CMO: Heather Swanson, M.D., Chief of Staff
Web address: www.albanyareahospital.com
| | 21 | 10 | 15 | 375 | 3 | 12798 | 62 | 7204 | 3023 | 80 |

ALBERT LEA—Freeborn County

☐ △ **ALBERT LEA MEDICAL CENTER**, 404 West Fountain Street, Zip 56007–2473; tel. 507/373–2384, (Total facility includes 61 beds in nursing home–type unit) (Nonreporting) **A**1 7 9 10 **S** Mayo Foundation, Rochester, MN
Primary Contact: Mark Ciota, M.D., Chief Executive Officer
Web address: www.almedcenter.org
| | 23 | 10 | 129 | — | — | — | — | — | — | — |

ALEXANDRIA—Douglas County

✠ ◯ **DOUGLAS COUNTY HOSPITAL**, 111 17th Avenue East, Zip 56308–3798; tel. 320/762–1511 **A**1 9 10 11 **F**2 4 9 11 12 22 23 26 27 30 33 34 37 46 47 50 51 52 53 54 55 59 60 61 62 63 64 65 69 73 74 75 77 81 82 84 86 88 93 94 95 96 106 108
Primary Contact: William G. Flaig, Administrator
CFO: Stan Greiner, Director Finance
Web address: www.dchospital.com
| | 13 | 10 | 99 | 4529 | 47 | 60206 | 587 | 55587 | 23041 | 459 |

ANOKA—Anoka County

☐ **ANOKA–METROPOLITAN REGIONAL TREATMENT CENTER**, 3301 Seventh Avenue, Zip 55303–1119; tel. 763/712–4000, (Nonreporting) **A**1 10
Primary Contact: Rod Kornrumpf, Regional Administrator
| | 12 | 22 | 247 | — | — | — | — | — | — | — |

APPLETON—Swift County

★ **APPLETON MUNICIPAL HOSPITAL AND NURSING HOME**, 30 South Behl Street, Zip 56208–1699; tel. 320/289–2422, (Total facility includes 84 beds in nursing home–type unit) **A**9 10 18 **F**11 26 27 28 29 33 51 52 54 58 59 60 63 65 69 88 91 92 94 97 108 **P**7
Primary Contact: Daniel J. Swenson, Chief Executive Officer and Administrator
CFO: Kyle Chase, Chief Financial Officer
Web address: www.appletonmedical.com
| | 14 | 10 | 131 | 352 | 81 | 12752 | 7 | 9219 | 4676 | 117 |

ARLINGTON—Sibley County

★ **SIBLEY MEDICAL CENTER**, 601 West Chandler Street, Zip 55307–4500, Mailing Address: P.O. Box 620, Zip 55307; tel. 507/964–2271 **A**9 10 18 **F**1 9 12 14 21 23 29 33 46 48 51 52 54 60 63 65 69 70 81 88 92 94 97 **P**6
Primary Contact: Jason Douglas, Administrator
COO: Sherry Reberg, Chief Operating Officer and Director of Nursing
CFO: Rhonda Matz, Chief Financial Officer
CMO: Dean Bergersen, M.D., Chief Medical Officer
CIO: David Davis, Information Technology Director
CHR: Nathan Lake, Director of Human Resources
Web address: www.sibleymedical.com
| | 14 | 10 | 17 | 359 | 3 | 24033 | 0 | 7301 | 3557 | 87 |

AURORA—St. Louis County

★ **WHITE COMMUNITY HOSPITAL**, 5211 Highway 110, Zip 55705–1599; tel. 218/229–2211, (Total facility includes 69 beds in nursing home–type unit) (Nonreporting) **A**9 10 18
Primary Contact: Paula Schaefbauer, Administrator and Chief Executive Officer
CFO: Chris DeVaney, Finance Director
Web address: www.whitech.org
| | 23 | 10 | 84 | — | — | — | — | — | — | — |

AUSTIN—Mower County

☐ **AUSTIN MEDICAL CENTER**, 1000 First Drive N.W., Zip 55912–2904; tel. 507/437–4551 **A**1 9 10 **F**2 4 11 12 23 27 28 33 36 37 42 46 47 48 51 52 53 54 55 57 58 59 60 61 62 63 64 65 66 69 70 71 72 73 75 76 77 81 82 84 85 88 93 94 106 107 108 **P**6 **S** Mayo Foundation, Rochester, MN
Primary Contact: Timothy Johnson, M.D., President
Web address: www.austinmedicalcenter.org
| | 23 | 10 | 73 | 3775 | 37 | 297570 | 414 | 81222 | 43080 | 882 |

MN

Hospital, Address, Telephone, Approval, Facility, and Physician Codes, Health Care System	Classi-fication Codes		Utilization Data					Expense (thousands) of dollars		
★ American Hospital Association (AHA) membership □ Joint Commission on Accreditation of Healthcare Organizations (JCAHO) accreditation ○ American Osteopathic Association (AOA) accreditation △ Commission on Accreditation of Rehabilitation Facilities (CARF) accreditation	Control	Service	Staffed Beds	Admissions	Census	Outpatient Visits	Births	Total	Payroll	Personnel

BAGLEY—Clearwater County

★ **CLEARWATER HEALTH SERVICES**, 203 Fourth Street N.W., Zip 56621–8307; tel. 218/694–6501, (Total facility includes 70 beds in nursing home–type unit) (Nonreporting) **A**9 10 18
Primary Contact: Larry Laudon, Chief Executive Officer
CFO: Gladys Luecken, Chief Financial Officer
CMO: Rudd Thabes, Chief Medical Staff
Web address: www.clearwaterhs.com

	13	10	95	—	—	—	—	—	—	—

BAUDETTE—Lake of the Woods County

★ **LAKEWOOD HEALTH CENTER**, 600 Main Avenue South, Zip 56623–2855; tel. 218/634–2120, (Total facility includes 50 beds in nursing home–type unit) **A**9 10 18 **F**2 6 8 9 11 12 22 23 24 26 27 28 29 33 36 39 41 45 46 48 51 52 59 63 64 69 81 88 92 94 97 98 **S** Catholic Health Initiatives, Denver, CO
Primary Contact: SharRay Palm, President and Chief Executive Officer
CFO: Lynn Ellis, Chief Financial Officer
Web address: www.lakewood–baudette.org

	21	10	65	359	53	10943	37	9504	3934	116

BEMIDJI—Beltrami County

★ △ **NORTH COUNTRY REGIONAL HOSPITAL**, 1300 Anne Street N.W., Zip 56601; tel. 218/751–5430, (Total facility includes 78 beds in nursing home–type unit) **A**7 9 10 19 20 **F**2 8 9 11 12 21 22 26 27 28 29 33 36 37 38 47 48 51 52 55 58 59 60 62 63 64 65 66 68 69 70 82 84 85 88 91 92 93 94 96 106 108 110 **P**6
Primary Contact: James F. Hanko, President and Chief Executive Officer
CFO: Vic Hagstrom, Vice President Finance
CMO: William Muller, M.D., President Medical Staff
CHR: Robert Verchota, Vice President of Ancillary Service and Human Resources
Web address: www.nchs.com

	23	10	194	5681	130	69904	972	62831	26648	517

BENSON—Swift County

★ **SWIFT COUNTY–BENSON HOSPITAL**, 1815 Wisconsin Avenue, Zip 56215–1653; tel. 320/843–4232 **A**9 10 18 **F**3 6 8 9 11 12 13 14 21 22 23 29 31 33 48 51 52 54 55 56 58 59 60 61 63 67 68 69 71 73 75 76 77 81 92 96 97 **P**6
Primary Contact: Frank Lawatsch, Chief Executive Officer
CFO: Jayne Thielke, Chief Financial Officer
CIO: Jayne Thielke, Chief Financial Officer
CHR: Stella Kalthoff, Quality Improvement Coordinator
Web address: www.scbh.org

	16	10	18	784	6	30269	8	7660	3036	74

BIGFORK—Itasca County

★ **BIG FORK VALLEY HOSPITAL**, 258 Pine Tree Drive, Zip 56628, Mailing Address: P.O. Box 258, Zip 56628–0258; tel. 218/743–3177, (Total facility includes 40 beds in nursing home–type unit) (Nonreporting) **A**9 10 18
Primary Contact: Daniel Odegaard, Chief Executive Officer
COO: Ken Westman, Chief Executive Officer
CMO: George Rounds, M.D., Chief of Staff
CHR: Sandra Le Blanc Boland, Human Resources Representative
Web address: www.bigforkvalley.org

	16	10	56	—	—	—	—	—	—	—

BLUE EARTH—Faribault County

⊞ **UNITED HOSPITAL DISTRICT**, 515 South Moore Street, Zip 56013–2158, Mailing Address: P.O. Box 160, Zip 56013–0160; tel. 507/526–3273 **A**1 9 10 **F**2 3 6 9 10 11 12 14 21 22 23 28 29 33 36 37 42 46 47 48 51 52 53 54 55 58 59 60 62 63 65 66 69 81 88 92 94 97 106 107 108 110 **P**6
Primary Contact: Chad Cooper, Chief Executive Officer
CFO: Steve Rozenboom, Chief Financial Officer
Web address: www.uhd.org

	16	10	48	969	22	41058	41	13865	5323	147

BRAINERD—Crow Wing County

□ **BRAINERD REGIONAL HUMAN SERVICES CENTER**, 1777 Highway 18 East, Zip 56401–7389; tel. 218/828–2201, (Total facility includes 28 beds in nursing home–type unit) (Nonreporting) **A**1 10
Primary Contact: Harvey G. Caldwell, Administrator and Chief Executive Officer

	12	22	293	—	—	—	—	—	—	—

□ **ST. JOSEPH'S MEDICAL CENTER**, 523 North Third Street, Zip 56401–3098; tel. 218/829–2861 **A**1 9 10 19 **F**2 3 4 9 10 11 12 21 22 23 26 27 28 29 33 34 35 36 46 47 48 50 51 52 55 58 59 60 61 62 63 64 65 66 69 71 73 74 75 76 77 78 81 82 84 85 86 88 94 95 96 108 110 **P**2 **S** Benedictine Health System, Duluth, MN
Primary Contact: Thomas K. Prusak, President
Web address: www.sjmcmn.org

	21	10	162	6908	73	139603	664	75296	33127	623

BRECKENRIDGE—Wilkin County

⊞ **ST. FRANCIS MEDICAL CENTER**, 415 Oak Street, Zip 56520–1298; tel. 218/643–3000, (Total facility includes 120 beds in nursing home–type unit) **A**1 5 9 10 20 **F**4 8 9 10 11 12 21 22 23 26 27 28 29 31 33 34 35 36 41 42 46 47 48 51 52 53 55 58 59 60 63 65 66 69 72 73 74 75 76 77 81 82 88 91 92 94 95 96 97 98 106 108 109 110 **S** Catholic Health Initiatives, Denver, CO
Primary Contact: David A. Nelson, President and Chief Executive Officer
CFO: Nancy Whitney, Chief Financial Officer
Web address: www.sfcare.org

	21	10	145	1575	124	44264	232	20995	9968	263

MN

Many Facility Codes have changed. Please refer to the AHA Guide Code Chart. © 2005 AHA Guide

Hospital, Address, Telephone, Approval, Facility, and Physician Codes, Health Care System	Classi-fication Codes		Utilization Data					Expense (thousands) of dollars		
★ American Hospital Association (AHA) membership □ Joint Commission on Accreditation of Healthcare Organizations (JCAHO) accreditation ○ American Osteopathic Association (AOA) accreditation △ Commission on Accreditation of Rehabilitation Facilities (CARF) accreditation	Control	Service	Staffed Beds	Admissions	Census	Outpatient Visits	Births	Total	Payroll	Personnel

BUFFALO—Wright County

☒ **BUFFALO HOSPITAL**, 303 Catlin Street, Zip 55313–1947; tel. 763/682–1212 **A**1 9 10 **F**2 9 11 12 14 21 23 27 28 29 33 35 38 46 48 55 58 59 61 62 63 64 65 66 69 81 84 88 93 94 95 106 107 108 **S** Allina Hospitals & Clinics, Minneapolis, MN
Primary Contact: Lenore Day, Interim President
COO: Lenore Day, Director Operations and Clinical Support
CFO: Joyce Dehmer, Director Finance
CHR: Stephen Bauman, Director of Human Resources
Web address: www.buffalohospital.org
— Control 23, Service 10, Staffed Beds 38, Admissions 2808, Census 20, Outpatient Visits 54745, Births 608, Total 33763, Payroll 15661, Personnel 274

BURNSVILLE—Dakota County

☒ **FAIRVIEW RIDGES HOSPITAL**, 201 East Nicollet Boulevard, Zip 55337–5799; tel. 952/892–2000 **A**1 9 10 **F**9 11 12 22 26 27 28 29 33 52 53 55 58 59 60 61 62 63 65 66 69 81 82 84 88 90 92 94 96 108 **S** Fairview Health Services, Minneapolis, MN
Primary Contact: Sara Criger, President and Chief Executive Officer
CFO: Laura DeNeui, Vice President, Finance and Quality Performance
CMO: Jamie Peters, M.D., Vice President, Medical Services
Web address: www.fairview.org
— Control 23, Service 10, Staffed Beds 147, Admissions 11456, Census 97, Outpatient Visits 92191, Births 2941, Total 95891, Payroll 51063, Personnel 776

CAMBRIDGE—Isanti County

☒ **CAMBRIDGE MEDICAL CENTER**, 701 South Dellwood Street, Zip 55008–1920; tel. 763/689–7700 **A**1 9 10 **F**2 3 4 9 11 12 21 22 23 24 26 27 28 29 31 33 34 37 39 44 46 47 48 52 54 55 57 58 59 60 61 62 63 64 65 66 69 70 71 72 73 74 75 76 77 81 82 84 88 91 93 94 95 96 98 106 108 109 110 **P**5 6 **S** Allina Hospitals & Clinics, Minneapolis, MN
Primary Contact: Dennis J. Doran, President
CFO: Kirk Nybakken, Finance Director
Web address: www.allina.com/ahs/cambridge.nsf
— Control 23, Service 10, Staffed Beds 81, Admissions 4103, Census 48, Outpatient Visits 297652, Births 494, Total 80774, Payroll 41032, Personnel 645

CANBY—Yellow Medicine County

★ **SIOUX VALLEY CANBY CAMPUS**, 112 St. Olaf Avenue South, Zip 56220–1433; tel. 507/223–7277, (Includes SENIOR HAVEN CONVALESCENT NURSING CENTER), (Total facility includes 75 beds in nursing home–type unit) **A**9 10 18 **F**2 5 6 8 9 11 12 21 23 26 27 28 29 32 33 41 45 48 49 51 52 55 59 63 69 81 91 92 94 97 107 108 **P**6 **S** Sioux Valley Hospitals and Health System, Sioux Falls, SD
Primary Contact: Robert J. Salmon, Chief Executive Officer
CFO: Allison Nelson, Controller
CMO: Maritza Lopez, M.D., Chief of Staff
CIO: Cheryl Ferguson, Associate Administrator
Web address: www.svcanbycampus.org
— Control 23, Service 10, Staffed Beds 100, Admissions 814, Census 79, Outpatient Visits 16686, Births 48, Total 13573, Payroll 6660, Personnel 197

CANNON FALLS—Goodhue County

★ **CANNON FALLS COMMUNITY HOSPITAL**, 1116 West Mill Street, Zip 55009–1898; tel. 507/263–4221, (Nonreporting) **A**9 10 18
Primary Contact: Glenn Christian, Interim Chief Executive Officer and Administrator
— Control 16, Service 10, Staffed Beds 14

CASS LAKE—Cass County

☒ **U. S. PUBLIC HEALTH SERVICE INDIAN HOSPITAL**, 7th Street and Grant Utley Avenue N.W., Zip 56633, Mailing Address: Rural Route 3, Box 211, Zip 56633; tel. 218/335–3200, (Nonreporting) **A**1 5 9 10 18 **S** U. S. Indian Health Service, Rockville, MD
Primary Contact: Jennifer Jenkins, Service Unit Director
CFO: Randall Jordan, Budget Analyst
— Control 47, Service 10, Staffed Beds 13

CLOQUET—Carlton County

★ **CLOQUET COMMUNITY MEMORIAL HOSPITAL**, 512 Skyline Boulevard, Zip 55720–1199; tel. 218/879–4641, (Total facility includes 88 beds in nursing home–type unit) **A**9 10 18 **F**2 9 11 12 21 23 28 48 52 55 58 59 60 62 63 64 65 66 92 94 95 96 97 108 109 **P**8
Primary Contact: Rick Breuer, Chief Executive Officer and Administrator
CFO: Brad Anderson, Chief Financial Officer
CIO: Jay Frohrip, Director Management Information Systems
Web address: www.cloquethospital.com
— Control 23, Service 10, Staffed Beds 114, Admissions 1666, Census 99, Outpatient Visits 43277, Births 104, Total 25463, Payroll 11770, Personnel 246

COOK—St. Louis County

★ **COOK HOSPITAL AND CONVALESCENT NURSING CARE UNIT**, 10 Fifth Street S.E., Zip 55723–9745; tel. 218/666–5945, (Total facility includes 41 beds in nursing home–type unit) **A**9 10 18 **F**1 9 12 26 27 28 29 33 41 44 46 52 60 69 81 84 88 92 94 95 97 108 110 **P**5
Primary Contact: Allen J. Vogt, Administrator
CFO: Mike Holmes, Chief Financial Officer
— Control 16, Service 10, Staffed Beds 55, Admissions 397, Census 41, Outpatient Visits 16904, Births 0, Total 6662, Payroll 3044, Personnel 99

COON RAPIDS—Anoka County

☒ **MERCY HOSPITAL**, 4050 Coon Rapids Boulevard, Zip 55433–2586; tel. 763/236–6000 **A**1 9 10 **F**2 9 10 11 14 15 17 19 21 22 23 26 27 28 29 30 31 33 37 38 41 48 54 55 56 58 59 60 61 62 63 64 66 69 70 71 73 74 75 77 78 81 82 84 88 90 94 96 98 106 108 **P**4 5 **S** Allina Hospitals & Clinics, Minneapolis, MN
Primary Contact: Venetia Kudrle, President
COO: Kathy Wilde, Vice President Operations and Patient Care
CFO: Lisa Kjentvet, Vice President Finance
CMO: Dennis O'Hare, M.D., Vice President Medical Affairs
CIO: Robert Plaszcz, Chief Information Officer
CHR: Patrick Drescich, Vice President Human Resources
Web address: www.allina.com
— Control 23, Service 10, Staffed Beds 266, Admissions 18299, Census 175, Outpatient Visits 144550, Births 2496, Total 215526, Payroll 89395, Personnel 1266

Hospital, Address, Telephone, Approval, Facility, and Physician Codes, Health Care System	Classi-fication Codes		Utilization Data					Expense (thousands) of dollars		
★ American Hospital Association (AHA) membership □ Joint Commission on Accreditation of Healthcare Organizations (JCAHO) accreditation ○ American Osteopathic Association (AOA) accreditation △ Commission on Accreditation of Rehabilitation Facilities (CARF) accreditation	Control	Service	Staffed Beds	Admissions	Census	Outpatient Visits	Births	Total	Payroll	Personnel

CROOKSTON—Polk County

★ **RIVERVIEW HEALTHCARE ASSOCIATION**, 323 South Minnesota Street,
Zip 56716–1600; tel. 218/281–9200, (Total facility includes 142 beds in nursing
home–type unit) **A**5 9 10 18 **F**1 2 3 4 5 8 9 11 12 21 26 27 28 29 30 31 33
34 35 36 37 38 39 44 47 48 51 52 53 55 58 59 60 61 62 63 64 65 66 69
70 75 81 82 85 88 92 93 94 95 96 97 106 107 108 110 **P**5 6 7
Primary Contact: Debra K. Boardman, President and Chief Executive Officer
COO: Jeannine F. Amon, R.N., Vice President and Chief Operating Officer
CFO: William Bennett, Chief Financial Officer
CMO: Theodore Olson, M.D., Chief of Staff
CIO: Nancie Hoerner, Information Management Coordinator
CHR: Jean Tate, Manager
Web address: www.riverviewhealth.org
| 23 | 10 | 194 | 1402 | 155 | 27819 | 157 | 33926 | 17479 | 444 |

CROSBY—Crow Wing County

★ **CUYUNA REGIONAL MEDICAL CENTER**, 320 East Main Street,
Zip 56441–1690; tel. 218/546–7000, (Total facility includes 130 beds in nursing
home–type unit) (Nonreporting) **A**9 10 18
Primary Contact: Thomas F. Reek, Chief Executive Officer
CFO: Kyle Bauer, Chief Financial Officer
CMO: David Goodwin, Chief of Staff
CHR: Theresa Sullivan, Administrator of Organizational Support
Web address: www.cuyunamed.org
| 16 | 10 | 155 | — | — | — | — | — | — | — |

DAWSON—Lac Qui Parle County

JOHNSON MEMORIAL HEALTH SERVICES, 1282 Walnut Street,
Zip 56232–2333; tel. 320/769–4323, (Total facility includes 70 beds in nursing
home–type unit) (Nonreporting) **A**9 10 18
Primary Contact: Glenn Haugo, Administrator
Web address: www.jmhsdawson.com
| 16 | 10 | 95 | — | — | — | — | — | — | — |

DEER RIVER—Itasca County

★ **DEER RIVER HEALTHCARE CENTER**, 1002 Comstock Drive, Zip 56636–9700;
tel. 218/246–2900, (Total facility includes 50 beds in nursing home–type unit)
(Nonreporting) **A**9 10 18
Primary Contact: Jeffry Stampohar, Chief Executive Officer
CFO: Steven Larson, Chief Financial Officer
CMO: David Goodall, M.D., Chief Medical Staff
CHR: Amy Lane Myers, Human Resources Manager
Web address: www.drhc.org
| 23 | 10 | 70 | — | — | — | — | — | — | — |

DETROIT LAKES—Becker County

⊠ **ST. MARY'S REGIONAL HEALTH CENTER**, 1027 Washington Avenue,
Zip 56501–3598; tel. 218/847–5611, (Total facility includes 100 beds in nursing
home–type unit) **A**1 9 10 **F**2 5 6 8 9 11 22 23 27 28 29 33 34 43 44 45 46
48 51 52 53 55 58 59 60 62 63 64 69 81 82 84 85 87 88 91 92 93 94 96
97 108 **P**5 **S** Benedictine Health System, Duluth, MN
Primary Contact: Thomas R. Thompson, Chief Executive Officer
CFO: Nate Meyer, Chief Financial Officer
CMO: James Christensen, M.D., Chief of Staff
CHR: Jean Evans, Director of Human Resources and Support Services
Web address: www.smrhc.com
| 21 | 10 | 154 | 2916 | 139 | 17614 | 464 | 29466 | 14652 | 273 |

DULUTH—St. Louis County

⊠ △ **MILLER–DWAN MEDICAL CENTER**, 502 East Second Street,
Zip 55805–1982; tel. 218/727–8762 **A**1 5 7 9 10 **F**3 4 8 9 13 22 26 27 28
29 31 40 44 46 50 52 55 58 60 61 63 65 66 68 71 72 73 74 75 76 77 78
79 88 94 96 108 110 **P**5 **S** St. Mary's/Duluth Clinic Health System, Duluth, MN
Primary Contact: Rocklon B. Chapin, Chief Operating Officer and Administrator
COO: Thomas H. Klassen, Executive Vice Persident and Chief Operating Officer
CFO: David H. Amundson, Chief Financial Officer
Web address: www.miller–dwan.com
| 23 | 10 | 152 | 4584 | 80 | 50146 | 0 | 54131 | 24613 | 476 |

⊠ △ **ST. LUKE'S HOSPITAL**, 915 East First Street, Zip 55805–2193;
tel. 218/249–5555 **A**1 2 3 5 7 9 10 **F**2 6 7 9 11 12 14 15 17 19 21 22 23 26
27 28 29 30 32 33 34 36 37 38 39 40 41 42 44 45 46 47 48 50 51 52 53
55 57 58 59 60 61 62 63 64 66 68 69 70 71 72 73 74 75 76 77 79 80 81
82 85 86 88 93 94 96 106 107 108 109 110 **P**1 6
Primary Contact: John Strange, President and Chief Executive Officer
CFO: Dennis Empey, Chief Financial Officer
CMO: Gary Peterson, M.D., Vice President Medical Affairs and Medical Director
CIO: Clark Averill, Director Information Technology
CHR: Dave Lucia, Director Human Resources
Web address: www.slhduluth.com
| 23 | 10 | 210 | 12538 | 150 | 155595 | 920 | 221973 | 104659 | 1491 |

⊠ **ST. MARY'S MEDICAL CENTER**, 407 East Third Street, Zip 55805–1984;
tel. 218/786–4000 **A**1 3 5 9 10 **F**2 9 10 11 14 15 17 19 21 22 23 26 27 28
29 33 34 35 36 38 39 43 46 50 51 52 53 55 56 57 58 59 61 62 63 64 67
69 81 82 84 87 88 93 94 96 106 107 108 109 **P**6 **S** St. Mary's/Duluth Clinic
Health System, Duluth, MN
Primary Contact: Susan E. McClernon, Chief Operating Officer
COO: Susan E. McClernon, Chief Operating Officer
CFO: David H. Amundson, Chief Financial Officer
CMO: Hugh Renier, M.D., Vice President Medical Affairs
CIO: Robert Bender, Director Information Technology Services
CHR: Glen Porter, Vice President Human Resources
Web address: www.smdc.org
| 23 | 10 | 315 | 18952 | 263 | 135462 | 1580 | 232868 | 90661 | 2101 |

Many Facility Codes have changed. Please refer to the AHA Guide Code Chart.

MN

Hospital, Address, Telephone, Approval, Facility, and Physician Codes, Health Care System	Classi-fication Codes		Utilization Data					Expense (thousands) of dollars		
★ American Hospital Association (AHA) membership □ Joint Commission on Accreditation of Healthcare Organizations (JCAHO) accreditation ○ American Osteopathic Association (AOA) accreditation △ Commission on Accreditation of Rehabilitation Facilities (CARF) accreditation	Control	Service	Staffed Beds	Admissions	Census	Outpatient Visits	Births	Total	Payroll	Personnel

EDINA—Hennepin County

⊞ **FAIRVIEW SOUTHDALE HOSPITAL**, 6401 France Avenue South, Zip 55435-2199; tel. 952/924-5000 **A**1 9 10 **F**2 4 9 10 11 12 14 15 17 19 21 22 23 26 27 28 29 31 33 37 38 39 40 46 47 48 49 52 54 55 57 58 59 61 62 63 66 69 71 73 75 79 81 82 83 84 85 86 88 90 92 93 94 95 96 98 106 108 109 110 **P**6 **S** Fairview Health Services, Minneapolis, MN
Primary Contact: Gary J. Strong, President
COO: Mary Bakken, Senior Vice President and Chief Operating Officer
CFO: Brent Wilde, Vice President
CMO: James Bishop, Director Medical Affairs
CHR: Robert Cocker, Director Human Resources
Web address: www.fairview.org

| | 23 | 10 | 329 | 21487 | 201 | 105504 | 3392 | 260787 | 115761 | 1579 |

ELBOW LAKE—Grant County

★ **ELEAH MEDICAL CENTER**, 930 First Street N.E., Zip 56531-4611; tel. 218/685-4461 **A**9 10 **F**6 12 21 23 27 28 33 34 36 41 46 48 51 52 60 61 62 63 69 70 81 84 88 96 97 106 **P**4
Primary Contact: Larry Rapp, M.D., Chief Medical and Executive Officer
COO: Larry Rapp, M.D., Chief Medical and Executive Officer
CMO: Larry Rapp, M.D., Chief Medical and Executive Officer
Web address: www.eleahmed.org

| | 23 | 10 | 20 | 510 | 6 | 840 | 1 | 5071 | 2037 | 54 |

ELY—St. Louis County

★ **ELY–BLOOMENSON COMMUNITY HOSPITAL**, 328 West Conan Street, Zip 55731-1198; tel. 218/365-3271, (Total facility includes 79 beds in nursing home-type unit) **A**9 10 18 **F**6 9 11 12 14 23 27 29 30 33 51 52 54 59 60 63 69 81 88 92 94 96 97 108 **P**6
Primary Contact: John Fossum, Chief Executive Officer and Administrator
CFO: Scott Kellerman, Chief Financial Officer
Web address: www.ebch.org

| | 23 | 10 | 104 | 648 | 79 | 9006 | 26 | 16577 | 7104 | 194 |

FAIRMONT—Martin County

⊞ **FAIRMONT MEDICAL CENTER–MAYO HEALTH SYSTEM**, 800 Medical Center Drive, Zip 56031-0800, Mailing Address: P.O. Box 835, Zip 56031-0835; tel. 507/238-8100, (Includes LUTZ WING CONVALESCENT AND NURSING CARE UNIT), (Total facility includes 40 beds in nursing home-type unit) **A**1 9 10 **F**9 11 12 14 23 26 27 28 29 33 35 36 37 39 41 42 46 48 49 51 52 53 58 59 60 62 63 65 66 69 70 72 73 74 75 76 77 81 82 84 87 88 92 93 94 95 96 97 106 107 108 110 **P**6 **S** Mayo Foundation, Rochester, MN
Primary Contact: Larry Gleason, Chief Administrative Officer
CFO: Kent Olson, Chief Financial Officer
Web address: www.fch.org

| | 23 | 10 | 97 | 2752 | 64 | 72436 | 302 | 37302 | 17385 | 539 |

FARIBAULT—Rice County

⊞ **DISTRICT ONE HOSPITAL**, 200 State Avenue, Zip 55021-6345; tel. 507/334-6451 **A**1 9 10 **F**2 9 11 12 23 27 29 30 33 34 36 46 47 48 53 54 55 58 59 61 62 63 64 65 66 69 81 88 94 95 96 106 108 109 110
Primary Contact: James N. Wolf, Chief Executive Officer
CFO: Patrick A. Justin, Chief Financial Officer
CIO: Patrick A. Justin, Chief Financial Officer
CHR: Rose Dube, Human Resource Manager
Web address: www.districtonehospital.com

| | 16 | 10 | 54 | 2271 | 20 | 35602 | 508 | 30504 | 12320 | 234 |

FERGUS FALLS—Otter Tail County

□ **FERGUS FALLS REGIONAL TREATMENT CENTER**, 1400 North Union Avenue, Zip 56537-1200; tel. 218/739-7200, (Nonreporting) **A**1 3 10
Primary Contact: Cynthia Skorick, Chief Executive Officer

| | 12 | 22 | 138 | — | — | — | — | — | — | — |

⊞ △ **LAKE REGION HEALTHCARE CORPORATION**, 712 South Cascade Street, Zip 56537-2900, Mailing Address: P.O. Box 728, Zip 56538-0728; tel. 218/736-8000, (Total facility includes 13 beds in nursing home-type unit) **A**1 7 9 10 20 **F**2 8 9 11 12 14 21 22 23 26 27 28 29 30 33 34 37 38 40 44 46 47 48 50 51 52 53 55 58 59 60 61 62 63 64 65 66 68 69 71 72 73 74 75 76 81 82 84 85 86 88 92 93 94 95 96 108 109 110
Primary Contact: Edward J. Mehl, Chief Executive Officer
CFO: Ed Strand, Assistant Administrator Finance and Chief Financial Officer
CMO: David Bjork, M.D., Chief of Staff
CHR: Cheryl Buck, Human Resource Manager
Web address: www.lrhc.org

| | 23 | 10 | 121 | 4369 | 52 | 52818 | 349 | 43247 | 21162 | 424 |

FOSSTON—Polk County

★ **FIRST CARE MEDICAL SERVICES**, 900 South Hilligoss Boulevard East, Zip 56542-1599; tel. 218/435-1133, (Total facility includes 50 beds in nursing home-type unit) **A**9 10 18 **F**1 3 6 8 11 12 13 14 21 23 24 29 30 31 33 34 35 36 39 41 44 45 46 47 48 51 52 53 54 55 56 58 59 60 61 62 63 67 68 69 70 71 81 82 87 88 92 94 96 97 106 108 110 **P**5
Primary Contact: Patricia Wangler, Chief Executive Officer
CFO: Kim Bodensteiner, Chief Financial Officer
CIO: Kris Dally, Business Office Manager
CHR: Diane Sundrud, Human Resource Director
Web address: www.firstcare.org

| | 23 | 10 | 76 | 883 | 54 | 68418 | 45 | 12345 | 6363 | 153 |

MN

Hospital, Address, Telephone, Approval, Facility, and Physician Codes, Health Care System	Classi-fication Codes		Utilization Data					Expense (thousands) of dollars		
★ American Hospital Association (AHA) membership □ Joint Commission on Accreditation of Healthcare Organizations (JCAHO) accreditation ○ American Osteopathic Association (AOA) accreditation △ Commission on Accreditation of Rehabilitation Facilities (CARF) accreditation	Control	Service	Staffed Beds	Admissions	Census	Outpatient Visits	Births	Total	Payroll	Personnel

MN

FRIDLEY—Anoka County

★ **UNITY HOSPITAL**, 550 Osborne Road N.E., Zip 55432–2799;
tel. 763/236–5000 **A**2 9 10 **F**2 3 4 9 10 11 12 15 21 22 26 27 28 29 30 33
37 48 52 54 55 56 58 59 60 61 63 64 66 69 70 79 81 82 84 88 89 90 94
96 106 108 **P**4 5 **S** Allina Hospitals & Clinics, Minneapolis, MN
Primary Contact: Venetia Kudrle, President
COO: Kathy Wilde, Vice President Operations and Patient Care
CFO: Lisa Kjentvet, Vice President Finance
CMO: Dennis O'Hare, M.D., Vice President Medical Affairs
CIO: Bob Plaszcz, Executive Vice President Information Services and Chief
Information Oficer
CHR: Patrick Drescich, Vice President Human Resources
Web address: www.allina.com
| | | 23 | 10 | 228 | 13203 | 141 | 69511 | 1919 | 145623 | 64512 | 973 |

GLENCOE—McLeod County

★ **GLENCOE REGIONAL HEALTH SERVICES**, 1805 Hennepin Avenue North,
Zip 55336–1416; tel. 320/864–3121, (Total facility includes 110 beds in nursing
home–type unit) **A**9 10 18 **F**1 6 9 11 12 14 21 23 26 27 28 33 44 52 55 58
59 60 63 65 66 69 70 81 88 91 92 94 96 97 108 **P**6 **S** Park Nicollet Health
Services, Saint Louis Park, MN
Primary Contact: Jon D. Braband, President and Chief Executive Officer
CFO: Cheryl Trippel, Finance Director
CMO: John H. Bergseng, M.D., D.O., Vice President Medical Affairs
CHR: Jill Hatlestad, Vice President Human Resources and Organizational Support
Web address: www.grhsonline.com
| | | 23 | 10 | 135 | 1741 | 120 | 22664 | 197 | 34839 | 16962 | 391 |

GLENWOOD—Pope County

★ **GLACIAL RIDGE HEALTH SYSTEM**, 10 Fourth Avenue S.E., Zip 56334–1898;
tel. 320/634–4521 **A**9 10 **F**6 9 11 14 23 29 33 34 36 41 46 47 48 51 52 59
63 94 96 97 108 **P**6
Primary Contact: Vern Silvernale, Administrator and Chief Executive Officer
COO: Vern Silvernale, Administrator and Chief Executive Officer
CFO: Michael Bruemmer, Controller
CHR: Gordon Paulson, Personnel Manager
Web address: www.glacialridge.org
| | | 16 | 10 | 34 | 699 | 6 | 11546 | 39 | 9351 | 4722 | 116 |

GOLDEN VALLEY—Hennepin County

✦ **REGENCY HOSPITAL OF MINNEAPOLIS**, (Formerly Golden Valley Health
Center), 1300 Hidden Lakes Parkway, Zip 55422–4299; tel. 612/588–2771,
(Nonreporting) **A**1 **S** Regency Hospital Company, Alpharetta, GA
Primary Contact: Douglas Beardsley, Administrator
| | | 33 | 80 | 15 | — | — | — | — | — | — | — |

GRACEVILLE—Big Stone County

GRACEVILLE HEALTH CENTER, 115 West Second Street, Zip 56240–0157,
Mailing Address: P.O. Box 157, Zip 56240–0157; tel. 320/748–7223, (Total
facility includes 90 beds in nursing home–type unit) (Nonreporting) **A**9 10 18
S Missionary Benedictine Sisters American Province, Norfolk, NE
Primary Contact: Helen Jorve, Chief Executive Officer
| | | 23 | 10 | 112 | | | | | | | |

GRAND MARAIS—Cook County

COOK COUNTY NORTH SHORE HOSPITAL, 515 West 5th Street,
Zip 55604–9716, Mailing Address: P.O. Box 10, Zip 55604–0010;
tel. 218/387–3040, (Total facility includes 47 beds in nursing home–type unit) **A**9
10 18 **F**6 8 11 12 23 33 51 59 69 81 92 94 97 **P**6
Primary Contact: Diane L. Pearson, Administrator
| | | 16 | 10 | 56 | 394 | 48 | 11921 | 3 | 9344 | 4376 | 113 |

GRAND RAPIDS—Itasca County

✦ **GRAND ITASCA CLINIC AND HOSPITAL**, 126 First Avenue S.E.,
Zip 55744–3698; tel. 218/326–3401, (Total facility includes 35 beds in nursing
home–type unit) **A**1 9 10 20 **F**9 10 11 14 22 23 25 27 33 34 44 51 52 55 59
62 63 68 81 82 83 88 92 94 95 96 108 109
Primary Contact: Dan McCormick, President and Chief Executive Officer
CFO: Steven Feltman, Chief Financial Officer
CMO: Jack Carlisle, M.D., Chief of Staff
CIO: Larry Friedman, Director Information Services
Web address: www.granditasca.org
| | | 23 | 10 | 107 | 2661 | 44 | 33655 | 383 | 32119 | 15927 | — |

GRANITE FALLS—Yellow Medicine County

★ **GRANITE FALLS MUNICIPAL HOSPITAL AND MANOR**, 345 Tenth Avenue,
Zip 56241–1499; tel. 320/564–3111, (Total facility includes 57 beds in nursing
home–type unit) (Nonreporting) **A**9 10 18
Primary Contact: George Gerlach, Administrator
CFO: LaVonne Koenen, Business Office Manager
Web address: www.gfmhm.com
| | | 14 | 10 | 77 | — | — | — | — | — | — | — |

HALLOCK—Kittson County

★ **KITTSON MEMORIAL HEALTHCARE CENTER**, 1010 South Birch Street,
Zip 56728–0700, Mailing Address: P.O. Box 700, Zip 56728–0700;
tel. 218/843–3612, (Total facility includes 77 beds in nursing home–type unit)
(Nonreporting) **A**9 10 18
Primary Contact: Richard J. Failing, Chief Executive Officer
CFO: Sandra Gjervold, Chief Financial Officer
| | | 23 | 10 | 92 | — | — | — | — | — | — | — |

HASTINGS—Dakota County

□ **REGINA MEDICAL CENTER**, 1175 Nininger Road, Zip 55033–1098;
tel. 651/480–4100, (Nonreporting) **A**1 9 10
Primary Contact: Mark D. Wilson, President and Chief Executive Officer
Web address: www.reginamedical.org
| | | 23 | 10 | 118 | — | — | — | — | — | — | — |

Many Facility Codes have changed. Please refer to the AHA Guide Code Chart. © 2005 AHA Guide

Hospital, Address, Telephone, Approval, Facility, and Physician Codes, Health Care System	Classi-fication Codes		Utilization Data					Expense (thousands) of dollars		
★ American Hospital Association (AHA) membership □ Joint Commission on Accreditation of Healthcare Organizations (JCAHO) accreditation ○ American Osteopathic Association (AOA) accreditation △ Commission on Accreditation of Rehabilitation Facilities (CARF) accreditation	Control	Service	Staffed Beds	Admissions	Census	Outpatient Visits	Births	Total	Payroll	Personnel

HENDRICKS—Lincoln County

★ **HENDRICKS COMMUNITY HOSPITAL**, 503 East Lincoln Street, Zip 56136–0106, Mailing Address: P.O. Box 1016, Zip 56136–0106; tel. 507/275–3134, (Total facility includes 70 beds in nursing home–type unit) **A**9 10 18 **F**1 6 8 9 11 12 14 21 23 27 28 29 33 36 41 46 51 55 59 60 63 69 88 91 92 94 97 108 **P**5
Primary Contact: Kirk Stensrud, Chief Executive Officer
Web address: www.hendrickshosp.org

| | 23 | 10 | 91 | 380 | 73 | 6411 | 14 | 7296 | 2793 | 103 |

HIBBING—St. Louis County

⊞ **FAIRVIEW UNIVERSITY MEDICAL CENTER–MESABI**, 750 East 34th Street, Zip 55746–4600; tel. 218/262–4881, (Nonreporting) **A**1 9 10 **S** Fairview Health Services, Minneapolis, MN
Primary Contact: Lawrence W. Pfaff, President and Chief Executive Officer
COO: Richard W. Dinter, M.D., Chief Operating Officer
CFO: John D. Kritz, Regional Financial Officer
CMO: Michael Heck, M.D., Chief Medical Officer
CIO: Joe Wivoda, Chief Information Officer
CHR: Jennifer Preston, Human Resources Director
Web address: www.range.fairview.org

| | 23 | 10 | 111 | — | — | — | — | — | — | — |

HUTCHINSON—McLeod County

⊞ **HUTCHINSON AREA HEALTH CARE**, 1095 Highway 15 South, Zip 55350–3182; tel. 320/234–5000, (Total facility includes 123 beds in nursing home–type unit) **A**1 9 10 **F**1 4 6 9 11 12 14 21 23 27 28 29 31 33 44 46 47 48 52 54 58 59 60 61 62 63 66 69 71 72 73 74 75 76 77 78 81 88 92 94 95 96 97 108 109 **S** Allina Hospitals & Clinics, Minneapolis, MN
Primary Contact: Philip G. Graves, President
CFO: Pamela Larson, Chief Financial Officer
CMO: Steven Mulder, M.D., Director Medical Affairs
CHR: Robyn Erickson, Division Director Support Services
Web address: www.hahc–hmc.com

| | 14 | 10 | 190 | 3142 | 144 | 71816 | 431 | 49084 | 22830 | 469 |

INTERNATIONAL FALLS—Koochiching County

⊞ **FALLS MEMORIAL HOSPITAL**, 1400 Highway 71, Zip 56649–2189; tel. 218/283–4481 **A**1 9 10 18 **F**2 9 11 12 14 21 23 26 27 28 29 33 46 48 52 59 63 64 69 81 88 97 107 **S** Quorum Health Resources, Plano, TX
Primary Contact: Ty W. Erickson, Chief Executive Officer
CFO: Nancy Treacy, Chief Financial Officer
Web address: www.fmh–mn.com

| | 23 | 10 | 25 | 1014 | 10 | 28618 | 89 | 12119 | 4844 | 129 |

IVANHOE—Lincoln County

DIVINE PROVIDENCE HEALTH CENTER/AVERA HEALTH, 312 East George Street, Zip 56142–0136, Mailing Address: P.O. Box 136, Zip 56142–0136; tel. 507/694–1414, (Total facility includes 38 beds in nursing home–type unit) **A**9 10 18 **F**1 6 9 22 23 33 44 46 47 48 51 52 54 58 63 66 69 70 88 89 91 92 94 96 97 108 **P**5 6 **S** Avera Health, Yankton, SD
Primary Contact: Mary Maertens, Interim Administrator
Web address: www.dphc.org

| | 23 | 10 | 56 | 165 | 36 | 4103 | 0 | 5260 | 2258 | — |

JACKSON—Jackson County

★ **JACKSON MEDICAL CENTER**, 1430 North Highway, Zip 56143–1098; tel. 507/847–2420 **A**9 10 18 **F**21 23 29 33 44 48 52 63 66 69 70 97 108 109 **S** Sioux Valley Hospitals and Health System, Sioux Falls, SD
Primary Contact: Mary Ruyter, Chief Executive Officer
CFO: Lori Johnson, Chief Financial Officer
Web address: www.jacksonmedical.org

| | 23 | 10 | 20 | 839 | 3 | 12148 | 0 | 5382 | 1839 | 60 |

LAKE CITY—Goodhue County

⊞ **LAKE CITY MEDICAL CENTER–MAYO**, 500 West Grant Street, Zip 55041–1143; tel. 651/345–3321, (Total facility includes 98 beds in nursing home–type unit) **A**1 9 10 18 **F**9 11 12 27 28 29 33 48 51 54 58 59 62 63 66 69 81 82 84 88 92 93 94 97 106 108 **S** Mayo Foundation, Rochester, MN
Primary Contact: Thomas J. Witt, M.D., President and Chief Executive Officer
COO: Mark Rinehardt, Chief Operating Officer
CFO: Sue Diercks, Chief Financial Officer
Web address: www.lakecitymedicalcenter.org

| | 23 | 10 | 116 | 775 | 100 | 13407 | 72 | 16299 | 7476 | 210 |

LE SUEUR—Le Sueur County

MINNESOTA VALLEY HEALTH CENTER, 621 South Fourth Street, Zip 56058–2298; tel. 507/665–3375, (Includes GARDENVIEW NURSING HOME), (Total facility includes 85 beds in nursing home–type unit) (Nonreporting) **A**9 10
Primary Contact: Jerry J. Boerboom, Chief Executive Officer and Administrator
Web address: www.mvhc.org

| | 23 | 10 | 102 | — | — | — | — | — | — | — |

LITCHFIELD—Meeker County

★ **MEEKER COUNTY MEMORIAL HOSPITAL**, 612 South Sibley Avenue, Zip 55355–3398; tel. 320/693–3242 **A**9 10 18 **F**9 11 12 23 28 33 44 46 47 48 53 55 59 61 63 76 81 88 94 96 97
Primary Contact: Michael Schramm, Chief Executive Officer
CFO: Gary Sogge, Chief Financial Officer
CMO: Debra G. Peterson, M.D., Chief of Staff
CIO: Connie Liimatta, Medical Records and Business Office Director
CHR: Cindi Twardy, Human Resources Department Manager
Web address: www.mcmh–litchfield.org

| | 13 | 10 | 38 | 1233 | 15 | 22280 | 151 | 14074 | 5704 | 117 |

MN

Hospital, Address, Telephone, Approval, Facility, and Physician Codes, Health Care System	Classi-fication Codes		Utilization Data					Expense (thousands) of dollars		
★ American Hospital Association (AHA) membership ☐ Joint Commission on Accreditation of Healthcare Organizations (JCAHO) accreditation ○ American Osteopathic Association (AOA) accreditation △ Commission on Accreditation of Rehabilitation Facilities (CARF) accreditation	Control	Service	Staffed Beds	Admissions	Census	Outpatient Visits	Births	Total	Payroll	Personnel

LITTLE FALLS—Morrison County

⊠ **ST. GABRIEL'S HOSPITAL**, 815 Second Street S.E., Zip 56345–3596; tel. 320/632–5441, (Total facility includes 150 beds in nursing home–type unit) **A**1 9 10 **F**1 2 8 9 11 12 21 22 27 28 33 36 37 48 51 52 55 58 59 60 62 63 64 65 66 69 81 82 87 88 92 94 95 96 97 108 **P**5 **S** Catholic Health Initiatives, Denver, CO
Primary Contact: Carl P. Vaagenes, President and Chief Executive Officer
CFO: Larry Novakoske, Vice President Finance
Web address: www.stgabriels.com

| | 21 | 10 | 199 | 1961 | 152 | 54000 | 245 | 36512 | 14913 | 409 |

LONG PRAIRIE—Todd County

★ **LONG PRAIRIE MEMORIAL HOSPITAL AND HOME**, 20 Ninth Street S.E., Zip 56347–1404; tel. 320/732–2141, (Total facility includes 95 beds in nursing home–type unit) **A**9 10 18 **F**1 6 11 12 14 21 26 27 28 33 45 46 48 52 53 59 60 63 69 81 84 88 92 94 97 108 **S** CentraCare Health System, Saint Cloud, MN
Primary Contact: Roger Oberg, Administrator
CFO: Larry Knutson, Finance Director
Web address: www.centracare.com

| | 23 | 10 | 120 | 894 | 101 | 19932 | 138 | 15024 | 6422 | 168 |

LUVERNE—Rock County

★ **SIOUX VALLEY LUVERNE MEDICAL CENTER**, (Formerly Luverne Community Hospital), 1600 North Kniss, Zip 56156–2519, Mailing Address: P.O. Box 1019, Zip 56156–2519; tel. 507/283–2321 **A**9 10 **F**3 4 6 9 11 12 14 21 22 23 24 27 28 29 33 36 37 38 44 46 48 52 53 58 59 60 61 63 65 69 70 81 84 86 88 93 95 96 97 106 108 109 110 **P**5 **S** Sioux Valley Hospitals and Health System, Sioux Falls, SD
Primary Contact: Gerald E. Carl, Chief Executive Officer
CFO: Stan Knobloch, Chief Financial Officer
CMO: Timothy S. Mulder, M.D., Chief of Staff
CIO: Diane Westenberg, Executive Assistant
CHR: Patty Winkels, Human Resources and Payroll Supervisor
Web address: www.luvernecommunityhospital.org

| | 23 | 10 | 28 | 999 | 9 | 16119 | 122 | 9983 | 4353 | 116 |

MADELIA—Watonwan County

⊠ **MADELIA COMMUNITY HOSPITAL**, 121 Drew Avenue S.E., Zip 56062–1899; tel. 507/642–3255 **A**1 9 10 18 **F**9 11 12 26 27 28 29 33 38 46 48 51 52 53 54 58 59 60 63 64 65 69 75 81 92 94 97 **P**6
Primary Contact: Candace Fenske, Administrator
CFO: Donna M. Klinkner, Business Manager
Web address: www.mchospital.org

| | 23 | 10 | 21 | 470 | 5 | 7430 | 40 | 5329 | 2234 | 58 |

MADISON—Lac Qui Parle County

MADISON HOSPITAL, 820 Third Avenue, Zip 56256–1014, Mailing Address: 900 Second Avenue, Zip 56256–1006; tel. 320/598–7556 **A**9 10 **F**8 9 12 21 22 27 28 33 46 48 51 52 54 60 63 69 70 81 84 88 91 92 94 97 109
Primary Contact: Thomas Richter, Chief Executive Officer
Web address: www.madisonlutheranhome.com

| | 23 | 10 | 111 | 599 | 93 | 22063 | 8 | 9831 | 5052 | 155 |

MAHNOMEN—Mahnomen County

★ **MAHNOMEN HEALTH CENTER**, 414 Jefferson Avenue, Zip 56557–4912, Mailing Address: P.O. Box 396, Zip 56557–0396; tel. 218/935–2511, (Total facility includes 48 beds in nursing home–type unit) (Nonreporting) **A**9 10 18 **S** MeritCare Health System, Fargo, ND
Primary Contact: Sue Klabo, Administrator
CFO: Nancy Buretta, Business Office Manager

| | 15 | 10 | 63 | — | — | — | — | — | — | — |

MANKATO—Blue Earth County

⊠ **IMMANUEL ST. JOSEPH'S—MAYO HEALTH SYSTEM**, 1025 Marsh Street, Zip 56002–8673, Mailing Address: P.O. Box 8673, Zip 56002–8673; tel. 507/625–4031 **A**1 3 5 9 10 19 **F**2 9 11 12 15 17 21 22 23 27 28 29 30 31 32 33 36 37 38 41 42 46 48 49 50 51 52 53 55 57 58 59 60 61 62 63 64 65 66 69 70 71 72 73 75 76 80 81 82 84 85 87 88 93 94 96 98 106 108 109 110 **P**6 **S** Mayo Foundation, Rochester, MN
Primary Contact: William Rupp, M.D., President and Chief Executive Officer
CFO: Gregory Burkel, Chief Financial Officer
CMO: Anthony Jaspers, President of the Medical Staff
CIO: Thomas Borowski, Director Information Systems
CHR: Julie Oliver, Chief Human Resources Officer
Web address: www.isj–mhs.org

| | 23 | 10 | 174 | 9206 | 99 | 232396 | 1375 | 140352 | 66964 | 1197 |

MARSHALL—Lyon County

⊠ **AVERA MARSHALL REGIONAL MEDICAL CENTER**, (Formerly Weiner Memorial Medical Center), 300 South Bruce Street, Zip 56258–3900; tel. 507/532–9661, (Total facility includes 76 beds in nursing home–type unit) **A**1 9 10 18 **F**1 2 9 11 12 14 21 23 26 27 28 33 37 41 45 46 48 51 52 53 55 58 59 61 62 63 65 69 81 84 85 88 92 93 94 96 97 106 108 110 **P**5 **S** Avera Health, Yankton, SD
Primary Contact: Bruce E. Roesler, Chief Executive Officer
CFO: Sharon Williams, Vice President Information and Financial Services
CMO: David Odland, M.D., Chief of Staff
CIO: Sharon Williams, Assistant Administrator Information and Financial Services
CHR: Brian Bohn, Vice President Human Resources
Web address: www.wmmc.org

| | 14 | 10 | 108 | 1618 | 86 | 21530 | 341 | 21017 | 11420 | 288 |

Many Facility Codes have changed. Please refer to the AHA Guide Code Chart.   © 2005 AHA Guide

Hospital, Address, Telephone, Approval, Facility, and Physician Codes, Health Care System	Classi-fication Codes		Utilization Data					Expense (thousands) of dollars		
★ American Hospital Association (AHA) membership □ Joint Commission on Accreditation of Healthcare Organizations (JCAHO) accreditation ○ American Osteopathic Association (AOA) accreditation △ Commission on Accreditation of Rehabilitation Facilities (CARF) accreditation	Control	Service	Staffed Beds	Admissions	Census	Outpatient Visits	Births	Total	Payroll	Personnel

MELROSE—Stearns County

★ **MELROSE AREA HOSPITAL – CENTRA CARE**, 11 North Fifth Avenue West, Zip 56352–1098; tel. 320/256–4231, (Total facility includes 75 beds in nursing home–type unit) **A**9 10 18 **F**1 5 11 12 23 26 27 29 33 44 52 53 55 58 59 60 61 62 63 69 80 81 88 91 92 94 96 97 110 **P**5 **S** CentraCare Health System, Saint Cloud, MN
Primary Contact: Joan Jackson, Administrator
CFO: Todd Stordahl, Chief Financial Officer
Web address: www.centracare.com

| 23 | 10 | 93 | 523 | 78 | 10998 | 69 | 10687 | 4539 | 135 |

MINNEAPOLIS—Hennepin County

⊠ **ABBOTT NORTHWESTERN HOSPITAL**, 800 East 28th Street, Zip 55407–3799; tel. 612/863–4000, (Includes SISTER KENNY REHABILITATION INSTITUTE) **A**1 2 3 5 8 9 10 **F**2 3 7 9 10 11 12 13 14 15 17 19 21 22 23 26 27 28 29 30 31 33 34 35 36 37 38 39 40 41 42 44 45 46 47 49 50 52 53 55 56 57 58 59 60 61 62 63 64 65 66 68 69 70 71 72 73 74 75 76 77 78 79 80 81 82 83 84 85 86 87 88 90 92 93 94 95 96 99 100 101 102 103 104 105 108 109 110 **P**2 5 6 **S** Allina Hospitals & Clinics, Minneapolis, MN
Primary Contact: Richard Sturgeon, M.D., Interim President
CFO: David Albright, Vice President Operations
CMO: Richard Sturgeon, M.D., Medical Affairs Vice President
CIO: Virginia Reed, Chief Information Officer
CHR: Al Johnson, Vice President Human Resources
Web address: www.allina.com

| 23 | 10 | 627 | 38075 | 468 | 192890 | 4673 | 609132 | 256740 | 3591 |

□ **CHILDREN'S HOSPITALS AND CLINICS**, 2525 Chicago Avenue South, Zip 55404–9976; tel. 612/813–6100 **A**1 2 3 5 9 10 **F**2 4 9 16 18 20 21 22 23 24 26 27 28 29 30 31 33 36 37 38 39 41 42 46 47 48 49 50 51 52 53 56 57 58 60 61 62 63 65 66 67 69 70 72 73 74 75 77 79 80 81 82 83 84 85 86 87 88 89 90 93 94 95 96 97 98 106 108 110 **P**1 5 6 **S** Children's Hospitals and Clinics of Minnesota, Minneapolis, MN
Primary Contact: Alan L. Goldbloom, M.D., President and Chief Executive Officer
Web address: www.childrenshc.org

| 23 | 50 | 173 | 7440 | 134 | 156419 | 0 | 218093 | 106550 | 1896 |

⊠ **HENNEPIN COUNTY MEDICAL CENTER**, 701 Park Avenue South, Zip 55415–1829; tel. 612/873–3000 **A**1 2 3 5 8 9 10 **F**2 4 6 9 10 11 12 13 14 15 17 19 21 22 23 24 26 27 28 29 30 31 32 33 34 35 37 39 40 42 44 45 46 47 48 50 52 53 55 56 57 58 59 60 61 62 63 64 65 66 67 68 69 70 71 72 73 74 75 76 77 78 79 81 82 84 85 87 88 90 93 94 95 96 98 101 106 107 108 109 110
Primary Contact: Jeff Spartz, Administrator
COO: Lynn Abrahamsen, Chief Operating Officer
CFO: Larry Kryzaniak, Chief Financial Officer
CMO: Michael Belzer, Medical Director
CIO: Joanne Sunquist, Chief Information Officer
CHR: Stephanie Secrest, Human Resources Director
Web address: www.hcmc.org

| 13 | 10 | 422 | 22173 | 305 | 451881 | 2795 | 404315 | 189384 | 3079 |

NORTH MEMORIAL HEALTH CARE See Robbinsdale

⊠ **PHILLIPS EYE INSTITUTE**, 2215 Park Avenue, Zip 55404–3756; tel. 612/336–6000 **A**1 9 10 **F**26 27 28 45 52 58 63 66 69 92 **S** Allina Hospitals & Clinics, Minneapolis, MN
Primary Contact: Shari E. Levy, President
CFO: Mark Bortnem, Director of Finance
Web address: www.allina.com

| 23 | 45 | 10 | 567 | 2 | 16907 | 0 | 20985 | 8843 | — |

□ **SHRINERS HOSPITALS FOR CHILDREN, TWIN CITIES**, 2025 East River Parkway, Zip 55414–3696; tel. 612/596–6100 **A**1 **F**9 21 26 27 29 47 48 52 58 62 63 65 66 69 88 94 96 108 **P**6 **S** Shriners Hospitals for Children, Tampa, FL
Primary Contact: Laurence E. Johnson, Administrator
Web address: www.shrinershq.org

| 23 | 57 | 40 | 427 | 4 | 5649 | 0 | — | — | 163 |

SISTER KENNY REHABILITATION INSTITUTE See Abbott Northwestern Hospital
ST. MARY'S HOSPITAL AND REHABILITATION CENTER See University of Minnesota Medical Center
UNIVERSITY OF MINNESOTA HOSPITAL AND CLINIC See University of Minnesota Medical Center

⊠ **UNIVERSITY OF MINNESOTA MEDICAL CENTER**, (Formerly Fairview–University Medical Center), 2450 Riverside Avenue, Zip 55454–1400; tel. 612/672–6000, (Includes FAIRVIEW RIVERSIDE HOSPITAL, 2312 South Sixth Street, Zip 55454; ST. MARY'S HOSPITAL AND REHABILITATION CENTER, 2414 South Seventh Street, Zip 55454; tel. 612/338–2229; UNIVERSITY OF MINNESOTA HOSPITAL AND CLINIC, 420 S.E. Delaware Street, Zip 55455–0392, Mailing Address: 420 S.E. Delaware Street, Box 502, Zip 55455–0392; tel. 612/626–3000), (Total facility includes 41 beds in nursing home–type unit) **A**1 3 5 8 9 10 **F**1 2 3 4 5 7 9 10 11 12 14 15 16 17 18 19 20 21 22 23 24 26 27 28 29 30 31 32 33 34 35 37 38 39 40 44 45 46 47 48 49 50 52 53 54 55 56 57 58 59 60 61 62 63 64 65 66 67 68 69 70 71 72 73 74 75 76 77 78 79 80 81 82 83 84 85 86 87 88 89 90 92 94 95 96 97 98 99 100 101 102 103 104 105 106 107 108 109 110 **P**5 **S** Fairview Health Services, Minneapolis, MN
Primary Contact: Gordon L. Alexander, President
CFO: Steven Hill, Vice President Finance
CIO: William Showalter, Vice President Chief Information Officer
CHR: Charles McIntosh, Senior Director Human Resources
Web address: www.fairview.org

| 23 | 10 | 829 | 34573 | 542 | 502305 | 2681 | 713969 | 275964 | 3843 |

Hospital, Address, Telephone, Approval, Facility, and Physician Codes, Health Care System	Classi-fication Codes		Utilization Data					Expense (thousands) of dollars		
★ American Hospital Association (AHA) membership □ Joint Commission on Accreditation of Healthcare Organizations (JCAHO) accreditation ○ American Osteopathic Association (AOA) accreditation △ Commission on Accreditation of Rehabilitation Facilities (CARF) accreditation	Control	Service	Staffed Beds	Admissions	Census	Outpatient Visits	Births	Total	Payroll	Personnel

⊠ △ **VETERANS AFFAIRS MEDICAL CENTER**, One Veterans Drive, Zip 55417–2399; tel. 612/725–2000, (Total facility includes 104 beds in nursing home–type unit) **A**1 2 3 5 7 8 **F**1 3 4 10 15 17 19 21 22 23 27 28 29 31 32 33 36 37 38 39 41 42 43 44 46 47 48 49 50 51 52 55 57 58 60 61 62 63 64 65 66 68 69 70 73 74 75 76 77 78 80 81 82 83 84 85 87 88 92 93 94 95 96 106 107 108 109 110 **S** Department of Veterans Affairs, Washington, DC Primary Contact: Steven Kleinglass, Director COO: Brian Stiller, Chief Operating Officer CFO: Paul Resel, Chief Financial Officer CMO: Jack Drucker, M.D., Chief of Staff CIO: Claire Stollie, Acting Chief Information Management Services CHR: Neil Falkner, Director Human Resources Services Web address: www.va.gov/sta/guide/home.asp	45	10	340	9200	340	500000	0	350000	175000	3010
MONTEVIDEO—Chippewa County										
★ **CHIPPEWA COUNTY–MONTEVIDEO HOSPITAL**, 824 North 11th Street, Zip 56265–1683; tel. 320/269–8877, (Nonreporting) **A**9 10 18 Primary Contact: Mark E. Paulson, Administrator CFO: Darlene Boike, Business Office Manager Web address: www.montevideomedical.com	15	10	25	—	—	—	—	—	—	—
MONTICELLO—Wright County										
⊠ **MONTICELLO BIG LAKE HOSPITAL**, 1013 Hart Boulevard, Zip 55362–8230; tel. 763/295–2945, (Total facility includes 91 beds in nursing home–type unit) **A**1 9 10 18 **F**3 6 9 11 12 13 14 26 27 33 52 55 56 59 61 62 63 67 68 71 81 88 92 93 94 108 Primary Contact: Barbara Schwientek, Chief Executive Officer COO: Chris Harff, Chief Operating Officer CFO: Nancy Friesen, Chief Financial Officer CMO: William Scheig, Chief of Staff CHR: Jody Smith, Organizational Support Officer Web address: www.mblch.com	16	10	107	1788	99	26426	536	32602	14481	243
MOOSE LAKE—Carlton County										
★ **MERCY HOSPITAL AND HEALTH CARE CENTER**, 710 South Kenwood Avenue, Zip 55767–9405; tel. 218/485–4481, (Total facility includes 94 beds in nursing home–type unit) **A**9 10 18 **F**1 2 6 8 9 11 12 21 23 26 27 28 29 33 34 41 45 46 48 51 52 53 55 58 59 60 63 65 66 69 81 88 92 94 96 97 106 107 108 **P**5 Primary Contact: Clayton R. Peterson, Chief Executive Officer CFO: John Unzen, Chief Financial Officer Web address: www.mercymooselake.org	16	10	125	1259	100	24076	152	30923	11816	262
MORA—Kanabec County										
⊠ **KANABEC HOSPITAL**, 301 South Highway 65, Zip 55051; tel. 320/679–1212 **A**1 9 10 18 **F**2 6 9 11 12 22 23 26 27 28 29 33 34 36 37 40 45 46 48 55 59 62 63 64 66 69 81 84 88 94 96 97 106 108 110 Primary Contact: Randy Ulseth, Chief Executive Officer COO: Christine M. Kimbler, R.N., Chief Operating Officer CFO: Gordy Forbort, Chief Financial Officer Web address: www.kanabechospital.org	13	10	25	1791	12	20538	188	19975	9340	193
MORRIS—Stevens County										
★ **STEVENS COMMUNITY MEDICAL CENTER**, 400 East First Street, Zip 56267–0660, Mailing Address: P.O. Box 660, Zip 56267–0660; tel. 320/589–1313 **A**9 10 18 **F**4 8 9 10 11 12 23 26 27 28 29 31 32 33 36 46 48 50 51 52 55 59 60 61 62 63 64 65 66 70 72 73 74 75 76 77 81 84 88 94 95 96 97 106 108 **P**6 Primary Contact: John Rau, President CFO: Kerrie Stageberg, Director Finance and Information Systems CIO: Kerrie Stageberg, Director Finance and Information Systems CHR: Karl Larson, Human Res Director Web address: www.scmcmorris.com	23	10	25	1257	12	127074	97	22740	11917	257
NEW PRAGUE—Scott County										
⊠ **QUEEN OF PEACE HOSPITAL**, 301 Second Street N.E., Zip 56071–1799; tel. 952/758–4431 **A**1 9 10 18 **F**9 11 12 14 22 23 28 29 30 32 33 36 37 41 46 48 51 52 53 55 58 59 60 61 62 63 66 68 69 70 81 84 88 91 93 95 96 106 108 109 **P**6 Primary Contact: Mary Klimp, Chief Executive Officer CFO: Paula Nelson, Chief Financial Officer and Associate Administrator CMO: John Berg, M.D., Chief of Staff CHR: Jeff Frank, Human Resource Director Web address: www.queenofpeacehospital.org	23	10	28	1475	10	37872	96	20179	9266	192
NEW ULM—Brown County										
⊠ **NEW ULM MEDICAL CENTER**, 1324 Fifth Street North, Zip 56073–1553, Mailing Address: P.O. Box 577, Zip 56073–0577; tel. 507/233–1000 **A**1 9 10 **F**2 3 4 6 9 11 12 14 21 23 26 27 28 29 30 33 34 36 37 38 44 51 52 53 54 55 58 59 60 61 62 63 64 69 70 71 72 73 74 75 76 77 78 81 84 88 89 94 95 96 97 106 107 108 109 110 **P**7 **S** Allina Hospitals & Clinics, Minneapolis, MN Primary Contact: Lori L. Wightman, Administrator CFO: Steve Hatkin, Director Finance CMO: Joan Krikava, M.D., Director Medical Affairs CIO: Steve Hatkin, Director Finance CHR: Diane Rasmussen, Director of Human Resources Web address: www.newulmmedicalcenter.com	23	10	47	2171	25	142062	349	44335	17029	375

Many Facility Codes have changed. Please refer to the AHA Guide Code Chart. © 2005 AHA Guide

Hospital, Address, Telephone, Approval, Facility, and Physician Codes, Health Care System	Classi-fication Codes		Utilization Data					Expense (thousands) of dollars		
	Control	Service	Staffed Beds	Admissions	Census	Outpatient Visits	Births	Total	Payroll	Personnel

★ American Hospital Association (AHA) membership
□ Joint Commission on Accreditation of Healthcare Organizations (JCAHO) accreditation
○ American Osteopathic Association (AOA) accreditation
△ Commission on Accreditation of Rehabilitation Facilities (CARF) accreditation

NORTHFIELD—Dakota County

☒ **NORTHFIELD HOSPITAL**, 2000 North Avenue, Zip 55057–1498; tel. 507/646–1000, (Includes LONG TERM CARE CENTER), (Total facility includes 40 beds in nursing home–type unit) **A**1 9 10 **F**2 5 6 11 12 22 23 27 28 30 33 36 46 48 51 52 53 54 55 58 59 60 61 62 63 64 66 69 70 81 84 85 87 88 92 93 94 95 96 97 107 108 109 110 **P**6
Primary Contact: Kendall C. Bank, President
CFO: Roger Stapek, Vice President and Chief Financial Officer
CHR: Mother Superior Dean Grotjohn, Director of Human Resources
Web address: www.northfieldhospital.org
| | 14 | 10 | 76 | 2421 | 55 | 29110 | 377 | 33345 | 14806 | 306 |

OLIVIA—Renville County

RENVILLE COUNTY HOSPITAL, 611 East Fairview Avenue, Zip 56277–0800; tel. 320/523–1261, (Nonreporting) **A**9 10 18
Primary Contact: Tim Middendorf, Administrator
Web address: www.renvillecountyhospital.org
| | 15 | 10 | 25 | — | — | — | — | — | — | — |

ONAMIA—Mille Lacs County

★ **MILLE LACS HEALTH SYSTEM**, 200 North Elm Street, Zip 56359–7978; tel. 320/532–3154, (Total facility includes 65 beds in nursing home–type unit) **A**9 10 18 20 **F**1 5 6 9 11 21 22 23 24 26 27 28 29 33 34 36 39 44 46 48 51 52 58 59 60 61 63 64 65 69 70 82 92 94 95 96 97 106 107 **P**6
Primary Contact: Daniel Reiner, Administrator and Chief Executive Officer
COO: Kathy Johnson, Chief Operating Officer
CFO: Chris Gross, Chief Financial Officer
CMO: Thomas H. Bracken, Chief of Staff
CHR: Sonya Towle, Human Resources Director
Web address: www.millelacshealth.com
| | 23 | 10 | 83 | 845 | 65 | 47274 | 71 | 20769 | 10408 | 246 |

ORTONVILLE—Big Stone County

★ **ORTONVILLE AREA HEALTH SERVICES**, 450 Eastvold Avenue, Zip 56278–1133; tel. 320/839–2502, (Total facility includes 74 beds in nursing home–type unit) (Nonreporting) **A**9 10 18 **S** Sioux Valley Hospitals and Health System, Sioux Falls, SD
Primary Contact: Kenneth W. Archer, Chief Executive Officer
CFO: James Foster, Finance Administrator
CMO: Mark Huntington, M.D., Medical Director
Web address: www.ortonvilleareahealth.org
| | 14 | 10 | 89 | — | — | — | — | — | — | — |

OWATONNA—Steele County

☒ **OWATONNA HOSPITAL**, 903 South Oak Street, Zip 55060–3234; tel. 507/451–3850 **A**1 9 10 **F**4 9 12 21 26 28 29 33 36 38 46 47 51 52 54 58 60 63 64 69 71 75 81 88 93 94 95 96 108 **S** Allina Hospitals & Clinics, Minneapolis, MN
Primary Contact: Dorothy Erdmann, President
CFO: Jeffrey Chestnut, Director Finance
Web address: www.allina.com
| | 23 | 10 | 48 | 2627 | 24 | 30894 | 550 | — | — | — |

PARK RAPIDS—Hubbard County

☒ **ST. JOSEPH'S AREA HEALTH SERVICES**, 600 Pleasant Avenue, Zip 56470–1432; tel. 218/732–3311 **A**1 9 10 20 **F**9 10 11 12 21 22 24 27 28 29 32 33 34 36 38 46 47 48 51 52 55 58 59 60 62 63 64 69 81 82 84 87 88 92 93 94 95 96 97 98 108 **S** Catholic Health Initiatives, Denver, CO
Primary Contact: Peter Jacobson, President and Chief Executive Officer
CFO: Brent Schmidt, Chief Financial Officer
Web address: www.sjahs.org
| | 21 | 10 | 43 | 2506 | 25 | 66443 | 139 | 29820 | 13082 | 296 |

PAYNESVILLE—Stearns County

★ **PAYNESVILLE AREA HEALTH CARE SYSTEM**, 200 West 1st Street, Zip 56362–1496; tel. 320/243–3767, (Total facility includes 64 beds in nursing home–type unit) **A**9 10 18 **F**1 6 8 11 12 14 23 27 28 33 44 45 52 58 59 63 81 88 91 92 94 96 97 108 110 **P**8
Primary Contact: Steven T. Moburg, Chief Executive Officer
COO: Thomas Kooiman, Chief Operating Officer
CFO: Kirk Johnson, Chief Financial Officer
CMO: Timothy Malling, M.D., Chief of Staff
CIO: Gary Smith, Information Technology Manager
CHR: Paulette Hagen, Human Resource Director
Web address: www.pahcs.com
| | 16 | 10 | 94 | 725 | 67 | 19968 | 136 | 25119 | 10253 | 194 |

PERHAM—Otter Tail County

☒ **PERHAM MEMORIAL HOSPITAL AND HOME**, 665 Third Street S.W., Zip 56573–1199; tel. 218/346–4500, (Total facility includes 102 beds in nursing home–type unit) (Nonreporting) **A**1 9 10 **S** MeritCare Health System, Fargo, ND
Primary Contact: Chuck Hofius, Administrator
CFO: Brad D. Wurgler, Chief Financial Officer
CIO: Jim Rieber, Director Information Systems
Web address: www.pmhh.com
| | 16 | 10 | 123 | — | — | — | — | — | — | — |

PINE CITY—Pine County

LAKESIDE MEDICAL CENTER, 129 East Sixth Avenue, Zip 55063; tel. 320/629–2542, (Nonreporting) **A**9 10
Primary Contact: Max Blaufuss, Administrator and Chief Executive Officer
| | 33 | 49 | 10 | — | — | — | — | — | — | — |

PIPESTONE—Pipestone County

PIPESTONE COUNTY MEDICAL CENTER/AVERA HEALTH, 916 4th Avenue S.W., Zip 56164–0370; tel. 507/825–6125, (Total facility includes 43 beds in nursing home–type unit) **A**9 10 **F**1 11 12 21 23 28 33 41 46 48 51 52 53 55 59 60 61 62 63 68 69 81 82 92 97 107 108 **P**4 **S** Avera Health, Yankton, SD
Primary Contact: Jody Jenner, Chief Executive Officer and Administrator
Web address: www.pcmchealth.org
| | 13 | 10 | 76 | 865 | 49 | 23272 | 82 | 13107 | 5398 | 160 |

MN

Hospital, Address, Telephone, Approval, Facility, and Physician Codes, Health Care System	Classi-fication Codes		Utilization Data					Expense (thousands) of dollars		
★ American Hospital Association (AHA) membership □ Joint Commission on Accreditation of Healthcare Organizations (JCAHO) accreditation ○ American Osteopathic Association (AOA) accreditation △ Commission on Accreditation of Rehabilitation Facilities (CARF) accreditation	Control	Service	Staffed Beds	Admissions	Census	Outpatient Visits	Births	Total	Payroll	Personnel

PRINCETON—Sherburne County

☒ **FAIRVIEW NORTHLAND REGIONAL HEALTH CARE**, 911 Northland Drive, Zip 55371–2173; tel. 763/389–1313 **A**1 9 10 **F**2 9 11 12 21 22 23 25 27 28 29 33 44 48 52 53 54 55 58 59 60 63 64 69 70 81 84 88 94 96 97 **P**6 **S** Fairview Health Services, Minneapolis, MN
Primary Contact: Michael Youso, President
CMO: Greg Schoen, M.D., Regional Medical Director
Web address: www.fairview.org/northland/

| 23 | 10 | 41 | 2772 | 20 | 33022 | 490 | 57031 | 31254 | 401 |

RED WING—Goodhue County

☒ **FAIRVIEW RED WING MEDICAL CENTER**, 701 Fairview Boulevard, Zip 55066–2848, Mailing Address: P.O. Box 95, Zip 55066–0095; tel. 651/267–5000, (Total facility includes 85 beds in nursing home–type unit) **A**1 9 10 **F**2 9 11 12 14 21 22 23 26 27 28 29 33 34 36 39 41 42 44 46 48 51 52 53 54 55 58 59 60 61 62 63 64 65 66 69 70 72 77 81 82 84 85 87 88 91 92 93 94 95 96 97 107 108 109 **P**1 **S** Fairview Health Services, Minneapolis, MN
Primary Contact: Scott Wordelman, President and Chief Executive Officer
COO: Beth Krehbrel, Chief Operating Officer
CFO: Mike Larson, Chief Financial Officer
CMO: Jack Alexander, M.D., Chief Medical Officer
CHR: Mary Kaphines, Human Resource Manager
Web address: www.fairview.org

| 23 | 10 | 135 | 2524 | 95 | 27621 | 384 | 71393 | 36371 | 504 |

REDLAKE—Beltrami County

☒ **U.S. PUBLIC HEALTH SERVICE INDIAN HOSPITAL**, Highway 1, Zip 56671, Mailing Address: P.O. Box 497, Zip 56671–0497; tel. 218/679–3912, (Nonreporting) **A**1 9 10 **S** U. S. Indian Health Service, Rockville, MD
Primary Contact: Essimae Stevens, Service Unit Director
CMO: John Robinson, Clinical Director

| 47 | 10 | 23 | | | | | | | |

REDWOOD FALLS—Redwood County

★ **REDWOOD AREA HOSPITAL**, 100 Fallwood Road, Zip 56283–1828; tel. 507/637–4500 **A**9 10 18 **F**1 2 9 11 12 21 23 26 33 36 37 38 46 47 48 51 52 53 55 58 59 60 61 63 65 66 69 82 85 93 94 96 97 106 108 **P**5
Primary Contact: James E. Schulte, Administrator
CFO: John Peyerl, Chief Financial Officer
CIO: Timothy Beske, Information Systems Manager
CHR: Jody Rindfleisch, Human Resource Manager
Web address: www.redwoodareahospital.org

| 14 | 10 | 30 | 773 | 7 | 11282 | 125 | 13113 | 5334 | 127 |

ROBBINSDALE—Hennepin County

☒ **NORTH MEMORIAL HEALTH CARE**, 3300 Oakdale Avenue North, Zip 55422–2926; tel. 763/520–5200 **A**1 2 3 5 9 10 **F**2 6 9 11 12 14 15 17 19 21 22 23 24 26 27 28 29 30 31 33 34 35 36 37 38 39 41 44 45 46 47 48 49 51 52 53 54 55 56 57 58 59 60 61 62 63 64 65 66 67 68 69 70 71 73 75 78 81 82 84 85 86 88 90 94 96 97 106 107 108 109 110 **P**6 8
Primary Contact: Scott R. Anderson, Chief Executive Officer
COO: David W. Cress, Vice President and Chief Operating Officer
CFO: Patrick Boran, Chief Financial Officer
CMO: Irfan Altafullah, M.D., Chief of Staff
CIO: Patrick Taffe, Vice President Information Services
CHR: James White, Vice President Human Resources
Web address: www.northmemorial.com

| 23 | 10 | 449 | 27420 | 304 | 251473 | 3067 | 447707 | 222239 | 3476 |

ROCHESTER—Olmsted County

★ **OLMSTED MEDICAL CENTER**, 1650 Fourth Street S.E., Zip 55904–4717, Mailing Address: 210 Ninth Street S.E., Zip 55904–4717; tel. 507/288–3443, (Nonreporting) **A**9 10
Primary Contact: Noel R. Peterson, M.D., MS, President and Chief Executive Officer
CFO: Troy D. Stafford, Assistant Administrator Finance
CMO: David E. Westgard, M.D., Chief Medical Officer
CIO: Susan M. Schuett, Assistant Administrator Information Systems
Web address: www.olmmed.org

| 23 | 10 | 63 | — | — | — | — | — | — | — |

☒ **ROCHESTER METHODIST HOSPITAL**, 201 West Center Street, Zip 55902–3084; tel. 507/266–7890, (Nonreporting) **A**1 3 5 9 10 **S** Mayo Foundation, Rochester, MN
Primary Contact: Lynn Frederick, Administrator
COO: Jeffrey Korsmo, Administrator
CFO: Lee Hecht, Chief Financial Officer
CMO: Michael Rock, M.D., Chair Hospital Practice Commitee
CIO: Abdul Bengali, Chairman Information Systems
Web address: www.mayoclinic.org

| 23 | 10 | 335 | — | — | — | — | — | — | — |

☒ **SAINT MARYS HOSPITAL**, 1216 Second Street S.W., Zip 55902–1970; tel. 507/255–5123, (Nonreporting) **A**1 3 5 8 9 10 **S** Mayo Foundation, Rochester, MN
Primary Contact: Lynn Frederick, Administrator
COO: Jeffrey Korsmo, Administrator
CFO: Lee Hecht, Chief Financial Officer
CMO: Michael Rock, M.D., Chair practice Commitee
CIO: Abdul Bengali, Chairman Foundation Information Technology
CHR: Ken Schneider, Chair, Department of Human Resources
Web address: www.mayoclinic.org

| 23 | 10 | 797 | — | — | — | — | — | — | — |

Many Facility Codes have changed. Please refer to the AHA Guide Code Chart. © 2005 AHA Guide

Hospital, Address, Telephone, Approval, Facility, and Physician Codes, Health Care System	Classi-fication Codes		Utilization Data					Expense (thousands) of dollars		
★ American Hospital Association (AHA) membership ☐ Joint Commission on Accreditation of Healthcare Organizations (JCAHO) accreditation ○ American Osteopathic Association (AOA) accreditation △ Commission on Accreditation of Rehabilitation Facilities (CARF) accreditation	Control	Service	Staffed Beds	Admissions	Census	Outpatient Visits	Births	Total	Payroll	Personnel

ROSEAU—Roseau County

⊞ **ROSEAU AREA HOSPITAL AND HOMES**, 715 Delmore Avenue, Zip 56751–1599; tel. 218/463–2500, (Total facility includes 124 beds in nursing home–type unit) **A**1 9 10 18 20 **F**2 6 8 9 11 12 21 22 23 24 26 27 28 29 33 34 36 37 38 39 41 44 46 47 48 51 52 58 59 60 63 64 65 66 69 77 81 85 88 92 94 95 96 97 106 108 **P**3 5
Primary Contact: Keith Okeson, Chief Executive Officer
COO: Susan C. Lisell, Senior Leader Patient Services
CFO: Cathy Huss, Chief Financial Officer
Web address: www.rahhinc.com

	23	10	149	958	127	38077	179	22392	10576	279

SAINT CLOUD—Stearns County

⊞ **ST. CLOUD HOSPITAL**, 1406 Sixth Avenue North, Zip 56303–1901; tel. 320/251–2700 **A**1 2 3 5 9 10 **F**2 4 9 10 11 12 14 15 17 19 21 22 23 26 27 28 29 31 32 33 34 35 36 37 39 40 42 43 44 46 47 48 49 50 51 52 53 54 55 56 57 58 59 60 61 62 63 64 65 66 67 68 69 70 71 72 73 74 75 76 77 78 79 80 81 82 84 85 86 87 88 90 91 93 94 96 98 106 107 108 109 110 **P**6 **S** CentraCare Health System, Saint Cloud, MN
Primary Contact: Craig J. Broman, President and Chief Executive Officer
CFO: John Seckinger, Vice President Corporate Services and Chief Financial Officer
CMO: Dan Whitlock, M.D., Chief Medical Officer
CIO: Chuck Dooley, Vice President Information Services
CHR: Duane Rasmusson, Human Resources Vice President
Web address: www.centracare.com

	23	10	425	24083	272	329303	2346	300419	129389	2783

⊞ **VETERANS AFFAIRS MEDICAL CENTER**, 4801 Veterans Drive, Zip 56303–2099; tel. 320/252–1670, (Total facility includes 228 beds in nursing home–type unit) **A**1 **F**1 2 3 4 12 21 22 23 26 27 28 29 32 36 37 38 39 41 42 44 45 47 48 50 52 53 58 60 61 63 66 69 70 71 73 76 77 78 88 92 94 96 106 107 108 109 110 **P**6 **S** Department of Veterans Affairs, Washington, DC
Primary Contact: Barry I. Bahl, Director
COO: Barry I. Bahl, Director
CFO: Mary Clausen, Chief Financial Officer
CMO: James Lukach, M.D., Chief of Staff
CIO: Robert Merchant, Chief Information Management
CHR: Lisa Rosendahl, Director, Human Resources
Web address: www.visn13.med.va.gov

	45	22	391	2283	336	203610	0	85942	58376	936

SAINT JAMES—Watonwan County

⊞ **ST. JAMES HEALTH SERVICES**, 1207 Sixth Avenue South, Zip 56081–2415, Mailing Address: P.O. Box 460, Zip 56081–0460; tel. 507/375–3261 **A**1 9 10 18 **F**2 3 9 11 12 13 14 21 22 23 24 26 27 28 29 33 34 35 36 46 47 48 51 52 53 55 56 58 59 60 63 64 65 66 67 68 69 70 71 75 81 85 92 94 96 97 107 108 109 **P**6 **S** Mayo Foundation, Rochester, MN
Primary Contact: Dawn L. Wells, Administrator
CFO: Pam Kunkel, Fiscal and Information Services Manager
CMO: Arshad Ahsan, M.D., Chief of Staff
CIO: Pam Kunkel, Fiscal and Information Services Manager
Web address: www.stjmc.org

	23	10	12	307	4	28908	22	7636	3182	101

SAINT LOUIS PARK—Hennepin County

★ △ **METHODIST HOSPITAL**, 6500 Excelsior Boulevard, Zip 55426–4702; tel. 952/993–5000 **A**2 7 9 10 **F**2 8 9 11 14 15 17 19 21 23 26 28 29 30 31 33 34 35 36 37 40 42 44 46 47 48 49 51 52 53 55 57 58 59 60 61 62 63 64 65 66 68 69 79 80 81 82 83 84 85 87 88 89 93 94 95 96 108 110 **S** Park Nicollet Health Services, Saint Louis Park, MN
Primary Contact: David K. Wessner, President and Chief Executive Officer
COO: John W. Herman, Chief Administrative Officer
CFO: David J. Cooke, Senior Vice President and Chief Financial Officer
CMO: Sam Carlson, M.D., Executive Vice President and Chief Medical Officer
CIO: Francis Cheung, Chief Information Officer
CHR: Arthur La Point, Vice President Human Resources
Web address: www.parknicollet.com

	23	10	382	26028	264	446861	3789	333989	128935	2121

SAINT PAUL—Ramsey County

⊞ △ **BETHESDA REHABILITATION HOSPITAL**, 559 Capitol Boulevard, Zip 55103–2101; tel. 651/232–2000 **A**1 7 10 **F**2 5 21 22 26 27 28 31 35 39 41 44 45 50 52 53 57 58 64 65 66 69 73 74 75 76 77 78 81 85 88 92 93 96 108 **S** HealthEast Care System, Saint Paul, MN
Primary Contact: Frank Indihar, M.D., Chief Executive Officer
COO: Ann M. Schrader, Vice President and Chief Operating Officer
CFO: Brian Johnson, Chief Financial Officer
CMO: Robert Beck, M.D., Vice President Medical Affairs
CIO: Ron Strachan, Chief Information Officer
CHR: Ginny Sullivan, Vice President Human Resources
Web address: www.healtheast.org

	23	80	172	1469	125	0	0	58604	31054	497

MN

	Classification Codes		Utilization Data					Expense (thousands) of dollars		
Hospital, Address, Telephone, Approval, Facility, and Physician Codes, Health Care System	Control	Service	Staffed Beds	Admissions	Census	Outpatient Visits	Births	Total	Payroll	Personnel

★ American Hospital Association (AHA) membership
□ Joint Commission on Accreditation of Healthcare Organizations (JCAHO) accreditation
○ American Osteopathic Association (AOA) accreditation
△ Commission on Accreditation of Rehabilitation Facilities (CARF) accreditation

MN

★ **CHILDREN'S HOSPITAL AND CLINICS**, 345 North Smith Avenue, Zip 55102–2392; tel. 651/220–6000 **A**3 5 9 10 **F**2 9 16 18 20 21 22 23 24 26 27 28 29 30 31 33 35 36 37 38 39 41 42 46 47 48 49 50 51 52 53 56 57 58 60 61 62 63 64 65 66 67 69 70 72 73 74 75 77 79 80 81 82 83 84 85 86 87 88 90 93 94 95 96 97 98 106 108 110 **P**1 5 6 **S** Children's Hospitals and Clinics of Minnesota, Minneapolis, MN
Primary Contact: Alan L. Goldbloom, M.D., President and Chief Executive Officer
COO: Julie Morath, Chief Operating Officer
CFO: Jerry Massmann, Chief Financial Officer
CMO: Phillip M. Kibort, M.D., Vice President Medical Affairs and Chief Medical Officer
CIO: Glenn Galloway, Director Information Technology
CHR: David Brumbaugh, Vice President Human Resources
Web address: www.childrenshc.org

Control	Service	Staffed Beds	Admissions	Census	Outpatient Visits	Births	Total	Payroll	Personnel
23	50	126	6036	91	229390	0	157560	79548	936

□ △ **GILLETTE CHILDREN'S SPECIALTY HEALTHCARE**, (PEDIATRIC SPECIALTY), 200 East University Avenue, Zip 55101–2598; tel. 651/291–2848 **A**1 5 7 9 10 **F**2 7 21 22 26 27 28 29 32 39 42 52 53 57 62 63 64 67 68 69 94 108 **P**6
Primary Contact: Margaret E. Perryman, Chief Executive Officer
Web address: www.gillettechildrens.org

Control	Service	Staffed Beds	Admissions	Census	Outpatient Visits	Births	Total	Payroll	Personnel
23	59	53	1580	23	84986	0	77550	34350	600

⊠ △ **REGIONS HOSPITAL**, 640 Jackson Street, Zip 55101–2595; tel. 651/254–3456 **A**1 2 3 5 7 8 9 10 12 13 **F**2 4 10 11 12 13 14 15 17 19 21 22 23 26 27 29 30 31 33 34 36 38 39 42 46 47 48 50 52 53 55 56 57 58 59 60 61 62 63 64 65 66 68 69 71 73 74 75 78 81 82 84 85 86 88 92 93 94 105 108 109 110 **P**1 8
Primary Contact: Brock D. Nelson, President and Chief Executive Officer
CFO: Greg Klugherz, Vice President and Chief Financial Officer
CIO: Kim LaReau, Vice President and Chief Information Officer
CHR: Linda Burgess, Director Human Resources
Web address: www.regionshospital.com

Control	Service	Staffed Beds	Admissions	Census	Outpatient Visits	Births	Total	Payroll	Personnel
23	10	396	24562	306	232036	2539	359139	215258	3181

⊠ **ST. JOHN'S HOSPITAL**, 1575 Beam Avenue, Zip 55109–1126; tel. 651/232–7000 **A**1 3 5 9 10 **F**2 11 12 21 22 23 26 27 28 29 30 31 33 34 35 39 40 42 46 47 48 49 50 52 53 55 56 57 58 59 60 61 62 63 64 65 66 69 73 75 77 79 80 81 82 84 85 87 88 92 94 95 96 107 108 109 **P**8 **S** HealthEast Care System, Saint Paul, MN
Primary Contact: Scott North, Chief Executive Officer
COO: Laura Kathahn, Associate Administrator
CMO: Thomas Lundsten, M.D., Medical Director
CIO: Ronald Strachahn, Chief Information Officer
Web address: www.stjohnshospital–mn.org
ST. JOHN'S HOSPITAL See

Control	Service	Staffed Beds	Admissions	Census	Outpatient Visits	Births	Total	Payroll	Personnel
23	10	189	14488	138	225540	2663	150153	63055	1022

⊠ **ST. JOSEPH'S HOSPITAL**, 69 West Exchange Street, Zip 55102–1053; tel. 651/232–3000 **A**1 3 5 9 10 **F**2 3 4 9 10 11 12 13 14 15 17 19 21 22 23 26 27 28 29 30 31 33 34 36 37 38 39 40 44 45 46 47 48 49 50 52 53 55 57 58 59 60 61 62 63 64 66 67 69 71 73 74 75 76 77 78 81 82 84 85 88 92 93 94 96 107 108 109 110 **P**8 **S** HealthEast Care System, Saint Paul, MN
Primary Contact: Scott Batulis, Chief Executive Officer
COO: Ann M. Schrader, Vice President and Chief Operating Officer
CFO: Robert D. Gill, Vice President and Chief Financial Officer
CMO: Bob Beck, Vice President Medical Affairs
CIO: Ron Strachan, Chief Information Officer
Web address: www.healtheast.org

Control	Service	Staffed Beds	Admissions	Census	Outpatient Visits	Births	Total	Payroll	Personnel
23	10	258	13999	164	104452	986	164071	67304	1276

⊠ △ **UNITED HOSPITAL**, 333 North Smith Avenue, Zip 55102–2389; tel. 651/220–8000, (Nonreporting) **A**1 2 3 5 7 9 10 **S** Allina Hospitals & Clinics, Minneapolis, MN
Primary Contact: Mark G. Mishek, President
CFO: John Bien, Vice President Finance
Web address: www.allina.com

Control	Service	Staffed Beds	Admissions	Census	Outpatient Visits	Births	Total	Payroll	Personnel
23	10	418	—	—	—	—	—	—	—

SAINT PETER—Nicollet County

★ **ST. PETER COMMUNITY HOSPITAL**, (Formerly St Peter Community Hospital and Heallth Care), 1900 North Sunrise Drive, Zip 56082–1327; tel. 507/931–2200 **A**9 10 18 **F**2 6 11 12 27 28 33 46 52 59 60 63 64 69 81 85 88 93 94 96 97 107
Primary Contact: Colleen A. Spike, Administrator
CFO: Kenneth D. Cornish, Chief Financial Officer
CMO: Benjamin Chaska, M.D., Chief Medical Staff
CIO: Paulette Redman, Health Information Management Manager
CHR: Val Campbell, Director of Human Resources
Web address: www.stpeterhealth.org

Control	Service	Staffed Beds	Admissions	Census	Outpatient Visits	Births	Total	Payroll	Personnel
14	10	17	724	4	27892	57	9988	4087	111

□ **ST. PETER REGIONAL TREATMENT CENTER**, 100 Freeman Drive, Zip 56082–1599; tel. 507/931–7100, (Nonreporting) **A**1 10
Primary Contact: Larry TeBrake, Site Director

Control	Service	Staffed Beds	Admissions	Census	Outpatient Visits	Births	Total	Payroll	Personnel
12	22	560	—	—	—	—	—	—	—

SANDSTONE—Pine County

★ **PINE MEDICAL CENTER**, 109 Court Avenue South, Zip 55072–5120; tel. 320/245–2212, (Total facility includes 69 beds in nursing home–type unit) **A**9 10 18 **F**6 9 22 27 28 29 33 44 46 52 63 81 84 88 92 97 107 **P**5 **S** St. Mary's/Duluth Clinic Health System, Duluth, MN
Primary Contact: Timothy Zwickey, Administrator and Chief Executive Officer
COO: Amy Hansen, Chief Operating Officer, Patient Care
CFO: Gregg Chartrand, Chief Financial Officer
CMO: Brian Barstad, M.D., Chief of Staff
Web address: www.pinemedical.org

Control	Service	Staffed Beds	Admissions	Census	Outpatient Visits	Births	Total	Payroll	Personnel
23	10	94	479	72	12849	0	10496	4091	164

Many Facility Codes have changed. Please refer to the AHA Guide Code Chart. © 2005 AHA Guide

Hospital, Address, Telephone, Approval, Facility, and Physician Codes, Health Care System	Classi-fication Codes		Utilization Data					Expense (thousands) of dollars		
	Control	Service	Staffed Beds	Admissions	Census	Outpatient Visits	Births	Total	Payroll	Personnel

★ American Hospital Association (AHA) membership
□ Joint Commission on Accreditation of Healthcare Organizations (JCAHO) accreditation
○ American Osteopathic Association (AOA) accreditation
△ Commission on Accreditation of Rehabilitation Facilities (CARF) accreditation

SAUK CENTRE—Stearns County

★ **ST. MICHAEL'S HOSPITAL AND NURSING HOME**, (Formerly St. Michael's Hospital), 425 North Elm Street, Zip 56378–1010; tel. 320/352–2221, (Total facility includes 60 beds in nursing home–type unit) (Nonreporting) **A**9 10 18
Primary Contact: Delano Christianson, Administrator
Web address: www.stmichaelshospital.org

Control 14, Service 10, Staffed Beds 85, Admissions —, Census —, Outpatient Visits —, Births —, Total —, Payroll —, Personnel —

SHAKOPEE—Scott County

✠ **ST. FRANCIS REGIONAL MEDICAL CENTER**, 1455 St. Francis Avenue, Zip 55379–3380; tel. 952/403–3000 **A**1 2 9 10 **F**2 9 11 12 21 22 23 27 29 31 33 37 38 39 45 46 47 48 53 54 55 58 59 60 61 62 63 65 66 69 81 84 85 88 94 95 96 106 107 108 **P**5 **S** Allina Hospitals & Clinics, Minneapolis, MN
Primary Contact: Thomas O'Connor, President
COO: Marcus Julian, Chief Operating Officer and Vice President Mission
CFO: Alan Lem, Vice President Finance
CMO: Brian Prokosch, M.D., Vice President Medical Affairs
CIO: Joe Delveaux, Manager Information Services
Web address: www.stfrancis–shakopee.com

Control 23, Service 10, Staffed Beds 61, Admissions 5175, Census 42, Outpatient Visits 98164, Births 1154, Total 65141, Payroll 27316, Personnel 471

SLAYTON—Murray County

★ **MURRAY COUNTY MEMORIAL HOSPITAL**, 2042 Juniper Avenue, Zip 56172–1016; tel. 507/836–6111 **A**9 10 18 **F**6 23 27 28 29 32 33 37 41 44 46 52 55 58 63 64 65 69 70 91 93 94 97 **P**5 **S** Sioux Valley Hospitals and Health System, Sioux Falls, SD
Primary Contact: Rick Nordahl, Administrator and Chief Executive Officer
CFO: Neil Frizzell, Chief Financial Officer
CHR: Angela Anderson, Human Resources Manager
Web address: www.murraycountymemorial.org

Control 13, Service 10, Staffed Beds 25, Admissions 429, Census 4, Outpatient Visits 12563, Births 0, Total 8459, Payroll 3124, Personnel 84

SLEEPY EYE—Brown County

SLEEPY EYE MEDICAL CENTER, 400 Fourth Avenue N.W., Zip 56085–1109, Mailing Address: P.O. Box 323, Zip 56085–0323; tel. 507/794–3571 **A**9 10 18 **F**11 12 29 33 46 48 54 59 63 69 81 93 94 97 **P**6
Primary Contact: Robert Van Meeteren, Chief Executive Officer
Web address: www.semedicalcenter.org

Control 14, Service 10, Staffed Beds 25, Admissions 428, Census 3, Outpatient Visits 7702, Births 5, Total 4656, Payroll 2240, Personnel 70

SPRINGFIELD—Brown County

□ **SPRINGFIELD MEDICAL CENTER–MAYO HEALTH SYSTEM**, 625 North Jackson Avenue, Zip 56087–1714, Mailing Address: P.O. Box 146, Zip 56087–0146; tel. 507/723–6201 **A**1 9 10 18 **F**11 12 23 27 28 30 33 34 46 48 58 59 63 64 69 70 81 92 96 97 106 **P**6 **S** Mayo Foundation, Rochester, MN
Primary Contact: Scott D. Thoreson, Administrator
Web address: www.smc–mhs.org

Control 23, Service 10, Staffed Beds 24, Admissions 569, Census 5, Outpatient Visits 21673, Births 37, Total 7883, Payroll 3890, Personnel 78

STAPLES—Wadena County

LAKEWOOD HEALTH SYSTEM, 401 Prairie Avenue N.E., Zip 56479–3201; tel. 218/894–1515, (Total facility includes 100 beds in nursing home–type unit) **A**9 10 18 **F**5 6 8 9 10 12 21 22 23 27 28 29 30 33 36 37 38 39 44 45 46 47 48 51 52 53 55 58 59 60 61 62 63 64 65 66 69 81 85 88 91 92 94 95 96 97 106 108 109 110 **P**7
Primary Contact: Tim Rice, President
Web address: www.lakewoodhealthsystem.com

Control 23, Service 10, Staffed Beds 125, Admissions 1186, Census 111, Outpatient Visits 183333, Births 137, Total 24910, Payroll 14957, Personnel 423

STARBUCK—Pope County

★ **MINNEWASKA DISTRICT HOSPITAL**, 610 West Sixth Street, Zip 56381–9782, Mailing Address: P.O. Box 160, Zip 56381–0160; tel. 320/239–2201, (Nonreporting) **A**9 10 18
Primary Contact: Bruce Harvey, Interim Chief Executive Officer
CFO: Bruce Harvey, Controller
CMO: Stacey Luetmer, M.D., Chief Medical Officer
CHR: Teresa Jergenson, Director of Human Resources
Web address: www.minnewaskahealth.com

Control 16, Service 10, Staffed Beds 19, Admissions —, Census —, Outpatient Visits —, Births —, Total —, Payroll —, Personnel —

STILLWATER—Washington County

✠ **LAKEVIEW HOSPITAL**, 927 West Churchill Street, Zip 55082–5930; tel. 651/439–5330 **A**1 5 9 10 **F**2 6 9 11 12 14 21 22 23 26 27 28 29 33 36 37 38 41 46 47 48 51 52 53 55 58 59 60 61 62 63 64 65 66 69 81 82 84 85 88 93 94 96 105 108 109
Primary Contact: Jeffrey J. Robertson, Chief Executive Officer
COO: Curt Geissler, Assistant Administrator and Chief Operating Officer
CFO: Doug Johnson, Chief Financial Officer
CIO: Bill Overby, Information Systems Manager
Web address: www.lakeview.org

Control 23, Service 10, Staffed Beds 52, Admissions 4247, Census 29, Outpatient Visits 81224, Births 736, Total 58424, Payroll 23710, Personnel 472

THIEF RIVER FALLS—Pennington County

★ **NORTHWEST MEDICAL CENTER**, 120 LaBree Avenue South, Zip 56701–2819, Mailing Address: P.O. Box 531, Zip 56701–0531; tel. 218/681–4240, (Total facility includes 90 beds in nursing home–type unit) **A**9 10 20 **F**9 10 11 12 21 22 23 27 29 31 33 41 44 46 47 48 52 55 59 60 61 62 63 64 65 69 71 72 74 75 76 77 81 84 88 92 94 95 96 106 107 108 109 **P**5
Primary Contact: Christine K. Harff, Chief Executive Officer
COO: Kevin J. Smith, Chief Operating Officer
CHR: Michael Parker, Human Resource Director
Web address: www.nwmc.org

Control 23, Service 10, Staffed Beds 158, Admissions 2068, Census 109, Outpatient Visits 19447, Births 283, Total 26710, Payroll 13766, Personnel 323

MN

Hospital, Address, Telephone, Approval, Facility, and Physician Codes, Health Care System	Classi-fication Codes		Utilization Data					Expense (thousands) of dollars		
	Control	Service	Staffed Beds	Admissions	Census	Outpatient Visits	Births	Total	Payroll	Personnel

★ American Hospital Association (AHA) membership
□ Joint Commission on Accreditation of Healthcare Organizations (JCAHO) accreditation
○ American Osteopathic Association (AOA) accreditation
△ Commission on Accreditation of Rehabilitation Facilities (CARF) accreditation

TRACY—Lyon County

★ **TRACY AREA MEDICAL SERVICES**, 251 Fifth Street East, Zip 56175–1536; tel. 507/629–3200, (Nonreporting) **A**9 10 18 **S** Sioux Valley Hospitals and Health System, Sioux Falls, SD
Primary Contact: Rick Nordahl, Administrator and Chief Executive Officer
CFO: Stacy Barstad, Chief Financial Officer
CHR: Angela Anderson, Human Resources Manager
Web address: www.tracyareamedical.org

Control	Service	Staffed Beds	Admissions	Census	Outpatient Visits	Births	Total	Payroll	Personnel
23	10	23	—	—	—	—	—	—	—

TWO HARBORS—Lake County

LAKE VIEW MEMORIAL HOSPITAL AND HOME, 325 11th Avenue, Zip 55616–1360; tel. 218/834–7300, (Total facility includes 50 beds in nursing home–type unit) **A**9 10 18 **F**4 8 9 14 27 28 29 33 41 48 52 58 60 62 63 66 69 73 81 82 88 92 94 97 107 **P**5
Primary Contact: Brian J. Carlson, FACHE, President and Chief Executive Officer
Web address: www.lvmhospital.com

| 23 | 10 | 68 | 306 | 47 | 13630 | 0 | 10043 | 4580 | 115 |

TYLER—Lincoln County

TYLER HEALTHCARE CENTER/AVERA HEALTH, 240 Willow Street, Zip 56178–0280, Mailing Address: P.O. Box 280, Zip 56178–0280; tel. 507/247–5521, (Total facility includes 43 beds in nursing home–type unit) (Nonreporting) **A**9 10 18 **S** Avera Health, Yankton, SD
Primary Contact: Dale Kruger, Chief Executive Officer & Chief Financial Officer

| 23 | 10 | 63 | — | — | — | — | — | — | — |

VIRGINIA—St. Louis County

△ **VIRGINIA REGIONAL MEDICAL CENTER**, 901 Ninth Street North, Zip 55792–2398; tel. 218/741–3340, (Total facility includes 116 beds in nursing home–type unit) **A**1 7 9 10 **F**2 6 9 11 12 21 22 26 27 28 29 33 34 37 38 40 44 48 52 55 57 58 59 63 66 68 70 81 82 84 88 92 93 94 96 108 110
Primary Contact: Keith D. Harvey, Chief Executive Officer
CFO: Georgia Day, Finance Director
CMO: Margaret Graebner, M.D., Chief of Staff
CIO: Doris Parenteau, Manager Business and Medical Records
CHR: Stephen Roskoski, Director of Human Resources
Web address: www.vrmc.org

| 14 | 10 | 199 | 3704 | 153 | 44519 | 302 | 43021 | 18677 | 436 |

WABASHA—Wabasha County

★ **SAINT ELIZABETH'S MEDICAL CENTER**, 1200 Grant Boulevard West, Zip 55981–1098; tel. 651/565–4531, (Total facility includes 159 beds in nursing home–type unit) **A**9 10 18 **F**1 4 5 8 9 10 11 12 14 21 22 27 28 29 33 34 39 41 44 45 46 48 51 52 55 58 59 60 63 66 69 72 73 74 76 77 81 88 91 92 94 96 97 106 107 108 109 110 **P**6 **S** Marian Health System, Tulsa, OK
Primary Contact: Thomas Crowley, President
CFO: John Wolfe, Chief Financial Officer
CMO: Kim Straub, M.D., President, Medical Staff
CHR: Jim Root, Director, Human Resources
Web address: www.stelizabethswabasha.org

| 21 | 10 | 179 | 896 | 149 | 28644 | 108 | 17868 | 8906 | 292 |

WACONIA—Carver County

⊞ **RIDGEVIEW MEDICAL CENTER**, 500 South Maple Street, Zip 55387–1791; tel. 952/442–2191 **A**1 2 9 10 **F**2 6 11 12 22 23 24 25 26 27 28 29 31 33 36 37 42 44 46 47 48 51 52 55 57 58 59 60 62 63 65 66 69 71 76 81 84 88 93 94 95 96 106 107 108 109
Primary Contact: Robert Stevens, President and Chief Executive Officer
COO: Rob Welch, Chief Operating Officer
CFO: Tim Gronseth, Vice President Finance
CIO: Marilyn Foss, Director Management Information Systems
CHR: Catherine Compton, Vice President
Web address: www.ridgeviewmedical.org

| 23 | 10 | 109 | 7020 | 61 | 117099 | 1209 | 87911 | 41529 | 830 |

WADENA—Wadena County

⊞ **TRI–COUNTY HOSPITAL**, 415 North Jefferson Street, Zip 56482–1297; tel. 218/631–3510 **A**1 9 10 18 **F**2 6 8 9 11 12 14 23 26 27 28 29 33 34 36 37 38 44 46 48 51 52 54 55 58 59 60 61 63 65 69 81 88 94 95 96 97 106 108 110
Primary Contact: Dennis C. Miley, Administrator
CFO: Joel Beiswenger, Director Financial Services
CMO: Tim Schmitt, M.D., Medical Staff President
CIO: Bill Blaha, Management Information Systems Manager
Web address: www.tricountyhospital.org

| 23 | 10 | 25 | 1592 | 17 | 71528 | 138 | 24972 | 11795 | 249 |

WARREN—Marshall County

★ **NORTH VALLEY HEALTH CENTER**, 109 South Minnesota Street, Zip 56762–1499; tel. 218/745–4211 **A**9 10 18 **F**6 12 23 26 27 28 33 41 45 51 52 60 63 81 84 88 94 97 **P**6
Primary Contact: Jon E. Linnell, Chief Executive Officer
CFO: Susan Butler, Chief Financial Officer
Web address: www.nvhc.net

| 23 | 10 | 20 | 295 | 2 | 29733 | 0 | 3430 | 1875 | 48 |

WASECA—Waseca County

□ **WASECA MEDICAL CENTER**, 501 North State Street, Zip 56093–2811; tel. 507/835–1210, (Nonreporting) **A**1 9 10 12 13 18 **S** Mayo Foundation, Rochester, MN
Primary Contact: Michael Milbrath, Executive Vice President
Web address: www.wmc–mhs.org

| 23 | 10 | 25 | — | — | — | — | — | — | — |

Many Facility Codes have changed. Please refer to the AHA Guide Code Chart.

© 2005 AHA Guide

Hospital, Address, Telephone, Approval, Facility, and Physician Codes, Health Care System	Classi-fication Codes		Utilization Data					Expense (thousands) of dollars		
	Control	Service	Staffed Beds	Admissions	Census	Outpatient Visits	Births	Total	Payroll	Personnel

★ American Hospital Association (AHA) membership
☐ Joint Commission on Accreditation of Healthcare Organizations (JCAHO) accreditation
○ American Osteopathic Association (AOA) accreditation
△ Commission on Accreditation of Rehabilitation Facilities (CARF) accreditation

WESTBROOK—Cottonwood County

★ **WESTBROOK HEALTH CENTER**, 920 Bell Avenue, Zip 56183–0188, Mailing Address: P.O. Box 188, Zip 56183–0188; tel. 507/274–6121, (Nonreporting) **A**9 10 18 **S** Sioux Valley Hospitals and Health System, Sioux Falls, SD
Primary Contact: Rick Nordahl, Administrator and Chief Executive Officer
COO: Rick Nordahl, Chief Operating Officer
CFO: Stacy Barstad, Chief Financial Officer
CHR: Angela Anderson, Human Resources Manager
Web address: www.westbrookhealthcenter.org
— Control 23, Service 10, Staffed Beds 13

WHEATON—Traverse County

WHEATON COMMUNITY HOSPITAL, 401 12th Street North, Zip 56296–1099; tel. 320/563–8226, (Nonreporting) **A**9 10 18
Primary Contact: Jesse Tischer, Administrator
— Control 14, Service 10, Staffed Beds 21

WILLMAR—Kandiyohi County

⊠ **RICE MEMORIAL HOSPITAL**, 301 Becker Avenue S.W., Zip 56201–3395; tel. 320/235–4543, (Total facility includes 77 beds in nursing home–type unit) **A**1 2 9 10 19 **F**6 9 10 11 12 21 22 23 27 30 33 36 37 38 45 46 47 48 49 52 53 55 58 59 60 61 62 63 65 66 69 71 73 74 75 76 77 78 79 81 82 84 87 88 92 93 94 95 96 106 108 109 110 **P**5
Primary Contact: Lawrence J. Massa, Chief Executive Officer
CFO: LeRoy Meyering, Associate Administrator Financial and Information Services
Web address: www.ricehospital.com
— Control 14, Service 10, Staffed Beds 199, Admissions 5133, Census 122, Outpatient Visits 85720, Births 816, Total 80662, Payroll 38343, Personnel 717

☐ **WILLMAR REGIONAL TREATMENT CENTER**, 1550 Highway 71 N.E., Zip 56201; tel. 320/231–5100, (Nonreporting) **A**1 10
Primary Contact: Sandra J. Butturff, Site Director
— Control 12, Service 22, Staffed Beds 164

WINDOM—Cottonwood County

★ **WINDOM AREA HOSPITAL**, 2150 Hospital Drive, Zip 56101–1287, Mailing Address: P.O. Box 339, Zip 56101–0339; tel. 507/831–2400 **A**9 10 18 **F**8 11 12 23 28 29 33 41 46 48 59 60 63 69 81 88 94 97 **S** Sioux Valley Hospitals and Health System, Sioux Falls, SD
Primary Contact: Geraldine Burmeister, Chief Executive Officer and Administrator
CFO: Kim Armstrong, Chief Financial Officer
CHR: Katie Slette, Communication Coordinator
Web address: www.windomareahospital.com
— Control 14, Service 10, Staffed Beds 25, Admissions 777, Census 6, Outpatient Visits 18320, Births 136, Total 8773, Payroll 3415, Personnel 86

WINONA—Winona County

★ **WINONA HEALTH**, 855 Mankato Avenue, Zip 55987–5377, Mailing Address: P.O. Box 5600, Zip 55987–0600; tel. 507/454–3650 **A**9 10 20 **F**2 4 9 11 12 21 22 27 28 29 30 31 33 37 39 40 41 44 46 47 48 49 52 55 58 59 60 62 63 65 66 69 71 72 73 74 75 76 77 81 84 85 88 92 93 94 95 96 106 108 110 **P**6
Primary Contact: Rachelle H. Schultz, President and Chief Executive Officer
COO: Rand G. Gettler, Chief Operating Officer
CFO: Michael Allen, Chief Financial Officer
CMO: Charles Shepard, M.D., Medical Director
CHR: Bill Gould, Chief People Resource Officer
Web address: www.winonahealth.org
— Control 23, Service 10, Staffed Beds 68, Admissions 2863, Census 30, Outpatient Visits 53260, Births 380, Total 39772, Payroll 19319, Personnel 436

WOODBURY—Washington County

⊠ **WOODWINDS HEALTH CAMPUS**, 1925 Woodwinds Drive, Zip 55125; tel. 651/232–0100 **A**1 9 10 **F**2 11 12 21 22 23 26 27 28 29 30 31 33 34 35 36 39 46 47 48 50 52 53 55 57 58 59 60 61 62 63 64 65 66 69 81 82 84 85 88 92 93 94 96 108 109 **P**8 **S** HealthEast Care System, Saint Paul, MN
Primary Contact: Julie A. Schmidt, Chief Executive Officer
CMO: Craig Svendsen, M.D., Medical Director
Web address: www.woodwinds.org
— Control 23, Service 10, Staffed Beds 53, Admissions 5481, Census 45, Outpatient Visits 77099, Births 1242, Total 66602, Payroll 26095, Personnel 426

WORTHINGTON—Nobles County

★ **WORTHINGTON REGIONAL HOSPITAL**, 1018 Sixth Avenue, Zip 56187–2202, Mailing Address: P.O. Box 997, Zip 56187–0997; tel. 507/372–2941 **A**10 **F**6 9 11 14 23 26 27 28 29 32 33 34 37 48 49 51 52 53 54 55 56 58 59 60 62 63 64 65 66 68 69 70 71 72 73 74 75 76 81 84 88 92 94 95 96 97 106 108 109 110 **S** Sioux Valley Hospitals and Health System, Sioux Falls, SD
Primary Contact: Melvin J. Platt, Chief Executive Officer
CFO: Bruce Viessman, Director Finance
Web address: www.worthingtonhospital.com
— Control 14, Service 10, Staffed Beds 66, Admissions 2317, Census 24, Outpatient Visits 39247, Births 398, Total 19841, Payroll 9595, Personnel 210

WYOMING—Chisago County

⊠ **FAIRVIEW LAKES REGIONAL HEALTH CARE**, 5200 Fairview Boulevard, Zip 55092–8013; tel. 651/982–7000 **A**1 9 10 **F**2 4 9 11 12 21 22 24 26 27 28 29 33 36 37 38 40 41 42 44 45 46 47 48 51 52 55 58 59 60 61 63 65 66 69 70 79 81 84 85 88 89 94 95 96 97 98 107 108 109 110 **P**6 8 **S** Fairview Health Services, Minneapolis, MN
Primary Contact: Daniel K. Anderson, President
CFO: Andy McCoy, Vice President Finance
CMO: Terry Martinson, M.D., Medical Director
CHR: Darci Tanberg, Director of Human Resources
Web address: www.fairview.org/lakes/flrmc.htm
— Control 23, Service 10, Staffed Beds 50, Admissions 4112, Census 30, Outpatient Visits 315846, Births 744, Total 99271, Payroll 48988, Personnel 760

MN

MISSISSIPPI

Hospital, Address, Telephone, Approval, Facility, and Physician Codes, Health Care System	Classi-fication Codes		Utilization Data					Expense (thousands) of dollars		
★ American Hospital Association (AHA) membership □ Joint Commission on Accreditation of Healthcare Organizations (JCAHO) accreditation ○ American Osteopathic Association (AOA) accreditation △ Commission on Accreditation of Rehabilitation Facilities (CARF) accreditation	Control	Service	Staffed Beds	Admissions	Census	Outpatient Visits	Births	Total	Payroll	Personnel

ABERDEEN—Monroe County

PIONEER COMMUNITY HOSPITAL OF ABERDEEN, 400 South Chestnut Street, Zip 39730–3335, Mailing Address: P.O. Box 548, Zip 39730–0747; tel. 662/369–2455 **A**9 10 18 **F**12 21 29 33 34 41 44 45 58 65 66 69 70 77 81 88 92 94 95 96 98 **S** Pioneer Health Services, Magee, MS Primary Contact: Steven M. Fontaine, Administrator Web address: www.pchaberdeen.com	33	10	25	227	2	8512	0	—	—	111

ACKERMAN—Choctaw County

CHOCTAW COUNTY MEDICAL CENTER, 148 West Cherry Street, Zip 39735–0417, Mailing Address: P.O. Box 417, Zip 39735–0417; tel. 662/285–3257, (Total facility includes 60 beds in nursing home–type unit) **A**9 10 18 **F**33 34 92 Primary Contact: Tami Jones, Administrator	33	10	72	594	61	0	0			48

AMORY—Monroe County

⊞ **GILMORE MEMORIAL HOSPITAL**, 1105 Earl Frye Boulevard, Zip 38821–0459, Mailing Address: P.O. Box 459, Zip 38821–0459; tel. 662/256–7111 **A**1 9 10 **F**11 12 14 21 26 28 29 33 34 41 55 56 58 59 60 63 65 66 67 68 69 81 82 84 88 92 94 97 109 110 **P**8 Primary Contact: Danny Spreitler, President and Chief Executive Officer CFO: Melinda McCrory, Vice President and Chief Financial Officer CMO: Danny Moore, M.D., Chief Medical Officer CIO: Nelson Breedlove, Vice President Support Services CHR: Mitzi Coleman, Director Human Resources Web address: www.gilmorehealth.com	23	10	95	3781	48	41718	764	35592	17482	471

BATESVILLE—Panola County

TRI–LAKES MEDICAL CENTER, 303 Medical Center Drive, Zip 38606–8608; tel. 662/563–5611 **A**9 10 **F**3 4 11 14 33 55 59 71 73 74 77 81 82 84 86 87 88 94 Primary Contact: Robert Corkern, M.D., Chief Executive Officer	13	10	53	2212	31	12932	208	—	—	303

BAY SAINT LOUIS—Hancock County

⊞ **HANCOCK MEDICAL CENTER**, 149 Drinkwater Boulevard, Zip 39521–2790, Mailing Address: P.O. Box 2790, Zip 39521–2790; tel. 228/467–8600 **A**1 9 10 **F**11 12 14 21 29 32 33 34 40 55 58 59 60 63 65 66 68 69 70 81 82 84 88 94 95 109 **S** Quorum Health Resources, Plano, TX Primary Contact: Hal W. Leftwich, FACHE, Administrator CFO: Brandon H. Slocum, Chief Financial Officer Web address: www.hmc.org	13	10	104	4390	54	63969	408	40242	17891	452

BAY SPRINGS—Jasper County

★ **JASPER GENERAL HOSPITAL**, 15 A South Sixth Street, Zip 39422–9738, Mailing Address: P.O. Box 527, Zip 39422–0527; tel. 601/764–2101, (Includes JASPER COUNTY NURSING HOME), (Total facility includes 110 beds in nursing home–type unit) **A**9 10 **F**51 66 92 94 Primary Contact: M. Kenneth Posey, FACHE, Administrator	13	10	126	67	110	0	0	4190	3524	52

BELZONI—Humphreys County

★ **HUMPHREYS COUNTY MEMORIAL HOSPITAL**, 500 CCC Road, Zip 39038–3806, Mailing Address: P.O. Box 510, Zip 39038–0510; tel. 662/247–3831 **A**9 10 18 20 **F**11 33 76 81 88 92 Primary Contact: Debra L. Griffin, Administrator CFO: Gaye Walker, Controller	13	10	25	491	3	7053	0	—	—	97

BILOXI—Harrison County

□ **BILOXI REGIONAL MEDICAL CENTER**, 150 Reynoir Street, Zip 39530–4199, Mailing Address: P.O. Box 128, Zip 39533–0128; tel. 228/432–1571 **A**1 9 10 **F**11 12 14 21 29 32 33 40 45 50 55 58 59 60 61 63 65 66 68 69 70 76 81 82 84 87 88 94 96 109 **P**4 **S** Health Management Associates, Naples, FL Primary Contact: Timothy W. Mitchell, Chief Executive Officer Web address: www.hmamississippi.com	33	10	153	6499	80	60920	592	—	—	510
⊞ **GULF COAST MEDICAL CENTER**, 180–A Debuys Road, Zip 39531–4405; tel. 228/388–6711, (Includes GULF OAKS HOSPITAL, 180–C Debuys Road, Zip 39531; tel. 601/388–0600) **A**1 9 10 **F**3 11 12 14 21 27 28 33 34 50 51 55 58 59 60 61 63 66 71 72 75 76 81 82 84 88 92 94 96 **S** TENET Healthcare Corporation, Dallas, TX Primary Contact: Micheal Terry, Chief Executive Officer CFO: Larry Holland, Chief Financial Officer CHR: Don Long, Director Human Resources Web address: www.gulfcoastmedicalcenter.com	33	10	189	4461	61	41549	315	43888	22323	441
□ **SELECT SPECIALTY HOSPITAL – BILOXI**, 648 Beach Boulevard, Zip 39530–4301; tel. 228/374–7474, (Nonreporting) **A**1 10 Primary Contact: James R. Foster, Chief Executive Officer	33	80	42	—	—	—	—	—	—	—

Many Facility Codes have changed. Please refer to the AHA Guide Code Chart.

© 2005 AHA Guide

Hospital, Address, Telephone, Approval, Facility, and Physician Codes, Health Care System	Classi-fication Codes		Utilization Data					Expense (thousands) of dollars		
	Control	Service	Staffed Beds	Admissions	Census	Outpatient Visits	Births	Total	Payroll	Personnel

★ American Hospital Association (AHA) membership
☐ Joint Commission on Accreditation of Healthcare Organizations (JCAHO) accreditation
○ American Osteopathic Association (AOA) accreditation
△ Commission on Accreditation of Rehabilitation Facilities (CARF) accreditation

⊞ VETERANS AFFAIRS GULF COAST VETERANS HEALTH CARE SYSTEM, 400 Veterans Avenue, Zip 39531–2410; tel. 228/523–5000, (Includes VETERANS AFFAIRS MEDICAL CENTER, GULFPORT DIVISION, 200 East Beach Boulevard, Gulfport, Zip 39507; tel. 228/563–2500), (Total facility includes 160 beds in nursing home–type unit) (Nonreporting) **A**1 3 5 **S** Department of Veterans Affairs, Washington, DC
Primary Contact: Julie A. Catellier, Director
COO: Christiane J. Jones, Associate Director
CFO: Wayne I. Deal, Chief Financial Officer
CMO: Gregg S. Parker, M.D., Chief of Staff
CIO: David D. Wagner, Chief Information Management Service
Web address: www.va.gov/sta/guide/home.asp
| 45 | 10 | 552 | — | — | — | — | — | — | — |

BOONEVILLE—Prentiss County
⊞ BAPTIST MEMORIAL HOSPITAL–BOONEVILLE, 100 Hospital Street, Zip 38829–3359; tel. 662/720–5000 **A**1 9 10 **F**12 14 26 27 28 29 32 33 34 41 55 58 63 65 66 70 71 73 76 81 82 84 88 94 96 **S** Baptist Memorial Health Care Corporation, Memphis, TN
Primary Contact: Al Sypniewski, Administrator and Chief Executive Officer
CFO: Diane Wilson, Chief Financial Officer
CMO: Joseph Wolfe, M.D., President Medical Staff
CIO: Linda Chaffin, Director Quality
Web address: www.bmhcc.org
| 21 | 10 | 66 | 1514 | 24 | 24262 | 0 | 16364 | 6403 | 205 |

BRANDON—Rankin County
☐ RANKIN MEDICAL CENTER, 350 Crossgates Boulevard, Zip 39042–2698; tel. 601/825–2811, (Nonreporting) **A**1 9 10 **S** Health Management Associates, Naples, FL
Primary Contact: Davis A. Richards, III, Chief Executive Officer
Web address: www.rankinmedcenter.com
| 33 | 10 | 134 | — | — | — | — | — | — | — |

BROOKHAVEN—Lincoln County
⊞ KING'S DAUGHTERS MEDICAL CENTER, 427 Highway 51 North, Zip 39601–2600, Mailing Address: P.O. Box 948, Zip 39602–0948; tel. 601/833–6011 **A**1 9 10 **F**3 11 12 13 14 21 27 28 29 32 33 40 50 55 58 59 60 63 65 67 68 69 71 81 82 84 88 92 94 95 96 107 109 **S** Quorum Health Resources, Plano, TX
Primary Contact: Phillip L. Grady, Chief Executive Officer
CFO: Dean Snider, Chief Financial Officer
CIO: Carl Smith, Director Information Systems
CHR: Celine Craig, Manager Human Resources
Web address: www.kdmc.org
| 23 | 10 | 109 | 3766 | 42 | 59697 | 534 | 34089 | 14615 | 424 |

CALHOUN CITY—Calhoun County
★ CALHOUN HEALTH SERVICES, 140 Burke–Calhoun City Road, Zip 38916–9690; tel. 662/628–6611, (Total facility includes 120 beds in nursing home–type unit) **A**9 10 **F**33 34 66 69 71 76 81 88 92 94
Primary Contact: James P. Franklin, Administrator
CFO: Mandy Suber, Controller
| 15 | 10 | 150 | 657 | 123 | 8037 | 0 | 10527 | 5547 | 225 |

CANTON—Madison County
MADISON COUNTY MEDICAL CENTER, Highway 16 East, Zip 39046–8823, Mailing Address: P.O. Box 1607, Zip 39046–1607; tel. 601/859–1331 **A**9 10 **F**11 12 21 32 33 34 59 60 63 66 69 81 88 94 **S** Health Management Associates, Naples, FL
Primary Contact: Daryl W. Weaver, Chief Executive Officer
| 33 | 10 | 34 | 1474 | 15 | 13764 | 294 | — | — | 116 |

CARTHAGE—Leake County
LEAKE MEMORIAL HOSPITAL, 300 Ellis Street, Zip 39051–0557, Mailing Address: P.O. Box 557, Zip 39051–0557; tel. 601/267–1100, (Total facility includes 44 beds in nursing home–type unit) **A**9 10 18 20 **F**26 28 33 34 63 66 69 81 88 92 94 **P**6
Primary Contact: Robert Faulkner, Administrator
| 13 | 10 | 69 | 736 | 52 | 13883 | 4 | 7365 | 3474 | 101 |

CENTREVILLE—Wilkinson County
⊞ FIELD MEMORIAL COMMUNITY HOSPITAL, 270 West Main Street, Zip 39631, Mailing Address: P.O. Box 639, Zip 39631–0639; tel. 601/645–5221 **A**1 9 10 18 20 **F**11 12 21 29 32 33 34 50 58 59 60 63 69 81 88 92 94 96
Primary Contact: Brock A. Slabach, Administrator
CFO: Chad Netterville, Assistant Administrator Finance
Web address: www.fmch.org
| 13 | 10 | 25 | 840 | 7 | 18105 | 80 | — | — | 154 |

CHARLESTON—Tallahatchie County
TALLAHATCHIE GENERAL HOSPITAL, 201 South Market, Zip 38921–2236, Mailing Address: P.O. Box 230, Zip 38921–0230; tel. 662/647–5535, (Total facility includes 68 beds in nursing home–type unit) **A**9 10 18 **F**32 33 66 81 92 94
Primary Contact: Bobby J. Brunson, Jr, Chief Executive Officer
| 13 | 10 | 77 | 317 | 66 | 3223 | 0 | — | — | 100 |

CLARKSDALE—Coahoma County
☐ NORTHWEST MISSISSIPPI REGIONAL MEDICAL CENTER, 1970 Hospital Drive, Zip 38614–7204, Mailing Address: P.O. Box 1218, Zip 38614–1218; tel. 662/627–3211, (Total facility includes 20 beds in nursing home–type unit) **A**1 9 10 19 **F**11 12 15 16 21 22 29 33 34 40 46 48 49 52 53 55 57 58 60 61 62 63 64 65 66 68 69 81 82 84 85 87 88 92 93 94 95 96 **S** Health Management Associates, Naples, FL
Primary Contact: Douglas Arnold, Chief Executive Officer
Web address: www.hmamississippi.com
| 33 | 10 | 175 | 6503 | 100 | 24965 | 904 | — | — | 495 |

MS

Hospital, Address, Telephone, Approval, Facility, and Physician Codes, Health Care System	Classi-fication Codes		Utilization Data					Expense (thousands) of dollars		
★ American Hospital Association (AHA) membership □ Joint Commission on Accreditation of Healthcare Organizations (JCAHO) accreditation ○ American Osteopathic Association (AOA) accreditation △ Commission on Accreditation of Rehabilitation Facilities (CARF) accreditation	Control	Service	Staffed Beds	Admissions	Census	Outpatient Visits	Births	Total	Payroll	Personnel

CLEVELAND—Bolivar County

☒ **BOLIVAR MEDICAL CENTER**, 901 Sunflower Road, Zip 38732–9722, Mailing Address: P.O. Box 1380, Zip 38732–1380; tel. 662/846–0061, (Total facility includes 35 beds in nursing home–type unit) **A**1 9 10 **F**28 32 33 34 40 48 55 59 62 63 64 66 69 70 81 82 88 92 94 96 108 **S** LifePoint Hospitals, Inc., Brentwood, TN
Primary Contact: Ruth A. McDaniel, Chief Executive Officer
CFO: Jim R. Williams, Chief Financial Officer
CMO: Don Blackwood, M.D., Chief Medical Staff
CIO: Doug Calvert, Director Information Systems
CHR: George Williams, Director Human Resources
Web address: www.bolivarmedical.com
| 33 | 10 | 143 | 5008 | 98 | 39593 | 601 | — | — | 396 |

COLLINS—Covington County

□ **COVINGTON COUNTY HOSPITAL**, Gerald McRaney Street, Zip 39428–3899, Mailing Address: P.O. Box 1149, Zip 39428–1149; tel. 601/765–6711 **A**1 9 10 **F**2 6 11 12 14 27 28 29 32 33 34 46 50 51 52 59 63 69 70 71 76 81 88 94 97 **P**4 5 6 7
Primary Contact: Clay Johnston, Administrator
| 13 | 10 | 50 | 1298 | 25 | 40000 | 87 | 9699 | 6575 | 192 |

COLUMBIA—Marion County

MARION GENERAL HOSPITAL, 1560 Sumrall Road, Zip 39429–2654, Mailing Address: P.O. Box 630, Zip 39429–0630; tel. 601/736–6303 **A**9 10 **F**12 21 29 32 33 50 51 55 63 66 69 70 81 82 88 94 95
Primary Contact: Jerry M. Howell, Chief Operating Officer
| 13 | 10 | 79 | 1748 | 22 | 33411 | 1 | 15088 | 7560 | 212 |

COLUMBUS—Lowndes County

☒ **BAPTIST MEMORIAL HOSPITAL–GOLDEN TRIANGLE**, 2520 Fifth Street North, Zip 39705–2095, Mailing Address: P.O. Box 1307, Zip 39703–1307; tel. 662/244–1000 **A**1 9 10 19 **F**3 4 11 12 13 14 21 27 28 29 32 33 34 40 41 45 50 55 56 58 59 60 61 63 65 66 67 68 69 70 71 73 75 76 77 78 81 82 84 86 87 88 92 94 95 96 98 107 109 **S** Baptist Memorial Health Care Corporation, Memphis, TN
Primary Contact: Jason Little, Administrator and Chief Executive Officer
COO: James Huffman, Chief Operating Officer and Chief Financial Officer
CFO: James Huffman, Chief Operating Officer and Chief Financial Officer
CIO: Sheila Bardwell, Director Information Systems
CHR: Bob McCallister, Director Human Resources
Web address: www.bmhcc.org
| 23 | 10 | 328 | 8107 | 121 | 89580 | 877 | — | — | 985 |

CORINTH—Alcorn County

□ **MAGNOLIA REGIONAL HEALTH CENTER**, 611 Alcorn Drive, Zip 38834–9368; tel. 662/293–1000 **A**1 9 10 19 **F**6 9 11 12 14 21 22 23 26 27 28 29 33 34 36 37 40 41 46 51 53 55 58 59 60 61 63 64 65 66 68 69 71 74 76 81 82 84 86 87 88 94 95 96 110
Primary Contact: Ricky D. Napper, Chief Executive Officer
Web address: www.mrhc.org
| 15 | 10 | 157 | 7146 | 88 | 102743 | 502 | 68045 | 26905 | 781 |

ELLISVILLE—Jones County

SOUTH CENTRAL EXTENDED CARE See South Central Regional Medical Center, Laurel

EUPORA—Webster County

☒ **NORTH MISSISSIPPI MEDICAL CENTER–EUPORA**, 500 Highway 9 South, Zip 39744–2215; tel. 662/258–6221, (Total facility includes 36 beds in nursing home–type unit) **A**1 9 10 **F**12 26 27 28 29 33 34 41 65 66 81 88 92 94 **S** North Mississippi Health Services, Inc., Tupelo, MS
Primary Contact: K. Michael Bailey, Ph.D., Administrator
CFO: Adonna Mitchell, Business Services Manager
CMO: David Booth, M.D., Chairman Medical Staff
CIO: Shirley Griffin, Manager
CHR: Dorothy Castle, Manager
| 23 | 10 | 74 | 1627 | 54 | 15723 | 0 | 12656 | 5290 | 151 |

FAYETTE—Jefferson County

JEFFERSON COUNTY HOSPITAL, 809 South Main Street, Zip 39069, Mailing Address: P.O. Box 577, Zip 39069–0577; tel. 601/786–3401 **A**9 10 **F**33 44 76 94
Primary Contact: Jerry Kennedy, Administrator
| 13 | 10 | 30 | 767 | 18 | 2099 | 0 | 5203 | 2110 | 62 |

FOREST—Scott County

S. E. LACKEY MEMORIAL HOSPITAL, 330 Broad Street, Zip 39074–0428, Mailing Address: P.O. Box 428, Zip 39074–0428; tel. 601/469–4151, (Total facility includes 30 beds in nursing home–type unit) **A**9 10 18 **F**4 9 12 21 27 28 29 32 33 34 44 46 63 65 69 73 77 78 81 82 84 88 92 94 95 97 106 **P**5 **S** Pioneer Health Services, Magee, MS
Primary Contact: Donna Riser, Administrator
Web address: www.selackey.com
| 23 | 10 | 55 | 1035 | 32 | 11628 | 0 | 9010 | 2930 | 116 |

GREENVILLE—Washington County

☒ **DELTA REGIONAL MEDICAL CENTER**, 1400 East Union Street, Zip 38703–3246, Mailing Address: P.O. Box 5247, Zip 38704–5247; tel. 662/378–3783 **A**1 9 10 19 **F**3 6 9 11 12 13 14 21 28 29 33 34 36 39 45 51 55 59 60 61 62 63 66 68 69 70 71 73 75 81 82 84 87 88 94 96 106 108 110 **P**6
Primary Contact: L. Ray Humphreys, Chief Executive Officer
COO: Allyson Williams, Chief Operating Officer
CFO: Courtney Phillips, Chief Financial Officer
CMO: Rodney Frothingham, M.D., Chief Medical Officer
CIO: Michael McEldowney, Director Information Services
CHR: Alphe Wells, Chief Human Resources Officer
Web address: www.deltaregional.com
| 13 | 10 | 166 | 8675 | 116 | 81341 | 732 | 82347 | 37852 | 876 |

Many Facility Codes have changed. Please refer to the AHA Guide Code Chart.   © 2005 AHA Guide

Hospital, Address, Telephone, Approval, Facility, and Physician Codes, Health Care System	Classi-fication Codes		Utilization Data					Expense (thousands) of dollars		
★ American Hospital Association (AHA) membership □ Joint Commission on Accreditation of Healthcare Organizations (JCAHO) accreditation ○ American Osteopathic Association (AOA) accreditation △ Commission on Accreditation of Rehabilitation Facilities (CARF) accreditation	Control	Service	Staffed Beds	Admissions	Census	Outpatient Visits	Births	Total	Payroll	Personnel
□ **THE KING'S DAUGHTERS HOSPITAL**, 300 Washington Avenue, Zip 38701–3614, Mailing Address: P.O. Box 1857, Zip 38702–1857; tel. 662/378–2020 **A**1 9 10 **F**11 12 21 29 33 55 59 63 66 68 69 70 71 76 81 82 84 88 94 107 109 Primary Contact: David W. Fuller, Chief Executive Officer Web address: www.tkdh.com	33	10	104	3288	40	43193	266	26089	10369	232
GREENWOOD—Leflore County										
⊠ △ **GREENWOOD LEFLORE HOSPITAL**, 1401 River Road, Zip 38930, Mailing Address: Drawer 1410, Zip 38935–1410; tel. 662/459–7000 **A**1 7 9 10 19 **F**11 12 14 21 23 28 29 32 33 34 37 41 50 55 57 58 59 60 62 63 64 65 66 68 69 71 76 81 82 84 87 88 92 93 94 95 96 109 110 **P**6 8 Primary Contact: Jerry W. Adams, Chief Executive Officer COO: Jeff Curtis, Chief Operating Officer CFO: James H. Jackson, Jr, Chief Financial Officer CMO: Melynda Noble, M.D., Chief Medical Staff CIO: Mark S. Hutson, Chief Information Officer CHR: Key Britt, Associate Director Web address: www.glh.org	15	10	175	8144	111	349604	704	80118	35555	776
GREENWOOD SPECIALTY HOSPITAL, 1401 River Road, 2nd Floor, Zip 38935; tel. 662/459–2681 **A**10 Primary Contact: Mark Edward Cunningham, Chief Executive Officer	33	80	15	6	1	0	0	—	—	12
GRENADA—Grenada County										
⊠ **GRENADA LAKE MEDICAL CENTER**, 960 Avent Drive, Zip 38901–5094; tel. 662/227–7000 **A**1 9 10 20 **F**6 11 12 14 15 21 23 29 33 34 37 41 45 48 49 50 51 55 57 58 59 61 62 63 68 69 70 81 82 84 87 88 92 93 94 108 109 **P**8 Primary Contact: Charles L. Denton, Chief Executive Officer CFO: Keith Heartsill, Chief Financial Officer CIO: Sarah Longest, Chief Information Officer Web address: www.glmc.net	13	10	142	4646	66	43612	640	34353	15709	477
GULFPORT—Harrison County										
⊠ **GARDEN PARK MEDICAL CENTER**, 15200 Community Road, Zip 39503–3085, Mailing Address: P.O. Box 1240, Zip 39502–1240; tel. 228/575–7000 **A**1 9 10 **F**11 12 21 26 27 28 29 33 34 39 40 41 45 46 49 52 53 55 58 59 60 62 63 66 68 69 70 71 76 81 82 84 86 87 88 94 108 110 **S** HCA, Nashville, TN Primary Contact: William E. Peaks, Chief Executive Officer CFO: Regina Ramazani, Chief Financial Officer Web address: www.gardenparkmedical.com	33	10	130	4290	58	39463	483	—	—	371
⊠ △ **MEMORIAL HOSPITAL AT GULFPORT**, 4500 13th Street, Zip 39501–2569, Mailing Address: P.O. Box 1810, Zip 39502–1810; tel. 228/867–4000, (Includes MEMORIAL BEHAVIORAL HEALTH, 11150 Highway 49 North, Zip 39503–4110; tel. 228/831–1700; Michael A. Zieman, Administrator) **A**1 2 7 9 10 **F**1 3 4 11 12 15 17 19 21 22 23 26 27 28 29 30 31 33 34 36 37 40 41 44 46 48 49 52 55 56 57 58 59 60 61 62 63 66 67 68 69 71 72 73 74 75 76 77 78 79 81 82 84 87 88 94 96 107 108 110 **P**3 8 Primary Contact: Gary G. Marchand, President and Chief Executive Officer COO: Jennifer H. Dumal, Vice President Patient Care Services CMO: Craig M. Slater, M.D., Senior Vice President, Medical Affairs Web address: www.gulfportmemorial.com VETERANS AFFAIRS MEDICAL CENTER, GULFPORT DIVISION See Veterans Affairs Gulf Coast Veterans Health Care System, Biloxi	15	10	445	16292	266	271781	1262	232156	100923	2043
HATTIESBURG—Forrest and Lamar County										
⊠ △ **FORREST GENERAL HOSPITAL**, 6051 U.S. Highway 49, Zip 39401–7243, Mailing Address: P.O. Box 16389, Zip 39404–6389; tel. 601/288–7000 **A**1 2 5 7 9 10 19 **F**3 4 10 11 12 14 15 17 19 21 22 23 26 27 28 29 33 34 39 40 41 47 48 49 51 53 55 56 58 59 60 61 63 64 65 66 68 69 71 72 73 74 75 77 78 79 81 82 84 87 88 93 94 95 96 106 108 109 **P**8 Primary Contact: William C. Oliver, President CFO: G Edward Tucker, Jr, Chief Financial Officer CMO: William H. Peters, M.D., Vice President of Medical Affairs CIO: G Edward Tucker, Jr, Chief Financial Officer CHR: Robert G. Stultz, Vice President Human Resources Web address: www.forrestgeneral.com	13	10	526	24627	332	124044	2576	255354	104422	2950
⊠ **REGENCY HOSPITAL OF HATTIESBURG**, 125 South 25th Avenue, Zip 39401; tel. 601/288–8510 **A**1 10 **F**28 **P**5 **S** Regency Hospital Company, Alpharetta, GA Primary Contact: James S. Kaigler, FACHE, Chief Executive Officer Web address: www.regencyhospital.com/hattiesburg.htm	32	80	37	383	27	0	0	—	—	92
⊠ **WESLEY MEDICAL CENTER**, 5001 Hardy Street, Zip 39402–1366, Mailing Address: P.O. Box 16509, Zip 39404–6509; tel. 601/268–8000 **A**1 9 10 19 **F**11 12 14 21 29 32 33 41 51 55 56 58 59 60 61 63 65 66 68 69 70 81 82 84 86 87 88 94 96 109 **S** Triad Hospitals, Inc., Plano, TX Primary Contact: Ronald T. Seal, Chief Executive Officer COO: Jim R. Kendrick, Chief Operating Officer CFO: Jeffrey L. Meigs, Chief Financial Officer CMO: Paul Talbot, M.D., President Medical Staff CIO: Debbie McMahan, Director Information Technology Web address: www.wesley.com	33	10	211	8526	120	74456	1033	—	—	931

MS

Hospital, Address, Telephone, Approval, Facility, and Physician Codes, Health Care System	Classi-fication Codes		Utilization Data					Expense (thousands) of dollars		
★ American Hospital Association (AHA) membership □ Joint Commission on Accreditation of Healthcare Organizations (JCAHO) accreditation ○ American Osteopathic Association (AOA) accreditation △ Commission on Accreditation of Rehabilitation Facilities (CARF) accreditation	Control	Service	Staffed Beds	Admissions	Census	Outpatient Visits	Births	Total	Payroll	Personnel

HAZLEHURST—Copiah County

★ **HARDY WILSON MEMORIAL HOSPITAL**, 233 Magnolia Street, Zip 39083–2229, Mailing Address: P.O. Box 889, Zip 39083–0889; tel. 601/894–4541 **A**9 10 **F**12 33 59 63 69 71 76 81 88 94 Primary Contact: John H. Phillips, Administrator and Chief Financial Officer	13	10	49	1245	24	11205	62	—	—	160

HOLLY SPRINGS—Marshall County

★ **ALLIANCE HEALTHCARE SYSTEM**, 1430 Highway 4 East, Zip 38635, Mailing Address: P.O. Box 6000, Zip 38634–6000; tel. 662/252–1212 **A**9 10 20 **F**12 21 27 28 29 33 34 44 45 58 63 66 71 76 77 81 88 94 96 Primary Contact: Perry E. Williams, Sr, Administrator and Chief Executive Officer COO: Perry E. Williams, Sr, Administrator CFO: Greg G. Underwood, Chief Financial Officer CMO: Peter Dews, M.D., Medical Director Web address: www.alliancehealth.us	33	10	40	1009	14	14314	0	—	—	119

HOUSTON—Chickasaw County

□ **TRACE REGIONAL HOSPITAL**, Highway 8 East, Zip 38851–9396, Mailing Address: P.O. Box 626, Zip 38851–0626; tel. 662/456–3700 **A**1 9 10 **F**12 14 29 33 34 50 55 58 63 68 69 71 74 76 81 84 88 92 94 **S** Sunlink Healthcare, Atlanta, GA Primary Contact: Gary L. Staten, Chief Executive Officer Web address: www.traceregional.com	33	10	84	1193	14	18348	0	—	—	167

INDIANOLA—Sunflower County

✚ **SOUTH SUNFLOWER COUNTY HOSPITAL**, 121 East Baker Street, Zip 38751–2498; tel. 662/887–5235 **A**1 9 10 20 **F**11 14 33 34 55 59 63 81 84 88 94 Primary Contact: H. J. Blessitt, Administrator CMO: Michael W. Montesi, M.D., Chief of Staff CIO: Julie Sterling, Information System Manager	13	10	49	2212	19	12784	342	15371	6846	145

IUKA—Tishomingo County

✚ **NORTH MISSISSIPPI MEDICAL CENTER–IUKA**, 1777 Curtis Drive, Zip 38852–1001, Mailing Address: P.O. Box 860, Zip 38852–0860; tel. 662/423–6051 **A**1 9 10 **F**6 14 21 26 27 28 29 33 34 41 55 58 63 65 66 68 69 81 82 88 94 96 98 **S** North Mississippi Health Services, Inc., Tupelo, MS Primary Contact: James R. Carter, Jr, Administrator CFO: Betty Moore, Business Manager Web address: www.nmhs.net	23	10	48	1895	25	13584	0	12692	5609	147

JACKSON—Hinds and Rankin County

□ **BRENTWOOD BEHAVIORAL HEALTHCARE OF MISSISSIPPI**, 3531 East Lakeland Drive, Zip 39296–9794; tel. 601/936–2024, (Nonreporting) **A**1 10 **S** Psychiatric Solutions, Franklin, TN Primary Contact: Michael J. Carney, Chief Executive Officer	33	22	107	—	—	—	—	—	—	—
□ **CENTRAL MISSISSIPPI MEDICAL CENTER**, 1850 Chadwick Drive, Zip 39204–3479, Mailing Address: P.O. Box 59001, Zip 39204–9001; tel. 601/376–1000 **A**1 2 9 10 **F**10 11 12 14 15 17 19 21 23 26 27 28 29 33 37 40 43 49 50 51 55 56 57 58 59 61 62 63 64 65 66 69 70 71 73 75 76 81 82 83 84 85 86 87 88 93 94 96 109 110 **P**8 **S** Health Management Associates, Naples, FL Primary Contact: John R. Finnegan, Chief Executive Officer Web address: www.centralmississippimedicalcenter.com	33	10	429	10469	159	44374	1400	120514	48856	1166
✚ **G.V. MONTGOMERY VETERANS AFFAIRS MEDICAL CENTER**, 1500 East Woodrow Wilson Drive, Zip 39216–5199; tel. 601/364–1201, (Total facility includes 120 beds in nursing home–type unit) (Nonreporting) **A**1 2 3 5 8 **S** Department of Veterans Affairs, Washington, DC Primary Contact: Richard J. Baltz, Director COO: Rebecca Wiley, R.N., Chief Operating Officer and Associate Director CMO: Kent Kirchner, M.D., Chief of Staff CIO: Robert Wolak, Chief Information Resource Management Service CHR: Sam Evans, Chief Human Resources Management Web address: www.va.gov	45	10	443	—	—	—	—	—	—	—
✚ △ **METHODIST REHABILITATION CENTER**, 1350 Woodrow Wilson Drive, Zip 39216–5198; tel. 601/981–2611, (Total facility includes 60 beds in nursing home–type unit) **A**1 7 8 9 10 **F**21 22 29 45 46 48 52 57 58 60 63 65 66 68 69 73 88 92 94 96 108 110 Primary Contact: Mark A. Adams, President and Chief Executive Officer COO: Joseph M. Morette, Executive Vice President CFO: Gary Armstrong, Executive Vice President CMO: Rahal Vohra, M.D., Medical Director CIO: Gary Armstrong, Executive Vice President CHR: Steve Hope, Vice President Corporate Services Web address: www.methodistrehab.org	23	46	184	2032	71	45264	0	42905	19950	400
✚ **MISSISSIPPI BAPTIST HEALTH SYSTEMS**, 1225 North State Street, Zip 39202–2002; tel. 601/968–1000 **A**1 2 3 5 9 10 **F**3 4 11 12 14 21 29 32 33 40 50 51 55 56 58 59 61 63 65 67 68 69 71 73 76 77 78 81 82 84 86 87 88 92 94 96 107 109 Primary Contact: Kurt W. Metzner, President and Chief Executive Officer CFO: Russell W. York, Vice President and Chief Financial Officer CMO: Eric A. McVey, Vice President and Chief Medical Officer Web address: www.mbhs.org	23	10	639	19205	290	123664	1079	—	—	2489

Many Facility Codes have changed. Please refer to the AHA Guide Code Chart.

© 2005 AHA Guide

Hospital, Address, Telephone, Approval, Facility, and Physician Codes, Health Care System	Classi-fication Codes		Utilization Data					Expense (thousands) of dollars		
★ American Hospital Association (AHA) membership □ Joint Commission on Accreditation of Healthcare Organizations (JCAHO) accreditation ○ American Osteopathic Association (AOA) accreditation △ Commission on Accreditation of Rehabilitation Facilities (CARF) accreditation	Control	Service	Staffed Beds	Admissions	Census	Outpatient Visits	Births	Total	Payroll	Personnel
□ **MISSISSIPPI HOSPITAL FOR RESTORATIVE CARE**, 1225 North State Street, Zip 39202–2097, Mailing Address: P.O. Box 23695, Zip 39225–3695; tel. 601/968–1000 **A**1 10 **F**21 44 92 94 Primary Contact: C. Gerald Cotton, Executive Director Web address: www.mbhs.org	23	80	25	243	21	0	0	—	—	79
⊠ **RIVER OAKS HOSPITAL**, 1030 River Oaks Drive, Zip 39232, Mailing Address: P.O. Box 5100, Zip 39296–5100; tel. 601/932–1030 **A**1 9 10 **F**11 12 15 17 21 29 32 33 34 55 56 59 61 62 63 66 68 69 81 82 87 88 92 93 94 109 **S** Health Management Associates, Naples, FL Primary Contact: John J. Cleary, President and Chief Executive Officer COO: Doug Self, Executive Vice President and Chief Operating Officer CFO: Jeff Bedford, Executive Vice President and Chief Financial Officer CMO: William G. Bush, M.D., Chief of Staff CIO: Pat Jones, Director Information Systems CHR: Warren Weed, Director Human Resources Web address: www.riveroakshospital.org	33	10	109	8241	89	49607	2018	71636	28278	686
□ **SELECT SPECIALTY HOSPITAL–JACKSON**, 1850 Chadwick Drive, 5th Floor, Zip 39204; tel. 601/376–1005 **A**1 10 **F**13 21 58 61 66 68 92 Primary Contact: Aaron Anothayanontha, Chief Executive Officer	33	80	40	395	32	0	0	—	—	123
⊠ **ST. DOMINIC–JACKSON MEMORIAL HOSPITAL**, 969 Lakeland Drive, Zip 39216–4699; tel. 601/200–2000 **A**1 2 3 5 9 10 **F**3 4 11 12 14 21 26 28 29 32 33 40 41 50 55 58 59 61 63 65 68 69 70 71 72 73 74 75 76 77 78 81 82 84 86 87 88 94 109 Primary Contact: Claude W. Harbarger, President CFO: Peter G. Koury, Executive Vice President Fiscal Services CMO: Tom Herrin, M.D., Medical Director CIO: Keith Van Camp, Vice President Information Services CHR: Lamar Nesbit, Senior Vice President Human Resources and Customer Services Web address: www.stdom.com	23	10	571	24167	360	70932	556	211119	86493	2174
⊠ **UNIVERSITY HOSPITALS AND CLINICS, UNIVERSITY OF MISSISSIPPI MEDICAL CENTER**, 2500 North State Street, Zip 39216–4505; tel. 601/984–1000, (Total facility includes 80 beds in nursing home–type unit) **A**1 2 3 5 8 9 10 **F**11 12 14 21 27 28 29 32 33 34 40 50 55 56 58 59 60 61 63 65 66 67 68 69 70 71 72 73 74 75 77 81 82 84 86 87 88 92 94 95 96 98 109 **S** Quorum Health Resources, Plano, TX Primary Contact: Frederick Woodrell, CHE, Chief Executive Officer COO: David G. Putt, CHE, Administrator CFO: Joe Amato, Chief Financial Officer CMO: Peggy Miller Davis, M.D., Chief Medical Officer CIO: Barbara Austin, Director Public Affairs CHR: Paul Trussel, Director Human Resources Web address: www.umc.edu	12	10	774	27870	591	253259	3379	399930	159556	4207
□ **WOMAN'S HOSPITAL AT RIVER OAKS**, 1026 North Flowood Drive, Zip 39232, Mailing Address: P.O. Box 4546, Zip 39296–4546; tel. 601/932–1000 **A**1 9 10 **F**11 12 21 29 32 56 59 63 66 88 92 94 109 **S** Health Management Associates, Naples, FL Primary Contact: Sherry J. Pitts, Administrator Web address: www.womanshospitalms.com	33	44	61	2663	26	13654	1537	—	—	201
KEESLER AFB—Harrison County										
⊠ **U. S. AIR FORCE MEDICAL CENTER KEESLER**, 301 Fisher Street, Suite 1A132, Zip 39534–2519; tel. 228/377–6510, (Nonreporting) **A**1 2 3 5 **S** Department of the Air Force, Washington, DC Primary Contact: Colonel Randy Borg, MSC, USAF, Administrator COO: Colonel Stanley F. Uchman, Deputy Commander CFO: Major David L. Johnson, Director, Medical Resource Management & Chief Financial Officer CMO: Colonel Thomas J. O'Donnell, Director Hospital Services Web address: www.81mdg06.keesler.af.mil/index.cgi	41	10	185	—	—	—	—	—	—	—
KILMICHAEL—Montgomery County										
★ **KILMICHAEL HOSPITAL**, 301 Lamar Avenue, Zip 39747–0188, Mailing Address: P.O. Box 188, Zip 39747–0188; tel. 662/262–4311 **A**9 10 **F**29 45 65 71 76 94 Primary Contact: Calvin D. Johnson, Chief Executive Officer	13	10	19	547	8	2539	0	—	—	59
KOSCIUSKO—Attala County										
★ **MONTFORT JONES MEMORIAL HOSPITAL**, 220 Highway 12 West, Zip 39090–3209, Mailing Address: P.O. Box 887, Zip 39090–0887; tel. 662/289–4311 **A**9 10 **F**12 14 27 32 33 34 44 55 63 67 68 69 76 81 82 87 88 94 Primary Contact: Richard W. Manning, Administrator CFO: James Thomas, Chief Financial Officer CHR: Paige Duke, Chief Human Resources and Marketing Web address: www.mjmh.com	13	10	71	1825	30	18287	0	14519	4796	155

MS

Hospital, Address, Telephone, Approval, Facility, and Physician Codes, Health Care System	Classi-fication Codes		Utilization Data					Expense (thousands) of dollars		
★ American Hospital Association (AHA) membership ☐ Joint Commission on Accreditation of Healthcare Organizations (JCAHO) accreditation ◯ American Osteopathic Association (AOA) accreditation △ Commission on Accreditation of Rehabilitation Facilities (CARF) accreditation	Control	Service	Staffed Beds	Admissions	Census	Outpatient Visits	Births	Total	Payroll	Personnel

LAUREL—Jones County

☒ **SOUTH CENTRAL REGIONAL MEDICAL CENTER**, 1220 Jefferson Street, Zip 39440–4374, Mailing Address: P.O. Box 607, Zip 39441–0607; tel. 601/426–4000, (Includes SOUTH CENTRAL EXTENDED CARE, Ivy Street, Ellisville, Zip 39437; tel. 601/477–9159), (Total facility includes 136 beds in nursing home–type unit) **A**1 9 10 19 20 **F**3 11 12 14 21 26 27 28 29 32 33 34 41 44 45 51 55 58 59 60 61 63 65 66 68 69 70 71 76 81 82 84 87 88 92 94 95 96 98 109 **P**6 8
Primary Contact: G. Douglas Higginbotham, Executive Director
CFO: Tom Canizaro, Associate Executive Director
CMO: Mark Nortom, M.D., President Medical Staff
CIO: Linda Gavin, Associate Executive Director Marketing and Physician Recruitment
CHR: Janet Staples, Director Human Resources
Web address: www.scrmc.com

| | 13 | 10 | 349 | 11002 | 280 | 161955 | 1163 | — | — | 1357 |

LEXINGTON—Holmes County

☒ **UNIVERSITY HOSPITAL AND CLINICS – HOLMES COUNTY**, 239 Bowling Green Road, Zip 39095–9332; tel. 662/834–1321 **A**1 9 10 12 18 20 **F**12 21 33 34 65 66 68 69 70 81 82 88 94 **S** Quorum Health Resources, Plano, TX
Primary Contact: Mary Ellen Pratt, Chief Executive Officer
CFO: Debbie McDonald, Manager Accounting

| | 12 | 10 | 42 | 1520 | 16 | 8591 | 0 | — | — | 129 |

LOUISVILLE—Winston County

WINSTON MEDICAL CENTER, 562 East Main Street, Zip 39339–2742, Mailing Address: P.O. Box 967, Zip 39339–0967; tel. 662/773–6211, (Total facility includes 120 beds in nursing home–type unit) **A**9 10 **F**12 14 33 34 55 63 76 81 88 92 94 97
Primary Contact: W. Dale Saulters, Administrator
Web address: www.winstonmedical.org

| | 23 | 10 | 185 | 645 | 114 | 21550 | 0 | 12271 | 4554 | 163 |

LUCEDALE—George County

GEORGE COUNTY HOSPITAL, 859 Winter Street, Zip 39452–6603, Mailing Address: P.O. Box 607, Zip 39452–0607; tel. 601/947–3161 **A**9 10 20 **F**11 12 14 33 34 41 55 59 63 69 76 81 82 84 88 94
Primary Contact: Paul A. Gardner, CPA, Administrator

| | 13 | 10 | 53 | 2689 | 26 | 31968 | 144 | — | — | 297 |

MACON—Noxubee County

★ **NOXUBEE GENERAL HOSPITAL**, 606 North Jefferson Street, Zip 39341–2236, Mailing Address: P.O. Box 480, Zip 39341–0480; tel. 662/726–4231, (Total facility includes 60 beds in nursing home–type unit) **A**9 10 18 **F**32 33 34 50 81 92 94
Primary Contact: Arthur Nester, Jr, Administrator

| | 13 | 10 | 85 | 601 | 61 | 5415 | 0 | 8466 | 3459 | 81 |

MAGEE—Simpson County

MAGEE GENERAL HOSPITAL, 300 Third Avenue, S.E., Zip 39111–3698; tel. 601/849–5070 **A**9 10 **F**11 12 26 27 28 33 59 63 76 81 82 84 88 94 95 96 97 110
Primary Contact: Althea H. Crumpton, Administrator

| | 23 | 10 | 56 | 2240 | 27 | 30628 | 128 | 14200 | 6139 | 215 |

MAGNOLIA—Pike County

BEACHAM MEMORIAL HOSPITAL, 205 North Cherry Street, Zip 39652–2819, Mailing Address: P.O. Box 351, Zip 39652–0351; tel. 601/783–2351 **A**9 10 **F**81 94
Primary Contact: Guy Geller, Administrator and Chief Executive Officer
Web address: www.beachammemhos.com

| | 23 | 10 | 37 | 1399 | 19 | 1994 | 0 | | | 97 |

MARKS—Quitman County

QUITMAN COUNTY HOSPITAL, 340 Getwell Drive, Zip 38646–9785; tel. 662/326–8031 **A**9 10 18 **F**29 33 34 65 66 69 71 76 81 88 94
Primary Contact: Sean Johnson, Administrator

| | 33 | 10 | 33 | 860 | 9 | 10549 | 1 | 5266 | 2492 | 99 |

MCCOMB—Pike County

☒ **SOUTHWEST MISSISSIPPI REGIONAL MEDICAL CENTER**, 215 Marion Avenue, Zip 39648–2798, Mailing Address: P.O. Box 1307, Zip 39649–1307; tel. 601/249–5500 **A**1 9 10 19 **F**11 12 14 15 17 19 21 23 26 27 28 33 40 41 44 45 46 47 48 49 51 52 55 58 59 61 62 63 64 65 66 68 69 71 76 78 79 80 81 82 84 85 87 88 94 95 96 97 106 109 **P**6
Primary Contact: Norman M. Price, FACHE, Administrator
COO: Philip Pandolph, Chief Operating Officer
CFO: Reece Nunnery, Chief Financial Officer
CMO: Ash Riad, M.D., Chief of Staff
CHR: Balfour Lipscomb, Administrative Director Human Resources
Web address: www.smrmc.com

| | 15 | 10 | 156 | 7397 | 88 | 69654 | 896 | 86513 | 38665 | 988 |

MEADVILLE—Franklin County

FRANKLIN COUNTY MEMORIAL HOSPITAL, Hospital Road, Zip 39653–4402, Mailing Address: P.O. Box 636, Zip 39653–0636; tel. 601/384–5801 **A**9 10 20 **F**21 29 33 34 44 45 63 65 69 71 76 78 81 88 94
Primary Contact: Lance Moak, Administrator
Web address: www.fcmh.net

| | 13 | 10 | 36 | 884 | 13 | 4176 | 0 | — | — | 87 |

MENDENHALL—Simpson County

SIMPSON GENERAL HOSPITAL, 1842 Simpson Highway 149, Zip 39114–3592; tel. 601/847–2221 **A**9 10 18 **F**29 33 41 44 50 63 65 66 68 69 71 73 74 75 76 81 82 88 94 96 98 **P**5
Primary Contact: Michael Nester, Administrator

| | 13 | 10 | 49 | 1042 | 15 | 10697 | 1 | — | — | 112 |

Many Facility Codes have changed. Please refer to the AHA Guide Code Chart.   © 2005 AHA Guide

Hospital, Address, Telephone, Approval, Facility, and Physician Codes, Health Care System	Classi-fication Codes		Utilization Data					Expense (thousands) of dollars		
★ American Hospital Association (AHA) membership □ Joint Commission on Accreditation of Healthcare Organizations (JCAHO) accreditation ○ American Osteopathic Association (AOA) accreditation △ Commission on Accreditation of Rehabilitation Facilities (CARF) accreditation	Control	Service	Staffed Beds	Admissions	Census	Outpatient Visits	Births	Total	Payroll	Personnel

MERIDIAN—Lauderdale County

□ **ALLIANCE HEALTH CENTER**, 5000 Highway 39 North, Zip 39301; tel. 601/483–6211 **A**1 9 10 **F**3 4 28 29 65 66 71 72 73 74 76 94 95 **S** Psychiatric Solutions, Franklin, TN
Primary Contact: William M. Patterson, Chief Executive Officer
Web address: www.alliancehealthcenter.com

| | 33 | 22 | 149 | 2338 | 87 | 589 | 0 | — | — | 252 |

EAST MISSISSIPPI STATE HOSPITAL, 4555 Highland Park Drive, Zip 39307–5498, Mailing Address: Box 4128, West Station, Zip 39304–4128; tel. 601/482–6186, (Total facility includes 226 beds in nursing home–type unit) **F**3 21 44 66 71 72 74 76 92 94 **S** Mississippi State Department of Mental Health, Jackson, MS
Primary Contact: Charles Carlisle, Director
Web address: www.emsh.state.ms.us

| | 12 | 22 | 543 | 1056 | 525 | 0 | 0 | — | — | 838 |

⊠ **JEFF ANDERSON REGIONAL MEDICAL CENTER**, 2124 14th Street, Zip 39301–4093; tel. 601/553–6000 **A**1 2 9 10 19 **F**11 12 14 21 26 27 28 29 32 33 34 41 50 55 56 58 59 60 61 63 65 66 67 68 69 71 81 82 86 87 88 94 95 96
Primary Contact: Mark D. McPhail, Chief Executive Officer
CFO: Larry Fortenberry, Controller
Web address: www.andersonhospital.com

| | 23 | 10 | 260 | 10506 | 155 | 70788 | 1105 | 111810 | 41122 | 1021 |

★ **REGENCY HOSPITAL OF MERIDIAN**, 1102 Constitution Avenue, 2nd Floor, Zip 39301, Mailing Address: 1102 Constitution Avenue, 2nd Floor, Zip 39301; tel. 601/484–7900 **A**10 **F**2 21 22 23 49 58 94 110 **S** Regency Hospital Company, Alpharetta, GA
Primary Contact: Benny Costello, Chief Executive Officer
Web address: www.ltac.com

| | 33 | 80 | 37 | 351 | 27 | 0 | 0 | 10233 | 3253 | 98 |

□ △ **RILEY HOSPITAL**, 1102 21st Avenue, Zip 39301–4096, Mailing Address: P.O. Box 1810, Zip 39301–1810; tel. 601/693–2511 **A**1 7 9 10 19 **F**11 12 19 21 26 29 55 56 58 59 60 61 63 64 65 66 68 69 81 82 87 88 92 94 95 96 106 108 109 110 **S** Health Management Associates, Naples, FL
Primary Contact: Stephen Nichols, Chief Executive Officer
Web address: www.hmamississippi.com

| | 33 | 10 | 120 | 4721 | 66 | 30264 | 653 | 44031 | 16179 | 409 |

⊠ **RUSH FOUNDATION HOSPITAL**, 1314 19th Avenue, Zip 39301–4195; tel. 601/483–0011 **A**1 9 10 19 **F**11 12 14 21 27 28 29 32 33 34 51 55 56 59 60 61 63 65 66 68 69 70 82 87 88 94 95 107 109 **S** Rush Health Systems, Meridian, MS
Primary Contact: Wallace Strickland, President and Chief Executive Officer
COO: Morris A. Reece, Executive Vice President and Chief Operating Officer
CFO: Darrell Wildman, Chief Financial Officer
CIO: Angela Sherrill, Director Information System
CHR: Donnie Smith, Director Human Resources
Web address: www.rushhealthsystems.org

| | 23 | 10 | 182 | 8546 | 108 | 35052 | 874 | — | — | 989 |

★ **SPECIALTY HOSPITAL OF MERIDIAN**, 1314 19th Avenue, Zip 39301–4116; tel. 601/703–4211 **A**10 **F**2 9 66 96 107 **S** Rush Health Systems, Meridian, MS
Primary Contact: Wallace Strickland, President and Chief Executive Officer
CFO: Lexie Fuller, Controller
CMO: Richmond Alexander, M.D., President and Medical Staff
CIO: Angela Sherrill, Corporate Director Information System
Web address: www.rushhealthsystems.org

| | 23 | 80 | 49 | 628 | 43 | — | 0 | 37345 | 9547 | 227 |

MONTICELLO—Lawrence County

LAWRENCE COUNTY HOSPITAL, Highway 84 East, Zip 39654–0788, Mailing Address: P.O. Box 788, Zip 39654–0788; tel. 601/587–4051 **A**9 10 18 **F**33 34 52 66 76 77 81 88 94
Primary Contact: Semmes Ross, Jr, Administrator

| | 13 | 10 | 25 | 672 | 6 | 9388 | 0 | 6473 | 2903 | 112 |

MORTON—Scott County

SCOTT REGIONAL HOSPITAL, 317 Highway 13 South, Zip 39117–3353, Mailing Address: P.O. Box 259, Zip 39117–0259; tel. 601/732–6301, (Nonreporting) **A**9 10
Primary Contact: Michael R. Edwards, Chief Executive Officer

| | 23 | 10 | 30 | — | — | — | — | — | — | — |

NATCHEZ—Adams County

□ **NATCHEZ COMMUNITY HOSPITAL**, 129 Jefferson Davis Boulevard, Zip 39120–5100, Mailing Address: P.O. Box 1203, Zip 39121–1203; tel. 601/445–6200 **A**1 9 10 **F**11 12 14 21 28 33 34 40 49 50 55 59 61 62 63 66 81 82 84 88 94 95 110 **S** Health Management Associates, Naples, FL
Primary Contact: J. Allen Tyra, Executive Director
Web address: www.hmamississippi.com

| | 33 | 10 | 101 | 4129 | 42 | 24080 | 407 | 23964 | 9975 | 256 |

⊠ △ **NATCHEZ REGIONAL MEDICAL CENTER**, Seargent S Prentiss Drive, Zip 39120–4726, Mailing Address: P.O. Box 1488, Zip 39121–1488; tel. 601/443–2100 **A**1 7 9 10 **F**11 12 14 33 34 55 59 66 67 68 76 77 81 82 84 86 88 94 **S** Quorum Health Resources, Plano, TX
Primary Contact: Jack F. Houghton, Chief Executive Officer
CFO: Walt Barlow, Interim Chief Financial Officer
CMO: Mallan G. Morgan, M.D., Chief of Staff
CIO: David Delaney, Director Information Management Systems
CHR: Eileen Richardson, Director Human Resources
Web address: www.natchezregional.com

| | 13 | 10 | 109 | 4401 | 60 | 31225 | 494 | — | — | 423 |

MS

Hospital, Address, Telephone, Approval, Facility, and Physician Codes, Health Care System	Classi-fication Codes		Utilization Data					Expense (thousands) of dollars		
★ American Hospital Association (AHA) membership □ Joint Commission on Accreditation of Healthcare Organizations (JCAHO) accreditation ○ American Osteopathic Association (AOA) accreditation △ Commission on Accreditation of Rehabilitation Facilities (CARF) accreditation	Control	Service	Staffed Beds	Admissions	Census	Outpatient Visits	Births	Total	Payroll	Personnel

NEW ALBANY—Union County

☒ **BAPTIST MEMORIAL HOSPITAL–UNION COUNTY**, 200 Highway 30 West, Zip 38652–3197; tel. 662/538–7631 **A**1 9 10 **F**2 6 9 11 12 21 27 29 32 33 37 47 55 57 58 59 60 61 62 63 65 66 69 81 82 84 87 88 92 93 94 96 108 109 **P**5 **S** Baptist Memorial Health Care Corporation, Memphis, TN
Primary Contact: Mitchell Johnson, Administrator and Chief Executive Officer
CFO: Kim High, Controller
CMO: H F. Mason, M.D., Chief of Staf
CIO: Missy Coltharp, Director
CHR: Lori Goode, Director Human Resources
Web address: www.bmhcc.org
| 23 | 10 | 153 | 4529 | 51 | 36364 | 928 | 33425 | 12779 | 366 |

NEWTON—Newton County

NEWTON REGIONAL HOSPITAL, (Formerly Rush Hospital–Newton), 202 South Main Street, Zip 39345–0299, Mailing Address: P.O. Box 299, Zip 39345–0299; tel. 601/683–2031 **A**9 10 **F**29 33 34 63 69 71 76 81 88 94 **P**6
Primary Contact: Timothy Thomas, Administrator
Web address: www.newtonregionalhospital.com
| 23 | 10 | 49 | 1257 | 10 | 10780 | 1 | 5861 | 2425 | 129 |

OCEAN SPRINGS—Jackson County

OCEAN SPRINGS HOSPITAL See Singing River Hospital System, Pascagoula

OLIVE BRANCH—De Soto County

□ **PARKWOOD BEHAVIORAL HEALTH SYSTEM**, 8135 Goodman Road, Zip 38654–2199; tel. 662/895–4900 **A**1 9 10 **F**3 4 21 26 27 28 29 45 58 60 65 66 71 72 73 74 75 77 78 92 94 **P**5 **S** Universal Health Services, Inc., King of Prussia, PA
Primary Contact: M. Andrew Mayo, Ph.D., Chief Executive Officer
Web address: www.parkwoodbhs.com
| 33 | 22 | 72 | 2106 | 54 | 0 | 0 | 11441 | 6211 | 139 |

OXFORD—Lafayette County

☒ **BAPTIST MEMORIAL HOSPITAL–NORTH MISSISSIPPI**, 2301 South Lamar Boulevard, Zip 38655–5373, Mailing Address: P.O. Box 946, Zip 38655–0946; tel. 662/232–8100 **A**1 9 10 19 **F**11 12 14 21 26 27 28 29 32 33 34 40 41 51 55 59 60 61 63 65 66 67 68 69 71 77 81 82 84 88 92 94 95 96 109 **S** Baptist Memorial Health Care Corporation, Memphis, TN
Primary Contact: Zachary Chandler, Administrator and Chief Executive Officer
CFO: Dana Williams, Assistant Administrator and Chief Financial Officer
CIO: Terri Campbell, Director Information Systems
CHR: Barry Wolfe, Director Human Resources
Web address: www.bmhcc.org
| 23 | 10 | 217 | 8858 | 126 | 24453 | 902 | — | — | 826 |

PASCAGOULA—Jackson County

☒ **SINGING RIVER HOSPITAL SYSTEM**, 2809 Denny Avenue, Zip 39581–5301; tel. 228/809–5000, (Includes OCEAN SPRINGS HOSPITAL, 3109 Bienville Boulevard, Ocean Springs, Zip 39564–4361; tel. 228/818–1111; SINGING RIVER HOSPITAL, tel. 228/809–5000), (Nonreporting) **A**1 2 9 10
Primary Contact: Lynn Truelove, Administrator
CFO: Robert Lewis, Chief Financial Officer
CIO: Carl Cloer, Director Information Systems
Web address: www.srhshealth.com
| 13 | 10 | 378 | — | — | — | — | — | — | — |

PHILADELPHIA—Neshoba County

☒ **CHOCTAW HEALTH CENTER**, 210 Hospital Circle, Zip 39350–6781; tel. 601/656–2211, (Nonreporting) **A**1 5 9 10 **S** U. S. Indian Health Service, Rockville, MD
Primary Contact: James D. Wallace, Executive Director
CFO: Donita Stephens, Administrative Assistant to Financial Services
CMO: Joann Coates, M.D., Chief of Staff
CHR: Linda McMillan, Patient Relations and Personnel Specialist
| 47 | 10 | 35 | — | — | — | — | — | — | — |

★ **NESHOBA COUNTY GENERAL HOSPITAL**, 1001 Holland Avenue, Zip 39350–2161, Mailing Address: P.O. Box 648, Zip 39350–0648; tel. 601/663–1200, (Total facility includes 148 beds in nursing home–type unit) **A**9 10 **F**12 21 33 34 44 45 50 55 63 68 76 81 88 92 94 **P**6 **S** Quorum Health Resources, Plano, TX
Primary Contact: Lawrence Graeber, Chief Executive Officer
CFO: Walt Barlow, Interim Chief Financial Officer
CMO: Walt Willis, M.D., Medical Director
CHR: Hedda Stewart, Director Human Resources
| 13 | 10 | 204 | 1795 | 168 | 29937 | 0 | 24572 | 11813 | 364 |

PICAYUNE—Pearl River County

CROSBY MEMORIAL HOSPITAL, 801 Goodyear Boulevard, Zip 39466–3221, Mailing Address: P.O. Box 909, Zip 39466–0909; tel. 601/798–4711 **A**9 10 **F**11 12 26 27 28 33 34 55 58 59 63 65 66 69 81 82 84 88 94 95 109
Primary Contact: Steve Grimm, CHE, Chief Executive Officer
Web address: www.crosbymh.com
| 33 | 10 | 61 | 2419 | 21 | 37239 | 293 | 25374 | 8371 | 240 |

PONTOTOC—Pontotoc County

☒ **NORTH MISSISSIPPI MEDICAL CENTER–PONTOTOC HOSPITAL AND NURSING HOME**, 176 South Main Street, Zip 38863–3311, Mailing Address: P.O. Box 790, Zip 38863–0790; tel. 662/488–7640, (Total facility includes 44 beds in nursing home–type unit) **A**1 9 10 18 **F**12 26 27 28 29 33 34 45 58 65 66 68 69 81 88 92 94 96 **S** North Mississippi Health Services, Inc., Tupelo, MS
Primary Contact: Fred B. Hood, Administrator
CFO: M Denise Heard, Director Business Services
Web address: www.nmhs.net
| 23 | 10 | 73 | 373 | 50 | 14642 | 0 | 11187 | 4656 | 145 |

Many Facility Codes have changed. Please refer to the AHA Guide Code Chart.

Hospital, Address, Telephone, Approval, Facility, and Physician Codes, Health Care System	Classi-fication Codes		Utilization Data					Expense (thousands) of dollars		
★ American Hospital Association (AHA) membership □ Joint Commission on Accreditation of Healthcare Organizations (JCAHO) accreditation ○ American Osteopathic Association (AOA) accreditation △ Commission on Accreditation of Rehabilitation Facilities (CARF) accreditation	Control	Service	Staffed Beds	Admissions	Census	Outpatient Visits	Births	Total	Payroll	Personnel

POPLARVILLE—Pearl River County

PEARL RIVER COUNTY HOSPITAL, 305 West Moody Street, Zip 39470–7242, Mailing Address: P.O. Box 392, Zip 39470–0392; tel. 601/795–4543, (Total facility includes 126 beds in nursing home–type unit) **A**9 10 **F**66 68 69 92 94
Primary Contact: Dorothy C. Bilbo, Administrator

| 13 | 10 | 150 | 361 | 88 | 0 | 0 | — | | 52 |

PORT GIBSON—Claiborne County

★ **CLAIBORNE COUNTY HOSPITAL**, 123 McComb Avenue, Zip 39150–2915, Mailing Address: P.O. Box 1004, Zip 39150–1004; tel. 601/437–5141 **A**9 10 18 **F**27 28 33 34 71 73 74 76 77 92 94
Primary Contact: Wanda C. Fleming, Administrator and Chief Executive Officer
CFO: Linda Caho–Mooney, Chief Financial Officer
CIO: Ada Ratliff, Chief Information Officer

| 13 | 10 | 32 | 550 | 9 | 9542 | 0 | 4434 | 2559 | 76 |

PRENTISS—Jefferson Davis County

JEFFERSON DAVIS COMMUNITY HOSPITAL, (Formerly Prentiss Regional Hospital and Extended Care Facilities), 1102 Rose Street, Zip 39474, Mailing Address: P.O. Box 1288, Zip 39474; tel. 601/792–4276, (Total facility includes 60 beds in nursing home–type unit) **A**9 10 **F**29 33 34 41 44 65 66 68 69 71 73 74 75 76 81 88 92 94 **S** Ameris Health Systems, Nashville, TN
Primary Contact: Mary Curtis, Administrator

| 23 | 10 | 101 | 831 | 70 | 8368 | 0 | — | | 117 |

PURVIS—Lamar County

□ **SOUTH MISSISSIPPI STATE HOSPITAL**, 823 Highway 589, Zip 39475–4194; tel. 601/794–0100 **A**1 10 **F**26 27 28 71 94 **P**6 **S** Mississippi State Department of Mental Health, Jackson, MS
Primary Contact: Wynona C. Winfield, Director
Web address: www.smsh.state.ms.us

| 12 | 22 | 50 | 511 | 43 | 0 | 0 | 6547 | 3356 | 105 |

QUITMAN—Clarke County

H. C. WATKINS MEMORIAL HOSPITAL, 605 South Archusa Avenue, Zip 39355–2398; tel. 601/776–6925, (Total facility includes 15 beds in nursing home–type unit) **A**9 10 18 20 **F**3 14 21 29 33 34 55 63 69 81 92 94 96
Primary Contact: Fred A. Truesdale, Jr, Chief Executive Officer

| 23 | 10 | 40 | 699 | 22 | 7005 | 0 | — | | 100 |

RICHTON—Perry County

PERRY COUNTY GENERAL HOSPITAL, 206 Bay Avenue, Zip 39476, Mailing Address: 206 Bay Avenue, Zip 39476; tel. 601/788–6316 **A**9 10 18 **F**33 51 68 69 81 88 92
Primary Contact: David Paris, Chief Executive Officer

| 32 | 10 | 22 | 523 | 4 | 4036 | 0 | — | — | 71 |

RIPLEY—Tippah County

▣ **TIPPAH COUNTY HOSPITAL**, 1005 City Avenue North, Zip 38663–0499, Mailing Address: P.O. Box 499, Zip 38663–0499; tel. 662/837–9221, (Total facility includes 40 beds in nursing home–type unit) **A**1 9 10 20 **F**6 9 12 21 22 29 33 34 41 55 63 81 82 88 92 94 97
Primary Contact: Jerry Green, Administrator
CFO: Janice Cross, Controller
CMO: Charles M. Elliott, M.D., Chief of Staff
CHR: Margaret Weeks, Manager Personnel

| 13 | 10 | 110 | 1173 | 53 | 17420 | 0 | 10535 | 5674 | 202 |

ROLLING FORK—Sharkey County

SHARKEY–ISSAQUENA COMMUNITY HOSPITAL, 108 South Fourth Street, Zip 39159–2612, Mailing Address: P.O. Box 339, Zip 39159–0339; tel. 662/873–4396 **A**9 10 20 **F**27 33 41 44 76 81 84 88 97
Primary Contact: Jerry Keever, Administrator

| 13 | 10 | 29 | 505 | 8 | 6981 | 0 | 5077 | 2870 | 67 |

RULEVILLE—Sunflower County

★ **NORTH SUNFLOWER MEDICAL CENTER**, (Formerly North Sunflower County Hospital), 840 North Oak Avenue, Zip 38771–0369, Mailing Address: P.O. Box 369, Zip 38771–0369; tel. 662/756–2711, (Total facility includes 52 beds in nursing home–type unit) **A**9 10 18 **F**2 3 21 26 27 29 33 34 39 45 46 48 51 52 53 58 60 63 68 69 70 74 81 88 92 94 96 97 98 108 110
Primary Contact: Billy Marlow, Administrator
COO: Sam Miller, Chief Operating Officer
CFO: Charlotte Townsend, Financial Manager
CMO: Adelo Aquino, M.D., Chief of Staff
CIO: Janet Fulgham, Director Information Services
CHR: Robbie Taylor, Director Human Resources

| 13 | 10 | 96 | 958 | 66 | 6084 | 0 | 8549 | 4138 | — |

SENATOBIA—Tate County

□ **NORTH OAK REGIONAL MEDICAL CENTER**, 401 Getwell Drive, Zip 38668–2213, Mailing Address: P.O. Box 648, Zip 38668–0648; tel. 662/562–3100 **A**1 9 10 **F**27 28 33 63 65 66 76 81 88 94
Primary Contact: James D. Tesar, Chief Executive Officer
Web address: www.normc.org

| 33 | 10 | 52 | 1009 | 15 | 12728 | 0 | — | — | 71 |

SOUTHAVEN—De Soto County

▣ △ **BAPTIST MEMORIAL HOSPITAL–DESOTO**, 7601 Southcrest Parkway, Zip 38671–4742; tel. 662/349–4000 **A**1 7 9 10 **F**11 12 14 21 29 33 34 40 45 50 55 59 60 61 63 65 66 68 69 75 81 82 84 86 87 88 92 94 95 96 109 **S** Baptist Memorial Health Care Corporation, Memphis, TN
Primary Contact: Randy King, Administrator and Chief Executive Officer
CFO: Micki Benefield, Chief Financial Officer
CMO: Brad Wolfe, M.D., President
CHR: Walter Banks, Director Human Resources
Web address: www.bmhcc.org

| 23 | 10 | 199 | 10764 | 155 | 69745 | 1597 | — | — | 921 |

Hospital, Address, Telephone, Approval, Facility, and Physician Codes, Health Care System	Classification Codes		Utilization Data					Expense (thousands) of dollars		
★ American Hospital Association (AHA) membership □ Joint Commission on Accreditation of Healthcare Organizations (JCAHO) accreditation ○ American Osteopathic Association (AOA) accreditation △ Commission on Accreditation of Rehabilitation Facilities (CARF) accreditation	Control	Service	Staffed Beds	Admissions	Census	Outpatient Visits	Births	Total	Payroll	Personnel

STARKVILLE—Oktibbeha County

☒ **OKTIBBEHA COUNTY HOSPITAL**, 400 Hospital Road, Zip 39759–2163, Mailing Address: Drawer 1506, Zip 39760–1506; tel. 662/323–4320 **A**1 9 10 **F**11 12 14 21 29 32 33 34 40 41 50 55 59 60 63 66 67 68 69 71 81 82 84 87 88 94 95 96
Primary Contact: Arthur C. Kelly, Administrator and Chief Executive Officer
COO: Mike Andrews, Assistant Administrator and Chief Operating Officer
CFO: Richard G. Hilton, Associate Administrator and Chief Financial Officer
CIO: Chamath Wijewardane, Director Information Technology
CHR: Mike Andrews, Assistant Administrator and Chief Operating Officer
Web address: www.och.org

| | 13 | 10 | 96 | 3342 | 34 | 135482 | 1127 | 36532 | 17920 | 456 |

TUPELO—Lee County

☒ **NORTH MISSISSIPPI MEDICAL CENTER – TUPELO**, 830 South Gloster Street, Zip 38801–4934; tel. 662/377–3000, (Total facility includes 107 beds in nursing home–type unit) **A**1 2 3 5 10 12 19 **F**3 4 11 12 14 21 26 27 28 29 33 34 40 41 44 50 51 55 56 58 59 60 61 63 65 66 67 68 69 70 71 72 73 74 76 77 78 81 82 84 86 87 88 92 94 95 96 98 109 **S** North Mississippi Health Services, Inc., Tupelo, MS
Primary Contact: John R. Heer, President and Chief Executive Officer
CFO: Gerald D. Wages, Executive Vice President Finance
Web address: www.nmhs.net

| | 23 | 10 | 757 | 30000 | 534 | 186307 | 2438 | 376843 | 134424 | 3664 |

□ **NORTH MISSISSIPPI STATE HOSPITAL**, 1937 Briar Ridge Road, Zip 38804; tel. 662/690–4200 **A**1 10 **F**2 12 45 66 71 74 76 94 96 **P**6 **S** Mississippi State Department of Mental Health, Jackson, MS
Primary Contact: Paul A. Callens, Ph.D., Director
Web address: www.nmsh.state.ms.us

| | 12 | 22 | 74 | 541 | 56 | 0 | 0 | 4221 | 4826 | 206 |

TYLERTOWN—Walthall County

★ **WALTHALL COUNTY GENERAL HOSPITAL**, 100 Hospital Drive, Zip 39667–2099; tel. 601/876–2122 **A**9 10 20 **F**27 33 34 63 66 69 76 81 88 94 **P**5
Primary Contact: Jimmy Graves, Administrator

| | 13 | 10 | 49 | 1442 | 16 | 18711 | 0 | 9963 | 4504 | 153 |

UNION—Newton County

□ **LAIRD HOSPITAL**, (Formerly Alliance–Laird Hospital), 25117 Highway 15, Zip 39365–9099; tel. 601/774–8214 **A**1 9 10 18 **F**12 21 29 33 34 55 63 66 81 88 94
Primary Contact: Thomas G. Bartlett, III, M.D., Administrator

| | 33 | 10 | 49 | 1455 | 14 | 14973 | 0 | — | — | 150 |

VICKSBURG—Warren County

PROMISE SPECIALTY HOSPITAL OF VICKSBURG, 1111 North Frontage Road, 2nd Floor, Zip 39180; tel. 601/619–3526 **A**10 **S** Promise Healthcare, Lafayette, LA
Primary Contact: Lee Huckaby, Chief Executive Officer
Web address: www.promise–vicksburg.com

| | 33 | 80 | 33 | 55 | 4 | 0 | 0 | — | — | 35 |

☒ **RIVER REGION HEALTH SYSTEM**, 2100 Highway 61 North, Zip 39183, Mailing Address: P.O. Box 590, Zip 39181–0590; tel. 601/883–5000, (Includes RIVER REGION MEDICAL CENTER, 2100 Highway 61 North, Mailing Address: P.O. Box 590, Zip 39181–0590; tel. 601/883–5000; RIVER REGION WEST CAMPUS, 1111 North Frontage Road, Zip 39180–5102; tel. 601/636–2611), (Total facility includes 19 beds in nursing home–type unit) (Nonreporting) **A**1 2 9 10 19 **S** Triad Hospitals, Inc., Plano, TX
Primary Contact: Phillip A. Clendenin, Chief Executive Officer
COO: Tim McManus, Administrator and Chief Operating Officer
CFO: Scott Pfister, Chief Financial Officer
CMO: W Briggs Hopson, M.D., Clinical Medical Director
CIO: J B. White, Chief Information Officer
CHR: Bill Holzmann, Director Human Resources
Web address: www.riverregion.com
VICKSBURG MEDICAL CENTER See River Region West Campus

| | 33 | 10 | 381 | — | | | | | | |

WATER VALLEY—Yalobusha County

YALOBUSHA GENERAL HOSPITAL, Highway 7 South, Zip 38965–3746, Mailing Address: P.O. Box 728, Zip 38965–0728; tel. 662/473–1411, (Total facility includes 77 beds in nursing home–type unit) **A**9 10 **F**21 45 60 81 88 92 94 **P**4
Primary Contact: Terry Varner, Administrator
Web address: www.watervalley.net/users/ygh

| | 13 | 10 | 103 | 696 | 82 | 9903 | 0 | — | — | 114 |

WAYNESBORO—Wayne County

□ **WAYNE GENERAL HOSPITAL**, 950 Matthew Drive, Zip 39367–2590, Mailing Address: P.O. Box 1249, Zip 39367–1249; tel. 601/735–5151 **A**1 9 10 20 **F**2 6 9 11 12 21 22 27 28 29 32 33 34 35 36 39 41 45 46 47 48 50 51 52 53 55 58 59 60 63 65 69 81 82 88 94 95 96 97 108 110
Primary Contact: Donald Hemeter, Administrator
Web address: www.waynegeneralhospital.org

| | 13 | 10 | 80 | 2928 | 38 | 30460 | 211 | 18783 | 9946 | 312 |

WEST POINT—Clay County

☒ **NORTH MISSISSIPPI MEDICAL CENTER–WEST POINT**, 835 Medical Center Drive, Zip 39773–9320; tel. 662/495–2300 **A**1 9 10 **F**11 12 14 21 26 27 28 29 32 33 41 45 55 58 59 61 63 65 66 68 69 70 81 82 84 88 94 95 96 109 **S** North Mississippi Health Services, Inc., Tupelo, MS
Primary Contact: Timothy H. Moore, Administrator

| | 23 | 10 | 60 | 3667 | 36 | 50910 | 440 | 24474 | 11393 | 287 |

MS

Many Facility Codes have changed. Please refer to the AHA Guide Code Chart.

© 2005 AHA Guide

Hospital, Address, Telephone, Approval, Facility, and Physician Codes, Health Care System	Classification Codes		Utilization Data					Expense (thousands) of dollars		
★ American Hospital Association (AHA) membership □ Joint Commission on Accreditation of Healthcare Organizations (JCAHO) accreditation ○ American Osteopathic Association (AOA) accreditation △ Commission on Accreditation of Rehabilitation Facilities (CARF) accreditation	Control	Service	Staffed Beds	Admissions	Census	Outpatient Visits	Births	Total	Payroll	Personnel

WHITFIELD—Rankin County

⊠ **MISSISSIPPI STATE HOSPITAL**, 3550 Highway 468 West, Zip 39193, Mailing Address: P.O. Box 157–A, Zip 39193–0157; tel. 601/351–8000, (Includes WHITFIELD MEDICAL SURGICAL HOSPITAL, Oak Circle, tel. 601/351–8023), (Total facility includes 479 beds in nursing home–type unit) **A**1 **F**3 26 28 32 58 71 72 92 **P**1 **S** Mississippi State Department of Mental Health, Jackson, MS
Primary Contact: James G. Chastain, CHE, Director
CFO: Warren Williams, CPA, Fiscal Services Director
CMO: Duncan Stone, M.D., Chief Medical Staff
CIO: James Dunaway, Director Information Management
CHR: Jarrod Ravencraft, Director Human Resources
Web address: www.msh.state.ms.us

| | 12 | 22 | 1303 | 2471 | 1091 | 7300 | 0 | 111479 | 64773 | 2374 |

WIGGINS—Stone County

STONE COUNTY HOSPITAL, 1434 East Central Avenue, Zip 39577; tel. 601/928–6600 **A**9 10 18 **F**12 21 26 27 28 29 33 34 63 66 81 88 94
Primary Contact: Carmen Reeves, Chief Executive Officer

| | 33 | 10 | 25 | 144 | 2 | 6765 | 0 | — | — | 85 |

WINONA—Montgomery County

TYLER HOLMES MEMORIAL HOSPITAL, 409 Tyler Holmes Drive, Zip 38967–1599; tel. 662/283–4114 **A**9 10 18 **F**29 33 34 63 66 81 88 94
Primary Contact: Rosamond M. Tyler, Administrator

| | 13 | 10 | 25 | 803 | 7 | 13081 | 0 | 6101 | 3172 | 118 |

YAZOO CITY—Yazoo County

KING'S DAUGHTERS HOSPITAL, 823 Grand Avenue, Zip 39194–3233; tel. 662/746–2261 **A**9 10 18 20 **F**12 21 33 41 63 66 69 81 82 88 94
Primary Contact: Noel W. Hart, Administrator
Web address: www.kdhyazoo.com

| | 23 | 10 | 25 | 1315 | 17 | 33438 | 13 | 11438 | 3855 | 128 |

MS

MISSOURI

Hospital, Address, Telephone, Approval, Facility, and Physician Codes, Health Care System	Classi-fication Codes		Utilization Data					Expense (thousands) of dollars		
★ American Hospital Association (AHA) membership □ Joint Commission on Accreditation of Healthcare Organizations (JCAHO) accreditation ○ American Osteopathic Association (AOA) accreditation △ Commission on Accreditation of Rehabilitation Facilities (CARF) accreditation	Control	Service	Staffed Beds	Admissions	Census	Outpatient Visits	Births	Total	Payroll	Personnel
ALBANY—Gentry County ★ **NORTHWEST MEDICAL CENTER**, 705 North College Street, Zip 64402–1499; tel. 660/726–3941, (Total facility includes 10 beds in nursing home–type unit) **A**9 10 **F**2 9 12 21 22 27 28 29 32 33 35 41 44 46 47 48 50 51 52 55 60 61 62 63 64 65 66 68 69 70 81 82 84 87 88 92 94 95 96 97 110 **P**6 Primary Contact: John W. Richmond, President and Chief Executive Officer CFO: Sheila Luke, Vice President Finance CIO: Linda Courtney, Director Health Information Web address: www.gcmh.org	23	10	35	1144	15	26970	—	8993	4172	129
APPLETON CITY—St. Clair County ★ **ELLETT MEMORIAL HOSPITAL**, 610 North Ohio Avenue, Zip 64724–1609, Mailing Address: P.O. Box 6, Zip 64724–0006; tel. 660/476–2111 **A**9 10 18 **F**6 9 27 33 46 63 69 81 84 88 94 97 **P**6 Primary Contact: Stephanie West, R.N., Administrator CMO: Imran Cheema, M.D., Chief Medical Officer Web address: www.ellettmemorial.com	16	10	25	410	4	2389	—	2875	1251	48
AURORA—Lawrence County ★ **ST. JOHN'S HOSPITAL – AURORA**, 500 Porter Street, Zip 65605–2399; tel. 417/678–2122 **A**9 10 18 **F**2 9 11 12 21 27 29 33 46 47 48 52 53 55 58 59 60 63 64 65 66 69 81 82 84 88 92 96 97 108 110 **P**6 **S** Sisters of Mercy Health System, Chesterfield, MO Primary Contact: Gary W. Jordan, President CFO: Marlyn Scheuen, Chief Financial Officer Web address: www.stjohns.com/aboutus/aurora.aspx	14	10	25	1097	10	26562	144	11251	6172	164
BELTON—Cass County ★ **RESEARCH BELTON HOSPITAL**, 17065 South 71 Highway, Zip 64012–2165; tel. 816/348–1200 **A**9 10 **F**2 12 22 27 29 33 35 37 39 46 48 52 53 55 57 58 60 62 63 64 66 69 81 82 84 88 92 93 94 96 106 108 110 **P**5 8 **S** HCA, Nashville, TN Primary Contact: Todd Krass, President and Chief Executive Officer CFO: Susan Shreeve, Chief Financial Officer CMO: Max G. Jackson, Vice President Medical Affairs CIO: Shahzad Fakhar, Chief Information Officer CHR: Kyla Stoltz, Director Human Resources Web address: www.researchbeltonhospital.com	23	10	38	2004	19	41661	0	27461	8813	138
BETHANY—Harrison County ★ **HARRISON COUNTY COMMUNITY HOSPITAL**, 2600 Miller Street, Zip 64424–2701, Mailing Address: P.O. Box 428, Zip 64424–0428; tel. 660/425–2211 **A**9 10 18 **F**2 9 12 21 26 27 28 29 33 35 37 41 45 46 47 48 51 52 55 58 60 63 66 68 69 81 82 84 87 88 92 93 94 97 108 110 **P**5 Primary Contact: Richard C. Hamilton, Administrator CFO: Christina Gillespie, Chief Financial Officer CHR: Brenda Gabrial, Director Human Resources Web address: www.hcchospital.org	16	10	20	480	4	33455	—	7446	3498	101
BLUE SPRINGS—Jackson County ⌧ **ST. MARY'S MEDICAL CENTER**, (Formerly St. Mary's Hospital of Blue Springs), 201 West R. D. Mize Road, Zip 64014–2533; tel. 816/228–5900 **A**1 9 10 **F**2 9 11 12 15 21 22 23 26 28 29 33 37 38 39 49 50 52 53 55 57 58 59 60 61 62 63 64 66 68 79 80 81 82 84 85 87 88 92 93 94 96 106 108 **S** Ascension Health, Saint Louis, MO Primary Contact: Gordon Docking, Chief Executive Officer CFO: Gary Clifton, Executive Vice President, Finance CMO: Steve Sanders, D.O., Vice President Medical Affairs CIO: Stewant Grant, Chief Information Officer CHR: Dawn Bryant, Vice President Organizational Development Web address: www.carondelethealth.org	23	10	134	6886	76	84888	1388	62412	25432	477
BOLIVAR—Polk County ⌧ **CITIZENS MEMORIAL HOSPITAL**, 1500 North Oakland Avenue, Zip 65613–3099; tel. 417/326–6000 **A**1 9 10 20 **F**2 6 9 11 12 15 17 21 22 26 27 28 29 30 31 32 33 34 35 36 37 39 41 44 45 46 47 48 51 52 53 55 58 59 60 62 63 64 65 66 68 69 70 71 73 75 76 77 81 82 84 88 93 94 95 96 97 106 108 109 110 **P**6 Primary Contact: Donald J. Babb, Chief Executive Officer COO: Allen Walldo, Chief Operating Officer CFO: Gary D. Fullbright, Comptroller CMO: Steven Butcher, D.O., Director Medical Affairs CIO: Denni McColm, Chief Information Officer Web address: www.citizensmemorial.com	16	10	74	3373	41	254692	450	55788	27554	791
BONNE TERRE—St. Francois County □ **PARKLAND HEALTH CENTER–BONNE TERRE**, 7245 Raider Road, Zip 63628; tel. 573/358–1400, (Nonreporting) **A**1 5 9 10 18 **S** BJC HealthCare, Saint Louis, MO Primary Contact: Richard L. Conklin, President Web address: www.parklandhealthcenter.org	23	10	3	—	—	—	—	—	—	—

Many Facility Codes have changed. Please refer to the AHA Guide Code Chart. © 2005 AHA Guide

Hospital, Address, Telephone, Approval, Facility, and Physician Codes, Health Care System	Classification Codes		Utilization Data					Expense (thousands) of dollars		
★ American Hospital Association (AHA) membership □ Joint Commission on Accreditation of Healthcare Organizations (JCAHO) accreditation ○ American Osteopathic Association (AOA) accreditation △ Commission on Accreditation of Rehabilitation Facilities (CARF) accreditation	Control	Service	Staffed Beds	Admissions	Census	Outpatient Visits	Births	Total	Payroll	Personnel

BOONVILLE—Cooper County

COOPER COUNTY MEMORIAL HOSPITAL, 17651 B Highway, Zip 65233–2839, Mailing Address: P.O. Box 88, Zip 65233–0088; tel. 660/882–7461, (Total facility includes 24 beds in nursing home–type unit) **A**5 9 10 20 **F**1 2 6 21 26 27 28 29 33 41 46 48 51 52 53 58 62 63 69 73 81 88 92 94 96 97 108 110 **S** University of Missouri Health Care, Columbia, MO
Primary Contact: Matt Waterman, Chief Executive Officer
| 13 | 10 | 49 | 919 | 33 | 24662 | 0 | 9806 | 3985 | 179 |

BRANSON—Taney County

⊞ **SKAGGS COMMUNITY HEALTH CENTER**, Business Highway 65 and Skaggs Road, Zip 65616–2035, Mailing Address: P.O. Box 650, Zip 65615–0650; tel. 417/335–7000, (Total facility includes 28 beds in nursing home–type unit) **A**1 9 10 20 **F**2 9 11 12 14 15 17 19 21 22 23 27 28 29 31 33 36 39 40 44 45 46 47 48 50 51 52 53 55 57 58 59 60 61 62 63 64 65 66 68 69 70 73 81 82 84 87 88 92 93 94 95 96 106 107 108 110 **P**6 8
Primary Contact: Bob D. Phillips, CHE, Administrator and Chief Executive Officer
COO: Michael L. Pierce, Chief Operating Officer
CFO: Sherry C. Day, CPA, Chief Financial Officer
CMO: Jerry Givens, M.D., Chief Medical Officer
CIO: Crystal Stallings, Chief Information Officer
CHR: Larry Dinges, Human Resources Director
Web address: www.skaggs.net
| 23 | 10 | 132 | 6873 | 88 | 230257 | 587 | 97911 | 38441 | 921 |

BRIDGETON—St. Louis County

⊞ △ **ALL SAINTS SPECIAL CARE HOSPITAL**, 12303 De Paul Drive, 2nd Floor, Zip 63044–2588; tel. 314/344–7830 **A**1 7 10 **F**2 21 22 27 37 94 110 **S** Dubuis Health System, Houston, TX
Primary Contact: David L. Adcock, Administrator
CMO: Anthony Masi, Medical Director
Web address: www.dubuis.org
| 23 | 80 | 20 | 231 | 18 | 0 | 0 | 7788 | 2921 | 54 |

BROOKFIELD—Linn County

GENERAL JOHN J. PERSHING MEMORIAL HOSPITAL, 130 East Lockling Avenue, Zip 64628–0130, Mailing Address: P.O. Box 408, Zip 64628–0408; tel. 660/258–2222 **A**9 10 18 **F**9 12 21 26 27 28 30 33 35 36 42 46 48 50 51 52 58 61 63 66 69 70 81 84 88 94 97 108 **P**6
Primary Contact: Phil Hamilton, R.N., Chief Executive Officer
| 23 | 10 | 25 | 931 | 9 | 53214 | — | 9867 | 3983 | 122 |

BUTLER—Bates County

★ **BATES COUNTY MEMORIAL HOSPITAL**, 615 West Nursery Street, Zip 64730–0370, Mailing Address: P.O. Box 370, Zip 64730–0370; tel. 660/200–7000, (Total facility includes 12 beds in nursing home–type unit) **A**9 10 20 **F**2 6 9 11 12 21 22 33 42 45 46 47 48 51 52 53 55 59 60 62 63 66 69 81 82 84 87 88 93 94 95 96 97
Primary Contact: Gaylon C. Lowery, CHE, Chief Executive Officer
CHR: Melinda Jackson, Director Human Resources
Web address: www.bcmhospital.com
| 13 | 10 | 60 | 2305 | 27 | 43817 | 43 | 24372 | 8435 | 246 |

CAMERON—Clinton County

CAMERON REGIONAL MEDICAL CENTER, 1600 East Evergreen, Zip 64429–1498, Mailing Address: P.O. Box 557, Zip 64429–0557; tel. 816/632–2101 **A**9 10 **F**2 9 12 14 21 23 27 28 29 30 32 33 36 37 44 45 46 47 48 50 51 52 55 57 58 60 61 62 63 64 66 68 69 71 73 76 77 81 88 92 93 94 95 97 108 110 **P**6
Primary Contact: Joseph F. Abrutz, Jr, Administrator
Web address: www.cameronregional.org
| 23 | 10 | 54 | 1339 | 34 | 139568 | — | 23889 | 9902 | 310 |

CAPE GIRARDEAU—Cape Girardeau County

⊞ **SAINT FRANCIS MEDICAL CENTER**, 211 St. Francis Drive, Zip 63703–8399; tel. 573/331–3000 **A**1 2 9 10 19 **F**2 7 9 10 11 12 14 15 17 19 21 22 23 24 26 27 28 29 32 33 34 35 37 38 39 41 42 46 47 48 49 50 51 52 53 55 56 57 58 59 60 61 62 63 64 65 66 67 68 69 81 82 84 85 87 88 93 94 95 96 106 107 108 109 **P**6
Primary Contact: Steven C. Bjelich, President and Chief Executive Officer
CFO: Tony Balsano, Vice President Finance
CIO: Diane Gammon, Director Information Systems
CHR: Teri Kreitzer, Director Human Resources
Web address: www.sfmc.net
| 23 | 10 | 243 | 10021 | 144 | 164373 | 440 | 163498 | 63234 | 1377 |

⊞ **SOUTHEAST MISSOURI HOSPITAL**, 1701 Lacey Street, Zip 63701–5299; tel. 573/334–4822 **A**1 2 9 10 19 **F**2 9 10 11 12 14 15 17 19 21 22 23 24 27 29 33 36 37 38 40 41 45 46 47 48 49 51 52 53 54 55 56 57 58 59 60 61 62 63 64 65 66 67 68 69 71 73 74 75 76 80 81 82 84 86 87 88 93 94 96 98 106 107 108 109 110
Primary Contact: James W. Wente, CPA, CHE, President and Chief Executive Officer
CFO: Jerry L. Sanders, CPA, Assistant Administrator
CMO: Morris H. Seligman, M.D., Director Medical Affairs
CIO: Jay McGuire, Director Information Systems
Web address: www.southeastmissourihospital.com
| 23 | 10 | 213 | 10667 | 132 | 177482 | 1340 | 156541 | 54760 | 1459 |

CARROLLTON—Carroll County

CARROLL COUNTY MEMORIAL HOSPITAL, 1502 North Jefferson Street, Zip 64633–1999; tel. 660/542–1695, (Total facility includes 32 beds in nursing home–type unit) **A**9 10 20 **F**1 2 8 9 12 21 27 33 41 44 46 48 51 52 58 60 68 81 84 88 91 92 94 97 **P**6
Primary Contact: Jerry Dover, Administrator and Chief Executive Officer
| 23 | 10 | 56 | 840 | 35 | 35139 | 0 | 7801 | 3455 | 95 |

MO

Hospital, Address, Telephone, Approval, Facility, and Physician Codes, Health Care System	Classi-fication Codes		Utilization Data					Expense (thousands) of dollars		
	Control	Service	Staffed Beds	Admissions	Census	Outpatient Visits	Births	Total	Payroll	Personnel

★ American Hospital Association (AHA) membership
□ Joint Commission on Accreditation of Healthcare Organizations (JCAHO) accreditation
○ American Osteopathic Association (AOA) accreditation
△ Commission on Accreditation of Rehabilitation Facilities (CARF) accreditation

CARTHAGE—Jasper County

★ **MCCUNE–BROOKS HOSPITAL,** 627 West Centennial Avenue, Zip 64836–0677; tel. 417/358–8121 **A**9 10 **F**2 6 9 12 22 28 29 33 38 39 41 44 46 48 51 53 54 55 58 62 63 66 71 76 81 92 93 94 95 96 97
Primary Contact: Robert Y. Copeland, Jr, FACHE, Chief Executive Officer
CFO: Tony Wright, Chief Financial Officer
CHR: Brenda Kaiser, Director Human Resources
Web address: www.mccune–brooks.org

| | 14 | 10 | 54 | 1732 | 24 | 40563 | 0 | 20173 | 8570 | 272 |

CASSVILLE—Barry County

★ **ST. JOHN'S HOSPITAL – CASSVILLE,** 94 Main Street, Zip 65625–1610; tel. 417/847–6000 **A**9 10 18 **F**26 27 28 **P**6 **S** Sisters of Mercy Health System, Chesterfield, MO
Primary Contact: Gary W. Jordan, President
CFO: Douglas Hoban, Chief Financial Officer
Web address: www.southbarrycountyhospital.com

| | 21 | 10 | 18 | 244 | 2 | 26242 | — | 7025 | 3815 | 97 |

CHESTERFIELD—St. Louis County

⊠ **ST. LUKE'S HOSPITAL,** 232 South Woods Mill Road, Zip 63017–3480; tel. 314/434–1500 **A**1 2 3 5 9 10 **F**2 8 9 10 11 12 14 15 17 19 21 22 23 24 27 28 29 30 32 33 35 37 38 39 41 42 44 46 47 48 49 50 52 53 54 55 57 58 59 60 61 62 63 64 65 66 68 69 70 79 80 81 82 84 85 87 88 89 90 91 92 94 95 96 106 107 108 109 110 **P**6 8
Primary Contact: Gary R. Olson, President and Chief Executive Officer
CFO: Brian Spillers, Chief Financial Officer
Web address: www.stlukes–stl.com

| | 23 | 10 | 513 | 19708 | 362 | 516188 | 2527 | 259884 | 129166 | 2650 |

CHILLICOTHE—Livingston County

⊠ **HEDRICK MEDICAL CENTER,** 100 Central Avenue, Zip 64601–1599; tel. 660/646–1480 **A**1 9 10 18 20 **F**2 9 11 12 21 22 23 27 28 29 31 32 33 36 37 39 46 48 51 52 54 55 58 59 63 64 65 66 68 69 70 81 84 88 92 94 96 97 106 107 108 **S** Saint Luke's Health System, Kansas City, MO
Primary Contact: James K. Johnson, Chief Executive Officer
CFO: Randy Brammer, Director Finance
CIO: Diane Havard, Information Systems Specialist
CHR: Lisa Hecker, Director Human Resources
Web address: www.saintlukeshealthsystem.org

| | 23 | 10 | 30 | 1148 | 15 | 80102 | 163 | 20647 | 9122 | 248 |

CLINTON—Henry County

⊠ **GOLDEN VALLEY MEMORIAL HOSPITAL,** 1600 North Second Street, Zip 64735–1297; tel. 660/885–5511, (Total facility includes 12 beds in nursing home–type unit) **A**1 9 10 20 **F**2 6 9 11 12 22 23 26 27 28 29 33 41 46 48 50 51 53 55 58 59 60 61 62 63 64 69 71 81 82 84 85 86 87 88 92 93 94 95 96 97 106 108 109 110
Primary Contact: Randy S. Wertz, Chief Executive Officer
CFO: Bruce B. Weddell, Chief Financial Officer
Web address: www.gvmh.org

| | 16 | 10 | 106 | 3769 | 49 | 63555 | 302 | 35984 | 17230 | 413 |

COLUMBIA—Boone County

⊠ **BOONE HOSPITAL CENTER,** 1600 East Broadway, Zip 65201–5897; tel. 573/815–8000, (Total facility includes 19 beds in nursing home–type unit) **A**1 2 3 5 9 10 **F**2 6 9 10 11 12 14 15 17 19 21 22 23 26 27 28 29 30 33 37 38 39 41 44 46 47 48 49 50 52 53 55 56 57 58 59 60 61 62 63 64 65 66 68 69 70 71 73 74 75 76 77 78 81 82 84 85 86 87 88 90 92 93 94 95 96 106 108 109 110 **S** BJC HealthCare, Saint Louis, MO
Primary Contact: Michael B. Shirk, President and Senior Executive Officer
COO: Randy Morrow, Vice President and Chief Operating Officer
CFO: Randy Morrow, Vice President and Chief Operating Officer
CMO: Carol Danuser, M.D., Chief Medical Officer
Web address: www.boone.org

| | 23 | 10 | 353 | 16742 | 240 | 141202 | 2137 | 205161 | 65476 | 1592 |

□ △ **COLUMBIA REGIONAL HOSPITAL,** 404 Keene Street, Zip 65201–6698; tel. 573/875–9000 **A**1 3 5 7 9 10 **F**2 9 11 12 15 17 21 22 26 27 28 33 39 40 41 44 49 52 53 55 56 57 58 59 61 62 63 64 65 66 68 69 71 76 81 82 84 88 89 90 93 94 95 107 108 **P**6 **S** University of Missouri Health Care, Columbia, MO
Primary Contact: James C. Poehling, Director
Web address: www.columbiaregional.org

| | 12 | 10 | 237 | 5791 | 82 | 67306 | 856 | 81772 | 26610 | 646 |

ELLIS FISCHEL CANCER CENTER See University of Missouri Hospitals and Clinics

⊠ **HARRY S. TRUMAN MEMORIAL VETERANS HOSPITAL,** 800 Hospital Drive, Zip 65201–5297; tel. 573/814–6000, (Total facility includes 41 beds in nursing home–type unit) **A**1 3 5 8 **F**2 3 4 14 15 17 19 21 22 23 26 28 29 32 33 35 36 37 38 42 44 47 48 50 51 52 55 57 58 60 61 62 63 64 65 66 68 69 70 71 73 74 75 76 77 78 81 82 84 87 88 92 93 94 96 106 107 108 109 110 **P**6 **S** Department of Veterans Affairs, Washington, DC
Primary Contact: Gary L. Campbell, CHE, Director
COO: Marie Weldon, FACHE, Associate Director
CFO: Curtis R. Russell, Chief Financial Officer
CMO: William Patterson, M.D., Chief of Staff
CIO: Rex Toles, Director Information Management Service Line
CHR: Thomas J. Patterson, Manager Human Resources
Web address: www.va.gov/sta/guide/home.asp

| | 45 | 10 | 118 | 3773 | 87 | 243712 | 0 | 118104 | 68162 | 935 |

MO

Many Facility Codes have changed. Please refer to the AHA Guide Code Chart.

© 2005 AHA Guide

Hospital, Address, Telephone, Approval, Facility, and Physician Codes, Health Care System	Classification Codes		Utilization Data					Expense (thousands) of dollars		
	Control	Service	Staffed Beds	Admissions	Census	Outpatient Visits	Births	Total	Payroll	Personnel

Classification Codes legend:
★ American Hospital Association (AHA) membership
□ Joint Commission on Accreditation of Healthcare Organizations (JCAHO) accreditation
○ American Osteopathic Association (AOA) accreditation
△ Commission on Accreditation of Rehabilitation Facilities (CARF) accreditation

Hospital	Control	Service	Staffed Beds	Admissions	Census	Outpatient Visits	Births	Total	Payroll	Personnel
⊠ △ **HOWARD A. RUSK REHABILITATION CENTER**, 315 Business Loop 70 West, Zip 65203–3248; tel. 573/817–2703 **A**1 5 7 10 **F**21 26 45 46 48 58 60 65 66 68 69 **S** HEALTHSOUTH Corporation, Birmingham, AL Primary Contact: Patrick N. Lee, CHE, Administrator CFO: Brian Winn, Controller CMO: Gregory Worsowicz, M.D., Medical Director CHR: Robin Prater, Director of Human Resources Web address: www.healthsouth.com	32	46	60	837	51	18545	0	15742	6708	174
□ **MID MISSOURI MENTAL HEALTH CENTER**, 3 Hospital Drive, Zip 65201–5296; tel. 573/884–1300 **A**1 3 5 10 **F**3 28 47 71 72 73 74 75 76 78 94 Primary Contact: Robert Reitz, Chief Operating Officer Web address: www.modmh.state.mo.us/mid_mo/	12	22	69	1995	65	—	—	16869	7653	260
□ **UNIVERSITY OF MISSOURI HOSPITALS AND CLINICS**, One Hospital Drive, Zip 65212–0001; tel. 573/882–4141, (Includes ELLIS FISCHEL CANCER CENTER, 115 Business Loop 70 West, Zip 65203; tel. 573/882–5460) **A**1 2 3 5 8 9 10 **F**2 6 7 9 11 12 13 14 15 16 17 18 19 20 21 22 23 24 26 27 28 29 30 31 32 33 34 37 38 39 40 44 46 47 48 49 50 52 53 55 56 57 58 59 60 61 62 63 64 65 66 67 69 70 73 74 75 77 79 80 81 84 85 86 87 88 89 90 93 94 95 96 98 101 105 107 108 109 110 **P**1 **S** University of Missouri Health Care, Columbia, MO Primary Contact: Cynthia M. Grueber, Director Web address: www.hsc.missouri.edu/~2000	12	10	260	11129	160	619120	444	284983	102101	2870

CREVE COEUR—St. Louis County
BARNES–JEWISH WEST COUNTY HOSPITAL See Saint Louis

CRYSTAL CITY—Jefferson County

Hospital	Control	Service	Staffed Beds	Admissions	Census	Outpatient Visits	Births	Total	Payroll	Personnel
○ **JEFFERSON MEMORIAL HOSPITAL**, Highway 61 South, Zip 63019, Mailing Address: P.O. Box 350, Zip 63019–0350; tel. 636/933–1000, (Total facility includes 18 beds in nursing home–type unit) **A**9 10 11 12 **F**2 3 4 6 9 10 11 12 15 17 19 21 22 26 27 28 29 33 35 36 37 38 39 40 41 42 45 46 47 48 51 52 55 57 58 59 60 62 63 64 65 66 68 69 70 71 72 73 74 75 76 77 78 81 82 84 86 87 88 92 93 94 95 96 106 108 109 110 Primary Contact: Mark S. Brodeur, Chief Executive Officer Web address: www.jeffersonmemorialhospital.org	23	10	228	9337	111	140720	793	75711	31604	915

DEXTER—Stoddard County

Hospital	Control	Service	Staffed Beds	Admissions	Census	Outpatient Visits	Births	Total	Payroll	Personnel
MISSOURI SOUTHERN HEALTHCARE, 1200 North One Mile Road, Zip 63841–1000; tel. 573/624–5566 **A**9 10 **F**2 9 12 14 21 27 28 32 33 41 44 46 48 51 52 53 55 60 63 64 65 66 68 69 81 82 84 88 92 93 94 96 97 108 **S** Sunlink Healthcare, Atlanta, GA Primary Contact: Jim Crawford, Chief Executive Officer Web address: www.msh–hospital.com	33	10	41	1783	15	77365	0	14224	7593	251

DONIPHAN—Ripley County

Hospital	Control	Service	Staffed Beds	Admissions	Census	Outpatient Visits	Births	Total	Payroll	Personnel
RIPLEY COUNTY MEMORIAL HOSPITAL, 109 Plum Street, Zip 63935–1299; tel. 573/996–2141 **A**9 10 **F**6 9 21 26 27 28 33 42 48 51 63 66 69 70 81 94 Primary Contact: Charles Ray Freeman, Chief Executive Officer	13	10	27	898	11	26808	0	7126	3837	70

EL DORADO SPRINGS—Cedar County

Hospital	Control	Service	Staffed Beds	Admissions	Census	Outpatient Visits	Births	Total	Payroll	Personnel
CEDAR COUNTY MEMORIAL HOSPITAL, 1401 South Park Street, Zip 64744–2037; tel. 417/876–2511 **A**9 10 18 **F**2 9 21 22 24 26 27 28 29 33 39 41 44 46 47 48 51 52 58 59 60 63 65 66 69 81 84 88 94 96 97 98 106 108 109 **P**6 Primary Contact: Jackie Boyles, Administrator Web address: www.ccmh.homestead.com	13	10	34	801	8	35150	100	8178	4118	119

ELLINGTON—Reynolds County

Hospital	Control	Service	Staffed Beds	Admissions	Census	Outpatient Visits	Births	Total	Payroll	Personnel
ADVANCED HEALTHCARE MEDICAL CENTER, (Formerly Reynolds County General Memorial Hospital), Highway 21 South, Zip 63638–7427, Mailing Address: Rural Route 4, Box 4269, Zip 63638–4269; tel. 573/663–2511 **A**9 10 18 **F**2 6 22 26 27 28 29 33 44 45 51 52 60 64 66 69 70 81 88 97 108 **P**4 Primary Contact: Greg Cerda, Chief Executive Officer	33	10	25	918	9	21226	—	18470	7422	132

EXCELSIOR SPRINGS—Clay County

Hospital	Control	Service	Staffed Beds	Admissions	Census	Outpatient Visits	Births	Total	Payroll	Personnel
⊠ **EXCELSIOR SPRINGS MEDICAL CENTER**, 1700 Rainbow Boulevard, Zip 64024–1190; tel. 816/630–6081, (Total facility includes 80 beds in nursing home–type unit) **A**1 9 10 18 **F**8 9 12 21 22 23 26 27 28 29 32 33 36 37 38 44 45 46 47 48 51 52 53 55 58 60 61 62 63 64 65 66 69 81 88 91 92 94 96 97 106 108 Primary Contact: Sally S. Nance, Chief Executive Officer CMO: Carl E. Ledbetter, D.O., President Medical Staff Web address: www.esmc.org	14	10	105	734	72	32358	0	15319	7054	191

FAIRFAX—Atchison County

Hospital	Control	Service	Staffed Beds	Admissions	Census	Outpatient Visits	Births	Total	Payroll	Personnel
★ **COMMUNITY HOSPITAL ASSOCIATION**, 405 East Main, Zip 64446–0107, Mailing Address: P.O. Box 107, Zip 64446–0107; tel. 660/686–2211 **A**9 10 18 **F**9 11 12 33 48 51 52 59 63 64 66 69 81 92 97 **S** Preferred Management Corporation, Shawnee, OK Primary Contact: Myra Evans, Administrator COO: Myra Evans, Administrator CFO: Suzanne Southard, Director Finance CMO: James Humphrey, Chief Medical Officer CIO: Toni Ray, Information Systems Supervisor CHR: Myra Evans, Administrator	23	10	25	742	10	18349	53	7669	3488	81

MO

Hospital, Address, Telephone, Approval, Facility, and Physician Codes, Health Care System	Classification Codes		Utilization Data					Expense (thousands) of dollars		
★ American Hospital Association (AHA) membership □ Joint Commission on Accreditation of Healthcare Organizations (JCAHO) accreditation ○ American Osteopathic Association (AOA) accreditation △ Commission on Accreditation of Rehabilitation Facilities (CARF) accreditation	Control	Service	Staffed Beds	Admissions	Census	Outpatient Visits	Births	Total	Payroll	Personnel

FARMINGTON—St. Francois County

○ **MINERAL AREA REGIONAL MEDICAL CENTER**, 1212 Weber Road, Zip 63640–3325; tel. 573/756–4581, (Total facility includes 10 beds in nursing home–type unit) **A**9 10 11 12 13 19 **F**2 9 11 12 21 22 23 26 27 28 33 35 46 48 51 52 55 58 59 60 61 62 63 64 65 66 69 73 77 81 82 84 85 87 88 92 93 94 95 96 108 **P**1
Primary Contact: Stephen L. Crain, President and Chief Executive Officer
Web address: www.marmc.org

| | 23 | 10 | 109 | 4011 | 46 | 156527 | 442 | 45336 | 22099 | 639 |

⊠ **PARKLAND HEALTH CENTER**, 1101 West Liberty Street, Zip 63640–1921; tel. 573/756–6451 **A**1 9 10 **F**2 9 11 12 21 22 27 28 29 30 32 33 35 37 39 40 41 42 46 48 49 50 52 53 54 55 58 59 60 61 62 63 64 65 66 69 71 76 81 82 84 85 87 88 93 94 95 96 106 108 **P**5 6 7 **S** BJC HealthCare, Saint Louis, MO
Primary Contact: Richard L. Conklin, President
CFO: Thomas P. Karl, Assistant Administrator Finance
CMO: Gary J. Grix, M.D., Chief of Staff
CHR: Sheri S. Graham, Director Human Resources and Administrative Services
Web address: www.parklandhealthcenter.org

| | 23 | 10 | 94 | 3789 | 40 | 68536 | 426 | 39234 | 15291 | 440 |

□ **SOUTHEAST MISSOURI MENTAL HEALTH CENTER**, 1010 West Columbia, Zip 63640–2997; tel. 573/218–6792 **A**1 10 **F**3 22 26 27 28 41 46 65 71 74 75 76
Primary Contact: Karen L. Adams, Chief Executive Officer
Web address: www.dmh.missouri.gov/southeast/

| | 12 | 22 | 160 | 1784 | 133 | 493 | 0 | 23389 | 9126 | 520 |

FORT LEONARD WOOD—Pulaski County

⊠ **GENERAL LEONARD WOOD ARMY COMMUNITY HOSPITAL**, 126 Missouri Avenue, Zip 65473–8952; tel. 573/596–0414 **A**1 **F**2 3 4 6 11 12 21 22 25 26 27 28 29 33 39 46 47 53 55 57 58 59 60 62 63 64 65 66 70 71 72 73 74 75 77 81 84 88 94 106 108 109 **S** Department of the Army, Office of the Surgeon General, Falls Church, VA
Primary Contact: Colonel Sharon DeRuvo, Commander
Web address: www.glwach.leonardwood.amedd.army.mil

| | 42 | 10 | 62 | 2723 | 35 | 361828 | 385 | 59377 | — | — |

FREDERICKTOWN—Madison County

MADISON MEDICAL CENTER, 611 West Main, Zip 63645–1111, Mailing Address: P.O. Box 431, Zip 63645–0431; tel. 573/783–3341, (Total facility includes 102 beds in nursing home–type unit) **A**9 10 18 **F**2 5 6 9 12 26 27 29 33 48 51 52 55 60 62 63 66 69 70 76 81 84 88 92 94 97 108
Primary Contact: Rodney D. Gross, Administrator
Web address: www.madisonmedicalcenter.net

| | 13 | 10 | 119 | 444 | 86 | 53665 | 0 | 12596 | 5894 | 263 |

FULTON—Callaway County

□ **CALLAWAY COMMUNITY HOSPITAL**, 10 South Hospital Drive, Zip 65251–2513; tel. 573/642–3376 **A**1 5 9 10 **F**2 9 11 12 21 27 28 33 46 48 51 52 55 59 62 63 64 65 69 70 81 82 84 88 92 93 97 106 108 **S** Sunlink Healthcare, Atlanta, GA
Primary Contact: John T. Graves, Chief Executive Officer
Web address: www.sunlinkhealth.com/callaway.html

| | 33 | 10 | 31 | 1061 | 10 | 34421 | 122 | 10641 | 3856 | 123 |

□ **FULTON STATE HOSPITAL**, 600 East Fifth Street, Zip 65251–1798; tel. 573/592–4100, (Total facility includes 16 beds in nursing home–type unit) **A**1 5 10 **F**2 3 9 22 32 35 39 44 45 46 48 58 65 66 71 73 74 76 94 96 106 108 **P**6
Primary Contact: Felix T. Vincenz, Ph.D., Chief Executive Officer
Web address: www.modmh.state.mo.us/fulton/history.htm

| | 12 | 22 | 464 | 624 | 452 | — | 0 | 63669 | 37309 | 1163 |

HANNIBAL—Marion County

⊠ **HANNIBAL REGIONAL HOSPITAL**, 6000 Hospital Drive, Zip 63401–6749, Mailing Address: P.O. Box 551, Zip 63401–0551; tel. 573/248–1300 **A**1 2 5 9 10 19 20 **F**2 9 11 12 15 16 17 18 19 20 22 23 26 27 28 29 31 32 33 37 45 46 47 48 49 50 51 52 55 57 58 59 60 61 62 63 64 65 66 68 69 70 71 72 73 74 75 76 77 79 80 81 82 84 86 87 88 93 94 95 96 100 102 103 104 105 106 107 108 109 110 **P**1
Primary Contact: John C. Grossmeier, President and Chief Executive Officer
CFO: Roger J. Dix, Senior Vice President and Chief Financial Officer
CIO: Phyllis Paris, Director
CHR: Penny Nunley, Vice President Human Resources
Web address: www.hrhonline.org

| | 23 | 10 | 105 | 5753 | 69 | 112727 | 621 | 63796 | 28269 | 724 |

HARRISONVILLE—Cass County

⊠ **CASS MEDICAL CENTER**, 1800 East Mechanic Street, Zip 64701–2017; tel. 816/380–3474 **A**1 9 10 18 **F**2 9 12 21 22 23 26 27 28 29 32 33 37 42 44 46 48 51 52 53 55 57 58 60 61 62 63 64 65 66 70 71 81 82 88 93 94 96 97 106 108 110 **P**6
Primary Contact: John Christopher Lang, Chief Executive Officer
CFO: Steve Klein, Assistant Administrator and Chief Financial Officer
CIO: Cynthia Miltenberger, Director Organizational Effectiveness
CHR: Carla Wallen, Manager Human Resources
Web address: www.cassmedicalcenter.com

| | 13 | 10 | 38 | 1762 | 21 | 88349 | 0 | 25617 | 10257 | 261 |

HAYTI—Pemiscot County

PEMISCOT MEMORIAL HEALTH SYSTEM, Highway 61 and Reed, Zip 63851–1245, Mailing Address: P.O. Box 489, Zip 63851–0489; tel. 573/359–1372, (Total facility includes 120 beds in nursing home–type unit) **A**9 10 **F**6 9 11 12 14 21 22 26 27 28 32 33 39 45 46 47 48 52 53 55 58 59 62 63 68 69 70 77 81 88 92 94 97 107 108 109 110 **P**6
Primary Contact: Kerry L. Noble, Administrator

| | 13 | 10 | 169 | 2899 | 89 | 57323 | 132 | 26859 | 12428 | 212 |

Many Facility Codes have changed. Please refer to the AHA Guide Code Chart.

MO

Hospital, Address, Telephone, Approval, Facility, and Physician Codes, Health Care System	Classi-fication Codes		Utilization Data					Expense (thousands) of dollars		
★ American Hospital Association (AHA) membership □ Joint Commission on Accreditation of Healthcare Organizations (JCAHO) accreditation ○ American Osteopathic Association (AOA) accreditation △ Commission on Accreditation of Rehabilitation Facilities (CARF) accreditation	Control	Service	Staffed Beds	Admissions	Census	Outpatient Visits	Births	Total	Payroll	Personnel

HERMANN—Gasconade County

★ **HERMANN AREA DISTRICT HOSPITAL**, Mailing Address: P.O. Box 470, Zip 65041–0470; tel. 573/486–2191 **A**9 10 18 20 **F**9 12 21 22 27 28 29 33 46 48 51 52 54 58 60 61 63 66 69 70 76 77 81 88 92 94 97 108 **P**6
Primary Contact: Dan McKinney, Administrator
CMO: Michael Mahoney, D.O., Chief of Staff
CIO: Cindy Corneli, Accountant
CHR: Carol Schaefer, Director Human Resources
Web address: www.hadh.org

| | 16 | 10 | 25 | 430 | 17 | 33175 | — | 9850 | 4515 | 145 |

HOUSTON—Texas County

TEXAS COUNTY MEMORIAL HOSPITAL, 1333 South Sam Houston Boulevard, Zip 65483–2046; tel. 417/967–3311 **A**5 9 10 20 **F**2 6 11 12 21 28 33 36 41 46 48 51 52 55 58 59 60 63 64 65 66 69 70 81 88 94 97 108 110 **P**6
Primary Contact: Wesley E. Murray, Chief Executive Officer
Web address: www.tcmh.org

| | 13 | 10 | 66 | 2147 | 23 | 136573 | 269 | 21454 | 11176 | 283 |

INDEPENDENCE—Jackson County

☒ **INDEPENDENCE REGIONAL HEALTH CENTER**, 1509 West Truman Road, Zip 64050–3498; tel. 816/836–8100, (Total facility includes 41 beds in nursing home–type unit) **A**1 2 9 10 12 **F**2 9 12 15 17 19 21 22 23 26 27 28 29 31 32 33 34 35 37 38 41 42 44 46 47 48 50 52 53 54 55 57 58 60 61 62 63 64 65 66 68 69 71 75 76 81 82 84 85 87 88 92 93 94 96 108 109 110 **P**6 **S** HCA, Nashville, TN
Primary Contact: Dan L. Jones, Jr, Chief Executive Officer
COO: Natalie Mussi, Cheif Operating Officer
Web address: www.independenceregionalhealthcenter.com

| | 33 | 10 | 213 | 8741 | 123 | 67318 | 0 | 93113 | 34840 | 567 |

☒ ○ **MEDICAL CENTER OF INDEPENDENCE**, 17203 East 23rd Street South, Zip 64057–1899; tel. 816/478–5000 **A**1 9 10 11 12 13 **F**2 9 11 12 14 15 17 21 22 23 26 27 28 29 33 35 37 39 44 46 47 48 50 52 54 55 58 59 60 61 62 63 64 65 66 69 73 75 81 82 84 85 88 92 94 95 96 108 109 110 **P**5 6 **S** HCA, Nashville, TN
Primary Contact: Dan L. Jones, Jr, Chief Executive Officer
Web address: www.medicalcenterofindependence.com

| | 33 | 10 | 123 | 6081 | 62 | 72994 | 1294 | 65919 | 24916 | 376 |

JEFFERSON CITY—Cole County

□ ○ △ **CAPITAL REGION MEDICAL CENTER**, 1125 Madison Street, Zip 65101–5227, Mailing Address: P.O. Box 1128, Zip 65102–1128; tel. 573/632–5000, (Total facility includes 20 beds in nursing home–type unit) **A**1 5 7 9 10 11 12 13 19 **F**2 4 6 9 11 12 15 17 19 21 22 23 24 27 29 30 31 33 41 42 44 46 47 48 50 51 52 54 55 57 58 59 60 61 62 63 64 66 68 69 72 73 75 77 79 81 82 85 87 88 92 93 94 95 96 106 107 108 109 **P**6 **S** University of Missouri Health Care, Columbia, MO
Primary Contact: Edward F. Farnsworth, FACHE, President
Web address: www.crmc.org

| | 23 | 10 | 134 | 8229 | 102 | 294065 | 644 | 105420 | 44246 | 1097 |

☒ **ST. MARYS HEALTH CENTER**, 100 St. Marys Medical Plaza, Zip 65101–1601; tel. 573/761–7000 **A**1 5 9 10 19 **F**2 9 11 12 15 17 19 21 22 23 26 27 28 29 30 31 32 33 37 39 46 47 48 50 52 55 57 58 59 60 61 62 63 64 65 66 68 69 70 71 73 74 75 76 77 78 80 81 82 84 85 87 88 92 93 94 96 106 108 109 110 **P**6 **S** SSM Health Care, Saint Louis, MO
Primary Contact: Elizabeth Aderholdt, President
COO: Marshall E. Smith, Executive Vice President and Chief Operating Officer
CFO: Tom Luebbering, Vice President Finance
CMO: John Lucio, D.O., President of Medical Staff
CHR: Ann Bollone, Vice President Organizational Effectiveness and Human Resources
Web address: www.stmarys–jeffcity.com

| | 23 | 10 | 167 | 10476 | 116 | 229764 | 956 | 111181 | 42739 | 1037 |

JOPLIN—Newton County

★ ○ **FREEMAN HEALTH SYSTEM**, 1102 West 32nd Street, Zip 64804–3599; tel. 417/347–1111, (Includes FREEMAN HOSPITAL EAST, 932 East 34th Street, Zip 64804–3999; FREEMAN HOSPITAL WEST, Mailing Address: 1102 West 32nd Street, Zip 64804–3599), (Total facility includes 32 beds in nursing home–type unit) **A**2 9 10 11 12 13 **F**2 9 11 12 14 15 17 19 21 22 23 24 26 27 28 29 30 32 33 34 35 37 38 39 42 44 46 47 48 49 50 51 52 53 55 56 57 58 59 60 61 62 63 64 65 66 68 69 70 71 73 75 76 81 82 84 88 90 92 93 94 95 96 106 107 108 109 110 **P**1 6 **S** Freeman Health System, Joplin, MO
Primary Contact: Gary D. Duncan, President and Chief Executive Officer
CFO: Steve W. Graddy, Chief Financial Officer
CMO: Charles H. Bentlage, M.D., Chief Medical Officer
CIO: Sue Annesser, Director Information Technology
CHR: Deborah Chiodo, Director Human Resources
Web address: www.freemanhealth.com

| | 23 | 10 | 320 | 17517 | 235 | 758001 | 2443 | 267974 | 133223 | 2645 |

MO

Hospital, Address, Telephone, Approval, Facility, and Physician Codes, Health Care System	Classi-fication Codes		Utilization Data					Expense (thousands) of dollars		
★ American Hospital Association (AHA) membership □ Joint Commission on Accreditation of Healthcare Organizations (JCAHO) accreditation ○ American Osteopathic Association (AOA) accreditation △ Commission on Accreditation of Rehabilitation Facilities (CARF) accreditation	Control	Service	Staffed Beds	Admissions	Census	Outpatient Visits	Births	Total	Payroll	Personnel
⊠ △ **ST. JOHN'S REGIONAL MEDICAL CENTER**, 2727 McClelland Boulevard, Zip 64804–1694; tel. 417/781–2727, (Total facility includes 10 beds in nursing home–type unit) **A**1 2 7 9 10 **F**2 4 6 9 10 11 12 14 15 17 19 21 22 23 26 27 28 29 31 32 33 34 35 36 37 38 39 40 42 46 47 48 49 50 51 52 53 54 55 57 58 59 60 61 62 63 64 65 66 68 69 70 71 72 73 74 75 76 77 78 79 80 81 82 84 86 88 92 93 94 95 96 98 106 107 108 109 110 **P**1 6 **S** Catholic Health Initiatives, Denver, CO Primary Contact: Gary L. Rowe, President and Chief Executive Officer COO: Debra Linnes, Chief Operating Officer CFO: Tony Noronha, Chief Financial Officer CMO: Dean Backstrom, M.D., Vice President Medical Affairs CIO: Jack L. Davis, Vice President Information Systems CHR: Gary Little, Vice President Human Resources Web address: www.stj.com	23	10	367	15460	203	229606	931	173063	70018	1816
KANSAS CITY—Jackson County										
⊠ **BAPTIST–LUTHERAN MEDICAL CENTER**, 6601 Rockhill Road, Zip 64131–1197; tel. 816/276–7000, (Total facility includes 23 beds in nursing home–type unit) **A**1 2 3 5 9 10 **F**2 3 9 11 12 15 17 19 21 22 23 26 27 28 29 30 32 33 37 38 39 40 41 42 44 45 50 52 55 57 58 59 60 61 62 63 65 66 68 69 70 71 73 74 75 77 78 81 82 84 86 87 88 92 93 94 95 96 105 108 109 110 **P**5 **S** HCA, Nashville, TN Primary Contact: Darrell W. Moore, President and Chief Executive Officer COO: Brian Lidiak, Chief Operating Officer CFO: James H. Brown, Chief Financial Officer CHR: Dennis Johnson, Director Human Resources Web address: www.b–lmc.com	23	10	265	6859	107	136512	636	121713	45249	745
⊠ **CHILDREN'S MERCY HOSPITAL**, 2401 Gillham Road, Zip 64108–4698; tel. 816/234–3000 **A**1 2 3 5 8 9 10 **F**2 7 9 13 14 15 16 17 18 19 20 21 22 23 24 27 28 29 30 32 33 34 35 37 38 39 42 46 47 48 49 50 51 52 53 56 57 58 60 61 62 63 64 65 66 67 68 69 70 71 72 73 77 81 82 84 85 87 88 90 94 95 96 98 99 101 102 107 108 110 **P**6 8 Primary Contact: Randall L. O'Donnell, Ph.D., President and Chief Executive Officer CFO: Dwight Hyde, Executive Vice President and Chief Financial Officer CMO: V Fred Burry, M.D., Executive Medical Director CIO: Jean Ann Breedlove, Chief Information Officer CHR: Dan Wright, Vice President Human Resources Web address: www.childrens–mercy.org	23	50	241	11242	174	288527	0	323445	165712	3486
□ **CRITTENTON CHILDREN'S CENTER**, (Formerly Crittenton), 10918 Elm Avenue, Zip 64134–4199; tel. 816/765–6600 **A**1 10 **F**4 21 22 26 27 28 29 31 47 58 60 65 66 71 72 73 74 75 77 92 94 96 108 **P**6 **S** Saint Luke's Health System, Kansas City, MO Primary Contact: Stephen W. Churchill, M.D., Chief Executive Officer and Medical Director Web address: www.saintlukeshealthsystem.org/app/hpcrittenton.asp	23	52	54	1436	29	19933	0	17266	10943	97
□ **KINDRED HOSPITAL KANSAS CITY**, 8701 Troost Avenue, Zip 64131–2767; tel. 816/995–2000 **A**1 10 **F**2 21 37 47 49 52 55 58 60 61 62 63 65 66 68 81 94 96 110 **S** Kindred Healthcare, Louisville, KY Primary Contact: Mark J. Stepanik, Chief Executive Officer Web address: www.kindredhospitalkc.com	33	80	94	608	66	755	0	24218	8806	205
⊠ **NORTH KANSAS CITY HOSPITAL**, 2800 Clay Edwards Drive, Zip 64116; tel. 816/691–2000, (Total facility includes 24 beds in nursing home–type unit) **A**1 2 9 10 **F**2 9 11 12 14 15 17 19 21 22 23 26 27 28 29 31 32 33 36 37 38 39 41 46 47 48 51 52 54 55 57 58 59 60 61 62 63 64 66 68 69 79 81 82 84 87 88 92 93 94 96 106 108 **P**6 Primary Contact: David R. Carpenter, FACHE, President and Chief Executive Officer COO: Nettie L. Agnew, R.N., Senior Vice President and Chief Operating Officer CFO: Jim McNey, Vice President Finance and Chief Financial Officer CIO: Art Fisk, Chief Information Officer CHR: Beverly Johnson, Vice President Human Resources Web address: www.nkch.org	14	10	351	22430	313	180053	2280	254473	102473	2195
⊠ **RESEARCH MEDICAL CENTER**, 2316 East Meyer Boulevard, Zip 64132–1199; tel. 816/276–4000, (Total facility includes 35 beds in nursing home–type unit) **A**1 2 3 5 9 10 **F**2 9 11 12 15 17 19 21 22 23 26 27 28 29 31 32 33 34 37 38 39 43 46 47 48 49 50 52 53 55 56 57 58 59 61 62 63 64 65 66 68 69 70 73 79 80 81 82 84 85 86 87 88 89 90 92 93 94 96 101 105 106 108 109 110 **P**5 6 **S** HCA, Nashville, TN Primary Contact: Niels P. Vernegaard, Chief Executive Officer COO: Ronald Lavater, Chief Operating Officer CFO: Susan Shreeve, Chief Financial Officer Web address: www.researchmedicalcenter.com	33	10	446	14245	240	144436	1537	255175	86690	1546
⊠ **RESEARCH PSYCHIATRIC CENTER**, 2323 East 63rd Street, Zip 64130–3495; tel. 816/444–8161 **A**1 10 **F**4 21 26 27 28 29 66 71 72 73 74 75 76 77 78 92 94 **S** HCA, Nashville, TN Primary Contact: Todd Krass, President and Chief Executive Officer CFO: James H. Brown, Chief Financial Officer Web address: www.researchpsychiatriccenter.com	23	22	100	2982	56	8838	0	15775	7526	134

MO

Many Facility Codes have changed. Please refer to the AHA Guide Code Chart. © 2005 AHA Guide

Hospital, Address, Telephone, Approval, Facility, and Physician Codes, Health Care System	Classi-fication Codes		Utilization Data					Expense (thousands) of dollars		
★ American Hospital Association (AHA) membership ☐ Joint Commission on Accreditation of Healthcare Organizations (JCAHO) accreditation ◯ American Osteopathic Association (AOA) accreditation △ Commission on Accreditation of Rehabilitation Facilities (CARF) accreditation	Control	Service	Staffed Beds	Admissions	Census	Outpatient Visits	Births	Total	Payroll	Personnel

Hospital	Control	Service	Staffed Beds	Admissions	Census	Outpatient Visits	Births	Total	Payroll	Personnel
⊠ **SAINT JOSEPH MEDICAL CENTER**, (Formerly Saint Joseph Health Center), 1000 Carondelet Drive, Zip 64114–4673; tel. 816/942–4400 **A**1 2 5 9 10 **F**2 9 11 12 15 17 19 21 22 23 26 28 29 30 33 37 38 39 44 46 47 48 50 52 53 55 56 57 58 59 60 61 62 63 64 65 66 68 81 82 84 85 87 88 92 93 94 96 106 108 109 **S** Ascension Health, Saint Louis, MO Primary Contact: Michele Schaefer, Chief Executive Officer CFO: Gary Clifton, Executive Vice President, Finance CMO: Steve Sanders, D.O., Vice President Medical Affairs CIO: Stewart Grant, Vice President and Chief Information Officer CHR: Dawn Bryant, Vice President Organizational Development Web address: www.carondelethealth.org	23	10	272	12329	167	130209	1281	147064	49781	1036
⊠ **SAINT LUKE'S HOSPITAL OF KANSAS CITY**, 4401 Wornall Road, Zip 64111–3238; tel. 816/932–2000 **A**1 2 3 5 8 9 10 **F**2 7 9 10 11 12 14 15 17 19 20 21 22 23 26 27 28 29 30 31 32 33 34 35 36 37 39 41 42 44 46 47 48 49 50 51 52 53 55 56 57 58 59 60 61 62 63 64 65 66 68 69 70 73 74 75 81 86 87 88 90 92 93 94 95 96 100 101 106 108 109 110 **S** Saint Luke's Health System, Kansas City, MO Primary Contact: G. Richard Hastings, Chief Executive Officer COO: Mark McPhee, M.D., Chief Operating Officer CFO: Jama Johnson, Chief Financial Officer CIO: John Wade, Chief Information Officer Web address: www.saintlukeshealthsystem.org/app/hpslh.asp	23	10	482	17909	269	205979	2732	334614	128772	2692
☐ **SAINT LUKE'S NORTHLAND HOSPITAL**, 5830 N.W. Barry Road, Zip 64154–2778; tel. 816/891–6000 **A**1 9 **F**2 9 11 12 21 22 23 24 26 27 28 29 30 31 33 35 37 38 39 44 45 46 47 48 49 55 56 59 63 64 65 69 81 82 84 88 90 92 93 94 95 96 98 106 107 108 110 **S** Saint Luke's Health System, Kansas City, MO Primary Contact: N. Gary Wages, President and Chief Executive Officer Web address: www.saint–lukes.org	23	10	79	3711	37	68213	875	53153	21829	440
SELECT SPECIALTY HOSPITAL – WESTERN MISSOURI, 2316 East Meyer Boulevard, 3–West, Zip 64132; tel. 816/276–9444 **A**10 **F**21 60 94 110 **P**8 **S** Select Medical Corporation, Mechanicsburg, PA Primary Contact: Jerry Janssen, Chief Executive Officer Web address: www.selectmedicalcorp.com	33	80	15	34	2	—	—	2309	962	—
THE CANCER INSTITUTE, 4401 Wornall Road, 5th Floor, Zip 64111; tel. 816/932–2823 **A**10 **F**2 12 23 27 28 29 46 48 52 61 64 79 80 86 88 92 94 96 99 108 **P**6 Primary Contact: Jeffrey Wieman, M.D., Chief Executive Officer Web address: www.saint–lukes.org	23	41	37	836	15	44421	—	35963	10511	159
⊠ **TRUMAN MEDICAL CENTER–HOSPITAL HILL**, 2301 Holmes Street, Zip 64108–2677; tel. 816/404–1000 **A**1 2 3 5 8 9 10 **F**2 9 10 11 12 14 15 21 22 23 26 27 28 29 31 32 33 34 35 37 39 44 45 46 47 48 50 51 52 53 55 56 57 58 59 60 61 62 63 65 66 69 70 81 82 84 87 88 89 90 92 93 94 95 96 98 106 108 109 110 **P**5 6 **S** Truman Medical Centers, Kansas City, MO Primary Contact: John W. Bluford, Chief Executive Officer COO: Catherine D. Disch, Chief Operating Officer CFO: Allen Johnson, Chief Financial Officer CMO: Mark Steele, M.D., Chief Medical Officer CIO: William McQuiston, Chief Information Officer CHR: Jim Jenkins, Director Human Resources Web address: www.trumanmed.org	23	10	206	12328	153	380225	2242	250317	116025	1858
★ △ **TRUMAN MEDICAL CENTER–LAKEWOOD**, 7900 Lee's Summit Road, Zip 64139–1246; tel. 816/404–7000, (Total facility includes 212 beds in nursing home–type unit) **A**3 5 7 9 10 **F**2 3 4 5 9 10 11 12 21 22 24 26 27 28 29 30 31 32 33 35 39 42 44 45 46 47 48 52 53 55 57 58 59 60 62 63 64 65 66 68 69 70 71 72 73 74 75 76 77 81 88 92 94 95 96 106 108 109 **P**5 6 **S** Truman Medical Centers, Kansas City, MO Primary Contact: Robin M. Schluter, Chief Operating Officer COO: Robin M. Schluter, Chief Operating Officer CFO: Daniel J. Williams, Chief Financial Officer CMO: Mark Steele, M.D., Chief Medical Officer CIO: William McQuiston, Chief Information Officer CHR: Jim Jenkins, Director Human Resources Web address: www.trumanmed.org	23	10	295	5980	293	394218	895	83439	38675	776
☐ **TWO RIVERS PSYCHIATRIC HOSPITAL**, 5121 Raytown Road, Zip 64133–2141; tel. 816/356–5688 **A**1 10 **F**3 4 21 22 26 27 28 29 31 47 58 65 66 71 72 74 75 76 77 78 94 96 98 **P**5 **S** Universal Health Services, Inc., King of Prussia, PA Primary Contact: Linda Berridge, Chief Executive Officer Web address: www.tworivershospital.com	33	22	76	2867	58	6652	0	12264	6060	159
⊠ **VETERANS AFFAIRS MEDICAL CENTER**, 4801 Linwood Boulevard, Zip 64128–2295; tel. 816/861–4700 **A**1 2 3 5 8 9 **F**1 3 4 27 55 62 63 71 73 74 75 76 77 92 110 **S** Department of Veterans Affairs, Washington, DC Primary Contact: Kent D. Hill, Director CFO: Charles Henning, Program Director Business Web address: www.va.gov/sta/guide/home.asp	45	10	155	5661	126	400204	0	180279	73726	698

MO

Hospital, Address, Telephone, Approval, Facility, and Physician Codes, Health Care System	Classi-fication Codes		Utilization Data					Expense (thousands) of dollars		
★ American Hospital Association (AHA) membership □ Joint Commission on Accreditation of Healthcare Organizations (JCAHO) accreditation ○ American Osteopathic Association (AOA) accreditation △ Commission on Accreditation of Rehabilitation Facilities (CARF) accreditation	Control	Service	Staffed Beds	Admissions	Census	Outpatient Visits	Births	Total	Payroll	Personnel
□ **WESTERN MISSOURI MENTAL HEALTH CENTER**, 1000 East 24th Street, Zip 64108–2776; tel. 816/512–7000 **A**1 3 5 10 **F**3 4 21 22 27 29 30 31 33 41 65 66 71 72 73 74 75 92 94 Primary Contact: Gloria Joseph, Superintendent Web address: www.dmhonline.dmh.state.mo.us	12	22	180	2520	140	8504	—	29880	18713	508
KENNETT—Dunklin County □ **TWIN RIVERS REGIONAL MEDICAL CENTER**, 1301 First Street, Zip 63857–2508, Mailing Address: P.O. Box 728, Zip 63857–0728; tel. 573/888–4522 **A**1 9 10 **F**2 6 11 12 14 21 22 23 26 27 28 29 33 37 39 40 44 46 48 49 52 53 55 59 60 61 62 63 64 68 71 75 88 94 106 108 109 **S** Health Management Associates, Naples, FL Primary Contact: John W. McClellan, Chief Executive Officer Web address: www.twinriversmedctr.com	33	10	116	4471	40	54296	—	27495	11377	343
KIRKSVILLE—Adair County ○ **NORTHEAST REGIONAL MEDICAL CENTER**, 315 South Osteopathy, Zip 63501–8599, Mailing Address: P.O. Box C8502, Zip 63501–8599; tel. 660/785–1000 **A**9 10 11 12 13 19 20 **F**2 11 12 21 22 27 28 29 33 34 37 40 41 46 47 48 49 51 52 53 55 58 59 60 63 64 65 66 68 69 81 82 84 87 88 93 94 96 97 106 108 109 110 **S** Community Health Systems, Inc., Brentwood, TN Primary Contact: Philip H. Walkley, Jr, Chief Executive Officer Web address: www.nermc.com	33	10	109	4622	50	81789	504	52134	18412	492
LAKE SAINT LOUIS—St. Charles County ⊞ **SSM ST. JOSEPH HOSPITAL WEST**, 100 Medical Plaza, Zip 63367–1395; tel. 636/625–5200 **A**1 9 10 **F**2 9 11 12 14 21 22 23 26 27 28 29 30 31 32 33 34 35 37 39 41 42 44 46 47 48 50 52 55 57 58 59 61 62 63 64 65 66 75 81 82 85 87 88 90 92 94 106 107 108 109 110 **P**6 8 **S** SSM Health Care, Saint Louis, MO Primary Contact: Paul Convery, M.D., Interim President and Chief Executive Officer COO: Pat Komoroski, MSN, R.N., Executive Vice President CFO: Carole Campbell, Director Finance CMO: James Freeman, M.D., Vice President Medical Affairs CIO: Marge Feilner, Manager Information Systems CHR: John Sarantakis, Director Human Resources Web address: www.ssmstjoseph.com	23	10	83	5544	48	92167	944	54738	26553	355
LAMAR—Barton County ★ **BARTON COUNTY MEMORIAL HOSPITAL**, 106 Gulf Street, Zip 64759–1077; tel. 417/682–6081 **A**9 10 20 **F**2 9 12 14 23 26 27 28 32 33 37 44 46 48 52 53 55 58 60 63 64 66 68 69 81 82 84 85 88 92 93 94 95 96 97 110 Primary Contact: Rudy C. Snedigar, Administrator and Chief Executive Officer COO: Virginia Rutledge, Assistant Administrator CFO: Wendy Duvall, Accountant CIO: Brad Butler, Network Administrator CHR: Sheila Boice, Director Human Resources Web address: www.bcmh.net	13	10	40	1226	15	48600	15	11293	4340	142
LEBANON—Laclede County ⊞ **ST. JOHN'S HOSPITAL – LEBANON**, 100 Hospital Drive, Zip 65536–9210; tel. 417/533–6100 **A**1 9 10 20 **F**2 3 4 9 11 12 21 22 27 29 30 33 37 39 41 46 48 52 53 55 58 59 60 62 63 64 65 66 68 69 81 84 88 93 94 95 96 97 106 108 110 **P**6 **S** Sisters of Mercy Health System, Chesterfield, MO Primary Contact: Timothy J. Johnsen, President COO: Jonathan Wade, Vice President CFO: Susan Mott, Vice President Finance CHR: Gary Moor, Director Human Resources Web address: www.stjohnslebanon.com	21	10	48	2619	26	47104	438	31613	15094	393
LEES SUMMIT—Jackson County ⊞ **LEE'S SUMMIT HOSPITAL**, 530 North Murray Road, Zip 64081–1497; tel. 816/969–6000 **A**1 9 10 **F**2 12 21 22 26 27 28 33 35 46 48 52 53 55 57 58 60 61 62 63 66 69 81 82 84 88 92 93 94 95 96 106 108 **P**5 **S** HCA, Nashville, TN Primary Contact: Carolyn W. Caldwell, Chief Executive Officer COO: Scott Montgomery, Vice President Operations CFO: Matthew Leary, Chief Financial Officer Web address: www.leessummithospital.com	33	10	83	4393	52	76775	0	49819	16590	284
LEXINGTON—Lafayette County ⊞ **LAFAYETTE REGIONAL HEALTH CENTER**, 1500 State Street, Zip 64067–1199; tel. 660/259–2203 **A**1 9 10 18 **F**9 12 21 23 27 28 33 48 52 55 58 60 62 63 64 66 69 81 84 86 88 94 97 **P**6 **S** HCA, Nashville, TN Primary Contact: Bret Kolman, CPA, Chief Executive Officer CHR: Lee Tagai, Director Human Resources Web address: www.lafayetteregionalhealthcenter.com	33	10	25	1256	13	75125	—	22071	8858	179
LIBERTY—Clay County ⊞ **LIBERTY HOSPITAL**, 2525 Glenn Hendren Drive, Zip 64068–9600, Mailing Address: P.O. Box 1002, Zip 64069–1002; tel. 816/781–7200, (Total facility includes 12 beds in nursing home–type unit) **A**1 2 9 10 **F**2 7 9 11 12 15 22 23 26 27 29 33 34 35 36 37 38 44 45 46 47 48 49 51 52 53 54 55 56 57 58 59 60 61 62 63 64 65 69 81 82 84 86 88 92 93 94 96 108 110 Primary Contact: Joseph W. Crossett, Administrator CHR: Patti Downey, Assistant Administrator Web address: www.Libertyhospital.org	16	10	229	12070	150	115243	784	111341	49011	984

Many Facility Codes have changed. Please refer to the AHA Guide Code Chart. © 2005 AHA Guide

Hospital, Address, Telephone, Approval, Facility, and Physician Codes, Health Care System	Classi-fication Codes		Utilization Data					Expense (thousands) of dollars		
★ American Hospital Association (AHA) membership □ Joint Commission on Accreditation of Healthcare Organizations (JCAHO) accreditation ○ American Osteopathic Association (AOA) accreditation △ Commission on Accreditation of Rehabilitation Facilities (CARF) accreditation	Control	Service	Staffed Beds	Admissions	Census	Outpatient Visits	Births	Total	Payroll	Personnel
LOUISIANA—Pike County ✠ **PIKE COUNTY MEMORIAL HOSPITAL**, 2305 West Georgia Street, Zip 63353–2559; tel. 573/754–5531 **A**1 9 10 20 **F**2 6 9 12 21 22 26 27 28 29 33 39 42 45 46 48 52 58 62 63 64 69 81 94 97 Primary Contact: Lorraine L. Harness, Administrator CFO: Tracie Matson, Chief Financial Officer CIO: Rich Yonker, Director Information Systems CHR: Layne Ebers, Director Human Resources	13	10	24	842	7	37723	—	8564	5002	137
MACON—Macon County ★ **SAMARITAN MEMORIAL HOSPITAL**, 1205 North Missouri Street, Zip 63552–2099; tel. 660/385–8700 **A**9 10 18 **F**2 6 9 11 21 22 23 26 27 28 29 30 31 33 36 37 38 39 41 46 47 48 49 50 51 52 53 57 58 60 61 62 63 64 65 66 69 70 81 84 88 92 94 95 96 97 108 109 **P**3 5 Primary Contact: Bernard A. Orman, Jr, Administrator CFO: Susan Spencer, Chief Financial Officer Web address: www.samaritanhospital.net	13	10	20	715	12	59125	—	14004	5565	173
MARSHALL—Saline County ★ **FITZGIBBON HOSPITAL**, 2305 South 65 Highway, Zip 65340–0250, Mailing Address: P.O. Box 250, Zip 65340–0250; tel. 660/886–7431 **A**9 10 20 **F**9 11 12 21 25 26 28 29 33 36 37 41 45 46 47 48 51 52 53 55 58 59 60 62 63 66 69 71 76 81 84 85 87 88 92 93 94 95 96 97 108 109 Primary Contact: Ronald A. Ott, Chief Executive Officer CFO: Nancy Harris, Chief Financial Officer CMO: Roy Elfrink, M.D., Chief of Staff CHR: Marilyn Ehlert, Director Human Resources Web address: www.fitzgibbon.org	23	10	52	2584	31	99217	332	25884	12088	429
MARYLAND HEIGHTS—St. Louis County ★ **RANKEN JORDAN**, (Pediatric Specialty Hospital), 11365 Dorsett Road, Zip 63043–3411; tel. 314/872–6400 **A**10 **F**2 13 21 29 35 39 52 65 66 68 69 92 94 108 110 **P**6 Primary Contact: Laureen K. Tanner, R.N., MSN, Chief Executive Officer COO: Laura Sease, R.N., Vice President and Chief Operating Officer CFO: Jean Bardwell, Vice President and Chief Financial Officer CMO: Nicholas Holekamp, M.D., Medical Director CIO: Jean Bardwell, Vice President and Chief Financial Officer Web address: www.rankenjordan.org	23	59	28	179	15	750	—	6798	3524	91
MARYVILLE—Nodaway County ✠ **ST. FRANCIS HOSPITAL AND HEALTH SERVICES**, 2016 South Main Street, Zip 64468–2693; tel. 660/562–2600 **A**1 9 10 20 **F**2 9 11 12 21 22 26 27 28 31 46 48 52 58 59 62 63 69 71 73 74 75 76 77 78 81 84 88 94 95 97 106 108 **P**6 **S** SSM Health Care, Saint Louis, MO Primary Contact: Michael Baumgartner, President COO: Cathy New, Vice President Clinical Services CFO: Jocelyn Skidmore, Finance Director CMO: James Bradley, M.D., Medical Staff President CIO: Dave Lewis, Information Services Director CHR: Martha Archer, Director Human Resources Web address: www.stfrancismaryville.com	21	10	55	2088	22	57630	319	37530	17637	408
MEMPHIS—Scotland County ★ **SCOTLAND COUNTY MEMORIAL HOSPITAL**, Sigler Avenue, Zip 63555–9767, Mailing Address: Rural Route 1, Box 53, Zip 63555–9767; tel. 660/465–8511 **A**9 10 18 **F**6 7 9 11 12 21 22 24 26 27 28 29 33 37 42 44 46 47 48 52 55 58 59 60 63 64 65 66 68 69 70 81 84 88 92 94 95 96 97 106 108 109 110 **P**6 Primary Contact: Marcia R. Dial, Chief Executive Officer CFO: Sheryl Templeton, Chief Financial Officer CIO: Angela Schmitter, Director Health Information Management Web address: www.scotlandcountyhospital.com	16	10	25	670	6	79394	66	8520	3941	121
MEXICO—Audrain County □ **AUDRAIN MEDICAL CENTER**, 620 East Monroe Street, Zip 65265–2963; tel. 573/582–5000 **A**1 2 5 9 10 19 20 **F**2 6 9 11 12 15 17 21 22 23 26 27 28 33 37 38 40 41 42 46 47 48 52 55 58 59 61 62 63 64 65 66 69 70 71 75 76 81 82 84 88 93 94 95 96 108 109 110 **P**6 Primary Contact: David A. Neuendorf, President and Chief Executive Officer Web address: www.audrainmedicalcenter.com	23	10	107	4163	42	160559	332	52499	22335	579
MILAN—Sullivan County ★ **SULLIVAN COUNTY MEMORIAL HOSPITAL**, 630 West Third Street, Zip 63556–1098; tel. 660/265–4212, (Total facility includes 14 beds in nursing home–type unit) **A**9 10 18 **F**21 24 27 28 29 33 41 46 47 48 52 58 60 63 65 66 70 81 84 88 92 110 **P**6 Primary Contact: Martha Gragg, R.N., MSN, Chief Executive Officer CFO: Amy Michael, Chief Financial Officer CMO: Tom Williams, M.D., Chief of Staff CIO: Kimberly Ray, Director Risk Management and Health Information CHR: Billie Ryals, Director Human Resources	13	10	39	373	24	16571	—	4607	2255	80

MO

Hospital, Address, Telephone, Approval, Facility, and Physician Codes, Health Care System	Classi-fication Codes		Utilization Data					Expense (thousands) of dollars		
★ American Hospital Association (AHA) membership ☐ Joint Commission on Accreditation of Healthcare Organizations (JCAHO) accreditation ○ American Osteopathic Association (AOA) accreditation △ Commission on Accreditation of Rehabilitation Facilities (CARF) accreditation	Control	Service	Staffed Beds	Admissions	Census	Outpatient Visits	Births	Total	Payroll	Personnel

MOBERLY—Randolph County

☐ **MOBERLY REGIONAL MEDICAL CENTER**, 1515 Union Avenue, Zip 65270–9449; tel. 660/263–8400, (Total facility includes 21 beds in nursing home–type unit) **A**1 5 9 10 12 13 **F**2 11 12 15 21 26 27 28 29 31 32 33 35 37 39 44 46 47 48 52 55 57 58 59 60 62 63 64 65 66 69 71 73 75 76 81 82 85 88 92 93 94 95 96 106 108 109 110 **S** Community Health Systems, Inc., Brentwood, TN
Primary Contact: Harold L. Siglar, Chief Executive Officer
Web address: www.moberlyhospital.com

| | 33 | 10 | 96 | 3334 | 46 | 38459 | 309 | 37536 | 12626 | 305 |

MONETT—Barry County

COX MONETT HOSPITAL, 801 Lincoln Avenue, Zip 65708–1698; tel. 417/235–3144 **A**9 10 **F**2 9 11 12 21 27 28 29 33 44 46 47 48 51 52 58 59 60 62 63 65 69 81 82 84 88 92 93 94 95 96 97 108 109 **P**1 **S** CoxHealth, Springfield, MO
Primary Contact: Gregory D. Johnson, Administrator and Chief Executive Officer
Web address: www.coxhealth.com

| | 23 | 10 | 47 | 1389 | 13 | 35461 | 359 | 20568 | 10305 | 326 |

MOUNT VERNON—Lawrence County

☐ △ **MISSOURI REHABILITATION CENTER**, 600 North Main, Zip 65712–1099; tel. 417/466–3711 **A**1 7 10 **F**2 4 9 22 41 45 46 48 52 55 68 69 88 93 94 108 **P**6 **S** University of Missouri Health Care, Columbia, MO
Primary Contact: Dennis Nicely, Director
Web address: www.muhealth.org/~rehab/

| | 12 | 80 | 139 | 460 | 58 | 47619 | — | 32928 | 17785 | 481 |

MOUNTAIN VIEW—Howell County

⊠ **ST. JOHN'S ST. FRANCIS HOSPITAL**, Highway 60, Zip 65548–7125, Mailing Address: P.O. Box 82, Zip 65548–0082; tel. 417/934–7000 **A**1 9 10 20 **F**2 9 12 21 22 26 27 28 33 46 52 58 63 68 69 81 84 88 96 97 108 **P**6 **S** Sisters of Mercy Health System, Chesterfield, MO
Primary Contact: Donald Swafford, President
CHR: Linda Divine, Manager Human Resources
Web address: www.stjohns.com/aboutus/stfrancis.aspx

| | 23 | 10 | 20 | 598 | 7 | 24890 | — | 7571 | 3723 | 128 |

NEOSHO—Newton County

★ **FREEMAN NEOSHO HOSPITAL**, 113 West Hickory Street, Zip 64850–1705; tel. 417/455–4352 **A**9 10 **F**2 6 9 12 14 21 22 23 26 27 28 29 33 34 35 44 46 47 48 52 55 58 60 61 62 63 65 66 68 69 70 81 87 88 92 94 95 96 97 108 110 **P**1 **S** Freeman Health System, Joplin, MO
Primary Contact: Phil Willcoxon, Chief Executive Officer
COO: Janice L. Walker, R.N., Chief Operating Officer
CFO: Steve W. Graddy, Chief Financial Officer
CMO: Rodney McFarland, M.D., Medical Director
CIO: Sue Annesser, Director Information Systems
CHR: Deborah Chiodo, Director Human Resourcesw
Web address: www.freemanhospitals.org

| | 23 | 10 | 63 | 2071 | 27 | 63335 | — | 25169 | 12128 | 255 |

NEVADA—Vernon County

☐ **HEARTLAND BEHAVIORAL HEALTH SERVICES**, 1500 West Ashland Street, Zip 64772–1710; tel. 417/667–2666, (Total facility includes 122 beds in nursing home–type unit) **A**1 9 10 **F**21 71 72 73 74 75 94 **S** Psychiatric Solutions, Franklin, TN
Primary Contact: Mike Ham, Chief Executive Officer
Web address: www.heartlandbhs.com

| | 33 | 22 | 159 | 699 | 75 | — | — | 8686 | 5150 | 181 |

⊠ **NEVADA REGIONAL MEDICAL CENTER**, 800 South Ash Street, Zip 64772–3223; tel. 417/667–3355 **A**1 9 10 **F**2 9 11 12 24 26 27 28 29 33 36 37 38 39 42 45 46 47 48 51 52 54 55 58 59 60 62 63 64 65 66 68 69 71 73 75 77 81 88 93 94 95 96 97 106 108 110 **S** Quorum Health Resources, Plano, TX
Primary Contact: Judith K. Feuquay, Chief Executive Officer
CFO: Cindy D. Buck, Vice President Business Office Group and Chief Financial Officer
CMO: Randy Booth, M.D., President Medical Staff
CHR: Pam Sweger, Director Human Resources
Web address: www.nrmchealth.com

| | 14 | 22 | 53 | 2320 | 26 | 44798 | 289 | 26823 | 10746 | 309 |

OSAGE BEACH—Camden County

⊠ **LAKE REGIONAL HEALTH SYSTEM**, 54 Hospital Drive, Zip 65065–3051; tel. 573/348–8000, (Total facility includes 16 beds in nursing home–type unit) **A**1 9 10 20 **F**2 9 11 12 14 15 17 19 21 22 23 26 27 28 29 32 33 34 37 39 41 46 47 48 51 52 53 55 57 58 59 60 61 62 63 64 65 66 69 81 82 84 85 87 88 92 93 94 95 96 106 108 **P**6
Primary Contact: Michael E. Henze, Chief Executive Officer
COO: Vicki L. Franklin, Senior Vice President Operations
CFO: Dan Probstfield, Senior Vice President Finance
CMO: Grant Barnum, M.D., Chief of Staff
CIO: Cindy Otradovec, Director Health Information Systems
CHR: Tom Williams, Director Human Resources
Web address: www.lakeregional.com

| | 23 | 10 | 140 | 6367 | 82 | 192881 | 771 | 105717 | 37470 | 995 |

OSCEOLA—St. Clair County

★ **SAC–OSAGE HOSPITAL**, Junction Highways 13 & Business 13, Zip 64776–0426, Mailing Address: P.O. Box 426, Zip 64776–0426; tel. 417/646–8181 **A**9 10 20 **F**2 6 9 12 22 23 27 28 33 46 47 48 50 52 55 58 60 61 63 65 66 68 69 81 88 92 94 97 108
Primary Contact: John Moran, Chief Executive Officer
Web address: www.sac-osagehospital.com

| | 16 | 10 | 47 | 1230 | 17 | 14660 | — | 9208 | 4657 | 137 |

Many Facility Codes have changed. Please refer to the AHA Guide Code Chart.

MO

Hospital, Address, Telephone, Approval, Facility, and Physician Codes, Health Care System	Classi-fication Codes		Utilization Data					Expense (thousands) of dollars		
★ American Hospital Association (AHA) membership □ Joint Commission on Accreditation of Healthcare Organizations (JCAHO) accreditation ○ American Osteopathic Association (AOA) accreditation △ Commission on Accreditation of Rehabilitation Facilities (CARF) accreditation	Control	Service	Staffed Beds	Admissions	Census	Outpatient Visits	Births	Total	Payroll	Personnel

PERRYVILLE—Perry County

⊠ **PERRY COUNTY MEMORIAL HOSPITAL**, 434 North West Street, Zip 63775–1398; tel. 573/547–2536 **A**1 9 10 18 **F**2 6 8 9 11 12 21 22 23 26 27 28 29 32 33 35 40 41 44 45 46 47 48 49 51 52 53 54 58 59 60 61 62 63 64 66 68 69 72 73 74 75 76 77 81 84 85 87 88 92 93 94 95 96 97 107 108 109
Primary Contact: William R. Alloy, Chief Executive Officer
COO: Patrick E. Carron, CHE, Vice President Operations
CFO: Randall Wolf, Vice President Finance
CMO: Mark Schabbing, Chief of Staff
CIO: Ron Heuring, Director Information Systems
CHR: Tina Lozier, Director Human Resources
Web address: www.pchmo.org
| 23 | 10 | 25 | 832 | 11 | 42050 | 167 | 19566 | 8870 | 243 |

POPLAR BLUFF—Butler County

⊠ **JOHN J. PERSHING VETERANS AFFAIRS MEDICAL CENTER**, 1500 North Westwood Boulevard, Zip 63901–3318; tel. 573/686–4151, (Total facility includes 40 beds in nursing home–type unit) **A**1 **F**2 4 9 12 21 22 27 28 31 32 33 41 42 44 45 48 50 51 52 58 60 62 63 65 66 68 69 70 73 74 77 81 82 84 88 92 94 106 107 108 109 110 **S** Department of Veterans Affairs, Washington, DC
Primary Contact: Nancy Arnold, R.N., Director
CFO: Edwin L. Ervin, Director Finance
CIO: Janice Vernon, Supervisory Information Technology Specialist
Web address: www.va.gov/sta/guide/home.asp
| 45 | 10 | 58 | 1761 | 56 | 108148 | — | 61881 | 47111 | 388 |

□ △ **POPLAR BLUFF REGIONAL MEDICAL CENTER**, 2620 North Westwood Boulevard, Zip 63901–2341, Mailing Address: P.O. Box 88, Zip 63901–2341; tel. 573/785–7721, (Includes THREE RIVERS HEALTHCARE–NORTH CAMPUS, 2620 North Westwood Boulevard, Mailing Address: P.O. Box 88, Zip 63901–2341; tel. 573/785–7721; THREE RIVERS HEALTHCARE–SOUTH CAMPUS, 621 Pine Boulevard, Zip 63901; tel. 573/686–4111), (Total facility includes 15 beds in nursing home–type unit) **A**1 2 7 9 10 19 **F**2 6 9 11 12 15 17 19 21 22 23 27 28 29 32 33 37 39 40 41 42 46 47 48 49 50 51 52 53 55 57 58 59 60 61 62 63 64 65 66 68 69 70 71 73 74 75 76 81 82 84 85 86 88 93 94 95 96 107 108 109 110 **P**6 **S** Health Management Associates, Naples, FL
Primary Contact: Joe B. Riley, Chief Executive Officer
Web address: www.three–rivershealthcare.com
| 33 | 10 | 257 | 11480 | 149 | 185658 | 1377 | 94548 | 35178 | 1081 |

POTOSI—Washington County

★ **WASHINGTON COUNTY MEMORIAL HOSPITAL**, 300 Health Way, Zip 63664–1499; tel. 573/438–5451 **A**9 10 18 **F**9 12 21 26 27 28 29 33 46 47 48 51 52 63 66 69 70 81 82 84 88 93 94 97 108 109 **P**3
Primary Contact: H. Clark Duncan, Jr, Administrator
COO: H Clark Duncan, Jr, Administrator
CFO: Allan Sucharski, Controller
CMO: Kelly Hartel, M.D., Chief of Staff
CIO: Greg Riddle, Information Systems Director
Web address: www.wcmhosp.org
| 13 | 10 | 25 | 475 | 5 | 60792 | — | 12049 | 4864 | 162 |

RICHMOND—Ray County

RAY COUNTY MEMORIAL HOSPITAL, 904 Wollard Boulevard, Zip 64085–2243; tel. 816/470–5432 **A**9 10 **F**9 12 21 27 33 36 37 51 52 58 63 69 81 84 94 97 108
Primary Contact: Tommy L. Hicks, Administrator
| 13 | 10 | 37 | 1150 | 14 | 13957 | — | 14854 | 5998 | 194 |

ROLLA—Phelps County

⊠ △ **PHELPS COUNTY REGIONAL MEDICAL CENTER**, 1000 West Tenth Street, Zip 65401–2905; tel. 573/458–8899, (Total facility includes 20 beds in nursing home–type unit) **A**1 5 7 9 10 19 20 **F**2 6 9 11 12 21 22 23 26 27 28 29 32 33 34 45 46 47 48 52 53 55 57 59 60 61 62 63 64 65 66 68 69 71 73 74 75 76 77 79 80 81 82 84 87 88 92 93 94 95 96 106 107 108 109 110
Primary Contact: John Denbo, Chief Executive Officer
CFO: Gerald Paule, Chief Financial Officer
CMO: Jay Crump, M.D., Director Medical Staff
CIO: Mary Crouch, Director Information Technologies
CHR: Frank Lazzaro, Administrative Director
Web address: www.pcrmc.com
| 13 | 10 | 198 | 8986 | 126 | 166572 | 904 | 100697 | 40150 | 982 |

SAINT CHARLES—St. Charles County

□ **CENTERPOINTE HOSPITAL**, 5931 Highway 94 South, Zip 63304–5611; tel. 636/441–7300 **A**1 10 **F**3 4 28 29 33 42 45 47 71 72 73 74 75 76 77 78 94
Primary Contact: Tariq F. Malik, CPA, Chief Executive Officer
Web address: www.centerpointehospital.com
| 33 | 52 | 84 | 2358 | 48 | 5459 | — | 11025 | 5999 | 184 |

MO

Hospital, Address, Telephone, Approval, Facility, and Physician Codes, Health Care System	Classi-fication Codes		Utilization Data					Expense (thousands) of dollars		
★ American Hospital Association (AHA) membership □ Joint Commission on Accreditation of Healthcare Organizations (JCAHO) accreditation ○ American Osteopathic Association (AOA) accreditation △ Commission on Accreditation of Rehabilitation Facilities (CARF) accreditation	Control	Service	Staffed Beds	Admissions	Census	Outpatient Visits	Births	Total	Payroll	Personnel

⊠ SSM ST. JOSEPH HEALTH CENTER, 300 First Capitol Drive, Zip 63301–2844; tel. 636/947–5000, (Total facility includes 10 beds in nursing home–type unit) **A**1 2 9 10 **F**2 3 4 9 11 12 14 15 17 19 21 22 23 26 27 28 29 30 31 32 33 34 35 37 39 41 42 44 45 46 47 48 50 52 55 57 58 59 61 62 63 64 65 66 68 70 71 72 73 74 75 76 77 78 81 82 84 85 87 88 90 92 93 94 95 96 98 106 108 109 110 **P**6 8 **S** SSM Health Care, Saint Louis, MO
Primary Contact: Paul Convery, M.D., Interim President and Chief Executive Officer
CFO: Carole Campbell, Director Finance
CMO: James Freeman, M.D., Vice President Medical Affairs
CIO: Marge Feilner, Director Information Services
CHR: John Sarantakis, Director Human Resources
Web address: www.ssmstjoseph.com

| | 23 | 10 | 276 | 14983 | 199 | 136072 | 704 | 135022 | 64438 | 1151 |

SAINT JOSEPH—Buchanan County

⊠ HEARTLAND REGIONAL MEDICAL CENTER, 5325 Faraon Street, Zip 64506–3398; tel. 816/271–6000, (Includes HEARTLAND HOSPITAL EAST), (Total facility includes 144 beds in nursing home–type unit) **A**1 2 5 9 10 20 **F**2 7 9 11 12 14 15 17 19 21 22 23 25 26 27 28 30 32 33 34 36 37 38 39 42 46 47 48 50 51 52 55 57 59 60 62 63 64 65 66 68 69 70 71 73 75 76 79 80 81 87 88 92 93 94 95 107 108 109 110 **P**6
Primary Contact: Lowell C. Kruse, President and Chief Executive Officer
COO: Curt Kretzinger, Chief Operating Officer
CFO: John P. Wilson, Chief Financial Officer
CMO: Charles Mullican, M.D., Chief Medical Officer
CIO: Helen Thompson, Chief Information Officer
Web address: www.heartland–health.com

| | 23 | 10 | 488 | 19004 | 289 | 529978 | 1647 | 286202 | 128802 | 2374 |

□ NORTHWEST MISSOURI PSYCHIATRIC REHABILITATION CENTER, 3505 Frederick Avenue, Zip 64506–2914; tel. 816/378–2300 **A**1 10 **F**3 21 31 39 46 47 48 58 60 65 66 70 71 74 75 76 94 106 108 **P**6
Primary Contact: Donna Buchanan, Ph.D., Chief Operating Officer

| | 12 | 22 | 111 | 59 | 111 | 28 | 0 | 18562 | 10349 | 299 |

SAINT LOUIS—St. Louis County

⊠ BARNES–JEWISH HOSPITAL, One Barnes–Jewish Hospital Plaza, Zip 63110–1094; tel. 314/747–3000 **A**1 2 3 5 8 9 10 **F**2 3 4 5 7 9 10 11 12 13 14 15 17 19 21 22 23 26 27 28 29 31 32 33 34 35 37 38 39 40 43 44 45 46 47 48 49 50 52 53 55 57 58 59 60 61 62 63 64 65 66 69 70 71 73 75 76 77 78 79 80 81 82 84 86 87 88 89 90 92 93 94 95 96 98 99 100 101 102 103 104 106 107 108 109 110 **P**1 5 6 7 **S** BJC HealthCare, Saint Louis, MO
Primary Contact: Andrew A. Ziskind, M.D., President and Chief Executive Officer
COO: Sharon O'Keefe, R.N., Chief Operating Officer
Web address: www.barnesjewish.org

| | 23 | 10 | 962 | 50558 | 777 | 332486 | 3456 | 989808 | 336517 | 9134 |

⊠ BARNES–JEWISH WEST COUNTY HOSPITAL, 12634 Olive Boulevard, Zip 63141–6337; tel. 314/996–8000, (Total facility includes 10 beds in nursing home–type unit) **A**1 3 5 9 10 **F**2 10 12 21 22 26 27 28 29 33 37 40 41 46 48 52 55 57 60 62 63 64 65 66 68 69 81 82 85 88 92 93 94 95 96 108 **P**1 4 5 7 8 **S** BJC HealthCare, Saint Louis, MO
Primary Contact: Mary Patricia Mohrman, R.N., MSN, President
COO: Ronald G. Evens, M.D., President and Senior Executive Officer
CFO: Diane M. Glen, Chief Financial Officer
CMO: Alan Londe, M.D., Chief of Staff
CIO: Jane Sterling, Director Information Systems
CHR: Horace Young, Manager Human Resources
Web address: www.bjc.org/bjwch.html

| | 23 | 10 | 74 | 3655 | 42 | 68581 | — | 57863 | 19664 | 423 |

⊠ CHRISTIAN HOSPITAL, (Formerly Christian Hospital Northeast–Northwest), 11133 Dunn Road, Zip 63136–6192; tel. 314/653–5000, (Total facility includes 24 beds in nursing home–type unit) **A**1 2 9 10 **F**1 2 6 9 12 15 17 19 21 22 23 26 28 29 33 37 39 40 41 42 44 46 48 49 52 54 55 57 58 60 61 62 63 64 65 66 68 69 71 74 76 77 78 79 81 82 84 85 86 87 88 92 93 94 96 106 108 110 **S** BJC HealthCare, Saint Louis, MO
Primary Contact: Paul E. Macek, President
CFO: Cheryl Matejka, Chief Financial Officer
CIO: Diane Tattich, Group Manager
Web address: www.bjc.org

| | 23 | 10 | 463 | 17238 | 295 | 173619 | 0 | 228238 | 89933 | 1817 |

★ ○ △ DES PERES HOSPITAL, 2345 Dougherty Ferry Road, Zip 63122–3313; tel. 314/821–5850 **A**7 9 10 11 12 13 **F**2 5 7 9 10 12 14 15 17 19 21 22 23 26 28 29 30 33 35 37 38 39 44 45 46 47 48 49 52 53 54 55 57 58 60 62 63 64 65 66 68 69 73 74 75 76 81 82 84 88 94 95 96 106 108 109 110 **S** TENET Healthcare Corporation, Dallas, TX
Primary Contact: Michele C. Meyer, Chief Executive Officer
COO: Barb Jacobsmeyer, Chief Operating Officer
CFO: Michael Kendrick, Chief Financial Officer
CMO: Karen Webb, M.D., Chief Medical Officer
CIO: Kay Hannon, Facility Information Systems Director
CHR: Ron Birlew, Director Human Resources
Web address: www.despereshospital.com

| | 33 | 10 | 127 | 8528 | 100 | 37474 | — | 90310 | 29747 | 666 |

MO

Many Facility Codes have changed. Please refer to the AHA Guide Code Chart. © 2005 AHA Guide

Hospital, Address, Telephone, Approval, Facility, and Physician Codes, Health Care System	Classi-fication Codes		Utilization Data					Expense (thousands) of dollars		
★ American Hospital Association (AHA) membership □ Joint Commission on Accreditation of Healthcare Organizations (JCAHO) accreditation ○ American Osteopathic Association (AOA) accreditation △ Commission on Accreditation of Rehabilitation Facilities (CARF) accreditation	Control	Service	Staffed Beds	Admissions	Census	Outpatient Visits	Births	Total	Payroll	Personnel
⊠ △ **FOREST PARK HOSPITAL**, 6150 Oakland Avenue, Zip 63139–3215; tel. 314/768–3000, (Total facility includes 20 beds in nursing home–type unit) **A**1 2 3 5 7 9 10 12 **F**2 9 11 12 14 15 17 19 21 22 23 26 27 28 33 34 35 39 40 44 45 46 47 48 52 53 55 56 57 58 59 60 61 62 63 64 68 69 70 71 73 74 75 76 77 79 80 81 84 87 88 92 94 95 96 107 108 109 110 **P**6 **S** Doctors Community Healthcare Corporation Primary Contact: John D. Hirsch, M.D., President and Chief Executive Officer CFO: Steven J. Weiss, Chief Financial Officer Web address: www.forestparkhospital.com	33	10	242	9155	122	148549	1090	106537	38665	975
□ **HAWTHORN CHILDREN PSYCHIATRIC HOSPITAL**, 1901 Pennsylvania, Zip 63133; tel. 314/512–7800 **A**1 **F**26 27 28 71 72 **P**6 Primary Contact: David Blue, Chief Executive Officer	12	52	52	261	41	—	—	10298	6488	216
⊠ **KINDRED HOSPITAL–ST. LOUIS**, 4930 Lindell Boulevard, Zip 63108–1510; tel. 314/361–8700 **A**1 10 **F**2 21 26 27 28 33 38 44 99 94 110 **S** Kindred Healthcare, Louisville, KY Primary Contact: Michael Moody, Interim Chief Executive Officer CFO: Jackie Bonness, Chief Financial Officer CMO: Neil Ettinger, M.D., Medical Director CHR: Denise Evans, Recruiter Human Resources Web address: www.kindredhealthcare.com	33	80	60	325	27	—	0	13945	5604	117
□ **METROPOLITAN ST. LOUIS PSYCHIATRIC CENTER**, 5351 Delmar, Zip 63112–3198; tel. 314/877–0500 **A**1 3 5 10 **F**3 26 27 28 71 75 **P**6 Primary Contact: MaryLois Lacey, Chief Executive Officer	12	22	112	2044	96	5596	—	—	—	419
MISSOURI BAPTIST MEDICAL CENTER See Town and Country										
⊠ **SAINT LOUIS UNIVERSITY HOSPITAL**, 3635 Vista at Grand Boulevard, Zip 63110–0250, Mailing Address: P.O. Box 15250, Zip 63110–0250; tel. 314/577–8000 **A**1 2 3 5 8 9 10 **F**2 5 7 9 12 14 15 17 19 21 22 23 26 27 28 29 30 31 33 34 35 37 38 39 42 44 46 47 48 49 50 52 53 54 55 57 58 60 61 62 63 64 65 66 69 70 71 73 74 75 76 77 79 80 81 82 84 85 86 87 88 94 95 96 99 100 101 102 104 105 106 107 108 109 **P**1 **S** TENET Healthcare Corporation, Dallas, TX Primary Contact: Crystal L. Haynes, Chief Executive Officer COO: Stephen Zieniewicz, Chief Operating Officer CFO: Raymond Alvey, Chief Financial Officer CMO: Karen Webb, M.D., Chief Medical Officer CIO: Beckie Patrick, Director Information System Technology CHR: Paula Just, Director Human Resources Web address: www.sluhospital.com	33	10	337	15310	258	113538	—	293535	81206	1508
□ **SELECT SPECIALTY HOSPITAL**, 6150 Oakland Avenue, 5th Floor, Zip 63139–3297; tel. 314/768–3000 **A**1 9 10 **F**21 57 94 110 Primary Contact: James Mikes, Administrator and Chief Executive Officer Web address: www.selectmedicalcorp.com	33	80	33	285	24	0	0	10494	4197	80
□ **SHRINERS HOSPITALS FOR CHILDREN, ST. LOUIS**, 2001 South Lindbergh Boulevard, Zip 63131–3597; tel. 314/432–3600 **A**1 3 5 **F**2 21 26 27 46 47 48 52 53 57 58 62 64 65 66 69 70 94 95 96 108 110 **S** Shriners Hospitals for Children, Tampa, FL Primary Contact: Josephine B. Holtz, R.N., Interim Administrator Web address: www.shrinershq.org	23	57	42	1843	14	11960	—	—	—	249
⊠ **SSM CARDINAL GLENNON CHILDREN'S HOSPITAL**, 1465 South Grand Boulevard, Zip 63104–1095; tel. 314/577–5600 **A**1 3 5 9 **F**2 9 16 18 20 21 22 23 24 26 27 28 29 30 31 32 33 34 35 37 38 39 42 46 47 48 49 50 52 56 57 58 60 61 62 63 65 66 67 68 69 70 72 73 74 75 77 81 84 87 88 90 92 93 94 95 96 98 99 100 101 102 103 104 105 107 108 110 **P**6 7 8 **S** SSM Health Care, Saint Louis, MO Primary Contact: Douglas A. Ries, FACHE, President COO: John S. Dubis, Executive Vice President CFO: Kelly Thompson, Director Finance CMO: Susan Heaney, M.D., Vice President Medical Affairs CIO: Joe Provaznik, Manager Information Systems CHR: Mary Pat Campbell, Director Human Resources Web address: www.cardinalglennon.com	23	50	164	5430	120	217590	—	141055	60792	1316
⊠ **SSM DEPAUL HEALTH CENTER**, 12303 DePaul Drive, Zip 63044–2588; tel. 314/344–6000, (Total facility includes 54 beds in nursing home–type unit) **A**1 9 10 **F**2 3 4 9 10 11 12 14 15 17 19 21 22 23 26 27 28 29 30 31 33 34 35 37 38 39 41 44 45 46 47 48 49 50 52 54 55 57 58 59 61 62 63 64 65 66 68 70 71 72 73 74 75 76 77 78 80 81 82 84 85 88 90 92 94 96 108 109 110 **P**6 8 **S** SSM Health Care, Saint Louis, MO Primary Contact: Melinda Clark, FACHE, President and Chief Executive Officer COO: Sean Hogan, Vice President and Chief Operating Officer CFO: Mark O'Connor, Chief Financial Officer CMO: Kevin Johnson, M.D., Vice President Medical Affairs CHR: Janet Olliges, Director Human Resources Web address: www.ssmdepaul.com	21	10	412	20399	276	155490	1841	188085	79745	1499
⊠ △ **SSM REHAB**, 6420 Clayton Road, Suite 600, Zip 63117–1811; tel. 314/768–5300 **A**1 7 9 10 **F**2 21 22 26 27 28 29 30 35 39 45 46 48 49 52 60 62 66 68 69 92 94 95 96 **P**6 **S** SSM Health Care, Saint Louis, MO Primary Contact: Steven P. Johnson, Ph.D., President Web address: www.ssmrehab.com	21	46	100	1684	68	132910	—	37747	27599	522

MO

Hospital, Address, Telephone, Approval, Facility, and Physician Codes, Health Care System	Classi-fication Codes		Utilization Data					Expense (thousands) of dollars		
★ American Hospital Association (AHA) membership □ Joint Commission on Accreditation of Healthcare Organizations (JCAHO) accreditation ○ American Osteopathic Association (AOA) accreditation △ Commission on Accreditation of Rehabilitation Facilities (CARF) accreditation	Control	Service	Staffed Beds	Admissions	Census	Outpatient Visits	Births	Total	Payroll	Personnel

SSM ST. JOSEPH HOSPITAL OF KIRKWOOD, 525 Couch Avenue,
Zip 63122–5536; tel. 314/966–1500 **A**1 9 10 **F**2 9 11 12 14 15 17 19 21 22
23 26 27 28 29 30 32 33 35 36 37 38 39 40 45 46 48 49 50 51 52 53 54
55 57 58 59 60 61 62 63 64 65 66 68 69 73 75 81 82 84 85 86 87 88 92
93 94 96 106 108 109 110 **P**6 8 **S** SSM Health Care, Saint Louis, MO
Primary Contact: Sherry Hausmann, President
COO: Brett Esrock, Executive Vice President and Chief Operating Officer
CFO: Alita Prosser, Director Finance
CMO: William Boyce, M.D., President Medical Staff
CIO: Leighton Wassilak, Director Information Systems
CHR: Kurt Delabar, Director Human Resources
Web address: www.st josephkirkwood.com
— Control 23, Service 10, Staffed Beds 202, Admissions 7816, Census 88, Outpatient Visits 84733, Births —, Total 85949, Payroll 36562, Personnel 728

SSM ST. MARY'S HEALTH CENTER, 6420 Clayton Road, Zip 63117–1872;
tel. 314/768–8000 **A**1 2 3 5 8 9 10 **F**2 9 11 12 14 15 17 19 21 22 23 26 27
28 29 31 33 35 37 38 39 44 45 46 47 48 49 52 55 56 57 58 59 61 62 63
64 65 66 68 69 71 73 75 76 78 81 82 84 88 90 92 94 96 106 108 109 110
S SSM Health Care, Saint Louis, MO
Primary Contact: Kenneth W. Lukhard, President
COO: Sister Susan K. Scholl, R.N., Executive Vice President and Chief Operating Officer
CFO: Mary Lococo, Director Finance
CMO: Howard Podolsky, M.D., Vice President and Chief Medical Officer
CIO: Bob Curran, Driector Health Information Management
CHR: Mary Kausch, Interim Director Human Resources
Web address: www.stlapps.ssmhc.com/intranet/home/smhcstl.nsf
— Control 23, Service 10, Staffed Beds 365, Admissions 25564, Census 306, Outpatient Visits 168872, Births 2824, Total 204139, Payroll 98297, Personnel 1696

△ **ST. ALEXIUS HOSPITAL**, 3933 South Broadway, Zip 63118–4601;
tel. 314/865–3333, (Includes SOUTHPOINTE HOSPITAL, 2639 Miami Street,
Zip 63118–3929; tel. 314/772–1456) **A**1 6 7 9 10 **F**2 10 12 15 21 22 28 29
31 32 33 35 44 45 46 48 49 52 53 55 57 60 61 62 63 65 66 68 69 70 71
74 75 76 77 78 81 82 87 88 93 95 108 109 **S** Doctors Community
Healthcare Corporation
Primary Contact: Doug Doris, Chief Executive Officer
COO: Robert S. Adcock, Chief Operating Officer
CFO: Johnny Watkins, Chief Financial Officer
CIO: Jennifer Schempp, Manager Information Systems
Web address: www.stalexiushospital.com
— Control 33, Service 10, Staffed Beds 319, Admissions 10533, Census 198, Outpatient Visits 61049, Births —, Total 94535, Payroll 48774, Personnel 847

ST. ANTHONY'S MEDICAL CENTER, 10010 Kennerly Road, Zip 63128–2185;
tel. 314/525–1000 **A**1 9 10 **F**2 3 4 9 11 12 14 15 17 19 21 22 23 26 27 28
29 31 33 34 36 37 38 39 41 42 44 45 46 47 48 49 50 51 52 53 54 55 56
57 58 59 60 61 62 63 64 65 66 68 69 70 71 72 73 74 75 76 77 78 80 81
82 84 87 88 93 94 95 96 106 107 108 110 **P**6
Primary Contact: Thomas H. Rockers, President and Chief Executive Officer
COO: Michalene D. Maringer, R.N., Executive Vice President and Chief Hospital Officer
CFO: John McGuire, Executive Vice President and Chief Financial Officer
CMO: Robert V. Griesbaum, M.D., Vice President Patient Care Quality
CIO: Gordon Lashmett, Chief Information Officer
CHR: Craig Mills, Vice President Human Resources
Web address: www.stanthonysmedcenter.com
— Control 23, Service 10, Staffed Beds 558, Admissions 28074, Census 385, Outpatient Visits 370450, Births 1410, Total 298492, Payroll 132102, Personnel 2991

△ **ST. JOHN'S MERCY MEDICAL CENTER**, 615 South New Ballas Road,
Zip 63141–8277; tel. 314/569–6000 **A**1 2 3 5 7 8 9 10 **F**2 4 7 9 11 12 13 14
15 17 19 20 21 22 23 24 26 27 28 29 30 31 32 33 34 37 40 41 42 44 45
46 47 48 49 50 52 53 54 55 56 57 58 59 61 62 63 64 65 66 67 68 69 70
71 72 73 74 75 76 77 78 79 80 81 82 84 86 87 88 89 90 93 94 95 96 98
108 109 110 **P**6 8 **S** Sisters of Mercy Health System, Chesterfield, MO
Primary Contact: Margaret Denielle DeNarvaez, President and Chief Executive Officer
COO: Mark S. Stauder, Executive Vice President and Chief Operating Officer
CFO: Randy Combs, Chief Financial Officer
CMO: Paul Hintze, M.D., Vice President Medical Affairs
CIO: Paul Merrywell, Vice President Information Services
CHR: Rocky Ruello, Vice President Human Resources
Web address: www.stjohnsmercy.org
— Control 23, Service 10, Staffed Beds 852, Admissions 37538, Census 565, Outpatient Visits 507272, Births 6969, Total 492111, Payroll 217692, Personnel 4878

△ **ST. LOUIS CHILDREN'S HOSPITAL**, One Children's Place,
Zip 63110–1081; tel. 314/454–6000 **A**1 3 5 7 8 9 10 **F**2 6 9 13 15 16 17 18
20 21 22 23 24 26 27 28 29 31 32 33 34 35 36 37 38 39 42 45 46 47 48
49 50 51 52 53 56 57 58 60 61 62 63 64 65 66 67 68 69 73 75 77 81 82
83 84 85 88 92 93 94 95 96 98 99 100 101 102 103 104 106 108 110
S BJC HealthCare, Saint Louis, MO
Primary Contact: Lee F. Fetter, President and Senior Executive Officer
Web address: www.stlouischildrens.org
— Control 23, Service 50, Staffed Beds 235, Admissions 10489, Census 175, Outpatient Visits 157162, Births —, Total 246815, Payroll 93584, Personnel 2082

□ **ST. LOUIS PSYCHIATRIC REHABILITATION CENTER**, 5300 Arsenal Street,
Zip 63139–1494; tel. 314/877–6500 **A**1 10 **F**9 22 28 32 39 41 45 58 65 66
71 73 74 94 96 108 **P**2 3 6
Primary Contact: MaryLois Lacey, Chief Executive Officer
Web address: www.dmh.missouri.gov
— Control 12, Service 22, Staffed Beds 212, Admissions 55, Census 203, Outpatient Visits —, Births —, Total 28741, Payroll 16533, Personnel 506

Many Facility Codes have changed. Please refer to the AHA Guide Code Chart.

Hospital, Address, Telephone, Approval, Facility, and Physician Codes, Health Care System	Classi-fication Codes		Utilization Data					Expense (thousands) of dollars		
★ American Hospital Association (AHA) membership □ Joint Commission on Accreditation of Healthcare Organizations (JCAHO) accreditation ○ American Osteopathic Association (AOA) accreditation △ Commission on Accreditation of Rehabilitation Facilities (CARF) accreditation	Control	Service	Staffed Beds	Admissions	Census	Outpatient Visits	Births	Total	Payroll	Personnel

⊠ **THE REHABILITATION INSTITUTE OF ST. LOUIS**, 4455 Duncan Avenue, Zip 63110–1111; tel. 314/658–3800 **A**1 10 **F**1 21 35 37 42 43 45 52 57 58 62 65 66 68 69 92 94 95 96 109 110 **S** HEALTHSOUTH Corporation, Birmingham, AL Primary Contact: Daniel J. Rothery, Administrator Web address: www.healthsouth.com	32	46	72	1411	60	44588	0	21259	10135	230
⊠ △ **VETERANS AFFAIRS MEDICAL CENTER**, 915 North Grand, Zip 63106; tel. 314/652–4100, (Total facility includes 121 beds in nursing home–type unit) **A**1 3 5 7 **F**2 3 4 6 7 12 15 17 21 22 29 32 33 36 37 38 39 42 44 45 47 48 49 50 51 52 53 55 57 58 60 61 62 63 65 66 68 69 70 71 73 74 75 76 77 78 81 82 84 88 92 93 94 96 106 108 109 110 **S** Department of Veterans Affairs, Washington, DC Primary Contact: Peter M. McBrady, Interim Director CFO: Gary Gardner, Director, Business Service Line CMO: Margarethe Hagemann, M.D., Chief of Staff CIO: James Daly, Director, Information Management Service Line CHR: Marie Lewis, Human Resources Liaison Web address: www.va.gov/sta/guide/home.asp	45	10	339	8482	275	485770	0	221360	133844	1941
SAINT PETERS—St. Charles County										
⊠ **BARNES–JEWISH ST. PETERS HOSPITAL**, 10 Hospital Drive, Zip 63376–1691; tel. 636/916–9000, (Total facility includes 8 beds in nursing home–type unit) **A**1 5 9 10 **F**2 9 11 12 15 17 21 22 23 26 27 28 29 33 37 46 47 48 50 52 55 58 59 60 61 62 63 64 65 66 68 69 81 82 84 88 92 93 94 96 106 108 109 **S** BJC HealthCare, Saint Louis, MO Primary Contact: David Ross, President CFO: Cindy Gross, Assistant Administrator, Finance CHR: Keith Bolton, Manager Web address: www.bjc.org/bjsph.html	23	10	90	6677	72	100672	699	70838	26263	617
SALEM—Dent County										
★ **SALEM MEMORIAL DISTRICT HOSPITAL**, Highway 72 North, Zip 65560–0774, Mailing Address: P.O. Box 774, Zip 65560–0774; tel. 573/729–6626, (Total facility includes 18 beds in nursing home–type unit) **A**9 10 18 20 **F**2 6 9 21 22 26 27 28 33 46 47 48 49 51 53 58 63 64 65 66 81 85 88 92 94 97 108 110 Primary Contact: Dennis P. Pryor, Administrator CFO: Kasey Lucas, Controller Web address: www.smdh.net	16	10	43	965	30	26488	—	11899	4659	181
SEDALIA—Pettis County										
⊠ **BOTHWELL REGIONAL HEALTH CENTER**, 601 East 14th Street, Zip 65301–1706, Mailing Address: P.O. Box 1706, Zip 65302–1706; tel. 660/826–8833, (Total facility includes 10 beds in nursing home–type unit) **A**1 9 10 19 20 **F**2 9 10 11 12 15 17 21 23 26 27 28 32 33 36 37 38 40 42 44 46 48 49 51 52 53 55 57 58 59 60 61 62 63 65 66 68 69 71 80 81 82 84 85 86 87 88 92 93 94 95 96 106 107 108 109 110 Primary Contact: John M. Dawes, Chief Executive Officer COO: Mark I. Hirshberg, Chief Operating Officer CFO: David Halsell, Chief Financial Officer CIO: Greg Collins, Information Systems Director CHR: Deb Clemmer, Vice President Human Resources Web address: www.brhc.org	14	10	153	6809	86	99864	604	67932	29469	787
SIKESTON—Scott County										
□ **MISSOURI DELTA MEDICAL CENTER**, 1008 North Main Street, Zip 63801–5099; tel. 573/471–1600 **A**1 9 10 19 20 **F**2 9 11 12 15 16 17 21 22 23 24 26 27 28 29 32 33 35 37 38 39 40 41 42 44 46 47 48 49 51 52 53 55 57 58 59 60 61 62 63 65 66 68 69 70 71 72 73 74 75 76 77 81 82 84 86 88 93 94 95 96 107 108 Primary Contact: Charles D. Ancell, President Web address: www.missouridelta.com	23	10	158	5474	69	169324	562	62514	28674	656
SMITHVILLE—Clay County										
★ △ **SAINT LUKE'S NORTHLAND HOSPITAL–SMITHVILLE CAMPUS**, 601 South 169 Highway, Zip 64089–9317; tel. 816/532–3700, (Total facility includes 8 beds in nursing home–type unit) **A**7 9 10 **F**9 21 22 26 27 28 29 30 31 33 35 37 38 41 44 45 46 47 48 52 54 58 60 65 68 69 71 72 73 74 75 76 77 78 92 94 95 96 98 107 108 110 **S** Saint Luke's Health System, Kansas City, MO Primary Contact: Don Sipes, Chief Executive Officer COO: Kevin Trimble, R.N., Senior Vice President and Chief Nursing Officer CFO: Julie Moorman, Chief Financial Officer CMO: George A. Pagels, M.D., Senior Vice President and Chief Medical Officer CIO: John Wade, Chief Information Officer CHR: Alan Abramovitz, Senior Director Human Resources Web address: www.saintlukeshealthsystem.org	23	10	40	1803	34	6668	0	12781	6648	139
SPRINGFIELD—Greene County										
○ **DOCTORS HOSPITAL OF SPRINGFIELD**, 2828 North National, Zip 65803–4306; tel. 417/837–4000 **A**9 10 11 **F**2 21 26 27 28 32 33 37 44 45 46 48 52 53 58 60 62 63 64 65 66 68 69 70 71 76 82 84 88 94 106 107 109 Primary Contact: Paul Taylor, Administrator	33	10	35	1174	18	89491	0	25504	9130	436

MO

Hospital, Address, Telephone, Approval, Facility, and Physician Codes, Health Care System	Classi-fication Codes		Utilization Data					Expense (thousands) of dollars		
★ American Hospital Association (AHA) membership □ Joint Commission on Accreditation of Healthcare Organizations (JCAHO) accreditation ○ American Osteopathic Association (AOA) accreditation △ Commission on Accreditation of Rehabilitation Facilities (CARF) accreditation	Control	Service	Staffed Beds	Admissions	Census	Outpatient Visits	Births	Total	Payroll	Personnel
□ **LAKELAND REGIONAL HOSPITAL**, 440 South Market Street, Zip 65806–2090; tel. 417/865–5581 **A**1 9 10 **F**27 28 33 58 71 72 74 75 94 **P**5 6 **S** Youth and Family Centered Services, Austin, TX Primary Contact: Stephen L. Spence, President and Chief Executive Officer Web address: www.yfcs.com	33	22	60	2078	51	—	—	7041	3885	213
⊠ △ **LESTER E. COX MEDICAL CENTERS**, 1423 North Jefferson Street, Zip 65802–1988; tel. 417/269–3000, (Includes LESTER E. COX MEDICAL CENTER NORTH; LESTER E. COX MEDICAL CENTER SOUTH, 3801 South National Avenue, Zip 65807; tel. 417/269–6000), (Total facility includes 43 beds in nursing home–type unit) **A**1 2 7 9 10 **F**2 3 4 6 9 10 11 12 14 15 17 19 21 22 23 24 26 27 28 29 30 32 33 34 35 37 38 39 40 41 42 44 45 46 47 48 49 50 51 52 53 54 55 56 57 58 59 60 61 62 63 64 65 66 67 68 69 70 71 72 76 79 80 81 82 84 86 87 88 89 90 92 93 94 95 96 106 107 108 109 110 **P**6 8 **S** CoxHealth, Springfield, MO Primary Contact: Robert H. Bezanson, President and Chief Executive Officer COO: Norb Bagley, Executive Vice President and Chief Operating Officer CFO: Jacob McWay, Senior Vice President and Chief Financial Officer CMO: James Coulter, M.D., Vice President Medical Affairs CIO: John Duff, M.D., Vice President Support Services and Chief Information Officer CHR: Donald Anderson, Vice President Human Resources Web address: www.coxhealth.com	23	10	719	31226	449	1226302	3624	585174	228748	5795
⊠ △ **ST. JOHN'S HOSPITAL**, 1235 East Cherokee Street, Zip 65804–2263; tel. 417/820–2000, (Total facility includes 26 beds in nursing home–type unit) **A**1 2 7 9 10 **F**2 3 4 5 6 7 9 11 12 13 14 15 17 19 21 22 23 25 26 27 28 29 30 31 32 33 34 35 36 37 38 39 40 41 42 44 45 46 47 48 49 50 51 52 53 55 56 57 58 59 60 61 62 63 64 65 66 67 68 69 70 71 72 73 74 75 76 77 79 80 81 82 84 86 87 88 90 92 93 94 95 96 98 99 106 107 108 109 110 **P**5 6 8 **S** Sisters of Mercy Health System, Chesterfield, MO Primary Contact: Robert T. Brodhead, President CFO: Kim Day, Chief Financial Officer CMO: Donald Wantuck, M.D., Chief of Staff CIO: Mark Pasquale, Vice President Information Systems CHR: Paul Elmore, Vice President Human Resources Web address: www.stjohns.com	23	10	601	32626	423	497586	2498	469240	180683	4635
□ **U. S. MEDICAL CENTER FOR FEDERAL PRISONERS**, 1900 West Sunshine Street, Zip 65807–2240, Mailing Address: P.O. Box 4000, Zip 65808–4000; tel. 417/862–7041, (Nonreporting) **A**1 Primary Contact: Bill Hedrick, Warden	48	10	587	—	—	—	—	—	—	—
STE. GENEVIEVE—Ste. Genevieve County										
★ **STE. GENEVIEVE COUNTY MEMORIAL HOSPITAL**, Highways 61 and 32, Zip 63670–0468, Mailing Address: P.O. Box 468, Zip 63670–0468; tel. 573/883–2751 **A**9 10 **F**2 9 11 12 21 23 26 28 29 31 32 33 44 46 47 48 51 52 55 58 59 60 61 62 63 64 65 66 69 81 84 88 93 94 95 96 97 106 108 109 **P**6 Primary Contact: Michael J. Laird, FACHE, Chief Executive Officer CFO: Susan Eckenfels, Director Finance CMO: Richard Pearson, M.D., Chief of Staff CIO: Marsha Norris, Director Information Systems CHR: Charles Pavlovsky, Director Human Resources Web address: www.stegenevievehospital.org	13	10	35	1507	15	87007	64	19348	8712	232
SULLIVAN—Crawford County										
★ **MISSOURI BAPTIST HOSPITAL–SULLIVAN**, 751 Sappington Bridge Road, Zip 63080–2354; tel. 573/468–4186 **A**9 10 **F**2 6 9 11 12 21 22 23 26 27 28 29 31 32 33 36 41 44 46 48 50 52 55 58 59 60 61 62 63 64 65 66 68 69 70 75 76 81 84 88 92 93 94 97 108 **P**6 **S** BJC HealthCare, Saint Louis, MO Primary Contact: Tony Schwarm, President CFO: Tonya Cottrell, Senior Financial Analyst CMO: Jaroslaw Michalik, M.D., Chief of Staff CHR: Lisa Lochner, Assistant Administrator Web address: www.bjc.org/mbhs.html	23	10	46	1927	25	54226	228	25983	10513	278
TOWN AND COUNTRY—St. Louis County										
⊠ **MISSOURI BAPTIST MEDICAL CENTER**, 3015 North Ballas Road, Zip 63131–2374; tel. 314/996–5000 **A**1 2 5 9 10 **F**2 9 11 12 14 15 17 19 21 22 23 26 27 28 29 33 38 42 46 47 48 49 50 52 53 55 57 58 59 60 61 62 63 64 65 66 68 69 79 80 81 82 84 86 87 88 92 94 95 96 108 109 110 **P**6 **S** BJC HealthCare, Saint Louis, MO Primary Contact: Carmelo J. Moceri, President CFO: Loren F. Chandler, Vice President Finance and Chief Financial Officer CMO: John Krettek, M.D., Vice President Medical Affairs and Chief Medical Officer CIO: Barb Campana, Director Information Systems CHR: Kristi Schmidt, Vice President Human Resources Web address: www.bjc.org/mbmc	23	10	379	22951	301	238944	4148	292186	98480	2497
TRENTON—Grundy County										
WRIGHT MEMORIAL HOSPITAL, 701 East First Street, Zip 64683–2402, Mailing Address: P.O. Box 628, Zip 64683–0628; tel. 660/359–5621 **A**9 10 18 **F**9 11 12 22 23 26 27 28 29 33 36 37 45 46 47 48 51 52 53 58 59 60 63 68 69 70 81 88 94 97 106 108 **P**1 **S** Saint Luke's Health System, Kansas City, MO Primary Contact: John Woodrich, Chief Executive Officer Web address: www.saintlukeshealthsystem.org	23	10	25	781	7	57846	203	12500	5951	152

MO

Many Facility Codes have changed. Please refer to the AHA Guide Code Chart. © 2005 AHA Guide

Hospital, Address, Telephone, Approval, Facility, and Physician Codes, Health Care System	Classi-fication Codes		Utilization Data					Expense (thousands) of dollars		
★ American Hospital Association (AHA) membership □ Joint Commission on Accreditation of Healthcare Organizations (JCAHO) accreditation ○ American Osteopathic Association (AOA) accreditation △ Commission on Accreditation of Rehabilitation Facilities (CARF) accreditation	Control	Service	Staffed Beds	Admissions	Census	Outpatient Visits	Births	Total	Payroll	Personnel

TROY—Lincoln County

□ **LINCOLN COUNTY MEDICAL CENTER**, 1000 East Cherry Street, Zip 63379–1599; tel. 636/528–8551 **A**1 9 10 18 **F**2 9 12 14 21 22 27 28 29 33 35 39 40 46 47 48 51 52 53 55 58 60 62 63 64 65 66 69 81 84 88 93 94 95 96 97 108
Primary Contact: Floyd B. Dowell, Jr, Administrator
Web address: www.lcmctroy.com

| | 13 | 10 | 25 | 1269 | 14 | 70617 | — | 22459 | 9680 | 253 |

UNIONVILLE—Putnam County

★ **PUTNAM COUNTY MEMORIAL HOSPITAL**, 1926 Oak Street, Zip 63565–1100, Mailing Address: P.O. Box 389, Zip 63565–0389; tel. 660/947–2411, (Total facility includes 10 beds in nursing home–type unit) **A**10 18 **F**23 33 46 48 61 81 88 92 97
Primary Contact: Ray Magers, Chief Executive Officer
COO: Katherine Smith, Chief Operating Officer
CFO: Tammy Wheeler, Controller
CMO: W Stephen Casady, M.D., Chief of Staff
CHR: Judy Green, Director Human Resources
Web address: www.pcmhosp.com

| | 13 | 10 | 35 | 374 | 12 | 34762 | — | 4791 | 2450 | 88 |

WARRENSBURG—Johnson County

□ **WESTERN MISSOURI MEDICAL CENTER**, 403 Burkarth Road, Zip 64093–3101; tel. 660/747–2500, (Total facility includes 11 beds in nursing home–type unit) **A**1 9 10 20 **F**2 9 11 12 14 21 22 23 24 26 27 28 33 37 46 47 48 50 52 53 55 58 59 60 62 63 64 68 69 75 81 82 84 88 92 93 94 95 96 97 106 108 109 110 **P**6
Primary Contact: Gregory B. Vinardi, President and Chief Executive Officer
Web address: www.wmmconline.org

| | 13 | 10 | 75 | 3534 | 35 | 72373 | 770 | 44318 | 21230 | 495 |

WASHINGTON—Franklin County

✠ **ST. JOHN'S MERCY HOSPITAL**, 901 East Fifth Street, Zip 63090; tel. 636/239–8000, (Total facility includes 22 beds in nursing home–type unit) **A**1 9 10 **F**2 9 10 11 12 21 22 24 26 27 28 29 33 34 37 39 40 46 48 50 52 55 57 58 59 62 63 64 68 69 70 81 84 85 86 87 88 89 92 93 94 95 96 98 106 108 109 110 **P**4 8 **S** Sisters of Mercy Health System, Chesterfield, MO
Web address: www.stjohnsmercy.org/sjmh/default.asp

| | 23 | 10 | 122 | 7139 | 71 | 121209 | 954 | 64272 | 27891 | 615 |

WENTZVILLE—St. Charles County

□ **CROSSROADS REGIONAL MEDICAL CENTER**, 500 Medical Drive, Zip 63385–3421; tel. 636/327–1000 **A**1 9 10 **F**2 9 10 11 12 21 22 26 28 33 37 44 46 47 48 52 55 58 59 60 62 63 65 66 68 69 70 71 75 76 81 82 84 87 88 94 96 106 108 109 110 **P**6 **S** Essent Healthcare, Nashville, TN
Primary Contact: Steve Wylie, Interim Chief Executive Officer
Web address: www.crossroadsregional.com

| | 33 | 10 | 73 | 2286 | 30 | 31176 | 152 | 26586 | 10008 | 257 |

WEST PLAINS—Howell County

✠ **OZARKS MEDICAL CENTER**, 1100 Kentucky Avenue, Zip 65775–1100, Mailing Address: P.O. Box 1100, Zip 65775–1100; tel. 417/256–9111, (Total facility includes 16 beds in nursing home–type unit) **A**1 9 10 19 20 **F**2 4 6 8 9 11 12 15 17 19 21 22 23 26 27 28 31 33 35 36 37 45 46 48 50 51 52 53 55 57 58 59 60 61 62 63 64 65 66 69 71 72 73 74 75 76 77 81 82 84 87 88 92 93 94 95 96 106 107 108 109 110 **P**8
Primary Contact: Philip D. Bagby, President and Chief Executive Officer
CFO: Michael Gross, Vice President Finance
CMO: Jeffrey L. Dryden, D.O., Vice President
CIO: Jim Johnson, Director Information Systems
CHR: Greg Shannon, Director Human Resources
Web address: www.ozarksmedicalcenter.com

| | 23 | 10 | 113 | 5542 | 59 | 200555 | 656 | 79358 | 35815 | 962 |

WINDSOR—Henry County

□ **ROYAL OAKS HOSPITAL**, 307 North Main, Zip 65360–1449; tel. 660/647–2182 **A**1 3 5 10 **F**29 31 52 58 71 72 73 74 75 76 77 94
Primary Contact: Jon L. Bair, Administrator
Web address: www.royal–oaks.com

| | 33 | 22 | 41 | 1498 | 32 | — | — | 10401 | 5851 | 137 |

MO

MONTANA

Hospital, Address, Telephone, Approval, Facility, and Physician Codes, Health Care System	Classi-fication Codes		Utilization Data					Expense (thousands) of dollars		
★ American Hospital Association (AHA) membership □ Joint Commission on Accreditation of Healthcare Organizations (JCAHO) accreditation ○ American Osteopathic Association (AOA) accreditation △ Commission on Accreditation of Rehabilitation Facilities (CARF) accreditation	Control	Service	Staffed Beds	Admissions	Census	Outpatient Visits	Births	Total	Payroll	Personnel

ANACONDA—Deer Lodge County

★ **COMMUNITY HOSPITAL OF ANACONDA**, 401 West Pennsylvania Street, Zip 59711–1999; tel. 406/563–8500, (Total facility includes 62 beds in nursing home–type unit) **A**9 10 18 20 **F**2 5 9 11 12 15 21 22 23 27 28 33 36 45 48 51 52 58 59 60 62 63 66 69 81 84 88 92 93 94 97 107 108 **P**6 **S** Providence Services, Spokane, WA
Primary Contact: Steve McNeece, Chief Executive Officer
CFO: Laura Austin, Chief Financial Officer
CIO: Laura Austin, Chief Financial Officer

| 23 | 10 | 87 | 1174 | 69 | 38770 | 45 | 14143 | 6160 | 183 |

BAKER—Fallon County

FALLON MEDICAL COMPLEX, 202 South 4th Street West, Zip 59313–0820, Mailing Address: P.O. Box 820, Zip 59313–0820; tel. 406/778–3331, (Total facility includes 40 beds in nursing home–type unit) **A**9 10 18 **F**9 12 23 24 26 27 28 30 33 44 46 47 48 51 54 58 61 63 69 70 81 88 92 94 95 96 97 **P**6
Primary Contact: David Espeland, Chief Executive Officer

| 23 | 10 | 52 | 239 | 38 | 16532 | 1 | 5590 | 2936 | 89 |

BIG SANDY—Chouteau County

★ **BIG SANDY MEDICAL CENTER**, Mailing Address: P.O. Box 530, Zip 59520–0530; tel. 406/378–2188, (Total facility includes 22 beds in nursing home–type unit) **A**9 10 18 **F**27 28 30 51 52 69 92 **P**2
Primary Contact: Harry Bold, Administrator

| 23 | 10 | 30 | 127 | 19 | 5223 | 0 | 1657 | 1180 | 31 |

BIG TIMBER—Sweet Grass County

★ **PIONEER MEDICAL CENTER**, 301 West Seventh Avenue, Zip 59011, Mailing Address: P.O. Box 1228, Zip 59011–1228; tel. 406/932–4603, (Total facility includes 52 beds in nursing home–type unit) **A**9 10 18 **F**1 6 8 9 24 29 33 36 44 46 48 52 54 60 63 69 70 75 92 94 95 97 106 109 110 **P**6
Primary Contact: Cody Langbehn, Chief Executive Officer
CMO: Kirby Peden, M.D., Chief of Staff
Web address: www.billingsclinic.com/bigtimber

| 13 | 10 | 60 | 183 | 38 | 8362 | 0 | 4736 | 1567 | 110 |

BILLINGS—Yellowstone County

⊞ **DEACONESS BILLINGS CLINIC**, 2800 10th Avenue North, Zip 59101–0799, Mailing Address: P.O. Box 37000, Zip 59107–7000; tel. 406/657–4000, (Total facility includes 125 beds in nursing home–type unit) **A**1 3 5 9 10 **F**2 6 7 8 9 11 12 14 15 17 19 21 22 23 24 26 27 28 29 30 31 33 34 35 36 37 38 39 40 42 44 45 46 47 48 49 50 52 53 55 56 57 58 59 60 61 62 63 64 65 66 69 70 71 72 73 74 75 76 77 78 81 82 87 88 89 92 93 94 95 96 98 106 107 108 109 110 **P**6
Primary Contact: Nicholas J. Wolter, M.D., President and Chief Executive Officer
CFO: Stan P. Moser, Chief Financial Officer
CMO: Mark C. Rumans, M.D., Chief of Staff
CIO: Chris E. Stevens, Chief Information Officer
CHR: Carlene Crall, Executive Director Human Resources
Web address: www.billingsclinic.com

| 23 | 10 | 350 | 13887 | 292 | 838081 | 1086 | 279922 | 137499 | 2511 |

⊞ △ **ST. VINCENT HEALTHCARE**, 1233 North 30th Street, Zip 59101–0165, Mailing Address: P.O. Box 35200, Zip 59107–5200; tel. 406/237–7000, (Total facility includes 28 beds in nursing home–type unit) **A**1 3 5 7 9 10 **F**2 9 10 11 12 14 15 17 19 21 22 24 26 27 28 29 30 31 33 34 35 37 38 39 40 44 45 46 47 48 49 50 52 55 56 57 58 59 60 61 62 63 64 65 66 67 68 69 70 72 73 74 76 77 81 82 85 88 92 93 94 95 96 98 106 107 108 109 **P**6 **S** Sisters of Charity of Leavenworth Health System, Lenexa, KS
Primary Contact: M. Michelle Hood, President and Chief Executive Officer
COO: Jack Bell, Executive Vice Persident and Chief Operating Officer
CFO: Steve Ballock, Chief Financial Officer
CIO: Jay McKiernan, Director, Information Systems
CHR: Harold Anderson, Vice President Human Resources
Web address: www.stvincenthealthcare.org

| 21 | 10 | 268 | 13249 | 159 | 374187 | 1280 | 182494 | 73283 | 1566 |

BOZEMAN—Gallatin County

★ **BOZEMAN DEACONESS HOSPITAL**, 915 Highland Boulevard, Zip 59715–6999; tel. 406/585–5000, (Nonreporting) **A**9 10 20
Primary Contact: John A. Nordwick, President and Chief Executive Officer

| 23 | 10 | 70 | — | — | — | — | — | — | — |

BROWNING—Glacier County

⊞ **U. S. PUBLIC HEALTH SERVICE BLACKFEET COMMUNITY HOSPITAL**, Mailing Address: P.O. Box 760, Zip 59417–0760; tel. 406/338–6100, (Nonreporting) **A**1 9 10 **S** U. S. Indian Health Service, Rockville, MD
Primary Contact: Jaloo Zelonis, Acting Director
Web address: www.phs.ihs.gov

| 47 | 10 | 25 | — | — | — | — | — | — | — |

MT

Many Facility Codes have changed. Please refer to the AHA Guide Code Chart. © 2005 AHA Guide

Hospital, Address, Telephone, Approval, Facility, and Physician Codes, Health Care System	Classi-fication Codes		Utilization Data					Expense (thousands) of dollars		
★ American Hospital Association (AHA) membership □ Joint Commission on Accreditation of Healthcare Organizations (JCAHO) accreditation ○ American Osteopathic Association (AOA) accreditation △ Commission on Accreditation of Rehabilitation Facilities (CARF) accreditation	Control	Service	Staffed Beds	Admissions	Census	Outpatient Visits	Births	Total	Payroll	Personnel

BUTTE—Silver Bow County

☒ **ST. JAMES HEALTHCARE**, 400 South Clark Street, Zip 59701–2328, Mailing Address: P.O. Box 3300, Zip 59702–3300; tel. 406/723–2500 **A**1 9 10 19 20 **F**2 9 11 12 15 17 21 22 23 27 28 29 33 34 37 40 41 44 46 49 52 55 56 58 59 60 61 63 66 69 79 80 81 82 84 85 87 88 92 93 94 95 **P**8 **S** Sisters of Charity of Leavenworth Health System, Lenexa, KS
Primary Contact: James Kiser, II, Chief Administrative Officer
CFO: Bruce Whitfield, Chief Financial Officer
CMO: Brett Kronenberger, M.D., Medical Staff President
CIO: Linda Barrett, Director Information Systems
CHR: Patrick Dudley, Director
Web address: www.stjameshealthcare.org

| | 23 | 10 | 69 | 4953 | 59 | 62636 | 492 | 54427 | 21408 | 493 |

CHESTER—Liberty County

★ **LIBERTY COUNTY HOSPITAL AND NURSING HOME**, Mailing Address: P.O. Box 705, Zip 59522–0705; tel. 406/759–5181, (Total facility includes 65 beds in nursing home–type unit) **A**9 10 18 20 **F**1 3 8 11 12 13 14 33 46 51 55 56 59 63 64 67 68 69 71 81 88 92 94 97 106 **P**6
Primary Contact: Walter S. Busch, Chief Executive Officer
CFO: Rich Moog, Chief Financial Officer
CMO: Anna Earl, M.D., Chief of Staff
Web address: www.lchnh.org

| | 23 | 10 | 76 | 251 | 37 | 6038 | 14 | 5945 | 3034 | 99 |

CHOTEAU—Teton County

★ **TETON MEDICAL CENTER**, 915 Fourth Street N.W., Zip 59422–9123; tel. 406/466–5763, (Total facility includes 36 beds in nursing home–type unit) **A**9 10 18 **F**1 5 9 12 26 27 28 29 33 36 41 44 45 46 47 48 51 52 65 69 92 94 95 97 108
Primary Contact: H. Ray Gibbons, FACHE, Chief Executive Officer
Web address: www.tetonmedicalcenter.net

| | 16 | 10 | 46 | 285 | 34 | 5302 | 0 | 2358 | 1362 | 62 |

CIRCLE—McCone County

MCCONE COUNTY HEALTH CENTER, Mailing Address: P.O. Box 48, Zip 59215–0048; tel. 406/485–3381, (Total facility includes 30 beds in nursing home–type unit) **A**9 10 18 **F**1 9 26 33 45 92 97 108
Primary Contact: Nancy Hansen, Administrator

| | 23 | 10 | 38 | 95 | 25 | 2769 | 0 | 2195 | 965 | 45 |

COLUMBUS—Stillwater County

STILLWATER COMMUNITY HOSPITAL, 44 West Fourth Avenue North, Zip 59019–7126, Mailing Address: P.O. Box 959, Zip 59019–0959; tel. 406/322–5316, (Total facility includes 10 beds in nursing home–type unit) **A**9 10 18 20 **F**8 12 21 24 27 29 33 44 46 48 51 53 54 58 63 69 92 94 97
Primary Contact: Tim Russell, Administrator

| | 23 | 10 | 23 | 231 | 13 | 6170 | 0 | 3487 | 1418 | 42 |

CONRAD—Pondera County

PONDERA MEDICAL CENTER, 805 Sunset Boulevard, Zip 59425–1721, Mailing Address: P.O. Box 758, Zip 59425–0757; tel. 406/271–3211, (Total facility includes 59 beds in nursing home–type unit) **A**9 10 18 **F**1 2 5 6 9 11 12 21 27 28 29 33 41 46 48 51 59 60 63 66 69 70 75 82 85 88 92 94 97 108 **P**6
Primary Contact: C. James Christensen, Chief Executive Officer
Web address: www.ourpmc.com

| | 23 | 10 | 79 | 459 | 59 | 15061 | 39 | 8748 | 4632 | 157 |

CROW AGENCY—Big Horn County

☒ **CROW/NORTHERN CHEYENNE HOSPITAL**, Mailing Address: P.O. Box 9, Zip 59022–0009; tel. 406/638–2626, (Nonreporting) **A**1 10 18 **S** U. S. Indian Health Service, Rockville, MD
Primary Contact: Kevin Stiffarm, Chief Executive Officer
COO: Curtis Brien, Administrative Officer
CMO: Clayton Bunt, M.D., Chief Medical Officer
CIO: Melanie Falls Down, Site Manager

| | 44 | 10 | 24 | — | — | — | — | — | — | — |

CULBERTSON—Roosevelt County

★ **ROOSEVELT MEMORIAL MEDICAL CENTER**, 818 Second Avenue East, Zip 59218, Mailing Address: P.O. Box 419, Zip 59218–0419; tel. 406/787–6281, (Total facility includes 34 beds in nursing home–type unit) **A**9 10 18 **F**1 6 9 21 24 26 27 29 33 39 44 45 46 48 52 54 66 69 70 84 92 94 97 **P**6
Primary Contact: Audrey Stromberg, Administrator
CFO: Carolyn Casterline, Financial Director
Web address: www.roosmem.org

| | 23 | 10 | 41 | 218 | 34 | 9591 | 0 | 3391 | 1890 | 65 |

CUT BANK—Glacier County

★ **NORTHERN ROCKIES MEDICAL CENTER**, 802 Second Street S.E., Zip 59427–3331; tel. 406/873–2251 **A**9 10 18 20 **F**9 21 33 39 48 52 58 59 60 63 69 70 81 82 84 88 94 97 108 **P**4
Primary Contact: Cherie Taylor, Chief Executive Officer
CFO: Nick Hinch, Chief Financial Officer
CMO: Clark Fultz, D.O., Chief Medical Staff
CHR: Kandie Lemieux, Administrative Assistant for Human Resources

| | 23 | 10 | 20 | 508 | 5 | 10713 | 59 | 7126 | 3041 | 58 |

DEER LODGE—Powell County

★ **POWELL COUNTY MEMORIAL HOSPITAL**, 1101 Texas Avenue, Zip 59722–1828; tel. 406/846–2212, (Total facility includes 16 beds in nursing home–type unit) **A**9 10 18 **F**2 9 10 11 24 26 27 28 29 33 46 48 52 58 63 81 88 92 97 **P**5
Primary Contact: John A. Cosco, Ph.D., FACHE, Chief Executive Officer
CFO: Jaena Richards, Chief Financial Officer
CIO: Chris Foster, Director Health Information Management
Web address: www.pcmh.org

| | 23 | 10 | 35 | 342 | 15 | 5911 | 15 | 4942 | 2032 | 57 |

MT

Hospital, Address, Telephone, Approval, Facility, and Physician Codes, Health Care System	Classi-fication Codes		Utilization Data					Expense (thousands) of dollars		
★ American Hospital Association (AHA) membership □ Joint Commission on Accreditation of Healthcare Organizations (JCAHO) accreditation ○ American Osteopathic Association (AOA) accreditation △ Commission on Accreditation of Rehabilitation Facilities (CARF) accreditation	Control	Service	Staffed Beds	Admissions	Census	Outpatient Visits	Births	Total	Payroll	Personnel

DILLON—Beaverhead County

★ **BARRETT HOSPITAL & HEALTHCARE**, 90 Highway 91 South, Zip 59725–3597; tel. 406/683–3000 **A**9 10 18 **F**2 9 11 12 21 22 24 26 27 28 29 31 33 35 36 37 38 39 46 47 48 51 52 53 55 58 59 60 62 63 65 69 81 82 85 87 88 92 94 95 96 97 106 108 109 110 **P**5 8 **S** Brim Healthcare, Inc., Brentwood, TN
Primary Contact: John M. Mootry, Chief Executive Officer
CFO: Dick Achter, Chief Operating Officer and Chief Financial Officer
CIO: Dick Achter, Chief Operating Officer and Chief Financial Officer
Web address: www.barretthospital.org

| | 16 | 10 | 20 | 895 | 7 | 22716 | 77 | 10256 | 4764 | 115 |

EKALAKA—Carter County

DAHL MEMORIAL MEDICAL ASSISTANCE FACILITY, Mailing Address: P.O. Box 46, Zip 59324–0046; tel. 406/775–8730, (Total facility includes 23 beds in nursing home–type unit) **A**9 10 18 **F**1 6 26 27 28 33 45 46 48 54 92 94 97 108 **P**6
Primary Contact: Nadine Elmore, Chief Executive Officer

| | 23 | 80 | 31 | 22 | 16 | 826 | 1 | 1179 | 716 | 41 |

ENNIS—Madison County

MADISON VALLEY HOSPITAL, 217 North Main Street, Zip 59729–0397, Mailing Address: P.O. Box 397, Zip 59729–0397; tel. 406/682–4222 **A**9 10 18 20 **F**14 33 46 48 70 97 **P**6
Primary Contact: Pete Brekhus, Chief Executive Officer
Web address: www.mvhospital–clinic.com

| | 16 | 10 | 9 | 146 | 2 | 13475 | 0 | 2311 | 1079 | 29 |

FORSYTH—Rosebud County

★ **ROSEBUD HEALTH CARE CENTER**, 383 North 17th Avenue, Zip 59327, Mailing Address: P.O. Box 268, Zip 59327–0268; tel. 406/346–2161, (Total facility includes 53 beds in nursing home–type unit) (Nonreporting) **A**9 10 18 20
Primary Contact: Gary W. Robertson, Chief Executive Officer
CFO: Kyle Gee, Chief Financial Officer
CHR: Karla Allies, Director Human Resources

| | 23 | 10 | 62 | — | — | — | — | — | — | — |

FORT BENTON—Chouteau County

★ **MISSOURI RIVER MEDICAL CENTER**, 1501 St. Charles Street, Zip 59442–0249, Mailing Address: P.O. Box 249, Zip 59442–0249; tel. 406/622–3331, (Total facility includes 45 beds in nursing home–type unit) **A**9 10 18 **F**1 8 12 28 33 36 45 46 48 51 52 54 60 69 92 94 97 106 107 108 **P**5 **S** Providence Services, Spokane, WA
Primary Contact: Jay Pottenger, Administrator
CFO: Lynn Asbeck, Business Office Manager
Web address: www.fortbenton.com/hospital.index.htm

| | 16 | 80 | 52 | 234 | 38 | 7187 | 0 | 4213 | 2378 | 84 |

FORT HARRISON—Lewis and Clark County

⊞ **VETERANS AFFAIRS MONTANA HEALTHCARE SYSTEM**, 1892 Williams Street, Zip 59636; tel. 406/442–6410, (Total facility includes 30 beds in nursing home–type unit) **A**1 **F**2 4 9 14 15 17 21 22 23 25 26 27 28 29 31 32 35 37 38 39 40 41 42 44 45 46 47 48 50 52 54 55 57 58 60 61 62 63 64 65 66 69 70 71 73 75 76 77 81 82 84 85 88 92 93 94 96 106 107 108 109 110 **P**6 **S** Department of Veterans Affairs, Washington, DC
Primary Contact: Joseph Underkofler, Director
CFO: Brian Gustafson, Chief Financial Officer
CMO: Faust M. Alvarez, M.D., Chief of Staff
CIO: Paul Gauthier, Chief Information Resources Management
CHR: Aggie Hamilton, Chief Human Resources
Web address: www.va.gov/sta/guide/home.asp

| | 45 | 10 | 80 | 2527 | 37 | 248662 | 0 | 96046 | 36959 | 576 |

GLASGOW—Valley County

⊞ **FRANCES MAHON DEACONESS HOSPITAL**, 621 Third Street South, Zip 59230–2699; tel. 406/228–3500 **A**1 9 10 18 **F**2 6 9 11 12 21 23 26 27 28 29 33 34 37 41 44 46 47 48 49 50 52 58 60 61 62 63 65 66 69 73 75 78 81 84 86 87 88 93 94 97 106 **P**6 7
Primary Contact: Randall G. Holom, Chief Executive Officer
COO: Ellen Guttenberg, Chief Operating Officer
CFO: Del Gienger, Director of Financial Services
CHR: Shelly Van Buren, Director, Human Resources
Web address: www.fmdh.org

| | 23 | 10 | 25 | 906 | 8 | 36869 | 140 | 15986 | 6813 | 205 |

GLENDIVE—Dawson County

★ **GLENDIVE MEDICAL CENTER**, 202 Prospect Drive, Zip 59330–1999; tel. 406/345–3306, (Total facility includes 75 beds in nursing home–type unit) **A**9 10 18 20 **F**2 8 9 11 12 22 23 26 27 29 31 33 34 36 37 44 45 46 48 50 51 52 54 55 58 59 60 61 62 63 66 69 71 72 75 76 81 82 84 88 92 94 95 96 97 107 108 109 **P**6 7 8
Primary Contact: Scott Duke, Chief Executive Officer
CFO: Barbara Markham, Chief Financial Officer
CIO: Mike Janeway, M.D., Executive Director Information Systems
CHR: Sandra McGovern, Executive Director Human Resources
Web address: www.gmc.org

| | 23 | 10 | 100 | 962 | 75 | 29653 | 52 | 17234 | 7682 | 236 |

MT

Many Facility Codes have changed. Please refer to the AHA Guide Code Chart.   © 2005 AHA Guide

Hospital, Address, Telephone, Approval, Facility, and Physician Codes, Health Care System	Classi-fication Codes		Utilization Data					Expense (thousands) of dollars		
★ American Hospital Association (AHA) membership □ Joint Commission on Accreditation of Healthcare Organizations (JCAHO) accreditation ○ American Osteopathic Association (AOA) accreditation △ Commission on Accreditation of Rehabilitation Facilities (CARF) accreditation	Control	Service	Staffed Beds	Admissions	Census	Outpatient Visits	Births	Total	Payroll	Personnel

GREAT FALLS—Cascade County

☒ △ **BENEFIS HEALTHCARE**, 1101 26th Street South, Zip 59405–5104; tel. 406/455–5000, (Includes BENEFIS HEALTH CARE–EAST CAMPUS, 1101 26th Street, Zip 59405; BENEFIS HEALTH CARE–WEST CAMPUS, 500 15th Avenue South, Zip 59405), (Total facility includes 146 beds in nursing home–type unit) **A**1 2 7 9 10 20 **F**2 3 4 5 9 10 11 12 14 15 16 17 18 19 21 22 23 26 27 28 29 31 33 34 36 37 38 39 42 44 45 46 47 48 49 50 51 52 55 56 57 58 59 60 61 62 63 64 65 66 67 68 69 70 71 73 74 75 76 77 78 79 80 81 82 84 85 88 90 92 93 94 95 96 98 106 107 108 109 110 **P**2 4 5 6 8 **S** Providence Services, Spokane, WA
Primary Contact: John H. Goodnow, President and Chief Executive Officer
COO: Laura Goldhahn Kowen, Chief Operating Officer and Senior Vice President
CFO: Wayne Dunn, Vice President Finance
CMO: Paul Dolan, M.D., Vice President Medical Affairs
CIO: Wayne Thompson, Manager Information Systems
CHR: Terry Olinger, Vice President Human Resources
Web address: www.benefis.org
| 23 | 10 | 470 | 14057 | 316 | 123763 | 1401 | 166954 | 71196 | 1687 |

CENTRAL MONTANA SURGICAL HOSPITAL, 1411 9th Street South, Zip 59405; tel. 406/727–5577, (Nonreporting) **A**9 10
Primary Contact: Anthony Peterschick, Administrator
| 33 | 13 | 20 | — | — | — | — | — | — | — |

HAMILTON—Ravalli County

★ **MARCUS DALY MEMORIAL HOSPITAL**, 1200 Westwood Drive, Zip 59840–2395; tel. 406/363–2211 **A**9 10 18 20 **F**9 11 12 26 27 28 29 33 36 38 46 47 48 51 54 55 59 60 62 63 65 66 69 70 75 81 84 88 94 95 96 107 108 109
Primary Contact: John M. Bartos, Chief Executive Officer
CFO: Donja Erdman, Chief Financial Officer
CIO: Pamela Chaplin, Data Processing Director
CHR: Debbie Morris, Director Human Resources
Web address: www.mdmh.org
| 23 | 10 | 48 | 1824 | 16 | 33698 | 187 | 25436 | 11711 | 266 |

HARDIN—Big Horn County

★ **BIG HORN COUNTY MEMORIAL HOSPITAL**, 17 North Miles Avenue, Zip 59034–0430; tel. 406/665–2310, (Total facility includes 73 beds in nursing home–type unit) **A**9 10 18 20 **F**1 8 9 11 12 21 26 27 28 29 33 39 46 48 59 60 63 68 69 81 88 91 92 94 97 98 106 108 **P**5
Primary Contact: Gary W. Robertson, Chief Executive Officer
CFO: Roxie Cain, Chief Financial Officer
CIO: David M. Peyok, Chief Executive Officer
| 23 | 10 | 89 | 397 | 54 | 4692 | 32 | 4757 | 2048 | 83 |

HARLEM—Blaine County

★ **U. S. PUBLIC HEALTH SERVICE INDIAN HOSPITAL**, Rural Route 1, Box 67, Zip 59526; tel. 406/353–3100 **A**10 18 **F**6 27 28 32 33 **P**5 **S** U. S. Indian Health Service, Rockville, MD
Primary Contact: Daryl A. Brockie, Director
CMO: Ethel L. Moore, M.D., Chief Medical Officer
CIO: Duane Stiffarm, Chief Information Officer
CHR: Mary H. Mount, Administrative Officer
| 47 | 10 | 6 | 212 | 1 | 18357 | 0 | — | — | 128 |

HARLOWTON—Wheatland County

★ **WHEATLAND MEMORIAL HOSPITAL**, 530 Third Street North East, Zip 59036, Mailing Address: P.O. Box 287, Zip 59036–0287; tel. 406/632–4351, (Total facility includes 33 beds in nursing home–type unit) **A**9 10 18 **F**12 14 22 24 27 28 29 33 44 45 46 47 48 50 52 60 62 64 66 69 70 88 92 94 96 97 108 109 **P**6
Primary Contact: Scot Mitchell, CHE, Chief Executive Officer
CFO: Kathie Newland, Accounting Manager
CHR: Patsy Eling, Director Human Resources
Web address: www.wheatlandmemorial.org
| 23 | 10 | 54 | 148 | 32 | 5015 | 0 | 3863 | 2056 | 62 |

HAVRE—Hill County

★ **NORTHERN MONTANA HOSPITAL**, 30 13th Street, Zip 59501–5222, Mailing Address: P.O. Box 1231, Zip 59501–1231; tel. 406/265–2211, (Total facility includes 136 beds in nursing home–type unit) **A**9 10 20 **F**8 9 11 12 27 28 29 31 33 36 37 38 39 44 46 48 49 51 52 53 55 58 59 60 62 63 69 70 71 72 74 75 76 77 78 81 82 84 88 92 93 94 96 97 106 108 110 **P**6
Primary Contact: David Henry, President and Chief Executive Officer
Web address: www.nmhcare.org
| 23 | 10 | 185 | 2834 | 148 | 74160 | 389 | 37585 | 19769 | 531 |

HELENA—Lewis and Clark County

☒ **SHODAIR CHILDREN'S HOSPITAL**, 2755 Colonial Drive, Zip 59601–4926, Mailing Address: P.O. Box 5539, Zip 59604–5539; tel. 406/444–7500 **A**1 9 10 **F**27 28 71 72 74 75 77 90 92 94 **P**6
Primary Contact: John P. Casey, Administrator
CFO: Jan Kalgaard, Chief Financial Officer
CHR: Gary Willis, Director Human Resources
Web address: www.shodairhospital.org
| 23 | 52 | 68 | 428 | 58 | 4571 | 0 | 11362 | 6313 | 169 |

☒ **ST. PETER'S HOSPITAL**, 2475 Broadway, Zip 59601–4999; tel. 406/442–2480, (Total facility includes 12 beds in nursing home–type unit) **A**1 2 9 10 20 **F**2 6 11 12 15 17 21 22 23 26 27 28 29 30 31 33 34 36 37 38 39 40 46 47 48 49 51 52 55 57 58 59 60 61 62 63 65 66 69 73 75 77 81 82 84 85 88 92 93 94 96 97 108 110 **P**4 8
Primary Contact: John H. Solheim, President and Chief Executive Officer
CFO: John Higgins, Chief Financial Officer
Web address: www.stpetes.org
| 23 | 10 | 99 | 5362 | 60 | 150379 | 690 | 68040 | 27628 | 536 |

MT

Hospital, Address, Telephone, Approval, Facility, and Physician Codes, Health Care System	Classi-fication Codes		Utilization Data					Expense (thousands) of dollars		
★ American Hospital Association (AHA) membership □ Joint Commission on Accreditation of Healthcare Organizations (JCAHO) accreditation ○ American Osteopathic Association (AOA) accreditation △ Commission on Accreditation of Rehabilitation Facilities (CARF) accreditation	Control	Service	Staffed Beds	Admissions	Census	Outpatient Visits	Births	Total	Payroll	Personnel

JORDAN—Garfield County

GARFIELD COUNTY HEALTH CENTER, 101 Levette Avenue, Zip 59337; tel. 406/557-2500, (Total facility includes 24 beds in nursing home–type unit) **A**9 10 18 **F**1 3 6 13 14 33 37 38 44 46 55 56 67 68 71 92 97 Primary Contact: Mark Pond, Administrator	13	10	28	44	16	316	0	1308	661	30

KALISPELL—Flathead County

HEALTH CENTER NORTHWEST, 320 Sunnyview Lane, Zip 59901; tel. 406/751-7500, (Nonreporting) **A**10 Primary Contact: Velinda Stevens, President	33	49	18	—	—	—	—	—	—	—
⊠ △ **KALISPELL REGIONAL MEDICAL CENTER**, 310 Sunnyview Lane, Zip 59901-3199; tel. 406/752-5111, (Includes PATHWAYS TREATMENT CENTER, 200 Heritage Way, Zip 59901; tel. 406/756-3950) **A**1 7 9 10 19 20 **F**2 3 4 6 11 15 17 19 21 22 23 26 27 28 29 32 33 34 36 46 47 48 51 52 53 55 56 57 58 59 61 62 63 64 65 66 68 69 71 72 73 74 75 76 77 78 79 80 81 82 84 85 88 94 96 108 110 Primary Contact: Velinda Stevens, President COO: Ted W. Hirsch, Chief Executive Officer CFO: Charles T. Pearce, Chief Financial and Information Officer CHR: Pat Wilson, Diector Human Resources Web address: www.krmc.org	23	10	149	6753	79	121397	838	84122	33554	871

LEWISTOWN—Fergus County

★ **CENTRAL MONTANA MEDICAL CENTER**, 408 Wendell Avenue, Zip 59457-2261; tel. 406/538-7711, (Total facility includes 85 beds in nursing home–type unit) **A**9 10 20 **F**1 2 6 9 11 12 21 23 26 27 28 29 33 34 36 37 39 41 44 45 46 48 51 52 57 58 59 60 61 62 63 65 69 73 75 78 81 82 87 88 92 93 94 95 96 97 98 106 108 110 **P**6 **S** Quorum Health Resources, Plano, TX Primary Contact: David M. Faulkner, Chief Executive Officer CFO: Alan Aldrich, Chief Financial Officer Web address: www.cmmccares.com	23	10	124	1483	86	34589	102	19204	9410	235

LIBBY—Lincoln County

★ **ST. JOHN'S LUTHERAN HOSPITAL**, 350 Louisiana Avenue, Zip 59923-2198; tel. 406/293-0100 **A**9 10 18 **F**2 8 9 11 12 14 21 22 23 28 29 33 36 37 38 44 46 48 51 52 53 55 58 59 60 62 63 69 70 75 81 85 88 92 94 95 96 97 106 107 108 109 110 Primary Contact: Bill Patten, Chief Executive Officer CFO: Ron Wiens, Chief Financial Officer CMO: Lance Ercanbrack, M.D., Chief of Staff CHR: Jeanie Gentry, Director Support Services Web address: www.sjlh.com	23	10	24	1030	10	26335	80	12880	6100	157

LIVINGSTON—Park County

★ **LIVINGSTON MEMORIAL HOSPITAL**, 504 South 13th Street, Zip 59047-3798; tel. 406/222-3541 **A**9 10 18 **F**11 12 14 21 23 26 27 28 29 33 34 36 37 39 51 52 53 55 59 60 61 62 63 64 65 66 69 81 82 88 95 97 **P**6 Primary Contact: Samuel G. Pleshar, Chief Executive Officer CIO: Sandra Harker, Director, Community Development	23	10	28	1160	11	27815	109	19206	10030	253

MALTA—Phillips County

PHILLIPS COUNTY MEDICAL CENTER, 417 South Fourth East, Zip 59538, Mailing Address: P.O. Box 640, Zip 59538-0640; tel. 406/654-1100 **A**9 10 18 **F**2 12 21 23 24 26 27 28 29 33 46 48 51 52 57 62 63 69 88 92 97 109 Primary Contact: Larry E. Putnam, Administrator	23	10	12	195	2	6792	0	3237	2008	56

MILES CITY—Custer County

⊠ **HOLY ROSARY HEALTHCARE**, 2600 Wilson Street, Zip 59301-5094; tel. 406/233-2600, (Total facility includes 100 beds in nursing home–type unit) **A**1 9 10 20 **F**2 11 12 14 21 22 23 27 28 29 33 36 45 46 48 52 55 58 59 61 62 63 64 66 68 69 81 82 84 85 88 92 94 95 96 97 107 108 110 **S** Sisters of Charity of Leavenworth Health System, Lenexa, KS Primary Contact: Greg Nielsen, Chief Administrative Officer CFO: Jeff Gollaher, Vice President Fiscal Servs CIO: Jana Anderson, Director Information Services CHR: Cathy Rodenbaugh, Human Resource Director Web address: www.hrh-mt.org	21	10	136	2130	90	33384	247	24168	10171	275

MISSOULA—Missoula County

⊠ △ **COMMUNITY MEDICAL CENTER**, 2827 Fort Missoula Road, Zip 59804-7408; tel. 406/728-4100 **A**1 5 7 9 10 19 **F**2 11 12 14 21 22 23 26 27 29 33 34 37 38 45 46 48 55 56 58 59 60 62 63 64 67 68 69 81 82 88 94 96 106 107 108 109 **P**6 Primary Contact: Thomas A. Moser, President and Chief Executive Officer CFO: David Richhart, Chief Financial Officer CMO: Frank Reed, M.D., Vice President Medical Staff Affairs CIO: Valerie Cole, Director Information Systems CHR: Betty Hilmo, Director Human Resources Web address: www.communitymed.org	23	10	146	6567	77	164740	1665	99383	47357	934

MT

Hospital, Address, Telephone, Approval, Facility, and Physician Codes, Health Care System	Classi- fication Codes		Utilization Data					Expense (thousands) of dollars		
★ American Hospital Association (AHA) membership □ Joint Commission on Accreditation of Healthcare Organizations (JCAHO) accreditation ○ American Osteopathic Association (AOA) accreditation △ Commission on Accreditation of Rehabilitation Facilities (CARF) accreditation	Control	Service	Staffed Beds	Admissions	Census	Outpatient Visits	Births	Total	Payroll	Personnel
✠ **ST. PATRICK HOSPITAL**, 500 West Broadway, Zip 59802–4096, Mailing Address: P.O. Box 4587, Zip 59806–4587; tel. 406/543–7271 **A**1 2 5 9 10 19 **F**2 3 4 9 10 12 15 16 17 18 19 20 21 22 23 26 27 28 29 30 31 32 33 34 35 37 38 39 40 41 43 46 47 48 49 50 52 53 55 57 58 60 61 62 63 64 65 67 69 70 71 72 73 74 75 76 77 78 79 80 81 82 83 84 85 86 87 88 92 93 94 95 96 104 106 108 109 110 **P**7 **S** Providence Services, Spokane, WA Primary Contact: Steve Witz, President CFO: Loren Jacobson, Vice President and Chief Financial Officer CIO: Arek Shennar, Director Information Services CHR: Lynn Brooks, Assistant Vice President Human Resources Web address: www.saintpatrick.org	21	10	200	9053	127	145260	0	146231	57198	1133
PHILIPSBURG—Granite County										
GRANITE COUNTY MEDICAL CENTER, Mailing Address: P.O. Box 729, Zip 59858–0729; tel. 406/859–3271, (Total facility includes 28 beds in nursing home–type unit) **A**9 10 18 **F**1 3 13 14 21 24 27 29 31 33 36 37 38 44 45 46 48 52 55 56 64 65 67 68 69 70 71 92 94 97 108 110 **P**6 Primary Contact: Doris White Gilbertson, Administrator	13	10	33	34	13	2352	0	1894	929	41
PLAINS—Sanders County										
★ **CLARK FORK VALLEY HOSPITAL**, Mailing Address: P.O. Box 768, Zip 59859–0768; tel. 406/826–3601, (Total facility includes 28 beds in nursing home–type unit) **A**9 10 18 **F**11 12 33 36 38 46 48 51 52 55 59 63 69 81 88 92 94 97 **P**6 Primary Contact: Lawrence L. White, Jr, Interim President and Chief Executive Officer CFO: Carla Neiman, Chief Financial Officer CMO: Dean O. French, M.D., Chief of Staff CIO: Carla Neiman, Chief Financial Officer CHR: Cheryl Kegel, Manager Human Resources Web address: www.cfvh.org	23	10	44	667	33	17461	40	9458	4459	131
PLENTYWOOD—Sheridan County										
SHERIDAN MEMORIAL HOSPITAL, 440 West Laurel Avenue, Zip 59254–1596; tel. 406/765–1420, (Total facility includes 78 beds in nursing home–type unit) **A**9 10 18 **F**2 6 9 11 12 22 29 33 36 46 51 55 59 60 63 69 81 88 92 94 97 108 **P**5 Primary Contact: Wayne Nelson, Chief Executive Officer Web address: www.sheridanhospital.org	23	10	110	491	76	6308	21	4518	3378	145
POLSON—Lake County										
✠ **ST. JOSEPH HOSPITAL**, 6 Thirteenth Avenue East, Zip 59860–5316, Mailing Address: P.O. Box 1010, Zip 59860–1010; tel. 406/883–5377 **A**1 9 10 18 **F**2 8 9 11 12 21 22 24 26 27 28 29 33 37 38 39 41 46 47 48 51 52 53 58 59 62 63 64 69 73 81 85 88 94 95 97 106 108 109 110 **P**7 **S** Providence Services, Spokane, WA Primary Contact: John W. Glueckert, President CFO: John Nadone, Vice President and Chief Financial Officer CMO: Maurice Brown, M.D., Chief of Staff Web address: www.saintjoes.org	21	10	22	831	5	68292	129	14115	4433	139
POPLAR—Roosevelt County										
POPLAR COMMUNITY HOSPITAL, H and Court Avenue, Zip 59255, Mailing Address: P.O. Box 38, Zip 59255; tel. 406/768–3452 **A**10 18 **F**6 26 27 28 33 39 45 46 48 52 58 62 63 81 92 94 97 110 **P**6 Primary Contact: Margaret B. Norgaard, Chief Executive Officer Web address: www.nemhs.net	23	10	20	326	12	6662	1	3326	1679	51
RED LODGE—Carbon County										
★ **BEARTOOTH HOSPITAL AND HEALTH CENTER**, 600 West 20th Street, Zip 59068, Mailing Address: P.O. Box 590, Zip 59068–0590; tel. 406/446–2345, (Total facility includes 30 beds in nursing home–type unit) **A**9 10 18 20 **F**9 11 12 14 21 22 32 33 36 37 38 39 41 44 46 47 48 51 52 53 59 60 63 65 66 68 69 70 88 92 94 95 97 108 **P**5 Primary Contact: Kelley Evans, Administrator CFO: Kyle Gee, Chief Financial Officer CMO: Jeff Zavala, M.D., Chief of Staff CIO: Mary Marks, Director Medical Records CHR: Tina Williamson, Director Human Resources	23	10	52	382	50	1693	38	4553	2686	92
RONAN—Lake County										
★ **ST. LUKE COMMUNITY HOSPITAL**, 107 Sixth Avenue S.W., Zip 59864–2634; tel. 406/676–4441, (Total facility includes 75 beds in nursing home–type unit) **A**9 10 18 **F**1 11 12 26 27 28 33 34 36 41 46 48 50 51 52 58 59 60 63 69 81 84 88 92 95 97 **P**6 Primary Contact: Shane H. Roberts, Chief Executive Officer CFO: Larry Robinson, Director Finance CMO: Steven M. Yoder, M.D., Chief of Staff CHR: Theresa Jones, Manager Human Resources Web address: www.stlukehealthnet.org	23	10	99	961	72	60737	136	18106	9151	232

MT

Hospital, Address, Telephone, Approval, Facility, and Physician Codes, Health Care System	Classi-fication Codes		Utilization Data					Expense (thousands) of dollars		
★ American Hospital Association (AHA) membership □ Joint Commission on Accreditation of Healthcare Organizations (JCAHO) accreditation ○ American Osteopathic Association (AOA) accreditation △ Commission on Accreditation of Rehabilitation Facilities (CARF) accreditation	Control	Service	Staffed Beds	Admissions	Census	Outpatient Visits	Births	Total	Payroll	Personnel

ROUNDUP—Musselshell County

★ **ROUNDUP MEMORIAL HEALTHCARE**, (Formerly Roundup Memorial Hospital), 1202 Third Street West, Zip 59072–1816, Mailing Address: P.O. Box 40, Zip 59072–0040; tel. 406/323–2302, (Total facility includes 37 beds in nursing home–type unit) **A**9 10 20 **F**1 9 26 29 33 46 69 70 88 92 94 97 108 **P**6 **S** Brim Healthcare, Inc., Brentwood, TN Primary Contact: Lee Rhodes, Chief Executive Officer CFO: Gary Bostrom, Chief Financial Officer CMO: Amed Madi, M.D., Chief Medical Officer CHR: Helen Rodeghiero, Manager Human Resources	23	10	48	411	29	5904	0	4852	2294	78

SCOBEY—Daniels County

DANIELS MEMORIAL HOSPITAL, 105 Fifth Avenue East, Zip 59263, Mailing Address: P.O. Box 400, Zip 59263–0400; tel. 406/487–2296, (Total facility includes 48 beds in nursing home–type unit) (Nonreporting) **A**9 10 18 20 Primary Contact: John L. Stindt, CHE, Chief Executive Officer	16	10	54	—	—	—	—	—	—	—

SHELBY—Toole County

★ **MARIAS MEDICAL CENTER**, 640 Park Drive, Zip 59474–1663, Mailing Address: P.O. Box P., Zip 59474–0915; tel. 406/434–3200, (Total facility includes 68 beds in nursing home–type unit) **A**9 10 18 20 **F**2 6 8 9 11 12 14 27 28 29 33 36 37 44 45 46 48 51 52 55 58 59 60 61 62 63 65 69 81 82 84 88 92 94 96 97 108 110 **P**6 Primary Contact: Mark A. Cross, Chief Executive Officer COO: Jamie Brownell, Clinic Chief Executive Officer CFO: Joshua Gilmore, Chief Financial Officer CMO: Daniel Rausch, M.D., Chief of Staff CIO: John McKeen, Information Technology Director Web address: www.mmcmt.org	13	10	88	527	51	14148	43	11174	4948	142

SHERIDAN—Madison County

RUBY VALLEY HOSPITAL, 220 East Crofoot Street, Zip 59749, Mailing Address: P.O. Box 336, Zip 59749–0336; tel. 406/842–5453 **A**9 10 18 **F**33 55 92 **P**5 6 Primary Contact: John M. Mootry, Interim Chief Executive Officer Web address: www.rvh@3rivers.net	16	12	7	168	1	791	0	1923	1375	30

SIDNEY—Richland County

SIDNEY HEALTH CENTER, 216 14th Avenue S.W., Zip 59270–3586; tel. 406/488–2100, (Total facility includes 93 beds in nursing home–type unit) **A**9 10 20 **F**1 2 6 8 11 12 14 21 22 23 27 28 29 33 36 41 46 48 51 52 54 58 59 60 63 64 65 69 70 81 82 84 85 88 90 92 93 94 95 97 106 108 109 110 **P**7 Primary Contact: Richard Haraldson, Chief Executive Officer Web address: www.sidneyhealth.org	23	10	130	1550	100	44788	93	25230	11162	368

SUPERIOR—Mineral County

★ **MINERAL COMMUNITY HOSPITAL**, 1208 6th Avenue East, Zip 59872–9603, Mailing Address: P.O. Box 66, Zip 59872–0066; tel. 406/822–4841, (Total facility includes 20 beds in nursing home–type unit) **A**9 10 18 20 **F**2 8 9 12 21 22 24 26 27 28 29 33 39 44 46 47 48 52 57 60 62 63 65 66 69 70 81 88 91 92 93 94 97 **P**6 **S** Brim Healthcare, Inc., Brentwood, TN Primary Contact: James P. Henshaw, Chief Executive Officer CFO: Cliff Case, Chief Financial Officer CMO: Yong Ho Park, M.D., Medical Director	23	10	41	210	20	6313	—	4663	1719	65

TERRY—Prairie County

★ **PRAIRIE COMMUNITY HEALTH CENTER**, (Formerly Prairie Community Medical Assistance Facility), 312 South Adams Avenue, Zip 59349–0156, Mailing Address: P.O. Box 156, Zip 59349–0156; tel. 406/635–5511, (Total facility includes 19 beds in nursing home–type unit) **A**9 10 18 **F**1 2 9 24 33 46 48 54 58 70 92 94 109 Primary Contact: Reed Reyman, Administrator CFO: Reed Reyman, Administrator CMO: Joseph M. Leal, Jr, M.D., Medical Director CIO: Henry Garrett, Chairman	16	80	21	89	1	2506	0	—	—	—

TOWNSEND—Broadwater County

BROADWATER HEALTH CENTER, 110 North Oak Street, Zip 59644–2399; tel. 406/266–3186, (Total facility includes 33 beds in nursing home–type unit) **A**9 10 18 20 **F**2 6 9 27 28 33 45 46 47 48 52 69 92 94 97 Primary Contact: Sam J. Allen, Chief Executive Officer	23	10	42	88	29	11098	0	3090	1034	52

WARM SPRINGS—Deer Lodge County

MONTANA STATE HOSPITAL, Zip 59756; tel. 406/693–7000 **A**10 **F**26 27 31 32 39 48 57 58 65 70 71 73 76 94 96 106 **P**6 Primary Contact: Ed Amberg, Administrator Web address: www.dphhs.state.mt.gov	12	22	205	581	165	0	0	21515	—	364

WHITE SULPHUR SPRINGS—Meagher County

★ **MOUNTAINVIEW MEDICAL CENTER**, 16 West Main Street, Zip 59645, Mailing Address: P.O. Box Q, Zip 59645; tel. 406/547–3321, (Total facility includes 31 beds in nursing home–type unit) **A**9 10 18 **F**2 23 26 27 29 33 36 37 38 44 48 51 52 58 69 70 77 92 96 97 108 109 110 **P**6 **S** Providence Services, Spokane, WA Primary Contact: Katharine Ann Campbell, Chief Executive Officer and Administrator CFO: Polly Hanson, Chief Financial Officer CMO: Marc Steinberg, M.D., Chief of Staff CHR: Lorna Fox, Director Human Resources Web address: www.mvmc.org	23	10	37	73	18	3476	0	3565	2132	35

Hospital, Address, Telephone, Approval, Facility, and Physician Codes, Health Care System	Classi-fication Codes		Utilization Data					Expense (thousands) of dollars		
★ American Hospital Association (AHA) membership □ Joint Commission on Accreditation of Healthcare Organizations (JCAHO) accreditation ○ American Osteopathic Association (AOA) accreditation △ Commission on Accreditation of Rehabilitation Facilities (CARF) accreditation	Control	Service	Staffed Beds	Admissions	Census	Outpatient Visits	Births	Total	Payroll	Personnel

WHITEFISH—Flathead County

★ **NORTH VALLEY HOSPITAL**, 6575 Highway 93 South, Zip 59937–2990; tel. 406/863–3500 **A**9 10 18 **F**2 9 11 12 21 22 23 29 33 37 39 44 46 48 52 53 55 58 59 60 62 63 64 65 66 70 81 84 85 88 92 93 94 95 96 97 108 **P**5 **S** Quorum Health Resources, Plano, TX Primary Contact: Craig E. Aasved, Chief Executive Officer CFO: Marilyn Hays, Chief Financial Officer CIO: Jay Adams, Chief Information Officer Web address: www.nvhosp.org	23	10	25	1504	14	37993	208	16110	6177	161

WOLF POINT—Roosevelt County

TRINITY HOSPITAL, (Total facility includes 60 beds in nursing home–type unit) **A**10 **F**1 2 5 6 11 12 21 23 26 27 28 33 39 44 45 46 48 52 54 55 58 59 61 62 63 64 88 91 92 94 97 110 **P**6 Primary Contact: Margaret B. Norgaard, Chief Executive Officer Web address: www.nemhs.net	23	10	80	761	56	10647	110	6094	3340	131

MT

NEBRASKA

Hospital, Address, Telephone, Approval, Facility, and Physician Codes, Health Care System	Classi-fication Codes		Utilization Data					Expense (thousands) of dollars		
★ American Hospital Association (AHA) membership □ Joint Commission on Accreditation of Healthcare Organizations (JCAHO) accreditation ○ American Osteopathic Association (AOA) accreditation △ Commission on Accreditation of Rehabilitation Facilities (CARF) accreditation	Control	Service	Staffed Beds	Admissions	Census	Outpatient Visits	Births	Total	Payroll	Personnel

AINSWORTH—Brown County

BROWN COUNTY HOSPITAL, 945 East Zero Street, Zip 69210–1547; tel. 402/387–2800 **A**9 10 18 **F**2 9 11 23 33 46 48 49 51 52 63 64 69 70 88 92 94 97 **P**6
Primary Contact: Neil Hilton, Chief Executive Officer

| 13 | 10 | 20 | 371 | 7 | 15450 | 10 | 4384 | 2284 | 76 |

ALBION—Boone County

★ **BOONE COUNTY HEALTH CENTER**, 723 West Fairview Street, Zip 68620–1725, Mailing Address: P.O. Box 151, Zip 68620–0151; tel. 402/395–2191 **A**9 10 18 **F**2 9 11 12 21 23 24 26 27 28 29 31 33 37 41 46 47 48 51 52 58 59 60 61 63 65 69 77 88 92 94 95 96 97 98 106 108 109 110 **P**5 6
Primary Contact: Victor Lee, FACHE, President and Chief Executive Officer
CFO: Carol Friesen, Chief Financial Officer
CIO: Shari Thompson, Chief Information Officer
CHR: Jennifer Beierman, Director Human Resources
Web address: www.boonecohealth.org

| 13 | 10 | 25 | 814 | 8 | 38230 | 74 | 12462 | 6048 | 176 |

ALLIANCE—Box Butte County

⊠ **BOX BUTTE GENERAL HOSPITAL**, 2101 Box Butte Avenue, Zip 69301–0810, Mailing Address: P.O. Box 810, Zip 69301–0810; tel. 308/762–6660 **A**1 5 9 10 18 20 **F**2 4 9 11 12 21 23 24 26 27 28 29 30 31 33 39 41 46 47 48 49 52 53 54 55 58 59 60 61 62 63 64 65 66 69 70 73 74 75 77 82 84 85 86 87 88 92 93 94 95 96 97 98 106 107 108 110
Primary Contact: Dan Griess, Chief Executive Officer
CFO: Tracy E. Jatczak, CPA, Chief Operating Officer
CIO: Jim Parks, Vice President Support Services
CHR: Lynn Placek, Payroll and Personnel Coordinator
Web address: www.bbgh.org

| 13 | 10 | 29 | 1178 | 10 | 28673 | 109 | 13599 | 6177 | 188 |

ALMA—Harlan County

★ **HARLAN COUNTY HEALTH SYSTEM**, 717 North Brown Street, Zip 68920–0836, Mailing Address: P.O. Box 836, Zip 68920–0836; tel. 308/928–2151 **A**9 10 18 **F**9 22 23 27 28 33 34 39 52 58 63 65 69 88 92 94 96 97 **S** Great Plains Health Alliance, Inc., Phillipsburg, KS
Primary Contact: Allen Van Driel, CHE, Administrator
CFO: Sharon Olson, Director Fiscal Services
Web address: www.gpha.com

| 13 | 10 | 25 | 274 | 7 | 7109 | 0 | 3417 | 1299 | 41 |

ATKINSON—Holt County

WEST HOLT MEMORIAL HOSPITAL, 406 West Neely Street, Zip 68713–0200; tel. 402/925–2811 **A**9 10 18 **F**11 23 25 27 28 33 34 37 46 48 59 63 69 81 88 94 97 **P**6 **S** Sioux Valley Hospitals and Health System, Sioux Falls, SD
Primary Contact: Mel L. Snow, Chief Executive Officer
Web address: www.westholtmed.org

| 23 | 10 | 18 | 421 | 4 | 12862 | 26 | 7751 | 3284 | 105 |

AUBURN—Nemaha County

★ **NEMAHA COUNTY HOSPITAL**, 2022 13th Street, Zip 68305–1799; tel. 402/274–4366 **A**9 10 18 **F**2 6 9 10 11 12 21 22 23 26 29 33 37 51 52 57 58 60 61 62 63 66 69 81 84 88 92 93 97 104 106 108 109
Primary Contact: Marty Fattig, Administrator and Chief Executive Officer
CFO: Mandy Price, Financial and Accounting Coordinator
CIO: Trisha Gerdes, Health Information Director
CHR: Susie Shupp, Director Human Resources
Web address: www.nemahacountyhospital.org

| 13 | 10 | 20 | 262 | 2 | 17213 | 0 | 6384 | 2533 | 74 |

AURORA—Hamilton County

★ **MEMORIAL HOSPITAL**, 1423 Seventh Street, Zip 68818–1197; tel. 402/694–3171, (Total facility includes 49 beds in nursing home–type unit) **A**9 10 18 **F**8 9 11 12 23 27 28 29 33 37 40 44 46 48 52 58 59 60 61 62 63 64 65 69 70 81 91 92 94 95 96 97 106 108 **P**6
Primary Contact: Diane R. Keller, Administrator
CFO: Phil Fendt, Chief Financial Officer
CMO: Timothy Widhalm, M.D., Chief of Staff
Web address: www.memorialcommunityhealth.org

| 23 | 10 | 75 | 552 | 47 | 16300 | 70 | 12739 | 7024 | 204 |

BASSETT—Rock County

ROCK COUNTY HOSPITAL, 102 East South Street, Zip 68714, Mailing Address: HC 75, Box 300, Zip 68714; tel. 402/684–3366, (Total facility includes 28 beds in nursing home–type unit) **A**9 10 18 **F**6 9 33 38 63 92 97
Primary Contact: Stacey Knox, Administrator
Web address: www.rockcountyhospital.com

| 13 | 10 | 45 | 188 | 27 | 3597 | 0 | 1945 | 1715 | 68 |

Many Facility Codes have changed. Please refer to the AHA Guide Code Chart.

© 2005 AHA Guide

NE

Hospital, Address, Telephone, Approval, Facility, and Physician Codes, Health Care System	Classi-fication Codes		Utilization Data					Expense (thousands) of dollars		
★ American Hospital Association (AHA) membership □ Joint Commission on Accreditation of Healthcare Organizations (JCAHO) accreditation ○ American Osteopathic Association (AOA) accreditation △ Commission on Accreditation of Rehabilitation Facilities (CARF) accreditation	Control	Service	Staffed Beds	Admissions	Census	Outpatient Visits	Births	Total	Payroll	Personnel

BEATRICE—Gage County

⊠ **BEATRICE COMMUNITY HOSPITAL AND HEALTH CENTER**, 1110 North Tenth Street, Zip 68310–2039, Mailing Address: P.O. Box 278, Zip 68310–0278; tel. 402/228–3344, (Total facility includes 71 beds in nursing home–type unit) **A**1 9 10 **F**9 11 12 21 22 23 27 28 29 33 36 37 40 41 46 48 51 52 53 54 55 58 59 60 61 62 63 64 65 66 69 70 81 82 84 85 87 88 92 94 96 97 106 108 109 110
Primary Contact: Thomas W. Sommers, President and Chief Executive Officer
CFO: Kathy Epp, Assistant Administrator Fiscal Services
CMO: Donald Weldon, M.D., Chief of Staff
CHR: Charlotte Campbell, Director Human Resources
Web address: www.beatricecommunityhospital.com
| | 23 | 10 | 118 | 1155 | 91 | 96020 | 113 | 27443 | 12233 | 347 |

BENKELMAN—Dundy County

★ **DUNDY COUNTY HOSPITAL**, 1313 North Cheyenne Street, Zip 69021, Mailing Address: P.O. Box 626, Zip 69021–0626; tel. 308/423–2204 **A**5 9 10 18 **F**11 12 21 22 23 26 27 28 33 39 44 46 48 55 58 59 61 62 63 65 69 81 92 97 **P**4
Primary Contact: Rita Jones, Chief Executive Officer
COO: Wendy Elkins, Director Operations
CFO: Sharon O'Brien, Director Administration
CMO: Shivaun Torres, M.D., Chief Medical Staff
CIO: Anna Elliot, Head Information Technology
CHR: Sandy Noffsinger, Executive Assistant
Web address: www.bwtelcom.net.dch
| | 13 | 10 | 14 | 241 | 2 | 9925 | 30 | 4756 | 2588 | 71 |

BLAIR—Washington County

MEMORIAL COMMUNITY HOSPITAL AND HEALTH SYSTEM, 810 North 22nd Street, Zip 68008–1199, Mailing Address: P.O. Box 250, Zip 68008–0250; tel. 402/426–2182 **A**9 10 18 **F**9 11 12 15 21 22 23 24 26 27 28 29 33 36 37 44 46 48 51 52 54 57 58 59 60 61 62 63 64 65 66 69 70 81 85 88 92 94 96 97 106 108 110 **P**6 **S** Alegent Health, Omaha, NE
Primary Contact: Sally Harvey, R.N., Regional Administrator
Web address: www.mchhs.org
| | 23 | 10 | 25 | 752 | 7 | 62703 | 67 | 16538 | 9464 | 169 |

BRIDGEPORT—Morrill County

MORRILL COUNTY COMMUNITY HOSPITAL, 1313 S Street, Zip 69336–0579, Mailing Address: P.O. Box 579, Zip 69336–0579; tel. 308/262–1616, (Nonreporting) **A**9 10 18
Primary Contact: Julia Morrow, Administrator
| | 13 | 10 | 20 | — | — | — | — | — | — | — |

BROKEN BOW—Custer County

JENNIE M. MELHAM MEMORIAL MEDICAL CENTER, 145 Memorial Drive, Zip 68822–1378, Mailing Address: P.O. Box 250, Zip 68822–0250; tel. 308/872–6891, (Total facility includes 65 beds in nursing home–type unit) (Nonreporting) **A**9 10
Primary Contact: Michael J. Steckler, President and Chief Executive Officer
| | 23 | 10 | 118 | — | — | — | — | — | — | — |

CALLAWAY—Custer County

★ **CALLAWAY DISTRICT HOSPITAL**, 211 Kimball, Zip 68825–0100, Mailing Address: P.O. Box 100, Zip 68825–0100; tel. 308/836–2228 **A**9 10 18 **F**12 14 23 26 27 28 33 52 55 63 88 97
Primary Contact: Marvin Neth, Administrator
Web address: www.calloway–ne.com/hospital
| | 16 | 10 | 12 | 172 | 1 | 7532 | 0 | 2144 | 915 | 31 |

CAMBRIDGE—Furnas County

★ **TRI–VALLEY HEALTH SYSTEM**, West Highway 6 and 34, Zip 69022–0488, Mailing Address: P.O. Box 488, Zip 69022–0488; tel. 308/697–3329, (Total facility includes 36 beds in nursing home–type unit) (Nonreporting) **A**9 10 18 **S** Brim Healthcare, Inc., Brentwood, TN
Primary Contact: Lynn Milnes, Chief Executive Officer
CIO: Matt Bamesbarger, Information Services Director
Web address: www.trivalleyhealth.com
| | 23 | 10 | 51 | — | — | — | — | — | — | — |

CENTRAL CITY—Merrick County

LITZENBERG MEMORIAL COUNTY HOSPITAL, 1715 26th Street, Zip 68826–9620, Mailing Address: Route 2, Box 1, Zip 68826–0001; tel. 308/946–3015, (Total facility includes 46 beds in nursing home–type unit) (Nonreporting) **A**5 9 10 18
Primary Contact: Michael R. Bowman, Administrator
| | 13 | 10 | 71 | — | — | — | — | — | — | — |

CHADRON—Dawes County

★ **CHADRON COMMUNITY HOSPITAL AND HEALTH SERVICES**, 821 Morehead Street, Zip 69337–2599; tel. 308/432–5586 **A**9 10 18 **F**8 9 11 12 21 23 24 27 28 29 31 33 36 37 46 48 49 50 51 55 58 59 60 61 63 64 69 81 84 88 91 92 94 95 96 97 108 **P**5 8
Primary Contact: Harold L. Krueger, Jr, Chief Executive Officer
CFO: Russ Bohnenkamp, Director Finance
Web address: www.chadronhospital.com
| | 23 | 10 | 25 | 701 | 6 | 13383 | 130 | 10682 | 4078 | 151 |

Hospital, Address, Telephone, Approval, Facility, and Physician Codes, Health Care System	Classi-fication Codes		Utilization Data					Expense (thousands) of dollars		
	Control	Service	Staffed Beds	Admissions	Census	Outpatient Visits	Births	Total	Payroll	Personnel

★ American Hospital Association (AHA) membership
□ Joint Commission on Accreditation of Healthcare Organizations (JCAHO) accreditation
○ American Osteopathic Association (AOA) accreditation
△ Commission on Accreditation of Rehabilitation Facilities (CARF) accreditation

COLUMBUS—Platte County

⊠ **COLUMBUS COMMUNITY HOSPITAL**, 4600 38th Street, Zip 68601, Mailing Address: P.O. Box 1800, Zip 68602–1800; tel. 402/564–7118, (Total facility includes 9 beds in nursing home–type unit) **A**1 9 10 20 **F**2 9 11 12 14 21 27 28 29 31 32 33 36 37 38 46 48 51 52 53 54 55 58 59 60 62 63 65 66 69 81 82 84 85 86 87 88 92 93 94 95 96 106 108 **P**3 8
Primary Contact: Gary W. Pulsipher, President and Chief Executive Officer
COO: James P. Goulet, Vice President Operations
CFO: J Joseph Barbaglia, Vice President Financial Services
CMO: Roselyn Remington, President, Medical Staff
CIO: J Joseph Barbaglia, Vice President Financial Services
Web address: www.columbushosp.org
... 23 10 54 2670 22 44041 569 36645 16150 394

COZAD—Dawson County

★ **COZAD COMMUNITY HOSPITAL**, 300 East 12th Street, Zip 69130–1505, Mailing Address: P.O. Box 108, Zip 69130–0108; tel. 308/784–2261 **A**9 10 18 **F**9 11 12 26 27 33 36 41 46 48 51 55 58 59 60 63 65 69 70 81 84 88 92 94 95 97 **P**6
Primary Contact: Lyle E. Davis, Administrator
Web address: www.cozadhealthcare.com
... 16 10 21 900 5 6761 58 6706 3698 92

CREIGHTON—Knox County

CREIGHTON AREA HEALTH SERVICES, 1503 Main Street, Zip 68729–0186, Mailing Address: P.O. Box 186, Zip 68729–0186; tel. 402/358–5700, (Total facility includes 46 beds in nursing home–type unit) **A**9 10 18 **F**1 9 10 21 23 27 28 29 33 36 39 44 45 46 48 51 52 58 60 61 63 65 69 70 92 94 96 97 106 108 **P**6
Primary Contact: Paul Hurd, CHE, Chief Executive Officer
Web address: www.cahs–ne.org
... 14 10 69 403 48 5419 0 5581 2911 105

CRETE—Saline County

★ **CRETE AREA MEDICAL CENTER**, 1540 Grove Street, Zip 68333–0220, Mailing Address: P.O. Box 220, Zip 68333–0220; tel. 402/826–6800, (Total facility includes 31 beds in nursing home–type unit) **A**9 10 18 **F**11 12 23 26 27 28 33 36 46 51 52 60 61 63 69 81
Primary Contact: Joseph W. Lohrman, Administrator
CFO: Terry Meinke, Faiclity Accountant
Web address: www.creteareamedicalcenter.com
... 23 10 56 505 33 — 68 14392 6112 192

DAVID CITY—Butler County

★ **BUTLER COUNTY HEALTH CARE CENTER**, 372 South Ninth Street, Zip 68632–2199; tel. 402/367–3115, (Nonreporting) **A**9 10 18
Primary Contact: Donald T. Naiberk, Administrator
CFO: Cindy Cherry, Chief Financial Officer
Web address: www.bchccnet.org
... 13 10 25 — — — — — — —

FAIRBURY—Jefferson County

★ **JEFFERSON COMMUNITY HEALTH CENTER**, 2200 H Street, Zip 68352–1119, Mailing Address: P.O. Box 277, Zip 68352–0277; tel. 402/729–3351, (Total facility includes 39 beds in nursing home–type unit) **A**9 10 18 **F**1 2 8 9 10 11 12 21 22 23 24 27 28 29 32 33 34 35 41 45 46 47 48 51 52 58 59 60 61 62 63 69 81 88 92 93 94 95 96 97 106 108
Primary Contact: William L. Welch, CHE, Chief Executive Officer
CFO: Chad Jurgens, Chief Financial Officer
CIO: Andy Rhine, Information Technology Specialist
Web address: www.jchc.us
... 23 10 64 639 43 18500 44 9651 4540 141

FALLS CITY—Richardson County

★ **COMMUNITY MEDICAL CENTER**, 2307 Barada Street, Zip 68355–1599, Mailing Address: P.O. Box 399, Zip 68355–0399; tel. 402/245–2428, (Nonreporting) **A**9 10 18
Primary Contact: Michael J. Ellis, Administrator and Chief Executive Officer
... 23 10 25 — — — — — — —

FRANKLIN—Franklin County

★ **FRANKLIN COUNTY MEMORIAL HOSPITAL**, 1406 Q Street, Zip 68939–0315, Mailing Address: P.O. Box 315, Zip 68939–0315; tel. 308/425–6221 **A**9 10 18 **F**9 14 22 23 26 27 28 29 33 34 36 39 46 47 48 52 58 60 62 63 69 70 94 96 97 **P**6
Primary Contact: Jerrell F. Gerdes, FACHE, Administrator
COO: Linda Bush, Chief Operating Officer
CMO: Linda Mazour, M.D., President
CIO: Cathy Webber, Chief Information Officer
Web address: www.franklincountymemorialhospital.org
... 13 10 12 210 3 6998 3 3659 2007 61

FREMONT—Dodge County

⊠ **FREMONT AREA MEDICAL CENTER**, 450 East 23rd Street, Zip 68025–2387; tel. 402/721–1610, (Total facility includes 162 beds in nursing home–type unit) **A**1 2 9 10 **F**2 9 11 12 14 15 17 21 22 23 27 28 29 33 36 37 41 44 45 46 47 48 51 52 53 55 58 59 60 61 62 63 64 65 66 69 79 80 81 82 85 88 92 93 94 95 96 108 **P**8
Primary Contact: D. Michael Leibert, FACHE, President and Chief Executive Officer
CFO: David G. Hanen, Vice President Fiscal Services and Chief Financial Officer
Web address: www.famc.org
... 13 10 262 4070 193 58531 527 61628 27919 677

FRIEND—Saline County

WARREN MEMORIAL HOSPITAL, 905 Second Street, Zip 68359–1198; tel. 402/947–2541, (Total facility includes 51 beds in nursing home–type unit) **A**9 10 18 **F**1 9 27 28 29 33 46 48 52 54 58 63 92 94 96 **P**6
Primary Contact: Amy Fish, Administrator
Web address: www.warrenmemorialhospital.org
... 14 10 63 49 45 5700 0 3352 1803 74

Many Facility Codes have changed. Please refer to the AHA Guide Code Chart. © 2005 AHA Guide

NE

Hospital, Address, Telephone, Approval, Facility, and Physician Codes, Health Care System	Classi-fication Codes		Utilization Data					Expense (thousands) of dollars		
★ American Hospital Association (AHA) membership □ Joint Commission on Accreditation of Healthcare Organizations (JCAHO) accreditation ○ American Osteopathic Association (AOA) accreditation △ Commission on Accreditation of Rehabilitation Facilities (CARF) accreditation	Control	Service	Staffed Beds	Admissions	Census	Outpatient Visits	Births	Total	Payroll	Personnel

GENEVA—Fillmore County

FILLMORE COUNTY HOSPITAL, 1325 H Street, Zip 68361–1325, Mailing Address: P.O. Box 193, Zip 68361–0193; tel. 402/759–3167, (Nonreporting) **A**9 10 18
Primary Contact: Larry Eichelberger, Administrator
Web address: www.fhsofgeneva.org

| | 13 | 10 | 25 | — | — | — | — | — | — | — |

GENOA—Nance County

GENOA COMMUNITY HOSPITAL, 706 Ewing Avenue, Zip 68640, Mailing Address: P.O. Box 310, Zip 68640–0310; tel. 402/993–2283, (Total facility includes 39 beds in nursing home–type unit) **A**9 10 18 **F**8 27 33 41 46 70 92 97 **P**6
Primary Contact: Shelli Cornwell, Administrator

| | 14 | 10 | 60 | 185 | 38 | 4873 | 0 | — | — | — |

GORDON—Sheridan County

★ **GORDON MEMORIAL HOSPITAL**, (Formerly Gordon Memorial Hospital District), 300 East Eighth Street, Zip 69343–9990; tel. 308/282–0401, (Total facility includes 40 beds in nursing home–type unit) **A**9 10 18 20 **F**1 8 11 12 14 21 23 29 33 45 48 51 55 58 59 62 63 69 81 85 88 92 97 **P**6 **S** Regional Health, Rapid City, SD
Primary Contact: Mehdi Merred, Chief Executive Officer
CFO: Jerry Wright, Chief Financial Officer
CMO: J F. Hutchins, M.D., Chief of Staff
CHR: Tina Mills, Personnel Director and Administrative Assistant
Web address: www.gordonhospital.org

| | 16 | 10 | 65 | 663 | 41 | — | 117 | 9152 | 5416 | 155 |

GOTHENBURG—Dawson County

★ **GOTHENBURG MEMORIAL HOSPITAL**, 910 20th Street, Zip 69138–1237, Mailing Address: P.O. Box 469, Zip 69138–0469; tel. 308/537–3661, (Total facility includes 37 beds in nursing home–type unit) **A**9 10 18 **F**2 9 11 12 26 27 28 29 33 41 46 47 48 52 58 59 60 63 65 68 69 70 88 92 95 96 97 **P**5
Primary Contact: John H. Johnson, Chief Executive Officer
CMO: Kayleen Jensen, Nursing Services Administrator
CIO: John H. Johnson, Chief Executive Officer
Web address: www.ghospital.org

| | 16 | 10 | 50 | 248 | 32 | 12440 | 37 | 5651 | 2274 | 91 |

GRAND ISLAND—Hall County

⊞ **SAINT FRANCIS MEDICAL CENTER**, 2620 West Faidley Avenue, Zip 68803–4297, Mailing Address: P.O. Box 9804, Zip 68802–9804; tel. 308/384–4600, (Includes SAINT FRANCIS MEMORIAL HEALTH CENTER, 2116 West Faidley Avenue, Zip 68803), (Total facility includes 36 beds in nursing home–type unit) **A**1 2 3 5 9 10 19 **F**2 3 4 9 10 11 12 13 14 15 17 21 22 23 26 27 28 29 31 33 36 37 38 41 44 45 46 47 48 51 52 53 55 56 57 58 59 61 62 63 64 65 67 68 71 77 78 88 92 94 96 98 106 108 110 **S** Catholic Health Initiatives, Denver, CO
Primary Contact: Michael R. Gloor, FACHE, President and Chief Executive Officer
COO: Dan McElligott, Chief Operating Officer
CIO: Vaughn Minton, Director for Information Systems
Web address: www.saintfrancisgi.org

| | 21 | 10 | 200 | 7912 | 101 | 210797 | 991 | 98134 | 40160 | 994 |

GRANT—Perkins County

PERKINS COUNTY HEALTH SERVICES, 900 Lincoln Avenue, Zip 69140–9799, Mailing Address: Rural Route 1, Box 26, Zip 69140–9799; tel. 308/352–7200, (Includes GOLDEN OURS CONVALESCENT HOME), (Total facility includes 64 beds in nursing home–type unit) (Nonreporting) **A**9 10 18
Primary Contact: Carol A. Kraus, Administrator and Chief Executive Officer

| | 16 | 10 | 84 | — | — | — | — | — | — | — |

HASTINGS—Adams County

HASTINGS REGIONAL CENTER, 4200 West Second Street, Zip 68901–9700, Mailing Address: P.O. Box 579, Zip 68902–0579; tel. 402/462–1971, (Nonreporting) **A**9 10
Primary Contact: William Gibson, Chief Executive Officer

| | 12 | 49 | 156 | — | — | — | — | — | — | — |

⊞ **MARY LANNING MEMORIAL HOSPITAL**, 715 North St. Joseph Avenue, Zip 68901–4497; tel. 402/461–5110 **A**1 2 9 10 19 **F**9 11 12 21 22 23 24 27 28 29 32 33 34 36 37 41 42 51 52 53 55 56 58 59 60 61 63 65 66 69 70 71 72 73 74 75 76 77 78 79 81 82 84 86 88 92 93 94 95 96 108 109 110 **P**6
Primary Contact: W. Michael Kearney, President and Chief Executive Officer
CFO: Mark A. Vincent, Vice President and Chief Financial Officer
CIO: George Sullivan, Director Management Information Systems
CHR: Bruce Cutright, Vice President Human Resources
Web address: www.mlmh.org

| | 23 | 10 | 165 | 5423 | 72 | 62733 | 702 | 68833 | 30334 | 811 |

HEBRON—Thayer County

★ **THAYER COUNTY HEALTH SERVICES**, 120 Park Avenue, Zip 68370–2019, Mailing Address: P.O. Box 49, Zip 68370–0049; tel. 402/768–6041 **A**9 10 18 **F**9 11 12 22 23 24 26 27 28 29 46 48 52 53 59 60 61 62 63 69 70 81 84 88 92 94 95 96 97 106 110 **P**4
Primary Contact: Joyce Beck, Administrator
COO: Jo Hacker, Director Nursing
CFO: Deb Craig, Chief Financial Officer
CMO: Stuart Embury, Medical Staff Director
Web address: www.thayercountyhealth.com

| | 13 | 10 | 14 | 530 | 4 | 1453 | 41 | 8636 | 4357 | 129 |

NE

Hospital, Address, Telephone, Approval, Facility, and Physician Codes, Health Care System	Classi-fication Codes		Utilization Data					Expense (thousands) of dollars		
★ American Hospital Association (AHA) membership □ Joint Commission on Accreditation of Healthcare Organizations (JCAHO) accreditation ○ American Osteopathic Association (AOA) accreditation △ Commission on Accreditation of Rehabilitation Facilities (CARF) accreditation	Control	Service	Staffed Beds	Admissions	Census	Outpatient Visits	Births	Total	Payroll	Personnel

HENDERSON—York County

HENDERSON HEALTH CARE SERVICES, 1621 Front Street, Zip 68371–0217; tel. 402/723–4512, (Total facility includes 40 beds in nursing home–type unit) (Nonreporting) **A**9 10 18 Primary Contact: Patricia Lundgren, Administrator Web address: www.telcoweb.net/health	23	10	56	—	—	—	—	—	—	—

HOLDREGE—Phelps County

★ **PHELPS MEMORIAL HEALTH CENTER**, 1215 Tibbals Street, Zip 68949–1280; tel. 308/995–2211 **A**1 10 **F**2 6 11 12 22 23 26 27 28 29 33 37 46 48 51 52 55 58 59 60 62 63 64 65 66 69 81 84 88 93 94 95 96 97 108 **S** Quorum Health Resources, Plano, TX Primary Contact: Joyce Grove Hein, Administrator and Chief Executive Officer CFO: Loren D. Schroder, Chief Financial Officer CMO: Stuart Embury, Medical Staff Director CIO: Loren D. Schroder, Chief Financial Officer CHR: Cindy Jackson, Director Human Resources Web address: www.phelpsmemorial.com	23	10	30	1517	17	26946	140	14578	6523	179

IMPERIAL—Chase County

CHASE COUNTY COMMUNITY HOSPITAL, 600 West 12th Street, Zip 69033–0819, Mailing Address: P.O. Box 819, Zip 69033–0819; tel. 308/882–7111, (Nonreporting) **A**9 10 18 Primary Contact: Lola Jones, R.N., Administrator Web address: www.chasecounty.com	13	10	25	—	—	—	—	—	—	—

KEARNEY—Buffalo County

★ △ **GOOD SAMARITAN HEALTH SYSTEMS**, 10 East 31st Street, Zip 68847–2926, Mailing Address: P.O. Box 1990, Zip 68848–1990; tel. 308/865–7100, (Total facility includes 20 beds in nursing home–type unit) **A**1 2 3 5 7 9 10 19 **F**1 2 6 7 9 11 12 15 17 19 21 22 23 26 27 28 29 30 32 33 34 35 36 39 41 46 48 49 51 52 53 54 55 57 58 59 60 61 62 63 64 66 68 69 79 80 81 82 84 85 87 88 92 93 94 95 96 98 106 108 110 **P**6 8 **S** Catholic Health Initiatives, Denver, CO Primary Contact: John Allen, President and Chief Executive Officer CFO: Doc Doulter, Interim Chief Financial Officer CMO: Robert Billerbeck, M.D., Vice President Medical Affairs CIO: Alan Bobyarchick, Director Information Services CHR: Mary Ann Mertz, Vice President Human Resources Web address: www.gshs.org	21	10	185	7753	155	62442	933	128774	54149	1258
★ **RICHARD H. YOUNG PSYCHIATRIC HOSPITAL**, 1755 Prairie View Place, Zip 68848; tel. 308/865–2000 **A**9 10 **F**21 22 26 27 28 31 35 39 48 53 58 66 71 72 73 74 75 76 77 78 92 94 **P**6 8 **S** Catholic Health Initiatives, Denver, CO Web address: www.gshs.org	21	22	43	795	23	125	—	8484	3806	63

KIMBALL—Kimball County

★ **KIMBALL HEALTH SERVICES**, 505 South Burg Street, Zip 69145–1398; tel. 308/235–1952 **A**9 10 18 **F**2 12 28 33 34 46 63 69 92 94 97 108 **P**4 Primary Contact: Kim Woods, R.N., President and Chief Executive Officer CMO: Dariusz Listopadzki, M.D., Chief of Staff Web address: www.kimballhealth.org	13	10	20	432	3	3241	0	5986	2973	97

LEXINGTON—Dawson County

★ **TRI–COUNTY AREA HOSPITAL**, 13th and Erie Streets, Zip 68850–0980, Mailing Address: P.O. Box 980, Zip 68850–0980; tel. 308/324–5651 **A**1 9 10 20 **F**2 6 9 11 12 23 26 33 36 41 46 48 51 52 53 59 62 63 65 69 81 88 91 92 94 97 106 Primary Contact: Calvin A. Hiner, Jr, Administrator CFO: Steve Lewis, Director Administrative Services CMO: Fran Acosta Carlson, M.D., Chief of Staff CHR: Carolyn Malzahn, Director Human Resources Web address: www.tricountyhospital.com	16	10	40	1256	13	33186	256	12427	5698	159

LINCOLN—Lancaster County

★ △ **BRYANLGH MEDICAL CENTER**, 1600 South 48th Street, Zip 68506–1299; tel. 402/489–0200, (Includes BRYANLGH MEDICAL CENTER–EAST, 1600 South 48th Street; BRYANLGH MEDICAL CENTER–WEST, 2300 South 16th Street, Zip 68502–3781; tel. 402/475–1011), (Total facility includes 16 beds in nursing home–type unit) **A**1 3 5 6 7 9 10 **F**2 3 4 11 12 14 15 17 19 21 22 23 26 27 28 31 33 34 37 41 43 46 47 48 50 51 52 53 55 57 58 59 61 62 63 64 65 66 68 69 71 72 73 74 75 76 77 78 79 80 81 82 83 84 85 87 88 92 93 94 95 96 98 100 106 108 Primary Contact: Craig M. Ames, President and Chief Operating Officer CFO: Jennifer Lesoing Lucs, Vice President and Chief Financial Officer CMO: Richard A. Morin, M.D., Vice President Medical Affairs CHR: Gary Moore, Vice President Human Resources Web address: www.bryanlgh.org LINCOLN DIVISION See Veterans Affairs Nebraska–Western Iowa Health Care System	23	10	396	25352	325	292267	2454	368443	153442	3393
□ **LINCOLN REGIONAL CENTER**, West Prospector Place and South Folsom, Zip 68522–2299, Mailing Address: P.O. Box 94949, Zip 68509–4949; tel. 402/471–4444, (Nonreporting) **A**1 9 10 Primary Contact: Barbara Ramsey, Ph.D., Chief Executive Officer	12	22	196	—	—	—	—	—	—	—

Many Facility Codes have changed. Please refer to the AHA Guide Code Chart. © 2005 AHA Guide

Hospital, Address, Telephone, Approval, Facility, and Physician Codes, Health Care System	Classi-fication Codes		Utilization Data					Expense (thousands) of dollars		
★ American Hospital Association (AHA) membership □ Joint Commission on Accreditation of Healthcare Organizations (JCAHO) accreditation ○ American Osteopathic Association (AOA) accreditation △ Commission on Accreditation of Rehabilitation Facilities (CARF) accreditation	Control	Service	Staffed Beds	Admissions	Census	Outpatient Visits	Births	Total	Payroll	Personnel
LINCOLN SURGICAL HOSPITAL, 1710 S. 70th Street, Suite 200, Zip 68506; tel. 402/484–9090, (Nonreporting) **A**10 Primary Contact: Robb Linafelter, Chief Executive Officer	33	49	7	—	—	—	—	—	—	—
★ △ **MADONNA REHABILITATION HOSPITAL**, 5401 South Street, Zip 68506–2134; tel. 402/489–7102, (Total facility includes 132 beds in nursing home–type unit) **A**7 9 10 **F**1 5 8 9 21 22 26 27 28 29 30 37 38 39 42 44 45 46 47 52 57 58 60 62 65 66 68 69 92 94 95 96 108 110 **P**6 Primary Contact: Marsha Lommel, President and Chief Executive Officer COO: Shirley J. Foster, Executive Vice President and Chief Operations Officer CFO: Victor J. Witkowicz, Senior Vice President and Chief Financial Officer CMO: Andrew Bohart, Vice President of Medical Affairs CIO: Lori Warner, Public Relations Manager CHR: Ann Koenig, Director Human Resources Web address: www.madonna.org	21	46	294	2665	231	28732	0	62090	39563	880
NEBRASKA HEART INSTITUTE, 1500 South 91st Street, Zip 68526; tel. 402/489–6555, (Nonreporting) **A**9 10 Primary Contact: Sheryl D. Dodds, Chief Executive Officer Web address: www.neheart.com	32	42	63	—	—	—	—	—	—	—
⊞ **SAINT ELIZABETH REGIONAL MEDICAL CENTER**, 555 South 70th Street, Zip 68510–2494; tel. 402/219–8000 **A**1 2 3 5 9 10 **F**9 11 12 13 14 15 17 19 21 22 26 27 28 29 33 36 38 42 46 47 48 51 52 55 56 57 58 59 60 61 62 63 66 69 81 82 84 85 87 88 93 94 95 96 106 107 108 110 **P**6 **S** Catholic Health Initiatives, Denver, CO Primary Contact: Robert J. Lanik, President and Chief Executive Officer CFO: Jeanette Wojtalewicz, Vice President Finance CIO: Robert Lench, Director Web address: www.saintelizabethonline.com	23	10	242	11994	144	132879	2511	163174	61436	1786
★ **VETERANS AFFAIRS NEBRASKA–WESTERN IOWA HEALTH CARE SYSTEM**, 600 South 70th Street, Zip 68510–2493; tel. 402/489–3802, (Includes LINCOLN DIVISION), (Nonreporting) **S** Department of Veterans Affairs, Washington, DC Primary Contact: Denise Harrison, Site Manager CFO: Russell Lloyd, Chief Financial Officer CMO: Rowen K. Zetterman, M.D., Chief of Staff CIO: David Daiker, Chief Information Resource Management CHR: David Peters, Chief Web address: www.va.gov/sta/guide/home.asp	45	10	186	—	—	—	—	—	—	—
LYNCH—Boyd County										
NIOBRARA VALLEY HOSPITAL, Mailing Address: P.O. Box 118, Zip 68746–0118; tel. 402/569–2451 **A**9 10 18 **F**1 33 41 45 46 63 64 69 70 81 92 97 **S** Sioux Valley Hospitals and Health System, Sioux Falls, SD Primary Contact: Bruce Purviance, Chief Executive Officer	23	10	20	102	1	3106	0	1833	663	27
MCCOOK—Red Willow County										
⊞ **COMMUNITY HOSPITAL**, 1301 East H Street, Zip 69001–1328, Mailing Address: P.O. Box 1328, Zip 69001–1328; tel. 308/345–2650 **A**1 9 10 20 **F**2 9 11 12 26 27 29 33 36 46 48 51 52 55 58 59 60 62 63 64 65 66 81 82 88 94 96 97 106 108 109 Primary Contact: Gary Bieganski, CHE, President CFO: Troy Bruntz, Chief Financial Officer CIO: Lori Beeby, Director Information Systems CHR: Tom Carpenter, Vice President Human Resources and Public Relations Web address: www.chmccook.org	23	10	44	1585	18	37364	153	19858	7646	181
MINDEN—Kearney County										
★ **KEARNEY COUNTY HEALTH SERVICES**, 727 East First Street, Zip 68959–1700; tel. 308/832–3400, (Total facility includes 50 beds in nursing home–type unit) (Nonreporting) **A**9 10 18 Primary Contact: John W. Rainey, Administrator CFO: Eldon Koepke, Chief Financial Officer Web address: www.kchs.org	13	10	75	—	—	—	—	—	—	—
NEBRASKA CITY—Otoe County										
★ **ST. MARY'S HOSPITAL**, 1314 Third Avenue, Zip 68410–1999; tel. 402/873–3321 **A**9 10 18 **F**9 11 12 14 28 33 52 53 54 55 58 59 61 63 66 81 87 88 92 93 96 97 **S** Catholic Health Initiatives, Denver, CO Primary Contact: Daniel J. Kelly, President and Chief Executive Officer CFO: Karl Vilums, Chief Financial Officer CMO: Brad Vasa, Chief of Staff Web address: www.stmaryshospitalnecity.org	21	10	18	567	4	25537	109	8263	3195	111
NELIGH—Antelope County										
★ **ANTELOPE MEMORIAL HOSPITAL**, 102 West Ninth Street, Zip 68756–0229, Mailing Address: P.O. Box 229, Zip 68756–0229; tel. 402/887–4151 **A**9 10 18 **F**6 9 11 12 29 30 33 36 41 44 46 48 50 51 52 53 59 63 69 81 92 94 95 97 109 **P**6 Primary Contact: Jack W. Green, Administrator CFO: Martha Nelson, Chief Financial Officer CIO: Jack W. Green, Administrator	23	10	25	541	9	31447	18	7639	3299	108

NE

Hospital, Address, Telephone, Approval, Facility, and Physician Codes, Health Care System	Classi-fication Codes		Utilization Data					Expense (thousands) of dollars		
	Control	Service	Staffed Beds	Admissions	Census	Outpatient Visits	Births	Total	Payroll	Personnel

★ American Hospital Association (AHA) membership
☐ Joint Commission on Accreditation of Healthcare Organizations (JCAHO) accreditation
◯ American Osteopathic Association (AOA) accreditation
△ Commission on Accreditation of Rehabilitation Facilities (CARF) accreditation

NORFOLK—Madison County

⊠ **FAITH REGIONAL HEALTH SERVICES**, 2700 Norfolk Avenue, Zip 68701, Mailing Address: P.O. BOX 869, Zip 68702–0869; tel. 402/644–7201, (Includes EAST CAMPUS, 1500 Koenigstein Avenue; WEST CAMPUS), (Total facility includes 99 beds in nursing home–type unit) **A**1 3 9 10 19 20 **F**2 4 8 11 12 15 17 19 21 22 23 24 26 27 28 29 32 33 34 35 36 37 39 40 41 42 44 45 46 47 48 49 51 52 53 55 57 58 59 60 61 62 63 64 65 66 68 69 71 72 73 74 75 76 77 79 81 82 84 85 86 87 88 92 93 94 95 96 106 108 109 110 **P**6 7 **S** Missionary Benedictine Sisters American Province, Norfolk, NE
Primary Contact: Robert L. Driewer, CHE, Chief Executive Officer
CFO: Dale Pohlman, Chief Financial Officer
CMO: Timothy Davy, M.D., Vice President Medical Affairs
CIO: Donald Cope, Director Information Systems
Web address: www.frhs.org

| | 23 | 10 | 222 | 6644 | 160 | 62697 | 983 | 78529 | 34025 | 960 |

NORFOLK REGIONAL CENTER, 1700 North Victory Road, Zip 68701–6859, Mailing Address: P.O. Box 1209, Zip 68702–1209; tel. 402/370–3400 **A**9 10 **F**1 4 27 45 71 73 74 77 78
Primary Contact: Richard B. Gamel, Chief Executive Officer

| | 12 | 22 | 180 | 464 | 174 | 2800 | 0 | 16495 | 9528 | 290 |

NORTH PLATTE—Lincoln County

⊠ **GREAT PLAINS REGIONAL MEDICAL CENTER**, 601 West Leota Street, Zip 69101–6598, Mailing Address: P.O. Box 1167, Zip 69103–1167; tel. 308/534–9310 **A**1 2 3 5 9 10 20 **F**2 4 9 11 12 21 22 23 27 29 33 36 37 40 46 48 51 52 55 58 59 60 61 62 63 64 66 69 71 72 73 75 76 77 78 80 81 82 84 85 87 88 93 94 95 96 108 110 **P**8 **S** Quorum Health Resources, Plano, TX
Primary Contact: Lucinda A. Bradley, Chief Executive Officer
COO: Mel McNea, Vice President Operations
CFO: Lana J. Webster, Vice President Finance
CIO: Jimmy Anderson, Director Information Systems
Web address: www.gprmc.com

| | 23 | 10 | 98 | 5108 | 49 | 199473 | 605 | 76427 | 33328 | 687 |

O'NEILL—Holt County

★ **AVERA ST. ANTHONY'S HOSPITAL**, Second and Adams Streets, Zip 68763–1569; tel. 402/336–2611 **A**9 10 18 **F**2 11 12 21 22 23 24 26 27 28 29 31 33 37 43 44 45 46 47 48 49 50 51 52 53 57 58 59 60 61 62 63 65 66 69 81 82 84 88 89 93 94 95 97 108 110 **P**6 **S** Avera Health, Yankton, SD
Primary Contact: Ronald J. Cork, President and Chief Executive Officer
CFO: Michael Garman, Chief Financial Officer
CMO: Jay Allison, President Medical Staff
CIO: Michael Garman, Chief Financial Officer
Web address: www.avera–sta.org

| | 21 | 10 | 27 | 1104 | 12 | 26572 | 100 | 13970 | 5340 | 152 |

OAKLAND—Burt County

★ **OAKLAND MEMORIAL HOSPITAL**, 601 East Second Street, Zip 68045–1499; tel. 402/685–5601 **A**9 10 18 **F**9 23 27 29 33 46 48 52 61 62 63 64 66 69 70 81 93 97 110 **P**5 6 **S** Trinity Health, Novi, MI
Primary Contact: Karen Vlach, Administrator
CFO: Mike Clymer, Chief Financial Officer
CHR: Karolyn McEnroy, Business Office Manager
Web address: www.oaklandhospital.org

| | 16 | 10 | 23 | 170 | 2 | 6117 | 0 | 3374 | 1508 | 47 |

OGALLALA—Keith County

★ **OGALLALA COMMUNITY HOSPITAL**, 2601 North Spruce Street, Zip 69153–2465; tel. 308/284–4011 **A**9 10 18 **F**11 12 14 21 22 29 33 42 46 48 51 55 59 60 63 65 69 70 77 81 88 93 94 96 107 **S** Banner Health, Phoenix, AZ
Primary Contact: Margie Molitor, R.N., Chief Executive Officer
CFO: Dena Klockman, Operations Administrator
CMO: Marlene Birkholtz, Chief of Staff

| | 23 | 10 | 18 | 850 | 9 | 64679 | 74 | 11594 | 5421 | — |

OMAHA—Douglas County

⊠ **ALEGENT HEALTH BERGAN MERCY MEDICAL CENTER**, 7500 Mercy Road, Zip 68124–2319; tel. 402/398–6060 **A**1 2 3 5 9 10 **F**1 2 9 11 12 14 15 17 19 21 22 23 24 26 27 28 29 30 31 32 33 34 35 36 37 38 39 40 42 44 45 46 47 48 49 50 51 52 53 55 56 58 59 60 61 62 63 64 65 66 70 73 79 80 81 83 84 85 86 87 88 90 92 94 95 96 97 98 107 108 109 110 **P**6 8 **S** Alegent Health, Omaha, NE
Primary Contact: Mary Kay Thalken, R.N., Interim Vice President and Chief Operating Officer
CIO: Dan Connolly, Chief Information Officer
Web address: www.alegent.com/bergan

| | 21 | 10 | 327 | 14917 | 182 | 191444 | 2689 | 223934 | 81053 | 1845 |

⊠ △ **ALEGENT HEALTH IMMANUEL MEDICAL CENTER**, 6901 North 72nd Street, Zip 68122–1799; tel. 402/572–2121, (Total facility includes 197 beds in nursing home–type unit) **A**1 2 3 5 7 9 10 **F**2 4 9 10 11 12 14 15 17 19 21 22 23 24 26 27 28 29 30 31 32 33 34 35 36 37 38 39 41 42 44 45 46 47 48 50 51 52 53 55 57 58 59 60 61 62 63 64 65 66 68 69 70 71 72 73 74 75 76 77 78 81 82 84 85 86 87 88 92 93 94 95 96 98 99 105 107 108 109 **P**6 8 **S** Alegent Health, Omaha, NE
Primary Contact: Barbara K. Goodrich, R.N., Vice President and Chief Operating Officer
CMO: Donald Manning, M.D., Chief Medical Officer
CIO: Ken Lawonn, Vice President, Information Technology
Web address: www.alegent.com/immanuel

| | 21 | 10 | 489 | 11967 | 196 | 101271 | 918 | 166760 | 61950 | 1388 |

Many Facility Codes have changed. Please refer to the AHA Guide Code Chart.

© 2005 AHA Guide

NE

Hospital, Address, Telephone, Approval, Facility, and Physician Codes, Health Care System	Classi-fication Codes		Utilization Data					Expense (thousands) of dollars		
★ American Hospital Association (AHA) membership □ Joint Commission on Accreditation of Healthcare Organizations (JCAHO) accreditation ○ American Osteopathic Association (AOA) accreditation △ Commission on Accreditation of Rehabilitation Facilities (CARF) accreditation	Control	Service	Staffed Beds	Admissions	Census	Outpatient Visits	Births	Total	Payroll	Personnel

★ ALEGENT HEALTH LAKESIDE HOSPITAL, 16901 Lakeside Hills Court, Zip 68130–2318; tel. 402/717–8000, (Nonreporting) **A**10 **S** Alegent Health, Omaha, NE
Primary Contact: Cindy Alloway, R.N., Vice President and Chief Operating Officer
Web address: www.alegent.org
`23 10 45 — — — — — — —`

BISHOP CLARKSON MEMORIAL HOSPITAL See Nebraska Medical Center

□ BOYS TOWN NATIONAL RESEARCH HOSPITAL, 555 North 30th Street, Zip 68131–2198; tel. 402/498–6511, (Nonreporting) **A**1 9 10
Primary Contact: John K. Arch, Administrator
Web address: www.boystownhospital.org
`23 50 14 — — — — — — —`

⊠ CHILDREN'S HOSPITAL, 8200 Dodge Street, Zip 68114–4113; tel. 402/955–5400 **A**1 3 5 9 10 **F**2 9 16 18 20 21 22 23 27 28 29 33 46 47 48 51 52 53 56 57 58 61 63 64 65 67 69 72 74 77 78 81 82 84 87 88 93 94 96 107 108 **P**8
Primary Contact: Gary A. Perkins, President and Chief Executive Officer
COO: Kathy L. English, R.N., Senior Vice President and Chief Operating Officer
CFO: Michael Brown, Vice President Finance and Chief Financial Officer
CMO: Steve Lazoritz, M.D., Vice President Medical Affairs
CIO: Janice Rowe, Director Information Resources
CHR: Corliss Lovstad, Director Human Resources
Web address: www.chsomaha.org
`23 50 142 6928 100 118800 0 125986 59971 1164`

⊠ CREIGHTON UNIVERSITY MEDICAL CENTER, 601 North 30th Street, Zip 68131–2197; tel. 402/449–5021, (Nonreporting) **A**1 3 5 8 9 10 **S** TENET Healthcare Corporation, Dallas, TX
Primary Contact: Philip P. Gustafson, Chief Executive Officer
CMO: Stephen Lanspa, M.D., Vice President Medical Affairs
Web address: www.saintjosephhospital.com
`33 10 278 — — — — — — —`

○ DOUGLAS COUNTY HEALTH CENTER, 4102 Woolworth Avenue, Zip 68105–1899; tel. 402/444–7000, (Total facility includes 254 beds in nursing home–type unit) **A**9 10 11 **F**8 39 44 52 69 71 77 78 92 94
Primary Contact: James C. Tourville, Administrator
Web address: www.co.douglas.ne.us
`13 22 308 979 248 18363 0 33191 18422 439`

⊠ NEBRASKA MEDICAL CENTER, 4350 Dewey Avenue, Zip 68198–7400, Mailing Address: 987400 Nebraska Medical Center, Zip 68198–7400; tel. 402/552–2000, (Includes BISHOP CLARKSON MEMORIAL HOSPITAL, 4350 Dewey Avenue, Zip 68105–1018; tel. 402/552–2000; UNIVERSITY HOSPITAL, UNIVERSITY OF NEBRASKA MEDICAL CENTER, 600 South 42nd Street, Zip 68198–4085; tel. 402/559–4000) **A**1 2 3 5 8 9 10 **F**2 5 6 9 10 11 12 13 14 15 16 17 18 19 20 21 22 23 26 27 28 29 30 31 32 33 34 35 37 38 39 40 41 42 44 46 47 48 49 50 52 53 55 56 57 58 59 61 62 63 64 65 66 67 69 70 71 72 73 74 75 76 77 79 80 81 82 84 85 86 87 88 90 92 93 94 95 96 99 100 101 102 103 105 106 107 108 109 110 **P**8
Primary Contact: Glenn A. Fosdick, FACHE, President and Chief Executive Officer
COO: Joe B. Graham, Chief Operating Officer
CFO: William S. Dinsmoor, Senior Vice President and Chief Financial Officer
CMO: Stephen B. Smith, M.D., Chief Medical Officer
CIO: Jim Veline, Interim Director Information Technology
Web address: www.nebraskamed.com
`23 10 516 21232 367 435178 2348 437244 167715 3915`

⊠ △ NEBRASKA METHODIST HOSPITAL, 8303 Dodge Street, Zip 68114–4199; tel. 402/354–4000 **A**1 2 3 5 7 9 10 **F**2 4 9 10 11 12 14 15 17 19 21 22 23 26 27 28 29 32 33 34 36 37 38 39 40 42 43 44 45 46 47 48 49 50 51 52 53 55 57 58 59 60 61 62 63 64 65 66 68 69 73 74 75 76 77 79 80 81 82 84 85 86 87 88 89 90 92 93 94 95 96 106 108 109 110 **P**8 **S** Nebraska Methodist Health System, Inc., Omaha, NE
Primary Contact: John M. Fraser, President and Chief Executive Officer
CFO: Raymond Stoupa, Vice President
CMO: William Shiffermiller, M.D., Vice President Medical Affairs
CIO: Charles Johnson, Vice President Information Technology
CHR: Holly Huerter, Vice President Human Resources
Web address: www.bestcare.org
`23 10 345 18306 235 252627 3828 266661 108941 1832`

NEBRASKA ORTHOPAEDIC HOSPITAL, 2808 South 143rd Plaza, Zip 68144; tel. 402/637–0600, (Nonreporting) **A**10
Primary Contact: Cindy Arbaugh, Chief Executive Officer
`33 47 24 — — — — — — —`

UNIVERSITY HOSPITAL, UNIVERSITY OF NEBRASKA MEDICAL CENTER See Nebraska Medical Center

⊠ VETERANS AFFAIRS MEDICAL CENTER, 4101 Woolworth Avenue, Zip 68105–1873; tel. 402/346–8800, (Total facility includes 76 beds in nursing home–type unit) (Nonreporting) **A**1 3 5 8 **S** Department of Veterans Affairs, Washington, DC
Primary Contact: Albert B. Washko, Director
CFO: Russell Lloyd, Chief Financial Officer
CHR: Dave Peters, Chief Human Resources Officer
Web address: www.va.gov/sta/guide/home.asp
`45 10 202 — — — — — — —`

ORD—Valley County

★ VALLEY COUNTY HOSPITAL, 217 Westridge Drive, Zip 68862–1675; tel. 308/728–3211, (Total facility includes 69 beds in nursing home–type unit) **A**9 10 18 **F**6 11 12 26 27 29 33 35 36 41 44 45 46 47 48 51 52 59 60 61 63 68 69 70 81 88 92 94 97 **P**6
Primary Contact: Neelam Bhardwaj, Chief Executive Officer and Administrator
CFO: Don Williamson, Chief Financial Officer
`13 10 95 611 58 13741 7 8628 4145 172`

Hospital, Address, Telephone, Approval, Facility, and Physician Codes, Health Care System	Classi-fication Codes		Utilization Data					Expense (thousands) of dollars		
★ American Hospital Association (AHA) membership □ Joint Commission on Accreditation of Healthcare Organizations (JCAHO) accreditation ○ American Osteopathic Association (AOA) accreditation △ Commission on Accreditation of Rehabilitation Facilities (CARF) accreditation	Control	Service	Staffed Beds	Admissions	Census	Outpatient Visits	Births	Total	Payroll	Personnel

OSCEOLA—Polk County

ANNIE JEFFREY MEMORIAL COUNTY HEALTH CENTER, 531 Beebe Street, Zip 68651, Mailing Address: P.O. Box 428, Zip 68651–0428; tel. 402/747–2031 **A**9 10 18 **F**1 9 11 21 26 27 28 29 33 41 46 47 48 52 54 58 59 60 63 66 69 70 92 94 95 97 106 **P**6
Primary Contact: Terry L. Hoffart, Administrator
Web address: www.anniejeffreyhospital.org

| | 13 | 10 | 21 | 270 | 2 | 9921 | 14 | 3256 | 1617 | 48 |

OSHKOSH—Garden County

GARDEN COUNTY HOSPITAL, 1100 West Second Street, Zip 69154, Mailing Address: P.O. Box 320, Zip 69154–0320; tel. 308/772–3283, (Total facility includes 40 beds in nursing home–type unit) **A**9 10 18 **F**6 9 26 27 33 34 48 52 69 91 92 94 95 97 98 108 109 **P**5
Primary Contact: Diana R. Stevens, Administrator

| | 13 | 10 | 50 | 161 | 35 | 2706 | 0 | 4699 | 2601 | — |

OSMOND—Pierce County

★ **OSMOND GENERAL HOSPITAL**, 5th and Maple Street, Zip 68765–0429, Mailing Address: P.O. Box 429, Zip 68765–0429; tel. 402/748–3393 **A**9 10 18 **F**1 9 26 27 28 33 45 46 54 62 63 64 97
Primary Contact: Celine M. Mlady, Chief Executive Officer
CFO: Jodi Aschoff, Chief Financial Officer
Web address: www.osmondhospital.com

| | 23 | 10 | 25 | 417 | 18 | 5253 | 0 | 3008 | 2540 | 71 |

PAPILLION—Sarpy County

☒ **ALEGENT–HEALTH MIDLANDS COMMUNITY HOSPITAL**, 11111 South 84th Street, Zip 68046–4157; tel. 402/593–3000 **A**1 2 9 10 **F**2 9 11 12 15 17 21 22 26 27 28 29 31 32 33 34 35 36 37 39 44 45 46 48 50 51 52 53 55 59 60 61 62 63 64 65 66 69 81 84 85 87 88 92 93 94 96 106 108 **P**6 8 **S** Alegent Health, Omaha, NE
Primary Contact: Kevin Nokels, Vice President and Chief Operating Officer
COO: Kevin Nokels, Vice President and Chief Operating Officer
CFO: Calvin J. Brummund, Operations Leader Financial Services
CIO: Dan Connolly, Chief Information Officer
Web address: www.alegent.org/midlands

| | 21 | 10 | 100 | 3141 | 37 | 55441 | 430 | 41094 | 19656 | 398 |

□ **SELECT SPECIALTY HOSPITAL–OMAHA**, 11111 South 84th Street, Zip 68046; tel. 402/898–2700, (Nonreporting) **A**1 9 10 **S** Select Medical Corporation, Mechanicsburg, PA
Primary Contact: Linda Mertz, Administrator
Web address: www.selectmedicalcorp.com

| | 33 | 80 | 30 | — | — | — | — | — | — | — |

PAWNEE CITY—Pawnee County

★ **PAWNEE COUNTY MEMORIAL HOSPITAL**, 600 I Street, Zip 68420–3001, Mailing Address: P.O. Box 313, Zip 68420–0313; tel. 402/852–2231, (Nonreporting) **A**9 10 18
Primary Contact: James A. Kubik, Administrator

| | 13 | 10 | 17 | — | — | — | — | — | — | — |

PENDER—Thurston County

★ **PENDER COMMUNITY HOSPITAL**, 603 Earl Street, Zip 68047–0100, Mailing Address: P.O. Box 100, Zip 68047–0100; tel. 402/385–3083, (Total facility includes 42 beds in nursing home–type unit) **A**9 10 18 **F**1 8 9 11 12 14 21 23 24 26 27 28 29 35 52 59 63 69 81 92 97 108 **S** Trinity Health, Novi, MI
CFO: Jean Kinney, Controller
CMO: Matt Felber, M.D., Medical Director
CIO: Teresa Heise, Management Information Systems Coordinator
Web address: www.pendercommunityhospital.com

| | 16 | 10 | 133 | 654 | 38 | 10385 | 63 | 7197 | 3099 | 138 |

PLAINVIEW—Pierce County

PLAINVIEW AREA HEALTH SYSTEM, 705 North Third Street, Zip 68769, Mailing Address: P.O. Box 489, Zip 68769–0489; tel. 402/582–4245, (Nonreporting) **A**9 10 18
Primary Contact: Becky Lambrecht, Administrator

| | 14 | 10 | 20 | — | — | — | — | — | — | — |

RED CLOUD—Webster County

WEBSTER COUNTY COMMUNITY HOSPITAL, Sixth Avenue and Franklin Street, Zip 68970–0465; tel. 402/746–2291 **A**9 10 18 **F**12 14 23 26 27 28 33 46 53 62 63 65 69 77 92 97 108 **P**6
Primary Contact: Robert L. Sheckler, Administrator
Web address: www.websterhospital.org

| | 13 | 10 | 16 | 294 | 4 | 5814 | 0 | 2535 | 1138 | 36 |

SAINT PAUL—Howard County

★ **HOWARD COUNTY COMMUNITY HOSPITAL**, 1113 Sherman Street, Zip 68873–1536, Mailing Address: P.O. Box 406, Zip 68873–0406; tel. 308/754–4421 **A**9 10 18 **F**2 9 11 21 26 33 46 48 52 59 63 66 81 94 97 108 **P**6
Primary Contact: Arthur H. Frable, Chief Executive Officer
CFO: Jeanine Soneson, Chief Financial Officer
CMO: Christopher Tom Have, M.D., Chief of Staff
CIO: Kari Pierson, Manager

| | 13 | 10 | 25 | 545 | 14 | 29273 | 35 | 7627 | 3802 | 120 |

SCHUYLER—Colfax County

★ **ALEGENT HEALTH–MEMORIAL HOSPITAL**, 104 West 17th Street, Zip 68661–1396; tel. 402/352–2441, (Nonreporting) **A**9 10 18 **S** Alegent Health, Omaha, NE
Primary Contact: Connie Peters, R.N., Regional Health Administrator
CFO: Jenice Detweiler, Operations Director Support Services
Web address: www.alegent.org

| | 21 | 10 | 15 | — | — | — | — | — | — | — |

NE

Many Facility Codes have changed. Please refer to the AHA Guide Code Chart. © 2005 AHA Guide

Hospital, Address, Telephone, Approval, Facility, and Physician Codes, Health Care System	Classi- fication Codes		Utilization Data					Expense (thousands) of dollars		
★ American Hospital Association (AHA) membership □ Joint Commission on Accreditation of Healthcare Organizations (JCAHO) accreditation ○ American Osteopathic Association (AOA) accreditation △ Commission on Accreditation of Rehabilitation Facilities (CARF) accreditation	Control	Service	Staffed Beds	Admissions	Census	Outpatient Visits	Births	Total	Payroll	Personnel

SCOTTSBLUFF—Scotts Bluff County

☒ △ **REGIONAL WEST MEDICAL CENTER**, 4021 Avenue B, Zip 69361–4695; tel. 308/635–3711, (Total facility includes 11 beds in nursing home–type unit) **A**1 2 3 5 7 9 10 19 20 **F**1 3 6 9 10 11 12 13 14 21 22 23 26 27 28 29 31 33 34 37 41 46 48 49 51 52 53 54 55 56 58 59 60 61 63 66 67 68 69 71 72 73 74 75 76 77 78 81 82 84 87 88 92 93 94 95 96 106 108 110 **P**5 6
Primary Contact: Todd Sorensen, M.D., Chief Executive Officer
CFO: Michael Goebel, Chief Financial Officer
CIO: Susan Heider, Vice President and Chief Information Officer
CHR: James Imler, Director Human Resources
Web address: www.rwmc.net

| | 23 | 10 | 95 | 7231 | 90 | 272012 | 781 | 103235 | 41063 | 971 |

SEWARD—Seward County

★ **MEMORIAL HEALTH CARE SYSTEMS**, 300 North Columbia Avenue, Zip 68434–9907; tel. 402/643–2971, (Total facility includes 115 beds in nursing home–type unit) **A**5 9 10 18 **F**8 11 12 27 28 33 52 58 63 81 88 92 97
Primary Contact: Roger J. Reamer, Chief Executive Officer
CFO: Greg Jerger, Chief Financial Officer
CMO: J B. Ketner, Medical Director
CIO: Carol Carlson, Director Marketing
Web address: www.mhcs–seward.org

| | 23 | 10 | 154 | 889 | 111 | 27630 | 101 | 20364 | 10437 | 337 |

SIDNEY—Cheyenne County

★ **MEMORIAL HEALTH CENTER**, 645 Osage Street, Zip 69162–1799; tel. 308/254–5825, (Total facility includes 64 beds in nursing home–type unit) (Nonreporting) **A**9 10 18 20
Primary Contact: Kent Aland, Chief Executive Officer
CFO: Sharon Lind, Chief Financial Officer
CMO: Clint Dorwart, M.D., Chief of Staff
CHR: Carnie Trost, Director Human Resources
Web address: www.memorialhealthcenter.org

| | 23 | 10 | 89 | — | — | — | — | — | — | — |

SUPERIOR—Nuckolls County

★ **BRODSTONE MEMORIAL HOSPITAL**, 520 East Tenth Street, Zip 68978–1225, Mailing Address: P.O. Box 187, Zip 68978–0187; tel. 402/879–3281 **A**9 10 18 **F**2 6 9 11 12 14 21 22 23 27 28 29 33 46 48 51 52 55 59 63 66 69 81 88 92 94 95 97 106 108 **P**5
Primary Contact: John E. Keelan, Administrator and Chief Executive Officer
CFO: Sandy Borden, Chief Financial Officer
CMO: Timothy Blecha, M.D., Medical Director
CIO: Gary Keeling, Chief Information Officer
CHR: Jodene Clabaugh, Human Resources Clerk
Web address: www.brodstonehospital.org

| | 23 | 10 | 25 | 693 | 10 | — | 45 | 10476 | 4844 | 146 |

SYRACUSE—Otoe County

★ **COMMUNITY MEMORIAL HOSPITAL**, 1579 Midland Street, Zip 68446–9732, Mailing Address: P.O. Box N, Zip 68446; tel. 402/269–2011 **A**9 10 18 **F**6 9 11 12 21 26 27 28 29 33 34 41 45 46 47 48 51 52 58 61 63 65 70 88 94 97 **P**6
Primary Contact: Al Klaasmeyer, Administrator
CFO: Cindi Mulcahy, Business Office Manager
CMO: Jean Louis Pare, M.D., Chief Medical Staff
CIO: Al Allen, Information Administrator
Web address: www.syracusecmh.org

| | 16 | 10 | 18 | 192 | 1 | 9560 | 19 | 4778 | 2236 | 64 |

TECUMSEH—Johnson County

★ **JOHNSON COUNTY HOSPITAL**, 202 High Street, Zip 68450–0599, Mailing Address: P.O. Box 599, Zip 68450–0599; tel. 402/335–3361, (Nonreporting) **A**9 10 18
Primary Contact: Diane Newman, Administrator
CIO: Shari Little, Inforamtion System Manager

| | 13 | 10 | 25 | — | — | — | — | — | — | — |

TILDEN—Antelope County

TILDEN COMMUNITY HOSPITAL, Second and Pine Streets, Zip 68781, Mailing Address: P.O. Box 340, Zip 68781–0340; tel. 402/368–5343, (Nonreporting) **A**9 10 18
Primary Contact: Julie Roemhildt, Administrator

| | 23 | 10 | 21 | — | — | — | — | — | — | — |

VALENTINE—Cherry County

★ **CHERRY COUNTY HOSPITAL**, Highway 12 and Green Street, Zip 69201–0410; tel. 402/376–2525 **A**9 10 18 **F**2 6 12 14 23 27 28 29 33 46 49 51 52 55 59 61 62 63 64 66 81 88 97 108 **P**6
Primary Contact: Brent A. Peterson, Administrator
CFO: Peggy Snell, Chief Finance Officer

| | 13 | 10 | 25 | 761 | 7 | 14478 | 125 | 9177 | 3906 | 112 |

WAHOO—Saunders County

★ **SAUNDERS COUNTY HEALTH SERVICE**, 805 West Tenth Street, Zip 68066–1102, Mailing Address: P.O. Box 185, Zip 68066–0185; tel. 402/443–4191, (Nonreporting) **A**9 10 18
Primary Contact: Earl N. Sheehy, President and Chief Executive Officer
CFO: Shannon Adams, Chief Financial Officer
CMO: Leo Meduna, M.D., Chief Medical Officer
CIO: Carrie Diller, Information Systems Coordinator
CHR: Cindy Barry, Coordinator Human Resources
Web address: www.saunders–health.org

| | 13 | 10 | 25 | — | — | — | — | — | — | — |

NE

Hospital, Address, Telephone, Approval, Facility, and Physician Codes, Health Care System	Classi-fication Codes		Utilization Data					Expense (thousands) of dollars		
★ American Hospital Association (AHA) membership □ Joint Commission on Accreditation of Healthcare Organizations (JCAHO) accreditation ○ American Osteopathic Association (AOA) accreditation △ Commission on Accreditation of Rehabilitation Facilities (CARF) accreditation	Control	Service	Staffed Beds	Admissions	Census	Outpatient Visits	Births	Total	Payroll	Personnel

WAYNE—Wayne County

★ **PROVIDENCE MEDICAL CENTER**, 1200 Providence Road, Zip 68787–1299; tel. 402/375–3800 **A**9 10 18 **F**6 11 12 22 23 26 27 28 33 36 41 51 54 58 61 63 64 66 69 79 81 88 94 95 97 **S** Missionary Benedictine Sisters American Province, Norfolk, NE
Primary Contact: Marcile Thomas, Administrator
Web address: www.providencemedical.com

21	10	25	866	11	11844	65	8886	4361	106

WEST POINT—Cuming County

★ **ST. FRANCIS MEMORIAL HOSPITAL**, 430 North Monitor Street, Zip 68788–1595; tel. 402/372–2404, (Total facility includes 70 beds in nursing home–type unit) **A**9 10 18 **F**9 11 12 21 22 23 27 29 33 36 37 41 48 51 52 53 58 59 60 61 62 63 64 68 69 75 81 85 88 92 95 96 97 108 110 **P**6
S Franciscan Sisters of Christian Charity HealthCare Ministry, Inc, Manitowoc, WI
Primary Contact: Ronald O. Briggs, FACHE, President and Chief Executive Officer
CFO: Dennis Dinslage, Vice President Finance and Chief Financial Officer
CMO: Brian Hass, M.D., Chief of Staff
CIO: Jean Meiergerd, Director Information Systems
Web address: www.fcswp.org

21	10	95	648	76	62306	81	14752	7725	186

WINNEBAGO—Thurston County

⊠ **U. S. PUBLIC HEALTH SERVICE INDIAN HOSPITAL**, Highway 7577, Zip 68071; tel. 402/878–2231, (Nonreporting) **A**1 9 10 **S** U. S. Indian Health Service, Rockville, MD
Primary Contact: Donald Lee, Service Unit Director
CFO: Audrey Parker, Budget Analyst

47	10	30	—	—	—	—	—	—	—

YORK—York County

★ **YORK GENERAL HEALTH CARE SERVICES**, 2222 North Lincoln Avenue, Zip 68467–1095; tel. 402/362–6671, (Total facility includes 120 beds in nursing home–type unit) **A**9 10 18 **F**2 8 9 11 12 21 23 29 33 37 40 41 44 45 46 48 49 51 52 53 55 58 59 60 61 62 63 64 65 66 69 81 82 84 86 87 88 91 92 93 94 95 96 97 108 110
Primary Contact: Charles K. Schulz, Chief Executive Officer
COO: Jane Thompson, Administrator and Chief Operating Officer
CFO: Bob McQuistan, Vice President Finance
CIO: John Temple, Director Information Systems
CHR: Barb Koester, Director Human Resources
Web address: www.yorkgeneral.org

23	10	154	1109	124	32140	140	24134	10722	312

NE

NEVADA

Hospital, Address, Telephone, Approval, Facility, and Physician Codes, Health Care System	Classi-fication Codes		Utilization Data					Expense (thousands) of dollars		
★ American Hospital Association (AHA) membership ☐ Joint Commission on Accreditation of Healthcare Organizations (JCAHO) accreditation ○ American Osteopathic Association (AOA) accreditation △ Commission on Accreditation of Rehabilitation Facilities (CARF) accreditation	Control	Service	Staffed Beds	Admissions	Census	Outpatient Visits	Births	Total	Payroll	Personnel

BATTLE MOUNTAIN—Lander County

BATTLE MOUNTAIN GENERAL HOSPITAL, 535 South Humboldt Street, Zip 89820–1988; tel. 775/635–2550, (Nonreporting) **A**9 10 18
Primary Contact: Kathy Ancho, Administrator
Web address: www.battlemtgeneralhospital.org

| | 16 | 10 | 25 | — | — | — | — | — | — | — |

BOULDER CITY—Clark County

BOULDER CITY HOSPITAL, 901 Adams Boulevard, Zip 89005–2213; tel. 702/293–4111, (Nonreporting) **A**9 10
Primary Contact: Kim O. Crandell, Chief Executive Officer and Administrator
Web address: www.bouldercityhospital.org

| | 23 | 10 | 67 | — | — | — | — | — | — | — |

CALIENTE—Lincoln County

GROVER C. DILS MEDICAL CENTER, Highway 93 North, Zip 89008, Mailing Address: P.O. Box 1010, Zip 89008–1010; tel. 775/726–3171, (Nonreporting) **A**9 10 20
Primary Contact: Shawn D. Wiscombe, Administrator
Web address: www.dilsmedicalcenter.org

| | 23 | 49 | 20 | | | | | | | |

CARSON CITY—Carson City County

△ **CARSON REHABILITATION CENTER**, 900 East Long Street, Zip 89706; tel. 775/881–7000, (Nonreporting) **A**7 9 10
Primary Contact: Edward L. Epperson, Chief Executive Officer

| | 23 | 46 | 30 | — | — | — | — | — | — | — |

✠ **CARSON TAHOE HOSPITAL**, 775 Fleischmann Way, Zip 89702–2995, Mailing Address: P.O. Box 2168, Zip 89702–2168; tel. 775/882–1361 **A**1 9 10 20 **F**2 3 4 9 10 11 15 17 21 22 23 27 29 31 33 35 42 46 47 48 53 55 58 59 60 61 63 66 69 71 72 73 74 75 76 77 78 79 81 82 84 85 86 88 94 96 106 107 108 109 110 **P**5
Primary Contact: Edward L. Epperson, Chief Executive Officer
COO: Kevin M. Stansbury, Chief Operating Officer
CFO: Sharon Johansson, Chief Financial Officer
CIO: Michael Blair, Chief Information Officer
CHR: Barbara Durham, Director Human Resources
Web address: www.carsontahoehospital.com

| | 23 | 10 | 131 | 8579 | 78 | 101629 | 849 | 110792 | 41559 | 798 |

ELKO—Elko County

✠ **NORTHEASTERN NEVADA REGIONAL HOSPITAL**, 2001 Errecart Boulevard, Zip 89801–3499; tel. 775/738–5151 **A**1 9 10 20 **F**9 11 12 21 22 23 33 46 48 52 58 59 61 62 63 65 66 69 81 82 84 88 93 106 110 **S** LifePoint Hospitals, Inc., Brentwood, TN
Primary Contact: David L. Henson, Chief Executive Officer
COO: Ann Cariker, Chief Operating Officer
CFO: Mike Long, Chief Financial Officer
CMO: Nanette Koupal Smith, Medical Records Director
CIO: Jeff Morgan, Information Systems Director
Web address: www.nnrhospital.com

| | 13 | 10 | 50 | 2299 | 18 | 41517 | 599 | 25816 | 9809 | — |

ELY—White Pine County

☐ **WILLIAM BEE RIRIE HOSPITAL**, 1500 Avenue H, Zip 89301–2699; tel. 775/289–3001 **A**1 9 10 18 **F**11 12 26 27 29 32 33 42 44 46 58 59 63 69 81 84 88 93 94 108 **P**8
Primary Contact: Robert A. Morasko, Chief Executive Officer
Web address: www.elynevadahospital.org

| | 13 | 10 | 29 | 1965 | 15 | — | — | — | — | 152 |

FALLON—Churchill County

✠ **BANNER CHURCHILL COMMUNITY HOSPITAL**, 801 East Williams Avenue, Zip 89406–3052; tel. 775/423–3151 **A**1 9 10 20 **F**2 6 9 11 12 21 22 23 29 33 34 46 47 48 51 52 58 60 61 62 63 65 66 69 70 81 82 84 88 94 107 108 110 **S** Banner Health, Phoenix, AZ
Primary Contact: Charles Myers, Chief Executive Officer
COO: Skip Reeves, Assistant Administrator Operations
CFO: Steven Fraker, Chief Financial Officer
Web address: www.churchillhospital.com

| | 23 | 10 | 40 | 1877 | 17 | 130591 | 408 | 36332 | 17323 | — |

GARDNERVILLE—Douglas County

CARSON VALLEY MEDICAL CENTER, 1107 Highway 395, Zip 89410; tel. 775/782–1600 **A**10 18 **F**2 12 21 23 27 28 33 37 38 46 48 52 53 58 60 63 64 69 81 84 85 88 94 108 **P**4 7
Primary Contact: Gerald Conley, Administrator

| | 23 | 10 | 15 | 529 | 4 | 35540 | 0 | 15788 | 5615 | 98 |

HAWTHORNE—Mineral County

MOUNT GRANT GENERAL HOSPITAL, First and A Street, Zip 89415, Mailing Address: P.O. Box 1510, Zip 89415–1510; tel. 775/945–2461, (Nonreporting) **A**9 10 18
Primary Contact: Richard Munger, Administrator

| | 23 | 10 | 11 | — | — | — | — | — | — | — |

HENDERSON—Clark County

✠ **HEALTHSOUTH REHABILITATION HOSPITAL – HENDERSON**, 10301 Jeffreys Street, Zip 89052; tel. 702/939–9400 **A**1 10 **F**21 29 45 51 52 68 69 110 **S** HEALTHSOUTH Corporation, Birmingham, AL
Primary Contact: Thomas Maher, Administrator

| | 33 | 46 | 60 | 1268 | 51 | 17298 | 0 | 13453 | — | 164 |

Hospital, Address, Telephone, Approval, Facility, and Physician Codes, Health Care System	Control	Service	Staffed Beds	Admissions	Census	Outpatient Visits	Births	Total	Payroll	Personnel

★ American Hospital Association (AHA) membership
□ Joint Commission on Accreditation of Healthcare Organizations (JCAHO) accreditation
○ American Osteopathic Association (AOA) accreditation
△ Commission on Accreditation of Rehabilitation Facilities (CARF) accreditation

Hospital	Control	Service	Staffed Beds	Admissions	Census	Outpatient Visits	Births	Total	Payroll	Personnel
⊠ **ST. ROSE DOMINICAN HOSPITALS – ROSE DE LIMA CAMPUS**, 102 East Lake Mead Parkway, Zip 89015–5524; tel. 702/616–5000 **A**1 10 **F**2 9 11 12 21 22 23 24 27 28 29 31 33 37 38 39 40 42 46 47 48 50 51 52 53 55 58 59 60 61 62 63 64 65 66 68 69 70 81 82 84 87 88 92 94 95 96 98 107 108 109 **S** Catholic Healthcare West, San Francisco, CA Primary Contact: Renato V. Baciarelli, President CFO: Parmod Garg, Chief Financial Officer CMO: Stephen K. Jones, M.D., Vice President Medical Staff Affairs CIO: Sharon Hester, Information Technology Site Manager CHR: Wayne Frangesch, Vice President Human Resources Web address: www.strosecares.com	23	10	138	7913	100	37013	1039	89309	39254	749
⊠ **ST. ROSE DOMINICAN HOSPITALS – SIENA CAMPUS**, 3001 St. Rose Parkway, Zip 89015; tel. 702/616–5000 **A**1 10 **F**2 3 9 11 12 13 14 15 16 17 18 19 21 22 23 24 27 28 29 31 33 35 37 38 39 41 42 46 47 48 51 52 53 55 56 57 58 59 60 61 62 63 64 65 66 67 68 69 70 71 81 82 84 85 88 92 94 95 96 98 106 107 108 109 **S** Catholic Healthcare West, San Francisco, CA Primary Contact: Rod A. Davis, President and Chief Executive Officer COO: Teressa Conley, Chief Operating Officer CFO: Parmod Garg, Chief Financial Officer CMO: Stephen K. Jones, M.D., Vice President Medical Staff Affairs CIO: Sharon Hester, Information Technology Site Manager CHR: Wayne Frangesch, Vice President Human Resources Web address: www.strosecares.com	23	10	214	15044	167	49022	2699	153047	52869	1051
INCLINE VILLAGE—Washoe County										
○ **INCLINE VILLAGE COMMUNITY HOSPITAL**, 880 Alder Avenue, Zip 89450; tel. 775/833–4100 **A**9 10 11 18 **F**12 33 46 51 52 69 81 82 88 93 Primary Contact: Fred A. Pritchard, Executive Director Web address: www.tfhd.com	16	10	4	39	1	—	—	—	—	—
LAS VEGAS—Clark County										
□ **DESERT SPRINGS HOSPITAL**, 2075 East Flamingo Road, Zip 89119–5121, Mailing Address: P.O. Box 19204, Zip 89132–9204; tel. 702/733–8800, (Nonreporting) **A**1 9 10 **S** Universal Health Services, Inc., King of Prussia, PA Primary Contact: Samuel Kaufman, Chief Executive Officer and Managing Director Web address: www.desertspringshosp.com	33	10	346	—	—	—	—	—	—	—
⊠ **HEALTHSOUTH HOSPITAL OF TENAYA**, 2500 North Tenaya, Zip 89128; tel. 702/562–2021 **A**1 10 **F**2 21 39 45 49 58 92 94 108 110 **S** HEALTHSOUTH Corporation, Birmingham, AL Primary Contact: Jerry Amato, Administrator COO: Jerry Amato, Chief Operating Officer and Administrator CFO: Marciano Patricio, Jr, Chief Financial Officer CMO: C Dean Milne, D.O., Medical Director CIO: Rose Mary Danuloff, Manager Medical Records CHR: Tovah D'Ambrosio, Manager Human Resources	33	80	70	907	59	0	0	21381	11779	185
⊠ **HEALTHSOUTH REHABILITATION HOSPITAL–LAS VEGAS**, (Formerly Rehabilitation Hospital), 1250 South Valley View Boulevard, Zip 89102–1861; tel. 702/877–8898, (Nonreporting) **A**1 10 **S** HEALTHSOUTH Corporation, Birmingham, AL Primary Contact: Gilbert Silbernagel, Administrator Web address: www.healthsouth.com	33	46	79	—	—	—	—	—	—	—
□ **HORIZON SPECIALTY HOSPITAL**, 640 Desert Lane, Zip 89106; tel. 702/382–3155, (Nonreporting) **A**1 10 Primary Contact: Sandra Rohlfing, R.N., Chief Executive Officer	33	46	25	—	—	—	—	—	—	—
□ **KINDRED HOSPITAL–LAS VEGAS**, 5110 West Sahara Avenue, Zip 89146–3406; tel. 702/871–1418, (Includes KINDRED HOSPITAL–FLAMINGO, 2250 East Flamingo Road, Zip 89119; tel. 702/784–4300) **A**1 10 **F**2 21 37 49 52 60 69 94 110 **S** Kindred Healthcare, Louisville, KY Primary Contact: Linn P. Billingsley, Chief Executive Officer Web address: www.kindredhealthcare.com	33	10	92	1094	81	1355	0	—	—	235
□ **MONTEVISTA HOSPITAL**, 5900 West Rochelle Avenue, Zip 89103–3327; tel. 702/364–1111, (Nonreporting) **A**1 9 **S** Psychiatric Solutions, Franklin, TN Primary Contact: Ingrid L. Whipple, Chief Executive Officer Web address: www.bhcmontevista.com	33	22	80	—	—	—	—	—	—	—
⊠ **MOUNTAINVIEW HOSPITAL**, 3100 North Tenaya Way, Zip 89128–0436; tel. 702/255–5000 **A**1 9 10 **F**2 10 11 12 15 17 19 21 22 23 27 28 33 38 46 47 48 53 55 58 59 60 61 62 63 64 69 81 82 84 88 94 96 108 109 **P**1 **S** HCA, Nashville, TN Primary Contact: Mark J. Howard, President and Chief Executive Officer COO: Tad A. Morley, Chief Operating Officer CFO: Joseph M. Richmond, Chief Financial Officer CMO: Sam Green, Chief of Staff CIO: Cae Swanger, Director Information Services CHR: Robert Nettles, Director Human Resources Web address: www.mountainview–hospital.com	33	10	199	16146	188	64713	2676	149949	50079	729
PROGRESSIVE HOSPITAL, 4015 South McLeod Drive, Zip 89121; tel. 702/433–2200 **A**10 **F**94 110 **P**8 Primary Contact: Rosemary Thiele, Chief Executive Officer	33	80	24	721	15	0	0	6022	3111	—

REHABILITATION HOSPITAL See HEALTHSOUTH Rehabilitation Hospital–Las Vegas

Hospital, Address, Telephone, Approval, Facility, and Physician Codes, Health Care System	Classi-fication Codes		Utilization Data					Expense (thousands) of dollars		
★ American Hospital Association (AHA) membership □ Joint Commission on Accreditation of Healthcare Organizations (JCAHO) accreditation ○ American Osteopathic Association (AOA) accreditation △ Commission on Accreditation of Rehabilitation Facilities (CARF) accreditation	Control	Service	Staffed Beds	Admissions	Census	Outpatient Visits	Births	Total	Payroll	Personnel
⊠ **SOUTHERN HILLS HOSPITAL AND MEDICAL CENTER**, 9300 West Sunset Road, Zip 89148; tel. 702/880–2100 **A**1 9 10 **F**2 12 15 17 21 22 23 26 27 28 29 33 39 44 46 48 49 53 57 58 59 61 62 63 64 69 70 81 82 84 85 88 92 94 108 **P**8 **S** HCA, Nashville, TN Primary Contact: Stephen E. Dixon, Chief Executive Officer COO: Jen Sweeney, Chief Operating Officer CFO: Steve Killian, Chief Financial Officer CMO: Arnold Way, M.D., Chief of Staff CIO: Cameron Bellamy, Director Information Technology and Systems CHR: Robert Brown, Director Human Resources Web address: www.southernhillshospital.com	33	10	130	2837	40	16272	299	44593	—	418
□ **SOUTHERN NEVADA ADULT MENTAL HEALTH SERVICES**, 6161 West Charleston Boulevard, Zip 89146; tel. 702/486–6000 **A**1 10 **F**21 27 28 29 31 33 71 73 74 75 76 77 94 **P**6 Primary Contact: Jonna Triggs, Chief Executive Officer Web address: www.mhds.state.nv.us	12	22	131	1491	72	139821	0	50992	17117	384
□ **SPRING VALLEY HOSPITAL MEDICAL CENTER**, 5400 South Rainbow Boulevard, Zip 89118; tel. 702/853–3333 **A**1 9 10 **F**2 12 15 17 21 33 46 52 55 59 62 63 64 66 81 82 84 85 88 92 94 108 109 **S** Universal Health Services, Inc., King of Prussia, PA Primary Contact: Karla Perez, Chief Executive Officer and Managing Director	33	10	90	7394	80	—	—	—	—	506
□ **SUMMERLIN HOSPITAL MEDICAL CENTER**, 657 Town Center Drive, Zip 89134; tel. 702/233–7000, (Nonreporting) **A**1 9 10 **S** Universal Health Services, Inc., King of Prussia, PA Primary Contact: Tim Hingtgen, Chief Executive Officer and Managing Director Web address: www.summerlinhospital.org	33	10	148	—	—	—	—	—	—	—
⊠ △ **SUNRISE HOSPITAL AND MEDICAL CENTER**, 3186 Maryland Parkway, Zip 89109–2306, Mailing Address: P.O. Box 98530, Zip 89193–8530; tel. 702/731–8000, (Includes INCLUDES SUNRISE CHILDREN'S HOSPITAL), (Nonreporting) **A**1 2 3 5 7 9 10 **S** HCA, Nashville, TN Primary Contact: Brian C. Robinson, Chief Executive Officer COO: Suzanne Cram, Chief Operating Officer CFO: John Peters, Chief Financial Officer CIO: Troy Sypien, Director Information Services Web address: www.sunrisehospital.com	33	10	655	—	—	—	—	—	—	—
⊠ **UNIVERSITY MEDICAL CENTER**, 1800 West Charleston Boulevard, Zip 89102–2386; tel. 702/383–2000 **A**1 2 3 5 9 10 **F**11 12 13 14 15 16 17 18 19 20 21 23 24 26 27 28 33 34 39 40 44 48 50 52 53 55 56 57 58 59 61 62 63 67 68 69 70 81 82 84 85 86 87 88 90 93 94 95 101 105 107 108 109 110 **P**6 Primary Contact: Lacy L. Thomas, CPA, Chief Executive Officer COO: Blain Claypool, Chief Operating Officer CFO: Michael T. Walsh, Chief Financial Officer CMO: John Ellerton, M.D., Chief of Staff CIO: Doug Northcutt, Chief Information Officer CHR: John Espinoza, Assistant Administrator Human Resources Web address: www.umc–cares.org	13	10	567	29560	459	645189	4098	396551	138285	3389
□ **VALLEY HOSPITAL MEDICAL CENTER**, 620 Shadow Lane, Zip 89106–4119; tel. 702/388–4000, (Nonreporting) **A**1 9 10 **S** Universal Health Services, Inc., King of Prussia, PA Primary Contact: Gregory E. Boyer, Chief Executive Officer Web address: www.valleyhospital.net	33	10	365	—	—	—	—	—	—	—
LOVELOCK—Pershing County										
★ **PERSHING GENERAL HOSPITAL**, 855 Sixth Street, Zip 89419, Mailing Address: P.O. Box 661, Zip 89419–0661; tel. 775/273–2621, (Total facility includes 30 beds in nursing home–type unit) **A**9 10 18 **F**26 27 33 46 48 60 70 81 84 88 92 94 97 110 Primary Contact: Matt Rees, Chief Executive Officer CFO: Marjorie Skinner, Director Finance CMO: Nancy Baker, D.O., Vice Chair Web address: www.pershinggenhospital.org	15	10	37	112	30	30330	0	7648	3355	65
MESQUITE—Clark County										
★ **MESA VIEW REGIONAL HOSPITAL**, 1299 Bertha Howe Avenue, Zip 89027; tel. 702/346–8040, (Nonreporting) **A**10 18 **S** Triad Hospitals, Inc., Plano, TX Primary Contact: Sue Conley, Chief Executive Officer Web address: www.mesaviewhospital.com	33	49	21	—	—	—	—	—	—	—
NELLIS AFB—Clark County										
⊠ **MIKE O'CALLAGHAN FEDERAL HOSPITAL**, 4700 Las Vegas Boulevard North, Suite 2419, Zip 89191–6601; tel. 702/653–2000, (Nonreporting) **A**1 **S** Department of the Air Force, Washington, DC Primary Contact: Colonel John Korlaske, MSC, Administrator CFO: Captain Tom Cunningham, Flight Commander Resource Management Officer CIO: Captain Dayton Rogalski, Executive Officer	41	10	94	—	—	—	—	—	—	—
NORTH LAS VEGAS—Clark County										
□ **NORTH VISTA HOSPITAL**, 1409 East Lake Mead Boulevard, Zip 89030–7197; tel. 702/649–7711, (Nonreporting) **A**1 9 10 13 **S** IASIS Healthcare, Franklin, TN Primary Contact: Anthony Marinello, Chief Executive Officer Web address: www.lakemeadhospital.com	31	10	198	—	—	—	—	—	—	—

NV

Hospital, Address, Telephone, Approval, Facility, and Physician Codes, Health Care System	Classi-fication Codes		Utilization Data					Expense (thousands) of dollars		
★ American Hospital Association (AHA) membership □ Joint Commission on Accreditation of Healthcare Organizations (JCAHO) accreditation ○ American Osteopathic Association (AOA) accreditation △ Commission on Accreditation of Rehabilitation Facilities (CARF) accreditation	Control	Service	Staffed Beds	Admissions	Census	Outpatient Visits	Births	Total	Payroll	Personnel
★ **VETERANS AFFAIRS SOUTHERN NEVADA HEALTHCARE SYSTEM**, Mailing Address: P.O. Box 360001, Zip 89036; tel. 702/636–3000, (Nonreporting) **A**5 **S** Department of Veterans Affairs, Washington, DC Primary Contact: John Hempel, Director COO: John Bright, Associate Director CFO: James R. Smith, Chief Fiscal Service CMO: Ramanujam Komanduri, M.D., Chief of Staff Web address: www.va.gov/sta/guide/home.asp	45	10	52	—	—	—	—	—	—	—
OWYHEE—Elko County										
⊠ **U. S. PUBLIC HEALTH SERVICE OWYHEE COMMUNITY HEALTH FACILITY**, Mailing Address: P.O. Box 130, Zip 89832–0130; tel. 775/757–2415, (Nonreporting) **A**1 10 18 **S** U. S. Indian Health Service, Rockville, MD Primary Contact: Alan J. Burgess, CHE, FAAMA, Administrator CFO: Noni Manning, Chief Financial Officer CMO: Gerard R. David, M.D., Clinical Director CIO: Alan J. Burgess, CHE, FAAMA, Administrator CHR: William Tandy, Driector Human Resources	46	10	15	—	—	—	—	—	—	—
RENO—Washoe County										
⊠ **SAINT MARY'S REGIONAL MEDICAL CENTER**, 235 West Sixth Street, Zip 89503; tel. 775/770–3000 **A**1 7 10 **F**2 10 11 12 14 15 16 17 18 19 21 22 23 24 27 28 29 33 36 37 38 42 44 46 47 48 49 50 51 52 53 55 56 57 58 59 60 61 62 63 64 65 66 68 69 75 79 80 81 82 83 84 85 87 88 92 94 95 96 107 108 109 110 **P**4 Primary Contact: Lawrence F. O'Brien, Chief Executive Officer CFO: Linda Herman, Vice President and Chief Financial Officer CMO: Peter Braimstein, M.D., Director Medical Affairs CIO: Chris Smith, Vice President and Chief Information Officer Web address: www.saintmarysreno.com	21	10	311	11897	167	425064	2680	212502	84369	1281
□ **TAHOE PACIFIC HOSPITALS**, 10405 Double R Boulevard, Zip 89512; tel. 775/355–5970, (Nonreporting) **A**1 10 **S** LifeCare Management Services, Plano, TX Primary Contact: Paul C. Miller, Chief Executive Officer Web address: www.lifecare–hospitals.com	33	80	29	—	—	—	—	—	—	—
⊠ **VETERANS AFFAIRS SIERRA NEVADA HEALTH CARE SYSTEM**, 1000 Locust Street, Zip 89502–2597; tel. 775/786–7200, (Total facility includes 60 beds in nursing home–type unit) **A**1 3 5 9 **F**2 4 7 9 12 15 21 22 23 26 28 29 31 32 33 35 36 37 38 39 42 44 45 46 47 48 50 51 52 53 55 57 58 60 61 62 63 64 65 66 69 70 71 73 74 75 76 77 78 81 82 84 85 87 88 92 93 94 96 106 107 108 109 110 **P**6 **S** Department of Veterans Affairs, Washington, DC Primary Contact: Kurt W. Schlegelmilch, M.D., CHE, Director COO: Jana R. Johnson, Associate Director CFO: Kathy Munday, Chief Business Service CMO: Thomas C. Barcia, M.D., Chief of Staff CIO: Jane Sullivan, Chief Information Resource Management Service CHR: Lorene Connel, Chief Human Resources Management Service Web address: www.va.gov/sta/guide/home.asp	45	10	113	2923	90	228871	0	114315	42505	729
⊠ **WASHOE MEDICAL CENTER**, 77 Pringle Way, Zip 89502–1474; tel. 775/982–4100 **A**1 2 3 5 9 10 **F**2 4 9 11 12 14 15 16 17 18 19 20 21 22 23 26 27 28 29 33 34 37 42 44 45 46 47 48 49 50 51 52 53 55 56 57 58 59 60 61 62 63 64 65 66 67 69 73 75 77 78 79 80 81 84 85 87 88 92 94 95 96 106 107 108 109 110 **P**6 **S** Washoe Health System, Reno, NV Primary Contact: James I. Miller, President and Chief Executive Officer CFO: Dennis Pettigrew, Chief Financial Officer CMO: Guy Gansert, M.D., Chief of Staff CIO: Charles Scully, Chief Information Officer CHR: Kris Novakovich, Vice President Human Resources Web address: www.washoehealth.com	23	10	529	23708	334	261548	4250	344704	140479	2244
□ **WASHOE MEDICAL CENTER REHABILITATION HOSPITAL**, 555 Gould Street, Zip 89502–1449; tel. 775/348–5500 **A**1 10 **F**21 26 27 28 45 68 69 110 **P**5 **S** Washoe Health System, Reno, NV Primary Contact: Michael R. Klepin, Administrator Web address: www.washoehealth.com	23	46	62	1063	50	—	0	11986	6488	—
WASHOE MEDICAL CENTER SOUTH MEADOWS, 10101 Double R Boulevard, Zip 89511; tel. 775/982–7000, (Nonreporting) **A**9 10 **S** Washoe Health System, Reno, NV Primary Contact: Alan C. Olive, Chief Executive Officer	33	10	36	—	—	—	—	—	—	—
□ **WEST HILLS HOSPITAL**, 1240 East Ninth Street, Zip 89512–2997, Mailing Address: P.O. Box 30012, Zip 89520–0012; tel. 775/323–0478 **A**1 3 5 9 10 **F**3 4 21 22 27 28 66 71 72 73 75 76 77 78 94 96 **S** Psychiatric Solutions, Franklin, TN Primary Contact: Edward J. Whitehouse, Interim Chief Executive Office Web address: www.bhcwesthills.com	33	22	95	2221	42	533	0	9787	4798	127
WILLOW SPRINGS RESIDENTIAL TREATMENT CENTER, 690 Edison Way, Zip 89502–4135; tel. 775/858–3303 **F**21 58 65 66 71 72 74 94 **S** Psychiatric Solutions, Franklin, TN Primary Contact: Nancy N. Dandliker, Executive Director Web address: www.bhcwillowsprings.com	33	52	74	300	63	0	0	—	—	84

Many Facility Codes have changed. Please refer to the AHA Guide Code Chart.

NV

Hospital, Address, Telephone, Approval, Facility, and Physician Codes, Health Care System	Classi-fication Codes		Utilization Data					Expense (thousands) of dollars		
★ American Hospital Association (AHA) membership ☐ Joint Commission on Accreditation of Healthcare Organizations (JCAHO) accreditation ○ American Osteopathic Association (AOA) accreditation △ Commission on Accreditation of Rehabilitation Facilities (CARF) accreditation	Control	Service	Staffed Beds	Admissions	Census	Outpatient Visits	Births	Total	Payroll	Personnel

SPARKS—Washoe County

☐ **NORTHERN NEVADA ADULT MENTAL HEALTH SERVICES**, 480 Galletti Way, Zip 89431–5574; tel. 775/688–2001 **A**1 3 5 10 **F**21 50 71 74 75 76 77 94
Primary Contact: Harold G. Cook, Agency Director
Web address: www.mhds.state.nv.us

| | 12 | 22 | 70 | 546 | 35 | — | 0 | — | — | — |

☐ **NORTHERN NEVADA MEDICAL CENTER**, 2375 East Prater Way, Zip 89434–9900; tel. 775/331–7000, (Nonreporting) **A**1 10 **S** Universal Health Services, Inc., King of Prussia, PA
Primary Contact: Margaret S. Cleary, Chief Executive Officer
Web address: www.nnmc.com

| | 33 | 10 | 100 | — | — | — | — | — | — | — |

TONOPAH—Nye County

★ **NYE REGIONAL MEDICAL CENTER**, 825 South Main Street, Zip 89049, Mailing Address: P.O. Box 391, Zip 89049–0391; tel. 775/482–6233, (Nonreporting) **A**9 10 20
Primary Contact: Richard L. Kilburn, Chief Executive Officer and Administrator
CFO: Karin Richardson, Chief Financial Officer
CMO: Vincent Scoccia, D.O., Chief Medical Staff

| | 33 | 10 | 44 | — | — | — | — | — | — | — |

WINNEMUCCA—Humboldt County

★ **HUMBOLDT GENERAL HOSPITAL**, 118 East Haskell Street, Zip 89445–3299; tel. 775/623–5222, (Total facility includes 30 beds in nursing home–type unit) (Nonreporting) **A**9 10 20
Primary Contact: James G. Parrish, FACHE, Chief Executive Officer
COO: Bill Barsanti, Operations Services Director
CFO: Eddy D. Davis, Chf Financial Officer and Administrative Service Director
CMO: Richard M. Ingle, M.D., Chief of Staff
CIO: Eddy D. Davis, Chf Financial Officer and Administrative Service Director
CHR: Rose Marie Green, Director Human Resources
Web address: www.hghospital.ws

| | 16 | 10 | 52 | — | — | — | — | — | — | — |

YERINGTON—Lyon County

SOUTH LYON MEDICAL CENTER, 213 South Whitacre, Zip 89447, Mailing Address: P.O. Box 940, Zip 89447–0940; tel. 775/463–2301, (Total facility includes 49 beds in nursing home–type unit) **A**9 10 20 **F**12 14 21 27 29 33 39 45 46 48 51 52 53 63 69 70 81 92 94 97 **P**6
Primary Contact: Joan S. Hall, R.N., Administrator
Web address: www.southlyonmedicalcenter.org

| | 23 | 10 | 63 | 380 | 45 | 37945 | 0 | — | — | 175 |

NV

NEW HAMPSHIRE

Hospital, Address, Telephone, Approval, Facility, and Physician Codes, Health Care System	Classification Codes		Utilization Data					Expense (thousands) of dollars		
	Control	Service	Staffed Beds	Admissions	Census	Outpatient Visits	Births	Total	Payroll	Personnel

★ American Hospital Association (AHA) membership
□ Joint Commission on Accreditation of Healthcare Organizations (JCAHO) accreditation
○ American Osteopathic Association (AOA) accreditation
△ Commission on Accreditation of Rehabilitation Facilities (CARF) accreditation

BERLIN—Coos County

ANDROSCOGGIN VALLEY HOSPITAL, 59 Page Hill Road, Zip 03570–3531; tel. 603/752–2200 **A**9 10 18 20 **F**9 11 12 14 22 26 27 28 32 33 34 36 37 46 47 48 50 51 52 55 58 59 60 62 63 64 67 69 71 76 81 82 88 92 93 94 96 97 108 **P**6
Primary Contact: Russell G. Keene, Chief Executive Officer
Web address: www.avhnh.com
| 23 | 10 | 59 | 2260 | 32 | 60276 | 96 | 33874 | 14722 | 308 |

CLAREMONT—Sullivan County

⊞ **VALLEY REGIONAL HOSPITAL**, 243 Elm Street, Zip 03743–2099; tel. 603/542–7771 **A**1 9 10 18 **F**1 2 9 11 12 21 27 28 29 31 33 36 37 39 40 41 42 46 48 51 52 53 55 57 58 59 60 61 62 63 64 66 69 70 71 73 74 75 76 77 78 81 82 88 94 96 97 108 109 **P**6
Primary Contact: Claire L. Bowen, Chief Executive Officer
COO: Frederick H. Kuriger, Senior Vice President and Chief Operating Officer
CFO: Dean Bither, Chief Financial Officer
CMO: Roy M. Barnes, M.D., President Medical Staff
CIO: Patty Witthaus, Director Information Services
CHR: Gregg Burdett, Vice President Human Resources
Web address: www.vrh.org
| 23 | 10 | 28 | 1606 | 16 | 60574 | 197 | 29259 | 13346 | 370 |

COLEBROOK—Coos County

★ **UPPER CONNECTICUT VALLEY HOSPITAL**, Corliss Lane, Zip 03576–9533, Mailing Address: Rural Route 2, Box 13, Zip 03576–9533; tel. 603/237–4971 **A**9 10 18 **F**6 12 22 23 26 27 28 29 33 36 39 44 46 47 48 50 51 52 53 55 58 60 61 63 64 66 69 73 75 81 88 92 94 97 98 106 110
Primary Contact: Clement Berry, Chief Executive Officer
COO: Kimberlee H. Daley, R.N., Chief Operating Officer
CMO: John Fothergill, M.D., Medical Director
Web address: www.hitchcock.org/pages/tha
| 23 | 10 | 16 | 597 | 6 | 26318 | 1 | 9658 | 3873 | 132 |

CONCORD—Merrimack County

⊞ **CONCORD HOSPITAL**, 250 Pleasant Street, Zip 03301–2598; tel. 603/225–2711 **A**1 2 3 5 9 10 13 **F**2 11 12 14 15 17 19 21 22 23 26 27 28 29 31 32 33 34 35 37 38 39 40 41 42 44 46 47 48 49 50 52 53 54 55 57 58 59 60 61 62 63 64 65 66 69 70 71 72 73 74 75 76 77 78 79 81 82 84 85 86 87 88 89 93 94 95 96 98 106 107 108 109 110 **P**6
Primary Contact: Michael B. Green, President and Chief Executive Officer
COO: Joseph M. Conley, Chief Operating Officer
CFO: Bruce R. Burns, Chief Financial Officer
CMO: David Green, M.D., Medical Staff President
CIO: Deane Morrison, Chief Information Officer
CHR: Leon Cornell, Vice President Human Resources
Web address: www.concordhospital.org
| 23 | 10 | 202 | 10890 | 143 | 360693 | 1451 | 192558 | 84648 | 2122 |

⊞ **HEALTHSOUTH REHABILITATION HOSPITAL**, 254 Pleasant Street, Zip 03301–2508; tel. 603/226–9800, (Nonreporting) **A**1 10 **S** HEALTHSOUTH Corporation, Birmingham, AL
Primary Contact: Lori Manor Underwood, Administrator
CFO: David Chin, Controller
CMO: Stuart Glassman, M.D., Medical Director
CHR: Erika Pouliot, Manager Human Resources
Web address: www.healthsouth.com
| 33 | 46 | 50 | — | — | — | — | — | — | — |

□ **NEW HAMPSHIRE HOSPITAL**, 36 Clinton Street, Zip 03301–3861; tel. 603/271–5200 **A**1 3 5 10 **F**2 11 21 22 26 27 28 32 44 50 53 57 58 60 65 66 71 72 74 76 94 106 108 **P**4 6
Primary Contact: Chester G. Batchelder, Superintendent
Web address: www.dhhs.state.nh.us./familyservice/nhhospital
| 12 | 22 | 230 | 1721 | 185 | 0 | 0 | 51180 | 29343 | 801 |

DERRY—Rockingham County

⊞ **PARKLAND MEDICAL CENTER**, One Parkland Drive, Zip 03038–2750; tel. 603/432–1500 **A**1 2 9 10 **F**2 10 11 12 15 17 21 23 26 27 28 29 33 34 37 39 40 42 45 46 48 52 55 57 58 59 61 62 63 65 66 69 70 81 82 84 86 88 92 93 94 96 108 109 **P**5 **S** HCA, Nashville, TN
Primary Contact: Anne Jamieson, Chief Executive Officer
CFO: Christopher Denton, Chief Financial Officer
CIO: Brad George, Director of Information Systems
CHR: Cynthia King, Administrative Director Human Resources
Web address: www.parklandmedicalcenter.com
| 33 | 10 | 82 | 2990 | 33 | 101121 | 474 | 60074 | 22837 | 407 |

DOVER—Strafford County

⊞ **WENTWORTH–DOUGLASS HOSPITAL**, 789 Central Avenue, Zip 03820–2589; tel. 603/742–5252 **A**1 2 9 10 **F**2 9 10 11 14 15 17 21 22 23 24 26 27 28 29 30 33 34 35 36 37 38 39 40 41 44 45 46 47 48 49 50 52 53 55 57 58 59 60 61 62 63 64 65 66 67 69 70 79 80 81 82 84 85 86 87 88 93 94 95 96 106 107 108 109 110 **P**5 7 8
Primary Contact: Gregory J. Walker, Chief Executive Officer
COO: Daniel N. Dunn, Vice President Operations
CFO: Peter Walcek, Vice President Finance
CIO: Robert Dullea, Chief Information Officer
CHR: William Irvine, Vice President Human Resources
Web address: www.wdhospital.com
| 23 | 10 | 115 | 5141 | 61 | 105315 | 830 | 111150 | 45683 | 885 |

NH

Hospital, Address, Telephone, Approval, Facility, and Physician Codes, Health Care System	Classification Codes		Utilization Data					Expense (thousands) of dollars		
★ American Hospital Association (AHA) membership □ Joint Commission on Accreditation of Healthcare Organizations (JCAHO) accreditation ○ American Osteopathic Association (AOA) accreditation △ Commission on Accreditation of Rehabilitation Facilities (CARF) accreditation	Control	Service	Staffed Beds	Admissions	Census	Outpatient Visits	Births	Total	Payroll	Personnel

EXETER—Rockingham County

⊠ **EXETER HOSPITAL**, 5 Alumni Drive, Zip 03833; tel. 603/778–7311 **A**1 2 9 10 **F**2 6 9 11 12 15 17 21 22 23 24 25 26 27 28 29 30 32 33 34 37 38 39 42 44 45 46 47 48 49 50 52 55 57 58 59 60 61 62 63 65 66 69 79 81 82 84 85 87 88 89 93 94 95 96 106 107 108 109 110
Primary Contact: Kevin J. Callahan, President and Chief Executive Officer
CFO: Kevin J. O'Leary, Senior Vice President and Chief Financial Officer
CIO: David Briden, Chief Information Officer
Web address: www.ehr.org

| | 23 | 10 | 88 | 4649 | 54 | 143720 | 712 | 108906 | 43712 | 961 |

FRANKLIN—Merrimack County

★ **FRANKLIN REGIONAL HOSPITAL**, 15 Aiken Avenue, Zip 03235–1299; tel. 603/934–2060 **A**9 10 18 **F**9 11 12 21 22 26 27 28 29 30 33 35 39 46 48 50 52 53 55 57 58 59 60 62 63 65 69 72 73 74 75 76 81 86 88 92 94 95 96 97 106 107 108 109 110 **P**6 8 **S** LRG Healthcare, Laconia, NH
Primary Contact: Thomas Clairmont, President
CFO: Henry D. Lipman, Executive Vice President and Chief Financial Officer
CMO: Peter Walkley, M.D., Chief of Staff
Web address: www.lrgh.org

| | 23 | 10 | 31 | 1492 | 21 | 54842 | 112 | 27543 | 14880 | 293 |

GREENFIELD—Hillsborough County

CROTCHED MOUNTAIN REHABILITATION CENTER, 1 Verney Drive, Zip 03047–5000; tel. 603/547–3311, (Total facility includes 62 beds in nursing home–type unit) **F**8 21 27 28 29 32 41 45 46 58 68 69 92 94 108 **P**6
Primary Contact: Donald L. Shumway, Chief Executive Officer
Web address: www.cmf.org

| | 23 | 46 | 146 | 56 | 124 | 5225 | 0 | 33539 | 18389 | 525 |

HAMPSTEAD—Rockingham County

□ **HAMPSTEAD HOSPITAL**, 218 East Road, Zip 03841–2228; tel. 603/329–5311, (Nonreporting) **A**1 9 10
Primary Contact: Phillip J. Kubiak, President
Web address: www.hampsteadhospital.com

| | 33 | 22 | 92 | — | — | — | — | — | — | — |

KEENE—Cheshire County

⊠ △ **CHESHIRE MEDICAL CENTER**, 580 Court Street, Zip 03431–1718; tel. 603/354–5400 **A**1 2 7 9 10 19 **F**2 11 12 14 15 21 22 23 24 25 28 29 30 31 33 34 35 37 38 40 41 46 47 48 50 52 53 55 57 58 59 60 61 62 63 64 65 66 68 69 71 72 73 74 75 76 77 78 79 81 82 84 87 88 93 94 95 96 97 106 108 109 110
Primary Contact: Arthur W. Nichols, President and Chief Executive Officer
CFO: Jill I. Batty, Chief Financial Officer
CMO: John Schlegelmilch, M.D., Medical Director for Healthcare Improvement Services
CIO: Michael House, Director Information Services
CHR: Julie Green, Vice President Human Resources
Web address: www.cheshire–med.com

| | 23 | 10 | 146 | 4763 | 72 | 116956 | 502 | 73168 | 30023 | 817 |

LACONIA—Belknap County

★ **LAKES REGION GENERAL HOSPITAL**, 80 Highland Street, Zip 03246–3298; tel. 603/524–3211 **A**9 10 19 **F**2 4 6 9 11 12 15 21 22 23 24 26 27 28 29 30 32 33 34 35 37 38 39 41 44 46 48 49 50 52 53 55 57 58 59 60 61 62 63 65 69 72 73 74 75 76 81 85 87 88 93 94 95 96 97 106 107 108 109 110 **P**6 8 **S** LRG Healthcare, Laconia, NH
Primary Contact: Thomas Clairmont, President
CFO: Henry D. Lipman, Executive Vice President and Chief Financial Officer
CMO: Peter Walkley, M.D., Chief of Staff
Web address: www.lrgh.org

| | 23 | 10 | 106 | 4947 | 63 | 49628 | 469 | 92250 | 41950 | 891 |

LANCASTER—Coos County

★ **WEEKS MEDICAL CENTER**, 173 Middle Street, Zip 03584–3561; tel. 603/788–4911 **A**9 10 18 **F**9 11 12 21 22 23 24 26 27 28 29 30 33 34 36 39 44 46 47 48 50 51 52 53 54 55 58 59 60 61 62 63 64 66 69 70 73 75 77 81 82 87 88 94 95 96 97 98 106 108 109 110 **P**6
Primary Contact: Scott W. Howe, Chief Executive Officer
CFO: Douglas McCaig, Controller
Web address: www.weeks.hitchcock.org

| | 23 | 10 | 25 | 1237 | 15 | 75013 | 143 | 26733 | 14895 | 306 |

LEBANON—Grafton County

★ **ALICE PECK DAY MEMORIAL HOSPITAL**, 125 Mascoma Street, Zip 03766–2650; tel. 603/448–3121, (Total facility includes 50 beds in nursing home–type unit) **A**9 10 18 **F**9 11 12 26 27 29 32 33 36 37 38 40 42 44 46 47 48 52 57 58 59 60 62 63 64 69 70 73 76 81 85 88 92 93 94 97 106 107 108 109 110 **P**5 6 8
Primary Contact: Harry G. Dorman, III, President and Chief Executive Officer
CFO: Theresa M. Koehler, Vice President Finance
CMO: Douglas A. Cedeno, M.D., Medical Director
CIO: John Gobel, Director Information Services
CHR: Donna Cramer, Director Human Resources
Web address: www.alicepeckday.org

| | 23 | 10 | 72 | 926 | 51 | 49955 | 223 | 28147 | 14072 | 354 |

NH

Hospital, Address, Telephone, Approval, Facility, and Physician Codes, Health Care System	Classi-fication Codes		Utilization Data					Expense (thousands) of dollars		
★ American Hospital Association (AHA) membership ☐ Joint Commission on Accreditation of Healthcare Organizations (JCAHO) accreditation ◯ American Osteopathic Association (AOA) accreditation △ Commission on Accreditation of Rehabilitation Facilities (CARF) accreditation	Control	Service	Staffed Beds	Admissions	Census	Outpatient Visits	Births	Total	Payroll	Personnel
☒ **MARY HITCHCOCK MEMORIAL HOSPITAL**, One Medical Center Drive, Zip 03756–0001; tel. 603/650–5000 **A**1 3 5 8 9 10 19 **F**2 6 7 9 10 11 12 14 15 16 17 18 19 20 21 22 23 24 26 27 28 29 32 33 34 35 36 37 38 39 40 43 44 45 46 47 48 49 50 52 53 55 56 57 58 59 60 61 62 63 64 65 66 67 69 70 71 72 73 74 75 76 77 78 79 80 81 82 84 85 86 87 88 89 90 92 93 94 95 96 99 101 104 105 106 108 109 110 **P**8 Primary Contact: James W. Varnum, President CFO: Richard H. Showalter, Senior Vice President Finance CMO: Lisabeth L. Maloney, M.D., Medical Director CIO: Peter A. Johnson, Vice President Information Services CHR: William Geraghty, Vice President Human Resources Web address: www.hitchcock.org	23	10	336	16853	271	175507	1166	480059	195000	3442
LITTLETON—Grafton County										
★ **LITTLETON REGIONAL HOSPITAL**, 600 Saint Johnsbury Road, Zip 03561–3436; tel. 603/444–9000 **A**9 10 18 **F**2 9 11 12 21 22 23 26 27 28 33 34 37 38 39 40 45 46 48 52 53 55 58 59 60 61 62 63 66 69 70 81 82 85 87 88 92 94 96 97 106 108 **P**6 **S** Quorum Health Resources, Plano, TX Primary Contact: William E. Holmes, Chief Executive Officer CFO: Christopher Lauer, Chief Financial Officer CMO: Clare Wilmot, M.D., President Medical Staff CIO: Peg Buckley, Information Services Coordinator CHR: Georgene Novak, Director Human Resources Web address: www.littletonhospital.org	23	10	25	1563	15	—	220	38007	16863	334
MANCHESTER—Hillsborough County										
☒ **CATHOLIC MEDICAL CENTER**, 100 McGregor Street, Zip 03102–3770; tel. 603/668–3545 **A**1 2 9 10 **F**2 7 9 10 11 12 15 17 19 21 22 23 24 26 27 28 29 30 31 32 33 35 36 37 38 39 41 45 46 47 48 49 50 52 53 55 57 58 59 60 61 62 63 64 65 66 68 69 71 73 75 77 78 81 82 84 85 87 88 93 94 95 96 98 106 107 108 109 110 **P**6 Primary Contact: Alyson Pitman Giles, President and Chief Executive Officer COO: Raymond J. Bonito, Senior Vice President and Chief Operating Officer CFO: George Allen, Chief Financial Officer CMO: Joseph Pepe, M.D., Medical Director CIO: Jack Santos, Chief Information Officer CHR: Margo Compagna, Vice President Human Resources Web address: www.catholicmedicalcenter.org	23	10	224	8889	133	90270	579	144144	60343	1152
☒ **ELLIOT HOSPITAL**, One Elliot Way, Zip 03103–3599; tel. 603/669–5300 **A**1 2 9 10 **F**2 9 10 11 12 14 15 17 21 22 24 26 27 28 29 31 32 33 34 35 37 38 39 40 41 42 44 45 46 47 48 49 50 52 53 55 56 57 58 59 60 61 62 63 64 65 66 69 70 71 73 74 75 76 78 79 81 82 84 85 86 87 88 89 90 93 94 95 96 106 108 109 110 **P**6 7 Primary Contact: Douglas F. Dean, Jr, President and Chief Executive Officer COO: Beth Hughes, Executive Vice President and Chief Operating Officer CFO: Richard Elwell, Senior Vice President and Chief Financial Officer CMO: Rick Phelps, M.D., Senior Vice President Medical Affairs CIO: Denise Purington, Vice President and Chief Information Officer CHR: Suzane Quain, Director Human Resources Web address: www.elliothospital.org	23	10	244	12025	143	198626	2418	169854	69785	1378
★ **VETERANS AFFAIRS MEDICAL CENTER**, 718 Smyth Road, Zip 03104–4098; tel. 603/624–4366, (Total facility includes 90 beds in nursing home–type unit) **A**5 **F**2 9 21 22 23 26 28 29 31 32 33 35 36 37 38 39 41 42 44 45 46 47 48 50 52 53 58 60 61 63 64 65 66 69 70 73 74 77 81 82 85 88 92 93 94 96 106 107 108 109 110 **P**6 **S** Department of Veterans Affairs, Washington, DC Primary Contact: Marc Levenson, Administrator COO: Susan Kimmey, Associate Director CFO: Frank Ryan, Chief Financial Officer CIO: Cynthia Obermiller, Chief Information Officer Web address: www.va.gov/sta/guide/home.asp	45	46	90	263	72	144169	0	34387	26510	517
NASHUA—Hillsborough County										
☒ **SOUTHERN NEW HAMPSHIRE MEDICAL CENTER**, 8 Prospect Street, Zip 03060–3925, Mailing Address: P.O. Box 2014, Zip 03061–2014; tel. 603/577–2000 **A**1 2 9 10 **F**1 2 10 11 12 15 17 21 22 23 26 27 28 29 31 33 34 39 40 43 46 47 48 50 55 56 58 59 60 61 63 64 65 66 69 70 71 73 75 76 77 78 81 82 84 86 87 88 89 93 94 95 96 106 107 108 109 110 **P**6 8 Primary Contact: Thomas E. Wilhelmsen, Jr, President and Chief Executive Officer CFO: Gary P. Marlow, Senior Vice President Finance and Chief Financial Officer CMO: Stephanie Wolf–Rosenblum, M.D., Vice President Medical Affairs CIO: Dwight Muller, Vice President Information Systems and Chief Information Officer CHR: Merryll Rosenfeld, Vice President Human Resources Web address: www.snhmc.org	23	10	180	9328	99	203929	1503	107109	54311	1038

NH

Many Facility Codes have changed. Please refer to the AHA Guide Code Chart.   © 2005 AHA Guide

Hospital, Address, Telephone, Approval, Facility, and Physician Codes, Health Care System	Classi-fication Codes		Utilization Data					Expense (thousands) of dollars		
★ American Hospital Association (AHA) membership ☐ Joint Commission on Accreditation of Healthcare Organizations (JCAHO) accreditation ○ American Osteopathic Association (AOA) accreditation △ Commission on Accreditation of Rehabilitation Facilities (CARF) accreditation	Control	Service	Staffed Beds	Admissions	Census	Outpatient Visits	Births	Total	Payroll	Personnel
⊞ △ **ST. JOSEPH HOSPITAL**, 172 Kinsley Street, Zip 03060–3688; tel. 603/882–3000 **A**1 2 7 9 10 **F**1 2 6 9 10 11 12 15 21 22 23 24 26 27 28 29 30 33 34 35 36 37 38 39 40 42 44 45 46 47 48 50 51 52 53 55 57 58 59 60 61 62 63 64 65 66 68 69 71 76 77 81 82 84 85 86 87 88 93 94 96 106 108 109 110 **P**6 8 **S** Covenant Health Systems, Inc., Lexington, MA Primary Contact: Peter B. Davis, President and Chief Executive Officer COO: Pam Duchene, R.N., Vice President Patient Care Services CFO: Richard Plamondon, Vice President Finance CMO: William Stephan, M.D., Vice President Medical Affairs CIO: Keith A. Choinka, Vice President Information Systems and Chief Information Officer CHR: Jacqueline Woolley, Vice President Human Resources Web address: www.stjosephhealthcare.com	21	10	144	5123	84	191409	677	102956	44932	904
NEW LONDON—Merrimack County										
★ **NEW LONDON HOSPITAL**, 273 County Road, Zip 03257–4570; tel. 603/526–2911, (Total facility includes 58 beds in nursing home–type unit) **A**9 10 18 **F**2 6 9 21 23 27 28 29 33 36 40 41 44 52 55 57 58 61 62 63 64 69 70 73 75 77 81 84 88 92 93 94 95 97 108 109 **P**6 Primary Contact: Bruce King, President and Chief Executive Officer CFO: Tina Naimie, Chief Financial Officer and Vice President Fiscal Services CMO: Timothy Wolfe, M.D., President Medical Staff Web address: www.newlondonhospital.org	23	10	75	753	62	166822	0	28770	11506	285
NORTH CONWAY—Carroll County										
MEMORIAL HOSPITAL, 3073 White Mountain Highway, Zip 03860–5001, Mailing Address: P.O. Box 5001, Zip 03860–5001; tel. 603/356–5461, (Total facility includes 45 beds in nursing home–type unit) **A**9 10 18 20 **F**1 2 9 11 12 21 22 26 27 28 29 33 34 46 48 55 58 59 60 61 62 63 65 66 69 81 82 83 84 85 87 88 92 94 95 96 97 98 106 108 109 **P**3 Primary Contact: Gary R. Poquette, FACHE, Executive Director Web address: www.thememorialhospital.org	23	10	80	1621	60	45997	258	30340	10870	254
PETERBOROUGH—Hillsborough County										
⊞ **MONADNOCK COMMUNITY HOSPITAL**, 452 Old Street Road, Zip 03458–1295; tel. 603/924–7191 **A**1 9 10 18 **F**2 7 11 12 21 22 23 26 27 28 29 30 31 32 33 35 37 39 41 44 46 47 48 52 55 57 58 59 60 61 62 63 64 65 66 69 70 71 73 74 75 76 77 81 82 85 88 92 94 95 96 97 106 108 109 110 **P**6 Primary Contact: Peter L. Gosline, Chief Executive Officer COO: Sarah Taylor, Chief Operating Officer CFO: Deborah A. Shipman, Chief Financial Officer CMO: E Ross Ramey, M.D., Medical Director CIO: Janice Greenyer, Vice President Planning and Information Technology CHR: Michael Blood, Vice President Human Resources Web address: www.monadnockhospital.org	23	10	35	1832	24	70250	388	42416	21178	472
PLYMOUTH—Grafton County										
★ **SPEARE MEMORIAL HOSPITAL**, 16 Hospital Road, Zip 03264–1199; tel. 603/536–1120 **A**9 10 18 20 **F**11 12 21 23 24 26 27 28 29 32 33 38 46 48 55 58 59 60 61 63 69 81 88 94 96 97 107 108 109 **P**8 Primary Contact: Michelle McEwen, President and Chief Executive Officer CFO: Peter Kritikos, Chief Financial Officer CMO: Jeffrey Reisert, M.D., President Medical Staff CIO: Jerry Coffey, Hardware Specialist CHR: Lauri Bolognani, Human Resources Officer Web address: www.spearehospital.com	23	10	28	1025	11	63241	146	23614	11341	229
PORTSMOUTH—Rockingham County										
⊞ **PORTSMOUTH REGIONAL HOSPITAL**, 333 Borthwick Avenue, Zip 03801–7004; tel. 603/436–5110 **A**1 9 10 **F**2 3 4 10 11 12 14 15 17 19 21 22 23 24 29 30 31 32 33 34 37 38 39 40 41 43 44 46 47 48 49 50 52 53 55 57 58 59 60 61 62 63 65 66 68 69 70 71 72 73 74 75 76 77 78 81 82 84 88 89 93 94 95 96 106 108 109 110 **P**1 **S** HCA, Nashville, TN Primary Contact: William J. Schuler, Chief Executive Officer COO: Stuart Hemming, Chief Operating Officer CFO: Richard Senger, Chief Financial Officer CIO: Ed Sovetskhy, Director Information Services CHR: Jackie Brayton, Vice President, Human Resources Web address: www.portsmouthhospital.com	33	10	165	7705	103	128178	898	—	—	775
ROCHESTER—Strafford County										
★ **FRISBIE MEMORIAL HOSPITAL**, 11 Whitehall Road, Zip 03867–3297; tel. 603/332–5211 **A**9 10 **F**2 6 9 11 14 15 16 21 23 24 26 27 28 29 33 37 39 44 46 47 48 52 53 55 58 59 60 61 63 65 66 69 70 71 76 77 78 81 84 86 87 88 93 94 96 106 107 108 109 **P**5 Primary Contact: Alvin D. Felgar, President and Chief Executive Officer CFO: John A. Marzinzik, Vice President Finance Web address: www.frisbiehospital.com	23	10	70	3457	40	95262	401	65171	26619	586
SALEM—Rockingham County										
☐ **NORTHEAST REHABILITATION HOSPITAL**, 70 Butler Street, Zip 03079–3925; tel. 603/893–2900 **A**1 10 **F**21 26 27 28 29 37 41 42 46 51 52 53 57 58 60 64 65 66 68 69 72 94 95 96 106 108 110 Primary Contact: John F. Prochilo, Chief Executive Officer and Administrator Web address: www.northeastrehab.com	33	46	80	1430	65	156275	0	34397	18244	390

NH

Hospital, Address, Telephone, Approval, Facility, and Physician Codes, Health Care System	Classi-fication Codes		Utilization Data					Expense (thousands) of dollars		
★ American Hospital Association (AHA) membership ☐ Joint Commission on Accreditation of Healthcare Organizations (JCAHO) accreditation ◯ American Osteopathic Association (AOA) accreditation △ Commission on Accreditation of Rehabilitation Facilities (CARF) accreditation	Control	Service	Staffed Beds	Admissions	Census	Outpatient Visits	Births	Total	Payroll	Personnel

WOLFEBORO—Carroll County

★ **HUGGINS HOSPITAL**, 240 South Main Street, Zip 03894–4455, Mailing Address: P.O. Box 912, Zip 03894–0912; tel. 603/569–7500, (Total facility includes 27 beds in nursing home–type unit) **A**9 10 18 20 **F**1 8 9 11 12 26 27 28 33 37 39 44 46 47 48 52 55 58 59 60 62 63 64 65 66 69 70 81 84 88 91 92 94 96 97 106 108 109 **P**8
Primary Contact: Leslie N. H. MacLeod, President
COO: David W. Tower, Chief Operating Officer
CFO: Daniel R. O'Neill, Vice President Finance
CMO: John Boornazian, M.D., Chief Medical Officer
CHR: Angela Closson, Director Human Resources
Web address: www.hugginshospital.org

	23	10	76	2022	44	89363	78	27090	11012	265

WOODSVILLE—Grafton County

★ **COTTAGE HOSPITAL**, Swiftwater Road, Zip 03785–2001, Mailing Address: P.O. Box 2001, Zip 03785–2001; tel. 603/747–2761 **A**2 9 10 18 **F**2 9 11 12 21 22 23 24 27 28 29 33 37 39 47 48 52 53 55 58 59 60 61 62 63 66 69 70 81 84 88 92 94 96 97 106 108 109 **P**8
Primary Contact: Reginald J. Lavoie, Administrator
Web address: www.cottagehospital.org

	23	10	25	1003	10	42108	101	19574	9510	191

NH

Many Facility Codes have changed. Please refer to the AHA Guide Code Chart.

NEW JERSEY

Hospital, Address, Telephone, Approval, Facility, and Physician Codes, Health Care System	Classi-fication Codes		Utilization Data					Expense (thousands) of dollars		
★ American Hospital Association (AHA) membership □ Joint Commission on Accreditation of Healthcare Organizations (JCAHO) accreditation ○ American Osteopathic Association (AOA) accreditation △ Commission on Accreditation of Rehabilitation Facilities (CARF) accreditation	Control	Service	Staffed Beds	Admissions	Census	Outpatient Visits	Births	Total	Payroll	Personnel

ANCORA—Camden County

□ **ANCORA PSYCHIATRIC HOSPITAL**, 202 Spring Garden Road, Zip 08037–9699; tel. 609/561–1700, (Nonreporting) **A**1 10 **S** Division of Mental Health Services, Department of Human Services, State of New Jersey, Trenton, NJ
Primary Contact: Latanya Wood, Chief Executive Officer
| | | 12 | 22 | 709 | — | — | — | — | — | — | — |

ATLANTIC CITY—Atlantic County

✠ **ATLANTICARE REGIONAL MEDICAL CENTER**, (Formerly Atlantic City Medical Center), 1925 Pacific Avenue, Zip 08401–6713; tel. 609/345–4000, (Includes ATLANTIC CITY MEDICAL CENTER–MAINLAND DIVISION, Jimmie Leeds Road, Pomona, Zip 08240; tel. 609/652–1000) **A**1 2 3 5 9 10 **F**2 4 6 7 9 10 11 12 14 15 17 19 21 22 23 24 26 27 28 29 31 32 33 34 35 39 42 44 45 46 47 48 49 50 51 52 53 55 56 57 58 59 60 61 62 63 64 65 66 69 70 71 72 73 74 75 76 77 78 79 80 81 82 84 85 87 88 90 94 95 96 98 106 108 109 110 **P**6 **S** AtlantiCare, Egg Harbor City, NJ
Primary Contact: David P. Tilton, President and Chief Executive Officer
CFO: Walter Grinier, Chief Financial Officer
CMO: Gary M. Siegelman, M.D., Vice President Medical Affairs
CIO: Larry Sharrott, President InfoShare
CHR: Fred J. Laquinta, Vice President, Corporate Human Resources
Web address: www.atlanticare.org
| | | 23 | 10 | 442 | 23349 | 311 | 220050 | 2102 | 328487 | 142774 | 2195 |

BAYONNE—Hudson County

✠ **BAYONNE MEDICAL CENTER**, 29 East 29th Street, Zip 07002–4699; tel. 201/858–5000 **A**1 2 6 9 10 **F**1 9 11 12 14 21 22 23 24 26 27 28 29 33 36 44 45 46 48 52 55 57 58 59 60 61 63 64 65 66 69 70 71 74 75 76 81 82 84 87 88 92 93 94 96 98 106 107 108 109
Primary Contact: Robert H. Evans, President and Chief Executive Officer
CFO: Kristin Kiessling, Vice President Finance and Chief Financial Officer
CIO: Marianne Wolenski, Director Information Systems
Web address: www.bayonnemedicalcenter.org
| | | 23 | 10 | 210 | 8178 | 152 | 151279 | 312 | 86609 | 58412 | 1134 |

BELLE MEAD—Somerset County

✠ **CARRIER CLINIC**, 252 County Route 601, Zip 08502–0147, Mailing Address: P.O. Box 147, Zip 08502–0147; tel. 908/281–1000 **A**1 3 5 9 10 **F**3 26 27 28 71 72 76 **P**6
Primary Contact: C. Richard Sarle, CPA, FACHE, President and Chief Executive Officer
COO: Mary Pawlikowski, Vice President
CFO: Randolph Jacobson, Chief Financial Officer
CMO: David Greenspan, M.D., Medical Director
CIO: Buddy Arriola, Information Services Manager
Web address: www.carrier.org
| | | 23 | 22 | 215 | 3887 | 177 | 0 | 0 | 40827 | 23185 | 487 |

EAST MOUNTAIN HOSPITAL, 40 East Mountain Road, Zip 08502; tel. 908/281–1545, (Nonreporting) **A**10
Primary Contact: Peter Casey, Acting Director
| | | 33 | 49 | 16 | — | — | — | — | — | — | — |

BELLEVILLE—Essex County

✠ **CLARA MAASS MEDICAL CENTER**, One Clara Maass Drive, Zip 07109–3557; tel. 973/450–2000 **A**1 2 9 10 **F**2 8 9 11 12 15 21 22 23 26 27 28 29 30 33 37 39 44 45 46 47 48 51 52 53 55 57 58 59 60 61 62 63 64 65 66 69 70 71 73 74 76 79 81 82 83 84 85 87 88 90 92 93 94 96 106 108 109 110 **P**5 **S** Saint Barnabas Health Care System, West Orange, NJ
Primary Contact: Thomas A. Biga, Executive Director
COO: Richard Salhany, Vice President Operations
CFO: Garrick J. Stoldt, Chief Financial Officer
CMO: Frank Mazzarella, M.D., Vice President Medical Affairs
CIO: Michael McTigue, Chief Information Officer
Web address: www.sbhcs.com
| | | 23 | 10 | 301 | 16569 | 226 | 295606 | 1446 | 148869 | 63229 | 591 |

SELECT SPECIALTY HOSPITAL–BELLEVILLE, One Clara Maas Drive, Zip 07109; tel. 973/450–2530, (Nonreporting) **A**10
Primary Contact: Robert Meyers, Chief Executive Officer
| | | 33 | 49 | 25 | — | — | — | — | — | — | — |

BERKELEY HEIGHTS—Union County

★ **RUNNELLS SPECIALIZED HOSPITAL OF UNION COUNTY**, 40 Watchung Way, Zip 07922–2618; tel. 908/771–5700, (Total facility includes 300 beds in nursing home–type unit) **A**9 10 **F**2 5 10 21 22 24 25 27 28 29 30 31 37 38 44 45 46 48 52 53 60 65 66 69 71 76 92 94 96 108 110 **P**6
Primary Contact: Joseph W. Sharp, Administrator
COO: Joan Wheeler, MSN, R.N., Associate Administrator
CFO: Michael Drummond, Chief Financial Officer
CMO: Raymond Lanza, D.O., Medical Director
CIO: Margaret A. Salisbury, Director Marketing
Web address: www.ucnj.org/runnells
| | | 13 | 80 | 369 | 1221 | 334 | 101 | 0 | 41636 | 26491 | 592 |

NJ

Hospital, Address, Telephone, Approval, Facility, and Physician Codes, Health Care System	Classi-fication Codes		Utilization Data					Expense (thousands) of dollars		
★ American Hospital Association (AHA) membership □ Joint Commission on Accreditation of Healthcare Organizations (JCAHO) accreditation ○ American Osteopathic Association (AOA) accreditation △ Commission on Accreditation of Rehabilitation Facilities (CARF) accreditation	Control	Service	Staffed Beds	Admissions	Census	Outpatient Visits	Births	Total	Payroll	Personnel

BERLIN—Camden County

VIRTUA WEST JERSEY HOSPITAL–BERLIN, 100 Townsend Avenue, Zip 08009–9035; tel. 856/322–3000, (Nonreporting) **S** Virtua Health, Marlton, NJ
Primary Contact: Gary L. Long, Vice President and Chief Operating Officer
Web address: www.virtua.org

| | 23 | 10 | 95 | — | — | — | — | — | — | — |

BLACKWOOD—Camden County

⊠ **CAMDEN COUNTY HEALTH SERVICES CENTER**, 20 Woodbury Turnersville Road, Zip 08012–2799; tel. 856/374–6600, (Total facility includes 291 beds in nursing home–type unit) **A**1 9 10 **F**3 26 27 28 38 44 66 71 74 76 92 94 108 110 **P**6
Primary Contact: Kevin G. Halpern, Chief Executive Officer
COO: Gene Lynam, Chief Operating Officer and Teasurer
CFO: Gene Lynam, Chief Operating Officer and Teasurer
CMO: Michael S. DeShields, M.D., Director Medical Affairs
Web address: www.cchsc.com

| | 13 | 80 | 449 | 1285 | 429 | 0 | 0 | 54060 | 23940 | 494 |

BOONTON TOWNSHIP—Morris County

SAINT CLARE'S HOSPITAL/BOONTON TOWNSHIP See Saint Clare's Hospital, Dover

BRICK TOWNSHIP—Ocean County

⊠ **OCEAN MEDICAL CENTER**, 425 Jack Martin Boulevard, Zip 08724; tel. 732/840–2200 **A**1 2 9 10 **F**1 2 4 5 9 11 12 14 15 17 21 22 23 24 26 27 28 29 33 35 37 38 40 41 44 46 48 49 50 52 53 54 55 57 58 59 60 61 62 63 64 65 66 69 70 73 74 75 79 80 81 82 84 88 92 93 94 96 98 106 107 108 109 110 **S** Meridian Health, Neptune, NJ
Primary Contact: W. Peter Daniels, President
COO: Richard Epstein, Vice President Operations
CFO: William Phillips, Senior Vice President Finance and Chief Financial Officer
CIO: Rebecca Weber, Vice President Information System and Chief Information Officer
CHR: John E. Sindoni, Senior Vice President Human Resources
Web address: www.meridianhealth.com

| | 23 | 10 | 210 | 13675 | 183 | 128821 | 1158 | 148136 | 63202 | 978 |

BRIDGETON—Cumberland County

⊠ **SOUTH JERSEY HEALTHCARE**, 333 Irving Avenue, Zip 08302–2100; tel. 856/575–4500, (Includes BRIDGETON HEALTH CENTER; ELMER HOSPITAL, West Front Street, Elmer, Zip 08318–1090, Mailing Address: P.O. Box 1090, Zip 08318–1090; tel. 856/363–1000; REGIONAL MEDICAL CENTER, 1505 West Sherman Avenue, Vineland, Zip 08360; tel. 856/841–8000; VINELAND HEALTH CENTER, 65 South State Street, Vineland, Zip 08360–4849; tel. 856/507–8500) **A**1 9 10 **F**2 9 10 11 12 14 15 21 22 26 27 28 29 31 33 35 37 39 42 46 47 48 49 52 53 55 57 58 59 60 61 62 63 64 65 66 69 71 72 73 74 75 76 77 78 80 81 82 84 85 87 88 94 95 96 98 108 109
Primary Contact: Chester B. Kaletkowski, President and Chief Executive Officer
COO: Wayne C. Schiffner, Executive Vice President
CFO: John A. DiAngelo, Senior Vice President Finance and Chief Financial Officer
CMO: Steven C. Linn, M.D., Vice President for Medical Affairs
CIO: Charles Rice, Chief Information Officer
CHR: Erich Florentine, Vice President Human Resources and Organizational Effectiveness
Web address: www.sjhs.com

| | 23 | 10 | 409 | 20361 | 287 | 228818 | 2298 | 229475 | 103908 | 2137 |

BROWNS MILLS—Burlington County

□ **DEBORAH HEART AND LUNG CENTER**, 200 Trenton Road, Zip 08015–1799; tel. 609/893–6611, (Nonreporting) **A**1 3 5 9 10 13
Primary Contact: John R. Ernst, Executive Director
Web address: www.deborah.org

| | 23 | 49 | 161 | — | — | — | — | — | — | — |

CAMDEN—Camden County

⊠ **COOPER HEALTH SYSTEM**, One Cooper Plaza, Zip 08103–1489; tel. 856/342–2000 **A**1 2 3 5 8 9 10 **F**7 9 11 12 14 15 16 17 18 19 20 21 22 23 24 26 27 28 29 30 32 33 34 42 44 45 46 47 48 49 50 52 53 55 56 57 58 59 60 61 62 63 65 66 67 69 70 71 72 73 81 82 84 87 88 93 94 95 96 98 108 109 110 **P**5
Primary Contact: Christopher Olivia, M.D., President and Chief Executive Officer
COO: Jeffrey N. Yarmel, Executive Vice Pfresident and Chief Operating Officer
CFO: Dennis Roemer, Executive Vice President and Chief Financial Officer
CMO: Stephen Rimar, M.D., Executive Vice President Medical Affairs
CIO: Karen Graham, Chief Information Officer
CHR: Joan H. Williams, Vice President Human Resources
Web address: www.cooperhealth.org

| | 23 | 10 | 400 | 23347 | 329 | 235398 | 2004 | 370471 | 136265 | 3937 |

⊠ △ **OUR LADY OF LOURDES MEDICAL CENTER**, 1600 Haddon Avenue, Zip 08103–3117; tel. 856/757–3500 **A**1 2 6 7 9 10 12 13 **F**2 9 10 11 12 14 15 17 19 21 22 23 24 27 28 29 30 31 32 33 35 37 38 39 44 46 47 48 49 50 52 53 55 56 57 58 59 61 62 63 64 65 66 68 69 70 73 75 81 82 84 85 87 88 90 94 96 98 101 102 105 106 108 109 **P**5 **S** Catholic Health East, Newtown Square, PA
Primary Contact: Mark T. Bateman, Chief Administrative Officer
CFO: Thomas J. Regner, Senior Vice President Finance and Chief Financial Officer
CMO: John P. Capelli, M.D., Vice President Medical Affairs
CIO: Maureen Hetu, Administrator, Information Services
CHR: Janet Moran, Vice President Human Resources
Web address: www.lourdesnet.org

| | 23 | 10 | 289 | 17305 | 268 | 174716 | 1269 | 229033 | 98770 | 1970 |

NJ

Many Facility Codes have changed. Please refer to the AHA Guide Code Chart.

© 2005 AHA Guide

Hospital, Address, Telephone, Approval, Facility, and Physician Codes, Health Care System	Classi-fication Codes		Utilization Data					Expense (thousands) of dollars		
	Control	Service	Staffed Beds	Admissions	Census	Outpatient Visits	Births	Total	Payroll	Personnel

★ American Hospital Association (AHA) membership
□ Joint Commission on Accreditation of Healthcare Organizations (JCAHO) accreditation
○ American Osteopathic Association (AOA) accreditation
△ Commission on Accreditation of Rehabilitation Facilities (CARF) accreditation

CAPE MAY COURT HOUSE—Cape May County

☒ **BURDETTE TOMLIN MEMORIAL HOSPITAL**, 2 Stone Harbor Boulevard, Zip 08210–9990; tel. 609/463–2000 **A**1 2 9 10 **F**2 9 11 12 21 22 23 26 27 28 29 32 33 35 37 39 41 45 46 47 48 52 55 57 59 60 61 62 63 64 65 66 69 70 79 80 81 87 88 94 96 106 108 110 **P**7
Primary Contact: Joanne Carrocino, FACHE, President and Chief Executive Officer
CFO: Mark Gill, Vice President Finance and Chief Financial Officer
CIO: Mike Cordi, Director Information Systems
CHR: Byron Hunter, Vice President Human Resources
Web address: www.btmh.com
— Control 23, Service 10, Staffed Beds 208, Admissions 10196, Census 137, Outpatient Visits 130749, Births 510, Total 92653, Payroll 41665, Personnel 932

CEDAR GROVE—Essex County

□ **ESSEX COUNTY HOSPITAL CENTER**, 125 Fairview Avenue, Zip 07009–1399; tel. 973/228–8000 **A**1 10 **F**26 27 28 31 32 44 50 58 65 66 71 74 76 94 96 **P**6
Primary Contact: Lucia A. Guarini, Administrator
— Control 13, Service 22, Staffed Beds 187, Admissions 110, Census 187, Outpatient Visits 0, Births 0, Total 42506, Payroll 23505, Personnel 425

CHERRY HILL—Camden County

★ ○ **KENNEDY MEMORIAL HOSPITALS–UNIVERSITY MEDICAL CENTER**, 2201 Chapel Avenue West, Zip 08002–2048; tel. 856/488–6500, (Includes KENNEDY MEMORIAL HOSPITAL, 18 East Laurel Road, Stratford, Zip 08084; tel. 609/346–6000; KENNEDY MEMORIAL HOSPITAL, 435 Hurffville–Cross Keys Road, Turnersville, Zip 08012; tel. 609/582–2500) **A**9 10 11 12 **F**2 3 4 6 9 10 11 12 15 17 21 22 23 24 26 27 28 29 31 32 33 35 37 38 39 44 45 46 47 48 49 50 51 52 53 55 56 57 58 59 61 62 63 64 65 66 69 70 71 72 73 74 75 76 77 78 79 80 81 82 84 85 87 88 90 92 93 94 95 96 98 106 108 109 110
Primary Contact: Joseph W. Devine, Vice President, Hospital Services
CFO: Joseph Lario, Senior Vice President Management Support Services
Web address: www.kennedyhealth.org
— Control 23, Service 10, Staffed Beds 471, Admissions 28125, Census 334, Outpatient Visits 334438, Births 1668, Total 268921, Payroll 117758, Personnel 2200

DENVILLE—Morris County

SAINT CLARE'S HOSPITAL/DENVILLE See Saint Clare's Hospital, Dover

DOVER—Morris County

KINDRED HOSPITAL–NEW JERSEY MORRIS COUNTY, 400 West Blackwell Street, Zip 07801; tel. 973/537–3818, (Nonreporting) **A**10
Primary Contact: Kay Peck, Chief Executive Officer
— Control 33, Service 49, Staffed Beds 45, Admissions —, Census —, Outpatient Visits —, Births —, Total —, Payroll —, Personnel —

☒ **SAINT CLARE'S HOSPITAL**, 400 West Blackwell Street, Zip 07801; tel. 973/625–6000, (Includes SAINT CLARE'S HOSPITAL/BOONTON TOWNSHIP, 130 Powerville Road, Boonton Township, Zip 07005; tel. 973/316–1800; SAINT CLARE'S HOSPITAL/DENVILLE, 25 Pocono Road, Denville, Zip 07834; tel. 973/625–6000; SAINT CLARE'S HOSPITAL/SUSSEX, 20 Walnut Street, Sussex, Zip 07461; tel. 973/702–2200), (Total facility includes 141 beds in nursing home–type unit) **A**1 2 9 10 **F**2 3 4 6 9 11 12 15 17 21 22 23 24 26 27 28 29 30 31 32 33 37 39 41 42 43 44 45 46 47 48 52 53 55 56 57 58 59 60 61 62 63 64 65 66 69 71 72 73 74 75 76 77 78 81 85 87 88 92 93 94 95 96 98 106 108 109 **P**5 **S** Marian Health System, Tulsa, OK
Primary Contact: David Lundquist, President and Chief Executive Officer
CFO: Peter Kisylia, Executive Vice President and Chief Financial Officer
CMO: Alma Ratcliffe, M.D., Executive Vice President
CIO: Richard Temple, Chief Information Officer
CHR: Joseph Marsicovete, Vice President Administrative and Regulatory Services
Web address: www.saintclares.org
— Control 23, Service 10, Staffed Beds 650, Admissions 20986, Census 426, Outpatient Visits 265276, Births 1906, Total 258387, Payroll 123308, Personnel 2513

EAST ORANGE—Essex County

□ **EAST ORANGE GENERAL HOSPITAL**, 300 Central Avenue, Zip 07019–2897; tel. 973/672–8400 **A**1 9 10 **F**3 4 21 22 25 26 27 28 29 31 33 46 48 49 52 55 61 63 66 69 70 71 72 73 74 75 77 78 81 82 88 94 108 **P**6
Primary Contact: Kevin Slavin, President and Chief Executive Officer
Web address: www.evh.org
— Control 23, Service 10, Staffed Beds 163, Admissions 6661, Census 140, Outpatient Visits —, Births 0, Total —, Payroll —, Personnel —

☒ **VETERANS AFFAIRS NEW JERSEY HEALTH CARE SYSTEM**, 385 Tremont Avenue, Zip 07018–1095; tel. 973/676–1000, (Includes EAST ORANGE DIVISION; LYONS DIVISION, 151 Knollcroft Road, Lyons, Zip 07939–9998; tel. 908/647–0180), (Total facility includes 360 beds in nursing home–type unit) **A**1 2 3 5 8 **F**1 2 3 4 5 9 12 14 21 22 23 25 29 30 31 32 33 37 38 41 42 44 45 46 47 48 49 50 51 52 53 55 57 58 60 61 62 63 65 66 69 70 71 73 75 76 77 78 81 84 88 92 93 94 96 106 108 109 110 **P**6 **S** Department of Veterans Affairs, Washington, DC
Primary Contact: Kenneth H. Mizrach, Director
COO: Kenneth H. Mizrach, Director
CFO: Nicholas DePiano, Chief Financial Officer
CMO: Christopher F. Terrence, M.D., Chief of Staff
CIO: Beverly Erhardt, Chief Information Management Services
CHR: Terry Stewart, Chief Management and Learning Resources
Web address: www.va.gov/visns/visn03/default.asp
— Control 45, Service 10, Staffed Beds 845, Admissions 5447, Census 280, Outpatient Visits 497830, Births 0, Total —, Payroll —, Personnel 2620

EATONTOWN—Monmouth County

★ **REHABILITATION HOSPITAL OF TINTON FALLS**, 2 Centre Plaza, Zip 07724; tel. 732/460–5320 **A**10 **F**21 22 27 28 29 39 44 45 46 52 53 57 58 61 62 65 66 68 69 73 74 76 88 92 109 110 **P**5 **S** HEALTHSOUTH Corporation, Birmingham, AL
Primary Contact: Linda A. Savino, Administrator
CFO: Lynne Freel, Finance Manager
CMO: Todd Cooperman, Medical Director
CHR: Anita Saum, Manager Human Resources
Web address: www.healthsouth.com
— Control 33, Service 46, Staffed Beds 60, Admissions 1268, Census 47, Outpatient Visits 8031, Births 0, Total 10924, Payroll 7088, Personnel —

NJ

Hospital, Address, Telephone, Approval, Facility, and Physician Codes, Health Care System	Classi-fication Codes		Utilization Data					Expense (thousands) of dollars		
★ American Hospital Association (AHA) membership □ Joint Commission on Accreditation of Healthcare Organizations (JCAHO) accreditation ○ American Osteopathic Association (AOA) accreditation △ Commission on Accreditation of Rehabilitation Facilities (CARF) accreditation	Control	Service	Staffed Beds	Admissions	Census	Outpatient Visits	Births	Total	Payroll	Personnel

EDISON—Middlesex County

★ △ **JFK JOHNSON REHABILITATION INSTITUTE**, 65 James Street, Zip 08818–3059; tel. 732/321–7050 **A**7 9 **F**21 22 26 27 28 29 30 35 37 39 41 44 46 47 52 53 57 60 62 65 66 68 69 94 95 96 **P**8 **S** Solaris Health System, Edison, NJ
Primary Contact: Anthony Cuzzola, Vice President Rehabilitation Services
CFO: Raymond F. Fredericks, Senior Vice President and Chief Financial Officer
CIO: Louis H. Hermans, Vice President Information Systems
Web address: www.solarishs.org
| | 23 | 46 | 92 | 2400 | 85 | 361014 | 0 | 53980 | 33130 | 437 |

⊠ **JFK MEDICAL CENTER**, 65 James Street, Zip 08818–3059; tel. 732/321–7000, (Nonreporting) **A**1 2 3 5 9 10 **S** Solaris Health System, Edison, NJ
Primary Contact: Scott Gebhard, Executive Vice President and Chief Executive Officer
CFO: Raymond F. Fredericks, Executive Vice President and Chief Financial Officer
CMO: William F. Oser, M.D., JD, Senior Vice President and Chief Medical Officer
CIO: Louis H. Hermans, Vice President Information Systems
Web address: www.solarishs.org
| | 23 | 10 | 325 | — | — | — | — | — | — | — |

ELIZABETH—Union County

⊠ **TRINITAS HOSPITAL–WILLIAMSON STREET CAMPUS**, 225 Williamson Street, Zip 07202–3600; tel. 908/994–5000, (Includes TRINITAS HOSPITAL – JERSEY STREET CAMPUS, 925 East Jersey Street, Zip 07201; tel. 908/994–5000; TRINITAS HOSPITAL – NEW POINT CAMPUS, 655 East Jersey Street, Zip 07206), (Total facility includes 142 beds in nursing home–type unit) **A**1 2 6 9 10 **F**2 4 6 9 11 12 15 17 21 22 23 24 26 27 28 29 31 33 35 37 38 39 41 42 44 46 47 48 49 50 52 55 57 58 59 61 63 66 69 70 71 72 73 74 75 76 77 78 80 81 82 83 84 85 87 88 92 93 94 96 98 108 109 110
Primary Contact: Gary S. Horan, FACHE, President and Chief Executive Officer
CFO: Paul C. Dabrowski, Senior Vice President and Chief Financial Officer
CMO: William McHugh, M.D., Chief Medical Officer
CIO: Judy Comitto, Vice President Information Services and Chief Information Officer
CHR: Glenn Nacion, Vice President Human Resources
Web address: www.trinitashospital.com
| | 23 | 10 | 467 | 15180 | 391 | 372625 | 1763 | 225239 | 101843 | 1905 |

ELMER—Salem County

ELMER HOSPITAL See South Jersey Healthcare, Bridgeton

ENGLEWOOD—Bergen County

⊠ **ENGLEWOOD HOSPITAL AND MEDICAL CENTER**, 350 Engle Street, Zip 07631–1898; tel. 201/894–3000 **A**1 2 3 5 9 10 **F**2 5 9 10 11 12 14 15 17 19 21 22 23 24 26 28 29 30 31 33 35 36 37 38 39 40 44 46 47 48 49 50 51 52 53 55 56 57 58 59 60 61 62 63 64 65 66 69 70 71 74 75 76 78 79 80 81 82 84 85 86 87 88 90 93 94 95 96 106 108 109 110 **P**5
Primary Contact: Douglas A. Duchak, President and Chief Executive Officer
CFO: Anthony T. Orlando, Senior Vice President Finance
CMO: Steven Weisholtz, M.D., President Medical Staff
CIO: Diane Caesar, Director
CHR: Elliot Brooks, Senior Vice President Human Resources
Web address: www.englewoodhospital.com
| | 23 | 10 | 331 | 15737 | 214 | 411567 | 2099 | 226746 | 101644 | 1800 |

FLEMINGTON—Hunterdon County

⊠ **HUNTERDON MEDICAL CENTER**, 2100 Wescott Drive, Zip 08822–4604; tel. 908/788–6100 **A**1 2 3 5 9 10 **F**2 4 9 11 12 15 17 21 22 23 24 26 27 28 29 31 33 37 38 41 42 44 46 47 48 49 50 51 52 55 57 58 59 60 61 62 63 64 65 66 69 70 71 72 73 74 75 76 77 78 79 80 81 82 85 88 93 94 95 96 98 106 108 109 110 **P**1 5
Primary Contact: Robert P. Wise, President and Chief Executive Officer
COO: Lawrence N. Grand, Vice President and Chief Operating Officer
CFO: Daniel J. Deets, Chief Financial Officer
CMO: Robert M. Pickoff, M.D., Vice President Medical Administration
CIO: Glenn Mamary, Chief Information Officer
CHR: Patrick Boyle, Director Human Resources
Web address: www.hunterdonhealthcare.org
| | 23 | 10 | 182 | 8409 | 107 | 460723 | 1389 | 150778 | 77783 | 1342 |

FREEHOLD—Monmouth County

⊠ **CENTRASTATE HEALTHCARE SYSTEM**, 901 West Main Street, Zip 07728–2549; tel. 732/431–2000 **A**1 2 9 10 **F**2 8 9 10 11 12 14 21 22 23 24 26 27 28 29 30 31 33 37 38 44 46 47 48 50 52 55 57 58 59 60 61 62 63 65 66 69 70 71 73 74 75 79 81 82 84 85 86 87 88 91 92 93 94 95 96 98 106 107 108 109 110 **P**1 5
Primary Contact: John T. Gribbin, President and Chief Executive Officer
COO: Daniel J. Messina, Senior Vice President and Chief Operating Officer
CFO: John Dellocono, Senior Vice President and Chief Financial Officer
CMO: Benjamin Weinstein, M.D., Senior Vice President and Medical Director
CIO: Indranil Ganguly, Vice President and Chief Information Officer
CHR: Fran Keane, Vice President Human Resources
Web address: www.centrastate.com
| | 23 | 10 | 262 | 14668 | 181 | 132849 | 1687 | 149163 | 65891 | 1606 |

GLEN GARDNER—Hunterdon County

□ **SENATOR GARRETT W. HAGEDORN PSYCHIATRIC HOSPITAL**, 200 Sanitorium Road, Zip 08826–3291; tel. 908/537–2141, (Nonreporting) **A**1 10 **S** Division of Mental Health Services, Department of Human Services, State of New Jersey, Trenton, NJ
Primary Contact: Debra A. Smith, Acting Chief Executive Officer
| | 12 | 22 | 181 | — | — | — | — | — | — | — |

Many Facility Codes have changed. Please refer to the AHA Guide Code Chart. © 2005 AHA Guide

NJ

Hospital, Address, Telephone, Approval, Facility, and Physician Codes, Health Care System	Classi-fication Codes		Utilization Data					Expense (thousands) of dollars		
★ American Hospital Association (AHA) membership □ Joint Commission on Accreditation of Healthcare Organizations (JCAHO) accreditation ○ American Osteopathic Association (AOA) accreditation △ Commission on Accreditation of Rehabilitation Facilities (CARF) accreditation	Control	Service	Staffed Beds	Admissions	Census	Outpatient Visits	Births	Total	Payroll	Personnel

HACKENSACK—Bergen County

⊠ **HACKENSACK UNIVERSITY MEDICAL CENTER**, 30 Prospect Avenue,
Zip 07601–1991; tel. 201/996–2000 **A**1 2 3 5 8 9 10 **F**1 2 3 4 5 7 8 9 10 11
12 13 14 15 17 19 21 22 23 24 25 26 27 28 29 30 31 32 33 34 35 36 37
38 39 40 41 42 44 45 46 47 48 49 50 51 52 53 54 55 56 57 59 60 61
62 63 64 65 66 67 68 69 70 71 72 73 74 75 76 77 78 79 80 81 82 83 84
85 86 87 88 89 90 92 93 94 95 96 98 99 101 104 105 106 107 108 109
110 **P**4 5 6 8
Primary Contact: John P. Ferguson, FACHE, President and Chief Executive Officer
COO: Robert C. Garrett, Executive Vice President and Chief Operating Officer
CFO: Harold P. Hogstrom, CPA, Executive Vice President Finance and Chief
Financial Officer
CMO: Peter DeMauro, M.D., Vice President and Chief Medical Officer
CIO: Lex Ferrauiola, Vice President Information Technology and Chief Information
Officer
CHR: Andre J. Ferullo, Senior Vice President Human Resources
Web address: www.humed.com
`23 10 661 66283 640 2286837 4469 850445 359906 6259`

HACKETTSTOWN—Warren County

⊠ **HACKETTSTOWN COMMUNITY HOSPITAL**, 651 Willow Grove Street,
Zip 07840–1792; tel. 908/852–5100 **A**1 9 10 **F**2 4 9 11 12 21 22 23 26 27
28 29 31 33 37 39 40 41 44 46 47 48 49 53 54 55 57 58 59 60 61 62 63
65 66 69 77 81 82 85 88 93 94 96 98 106 108 109 110 **S** Adventist
HealthCare, Rockville, MD
Primary Contact: Gene C. Milton, President and Chief Executive Officer
COO: Jason Coe, Chief Operating Officer
CFO: Stella Visaggio, Chief Financial Officer
CMO: Patrick Caruso, M.D., President Medical Staff
CIO: Dorothy Cox, Manager Information Systems
CHR: Jeanne Jepson, Director Human Resources
Web address: www.hch.org
`21 10 92 4876 54 58576 783 60599 27637 703`

HAMILTON—Mercer County

⊠ **ROBERT WOOD JOHNSON UNIVERSITY HOSPITAL AT HAMILTON**, One
Hamilton Health Place, Zip 08690–3599; tel. 609/586–7900 **A**1 2 9 10 **F**1 2 7
9 10 11 12 14 15 17 21 22 23 24 26 27 28 29 30 32 33 35 36 37 38 39 40
41 42 44 45 46 47 48 49 50 52 53 54 55 57 58 59 60 61 62 63 64 65 66
69 70 73 75 76 79 80 81 82 84 85 86 87 88 92 93 94 95 96 98 106 107
108 109 110 **P**6 7 **S** Robert Wood Johnson Health System & Network, New
Brunswick, NJ
Primary Contact: Christy Stephenson, Chief Executive Officer
COO: Deborah Cardello, Chief Operating Officer
CFO: Peter Newell, Senior Vice President Finance and Chief Financial Officer
CMO: Feroz Safdar, M.D., Chief of Staff
CIO: Pam Jenner, Director Information Systems
CHR: Richard Lovering, Senior Vice President Human Resources and Health
Promotion
Web address: www.rwjhamilton.org
`23 10 204 13163 169 228260 1063 156935 71280 1528`

HAMMONTON—Atlantic County

□ **WILLIAM B. KESSLER MEMORIAL HOSPITAL**, 600 South White Horse Pike,
Zip 08037–2099; tel. 609/561–6700 **A**1 9 10 **F**2 9 14 21 26 27 28 30 32 33
37 41 45 46 48 49 50 52 53 55 58 60 62 63 64 65 66 69 70 82 87 88 93
94 95 96 106 108 110
Primary Contact: Michael J. Gonnella, President and Chief Executive Officer
Web address: www.kesslerhospital.org
`23 10 86 3739 53 — 0 — — —`

HOBOKEN—Hudson County

⊠ **ST. MARY HOSPITAL**, 308 Willow Avenue, Zip 07030–3889;
tel. 201/418–1000, (Nonreporting) **A**1 3 5 9 10 **S** Bon Secours Health System,
Inc., Marriottsville, MD
Primary Contact: Michael J. Sniffen, Interim President and Chief Executive Officer
COO: Marie T. Droege, Executive Vice President Operations
CFO: John Barone, Vice President Finance and Chief Financial Officer
CMO: Christopher Valerian, D.O., Vice President Medical Affairs
Web address: www.bonsecoursnj.org
`21 10 401 — — — — — — —`

HOLMDEL—Monmouth County

⊠ **BAYSHORE COMMUNITY HOSPITAL**, 727 North Beers Street,
Zip 07733–1598; tel. 732/739–5900 **A**1 2 9 10 **F**2 9 12 15 21 22 23 26 27
28 29 33 34 36 37 39 40 42 44 46 47 48 49 52 53 54 55 57 58 60 61 62
63 64 65 66 69 81 82 84 85 87 88 92 93 94 96 106 108 110 **P**6 7
Primary Contact: Raimonda Clark, President and Chief Executive Officer
CFO: Jane Kaye, Vice President Finance
CMO: Gerald Costa, M.D., Vice President Medical Affairs
CIO: Linda Woods, Vice President Information Services
CHR: Emro Krasovec, Vice President Human Resources
Web address: www.bchs.com
`23 10 181 9131 145 86445 0 91171 43200 942`

Hospital, Address, Telephone, Approval, Facility, and Physician Codes, Health Care System	Classi-fication Codes		Utilization Data					Expense (thousands) of dollars		
★ American Hospital Association (AHA) membership □ Joint Commission on Accreditation of Healthcare Organizations (JCAHO) accreditation ○ American Osteopathic Association (AOA) accreditation △ Commission on Accreditation of Rehabilitation Facilities (CARF) accreditation	Control	Service	Staffed Beds	Admissions	Census	Outpatient Visits	Births	Total	Payroll	Personnel

IRVINGTON—Essex County

☒ **IRVINGTON GENERAL HOSPITAL**, 832 Chancellor Avenue, Zip 07111–0709; tel. 973/399–6000 **A**1 9 10 **F**2 9 21 22 23 26 27 28 29 33 35 39 46 47 48 53 57 58 60 61 62 63 64 66 69 81 88 92 94 96 108 **P**8 **S** Saint Barnabas Health Care System, West Orange, NJ
Primary Contact: Patricia Carroll, Executive Director
CMO: Mahesh Desai, M.D., Vice President Medical Affairs
CIO: Angelo Schittone, Chief Information Officer
CHR: Sharyn Matthews, Vice President Human Resources
Web address: www.sbhcs.com

| 23 | 10 | 111 | 4763 | 88 | 37416 | 0 | 54466 | 25768 | 394 |

JERSEY CITY—Hudson County

☒ **CHRIST HOSPITAL**, 176 Palisade Avenue, Zip 07306–1196, Mailing Address: P.O. Box J–1, Zip 07306–1196; tel. 201/795–8200 **A**1 2 6 9 10 **F**2 3 4 9 10 11 12 15 21 22 23 26 27 28 29 31 33 36 37 38 43 44 45 46 47 48 49 50 51 52 53 55 57 58 59 60 61 62 63 64 65 66 69 70 71 72 73 74 75 76 77 78 79 80 81 82 83 84 85 87 88 92 93 94 95 96 98 106 107 108 109 110
Primary Contact: Peter A. Kelly, President and Chief Executive Officer
CFO: Michael D. Ayres, Senior Vice President and Chief Financial Officer
CMO: Oscar Pizzard, M.D., President Medical Staff
CIO: Marty Grossman, Director Information Technology
CHR: Eileen Clyne, Director Human Resources
Web address: www.christhospital.org

| 23 | 10 | 313 | 13780 | 271 | 243899 | 1146 | 161042 | 73862 | 1333 |

☒ **LIBERTYHEALTH–GREENVILLE HOSPITAL**, (Formerly Greenville Hospital), 1825 John F. Kennedy Boulevard, Zip 07305–2198; tel. 201/547–6100 **A**1 10 **F**2 12 14 21 22 23 27 28 29 33 37 38 39 46 48 49 53 55 60 63 64 69 81 82 85 87 88 94 108 109 **S** LibertyHealth, Jersey City, NJ
Primary Contact: Jean A. Murray, Administrator and Senior Vice President of Operations
COO: E Stephen Kirby, Chief Operating Officer
CFO: E Stephen Kirby, Senior Vice President Finance, Chief Financial Officer and Chief Operating Officer
CMO: Bhavani P. Mekala, M.D., President Medical Staff
CIO: William Dauster, Vice President Public Affairs
CHR: Ronald Brooks, Vice President Human Resources
Web address: www.libertyhcs.org

| 23 | 10 | 100 | 3444 | 72 | 14175 | 0 | 29978 | 13432 | 176 |

□ **LIBERTYHEALTH–JERSEY CITY MEDICAL CENTER**, (Formerly Jersey City Medical Center), 355 Grand Street, Zip 07302; tel. 201/915–2000, (Nonreporting) **A**1 2 3 5 9 10 **S** LibertyHealth, Jersey City, NJ
Primary Contact: Jonathan M. Metsch, Dr.PH, President and Chief Executive Officer
Web address: www.libertyhcs.org

| 23 | 10 | 366 | — | — | — | — | — | — | — |

LAKEWOOD—Ocean County

☒ **KIMBALL MEDICAL CENTER**, 600 River Avenue, Zip 08701–4281; tel. 732/363–1900, (Nonreporting) **A**1 2 9 10 **S** Saint Barnabas Health Care System, West Orange, NJ
Primary Contact: Joe Hicks, Executive Director
COO: Tony Cava, Vice President Operations
CFO: Paul Rouvell, Vice President Finance
CMO: Tony Lombardino, Vice President Medical Affairs
CIO: Kathryn Collins, Vice President Information Systems
Web address: www.sbhcs.com

| 23 | 10 | 302 | — | — | — | — | — | — | — |

LIVINGSTON—Essex County

☒ **SAINT BARNABAS MEDICAL CENTER**, 94 Old Short Hills Road, Zip 07039–5668; tel. 973/322–5000 **A**1 2 3 5 8 9 10 12 13 **F**9 10 11 12 13 14 15 17 19 21 22 23 24 26 27 28 29 30 33 35 37 39 41 44 45 46 47 48 49 50 52 53 55 56 57 58 59 61 62 63 65 66 67 69 70 73 81 82 84 87 88 93 94 96 97 98 101 105 106 108 110 **P**5 **S** Saint Barnabas Health Care System, West Orange, NJ
Primary Contact: John F. Bonamo, M.D., Executive Director
COO: Gregory Rokosz, D.O., Senior Vice President Medical and Academic Affairs
CFO: Patrick Ahearn, Senior Vice President Finance and Administrative Services
CIO: John Moustakakis, Chief Information Officer
CHR: Arnie Manzo, Vice President Human Resources
Web address: www.sbhcs.com

| 23 | 10 | 592 | 39552 | 510 | 70936 | 7094 | 416953 | 167196 | — |

LONG BRANCH—Monmouth County

☒ **MONMOUTH MEDICAL CENTER**, 300 Second Avenue, Zip 07740–6303; tel. 732/222–5200 **A**1 2 3 5 8 9 10 **F**2 4 9 10 11 12 15 17 21 22 23 24 26 27 28 29 30 31 32 33 35 36 37 38 39 40 41 42 44 45 46 47 48 49 50 52 53 55 56 57 58 59 60 61 62 63 64 65 66 69 70 71 72 73 74 75 76 77 78 79 80 81 82 83 84 85 86 88 89 90 92 93 94 95 96 97 98 106 107 108 109 110 **P**1 5 6 7 **S** Saint Barnabas Health Care System, West Orange, NJ
Primary Contact: Frank J. Vozos, M.D., FACS, Executive Director
CFO: Gerald Tofani, Chief Financial Officer
CMO: Eric Burkett, M.D., Vice President Medical Affairs
CIO: Richard Wheatley, Vice President Information Services
CHR: Bruce Pardo, Vice President Human Resources
Web address: www.sbhcs.com

| 23 | 10 | 232 | 16757 | 232 | 139315 | 3347 | 213436 | 91282 | 1590 |

NJ

Many Facility Codes have changed. Please refer to the AHA Guide Code Chart. © 2005 AHA Guide

Hospital, Address, Telephone, Approval, Facility, and Physician Codes, Health Care System	Classi-fication Codes		Utilization Data					Expense (thousands) of dollars		
★ American Hospital Association (AHA) membership □ Joint Commission on Accreditation of Healthcare Organizations (JCAHO) accreditation ○ American Osteopathic Association (AOA) accreditation △ Commission on Accreditation of Rehabilitation Facilities (CARF) accreditation	Control	Service	Staffed Beds	Admissions	Census	Outpatient Visits	Births	Total	Payroll	Personnel
SPECIALTY HOSPITAL AT MONMOUTH, 300 Second Avenue, Zip 07740; tel. 732/923–5037, (Nonreporting) **A**10 Primary Contact: Violeta Peters, Chief Executive Officer	33	49	25	—	—	—	—	—	—	—

LYONS—Somerset County

LYONS DIVISION See Veterans Affairs New Jersey Health Care System, East Orange

MANAHAWKIN—Ocean County

⊠ **SOUTHERN OCEAN COUNTY HOSPITAL**, 1140 Route 72 West, Zip 08050–2499; tel. 609/978–8900 **A**1 2 9 10 **F**2 9 11 12 15 21 22 23 24 26 27 28 29 33 34 35 36 37 38 39 40 41 42 44 46 47 48 51 52 53 55 57 58 59 60 61 62 63 64 65 66 69 81 82 84 86 87 88 92 93 94 96 98 106 108 109 110 **P**5 7 8 Primary Contact: Joseph P. Coyle, President and Chief Executive Officer COO: Stephanie L. Bloom, Chief Operating Officer CFO: Richard A. Hand, Vice President Information and Chief Financial Officer CMO: Edward Niewiadomski, M.D., Vice President Medical Affairs CIO: Kevin Bryant, Vice President Information CHR: Raymond Green, Vice President Human Resources Web address: www.soch.com	23	10	142	7975	116	152089	321	91346	35381	812

MARLTON—Burlington County

□ **MARLTON REHABILITATION HOSPITAL**, 92 Brick Road, Zip 08053–2020; tel. 856/988–8778, (Nonreporting) **A**1 10 **S** VIBRA Healthcare, Mechanicsburg, PA Primary Contact: Christopher Gillies, Chief Executive Officer	33	46	46	—	—	—	—	—	—	—
⊠ **VIRTUA WEST JERSEY HOSPITAL–MARLTON**, 90 Brick Road, Zip 08053–9697; tel. 856/355–6000, (Nonreporting) **A**1 10 **S** Virtua Health, Marlton, NJ Primary Contact: Ellen Guarnieri, Vice President and Chief Operating Officer COO: Ellen Guarnieri, Vice President and Chief Operating Officer CFO: Brian Malone, Director Finance Web address: www.virtua.org	23	10	165	—	—	—	—	—	—	—
□ **WEISMAN CHILDREN'S REHABILITATION HOSPITAL**, 92 Brick Road, 3rd Floor, Zip 08053; tel. 856/589–4520, (Nonreporting) **A**1 10 Primary Contact: Richard W. Shepherd, Chief Executive Officer	33	46	30	—	—	—	—	—	—	—

MONTCLAIR—Essex County

⊠ **MOUNTAINSIDE HOSPITAL**, 1 Bay Avenue, Zip 07042–4898; tel. 973/429–6000, (Total facility includes 18 beds in nursing home–type unit) **A**1 2 3 5 6 8 9 10 **F**2 4 6 9 10 11 12 14 15 17 21 22 23 26 27 28 30 31 32 33 37 38 41 45 46 48 49 50 52 53 55 57 58 59 60 61 62 63 64 66 69 71 72 73 74 75 77 78 79 80 81 82 84 85 86 87 88 92 93 94 95 96 97 106 108 109 110 **P**5 6 **S** Atlantic Health System, Florham Park, NJ Primary Contact: Joseph A. Trunfio, Ph.D., President and Chief Executive Officer COO: Joanne M. Conroy, M.D., Executive Vice President and Chief Operating Officer CFO: Kevin Shanley, Vice President Finance and Chief Financial Officer CMO: Joanne M. Conroy, M.D., Executive Vice President and Chief Operating Officer CIO: Linda Reed, Vice President and Chief Information Officer CHR: Andrew Kovach, Vice President Human Resources and Shared Services Web address: www.atlantichealth.org/cons/hospitals/at_MSH	23	10	261	11956	182	144308	781	159599	75613	1390

MORRIS PLAINS—Morris County

□ **GREYSTONE PARK PSYCHIATRIC HOSPITAL**, Central Avenue, Zip 07950–1005, Mailing Address: P.O. Box A, Zip 07950–1005; tel. 973/538–1800 **A**1 10 **F**27 28 32 45 46 58 71 94 108 **P**6 **S** Division of Mental Health Services, Department of Human Services, State of New Jersey, Trenton, NJ Primary Contact: Janet Monroe, Chief Executive Officer Web address: www.state.nj.us/humanservices/pfnurse/greystone.htm	12	22	578	348	540	4522	0	—	—	1303

MORRISTOWN—Morris County

⊠ △ **MORRISTOWN MEMORIAL HOSPITAL**, 100 Madison Avenue, Zip 07962–1956; tel. 973/971–5000, (Includes REHABILITATION INSTITUTE AT THE MOUNT KEMBLE DIVISION), (Total facility includes 40 beds in nursing home–type unit) **A**1 2 3 5 7 8 9 10 **F**2 4 9 10 11 12 14 15 17 19 21 22 23 24 26 27 28 29 30 31 32 33 34 35 37 39 41 42 46 47 48 49 50 52 53 54 55 56 57 58 59 60 61 62 63 64 65 66 67 68 69 70 71 72 73 74 75 76 77 79 80 81 82 83 84 85 86 87 88 90 92 93 94 95 96 98 106 107 108 110 **P**5 6 **S** Atlantic Health System, Florham Park, NJ Primary Contact: Joseph A. Trunfio, Ph.D., President and Chief Executive Officer COO: Joanne M. Conroy, M.D., Executive Vice President and Chief Operating Officer CFO: Kevin Shanley, Vice President Finance and Chief Financial Officer CMO: Joanne M. Conroy, M.D., Executive Vice President and Chief Operating Officer CIO: Linda Reed, Vice President and Chief Information Officer CHR: Andrew Kovach, Vice President Human Resources and Shared Services Web address: www.atlantichealth.org/cons/hospitals/at_MMH	23	10	601	33219	484	284506	4114	475753	221924	3995

NJ

Hospital, Address, Telephone, Approval, Facility, and Physician Codes, Health Care System	Classi-fication Codes		Utilization Data					Expense (thousands) of dollars		
★ American Hospital Association (AHA) membership □ Joint Commission on Accreditation of Healthcare Organizations (JCAHO) accreditation ○ American Osteopathic Association (AOA) accreditation △ Commission on Accreditation of Rehabilitation Facilities (CARF) accreditation	Control	Service	Staffed Beds	Admissions	Census	Outpatient Visits	Births	Total	Payroll	Personnel

MOUNT HOLLY—Burlington County

□ **HAMPTON HOSPITAL**, 650 Rancocas Road, Zip 08060–5613, Mailing Address: P.O. Box 7000, Rancocas, Zip 08073–7000; tel. 609/267–7000, (Nonreporting) **A**1 9 10 **S** Universal Health Services, Inc., King of Prussia, PA Primary Contact: James P. Gallagher, Chief Executive Officer Web address: www.hamptonhospital.com	33	22	83	—	—	—	—			
□ **VIRTUA MEMORIAL HOSPITAL BURLINGTON COUNTY**, 175 Madison Avenue, Zip 08060–2099; tel. 609/267–0700 **A**1 3 5 9 10 **F**4 11 14 15 17 21 22 23 27 28 33 37 45 49 55 59 61 63 64 66 69 71 72 73 75 81 84 86 88 90 93 94 96 108 109 110 **S** Virtua Health, Marlton, NJ Primary Contact: Stephen Kolesk, M.D., Vice President and Chief Operating Officer Web address: www.virtua.org	23	10	296	16356	193	—	2098	99891	56599	—

MOUNTAINSIDE—Union County

□ △ **CHILDREN'S SPECIALIZED HOSPITAL**, 150 New Providence Road, Zip 07092–2590; tel. 908/233–3720, (Includes CHILDREN'S SPECIALIZED HOSPITAL–TOMS RIVER, 94 Stevens Road, Toms River, Zip 08755–1237; tel. 732/914–1100), (Total facility includes 62 beds in nursing home–type unit) **A**1 5 7 9 10 **F**28 52 57 68 69 70 72 73 92 **P**6 **S** Robert Wood Johnson Health System & Network, New Brunswick, NJ Primary Contact: Amy B. Mansue, President and Chief Executive Officer Web address: www.childrens–specialized.org	23	56	109	346	103	130049	0	68593	40290	799

NEPTUNE—Monmouth County

✠ **JERSEY SHORE UNIVERSITY MEDICAL CENTER**, 1945 Route 33, Zip 07754–0397; tel. 732/775–5500 **A**1 2 3 5 8 9 10 **F**2 4 9 10 11 12 14 15 17 19 21 22 23 24 26 27 28 32 33 34 37 38 39 40 42 46 48 49 50 52 53 55 56 57 58 59 61 62 63 64 65 66 67 69 70 71 72 73 74 75 76 77 78 80 81 82 84 85 86 88 92 93 94 95 96 106 108 109 110 **S** Meridian Health, Neptune, NJ Primary Contact: Steven G. Littleson, President COO: Jill Ostrem, Vice President Operations CFO: William Phillips, Senior Vice President Finance and Chief Financial Officer CMO: Carl M. Marchetti, M.D., Senior Vice President Medical Affairs CIO: Rebecca Weber, Vice President Information Technology CHR: John Sinnoni, Senior Vice President Human Resources Web address: www.meridianhealth.com	23	10	446	26593	367	183485	2031	351439	136384	2232

NEW BRUNSWICK—Middlesex County

✠ **ROBERT WOOD JOHNSON UNIVERSITY HOSPITAL**, 1 Robert Wood Johnson Place, Zip 08903–2601; tel. 732/828–3000, (Nonreporting) **A**1 2 3 5 8 9 10 **S** Robert Wood Johnson Health System & Network, New Brunswick, NJ Primary Contact: Clifton R. Lacy, M.D., President and Chief Executive Officer CFO: John Gantner, Treasurer Web address: www.rwjuh.edu	23	10	482	—	—	—	—	—	—	—
✠ **SAINT PETER'S UNIVERSITY HOSPITAL**, 254 Easton Avenue, Zip 08901–1780, Mailing Address: P.O. Box 591, Zip 08903–0591; tel. 732/745–8600, (Total facility includes 20 beds in nursing home–type unit) **A**1 2 3 5 8 9 10 **F**1 2 9 11 12 14 15 17 21 22 23 24 26 27 28 29 32 33 37 38 39 40 42 44 45 46 47 48 49 50 52 53 55 56 57 58 59 61 62 63 64 65 66 67 69 70 79 80 81 82 84 85 87 88 90 92 93 94 95 96 98 106 108 109 110 **P**1 6 7 Primary Contact: Sheryl A. Slonim, President and Chief Executive Officer COO: John Grangeia, Senior Vice President Operations CFO: John Calandriello, Chief Financial Officer CIO: Robert Babin, Acting Chief Information Officer CHR: Kevin Kerner, Vice President Human Resources Web address: www.stpetersuh.com	21	10	421	24348	337	301459	6386	—	—	2555

NEWARK—Essex County

□ **COLUMBUS HOSPITAL**, 495 North 13th Street, Zip 07107–1397; tel. 973/268–1400 **A**1 5 9 10 **F**11 12 21 22 23 30 33 38 39 40 45 46 48 49 53 55 57 58 59 61 63 64 66 70 76 77 81 84 88 90 93 94 96 108 110 **S** Cathedral Healthcare System, Inc., Newark, NJ Primary Contact: Richard Giorgino, Administrator	23	10	169	8925	130	—	0	—	—	—
MT. CARMEL BEHAVIORAL HEALTHCARE SYSTEM, 1160 Raymond Boulevard, Zip 07102; tel. 973/596–4100, (Nonreporting) **A**9 10 Primary Contact: Ronald A. Finch, Ed.D., Director Healthcare	21	22	20	—	—	—	—	—	—	—
✠ **NEWARK BETH ISRAEL MEDICAL CENTER**, 201 Lyons Avenue, Zip 07112–2027; tel. 973/926–7000 **A**1 2 3 5 8 9 10 12 13 **F**1 2 4 7 9 10 11 12 14 15 16 17 18 19 20 21 22 23 24 26 27 28 29 30 31 32 33 35 37 38 39 41 42 44 45 46 47 48 49 50 52 53 55 56 57 58 59 60 61 62 63 64 65 66 67 69 70 71 72 73 74 75 76 77 78 79 81 82 84 85 87 88 90 92 94 95 96 97 98 100 101 105 106 108 109 110 **P**8 **S** Saint Barnabas Health Care System, West Orange, NJ Primary Contact: Paul A. Mertz, Executive Director COO: Kenneth L. Tyson, Senior Vice President Operations CFO: Veronica Zeichner, Chief Financial Officer CMO: Murray Belsky, M.D., Vice President Medical Affairs CHR: Zach Lipner, Vice President Human Resources Web address: www.sbhcs.com	23	10	567	21259	399	237420	2022	363034	170655	2911

Many Facility Codes have changed. Please refer to the AHA Guide Code Chart. © 2005 AHA Guide

NJ

Hospital, Address, Telephone, Approval, Facility, and Physician Codes, Health Care System	Classi-fication Codes		Utilization Data					Expense (thousands) of dollars		
★ American Hospital Association (AHA) membership □ Joint Commission on Accreditation of Healthcare Organizations (JCAHO) accreditation ○ American Osteopathic Association (AOA) accreditation △ Commission on Accreditation of Rehabilitation Facilities (CARF) accreditation	Control	Service	Staffed Beds	Admissions	Census	Outpatient Visits	Births	Total	Payroll	Personnel
□ **SAINT JAMES HOSPITAL OF NEWARK**, 155 Jefferson Street, Zip 07105–1791; tel. 973/589–1300, (Nonreporting) **A**1 9 10 **S** Cathedral Healthcare System, Inc., Newark, NJ Primary Contact: Ceu Cirne–Neves, Administrator Web address: www.cathedralhealth.org	21	10	189	—	—	—	—	—	—	—
□ **SAINT MICHAEL'S MEDICAL CENTER**, 268 Dr. Martin Luther King Jr. Boulevard, Zip 07102–2094; tel. 973/877–5000 **A**1 3 5 9 10 12 13 **F**2 3 4 9 12 14 15 17 19 21 22 23 26 27 28 29 31 33 37 39 40 43 46 47 48 49 50 52 53 55 57 58 61 62 63 64 65 66 69 70 71 73 74 75 77 78 79 80 81 82 84 86 87 88 92 93 94 96 108 109 110 **S** Cathedral Healthcare System, Inc., Newark, NJ Primary Contact: Felicia Karsos, Acting Administrator Web address: www.cathedralhealthcare.org	21	10	223	11461	178	69258	0	199037	72676	1309
✠ **UNIVERSITY OF MEDICINE AND DENTISTRY OF NEW JERSEY–UNIVERSITY HOSPITAL**, 150 Bergen Street, Zip 07103–2496; tel. 973/972–4300 **A**1 2 3 5 8 9 10 12 **F**2 3 6 9 10 12 14 15 17 19 21 22 23 24 27 28 29 30 31 32 33 34 35 37 38 39 42 44 45 46 48 50 52 53 55 56 57 58 59 60 61 62 63 66 67 69 70 71 73 75 79 80 81 82 83 84 85 86 87 88 90 92 94 95 96 98 102 105 106 107 108 109 110 Primary Contact: Darlene L. Cox, President and Chief Executive Officer COO: Derrick Johnson, Vice President Operations CFO: James P. Lawler, CPA, Vice President Finance CMO: Suzanne Atkin, M.D., Chief of Staff and Associate Dean Clinical Affairs CIO: Richard Calman, Director Information Systems Technology and Health Management Information Systems CHR: Maryann Master, Vice President Human Resources Web address: www.umdnj.edu	12	10	488	19068	354	278519	2039	504245	257158	—
NEWTON—Sussex County ✠ **NEWTON MEMORIAL HOSPITAL**, 175 High Street, Zip 07860–1004; tel. 973/383–2121 **A**1 2 9 10 **F**2 4 9 10 11 12 21 22 23 24 27 28 29 31 32 33 37 45 46 47 48 49 50 51 52 53 55 57 58 59 60 61 62 63 64 65 66 68 69 70 71 72 73 74 75 76 77 78 81 82 87 88 93 94 95 96 106 107 108 110 Primary Contact: Dennis H. Collette, President and Chief Executive Officer COO: Barbara Gentile, Assistant Vice President Patient Care Services CFO: David Rikkola, Vice President Finance and Chief Financial Officer CMO: David J. Meltz, Vice President Medical Affairs CIO: Eileen Griffiths, Director Information Technology CHR: Robert Chianese, Vice President Human Resources Web address: www.nmhnj.org	23	10	146	11152	107	222387	702	95262	46721	739
NORTH BERGEN—Hudson County ✠ **PALISADES MEDICAL CENTER**, 7600 River Road, Zip 07047–6217; tel. 201/854–5000, (Nonreporting) **A**1 10 **S** New York Presbyterian Healthcare System, New York, NY Primary Contact: Bruce J. Markowitz, President and Chief Executive Officer CFO: Richard Salvia, Vice President Finance and Chief Financial Officer CMO: Maria E. Boria, M.D., Vice President Medical Staff CIO: Alison Romaine, Director Management Information Systems CHR: Donna Cahill, Director Human Resources Web address: www.palisadesmedical.org	23	10	202	—	—	—	—	—	—	—
NORTH PLAINFIELD—Somerset County ✠ **MUHLENBERG REGIONAL MEDICAL CENTER**, Park Avenue and Randolph Road, Zip 07060; tel. 908/668–2000, (Total facility includes 23 beds in nursing home–type unit) (Nonreporting) **A**1 2 3 5 6 9 10 **S** Solaris Health System, Edison, NJ Primary Contact: Nancy A. Fiamingo, Senior Vice President and Chief Operating Officer COO: Nancy A. Fiamingo, Senior Vice President and Chief Operating Officer CFO: Raymond F. Fredericks, Executive Vice President and Chief Financial Officer CMO: Robert Bayly, M.D., Vice President Medical Affairs CIO: Louis H. Hermans, Vice President Information Systems and Chief Information Officer CHR: Shirley Higgins–Bowers, Vice President Human Resources Web address: www.solarishs.org	23	10	301	—	—	—	—	—	—	—
OLD BRIDGE—Middlesex County OLD BRIDGE DIVISION See Raritan Bay Medical Center, Perth Amboy										
PARAMUS—Bergen County ✠ **BERGEN REGIONAL MEDICAL CENTER**, 230 East Ridgewood Avenue, Zip 07652–4131; tel. 201/967–4000, (Total facility includes 610 beds in nursing home–type unit) (Nonreporting) **A**1 3 5 9 10 Primary Contact: Joseph Gallagher, President and Chief Executive Officer COO: Guy A. Barg, Executive Vice President and Chief Operating Officer CFO: Robert A. Pudlak, Executive Vice President and Chief Financial Officer CMO: Robert M. Harris, M.D., President Medical and Dental Staff CIO: Ronald Li, Vice President Management Information Systems Web address: www.bergenregional.com	13	22	1039	—	—	—	—	—	—	—

NJ

Hospital, Address, Telephone, Approval, Facility, and Physician Codes, Health Care System	Classi-fication Codes		Utilization Data					Expense (thousands) of dollars		
★ American Hospital Association (AHA) membership □ Joint Commission on Accreditation of Healthcare Organizations (JCAHO) accreditation ○ American Osteopathic Association (AOA) accreditation △ Commission on Accreditation of Rehabilitation Facilities (CARF) accreditation	Control	Service	Staffed Beds	Admissions	Census	Outpatient Visits	Births	Total	Payroll	Personnel

PASSAIC—Passaic County

⊠ **PBI REGIONAL MEDICAL CENTER**, 70 Parker Avenue, Zip 07055–7000; tel. 973/365–5000 **A**1 9 10 **F**2 4 12 15 17 19 22 23 27 28 29 36 37 38 39 44 45 46 47 48 49 52 53 55 57 58 59 60 61 62 63 65 66 69 78 79 81 87 88 93 94 95 96 97 98 106 108 109 110
Primary Contact: Jeffrey S. Moll, President and Chief Executive Officer
CFO: Joe Aquilante, Vice President Finance
Web address: www.pbih.org
| 23 | 10 | 264 | 11743 | 178 | 163553 | 1028 | 145777 | 61407 | 823 |

⊠ **ST. MARY'S HOSPITAL**, 211 Pennington Avenue, Zip 07055–4698; tel. 973/470–3000 **A**1 10 **F**2 11 12 14 21 22 23 24 26 27 28 29 31 33 37 42 44 45 46 47 48 50 52 55 57 58 59 60 61 62 63 64 65 66 69 70 71 72 73 74 75 76 77 78 81 82 85 87 88 93 94 96 108 110 **P**1 5
Primary Contact: Patricia Peterson, President and Chief Executive Officer
CFO: Jolanta Londene, Vice President Finance and Chief Financial Officer
CMO: Ronald Poblete, M.D., President Medical and Dental Staff
CIO: Shafiq Rab, Chief Information Officer
CHR: Linda Faison, Director Human Resources
Web address: www.smh–passaic.org
| 21 | 10 | 200 | 5431 | 86 | 143152 | 917 | 69066 | 32793 | 878 |

PATERSON—Passaic County

⊠ **BARNERT HOSPITAL**, 680 Dr. Martin Luther King Jr. Way, Zip 07514–1472; tel. 973/977–6600 **A**1 9 10 12 13 **F**1 2 4 10 11 12 21 23 26 27 28 29 31 33 44 45 46 48 50 52 53 55 57 58 59 60 61 62 63 65 69 70 71 72 73 74 75 76 77 78 81 84 85 87 88 93 94 96 106 108 109 110 **P**5
Primary Contact: Joseph S. Orlando, Interim Chief Executive Officer
COO: M Raymond Alvarez, Vice President Ancillary
CFO: Alfred R. Fetter, Vice President Finance
CMO: Nazmi Elrabie, M.D., President Medical Staff
CIO: Michael Piro, Vice President Facilities and Management Information Systems
CHR: Santo Sacco, Vice President Human Resources
Web address: www.barnerthosp.com
| 23 | 10 | 166 | 6468 | 99 | 155113 | 910 | 77675 | 33624 | 633 |

⊠ ○ **ST. JOSEPH'S REGIONAL MEDICAL CENTER**, 703 Main Street, Zip 07503–2691; tel. 973/754–2000 **A**1 2 3 5 9 10 11 12 13 **F**2 4 10 11 12 13 14 15 16 17 18 19 20 21 22 23 24 27 28 29 31 32 33 34 35 36 37 38 39 42 44 46 47 48 49 50 51 52 53 55 56 57 58 59 60 61 62 63 64 65 66 67 69 70 71 72 73 74 75 76 77 78 79 80 81 82 83 84 85 86 88 90 92 94 95 96 97 98 99 106 107 108 109 **P**5 **S** St. Joseph's Healthcare System, Paterson, NJ
Primary Contact: William A. McDonald, Interim Chief Executive Officer
CFO: Rick Annis, Senior Vice President and Chief Financial Officer
CMO: James Labagnara, M.D., Interim Chief Medical Officer
CIO: James Cavanagh, Chief Information Officer
Web address: www.sjhmc.org
| 21 | 10 | 651 | 24081 | 340 | 2056382 | 3261 | 419067 | 180481 | 3892 |

PEAPACK—Somerset County

□ **MATHENY MEDICAL AND EDUCATIONAL CENTER**, (Formerly Matheny School and Hospital), Main Street, Zip 07977, Mailing Address: P.O. Box 339, Zip 07977–0339; tel. 908/234–0011 **A**1 5 10 **F**1 21 29 32 37 52 57 58 65 66 69 73 92 94 96 108 109 110 **P**6
Primary Contact: Steven M. Proctor, President
Web address: www.matheny.org
| 23 | 48 | 99 | 40 | 91 | 1460 | 0 | 27876 | 15926 | 418 |

PERTH AMBOY—Middlesex County

⊠ **RARITAN BAY MEDICAL CENTER**, 530 New Brunswick Avenue, Zip 08861; tel. 732/442–3700, (Includes OLD BRIDGE DIVISION, One Hospital Plaza, Old Bridge, Zip 08857; tel. 732/360–1000; PERTH AMBOY DIVISION, 530 New Brunswick Avenue, Zip 08861–3685; tel. 732/442–3700) **A**1 2 6 9 10 **F**2 3 4 6 9 10 11 12 13 14 15 21 22 23 26 27 28 29 31 33 37 38 39 42 44 45 46 48 49 50 52 53 54 55 58 59 60 61 62 63 64 65 66 67 68 69 70 71 75 76 77 81 82 84 85 86 87 88 93 94 96 98 108 109 110 **P**5 7
Primary Contact: Michael R. D'Agnes, President and Chief Executive Officer
COO: Ronald D. Esser, Senior Vice President and Chief Operating Officer
CFO: Thomas Shanahan, Chief Financial Officer and Senior Vice President
CMO: John Middleton, M.D., Chief Medical Officer
CHR: Vincent Costantino, Vice President Human Resources
Web address: www.rbmc.org
| 23 | 10 | 402 | 17292 | 297 | 258745 | 1099 | 209961 | 104260 | 1861 |

PHILLIPSBURG—Warren County

⊠ **WARREN HOSPITAL**, 185 Roseberry Street, Zip 08865–9955; tel. 908/859–6700 **A**1 2 3 5 9 10 12 13 **F**4 9 11 12 21 22 23 26 27 28 29 32 33 37 41 42 44 47 48 50 52 53 55 58 59 60 61 63 65 66 69 70 71 73 75 76 81 84 88 93 94 95 96 98 108 110 **P**7
Primary Contact: Jeffrey C. Goodwin, President and Chief Executive Officer
COO: Jeffrey W. Kelly, Senior Vice President Administration
CFO: Carl M. Alberto, Vice Prersident Finance
CMO: Frank Gilly, M.D., Vice President Medical Affairs
CHR: William Durett, Director Human Resources
Web address: www.warrenhospital.org
| 23 | 10 | 148 | 6237 | 88 | — | 401 | — | — | — |

PISCATAWAY—Middlesex County

UNIVERSITY OF MEDICINE AND DENTISTRY OF NEW JERSEY, UNIVERSITY BEHAVIORAL HEALTHCARE, 671 Hoes Lane, Zip 08855, Mailing Address: P.O. Box 1392, Zip 08855–1392; tel. 732/235–5900 **A**3 10 **F**1 4 5 21 28 29 31 33 44 47 66 71 72 74 75 76 77 78 94 96 98 **P**6
Primary Contact: Christopher O. Kosseff, President and Chief Executive Officer
Web address: www.umdnj.edu
| 12 | 22 | 48 | 1534 | 38 | 253755 | 0 | 99460 | 52641 | 1165 |

Many Facility Codes have changed. Please refer to the AHA Guide Code Chart. © 2005 AHA Guide

Hospital, Address, Telephone, Approval, Facility, and Physician Codes, Health Care System	Classi-fication Codes		Utilization Data					Expense (thousands) of dollars		
★ American Hospital Association (AHA) membership □ Joint Commission on Accreditation of Healthcare Organizations (JCAHO) accreditation ○ American Osteopathic Association (AOA) accreditation △ Commission on Accreditation of Rehabilitation Facilities (CARF) accreditation	Control	Service	Staffed Beds	Admissions	Census	Outpatient Visits	Births	Total	Payroll	Personnel

POMONA—Atlantic County

★ △ **BACHARACH INSTITUTE FOR REHABILITATION**, 61 West Jimmy Leeds Road, Zip 08240–0723, Mailing Address: P.O. Box 723, Zip 08240–0723; tel. 609/652–7000, (Nonreporting) **A**1 7 9 10

| | 23 | 46 | 80 | — | — | — | — | — | — | — |

Primary Contact: Richard J. Kathrins, Administrator and Chief Executive Officer
CFO: Frank Scudese, Director Fiscal Services
CMO: Craig Anmuth, M.D., Medical Director
CIO: Jeff Rees, Director Information Systems
CHR: Diane Croshaw, Vice President Human Resources
Web address: www.bacharach.org

POMPTON PLAINS—Morris County

★ **CHILTON MEMORIAL HOSPITAL**, 97 West Parkway, Zip 07444–1696; tel. 973/831–5000 **A**1 2 9 10 **F**2 9 10 11 12 15 21 22 23 24 25 26 27 28 29 33 35 37 38 39 42 45 46 47 48 49 52 55 57 58 59 60 61 62 63 64 65 66 69 70 71 72 73 75 76 79 80 81 82 83 84 85 86 87 88 92 93 94 95 96 106 108 110

| | 23 | 10 | 260 | 11329 | 150 | 126619 | 1297 | 127527 | 56715 | 1070 |

Primary Contact: Deborah K. Zastocki, FACHE, President and Chief Executive Officer
COO: Patrick Gavin, Chief Operating Officer
CFO: Michael Richetti, Chief Financial Officer
CMO: Charles Ross, M.D., Vice President Medical Affairs
CIO: Karen S. Smith, Director Information Services
CHR: Julia McGovern, Vice President Human Resources
Web address: www.chiltonmemorial.org

PRINCETON—Mercer County

★ △ **UNIVERSITY MEDICAL CENTER AT PRINCETON**, 253 Witherspoon Street, Zip 08540–3213; tel. 609/497–4000, (Includes ACUTE GENERAL HOSPITAL, MERWICK UNIT–EXTENDED CARE AND REHABILITATION, PRINCETON HOUSE UNIT–COMMUNITY MENTAL HEALTH AND SUBSTANCE ABUSE), (Total facility includes 93 beds in nursing home–type unit) **A**1 2 3 5 7 8 9 10 **F**2 3 4 9 10 11 12 14 15 21 22 23 26 27 28 29 33 36 37 40 41 45 46 48 49 51 52 53 55 57 58 59 60 61 62 63 64 66 68 69 70 71 72 73 74 75 76 77 78 79 80 81 82 84 87 88 92 93 94 96 98 108 110

| | 23 | 10 | 378 | 16254 | 209 | 450422 | 1824 | 194379 | 90269 | 1905 |

Primary Contact: Barry S. Rabner, President and Chief Executive Officer
CFO: Bruce Traub, Vice President Finance
Web address: www.mcp.org

RAHWAY—Union County

★ **ROBERT WOOD JOHNSON UNIVERSITY HOSPITAL AT RAHWAY**, 865 Stone Street, Zip 07065–2797; tel. 732/381–4200, (Total facility includes 16 beds in nursing home–type unit) **A**1 9 10 **F**2 9 12 14 15 21 22 23 26 27 28 29 31 33 36 37 39 40 44 45 46 47 48 52 53 55 57 58 60 61 62 63 65 66 69 70 73 74 75 81 82 84 87 88 92 94 96 98 107 108 109 **P**5 **S** Robert Wood Johnson Health System & Network, New Brunswick, NJ

| | 23 | 10 | 157 | 7594 | 133 | 58939 | 0 | 93586 | 43171 | 772 |

Primary Contact: Kirk C. Tice, President and Chief Executive Officer
CFO: Peter Bihuniak, Vice President Finance
CMO: Paul Schackman, M.D., President Medical Staff
CIO: Kathleen O'Connell, Site Manager Information Systems
Web address: www.rahwayhospital.com

RED BANK—Monmouth County

★ △ **RIVERVIEW MEDICAL CENTER**, 1 Riverview Plaza, Zip 07701–9982; tel. 732/741–2700 **A**1 2 7 9 10 **F**2 4 9 11 12 14 15 17 21 22 23 24 26 27 28 29 31 33 35 37 38 46 47 48 49 50 52 53 55 57 58 59 61 62 63 64 65 66 69 70 71 72 73 74 75 76 77 78 79 80 81 82 84 85 87 88 92 93 94 96 97 106 108 109 110 **S** Meridian Health, Neptune, NJ

| | 23 | 10 | 282 | 15560 | 207 | 111974 | 2136 | 148375 | 67737 | 988 |

Primary Contact: Timothy J. Hogan, President
CFO: Chitra Kasinathan, Finance Site Manager
CMO: Lynn Helmer, M.D., Senior Vice President Medical Affairs
CIO: Diane Gribbin, Communications and Marketing Manager
CHR: Sheila Hintze, Manager
Web address: www.meridianhealth.com

RIDGEWOOD—Bergen County

★ **VALLEY HOSPITAL**, 223 North Van Dien Avenue, Zip 07450–9982; tel. 201/447–8000 **A**1 2 5 9 10 **F**2 9 10 11 12 14 15 17 19 21 22 23 24 26 27 28 29 30 31 32 33 37 38 39 40 41 42 44 45 46 47 48 49 50 52 53 54 55 56 57 58 59 60 61 62 63 64 65 66 67 69 70 73 74 75 76 79 80 81 82 84 85 86 87 88 89 90 93 94 95 96 98 106 108 109 110 **P**7

| | 23 | 10 | 420 | 24699 | 341 | 236250 | 3263 | 355988 | 167514 | 2816 |

Primary Contact: Audrey Meyers, President and Chief Executive Officer
CFO: Richard Keenan, Senior Vice President Finance
CMO: Arthur DeSimone, M.D., Vice President Medical Affairs
CHR: Anne Raftery, Vice President Human Resources
Web address: www.valleyhealth.com

SALEM—Salem County

□ **MEMORIAL HOSPITAL OF SALEM COUNTY**, 310 Woodstown Road, Zip 08079–2080; tel. 856/935–1000 **A**1 2 9 10 **F**2 9 11 12 14 21 22 23 27 33 34 36 37 39 40 41 46 48 49 51 54 55 58 59 60 61 62 63 64 66 69 75 81 82 84 88 93 94 96 106 108 109 110 **P**5 6 7 **S** Community Health Systems, Inc., Brentwood, TN

| | 33 | 10 | 110 | 5431 | 60 | 92590 | 383 | 58226 | 23832 | 460 |

Primary Contact: Robert W. Allen, Chief Executive Officer
Web address: www.salemhospitalnj.org

NJ

Hospital, Address, Telephone, Approval, Facility, and Physician Codes, Health Care System	Classi-fication Codes		Utilization Data					Expense (thousands) of dollars		
★ American Hospital Association (AHA) membership □ Joint Commission on Accreditation of Healthcare Organizations (JCAHO) accreditation ○ American Osteopathic Association (AOA) accreditation △ Commission on Accreditation of Rehabilitation Facilities (CARF) accreditation	Control	Service	Staffed Beds	Admissions	Census	Outpatient Visits	Births	Total	Payroll	Personnel

SECAUCUS—Hudson County

□ **LIBERTYHEALTH–MEADOWLANDS HOSPITAL MEDICAL CENTER**, (Formerly Meadowlands Hospital Medical Center), 55 Meadowland Parkway, Zip 07096–1580; tel. 201/392–3100 **A**1 9 10 **F**3 11 12 14 15 21 25 27 29 30 33 41 44 45 46 48 49 52 55 58 59 61 62 63 64 66 68 73 81 82 87 88 89 93 94 95 96 106 108 109 **S** LibertyHealth, Jersey City, NJ
Primary Contact: Martin W. Baicker, CHE, Senior Vice President and Administrator
Web address: www.libertyhcs.com

| | 23 | 10 | 147 | 5725 | 99 | 22341 | 748 | 62668 | 25419 | 197 |

SOMERS POINT—Atlantic County

⊞ **SHORE MEMORIAL HOSPITAL**, 1 East New York Avenue, Zip 08244–2387; tel. 609/653–3500 **A**1 2 9 10 **F**2 9 11 12 14 15 21 22 23 26 27 28 29 33 35 37 39 45 46 47 48 49 50 52 53 55 57 58 59 60 61 62 63 64 65 66 69 79 81 82 84 85 87 88 92 94 96 106 108 109 110 **P**5
Primary Contact: Albert Gutierrez, President and Chief Executive Officer
COO: Ronald Johnson, Vice President Operations and Chief Operating Officer
CFO: James T. Foley, Vice President and Chief Financial Officer
CMO: Peter R. Jungblut, M.D., Vice President Medical Affairs and Chief Medical Officer
CIO: Ronald Johnson, Vice President Operations and Chief Operating Officer
CHR: Alan Beatty, Vice President Human Resources
Web address: www.shorememorial.org

| | 23 | 10 | 208 | 11953 | 162 | 124649 | 1535 | 157764 | 70414 | 1351 |

SOMERVILLE—Somerset County

⊞ **SOMERSET MEDICAL CENTER**, 110 Rehill Avenue, Zip 08876–2598; tel. 908/685–2200 **A**1 2 3 5 9 10 **F**2 6 10 11 12 15 17 21 22 23 26 27 28 29 33 37 41 44 46 47 48 49 50 52 55 57 58 59 60 61 62 63 66 69 70 71 72 73 74 75 76 77 78 81 84 86 87 88 93 94 95 96 97 106 108 109
Primary Contact: Kenneth Bateman, President and Chief Executive Officer
COO: Kathy Van Camp, Senior Vice President and Chief Operating Officer
CFO: Brian O'Neill, Vice President Finance
CMO: William Cors, M.D., Senior Vice President Medical Affairs
CIO: Dave Dyer, Vice President and Chief Information Officer
CHR: Mary Ann Bross, Vice President Human Resources
Web address: www.smchealthwise.com

| | 23 | 10 | 361 | 15016 | 193 | 111726 | 1392 | 184951 | 83963 | 1577 |

STRATFORD—Camden County

KENNEDY MEMORIAL HOSPITAL See Kennedy Memorial Hospitals–University Medical Center, Cherry Hill

SUMMIT—Union County

⊞ **OVERLOOK HOSPITAL**, 99 Beauvoir Avenue, Zip 07902–0220; tel. 908/522–2000 **A**1 2 3 5 8 9 10 12 13 **F**2 9 10 11 12 14 15 21 22 23 26 27 28 29 31 32 33 36 37 38 39 40 41 42 43 44 45 46 47 48 49 51 52 53 55 56 57 58 59 60 61 62 63 64 65 66 69 70 71 72 73 74 75 76 77 78 79 81 82 83 84 85 86 87 88 89 90 92 93 94 96 97 106 107 108 109 110 **P**5 6 **S** Atlantic Health System, Florham Park, NJ
Primary Contact: Joseph A. Trunfio, Ph.D., President and Chief Executive Officer
COO: Alan R. Lieber, Chief Operating Officer
CFO: Kevin Shanley, Vice President Finance and Chief Financial Officer
CMO: Joanne M. Conroy, M.D., Executive Vice President and Chief Operating Officer
CIO: Linda Reed, Vice President and Chief Information Officer
CHR: Andrew Kovach, Vice President Human Resources and Shared Services
Web address: www.atlantichealth.org/cons/hospitals/at_OH

| | 23 | 10 | 363 | 17487 | 253 | 141908 | 2510 | 248318 | 125515 | 2287 |

□ **SUMMIT HOSPITAL**, 19 Prospect Street, Zip 07902–0100; tel. 908/522–7000, (Nonreporting) **A**1 9 10 **S** Psychiatric Solutions, Franklin, TN
Primary Contact: James E. Ledbetter, Ph.D., Chief Executive Officer

| | 33 | 22 | 90 | — | — | — | — | — | — | — |

SUSSEX—Sussex County

SAINT CLARE'S HOSPITAL/SUSSEX See Saint Clare's Hospital, Dover

TEANECK—Bergen County

⊞ **HOLY NAME HOSPITAL**, 718 Teaneck Road, Zip 07666–4281; tel. 201/833–3000 **A**1 2 6 9 10 **F**1 2 9 10 11 12 15 21 22 23 24 26 27 28 29 30 32 33 36 37 42 44 45 46 47 48 49 51 52 53 55 57 58 59 60 61 62 63 65 66 69 70 71 73 75 76 79 81 82 84 86 87 88 93 94 96 106 107 108 109 110
Primary Contact: Michael Maron, President and Chief Executive Officer
CFO: Gregory Adams, Senior Vice President and Chief Financial Officer
CMO: Paul Mendelowitz, Senior Vice President for Medical Affairs
CIO: Paul Garrin, Vice President Information Systems and Chief Information Officer
CHR: Anthony Pellicano, Vice President Human Resources
Web address: www.holyname.org

| | 23 | 10 | 318 | 16574 | 207 | 271991 | 1314 | 166215 | 80197 | 1609 |

TOMS RIVER—Ocean County

CHILDREN'S SPECIALIZED HOSPITAL–TOMS RIVER See Children's Specialized Hospital, Mountainside

NJ

Many Facility Codes have changed. Please refer to the AHA Guide Code Chart.
© 2005 AHA Guide

Hospital, Address, Telephone, Approval, Facility, and Physician Codes, Health Care System	Classi-fication Codes		Utilization Data					Expense (thousands) of dollars		
★ American Hospital Association (AHA) membership □ Joint Commission on Accreditation of Healthcare Organizations (JCAHO) accreditation ○ American Osteopathic Association (AOA) accreditation △ Commission on Accreditation of Rehabilitation Facilities (CARF) accreditation	Control	Service	Staffed Beds	Admissions	Census	Outpatient Visits	Births	Total	Payroll	Personnel
✦ **COMMUNITY MEDICAL CENTER**, 99 Route 37 West, Zip 08755–6423; tel. 732/557–8000 **A**1 2 9 10 **F**1 2 9 10 11 12 14 15 21 22 23 24 26 27 28 29 31 33 35 36 37 38 39 41 44 45 46 47 48 49 50 51 52 53 54 55 57 58 59 60 61 62 63 64 65 66 69 70 73 79 80 81 82 83 84 85 87 88 92 93 94 95 96 97 98 106 108 109 110 **P**5 **S** Saint Barnabas Health Care System, West Orange, NJ Primary Contact: Nancy L. Wollen, R.N., CHE, Executive Director and Chief Administrative Officer COO: Frank Gelormini, Vice President Support Services CFO: Thomas Percello, Vice President Financial Services CMO: John Crisanti, M.D., Vice President Medical Affairs CIO: Richard Wheatley, Vice President Information Services CHR: Jane Palaia, Vice President Human Resources Web address: www.sbhcs.com	23	10	494	27591	398	323586	1907	277941	122593	2151
✦ **HEALTHSOUTH REHABILITATION HOSPITAL OF NEW JERSEY**, 14 Hospital Drive, Zip 08755–6470; tel. 732/244–3100 **A**1 9 10 **F**21 37 42 53 58 62 65 66 68 69 88 92 94 96 108 109 110 **P**5 **S** HEALTHSOUTH Corporation, Birmingham, AL Primary Contact: Patricia Ostaszewski, Administrator CFO: Patricia Brustman, Chief Financial Officer CMO: Joseph Stillo, M.D., Medical Director CIO: Linda Sanchez, Health Information Management Manager CHR: Michael McGowan, Director Human Resources Web address: www.healthsouth.com	33	46	125	2408	119	45015	0	32068	19595	410
TRENTON—Mercer County										
✦ **CAPITAL HEALTH SYSTEM AT FULD**, 750 Brunswick Avenue, Zip 08638–4174; tel. 609/394–6000 **A**1 2 3 5 6 9 10 **F**2 4 6 12 14 21 22 23 24 26 27 28 29 31 33 34 35 37 38 39 40 42 44 45 46 47 48 49 50 52 53 54 55 57 58 60 61 62 63 65 66 69 70 71 72 73 74 75 76 77 78 81 82 84 85 87 88 93 94 95 96 98 106 107 108 109 **S** Capital Health System, Trenton, NJ Primary Contact: Al Maghazehe, Chief Executive Officer COO: Larry DiSanto, Executive Vice President and Chief Operating Officer CFO: Ronald J. Guy, Chief Financial Officer CMO: Norman Coopersmith, M.D., Vice President Medical Affairs CIO: Gene Grochala, Vice President Information Systems CHR: Scott Clemmensen, Vice President Human Resources and Leadership Enhancement Web address: www.capitalhealth.org	23	10	186	7758	141	150000	0	143062	67026	1137
✦ **CAPITAL HEALTH SYSTEM AT MERCER**, 446 Bellevue Avenue, Zip 08618–4597, Mailing Address: P.O. Box 1658, Zip 08607–1658; tel. 609/394–4000 **A**1 2 6 9 10 **F**1 2 6 7 11 12 14 15 17 21 22 23 24 26 27 28 29 30 31 33 34 36 37 38 39 40 44 45 46 47 48 49 50 52 53 54 55 56 57 58 59 60 61 62 63 64 65 66 69 70 73 74 79 80 81 82 83 85 86 87 88 90 93 94 95 96 98 106 107 108 109 110 **S** Capital Health System, Trenton, NJ Primary Contact: Al Maghazehe, Chief Executive Officer COO: Larry DiSanto, Executive Vice President and Chief Operating Officer CFO: Ronald J. Guy, Chief Financial Officer CMO: Norman Coopersmith, M.D., Vice President Medical Affairs CIO: Gene Grochala, Vice President Information Systems CHR: Scott Clemmensen, Vice President Human Resources and Leadership Enhancement Web address: www.capitalhealth.org	23	10	260	12639	167	180000	2908	154210	74470	1196
✦ **ST. FRANCIS MEDICAL CENTER**, 601 Hamilton Avenue, Zip 08629–1986; tel. 609/599–5000 **A**1 2 6 9 10 12 13 **F**2 6 9 10 12 14 15 17 19 21 22 23 26 27 28 29 33 36 37 39 42 44 45 46 47 48 49 50 51 52 53 54 55 57 58 60 61 62 63 65 66 69 70 71 73 74 75 77 78 79 81 82 86 87 88 93 94 96 98 107 108 109 110 **P**5 **S** Catholic Health East, Newtown Square, PA Primary Contact: Gerald J. Jablonowski, President and Chief Executive Officer COO: Joseph Flamini, Vice President Operations CFO: Gail Kosyla, Vice President Finance and Chief Financial Officer CMO: C James Romano, M.D., President Medical Staff CIO: Richard Dowgun, Chief Information Officer CHR: Laura James, Director Human Resources Web address: www.stfrancismedical.com	21	10	165	6442	97	96514	0	100209	45160	770
✦ **ST. LAWRENCE REHABILITATION CENTER**, 2381 Lawrenceville Road, Zip 08648–2024; tel. 609/896–9500, (Total facility includes 30 beds in nursing home–type unit) (Nonreporting) **A**1 10 Primary Contact: Charles L. Brennan, President and Chief Executive Officer CFO: Thomas W. Boyle, Chief Financial Officer CIO: Jane Millner, Director Community Relations and Development Web address: www.slrc.org	21	46	116	—	—	—	—	—	—	—

NJ

Hospital, Address, Telephone, Approval, Facility, and Physician Codes, Health Care System	Classi-fication Codes		Utilization Data					Expense (thousands) of dollars		
★ American Hospital Association (AHA) membership □ Joint Commission on Accreditation of Healthcare Organizations (JCAHO) accreditation ○ American Osteopathic Association (AOA) accreditation △ Commission on Accreditation of Rehabilitation Facilities (CARF) accreditation	Control	Service	Staffed Beds	Admissions	Census	Outpatient Visits	Births	Total	Payroll	Personnel

⊠ **TRENTON PSYCHIATRIC HOSPITAL**, Route 29 and Sullivan Way, Zip 08628–3425, Mailing Address: P.O. Box 7500, West Trenton, Zip 08628–7500; tel. 609/633–1500 **A**1 10 **F**9 21 22 27 28 29 32 35 37 38 44 45 46 53 58 60 65 66 73 74 94 108 109 **S** Division of Mental Health Services, Department of Human Services, State of New Jersey, Trenton, NJ Primary Contact: Gregory P. Roberts, Chief Executive Officer COO: William J. May, Deputy Chief Executive Officer CFO: Gregory Love, Business Manager CMO: Nazimuddin Qazi, M.D., Chief Medicine CIO: Christopher Morrison, Director Information Technology CHR: John Lubitsky, Director Human Resources	12	22	511	1106	483	0	0	—	—	1213
TURNERSVILLE—Camden County KENNEDY MEMORIAL HOSPITAL See Kennedy Memorial Hospitals–University Medical Center, Cherry Hill										
UNION—Union County ⊠ **UNION HOSPITAL**, 1000 Galloping Hill Road, Zip 07083–1652; tel. 908/687–1900 **A**1 2 9 10 12 13 **F**1 2 9 14 21 22 23 26 27 28 29 32 33 44 45 46 47 48 50 53 55 58 60 62 63 65 66 69 81 82 84 85 88 92 94 95 108 **S** Saint Barnabas Health Care System, West Orange, NJ Primary Contact: Kathryn W. Coyne, Executive Director COO: Kathryn W. Coyne, Executive Director CFO: Patrick Ahearn, Senior Vice President Finance and Administrative Services CMO: James Agresti, D.O., Vice President Medical Affairs CIO: Joseph Sullivan, Senior Vice President Information Systems CHR: James Masterson, Vice President Human Resources Web address: www.sbhcs.com	23	10	142	7006	106	48367	0	79993	34992	761
VINELAND—Cumberland County **REHABILITATION HOSPITAL OF SOUTH JERSEY**, 1237 West Sherman Avenue, Zip 08360; tel. 856/696–7100, (Nonreporting) **A**10 Primary Contact: Frank Bonner, M.D., Chief Executive Officer VINELAND HEALTH CENTER See South Jersey Healthcare, Bridgeton	33	46	30	—	—	—	—	—	—	—
VOORHEES—Camden County **VIRTUA WEST JERSEY HOSPITAL–VOORHEES**, 101 Carnie Boulevard, Zip 08043–1597; tel. 856/325–3000, (Nonreporting) **A**3 5 9 10 **S** Virtua Health, Marlton, NJ Primary Contact: Michael S. Kotzen, Vice President and Chief Operating Officer Web address: www.virtua.org	23	10	260	—	—	—	—	—	—	—
WAYNE—Passaic County ⊠ **ST. JOSEPH'S WAYNE HOSPITAL**, 224 Hamburg Turnpike, Zip 07470–2100; tel. 973/942–6900 **A**1 9 10 **F**2 9 11 12 14 15 17 21 22 23 26 27 28 29 33 35 36 37 39 44 46 48 50 51 52 55 58 60 61 62 63 64 65 66 68 69 81 82 84 85 87 88 93 94 96 106 108 **P**5 8 **S** St. Joseph's Healthcare System, Paterson, NJ Primary Contact: William A. McDonald, Interim Chief Executive Officer CFO: Stuart May, Vice President Finance and Chief Financial Officer CMO: James Labagnara, M.D., Vice President Medical Affairs CIO: Gail Keyser, Director Information Technology Services Web address: www.sjwh.net	23	10	122	6692	114	60137	198	73216	31144	514
WEST ORANGE—Essex County ⊠ △ **KESSLER INSTITUTE FOR REHABILITATION**, 1199 Pleasant Valley Way, Zip 07052–1419; tel. 973/731–3600, (Includes EAST ORANGE FACILITY, WEST ORANGE FACILITY, SADDLE BROOK FACILITY AND CHESTER FACILITY), (Nonreporting) **A**1 3 5 7 9 10 **S** Select Medical Corporation, Mechanicsburg, PA Primary Contact: Robert Brehm, President CFO: Ted Bolcavage, Regiional Controller CMO: Bruce M. Gans, M.D., Executive Vice President and Chief Medical Officer CIO: James Talalai, Chief Information Officer CHR: Frank Fritsch, Chief Human Resources Officer Web address: www.kessler-rehab.com	33	46	322	—	—	—	—	—	—	—
WESTWOOD—Bergen County ⊠ **PASCACK VALLEY HOSPITAL**, 250 Old Hook Road, Zip 07675–3181; tel. 201/358–3000 **A**1 2 10 **F**2 9 10 11 12 14 15 17 21 22 23 26 27 28 29 32 33 36 37 41 45 46 47 48 49 50 51 52 53 54 55 57 58 59 60 61 62 63 65 66 69 70 73 79 81 82 84 86 88 89 90 93 94 95 96 98 106 108 109 **P**5 Primary Contact: Sidney E. Mitchell, President and Chief Executive Officer CFO: Brian McIndoe, Senior Vice President Finance Web address: www.pvhospital.org	23	10	146	15983	112	158153	1175	131176	58515	957
WILLINGBORO—Burlington County ⊠ **LOURDES MEDICAL CENTER OF BURLINGTON COUNTY**, 218–A Sunset Road, Zip 08046–1162; tel. 609/835–2900 **A**1 2 9 10 13 **F**2 4 9 10 11 12 14 15 21 22 23 27 28 29 30 31 32 33 35 37 39 44 46 47 48 49 50 52 53 55 57 58 59 61 62 63 64 65 66 69 70 71 73 75 77 78 81 82 83 84 85 87 88 90 93 94 96 106 108 109 110 **P**5 **S** Catholic Health East, Newtown Square, PA Primary Contact: John L. Nespoli, Chief Administrative Officer COO: Robert Ruggero, Senior Vice President Operations CFO: Thomas J. Regner, Senior Vice President Finance and Chief Financial Officer CMO: Nathan Zuckerman, M.D., Vice President Medical Affairs CIO: Mike Elfert, Director Information Services CHR: Janet Moran, Vice President Human Resources Web address: www.lourdesnet.org	23	10	165	8468	114	108634	1107	100684	47700	605

Hospital, Address, Telephone, Approval, Facility, and Physician Codes, Health Care System	Classi-fication Codes		Utilization Data					Expense (thousands) of dollars		
★ American Hospital Association (AHA) membership □ Joint Commission on Accreditation of Healthcare Organizations (JCAHO) accreditation ○ American Osteopathic Association (AOA) accreditation △ Commission on Accreditation of Rehabilitation Facilities (CARF) accreditation	Control	Service	Staffed Beds	Admissions	Census	Outpatient Visits	Births	Total	Payroll	Personnel
WOODBRIDGE—Middlesex County										
WOODBRIDGE DEVELOPMENT CENTER, Rahway Avenue, Zip 07095–3697, Mailing Address: P.O. Box 189, Zip 07095–0189; tel. 732/499–5951, (Nonreporting) Primary Contact: Amy R. Bailon, M.D., Medical Director	12	12	125	—	—	—	—	—	—	—
WOODBURY—Gloucester County										
✠ **UNDERWOOD–MEMORIAL HOSPITAL**, 509 North Broad Street, Zip 08096–1697, Mailing Address: P.O. Box 359, Zip 08096–7359; tel. 856/845–0100 **A**1 3 5 9 10 **F**2 9 10 11 12 14 15 21 23 27 28 29 31 32 33 37 39 44 45 46 48 50 51 52 55 57 58 59 60 61 62 63 64 69 70 71 72 75 76 77 78 81 87 88 92 93 94 96 106 108 109 110 **P**6 Primary Contact: Steven W. Jackmuff, President and Chief Executive Officer COO: Eileen K. Cardile, Executive Vice President and Chief Operating Officer CFO: James R. Brant, Senior Vice President Finance and Chief Financial Officer CIO: Michael E. Baker, Director Information Systems CHR: Anthony DeBartolo, Director Human Resources Web address: www.umhospital.org	23	10	240	13266	191	115801	1197	132264	66743	1332
WYCKOFF—Bergen County										
✠ **CHRISTIAN HEALTH CARE CENTER**, 301 Sicomac Avenue, Zip 07481–2194; tel. 201/848–5200, (Total facility includes 252 beds in nursing home–type unit) **A**1 10 **F**1 8 9 21 22 26 28 29 36 37 38 44 52 53 58 69 71 72 73 74 76 77 78 91 92 108 110 **P**6 Primary Contact: Douglas A. Struyk, President and Chief Executive Officer COO: Denise Ratcliffe, Executive Vice President and Chief Operating Officer CFO: Kevin Stagg, Vice President Finance and Chief Financial Officer CMO: Howard Gilman, Medical Executive CHR: Bob Zierold, Vice President Human Resources Web address: www.chccnj.org	23	22	507	1321	494	36569	0	49316	29013	648

NJ

NEW MEXICO

Hospital, Address, Telephone, Approval, Facility, and Physician Codes, Health Care System	Classi-fication Codes		Utilization Data					Expense (thousands) of dollars		
★ American Hospital Association (AHA) membership □ Joint Commission on Accreditation of Healthcare Organizations (JCAHO) accreditation ○ American Osteopathic Association (AOA) accreditation △ Commission on Accreditation of Rehabilitation Facilities (CARF) accreditation	Control	Service	Staffed Beds	Admissions	Census	Outpatient Visits	Births	Total	Payroll	Personnel

ALAMOGORDO—Otero County

☒ **GERALD CHAMPION REGIONAL MEDICAL CENTER**, 2669 North Scenic Drive, Zip 88310–8799; tel. 505/439–6100 **A**1 9 10 20 **F**2 11 12 21 22 26 27 28 33 46 48 52 55 59 62 63 64 66 81 82 84 85 88 92 93 94 106 108 109 **P**2 5 **S** Quorum Health Resources, Plano, TX
Primary Contact: Carl W. Mantey, Chief Executive Officer
CMO: Michael Hickey, M.D., Medical Director
Web address: www.gcrmc.org
— 23 10 99 4183 51 78487 741 53103 19729 506

ALBUQUERQUE—Bernalillo County

□ **ALBUQUERQUE REGIONAL MEDICAL CENTER**, 601 Martin Luther King Jr. Avenue N.E., Zip 87102–3670, Mailing Address: P.O. Box 25555, Zip 87125–0555; tel. 505/727–8000, (Nonreporting) **A**1 2 9 10 **S** Ardent Health Services, Nashville, TN
Primary Contact: Michael F. O'Keefe, FACHE, Chief Executive Officer
Web address: www.albuquerquehospital.com
— 33 10 128 — — — — — — —

★ **CARRIE TINGLEY HOSPITAL**, 1127 University Boulevard N.E., Zip 87102–1715; tel. 505/272–5200, (Nonreporting) **A**3 5 9 10 **S** University of New Mexico, Albuquerque, NM
Primary Contact: Barbara Ohm, Executive Director
CFO: Nancy Brandt, Chief Financial Officer
CMO: Frederick C. Sherman, M.D., Medical Director
CIO: Ron Margolis, Chief Information Officer
CHR: Jim Pendergast, Human Resources Administrator
Web address: www.hospitals.unm.edu/cth/index.shtml
— 12 57 30 — — — — — — —

DESERT HILLS HOSPITAL, 5310 Sequoia Road N.W., Zip 87120–1249; tel. 505/836–7330 **F**21 28 71 72 77 78 **P**5
Primary Contact: Carol Bickelman, President and Chief Executive Officer
Web address: www.yfcs.com
— 33 22 88 542 79 14379 — 9421 5467 5447500

☒ **HEALTHSOUTH REHABILITATION CENTER**, 7000 Jefferson N.E., Zip 87109–4357; tel. 505/344–9478, (Nonreporting) **A**1 10 **S** HEALTHSOUTH Corporation, Birmingham, AL
Primary Contact: Sylvia K. Kelly, Administrator
CFO: Phil Lowe, Controller
CMO: Altaf Ahmed, M.D., Medical Director
Web address: www.healthsouth.com
— 33 46 60 — — — — — — —

☒ **HEART HOSPITAL OF NEW MEXICO**, 504 Elm Street, Zip 87102; tel. 505/724–2000 **A**1 9 10 **F**14 15 17 19 21 22 28 29 33 37 39 45 46 47 48 49 52 53 58 63 64 65 66 81 82 88 108 **S** MedCath, Inc., Charlotte, NC
Primary Contact: Phil Shaw, Interim President and Chief Executive Officer
COO: Terry Odom, Vice President Clinical Services
CMO: Harvey White, Medical Director
CHR: Michelle Garcia, Human Resources
Web address: www.hearthospitalnm.com
— 33 10 55 3916 40 — 0 50025 15680 —

□ **INTEGRATED SPECIALTY HOSPITAL OF ALBUQUERQUE**, 235 Elm Street N.E., Zip 87102; tel. 505/842–5550, (Nonreporting) **A**1 10
Primary Contact: Kathi Gleim, Chief Executive Officer
— 33 49 25 — — — — — — —

□ **KINDRED HOSPITAL – ALBUQUERQUE**, 700 High Street N.E., Zip 87102–2565; tel. 505/242–4444 **A**1 10 **F**21 37 38 58 60 94 110 **P**8 **S** Kindred Healthcare, Louisville, KY
Primary Contact: Laura S. Wills, Chief Executive Officer
Web address: www.kindredhealthcare.com
— 33 80 61 333 27 0 0 13070 4980 —

□ **LOVELACE MEDICAL CENTER**, 5400 Gibson Boulevard S.E., Zip 87108–4763; tel. 505/262–7000, (Total facility includes 16 beds in nursing home–type unit) (Nonreporting) **A**1 2 3 5 9 10 **S** Ardent Health Services, Nashville, TN
Primary Contact: Richard Rolston, M.D., President and Chief Executive Officer
Web address: www.lovelace.com
— 33 10 212 — — — — — — —

□ **MEMORIAL PSYCHIATRIC HOSPITAL**, 806 Central Avenue S.E., Zip 87102–3671, Mailing Address: P.O. Box 26568, Zip 87125–6568; tel. 505/247–0220, (Nonreporting) **A**1 9 10 **S** Youth and Family Centered Services, Austin, TX
Primary Contact: Kay DeLage, Chief Executive Officer
Web address: www.yfcs.com
— 33 22 58 — — — — — — —

☒ **PRESBYTERIAN HOSPITAL**, 1100 Central Avenue S.E., Zip 87106–4934, Mailing Address: P.O. Box 26666, Zip 87125–6666; tel. 505/841–1234 **A**1 2 5 9 10 **F**2 6 9 11 14 15 16 17 18 19 20 21 22 23 26 27 28 33 46 49 53 55 56 57 58 59 60 61 62 63 64 65 66 67 69 70 81 82 84 85 87 88 92 94 95 96 102 105 107 108 109 110 **P**6 **S** Presbyterian Healthcare Services, Albuquerque, NM
Primary Contact: Mark W. Reifsteck, Senior Vice President and Chief Operating Officer
COO: Mark W. Reifsteck, Senior Vice President and Chief Operating Officer
CFO: Paul Briggs, Senior Vice President and Chief Financial Officer
CMO: Eddie Benge, M.D., Vice President Medical Staff Affairs
CIO: Bob Skinner, Chief Information Officer
CHR: Renee Reimer, Vice President Human Resources
Web address: www.phs.org
— 23 10 349 25361 349 1105794 5178 421691 220969 3539

NM

Many Facility Codes have changed. Please refer to the AHA Guide Code Chart. © 2005 AHA Guide

Hospital, Address, Telephone, Approval, Facility, and Physician Codes, Health Care System	Classi-fication Codes		Utilization Data					Expense (thousands) of dollars		
★ American Hospital Association (AHA) membership □ Joint Commission on Accreditation of Healthcare Organizations (JCAHO) accreditation ○ American Osteopathic Association (AOA) accreditation △ Commission on Accreditation of Rehabilitation Facilities (CARF) accreditation	Control	Service	Staffed Beds	Admissions	Census	Outpatient Visits	Births	Total	Payroll	Personnel
⊠ **PRESBYTERIAN KASEMAN HOSPITAL**, 8300 Constitution Avenue N.E., Zip 87110–7624, Mailing Address: P.O. Box 26666, Zip 87125–6666; tel. 505/291–2000 **A**1 9 10 **F**2 4 12 21 22 26 27 28 33 36 37 38 39 53 58 62 63 69 71 72 73 74 75 77 78 79 81 82 88 92 93 94 98 108 110 **S** Presbyterian Healthcare Services, Albuquerque, NM Primary Contact: Robert A. Garcia, Administrative Director COO: Mark W. Reifsteck, Senior Vice President and Chief Operating Officer CFO: Liz Alhand, Senior Vice President Finance CMO: Eddie Benge, M.D., Vice President Medical Staff Affairs CIO: Bob Skinner, Chief Information Officer CHR: Renee Reimer, Vice President Human Resources Web address: www.phs.org	23	10	115	3971	70	115461	0	59238	27149	673
★ **PUBLIC HEALTH SERVICE INDIAN HOSPITAL**, 801 Vassar Drive N.E., Zip 87106–2799; tel. 505/248–4000, (Nonreporting) **A**10 **S** U. S. Indian Health Service, Rockville, MD Primary Contact: Maria Rickert, Chief Executive Officer CFO: Kurt Riley, Administrative Officer CIO: Kathy Lewis, Director Information Management Services	47	10	28	—	—	—	—	—	—	—
△ **REHABILITATION HOSPITAL OF NEW MEXICO**, 505 Elm Street N.E., Zip 87102–2500, Mailing Address: P.O. Box 25555, Zip 87125–5555; tel. 505/727–4700, (Total facility includes 17 beds in nursing home–type unit) (Nonreporting) **A**7 10 **S** Ardent Health Services, Nashville, TN Primary Contact: Dale Olson, Chief Executive Officer Web address: www.sjhs.org	21	46	62	—	—	—	—	—	—	—
⊠ **UNIVERSITY HOSPITAL**, 2211 Lomas Boulevard N.E., Zip 87106–2745; tel. 505/272–2111, (Includes MENTAL HEALTH CENTER, 2600 Marble N.E., Zip 87131–2600; tel. 505/272–2800; UNIVERSITY OF NEW MEXICO CHILDREN'S PSYCHIATRIC HOSPITAL, 1001 Yale Boulevard N.E., Zip 87131–3830; tel. 505/272–2890) **A**1 2 3 5 8 9 10 12 13 **F**2 7 9 11 12 15 16 17 18 19 21 22 26 27 28 29 30 31 33 34 35 36 37 38 39 40 44 46 47 48 49 50 52 53 55 56 57 58 59 60 61 62 63 64 65 66 67 69 70 73 74 79 80 81 82 83 84 85 86 87 88 89 90 93 94 95 96 98 101 106 108 109 110 **P**5 **S** University of New Mexico, Albuquerque, NM Primary Contact: Stephen W. McKernan, Chief Executive Officer CFO: Nancy Brandt, Chief Financial Officer CIO: Ron Margolis, Chief Information Officer CHR: Jim Pendergast, Human Resources Administrator Web address: www.unm.edu	12	10	292	18890	291	413946	3555	269251	139370	4156
⊠ △ **VETERANS AFFAIRS MEDICAL CENTER**, 1501 San Pedro S.E., Zip 87108–5138; tel. 505/265–1711, (Total facility includes 36 beds in nursing home–type unit) **A**1 2 3 5 7 8 **F**3 4 9 10 12 14 15 17 19 21 22 23 25 27 29 31 32 33 35 37 38 39 40 44 45 46 47 48 49 50 51 52 53 55 57 58 60 61 62 63 64 65 66 68 69 70 71 73 74 75 76 77 78 81 82 83 84 85 86 87 88 94 96 106 108 109 110 **S** Department of Veterans Affairs, Washington, DC Primary Contact: Mary A. Dowling, Director CFO: Michael McNeill, Chief Fiscal Service CMO: David Groeber, M.D., Chief of Staff CIO: John Hena, Chief Information Management Web address: www.va.gov/sta/guide/home.asp	45	10	181	6730	143	510637	0	227801	100645	1705
WEST MESA MEDICAL CENTER, 10501 Golf Course Road N.W., Zip 87114–5000, Mailing Address: P.O. Box 25555, Zip 87125–0555; tel. 505/727–2000, (Total facility includes 22 beds in nursing home–type unit) (Nonreporting) **A**9 10 **S** Ardent Health Services, Nashville, TN Primary Contact: Angela M. Marchi, Chief Executive Officer Web address: www.lovelacesandiahealthsystem.com	21	10	48	—	—	—	—	—	—	—
WOMEN'S HOSPITAL, (Formerly Northeast Heights Medical Center), 4701 Montgomery Boulevard N.E., Zip 87109–1251, Mailing Address: P.O. Box 25555, Zip 87125–0555; tel. 505/727–7800, (Nonreporting) **A**9 10 **S** Ardent Health Services, Nashville, TN Primary Contact: Sheri Milone, Chief Executive Officer and Administrator Web address: www.lovelacesandia.com	21	10	84	—	—	—	—	—	—	—
ARTESIA—Eddy County										
★ **ARTESIA GENERAL HOSPITAL**, 702 North 13th Street, Zip 88210–1199; tel. 505/748–3333 **A**9 10 20 **F**2 9 21 22 28 29 32 33 46 48 52 58 63 66 81 88 93 94 97 **P**6 Primary Contact: Claude E. Camp, III, Chief Executive Officer CMO: Joe Salgado, Chief of Staff CIO: David Neal, Information Systems Coordinator Web address: www.artesiageneral.com	23	10	20	728	6	18607	4	11311	4440	143
CARLSBAD—Eddy County										
⊠ **CARLSBAD MEDICAL CENTER**, 2430 West Pierce Street, Zip 88220–3597; tel. 505/887–4100 **A**1 9 10 19 20 **F**12 15 17 21 22 26 27 28 29 32 33 35 40 46 47 48 52 58 59 60 61 63 65 66 68 69 73 81 82 84 87 88 92 94 **S** Triad Hospitals, Inc., Plano, TX Primary Contact: Fred Woody, Chief Executive Officer COO: Bradley McGrath, Chief Operating Officer CFO: Janet Carbary, Chief Financial Officer CIO: Kenneth Kemp, Director Information Systems Web address: www.triadhospitals.com	33	10	127	3763	37	69703	596	37375	14567	467

NM

Hospital, Address, Telephone, Approval, Facility, and Physician Codes, Health Care System	Classi-fication Codes		Utilization Data					Expense (thousands) of dollars		
★ American Hospital Association (AHA) membership □ Joint Commission on Accreditation of Healthcare Organizations (JCAHO) accreditation ○ American Osteopathic Association (AOA) accreditation △ Commission on Accreditation of Rehabilitation Facilities (CARF) accreditation	Control	Service	Staffed Beds	Admissions	Census	Outpatient Visits	Births	Total	Payroll	Personnel

CLAYTON—Union County

★ **UNION COUNTY GENERAL HOSPITAL**, 301 Harding Street, Zip 88415–3321, Mailing Address: P.O. Box 489, Zip 88415–0489; tel. 505/374–2585 **A**9 10 18 **F**9 11 12 14 21 23 28 29 33 39 46 48 51 52 55 59 62 63 64 66 69 70 81 85 88 96 97 107 **S** Brim Healthcare, Inc., Brentwood, TN
Primary Contact: Stephen J. Campbell, Administrator
CFO: Texas Davis, Controller
CHR: Jill Swagerty, Director Human Resources
Web address: www.unioncountygeneral.com

| 23 | 10 | 21 | 479 | 4 | 10061 | 33 | 5506 | 2312 | 61 |

CLOVIS—Curry County

✉ **PLAINS REGIONAL MEDICAL CENTER**, 2100 Martin Luther King, Jr. Boulevard, Zip 88101–9412, Mailing Address: P.O. Box 1688, Zip 88101–1688; tel. 505/769–2141 **A**1 9 10 20 **F**2 9 11 12 21 22 23 26 27 28 29 33 36 37 39 40 41 44 46 49 50 51 52 53 54 55 58 59 60 61 62 63 64 66 69 70 79 80 81 82 84 85 87 88 94 96 97 106 107 108 109 110 **P**6 **S** Presbyterian Healthcare Services, Albuquerque, NM
Primary Contact: Brian S. Bentley, Administrator
CFO: Wesley White, Chief Financial Officer
Web address: www.phs.org

| 23 | 10 | 106 | 5506 | 53 | 165940 | 1345 | 58966 | 24647 | 569 |

CROWNPOINT—McKinley County

★ **U. S. PUBLIC HEALTH SERVICE INDIAN HOSPITAL**, Mailing Address: P.O. Box 358, Zip 87313–0358; tel. 505/786–5291 **A**10 **F**2 6 11 12 21 24 26 27 28 29 31 32 33 35 39 41 45 46 47 48 51 52 53 58 59 66 69 70 74 77 94 96 97 98 106 107 109 110 **P**6 **S** U. S. Indian Health Service, Rockville, MD
Primary Contact: Anita Muneta, Chief Executive Officer
COO: Mary Ann O'Neal, Administrative Officer
CFO: Fawn Tsosie, Finance Manager
CMO: Alexander Vujan, M.D., Acting Clinical Director
CIO: Anita Muneta, Chief Executive Officer
CHR: Victoria Pablo, Human Resource Specialist
Web address: www.ihs.gov

| 47 | 10 | 25 | 974 | 8 | 79675 | 86 | 23522 | 13966 | 275 |

DEMING—Luna County

★ **MIMBRES MEMORIAL HOSPITAL**, 900 West Ash Street, Zip 88030–4098, Mailing Address: P.O. Box 710, Zip 88031–0710; tel. 505/546–2761, (Total facility includes 70 beds in nursing home–type unit) (Nonreporting) **A**9 10 20 **S** Community Health Systems, Inc., Brentwood, TN
Primary Contact: Derrick Yu, Chief Executive Officer
CFO: Remer DeLoach, Chief Financial Officer
CHR: Kevin Driver, Human Resource Director
Web address: www.mimbresmemorial.com

| 33 | 10 | 119 | — | — | — | — | — | — | — |

ESPANOLA—Rio Arriba County

✉ **ESPANOLA HOSPITAL**, 1010 Spruce Street, Zip 87532–2746; tel. 505/753–7111 **A**1 9 10 20 **F**6 9 11 12 21 22 26 27 28 29 33 46 47 48 51 52 53 55 58 59 60 62 63 65 66 69 70 81 82 84 85 88 93 94 96 106 107 108 109 110 **P**3 8 **S** Presbyterian Healthcare Services, Albuquerque, NM
Primary Contact: Marcella A. Romero, Administrator
Web address: www.phs.org

| 23 | 10 | 80 | 2469 | 21 | 89456 | 341 | 34654 | 16960 | 330 |

FARMINGTON—San Juan County

✉ **SAN JUAN REGIONAL MEDICAL CENTER**, 801 West Maple Street, Zip 87401–5698; tel. 505/325–5011, (Includes SAN JUAN REGIONAL MEDICAL CENTER REHABILITATION HOSPITAL, 525 South Schwartz, Zip 87401; tel. 505/327–3422) **A**1 2 5 9 10 19 20 **F**6 9 11 12 21 22 24 26 27 28 29 33 34 45 47 48 49 52 53 55 57 58 59 61 62 63 66 69 70 71 72 73 75 79 81 82 84 85 87 88 94 106 107 108 110 **P**5
Primary Contact: Steve Altmiller, President and Chief Executive Officer
CFO: Mike Phillips, Chief Strategy Officer
CIO: Jim Holmes, Chief Information Officer
CHR: Elizabeth Childs, Human Resources Manager
Web address: www.sanjuanregional.com

| 23 | 10 | 168 | 9450 | 107 | 171105 | 1315 | 128666 | 57944 | 1193 |

GALLUP—McKinley County

✉ **GALLUP INDIAN MEDICAL CENTER**, 516 East Nizhoni Boulevard, Zip 87301–5748, Mailing Address: P.O. Box 1337, Zip 87305–1337; tel. 505/722–1000, (Nonreporting) **A**1 9 10 **S** U. S. Indian Health Service, Rockville, MD
Primary Contact: Floyd Thompson, Chief Executive Officer
COO: Bennie C. Yazzie, Administratrative Officer
CFO: Earleen Yazzie, Financial Manager
CIO: Harriett Beyuka, Management Informatom Systems Manager
CHR: Joan Davis, Human Resources Director
Web address: www.ihs.gov

| 47 | 10 | 99 | — | — | — | — | — | — | — |

✉ **REHOBOTH MCKINLEY CHRISTIAN HOSPITAL**, 1901 Red Rock Drive, Zip 87301–1901; tel. 505/863–7000 **A**1 5 9 10 20 **F**2 3 4 9 11 12 22 23 24 26 27 28 29 31 33 36 38 39 42 44 46 48 49 51 53 55 58 59 60 61 62 63 64 65 66 69 70 72 73 74 75 77 81 84 88 93 94 96 106 108 109 **P**5 6 8
Primary Contact: David J. Baltzer, President
CFO: Robert C. Tyk, Vice President Finance
CMO: Mary L. Poel, M.D., Vice President Medical Affairs
Web address: www.rmch.org

| 23 | 10 | 89 | 3788 | 48 | 245500 | 529 | 62053 | 30472 | 600 |

NM

Many Facility Codes have changed. Please refer to the AHA Guide Code Chart.   © 2005 AHA Guide

Hospital, Address, Telephone, Approval, Facility, and Physician Codes, Health Care System	Classi-fication Codes		Utilization Data					Expense (thousands) of dollars		
★ American Hospital Association (AHA) membership □ Joint Commission on Accreditation of Healthcare Organizations (JCAHO) accreditation ○ American Osteopathic Association (AOA) accreditation △ Commission on Accreditation of Rehabilitation Facilities (CARF) accreditation	Control	Service	Staffed Beds	Admissions	Census	Outpatient Visits	Births	Total	Payroll	Personnel

GRANTS—Cibola County

✠ **CIBOLA GENERAL HOSPITAL**, 1016 Roosevelt Avenue, Zip 87020–2104; tel. 505/287–4446 **A**1 9 10 20 **F**2 9 11 12 21 22 29 32 33 46 48 52 53 55 58 59 63 64 69 81 84 88 93 94 95 108 **P**8 **S** Quorum Health Resources, Plano, TX Primary Contact: Vincent Ashley, Chief Executive Officer CFO: Jeff Rimel, Chief Financial Officer CIO: Norman Wilder, Director Information Services Web address: www.cibolahospital.com	13	10	25	984	7	20071	252	12623	5019	127

HOBBS—Lea County

✠ **LEA REGIONAL MEDICAL CENTER**, 5419 North Lovington Highway, Zip 88240–9125, Mailing Address: P.O. Box 3000, Zip 88240–3000; tel. 505/492–5000 **A**1 9 10 19 20 **F**2 11 12 14 17 21 26 28 29 33 44 46 48 52 55 59 60 62 63 66 68 69 71 73 75 77 81 84 88 92 94 95 108 109 **S** Triad Hospitals, Inc., Plano, TX Primary Contact: Larry C. Bozeman, Chief Executive Officer CFO: Julie Soekoro, Chief Financial Officer CMO: Truett Maddox, M.D., Chief of Staff CIO: Tom Motejzik, Director of Information Services CHR: Linda Wallace, Director of Human Resources Web address: www.learegionalmedicalcenter.com	33	10	214	5397	51	60298	867	44089	17604	463

LAS CRUCES—Dona Ana County

✠ **MEMORIAL MEDICAL CENTER**, 2450 South Telshor Boulevard, Zip 88011–5076; tel. 505/522–8641, (Nonreporting) **A**1 3 5 9 10 20 **S** LifePoint Hospitals, Inc., Brentwood, TN Primary Contact: Paul F. Herzog, Chief Executive Officer COO: David B. Darden, Chief Executive Officer CFO: Phillip Rivera, Chief Financial Officer CMO: Bruce San Filippo, M.D., Vice President and Chief Medical Officer CHR: Laura Pierce, Human Resources Director Web address: www.mmclc.org	23	10	240	—	—	—	—	—	—	—
□ **MESILLA VALLEY HOSPITAL**, 3751 Del Rey Boulevard, Zip 88012–8526; tel. 505/382–3500 **A**1 9 10 **F**3 21 27 28 29 31 37 39 47 71 72 73 74 75 76 77 94 96 **S** Psychiatric Solutions, Franklin, TN Primary Contact: Robert Mansfield, Chief Executive Officer Web address: www.mesillavalleyhospital.com	33	22	125	1375	27	0	0	12612	7154	216
✠ **MOUNTAINVIEW REGIONAL MEDICAL CENTER**, 4311 East Lohman Avenue, Zip 88011; tel. 505/556–7600 **A**1 9 10 **F**2 11 12 14 15 17 19 21 22 26 27 28 29 33 37 38 45 46 47 48 49 52 53 55 57 58 59 60 62 63 64 65 68 69 75 81 82 84 85 87 88 94 95 108 109 110 **P**8 **S** Triad Hospitals, Inc., Plano, TX Primary Contact: John L. Hummer, Chief Executive Officer COO: Edmundo Castaneda, Chief Operating Officer Web address: www.mountainviewregional.com	33	10	163	5890	69	57969	909	61006	22221	503

LAS VEGAS—San Miguel County

□ **ALTA VISTA REGIONAL HOSPITAL**, 104 Legion Drive, Zip 87701, Mailing Address: P.O. Box 248, Zip 87701; tel. 505/426–3500 **A**1 9 10 20 **F**2 9 11 12 15 21 26 27 28 29 33 46 48 52 55 57 59 62 63 64 65 69 81 82 84 85 87 88 93 97 108 109 **P**5 6 **S** Community Health Systems, Inc., Brentwood, TN Primary Contact: Benjamin J. Everett, Chief Executive Officer Web address: www.altavistaregionalhospital.com	33	10	54	2000	17	33936	335	27081	10399	—
□ **LAS VEGAS MEDICAL CENTER**, 3695 Hot Springs Boulevard, Zip 87701–9575; tel. 505/454–2100, (Total facility includes 176 beds in nursing home–type unit) **A**1 9 10 **F**21 26 27 28 29 31 44 60 66 69 71 72 73 74 75 76 77 92 94 108 **P**6 Primary Contact: Brian A. Brozost, M.D., Executive Director and Administrator Web address: www.health.state.nm.us	12	22	382	888	295	800	0	40594	—	992

LOS ALAMOS—Los Alamos County

✠ **LOS ALAMOS MEDICAL CENTER**, 3917 West Road, Zip 87544–2293; tel. 505/662–4201 **A**1 9 10 20 **F**2 26 33 37 40 46 48 52 55 58 59 61 62 63 64 70 81 82 84 87 88 93 94 95 97 107 108 **P**8 **S** LifePoint Hospitals, Inc., Brentwood, TN Primary Contact: Gary A. Nicholds, FACHE, Chief Executive Officer CFO: Heather Teter, Chief Financial Officer CMO: Mary Ellen Csanadi, M.D., Chief of Staff CIO: Steven Santistevan, Director Information Systems CHR: Jacqueline Carroll, Director Human Resources Web address: www.losalamosmedicalcenter.com	33	10	36	1547	13	72228	332	31821	11357	258

LOVINGTON—Lea County

★ **NOR–LEA GENERAL HOSPITAL**, 1600 North Main Avenue, Zip 88260–2871; tel. 505/396–6611 **A**9 10 18 **F**2 7 9 12 21 22 24 26 27 28 29 33 36 39 46 48 51 52 58 63 76 81 84 88 94 97 109 **P**6 **S** Covenant Health System, Lubbock, TX Primary Contact: David B. Shaw, Chief Executive Officer and Administrator CFO: Allyson Roberts, CPA, Chief Financial Officer CMO: Ronald Hopkins, D.O., Chief of Staff Web address: www.nlgh.org	16	10	12	492	4	98508	0	13163	5800	166

NM

Hospital, Address, Telephone, Approval, Facility, and Physician Codes, Health Care System	Classi-fication Codes		Utilization Data					Expense (thousands) of dollars		
★ American Hospital Association (AHA) membership □ Joint Commission on Accreditation of Healthcare Organizations (JCAHO) accreditation ○ American Osteopathic Association (AOA) accreditation △ Commission on Accreditation of Rehabilitation Facilities (CARF) accreditation	Control	Service	Staffed Beds	Admissions	Census	Outpatient Visits	Births	Total	Payroll	Personnel

MESCALERO—Otero County

⊞ U. S. PUBLIC HEALTH SERVICE INDIAN HOSPITAL, Mailing Address: Box 210, Zip 88340–0210; tel. 505/671–4441, (Nonreporting) **A**1 9 10 **S** U. S. Indian Health Service, Rockville, MD
Primary Contact: Matthew Anderson, Administrator
CFO: Greg Powers, Administrative Officer
CIO: Raymond Little, Site Manager

| | 44 | 10 | 11 | — | — | — | — | — | — | — |

PORTALES—Roosevelt County

ROOSEVELT GENERAL HOSPITAL, 14121 U.S. Highway 70, Zip 88130, Mailing Address: P.O. Box 868, Zip 88130–0868; tel. 505/359–1800 **A**9 10 **F**2 9 21 22 27 28 33 46 51 58 63 66 69 81 82 84 88 94 95 106 **S** Covenant Health System, Lubbock, TX
Primary Contact: James P. D'Agostino, Chief Executive Officer

| | 16 | 10 | 22 | 821 | 7 | 25458 | 0 | 11788 | 4264 | 132 |

RATON—Colfax County

★ MINERS' COLFAX MEDICAL CENTER, 200 Hospital Drive, Zip 87740–2099; tel. 505/445–3661, (Includes MINERS' HOSPITAL OF NEW MEXICO), (Total facility includes 47 beds in nursing home–type unit) **A**9 10 20 **F**2 5 9 11 12 23 27 29 33 41 46 48 55 59 61 63 64 65 81 82 88 92 94 96 97 108
Primary Contact: Donald R. Holl, Chief Executive Officer
CFO: Gary Gabriele, Director Budget and Finance
CIO: Richard Laner, Jr, Information Systems Manager
Web address: www.minershosp.com

| | 12 | 10 | 80 | 1303 | 36 | 25227 | 131 | 16846 | 6793 | 225 |

ROSWELL—Chaves County

□ EASTERN NEW MEXICO MEDICAL CENTER, 405 West Country Club Road, Zip 88201–9981; tel. 505/622–8170, (Nonreporting) **A**1 3 5 9 10 19 20 **S** Community Health Systems, Inc., Brentwood, TN
Primary Contact: Richard H. Robinson, Chief Executive Officer
Web address: www.enmmc.com

| | 13 | 10 | 149 | — | — | — | — | — | — | — |

□ NEW MEXICO REHABILITATION CENTER, 31 Gail Harris Avenue, Zip 88203–8134; tel. 505/347–3400, (Includes PECOS VALLEY LODGE) **A**1 10 **F**3 4 26 27 28 68 69
Primary Contact: Laurie Brannigan, Administrator

| | 12 | 46 | 41 | 606 | 29 | — | 0 | 4817 | 3490 | 117 |

RUIDOSO—Lincoln County

⊞ LINCOLN COUNTY MEDICAL CENTER, 211 Sudderth Drive, Zip 88345–6043, Mailing Address: P.O. Box 8000, Zip 88345–8000; tel. 505/257–7381 **A**1 9 10 20 **F**1 6 9 11 12 21 26 27 28 29 32 33 41 44 46 48 52 55 59 60 61 63 69 76 79 81 84 88 96 **P**5 6 **S** Presbyterian Healthcare Services, Albuquerque, NM
Primary Contact: James P. Gibson, Administrator
CFO: Dudley McCauley, Chief Financial Officer
CMO: Dennis Worthington, M.D., Chief of Staff
Web address: www.phs.org

| | 23 | 10 | 25 | 1075 | 7 | 59371 | 303 | 20783 | 9043 | 297 |

SAN FIDEL—Cibola County

⊞ ACOMA–CANONCITO–LAGUNA HOSPITAL, Mailing Address: P.O. Box 130, Zip 87049–0130; tel. 505/552–5300 **A**1 10 **F**4 6 12 21 24 26 28 31 32 33 39 52 58 69 70 72 77 88 94 107 **P**1 **S** U. S. Indian Health Service, Rockville, MD
Primary Contact: R. C. Begay, Chief Executive Officer

| | 47 | 10 | 14 | 392 | 5 | 57890 | 0 | — | — | 215 |

SANTA FE—Santa Fe County

⊞ PHS SANTA FE INDIAN HOSPITAL, 1700 Cerrillos Road, Zip 87505–3554; tel. 505/988–9821 **A**1 10 **F**2 4 11 21 24 26 27 28 29 32 37 39 42 46 48 52 53 58 59 63 65 69 70 72 73 77 78 94 98 106 107 109 **S** U. S. Indian Health Service, Rockville, MD
Primary Contact: Richard L. Zephier, Ph.D., Chief Executive Officer
COO: Leonard Montoya, Administrative Officer
CMO: Bret Smoker, Clinical Director
CIO: Vernita Jones, Site Manager

| | 44 | 10 | 39 | 960 | 8 | — | — | — | — | — |

⊞ △ ST. VINCENT HOSPITAL, 455 St. Michael's Drive, Zip 87505–7663, Mailing Address: P.O. Box 2107, Zip 87504–2107; tel. 505/983–3361, (Nonreporting) **A**1 2 3 5 7 9 10 20
Primary Contact: J. Alex Valdez, JD, Chief Executive Officer
COO: Gary Williams, Chief Operating Officer and Chief Nursing Officer
CFO: Rick Doxtator, Chief Financial Officer
CMO: Gary Frank, M.D., Chief Medical Officer
CIO: Don Butterfield, Marketing and Public Relations Specialist
Web address: www.stvin.org

| | 23 | 10 | 164 | — | — | — | — | — | — | — |

SANTA ROSA—Guadalupe County

GUADALUPE COUNTY HOSPITAL, 535 Lake Drive, Zip 88435–2542, Mailing Address: P.O. Box 500, Zip 88435–0500; tel. 505/472–3246 **A**9 10 20 **F**26 27 28 33 46 52 53 58 60 64 65 66 81 82 88 **P**5
Primary Contact: Christina Campos, Administrator

| | 13 | 10 | 10 | 228 | 1 | 3477 | 0 | 2796 | 736 | 29 |

SANTA TERESA—Dona Ana County

□ PEAK BEHAVIORAL HEALTH SERVICES, (Formerly Peak Psychiactric Hospital), 5065 McNut Road, Zip 88008; tel. 505/589–3000, (Nonreporting) **A**1 10 **S** Psychiatric Solutions, Franklin, TN
Primary Contact: James Baca, Chief Executive Officer

| | 33 | 22 | 36 | — | — | — | — | — | — | — |

NM

Hospital, Address, Telephone, Approval, Facility, and Physician Codes, Health Care System	Classi-fication Codes		Utilization Data					Expense (thousands) of dollars		
★ American Hospital Association (AHA) membership □ Joint Commission on Accreditation of Healthcare Organizations (JCAHO) accreditation ○ American Osteopathic Association (AOA) accreditation △ Commission on Accreditation of Rehabilitation Facilities (CARF) accreditation	Control	Service	Staffed Beds	Admissions	Census	Outpatient Visits	Births	Total	Payroll	Personnel

SHIPROCK—San Juan County

☒ **NORTHERN NAVAJO MEDICAL CENTER**, Mailing Address: P.O. Box 160, Zip 87420–0160; tel. 505/368–6001, (Nonreporting) **A**1 10 **S** U. S. Indian Health Service, Rockville, MD
Primary Contact: Carla Baha–Alchesay, Chief Executive Officer
CFO: Josie Atcitty, Finance Officer
CMO: George Baacke, M.D., Clinical Director
CIO: Roland Chapman, Chief Information Officer
CHR: Cecelia A. Anderson, Clinical Director
Web address: www.home.nnmc.ihs.gov

| 44 | 10 | 64 | — | — | — | — | — | — | — |

SILVER CITY—Grant County

☒ **GILA REGIONAL MEDICAL CENTER**, 1313 East 32nd Street, Zip 88061; tel. 505/538–4000 **A**1 9 10 20 **F**2 6 9 11 12 22 23 26 27 28 29 33 34 36 41 48 51 52 55 57 58 59 60 61 62 63 64 66 69 71 73 75 76 81 82 84 85 88 93 94 **P**5 **S** Quorum Health Resources, Plano, TX
Primary Contact: John Rossfeld, Chief Executive Officer
CFO: Clifford Lee Olsson, Chief Financial Officer
CMO: Jean Remillard, M.D., Chief Medical Officer
CIO: Edie Steed, Chief Information Officer
CHR: Barbara Barela, Human Resources Director
Web address: www.grmc.org

| 13 | 10 | 68 | 3695 | 33 | 86656 | 431 | 45516 | 19379 | 507 |

SOCORRO—Socorro County

☒ **SOCORRO GENERAL HOSPITAL**, 1202 Highway 60 West, Zip 87801, Mailing Address: P.O. Box 1009, Zip 87801–1009; tel. 505/835–1140, (Nonreporting) **A**1 9 10 18 20 **S** Presbyterian Healthcare Services, Albuquerque, NM
Primary Contact: Hoyt Skabelund, Administrator
CFO: Denise Irion, Controller
Web address: www.phs.org/facilities/facsocorro.htm

| 23 | 10 | 15 | — | — | — | — | — | — | — |

TAOS—Taos County

★ **HOLY CROSS HOSPITAL**, 1397 Weimer Road, Zip 87571–6284, Mailing Address: P.O. Box DD, Zip 87571–6284; tel. 505/758–8883 **A**5 9 10 20 **F**2 9 11 12 15 21 22 27 29 33 40 46 47 48 52 55 58 59 62 63 64 65 66 69 81 82 84 85 88 96 106 108 110 **P**8 **S** Quorum Health Resources, Plano, TX
Primary Contact: Warren K. Spellman, Chief Executive Officer
CFO: Richard Eisenring, Chief Financial Officer
CMO: Ellen Warren, M.D., Chief of Staff
CIO: Rosemary Hammer, Information System Director
CHR: James Arkens, Human Resource Director
Web address: www.taoshospital.org

| 23 | 10 | 49 | 2572 | 24 | 46809 | 249 | 32998 | 13066 | 328 |

TRUTH OR CONSEQUENCES—Sierra County

☒ **SIERRA VISTA HOSPITAL**, 800 East Ninth Avenue, Zip 87901–1961; tel. 505/894–2111 **A**1 9 10 18 **F**4 9 21 22 27 29 31 33 52 63 69 73 77 94 97
Primary Contact: James J. Cliborne, Jr, Chief Executive Officer and Administrator
COO: Milton Wilhite, Chief Operating Officer
CMO: James F. Malcolmson, M.D., Chief of Staff
CIO: Dan Morrell, Information System Manager
CHR: Esmeralda Graham, Human Resources and People Services

| 15 | 10 | 25 | 375 | 4 | 23344 | — | 11282 | 4892 | 107 |

TUCUMCARI—Quay County

★ **DR. DAN C. TRIGG MEMORIAL HOSPITAL**, 301 East Miel De Luna Avenue, Zip 88401–3810, Mailing Address: P.O. Box 608, Zip 88401–0608; tel. 505/461–0141 **A**9 10 18 **F**2 9 11 12 21 26 27 28 29 33 34 48 51 53 59 63 68 69 81 88 92 93 94 97 108 **P**5 **S** Presbyterian Healthcare Services, Albuquerque, NM
Primary Contact: Bo Beames, Administrator
CFO: Ruth Jones, Comptroller
CIO: Bob Skinner, Vice President Information Services
Web address: www.phs.org

| 23 | 10 | 25 | 797 | 7 | 23737 | 55 | 10683 | 3926 | 103 |

ZUNI—McKinley County

☒ **U. S. PUBLIC HEALTH SERVICE INDIAN HOSPITAL**, Route 301 North B. Street, Zip 87327, Mailing Address: P.O. Box 467, Zip 87327–0467; tel. 505/782–4431 **A**1 10 **F**11 12 26 27 28 32 33 37 48 53 59 66 74 75 76 77 88 **S** U. S. Indian Health Service, Rockville, MD
Primary Contact: Jean Othole, Service Unit Director
CMO: David Kessler, Clinical Director
CHR: Cynthia Tsalate, Human Resource Specialist

| 47 | 10 | 29 | 652 | 8 | 82278 | 115 | — | — | — |

NM

NEW YORK

Hospital, Address, Telephone, Approval, Facility, and Physician Codes, Health Care System	Classi- fication Codes		Utilization Data					Expense (thousands) of dollars		
★ American Hospital Association (AHA) membership □ Joint Commission on Accreditation of Healthcare Organizations (JCAHO) accreditation ○ American Osteopathic Association (AOA) accreditation △ Commission on Accreditation of Rehabilitation Facilities (CARF) accreditation	Control	Service	Staffed Beds	Admissions	Census	Outpatient Visits	Births	Total	Payroll	Personnel

ALBANY—Albany County

□ **ALBANY MEDICAL CENTER**, 43 New Scotland Avenue, Zip 12208–3478; tel. 518/262–3125, (Includes ALBANY MEDICAL CENTER SOUTH–CLINICAL CAMPUS, 25 Hackett Boulevard, Zip 12208–3499; tel. 518/242–1200; Timothy W. Duffy, General Director) **A**1 2 3 5 8 9 10 12 13 **F**5 9 10 11 12 14 15 16 17 18 19 20 21 22 23 24 26 27 28 29 33 34 37 39 44 46 47 49 50 52 53 55 56 57 58 59 60 61 62 63 64 65 66 67 68 69 70 71 72 73 75 76 77 78 79 80 81 82 83 84 85 86 87 88 89 90 94 101 102 104 105 108
Primary Contact: James J. Barba, President and Chief Executive Officer
Web address: www.amc.edu
| 23 | 10 | 584 | 25728 | 461 | 341016 | 2128 | 409290 | 143373 | 3711

□ **ALBANY MEMORIAL HOSPITAL**, 600 Northern Boulevard, Zip 12204–1083; tel. 518/471–3221, (Nonreporting) **A**1 5 6 9 10
Primary Contact: Norman E. Dascher, Jr, Chief Executive Officer
Web address: www.nehealth.com
| 23 | 10 | 165 | — | — | — | — | — | — | —

□ **CAPITAL DISTRICT PSYCHIATRIC CENTER**, 75 New Scotland Avenue, Zip 12208–3474; tel. 518/447–9611, (Nonreporting) **A**1 3 5 10 **S** New York State Office of Mental Health, Albany, NY
Primary Contact: Lou Campbell, Acting Executive Director
| 12 | 22 | 200 | | | | | | |

⊞ **ST. PETER'S HOSPITAL**, 315 South Manning Boulevard, Zip 12208–1789; tel. 518/525–1550, (Nonreporting) **A**1 2 3 5 9 10 12 **S** Catholic Health East, Newtown Square, PA
Primary Contact: Steven P. Boyle, President and Chief Executive Officer
CFO: Gary Lang, Chief Financial Officer
CMO: William F. Conway, M.D., Senior Vice President, Medical Staff Affairs
CIO: Jonathan Goldberg, Chief Information Officer
CHR: Tony Bongiovanni, Vice President Human Resources
Web address: www.stpetershealthcare.org
| 23 | 10 | 442 | — | — | — | — | — | — | —

⊞ △ **VETERANS AFFAIRS MEDICAL CENTER**, 113 Holland Avenue, Zip 12208–3473; tel. 518/626–5000 **A**1 2 3 5 7 8 9 **F**1 4 12 14 15 17 21 22 23 26 27 28 29 32 33 36 37 38 39 41 44 45 46 47 48 49 50 51 55 57 58 60 61 62 63 65 66 69 70 71 73 75 77 81 82 84 88 92 94 96 106 108 109 110 **S** Department of Veterans Affairs, Washington, DC
Primary Contact: Mary–Ellen Piche, Director
COO: Douglas Erickson, Associate Director
CFO: Royce Calhoun, Fiscal Officer
CMO: Barbara Bates, M.D., Chief Medical Oficer
CIO: Mike Mullahey, Operations Manager
CHR: Douglas Bender, Human Resource Manager
Web address: www.va.gov/sta/guide/home.asp
| 45 | 10 | 133 | 2970 | 56 | 254977 | — | 119817 | 63581 | 1065

ALEXANDRIA BAY—Jefferson County

RIVER HOSPITAL, 4 Fuller Street, Zip 13607; tel. 315/482–2511, (Total facility includes 27 beds in nursing home–type unit) (Nonreporting) **A**9 10 18
Primary Contact: Michael J. McLean, Chief Executive Officer
Web address: www.riverhospital.org
| 23 | 10 | 51 | — | — | — | — | — | — | —

AMITYVILLE—Suffolk County

□ **BRUNSWICK GENERAL HOSPITAL**, 366 Broadway, Zip 11701–9820; tel. 631/789–7000, (Includes BRUNSWICK HALL, 80 Louden Avenue, Zip 11701–2735; tel. 516/789–7100; BRUNSWICK PHYSICAL MEDICINE AND REHABILITATION HOSPITAL, 366 Broadway), (Total facility includes 94 beds in nursing home–type unit) (Nonreporting) **A**1 9 10
Primary Contact: Amar Jit Singh, M.D., Chief Executive Officer
Web address: www.brunswickhospital.com
| 33 | 10 | 275 | — | — | — | — | — | — | —

□ **SOUTH OAKS HOSPITAL**, 400 Sunrise Highway, Zip 11701–2508; tel. 631/264–4000, (Nonreporting) **A**1 10
Primary Contact: Robert E. Detor, Chief Executive Officer
Web address: www.southoaks.com
| 23 | 22 | 145 | — | — | — | — | — | — | —

AMSTERDAM—Montgomery County

★ ○ **AMSTERDAM MEMORIAL HOSPITAL**, 4988 State Highway 30, Zip 12010–1699; tel. 518/842–3100, (Total facility includes 160 beds in nursing home–type unit) **A**9 10 11 **F**1 2 9 12 21 22 25 26 27 28 29 41 42 44 48 50 52 58 60 63 66 68 69 70 81 82 84 85 88 92 93 94 95 96 98 107 108 109 110 **P**6
Primary Contact: Donald W. Massey, President and Chief Executive Officer
COO: Jennifer Gilston, Chief Operating Officer and Corporate Compliance Officer
CFO: Joseph Miller, Chief Financial Officer
CMO: Kevin P. Cope, M.D., Chief Medical Director
CIO: Ivan Antonyuk, Director Information Technology
CHR: Maureen Fowler, Director, Human Resources
Web address: www.amsterdammemorial.org
| 23 | 10 | 199 | 512 | 168 | 80097 | 0 | 31357 | 13410 | 427

NY

Hospital, Address, Telephone, Approval, Facility, and Physician Codes, Health Care System	Classi-fication Codes		Utilization Data					Expense (thousands) of dollars		
★ American Hospital Association (AHA) membership □ Joint Commission on Accreditation of Healthcare Organizations (JCAHO) accreditation ○ American Osteopathic Association (AOA) accreditation △ Commission on Accreditation of Rehabilitation Facilities (CARF) accreditation	Control	Service	Staffed Beds	Admissions	Census	Outpatient Visits	Births	Total	Payroll	Personnel

⊠ **ST. MARY'S HOSPITAL**, 427 Guy Park Avenue, Zip 12010–1095; tel. 518/842–1900 **A**1 9 10 **F**2 3 4 9 11 12 14 21 22 23 26 27 28 29 30 31 33 36 37 38 39 42 45 46 47 48 49 50 52 53 55 57 58 59 60 61 62 63 65 66 69 70 71 72 73 74 75 76 77 78 81 82 84 85 88 94 96 106 108 109 **S** Ascension Health, Saint Louis, MO Primary Contact: Victor Giulianelli, President and Chief Executive Officer COO: Scott Bruce, Vice President of Operations CFO: Bernard Burns, Vice President Finance CMO: Timothy Shoen, M.D., Vice President Medical Staff Services CIO: Frank Negro, Vice President Information Services CHR: Beth Stevens, Vice President of Human Resources Web address: www.smha.org	23	10	143	6306	102	228444	530	66231	35641	1054
AUBURN—Cayuga County										
⊠ **AUBURN MEMORIAL HOSPITAL**, 17 Lansing Street, Zip 13021–1943; tel. 315/255–7011, (Total facility includes 80 beds in nursing home–type unit) **A**1 9 10 19 **F**2 9 10 11 12 14 21 22 23 26 27 28 29 33 36 38 42 46 48 52 53 55 58 59 61 62 63 64 69 71 73 75 81 82 88 92 93 94 96 107 108 110 Primary Contact: Brendan P. McGrath, Administrator CFO: John A. Rovelli, Chief Financial Officer CMO: Frank P. LoTurco, D.O., Medical Director CHR: Lisa Dittrich, Manager, Employee Relations Web address: www.auburnhospital.org	23	10	243	6127	169	123211	485	66772	32184	717
BATAVIA—Genesee County										
⊠ **UNITED MEMORIAL MEDICAL CENTER**, 127 North Street, Zip 14020–2260; tel. 585/343–6030, (Includes UNITED MEMORIAL MEDICAL CENTER–BANK STREET; UNITED MEMORIAL MEDICAL CENTER–NORTH STREET, 16 Banks Street, Zip 14020–1697; tel. 585/343–6030), (Nonreporting) **A**1 9 10 Primary Contact: Karen Peters, Interim Chief Executive Officer CFO: Jeanne La Chance, Vice President Finance CMO: Louis Green, Jr, M.D., Vice President Medical Affairs CIO: Robert J. Duthe, Director Information Services CHR: Sonja Gonyea, Director of Human Resources Web address: www.ummc.org	23	10	126	—	—	—	—	—	—	—
★ **VETERANS AFFAIRS WESTERN NEW YORK HEALTHCARE SYSTEM–BATAVIA DIVISION**, 222 Richmond Avenue, Zip 14020–1288; tel. 585/343–7500, (Total facility includes 70 beds in nursing home–type unit) (Nonreporting) **A**5 9 **S** Department of Veterans Affairs, Washington, DC Primary Contact: Michael S. Finegan, Director Web address: www.va.gov/sta/guide/home.asp	45	10	158	—	—	—	—	—	—	—
BATH—Steuben County										
⊠ **IRA DAVENPORT MEMORIAL HOSPITAL**, 7571 State Route 54, Zip 14810–9590; tel. 607/776–8500, (Total facility includes 120 beds in nursing home–type unit) (Nonreporting) **A**1 9 10 Primary Contact: James B. Watson, Chief Executive Officer CFO: James Smith, Chief Financial Officer CMO: Dennis O'Connor, M.D., Medical Director CIO: Ben Younker, Information Systems Manager CHR: Marybess Hazelett, Human Resources Director Web address: www.davenportandtaylor.org	23	10	186	—	—	—	—	—	—	—
⊠ **VETERANS AFFAIRS MEDICAL CENTER**, 76 Veterans Avenue, Zip 14810–0842; tel. 607/664–4000, (Total facility includes 140 beds in nursing home–type unit) **A**1 **F**2 4 6 21 22 26 27 28 29 32 33 37 38 41 44 45 46 47 52 57 58 60 62 65 66 69 70 77 81 88 92 94 96 106 108 109 110 **S** Department of Veterans Affairs, Washington, DC Primary Contact: Linda Weiss, Acting Director CFO: Jill Haynes, Financial Coach CMO: Alan Fantuzzo, D.O., Chief of Staff CIO: Rory White, Information Systems Operations Manager CHR: Char Taft, Service Line and Human Resources Management Manager Web address: www.va.gov/sta/guide/home.asp	45	10	360	2455	328	—	0	—	—	588
BAY SHORE—Suffolk County										
⊠ **SOUTHSIDE HOSPITAL**, 301 East Main Street, Zip 11706–8458; tel. 631/968–3000 **A**1 2 3 5 9 10 **F**2 3 9 10 11 12 14 15 16 17 21 22 23 26 27 28 29 30 33 34 35 36 37 38 39 42 44 46 47 48 49 50 51 52 53 55 57 58 59 60 61 62 63 64 65 66 68 69 70 71 73 74 75 76 77 79 81 82 84 87 88 90 92 94 95 96 98 106 108 109 110 **S** North Shore–LIJ Health System, Great Neck, NY Primary Contact: Michael L. Nolan, Prseident and Chief Executive Officer COO: Winnie Mack, Vice President CFO: Jeffrey Morgan, Chief Financial Officer CMO: Michael Delman, Senior Vice President Medical Affairs CIO: Lowney Mincy, Director Information Systems CHR: Anne Barrett, Director Human Resources Web address: www.southsidehospital.org	23	10	371	16610	293	154246	2836	212390	103102	1834
BEACON—Dutchess County SAINT FRANCIS HOSPITAL See Saint Francis Hospital, Poughkeepsie **BELLEROSE—Queens County, See New York City**										

Hospital, Address, Telephone, Approval, Facility, and Physician Codes, Health Care System	Classification Codes		Utilization Data					Expense (thousands) of dollars		
★ American Hospital Association (AHA) membership □ Joint Commission on Accreditation of Healthcare Organizations (JCAHO) accreditation ○ American Osteopathic Association (AOA) accreditation △ Commission on Accreditation of Rehabilitation Facilities (CARF) accreditation	Control	Service	Staffed Beds	Admissions	Census	Outpatient Visits	Births	Total	Payroll	Personnel

BETHPAGE—Nassau County

□ **NEW ISLAND HOSPITAL**, 4295 Hempstead Turnpike, Zip 11714–5769; tel. 516/579–6000, (Nonreporting) **A**1 9 10
Primary Contact: Paul E. Seale, Chief Executive Officer
Web address: www.newislandhospital.com

| | | 23 | 10 | 147 | — | — | — | — | — | — | — |

BINGHAMTON—Broome County

BINGHAMTON GENERAL HOSPITAL See United Health Services Hospitals–Binghamton

□ **GREATER BINGHAMTON HEALTH CENTER**, 425 Robinson Street, Zip 13901–4198; tel. 607/724–1391 **A**1 10 **F**21 22 29 32 58 71 72 76 77 78 94 96 108 **S** New York State Office of Mental Health, Albany, NY
Primary Contact: Margaret R. Dugan, Executive Director

| | | 12 | 22 | 154 | 93 | 145 | — | 0 | — | — | 414 |

⊠ **OUR LADY OF LOURDES MEMORIAL HOSPITAL**, 169 Riverside Drive, Zip 13905–4198; tel. 607/798–5111 **A**1 2 9 10 **F**2 7 8 9 11 12 21 22 23 26 27 28 29 33 36 37 38 39 41 42 44 46 47 48 51 52 53 54 55 57 58 59 60 61 62 63 65 66 69 70 79 81 82 83 84 85 87 88 93 94 95 98 107 108 109 110 **P**7 **S** Ascension Health, Saint Louis, MO
Primary Contact: John D. O'Neil, President and Chief Executive Officer
CFO: Brian Regan, Senior Vice President Finance and Chief Financial Officer
CMO: Robert Taylor, III, M.D., Vice President Medical Affairs
CIO: John Laliberte, Director Information Services
CHR: Patricia Folts, Assistant Vice President and Human Resources
Web address: www.lourdes.com

| | | 21 | 10 | 159 | 9184 | 111 | 1104792 | 1198 | 160853 | 67393 | 1515 |

⊠ **UNITED HEALTH SERVICES HOSPITALS–BINGHAMTON**, 10–42 Mitchell Avenue, Zip 13903–1678; tel. 607/763–6000, (Includes BINGHAMTON GENERAL HOSPITAL, 10–42 Mitchell Avenue, Zip 13903; MEDICENTER, 600 High Avenue, Endicott, Zip 13760; tel. 607/754–7171; WILSON MEMORIAL REGIONAL MEDICAL CENTER, 33–57 Harrison Street, Johnson City, Zip 13790) **A**1 2 8 9 10 **F**2 3 4 9 10 11 12 14 15 17 19 21 22 23 24 26 27 28 29 31 32 33 34 39 40 44 47 48 49 50 52 53 55 56 57 58 59 60 61 62 63 64 65 66 68 69 70 71 73 74 75 76 77 81 82 85 87 88 89 92 93 94 95 96 106 108 109 110 **P**6 **S** United Health Services, Binghamton, NY
Primary Contact: Matthew J. Salanger, President and Chief Executive Officer
Web address: www.uhs.net

| | | 23 | 10 | 425 | 17023 | 294 | 259378 | 1347 | 273817 | 109322 | 2478 |

BRENTWOOD—Suffolk County

PILGRIM PSYCHIATRIC CENTER, 998 Crooked Hill Road, Zip 11717–1087; tel. 631/761–3500, (Includes KINGS PARK PSYCHIATRIC CENTER, 998 Crooked Hill Road, tel. 516/761–3500), (Nonreporting) **A**10 **S** New York State Office of Mental Health, Albany, NY
Primary Contact: Dean R. Weinstock, R.N., Acting Executive Director

| | | 12 | 22 | 744 | — | — | — | — | — | — | — |

BROCKPORT—Monroe County

⊠ **LAKESIDE MEMORIAL HOSPITAL**, 156 West Avenue, Zip 14420–1286; tel. 585/395–6095 **A**1 9 10 **F**2 9 11 12 21 27 28 29 33 36 39 47 48 53 55 58 59 60 63 65 66 69 81 84 88 92 94 96 106 107
Primary Contact: Charles W. Smith, Jr, President and Chief Executive Officer
CFO: Kevin C. Nacy, Executive Vice President
CMO: William T. Cave, M.D., Vice President for Medical Affairs
Web address: www.lakesidehealth.com

| | | 23 | 10 | 61 | 2748 | 45 | — | 297 | — | — | — |

BRONX—Bronx County, See New York City

BRONXVILLE—Westchester County

⊠ **LAWRENCE HOSPITAL CENTER**, 55 Palmer Avenue, Zip 10708–3491; tel. 914/787–1000 **A**1 2 5 9 10 **F**2 9 11 12 14 21 22 23 26 29 33 35 36 37 38 39 40 46 47 48 49 51 52 53 54 55 56 57 58 59 61 62 63 64 66 69 73 81 82 84 85 88 90 94 95 96 106 108
Primary Contact: Edward M. Dinan, President and Chief Executive Officer
CFO: Murray Askinazi, Vice President Finance
CMO: Werner Roeder, M.D., Vice President Medical Affairs
CHR: Deborah Gogliettino, Vice President Human Resources
Web address: www.lawrencehealth.org

| | | 23 | 10 | 182 | 10999 | 148 | 154188 | 1805 | 110266 | 52426 | 878 |

BROOKLYN—Kings County, See New York City

BUFFALO—Erie County

BRYLIN HOSPITALS, 1263 Delaware Avenue, Zip 14209–2497; tel. 716/886–8200, (Nonreporting) **A**10
Primary Contact: Eric D. Pleskow, President and Chief Executive Officer
Web address: www.brylin.com

| | | 33 | 22 | 150 | — | — | — | — | — | — | — |

⊠ **BUFFALO GENERAL HOSPITAL**, 100 High Street, Zip 14203–1154; tel. 716/859–5600, (Includes DE GRAFF MEMORIAL HOSPITAL, 445 Tremont Street, North Tonawanda, Zip 14120–0750, Mailing Address: P.O. Box 0750, Zip 14120–0750; tel. 716/694–4500; Christopher Lane, President; MILLARD FILLMORE GATES CIRCLE HOSPITAL, 3 Gates Circle, Zip 14209–9986; tel. 716/887–4600; Michael Nagowski, President; MILLARD FILLMORE SUBURBAN HOSPITAL, 1540 Maple Road, Williamsville, Zip 14221; tel. 716/688–3100), (Total facility includes 557 beds in nursing home–type unit) (Nonreporting) **A**1 3 5 8 9 10 **S** KALEIDA Health, Buffalo, NY
Primary Contact: William D. McGuire, Chief Executive Officer
COO: James R. Kaskie, President and Chief Operating Officer
CFO: Robert Glenning, Executive Vice President and Chief Financial Officer
CMO: Margaret Paroski, M.D., Executive Vice President and Chief Medical Officer
CIO: Francis Meyer, Vice President Information Systems Technology
CHR: Robert Nolan, Vice President and General Counsel
Web address: www.kaleidahealth.org

| | | 23 | 10 | 1691 | — | — | — | — | — | — | — |

Many Facility Codes have changed. Please refer to the AHA Guide Code Chart.   © 2005 AHA Guide

Hospital, Address, Telephone, Approval, Facility, and Physician Codes, Health Care System	Classi-fication Codes		Utilization Data					Expense (thousands) of dollars		
★ American Hospital Association (AHA) membership □ Joint Commission on Accreditation of Healthcare Organizations (JCAHO) accreditation ○ American Osteopathic Association (AOA) accreditation △ Commission on Accreditation of Rehabilitation Facilities (CARF) accreditation	Control	Service	Staffed Beds	Admissions	Census	Outpatient Visits	Births	Total	Payroll	Personnel
□ **BUFFALO PSYCHIATRIC CENTER**, 400 Forest Avenue, Zip 14213–1298; tel. 716/885–2261, (Nonreporting) **A**1 10 **S** New York State Office of Mental Health, Albany, NY Primary Contact: Thomas Dodson, Executive Director Web address: www.omh.state.ny.us	12	22	240	—	—	—	—	—	—	—
□ **ERIE COUNTY MEDICAL CENTER**, 462 Grider Street, Zip 14215–3098; tel. 716/898–3000, (Total facility includes 794 beds in nursing home–type unit) (Nonreporting) **A**1 3 5 9 10 Primary Contact: Michael A. Young, FACHE, Chief Executive Officer Web address: www.ecmc.edu	13	10	1200	—	—	—	—	—	—	—
⊞ **MERCY HOSPITAL**, 565 Abbott Road, Zip 14220–2095; tel. 716/826–7000, (Total facility includes 74 beds in nursing home–type unit) **A**1 3 5 9 10 **F**2 11 12 14 15 17 19 21 22 23 29 33 36 42 52 53 55 56 58 59 62 63 64 66 68 81 88 92 93 94 108 **S** Catholic Health System, Buffalo, NY Primary Contact: John P. Davanzo, President and Chief Executive Officer CFO: Jim Dunop, Vice President Finance CMO: Richard Ruh, M.D., Vice President Medical Affairs and Medical Director CHR: Wendi Bazemore, Senior Operations Manager Human Resources Web address: www.chsbuffalo.org	21	10	389	18368	327	367947	2941	184028	79191	—
⊞ **ROSWELL PARK CANCER INSTITUTE**, Elm and Carlton Streets, Zip 14263–0001; tel. 716/845–5770 **A**1 2 3 5 8 9 10 **F**2 9 12 15 21 22 23 24 26 27 28 29 30 31 32 35 36 37 38 39 42 43 46 47 48 49 50 52 53 55 57 58 60 61 62 63 64 65 66 67 68 69 70 73 79 80 81 82 84 85 86 87 88 90 92 94 96 99 104 106 108 109 110 **P**6 Primary Contact: David C. Hohn, M.D., President and Chief Executive Officer CFO: Gregory McDonald, Vice President of Finance and Chief Financial Officer CMO: Judy Smith, Medical Director CIO: JoAnne Ruh, Vice President Information Technology CHR: Rick Paris, Vice President, Human Resources Web address: www.roswellpark.org	16	41	101	4250	80	136867	0	299523	121486	2592
SHEEHAN MEMORIAL HOSPITAL, 425 Michigan Avenue, Zip 14203–2297; tel. 716/848–2000, (Nonreporting) **A**9 10 Primary Contact: Sheila Kee, President and Chief Executive Officer Web address: www.smhhealth.org	23	10	109	—	—	—	—	—	—	—
⊞ **SISTERS OF CHARITY HOSPITAL OF BUFFALO**, 2157 Main Street, Zip 14214–2692; tel. 716/862–1000, (Total facility includes 80 beds in nursing home–type unit) **A**1 2 3 5 9 10 12 13 **F**2 4 6 10 11 12 21 22 23 26 27 28 29 30 32 33 36 37 38 39 41 42 46 48 49 51 52 53 55 56 57 58 59 61 62 63 64 66 68 69 70 81 82 85 88 89 92 94 96 108 109 **P**8 **S** Catholic Health System, Buffalo, NY Primary Contact: Harry Smith, Jr, President and Senior Administrative Officer COO: Matthew Hamp, Chief Operating Officer CFO: K David Crane, Chief Financial Officer CMO: Nady Shehata, Vice President Medical Affairs CIO: Jeffrey Baughan, Vice President Information Technology Web address: www.chsbuffalo.org	21	10	307	13183	226	233869	2979	138504	62205	1375
⊞ **VETERANS AFFAIRS WESTERN NEW YORK HEALTHCARE SYSTEM–BUFFALO DIVISION**, 3495 Bailey Avenue, Zip 14215–1129; tel. 716/834–9200, (Total facility includes 120 beds in nursing home–type unit) (Nonreporting) **A**1 2 3 5 8 9 **S** Department of Veterans Affairs, Washington, DC Primary Contact: Michael S. Finegan, Director CFO: Royce Calhoun, Business Manager CMO: Avery Ellis, M.D., Chief of Staff CIO: Margaret Owzcarzak, Chief Information Systems CHR: Teresa Switek, Manager Human Resources Web address: www.va.gov/visn/visn02	45	10	233	—	—	—	—	—	—	—
□ **WESTERN NEW YORK CHILDREN'S PSYCHIATRIC CENTER**, 1010 East and West Road, Zip 14224–3698; tel. 716/674–9730, (Nonreporting) **A**1 **S** New York State Office of Mental Health, Albany, NY Primary Contact: David Heffler, Ph.D., Executive Director Web address: www.omh.state.ny.us	12	52	46	—	—	—	—	—	—	—
WOMEN AND CHILDREN'S HOSPITAL, 219 Bryant Street, Zip 14222–2099; tel. 716/878–7000, (Nonreporting) **A**3 5 9 **S** KALEIDA Health, Buffalo, NY Primary Contact: Cheryl Klass, President	23	49	200	—	—	—	—	—	—	—
CANANDAIGUA—Ontario County										
⊞ **THOMPSON HEALTH**, 350 Parrish Street, Zip 14424–1793; tel. 585/396–6000, (Total facility includes 180 beds in nursing home–type unit) **A**1 9 10 **F**2 7 9 11 12 21 22 23 24 25 26 27 28 29 30 33 37 38 46 47 48 52 53 55 57 58 59 60 61 62 63 64 65 66 69 70 73 81 82 85 88 92 93 94 95 96 98 106 107 108 109 Primary Contact: Linda M. Janczak, President and Chief Executive Officer COO: Deborah Weymouth, Senior Vice President Operations and Chief Financial Officer CFO: Deborah Weymouth, Senior Vice President Operations and Chief Financial Officer CMO: Martin Lustick, M.D., Senior Vice President Medical Services CIO: Mark Halladay, Director Information Services CHR: Jennifer DeVault, Director Associate Services Web address: www.thompsonhealth.com	23	10	278	4338	232	616332	669	72698	37617	969

NY

Hospital, Address, Telephone, Approval, Facility, and Physician Codes, Health Care System	Classi-fication Codes		Utilization Data					Expense (thousands) of dollars		
★ American Hospital Association (AHA) membership □ Joint Commission on Accreditation of Healthcare Organizations (JCAHO) accreditation ○ American Osteopathic Association (AOA) accreditation △ Commission on Accreditation of Rehabilitation Facilities (CARF) accreditation	Control	Service	Staffed Beds	Admissions	Census	Outpatient Visits	Births	Total	Payroll	Personnel

⊠ **VETERANS AFFAIRS MEDICAL CENTER,** (Primary Care, NHCU, Behavioral), 400 Fort Hill Avenue, Zip 14424–1197; tel. 585/394–2000, (Total facility includes 138 beds in nursing home–type unit) **A**1 5 **F**1 3 4 5 8 21 22 26 27 28 29 30 31 32 36 38 39 41 42 44 45 46 47 48 50 51 52 53 57 58 60 65 66 69 70 71 73 74 76 77 78 81 88 92 94 96 106 108 109 **P**6 **S** Department of Veterans Affairs, Washington, DC
Primary Contact: W. David Smith, Director
CMO: Robert Babcock, M.D., Chief of Staff
CIO: Patricia Simon, Manager Information Systems
Web address: www.va.gov/visns/visn02/can_nf.html

| | 45 | 49 | 238 | 452 | 141 | 182001 | 0 | 75915 | 37540 | 802 |

CARMEL—Putnam County

ARMS ACRES, 75 Seminary Hill Road, Zip 10512–1921; tel. 845/225–3400, (Nonreporting)
Primary Contact: Patrice Wallace–Moore, Executive Director
Web address: www.armsacres.com

| | 33 | 82 | 129 | — | — | — | — | — | — | — |

□ **PUTNAM HOSPITAL CENTER,** 670 Stoneleigh Avenue, Zip 10512–9948; tel. 845/279–5711 **A**1 9 10 **F**9 10 11 12 21 23 27 28 29 33 37 40 46 48 49 51 55 57 58 59 61 62 63 64 65 66 69 70 71 75 78 81 84 88 93 94 96 106 107 108 110 **P**6 **S** Health Quest, Poughkeepsie, NY
Primary Contact: Michael T. Weber, President and Chief Executive Officer
Web address: www.putnamhospital.org

| | 23 | 10 | 144 | 7021 | 98 | 165947 | 607 | 97158 | 38517 | 733 |

CARTHAGE—Jefferson County

□ **CARTHAGE AREA HOSPITAL,** 1001 West Street, Zip 13619–9703; tel. 315/493–1000, (Total facility includes 30 beds in nursing home–type unit) **A**1 9 10 20 **F**9 11 12 21 22 26 27 28 29 31 32 33 36 37 38 44 46 47 48 52 58 59 60 62 63 64 65 68 69 81 88 92 94 96 97 98 106 108 109
Primary Contact: Walter S. Becker, Chief Executive Officer
Web address: www.carthagehospital.com

| | 23 | 10 | 78 | 2079 | 56 | 87202 | 299 | 23056 | 10716 | 263 |

CASTLE POINT—Dutchess County

VETERAN AFFAIRS HUDSON VALLEY HEALTH CARE SYSTEM–CASTLE POINT DIVISION See Veterans Affairs Hudson Valley Health Care System–F.D. Roosevelt Hospital, Montrose

CATSKILL—Columbia County

COLUMBIA–GREENE LONG TERM CARE See Columbia Memorial Hospital, Hudson

CHEEKTOWAGA—Erie County

⊠ **ST. JOSEPH HOSPITAL,** 2605 Harlem Road, Zip 14225–4097; tel. 716/891–2400 **A**1 9 10 **F**12 21 22 26 27 28 33 37 38 39 41 42 48 52 53 55 58 62 63 64 65 66 69 70 81 82 88 92 93 94 96 99 104 108 **S** Catholic Health System, Buffalo, NY
Primary Contact: James M. Millard, President and Senior Administrative Officer
COO: James M. Millard, President and Senior Administrative Officer
CMO: Rajinder Sachar, M.D., Vice President, Medical Affairs
CIO: Jeffrey Baughan, Chief Information Officer
CHR: Kimberly Juzdowski, Manager, Human Resources
Web address: www.chsbuffalo.org

| | 23 | 10 | 132 | 5837 | 92 | 201527 | 0 | 59803 | 25111 | 588 |

CLIFTON SPRINGS—Ontario County

⊠ **CLIFTON SPRINGS HOSPITAL AND CLINIC,** 2 Coulter Road, Zip 14432–1189; tel. 315/462–1311, (Total facility includes 108 beds in nursing home–type unit) **A**1 9 10 **F**3 4 9 10 12 21 22 26 27 28 29 31 33 37 38 42 43 44 45 46 47 48 52 53 55 58 60 63 65 66 69 70 71 73 74 75 76 77 78 81 82 86 88 92 94 96 108 110 **P**5
Primary Contact: John P. Galati, President and Chief Executive Officer
COO: Arthur Dehey, Senior Vice President and Chief Financial Officer
CFO: Trisha Koczent, Controller
Web address: www.cliftonspringshospital.org

| | 23 | 10 | 262 | 3648 | 172 | 149730 | 0 | 47228 | 23409 | — |

COBLESKILL—Schoharie County

□ **BASSETT HOSPITAL OF SCHOHARIE COUNTY,** 178 Grandview Drive, Zip 12043–1331; tel. 518/254–3456, (Nonreporting) **A**1 9 10
Primary Contact: Eric H. Stein, FACHE, Administrator and Chief Executive Officer
Web address: www.bhsc.org

| | 23 | 10 | 40 | — | — | — | — | — | — | — |

COOPERSTOWN—Otsego County

⊠ **MARY IMOGENE BASSETT HOSPITAL,** One Atwell Road, Zip 13326–1394; tel. 607/547–3100 **A**1 2 3 5 8 10 12 19 20 **F**2 10 11 12 15 17 19 21 22 23 24 26 27 28 29 32 33 34 40 41 42 46 47 48 49 50 52 53 55 57 58 59 60 61 62 63 65 66 69 70 71 72 73 74 75 76 77 80 81 82 84 85 87 88 93 94 95 96 105 106 107 108 109 110 **P**6
Primary Contact: William F. Streck, M.D., President and Chief Executive Officer
COO: Bertine C. McKenna, Ph.D., Executive Vice President and Chief Operating Officer
CFO: Nicholas Nicoletta, Vice President Finance and Chief Financial Officer
CMO: Gerald D. Groff, M.D., Vice President Medical Affairs
CIO: Kenneth R. Deans, Jr, Vice President Information Services and Chief Information Officer
CHR: Robin A. Moore, Vice President Human Resources
Web address: www.bassethealthcare.org/

| | 23 | 10 | 148 | 8201 | 108 | 517214 | 617 | 226558 | 120718 | 2310 |

NY

Many Facility Codes have changed. Please refer to the AHA Guide Code Chart. © 2005 AHA Guide

Hospital, Address, Telephone, Approval, Facility, and Physician Codes, Health Care System	Classi-fication Codes		Utilization Data					Expense (thousands) of dollars		
★ American Hospital Association (AHA) membership □ Joint Commission on Accreditation of Healthcare Organizations (JCAHO) accreditation ○ American Osteopathic Association (AOA) accreditation △ Commission on Accreditation of Rehabilitation Facilities (CARF) accreditation	Control	Service	Staffed Beds	Admissions	Census	Outpatient Visits	Births	Total	Payroll	Personnel

CORNING—Steuben County

★ **CORNING HOSPITAL**, 176 Denison Parkway East, Zip 14830–2899; tel. 607/937–7200 **A**1 9 10 **F**2 9 11 12 21 22 23 26 27 29 31 33 35 37 39 41 46 48 52 55 58 59 60 61 62 63 66 69 73 81 82 84 88 92 93 94 95 96 106 108 109 **S** Guthrie Healthcare System, Sayre, PA
Primary Contact: Marilyn J. Custer–Mitchell, Chief Operating Officer
COO: Marilyn J. Custer–Mitchell, President and Chief Executive Officer
CFO: Francis M. Macafee, Vice President Finance
CHR: James J. Cummings, Administrative Director, Human Resources
Web address: www.corninghospital.com

	23	10	99	4521	52	123491	412	62439	22858	443

CORTLAND—Cortland County

★ **CORTLAND MEMORIAL HOSPITAL**, 134 Homer Avenue, Zip 13045–0960; tel. 607/756–3500, (Total facility includes 82 beds in nursing home–type unit) **A**1 9 10 20 **F**1 2 9 11 12 22 27 29 33 37 39 41 44 46 48 51 52 53 55 59 60 62 63 64 65 66 69 71 73 75 81 82 84 85 87 88 92 93 94 95 96 97 106 107 108 109 110
Primary Contact: Brian R. Mitteer, Chief Executive Officer
CFO: David Hardy, Senior Vice President Operations and Chief Financial Officer
CMO: Tyson Smith, M.D., Senior Vice President Medical Affairs and Strategic Planning
CIO: Thomas Hallisey, Vice President Information Management
CHR: Andrew Nottige, Vice President Human Resources
Web address: www.cortlandhospital.org

	23	10	202	4698	156	125062	502	56479	26128	681

CORTLANDT MANOR—Westchester County

★ **HUDSON VALLEY HOSPITAL CENTER**, 1980 Crompond Road, Zip 10567–4182; tel. 914/737–9000 **A**1 9 10 **F**2 7 9 11 12 21 22 23 26 27 28 29 30 31 33 37 38 41 42 44 46 47 48 52 53 55 56 57 58 59 60 61 62 63 64 65 66 69 70 75 81 82 84 85 86 87 88 94 95 96 97 106 108
Primary Contact: John C. Federspiel, President and Chief Executive Officer
CFO: Mark Webster, Vice President Finance
CMO: Marc Napp, M.D., Vice President Medical Staff
CIO: Chryl Pynn, Director Management Information Systems
Web address: www.hvhc.org

	23	10	109	5902	78	95138	958	78852	34764	706

CUBA—Allegany County

CUBA MEMORIAL HOSPITAL, 140 West Main Street, Zip 14727–1398; tel. 585/968–2000, (Total facility includes 61 beds in nursing home–type unit) (Nonreporting) **A**9 10 18
Primary Contact: Andrew Boser, Chief Executive Officer
Web address: www.cuba.memorialhospital.org

	23	49	81	—	—	—	—	—	—	—

DANSVILLE—Livingston County

★ **NICHOLAS H. NOYES MEMORIAL HOSPITAL**, 111 Clara Barton Street, Zip 14437–9527; tel. 585/335–6001 **A**1 9 10 **F**6 9 11 12 15 17 21 23 28 29 33 36 41 42 43 45 47 48 49 50 51 52 54 55 58 59 60 62 63 65 66 69 70 73 74 75 77 81 84 85 88 93 94 96 97 108
Primary Contact: James Wissler, President and Chief Executive Officer
CFO: Jay T. Maslyn, Chief Financial Officer
CMO: Douglas Mayhle, M.D., Medical Director
CHR: Denise Morley, Director of Human Resources
Web address: www.noyes–health.org

	23	10	72	3129	35	148243	369	35124	14579	399

DELHI—Delaware County

□ **O'CONNOR HOSPITAL**, 460 Andes Road, Route 28, Zip 13753; tel. 607/746–0300 **A**1 9 10 18 **F**12 21 27 28 29 33 46 47 48 52 58 60 62 63 65 66 69 81 88 89 94 96 97 109
Web address: www.oconnor–hospital.org

	23	10	16	217	5	25535	0	9735	3270	93

DOBBS FERRY—Westchester County

□ **COMMUNITY HOSPITAL AT DOBBS FERRY**, 128 Ashford Avenue, Zip 10522–1896; tel. 914/693–0700, (Nonreporting) **A**1 9 10
Primary Contact: Ronald Corti, President and Chief Executive Officer
Web address: www.riversidehealth.org

	23	10	50	—	—	—	—	—	—	—

DUNKIRK—Chautauqua County

★ **BROOKS MEMORIAL HOSPITAL**, 529 Central Avenue, Zip 14048–2599; tel. 716/366–1111 **A**1 9 10 19 **F**2 9 11 12 21 26 27 28 29 33 43 44 46 47 48 49 52 53 54 55 58 59 61 62 63 65 66 69 70 80 81 82 84 85 88 93 94 95 96 106 108 109 **P**5
Primary Contact: Richard H. Ketcham, President
CFO: Ralph Webdale, Vice President Finance
CIO: Kathy Kucharski, Director Management Information Systems
CHR: Joan VanDette, Vice President, Human Resources
Web address: www.brookshospital.org

	23	10	69	2914	39	102404	465	30185	13176	364

EAST MEADOW—Nassau County

★ **NASSAU UNIVERSITY MEDICAL CENTER**, 2201 Hempstead Turnpike, Zip 11554–1854; tel. 516/572–6011 **A**1 2 3 5 8 9 10 12 13 **F**2 3 6 9 10 11 12 13 14 15 21 22 23 24 28 29 31 32 33 34 37 39 42 45 48 49 50 52 53 55 56 57 58 59 60 61 62 63 66 67 68 69 70 71 72 73 74 75 76 77 80 81 82 84 85 88 89 90 94 96 108 110
Primary Contact: Daniel A. Kane, Acting President and Chief Executive Officer
CFO: Gary Bie, Senior Vice President for Finance and Administration and Chief Financial Officer
CMO: Leonard Barrett, M.D., Acting Medical Director
CIO: Christine Forman, Vice President and Chief Information Officer
CHR: George Boerum, Vice President for Human Resources
Web address: www.numc.edu

	23	10	631	21120	380	279446	1608	335005	163036	2641

NY

Hospital, Address, Telephone, Approval, Facility, and Physician Codes, Health Care System	Classi-fication Codes		Utilization Data					Expense (thousands) of dollars		
★ American Hospital Association (AHA) membership □ Joint Commission on Accreditation of Healthcare Organizations (JCAHO) accreditation ○ American Osteopathic Association (AOA) accreditation △ Commission on Accreditation of Rehabilitation Facilities (CARF) accreditation	Control	Service	Staffed Beds	Admissions	Census	Outpatient Visits	Births	Total	Payroll	Personnel

ELIZABETHTOWN—Essex County

⊠ **ELIZABETHTOWN COMMUNITY HOSPITAL**, Park Street, Zip 12932–0277, Mailing Address: P.O. Box 277, Zip 12932–0277; tel. 518/873–6377, (Nonreporting) **A**1 9 10 18
Primary Contact: Rodney C. Boula, Administrator
CFO: Sarah Stradley, Director Finance
Web address: www.ech.org
| 23 | 10 | 25 | — | — | — | — | — | — | — |

ELLENVILLE—Ulster County

ELLENVILLE REGIONAL HOSPITAL, Route 209, Zip 12428–0668, Mailing Address: P.O. Box 668, Zip 12428–0668; tel. 845/647–6400 **A**9 10 18 **F**21 29 33 36 37 46 52 58 63 69 81 82 88 94 108
Primary Contact: Steven L. Kelley, President and Chief Executive Officer
Web address: www.ellenvilleregional.org
| 23 | 10 | 25 | 716 | 11 | 12000 | 1 | — | — | 117 |

ELMHURST—Queens County, See New York City

ELMIRA—Chemung County

⊠ **ARNOT OGDEN MEDICAL CENTER**, 600 Roe Avenue, Zip 14905–1629; tel. 607/737–4100, (Total facility includes 40 beds in nursing home–type unit) **A**1 2 6 9 10 **F**2 9 10 11 12 17 19 21 22 23 24 26 27 28 29 30 33 34 35 37 39 41 42 44 45 46 47 48 49 50 52 53 55 56 57 58 59 60 61 62 63 64 65 66 69 70 73 77 79 81 82 84 85 86 87 88 92 93 94 95 96 98 106 107 108 109 110 **P**6
Primary Contact: Anthony J. Cooper, FACHE, President and Chief Executive Officer
COO: H Fred Farley, FACHE, Ph.D., Chief Operating Officer
CFO: Ronald J. Kintz, Vice President and Treasurer
CMO: Stephen Martyak, M.D., JD, Interim Vice President Medical Affairs
CIO: Gregg Martin, Manager Management Information Systems
CHR: Brian Forrest, Director of Human Resources
Web address: www.aomc.org
| 23 | 10 | 256 | 9550 | 175 | 274872 | 1352 | 140954 | 66487 | 1539 |

□ **ELMIRA PSYCHIATRIC CENTER**, 100 Washington Street, Zip 14901–2898; tel. 607/737–4739, (Nonreporting) **A**1 9 10 **S** New York State Office of Mental Health, Albany, NY
Primary Contact: William Benedict, Executive Director
Web address: www.omh.state.ny.us/omhweb/facilities/elpc/facility.htm
| 12 | 22 | 93 | — | — | — | — | — | — | — |

⊠ **ST. JOSEPH'S HOSPITAL**, 555 East Market Street, Zip 14902–1512; tel. 607/733–6541, (Includes TWIN TIERS REHABILITATION CENTER), (Total facility includes 71 beds in nursing home–type unit) **A**1 9 10 **F**3 4 9 12 13 21 22 26 27 28 29 33 36 37 38 39 40 45 46 47 48 50 52 53 55 58 60 62 63 66 68 69 70 71 75 81 82 84 87 88 92 93 94 96 107 108 109
Primary Contact: Sister Marie Castagnaro, President and Chief Executive Officer
COO: Albert A. Barto, Vice President Operations
CFO: Robert McNamara, Vice President Finance
CIO: Albert A. Barto, Vice President Operations
CHR: Roger Rockwell, Director of Human Resources
Web address: www.stjosephs.org
| 21 | 10 | 250 | 6279 | 207 | — | 0 | — | — | 770 |

ENDICOTT—Broome County

MEDICENTER See United Health Services Hospitals–Binghamton, Binghamton

FAR ROCKAWAY—Queens County, See New York City

FLUSHING—Queens County, See New York City

FOREST HILLS—Queens County, See New York City

FULTON—Oswego County

⊠ **ALBERT LINDLEY LEE MEMORIAL HOSPITAL**, 510 South Fourth Street, Zip 13069–2994; tel. 315/591–9400 **A**1 9 10 **F**9 12 21 27 28 33 42 46 48 52 55 60 62 63 64 65 69 70 81 82 84 85 87 88 93 94 96 108
Primary Contact: Dennis A. Casey, Executive Director
CFO: Gregory Fernandez, Chief Financial Officer
CMO: Anurag Sahai, M.D., Medical Director
CIO: David Markant, Information Systems Manager
CHR: M Rita Tickle, Director, Human Resources
Web address: www.allee.org
| 23 | 10 | 67 | 625 | 37 | 62116 | 0 | 25457 | 11973 | 337 |

GENEVA—Ontario County

⊠ △ **GENEVA GENERAL HOSPITAL**, 196 North Street, Zip 14456–1694; tel. 315/787–4000 **A**1 7 9 10 **F**2 3 9 11 12 21 22 23 24 26 27 28 29 33 37 42 46 47 48 49 50 52 53 54 55 58 59 60 61 62 63 65 66 68 69 73 75 81 82 84 88 92 93 94 96 108 109
Primary Contact: James J. Dooley, President and Chief Executive Officer
COO: Mary Ann Eldred, Executive Vice President and Chief Operating Officer
CFO: Lawrence J. Farnand, Treasurer and Chief Financial Officer
CMO: Jose Acevedo, M.D., Vice President Medical Affairs and Chief Medical Officer
CIO: Daniel Pletcher, Director Information System
CHR: Jack Linsky, Vice President, Human Resources
Web address: www.flhealth.org
| 23 | 10 | 132 | 4300 | 54 | 425794 | 578 | 52107 | 27942 | 717 |

NY

Many Facility Codes have changed. Please refer to the AHA Guide Code Chart. © 2005 AHA Guide

Hospital, Address, Telephone, Approval, Facility, and Physician Codes, Health Care System	Classi-fication Codes		Utilization Data					Expense (thousands) of dollars		
★ American Hospital Association (AHA) membership □ Joint Commission on Accreditation of Healthcare Organizations (JCAHO) accreditation ○ American Osteopathic Association (AOA) accreditation △ Commission on Accreditation of Rehabilitation Facilities (CARF) accreditation	Control	Service	Staffed Beds	Admissions	Census	Outpatient Visits	Births	Total	Payroll	Personnel

GLEN COVE—Nassau County

☒ **GLEN COVE HOSPITAL**, (Formerly North Shore University Hospital at Glen Cove), 101 St. Andrews Lane, Zip 11542–2254; tel. 516/674–7300 **A**1 2 3 5 9 10 **F**2 4 7 9 10 12 14 21 22 23 24 25 26 27 28 29 30 31 32 33 35 36 37 38 39 42 44 45 46 47 48 49 50 51 52 53 54 55 57 58 60 61 62 63 64 65 66 68 69 70 71 73 74 75 76 77 80 81 82 85 87 88 90 92 94 95 96 98 106 108 109 110 **P**6 **S** North Shore–LIJ Health System, Great Neck, NY
Primary Contact: Dennis Connors, Executive Director
CFO: Jon Sendach, Associate Executive Director Finance
CMO: George Dunn, M.D., Senior Vice President Medical Affairs
Web address: www.northshorelij.com
| | 23 | 10 | 210 | 10181 | 204 | 154247 | 79 | 128213 | 61428 | 835 |

GLEN OAKS—Queens County, See New York City

GLENS FALLS—Warren County

☒ **GLENS FALLS HOSPITAL**, 100 Park Street, Zip 12801; tel. 518/926–1000 **A**1 2 9 10 **F**2 4 9 11 12 14 15 17 21 22 23 27 28 29 30 31 32 33 38 39 41 42 45 46 48 49 52 53 55 57 58 59 60 61 62 63 64 65 66 68 69 70 71 72 73 74 75 77 79 81 82 85 87 88 93 94 95 96 97 106 107 108 109 **P**6
Primary Contact: David G. Kruczlnicki, President and Chief Executive Officer
COO: James W. Connolly, Executive Vice President and Chief Operating Officer
CFO: D Michael Niles, Vice President Finance
CMO: Robert W. Pringle, M.D., Vice President Medical Affairs and Medical Director
CHR: Marcy Dreimiller, Vice President Human Resources and Support Services
Web address: www.glensfallshospital.org
| | 23 | 10 | 304 | 13331 | 201 | 624280 | 1410 | 180711 | 92157 | 2209 |

GLOVERSVILLE—Fulton County

□ **NATHAN LITTAUER HOSPITAL AND NURSING HOME**, 99 East State Street, Zip 12078–1293; tel. 518/725–8621, (Total facility includes 84 beds in nursing home–type unit) **A**1 5 9 10 **F**2 9 11 12 21 22 23 24 26 27 28 29 30 33 39 41 42 46 47 48 50 52 53 55 57 58 59 60 61 62 63 64 65 66 69 70 81 82 87 88 92 94 96 106 108 109 **P**6
Primary Contact: Laurence E. Kelly, President and Chief Executive Officer
Web address: www.nlh.org
| | 23 | 10 | 170 | 3791 | 129 | 187871 | 378 | 55715 | 29438 | 680 |

GOSHEN—Orange County

ORANGE REGIONAL MEDICAL CENTER–ARDEN HILL CAMPUS See Orange Regional Medical Center, Middletown

GOUVERNEUR—St. Lawrence County

□ **EDWARD JOHN NOBLE HOSPITAL OF GOUVERNEUR**, 77 West Barney Street, Zip 13642–1090; tel. 315/287–1000, (Total facility includes 40 beds in nursing home–type unit) **A**1 9 10 20 **F**2 6 9 11 12 21 22 24 26 27 28 29 30 31 32 33 37 42 44 45 46 47 48 50 52 55 58 59 60 61 62 63 64 65 66 69 70 81 82 84 88 92 94 95 97 106 108 109 **P**6
Primary Contact: Charles P. Conole, FACHE, Chief Executive Officer
Web address: www.ejnoble.com
| | 23 | 10 | 87 | 1351 | 53 | 47053 | 88 | 16786 | 7834 | 256 |

GOWANDA—Cattaraugus County

○ **TRI–COUNTY MEMORIAL HOSPITAL**, 100 Memorial Drive, Zip 14070–1194; tel. 716/532–3377, (Nonreporting) **A**9 10 11
Primary Contact: Ronald J. Krawiec, President and Chief Executive Officer
Web address: www.tlchealth.org
| | 23 | 10 | 65 | — | — | — | — | — | — | — |

GREENPORT—Suffolk County

☒ **EASTERN LONG ISLAND HOSPITAL**, 201 Manor Place, Zip 11944–1298; tel. 631/477–1000 **A**1 9 10 **F**2 3 4 9 12 14 21 22 23 28 29 33 36 37 39 41 44 46 48 52 53 55 57 58 62 63 65 66 69 71 75 76 81 82 84 88 94 95 96 106 108
Primary Contact: Paul J. Connor, III, President and Chief Executive Officer
CFO: Drew Pallas, Vice President Finance
CIO: Blake Benz, Director Data Processing
Web address: www.elih.org
| | 23 | 10 | 80 | 3086 | 63 | 23682 | 5 | 28935 | 12693 | 250 |

HAMILTON—Madison County

☒ **COMMUNITY MEMORIAL HOSPITAL**, 150 Broad Street, Zip 13346–9518; tel. 315/824–1100, (Total facility includes 40 beds in nursing home–type unit) (Nonreporting) **A**1 10
Primary Contact: David Felton, President and Chief Executive Officer
CFO: Richard S. Kirby, Executive Vice President and Chief Financial Officer
CMO: Michael S. Jastremski, M.D., Vice President Medical Affairs and Director Emergency Services
Web address: www.communitymemorial.org
| | 23 | 10 | 84 | — | — | — | — | — | — | — |

HARRIS—Sullivan County

☒ **CATSKILL REGIONAL MEDICAL CENTER**, 68 Harris Bushville Road, Zip 12742–5030, Mailing Address: P.O. Box 800, Zip 12742–0800; tel. 845/794–3300, (Total facility includes 64 beds in nursing home–type unit) **A**1 2 9 10 18 19 20 **F**1 2 3 9 11 12 14 21 22 23 24 27 28 29 30 32 33 37 39 40 41 42 44 45 46 47 48 49 50 52 53 55 57 58 59 60 61 62 63 64 65 66 68 69 70 71 73 75 76 81 82 84 85 88 92 94 96 97 98 108 109 110 **P**6
Primary Contact: Arthur L. Brien, President and Chief Executive Officer
COO: Larry Cafasso, Senior Vice President and Chief Operating Officer
CFO: Nicholas Lanza, Interim Chief Financial Officer
CMO: Regina Olasin, Senior Vice President Director of Medical Affairs
CIO: Sue Sandell, Director Information Services
CHR: Deborah McClure, Director Human Resources
Web address: www.catskillregional.org
| | 23 | 10 | 274 | 5921 | 146 | 130513 | 490 | 92723 | 41598 | 845 |

HOLLISWOOD—Queens County, See New York City

NY

Hospital, Address, Telephone, Approval, Facility, and Physician Codes, Health Care System	Classi-fication Codes		Utilization Data					Expense (thousands) of dollars		
★ American Hospital Association (AHA) membership □ Joint Commission on Accreditation of Healthcare Organizations (JCAHO) accreditation ○ American Osteopathic Association (AOA) accreditation △ Commission on Accreditation of Rehabilitation Facilities (CARF) accreditation	Control	Service	Staffed Beds	Admissions	Census	Outpatient Visits	Births	Total	Payroll	Personnel

HORNELL—Steuben County

☒ **ST. JAMES MERCY HOSPITAL**, 411 Canisteo Street, Zip 14843–2197; tel. 607/324–8000, (Total facility includes 120 beds in nursing home–type unit) **A**1 9 10 20 **F**1 2 3 4 15 21 22 26 27 28 29 32 33 49 55 59 60 62 63 64 69 71 72 78 81 88 92 93 94 96 107 108 **P**4 **S** Catholic Health East, Newtown Square, PA
Primary Contact: Clarence R. La Liberty, Jr, President and Chief Executive Officer
COO: Pamela Urban, Senior Vice President Operations
CFO: David Capone, Senior Vice President Finance and Chief Financial Officer
CMO: Sue Wesley, M.D., Senior Vice President Medical Staff Affiars
CIO: Pam Caskey, Director Information Systems
Web address: www.stjamesmercy.org
| | 23 | 10 | 225 | 4705 | 188 | 236684 | 305 | 54817 | 26998 | 770 |

HUDSON—Columbia County

□ **COLUMBIA MEMORIAL HOSPITAL**, 71 Prospect Avenue, Zip 12534–2900; tel. 518/828–7601, (Includes COLUMBIA–GREENE LONG TERM CARE, 161 Jefferson Heights, Catskill, Zip 12414; tel. 518/943–6363), (Total facility includes 120 beds in nursing home–type unit) **A**1 9 10 19 **F**9 11 12 21 26 27 28 29 33 34 36 37 42 44 46 48 52 55 59 60 63 65 66 69 70 71 75 78 81 82 88 92 94 106 107 108 109 110
Primary Contact: Jane Ehrlich, President and Chief Executive Officer
Web address: www.columbiamemorial.com
| | 23 | 10 | 245 | 6505 | 213 | — | — | — | — | 998 |

HUNTINGTON—Suffolk County

☒ **HUNTINGTON HOSPITAL**, 270 Park Avenue, Zip 11743–2799; tel. 631/351–2200 **A**1 2 9 10 **F**2 9 10 11 12 14 17 21 22 23 26 27 28 29 30 31 33 34 37 42 46 47 48 49 50 52 53 54 55 57 58 59 61 62 63 64 65 69 70 71 73 74 75 76 77 80 81 82 85 88 92 94 95 96 106 108 109 **S** North Shore–LIJ Health System, Great Neck, NY
Primary Contact: J. Ronald Gaudreault, President and Chief Executive Officer
CFO: Kevin Lawlor, Senior Vice President and Chief Financial Officer
CMO: Michael Grosso, M.D., Vice President Medical Affairs
CIO: Linda Fisher, Director Information Services
CHR: Michael J. Quartier, Vice President, Administrative Services
Web address: www.hunthosp.org
| | 23 | 10 | 259 | 14583 | 231 | 117355 | 1983 | 175821 | 89383 | 1483 |

HUNTINGTON STATION—Suffolk County

□ **SAGAMORE CHILDREN'S PSYCHIATRIC CENTER**, 197 Half Hollow Road, Zip 11746–5861; tel. 631/673–7700, (Nonreporting) **A**1 **S** New York State Office of Mental Health, Albany, NY
Primary Contact: Dennis Dubey, Ph.D., Executive Director
Web address: www.omh.state.ny.us/ombweb/facilities/scpc/facility.htm
| | 12 | 52 | 69 | — | — | — | — | — | — | — |

IRVING—Chautauqua County

○ **LAKE SHORE HEALTH CARE CENTER**, 845 Route 5 and 20, Zip 14081–9716; tel. 716/934–2654, (Total facility includes 40 beds in nursing home–type unit) **A**10 11 **F**1 2 3 4 9 12 21 23 26 27 28 29 32 33 39 44 45 46 48 51 55 57 58 61 62 63 64 69 71 74 75 76 77 81 82 88 92 94 96 108 110
Primary Contact: Ronald J. Krawiec, President and Chief Executive Officer
Web address: www.tlchealth.org
| | 23 | 10 | 244 | 3319 | 180 | — | 0 | 40932 | 20281 | — |

ITHACA—Tompkins County

☒ **CAYUGA MEDICAL CENTER AT ITHACA**, 101 Dates Drive, Zip 14850–1383; tel. 607/274–4011 **A**1 2 5 9 10 19 **F**2 9 10 11 12 15 21 22 23 26 27 28 31 33 37 38 40 41 42 46 47 48 50 52 53 55 56 57 58 59 60 61 62 63 64 65 66 68 69 71 72 73 75 76 81 82 84 85 86 87 88 93 94 95 96 97 106 107 108 109 110 **P**6
Primary Contact: D. Rob Mackenzie, M.D., President and Chief Executive Officer
CFO: John Rudd, Chief Financial Officer
CMO: Anthony Greer, M.D., Vice President Medical Affairs
CHR: Alan Pedersen, Vice President Human Resources
Web address: www.cayugamed.org
| | 23 | 10 | 166 | 7045 | 94 | 186179 | 892 | 87406 | 35324 | 862 |

JACKSON HEIGHTS—Queens County, See New York City

JAMAICA—Queens County, See New York City

JAMESTOWN—Chautauqua County

☒ **WOMAN'S CHRISTIAN ASSOCIATION HOSPITAL**, 207 Foote Avenue, Zip 14702–9975, Mailing Address: P.O. Box 840, Zip 14702–0840; tel. 716/487–0141 **A**1 2 9 10 19 **F**3 4 9 11 12 15 22 23 24 26 27 28 29 31 33 37 38 42 45 46 47 48 49 50 52 53 55 57 58 59 60 61 63 65 66 68 69 70 71 72 73 74 75 76 77 81 82 84 85 86 88 93 94 95 96 98 106 108 109 **P**5
Primary Contact: Betsy T. Wright, President and Chief Executive Officer
CFO: Charles Iverson, Vice President Finance and Chief Financial Officer
CMO: Marlene Garone, M.D., Vice President Medical Affairs and Medical Director
CIO: Keith Robison, Chief Information Officer
CHR: Barry Nateman, Director Human Resources
Web address: www.wcahospital.org
| | 23 | 10 | 276 | 8514 | 141 | 251109 | 659 | 88983 | 42435 | 1222 |

JOHNSON CITY—Broome County

WILSON MEMORIAL REGIONAL MEDICAL CENTER See United Health Services Hospitals–Binghamton, Binghamton

Many Facility Codes have changed. Please refer to the AHA Guide Code Chart. © 2005 AHA Guide

Hospital, Address, Telephone, Approval, Facility, and Physician Codes, Health Care System	Classi-fication Codes		Utilization Data					Expense (thousands) of dollars		
★ American Hospital Association (AHA) membership □ Joint Commission on Accreditation of Healthcare Organizations (JCAHO) accreditation ○ American Osteopathic Association (AOA) accreditation △ Commission on Accreditation of Rehabilitation Facilities (CARF) accreditation	Control	Service	Staffed Beds	Admissions	Census	Outpatient Visits	Births	Total	Payroll	Personnel

KATONAH—Westchester County

⊠ **FOUR WINDS HOSPITAL**, 800 Cross River Road, Zip 10536–3549; tel. 914/763–8151 **A**1 10 **F**21 22 27 28 29 44 45 53 58 71 72 73 74 75 76 78 94 96 108
Primary Contact: Samuel C. Klagsbrun, M.D., Executive Medical Director
COO: Janet Z. Segal, Chief Operating Officer
CFO: Barry S. Weinstein, Chief Financial Officer
CMO: Jonathan Bauman, Medical Director
Web address: www.fourwindshospital.com

| 33 | 22 | 175 | 3053 | 165 | 8213 | 0 | — | — | 470 |

KENMORE—Erie County

⊠ **KENMORE MERCY HOSPITAL**, 2950 Elmwood Avenue, Zip 14217–1390; tel. 716/447–6100, (Total facility includes 160 beds in nursing home–type unit) **A**1 9 10 **F**14 21 22 26 27 28 33 42 48 49 53 55 58 60 61 62 63 65 66 68 69 70 81 82 88 92 94 95 96 108 **S** Catholic Health System, Buffalo, NY
Primary Contact: Mary Hoffman, President and Senior Administrative Officer
CFO: Dave Coone, Chief Financial Officer
CMO: Michael Sullivan, Medical Director
CIO: Jeffrey Baughan, Vice President Information Technology
CHR: Pam Nicastro, Director Human Resources
Web address: www.chsbuffalo.org

| 23 | 10 | 308 | 8106 | 259 | 147039 | 0 | 90364 | 38062 | 745 |

KINGSTON—Ulster County

⊠ **BENEDICTINE HOSPITAL**, 105 Marys Avenue, Zip 12401–5894; tel. 845/338–2500 **A**1 2 9 10 12 13 19 **F**4 6 9 11 12 17 22 23 27 28 29 30 33 36 37 38 42 44 45 46 48 53 55 57 58 59 61 62 63 66 68 69 71 72 75 77 78 79 81 88 93 94 96 106 108 109 110 **P**7
Primary Contact: Thomas A. Dee, President and Chief Executive Officer
CFO: Daniel Rinaldi, Senior Vice President Finance and Chief Financial Officer
CMO: Rafael Olazagasti, M.D., Vice President Medical Affairs and Network Development
CIO: John Finch, Vice President Corporate Development
CHR: Heidi Rosborough, Manager, Human Resources
Web address: www.benedictine.org

| 21 | 10 | 190 | 6896 | 119 | 43819 | 347 | 70239 | 32830 | 726 |

□ **KINGSTON HOSPITAL**, 396 Broadway, Zip 12401–4692; tel. 845/331–3131 **A**1 9 10 19 **F**2 3 4 9 11 12 15 21 22 23 26 27 28 29 30 33 36 37 39 42 44 46 48 49 53 55 57 58 59 60 61 62 63 64 65 66 68 69 81 82 84 85 87 88 93 94 95 96 106 108 109
Primary Contact: Michael S. Kaminski, President and Chief Executive Officer
Web address: www.kingstonregionalhealth.org

| 23 | 10 | 160 | 6954 | 106 | 121363 | 448 | 72999 | 29890 | 633 |

LEWISTON—Niagara County

⊠ **MOUNT ST. MARY'S HOSPITAL AND HEALTH CENTER**, 5300 Military Road, Zip 14092–1997; tel. 716/297–4800, (Nonreporting) **A**1 9 10 **S** Ascension Health, Saint Louis, MO
Primary Contact: Angelo G. Calbone, President and Chief Executive Officer
CFO: Paul E. Belter, Vice President Finance and Chief Financial Officer
CIO: Richard J. Witkowski, Director Management Information Systems
Web address: www.msmh.org

| 21 | 10 | 175 | — | — | — | — | — | — | — |

LITTLE FALLS—Herkimer County

⊠ **LITTLE FALLS HOSPITAL**, 140 Burwell Street, Zip 13365–1725; tel. 315/823–1000, (Total facility includes 34 beds in nursing home–type unit) (Nonreporting) **A**1 10 18
Primary Contact: Jonathan I. Lawrence, President and Chief Executive Offier
CFO: James Vielkind, Chief Financial Officer
CMO: Laurance C. Lee, M.D., Medical Director
CIO: Richard L. Ervin, Chief Information Officer
Web address: www.lfhny.org

| 23 | 10 | 59 | — | — | — | — | — | — | — |

LITTLE NECK—Queens County, See New York City

LOCKPORT—Niagara County

LOCKPORT MEMORIAL HOSPITAL, 521 East Avenue, Zip 14094–3299; tel. 716/514–5700 **A**9 10 **F**2 3 9 10 11 12 26 27 28 29 37 42 46 47 48 52 55 59 60 61 62 63 65 66 69 70 81 84 88 94 106 108 109
Primary Contact: Clare A. Haar, Chief Executive Officer

| 23 | 10 | 112 | 4310 | 71 | 68805 | 388 | 20541 | 13130 | 337 |

LONG BEACH—Nassau County

⊠ **LONG BEACH MEDICAL CENTER**, 455 East Bay Drive, Zip 11561–2300, Mailing Address: P.O. Box 300, Zip 11561–2300; tel. 516/897–1000, (Total facility includes 200 beds in nursing home–type unit) **A**1 9 10 12 13 **F**2 3 4 7 9 12 14 15 21 22 23 26 27 28 29 30 31 32 33 37 39 41 42 44 45 46 47 48 49 50 51 52 53 55 57 58 61 62 63 64 65 66 68 69 70 71 72 73 74 75 76 77 81 82 84 85 87 88 92 93 94 95 96 98 106 108 110
Primary Contact: Douglas L. Melzer, Chief Executive Officer
CFO: Lewis Z. Cohn, Jr, Chief Financial Officer
CMO: Harish Sood, M.D., Medical Director
CIO: Peter Genova, Chief Information Officer
CHR: John Sikoryak, Director Human Resources
Web address: www.lbmc.org

| 23 | 10 | 334 | 6640 | 301 | 136312 | 0 | 90079 | 44823 | 1006 |

LONG ISLAND CITY—Queens County, See New York City

NY

Hospital, Address, Telephone, Approval, Facility, and Physician Codes, Health Care System	Classi-fication Codes		Utilization Data					Expense (thousands) of dollars		
★ American Hospital Association (AHA) membership □ Joint Commission on Accreditation of Healthcare Organizations (JCAHO) accreditation ○ American Osteopathic Association (AOA) accreditation △ Commission on Accreditation of Rehabilitation Facilities (CARF) accreditation	Control	Service	Staffed Beds	Admissions	Census	Outpatient Visits	Births	Total	Payroll	Personnel

LOWVILLE—Lewis County

☒ **LEWIS COUNTY GENERAL HOSPITAL**, 7785 North State Street, Zip 13367–1297; tel. 315/376–5200, (Total facility includes 160 beds in nursing home–type unit) **A**1 9 10 20 **F**1 2 5 9 11 12 21 22 26 27 28 29 33 37 44 45 46 48 52 55 58 59 60 62 63 65 66 69 70 81 82 84 87 88 92 94 95 96 97 108 109 **P**8
Primary Contact: Mark J. Rappaport, Chief Executive Officer
CFO: Eric Burch, Chief Financial Officer
CMO: Catherine Williams, M.D., Medical Director
CIO: Rob Uttendorfsky, Director Information Management
CHR: Timothy Ryan, Director, Human Resources
Web address: www.lcgh.net

| 13 | 10 | 214 | 1669 | 173 | 72162 | 161 | 31218 | 13114 | 367 |

MALONE—Franklin County

☒ **ALICE HYDE MEDICAL CENTER**, 133 Park Street, Zip 12953–0729, Mailing Address: P.O. Box 729, Zip 12953–0729; tel. 518/483–3000, (Total facility includes 75 beds in nursing home–type unit) **A**1 9 10 20 **F**2 6 9 11 12 21 23 26 27 28 29 32 33 36 37 46 47 48 49 52 53 55 58 59 61 62 63 64 66 69 70 79 81 82 84 85 86 87 88 92 93 94 96 106 108 109
Primary Contact: John W. Johnson, President and Chief Executive Officer
CFO: Sandra MacDonald, Acting Vice President of Finance
CMO: Jan Close, M.D., Chief Medical Officer
Web address: www.alicehyde.com

| 23 | 10 | 151 | 3282 | 108 | 120640 | 260 | 42835 | 20240 | 489 |

MANHASSET—Nassau County

MANHASSET AMBULATORY CARE PAVILION See Long Island Jewish Medical Center, New York

☒ **NORTH SHORE UNIVERSITY HOSPITAL**, 300 Community Drive, Zip 11030–3876; tel. 516/562–0100, (Includes SCHNEIDER CHILDRENS HOSPITAL AT NORTH SHORE UNIVERSITY HOSPITAL, 300 Community Drive, Zip 11030) **A**1 2 3 5 8 9 10 **F**2 4 6 7 9 10 11 12 14 15 17 19 21 23 24 26 27 28 29 30 31 32 33 34 35 36 37 38 39 40 42 44 45 46 47 48 49 50 51 52 53 54 55 56 57 58 59 60 61 62 63 64 65 66 67 69 70 71 72 73 74 75 76 77 79 80 81 82 84 85 86 87 88 89 90 92 93 94 96 98 99 104 106 108 109 110 **P**6 **S** North Shore–LIJ Health System, Great Neck, NY
Primary Contact: Dennis Dowling, Executive Director
COO: Mary Jo La Posta, Deputy Executive Director
CFO: Michael Di Taranto, Associate Executive Director
CMO: Paul Gitman, M.D., Medical Director
CHR: Ronald Stone, Regional Chief Human Resource Officer
Web address: www.northshorelij.com

| 23 | 10 | 788 | 47264 | 747 | 491792 | 5780 | 1004545 | 472657 | 5770 |

MANHATTAN—New York County, See New York City

MARCY—Oneida County

□ **CENTRAL NEW YORK PSYCHIATRIC CENTER**, Mailing Address: P.O. Box 300, Zip 13403–0300; tel. 315/736–8271 **A**1 5 **F**2 3 32 33 45 48 50 52 53 58 60 65 66 71 72 73 74 75 76 77 94 96 106 108 **S** New York State Office of Mental Health, Albany, NY
Primary Contact: Hal E. Smith, Executive Director

| 12 | 22 | 206 | 861 | 176 | 147000 | 0 | — | — | 495 |

MARGARETVILLE—Delaware County

□ **MARGARETVILLE MEMORIAL HOSPITAL**, 42084 State Highway 28, Zip 12455–0200; tel. 845/586–2631 **A**1 9 10 18 **F**6 9 12 21 33 36 52 60 61 69 70 81 82 94 109
Primary Contact: Joseph A. DiPalo, Chief Executive Officer
Web address: www.margaretvillehospital.org

| 23 | 10 | 15 | 458 | 6 | — | 0 | — | — | 108 |

MASSENA—St. Lawrence County

☒ **MASSENA MEMORIAL HOSPITAL**, One Hospital Drive, Zip 13662–1097; tel. 315/764–1711 **A**1 10 **F**2 9 11 12 14 15 21 23 26 27 28 29 33 37 40 44 46 48 49 52 55 59 61 63 64 65 66 69 70 81 82 83 84 85 86 87 88 90 94 96 106 108 109
Primary Contact: Charles F. Fahd, II, Chief Executive Officer
CFO: Kelley Tierman, Chief Financial Officer
CMO: Nimesh Desai, M.D., Medical Director
CIO: Jana Grose, Director Management Information Systems
CHR: Tanya Griffin, Senior Director, Human Resources
Web address: www.massenahospital.org

| 14 | 10 | 50 | 3196 | 36 | 107935 | 242 | 31617 | 13781 | 318 |

MEDINA—Orleans County

☒ △ **MEDINA MEMORIAL HOSPITAL**, 200 Ohio Street, Zip 14103–1095; tel. 585/798–2000, (Total facility includes 30 beds in nursing home–type unit) **A**1 7 9 10 **F**3 9 11 12 13 14 21 22 23 24 26 27 28 29 30 31 33 36 42 46 47 48 49 51 52 53 55 56 58 59 60 62 63 67 68 69 70 71 76 81 82 86 88 92 94 96 97 108 109 110 **P**5
Primary Contact: James Sinner, Chief Executive Officer
COO: Mary Kargbo, Chief Operating Officer
CFO: Raj Mehta, Chief Financial Officer
CMO: Amrit Singh, M.D., Medical Staff President
CHR: David McCarroll, Nursing Home Administrator
Web address: www.medinamemorial.org

| 23 | 10 | 101 | 2051 | 59 | 98796 | 154 | 27287 | 13205 | 459 |

MIDDLETOWN—Orange County

□ **MIDDLETOWN PSYCHIATRIC CENTER**, 122 Dorothea Dix Drive, Zip 10940–6198; tel. 845/342–5511, (Nonreporting) **A**1 10 **S** New York State Office of Mental Health, Albany, NY
Primary Contact: James H. Bopp, Executive Director
Web address: www.omh.state.ny.us/omhweb/facilities/mipc/facility.htm

| 12 | 22 | 112 | — | — | — | — | — | — | — |

NY

Many Facility Codes have changed. Please refer to the AHA Guide Code Chart. © 2005 AHA Guide

Hospital, Address, Telephone, Approval, Facility, and Physician Codes, Health Care System	Classi-fication Codes		Utilization Data					Expense (thousands) of dollars		
★ American Hospital Association (AHA) membership □ Joint Commission on Accreditation of Healthcare Organizations (JCAHO) accreditation ○ American Osteopathic Association (AOA) accreditation △ Commission on Accreditation of Rehabilitation Facilities (CARF) accreditation	Control	Service	Staffed Beds	Admissions	Census	Outpatient Visits	Births	Total	Payroll	Personnel

✦ △ **ORANGE REGIONAL MEDICAL CENTER**, 60 Prospect Avenue, Zip 10940–4133; tel. 845/343–2424, (Includes ORANGE REGIONAL MEDICAL CENTER–ARDEN HILL CAMPUS, 4 Harriman Drive, Goshen, Zip 10924–2499; tel. 845/294–5441) **A**1 2 7 9 10 **F**2 4 6 9 10 11 12 14 15 21 22 23 26 27 28 29 33 37 40 42 46 47 48 49 52 53 55 57 58 59 60 61 62 63 65 66 68 69 71 72 73 74 75 76 77 78 79 80 81 82 84 85 86 87 88 90 92 93 94 96 106 108 109 110 Primary Contact: Jeffrey D. Hirsch, President and Chief Executive Officer COO: Robert G. Wolleben, Chief Operating Officer CFO: Mitch Amodo, Executive Vice President and Chief Financial Officer CMO: Norman Stein, M.D., Vice President Medical Affairs and Medical Director CIO: Robert Diamond, Vice President Information Technology and Chief Information Officer CHR: Deborah Carr, Vice President Human Resources Web address: www.ormc.org	23	10	343	19885	299	217778	1916	226199	107353	1978
MINEOLA—Nassau County										
✦ **WINTHROP–UNIVERSITY HOSPITAL**, 259 First Street, Zip 11501–3987; tel. 516/663–0333 **A**1 2 3 5 8 9 10 **F**4 9 10 11 12 14 15 17 19 21 22 23 24 26 27 28 29 31 33 34 37 44 46 47 48 49 50 51 52 53 54 55 56 57 58 59 60 61 62 63 65 66 67 69 79 81 82 84 86 87 88 93 94 96 98 106 108 109 **P**4 5 6 Primary Contact: Daniel P. Walsh, President and Chief Executive Officer CMO: Joseph Greensher, M.D., Medical Director CIO: Nicholas Casabona, Director Management Information Services CHR: George Rasner, Vice President, Human Resources Web address: www.winthrop.org	23	10	507	30367	485	292999	4758	451843	202674	3984
MONTOUR FALLS—Schuyler County										
□ **SCHUYLER HOSPITAL**, 220 Steuben Street, Zip 14865–9709; tel. 607/535–7121, (Total facility includes 120 beds in nursing home–type unit) **A**1 9 10 **F**9 11 12 21 22 26 27 28 33 37 42 46 48 54 55 58 59 60 63 66 69 70 81 84 88 93 94 96 97 108 109 **P**5 6 7 Primary Contact: Donald C. Lewis, President and Chief Executive Officer Web address: www.schuylerhospital.org	23	10	166	1399	137	121044	164	21313	10495	337
MONTROSE—Westchester County										
✦ **VETERANS AFFAIRS HUDSON VALLEY HEALTH CARE SYSTEM–F.D. ROOSEVELT HOSPITAL**, Mailing Address: P.O. Box 100, Zip 10548–0110; tel. 914/737–4400, (Includes VETERAN AFFAIRS HUDSON VALLEY HEALTH CARE SYSTEM–CASTLE POINT DIVISION, Castle Point, Zip 12511–9999; tel. 914/831–2000; VETERANS AFFAIRS HUDSON VALLEY HEALTH CARE SYSTEM–MONTROSE DIVISION, Zip 10548), (Total facility includes 180 beds in nursing home–type unit) (Nonreporting) **A**1 3 5 **S** Department of Veterans Affairs, Washington, DC Primary Contact: Michael A. Sabo, Director CFO: John Walsh, Chief Fiscal Services Web address: www.va.gov/sta/guide/home.asp	45	22	413	—	—	—	—	—	—	—
MOUNT KISCO—Westchester County										
✦ **NORTHERN WESTCHESTER HOSPITAL**, 400 East Main Street, Zip 10549–3477; tel. 914/666–1200, (Nonreporting) **A**1 2 9 10 Primary Contact: Joel Seligman, President and Chief Executive Officer COO: Warren Geller, Senior Vice President, Administration CFO: John Partenza, Vice President and Treasurer CMO: Marla Koroly, Chief Medical Officer and Senior Vice President Medical Affairs CIO: Barbara Santoro, Director Information Systems CHR: Kerry Flynn, Vice President Human Resources Web address: www.nwhc.net	23	10	195	—	—	—	—	—	—	—
MOUNT VERNON—Westchester County										
□ **MOUNT VERNON HOSPITAL**, 12 North Seventh Avenue, Zip 10550–2098; tel. 914/664–8000, (Nonreporting) **A**1 3 5 9 10 Primary Contact: John R. Spicer, President and Chief Executive Officer Web address: www.ssmc.org	23	10	128	—	—	—	—	—	—	—
NEW HAMPTON—Orange County										
□ **MID–HUDSON FORENSIC PSYCHIATRIC CENTER**, Route 17M, Zip 10958, Mailing Address: P.O. Box 158, Zip 10958–0158; tel. 845/374–3171, (Nonreporting) **A**1 10 **S** New York State Office of Mental Health, Albany, NY Primary Contact: Howard Holanchock, Executive Director Web address: www.omh.state.ny.us	12	22	268	—	—	—	—	—	—	—
NEW HYDE PARK—Queens County, See New York City										

NY

Hospital, Address, Telephone, Approval, Facility, and Physician Codes, Health Care System	Classi-fication Codes		Utilization Data					Expense (thousands) of dollars		
★ American Hospital Association (AHA) membership □ Joint Commission on Accreditation of Healthcare Organizations (JCAHO) accreditation ○ American Osteopathic Association (AOA) accreditation △ Commission on Accreditation of Rehabilitation Facilities (CARF) accreditation	Control	Service	Staffed Beds	Admissions	Census	Outpatient Visits	Births	Total	Payroll	Personnel

NEW ROCHELLE—Westchester County

⊠ **SOUND SHORE MEDICAL CENTER OF WESTCHESTER**, 16 Guion Place, Zip 10801–5500; tel. 914/632–5000, (Total facility includes 150 beds in nursing home–type unit) **A**1 2 3 5 8 9 10 **F**1 2 3 9 10 11 12 15 21 22 23 24 26 27 28 29 30 31 33 34 35 37 38 39 44 46 47 48 50 52 53 55 57 58 59 60 61 62 63 64 65 66 68 69 70 72 73 74 77 81 82 83 85 87 88 92 93 94 95 96 98 106 108 **P**8
Primary Contact: John R. Spicer, President and Chief Executive Officer
COO: Douglas O. Landy, Executive Vice President and Chief Operating Officer
CMO: Jeffrey Stier, M.D., Medical Director
CHR: Dennis Ashley, Vice President Human Resources
Web address: www.sshsw.org

| | 23 | 10 | 403 | 11266 | 273 | 128367 | 1536 | 149090 | 73794 | 1305 |

NEW YORK (Includes all hospitals located within the five boroughs)

   BRONX - Bronx County (Mailing Address - Bronx)
   BROOKLYN - Kings County (Mailing Address - Brooklyn)
   MANHATTAN - New York County (Mailing Address - New York)
   QUEENS - Queens County (Mailing Addresses - Bellerose, Elmhurst, Far Rockaway, Flushing, Forest Hills, Glen Oaks, Holliswood, Jackson Heights, Jamaica, Little Neck, Long Island City, New Hyde Park, and Queens Village)
   RICHMOND VALLEY - Richmond County (Mailing Address - Staten Island)
   BAYLEY SETON CAMPUS See St. Vincent's Hospital

⊠ **BELLEVUE HOSPITAL CENTER**, 462 First Avenue, Zip 10016–9198; tel. 212/562–4141, (Includes BELLEVUE COMPREHENSIVE GENERAL CARE, BELLEVUE PHYSICAL MEDICINE AND REHABILITATION SERVICES, BELLEVUE PSYCHIATRIC SERVICES, BELLEVUE TUBERCULOSIS SERVICES, COMPREHENSIVE AMBULATORY CARE SERVICES: LEVEL I TRAUMA CENTER), (Nonreporting) **A**1 2 3 5 8 9 10 **S** New York City Health and Hospitals Corporation, New York, NY
Primary Contact: Linda Curtis, Acting Executive Director
CFO: Aaron Cohen, Chief Financial Officer
CMO: Eric Manheimer, M.D., Medical Director
CIO: Mary McKenna, Chief Information Officer
CHR: Brenda Chapman, Director Human Resources
Web address: www.nyc.gov/bellevue

| | 14 | 10 | 771 | — | — | — | — | — | — | — |

⊠ **BETH ISRAEL MEDICAL CENTER**, First Avenue and 16th Street, Zip 10003–3803; tel. 212/420–2000, (Includes BETH ISRAEL MEDICAL CENTER–KINGS HIGHWAY DIVISION, 3201 Kings Highway, Zip 11234; tel. 718/252–3000) **A**1 3 5 8 9 10 **F**2 3 4 6 7 9 10 11 12 14 15 17 19 21 22 23 24 25 26 27 28 29 30 31 32 33 35 36 37 38 39 40 42 44 45 46 47 48 49 50 52 53 55 56 57 58 59 60 61 62 63 64 65 66 67 68 69 70 71 72 73 74 75 76 77 79 80 81 82 84 85 86 87 88 89 90 94 95 96 98 104 105 106 107 108 109 110 **S** Continuum Health Partners, New York, NY
Primary Contact: David Shulkin, M.D., President and Chief Executive Officer
COO: Jeffrey Menkes, Executive Vice President and Chief Operating Officer
CFO: Brendan Loughlin, Senior Vice President
CMO: Donald Hoskins, M.D., Chief Medical Officer
CIO: Marc Milstein, Vice President and Chief Information Systems
CHR: Bart Metzger, Vice President Human Resources
Web address: www.bethisraelny.org

| | 23 | 10 | 821 | 50677 | 821 | 644350 | 3839 | 1019721 | 483954 | 7854 |

□ **BRONX CHILDREN'S PSYCHIATRIC CENTER**, 1000 Waters Place, Bronx, Zip 10461–2799; tel. 718/239–3600, (Nonreporting) **A**1 **S** New York State Office of Mental Health, Albany, NY
Primary Contact: Mark D. Bienstock, Executive Director

| | 12 | 52 | 75 | | | | | | | |

□ **BRONX PSYCHIATRIC CENTER**, 1500 Waters Place, Bronx, Zip 10461–2796; tel. 718/931–0600, (Nonreporting) **A**1 3 5 10 **S** New York State Office of Mental Health, Albany, NY
Primary Contact: LeRoy Carmichael, Executive Director
Web address: www.omh.state.ny.us

| | 12 | 22 | 450 | — | — | — | — | — | — | — |

⊠ **BRONX–LEBANON HOSPITAL CENTER**, 1276 Fulton Avenue, Bronx, Zip 10456–3499; tel. 718/590–1800, (Includes CONCOURSE DIVISION, 1650 Grand Concourse, Zip 10457; tel. 718/590–1800; FULTON DIVISION), (Total facility includes 240 beds in nursing home–type unit) (Nonreporting) **A**1 2 3 5 8 9 10
Primary Contact: Miguel A. Fuentes, Jr, President and Chief Executive Officer
COO: Steven Anderman, Senior Vice President and Chief Operating Officer
CFO: Victor DeMarco, Senior Vice President and Chief Financial Officer
CMO: Milton A. Gumbs, M.D., Vice President Medical Affairs and Medical Director
CIO: Steven Anderman, Senior Vice President and Chief Operating Officer
CHR: Sheldon Ortsman, Vice President, Operations and Human Resources
Web address: www.bronxcare.org

| | 23 | 10 | 784 | — | — | — | — | — | — | — |

□ **BROOKDALE HOSPITAL MEDICAL CENTER**, Linden Boulevard at Brookdale Plaza, Brooklyn, Zip 11212–3198; tel. 718/240–5000, (Total facility includes 448 beds in nursing home–type unit) **A**1 3 5 8 9 10 12 **F**1 4 6 8 10 11 12 14 15 19 20 21 22 23 24 26 27 28 29 31 32 33 34 36 37 39 42 44 45 48 49 50 51 52 53 55 56 57 58 59 60 61 62 63 66 67 69 70 71 72 73 74 75 76 77 78 81 82 84 87 88 92 94 96 97 98 108 110 **P**5 7
Primary Contact: David P. Rosen, President and Chief Executive Officer
Web address: www.brookdalehospital.com

| | 23 | 10 | 960 | 22106 | 843 | 307687 | 2099 | 451630 | 213012 | 3925 |

NY

Many Facility Codes have changed. Please refer to the AHA Guide Code Chart.

Hospital, Address, Telephone, Approval, Facility, and Physician Codes, Health Care System	Classi-fication Codes		Utilization Data					Expense (thousands) of dollars		
★ American Hospital Association (AHA) membership □ Joint Commission on Accreditation of Healthcare Organizations (JCAHO) accreditation ○ American Osteopathic Association (AOA) accreditation △ Commission on Accreditation of Rehabilitation Facilities (CARF) accreditation	Control	Service	Staffed Beds	Admissions	Census	Outpatient Visits	Births	Total	Payroll	Personnel
□ **BROOKLYN HOSPITAL CENTER**, 121 DeKalb Avenue, Brooklyn, Zip 11201–5493; tel. 718/250–8000, (Nonreporting) **A**1 2 3 5 8 9 10 **S** New York Presbyterian Healthcare System, New York, NY Primary Contact: Samuel Lehrfeld, President and Chief Executive Officer Web address: www.tbh.org	23	10	653	—	—	—	—	—	—	—
□ **CABRINI MEDICAL CENTER**, 227 East 19th Street, Zip 10003–2600; tel. 212/995–6000 **A**1 3 5 8 9 10 **F**2 3 4 6 12 14 21 22 23 26 27 28 29 30 33 34 36 37 38 40 42 44 45 46 47 48 49 50 51 52 53 55 57 58 60 61 62 63 64 66 68 69 70 71 73 74 75 76 77 79 80 81 82 84 85 88 94 96 106 107 108 109 110 **P**5 8 Primary Contact: Robert S. Chaloner, President and Chief Executive Officer Web address: www.cabrininy.org	23	10	234	10803	234	158844	0	161287	77914	1225
★ **CALVARY HOSPITAL**, 1740 Eastchester Road, Bronx, Zip 10461–2392; tel. 718/863–6900 **A**1 9 10 **F**21 22 23 29 32 36 37 38 39 51 52 53 58 61 66 79 88 94 96 98 108 110 **P**6 Primary Contact: Frank A. Calamari, President and Chief Executive Officer COO: Richard J. Kutilek, Chief Operating Officer CFO: Frank J. Locaparra, Chief Financial Officer CMO: Michael J. Brescia, Executive Medical Director CIO: Patrick Martin, Director of Information Systems CHR: Mary Kelly, Director of Human Resources Web address: www.calvaryhospital.org	21	80	200	2724	186	40000	0	77972	41007	705
★ △ **COLER–GOLDWATER SPECIALTY HOSPITAL AND NURSING FACILITY**, One Main Street, Zip 10044; tel. 212/318–8000, (Includes COLER MEMORIAL HOSPITAL, Roosevelt Island, tel. 212/848–6000; GOLDWATER MEMORIAL HOSPITAL, Franklin D. Roosevelt Island, tel. 212/318–8000), (Total facility includes 1389 beds in nursing home–type unit) **A**1 3 5 7 10 **F**2 9 12 22 25 26 27 28 31 32 44 46 48 50 53 57 58 60 62 66 68 73 81 88 92 94 96 106 108 110 **P**5 **S** New York City Health and Hospitals Corporation, New York, NY Primary Contact: Claude Ritman, Executive Director COO: Robert Hughes, Chief Operating Officer CFO: Gloria Ranghelli, Deputy Chief Financial Officer CMO: Yolanda Bruno, M.D., Medical Director CHR: Howard Kritz, Director Web address: www.coler–goldwater.org	15	80	2016	2828	1906	0	0	234417	166241	3191
CONCOURSE DIVISION See Bronx–Lebanon Hospital Center										
★ **CONEY ISLAND HOSPITAL**, 2601 Ocean Parkway, Brooklyn, Zip 11235–7795; tel. 718/616–3000, (Nonreporting) **A**1 3 5 8 9 10 **S** New York City Health and Hospitals Corporation, New York, NY Primary Contact: Peter Wolf, Executive Director COO: Jerry Cammarata, Ph.D., Sc.D., Associate Executive Director Web address: www.ci.nyc.ny.us/html/hhc/html/coneyisland.html	14	10	376	—	—	—	—	—	—	—
CORNERSTONE OF MEDICAL ARTS CENTER HOSPITAL, 57 West 57th Street, Zip 10019–2802; tel. 212/755–0200, (Nonreporting) **S** Cornerstone Healthcare Group, Austin, TX Primary Contact: Norman J. Sokolow, Chairman and Chief Executive Officer Web address: www.cornerstoneny.com	33	82	162	—	—	—	—	—	—	—
□ **CREEDMOOR PSYCHIATRIC CENTER**, Jamaica, Mailing Address: 80–45 Winchester Boulevard, Queens Village, Zip 11427–2199; tel. 718/264–3600, (Nonreporting) **A**1 10 **S** New York State Office of Mental Health, Albany, NY Primary Contact: Charlotte Seltzer, Executive Director Web address: www.omh.state.ny.us	12	22	456	—	—	—	—	—	—	—
★ **ELMHURST HOSPITAL CENTER**, 79–01 Broadway, Flushing, Zip 11373–1368; tel. 718/334–4000 **A**1 2 3 5 8 10 **F**4 7 11 12 14 15 16 17 18 21 22 23 24 26 27 28 29 31 33 34 39 40 41 44 45 46 47 48 49 50 52 53 55 56 57 58 59 60 61 62 63 65 66 67 68 69 70 71 72 73 74 75 76 77 78 79 81 82 88 92 94 95 96 98 **P**6 **S** New York City Health and Hospitals Corporation, New York, NY Primary Contact: Chris D. Constantino, Executive Director CFO: Julius Wool, Chief Financial Officer CMO: Jasmin Moshirpur, Dean and Medical Director CIO: Alfred Marino, Chief Information Officer CHR: Carol White, Associate Executive Director Web address: www.elmhursthospitalcenter.org	14	10	525	24446	457	713848	4274	387287	167831	3374
□ **FLUSHING HOSPITAL MEDICAL CENTER**, 45th Avenue at Parsons Boulevard, Flushing, Zip 11355–2100; tel. 718/670–5000 **A**1 3 5 9 10 **F**2 3 4 6 9 11 12 14 21 22 23 24 26 27 28 29 30 32 33 37 38 39 42 44 46 48 49 50 52 53 55 56 57 58 59 61 62 63 66 69 70 71 73 74 75 76 77 81 82 88 94 96 106 108 109 **P**5 7 Primary Contact: David P. Rosen, President and Chief Executive Officer Web address: www.flushinghospital.org	23	10	293	14945	224	156308	2141	152237	83862	1438
FULTON DIVISION See Bronx–Lebanon Hospital Center										
GOLDWATER MEMORIAL HOSPITAL See Coler–Goldwater Specialty Hospital and Nursing Facility										
□ **GRACIE SQUARE HOSPITAL**, 420 East 76th Street, Zip 10021–3104; tel. 212/988–4400 **A**1 10 **F**21 29 31 37 44 46 48 58 60 66 71 73 74 76 86 94 96 **S** New York Presbyterian Healthcare System, New York, NY Primary Contact: Frank Bruno, Chief Executive Officer Web address: www.nygsh.org	23	22	157	3139	150	0	0	—	—	249

NY

Hospital, Address, Telephone, Approval, Facility, and Physician Codes, Health Care System	Classi-fication Codes		Utilization Data					Expense (thousands) of dollars		
★ American Hospital Association (AHA) membership □ Joint Commission on Accreditation of Healthcare Organizations (JCAHO) accreditation ○ American Osteopathic Association (AOA) accreditation △ Commission on Accreditation of Rehabilitation Facilities (CARF) accreditation	Control	Service	Staffed Beds	Admissions	Census	Outpatient Visits	Births	Total	Payroll	Personnel
✱ △ **HARLEM HOSPITAL CENTER**, 506 Lenox Avenue, Zip 10037–1894; tel. 212/939–1000, (Includes HARLEM GENERAL CARE UNIT AND HARLEM PSYCHIATRIC UNIT), (Nonreporting) **A**1 2 3 5 7 8 9 10 **S** New York City Health and Hospitals Corporation, New York, NY Primary Contact: John M. Palmer, Ph.D., Executive Director CFO: Jeffrey Rogoff, Deputy Executive Director Web address: www.nyclink.org/hhc	14	10	275	—	—	—	—	—	—	—
□ **HOLLISWOOD HOSPITAL**, 87–37 Palermo Street, Jamaica, Zip 11423–1209; tel. 718/776–8181 **A**1 10 **F**21 27 28 44 71 72 73 74 75 76 78 94 **S** Liberty Management Group, Inc., Ramsey, NJ Primary Contact: Jeffrey Borenstein, M.D., Chief Executive Officer and Medical Director Web address: www.holliswoodhospital.com	33	22	110	2493	100	0	0	21023	9654	188
✱ △ **HOSPITAL FOR JOINT DISEASES ORTHOPAEDIC INSTITUTE**, 301 East 17th Street, Zip 10003–3890; tel. 212/598–6000 **A**1 3 5 7 8 9 10 **F**2 7 9 21 22 26 27 28 29 30 37 39 41 44 46 47 48 51 52 53 55 57 58 60 61 62 63 64 65 66 68 69 70 81 82 84 85 87 88 92 94 95 96 107 108 109 110 **P**5 Primary Contact: David A. Dibner, FACHE, Chief Executive Officer CFO: Gerald R. Ferlisi, Vice President Finance CMO: H Michael Belmont, M.D., Medical Director CIO: Stuart Sugarman, Senior Vice President and Chief Information Officer CHR: Austin Bender, Director Human Resources Web address: www.jointdiseases.com	23	47	175	6717	107	121117	0	169613	72467	1055
✱ **HOSPITAL FOR SPECIAL SURGERY**, 535 East 70th Street, Zip 10021–4898; tel. 212/606–1000 **A**1 3 5 8 9 10 **F**2 7 21 22 24 25 26 27 28 29 30 34 35 37 39 41 42 44 46 47 52 53 57 58 60 62 63 65 66 69 70 73 79 80 81 82 83 84 85 86 87 88 94 95 96 98 104 105 108 109 **P**4 8 **S** New York Presbyterian Healthcare System, New York, NY Primary Contact: John R. Reynolds, President and Chief Executive Officer COO: Lisa Goldstein, Vice President and Chief Operating Officer CFO: Stacey Malakoff, Chief Financial Officer CMO: Thomas P. Sculco, M.D., Chief Medical Officer CIO: John Cox, Assistant Vice President and Chief Information Officer CHR: Stephen A. Reday, Vice President of Human Resources Web address: www.hss.edu	23	47	142	9524	117	234940	0	314047	130518	2264
□ **INTERFAITH MEDICAL CENTER**, 1545 Atlantic Avenue, Brooklyn, Zip 11213; tel. 718/613–4000, (Nonreporting) **A**1 3 5 9 10 Primary Contact: Edward J. Glicksman, Chief Executive Officer Web address: www.interfaithmedical.com	23	10	287	—	—	—	—	—	—	—
JACK D WEILER HOSPITAL OF ALBERT EINSTEIN COLLEGE OF MEDICINE See Montefiore Medical Center										
✱ **JACOBI MEDICAL CENTER**, Pelham Parkway South and Eastchester Road, Bronx, Zip 10461–1197; tel. 718/918–5000 **A**1 3 5 8 9 10 **F**2 3 4 6 9 10 11 12 13 14 21 22 23 24 26 27 28 29 30 31 32 33 34 35 37 38 39 40 41 42 45 46 47 48 49 50 51 52 53 55 56 57 58 59 60 61 62 63 64 65 66 67 68 69 70 71 72 73 74 75 76 77 81 82 83 84 85 86 87 88 89 90 94 95 96 98 106 107 108 109 110 **P**6 **S** New York City Health and Hospitals Corporation, New York, NY Primary Contact: William P. Walsh, Executive Director COO: Arthur Wagner, Chief Operating Officer CFO: Nancy Guzman, Chief Financial Officer CIO: Daniel Morreale, Chief Information Officer CHR: Dolores Leite, Chief Human Resource Exec Web address: www.ci.nyc.ny.us/html/hhc/html/jacobi.html	14	10	556	21027	415	840091	2336	447230	184748	3303
✱ **JAMAICA HOSPITAL MEDICAL CENTER**, 8900 Van Wyck Expressway, Jamaica, Zip 11418–2832; tel. 718/206–6000, (Total facility includes 204 beds in nursing home–type unit) **A**1 3 5 9 10 12 13 **F**2 6 9 11 12 14 15 21 22 23 27 28 29 30 32 33 34 35 37 38 39 41 42 44 45 46 47 48 49 50 51 52 53 55 56 57 58 59 60 61 62 63 64 65 66 67 68 69 70 71 73 74 75 76 77 81 82 84 85 87 88 89 90 92 94 95 96 98 106 107 108 109 **P**5 7 Primary Contact: David P. Rosen, President CFO: Mounir F. Doss, Executive Vice President and Chief Financial Officer CMO: Anthony Di Maria, M.D., Chief Medical Officer CIO: Richard Hlavenka, Director Management Information Systems CHR: Max Sclair, Vice President Web address: www.Jamaicahospital.org	23	10	588	20559	554	486375	3227	302270	148551	3040
✱ **KINGS COUNTY HOSPITAL CENTER**, 451 Clarkson Avenue, Brooklyn, Zip 11203–2097; tel. 718/245–3131, (Nonreporting) **A**1 2 3 5 8 9 10 **S** New York City Health and Hospitals Corporation, New York, NY Primary Contact: Jean G. Leon, R.N., Senior Vice President COO: George Proctor, Chief Operating Officer and Chief Financial Officer CFO: George Proctor, Chief Operating Officer and Chief Financial Officer CMO: Kathie Rones, M.D., Medical Director CIO: Al Porco, Chief Information Officer CHR: Stephen Small Warner, Deputy Executive Director, Network Human Resources Web address: www.ci.nyc.ny.us/html/hhc/html/kings.html	14	10	627	—	—	—	—	—	—	—

NY

Many Facility Codes have changed. Please refer to the AHA Guide Code Chart.

© 2005 AHA Guide

Hospital, Address, Telephone, Approval, Facility, and Physician Codes, Health Care System	Classi-fication Codes		Utilization Data					Expense (thousands) of dollars		
★ American Hospital Association (AHA) membership □ Joint Commission on Accreditation of Healthcare Organizations (JCAHO) accreditation ○ American Osteopathic Association (AOA) accreditation △ Commission on Accreditation of Rehabilitation Facilities (CARF) accreditation	Control	Service	Staffed Beds	Admissions	Census	Outpatient Visits	Births	Total	Payroll	Personnel
□ **KINGSBORO PSYCHIATRIC CENTER**, 681 Clarkson Avenue, Brooklyn, Zip 11203–2199; tel. 718/221–7395 **A**1 3 5 10 **F**22 29 32 58 71 77 94 **S** New York State Office of Mental Health, Albany, NY Primary Contact: Martin Darcy, Acting Executive Director Web address: www.omh.state.ny.us/omhweb/facilities/kbpc/facility/htm	12	22	290	317	279	0	0	28600	22000	656
✠ △ **KINGSBROOK JEWISH MEDICAL CENTER**, 585 Schenectady Avenue, Brooklyn, Zip 11203–1891; tel. 718/604–5000, (Total facility includes 538 beds in nursing home–type unit) **A**1 3 5 7 9 10 **F**1 6 12 14 21 22 27 28 29 32 33 40 42 44 45 46 48 49 51 52 55 57 58 60 62 63 65 66 68 69 70 71 73 74 75 76 77 81 82 84 87 88 92 93 94 108 109 110 Primary Contact: Linda Brady, M.D., President and Chief Executive Officer CFO: Mohamed Hebela, CPA, Vice President Finance and Chief Financial Officer CMO: Georges J. Casimir, M.D., Vice President Medical Affairs CHR: John McKeon, Vice President Human Resources Web address: www.kingsbrook.org	23	10	864	9404	774	—	0	—	—	—
✠ **LENOX HILL HOSPITAL**, 100 East 77th Street, Zip 10021–1883; tel. 212/434–2000 **A**1 3 5 8 9 10 **F**14 27 28 55 56 59 67 71 Primary Contact: Gladys George, President and Chief Executive Officer COO: Terence M. O'Brien, Executive Vice President and Chief Operating Officer CFO: Thomas E. Poccia, Vice President and Chief Financial Officer CIO: Louis Ajamy, Vice President and Chief Information Officer Web address: www.lenoxhillhospital.org	23	10	531	30673	458	—	—	—	—	2724
✠ **LINCOLN MEDICAL AND MENTAL HEALTH CENTER**, 234 East 149th Street, Bronx, Zip 10451–9998; tel. 718/579–5700, (Nonreporting) **A**1 3 8 9 10 **S** New York City Health and Hospitals Corporation, New York, NY Primary Contact: Jose R. Sanchez, Executive Director CFO: Victor Bakker, Chief Financial Officer CMO: Melissa Schori, M.D., Medical Director CIO: Suzanne Carter, Ed.D., Chief Information Officer CHR: Herman Smith, Senior Assistant Executive Director	14	10	322	—	—	—	—	—	—	—
LOEB CENTER NURSING REHABILITATION See Montefiore Medical Center										
✠ **LONG ISLAND COLLEGE HOSPITAL**, 339 Hicks Street, Brooklyn, Zip 11201–5509; tel. 718/780–1000 **A**1 2 3 5 8 9 10 **F**4 6 7 11 12 14 21 22 23 24 26 27 28 29 31 32 33 36 37 38 39 40 42 44 46 47 48 49 50 51 52 53 55 56 57 58 59 60 61 62 63 64 65 66 67 68 69 70 71 72 73 74 75 76 77 78 79 81 82 84 85 87 88 93 94 96 98 108 109 110 **S** Continuum Health Partners, New York, NY Primary Contact: Rita Battles, President and Chief Executive Officer CFO: Tomas Del Rio, Vice President Finance CIO: Hal Wachter, Director Information Systems Web address: www.wehealny.org	23	10	432	20271	332	259266	2871	—	—	2567
✠ **LONG ISLAND JEWISH MEDICAL CENTER**, 270–05 76th Avenue, New Hyde Park, Zip 11040–1496; tel. 718/470–7000, (Includes MANHASSET AMBULATORY CARE PAVILION, 1554 Northern Boulevard, Manhasset, Zip 11030; tel. 516/365–2070; SCHNEIDER CHILDREN'S HOSPITAL, 270–05 76th Avenue, Zip 11040; tel. 718/470–3000; ZUCKER HILLSIDE HOSPITAL, 75–59 263rd Street, Glen Oaks, Zip 11004; tel. 718/470–8000) **A**1 2 3 5 8 9 10 12 13 **F**1 2 4 7 8 9 10 11 12 14 15 16 17 18 19 20 21 22 23 24 26 27 28 29 30 31 32 33 34 35 37 38 39 40 42 44 45 46 47 48 49 50 51 52 53 55 56 57 58 59 60 61 62 63 64 65 66 67 69 70 71 72 73 74 75 76 77 78 79 80 81 82 84 85 87 88 89 90 92 93 94 95 96 98 99 106 107 108 109 110 **P**6 **S** North Shore–LIJ Health System, Great Neck, NY Primary Contact: Dennis Dowling, Executive Director CFO: Lora Myers, Associate Executive Director CMO: Jon R. Cohen, M.D., Chief Medical Officer CIO: Patrick Carney, Chief Information Officer Web address: www.lij.edu	23	10	795	41585	784	643894	5547	909252	440515	5872
✠ **LUTHERAN MEDICAL CENTER**, 150 55th Street, Brooklyn, Zip 11220–2570; tel. 718/630–7000 **A**1 3 5 9 10 12 13 **F**2 3 4 6 7 9 10 11 12 14 21 22 23 24 26 27 28 29 30 31 32 33 34 37 39 40 42 44 45 46 47 48 49 50 51 52 53 54 55 56 57 58 59 60 61 62 63 64 65 66 68 69 70 71 73 74 75 76 77 79 80 81 82 84 85 87 88 91 92 93 94 95 96 108 109 110 **P**8 Primary Contact: Wendy Z. Goldstein, President and Chief Executive Officer COO: Claudia Caine, Executive Vice President and Chief Operating Officer CFO: Richard Langfelder, Executive Vice President and Chief Financial Officer CMO: Victor R. Hrehorovich, M.D., Executive Vice President and Medical Director CIO: Steve Art, Senior Vice President and Chief Information Officer CHR: Frank Scheets, Vice President Web address: www.lmcmc.com	21	10	476	20734	331	47879	3667	367564	170731	2825
✠ **MAIMONIDES MEDICAL CENTER**, 4802 Tenth Avenue, Brooklyn, Zip 11219–2916; tel. 718/283–6000 **A**1 3 5 8 9 10 12 13 **F**1 2 6 7 9 10 11 12 14 15 17 19 21 22 23 24 26 27 28 29 31 32 33 35 37 38 39 42 44 46 48 50 52 53 55 56 57 58 59 60 61 62 63 64 66 67 69 70 71 72 73 74 75 76 77 78 81 82 83 84 85 87 88 89 90 93 94 95 96 98 106 108 109 110 **P**4 5 6 7 8 Primary Contact: Pamela S. Brier, President and Chief Executive Officer COO: Mark McDougle, Executive Vice President and Chief Operating Officer CFO: Robert Naldi, Chief Financial Officer CMO: Samuel Kopel, M.D., Medical Director CIO: Walter Fahey, Acting Chief Information Officer CHR: Marc Leff, Vice President, Human Resources Web address: www.maimonidesmed.org	23	10	610	32639	558	252694	6371	649551	324935	4703

NY

Hospital, Address, Telephone, Approval, Facility, and Physician Codes, Health Care System	Classi-fication Codes		Utilization Data					Expense (thousands) of dollars		
★ American Hospital Association (AHA) membership ☐ Joint Commission on Accreditation of Healthcare Organizations (JCAHO) accreditation ○ American Osteopathic Association (AOA) accreditation △ Commission on Accreditation of Rehabilitation Facilities (CARF) accreditation	Control	Service	Staffed Beds	Admissions	Census	Outpatient Visits	Births	Total	Payroll	Personnel
✠ **MANHATTAN EYE, EAR AND THROAT HOSPITAL**, 210 East 64th Street, Zip 10021–9885; tel. 212/838–9200 **A**1 3 5 9 10 **F**2 6 9 21 22 24 26 27 28 29 32 33 35 37 39 46 47 48 58 60 62 63 65 66 73 93 94 95 96 97 108 109 **P**8 Primary Contact: Philip Rosenthal, Executive Director COO: Terence M. O'Brien, Executive Vice President and Chief Operating Officer CFO: Tom Poccia, Chief Financial Officer CIO: Louis Ajamy, Vice President and Chief Information Officer CHR: Glen Courounis, Vice President Human Resources Web address: www.meeth.org	23	45	29	1224	5	44688	0	41699	14369	226
☐ **MANHATTAN PSYCHIATRIC CENTER–WARD'S ISLAND**, 600 East 125th Street, Zip 10035–9998; tel. 212/369–0500, (Nonreporting) **A**1 3 5 10 **S** New York State Office of Mental Health, Albany, NY Primary Contact: Eileen Consilvio, R.N., MS, Executive Director MARY IMMACULATE HOSPITAL See Saint Vincents Catholic Medical Centers of New York	12	22	745	—	—	—	—	—	—	—
✠ **MEMORIAL SLOAN–KETTERING CANCER CENTER**, 1275 York Avenue, Zip 10021–6094; tel. 212/639–2000 **A**1 2 3 5 8 9 10 **F**2 9 12 21 22 23 24 26 27 28 29 30 32 35 37 38 39 42 44 46 47 48 49 50 52 53 55 57 58 60 61 62 63 64 65 66 69 72 73 77 79 80 81 82 84 85 86 87 88 90 94 96 99 106 107 108 109 **P**1 Primary Contact: Harold Varmus, M.D., President and Chief Executive Officer COO: Kathryn Martin, Senior Vice President, Hospital Administrator CFO: Michael Gutnick, Senior Vice President Finance CMO: Robert E. Wittes, M.D., Physician in Chief CIO: Patricia Skarulis, Vice President Information Systems Web address: www.mskcc.org	23	41	425	20064	371	870594	0	1124125	353539	6977
✠ **METROPOLITAN HOSPITAL CENTER**, 1901 First Avenue, Zip 10029–7496; tel. 212/423–6262, (Includes METROPOLITAN GENERAL CARE UNIT, METROPOLITAN DRUG DETOXIFICATION AND METROPOLITAN PSYCHIATRIC UNIT), (Nonreporting) **A**1 3 5 8 9 10 **S** New York City Health and Hospitals Corporation, New York, NY Primary Contact: Louis Martir, Executive Director CFO: Albert L. Bigott, Chief Financial Officer CMO: Richard Stone, M.D., Medical Director CIO: Suzanne Carter, Ed.D., Chief Information Officer MONSIGNOR JAMES H FITZPATRICK PAVILION FOR SKILLED NURSING CARE See Saint Vincents Catholic Medical Centers of New York	15	10	325	—	—	—	—	—	—	—
✠ **MONTEFIORE MEDICAL CENTER**, 111 East 210th Street, Bronx, Zip 10467–2490; tel. 718/920–4321, (Includes JACK D WEILER HOSPITAL OF ALBERT EINSTEIN COLLEGE OF MEDICINE, 1825 Eastchester Road, Zip 10461–2373; tel. 718/904–2000; LOEB CENTER NURSING REHABILITATION) **A**1 3 5 8 9 10 **F**1 4 9 10 11 12 14 15 16 17 18 19 20 21 22 23 24 26 27 28 29 32 33 35 36 37 38 39 40 42 44 46 47 48 49 50 51 52 53 55 56 57 58 59 60 61 62 63 64 65 66 67 68 69 70 71 72 73 74 75 76 77 79 81 82 84 85 87 88 89 90 92 93 94 96 98 99 100 101 106 107 108 109 110 **P**5 Primary Contact: Spencer Foreman, M.D., President COO: Robert B. Conaty, Executive Vice President Operations CFO: Joel A. Perlman, Senior Vice President Finance CMO: Steven M. Safyer, M.D., Senior Vice President and Chief Medical Officer CIO: Jack Wolf, Vice President Management Information Systems Web address: www.montefiore.org MORGAN STANLEY CHILDREN'S HOSPITAL OF NEW YORK–PRESBYTERIAN See New York–Presbyterian Hospital	23	10	1003	57541	900	1418496	4202	1676026	753196	11496
✠ △ **MOUNT SINAI HOSPTIAL**, One Gustave L. Levy Place, Zip 10029–6574; tel. 212/241–6500 **A**1 3 5 7 8 9 10 **F**1 2 4 5 6 9 10 11 12 13 14 15 16 17 18 19 20 21 22 23 24 26 27 28 29 30 31 32 33 35 37 38 39 40 42 43 44 45 46 47 48 49 50 52 53 55 56 57 58 59 60 61 62 63 64 65 66 67 68 69 70 71 72 73 74 75 76 77 79 80 81 82 83 84 85 86 87 88 89 90 93 94 95 96 98 99 100 101 102 103 104 105 106 107 108 109 110 **P**5 Primary Contact: Burton P. Drayer, M.D., President COO: Wayne Keathley, M.P.H., Chief Operating Officer CFO: Donald Scanlon, Chief Financial Officer CMO: Derborah Marin, M.D., Chief Medical Officer CIO: Jack Nelson, Senior Vice President and Chief Information Officer CHR: Jane Maksoud, Director, Human Resources Web address: www.mountsinai.org	23	10	938	45421	812	461526	4304	946173	376847	—
☐ **NEW YORK COMMUNITY HOSPITAL**, 2525 Kings Highway, Brooklyn, Zip 11229–1798, Mailing Address: 2513 Avenue O, Zip 11210; tel. 718/692–5300, (Nonreporting) **A**1 5 9 10 **S** New York Presbyterian Healthcare System, New York, NY Primary Contact: Lin H. Mo, President and Chief Executive Officer Web address: www.nycommunityhospital.com	23	10	125	—	—	—	—	—	—	—

NY

Hospital, Address, Telephone, Approval, Facility, and Physician Codes, Health Care System	Classi-fication Codes		Utilization Data					Expense (thousands) of dollars		
★ American Hospital Association (AHA) membership □ Joint Commission on Accreditation of Healthcare Organizations (JCAHO) accreditation ○ American Osteopathic Association (AOA) accreditation △ Commission on Accreditation of Rehabilitation Facilities (CARF) accreditation	Control	Service	Staffed Beds	Admissions	Census	Outpatient Visits	Births	Total	Payroll	Personnel

	Control	Service	Staffed Beds	Admissions	Census	Outpatient Visits	Births	Total	Payroll	Personnel
⊠ **NEW YORK EYE AND EAR INFIRMARY**, 310 East 14th Street, Zip 10003–4201; tel. 212/979–4000 **A**1 3 5 9 10 **F**9 21 22 26 27 28 29 34 35 37 39 42 46 47 48 52 53 57 63 64 65 69 81 88 92 93 94 96 99 105 108 **P**8 **S** Continuum Health Partners, New York, NY Primary Contact: Joseph P. Corcoran, President and Chief Executive Officer COO: Raymond Minicus, Vice President and Chief Operating Officer CFO: Vincent R. Raab, Vice President Finance and Chief Financial Officer CMO: J Robert Rosenthal, M.D., Vice President, Medical Affairs CIO: Don Ushak, Director of Information Systems CHR: Susan Singer, Director, Human Resources Web address: www.nyee.edu	23	45	32	921	8	185056	0	74360	35626	651
□ **NEW YORK HOSPITAL MEDICAL CENTER OF QUEENS**, 56–45 Main Street, Flushing, Zip 11355–5000; tel. 718/670–1231, (Nonreporting) **A**1 2 3 5 9 10 **S** New York Presbyterian Healthcare System, New York, NY Primary Contact: Stephen S. Mills, President and Chief Executive Officer Web address: www.nyhq.org	23	10	439	—	—	—	—	—	—	—
⊠ **NEW YORK METHODIST HOSPITAL**, 506 Sixth Street, Brooklyn, Zip 11215–3645; tel. 718/780–3000 **A**1 2 3 5 8 9 10 **F**2 7 9 10 11 12 14 21 22 26 27 28 29 32 33 35 37 38 39 40 42 44 46 47 48 49 50 52 53 55 56 57 58 59 60 61 62 63 65 66 67 68 70 71 73 75 76 77 79 81 82 83 84 87 88 90 93 94 96 106 108 109 **P**6 **S** New York Presbyterian Healthcare System, New York, NY Primary Contact: Mark J. Mundy, President and Chief Executive Officer CFO: Edward A. Zaidberg, Senior Vice President Finance CMO: Stanley Sherbell, Executive Vice President for Medical Affairs Web address: www.nym.org	23	10	570	27862	490	—	—	—	—	—
□ **NEW YORK STATE PSYCHIATRIC INSTITUTE**, 1051 Riverside Drive, Zip 10032–2695; tel. 212/543–5000 **A**1 3 5 10 **F**26 27 28 52 71 72 74 76 77 84 87 94 **S** New York State Office of Mental Health, Albany, NY Primary Contact: Jeffrey A. Lieberman, M.D., Executive Director Web address: www.nyspi.org	12	22	58	514	50	50631	—	—	—	—
⊠ △ **NEW YORK UNIVERSITY MEDICAL CENTER**, 550 First Avenue, Zip 10016–4576; tel. 212/263–7300, (Includes RUSK INSTITUTE) **A**1 3 5 7 8 9 10 **F**2 5 6 9 10 11 12 14 15 16 17 18 19 20 21 22 23 24 26 27 28 29 30 31 32 33 34 35 37 38 39 41 42 43 44 46 47 48 49 50 52 53 55 56 57 58 59 60 61 62 63 64 65 66 67 68 69 70 71 72 73 74 75 76 77 79 80 81 82 84 85 87 88 89 90 93 94 95 96 98 99 101 102 104 105 106 108 109 110 **P**5 Primary Contact: Eric Rackow, M.D., President and Chief Executive Officer COO: Mona Sonnenshein, Senior Vice President for Hospital Administration CFO: Richard Miller, Senior Vice President Finance CMO: Max M. Cohen, M.D., Chief Medical Officer CIO: Stuart Sugarman, Senior Vice President and Chief Information Officer CHR: Ira Warm, Senior Vice President Human Resources Web address: www.nyumedicalcenter.org	23	10	731	31996	644	490370	4759	675918	318792	6126
□ **NEW YORK WESTCHESTER SQUARE MEDICAL CENTER**, 2475 St. Raymond Avenue, Bronx, Zip 10461–3198; tel. 718/430–7300 **A**1 5 9 10 **F**2 12 14 21 23 29 33 39 46 49 52 53 55 57 58 61 62 63 66 69 70 75 81 82 84 88 94 108 **S** New York Presbyterian Healthcare System, New York, NY Primary Contact: Alan Kopman, President and Chief Executive Officer Web address: www.nywsmc.org	12	10	165	7329	128	52869	0	—	—	—
⊠ △ **NEW YORK–PRESBYTERIAN HOSPITAL**, 525 East 68th Street, Zip 10021–4885; tel. 212/746–5454, (Includes MORGAN STANLEY CHILDREN'S HOSPITAL OF NEW YORK–PRESBYTERIAN, 3959 Broadway, Zip 10032–3784; tel. 212/305–2500; NEW YORK–PRESBYTERIAN HOSPITAL, WESTCHESTER DIVISION, Zip 10605; NEW YORK–PRESBYTERIAN HOSPITAL/WEILL CORNELL MEDICAL CENTER; NEW YORK–PRESBYTERIAN/COLUMBIA UNIVERSITY MEDICAL CENTER, 161 Fort Washington Avenue, Zip 10032; tel. 212/305–2500; PAYNE WHITNEY PSYCHIATRIC CLINIC; THE ALLEN PAVILION, 5141 Broadway, Zip 10032; tel. 212/932–5000) **A**1 2 3 5 7 8 9 10 **F**1 2 3 4 5 6 7 9 10 11 12 13 14 15 16 17 18 19 20 21 22 23 24 26 27 28 29 30 31 32 33 34 35 37 38 39 40 41 42 43 44 45 46 47 48 49 50 52 53 55 56 57 58 59 60 61 62 63 64 65 66 67 68 69 70 71 72 73 74 75 76 77 78 79 80 81 82 84 85 86 87 88 89 90 92 93 94 95 96 98 99 100 101 102 103 104 105 106 107 108 109 110 **P**5 **S** New York Presbyterian Healthcare System, New York, NY Primary Contact: Herbert Pardes, M.D., President and Chief Executive Officer CFO: Phyllis R. Lantos, Senior Vice President, Chief Financial Officer and Treasurer CMO: Laura Forese, Senior Vice President and Chief Medical Officer CIO: Aurelia Boyer, Senior Vice President and Chief Information Officer CHR: Thomas Ferguson, Senior Vice President and Chief Human Resources Officer Web address: www.nyp.org NEW YORK–PRESBYTERIAN HOSPITAL/WEILL CORNELL MEDICAL CENTER See New York–Presbyterian Hospital NEW YORK–PRESBYTERIAN/COLUMBIA UNIVERSITY MEDICAL CENTER See New York–Presbyterian Hospital	23	10	2095	93241	1802	1661128	12425	2337821	1070809	17507

Hospital, Address, Telephone, Approval, Facility, and Physician Codes, Health Care System	Classification Codes		Utilization Data					Expense (thousands) of dollars		
★ American Hospital Association (AHA) membership □ Joint Commission on Accreditation of Healthcare Organizations (JCAHO) accreditation ○ American Osteopathic Association (AOA) accreditation △ Commission on Accreditation of Rehabilitation Facilities (CARF) accreditation	Control	Service	Staffed Beds	Admissions	Census	Outpatient Visits	Births	Total	Payroll	Personnel

★ **NORTH CENTRAL BRONX HOSPITAL**, 3424 Kossuth Avenue, Bronx, Zip 10467–2489; tel. 718/519–3500 **A**1 8 9 10 **F**2 4 6 9 12 21 22 24 26 27 28 29 30 31 32 33 35 39 42 46 47 48 50 52 53 55 56 58 59 60 61 62 63 65 66 69 70 71 72 73 74 75 76 77 78 81 82 87 88 89 93 94 95 96 98 106 108 **P**6 **S** New York City Health and Hospitals Corporation, New York, NY Primary Contact: William P. Walsh, Executive Director COO: Arthur Wagner, Chief Operating Officer CFO: Nancy Guzman, Chief Financial Officer CIO: Daniel Morreale, Chief Information Officer CHR: Dolores Leite, Chief Human Resource Exec Web address: www.ci.nyc.ny.us/html/hhc/html/northcentralbronx.html	14	10	210	7792	190	258345	1727	159646	61284	1193
★ **NORTH GENERAL HOSPITAL**, 1879 Madison Avenue, Zip 10035–2745; tel. 212/423–4000 **A**1 3 5 9 10 **F**2 3 4 10 12 21 23 29 30 32 33 34 37 39 44 46 48 49 50 52 53 55 57 58 61 62 63 64 66 69 71 72 73 77 81 88 94 96 106 107 109 110 Primary Contact: Samuel J. Daniel, M.D., President and Chief Executive Officer COO: Michael Greene, Chief Operating Officer CFO: Francis Hagan, Chief Financial Officer CMO: Valentine Burroughs, M.D., Medical Director CIO: Michele Prisco, Director CHR: Donald Ray, Attorney Web address: www.northgeneral.org	23	10	159	8136	147	118865	—	—	—	978
★ **NORTH SHORE UNIVERSITY HOSPITAL–FOREST HILLS**, Flushing, Mailing Address: 102–01 66th Road, Zip 11375–2029; tel. 718/830–4000 **A**1 2 5 9 10 **F**2 10 11 12 21 22 23 26 27 28 29 31 33 34 35 37 38 39 40 42 45 46 47 48 49 52 53 55 57 59 61 62 63 64 65 66 70 73 81 88 92 94 96 106 108 109 **S** North Shore–LIJ Health System, Great Neck, NY Primary Contact: Robert T. Hettenbach, Executive Director Web address: www.northshorelij.com	23	10	223	12996	193	50801	1826	117238	53041	832
□ **NYU DOWNTOWN HOSPITAL**, 170 William Street, Zip 10038–2649; tel. 212/312–5000, (Nonreporting) **A**1 3 5 9 10 Primary Contact: Bruce D. Logan, M.D., President and Chief Executive Officer Web address: www.nyudh.med.nyu.edu	23	10	162	—						
□ **OUR LADY OF MERCY MEDICAL CENTER**, 600 East 233rd Street, Bronx, Zip 10466–2697; tel. 718/920–9000 **A**1 2 3 5 8 9 10 **F**2 3 6 9 11 12 14 21 22 23 24 26 27 28 29 32 33 34 39 42 44 46 48 49 52 53 55 56 57 58 59 60 61 62 63 66 69 70 71 72 73 74 75 76 77 81 82 83 84 88 94 96 108 110 Primary Contact: Richard Celiberti, President and Chief Executive Officer Web address: www.ourladyofmercy.com	21	10	377	15277	221	—	1829	—	—	1833
□ **PARKWAY HOSPITAL**, 70–35 113th Street, Flushing, Zip 11375–4699; tel. 718/990–4100 **A**1 9 10 **F**6 12 14 21 33 36 37 49 55 65 66 81 82 88 93 94 106 Primary Contact: Alan P. Zeitlin, M.D., Chief Executive Officer	33	10	180	9450	156	—	—	—	—	
PAYNE WHITNEY PSYCHIATRIC CLINIC See New York–Presbyterian Hospital										
□ ○ **PENINSULA HOSPITAL CENTER**, 51–15 Beach Channel Drive, Far Rockaway, Zip 11691–1074; tel. 718/734–2000, (Nonreporting) **A**1 9 10 11 12 13 Primary Contact: Robert V. Levine, President and Chief Executive Officer	23	10	190							
□ **QUEENS CHILDREN'S PSYCHIATRIC CENTER**, 74–03 Commonwealth Boulevard, Jamaica, Zip 11426–1890; tel. 718/264–4506 **A**1 **F**21 71 72 77 78 94 **P**6 **S** New York State Office of Mental Health, Albany, NY Primary Contact: Keith Little, Acting Executive Director Web address: www.omh.state.ny.us	12	52	84	125	72	32000	0	—	—	300
★ **QUEENS HOSPITAL CENTER**, 82–68 164th Street, Jamaica, Zip 11432–1104; tel. 718/883–3000 **A**1 2 3 5 8 9 10 **F**3 4 9 12 22 23 24 26 27 28 29 31 32 33 39 44 46 52 53 55 56 59 63 68 69 70 71 72 73 75 76 77 78 81 84 93 94 98 108 109 **P**6 **S** New York City Health and Hospitals Corporation, New York, NY Primary Contact: Antonio D. Martin, Executive Director CFO: Julius Wool, Chief Financial Officer CIO: Alfred Marino, Chief Information Officer Web address: www.ci.nyc.ny.us/html/hhc/html/facilities/queens/shtml	14	10	248	13546	196	377498	1770	219291	92080	1903
□ **ROCKEFELLER UNIVERSITY HOSPITAL**, (Clinical Research), 1230 York Avenue, Zip 10021–6399; tel. 212/327–8000 **A**1 10 **F**2 94 Primary Contact: Emil Gotschlich, M.D., Vice President Medical Sciences Web address: www.clinfo.rockefeller.edu	23	49	40	248	7	5304	0	—	—	62
ROOSEVELT HOSPITAL See St. Luke's–Roosevelt Hospital Center										
RUSK INSTITUTE See New York University Medical Center										
★ **SAINT VINCENT'S HOSPITAL – MANHATTAN**, 170 West 12th Street, Zip 10011–8397; tel. 212/604–7000, (Nonreporting) **A**1 2 8 9 10 **S** Saint Vincent Catholic Medical Centers, New York, NY Primary Contact: Kathleen Galvin, Executive Director CFO: Timothy Weis, Chief Financial Officer Web address: www.svcmcny.org	21	10	978	—	—	—	—	—	—	—

Hospital, Address, Telephone, Approval, Facility, and Physician Codes, Health Care System	Classi-fication Codes		Utilization Data					Expense (thousands) of dollars		
★ American Hospital Association (AHA) membership □ Joint Commission on Accreditation of Healthcare Organizations (JCAHO) accreditation ○ American Osteopathic Association (AOA) accreditation △ Commission on Accreditation of Rehabilitation Facilities (CARF) accreditation	Control	Service	Staffed Beds	Admissions	Census	Outpatient Visits	Births	Total	Payroll	Personnel
✦ **SAINT VINCENTS CATHOLIC MEDICAL CENTERS OF NEW YORK**, 88–25 153rd Street, Jamaica, Zip 11432–3731; tel. 718/558–6900, (Includes HOLY FAMILY HOME, 1740 84th Street, Brooklyn, Zip 11214; tel. 718/232–3666; MARY IMMACULATE HOSPITAL, 152–11 89th Avenue, Zip 11432; tel. 718/558–2000; MONSIGNOR JAMES H FITZPATRICK PAVILION FOR SKILLED NURSING CARE, 152–11 89th Avenue, Zip 11432; tel. 718/558–2800; ST. JOSEPH'S HOSPITAL, 158–40 79th Avenue, Flushing, Zip 11366; tel. 718/558–6200; ST. MARY'S HOSPITAL OF BROOKLYN, 170 Buffalo Avenue, Brooklyn, Zip 11213; tel. 718/221–3000), (Total facility includes 603 beds in nursing home–type unit) (Nonreporting) **A**1 2 9 10 **S** Saint Vincent Catholic Medical Centers, New York, NY Primary Contact: Rose Britt, Executive Director CFO: Daniel Rinaldi, Vice President and Chief Financial Officer CIO: Malcolm Murray, Vice President Information Services Web address: www.svcmc.org SCHNEIDER CHILDREN'S HOSPITAL See Long Island Jewish Medical Center	21	10	1584	—	—	—	—	—	—	—
□ **SOUTH BEACH PSYCHIATRIC CENTER**, 777 Seaview Avenue, Staten Island, Zip 10305–3499; tel. 718/667–2300, (Nonreporting) **A**1 10 **S** New York State Office of Mental Health, Albany, NY Primary Contact: William Henri, Executive Director Web address: www.omh.state.ny.us ST VINCENT'S CAMPUS See St. Vincent's Hospital	12	22	325	—	—	—	—	—	—	—
□ **ST. BARNABAS HOSPITAL**, 183rd Street & Third Avenue, Bronx, Zip 10457–9998; tel. 718/960–9000, (Includes UNION HOSPITAL OF THE BRONX, 260 East 188th Street, Zip 10458; tel. 718/220–2020), (Total facility includes 199 beds in nursing home–type unit) (Nonreporting) **A**1 3 5 9 10 12 13 Primary Contact: Ronald Gade, M.D., President Web address: www.stbarnabashospital.org	23	10	645	—	—	—	—	—	—	—
□ ○ **ST. JOHN'S EPISCOPAL HOSPITAL–SOUTH SHORE**, 327 Beach 19th Street, Far Rockaway, Zip 11691–4424; tel. 718/869–7000, (Nonreporting) **A**1 3 5 9 10 11 12 13 Primary Contact: Luis Hernandez, Chief Executive Officer ST. JOSEPH'S HOSPITAL See Saint Vincents Catholic Medical Centers of New York	21	10	240	—	—	—	—	—	—	—
✦ **ST. LUKE'S–ROOSEVELT HOSPITAL CENTER**, 1000 Tenth Avenue, Zip 10019; tel. 212/523–4000, (Includes ROOSEVELT HOSPITAL, 1000 Tenth Avenue, tel. 212/523–5700; ST. LUKE'S HOSPITAL CENTER) **A**1 3 5 8 9 10 **F**2 3 4 6 9 10 11 12 14 15 17 19 21 22 23 24 26 27 28 29 31 32 33 34 35 36 37 38 39 42 43 44 46 47 48 49 50 52 53 55 56 57 58 59 60 61 62 63 64 65 66 67 68 69 70 71 72 73 74 75 76 77 78 79 80 81 82 83 84 85 87 88 89 90 94 95 96 97 98 101 106 108 109 **P**6 8 **S** Continuum Health Partners, New York, NY Primary Contact: Richard F. Daines, M.D., President and Chief Executive Officer CFO: Brendan Loughlin, Executive Vice President and Chief Financial Officer CMO: Peter Tesler, M.D., Associate Medical Director CIO: Marc Milstein, Chief Information Officer CHR: Bart Metzger, Vice President Human Resources Web address: www.slrhc.org ST. MARY'S HOSPITAL OF BROOKLYN See Saint Vincents Catholic Medical Centers of New York	23	10	718	41665	668	602916	5225	838524	410978	5754
✦ **ST. VINCENT'S HOSPITAL**, (Formerly St. Vincent's Catholic Medical Center, Staten Island Region), 355 Bard Avenue, Staten Island, Zip 10310–1699; tel. 718/818–1234, (Includes BAYLEY SETON CAMPUS, 75 Vanderbilt Avenue, Zip 10304–3850; tel. 718/818–6000; ST VINCENT'S CAMPUS), (Nonreporting) **A**1 2 3 5 9 10 **S** Saint Vincent Catholic Medical Centers, New York, NY Primary Contact: Dawn M. Gideon, Executive Director CFO: Robert Zupa, Vice President Finance Web address: www.svcmc.org/statenisland/	21	10	449	—	—	—	—	—	—	—
□ **ST. VINCENT'S MIDTOWN HOSPITAL**, 415 West 51st Street, Zip 10019–6394; tel. 212/459–8000 **A**1 9 10 12 **F**2 4 6 14 21 22 29 32 33 37 42 44 46 48 49 50 52 53 55 56 57 60 61 62 63 65 66 69 71 73 74 81 88 92 94 108 110 Primary Contact: Len Walsh, Chief Executive Officer Web address: www.svcmc.org/midtown	21	10	143	7164	88	91156	0	77460	40102	711
✦ △ **STATEN ISLAND UNIVERSITY HOSPITAL**, 475 Seaview Avenue, Staten Island, Zip 10305–9998; tel. 718/226–9000 **A**1 2 3 5 7 8 9 10 **F**2 3 4 5 6 9 10 11 12 13 14 15 17 19 21 22 23 24 26 27 28 29 30 32 33 34 36 37 38 39 40 42 44 45 46 47 48 49 50 53 55 56 57 58 59 61 62 63 64 66 67 68 69 70 71 73 74 76 77 78 79 81 82 84 85 86 87 88 89 90 93 94 96 98 99 106 107 108 109 110 **S** North Shore–LIJ Health System, Great Neck, NY Primary Contact: Anthony C. Ferreri, President and Chief Executive Officer COO: Al Glover, Chief Operating Officer CFO: Jack Costello, Senior Vice President Finance and Chief Financial Officer CMO: Mark Jarrett, M.D., Chief Medical Officer CIO: Frank Di Sanzo, Vice President and Chief Information Officer CHR: Margaret Dialto, Vice President Human Resources Web address: www.siuh.edu	23	10	686	39649	592	285861	3009	567850	255956	4732

NY

Hospital, Address, Telephone, Approval, Facility, and Physician Codes, Health Care System	Classi-fication Codes		Utilization Data					Expense (thousands) of dollars		
★ American Hospital Association (AHA) membership □ Joint Commission on Accreditation of Healthcare Organizations (JCAHO) accreditation ○ American Osteopathic Association (AOA) accreditation △ Commission on Accreditation of Rehabilitation Facilities (CARF) accreditation	Control	Service	Staffed Beds	Admissions	Census	Outpatient Visits	Births	Total	Payroll	Personnel

□ **STATEN ISLAND UNIVERSITY HOSPITAL–CONCORD**, 1050 Targee Street, Staten Island, Zip 10304–4499; tel. 718/390–1400, (Nonreporting) **A**1 9 10 Primary Contact: Anthony C. Ferreri, President and Chief Executive Officer Web address: www.siuh.edu	23	10	117	—	—	—	—	—	—	—
⊠ **SUNY DOWNSTATE MEDICAL CENTER UNIVERSITY HOSPITAL**, 445 Lenox Road, Brooklyn, Zip 11203–2098; tel. 718/270–1000 **A**1 2 3 5 8 9 10 **F**6 11 12 14 15 16 17 18 19 20 21 22 23 24 26 27 28 29 31 32 33 37 40 41 42 44 45 46 47 48 49 50 52 55 56 57 58 59 60 61 62 63 65 66 67 68 69 70 71 72 73 74 75 76 77 78 81 82 84 86 87 88 93 94 95 96 97 101 107 108 109 **P**5 Primary Contact: Robert P. Jacobs, M.D., Chief Executive Officer COO: Debra D. Carey, Chief Administrative Officer CFO: Gerry Dantis, Assistant Vice President Finance CMO: Richard Freeman, M.D., Chief Medical Officer CIO: Bert Robles, Chief Information Officer CHR: Stephan Kass, Vice President for Human Resources Web address: www.downstate.edu	12	10	324	15447	233	321215	1470	377408	171872	2731
THE ALLEN PAVILION See New York–Presbyterian Hospital										
THE MOUNT SINAI HOSPITAL OF QUEENS, 25–10 30th Avenue, Long Island City, Zip 11102–2495; tel. 718/932–1000 **A**10 **F**2 12 21 22 23 24 27 28 29 33 36 37 38 39 42 44 46 47 48 49 52 53 55 57 58 61 62 63 64 65 66 69 70 73 76 77 79 81 82 87 88 94 95 96 97 106 107 108 **P**6 Primary Contact: Caryn A. Schwab, Executive Director Web address: www.mshq.org	23	10	196	10456	168	70575	0	102971	53218	872
UNION HOSPITAL OF THE BRONX See St. Barnabas Hospital										
⊠ **VETERANS ADMINISTRATION NEW YORK HARBOR HEALTHCARE SYSTEM**, 800 Poly Place, Brooklyn, Zip 11209–7104; tel. 718/630–3500, (Includes VETERANS AFFAIRS MEDICAL CENTER; VETERANS AFFAIRS MEDICAL CENTER, 423 East 23rd Street, New York, Zip 10010–5050; tel. 212/686–7500), (Total facility includes 231 beds in nursing home–type unit) **A**1 2 3 5 8 **F**1 2 3 4 6 7 12 14 15 17 19 21 22 23 28 29 31 32 33 36 37 38 41 42 44 45 46 47 48 49 50 51 52 53 55 57 58 60 61 62 63 64 65 66 68 69 70 71 73 74 75 76 77 78 79 80 81 82 83 84 85 87 88 92 94 96 106 108 109 110 **P**6 **S** Department of Veterans Affairs, Washington, DC Primary Contact: John J. Donnellan, Jr, Director CFO: Daniel Downey, Chief Fiscal Service CIO: Maria Schay, Chief Information Officer Web address: www.vaww.va.gov	45	10	549	9939	458	672693	0	462093	228238	3448
⊠ △ **VETERANS AFFAIRS MEDICAL CENTER**, 130 West Kingsbridge Road, Bronx, Zip 10468–3992; tel. 718/584–9000, (Total facility includes 112 beds in nursing home–type unit) **A**1 2 3 5 7 8 **F**2 4 5 7 9 12 14 15 17 21 22 23 25 26 27 28 29 30 31 32 33 36 37 38 39 40 42 43 44 45 47 48 49 50 52 53 55 57 58 60 61 62 63 64 65 66 68 69 70 71 73 74 75 76 77 78 79 80 81 82 84 85 87 88 92 94 96 106 107 108 109 110 **S** Department of Veterans Affairs, Washington, DC Primary Contact: Maryann Musumeci, Director CFO: Gregory Angelo, Chief Fiscal Program CMO: Clive Rosendorff, M.D., Chief Medical Program CIO: Linda Bund, Chief Information Officer, Director of Education CHR: Peter Tinker, Chief, Human Resources Web address: www.va.gov/sta/guide/home.asp	45	10	326	4681	224	273242	0	162607	107647	1758
□ **VICTORY MEMORIAL HOSPITAL**, 9036 Seventh Avenue, Brooklyn, Zip 11228–3625; tel. 718/567–1234, (Nonreporting) **A**1 9 10 Primary Contact: Krishin L. Bhatia, Administrator Web address: www.vmhny.org	23	10	346	—	—	—	—	—	—	—
⊠ **WOODHULL MEDICAL AND MENTAL HEALTH CENTER**, 760 Broadway Street, Brooklyn, Zip 11206–5383; tel. 718/963–8000, (Nonreporting) **A**1 8 9 10 **S** New York City Health and Hospitals Corporation, New York, NY Primary Contact: Lynda D. Curtis, Executive Director COO: Candis Best, Chief Information Officer and Chief Operating Officer CFO: Milton Nunez, Chief Financial Officer CMO: Edward Fishkin, M.D., Medical Director CIO: Candis Best, Chief Information Officer and Chief Operating Officer CHR: Yvette Villanueva, Senior Associate Executive Director Web address: www.nyc.gov/html/hhc/home/html	14	10	406	—	—	—	—	—	—	—
⊠ ○ **WYCKOFF HEIGHTS MEDICAL CENTER**, 374 Stockholm Street, Brooklyn, Zip 11237–4099; tel. 718/963–7272 **A**1 3 5 9 10 11 12 13 **F**6 11 12 14 21 22 23 26 27 28 29 32 33 37 39 42 44 45 46 47 48 49 50 52 53 55 56 57 58 59 61 62 63 64 65 66 69 70 81 82 84 85 88 90 92 94 96 106 108 109 110 **P**4 6 **S** New York Presbyterian Healthcare System, New York, NY Primary Contact: Dominick J. Gio, President and Chief Executive Officer COO: Harold E. McDonald, Executive Vice President and Chief Operating Officer CFO: Hal McNeil, Vice President and Chief Financial Officer CMO: Nirmal K. Mattoo, M.D., Senior Vice President and Medical Director CIO: Sid Kaul, Chief Information Officer CHR: Fred Eisgrub, Vice President, Human Resources Web address: www.wyckoffhospital.org	23	10	305	19355	284	260403	1816	238467	98446	1790
ZUCKER HILLSIDE HOSPITAL See Long Island Jewish Medical Center										

NY

Many Facility Codes have changed. Please refer to the AHA Guide Code Chart. © 2005 AHA Guide

Hospital, Address, Telephone, Approval, Facility, and Physician Codes, Health Care System	Classi-fication Codes		Utilization Data					Expense (thousands) of dollars		
★ American Hospital Association (AHA) membership □ Joint Commission on Accreditation of Healthcare Organizations (JCAHO) accreditation ○ American Osteopathic Association (AOA) accreditation △ Commission on Accreditation of Rehabilitation Facilities (CARF) accreditation	Control	Service	Staffed Beds	Admissions	Census	Outpatient Visits	Births	Total	Payroll	Personnel

NEWARK—Wayne County

□ **NEWARK–WAYNE COMMUNITY HOSPITAL**, Driving Park Avenue, Zip 14513, Mailing Address: P.O. Box 111, Zip 14513–0111; tel. 315/332–2022, (Total facility includes 180 beds in nursing home–type unit) **A**1 9 10 **F**1 2 8 9 10 11 12 21 22 27 28 30 31 33 35 39 44 46 47 48 52 53 55 57 58 59 60 62 63 64 65 66 69 71 75 81 84 88 92 94 96 106 108 109 110 **P**5 **S** ViaHealth, Rochester, NY
Primary Contact: W. Neil Stroman, Administrator
Web address: www.viahealth.org

| | 23 | 10 | 275 | 3603 | 223 | 144835 | 434 | — | — | 539 |

NEWBURGH—Orange County

⊞ **ST. LUKE'S CORNWALL HOSPITAL – NEWBURGH CAMPUS**, 70 Dubois Street, Zip 12550–4898; tel. 845/561–4400, (Includes ST. LUKE'S CORNWALL HOSPITAL – CORNWALL CAMPUS, 19 Laurel Avenue, Cornwall, Zip 12518–1499; tel. 845/534–7711; ST. LUKE'S HOSPITAL) **A**1 2 9 10 **F**2 4 9 11 12 21 23 26 27 28 29 30 33 37 39 40 42 45 46 47 48 49 52 53 55 56 57 58 59 60 61 62 63 64 65 66 69 71 73 75 78 81 82 84 87 88 94 96 106 108 110
Primary Contact: Allan E. Atzrott, President and Chief Executive Officer
COO: Robert Ross, Vice President Operations
CFO: Mary Elizabeth Duffy, Vice President and Chief Financial Officer
CMO: Christine Jelalian, M.D., Medical Director
CIO: Jane Lake, Director, Information Technology
CHR: Deborah Turner, Vice President Human Resources
Web address: www.stlukescornwallhospital.org

| | 23 | 10 | 268 | 13713 | 176 | 61873 | 1177 | 126532 | 60888 | 1290 |

NEWFANE—Niagara County

★ **INTER–COMMUNITY MEMORIAL HOSPITAL**, 2600 William Street, Zip 14108–1093; tel. 716/778–5111 **A**9 10 **F**9 11 12 14 26 27 28 29 32 33 37 42 44 46 47 48 52 55 58 59 60 62 63 65 66 69 70 81 82 84 88 92 94 106 107 108 109
Primary Contact: Clare A. Haar, Chief Executive Officer
COO: David J. Di Bacco, Chief Operating Officer
CFO: Donald L. Kepner, Chief Financial Officer
CMO: Norbert J. Szymula, M.D., Medical Director
CHR: Laura E. Clark, Director of Human Resources

| | 23 | 10 | 71 | 2445 | 32 | 64568 | 120 | 18466 | 9280 | 252 |

NIAGARA FALLS—Niagara County

NIAGARA FALLS MEMORIAL MEDICAL CENTER, 621 Tenth Street, Zip 14302–0708, Mailing Address: P.O. Box 708, Zip 14302–0708; tel. 716/278–4000, (Nonreporting) **A**3 5 9 10
Primary Contact: Joseph A. Ruffolo, President and Chief Executive Officer
Web address: www.nfmmc.org

| | 23 | 10 | 288 | — | — | — | — | — | — | — |

NORTH TONAWANDA—Niagara County

DE GRAFF MEMORIAL HOSPITAL See Buffalo General Hospital, Buffalo

NORTHPORT—Suffolk County

⊞ △ **VETERANS AFFAIRS MEDICAL CENTER**, 79 Middleville Road, Zip 11768–2293; tel. 631/261–4400 **A**1 2 3 5 7 8 **F**2 3 4 10 15 21 22 23 26 27 28 29 31 32 33 35 36 37 38 39 41 44 46 47 48 49 50 52 53 55 57 58 60 61 62 63 65 66 68 69 70 71 73 74 75 76 77 78 79 81 82 84 86 87 88 92 93 94 96 106 107 108 109 110 **P**6 **S** Department of Veterans Affairs, Washington, DC
Primary Contact: Robert Schuster, Director
CFO: Nancy Mirone, Business Manager
CMO: Edward Mack, M.D., Chief of Staff
CIO: Robert Ziskin, Chief Information Officer
Web address: www.va.gov/sta/guide/home.asp

| | 45 | 10 | 332 | 3046 | 241 | 306037 | 0 | 188257 | — | 1473 |

NORWICH—Chenango County

□ ○ **CHENANGO MEMORIAL HOSPITAL**, 179 North Broad Street, Zip 13815–1097; tel. 607/337–4111, (Total facility includes 80 beds in nursing home–type unit) (Nonreporting) **A**1 10 11 **S** United Health Services, Binghamton, NY
Primary Contact: Frank W. Mirabito, President
Web address: www.uhs.net/aboutus/hospitals/chenango/index.asp

| | 23 | 10 | 138 | — | — | — | — | — | — | — |

NYACK—Rockland County

□ **NYACK HOSPITAL**, 160 North Midland Avenue, Zip 10960–1998; tel. 845/348–2000 **A**1 2 5 9 10 **F**2 3 4 9 11 12 21 22 23 24 27 28 29 30 31 32 33 34 36 37 38 39 40 46 47 48 49 50 51 52 53 55 57 58 59 60 61 62 63 64 65 66 69 81 82 84 85 86 87 88 92 93 94 95 96 106 107 108 109 110
Primary Contact: David H. Freed, President and Chief Executive Officer
Web address: www.nyackhospital.org

| | 23 | 10 | 375 | 14173 | 202 | 155489 | 2100 | 138843 | 67375 | 1204 |

OCEANSIDE—Nassau County

⊞ **SOUTH NASSAU COMMUNITIES HOSPITAL**, One Healthy Way, Zip 11572–1500, Mailing Address: P.O. Box 9007, Zip 11572–9007; tel. 516/632–3000 **A**1 2 3 5 9 10 **F**2 4 9 10 11 12 14 15 17 21 22 23 26 27 28 29 31 33 34 37 38 39 42 43 44 45 46 47 48 49 50 51 52 53 54 55 57 58 59 60 61 62 63 64 65 66 69 70 71 72 73 74 75 76 77 78 79 80 81 82 83 84 85 87 88 89 90 94 95 96 106 108 109 110
Primary Contact: Joseph A. Quagliata, President and Chief Executive Officer
COO: Akram Boutros, M.D., Executive Vice President and Chief Medical Officer
CFO: Gerard Haas, Senior Vice President and Chief Financial Officer
CMO: Akram Boutros, M.D., Executive Vice President and Chief Medical Officer
CIO: John Mertz, Director Information Services
CHR: Paul Giordano, Vice President and Human Resources
Web address: www.southnassau.org

| | 23 | 10 | 350 | 15996 | 312 | 330533 | 1376 | 212802 | 99666 | 1720 |

NY

Hospital, Address, Telephone, Approval, Facility, and Physician Codes, Health Care System	Classi-fication Codes		Utilization Data					Expense (thousands) of dollars		
	Control	Service	Staffed Beds	Admissions	Census	Outpatient Visits	Births	Total	Payroll	Personnel

★ American Hospital Association (AHA) membership
□ Joint Commission on Accreditation of Healthcare Organizations (JCAHO) accreditation
○ American Osteopathic Association (AOA) accreditation
△ Commission on Accreditation of Rehabilitation Facilities (CARF) accreditation

OGDENSBURG—St. Lawrence County

⊠ **CLAXTON–HEPBURN MEDICAL CENTER**, 214 King Street, Zip 13669–1192; tel. 315/393–3600, (Total facility includes 29 beds in nursing home–type unit) **A**1 9 10 20 **F**2 9 11 12 21 22 23 26 27 28 29 30 31 33 35 39 40 41 42 44 46 47 48 49 50 52 58 59 60 61 62 63 64 65 66 68 69 70 71 73 74 75 80 81 82 84 86 87 88 92 93 94 95 96 97 98 106 108 109 110
Primary Contact: Mark Webster, President
CFO: Frederick Morey, Chief Financial Officer
CMO: Ravinder Agarwal, M.D., Medical Director
CIO: Christiana Kalvaitis, Manager Management Information Systems
CHR: John Ziegler, Director Human Resources
Web address: www.chmed.org
— 23 10 | 159 | 4914 | 108 | 133930 | 393 | 56445 | 23808 | 540

□ **ST. LAWRENCE PSYCHIATRIC CENTER**, 1 Chimney Point Drive, Zip 13669–2291; tel. 315/541–2001, (Nonreporting) **A**1 10 **S** New York State Office of Mental Health, Albany, NY
Primary Contact: Jim Spooner, Executive Director
— 12 22 | 114 | — | — | — | — | — | — | —

OLEAN—Cattaraugus County

⊠ **OLEAN GENERAL HOSPITAL**, 515 Main Street, Zip 14760–9912; tel. 716/373–2600 **A**1 9 10 19 **F**2 9 11 12 21 22 23 27 28 31 33 39 40 45 46 48 49 52 55 58 59 60 62 63 65 66 69 71 73 75 77 78 81 82 84 85 87 88 93 94 95 106 108
Primary Contact: Bruce D. Cummings, President and Chief Executive Officer
CFO: Lou Inzana, Vice President Finance and Chief Financial Officer
CIO: Daniel Rissi, M.D., Vice President Medical Affairs
CHR: John Snyder, Vice President Human Resources
Web address: www.ogh.org
— 23 10 | 141 | 7518 | 99 | 118000 | 691 | 62838 | 26946 | 682

ONEIDA—Madison County

⊠ **ONEIDA HEALTHCARE CENTER**, 321 Genesee Street, Zip 13421–0321; tel. 315/363–6000, (Total facility includes 160 beds in nursing home–type unit) **A**1 10 **F**2 11 12 26 27 28 33 46 47 55 58 59 60 62 63 65 66 69 81 82 84 86 87 88 92 93 94 108 **P**1
Primary Contact: Richard G. Smith, Chief Executive Officer
COO: Paul A. Scopac, Chief Operating Officer
CFO: Vincent S. Maneen, Chief Financial Officer
CMO: Alberto Del Pino, M.D., Chief of Staff
CIO: Mary Fox, Director Information Systems
CHR: John G. Margo, Human Resources Director
Web address: www.oneidahealthcare.org
— 23 10 | 261 | 3685 | 197 | 131396 | 492 | 52785 | 25428 | 731

ONEONTA—Otsego County

⊠ **AURELIA OSBORN FOX MEMORIAL HOSPITAL**, 1 Norton Avenue, Zip 13820–2697; tel. 607/432–2000, (Total facility includes 131 beds in nursing home–type unit) **A**1 9 10 19 20 **F**1 9 11 12 14 21 22 23 26 27 28 29 31 32 33 37 39 40 41 42 44 46 47 48 52 53 55 57 58 59 60 61 62 63 65 66 69 70 71 72 73 74 75 76 81 82 87 88 92 94 96 106 107 108 109 **P**5
Primary Contact: John R. Remillard, President
CMO: David M. Evelyn, M.D., Vice President Medical Affairs
CIO: Joseph Phillips, Director Information Systems
CHR: Keith Valk, Vice President, Human Resources
Web address: www.foxcarenetwork.com
— 23 10 | 247 | 4714 | 200 | — | — | — | — | 683

ORANGEBURG—Rockland County

□ **ROCKLAND CHILDREN'S PSYCHIATRIC CENTER**, 599 Convent Road, Zip 10962; tel. 845/359–7400, (Nonreporting) **A**1 10 **S** New York State Office of Mental Health, Albany, NY
Primary Contact: Barry Kutok, Interim Executive Director
— 12 52 | 54 | — | — | — | — | — | — | —

□ **ROCKLAND PSYCHIATRIC CENTER**, 140 Old Orangeburg Road, Zip 10962–0071; tel. 845/359–1000, (Nonreporting) **A**1 5 10 **S** New York State Office of Mental Health, Albany, NY
Primary Contact: James H. Bopp, Executive Director
— 12 22 | 525 | — | — | — | — | — | — | —

OSSINING—Westchester County

OSSINING CORRECTIONAL FACILITIES HOSPITAL, 354 Hunter Street, Zip 10562–5498; tel. 914/941–0108, (Nonreporting)
Primary Contact: John Perilli, M.D., Health Services Director
— 12 11 | 25 | — | — | — | — | — | — | —

STONY LODGE HOSPITAL, 40 Croton Dam Road, Zip 10562–2644, Mailing Address: P.O. Box 1250, Briarcliff Manor, Zip 10510–1250; tel. 914/941–7400 **A**9 10 **F**71 72 73 75 77 78 **P**6
Primary Contact: Kevin F. Czipo, Executive Director
Web address: www.stonylodge.com
— 33 22 | 61 | 720 | 59 | 5857 | 0 | 13786 | 7615 | 197

OSWEGO—Oswego County

⊠ **OSWEGO HOSPITAL**, 110 West Sixth Street, Zip 13126–9985; tel. 315/349–5511 **A**1 9 10 **F**2 4 9 11 12 14 21 26 27 28 31 33 37 38 39 47 51 52 53 55 57 58 59 60 61 62 63 64 65 66 68 69 70 71 72 73 74 75 76 77 78 81 82 85 87 88 92 94 96 106 108 110
Primary Contact: Corte J. Spencer, Chief Executive Officer
COO: Gail Greenwood, Chief Operating Officer
CFO: Paul Snyder, Chief Financial Officer
CMO: Patsy Iannolo, M.D., Director of Medical Affairs
CIO: Richard Morgan, Chief Information Officer
CHR: Michael Russell, Director of Human Resources
Web address: www.oswegohealth.org
— 23 10 | 74 | 5076 | 68 | 228838 | 610 | 49802 | 24823 | 603

NY

Many Facility Codes have changed. Please refer to the AHA Guide Code Chart.   © 2005 AHA Guide

Hospital, Address, Telephone, Approval, Facility, and Physician Codes, Health Care System	Classi-fication Codes		Utilization Data					Expense (thousands) of dollars		
★ American Hospital Association (AHA) membership □ Joint Commission on Accreditation of Healthcare Organizations (JCAHO) accreditation ○ American Osteopathic Association (AOA) accreditation △ Commission on Accreditation of Rehabilitation Facilities (CARF) accreditation	Control	Service	Staffed Beds	Admissions	Census	Outpatient Visits	Births	Total	Payroll	Personnel

PATCHOGUE—Suffolk County

☒ **BROOKHAVEN MEMORIAL HOSPITAL MEDICAL CENTER**, 101 Hospital Road, Zip 11772–4897; tel. 631/654–7100 **A**1 9 10 **F**2 4 11 12 14 21 22 23 26 27 28 29 33 34 36 37 41 46 47 48 49 50 51 52 53 54 55 57 59 61 62 63 64 65 66 70 71 72 73 74 75 76 77 81 82 84 85 88 93 94 96 97 106 108 109 **P**5
Primary Contact: Thomas Ockers, President and Chief Executive Officer
CFO: Ronald A. Giraulo, Vice President Finance and Administration
CMO: Anthony J. Shallash, M.D., Chief Medical Officer
CIO: Donald Fleming, Chief Information Officer
CHR: Virginia Raffaele, Vice President Human Resources
Web address: www.bmhmc.org

23	10	321	13661	228	—	593	200590	95299	1513

PENN YAN—Yates County

☒ **SOLDIERS AND SAILORS MEMORIAL HOSPITAL OF YATES COUNTY**, 418 North Main Street, Zip 14527–1085; tel. 315/531–2000, (Total facility includes 151 beds in nursing home–type unit) **A**1 9 10 **F**1 2 9 12 21 26 27 28 29 33 42 44 46 48 52 53 55 58 60 62 63 66 69 70 71 72 73 74 75 76 77 81 88 92 94 96 97 108 109
Primary Contact: James J. Dooley, President and Chief Executive Officer
COO: Mary Ann Eldred, Executive Vice President and Chief Operating Officer
CFO: Lawrence J. Farnand, Treasurer and Chief Financial Officer
CMO: Jose Acevedo, M.D., Vice President Medical Affairs and Chief Medical Officer
CIO: Daniel Pletcher, Director Information System
CHR: Jack Linsky, Vice President, Human Resources
Web address: www.flhealth.org

23	10	205	1600	170	70001	0	26253	13492	397

PLAINVIEW—Nassau County

☒ **NORTH SHORE UNIVERSITY HOSPITAL AT PLAINVIEW**, 888 Old Country Road, Zip 11803–4978; tel. 516/719–3000 **A**1 2 9 10 12 13 **F**2 7 11 12 21 22 23 26 27 28 29 30 31 33 35 39 46 47 48 49 52 53 54 55 57 58 59 61 62 63 64 65 66 70 74 75 81 82 84 88 92 94 96 106 108 **P**6 **S** North Shore–LIJ Health System, Great Neck, NY
Primary Contact: Deborah Tascone, R.N., MS, Executive Director
CFO: Michael Fener, Associate Executive Director Finance
CMO: Abdallah Mishrick, M.D., Senior Vice President Medical Affairs
CIO: Nick O'Connor, Vice President and Chief Information Officer
Web address: www.northshorelij.com

23	10	211	12999	199	49145	1117	127979	64836	958

PLATTSBURGH—Clinton County

☒ **CHAMPLAIN VALLEY PHYSICIANS HOSPITAL MEDICAL CENTER**, 75 Beekman Street, Zip 12901–1493; tel. 518/561–2000, (Total facility includes 64 beds in nursing home–type unit) **A**1 2 5 9 10 19 20 **F**6 9 11 12 14 15 17 19 21 22 23 24 27 28 29 30 31 32 33 34 35 37 39 40 41 42 46 47 48 49 50 52 55 57 58 59 60 61 62 63 64 65 66 69 70 71 72 73 74 75 79 81 82 84 86 88 92 93 94 95 96 106 107 108 109 110 **P**5
Primary Contact: Stephens M. Mundy, President and Chief Executive Officer
COO: Charles Gijanto, Executive Vice President and Chief Operating Officer
CFO: Joyce Rafferty, Vice President Finance
CMO: Wouter Rietsema, M.D., Medical Director
CIO: Rosemary Miller, Associate Vice President Information Systems Services
CHR: Noreen Brady, Vice President of Human Resources
Web address: www.cvph.org

23	10	405	10092	246	278425	977	152151	75189	1644

POMONA—Rockland County

□ **DOCTOR ROBERT L. YEAGER HEALTH CENTER**, 50 Sanatorium Road, Zip 10970–3554; tel. 845/364–2700, (Includes SUMMIT PARK HOSPITAL–ROCKLAND COUNTY INFIRMARY), (Total facility includes 300 beds in nursing home–type unit) (Nonreporting) **A**1 10
Primary Contact: Anjan Bhattacharyya, Commissioner
Web address: www.co.rockland.ny.us

13	49	408	—	—	—	—	—	—	—

PORT CHESTER—Westchester County

□ **NEW YORK UNITED HOSPITAL MEDICAL CENTER**, 406 Boston Post Road, Zip 10573–7300; tel. 914/934–3000, (Total facility includes 70 beds in nursing home–type unit) (Nonreporting) **A**1 5 9 10 12 13 **S** New York Presbyterian Healthcare System, New York, NY
Primary Contact: Philip G. Dionne, President and Chief Executive Officer
Web address: www.uhmc.com

23	10	203	—	—	—	—	—	—	—

PORT JEFFERSON—Suffolk County

☒ **JOHN T. MATHER MEMORIAL HOSPITAL**, 75 North Country Road, Zip 11777–2190; tel. 631/473–1320 **A**1 2 9 10 **F**4 9 10 12 14 21 23 26 27 28 29 30 31 33 35 37 44 45 46 48 49 52 54 55 58 60 61 63 64 65 66 69 71 72 75 76 77 78 81 82 84 85 87 88 89 90 93 94 96 106 108 109 110 **P**6
Primary Contact: Kenneth D. Roberts, President
CFO: Frank Lettera, Vice President Finance
CIO: Thomas Heiman, Assistant Vice President of Information Services
CHR: Diane Marotta, Vice President for Human Resources
Web address: www.matherhospital.com

23	10	248	11761	218	137819	0	155041	76231	1546

□ **ST. CHARLES HOSPITAL**, 200 Belle Terre Road, Zip 11777–1928; tel. 631/474–6000, (Nonreporting) **A**1 2 9 10 **S** Catholic Health Services of Long Island, Rockville Centre, NY
Primary Contact: James O'Connor, President and Chief Executive Officer
Web address: www.stcharleshospital.chsli.org

21	10	289	—	—	—	—	—	—	—

NY

Hospital, Address, Telephone, Approval, Facility, and Physician Codes, Health Care System	Classi-fication Codes		Utilization Data					Expense (thousands) of dollars		
★ American Hospital Association (AHA) membership □ Joint Commission on Accreditation of Healthcare Organizations (JCAHO) accreditation ○ American Osteopathic Association (AOA) accreditation △ Commission on Accreditation of Rehabilitation Facilities (CARF) accreditation	Control	Service	Staffed Beds	Admissions	Census	Outpatient Visits	Births	Total	Payroll	Personnel

PORT JERVIS—Orange County

☒ **BON SECOURS COMMUNITY HOSPITAL**, 160 East Main Street,
Zip 12771–2245, Mailing Address: P.O. Box 1014, Zip 12771–1014;
tel. 845/858–7000, (Total facility includes 46 beds in nursing home–type unit)
(Nonreporting) **A**1 2 9 10 **S** Bon Secours Health System, Inc., Marriottsville, MD
Primary Contact: Thomas R. Brunelle, Executive Vice President and Administrator
COO: Gaynor Rosenstein, Vice President Operations
CFO: John Whitesel, Senior Vice President and Chief Financial Officer
CMO: Jeffrey Auerbach, D.O., Medical Director
CHR: Kim Hirkaler, Director of Human Resources
Web address: www.bonsecourscommunityhosp.org

	Control	Service	Staffed Beds	Admissions	Census	Outpatient Visits	Births	Total	Payroll	Personnel
BON SECOURS COMMUNITY HOSPITAL	21	10	187	—	—	—	—	—		

POTSDAM—St. Lawrence County

☒ **CANTON–POTSDAM HOSPITAL**, 50 Leroy Street, Zip 13676–1799;
tel. 315/265–3300 **A**1 9 10 **F**3 4 11 12 21 22 26 27 28 33 34 42 46 47 48
58 59 63 66 69 79 81 82 84 85 86 87 88 93 94 95 96 106 110
Primary Contact: Richard J. Krasnauskas, President and Chief Executive Officer
CMO: Robert T. Rogers, II, M.D., Medical Director
CIO: Stephen W. Potter, Chief Information Officer
CHR: Julie Kuenzler, Director Human Resources
Web address: www.cphospital.net

	Control	Service	Staffed Beds	Admissions	Census	Outpatient Visits	Births	Total	Payroll	Personnel
CANTON–POTSDAM HOSPITAL	23	10	94	3919	52	161201	395	43408	18913	509

POUGHKEEPSIE—Dutchess County

□ **HUDSON RIVER PSYCHIATRIC CENTER**, 10 Ross Circle, Zip 12601–1078;
tel. 845/452–8000, (Nonreporting) **A**1 5 10 **S** New York State Office of Mental
Health, Albany, NY
Primary Contact: Jean L. Wolfersteig, Acting Executive Director
Web address: www.omh.state.ny.us

	Control	Service	Staffed Beds	Admissions	Census	Outpatient Visits	Births	Total	Payroll	Personnel
HUDSON RIVER PSYCHIATRIC CENTER	12	22	460	—	—	—	—	—		

□ △ **SAINT FRANCIS HOSPITAL**, 241 North Road, Zip 12601–1399;
tel. 845/483–5000, (Includes SAINT FRANCIS HOSPITAL, 11 Hastings Drive,
Beacon, Zip 12508; tel. 845/838–4500) **A**1 2 7 9 10 **F**2 3 4 9 12 14 21 22 23
24 26 27 28 29 30 32 33 34 37 40 44 45 46 47 48 49 51 52 53 55 57 58
60 61 62 63 65 66 68 69 71 72 73 74 75 76 77 81 82 84 85 87 88 93 94
95 96 97 106 108 110
Primary Contact: Robert L. Savage, President and Chief Executive Officer
Web address: www.sfhhc.com

	Control	Service	Staffed Beds	Admissions	Census	Outpatient Visits	Births	Total	Payroll	Personnel
SAINT FRANCIS HOSPITAL	21	10	319	9978	220	222055	0	—	—	1281

☒ **VASSAR BROTHERS MEDICAL CENTER**, 45 Reade Place, Zip 12601–3990;
tel. 845/454–8500 **A**1 2 9 10 **F**9 11 12 14 15 17 19 21 23 24 26 27 28 29
30 31 32 33 36 37 38 42 44 45 46 48 51 52 53 55 56 57 58 59 61 62 63
64 65 66 69 70 79 81 82 84 85 88 90 93 94 95 96 97 106 108 109 110 **P**6
S Health Quest, Poughkeepsie, NY
Primary Contact: Daniel Z. Aronzon, M.D., Acting President and Chief Executive
Officer
CFO: Donna McGregor, Chief Financial Officer
CIO: Nicholas Christiano, Chief Information Officer
CHR: Mark Kochanowski, Vice President Human Resources
Web address: www.vassarbrothers.org

	Control	Service	Staffed Beds	Admissions	Census	Outpatient Visits	Births	Total	Payroll	Personnel
VASSAR BROTHERS MEDICAL CENTER	23	10	315	17345	252	160823	2431	217266	90608	1498

QUEENS—Queens County, See New York City

QUEENS VILLAGE—Queens County, See New York City

RHINEBECK—Dutchess County

□ △ **NORTHERN DUTCHESS HOSPITAL**, 6511 Springbrook Avenue,
Zip 12572–5002, Mailing Address: P.O. Box 5002, Zip 12572–5002;
tel. 845/876–3001 **A**1 7 9 10 **F**7 9 11 12 21 29 30 32 33 37 41 42 48 55 58
59 62 63 64 66 68 69 81 84 88 93 94 95 96 106 108 109 **P**6 **S** Health
Quest, Poughkeepsie, NY
Primary Contact: Michael Mimoso, President and Chief Executive Officer
Web address: www.ndhosp.com

	Control	Service	Staffed Beds	Admissions	Census	Outpatient Visits	Births	Total	Payroll	Personnel
NORTHERN DUTCHESS HOSPITAL	23	10	68	2892	38	79252	713	36572	15373	283

RICHMOND VALLEY—Richmond County, See New York City

RIVERHEAD—Suffolk County

□ **CENTRAL SUFFOLK HOSPITAL**, 1300 Roanoke Avenue, Zip 11901–2028;
tel. 631/548–6000, (Total facility includes 60 beds in nursing home–type unit) **A**1
9 10 **F**2 9 10 11 12 21 22 33 40 41 42 45 46 48 49 51 52 53 55 57 59 60
61 62 63 66 69 81 84 88 92 94 96 106 107 108 110
Primary Contact: Andrew J. Mitchell, President and Chief Executive Officer
Web address: www.centralsuffolkhospital.org

	Control	Service	Staffed Beds	Admissions	Census	Outpatient Visits	Births	Total	Payroll	Personnel
CENTRAL SUFFOLK HOSPITAL	23	10	104	5656	74	—	—	—	—	

ROCHESTER—Monroe County

☒ **HIGHLAND HOSPITAL OF ROCHESTER**, 1000 South Avenue, Zip 14620–2782;
tel. 585/473–2200 **A**1 3 5 9 10 **F**3 4 9 10 11 12 21 22 23 24 26 27 28 29
32 33 35 36 37 39 44 46 47 48 49 50 52 53 55 57 58 59 60 61 62 63 65
66 69 70 73 74 79 81 82 84 87 88 92 94 96 108 109 110 **P**6 **S** Strong
Memorial Hospital, Rochester, NY
Primary Contact: Steven I. Goldstein, President and Chief Executive Officer
COO: Cindy Becker, Vice President and Chief Operating Officer
CFO: Leonard J. Shute, Chief Financial Officer
CMO: Raymond Mayewski, M.D., Chief Medical Officer
CIO: Jerry Powell, Chief Information Officer
Web address: www.stronghealth.com

	Control	Service	Staffed Beds	Admissions	Census	Outpatient Visits	Births	Total	Payroll	Personnel
HIGHLAND HOSPITAL OF ROCHESTER	23	10	241	13632	168	—	—	—	—	

Hospital, Address, Telephone, Approval, Facility, and Physician Codes, Health Care System	Classi-fication Codes		Utilization Data					Expense (thousands) of dollars		
★ American Hospital Association (AHA) membership □ Joint Commission on Accreditation of Healthcare Organizations (JCAHO) accreditation ○ American Osteopathic Association (AOA) accreditation △ Commission on Accreditation of Rehabilitation Facilities (CARF) accreditation	Control	Service	Staffed Beds	Admissions	Census	Outpatient Visits	Births	Total	Payroll	Personnel
⊠ **PARK RIDGE HOSPITAL**, 1555 Long Pond Road, Zip 14626–4182; tel. 585/723–7000 **A**1 3 5 9 10 **F**1 2 3 4 8 9 11 12 15 17 21 22 23 26 27 28 29 31 32 33 34 35 37 39 44 45 46 47 48 49 50 51 52 55 57 58 59 60 61 62 63 64 65 66 68 69 70 71 72 73 74 75 76 77 78 82 87 88 91 92 93 94 95 96 98 106 107 108 109 **P**5 6 Primary Contact: Martin E. Carlin, President COO: Stewart Putnam, Executive Vice President, Cod Unity Health CFO: Warren Hern, Executive Vice President and Chief Financial Officer CMO: Joseph Salipante, M.D., Vice President Medical Affairs CHR: Paula Dolan, Vice President Human Resources Web address: www.unityhealth.org	23	10	441	12256	178	1015399	1201	256330	129307	2057
□ **ROCHESTER GENERAL HOSPITAL**, 1425 Portland Avenue, Zip 14621–3099; tel. 585/922–4000 **A**1 2 3 5 8 9 10 **F**2 4 9 10 11 12 14 15 17 19 21 22 23 24 27 28 29 30 31 32 33 34 35 37 39 42 44 46 47 48 49 51 52 53 55 57 58 59 60 61 62 63 64 65 66 68 69 70 71 72 73 74 75 76 77 78 79 81 82 84 86 87 88 90 92 94 95 96 98 106 108 109 110 **S** ViaHealth, Rochester, NY Primary Contact: Samuel R. Huston, President and Chief Executive Officer Web address: www.viahealth.org/	23	10	492	24959	424	926400	2469	—	—	4274
□ **ROCHESTER PSYCHIATRIC CENTER**, 1111 Elmwood Avenue, Zip 14620–3005; tel. 585/473–3230, (Nonreporting) **A**1 3 5 9 10 **S** New York State Office of Mental Health, Albany, NY Primary Contact: Michael P. Zuber, Ph.D., Executive Director Web address: www.omh.state.ny.us/omhweb/facilities/ropc/facility.htm	12	22	180	—	—	—	—	—	—	—
⊠ △ **STRONG MEMORIAL HOSPITAL OF THE UNIVERSITY OF ROCHESTER**, 601 Elmwood Avenue, Zip 14642–0002; tel. 585/275–2100 **A**1 3 5 7 8 9 10 **F**2 3 4 5 7 9 10 11 12 13 14 15 16 17 18 19 20 21 22 23 24 26 27 28 29 30 31 32 33 34 35 36 37 38 39 40 41 42 43 44 45 46 47 48 49 50 51 52 53 55 56 57 58 59 60 61 62 63 64 65 66 67 68 69 70 71 72 73 74 75 76 77 78 79 80 81 82 84 85 87 88 89 90 92 93 94 95 96 98 99 100 101 102 104 105 106 107 108 109 110 **P**5 6 **S** Strong Memorial Hospital, Rochester, NY Primary Contact: Steven I. Goldstein, General Director and Chief Executive Officer CFO: Leonard J. Shute, Senior Director Finance CIO: D Jerome Powell, Director Information Services Web address: www.urmc.rochester.edu	23	10	695	34969	638	1107819	3326	646761	269048	6245
ROCKVILLE CENTRE—Nassau County										
□ **MERCY MEDICAL CENTER**, 1000 North Village Avenue, Zip 11570–1098; tel. 516/705–2525, (Nonreporting) **A**1 2 9 10 **S** Catholic Health Services of Long Island, Rockville Centre, NY Primary Contact: Martin A. Bieber, President and Chief Executive Officer Web address: www.mercymedicalcenter.org	21	10	387	—	—	—	—	—	—	—
ROME—Oneida County										
⊠ △ **ROME MEMORIAL HOSPITAL**, 1500 North James Street, Zip 13440–2898; tel. 315/338–7000, (Total facility includes 82 beds in nursing home–type unit) **A**1 7 9 10 **F**2 4 11 12 21 24 26 27 28 29 33 37 44 46 47 48 50 52 55 58 59 60 61 62 63 65 66 68 69 70 71 76 81 82 87 88 92 93 94 95 106 108 109 **P**6 Primary Contact: Darlene A. Burns, R.N., President and Chief Executive Officer CFO: Nick Mayhew, Vice President and Chief Financial Officer CMO: Marybeth McCall, Chief Medical Officer CIO: Tony Laria, Director Management Information Systems CHR: Gina Chambers, Human Resource Manager Web address: www.romehospital.org	23	10	195	5496	156	144576	606	56777	29231	851
ROSLYN—Nassau County										
⊠ **ST. FRANCIS HOSPITAL**, 100 Port Washington Boulevard, Zip 11576–1348; tel. 516/562–6000, (Nonreporting) **A**1 9 10 **S** Catholic Health Services of Long Island, Rockville Centre, NY Primary Contact: Alan D. Guerci, M.D., Chief Executive Officer COO: Ruth Hennessey, Senior Vice President and Chief Operating Officer CFO: William C. Armstrong, Vice President and Chief Financial Officer CMO: Lawrence A. Reduto, M.D., Executive Vice President Medical Affairs CHR: Miles H. Kucker, Vice President, Human Resources Web address: www.stfrancisheartcenter.chsli.org	23	49	321	—	—	—	—	—	—	—
RYE—Westchester County										
⊠ **RYE HOSPITAL CENTER**, 754 Boston Post Road, Zip 10580–2724; tel. 914/967–4567 **A**1 10 **F**71 72 74 76 94 Primary Contact: Jack C. Schoenholtz, M.D., Medical Director, Administrator, President and Chief Executive Officer CFO: John Marcogliese, Vice President for Financial Operations Web address: www.ryehospitalcenter.com	33	22	34	187	28	—	0	—	—	59
SARANAC LAKE—Franklin County										
⊠ **ADIRONDACK MEDICAL CENTER**, 2233 State Route 86, Zip 12983, Mailing Address: P.O. Box 471, Zip 12983–0471; tel. 518/891–4141 **A**1 9 10 20 **F**2 9 10 11 12 21 22 23 26 27 28 29 32 33 34 37 44 46 47 48 49 52 55 57 58 59 60 61 62 63 64 65 69 70 71 81 82 83 84 86 87 88 93 94 95 96 97 106 108 109 **P**1 5 **S** Brim Healthcare, Inc., Brentwood, TN Primary Contact: Chandler M. Ralph, President and Chief Executive Officer CFO: Patrick M. Facteau, Vice President Finance CMO: Paul Seward, M.D., Vice President Medical Affairs CIO: Paul Johnson, Director, Information Systems CHR: Chris Walker, Vice President Human Resources Web address: www.amccares.org	23	10	77	3198	42	116108	229	50297	22779	490

NY

Hospital, Address, Telephone, Approval, Facility, and Physician Codes, Health Care System	Classi-fication Codes		Utilization Data					Expense (thousands) of dollars		
★ American Hospital Association (AHA) membership □ Joint Commission on Accreditation of Healthcare Organizations (JCAHO) accreditation ○ American Osteopathic Association (AOA) accreditation △ Commission on Accreditation of Rehabilitation Facilities (CARF) accreditation	Control	Service	Staffed Beds	Admissions	Census	Outpatient Visits	Births	Total	Payroll	Personnel

SARATOGA SPRINGS—Saratoga County

□ **FOUR WINDS HOSPITAL**, 30 Crescent Avenue, Zip 12866; tel. 518/584–3600, (Nonreporting) **A**1 9 10
Primary Contact: Michael O'Neil, Administrator

	33	49	83	—						

✠ **SARATOGA HOSPITAL**, 211 Church Street, Zip 12866–1003; tel. 518/587–3222, (Total facility includes 72 beds in nursing home–type unit) **A**1 9 10 **F**2 11 12 14 15 21 22 26 28 29 31 33 36 37 44 46 48 52 53 55 57 58 59 60 61 62 63 64 66 69 70 71 72 73 74 75 76 81 82 84 85 86 88 92 94 95 96 106 107 108 109
Primary Contact: David Andersen, President and Chief Executive Officer
CFO: James M. Gavin, Vice President and Chief Financial Officer
CMO: Jeffrey Paug, President of Medical Staff
CIO: John Mangona, Chief Information Officer
CHR: James E. Marco, Jr, Vice President, Chief Human Resources Officer
Web address: www.saratogacare.org

	23	10	211	7919	185	155465	811	95682	46044	1107

SCHENECTADY—Schenectady County

□ **BELLEVUE WOMAN'S HOSPITAL**, 2210 Troy Road, Zip 12309–4797; tel. 518/346–9400, (Nonreporting) **A**1 9 10
Primary Contact: Anne Saile, President and Chief Executive Officer
Web address: www.bellevuewoman.com

	33	44	55	—						

CONIFER PARK, 79 Glenridge Road, Zip 12302–4523; tel. 518/399–6446 **A**9 **F**3 4 28 70 94 96 109
Primary Contact: Jack Duffy, Executive Director
Web address: www.libertymgt.com

	33	82	225	3536	195	100	0	18446	11749	296

✠ **ELLIS HOSPITAL**, 1101 Nott Street, Zip 12308–2487; tel. 518/243–4000, (Total facility includes 82 beds in nursing home–type unit) (Nonreporting) **A**1 2 3 5 9 10
Primary Contact: Robert E. Smanik, FACHE, President and Chief Executive Officer
COO: Dianne Shugrue, Executive Vice President Operations and Chief Operating Officer
CFO: Gordon A. King, Interim Vice President Financial Services
CMO: David Liebers, M.D., Interim Chief Medical Officer
CIO: William Young, Chief Information Officer
CHR: David A. Homyk, Vice President Human Resources
Web address: www.ellishospital.org

	23	10	351	—						

□ **ST. CLARE'S HOSPITAL OF SCHENECTADY**, 600 McClellan Street, Zip 12304–1090; tel. 518/382–2000, (Nonreporting) **A**1 3 5 9 10 12
Primary Contact: Peter E. Capobianco, President and Chief Executive Officer

	21	10	200	—						

✠ △ **SUNNYVIEW REHABILITATION HOSPITAL**, 1270 Belmont Avenue, Zip 12308–2104; tel. 518/382–4500 **A**1 3 5 7 9 10 **F**9 10 21 27 37 41 44 46 52 60 62 68 69 94 96 108 **P**5 6
Primary Contact: Robert J. Bylancik, CHE, President and Chief Executive Officer
COO: Edward Eisenman, Vice President Finance
CFO: Edward Eisenman, Vice President Finance
CMO: Gary Williams, M.D., Chief Medical Staff
CIO: Patrick Clark, Manager Information Technology
Web address: www.sunnyview.org

	23	46	104	1950	68	45769	0	31764	19173	521

SLEEPY HOLLOW—Westchester County

✠ **PHELPS MEMORIAL HOSPITAL CENTER**, 701 North Broadway, Zip 10591–1096; tel. 914/366–3000 **A**1 9 10 **F**2 3 4 6 7 9 11 12 14 21 22 23 24 26 27 28 29 32 33 36 37 38 39 42 44 45 46 47 48 50 52 53 54 55 57 58 59 60 61 62 63 64 65 66 68 69 70 71 74 75 76 77 81 82 85 87 88 90 92 93 94 95 96 106 107 108 109 110 **P**1 5 8
Primary Contact: Keith F. Safian, President and Chief Executive Officer
COO: Bruce B. Davidow, Senior Vice President and Chief Operating Officer
CFO: Vincent DeSantis, Vice President Finance
CMO: Lawrence L. Faltz, M.D., Senior Vice President for Medical Affairs and Medical Director
CHR: Kevin T. Byrne, Vice President Human Resources
Web address: www.phelpshospital.org

	23	10	235	8252	147	216518	1145	113972	56921	926

SMITHTOWN—Suffolk County

□ **ST. CATHERINE OF SIENA MEDICAL CENTER**, 50 Route 25–A, Zip 11787–1398; tel. 631/862–3000, (Total facility includes 240 beds in nursing home–type unit) **A**1 9 10 **F**3 9 11 12 14 21 22 23 26 27 28 29 33 36 37 39 45 46 48 49 52 53 55 57 58 59 61 62 63 65 66 69 70 71 75 76 81 84 88 91 92 94 96 106 108 109 110 **S** Catholic Health Services of Long Island, Rockville Centre, NY
Primary Contact: Vincent DiRubbio, President and Chief Executive Officer
Web address: www.stcatherinemedicalcenter.org

	21	10	490	13995	467	—	—	—	—	1404

SOUTHAMPTON—Suffolk County

□ **SOUTHAMPTON HOSPITAL**, 240 Meeting House Lane, Zip 11968–5090; tel. 631/726–8555, (Nonreporting) **A**1 9 10
Primary Contact: Annette B. Leahy, President and Chief Executive Officer
Web address: www.southamptonhospital.org

	23	10	127	—						

SPRINGVILLE—Erie County

BERTRAND CHAFFEE HOSPITAL, 224 East Main Street, Zip 14141–1497; tel. 716/592–2871, (Total facility includes 80 beds in nursing home–type unit) **A**9 10 **F**2 12 14 21 27 28 33 34 36 42 48 54 58 59 60 63 65 69 81 82 84 88 92 94 109
Primary Contact: Steve Krisiak, Chief Executive Officer
Web address: www.chaffeehospitalandhome.org

	23	10	114	1471	94	—	0	—	—	228

Many Facility Codes have changed. Please refer to the AHA Guide Code Chart. © 2005 AHA Guide

Hospital, Address, Telephone, Approval, Facility, and Physician Codes, Health Care System	Classi-fication Codes		Utilization Data					Expense (thousands) of dollars		
★ American Hospital Association (AHA) membership □ Joint Commission on Accreditation of Healthcare Organizations (JCAHO) accreditation ○ American Osteopathic Association (AOA) accreditation △ Commission on Accreditation of Rehabilitation Facilities (CARF) accreditation	Control	Service	Staffed Beds	Admissions	Census	Outpatient Visits	Births	Total	Payroll	Personnel

STAR LAKE—St. Lawrence County

★ **CLIFTON–FINE HOSPITAL**, (Critical Access Hosital), Oswegatchie Trail, Zip 13690, Mailing Address: P.O. Box 10, Zip 13690–0010; tel. 315/848–3351, (Total facility includes 11 beds in nursing home–type unit) **A**9 10 18 **F**6 9 12 21 28 29 33 46 48 52 69 81 88 92 94 97 106 **P**6
Primary Contact: Roger A. Masse, Chief Executive Officer
Web address: www.northnet.org

| | 23 | 49 | 20 | 163 | 13 | 12781 | 0 | 5534 | 2733 | 66 |

STATEN ISLAND—Richmond County, See New York City

STONY BROOK—Suffolk County

★ **STONY BROOK UNIVERSITY HOSPITAL**, State University of New York, Zip 11794–8410; tel. 631/689–8333 **A**1 2 3 5 8 9 10 **F**2 5 6 9 10 11 12 13 14 15 16 17 18 19 20 21 22 23 24 28 29 30 32 33 34 37 39 40 43 44 45 46 47 48 49 50 52 53 55 56 57 58 59 60 61 62 63 64 65 66 67 70 71 72 73 74 75 76 78 79 81 82 84 85 86 88 89 90 93 94 95 96 99 101 104 106 107 108 110
Primary Contact: Bruce Schroffel, Director and Chief Executive Officer
COO: Amir Dan Rubin, Chief Operating Officer
CFO: Dennis Mitchell, Acting Chief Financial Officer
CMO: Thomas Biancaniello, Chief Medical Officer
CIO: Dennis Proul, Chief Information Officer
Web address: www.stonybrookhospital.com

| | 12 | 10 | 504 | 27631 | 455 | 358024 | 3160 | 607355 | 222613 | 4114 |

SUFFERN—Rockland County

★ **GOOD SAMARITAN HOSPITAL**, 255 Lafayette Avenue, Zip 10901–4869; tel. 845/368–5000, (Nonreporting) **A**1 2 9 10 **S** Bon Secours Health System, Inc., Marriottsville, MD
Primary Contact: Michael H. Schnieders, Executive Vice President and Administrator
CFO: John Whitesel, Senior Vice President and Chief Financial Officer
CMO: James Luciano, M.D., Vice President Medical Affairs
CIO: Leonard Ptak, Executive Vice President Information Systems
CHR: Elizabeth Savage, Senior Vice President Human Resources
Web address: www.goodsamhosp.org

| | 21 | 10 | 308 | — | — | — | — | — | — | — |

SYOSSET—Nassau County

★ **NORTH SHORE UNIVERSITY HOSPITAL AT SYOSSET**, 221 Jericho Turnpike, Zip 11791–4567; tel. 516/496–6400 **A**1 9 10 **F**2 10 12 21 22 26 27 28 29 30 31 33 35 37 39 46 47 48 52 53 55 57 58 62 63 64 66 70 71 73 74 75 81 82 88 92 94 96 106 108 **P**6 **S** North Shore–LIJ Health System, Great Neck, NY
Primary Contact: Deborah Tascone, R.N., MS, Executive Director
CFO: Richard Reilly, Assistant Administratior, Finance
CMO: Abdallah Mishrick, M.D., Senior Vice President Medical Affairs
CIO: Charles M. Trunz, III, Chief Information Officer and Chief Administrative Officer
CHR: Rosemarie Milano, Chief Human Resources Director
Web address: www.northshorelij.com

| | 23 | 10 | 64 | 4297 | 61 | 35143 | 0 | 75561 | 34125 | 470 |

SYRACUSE—Onondaga County

★ **COMMUNITY–GENERAL HOSPITAL OF GREATER SYRACUSE**, 4900 Broad Road, Zip 13215–2293; tel. 315/492–5011, (Total facility includes 50 beds in nursing home–type unit) **A**1 3 5 9 10 **F**2 9 11 12 21 22 23 26 27 28 33 39 46 47 48 52 53 55 57 58 59 60 61 62 63 65 68 69 71 81 82 85 87 88 92 93 94 106 108 110
Primary Contact: Thomas P. Quinn, President and Chief Executive Officer
CFO: Pamela Johnson, Corporate Vice President and Chief Financial Officer
CMO: Daniel Carlson, M.D., Senior Vice President Medical Affairs
CIO: Mitchell P. Rozonkiewiecz, Corporate Vice President Information Systems
CHR: John Van Epps, Director Human Resources
Web address: www.cgh.org

| | 23 | 10 | 278 | 9058 | 177 | 83783 | 1166 | 100551 | 45846 | 1315 |

★ **CROUSE HOSPITAL**, 736 Irving Avenue, Zip 13210–1690; tel. 315/470–7111 **A**1 3 5 9 10 12 **F**2 3 4 9 10 11 12 21 22 23 26 27 28 29 30 31 32 33 34 35 37 38 39 40 42 45 46 47 48 49 50 52 53 55 56 57 58 59 60 61 62 63 65 66 69 70 73 81 82 84 88 94 96 106 107 108 109 110 **P**6 8
Primary Contact: Paul J. Kronenberg, M.D., President and Chief Executive Officer
COO: Lisa Speach, Chief Operating Officer
CFO: Kim Baynton, Chief Financial Officer
CIO: Robert Allen, Director Communications
CHR: Steve Simmons, Vice President, Human Resources
Web address: www.crouse.org

| | 23 | 10 | 482 | 18420 | 265 | 290987 | 3854 | — | — | — |

□ **FOUR WINDS SYRACUSE**, 650 South Salina Street, Zip 13202–3524; tel. 315/476–2161, (Nonreporting) **A**1 9 10
Primary Contact: James P. Hackett, Jr, Administrator and Chief Executive Officer
Web address: www.fourwindshospital.com

| | 32 | 22 | 71 | — | — | — | — | — | — | — |

□ **RICHARD H. HUTCHINGS PSYCHIATRIC CENTER**, 620 Madison Street, Zip 13210–2319; tel. 315/473–4980, (Nonreporting) **A**1 3 5 10 **S** New York State Office of Mental Health, Albany, NY
Primary Contact: Colleen Zackoski, Executive Director
Web address: www.omh.state.ny.us

| | 12 | 22 | 131 | — | — | — | — | — | — | — |

NY

Hospital, Address, Telephone, Approval, Facility, and Physician Codes, Health Care System	Classification Codes		Utilization Data					Expense (thousands) of dollars		
★ American Hospital Association (AHA) membership □ Joint Commission on Accreditation of Healthcare Organizations (JCAHO) accreditation ○ American Osteopathic Association (AOA) accreditation △ Commission on Accreditation of Rehabilitation Facilities (CARF) accreditation	Control	Service	Staffed Beds	Admissions	Census	Outpatient Visits	Births	Total	Payroll	Personnel
□ **ST. JOSEPH'S HOSPITAL HEALTH CENTER**, 301 Prospect Avenue, Zip 13203–1895; tel. 315/448–5111, (Nonreporting) **A**1 3 5 9 10 **S** Sisters of Saint Francis, Syracuse, NY Primary Contact: Theodore M. Pasinski, President Web address: www.SJHSYR.ORG	23	10	431	—	—	—	—	—	—	—
✠ **UPSTATE MEDICAL UNIVERSITY**, 750 East Adams Street, Zip 13210–2399; tel. 315/464–5540 **A**1 2 8 9 10 **F**2 7 9 10 12 13 14 15 17 19 20 21 22 23 27 28 29 31 32 33 34 35 37 38 39 40 42 43 44 46 47 48 49 50 52 53 55 57 58 60 61 62 63 65 66 67 68 69 70 71 72 73 74 75 76 77 80 81 82 84 85 87 88 89 90 94 95 96 98 99 101 105 108 109 110 **P**7 Primary Contact: Phillip S. Schaengold, JD, Executive Director COO: Phillip S. Schaengold, JD, Chief Operating Officer CFO: Tom Donovan, Chief Financial Officer CIO: Terry Wagner, Chief Information Officer Web address: www.universityhospital.org/	12	10	355	16044	287	332215	0	412648	149355	3507
✠ △ **VETERANS AFFAIRS MEDICAL CENTER**, 800 Irving Avenue, Zip 13210–2796; tel. 315/425–4400, (Total facility includes 48 beds in nursing home–type unit) **A**1 3 5 7 8 **F**2 4 14 15 22 23 26 29 30 31 32 33 35 36 37 38 39 40 42 44 48 49 50 51 52 55 57 58 60 61 62 63 64 65 66 68 69 70 71 76 77 81 82 84 87 88 92 93 94 96 106 108 109 **P**8 **S** Department of Veterans Affairs, Washington, DC Primary Contact: James Cody, Director COO: Michael J. Swartz, Associate Medical Center Director CFO: Bob Alsheimer, Chief Financial Officer CMO: E Jackson Allison, M.D., Chief of Staff CIO: Mike Leroy, Information Resource Manager CHR: Mark Antinelli, Human Resources Manager Web address: www.va.gov/sta/guide/home.asp	45	10	154	4605	120	352252	0	148619	68724	1081
TICONDEROGA—Essex County										
★ **MOSES LUDINGTON HOSPITAL**, 1019 Wicker Street, Zip 12883–1097; tel. 518/585–2831, (Nonreporting) **A**9 10 18 Primary Contact: Diane M. Hart, Interim Chief Executive Officer COO: Diane M. Hart, Interim Chief Executive Officer CFO: Vicki DeLong, Interim Chief Financial Officer CMO: Robert Holterman, M.D., Medical Director CIO: Lisa Busby, Information Systems Manager CHR: Tamara Chagnon, Human Resource Coordinator Web address: www.mosesludington.com	23	10	15	—	—	—	—	—	—	—
TROY—Rensselaer County										
□ **SAMARITAN HOSPITAL**, 2215 Burdett Avenue, Zip 12180–2475; tel. 518/271–3300, (Nonreporting) **A**1 5 9 10 Primary Contact: Paul A. Milton, Chief Operating Officer Web address: www.nehealth.com	23	10	238	—	—	—	—	—	—	—
✠ **SETON HEALTH SYSTEM**, 1300 Massachusetts Avenue, Zip 12180–1695; tel. 518/268–5000, (Includes SETON HEALTH SYSTEM–ST. MARY'S HOSPITAL) **A**1 9 10 **F**1 2 3 6 9 11 12 14 21 22 23 24 27 28 29 31 32 33 36 37 38 39 40 42 44 46 48 49 50 51 52 53 55 57 58 59 60 61 62 63 64 65 66 69 70 81 82 84 85 88 92 93 94 95 96 98 106 107 108 109 **P**6 **S** Ascension Health, Saint Louis, MO Primary Contact: Gino J. Pazzaglini, FACHE, President and Chief Executive Officer CFO: Scott St George, Chief Financial Officer CMO: William Grattan, M.D., Chief Medical Officer CIO: Robert Charbonneau, Senior Vice President and Chief Information Officer CHR: Kathleen Occhiogrosso, Vice President Human Resources Web address: www.setonhealth.org	21	10	179	8259	117	456062	596	100568	51469	1103
UTICA—Oneida County										
✠ △ **FAXTON–ST. LUKE'S HEALTHCARE**, 1676 Sunset Avenue, Zip 13502–5475, Mailing Address: P.O. Box 479, Zip 13503–0479; tel. 315/624–6000, (Includes FAXTON CAMPUS, 1676 Sunset Avenue, tel. 315/624–6200; ST. LUKE'S CAMPUS, Mailing Address: P.O. Box 479, Zip 13503–0479; tel. 315/624–6000), (Total facility includes 72 beds in nursing home–type unit) **A**1 2 7 10 **F**1 4 9 11 12 14 21 26 27 28 29 32 33 37 42 44 47 48 49 52 53 54 55 58 59 60 61 63 65 66 68 69 70 71 72 75 76 79 81 82 86 87 88 92 94 96 106 107 108 109 **P**5 Primary Contact: Keith A. Fenstemacher, President and Chief Executive Officer COO: Scott H. Perra, Executive Vice President and Chief Operating Officer CFO: Michael Haile, Senior Vice President Finance CMO: Frederick Goldberg, M.D., Senior Vice President and Medical Director CIO: Mary Ford, Vice President and Chief Information Officer CHR: Tony Scibelli, Vice President Human Resources Web address: www.mvnhealth.com	23	10	430	16871	313	250791	2094	187933	83771	2195
□ **MOHAWK VALLEY PSYCHIATRIC CENTER**, 1400 Noyes Street, Zip 13502–3803; tel. 315/797–6800, (Nonreporting) **A**1 10 **S** New York State Office of Mental Health, Albany, NY Primary Contact: Maureen L. Ruben, Executive Director	12	22	614	—	—	—	—	—	—	—

Many Facility Codes have changed. Please refer to the AHA Guide Code Chart.

Hospital, Address, Telephone, Approval, Facility, and Physician Codes, Health Care System	Classi-fication Codes		Utilization Data					Expense (thousands) of dollars		
★ American Hospital Association (AHA) membership □ Joint Commission on Accreditation of Healthcare Organizations (JCAHO) accreditation ○ American Osteopathic Association (AOA) accreditation △ Commission on Accreditation of Rehabilitation Facilities (CARF) accreditation	Control	Service	Staffed Beds	Admissions	Census	Outpatient Visits	Births	Total	Payroll	Personnel
★□ **ST. ELIZABETH MEDICAL CENTER**, 2209 Genesee Street, Zip 13501–5999; tel. 315/798–8100 **A**1 10 12 **F**2 9 10 12 14 15 17 19 21 22 23 24 26 27 28 33 34 39 46 48 50 51 52 53 55 57 58 60 61 62 63 64 66 69 70 71 72 73 75 76 81 82 85 87 88 92 93 94 95 96 108 109 110 **P**6 **S** Sisters of Saint Francis, Syracuse, NY Primary Contact: Sister M. Johanna DeLelys, President and Chief Executive Officer COO: Matthew D. Babcock, Chief Operating Officer CFO: Louis Aiello, Chief Financial Officer CMO: Albert D'Accurzio, Medical Director CIO: Robert Gillette, Chief Information Officer CHR: Patrick Buckley, Director of Human Resources Web address: www.stemc.org	21	10	190	10919	169	406330	0	147609	—	1609
ST. LUKE'S CAMPUS See Faxton–St. Luke's Healthcare										
VALHALLA—Westchester County										
★□ **BLYTHEDALE CHILDREN'S HOSPITAL**, 95 Bradhurst Avenue, Zip 10595–1697; tel. 914/592–7555 **A**1 10 **F**21 26 27 28 29 37 38 39 46 52 57 58 62 65 67 68 69 72 77 90 94 Primary Contact: Larry L. Levine, President and Chief Executive Officer CFO: Kathryn Malon, Chief Fiscal Officer Web address: www.blythedale.org	23	56	92	336	76	33656	0	34101	20118	377
□ **WESTCHESTER MEDICAL CENTER**, Valhalla Campus, Zip 10595–1696; tel. 914/493–7000, (Total facility includes 236 beds in nursing home–type unit) **A**1 3 8 9 10 **F**2 4 6 9 10 12 13 14 15 21 22 29 30 31 32 33 34 36 37 38 39 40 44 46 48 49 50 52 53 55 56 57 58 59 60 61 62 63 65 66 67 68 69 70 71 72 73 74 75 76 77 81 82 84 86 87 88 92 94 95 96 98 106 108 109 110 Primary Contact: John R. Spicer, Interim President and Chief Executive Officer Web address: www.wcmc.com	16	10	871	23421	726	—	—	—	—	3255
VALLEY STREAM—Nassau County										
★□ **FRANKLIN HOSPITAL MEDICAL CENTER**, 900 Franklin Avenue, Zip 11580–2190; tel. 516/256–6000, (Total facility includes 120 beds in nursing home–type unit) **A**1 2 9 10 **F**1 2 9 10 12 14 21 22 23 26 27 28 29 31 33 36 37 39 40 44 45 46 48 49 51 52 53 55 57 58 59 60 61 62 63 65 66 70 71 81 84 88 92 94 96 98 108 109 110 **P**6 **S** North Shore–LIJ Health System, Great Neck, NY Primary Contact: Joseph Lamantia, Executive Director CFO: Elizabeth Zubko, Finance Administrator CMO: Ira Klonsky, M.D., Medical Director CHR: Angela Fisher, Director Human Resources Web address: www.fhmc.org	23	10	370	11518	321	211815	494	136871	70337	1174
WALTON—Delaware County										
DELAWARE VALLEY HOSPITAL, 1 Titus Place, Zip 13856–1498; tel. 607/865–2100 **A**9 10 18 **F**3 9 11 12 21 26 27 28 29 33 42 45 46 48 58 60 63 66 69 70 81 88 94 97 106 108 109 **P**6 **S** United Health Services, Binghamton, NY Primary Contact: David J. Polge, President and Chief Executive Officer Web address: www.uhs.net	23	10	33	973	15	95046	0	12103	6982	165
WARSAW—Wyoming County										
□ **WYOMING COUNTY COMMUNITY HOSPITAL**, 400 North Main Street, Zip 14569–1097; tel. 585/786–2233, (Total facility includes 160 beds in nursing home–type unit) **A**1 9 10 20 **F**2 9 11 12 21 23 24 27 28 29 31 37 46 47 48 55 59 60 61 62 63 65 68 69 70 71 73 74 75 76 77 81 82 88 92 96 97 106 108 109 110 Primary Contact: Lucille K. Sheedy, Administrator and Chief Executive Officer Web address: www.wcch.net	13	10	206	3490	195	103195	360	—	—	565
WARWICK—Orange County										
★□ **ST. ANTHONY COMMUNITY HOSPITAL**, 15 Maple Avenue, Zip 10990–5180; tel. 845/987–5173 **A**1 9 10 **F**2 11 12 14 21 22 23 27 28 29 30 33 37 38 46 48 52 53 55 57 58 59 61 62 63 64 65 66 69 81 82 84 88 92 93 94 96 106 108 109 110 **S** Bon Secours Health System, Inc., Marriottsville, MD Primary Contact: Leah Cerkvenik, Executive Vice President, Administrator and Chief Executive Officer CFO: John Whitesel, Senior Vice President and Chief Financial Officer Web address: www.stanthonycommunityhosp.org	21	10	61	2836	35	50826	577	32841	14436	239
WATERTOWN—Jefferson County										
□ **SAMARITAN MEDICAL CENTER**, 830 Washington Street, Zip 13601–4066; tel. 315/785–4121 **A**1 10 12 13 19 **F**4 11 12 15 21 22 23 27 28 29 33 40 46 49 52 53 55 57 58 59 60 61 62 63 66 68 69 70 71 72 73 75 76 77 81 82 84 86 88 93 94 108 109 **P**6 Primary Contact: Thomas H. Carman, President and Chief Executive Officer Web address: www.samaritanhealth.com	23	10	221	7915	134	209031	1276	106378	51700	1156
WELLSVILLE—Allegany County										
★□ **JONES MEMORIAL HOSPITAL**, 191 North Main Street, Zip 14895–1197, Mailing Address: P.O. Box 72, Zip 14895–0072; tel. 585/593–1100 **A**1 9 10 20 **F**9 11 12 14 21 22 23 26 27 28 29 31 33 34 37 50 52 55 58 59 60 61 62 63 64 65 69 70 81 88 89 95 96 97 106 108 109 Primary Contact: Ann C. Gilpin, President and Chief Executive Officer CHR: Susan Nicol, Director of Human Resources Web address: www.jmhny.org	23	10	70	2804	28	127365	367	28506	13494	330

NY

Hospital, Address, Telephone, Approval, Facility, and Physician Codes, Health Care System	Classi-fication Codes		Utilization Data					Expense (thousands) of dollars		
★ American Hospital Association (AHA) membership □ Joint Commission on Accreditation of Healthcare Organizations (JCAHO) accreditation ○ American Osteopathic Association (AOA) accreditation △ Commission on Accreditation of Rehabilitation Facilities (CARF) accreditation	Control	Service	Staffed Beds	Admissions	Census	Outpatient Visits	Births	Total	Payroll	Personnel

WEST HAVERSTRAW—Rockland County

□ △ **HELEN HAYES HOSPITAL**, Route 9W, Zip 10993–1195; tel. 845/786–4000, (Total facility includes 25 beds in nursing home–type unit) **A**1 5 7 10 **F**7 21 22 26 27 28 29 30 32 35 41 47 48 52 57 58 60 62 63 65 66 68 69 70 73 92 94 95 96 108 109 110 **P**6
Primary Contact: Magdalena Ramirez, Chief Executive Officer
Web address: www.helenhayeshospital.org

| 12 | 46 | 155 | 2976 | 138 | — | 0 | 65490 | 31366 | 622 |

WEST ISLIP—Suffolk County

□ **GOOD SAMARITAN HOSPITAL MEDICAL CENTER**, 1000 Montauk Highway, Zip 11795–4958; tel. 631/376–3000, (Total facility includes 100 beds in nursing home–type unit) **A**1 2 9 10 12 13 **F**2 9 10 11 12 14 21 22 23 24 26 27 28 29 31 32 33 34 37 38 39 42 44 46 47 48 49 50 51 52 53 54 55 56 57 58 59 60 61 62 63 65 66 67 69 70 73 75 79 81 82 84 85 87 88 92 93 94 95 96 98 106 108 109 110 **P**8 **S** Catholic Health Services of Long Island, Rockville Centre, NY
Primary Contact: Richard J. Murphy, President and Chief Executive Officer
Web address: www.good–samaritan–hospital.org

| 21 | 10 | 531 | 25362 | 468 | 281687 | 2998 | 305665 | 164037 | 2661 |

WEST POINT—Orange County

⊠ **KELLER ARMY COMMUNITY HOSPITAL**, U.S. Military Academy, Zip 10996–1197; tel. 845/938–5169, (Nonreporting) **A**1 **S** Department of the Army, Office of the Surgeon General, Falls Church, VA
Primary Contact: Colonel Peter G. Torok, Commander
COO: Lieutenant Colonel Scott F. Cass, Deputy Commander of Administration
CFO: Major Joseph Rheney, Chief, Resources Management Division
CMO: Lieutenant Colonel Italo Bastianelli, Deputy Commander for Clinical Services
CIO: Patrick McGuinness, Chief Information Management
CHR: Captain Alex L. Hayman, Chief Human Resources
Web address: www.wramc.amedd.army.mil/wp

| 42 | 10 | 35 | — | — | — | — | | | |

WESTFIELD—Chautauqua County

★ **WESTFIELD MEMORIAL HOSPITAL**, 189 East Main Street, Zip 14787–1195; tel. 716/326–4921 **A**9 10 **F**9 11 12 21 26 27 28 29 33 36 39 52 59 63 69 81 85 88 95 106 109 **S** St. Vincent Health System, Erie, PA
Primary Contact: Stuart W. Williams, President and Chief Executive Officer
CFO: Henry J. Ward, Vice President Finance and Chief Financial Officer
CMO: Russell Elwell, M.D., Medical Director
CIO: Cindy Harper, Director Information Systems
Web address: www.wmhinc.org

| 23 | 10 | 19 | 901 | 8 | 22257 | 192 | 8271 | 3821 | 97 |

WHITE PLAINS—Westchester County

⊠ △ **BURKE REHABILITATION HOSPITAL**, 785 Mamaroneck Avenue, Zip 10605–2593; tel. 914/597–2500, (Nonreporting) **A**1 5 7 9 10
Primary Contact: Mary Beth Walsh, M.D., Chief Executive Officer
Web address: www.burke.org

| 23 | 46 | 150 | — | — | — | — | — | — | — |

NEW YORK–PRESBYTERIAN HOSPITAL, WESTCHESTER DIVISION See New York–Presbyterian Hospital, New York

⊠ **WHITE PLAINS HOSPITAL CENTER**, Davis Avenue and Post Road, Zip 10601–4699; tel. 914/681–0600 **A**1 2 9 10 **F**2 4 9 10 11 12 14 21 22 23 26 27 28 29 30 33 37 38 44 46 47 48 50 51 52 53 54 55 58 59 60 61 62 63 65 66 69 70 71 72 73 75 77 79 81 82 84 85 86 87 88 93 94 96 108 110 **P**2 5 8
Primary Contact: Jon B. Schandler, President and Chief Executive Officer
CFO: John Sciurba, Vice President and Chief Financial Officer
CMO: Lawrence J. Kadish, M.D., Executive Vice President and Medical Director
CHR: Michael Pagliaro, Vice President for Human Resources
Web address: www.wphospital.org

| 23 | 10 | 226 | 14423 | 226 | 250000 | 2467 | — | — | 1597 |

WILLIAMSVILLE—Erie County

MILLARD FILLMORE SUBURBAN HOSPITAL See Buffalo General Hospital, Buffalo

YONKERS—Westchester County

⊠ **ST. JOHN'S RIVERSIDE HOSPITAL**, 967 North Broadway, Zip 10701–1399; tel. 914/964–4444, (Includes ANDRUS PAVILION, 967 North Broadway, tel. 914/964–4444; PARKCARE PAVILION, Two Park Avenue, Zip 10703–3497; tel. 914/964–7300), (Total facility includes 120 beds in nursing home–type unit) (Nonreporting) **A**1 9 10
Primary Contact: James Foy, President and Chief Executive Officer
COO: Lynn M. Nelson, R.N., Chief Operating Officer
CFO: Dave Scarpino, Vice President Finance and Chief Financial Officer
CMO: Jay Izes, M.D., Vice President Medical Affairs
CIO: Peter Weidner, Director Management Information Systems
CHR: Pam LaFrance, Vice President of Human Resources
Web address: www.riversidehealth.org

| 23 | 10 | 517 | — | — | — | — | | | |

⊠ **ST. JOSEPH'S MEDICAL CENTER**, 127 South Broadway, Zip 10701–4080; tel. 914/378–7000, (Total facility includes 200 beds in nursing home–type unit) **A**1 3 5 9 10 **F**1 2 3 4 9 10 12 21 22 23 24 26 27 28 29 31 32 33 34 35 37 39 42 44 45 46 48 49 50 51 52 55 57 58 60 61 62 63 66 69 70 71 73 75 76 77 78 81 82 88 92 94 106 107 108
Primary Contact: Michael J. Spicer, President and Chief Executive Officer
CFO: James J. Curcuruto, Senior Vice President Finance
CMO: Nicholas De Robertis, M.D., Medical Director
CIO: Deborah Di Bernardo, Chief Information Officer
Web address: www.saintjosephs.org

| 23 | 10 | 363 | 7300 | 319 | — | 0 | — | — | 1161 |

Many Facility Codes have changed. Please refer to the AHA Guide Code Chart.

NORTH CAROLINA

Hospital, Address, Telephone, Approval, Facility, and Physician Codes, Health Care System	Classi-fication Codes		Utilization Data					Expense (thousands) of dollars		
	Control	Service	Staffed Beds	Admissions	Census	Outpatient Visits	Births	Total	Payroll	Personnel

★ American Hospital Association (AHA) membership
☐ Joint Commission on Accreditation of Healthcare Organizations (JCAHO) accreditation
○ American Osteopathic Association (AOA) accreditation
△ Commission on Accreditation of Rehabilitation Facilities (CARF) accreditation

AHOSKIE—Hertford County

✠ **ROANOKE–CHOWAN HOSPITAL**, 500 South Academy Street, Zip 27910–3261, Mailing Address: P.O. Box 1385, Zip 27910–1385; tel. 252/209–3000 **A**1 9 10 **F**9 11 12 21 22 23 24 27 28 29 32 33 36 38 41 46 48 55 57 59 60 61 62 63 64 66 69 70 71 73 75 76 77 81 82 85 87 88 92 93 94 96 106 107 108 109 **P**7 **S** University Health Systems of Eastern Carolina, Greenville, NC
Primary Contact: Susan S. Lassiter, President
CFO: Lynn T. Lanier, Vice President Finance and Chief Financial Officer
CMO: Robert C. Kahn, Chief of Staff
Web address: www.uhseast.com
| 23 | 10 | 105 | 4953 | 67 | 206423 | 462 | 41675 | 16192 | 596 |

ALBEMARLE—Stanly County

✠ **STANLY MEMORIAL HOSPITAL**, 301 Yadkin Street, Zip 28001–3448, Mailing Address: P.O. Box 1489, Zip 28002–1489; tel. 704/984–4000 **A**1 9 10 **F**2 9 10 11 12 14 15 21 22 23 27 29 32 33 44 46 47 48 49 50 51 52 53 55 57 58 59 60 61 62 63 65 66 68 69 70 71 72 73 74 75 76 77 81 82 84 88 93 94 95 96 106 108 110 **P**5 6
Primary Contact: Roy M. Hinson, FACHE, President and Chief Executive Officer
COO: Debra B. Smith, Senior Vice President and Chief Operating Officer
CFO: Randy Medlin, Vice President Fiscal Services
CMO: Peter B. Gusmer, Chief of Staff
CIO: Brian Freeman, Director Management Information Systems
CHR: Sue Barbee, Director Human Resources
Web address: www.stanly.org
| 23 | 10 | 119 | 6139 | 67 | 172140 | 768 | 78017 | 28223 | 906 |

ASHEBORO—Randolph County

✠ **RANDOLPH HOSPITAL**, 364 White Oak Street, Zip 27203–5400, Mailing Address: P.O. Box 1048, Zip 27204–1048; tel. 336/625–5151 **A**1 9 10 **F**2 7 11 12 17 21 22 26 27 28 29 32 33 37 38 39 41 46 47 48 50 51 52 53 55 57 58 59 60 62 63 64 65 66 69 81 82 85 87 88 94 96 106 108 110 **P**6
Primary Contact: Robert E. Morrison, President
CMO: Thomas Whyte, M.D., Chief of Staff
Web address: www.randolphhospital.org
| 23 | 10 | 107 | 6745 | 66 | 130235 | 803 | 66178 | 28845 | 745 |

ASHEVILLE—Buncombe County

ASHEVILLE SPECIALTY HOSPITAL, 428 Biltmore Avenue, 4th Floor, Zip 28802; tel. 828/213–5400, (Nonreporting) **A**10
Primary Contact: Jay Cutspec, President and Chief Executive Officer
| 33 | 49 | 34 | — | — | — | — | — | — | — |

✠ **MISSION HOSPITALS**, 509 Biltmore Avenue, Zip 28801–4690; tel. 828/213–1111, (Includes MEMORIAL MISSION HOSPITAL; ST. JOSEPH'S HOSPITAL, 428 Biltmore Avenue, Zip 28801–9839) **A**1 2 3 5 9 10 11 **F**2 6 9 10 11 12 14 15 17 19 21 22 23 24 26 27 28 29 32 33 34 35 37 38 39 40 41 42 44 45 46 47 48 49 50 52 53 55 56 57 58 59 60 61 62 63 64 65 66 67 69 70 71 72 73 74 75 76 77 78 79 80 81 82 84 85 86 87 88 89 90 93 94 95 96 98 106 107 108 109 110 **P**6
Primary Contact: Joseph F. Damore, President and Chief Executive Officer
COO: David S. Spillers, Chief Operating Officer
CFO: Lonnie D. Younger, Senior Vice President and Chief Financial Officer
CMO: George M. Bilbrey, M.D., Chief of Staff
CIO: D Arlo Jennings, Chief Information Officer
CHR: Bill Mance, Vice President Human Resources
Web address: www.missionhospitals.org/
| 23 | 10 | 721 | 34765 | 462 | 392581 | 3494 | 277735 | 215894 | 5703 |

✠ △ **THOMS REHABILITATION HOSPITAL**, 68 Sweeten Creek Road, Zip 28803–1599, Mailing Address: P.O. Box 5779, Zip 28813–5779; tel. 828/274–2400 **A**1 7 10 **F**1 21 22 28 30 36 37 38 44 45 46 47 48 51 53 58 60 62 65 66 68 69 94 95 96 108 110
Primary Contact: Charles D. Norvell, President and Chief Executive Officer
COO: Tracy Buchanan, Chief Operating Officer
CFO: Diann Bolick, Chief Financial Officer
CIO: Janise Donovan, Chief Information Officer
CHR: Karen Vernon–Young, Vice President Human Resources and Communications
Web address: www.thoms.org
| 23 | 46 | 107 | 1820 | 72 | 67926 | 0 | 52664 | 31051 | 633 |

✠ **VETERANS AFFAIRS MEDICAL CENTER**, 1100 Tunnel Road, Zip 28805–2087; tel. 828/298–7911, (Total facility includes 120 beds in nursing home–type unit) **A**1 3 5 **F**2 3 4 9 14 15 16 17 19 21 22 23 26 28 29 32 33 37 38 39 44 45 50 52 55 57 58 61 62 63 64 65 66 68 69 70 71 73 77 81 82 84 85 87 88 92 94 97 106 107 108 109 110 **P**6 **S** Department of Veterans Affairs, Washington, DC
Primary Contact: James A. Christian, Director
CMO: James W. Martin, D.D.S., Interim Chief of Staff
CIO: Carla McLendon, Director Information Resource Management Services
CHR: Melissa Bragg, Chief Human Resources Management
Web address: www.va.gov/sta/guide/home.asp
| 45 | 10 | 297 | 3978 | 194 | 226076 | 0 | — | — | — |

NC

Hospital, Address, Telephone, Approval, Facility, and Physician Codes, Health Care System	Classi-fication Codes		Utilization Data					Expense (thousands) of dollars		
★ American Hospital Association (AHA) membership □ Joint Commission on Accreditation of Healthcare Organizations (JCAHO) accreditation ○ American Osteopathic Association (AOA) accreditation △ Commission on Accreditation of Rehabilitation Facilities (CARF) accreditation	Control	Service	Staffed Beds	Admissions	Census	Outpatient Visits	Births	Total	Payroll	Personnel

BELHAVEN—Beaufort County

PUNGO DISTRICT HOSPITAL, 202 East Water Street, Zip 27810–9998; tel. 252/943–2111, (Total facility includes 10 beds in nursing home–type unit) **A**9 10 18 **F**9 12 21 22 26 27 28 33 45 46 52 58 60 63 66 69 81 88 92 93 94 97
Primary Contact: Kenneth E. Ragland, Chief Executive Officer

| | 23 | 10 | 35 | 1183 | 25 | 14449 | 0 | 9993 | 4917 | 146 |

BLACK MOUNTAIN—Buncombe County

JULIAN F. KEITH ALCOHOL AND DRUG ABUSE TREATMENT CENTER, 201 Tabernacle Road, Zip 28711–2599; tel. 828/669–3400, (Nonreporting) **A**10
Primary Contact: William A. Rafter, Director
Web address: www.jfkadatc.net

| | 12 | 82 | 110 | — | — | — | — | — | — | — |

BLOWING ROCK—Watauga County

⊠ **BLOWING ROCK HOSPITAL**, Chestnut Street, Zip 28605–0148, Mailing Address: Box 148, Zip 28605–0148; tel. 828/295–3136, (Includes DAVANT REHABILITATION AND EXTENDED CARE CENTER), (Total facility includes 72 beds in nursing home–type unit) **A**1 9 10 18 **F**1 33 51 52 69 81 88 92 96 107 **P**5
Primary Contact: Alice Salthouse, Administrator and Chief Executive Officer
CFO: Linda Heaton, Chief Financial Officer
CMO: Charles Davant, III, M.D., Chief Medical Officer
CHR: Pam Pitts, Director Personnel
Web address: www.blowingrockhospital.org

| | 23 | 10 | 100 | 429 | 65 | 8483 | 0 | 11202 | 4769 | 150 |

BOILING SPRINGS—Cleveland County

CRAWLEY MEMORIAL HOSPITAL, 315 West College Avenue, Zip 28017, Mailing Address: P.O. Box 996, Zip 28017–0996; tel. 704/434–9466, (Nonreporting) **A**9 10 **S** Carolinas HealthCare System, Charlotte, NC
Primary Contact: Gail McKillop, President
Web address: www.carolinas.org

| | 23 | 10 | 60 | — | — | — | — | — | — | — |

BOONE—Watauga County

⊠ **WATAUGA MEDICAL CENTER**, Deerfield Road, Zip 28607–2600, Mailing Address: P.O. Box 2600, Zip 28607–2600; tel. 828/262–4100 **A**1 2 9 10 19 **F**2 4 11 12 14 15 21 22 23 26 27 28 29 31 33 37 39 41 42 46 48 49 51 52 55 57 58 59 60 61 63 65 66 69 81 82 84 87 88 93 94 95 96 98 106 108 110 **P**8
Primary Contact: Richard G. Sparks, President
COO: Tim Ford, Senior Vice President Operations
CFO: Will Grant, Senior Vice President Finance
Web address: www.wataugamc.org

| | 23 | 10 | 95 | 5437 | 66 | 79151 | 544 | 64741 | 28738 | 773 |

BREVARD—Transylvania County

⊠ **TRANSYLVANIA COMMUNITY HOSPITAL**, Hospital Drive, Zip 28712–1116, Mailing Address: Box 1116, Zip 28712–1116; tel. 828/884–9111 **A**1 2 9 10 **F**2 9 11 12 21 22 24 26 27 28 29 33 36 46 47 48 51 52 55 59 60 62 63 70 81 82 85 88 92 94 96 97 106 108 109 **P**1 5
Primary Contact: Robert J. Bednarek, President and Chief Executive Officer
COO: Rebecca W. Carter, MSN, Chief Operating Officer
CFO: Theresa Parker, Chief Financial Officer
CMO: Barry Bodie, M.D., Chief of Staff
CIO: Pat Perry, Manager Information Systems
Web address: www.tchospital.org

| | 23 | 10 | 54 | 1969 | 23 | 36523 | 191 | 31257 | 12520 | 362 |

BRYSON CITY—Swain County

★ **SWAIN COUNTY HOSPITAL**, 45 Plateau Street, Zip 28713–6784; tel. 828/488–4013 **A**9 10 18 **F**9 12 21 22 26 27 28 29 33 35 36 37 38 46 48 51 53 58 60 62 63 64 69 81 88 93 94 97 108 110 **P**5 7 **S** WestCare Health System, Sylva, NC
Primary Contact: Ronald A. Sloan, Administrator
COO: Mark T. Leonard, Chief Executive Officer
CFO: Pam Buchanan, Chief Financial Officer
CMO: Randy Savell, M.D., Chief of Staff
CIO: Shawn Remacle, Chief Information Officer
Web address: www.westcare.org

| | 23 | 10 | 25 | 676 | 5 | 21806 | 0 | 8974 | 3288 | 83 |

BURGAW—Pender County

⊠ **PENDER MEMORIAL HOSPITAL**, 507 Freemont Street, Zip 28425–5131; tel. 910/259–5451, (Total facility includes 43 beds in nursing home–type unit) **A**1 9 10 18 **F**2 9 12 21 26 27 28 29 33 44 46 48 51 52 53 55 60 63 69 81 84 85 88 92 94 96 97 106 108 **S** New Hanover Health Network, Wilmington, NC
Primary Contact: Matthew Mendez, Administrator
CFO: George Sprinkel, Financial Officer
CMO: Naseem Nasrallah, M.D., Chief of Staff
CHR: Holly Horton, Director Human Resources
Web address: www.nhhn.org

| | 13 | 10 | 68 | 1241 | 45 | 29396 | 0 | 14217 | 7370 | 218 |

BURLINGTON—Alamance County

⊠ **ALAMANCE REGIONAL MEDICAL CENTER**, 1240 Huffman Mill Road, Zip 27216–0202, Mailing Address: P.O. Box 202, Zip 27216–0202; tel. 336/538–7000 **A**1 2 9 10 **F**2 4 9 10 11 12 15 17 21 22 23 26 27 28 29 30 31 32 33 37 39 42 44 45 46 47 48 50 51 52 53 55 57 58 59 60 61 62 63 64 65 66 68 69 70 71 73 74 75 76 77 78 79 81 82 84 85 86 87 88 92 93 94 95 96 98 106 108 109 **P**6
Primary Contact: Thomas E. Ryan, President
CFO: Rex Street, Vice President Finance
CIO: Angie Counts, Director Public Relations
Web address: www.armc.com

| | 23 | 10 | 210 | 9890 | 122 | 141000 | 1199 | 128686 | 52937 | 1333 |

Many Facility Codes have changed. Please refer to the AHA Guide Code Chart.   © 2005 AHA Guide

Hospital, Address, Telephone, Approval, Facility, and Physician Codes, Health Care System	Classi-fication Codes		Utilization Data					Expense (thousands) of dollars		
★ American Hospital Association (AHA) membership □ Joint Commission on Accreditation of Healthcare Organizations (JCAHO) accreditation ○ American Osteopathic Association (AOA) accreditation △ Commission on Accreditation of Rehabilitation Facilities (CARF) accreditation	Control	Service	Staffed Beds	Admissions	Census	Outpatient Visits	Births	Total	Payroll	Personnel

BURNSVILLE—Yancey County

YANCEY COMMUNITY MEDICAL CENTER, 320 Pensacola Road, Zip 28714; tel. 828/682–6136, (Nonreporting) **A**9 10 18
Primary Contact: Dena Hensley, Administrator

| | 23 | 10 | 6 | — | — | — | — | — | — | — |

BUTNER—Granville County

□ **JOHN UMSTEAD HOSPITAL**, 1003 12th Street, Zip 27509–1626; tel. 919/575–7211, (Includes ALCOHOL AND DRUG ABUSE TREATMENT CENTER, 205 West E Street, Zip 27509; tel. 919/575–7928; Cliff Hood, Director) **A**1 3 5 10 **F**2 22 26 32 45 46 58 60 71 72 74 75 76 92 94 106 108 **P**6
Primary Contact: Patricia L. Christian, Ph.D., R.N., Chief Executive Officer
Web address: www.juh.dhhs.state.nc.us

| | 12 | 22 | 433 | 6002 | 306 | 6260 | 0 | 96420 | 43399 | 1083 |

CAMP LEJEUNE—Onslow County

✠ **NAVAL HOSPITAL**, Mailing Address: P.O. Box 10100, Zip 28547–0100; tel. 910/450–4300 **A**1 **F**4 11 12 21 22 24 25 26 27 28 29 32 33 37 40 41 42 47 48 52 53 55 58 59 60 62 63 64 66 69 70 71 72 73 75 77 78 81 82 83 84 85 87 88 94 95 106 108 **P**1 **S** Bureau of Medicine and Surgery, Department of the Navy, Washington, DC
Primary Contact: Captain R. C. Welton, Chief Commander
Web address: www.nhcl.med.navy.mil

| | 43 | 10 | 76 | 4962 | 36 | 359797 | 515 | 74700 | 70315 | 1688 |

CARY—Wake County

★ △ **WAKEMED CARY HOSPITAL**, 1900 Kildaire Farm Road, Zip 27511; tel. 919/233–2300, (Includes SOUTHERN WAKE HOSPITAL, 400 West Ranson Street, Fuquay–Varina, Zip 27526; tel. 919/552–2206), (Total facility includes 36 beds in nursing home–type unit) **A**7 9 10 **F**2 9 11 12 15 17 19 22 23 27 28 29 33 35 37 39 46 47 48 50 52 53 55 56 57 58 59 60 61 62 63 64 65 69 81 82 85 87 88 92 94 95 96 108 109 **S** WakeMed, Raleigh, NC
Web address: www.wakemed.org

| | 23 | 10 | 150 | 7892 | 110 | 181510 | 2280 | 79121 | 40397 | 871 |

CHAPEL HILL—Orange County

✠ △ **UNIVERSITY OF NORTH CAROLINA HOSPITALS**, 101 Manning Drive, Zip 27514–4220; tel. 919/966–4131, (Includes NORTH CAROLINA CHILDREN'S AND WOMEN'S HOSPITAL ; NORTH CAROLINA NEUROSCIENCES HOSPITAL) **A**1 2 3 5 7 8 9 10 **F**2 3 4 6 7 9 10 11 12 13 14 15 16 17 18 19 20 21 22 23 24 26 27 28 29 30 31 32 33 34 35 36 37 38 39 41 42 44 45 46 47 48 49 50 51 52 53 55 56 57 58 59 60 61 62 63 64 65 66 67 68 69 70 71 72 73 74 75 76 77 78 79 80 81 82 84 85 86 87 88 89 90 93 94 95 96 98 99 100 101 102 103 104 105 106 107 108 109 110
Primary Contact: Gary L. Park, President and Chief Executive Officer
COO: Todd L. Peterson, Executive Vice President and Chief Operating Officer
CMO: Brian Goldstein, M.D., Chief of Staff
CIO: J P. Kichak, Vice President Information Services
CHR: Peter Barnes, Senior Vice President Human Resources
Web address: www.unchealthcare.org

| | 12 | 10 | 688 | 30831 | 548 | 1116641 | 3554 | 586453 | 285752 | 5304 |

CHARLOTTE—Mecklenburg County

✠ **CAROLINAS MEDICAL CENTER**, 1000 Blythe Boulevard, Zip 28203–5871, Mailing Address: P.O. Box 32861, Zip 28232–2861; tel. 704/355–2000 **A**1 2 3 5 8 9 10 **F**2 6 7 9 10 11 12 14 15 16 17 18 19 20 21 22 23 24 27 28 29 30 31 32 33 34 35 37 38 39 42 44 45 46 47 48 49 50 51 52 53 55 56 57 58 59 62 63 64 65 66 67 70 71 72 73 74 75 76 77 78 79 80 81 82 84 85 86 87 88 89 90 92 93 94 95 96 98 100 101 102 105 106 107 108 109 110 **P**2 6 **S** Carolinas HealthCare System, Charlotte, NC
Primary Contact: Suzanne H. Freeman, R.N., President
COO: Phyllis Wingate–Jones, Senior Vice President Operations
CFO: Greg A. Gombar, Chief Financial Officer
CMO: Stephen L. Moore, M.D., Vice President, Medical Management & Medical Director
CIO: John J. Knox, III, Vice President and Chief Information Officer
CHR: F Traylor Renfro, Senior Vice President Human Resources
Web address: www.carolinashealthcare.org

| | 16 | 10 | 861 | 45017 | 668 | 798034 | 7281 | 963825 | 377953 | 7922 |

CAROLINAS MEDICAL CENTER– PINEVILLE See

✠ △ **CAROLINAS MEDICAL CENTER–MERCY**, 2001 Vail Avenue, Zip 28207–1289; tel. 704/379–5000, (Includes CAROLINAS MEDICAL CENTER–PINEVILLE, 10628 Park Road, Zip 28210; tel. 704/543–2025; William K. Brown, Vice President and Administrator) **A**1 6 7 9 10 **F**3 14 15 17 19 21 22 23 27 28 33 35 37 38 39 46 48 49 52 53 55 57 61 62 63 64 66 68 69 81 82 84 85 87 88 93 94 108 110 **S** Carolinas HealthCare System, Charlotte, NC
Primary Contact: C. Curtis Copenhaver, President
COO: Thomas E. Hassett, Vice President
CFO: David Thomas, Chief Financial Officer
CMO: Charles Harr, M.D., President Medical Staff
CHR: Stephanie McGary, Regional Director Human Resources
Web address: www.carolinashealthcare.org

| | 16 | 10 | 224 | 7141 | 121 | 52938 | 0 | 96666 | 35215 | 641 |

✠ **CAROLINAS MEDICAL CENTER–PINEVILLE**, 10628 Park Road, Zip 28210; tel. 704/543–2025 **A**1 9 10 **F**11 15 21 22 27 28 29 33 35 37 39 46 48 52 53 55 56 59 62 63 64 66 69 81 82 84 87 88 93 94 108 **S** Carolinas HealthCare System, Charlotte, NC
Primary Contact: William K. Brown, Vice President and Administrator
Web address: www.carolinashealthcare.org

| | 16 | 10 | 108 | 6320 | 65 | 83450 | 1969 | 64148 | 25892 | 522 |

NC

Hospital, Address, Telephone, Approval, Facility, and Physician Codes, Health Care System	Classification Codes		Utilization Data					Expense (thousands) of dollars		
★ American Hospital Association (AHA) membership □ Joint Commission on Accreditation of Healthcare Organizations (JCAHO) accreditation ○ American Osteopathic Association (AOA) accreditation △ Commission on Accreditation of Rehabilitation Facilities (CARF) accreditation	Control	Service	Staffed Beds	Admissions	Census	Outpatient Visits	Births	Total	Payroll	Personnel

⊠ **CAROLINAS MEDICAL CENTER–UNIVERSITY**, 8800 North Tryon Street, Zip 28262–8415, Mailing Address: P.O. Box 560727, Zip 28256–0727; tel. 704/548–6000 **A**1 9 10 **F**11 15 21 22 23 27 28 33 35 37 39 46 48 52 53 55 58 59 61 62 63 64 66 69 81 82 84 85 87 88 93 94 108 **S** Carolinas HealthCare System, Charlotte, NC Primary Contact: W. Spencer Lilly, Administrator Web address: www.carolinashealthcare.org	16	10	122	6123	62	119642	1422	79020	31046	619
⊠ △ **CHARLOTTE INSTITUTE OF REHABILITATION**, 1100 Blythe Boulevard, Zip 28203–5864; tel. 704/355–4300 **A**1 7 10 **F**26 27 28 52 68 69 94 108 **P**1 **S** Carolinas HealthCare System, Charlotte, NC Primary Contact: Thomas M. Nojunas, Vice President and Administrator CFO: William Hopkins, Director Finance CMO: James McDeavitt, M.D., Chief Medical Staff Web address: www.carolinashealthcare.org	23	46	120	1685	76	28922	—	32120	18303	—
⊠ **PRESBYTERIAN HOSPITAL**, 200 Hawthorne Lane, Zip 28204–2528, Mailing Address: P.O. Box 33549, Zip 28233–3549; tel. 704/384–4000 **A**1 2 9 10 **F**2 4 9 10 11 12 14 15 17 19 21 22 23 24 26 27 28 29 30 31 33 36 37 38 39 41 42 43 44 45 46 47 48 49 50 51 52 53 55 56 57 58 59 61 63 64 65 66 67 69 71 72 73 74 75 76 77 78 79 81 82 84 86 87 88 90 93 94 96 105 106 108 109 110 **P**6 **S** Novant Health, Winston–Salem, NC Primary Contact: Carl Armato, President COO: Lynn Ingram Boggs, Executive Vice President and Chief Operating Officer CFO: Patrick Easterling, Vice President and Chief Financial Officer CMO: Stephen Wallenhaupt, M.D., Executive Vice President Medical Affairs CIO: Rich B. McKnight, Interim Senior Vice President Information Technology CHR: Jacqueline D. Gattis, Senior Vice President Human Resources Web address: www.presbyterian.org	23	10	547	25782	547	173520	3748	—	—	2977
★ **PRESBYTERIAN–ORTHOPAEDIC HOSPITAL**, 1901 Randolph Road, Zip 28207–1195; tel. 704/375–6792 **A**9 10 **F**2 9 21 22 26 28 35 37 38 39 52 53 58 62 63 65 66 69 92 94 95 96 **S** Novant Health, Winston–Salem, NC Primary Contact: Tanya Blackmon, Executive Director Orthopaedic Services CFO: Tammy Geist, Chief Financial Officer CIO: Shelia Cook, Director Information Systems Web address: www.novanthealth.org	23	47	76	3989	72	18950	0	—	—	309
CHEROKEE—Swain County										
⊠ **CHEROKEE INDIAN HOSPITAL AUTHORITY**, Hospital Road, Zip 28719, Mailing Address: Caller Box C–26, Zip 28719; tel. 828/497–9163, (Nonreporting) **A**1 10 **S** U. S. Indian Health Service, Rockville, MD Primary Contact: Arnold Wachacha, Administrator CFO: Shirley Hilton, Budget Analyst	47	10	28	—	—	—	—	—	—	—
CHERRY POINT—Craven County										
⊠ **NAVAL HOSPITAL**, Mailing Address: PSC Box 8023, Zip 28533–0023; tel. 252/466–0266, (Nonreporting) **A**1 **S** Bureau of Medicine and Surgery, Department of the Navy, Washington, DC Primary Contact: Captain Donald Thompson, Commanding Officer COO: Captain M H. Anderson, MC, USN, Executive Officer CFO: Lieutenant D E. Quance, MSC, USNR, Director Resources CMO: Captain C R. Armstrong, MC, USN, Director Outpatient Care CIO: Jacqueline Buntyn, Head Management Information Web address: www.cpoint–www.med.navy.mil	43	10	23	—	—	—	—	—	—	—
CLINTON—Sampson County										
⊠ **SAMPSON REGIONAL MEDICAL CENTER**, 607 Beaman Street, Zip 28328–2697, Mailing Address: P.O. Box 260, Zip 28329–0260; tel. 910/592–8511, (Total facility includes 30 beds in nursing home–type unit) (Nonreporting) **A**1 9 10 Primary Contact: Larry H. Chewning, III, Chief Executive Officer COO: Wanda L. Boyette, R.N., Senior Vice President and Chief Operating Officer CFO: Jerry Heinzman, Senior Vice President and Chief Financial Officer CMO: W Alexander Huff, M.D., President Medical Staff CIO: David Ziolkowski, Chief Information Officer CHR: Patricia Britt–Boyette, Vice President Human Resources Web address: www.sampsonrmc.org	13	10	146	—	—	—	—	—	—	—
CLYDE—Haywood County										
⊠ **HAYWOOD REGIONAL MEDICAL CENTER**, 262 Leroy George Drive, Zip 28721–9434; tel. 828/456–7311, (Total facility includes 20 beds in nursing home–type unit) **A**1 9 10 **F**9 11 12 17 21 26 27 28 29 33 36 41 44 46 47 48 51 55 60 61 63 65 69 73 81 82 84 88 92 93 94 95 96 107 108 109 110 **P**8 Primary Contact: David O. Rice, President COO: Alton T. Byers, Chief Operating Officer CFO: Gwen Evans, Chief Financial Officer CMO: David Love, M.D., Chief Medical Officer CIO: John Olivier, Director Information Systems CHR: Gary Arrington, Director Human Resources Web address: www.haymed.org	16	10	125	6072	65	148252	283	61813	28782	808
COLUMBUS—Polk County										
□ **ST. LUKE'S HOSPITAL**, 101 Hospital Drive, Zip 28722–9473; tel. 828/894–3311 **A**1 9 10 **F**2 9 12 21 22 26 27 28 29 33 44 46 48 51 55 58 60 62 63 64 69 71 76 81 82 85 88 94 97 106 108 110 Primary Contact: C. Cameron Highsmith, President and Chief Executive Officer Web address: www.saintlukeshospital.com	23	10	63	1964	39	46403	0	18218	8246	285

Many Facility Codes have changed. Please refer to the AHA Guide Code Chart.

Hospital, Address, Telephone, Approval, Facility, and Physician Codes, Health Care System	Classi-fication Codes		Utilization Data					Expense (thousands) of dollars		
★ American Hospital Association (AHA) membership □ Joint Commission on Accreditation of Healthcare Organizations (JCAHO) accreditation ○ American Osteopathic Association (AOA) accreditation △ Commission on Accreditation of Rehabilitation Facilities (CARF) accreditation	Control	Service	Staffed Beds	Admissions	Census	Outpatient Visits	Births	Total	Payroll	Personnel

CONCORD—Cabarrus County

☒ **NORTHEAST MEDICAL CENTER**, 920 Church Street North, Zip 28025–2983; tel. 704/783–3000 **A**1 2 9 10 **F**2 4 6 7 9 10 11 12 14 21 22 23 24 26 27 28 29 30 31 32 33 34 35 36 37 38 40 41 42 44 45 46 47 48 49 50 51 52 53 54 55 57 58 59 60 61 62 63 65 66 67 69 70 71 72 73 74 75 76 77 78 79 81 82 83 84 85 86 87 88 89 93 94 95 96 97 98 106 107 108 109 110 **P**6
Primary Contact: Laurence C. Hinsdale, President and Chief Executive Officer
COO: Dari Caldwell, Executive Vice President and Chief Operating Officer
CFO: Mark Nantz, Chief Financial Officer
CIO: Keith McNeice, Vice President and Chief Information Officer
Web address: www.northeastmedical.org
| 23 | 10 | 357 | 18676 | 238 | 695462 | 2712 | 318506 | 147965 | 3377 |

DANBURY—Stokes County

☒ **STOKES–REYNOLDS MEMORIAL HOSPITAL**, 1570 Highway 8 and 89 North, Zip 27016, Mailing Address: P.O. Box 10, Zip 27016–0010; tel. 336/593–2831, (Total facility includes 40 beds in nursing home–type unit) **A**1 9 10 18 **F**2 12 26 27 28 29 33 34 36 42 46 47 48 52 55 63 64 69 70 81 88 92 94 97 107 **P**6 **S** North Carolina Baptist Hospital, Winston–Salem, NC
Primary Contact: Lance C. Labine, President
CFO: Jim Chatman, Chief Financial Officer
CMO: Samuel C. Newsome, M.D., President, Medical Staff
Web address: www.wfubmc.edu/stokes
| 21 | 10 | 65 | 598 | 65 | 30630 | 0 | 13979 | 6623 | 187 |

DUNN—Harnett County

□ **BETSY JOHNSON REGIONAL HOSPITAL**, 800 Tilghman Drive, Zip 28334–5599, Mailing Address: Drawer 1706, Zip 28335–1706; tel. 910/892–7161 **A**1 9 10 **F**2 9 11 12 22 27 28 29 32 33 37 44 46 48 53 55 58 59 60 61 62 63 64 65 69 81 82 85 87 88 93 94 96 110
Primary Contact: Alfred P. Taylor, Chief Executive Officer
Web address: www.bjrh.org
| 16 | 10 | 78 | 4597 | 53 | 79090 | 664 | 43174 | 20878 | 467 |

DURHAM—Durham County

☒ **DUKE UNIVERSITY HOSPITAL**, Erwin Road, Zip 27710–0001, Mailing Address: P.O. Box 3708, Zip 27710–3708; tel. 919/684–8111, (Includes DUKE UNIVERSITY HOSPITAL) **A**1 2 8 9 10 13 **F**2 5 6 9 10 11 12 14 15 16 17 18 19 20 21 22 23 24 26 27 28 29 30 31 32 33 34 35 37 38 39 42 44 46 47 48 49 50 52 53 55 56 57 58 59 60 61 62 63 64 65 66 67 69 70 71 73 75 76 77 79 80 81 82 84 85 86 87 88 89 90 93 94 95 96 98 99 100 101 102 103 104 105 106 108 109 110 **P**1 **S** Duke University Health System, Durham, NC
Primary Contact: William J. Fulkerson, M.D., Chief Executive Officer
COO: Kevin W. Sowers, R.N., MSN, Chief Operating Officer
CFO: Mark F. Miller, Chief Financial Officer
CMO: William J. Fulkerson, M.D., Chief Executive Officer
CIO: Asif Ahmad, Chief Information Officer
CHR: Stephen R. Smith, Vice President Human Resources
Web address: www.mc.duke.edu
| 23 | 10 | 753 | 36879 | 608 | 676642 | 2988 | 866661 | 375546 | 6927 |

☒ **DURHAM REGIONAL HOSPITAL**, 3643 North Roxboro Road, Zip 27704–2763; tel. 919/470–4000 **A**1 3 5 6 9 10 **F**2 9 10 11 12 14 15 17 19 21 22 23 27 28 29 33 35 39 40 44 46 47 48 49 50 52 53 55 57 58 59 60 61 62 63 64 65 66 68 69 71 73 75 76 78 81 82 84 85 87 88 93 94 95 96 106 108 110 **P**6 **S** Duke University Health System, Durham, NC
Primary Contact: David P. McQuaid, Chief Executive Officer
COO: Ernest Baptiste, Chief Operating Officer
CFO: G Gregory Damron, Chief Financial Officer
CMO: Edward N. LaMay, M.D., Chief Medical Officer
CIO: Terry Mears, Director Information Systems
CHR: Richard J. Walsh, Ph.D., Chief Human Resources Officer
Web address: www.durhamregional.org
| 23 | 10 | 269 | 15495 | 215 | 122552 | 2160 | 187182 | 81825 | 1964 |

☒ **DURHAM VETERANS AFFAIRS MEDICAL CENTER**, 508 Fulton Street, Zip 27705–3897; tel. 919/286–0411, (Total facility includes 90 beds in nursing home–type unit) (Nonreporting) **A**1 3 5 8 **S** Department of Veterans Affairs, Washington, DC
Primary Contact: Alan K. Begbie, Acting Director
COO: Alan K. Begbie, Associate Director
CMO: John D. Shelburne, M.D., Chief of Staff
CIO: Conrad Raber, Chief, Information Resources Management Service
Web address: www.va.gov/sta/guide/facility.asp?id=43
| 45 | 10 | 232 | — | — | — | — | — | — | — |

NORTH CAROLINA EYE AND EAR HOSPITAL, 1110 West Main Street, Zip 27701–2000; tel. 919/682–9341, (Nonreporting) **A**9 10
Primary Contact: Robert C. Miner, Chief Executive Officer
| 32 | 45 | 24 | — | — | — | — | — | — | — |

NORTH CAROLINA SPECIALTY HOSPITAL, 1110 West Main Street, Zip 27701–2000; tel. 919/956–9300, (Nonreporting) **A**9 10 **S** National Surgical Hospitals, Chicago, IL
| 33 | 49 | 14 | — | — | — | — | — | — | — |

□ **SELECT SPECIALTY HOSPITAL OF DURHAM**, 3643 North Roxboro Road, 6th Floor, Zip 27704; tel. 919/470–9000, (Nonreporting) **A**1 10
Primary Contact: Matthew Womble, Chief Executive Officer
| 33 | 49 | 30 | — | — | — | — | — | — | — |

EDEN—Rockingham County

☒ **MOREHEAD MEMORIAL HOSPITAL**, 117 East King's Highway, Zip 27288–5299; tel. 336/623–9711, (Total facility includes 134 beds in nursing home–type unit) **A**1 2 9 10 **F**2 9 11 12 21 22 23 28 29 30 33 37 38 44 46 47 48 51 52 55 57 58 59 60 61 62 63 69 70 79 81 82 84 85 87 88 92 93 94 95 96 98 106 108 109 110 **P**6 8 **S** Quorum Health Resources, Plano, TX
Primary Contact: Robert Enders, President
CFO: Tom Gillespie, Vice President Finance
Web address: www.morehead.org
| 23 | 10 | 242 | 6267 | 182 | 138448 | 534 | 61230 | 28742 | 696 |

NC

Hospital, Address, Telephone, Approval, Facility, and Physician Codes, Health Care System	Classi-fication Codes		Utilization Data					Expense (thousands) of dollars		
★ American Hospital Association (AHA) membership □ Joint Commission on Accreditation of Healthcare Organizations (JCAHO) accreditation ○ American Osteopathic Association (AOA) accreditation △ Commission on Accreditation of Rehabilitation Facilities (CARF) accreditation	Control	Service	Staffed Beds	Admissions	Census	Outpatient Visits	Births	Total	Payroll	Personnel

EDENTON—Chowan County

⊠ **CHOWAN HOSPITAL**, 211 Virginia Road, Zip 27932–0629, Mailing Address: P.O. Box 629, Zip 27932–0629; tel. 252/482–8451, (Total facility includes 39 beds in nursing home–type unit) **A**1 9 10 18 **F**2 9 11 12 21 22 23 26 27 28 29 33 37 44 46 48 51 52 55 58 59 60 61 62 63 64 69 81 82 85 88 92 94 96 97 106 108 109 **P**6 **S** University Health Systems of Eastern Carolina, Greenville, NC
Primary Contact: Jeffrey N. Sackrison, CHE, President
CFO: Brian A. Bunch, Vice President Financial Services
CHR: Debbie Swicegood, Director Human Resources
Web address: www.uhseast.com

| 23 | 10 | 76 | 2255 | 51 | 30115 | 354 | 29108 | 12798 | 429 |

ELIZABETH CITY—Pasquotank County

⊠ **ALBEMARLE HOSPITAL**, 1144 North Road Street, Zip 27909, Mailing Address: P.O. Box 1587, Zip 27906–1587; tel. 252/335–0531 **A**1 9 10 19 20 **F**2 11 12 14 15 21 22 23 26 27 28 29 32 33 38 41 45 46 47 48 52 53 55 57 58 59 60 61 62 63 65 66 69 79 81 82 84 87 88 93 94 96 108 109 110
Primary Contact: Sharon M. Tanner, President and Chief Executive Officer
CFO: John Wiggins, Vice President Finance and Chief Financial Officer
CMO: David Carter, M.D., Chief of Staff
CHR: Jan King Robinson, Vice President Human Resources and Organizational Development
Web address: www.albemarlehosp.org

| 16 | 10 | 150 | 8059 | 102 | 116088 | 684 | 83415 | 37864 | 858 |

ELIZABETHTOWN—Bladen County

⊠ **BLADEN COUNTY HOSPITAL**, 501 South Poplar Street, Zip 28337–0398, Mailing Address: P.O. Box 398, Zip 28337–0398; tel. 910/862–5100, (Total facility includes 10 beds in nursing home–type unit) **A**1 9 10 18 **F**9 11 12 21 22 26 27 28 33 52 55 59 60 63 64 66 69 81 88 92 98 107 108 109 **P**6
Primary Contact: David J. Masterson, Chief Executive Officer
COO: Carl Gyczynski, Vice President Operations
CFO: Bruce Brooks, Chief Financial Officer
CMO: Susan Aycock, M.D., President Medical Staff
CIO: Ken Pervine, Management Information Systems Director
Web address: www.bchn.org

| 13 | 10 | 35 | 1424 | 31 | 16067 | 183 | 19370 | 9304 | 271 |

ELKIN—Surry County

⊠ **HUGH CHATHAM MEMORIAL HOSPITAL**, 180 Parkwood Drive, Zip 28621–0560, Mailing Address: P.O. Box 560, Zip 28621–0560; tel. 336/527–7000, (Total facility includes 147 beds in nursing home–type unit) (Nonreporting) **A**1 2 9 10 **S** Quorum Health Resources, Plano, TX
Primary Contact: Richard D. Osmus, Chief Executive Officer
CFO: Donald E. Trippel, Chief Financial Officer
CMO: Tony Canupp, M.D., Chief of Staff
CHR: Jeff Seaford, Director Human Resources
Web address: www.hughchatham.org

| 23 | 10 | 220 | — | — | — | — | — | — | — |

ERWIN—Harnett County

⊠ **GOOD HOPE HOSPITAL**, 410 Denim Drive, Zip 28339–0668; tel. 910/897–6151, (Nonreporting) **A**1 9 10 **S** Quorum Health Resources, Plano, TX
Primary Contact: Donald E. Annis, Chief Executive Officer
COO: Amy Hamby, R.N., Chief Clinical Officer
CFO: Denise Smith, Chief Executive Officer
CMO: Marcos Rosado, M.D., Chief of Staff
CIO: Jim Shaver, Director Information Systems
CHR: Michele Baker, Director Human Resources
Web address: www.goodhopehospital.org

| 23 | 10 | 47 | — | — | — | — | — | — | — |

FAYETTEVILLE—Cumberland County

BEHAVIORAL HEALTH CARE OF CAPE FEAR VALLEY HEALTH SYSTEM, 3425 Melrose Road, Zip 28304–1695; tel. 910/609–3000 **A**10 **F**3 21 26 27 28 33 71 72 74 75 77 78 93 **P**1 8 **S** Cumberland County Hospital System, Fayetteville, NC
Primary Contact: Stanley D. Dodson, Director for Psychiatric Services
Web address: www.capefearvalley.com

| 13 | 22 | 32 | 1476 | 20 | 6907 | 0 | — | — | 108 |

⊠ △ **CAPE FEAR VALLEY HEALTH SYSTEM**, 1638 Owen Drive, Zip 28304–3431, Mailing Address: P.O. Box 2000, Zip 28302–2000; tel. 910/609–4000, (Includes SOUTHEASTERN REGIONAL REHABILITATION CENTER ; HIGHSMITH–RAINEY MEMORIAL HOSPITAL, 150 Robeson Street, Zip 28301–5570; tel. 910/609–1000; Walt Rose, Vice President) **A**1 2 7 9 10 **F**4 6 10 11 12 14 15 17 19 21 22 23 26 27 28 29 30 31 32 33 36 37 38 39 40 41 44 45 46 47 48 49 50 51 52 53 55 56 57 58 59 60 61 62 63 64 65 66 67 68 69 70 71 72 73 74 75 76 77 78 79 81 82 83 84 85 86 88 92 93 94 95 96 106 107 108 109 110 **P**5 6 **S** Cumberland County Hospital System, Fayetteville, NC
Primary Contact: Richard H. Parks, FACHE, Chief Executive Officer
COO: Joyce P. Korzen, R.N., Senior Vice President and Chief Operating Officer
CFO: Torrey M. Johnson, Jr, Chief Financial Officer
CIO: William Avenel, Vice President Information Systems and Chief Information Officer
CHR: Steve Thomas, Vice President Human Resources
Web address: www.capefearvalley.com

| 23 | 10 | 581 | 28826 | 441 | 434097 | 3980 | 403200 | 167692 | 3804 |

NC

Many Facility Codes have changed. Please refer to the AHA Guide Code Chart.   © 2005 AHA Guide

Hospital, Address, Telephone, Approval, Facility, and Physician Codes, Health Care System	Classi-fication Codes		Utilization Data					Expense (thousands) of dollars		
★ American Hospital Association (AHA) membership □ Joint Commission on Accreditation of Healthcare Organizations (JCAHO) accreditation ○ American Osteopathic Association (AOA) accreditation △ Commission on Accreditation of Rehabilitation Facilities (CARF) accreditation	Control	Service	Staffed Beds	Admissions	Census	Outpatient Visits	Births	Total	Payroll	Personnel
⊠ **VETERANS AFFAIRS MEDICAL CENTER**, 2300 Ramsey Street, Zip 28301–3899; tel. 910/822–7059, (Total facility includes 69 beds in nursing home–type unit) **A**1 **F**2 4 21 22 26 27 28 29 32 33 36 37 38 39 42 44 45 46 48 50 51 52 53 55 57 58 60 62 63 64 66 69 70 71 73 74 75 77 81 82 84 88 92 93 94 96 106 108 109 110 **P**6 **S** Department of Veterans Affairs, Washington, DC Primary Contact: Janet S. Stout, Director CFO: Joseph Albanese, Chief Fiscal Services CIO: Clint Nordan, Chief Information Resource Management Web address: www.va.gov/sta/guide/home.asp	45	10	159	3476	118	322185	0	60778	53831	893
FLETCHER—Henderson County										
⊠ ○ **PARK RIDGE HOSPITAL**, Naples Road, Zip 28732, Mailing Address: P.O. Box 1569, Zip 28732–1569; tel. 828/684–8501 **A**1 9 10 11 19 **F**2 9 10 11 12 21 22 23 26 27 28 29 33 38 39 48 51 53 55 58 59 61 62 63 69 71 75 76 78 81 82 84 88 92 93 94 95 96 97 105 106 107 108 110 **P**6 **S** Adventist Health System Sunbelt Health Care Corporation, Winter Park, FL Primary Contact: Michael H. Schultz, Chief Executive Officer CFO: Kelly J. Pettijohn, Vice President Finance CMO: Donald Culver, M.D., Chief of Staff CHR: Charlotte Lyda, Director Human Resources Web address: www.parkridgehospital.org	23	10	98	4494	66	178174	549	61255	25952	688
FORT BRAGG—Cumberland County										
⊠ **WOMACK ARMY MEDICAL CENTER**, Normandy Drive, Zip 28307–5000; tel. 910/907–6000 **A**1 3 5 **F**2 4 6 9 10 11 12 21 22 23 24 25 26 27 28 29 31 33 34 35 37 39 40 42 46 47 48 52 53 55 56 57 58 59 60 61 62 63 66 69 70 71 73 75 77 81 82 84 85 87 88 94 96 106 107 108 109 **S** Department of the Army, Office of the Surgeon General, Falls Church, VA Primary Contact: Colonel Ronald Maul, Commander Web address: www.wamc.amedd.army.mil/	42	10	129	8931	74	906005	2909	—	—	—
FRANKLIN—Macon County										
⊠ **ANGEL MEDICAL CENTER**, Riverview and White Oak Streets, Zip 28734, Mailing Address: P.O. Box 1209, Zip 28744; tel. 828/524–8411 **A**1 9 10 **F**9 11 12 21 22 23 27 29 33 36 37 38 40 46 48 51 52 53 55 57 58 59 60 61 62 63 66 69 70 81 82 84 88 93 96 97 106 107 108 109 **S** Quorum Health Resources, Plano, TX Primary Contact: Michael E. Zuliani, Chief Executive Officer CFO: Donald Wade, Chief Financial Officer CIO: Gary Hanold, Director Management Information Systems Web address: www.angelmed.org	23	10	59	1561	15	49096	187	34580	14274	387
FUQUAY–VARINA—Wake County										
SOUTHERN WAKE HOSPITAL See WakeMed Cary Hospital, Cary										
GASTONIA—Gaston County										
⊠ **GASTON MEMORIAL HOSPITAL**, 2525 Court Drive, Zip 28054–2142, Mailing Address: P.O. Box 1747, Zip 28053–1747; tel. 704/834–2000 **A**1 2 9 10 **F**2 11 12 14 15 17 19 21 22 23 26 27 28 29 33 37 39 41 49 53 55 56 57 58 59 61 62 63 64 66 69 71 72 75 79 80 81 84 86 88 92 93 94 95 96 108 109 110 Primary Contact: Wayne F. Shovelin, President and Chief Executive Officer COO: Terry L. Jones, Executive Vice President and Chief Operating Officer CFO: Dave Willie, Chief Financial Officer and Vice President Fiscal Services CIO: Mike Johnson, Director Information Systems CHR: Bob Henderson, Vice President Human Resources Web address: www.caromont.org	23	10	378	21680	279	338732	2626	226123	92873	1953
GOLDSBORO—Wayne County										
□ **CHERRY HOSPITAL**, 201 Stevens Mill Road, Zip 27530–1057; tel. 919/731–3200, (Total facility includes 65 beds in nursing home–type unit) **A**1 10 **F**2 22 26 27 28 32 44 53 66 71 72 76 92 94 108 **P**6 Primary Contact: Liston G. Edwards, Director Web address: www.dhhs.state.nc.us/mhddsas/cherry	12	22	403	3628	306	0	0	64782	40753	1054
⊠ **WAYNE MEMORIAL HOSPITAL**, 2700 Wayne Memorial Drive, Zip 27534, Mailing Address: P.O. Box 8001, Zip 27533; tel. 919/736–1110 **A**1 2 9 10 19 **F**2 11 12 15 21 22 23 26 27 29 33 37 44 46 47 48 49 50 52 53 55 56 57 58 59 60 61 62 63 65 66 69 71 72 73 74 75 76 78 81 82 84 85 86 87 88 93 94 95 96 106 108 Primary Contact: J. William Paugh, President and Chief Executive Officer COO: Thomas A. Bradshaw, Vice President Operations CFO: Rebecca W. Craig, Vice President and Chief Financial Officer CMO: Christopher P. Griffin, M.D., President Medical Staff CIO: Lori Cole, Director Information Management Web address: www.waynehealth.org	23	10	270	13589	188	156320	1437	126418	56746	1263
GREENSBORO—Guilford County										
BEHAVIORAL HEALTH CENTER, 700 Walter Reed Drive, Zip 27403–1129; tel. 336/852–4821, (Nonreporting) **S** Moses Cone Health System, Greensboro, NC Primary Contact: Paul A. Jeffrey, Vice President Web address: www.mosescone.com	23	22	80	—	—	—	—	—	—	—

NC

Hospital, Address, Telephone, Approval, Facility, and Physician Codes, Health Care System	Classi-fication Codes		Utilization Data					Expense (thousands) of dollars		
★ American Hospital Association (AHA) membership □ Joint Commission on Accreditation of Healthcare Organizations (JCAHO) accreditation ○ American Osteopathic Association (AOA) accreditation △ Commission on Accreditation of Rehabilitation Facilities (CARF) accreditation	Control	Service	Staffed Beds	Admissions	Census	Outpatient Visits	Births	Total	Payroll	Personnel

□ KINDRED HOSPITAL–GREENSBORO, 2401 Southside Boulevard, Zip 27406–3311; tel. 336/271–2800, (Total facility includes 23 beds in nursing home–type unit) **A**1 9 10 **F**2 21 27 49 52 55 60 63 69 81 88 92 94 110 **S** Kindred Healthcare, Louisville, KY
Primary Contact: David M. Polunas, Chief Executive Officer
Web address: www.kindredhealthcare.com/hospitals/greensboro

| | 33 | 10 | 124 | 583 | 88 | 226 | 0 | 30115 | 14422 | 261 |

⊠ △ MOSES CONE HEALTH SYSTEM, 1200 North Elm Street, Zip 27401–1020; tel. 336/832–7000, (Includes MOSES H. CONE MEMORIAL HOSPITAL; WESLEY LONG COMMUNITY HOSPITAL, 501 North Elam Avenue, Zip 27403; tel. 336/832–1000; WOMEN'S HOSPITAL OF GREENSBORO, 801 Green Valley Road, Zip 27408; tel. 336/832–6500), (Total facility includes 395 beds in nursing home–type unit) **A**1 2 3 5 7 9 10 **F**2 4 6 9 10 11 12 14 15 17 19 21 22 23 24 26 27 28 29 32 33 34 35 36 37 38 39 40 42 44 46 47 48 49 50 51 52 53 55 56 57 58 59 60 61 62 63 64 65 66 67 69 70 71 72 73 74 75 76 77 79 80 81 82 84 85 86 87 88 89 90 92 93 94 95 96 98 106 107 108 109 110 **P**6 8 **S** Moses Cone Health System, Greensboro, NC
Primary Contact: R. Timothy Rice, President and Chief Executive Officer
COO: Glenn D. Waters, Chief Operating Officer
CFO: Beth Ward, Vice President and Chief Financial Officer
CIO: John Jenkins, Vice President and Chief Information Officer
CHR: Noel Burt, Ph.D., Vice President Human Resources
Web address: www.mosescone.com

| | 23 | 10 | 1324 | 47576 | 977 | 565187 | 5976 | 603505 | 261293 | 6451 |

GREENVILLE—Pitt County

⊠ △ PITT COUNTY MEMORIAL HOSPITAL, 2100 Stantonsburg Road, Zip 27834, Mailing Address: P.O. Box 6028, Zip 27835–6028; tel. 252/847–4100 **A**1 2 3 5 7 8 9 10 19 **F**2 6 10 11 12 14 15 16 17 18 19 20 21 22 23 25 26 27 28 29 31 32 33 34 35 36 37 38 39 40 42 43 44 45 46 47 48 49 50 52 53 55 56 57 58 59 60 61 62 63 64 65 66 67 68 69 70 71 72 73 74 75 76 77 79 81 82 84 85 86 87 88 89 90 93 94 95 96 99 101 107 108 109 110 **P**8 **S** University Health Systems of Eastern Carolina, Greenville, NC
Primary Contact: Deborah W. Davis, President
CFO: Jack W. Holsten, Chief Financial Officer
CIO: Edward McFall, Chief Information Officer
Web address: www.uhseast.com

| | 23 | 10 | 745 | 36614 | 585 | 273103 | 3554 | 562950 | 220487 | 5091 |

WALTER B. JONES ALCOHOL AND DRUG ABUSE TREATMENT CENTER, 2577 West Fifth Street, Zip 27834–7813; tel. 252/830–3426, (Nonreporting) **A**9 10
Primary Contact: Theresa Edmondson, Director

| | 12 | 82 | 77 | — | — | — | — | — | — | — |

HAMLET—Richmond County

□ SANDHILLS REGIONAL MEDICAL CENTER, 1000 West Hamlet Avenue, Zip 28345–4522, Mailing Address: P.O. Box 1109, Zip 28345–1109; tel. 910/205–8000 **A**1 9 10 **F**2 12 15 21 22 26 27 28 33 37 39 46 49 53 55 58 62 63 64 69 71 75 77 78 81 82 84 85 88 93 94 108 110 **S** Health Management Associates, Naples, FL
Primary Contact: William H. Leonard, Chief Executive Officer
Web address: www.hma–corp.com

| | 33 | 10 | 64 | 3557 | 41 | — | 0 | — | — | 267 |

HENDERSON—Vance County

⊠ △ MARIA PARHAM MEDICAL CENTER, 566 Ruin Creek Road, Zip 27536–2957; tel. 252/438–4143 **A**1 7 9 10 **F**2 9 11 12 15 21 22 23 27 28 29 30 31 33 35 37 39 42 46 47 48 50 51 52 53 55 58 59 60 61 62 63 65 66 68 69 70 81 82 84 88 93 94 95 96 106 108 109 110 **P**3 8
Primary Contact: Michael L. Shields, President and Chief Executive Officer
CFO: Jon Carpenter, Vice President Finance and Chief Financial Officer
CMO: James O. Goodwin, M.D., Vice President Medical Affairs
CIO: Randy Williams, Director Management Information Systems
CHR: Edward Raymond, Vice President Human Resources
Web address: www.mphosp.org

| | 23 | 10 | 102 | 5765 | 66 | 148220 | 674 | 53886 | 21837 | 661 |

HENDERSONVILLE—Henderson County

⊠ MARGARET R. PARDEE MEMORIAL HOSPITAL, 800 North Justice Street, Zip 28791–2563; tel. 828/696–1000, (Total facility includes 20 beds in nursing home–type unit) **A**1 2 9 10 **F**1 2 9 10 11 12 14 21 22 23 24 26 27 28 29 32 33 35 36 37 38 39 40 41 46 47 48 51 52 53 54 55 57 58 59 60 61 62 63 65 66 69 70 71 73 74 75 76 81 82 84 87 88 92 93 94 95 96 106 107 108 109 110 **P**6
Primary Contact: Robert P. Goodwin, President and Chief Executive Officer
COO: Sandy Smith, R.N., Senior Vice President Operations
CIO: Sherman Moore, Director Information Systems
Web address: www.pardeehospital.org

| | 13 | 10 | 181 | 9373 | 124 | 175220 | 572 | 105441 | 38913 | 1039 |

HICKORY—Catawba County

⊠ △ CATAWBA VALLEY MEDICAL CENTER, 810 Fairgrove Church Road S.E., Zip 28602–9643; tel. 828/326–3000 **A**1 2 5 7 9 10 **F**2 4 9 10 11 12 15 17 21 22 23 26 27 28 29 30 32 33 35 37 38 39 40 41 42 44 45 46 47 48 50 52 53 55 57 58 59 60 61 62 63 64 65 66 68 69 70 71 73 74 75 76 77 78 79 80 81 82 83 84 85 86 87 88 93 94 95 96 106 107 108 109 110 **P**8
Primary Contact: J. Anthony Rose, President and Chief Executive Officer
COO: Scott Echelberger, Vice President Operations
CIO: John Putnick, Director Information Systems
CHR: Phyllis Johnston, Director
Web address: www.catawbavalleymc.org

| | 13 | 10 | 213 | 8638 | 125 | 164664 | 1321 | 122396 | 55502 | 1068 |

NC

Many Facility Codes have changed. Please refer to the AHA Guide Code Chart.   © 2005 AHA Guide

Hospital, Address, Telephone, Approval, Facility, and Physician Codes, Health Care System	Classi-fication Codes		Utilization Data					Expense (thousands) of dollars		
★ American Hospital Association (AHA) membership □ Joint Commission on Accreditation of Healthcare Organizations (JCAHO) accreditation ○ American Osteopathic Association (AOA) accreditation △ Commission on Accreditation of Rehabilitation Facilities (CARF) accreditation	Control	Service	Staffed Beds	Admissions	Census	Outpatient Visits	Births	Total	Payroll	Personnel
⊠ **FRYE REGIONAL MEDICAL CENTER**, 420 North Center Street, Zip 28601–5049; tel. 828/322–6070, (Includes FRYE REGIONAL MEDICAL CENTER–SOUTH CAMPUS, tel. 704/328–2226), (Total facility includes 17 beds in nursing home–type unit) (Nonreporting) **A**1 2 9 10 **S** TENET Healthcare Corporation, Dallas, TX Primary Contact: Dennis Ray Bruns, Chief Executive Officer CFO: David O'Connor, Chief Financial Officer CMO: James Hodges, M.D., Chief of Staff CIO: Nathan White, Admin Director Information Systems Web address: www.fryemedctr.com	33	10	355	—	—	—	—	—	—	—
HIGH POINT—Guilford County										
⊠ △ **HIGH POINT REGIONAL HEALTH SYSTEM**, 601 North Elm Street, Zip 27262–4398, Mailing Address: P.O. Box HP–5, Zip 27261; tel. 336/878–6000, (Total facility includes 18 beds in nursing home–type unit) **A**1 2 7 9 10 **F**2 3 4 6 7 9 10 11 12 14 15 17 19 21 22 23 26 27 28 29 30 32 33 37 38 39 40 41 42 46 47 48 49 50 52 53 55 57 58 59 60 61 62 63 64 65 66 68 69 71 73 74 75 76 77 79 80 81 82 84 85 86 87 88 92 93 94 96 106 107 108 109 110 Primary Contact: Jeffrey S. Miller, President and Chief Executive Officer CFO: Bob Duncan, Vice President Finance CMO: Gregory W. Taylor, M.D., Senior Vice President and Chief Medical Director CIO: Eugene Roth, Chief Information Officer CHR: Angela Culler, Chief Human Resources Officer Web address: www.highpointregional.com	23	10	345	16377	250	111698	1836	187880	79011	1812
HIGHLANDS—Macon County										
⊠ **HIGHLANDS–CASHIERS HOSPITAL**, 190 Hospital Drive, Zip 28741–7600, Mailing Address: P.O. Drawer 190, Zip 28741–0190; tel. 828/526–1200, (Total facility includes 80 beds in nursing home–type unit) **A**1 9 10 18 **F**2 9 12 21 22 27 33 36 37 41 46 48 54 60 62 63 81 88 92 94 97 106 108 Primary Contact: H. James Graham, Administrator CFO: Joan Cabe, Vice President Operations CIO: Frank Leslie, Corporate Compliance Officer Web address: www.hchospital.org	23	10	104	723	81	92472	0	17121	7505	207
HUNTERSVILLE—Mecklenburg County										
PRESBYTERIAN HOSPITAL HUNTERSVILLE, 10030 Gilead Road, Zip 28078, Mailing Address: P.O. Box 3508, Zip 28070–3508; tel. 704/316–4000, (Nonreporting) **A**9 10 **S** Novant Health, Winston–Salem, NC Primary Contact: Denise B. Mihal, R.N., Chief Executive Officer	23	49	50	—	—	—	—	—	—	—
JACKSONVILLE—Onslow County										
□ **BRYNN MARR BEHAVIORAL HEALTHCARE SYSTEM**, 192 Village Drive, Zip 28546–7299; tel. 910/577–1400 **A**1 10 **F**28 29 31 46 47 48 71 72 74 75 76 94 96 **P**6 **S** Psychiatric Solutions, Franklin, TN Primary Contact: Sarah Wiltgen, Chief Executive Officer Web address: www.brynnmarr.org	33	22	88	1488	64	0	0	—	—	195
⊠ **ONSLOW MEMORIAL HOSPITAL**, 317 Western Boulevard, Zip 28540–6379, Mailing Address: P.O. Box 1358, Zip 28540–1358; tel. 910/577–2345 **A**1 9 10 20 **F**2 6 9 11 12 14 15 22 27 28 31 33 37 38 40 46 47 48 49 52 55 56 57 58 59 60 61 62 63 64 65 69 81 82 84 85 88 93 94 96 108 110 **P**8 Primary Contact: Ed Piper, Chief Executive Officer CFO: Roy Smith, Chief Financial Officer CHR: Tina McClatchy, Director Human Resources Web address: www.onslowmemorial.org	16	10	133	8136	81	—	1410	75366	31638	789
JEFFERSON—Ashe County										
⊠ **ASHE MEMORIAL HOSPITAL**, 200 Hospital Avenue, Zip 28640–9244; tel. 336/846–7101, (Total facility includes 60 beds in nursing home–type unit) **A**1 9 10 20 **F**2 9 11 12 22 26 27 28 29 33 41 46 47 48 52 58 59 63 65 69 81 82 88 92 94 96 97 107 108 **S** Quorum Health Resources, Plano, TX Primary Contact: R. D. Williams, Administrator and Chief Executive Officer COO: Joe Thore, Chief Operating Officer CFO: Joy McClure, Chief Financial Officer CMO: Vickie Ingledue, M.D., Chief of Staff CIO: William Baldwin, Chief Information Officer CHR: Sherry Cox, Chief Human Resources Officer Web address: www.ashememorial.org	23	10	115	1684	74	36876	82	20548	9131	284
KENANSVILLE—Duplin County										
⊠ **DUPLIN GENERAL HOSPITAL**, 401 North Main Street, Zip 28349–9989, Mailing Address: P.O. Box 278, Zip 28349–0278; tel. 910/296–0941, (Total facility includes 20 beds in nursing home–type unit) **A**1 9 10 **F**9 11 12 21 22 26 27 28 29 33 44 46 50 53 55 58 59 63 69 70 71 74 75 76 81 82 84 88 92 93 94 108 109 **P**6 Primary Contact: J. Douglas Yarbrough, Chief Executive Officer CFO: Lucinda Maready, Chief Financial Officer CMO: Steven Takas, M.D., Chief Medical Staff CIO: Lucinda Maready, Chief Financial Officer Web address: www.dgh.org	13	10	89	3695	61	48701	780	24882	13850	384

NC

Hospital, Address, Telephone, Approval, Facility, and Physician Codes, Health Care System	Classi-fication Codes		Utilization Data						Expense (thousands) of dollars		
★ American Hospital Association (AHA) membership □ Joint Commission on Accreditation of Healthcare Organizations (JCAHO) accreditation ○ American Osteopathic Association (AOA) accreditation △ Commission on Accreditation of Rehabilitation Facilities (CARF) accreditation	Control	Service	Staffed Beds	Admissions	Census	Outpatient Visits	Births	Total	Payroll	Personnel

KINGS MOUNTAIN—Cleveland County

☒ **KINGS MOUNTAIN HOSPITAL**, 706 West King Street, Zip 28086–2708; tel. 704/739–3601, (Total facility includes 10 beds in nursing home–type unit) (Nonreporting) **A**1 9 10 **S** Carolinas HealthCare System, Charlotte, NC
Primary Contact: John E. Young, President and Chief Executive Officer
CFO: Terry Edwards, Controller
CMO: Inderjeet Singh, M.D., Chief of Staff
CHR: Betty Batchler, Director Human Resources
Web address: www.carolinas.org

| | 16 | 10 | 72 | — | — | — | — | — | — | — |

KINSTON—Lenoir County

CASWELL CENTER, 2415 West Vernon Avenue, Zip 28504–3321; tel. 252/208–4000, (Nonreporting)
Primary Contact: Michael Moseley, Director
Web address: www.caswellcenter.org

| | 12 | 62 | 813 | — | — | — | — | — | — | — |

☒ **LENOIR MEMORIAL HOSPITAL**, 100 Airport Road, Zip 28501–1634, Mailing Address: P.O. Box 1678, Zip 28503–1678; tel. 252/522–7000, (Total facility includes 26 beds in nursing home–type unit) **A**1 2 9 10 19 20 **F**2 9 10 11 15 21 22 23 27 28 29 31 33 34 37 39 41 43 44 45 46 47 48 49 50 52 53 55 57 58 59 60 61 62 63 64 65 66 68 69 75 79 81 82 84 85 87 88 92 93 94 96 98 106 108 110
Primary Contact: Gary E. Black, President and Chief Executive Officer
CFO: Sarah Mayo, Vice President Financial and Information Services
CMO: George West, M.D., President Medical Staff
CIO: Mary Jo Nimmo, Director Management Information Systems
CHR: Jim Dobbins, Vice President Human Resources
Web address: www.lenoirmemorial.org

| | 23 | 10 | 219 | 11088 | 158 | 85261 | 696 | 90028 | 37649 | 859 |

LAURINBURG—Scotland County

☒ **SCOTLAND MEMORIAL HOSPITAL**, 500 Lauchwood Drive, Zip 28352–5599; tel. 910/291–7000, (Total facility includes 50 beds in nursing home–type unit) **A**1 9 10 **F**2 3 4 9 11 12 21 22 23 26 27 29 32 33 37 42 45 46 47 48 52 55 57 58 59 60 61 62 63 64 65 66 68 69 70 73 79 81 82 84 85 88 92 94 96 106 107 108 109 110 **P**2 8
Primary Contact: Gregory C. Wood, Chief Executive Officer
CFO: Matthew Pracht, Vice President Finance
CIO: Larry Pergerson, Director Information Systems
CHR: Ann Locklear, Director Human Resources
Web address: www.scotlandhealth.org

| | 23 | 10 | 159 | 6550 | 123 | 134118 | 745 | 77990 | 32061 | 789 |

LENOIR—Caldwell County

☒ **CALDWELL MEMORIAL HOSPITAL**, 321 Mulberry Street S.W., Zip 28645–5720, Mailing Address: P.O. Box 1890, Zip 28645–1890; tel. 828/757–5100 **A**1 2 9 10 **F**7 9 11 12 17 21 22 23 27 33 37 38 41 42 46 48 55 59 61 62 63 65 69 70 81 88 92 93 94 95 96 106 108 **P**4 6 8
Primary Contact: Laura J. Easton, President and Chief Executive Officer
CFO: Donald F. Gardner, Vice President Fiscal Services
CMO: Mark Batts, M.D., Chief of Staff
CIO: Tim Palmer, Director Information Systems
CHR: Rebecca Smith, Vice President
Web address: www.caldwell–mem.org

| | 23 | 10 | 72 | 4143 | 38 | 94341 | 663 | — | — | — |

LEXINGTON—Davidson County

☒ **LEXINGTON MEMORIAL HOSPITAL**, 250 Hospital Drive, Zip 27292–6728, Mailing Address: P.O. Box 1817, Zip 27293–1817; tel. 336/248–5161, (Nonreporting) **A**1 9 10
Primary Contact: John A. Cashion, FACHE, President
CFO: Harold R. Trader, Vice President and Chief Financial Officer
CMO: Paul F. Meyer, M.D., Chief of Staff
CIO: Kevin Buchanan, Director Management Information Systems
CHR: Dolly Mayerchak, Director Human Resources
Web address: www.lexingtonmemorial.com

| | 23 | 10 | 87 | — | — | — | — | — | — | — |

LINCOLNTON—Lincoln County

☒ **LINCOLN MEDICAL CENTER**, 200 Gamble Drive, Zip 28092–4421, Mailing Address: Box 677, Zip 28093–0677; tel. 704/735–3071 **A**1 9 10 **F**7 9 10 11 12 21 22 24 28 29 33 34 35 37 39 40 46 47 48 51 52 53 54 55 57 58 59 60 63 65 66 69 81 85 86 88 93 94 95 96 106 108 110 **S** Carolinas HealthCare System, Charlotte, NC
Primary Contact: Peter W. Acker, President and Chief Executive Officer
CFO: James Ramsey, Vice President Finance and Chief Financial Officer
CIO: Wendy Isaac, Director Management Information
CHR: Lesley Chawbless, Assistant Vice President Human Resources
Web address: www.lincolnmedical.org

| | 23 | 10 | 87 | 3357 | 43 | 75086 | 478 | 41333 | 18495 | 534 |

LINVILLE—Avery County

□ **CHARLES A. CANNON JR. MEMORIAL HOSPITAL**, 434 Hospital Drive, Zip 28646, Mailing Address: P.O. Box 767, Zip 28646; tel. 828/737–7000, (Total facility includes 10 beds in nursing home–type unit) (Nonreporting) **A**1 9 10
Primary Contact: Edward C. Greene, Jr, President
Web address: www.cannonmh.org

| | 23 | 10 | 70 | — | — | — | — | — | — | — |

Many Facility Codes have changed. Please refer to the AHA Guide Code Chart. © 2005 AHA Guide

Hospital, Address, Telephone, Approval, Facility, and Physician Codes, Health Care System	Classi-fication Codes		Utilization Data					Expense (thousands) of dollars		
★ American Hospital Association (AHA) membership □ Joint Commission on Accreditation of Healthcare Organizations (JCAHO) accreditation ○ American Osteopathic Association (AOA) accreditation △ Commission on Accreditation of Rehabilitation Facilities (CARF) accreditation	Control	Service	Staffed Beds	Admissions	Census	Outpatient Visits	Births	Total	Payroll	Personnel

LOUISBURG—Franklin County

□ **FRANKLIN REGIONAL MEDICAL CENTER**, 100 Hospital Drive, Zip 27549–2256, Mailing Address: P.O. Box 609, Zip 27549–0609; tel. 919/497–8401 **A**1 9 10 **F**9 10 12 15 21 22 26 27 29 33 37 46 47 48 53 55 57 58 60 62 63 65 66 69 73 74 75 81 84 85 88 93 94 108 **P**4 6 **S** Health Management Associates, Naples, FL
Primary Contact: Thomas Dunning, Executive Director
Web address: www.franklinregionalmedicalctr.com

| | 33 | 10 | 56 | 2621 | 29 | 39506 | 0 | 27605 | 11835 | 323 |

LUMBERTON—Robeson County

☒ **SOUTHEASTERN REGIONAL MEDICAL CENTER**, 300 West 27th Street, Zip 28358–3017, Mailing Address: P.O. Box 1408, Zip 28359–1408; tel. 910/671–5000, (Total facility includes 115 beds in nursing–type unit) **A**1 9 10 12 13 19 20 **F**2 4 11 15 17 21 22 23 27 28 29 33 36 37 38 39 41 46 47 48 49 51 53 55 57 58 59 60 61 62 63 64 66 69 70 71 79 81 82 84 85 88 92 93 94 95 96 108 110 **P**8
Primary Contact: J. L. Welsh, Jr, President and Chief Executive Officer
CFO: C Thomas Johnson, III, Vice President Finance
CMO: George W. Mozingo, M.D., Chief Medical Staff
CIO: Ann Stephen, Director Public Relations
CHR: Joseph W. Glezen, Director Human Resources
Web address: www.srmc.org

| | 23 | 10 | 403 | 15193 | 320 | 260932 | 1431 | 161221 | 69737 | 1571 |

MARION—McDowell County

☒ **MCDOWELL HOSPITAL**, 430 Rankin Drive, Zip 28752–4989, Mailing Address: P.O. Box 730, Zip 28752–0730; tel. 828/659–5000 **A**1 9 10 **F**2 9 11 12 21 22 23 27 29 33 34 37 42 46 48 52 53 55 58 59 61 62 63 65 66 69 81 82 88 94 96 108 109 110 **P**6
Primary Contact: Sonya Greck, Chief Executive Officer
Web address: www.mcdhospital.org

| | 23 | 10 | 65 | 2386 | 25 | 67525 | 267 | 25202 | 11706 | 313 |

MATTHEWS—Mecklenburg County

★ **PRESBYTERIAN HOSPITAL–MATTHEWS**, 1500 Matthews Township Parkway, Zip 28105–4656, Mailing Address: P.O. Box 3310, Zip 28106–3310; tel. 704/384–6500, (Nonreporting) **A**9 10 **S** Novant Health, Winston–Salem, NC
Primary Contact: Paula Vincent, Vice President Community Acute Services
COO: Lynn Ingram Boggs, Executive Vice President and Chief Operating Officer
CFO: Greg Klein, Director Finance
CMO: Stephen Wallenhaupt, M.D., Executive Vice President Medical Affairs
Web address: www.presbyterian.org

| | 23 | 10 | 94 | — | — | — | — | — | — | — |

MCCAIN—Hoke County

MCCAIN CORRECTIONAL HOSPITAL, Mailing Address: P.O. Box 5118, Zip 28361–5118; tel. 910/944–2351, (Nonreporting)
Primary Contact: F. David Hubbard, Superintendent

| | 12 | 11 | 81 | — | — | — | — | — | — | — |

MOCKSVILLE—Davie County

☒ **DAVIE COUNTY HOSPITAL**, 223 Hospital Street, Zip 27028–2038, Mailing Address: P.O. Box 1209, Zip 27028–1209; tel. 336/751–8100 **A**1 9 10 18 **F**2 9 12 27 28 29 33 46 48 52 60 62 63 64 69 81 88 94 97 107
Primary Contact: Lynne T. Doss, Administrator
CFO: Terry R. Bowman, Chief Financial Officer
CMO: Melissa Seagle, M.D., President Medical Staff
CHR: Linda Pate, Director Human Resources
Web address: www.daviehospital.org

| | 23 | 10 | 25 | 323 | 3 | 18571 | 0 | 8100 | 3574 | 92 |

MONROE—Union County

☒ **UNION REGIONAL MEDICAL CENTER**, 600 Hospital Drive, Zip 28112–6000, Mailing Address: P.O. Box 5003, Zip 28111–5003; tel. 704/283–3100, (Total facility includes 66 beds in nursing home–type unit) **A**1 9 10 **F**2 3 4 9 11 12 15 21 22 23 26 27 29 32 33 37 39 44 46 47 48 51 52 55 57 58 59 60 61 62 63 64 65 66 69 79 81 82 84 87 88 92 93 94 96 106 108 109 110 **S** Carolinas HealthCare System, Charlotte, NC
Primary Contact: John W. Roberts, President and Chief Executive Officer
COO: Dave Anderson, Vice President Operations
CFO: Carol Davis, Vice President Financial Services
CMO: Robert Austin, M.D., President Medical Staff
CIO: Chris Bowen, Director Information Services
CHR: Sandra Butler, Vice President Human Resources
Web address: www.unionregional.org

| | 16 | 10 | 215 | 8214 | 152 | 126299 | 1360 | 95552 | 38978 | 1007 |

MOORESVILLE—Iredell County

□ **LAKE NORMAN REGIONAL MEDICAL CENTER**, 171 Fairview Road, Zip 28117–9500, Mailing Address: P.O. Box 3250, Zip 28117–3250; tel. 704/660–4000 **A**1 9 10 **F**2 11 12 15 21 22 23 28 29 33 46 47 48 51 52 55 57 58 59 60 62 63 64 65 69 81 82 83 84 88 93 94 95 96 106 108 109 110 **P**8 **S** Health Management Associates, Naples, FL
Primary Contact: P. Paul Smith, Jr, Executive Director
Web address: www.lnrmc.com

| | 33 | 10 | 129 | 6905 | 81 | 95067 | 932 | — | — | 824 |

NC

Hospital, Address, Telephone, Approval, Facility, and Physician Codes, Health Care System	Classi-fication Codes		Utilization Data					Expense (thousands) of dollars		
★ American Hospital Association (AHA) membership ☐ Joint Commission on Accreditation of Healthcare Organizations (JCAHO) accreditation ◯ American Osteopathic Association (AOA) accreditation △ Commission on Accreditation of Rehabilitation Facilities (CARF) accreditation	Control	Service	Staffed Beds	Admissions	Census	Outpatient Visits	Births	Total	Payroll	Personnel

MOREHEAD CITY—Carteret County

☒ **CARTERET GENERAL HOSPITAL**, 3500 Arendell Street, Zip 28557–1619, Mailing Address: P.O. Box 1619, Zip 28557–1619; tel. 252/808–6000, (Total facility includes 104 beds in nursing home–type unit) **A**1 9 10 19 20 **F**6 9 10 11 12 21 22 23 26 27 28 29 33 36 37 42 45 46 48 51 52 53 58 59 61 62 63 64 65 66 70 81 82 84 88 92 93 94 96 106 108 110
Primary Contact: Frederick A. Odell, III, FACHE, President
CFO: Riley Gray, Vice President Fiscal Services
CIO: Robert Walker, Manager Information Services
CHR: Elizabeth Beswick, Vice President Human Resources
Web address: www.ccgh.org

| | 13 | 10 | 221 | 7143 | 155 | 101055 | 572 | 68885 | 31922 | 852 |

MORGANTON—Burke County

☐ **BROUGHTON HOSPITAL**, 1000 South Sterling Street, Zip 28655–3999; tel. 828/433–2111, (Nonreporting) **A**1 5 10
Primary Contact: Seth P. Hunt, Jr, Director and Chief Executive Officer
Web address: www.broughtonhospital.org

| | 12 | 22 | 370 | — | — | — | — | — | — | — |

☒ **GRACE HOSPITAL**, 2201 South Sterling Street, Zip 28655–4058; tel. 828/580–5000, (Total facility includes 120 beds in nursing home–type unit) **A**1 2 9 10 **F**2 9 11 12 21 22 23 26 27 28 29 33 37 41 44 45 46 47 48 51 52 53 54 55 58 59 60 61 62 63 65 66 69 71 73 74 75 76 77 78 79 81 82 83 85 86 87 88 92 94 95 96 97 106 107 108 109 110 **P**8 **S** Carolinas HealthCare System, Charlotte, NC
Primary Contact: Kenneth W. Wood, President and Chief Executive Officer
CFO: Robert Fritts, Chief Financial Officer
CIO: Jamey Pennington, Director Information Systems
CHR: Phil Satey, Vice President Human Resources
Web address: www.gracehcs.org

| | 23 | 10 | 269 | 7186 | 186 | 118685 | 939 | 73983 | 32744 | 722 |

MOUNT AIRY—Surry County

☒ **NORTHERN HOSPITAL OF SURRY COUNTY**, 830 Rockford Street, Zip 27030–5365, Mailing Address: P.O. Box 1101, Zip 27030–1101; tel. 336/719–7000, (Total facility includes 33 beds in nursing home–type unit) **A**1 9 10 **F**2 9 11 12 15 21 22 23 27 28 29 33 36 37 38 39 40 44 46 47 48 51 52 53 55 57 58 59 60 62 63 64 65 66 69 75 81 82 84 85 87 88 92 93 94 95 96 97 108 109 **S** Quorum Health Resources, Plano, TX
Primary Contact: William B. James, Chief Executive Officer
CFO: Robert G. Hetrick, Chief Financial Officer
CMO: Cecil Thoppil, M.D., Chief of Staff
CHR: Bill Hancock, Director Human Resources
Web address: www.northernhospital.com

| | 16 | 10 | 113 | 4603 | 76 | 174895 | 585 | 54060 | 23111 | 584 |

MURPHY—Cherokee County

☒ **MURPHY MEDICAL CENTER**, 4130 U.S. Highway 64 East, Zip 28906–7917; tel. 828/837–8161, (Total facility includes 134 beds in nursing home–type unit) **A**1 9 10 **F**2 5 9 11 12 22 23 27 28 29 33 35 36 38 41 42 46 48 51 52 53 55 58 60 61 63 64 69 79 81 82 84 85 88 92 94 96 107 108 110
Primary Contact: Mike Stevenson, Administrator
CFO: Steve Gilgen, Assistant Administrator Fiscal Services
Web address: www.grove.net/~mmc

| | 23 | 10 | 184 | 2872 | 154 | 78981 | 270 | 38913 | 19735 | 594 |

NAGS HEAD—Dare County

☒ **THE OUTER BANKS HOSPITAL**, 4800 South Croatan Highway, Zip 27959–9704; tel. 252/449–4500 **A**1 9 10 **F**2 10 11 12 21 27 28 29 33 44 46 48 52 53 58 59 60 62 63 68 69 81 84 85 88 94 108 **S** University Health Systems of Eastern Carolina, Greenville, NC
Primary Contact: Roger Robinson, Interim President
CFO: Todd Warlitner, Vice President of Business Operations
CMO: Brian Baxter, M.D., President Medical Staff
CHR: Melody Clopton, Director Human Resources
Web address: www.theouterbankshospital.com

| | 23 | 10 | 19 | 1689 | 12 | 32444 | 427 | 22863 | 7797 | 193 |

NEW BERN—Craven County

☒ △ **CRAVEN REGIONAL MEDICAL CENTER**, 2000 Neuse Boulevard, Zip 28560–3499, Mailing Address: P.O. Box 12157, Zip 28561–2157; tel. 252/633–8111 **A**1 2 7 9 10 19 20 **F**6 9 11 12 14 15 17 19 21 22 23 42 46 47 48 49 51 52 53 55 57 58 59 61 62 63 68 69 71 79 81 84 86 88 92 93 94 96 107 108 110
Primary Contact: Raymond Budrys, Chief Executive Officer
COO: Rosanne Leahy, Vice President Nursing Services
CFO: John B. Satterfield, Jr, Vice President Finance
CMO: Ronald B. May, Vice President, Medical Affairs
CIO: G Raymond Leggett, Vice President, Administration
CHR: Bruce A. Martin, Vice President Human Resources
Web address: www.cravenhealthcare.org

| | 16 | 10 | 284 | 16150 | 239 | — | — | — | — | — |

NORTH WILKESBORO—Wilkes County

☒ **WILKES REGIONAL MEDICAL CENTER**, 1370 West D Street, Zip 28659–3506, Mailing Address: P.O. Box 609, Zip 28659–0609; tel. 336/651–8100, (Total facility includes 10 beds in nursing home–type unit) (Nonreporting) **A**1 9 10
Primary Contact: Ted G. Chapin, Chief Executive Officer
CFO: Anthony C. Rispoli, Chief Financial Officerf
CMO: David Sargent, M.D., Chief Medical Officer
CIO: Mark Cullison, Director Facility Services
Web address: www.wfubmc.edu

| | 16 | 10 | 130 | — | — | — | — | — | — | — |

NC

Many Facility Codes have changed. Please refer to the AHA Guide Code Chart.

Hospital, Address, Telephone, Approval, Facility, and Physician Codes, Health Care System	Classi-fication Codes		Utilization Data					Expense (thousands) of dollars		
★ American Hospital Association (AHA) membership □ Joint Commission on Accreditation of Healthcare Organizations (JCAHO) accreditation ○ American Osteopathic Association (AOA) accreditation △ Commission on Accreditation of Rehabilitation Facilities (CARF) accreditation	Control	Service	Staffed Beds	Admissions	Census	Outpatient Visits	Births	Total	Payroll	Personnel

OXFORD—Granville County

☒ **GRANVILLE MEDICAL CENTER**, 1010 College Street, Zip 27565–2507, Mailing Address: P.O. Box 947, Zip 27565–0947; tel. 919/690–3000, (Total facility includes 80 beds in nursing home–type unit) **A**1 9 10 **F**1 2 9 11 12 21 23 27 29 31 32 33 37 39 44 45 46 47 48 52 55 58 59 60 61 62 63 64 65 69 73 74 76 77 81 82 84 85 87 88 92 93 94 96 97 108 109 110 **P**1 **S** Quorum Health Resources, Plano, TX
Primary Contact: Ronald J. Vigus, Chief Executive Officer
CFO: Sherry Jensen, Chief Financial Officer
CMO: Stacy Lewis, M.D., Chief Medical Staff
CHR: Tonya Jones, Director Human Resourced
Web address: www.granvillemedical.com

| | 13 | 10 | 142 | 2433 | 91 | 31961 | 416 | 26225 | 11953 | 273 |

PINEHURST—Moore County

☒ △ **FIRSTHEALTH MOORE REGIONAL HOSPITAL**, 155 Memorial Drive, Zip 28374–8710, Mailing Address: P.O. Box 3000, Zip 28374–3000; tel. 910/215–1000 **A**1 2 7 9 10 19 **F**3 4 9 10 11 12 14 15 17 19 21 22 23 26 27 28 29 30 33 35 37 39 40 41 42 44 45 46 47 48 49 52 53 55 56 57 58 59 60 61 62 63 65 66 68 69 71 72 73 74 75 76 77 78 79 81 82 84 85 86 87 88 93 94 96 98 106 107 108 109 **S** FirstHealth of the Carolinas, Pinehurst, NC
Primary Contact: Stuart Voelpel, Senior Vice President Operations Hospital and Chief Operating Officer
COO: Stuart Voelpel, Senior Vice President Operations Hospital and Chief Operating Officer
CFO: Lynn S. DeJaco, Senior Vice President and Chief Financial Officer
CMO: Michael Lachina, M.D., Senior Vice President and Chief Medical Officer
CIO: David B. Dillehunt, Vice President Information Systems and Chief Information Officer
CHR: Dan Biediger, Vice President Human Resources
Web address: www.firsthealth.org

| | 23 | 10 | 356 | 20947 | 260 | 163461 | 1596 | 232162 | 95020 | 2439 |

PLYMOUTH—Washington County

☐ **WASHINGTON COUNTY HOSPITAL**, 958 U.S. Highway 64 East, Zip 27962–9591; tel. 252/793–4135 **A**1 9 10 18 **F**6 9 21 22 23 26 27 28 33 47 52 63 65 66 70 81 88 97
Primary Contact: William M. Donohoo, FACHE, Chief Executive Officer
Web address: www.wchonline.com

| | 13 | 10 | 25 | 811 | 8 | 21874 | 0 | 11544 | 4989 | — |

RALEIGH—Wake County

CENTRAL PRISON HOSPITAL, 1300 Western Boulevard, Zip 27606–2148; tel. 919/733–0800, (Nonreporting)
Primary Contact: Thomas J. Hawkins, Hospital Services Administrator

| | 12 | 11 | 230 | — | — | — | — | — | — | — |

☐ **DOROTHEA DIX HOSPITAL**, 3601 Mail Service Center, Zip 27699–3601; tel. 919/733–5540, (Nonreporting) **A**1 3 5 10
Primary Contact: Walter Stelle, Ph.D., Director

| | 12 | 22 | 443 | — | — | — | — | — | — | — |

☒ **DUKE HEALTH RALEIGH HOSPITAL**, (Formerly Raleigh Community Hospital), 3400 Wake Forest Road, Zip 27609–7373, Mailing Address: P.O. Box 28280, Zip 27611–8280; tel. 919/954–3000 **A**1 9 10 **F**3 9 11 12 13 14 15 21 22 23 26 28 29 32 33 37 38 41 46 48 52 55 56 57 58 59 60 61 62 63 66 67 68 69 71 79 80 81 82 83 84 85 87 88 92 93 94 95 96 99 100 101 102 103 104 106 108 **P**6 **S** Duke University Health System, Durham, NC
Primary Contact: James P. Knight, Chief Executive Officer
COO: Thomas Hanenburg, Vice President and Chief Operating Officer
CFO: Terri Newsom, Vice President and Chief Financial Officer
Web address: www.dukehealthraleigh.org

| | 23 | 10 | 150 | 6863 | 84 | 90940 | 997 | 103693 | 37992 | 653 |

☐ **HOLLY HILL HOSPITAL**, 3019 Falstaff Road, Zip 27610–1812; tel. 919/250–7000, (Nonreporting) **A**1 10 **S** Psychiatric Solutions, Franklin, TN
Primary Contact: Thomas L. Ryba, Chief Executive Officer
Web address: www.hollyhillhospital.com

| | 33 | 22 | 105 | — | — | — | — | — | — | — |

LARRY B. ZIEVERINK, SR. ALCOHOLISM TREATMENT CENTER, (Formerly Wake County Alcoholism Treatment Center), 3000 Falstaff Road, Zip 27610–1897; tel. 919/250–1500 **A**9 10 **F**3 4 21 28 45 73 75 77 94 96 **P**5
Primary Contact: Roy C. Nickell, Jr, Director Substance Abuse Services
Web address: www.wakegov.com/county/family/atc

| | 13 | 82 | 34 | 830 | 25 | 18709 | 0 | 3136 | — | 129 |

☒ △ **REX HEALTHCARE**, 4420 Lake Boone Trail, Zip 27607–6599; tel. 919/784–3100, (Total facility includes 227 beds in nursing home–type unit) **A**1 2 7 9 10 **F**1 2 6 9 11 12 14 15 17 19 21 22 23 26 27 28 29 31 33 36 37 38 39 40 41 42 44 45 46 47 48 49 50 51 52 53 54 55 57 58 59 60 61 62 63 64 65 66 69 70 73 79 81 82 84 85 86 87 88 90 92 93 94 96 106 107 108 109 110 **P**6
Primary Contact: David W. Strong, President
CFO: John P. Lewis, Vice President Finance and Chief Financial Officer
CMO: David Boerner, Medical Director
CIO: Dave Rowley, Vice President Information Technology and Chief Information Officer
CHR: Stephen W. Burris, Vice President Human Resources
Web address: www.rexhealth.com

| | 23 | 10 | 621 | 24652 | 472 | — | 5173 | 327511 | 137395 | 3073 |

NC

Hospital, Address, Telephone, Approval, Facility, and Physician Codes, Health Care System	Classi-fication Codes		Utilization Data					Expense (thousands) of dollars		
★ American Hospital Association (AHA) membership □ Joint Commission on Accreditation of Healthcare Organizations (JCAHO) accreditation ○ American Osteopathic Association (AOA) accreditation △ Commission on Accreditation of Rehabilitation Facilities (CARF) accreditation	Control	Service	Staffed Beds	Admissions	Census	Outpatient Visits	Births	Total	Payroll	Personnel
⌧ △ **WAKEMED RALEIGH CAMPUS**, (Formerly WakeMed New Bern Campus), 3000 New Bern Avenue, Zip 27610–1295; tel. 919/350–8000, (Total facility includes 19 beds in nursing home–type unit) **A**1 3 5 7 9 10 **F**2 6 7 9 10 11 12 14 15 17 19 21 22 23 24 27 28 29 32 33 34 35 37 39 41 42 44 45 46 47 48 49 50 51 52 53 55 56 57 58 59 60 61 62 63 64 65 67 68 69 70 77 81 82 84 85 87 88 92 93 94 95 96 106 108 109 110 **P**6 **S** WakeMed, Raleigh, NC Primary Contact: William K. Atkinson, II, Ph.D., President and Chief Executive Officer Web address: www.wakemed.org	23	10	602	30122	488	703391	4757	488354	237456	4418
REIDSVILLE—Rockingham County										
★ **ANNIE PENN HOSPITAL**, 618 South Main Street, Zip 27320–5094; tel. 336/951–4000, (Total facility includes 92 beds in nursing home–type unit) (Nonreporting) **A**9 10 **S** Moses Cone Health System, Greensboro, NC Primary Contact: Susan H. Fitzgibbon, President and Executive Vice President COO: Susan H. Fitzgibbon, President CFO: Lena Medley, Director Financial Services CMO: Mike Rourk, Chief Medical Services CIO: Harvey Beck, Director Information Systems CHR: Grace B. Moffitt, Vice President Human Resources and Support Services Web address: www.mosescone.com	23	10	179	—		—	—	—	—	—
ROANOKE RAPIDS—Halifax County										
⌧ **HALIFAX REGIONAL MEDICAL CENTER**, 250 Smith Church Road, Zip 27870, Mailing Address: P.O. Box 1089, Zip 27870; tel. 252/535–8011 **A**1 9 10 20 **F**2 9 11 12 15 21 26 27 29 33 37 39 41 42 46 47 48 49 50 52 53 54 55 58 59 60 61 62 63 64 65 69 70 71 74 75 76 81 82 85 88 93 94 96 108 **P**6 8 Primary Contact: M. E. Gilstrap, President and Chief Executive Officer COO: Paul G. Sherwood, Senior Vice President and Chief Operating Officer CFO: Lee Boles, Chief Financial Officer CIO: Samuel Johnson, Information Systems Manager CHR: Val Short, Vice President Human Resources Web address: www.halifaxmedicalcenter.org	23	10	138	7775	107	88621	734	61880	26770	748
ROCKINGHAM—Richmond County										
⌧ **FIRSTHEALTH RICHMOND MEMORIAL HOSPITAL**, 925 Long Drive, Zip 28379–4815; tel. 910/417–3000, (Total facility includes 51 beds in nursing home–type unit) **A**1 9 10 **F**11 12 15 21 22 24 26 27 28 29 33 37 44 46 47 48 52 53 55 58 59 62 63 65 66 69 81 84 88 92 93 94 96 106 107 108 109 **S** FirstHealth of the Carolinas, Pinehurst, NC Primary Contact: John J. Jackson, Vice President Operations COO: Cindy McNeill McDonald, Chief Operating Officer and Chief Nursing Officer CFO: John D. Price, Chief Financial Officer CMO: George Bussey, M.D., Chief Medical Officer Web address: www.firsthealth.org	23	10	141	4342	81	42441	476	32739	16333	380
ROCKY MOUNT—Nash County										
□ **LIFECARE HOSPITALS OF NORTH CAROLINA**, 1051 Noell Lane, Zip 27804–1761; tel. 252/451–2300 **A**1 10 **F**21 58 62 64 94 110 **S** LifeCare Management Services, Plano, TX Primary Contact: Kevin S. Cooper, R.N., Chief Executive Officer and Administrator Web address: www.lifecare-hospitals.com	32	80	43	477	37	0	0	—	—	—
⌧ △ **NASH HEALTH CARE SYSTEMS**, 2460 Curtis Ellis Drive, Zip 27804–2297; tel. 252/443–8000 **A**1 2 7 9 10 19 **F**2 3 4 9 11 12 15 21 22 23 26 27 28 29 31 33 36 37 39 41 46 47 48 49 52 54 55 57 59 60 61 62 63 64 65 66 68 69 71 72 73 74 75 76 77 80 81 82 84 85 87 88 93 94 95 96 106 107 108 109 110 **P**7 Primary Contact: Richard Kirk Toomey, President and Chief Executive Officer COO: Brad Weisner, Executive Vice President and Chief Operating Officer CFO: Al Hooks, Senior Vice President and Chief Financial Officer CMO: Rick Guarino, M.D., Senior Vice President and Chief Medical Officer CIO: David Hinkle, Vice President and Chief Information Officer CHR: Cam Blalock, Senior Vice President Corporate Services Web address: www.nhcs.org	16	10	300	14858	214	194845	1291	156292	72381	1618
ROXBORO—Person County										
⌧ **PERSON MEMORIAL HOSPITAL**, 615 Ridge Road, Zip 27573–4630; tel. 336/599–2121, (Total facility includes 60 beds in nursing home–type unit) **A**1 9 10 **F**9 11 12 21 23 26 27 28 29 33 37 38 46 48 52 55 58 59 60 61 62 63 65 69 76 77 81 82 88 92 93 94 96 108 **S** Duke University Health System, Durham, NC Primary Contact: Craig B. James, Chief Executive Officer CFO: James L. Leis, Jr, Chief Financial Officer CIO: Keith Gravitt, Information Systems Manager CHR: Mary Paylor, Director Human Resources Web address: www.personhospital.com	23	10	110	2705	83	48788	188	27513	11512	311

NC

Hospital, Address, Telephone, Approval, Facility, and Physician Codes, Health Care System	Classi-fication Codes		Utilization Data					Expense (thousands) of dollars		
★ American Hospital Association (AHA) membership □ Joint Commission on Accreditation of Healthcare Organizations (JCAHO) accreditation ○ American Osteopathic Association (AOA) accreditation △ Commission on Accreditation of Rehabilitation Facilities (CARF) accreditation	Control	Service	Staffed Beds	Admissions	Census	Outpatient Visits	Births	Total	Payroll	Personnel

RUTHERFORDTON—Rutherford County

✠ **RUTHERFORD HOSPITAL**, 288 South Ridgecrest Avenue, Zip 28139–3097; tel. 828/286–5000 **A**1 2 9 10 19 **F**2 9 11 12 15 21 22 23 26 27 28 29 33 35 37 39 41 42 43 44 46 47 48 51 52 55 57 58 59 60 61 62 63 64 65 66 69 70 71 73 74 75 77 81 82 84 86 87 88 93 94 95 96 106 107 108 109 110 **S** Quorum Health Resources, Plano, TX
Primary Contact: Robert D. Jones, President
CFO: James B. Bross, Vice President and Chief Financial Officer
CMO: Lee Baker, M.D., Vice President Medical Affairs
CIO: Tommy Finley, Chief Information Officer
CHR: James Rowell, Vice President Human Resources
Web address: www.rutherfordhosp.org
| 23 | 10 | 143 | 6129 | 63 | 133398 | 687 | 60089 | 28011 | 725 |

SALISBURY—Rowan County

✠ **ROWAN REGIONAL MEDICAL CENTER**, 612 Mocksville Avenue, Zip 28144–2799; tel. 704/210–5000 **A**1 9 10 **F**2 4 9 11 12 14 17 21 22 23 26 29 33 36 37 42 46 48 49 50 51 52 53 55 57 58 59 61 62 63 65 66 68 69 71 78 81 82 84 85 87 88 94 96 108 109 110 **P**6
Primary Contact: Charles W. Elliott, Jr, Chief Executive Officer
COO: Lee Roy Kirk, Jr, Senior Vice President and Chief Operating Officer
CFO: Marlin Markham, Vice President and Chief Financial Officer
CMO: David N. Smith, M.D., Vice President, Medical Affairs
CIO: Jerry Reardon, Director Information Systems
CHR: Jerry Clevenger, Vice President Human Resources
Web address: www.rowan.org
| 23 | 10 | 188 | 9846 | 122 | 196993 | 947 | 128363 | 54842 | 1246 |

✠ **VETERANS AFFAIRS MEDICAL CENTER**, 1601 Brenner Avenue, Zip 28144–2559; tel. 704/638–9000, (Total facility includes 270 beds in nursing home–type unit) **A**1 5 **F**3 4 12 21 22 33 36 37 38 41 42 44 48 50 51 55 57 58 60 61 62 63 65 66 69 70 71 74 75 76 77 78 81 84 88 93 94 96 106 107 108 109 110 **S** Department of Veterans Affairs, Washington, DC
CFO: Richard L. Terrell, Chief Financial Officer
Web address: www.va.gov/sta/guide/home.asp
| 45 | 10 | 429 | 2771 | 269 | 319311 | 0 | — | — | — |

SANFORD—Lee County

✠ **CENTRAL CAROLINA HOSPITAL**, 1135 Carthage Street, Zip 27330–4111; tel. 919/774–2100, (Nonreporting) **A**1 9 10 **S** TENET Healthcare Corporation, Dallas, TX
Primary Contact: Dale Armstrong, Chief Executive Officer
COO: Scott Ansede, Chief Operating Officer
CMO: Richard Ebken, M.D.
CIO: Jimmy Whitaker, Director Information Systems
CHR: El Reta Pizzutelli, Director Human Resources
Web address: www.centralcarolinahosp.com
| 33 | 10 | 137 | — | — | — | — | — | — | — |

SCOTLAND NECK—Halifax County

OUR COMMUNITY HOSPITAL, 921 Junior High Road, Zip 27874–0405, Mailing Address: Box 405, Zip 27874–0405; tel. 252/826–4144, (Total facility includes 65 beds in nursing home–type unit) (Nonreporting) **A**9 10 18
Primary Contact: Thomas K. Majure, Administrator
Web address: www.och-bltc.com
| 23 | 10 | 70 | — | — | — | — | — | — | — |

SHELBY—Cleveland County

✠ **CLEVELAND REGIONAL MEDICAL CENTER**, 201 East Grover Street, Zip 28150; tel. 704/487–3000, (Total facility includes 120 beds in nursing home–type unit) **A**1 2 9 10 19 **F**9 11 12 15 21 22 23 24 26 27 28 29 31 32 33 34 35 37 39 40 42 44 45 46 47 48 50 52 55 58 59 60 61 62 63 64 65 66 69 75 77 79 80 81 82 84 85 86 87 88 92 93 94 96 108 109 110 **S** Carolinas HealthCare System, Charlotte, NC
Primary Contact: John E. Young, President and Chief Executive Officer
COO: Veronica Poole Adams, Vice President, Chief Operating Officer and Chief Nursing Executive
CFO: Rose Coyne, Vice President and Chief Financial Officer
CMO: Johnson Kelly, M.D., Vice President and Chief Medical Officer
CIO: Craig Richardville, Chief Information Officer
CHR: Debbie Kale, Assistant Vice President Human Resources
Web address: www.carolinas.org
| 16 | 10 | 306 | 10253 | 226 | 98327 | 1026 | 122037 | 47639 | 1173 |

SILER CITY—Chatham County

✠ **CHATHAM HOSPITAL**, West Third Street and Ivy Avenue, Zip 27344–2343, Mailing Address: P.O. Box 649, Zip 27344; tel. 919/663–2113 **A**1 5 9 10 18 **F**9 12 14 15 21 27 28 29 33 46 48 53 58 61 63 69 81 84 88 93 94 97 108 **S** Quorum Health Resources, Plano, TX
Primary Contact: Woodrow W. Hathaway, Jr, Chief Executive Officer
CFO: Burt Barnette, Chief Financial Officer
CHR: Kathy Thomas, Director Human Resources
Web address: www.chathamhospital.org
| 23 | 10 | 25 | 775 | 8 | 21666 | 0 | 11870 | 4886 | 158 |

SMITHFIELD—Johnston County

✠ **JOHNSTON MEMORIAL HOSPITAL**, 509 North Bright Leaf Boulevard, Zip 27577–1376, Mailing Address: P.O. Box 1376, Zip 27577–1376; tel. 919/934–8171 **A**1 9 10 19 **F**2 9 11 12 15 21 22 23 26 27 28 29 32 33 34 36 37 41 42 46 48 51 52 55 57 58 59 60 62 63 64 65 69 71 72 73 75 76 81 82 87 88 93 94 106 107 108 109 **P**6 **S** Quorum Health Resources, Plano, TX
Primary Contact: Leland E. Farnell, President
CFO: Ed Simpson, Vice President Finance
CHR: James Coleman, Vice President Human Resources
Web address: www.johnstonmemorial.org
| 13 | 10 | 160 | 7941 | 99 | 159881 | 1149 | 71227 | 35540 | 950 |

NC

Hospital, Address, Telephone, Approval, Facility, and Physician Codes, Health Care System	Classi-fication Codes		Utilization Data					Expense (thousands) of dollars		
★ American Hospital Association (AHA) membership ☐ Joint Commission on Accreditation of Healthcare Organizations (JCAHO) accreditation ○ American Osteopathic Association (AOA) accreditation △ Commission on Accreditation of Rehabilitation Facilities (CARF) accreditation	Control	Service	Staffed Beds	Admissions	Census	Outpatient Visits	Births	Total	Payroll	Personnel

SOUTHPORT—Brunswick County

⊞ **J. ARTHUR DOSHER MEMORIAL HOSPITAL**, 924 Howe Street, Zip 28461–3099; tel. 910/457–3800, (Total facility includes 64 beds in nursing home–type unit) (Nonreporting) **A**1 9 10
Primary Contact: Edgar Haywood, III, Administrator
CFO: James Shomaker, CPA, Assistant Administrator and Chief Financial Officer
CMO: Brad L. Hilaman, M.D., Chief of Staff
CIO: Susan Shomaker, Director Information Management Systems
CHR: Kelley Richards, Director Human Resources
Web address: www.dosher.org

| | 16 | 10 | 100 | — | — | — | — | — | — | — |

SPARTA—Alleghany County

⊞ **ALLEGHANY MEMORIAL HOSPITAL**, 233 Doctors Street, Zip 28675–0009, Mailing Address: P.O. Box 9, Zip 28675–0009; tel. 336/372–5511 **A**1 9 10 18 20 **F**1 2 11 12 21 22 26 27 28 29 33 34 37 48 51 52 59 62 63 66 69 70 81 84 88 92 93 94 97 106 108 **P**5 **S** Quorum Health Resources, Plano, TX
Primary Contact: Kevin Harlan, Chief Executive Officer
CFO: Ralph Castillo, Chief Financial Officer
CMO: Denise Absher, M.D., Chief Medical Staff
CIO: Darlene Keith, Chief Information Systems
CHR: John Spencer, Director Human Resources
Web address: www.amhsparta.org

| | 23 | 10 | 46 | 1123 | 9 | 16645 | 59 | 11058 | 4912 | 135 |

SPRUCE PINE—Mitchell County

☐ **SPRUCE PINE COMMUNITY HOSPITAL**, 125 Hospital Drive, Zip 28777, Mailing Address: P.O. Drawer 9, Zip 28777; tel. 828/765–4201 **A**1 9 10 20 **F**11 12 21 22 23 26 27 28 29 32 33 41 46 51 55 58 60 61 62 63 69 70 81 84 85 88 93 94 97 107 108 **P**8
Primary Contact: Keith S. Holtsclaw, Chief Executive Officer
Web address: www.spchospital.org

| | 23 | 10 | 40 | 2219 | 20 | 61106 | 141 | 21044 | 10172 | 283 |

STATESVILLE—Iredell County

☐ **DAVIS REGIONAL MEDICAL CENTER**, 218 Old Mocksville Road, Zip 28625–1930, Mailing Address: P.O. Box 1823, Zip 28687–1823; tel. 704/873–0281 **A**1 9 10 **F**2 11 12 15 21 22 23 27 28 29 30 31 33 35 37 38 39 41 46 47 48 49 50 52 53 55 57 58 59 60 61 62 63 64 65 66 69 70 71 73 74 75 76 81 82 85 87 88 92 93 94 95 96 108 110 **S** Health Management Associates, Naples, FL
Primary Contact: Vincent T. Cherry, Jr, Chief Executive Director
Web address: www.davisregional.com

| | 33 | 10 | 123 | 5894 | 71 | 66161 | 582 | — | — | 586 |

⊞ **IREDELL MEMORIAL HOSPITAL**, 557 Brookdale Drive, Zip 28677–1828, Mailing Address: P.O. Box 1828, Zip 28687–1828; tel. 704/873–5661, (Total facility includes 48 beds in nursing home–type unit) **A**1 2 9 10 **F**2 9 11 12 14 15 21 22 23 24 26 27 28 29 33 37 39 44 46 47 48 49 50 51 53 55 57 59 60 61 62 63 64 65 66 69 70 72 73 74 75 76 78 79 80 81 82 84 85 87 88 92 94 96 106 108 109 110
Primary Contact: Ed Rush, President and Chief Executive Officer
CFO: Fred W. Karnap, Vice President Finance
CMO: Roger Hatharasinghe, M.D., President Medical Staff
CIO: Myers M. David, Chief Information Officer
CHR: Elaine Allison, Director Human Resources
Web address: www.iredellmemorial.org

| | 23 | 10 | 203 | 9397 | 157 | 145164 | 810 | 117963 | 57450 | 1239 |

SUPPLY—Brunswick County

⊞ **BRUNSWICK COMMUNITY HOSPITAL**, 1 Medical Center Drive, Zip 28462–3350, Mailing Address: P.O. Box 139, Zip 28462–0139; tel. 910/755–8121 **A**1 9 10 **F**2 9 11 12 21 22 26 27 28 29 33 44 46 48 52 58 62 63 66 69 81 82 87 88 93 94 96 106 108 109 **P**5 **S** HCA, Nashville, TN
Primary Contact: Hugh Brown, Chief Executive Officer
CFO: Joan Thomas, Chief Financial Officer
CMO: Robert Hassler, M.D., Director Medical Affairs
CIO: Pamela Parrish, Information Systems Director
Web address: www.brunswickcommunityhospital.com

| | 33 | 10 | 60 | 3458 | 32 | 31206 | 196 | 44803 | 12497 | — |

SYLVA—Jackson County

⊞ **HARRIS REGIONAL HOSPITAL**, 68 Hospital Road, Zip 28779–2795; tel. 828/586–7000, (Total facility includes 114 beds in nursing home–type unit) **A**1 9 10 **F**1 2 6 9 11 12 21 22 23 27 28 29 33 34 36 38 39 45 47 51 52 53 55 56 58 59 60 61 62 63 64 65 66 69 81 82 84 87 88 92 93 94 95 108 109 110 **P**5 7 **S** WestCare Health System, Sylva, NC
Primary Contact: Mark T. Leonard, Chief Executive Officer
CFO: Pam Buchanan, Chief Financial Officer
CMO: Randy Savell, M.D., Chief of Staff
CIO: Shawn Remacle, Chief Information Officer
CHR: Janet Millsaps, Staff Services Manager
Web address: www.westcare.org

| | 23 | 10 | 201 | 5028 | 201 | 62263 | 710 | 51618 | 25412 | 818 |

TARBORO—Edgecombe County

⊞ **HERITAGE HOSPITAL**, 111 Hospital Drive, Zip 27886–2011; tel. 252/641–7700, (Total facility includes 10 beds in nursing home–type unit) **A**1 9 10 **F**2 9 11 12 21 22 23 26 27 28 32 33 37 39 46 48 54 55 58 59 61 62 63 64 66 68 69 81 88 92 94 95 96 97 108 **S** University Health Systems of Eastern Carolina, Greenville, NC
Primary Contact: Wendell H. Baker, Jr, President
CFO: Charles Alford, Vice President Financial Services
CMO: Barry Bunn, M.D., Chief of Staff
CHR: Arenda Battle, Director Human Resources
Web address: www.heritage.uhseast.com

| | 23 | 10 | 127 | 4298 | 52 | 49099 | 592 | 41013 | 15231 | 429 |

NC

Many Facility Codes have changed. Please refer to the AHA Guide Code Chart.

© 2005 AHA Guide

Hospital, Address, Telephone, Approval, Facility, and Physician Codes, Health Care System	Classi-fication Codes		Utilization Data					Expense (thousands) of dollars		
★ American Hospital Association (AHA) membership □ Joint Commission on Accreditation of Healthcare Organizations (JCAHO) accreditation ○ American Osteopathic Association (AOA) accreditation △ Commission on Accreditation of Rehabilitation Facilities (CARF) accreditation	Control	Service	Staffed Beds	Admissions	Census	Outpatient Visits	Births	Total	Payroll	Personnel

TAYLORSVILLE—Alexander County

FRYE REGIONAL MEDICAL CENTER–ALEXANDER CAMPUS, 326 Third Street S.W., Zip 28681; tel. 828/635–4200, (Nonreporting) **A**9 10 18 Primary Contact: Jan Butler, Administrator	33	49	4	—	—	—	—	—	—	—

THOMASVILLE—Davidson County

✠ **THOMASVILLE MEDICAL CENTER**, 207 Old Lexington Road, Zip 27360–3428, Mailing Address: P.O. Box 789, Zip 27361–0789; tel. 336/472–2000 **A**1 9 10 **F**11 12 21 22 27 28 29 33 44 46 48 52 55 57 58 59 60 61 62 63 64 65 66 68 69 71 76 81 82 85 87 88 93 96 106 108 109 **P**5 **S** Novant Health, Winston–Salem, NC Primary Contact: Gabrielle K. Causby, President CFO: Tom Pogue, Vice President CHR: Andrea West, Manager Human Resources Web address: www.thomasvillemedicalcenter.org	23	10	81	4032	50	65069	567	37093	16149	400

TROY—Montgomery County

✠ **FIRSTHEALTH MONTGOMERY MEMORIAL HOSPITAL**, 520 Allen Street, Zip 27371–2802, Mailing Address: P.O. Box 486, Zip 27371–0486; tel. 910/572–1301, (Total facility includes 30 beds in nursing home–type unit) (Nonreporting) **A**1 9 10 18 **S** FirstHealth of the Carolinas, Pinehurst, NC Primary Contact: Kerry A. Hensley, R.N., Vice President Operations CHR: Ellie Wiles, Manager Human Resources Web address: www.firsthealth.org	23	10	55	—	—	—	—	—	—	—

VALDESE—Burke County

✠ **VALDESE GENERAL HOSPITAL**, 720 Malcolm Boulevard, Zip 28690, Mailing Address: P.O. Box 700, Zip 28690–0700; tel. 828/874–2251, (Total facility includes 120 beds in nursing home–type unit) **A**1 2 9 10 **F**2 9 10 12 17 21 22 23 26 27 28 29 33 37 38 43 44 45 46 48 52 53 55 58 60 61 62 63 65 66 69 79 81 82 83 85 86 87 88 91 92 94 106 108 109 **P**8 **S** Carolinas HealthCare System, Charlotte, NC Primary Contact: Lloyd E. Wallace, President and Chief Executive Officer CFO: Robert Fritts, Chief Financial Officer CMO: Franklin W. Steele, President of Valdese Hospital Medical Staff CIO: Jeryl Davis, Vice President Marketing and Public Affairs CHR: Phil Satey, Vice President Human Resources Web address: www.blueridgehealth.org	16	10	199	3471	146	46522	110	44153	18989	363

WADESBORO—Anson County

✠ **ANSON COMMUNITY HOSPITAL**, 500 Morven Road, Zip 28170–2745; tel. 704/694–5131, (Total facility includes 95 beds in nursing home–type unit) **A**1 9 10 **F**9 12 21 22 26 27 28 29 33 44 46 47 48 51 52 60 63 65 66 69 81 88 92 94 96 97 106 108 **P**5 **S** Carolinas HealthCare System, Charlotte, NC Primary Contact: Frederick G. Thompson, Ph.D., Administrator and Chief Executive Officer CFO: Dale Spencer, Chief Financial Officer Web address: www.carolinashealthcare.org	16	10	125	1771	112	29732	0	21299	10232	342

WASHINGTON—Beaufort County

✠ **BEAUFORT COUNTY HOSPITAL**, 628 East 12th Street, Zip 27889–3498; tel. 252/975–4100 **A**1 9 10 **F**2 6 11 21 22 23 26 27 28 29 33 41 45 46 47 48 51 52 53 55 58 61 62 63 64 65 66 70 71 73 74 75 76 81 82 84 85 88 93 94 96 107 108 Primary Contact: Bill R. Bedsole, Chief Executive Officer COO: Susan Gerard, Assistant Administrator CMO: Kenny Nall, M.D., Chief of Staff CIO: Amy Boyd, Manager Information Systems CHR: Penny Leggett, Manager Human Resources Web address: www.beaufortcountyhospital.org	16	10	99	3935	43	105232	419	45543	19422	544

WHITEVILLE—Columbus County

✠ **COLUMBUS COUNTY HOSPITAL**, 500 Jefferson Street, Zip 28472–9987; tel. 910/642–8011 **A**1 9 10 19 **F**2 9 11 12 15 21 22 23 26 27 28 29 33 40 46 47 49 53 55 57 58 59 62 63 65 66 69 81 84 85 88 93 94 95 96 108 109 110 **P**8 **S** Quorum Health Resources, Plano, TX Primary Contact: William S. Clark, Chief Executive Officer COO: Hardy Ledbetter, Chief Operating Officer CFO: George Harms, Chief Financial Officer CMO: Ron Walters, M.D., Chief of Staff CIO: Lisa Ward, Director Management Information Systems CHR: Ginger Scott, Director Human Resources Web address: www.cchospital.com	23	10	113	6186	77	—	511	—	—	554

WILLIAMSTON—Martin County

□ **MARTIN GENERAL HOSPITAL**, 310 South McCaskey Road, Zip 27892–2150, Mailing Address: P.O. Box 1128, Zip 27892–1128; tel. 252/809–6179, (Nonreporting) **A**1 9 10 **S** Community Health Systems, Inc., Brentwood, TN Primary Contact: David S. Sanders, Chief Executive Officer Web address: www.martingeneral.com	13	10	49	—	—	—	—	—	—	—

NC

Hospital, Address, Telephone, Approval, Facility, and Physician Codes, Health Care System	Classi-fication Codes		Utilization Data					Expense (thousands) of dollars		
★ American Hospital Association (AHA) membership □ Joint Commission on Accreditation of Healthcare Organizations (JCAHO) accreditation ○ American Osteopathic Association (AOA) accreditation △ Commission on Accreditation of Rehabilitation Facilities (CARF) accreditation	Control	Service	Staffed Beds	Admissions	Census	Outpatient Visits	Births	Total	Payroll	Personnel

WILMINGTON—New Hanover County

⊞ △ **NEW HANOVER REGIONAL MEDICAL CENTER**, 2131 South 17th Street, Zip 28401–7483, Mailing Address: P.O. Box 9000, Zip 28402–9000; tel. 910/343–7000, (Includes CAPE FEAR HOSPITAL, 5301 Wrightsville Avenue, Zip 28403–6599; tel. 910/452–8100) **A**1 2 3 5 7 9 10 12 13 **F**2 6 9 10 11 12 14 15 16 17 18 19 20 21 22 23 26 28 29 30 31 33 34 37 38 39 42 44 45 46 47 48 49 50 52 53 55 56 57 58 59 60 61 62 63 64 65 66 68 69 70 71 74 75 76 78 79 81 82 84 85 86 87 88 93 94 96 98 106 108 109 **P**6 **S** New Hanover Health Network, Wilmington, NC
Primary Contact: John K. Barto, Jr, Chief Executive Officer
COO: Donna Bost, R.N., Vice President and Cape Fear Hospital Administrator
CFO: Edwin J. Ollie, Senior Vice President and Chief Financial Officer
CMO: Thaddeus Dunn, M.D., President Medical Staff
CIO: Avery Cloud, Vice President and Chief Information Officer
CHR: Peter Rzeminski, Vice President Human Resources
Web address: www.nhhn.org
| | 13 | 10 | 655 | 33461 | 490 | 117068 | 3518 | 450192 | 180040 | 4136 |

WILMINGTON TREATMENT CENTER, 2520 Troy Drive, Zip 28401–7643; tel. 910/762–2727, (Nonreporting) **A**10
Primary Contact: Charles S. Sharp, Chief Executive Officer
Web address: www.wilmtreatment.com
| | 33 | 82 | 44 | — | — | — | — | — | — | — |

WILSON—Wilson County

⊞ **WILSON MEDICAL CENTER**, 1705 South Tarboro Street, Zip 27893–3428; tel. 252/399–8040 **A**1 9 10 19 **F**2 9 11 12 15 21 22 23 27 28 32 33 38 46 47 49 52 55 57 58 59 60 61 62 63 64 65 66 69 71 74 75 76 80 81 82 84 85 86 88 92 93 94 96 108 **P**6
Primary Contact: Christopher T. Durrer, President and Chief Executive Officer
CFO: D Ronald Tomlinson, Executive Vice President and Chief Financial Officer
CIO: Rex Burnworth, Director Information Systems
CHR: Lynne Gallimore, Vice President
Web address: www.wilmed.org
| | 23 | 10 | 220 | 8223 | 98 | 159724 | 1175 | 90404 | 40379 | 954 |

WINDSOR—Bertie County

⊞ **BERTIE MEMORIAL HOSPITAL**, 1403 South King Street, Zip 27983–1726, Mailing Address: P.O. Box 40, Zip 27983–1726; tel. 252/794–6600 **A**1 9 10 18 **F**12 26 27 33 46 52 60 63 81 88 108 109 **S** University Health Systems of Eastern Carolina, Greenville, NC
Primary Contact: Jeffrey N. Sackrison, CHE, President
CFO: Brian A. Bunch, Vice President Financial Services
Web address: www.bertie.uhseast.com
| | 23 | 10 | 6 | 353 | 3 | 17146 | 0 | 10042 | 4098 | 108 |

WINSTON–SALEM—Forsyth County

⊞ **FORSYTH MEDICAL CENTER**, 3333 Silas Creek Parkway, Zip 27103–3090; tel. 336/718–5000, (Total facility includes 20 beds in nursing home–type unit) **A**1 2 3 5 9 10 **F**2 4 6 7 10 11 14 15 17 19 21 22 23 24 25 26 27 28 29 30 31 33 34 37 38 39 41 43 44 45 46 47 48 49 50 51 52 53 54 55 56 57 58 59 60 61 62 63 64 65 66 68 69 70 71 72 73 74 75 76 77 78 79 80 81 82 84 85 86 87 88 92 97 108 109 110 **P**6 **S** Novant Health, Winston–Salem, NC
Primary Contact: Gregory J. Beier, President
COO: Sallye A. Liner, Executive Vice President and Chief Operating Officer
CFO: Dean Swindle, Chief Financial Officer
CMO: Elms Allen, M.D., Senior Vice President Medical Affairs
CHR: Jacqueline D. Gattis, Senior Vice President Human Resources
Web address: www.novanthealth.org
| | 23 | 10 | 776 | 39815 | 634 | 112321 | 6500 | 399861 | 161864 | 3543 |

★ **MEDICAL PARK HOSPITAL**, 1950 South Hawthorne Road, Zip 27103–3993, Mailing Address: P.O. Box 24728, Zip 27114–4728; tel. 336/718–0600 **A**2 9 10 **F**2 21 26 27 28 29 37 45 52 53 58 61 62 63 66 92 94 108 **S** Novant Health, Winston–Salem, NC
Primary Contact: Timothy S. Shelton, Administrator
Web address: www.novanthealth.org
| | 23 | 10 | 40 | 1538 | 15 | 12798 | 0 | 33863 | 10858 | 271 |

⊞ △ **NORTH CAROLINA BAPTIST HOSPITAL (WAKE FOREST UNIVERSITY BAPTIST MEDICAL CENTER)**, Medical Center Boulevard, Zip 27157–0001; tel. 336/716–2011, (Total facility includes 170 beds in nursing home–type unit) **A**1 2 7 8 9 10 **F**2 6 7 9 10 12 13 14 15 16 17 18 19 20 21 22 23 24 26 27 28 29 31 32 33 34 35 37 38 39 40 41 43 44 45 46 47 48 49 50 51 52 53 55 56 57 58 60 61 62 63 64 65 66 67 68 69 70 71 72 73 74 75 76 77 78 79 80 81 82 84 85 86 87 88 92 93 94 95 96 98 99 100 101 104 105 106 107 108 109 110 **P**1 6 **S** North Carolina Baptist Hospital, Winston–Salem, NC
Primary Contact: Len B. Preslar, Jr, President and Chief Executive Officer
COO: Donny C. Lambeth, Senior Vice President and Chief Operating Officer
CFO: Gina B. Ramsey, Vice President Financial Services and Chief Financial Officer
CMO: Patricia L. Adams, M.D., Chief Professional Services
CIO: Paul M. LoRusso, Vice President Information Services, Chief Information Officer
CHR: Kerry A. Garrigan, Vice President Human Resources
Web address: www.wfubmc.edu
| | 23 | 10 | 937 | 34378 | 747 | 215715 | 1 | 698436 | 302260 | 7046 |

OLD VINEYARD YOUTH SERVICES, (Formerly Wake Forest University – Baptist Behavioral Health), 3637 Old Vineyard Road, Zip 27104–4835; tel. 336/794–3550, (Nonreporting) **A**5
Primary Contact: Ted Brewer, Chief Executive Officer
Web address: www.keystoneyouth.com
| | 23 | 22 | 99 | — | — | — | — | — | — | — |

NC

Many Facility Codes have changed. Please refer to the AHA Guide Code Chart. © 2005 AHA Guide

Hospital, Address, Telephone, Approval, Facility, and Physician Codes, Health Care System	Classi-fication Codes		Utilization Data					Expense (thousands) of dollars		
★ American Hospital Association (AHA) membership □ Joint Commission on Accreditation of Healthcare Organizations (JCAHO) accreditation ○ American Osteopathic Association (AOA) accreditation △ Commission on Accreditation of Rehabilitation Facilities (CARF) accreditation	Control	Service	Staffed Beds	Admissions	Census	Outpatient Visits	Births	Total	Payroll	Personnel
□ **SELECT SPECIALTY HOSPITAL OF WINSTON–SALEM**, 3333 Silas Creek Parkway, 6th Floor, Zip 27103; tel. 336/718–6300, (Nonreporting) **A**1 10 Primary Contact: Dan Epley, Chief Executive Officer	33	49	52	—	—	—	—	—	—	—
YADKINVILLE—Yadkin County										
✶ **HOOTS MEMORIAL HOSPITAL**, 624 West Main Street, Zip 27055–7804, Mailing Address: P.O. Box 68, Zip 27055–0068; tel. 336/679–2041 **A**1 9 10 18 **F**2 9 12 21 22 27 28 29 33 34 39 44 46 48 52 63 64 68 69 70 81 88 94 97 108 **P**6 **S** North Carolina Baptist Hospital, Winston–Salem, NC Primary Contact: Lance C. Labine, President CFO: Jim Chatman, Chief Financial Officer Web address: www.bgsm.edu/hoots/	23	10	22	143	3	18804	0	7008	3163	92

NC

NORTH DAKOTA

Hospital, Address, Telephone, Approval, Facility, and Physician Codes, Health Care System	Classi-fication Codes		Utilization Data					Expense (thousands) of dollars		
★ American Hospital Association (AHA) membership □ Joint Commission on Accreditation of Healthcare Organizations (JCAHO) accreditation ○ American Osteopathic Association (AOA) accreditation △ Commission on Accreditation of Rehabilitation Facilities (CARF) accreditation	Control	Service	Staffed Beds	Admissions	Census	Outpatient Visits	Births	Total	Payroll	Personnel

ASHLEY—McIntosh County

★ **ASHLEY MEDICAL CENTER**, 612 North Center Avenue, Zip 58413–0556, Mailing Address: P.O. Box 450, Zip 58413–0450; tel. 701/288-3433, (Total facility includes 44 beds in nursing home–type unit) **A**9 10 18 **F**2 9 12 23 24 26 27 28 29 33 34 36 37 38 39 41 44 45 46 48 51 52 53 55 58 60 63 64 65 66 69 70 81 91 92 94 95 96 97 108 109 110 **P**6
Primary Contact: Kathleen Hoeft, Administrator and Chief Executive Officer
CFO: Jerry Lepp, Chief Financial Officer
CMO: Udom Tinsa, Medical Director
Web address: www.amctoday.org
`23 10 64 281 45 5536 0 4753 2550 108`

BELCOURT—Rolette County

✉ **U. S. PUBLIC HEALTH SERVICE INDIAN HOSPITAL**, Mailing Address: P.O. Box 160, Zip 58316–0160; tel. 701/477–6111, (Nonreporting) **A**1 10 **S** U. S. Indian Health Service, Rockville, MD
Primary Contact: Linus Everling, JD, M.P.H., Chief Executive Officer
CFO: Lynn Davis, Chief Financial Officer
`44 10 27 — — — — — — —`

BISMARCK—Burleigh County

✉ △ **MEDCENTER ONE**, 300 North Seventh Street, Zip 58501–4439, Mailing Address: P.O. Box 5525, Zip 58506–5525; tel. 701/323–6000, (Total facility includes 22 beds in nursing home–type unit) **A**1 2 3 5 7 9 10 **F**2 7 9 10 11 12 14 15 17 19 21 22 23 24 27 28 29 33 34 35 36 37 38 39 40 41 44 46 47 48 49 50 51 52 54 55 56 57 58 59 60 61 62 63 64 65 66 67 68 69 70 71 72 73 74 75 76 77 78 81 82 84 85 86 88 89 92 93 94 95 96 98 101 107 108 109 110 **P**6
Primary Contact: James C. Cooper, President and Chief Executive Officer
CFO: Paul Morth, Vice President Finance
CMO: Craig Lambrecht, M.D., Medical Director
CIO: John Miller, Vice President Information Services
CHR: Scott Boehm, vice President Human Resources
Web address: www.medcenterone.com
`23 10 188 8568 116 529893 717 180700 93494 1530`

✉ △ **ST. ALEXIUS MEDICAL CENTER**, 900 East Broadway, Zip 58501–4586, Mailing Address: P.O. Box 5510, Zip 58506–5510; tel. 701/530–7000, (Total facility includes 19 beds in nursing home–type unit) **A**1 2 3 5 7 9 10 **F**2 7 9 10 11 12 14 15 17 19 20 21 22 23 24 25 26 27 28 29 30 31 33 34 36 37 41 43 44 46 47 48 49 51 52 53 55 56 57 58 59 61 62 63 67 68 69 71 72 73 74 75 76 77 78 81 84 86 88 92 93 94 95 96 97 106 108 109 110 **P**8
S Benedictine Sisters of the Annunciation, Bismarck, ND
Primary Contact: Richard A. Tschider, FACHE, President and Chief Executive Officer
CFO: Gary Miller, Senior Vice President and Chief Financial Officer
CMO: Shiraz Hyder, M.D., Director Medical Affairs
CIO: Ron Hindt, Chief Information Officer
CHR: Wanda Pfaff, Vice President Human Resources
Web address: www.st.alexius.org
`21 10 282 10301 141 161214 1084 139753 60857 1599`

BOTTINEAU—Bottineau County

ST. ANDREW'S HEALTH CENTER, 316 Ohmer Street, Zip 58318–1018; tel. 701/228–9300 **A**5 9 10 18 **F**12 14 22 23 27 28 33 34 39 46 48 52 63 91 94 97 108 **P**1 **S** Sisters of Mary of the Presentation Health System, Fargo, ND
Primary Contact: Jodi Atkinson, President and Chief Executive Officer
Web address: www.standrewshealth.com
`23 10 25 140 1 6950 0 3971 1629 73`

BOWMAN—Bowman County

SOUTHWEST HEALTHCARE SERVICES, 202 Sixth Avenue S.W., Zip 58623–0009, Mailing Address: P.O. Drawer C, Zip 58623; tel. 701/523–5265, (Total facility includes 67 beds in nursing home–type unit) **A**9 10 18 **F**1 6 8 9 23 29 30 33 45 46 48 51 63 81 84 88 91 92 94 96 97 106 108
Primary Contact: Darrold Bertsch, Administrator
Web address: www.swhealthcare.net
`23 10 90 192 67 — 0 7038 4183 —`

CANDO—Towner County

★ **TOWNER COUNTY MEDICAL CENTER**, Highway 281 N, Box 688, Zip 58324–0688; tel. 701/968–4411, (Total facility includes 54 beds in nursing home–type unit) **A**5 9 10 20 **F**3 4 9 11 12 23 25 29 30 33 34 39 46 48 52 54 59 63 66 69 70 91 92 96 97 **P**6
Primary Contact: Les Wietstock, Chief Executive Officer
CFO: Sandra Teubner, Chief Financial Officer
CHR: Pat Klingenberg, Director Human Resources
Web address: www.tcmedcenter.com
`23 10 98 432 51 18093 12 7227 3899 133`

Many Facility Codes have changed. Please refer to the AHA Guide Code Chart.

© 2005 AHA Guide

Hospital, Address, Telephone, Approval, Facility, and Physician Codes, Health Care System	Classi-fication Codes		Utilization Data					Expense (thousands) of dollars		
★ American Hospital Association (AHA) membership □ Joint Commission on Accreditation of Healthcare Organizations (JCAHO) accreditation ○ American Osteopathic Association (AOA) accreditation △ Commission on Accreditation of Rehabilitation Facilities (CARF) accreditation	Control	Service	Staffed Beds	Admissions	Census	Outpatient Visits	Births	Total	Payroll	Personnel

CARRINGTON—Foster County

★ **CARRINGTON HEALTH CENTER**, 800 North Fourth Street, Zip 58421–1217; tel. 701/652–3141, (Total facility includes 24 beds in nursing home–type unit) **A**5 9 10 18 **F**6 8 9 11 12 21 22 23 29 33 34 36 38 39 46 47 48 52 58 60 63 65 69 81 84 85 88 94 96 97 106 108 110 **S** Catholic Health Initiatives, Denver, CO
Primary Contact: Johnson L. Smith, Interim President and Chief Executive Officer
CFO: Jane Bissel, Chief Financial Officer
CMO: Michael J. Page, M.D., Chief Medical Officer
Web address: www.carringtonhealthcenter.com

| | 21 | 10 | 49 | 702 | 27 | 17844 | 33 | — | — | — |

CAVALIER—Pembina County

★ **PEMBINA COUNTY MEMORIAL HOSPITAL AND WEDGEWOOD MANOR**, 301 Mountain Street East, Zip 58220–4015, Mailing Address: P.O. Box 380, Zip 58220–0380; tel. 701/265–8461, (Total facility includes 60 beds in nursing home–type unit) **A**5 9 10 18 **F**2 9 21 23 27 33 34 37 38 39 44 48 53 59 61 63 64 65 66 69 70 81 84 88 92 94 95 96 97 106 108 **P**5
Primary Contact: Sarah Voss, Chief Executive Officer
CFO: Sarah S. Gustafson, Director Finance
CMO: Hassan Khoudoud, M.D., Chief of Staff
CIO: Robert Heidt, Director Information Systems
Web address: www.cavalierhospital.com

| | 23 | 10 | 85 | 447 | 61 | 16196 | 5 | 8087 | 3747 | 132 |

COOPERSTOWN—Griggs County

COOPERSTOWN MEDICAL CENTER, 1200 Roberts Avenue, Zip 58425, Mailing Address: 1299 Roberts Avenue, Zip 58425; tel. 701/797–2221, (Nonreporting) **A**10 18
Primary Contact: Gregory Stomp, Chief Executive Officer
Web address: www.coopermedicalcenter.org

| | 23 | 10 | 10 | — | — | — | — | — | — | — |

CROSBY—Divide County

ST. LUKE'S HOSPITAL, 702 First Street Southwest, Zip 58730–0010; tel. 701/965–6384 **A**5 9 10 18 **F**9 14 26 33 47 48 54 60 63 65 66 69 97 **P**6
Primary Contact: Leslie O. Urvand, Administrator

| | 23 | 10 | 12 | 145 | 1 | 5278 | 0 | 2928 | 1576 | 48 |

DEVILS LAKE—Ramsey County

⊠ **MERCY HOSPITAL**, 1031 Seventh Street N.E., Zip 58301–2798; tel. 701/662–2131 **A**1 5 9 10 20 **F**2 9 11 14 22 26 27 28 29 30 33 34 36 37 46 47 48 51 55 58 59 61 63 65 66 69 81 82 84 88 94 96 97 106 **P**5 **S** Catholic Health Initiatives, Denver, CO
Primary Contact: Marlene J. Krein, President and Chief Executive Officer
COO: Jerry S. Lindell, Senior Vice President
CFO: Michael Loff, Vice President Finance
Web address: www.mercyhospitaldl.com

| | 23 | 10 | 35 | 1466 | 14 | 20181 | 240 | 12502 | 5596 | 180 |

DICKINSON—Stark County

⊠ **ST. JOSEPH'S HOSPITAL AND HEALTH CENTER**, 30 Seventh Street West, Zip 58601–4399; tel. 701/456–4000 **A**1 5 9 10 20 **F**2 9 11 12 21 22 23 27 28 29 32 33 34 36 37 38 40 41 46 47 48 49 51 52 54 55 56 57 58 59 60 61 62 63 64 66 69 70 71 72 74 75 76 77 78 79 81 82 84 85 86 87 88 93 94 95 96 97 108 **S** Catholic Health Initiatives, Denver, CO
Primary Contact: Allan C. Sonduck, President and Chief Executive Officer
CFO: Wayne J. Fuhrman, Chief Financial Officer
Web address: www.stjoeshospital.org

| | 21 | 10 | 83 | 2816 | 39 | 41068 | 313 | 33863 | 15620 | 348 |

ELGIN—Grant County

JACOBSON MEMORIAL HOSPITAL CARE CENTER, 601 East Street North, Zip 58533–0376; tel. 701/584–2792, (Total facility includes 25 beds in nursing home–type unit) (Nonreporting) **A**9 10 18
Primary Contact: Kurt Waldbillig, Chief Executive Officer

| | 23 | 10 | 46 | — | — | — | — | — | — | — |

FARGO—Cass County

HEARTLAND HEALTH SYSTEM See MeritCare South University

⊠ **INNOVIS HEALTH**, 3000 32nd Avenue South, Zip 58103; tel. 701/364–8000 **A**1 9 10 **F**2 10 11 12 14 15 17 19 20 21 22 23 25 27 28 29 33 34 35 37 38 39 55 56 57 58 59 60 61 62 63 65 66 69 81 82 84 85 86 88 89 94 96 108 109 110
Primary Contact: Paul J. Wilson, Chief Executive Officer
CFO: Stacie Heiden, Chief Financial Officer
CIO: Ken Gilles, Director of Information Systems
CHR: Carol Berndt, Administrator Human Resources
Web address: www.innovishealth.com

| | 23 | 10 | 74 | 6026 | 60 | 15413 | 898 | 66643 | 21327 | 580 |

⊠ △ **MERITCARE MEDICAL CENTER**, (Formerly MeritCare Hospital), 720 Fourth Street North, Zip 58122; tel. 701/234–6000, (Includes MERITCARE SOUTH UNIVERSITY, 1720 South University Drive, Zip 58103–4994; tel. 701/280–4100; Darla Dobberstein, Executive Partner), (Total facility includes 33 beds in nursing home–type unit) **A**1 2 3 5 7 8 9 10 **F**2 4 7 9 10 11 14 15 16 17 18 19 20 21 22 23 26 27 28 29 33 34 35 36 37 38 39 40 41 42 43 44 49 50 51 52 53 55 56 57 58 59 61 62 63 64 66 67 68 69 71 72 74 75 77 78 79 80 81 82 84 85 86 87 88 92 93 94 95 101 105 106 108 110 **S** MeritCare Health System, Fargo, ND
Primary Contact: Roger L. Gilbertson, M.D., President
COO: John Doherty, Chief Operating Officer
CFO: Lisa Carlson, Chief Financial Officer
CMO: Gregory Post, M.D., Senior Executive and Chief of Staff
CIO: Craig Hewit, Executive Partner Information Management
CHR: Harriette McCaul, Executive Partner Human Resources
Web address: www.meritcare.com

| | 21 | 10 | 522 | 19453 | 289 | 259769 | 2252 | 271577 | 105542 | 2336 |

Hospital, Address, Telephone, Approval, Facility, and Physician Codes, Health Care System	Classi-fication Codes		Utilization Data					Expense (thousands) of dollars		
★ American Hospital Association (AHA) membership □ Joint Commission on Accreditation of Healthcare Organizations (JCAHO) accreditation ○ American Osteopathic Association (AOA) accreditation △ Commission on Accreditation of Rehabilitation Facilities (CARF) accreditation	Control	Service	Staffed Beds	Admissions	Census	Outpatient Visits	Births	Total	Payroll	Personnel
□ **PRAIRIE AT ST. JOHN'S**, 510 4th Street South, Zip 58103–1914; tel. 701/476–7200 **A**1 9 10 **F**3 22 27 28 29 33 41 44 45 71 72 73 74 75 76 77 78 94 **P**6 Primary Contact: Marshall Korman, Chief Executive Officer	33	22	67	1414	40	12726	0	—	—	—
□ **SCCI HOSPITAL – FARGO**, 1720 University Drive South, Zip 58103; tel. 701/241–9099, (Nonreporting) **A**1 9 10 Primary Contact: Custer Huseby, Chief Executive Officer	33	49	31							
⊠ **VETERANS AFFAIRS MEDICAL AND REGIONAL OFFICE CENTER**, 2101 Elm Street, Zip 58102–2498; tel. 701/232–3241, (Total facility includes 28 beds in nursing home–type unit) **A**1 2 3 5 **F**2 4 9 10 21 22 23 29 31 32 36 37 38 45 46 47 48 49 50 52 55 57 58 60 61 62 63 64 65 66 68 69 70 71 73 74 75 76 77 78 81 82 85 87 88 92 93 94 96 106 107 108 109 110 **S** Department of Veterans Affairs, Washington, DC Primary Contact: Douglas M. Kenyon, Director CFO: Roger Saylor, Finance Officer CMO: William K. Becker, M.D., Chief of Staff and Medical Director CIO: Dennis Gilbertson, Chief Information Resource Management CHR: David J. Kirk, Chief Human Resources Management Service Web address: www.va.gov/sta/guide/home.asp	45	10	71	2205	61	129472	0	60869	46603	668
FORT YATES—Sioux County										
⊠ **U. S. PUBLIC HEALTH SERVICE INDIAN HOSPITAL**, N 10 North River Road, Zip 58538, Mailing Address: P.O. Box J, Zip 58538; tel. 701/854–3831, (Nonreporting) **A**1 5 9 10 **S** U. S. Indian Health Service, Rockville, MD Primary Contact: Tim Yellow, Director CFO: William Condon, Deputy Administrative Officer	47	10	14							
GARRISON—McLean County										
★ **GARRISON MEMORIAL HOSPITAL**, 407 Third Avenue S.E., Zip 58540–0039; tel. 701/463–2275, (Total facility includes 24 beds in nursing home–type unit) (Nonreporting) **A**5 9 10 18 20 **S** Benedictine Sisters of the Annunciation, Bismarck, ND Primary Contact: Dennis Goebel, President and Chief Executive Officer CFO: Tod Graeber, Controller	21	10	46	—	—	—	—	—	—	—
GRAFTON—Walsh County										
★ **UNITY MEDICAL CENTER**, 164 West 13th Street, Zip 58237–1896; tel. 701/352–1620 **A**5 9 10 18 **F**9 11 14 24 29 33 34 46 48 52 58 59 60 63 66 69 70 94 96 97 108 **P**4 Primary Contact: Everett A. Butler, Chief Executive Officer CFO: Rachel Ray, Chief Financial Officer Web address: www.unitymedcenter.com	23	10	17	362	6	39707	23	5482	3019	75
GRAND FORKS—Grand Forks County										
⊠ △ **ALTRU HEALTH SYSTEM**, 1000 South Columbia Road, Zip 58201–4032; tel. 701/780–5000, (Includes ALTRU HEALTH INSTITUTE, 1300 South Columbia Road, Zip 58201; tel. 701/780–2311; ALTRU HOSPITAL, 1200 South Columbia Road, Zip 58201; tel. 701/780–5000) **A**1 2 3 5 7 9 10 20 **F**2 3 4 6 8 9 10 11 12 14 15 16 17 18 19 21 22 23 24 28 29 30 31 33 34 35 36 37 38 39 41 44 45 46 47 48 49 50 51 52 53 54 55 56 57 58 59 60 61 62 63 64 65 66 68 69 70 71 72 73 74 75 76 77 78 79 81 82 83 84 85 87 88 89 91 93 94 96 106 107 108 109 110 **P**6 Primary Contact: Greg Gerloff, Chief Executive Officer COO: David Molmen, Chief Operating Officer CFO: Dwight Thompson, Chief Financial Officer CMO: James Van Looy, M.D., Chief Medical Executive CIO: Marv Meier, Administrative Director Information Services Web address: www.altru.org	23	10	264	11697	149	107186	1427	269198	143868	2657
RICHARD P. STADTER PSYCHIATRIC CENTER, 1451 44th Avenue South, Zip 58208; tel. 701/775–2500, (Nonreporting) **A**9 10 Primary Contact: Thomas Peterson, Chief Executive Officer	33	49	34	—	—	—	—	—	—	—
HARVEY—Wells County										
★ **ST. ALOISIUS MEDICAL CENTER**, 325 East Brewster Street, Zip 58341–1605; tel. 701/324–4651, (Total facility includes 106 beds in nursing home–type unit) **A**5 9 10 18 **F**11 12 22 23 33 44 46 48 55 60 61 63 69 91 92 94 96 97 108 109 **S** Sisters of Mary of the Presentation Health System, Fargo, ND Primary Contact: Ronald J. Volk, President and Chief Executive Officer Web address: www.staloisius.com	21	10	131	719	107	7818	14	9604	4974	241
HAZEN—Mercer County										
★ **SAKAKAWEA MEDICAL CENTER**, 510 Eighth Avenue N.E., Zip 58545–4637; tel. 701/748–2225 **A**5 9 10 18 **F**2 9 11 12 14 33 36 37 44 46 48 51 55 58 59 60 63 65 68 81 84 88 91 94 95 96 97 106 108 **P**6 CFO: Renae Snyder, Business Office Manager Web address: www.sakmedcenter.com	23	10	25	210	2	15400	1	4431	2477	79
HETTINGER—Adams County										
□ **WEST RIVER REGIONAL MEDICAL CENTER**, 1000 Highway 12, Zip 58639–7530; tel. 701/567–4561 **A**1 5 9 10 18 **F**2 6 7 8 9 11 12 14 21 23 24 27 28 29 31 33 35 37 38 39 41 44 45 46 47 48 51 52 55 58 59 60 61 63 64 65 66 70 76 77 81 82 84 85 87 88 91 93 94 95 96 97 98 105 106 108 109 110 **P**3 Primary Contact: James K. Long, CPA, Administrator and Chief Executive Officer Web address: www.wrhs.com	23	10	40	1212	13	72762	77	17112	6472	235

Many Facility Codes have changed. Please refer to the AHA Guide Code Chart.   © 2005 AHA Guide

Hospital, Address, Telephone, Approval, Facility, and Physician Codes, Health Care System	Classi-fication Codes		Utilization Data					Expense (thousands) of dollars		
★ American Hospital Association (AHA) membership □ Joint Commission on Accreditation of Healthcare Organizations (JCAHO) accreditation ○ American Osteopathic Association (AOA) accreditation △ Commission on Accreditation of Rehabilitation Facilities (CARF) accreditation	Control	Service	Staffed Beds	Admissions	Census	Outpatient Visits	Births	Total	Payroll	Personnel

HILLSBORO—Traill County

★ **HILLSBORO MEDICAL CENTER**, 12 Third Street S.E., Zip 58045–4821, Mailing Address: P.O. Box 609, Zip 58045–0609; tel. 701/636–4501, (Total facility includes 48 beds in nursing home–type unit) **A**5 9 10 18 20 **F**1 2 6 9 33 41 44 45 60 81 84 88 92 94 97 107
Primary Contact: Bruce D. Bowersox, Administrator
CFO: Darlene Swanson, Business Manager
Web address: www.hillsboromedicalcenter.com

| | 23 | 10 | 68 | 261 | 51 | 14904 | 0 | — | — | 80 |

JAMESTOWN—Stutsman County

⊠ **JAMESTOWN HOSPITAL**, 419 Fifth Street N.E., Zip 58401–3360; tel. 701/252–1050 **A**1 5 9 10 20 **F**2 9 10 11 12 14 23 27 28 29 30 33 34 36 37 38 41 46 47 48 51 52 54 55 58 59 60 63 64 65 66 69 81 82 84 87 88 94 96 97 106 108
Primary Contact: Martin I. Richman, President and Chief Executive Officer
COO: Mary Ellen Frey, Chief Operating Officer
CFO: Wes Smith, Chief Financial Officer
Web address: www.jamestownhospital.com

| | 23 | 10 | 56 | 2029 | 17 | 23278 | 231 | 20060 | 9617 | 255 |

□ **NORTH DAKOTA STATE HOSPITAL**, 2605 Circle Drive, Zip 58401–6905; tel. 701/253–3964, (Nonreporting) **A**1 5 10
Primary Contact: Alex Schweitzer, Superintendent and Chief Executive Officer

| | 12 | 22 | 200 | — | | | | | | |

KENMARE—Ward County

★ **KENMARE COMMUNITY HOSPITAL**, 317 First Avenue N.W., Zip 58746–7104, Mailing Address: P.O. Box 697, Zip 58746–0697; tel. 701/385–4296, (Nonreporting) **A**10 18
Primary Contact: Margaret Shawn Smothers, Administrator
COO: Bev Heninger, Director Nursing
CFO: Kevin Seehafer, Chief Financial Officer
CMO: Srinivasa Madala, M.D., Physician
CIO: Alan Okerson, Information Technology Director
CHR: Ranae Ehlke, Administrative Secretary and Risk Management and Human Resources Coordinator

| | 23 | 10 | 25 | | | | | | | |

LANGDON—Cavalier County

★ **CAVALIER COUNTY MEMORIAL HOSPITAL**, 909 Second Street, Zip 58249–2499; tel. 701/256–6100 **A**5 9 10 18 **F**2 6 12 33 52 53 55 58 61 63 69 94 97 **P**7
Primary Contact: Lawrence Blue, Administrator and Chief Executive Officer
COO: Lawrence Blue, Administrator and Chief Executive Officer
CFO: Julie Feil, Accountant
CMO: Ahsan Khalid, Medical Director
CHR: Christie Sauer, Human Resources Officer
Web address: www.cavaliercountyhospital.com

| | 23 | 10 | 25 | 313 | 4 | 25366 | 0 | 4454 | 2522 | 81 |

LINTON—Emmons County

LINTON HOSPITAL, 518 North Broadway, Zip 58552–7308, Mailing Address: P.O. Box 850, Zip 58552–0850; tel. 701/254–4511, (Nonreporting) **A**5 9 10 18 20
Primary Contact: Roger R. Unger, Administrator

| | 23 | 10 | 25 | — | — | — | — | — | — | — |

LISBON—Ransom County

★ **LISBON AREA HEALTH SERVICES**, 905 Main Street, Zip 58054–0353, Mailing Address: P.O. Box 353, Zip 58054–0353; tel. 701/683–5241, (Total facility includes 45 beds in nursing home–type unit) (Nonreporting) **A**5 9 10 18
S Catholic Health Initiatives, Denver, CO
Primary Contact: Bradley D. Burris, President and Chief Executive Officer
COO: Diane Weispfenning, Chief Operating Officer
CFO: Donald Kapfer, Finance Director
Web address: www.lhsnet.com

| | 23 | 10 | 65 | — | | | | | | |

MAYVILLE—Traill County

★ **UNION HOSPITAL**, 42 Sixth Avenue S.E., Zip 58257–1598; tel. 701/786–3800 **A**5 9 10 18 **F**11 12 26 27 28 33 34 41 44 51 52 58 59 63 89 94
Primary Contact: Roger Baier, Chief Executive Officer
Web address: www.unionhospital.com

| | 23 | 10 | 25 | 247 | 1 | 6557 | 0 | — | — | 44 |

MCVILLE—Nelson County

NELSON COUNTY HEALTH SYSTEM, 200 Main Street, Zip 58254–4002, Mailing Address: P.O. Box 367, Zip 58254–0367; tel. 701/322–4328, (Nonreporting) **A**9 10 18
Primary Contact: Cathy Swenson, Chief Executive Officer

| | 23 | 10 | 19 | — | | | | | | |

MINOT—Ward County

⊠ △ **TRINITY HEALTH**, One Burdick Expressway West, Zip 58701, Mailing Address: P.O. Box 5020, Zip 58701–5020; tel. 701/857–5000, (Includes TRINITY HOSPITAL–ST. JOSEPH'S), (Total facility includes 294 beds in nursing home–type unit) **A**1 2 3 5 7 9 10 19 **F**2 3 4 6 9 11 12 14 15 17 19 21 22 23 27 28 29 30 31 33 34 35 36 37 38 39 40 42 44 45 46 47 48 49 51 52 55 56 57 58 59 60 61 62 63 64 65 66 68 69 70 71 72 73 74 75 76 77 78 79 80 81 82 84 85 86 87 88 89 90 91 92 93 94 95 96 98 106 107 108 109 110 **P**6
Primary Contact: Terry G. Hoff, President
CFO: Kevin Seehafer, Controller
Web address: www.trinityhealth.org

| | 23 | 10 | 586 | 9496 | 417 | 141189 | 1238 | 199103 | 99062 | 2172 |

Hospital, Address, Telephone, Approval, Facility, and Physician Codes, Health Care System	Classi-fication Codes		Utilization Data					Expense (thousands) of dollars		
★ American Hospital Association (AHA) membership □ Joint Commission on Accreditation of Healthcare Organizations (JCAHO) accreditation ○ American Osteopathic Association (AOA) accreditation △ Commission on Accreditation of Rehabilitation Facilities (CARF) accreditation	Control	Service	Staffed Beds	Admissions	Census	Outpatient Visits	Births	Total	Payroll	Personnel
NORTHWOOD—Grand Forks County										
★ **NORTHWOOD DEACONESS HEALTH CENTER**, 4 North Park Street, Zip 58267–0190; tel. 701/587–6060, (Total facility includes 77 beds in nursing home–type unit) **A**5 9 10 18 **F**6 9 22 28 29 33 37 38 41 44 45 46 47 48 52 54 58 60 63 69 70 88 91 92 94 97 108 109 **P**5 Primary Contact: Pete Antonson, Chief Executive Officer CMO: Jon Berg, M.D., Chief of Staff CIO: Chad Peterson, Chief Information Officer Web address: www.ndhc.net	21	10	89	375	76	2362	0	7242	3619	115
OAKES—Dickey County										
★ **OAKES COMMUNITY HOSPITAL**, 314 South Eighth Street, Zip 58474–2099; tel. 701/742–3291, (Nonreporting) **A**5 9 10 18 **S** Catholic Health Initiatives, Denver, CO Primary Contact: Bradley D. Burris, President and Chief Executive Officer COO: Diane Weispfenning, Vice President of Operations CFO: Don Kapfer, Chief Financial Officer CMO: Vani Nagala, M.D., Chief Medical Officer CIO: Terry Engel, Information Technology Manager CHR: Julie Entzminger, Manager Human Resources	21	10	25	—	—	—	—	—	—	—
PARK RIVER—Walsh County										
★ **FIRST CARE HEALTH CENTER**, 115 Vivian Street, Zip 58270–0708; tel. 701/284–7500 **A**9 10 18 **F**10 11 21 22 23 27 28 33 63 81 84 88 97 **P**4 Primary Contact: Louise Dryburgh, Administrator CFO: Layne Ensrude, Chief Financial Officer CMO: K J. Midgarden, M.D., Chief Medical Staff Web address: www.firstcarehc.org	23	10	14	396	6	15687	36	5053	2339	65
RICHARDTON—Stark County										
RICHARDTON HEALTH CENTER, 212 Third Avenue West, Zip 58652–7103, Mailing Address: P.O. Box H, Zip 58652; tel. 701/974–3304, (Nonreporting) **A**9 10 18 Primary Contact: Bruce Howe, Jr, Chief Executive Officer	23	49	25	—	—	—	—	—	—	—
ROLLA—Rolette County										
PRESENTATION MEDICAL CENTER, 213 Second Avenue N.E., Zip 58367–7153, Mailing Address: P.O. Box 759, Zip 58367–0759; tel. 701/477–3161 **A**9 10 18 **F**9 10 11 12 22 23 27 29 33 44 46 48 52 59 60 61 63 66 69 70 81 84 88 94 95 97 109 **P**6 **S** Sisters of Mary of the Presentation Health System, Fargo, ND Primary Contact: Kimber Wraalstad, President and Chief Executive Officer Web address: www.pmc-rolla.com	21	10	25	636	8	8360	82	7402	3337	115
RUGBY—Pierce County										
★ **HEART OF AMERICA MEDICAL CENTER**, 800 Main Avenue South, Zip 58368–2198; tel. 701/776–5261, (Total facility includes 160 beds in nursing home–type unit) **A**5 9 10 20 **F**6 9 11 22 23 33 36 38 41 44 50 52 55 58 59 60 63 69 81 88 91 92 94 95 96 97 108 **P**2 Primary Contact: Jerry E. Jurena, Executive Director CFO: Bonnie Kuehnemund, Comptroller Web address: www.hamc.com	23	10	180	1080	140	20606	57	13450	6801	—
STANLEY—Mountrail County										
MOUNTRAIL COUNTY MEDICAL CENTER, 615 6th Street S.E., Zip 58784–4323, Mailing Address: P.O. Box 399, Zip 58784–0399; tel. 701/628–2424 **A**9 10 18 **F**9 24 27 33 46 48 52 53 63 69 70 94 97 **P**6 Primary Contact: Mitch Leupp, Administrator Web address: www.stanleynd.com/health	23	10	11	175	5	6110	0	2430	370	13
TIOGA—Williams County										
★ **TIOGA MEDICAL CENTER**, 810 North Welo Street, Zip 58852–0159, Mailing Address: P.O. Box 159, Zip 58852–0159; tel. 701/664–3305, (Total facility includes 30 beds in nursing home–type unit) (Nonreporting) **A**5 9 10 18 Primary Contact: Randall K. Pederson, Chief Executive Officer CMO: Mukesh Patel, M.D., Chief of Staff	23	10	55	—	—	—	—	—	—	—
TURTLE LAKE—McLean County										
COMMUNITY MEMORIAL HOSPITAL, 220 Fifth Avenue, Zip 58575–4005, Mailing Address: P.O. Box 280, Zip 58575–0280; tel. 701/448–2331, (Nonreporting) **A**9 10 18 Primary Contact: Dennis Goebel, Administrator	21	10	25	—	—	—	—	—	—	—
VALLEY CITY—Barnes County										
★ **MERCY HOSPITAL**, 570 Chautauqua Boulevard, Zip 58072–3199; tel. 701/845–6400 **A**5 9 10 18 **F**2 9 11 14 21 22 23 24 28 33 34 44 47 48 51 52 55 58 59 60 63 64 65 69 81 94 95 96 97 108 110 **S** Catholic Health Initiatives, Denver, CO Primary Contact: Johnson L. Smith, President and Chief Executive Officer CFO: Jane Bissel, Chief Financial Officer Web address: www.mercyhospital.biz	21	10	25	838	11	17942	80	9177	4848	133
WATFORD CITY—McKenzie County										
★ **MCKENZIE COUNTY HEALTHCARE SYSTEM**, 516 North Main Street, Zip 58854–0548; Mailing Address: P.O. Box 548, Zip 58854–0548; tel. 701/842–3000, (Nonreporting) **A**9 10 18 Primary Contact: Kris Pacheco, Chief Executive Officer CFO: Mark Thorland, Chief Financial Officer	23	10	24	—	—	—	—	—	—	—

Many Facility Codes have changed. Please refer to the AHA Guide Code Chart. © 2005 AHA Guide

Hospital, Address, Telephone, Approval, Facility, and Physician Codes, Health Care System	Classi-fication Codes		Utilization Data					Expense (thousands) of dollars		
★ American Hospital Association (AHA) membership ☐ Joint Commission on Accreditation of Healthcare Organizations (JCAHO) accreditation ○ American Osteopathic Association (AOA) accreditation △ Commission on Accreditation of Rehabilitation Facilities (CARF) accreditation	Control	Service	Staffed Beds	Admissions	Census	Outpatient Visits	Births	Total	Payroll	Personnel

WILLISTON—Williams County

⊞ **MERCY MEDICAL CENTER**, 1301 15th Avenue West, Zip 58801–3896; tel. 701/774–7400 **A**1 5 9 10 20 **F**2 4 9 11 12 21 22 23 26 27 29 33 34 36 37 41 44 45 46 48 51 55 58 59 60 61 62 63 64 69 70 71 72 77 78 79 81 84 86 88 92 93 94 95 96 97 106 108 110 **P**6 **S** Catholic Health Initiatives, Denver, CO
Primary Contact: Kimberly J. Miller, CHE, President and Chief Executive Officer
CFO: Kerry Monson, Vice President Finance and Chief Financial Officer
CMO: Beverly Tong, M.D., Chief of Staff
CIO: Sean Key, Director Information Technology
Web address: www.mercy–williston.org

| | 21 | 10 | 45 | 1937 | 21 | 55460 | 282 | 34257 | 16190 | 422 |

WISHEK—McIntosh County

★ **WISHEK COMMUNITY HOSPITAL AND CLINICS**, 1007 Fourth Avenue South, Zip 58495–7527, Mailing Address: P.O. Box 647, Zip 58495–0647; tel. 701/452–2326, (Nonreporting) **A**5 9 10 18
Primary Contact: Derrick A. Jones, Administrator
CFO: Beverly Vilhauer, Director Finance
Web address: www.wishekhospital.com

| | 23 | 10 | 20 | — | — | — | — | — | — | — |

OH

OHIO

Hospital, Address, Telephone, Approval, Facility, and Physician Codes, Health Care System	Classi-fication Codes		Utilization Data					Expense (thousands) of dollars		
★ American Hospital Association (AHA) membership □ Joint Commission on Accreditation of Healthcare Organizations (JCAHO) accreditation ○ American Osteopathic Association (AOA) accreditation △ Commission on Accreditation of Rehabilitation Facilities (CARF) accreditation	Control	Service	Staffed Beds	Admissions	Census	Outpatient Visits	Births	Total	Payroll	Personnel

AKRON—Summit County

★ **AKRON CHILDREN'S HOSPITAL**, One Perkins Square, Zip 44308–1062; tel. 330/543–1000 **A**1 2 3 5 8 9 10 **F**2 6 13 16 18 20 21 22 26 27 28 29 30 31 32 33 34 35 37 38 39 45 46 47 48 49 50 51 52 53 56 57 58 61 62 63 65 66 67 69 70 71 72 73 74 75 77 78 81 82 84 87 88 90 93 94 95 96 98 105 107 108 109 110 **P**6
Primary Contact: William H. Considine, President
CFO: Ernest Douglas, Treasurer
CMO: Daniel McMahon, M.D., President Medical Staff
CIO: Jeffrey Hale, Vice President Information Services
CHR: Ruth Swan, Director
Web address: www.akronchildrens.org
AKRON CITY HOSPITAL See Summa Health System
| | 23 | 50 | 218 | 8458 | 116 | 187508 | 0 | 230331 | 114175 | 1835 |

★ **AKRON GENERAL MEDICAL CENTER**, 400 Wabash Avenue, Zip 44307–2433; tel. 330/344–6000 **A**1 2 3 5 8 9 10 **F**2 4 6 9 10 11 12 14 15 17 19 21 22 23 26 27 28 29 30 31 32 33 34 35 36 37 38 39 40 41 42 44 45 46 47 48 49 50 51 52 53 55 57 58 59 60 61 62 63 64 65 66 69 70 71 73 74 75 76 77 78 79 81 82 83 84 85 86 87 88 89 90 92 93 94 95 96 98 106 108 109 110 **P**1 6 7 **S** Akron General Health System, Akron, OH
Primary Contact: Alan J. Bleyer, President
COO: Cathy M. Ceccio, MSN, Executive Vice President and Chief Operating Officer
CFO: Alan House, Interim Vice President Finance and Accounting
CMO: Richard J. Streck, M.D., Senior Vice President Medical Affairs
CIO: Nancy Jones, Chief Information Officer
CHR: Maureen Van Duser, Vice President Human Resources
Web address: www.akrongeneral.org
| | 23 | 10 | 462 | 23322 | 308 | 456765 | 2813 | 346279 | 143073 | 3120 |

★ △ **EDWIN SHAW HOSPITAL FOR REHABILITATION**, 1621 Flickinger Road, Zip 44312–4495; tel. 330/784–1271, (Total facility includes 49 beds in nursing home–type unit) (Nonreporting) **A**1 5 7 9 10
Primary Contact: Cathy M. Ceccio, MSN, Executive Director
Web address: www.edwinshaw.com
| | 13 | 46 | 161 | — | — | — | — | — | — | — |

□ **SELECT SPECIALTY HOSPITAL–AKRON**, 525 East Market Street, Zip 44309; tel. 330/375–4390, (Nonreporting) **A**1 10
Primary Contact: Gregory T. Storer, Chief Executive Officer
| | 33 | 80 | 34 | — | — | — | — | — | — | — |

□ **SELECT SPECIALTY HOSPITAL–NORTHEAST OHIO**, 400 Wabash Avenue, 9th Floor, Zip 44307; tel. 330/344–6910, (Nonreporting) **A**1 10
Primary Contact: Pat Mahovich, Chief Executive Officer
| | 33 | 80 | 31 | — | — | — | — | — | — | — |

★ **SUMMA HEALTH SYSTEM**, (Includes AKRON CITY HOSPITAL, 525 East Market Street, Zip 44309–2090, Mailing Address: P.O. Box 2090, Zip 44309–2090; tel. 330/375–3000; SAINT THOMAS HOSPITAL, 444 North Main Street, Zip 44310; tel. 330/375–3000), (Total facility includes 10 beds in nursing home–type unit) **A**1 2 3 5 8 9 10 **F**2 3 4 6 7 9 10 11 12 14 15 17 19 21 22 23 26 27 28 29 30 31 32 33 34 35 36 37 38 39 40 41 42 44 45 46 47 48 49 50 51 52 53 55 56 57 58 59 60 61 62 63 64 65 66 68 69 70 71 73 74 75 76 77 78 79 81 82 83 84 85 86 87 88 89 90 92 93 94 95 96 97 101 106 107 108 109 110 **P**8
Primary Contact: Thomas J. Strauss, President and Chief Executive Officer
COO: Robert Harrigan, President and Chief Operating Officer
CFO: Michael Rutherford, Chief Financial Officer
CMO: Dale Murphy, M.D., Vice President Medical Affairs
CIO: Charles Ross, M.D., Vice President Information Technology System and Chief Information Officer
CHR: Kyle Klawitter, Vice President Human Resources
Web address: www.summahealth.org
| | 23 | 10 | 485 | 35394 | 460 | 400073 | 3471 | 444199 | 182222 | 4247 |

ALLIANCE—Stark County

□ **ALLIANCE COMMUNITY HOSPITAL**, 264 East Rice Street, Zip 44601–4399; tel. 330/829–4000, (Total facility includes 72 beds in nursing home–type unit) **A**1 2 9 10 **F**9 11 12 21 22 27 28 29 33 34 36 37 39 40 44 45 46 47 48 49 51 52 54 55 58 59 60 62 63 65 66 68 69 71 76 81 82 84 85 87 88 92 93 94 96 107 108 109 **P**8
Primary Contact: Stanley W. Jonas, Chief Executive Officer
Web address: www.achosp.org
| | 23 | 10 | 210 | 4865 | 116 | 171660 | 381 | 63970 | 30518 | 732 |

AMHERST—Lorain County

□ **THE HOSPITAL FOR ORTHOPAEDIC AND SPECIALTY SERVICES**, 254 Cleveland Avenue, Zip 44001–1699; tel. 440/988–6000 **A**1 9 10 **F**21 26 33 35 39 46 47 48 52 60 62 63 65 69 81 85 88 93 94
Primary Contact: Kevin C. Martin, President and Chief Executive Officer
Web address: www.emh–healthcare.org
| | 23 | 10 | 36 | 1437 | 16 | 14550 | 0 | 17900 | 6088 | 124 |

ASHLAND—Ashland County

★ **SAMARITAN REGIONAL HEALTH SYSTEM**, 1025 Center Street, Zip 44805–4098; tel. 419/289–0491, (Nonreporting) **A**1 9 10
Primary Contact: Danny L. Boggs, President and Chief Executive Officer
CFO: David Boyer, Vice President Finance and Chief Financial Officer
CIO: Sharon Neura, Vice President Marketing and Public Relations
CHR: Alyce Legg, Vice President Human Resources
Web address: www.samaritanhospital.org
| | 23 | 10 | 70 | — | — | — | — | — | — | — |

Many Facility Codes have changed. Please refer to the AHA Guide Code Chart. © 2005 AHA Guide

OH

Hospital, Address, Telephone, Approval, Facility, and Physician Codes, Health Care System	Classi-fication Codes		Utilization Data					Expense (thousands) of dollars		
★ American Hospital Association (AHA) membership □ Joint Commission on Accreditation of Healthcare Organizations (JCAHO) accreditation ○ American Osteopathic Association (AOA) accreditation △ Commission on Accreditation of Rehabilitation Facilities (CARF) accreditation	Control	Service	Staffed Beds	Admissions	Census	Outpatient Visits	Births	Total	Payroll	Personnel

ASHTABULA—Ashtabula County

□ **ASHTABULA COUNTY MEDICAL CENTER**, 2420 Lake Avenue, Zip 44004–4993; tel. 440/997–2262, (Total facility includes 15 beds in nursing home–type unit) **A**1 9 10 19 **F**2 3 4 9 11 12 14 21 22 26 27 28 29 31 33 34 36 37 40 46 48 51 52 53 55 57 58 59 60 62 63 64 66 69 70 71 73 75 76 77 78 81 82 84 87 88 92 94 96 106 108 **P**6
Primary Contact: Kevin J. Miller, FACHE, President and Chief Executive Officer
Web address: www.acmchealth.org

23	10	192	6294	85	118074	546	58044	23383	544

ATHENS—Athens County

✠ **O'BLENESS MEMORIAL HOSPITAL**, 55 Hospital Drive, Zip 45701–2302; tel. 740/593–5551 **A**1 9 10 12 13 19 **F**2 9 11 12 23 26 29 32 33 34 35 36 37 44 46 48 50 51 52 55 57 58 59 60 61 62 63 64 65 66 69 70 75 81 82 84 85 87 88 94 96 107 108
Primary Contact: Richard F. Castrop, President
CFO: Ward Howe, CPA, Vice President Finance
CIO: Kristine Furner, Director Management Information Systems
CHR: Sandie Leasure, Senior Vice President Human Resources
Web address: www.obleness.org

23	10	58	2620	28	81269	565	40731	15842	389

BARBERTON—Summit County

✠ △ **BARBERTON CITIZENS HOSPITAL**, 155 Fifth Street N.E., Zip 44203–3398; tel. 330/745–1611, (Total facility includes 50 beds in nursing home–type unit) **A**1 2 3 5 7 9 10 **F**2 3 10 11 12 13 14 15 17 19 21 22 23 26 27 28 29 32 33 37 40 41 44 46 47 48 49 52 53 55 56 57 58 59 60 61 62 63 64 65 66 67 68 69 70 71 75 81 84 86 88 92 93 94 95 96 106 108 109 110 **P**4 **S** Triad Hospitals, Inc., Plano, TX
Primary Contact: Willard P. Roderick, Chief Executive Officer
COO: Thomas DeBord, Chief Operating Officer
CFO: Nathan Van Laningham, Vice President and Chief Financial Officer
CMO: Mark Parker, M.D., Medical Director
CIO: David Lynch, Director Information Systems
Web address: www.barbertonhospital.com

33	10	226	8212	138	313912	715	—	—	1002

✠ **REGENCY HOSPITAL OF AKRON**, 155 Fifth Street N.E., Zip 44203; tel. 330/861–2065, (Nonreporting) **A**1 10 **S** Regency Hospital Company, Alpharetta, GA
Primary Contact: Richard L. Adams, Chief Executive Officer
CFO: Gene Winters, Chief Financial Officer
CMO: Akram Dar, M.D., Medical Director
Web address: www.regencyhospital.com

33	49	36	—	—	—	—	—	—	—

BARNESVILLE—Belmont County

✠ **BARNESVILLE HOSPITAL ASSOCIATION**, 639 West Main Street, Zip 43713–0309, Mailing Address: P.O. Box 309, Zip 43713–0309; tel. 740/425–3941 **A**1 5 9 10 18 **F**2 9 12 14 21 22 23 26 27 28 29 32 33 46 47 48 51 52 54 55 57 58 60 61 62 63 64 65 66 69 81 82 84 85 88 92 94 97 106 108 **P**6
Primary Contact: Richard L. Doan, CHE, Chief Executive Officer
CFO: Willie Cooper–Lohr, Chief Financial Officer
CMO: David J. Hilliard, D.O., Chief of Staff
CIO: Tiffany Gramby, Director Health Information Management and Privacy Officer
CHR: Beth Brill, Director Human Resources
Web address: www.barnesvillehospital.com

23	10	25	1830	19	46723	0	15407	7364	219

BATAVIA—Clermont County

✠ **MERCY HOSPITAL CLERMONT**, 3000 Hospital Drive, Zip 45103–1998; tel. 513/732–8200 **A**1 2 9 10 **F**2 12 21 22 23 26 28 29 33 38 39 45 46 47 48 52 53 55 57 58 61 62 63 65 66 69 70 71 75 79 81 84 88 95 96 108 110 **P**6 **S** Catholic Healthcare Partners, Cincinnati, OH
Primary Contact: Mark D. Shugarman, President and Chief Executive Officer
COO: Brad Bertke, Vice President Support Services
CFO: Edward Roeber, Vice President Finance
CMO: Dogan Temizer, M.D., Chief of Staff
CIO: Ray Pierangeli, Regional Vice President Information Services
CHR: Shirley Walker, Director Human Resources
Web address: www.e–mercy.com

21	10	124	6426	67	58788	0	52313	20198	456

BEDFORD—Cuyahoga County

✠ **UHHS BEDFORD MEDICAL CENTER**, 44 Blaine Avenue, Zip 44146–2799; tel. 440/735–3900 **A**1 2 9 10 **F**2 9 11 12 21 22 26 27 28 29 31 33 35 36 37 39 40 44 46 47 48 52 53 55 57 58 59 60 61 62 63 64 65 66 69 75 81 85 87 88 92 93 94 106 108 109 110 **S** University Hospitals Health System, Cleveland, OH
Primary Contact: Sean McKibben, President
COO: Michelle Giltner, Director Patient Care Services
CFO: Sonia Salvino, Director Finance
CMO: Marwan Hilal, M.D., Chief of Staff
CHR: Donna Kwiecien, Manager Human Resources
Web address: www.uhhsbmc.com

23	10	103	4316	52	160588	426	41423	18414	367

Hospital, Address, Telephone, Approval, Facility, and Physician Codes, Health Care System	Classi-fication Codes		Utilization Data					Expense (thousands) of dollars		
★ American Hospital Association (AHA) membership □ Joint Commission on Accreditation of Healthcare Organizations (JCAHO) accreditation ○ American Osteopathic Association (AOA) accreditation △ Commission on Accreditation of Rehabilitation Facilities (CARF) accreditation	Control	Service	Staffed Beds	Admissions	Census	Outpatient Visits	Births	Total	Payroll	Personnel

BELLAIRE—Belmont County

★ **BELMONT COMMUNITY HOSPITAL**, 4697 Harrison Street, Zip 43906–1338, Mailing Address: P.O. Box 653, Zip 43906–0653; tel. 740/671–1200 **A**1 9 10 **F**9 12 27 29 32 33 42 46 48 52 55 63 68 69 71 75 78 81 84 86 88 94 108 **P**6
Primary Contact: Gary R. Gould, FACHE, Chief Executive Officer
CFO: James Holden, Chief Financial Officer
CMO: C N. Patel, M.D., Chief of Staff
CHR: Donna McGee, Director Human Resources
| | | 23 | 10 | 72 | 2176 | 37 | 44563 | 0 | 19953 | 8884 | 272 |

BELLEFONTAINE—Logan County

★ **MARY RUTAN HOSPITAL**, 205 Palmer Avenue, Zip 43311–2298; tel. 937/592–4015 **A**1 3 5 9 10 **F**2 9 11 12 15 21 22 23 27 28 33 36 37 42 46 48 51 53 55 58 59 60 61 63 64 65 66 69 79 81 82 84 87 88 93 94 96 106 108 109
Primary Contact: Mandy C. Goble, President & Chief Executive Officer
CFO: Ron Carmin, Vice President Fiscal Affairs
CMO: Grant Varian, M.D., Medical Director
CIO: Jerome Hickerson, Director Information Systems
CHR: Tim Froebe, Vice President Human Resources
Web address: www.maryrutan.org
| | | 23 | 10 | 110 | 3420 | 37 | 115769 | 525 | 54848 | 20253 | 530 |

BELLEVUE—Sandusky County

★ **BELLEVUE HOSPITAL**, 1400 West Main Street, Zip 44811, Mailing Address: P.O. Box 8004, Zip 44811–8004; tel. 419/483–4040 **A**1 2 5 9 10 **F**2 9 11 12 23 27 28 29 30 33 37 39 44 45 46 48 50 53 55 57 58 59 60 62 63 69 76 81 82 87 88 93 94 95 96 97 106 108 **P**8
Primary Contact: Michael K. Winthrop, President
CFO: Alan Ganci, Executive Vice President
CMO: Roger Garcia, D.O., Medical Staff President
CIO: Laura Collier, Data Processing Coordinator
CHR: Deborah Ganci, Vice President Human Resources
Web address: www.bellevuehospital.com
| | | 23 | 10 | 48 | 2344 | 24 | 66329 | 322 | 31702 | 12878 | 331 |

BLUFFTON—Allen County

BLANCHARD VALLEY REGIONAL HEALTH CENTER–BLUFFTON CAMPUS See Blanchard Valley Health Association, Findlay

BOARDMAN—Portage County

GREENBRIAR REHABILITATION HOSPITAL, 8064 South Avenue, Suite One, Zip 44512; tel. 330/726–3700, (Nonreporting) **A**10
Primary Contact: Daphne Bonner, Administrator
| | | 33 | 46 | 29 | — | | — | | — | — | — |

BOWLING GREEN—Wood County

★ **WOOD COUNTY HOSPITAL**, 950 West Wooster Street, Zip 43402–2699; tel. 419/354–8900 **A**1 5 9 10 **F**2 9 10 11 12 14 27 33 39 46 48 53 54 55 58 59 60 62 63 64 69 81 84 85 87 88 93 94 95 96 106 108 109 **P**8
Primary Contact: Stanley R. Korducki, President
COO: Daniel A. Colon, Vice President Operations
CFO: Karol Bortel, Vice President Financial Services
CIO: Joanne White, Chief Information Officer
CHR: Frank Day, Vice President Patient Services
Web address: www.wch.net
| | | 23 | 10 | 97 | 3858 | 35 | 121100 | 574 | 44597 | 20012 | 507 |

BRYAN—Williams County

□ **COMMUNITY HOSPITALS AND WELLNESS CENTERS**, (Formerly Community Hospitals of Williams County), 433 West High Street, Zip 43506–1680; tel. 419/636–1131, (Includes ARCHBOLD HOSPITAL, 121 Westfield Drive, Archbold, Zip 43502; tel. 419/445–4415; BRYAN HOSPITAL; MONTPELIER HOSPITAL, 909 East Snyder Avenue, Montpelier, Zip 43543; tel. 419/485–3154), (Nonreporting) **A**1 2 5 9 10 19
Primary Contact: Philip L. Ennen, Vice President and Chief Executive Officer
Web address: www.chwchospital.com
| | | 23 | 10 | 113 | — | | — | | — | — | — |

BUCYRUS—Crawford County

★ **BUCYRUS COMMUNITY HOSPITAL**, 629 North Sandusky Avenue, Zip 44820–0627; tel. 419/562–4677 **A**1 9 10 18 **F**2 9 12 14 21 23 27 28 29 33 34 37 44 46 47 48 58 60 61 62 63 64 65 69 81 82 85 88 95 96 97 106 108 **P**6
Primary Contact: Gerard D. Klein, President and Chief Executive Officer
CFO: Gerald H. Klein, Vice President Finance
CMO: Michael A. Johnson, M.D., Chief of Staff
CIO: Cathy Brown, Information Systems Manager
CHR: Marsha Gathright, Human Resources Manager
Web address: www.bchonline.org
| | | 23 | 10 | 25 | 965 | 10 | 46427 | — | 20509 | 8093 | 236 |

CADIZ—Harrison County

★ **HARRISON COMMUNITY HOSPITAL**, 951 East Market Street, Zip 43907–9749; tel. 740/942–4631 **A**1 9 10 18 **F**6 8 9 12 14 21 22 24 25 27 28 29 32 33 37 41 44 45 46 48 51 52 53 55 57 58 60 63 65 66 68 69 70 81 82 85 88 92 93 94 95 96 97 98 106 108 109
Primary Contact: Terry M. Carson, Chief Executive Officer
CFO: Sally Huff, Controller
CMO: Isam Tabbah, M.D., Chief of Staff
CHR: Marcella Evans, Director Human Resources
Web address: www.harrisoncommunity.com
| | | 23 | 10 | 25 | 637 | 15 | 13348 | 0 | 10546 | 4815 | 166 |

Many Facility Codes have changed. Please refer to the AHA Guide Code Chart.

Hospital, Address, Telephone, Approval, Facility, and Physician Codes, Health Care System	Classification Codes		Utilization Data					Expense (thousands) of dollars		
★ American Hospital Association (AHA) membership □ Joint Commission on Accreditation of Healthcare Organizations (JCAHO) accreditation ○ American Osteopathic Association (AOA) accreditation △ Commission on Accreditation of Rehabilitation Facilities (CARF) accreditation	Control	Service	Staffed Beds	Admissions	Census	Outpatient Visits	Births	Total	Payroll	Personnel

CAMBRIDGE—Guernsey County

□ **APPALACHIAN BEHAVIORAL HEALTHCARE**, 66737 Old 21 Road North, Zip 43725–9298; tel. 740/439–1371, (Nonreporting) **A**1 10
Primary Contact: Jane E. Krason, R.N., Chief Executive Officer
Web address: www.mh.state.oh.us

| | 12 | 22 | 224 | — | — | — | — | — | — | — |

▣ **SOUTHEASTERN OHIO REGIONAL MEDICAL CENTER**, 1341 North Clark Street, Zip 43725–0610, Mailing Address: P.O. Box 610, Zip 43725–0610; tel. 740/439–3561, (Total facility includes 20 beds in nursing home–type unit) **A**1 2 5 9 10 **F**2 6 9 11 12 15 21 22 23 26 27 28 29 33 34 46 47 48 49 51 52 55 58 59 60 62 63 64 65 66 69 81 84 87 88 92 93 94 95 96 106 108 109 110 **P**6 8
Primary Contact: James W. Keller, M.D., President, Chief Executive Officer and Chief Medical Officer
COO: Raymond Chorey, Chief Operating Officer
CFO: Donald P. Huelskamp, Vice President Finance and Chief Financial Officer
CMO: James W. Keller, M.D., President, Chief Executive Officer and Chief Medical Officer
CHR: Patricia Grubbs, Human Resources Director
Web address: www.seormc.org

| | 23 | 10 | 140 | 5862 | 51 | 84972 | 447 | 59068 | 24467 | 693 |

CANTON—Stark County

ACUTE CARE SPECIALTY HOSPITAL OF AULTMAN, 2600 Sixth Street, S.W., Zip 44710; tel. 330/363–4000, (Nonreporting) **A**10
Primary Contact: Jackie Toth, Administrator

| | 33 | 80 | 30 | — | — | — | — | — | — | — |

▣ △ **AULTMAN HOSPITAL**, 2600 Sixth Street S.W., Zip 44710–1799; tel. 330/452–9911, (Total facility includes 60 beds in nursing home–type unit) **A**1 2 3 5 6 7 8 9 10 **F**2 6 9 10 11 12 14 15 17 19 21 22 23 26 27 28 29 32 33 34 35 36 37 38 39 40 41 42 44 45 46 47 48 49 50 51 52 53 55 56 57 58 59 60 61 62 63 64 65 66 68 69 70 71 75 76 78 80 81 82 83 84 85 87 88 90 92 93 94 95 96 97 98 106 107 108 109 110 **P**3 7
Primary Contact: Edward J. Roth, III, President
CFO: Mark J. Wright, Vice President and Chief Financial Officer
CIO: Tim Oberschlake, Associate Vice President Information Systems
CHR: Vi Leggett, Vice President
Web address: www.aultman.com

| | 23 | 10 | 581 | 29802 | 445 | 446247 | 2667 | — | — | 4001 |

▣ △ **MERCY MEDICAL CENTER**, 1320 Mercy Drive N.W., Zip 44708–2641; tel. 330/489–1000 **A**1 2 3 5 7 9 10 **F**2 4 9 11 12 14 15 17 19 21 22 23 26 27 28 29 34 35 36 37 40 41 42 44 46 47 48 49 51 52 53 55 58 59 60 61 62 63 64 65 66 68 69 70 71 72 73 74 75 76 77 80 81 82 84 85 86 87 88 93 94 95 96 106 107 108 109 110 **P**6 7 **S** Sisters of Charity of St. Augustine Health System, Cleveland, OH
Primary Contact: Thomas E. Cecconi, President and Chief Executive
COO: Jeffrey Smith, Senior Vice President and Chief Operating Officer
CMO: David Gormsen, D.O., Chief Medical Officer
CIO: James H. Carroll, Manager Information Systems
CHR: Sandi Arnold, Director Human Resources
Web address: www.thequalityhospital.com

| | 23 | 10 | 352 | 17170 | 230 | 526195 | 1683 | 205037 | 87424 | 1958 |

CHAGRIN FALLS—Cuyahoga County

□ **WINDSOR HOSPITAL**, 115 East Summit Street, Zip 44022–2750; tel. 440/247–5300, (Nonreporting) **A**1 9 10 **S** Psychiatric Solutions, Franklin, TN
Primary Contact: Richard Warden, Chief Executive Officer
Web address: www.bhcwindsor.com

| | 33 | 22 | 47 | — | — | — | — | — | — | — |

CHARDON—Geauga County

□ **HEATHER HILL HOSPITAL AND HEALTH PARTNERSHIP**, (Formerly Heather Hill Hospital, Health and Care Center), 12340 Bass Lake Road, Zip 44024–8327; tel. 440/285–4040, (Total facility includes 264 beds in nursing home–type unit) **A**1 9 10 **F**1 5 8 21 22 26 27 28 32 36 38 41 44 45 46 48 49 52 60 69 88 92 94 108 110 **S** University Hospitals Health System, Cleveland, OH
Primary Contact: Richard J. Frenchie, President and Chief Executive Officer
Web address: www.healtherhill.org

| | 23 | 80 | 320 | 1253 | 256 | 8096 | 0 | 32036 | 13611 | 401 |

▣ **UHHS GEAUGA REGIONAL HOSPITAL**, 13207 Ravenna Road, Zip 44024–9012; tel. 440/269–6000, (Total facility includes 21 beds in nursing home–type unit) **A**1 2 9 10 **F**2 9 11 12 14 15 21 22 23 26 27 28 29 32 33 35 37 39 44 45 46 48 52 55 57 58 59 60 61 62 63 64 65 66 69 71 73 74 75 76 81 82 84 87 88 92 94 95 96 108 109 **S** University Hospitals Health System, Cleveland, OH
Primary Contact: Richard J. Frenchie, President and Chief Executive Officer
COO: Sally J. Klock, Chief Operating Officer
CFO: Sharon McGowan, Director Finance
CMO: Martin Macklin, M.D., Ph.D., Vice President Medical Affairs
CIO: Lou Ciraldo, Community Hospitals Representative Information Services
Web address: www.uhhsgrh.com

| | 23 | 10 | 125 | 6568 | 79 | 75477 | 1070 | 58049 | 23139 | 453 |

Hospital, Address, Telephone, Approval, Facility, and Physician Codes, Health Care System	Classi-fication Codes		Utilization Data					Expense (thousands) of dollars		
	Control	Service	Staffed Beds	Admissions	Census	Outpatient Visits	Births	Total	Payroll	Personnel

★ American Hospital Association (AHA) membership
□ Joint Commission on Accreditation of Healthcare Organizations (JCAHO) accreditation
○ American Osteopathic Association (AOA) accreditation
△ Commission on Accreditation of Rehabilitation Facilities (CARF) accreditation

CHILLICOTHE—Ross County

⊠ **ADENA HEALTH SYSTEM**, 272 Hospital Road, Zip 45601–9031; tel. 740/779–7500 **A**1 2 9 10 19 **F**2 4 11 12 15 17 21 22 23 24 26 27 28 29 30 33 36 37 39 40 42 44 46 47 48 50 51 52 53 55 57 58 59 60 61 62 63 64 65 66 68 69 70 71 72 73 74 75 76 77 81 82 84 85 87 88 89 93 94 95 96 97 98 106 107 108 109 110 **P**6 Primary Contact: Mark H. Shuter, President and Chief Executive Officer COO: Kenneth E. Bryan, Chief Operating Officer CFO: Ralph W. Sorrell, Sr, Chief Financial Officer CMO: John Gabis, M.D., Medical Director CIO: Dennis Vogt, Director Information Services CHR: Brandt Lippert, Vice President Human Resources Web address: www.adena.org	23	10	190	10387	103	356746	1067	169414	73313	1534
⊠ **VETERANS AFFAIRS MEDICAL CENTER**, 17273 State Route 104, Zip 45601–0999; tel. 740/773–1141, (Total facility includes 162 beds in nursing home–type unit) **A**1 5 **F**2 4 9 21 22 28 29 31 32 35 36 37 38 39 42 44 45 46 47 48 50 51 52 57 58 60 62 63 65 66 69 70 71 73 75 76 77 78 81 88 92 93 94 96 106 108 109 **P**6 **S** Department of Veterans Affairs, Washington, DC Primary Contact: Douglas A. Moorman, Medical Center Director COO: Keith Sullivan, Acting Associate Director CFO: Rick Deckard, Chief, Fiscal Service CMO: Murali K. Chitluri, M.D., Chief of Staff CIO: Joseph Enderle, Chief Information Officer CHR: Angela Young, Human Resources Officer Web address: www.va.gov/sta/guide/home.asp	45	22	297	4318	229	204964	0	107320	72241	1100

CINCINNATI—Hamilton County

□ **BETHESDA NORTH HOSPITAL**, 10500 Montgomery Road, Zip 45242–4415; tel. 513/745–1111 **A**1 2 3 5 9 10 **F**2 9 10 11 12 14 15 17 19 21 22 23 26 27 28 29 30 32 33 34 35 37 38 39 41 42 44 45 46 47 48 50 52 53 55 57 58 59 61 62 63 64 65 66 68 69 70 73 75 81 82 84 85 87 88 90 92 93 94 95 96 108 109 110 **P**6 Primary Contact: John S. Prout, President and Chief Executive Officer Web address: www.trihealth.com	23	10	290	22891	236	233135	4375	257960	117392	1556
⊠ △ **CHILDREN'S HOSPITAL MEDICAL CENTER**, 3333 Burnet Avenue, Zip 45229–3039; tel. 513/636–4200, (Includes DIVISION OF ADOLESCENT MEDICINE, CINCINNATI CENTER FOR DEVELOPMENTAL DISORDERS, AND CONVALESCENT HOSPITAL FOR CHILDREN ; CHILDREN'S HOSPITAL) **A**1 2 3 5 7 8 9 10 **F**2 4 6 7 9 10 14 16 18 20 21 22 23 24 26 27 28 29 30 31 32 33 34 35 36 37 38 39 40 42 46 47 48 49 50 51 52 53 56 57 58 60 61 62 63 64 65 66 67 68 69 70 71 72 73 74 75 77 78 81 82 84 85 86 87 88 93 94 95 96 98 99 100 101 102 104 105 106 107 108 110 **P**1 Primary Contact: James M. Anderson, President and Chief Executive Officer CFO: Scott J. Hamlin, Chief Financial Officer CIO: Marianne Speight, Vice President Information System and Chief Information Officer CHR: Ronald McKinley, Ph.D., Vice President Human Resources Web address: www.chmcc.org	23	50	413	15692	248	745790	0	546841	191822	7782
⊠ △ **CHRIST HOSPITAL**, 2139 Auburn Avenue, Zip 45219–2989; tel. 513/585–2000 **A**1 2 3 5 6 7 9 10 **F**2 4 6 9 10 11 12 14 15 17 19 21 22 23 26 27 28 29 30 33 35 37 38 39 44 45 46 47 48 49 50 52 53 55 57 58 59 60 61 62 63 64 65 66 68 69 70 71 72 73 76 77 78 79 80 81 82 84 85 86 87 88 89 92 94 95 96 101 106 108 109 110 **S** Health Alliance of Greater Cincinnati, Cincinnati, OH Primary Contact: Susan Croushore, Executive Director and Senior Vice President COO: Victor DiPilla, Vice President CFO: John K. Renner, Finance Director CMO: William Dirkes, M.D., President, Medical Staff CIO: Debbie Hayes, Vice President CHR: Alan Jones, Director Web address: www.health–alliance.com/hospitals/christ_control.html	23	10	440	25667	302	201226	3336	338615	118667	2331
□ △ **DEACONESS HOSPITAL**, 311 Straight Street, Zip 45219–1099; tel. 513/559–2100 **A**1 7 9 10 **F**2 7 9 10 12 14 15 17 19 21 22 23 26 27 28 29 33 36 37 41 44 45 46 47 48 49 52 53 55 57 58 60 61 62 63 64 65 66 68 69 70 71 73 74 75 76 77 81 82 84 88 92 94 95 96 108 110 Primary Contact: Richard Gandersman, Chief Executive Officer Web address: www.Deaconess–healthcare.com	23	10	177	5408	85	41859	0	60222	24474	654
□ △ **DRAKE CENTER**, 151 West Galbraith Road, Zip 45216–1096; tel. 513/948–2500, (Total facility includes 204 beds in nursing home–type unit) (Nonreporting) **A**1 5 7 9 10 Primary Contact: Roberta J. Bradford, President and Chief Executive Officer Web address: www.drakecenter.com	23	10	288	—	—	—	—	—	—	—
□ **DRAKE PAVILION**, 2139 Auburn Avenue, Zip 45219; tel. 513/585–0300, (Nonreporting) **A**1 10 Primary Contact: Doreen Jackson, Chief Executive Officer	33	49	30	—	—	—	—	—	—	—

Many Facility Codes have changed. Please refer to the AHA Guide Code Chart. © 2005 AHA Guide

Hospital, Address, Telephone, Approval, Facility, and Physician Codes, Health Care System	Classi-fication Codes		Utilization Data					Expense (thousands) of dollars		
★ American Hospital Association (AHA) membership □ Joint Commission on Accreditation of Healthcare Organizations (JCAHO) accreditation ○ American Osteopathic Association (AOA) accreditation △ Commission on Accreditation of Rehabilitation Facilities (CARF) accreditation	Control	Service	Staffed Beds	Admissions	Census	Outpatient Visits	Births	Total	Payroll	Personnel

⊠ △ GOOD SAMARITAN HOSPITAL, 375 Dixmyth Avenue, Zip 45220–2489; tel. 513/872–1400, (Total facility includes 11 beds in nursing home–type unit) **A**1 3 5 6 7 8 9 10 **F**2 4 9 10 11 12 14 15 17 19 21 22 23 26 27 28 29 30 32 33 35 37 38 39 41 42 44 45 46 47 48 49 50 52 53 55 56 57 58 59 61 62 63 64 65 66 68 69 70 71 72 73 75 76 77 78 79 80 81 82 84 85 87 88 90 92 93 94 95 96 104 108 109 110 **P**6 **S** Catholic Health Initiatives, Denver, CO
Primary Contact: John S. Prout, President and Chief Executive Officer
COO: Claus von Zychlin, Executive Vice President and Chief Operating Officer
CFO: Robert Halonen, Ph.D., Senior Vice President and Chief Financial Officer
CMO: Kathleen Forbes, M.D., Senior Vice President Medical Affairs, Chief Quality Officer
CIO: Rick Moore, Vice President and Chief Information Officer
CHR: Walter McLarty, Vice President Human Resources
Web address: www.trihealth.com
`21  10  468  25706  338  170813  6273  280789  120321  2276`

⊠ JEWISH HOSPITAL, 4777 East Galbraith Road, Zip 45236–2725; tel. 513/686–3000 **A**1 2 3 5 9 10 **F**2 9 10 12 14 15 17 19 21 22 23 25 26 27 28 29 30 32 33 35 37 39 42 44 46 47 48 49 52 53 55 57 58 61 62 63 64 65 66 69 70 79 80 81 82 84 85 87 88 92 94 95 96 99 108 110 **S** Health Alliance of Greater Cincinnati, Cincinnati, OH
Primary Contact: M. Aurora Lambert, Senior Vice President
CFO: Ronald Long, Chief Financial Officer
Web address: www.health–alliance.com/jewish.html
`23  10  200  13450  161  150011  0  156649  59069  1284`

⊠ MERCY FRANCISCAN HOSPITAL MOUNT AIRY, 2446 Kipling Avenue, Zip 45239–6650; tel. 513/853–5000, (Total facility includes 20 beds in nursing home–type unit) (Nonreporting) **A**1 2 9 10 **S** Catholic Healthcare Partners, Cincinnati, OH
Primary Contact: James Gravell, President and Chief Executive Officer
COO: James Gravell, Executive Vice President
CFO: Edward Roeber, Senior Vice President Finance and Chief Financial Officer
CMO: Leonard M. Randolph, Jr, M.D., Chief Medical Officer
CIO: Ray Pierangeli, Regional Vice President Information Services
CHR: Chris Browning, Regional Vice President Human Resources
Web address: www.mercy.health–partners.org
`21  10  246  —  —  —  —  —  —  —`

⊠ MERCY FRANCISCAN HOSPITAL–WESTERN HILLS, 3131 Queen City Avenue, Zip 45238–2396; tel. 513/389–5000, (Total facility includes 20 beds in nursing home–type unit) (Nonreporting) **A**1 2 9 10 **S** Catholic Healthcare Partners, Cincinnati, OH
Primary Contact: James Chadwick Patrick, President and Chief Executive Officer
COO: Patrick Kowalski, Chief Financial Officer
Web address: www.mercy.health–partners.org
`21  10  163  —  —  —  —  —  —  —`

⊠ MERCY HOSPITAL ANDERSON, 7500 State Road, Zip 45255–2492; tel. 513/624–4500, (Nonreporting) **A**1 2 9 10 **S** Catholic Healthcare Partners, Cincinnati, OH
Primary Contact: Patricia A. Schroer, President and Chief Executive Officer
COO: Adam Dittman, Vice President Professional and Support Services
CFO: Edward Roeber, Vice President Finance
CIO: Ray Pierangeli, Vice President and Chief Information Officer
CHR: Sandie Ferrigno, Human Resoures Director
Web address: www.mercy.health–partners.org
`21  10  160  —  —  —  —  —  —  —`

□ SELECT SPECIALTY HOSPITAL, 322 Dixmyth Avenue, Zip 45220; tel. 513/487–4105, (Nonreporting) **A**1 9 10
Primary Contact: John Baird, Administrtor and Chief Executive Officer
Web address: www.selectmedicalcorp.com
`33  80  36  —  —  —  —  —  —  —`

□ SHRINERS HOSPITALS FOR CHILDREN, SHRINERS BURNS HOSPITAL, CINCINNATI, (Pediatric Burn Injuries), 3229 Burnet Avenue, Zip 45229–3095; tel. 513/872–6000 **A**1 **F**13 21 41 45 46 52 53 58 60 63 69 94 96 108 **S** Shriners Hospitals for Children, Tampa, FL
Primary Contact: Ronald R. Hitzler, Administrator
Web address: www.shrinershq.org
`23  59  30  1017  14  3936  0  —  —  312`

□ SUMMIT BEHAVIORAL HEALTHCARE, 1101 Summit Road, Zip 45237–2652; tel. 513/948–3600 **A**1 9 10 **F**4 21 22 26 27 29 31 32 42 45 58 60 65 66 71 72 73 74 76 77 94 96 106 108 **P**6
Primary Contact: Elizabeth Banks, Chief Executive Officer
Web address: www.prime/prime.htm
`12  22  274  461  231  0  0  33934  19421  388`

⊠ UNIVERSITY HOSPITAL, 234 Goodman Street, Zip 45219–2316; tel. 513/584–1000 **A**1 2 3 5 8 9 10 **F**2 6 7 9 10 11 12 13 14 15 17 19 21 22 23 26 27 28 29 30 31 32 33 34 35 37 38 39 41 43 44 45 46 47 48 49 50 52 53 55 57 58 59 61 62 63 64 65 66 69 70 71 73 74 75 76 77 79 80 81 82 84 85 86 87 88 90 92 94 95 96 98 100 101 102 103 104 105 107 108 109 110 **S** Health Alliance of Greater Cincinnati, Cincinnati, OH
Primary Contact: James A. Kingsbury, Executive Director and Senior Vice President
CFO: Sean Gallagher, Vice President Finance
CMO: Michael Nussbaum, M.D., Chief of Staff
CIO: Alex Rodriguez, Senior Vice President and Chief Information Officer
CHR: Jonathan Small, Vice President Human Resources
Web address: www.health–alliance.com/Univ_control.html
`23  10  448  26308  354  405100  2092  430558  156400  3111`

Hospital, Address, Telephone, Approval, Facility, and Physician Codes, Health Care System	Classi-fication Codes		Utilization Data					Expense (thousands) of dollars		
★ American Hospital Association (AHA) membership □ Joint Commission on Accreditation of Healthcare Organizations (JCAHO) accreditation ○ American Osteopathic Association (AOA) accreditation △ Commission on Accreditation of Rehabilitation Facilities (CARF) accreditation	Control	Service	Staffed Beds	Admissions	Census	Outpatient Visits	Births	Total	Payroll	Personnel
☒ **VETERANS AFFAIRS MEDICAL CENTER**, 3200 Vine Street, Zip 45220–2288; tel. 513/861–3100, (Total facility includes 64 beds in nursing home–type unit) **A**1 3 5 8 **F**2 3 4 14 15 17 21 22 23 26 27 28 29 30 31 32 33 35 37 39 41 42 44 46 47 48 49 50 51 52 53 55 57 58 60 61 62 63 64 65 66 69 70 71 73 74 75 76 77 78 81 82 85 88 92 93 94 95 96 106 107 108 109 110 **S** Department of Veterans Affairs, Washington, DC Primary Contact: Carlos B. Lott, Jr, Director COO: Thomas P. Pishioneri, Associate Director CFO: Richard Benjamin, Chief Fiscal Services CMO: Creighton Wright, M.D., Chief of Staff CIO: Debra Luttjohann, Chief Information Officer Web address: www.va.gov/sta/guide/home.asp	45	10	113	5448	108	318855	0	124934	102746	1441
CIRCLEVILLE—Pickaway County										
☒ △ **BERGER HEALTH SYSTEM**, 600 North Pickaway Street, Zip 43113–1499; tel. 740/474–2126 **A**1 7 9 10 **F**2 9 11 12 17 21 22 23 26 27 28 29 30 33 36 37 39 42 44 45 46 47 48 49 51 52 53 55 57 58 59 60 61 62 63 65 66 68 69 81 82 84 86 88 93 94 95 96 97 106 108 109 110 Primary Contact: Larry Thornhill, President and Chief Executive Officer COO: Sandra Rudawsky, Corporate Senior Vice President and Chief Operating Officer CFO: Tim Colburn, Corporate Vice President Finance CMO: James Sardo, Chief of Staff CIO: Andy Chileski, Corporate Vice President Management Information Systems CHR: Suzanne Welker, Corporate Vice President Human Resources Web address: www.bergerhealth.com	15	10	85	3290	38	89640	403	52699	18815	476
CLEVELAND—Cuyahoga County										
CLEVELAND CAMPUS See Northcoast Behavioral Healthcare System, Northfield										
□ △ **CLEVELAND CLINIC CHILDREN'S HOSPITAL FOR REHABILITATION**, Mailing Address: 2801 Martin Luther King Jr. Drive, Zip 44104–3865; tel. 216/721–5400 **A**1 7 9 10 **F**21 24 26 27 28 29 45 58 65 66 68 69 72 92 94 96 108 **S** Cleveland Clinic Health System, Cleveland, OH Primary Contact: David Kenogy, M.D., Medical Director Web address: www.clevelandclinic.org/childrensrehab	23	56	47	225	18	27236	0	18857	11524	230
☒ △ **CLEVELAND CLINIC FOUNDATION**, 9500 Euclid Avenue, Zip 44195–5108; tel. 216/444–2200 **A**1 2 3 5 7 8 9 10 13 **F**2 3 4 5 6 7 9 10 11 12 14 15 16 17 18 19 20 21 22 23 24 26 27 28 29 30 31 32 33 35 37 38 39 40 41 42 43 44 45 46 47 48 49 50 52 53 55 56 57 58 59 60 61 62 63 64 65 66 67 69 70 71 72 73 74 75 76 77 78 79 80 81 82 84 85 86 87 88 89 90 92 93 94 95 96 98 99 100 101 102 103 104 105 106 107 108 109 110 **P**1 3 **S** Cleveland Clinic Health System, Cleveland, OH Primary Contact: Delos Cosgrove, M.D., President and Chief Executive Officer COO: Michael P. O'Boyle, Chief Operating Officer CFO: Steven Glass, Interim Chief Financial Officer CMO: Robert Kay, M.D., Chief of Staff CIO: C Martin Harris, M.D., Chief Information Officer CHR: Roberto Llamas, Chief Human Resources Officer Web address: www.clevelandclinic.org	23	10	1032	55406	911	2875388	2016	2105458	997191	16410
□ **FAIRVIEW HOSPITAL**, 18101 Lorain Avenue, Zip 44111–5656; tel. 216/476–7000 **A**1 2 3 5 9 10 **F**1 11 12 14 15 17 19 21 22 23 24 26 27 28 29 33 34 36 37 41 44 46 47 48 49 52 54 55 56 57 58 59 60 61 62 63 65 66 68 69 70 73 75 79 80 81 82 84 87 88 92 94 96 107 108 109 **S** Cleveland Clinic Health System, Cleveland, OH Primary Contact: Fred M. DeGrandis, Chief Executive Officer Web address: www.fairviewhospital.org	23	10	414	17739	245	273805	3183	229137	107441	1199
☒ **GRACE HOSPITAL**, 2307 West 14th Street, Zip 44113–3698; tel. 216/687–1500 **A**1 10 **F**26 27 28 44 58 64 65 66 94 110 **P**8 Primary Contact: Rajive Khanna, Chief Executive Officer COO: Rajive Khanna, Chief Operating Officer CMO: John Nickels, M.D., President Medical Staff CIO: Mary Zimpfer, Vice President Quality Management Web address: www.gracehospital.org	23	80	104	815	63	0	0	26235	11652	267
HANNA HOUSE SKILLED NURSING FACILITY See University Hospitals of Cleveland										
□ **HILLCREST HOSPITAL**, 6780 Mayfield Road, Zip 44124–2202; tel. 440/449–4500 **A**1 2 9 10 **F**9 11 12 14 15 16 17 18 19 20 21 23 26 27 28 29 31 33 34 37 38 39 45 46 47 48 49 52 54 55 56 58 59 60 61 63 65 66 69 70 73 81 82 84 86 87 88 89 90 92 93 94 95 96 98 106 107 108 109 **S** Cleveland Clinic Health System, Cleveland, OH Primary Contact: Glenn Levy, Chief Administrative Officer Web address: www.meridia.com	23	10	431	17500	225	293346	2818	232137	102354	2051
□ **HURON HOSPITAL**, 13951 Terrace Road, Zip 44112–4399; tel. 216/761–3300 **A**1 2 6 9 10 **F**3 4 9 11 12 15 16 17 18 19 20 21 24 26 27 28 29 33 34 37 38 39 44 45 46 48 49 50 52 55 56 58 59 60 61 62 63 66 69 70 71 77 78 81 84 88 89 92 94 95 96 98 108 109 110 **S** Cleveland Clinic Health System, Cleveland, OH Primary Contact: A. Gus Kious, M.D., Chief Administrative Officer Web address: www.meridia.org	23	10	183	9423	131	75327	874	93210	52573	1029

Many Facility Codes have changed. Please refer to the AHA Guide Code Chart.

© 2005 AHA Guide

Hospital, Address, Telephone, Approval, Facility, and Physician Codes, Health Care System	Classification Codes		Utilization Data					Expense (thousands) of dollars		
★ American Hospital Association (AHA) membership □ Joint Commission on Accreditation of Healthcare Organizations (JCAHO) accreditation ○ American Osteopathic Association (AOA) accreditation △ Commission on Accreditation of Rehabilitation Facilities (CARF) accreditation	Control	Service	Staffed Beds	Admissions	Census	Outpatient Visits	Births	Total	Payroll	Personnel

□ **KINDRED HOSPITAL–CLEVELAND**, 2351 East 22nd Street, 7th Floor, Zip 44115; tel. 216/363–2671, (Nonreporting) **A**1 5
Primary Contact: Rick Pletz, Chief Executive Officer

| | 33 | 10 | 75 | — | — | — | — | — | — | — |

□ **LUTHERAN HOSPITAL**, 1730 West 25th Street, Zip 44113–3170; tel. 216/696–4300 **A**1 9 10 **F**7 21 23 25 26 27 28 29 33 37 44 45 46 47 48 49 52 55 58 60 62 63 65 66 68 69 70 71 73 74 76 77 81 82 84 88 92 94 95 96 106 108 **S** Cleveland Clinic Health System, Cleveland, OH
Primary Contact: Steve Ruwoldt, Chief Administrative Officer
Web address: www.lutheranhospital.org

| | 23 | 10 | 185 | 6594 | 111 | 83104 | 0 | 68516 | 33726 | 529 |

▣ △ **METROHEALTH MEDICAL CENTER**, 2500 MetroHealth Drive, Zip 44109–1998; tel. 216/778–7800, (Total facility includes 441 beds in nursing home–type unit) **A**1 2 3 5 7 8 9 10 13 **F**1 2 4 5 6 7 9 10 11 12 13 14 15 17 19 21 22 23 24 27 28 29 30 31 32 33 34 35 36 37 38 39 41 42 44 45 46 47 48 49 50 52 53 55 56 57 58 59 60 61 62 63 64 65 66 67 68 69 70 71 72 73 74 75 76 77 78 79 80 81 82 84 85 86 87 88 89 90 92 93 94 95 96 98 106 107 108 109 110 **P**6
Primary Contact: John Sideras, President
CFO: Nancy Fisher Crum, Chief Financial Officer
CMO: Ben H. Brouhard, M.D., Executive Vice President and Chief of Staff
CHR: Paul Monahan, General Manager, Labor Relations and Employment
Web address: www.metrohealth.org
RAINBOW BABIES AND CHILDREN'S HOSPITAL See University Hospitals of Cleveland
SAINT LUKE'S MEDICAL CENTER See St. Vincent Charity Hospital

| | 13 | 10 | 1001 | 24549 | 749 | 765769 | 3339 | 544287 | 304150 | 5292 |

▣ ○ **ST. JOHN WEST SHORE HOSPITAL**, 29000 Center Ridge Road, Zip 44145–5219; tel. 440/835–8000, (Nonreporting) **A**1 2 9 10 11 12 13 **S** Sisters of Charity of St. Augustine Health System, Cleveland, OH
Primary Contact: Keith R. Poisson, President
COO: Rick Cicero, Vice President Business Development
CFO: David K. Stewart, Vice President Finance
CMO: Robert B. Daroff, M.D., Chief of Staff and Senior Vice President Academic Affairs
CHR: Gary Lazroff, Vice President Human Resources
Web address: www.sjws.net

| | 23 | 10 | 160 | — | — | — | — | — | — | — |

▣ **ST. VINCENT CHARITY HOSPITAL**, 2351 East 22nd Street, Zip 44115–3111; tel. 216/861–6200, (Includes SAINT LUKE'S MEDICAL CENTER, 11311 Shaker Boulevard, Zip 44104–3805; tel. 216/368–7000), (Total facility includes 22 beds in nursing home–type unit) **A**1 2 3 5 9 10 **F**2 4 5 7 9 10 12 14 15 17 19 21 22 23 25 26 27 28 29 30 31 32 33 35 36 37 38 39 42 43 44 45 46 47 48 49 50 52 53 55 57 58 60 61 62 63 65 66 69 70 71 72 73 74 75 76 77 78 81 82 84 85 87 88 92 93 94 95 96 98 106 107 108 109 110 **P**7 **S** Sisters of Charity of St. Augustine Health System, Cleveland, OH
Primary Contact: Jeffrey S. Jeney, President and Chief Executive Officer
CFO: David K. Stewart, Vice President Financial Operations
CMO: John B. Marshall, M.D., Vice President Clinical Integration
CIO: James H. Carroll, Manager Information Systems
CHR: Gary Lazroff, Vice President Human Resources
Web address: www.svch.net

| | 23 | 10 | 222 | 10073 | 138 | 183557 | 0 | 125895 | 53033 | 1041 |

▣ △ **UNIVERSITY HOSPITALS OF CLEVELAND**, 11100 Euclid Avenue, Zip 44106–2602; tel. 216/844–1000, (Includes ALFRED AND NORMA LERNER TOWER, BOLWELL HEALTH CENTER, HANNA PAVILION, LAKESIDE HOSPITAL, SAMUEL MATHER PAVILION ; HANNA HOUSE SKILLED NURSING FACILITY; RAINBOW BABIES AND CHILDREN'S HOSPITAL; UNIVERSITY MACDONALD WOMEN'S HOSPITAL), (Total facility includes 60 beds in nursing home–type unit) **A**1 2 3 5 7 8 9 10 **F**2 4 5 6 7 9 10 11 12 14 15 16 17 18 19 20 21 22 23 24 26 27 28 29 30 31 32 33 34 35 36 37 38 39 40 41 42 43 44 45 46 47 48 49 50 51 52 53 54 55 56 57 58 59 60 61 62 63 64 65 66 67 68 69 70 71 72 73 74 75 76 77 78 79 80 81 82 83 84 85 86 87 88 89 90 92 93 94 95 96 98 99 100 101 102 103 104 105 106 107 108 109 110 **S** University Hospitals Health System, Cleveland, OH
Primary Contact: Fred C. Rothstein, M.D., President and Chief Executive Officer
CFO: Michael Szubski, Senior Vice President and Chief Financial Officer
CMO: Nathan Levitan, M.D., Chief Medical Officer and Senior Vice President Academic Affairs
CIO: Edward Marx, Vice President and Chief Information Officer
CHR: Dave Pasco, Vice President Human Resources
Web address: www.uhhs.com

| | 23 | 10 | 580 | 36204 | 550 | 987781 | 4133 | 713118 | 257854 | 5790 |

▣ △ **VETERANS AFFAIRS MEDICAL CENTER**, 10701 East Boulevard, Zip 44106–1702; tel. 216/791–3800, (Total facility includes 190 beds in nursing home–type unit) (Nonreporting) **A**1 3 5 7 8 **S** Department of Veterans Affairs, Washington, DC
Primary Contact: William D. Montague, Director
CFO: Gene DeAngelis, Chief Fiscal Service
CIO: Michael Hickman, Chief Information Resource Management
Web address: www.va.gov/sta/guide/home.asp

| | 45 | 10 | 459 | — | — | — | — | — | — | — |

OH

Hospital, Address, Telephone, Approval, Facility, and Physician Codes, Health Care System	Classi-fication Codes		Utilization Data					Expense (thousands) of dollars		
★ American Hospital Association (AHA) membership □ Joint Commission on Accreditation of Healthcare Organizations (JCAHO) accreditation ○ American Osteopathic Association (AOA) accreditation △ Commission on Accreditation of Rehabilitation Facilities (CARF) accreditation	Control	Service	Staffed Beds	Admissions	Census	Outpatient Visits	Births	Total	Payroll	Personnel

COLDWATER—Mercer County

✠ **MERCER COUNTY JOINT TOWNSHIP COMMUNITY HOSPITAL**, 800 West Main Street, Zip 45828–1698; tel. 419/678–2341 **A**1 5 9 10 **F**6 9 11 12 21 22 23 27 28 29 30 33 37 46 48 51 55 58 59 60 61 62 63 64 66 69 81 82 84 85 88 93 94 95 96 97 106 107 108 110 **P**3
Primary Contact: Terrance J. Padden, Chief Executive Officer
CFO: James A. Wermert, Chief Financial Officer
CMO: James Schwieterman, Chief of Staff
CIO: Rich Branch, Director Information Systems
CHR: George Braid, Director of Human Resources
Web address: www.mercerhospital.com
| 16 | 10 | 60 | 1976 | 18 | 57750 | 354 | 29674 | 11797 | 325 |

COLUMBUS—Franklin County

✠ △ **CHILDREN'S HOSPITAL**, 700 Children's Drive, Zip 43205–2696; tel. 614/722–2000 **A**1 2 3 5 7 9 10 **F**2 6 10 13 14 15 16 17 18 19 20 21 22 23 24 27 29 32 33 34 35 36 37 39 41 42 45 46 47 48 49 50 51 52 53 56 57 58 60 61 62 63 64 65 66 67 68 69 70 72 73 74 75 76 77 81 82 84 85 87 88 90 93 94 95 96 97 98 99 101 107 108 110 **P**6 8
Primary Contact: Thomas N. Hansen, M.D., Chief Executive Officer
COO: Keith D. Goodwin, Chief Operating Officer
CFO: Tim Robinson, Chief Financial Officer and Treasurer
CMO: David J. Fisher, M.D., Medical Director
CIO: Rick Miller, Corporate Director Human Resources and Information Services
CHR: Rick Miller, Corporate Director Human Resources and Information Services
Web address: www.childrenscolumbus.org
| 23 | 50 | 353 | 13997 | 238 | 598795 | 0 | 344632 | 139746 | 4249 |

✠ ○ **DOCTORS HOSPITAL**, 5100 West Broad Street, Zip 43228; tel. 614/544–1000 **A**1 2 9 10 11 12 13 **F**9 11 12 14 15 17 19 21 22 23 26 27 28 29 33 36 37 42 48 49 50 52 53 55 57 58 59 61 62 63 66 69 70 71 73 74 75 77 81 82 84 85 86 87 88 92 93 96 107 108 109 **P**5 6 8
S OhioHealth, Columbus, OH
Primary Contact: Kreg Gruber, President
CFO: Nathan Van Laningham, Vice President and Chief Financial Officer
CMO: Francis V. Dono, D.O., Vice President Medical Affairs
CHR: Barbara Otey, Vice President Human Resources
Web address: www.ohiohealth.com
| 21 | 10 | 209 | 10649 | 130 | 162697 | 1218 | 148797 | 61466 | 948 |

✠ △ **GRANT MEDICAL CENTER**, 111 South Grant Avenue, Zip 43215–1898; tel. 614/566–9000 **A**1 7 8 9 10 **F**1 2 11 12 14 15 17 18 19 21 22 23 25 26 27 28 29 30 31 33 34 36 37 38 41 42 45 46 48 49 50 52 53 55 56 57 58 59 61 62 63 64 66 68 69 70 78 81 82 84 85 87 88 89 90 92 93 94 95 96 97 98 106 107 108 109 110 **P**5 6 8 **S** OhioHealth, Columbus, OH
Primary Contact: Robert Falcone, M.D., President
COO: Robert Falcone, M.D., Senior Operations Officer
CFO: Michael Louge, Senior Vice President and Chief Financial Officer
CIO: William Winnenberg, Vice President Information Services
Web address: www.ohiohealth.com
| 21 | 10 | 385 | 20415 | 254 | 174509 | 2252 | 294961 | 117110 | 2000 |

✠ △ **MOUNT CARMEL**, Mailing Address: 793 West State Street, Zip 43222–1551; tel. 614/234–5000, (Includes MOUNT CARMEL EAST HOSPITAL, 6001 East Broad Street, Zip 43213; tel. 614/234–6000; MOUNT CARMEL WEST HOSPITAL) **A**1 2 3 5 7 9 10 **F**2 9 10 11 12 15 17 19 21 22 23 26 27 28 29 33 34 35 38 39 40 47 48 52 53 55 56 57 58 59 61 62 63 64 65 66 68 70 71 73 75 77 78 79 80 81 82 83 84 85 87 88 90 94 106 108 109 110 **S** Trinity Health, Novi, MI
Primary Contact: Joseph T. Calvaruso, President and Chief Executive Officer
CFO: Russell W. Gardner, Chief Financial Officer
CIO: Cindy Sheets, Chief Information Officer
Web address: www.mountcarmelhealth.com
| 21 | 10 | 843 | 38225 | 525 | 441302 | 4562 | 522217 | 181634 | — |

✠ **OHIO STATE UNIVERSITY HOSPITALS EAST**, 1492 East Broad Street, Zip 43205–1546; tel. 614/257–3000 **A**1 3 5 9 10 **F**2 3 4 6 12 15 21 22 26 27 28 29 33 35 37 39 46 47 48 49 52 53 55 57 58 60 61 62 63 64 65 66 69 70 73 81 82 84 88 92 94 96 98 108 110 **P**2 6 **S** Ohio State University Health System, Columbus, OH
Primary Contact: Karen Mlawsky, Executive Director
CFO: Patrick Robertson, Chief Financial Officer
Web address: www.medicalcenter.osu.edu
| 12 | 10 | 175 | 9492 | 125 | 91243 | 0 | 111400 | 42049 | 2003 |

✠ **OHIO STATE UNIVERSITY JAMES CANCER HOSPITAL**, 300 West Tenth Avenue, Zip 43210–1240; tel. 614/293–5485 **A**1 2 3 5 8 9 10 **F**2 4 6 7 9 10 11 12 14 15 17 19 21 22 23 24 25 26 27 28 29 30 31 32 33 34 35 36 37 38 39 40 41 42 43 44 46 47 48 49 50 52 53 55 57 58 60 61 62 63 64 65 66 68 69 70 72 73 74 75 76 77 78 79 80 81 82 84 85 86 87 88 89 90 92 93 94 95 96 98 99 100 101 102 103 104 105 106 107 108 109 110 **P**2 6 **S** Ohio State University Health System, Columbus, OH
Primary Contact: David E. Schuller, M.D., Chief Executive Officer
CFO: Bell Julian, Administrator Fiscal Services
Web address: www.jamesline.com
| 12 | 41 | 156 | 6992 | 134 | 147479 | 0 | 223342 | 52393 | 2420 |

Many Facility Codes have changed. Please refer to the AHA Guide Code Chart. © 2005 AHA Guide

Hospital, Address, Telephone, Approval, Facility, and Physician Codes, Health Care System	Classi-fication Codes		Utilization Data					Expense (thousands) of dollars		
★ American Hospital Association (AHA) membership □ Joint Commission on Accreditation of Healthcare Organizations (JCAHO) accreditation ○ American Osteopathic Association (AOA) accreditation △ Commission on Accreditation of Rehabilitation Facilities (CARF) accreditation	Control	Service	Staffed Beds	Admissions	Census	Outpatient Visits	Births	Total	Payroll	Personnel
⊞ △ **OHIO STATE UNIVERSITY MEDICAL CENTER**, 410 West 10th Avenue, Zip 43210–1240; tel. 614/293–8000 **A**1 3 5 7 8 9 10 **F**2 4 6 7 9 10 11 12 13 14 15 17 19 21 22 23 25 26 27 28 29 30 31 32 33 34 35 37 38 39 40 41 42 43 44 46 47 48 49 50 52 53 55 56 57 58 59 60 61 62 63 64 65 66 68 69 70 71 72 73 74 75 76 77 78 79 80 81 82 84 85 86 87 88 89 90 92 93 94 95 96 98 99 100 101 102 103 104 105 106 107 108 109 110 **P**2 6 **S** Ohio State University Health System, Columbus, OH Primary Contact: Peter E. Geier, Chief Executive Officer CFO: Richard Schrock, Chief Financial Officer CMO: Hagop Mekhjian, M.D., Medical Director CIO: Jeff Wilkins, Interim Chief Information Officer CHR: Les Ridout, Interim Human Resources Officer Web address: www.osumedcenter.edu	12	10	654	29200	483	612584	4103	593112	220057	5911
⊞ **RIVERSIDE METHODIST HOSPITAL**, 3535 Olentangy River Road, Zip 43214–3998; tel. 614/566–5000 **A**1 2 9 10 **F**1 2 4 7 9 10 11 12 14 15 17 19 21 22 23 26 27 28 29 30 31 33 34 35 36 37 38 39 41 42 43 44 45 46 48 49 50 52 53 55 56 57 58 59 60 61 62 63 64 65 66 69 70 71 73 74 75 76 77 78 79 80 81 82 84 85 86 87 88 89 90 92 93 94 95 96 97 106 108 109 **P**5 6 7 8 **S** OhioHealth, Columbus, OH Primary Contact: Bruce P. Hagen, President COO: Bruce P. Hagen, President CFO: Vinson Yates, Vice President Finance CMO: Mark Vary, M.D., Chief Medical Officer CIO: William Winnenberg, Vice President Information Services CHR: Paul N. Patton, Vice President Human Resources Web address: www.ohiohealth.com	21	10	813	42387	516	618527	6433	618609	243588	3718
□ **SELECT SPECIALTY HOSPITAL–COLUMBUS**, 410 West 10th Avenue, 11th Floor, Zip 43210; tel. 614/293–6931, (Nonreporting) **A**1 10 Primary Contact: Dan West, Chief Executive Officer	33	80	50	—	—	—	—	—	—	—
□ **SELECT SPECIALTY HOSPITAL–COLUMBUS**, 111 South Grant Avenue, 5th Floor, Zip 43215; tel. 614/566–8211, (Nonreporting) **A**1 10 Primary Contact: Albert Wright, Chief Executive Officer	33	80	37	—	—	—	—	—	—	—
□ **SELECT SPECIALTY HOSPITAL–COLUMBUS**, 1492 East Broad Street, 8th Floor, Zip 43205; tel. 614/252–4440, (Nonreporting) **A**1 10 Primary Contact: Albert Wright, Chief Executive Officer	33	80	44	—	—	—	—	—	—	—
⊞ **TWIN VALLEY BEHAVIORAL HEALTHCARE–COLUMBUS CAMPUS**, (Formerly Twin Valley Psychiatric System/Columbus Campus), 2200 West Broad Street, Zip 43223–1295; tel. 614/752–0333, (Nonreporting) **A**1 9 10 Primary Contact: James Ignelzi, Chief Executive Officer	12	22	338	—	—	—	—	—	—	—
CONNEAUT—Ashtabula County										
⊞ **UHHS BROWN MEMORIAL HOSPITAL**, 158 West Main Road, Zip 44030–2039; tel. 440/593–1131 **A**1 9 10 18 **F**2 6 9 12 21 26 27 28 29 33 40 46 47 48 52 53 55 58 61 62 63 65 66 69 81 88 94 96 97 108 109 **P**7 **S** University Hospitals Health System, Cleveland, OH Primary Contact: William P. Lawrence, President CFO: Rob David, Director Finance Services CMO: Gary Huston, D.O., Director Medical Affairs CIO: Alnita B. Russell, Director Quality and Access Services Web address: www.uhhs.com	23	10	25	953	11	103436	147	17718	6810	149
COSHOCTON—Coshocton County										
□ **COSHOCTON COUNTY MEMORIAL HOSPITAL**, 1460 Orange Street, Zip 43812–6330, Mailing Address: P.O. Box 1330, Zip 43812–6330; tel. 740/622–6411, (Total facility includes 61 beds in nursing home–type unit) **A**1 9 10 20 **F**11 21 23 26 27 33 34 45 46 55 58 60 61 62 63 69 79 81 82 84 85 86 88 92 93 94 96 107 108 109 110 **P**7 Primary Contact: Gregory M. Nowak, Administrator and Chief Executive Officer Web address: www.ccmh.com	23	10	135	3966	89	59509	353	45423	15082	493
CUYAHOGA FALLS—Summit County										
○ **CUYAHOGA FALLS GENERAL HOSPITAL**, 1900 23rd Street, Zip 44223–1499; tel. 330/971–7000 **A**9 10 11 12 13 **F**1 11 12 21 23 27 28 33 36 37 46 49 52 55 57 58 59 60 61 62 63 64 69 70 81 82 84 88 92 93 108 109 **P**8 Primary Contact: Kathleen A. Rice, President and Chief Operating Officer Web address: www.summahealth.org	23	10	105	4535	45	97872	661	58642	24399	531
DAYTON—Montgomery County										
□ **CHILDREN'S MEDICAL CENTER**, One Children's Plaza, Zip 45404–1815; tel. 937/641–3000 **A**1 2 3 5 8 9 10 **F**2 6 9 16 21 22 23 24 26 27 28 29 32 33 34 35 36 37 38 39 42 46 47 48 49 50 51 52 56 57 58 60 61 62 63 64 65 66 67 69 70 81 84 88 90 93 94 96 98 106 107 108 **P**6 Primary Contact: David Kinsaul, President and Chief Executive Officer Web address: www.childrensdayton.org	23	12	123	6010	72	221738	0	116991	52545	1198
DAYTON CAMPUS, 2611 Wayne Avenue, Zip 45420–1800; tel. 937/258–0440, (Nonreporting) **A**10 Primary Contact: James Ignelzi, Chief Executive Officer Web address: www.mh.state.oh.us	12	22	110	—	—	—	—	—	—	—
⊞ **DAYTON HEART HOSPITAL**, 707 South Edwin C. Moses Boulevard, Zip 45408; tel. 937/221–8000, (Nonreporting) **A**1 9 10 **S** MedCath, Inc., Charlotte, NC Primary Contact: Chad Carpenter, President and Chief Executive Officer Web address: www.daytonhearthospital.com	33	42	47	—	—	—	—	—	—	—

OH

Hospital, Address, Telephone, Approval, Facility, and Physician Codes, Health Care System	Classification Codes		Utilization Data					Expense (thousands) of dollars		
★ American Hospital Association (AHA) membership □ Joint Commission on Accreditation of Healthcare Organizations (JCAHO) accreditation ○ American Osteopathic Association (AOA) accreditation △ Commission on Accreditation of Rehabilitation Facilities (CARF) accreditation	Control	Service	Staffed Beds	Admissions	Census	Outpatient Visits	Births	Total	Payroll	Personnel
⊠ **GOOD SAMARITAN HOSPITAL**, 2222 Philadelphia Drive, Zip 45406–1813; tel. 937/278–2612 **A**1 2 3 5 10 **F**2 4 9 11 12 14 15 17 19 21 22 23 26 28 29 30 31 33 34 37 38 42 44 46 47 48 49 50 52 53 55 57 58 59 60 61 62 63 64 65 66 69 70 71 73 74 75 76 78 79 80 81 82 84 85 87 88 92 93 94 95 96 106 107 108 109 **P**8 **S** Catholic Health Initiatives, Denver, CO Primary Contact: James R. Pancoast, President and Chief Executive Officer CFO: Thomas Duncan, Vice President and Chief Financial Officer CMO: Daniel L. Schoulties, M.D., Vice President Medical Affairs CIO: Mikki Clancy, Vice President and Chief Information Officer CHR: William Linesch, Vice President Human Resources Web address: www.goodsamdayton.com	21	10	348	18589	236	432036	1344	277446	127598	3394
★ ○ △ **GRANDVIEW HOSPITAL AND MEDICAL CENTER**, 405 Grand Avenue, Zip 45405–4796; tel. 937/226–3200, (Includes SOUTHVIEW HOSPITAL AND FAMILY HEALTH CENTER, 1997 Miamisburg–Centerville Road, Zip 45459–3800; tel. 937/439–6000) **A**7 9 10 11 12 13 **F**2 3 4 9 10 11 12 14 15 17 19 21 22 23 24 26 27 28 29 30 31 32 33 35 36 37 38 39 41 42 46 47 48 49 50 51 52 53 55 56 57 58 59 60 61 62 63 64 65 66 68 69 70 71 73 74 75 76 77 78 81 82 84 85 87 88 92 93 94 95 96 104 106 107 108 109 110 **P**7 8 **S** Kettering Medical Center–Network, Dayton, OH Primary Contact: Roy G. Chew, Ph.D., President COO: Peter J. King, Senior Vice President and Chief Financial Officer CFO: Russell Wetherell, Vice Preesident Finance and Operations CMO: Tom Hardy, D.O., Vice President Medical Affairs CIO: Frank R. Engler, Jr, Director Administrative Services Web address: www.kmcnetwork.org	21	10	330	12775	168	187639	1674	186019	78647	1532
KETTERING YOUTH SERVICES See Sycamore Hospital, Miamisburg										
KINDRED HOSPITAL–DAYTON, One Elizabeth Place, 5th Floor, Zip 45408; tel. 937/222–5963, (Nonreporting) **A**10 Primary Contact: Mark K. Floro, Chief Executive Officer	33	49	67	—	—	—	—	—	—	—
⊠ △ **MIAMI VALLEY HOSPITAL**, One Wyoming Street, Zip 45409–2793; tel. 937/208–8000 **A**1 2 3 5 7 8 10 **F**1 2 4 11 12 13 14 15 17 19 21 22 23 26 27 28 29 31 32 33 34 35 37 38 39 41 42 44 45 46 47 48 49 50 52 55 56 57 58 59 60 61 62 63 64 65 66 68 69 71 73 74 75 76 77 78 79 81 82 84 85 86 87 88 89 90 93 94 95 96 98 99 101 106 108 109 110 **P**8 Primary Contact: William M. Thornton, President and Chief Executive Officer COO: Mary H. Boosalis, Executive Vice President and Chief Operating Officer CFO: Timothy D. Jackson, Executive Vice President and Chief Financial Officer CMO: Gary Collier, M.D., Vice President and Chief Medical Officer, Medical Affairs CIO: Mikki Clancy, Vice President and Chief Information Officer CHR: William Linesch, Vice President Human Resources Web address: www.miamivalleyhospital.org	23	10	641	29601	446	647263	4941	470203	213340	4672
SOUTHVIEW HOSPITAL AND FAMILY HEALTH CENTER See Grandview Hospital and Medical Center										
⊠ **VETERANS AFFAIRS MEDICAL CENTER**, 4100 West Third Street, Zip 45428–1002; tel. 937/268–6511, (Total facility includes 265 beds in nursing home–type unit) **A**1 2 3 5 8 **F**2 4 5 9 15 17 21 22 23 29 31 32 33 35 36 37 38 39 41 42 44 45 46 47 48 49 50 51 52 55 57 58 60 61 62 63 65 66 69 70 71 73 74 76 77 81 82 87 88 92 93 94 96 106 107 108 109 **P**6 **S** Department of Veterans Affairs, Washington, DC Primary Contact: Steven M. Cohen, M.D., Director CFO: Lawrence Andrews, Chief Fiscal Services CMO: Edward E. Sperber, Chief of Staff CIO: Susan Sherer, Chief Information Resource Management Web address: www.va.gov/sta/guide/home.asp	45	10	500	5981	391	330334	0	163811	97194	1721
DEFIANCE—Defiance County										
⊠ **DEFIANCE REGIONAL MEDICAL CENTER**, 1200 Ralston Avenue, Zip 43512–1396; tel. 419/783–6955 **A**1 5 9 10 18 **F**2 9 11 12 15 23 27 28 33 34 37 46 47 48 52 55 58 59 60 61 62 63 65 66 69 71 73 74 75 76 77 78 81 82 84 87 88 93 94 96 106 108 109 **P**6 **S** ProMedica Health System, Toledo, OH Primary Contact: John E. Horns, President COO: Dan Schwanke, Executive Director CFO: Bernie Nawrocki, Director Fiscal Services CMO: Kermit Erwin, M.D., Medical Director CIO: Kevin Wietrzykowski, Information Mangement Systems Director CHR: Linda Shaffer, Director Human Resources Web address: www.promedica.org	23	10	61	3999	36	20636	646	37196	12855	295
★ **MERCY HOSPITAL OF DEFIANCE**, 1404 East Second Street, Zip 43512; tel. 419/782–8444, (Nonreporting) **A**9 10 **S** Catholic Healthcare Partners, Cincinnati, OH Primary Contact: Chad Peter, Administrator Web address: www.ehealthconnection.com/regions/toledo/	23	10	23	—	—	—	—	—	—	—
DELAWARE—Delaware County										
□ △ **GRADY MEMORIAL HOSPITAL**, 561 West Central Avenue, Zip 43015–1485; tel. 740/369–8711, (Nonreporting) **A**1 2 5 7 9 10 **S** OhioHealth, Columbus, OH Primary Contact: Everett P. Weber, Jr, President and Chief Executive Officer Web address: www.gradyhospital.com	23	10	75	—	—	—	—	—	—	—

Many Facility Codes have changed. Please refer to the AHA Guide Code Chart. © 2005 AHA Guide

Hospital, Address, Telephone, Approval, Facility, and Physician Codes, Health Care System	Classification Codes		Utilization Data					Expense (thousands) of dollars		
★ American Hospital Association (AHA) membership □ Joint Commission on Accreditation of Healthcare Organizations (JCAHO) accreditation ○ American Osteopathic Association (AOA) accreditation △ Commission on Accreditation of Rehabilitation Facilities (CARF) accreditation	Control	Service	Staffed Beds	Admissions	Census	Outpatient Visits	Births	Total	Payroll	Personnel

DENNISON—Tuscarawas County

⊞ **TWIN CITY HOSPITAL**, 819 North First Street, Zip 44621–1098; tel. 740/922–2800, (Nonreporting) **A**1 9 10 18
Primary Contact: Marge Jentes, Interim Chief Executive Officer
CFO: Jud Love, Director Finance
CMO: Rey Marquino, M.D., Chief of Staff
CHR: Laura Spinell, Director Human Resources
Web address: www.twincityhospital.org

| | 23 | 10 | 25 | — | — | — | — | — | — | — |

DOVER—Tuscarawas County

⊞ **UNION HOSPITAL**, 659 Boulevard, Zip 44622–2077; tel. 330/343–3311 **A**1 9 10 19 **F**2 9 11 12 15 21 23 26 27 28 29 33 37 39 41 46 47 48 51 52 55 58 59 60 61 62 63 64 65 69 80 81 82 87 88 93 94 95 96 108 **P**8
Primary Contact: William W. Harding, President and Chief Executive Officer
CFO: Eugene A. Thorn, III, Vice President, Finance and Chief Financial Officer
CMO: Thomas J. Kelly, M.P.H., D.O., Vice President Medical Affairs
CIO: David Baumgardner, Director Information Services
CHR: Darwin K. Smith, Vice President, Human Resources
Web address: www.unionhospital.org

| | 23 | 10 | 139 | 6267 | 72 | 266894 | 785 | 79298 | 31933 | 820 |

EAST LIVERPOOL—Columbiana County

⊞ **EAST LIVERPOOL CITY HOSPITAL**, 425 West Fifth Street, Zip 43920–2498; tel. 330/385–7200, (Total facility includes 20 beds in nursing home–type unit) **A**1 9 10 **F**2 9 11 12 15 21 22 23 24 27 28 29 32 33 35 39 40 41 46 48 49 51 52 55 57 58 59 60 61 62 63 64 65 66 69 81 82 85 88 92 94 96 106 108 110
Primary Contact: Melvin R. Creeley, President
CFO: Michael H. Winiarski, Vice President Finance
CMO: Vern Orlang, M.D., Medical Director
CIO: Frank Mader, Director Information Services
Web address: www.elch.org

| | 23 | 10 | 143 | 6684 | 81 | 102833 | 246 | 49808 | 21202 | 526 |

ELYRIA—Lorain County

⊞ **EMH REGIONAL MEDICAL CENTER**, 630 East River Street, Zip 44035–5902; tel. 440/329–7500 **A**1 2 9 10 **F**2 9 11 12 14 15 17 19 21 22 26 28 29 33 37 39 41 46 47 48 51 52 55 57 58 59 60 61 62 63 64 65 66 69 71 81 82 84 85 87 88 93 94 95 108 **P**6 7
Primary Contact: Kevin C. Martin, President and Chief Executive Officer
CFO: Dave Cook, Vice President and Chief Financial Officer
CMO: Donald Sheldon, M.D., Vice President Medical Affairs
CIO: Scott Smith, Director Information Systems
CHR: Daniel Miller, Vice President Human Resources
Web address: www.emh–healthcare.org

| | 23 | 10 | 262 | 13987 | 154 | 188988 | 1067 | 161861 | 55565 | 1189 |

EUCLID—Cuyahoga County

□ △ **EUCLID HOSPITAL**, 18901 Lake Shore Boulevard, Zip 44119–1090; tel. 216/531–9000 **A**1 2 7 10 **F**9 12 14 15 17 21 26 27 28 29 32 33 37 44 46 48 55 60 61 62 63 66 68 69 71 76 77 78 81 84 88 92 94 95 108 109 **S** Cleveland Clinic Health System, Cleveland, OH
Primary Contact: Lauren Rock, Chief Administrative Officer
Web address: www.meridia.org

| | 23 | 10 | 219 | 8539 | 151 | 73410 | 0 | 77019 | 39614 | 823 |

FAIRFIELD—Butler County

⊞ **MERCY HOSPITAL FAIRFIELD**, 3000 Mack Road, Zip 45014; tel. 513/870–7000 **A**1 2 9 10 **F**2 9 11 12 14 19 21 22 23 27 28 33 38 41 48 49 52 55 57 58 59 60 61 62 63 64 66 69 81 82 84 85 87 88 92 94 95 96 97 108 109 110 **S** Catholic Healthcare Partners, Cincinnati, OH
Primary Contact: Jeffrey A. Ashin, Interim President and Chief Executive Officer
COO: Glenda Wharton, Vice President Nursing
CFO: Edward Roeber, Senior Vice President Finance and Chief Financial Officer
CMO: Leonard M. Randolph, Jr, M.D., Chief Medical Officer
CIO: Ray Pierangeli, Senior Vice President and Chief Information Officer
CHR: Christine Browning, Regional Vice President Human Resources
Web address: www.e–mercy.com

| | 23 | 10 | 168 | 11112 | 111 | 164703 | 1668 | 111720 | 38134 | 896 |

FINDLAY—Hancock County

⊞ **BLANCHARD VALLEY HEALTH ASSOCIATION**, 145 West Wallace Street, Zip 45840–1299; tel. 419/423–4500, (Includes BLANCHARD VALLEY REGIONAL HEALTH CENTER–BLUFFTON CAMPUS, 139 Garau Street, Bluffton, Zip 45817–0048; tel. 419/358–9010; BLANCHARD VALLEY REGIONAL HEALTH CENTER–FINDLAY CAMPUS, John L. Bookmyer, Executive Vice President and Chief Operating Officer) **A**1 9 10 18 19 **F**9 10 11 12 26 27 28 29 33 34 37 38 44 48 49 50 52 55 57 58 59 61 62 63 64 65 66 69 70 71 76 81 82 84 85 86 87 88 92 93 94 95 96 98 106 108 109 **P**5
Primary Contact: Scott C. Malaney, President and Chief Executive Officer
COO: John L. Bookmyer, Executive Vice President and Chief Operating Officer
CFO: Duane Donaldson, Chief Financial Officer
CMO: Bill Kose, M.D., Senior Vice President Medical Affairs
CIO: Annette Elchert, Director Information Services
CHR: Donald Holtvoigt, Director Human Resources
Web address: www.bvha.org

| | 23 | 10 | 104 | 8066 | 78 | 264067 | 1289 | 108462 | 47798 | 1056 |

OH

Hospital, Address, Telephone, Approval, Facility, and Physician Codes, Health Care System	Classi-fication Codes		Utilization Data					Expense (thousands) of dollars		
★ American Hospital Association (AHA) membership □ Joint Commission on Accreditation of Healthcare Organizations (JCAHO) accreditation ○ American Osteopathic Association (AOA) accreditation △ Commission on Accreditation of Rehabilitation Facilities (CARF) accreditation	Control	Service	Staffed Beds	Admissions	Census	Outpatient Visits	Births	Total	Payroll	Personnel

FOSTORIA—Hancock County

☒ **FOSTORIA COMMUNITY HOSPITAL**, 501 Van Buren Street, Zip 44830–0907, Mailing Address: P.O. Box 907, Zip 44830–0907; tel. 419/435–7734 **A**1 5 9 10 18 **F**2 9 11 12 23 26 27 28 29 33 45 46 48 51 52 54 55 58 59 60 61 62 63 65 69 70 81 82 84 87 88 92 93 94 95 96 97 106 108 109 **P**7 **S** ProMedica Health System, Toledo, OH
Primary Contact: Timothy Jakacki, President
CFO: Ken Swint, Vice President Finance and Chief Financial Officer
CIO: Dave Selman, Corporate Vice President Information Systems
Web address: www.fchosp.org | 23 | 10 | 25 | 1412 | 11 | 46219 | 185 | 25716 | 9469 | 240 |

FREMONT—Sandusky County

☒ **MEMORIAL HOSPITAL**, 715 South Taft Avenue, Zip 43420–3200; tel. 419/332–7321 **A**1 5 9 10 **F**2 9 11 12 21 22 23 24 26 27 28 29 31 33 36 37 38 44 45 46 47 48 51 52 53 54 55 57 58 59 60 61 62 63 64 65 66 69 71 72 73 75 77 78 81 82 84 88 94 96 98 106 108 109 110 **P**1 5 6
S Quorum Health Resources, Plano, TX
Primary Contact: John A. Gorman, Chief Executive Officer
COO: Sandra J. Foster, Chief Patient Services Officer
CFO: Rick Ruppel, Chief Financial Officer
CIO: John Allen, Chief Information Officer
Web address: www.fremontmemorial.org | 23 | 10 | 120 | 3259 | 30 | 110993 | 483 | 46571 | 18624 | 413 |

GALION—Crawford County

☒ **GALION COMMUNITY HOSPITAL**, 269 Portland Way South, Zip 44833–2399; tel. 419/468–4841, (Total facility includes 33 beds in nursing home–type unit) **A**1 9 10 18 **F**2 9 11 12 21 23 26 27 28 29 33 37 39 41 46 48 52 53 54 55 58 59 60 61 62 63 66 68 69 81 82 85 87 88 92 93 94 95 96 97 106 108 109 **P**3
Primary Contact: LaMar L. Wyse, President and Chief Executive Officer
CFO: Robert V. Melaragno, Vice President and Chief Financial Officer
Web address: www.galionhospital.org | 23 | 10 | 126 | 2092 | 54 | 50426 | 411 | 29856 | 11852 | 315 |

GALLIPOLIS—Gallia County

□ △ **HOLZER MEDICAL CENTER**, 100 Jackson Pike, Zip 45631–1563; tel. 740/446–5000, (Nonreporting) **A**1 2 5 7 9 10 19
Primary Contact: James R. Phillipe, President
Web address: www.holzer.org | 23 | 10 | 25 | — | — | — | — | — | — | — |

GARFIELD HEIGHTS—Cuyahoga County

□ △ **MARYMOUNT HOSPITAL**, 12300 McCracken Road, Zip 44125–2975; tel. 216/581–0500 **A**1 2 7 9 10 12 **F**9 11 12 15 21 23 26 27 28 29 31 32 33 35 37 39 40 41 42 44 45 46 47 48 50 52 53 54 55 57 58 59 60 61 62 63 66 69 70 71 72 73 74 75 76 77 78 81 82 84 85 87 88 92 93 94 95 96 107 108 109 **S** Cleveland Clinic Health System, Cleveland, OH
Primary Contact: David J. Kilarski, President and Chief Executive Officer
Web address: www.marymount.org | 23 | 10 | 237 | 12326 | 184 | 162296 | 710 | 128380 | 62881 | 1307 |

GENEVA—Ashtabula County

☒ **UHHS–MEMORIAL HOSPITAL OF GENEVA**, 870 West Main Street, Zip 44041–1295; tel. 440/466–1141 **A**1 9 10 18 **F**2 6 9 12 15 21 26 27 28 29 33 37 45 46 47 48 52 53 55 58 60 61 63 65 66 69 81 93 94 96 97 108 109 **P**7 **S** University Hospitals Health System, Cleveland, OH
Primary Contact: Laurie Delgado, President and Chief Executive Officer
COO: Laurie Delgado, Vice President and Chief Operating Officer
CFO: Rob David, Director Finance Services
Web address: www.uhhs.com/geneva | 23 | 10 | 25 | 1203 | 13 | 141258 | 0 | 20222 | 7423 | 124 |

GEORGETOWN—Brown County

☒ **BROWN COUNTY GENERAL HOSPITAL**, 425 Home Street, Zip 45121–1407; tel. 937/378–7500 **A**1 9 10 **F**9 11 12 21 23 26 27 28 33 46 48 51 52 55 58 59 60 61 62 63 65 66 69 70 81 82 83 85 86 87 88 94 107 108 **P**6
S Quorum Health Resources, Plano, TX
Primary Contact: Bruce A. Bennett, Chief Executive Officer
CFO: R Jeffrey Fels, Vice President Finance and Support Services
CHR: Mike Sterling, Director Human Resources
Web address: www.browncountygeneralhospital.org | 13 | 10 | 59 | 1777 | 15 | 58603 | 405 | 17956 | 14735 | 364 |

GREEN SPRINGS—Sandusky County

☒ △ **ST. FRANCIS HEALTH CARE CENTRE**, 401 North Broadway, Zip 44836–9653; tel. 419/639–2626, (Total facility includes 148 beds in nursing home–type unit) **A**1 7 9 10 **F**2 21 22 26 27 28 52 69 92 94 96 108 110
S VIBRA Healthcare, Mechanicsburg, PA
Primary Contact: Kim D. Eicher, Chief Executive Officer
CFO: Douglas Morris, Chief Financial Officer
CMO: John Yuhas, D.O., Medical Director
CHR: Joan E. Schmidt, Director, Human Resources
Web address: www.sfhcc.org | 21 | 80 | 184 | 648 | 109 | 10101 | 0 | 16507 | 5805 | 141 |

GREENFIELD—Highland County

□ △ **GREENFIELD AREA MEDICAL CENTER**, 550 Mirabeau Street, Zip 45123–1617; tel. 937/981–9400 **A**1 7 10 18 **F**2 12 28 33 52 53 58 60 62 63 66 69 81 82 88 92 94 97 110 **P**5
Primary Contact: Jeff Graham, Chief Executive Officer
Web address: www.adena.org | 23 | 10 | 25 | 736 | 12 | 40611 | 0 | 8873 | 4107 | 118 |

Hospital, Address, Telephone, Approval, Facility, and Physician Codes, Health Care System	Classi-fication Codes		Utilization Data					Expense (thousands) of dollars		
★ American Hospital Association (AHA) membership □ Joint Commission on Accreditation of Healthcare Organizations (JCAHO) accreditation ○ American Osteopathic Association (AOA) accreditation △ Commission on Accreditation of Rehabilitation Facilities (CARF) accreditation	Control	Service	Staffed Beds	Admissions	Census	Outpatient Visits	Births	Total	Payroll	Personnel

GREENVILLE—Darke County

★ **WAYNE HOSPITAL**, 835 Sweitzer Street, Zip 45331–1077; tel. 937/548–1141 **A**1 9 10 **F**2 9 10 11 12 22 26 27 28 29 33 36 37 38 46 47 48 52 53 54 55 58 59 60 61 62 63 65 66 69 81 82 84 87 88 93 94 96 97 106 107 108 110 **P**1
Primary Contact: Raymond E. Laughlin, Jr, President and Chief Executive Officer
CFO: Marvella Fletcher, Vice President Fiscal Services
Web address: www.waynehospital.com
| 23 | 10 | 73 | 2570 | 23 | 91627 | 395 | 34283 | 15946 | 347 |

HAMILTON—Butler County

★ **FORT HAMILTON HOSPITAL**, 630 Eaton Avenue, Zip 45013–2770; tel. 513/867–2000 **A**1 2 9 10 **F**2 9 10 11 12 15 21 22 23 24 26 27 28 29 30 32 33 35 37 38 39 40 44 46 47 48 50 52 53 55 57 58 59 60 61 62 63 64 65 66 68 69 71 72 73 74 75 76 77 78 81 82 84 85 87 88 92 93 94 95 96 98 106 108 109 110 **S** Health Alliance of Greater Cincinnati, Cincinnati, OH
Primary Contact: Lynn M. Oswald, R.N., Senior Vice President
CFO: Rick Hinds, Vice President and Chief Financial Officer
Web address: www.health–alliance.com/forthamilton.html
| 23 | 10 | 181 | 11362 | 127 | 98675 | 1266 | 89187 | 38288 | 892 |

HICKSVILLE—Defiance County

★ **COMMUNITY MEMORIAL HOSPITAL**, 208 North Columbus Street, Zip 43526–1299; tel. 419/542–6692 **A**1 9 10 18 **F**2 9 11 12 21 22 26 27 29 33 41 45 46 48 59 60 63 66 69 70 81 88 92 93 94 97 107 108 **P**6
Primary Contact: Melvin H. Fahs, Chief Executive Officer
COO: Michelle Waggoner, Chief Operating Officer
CHR: Michelle Waggoner, Chief Operating Officer
Web address: www.cmhosp.com
| 16 | 10 | 25 | 473 | 4 | 19879 | 74 | 10221 | 4501 | 136 |

HILLSBORO—Highland County

★ **HIGHLAND DISTRICT HOSPITAL**, 1275 North High Street, Zip 45133–8571; tel. 937/393–6100 **A**1 9 10 **F**9 11 12 21 22 23 26 27 28 29 33 46 48 51 52 53 57 59 60 61 62 63 64 65 66 69 71 76 81 84 88 94 95 96 106 108 110 **P**3
Primary Contact: Paula J. Detterman, President and Chief Executive Officer
CFO: Robert Kerr, Chief Financial Officer
CMO: Paul Schreiban, M.D., Chief of Staff
CIO: Randy Houck, Information Technology Manager
CHR: Earlean Christensen, Director Human Resources
Web address: www.hdh.org
| 16 | 10 | 55 | 2436 | 28 | 79607 | 347 | 35998 | 14559 | 385 |

JACKSON—Jackson County

□ **HOLZER MEDICAL CENTER – JACKSON**, 500 Burlington Road, Zip 45640–9360; tel. 740/395–8500, (Nonreporting) **A**1 9 10 18
Primary Contact: Ross Matlack, President and Chief Executive Officer
| 33 | 49 | 29 | — | — | — | — | — | — | — |

KENTON—Hardin County

★ **HARDIN MEMORIAL HOSPITAL**, 921 East Franklin Street, Zip 43326–2099, Mailing Address: P.O. Box 710, Zip 43326–0710; tel. 419/673–0761 **A**1 9 10 18 **F**9 12 21 22 26 27 28 33 36 46 47 48 50 51 54 58 60 61 62 63 65 66 69 70 75 81 82 88 93 94 97 108 **S** OhioHealth, Columbus, OH
Primary Contact: Mark R. Seckinger, Administrator and Chief Executive Officer
CFO: Ron Snyder, Chief Financial Officer
Web address: www.hardinmemorial.org
| 23 | 10 | 25 | 1529 | 16 | 63109 | 0 | 17841 | 8968 | 229 |

KETTERING—Montgomery County

★ △ **CHARLES F. KETTERING MEMORIAL HOSPITAL**, 3535 Southern Boulevard, Zip 45429; tel. 937/298–4331, (Total facility includes 100 beds in nursing home–type unit) **A**1 2 3 5 7 8 9 10 **F**2 3 4 5 8 9 10 11 12 14 15 17 19 21 22 23 24 26 27 28 29 30 31 32 33 35 36 37 38 39 40 41 42 43 44 45 46 47 48 49 50 51 52 53 55 56 57 58 59 60 61 62 63 64 65 66 68 69 70 71 72 73 74 75 76 77 79 80 81 82 84 85 86 87 88 89 91 92 93 94 95 96 98 104 106 108 109 110 **P**7 8 **S** Kettering Medical Center–Network, Dayton, OH
Primary Contact: Fred M. Manchur, President
COO: Terry Burns, Chief Operating Officer
CMO: Gregory Wise, M.D., Vice President Medical Affiars
Web address: www.kmcnetwork.org
| 21 | 10 | 521 | 21709 | 341 | 187608 | 2260 | 311252 | 130734 | 2635 |

LAKEWOOD—Cuyahoga County

□ △ **LAKEWOOD HOSPITAL**, 14519 Detroit Avenue, Zip 44107–4383; tel. 216/521–4200, (Total facility includes 45 beds in nursing home–type unit) **A**1 2 7 9 10 **F**1 11 12 14 15 17 19 21 22 24 26 27 28 33 34 40 42 44 46 47 48 49 50 51 52 53 54 55 56 58 59 60 62 63 65 66 68 69 70 71 72 73 74 75 76 77 78 81 82 84 87 88 92 94 96 98 107 108 109 **S** Cleveland Clinic Health System, Cleveland, OH
Primary Contact: Jack D. Gustin, Chief Administrative Officer
Web address: www.lakewoodhospital.org
| 23 | 10 | 334 | 12945 | 193 | 117990 | 789 | 113598 | 53610 | 769 |

LANCASTER—Fairfield County

★ △ **FAIRFIELD MEDICAL CENTER**, 401 North Ewing Street, Zip 43130–3371; tel. 740/687–8000 **A**1 2 5 7 9 10 **F**2 9 11 12 15 17 19 21 22 26 27 28 29 30 31 33 35 37 38 41 42 46 48 51 52 55 57 58 59 60 61 62 63 64 66 69 70 71 75 77 81 82 84 85 87 88 94 95 96 106 108 109 110 **P**4
Primary Contact: Mina H. Ubbing, President and Chief Executive Officer
COO: Howard Sniderman, Vice President Professional and Support Services
CFO: Sky Gettys, Vice President Finance
CMO: Jerome J. Roche, Chief Medical Officer
CHR: Dominic Prunte, Director Human Resources
Web address: www.fmchealth.org
| 23 | 10 | 222 | 12673 | 147 | 221367 | 1231 | 149824 | 65483 | 1581 |

Hospital, Address, Telephone, Approval, Facility, and Physician Codes, Health Care System	Classi-fication Codes		Utilization Data					Expense (thousands) of dollars		
★ American Hospital Association (AHA) membership □ Joint Commission on Accreditation of Healthcare Organizations (JCAHO) accreditation ○ American Osteopathic Association (AOA) accreditation △ Commission on Accreditation of Rehabilitation Facilities (CARF) accreditation	Control	Service	Staffed Beds	Admissions	Census	Outpatient Visits	Births	Total	Payroll	Personnel

LIMA—Allen County

⊞ INSTITUTE FOR ORTHOPAEDIC SURGERY, 801 Medical Drive, Suite B., Zip 45804; tel. 419/224–7586, (Nonreporting) **A**1 9 10 **S** Catholic Healthcare Partners, Cincinnati, OH
Primary Contact: Cindy Hauck, Administrator

| | 32 | 47 | 3 | — | — | — | — | — | — | — |

⊞ LIMA MEMORIAL HEALTH SYSTEM, 1001 Bellefontaine Avenue, Zip 45804–2899; tel. 419/228–3335 **A**1 2 9 10 **F**2 9 11 12 14 15 17 19 21 22 23 26 27 28 29 33 34 37 38 40 41 42 43 46 47 48 49 51 52 53 54 55 57 58 59 60 61 62 63 64 65 66 68 69 70 79 81 82 84 86 87 88 92 93 94 95 96 98 106 108 109 110 **P**8
Primary Contact: Michael D. Swick, President and Chief Executive Officer
COO: Robert Armstrong, Senior Vice President and Chief Operating Officer
CFO: Eric Pohjala, Vice President and Chief Financial Officer
CMO: Lynn Thompson, M.D., Vice President and Chief Medical Officer
CIO: Cheryl Homan, Administrative Director
CHR: Theresa Bowen, Administrative Director
Web address: www.limamemorial.org

| | 23 | 10 | 248 | 10767 | 112 | 221181 | 612 | 114744 | 45060 | 1105 |

□ OAKWOOD CORRECTIONAL FACILITY, 3200 North West Street, Zip 45801–2000; tel. 419/225–8052 **A**1 **F**21 22 28 45 46 47 48 50 58 60 65 66 71 72 74 75 76 78 94 96 106 108 109 **P**5
Primary Contact: Christopher Yanai, Warden and Chief Executive Officer
Web address: www.drc.state.oh.us/public/ocf.htm

| | 12 | 22 | 131 | 225 | 73 | 36 | 0 | 21612 | 18800 | 336 |

□ SCCI HOSPITAL – LIMA, 730 West Market Street, Zip 45801; tel. 419/224–1888, (Nonreporting) **A**1 9 10
Primary Contact: Karen Caywood, Chief Executive Officer

| | 33 | 49 | 12 | — | — | — | — | — | — | — |

⊞ △ ST. RITA'S MEDICAL CENTER, 730 West Market Street, Zip 45801–4670; tel. 419/227–3361 **A**1 2 7 9 10 **F**3 4 7 9 11 12 14 15 17 19 21 22 23 24 26 27 28 29 30 31 32 33 34 36 37 38 39 41 44 46 47 48 49 50 51 52 53 55 56 57 58 59 61 62 63 64 65 66 68 69 70 71 72 73 74 75 76 77 78 79 81 82 84 85 86 87 88 92 94 95 96 106 107 108 109 110 **P**8 **S** Catholic Healthcare Partners, Cincinnati, OH
Primary Contact: James P. Reber, President and Chief Executive Officer
COO: Brian Smith, Executive Vice President and Chief Operating Officer
CMO: Herbert Schumm, M.D., Vice Persident Medical Affairs
CHR: Will Cason, Vice President, Human Resources
Web address: www.stritas.org

| | 21 | 10 | 383 | 14683 | 191 | 385866 | 1936 | 247633 | 98576 | 2223 |

LODI—Medina County

□ LODI COMMUNITY HOSPITAL, 225 Elyria Street, Zip 44254–1096; tel. 330/948–1222 **A**1 5 10 18 **F**9 12 22 27 28 29 30 33 37 48 58 60 63 69 81 88 94 96 97 108 **P**1 6 **S** Akron General Health System, Akron, OH
Primary Contact: Thomas Whelan, President
Web address: www.lodihospital.com

| | 23 | 10 | 23 | 430 | 9 | 26674 | 0 | 10302 | 4429 | 100 |

LOGAN—Hocking County

⊞ HOCKING VALLEY COMMUNITY HOSPITAL, 601 State Route 664 North, Zip 43138–0966, Mailing Address: P.O. Box 966, Zip 43138–0966; tel. 740/380–8000, (Total facility includes 30 beds in nursing home–type unit) **A**1 9 10 18 **F**2 9 11 12 21 22 23 26 27 28 33 44 46 48 52 58 59 60 61 62 63 64 65 69 71 76 81 84 87 88 92 93 94 106 107 108 109 110 **P**1 3
Primary Contact: Clifford K. Harmon, President
CFO: LeeAnn Lucas–Helber, Vice President Finance
CMO: James Haywood, D.O., Medical Director
CHR: Shelia Roberts, Director Human Resources
Web address: www.hvch.org

| | 13 | 10 | 92 | 1766 | 45 | 53551 | 154 | 24432 | 9696 | 169 |

LONDON—Madison County

⊞ MADISON COUNTY HOSPITAL, 210 North Main Street, Zip 43140–1115; tel. 740/852–1372, (Total facility includes 11 beds in nursing home–type unit) **A**1 9 10 **F**9 11 12 14 21 23 26 27 28 29 31 33 36 37 38 41 42 44 46 47 48 50 51 52 55 57 58 59 60 61 62 63 64 65 66 68 69 71 73 74 75 76 77 78 81 82 88 92 93 94 95 96 98 106 108 109 110 **P**5
Primary Contact: Fred L. Kolb, Chief Executive Officer
CFO: Eric Young, Chief Financial Officer
CMO: Steven Richardson, M.D., Chief Medical Staff
CIO: George Shaffer, Director Information Technology
CHR: Becky Rozell, Director Human Resources
Web address: www.mch-ohio.org

| | 23 | 10 | 43 | 1541 | 25 | 33320 | 198 | 26218 | 10985 | 237 |

LORAIN—Lorain County

⊞ △ COMMUNITY HEALTH PARTNERS REGIONAL MEDICAL CENTER, (Formerly Community Health Partners Hospital and Surgical Center), 3700 Kolbe Road, Zip 44053–1697; tel. 440/960–4000, (Nonreporting) **A**1 2 7 9 10 **S** Catholic Healthcare Partners, Cincinnati, OH
Primary Contact: Gary Wengard, Interim President and Chief Executive Officer
COO: Michael S. Deming, Chief Operating Officer
CFO: Gary Wengerd, Vice President Finance and Chief Financial Officer
CMO: Donald Blanford, M.D., Chief Medical Officer
CIO: Robin Stursa, Director Information Systems
Web address: www.community–health–partners.com

| | 21 | 10 | 318 | — | — | — | — | — | — | — |

Many Facility Codes have changed. Please refer to the AHA Guide Code Chart. © 2005 AHA Guide

Hospital, Address, Telephone, Approval, Facility, and Physician Codes, Health Care System	Classi-fication Codes		Utilization Data					Expense (thousands) of dollars		
★ American Hospital Association (AHA) membership □ Joint Commission on Accreditation of Healthcare Organizations (JCAHO) accreditation ○ American Osteopathic Association (AOA) accreditation △ Commission on Accreditation of Rehabilitation Facilities (CARF) accreditation	Control	Service	Staffed Beds	Admissions	Census	Outpatient Visits	Births	Total	Payroll	Personnel

□ **SPECIALTY HOSPITAL OF LORAIN**, 205 West 20th Street, Suite 200, Zip 44052; tel. 440/204–3500, (Nonreporting) **A**1 10 **S** Cornerstone Healthcare Group, Austin, TX Primary Contact: Julia M. Meeks, President and Chief Executive Officer Web address: www.specialtyhospitaloflorain.com	33	80	30	—	—	—	—	—	—	—
MANSFIELD—Richland County										
✠ **MEDCENTRAL HEALTH SYSTEM**, 335 Glessner Avenue, Zip 44903–2265; tel. 419/526–8000, (Includes MANSFIELD HOSPITAL; SHELBY HOSPITAL, 20 Morris Road, Shelby, Zip 44875; tel. 419/342–5015; Ron Distl, Vice President and Chief Operating Officer) **A**1 2 6 9 10 **F**2 14 27 28 55 59 63 68 71 Primary Contact: James E. Meyer, President and Chief Executive Officer CFO: John Kastelic, Vice President Finance CMO: Terry Weston, M.D., Vice President Medical Affairs CIO: Jack Barrett, Director Data Processing CHR: Bruce Engle, Vice President Human Resources Web address: www.medcentral.org	23	10	328	16856	245	221688	1297	222776	90978	2064
□ **SCCI – MANSFIELD**, 335 Glessner Avenue, Zip 44903; tel. 419/526–0777, (Nonreporting) **A**1 10 Primary Contact: Karen Caywood, Chief Executive Officer	33	49	17	—	—	—	—	—	—	—
MARIETTA—Washington County										
✠ △ **MARIETTA MEMORIAL HOSPITAL**, 401 Matthew Street, Zip 45750–1699; tel. 740/374–1400 **A**1 2 7 9 10 **F**2 3 4 9 11 12 15 21 22 23 26 27 28 29 33 36 37 38 40 41 44 45 46 47 48 50 51 52 53 55 58 59 60 61 62 63 65 66 68 69 71 73 74 75 76 78 79 81 82 84 85 86 87 88 93 94 96 108 109 110 **P**8 Primary Contact: Larry J. Unroe, President COO: J Scott Cantley, Vice President and Chief Operating Officer CFO: Orvie E. Fischer, Senior Vice President and Chief Financial Officer CIO: Charles Morgan, Director Information Technology CHR: Dee Ann Gehlauf, Administrative Director, Human Resources Web address: www.mmhospital.org	23	10	168	6634	76	188050	607	103327	41471	718
★ ○ **SELBY GENERAL HOSPITAL**, 1106 Colegate Drive, Zip 45750–1323; tel. 740/568–2000 **A**9 10 11 12 13 18 **F**2 9 12 21 22 24 27 28 29 30 33 37 39 42 44 46 47 48 52 54 55 58 61 62 63 64 66 69 70 81 82 87 88 95 96 97 98 106 108 109 **S** Quorum Health Resources, Plano, TX Primary Contact: Kevin P. Calhoun, Chief Executive Officer CFO: Thomas Kelly, Chief Financial Officer CMO: Isidro Amigo, D.O., Chief of Staff CHR: Cindy Tornes, Coordinator Human Resources Web address: www.selbygeneralhospital.com	23	10	25	1148	12	46742	0	16765	6395	189
MARION—Marion County										
✠ △ **MARION GENERAL HOSPITAL**, 1000 McKinley Park Drive, Zip 43302–6397; tel. 740/383–8400 **A**1 2 5 7 9 10 19 **F**2 3 9 11 12 13 14 15 21 22 23 27 33 36 48 49 51 53 55 56 57 58 59 61 62 63 66 67 68 71 77 78 81 84 85 88 92 94 96 106 108 **S** OhioHealth, Columbus, OH Primary Contact: Ronald J. Bachman, President and Chief Executive Officer CFO: Jerry G. Feyh, Vice President Financial Services CMO: Carol M. Solie, M.D., Vice President Medical Affairs CIO: Chuck Tudor, Information Services Director CHR: Debra K. Rapert, Director Human Resources Web address: www.mariongeneral.com	23	10	131	9074	95	102811	1076	84854	34472	951
MARTINS FERRY—Belmont County										
✠ **EAST OHIO REGIONAL HOSPITAL**, 90 North Fourth Street, Zip 43935–1648; tel. 740/633–1100, (Total facility includes 94 beds in nursing home–type unit) **A**1 9 10 **F**2 9 11 12 15 21 23 26 27 28 29 33 34 35 39 41 46 47 48 51 52 53 55 57 58 59 60 62 63 64 65 66 69 81 82 85 87 88 92 93 94 95 96 106 107 108 110 **P**5 **S** Ohio Valley Health Services and Education Corporation, Wheeling, WV Primary Contact: Brian K. Felici, President and Chief Executive Officer COO: Anne Hellstern, Associate Administrator and Chief Operating Officer CFO: David T. Baranik, Senior Vice President and Chief Financial Officer CIO: Bob Panichi, Chief Information Officer CHR: James R. Stultz, Senior Vice President, Human Resources Web address: www.eastohioregionalhospital.com	23	10	172	5358	142	176804	412	64050	26232	713
MARYSVILLE—Union County										
✠ **MEMORIAL HOSPITAL OF UNION COUNTY**, 500 London Avenue, Zip 43040–1594; tel. 937/644–6115, (Nonreporting) **A**1 5 9 10 Primary Contact: Olas A. Hubbs, III, President and Chief Executive Officer COO: Laurie A. Whittington, Chief Operating Officer CFO: Jeffrey Ehlers, Vice President Finance and Information Services CMO: William McLemore, M.D., Chief of Staff CIO: Carl Zani, Director Information Systems CHR: Carman Wirtz, Vice President Human Resources Web address: www.memorialhosp.org	13	10	193	—	—	—	—	—	—	—

OH

Hospital, Address, Telephone, Approval, Facility, and Physician Codes, Health Care System	Classi-fication Codes		Utilization Data					Expense (thousands) of dollars		
★ American Hospital Association (AHA) membership ☐ Joint Commission on Accreditation of Healthcare Organizations (JCAHO) accreditation ◯ American Osteopathic Association (AOA) accreditation △ Commission on Accreditation of Rehabilitation Facilities (CARF) accreditation	Control	Service	Staffed Beds	Admissions	Census	Outpatient Visits	Births	Total	Payroll	Personnel

MASSILLON—Stark County

★ ◯ △ **DOCTORS HOSPITAL OF STARK COUNTY**, 400 Austin Avenue N.W., Zip 44646–3554; tel. 330/837–7200 **A**2 7 9 10 11 12 13 **F**2 11 12 15 17 19 21 23 26 27 28 29 33 34 37 40 44 46 47 48 52 55 58 59 60 61 62 63 64 65 66 68 69 70 71 73 74 76 81 82 84 87 88 94 95 96 106 108 109 110 **P**8 **S** Triad Hospitals, Inc., Plano, TX
Primary Contact: Janie Sinacore–Jaberg, R.N., MS, FACHE, Chief Executive Officer
CFO: Tom Ramsey, Chief Financial Officer
CMO: Brian E. Wind, D.O., Chief of Staff
CIO: William J. Mars, Vice President and Chief Information Officer
CHR: Angie Boyle, Director Human Resources
Web address: www.drshospital.com
| 33 | 10 | 133 | 3096 | 48 | 56793 | 239 | 55091 | 20980 | 486 |

☐ **HEARTLAND BEHAVIORAL HEALTHCARE**, 3000 Erie Street, Zip 44646–7993, Mailing Address: Box 540, Zip 44648–0540; tel. 330/833–3135, (Nonreporting) **A**1 9 10
Primary Contact: Helen L. Stevens, Chief Executive Officer
| 12 | 22 | 184 | — | — | — | — | — | — | — |

✶ △ **MASSILLON COMMUNITY HOSPITAL**, 875 Eighth Street N.E., Zip 44646–8503, Mailing Address: P.O. Box 805, Zip 44648–8503; tel. 330/832–8761, (Total facility includes 16 beds in nursing home–type unit) **A**1 7 9 10 **F**2 3 4 9 12 21 22 23 26 29 32 33 35 39 41 44 46 47 48 50 52 53 55 58 60 62 63 64 65 66 68 69 71 72 76 77 78 81 87 88 92 93 94 96 106 108 110 **S** Akron General Health System, Akron, OH
Primary Contact: Michael L. Reichfield, President
COO: Elizabeth Pruitt, Vice President Operations
CFO: James Miltner, Vice President, Finance
CIO: Stacey Malcolm, Director Information Systems
Web address: www.mchosp.org
| 23 | 10 | 139 | 3859 | 63 | 103788 | 0 | 46764 | 20527 | 582 |

MAUMEE—Lucas County

☐ **FOCUS HEALTHCARE OF OHIO**, 1725 Timber Line Road, Zip 43537–4015; tel. 419/891–9333, (Nonreporting) **A**1 10
Primary Contact: Carey W. Plummer, Chief Executive Officer
Web address: www.focushealthcare.com
| 33 | 49 | 42 | — | — | — | — | — | — | — |

✶ **ST. LUKE'S HOSPITAL**, 5901 Monclova Road, Zip 43537–1899; tel. 419/893–5911 **A**1 2 9 10 **F**2 9 10 11 12 14 15 17 19 21 22 23 26 27 28 29 33 37 45 46 48 52 53 54 55 57 59 60 61 62 63 64 65 66 68 69 73 81 82 84 85 87 88 93 94 95 96 98 106 108 109 **P**8
Primary Contact: Frank J. Bartell, III, President and Chief Executive Officer
CFO: David M. Oppenlander, Vice President and Treasurer
CMO: Daniel G. Williams, M.D., Chief of Staff
CIO: Lawrence C. Loehrke, Chief Information Officer
CHR: Debra A. Ball, Vice President Human Resources
Web address: www.stlukeshospital.com
| 23 | 10 | 229 | 10266 | 117 | 152117 | 577 | 132790 | 53557 | 1109 |

MEDINA—Medina County

☐ △ **MEDINA GENERAL HOSPITAL**, 1000 East Washington Street, Zip 44256–2170; tel. 330/725–1000 **A**1 2 7 9 10 **F**2 6 11 12 21 22 23 27 29 33 46 47 48 51 52 55 57 58 59 60 61 62 63 65 69 70 81 82 84 85 87 88 93 94 95 96 107 108 109 **P**8
Primary Contact: Gary D. Hallman, President and Chief Executive Officer
Web address: www.medinahospital.org
| 23 | 10 | 118 | 5459 | 62 | 171241 | 1006 | 82125 | 36623 | 789 |

MIAMISBURG—Montgomery County

☐ **LIFECARE HOSPITAL OF DAYTON**, 2150 Leiter Road, Zip 45342; tel. 937/384–8300, (Nonreporting) **A**1 10 **S** LifeCare Management Services, Plano, TX
Primary Contact: Ken D'Amico, Chief Executive Officer
| 33 | 80 | 42 | — | — | — | — | — | — | — |

★ **SYCAMORE HOSPITAL**, 2150 Leiter Road, Zip 45342; tel. 937/866–0551, (Includes KETTERING YOUTH SERVICES, 5350 Lamme Road, Dayton, Zip 45439; tel. 513/299–9511) **A**9 10 **F**2 3 4 9 10 14 21 22 24 26 27 28 29 30 31 32 33 35 36 37 38 39 41 42 44 46 47 48 49 50 51 52 53 55 57 58 60 61 62 63 64 65 66 69 70 71 72 73 74 75 77 78 81 82 84 85 87 88 91 92 94 95 96 98 104 106 108 109 110 **P**7 8 **S** Kettering Medical Center–Network, Dayton, OH
Primary Contact: Richard Haas, Senior Executive Officer
COO: Richard Haas, Senior Executive Officer
CFO: Terry Burns, Vice President Finance and Operations
CMO: Gregory Wise, M.D., Vice President Medical Affiars
CIO: Nyle Morgan, Director Information Systems
CHR: Beverly Morris, Vice President Human Resources
Web address: www.kmcnetwork.org
| 21 | 10 | 142 | 5491 | 78 | 75489 | 0 | 63598 | 23853 | 530 |

MIDDLEBURG HEIGHTS—Cuyahoga County

☐ **SOUTHWEST GENERAL HEALTH CENTER**, 18697 Bagley Road, Zip 44130–3497; tel. 440/816–8000 **A**1 2 9 10 **F**2 4 6 9 11 12 14 15 17 19 21 22 23 24 26 27 29 31 32 33 34 35 36 37 39 40 41 42 44 45 46 47 48 49 51 52 53 55 57 58 59 60 61 62 63 65 66 69 70 71 72 73 74 75 76 77 78 81 82 84 85 86 87 88 92 93 94 95 96 98 107 108 109 110 **P**6 **S** University Hospitals Health System, Cleveland, OH
Primary Contact: L. Jon Schurmeier, President and Chief Executive Officer
Web address: www.swgeneral.com
| 23 | 10 | 297 | 16113 | 216 | 388581 | 1517 | 206685 | 84374 | 2179 |

Many Facility Codes have changed. Please refer to the AHA Guide Code Chart.

Hospital, Address, Telephone, Approval, Facility, and Physician Codes, Health Care System	Classi-fication Codes		Utilization Data					Expense (thousands) of dollars		
★ American Hospital Association (AHA) membership □ Joint Commission on Accreditation of Healthcare Organizations (JCAHO) accreditation ○ American Osteopathic Association (AOA) accreditation △ Commission on Accreditation of Rehabilitation Facilities (CARF) accreditation	Control	Service	Staffed Beds	Admissions	Census	Outpatient Visits	Births	Total	Payroll	Personnel

MIDDLETOWN—Butler County

□ △ **MIDDLETOWN REGIONAL HOSPITAL**, 105 McKnight Drive, Zip 45044–4838; tel. 513/424–2111 **A**1 2 7 9 10 **F**8 9 10 11 12 14 15 21 22 23 26 27 28 33 34 36 46 48 49 51 53 54 55 57 58 59 60 61 62 63 66 68 69 71 72 73 74 75 76 77 78 81 84 85 86 87 88 94 95 96 108 109
Primary Contact: Douglas W. McNeill, FACHE, President and Chief Executive Officer
Web address: www.middletownhospital.org

| | | 23 | 10 | 310 | 10884 | 127 | 177860 | 1001 | 131041 | 52234 | 1329 |

MILLERSBURG—Holmes County

□ **POMERENE HOSPITAL**, 981 Wooster Road, Zip 44654–1094; tel. 330/674–1015 **A**1 9 10 **F**2 9 11 12 22 27 29 33 37 45 46 48 53 55 58 59 60 62 63 64 69 81 82 84 85 87 88 93 94 95 106 108 109 **P**1
Primary Contact: P. W. Smith, Jr, Administrator and Chief Executive Officer
Web address: www.pomerenehospital.org

| | | 13 | 10 | 40 | 1951 | 17 | 46587 | 476 | 23433 | 9660 | 242 |

MONTPELIER—Williams County

△ **COMMUNITY HOSPITAL**, 909 East Snyder Avenue, Zip 43543; tel. 419/636–1131, (Nonreporting) **A**7 10 18
Primary Contact: Rusty O. Brunicardi, President
MONTPELIER HOSPITAL See Community Hospitals and Wellness Centers, Bryan

| | | 33 | 49 | 35 | — | — | — | — | — | — | — |

MOUNT GILEAD—Morrow County

✠ **MORROW COUNTY HOSPITAL**, 651 West Marion Road, Zip 43338–1096; tel. 419/946–5015, (Total facility includes 38 beds in nursing home–type unit) (Nonreporting) **A**1 9 10 18 **S** OhioHealth, Columbus, OH
Primary Contact: Diana D. Fisher, President and Chief Executive Officer
CFO: Joe Schueler, Chief Financial Officer
Web address: www.morrowcountyhospital.com

| | | 13 | 10 | 53 | — | — | — | — | — | — | — |

MOUNT VERNON—Knox County

✠ **KNOX COMMUNITY HOSPITAL**, 1330 Coshocton Road, Zip 43050–1495; tel. 740/393–9000 **A**1 5 9 10 **F**2 9 11 12 15 17 21 22 23 26 27 28 29 33 34 37 38 40 46 47 48 52 53 54 55 58 59 60 61 62 63 65 66 69 81 82 84 85 88 93 94 108 109 110 **S** Quorum Health Resources, Plano, TX
Primary Contact: Kevin L. Rogols, Chief Executive Officer
COO: Kevin L. Rogols, Chief Executive Officer
CFO: Christine Martin, Chief Financial Officer
CIO: Kwi Holland, Director Information Services
CHR: Betty Lucci, Vice President Human Resources
Web address: www.knoxcommhosp.org

| | | 23 | 10 | 82 | 3963 | 38 | 71295 | 373 | 45143 | 19741 | 460 |

NAPOLEON—Henry County

✠ **HENRY COUNTY HOSPITAL**, 11600 State Route 424, Zip 43545–9399; tel. 419/592–4015 **A**1 5 9 10 18 **F**2 4 9 11 12 21 23 27 28 30 33 37 41 46 48 52 53 58 59 61 62 63 65 66 69 72 73 74 77 81 82 84 87 88 94 95 96 97 106 108
Primary Contact: Kimberly Bordenkircher, Chief Executive Officer
CFO: Mary Clapp, Controller
CHR: Jennifer Fisher, Manager Human Resources
Web address: www.henrycountyhospital.org

| | | 23 | 10 | 25 | 817 | 9 | 33302 | 90 | 17731 | 7560 | 167 |

NELSONVILLE—Athens County

★ ○ **DOCTORS HOSPITAL NELSONVILLE**, 1950 Mount Saint Mary Drive, Zip 45764–1193; tel. 740/753–1931, (Total facility includes 45 beds in nursing home–type unit) **A**9 10 11 18 **F**2 12 21 23 27 28 33 46 48 55 58 62 63 64 81 82 85 87 92 94 97 108 **S** OhioHealth, Columbus, OH
Primary Contact: Steve Swart, Administrator
CFO: Neal Allison, Chief Financial Officer
CHR: Shannon Atha, Human Resource and Compliance Director
Web address: www.ohiohealth.com

| | | 23 | 10 | 70 | 907 | 52 | 27056 | 0 | 15146 | 6912 | 226 |

NEW ALBANY—Franklin County

□ **NEW ALBANY SURGICAL HOSPITAL**, 7333 Smith's Mill Road, Zip 43054; tel. 614/775–6600 **A**1 10 **F**2 21 27 47 62 63 64 65 81 84 88 95 108 **P**2
Primary Contact: Richard D'Enbeau, President and Chief Executive Officer
Web address: www.newalbanysurgicalhospital.com

| | | 32 | 13 | 42 | 2510 | 15 | 3708 | 0 | — | — | 191 |

NEWARK—Licking County

□ **LICKING MEMORIAL HOSPITAL**, 1320 West Main Street, Zip 43055–3699; tel. 740/348–4000 **A**1 2 5 9 10 **F**2 3 4 11 12 21 23 24 26 27 28 29 33 37 39 46 47 48 51 52 53 55 57 58 59 60 61 63 64 65 66 69 70 71 73 74 75 77 78 82 84 85 88 93 94 96 106 107 108 110 **P**6
Primary Contact: William J. Andrews, President
Web address: www.lmhealth.org

| | | 23 | 10 | 233 | 7242 | 61 | 227284 | 1058 | 90629 | 39191 | 951 |

NORTHFIELD—Summit County

□ **NORTHCOAST BEHAVIORAL HEALTHCARE SYSTEM**, 1756 Sagamore Road, Zip 44067–1086; tel. 330/467–7131, (Includes CLEVELAND CAMPUS, 1708 Southpoint Drive, Cleveland, Zip 44109–1999; tel. 216/787–0500; NORTHFIELD CAMPUS; TOLEDO CAMPUS, 930 South Detroit Avenue, Toledo, Zip 43614–2701; tel. 419/381–1881), (Nonreporting) **A**1 5 10
Primary Contact: Thomas M. Cheek, Chief Executive Officer

| | | 12 | 22 | 376 | — | — | — | — | — | — | — |

OH

Hospital, Address, Telephone, Approval, Facility, and Physician Codes, Health Care System	Classi-fication Codes		Utilization Data					Expense (thousands) of dollars		
★ American Hospital Association (AHA) membership □ Joint Commission on Accreditation of Healthcare Organizations (JCAHO) accreditation ○ American Osteopathic Association (AOA) accreditation △ Commission on Accreditation of Rehabilitation Facilities (CARF) accreditation	Control	Service	Staffed Beds	Admissions	Census	Outpatient Visits	Births	Total	Payroll	Personnel

NORWALK—Huron County

☒ ○ **FISHER–TITUS MEDICAL CENTER**, 272 Benedict Avenue, Zip 44857–2374; tel. 419/668–8101, (Total facility includes 69 beds in nursing home–type unit) **A**1 2 9 10 11 19 **F**2 8 9 11 12 21 23 26 27 28 29 30 32 33 37 39 40 44 46 47 48 51 52 54 55 57 58 59 60 61 62 63 64 65 66 69 81 82 84 85 86 87 88 91 92 93 94 95 96 106 108 109 **P**7
Primary Contact: Patrick J. Martin, President and Chief Executive Officer
CFO: Wendy Melching, CPA, Vice President Finance
CIO: John Britton, Director of Information Services
CHR: Stan Hire, Vice President Human Resources
Web address: www.fisher–titus.com
| 23 | 10 | 140 | 4317 | 104 | 128804 | 697 | 67588 | 28660 | 686 |

OBERLIN—Lorain County

□ **ALLEN MEDICAL CENTER**, 200 West Lorain Street, Zip 44074–1077; tel. 440/775–1211, (Nonreporting) **A**1 9 10 18 **S** Catholic Healthcare Partners, Cincinnati, OH
Primary Contact: Edwin M. Oley, President and Chief Executive Officer
Web address: www.ehealthconnection.com/lorain
| 23 | 10 | 25 | — | — | — | — | — | — | — |

OREGON—Lucas County

☒ **BAY PARK COMMUNITY HOSPITAL**, 2801 Bay Park Drive, Zip 43616; tel. 419/690–7900 **A**1 9 10 **F**2 9 11 12 15 21 22 23 26 27 28 29 33 35 37 39 46 47 48 49 52 53 55 57 58 59 60 61 62 63 64 65 66 69 81 82 84 85 88 92 93 94 95 96 106 108 109 110 **P**6 **S** ProMedica Health System, Toledo, OH
Primary Contact: Terri L. McLain, R.N., MSN, CHE, President
Web address: www.promedica.org
| 23 | 10 | 70 | 3567 | 41 | 73086 | 474 | 50590 | 17946 | 345 |

☒ **ST. CHARLES MERCY HOSPITAL**, 2600 Navarre Avenue, Zip 43616–3297; tel. 419/696–7200 **A**1 2 5 9 10 **F**4 6 9 10 11 12 21 22 23 26 27 28 29 30 33 34 37 41 42 44 45 46 48 50 52 55 59 60 61 62 63 64 68 69 71 72 73 74 75 76 77 78 79 80 81 82 83 84 85 86 87 88 93 94 95 96 99 108 109 110 **P**1 **S** Catholic Healthcare Partners, Cincinnati, OH
Primary Contact: David J. Ameen, President and Chief Executive Officer
CFO: Todd Warner, Interim Chief Financial Officer
CMO: Nagi Bishara, M.D., Chief of Staff
CIO: James Albin, Regional Vice President and Chief Information Officer
CHR: Gary George, Regional Vice President Human Resources
Web address: www.mercyweb.org
| 21 | 10 | 390 | 9790 | 163 | 172855 | 696 | — | — | 1166 |

ORRVILLE—Wayne County

☒ **DUNLAP MEMORIAL HOSPITAL**, 832 South Main Street, Zip 44667–2208; tel. 330/682–3010, (Nonreporting) **A**1 9 10 18
Primary Contact: Lynn V. Horner, President and Chief Executive Officer
CFO: Randall S. Evans, Vice President Finance
Web address: www.dunlaphospital.org
| 23 | 10 | 25 | — | — | — | — | — | — | — |

OXFORD—Butler County

○ **MCCULLOUGH–HYDE MEMORIAL HOSPITAL**, 110 North Poplar Street, Zip 45056–1292; tel. 513/523–2111 **A**9 10 11 **F**2 9 11 12 21 22 23 24 26 27 28 29 33 45 46 47 48 52 54 55 58 59 60 61 62 63 64 65 69 81 84 87 88 93 94 95 96 106 107 108 109
Primary Contact: Richard A. Daniels, President and Chief Executive Officer
Web address: www.mhmh.org
| 23 | 10 | 45 | 2389 | 23 | 79673 | 515 | 38401 | 15762 | 358 |

PAINESVILLE—Lake County

☒ **LAKE HOSPITAL SYSTEM**, 10 East Washington, Zip 44077–3472; tel. 440/354–2400, (Total facility includes 8 beds in nursing home–type unit) **A**1 2 9 10 **F**9 11 12 15 17 19 21 22 23 26 27 28 29 33 35 36 37 39 40 42 44 45 46 47 48 49 51 52 53 54 55 57 58 59 60 62 63 65 66 68 69 71 76 81 82 84 85 86 88 92 93 94 95 96 106 107 108 109 **P**1
Primary Contact: Cynthia Ann Moore–Hardy, President and Chief Executive Officer
CFO: Robert Tracz, Chief Financial Officer
CMO: Theodore Nichols, M.D., Senior Vice President Medical Affairs
Web address: www.lhs.net
| 23 | 10 | 318 | 16111 | 197 | 277389 | 1836 | 195667 | 78489 | 1891 |

PARMA—Cuyahoga County

☒ △ **PARMA COMMUNITY GENERAL HOSPITAL**, 7007 Powers Boulevard, Zip 44129–5495; tel. 440/743–3000, (Total facility includes 27 beds in nursing home–type unit) **A**1 2 7 10 **F**1 2 8 9 10 11 12 14 15 17 19 21 22 23 24 26 28 29 30 33 35 36 37 38 39 40 41 44 45 46 47 48 51 52 53 54 55 57 58 59 60 61 62 63 64 65 66 68 69 71 79 80 81 82 84 85 88 92 94 95 96 98 106 107 108 110 **P**6
Primary Contact: Patricia A. Ruflin, President and Chief Executive Officer
CFO: Barry L. Franklin, Executive Vice President and Chief Financial Officer
CMO: Donn Wolfson, M.D., Vice President Medical Affairs
CIO: Terry Deis, Vice President General Services and Chief Information Officer
CHR: Larry Jeffries, Senior Director Human Resources
Web address: www.parmahospital.org
| 23 | 10 | 307 | 17832 | 253 | 293868 | 572 | 178271 | 76285 | 1685 |

PAULDING—Paulding County

□ **PAULDING COUNTY HOSPITAL**, 1035 West Wayne Street, Zip 45879–9220; tel. 419/399–4080 **A**1 9 10 18 **F**2 9 11 12 21 22 28 33 41 45 46 48 51 52 53 54 58 59 60 62 63 69 70 81 82 84 88 92 93 94 97 106 108
Primary Contact: Gary W. Adkins, Chief Executive Officer
Web address: www.pauldingcountyhospital.com
| 13 | 10 | 25 | 634 | 6 | 60183 | 85 | 14799 | 7186 | 172 |

Many Facility Codes have changed. Please refer to the AHA Guide Code Chart.   © 2005 AHA Guide

Hospital, Address, Telephone, Approval, Facility, and Physician Codes, Health Care System	Classi-fication Codes		Utilization Data					Expense (thousands) of dollars		
★ American Hospital Association (AHA) membership □ Joint Commission on Accreditation of Healthcare Organizations (JCAHO) accreditation ○ American Osteopathic Association (AOA) accreditation △ Commission on Accreditation of Rehabilitation Facilities (CARF) accreditation	Control	Service	Staffed Beds	Admissions	Census	Outpatient Visits	Births	Total	Payroll	Personnel

PORT CLINTON—Ottawa County

□ **H. B. MAGRUDER MEMORIAL HOSPITAL**, 615 Fulton Street, Zip 43452–2034; tel. 419/734–3131 **A**1 5 9 10 18 **F**2 9 12 21 23 26 27 28 29 33 39 40 46 47 48 52 54 55 58 61 62 63 64 65 66 69 70 81 82 87 88 94 95 96 97 108 110 **P**6 8
Primary Contact: David R. Norwine, FACHE, President and Chief Executive Officer
Web address: www.magruderhospital.com

| 23 | 10 | 25 | 1280 | 13 | 82787 | 0 | 29636 | 12007 | 299 |

PORTSMOUTH—Scioto County

⊠ △ **SOUTHERN OHIO MEDICAL CENTER**, 1805 27th Street, Zip 45662–2400; tel. 740/354–5000, (Includes MERCY HOSPITAL, 1248 Kinneys Lane, Zip 45662; SCIOTO MEMORIAL HOSPITAL, 1805 27th Street, Zip 45662) **A**1 5 7 9 10 12 13 19 **F**2 9 11 12 15 17 21 22 23 26 27 28 29 30 31 32 33 36 37 38 39 41 42 44 46 47 48 50 51 52 53 55 57 58 59 60 61 62 63 64 65 66 68 73 75 81 82 84 85 87 88 91 93 94 95 96 98 106 107 108 109 110 **P**3 **S** OhioHealth, Columbus, OH
Primary Contact: Randal M. Arnett, President and Chief Executive Officer
COO: Claudia Burchett, Vice President Patient Services
CFO: Dean Wray, Vice President Finance
CMO: Kendall Stewart, M.D., Medical Director
CIO: Brent Richard, Director Information Systems
CHR: Bane Sylvia, Vice President Human Resources
Web address: www.somc.org

| 23 | 10 | 222 | 11594 | 144 | 295803 | 1413 | 155965 | 61264 | 1601 |

RAVENNA—Portage County

★ **REGENCY HOSPITAL OF RAVENNA**, 6847 North Chestnut Street, Zip 44266; tel. 330/296–2350, (Nonreporting) **S** Regency Hospital Company, Alpharetta, GA
Primary Contact: Robert A. Leonhard, Jr, Chief Executive Officer

| 33 | 80 | 19 | — | — | — | — | — | — | — |

□ **ROBINSON MEMORIAL HOSPITAL**, 6847 North Chestnut Street, Zip 44266–1204, Mailing Address: P.O. Box 1204, Zip 44266–1204; tel. 330/297–0811 **A**1 2 3 5 9 10 **F**2 9 11 12 14 15 17 21 22 23 24 26 27 28 29 33 34 35 36 37 38 39 40 42 44 46 47 48 50 51 52 55 57 58 59 60 61 62 63 64 65 66 69 70 73 79 80 81 82 84 85 87 88 93 94 95 96 106 107 108 109 110 **P**6 8
Primary Contact: Stephen Colecchi, President and Chief Executive Officer
Web address: www.robinsonmemorial.org

| 13 | 10 | 118 | 8410 | 92 | 128214 | 595 | 120395 | 48503 | 1119 |

RICHMOND HEIGHTS—Cuyahoga County

★ ○ **UHHS RICHMOND HEIGHTS HOSPITAL**, 27100 Chardon Road, Zip 44143–1198; tel. 440/585–6500, (Nonreporting) **A**9 10 11 12 13 **S** University Hospitals Health System, Cleveland, OH
Primary Contact: William P. Lawrence, President
CFO: Kris Bennett, Finance Director
CMO: Michael Devereaux, M.D., Medical Director and Vice President Clinical Integration
CHR: Marti Newman, Acting Manager Human Resources
Web address: www.uhhsrh.org

| 23 | 10 | 100 | | | | | | | |

ROCK CREEK—Ashtabula County

GLENBEIGH HOSPITAL AND OUTPATIENT CENTERS, Route 45, Zip 44084, Mailing Address: P.O. Box 298, Zip 44084–0298; tel. 440/563–3400 **A**10 **F**3 4 26 27 28 **P**5
Primary Contact: Patricia Weston–Hall, Executive Director
Web address: www.glenbeigh.com

| 23 | 82 | 85 | 1709 | 30 | 28127 | 0 | — | — | 104 |

SAINT CLAIRSVILLE—Belmont County

□ **FOX RUN HOSPITAL**, 67670 Traco Drive, Zip 43950–9375; tel. 740/695–2131 **A**1 10 **F**21 26 27 28 66 71 72 74 77 94 **P**6 **S** Psychiatric Solutions, Franklin, TN
Primary Contact: Karen Maxwell, Chief Executive Officer
Web address: www.bhcfoxrun.com

| 33 | 22 | 74 | 992 | 63 | 351 | 0 | 7116 | 3813 | 131 |

SAINT MARYS—Auglaize County

⊠ **JOINT TOWNSHIP DISTRICT MEMORIAL HOSPITAL**, 200 St. Clair Street, Zip 45885–2400; tel. 419/394–3387, (Total facility includes 15 beds in nursing home–type unit) **A**1 9 10 **F**2 6 9 11 12 21 23 27 28 29 33 37 40 46 48 51 52 53 58 59 60 61 62 63 65 66 68 69 70 81 82 88 92 94 95 96 106 108 109 110
Primary Contact: James R. Chick, President
CFO: Jeffrey W. Vossler, Vice President Financial Services
CIO: DeWayne Marsee, Director Information Systems
CHR: Art Swain, Vice President Support Services
Web address: www.jtdmh.org

| 23 | 10 | 90 | 4204 | 50 | 76289 | 262 | 45300 | 16825 | 439 |

SALEM—Columbiana County

⊠ **SALEM COMMUNITY HOSPITAL**, 1995 East State Street, Zip 44460–0121; tel. 330/332–1551, (Total facility includes 15 beds in nursing home–type unit) **A**1 5 9 10 **F**9 11 12 15 17 21 22 23 26 27 28 33 37 40 46 48 52 54 55 57 58 59 60 61 62 63 64 69 81 82 84 85 87 88 92 93 94 96 106 108 110
Primary Contact: Howard E. Rohleder, President and Chief Executive Officer
CFO: Mike Giangardella, Vice President Finance and Administration
CIO: Mark L'Italien, Director Information Services
Web address: www.salemhosp.com

| 23 | 10 | 140 | 6313 | 80 | 145862 | 620 | 71232 | 32776 | 784 |

Hospital, Address, Telephone, Approval, Facility, and Physician Codes, Health Care System	Classi-fication Codes		Utilization Data					Expense (thousands) of dollars		
★ American Hospital Association (AHA) membership □ Joint Commission on Accreditation of Healthcare Organizations (JCAHO) accreditation ○ American Osteopathic Association (AOA) accreditation △ Commission on Accreditation of Rehabilitation Facilities (CARF) accreditation	Control	Service	Staffed Beds	Admissions	Census	Outpatient Visits	Births	Total	Payroll	Personnel

SANDUSKY—Erie County

□ ○ △ **FIRELANDS REGIONAL HEALTH SYSTEM**, 1101 Decatur Street, Zip 44870–3335; tel. 419/626–7400, (Includes FIRELANDS REGIONAL MEDICAL CENTER – MAIN CAMPUS, 1101 Decatur Street, Zip 44870–8005; tel. 419/626–7400; FIRELANDS REGIONAL MEDICAL CENTER SOUTH CAMPUS, 1912 Hayes Avenue, Zip 44870–4736; tel. 419/621–7000; Charles A. Stark, CHE, President and Chief Executive Officer), (Nonreporting) **A**1 2 6 7 9 10 11 12 13 19
Primary Contact: Charles A. Stark, CHE, President and Chief Executive Officer
Web address: www.firelands.com
    23 10 211 — — — — — — —

SHELBY—Richland County

SHELBY HOSPITAL See MedCentral Health System, Mansfield

SIDNEY—Shelby County

⊞ **WILSON MEMORIAL HOSPITAL**, 915 West Michigan Street, Zip 45365–2491; tel. 937/498–2311 **A**1 9 10 **F**2 6 9 10 11 12 15 21 22 23 26 27 28 33 36 44 46 48 49 51 52 53 55 59 60 61 62 63 64 65 66 69 71 76 81 82 88 93 94 96 108 109 **P**6
Primary Contact: Thomas J. Boecker, President and Chief Executive Officer
CFO: Douglas Bomba, Vice President Finance
CMO: Randall Welsh, M.D., Chief of Staff
CIO: Jeff Partee, Chief Information Officer
CHR: Bill McCaskey, Director Human Resources
Web address: www.wilsonhospital.com
    23 10 90 3598 39 163106 637 54178 21513 567

SPRINGFIELD—Clark County

⊞ **COMMUNITY HOSPITAL**, 2615 East High Street, Zip 45505–1422, Mailing Address: Box 1228, Zip 45501–1228; tel. 937/325–0531, (Total facility includes 26 beds in nursing home–type unit) **A**1 6 9 10 **F**2 9 11 12 14 15 17 19 21 22 26 27 28 29 30 33 36 37 39 41 46 47 48 49 50 52 54 55 57 58 59 60 61 62 63 65 66 68 69 82 84 85 87 88 92 93 94 96 106 108 109 110 **S** Catholic Healthcare Partners, Cincinnati, OH
Primary Contact: Andrew R. McCulloch, President and Chief Executive Officer
CFO: Dana E. Engle, Vice President Finance
CMO: Kamel Abraham, M.D., Chief of Staff
Web address: www.communityhospital.com
    21 10 204 9760 122 173443 1593 119236 47780 1268

⊞ **MERCY MEDICAL CENTER**, 1343 North Fountain Boulevard, Zip 45501–1380; tel. 937/390–5000 **A**1 2 5 9 10 **F**2 4 9 12 14 15 17 19 21 22 24 26 27 28 29 31 33 36 37 38 42 44 46 48 49 50 51 52 53 55 57 58 60 62 63 65 66 68 69 81 82 84 85 87 88 93 94 96 98 106 108 109 110 **S** Catholic Healthcare Partners, Cincinnati, OH
Primary Contact: Andrew R. McCulloch, President and Chief Executive Officer
CFO: David Wilhoite, Chief Financial Officer
CMO: Donald Johnson, M.D., Chief Medical Officer
CIO: Steve Sarros, Interim Director Information Systems
CHR: Cheryl Lamhorn, Director Human Resources
Web address: www.mercy–health.org
    21 10 158 8541 112 115228 0 56900 40519 917

STEUBENVILLE—Jefferson County

⊞ **TRINITY HEALTH SYSTEM**, 380 Summit Avenue, Zip 43952–2699; tel. 740/283–7000, (Includes TRINITY MEDICAL CENTER EAST; TRINITY MEDICAL CENTER WEST, 4000 Johnson Road, Zip 43952–2393; tel. 740/264–8000), (Nonreporting) **A**1 2 6 9 10 **S** Franciscan Services Corporation, Sylvania, OH
Primary Contact: Fred B. Brower, President and Chief Executive Officer
CIO: Tom Kiger, Director Information Systems
Web address: www.trinityhealth.com
    21 10 350 — — — — — — —

SYLVANIA—Lucas County

⊞ **FLOWER HOSPITAL**, 5200 Harroun Road, Zip 43560–2196; tel. 419/824–1444 **A**1 2 9 10 **F**2 9 11 12 15 17 19 21 22 23 26 27 28 29 30 31 33 37 39 44 45 46 47 48 52 53 55 58 59 60 61 62 63 64 65 66 68 69 70 71 73 74 75 76 79 80 81 82 83 84 85 87 88 92 93 94 95 96 106 108 109 **S** ProMedica Health System, Toledo, OH
Primary Contact: Kevin C. Webb, FACHE, President
CFO: Alan Sattler, Senior Vice President, Finance
CIO: David G. Selman, Vice President Information
Web address: www.promedica.org
    23 10 252 11074 168 110927 923 120354 55150 1356

TIFFIN—Seneca County

⊞ **MERCY HOSPITAL OF TIFFIN**, 485 West Market Street, Zip 44883–0727; tel. 419/447–3130 **A**1 5 9 10 **F**2 9 11 12 21 22 23 26 27 28 29 30 33 37 38 39 44 45 46 47 48 50 52 53 55 57 58 59 60 61 62 63 64 65 66 70 79 80 81 82 84 85 86 87 88 90 92 93 94 96 98 106 108 109 110 **P**8 **S** Catholic Healthcare Partners, Cincinnati, OH
Primary Contact: Dale E. Thornton, M.P.H., CHE, President and Chief Executive Officer
CFO: Thomas Poulson, Vice President Finance
CIO: Catherine Marvin, Manager of Application Services
CHR: Diana Olson, Chief Human Resources Officer
Web address: www.mhsnr.org
    21 10 65 2276 29 94862 456 39108 16241 448

Hospital, Address, Telephone, Approval, Facility, and Physician Codes, Health Care System	Classi-fication Codes		Utilization Data					Expense (thousands) of dollars		
★ American Hospital Association (AHA) membership □ Joint Commission on Accreditation of Healthcare Organizations (JCAHO) accreditation ○ American Osteopathic Association (AOA) accreditation △ Commission on Accreditation of Rehabilitation Facilities (CARF) accreditation	Control	Service	Staffed Beds	Admissions	Census	Outpatient Visits	Births	Total	Payroll	Personnel

TOLEDO—Lucas County

□ △ **MEDICAL COLLEGE OF OHIO HOSPITALS**, 3000 Arlington Avenue, Zip 43614–5805; tel. 419/383–4000 **A**1 2 3 5 7 8 9 10 **F**2 7 9 10 12 15 17 19 21 22 23 24 26 27 28 29 32 33 34 37 38 39 40 41 42 43 44 46 47 48 49 50 52 53 55 57 58 60 61 62 63 64 65 66 68 69 70 71 72 73 74 75 76 77 78 79 80 81 82 83 84 85 86 87 88 89 90 92 94 95 96 98 101 102 106 108 109 110 **P**4
Primary Contact: Lloyd A. Jacobs, M.D., President
Web address: www.mco.edu

| 12 | 10 | 233 | 10156 | 157 | 193926 | 0 | 175627 | 75260 | 1559 |

★ ○ **ST. ANNE MERCY HOSPITAL**, 3404 West Sylvania Avenue, Zip 43623; tel. 419/407–2663 **A**1 2 9 10 11 **F**2 11 12 21 22 23 26 27 28 29 30 31 33 38 42 44 46 47 48 52 53 55 57 58 59 61 62 63 64 65 66 69 81 82 84 85 87 88 94 95 96 108 109 **P**1 **S** Catholic Healthcare Partners, Cincinnati, OH
Primary Contact: Karen H. Connors, President and Chief Executive Officer
CFO: Samantha Platyke, Chief Financial Officer
CIO: James Albin, Regional Vice President and Chief Information Officer
CHR: Gary George, Regional Vice President Human Resources
Web address: www.mercyweb.org

| 21 | 10 | 142 | 5128 | 70 | 147797 | 477 | — | — | 645 |

★ ○ **ST. VINCENT MERCY MEDICAL CENTER**, 2213 Cherry Street, Zip 43608–2691; tel. 419/251–3232, (Includes MERCY CHILDREN'S HOSPITAL, tel. 419/251–8000; Richard R. Evens, President) **A**1 2 3 5 9 10 11 12 13 **F**2 6 9 10 11 12 13 14 15 16 17 18 19 20 21 22 23 24 26 27 28 29 30 31 33 34 35 37 38 39 40 42 44 46 47 48 49 50 52 53 55 56 57 58 59 60 61 62 63 64 65 66 67 69 70 71 73 74 75 76 77 78 80 81 82 83 84 85 86 87 88 92 93 94 95 96 98 99 104 106 108 109 110 **P**8 **S** Catholic Healthcare Partners, Cincinnati, OH
Primary Contact: Jeffrey D. Peterson, President and Chief Executive Officer
CFO: Samantha M. Platzke, Senior Vice President Finance and Chief Financial Officer
CMO: David R. Franzblau, M.D., Chief Medical Officer
CIO: James Albin, Regional Vice President and Chief Information Officer
CHR: Gary George, Regional Vice President Human Resources
Web address: www.mercyweb.org

| 21 | 10 | 556 | 19225 | 283 | 334845 | 1218 | — | — | 2743 |

★ **THE TOLEDO HOSPITAL**, 2142 North Cove Boulevard, Zip 43606–3896; tel. 419/291–4000, (Includes TOLEDO CHILDREN'S HOSPITAL, Janice E. McBride, President), (Total facility includes 25 beds in nursing home–type unit) **A**1 3 9 10 12 13 **F**2 3 4 7 9 11 12 14 15 16 17 18 19 20 21 22 23 24 26 27 28 29 30 31 32 33 34 37 38 39 40 41 42 46 47 48 49 52 53 55 56 57 58 59 60 61 62 63 64 65 66 67 69 70 71 72 73 74 75 77 78 80 81 82 83 84 85 87 88 89 90 92 93 94 95 96 98 106 108 109 110 **S** ProMedica Health System, Toledo, OH
Primary Contact: Barbara Steele, President
CFO: Lori Johnston, Vice President Finance
CMO: Ronald Wainz, M.D., Vice President Medical Affairs
CIO: David G. Selman, Corporate Vice President Information Resources
CHR: Charles McDowell, Corporate Vice President Human Resources
Web address: www.promedica.org
TOLEDO CAMPUS See Northcoast Behavioral Healthcare System, Northfield

| 23 | 10 | 610 | 29964 | 401 | 508772 | 4520 | 440772 | 180495 | 4295 |

TROY—Miami County

□ △ **UPPER VALLEY MEDICAL CENTER**, 3130 North Dixie Highway, Zip 45373–1309; tel. 937/440–4000, (Includes DETTMER HOSPITAL, tel. 937/440–7500) **A**1 2 3 5 7 9 10 **F**2 3 6 11 12 15 19 21 22 23 24 26 27 28 29 33 35 37 39 40 41 42 43 46 47 48 50 51 52 53 55 58 59 60 61 62 63 64 65 66 68 69 71 72 73 74 75 76 77 81 82 84 87 88 92 93 94 95 96 98 106 108 109 110 **P**6
Primary Contact: David J. Meckstroth, President and Chief Executive Officer
Web address: www.uvmc.com

| 23 | 10 | 178 | 9260 | 114 | 304000 | 1090 | 112419 | 50045 | 1257 |

UPPER SANDUSKY—Wyandot County

★ **WYANDOT MEMORIAL HOSPITAL**, 885 North Sandusky Avenue, Zip 43351–1098; tel. 419/294–4991 **A**5 9 10 18 **F**2 9 11 12 14 21 23 27 28 33 46 48 52 59 60 61 62 63 64 65 66 81 82 87 88 93 97 106 108 **P**6
Primary Contact: Joseph A. D'Ettorre, Chief Executive Officer
COO: Ty Shaull, Chief Operating Officer
CFO: Alan H. Yeates, Vice President Fiscal Services
CMO: Joseph G. Sberna, M.D., Chief of Staff
Web address: www.wyandotmemorial.com

| 16 | 10 | 25 | 984 | 10 | 45540 | 151 | 18105 | 7356 | 173 |

URBANA—Champaign County

★ **MERCY MEMORIAL HOSPITAL**, 904 Scioto Street, Zip 43078–2200; tel. 937/653–5231 **A**9 10 18 **F**2 4 12 21 22 24 26 27 28 29 33 46 48 53 55 58 60 62 63 64 66 69 81 84 88 94 97 98 106 108 **P**2 **S** Catholic Healthcare Partners, Cincinnati, OH
Primary Contact: Karl Zalar, Administrator and Chief Executive Officer
Web address: www.mercy–health.org

| 21 | 10 | 12 | 941 | 8 | 50479 | 0 | 15627 | 5703 | 126 |

VAN WERT—Van Wert County

★ **VAN WERT COUNTY HOSPITAL**, 1250 South Washington Street, Zip 45891–2599; tel. 419/238–2390 **A**1 5 9 10 **F**11 12 21 26 27 28 29 33 41 42 44 46 48 49 52 55 59 60 62 63 66 69 81 82 84 88 93 94 95 108 **P**8
Primary Contact: Mark J. Minick, President and Chief Executive Officer
CFO: Michael T. Holliday, Vice President Fiscal and Administrative Services
CHR: Joyce Pothast, Vice President Human and Environmental Services
Web address: www.vanwerthospital.org

| 23 | 10 | 80 | 1664 | 17 | 49680 | 301 | 28372 | 10060 | 217 |

Hospital, Address, Telephone, Approval, Facility, and Physician Codes, Health Care System	Classi-fication Codes		Utilization Data					Expense (thousands) of dollars		
	Control	Service	Staffed Beds	Admissions	Census	Outpatient Visits	Births	Total	Payroll	Personnel

★ American Hospital Association (AHA) membership
□ Joint Commission on Accreditation of Healthcare Organizations (JCAHO) accreditation
○ American Osteopathic Association (AOA) accreditation
△ Commission on Accreditation of Rehabilitation Facilities (CARF) accreditation

WADSWORTH—Medina County

□ **WADSWORTH–RITTMAN HOSPITAL**, 195 Wadsworth Road, Zip 44281–9505; tel. 330/334–1504, (Nonreporting) **A**1 5 9 10
Primary Contact: James W. Pope, FACHE, President and Chief Executive Officer
Web address: www.wrhospital.com
— Control 23, Service 10, Staffed Beds 77

WARREN—Trumbull County

□ **FORUM HEALTH TRUMBULL MEMORIAL HOSPITAL**, 1350 East Market Street, Zip 44482–6628; tel. 330/841–9011, (Nonreporting) **A**1 2 3 5 9 10 **S** Forum Health, Youngstown, OH
Primary Contact: N. Kristopher Hoce, President and Chief Executive Officer
Web address: www.forumhealth.org
— Control 23, Service 10, Staffed Beds 292

□ △ **FORUM HILLSIDE REHABILITATION HOSPITAL**, 8747 Squires Lane N.E., Zip 44484–1649; tel. 330/841–3700, (Nonreporting) **A**1 5 7 9 10 **S** Forum Health, Youngstown, OH
Primary Contact: Rodney Jones, Chief Operating Officer
Web address: www.forumhealth.org
— Control 13, Service 46, Staffed Beds 47

⊠ ○ **ST. JOSEPH HEALTH CENTER**, 667 Eastland Avenue S.E., Zip 44484–4531; tel. 330/841–4000, (Total facility includes 11 beds in nursing home–type unit) **A**1 9 10 11 12 13 **F**2 4 9 10 11 12 21 22 23 26 27 28 29 33 34 35 37 38 39 40 41 42 43 44 45 46 48 49 50 52 54 55 58 59 60 61 62 63 64 65 66 69 70 71 72 73 74 75 76 77 79 80 81 82 83 84 85 86 87 88 92 93 94 96 107 108 109 110 **S** Catholic Healthcare Partners, Cincinnati, OH
Primary Contact: Robert W. Shroder, President and Chief Executive Officer
COO: William A. Young, Jr, Chief Operating Officer
CFO: R Andrew Brothers, Senior Vice President Finance
CIO: Charles Folkwein, Vice President Ancillary Services and Information Technology
CHR: Molly Seals, Senior Vice President Human Resources and Organizational Development
Web address: www.hmpartners.org
— Control 21, Service 10, Staffed Beds 158, Admissions 8205, Census 103, Outpatient Visits 155326, Births 860, Total 95343, Payroll 34690, Personnel 917

WARRENSVILLE HEIGHTS—Morgan County

□ ○ **SOUTH POINTE HOSPITAL**, 4110 Warrensville Center Road, Zip 44122–7099; tel. 216/491–6000 **A**1 2 10 11 12 13 **F**9 12 21 22 23 24 26 27 28 29 30 31 32 33 35 37 38 40 41 45 46 47 48 49 50 52 54 55 60 61 62 63 66 68 69 70 71 72 73 74 75 76 77 78 81 82 84 86 87 88 89 92 94 95 96 98 106 107 108 109 **S** Cleveland Clinic Health System, Cleveland, OH
Primary Contact: Beverly Lozar, Chief Administrative Officer
Web address: www.southpointehospital.org
— Control 23, Service 10, Staffed Beds 234, Admissions 10353, Census 169, Outpatient Visits 169907, Births 0, Total 121372, Payroll 60077, Personnel 1231

WASHINGTON COURT HOUSE—Lucas County

⊠ **FAYETTE COUNTY MEMORIAL HOSPITAL**, 1430 Columbus Avenue, Zip 43160–1791; tel. 740/335–1210 **A**1 5 9 10 **F**2 9 10 11 12 21 23 27 28 29 32 33 37 46 47 48 51 52 53 54 55 57 58 59 60 61 62 63 64 65 66 69 70 75 81 88 94 95 96 108 **S** Trinity Health, Novi, MI
Primary Contact: Francis G. Albarano, Chief Executive Officer
CFO: Chris Peters, Vice President Finance
CMO: Frank Klamet, Chief of Staff
CIO: Bruce Denen, Data Processing Manager
CHR: Tina Powers, Human Resource Directpr
Web address: www.fcmh.org
— Control 13, Service 10, Staffed Beds 34, Admissions 1603, Census 14, Outpatient Visits —, Births 341, Total 27370, Payroll 10578, Personnel 276

WAUSEON—Fulton County

⊠ **FULTON COUNTY HEALTH CENTER**, 725 South Shoop Avenue, Zip 43567–1701; tel. 419/335–2015, (Total facility includes 71 beds in nursing home–type unit) **A**1 2 9 10 **F**8 9 11 12 21 23 26 27 33 41 46 48 54 55 58 59 60 61 62 63 66 69 71 74 75 76 77 78 81 82 84 87 88 91 92 93 94 95 96 106 108
Primary Contact: E. Dean Beck, Administrator
COO: Patti Finn, Assistant Administrator
CFO: Darrell Topmiller, Director Finance
CHR: Kristy Synder, Human Resources Director
Web address: www.fultoncountyhealthcenter.org
— Control 23, Service 10, Staffed Beds 172, Admissions 2742, Census 107, Outpatient Visits 142787, Births 297, Total 46913, Payroll 20640, Personnel 583

WAVERLY—Pike County

□ **PIKE COMMUNITY HOSPITAL**, 100 Dawn Lane, Zip 45690–9664; tel. 740/947–2186 **A**1 9 10 **F**9 12 26 27 29 33 35 39 44 46 47 48 52 53 55 58 62 63 65 69 70 81 82 83 84 87 88 93 94 97 108 109 110 **P**6
Primary Contact: Richard E. Sobota, President and Chief Executive Officer
Web address: www.pikecommunityhospital.org
— Control 23, Service 10, Staffed Beds 33, Admissions 1284, Census 10, Outpatient Visits 43672, Births 0, Total 14268, Payroll 6871, Personnel 246

WEST UNION—Adams County

□ **ADAMS COUNTY HOSPITAL**, 210 North Wilson Drive, Zip 45693–1574; tel. 937/544–5571 **A**1 9 10 18 **F**9 12 21 22 23 26 27 28 29 33 36 37 38 41 46 48 51 52 53 58 60 61 62 63 65 66 69 81 84 88 93 94 95 97 106 108 109 110
Primary Contact: Linda Niles, Chief Executive Officer
Web address: www.bright.net/~ach
— Control 13, Service 10, Staffed Beds 25, Admissions 1696, Census 17, Outpatient Visits 44381, Births 0, Total 17852, Payroll 7593, Personnel 234

WESTERVILLE—Franklin County

⊠ **MOUNT CARMEL ST. ANN'S**, 500 South Cleveland Avenue, Zip 43081–8998; tel. 614/898–4000 **A**1 3 9 10 **F**2 9 11 12 15 17 19 21 22 23 26 27 28 29 33 35 36 37 38 39 40 48 51 52 53 55 56 57 58 59 61 62 63 64 65 66 70 79 80 81 82 83 84 85 87 88 90 94 106 108 109 110 **S** Trinity Health, Novi, MI
Primary Contact: Joseph T. Calvaruso, Chief Executive Officer
Web address: www.mountcarmelhealth.com
— Control 21, Service 10, Staffed Beds 272, Admissions 13682, Census 164, Outpatient Visits 180070, Births 4359, Total 156709, Payroll 60979, Personnel —

Many Facility Codes have changed. Please refer to the AHA Guide Code Chart.
© 2005 AHA Guide

Hospital, Address, Telephone, Approval, Facility, and Physician Codes, Health Care System	Classi-fication Codes		Utilization Data					Expense (thousands) of dollars		
★ American Hospital Association (AHA) membership □ Joint Commission on Accreditation of Healthcare Organizations (JCAHO) accreditation ○ American Osteopathic Association (AOA) accreditation △ Commission on Accreditation of Rehabilitation Facilities (CARF) accreditation	Control	Service	Staffed Beds	Admissions	Census	Outpatient Visits	Births	Total	Payroll	Personnel

WILLARD—Huron County

☒ **MERCY HOSPITAL OF WILLARD**, 110 East Howard Street, Zip 44890–1611; tel. 419/964–5000 **A**1 5 9 10 18 **F**4 11 12 22 28 29 33 45 46 47 48 51 52 54 55 58 59 60 61 62 63 66 69 77 81 84 88 92 94 96 97 108 109 **P**8 **S** Catholic Healthcare Partners, Cincinnati, OH
Primary Contact: Robert E. Gospodarek, President and Chief Executive Officer
CFO: Thomas Poulson, Vice President Finance
CMO: James Rosso, M.D., Chief of Staff
CHR: Diana Olson, Chief Human Resources Officer
Web address: www.mhsnr.org

| | 21 | 10 | 25 | 758 | 10 | 53825 | 144 | 19557 | 8333 | 181 |

WILLOUGHBY—Lake County

□ **LAURELWOOD HOSPITAL**, (Formerly UHHS Laurelwood Hospital), 35900 Euclid Avenue, Zip 44094–4648; tel. 440/953–3000 **A**1 9 10 **F**3 4 26 27 28 29 30 52 66 71 72 73 74 75 77 78 94 108 **P**6
Primary Contact: Farshid Afsarifard, Ph.D., CHE, President and Chief Executive Officer
Web address: www.laurelwoodhospital.com

| | 23 | 22 | 116 | 3558 | 67 | 31084 | 0 | 18881 | 10934 | 307 |

WILMINGTON—Clinton County

☒ △ **CLINTON MEMORIAL HOSPITAL**, 610 West Main Street, Zip 45177–0600; tel. 937/382–6611, (Total facility includes 12 beds in nursing home–type unit) **A**1 2 3 5 7 9 10 **F**9 11 12 15 21 22 27 28 29 31 32 33 39 41 42 44 46 47 48 51 52 53 54 55 57 58 59 60 61 62 63 65 66 68 69 70 81 82 84 88 92 94 95 96 107 108 109 **P**1
Primary Contact: Timothy J. Crowley, President and Chief Executive Officer
CFO: William E. Baecker, Vice President and Chief Financial Officer
CMO: Philip C. Aschi, D.O., Chief of Staff
CHR: Charles Snider, Director Human Resources
Web address: www.cmhregional.com

| | 13 | 10 | 87 | 4441 | 43 | 206686 | 686 | 78662 | 33128 | 778 |

WOOSTER—Wayne County

☒ **WOOSTER COMMUNITY HOSPITAL**, 1761 Beall Avenue, Zip 44691–2342; tel. 330/263–8100 **A**1 2 9 10 19 **F**2 9 11 12 15 21 22 23 24 26 27 28 29 33 40 41 45 46 48 50 51 52 55 57 58 59 60 61 62 63 64 65 66 69 81 82 84 85 86 87 88 93 94 96 106 108 109 110 **P**8 **S** Quorum Health Resources, Plano, TX
Primary Contact: William E. Sheron, Chief Executive Officer
Web address: www.woosterhospital.org

| | 14 | 10 | 114 | 5574 | 53 | 156663 | 1004 | 66064 | 27610 | 659 |

WRIGHT–PATTERSON AFB—Greene County

☒ **WRIGHT PATTERSON MEDICAL CENTER**, 4881 Sugar Maple Drive, Zip 45433–5529; tel. 937/257–0837, (Nonreporting) **A**1 2 3 5 **S** Department of the Air Force, Washington, DC
Primary Contact: Colonel Loretta Bailey, Administrator
CFO: Major Brenda Hanes, Flight Commander Resource Management
CIO: Matt Osborne, Medical Information Systems Flight Chief
Web address: www.wpmc1.wpafb.af.mil

| | 41 | 10 | 70 | — | — | — | — | — | — | — |

XENIA—Greene County

☒ △ **GREENE MEMORIAL HOSPITAL**, 1141 North Monroe Drive, Zip 45385–1600; tel. 937/352–2000 **A**1 2 5 7 9 10 **F**2 4 9 11 12 21 22 23 27 28 29 33 34 35 37 38 39 42 44 45 46 48 49 51 52 53 54 55 57 58 59 60 61 62 63 64 65 66 68 69 70 71 72 73 74 75 76 77 78 80 81 82 87 88 92 93 94 95 96 107 108 109
Primary Contact: Michael R. Stephens, President
COO: Timothy Ols, Vice President and Chief Operating Officer
CFO: Timothy J. Pollard, Chief Financial Officer
CMO: David Goldberg, M.D., Medical Director
CIO: David Arose, Director Management Information Systems
CHR: Barbara Coalter, Director Human Resources
Web address: www.greenehealth.org

| | 23 | 10 | 111 | 4310 | 55 | 113133 | 293 | 58794 | 22751 | 680 |

YOUNGSTOWN—Mahoning County

□ **BELMONT PINES HOSPITAL**, 615 Churchill–Hubbard Road, Zip 44505–1379; tel. 330/759–2700, (Nonreporting) **A**1 9 10 **S** Psychiatric Solutions, Franklin, TN
Primary Contact: George H. Perry, Ph.D., Chief Executive Officer
Web address: www.belmontpines.com

| | 33 | 22 | 46 | — | — | — | — | — | — | — |

□ **MAHONING VALLEY HOSPITAL**, 345 Oak Hill Avenue, Suite 210, Zip 44502; tel. 330/480–1250, (Nonreporting) **A**1 10
Primary Contact: Michael Senchak, President and Chief Executive Officer
NORTHSIDE MEDICAL CENTER See Western Reserve Care System

| | 33 | 49 | 45 | — | — | — | — | — | — | — |

□ **SELECT SPECIALTY HOSPITAL–YOUNGSTOWN**, 1044 Belmont Avenue, Zip 44501; tel. 330/480–2349, (Nonreporting) **A**1 10
Primary Contact: Major MaryJo Shuntich, Chief Executive Officer

| | 33 | 80 | 31 | — | — | — | — | — | — | — |

Hospital, Address, Telephone, Approval, Facility, and Physician Codes, Health Care System	Classi-fication Codes		Utilization Data					Expense (thousands) of dollars		
★ American Hospital Association (AHA) membership □ Joint Commission on Accreditation of Healthcare Organizations (JCAHO) accreditation ○ American Osteopathic Association (AOA) accreditation △ Commission on Accreditation of Rehabilitation Facilities (CARF) accreditation	Control	Service	Staffed Beds	Admissions	Census	Outpatient Visits	Births	Total	Payroll	Personnel
✶ △ **ST. ELIZABETH HEALTH CENTER**, 1044 Belmont Avenue, Zip 44504–1096, Mailing Address: P.O. Box 1790, Zip 44501–1790; tel. 330/746–7211, (Total facility includes 30 beds in nursing home–type unit) **A**1 3 5 7 8 9 10 **F**2 6 9 10 11 12 14 15 17 19 21 22 23 26 27 28 29 32 33 34 35 37 38 39 40 41 42 43 44 45 46 47 48 49 50 52 53 54 55 56 57 58 59 60 61 62 63 64 65 66 68 69 70 71 72 73 74 75 76 77 79 80 81 82 83 84 85 86 87 88 92 93 94 95 96 101 106 108 109 110 **S** Catholic Healthcare Partners, Cincinnati, OH Primary Contact: Robert W. Shroder, President and Chief Executive Officer COO: James R. Davis, Executive Vice President and Chief Operating Officer CFO: R Andrew Brothers, Senior Vice President Finance and Chief Financial Officer CIO: Charles Folkwein, Senior Vice President Ancillary Services and Information Technology CHR: Molly Seals, Senior Vice President Human Resources and Organizational Development Web address: www.hmpartners.org	21	10	482	21634	341	338842	1747	286515	108325	2572
TOD CHILDREN'S HOSPITAL See Western Reserve Care System										
□ **WESTERN RESERVE CARE SYSTEM**, 500 Gypsy Lane, Zip 44501–0240, Mailing Address: P.O. Box 990, Zip 44501–0990; tel. 330/747–1444, (Includes NORTHSIDE MEDICAL CENTER, tel. 330/747–1444; TOD CHILDREN'S HOSPITAL, tel. 330/747–6700), (Nonreporting) **A**1 2 3 5 8 10 **S** Forum Health, Youngstown, OH Primary Contact: N. Kristopher Hoce, President and Chief Executive Officer Web address: www.forumhealth.org	23	10	373	—	—	—	—	—	—	—
ZANESVILLE—Muskingum County										
✶ △ **GENESIS HEALTHCARE SYSTEM**, 2951 Maple Avenue, Zip 43701–2881; tel. 740/454–5000, (Includes BETHESDA HOSPITAL, 2951 Maple Avenue, Zip 43701–1465; tel. 614/454–4000; GOOD SAMARITAN MEDICAL AND REHABILITATION CENTER, 800 Forest Avenue), (Total facility includes 17 beds in nursing home–type unit) **A**1 2 7 9 10 19 **F**2 4 9 11 12 14 15 17 19 21 22 23 24 26 27 28 29 30 33 35 36 37 38 39 40 42 43 44 46 47 48 49 52 53 55 57 58 59 60 61 62 63 64 65 66 68 69 70 71 72 73 74 75 76 77 78 79 80 81 82 84 85 86 87 88 92 93 94 96 106 107 108 109 110 **P**8 **S** Franciscan Sisters of Christian Charity HealthCare Ministry, Inc, Manitowoc, WI Primary Contact: Thomas L. Sieber, President and Chief Executive Officer CFO: Paul Masterson, Chief Financial Officer CIO: Ed Romito, Director Information Systems Web address: www.genesishcs.org	23	10	405	16136	224	237384	1633	199342	81749	2345
□ **SELECT SPECIALTY HOSPITAL–ZANESVILLE**, 800 Forest Avenue, 6th Floor, Zip 43701; tel. 740/454–5000, (Nonreporting) **A**1 10 Primary Contact: Tom Seiber, Chief Executive Officer	33	80	25	—	—	—	—	—	—	—

Many Facility Codes have changed. Please refer to the AHA Guide Code Chart.

OKLAHOMA

Hospital, Address, Telephone, Approval, Facility, and Physician Codes, Health Care System	Classification Codes		Utilization Data					Expense (thousands) of dollars		
	Control	Service	Staffed Beds	Admissions	Census	Outpatient Visits	Births	Total	Payroll	Personnel

★ American Hospital Association (AHA) membership
□ Joint Commission on Accreditation of Healthcare Organizations (JCAHO) accreditation
○ American Osteopathic Association (AOA) accreditation
△ Commission on Accreditation of Rehabilitation Facilities (CARF) accreditation

ADA—Pontotoc County

⊠ **CHICKASAW NATION HEALTH SYSTEM**, 1001 North Country Club Road, Zip 74820–2847; tel. 580/436–3980 **A**1 10 **F**6 21 22 26 27 28 33 52 55 58 59 62 63 68 88 94 108 **P**6 **S** U. S. Indian Health Service, Rockville, MD
Primary Contact: Bill Lance, Administrator
COO: Sandi Sanders, Chief Operating Officer
CFO: Jenny Trett, Chief Financial Officer
CMO: Tina Cooper, M.D., Medical Director
CIO: Terry Clark, Chief Information Officer
CHR: Jalinda Kelley, Director
Web address: www.ihs.gov — 47 10 52 2761 31 329456 574 68958 — 663

□ **ROLLING HILLS HOSPITAL**, 1000 Rolling Hills Lane, Zip 74820–9415; tel. 580/436–3600, (Nonreporting) **A**1 10 **S** Liberty Management Group, Inc., Ramsey, NJ
Primary Contact: Darnell Powell, Executive Director
Web address: www.rollinghillshospital.com — 33 22 40 — — — — — — —

⊠ △ **VALLEY VIEW REGIONAL HOSPITAL**, 430 North Monta Vista, Zip 74820–4610; tel. 580/332–2323 **A**1 2 7 9 10 19 20 **F**2 6 9 11 12 15 22 23 26 28 29 33 40 49 51 52 53 54 55 56 57 58 59 60 61 62 63 64 65 66 68 81 82 84 88 92 93 94 95 108 110
Primary Contact: Ronald W. Webb, President and Chief Executive Officer
CFO: Rory Ward, Chief Financial Officer
CIO: Dennis Jackson, Director Management Information Systems
CHR: David Jordan, Vice President Human Resources
Web address: www.valleyviewregional.com — 23 10 156 6086 74 52141 526 53823 21714 693

ALTUS—Jackson County

⊠ **JACKSON COUNTY MEMORIAL HOSPITAL**, 1200 East Pecan Street, Zip 73521–6192, Mailing Address: Box 8190, Zip 73522–8190; tel. 580/482–4781, (Total facility includes 25 beds in nursing home–type unit) **A**1 9 10 19 20 **F**2 8 9 11 12 21 22 23 27 29 33 36 46 47 48 49 51 52 53 55 58 59 60 61 62 63 64 65 66 69 72 73 74 76 77 81 82 84 88 91 92 93 94 96 106 108 109 110 **P**6
Primary Contact: William G. Wilson, President and Chief Executive Officer
COO: Jim King, Executive Vice President and Chief Operating Officer
CFO: Nancy Davidson, Senior Vice President and Chief Financial Officer
CMO: John Glasgow, M.D., Chief of Staff
CIO: David Parker, Director Information Systems
CHR: Jeff Pierce, Vice President Human Resources
Web address: www.jcmh.com — 16 10 101 5585 79 85572 537 52764 24787 619

ALVA—Woods County

★ **SHARE MEDICAL CENTER**, 800 Share Drive, Zip 73717–3699, Mailing Address: P.O. Box 727, Zip 73717–0727; tel. 580/327–2800, (Total facility includes 72 beds in nursing home–type unit) **A**9 10 20 **F**1 12 21 26 27 28 29 33 34 36 46 51 52 54 62 63 81 82 83 88 92 94 108 **S** Quorum Health Resources, Plano, TX
Primary Contact: Barbara Oestmann, Chief Executive Officer
CFO: Denise Reed, Chief Financial Officer
CMO: Scott Burk, Chief of Staff
CHR: Kristi Moorman, Supervisor Human Resources
Web address: www.smcok.com — 16 10 117 769 76 16464 0 8529 4245 167

ANADARKO—Caddo County

PHYSICIANS' HOSPITAL IN ANADARKO, 1002 Central Boulevard East, Zip 73005–4496; tel. 405/247–2551, (Nonreporting) **A**9 10 18
Primary Contact: Lee Youngblood, Administrator — 32 49 25 — — — — — — —

ANTLERS—Pushmataha County

PUSHMATAHA COUNTY–TOWN OF ANTLERS HOSPITAL AUTHORITY, 510 East Main Street, Zip 74523–3262, Mailing Address: P.O. Box 518, Zip 74523–3262; tel. 580/298–3342 **A**9 10 **F**9 26 27 28 33 34 51 59 63 81 82 84 88 **P**3
Primary Contact: Dennis Franks, Chief Executive Officer — 44 10 37 1376 14 — 0 5685 3504 117

ARDMORE—Carter County

⊠ **MERCY MEMORIAL HEALTH CENTER**, 1011 14th Street N.W., Zip 73401–1889; tel. 580/223–5400 **A**1 9 10 19 **F**2 9 11 12 15 21 22 26 27 28 29 32 33 34 44 46 47 50 51 52 55 59 60 61 63 65 66 68 69 79 81 82 84 86 88 93 94 96 107 110 **P**6 8 **S** Sisters of Mercy Health System, Chesterfield, MO
Primary Contact: Bobby G. Thompson, President and Chief Executive Officer
CMO: David Hamblin, M.D., Vice President of Medical Affairs
Web address: www.mercyok.com — 21 10 199 8329 120 103606 823 69234 — 767

ATOKA—Atoka County

★ **ATOKA MEMORIAL HOSPITAL**, 1501 South Virginia Avenue, Zip 74525–3298; tel. 580/889–3333 **A**9 10 18 **F**2 6 9 21 33 51 81 88 97
Primary Contact: Jason Anglin, Chief Executive Officer
CIO: Paul David Moore, Administrator
Web address: www.atoka–hosp.otnnet.net — 16 10 25 828 9 — 0 5719 3290 47

Hospital, Address, Telephone, Approval, Facility, and Physician Codes, Health Care System	Classi-fication Codes		Utilization Data					Expense (thousands) of dollars		
★ American Hospital Association (AHA) membership □ Joint Commission on Accreditation of Healthcare Organizations (JCAHO) accreditation ○ American Osteopathic Association (AOA) accreditation △ Commission on Accreditation of Rehabilitation Facilities (CARF) accreditation	Control	Service	Staffed Beds	Admissions	Census	Outpatient Visits	Births	Total	Payroll	Personnel

BARTLESVILLE—Washington County

CONTINUOUS CARE CENTERS OF BARTLESVILLE, 3500 East Frank Phillips Boulevard, 4 Tower, Zip 74006; tel. 918/331–1452 **A**10 **F**21 23 37 60 94 110 **P**8 Primary Contact: Sue Stence, Administrator Web address: www.cccok.com	23	80	16	165	12	0	0	4105	1515	35
⊞ **JANE PHILLIPS MEDICAL CENTER**, 3500 East Frank Phillips Boulevard, Zip 74006–2409; tel. 918/333–7200 **A**1 2 3 5 9 10 19 **F**9 11 12 14 15 17 21 22 23 26 27 28 33 34 36 37 40 41 49 50 51 52 57 58 59 60 61 62 63 64 65 66 68 69 71 72 73 74 75 76 79 81 82 84 86 87 88 93 94 95 96 97 106 108 110 **P**4 7 **S** Marian Health System, Tulsa, OK Primary Contact: David R. Stire, Chief Executive Officer CFO: Mike Moore, Chief Financial Officer CMO: John Smithson, Jr, M.D., Vice President CIO: Rob Poole, Director CHR: Jennifer Workman, Director Human Resources Web address: www.jpmc.org	21	10	132	6795	80	61325	823	70673	25472	0

BEAVER—Beaver County

BEAVER COUNTY MEMORIAL HOSPITAL, 212 East Eighth Street, Zip 73932, Mailing Address: P.O. Box 640, Zip 73932–0640; tel. 580/625–4551, (Nonreporting) **A**9 10 18 20 Primary Contact: Brent Meyers, Administrator	16	10	15	—	—	—	—	—	—	—

BLACKWELL—Kay County

⊞ **INTEGRIS BLACKWELL REGIONAL HOSPITAL**, 710 South 13th Street, Zip 74631–3700; tel. 580/363–2311, (Nonreporting) **A**1 9 10 **S** INTEGRIS Health, Oklahoma City, OK Primary Contact: Jeffrey S. Tarrant, CHE, Chief Executive Officer CFO: Rex Van Meter, Chief Financial Officer CMO: Paul Briggs, M.D., Chief of Staff Web address: www.integris–health.com	23	10	34	—	—	—	—	—	—	—

BOISE CITY—Cimarron County

★ **CIMARRON MEMORIAL HOSPITAL**, 100 South Ellis Street, Zip 73933; tel. 580/544–2501, (Nonreporting) **A**9 10 18 Primary Contact: Paul Miller, Interim Chief Executive Officer	13	10	20	—	—	—	—	—	—	—

BRISTOW—Creek County

★ **BRISTOW MEMORIAL HOSPITAL**, 700 West 7th Street, Suite 6, Zip 74010; tel. 918/367–2215 **A**9 10 **F**2 10 27 28 29 33 36 39 46 51 62 63 69 81 97 **P**1 6 7 **S** Hillcrest HealthCare System, Tulsa, OK Primary Contact: Ryan Gehrig, Chief Executive Officer CFO: Della Allison, Chief Financial Officer Web address: www.bristowmedicalcenter.com	23	10	17	452	3	—	0	4412	2171	60

BROKEN ARROW—Tulsa County

⊞ △ **SAINT FRANCIS HOSPITAL AT BROKEN ARROW**, 3000 South Elm Place, Zip 74012–7952; tel. 918/455–3535 **A**1 7 9 10 **F**2 12 21 22 26 27 28 33 34 46 48 52 53 55 58 59 60 62 63 64 68 69 81 82 84 88 94 108 **S** Saint Francis Health System, Tulsa, OK Primary Contact: Joseph H. Neely, Senior Vice President and Administrator Web address: www.stfrancis.com	23	10	74	2371	40	22077	0	16828	12916	242

BUFFALO—Harper County

★ **HARPER COUNTY COMMUNITY HOSPITAL**, Highway 64 North, Zip 73834, Mailing Address: P.O. Box 60, Zip 73834–0060; tel. 580/735–2555 **A**9 10 18 20 **F**27 28 59 63 69 70 94 97 Primary Contact: Karen Ives, Interim Administrator CIO: Kim Hudson, Chief Information Officer	13	10	25	274	3	985	23	1542	827	34

CARNEGIE—Caddo County

★ **CARNEGIE TRI–COUNTY MUNICIPAL HOSPITAL**, 102 North Broadway, Zip 73015, Mailing Address: P.O. Box 97, Zip 73015–0097; tel. 580/654–1050 **A**9 10 20 **F**6 26 27 28 29 33 48 63 81 97 Primary Contact: Shane Dunning, Administrator	14	10	15	604	6	5371	0	2611	1299	59

CHEYENNE—Roger Mills County

★ **ROGER MILLS MEMORIAL HOSPITAL**, Fifth and L. L Males Avenue, Zip 73628, Mailing Address: P.O. Box 219, Zip 73628–0219; tel. 580/497–3336 **A**9 10 18 **F**6 27 28 29 33 46 48 94 97 Primary Contact: Marilyn Bryan, Administrator CFO: Lois Wilson, Controller	16	10	15	155	1	28909	0	2915	1502	36

CHICKASHA—Grady County

⊞ **GRADY MEMORIAL HOSPITAL**, 2220 West Iowa Avenue, Zip 73018–2738; tel. 405/224–2300 **A**1 9 10 19 20 **F**2 11 21 22 26 27 28 55 59 62 63 64 69 81 84 88 93 94 96 106 108 109 Primary Contact: E. Michael Nunamaker, Chief Executive Officer CFO: Linda Hart, Vice President Finance CMO: Virginia Harr, M.D., Chief of Staff CIO: Sylvia Ho, Director Information Services CHR: Steve Hutchens, Vice President General Services Web address: www.gradymem.org	16	10	99	3161	31	34904	425	35362	17307	402

Hospital, Address, Telephone, Approval, Facility, and Physician Codes, Health Care System	Classi-fication Codes		Utilization Data					Expense (thousands) of dollars		
★ American Hospital Association (AHA) membership □ Joint Commission on Accreditation of Healthcare Organizations (JCAHO) accreditation ○ American Osteopathic Association (AOA) accreditation △ Commission on Accreditation of Rehabilitation Facilities (CARF) accreditation	Control	Service	Staffed Beds	Admissions	Census	Outpatient Visits	Births	Total	Payroll	Personnel

CLAREMORE—Rogers County

⊞ **CLAREMORE REGIONAL HOSPITAL**, 1202 North Muskogee Place, Zip 74017–3036; tel. 918/341–2556 **A**1 9 10 **F**2 12 27 28 32 33 52 55 59 63 69 70 81 88 **P**6 **S** Triad Hospitals, Inc., Plano, TX Primary Contact: David Chaussard, Chief Executive Officer CFO: Cheryl Patterson, Chief Financial Officer CHR: Pat Goad, Human Resources Director Web address: www.claremorereghospital.com	47	10	46	1526	19	172451	345	32625	16485	343
⊞ **U. S. PUBLIC HEALTH SERVICE COMPREHENSIVE INDIAN HEALTH FACILITY**, 101 South Moore Avenue, Zip 74017–5091; tel. 918/342–6434 **A**1 5 10 **F**2 12 27 28 32 33 52 55 59 63 69 70 81 88 **P**6 **S** U. S. Indian Health Service, Rockville, MD Primary Contact: James F. Cussen, Director CFO: LaLana Spears, Supervisor Accounting CMO: Paul Mobley, D.O., Clinical Director CIO: Mark Rives, Information Technology Officer	47	10	46	1526	19	172451	345	32625	16485	343

CLEVELAND—Pawnee County

★ **CLEVELAND AREA HOSPITAL**, 1401 West Pawnee Street, Zip 74020–3019; tel. 918/358–2501 **A**9 10 18 **F**9 12 21 30 33 41 51 52 63 68 69 71 76 81 88 92 97 108 **S** Hillcrest HealthCare System, Tulsa, OK Primary Contact: Samuel T. Guild, Chief Executive Officer CFO: David Ward, Business Manager Web address: www.hillcrest.com	33	10	17	300	4	14488	0	5265	2477	80

CLINTON—Custer County

⊞ **INTEGRIS CLINTON REGIONAL HOSPITAL**, 100 North 30th Street, Zip 73601–3117, Mailing Address: P.O. Box 1569, Zip 73601–1569; tel. 580/323–2363 **A**1 9 10 **F**2 9 11 12 21 22 23 26 27 28 33 36 46 47 48 51 52 53 55 58 59 60 61 63 68 69 80 81 82 85 88 94 95 97 108 109 110 **S** INTEGRIS Health, Oklahoma City, OK Primary Contact: Jerry Jones, Administrator CFO: Richard Foster, CHE, Chief Financial Officer CHR: Karen Hunter, Director Human Resources Web address: www.integris–health.com	23	10	49	2321	22	15862	161	18673	7389	179
⊞ **U. S. PUBLIC HEALTH SERVICE INDIAN HOSPITAL**, Mailing Address: Route 1, Box 3060, Zip 73601–9303; tel. 580/323–2884, (Nonreporting) **A**1 10 **S** U. S. Indian Health Service, Rockville, MD Primary Contact: Terri Schmidt, Director CFO: Millie Blackmon, Administrative Officer CMO: Dolly R. Garcia, M.D., Clinical Director Web address: www.ihs.gov	47	10	11	—	—	—	—	—	—	—

COALGATE—Coal County

★ **COAL COUNTY GENERAL HOSPITAL**, (Formerly Hurley Health Center), 6 North Covington Street, Zip 74538–2002, Mailing Address: P.O. Box 326, Zip 74538; tel. 580/927–2327, (Total facility includes 75 beds in nursing home–type unit) **A**9 10 18 20 **F**26 27 36 51 81 88 92 97 Primary Contact: Dan A. Clements, Chief Executive Officer CFO: Jamie Massie, Chief Financial Officer Web address: www.hillcrest.com	23	10	95	867	74	5038	0	—	—	47

CORDELL—Washita County

★ **CORDELL MEMORIAL HOSPITAL**, 1220 North Glenn English Street, Zip 73632–2099; tel. 580/832–3339 **A**9 10 18 **F**6 27 33 46 48 63 81 92 97 **P**6 Primary Contact: Charles H. Greene, Jr, Administrator CFO: Sue Kelley, Chief Financial Officer	14	10	25	329	3	3721	0	2114	1023	39

CUSHING—Payne County

⊞ **CUSHING REGIONAL HOSPITAL**, 1027 East Cherry Street, Zip 74023–4101, Mailing Address: P.O. Box 1409, Zip 74023–1409; tel. 918/225–2915, (Nonreporting) **A**1 9 10 **S** Hillcrest HealthCare System, Tulsa, OK Primary Contact: Ron Cackler, President and Chief Executive Officer CFO: Lorene Cook, Vice President Financial and Information Services Web address: www.hillcrest.com	14	10	75	—	—	—	—	—	—	—

DRUMRIGHT—Creek County

DRUMRIGHT REGIONAL HOSPITAL, 610 West Bypass Street, Zip 74030; tel. 918/382–2300, (Nonreporting) **A**10 18 Primary Contact: Davis D. Skinner, Chief Executive Officer	23	49	15	—	—	—	—	—	—	—

DUNCAN—Stephens County

⊞ **DUNCAN REGIONAL HOSPITAL**, 1407 North Whisenant Drive, Zip 73533–1650, Mailing Address: P.O. Box 2000, Zip 73534–2000; tel. 580/252–5300, (Total facility includes 16 beds in nursing home–type unit) **A**1 9 10 20 **F**2 9 11 12 14 21 22 26 28 29 32 33 34 36 41 46 47 48 51 52 55 58 59 60 62 63 66 69 81 82 84 87 88 92 94 95 96 108 110 **P**6 8 Primary Contact: Scott Street, President and Chief Executive Officer CFO: Melissa Walker, Vice President and Chief Financial Officer CIO: Roger Neal, Director Information Technology Web address: www.duncanregional.com	23	10	98	4527	51	85045	450	43135	18851	560

Hospital, Address, Telephone, Approval, Facility, and Physician Codes, Health Care System	Classi-fication Codes		Utilization Data					Expense (thousands) of dollars		
★ American Hospital Association (AHA) membership □ Joint Commission on Accreditation of Healthcare Organizations (JCAHO) accreditation ○ American Osteopathic Association (AOA) accreditation △ Commission on Accreditation of Rehabilitation Facilities (CARF) accreditation	Control	Service	Staffed Beds	Admissions	Census	Outpatient Visits	Births	Total	Payroll	Personnel

DURANT—Bryan County

☒ **MEDICAL CENTER OF SOUTHEASTERN OKLAHOMA**, 1800 University Boulevard, Zip 74701–3006, Mailing Address: P.O. Box 1207, Zip 74702–1207; tel. 580/924–3080 **A**1 9 10 12 13 19 **F**2 9 10 11 12 15 21 26 27 32 33 34 37 38 40 46 48 51 55 57 58 59 62 63 64 65 66 69 81 82 84 88 93 94 95 96 108 109 **P**8 **S** Health Management Associates, Naples, FL
Primary Contact: Jacquelyn Harms, R.N., Executive Director
CMO: Chris Sturch, M.D., Chief of Staff
CIO: Katy Stinson, Director Information Services
Web address: www.mcsohealth.com

| | 33 | 10 | 120 | 7395 | 71 | 48969 | 933 | — | — | 423 |

EDMOND—Oklahoma County

☒ **EDMOND MEDICAL CENTER**, 1 South Bryant Street, Zip 73034–4798; tel. 405/341–6100 **A**1 5 9 10 **F**2 9 10 12 15 17 21 23 28 29 32 33 44 46 48 49 52 53 55 57 58 60 61 62 63 64 66 69 70 71 75 76 81 82 84 85 88 93 94 95 96 106 108 **P**5 **S** HCA, Nashville, TN
Primary Contact: Ed Gray, Chief Executive Officer
CFO: Lavaughn Carey, Chief Financial Officer
CMO: Stephen Mihalsky, Chief of Staff
CIO: Farrell Maier, Ethics and Compliance and Chief Information
CHR: Michael Rhoades, Chief Human Resources Officer
Web address: www.edmondhospital.com

| | 33 | 10 | 87 | 3282 | 47 | 47065 | 0 | 48704 | 15061 | 362 |

□ **EDMOND SPECIALTY HOSPITAL**, 1100 East Ninth Street, Zip 73034–5755; tel. 405/341–8150, (Total facility includes 8 beds in nursing home–type unit) **A**1 10 **F**2 21 23 37 44 45 53 57 58 60 62 69 94 110 **S** Integrated Health Services, Sparks Glencoe, MD
Primary Contact: Gayla Campbell, Executive Director
Web address: www.thicare.com/EdmondSpecialty/

| | 33 | 80 | 42 | 393 | 30 | 332 | 0 | 5001 | 4338 | 87 |

□ **RENAISSANCE WOMEN'S HOSPITAL OF EDMOND**, 1800 South Renaissance Boulevard, Zip 73013; tel. 405/359–9800, (Nonreporting) **A**1 9 10
Primary Contact: Steve Powell, Administrator

| | 33 | 49 | 14 | — | — | — | — | — | — | — |

EL RENO—Canadian County

★ **PARKVIEW HOSPITAL**, 2115 Parkview Drive, Zip 73036–2199, Mailing Address: P.O. Box 129, Zip 73036–0129; tel. 405/262–2640 **A**9 10 **F**2 9 11 21 22 25 26 27 28 29 32 33 46 47 48 51 52 55 58 59 63 65 69 75 81 88 94 96 108 109 110
Primary Contact: Lex Smith, Administrator
CFO: Rod Shook, Controller
CHR: Wendy Finnen, Director Human Resources
Web address: www.parkview–hospital.com

| | 16 | 10 | 54 | 1499 | 14 | 23211 | 150 | 12705 | 7068 | 229 |

ELK CITY—Beckham County

☒ **GREAT PLAINS REGIONAL MEDICAL CENTER**, 1705 West Second Street, Zip 73644–4496, Mailing Address: P.O. Box 2339, Zip 73648–2339; tel. 580/225–2511 **A**1 9 10 **F**2 9 11 12 15 17 19 21 22 23 26 27 28 29 32 33 34 35 37 39 40 44 45 46 47 48 51 53 55 57 58 59 60 61 62 63 64 65 66 69 70 71 73 74 75 76 80 81 82 84 85 87 88 92 93 94 95 96 97 106 108 109 110 **P**6 8
Primary Contact: Robin E. Lake, Chief Executive Officer
COO: Pat James, Chief Operating Officer
CMO: Craig Phelps, M.D., Chief of Staff
CIO: Terry Davis, Chief Information Officer
CHR: Bill Barrett, Director Human Resources
Web address: www.gprmc–ok.com

| | 23 | 10 | 66 | 3195 | 36 | 59348 | 374 | 27304 | 12211 | 300 |

ENID—Garfield County

☒ **INTEGRIS BASS BAPTIST HEALTH CENTER**, 600 South Monroe Street, Zip 73701–7211, Mailing Address: P.O. Box 3168, Zip 73702–3168; tel. 580/233–2300, (Includes INTEGRIS BASS BEHAVIORAL HEALTH SYSTEM, 2216 South Van Buren Street, Zip 73703–8299; tel. 580/234–2220) **A**1 3 5 9 10 **F**2 9 11 12 14 15 16 17 19 21 22 23 27 28 33 37 42 44 46 48 49 51 52 53 54 55 58 59 60 61 62 63 65 66 69 70 71 72 73 75 76 80 81 82 84 85 92 95 96 107 108 109 110 **P**6 **S** INTEGRIS Health, Oklahoma City, OK
Primary Contact: Karl Weinmeister, Interim Administrator
CHR: Bennie Salkil, Director Human Resources
Web address: www.integris–health.com

| | 23 | 10 | 151 | 5978 | 107 | 47168 | 686 | 66678 | 28552 | 646 |

□ **INTEGRIS BASS PAVILION**, 491 South Third, Zip 73701; tel. 580/233–2300 **A**1 10 **F**9 21 22 23 27 28 34 37 46 53 54 58 60 64 65 66 95 96 108 110 **P**6
Web address: www.integris–health.com/integris/en–us/locations/bass–enid

| | 23 | 10 | 18 | 195 | 14 | 2482 | 0 | 7211 | 2957 | 57 |

□ △ **ST. MARY'S REGIONAL MEDICAL CENTER**, 305 South Fifth Street, Zip 73701–5899, Mailing Address: Box 232, Zip 73702–0232; tel. 580/233–6100 **A**1 2 7 9 10 **F**2 9 10 11 12 15 17 19 21 22 23 26 27 28 29 31 32 33 37 41 42 46 47 48 50 52 53 54 55 56 57 58 59 60 61 62 63 65 68 69 79 81 82 84 85 86 87 88 92 93 94 95 96 108 109 110 **S** Universal Health Services, Inc., King of Prussia, PA
Primary Contact: Rick Wallace, FACHE, Chief Executive Officer
Web address: www.stmarysregional.com

| | 33 | 10 | 160 | 6861 | 113 | 55248 | 437 | 67569 | 23159 | 488 |

EUFAULA—Mcintosh County

COMMUNITY HOSPITAL–LAKEVIEW, 1 Hospital Drive, Zip 74432–4010, Mailing Address: P.O. Box 629, Zip 74432–0629; tel. 918/689–2535 **A**9 10 **F**2 27 33 48 51 58 63 108
Primary Contact: Daniel J. Schaetzle, Administrator
Web address: www.swnd@cwis.com

| | 33 | 10 | 33 | 202 | 2 | 5509 | 1 | 4884 | 1109 | 40 |

OK

Hospital, Address, Telephone, Approval, Facility, and Physician Codes, Health Care System	Classi-fication Codes		Utilization Data					Expense (thousands) of dollars		
★ American Hospital Association (AHA) membership □ Joint Commission on Accreditation of Healthcare Organizations (JCAHO) accreditation ○ American Osteopathic Association (AOA) accreditation △ Commission on Accreditation of Rehabilitation Facilities (CARF) accreditation	Control	Service	Staffed Beds	Admissions	Census	Outpatient Visits	Births	Total	Payroll	Personnel

FAIRFAX—Osage County

★ **FAIRFAX MEMORIAL HOSPITAL**, Taft Avenue and Highway 18, Zip 74637–4028, Mailing Address: P.O. Box 219, Zip 74637–0219; tel. 918/642–3291, (Nonreporting) **A**9 10 18
Primary Contact: Emery Brautigan, Chief Executive Officer
CFO: Emery Brautigan, Chief Executive Officer
Web address: www.hillcrest.com

| | 23 | 10 | 15 | — | | | | | | |

FAIRVIEW—Major County

FAIRVIEW HOSPITAL, 523 East State Road, Zip 73737–1498, Mailing Address: P.O. Box 548, Zip 73737–0548; tel. 580/227–3721, (Nonreporting) **A**9 10 18
Primary Contact: David Abercrombie, Chief Executive Officer
Web address: www.fairviewhospital.net

| | 14 | 10 | 25 | — | | | | | | |

FORT SILL—Comanche County

☒ **REYNOLDS ARMY COMMUNITY HOSPITAL**, 4301 Mow–way Street, Zip 73503–6300; tel. 580/458–3000 **A**1 **F**2 4 6 10 11 12 21 22 24 25 26 27 28 29 31 32 33 34 35 39 42 44 45 46 47 48 52 53 55 57 58 59 60 62 63 64 66 69 70 73 74 75 77 81 82 88 89 90 92 94 95 96 106 107 108 109 **S** Department of the Army, Office of the Surgeon General, Falls Church, VA
Primary Contact: Colonel Frederick A. Swiderski, Commander
COO: Major Paul Roberts, Chief of Staff
CFO: Darleen Snyder, Chief Business Analysis Division
CMO: Colonel Larry Godfrey, Deputy Commander Clinical Services
CIO: Major Eric McClurg, Chief Information Management Division
CHR: Homer Williams, Chief Civilian Personnel Branch
Web address: www.rach.sill.amedd.army.mil

| | 42 | 10 | 32 | 2838 | 18 | 402748 | 645 | — | — | 929 |

FREDERICK—Tillman County

★ **MEMORIAL HOSPITAL AND PHYSICIAN GROUP**, 319 East Josephine, Zip 73542–2299; tel. 580/335–7565, (Total facility includes 30 beds in nursing home–type unit) **A**9 10 20 **F**9 21 27 29 33 48 51 52 63 69 81 88 92 97 110 **P**6
Primary Contact: Al Allee, Chief Executive Officer
CFO: Lisa Hart, Controller
CHR: Cindy Duncan, Director Human Resources

| | 16 | 10 | 55 | 805 | 35 | 26668 | 2 | 5791 | 2452 | 118 |

GROVE—Delaware County

☒ **INTEGRIS GROVE GENERAL HOSPITAL**, 1310 South Main Street, Zip 74344–1310; tel. 918/786–2243 **A**1 9 10 20 **F**9 11 21 23 28 42 51 52 55 59 60 61 62 63 64 81 88 93 108 109 110 **S** INTEGRIS Health, Oklahoma City, OK
Primary Contact: Greg Martin, Administrator and Chief Executive Officer
CFO: Kevin Cox, Chief Financial Officer
Web address: www.integris–health.com

| | 23 | 10 | 50 | 3502 | 28 | 71294 | 241 | 31256 | 11053 | 278 |

GUTHRIE—Logan County

★ **LOGAN MEDICAL CENTER**, (Formerly Logan Hospital and Medical Center), Highway 33 West at Academy Road, Zip 73044–3700, Mailing Address: P.O. Box 1017, Zip 73044–1017; tel. 405/282–6700 **A**9 10 18 **F**9 21 26 28 29 32 33 46 48 51 58 63 69 70 81 84 97 **P**6 7 **S** Quorum Health Resources, Plano, TX
Primary Contact: Shawn Morrow, Chief Executive Officer
CFO: Steve Taylor, Chief Financial Officer
CMO: Todd Krehbill, M.D., Chief of Staff
CHR: Mary Jo Messelt, Director Human Resources
Web address: www.loganhosp.com

| | 16 | 10 | 25 | 691 | 7 | 26208 | 0 | 11608 | 5554 | 194 |

GUYMON—Texas County

★ **MEMORIAL HOSPITAL OF TEXAS COUNTY**, 520 Medical Drive, Zip 73942–4438; tel. 580/338–6515 **A**9 10 20 **F**2 9 11 12 21 24 26 27 28 29 31 34 36 46 48 51 52 53 54 58 59 63 64 66 70 81 82 84 88 94 97 108 109 **P**6
Primary Contact: Tim Starkey, Chief Executive Officer
COO: Tim Starkey, Chief Executive Officer
CFO: Ben Helm, Chief Financial Officer
CMO: R Kelly McMurray, D.O., Chief of Staff
CHR: Julie West, Chief Administrative Officer
Web address: www.mhtcguymon.org

| | 13 | 10 | 47 | 2403 | 20 | 18823 | 417 | 15558 | 6484 | 180 |

HENRYETTA—Okmulgee County

☒ **HENRYETTA MEDICAL CENTER**, Dewey Bartlett and Main Streets, Zip 74437–6820, Mailing Address: P.O. Box 1269, Zip 74437–1269; tel. 918/652–4463, (Nonreporting) **A**1 9 10 **S** Hillcrest HealthCare System, Tulsa, OK
Primary Contact: Dee Renshaw, Chief Executive Officer
CFO: Loren Rials, Chief Financial Officer
Web address: www.henryetta.org/medical

| | 23 | 10 | 42 | — | — | — | — | — | — | — |

HOBART—Kiowa County

★ **ELKVIEW GENERAL HOSPITAL**, 429 West Elm Street, Zip 73651–1699; tel. 580/726–3324 **A**9 10 **F**2 11 12 21 23 33 51 61 62 63 64 75 81 82 85 87 88 97 **P**6 7
Primary Contact: J. W. Finch, Jr, Administrator
CFO: Sandra Strain, Controller

| | 16 | 10 | 38 | 1640 | 19 | 11711 | 96 | 9522 | 5202 | 259 |

Hospital, Address, Telephone, Approval, Facility, and Physician Codes, Health Care System	Classi-fication Codes		Utilization Data					Expense (thousands) of dollars		
★ American Hospital Association (AHA) membership □ Joint Commission on Accreditation of Healthcare Organizations (JCAHO) accreditation ○ American Osteopathic Association (AOA) accreditation △ Commission on Accreditation of Rehabilitation Facilities (CARF) accreditation	Control	Service	Staffed Beds	Admissions	Census	Outpatient Visits	Births	Total	Payroll	Personnel

HOLDENVILLE—Hughes County

★ **HOLDENVILLE GENERAL HOSPITAL**, 100 McDougal Drive, Zip 74848–9700; tel. 405/379–4200, (Nonreporting) **A**9 10 18 **S** Brim Healthcare, Inc., Brentwood, TN Primary Contact: Deryl E. Gulliford, Ph.D., Chief Executive Officer CFO: Chris Dover, CPA, Chief Financial Officer	16	10	25	—	—	—	—	—	—	—

HOLLIS—Harmon County

★ **HARMON MEMORIAL HOSPITAL**, 400 East Chestnut Street, Zip 73550–2030, Mailing Address: P.O. Box 791, Zip 73550–0791; tel. 580/688–3363, (Nonreporting) **A**9 10 20 Primary Contact: Billy Burge, Chief Executive Officer CFO: Ruthie Matheson, Chief Financial Officer CHR: Marti Taylor, Human Resources Director	16	10	20	—	—	—	—	—	—	—

HUGO—Choctaw County

★ **CHOCTAW MEMORIAL HOSPITAL**, 1405 East Kirk Road, Zip 74743–3603; tel. 580/326–6414 **A**9 10 **F**26 27 28 33 46 47 51 52 58 63 66 81 88 94 97 **P**5 **S** Quorum Health Resources, Plano, TX Primary Contact: Steven K. Jacobson, Chief Executive Officer and Administrator CFO: Mary Stinson, Chief Financial Officer CHR: Darlene Galyon, Administrator Human Resources	16	10	34	1947	21	11148	0	5792	2879	140
LANE FROST HEALTH AND REHABILITATION CENTER, (Formerly Destiny: Future Quest), 2815 East Jackson Street, Zip 74743; tel. 580/326–9200, (Nonreporting) **A**10	23	49	60	—	—	—	—	—	—	—

IDABEL—Mccurtain County

★ **MCCURTAIN MEMORIAL HOSPITAL**, 1301 Lincoln Road, Zip 74745–7341; tel. 580/286–7623 **A**9 10 20 **F**9 11 12 21 22 26 27 33 46 51 55 59 63 69 71 76 81 84 88 93 94 97 **P**8 Primary Contact: Bristol Messer, Chief Executive Officer CFO: Ray B. Whitmore, Chief Financial Officer CMO: Jon Maxwell, D.O., Chief of Staff CHR: Doris Brown, Assistant Administrator and Director Human Resources	23	10	73	2665	27	38641	320	15334	7561	243

KINGFISHER—Kingfisher County

★ **KINGFISHER REGIONAL HOSPITAL**, 500 South Ninth Street, Zip 73750–3528, Mailing Address: P.O. Box 59, Zip 73750–0059; tel. 405/375–3141 **A**9 10 18 **F**9 11 12 46 48 52 59 60 63 69 81 88 94 97 108 **S** Quorum Health Resources, Plano, TX Primary Contact: Damon Benson, Chief Executive Officer CFO: Doran Hammett, Chief Financial Officer CIO: Rose Sherwood, Information Technology Specialist CHR: Carolyn Bjerke, Human Resources Director Web address: www.kingfisherhospital.com	23	10	25	1184	3	3313	90	7263	—	0

LAWTON—Comanche County

✳ △ **COMANCHE COUNTY MEMORIAL HOSPITAL**, 3401 West Gore Boulevard, Zip 73505–0129, Mailing Address: P.O. Box 129, Zip 73502–0129; tel. 580/355–8620 **A**1 2 3 5 7 9 10 **F**2 6 9 11 12 14 15 17 19 21 22 23 24 27 28 32 33 34 37 40 44 46 47 48 49 50 51 52 53 55 57 58 59 60 61 62 63 64 65 66 68 69 70 71 72 74 75 76 78 81 82 84 87 88 92 93 94 95 96 97 106 107 108 109 110 Primary Contact: Randall K. Segler, Chief Executive Officer COO: Douglas K. Weaver, Chief Operating Officer CFO: David Blackmon, Chief Financial Officer CIO: James Porter, Director Information Services Web address: www.memorialhealthsource.com	16	10	283	10381	140	105361	1088	119546	57701	1364
JIM TALIAFERRO COMMUNITY MENTAL HEALTH, 602 S.W. 37th Street, Zip 73505; tel. 580/248–5780 **A**10 **F**4 21 46 71 72 73 74 75 77 78 94 108 Primary Contact: Jim Regan, Interim Executive Director	12	22	22	1240	10	18000	0	—	—	43
✳ △ **SOUTHWESTERN MEDICAL CENTER**, 5602 S.W. Lee Boulevard, Zip 73505–9635, Mailing Address: P.O. Box 7290, Zip 73506–7290; tel. 580/531–4700 **A**1 2 3 5 7 9 10 **F**2 9 11 21 22 23 27 28 29 44 46 48 49 52 55 57 59 60 61 63 68 69 70 71 72 75 76 77 80 81 82 84 85 87 88 93 94 96 97 108 109 110 **P**1 **S** HCA, Nashville, TN Primary Contact: Thomas L. Rine, President and Chief Executive Officer CFO: Ken Pannell, Chief Financial Officer CMO: J Shane Ross, Chief of Staff CIO: Steve O'Connor, Director of Information Services CHR: Helen Hooper, Director Human Resources Web address: www.swmconline.com	33	10	162	5375	107	42442	430	62909	20449	504
✳ **U. S. PUBLIC HEALTH SERVICE INDIAN HOSPITAL**, 1515 Lawrie Tatum Road, Zip 73507–3099; tel. 580/353–0350, (Nonreporting) **A**1 10 **S** U. S. Indian Health Service, Rockville, MD Primary Contact: Hickory Starr, Jr, Chief Executive Officer COO: Jacqueline Curley, Supervisory Accountant CFO: Jacqueline Curley, Supervisory Accountant CMO: Bryce Poolaw, Clinical Director CIO: Steve Barse, Chief Information Officer CHR: Twylla Jimboy, Supervisor Human Resources	47	10	44	—	—	—	—	—	—	—

Many Facility Codes have changed. Please refer to the AHA Guide Code Chart.

© 2005 AHA Guide

OK

Hospital, Address, Telephone, Approval, Facility, and Physician Codes, Health Care System	Classification Codes		Utilization Data					Expense (thousands) of dollars		
★ American Hospital Association (AHA) membership □ Joint Commission on Accreditation of Healthcare Organizations (JCAHO) accreditation ○ American Osteopathic Association (AOA) accreditation △ Commission on Accreditation of Rehabilitation Facilities (CARF) accreditation	Control	Service	Staffed Beds	Admissions	Census	Outpatient Visits	Births	Total	Payroll	Personnel
LINDSAY—Garvin County										
LINDSAY MUNICIPAL HOSPITAL, Highway 19 West, Zip 73052, Mailing Address: P.O. Box 888, Zip 73052–0888; tel. 405/756–1404 **A**9 10 **F**33 64 81 Primary Contact: James E. Koulovatos, Chief Executive Officer	16	10	26	692	12	3216	0	4540	2148	83
MADILL—Marshall County										
★□ **INTEGRIS MARSHALL COUNTY MEDICAL CENTER**, 1 Hospital Drive, Zip 73446, Mailing Address: P.O. Box 827, Zip 73446–0827; tel. 580/795–3384 **A**1 9 10 18 **F**2 9 21 22 27 29 33 36 37 38 46 48 62 63 69 81 84 85 88 94 95 96 97 106 108 **P**6 **S** INTEGRIS Health, Oklahoma City, OK Primary Contact: C. David Hill, Chief Executive Officer CFO: Oneida Bull, Controller CMO: Joe Potter, M.D., Chief of Staff Web address: www.integris–health.com	23	10	20	970	7	11705	0	7513	3341	79
MANGUM—Greer County										
MANGUM CITY HOSPITAL, One Wickersham Drive, Zip 73554–9116, Mailing Address: P.O. Box 280, Zip 73554–0280; tel. 580/782–3353, (Nonreporting) **A**9 10 18 20 Primary Contact: Michael Ulm, Chief Executive Officer Web address: www.mangumhospital.org	14	10	17	—	—	—	—	—	—	—
MARIETTA—Love County										
★ **MERCY HEALTH LOVE COUNTY**, 300 Wanda Street, Zip 73448–1200; tel. 580/276–3347, (Nonreporting) **A**9 10 18 Primary Contact: Richard Barker, Administrator	13	10	25	—	—	—	—	—	—	—
MCALESTER—Pittsburg County										
CARL ALBERT COMMUNITY MENTAL HEALTH CENTER, 1101 East Monroe Avenue, Zip 74501–4826; tel. 918/426–1000, (Nonreporting) **A**10 Primary Contact: George R. Jones, Director Web address: www.odmhsas.org	12	22	20	—	—	—	—	—	—	—
★□ △ **MCALESTER REGIONAL HEALTH CENTER**, One Clark Bass Boulevard, Zip 74501–4267, Mailing Address: P.O. Box 1228, Zip 74502–1228; tel. 918/426–1800 **A**1 7 9 10 19 20 **F**8 9 11 12 15 17 21 22 23 29 31 32 33 37 38 40 41 46 47 48 49 50 54 55 58 59 62 63 64 65 66 68 69 73 81 82 84 88 93 94 95 96 98 106 108 109 110 Primary Contact: Shaun Beggs, Interim Chief Executive Officer CFO: Shaun Beggs, Controller CIO: Roger Allen, Director Management Information Systems CHR: Emily Mouser, Vice President Human Resources and Organizational Development Web address: www.mrhcok.com	16	10	163	6510	98	57376	701	29782	21627	727
MIAMI—Ottawa County										
★□ **INTEGRIS BAPTIST REGIONAL HEALTH CENTER**, 200 Second Street S.W., Zip 74354–6830, Mailing Address: P.O. Box 1207, Zip 74355–1207; tel. 918/542–6611 **A**1 9 10 20 **F**2 4 6 9 11 12 21 22 26 27 28 33 34 35 36 39 40 44 46 47 48 49 51 52 53 54 55 58 59 60 62 63 64 65 68 69 71 73 74 75 76 77 81 82 88 91 92 94 95 96 97 108 110 **P**5 7 **S** INTEGRIS Health, Oklahoma City, OK Primary Contact: Joel A. Hart, FACHE, Chief Executive Officer CFO: Karen Reynolds, Chief Financial Officer CMO: Duane G. Koehler, Chief of Staff CHR: Ginger Ratliff, Director Human Resources Web address: www.integris–health.com	23	10	100	4797	59	57505	344	41150	18999	493
★ **WILLOW CREST HOSPITAL**, 130 A Street S.W., Zip 74354–6800; tel. 918/542–1836 **A**10 **F**71 72 74 75 97 **P**6 Primary Contact: Anne G. Anthony, Administrator and Chief Executive Officer COO: Nelson L. Sutton, Chief Operating Officer CFO: Cindy Bell, Director Finance CMO: Mark Elkington, M.D., Chief Medical Officer CIO: Steven Goodman, Chief Information Officer CHR: Kathy Henderson, Director Human Resources Web address: www.willowcresthospital.com	33	52	75	458	70	0	0	7721	5015	133
MIDWEST CITY—Oklahoma County										
★□ **MIDWEST REGIONAL MEDICAL CENTER**, 2825 Parklawn Drive, Zip 73110–4258; tel. 405/610–4411 **A**1 2 9 10 **F**2 6 9 11 12 14 15 17 19 21 22 23 26 27 28 33 34 35 39 45 46 47 48 51 52 55 57 58 59 60 61 62 63 64 65 66 69 70 71 73 74 75 81 82 84 87 88 93 94 95 96 108 109 **S** Health Management Associates, Naples, FL Primary Contact: Brian L. Clemens, Chief Executive Officer CFO: Brian D. Steines, Chief Financial Officer CMO: Thomas Bryant, M.D., Chief of Staff CHR: Richard Baranek, Director Human Resources Web address: www.midwestregional.com	33	10	255	15836	180	126000	1052	109278	46429	—
★□ **SPECIALTY HOSPITAL OF MIDWEST CITY**, 8210 National Avenue, Zip 73110; tel. 405/739–0800, (Nonreporting) **A**1 10 **S** Integrated Health Services, Sparks Glencoe, MD Primary Contact: Jerry Pyron, Chief Executive Officer CFO: Vince Bridges, Controller	33	10	42	—	—	—	—	—	—	—

Hospital, Address, Telephone, Approval, Facility, and Physician Codes, Health Care System	Classi-fication Codes		Utilization Data					Expense (thousands) of dollars		
★ American Hospital Association (AHA) membership □ Joint Commission on Accreditation of Healthcare Organizations (JCAHO) accreditation ○ American Osteopathic Association (AOA) accreditation △ Commission on Accreditation of Rehabilitation Facilities (CARF) accreditation	Control	Service	Staffed Beds	Admissions	Census	Outpatient Visits	Births	Total	Payroll	Personnel

MUSKOGEE—Muskogee County

✠ **MUSKOGEE REGIONAL MEDICAL CENTER**, 300 Rockefeller Drive, Zip 74401–5081; tel. 918/682–5501 **A**1 2 9 10 19 **F**2 9 11 12 21 22 23 27 28 33 34 37 40 42 43 46 48 49 51 53 55 57 58 59 60 61 62 63 64 65 66 68 69 71 73 75 76 77 78 79 81 82 84 87 88 93 94 95 96 106 107 108 110 Primary Contact: Anthony W. Armstrong, Chief Executive Officer and President CFO: Jim Blair, Senior Vice President, Chief Financial Officer CMO: Lee Taylor, Vice President, Medical and Clinical Services CIO: Paul J. Julian, Vice President, Chief Information Officer CHR: Phyllis Spriggs, Vice President, Human Resources Web address: www.muskogeehealth.com	16	10	254	11847	163	93496	597	—	—	1050
✠ **VETERANS AFFAIRS MEDICAL CENTER**, 1011 Honor Heights Drive, Zip 74401–1399; tel. 918/683–3261 **A**1 5 **F**2 4 9 12 21 22 23 26 27 28 29 30 31 32 36 37 38 39 42 45 46 47 48 49 50 52 55 58 60 61 62 63 65 66 69 70 73 74 75 76 77 81 82 88 94 96 106 107 108 109 110 **S** Department of Veterans Affairs, Washington, DC Primary Contact: Benjamin Campeau, Interim Director COO: Benjamin Campeau, Associate Director CFO: Donna Fuerstenberg, Chief Fiscal Services CMO: William F. Dubbs, M.D., Chief of Staff CIO: Gary Duvall, Chief Information Resource Management CHR: Freida Nan Haynes, Chief Web address: www.va.gov/sta/guide/home.asp	45	10	50	3007	43	313373	0	113986	39291	668

NORMAN—Cleveland County

□ **GRIFFIN MEMORIAL HOSPITAL**, 900 East Main Street, Zip 73071–5305, Mailing Address: P.O. Box 151, Zip 73070–0151; tel. 405/321–4880 **A**1 3 5 10 **F**22 33 71 75 76 94 106 108 **P**6 **S** Oklahoma State Department of Mental Health and Substance Abuse Services, Oklahoma City, OK Primary Contact: Don Bowen, Executive Director Web address: www.odmhsas.org	12	22	150	2922	127	—	0	22929	12831	425
J. D. MCCARTY CENTER FOR CHILDREN WITH DEVELOPMENTAL DISABILITIES, (pediatric rehabilitation), 2002 East Robinson, Zip 73071–5264; tel. 405/307–2800 **A**10 **F**32 58 68 69 94 108 Primary Contact: Curtis A. Peters, Chief Executive Officer Web address: www.jdmc.org	12	59	24	117	20	2220	0	—	—	184
✠ △ **NORMAN REGIONAL HOSPITAL**, 901 North Porter Street, Zip 73071–6482, Mailing Address: P.O. Box 1308, Zip 73070–1308; tel. 405/307–1000 **A**1 2 7 9 10 **F**2 6 9 10 11 12 14 21 22 23 26 27 28 29 31 32 33 34 37 41 45 46 47 48 52 53 54 55 56 57 58 59 60 61 62 63 64 65 66 68 69 70 71 73 74 76 77 79 80 81 82 83 84 85 87 88 92 93 94 95 96 106 107 108 109 110 **P**1 7 Primary Contact: David D. Whitaker, FACHE, President and Chief Executive Officer COO: Greg Terrell, Vice President Operations CFO: Melvin Alexander, Vice President and Chief Financial Officer CMO: Jerry Leu, M.D., Vice President Medical Affairs CHR: Carolyn Shockey, Director Human Resources Web address: www.normanregional.com	16	10	324	17019	229	217329	2132	166179	71715	1418

NOWATA—Nowata County

JANE PHILLIPS NOWATA HEALTH CENTER, 237 South Locust Street, Zip 74048–0426, Mailing Address: P.O. Box 426, Zip 74048–0426; tel. 918/273–3102 **A**9 10 18 **F**34 88 92 97 108 Primary Contact: Maggie Blevins, Administrator Web address: www.jpmc.org	23	10	10	205	4	2622	0	1874	1010	32

OKEENE—Blaine County

★ **OKEENE MUNICIPAL HOSPITAL**, (Critical Access Hospital), 207 East F Street, Zip 73763, Mailing Address: P.O. Box 489, Zip 73763–0489; tel. 580/822–4417, (Total facility includes 20 beds in nursing home–type unit) **A**9 10 18 **F**2 11 21 27 28 33 46 47 48 52 53 59 60 63 64 66 92 97 Primary Contact: Shelly Dunham, Administrator COO: Pat Lorenz, Assistant Administrator CIO: Marsha Price, Supervisor Medical Records Web address: www.okeenehospital.com	16	49	35	405	21	8426	52	2951	1486	49

OKEMAH—Okfuskee County

★ **CREEK NATION COMMUNITY HOSPITAL**, 309 North 14th Street, Zip 74859–2099; tel. 918/623–1424, (Nonreporting) **A**9 10 **S** U. S. Indian Health Service, Rockville, MD Primary Contact: Jo Ann Skaggs, Chief Executive Officer CFO: Jerry Mitchum, Chief Financial Officer CMO: Lawrence Vark, Chief Medical Officer CHR: Russell Torbett, Manager	47	10	34	—						

OKLAHOMA CITY—Oklahoma County

★ **ADVANCE CARE HOSPITAL OF OKLAHOMA CITY**, 4300 West Memorial Road, 5th Floor, Zip 73120; tel. 405/486–8800, (Nonreporting) **A**10 **S** Dubuis Health System, Houston, TX Primary Contact: George H. Dashner, FACHE, Administrator Web address: www.dubuis.org	22	80	34	—	—	—	—	—	—	—

Many Facility Codes have changed. Please refer to the AHA Guide Code Chart.   © 2005 AHA Guide

Hospital, Address, Telephone, Approval, Facility, and Physician Codes, Health Care System	Classification Codes		Utilization Data					Expense (thousands) of dollars		
	Control	Service	Staffed Beds	Admissions	Census	Outpatient Visits	Births	Total	Payroll	Personnel

★ American Hospital Association (AHA) membership
□ Joint Commission on Accreditation of Healthcare Organizations (JCAHO) accreditation
○ American Osteopathic Association (AOA) accreditation
△ Commission on Accreditation of Rehabilitation Facilities (CARF) accreditation

OK

☒ △ **BONE AND JOINT HOSPITAL**, 1111 North Dewey Avenue, Zip 73103–2615; tel. 405/552–9100 **A**1 3 5 7 9 10 **F**2 7 9 21 22 33 37 42 53 58 60 62 63 64 68 92 94 95 108 **S** SSM Health Care, Saint Louis, MO Primary Contact: James A. Hyde, Administrator COO: Janet Farhood, Executive Vice President and Chief Operating Officer CFO: Eric Ericson, Director of Finance CMO: Thomas Tkach, M.D., Chief of Staff CIO: Kevin Olson, Director of Information Systems CHR: Cheryl McConnell, Director Human Resources Web address: www.boneandjoint.com	21	47	80	3996	55	4643	0	40970	14732	283
□ **CENTRIS**, 4401 South Western Avenue, 7th Floor, Zip 73109; tel. 405/644–5007 **A**1 10 **F**21 37 49 64 94 110 Primary Contact: Connie Strickland, Administrator	23	80	26	277	20	0	0	—	—	43
CHILDREN'S HOSPITAL OF OKLAHOMA See OU Medical Center										
☒ △ **DEACONESS HOSPITAL**, 5501 North Portland Avenue, Zip 73112–2099; tel. 405/604–6000 **A**1 2 7 9 10 **F**2 9 11 12 15 17 19 21 22 26 28 33 39 46 48 49 51 52 55 58 59 61 62 63 64 65 68 69 70 71 75 76 79 81 84 88 92 93 94 96 108 109 110 **P**8 **S** Triad Hospitals, Inc., Plano, TX Primary Contact: Paul Dougherty, President and Chief Executive Officer COO: R Andrew Wachtel, Vice President Operations CFO: John Hackbarth, CPA, CHE, Vice President Finance CMO: Kenneth W. Whittington, M.D., Vice President Medical Affairs CIO: R Andrew Wachtel, Vice President Operations CHR: M L. Wood, Vice President Human Resources Web address: www.deaconessokc.org	21	10	267	12853	180	—	1681	120693	47426	1254
EVERETT TOWER See OU Medical Center										
☒ **INTEGRIS BAPTIST MEDICAL CENTER**, 3300 N.W. Expressway, Zip 73112–4481; tel. 405/949–3011, (Includes INTEGRIS MENTAL HEALTH SYSTEM–SPENCER, 2601 North Spencer Road, Spencer, Zip 73084–3699, Mailing Address: P.O. Box 11137, Oklahoma City, Zip 73136–0137; tel. 405/717–9800; R. Murali Krishna, M.D., President and Chief Operating Officer) **A**1 2 3 5 9 10 **F**2 9 11 12 13 14 15 17 19 20 21 22 23 26 27 28 29 30 33 34 39 40 41 42 49 51 52 53 55 56 57 58 59 60 61 62 63 64 65 66 67 69 70 73 79 80 81 82 83 84 85 86 87 88 89 90 92 93 94 96 99 101 102 103 104 105 108 109 110 **P**6 7 8 **S** INTEGRIS Health, Oklahoma City, OK Primary Contact: C. Bruce Lawrence, President and Chief Operating Officer COO: C Bruce Lawrence, President and Chief Operating Officer CFO: Wentz J. Miller, Jr, Managing Director and Chief Financial Officer CMO: James P. White, M.D., Chief Medical Officer CIO: Harry McQueen, Vice President and Chief Information Officer CHR: Robert Quiring, Vice President Human Resources Web address: www.integris–health.com	23	10	483	22623	327	374794	2147	336242	120402	2767
☒ △ **INTEGRIS SOUTHWEST MEDICAL CENTER**, 4401 South Western, Zip 73109–3441; tel. 405/636–7000 **A**1 2 7 9 10 **F**2 9 11 12 15 17 19 21 22 23 26 27 28 29 33 34 35 37 44 45 46 47 48 49 50 52 53 54 55 57 58 59 60 61 62 63 64 65 66 68 69 70 79 81 82 84 85 86 87 88 92 93 94 96 108 109 110 **P**6 7 8 **S** INTEGRIS Health, Oklahoma City, OK Primary Contact: C. Bruce Lawrence, President and Chief Operating Officer COO: Chris Hammes, Administrator CFO: Errol Mitchell, Vice President CMO: Marty McBee, D.O., Chief of Staff Web address: www.integris–health.com	23	10	361	16505	248	—	1527	—	—	1466
□ **KINDRED HOSPITAL– OKLAHOMA CITY**, 1407 North Robinson Avenue, Zip 73103; tel. 405/232–8000, (Nonreporting) **A**1 10 **S** Kindred Healthcare, Louisville, KY Primary Contact: Kenneth R. Ross, Chief Executive Officer Web address: www.kindredhealthcare.com	33	49	59	—	—	—	—	—	—	—
□ **LAKESIDE WOMEN'S HOSPITAL**, 11200 North Portland Avenue, Zip 73120; tel. 405/936–1500, (Nonreporting) **A**1 9 10 Primary Contact: Kelley Brewer, Chief Executive Officer	33	49	14	—	—	—	—	—	—	—
☒ △ **MERCY HEALTH CENTER**, 4300 West Memorial Road, Zip 73120–8362; tel. 405/755–1515 **A**1 2 7 9 10 **F**2 9 11 12 14 15 17 19 21 22 27 28 29 30 32 33 36 37 38 39 41 42 44 46 47 48 50 51 52 53 54 55 56 57 58 59 60 61 62 63 64 68 69 70 79 80 81 82 83 84 85 87 88 93 94 95 96 106 107 108 109 110 **P**7 **S** Sisters of Mercy Health System, Chesterfield, MO Primary Contact: Michael J. Packnett, President and Chief Executive Officer COO: Jeff Johnston, Chief Operating Officer CFO: Mark A. Nafziger, Senior Vice President and Chief Financial Officer CMO: Mark Johnson, M.D., Chief Medical Officer CHR: Cathy Withiam, Vice President Human Resources Web address: www.mhso.okla.smhs.com	21	10	351	14615	215	198907	1464	177867	75957	2162
□ **NORTHWEST SURGICAL HOSPITAL**, 9204 North May Avenue, Zip 73120–4419; tel. 405/848–1918 **A**1 10 **F**26 27 33 62 63 84 Primary Contact: Jerry Forehand, R.N., Chief Executive Officer	33	13	9	678	6	—	0	12813	2722	48
□ **OKLAHOMA CENTER FOR ORTHOPEDIC AND MULTI–SPECIALTY SURGERY**, 8100 South Walker, Suite C., Zip 73139; tel. 405/602–6500, (Nonreporting) **A**1 9 10 **S** United Surgical Partners International, Addison, TX Primary Contact: Teri Philbrick, Chief Executive Officer	33	47	10	—	—	—	—	—	—	—

OK

Hospital, Address, Telephone, Approval, Facility, and Physician Codes, Health Care System	Classi-fication Codes		Utilization Data					Expense (thousands) of dollars		
★ American Hospital Association (AHA) membership □ Joint Commission on Accreditation of Healthcare Organizations (JCAHO) accreditation ○ American Osteopathic Association (AOA) accreditation △ Commission on Accreditation of Rehabilitation Facilities (CARF) accreditation	Control	Service	Staffed Beds	Admissions	Census	Outpatient Visits	Births	Total	Payroll	Personnel
□ **OKLAHOMA HEART HOSPITAL**, 4050 West Memorial Road, Zip 73120; tel. 405/608–3200 **A**1 9 10 **F**2 14 15 19 21 22 26 27 28 29 33 46 47 48 49 52 58 60 63 64 66 81 88 94 108 Primary Contact: Michael J. Packnett, President and Chief Executive Officer Web address: www.okheart.com	32	10	78	7850	65	11475	0	90247	25188	617
OKLAHOMA SPINE HOSPITAL, 14101 Parkway Commons Drive, Zip 73134; tel. 405/749–2700, (Nonreporting) **A**10 Primary Contact: Kevin Blaylock, Chief Executive Officer	33	49	12	—	—	—	—	—	—	—
✠ **OU MEDICAL CENTER**, (Formerly Oklahoma University Medical Center), 1200 Everett Drive, Zip 73104–5047, Mailing Address: P.O. Box 26307, Zip 73126; tel. 405/271–4700, (Includes CHILDREN'S HOSPITAL OF OKLAHOMA; EVERETT TOWER; PRESBYTERIAN TOWER) **A**1 2 3 5 8 9 10 **F**1 2 7 9 11 12 14 15 16 17 18 19 20 21 22 23 24 26 27 28 29 30 32 33 34 37 40 41 42 43 44 45 46 47 48 49 50 52 53 55 56 57 58 59 60 61 62 63 65 66 67 68 69 70 71 73 74 75 76 81 84 87 88 89 90 94 95 96 100 103 106 107 108 109 110 **S** HCA, Nashville, TN Primary Contact: Gerald J. Maier, FACHE, Chief Executive Officer COO: Rebecca Benoit, Chief Operating Officer CFO: Jim Watson, Chief Financial Officer CMO: J Andy Sullivan, M.D., Chief Medical Officer CIO: Larry Forsyth, Director Information Services CHR: Laura Land, Chief Human Resources Officer Web address: www.oumedcenter.com	33	10	578	26911	421	223805	3916	365989	124649	2548
□ **PHYSICIANS HOSPITAL**, 3100 S.W. 89th Street, Zip 73159–7900; tel. 405/378–3755, (Nonreporting) **A**1 10 Primary Contact: Thomas R. Rice, FACHE, President and Chief Operating Officer PRESBYTERIAN TOWER See OU Medical Center	32	49	51	—	—	—	—	—	—	—
□ **SELECT SPECIALTY HOSPITAL–OKLAHOMA CITY EAST**, 3300 N.W. Expressway Street, Zip 73112; tel. 405/951–8100, (Nonreporting) **A**1 10 Primary Contact: Madelene Roedl, President	33	80	38	—	—	—	—	—	—	—
□ **SELECT SPECIALTY HOSPITAL–OKLAHOMA CITY WEST**, 3613 N.W. 56th Street, Suite 100, Zip 73112; tel. 405/604–4016, (Nonreporting) **A**1 10 Primary Contact: Connie Strickland, Administrator	33	49	32	—	—	—	—	—	—	—
✠ △ **ST. ANTHONY HOSPITAL**, 1000 North Lee Street, Zip 73102–1080, Mailing Address: P.O. Box 205, Zip 73101–0205; tel. 405/272–7000, (Includes ST. MICHAEL HOSPITAL, 2129 S.W. 59th Street, Zip 73119–7001; tel. 405/713–5700) **A**1 2 3 5 7 9 10 12 13 **F**1 2 3 4 10 11 12 14 15 17 19 21 22 23 27 28 29 32 33 34 36 37 40 44 46 47 48 49 52 53 55 57 59 60 61 62 63 64 65 68 69 70 71 72 73 74 75 76 77 78 81 82 84 85 87 88 92 93 94 95 99 103 106 108 **P**1 6 7 **S** SSM Health Care, Saint Louis, MO Primary Contact: Joe Hodges, President CFO: Greg Simia, Vice President Finance CMO: Kersey Winfree, M.D., Chief Medical Officer Web address: www.saintsok.com	21	10	543	16469	351	90717	1144	189641	76763	1878
□ **SURGICAL HOSPITAL OF OKLAHOMA**, 100 S.E. 59th Street, Zip 73129; tel. 405/634–9300 **A**1 10 **F**2 26 27 28 33 63 82 84 85 Primary Contact: Phil Ross, Chief Executive Officer	32	13	12	350	2	7053	0	12450	4042	95
□ **VALIR REHABILITATION HOSPITAL**, 700 N.W. Seventh Street, Zip 73102–1295; tel. 405/236–3131 **A**1 10 **F**21 22 27 28 29 33 52 53 58 60 68 69 94 95 Primary Contact: Stacy Smith, Chief Executive Officer Web address: www.valir.com	33	46	56	494	17	2732	0	5684	3143	53
✠ △ **VETERANS AFFAIRS MEDICAL CENTER**, 921 N.E. 13th Street, Zip 73104–5028; tel. 405/270–0501, (Nonreporting) **A**1 3 5 7 8 **S** Department of Veterans Affairs, Washington, DC Primary Contact: Steven J. Gentling, FACHE, Director COO: Kathleen Fogarty, MS, Associate Director CFO: Haze McDougal, Chief Fiscal Service CMO: Robert McCaffree, M.D., Chief of Staff CIO: Leigh Mulanax, Chief Information Management Services CHR: Nicole Craven, Acting Chief, Human Resources Web address: www.va.gov/sta/guide/home.asp	45	10	169	—	—	—	—	—	—	—
OKMULGEE—Okmulgee County										
GEORGE NIGH REHABILITATION CENTER, 900 East Airport Road, Zip 74447–9762, Mailing Address: P.O. Box 1118, Zip 74447–1118; tel. 918/756–9211, (Total facility includes 13 beds in nursing home–type unit) (Nonreporting) **A**10 Primary Contact: Gala McBee, Administrator Web address: www.gnrc.ouhsc.edu	23	46	39	—	—	—	—	—	—	—
OKMULGEE MEMORIAL HOSPITAL, 1401 Morris Drive, Zip 74447–6419, Mailing Address: P.O. Box 1038, Zip 74447–1038; tel. 918/756–4233 **A**9 10 **F**2 9 11 21 22 27 28 33 44 46 51 52 58 59 62 63 66 71 76 77 81 82 83 87 88 94 97 108 Primary Contact: Rex Jones, Interim Chief Executive Officer Web address: www.okmulgeehospital.com	23	49	66	2368	27	32929	308	15051	8001	245

Many Facility Codes have changed. Please refer to the AHA Guide Code Chart. © 2005 AHA Guide

★	American Hospital Association (AHA) membership	
□	Joint Commission on Accreditation of Healthcare Organizations (JCAHO) accreditation	
○	American Osteopathic Association (AOA) accreditation	
△	Commission on Accreditation of Rehabilitation Facilities (CARF) accreditation	

Hospital, Address, Telephone, Approval, Facility, and Physician Codes, Health Care System	Control	Service	Staffed Beds	Admissions	Census	Outpatient Visits	Births	Total	Payroll	Personnel
PAULS VALLEY—Garvin County										
★ **PAULS VALLEY GENERAL HOSPITAL**, 100 Valley Drive, Zip 73075–0368, Mailing Address: Box 368, Zip 73075–0368; tel. 405/238–5501, (Total facility includes 8 beds in nursing home–type unit) **A**9 10 20 **F**6 9 11 12 21 33 36 37 38 44 46 51 55 59 60 63 69 81 88 92 96 97 107 Primary Contact: Charles Johnston, Administrator CFO: Brent Mynhier, Chief Financial Officer Web address: www.pvgh.net	15	10	50	1798	25	—	101	13024	6433	0
PAWHUSKA—Osage County										
PAWHUSKA HOSPITAL, 1101 East 15th Street, Zip 74056–1920; tel. 918/287–3232 **A**9 10 18 **F**2 9 21 33 41 69 81 92 97 108 Primary Contact: Ron Dunkle, Administrator	14	10	15	234	4	0	0	2368	824	16
PAWNEE—Pawnee County										
★ **PAWNEE MUNICIPAL HOSPITAL**, 1212 Fourth Street, Zip 74058–4046, Mailing Address: P.O. Box 467, Zip 74058–0467; tel. 918/762–2577 **A**9 10 **F**9 12 21 26 27 30 33 36 51 63 68 69 81 92 97 108 **S** Hillcrest HealthCare System, Tulsa, OK Primary Contact: Samuel T. Guild, Chief Executive Officer CFO: Tina Steele, Chief Financial Officer CMO: Jim Riemer, Medical Director CHR: Virginia Rogers, Human Resources Director Web address: www.hillcrest.com	33	10	20	1111	9	6007	0	4407	2199	70
PERRY—Noble County										
★ **PERRY MEMORIAL HOSPITAL**, 501 14th Street, Zip 73077–5099; tel. 580/336–3541 **A**9 10 20 **F**2 9 12 21 22 26 27 28 33 46 48 51 52 62 63 64 69 81 88 94 97 108 110 **S** Quorum Health Resources, Plano, TX Primary Contact: Joe Duerr, Chief Executive Officer CFO: Milena Davis, Chief Financial Officer CIO: Vanessa Sigler, Director of Health Information Management CHR: Shellie Seabolt, Director Human Resources Web address: www.pmh-ok.org	16	10	26	771	11	19017	0	5479	2607	87
PONCA CITY—Kay County										
⊞ **VIA CHRISTI OKLAHOMA REGIONAL MEDICAL CENTER**, 1900 North 14th Street, Zip 74601–2035, Mailing Address: P.O. Box 1270, Zip 74602–1270; tel. 580/765–3321, (Total facility includes 12 beds in nursing home–type unit) **A**1 9 10 19 **F**2 11 12 15 21 22 24 26 27 28 29 31 33 34 37 38 39 41 44 46 47 48 50 51 52 53 55 57 58 59 60 61 62 63 65 66 69 71 73 74 76 81 84 85 86 88 92 93 94 95 96 106 108 109 **P**5 **S** Via Christi Health System, Wichita, KS Primary Contact: W. Charles Waters, President and Chief Executive Officer CFO: Rick Snyder, Vice President and Chief Financial Officer CIO: Lynn Hampton, Director Information Systems CHR: Keith Hufnagel, Director Human Resources Web address: www.viachristiok.org	21	10	97	3560	39	72894	336	35020	13659	365
POTEAU—Le Flore County										
⊞ **EASTERN OKLAHOMA MEDICAL CENTER**, 105 Wall Street, Zip 74953–4428, Mailing Address: P.O. Box 1148, Zip 74953–1148; tel. 918/647–8161 **A**1 9 10 20 **F**9 12 21 22 33 39 44 46 48 51 52 53 55 58 59 63 69 70 76 77 81 82 84 87 88 108 **P**6 Primary Contact: Terry Buckner, Chief Executive Officer CFO: Nancy Frier, Chief Financial Officer CIO: Michael C. Huggins, Network System Administrator CHR: Michele Oglesby, Human Resources Manager	23	10	72	2874	28	—	438	15515	6049	210
PRAGUE—Lincoln County										
★ **PRAGUE MUNICIPAL HOSPITAL**, 1322 Klabzuba Avenue, Zip 74864–9005, Mailing Address: P.O. Drawer S, Zip 74864–9005; tel. 405/567–4922 **A**9 10 18 **F**9 33 34 46 48 52 53 63 70 75 81 92 97 108 **P**1 6 Primary Contact: Joan Walters, Interim Chief Executive Officer CFO: Doug Erickson, Chief Financial Officer Web address: www.hillcrest.com	14	10	19	164	2	7118	0	2594	1219	30
PRYOR—Mayes County										
⊞ **INTEGRIS MAYES COUNTY MEDICAL CENTER**, 111 North Bailey Street, Zip 74361–4211, Mailing Address: P.O. Box 278, Zip 74362–0278; tel. 918/825–1600 **A**1 9 10 **F**2 9 11 12 21 22 28 29 32 33 34 36 44 46 48 51 52 58 59 63 65 66 69 81 85 88 94 96 97 106 108 **S** INTEGRIS Health, Oklahoma City, OK Primary Contact: W. Charles Jordan, Administrator CFO: Kristy McCollough, Assistant Administrator and Chief Financial Officer CMO: Paul Battles, M.D., Chief Medical Staff CHR: James Chronister, Human Resources Director	23	10	52	1426	13	15395	0	15103	5945	177
PURCELL—McClain County										
★ **PURCELL MUNICIPAL HOSPITAL**, 1500 North Green Avenue, Zip 73080–1699, Mailing Address: P.O. Box 511, Zip 73080–0511; tel. 405/527–6524 **A**9 10 **F**2 9 11 21 22 26 29 33 46 48 52 58 59 60 63 65 66 69 81 88 93 94 96 97 **P**8 **S** Quorum Health Resources, Plano, TX Primary Contact: Curtis R. Pryor, Chief Executive Officer CFO: Jennifer Warren, Chief Financial Officer CMO: Jill Watson, Chief of Staff CIO: Jennifer Patterson, Information Technology Coordinator CHR: Fran Ray, Manager Human Resources Web address: www.purcellhospital.com	14	10	30	1591	16	33170	66	10293	4456	142

Hospital, Address, Telephone, Approval, Facility, and Physician Codes, Health Care System	Classi-fication Codes		Utilization Data					Expense (thousands) of dollars		
★ American Hospital Association (AHA) membership □ Joint Commission on Accreditation of Healthcare Organizations (JCAHO) accreditation ○ American Osteopathic Association (AOA) accreditation △ Commission on Accreditation of Rehabilitation Facilities (CARF) accreditation	Control	Service	Staffed Beds	Admissions	Census	Outpatient Visits	Births	Total	Payroll	Personnel
SALLISAW—Sequoyah County **SEQUOYAH MEMORIAL HOSPITAL**, 213 East Redwood Street, Zip 74955–2811, Mailing Address: P.O. Box 505, Zip 74955–0505; tel. 918/774–1100 **A**9 10 **F**9 24 27 28 29 33 36 37 38 48 51 63 69 81 88 96 106 108 Primary Contact: Charles Wade, Interim Administrator Web address: www.smhok.com	15	10	41	796	8	19191	0	8083	3863	191
SAPULPA—Creek County ★ **ST. JOHN SAPULPA**, 519 South Division Street, Zip 74066–4501, Mailing Address: P.O. Box 1368, Zip 74067–1368; tel. 918/224–4280 **A**9 10 18 **F**2 12 21 22 23 26 27 33 52 63 69 81 88 97 108 **P**5 **S** Marian Health System, Tulsa, OK Primary Contact: Raymond L. Replogle, President and Chief Executive Officer CFO: Donna Nagel, Senior Director Operations CMO: Roger D. Wilson, M.D., Medical Director Web address: www.sjmc.org	21	10	25	1389	13	19292	0	16369	4460	128
SAYRE—Beckham County ★ **SAYRE MEMORIAL HOSPITAL**, 501 East Washington Street, Zip 73662–1337; tel. 580/928–5541 **A**9 10 **F**21 28 34 44 51 64 66 69 81 88 92 94 97 **P**6 **S** Quorum Health Resources, Plano, TX Primary Contact: Rex Jones, Chief Executive Officer CFO: Monica Scott, Chief Financial Officer	23	10	35	1227	15	10593	17	4964	2139	83
SEILING—Dewey County **SEILING HOSPITAL**, Highway 60 N.E., Zip 73663, Mailing Address: P.O. Box 720, Zip 73663–0720; tel. 580/922–7361 **A**9 10 20 **F**33 51 81 84 88 97 **P**5 Primary Contact: Charlotte Billings, Interim Chief Executive Officer	14	10	18	355	4	4320	0	—	—	44
SEMINOLE—Seminole County **SEMINOLE MEDICAL CENTER**, (Formerly Seminole Municipal Hospital), 2401 Wrangler Boulevard, Zip 74868–1917; tel. 405/303–4000, (Nonreporting) **A**9 10 Primary Contact: LaDonna McAlvain, R.N., Administrator Web address: www.seminolemedicalcenter.com	14	10	29	—	—	—	—	—	—	—
SHATTUCK—Ellis County ★ **NEWMAN MEMORIAL HOSPITAL**, 905 South Main Street, Zip 73858–9802; tel. 580/938–2551 **A**9 10 20 **F**2 9 11 12 21 22 24 27 28 29 32 33 41 48 51 54 59 62 63 66 69 81 84 88 92 94 97 108 Primary Contact: Gary W. Mitchell, Chief Executive Officer COO: Kevin O'Brien, Chief Operating Officer Web address: www.newmanmemorialhospital.org	23	10	27	816	7	34929	121	6536	2679	88
SHAWNEE—Pottawatomie County ✠ **UNITY HEALTH CENTER**, 1102 West MacArthur Street, Zip 74804–1744; tel. 405/273–2270 **A**1 2 9 10 **F**9 11 12 15 21 22 23 26 27 28 29 33 34 37 55 56 59 68 81 82 84 88 93 94 95 96 107 108 109 **P**5 Primary Contact: Charles E. Skillings, President and Chief Executive Officer COO: Gray Cox, President CFO: Vicky Fine, Vice President and Chief Financial Officer CIO: Linda E. Brown, R.N., Vice President Clinical Support Web address: www.unityhealthcenter.com	23	10	104	5706	58	86943	762	45824	20464	293
STIGLER—Haskell County ★ **HASKELL COUNTY HEALTHCARE SYSTEM**, 401 N.W. H Street, Zip 74462–1625; tel. 918/967–4682, (Nonreporting) **A**9 10 20 **S** Quorum Health Resources, Plano, TX Primary Contact: Mark Harrel, Chief Executive Officer CFO: Tammy Shaw, Chief Financial Officer CMO: Mark McCurry, M.D., Chief of Staff CIO: Tammy Shaw, Chief Financial Officer	13	10	29	—	—	—	—	—	—	—
STILLWATER—Payne County ✠ **STILLWATER MEDICAL CENTER**, 1323 West Sixth Avenue, Zip 74074–4399, Mailing Address: P.O. Box 2408, Zip 74076–2408; tel. 405/372–1480, (Total facility includes 9 beds in nursing home–type unit) **A**1 9 10 19 20 **F**2 9 11 12 15 27 28 29 32 33 34 41 51 54 55 58 59 62 63 64 66 68 69 78 81 82 84 85 88 92 93 94 95 106 108 **P**6 7 Primary Contact: Jerry G. Moeller, President and Chief Executive Officer CMO: Terry N. Brown, M.D., Medical Director Web address: www.stillwater–medical.org	16	10	109	4936	53	76354	905	55740	22056	631
STILWELL—Adair County ★ **MEMORIAL HOSPITAL**, 1401 West Locust, Zip 74960, Mailing Address: P.O. Box 272, Zip 74960; tel. 918/696–3101 **A**9 10 20 **F**9 28 33 51 62 81 88 **P**6 Primary Contact: Alan L. Adams, President	23	10	31	1686	14	6736	31	8961	4835	156
STROUD—Lincoln County **STROUD REGIONAL MEDICAL CENTER**, Highway 66 West, Zip 74079, Mailing Address: P.O. Box 530, Zip 74079–0530; tel. 918/968–3571, (Nonreporting) **A**9 10 18 Primary Contact: Beverly Ash, Administrator	23	10	25	—	—	—	—	—	—	—
SULPHUR—Murray County **ARBUCKLE MEMORIAL HOSPITAL**, 2011 West Broadway Street, Zip 73086–4221; tel. 580/622–2161, (Nonreporting) **A**9 10 18 **S** Preferred Management Corporation, Shawnee, OK Primary Contact: Darin Farrell, Chief Executive Officer	13	10	25	—	—	—	—	—	—	—

Many Facility Codes have changed. Please refer to the AHA Guide Code Chart.

© 2005 AHA Guide

OK

Hospital, Address, Telephone, Approval, Facility, and Physician Codes, Health Care System	Classi-fication Codes		Utilization Data					Expense (thousands) of dollars		
★ American Hospital Association (AHA) membership □ Joint Commission on Accreditation of Healthcare Organizations (JCAHO) accreditation ○ American Osteopathic Association (AOA) accreditation △ Commission on Accreditation of Rehabilitation Facilities (CARF) accreditation	Control	Service	Staffed Beds	Admissions	Census	Outpatient Visits	Births	Total	Payroll	Personnel

TAHLEQUAH—Cherokee County

□ **TAHLEQUAH CITY HOSPITAL**, 1400 East Downing Street, Zip 74464–3324, Mailing Address: P.O. Box 1008, Zip 74465–1008; tel. 918/456–0641, (Nonreporting) **A**1 9 10 20
Primary Contact: Brian K. Woodliff, Chief Executive Officer
Web address: www.tch–ok.org

| 16 | 10 | 97 | — | — | — | — | — | — | — |

⊠ **WILLIAM W. HASTINGS INDIAN HOSPITAL**, 100 South Bliss Avenue, Zip 74464–3399; tel. 918/458–3100, (Nonreporting) **A**1 10 **S** U. S. Indian Health Service, Rockville, MD
Primary Contact: Hickory Starr, Jr, Administrator

| 47 | 10 | 60 | — | — | — | — | — | — | — |

TALIHINA—La Flore County

⊠ **CHOCTAW NATION HEALTH CARE CENTER**, One Choctaw Way, Zip 74571–9517; tel. 918/567–7000 **A**1 10 **F**2 4 5 11 12 21 24 26 27 28 29 32 33 35 37 39 41 42 44 45 46 47 48 50 52 58 59 62 63 64 65 66 69 70 71 72 74 75 77 81 88 89 94 106 107 109 110 **P**6 **S** U. S. Indian Health Service, Rockville, MD
Primary Contact: Reece Sherrill, Administrator
COO: Todd Hallmark, Chief Operating Officer
CFO: Teresa Jackson, Chief Financial Officer
CMO: Tom Bonin, M.D., Medical Director
CIO: Skip Leader, Chief Information Officer
CHR: Evelyn Jones, Director Human Resources
Web address: www.choctawnationhealth.com

| 47 | 10 | 37 | 1690 | 14 | 93399 | 391 | 55082 | 21632 | 466 |

TISHOMINGO—Johnston County

JOHNSTON MEMORIAL HOSPITAL, 1000 South Byrd Street, Zip 73460–3299; tel. 580/371–2327 **A**9 10 18 **F**2 33 81 88 97
Primary Contact: Mary Owen, R.N., Interim Administrator

| 31 | 10 | 25 | 561 | 4 | 5560 | 0 | 345956 | 133 | 36 |

TULSA—Tulsa County

BROOKHAVEN HOSPITAL, 201 South Garnett Road, Zip 74128–1800; tel. 918/438–4257 **A**10 **F**3 4 27 28 31 71 74 75 77 78 94 96 **P**8
Primary Contact: Rolf B. Gainer, Chief Executive Officer and Administrator
Web address: www.brookhavenhospital.com

| 33 | 22 | 40 | 683 | 30 | 0 | 0 | 6554 | 2645 | 76 |

★ **CONTINUOUS CARE CENTER OF TULSA**, 1924 South Utica Avenue, Zip 74105–6510; tel. 918/749–8930 **A**10 **F**21 33 37 38 60 64 94 110 **P**8
Primary Contact: Raymond L. Replogle, President and Chief Executive Officer
COO: Mike Harris, Chief Operating Officer
CFO: Basil Wyatt, Chief Financial Officer
CMO: Gordon Lantz, M.D., Medical Director
CIO: Dana Jetton, Chief Information Officer
CHR: Sunny Benjamin, Director Human Resources
Web address: www.cccok.com

| 23 | 80 | 46 | 473 | 36 | 0 | 0 | 15000 | 6121 | 105 |

⊠ **HILLCREST MEDICAL CENTER**, 1120 South Utica, Zip 74104–4090; tel. 918/579–1000 **A**1 3 5 9 10 **F**2 9 10 11 12 13 14 15 17 19 21 22 23 24 26 27 28 29 32 33 34 37 39 41 44 46 47 48 49 50 51 52 53 55 56 57 58 59 60 61 62 63 64 65 66 67 68 69 71 73 74 75 77 78 81 82 83 84 86 88 89 92 93 94 95 96 99 106 108 109 110 **S** Hillcrest HealthCare System, Tulsa, OK
Primary Contact: Steve Dobbs, Chief Executive Officer
COO: Jody Abbott, Chief Operating Officer
CFO: Donald Baker, Vice President Finance
CMO: Steven Landgarten, M.D., Senior Vice President Medical Staff Affairs
CHR: Claudia Underwood, Vice President Human Resources
Web address: www.hillcrest.com

| 23 | 10 | 432 | 21334 | 280 | 306354 | 4187 | 152676 | — | 1595 |

⊠ **HILLCREST SPECIALTY HOSPITAL**, (Formerly Specialty Hospital of Tulsa), 744 West 9th Street, Zip 74127–9028; tel. 918/599–4000 **A**1 10 **F**2 21 22 33 44 45 58 60 64 66 73 92 94 **S** Ardent Health Services, Nashville, TN
Primary Contact: Kenneth Noteboom, Chief Executive Officer
CFO: Bryan Fissel, Director of Finance
Web address: www.hillcrestspecialty.com

| 33 | 80 | 100 | 895 | 72 | 0 | 0 | 31335 | 7733 | 105 |

⊠ **LAUREATE PSYCHIATRIC CLINIC AND HOSPITAL**, 6655 South Yale Avenue, Zip 74136–3329; tel. 918/481–4000 **A**1 3 5 10 **F**3 4 26 27 28 71 72 73 74 75 76 77 78 **P**6 **S** Saint Francis Health System, Tulsa, OK
Primary Contact: Reese Jackson, Senior Vice President and Administrator
Web address: www.laureate.com

| 23 | 22 | 75 | 2983 | 54 | 0 | 0 | 22650 | 13706 | 271 |

□ **MEADOWBROOK REHABILITATION HOSPITAL OF TULSA**, 3219 South 79th East Avenue, Zip 74145–1312; tel. 918/663–8183, (Nonreporting) **A**1 10
Primary Contact: Shirley Brister, Chief Executive Officer

| 32 | 46 | 60 | — | — | — | — | — | — | — |

ORTHOPEDIC HOSPITAL OF OKLAHOMA, 2408 East 81st Street, Suite 300, Zip 74137; tel. 918/477–5000, (Nonreporting) **A**10
Primary Contact: Don Burman, Chief Executive Officer

| 33 | 49 | 27 | — | — | — | — | — | — | — |

PARKSIDE HOSPITAL, 1620 East 12th Street, Zip 74120–5499; tel. 918/582–2131, (Nonreporting) **A**3 5 10
Primary Contact: Debra Moore, Chief Executive Officer
Web address: www.parksideinc.org

| 23 | 22 | 40 | — | — | — | — | — | — | — |

□ **SAINT FRANCIS HEART HOSPITAL**, 10501 East 91st Street South, Zip 74133; tel. 918/307–6000 **A**1 10 **F**9 14 33 46 48 58 81 85 88 94 108 **S** Saint Francis Health System, Tulsa, OK
Primary Contact: Robert S. Dolan, Chief Executive Officer
Web address: www.saintfrancisheart.com

| 32 | 42 | 52 | 1439 | 12 | 2538 | 0 | 26430 | 7614 | 233 |

Hospital, Address, Telephone, Approval, Facility, and Physician Codes, Health Care System	Classi-fication Codes		Utilization Data					Expense (thousands) of dollars		
★ American Hospital Association (AHA) membership □ Joint Commission on Accreditation of Healthcare Organizations (JCAHO) accreditation ○ American Osteopathic Association (AOA) accreditation △ Commission on Accreditation of Rehabilitation Facilities (CARF) accreditation	Control	Service	Staffed Beds	Admissions	Census	Outpatient Visits	Births	Total	Payroll	Personnel

⊠ △ **SAINT FRANCIS HOSPITAL**, 6161 South Yale Avenue, Zip 74136–1902; tel. 918/494–2200, (Total facility includes 40 beds in nursing home–type unit) **A**1 2 3 5 7 9 10 **F**2 6 9 10 11 12 13 14 15 16 17 18 19 21 22 23 24 27 28 29 32 33 34 35 37 38 39 40 41 44 45 46 47 48 49 50 52 53 54 55 56 57 58 59 60 61 62 63 64 65 66 67 69 79 80 81 82 84 85 86 87 88 90 92 93 94 95 96 99 100 101 104 106 107 108 109 110 **P**1 6 8 **S** Saint Francis Health System, Tulsa, OK Primary Contact: Reese Jackson, Senior Vice President and Administrator COO: Reese Jackson, Chief Operating Officer CFO: Barry L. Steichen, Senior Vice President and Chief Financial Officer CMO: Thomas David, M.D., Senior Vice President and Chief Medical Officer CIO: Mark Stastny, Vice President Information Technology CHR: Joseph H. Neely, Senior Vice President and Administrator Web address: www.saintfrancis.com	23	10	666	37976	510	661134	3118	264859	147880	3971
□ **SELECT SPECIALTY HOSPITAL – TULSA**, 744 West Ninth Street, Zip 74127–9096; tel. 918/502–1400, (Nonreporting) **A**1 10 **S** Select Medical Corporation, Mechanicsburg, PA Primary Contact: David Bennett, Chief Executive Officer	33	80	32	—	—	—	—	—	—	—
□ **SHADOW MOUNTAIN BEHAVIORAL HEALTH SYSTEM**, 6262 South Sheridan Road, Zip 74133–4099; tel. 918/492–8200, (Nonreporting) **A**1 **S** Psychiatric Solutions, Franklin, TN Primary Contact: Sharon Worsham, Chief Executive Officer	33	52	100	—	—	—	—	—	—	—
⊠ **SOUTHCREST HOSPITAL**, 8801 South 101st East Avenue, Zip 74133; tel. 918/294–4000 **A**1 9 10 **F**9 10 11 12 15 17 19 21 22 23 27 29 41 43 46 48 52 53 55 59 61 62 63 64 66 69 70 81 82 84 88 94 96 108 109 **S** Triad Hospitals, Inc., Plano, TX Primary Contact: Anthony R. Young, Chief Executive Officer COO: Terri Jacobs, Administrator CFO: Matt Romero, Vice President Finance and Chief Financial Officer CIO: Brenda Crawford, Process Leader Management of Information CHR: Shelia Nelson, Process Leader Human Resources Web address: www.southcresthospital.com	33	10	180	8179	86	—	1480	—	—	592
□ **SOUTHWESTERN REGIONAL MEDICAL CENTER**, 2408 East 81st Street, Zip 74137–4210; tel. 918/496–5000, (Nonreporting) **A**1 2 9 10 **S** Cancer Treatment Centers of America, Arlington Heights, IL Primary Contact: James H. Bruer, President and Chief Executive Officer Web address: www.cancercenter.com	33	49	40	—	—	—	—	—	—	—
⊠ **ST. JOHN MEDICAL CENTER**, 1923 South Utica Avenue, Zip 74104–5445; tel. 918/744–2345, (Total facility includes 24 beds in nursing home–type unit) **A**1 2 3 5 9 10 **F**2 6 9 10 11 14 15 16 17 18 19 20 21 22 23 26 27 28 29 35 36 37 38 39 40 41 42 44 45 46 47 48 49 50 51 52 53 55 56 57 58 59 60 61 62 63 64 65 66 67 68 69 71 73 74 75 76 77 78 79 80 81 82 84 85 86 87 88 92 93 94 95 96 99 103 105 106 107 108 109 110 **P**5 6 7 **S** Marian Health System, Tulsa, OK Primary Contact: David Pynn, President and Chief Executive Officer CFO: Lex S. Anderson, Executive Vice President CMO: William Allred, M.D., Vice President of Medical Affairs CIO: Mike Reeves, Vice President CHR: Howard Peterson, Senior Vice President Web address: www.sjmc.org	21	10	557	30489	425	144924	2114	317659	108736	2811
⊠ ○ **TULSA REGIONAL MEDICAL CENTER**, 744 West Ninth Street, Zip 74127–9990; tel. 918/587–2561 **A**1 9 10 11 12 13 **F**2 9 10 11 12 14 15 17 19 21 22 23 26 27 28 29 30 33 34 39 40 44 45 46 47 48 50 52 55 56 57 58 59 60 61 62 63 64 65 66 69 70 71 72 73 74 75 76 78 81 82 84 85 87 88 93 94 95 96 98 106 107 108 110 **P**5 8 **S** Hillcrest HealthCare System, Tulsa, OK Primary Contact: Dan Fieker, Chief Executive Officer CFO: David Jamin, Administrative Director Finance CMO: Dan Fieker, Chief Executive Officer Web address: www.hillcrest.com	33	10	212	12864	211	39541	1122	120409	51694	1216
⊠ **TULSA SPINE HOSPITAL**, 6901 South Olympia Avenue, Zip 74132; tel. 918/388–5701 **A**1 10 **F**2 21 22 26 27 28 33 62 63 66 81 82 84 85 88 Primary Contact: Terry L. Woodbeck, Administrator Web address: www.tulsaspinehospital.com	32	13	21	1438	10	3957	0	—	—	129
VINITA—Craig County										
★ **CRAIG GENERAL HOSPITAL**, 735 North Foreman Street, Zip 74301–1418, Mailing Address: Box 326, Zip 74301–0326; tel. 918/256–7551 **A**9 10 20 **F**9 11 22 23 27 33 46 48 55 59 60 63 69 71 76 77 81 82 84 88 92 93 94 97 108 **P**6 Primary Contact: B. Joe Gunn, Ed.D., FACHE, Administrator and Chief Executive Officer CFO: Terry W. Shambles, Chief Financial Officer CMO: Ed Allensworth, M.D., Medical Director CIO: Terry W. Shambles, Chief Financial Officer CHR: Marsha Emerson, Administrator for Support Services Web address: www.craiggeneralhospital.com	13	10	58	1537	19	27176	80	11870	5304	147

Many Facility Codes have changed. Please refer to the AHA Guide Code Chart.

© 2005 AHA Guide

OK

Hospital, Address, Telephone, Approval, Facility, and Physician Codes, Health Care System	Classi-fication Codes		Utilization Data					Expense (thousands) of dollars		
★ American Hospital Association (AHA) membership □ Joint Commission on Accreditation of Healthcare Organizations (JCAHO) accreditation ○ American Osteopathic Association (AOA) accreditation △ Commission on Accreditation of Rehabilitation Facilities (CARF) accreditation	Control	Service	Staffed Beds	Admissions	Census	Outpatient Visits	Births	Total	Payroll	Personnel
OKLAHOMA FORENSIC CENTER, Mailing Address: P.O. Box 69, Zip 74301–0069; tel. 918/256–7841, (Nonreporting) **S** Oklahoma State Department of Mental Health and Substance Abuse Services, Oklahoma City, OK Primary Contact: William T. Burkett, Chief Executive Officer	12	22	221	—	—	—	—	—	—	—
WAGONER—Wagoner County										
★ **WAGONER COMMUNITY HOSPITAL**, 1200 West Cherokee, Zip 74467–4681, Mailing Address: Box 407, Zip 74477–0407; tel. 918/485–5514, (Nonreporting) **A**9 10 **S** Hillcrest HealthCare System, Tulsa, OK Primary Contact: John W. Crawford, Chief Executive Officer CFO: Loren Rials, Chief Financial Officer CHR: Barnetta Webb, Director	23	10	100	—	—	—	—	—	—	—
WATONGA—Blaine County										
★ **WATONGA MUNICIPAL HOSPITAL**, 500 North Nash Boulevard, Zip 73772–0370, Mailing Address: Box 370, Zip 73772–0370; tel. 580/623–7211 **A**9 10 18 **F**6 9 22 27 28 29 33 46 48 52 53 60 69 81 84 88 92 97 Primary Contact: Brenda K. Doyel, Chief Executive Officer CFO: Brenda K. Doyel, Chief Executive Officer CMO: Curtis Schenk, M.D., Chief of Staff CIO: Kathy Vermillion, Medical Records Supervisor CHR: Linda McSperitt, Accounting Supervisor Web address: www.watongahospital.com	16	10	21	389	3	16288	1	3089	1549	52
WAURIKA—Jefferson County										
★ **JEFFERSON COUNTY HOSPITAL**, Highway 70 and 81, Zip 73573–3075, Mailing Address: P.O. Box 90, Zip 73573–0090; tel. 580/228–2344 **A**9 10 18 **F**9 33 46 69 81 84 88 97 Primary Contact: Jane McDowell, Administrator CFO: Richard Tallon, Chief Financial Officer CMO: Steve Hinshaw, M.D., Chief of Staff CIO: Nikki McGahey, Information Officer	13	10	25	384	5	12274	0	2750	1516	44
WEATHERFORD—Custer County										
★ **SOUTHWESTERN MEMORIAL HOSPITAL**, 215 North Kansas Street, Zip 73096–5499; tel. 580/772–5551 **A**9 10 18 **F**2 9 11 12 21 23 27 28 33 45 47 52 53 58 59 63 65 81 82 88 97 107 Primary Contact: Debbie Howe, Chief Executive Officer CFO: Donna Avant, Chief Financial Officer CMO: Mike Aaron, M.D., Chief of Staff CIO: Stephanie Helton, Director Health Information Management CHR: Jane Karlin, Director Human Resources Web address: www.smhospital.com	16	10	25	1089	7	25223	238	6709	3523	133
WILBURTON—Latimer County										
LATIMER COUNTY GENERAL HOSPITAL, 806 Highway 2 North, Zip 74578–3698; tel. 918/465–2391, (Nonreporting) **A**9 10 Primary Contact: M. Sue Mings, Administrator	13	10	26	—	—	—	—	—	—	—
WOODWARD—Woodward County										
NORTHWESTERN CENTER FOR BEHAVIORAL HEALTH, 1222 10th Street, Suite 211, Zip 73801; tel. 580/571–3233 **A**10 **F**4 71 72 73 74 75 76 77 78 **P**6 **S** Oklahoma State Department of Mental Health and Substance Abuse Services, Oklahoma City, OK Primary Contact: Steve Norwood, Executive Director	12	22	84	947	70	0	0	13453	7098	214
✠ **WOODWARD REGIONAL HOSPITAL**, 900 17th Street, Zip 73801–2423; tel. 580/256–5511 **A**1 9 10 20 **F**9 11 12 21 22 23 26 27 29 33 36 46 51 54 55 59 60 62 63 64 76 81 84 85 88 93 94 96 97 106 108 **S** Triad Hospitals, Inc., Plano, TX Primary Contact: Troy Taubenheim, Chief Executive Officer CFO: Stephen Thames, Chief Financial Officer Web address: www.woodwardhospital.com	33	10	68	2159	24	34079	279	24550	9065	282
YUKON—Canadian County										
✠ **INTEGRIS CANADIAN VALLEY REGIONAL HOSPITAL**, 1201 Health Center Parkway, Zip 73099; tel. 405/717–6800 **A**1 9 10 **F**9 11 12 21 22 26 27 28 33 48 52 59 62 63 66 69 70 81 108 **S** INTEGRIS Health, Oklahoma City, OK Primary Contact: James D. Moore, FACHE, Chief Executive Officer and Administrator CFO: Cindy White, Chief Financial Officer CMO: Curtis Brown, M.D., Chief of Staff CHR: Lynn Ketch, Manager Human Resources and Volunteer Services Web address: www.integris–health.com	23	10	40	2227	16	27722	429	16218	6164	145

OREGON

Hospital, Address, Telephone, Approval, Facility, and Physician Codes, Health Care System	Classification Codes		Utilization Data					Expense (thousands) of dollars		
★ American Hospital Association (AHA) membership □ Joint Commission on Accreditation of Healthcare Organizations (JCAHO) accreditation ○ American Osteopathic Association (AOA) accreditation △ Commission on Accreditation of Rehabilitation Facilities (CARF) accreditation	Control	Service	Staffed Beds	Admissions	Census	Outpatient Visits	Births	Total	Payroll	Personnel

ALBANY—Linn County

⊠ **SAMARITAN ALBANY GENERAL HOSPITAL**, 1046 West Sixth Avenue, Zip 97321–1999; tel. 541/812–4000 **A**1 9 10 **F**2 9 11 12 21 22 26 27 28 29 33 34 36 41 46 47 48 50 52 55 58 59 63 64 65 66 69 81 84 88 92 94 95 96 106 108 109 110 **S** Samaritan Health Services, Corvallis, OR
Primary Contact: David G. Triebes, Chief Executive Officer
CFO: Dan Smith, Vice President Finance
Web address: www.samhealth.org

| 23 | 10 | 63 | 3796 | 29 | 66166 | 671 | 50749 | 23104 | 475 |

ASHLAND—Jackson County

⊠ **ASHLAND COMMUNITY HOSPITAL**, 280 Maple Street, Zip 97520–1593, Mailing Address: P.O. Box 98, Zip 97520–0098; tel. 541/482–2441 **A**1 9 10 **F**9 10 11 12 21 26 27 28 29 33 34 36 37 38 48 51 52 54 55 57 58 59 60 62 63 64 65 66 69 81 88 92 94 95 96 106 109 110
Primary Contact: Mark E. Marchetti, President and Chief Executive Officer
CFO: Ron Telles, Chief Financial Officer
CMO: Jean Keevil, M.D., Chief Medical Staff
CIO: Reggie Thornton, Chief Information Officer
CHR: Karen Herwig, Director Human Resources
Web address: www.ashlandhospital.org

| 23 | 10 | 31 | 1938 | 17 | 61025 | 388 | 35094 | 14772 | 315 |

ASTORIA—Clatsop County

⊠ **COLUMBIA MEMORIAL HOSPITAL**, 2111 Exchange Street, Zip 97103–3329; tel. 503/325–4321 **A**1 9 10 18 **F**2 9 11 12 21 22 27 28 29 30 33 34 36 46 47 48 51 55 58 59 62 63 65 66 69 70 81 82 84 85 88 94 95 106 109 110 **P**5 6
Primary Contact: Terry O. Finklein, Chief Executive Officer
CFO: Erik Thorsen, Chief Financial Officer
CHR: Starla Niemann, Director Human Resources
Web address: www.columbiamemorial.org

| 23 | 10 | 25 | 1942 | 16 | 71608 | 308 | 26889 | 12434 | 265 |

BAKER CITY—Baker County

⊠ **ST. ELIZABETH HEALTH SERVICES**, 3325 Pocahontas Road, Zip 97814–1464; tel. 541/523–6461, (Total facility includes 50 beds in nursing home–type unit) **A**1 9 10 18 20 **F**9 11 12 14 21 22 26 27 29 33 34 45 46 48 52 53 55 58 59 60 62 63 66 69 70 81 85 88 92 94 95 96 97 108 109 110 **P**5 **S** Catholic Health Initiatives, Denver, CO
Primary Contact: George Winn, President and Chief Executive Officer
CFO: Jeff Daniels, Vice President Finance and Chief Financial Officer
CHR: Jerry Nickell, Vice President Human Resource and Mission
Web address: www.stelizabethhealth.com

| 23 | 10 | 75 | 1373 | 56 | 27146 | 95 | 20445 | 8406 | 195 |

BANDON—Coos County

★ **SOUTHERN COOS HOSPITAL AND HEALTH CENTER**, 900 11th Street S.E., Zip 97411–9114; tel. 541/347–2426 **A**9 10 18 **F**2 9 12 21 22 27 28 29 33 37 39 42 46 48 51 52 53 58 60 63 64 66 81 88 96 97 108 109 110
Primary Contact: James A. Wathen, Chief Executive Officer
CFO: Randall J. Scholten, Chief Financial Officer
Web address: www.southerncoos.com

| 16 | 10 | 18 | 368 | 3 | 13219 | 0 | 7469 | 3195 | 93 |

BEND—Deschutes County

⊠ **ST. CHARLES MEDICAL CENTER – BEND**, 2500 N.E. Neff Road, Zip 97701–6015; tel. 541/382–4321 **A**1 2 3 5 9 10 19 **F**9 10 11 15 16 17 18 19 20 21 22 23 26 27 28 29 33 34 36 37 38 39 46 47 48 49 51 52 53 55 56 57 58 59 60 61 62 63 64 65 68 69 73 75 78 79 80 81 82 83 85 87 88 92 93 94 96 106 108 109 110 **P**5 **S** Cascade Healthcare Community, Bend, OR
Primary Contact: Jim R. Hobbs, President and Chief Executive Officer
COO: Rick Martin, Senior Vice President Operations
CFO: Thomas Safley, Vice President Finance and Chief Financial Officer
CMO: Dean Sharpe, Vice President Medical Affairs
CIO: Todd Sprague, Marketing and Community Relations Director
CHR: Jim Dover, Vice President Human Resources
Web address: www.scmc.org

| 23 | 10 | 172 | 12288 | 135 | 115244 | 1578 | 194298 | 83581 | 1436 |

BURNS—Harney County

HARNEY DISTRICT HOSPITAL, 557 West Washington Street, Zip 97720–1497; tel. 541/573–7281 **A**9 10 18 **F**6 11 12 27 28 29 33 34 52 59 63 69 71 75 81 88 97 **P**5
Primary Contact: Jim Bishop, Interim Administrator
Web address: www.harneydistricthospital.com

| 16 | 10 | 20 | 781 | 5 | 19651 | 46 | 7457 | 3435 | 93 |

CLACKAMAS—Clackamas County

⊠ **KAISER SUNNYSIDE MEDICAL CENTER**, 10180 S.E. Sunnyside Road, Zip 97015–9303; tel. 503/652–2880 **A**1 2 10 **F**2 9 10 11 12 22 23 26 27 28 33 38 41 47 50 51 52 55 56 57 58 59 60 61 62 63 64 65 66 69 75 81 82 84 85 87 88 92 94 95 107 108 109 **P**6 **S** Kaiser Foundation Hospitals, Oakland, CA
Primary Contact: Jesse M. Gamez, Administrator
CFO: Frank Hemeon, Vice President Financial Administration
CMO: Rick Olson, Chief of Staff
CIO: Larry Wheeler, Vice President Communications and External Affairs
CHR: Tricia Peters, Vice President Human Resources
Web address: www.kaiserpermanente.org

| 23 | 10 | 185 | 13243 | 141 | 268435 | 1398 | — | — | 1506 |

Many Facility Codes have changed. Please refer to the AHA Guide Code Chart.

OR

Hospital, Address, Telephone, Approval, Facility, and Physician Codes, Health Care System	Classi-fication Codes		Utilization Data					Expense (thousands) of dollars		
★ American Hospital Association (AHA) membership □ Joint Commission on Accreditation of Healthcare Organizations (JCAHO) accreditation ○ American Osteopathic Association (AOA) accreditation △ Commission on Accreditation of Rehabilitation Facilities (CARF) accreditation	Control	Service	Staffed Beds	Admissions	Census	Outpatient Visits	Births	Total	Payroll	Personnel

COOS BAY—Coos County

☒ **BAY AREA HOSPITAL**, 1775 Thompson Road, Zip 97420–2198;
tel. 541/269–8111 **A**1 9 10 19 **F**2 9 10 11 12 22 23 26 27 28 33 34 40 51
55 57 58 59 60 61 62 63 64 69 71 72 75 79 81 82 84 88 93 94 96 106
108 110 **P**5
Primary Contact: Daniel L. Smith, President and Chief Executive Officer
CFO: Tim Salisbury, Vice President Finance
CMO: Terry Bach, M.D., Director Medical Affairs
CIO: Bob Adams, Information Services Manager
CHR: Tom Shine, Vice President Human Resources
Web address: www.bayareahospital.org
| 16 | 10 | 127 | 8097 | 86 | 61701 | 610 | 81150 | 38918 | 776 |

COQUILLE—Coos County

★ **COQUILLE VALLEY HOSPITAL**, 940 East Fifth Street, Zip 97423–1699;
tel. 541/396–3101 **A**9 10 18 **F**11 12 21 26 27 33 34 46 47 51 59 63 65 66
70 75 81 84 88 92 97 106 110
Primary Contact: Dennis G. Zielinski, Chief Executive Officer
CFO: Gail Ludington, Chief Financial Officer
CMO: James Sinnott, M.D., Chief of Medical Staff
Web address: www.cvhospital.org
| 16 | 10 | 15 | 727 | 5 | 18193 | 48 | 8900 | 3353 | 56 |

CORVALLIS—Benton County

☒ **GOOD SAMARITAN REGIONAL MEDICAL CENTER**, 3600 N.W. Samaritan
Drive, Zip 97330–3737, Mailing Address: P.O. Box 1068, Zip 97339–1068;
tel. 541/768–5111 **A**1 2 9 10 19 **F**2 4 10 11 12 15 17 18 19 21 22 23 26 27
28 29 30 33 34 37 41 48 49 51 52 53 55 57 58 59 60 61 62 63 64 65 66
69 70 71 73 74 75 76 77 79 80 81 82 84 88 92 93 94 95 96 106 108 109
110 **P**7 **S** Samaritan Health Services, Corvallis, OR
Primary Contact: Steven W. Jasperson, Chief Executive Officer
COO: Steven W. Jasperson, Executive Vice President Operations and Chief
Operating Officer
CFO: Daniel B. Smith, Vice President Finance
CIO: Robert French, Vice President Information Services
Web address: www.samhealth.org
| 23 | 10 | 134 | 8033 | 92 | 224814 | 993 | 149356 | 63394 | 1078 |

COTTAGE GROVE—Lane County

★ **COTTAGE GROVE COMMUNITY HOSPITAL**, 1515 Village Drive, Zip 97424;
tel. 541/942–0511 **A**9 10 18 **F**12 24 33 44 52 58 69 70 81 88 109
S PeaceHealth, Bellevue, WA
Primary Contact: Tim Herrmann, Administrator
| 33 | 10 | 14 | 354 | 3 | 32355 | 0 | 8163 | 3567 | 61 |

DALLAS—Polk County

WEST VALLEY HOSPITAL, 550 S.E. Clay Street, Zip 97338–2899, Mailing
Address: P.O. Box 378, Zip 97338–0378; tel. 503/623–8301 **A**9 10 18 **F**2 9
12 21 26 27 28 29 33 34 39 45 46 48 52 53 58 60 62 63 68 69 81 82 84
88 95 97 108 110
Primary Contact: Eric Buckland, CHE, Site Administrator
Web address: www.westvalleyhospital.org
| 23 | 10 | 6 | 151 | 1 | 48429 | 0 | 11112 | 4905 | 99 |

ENTERPRISE—Wallowa County

★ **WALLOWA MEMORIAL HOSPITAL**, 401 N.E. 1st Street, Zip 97828–1167;
tel. 541/426–3111, (Total facility includes 32 beds in nursing home–type unit) **A**5
9 10 18 **F**2 6 9 11 12 14 22 23 26 27 28 29 33 34 36 38 44 45 48 51 53
58 59 61 62 63 64 66 68 69 75 81 88 92 95 96 97 106 108
Primary Contact: Larry Davy, Administrator and Chief Executive Officer
CFO: Randal Anderson, Chief Financial Officer
CMO: Kaare Tingelstad, D.O., Chief Medical Staff
CHR: Nancy Waters, Director Human Resources
Web address: www.wchcd.org
| 16 | 10 | 57 | 627 | 33 | 13576 | 53 | 8880 | 4196 | 142 |

EUGENE—Lane County

☒ △ **SACRED HEART MEDICAL CENTER**, 1255 Hilyard Street,
Zip 97401–3700, Mailing Address: P.O. Box 10905, Zip 97440–0905;
tel. 541/686–7300 **A**1 7 9 10 **F**2 9 11 15 19 21 22 23 26 27 28 29 33 34 36
37 38 39 40 46 47 48 49 52 53 55 56 57 58 59 61 62 63 64 65 68 69 71
72 73 74 75 76 77 81 82 85 88 93 94 96 108 109 110 **P**6 **S** PeaceHealth,
Bellevue, WA
Primary Contact: Jill Hoggard Green, R.N., Ph.D., Administrator
COO: Jill Hoggard Green, R.N., Ph.D., Assistant Vice President
CFO: Karen Shepard, Vice President Finance
CMO: Vern Katz, M.D., Chief of Staff
CIO: Don McMillan, Chief Information Officer
CHR: Barb Dember, Regional Vice President Joint Venture Relations
Web address: www.peacehealth.org
| 21 | 10 | 463 | 25898 | 301 | 106213 | 2541 | 323510 | 133180 | 2573 |

SERENITY LANE, 616 East 16th, Zip 97401–4357;
tel. 541/687–1110, (Nonreporting)
Primary Contact: Neil H. McNaughton, Executive Director and Administrator
Web address: www.serenitylane.org
| 23 | 82 | 55 | — | | — | | — | — | — |

FLORENCE—Lane County

☒ **PEACE HARBOR HOSPITAL**, 400 Ninth Street, Zip 97439–7398;
tel. 541/997–8412 **A**1 9 10 18 **F**4 9 11 12 22 27 28 29 33 34 36 37 38 39
46 48 51 55 59 63 69 81 82 84 87 88 96 **S** PeaceHealth, Bellevue, WA
Primary Contact: James R. Barnhart, Chief Executive Officer
CFO: Rick Yecny, Vice President and Chief Financial Officer
CMO: Sharon F. Catlin, D.O., Regional Medical Director
CIO: Ginni Boughal, Health Information Manager
CHR: Don Bourland, Vice President, Human Resources
Web address: www.peacehealth.org
| 21 | 10 | 21 | 1577 | 14 | 36900 | 77 | 24289 | 11096 | 223 |

Hospital, Address, Telephone, Approval, Facility, and Physician Codes, Health Care System	Classi-fication Codes		Utilization Data					Expense (thousands) of dollars		
★ American Hospital Association (AHA) membership ☐ Joint Commission on Accreditation of Healthcare Organizations (JCAHO) accreditation ○ American Osteopathic Association (AOA) accreditation △ Commission on Accreditation of Rehabilitation Facilities (CARF) accreditation	Control	Service	Staffed Beds	Admissions	Census	Outpatient Visits	Births	Total	Payroll	Personnel

FOREST GROVE—Washington County

TUALITY FOREST GROVE HOSPITAL See Tuality Healthcare, Hillsboro

GOLD BEACH—Curry County

	12	10	24	745	5	54197	69	11999	4916	115

CURRY GENERAL HOSPITAL, 94220 Fourth Street, Zip 97444–9990; tel. 541/247–6621 **A**9 10 18 20 **F**8 11 12 33 45 46 48 52 55 58 59 63 81 84 88 91 96
Primary Contact: Ginny Hochberg, Chief Executive Officer and Clinical Administrator
Web address: www.currygeneralhospital.com

GRANTS PASS—Josephine County

	23	10	98	7706	70	182107	779	78175	30762	648

✠ **THREE RIVERS COMMUNITY HOSPITAL AND HEALTH CENTER**, 500 S.W. Ramsey Avenue, Zip 97527; tel. 541/472–7000 **A**1 9 10 20 **F**2 9 11 12 21 22 26 27 28 29 30 32 33 34 37 41 42 44 45 46 47 48 51 52 55 58 59 60 62 63 64 66 69 73 75 80 81 82 84 87 88 94 96 106 107 108 109 110 **P**6
S Asante Health System, Medford, OR
Primary Contact: Paul Janke, Senior Vice President
CFO: Marvin Haas, Senior Vice President Finance
CMO: Theo Powell, M.D., Medical Director
CIO: Mark Hetz, Chief Information Officer
Web address: www.asante.org

GRESHAM—Multnomah County

	23	10	55	4750	42	91859	958	49823	21370	425

✠ **LEGACY MOUNT HOOD MEDICAL CENTER**, 24800 S.E. Stark, Zip 97030–0154; tel. 503/667–1122 **A**1 9 10 **F**2 9 11 12 15 21 22 23 24 26 27 28 29 31 33 35 37 39 44 46 48 49 52 53 55 57 58 59 60 61 62 63 64 65 66 69 73 74 75 79 81 82 84 85 87 88 92 94 96 108 109 **P**8 **S** Legacy Health System, Portland, OR
Primary Contact: Thomas S. Parker, Site Administrator
Web address: www.legacyhealth.org

HEPPNER—Morrow County

	16	10	10	164	5	4657	0	4639	—	46

PIONEER MEMORIAL HOSPITAL, 564 East Pioneer Drive, Zip 97836, Mailing Address: P.O. Box 9, Zip 97836; tel. 541/676–9133, (Total facility includes 4 beds in nursing home–type unit) **A**9 10 18 **F**6 9 14 29 33 36 44 45 48 51 52 54 58 81 88 97 **P**6
Primary Contact: Victor Vander Does, Administrator
Web address: www.victorlvd@centurytel.net

HERMISTON—Umatilla County

	23	10	45	2656	22	65205	572	30856	13447	373

✠ **GOOD SHEPHERD HEALTHCARE SYSTEM**, 610 N.W. 11th Street, Zip 97838–9696; tel. 541/667–3400 **A**1 9 10 20 **F**2 9 11 12 21 22 26 33 34 36 37 39 41 46 47 48 51 52 55 58 59 60 63 64 65 66 69 70 81 82 84 85 88 94 96 97 106 107 108 **P**6 7
Primary Contact: Dennis E. Burke, President
COO: David T. Hughes, FACHE, Senior Vice President Operations
CFO: Jack Esp, Chief Fiscal Services
CMO: Winn Gregory, M.D., Medical Staff President
CHR: Vickie Hendricks, Director Human Resources
Web address: www.gshealth.org

HILLSBORO—Washington County

	23	10	143	6719	75	165064	1452	116248	53514	1063

✠ **TUALITY HEALTHCARE**, 335 S.E. Eighth Avenue, Zip 97123–4246; tel. 503/681–1111, (Includes TUALITY COMMUNITY HOSPITAL, Mailing Address: P.O. Box 309, Zip 97123; TUALITY FOREST GROVE HOSPITAL, 1809 Maple Street, Forest Grove, Zip 97116–1995; tel. 503/357–2173) **A**1 10 **F**2 9 11 12 14 15 17 19 21 22 23 24 27 28 29 30 33 35 39 42 44 45 46 47 48 51 52 53 55 57 58 59 60 61 62 63 64 65 66 69 70 71 73 76 77 81 82 84 85 87 88 94 95 96 106 107 108 109 110 **P**1 6 7
Primary Contact: Richard Stenson, President and Chief Executive Officer
COO: Manuel S. Berman, Chief Operating Officer
CFO: Tim Fleischmann, Chief Financial Officer
CMO: Nicholas Orfanakis, M.D., Chief of Staff
CIO: John Stoneburg, Chief Information Officer
CHR: Daryl Gohl, Director Human Resources
Web address: www.tuality.com

HOOD RIVER—Hood River County

	21	10	25	1578	12	91900	383	35355	14048	309

✠ **PROVIDENCE HOOD RIVER MEMORIAL HOSPITAL**, 811 13th Street, Zip 97031–1204, Mailing Address: P.O. Box 149, Zip 97031–0149; tel. 541/386–3911 **A**1 9 10 18 **F**1 4 8 9 11 12 22 27 28 29 33 34 41 42 44 45 46 47 51 53 55 58 59 60 63 65 70 72 73 74 75 77 81 82 84 88 91 96 97 98 106 107 108 **S** Providence Health System, Seattle, WA
Primary Contact: James Arp, Chief Executive Officer
CFO: Ron Guth, Chief Financial Officer
CIO: Barbara Young, Director Community Relations
CHR: Catherine Bourgault, Director Human Resources
Web address: www.providence.org/hoodriver

Many Facility Codes have changed. Please refer to the AHA Guide Code Chart. © 2005 AHA Guide

Hospital, Address, Telephone, Approval, Facility, and Physician Codes, Health Care System	Classi-fication Codes		Utilization Data					Expense (thousands) of dollars		
★ American Hospital Association (AHA) membership □ Joint Commission on Accreditation of Healthcare Organizations (JCAHO) accreditation ○ American Osteopathic Association (AOA) accreditation △ Commission on Accreditation of Rehabilitation Facilities (CARF) accreditation	Control	Service	Staffed Beds	Admissions	Census	Outpatient Visits	Births	Total	Payroll	Personnel

JOHN DAY—Grant County

★ **BLUE MOUNTAIN HOSPITAL**, 170 Ford Road, Zip 97845–2009; tel. 541/575–1311, (Total facility includes 52 beds in nursing home–type unit) **A**9 10 18 **F**1 2 6 9 11 12 14 21 22 23 27 29 30 33 34 37 44 45 46 47 48 51 52 53 55 58 59 63 65 66 69 81 84 88 92 94 95 96 97 110 **S** Brim Healthcare, Inc., Brentwood, TN
Primary Contact: Robert Houser, Chief Executive Officer
CFO: Judy Lenz, Chief Financial Officer
CMO: Jack Jackson, M.D., Chief of Staff
CHR: Verlene Davis, Human Resources Director
Web address: www.bluemountainhospital.org
| | 16 | 10 | 68 | 314 | 26 | 19786 | 48 | 10256 | 4147 | 98 |

KLAMATH FALLS—Klamath County

✸ **MERLE WEST MEDICAL CENTER**, 2865 Daggett Street, Zip 97601–1180; tel. 541/882–6311 **A**1 2 3 5 9 10 19 20 **F**2 9 10 11 12 15 17 21 23 26 27 28 29 33 34 35 39 41 42 45 46 47 48 49 51 52 53 55 57 58 59 60 61 63 64 65 66 69 70 79 80 81 82 84 85 86 87 88 94 96 106 107 108 110 **P**6
Primary Contact: Paul R. Stewart, President and Chief Executive Officer
CFO: S Andrew Rybolt, Vice President and Chief Financial Officer
CMO: Rick Zwartverwer, M.D., Vice President Medical Affairs
CIO: David Chabner, Director Information Services
CHR: Don York, Vice President Human Resources
Web address: www.mwmc.org
| | 23 | 10 | 133 | 6449 | 62 | 210990 | 779 | 97295 | 38899 | 857 |

LA GRANDE—Union County

✸ **GRANDE RONDE HOSPITAL**, 900 Sunset Drive, Zip 97850–1362, Mailing Address: P.O. Box 3290, Zip 97850–3290; tel. 541/963–8421 **A**1 9 10 18 20 **F**2 9 11 12 14 21 22 23 24 28 33 34 36 37 38 41 46 47 48 51 53 55 58 59 60 61 63 64 65 69 70 81 82 84 87 88 92 94 96 97 108 110
Primary Contact: James A. Mattes, President
CFO: Robert N. Whinery, Vice President Finance
CIO: Fred Thornton, Director Information Systems
CHR: Kristi Puckett, Director of Human Resources
Web address: www.grh.org
| | 23 | 10 | 63 | 2367 | 19 | 43325 | 304 | 26987 | 13401 | 265 |

LAKEVIEW—Lake County

★ **LAKE DISTRICT HOSPITAL**, 700 South J Street, Zip 97630–1679; tel. 541/947–2114 **A**5 9 10 18 **F**3 9 11 12 14 26 27 28 33 34 36 47 48 51 52 53 55 59 63 71 75 81 88 92 94 96 97 108 110 **P**4
Primary Contact: Gordon Ensley, Chief Executive Officer
CFO: Ken Landau, Chief Financial Officer
CMO: Timothy Gallagher, M.D., Chief of Staff
CHR: Linda Michaelson, Director Human Resources
Web address: www.lake–health.com
| | 16 | 10 | 68 | 707 | 35 | 21435 | 47 | 9823 | 4348 | 121 |

LEBANON—Linn County

✸ **SAMARITAN LEBANON COMMUNITY HOSPITAL**, 525 North Santiam Highway, Zip 97355–4363, Mailing Address: P.O. Box 739, Zip 97355–0739; tel. 541/258–2101 **A**1 9 10 **F**2 3 9 11 12 13 14 21 22 23 26 27 28 29 33 34 35 36 39 41 47 48 52 53 55 56 58 59 61 62 63 64 65 66 67 68 69 70 71 81 84 88 92 94 96 97 106 107 108 109 110 **P**5 6 **S** Samaritan Health Services, Corvallis, OR
Primary Contact: Becky A. Pape, R.N., Chief Executive Officer
CFO: Dan Smith, Vice President Finance
CMO: Mark Donnelly, M.D., President Medical Staff
CIO: Robert French, Vice President Information Services
CHR: Connie Erwin, Manager
Web address: www.samhealth.org
| | 23 | 10 | 49 | 2570 | 23 | 71345 | 300 | 40385 | 17426 | 340 |

LINCOLN CITY—Lincoln County

✸ **SAMARITAN NORTH LINCOLN HOSPITAL**, 3043 N.E. 28th Street, Zip 97367–4523, Mailing Address: P.O. Box 767, Zip 97367–0767; tel. 541/994–3661 **A**1 9 10 18 **F**2 9 11 12 21 22 26 27 28 29 33 34 39 46 47 48 51 52 53 55 58 59 63 65 66 69 70 82 85 88 94 96 97 106 107 108 **S** Samaritan Health Services, Corvallis, OR
Primary Contact: Jack T. Flaig, Chief Executive Officer
CFO: Mark Christensen, Director Finance
CMO: David Rosencrantz, M.D., President Medical Staff
CIO: Robert French, Director Information Services
CHR: Penny Dunne, R.N., Human Resource Director
Web address: www.samhealth.org
| | 23 | 10 | 25 | 1594 | 15 | 47586 | 168 | 30288 | 15010 | 232 |

MADRAS—Jefferson County

★ **MOUNTAIN VIEW HOSPITAL DISTRICT**, 470 N.E. A Street, Zip 97741–1844; tel. 541/475–3882, (Total facility includes 47 beds in nursing home–type unit) **A**9 10 20 **F**9 11 12 21 26 27 28 29 33 34 36 38 39 44 47 48 51 55 59 60 63 69 75 81 88 92 96 97 107
Primary Contact: Susan McGough, Administrator
CFO: Rick Lee Nader, Chief Financial Officer
CMO: Jonathan Sidell, M.D., Chief Medical Officer
Web address: www.mvhd.org
| | 16 | 10 | 78 | 1164 | 35 | 28136 | 198 | 15725 | 7319 | 185 |

Hospital, Address, Telephone, Approval, Facility, and Physician Codes, Health Care System	Classification Codes		Utilization Data					Expense (thousands) of dollars		
★ American Hospital Association (AHA) membership □ Joint Commission on Accreditation of Healthcare Organizations (JCAHO) accreditation ○ American Osteopathic Association (AOA) accreditation △ Commission on Accreditation of Rehabilitation Facilities (CARF) accreditation	Control	Service	Staffed Beds	Admissions	Census	Outpatient Visits	Births	Total	Payroll	Personnel
MCMINNVILLE—Yamhill County										
✠ **WILLAMETTE VALLEY MEDICAL CENTER**, 2700 S.E. Stratus Avenue, Zip 97128–6498; tel. 503/472–6131 **A**1 9 10 **F**2 9 11 12 21 22 26 27 28 29 33 34 44 46 48 49 52 55 57 58 59 60 61 62 63 66 68 69 81 82 84 88 93 94 96 106 108 109 **P**5 6 **S** Triad Hospitals, Inc., Plano, TX Primary Contact: Rosemari Davis, Chief Executive Officer COO: Robb Childs, Chief Operating Officer CFO: Jeffrey VanHorn, Chief Financial Officer CIO: Frank Evans, Information Systems Services Manager CHR: Cheryl Gebhart, Human Resources Director Web address: www.wvmcweb.com	33	10	67	4487	42	73691	681	48427	19829	378
MEDFORD—Jackson County										
✠ **PROVIDENCE MEDFORD MEDICAL CENTER**, 1111 Crater Lake Avenue, Zip 97504–6241; tel. 541/732–5000 **A**1 2 9 10 **F**1 2 11 12 15 21 22 23 24 29 33 34 36 37 38 39 40 44 45 46 47 48 49 50 51 52 53 55 57 58 59 60 61 63 64 65 66 68 69 75 79 80 81 84 87 88 94 96 108 109 **P**6 **S** Providence Health System, Seattle, WA Primary Contact: Charles T. Wright, Chief Executive, Southern Oregon Service Area CFO: Michael Strasser, Assistant Administrator Fiscal Services Web address: www.providence.org	21	10	127	6275	72	369583	459	—	—	—
✠ **ROGUE VALLEY MEDICAL CENTER**, 2825 East Barnett Road, Zip 97504–8332; tel. 541/789–7000 **A**1 2 9 10 **F**9 11 12 14 15 16 17 18 19 20 21 22 23 24 26 27 28 29 30 31 33 34 36 37 40 45 46 47 48 49 51 52 55 56 57 58 59 61 62 63 65 66 69 71 73 75 79 81 82 88 92 93 94 96 108 109 **P**6 **S** Asante Health System, Medford, OR Primary Contact: Roseanne McLaren, Administrator CFO: Marvin Haas, Senior Vice President, Administration and Finance CIO: Mark Hetz, Chief Information Officer CHR: Michael Hancock, Interim Vice President Human Resources Web address: www.asante.org	23	10	260	14841	170	323048	1371	207501	72709	1604
MILWAUKIE—Clackamas County										
✠ **PROVIDENCE MILWAUKIE HOSPITAL**, 10150 S.E. 32nd Avenue, Zip 97222–6593; tel. 503/513–8300 **A**1 2 3 5 9 10 **F**2 11 12 21 22 23 26 27 28 29 30 32 33 35 36 37 38 39 42 44 46 47 48 51 52 53 55 57 58 59 60 61 62 63 64 65 66 69 70 73 76 78 81 82 84 88 92 93 94 95 96 97 106 108 109 110 **S** Providence Health System, Seattle, WA Primary Contact: Jacquelyn Gaines, Administrator COO: Richard Smith, Assistant Administrator Web address: www.providence.org	21	10	56	3381	29	146689	598	54267	22243	364
NEWBERG—Yamhill County										
✠ **PROVIDENCE NEWBERG HOSPITAL**, 501 Villa Road, Zip 97132–1832; tel. 503/537–1555 **A**1 9 10 **F**1 2 9 11 12 21 22 23 26 27 28 29 33 34 35 37 46 48 51 52 55 58 59 60 61 62 63 64 65 66 69 73 81 82 84 85 86 87 88 93 94 96 106 108 109 110 **S** Providence Health System, Seattle, WA Primary Contact: Larry Bowe, Chief Executive, Yamhill Service Area CFO: Jack R. Sumner, Assistant Administrator Finance CIO: Rick Skinner, Vice President Information Services and Chief Information Officer CHR: Joannia Mikutic, Director Human Resources Web address: www.phsor.org	21	10	36	1625	14	113076	338	36871	16631	248
NEWPORT—Lincoln County										
✠ **SAMARITAN PACIFIC COMMUNITIES HOSPITAL**, 930 S.W. Abbey Street, Zip 97365–4820, Mailing Address: P.O. Box 945, Zip 97365–4820; tel. 541/265–2244 **A**1 9 10 18 20 **F**27 33 34 35 36 39 45 51 52 55 58 59 60 61 62 63 69 70 81 82 88 92 94 96 97 108 109 110 **P**6 **S** Samaritan Health Services, Corvallis, OR Primary Contact: David C. Bigelow, Chief Executive Officer CFO: Mark Christensen, Director Finance CHR: Penny Dunne, R.N., Human Resource Director Web address: www.samhealth.org/pch	21	10	42	1536	12	70889	231	34308	16505	366
ONTARIO—Malheur County										
✠ **HOLY ROSARY MEDICAL CENTER**, 351 S.W. Ninth Street, Zip 97914–2693; tel. 541/881–7000 **A**1 5 9 10 **F**2 10 11 12 22 26 27 28 29 33 34 36 37 39 40 42 43 44 46 48 50 51 53 55 58 59 60 62 63 64 69 70 81 82 85 88 93 94 95 96 97 106 107 108 110 **S** Catholic Health Initiatives, Denver, CO Primary Contact: Mark F. Dalley, President and Chief Executive Officer CHR: Karen Kosowan, Vice President, Human Resources Web address: www.holyrosary–ontario.org	21	10	49	3536	27	64850	712	44879	16749	371
OREGON CITY—Clackamas County										
✠ **WILLAMETTE FALLS HOSPITAL**, 1500 Division Street, Zip 97045–1597; tel. 503/656–1631 **A**1 2 9 10 **F**9 11 12 32 33 36 42 46 47 48 52 53 55 59 60 61 63 65 69 70 81 82 84 87 88 94 96 107 108 Primary Contact: Russ Reinhard, President CFO: Tim Blanchard, Vice President Finance Web address: www.willamettefallshospital.org	23	10	91	5845	43	84797	1004	69995	31432	554

Hospital, Address, Telephone, Approval, Facility, and Physician Codes, Health Care System	Classi- fication Codes		Utilization Data					Expense (thousands) of dollars		
	Control	Service	Staffed Beds	Admissions	Census	Outpatient Visits	Births	Total	Payroll	Personnel

★ American Hospital Association (AHA) membership
□ Joint Commission on Accreditation of Healthcare Organizations (JCAHO) accreditation
○ American Osteopathic Association (AOA) accreditation
△ Commission on Accreditation of Rehabilitation Facilities (CARF) accreditation

PENDLETON—Umatilla County

EASTERN OREGON PSYCHIATRIC CENTER, 2575 Westgate, Zip 97801–9613; tel. 541/276–4511, (Nonreporting) **A**10
Primary Contact: Maxine Stone, Superintendent

| | 12 | 22 | 60 | — | — | — | — | — | — | — |

★ **ST. ANTHONY HOSPITAL**, 1601 S.E. Court Avenue, Zip 97801–3297; tel. 541/276–5121 **A**1 2 5 9 10 18 20 **F**11 12 21 22 26 27 28 29 32 33 34 36 37 38 40 44 46 47 48 51 52 53 58 59 60 61 62 63 66 69 70 81 82 84 87 88 94 96 97 108 **S** Catholic Health Initiatives, Denver, CO
Primary Contact: Jeffrey S. Drop, President and Chief Executive Officer
CFO: Steven Taylor, Vice President and Chief Financial Officer
CMO: Jonathan Hitzman, M.D., Chief of Staff
CHR: Jon Oravec, Vice President Human Resources
Web address: www.sahpendleton.org

| | 21 | 10 | 25 | 1811 | 15 | 30867 | 321 | 27708 | 10142 | 240 |

PORTLAND—Multnomah County

★ **ADVENTIST MEDICAL CENTER**, 10123 S.E. Market Street, Zip 97216–2599; tel. 503/257–2500 **A**1 2 10 **F**2 3 **F**2 9 41 42 46 47 48 49 51 52 53 55 57 58 59 60 61 62 63 65 66 69 71 79 81 82 84 85 87 88 93 94 95 96 106 107 108 109 **P**6 7 **S** Adventist Health, Roseville, CA
Primary Contact: Deryl L. Jones, President and Chief Executive Officer
CFO: V Mark Perry, Chief Financial Officer
CIO: David Eastman, Regional Chief Information Officer
CHR: Herbert Hill, Director, Human Resources
Web address: www.adventisthealthnw.com

| | 21 | 10 | 252 | 10841 | 134 | 426582 | 1296 | 174253 | 83760 | 1794 |

DOERNBECHER CHILDREN'S HOSPITAL See OHSU Hospital
GOOD SAMARITAN HOSPITAL AND MEDICAL CENTER See Legacy Good Samaritan Hospital and Medical Center

★ △ **LEGACY EMANUEL HOSPITAL AND HEALTH CENTER**, 2801 North Gantenbein Avenue, Zip 97227–1674; tel. 503/413–2200 **A**1 3 5 7 9 10 **F**2 9 11 12 13 15 16 17 18 19 20 21 22 23 24 26 27 28 29 31 33 34 35 37 39 40 41 42 44 46 47 48 49 50 52 53 55 56 57 58 59 60 61 62 63 64 65 66 67 69 70 71 72 73 74 75 78 81 82 84 85 87 88 92 94 108 109 110 **P**8 **S** Legacy Health System, Portland, OR
Primary Contact: Stephani White, Vice President and Site Administrator
CFO: Pamela S. Vukovich, Senior Vice President and Chief Financial Officer
CMO: Keith I. Marton, M.D., Senior Vice President and Chief Medical Officer
CIO: Carol Edwards, Vice President and Chief Information Officer
Web address: www.legacyhealth.org

| | 23 | 10 | 403 | 19078 | 280 | 216646 | 2146 | 337997 | 154411 | 3015 |

★ **LEGACY GOOD SAMARITAN HOSPITAL AND MEDICAL CENTER**, 1015 N.W. 22nd Avenue, Zip 97210–3099; tel. 503/413–7711, (Includes GOOD SAMARITAN HOSPITAL AND MEDICAL CENTER; REHABILITATION INSTITUTE OF OREGON) **A**1 3 5 9 10 **F**2 9 10 11 12 15 16 17 19 20 21 22 23 24 26 27 28 29 31 33 35 37 39 41 42 44 46 47 49 50 52 53 55 57 58 59 60 61 62 63 64 65 66 68 69 70 71 73 74 75 76 79 81 82 84 85 87 88 92 93 94 96 99 101 105 107 108 109 **P**8 **S** Legacy Health System, Portland, OR
Primary Contact: Robert Pallari, President and Chief Executive Officer
COO: Robert Pallari, President and Chief Executive Officer
CFO: Pamela S. Vukovich, Vice President Financial Services
CMO: Keith I. Marton, M.D., Senior Vice President and Chief Medical Officer
CIO: C Matthew Calais, Senior Vice President and Chief Information Officer
CHR: Sonja Steves, Vice President Marketing
Web address: www.legacyhealth.org

| | 23 | 10 | 274 | 13323 | 165 | 199724 | 1487 | 194635 | 76693 | 1500 |

★ **OHSU HOSPITAL**, 3181 S.W. Sam Jackson Park Road, Zip 97201–3098; tel. 503/494–8311, (Includes DOERNBECHER CHILDREN'S HOSPITAL) **A**1 2 3 5 8 9 10 **F**2 4 7 9 10 11 12 14 15 16 17 18 19 20 21 22 23 24 26 27 28 29 30 31 32 33 34 35 37 38 39 41 42 43 44 46 47 48 50 52 53 55 56 57 58 59 60 61 62 63 64 65 66 67 69 70 71 72 73 74 75 76 77 79 80 81 82 84 85 86 87 88 89 90 93 94 95 96 98 99 100 101 102 104 105 106 107 108 109 **P**1
Primary Contact: Peter F. Rapp, Vice President and Executive Director
CFO: Brad King, Vice President and Chief Financial Officer
CMO: A Roy Magnusson, M.D., Chief Medical Officer
CIO: John Kenagy, Chief Information Officer
CHR: Rick Bentzinger, Vice President of Human Resources
Web address: www.ohsu.edu

| | 16 | 10 | 449 | 24719 | 365 | 596206 | 2635 | 561517 | 213487 | 5628 |

★ **PROVIDENCE PORTLAND MEDICAL CENTER**, 4805 N.E. Glisan Street, Zip 97213–2967; tel. 503/215–1111 **A**1 2 3 5 9 10 **F**2 3 4 7 11 12 14 15 17 19 21 22 23 26 27 28 29 30 31 33 35 36 37 38 39 40 41 42 43 44 46 47 48 49 50 51 52 53 55 57 58 59 60 61 62 63 64 65 66 68 69 70 71 72 73 76 77 78 79 80 81 82 83 84 85 86 87 88 92 93 94 95 96 97 99 100 106 108 109 110 **S** Providence Health System, Seattle, WA
Primary Contact: David T. Underriner, Administrator
CFO: Dave Hilton, Director Financial Services
Web address: www.providence.org

| | 21 | 10 | 402 | 21059 | 261 | 1081553 | 2403 | 396578 | 147841 | 2613 |

OR

Hospital, Address, Telephone, Approval, Facility, and Physician Codes, Health Care System	Classi-fication Codes		Utilization Data					Expense (thousands) of dollars		
★ American Hospital Association (AHA) membership □ Joint Commission on Accreditation of Healthcare Organizations (JCAHO) accreditation ○ American Osteopathic Association (AOA) accreditation △ Commission on Accreditation of Rehabilitation Facilities (CARF) accreditation	Control	Service	Staffed Beds	Admissions	Census	Outpatient Visits	Births	Total	Payroll	Personnel
⊞ **PROVIDENCE ST. VINCENT MEDICAL CENTER**, 9205 S.W. Barnes Road, Zip 97225–6661; tel. 503/216–1234 **A**1 2 3 5 9 10 **F**2 4 11 12 14 15 17 19 21 22 23 26 27 28 29 30 31 33 35 36 37 38 39 40 41 42 44 46 47 48 49 50 51 52 53 55 56 57 58 59 60 61 62 63 64 65 66 69 70 71 73 76 77 78 79 80 81 82 83 84 85 86 87 88 92 93 94 95 96 97 100 106 108 109 110 **S** Providence Health System, Seattle, WA Primary Contact: Donald Elsom, Administrator CFO: William Olson, Director Finance CIO: Kate Chester, Senior Public Relations Coordinator Web address: www.providence.org/portland/hospitals REHABILITATION INSTITUTE OF OREGON See Legacy Good Samaritan Hospital and Medical Center	21	10	483	30560	334	488966	5873	486040	—	3065
□ **SHRINERS HOSPITALS FOR CHILDREN, PORTLAND**, 3101 S.W. Sam Jackson Park Road, Zip 97239; tel. 503/241–5090, (Nonreporting) **A**1 3 5 **S** Shriners Hospitals for Children, Tampa, FL Primary Contact: C. Thomas D'Esmond, Administrator Web address: www.shcc.org	23	57	40	—	—	—	—	—	—	—
⊞ **VETERANS AFFAIRS MEDICAL CENTER**, 3710 S.W. U.S. Veterans Hospital Road, Zip 97201; tel. 503/220–8262, (Total facility includes 72 beds in nursing home–type unit) **A**1 2 3 5 8 **F**2 3 4 5 7 10 14 15 17 19 21 22 23 26 28 29 30 31 32 33 35 36 37 38 39 41 42 43 44 45 46 47 48 49 50 51 52 55 57 58 60 61 62 63 64 65 66 68 69 70 71 73 74 75 76 77 78 81 82 83 84 85 88 89 90 92 93 94 96 99 101 102 104 106 108 109 110 **P**6 **S** Department of Veterans Affairs, Washington, DC Primary Contact: James Tuchschmidt, M.D., Director CFO: Susan P. Heublein, Associate Director for Financial Services CMO: Richard F. Davis, M.D., Chief of Staff CIO: David M. Smith, M.D., Associate Director Information Management CHR: Patrice Craig, Chief Human Resources Management Division Web address: www.va.gov/sta/guide/home.asp	45	10	221	7294	111	528101	0	326658	139839	2339
PRINEVILLE—Crook County										
PIONEER MEMORIAL HOSPITAL, 1201 N.E. Elm Street, Zip 97754–1206; tel. 541/447–6254 **A**9 10 18 **F**2 9 11 12 21 29 33 34 36 38 46 48 51 52 53 55 58 59 62 63 66 81 85 88 94 96 97 108 Primary Contact: Donald J. Wee, Executive Director Web address: www.pmhprineville.org	23	10	25	911	7	101863	119	16230	6759	143
REDMOND—Deschutes County										
⊞ **ST. CHARLES MEDICAL CENTER – REDMOND**, 1253 North Canal Boulevard, Zip 97756–1395; tel. 541/548–8131 **A**1 9 10 20 **F**9 11 12 21 22 26 27 28 33 34 37 46 47 48 50 51 52 55 58 59 63 65 69 75 81 82 88 94 95 106 108 109 110 **P**7 **S** Cascade Healthcare Community, Bend, OR Primary Contact: Jim R. Hobbs, President and Chief Executive Officer CFO: Thomas Safley, Vice President Finance Web address: www.codh.org	23	10	48	2541	19	45538	367	24508	11519	220
REEDSPORT—Douglas County										
LOWER UMPQUA HOSPITAL DISTRICT, 600 Ranch Road, Zip 97467–1795; tel. 541/271–2171, (Total facility includes 35 beds in nursing home–type unit) **A**9 10 18 20 **F**2 6 9 12 22 23 27 28 29 33 34 36 37 38 39 44 45 46 47 48 51 52 53 55 58 60 62 63 66 69 81 88 92 94 96 97 106 108 110 Primary Contact: Sandra Reese, Administrator Web address: www.lowerumpquahospital.com	16	10	49	875	36	21636	0	14559	6368	154
ROSEBURG—Douglas County										
⊞ **MERCY MEDICAL CENTER**, 2700 Stewart Parkway, Zip 97470–1297; tel. 541/673–0611 **A**1 2 9 10 20 **F**2 9 10 11 12 14 15 22 23 26 27 28 29 33 34 35 36 37 38 39 42 44 45 46 48 49 50 51 52 53 55 57 58 59 60 61 62 63 64 65 66 69 71 72 73 74 75 76 77 81 82 84 85 87 88 91 93 94 96 106 108 109 110 **P**6 **S** Catholic Health Initiatives, Denver, CO Primary Contact: Victor J. Fresolone, FACHE, President and Chief Executive Officer CFO: John Kasberger, Vice President, Chief Financial Officer and Corporate Responsibility Officer CMO: Mark Herscher, M.D., Chief of Staff CIO: Kathleen Nickel, Director Communications CHR: Deb Lightcap, Director Human Resources Web address: www.mercyrose.org	21	10	153	10641	118	227004	950	109871	44707	1011
⊞ **VETERANS AFFAIRS ROSEBURG HEALTHCARE SYSTEM**, 913 N.W. Garden Valley Boulevard, Zip 97470–6513; tel. 541/440–1000 **A**1 **F**2 3 9 21 22 26 27 28 29 31 32 33 35 36 38 39 42 44 46 47 48 50 51 55 58 60 62 63 64 65 66 69 70 71 73 75 76 77 82 85 87 88 92 93 94 96 106 108 110 **P**6 **S** Department of Veterans Affairs, Washington, DC Primary Contact: George Marnell, Director Web address: www.va.gov/sta/guide/home.asp	45	10	143	2624	62	259600	0	50620	36307	688
SALEM—Marion County										
□ **OREGON STATE HOSPITAL**, 2600 Center Street N.E., Zip 97301–2682; tel. 503/945–2870 **A**1 3 5 10 **F**2 21 22 26 29 32 37 38 39 41 44 48 53 58 65 66 70 71 72 73 74 76 94 96 106 108 **P**6 Primary Contact: Marvin D. Fickle, M.D., Superintendent Web address: www.oregon.gov/dhs/mentalhealth/osh/main.shtml	12	22	745	697	723	0	0	92097	48519	1092

Many Facility Codes have changed. Please refer to the AHA Guide Code Chart.

© 2005 AHA Guide

Hospital, Address, Telephone, Approval, Facility, and Physician Codes, Health Care System	Classi-fication Codes		Utilization Data					Expense (thousands) of dollars		
★ American Hospital Association (AHA) membership ☐ Joint Commission on Accreditation of Healthcare Organizations (JCAHO) accreditation ○ American Osteopathic Association (AOA) accreditation △ Commission on Accreditation of Rehabilitation Facilities (CARF) accreditation	Control	Service	Staffed Beds	Admissions	Census	Outpatient Visits	Births	Total	Payroll	Personnel

⊞ **SALEM HOSPITAL**, 665 Winter Street S.E., Zip 97301–3959, Mailing Address: P.O. Box 14001, Zip 97309–5014; tel. 503/561–5200, (Includes PSYCHIATRIC MEDICINE CENTER, 1127 Oak Street S.E., Zip 97301; REGIONAL REHABILITATION CENTER, 2561 Center Street N.E., Zip 97301; tel. 503/370–5986) **A**1 2 9 10 **F**2 9 11 12 14 15 17 19 21 22 23 24 26 27 28 29 33 34 35 37 38 39 41 44 45 46 47 48 50 51 52 53 55 56 57 58 59 60 61 62 63 64 65 66 68 69 71 72 73 74 75 76 77 78 79 80 81 82 83 84 85 87 88 93 94 95 96 104 106 107 108 110 Primary Contact: Norman F. Gruber, President and Chief Executive Officer COO: Jeffrey Cushing, Executive Vice President Operations CFO: Aaron Crane, Chief Financial Officer CMO: George Miller, M.D., Vice President Medical Affairs CIO: Dennis Sato, Chief Information Officer CHR: Beverly Bow, Vice President Human Resources Web address: www.salemhospital.org	23	10	417	18386	235	365808	3265	282408	132798	2554
SEASIDE—Clatsop County										
⊞ **PROVIDENCE SEASIDE HOSPITAL**, 725 South Wahanna Road, Zip 97138–7735; tel. 503/717–7000, (Total facility includes 20 beds in nursing home–type unit) **A**1 9 10 18 **F**2 9 10 11 12 14 22 23 24 26 27 28 29 33 42 46 47 48 51 52 55 58 59 60 62 63 64 65 66 69 70 81 88 92 94 96 97 106 108 109 **P**6 **S** Providence Health System, Seattle, WA Primary Contact: William P. Sexton, Chief Executive CFO: Pamela Cooper, Director Finance CMO: Lisa Huddleston, M.D., Chief of Staff CHR: Martie Teske, Human Resources Director Web address: www.providence.org	21	10	47	1183	30	91111	147	20756	13950	223
SILVERTON—Marion County										
★ **SILVERTON HOSPITAL**, 342 Fairview Street, Zip 97381–1993; tel. 503/873–1500 **A**9 10 **F**2 9 11 12 21 22 26 28 29 33 34 39 41 42 45 46 47 48 52 53 55 58 59 60 62 63 64 65 66 69 81 84 88 94 96 97 106 107 108 109 110 Primary Contact: William E. Winter, Administrative Director COO: Jeffrey D. Lorenz, Chief Operating Officer CFO: Jeff Fritsche, Chief Financial Officer CMO: Rob Rosborough, M.D., President Medical Staff CIO: Peter Vanden Berg, Information Services Specialist CHR: Jim Washam, Human Resources Manager Web address: www.silvertonhospital.org	23	10	48	3259	24	84977	1667	45009	22078	439
SPRINGFIELD—Lane County										
⊞ **MCKENZIE–WILLAMETTE MEDICAL CENTER**, (Formerly McKenzie–Willamette Hospital), 1460 G Street, Zip 97477–4197; tel. 541/726–4400 **A**1 9 10 **F**11 15 21 27 28 29 30 33 34 44 46 47 48 55 58 59 63 65 69 81 82 87 88 94 96 108 109 **P**6 **S** Triad Hospitals, Inc., Plano, TX Primary Contact: Roy J. Orr, Chief Executive Officer COO: Kathleen M. Deacon, R.N., Chief Operating Officer CFO: Karen Francis, Vice President Finance CIO: Amy Lathrop, Director Information Technology Web address: www.mckweb.com	33	10	105	5555	49	65770	963	64053	29380	539
STAYTON—Marion County										
⊞ **SANTIAM MEMORIAL HOSPITAL**, 1401 North 10th Avenue, Zip 97383–1399; tel. 503/769–2175 **A**1 9 10 **F**2 6 9 11 12 21 22 26 27 28 33 34 37 39 45 59 62 63 66 81 88 94 97 106 Primary Contact: Terry L. Fletchall, Administrator COO: Maggie Hudson, Director Operations and Financial Services CFO: Betty Emery, Chief Financial Officer CMO: Thomas VanVeen, M.D., Chief Medical Officer Web address: www.santiamhospital.com	23	10	40	1078	8	31059	214	13847	5439	123
THE DALLES—Wasco County										
⊞ **MID-COLUMBIA MEDICAL CENTER**, 1700 East 19th Street, Zip 97058–3316; tel. 541/296–1111 **A**1 9 10 19 20 **F**8 9 11 12 14 21 24 27 28 29 30 33 34 40 41 42 44 46 47 48 50 51 52 55 58 59 60 61 63 65 66 69 70 81 82 84 88 91 93 94 96 98 106 108 109 Primary Contact: Duane Francis, President Web address: www.mcmc.net	23	10	49	2506	24	104414	268	47252	20899	411
TILLAMOOK—Tillamook County										
★ **TILLAMOOK COUNTY GENERAL HOSPITAL**, 1000 Third Street, Zip 97141–3430; tel. 503/842–4444 **A**9 10 18 20 **F**1 2 6 11 12 14 21 22 26 27 28 29 33 34 36 37 38 39 46 48 51 52 53 58 59 60 62 63 65 66 69 75 81 82 84 85 88 94 96 97 106 108 110 **S** Adventist Health, Roseville, CA Primary Contact: Wendell Hesseltine, President and Chief Executive Officer Web address: www.tcgh.com	21	10	25	1522	12	13577	175	32341	13056	258

Hospital, Address, Telephone, Approval, Facility, and Physician Codes, Health Care System	Classi-fication Codes		Utilization Data					Expense (thousands) of dollars		
★ American Hospital Association (AHA) membership □ Joint Commission on Accreditation of Healthcare Organizations (JCAHO) accreditation ○ American Osteopathic Association (AOA) accreditation △ Commission on Accreditation of Rehabilitation Facilities (CARF) accreditation	Control	Service	Staffed Beds	Admissions	Census	Outpatient Visits	Births	Total	Payroll	Personnel

TUALATIN—Clackamas County

☒ **LEGACY MERIDIAN PARK HOSPITAL**, 19300 S.W. 65th Avenue, Zip 97062–9741; tel. 503/692–1212 **A**1 9 10 **F**2 4 9 11 12 15 17 21 22 23 24 26 27 28 29 31 33 35 37 39 44 46 47 48 49 52 53 55 57 58 59 60 61 62 63 64 65 69 73 74 75 81 82 84 85 87 88 92 93 94 96 108 109 **P**8 **S** Legacy Health System, Portland, OR
Primary Contact: Allyson Anderson, Vice President and Administrator
COO: Barbara Zappas, Senior Vice President Clinical Operations
CFO: Pamela S. Vukovich, Senior Vice President and Chief Financial Officer
CMO: Keith I. Marton, M.D., Senior Vice President and Chief Medical Officer
CIO: C Matthew Calais, Senior Vice President and Chief Information Officer
Web address: www.legacyhealth.org

Control	Service	Staffed Beds	Admissions	Census	Outpatient Visits	Births	Total	Payroll	Personnel
23	10	133	7538	69	119412	1404	79921	31046	595

Many Facility Codes have changed. Please refer to the AHA Guide Code Chart. © 2005 AHA Guide

PENNSYLVANIA

Hospital, Address, Telephone, Approval, Facility, and Physician Codes, Health Care System	Classi-fication Codes		Utilization Data					Expense (thousands) of dollars		
★ American Hospital Association (AHA) membership □ Joint Commission on Accreditation of Healthcare Organizations (JCAHO) accreditation ○ American Osteopathic Association (AOA) accreditation △ Commission on Accreditation of Rehabilitation Facilities (CARF) accreditation	Control	Service	Staffed Beds	Admissions	Census	Outpatient Visits	Births	Total	Payroll	Personnel

ABINGTON—Montgomery County

⊞ **ABINGTON MEMORIAL HOSPITAL**, 1200 Old York Road, Zip 19001–3720; tel. 215/481–2000 **A**1 2 3 5 6 9 10 12 **F**1 2 9 11 12 14 15 17 19 21 22 23 24 25 26 27 28 29 30 31 32 33 34 35 36 37 38 39 41 42 44 45 46 47 48 49 50 51 52 53 55 56 57 58 59 60 61 62 63 64 65 66 68 69 70 71 72 73 74 75 76 77 78 79 80 81 82 84 85 87 88 89 90 92 93 94 95 96 98 106 108 109 110 **P**6 7
Primary Contact: Richard L. Jones, Jr, FACHE, President and Chief Executive Officer
COO: Margaret M. McGoldrick, Executive Vice President and Administrator
CFO: Michael Walsh, Vice President Finance
CMO: John J. Kelly, M.D., Chief of Staff
CIO: Alison Ferren, Director Information Services
CHR: Meghan Patton, Vice President Human Resources
Web address: www.amh.org — 23 10 505 33309 431 525856 4840 411403 182136 3946

ALIQUIPPA—Beaver County

★ **ALIQUIPPA COMMUNITY HOSPITAL**, 2500 Hospital Drive, Zip 15001–2191; tel. 724/857–1212, (Nonreporting) **A**9 10 — 21 10 208 — — — — — — —
Primary Contact: Anthony Puorro, Chief Executive Officer
CIO: James Stafford, Director Information Systems
Web address: www.aclonline.org

ALLENTOWN—Lehigh County

□ **ALLENTOWN STATE HOSPITAL**, 1600 Hanover Avenue, Zip 18103–2408; tel. 610/740–3200, (Nonreporting) **A**1 10 — 12 22 181 — — — — — — —
Primary Contact: Gregory M. Smith, Chief Executive Officer

□ △ **GOOD SHEPHERD REHABILITATION HOSPITAL**, 501 St. John Street, Zip 18103–3231, Mailing Address: 543 St. John Street, Zip 18103–3231; tel. 610/776–3299 **A**1 7 9 10 **F**9 21 22 26 27 28 29 30 37 53 58 60 68 69 92 94 96 108 110 **P**6 — 23 46 75 1951 55 126576 0 39511 15761 966
Primary Contact: Sally Gammon, President and Chief Executive Officer
Web address: www.goodshepherdrehab.org

GOOD SHEPHERD SPECIALTY HOSPITAL, Cedar Crest Boulevard, 1st Floor, Zip 18105; tel. 610/402–8962, (Nonreporting) **A**10 — 33 49 32 — — — — — — —
Primary Contact: Pam Miles, Administrator

⊞ **LEHIGH VALLEY HOSPITAL**, 1200 South Cedar Crest Boulevard, Zip 18105–6248, Mailing Address: P.O. Box 689, Zip 18105–0689; tel. 610/402–8000, (Total facility includes 42 beds in nursing home–type unit) **A**1 2 3 5 8 9 10 12 13 **F**2 5 6 7 9 10 11 12 13 14 15 17 19 21 22 23 24 26 27 28 29 30 31 32 33 34 35 36 37 38 39 40 41 42 44 45 46 47 48 49 50 51 52 53 55 56 57 58 59 60 61 62 63 64 65 66 67 69 70 71 72 73 74 75 76 77 78 79 80 81 82 83 84 85 86 87 88 89 90 92 93 94 95 96 98 101 105 106 107 108 109 110 **P**4 5 6 7 8 — 23 10 651 37058 540 272109 3135 505137 177565 4650
Primary Contact: Elliot J. Sussman, M.D., President and Chief Executive Officer
COO: Louis L. Liebhaber, Chief Operating Officer
CFO: Vaughn C. Gower, Senior Vice President and Chief Financial Officer
CMO: Ronald W. Swinfard, M.D., Chief Medical Officer
CIO: Harry Lukens, Senior Vice President and Chief Information Officer
CHR: Mary Kay Grim, Senior Vice President Human Resources
Web address: www.lvhhn.org

□ △ **SACRED HEART HOSPITAL**, 421 Chew Street, Zip 18102–3490; tel. 610/776–4500, (Total facility includes 22 beds in nursing home–type unit) **A**1 2 3 5 7 9 10 12 13 **F**2 10 11 12 14 15 17 19 21 22 23 24 26 27 28 29 32 33 36 37 38 39 41 42 44 45 46 47 48 50 51 52 55 57 58 59 60 61 62 63 64 65 66 69 70 71 73 74 75 76 79 81 84 85 88 92 93 94 96 106 107 108 109 110 **P**6 7 8 — 23 10 249 7856 103 161800 523 102003 47167 1388
Primary Contact: James M. Seitzinger, President and Chief Executive Officer
Web address: www.shh.org
ST LUKE'S HOSPITAL–ALLENTOWN CAMPUS See St. Luke's Hospital – Bethlehem Campus, Bethlehem

ALTOONA—Blair County

ALTOONA CENTER, 1515 Fourth Street, Zip 16601–4595; tel. 814/946–6900, (Nonreporting) **A**9 — 12 62 138 — — — — — — —
Primary Contact: Barry C. Benford, Director

⊞ ○ **ALTOONA HOSPITAL CAMPUS**, (Formerly Altoona Hospital), 620 Howard Avenue, Zip 16601–4899; tel. 814/946–2011 **A**1 2 9 10 11 12 13 **F**2 3 4 9 10 11 12 15 17 19 21 22 23 24 26 27 28 29 31 33 34 37 38 39 40 42 43 44 46 48 49 52 53 55 57 58 59 60 61 62 63 64 65 69 71 72 73 74 75 76 77 79 80 81 82 84 86 87 88 90 93 94 95 96 106 108 109 110 **P**8 — 23 10 173 14572 173 362049 1359 182987 71011 1448
Primary Contact: James W. Barner, President and Chief Executive Officer
CFO: Charles Zorger, Senior Vice President Finance
CMO: Michael Gerard Moncman, D.O., President, Medical Staff
CIO: David J. Duncan, Ph.D., FACHE, Senior Vice President
CHR: Gary Naugle, Vice President Human Resources
Web address: www.altoonahospital.org

Hospital, Address, Telephone, Approval, Facility, and Physician Codes, Health Care System	Classi-fication Codes		Utilization Data					Expense (thousands) of dollars		
★ American Hospital Association (AHA) membership □ Joint Commission on Accreditation of Healthcare Organizations (JCAHO) accreditation ○ American Osteopathic Association (AOA) accreditation △ Commission on Accreditation of Rehabilitation Facilities (CARF) accreditation	Control	Service	Staffed Beds	Admissions	Census	Outpatient Visits	Births	Total	Payroll	Personnel
★ **BON SECOURS HOSPITAL CAMPUS**, (Formerly Bon Secours–Holy Family Regional Health System), 2500 Seventh Avenue, Zip 16602–2099; tel. 814/944–1681, (Total facility includes 17 beds in nursing home–type unit) **A**2 9 10 **F**2 9 12 15 17 19 21 22 23 24 26 27 28 29 30 33 36 37 38 39 46 47 48 49 50 52 53 55 57 58 60 61 62 63 64 66 68 69 71 73 76 80 81 82 84 88 92 93 94 95 96 106 108 110 CFO: David J. McConnell, Chief Financial Officer CMO: Frank E. Sangiorgio, M.D., President Medical Staff CIO: Michael Corso, Chief Information Officer Web address: www.bonsecoursholyfamily.org	23	10	130	4810	78	122027	0	66867	27583	568
✦ **HEALTHSOUTH REHABILITATION HOSPITAL OF ALTOONA**, 2005 Valley View Boulevard, Zip 16602–4598; tel. 814/944–3535 **A**1 10 **F**1 21 26 27 28 39 44 45 46 48 49 58 62 68 69 95 96 **S** HEALTHSOUTH Corporation, Birmingham, AL Primary Contact: Scott Filler, Administrator CFO: Michael Zenone, Controller CMO: Rakesh Patel, D.O., Medical Director CHR: Christine Filer, Director Human Resources Web address: www.healthsouth.com	33	46	70	1586	62	55472	0	20423	10970	268
✦ **JAMES E. VAN ZANDT VETERANS AFFAIRS MEDICAL CENTER**, 2907 Pleasant Valley Boulevard, Zip 16602–4377; tel. 814/943–8164, (Total facility includes 40 beds in nursing home–type unit) **A**1 9 **F**4 12 21 22 29 32 33 35 36 37 42 44 45 47 48 50 51 52 55 57 58 60 63 65 66 69 70 73 77 81 85 88 92 94 96 106 108 109 110 **P**6 **S** Department of Veterans Affairs, Washington, DC Primary Contact: Gerald L. Williams, Director CFO: Charles T. Becker, Manager Resources Web address: www.va.gov/sta/guide/home.asp	45	10	68	1344	52	191039	0	66036	24273	448
AMBLER—Montgomery County										
□ **HORSHAM CLINIC**, 722 East Butler Pike, Zip 19002–2310; tel. 215/643–7800, (Nonreporting) **A**1 9 10 **S** Universal Health Services, Inc., King of Prussia, PA Primary Contact: Phyllis Weisfield, Interim Chief Executive Officer Web address: www.horshamclinic.com	31	22	138	—	—	—	—	—	—	—
ASHLAND—Schuylkill County										
✦ **ASHLAND REGIONAL MEDICAL CENTER**, 101 Broad Street, Zip 17921–0000; tel. 570/875–2000, (Total facility includes 40 beds in nursing home–type unit) **A**1 9 10 **F**2 9 21 26 27 33 39 44 46 47 48 52 53 55 58 62 63 69 81 82 87 88 92 94 108 109 **P**6 **S** LifePoint Hospitals, Inc., Brentwood, TN Primary Contact: Cindy Gorr, Chief Executive Officer CFO: Jeffrey Chilson, Chief Financial Officer CMO: Yasser Khoudeir, M.D., Medical Staff President CHR: Laura LaBuda, Director Human Resources Web address: www.ashlandregional.com	32	10	123	2213	51	22164	0	16856	8258	195
BEAVER—Beaver County										
□ **KINDRED HOSPITAL–HERITAGE VALLEY**, 1000 Dutch Ridge Road, Zip 15009; tel. 724/773–8210, (Nonreporting) **A**1 9 10 Primary Contact: Susan Colpo, Chief Executive Officer	33	49	35	—	—	—	—	—	—	—
□ **THE MEDICAL CENTER, BEAVER**, 1000 Dutch Ridge Road, Zip 15009–9727; tel. 724/728–7000, (Nonreporting) **A**1 9 10 12 13 **S** Heritage Valley Health System, Beaver, PA Primary Contact: Norman F. Mitry, President and Chief Executive Officer Web address: www.heritagevalley.org	23	10	359	—	—	—	—	—	—	—
BENSALEM—Bucks County										
LIVENGRIN FOUNDATION, 4833 Hulmeville Road, Zip 19020–3099; tel. 215/638–5200, (Nonreporting) **A**9 Primary Contact: Richard M. Pine, President and Chief Executive Officer Web address: www.livengrin.org	23	82	76	—	—	—	—	—	—	—
BERWICK—Columbia County										
□ **BERWICK HOSPITAL CENTER**, 701 East 16th Street, Zip 18603–2397; tel. 570/759–5000, (Total facility includes 240 beds in nursing home–type unit) **A**1 9 10 **F**2 11 12 15 21 23 26 27 28 32 33 34 36 37 38 44 46 48 51 52 55 59 60 61 62 63 64 69 71 73 74 75 76 81 82 84 87 88 92 93 94 96 108 109 110 **P**6 **S** Community Health Systems, Inc., Brentwood, TN Primary Contact: Alex M. Poirier, Chief Executive Officer Web address: www.berwick–hospital.com	33	10	341	3840	235	73198	156	—	—	511
BETHLEHEM—Lehigh County										
✦ **LEHIGH VALLEY HOSPITAL–MUHLENBERG**, 2545 Schoenersville Road, Zip 18017–7384; tel. 484/884–2201 **A**1 9 10 12 13 **F**2 9 12 14 15 17 19 21 22 23 26 27 28 29 30 31 32 33 35 36 37 38 39 40 41 44 46 47 48 49 51 52 53 55 57 58 60 61 62 63 64 65 66 69 70 75 81 82 83 84 85 87 88 89 90 92 93 94 95 106 108 110 **P**4 5 7 8 Primary Contact: Elliot J. Sussman, M.D., President and Chief Executive Officer COO: Louis L. Liebhaber, Chief Operating Officer CFO: Vaughn C. Gower, Senior Vice President Finance and Chief Financial Officer CMO: Ronald W. Swinfard, M.D., Chief Medical Officer CIO: Harry Lukens, Senior Vice President and Chief Information Officer CHR: Mary Kay Grim, Senior Vice President Human Resources Web address: www.lvhhn.org	23	10	116	7795	88	143798	0	99789	38211	882

Many Facility Codes have changed. Please refer to the AHA Guide Code Chart. © 2005 AHA Guide

Hospital, Address, Telephone, Approval, Facility, and Physician Codes, Health Care System	Classification Codes		Utilization Data					Expense (thousands) of dollars		
★ American Hospital Association (AHA) membership □ Joint Commission on Accreditation of Healthcare Organizations (JCAHO) accreditation ○ American Osteopathic Association (AOA) accreditation △ Commission on Accreditation of Rehabilitation Facilities (CARF) accreditation	Control	Service	Staffed Beds	Admissions	Census	Outpatient Visits	Births	Total	Payroll	Personnel

□ **ST. LUKE'S HOSPITAL – BETHLEHEM CAMPUS**, 801 Ostrum Street, Zip 18015–1065; tel. 610/954–4000, (Includes ST LUKE'S HOSPITAL–ALLENTOWN CAMPUS, 1736 Hamilton Street, Allentown, Zip 18104–5656; tel. 610/770–8300; Elaine Thompson, Ph.D., Executive Vice President and Chief Operating Officer) **A**1 2 3 5 6 8 9 10 12 13 **F**2 7 9 10 11 12 14 15 17 19 21 22 23 24 27 28 29 30 31 32 33 34 35 36 37 38 39 40 41 42 44 46 47 48 49 50 52 55 56 57 58 59 60 61 62 63 64 65 66 69 71 72 73 74 75 76 77 78 79 80 81 82 83 84 85 86 87 88 93 94 95 96 97 98 106 107 108 109 110 **P**8
Primary Contact: Richard A. Anderson, President and Chief Executive Officer
Web address: www.slhn–lehighvalley.org

| | 23 | 10 | 435 | 30925 | 371 | 399566 | 4262 | 348716 | 144924 | 3260 |

BLOOMSBURG—Columbia County

★ **BLOOMSBURG HOSPITAL**, 549 Fair Street, Zip 17815–0340; tel. 570/387–2100 **A**9 10 **F**2 9 11 12 21 22 26 27 29 30 33 35 37 39 44 46 47 48 52 53 55 58 59 60 62 63 64 66 71 72 74 75 76 81 82 84 87 88 93 94 96 106
Primary Contact: Regis Cabonor, Administrator
CFO: Joseph M. DeVito, Chief Financial Officer
CMO: Aldo Suraci, M.D., President Medical Staff
CIO: Robert Theiss, Chief Information Officer
CHR: Thomas Conlin, Vice President Human Resources
Web address: www.tbhonline.org

| | 23 | 10 | 68 | 2575 | 28 | 79104 | 311 | 29272 | 12049 | 338 |

BRADDOCK—Allegheny County

□ **UPMC BRADDOCK**, 400 Holland Avenue, Zip 15104–1598; tel. 412/636–5000, (Total facility includes 23 beds in nursing home–type unit) (Nonreporting) **A**1 9 10 **S** University of Pittsburgh Medical Center, Pittsburgh, PA
Primary Contact: Mark Sevco, President
Web address: www.upmc.edu

| | 23 | 10 | 133 | — | — | — | — | — | — | — |

BRADFORD—McKean County

✠ **BRADFORD REGIONAL MEDICAL CENTER**, 116 Interstate Parkway, Zip 16701–0218; tel. 814/368–4143, (Total facility includes 95 beds in nursing home–type unit) **A**1 9 10 **F**9 11 12 15 21 23 26 27 28 29 32 33 36 37 39 41 44 46 48 51 52 55 58 59 60 61 62 63 64 65 66 69 70 71 73 74 75 76 77 78 81 82 84 87 88 92 93 94 95 96 106 108 109 **P**8
Primary Contact: George E. Leonhardt, CHE, President and Chief Executive Officer
COO: Glen Washington, Senior Vice President Operations
CFO: James Tarasovitch, Senior Vice President and Chief Financial Officer
CMO: David Godfrey, M.D., Vice President Medical Affairs
CIO: Terry Palmer, Chief Informaiton Officer
CHR: Timothy A. Hays, Vice President Human Resources
Web address: www.brmc.com

| | 23 | 10 | 180 | 4754 | 146 | 110413 | 358 | 54510 | 23326 | 687 |

BRIDGEVILLE—Allegheny County

□ **MAYVIEW STATE HOSPITAL**, 1601 Mayview Road, Zip 15017–1547; tel. 412/257–6500, (Nonreporting) **A**1 5 10
Primary Contact: Richard Kuppelweiser, Chief Executive Officer

| | 12 | 22 | 438 | — | — | — | — | — | — | — |

BRISTOL—Bucks County

□ **LOWER BUCKS HOSPITAL**, 501 Bath Road, Zip 19007–3190; tel. 215/785–9200 **A**1 5 9 10 **F**9 11 12 14 15 17 19 21 22 26 27 28 31 33 37 41 42 46 47 48 51 52 55 56 58 59 60 61 63 65 66 69 71 73 74 75 81 82 84 88 93 94 95 96 108 109 110
Primary Contact: Austin B. Cleveland, President and Chief Executive Officer
Web address: www.lowerbuckshospital.org

| | 23 | 10 | 163 | 8023 | 110 | 131574 | 673 | 98617 | 37865 | 844 |

BROOKVILLE—Jefferson County

★ **BROOKVILLE HOSPITAL**, 100 Hospital Road, Zip 15825–1367; tel. 814/849–2312 **A**9 10 **F**2 11 12 14 15 21 22 26 27 28 29 32 33 46 48 51 58 59 60 61 63 65 69 71 76 81 82 87 88 93 94 95 97 108 110 **P**5
Primary Contact: Robert E. Fisher, President and Chief Executive Officer
CFO: Julie Peer, Vice President Finance
CHR: Deborah Momeyer, Director Human Resources
Web address: www.brookvillehospital.org

| | 23 | 10 | 62 | 2328 | 27 | 82913 | 120 | 24963 | 8935 | 310 |

BROWNSVILLE—Fayette County

★ **BROWNSVILLE GENERAL HOSPITAL**, 125 Simpson Road, Zip 15417–9699; tel. 724/785–7200 **A**9 10 **F**9 12 21 22 27 28 29 33 37 41 44 52 58 60 61 62 63 65 66 68 69 70 71 74 75 76 77 78 81 82 84 86 88 93 94 96 108 110
Primary Contact: Michael J. Evans, Chief Executive Officer
COO: Karl T. Skrypak, Executive Vice President and Chief Operating Officer
CFO: Michael Conte, Financial Consultant
CMO: Bhagwan Wadhwani, M.D., Chief of Staff
CIO: Lisa Orris, Director Laboratory, Cardiopulmonary and Information Systems
CHR: Raymond Royesky, Director Human Resources
Web address: www.bghlink.com

| | 23 | 10 | 51 | 2097 | 41 | 55273 | 0 | 19258 | 8126 | 192 |

BRYN MAWR—Montgomery County

□ **BRYN MAWR HOSPITAL**, 130 South Bryn Mawr Avenue, Zip 19010–3160; tel. 610/526–3000, (Total facility includes 17 beds in nursing home–type unit) **A**1 2 3 5 9 10 **F**2 6 9 11 12 14 15 17 19 21 22 23 26 27 28 29 33 36 37 38 44 46 47 48 50 52 55 56 57 58 59 60 61 62 63 64 65 66 69 71 72 73 75 76 77 78 79 80 81 82 84 87 88 89 90 94 96 108 109 110 **P**2 6 7 **S** Jefferson Health System, Wayne, PA
Primary Contact: Andrea F. Gilbert, CHE, President
Web address: www.brynmawrhospital.org

| | 23 | 10 | 320 | 17096 | 211 | 147781 | 1936 | 190426 | 72628 | 1259 |

Hospital, Address, Telephone, Approval, Facility, and Physician Codes, Health Care System	Classi-fication Codes		Utilization Data					Expense (thousands) of dollars		
★ American Hospital Association (AHA) membership □ Joint Commission on Accreditation of Healthcare Organizations (JCAHO) accreditation ○ American Osteopathic Association (AOA) accreditation △ Commission on Accreditation of Rehabilitation Facilities (CARF) accreditation	Control	Service	Staffed Beds	Admissions	Census	Outpatient Visits	Births	Total	Payroll	Personnel

BUTLER—Butler County

☒ **BUTLER HEALTH SYSTEM**, 911 East Brady Street, Zip 16001–4697; tel. 724/283–6666, (Total facility includes 23 beds in nursing home–type unit) **A**1 9 10 **F**3 4 11 12 14 15 17 19 21 23 24 26 27 28 29 33 37 46 48 55 57 59 62 63 64 66 71 73 76 81 82 84 86 87 88 92 93 94 96 106 108 109
Primary Contact: Joseph A. Stewart, Chief Executive Officer
CFO: Anne Krebs, Chief Financial Officer
CMO: Mike Swank, Executive Director Physician Network Development
CIO: Mark Maddamma, Executive Director Information Systems
CHR: Lin Sorber, Vice President Human Resources
Web address: www.butlerhealthsystem.org — **23 10 248 13685 181 367527 900 122672 52080 1312**

☒ △ **VETERANS AFFAIRS MEDICAL CENTER**, 325 New Castle Road, Zip 16001–2480; tel. 724/287–4781, (Total facility includes 86 beds in nursing home–type unit) **A**1 7 9 **F**1 2 4 10 21 22 25 26 28 31 32 36 37 38 39 41 44 45 46 48 51 52 57 58 60 65 66 69 70 77 88 92 94 96 106 107 108 109 **P**6 **S** Department of Veterans Affairs, Washington, DC
Primary Contact: David Wood, Director
COO: Richard W. Cotter, Chief Operating Officer
CFO: Doug George, Financial Manager
CMO: Varsha Mehta, M.D., Chief of Staff
CIO: Kenneth Kalberer, Information System Manager
CHR: Stanley Pakutz, Manager Business Office
Web address: www.va.gov/station/529–butler — **45 80 149 1010 127 112535 0 62889 33290 511**

CAMP HILL—Cumberland County

☒ **HOLY SPIRIT HOSPITAL**, 503 North 21st Street, Zip 17011–2288; tel. 717/763–2100 **A**1 5 9 10 **F**2 4 9 11 12 14 15 17 19 21 22 23 26 27 28 29 31 33 35 39 46 47 48 50 52 55 56 57 58 59 60 61 62 63 64 65 66 69 71 72 73 74 75 76 77 78 81 82 84 85 87 88 93 94 96 98 107 108 110
Primary Contact: Sister Romaine Niemeyer, President and Chief Executive Officer
CFO: Karl Waltman, Vice President Finance
CMO: Charles A. DeLone, M.D., Vice President Medical Affairs
CHR: William Shartle, Vice President Human Resources
Web address: www.hsh.org — **21 10 311 15667 233 213432 1107 177730 84100 1989**

□ **SELECT SPECIALTY HOSPITAL–CAMP HILL**, 503 North 21st Street, 5th Floor, Zip 17011; tel. 717/972–4560, (Nonreporting) **A**1 9 10
Primary Contact: Marcia Medlin, Chief Executive Officer — **33 49 31 — — — — — — —**

STATE CORRECTIONAL INSTITUTION AT CAMP HILL, 2500 Lisbon Road, Zip 17011, Mailing Address: P.O. Box 200, Zip 17011–0200; tel. 717/737–4531, (Nonreporting)
Primary Contact: Kathy Montag, Administrator Health Care — **12 49 34 — — — — — — —**

CANONSBURG—Washington County

☒ **CANONSBURG GENERAL HOSPITAL**, 100 Medical Boulevard, Zip 15317–9762; tel. 724/745–6100 **A**1 9 10 **F**2 6 9 12 21 22 23 24 26 27 28 29 33 45 46 47 48 52 53 55 58 60 61 62 63 68 81 85 87 88 93 94 106 108 **P**6 **S** West Penn Allegheny Health System, Pittsburgh, PA
Primary Contact: Kim Malinky, President and Chief Executive Officer
CFO: Gene Trout, Chief Financial Officer
CMO: William Thomeier, M.D., President Medical Staff
CIO: Lisa Carrigan, Director Information Systems
CHR: Martha L. Clister, Director Human Resources
Web address: www.wpahs.org — **23 10 104 4962 68 82625 0 41320 17570 419**

CARBONDALE—Lackawanna County

☒ **MARIAN COMMUNITY HOSPITAL**, 100 Lincoln Avenue, Zip 18407–2198; tel. 570/281–1000 **A**1 9 10 **F**21 22 23 28 33 45 48 51 52 53 55 57 58 61 62 63 65 71 81 82 84 88 93 94 96 108 **P**4 **S** Catholic Health East, Newtown Square, PA
Primary Contact: Sister Jean Coughlin, President and Chief Executive Officer
CFO: Thomas Heron, Chief Financial Officer
CMO: Patrick McAndrew, D.O., President Medical Staff
CIO: Doug Tippins, Director Information Services
CHR: Joseph Casarella, Director Human Resources
Web address: www.marianhospital.org — **21 10 104 4019 54 62925 0 32957 13782 376**

CARLISLE—Cumberland County

☒ **CARLISLE REGIONAL MEDICAL CENTER**, 246 Parker Street, Zip 17013–3661; tel. 717/249–1212 **A**1 9 10 **F**2 11 12 15 21 22 23 26 27 28 29 33 37 38 39 42 46 48 51 52 55 57 58 59 60 61 62 63 64 65 66 68 69 79 81 82 83 84 85 88 94 96 108 109 110 **P**8 **S** Health Management Associates, Naples, FL
COO: Rick Schaffner, Associate Executive Director and Chief Operating Officer
CFO: Jeff Morgan, Associate Executive Director and Chief Financial Officer
CMO: Howard Alster, M.D., President, Medical Staff
CIO: Kemp Beatty, Director Information Management
Web address: www.carlislermc.com — **33 10 133 6986 86 88622 518 — — 591**

CENTRE HALL—Centre County

□ **MEADOWS PSYCHIATRIC CENTER**, 132 The Meadows Drive, Zip 16828–9798; tel. 814/364–2161 **A**1 9 10 **F**27 71 72 75 76 77 78 **P**6 **S** Universal Health Services, Inc., King of Prussia, PA
Primary Contact: Felicia Stehley, Chief Executive Officer
Web address: www.themeadow.net — **33 22 101 2687 76 0 0 11428 5725 179**

Many Facility Codes have changed. Please refer to the AHA Guide Code Chart. © 2005 AHA Guide

PA

Hospital, Address, Telephone, Approval, Facility, and Physician Codes, Health Care System	Classification Codes		Utilization Data					Expense (thousands) of dollars		
★ American Hospital Association (AHA) membership □ Joint Commission on Accreditation of Healthcare Organizations (JCAHO) accreditation ○ American Osteopathic Association (AOA) accreditation △ Commission on Accreditation of Rehabilitation Facilities (CARF) accreditation	Control	Service	Staffed Beds	Admissions	Census	Outpatient Visits	Births	Total	Payroll	Personnel

CHAMBERSBURG—Franklin County

✠ **CHAMBERSBURG HOSPITAL**, 112 North Seventh Street, Zip 17201–0187, Mailing Address: P.O. Box 6005, Zip 17201–6005; tel. 717/267–3000 **A**1 2 9 10 19 **F**2 9 11 12 14 15 17 21 22 23 26 27 28 29 30 33 37 38 39 41 42 44 46 47 48 50 52 53 55 56 57 58 59 60 61 62 63 64 65 66 68 69 70 71 72 73 74 75 76 77 79 81 82 84 85 87 88 92 93 94 95 96 106 107 108 109 **P**6 7 8 **S** Summit Health, Chambersburg, PA
Primary Contact: Norman B. Epstein, CHE, President
COO: John P. Massimilla, Vice President Administration
CFO: Patrick W. O'Donnell, CPA, Vice President Finance
CMO: David J. Carlson, D.O., Vice President Medical Affairs
CIO: Michael Zeigler, Vice President and Chief Information Officer
CHR: Lou Gregorio, Vice President Human Resources
Web address: www.summithealth.org
Codes: 23 10 | 231 | 12433 | 167 | 287671 | 1277 | 141816 | 64597 | 1330

CHESTER—Delaware County

KEYSTONE CENTER, 2001 Providence Avenue, Zip 19013–5504; tel. 610/876–9000, (Nonreporting) **A**9 **S** Universal Health Services, Inc., King of Prussia, PA
Primary Contact: Billy Young, Chief Executive Officer
Web address: www.keystonecenter.net
Codes: 33 82 | 84 | — | — | — | — | — | — | —

CLARION—Clarion County

★ ○ **CLARION HOSPITAL**, One Hospital Drive, Zip 16214–8599; tel. 814/226–9500 **A**9 10 11 12 13 19 **F**6 11 12 21 22 23 29 33 34 41 46 48 52 55 59 60 61 62 63 81 82 84 88 92 93 94 108 110 **P**7 **S** Quorum Health Resources, Plano, TX
Primary Contact: Edward J. Hannon, President and Chief Executive Officer
CFO: Vincent M. Lamorella, Chief Financial Officer
Web address: www.clarionhospital.org
Codes: 23 10 | 83 | 3891 | 40 | 100161 | 341 | 37811 | 14301 | 448

□ **CLARION PSYCHIATRIC CENTER**, 2 Hospital Drive, Zip 16214–9424; tel. 814/226–9545, (Nonreporting) **A**1 9 10 **S** Universal Health Services, Inc., King of Prussia, PA
Primary Contact: Jeffrey Barnett, Chief Executive Officer
Web address: www.clarioncenter.com
Codes: 31 22 | 52 | — | — | — | — | — | — | —

CLARKS SUMMIT—Lackawanna County

□ **CLARKS SUMMIT STATE HOSPITAL**, 1451 Hillside Drive, Zip 18411–9504; tel. 570/586–2011 **A**1 10 **F**22 26 28 30 32 37 38 44 45 46 48 50 53 58 60 65 66 71 73 74 75 76 94 96 106 108 **P**6
Primary Contact: Thomas P. Comerford, Jr, Superintendent
Codes: 12 22 | 265 | 98 | 226 | 0 | 0 | 35096 | 20491 | 475

CLEARFIELD—Clearfield County

CLEARFIELD HOSPITAL, 809 Turnpike Avenue, Zip 16830–1232, Mailing Address: P.O. Box 992, Zip 16830–0992; tel. 814/765–5341 **A**9 10 **F**2 9 11 12 15 21 22 23 26 27 28 29 33 36 39 46 47 48 51 52 55 58 59 60 61 62 63 64 65 66 69 70 73 74 76 77 81 82 84 85 87 88 93 94 95 96 97 106 108 110 **P**5
Primary Contact: Robert B. Murray, III, CHE, President and Chief Executive Officer
Web address: www.clearfieldhosp.org
Codes: 23 10 | 83 | 3715 | 40 | 206361 | 253 | 50859 | 21545 | 614

COAL TOWNSHIP—Northumberland County

★ **SHAMOKIN AREA COMMUNITY HOSPITAL**, 4200 Hospital Road, Zip 17866–9697; tel. 570/644–4200, (Total facility includes 15 beds in nursing home–type unit) **A**9 10 **F**2 8 9 12 21 22 26 27 28 29 30 31 33 37 39 40 44 46 48 52 53 55 58 60 62 63 64 66 69 71 73 76 81 82 84 88 92 94 95 96 106 108
Primary Contact: John P. Wiercinski, President and Chief Executive Officer
CFO: Kathleen Chapman, Vice President and Chief Financial Officer
CIO: Kimberly Chaundy, Information Systems Manager
CHR: Rick Flynn, Vice President Human Resources
Web address: www.shamokinhospital.org
Codes: 23 10 | 70 | 3360 | 47 | 67997 | 0 | 24222 | 9921 | 263

COALDALE—Schuylkill County

□ **ST. LUKE'S MINER'S MEMORIAL HOSPITAL**, 360 West Ruddle Street, Zip 18218–1099; tel. 570/645–2131, (Total facility includes 48 beds in nursing home–type unit) **A**1 9 10 **F**2 6 12 21 22 23 26 27 28 32 33 36 37 41 44 45 46 48 51 52 54 55 57 58 60 61 62 63 65 66 69 81 84 88 92 94 95 96 107 108 110
Primary Contact: William J. Crossin, President and Chief Executive Officer
Web address: www.slhhn.org
Codes: 23 10 | 93 | 2198 | 73 | 61474 | 0 | 30468 | 13778 | 318

COATESVILLE—Chester County

□ **BRANDYWINE HOSPITAL**, 201 Reeceville Road, Zip 19320–1536; tel. 610/383–8000, (Nonreporting) **A**1 2 6 9 10 **S** Community Health Systems, Inc., Brentwood, TN
Primary Contact: Warren E. Callaway, FACHE, Chief Executive Officer
Web address: www.brandywinehospital.com
Codes: 33 10 | 164 | — | — | — | — | — | — | —

PA

Hospital, Address, Telephone, Approval, Facility, and Physician Codes, Health Care System	Classi-fication Codes		Utilization Data					Expense (thousands) of dollars		
★ American Hospital Association (AHA) membership □ Joint Commission on Accreditation of Healthcare Organizations (JCAHO) accreditation ○ American Osteopathic Association (AOA) accreditation △ Commission on Accreditation of Rehabilitation Facilities (CARF) accreditation	Control	Service	Staffed Beds	Admissions	Census	Outpatient Visits	Births	Total	Payroll	Personnel

VETERANS AFFAIRS MEDICAL CENTER, 1400 Black Horse Hill Road, Zip 19320–2040; tel. 610/384–7711, (Total facility includes 218 beds in nursing home–type unit) **A**1 9 **F**2 3 4 5 8 9 10 21 22 26 27 28 29 31 32 35 36 37 38 39 41 42 44 45 46 47 48 50 51 52 53 57 58 60 62 64 65 66 69 70 71 73 74 76 77 78 79 81 88 92 94 96 106 107 108 109 110 **P**6 **S** Department of Veterans Affairs, Washington, DC
Primary Contact: Gary W. Devansky, Director
CFO: Thomas Robinson, Chief Financial Officer
CMO: James F. Tischler, M.D., Chief of Staff
CIO: Eugene Doria, Chief Information Officer
CHR: George Pearson, Director Human Resources Management Service
Web address: www.va.gov/sta/guide/home.asp
— 45 82 526 3020 463 144251 0 124420 79411 1171

CONNELLSVILLE—Fayette County

HIGHLANDS HOSPITAL, 401 East Murphy Avenue, Zip 15425–2700; tel. 724/628–1500 **A**9 10 **F**2 9 10 12 21 22 28 29 30 32 33 35 39 41 44 45 46 47 48 50 52 55 58 60 62 64 66 69 71 72 73 74 75 76 81 82 85 87 88 94 96 97 108
Primary Contact: Michelle P. Cunningham, Chief Executive Officer
Web address: www.highlandshospital.org
— 23 10 87 2930 36 64531 0 23009 9113 278

CORRY—Erie County

CORRY MEMORIAL HOSPITAL, 612 West Smith Street, Zip 16407–1196; tel. 814/664–4641 **A**9 10 18 **F**11 12 33 36 47 51 58 60 62 63 64 65 69 76 81 82 88 94 96 97 105 109
Primary Contact: Barbara Nichols, R.N., President and Chief Executive Officer
Web address: www.corryhospital.com
— 23 10 25 2237 25 — 0 — — 252

COUDERSPORT—Potter County

CHARLES COLE MEMORIAL HOSPITAL, 1001 East Second Street, Zip 16915–9762; tel. 814/274–9300, (Total facility includes 49 beds in nursing home–type unit) **A**1 9 10 20 **F**2 8 9 11 12 14 21 22 23 28 29 33 36 41 46 48 51 52 59 60 61 62 63 66 68 69 71 76 81 84 88 92 94 96 97 106 108 109 110
Primary Contact: David B. Acker, FACHE, Chief Executive Officer
COO: Linda Summers, Chief Operating Officer
CFO: Edwin Szewczyk, Chief Financial Officer
CMO: Howard J. Miller, M.D., Medical Staff President
CHR: J Thomas Noe, Director Human Resources
Web address: www.charlescolehospital.com
— 23 10 124 3108 83 152481 291 47910 16337 461

CRANBERRY—Butler County

UPMC PASSAVANT CRANBERRY, One St. Francis Way, Zip 16066; tel. 724/772–5300, (Total facility includes 150 beds in nursing home–type unit) (Nonreporting) **A**9 10 **S** University of Pittsburgh Medical Center, Pittsburgh, PA
Primary Contact: Teresa A. Petrick, Chief Executive Officer
— 23 10 185 — — — — — — —

DANVILLE—Montour County

DANVILLE STATE HOSPITAL, 200 State Hospital Drive, Zip 17821–9198; tel. 570/271–4500 **A**1 10 **F**26 71 94 108 **P**6
Primary Contact: Donna M. Ashbridge, Chief Executive Officer
— 12 22 150 106 135 0 0 27482 16118 341

GEISINGER HEALTHSOUTH REHABILITATION HOSPITAL, 2 Rehab Lane, Zip 17821; tel. 570/271–6733 **A**1 9 10 **F**21 45 48 68 69 95 96 109 **P**1 **S** HEALTHSOUTH Corporation, Birmingham, AL
Primary Contact: Lorie Dillon, Administrator
CFO: Sally Morgante, Controller
CMO: Charles Sawyer, M.D., Medical Director
CHR: Christian Shirley, Director Human Resources
Web address: www.healthsouth.com
— 32 46 40 812 31 41582 0 9499 5946 109

GEISINGER MEDICAL CENTER, 100 North Academy Avenue, Zip 17822–2201; tel. 570/271–6211 **A**1 2 3 5 8 10 12 13 19 **F**2 6 7 9 10 11 12 14 15 16 17 18 19 20 21 22 23 24 26 28 29 30 31 32 33 34 37 38 39 40 44 46 47 48 49 50 52 53 55 56 57 58 59 61 62 63 64 65 66 67 69 70 71 72 73 74 75 76 77 78 79 80 81 82 84 85 86 87 88 89 93 94 95 96 99 101 104 105 106 107 108 109 110 **P**4 **S** Geisinger Health System, Danville, PA
Primary Contact: Louis A. Shapiro, Chief Operating Officer, Clinical Enterprise
COO: Frank J. Trembulak, Executive Vice President and Chief Operating Officer
CFO: Kevin F. Brennan, Executive Vice President and Chief Financial Officer
CMO: Bruce H. Hamory, M.D., Executive Vice President and Chief Medical Officer
CIO: Frank Richards, Chief Information Officer
CHR: Richard E. Merkle, Chief Human Resources Officer
Web address: www.geisinger.org
— 23 10 368 20271 273 481342 1489 309806 105280 2839

SELECT SPECIALTY HOSPITAL–DANVILLE, 100 North Academy Avenue, 3rd Floor, Zip 17822–3050; tel. 570/214–9657, (Nonreporting) **A**9 10 **S** Select Medical Corporation, Mechanicsburg, PA
Primary Contact: Lori Metzer, Chief Executive Officer
— 33 80 30 — — — — — — —

DARBY—Delaware County

KINDRED HOSPITAL – DELAWARE COUNTY, 1500 Lansdowne Avenue, 6th Floor, Zip 19023; tel. 610/237–5780, (Nonreporting) **A**1 9 10
Primary Contact: Cathy Pusey, Chf Executive Officer
— 33 49 43 — — — — — — —

Many Facility Codes have changed. Please refer to the AHA Guide Code Chart.

Hospital, Address, Telephone, Approval, Facility, and Physician Codes, Health Care System	Classi-fication Codes		Utilization Data					Expense (thousands) of dollars		
★ American Hospital Association (AHA) membership □ Joint Commission on Accreditation of Healthcare Organizations (JCAHO) accreditation ○ American Osteopathic Association (AOA) accreditation △ Commission on Accreditation of Rehabilitation Facilities (CARF) accreditation	Control	Service	Staffed Beds	Admissions	Census	Outpatient Visits	Births	Total	Payroll	Personnel

▣ △ **MERCY CATHOLIC MEDICAL CENTER**, 1500 South Lansdowe Avenue, Zip 19023; tel. 610/237–4000, (Includes MERCY FITZGERALD HOSPITAL, 1500 South Lansdowne Avenue, tel. 610/237–4000; MERCY HOSPITAL OF PHILADELPHIA, 501 South 54th Street, Philadelphia, Zip 19143; tel. 215/748–9000), (Total facility includes 22 beds in nursing home–type unit) **A**1 2 7 9 10 12 13 **F**2 3 4 6 9 12 14 15 17 19 21 22 23 26 27 28 29 31 33 36 37 38 39 40 41 42 44 46 47 48 50 51 52 55 58 60 61 62 63 64 65 66 68 69 70 71 73 74 75 76 77 81 82 84 85 87 88 92 93 94 96 106 108 109 110 **P**6 **S** Catholic Health East, Newtown Square, PA
Primary Contact: R. Alan Larson, Chief Executive Officer
COO: Marsha Rowe, Chief Operating Officer
CFO: Taylor McCormick, Chief Financial Officer
CMO: Mark J. Baumel, M.D., MS, Chief Medical Officer and Senior Vice President Medical Management
CIO: Steve Czapla, Vice President Information Technical Technology
CHR: Gregory Papa, Vice President Human Resources
Web address: www.mercyhealth.org
— **21 10 470 23140 382 212278 0 255489 111114 2279**

DOWNINGTOWN—Chester County
ST. JOHN VIANNEY HOSPITAL, 151 Woodbine Road, Zip 19335–3057; tel. 610/269–2600, (Nonreporting) **A**9
Primary Contact: Thomas F. Dugan, Administrator
Web address: www.sjvcenter.org
— **21 22 42 — — — — — — — —**

DOYLESTOWN—Bucks County
▣ △ **DOYLESTOWN HOSPITAL**, 595 West State Street, Zip 18901–2597; tel. 215/345–2200, (Total facility includes 129 beds in nursing home–type unit) **A**1 2 7 9 10 **F**2 8 9 10 11 12 14 15 17 19 21 22 23 24 26 27 28 29 30 31 32 33 36 37 38 41 42 44 45 46 47 48 50 51 52 53 55 56 57 58 59 60 61 62 63 64 65 66 68 69 75 81 82 84 85 88 91 92 94 96 98 106 108 109 **P**5 8
Primary Contact: Richard A. Reif, President and Chief Executive Officer
CFO: Robert Bauer, Vice President Finance and Chief Financial Officer
CMO: Scott S. Levy, M.D., Vice President and Chief Medical Officer
CHR: Barbara Hebel, Director Human Resources
Web address: www.dh.org
— **23 10 324 12713 279 277456 1501 175112 70658 1822**

□ **FOUNDATIONS BEHAVIORAL HEALTH**, 833 East Butler Avenue, Zip 18901–2280; tel. 215/345–0444, (Total facility includes 40 beds in nursing home–type unit) **A**1 10 **F**21 22 42 47 51 52 58 65 66 70 71 72 74 77 78 94 98 **P**6
Primary Contact: Ronald T. Bernstein, President and Chief Executive Officer
Web address: www.fbh.com
— **23 52 94 614 76 201064 0 16313 8099 209**

DREXEL HILL—Delaware County
▣ ○ △ **DELAWARE COUNTY MEMORIAL HOSPITAL**, 501 North Lansdowne Avenue, Zip 19026–1114; tel. 610/284–8100 **A**1 2 3 5 7 9 10 11 12 **F**2 6 9 11 12 14 21 22 23 26 27 28 29 30 33 35 36 39 40 44 45 46 48 50 51 52 53 55 56 57 58 59 60 61 62 63 64 65 66 68 69 70 73 79 80 81 82 83 84 85 86 87 88 89 90 94 95 96 97 98 108 109 110 **P**6 **S** Crozer–Keystone Health System, Springfield, PA
Primary Contact: Joan K. Richards, Chief Executive Officer
COO: William McCune, Chief Operating Officer
CFO: Richard I. Bennett, Senior Vice President and Chief Financial Officer
CMO: Seth Malin, M.D., President Medical and Dental Staff
CIO: Robert E. Wilson, Vice President and Chief Information Officer
CHR: Eugene Zegar, Vice President Human Resources
Web address: www.crozer.org
— **23 10 215 11173 170 96658 1405 129097 54291 982**

DU BOIS—Clearfield County
□ **DU BOIS REGIONAL MEDICAL CENTER**, 100 Hospital Avenue, Zip 15801–1440, Mailing Address: P.O. Box 447, Zip 15801–0447; tel. 814/371–2200, (Nonreporting) **A**1 2 9 10
Primary Contact: Raymond A. Graeca, President and Chief Executive Officer
Web address: www.drmc.org
— **23 10 203 — — — — — — — —**

EAGLEVILLE—Montgomery County
★ **EAGLEVILLE HOSPITAL**, 100 Eagleville Road, Zip 19408–0045, Mailing Address: P.O. Box 45, Zip 19408–0045; tel. 610/539–6000 **A**9 10 **F**2 3 21 26 27 28 29 39 45 47 50 53 58 65 71 73 74 76 94 96 98 108 109 **P**6
Primary Contact: Kendria McWilliams, Chief Executive Officer
CFO: Hon–Chung Tong, Chief Financial Officer
CMO: Robert Wilson, D.O., Director Medical Services
CIO: Richard R. Mitchell, Network Administrator
Web address: www.eaglevillehospital.org
— **23 82 351 3313 224 0 0 22405 10871 315**

EAST STROUDSBURG—Monroe County
▣ △ **POCONO MEDICAL CENTER**, 206 East Brown Street, Zip 18301–3006; tel. 570/421–4000 **A**1 2 7 9 10 20 **F**2 9 11 12 14 21 22 23 24 26 27 28 29 31 32 33 37 39 42 44 46 47 48 50 52 55 57 58 59 60 61 62 63 64 65 66 69 70 71 73 74 75 76 79 80 81 82 84 85 87 88 94 96 106 108 110
Primary Contact: Joseph S. Bonanno, Interim President and Chief Executive Officer
CFO: Edward J. Walsh, Vice President Financial Services
CMO: Richard F. Lain, M.D., Vice President Medical Affairs
CIO: Marian Moran, Vice President and Chief Information Officer
CHR: John Delaney, Vice President Human Resources
Web address: www.pmchealthsystem.org
— **23 10 192 11821 143 194246 752 119629 51120 979**

Hospital, Address, Telephone, Approval, Facility, and Physician Codes, Health Care System	Classi-fication Codes		Utilization Data					Expense (thousands) of dollars		
★ American Hospital Association (AHA) membership □ Joint Commission on Accreditation of Healthcare Organizations (JCAHO) accreditation ○ American Osteopathic Association (AOA) accreditation △ Commission on Accreditation of Rehabilitation Facilities (CARF) accreditation	Control	Service	Staffed Beds	Admissions	Census	Outpatient Visits	Births	Total	Payroll	Personnel

EASTON—Northampton County

□ **EASTON HOSPITAL**, 250 South 21st Street, Zip 18042–3892; tel. 610/250–4000, (Nonreporting) **A**1 2 3 5 9 10 12 13 **S** Community Health Systems, Inc., Brentwood, TN
Primary Contact: Cornelio R. Catena, President and Chief Executive Officer
Web address: www.easton–hospital.com

| | 23 | 10 | 231 | — | — | — | — | — | — | — |

□ **SCCI HOSPITAL – EASTON**, 250 South 21st Street, Zip 18042; tel. 610/250–4709, (Nonreporting) **A**1 9 10
Primary Contact: Linda Luther, Chief Executive Officer

| | 33 | 49 | 31 | — | — | — | — | — | — | — |

ELKINS PARK—Montgomery County

△ **MOSS REHAB, EINSTEIN AT ELKINS PARK**, 60 East Township Line Road, Zip 19027–2220; tel. 215/663–6000, (Nonreporting) **A**3 5 7 9 10 **S** Albert Einstein Healthcare Network, Philadelphia, PA
Primary Contact: Ruth Lefton, Chief Operating Officer

| | 23 | 10 | 158 | — | — | — | — | — | — | — |

ELLWOOD CITY—Lawrence County

ELLWOOD CITY HOSPITAL, 724 Pershing Street, Zip 16117–1474; tel. 724/752–0081, (Total facility includes 23 beds in nursing home–type unit) (Nonreporting) **A**9 10
Primary Contact: Herbert S. Skuba, President and Chief Executive Officer

| | 23 | 10 | 118 | — | — | — | — | — | — | — |

EPHRATA—Lancaster County

□ **EPHRATA COMMUNITY HOSPITAL**, 169 Martin Avenue, Zip 17522–1002, Mailing Address: P.O. Box 1002, Zip 17522–1002; tel. 717/733–0311 **A**1 9 10 **F**9 11 12 21 22 23 26 27 28 29 30 33 37 40 42 46 47 48 50 51 52 54 55 57 58 59 60 61 62 63 64 65 66 68 70 71 72 73 74 75 76 77 81 82 84 86 87 88 93 94 96 106 108 109 110 **P**6 8
Primary Contact: John M. Porter, Jr, President and Chief Executive Officer
Web address: www.ephratahospital.org

| | 23 | 10 | 133 | 8179 | 85 | 311383 | 879 | 123015 | 57006 | 1216 |

ERIE—Erie County

□ **HAMOT MEDICAL CENTER**, 201 State Street, Zip 16550–0002; tel. 814/877–6000 **A**1 2 3 5 8 9 10 12 13 **F**2 9 10 11 14 15 17 19 21 22 23 26 27 28 29 30 31 33 34 35 36 37 38 39 40 46 47 48 49 50 52 53 55 56 57 58 59 60 61 62 63 64 65 69 75 81 82 84 85 87 88 90 94 95 96 106 107 108 109 110 **P**6 8
Primary Contact: John T. Malone, President and Chief Executive Officer
Web address: www.hamot.org

| | 23 | 10 | 349 | 16699 | 210 | 126755 | 1532 | 193211 | 72560 | 1796 |

⊠ **HEALTHSOUTH REHABILITATION HOSPITAL OF ERIE**, 143 East Second Street, Zip 16507–1501; tel. 814/878–1200, (Nonreporting) **A**1 10 **S** HEALTHSOUTH Corporation, Birmingham, AL
Primary Contact: Louis M. Condrasky, Administrator
CFO: Lori Gibben, Assistant Controller
CMO: John Wyatt, M.D., Medical Director
CIO: Lynn Braendel, Director Health Information Management Systems
CHR: William Robinson, Director Human Resources
Web address: www.healthsouth.com

| | 33 | 46 | 108 | — | — | — | — | — | — | — |

○ **MILLCREEK COMMUNITY HOSPITAL**, 5515 Peach Street, Zip 16509–2695; tel. 814/864–4031, (Total facility includes 33 beds in nursing home–type unit) **A**9 10 11 12 13 **F**2 3 10 11 12 15 17 25 26 32 33 39 52 53 55 57 58 59 62 63 64 66 70 71 72 73 74 75 81 84 88 92 94 106 107 108 110
Primary Contact: Mary L. Eckert, President and Chief Executive Officer
Web address: www.millcreekcommunityhospital.com

| | 23 | 10 | 168 | 4088 | 82 | 37855 | 188 | 24657 | 11359 | 313 |

⊠ **SAINT VINCENT HEALTH CENTER**, 232 West 25th Street, Zip 16544–0002; tel. 814/452–5000, (Total facility includes 14 beds in nursing home–type unit) **A**1 9 10 12 13 **F**2 4 9 11 12 14 15 17 19 21 22 23 26 27 28 30 31 32 33 35 36 39 40 42 43 47 48 49 50 52 53 55 56 57 58 59 60 61 62 63 64 65 66 68 71 73 74 75 76 77 81 82 84 85 86 87 88 89 92 93 94 95 96 97 106 107 108 109 110 **P**6 **S** St. Vincent Health System, Erie, PA
Primary Contact: C. Angela Bontempo, President and Chief Executive Officer
CMO: Richard Cogley, M.D., Senior Vice President Medical Affairs
CIO: Kerry Kerlin, Vice President Information Technology
Web address: www.svhs.org

| | 23 | 10 | 456 | 16133 | 235 | 155866 | 1655 | 194237 | 66616 | 2106 |

□ **SELECT SPECIALTY HOSPITAL–ERIE**, 201 State Street, Zip 16550; tel. 814/877–2774, (Nonreporting) **A**1 9 10
Primary Contact: Anne Frew, Chief Executive Officer

| | 33 | 49 | 35 | — | — | — | — | — | — | — |

□ **SHRINERS HOSPITALS FOR CHILDREN, ERIE**, 1645 West 8th Street, Zip 16505–5007; tel. 814/875–8700 **A**1 **F**27 28 29 46 48 52 58 60 62 63 64 65 66 67 69 88 94 108 **P**8 **S** Shriners Hospitals for Children, Tampa, FL
Primary Contact: Richard W. Brzuz, FACHE, Administrator
Web address: www.shrinershq.org

| | 23 | 57 | 30 | 792 | 6 | 8778 | 0 | — | — | 161 |

⊠ **VETERANS AFFAIRS MEDICAL CENTER**, 135 East 38th Street, Zip 16504–1596; tel. 814/860–2576, (Total facility includes 52 beds in nursing home–type unit) (Nonreporting) **A**1 9 **S** Department of Veterans Affairs, Washington, DC
Primary Contact: Michael Adelman, M.D., Acting Director
CFO: William Berg, Financial Manager
CMO: Michael Adelman, M.D., Chief of Staff
CIO: Brian Wilshire, Supervisor Information Systems
CHR: Lynn Nies, Human Resources Officer
Web address: www.va.gov/sta/guide/home.asp

| | 45 | 10 | 78 | — | — | — | — | — | — | — |

Many Facility Codes have changed. Please refer to the AHA Guide Code Chart. © 2005 AHA Guide

Hospital, Address, Telephone, Approval, Facility, and Physician Codes, Health Care System	Classi-fication Codes		Utilization Data					Expense (thousands) of dollars		
★ American Hospital Association (AHA) membership □ Joint Commission on Accreditation of Healthcare Organizations (JCAHO) accreditation ○ American Osteopathic Association (AOA) accreditation △ Commission on Accreditation of Rehabilitation Facilities (CARF) accreditation	Control	Service	Staffed Beds	Admissions	Census	Outpatient Visits	Births	Total	Payroll	Personnel

EVERETT—Bedford County

□ **UPMC BEDFORD MEMORIAL**, 10455 Lincoln Highway, Zip 15537–7046; tel. 814/623–6161 **A**1 9 10 20 **F**2 9 11 12 15 21 22 26 27 28 29 32 33 37 39 40 44 46 47 48 50 52 53 55 57 58 59 60 61 62 63 64 65 66 69 70 75 77 81 82 84 88 93 94 95 96 97 106 108 110 **S** University of Pittsburgh Medical Center, Pittsburgh, PA
Primary Contact: Roger P. Winn, President
Web address: www.bedford.org

| 23 | 10 | 27 | 2466 | 19 | 94616 | 249 | 26740 | 10756 | 325 |

FARRELL—Mercer County

SHENANGO VALLEY CAMPUS See UPMC Horizon, Greenville

FORT WASHINGTON—Montgomery County

□ **BROOKE GLEN BEHAVIORAL HOSPITAL**, (Formerly Northwestern Institute of Psychiatry), 7170 Lafayette Avenue, Zip 19034–0209; tel. 215/641–5300, (Nonreporting) **A**1 9 10 **S** Ardent Health Services, Nashville, TN
Primary Contact: Robert Fleming, Administrator

| 33 | 22 | 146 | — | — | — | — | — | — | — |

GETTYSBURG—Adams County

⊠ **GETTYSBURG HOSPITAL**, 147 Gettys Street, Zip 17325–2534; tel. 717/334–2121, (Total facility includes 19 beds in nursing home–type unit) **A**1 9 10 **F**2 9 11 12 15 21 22 23 24 26 27 28 29 30 33 37 42 46 48 51 52 53 55 58 59 60 61 63 64 66 69 81 82 84 88 92 93 94 95 96 106 108 109 **P**8 **S** WellSpan Health, York, PA
Primary Contact: Kevin H. Mosser, M.D., Chief Executive Officer
COO: Joseph H. Edgar, Senior Vice President Operations
CFO: Richard A. Harley, Senior Vice President Finance and Chief Financial Officer
CIO: Robin Kimple, Director Information Services
Web address: www.wellspan.org

| 23 | 10 | 95 | 4780 | 56 | 142087 | 505 | 58098 | 25206 | 567 |

GLENSIDE—Montgomery County

⊠ △ **CHESTNUT HILL REHABILITATION HOSPITAL**, 8601 Stenton Avenue, Zip 19038–8395; tel. 215/233–6200 **A**1 7 10 **F**1 2 7 8 26 27 28 29 30 32 37 44 45 46 51 52 54 58 60 66 68 69 73 75 76 88 91 94 95 96 108 110 **P**4
Primary Contact: Steven Carp, Director of Rehabilitation Services
CFO: Stuart Moss, Executive Vice President and Chief Financial Officer
CMO: Matthew Schwartz, M.D., Medical Director
CIO: Jack Nash, Vice President and Chief Information Officer
CHR: Paul Cavanaugh, Director Human Resources
Web address: www.chh.org

| 23 | 46 | 48 | 1291 | 34 | 24000 | 0 | 15293 | 6300 | 269 |

GREENSBURG—Westmoreland County

□ **EXCELA WESTMORELAND REGIONAL HOSPITAL**, (Formerly Westmoreland Regional Hospital), 532 West Pittsburgh Street, Zip 15601–2282; tel. 724/832–4000, (Total facility includes 46 beds in nursing home–type unit) **A**1 2 9 10 **F**2 4 7 9 10 11 12 14 15 17 19 21 22 24 26 28 29 30 31 32 33 35 36 37 39 40 44 45 46 47 48 50 51 52 53 55 57 58 59 60 61 62 63 64 65 66 68 69 70 71 72 73 74 75 76 77 78 79 80 81 82 84 86 87 88 92 93 94 95 96 98 106 108 109 110 **S** Excela Health, Greensburg, PA
Primary Contact: David S. Gallatin, Chief Executive Officer
Web address: www.excelahealth.org

| 23 | 10 | 290 | 15284 | 208 | 299432 | 1178 | 136024 | 55611 | 1562 |

□ **SELECT SPECIALTY HOSPITAL OF GREENSBURG**, 532 West Pittsburgh Street, Zip 15601; tel. 724/832–4210, (Nonreporting) **A**1 10
Primary Contact: Anthony Martino, Chief Executive Officer

| 33 | 49 | 31 | — | — | — | — | — | — | — |

GREENVILLE—Mercer County

□ **UPMC HORIZON**, (Includes GREENVILLE CAMPUS, 110 North Main Street, Zip 16125–1795; tel. 724/588–2100; SHENANGO VALLEY CAMPUS, 2200 Memorial Drive, Farrell, Zip 16121–1398; tel. 724/981–3500), (Total facility includes 36 beds in nursing home–type unit) **A**1 2 9 10 12 13 **F**1 2 7 9 10 11 12 15 21 22 23 24 26 27 28 29 30 32 33 34 35 37 39 41 42 44 45 46 47 48 52 53 55 57 58 59 60 61 62 63 64 65 66 68 69 70 81 82 84 85 87 88 92 93 94 95 96 97 106 108 109 110 **P**8 **S** University of Pittsburgh Medical Center, Pittsburgh, PA
Primary Contact: Dean Eckenrode, Chief Executive Officer
Web address: www.horizon.upmc.com

| 23 | 10 | 212 | 9363 | 125 | 197444 | 745 | 91407 | 37400 | 1070 |

GROVE CITY—Mercer County

○ **UNITED COMMUNITY HOSPITAL**, 631 North Broad Street Extension, Zip 16127–9703; tel. 724/458–5442, (Total facility includes 20 beds in nursing home–type unit) **A**9 10 11 **F**2 11 12 23 26 27 28 29 33 37 39 42 48 49 51 52 55 58 59 61 62 63 66 69 81 82 84 85 87 88 92 93 94 96 106 108 109 110
Primary Contact: Robert Jackson, Jr, Interim Chief Executive Officer
Web address: www.uchpa.org

| 23 | 10 | 101 | 3212 | 40 | — | 258 | — | — | 411 |

HANOVER—York County

□ **HANOVER HOSPITAL**, 300 Highland Avenue, Zip 17331–2297; tel. 717/637–3711 **A**1 9 10 **F**2 9 11 12 15 21 22 23 24 26 27 28 29 32 33 38 39 40 41 42 44 45 46 48 50 52 55 57 58 59 60 61 62 63 64 65 68 69 81 82 84 85 87 88 93 94 95 96 98 106 108 109 110 **P**8
Primary Contact: William R. Walb, CHE, President and Chief Executive Officer
Web address: www.hanoverhospital.org

| 23 | 10 | 119 | 5576 | 59 | 210282 | 683 | 78274 | 33511 | 917 |

HARRISBURG—Dauphin County

□ **HARRISBURG STATE HOSPITAL**, 2101 Cameron Street, Zip 17105–1300, Mailing Address: P.O. Box 61260, Zip 17106–1260; tel. 717/772–7455 **A**1 5 10 **F**21 22 30 32 45 58 66 71 74 76 94 106 108 **P**6
Primary Contact: Gregory M. Smith, Chief Executive Officer

| 12 | 22 | 264 | 119 | 264 | 0 | 0 | 42244 | — | 542 |

PA

Hospital, Address, Telephone, Approval, Facility, and Physician Codes, Health Care System	Classi-fication Codes		Utilization Data					Expense (thousands) of dollars		
★ American Hospital Association (AHA) membership □ Joint Commission on Accreditation of Healthcare Organizations (JCAHO) accreditation ○ American Osteopathic Association (AOA) accreditation △ Commission on Accreditation of Rehabilitation Facilities (CARF) accreditation	Control	Service	Staffed Beds	Admissions	Census	Outpatient Visits	Births	Total	Payroll	Personnel
□ **PINNACLEHEALTH SYSTEM**, 101 South Front Street, Zip 17101, Mailing Address: P.O. Box 8700, Zip 17105–8700; tel. 717/782-3131, (Includes PINNACLEHEALTH AT COMMUNITY GENERAL OSTEOPATHIC HOSPITAL, 4300 Londonderry Road, Zip 17109–5397; tel. 717/652–3000; PINNACLEHEALTH AT HARRISBURG HOSPITAL, 111 South Front Street, Zip 17101–2099; tel. 717/782–3131; PINNACLEHEALTH AT POLYCLINIC HOSPITAL, 2601 North Third Street, Zip 17110–2098; tel. 717/782–4141; PINNACLEHEALTH AT SEIDLE MEMORIAL HOSPITAL, 120 South Filbert Street, Mechanicsburg, Zip 17055–6591; tel. 717/795–6760), (Total facility includes 79 beds in nursing home–type unit) **A**1 2 3 5 9 10 12 13 **F**2 6 9 10 11 12 14 15 17 19 21 22 23 24 26 28 29 33 35 36 37 38 39 42 44 46 47 48 50 51 52 53 55 56 57 58 59 60 61 62 63 64 65 66 68 69 70 71 72 73 74 76 77 78 79 80 81 82 84 85 87 88 92 93 94 98 101 102 105 106 107 108 109 110 Primary Contact: Roger Longenderfer, M.D., President and Chief Executive Officer Web address: www.pinnaclehealth.org	23	10	700	32399	513	491957	4033	399864	154232	3751
□ **SCCI HOSPITAL – HARRISBURG**, 2601 North Third Street, Zip 17110; tel. 717/213–9944, (Nonreporting) **A**1 10 Primary Contact: Tammy Carben, Interim Chief Executive Officer	33	49	22	—	—	—	—	—	—	—
HASTINGS—Cambria County										
MINERS MEDICAL CENTER, 290 Haida Avenue, Zip 16646, Mailing Address: P.O. Box 689, Zip 16646-0689; tel. 814/247-3100 **A**9 10 20 **F**2 12 21 22 23 26 27 29 30 33 44 46 48 52 55 58 61 62 63 65 70 75 81 82 88 94 95 96 97 107 108 **P**8 Primary Contact: Michael K. Lauf, President Web address: www.minershosp.org	23	10	30	1212	13	46685	0	14101	4410	141
HAZLETON—Luzerne County										
⊞ △ **HAZLETON GENERAL HOSPITAL**, 700 East Broad Street, Zip 18201–6897; tel. 570/501–4000 **A**1 7 9 10 **F**2 9 21 23 26 27 28 29 33 35 37 39 45 46 47 48 49 52 53 54 55 58 59 61 62 63 65 66 68 72 81 87 88 93 94 108 110 **S** Greater Hazleton Health Alliance, Hazleton, PA Primary Contact: James Edwards, President COO: Lowell W. Johnson, Senior Vice President and Chief Operating Officer CFO: William Bauer, Vice President Finance and Chief Financial Officer CMO: Anthony Valente, M.D., Vice President Medical Affairs CIO: Carl Shoener, Chief Information Officer CHR: Timothy Farley, Vice President Human Resources Web address: www.ghha.org	23	10	127	5760	81	46357	546	—	—	—
⊞ **HAZLETON–ST. JOSEPH MEDICAL CENTER**, 687 North Church Street, Zip 18201–3198; tel. 570/501–6000 **A**1 9 10 **F**9 12 21 22 23 24 26 27 28 29 33 35 37 39 40 41 45 46 47 48 51 52 53 55 58 60 61 62 63 65 66 69 70 81 82 87 88 94 108 109 110 **S** Greater Hazleton Health Alliance, Hazleton, PA Primary Contact: James Edwards, President COO: Lowell W. Johnson, Senior Vice President and Chief Operating Officer CFO: William Bauer, Vice President Finance and Chief Financial Officer CMO: Anthony Valente, M.D., Vice President Medical Affairs CIO: Carl Shoener, Chief Information Officer CHR: Timothy Farley, Vice President Human Resources Web address: www.ghha.org	23	10	34	2702	34	77728	0	—	—	344
HERSHEY—Dauphin County										
⊞ △ **PENN STATE MILTON S. HERSHEY MEDICAL CENTER**, 500 University Drive, Zip 17033–0850, Mailing Address: P.O. Box 850, Zip 17033–0850; tel. 717/531–8521 **A**1 2 3 5 7 8 9 10 **F**2 6 7 10 11 12 15 16 17 18 19 20 21 22 23 24 26 28 29 30 33 34 35 37 38 39 40 41 42 44 46 47 48 49 50 52 53 55 56 57 58 59 60 61 62 63 64 65 66 67 68 69 70 71 72 73 74 75 76 77 78 79 80 81 82 83 84 85 86 87 88 89 90 92 93 94 95 96 98 99 100 101 105 106 108 109 110 **P**6 Primary Contact: Darrell G. Kirch, M.D., Chief Executive Officer COO: David Hefner, Executive Director and Chief Operating Officer CFO: Kevin Haley, Interim Chief Financial Officer CMO: Michael Weitekamp, M.D., Chief Medical Officer CIO: Thomas Abendroth, M.D., Chief Information Officer Web address: www.hmc.psu.edu	23	10	411	22359	344	476142	1328	424447	193185	5641
HONESDALE—Wayne County										
⊞ **WAYNE MEMORIAL HOSPITAL**, 601 Park Street, Zip 18431–1445; tel. 570/253–8100 **A**1 9 10 **F**9 11 12 23 26 27 28 29 30 32 33 36 41 42 44 46 48 50 51 52 58 59 60 61 62 63 65 69 77 81 82 84 88 94 95 96 97 98 106 108 **P**8 Primary Contact: David L. Hoff, Executive Director COO: John Conte, Director Facility Services CFO: Michael J. Clifford, Director Finance CMO: George Tietjen, M.D., Chief of Staff CIO: Tom Hoffman, Information Systems Manager CHR: Elizabeth McDonald, Director Human Resources Web address: www.wmh.org	23	10	90	4854	60	133770	430	49491	18529	489

Many Facility Codes have changed. Please refer to the AHA Guide Code Chart.

© 2005 AHA Guide

Hospital, Address, Telephone, Approval, Facility, and Physician Codes, Health Care System	Classi-fication Codes		Utilization Data					Expense (thousands) of dollars		
★ American Hospital Association (AHA) membership □ Joint Commission on Accreditation of Healthcare Organizations (JCAHO) accreditation ○ American Osteopathic Association (AOA) accreditation △ Commission on Accreditation of Rehabilitation Facilities (CARF) accreditation	Control	Service	Staffed Beds	Admissions	Census	Outpatient Visits	Births	Total	Payroll	Personnel

HUNTINGDON—Huntingdon County

⊠ **J. C. BLAIR MEMORIAL HOSPITAL**, 1225 Warm Springs Avenue, Zip 16652–2398; tel. 814/643–2290 **A**1 9 10 **F**2 9 11 12 21 26 27 28 29 33 46 47 48 52 53 55 59 63 64 65 66 71 72 75 76 78 81 82 84 87 88 93 94 96 97 106 108 **P**6 **S** Quorum Health Resources, Plano, TX
Primary Contact: Roger D. Feldt, FACHE, Interim President and Chief Executive Officer
CFO: Charles T. Glanville, Interim Chief Financial Officer
CMO: Daniel Delp, M.D., Chief of Staff
CIO: Steve Gildea, Director Management Information Systems
CHR: Michael Hubert, Vice President Human Resources
Web address: www.jcblair.org

| 23 | 10 | 71 | 3342 | 40 | 109401 | 293 | 33335 | 12988 | 337 |

INDIANA—Indiana County

★ **INDIANA REGIONAL MEDICAL CENTER**, 835 Hospital Road, Zip 15701–0788; Mailing Address: P.O. Box 788, Zip 15701–0788; tel. 724/357–7000 **A**2 9 10 20 **F**2 9 12 15 21 22 23 26 27 28 29 32 33 35 37 38 41 44 46 48 52 55 57 58 59 60 61 62 63 64 66 68 69 71 76 79 80 81 82 84 88 93 94 96 108 110
Primary Contact: Stephen A. Wolfe, President and Chief Executive Officer
COO: Dominic Paccapaniccia, Senior Vice President Operations
CFO: Larry J. Marshall, CPA, Senior Vice President Finance
CMO: Bruce A. Bush, M.D., Vice President Medical Affairs
CIO: Gene Burd, Management Information Systems Director
CHR: Matt Reading, Director Human Resources
Web address: www.indianarmc.org

| 23 | 10 | 162 | 7705 | 95 | 225874 | 660 | 80295 | 34334 | 864 |

JEANNETTE—Westmoreland County

⊠ **MERCY JEANNETTE HOSPITAL**, 600 Jefferson Avenue, Zip 15644–2599; tel. 724/527–3551, (Total facility includes 11 beds in nursing home–type unit) **A**1 9 10 **F**2 9 10 11 12 14 21 22 23 26 27 28 29 31 33 35 37 38 39 42 44 45 46 48 49 52 53 55 57 58 59 61 62 63 64 65 66 68 69 71 73 74 75 76 81 82 84 87 88 92 94 96 106 108 109 110 **P**6 7 **S** Catholic Health East, Newtown Square, PA
Primary Contact: Julie A. Hester, Administrator
CFO: Kevin B. May, Executie Director Finance
CMO: Bassam K. Kharma, M.D., Chairman, Department of Medicine
CIO: Laurel Bistko, Director Information Systems
CHR: Theresa Drye, Manager Human Resources
Web address: www.jdmh.org/

| 23 | 10 | 138 | 5586 | 70 | 131054 | 552 | 49892 | 19956 | 479 |

MONSOUR MEDICAL CENTER, 70 Lincoln Way East, Zip 15644–3185; tel. 724/527–1511 **A**10 **F**2 3 9 12 13 14 21 25 27 28 29 31 33 37 40 42 44 51 52 55 56 57 58 61 62 63 67 68 71 72 73 74 75 76 81 82 88 92 94 106 107 108 **P**2
Primary Contact: John Bukovac, Chief Executive Officer

| 23 | 10 | 139 | 1752 | 37 | 19927 | 0 | 18167 | 7529 | 177 |

JENKINTOWN—Montgomery County

⊠ **HOLY REDEEMER HOSPITAL AND MEDICAL CENTER**, 1648 Huntingdon Pike, Zip 19046–8001; tel. 215/947–3000, (Total facility includes 31 beds in nursing home–type unit) **A**1 5 9 10 **F**2 8 9 11 12 14 15 17 21 22 23 24 26 27 28 29 32 33 36 37 38 39 41 44 45 46 47 48 50 51 52 54 55 56 57 58 59 60 61 62 63 64 65 66 69 70 71 73 76 80 81 82 85 88 92 93 94 95 96 98 106 108 109 110
Primary Contact: Michael B. Laign, President and Chief Executive Officer
COO: Mark T. Jones, Executive Vice President and System Chief Executive Officer
CFO: Russell R. Wagner, Senior Vice President Finance
CMO: Steven Ockrymiek, M.D., Senior Vice President
CIO: Anne Searle, Vice President and Chief Information Officer
CHR: Joseph J. Cassidy, R.N., Interim Vice President
Web address: www.holyredeemer.com

| 23 | 10 | 272 | 15725 | 197 | 337546 | 2280 | 150762 | 60532 | 1429 |

JERSEY SHORE—Lycoming County

⊠ **JERSEY SHORE HOSPITAL**, 1020 Thompson Street, Zip 17740–1794; tel. 570/398–0100 **A**1 9 10 18 **F**9 12 14 21 22 26 27 28 29 33 37 46 47 48 52 55 58 60 62 63 64 65 69 70 81 82 84 85 87 88 94 95 96 97 106 108 110 **P**6 **S** Quorum Health Resources, Plano, TX
Primary Contact: Louis A. Ditzel, Jr, President and Chief Executive Officer
COO: Mark A. O'Neill, Senior Vice President and Chief Financial Officer
CFO: Kurt Williams, Controller and Vice President Financial Services
CMO: Carmen Spinney, M.D., President Medical and Dental Staff
CHR: Trudi Alexander, Director Human Resources
Web address: www.jsh.org

| 23 | 10 | 25 | 1260 | 14 | 58288 | 0 | 17307 | 6837 | 224 |

JOHNSTOWN—Cambria County

⊠ **MEMORIAL MEDICAL CENTER**, (Formerly Conemaugh Memorial Medical Center), 1086 Franklin Street, Zip 15905–4398; tel. 814/534–9000, (Includes GOOD SAMARITAN MEDICAL CENTER, 1020 Franklin Street, Zip 15905–4186; tel. 814/533–1000) **A**1 2 3 5 6 9 10 12 **F**2 4 9 10 11 12 15 17 19 21 22 23 24 26 27 28 29 31 32 33 34 35 37 38 39 40 41 42 44 45 46 47 48 50 51 52 53 55 56 57 58 59 60 61 62 63 64 65 66 68 69 70 71 72 73 74 76 77 79 81 82 84 86 87 88 92 93 94 95 96 98 106 108 109 110 **P**5 7 8
Primary Contact: Steven E. Tucker, President
CFO: Edward De Pasquale, Chief Financial Officer
CMO: Scott A. Becker, Chief Executive Officer
CIO: Jim Perez, Interim Chief Information Officer
CHR: Susan Benya, Vice President
Web address: www.conemaugh.org

| 23 | 10 | 366 | 18153 | 256 | 418633 | 931 | 220200 | 81937 | 2482 |

Hospital, Address, Telephone, Approval, Facility, and Physician Codes, Health Care System	Classi-fication Codes		Utilization Data					Expense (thousands) of dollars		
★ American Hospital Association (AHA) membership □ Joint Commission on Accreditation of Healthcare Organizations (JCAHO) accreditation ○ American Osteopathic Association (AOA) accreditation △ Commission on Accreditation of Rehabilitation Facilities (CARF) accreditation	Control	Service	Staffed Beds	Admissions	Census	Outpatient Visits	Births	Total	Payroll	Personnel

□ **SELECT SPECIALTY HOSPITAL OF JOHNSTOWN**, 1086 Franklin Street, 6th Floor, Zip 15905; tel. 814/534–5000, (Nonreporting) **A**1 9 10	33	49	38	—	—	—	—	—	—	—
□ **UPMC LEE REGIONAL**, 320 Main Street, Zip 15901–1694; tel. 814/533–0123, (Total facility includes 18 beds in nursing home–type unit) **A**1 2 9 10 **F**6 9 11 12 14 21 22 26 27 28 29 31 33 36 37 41 42 44 45 46 48 51 52 55 56 57 58 59 60 62 63 65 68 69 70 75 81 82 84 88 89 92 93 94 96 106 107 108 109 110 **P**8 **S** University of Pittsburgh Medical Center, Pittsburgh, PA Primary Contact: Roger P. Winn, President Web address: www.upmc.edu/lee	23	10	209	7778	100	150257	708	92463	35753	1010
KANE—McKean County										
KANE COMMUNITY HOSPITAL, 4372 Route 5, Zip 16735, Mailing Address: 4372 Route 6, Zip 16735; tel. 814/837–8585 **A**9 10 20 **F**2 3 9 12 14 21 22 29 30 33 46 48 51 52 53 55 58 60 62 63 64 69 81 82 84 85 88 92 94 95 96 97 107 108 109 **P**4 Primary Contact: J. Gary Rhodes, Chief Executive Officer Web address: www.kanehosp.com	23	10	31	1607	16	33521	0	17613	7202	178
KINGSTON—Luzerne County										
□ **FIRST HOSPITAL WYOMING VALLEY**, 562 Wyoming Avenue, Zip 18704; tel. 570/552–3900, (Nonreporting) **A**1 9 10 Primary Contact: Joseph H. Knecht, Chief Executive Officer Web address: www.wvhcs.org	33	22	96	—	—	—	—	—	—	—
KITTANNING—Armstrong County										
ARMSTRONG COUNTY MEMORIAL HOSPITAL, One Nolte Drive, Zip 16201–8808; tel. 724/543–8500, (Total facility includes 17 beds in nursing home–type unit) **A**2 9 10 19 **F**9 11 12 14 15 21 22 23 26 27 28 29 33 37 39 40 46 47 48 52 55 58 59 60 61 62 63 64 66 68 69 70 71 73 74 75 76 79 80 81 82 83 84 85 86 87 88 92 93 94 95 96 108 110 Primary Contact: John I. Lewis, Chief Executive Officer Web address: www.acmh.org	23	10	147	7299	105	155473	647	65250	32234	781
LAFAYETTE HILL—Montgomery County										
EUGENIA HOSPITAL, 660 Thomas Road, Zip 19444–1199; tel. 215/836–7700, (Nonreporting) **A**9 10 **S** Progressions Group, Inc., Lafayette Hill, PA	33	22	126	—	—	—	—	—	—	—
LANCASTER—Lancaster County										
★ **LANCASTER GENERAL HOSPITAL**, 555 North Duke Street, Zip 17604–3555, Mailing Address: P.O. Box 3555, Zip 17604–3555; tel. 717/290–5511 **A**1 2 3 5 6 9 10 **F**2 9 11 12 15 17 19 21 22 23 24 26 27 28 29 32 33 34 35 37 39 42 43 44 46 47 48 49 50 52 53 55 56 57 58 59 60 61 62 63 64 65 66 68 69 70 71 75 79 80 81 82 85 86 87 88 92 93 94 96 106 108 109 110 **P**6 Primary Contact: Thomas E. Beeman, President and Chief Executive Officer CFO: F Joseph Byorick, Senior Vice President Finance CMO: Bruce H. Pokorney, M.D., Senior Vice President Medical Affairs CIO: Leonard Martin, Vice President Information Services Web address: www.lancastergeneral.org	23	10	521	31086	420	1064438	4697	452420	177522	3993
□ △ **LANCASTER REGIONAL MEDICAL CENTER**, 250 College Avenue, Zip 17603, Mailing Address: P.O. Box 3434, Zip 17604–3434; tel. 717/291–8211, (Total facility includes 21 beds in nursing home–type unit) (Nonreporting) **A**1 7 9 10 **S** Health Management Associates, Naples, FL Primary Contact: Brad K. Nurkin, Chief Executive Officer	23	10	226	—	—	—	—	—	—	—
□ **SELECT SPECIALTY HOSPITAL–LANCASTER**, 555 North Duke Street, Zip 17604; tel. 717/544–5401, (Nonreporting) **A**1 10 Primary Contact: Terrie Dittmeyer, Chief Executive Officer	33	49	30	—	—	—	—	—	—	—
LANGHORNE—Bucks County										
BUCKS COUNTY CAMPUS See Frankford Hospital of the City of Philadelphia, Philadelphia										
★ **ST. MARY MEDICAL CENTER**, Langhorne–Newtown Road, Zip 19047–1295; tel. 215/710–2000, (Nonreporting) **A**1 2 9 10 **S** Catholic Health East, Newtown Square, PA Primary Contact: Gregory T. Wozniak, President and Chief Executive Officer CFO: Edward Maher, Chief Financial Officer and Vice President Finance CMO: Joseph Conroy, M.D., Vice President Medical Affairs CIO: Kirk Erwin, Director Information Technology and Communications CHR: Marcia Telthorster, Vice President Human Resources Web address: www.stmaryhealthcare.org	21	10	262	—	—	—	—	—	—	—
LANSDALE—Montgomery County										
□ **CENTRAL MONTGOMERY MEDICAL CENTER**, 100 Medical Campus Drive, Zip 19446–1200; tel. 215/368–2100 **A**1 2 9 10 **F**2 9 11 12 14 21 22 23 26 27 28 29 32 33 37 57 59 60 61 62 63 68 69 81 82 88 94 96 108 110 **S** Universal Health Services, Inc., King of Prussia, PA Primary Contact: George E. Miller, Chief Executive Officer Web address: www.cmmc–uhs.com	31	10	119	5520	73	—	502	—	—	499

Hospital, Address, Telephone, Approval, Facility, and Physician Codes, Health Care System	Classi-fication Codes		Utilization Data					Expense (thousands) of dollars		
★ American Hospital Association (AHA) membership □ Joint Commission on Accreditation of Healthcare Organizations (JCAHO) accreditation ○ American Osteopathic Association (AOA) accreditation △ Commission on Accreditation of Rehabilitation Facilities (CARF) accreditation	Control	Service	Staffed Beds	Admissions	Census	Outpatient Visits	Births	Total	Payroll	Personnel

LATROBE—Westmoreland County

★ **EXCELA LATROBE AREA HOSPITAL**, (Formerly Latrobe Area Hospital), 121 West Second Avenue, Zip 15650–1096; tel. 724/537–1000, (Total facility includes 20 beds in nursing home–type unit) **A**1 2 3 5 9 10 **F**2 6 9 10 11 12 15 17 19 21 22 24 26 27 28 29 31 33 35 36 37 39 40 41 42 45 46 47 48 51 52 53 55 57 58 59 60 61 62 63 64 65 66 69 70 71 72 73 74 75 76 77 78 80 81 82 84 85 87 88 92 93 94 96 106 108 109 110 **P**6 **S** Excela Health, Greensburg, PA
Primary Contact: Douglas A. Clark, FACHE, President
COO: Louis A. Sciullo, Associate Director Operations
CFO: Robert S. Thornton, Associate Director and Chief Financial Officer
CIO: Joseph Dado, Associate Director and Chief Information Officer
CHR: Jill Clements, Associate Director and Chief Human Resources Officer
Web address: www.lah.com
— 23 10 188 11122 141 381330 548 118383 56948 1186

LEBANON—Lebanon County

★ **THE GOOD SAMARITAN HOSPITAL**, Fourth and Walnut Streets, Zip 17042–1281, Mailing Address: P.O. Box 1281, Zip 17042–1281; tel. 717/270–7500, (Total facility includes 19 beds in nursing home–type unit) **A**1 3 5 9 10 13 **F**2 9 11 12 21 22 23 26 27 28 29 30 32 33 36 37 40 41 48 49 51 52 53 55 58 59 60 61 63 66 68 69 81 82 84 85 87 88 92 93 94 96 106 107 108 110 **P**8
Primary Contact: Robert J. Longo, CHE, President and Chief Executive Officer
COO: Stephanie Thompson, Vice President Nursing Services
CFO: Robert J. Richards, Vice President Finance and Chief Financial Officer
CMO: Mark Jacobson, D.O., Vice President Medical Affairs
CIO: Richard Follett, Director Information Services
CHR: Kimberly Feeman, Vice President Human Resources
Web address: www.gshleb.org
— 23 10 176 9800 124 221113 1040 103045 42000 1211

★ **VETERANS AFFAIRS MEDICAL CENTER**, 1700 South Lincoln Avenue, Zip 17042–7529; tel. 717/272–6621, (Total facility includes 144 beds in nursing home–type unit) **A**1 3 5 9 **F**2 3 4 21 22 23 26 27 28 29 32 33 35 36 37 38 39 41 42 44 45 46 47 48 51 52 53 55 57 58 60 61 62 63 65 66 69 70 71 72 73 75 76 77 78 81 88 92 94 96 106 107 108 109 110 **P**6 **S** Department of Veterans Affairs, Washington, DC
Primary Contact: Terry M. Gerigk, Director
COO: Steven Gallerizzo, Acting Associate Director
CFO: Jeffrey Beiler, Financial Manager
CMO: Ana Mello, M.D., Chief of Staff
CIO: Ray Bush, Manager Information Management
CHR: Ray Kent, Human Resources Manager
Web address: www.va.gov/sta/guide/home.asp
— 45 10 257 3040 214 259435 0 136755 54471 1107

LEHIGHTON—Carbon County

★ △ **GNADEN HUETTEN MEMORIAL HOSPITAL**, 211 North 12th Street, Zip 18235–1138; tel. 610/377–1300, (Total facility includes 91 beds in nursing home–type unit) **A**1 7 9 10 **F**2 9 11 12 21 22 26 27 28 29 32 33 37 41 42 44 46 47 48 49 51 52 53 54 55 57 58 59 60 62 63 65 66 68 69 70 71 72 73 74 75 76 78 81 82 84 86 88 92 94 95 96 106 108 109 110 **P**8 **S** Blue Mountain Health System, Lehighton, PA
Primary Contact: Robert J. Clark, FACHE, President and Chief Executive Officer
CFO: Richard J. Hager, Senior Vice President and Chief Financial Officer
CIO: George Sanchez, Director Information Services
CHR: Terry Purcell, Vice President Human Resources
Web address: www.bluemountainhealthsystem.org
— 23 10 202 4442 150 138528 293 46755 18868 529

LEWISBURG—Union County

EVANGELICAL COMMUNITY HOSPITAL, One Hospital Drive, Zip 17837–9314; tel. 570/522–2000 **A**9 10 19 **F**2 6 9 10 11 12 14 21 23 24 27 29 32 33 36 37 38 40 41 42 44 45 46 47 48 51 52 55 57 58 59 60 61 62 63 65 68 69 70 79 81 82 84 85 86 87 88 92 93 94 95 96 106 108 109 110 **P**3 5
Primary Contact: Michael N. O'Keefe, President and Chief Executive Officer
Web address: www.evanhospital.com
— 23 10 136 6817 72 197577 925 78730 34019 867

U. S. PENITENTIARY INFIRMARY, Route 7, Zip 17837–9303; tel. 570/523–1251, (Nonreporting)
Primary Contact: Arnold Reyes, Administrator
— 48 11 17 — — — — — — —

LEWISTOWN—Mifflin County

★ **LEWISTOWN HOSPITAL**, 400 Highland Avenue, Zip 17044–1198; tel. 717/248–5411 **A**1 2 5 9 10 19 **F**2 9 11 12 14 21 22 23 26 27 28 29 33 36 37 39 40 44 46 48 51 52 53 55 57 58 59 60 61 62 63 64 65 66 69 70 71 72 73 74 75 76 77 80 81 82 84 85 86 87 88 93 94 96 106 108 109 110 **P**6
Primary Contact: A. Gordon McAleer, FACHE, President and Chief Executive Officer
CFO: Randy Tewksbury, Vice President Finance
CIO: Ron Cowan, Chief Information Officer
CHR: N Sue Reinke, Vice President Human Resources
Web address: www.lewistownhospital.org
— 23 10 123 7498 84 205079 556 62602 26433 657

LITITZ—Lancaster County

□ **HEART OF LANCASTER REGIONAL MEDICAL CENTER**, 1500 Highlands Avenue, Zip 17543; tel. 717/625–5000, (Nonreporting) **A**1 9 10 12 13 **S** Health Management Associates, Naples, FL
Primary Contact: Lee Christenson, Chief Executive Officer
Web address: www.chol.org
— 33 10 139 — — — — — — —

Hospital, Address, Telephone, Approval, Facility, and Physician Codes, Health Care System	Classi-fication Codes		Utilization Data					Expense (thousands) of dollars		
★ American Hospital Association (AHA) membership □ Joint Commission on Accreditation of Healthcare Organizations (JCAHO) accreditation ○ American Osteopathic Association (AOA) accreditation △ Commission on Accreditation of Rehabilitation Facilities (CARF) accreditation	Control	Service	Staffed Beds	Admissions	Census	Outpatient Visits	Births	Total	Payroll	Personnel

LOCK HAVEN—Clinton County

□ **LOCK HAVEN HOSPITAL**, 24 Cree Drive, Zip 17745–2699; tel. 570/893–5000, (Total facility includes 120 beds in nursing home–type unit) (Nonreporting) **A**1 9 10 **S** Community Health Systems, Inc., Brentwood, TN
Primary Contact: John C. Yanes, Chief Executive Officer
Web address: www.lhhospital.com

| | 33 | 10 | 195 | — | — | — | — | — | — | — |

MALVERN—Chester County

□ △ **BRYN MAWR REHABILITATION HOSPITAL**, 414 Paoli Pike, Zip 19355–3300, Mailing Address: P.O. Box 3007, Zip 19355–3300; tel. 610/251–5400 **A**1 7 10 **F**21 26 27 28 29 37 42 44 52 57 60 61 62 65 66 68 69 92 94 96 108 110 **P**5 **S** Jefferson Health System, Wayne, PA
Primary Contact: Donna Phillips, President
Web address: www.mainlinehealth.org

| | 23 | 46 | 143 | 3852 | 132 | 28855 | 0 | 43612 | 21959 | 493 |

□ **DEVEREUX CHILDREN'S BEHAVIORAL HEALTH CENTER**, 655 Sugartown Road, Zip 19355–0275, Mailing Address: P.O. Box 275, Zip 19355–0275; tel. 484/595–6777, (Nonreporting) **A**1 **S** Devereux, Villanova, PA
Primary Contact: Walter J. Grono, Executive Director
Web address: www.devereux.org

| | 23 | 22 | 13 | — | — | — | — | — | — | — |

MALVERN INSTITUTE, 940 King Road, Zip 19355–3167; tel. 610/647–0330, (Nonreporting) **A**9 **S** Progressions Group, Inc., Lafayette Hill, PA
Primary Contact: Richard Mangano, Administrator and Chief Executive Officer

| | 33 | 82 | 40 | — | — | — | — | — | — | — |

MCCONNELLSBURG—Fulton County

★ **FULTON COUNTY MEDICAL CENTER**, 216 South First Street, Zip 17233–1399; tel. 717/485–3155, (Total facility includes 57 beds in nursing home–type unit) **A**9 10 18 **F**2 9 12 21 26 27 28 33 39 46 48 51 52 53 55 58 60 63 66 69 81 84 85 88 92 94 96 97 106 108 110 **P**6
Primary Contact: Jason F. Hawkins, Interim President and Chief Executive
CFO: Jason F. Hawkins, Chief Financial Officer
CMO: James N. Rintoul, M.D., President Medical Staff
CIO: Harold M. Gress, Jr, Manager Management Information Systems
CHR: Lynne M. Hixson, Manager Human Resources
Web address: www.fcmc–pa.org

| | 23 | 10 | 82 | 1262 | 69 | 43531 | 0 | 18974 | 9494 | 269 |

MCKEES ROCKS—Allegheny County

✠ **OHIO VALLEY GENERAL HOSPITAL**, 25 Heckel Road, Zip 15136–1694; tel. 412/777–6161 **A**1 6 9 10 **F**2 8 11 12 15 21 22 28 33 37 40 46 48 49 55 58 59 60 62 63 64 68 69 81 82 84 85 87 88 93 94 108 110 **P**6 **S** Quorum Health Resources, Plano, TX
Primary Contact: William F. Provenzano, President and Chief Executive Officer
CFO: William J. Day, Vice President Finance
CIO: Joyce Polovich, Director Information Mangement
CHR: Vicki Mell, Vice President Human Resources
Web address: www.ohiovalleyhospital.org

| | 23 | 10 | 89 | 4731 | 67 | 119434 | 279 | 52425 | 19006 | 453 |

MCKEESPORT—Allegheny County

□ **UPMC MCKEESPORT**, 1500 Fifth Avenue, Zip 15132–2482; tel. 412/664–2000, (Total facility includes 19 beds in nursing home–type unit) **A**1 3 5 9 10 12 13 **F**2 9 12 14 15 21 22 23 24 26 27 28 29 33 39 42 44 45 46 47 48 49 50 51 52 53 55 57 58 60 61 62 63 65 66 68 69 70 71 74 75 76 79 80 81 82 84 88 92 93 94 95 96 98 106 108 109 110 **S** University of Pittsburgh Medical Center, Pittsburgh, PA
Primary Contact: Ronald H. Ott, President
Web address: www.mckeesport.upmc.com

| | 23 | 10 | 181 | 9653 | 162 | — | 0 | — | — | 972 |

MEADVILLE—Crawford County

✠ **MEADVILLE MEDICAL CENTER**, 751 Liberty Street, Zip 16335–2555; tel. 814/333–5000, (Total facility includes 32 beds in nursing home–type unit) **A**1 2 9 10 12 13 19 20 **F**2 3 4 9 10 11 12 15 21 22 23 24 27 28 29 30 31 33 36 37 41 44 45 46 48 49 51 52 55 57 58 59 60 61 62 63 64 65 66 68 69 71 73 74 75 76 81 84 87 88 92 93 94 95 96 106 108 109 110 **P**6
Primary Contact: Anthony J. DeFail, FACHE, President and Chief Executive Officer
CFO: Dave Poland, Chief Financial Officer
CMO: David McNamara, M.D., Medical Director
CIO: Mark Mahoney, Manager Information Systems
Web address: www.mmchs.org

| | 23 | 10 | 248 | 8519 | 132 | 161017 | 531 | 79413 | 32163 | 913 |

MECHANICSBURG—Cumberland County

✠ **HEALTHSOUTH REGIONAL SPECIALTY HOSPITAL**, (Formerly HEALTHSOUTH Rehabilitation for Special Services), 4950 Wilson Lane, Zip 17055; tel. 717/697–7706, (Nonreporting) **A**1 9 10 **S** HEALTHSOUTH Corporation, Birmingham, AL
Primary Contact: Brent Burger, Administrator

| | 33 | 46 | 46 | — | — | — | — | — | — | — |

✠ **HEALTHSOUTH REHABILITATION OF MECHANICSBURG**, 175 Lancaster Boulevard, Zip 17055–0736, Mailing Address: P.O. Box 2016, Zip 17055–2016; tel. 717/691–3700, (Nonreporting) **A**1 9 10 **S** HEALTHSOUTH Corporation, Birmingham, AL
Primary Contact: Gregory P. Toot, Administrator and Chief Executive Officer
CMO: Michael Lupinacci, M.D., Medical Director
CHR: Joe Powell, Director Human Resources
Web address: www.healthsouth.com

| | 33 | 46 | 103 | — | — | — | — | — | — | — |

PINNACLEHEALTH AT SEIDLE MEMORIAL HOSPITAL See PinnacleHealth System, Harrisburg

Hospital, Address, Telephone, Approval, Facility, and Physician Codes, Health Care System	Classification Codes		Utilization Data					Expense (thousands) of dollars		
★ American Hospital Association (AHA) membership ☐ Joint Commission on Accreditation of Healthcare Organizations (JCAHO) accreditation ◯ American Osteopathic Association (AOA) accreditation △ Commission on Accreditation of Rehabilitation Facilities (CARF) accreditation	Control	Service	Staffed Beds	Admissions	Census	Outpatient Visits	Births	Total	Payroll	Personnel

MEDIA—Delaware County

✠ **RIDDLE MEMORIAL HOSPITAL**, 1068 West Baltimore Pike, Zip 19063–5177; tel. 610/566–9400, (Total facility includes 23 beds in nursing home–type unit) **A**1 2 9 10 **F**2 4 6 9 11 12 21 22 23 24 26 27 28 29 30 32 33 35 37 39 41 44 46 48 50 51 52 53 55 56 57 58 59 60 61 62 63 65 66 69 70 73 81 82 84 85 86 87 88 91 92 93 94 95 96 98 106 108 109 110 **P**6 7
Primary Contact: Daniel E. Kennedy, President and Chief Executive Officer
COO: Robert J. Santilli, Vice President and Chief Operating Officer
CFO: Ronald W. Eyler, Vice President and Chief Financial Officer
CMO: George Lieb, M.D., President Medical Executive Committee
CIO: Denis Tucker, Director Information Services
CHR: Thom Rossi, Director Human Resources
Web address: www.riddlehospital.org
| 23 | 10 | 189 | 11697 | 158 | 111678 | 1270 | 102919 | 45801 | 1049 |

MEYERSDALE—Somerset County

☐ **MEYERSDALE MEDICAL CENTER**, 200 Hospital Drive, Zip 15552–1249; tel. 814/634–5911 **A**1 9 10 18 **F**12 21 26 33 46 48 52 60 63 64 81 88 94 96 97
Primary Contact: Mary L. Libengood, President
Web address: www.conemaugh.org
| 23 | 10 | 20 | 625 | 7 | 26959 | 0 | 6520 | 2565 | 92 |

MONONGAHELA—Washington County

✠ **MONONGAHELA VALLEY HOSPITAL**, 1163 Country Club Road, Rt 88, Zip 15063–1095; tel. 724/258–1000 **A**1 2 9 10 **F**2 7 9 10 11 12 14 15 17 21 22 23 24 26 27 28 29 32 33 37 39 42 44 46 47 48 50 52 53 55 57 58 59 60 61 62 63 64 65 66 68 69 71 73 74 75 76 79 80 81 82 85 87 88 93 94 95 96 106 108 109 110 **P**8
Primary Contact: Louis J. Panza, Jr, President and Chief Executive Officer
COO: Patrick J. Alberts, Senior Vice President and Chief Operating Officer
CFO: Daniel F. Simmons, Chief Financial Officer
CIO: Sandra Osborne, Director Information Systems
CHR: David Clark, Vice President Human Resources
Web address: www.monvalleyhospital.com
| 23 | 10 | 253 | 11165 | 156 | 232605 | 531 | 90967 | 40274 | 1012 |

MONROEVILLE—Allegheny County

✠ **FORBES REGIONAL HOSPITAL**, 2570 Haymaker Road, Zip 15146–3592; tel. 412/858–2000 **A**1 3 5 9 10 **F**9 10 11 12 15 16 21 22 23 26 27 28 29 33 35 36 37 38 39 41 44 45 46 48 52 53 54 55 57 58 59 61 62 63 65 66 68 69 71 75 76 77 81 82 84 85 86 87 88 94 96 106 108 **S** West Penn Allegheny Health System, Pittsburgh, PA
Primary Contact: Thomas J. Senker, President and Chief Executive Officer
COO: Darlette Tice, Vice President Operations and Chief Nursing Executive
CFO: Richard C. Chesnos, Vice President Operations and Chief Financial Officer
CMO: Joseph Grennan, M.D., Medical Director and Vice President Clinical Quality and Resource Management
CIO: Sharon Lewis, Client Service Manager
CHR: Rebecca Trumble, Director Human Resources
Web address: www.wpahs.org
| 23 | 10 | 231 | 13527 | 185 | 201591 | 1011 | 106372 | 43179 | 1289 |

✠ **HEALTHSOUTH HOSPITAL OF PITTSBURGH**, (Formerly HEALTHSOUTH Rehabilitation Hospital of Greater Pittsburgh), 2380 McGinley Road, Zip 15146–4400; tel. 412/856–2400 **A**1 9 10 **F**7 21 26 28 29 42 45 52 58 60 62 65 66 69 88 94 95 96 108 110 **S** HEALTHSOUTH Corporation, Birmingham, AL
Primary Contact: Timothy Bugin, Chief Operating Officer
CMO: Herbert Kunkel, Jr, M.D., Medical Director
CIO: Justin Armstrong, Chief Information Officer
CHR: Leslie Cunningham, Chief Human Resources Officer
Web address: www.healthsouth.com
| 33 | 80 | 89 | 848 | 58 | 33857 | 0 | 22628 | 11081 | 264 |

MONTROSE—Susquehanna County

ENDLESS MOUNTAIN HEALTH SYSTEMS, 1 Grow Avenue, Zip 18801–1199; tel. 570/278–3801 **A**9 10 18 **F**21 26 28 29 33 41 44 46 48 55 58 63 69 81 88 94 96 97 106 **P**4
Primary Contact: Rex Catlin, Administrator
Web address: www.endlesscare.org
| 23 | 10 | 22 | 1105 | 11 | 61099 | 0 | 9225 | 3929 | 138 |

MOUNT GRETNA—Lebanon County

☐ **PHILHAVEN, BEHAVIORAL HEALTHCARE SERVICES**, 283 South Butler Road, Zip 17064–0550, Mailing Address: P.O. Box 550, Zip 17064–0550; tel. 717/273–8871 **A**1 9 10 **F**26 27 71 72 73 74 75 76 77 78 94 108 **P**6
Primary Contact: LaVern J. Yutzy, Chief Executive Officer
Web address: www.philhaven.com
| 21 | 22 | 83 | 2155 | 55 | 77498 | 0 | 35258 | 23899 | 737 |

MOUNT PLEASANT—Westmoreland County

✠ **EXCELA FRICK HOSPITAL**, (Formerly Frick Hospital), 508 South Church Street, Zip 15666–1790; tel. 724/547–1500, (Total facility includes 18 beds in nursing home–type unit) **A**1 2 9 10 **F**1 2 9 11 12 14 21 22 26 27 28 29 31 32 33 37 44 45 46 47 48 50 51 52 55 57 58 59 60 61 62 63 64 65 66 69 81 82 84 87 88 92 93 94 95 96 98 106 108 **S** Excela Health, Greensburg, PA
Primary Contact: David S. Gallatin, Chief Executive Officer
COO: Samuel Raneri, Chief Operating Officer
CFO: Richard Caruso, Vice President Finance
CMO: Angelo DeMezza, M.D., Senior Vice President Medical Affairs
CIO: Joseph Dado, Associate Director and Chief Information Officer
CHR: Mark P. Frick, Vice President Human Resources
Web address: www.frickhospital.org
| 23 | 10 | 100 | 5492 | 70 | 92072 | 143 | 42007 | 18059 | 466 |

Hospital, Address, Telephone, Approval, Facility, and Physician Codes, Health Care System	Classi-fication Codes		Utilization Data					Expense (thousands) of dollars		
★ American Hospital Association (AHA) membership □ Joint Commission on Accreditation of Healthcare Organizations (JCAHO) accreditation ○ American Osteopathic Association (AOA) accreditation △ Commission on Accreditation of Rehabilitation Facilities (CARF) accreditation	Control	Service	Staffed Beds	Admissions	Census	Outpatient Visits	Births	Total	Payroll	Personnel

MUNCY—Lycoming County

MUNCY VALLEY HOSPITAL See Susquehanna Health System, Williamsport

NANTICOKE—Luzerne County

★ **MERCY SPECIAL CARE HOSPITAL**, 128 West Washington Street, Zip 18634–3113; tel. 570/735–5000 **A**9 10 **F**9 21 22 26 27 28 36 37 38 42 44 46 52 58 71 74 75 76 77 78 91 93 94 96 107 108 110 **S** Catholic Healthcare Partners, Cincinnati, OH
Primary Contact: Robert D. Williams, Vice President and Administrator
CFO: Stephen Franko, Chief Financial Officer
Web address: www.mhs–nepa.com

| 21 | 10 | 56 | 645 | 48 | — | 0 | — | — | 127 |

NATRONA HEIGHTS—Allegheny County

⊠ **ALLE–KISKI MEDICAL CENTER**, 1301 Carlisle Street, Zip 15065–1192; tel. 724/224–5100 **A**1 2 9 10 **F**2 9 11 12 14 15 19 21 22 23 27 28 29 31 32 33 34 36 37 40 42 44 45 46 47 48 52 53 55 57 58 59 60 61 62 63 64 65 66 69 71 73 74 75 76 79 80 81 82 83 84 85 86 87 88 92 93 94 95 96 97 106 107 108 109 110 **S** West Penn Allegheny Health System, Pittsburgh, PA
Primary Contact: Cindy K. Schamp, President
CFO: George Sandora, Director Finance
CIO: Linda Fergus, Director Information Systems
Web address: www.wpahs.org

| 23 | 10 | 250 | 11915 | 159 | 166466 | 482 | 94369 | 38381 | 1161 |

NEW CASTLE—Lawrence County

⊠ **JAMESON HOSPITAL**, 1211 Wilmington Avenue, Zip 16105–2595; tel. 724/658–9001, (Total facility includes 20 beds in nursing home–type unit) **A**1 2 6 9 10 **F**2 8 9 11 12 15 17 21 22 23 24 26 27 28 29 31 33 34 36 37 40 44 46 47 48 51 52 53 55 58 59 60 63 65 66 68 69 71 74 75 76 78 81 82 84 85 87 88 92 93 94 96 106 108 109 110
Primary Contact: Thomas White, President and Chief Executive Officer
COO: Donald E. Melonio, Executive Vice President and Chief Operating Officer
CFO: James Aubel, Chief Financial Officer
CMO: William Gilleland, Jr, M.D., Medical Staff President
CIO: James Aubel, Director Fiscal Services and Information Management Services
CHR: Neil A. Chessin, Vice President
Web address: www.jamesonhealthsystem.com

| 23 | 10 | 238 | 12603 | 173 | 270361 | 566 | 99841 | 44445 | 1264 |

NORRISTOWN—Montgomery County

⊠ ○ **MERCY SUBURBAN HOSPITAL**, 2701 DeKalb Pike, Zip 19401–1820; tel. 610/278–2000 **A**1 2 9 10 11 12 13 **F**2 9 11 12 21 22 23 26 27 28 29 30 31 32 33 35 36 37 38 39 44 46 48 50 51 52 55 57 58 59 60 61 62 63 64 66 69 70 71 74 76 79 81 82 84 85 86 87 88 92 94 96 106 108 109 110 **P**7 **S** Catholic Health East, Newtown Square, PA
Primary Contact: Mark C. Barabas, President and Chief Executive Officer
CFO: Peter B. Kenniff, CPA, Chief Financial Officer
CMO: Bernard C. McDonnell, D.O., Vice President Medical Affairs
Web address: www.mercyhealth.org

| 21 | 10 | 141 | 7509 | 95 | 93151 | 786 | 81829 | — | 778 |

MONTGOMERY COUNTY EMERGENCY SERVICE, 50 Beech Drive, Zip 19403–5421; tel. 610/279–6100 **A**9 10 **F**3 4 6 21 27 29 31 52 71 72 73 74 75 76 77 94 **P**6
Primary Contact: Rocio Nell, M.D., Chief Executive Officer and Medical Director
Web address: www.mces.org

| 23 | 22 | 80 | 2881 | 68 | 3248 | 0 | 13742 | 8520 | 204 |

⊠ **MONTGOMERY HOSPITAL MEDICAL CENTER**, 1301 Powell Street, Zip 19401–3377, Mailing Address: P.O. Box 992, Zip 19404–0992; tel. 610/270–2000 **A**1 2 3 5 9 10 **F**2 9 11 12 14 21 22 23 26 27 28 29 33 35 36 37 39 40 43 44 45 46 47 48 49 51 52 53 55 57 58 59 60 61 62 63 64 66 69 70 71 72 73 74 75 76 78 80 81 82 84 85 88 93 94 96 106 108 109 110 **P**6
Primary Contact: Timothy M. Casey, President and Chief Executive Officer
CFO: Edward Ladely, Senior Vice President and Chief Financial Officer
CIO: Ed Hemschoot, Director Information Systems
CHR: Dan B. Williams, Senior Vice President and Chief Human Resources Officer
Web address: www.montgomeryhospital.com

| 23 | 10 | 166 | 8419 | 100 | 175922 | 659 | 80929 | 38511 | 788 |

□ **NORRISTOWN STATE HOSPITAL**, 1001 Sterigere Street, Zip 19401–5300; tel. 610/270–1000, (Nonreporting) **A**1 5 9 10
Primary Contact: Marguerite M. Conley, Chief Executive Officer

| 12 | 22 | 664 | — | — | — | — | — | — | — |

⊠ **VALLEY FORGE MEDICAL CENTER AND HOSPITAL**, 1033 West Germantown Pike, Zip 19403–3998; tel. 610/539–8500 **A**1 10 **F**2 3 21 27 28 33 50 53 58 73 94 96 **P**6
Primary Contact: Marian W. Colcher, President
CFO: Gregg Y. Slocum, Chief Financial Officer
CMO: Robert E. Colcher, M.D., Medical Director
Web address: www.vfmc.net

| 33 | 82 | 78 | 1554 | 68 | 21 | 0 | 10937 | 6345 | 136 |

OAKDALE—Allegheny County

⊠ **KINDRED HOSPITAL-PITTSBURGH**, 7777 Steubenville Pike, Zip 15071–3409; tel. 412/494–5500, (Nonreporting) **A**1 9 10 **S** Kindred Healthcare, Louisville, KY
Primary Contact: Gregory J. Kuntz, Chief Executive Officer
COO: Susan Colpo, Chief Operating Officer
CFO: Kevin Varley, Chief Financial Officer
CMO: Mark Lega, M.D., Medical Director
CIO: Kurt Segeleon, Director Health Information Management
CHR: Nancy Smocynski, Payroll/Personnel and Human Resource Director
Web address: www.kindredhealthcare.com

| 33 | 49 | 63 | — | — | — | — | — | — | — |

Many Facility Codes have changed. Please refer to the AHA Guide Code Chart.   © 2005 AHA Guide

Hospital, Address, Telephone, Approval, Facility, and Physician Codes, Health Care System	Classi-fication Codes		Utilization Data					Expense (thousands) of dollars		
★ American Hospital Association (AHA) membership □ Joint Commission on Accreditation of Healthcare Organizations (JCAHO) accreditation ○ American Osteopathic Association (AOA) accreditation △ Commission on Accreditation of Rehabilitation Facilities (CARF) accreditation	Control	Service	Staffed Beds	Admissions	Census	Outpatient Visits	Births	Total	Payroll	Personnel

OREFIELD—Lehigh County

KIDSPEACE CHILDREN'S HOSPITAL, (Formerly National Hospital for Kids in Crisis), 5300 Kids Peace Drive, Zip 18069–9101; tel. 610/799–8800 **A**9 10 **F**71 72 Primary Contact: Charles Thomas O'Donnell, President and Chief Executive Officer Web address: www.kidspeace.org	23	52	56	1228	44	0	0	—	—	141

PALMERTON—Carbon County

□ **PALMERTON HOSPITAL**, 135 Lafayette Avenue, Zip 18071–1596; tel. 610/826–3141 **A**1 9 10 **F**1 8 9 11 12 21 22 24 27 28 29 33 37 41 46 48 49 51 52 53 55 58 59 62 63 64 65 66 69 70 81 82 84 88 93 94 96 108 **P**8 **S** Blue Mountain Health System, Lehighton, PA Primary Contact: Robert J. Clark, FACHE, President and Chief Executive Officer Web address: www.palmertonhospital.com	23	10	70	2847	36	—	0	—	—	267

PAOLI—Chester County

PAOLI HOSPITAL, 255 West Lancaster Avenue, Zip 19301–1792; tel. 610/648–1000, (Nonreporting) **A**2 9 10 **S** Jefferson Health System, Wayne, PA Primary Contact: Barbara J. Tachovsky, President Web address: www.mainlinehealth.org	23	10	147	—	—	—	—	—	—	—

PECKVILLE—Lackawanna County

MID–VALLEY HOSPITAL, 1400 Main Street, Zip 18452–2098; tel. 570/383–5500 **A**9 10 **F**2 6 9 12 21 26 27 28 29 33 36 38 39 45 46 48 53 55 58 62 63 66 69 81 82 88 94 106 108 **P**8 Primary Contact: Ann Marie Stevens, Director of Operations Web address: www.mth.org	23	10	38	1104	14	37864	0	10517	4621	131

PHILADELPHIA—Philadelphia County

□ **ALBERT EINSTEIN MEDICAL CENTER**, 5501 Old York Road, Zip 19141–3098; tel. 215/456–7890, (Includes MOSS REHAB, 1200 West Tabor Road, Zip 19141–3099; tel. 215/456–9070), (Total facility includes 102 beds in nursing home–type unit) (Nonreporting) **A**1 2 3 5 8 9 10 12 13 **S** Albert Einstein Healthcare Network, Philadelphia, PA Primary Contact: Barry R. Freedman, President and Chief Executive Officer Web address: www.einstein.edu	23	10	701	—	—	—	—	—	—	—
□ **BELMONT CENTER FOR COMPREHENSIVE TREATMENT**, 4200 Monument Road, Zip 19131–1625; tel. 215/877–2000, (Nonreporting) **A**1 9 10 **S** Albert Einstein Healthcare Network, Philadelphia, PA Primary Contact: Sharon A. Bergen, Chief Operating Officer Web address: www.einstein.edu	23	22	146	—	—	—	—	—	—	—
★ **CHESTNUT HILL HEALTH SYSTEM**, (Formerly Chestnut Hill HealthCare), 8835 Germantown Avenue, Zip 19118–2765; tel. 215/248–8200, (Nonreporting) **A**1 3 5 9 10 **S** Community Health Systems, Inc., Brentwood, TN Primary Contact: Rodney D. Reider, Chief Executive Officer CFO: Stuart Moss, Vice President Finance and Chief Financial Officer CMO: Robert J. Gillesby, M.D., Executive Vice President Clinical Services and Chief Medical Officer CIO: Jack Nash, Interim Director Information Systems CHR: Rita Guzewski, Director Human Resources Web address: www.chh.org	23	10	212	—	—	—	—	—	—	—
★ **CHILDREN'S HOSPITAL OF PHILADELPHIA**, 34th Street and Civic Center Boulevard, Zip 19104–4304; tel. 215/590–1000 **A**1 3 5 8 9 10 **F**2 9 14 15 16 18 19 20 21 22 23 24 26 27 28 29 31 32 33 34 35 37 38 39 42 46 47 48 49 50 51 52 56 57 58 60 61 62 63 64 65 66 67 68 69 70 72 73 74 75 77 81 82 84 85 87 88 90 93 94 95 96 98 99 100 101 102 103 107 108 110 **P**6 Primary Contact: Steven M. Altschuler, President and Chief Executive Officer COO: Gavin R. Kerr, Executive Vice President and Chief Operating Officer CFO: Thomas Todorow, Chief Financial Officer CMO: James Steven, M.D., Chief Medical Officer CIO: Charles Enicks, Vice President and Chief Information Officer CHR: Meg Jones, Vice President Human Resources Web address: www.chop.edu	23	50	381	23251	319	987342	0	642641	300187	6869
□ **FAIRMOUNT BEHAVIORAL HEALTH SYSTEM**, 561 Fairthorne Avenue, Zip 19128–2499; tel. 215/487–4000 **A**1 9 10 **F**3 28 33 71 72 75 78 94 **P**6 **S** Universal Health Services, Inc., King of Prussia, PA Primary Contact: Geoff Botak, Chief Executive Officer Web address: www.fairmountbhs.com	33	22	180	4331	160	6972	0	—	—	—
★ **FOX CHASE CANCER CENTER–AMERICAN ONCOLOGIC HOSPITAL**, 333 Cottman Avenue, Zip 19111; tel. 215/728–6900 **A**1 2 3 5 8 9 10 **F**2 9 12 21 22 23 26 27 28 29 30 32 36 37 38 39 41 46 47 48 49 50 51 52 53 55 57 58 60 61 62 63 64 65 66 69 73 79 80 81 82 83 84 85 86 87 88 90 94 96 108 109 **P**6 Primary Contact: James F. Lynch, Vice President, Hospital Administration COO: R Donald Leedy, Chief Operating Officer CFO: Anthony Diasio, Vice President Finance and Chief Financial Officer CMO: Robert F. Ozols, Ph.D., Senior Vice President Medical Sciences CIO: J Robert Beck, M.D., Vice President Information Services and Chief Information Officer CHR: Gary Weyhmuller, Vice President Human Resources Web address: www.fccc.edu	23	41	74	3946	57	63406	0	117708	35644	788

Hospital, Address, Telephone, Approval, Facility, and Physician Codes, Health Care System	Classi- fication Codes		Utilization Data					Expense (thousands) of dollars		
★ American Hospital Association (AHA) membership □ Joint Commission on Accreditation of Healthcare Organizations (JCAHO) accreditation ○ American Osteopathic Association (AOA) accreditation △ Commission on Accreditation of Rehabilitation Facilities (CARF) accreditation	Control	Service	Staffed Beds	Admissions	Census	Outpatient Visits	Births	Total	Payroll	Personnel
□ △ **FRANKFORD HOSPITAL OF THE CITY OF PHILADELPHIA**, Knights and Red Lion Roads, Zip 19114–4208; tel. 215/612–4000, (Includes BUCKS COUNTY CAMPUS, 380 North Oxford Valley Road, Langhorne, Zip 19047–8399; tel. 215/949–5000; FRANKFORD CAMPUS, Frankford Avenue and Wakeling Street, Zip 19124; tel. 215/831–2000), (Total facility includes 35 beds in nursing home–type unit) **A**1 3 5 6 7 8 9 10 12 13 **F**2 4 9 11 12 15 17 19 21 22 23 24 26 27 28 29 30 32 33 34 41 42 44 45 46 47 48 50 51 52 53 54 55 56 57 58 59 60 61 62 63 64 65 66 69 70 71 73 75 76 77 78 79 80 81 82 85 86 88 92 93 94 95 96 106 107 108 109 **P**6 **S** Jefferson Health System, Wayne, PA Primary Contact: Roy A. Powell, President Web address: www.frankfordhospitals.org	23	10	436	26895	384	329321	1626	—	—	2729
✠ **FRIENDS BEHAVIORAL HEALTH SYSTEM**, (Formerly Friends Hospital), 4641 Roosevelt Boulevard, Zip 19124–2399; tel. 215/831–4600 **A**1 3 5 9 10 **F**21 22 27 33 44 71 72 73 74 75 76 94 **P**5 6 **S** Horizon Health Corporation, Lewisville, TX Primary Contact: Joseph Pyle, Executive Vice President and Chief Operating Officer COO: Joseph Pyle, Executive Vice President and Chief Operating Officer CFO: Arris S. Veronie, Chief Financial Officer CMO: James Varrell, M.D., Medical Director CIO: Peter Schwartz, Chief Information Officer Web address: www.friendshospitalonline.org	23	22	192	6438	167	15370	0	39567	17253	436
GIRARD MEDICAL CENTER See North Philadelphia Health System										
✠ **GRADUATE HOSPITAL**, One Graduate Plaza, Zip 19146–1407; tel. 215/893–2000, (Total facility includes 24 beds in nursing home–type unit) (Nonreporting) **A**1 2 3 5 8 9 10 12 **S** TENET Healthcare Corporation, Dallas, TX Primary Contact: Brian Finestein, President COO: John Kristel, Chief Operating Officer CFO: Robert Amon, Interim Chief Financial Officer Web address: www.graduatehospital.com	33	10	181	—	—	—	—	—	—	—
✠ **HAHNEMANN UNIVERSITY HOSPITAL**, Broad and Vine Streets, Zip 19102–1192; tel. 215/762–7000 **A**1 2 3 5 8 9 10 **F**2 10 11 12 14 15 17 19 21 22 23 26 27 28 29 33 34 42 46 48 55 56 59 61 62 63 64 71 75 76 78 93 94 96 99 100 101 102 103 108 110 **P**6 **S** TENET Healthcare Corporation, Dallas, TX Primary Contact: Michael P. Halter, Chief Executive Officer CFO: Brian Reilly, Chief Financial Officer CMO: George Amrom, M.D., Vice President Medical Affairs CIO: Paula Hudson, Chief Information Officer CHR: Douglas Allen, Chief Human Resources Officer Web address: www.hahnemannhospital.com	33	10	447	17863	316	71189	2258	—	—	2689
✠ △ **HOSPITAL OF THE UNIVERSITY OF PENNSYLVANIA**, 3400 Spruce Street, Zip 19104–4283; tel. 215/662–4000 **A**1 3 5 7 8 9 10 **F**2 7 9 10 11 12 13 14 15 17 19 21 22 23 26 27 28 29 30 31 32 33 34 35 37 38 39 40 42 44 45 46 47 48 49 50 51 52 53 55 56 57 58 59 60 61 62 63 64 65 66 68 69 70 71 72 73 74 75 76 77 79 80 81 82 83 84 85 86 87 88 89 90 92 93 94 95 96 98 99 100 101 102 103 104 105 106 107 108 109 110 **S** University of Pennsylvania Health System, Philadelphia, PA Primary Contact: Ralph W. Muller, President and Chief Executive Officer COO: Albert Black, Jr, Chief Operating Officer CFO: Andrew Devoe, Senior Vice President and Chief Financial Officer CMO: David E. Longnecker, M.D., Senior Vice President and Chief Medical Officer CIO: George M. Brenckle, Ph.D., Chief Information Officer Web address: www.med.upenn.edu	23	10	624	34955	557	713455	3776	773202	251854	7455
✠ **JEANES HOSPITAL**, 7600 Central Avenue, Zip 19111–2499; tel. 215/728–2000 **A**1 5 9 10 **F**2 9 11 12 21 22 23 26 27 28 29 32 33 35 37 44 46 48 49 51 52 53 55 56 57 58 59 60 61 62 63 66 68 69 81 82 84 86 88 93 94 96 106 108 109 110 **P**6 **S** Temple University Health System, Philadelphia, PA Primary Contact: Linda J. Grass, Executive Director and Chief Executive Officer CFO: Gerald P. Oetzel, Chief Financial Officer CMO: Joel Weissman, M.D., Chief Medical Officer Web address: www.jeanes.com	23	10	207	10726	145	110113	922	111528	45261	857
JOHN F. KENNEDY MEMORIAL HOSPITAL, Langdon Street and Cheltenham Avenue, Zip 19124–1098; tel. 215/831–7000, (Nonreporting) Primary Contact: Stephen H. Saks, Chief Executive Officer	23	10	141	—	—	—	—	—	—	—
□ **KENSINGTON HOSPITAL**, 136 West Diamond Street, Zip 19122–1721; tel. 215/426–8100 **A**1 9 10 **F**2 3 4 12 21 24 27 28 29 32 45 48 50 52 53 58 63 70 73 94 106 109 110 **P**6 Primary Contact: Eileen Hause, Chief Executive Officer	12	10	45	2122	29	11834	0	6341	3763	124
□ **KINDRED HOSPITAL–PHILADELPHIA**, 6129 Palmetto Street, Zip 19111–5729; tel. 215/722–8555, (Nonreporting) **A**1 9 10 **S** Kindred Healthcare, Louisville, KY Primary Contact: Margaret M. Murphy, Chief Executive Officer Web address: www.kindredhealthcare.com	33	49	52	—	—	—	—	—	—	—
✠ △ **MAGEE REHABILITATION HOSPITAL**, 1513 Race Street, Zip 19102–1177; tel. 215/587–3000 **A**1 3 5 7 10 **F**9 21 22 26 29 37 42 46 53 58 60 65 68 69 94 96 108 **P**4 **S** Jefferson Health System, Wayne, PA Primary Contact: William E. Staas, Jr, M.D., President, Chief Executive Officer and Medical Director CFO: Patricia A. Underwood, Chief Financial Officer Web address: www.mageerehab.org	23	46	96	1730	75	26476	0	37022	19009	432

Many Facility Codes have changed. Please refer to the AHA Guide Code Chart.

Hospital, Address, Telephone, Approval, Facility, and Physician Codes, Health Care System	Classi-fication Codes		Utilization Data					Expense (thousands) of dollars		
★ American Hospital Association (AHA) membership □ Joint Commission on Accreditation of Healthcare Organizations (JCAHO) accreditation ○ American Osteopathic Association (AOA) accreditation △ Commission on Accreditation of Rehabilitation Facilities (CARF) accreditation	Control	Service	Staffed Beds	Admissions	Census	Outpatient Visits	Births	Total	Payroll	Personnel

MERCY HOSPITAL OF PHILADELPHIA See Mercy Catholic Medical Center, Darby
METHODIST HOSPITAL See Thomas Jefferson University Hospital
MOSS REHAB See Albert Einstein Medical Center

⊠ △ **NAZARETH HOSPITAL**, 2601 Holme Avenue, Zip 19152–2096; tel. 215/335–6000, (Total facility includes 28 beds in nursing home–type unit) **A**1 7 9 10 **F**2 9 12 14 21 22 23 26 27 28 29 32 33 37 38 41 44 45 46 47 48 52 53 55 57 58 60 61 62 63 64 65 66 68 69 73 81 82 84 85 88 92 94 95 96 106 108 **P**6 **S** Catholic Health East, Newtown Square, PA Primary Contact: Patricia B. DeAngelis, President and Chief Executive Officer COO: Christina Fitz–Patrick, R.N., Chief Operating Officer CFO: David Wajda, Chief Financial Officer CMO: Dale Mandel, M.D., Chief Medical Officer CHR: Mary Ellen Cockerham, Vice President Human Resoruces Web address: www.nazarethhospital.org	23	10	233	11997	192	165949	0	103479	47131	947
⊠ **NORTH PHILADELPHIA HEALTH SYSTEM**, 1524 West Girard Avenue, Zip 19130–1615; tel. 215/787–9000, (Includes GIRARD MEDICAL CENTER, Girard Avenue at Eighth Street, Zip 19122; tel. 215/787–2000; ST. JOSEPH'S HOSPITAL, Catherine Kutzler, R.N., Senior Vice President and Chief Executive Officer), (Nonreporting) **A**1 9 10 Primary Contact: George J. Walmsley, III, CPA, President and Chief Executive Officer CFO: Ronald Kaplan, Chief Financial Officer CIO: Tony Iero, Director Management Information Systems CHR: James Gloner, Senior Vice President Web address: www.nphs.com	23	10	315	—	—	—	—	—	—	—
⊠ **PENNSYLVANIA HOSPITAL**, 800 Spruce Street, Zip 19107–6192; tel. 215/829–3000 **A**1 3 5 9 10 **F**2 7 9 10 11 12 14 15 17 19 21 22 23 26 27 28 29 30 31 33 35 37 38 39 41 42 46 47 48 49 50 52 53 55 56 57 58 59 60 61 62 63 64 65 66 68 69 70 71 72 73 74 75 77 79 81 82 84 85 86 87 88 89 90 92 93 94 95 96 98 99 104 106 108 109 **P**6 **S** University of Pennsylvania Health System, Philadelphia, PA Primary Contact: Timothy O. Morgan, Executive Director COO: Kathleen Kinslow, Chief Operating Officer CFO: Frank Anastasi, Director Finance CMO: R Michael Buckley, M.D., Chief Medical Officer Web address: www.pahosp.com	23	10	409	22404	306	202118	4622	282353	116267	2074
⊠ **PRESBYTERIAN MEDICAL CENTER OF THE UNIVERSITY OF PENNSYLVANIA HEALTH SYSTEM**, 39th and Market Street, Zip 19104–2699; tel. 215/662–8000, (Total facility includes 26 beds in nursing home–type unit) **A**1 3 5 9 10 **F**2 3 4 7 9 10 12 14 15 17 19 21 22 23 26 27 28 29 30 31 32 33 35 37 38 39 42 44 45 46 48 49 50 51 52 53 55 58 60 61 62 63 64 65 69 70 71 73 75 77 78 81 82 84 85 87 88 92 93 94 95 96 104 105 108 110 **P**6 **S** University of Pennsylvania Health System, Philadelphia, PA Primary Contact: Michele M. Volpe, Executive Director and Chief Executive Officer CFO: Andrew Devoe, Chief Financial Officer CMO: Ana Pujols–McKee, M.D., Chief Medical Officer and Associate Executive Director CIO: Rene Donnard, Director Marketing and Public Relations CHR: Christine Lynch, Associate Vice President Human Resources Web address: www.health.upenn.edu/pmc	23	10	277	13991	204	138772	0	243657	82363	1682
⊠ △ **ROXBOROUGH MEMORIAL HOSPITAL**, 5800 Ridge Avenue, Zip 19128–1737; tel. 215/483–9900 **A**1 6 7 9 10 **F**15 21 23 26 27 28 33 39 45 48 49 52 55 57 58 60 61 62 63 66 68 69 71 76 77 78 81 84 88 93 94 108 110 **S** TENET Healthcare Corporation, Dallas, TX Primary Contact: John J. Donnelly, Jr, Chief Executive Officer CFO: Michael Metts, Chief Financial Officer Web address: www.roxboroughmemorial.com	33	10	125	6116	102	45648	0	45312	24395	511
□ **SHRINERS HOSPITALS FOR CHILDREN, PHILADELPHIA**, 3551 North Broad Street, Zip 19140–4131; tel. 215/430–4000, (Nonreporting) **A**1 3 5 **S** Shriners Hospitals for Children, Tampa, FL Primary Contact: Sharon J. Rajnic, Administrator Web address: www.shrinershq.org	23	57	80	—	—	—	—	—	—	—
⊠ **ST. AGNES CONTINUING CARE CENTER**, 1900 South Broad Street, Zip 19145–2304; tel. 215/339–4100, (Total facility includes 19 beds in nursing home–type unit) **A**1 3 5 9 10 12 13 **F**13 21 22 27 28 29 33 41 48 55 58 61 62 63 68 69 81 84 88 92 94 108 109 110 **S** Catholic Health East, Newtown Square, PA Primary Contact: James J. Flowers, D.O., President and Chief Executive Officer COO: Ernest N. Perilli, Chief Operating Officer CFO: Teresa A. Gresko, Chief Financial Officer CIO: Charles Schechterly, Director Information Systems CHR: Maryann Kenkelen, Vice President Human Resources and Tenant Services Web address: www.stagnesphila.org	21	10	172	8728	166	100610	0	111356	45092	586

Hospital, Address, Telephone, Approval, Facility, and Physician Codes, Health Care System	Classi-fication Codes		Utilization Data					Expense (thousands) of dollars		
★ American Hospital Association (AHA) membership □ Joint Commission on Accreditation of Healthcare Organizations (JCAHO) accreditation ○ American Osteopathic Association (AOA) accreditation △ Commission on Accreditation of Rehabilitation Facilities (CARF) accreditation	Control	Service	Staffed Beds	Admissions	Census	Outpatient Visits	Births	Total	Payroll	Personnel
⊠ **ST. CHRISTOPHER'S HOSPITAL FOR CHILDREN**, Erie Avenue at Front Street, Zip 19134–1095; tel. 215/427–5000, (Nonreporting) **A**1 3 5 8 9 10 **S** TENET Healthcare Corporation, Dallas, TX Primary Contact: Jill Tillman, Chief Executive Officer COO: Jill Tillman, Chief Executive Officer CFO: Gil Cottle, Chief Financial Officer CMO: Maureen Fee, M.D., Chief Medical Officer CIO: Steve Landis, Director Information Services CHR: Maria Sceenna, Chief Human Resources Officer Web address: www.stchristophershospital.com	23	50	178	—	—	—	—	—	—	—
ST. JOSEPH'S HOSPITAL See North Philadelphia Health System										
⊠ **TEMPLE EAST, NORTHEASTERN HOSPITAL**, 2301 East Allegheny Avenue, Zip 19134–4497; tel. 215/291–3000 **A**1 3 5 6 9 10 **F**1 2 11 12 14 21 22 23 26 27 28 29 33 35 38 39 42 44 45 46 48 52 53 55 58 59 60 61 62 63 66 69 81 84 87 88 93 94 96 108 109 **S** Temple University Health System, Philadelphia, PA Primary Contact: John J. Buckley, Executive Director and Chief Executive Officer COO: Dale Schlegel, Associate Hospital Director Operations CFO: Thomas A. Bielecki, Chief Financial Officer CMO: Marc P. Hurowitz, D.O., Chief Medical Officer CIO: Andrew J. Cymerman, Chief Information Officer CHR: David Brodar, Associate Director Human Resources Web address: www.health.temple.edu/northeastern.html	23	10	185	10954	134	86319	1124	94645	37632	762
⊠ **TEMPLE UNIVERSITY CHILDREN'S MEDICAL CENTER**, 3509 North Broad Street, Zip 19140; tel. 215/707–6038 **A**1 3 9 10 **F**2 6 9 10 21 24 26 27 28 29 31 32 33 34 37 39 42 46 47 48 50 52 53 57 58 61 62 63 65 66 67 70 72 73 75 81 88 93 94 95 96 98 107 108 **P**2 6 **S** Temple University Health System, Philadelphia, PA Primary Contact: Raymond W. Uhlhorn, Executive Director and Chief Executive Officer CFO: William Stute, Chief Financial Officer CMO: Ernest G. Bertha, M.D., Chief Medical Officer CIO: Michael Prushan, Chief Learning Officer CHR: David Molotsky, Associate Director Human Resources Web address: www.health.temple.edu/tucmc/index.htm	23	10	68	3727	26	56563	0	55522	12992	348
⊠ **TEMPLE UNIVERSITY HOSPITAL**, Broad and Ontario Streets, Zip 19140–5192; tel. 215/707–2000, (Includes TEMPLE UNIVERSITY HOSPITAL – EPISCOPAL DIVISION, 100 East Lehigh Avenue, Zip 19125–1098; tel. 215/427–7000) **A**1 2 3 5 6 8 9 10 **F**2 4 9 10 11 12 13 14 15 17 19 21 22 23 26 27 28 29 31 32 33 34 35 36 37 38 39 41 44 46 47 48 49 50 52 53 55 56 57 58 59 60 61 62 63 64 65 66 68 69 71 72 73 74 75 76 77 78 81 82 84 85 87 88 90 93 94 95 96 99 100 101 103 104 105 106 107 108 109 110 **P**4 **S** Temple University Health System, Philadelphia, PA Primary Contact: Daniel J. Sinnott, Executive Director and Chief Executive Officer CFO: Edward Chabalowski, Chief Financial Officer CMO: Howard Grant, M.D., Chief Medical Officer CIO: Arthur Papacostas, M.D., Vice President and Chief Information Officer Web address: www.health.temple.edu/tuh/	23	10	640	29794	533	233116	2722	542991	200468	3989
□ △ **THOMAS JEFFERSON UNIVERSITY HOSPITAL**, 111 South 11th Street, Zip 19107–5096; tel. 215/955–6000, (Includes METHODIST HOSPITAL, 2301 South Broad Street, Zip 19148; tel. 215/952–9000; THOMAS JEFFERSON UNIVERSITY HOSPITAL–FORD ROAD CAMPUS, 3905 Ford Road, Zip 19131; tel. 215/578–3630) **A**1 2 3 5 6 7 8 9 10 **F**2 4 5 6 7 9 10 11 12 14 15 16 17 18 19 20 21 22 23 24 26 27 28 29 30 31 32 33 34 35 36 37 38 39 40 42 43 44 45 46 47 48 50 51 52 53 55 56 57 58 59 60 61 62 63 64 65 66 68 69 70 71 72 73 75 76 77 79 80 81 82 83 84 85 86 87 88 89 90 92 93 94 95 96 98 99 101 102 104 105 106 108 109 110 **P**2 8 **S** Jefferson Health System, Wayne, PA Primary Contact: Thomas J. Lewis, CHE, President and Chief Executive Officer Web address: www.jeffersonhospital.org	23	10	905	39314	690	445954	2136	797913	316965	6190
⊠ △ **VETERANS AFFAIRS MEDICAL CENTER**, University and Woodland Avenues, Zip 19104–4594; tel. 215/823–5800, (Total facility includes 240 beds in nursing home–type unit) (Nonreporting) **A**1 3 5 7 8 9 **S** Department of Veterans Affairs, Washington, DC Primary Contact: Michael J. Sullivan, Director CFO: Vinh Tran, Chief Financial Officer CMO: Martin F. Heyworth, M.D., Chief of Staff CIO: Adrienne Ficchi, Vice President Information Management CHR: Gerald Morelli, Director Human Resources Web address: www.va.gov/sta/guide/home.asp	45	10	389	—	—	—	—	—	—	—
□ **WILLS EYE HOSPITAL**, 840 Walnut Street, Zip 19107–5109; tel. 215/928–3000, (Nonreporting) **A**1 9 10 Primary Contact: James J. Mulvihill, Chief Executive Officer Web address: www.atwills.com	23	49	40	—	—	—	—	—	—	—
PHILIPSBURG—Clearfield County										
PHILIPSBURG AREA HOSPITAL, 210 Loch Lomond Road, Zip 16866; tel. 814/342–7112, (Nonreporting) **A**9 10 Primary Contact: Michael Loomis, Chief Executive Officer Web address: www.philipsburghospital.com	33	49	50	—	—	—	—	—	—	—

PA

Many Facility Codes have changed. Please refer to the AHA Guide Code Chart.

© 2005 AHA Guide

Hospital, Address, Telephone, Approval, Facility, and Physician Codes, Health Care System	Classi-fication Codes		Utilization Data					Expense (thousands) of dollars		
★ American Hospital Association (AHA) membership □ Joint Commission on Accreditation of Healthcare Organizations (JCAHO) accreditation ○ American Osteopathic Association (AOA) accreditation △ Commission on Accreditation of Rehabilitation Facilities (CARF) accreditation	Control	Service	Staffed Beds	Admissions	Census	Outpatient Visits	Births	Total	Payroll	Personnel

PHOENIXVILLE—Chester County

☒ **PHOENIXVILLE HOSPITAL**, 140 Nutt Road, Zip 19460–3900; tel. 610/983–1000 **A**1 9 10 **F**2 9 11 12 14 15 17 19 21 23 24 26 27 28 29 30 31 32 33 37 40 44 46 48 50 52 55 56 57 58 59 60 61 62 63 64 65 66 69 73 75 81 82 87 88 94 96 98 106 108 109 110 **S** Community Health Systems, Inc., Brentwood, TN
Primary Contact: Steven M. Tullman, Chief Executive Officer
CFO: Roy Boyd, Chief Financial Officer
CMO: David Stepansky, M.D., Chief Medical Officer
CIO: Terrie Hiltunen, Director Information Systems
CHR: Grant Hoffman, Director Human Resources
Web address: www.pennhealth.com/phoenix

| 23 | 10 | 136 | 8082 | 91 | 160306 | 1184 | 95540 | 35525 | 814 |

PITTSBURGH—Allegheny County

☒ **ALLEGHENY GENERAL HOSPITAL**, 320 East North Avenue, Zip 15212–4756; tel. 412/359–3131, (Includes SUBURBAN GENERAL HOSPITAL, 100 South Jackson Avenue, Zip 15202–3499; tel. 412/734–6000; Margaret Hardt, President and Chief Executive Officer) **A**1 2 3 5 8 9 10 **F**2 6 7 9 10 11 12 14 15 17 19 21 22 23 24 26 27 28 29 30 31 32 33 34 35 37 39 40 41 42 43 45 46 47 48 49 50 51 52 53 55 56 57 58 59 60 61 62 63 64 65 66 67 69 70 71 72 73 74 75 76 77 78 79 80 81 82 83 84 85 87 88 89 90 93 94 95 96 98 100 101 105 106 108 109 110 **P**6 **S** West Penn Allegheny Health System, Pittsburgh, PA
Primary Contact: Connie M. Cibrone, President and Chief Executive Officer
COO: Frank G. DeLisi, III, CHE, Senior Vice President and Chief Operating Officer
CFO: Dawn Javersack, Vice President and Chief Financial Officer
CMO: Michael White, M.D., President, Medical Staff
CIO: Nicholas J. Valadja, Vice President Information Systems
Web address: www.wpahs.org

| 23 | 10 | 426 | 27288 | 405 | 486365 | 1362 | 475747 | 165962 | 4029 |

★ **CHILDREN'S HOME OF PITTSBURGH**, 5618 Kentucky Avenue, Zip 15232–2606; tel. 412/441–4884 **A**9 10 **F**2 21 26 27 28 36 58 65 94
Primary Contact: Pamela R. Schanwald, Chief Executive Officer
COO: Karen Schneider, Chief Operating Officer
CFO: Kim Phillips, Director Finance
Web address: www.childrenshomepgh.org

| 23 | 50 | 11 | 166 | 9 | 0 | 0 | 3967 | 2174 | 42 |

□ **CHILDREN'S HOSPITAL OF PITTSBURGH OF UPMC**, 3705 Fifth Avenue at De Soto Street, Zip 15213–2583; tel. 412/692–5325 **A**1 3 5 8 9 10 **F**2 6 10 14 16 18 20 21 22 23 24 29 30 32 33 34 37 38 39 42 43 46 47 49 50 51 52 53 56 57 58 60 61 62 63 64 65 66 67 69 70 73 79 80 81 82 83 84 85 86 87 88 93 94 96 97 98 99 100 101 102 103 104 106 108 110 **P**4 **S** University of Pittsburgh Medical Center, Pittsburgh, PA
Primary Contact: Roger A. Oxendale, President and Chief Executive Officer
Web address: www.chp.edu

| 23 | 50 | 260 | 12409 | 182 | 144856 | 0 | 259015 | 91924 | 2749 |

EYE AND EAR HOSPITAL OF PITTSBURGH See UPMC Presbyterian

☒ **HEALTHSOUTH HARMARVILLE REHABILITATION HOSPITAL**, Guys Run Road, Zip 15238–0460, Mailing Address: P.O. Box 11460, Zip 15238–0460; tel. 412/828–1300 **A**1 10 **F**2 21 22 26 29 37 51 52 57 58 60 62 65 66 68 69 81 88 95 96 108 110 **S** HEALTHSOUTH Corporation, Birmingham, AL
Primary Contact: Sharon Noro, Administrator
COO: Cynthia Eiseman, Chief Operating Officer
CFO: Jim Steinkirchner, Regional Controller
Web address: www.healthsouth.com

| 33 | 46 | 202 | 2386 | 131 | 28074 | 0 | 28352 | 16968 | 473 |

□ **JEFFERSON REGIONAL MEDICAL CENTER**, 565 Coal Valley Road, Zip 15236–0119, Mailing Address: Box 18119, Zip 15236–0119; tel. 412/469–5000, (Nonreporting) **A**1 9 10
Primary Contact: Thomas P. Timcho, President and Chief Executive Officer
Web address: www.shhspgh.org

| 23 | 10 | 343 | — | — | — | — | — | — | — |

□ **LIFECARE HOSPITALS OF PITTSBURGH**, 225 Penn Avenue, Zip 15221–2173; tel. 412/247–2424 **A**1 9 10 **F**21 26 46 52 54 58 60 64 69 71 76 81 94 96 108 110 **S** LifeCare Management Services, Plano, TX
Primary Contact: Clifton Neal Orme, FACHE, Administrator and Chief Executive Officer
Web address: www.lifecare–hospitals.com

| 33 | 10 | 132 | 1264 | 97 | 0 | 0 | — | — | — |

☒ **MAGEE–WOMENS HOSPITAL OF UPMC**, 300 Halket Street, Zip 15213–3180; tel. 412/641–1000, (Nonreporting) **A**1 2 3 5 8 9 10 **S** University of Pittsburgh Medical Center, Pittsburgh, PA
Primary Contact: Leslie C. Davis, President
CFO: Sue McCarthy, Chief Financial Officer
CMO: Dennis English, M.D., Director Health Management
CIO: Bruce Haviland, Chief Information Officer
CHR: Jane Tibbott, Director
Web address: www.magee.edu

| 23 | 44 | 205 | — | — | — | — | — | — | — |

Hospital, Address, Telephone, Approval, Facility, and Physician Codes, Health Care System	Classi-fication Codes		Utilization Data					Expense (thousands) of dollars		
★ American Hospital Association (AHA) membership ☐ Joint Commission on Accreditation of Healthcare Organizations (JCAHO) accreditation ◯ American Osteopathic Association (AOA) accreditation △ Commission on Accreditation of Rehabilitation Facilities (CARF) accreditation	Control	Service	Staffed Beds	Admissions	Census	Outpatient Visits	Births	Total	Payroll	Personnel
⊠ △ **MERCY HOSPITAL OF PITTSBURGH**, 1400 Locust Street, Zip 15219–5166; tel. 412/232–8111, (Total facility includes 34 beds in nursing home–type unit) **A**1 2 3 5 6 7 8 9 10 12 13 **F**2 3 11 12 13 15 17 19 21 22 23 24 26 27 28 29 30 33 34 35 37 38 39 40 42 44 45 46 47 48 49 50 51 52 53 55 56 57 58 59 60 61 62 63 64 65 66 68 69 70 71 75 76 77 79 80 81 82 84 86 88 90 92 93 94 96 98 106 107 108 109 110 **S** Catholic Health East, Newtown Square, PA Primary Contact: Kenneth A. Eshak, President and Chief Executive Officer CFO: Jack Gaenzle, Senior Vice President Finance and Administration CMO: A. J. Pinevich, M.D., Vice President Quality and Patient Safety CIO: Stephen D. Adams, Executive Vice President and Chief Executive Officer CHR: Kristen Bell, Director Human Resources Web address: www.mercylink.org	23	10	495	22231	357	217901	1592	259921	98427	2428
⊠ **MERCY HOSPITAL–NORTH SHORE CAMPUS**, 1004 Arch Street, Zip 15212–5235; tel. 412/323–5600, (Nonreporting) **A**1 9 10 **S** Catholic Health East, Newtown Square, PA Primary Contact: Mary Anne Foley, Aministrator CFO: Edwin Ellis, Jr, Executive Vice President and Chief Financial Officer CMO: Joanne V. Narduzzi, M.D., Vice President Academic Affairs CIO: Stephen D. Adams, Chief Information Officer Web address: www.mercylink.org	21	22	132	—	—	—	—	—	—	—
MONTEFIORE HOSPITAL See UPMC Presbyterian										
☐ **SELECT SPECIALTY HOSPITAL**, 200 Lothrop Street, E824, Zip 15213; tel. 412/586–9819, (Nonreporting) **A**1 10 Primary Contact: Keith J. Weinhold, Chief Executive Officer	33	49	32	—	—	—	—	—	—	—
☐ **SELECT SPECIALTY HOSPITAL–PITTSBURGH**, 1400 Locust Street, Zip 15219; tel. 412/485–4500, (Nonreporting) **A**1 9 10 Primary Contact: Regina Vercilla, Chief Executive Officer	33	49	41	—	—	—	—	—	—	—
☐ **SOUTHWOOD PSYCHIATRIC HOSPITAL**, 2575 Boyce Plaza Road, Zip 15241–3925; tel. 412/257–2290 **A**1 9 **F**71 72 **P**6 **S** Youth and Family Centered Services, Austin, TX Primary Contact: Lynne M. Struble, MSN, Chief Executive Officer Web address: www.southwoodhospital.com	33	52	119	1165	95	21009	0	10440	6328	238
☐ **ST. CLAIR MEMORIAL HOSPITAL**, 1000 Bower Hill Road, Zip 15243–1873; tel. 412/344–6600, (Total facility includes 14 beds in nursing home–type unit) **A**1 2 9 10 **F**2 9 11 12 14 15 17 19 21 22 23 24 26 27 28 29 31 33 35 38 39 40 41 42 44 45 46 47 48 49 50 52 55 57 58 59 60 61 62 63 64 65 66 68 69 71 73 74 75 76 78 81 82 84 85 86 87 88 92 93 94 96 98 106 108 109 110 Primary Contact: Benjamin E. Snead, President and Chief Executive Officer Web address: www.stclair.org	23	10	295	15492	220	265270	1249	146084	61440	1372
STATE CORRECTIONAL INSTITUTION HOSPITAL, Doerr Street, Zip 15233, Mailing Address: P.O. Box 99901, Zip 15233; tel. 412/761–1955, (Nonreporting) Primary Contact: Joan Delie, Administrator	12	11	27	—	—	—	—	—	—	—
⊠ △ **THE CHILDREN'S INSTITUTE OF PITTSBURGH**, 6301 Northumberland Street, Zip 15217–1396; tel. 412/420–2400 **A**1 7 9 10 **F**21 22 26 27 28 29 52 65 66 68 69 72 94 108 Primary Contact: David K. Miles, President and Chief Executive Officer CFO: Jody Mulvihill, Assistant Controller CMO: Jamie Calabrese, M.D., Medical Director CIO: Sharon Dorogy, Director Information Systems CHR: Bob Brown, Director Human Resources Web address: www.amazingkids.org	23	56	39	286	26	42189	0	18090	9323	221
☐ **UPMC PASSAVANT**, 9100 Babcock Boulevard, Zip 15237–5815; tel. 412/367–6700 **A**1 9 10 **F**2 9 12 15 17 19 21 22 23 26 27 28 29 33 36 37 40 44 46 47 48 51 52 53 55 57 58 60 61 62 63 65 66 68 69 73 79 81 84 85 87 88 92 93 94 96 106 108 110 **S** University of Pittsburgh Medical Center, Pittsburgh, PA Primary Contact: Teresa A. Petrick, President Web address: www.upmc.edu/passavant	23	10	258	13339	179	336123	0	151563	57483	1504
☐ **UPMC PRESBYTERIAN**, 200 Lothrop Street, Zip 15213–2585; tel. 412/647–2345, (Includes EYE AND EAR HOSPITAL OF PITTSBURGH, 200 Lothrop Street, Zip 15213–2592; tel. 412/647–2345; MONTEFIORE HOSPITAL, 200 Lothrop Street, Zip 15213; tel. 412/647–2345; UPMC PRESBYTERIAN HOSPITAL; UPMC SHADYSIDE, 5230 Centre Avenue, Zip 15232–1381; tel. 412/623–2121; WESTERN PSYCHIATRIC INSTITUTE AND CLINIC, 3811 O'Hara Street, Zip 15213–2593; tel. 412/624–2100), (Total facility includes 30 beds in nursing home–type unit) **A**1 2 3 5 6 8 9 10 13 **F**1 2 4 5 6 7 8 9 10 11 12 14 15 17 19 21 22 23 24 25 26 27 28 29 30 31 33 34 35 36 37 38 39 40 41 42 43 44 45 46 47 48 49 50 51 52 53 54 55 57 58 59 60 61 62 63 64 65 66 69 70 71 72 73 74 75 76 77 78 79 80 81 82 83 84 85 86 87 88 89 90 92 93 94 95 96 98 99 100 101 102 103 104 105 106 108 109 110 **P**6 **S** University of Pittsburgh Medical Center, Pittsburgh, PA Primary Contact: Elizabeth B. Concordia, President Web address: www.upmc.edu	23	10	1412	64678	1105	667071	958	1306530	420745	11507
☐ △ **UPMC SOUTH SIDE**, 2000 Mary Street, Zip 15203–2095; tel. 412/488–5550 **A**1 7 9 10 **F**2 12 19 21 22 28 29 33 35 45 46 48 52 53 58 63 64 66 68 69 71 74 75 76 81 82 88 92 93 94 96 106 108 110 **P**1 **S** University of Pittsburgh Medical Center, Pittsburgh, PA Primary Contact: Nancy Magee, President Web address: www.upmc.edu/southside/	23	10	126	5821	93	80004	0	54940	19883	531

Many Facility Codes have changed. Please refer to the AHA Guide Code Chart. © 2005 AHA Guide

PA

Hospital, Address, Telephone, Approval, Facility, and Physician Codes, Health Care System	Classi-fication Codes		Utilization Data					Expense (thousands) of dollars		
★ American Hospital Association (AHA) membership □ Joint Commission on Accreditation of Healthcare Organizations (JCAHO) accreditation ○ American Osteopathic Association (AOA) accreditation △ Commission on Accreditation of Rehabilitation Facilities (CARF) accreditation	Control	Service	Staffed Beds	Admissions	Census	Outpatient Visits	Births	Total	Payroll	Personnel
□ **UPMC ST. MARGARET**, 815 Freeport Road, Zip 15215–3399; tel. 412/784–4000 **A**1 2 3 5 6 9 10 12 13 **F**2 5 7 9 10 12 21 22 23 26 27 28 29 33 35 36 37 38 39 40 41 42 44 46 47 48 49 50 52 53 55 57 58 60 61 62 63 64 65 66 68 69 70 75 76 77 79 81 82 83 84 85 87 88 93 94 95 96 98 106 108 **P**8 **S** University of Pittsburgh Medical Center, Pittsburgh, PA Primary Contact: David T. Martin, President Web address: www.upmc.edu/stmargaret	23	10	208	12847	166	181722	0	148668	51929	1354
✦ **VETERANS AFFAIRS PITTSBURGH HEALTHCARE SYSTEM**, (Med/Surg/Psych/LTC), Delafield Road, Zip 15240–1001; tel. 412/688–6000, (Includes VETERANS AFFAIRS MEDICAL CENTER, 7180 Highland Drive, Zip 15206–1297; tel. 412/365–4900; VETERANS AFFAIRS MEDICAL CENTER, University Drive C, tel. 412/688–6000), (Total facility includes 336 beds in nursing home–type unit) **A**1 2 8 9 **F**1 2 3 4 5 7 9 10 14 15 17 19 21 22 23 28 29 30 31 32 33 36 37 38 39 42 44 45 47 48 49 50 51 52 53 55 57 58 60 61 62 63 64 65 66 68 69 70 71 73 74 75 76 77 81 82 84 87 88 92 93 94 96 101 105 106 107 108 109 110 **P**6 **S** Department of Veterans Affairs, Washington, DC Primary Contact: Michael E. Moreland, Director COO: Patricia Nealon, Acting Associate Director CFO: James Baker, Vice President Business Support Services CMO: Rajiv Jain, M.D., Chief of Staff CIO: Angelo Baiocchi, Vice President Information Management CHR: William Mills, Program Manager Human Resources Web address: www.va.gov/pittsburgh	45	49	692	8427	550	450710	0	—	—	—
✦ **WESTERN PENNSYLVANIA HOSPITAL**, 4800 Friendship Avenue, Zip 15224–1722; tel. 412/578–5000 **A**1 2 3 5 6 8 9 10 12 13 **F**1 2 7 9 10 11 12 13 14 15 17 19 21 22 23 24 26 27 28 29 30 32 33 35 37 38 39 40 42 43 44 46 47 48 49 50 51 52 53 55 56 57 58 59 60 61 62 63 64 65 66 68 69 70 71 74 75 76 79 80 81 82 84 85 86 87 88 89 90 93 94 95 96 99 106 108 109 110 **P**6 7 **S** West Penn Allegheny Health System, Pittsburgh, PA Primary Contact: James M. Collins, President and Chief Executive Officer COO: Edward M. Klaman, Senior Vice President and Chief Operating Officer CFO: Richard C. Chesnos, Vice President Operations and Director Finance CMO: E Douglas Newton, M.D., President Medical Staff CIO: Christine B. Middlemiss, Senior Director Information Services CHR: Tanya Ulrich, Director Human Resources Web address: www.wpahs.org WESTERN PSYCHIATRIC INSTITUTE AND CLINIC See UPMC Presbyterian	23	10	479	21175	314	179817	2058	325333	124015	2434
PLEASANT GAP—Centre County										
✦ **HEALTHSOUTH NITTANY VALLEY REHABILITATION HOSPITAL**, 550 West College Avenue, Zip 16823–7416; tel. 814/359–3421 **A**1 9 10 **F**21 45 48 52 68 69 96 97 **P**5 **S** HEALTHSOUTH Corporation, Birmingham, AL Primary Contact: Susan Hartman, Administrator CFO: Steven Alwine, Controller CMO: Richard Allatt, M.D., Medical Director CHR: Kirstin Brown, Director Human Resources Web address: www.healthsouth.com	33	46	85	1228	50	45823	0	—	—	181
POTTSTOWN—Montgomery County										
□ **POTTSTOWN MEMORIAL MEDICAL CENTER**, 1600 East High Street, Zip 19464–5093; tel. 610/327–7000, (Total facility includes 21 beds in nursing home–type unit) **A**1 2 9 10 **F**9 11 12 15 21 22 23 27 28 29 32 33 39 41 42 44 46 48 49 51 52 53 55 57 58 59 60 61 62 63 66 68 69 71 75 76 81 82 87 88 92 94 96 108 109 **P**6 **S** Community Health Systems, Inc., Brentwood, TN Primary Contact: Martin D. Smith, Chief Executive Officer Web address: www.pmmctr.org	33	10	222	9305	104	140200	840	105903	41084	915
POTTSVILLE—Schuylkill County										
✦ **GOOD SAMARITAN REGIONAL MEDICAL CENTER**, 700 East Norwegian Street, Zip 17901–2798; tel. 570/621–4000 **A**1 2 9 10 **F**4 9 12 15 21 22 23 26 27 28 32 33 37 44 46 48 50 52 55 58 60 61 62 63 64 65 66 68 69 81 82 84 85 88 93 94 96 106 108 109 110 **P**6 **S** Ascension Health, Saint Louis, MO Primary Contact: Peter Bergmann, President and Chief Executive Officer CFO: Daniel A. Kochie, CPA, Senior Vice President and Chief Financial Officer CMO: Thomas McLaughlin, M.D., Chief Medical Officer CIO: David Schneck, Director Health Information Management and Technology CHR: Denis Orthaus, Director Human Resources Web address: www.gsrmc.com	21	10	147	6888	109	133348	0	62099	26410	662
✦ △ **POTTSVILLE HOSPITAL AND WARNE CLINIC**, 420 South Jackson Street, Zip 17901–3692; tel. 570/621–5000 **A**1 2 6 7 9 10 19 **F**2 9 11 12 21 22 24 26 27 28 29 31 32 33 37 39 40 44 46 48 50 51 52 53 55 57 58 59 60 61 62 63 64 65 68 69 71 72 74 75 76 77 78 81 82 84 85 86 88 93 94 95 108 109 110 Primary Contact: John E. Simodejka, President and Chief Executive Officer CFO: Craig P. Hunt, Vice President Operations and Finance CHR: Martin Treasure, Director Human Resources Web address: www.pottsvillehospital.com	23	10	200	8316	123	98380	1072	64596	27656	725

PA

Hospital, Address, Telephone, Approval, Facility, and Physician Codes, Health Care System	Classi-fication Codes		Utilization Data					Expense (thousands) of dollars		
★ American Hospital Association (AHA) membership □ Joint Commission on Accreditation of Healthcare Organizations (JCAHO) accreditation ○ American Osteopathic Association (AOA) accreditation △ Commission on Accreditation of Rehabilitation Facilities (CARF) accreditation	Control	Service	Staffed Beds	Admissions	Census	Outpatient Visits	Births	Total	Payroll	Personnel

PUNXSUTAWNEY—Jefferson County

★ **PUNXSUTAWNEY AREA HOSPITAL**, 81 Hillcrest Drive, Zip 15767–2616; tel. 814/938–1800 **A**9 10 **F**2 11 12 21 22 23 26 27 28 29 31 33 37 39 40 42 46 47 48 49 50 51 53 55 57 58 59 60 62 63 64 65 69 77 81 82 84 85 86 87 88 94 97 110 **P**6 7
Primary Contact: Daniel D. Blough, Jr, Chief Executive Officer
CFO: Jack Sisk, Chief Financial Officer
CMO: Charles Lambiotte, M.D., Medical Staff President
CIO: Chuck States, Director Information Systems
CHR: Barbara Kostok, Manager Human Resources
Web address: www.pah.org
→ 23 | 10 | 44 | 2216 | 25 | 91581 | 203 | 23665 | 11049 | 305

QUAKERTOWN—Bucks County

□ **ST. LUKE'S QUAKERTOWN HOSPITAL**, 1021 Park Avenue, Zip 18951–9003; tel. 215/538–4510 **A**1 2 9 10 **F**2 6 9 12 21 22 23 24 26 27 28 29 31 33 36 37 38 39 40 44 45 46 47 48 49 50 52 54 55 57 58 60 61 62 63 64 65 66 69 70 71 72 73 74 75 76 77 81 82 84 88 93 94 95 96 97 98 106 107 108 109 110 **P**6 8
Primary Contact: Edward Nawrocki, President
Web address: www.slhhn.org
→ 23 | 10 | 57 | 2995 | 35 | 62384 | 0 | 28836 | 10969 | 310

READING—Berks County

⊠ **HEALTHSOUTH READING REHABILITATION HOSPITAL**, 1623 Morgantown Road, Zip 19607–9455; tel. 610/796–6000 **A**1 9 10 **F**2 7 10 21 22 26 27 28 29 37 42 44 45 48 52 57 58 62 65 66 68 69 76 77 94 95 96 108 110
S HEALTHSOUTH Corporation, Birmingham, AL
Primary Contact: Tammy L. Ober, Administrator
CFO: Barbara Bennett, Controller
CMO: Patti Brown, Medical Director
CHR: Lynne Rendle, Regional Director Human Resources
Web address: www.healthsouth.com
→ 33 | 46 | 95 | 1519 | 60 | 40032 | 0 | 15893 | 10895 | 234

⊠ **ST. JOSEPH MEDICAL CENTER**, 215 North 12th Street, Zip 19604, Mailing Address: P.O. Box 316, Zip 19603–0316; tel. 610/378–2000, (Total facility includes 24 beds in nursing home–type unit) **A**1 2 9 10 12 13 **F**1 2 9 10 11 12 15 17 19 21 22 23 24 26 27 28 29 30 31 32 33 35 37 38 39 40 41 42 44 46 47 48 50 52 53 55 56 57 58 59 60 61 62 63 64 65 66 69 70 71 72 73 74 75 76 77 78 79 81 82 84 85 86 87 88 92 93 94 95 96 97 106 108 109 110 **P**6 **S** Catholic Health Initiatives, Denver, CO
Primary Contact: John R. Morahan, President and Chief Executive Officer
CFO: Patrick Richards, Vice President Finance and Chief Financial Officer
CMO: Samuel Alfaro, M.D., Vice President Medical Affairs
CIO: Mary Babb, Director Information Technology
CHR: Scott Mengle, Vice President Human Resources
Web address: www.sjmcberks.org
→ 21 | 10 | 267 | 12268 | 161 | 288742 | 860 | 134019 | 55317 | 1206

RENOVO—Clinton County

BUCKTAIL MEDICAL CENTER, 1001 Pine Street, Zip 17764–1620; tel. 570/923–1000, (Total facility includes 41 beds in nursing home–type unit) (Nonreporting) **A**9 10 18
Primary Contact: Anita L. Rathgeber, Administrator
→ 23 | 10 | 50 | — | — | — | — | — | — | —

RIDLEY PARK—Delaware County

TAYLOR HOSPITAL See Crozer–Chester Medical Center, Upland

ROARING SPRING—Blair County

⊠ **NASON HOSPITAL**, 105 Nason Drive, Zip 16673–1202; tel. 814/224–2141 **A**1 9 10 **F**2 9 11 12 21 22 26 27 28 33 36 37 39 40 46 48 51 52 53 55 58 59 60 63 64 66 81 82 84 85 87 88 94 96 97 106 108 **P**3
Primary Contact: Garrett W. Hoover, President and Chief Executive Officer
CFO: Raymond C. Askey, Vice President Fiscal Services
CIO: Brian Lilly, Director Information Systems
CHR: Patricia McGraw, Director Human Resources
→ 23 | 10 | 42 | 2155 | 21 | 82435 | 377 | 20696 | 7956 | 252

SAINT MARYS—Elk County

⊠ **ELK REGIONAL HEALTH CENTER**, 763 Johnsonburg Road, Zip 15857–3498; tel. 814/788–8000, (Total facility includes 138 beds in nursing home–type unit) **A**1 9 10 20 **F**2 11 12 21 22 23 26 27 28 29 31 33 35 37 38 46 47 48 55 59 60 61 62 63 64 65 66 69 70 81 82 88 92 94 95 96 97 106 107 108 109 110 **P**6
Primary Contact: Scott A. Berlucchi, President and Chief Executive Officer
CFO: James Byham, Vice President Financial Services
CMO: Jayant L. Patankar, M.D., President Medical Staff
Web address: www.elkregional.org
→ 23 | 10 | 221 | 3314 | 147 | 128364 | 250 | 47448 | 21097 | 754

SAYRE—Bradford County

⊠ **ROBERT PACKER HOSPITAL**, 1 Guthrie Square, Zip 18840–1698; tel. 570/888–6666 **A**1 2 3 5 9 10 12 13 19 **F**2 10 11 12 14 15 17 19 21 22 23 26 27 28 31 33 34 37 39 40 45 46 48 49 50 52 53 55 57 58 59 60 61 62 63 64 65 66 67 69 71 72 73 74 75 76 77 78 79 80 81 82 84 85 86 87 89 92 93 94 95 96 105 107 108 109 110 **P**1 **S** Guthrie Healthcare System, Sayre, PA
Primary Contact: William F. Vanaskie, CHE, President and Chief Executive Officer
COO: Mary N. Mannix, Senior Vice President and Chief Information Officer
CFO: Minh Dang, Vice President Finance
CIO: Mary N. Mannix, Senior Vice President and Chief Operating Officer
CHR: Russ Keffer, Senior Vice President
Web address: www.guthrie.org
→ 23 | 10 | 222 | 11364 | 139 | 153963 | 857 | 149806 | 47442 | 1216

Many Facility Codes have changed. Please refer to the AHA Guide Code Chart. © 2005 AHA Guide

Hospital, Address, Telephone, Approval, Facility, and Physician Codes, Health Care System	Classi-fication Codes		Utilization Data					Expense (thousands) of dollars		

	Control	Service	Staffed Beds	Admissions	Census	Outpatient Visits	Births	Total	Payroll	Personnel

★ American Hospital Association (AHA) membership
□ Joint Commission on Accreditation of Healthcare Organizations (JCAHO) accreditation
○ American Osteopathic Association (AOA) accreditation
△ Commission on Accreditation of Rehabilitation Facilities (CARF) accreditation

SCRANTON—Lackawanna County

✠ △ **ALLIED SERVICES REHABILITATION HOSPITAL**, 475 Morgan Highway, Zip 18501–1103, Mailing Address: P.O. Box 1103, Zip 18501–1103; tel. 570/348–1300 **A**1 7 10 **F**9 21 22 26 28 29 41 44 45 46 52 58 60 61 62 65 66 68 69 94 95 96 108 109 110 Primary Contact: James L. Brady, President CFO: Michael Avvisato, Vice President and Chief Financial Officer CMO: Michael Armica, M.D., Vice President CIO: John Kravitz, Chief Information Officer Web address: www.allied–services.org	23	46	117	2470	77	19240	0	33475	14542	419
✠ **COMMUNITY MEDICAL CENTER**, 1800 Mulberry Street, Zip 18510–2523, Mailing Address: P.O. Box 2037, Zip 18501–2037; tel. 570/969–8000, (Total facility includes 20 beds in nursing home–type unit) **A**1 9 10 **F**2 9 10 11 12 14 15 17 19 21 22 23 26 27 28 29 33 34 35 37 39 44 46 47 48 50 52 53 55 56 57 58 59 60 61 62 63 64 65 66 69 70 71 73 75 76 78 81 82 83 85 87 88 90 92 93 94 96 108 109 110 Primary Contact: C. Richard Hartman, M.D., President and Chief Executive Officer COO: Allen C. Minor, Vice President Operations CFO: Manuel Evans, Chief Financial Officer CIO: Joseph Fisne, Chief Information Officer Web address: www.cmchealthsys.org	23	10	275	12967	178	99114	1354	133926	53062	1123
✠ △ **MERCY HOSPITAL OF SCRANTON**, 746 Jefferson Avenue, Zip 18501–1697; tel. 570/348–7100 **A**1 2 3 5 7 9 10 12 **F**9 11 12 14 15 19 21 22 23 24 26 27 28 29 32 33 35 36 38 39 41 42 43 46 47 48 49 50 51 52 53 55 57 58 59 61 62 63 65 66 69 70 79 81 82 84 88 92 93 94 96 108 109 110 **P**6 **S** Catholic Healthcare Partners, Cincinnati, OH Primary Contact: C. J. Urlaub, Chief Administrative Officer COO: C J Urlaub, Chief Administrative Officer CFO: Stephen Franko, Vice President Finance and Chief Financial Officer CMO: E Donald Kotchick, M.D., Vice President Medical Affairs CIO: John Honells, Chief Information Officer Web address: www.mhs–nepa.com	21	10	251	10220	129	194984	338	120001	46429	1010
✠ △ **MOSES TAYLOR HOSPITAL**, 700 Quincy Avenue, Zip 18510–1798; tel. 570/340–2100, (Total facility includes 32 beds in nursing home–type unit) **A**1 3 5 7 9 10 **F**2 9 11 12 21 22 23 26 27 28 33 37 40 44 47 49 50 51 52 53 55 56 57 58 59 60 61 62 63 64 65 66 69 71 76 81 82 85 88 92 93 94 96 108 109 110 **P**6 Primary Contact: Harold E. Anderson, Chief Executive Officer CFO: William Roe, Chief Financial Officer CMO: Carmen A. Brutico, M.D., Chief Medical Officer CIO: Edward Roman, Assistant Vice President and Chief Information Officer CHR: Paul Gionfriddo, Vice President Human Resources Web address: www.mth.org	23	10	204	9332	158	142918	1134	104041	39484	1066

SELLERSVILLE—Bucks County

✠ △ **GRAND VIEW HOSPITAL**, 700 Lawn Avenue, Zip 18960–1576, Mailing Address: P.O. Box 902, Zip 18960–0902; tel. 215/453–4000 **A**1 2 5 7 9 10 **F**2 6 9 11 12 21 22 23 24 26 27 28 29 33 35 36 37 39 44 46 47 48 50 51 52 53 55 57 59 60 61 62 63 64 65 66 69 71 73 74 76 79 80 81 82 84 85 87 88 94 95 96 106 108 109 110 Primary Contact: Stuart H. Fine, Chief Executive Officer CFO: Gregory Wuerstle, Vice President Finance CIO: Jane Doll Loveless, Vice President Information Services Web address: www.gvh.org	23	10	198	9036	122	260148	1323	109201	55868	1160

SENECA—Venango County

□ **UPMC NORTHWEST**, 100 Fairfield Drive, Zip 16346; tel. 814/676–7600, (Total facility includes 16 beds in nursing home–type unit) **A**1 2 9 10 **F**4 9 11 12 22 26 27 29 33 34 37 48 52 54 55 57 58 59 60 61 62 63 65 66 68 69 70 71 75 77 78 82 84 87 88 92 93 94 95 107 108 110 **S** University of Pittsburgh Medical Center, Pittsburgh, PA Primary Contact: Neil E. Todhunter, President Web address: www.upmc.com	23	10	209	7799	95	177146	399	63417	26540	816

SEWICKLEY—Allegheny County

✠ **HEALTHSOUTH REHABILITATION HOSPITAL**, 303 Camp Meeting Road, Zip 15143–8322; tel. 412/741–9500, (Nonreporting) **A**1 10 **S** HEALTHSOUTH Corporation, Birmingham, AL Primary Contact: Sharon Noro, Administrator CFO: Tony Bodnar, Assistant Controller CMO: Mark Mitros, M.D., Medical Director CIO: Daryl Ault, Director Information Services CHR: Leslie Cunningham, Director Human Resources Web address: www.healthsouth.com	33	46	44	—	—	—	—	—	—	—
□ **SEWICKLEY VALLEY HOSPITAL, (A DIVISION OF VALLEY MEDICAL FACILITIES)**, 720 Blackburn Road, Zip 15143–1459; tel. 412/741–6600, (Nonreporting) **A**1 6 9 10 **S** Heritage Valley Health System, Beaver, PA Primary Contact: Norman F. Mitry, President and Chief Executive Officer Web address: www.heritagevalley.org	23	10	182	—	—	—	—	—	—	—

PA

Hospital, Address, Telephone, Approval, Facility, and Physician Codes, Health Care System	Classi-fication Codes		Utilization Data					Expense (thousands) of dollars		
★ American Hospital Association (AHA) membership □ Joint Commission on Accreditation of Healthcare Organizations (JCAHO) accreditation ○ American Osteopathic Association (AOA) accreditation △ Commission on Accreditation of Rehabilitation Facilities (CARF) accreditation	Control	Service	Staffed Beds	Admissions	Census	Outpatient Visits	Births	Total	Payroll	Personnel

PA

SHARON—Mercer County

⊞ **SHARON REGIONAL HEALTH SYSTEM**, 740 East State Street, Zip 16146–3395; tel. 724/983–3911, (Total facility includes 38 beds in nursing home–type unit) **A**1 2 6 9 10 **F**2 4 9 11 12 14 15 17 19 21 22 23 24 27 28 29 31 33 34 35 36 37 39 40 41 42 44 46 47 48 49 51 52 55 57 58 59 60 61 62 63 64 65 66 68 69 71 72 73 74 75 76 77 78 80 81 82 84 85 86 87 88 92 93 94 95 96 98 106 108 109 110 **P**6 7 8
Primary Contact: Wayne W. Johnston, President and Chief Executive Officer
COO: John A. Zidansek, Executive Vice President
CFO: Raymond W. Schauer, Vice President Finance
CIO: Jack Janoso, Chief Information Officer
CHR: John Davidson, Vice President Human Resources
Web address: www.sharonregional.com
| | 23 | 10 | 237 | 11113 | 169 | 328552 | 414 | 126197 | 51797 | 1422 |

SHICKSHINNY—Luzerne County

CLEAR BROOK LODGE, 890 Bethel Road, Zip 18655; tel. 570/864–3116, (Nonreporting)
Primary Contact: Nicholas Colangelo, Chief Executive Officer
| | 23 | 82 | 65 | — | — | — | — | — | — | — |

SOMERSET—Somerset County

⊞ **SOMERSET HOSPITAL CENTER FOR HEALTH**, 225 South Center Avenue, Zip 15501–2088; tel. 814/443–5000, (Total facility includes 15 beds in nursing home–type unit) **A**1 9 10 **F**2 3 4 9 11 12 15 17 21 22 24 26 27 28 29 30 32 33 36 37 38 44 46 47 48 50 51 52 53 55 58 59 60 62 63 65 66 69 71 72 73 74 75 76 77 81 82 84 88 92 93 94 95 96 98 106 108 109 110 **P**6
Primary Contact: Michael J. Farrell, CHE, Chief Executive Officer
COO: Cheryl Brill, Vice President, Chief Nursing Officer and Chief Operating Officer
CFO: Ron Park, Chief Financial Officer
CIO: Robert McNelly, Information Services Director
CHR: Sharon Glover, Director Human Resources
Web address: www.somersethospital.com
| | 23 | 10 | 173 | 5090 | 73 | 158774 | 417 | 47384 | 18858 | 556 |

SPRINGFIELD—Delaware County

SPRINGFIELD HOSPITAL See Crozer–Chester Medical Center, Upland

STATE COLLEGE—Centre County

⊞ **MOUNT NITTANY MEDICAL CENTER**, 1800 Park Avenue, Zip 16803–6797; tel. 814/231–7000 **A**1 2 9 10 **F**2 9 11 12 14 15 21 22 23 26 27 28 29 33 36 37 45 46 48 52 53 55 57 58 59 60 61 62 63 64 66 69 71 72 73 74 75 79 81 82 84 85 87 88 93 94 96 106 107 108 110
Primary Contact: Thomas J. Murray, FACHE, President and Chief Executive Officer
COO: David B. Peterson, Executive Vice President and Chief Operating Officer
CFO: Richard Wisniewski, Senior Vice President Finance and Chief Financial Officer
CMO: Francis X. Speidel, M.D., Senior Vice President Medical Affairs and Chief Quality Officer
CIO: Kenneth Bixel, Senior Vice President and Chief Information Officer
CHR: Jerry Dittmann, Vice President Human Resources
Web address: www.mountnittany.org
| | 23 | 10 | 172 | 9260 | 109 | 180184 | 1304 | 87621 | 38272 | 846 |

SUNBURY—Northumberland County

★ **SUNBURY COMMUNITY HOSPITAL**, 350 North Eleventh Street, Zip 17801–0737; tel. 570/286–3333, (Total facility includes 29 beds in nursing home–type unit) (Nonreporting) **A**9 10
Primary Contact: Edwin L. Hansen, Chief Executive Officer
CFO: Randy B. Morris, Chief Financial Officer
CHR: Colleen Albright, Vice President Administration and Human Relations
Web address: www.schopc.org
| | 23 | 10 | 105 | — | — | — | — | — | — | — |

SUSQUEHANNA—Susquehanna County

BARNES–KASSON COUNTY HOSPITAL, 400 Turnpike Street, Zip 18847–1638; tel. 570/853–3135, (Total facility includes 58 beds in nursing home–type unit) **A**9 10 **F**2 11 12 27 28 32 33 45 51 52 53 54 55 59 81 84 88 92 94 96 97 106 109 110
Primary Contact: Sara C. Iveson, Executive Director
Web address: www.barnes–kasson.org
| | 23 | 10 | 99 | 1603 | 78 | 26628 | 25 | 16695 | 7395 | 262 |

TITUSVILLE—Crawford County

★ **TITUSVILLE AREA HOSPITAL**, 406 West Oak Street, Zip 16354–1404; tel. 814/827–1851 **A**9 10 **F**9 11 12 22 23 27 28 32 33 37 45 46 48 51 55 58 59 60 61 63 65 69 81 82 84 87 88 97 106 110
Primary Contact: Anthony J. Nasralla, FACHE, President and Chief Executive Officer
CFO: Paul Mattis, Vice President Finance
CMO: William Sonnenberg, M.D., Medical Staff President
CIO: Deanna Callahan, Director Information Systems
CHR: Jeffrey Saintz, Vice President Human Resources
Web address: www.titusvillehospital.org
| | 23 | 10 | 56 | 2755 | 32 | 77116 | 266 | 27229 | 11472 | 273 |

TORRANCE—Westmoreland County

□ **TORRANCE STATE HOSPITAL**, Torrance Road, Zip 15779–0111, Mailing Address: P.O. Box 111, Zip 15779–0111; tel. 724/459–8000 **A**1 10 **F**2 12 21 22 26 27 28 29 30 31 32 45 53 58 60 71 74 76 94 96 106 108
Primary Contact: Edna I. McCutcheon, Chief Executive Officer
| | 12 | 22 | 233 | 126 | 222 | 0 | 0 | 39189 | 23677 | 471 |

Hospital, Address, Telephone, Approval, Facility, and Physician Codes, Health Care System	Classi-fication Codes		Utilization Data					Expense (thousands) of dollars		
	Control	Service	Staffed Beds	Admissions	Census	Outpatient Visits	Births	Total	Payroll	Personnel

★ American Hospital Association (AHA) membership
☐ Joint Commission on Accreditation of Healthcare Organizations (JCAHO) accreditation
○ American Osteopathic Association (AOA) accreditation
△ Commission on Accreditation of Rehabilitation Facilities (CARF) accreditation

TOWANDA—Bradford County

✠ **MEMORIAL HOSPITAL**, One Hospital Drive, Zip 18848–9702; tel. 570/265–2191, (Total facility includes 119 beds in nursing home–type unit) **A**1 9 10 **F**6 8 9 11 12 21 22 27 29 30 33 36 37 38 39 45 46 48 51 52 55 58 59 60 62 63 64 65 66 69 81 82 84 85 88 92 93 94 95 97 106 108 110 **S** Quorum Health Resources, Plano, TX
Primary Contact: Gary A. Baker, President
CFO: William K. Rohrbach, Vice President Fiscal Affairs
CMO: Joseph Biancarelli, M.D., President Medical Staff
CIO: Karen Brown, Director Information Systems
CHR: Linda Berry, Vice President Human Resources
Web address: www.memorialhospital.org
`23 10 162 2355 141 55070 176 27650 13022 430`

TROY—Bradford County

★ ○ **TROY COMMUNITY HOSPITAL**, 100 John Street, Zip 16947–0036; tel. 570/297–2121 **A**9 10 11 18 **F**9 12 21 22 26 27 28 29 33 39 44 48 53 63 66 81 88 92 94 97 108 **P**8 **S** Guthrie Healthcare System, Sayre, PA
Primary Contact: Staci Covey, Administrator
CFO: Bernie Smith, Chief Financial Officer
CMO: Vance A. Good, M.D., Chief Medical Staff
Web address: www.guthrie.org
`23 10 30 597 19 21353 0 8516 3806 96`

TUNKHANNOCK—Wyoming County

✠ **TYLER MEMORIAL HOSPITAL**, 880 State Road 6 West, Zip 18657–6149; tel. 570/836–2161 **A**1 9 10 **F**22 23 26 27 28 33 48 52 53 55 58 59 60 61 63 66 69 81 88 96 97 106 108
Primary Contact: William M. Milligan, Jr, President and Chief Executive Officer
CFO: Thomas Dougherty, Chief Financial Officer
CIO: Dan Diljak, Chief Information Officer
CHR: Jill Smith, Director Human Resources
Web address: www.tylerhospital.com
`23 10 58 2456 25 48303 232 22280 7981 305`

TYRONE—Blair County

★ **TYRONE HOSPITAL**, One Hospital Drive, Zip 16686–1810; tel. 814/684–1255 **A**9 10 18 **F**12 21 33 59 63 69 81 84 88 94 97 108 110 **P**5 **S** Quorum Health Resources, Plano, TX
Primary Contact: Walter S. Van Dyke, Chief Executive Officer
CFO: George Berger, Chief Financial Officer
CIO: Steve Gildea, Director Management Information Systems
CHR: Leeann Price, Director Human Resources
Web address: www.tyronehospital.org
`23 10 59 1508 13 8725 130 12563 5014 126`

UNIONTOWN—Fayette County

✠ **UNIONTOWN HOSPITAL**, 500 West Berkeley Street, Zip 15401–5596; tel. 724/430–5000, (Total facility includes 19 beds in nursing home–type unit) **A**1 2 9 10 **F**9 11 12 15 17 21 26 27 28 29 33 40 48 52 55 57 58 59 61 62 63 68 69 81 82 84 85 87 88 92 93 94 96 106 108
Primary Contact: Paul Bacharach, President and Chief Executive Officer
CFO: Steven P. Handy, CPA, Senior Vice President, Chief Financial Officer and Chief Information Officer
CIO: Steven P. Handy, CPA, Senior Vice President, Chief Financial Officer and Chief Information Officer
Web address: www.uniontownhospital.com
`23 10 206 10024 137 194838 773 84446 33653 986`

UPLAND—Delaware County

✠ ○ △ **CROZER–CHESTER MEDICAL CENTER**, One Medical Center Boulevard, Zip 19013–3995; tel. 610/447–2000, (Includes SPRINGFIELD HOSPITAL, 190 West Sproul Road, Springfield, Zip 19064–2097; tel. 610/328–8700; TAYLOR HOSPITAL, 175 East Chester Pike, Ridley Park, Zip 19078–2212; tel. 610/595–6000) **A**1 2 3 5 7 8 9 10 11 12 **F**1 2 5 6 9 10 11 12 13 14 15 17 19 21 22 23 24 26 27 28 29 30 31 33 34 35 36 37 39 40 42 44 45 46 48 50 51 52 53 55 56 57 58 59 60 61 62 63 64 65 66 68 69 70 71 72 73 74 75 76 77 78 79 80 81 82 83 84 85 86 87 88 89 90 93 94 95 96 97 98 108 109 110 **P**6 **S** Crozer–Keystone Health System, Springfield, PA
Primary Contact: Joan K. Richards, Chief Executive Officer
COO: Joseph Saunders, Chief Operating Officer
CFO: Richard I. Bennett, Senior Vice President and Chief Financial Officer
CMO: Gary D. Wendell, M.D., President Medical and Dental Staff
CIO: Robert E. Wilson, Vice President and Chief Information Officer
CHR: Eugene Zegar, Vice President Human Resources
Web address: www.crozer.org
`23 10 600 27896 450 347734 2006 421116 177141 3051`

WARMINSTER—Bucks County

✠ **WARMINSTER HOSPITAL**, 225 Newtown Road, Zip 18974–5221; tel. 215/441–6600 **A**1 3 5 9 10 **F**2 12 15 21 23 26 29 31 33 44 46 48 52 53 55 62 63 64 68 69 71 75 76 81 82 84 88 94 96 106 108 110 **S** TENET Healthcare Corporation, Dallas, TX
Primary Contact: Andrew E. Harris, Chief Executive Officer
CFO: Anthony Zumpano, Chief Financial Officer
Web address: www.warminsterhospital.com
`33 10 151 4704 69 61379 0 50459 20066 469`

Hospital, Address, Telephone, Approval, Facility, and Physician Codes, Health Care System	Classi-fication Codes		Utilization Data					Expense (thousands) of dollars		
★ American Hospital Association (AHA) membership □ Joint Commission on Accreditation of Healthcare Organizations (JCAHO) accreditation ○ American Osteopathic Association (AOA) accreditation △ Commission on Accreditation of Rehabilitation Facilities (CARF) accreditation	Control	Service	Staffed Beds	Admissions	Census	Outpatient Visits	Births	Total	Payroll	Personnel

WARREN—Warren County

WARREN GENERAL HOSPITAL, Two Crescent Park West, Zip 16365–0068, Mailing Address: P.O. Box 68, Zip 16365–0068; tel. 814/723–4973, (Total facility includes 16 beds in nursing home–type unit) **A**9 10 **F**9 11 12 21 22 23 26 27 28 32 33 36 37 42 46 48 51 52 53 55 58 59 60 61 62 63 64 69 70 71 72 75 76 79 80 81 82 85 87 88 92 94 95 96 106 108 110
Primary Contact: John P. Papalia, CHE, Chief Executive Officer
Web address: www.wgh.org
| 23 | 10 | 105 | 3590 | 54 | 124449 | 335 | 44427 | 20181 | 510 |

□ **WARREN STATE HOSPITAL**, 33 Main Drive, Zip 16365–5001; tel. 814/723–5500 **A**1 10 **F**2 22 32 45 58 60 66 71 94 108
Primary Contact: Carmen N. Ferranto, Chief Executive Officer
| 12 | 22 | 250 | 242 | 210 | 0 | 0 | 38523 | 22517 | 492 |

WASHINGTON—Washington County

✚ **WASHINGTON HOSPITAL**, 155 Wilson Avenue, Zip 15301–3398; tel. 724/225–7000, (Total facility includes 17 beds in nursing home–type unit) **A**1 2 3 5 6 9 10 12 13 **F**2 4 9 11 12 15 17 19 21 22 23 24 26 27 28 29 30 31 32 33 36 37 38 39 41 42 44 46 47 48 49 50 52 55 57 58 59 60 61 62 63 64 65 68 69 70 71 72 73 74 75 76 79 80 81 82 84 85 86 87 88 92 93 94 96 98 106 107 108 109 **P**1 7
Primary Contact: Telford W. Thomas, President and Chief Executive Officer
COO: Gary B. Weinstein, Executive Vice President
CFO: Michael J. Roney, Vice President Finance and Chief Financial Officer
CMO: William P. Pearson, M.D., Vice President Medical Affairs
CIO: Rodney Louk, Vice President Information Systems
CHR: William H. Cline, Vice President Human Resources
Web address: www.washingtonhospital.org
| 23 | 10 | 265 | 14582 | 190 | 650261 | 1084 | 168521 | 74297 | 1638 |

WAYNESBORO—Franklin County

✚ **WAYNESBORO HOSPITAL**, 501 East Main Street, Zip 17268–2394; tel. 717/765–4000 **A**1 9 10 19 **F**2 9 11 12 21 22 23 27 28 33 42 46 47 48 52 53 57 58 59 60 61 62 63 64 65 66 69 81 82 84 87 88 93 94 95 96 97 106 108 109 110 **P**8 **S** Summit Health, Chambersburg, PA
Primary Contact: Kenneth L. Shur, Vice President and Chief Operating Officer
CFO: Patrick W. O'Donnell, CPA, Vice President Finance
Web address: www.summithealth.org
| 23 | 10 | 62 | 3082 | 35 | 98826 | 397 | 37701 | 18979 | 445 |

WAYNESBURG—Greene County

★ **GREENE COUNTY MEMORIAL HOSPITAL**, Seventh Street and Bonar Avenue, Zip 15370–1697; tel. 724/627–3101, (Total facility includes 20 beds in nursing home–type unit) **A**9 10 **F**2 9 12 21 26 27 28 33 37 41 46 47 48 51 58 60 63 64 65 66 69 81 83 84 85 86 87 88 92 94 96 106 **P**6
Primary Contact: Raoul M. Walsh, Chief Executive Officer
CFO: Gina Barrett, Chief Financial Officer
CIO: Brad Cumberledge, Director Information Services
Web address: www.gcmhcare.com
| 23 | 10 | 45 | 2531 | 34 | 52106 | 0 | 24546 | 11163 | 288 |

WELLSBORO—Tioga County

✚ **SOLDIERS AND SAILORS MEMORIAL HOSPITAL**, 32–36 Central Avenue, Zip 16901–1899; tel. 570/724–1631 **A**1 9 10 20 **F**2 9 11 12 14 27 28 33 52 55 58 59 62 63 64 66 69 71 75 76 81 82 84 87 88 92 93 94 108 **P**7
Primary Contact: Jan E. Fisher, President and Chief Executive Officer
CFO: Ronald Gilbert, Jr, Chief Financial Officer
CMO: F Ardell Thomas, M.D., Chief Medical Officer
CIO: Joe Bubacz, Director Information Resources
CHR: Gene Yajko, Director Human Resources
Web address: www.laurelhs.org
| 23 | 10 | 83 | 2925 | 34 | 93287 | 304 | 30662 | 13320 | 410 |

WERNERSVILLE—Berks County

□ **WERNERSVILLE STATE HOSPITAL**, Route 422, Zip 19565–0300, Mailing Address: P.O. Box 300, Zip 19565–0300; tel. 610/678–3411 **A**1 10 **F**21 22 32 41 45 46 53 57 58 60 62 65 66 71 73 74 76 94 96 106 108 110 **P**1
Primary Contact: Irene Taylor, Chief Executive Officer
| 12 | 22 | 182 | 115 | 174 | 0 | 0 | 32984 | 19517 | 392 |

WEST CHESTER—Chester County

✚ **CHESTER COUNTY HOSPITAL**, 701 East Marshall Street, Zip 19380–4412; tel. 610/431–5000 **A**1 2 5 9 10 **F**2 9 11 12 14 15 17 19 21 23 24 26 27 28 29 33 36 37 38 39 41 44 46 47 48 51 52 53 54 55 56 58 59 60 61 62 63 64 65 66 70 79 80 81 82 84 87 88 90 94 95 96 98 106 108 109 110 **P**3 4 6
Primary Contact: H. L. Perry Pepper, FACHE, President
COO: Michael Barber, Senior Vice President Operations
CFO: Kenneth E. Flickinger, Corporate Vice President Finance
CMO: Richard D. Donze, D.O., Senior Vice President Medical Affairs
CIO: Mary Buckley, Vice President Information Technology
Web address: www.cchosp.com
| 23 | 10 | 219 | 13457 | 154 | 389861 | 1921 | 123134 | 54610 | 1269 |

WEST GROVE—Chester County

□ **JENNERSVILLE REGIONAL HOSPITAL**, 1015 West Baltimore Pike, Zip 19390–9499; tel. 610/869–1000 **A**1 2 9 10 **F**2 9 11 12 21 23 27 28 33 36 39 40 48 51 55 59 60 61 63 66 69 81 82 84 85 88 93 94 95 96 97 108 109 **S** Community Health Systems, Inc., Brentwood, TN
Primary Contact: Bryan J. Hargis, President and Chief Executive Officer
Web address: www.jennersville.com
| 33 | 10 | 59 | 3681 | 35 | 17264 | 383 | 39006 | 15308 | 329 |

Many Facility Codes have changed. Please refer to the AHA Guide Code Chart. © 2005 AHA Guide

Hospital, Address, Telephone, Approval, Facility, and Physician Codes, Health Care System	Classi-fication Codes		Utilization Data					Expense (thousands) of dollars		
★ American Hospital Association (AHA) membership □ Joint Commission on Accreditation of Healthcare Organizations (JCAHO) accreditation ○ American Osteopathic Association (AOA) accreditation △ Commission on Accreditation of Rehabilitation Facilities (CARF) accreditation	Control	Service	Staffed Beds	Admissions	Census	Outpatient Visits	Births	Total	Payroll	Personnel

WEST READING—Berks County

☒ △ **READING HOSPITAL AND MEDICAL CENTER**, Sixth Avenue and Spruce Street, Zip 19611–1428, Mailing Address: P.O. Box 16052, Zip 19612–6052; tel. 610/988–8000 **A**1 2 3 5 6 7 9 10 12 **F**2 4 9 10 11 12 15 17 19 21 22 23 26 27 28 29 33 36 37 38 41 42 44 46 47 48 50 51 52 53 55 56 57 58 59 60 61 62 63 64 65 66 68 69 70 71 72 73 74 75 76 77 78 79 80 81 82 84 85 87 88 89 90 92 93 94 96 98 106 108 109 **P**8
Primary Contact: Charles Sullivan, President and Chief Executive Officer
COO: Scott R. Wolfe, CPA, Senior Vice President and Chief Operating Officer
CFO: Steven Finkel, Vice President and Treasurer
CMO: Gerald Malick, M.D., Vice President and Medical Director
CIO: Jayashree Raman, Vice President and Chief Information Officer
Web address: www.readinghospital.org | 23 | 10 | 598 | 29017 | 441 | 787871 | 3320 | 391109 | 167013 | 3806 |

WILKES–BARRE—Luzerne County

CLEAR BROOK MANOR, 1100 East Northampton Street, Zip 18702–9803; tel. 570/823–1171, (Nonreporting)
Primary Contact: Robert Piccone, President | 23 | 82 | 50 | — | — | — | — | — | — | — |

☒ **GEISINGER WYOMING VALLEY MEDICAL CENTER**, 1000 East Mountain Drive, Zip 18711–0027; tel. 570/826–7300 **A**1 2 9 10 **F**6 9 10 11 12 14 15 17 19 23 26 27 28 32 33 35 37 40 45 46 47 48 52 53 57 58 59 60 61 62 63 64 65 66 68 69 72 75 79 80 81 82 84 85 86 87 88 89 93 94 95 96 106 107 108 **S** Geisinger Health System, Danville, PA
Primary Contact: Lissa Bryan–Smith, Chief Administrative Officer
CFO: Jeffrey T. Wright, Chief Financial Officer
CMO: Jeffrey R. Folk, M.D., Medical Director
CIO: Frank Richards, Chief Information Officer
CHR: Margaret Heffers, Assistant Vice President Human Resources
Web address: www.geisinger.org | 23 | 10 | 138 | 7787 | 101 | 273974 | 696 | 96662 | 28903 | 904 |

☒ △ **JOHN HEINZ INSTITUTE OF REHABILITATION MEDICINE**, 150 Mundy Street, Zip 18702; tel. 570/826–3800 **A**1 7 9 10 **F**2 9 21 22 24 26 27 28 29 37 42 45 46 48 51 52 53 58 60 65 68 69 94 95 96 108 110
Primary Contact: Thomas E. Pugh, Chief Executive Officer
CFO: Mike Avvisato, Vice President and Chief Financial Officer
CIO: John Regula, Chief Information Officer
Web address: www.allied–services.org | 23 | 46 | 94 | 2217 | 81 | 131536 | 0 | 29034 | 14541 | 431 |

□ **KINDRED HOSPITAL–WOMING VALLEY**, 575 North River Street, 7th Floor, Zip 18764; tel. 570/552–7620, (Nonreporting) **A**1 10
Primary Contact: Erin Pica, Chief Executive Officer | 33 | 49 | 36 | — | — | — | — | — | — | — |

☒ **MERCY HOSPITAL OF WILKES–BARRE**, 25 Church Street, Zip 18765–0999, Mailing Address: P.O. Box 658, Zip 18765–0658; tel. 570/826–3100, (Total facility includes 20 beds in nursing home–type unit) (Nonreporting) **A**1 9 10 **S** Catholic Healthcare Partners, Cincinnati, OH
Primary Contact: Eugene Bassett, Chief Administrative Officer
COO: Eugene Bassett, Chief Administrative Officer
CFO: Stephen Franko, Vice President Finance and Chief Financial Officer
CMO: Gerald Maloney, D.O., Chief Medical Officer
CHR: Maggie Lund, Vice President Human Resources
Web address: www.mhs–nepa.com | 21 | 10 | 188 | — | — | — | — | — | — | — |

☒ △ **VETERANS AFFAIRS MEDICAL CENTER**, 1111 East End Boulevard, Zip 18711–0026; tel. 570/824–3521, (Total facility includes 108 beds in nursing home–type unit) **A**1 2 3 5 7 9 **F**2 3 4 5 8 9 10 21 22 23 26 27 28 29 31 32 33 35 36 37 38 39 41 42 43 44 45 46 47 48 49 50 51 52 53 55 57 58 60 61 62 63 65 66 69 70 71 73 74 75 76 77 81 85 87 88 92 93 94 96 106 108 109 110 **P**6 **S** Department of Veterans Affairs, Washington, DC
Primary Contact: Roland E. Moore, Director
COO: C Gene Molino, Acting Chief Operating Officer
CFO: Donald E. Foote, Fiscal Officer
CMO: William K. Grossman, M.D., Chief of Staff
Web address: www.va.gov/sta/guide/home.asp | 45 | 10 | 184 | 2119 | 143 | 351634 | 0 | 130154 | 52695 | 1052 |

□ **WYOMING VALLEY HEALTH CARE SYSTEM**, 575 North River Street, Zip 18764–0001; tel. 570/829–8111, (Includes WILKES–BARRE GENERAL HOSPITAL), (Total facility includes 26 beds in nursing home–type unit) **A**1 2 9 10 **F**2 3 9 11 12 14 15 17 19 21 22 23 26 28 33 35 39 41 42 43 44 46 47 48 50 52 55 57 58 59 61 62 63 65 66 69 79 81 82 84 85 86 87 88 92 94 96 108 109 110
Primary Contact: William R. Host, M.D., President and Chief Executive Officer
Web address: www.wvhc.org | 23 | 10 | 353 | 18054 | 268 | 533164 | 1310 | 184118 | 70647 | 1752 |

WILLIAMSBURG—Blair County

COVE FORGE BEHAVIORAL HEALTH SYSTEM, New Beginnings Road, P.O. Box B, Zip 16693; tel. 814/832–2121, (Nonreporting)
Primary Contact: Mark Sarneso, Chief Executive Officer | 33 | 82 | 100 | — | — | — | — | — | — | — |

PA

Hospital, Address, Telephone, Approval, Facility, and Physician Codes, Health Care System	Classi-fication Codes		Utilization Data					Expense (thousands) of dollars		
★ American Hospital Association (AHA) membership □ Joint Commission on Accreditation of Healthcare Organizations (JCAHO) accreditation ○ American Osteopathic Association (AOA) accreditation △ Commission on Accreditation of Rehabilitation Facilities (CARF) accreditation	Control	Service	Staffed Beds	Admissions	Census	Outpatient Visits	Births	Total	Payroll	Personnel

WILLIAMSPORT—Lycoming County

☒ △ **SUSQUEHANNA HEALTH SYSTEM**, 777 Rural Avenue, Zip 17701–3198; tel. 570/321–1000, (Includes DIVINE PROVIDENCE HOSPITAL, 1100 Grampian Boulevard, Zip 17701–1995; tel. 570/326–8000; MUNCY VALLEY HOSPITAL, 215 East Water Street, Muncy, Zip 17756–8700; tel. 570/546–8282; WILLIAMSPORT HOSPITAL AND MEDICAL CENTER, 777 Rural Avenue, tel. 570/321–1000; Linda S. Widra, FACHE, Ph.D., R.N., Administrator), (Total facility includes 139 beds in nursing home–type unit) **A**1 2 7 9 10 13 **F**1 6 7 9 10 11 12 14 15 17 19 21 22 23 24 26 27 28 29 32 33 35 36 37 38 39 40 41 42 44 45 46 47 48 49 50 51 52 53 55 57 58 59 60 61 62 63 65 66 68 69 70 71 72 73 76 77 79 81 82 84 86 88 89 92 93 94 95 96 97 98 106 107 108 109 110 **P**3 7 8
Primary Contact: Steven P. Johnson, President and Chief Executive Officer
COO: Steven P. Johnson, Senior Vice President and Chief Operating Officer
CFO: Charles J. Santangelo, CPA, Senior Vice President and Chief Financial Officer
CMO: George Manchester, M.D., Senior Vice President Medical Affairs
CIO: Pamela R. Wirth, Vice President and Chief Information Officer
Web address: www.shscares.org — 23 10 414 14022 291 434048 1281 201503 87362 2567

WINDBER—Somerset County

☒ **WINDBER MEDICAL CENTER**, 600 Somerset Avenue, Zip 15963–1331; tel. 814/467–3000 **A**1 9 10 **F**2 10 11 12 21 22 23 26 27 28 29 30 33 36 37 38 41 42 45 46 47 48 51 52 53 55 58 59 60 62 63 64 65 66 69 73 81 82 85 86 87 88 90 92 94 95 96 106 108 109
Primary Contact: Nicholas Jacobs, FACHE, President
COO: James Eckenrode, M.D., Chief Operating Officer and Chief Medical Officer
CFO: Linda Fanale, Principal Partner
CMO: James Eckenrode, M.D., Chief Operating Officer and Chief Medical Officer
CIO: Steve Ahern, Chief Information Officer
CHR: Tonia Gordon, Principal Partner
Web address: www.windbercare.com — 23 10 63 2055 19 82907 74 30911 12324 376

WYNNEWOOD—Montgomery County

LANKENAU HOSPITAL, 100 Lancaster Avenue West, Zip 19096–3411; tel. 610/645–2000 **A**2 3 5 9 10 12 13 **F**2 11 12 14 15 17 19 20 21 22 23 24 27 28 29 30 31 32 33 35 36 37 38 39 40 41 42 44 45 46 47 48 52 55 56 57 58 59 60 61 62 63 64 65 66 69 70 79 80 81 82 84 85 86 87 88 90 92 93 94 95 96 98 100 101 106 108 110 **P**7 **S** Jefferson Health System, Wayne, PA
Primary Contact: Gail A. Egan, President
Web address: www.jeffersonhealth.org — 23 10 330 19793 257 167602 2344 265401 90336 1663

YORK—York County

☒ **HEALTHSOUTH REHABILITATION HOSPITAL OF YORK**, 1850 Normandie Drive, Zip 17404–1534; tel. 717/767–6941 **A**1 9 10 **F**2 21 28 37 51 52 58 65 66 68 69 94 96 108 110 **S** HEALTHSOUTH Corporation, Birmingham, AL
Primary Contact: Cheryl Fleming, Administrator
COO: Cheryl Kuhn, Director Marketing Operations
CFO: Jay Shoen, Chief Financial Officer
CMO: Bruce Sicilia, M.D., Medical Director
CHR: Sarah Arthur, Director Human Resources
Web address: www.healthsouth.com — 33 46 90 1936 72 69076 0 22345 12436 —

★ ○ **MEMORIAL HOSPITAL**, 325 South Belmont Street, Zip 17403–2609, Mailing Address: P.O. Box 15118, Zip 17405–5118; tel. 717/843–8623 **A**9 10 11 12 13 **F**2 6 9 11 12 15 21 22 23 26 27 28 29 33 36 37 39 44 46 47 48 50 51 52 53 55 58 59 60 61 62 63 64 65 66 69 77 82 84 87 88 93 94 95 96 106 107 108 110 **P**6
Primary Contact: Sally J. Dixon, President and Chief Executive Officer
COO: Tom Harlow, Vice President Operations
CFO: Richard Imbimbo, Chief Financial Officer
CMO: Anthony Minissale, M.D., Vice President Medical Affairs
CIO: Clifford Weaver, Management Information Systems Director
Web address: www.mhyork.org — 23 10 100 5544 61 122207 764 61286 29815 770

☒ **YORK HOSPITAL**, 1001 South George Street, Zip 17405–3645; tel. 717/851–2345 **A**1 2 3 5 9 10 **F**2 6 9 10 11 12 14 15 17 19 21 22 23 24 26 27 28 29 30 32 33 34 35 37 38 39 42 43 44 46 47 48 49 50 52 53 55 56 57 58 59 60 61 62 63 64 65 66 69 70 71 72 73 74 75 76 77 78 79 80 81 82 84 85 87 88 90 93 94 95 96 98 106 107 108 109 110 **P**8 **S** WellSpan Health, York, PA
Primary Contact: Richard L. Seim, President and Chief Executive Officer
COO: Raymond Rosen, Vice President Operations
CFO: Michael F. O'Connor, Senior Vice President Finance
CMO: Peter M. Hartmann, M.D., Vice President Medical Affairs
CIO: William J. Gillespie, Vice President and Chief Information Officer
CHR: Robert J. Batory, Vice President Human Resources
Web address: www.wellspan.org — 23 10 460 29157 369 806846 2885 380721 149449 3271

RHODE ISLAND

Hospital, Address, Telephone, Approval, Facility, and Physician Codes, Health Care System	Classi- fication Codes		Utilization Data					Expense (thousands) of dollars		
★ American Hospital Association (AHA) membership □ Joint Commission on Accreditation of Healthcare Organizations (JCAHO) accreditation ○ American Osteopathic Association (AOA) accreditation △ Commission on Accreditation of Rehabilitation Facilities (CARF) accreditation	Control	Service	Staffed Beds	Admissions	Census	Outpatient Visits	Births	Total	Payroll	Personnel
CRANSTON—Providence County										
□ **ELEANOR SLATER HOSPITAL**, John O. Pastore Center, 111 Howard Avenue, Zip 02920–0269, Mailing Address: P.O. Box 8269, Zip 02920–8269; tel. 401/462–3085 **A**1 10 **F**27 28 32 37 44 45 46 48 50 58 60 65 66 71 73 74 76 94 96 108 110 **P**6 Primary Contact: Richard H. Freeman, Chief Executive Officer Web address: www.mhrh.state.ri.us	12	80	370	130	369	0	0	—	—	—
EAST PROVIDENCE—Providence County										
□ **EMMA PENDLETON BRADLEY HOSPITAL**, 1011 Veterans Memorial Parkway, Zip 02915–5099; tel. 401/432–1000, (Nonreporting) **A**1 3 5 9 10 **S** Lifespan Corporation, Providence, RI Primary Contact: Daniel J. Wall, President and Chief Executive Officer Web address: www.lifespan.org	23	52	51	—	—	—	—	—	—	—
NEWPORT—Newport County										
□ △ **NEWPORT HOSPITAL**, 11 Friendship Street, Zip 02840–2299; tel. 401/846–6400, (Total facility includes 19 beds in nursing home–type unit) **A**1 2 7 9 10 **F**9 11 12 21 22 23 26 27 28 29 33 40 44 46 47 48 49 52 53 55 57 58 59 60 61 62 63 64 65 68 69 70 71 73 75 78 81 82 84 87 88 92 93 94 96 106 108 109 **S** Lifespan Corporation, Providence, RI Primary Contact: Arthur J. Sampson, President and Chief Executive Officer Web address: www.newporthospital.org	23	10	130	6599	92	107749	687	86890	33956	589
NORTH PROVIDENCE—Providence County										
□ **ST. JOSEPH HEALTH SERVICES OF RHODE ISLAND**, 200 High Service Avenue, Zip 02904–5199; tel. 401/456–3000, (Includes OUR LADY OF FATIMA HOSPITAL, 200 High Service Avenue, Zip 02904; ST. JOSEPH HOSPITAL FOR SPECIALTY CARE, 21 Peace Street, Providence, Zip 02907; tel. 401/456–3000), (Total facility includes 24 beds in nursing home–type unit) **A**1 2 6 9 10 **F**8 9 12 21 22 23 24 26 28 29 32 33 39 40 44 45 46 48 49 52 53 57 58 60 61 62 63 66 68 69 71 73 75 76 77 78 81 82 84 88 91 92 93 94 96 107 108 109 110 **P**5 Primary Contact: H. John Keimig, President and Chief Executive Officer Web address: www.saintjosephri.com	21	10	295	11920	235	237956	0	145864	71935	1543
NORTH SMITHFIELD—Providence County										
LANDMARK MEDICAL CENTER–FOGARTY UNIT See Landmark Medical Center, Woonsocket										
□ **REHABILITATION HOSPITAL OF RHODE ISLAND**, 116 Eddie Dowling Highway, Zip 02896; tel. 401/766–0800, (Nonreporting) **A**1 10 Primary Contact: Lisa LaDew, Chief Executive Officer Web address: www.rhri.net	32	46	70	—	—	—	—	—	—	—
PAWTUCKET—Providence County										
⊞ △ **MEMORIAL HOSPITAL OF RHODE ISLAND**, 111 Brewster Street, Zip 02860–4499; tel. 401/729–2000 **A**1 2 3 5 7 8 9 10 **F**2 9 11 12 14 15 21 23 24 26 27 28 29 32 33 37 38 39 40 42 44 45 46 48 49 50 51 52 53 54 55 57 58 59 60 61 62 63 64 65 68 69 70 81 82 84 87 88 92 93 94 95 96 106 107 108 109 **P**6 8 Primary Contact: Francis R. Dietz, President COO: Shelley MacDonald, R.N., Senior Vice President Operations CFO: Michael Ryan, Senior Vice President Finance CMO: Andrew Artenstein, Physician in Chief, Medicine CIO: Raymond Ortelt, Director Information Systems Web address: www.mhri.org	23	10	159	7888	107	199818	644	149900	75594	1418
PROVIDENCE—Providence County										
⊞ **BUTLER HOSPITAL**, 345 Blackstone Boulevard, Zip 02906–4829; tel. 401/455–6200 **A**1 3 5 9 10 **F**3 4 22 26 27 29 31 33 35 44 47 53 57 65 71 72 74 75 76 77 78 94 96 106 108 **P**8 **S** Care New England Health System, Providence, RI Primary Contact: Patricia R. Recupero, JD, M.D., President and Chief Executive Officer COO: Walter Dias, Vice President and Chief Operating Officer CFO: Bonnie Baker, Vice President Finance and Chief Financial Officer CMO: Steven Rasmussen, M.D., Medical Director CIO: Bruce A. Reirden, Vice President and Chief Information Officer CHR: Timothy Bigelow, Director of Human Resources Web address: www.butler.org	23	22	113	4242	100	30406	0	51293	31084	542
□ **MIRIAM HOSPITAL**, 164 Summit Avenue, Zip 02906–2895; tel. 401/793–2500 **A**1 2 3 5 8 9 10 **F**12 14 15 17 19 21 22 26 27 29 33 42 46 47 48 52 53 55 57 58 60 62 63 66 69 70 81 82 84 87 88 92 94 96 106 108 **P**3 5 6 7 **S** Lifespan Corporation, Providence, RI Primary Contact: Kathleen C. Hittner, M.D., President and Chief Executive Officer Web address: www.lifespan.org	23	10	208	13216	181	81530	0	256145	102308	1552

Hospital, Address, Telephone, Approval, Facility, and Physician Codes, Health Care System	Classi-fication Codes		Utilization Data					Expense (thousands) of dollars		
★ American Hospital Association (AHA) membership ☐ Joint Commission on Accreditation of Healthcare Organizations (JCAHO) accreditation ○ American Osteopathic Association (AOA) accreditation △ Commission on Accreditation of Rehabilitation Facilities (CARF) accreditation	Control	Service	Staffed Beds	Admissions	Census	Outpatient Visits	Births	Total	Payroll	Personnel
☐ **RHODE ISLAND HOSPITAL**, 593 Eddy Street, Zip 02903–4900; tel. 401/444–4000 **A**1 2 3 5 8 9 10 **F**12 14 15 16 17 18 19 20 21 22 23 24 27 29 32 33 34 37 38 40 41 42 43 46 47 48 49 50 52 53 55 57 58 60 61 62 63 65 66 67 69 71 73 74 75 76 77 78 79 81 82 84 86 88 92 93 94 95 96 98 101 106 107 108 110 **P**3 5 6 **S** Lifespan Corporation, Providence, RI Primary Contact: Joseph F. Amaral, M.D., President and Chief Executive Officer Web address: www.lifespan.org	23	10	579	29964	455	281376	0	656486	268472	4321
✦ **ROGER WILLIAMS MEDICAL CENTER**, 825 Chalkstone Avenue, Zip 02908–4735; tel. 401/456–2000, (Total facility includes 16 beds in nursing home–type unit) **A**1 2 3 5 8 9 10 **F**4 6 8 9 12 15 17 21 22 23 26 27 28 29 33 40 44 46 47 48 50 51 52 53 55 58 60 61 62 63 65 66 69 70 71 73 76 77 78 81 82 84 87 88 92 93 94 96 108 109 110 **P**3 5 8 Primary Contact: Robert A. Urciuoli, President and Chief Executive Officer CFO: Joseph Iannoni, Chief Financial Officer CMO: Thomas DeNucci, M.D., President Medical Staff CIO: Susan Cerrone Abely, Vice President and Chief Information Officer CHR: Joseph Eastman, Director Human Resources Web address: www.rwmc.com ST. JOSEPH HOSPITAL FOR SPECIALTY CARE See St. Joseph Health Services of Rhode Island, North Providence	23	10	151	8556	124	206297	0	121886	52783	1320
✦ **VETERANS AFFAIRS MEDICAL CENTER**, 830 Chalkstone Avenue, Zip 02908–4799; tel. 401/457–3042 **A**1 3 5 **F**2 4 21 22 23 26 27 28 31 32 33 34 37 39 40 44 45 47 48 49 50 51 52 55 57 58 60 61 62 63 64 65 66 69 70 71 73 74 75 76 77 81 82 85 87 88 92 94 96 106 108 109 110 **S** Department of Veterans Affairs, Washington, DC Primary Contact: Vincent Ng, Director Web address: www.va.gov/sta/guide/home.asp	45	10	75	3187	60	271388	0	109568	59376	720
✦ **WOMEN AND INFANTS HOSPITAL OF RHODE ISLAND**, 101 Dudley Street, Zip 02905–2499; tel. 401/274–1100 **A**1 2 3 5 8 9 10 **F**2 4 9 11 12 21 22 23 26 27 28 29 30 33 35 36 37 38 39 45 46 47 48 52 53 56 58 59 61 63 64 65 66 70 73 74 77 78 81 88 89 90 94 96 98 106 108 109 **P**5 6 8 **S** Care New England Health System, Providence, RI Primary Contact: Constance A. Howes, President and Chief Executive Officer COO: Dick Argys, Executive Vice President and Chief Operating Officer CFO: John M. Sutherland, III, Vice President Finance CIO: Bruce A. Reirden, Vice President Information Services Web address: www.womenandinfants.org	23	44	197	14496	185	—	9654	242871	118248	2068
WAKEFIELD—Washington County										
✦ **SOUTH COUNTY HOSPITAL**, 100 Kenyon Avenue, Zip 02879–4299; tel. 401/782–8000, (Nonreporting) **A**1 2 9 10 Primary Contact: Louis R. Giancola, President and Chief Executive Officer CFO: Michael J. Koziol, Vice President and Chief Financial Officer CMO: Joseph J. O'Neill, Vice President, Medical Affairs CIO: Gary Croteau, Chief Information Officer CHR: Maggie Thomas, Chief Human Resources Officer Web address: www.schospital.com	23	10	83	—	—	—	—	—	—	—
WARWICK—Kent County										
✦ △ **KENT COUNTY MEMORIAL HOSPITAL**, 455 Tollgate Road, Zip 02886–2770; tel. 401/737–7000 **A**1 2 7 9 10 **F**2 9 11 12 15 21 22 23 24 26 27 28 29 30 32 33 36 37 38 39 40 44 45 46 47 48 49 50 53 55 57 58 59 60 61 62 63 64 65 66 68 69 70 71 73 75 76 81 82 84 85 87 88 93 94 95 96 108 109 110 **P**6 8 **S** Care New England Health System, Providence, RI Primary Contact: Robert E. Baute, M.D., President and Chief Executive Officer CFO: Paul Beaudoin, Vice President Finance and Chief Financial Officer CMO: John R. Audett, M.D., Vice President, Medical Director CIO: Bruce A. Reirden, Vice President and Chief Information Officer CHR: Michael Dacey, Vice President Human Resources Web address: www.kentri.org	23	10	320	15162	231	233914	1133	192107	95245	1788
WESTERLY—Washington County										
✦ **WESTERLY HOSPITAL**, 25 Wells Street, Zip 02891–2934; tel. 401/596–6000 **A**1 9 10 **F**2 9 11 12 15 21 22 23 26 28 29 33 36 37 40 44 46 47 48 49 50 52 55 57 58 59 60 61 62 63 65 66 69 70 73 75 81 82 84 85 87 88 89 94 95 96 98 106 107 108 109 110 **P**1 Primary Contact: Charles S. Kinney, President and Chief Executive Officer CFO: Jeanne LaChance, Vice President Finance and Chief Financial Officer CIO: Crystal Pilon, Chief Information Officer Web address: www.westerlyhospital.org	23	10	125	4686	50	444038	444	65918	30106	421
WOONSOCKET—Providence County										
☐ **LANDMARK MEDICAL CENTER**, 115 Cass Avenue, Zip 02895–4731; tel. 401/769–4100, (Includes LANDMARK MEDICAL CENTER–FOGARTY UNIT, Eddie Dowling Highway, North Smithfield, Zip 02896; tel. 401/766–0800; LANDMARK MEDICAL CENTER–WOONSOCKET UNIT), (Nonreporting) **A**1 2 9 10 Primary Contact: Gary J. Gaube, President Web address: www.landmarkmedical.org	23	10	133	—	—	—	—	—	—	—

Many Facility Codes have changed. Please refer to the AHA Guide Code Chart.

© 2005 AHA Guide

SOUTH CAROLINA

Hospital, Address, Telephone, Approval, Facility, and Physician Codes, Health Care System	Classification Codes		Utilization Data					Expense (thousands) of dollars		
★ American Hospital Association (AHA) membership □ Joint Commission on Accreditation of Healthcare Organizations (JCAHO) accreditation ○ American Osteopathic Association (AOA) accreditation △ Commission on Accreditation of Rehabilitation Facilities (CARF) accreditation	Control	Service	Staffed Beds	Admissions	Census	Outpatient Visits	Births	Total	Payroll	Personnel

ABBEVILLE—Abbeville County

☒ **ABBEVILLE COUNTY MEMORIAL HOSPITAL**, 901 West Greenwood Street, Zip 29620–0887, Mailing Address: P.O. Box 887, Zip 29620–0887; tel. 864/366–5011 **A**1 9 10 18 **F**2 11 12 14 21 28 29 33 41 44 46 48 51 52 55 57 58 59 60 62 63 64 66 69 81 87 91 93 96 107 108 **P**8 **S** Quorum Health Resources, Plano, TX
Primary Contact: Alvin Hoover, CHE, Chief Executive Officer
CFO: Sheldon Bontreger, Chief Financial Officer
CMO: Juan Bonetti, Chief of Staff
CHR: Libba Deery, Human Resource Manager
| 13 | 10 | 40 | 1183 | 10 | 25610 | 118 | 15244 | 6531 | 220 |

AIKEN—Aiken County

□ **AIKEN REGIONAL MEDICAL CENTERS**, 302 University Parkway, Zip 29801–2757, Mailing Address: P.O. Box 1117, Zip 29802–1117; tel. 803/641–5000, (Includes AURORA PAVILION, 655 Medical Park Drive, Zip 29801; tel. 803/641–5900) **A**1 9 10 **F**4 9 12 14 15 17 19 21 23 27 29 33 37 42 44 46 47 48 52 55 59 61 62 63 64 65 66 68 71 72 73 74 75 76 77 78 79 80 81 83 84 87 91 92 93 95 107 108 **S** Universal Health Services, Inc., King of Prussia, PA
Primary Contact: Kathryn D. Justyn, Chief Executive Officer
Web address: www.aikenregional.com
| 33 | 10 | 269 | 11635 | 148 | 126374 | 963 | 124409 | 44585 | 709 |

ANDERSON—Anderson County

☒ **ANMED HEALTH MEDICAL CENTER**, (Formerly Anderson Area Medical Center), 800 North Fant Street, Zip 29621–5793; tel. 864/261–1000, (Includes ANMED HEALTH WOMEN'S AND CHILDREN'S HOSPITAL, 2000 East Greenville Street, Zip 29621; tel. 864/261–1000), (Total facility includes 10 beds in nursing home–type unit) **A**1 2 3 5 9 10 **F**2 9 11 12 14 15 17 19 21 22 23 26 27 28 29 32 33 37 39 40 42 44 46 47 48 49 50 51 52 53 55 57 58 59 60 61 62 63 64 65 66 70 71 72 73 74 75 76 77 80 81 82 84 85 86 87 88 92 94 95 96 106 107 108 109 110 **P**7 8
Primary Contact: John A. Miller, Jr, FACHE, President
COO: William T. Manson, III, Executive Vice President
CFO: Jerry A. Parrish, Vice President
CMO: Mike Tillirson, Executive Vice President
CIO: Darrell Hickman, Director Information Services
CHR: Doug Douglas, Vice President Human Resources
Web address: www.anmed.com
| 23 | 10 | 412 | 18580 | 259 | 597513 | 1863 | — | — | 2759 |

☒ **ANMED HEALTHOUTH REHABILITATION HOSPITAL**, 1 Spring Back Way, Zip 29621; tel. 864/716–2600, (Total facility includes 10 beds in nursing home–type unit) (Nonreporting) **A**1 10 **S** HEALTHSOUTH Corporation, Birmingham, AL
Primary Contact: Michele M. Skripps, Administrator
| 32 | 46 | 40 | — | — | — | — | — | — | — |

□ **PATRICK B. HARRIS PSYCHIATRIC HOSPITAL**, 130 Highway 252, Zip 29622; tel. 864/231–2600 **A**1 10 **F**26 27 28 29 46 65 66 71 73 74 75 76 93 105 107
Primary Contact: John Fletcher, Chief Executive Officer
Web address: www.patrickbharrispsychiatrichospital.com/index.htm
| 12 | 22 | 154 | 1179 | 118 | — | — | 16980 | 9545 | 342 |

BAMBERG—Bamberg County

☒ **BAMBERG COUNTY MEMORIAL HOSPITAL AND NURSING CENTER**, 509 North Street, Zip 29003–0507, Mailing Address: P.O. Box 507, Zip 29003–0507; tel. 803/245–4321, (Total facility includes 88 beds in nursing home–type unit) **A**1 9 10 **F**9 12 21 22 28 33 37 45 46 48 49 58 59 60 63 66 69 81 88 92 97
Primary Contact: Warren E. Hammett, Administrator
CFO: Barney E. Osborne, Jr, Chief Financial Officer
CMO: Danette McAlhaney, M.D., Chief of Staff
CHR: Susan Hiers, Director of Human Resources
| 13 | 10 | 128 | 1627 | 104 | 17250 | 100 | 23280 | 9384 | 177 |

BARNWELL—Barnwell County

☒ **BARNWELL COUNTY HOSPITAL**, 811 Reynolds Road, Zip 29812–1555; tel. 803/259–1000 **A**1 9 10 20 **F**2 12 21 27 28 29 33 46 48 52 55 63 65 66 69 81 87 92 107
Primary Contact: Robert E. Waters, Chief Executive Officer
CFO: Jessica Burriss, Chief Financial Officer
CMO: Richard E. Boyles, M.D., Chief of Medical Staff
CIO: Randal Padgett, Information Systems Manager
CHR: Sherry Donaldson, Director of Human Resources
| 13 | 10 | 33 | 1165 | 14 | 14671 | 0 | 10137 | 4984 | 140 |

BEAUFORT—Beaufort County

☒ **BEAUFORT MEMORIAL HOSPITAL**, 955 Ribaut Road, Zip 29902–5441; tel. 843/522–5200 **A**1 9 10 20 **F**2 9 11 12 15 21 22 23 26 27 28 29 33 37 39 40 41 46 47 48 49 51 52 54 55 57 58 59 60 61 62 63 64 65 66 68 69 71 73 74 75 76 77 81 82 84 85 88 92 94 96 98 106 108 109 110
Primary Contact: David E. Brown, President and Chief Executive Officer
Web address: www.bmhsc.org
| 13 | 10 | 193 | 12142 | 146 | 41864 | 1823 | 94271 | 39463 | 971 |

Hospital, Address, Telephone, Approval, Facility, and Physician Codes, Health Care System	Classi- fication Codes		Utilization Data					Expense (thousands) of dollars		
★ American Hospital Association (AHA) membership □ Joint Commission on Accreditation of Healthcare Organizations (JCAHO) accreditation ○ American Osteopathic Association (AOA) accreditation △ Commission on Accreditation of Rehabilitation Facilities (CARF) accreditation	Control	Service	Staffed Beds	Admissions	Census	Outpatient Visits	Births	Total	Payroll	Personnel
⊠ **NAVAL HOSPITAL**, 1 Pinckney Boulevard, Zip 29902–6148; tel. 843/228–5301, (Nonreporting) **A**1 5 **S** Bureau of Medicine and Surgery, Department of the Navy, Washington, DC Primary Contact: Captain James Hoffower, Commanding Officer CIO: Lieutenant Dallas Jones, Head Management Information	43	10	20	—	—	—	—	—	—	—
BENNETTSVILLE—Marlboro County										
□ **MARLBORO PARK HOSPITAL**, 1138 Cheraw Highway, Zip 29512–0738, Mailing Address: P.O. Box 738, Zip 29512–0738; tel. 843/479–2881 **A**1 9 10 **F**2 11 12 21 27 29 33 36 46 48 50 55 58 60 62 63 65 66 69 71 74 76 81 82 86 88 92 94 97 108 109 **P**8 **S** Community Health Systems, Inc., Brentwood, TN Primary Contact: Bobby Ginn, Chief Executive Officer Web address: www.marlboroparkhospital.com	32	10	98	2147	25	14142	179	20090	7248	165
CAMDEN—Kershaw County										
⊠ **KERSHAW COUNTY MEDICAL CENTER**, 1315 Roberts Street, Zip 29020–7003, Mailing Address: P.O. Box 7003, Zip 29020–7003; tel. 803/432–4311, (Total facility includes 88 beds in nursing home–type unit) **A**1 9 10 **F**2 6 9 11 12 19 21 22 23 24 26 27 28 29 32 33 35 36 39 40 41 42 44 45 46 47 48 50 51 52 53 55 58 59 60 61 62 63 64 65 66 69 70 81 82 84 87 88 92 93 94 96 108 109 Primary Contact: Donnie J. Weeks, President and Chief Executive Officer Web address: www.kcmc.org	13	10	195	5271	154	89694	426	67629	27642	729
CHARLESTON—Charleston County										
⊠ **BON SECOURS–ST. FRANCIS XAVIER HOSPITAL**, 2095 Henry Tecklenburg Drive, Zip 29414–0001, Mailing Address: P.O. Box 160001, Zip 29414–0001; tel. 843/402–1000 **A**1 9 10 **F**2 6 11 12 15 21 22 26 27 28 29 33 37 39 40 46 48 49 52 53 55 57 58 59 60 62 63 64 65 66 69 73 81 83 86 87 92 93 94 95 107 108 109 **S** Carolinas HealthCare System, Charlotte, NC Primary Contact: Allen P. Carroll, Chief Executive Officer CFO: Bret Johnson, Chief Financial Officer CMO: Gerald Shealy, M.D., Chief CIO: Michael Taylor, Chief Information Officer CHR: Doug Harrison, Vice President Human Resources Web address: www.ropersaintfrancis.com	23	10	145	8889	111	122128	1382	82272	32833	783
★ **CHARLESTON MEMORIAL HOSPITAL**, 326 Calhoun Street, Zip 29401–1189; tel. 843/792–2300 **A**9 10 **F**2 12 22 27 28 33 87 93 **S** MUSC Medical Center of Medical University of South Carolina, Charleston, SC Primary Contact: Thomas F. Moore, Administrator COO: W Stuart Smith, Vice President of Clinical Operations and Executive Director CFO: Todd Nimmich, Fiscal Services Manager CMO: John Heffner, Executive Medical Director CIO: Sid McMahon, Assistant Administrator Information Management CHR: Helena G. Bastian, Director Human Resource Services Web address: www.musc.edu	12	10	20	262	17	15400	0	20267	6292	146
⊠ **HEALTHSOUTH REHABILITATION HOSPITAL OF CHARLESTON**, 9181 Medcom Street, Zip 29406–9168; tel. 843/820–7777, (Nonreporting) **A**1 10 **S** HEALTHSOUTH Corporation, Birmingham, AL Primary Contact: Troy Powell, Administrator Web address: www.healthsouth.com	33	46	46	—	—	—	—	—	—	—
□ **KINDRED HOSPITAL–CHARLESTON**, 326 Calhoun Street, 3rd Floor, Zip 29401; tel. 843/876–8670 **A**1 10 **F**2 21 68 92 93 109 Primary Contact: Joey Fisher, Chief Executive Officer Web address: www.khcharleston.com	33	80	39	330	28	0	0	—	—	84
⊠ **MUSC MEDICAL CENTER OF MEDICAL UNIVERSITY OF SOUTH CAROLINA**, 169 Ashley Avenue, Zip 29425; tel. 843/792–2300 **A**1 2 3 5 8 9 10 **F**2 3 4 6 10 11 12 14 15 16 17 18 19 **20 21** 22 23 26 27 28 29 33 34 35 37 38 39 45 46 48 49 50 52 53 55 56 57 58 59 61 62 63 64 65 66 69 71 72 73 74 75 76 77 78 79 80 81 83 84 87 89 91 92 93 98 99 100 101 103 106 107 108 109 **S** MUSC Medical Center of Medical University of South Carolina, Charleston, SC Primary Contact: Stuart Smith, Vice President Clinical Operations and Executive Director CFO: Lisa P. Montgomery, Administrator Finance CMO: John Heffner, Medical Director CIO: Frank Clark, Chief Information Officer CHR: Betts Ellis, Administrator, Institutional Relations Web address: www.musc.edu	12	10	590	28212	466	647480	2188	595861	207249	4611
NAVAL HOSPITAL See North Charleston										
□ **PALMETTO LOWCOUNTRY BEHAVIORAL HEALTH SYSTEM**, 2777 Speissegger Drive, Zip 29405–8299; tel. 843/747–5830 **A**1 9 10 **F**3 4 21 27 28 29 65 66 71 72 74 75 76 77 78 92 93 95 **S** Psychiatric Solutions, Franklin, TN Primary Contact: Anne Battin, Administrator Web address: www.plbhs.com	33	22	70	2291	42	7186	0	—	—	179

Many Facility Codes have changed. Please refer to the AHA Guide Code Chart.

© 2005 AHA Guide

Hospital, Address, Telephone, Approval, Facility, and Physician Codes, Health Care System	Classi-fication Codes		Utilization Data					Expense (thousands) of dollars		
★ American Hospital Association (AHA) membership □ Joint Commission on Accreditation of Healthcare Organizations (JCAHO) accreditation ○ American Osteopathic Association (AOA) accreditation △ Commission on Accreditation of Rehabilitation Facilities (CARF) accreditation	Control	Service	Staffed Beds	Admissions	Census	Outpatient Visits	Births	Total	Payroll	Personnel
⊠ **RALPH H. JOHNSON VETERANS AFFAIRS MEDICAL CENTER**, 109 Bee Street, Zip 29401–5703; tel. 843/577–5011 **A**1 2 3 5 8 **F**1 2 4 13 14 15 17 19 21 22 23 26 27 28 29 31 32 36 37 38 42 44 46 47 48 49 50 51 52 53 54 55 58 60 61 62 63 64 65 66 70 71 73 74 75 76 77 78 79 80 81 83 87 91 92 93 95 98 107 108 109 **S** Department of Veterans Affairs, Washington, DC Primary Contact: William A. Mountcastle, CHE, Director COO: Johnetta McKinley, Associate Director CFO: Marcia Balonis, Chief Financial Officer CMO: Florence N. Hutchison, M.D., Chief of Staff CIO: Michael Cortright, Chief Information Officer CHR: Joyce Cornett, Human Resources Officer Web address: www.va.gov/sta/guide/home.asp	45	10	85	4003	73	17514	0	140126	87653	1051
⊠ **ROPER HOSPITAL**, 316 Calhoun Street, Zip 29401–1125; tel. 843/724–2000 **A**1 2 3 5 9 10 **F**2 6 9 11 12 14 15 17 19 21 22 23 26 27 28 29 33 39 40 41 42 45 46 47 48 49 50 51 52 54 55 57 58 59 60 61 62 63 64 65 66 68 69 73 79 80 81 83 84 85 86 87 91 92 93 94 95 98 106 107 108 109 **S** Carolinas HealthCare System, Charlotte, NC Primary Contact: Matthew J. Severance, Chief Executive Officer CFO: Bret Johnson, Chief Financial Officer CMO: Steven D. Shapiro, M.D., Interim Vice President for Medical Affairs CIO: Michael Taylor, Chief Information Officer CHR: Douglas Harrison, Vice President for Human Resources Web address: www.carealliance.com	23	10	345	16836	276	264349	846	247422	91040	2199
⊠ **TRIDENT MEDICAL CENTER**, 9330 Medical Plaza Drive, Zip 29406–9195; tel. 843/797–7000, (Total facility includes 25 beds in nursing home–type unit) **A**1 2 9 10 **F**6 11 12 15 17 19 21 22 23 28 29 33 42 46 47 48 49 50 52 55 56 57 58 59 60 61 62 63 65 66 69 79 80 81 82 84 85 87 88 92 94 95 96 108 109 **S** HCA, Nashville, TN Primary Contact: Terry J. Gunn, President and Chief Executive Officer COO: Jim Rardin, Chief Operating Officer CFO: Karl E. Gorrell, Chief Financial Officer CIO: Steve Burns, Driector Information Services Web address: www.tridenthealthsystem.com	33	10	275	16037	224	195509	2175	206275	—	1028
CHERAW—Chesterfield County										
□ **CHESTERFIELD GENERAL HOSPITAL**, 711 Chesterfield Highway, Zip 29520, Mailing Address: P.O. Box 151, Zip 29520–0151; tel. 843/537–7881 **A**1 9 10 **F**2 9 11 12 21 24 28 29 33 46 48 50 52 55 58 59 62 63 64 65 66 81 82 85 88 89 94 97 108 **P**6 **S** Community Health Systems, Inc., Brentwood, TN Primary Contact: Vance Reynolds, Chief Executive Officer Web address: www.chesterfieldgeneral.com	33	10	59	2473	24	41249	174	22004	8462	221
CHESTER—Chester County										
⊠ **CHESTER COUNTY HOSPITAL AND NURSING CENTER**, 1 Medical Park Drive, Zip 29706–9799; tel. 803/581–3151, (Total facility includes 100 beds in nursing home–type unit) (Nonreporting) **A**1 9 10 **S** Health Management Associates, Naples, FL Primary Contact: William H. Bundy, Chief Executive Officer CIO: Lannie Atkinson, Chf Information Officer Web address: www.chospital.org	12	10	154	—	—	—	—	—	—	—
CLINTON—Laurens County										
⊠ **LAURENS COUNTY HEALTHCARE SYSTEM**, Highway 76 East, Zip 29325–2331, Mailing Address: P.O. Box 976, Zip 29325–0976; tel. 864/833–9100, (Includes LAURENS COUNTY HOSPITAL, Mailing Address: P.O. Box 976, Zip 29325; tel. 803/833–9100), (Total facility includes 14 beds in nursing home–type unit) **A**1 9 10 **F**2 9 11 12 14 21 22 23 24 26 27 28 29 33 40 46 48 50 52 55 58 59 60 61 62 63 64 65 69 81 82 84 88 92 93 94 96 106 109 110 **P**8 **S** Quorum Health Resources, Plano, TX Primary Contact: Richard E. D'Alberto, FACHE, Chief Executive Officer CFO: Dan Elmer, Chief Financial Officer CMO: Jay Montgomery, Chief of Staff CIO: Wade Williams, Information Systems Director CHR: Brent O'Shields, Human Resources Director Web address: www.lchcs.org	16	10	90	3409	57	68359	387	40457	15588	394
WHITTEN CENTER, Highway 76 East, Zip 29325, Mailing Address: P.O. Box 239, Zip 29325; tel. 864/833–2733, (Nonreporting) Primary Contact: William Killion, Chief Executive Officer	12	62	22	—	—	—	—	—	—	—
COLUMBIA—Richland County										
□ **G. WERBER BRYAN PSYCHIATRIC HOSPITAL**, 220 Faison Drive, Zip 29203–3295; tel. 803/935–7146 **A**1 10 **F**21 22 26 27 28 31 41 44 46 48 65 66 71 74 75 76 93 98 107 Primary Contact: W. Russell Hughes, Ph.D., Director Web address: www.state.sc.us/dmh/bryan	12	22	245	1979	238	0	0	26554	16440	556
⊠ **HEALTHSOUTH REHABILITATION HOSPITAL**, 2935 Colonial Drive, Zip 29203–6811; tel. 803/254–7777 **A**1 10 **F**21 26 28 29 44 52 58 60 65 66 68 69 93 94 95 105 **P**5 **S** HEALTHSOUTH Corporation, Birmingham, AL Primary Contact: Candace Knox, Administrator CFO: Susan Bregin, Controller CMO: Devin Thayer, M.D., Medical Director CHR: Christine Butts, Human Resources Director Web address: www.healthsouth.com	33	46	96	1545	71	0	0	16880	9377	199

SC

SC

Hospital, Address, Telephone, Approval, Facility, and Physician Codes, Health Care System	Classi-fication Codes		Utilization Data					Expense (thousands) of dollars		
★ American Hospital Association (AHA) membership □ Joint Commission on Accreditation of Healthcare Organizations (JCAHO) accreditation ○ American Osteopathic Association (AOA) accreditation △ Commission on Accreditation of Rehabilitation Facilities (CARF) accreditation	Control	Service	Staffed Beds	Admissions	Census	Outpatient Visits	Births	Total	Payroll	Personnel
INTERMEDICAL HOSPITAL OF SOUTH CAROLINA, Taylor at Marion Street, Zip 29220; tel. 803/296–3097 **A**10 **F**2 21 22 26 28 93	23	10	35	188	22	0	0	8422	2336	75
MIDLANDS CENTER, 8301 Farrow Road, Zip 29203–3294; tel. 803/935–7508, (Nonreporting) Primary Contact: Ronald P. Childs, FACHE, Health Services Administrator	12	12	24	—	—	—	—	—	—	—
⊠ **PALMETTO HEALTH BAPTIST/COLUMBIA**, Taylor at Marion Street, Zip 29220–0001; tel. 803/296–5010, (Total facility includes 22 beds in nursing home–type unit) **A**1 2 3 5 9 10 **F**2 10 11 12 14 15 21 22 23 26 27 28 29 33 36 37 40 42 50 51 52 53 55 56 57 58 59 60 61 62 63 64 65 66 69 71 72 73 74 75 76 77 78 81 82 84 85 86 88 92 94 96 108 109 110 **S** Palmetto Health Alliance, Columbia, SC Primary Contact: James M. Bridges, Executive Vice President and Chief Operating Officer COO: James M. Bridges, Executive Vice President and Chief Operating Officer CFO: Paul K. Duane, Executive Vice President and Chief Financial Officer CMO: Mark James Mayson, M.D., Chief of Staff CIO: David Garrett, Executive Vice President for Information Technology CHR: Trip Gregory, Senior Vice President of Human Resources Web address: www.palmettohealth.org	23	10	409	20613	306	206644	3780	244293	102690	2182
⊠ **PALMETTO HEALTH RICHLAND**, Five Richland Medical Park Drive, Zip 29203–6897, Mailing Address: P.O. Box 2266, Zip 29203–2266; tel. 803/434–7000 **A**1 2 3 5 8 9 10 **F**1 2 4 5 9 11 12 14 15 17 19 21 22 23 24 26 27 28 29 32 33 34 42 43 44 46 47 48 49 50 52 53 55 56 58 59 60 61 62 63 65 66 69 70 71 72 73 74 75 76 77 78 79 81 83 84 86 87 89 91 92 93 94 95 97 98 105 107 108 109 **S** Palmetto Health Alliance, Columbia, SC Primary Contact: James E. Lathren, Executive Vice President and Chief Operating Officer COO: James E. Lathren, Executive Vice President and Chief Operating Officer CFO: Paul K. Duane, Executive Vice President and Chief Financial Officer CMO: Greta Harper, M.D., Chief of Staff CIO: David Garrett, Executive Vice President for Information Technology CHR: Trip Gregory, Senior Vice President of Human Resources Web address: www.palmettohealth.org	23	10	633	32967	494	486688	2337	432089	161440	3859
⊠ **SISTERS OF CHARITY PROVIDENCE HOSPITALS**, 2435 Forest Drive, Zip 29204–2098; tel. 803/865–4500, (Includes PROVIDENCE HOSPITAL NORTHEAST, 120 Gateway Corporate Boulevard, Zip 29203–9611; tel. 803/865–4500; Debbie Johnson, Vice President) **A**1 9 10 **F**2 9 14 15 17 19 21 22 26 27 28 29 32 33 42 46 47 48 49 50 52 53 55 57 62 63 64 65 66 69 73 81 83 84 86 87 92 93 95 107 108 **P**7 **S** Sisters of Charity of St. Augustine Health System, Cleveland, OH Primary Contact: Stephen A. Purves, CHE, President and Chief Executive Officer COO: Michael L. McEachern, Senior Vice President and Chief Operating Officer CFO: James S. Green, Senior Vice President and Chief Financial Officer CMO: Robert L. Mobley, Vice President, Medical Affairs CIO: Lib Cumbee, Director Information Systems CHR: Richard Grooms, Vice President, Human Resources Web address: www.provhosp.org	21	10	251	12870	186	78866	0	171012	54509	1138
SOUTH CAROLINA STATE HOSPITAL, 2100 Bull Street, Zip 29201–2104, Mailing Address: P.O. Box 119, Zip 29202–0119; tel. 803/898–2261 **F**2 22 26 27 28 32 44 71 73 74 75 76 83 107 Primary Contact: Peter Getz, Administrator Web address: www.state.sc.us/dmh	12	22	117	73	79	7803	0	9337	3967	72
□ **WILLIAM S. HALL PSYCHIATRIC INSTITUTE**, 1800 Colonial Drive, Zip 29203–6827, Mailing Address: P.O. Box 119, Zip 29202–0119; tel. 803/898–1693 **A**1 3 5 10 **F**1 2 26 27 28 41 60 65 69 71 72 73 74 75 77 92 93 105 107 108 Primary Contact: W. Russell Hughes, Ph.D., Director Web address: www.state.sc.us/dmh	12	22	85	435	66	10027	0	20077	12882	352
⊠ **WM. JENNINGS BRYAN DORN VETERANS AFFAIRS MEDICAL CENTER**, 6439 Garners Ferry Road, Zip 29209–1639; tel. 803/776–4000, (Total facility includes 78 beds in nursing home–type unit) **A**1 2 3 5 **F**2 4 8 12 15 21 22 23 26 27 28 29 32 37 41 42 44 45 46 47 48 49 50 51 52 55 58 60 61 62 63 65 66 69 70 71 73 74 75 76 77 81 82 84 85 87 88 92 94 96 107 108 109 **S** Department of Veterans Affairs, Washington, DC Primary Contact: Brian Heckert, Chief Executive Officer COO: Terrence Hannigan, Chief Operating Officer CFO: James Cavanaugh, Chief Fiscal Officer CMO: Alfred Boykin, Chief Medical Officer CIO: David C. Owings, Director Information Management Service Line Web address: www.va.gov/sta/guide/home.asp	45	10	180	5725	165	536130	0	—	—	1365

Many Facility Codes have changed. Please refer to the AHA Guide Code Chart.

© 2005 AHA Guide

Hospital, Address, Telephone, Approval, Facility, and Physician Codes, Health Care System	Classi-fication Codes		Utilization Data					Expense (thousands) of dollars		
★ American Hospital Association (AHA) membership □ Joint Commission on Accreditation of Healthcare Organizations (JCAHO) accreditation ○ American Osteopathic Association (AOA) accreditation △ Commission on Accreditation of Rehabilitation Facilities (CARF) accreditation	Control	Service	Staffed Beds	Admissions	Census	Outpatient Visits	Births	Total	Payroll	Personnel

CONWAY—Horry County

☒ **CONWAY MEDICAL CENTER**, 300 Singleton Ridge Road, Zip 29526–9175, Mailing Address: P.O. Box 829, Zip 29528–0829; tel. 843/347–7111, (Total facility includes 88 beds in nursing home–type unit) **A**9 10 **F**2 9 10 11 12 15 21 22 27 28 29 33 40 41 42 46 47 48 49 50 55 58 59 60 62 63 65 66 69 81 82 84 86 87 88 92 93 94 96 108 109
Primary Contact: Philip A. Clayton, President and Chief Executive Officer
CFO: Bret Barr, Vice President Fiscal Services
CMO: D Mark Wilson, M.D., Chief of Staff
CIO: Mickey Waters, Director Information Technology
CHR: Craig Hyman, Vice President Human Resources
Web address: www.conwaymedicalcenter.com
| 23 | 10 | 244 | 9614 | 179 | 112295 | 1255 | — | — | 826 |

DARLINGTON—Darlington County

MCLEOD MEDICAL CENTER–DARLINGTON See McLeod Health, Florence

DILLON—Dillon County

☒ **MCLEOD MEDICAL CENTER–DILLON**, (Formerly Saint Eugene Medical Center), 301 East Jackson Street, Zip 29536–2509, Mailing Address: P.O. Box 1327, Zip 29536–1327; tel. 843/774–4111 **A**1 9 10 **F**2 9 11 12 21 22 24 26 27 28 29 33 37 39 41 46 47 48 53 55 58 59 60 62 63 64 66 69 81 82 84 88 94 96 98 106 108 109
Primary Contact: Donald D. Sandoval, FACHE, Administrator
CFO: Fulton Ervin, Controller
CMO: Paul D. Freel, M.D., Chief of Staff
CIO: Edna Hale, Director Information System
CHR: Cynthia Causey, Associate Administrator Human and Mission Services
Web address: www.mcleodhealth.org
| 23 | 10 | 86 | 4944 | 42 | 38138 | 273 | 28603 | 12437 | 257 |

EASLEY—Pickens County

☒ **PALMETTO HEALTH BAPTIST EASLEY**, 200 Fleetwood Drive, Zip 29640–2076, Mailing Address: P.O. Box 2129, Zip 29641–2129; tel. 864/442–7200 **A**1 9 10 **F**2 9 11 12 15 21 22 28 29 32 33 44 46 48 52 55 58 59 62 63 65 66 68 81 82 84 88 94 96 108 109 **S** Palmetto Health Alliance, Columbia, SC
Primary Contact: Roddey E. Gettys, III, Executive Vice President and Chief Operating Officer
CFO: J Larry Pope, Vice President Finance
Web address: www.palmettohealth.org
| 23 | 10 | 79 | 5116 | 52 | 37035 | 563 | 56805 | 21796 | 641 |

EDGEFIELD—Edgefield County

☒ **EDGEFIELD COUNTY HOSPITAL**, 300 Ridge Medical Plaza, Zip 29824; tel. 803/637–3174 **A**1 9 10 18 **F**2 9 26 27 28 29 33 36 44 46 48 53 58 60 63 69 70 83 87 93 95 96
Primary Contact: Samuel S. Gregory, Chief Executive Officer
CFO: Troy Pickens, Chief Financial Officer
CMO: George Rainsford, M.D., Chief of Medical Staff
CIO: Leslie Seigler, Public Relations
CHR: Sylvia Byrd, Director Human Resources
| 13 | 10 | 40 | 869 | 8 | 10916 | 0 | 7999 | 3931 | 131 |

FAIRFAX—Allendale County

★ **ALLENDALE COUNTY HOSPITAL**, 1787 Allendale Fairfax Highway, Zip 29827–0278, Mailing Address: Box 218, Zip 29827–0218; tel. 803/632–3311, (Total facility includes 44 beds in nursing home–type unit) **A**9 10 18 **F**11 12 27 28 29 33 36 46 48 50 52 59 63 65 66 69 70 81 88 92 94 97 109 **P**6
Primary Contact: M. K. Hiatt, Administrator
CFO: Julie Allen, Chief Financial Officer
| 16 | 10 | 69 | 563 | 46 | 39004 | 104 | 9854 | 4392 | 127 |

FLORENCE—Florence County

☒ △ **CAROLINAS HOSPITAL SYSTEM**, 805 Pamplico Highway, Zip 29505–6050, Mailing Address: P.O. Box 100550, Zip 29501–0550; tel. 843/674–5000 **A**1 7 9 10 **F**3 4 21 29 52 58 65 66 68 83 93 105 107 **S** Triad Hospitals, Inc., Plano, TX
Primary Contact: James O'Laughlin, Chief Executive Officer
COO: Lance Jones, Chief Operating Officer
CFO: Paul Morris, Chief Financial Officer
CMO: Thomas Phillips, Chief of Staff
CIO: Larry McElveen, Chief Information Officer
CHR: John Coker, Director, Human Resource
Web address: www.carolinashospital.com
| 33 | 46 | 66 | 1315 | 35 | — | — | 10729 | 5758 | 207 |

☒ **HEALTHSOUTH REHABILITATION HOSPITAL**, 900 East Cheves Street, Zip 29506–2704; tel. 843/679–9000, (Nonreporting) **A**1 10 **S** HEALTHSOUTH Corporation, Birmingham, AL
Primary Contact: James Scott Rowe, Administrator
CFO: Robert Wheeler, Controller
CMO: Adora Matthews, M.D., Medical Director
CHR: Susan Trantham, Director of Human Resources
Web address: www.healthsouth.com
| 33 | 46 | 88 | — | — | — | — | — | — | — |

Hospital, Address, Telephone, Approval, Facility, and Physician Codes, Health Care System	Classi-fication Codes		Utilization Data					Expense (thousands) of dollars		
★ American Hospital Association (AHA) membership □ Joint Commission on Accreditation of Healthcare Organizations (JCAHO) accreditation ○ American Osteopathic Association (AOA) accreditation △ Commission on Accreditation of Rehabilitation Facilities (CARF) accreditation	Control	Service	Staffed Beds	Admissions	Census	Outpatient Visits	Births	Total	Payroll	Personnel
✠ **MCLEOD HEALTH**, 555 East Cheves Street, Zip 29506–2617, Mailing Address: P.O. Box 100551, Zip 29501–0551; tel. 843/777–2000, (Includes MCLEOD MEDICAL CENTER–DARLINGTON, 701 Cashua Ferry Road, Darlington, Zip 29532, Mailing Address: P.O. Box 1859, Zip 29540; tel. 843/395–1100; Pat Godbold, Administrator), (Nonreporting) **A**1 2 3 5 9 10 Primary Contact: Robert L. Colones, President and Chief Executive Officer CFO: Michael Browning, Senior Vice President and Chief Financial Officer CMO: Alva W. Whitehead, M.D., Vice President Medical Services CIO: Janice Castle, Vice President and Chief Information Officer CHR: Jeannette Glenn, Vice President, Human Resources and Education and Training Web address: www.mcleodhealth.org	23	10	411	—	—	—	—	—	—	—
✠ **REGENCY HOSPITAL OF FLORENCE**, 121 East Cedar Street, Zip 29506; tel. 843/661–3499, (Nonreporting) **A**1 10 **S** Regency Hospital Company, Alpharetta, GA Primary Contact: Daniel C. Dunmyer, Chief Executive Officer Web address: www.regencyhospital.com	33	80	28	—	—	—	—	—	—	—
FORT JACKSON—Richland County										
✠ **MONCRIEF ARMY COMMUNITY HOSPITAL**, 4500 Stuart Street, Zip 29207–5720; tel. 803/751–2284, (Nonreporting) **A**1 2 5 **S** Department of the Army, Office of the Surgeon General, Falls Church, VA Primary Contact: Colonel James M. Baunchalk, Commander COO: Lieutenant Colonel Daniel Jimenez, Deputy Commander for Clinical Services CFO: Major Jeffery Rimmer, Chief Resource Management Division CMO: Colonel Daniel R. Davidson, Deputy Commander for Clinical Services CIO: Captain Eric C. Drynan, Deputy Commander Information Management CHR: Major Jeffery Rimmer, Chief Resource Management Division Web address: www.moncrief.amedd.army.mil	42	10	60	—	—	—	—	—	—	—
GAFFNEY—Cherokee County										
□ **UPSTATE CAROLINA MEDICAL CENTER**, 1530 North Limestone Street, Zip 29340–4738; tel. 864/487–4271 **A**1 9 10 **F**2 6 9 11 12 21 22 28 29 33 40 46 48 52 55 58 59 60 62 63 65 66 69 81 87 93 94 107 108 **P**8 **S** Health Management Associates, Naples, FL Primary Contact: Joe D. Howell, Executive Director Web address: www.upstatecarolina.org	33	10	125	4633	48	56159	338	31123	13425	364
GEORGETOWN—Georgetown County										
✠ **GEORGETOWN MEMORIAL HOSPITAL**, 606 Black River Road, Zip 29440–3368, Mailing Address: Drawer 1718, Zip 29442–1718; tel. 843/527–7000 **A**1 2 9 10 19 20 **F**2 9 10 11 12 14 15 17 21 22 23 24 28 29 32 33 37 38 39 40 41 42 44 46 47 48 49 50 52 53 55 57 58 59 60 61 62 63 64 65 66 69 70 73 75 81 82 83 84 86 87 92 93 94 95 98 107 108 109 **S** Quorum Health Resources, Plano, TX Primary Contact: Bruce P. Bailey, Chief Executive Officer CFO: Terry L. Kiser, Chief Financial Officer CMO: Charles J. Cohn, M.D., Chief of Staff CHR: Beth Samples, Human Resource Director Web address: www.gmhsc.com	23	10	135	7427	98	103080	436	86841	29634	633
GREENVILLE—Greenville County										
✠ △ **BON SECOURS ST. FRANCIS HEALTH SYSTEM**, One St. Francis Drive, Zip 29601–3207; tel. 864/255–1000, (Total facility includes 12 beds in nursing home–type unit) **A**1 2 7 9 10 **F**2 12 14 15 17 19 21 22 23 27 28 29 33 36 37 38 40 41 46 47 48 49 51 52 53 55 57 58 60 61 62 63 65 66 68 69 81 82 84 87 88 92 94 96 99 106 108 109 110 **P**1 **S** Bon Secours Health System, Inc., Marriottsville, MD Primary Contact: Valinda Rutledge, Chief Executive Officer CFO: Ronnie Hyatt, Vice Pres Finance CMO: Mary Jo Cagle, Acting Chief Medical Officer CIO: Jeff Burke, Chief Information Officer CHR: Lisa Slayton, Vice President Human Resources Web address: www.stfrancishealth.org	23	10	237	9610	151	86556	0	137916	50082	1091
✠ △ **GREENVILLE MEMORIAL HOSPITAL**, 701 Grove Road, Zip 29605–4295; tel. 864/455–7000, (Includes MARSHALL I. PICKENS HOSPITAL; ROGER C. PEACE REHABILITATION HOSPITAL) **A**1 2 3 5 7 8 9 10 **F**2 4 9 11 12 14 15 17 19 21 22 23 24 26 27 28 29 30 31 32 33 34 35 37 39 40 41 42 44 46 47 48 49 50 52 53 55 56 57 58 59 60 61 62 63 64 65 66 67 68 69 70 71 72 73 74 75 76 77 78 81 82 84 85 87 88 89 92 93 94 95 96 98 106 108 109 110 **P**6 7 8 **S** Greenville Hospital System, Greenville, SC Primary Contact: Greg Rusnak, Vice President Web address: www.ghs.org	23	10	806	38123	662	434086	5122	593609	207583	4362
□ **SHRINERS HOSPITALS FOR CHILDREN, GREENVILLE**, 950 West Faris Road, Zip 29605–4277; tel. 864/271–3444 **A**1 3 5 **F**9 26 37 46 47 48 52 53 58 60 62 63 64 65 67 69 70 71 89 92 93 105 107 109 **S** Shriners Hospitals for Children, Tampa, FL Primary Contact: Gary F. Fraley, Administrator Web address: www.shrinershq.org	23	57	50	1078	15	25242	0	21032	11072	219
W. J. BARGE MEMORIAL HOSPITAL, Wade Hampton Boulevard, Zip 29614; tel. 864/242–5100, (Nonreporting) Primary Contact: Aras Pundys, Administrator	23	11	79	—	—	—	—	—	—	—

Many Facility Codes have changed. Please refer to the AHA Guide Code Chart.

© 2005 AHA Guide

Hospital, Address, Telephone, Approval, Facility, and Physician Codes, Health Care System	Classi-fication Codes		Utilization Data					Expense (thousands) of dollars		
★ American Hospital Association (AHA) membership □ Joint Commission on Accreditation of Healthcare Organizations (JCAHO) accreditation ○ American Osteopathic Association (AOA) accreditation △ Commission on Accreditation of Rehabilitation Facilities (CARF) accreditation	Control	Service	Staffed Beds	Admissions	Census	Outpatient Visits	Births	Total	Payroll	Personnel

GREENWOOD—Greenwood County

⊠ **SELF REGIONAL HEALTHCARE**, 1325 Spring Street, Zip 29646–3860; tel. 864/227–4111, (Total facility includes 27 beds in nursing home–type unit) **A**1 2 3 5 9 10 19 **F**2 9 10 11 12 14 15 17 19 22 23 24 26 27 28 29 31 32 33 37 39 41 42 46 47 48 49 51 52 53 55 56 57 58 59 60 61 62 63 65 66 69 70 71 72 73 74 75 76 77 78 81 82 84 87 88 93 94 95 96 98 106 107 108 109 110 **P**8
Primary Contact: M. John Heydel, President and Chief Executive Officer
COO: Fred L. Latham, Executive Vice President and Chief Operating Officer
CFO: Anita Lockridge, Senior Vice President and Chief Financial Officer
CMO: Mark Robirds, Director of Medical Staff
CIO: Patrick Stewart, Vice President of Information Systems
CHR: Susan Jones, Vice President of Human Resources
Web address: www.selfregional.org
| | 23 | 10 | 351 | 15209 | 214 | 212860 | 1478 | 204904 | 81975 | 1839 |

GREER—Greenville County

★ **ALLEN BENNETT HOSPITAL**, 313 Memorial Drive, Zip 29650–1521; tel. 864/848–8200, (Includes ROGER HUNTINGTON NURSING CENTER), (Total facility includes 10 beds in nursing home–type unit) **A**9 10 **F**2 9 11 12 21 22 26 27 28 29 33 35 37 39 40 46 47 48 50 52 53 55 59 62 63 64 65 66 69 81 84 85 88 92 94 108 109 **P**6 7 8 **S** Greenville Hospital System, Greenville, SC
Primary Contact: Phil Feisal, Administrator
Web address: www.ghs.org
| | 23 | 10 | 68 | 3397 | 53 | 95489 | 463 | 43062 | 17612 | 262 |

□ **CAROLINA CENTER FOR BEHAVIORAL HEALTH**, 2700 East Phillips Road, Zip 29650–4816; tel. 864/968–6300, (Nonreporting) **A**1 9 10 **S** Universal Health Services, Inc., King of Prussia, PA
Primary Contact: John Willingham, Chief Executive Officer
Web address: www.thecarolinacenter.com
| | 33 | 22 | 66 | — | — | — | — | — | — | — |

HARDEEVILLE—Beaufort County

★ **COASTAL CAROLINA MEDICAL CENTER**, 1000 Medical Center Drive, Zip 29926, Mailing Address: P.O. Box 1758, Zip 29927–1758; tel. 843/784–8000, (Nonreporting) **A**10 **S** LifePoint Hospitals, Inc., Brentwood, TN
Primary Contact: Eric Deaton, Chief Executive Officer
Web address: www.coastalcarolinamedicalcenter.com
| | 33 | 10 | 41 | — | — | — | — | — | — | — |

HARTSVILLE—Darlington County

□ **CAROLINA PINES REGIONAL MEDICAL CENTER**, 1304 West BoBo Newsom Highway, Zip 29550–4710; tel. 843/339–2100 **A**1 9 10 **F**2 11 12 15 21 26 27 28 29 33 46 48 52 54 55 57 58 59 62 63 64 65 66 69 81 83 84 86 87 91 93 95 98 107 108 109 **S** Health Management Associates, Naples, FL
Primary Contact: David L. Castleberry, Chief Executive Officer
Web address: www.cprmc.com
| | 33 | 10 | 120 | 8679 | 99 | 59231 | 638 | 51316 | 20541 | 463 |

HILTON HEAD ISLAND—Beaufort County

⊠ △ **HILTON HEAD REGIONAL MEDICAL CENTER**, 25 Hospital Center Boulevard, Zip 29926–2738, Mailing Address: P.O. Box 21117, Zip 29925–1117; tel. 843/681–6122 **A**1 7 9 10 20 **F**2 8 9 10 11 12 14 15 17 19 21 22 23 28 29 33 39 42 44 45 46 47 48 50 52 53 55 57 59 60 61 62 63 64 65 66 69 72 73 74 75 76 81 82 84 85 88 92 94 95 96 106 107 108 109 110 **S** TENET Healthcare Corporation, Dallas, TX
Primary Contact: Elizabeth Lamkin, President and Chief Executive Officer
CFO: Todd Lockcuff, Chief Financial Officer
CIO: Stephen Brendler, Director Information Systems
Web address: www.hiltonheadmedctr.com
| | 32 | 10 | 93 | 5198 | 57 | 90402 | 507 | 68103 | 20430 | 445 |

KINGSTREE—Williamsburg County

★ **WILLIAMSBURG REGIONAL HOSPITAL**, 500 Nelson Boulevard, Zip 29556–4027, Mailing Address: P.O. Drawer 568, Zip 29556–0568; tel. 843/355–8888 **A**9 10 18 **F**2 6 9 11 12 21 22 26 27 28 29 33 35 39 44 46 48 52 54 59 60 63 65 66 69 87 92 96 105 107 108
Primary Contact: John C. Hales, Jr, FACHE, Chief Executive Officer
COO: Dan Harrington, Chief Operating Officer and Human Resources Director
CMO: Raymond K. Allen, M.D., Chief of Medical Staff
CIO: Jamie Newsom, Director of Information Systems
Web address: www.w–rh.org
| | 23 | 10 | 34 | 1500 | 14 | 30154 | 195 | 15356 | 6293 | 184 |

LAKE CITY—Florence County

⊠ **LAKE CITY COMMUNITY HOSPITAL**, (Formerly Carolinas Hospital System–Lake City), 258 North Ron McNair Boulevard, Zip 29560–1029, Mailing Address: P.O. Box 1479, Zip 29560–1479; tel. 843/374–2036 **A**1 9 10 **F**12 21 22 27 28 29 33 39 44 46 48 50 52 54 58 60 62 63 65 69 83 87 92 93 94 96 107 108 **S** Quorum Health Resources, Plano, TX
Primary Contact: Clarence W. Bowman, Chief Executive Officer
COO: Deborah Mills, Chief Nursing Officer
CFO: Beth Huggins, Controller
CIO: David Fuller, Director Radiology and Information Systems
| | 33 | 10 | 40 | 1022 | 15 | 36423 | 0 | 15635 | 6690 | 168 |

LANCASTER—Lancaster County

□ △ **SPRINGS MEMORIAL HOSPITAL**, 800 West Meeting Street, Zip 29720–2298; tel. 803/286–1214, (Total facility includes 14 beds in nursing home–type unit) **A**1 5 7 9 10 19 20 **F**2 3 4 9 11 12 14 21 14 21 26 27 28 29 33 36 37 46 48 50 51 52 55 59 60 62 63 65 68 69 81 82 84 88 92 93 94 108 109 **S** Community Health Systems, Inc., Brentwood, TN
Primary Contact: Daniel E. McKay, Chief Executive Officer
Web address: www.springsmemorial.com
| | 33 | 10 | 194 | 7950 | 105 | 33073 | 689 | — | — | 625 |

Hospital, Address, Telephone, Approval, Facility, and Physician Codes, Health Care System	Classi-fication Codes		Utilization Data					Expense (thousands) of dollars		
★ American Hospital Association (AHA) membership □ Joint Commission on Accreditation of Healthcare Organizations (JCAHO) accreditation ○ American Osteopathic Association (AOA) accreditation △ Commission on Accreditation of Rehabilitation Facilities (CARF) accreditation	Control	Service	Staffed Beds	Admissions	Census	Outpatient Visits	Births	Total	Payroll	Personnel

LORIS—Horry County

⊠ **LORIS COMMUNITY HOSPITAL**, 3655 Mitchell Street, Box 690001, Zip 29569–9601; tel. 843/716–7000, (Total facility includes 88 beds in nursing home–type unit) **A**1 9 10 **F**2 9 11 12 21 22 23 24 26 27 28 29 33 37 39 41 42 46 47 48 49 50 52 53 55 57 58 59 60 62 63 64 65 66 69 81 82 84 88 92 93 94 95 96 98 106 108 109 110
Primary Contact: J. Timothy Browne, President and Chief Executive Officer
CFO: Fred O. Todd, Vice President, Finance
CMO: James Wright, M.D., Vice President Medical Affairs
Web address: www.lorishealthcaresystem.com
   16 10 193 4901 125 101025 350 62397 24693 647

MANNING—Clarendon County

⊠ **CLARENDON MEMORIAL HOSPITAL**, 10 Hospital Street, Zip 29102–3153, Mailing Address: P.O. Box 550, Zip 29102–0550; tel. 803/435–8463 **A**1 9 10 **F**2 6 9 11 12 21 22 26 27 28 29 32 33 37 39 41 42 44 46 48 50 51 52 55 58 59 60 63 64 65 69 73 81 83 86 87 91 92 93 95 98 105 107 108
Primary Contact: Edward R. Frye, Jr, Chief Executive Officer
COO: Susan C. Shugart, Chief Operating Officer
CFO: Richard Stokes, CPA, Chief Financial Officer
CMO: David C. Gaines, M.D., Chief of Staff
CIO: Dorinda Wise, Information Technology Manager
CHR: Gail Duke, Director of Human Resources
Web address: www.clarendonmemorial.com
   16 10 56 2592 30 99349 527 — — 367

MOUNT PLEASANT—Charleston County

⊠ **EAST COOPER REGIONAL MEDICAL CENTER**, 1200 Johnnie Dodds Boulevard, Zip 29464–3294; tel. 843/881–0100 **A**1 5 9 10 **F**2 11 12 21 23 26 28 29 33 37 46 48 52 55 57 58 59 60 61 62 63 64 65 69 81 84 86 87 91 92 93 94 98 107 108 109 **S** TENET Healthcare Corporation, Dallas, TX
Primary Contact: Andrea L. Wozniak, R.N., Chief Executive Officer
COO: T William Cone, Jr, Executive Vice President
CFO: Steve Woodford, Chief Financial Officer
CIO: Jack Goynes, Director Information Resources
CHR: Shannon Iriel, Director, Human Resources
Web address: www.eastcoopermedctr.com
   33 10 106 5276 54 25262 1561 63345 23346 499

MULLINS—Marion County

⊠ **MARION COUNTY MEDICAL CENTER**, 2829 East Highway 76, Zip 29574–6035, Mailing Address: P.O. Drawer 1150, Marion, Zip 29571–1150; tel. 843/431–2000, (Nonreporting) **A**1 9 10 20
Primary Contact: Gene Tucker, Interim Chief Executive Officerf
CFO: Gene Tucker, Chief Financial Officer
CMO: John Odom, M.D., Chief of Medical Staff
CIO: Pat Strickland, Information Systems Manager
Web address: www.marioncountymedical.com
   23 10 124 —

MURRELLS INLET—Georgetown County

⊠ **WACCAMAW COMMUNITY HOSPITAL**, 4070 Highway 17 Bypass, Zip 29576, Mailing Address: P.O. Drawer 3350, Zip 29576; tel. 843/652–1000 **A**1 9 10 **F**2 9 10 11 12 14 21 22 23 24 28 29 32 33 37 38 39 40 44 49 50 53 55 57 58 59 60 61 62 63 64 65 66 68 70 73 75 81 82 83 84 86 87 92 93 107 108 109 **S** Quorum Health Resources, Plano, TX
Primary Contact: Gayle L. Resetar, Chief Operating Officer
CFO: Terry L. Kiser, Chief Financial Officer
CIO: Bruce Hojnacki, Chief Information Officer
CHR: Beth Samples, Human Resource Director
Web address: www.gmhsc.com
   23 10 83 5052 71 37600 357 49731 14635 285

MYRTLE BEACH—Horry County

⊠ **GRAND STRAND REGIONAL MEDICAL CENTER**, 809 82nd Parkway, Zip 29572–1413; tel. 843/692–1000 **A**1 2 9 10 19 **F**2 9 11 12 14 15 17 19 21 22 23 26 27 28 29 32 33 37 39 42 46 47 48 49 52 55 57 58 59 60 61 62 63 64 65 66 81 82 84 85 86 87 88 92 93 94 96 106 108 109 **P**6 **S** HCA, Nashville, TN
Primary Contact: Doug White, Chief Executive Officer
CFO: Turner Wortham, Chief Financial Officer
Web address: www.grandstrandmed.com
   33 10 219 10777 135 164782 968 — — 909

NEWBERRY—Newberry County

⊠ **NEWBERRY COUNTY MEMORIAL HOSPITAL**, 2669 Kinard Street, Zip 29108–0497, Mailing Address: P.O. Box 497, Zip 29108–0497; tel. 803/276–7570, (Total facility includes 12 beds in nursing home–type unit) **A**1 9 10 20 **F**2 6 9 11 12 14 21 22 24 26 28 29 33 37 41 44 45 46 47 48 52 53 55 58 59 60 62 63 64 65 66 69 77 78 81 82 84 88 92 93 94 108 109 **S** Quorum Health Resources, Plano, TX
Primary Contact: Lynn W. Beasley, President and Chief Executive Officer
Web address: www.newberryhospital.org
   13 10 77 2991 40 52438 309 30908 12893 395

NORTH CHARLESTON—Charleston County

HEALTHSOUTH REHABILITATION HOSPITAL–CHARLESTON, 9181 Ned Com Street, Zip 29406; tel. 843/820–7777 **A**10 **F**7 21 27 28 29 37 42 44 46 48 52 57 60 62 65 68 69 95 105
Primary Contact: Troy Powell, Administrator
Web address: www.healthsouth.com
   33 46 46 942 40 — 0 9861 5362 150

Hospital, Address, Telephone, Approval, Facility, and Physician Codes, Health Care System	Classi-fication Codes		Utilization Data					Expense (thousands) of dollars		
★ American Hospital Association (AHA) membership ☐ Joint Commission on Accreditation of Healthcare Organizations (JCAHO) accreditation ◯ American Osteopathic Association (AOA) accreditation △ Commission on Accreditation of Rehabilitation Facilities (CARF) accreditation	Control	Service	Staffed Beds	Admissions	Census	Outpatient Visits	Births	Total	Payroll	Personnel

★ **NAVAL HOSPITAL**, 3600 Rivers Avenue, Zip 29405; tel. 843/743–7000, (Nonreporting) **A**3 5 **S** Bureau of Medicine and Surgery, Department of the Navy, Washington, DC Primary Contact: Captain Margaret Allard, Commanding Officer CFO: Scott F. Hall, Comptroller CMO: Commander Shawn Niemann, M.D., Medical Director CIO: Bo Knight, Management Information Department Head Web address: www.nhchasn.med.navy.mil	43	10	15	—	—	—	—	—	—	—

ORANGEBURG—Orangeburg County

✠ **REGIONAL MEDICAL CENTER OF ORANGEBURG AND CALHOUN COUNTIES**, 3000 St. Matthews Road, Zip 29118–1470; tel. 803/395–2200 **A**1 2 9 10 19 **F**2 9 11 12 14 15 21 22 23 24 27 28 29 33 35 36 37 38 41 46 47 48 49 50 51 53 55 57 58 59 60 61 62 63 64 65 66 68 69 71 73 74 75 76 79 81 82 83 84 86 87 91 92 93 94 95 97 98 107 108 109 **S** Quorum Health Resources, Plano, TX Primary Contact: Thomas C. Dandridge, President COO: David Bixler, Senior Vice President CFO: Lisa Goodlett, Vice President Finance CIO: Dale Kerwin, Information Director CHR: Howard Harris, Vice President Human Resources Web address: www.regmed.com	13	10	286	10321	162	63603	1302	135642	57223	1148

PICKENS—Pickens County

✠ **CANNON MEMORIAL HOSPITAL**, 123 West G. Acker Drive, Zip 29671–2739, Mailing Address: P.O. Box 188, Zip 29671–0188; tel. 864/878–4791 **A**1 10 **F**2 9 12 14 21 24 26 27 28 29 33 40 41 44 46 48 50 52 55 58 62 63 64 65 69 81 87 92 93 98 107 **P**8 Primary Contact: Norman G. Rentz, President and Chief Executive Officer CFO: Mary F. Arnette, Chief Financial Officer CMO: C Richard Curry, M.D., Chief of Staff CIO: Amanda Dow, Director Community Relations CHR: Lisa G. Bryant, Director of Human Resources Web address: www.cannonhospital.org	23	10	42	1367	17	36814	0	14778	6333	213

ROCK HILL—York County

✠ **HEALTHSOUTH REHABILITATION HOSPITAL**, 1795 Frank Gaston Boulevard, Zip 29732; tel. 803/362–3500 **A**1 10 **F**2 21 27 28 44 58 65 68 69 109 **S** HEALTHSOUTH Corporation, Birmingham, AL Primary Contact: Anthony W. Jackson, Administrator Web address: www.healthsouth.org	33	46	34	670	30	0	0	7209	4032	98
✠ **PIEDMONT HEALTHCARE SYSTEM**, 222 Herlong Avenue, Zip 29732–1952; tel. 803/329–1234 **A**1 9 10 **F**2 6 9 10 11 12 14 15 17 19 21 22 23 26 27 28 29 33 41 45 46 47 48 49 50 52 55 57 58 59 60 62 63 65 66 69 71 73 74 75 81 83 85 87 92 93 95 107 108 **S** TENET Healthcare Corporation, Dallas, TX Primary Contact: Charles F. Miller, President and Chief Executive Officer CFO: Neal Saul, Vice President Finance Web address: www.piedmonthealth.com	33	10	266	16431	213	131802	2083	186416	59553	1399

SENECA—Oconee County

✠ **OCONEE MEMORIAL HOSPITAL**, 298 Memorial Drive, Zip 29672–9499; tel. 864/882–3351, (Includes LILA DOYLE NURSING CARE FACILITY), (Total facility includes 79 beds in nursing home–type unit) **A**1 10 **F**2 6 9 11 12 15 21 22 23 24 26 27 28 29 33 36 37 41 42 44 45 46 47 48 50 51 52 55 57 58 59 60 61 62 63 64 65 66 69 70 73 75 81 82 88 92 93 94 95 96 106 108 110 **P**8 Primary Contact: Jeanne L. Ward, President CFO: Greg Scarbrough, Senior Vice President Finance and Chief Financial Officer CMO: Conrad K. Shuler, M.D., Chief Medical Officer CIO: Jay Hansen, Director Information Services CHR: Carolyn J. Cobb, Director, Human Resources Web address: www.oconeememorial.org	23	10	201	7468	202	127798	530	100194	39964	923

SHAW AFB—Sumter County

★ **U. S. AIR FORCE HOSPITAL SHAW**, 431 Meadowlark Street, Zip 29152–5019; tel. 803/895–6324, (Nonreporting) **S** Department of the Air Force, Washington, DC Primary Contact: Colonel Troy Molnar, Commander CFO: Captain W Lance Rodgers, Manager Managed Care Flight Commander CIO: Lieutenant Kenneth W. Whitlock, Medical Information Services Flight Commander Web address: www.shaw.af.mil	41	44	11	—	—	—	—	—	—	—

SIMPSONVILLE—Greenville County

★ **HILLCREST HOSPITAL**, 729 S.E. Main Street, Zip 29681–3280; tel. 864/967–6100 **A**9 10 **F**2 9 10 12 21 22 26 27 28 29 33 35 37 39 41 48 50 52 55 62 63 64 65 83 84 87 91 92 93 95 107 **P**6 7 8 **S** Greenville Hospital System, Greenville, SC Primary Contact: Dennis R. Burns, FACHE, Administrator CFO: Pam DeVore, Financial Manager Web address: www.ghs.org	23	10	43	1952	27	90367	0	31554	11323	219

SC

Hospital, Address, Telephone, Approval, Facility, and Physician Codes, Health Care System	Classi-fication Codes		Utilization Data					Expense (thousands) of dollars		
★ American Hospital Association (AHA) membership □ Joint Commission on Accreditation of Healthcare Organizations (JCAHO) accreditation ○ American Osteopathic Association (AOA) accreditation △ Commission on Accreditation of Rehabilitation Facilities (CARF) accreditation	Control	Service	Staffed Beds	Admissions	Census	Outpatient Visits	Births	Total	Payroll	Personnel

SPARTANBURG—Spartanburg County

☒ △ **MARY BLACK HEALTH SYSTEM**, 1700 Skylyn Drive, Zip 29307–1061, Mailing Address: P.O. Box 3217, Zip 29304–3217; tel. 864/573–3000 **A**1 7 9 10 **F**2 9 11 12 15 21 23 26 27 28 29 33 39 42 45 46 48 52 55 58 59 60 61 62 63 64 65 66 68 69 71 76 81 83 84 86 87 92 93 107 108 109 **P**5 8 **S** Triad Hospitals, Inc., Plano, TX
Primary Contact: Glenn A. Robinson, Chief Executive Officer
COO: Michael Lutes, Chief Operating Officer
CFO: Jay R. Johnson, Chief Operating Officer
CIO: Jim Leonard, Chief Information Officer
CHR: Beth VanOrsdale, Manager, Human Resources
Web address: www.maryblack.org
— 33 10 168 7247 102 99742 1169 85630 32091 771

☒ **SPARTANBURG HOSPITAL FOR RESTORATIVE CARE**, 389 Serpentine Drive, Zip 29303–3026; tel. 864/560–3280, (Nonreporting) **A**1 9 10 **S** Spartanburg Regional Healthcare System, Spartanburg, SC
Primary Contact: Anita M. Butler, Chief Executive Officer
Web address: www.srhs.com
— 16 80 82 — — — — — — —

☒ **SPARTANBURG REGIONAL MEDICAL CENTER**, 101 East Wood Street, Zip 29303–3016; tel. 864/560–6000 **A**1 2 3 5 9 10 12 13 **F**2 6 9 10 11 12 14 15 17 19 21 22 23 26 27 28 29 30 31 32 33 36 37 38 40 42 44 45 46 47 48 49 50 51 52 53 55 56 57 58 59 60 61 62 63 65 66 69 70 71 72 73 74 75 76 77 78 79 80 81 83 84 85 86 87 91 92 93 94 95 98 105 107 108 109 **P**5 **S** Spartanburg Regional Healthcare System, Spartanburg, SC
Primary Contact: Ingo Angermeier, FACHE, President and Chief Executive Officer
COO: Charles Townson, Chief Operating Officer
CFO: Larry Barnette, Senior Vice President Finance
CMO: Robert Riehle, M.D., Chief Medical Officer
CIO: Raymond Shingler, Vice President Information System
CHR: James R. Walker, Vice President of Human Resources
Web address: www.spartanburgregional.com
— 16 10 465 30861 389 343662 2455 448897 186541 4300

SUMMERVILLE—Dorchester County

★ **SUMMERVILLE MEDICAL CENTER**, 295 Midland Parkway, Zip 29485–8104; tel. 843/832–5000, (Total facility includes 14 beds in nursing home–type unit) **A**9 **F**11 12 21 22 28 29 33 44 46 47 48 52 55 58 59 60 62 63 65 66 69 81 82 84 85 87 88 94 96 108 109
Primary Contact: Pearce W. Fleming, Jr, CHE, Chief Executive Officer
CFO: Karl E. Gorrell, Chief Financial Officer
CIO: Steve Burns, Driector Information Services
Web address: www.tridenthealthsystem.com
— 33 10 80 5460 71 90897 897 225825 — 290

SUMTER—Sumter County

☒ **TUOMEY HEALTHCARE SYSTEM**, 129 North Washington Street, Zip 29150–4983; tel. 803/778–9000, (Total facility includes 18 beds in nursing home–type unit) **A**1 9 10 19 **F**2 11 12 15 17 21 22 23 24 26 27 28 29 33 36 40 42 44 46 47 48 49 51 52 53 55 58 59 60 61 62 63 64 65 66 68 69 75 79 81 82 84 85 86 88 92 93 94 95 96 106 107 108 109 110
Primary Contact: Jay Cox, President and Chief Executive Officer
CFO: William Johnson, Vice President and Chief Financial Officer
CMO: Gene Dickerson, M.D., Vice President of Medical Affairs
CHR: Paul Schumacher, Administrative Director
Web address: www.tuomey.com
— 23 10 246 8263 187 138880 1407 141952 54222 1262

TRAVELERS REST—Greenville County

NORTH GREENVILLE HOSPITAL, 807 North Main Street, Zip 29690–0628; tel. 864/834–5132 **A**9 10 **F**2 21 24 26 27 28 29 33 35 37 39 42 44 46 47 48 49 52 55 58 62 64 65 66 70 92 93 107 109 **P**6 7 8
Primary Contact: Scott R. Jones, Chief Executive Officer
Web address: www.ghs.org
— 23 10 25 241 17 40511 0 14297 5839 126

□ **SPRINGBROOK BEHAVIORAL HEALTH SYSTEM**, One Havenwood Lane, Zip 29690–1005, Mailing Address: P.O. Box 1005, Zip 29690–1005; tel. 864/834–8013 **A**1 9 10 **F**27 65 71 72 73 74 75 76 92 93
Primary Contact: Thomas J. De Martini, Chief Executive Officer
Web address: www.springbrookbehavioral.com
— 33 22 20 271 7 0 0 7258 3526 112

UNION—Union County

☒ **WALLACE THOMSON HOSPITAL**, 322 West South Street, Zip 29379–2857, Mailing Address: P.O. Box 789, Zip 29379–0789; tel. 864/429–2600, (Total facility includes 113 beds in nursing home–type unit) **A**1 9 10 **F**2 6 11 12 21 27 28 29 33 43 46 48 52 54 55 58 59 62 63 65 66 81 84 88 92 94 108 109 **S** Quorum Health Resources, Plano, TX
Primary Contact: Karen A. Fiducia, Interim Chief Executive Officer
CFO: Robert G. Tusler, Chief Financial Officer
Web address: www.wallacethomson.com
— 16 10 220 3804 160 36132 123 34112 11003 270

VARNVILLE—Hampton County

★ **HAMPTON REGIONAL MEDICAL CENTER**, 503 Carolina Avenue West, Zip 29944, Mailing Address: P.O. Box 338, Zip 29944–0338; tel. 803/943–2771 **A**9 10 20 **F**10 12 27 29 33 46 48 52 60 63 69 81 84 87 92 93 107 **P**5
Primary Contact: Dave H. Hamill, President and Chief Executive Officer
— 23 10 25 1011 10 27845 0 10137 4442 134

Many Facility Codes have changed. Please refer to the AHA Guide Code Chart.

© 2005 AHA Guide

Hospital, Address, Telephone, Approval, Facility, and Physician Codes, Health Care System	Classi-fication Codes		Utilization Data					Expense (thousands) of dollars		
★ American Hospital Association (AHA) membership □ Joint Commission on Accreditation of Healthcare Organizations (JCAHO) accreditation ○ American Osteopathic Association (AOA) accreditation △ Commission on Accreditation of Rehabilitation Facilities (CARF) accreditation	Control	Service	Staffed Beds	Admissions	Census	Outpatient Visits	Births	Total	Payroll	Personnel

WALTERBORO—Colleton County

✠ **COLLETON MEDICAL CENTER**, 501 Robertson Boulevard, Zip 29488–5714; tel. 843/549–2000 **A**1 9 10 20 **F**2 9 11 12 21 22 24 26 27 28 29 30 33 37 41 44 46 48 49 52 55 58 59 60 62 63 65 66 68 69 70 81 82 84 88 92 93 94 95 96 98 108 109 110 **S** HCA, Nashville, TN
Primary Contact: Rebecca T. Brewer, FACHE, Chief Executive Officer
CFO: Jimmy Hiott, Chief Financial Officer
CMO: Andrew Calcutt, Chief of Medical Staff
CHR: Patricia Hendrick, Human Resources Director
Web address: www.colletonmedical.com

| 33 | 10 | 131 | 4938 | 71 | 60210 | 445 | 49640 | 17997 | 392 |

WEST COLUMBIA—Lexington County

✠ **LEXINGTON MEDICAL CENTER**, 2720 Sunset Boulevard, Zip 29169–4816; tel. 803/791–2000 **A**1 9 10 **F**2 9 10 12 15 21 22 23 24 26 27 28 29 31 32 33 37 40 44 46 48 49 50 52 53 55 57 58 59 60 61 62 63 64 65 66 69 79 81 83 87 92 93 94 95 98 107 108 **P**6
Primary Contact: Michael J. Biediger, President and Chief Executive Officer
COO: Tod Augsburger, Senior Vice President and Chief Operating Officer
CFO: Melinda Kruzner, Chief Financial Officer
CMO: Bruce H. Truesdale, M.D., Chief of Staff
CIO: George Evans, Director Information Services
CHR: Shawn Martin Lyde, Human Resources Director
Web address: www.lexmed.com

| 16 | 10 | 312 | 19424 | 263 | 377847 | 2579 | 229589 | 87511 | 2166 |

□ **THREE RIVERS CENTER FOR BEHAVIORAL HEALTH**, 2900 Sunset Boulevard, Zip 29169–3422; tel. 803/796–9911 **A**1 9 10 **F**3 4 29 46 65 71 72 73 74 75 76 77 78 92
Primary Contact: R. Andy Hanner, Chief Executive Officer
Web address: www.threeriversbehavioral.org

| 33 | 22 | 66 | 1917 | 48 | 0 | 0 | 10213 | 4955 | 165 |

WINNSBORO—Fairfield County

✠ **FAIRFIELD MEMORIAL HOSPITAL**, 102 U.S. Highway 321 By–Pass North, Zip 29180–9251; Mailing Address: P.O. Box 620, Zip 29180–0620; tel. 803/635–5548 **A**1 5 9 10 18 **F**9 12 23 26 27 28 29 33 44 46 48 51 52 58 60 61 62 63 65 66 69 81 87 92 93 95 105 107
Primary Contact: J. Larry Dozier, Jr, FACHE, Chief Executive Officer
CFO: David Kline, Chief Financial Officer
CMO: Deborah Stuck, M.D., Chief Medical Officer
CIO: Jeff Betsch, Director
CHR: Shawna Martin Lyde, Director
Web address: www.fairfieldmemorial.org

| 13 | 10 | 25 | 760 | 10 | — | 0 | 11757 | 5185 | 176 |

SC

SOUTH DAKOTA

Hospital, Address, Telephone, Approval, Facility, and Physician Codes, Health Care System	Classi-fication Codes		Utilization Data					Expense (thousands) of dollars		
★ American Hospital Association (AHA) membership □ Joint Commission on Accreditation of Healthcare Organizations (JCAHO) accreditation ○ American Osteopathic Association (AOA) accreditation △ Commission on Accreditation of Rehabilitation Facilities (CARF) accreditation	Control	Service	Staffed Beds	Admissions	Census	Outpatient Visits	Births	Total	Payroll	Personnel

ABERDEEN—Brown County

⊠ △ **AVERA ST. LUKE'S**, 305 South State Street, Zip 57402–4450; tel. 605/622–5000, (Total facility includes 143 beds in nursing home–type unit) **A**1 2 7 9 10 19 20 **F**1 2 4 6 8 9 11 12 14 15 21 22 23 24 26 27 28 29 30 32 33 36 37 40 44 46 48 49 50 51 52 53 55 57 58 59 60 61 62 63 64 65 66 68 69 70 71 72 73 74 75 76 77 78 79 80 81 82 84 85 87 88 91 92 93 94 95 96 97 106 108 109 110 **S** Avera Health, Yankton, SD
Primary Contact: Ronald L. Jacobson, President and Chief Executive Officer
COO: K. C. DeBoer, Vice President Hospital Division
CFO: Geoff Durst, Vice President Finance
CMO: John Fritz, D.O., Vice President Outreach and Referral Services
CIO: Julie Kusler, Information Services Manager
CHR: Mary Davis, Vice President
Web address: www.averastlukes.org
    21 10 269 6762 219 216207 707 100683 44206 1118

DAKOTA PLAINS SURGICAL CENTER, 701 8th Avenue N.W., Suite C., Zip 57401; tel. 605/225–3300, (Nonreporting) **A**10
Primary Contact: Charles Livingston, Administrator
    33 13 8 — — — — — — —

ARMOUR—Douglas County

DOUGLAS COUNTY MEMORIAL HOSPITAL, 708 Eighth Street, Zip 57313–2102; tel. 605/724–2159 **A**9 10 18 **F**2 6 8 9 11 12 26 27 28 29 33 36 41 46 48 51 52 54 59 60 61 63 69 81 84 88 95 97
Primary Contact: Heath Brouwer, Administrator
Web address: www.dcmhsd.org
    23 10 11 273 2 5895 20 3937 1779 65

BOWDLE—Edmunds County

BOWDLE HOSPITAL, 8001 West Fifth Street, Zip 57428–0566; tel. 605/285–6146, (Total facility includes 38 beds in nursing home–type unit) **A**9 10 18 **F**6 8 9 27 33 41 45 48 52 92 94 97
Primary Contact: Kathy Gerdes, Administrator
Web address: www.bowdlehealthcarecenter.com
    14 10 54 174 39 6106 0 3421 1784 74

BRITTON—Marshall County

★ **MARSHALL COUNTY HEALTHCARE CENTER/AVERA HEALTH**, 413 Ninth Street, Zip 57430; tel. 605/448–2253 **A**9 10 18 **F**8 9 21 26 27 28 29 33 46 47 48 51 52 65 66 69 97 **P**5 **S** Avera Health, Yankton, SD
Primary Contact: Stephanie Reasy, Administrator
Web address: www.avera.org
    23 10 20 384 5 10027 0 3463 1514 54

BROOKINGS—Brookings County

★ **BROOKINGS HEALTH SYSTEM**, (Formerly Brookings Hospital), 300 22nd Avenue, Zip 57006–2496; tel. 605/696–9000, (Total facility includes 79 beds in nursing home–type unit) **A**9 10 **F**6 9 11 21 23 27 29 33 36 44 45 46 48 51 54 55 58 59 63 65 66 81 84 88 92 96 97 108
Primary Contact: Vern Carda, Administrator and Chief Executive Officer
CFO: Kevin Coffey, Chief Financial Officer
CHR: Sheila Maffett, Chief Human Resources and Public Relations Officer
Web address: www.brookingshospital.org
    14 10 140 1337 86 49496 239 14822 7558 247

BURKE—Gregory County

★ **COMMUNITY MEMORIAL HOSPITAL**, (Rural Critical Access Hospital), Eighth and Jackson, Zip 57523, Mailing Address: P.O. Box 319, Zip 57523–0319; tel. 605/775–2621 **A**9 10 18 **F**2 9 21 23 26 27 28 29 33 46 47 48 52 92 94 97 **P**6 **S** Sioux Valley Hospitals and Health System, Sioux Falls, SD
Primary Contact: Michelle Murphy, Chief Executive Officer
COO: Michelle Murphy, Chief Executive Officer
CFO: Jim Frank, Chief Financial Officer
CMO: Teresa Marts, M.D., Chief of Medical Staff
CHR: Becky Jacobson, Manager Business Office and Human Resources
    23 49 16 307 1 1855 0 2779 1330 59

CANTON—Lincoln County

★ **CANTON–INWOOD MEMORIAL HOSPITAL**, 440 North Hiawatha Drive, Zip 57013–9404; tel. 605/987–2621 **A**9 10 18 **F**8 27 28 33 46 48 52 59 60 63 69 94 **S** Sioux Valley Hospitals and Health System, Sioux Falls, SD
Primary Contact: Eric Hilmoe, Chief Executive Officer
CFO: Paul Gerhart, Chief Financial Off
Web address: www.cantoninwoodhospital.org
    23 10 18 431 4 16354 22 4034 1968 68

CHAMBERLAIN—Brule County

★ **MID DAKOTA MEDICAL CENTER**, 300 South Byron Boulevard, Zip 57325–9741; tel. 605/234–5511, (Total facility includes 45 beds in nursing home–type unit) **A**9 10 18 20 **F**2 11 12 21 23 27 28 29 33 46 48 55 58 59 60 63 64 65 69 81 88 92 94 95 97 **P**6 **S** Sioux Valley Hospitals and Health System, Sioux Falls, SD
Primary Contact: Maureen Cadwell, Chief Executive Officer
CFO: Tom Pitlick, Chief Financial Officer
CMO: Gary Van Ert, M.D., Chief Medical Staff
CHR: Dotty Hieb, Human Resource Director
Web address: www.middakotamedicalcenter.org
    23 10 70 1031 48 8334 23 9862 4607 174

Many Facility Codes have changed. Please refer to the AHA Guide Code Chart. © 2005 AHA Guide

SD

Hospital, Address, Telephone, Approval, Facility, and Physician Codes, Health Care System	Classi-fication Codes		Utilization Data					Expense (thousands) of dollars		
★ American Hospital Association (AHA) membership □ Joint Commission on Accreditation of Healthcare Organizations (JCAHO) accreditation ○ American Osteopathic Association (AOA) accreditation △ Commission on Accreditation of Rehabilitation Facilities (CARF) accreditation	Control	Service	Staffed Beds	Admissions	Census	Outpatient Visits	Births	Total	Payroll	Personnel

CLEAR LAKE—Deuel County

★ **DEUEL COUNTY MEMORIAL HOSPITAL**, 701 Third Avenue South, Zip 57226–2016; tel. 605/874–2141 **A**9 10 18 **F**9 21 23 24 26 27 28 29 33 37 39 41 46 47 48 51 52 53 63 65 70 92 97 106 107 109 **P**6 **S** Sioux Valley Hospitals and Health System, Sioux Falls, SD Primary Contact: Robert J. Salmon, Chief Executive Officer CFO: Allison Nelson, Chief Financial Officer CMO: Dorota Malinowska, M.D., Medical Staff Chairman Web address: www.siouxvalley.org	23	10	20	209	3	20424	0	3448	2079	57

CUSTER—Custer County

★ **CUSTER COMMUNITY HOSPITAL**, 1039 Montgomery Street, Zip 57730–1397; tel. 605/673–2229, (Total facility includes 76 beds in nursing home–type unit) **A**9 10 18 **F**8 11 21 26 27 33 44 46 52 58 59 60 69 70 88 92 94 97 110 **P**8 **S** Regional Health, Rapid City, SD Primary Contact: Jason Petik, Chief Executive Officer Web address: www.custerhospital.org	23	10	87	354	80	12053	12	8721	4979	153

DAKOTA DUNES—Union County

SIOUXLAND SURGERY CENTER, 600 North Sioux Point Road, Zip 57049–5000; tel. 605/232–3332, (Nonreporting) **A**9 10 Primary Contact: Greg Miner, Administrator	33	49	10	—	—	—	—	—	—	—

DE SMET—Kingsbury County

DE SMET MEMORIAL HOSPITAL, 306 Prairie Avenue S.W., Zip 57231–9499; tel. 605/854–3329 **A**9 10 18 20 **F**12 26 27 28 33 46 48 52 69 97 Primary Contact: John L. Single, Chief Executive Officer and Administrator	14	10	14	231	2	7559	0	1782	945	18

DEADWOOD—Lawrence County

★ **NORTHERN HILLS GENERAL HOSPITAL**, 61 Charles Street, Zip 57732–1303; tel. 605/722–6101 **A**9 10 18 **F**2 6 11 12 21 23 33 46 48 54 55 58 59 60 63 66 68 69 70 81 88 92 97 **P**6 **S** Regional Health, Rapid City, SD Primary Contact: Don A. Nelson, Chief Executive Officer CMO: James Holloway, M.D., President Medical Staff CHR: Kathryn L. Shockey, Director Human Resources Web address: www.rcrh.org	23	10	18	426	6	13026	16	9566	4589	113

DELL RAPIDS—Minnehaha County

★ **DELLS AREA HEALTH CENTER**, 909 North Iowa Avenue, Zip 57022–1231; tel. 605/428–5431 **A**10 18 **F**9 11 12 27 33 41 48 63 69 97 **S** Avera Health, Yankton, SD Primary Contact: James A. Faulwell, Chief Executive Officer and Administrator CFO: Allison Bolger, Chief Financial Officer CMO: Valorie Larson, M.D., Chief of Staff CHR: Dawn Ingalls, Human Resources Regional Representative	21	10	20	539	6	7862	33	4066	1987	46

EAGLE BUTTE—Dewey County

⊠ **U. S. PUBLIC HEALTH SERVICE INDIAN HOSPITAL**, Mailing Address: P.O. Box 1012, Zip 57625–1012; tel. 605/964–7724 **A**1 10 **F**6 21 26 27 28 33 39 45 47 50 52 70 88 92 106 107 109 110 **P**8 **S** U. S. Indian Health Service, Rockville, MD Primary Contact: Donald D. Annis, Service Unit Director CFO: Lisa Deal, Budget Analyst	47	10	11	248	3	59653	1	14300	4521	31

EUREKA—McPherson County

★ **EUREKA COMMUNITY HEALTH SERVICES/AVERA HEALTH**, 410 Ninth Street, Zip 57437–0517, Mailing Address: P.O. Box 517, Zip 57437–0517; tel. 605/284–2661 **A**9 10 18 **F**8 26 27 28 29 33 48 51 60 63 69 97 **S** Avera Health, Yankton, SD Primary Contact: Robert A. Dockter, Administrator CFO: Joyce Schwingler, Finance Officer Web address: www.avera.org/facilities/eureka.htm	23	10	6	179	2	7673	0	1681	686	35

FAULKTON—Faulk County

FAULK COUNTY MEMORIAL HOSPITAL, 911 St. John Street, Zip 57438, Mailing Address: P.O. Box 100, Zip 57438–0100; tel. 605/598–6263 **A**9 10 18 **F**8 14 21 25 28 33 48 60 69 70 92 97 **P**5 Primary Contact: Jay Jahnig, Chief Executive Officer	13	10	19	169	2	7466	0	1944	915	33

FLANDREAU—Moody County

★ **FLANDREAU MEDICAL CENTER/AVERA HEALTH**, 214 North Prairie Avenue, Zip 57028–1243; tel. 605/997–2433 **A**9 10 18 **F**9 21 23 27 28 29 33 36 37 38 46 47 48 51 52 53 58 61 63 65 69 70 88 92 94 96 97 107 109 110 **S** Avera Health, Yankton, SD Primary Contact: Randy Anderson, Administrator and Chief Executive Officer COO: Marie Myers, Director of Patient Care Services CIO: Melissa Jones, Director of Health Information Web address: www.flandreaumedical.org	23	10	18	377	4	12829	1	3159	1360	37

Hospital, Address, Telephone, Approval, Facility, and Physician Codes, Health Care System	Classi-fication Codes		Utilization Data					Expense (thousands) of dollars		
★ American Hospital Association (AHA) membership □ Joint Commission on Accreditation of Healthcare Organizations (JCAHO) accreditation ○ American Osteopathic Association (AOA) accreditation △ Commission on Accreditation of Rehabilitation Facilities (CARF) accreditation	Control	Service	Staffed Beds	Admissions	Census	Outpatient Visits	Births	Total	Payroll	Personnel

FORT MEADE—Meade County

✠ **VETERANS AFFAIRS BLACK HILLS HEALTH CARE SYSTEM**, 113 Comanche Road, Zip 57741–1099; tel. 605/347–2511, (Includes VETERANS AFFAIRS MEDICAL CENTER, 500 North Fifth Street, Hot Springs, Zip 57747; tel. 605/745–2052), (Total facility includes 104 beds in nursing home–type unit) **A**1 5 **F**2 5 9 10 12 21 22 23 26 29 32 33 36 37 38 39 42 44 45 46 47 48 49 50 51 52 53 55 57 58 60 61 62 63 65 66 69 70 71 75 76 77 78 81 82 84 88 92 93 94 96 106 107 108 109 110 **S** Department of Veterans Affairs, Washington, DC
Primary Contact: Peter P. Henry, CHE, Director
COO: Stephen R. DiStasio, Associate Director for Operations
CFO: Bill Gambill, Chief Financial Officer
CIO: James W. Ross, Chief Information Officer
CHR: Timothy McGuigan, Chief Human Resources Management Service
Web address: www.va.gov/sta/guide/home.asp
| 45 | 10 | 351 | 2511 | 121 | 240977 | — | 120625 | 54186 | 934 |

FREEMAN—Hutchinson County

★ **FREEMAN REGIONAL HEALTH SERVICES**, (Formerly Freeman Community Hospital), 510 East Eighth Street, Zip 57029–0370, Mailing Address: P.O. Box 370, Zip 57029–0370; tel. 605/925–4000, (Total facility includes 59 beds in nursing home–type unit) **A**9 10 18 **F**1 2 9 11 22 23 26 27 28 29 33 37 39 44 45 46 47 48 52 53 54 55 58 59 60 61 62 63 65 68 81 88 91 92 94 96 97 108
Primary Contact: Daniel Gran, Chief Executive Officer
Web address: www.freemanregional.com
| 23 | 10 | 84 | 326 | 45 | 8252 | 25 | 5584 | 2705 | 95 |

GETTYSBURG—Potter County

★ **GETTYSBURG MEDICAL CENTER**, 606 East Garfield Avenue, Zip 57442–1398; tel. 605/765–2480, (Total facility includes 48 beds in nursing home–type unit) **A**9 10 18 **F**2 5 9 21 22 29 30 33 37 39 47 48 52 60 62 63 65 66 69 91 92 94 96 97 108 **S** Catholic Health Initiatives, Denver, CO
Primary Contact: Mark Schmidt, President and Chief Executive Officer
Web address: www.catholichealthinit.org
| 21 | 10 | 58 | 246 | 45 | 4947 | 0 | 3583 | 1802 | 65 |

GREGORY—Gregory County

★ **AVERA GREGORY HEALTHCARE CENTER**, 400 Park Avenue, Zip 57533–0400, Mailing Address: P.O. Box 408, Zip 57533–0408; tel. 605/835–8394, (Total facility includes 55 beds in nursing home–type unit) **A**9 10 **F**1 5 11 12 14 21 22 26 27 28 29 33 34 36 37 44 45 46 47 48 49 51 53 58 59 60 61 62 63 65 66 81 92 93 94 95 96 97 109 **S** Avera Health, Yankton, SD
Primary Contact: Mark Klosterman, Chief Executive Officer
CFO: Trish Keiser, Comptroller
CIO: Doug Williamson, Director of Support Services
Web address: www.gregoryhealthcare.org
| 21 | 10 | 94 | 881 | 62 | 17373 | 25 | 7140 | 3124 | 114 |

HOT SPRINGS—Fall River County

★ **FALL RIVER HOSPITAL**, 209 North 16th Street, Zip 57747–1375; tel. 605/745–3159, (Includes CASTLE MANOR), (Total facility includes 61 beds in nursing home–type unit) **A**9 10 18 **F**8 27 28 33 45 52 63 69 81 88 92 **P**6
Primary Contact: John B. Miller, Administrator
CMO: Pat Mitchel, M.D., Medical Director
CIO: Dwayne Heafner, Chief Information Officer
VETERANS AFFAIRS MEDICAL CENTER See Veterans Affairs Black Hills Health Care System, Fort Meade
| 23 | 10 | 70 | 207 | 64 | 9719 | 0 | 4938 | 2237 | 110 |

HOVEN—Potter County

HOLY INFANT HOSPITAL, Main Street, Zip 57450–0158, Mailing Address: P.O. Box 158, Zip 57450–0158; tel. 605/948–2262 **A**9 10 20 **F**8 14 27 33 55 60 63 69 92 97
Primary Contact: Jay Duenwald, Interim Administrator
| 23 | 10 | 26 | 90 | 1 | 457 | 0 | 1038 | 486 | 30 |

HURON—Beadle County

★ **HURON REGIONAL MEDICAL CENTER**, 172 Fourth Street S.E., Zip 57350–2590; tel. 605/353–6200 **A**9 10 18 20 **F**2 9 11 21 22 23 26 27 28 29 33 34 36 46 48 49 51 52 55 58 59 60 62 63 65 69 75 81 82 84 87 88 93 94 97 108 **S** Quorum Health Resources, Plano, TX
Primary Contact: John L. Single, Chief Executive Officer
CFO: Marcia Zwanziger, Vice President Finance
CMO: Jim Schwaiger, M.D., Chief of Staff
CHR: Rhonda Hanson, Director Human Resources
Web address: www.huronregional.org
| 23 | 10 | 61 | 1501 | 16 | 48421 | 242 | 21580 | 8990 | 204 |

LEMMON—Perkins County

FIVE COUNTIES HOSPITAL, 405 Sixth Avenue West, Zip 57638–1318, Mailing Address: P.O. Box 479, Zip 57638–0479; tel. 605/374–3871, (Total facility includes 43 beds in nursing home–type unit) **A**9 10 18 **F**8 9 21 28 33 91 92 97 108 **P**5 **S** Regional Health, Rapid City, SD
Primary Contact: Jannette Van Beek, Chief Executive Officer
Web address: www.rcrh.org/facilities/hospitals/fivecounties.asp
| 23 | 10 | 47 | 51 | 43 | 602 | 0 | 2299 | 943 | 58 |

MADISON—Lake County

★ **MADISON COMMUNITY HOSPITAL**, 917 North Washington Avenue, Zip 57042–1696; tel. 605/256–6551 **A**9 10 18 20 **F**6 9 11 12 23 26 27 28 29 33 45 46 48 51 52 55 58 59 60 63 64 69 81 82 88 92 97 106 108
Primary Contact: Tamara Miller, Administrator
Web address: www.madisonhospital.com
| 23 | 10 | 25 | 585 | 9 | 27664 | 57 | 8050 | 4172 | 116 |

Many Facility Codes have changed. Please refer to the AHA Guide Code Chart. © 2005 AHA Guide

Hospital, Address, Telephone, Approval, Facility, and Physician Codes, Health Care System	Classi-fication Codes		Utilization Data					Expense (thousands) of dollars		
★ American Hospital Association (AHA) membership □ Joint Commission on Accreditation of Healthcare Organizations (JCAHO) accreditation ○ American Osteopathic Association (AOA) accreditation △ Commission on Accreditation of Rehabilitation Facilities (CARF) accreditation	Control	Service	Staffed Beds	Admissions	Census	Outpatient Visits	Births	Total	Payroll	Personnel

MARTIN—Bennett County

BENNETT COUNTY HEALTHCARE CENTER, 102 Major Allen Street, Zip 57551, Mailing Address: P.O. Box 70–D, Zip 57551; tel. 605/685–6622, (Total facility includes 42 beds in nursing home–type unit) **A**9 10 18 **F**6 8 27 33 44 46 48 51 60 69 88 92 94 97 Primary Contact: Marlene Christman, Administrator Web address: www.bchospital.com	13	10	62	157	42	5722	0	3477	1932	73

MILBANK—Grant County

★ **MILBANK AREA HOSPITAL/AVERA HEALTH**, 901 East Virgil Avenue, Zip 57252; tel. 605/432–4538, (Includes ST. WILLIAM HOME FOR THE AGED) **A**10 18 **F**11 12 22 23 26 27 28 33 36 51 55 59 60 63 69 81 88 92 94 97 106 107 109 110 **S** Avera Health, Yankton, SD Primary Contact: Jeffrey M. Lang, Administrator CFO: Allison Bolger, Chief Financial Officer	23	10	25	680	8	16828	52	5521	2093	56

MILLER—Hand County

★ **HAND COUNTY MEMORIAL HOSPITAL/AVERA HEALTH**, 300 West Fifth Street, Zip 57362–1238; tel. 605/853–2421, (Total facility includes 23 beds in nursing home–type unit) **A**9 10 20 **F**6 8 9 14 24 26 27 28 29 33 34 41 44 46 47 48 51 52 54 57 58 60 63 65 69 81 88 92 96 97 108 109 110 **P**5 **S** Avera Health, Yankton, SD Primary Contact: Bryan Breitling, Administrator CFO: Debbie Pullman, Business Manager CMO: Joel Huber, M.D., Chief of Staff CIO: Janice Purrington, Medical Records Coordinator CHR: Debbie Pullman, Business Manager Web address: www.avera.org	23	10	44	373	5	7738	0	3458	1629	67

MITCHELL—Davison County

⊠ **AVERA QUEEN OF PEACE**, 525 North Foster, Zip 57301–2999; tel. 605/995–2000, (Total facility includes 114 beds in nursing home–type unit) **A**1 9 10 **F**2 8 9 11 12 21 22 23 26 27 28 29 32 33 34 36 37 39 41 44 46 48 51 52 54 55 58 59 60 61 62 63 64 65 69 75 80 81 82 84 88 91 92 93 94 95 96 97 106 108 109 110 **S** Avera Health, Yankton, SD Primary Contact: Thomas P. Rasmusson, President and Chief Executive Officer CFO: Patrick Clark, Senior Vice President Finance and Support Services CIO: Patti Brooks, Director Information Systems CHR: Chris Nelson, Director Human Resources Web address: www.averaqueenofpeace.org	21	10	213	3689	147	104496	492	52777	24250	428

MOBRIDGE—Walworth County

★ **MOBRIDGE REGIONAL HOSPITAL**, 1401 Tenth Avenue West, Zip 57601–1199, Mailing Address: P.O. Box 580, Zip 57601–0580; tel. 605/845–3693 **A**9 10 18 **F**2 6 8 9 11 12 23 27 28 29 33 42 44 46 48 51 52 55 59 63 69 81 88 91 92 94 97 **P**6 Primary Contact: Angelia K. Svihovec, Chief Executive Officer CFO: Renae Tisdall, Chief Financial Officer CHR: Jodi Lemke, Director of Human Resources Web address: www.mrhonline.org	23	10	31	811	8	23534	74	5999	2929	134

PARKSTON—Hutchinson County

★ **AVERA ST. BENEDICT HEALTH CENTER**, 401 Glynn Drive, Zip 57366–2031; tel. 605/928–3311, (Total facility includes 75 beds in nursing home–type unit) **A**9 10 18 **F**1 8 11 12 21 22 23 24 26 27 28 29 33 36 37 41 46 47 48 51 52 53 54 55 59 61 63 65 70 81 88 91 92 94 95 96 97 106 108 110 **S** Avera Health, Yankton, SD Primary Contact: Gale Walker, President and Chief Executive Officer CFO: Rita Mohnen, Assistant Administrator and Chief Financial Officer CMO: Antoinette VanderPol, Chief of Staff CIO: Shellie Goldammer, Information Systems CHR: Phyllis Ehler, Human Resource Director Web address: www.averastbenedict.org	21	10	100	644	78	23828	45	11192	5579	167

PHILIP—Haakon County

★ **HANS P. PETERSON MEMORIAL HOSPITAL**, 503 West Pine Street, Zip 57567, Mailing Address: P.O. Box 790, Zip 57567–0790; tel. 605/859–2511, (Total facility includes 30 beds in nursing home–type unit) **A**9 10 18 **F**8 9 27 28 33 41 51 69 81 92 95 97 **P**6 **S** Regional Health, Rapid City, SD Primary Contact: David Dick, Chief Executive Officer Web address: www.rcrh.org/Facilities/Hospitals/HPPMemorial.asp	23	10	48	185	30	1805	0	4904	2579	93

PIERRE—Hughes County

⊠ **ST. MARY'S HEALTHCARE CENTER**, 800 East Dakota Avenue, Zip 57501–3313; tel. 605/224–3100, (Total facility includes 105 beds in nursing home–type unit) **A**1 9 10 20 **F**2 9 11 12 22 23 26 27 28 31 33 36 37 38 48 49 51 52 55 59 60 61 63 64 65 69 81 84 88 91 92 94 95 97 106 108 **P**5 **S** Catholic Health Initiatives, Denver, CO Primary Contact: James D. M. Russell, President and Chief Executive Officer CFO: Dalton Huber, Vice President Fiscal Services CMO: Tom Nuber, M.D., Chief of Staff CIO: Chris Harrison, Director Information Services CHR: Paul Marso, Vice President Human Resources Web address: www.st-marys.com	23	10	165	2751	118	20688	539	30903	14250	390

SD

Hospital, Address, Telephone, Approval, Facility, and Physician Codes, Health Care System	Classification Codes		Utilization Data					Expense (thousands) of dollars		
★ American Hospital Association (AHA) membership □ Joint Commission on Accreditation of Healthcare Organizations (JCAHO) accreditation ○ American Osteopathic Association (AOA) accreditation △ Commission on Accreditation of Rehabilitation Facilities (CARF) accreditation	Control	Service	Staffed Beds	Admissions	Census	Outpatient Visits	Births	Total	Payroll	Personnel

PINE RIDGE—Shannon County

⊠ **U. S. PUBLIC HEALTH SERVICE INDIAN HOSPITAL**, Mailing Address: P.O. Box 1201, Zip 57770–1201; tel. 605/867–5131, (Nonreporting) **A**1 10 **S** U. S. Indian Health Service, Rockville, MD
Primary Contact: Vern F. Donnell, Service Unit Director

| 44 | 10 | 45 | — | — | — | — | — | — | — |

PLATTE—Charles Mix County

★ **PLATTE HEALTH CENTER/AVERA HEALTH**, 601 East Seventh, Zip 57369–2123, Mailing Address: P.O. Box 200, Zip 57369–0200; tel. 605/337–3364, (Total facility includes 48 beds in nursing home–type unit) **A**9 10 18 **F**1 8 26 27 28 33 48 51 54 58 63 69 81 88 92 **P**6 **S** Avera Health, Yankton, SD
Primary Contact: Mark Burket, Chief Executive Officer
CFO: Jerry Hoffman, Chief Financial Officer
Web address: www.phcavera.org

| 23 | 10 | 63 | 304 | 51 | 9655 | 12 | 5765 | 3137 | 42 |

RAPID CITY—Pennington County

BLACK HILLS SURGERY CENTER, 216 Anamaria Drive, Zip 57701, Mailing Address: 1868 Lombardy Drive, Zip 57701; tel. 605/721–4900, (Nonreporting) **A**9 10
Primary Contact: Franklin Shobe, Administrator and Chief Executive Officer

| 32 | 10 | 26 | — | — | — | — | — | — | — |

⊠ **INDIAN HEALTH SERVICE HOSPITAL**, 3200 Canyon Lake Drive, Zip 57702–8197; tel. 605/355–2280 **A**1 10 **F**2 4 12 24 26 27 28 29 30 31 32 33 37 39 41 45 46 48 50 52 53 58 65 71 72 73 74 75 76 77 78 92 94 96 106 107 110 **S** U. S. Indian Health Service, Rockville, MD
Primary Contact: Ray Grandbois, M.P.H., Director
CFO: Helen Thompson, Administrative Officer
Web address: www.ihs.gov

| 47 | 10 | 32 | 465 | 7 | 74482 | 0 | 19512 | 7818 | 166 |

⊠ **RAPID CITY REGIONAL HOSPITAL SYSTEM OF CARE**, 353 Fairmont Boulevard, Zip 57701–7393, Mailing Address: P.O. Box 6000, Zip 57709–6000; tel. 605/719–1000 **A**1 2 3 5 9 10 **F**2 4 8 9 10 11 12 14 15 17 19 21 22 23 26 27 28 29 30 31 33 35 36 37 40 44 45 46 47 48 49 51 52 53 55 56 57 58 59 60 61 62 63 64 65 66 67 68 69 71 72 73 74 75 77 79 80 81 82 84 85 86 87 88 93 94 95 96 104 106 108 110 **P**1 6 7 **S** Regional Health, Rapid City, SD
Primary Contact: Timothy H. Sughrue, Chief Executive Officer
CFO: David Goehring, Interim Vice President Financial Services
CMO: Robert Allen, M.D., Medical Staff Liaison Officer
CIO: Richard Latuchie, Vice President Business Development
CHR: Robert McGlone, Vice President of Human Resources
Web address: www.rcrh.org

| 23 | 10 | 371 | 16689 | 241 | 170170 | 2146 | 256775 | 112352 | 2339 |

SAME DAY SURGERY CENTER, 651 Cathedral Drive, Zip 57701; tel. 605/719–5000, (Nonreporting) **A**9 10
Primary Contact: Doris Fritts, Director

| 33 | 13 | 8 | — | — | — | — | — | — | — |

REDFIELD—Spink County

COMMUNITY MEMORIAL HOSPITAL, 110 West Tenth Avenue, Zip 57469–0420, Mailing Address: P.O. Box 420, Zip 57469–0420; tel. 605/472–1111 **A**9 10 18 **F**2 6 8 9 14 27 28 29 33 41 44 46 48 51 52 54 57 58 60 63 64 69 70 88 92 94 95 97 108 **P**6
Primary Contact: Terry Dejong, Chief Executive Officer

| 14 | 10 | 25 | 525 | 7 | 20033 | 0 | 6318 | 3531 | 98 |

ROSEBUD—Todd County

⊠ **U. S. PUBLIC HEALTH SERVICE INDIAN HOSPITAL**, Highway 18, Soldier Creek Road, Zip 57570; tel. 605/747–2231 **A**1 10 **F**2 11 12 21 27 28 29 31 32 33 39 47 48 50 52 53 58 59 63 64 65 66 69 70 73 81 88 94 106 108 109 **P**6 **S** U. S. Indian Health Service, Rockville, MD
Primary Contact: Dixie Gaikowski, Acting Chief Executive Officer
COO: Romeo Vivit, Chief Surgeon
CFO: Myrna Knox, Budget Analyst
CMO: Tim Ryschon, Clinical Director

| 47 | 10 | 35 | 1084 | 9 | 71221 | 180 | 15278 | 12116 | 219 |

SCOTLAND—Bon Homme County

★ **LANDMANN–JUNGMAN MEMORIAL HOSPITAL**, 600 Billars Street, Zip 57059–2026; tel. 605/583–2226 **A**9 10 18 **F**9 23 26 27 28 29 32 33 36 41 46 48 51 52 63 66 69 88 91 94 96 97 108 **S** Avera Health, Yankton, SD
Primary Contact: Jay Plucker, Administrator
CFO: Darcy Kepplinger, Business Office Manager
CMO: Nibal A. Harati, M.D., Chief of Staff
CHR: Sandy Viau Zeeb, Employee and Community Relations
Web address: www.ljmh.org

| 23 | 10 | 19 | 398 | 4 | 4367 | 0 | 2144 | 1701 | 51 |

SIOUX FALLS—Minnehaha County

⊠ **AVERA HEART HOSPITAL OF SOUTH DAKOTA**, (Formerly Heart Hospital of South Dakota), 4500 West 69th Street, Zip 57108–8148; tel. 605/977–7000 **A**1 9 10 **F**2 9 15 17 19 21 22 26 29 33 41 46 47 48 49 52 58 63 65 66 81 82 87 88 92 94 108 **S** MedCath, Inc., Charlotte, NC
Primary Contact: Jon Soderholm, President
CFO: Jean White, Vice President of Finance
Web address: www.southdakotaheart.com

| 32 | 10 | 55 | 4025 | 38 | 3807 | 0 | 41906 | 13673 | 332 |

SD

Hospital, Address, Telephone, Approval, Facility, and Physician Codes, Health Care System	Classi-fication Codes		Utilization Data					Expense (thousands) of dollars		
★ American Hospital Association (AHA) membership □ Joint Commission on Accreditation of Healthcare Organizations (JCAHO) accreditation ○ American Osteopathic Association (AOA) accreditation △ Commission on Accreditation of Rehabilitation Facilities (CARF) accreditation	Control	Service	Staffed Beds	Admissions	Census	Outpatient Visits	Births	Total	Payroll	Personnel

⊠ △ **AVERA McKENNAN HOSPITAL AND UNIVERSITY HEALTH CENTER**, (Formerly Avera McKennan Hospital), 800 East 21st Street, Zip 57105–1096, Mailing Address: P.O. Box 5045, Zip 57117–5045; tel. 605/322–8000, (Total facility includes 196 beds in nursing home–type unit) **A**1 2 3 5 7 9 10 **F**2 4 6 8 9 10 11 12 13 15 16 17 18 19 21 22 23 24 27 28 29 30 31 33 34 35 36 37 38 39 41 42 44 45 46 47 48 49 50 51 52 53 55 56 57 58 59 60 61 62 63 64 65 66 67 68 69 70 71 72 73 74 75 76 77 78 79 81 82 84 85 87 88 90 91 92 93 94 95 96 98 99 101 104 105 106 108 109 110 **P**6 **S** Avera Health, Yankton, SD Primary Contact: Fredrick Slunecka, Regional President CFO: Ron Farr, Senior Vice President Finance CMO: David Kapaska, D.O., Senior Vice President Medical Affairs CIO: Kristin Gross, Director Information Technology Center CHR: Bill McLean, Senior Vice President Human Resources Web address: www.averamckennan.org	21	10	651	18270	328	143519	1428	318508	147848	3479
△ **CHILDRENS CARE HOSPITAL AND SCHOOL**, 2501 West 26th Street, Zip 57105–2498; tel. 605/782–2300 **A**7 9 10 **F**9 21 26 27 28 29 42 45 52 58 65 68 69 72 92 94 108 Primary Contact: Charisse S. Oland, President and Chief Executive Officer Web address: www.cchs.org	23	56	114	45	84	17561	0	17911	10745	337
⊠ **ROYAL C. JOHNSON VETERANS MEMORIAL HOSPITAL**, 2501 West 22nd Street, Zip 57105–9920, Mailing Address: P.O. Box 5046, Zip 57117–5046; tel. 605/336–3230, (Total facility includes 58 beds in nursing home–type unit) **A**1 3 5 **F**4 9 21 25 28 32 35 36 37 38 39 44 48 49 50 51 55 57 58 60 61 62 65 66 69 70 71 73 75 76 77 78 79 81 82 88 93 94 106 107 108 109 **P**6 **S** Department of Veterans Affairs, Washington, DC Primary Contact: Joseph M. Dalpiaz, Director CFO: Richard Jamison, Chief Financial Officer CMO: Rachel McCracken, M.D., Acting Chief of Staff CHR: Betsy Geiver, Chief Human Resources Web address: www.visn23.med.va.gov	45	10	103	3808	103	135666	0	39287	30585	675
□ **SELECT SPECIALTY HOSPITAL–SIOUX FALLS**, 800 East 21 Street, Suite 3300, Zip 57105; tel. 605/322–3500, (Nonreporting) **A**1 9 10 Primary Contact: Carol Ulmer, Chief Executive Officer	33	49	24	—	—	—	—	—	—	—
★ **SIOUX FALLS SURGICAL CENTER**, 910 East 20th Street, Zip 57105; tel. 605/334–6730, (Nonreporting) **A**9 10 Primary Contact: Douglas V. Johnson, Executive Director CFO: Kyle Goldammer, Chief Financial Officer CMO: Donald A. Schellpfeffer, M.D., Medical Director Web address: www.sfsurgical.com	33	49	31	—	—	—	—	—	—	—
⊠ △ **SIOUX VALLEY HOSPITAL UNIVERSITY MEDICAL CENTER**, 1305 West 18th Street, Zip 57105–0496, Mailing Address: P.O. Box 5039, Zip 57117–5039; tel. 605/333–1000 **A**1 2 3 5 7 8 9 10 **F**2 7 9 10 11 12 14 15 16 17 18 19 20 21 22 23 24 26 27 28 29 30 33 34 35 36 37 38 39 41 42 43 44 45 46 47 48 49 50 51 52 53 55 56 57 58 59 60 61 62 63 64 65 66 67 68 69 70 71 72 73 74 75 76 77 78 79 80 81 82 84 85 86 87 88 89 90 92 93 94 95 96 104 106 107 108 109 110 **P**6 **S** Sioux Valley Hospitals and Health System, Sioux Falls, SD Primary Contact: Becky Nelson, President CFO: Jeff Sandene, Chief of Finance CMO: Ken Aspaas, Chief Medical Officer CIO: Arlyn Broekhuis, Director Information Systems CHR: Evan Burkett, Chief Human Resource Officer Web address: www.siouxvalley.org	23	10	492	22241	296	262252	2953	284411	132116	3050
SISSETON—Roberts County										
★ **COTEAU DES PRAIRIES HOSPITAL**, 205 Orchard Drive, Zip 57262–2398; tel. 605/698–7647 **A**9 10 20 **F**11 23 27 28 29 33 41 46 47 48 51 52 55 58 59 60 63 65 68 69 88 97 **P**6 Primary Contact: Bill Nelson, Administrator and Chief Executive Officer Web address: www.cdphospital.com	23	10	27	584	5	22266	138	5987	3136	87
⊠ **U. S. PUBLIC HEALTH SERVICE INDIAN HOSPITAL**, Chestnut Street, Zip 57262, Mailing Address: P.O. Box 189, Zip 57262–0189; tel. 605/698–7606 **A**1 10 **F**26 27 28 32 33 48 52 94 107 108 **S** U. S. Indian Health Service, Rockville, MD Primary Contact: Richard Huff, Administrator CFO: Ramona Owen, Administrative Officer Web address: www.home.aberdeen.his.gov	47	10	11	104	1	25362	0	4115	3208	23
SPEARFISH—Lawrence County										
★ **LOOKOUT MEMORIAL HOSPITAL**, 1440 North Main Street, Zip 57783–1504; tel. 605/644–4000 **A**10 **F**2 9 11 12 21 23 26 27 28 33 36 38 46 48 51 55 58 59 62 63 64 69 70 81 82 84 88 92 93 94 96 97 106 108 109 110 **P**6 **S** Regional Health, Rapid City, SD Primary Contact: Larry W. Veitz, Chief Executive Officer Web address: www.rcrh.org	23	10	40	1645	13	26239	400	21309	10045	248
SPEARFISH SURGERY CENTER, 1316 10th Street, Zip 57783; tel. 605/642–3113, (Nonreporting) **A**9 10	33	49	4	—	—	—	—	—	—	—

SD

Hospital, Address, Telephone, Approval, Facility, and Physician Codes, Health Care System	Classi-fication Codes		Utilization Data					Expense (thousands) of dollars		
★ American Hospital Association (AHA) membership □ Joint Commission on Accreditation of Healthcare Organizations (JCAHO) accreditation ○ American Osteopathic Association (AOA) accreditation △ Commission on Accreditation of Rehabilitation Facilities (CARF) accreditation	Control	Service	Staffed Beds	Admissions	Census	Outpatient Visits	Births	Total	Payroll	Personnel

STURGIS—Meade County

★ **STURGIS COMMUNITY HEALTH CARE CENTER**, 949 Harmon Street, Zip 57785–2452; tel. 605/347–2536, (Total facility includes 84 beds in nursing home–type unit) **A**10 18 **F**9 11 12 21 26 27 28 33 36 37 51 59 60 63 69 81 88 92 96 97 **S** Regional Health, Rapid City, SD
Primary Contact: Van Hyde, Chief Executive Officer
CFO: Jodie Mitchell, Facility Financial Director
CMO: Chuck Lewis, D.O., Chief of Staff
Web address: www.rcrh.org/Facilities/Hospitals/SCHCC/Default.asp

| 23 | 10 | 109 | 983 | 91 | 14289 | 61 | 11927 | 6032 | 101 |

TYNDALL—Bon Homme County

★ **ST. MICHAEL'S HOSPITAL**, 410 West 16th Avenue, Zip 57066, Mailing Address: P.O. Box 27, Zip 57066–0027; tel. 605/589–3341, (Total facility includes 9 beds in nursing home–type unit) **A**9 10 18 **F**12 26 27 28 33 41 48 51 55 63 65 81 84 88 92 95 97 **P**6 **S** Avera Health, Yankton, SD
Primary Contact: Carol Deurmier, Chief Executive Officer
CFO: Lisa Ronke, Director of Finance and Business Office
CMO: Herbert A. Saloum, M.D., Medical Director

| 21 | 10 | 34 | 314 | 12 | 9775 | 0 | 4282 | 2295 | 61 |

VERMILLION—Clay County

★ **SIOUX VALLEY VERMILLION MEDICAL CENTER**, 20 South Plum Street, Zip 57069–3346; tel. 605/624–2611, (Total facility includes 66 beds in nursing home–type unit) **A**9 10 18 **F**12 26 29 33 48 53 58 59 63 69 70 81 88 93 94 95 96 106 **P**8 **S** Sioux Valley Hospitals and Health System, Sioux Falls, SD
Primary Contact: Timothy J. Tracy, Chief Executive Officer
CFO: Valerie Osterberg, Chief Financial Officer
CMO: Thomas Olson, M.D., Chief of Staff
Web address: www.siouxvalleyvermillion.org

| 23 | 10 | 116 | 474 | 67 | 17692 | 84 | 10722 | 5323 | 185 |

VIBORG—Turner County

★ **PIONEER MEMORIAL HOSPITAL AND HEALTH SERVICES**, 315 North Washington Street, Zip 57070–2002, Mailing Address: P.O. Box 368, Zip 57070–0368; tel. 605/326–5161, (Total facility includes 52 beds in nursing home–type unit) **A**9 10 18 **F**1 8 12 22 26 27 28 33 36 41 44 46 48 54 58 62 63 70 81 84 88 91 92 94 96 97 **P**6 **S** Sioux Valley Hospitals and Health System, Sioux Falls, SD
Primary Contact: Georgia Pokorney, Chief Executive Officer
CFO: Anne Christiansen, Chief Financial Officer
CMO: Francisco P. Cruz, M.D., Chief Medical Officer
Web address: www.pioneermemorial.org

| 23 | 10 | 64 | 353 | 52 | 18740 | 0 | 8340 | 4187 | 133 |

WAGNER—Charles Mix County

★ **WAGNER COMMUNITY MEMORIAL HOSPITAL**, Third and Walnut, Zip 57380, Mailing Address: P.O. Box 280, Zip 57380–0280; tel. 605/384–3611 **A**9 10 18 **F**9 14 23 27 28 33 34 44 46 48 52 55 63 69 70 88 91 92 94 97 110 **P**6 **S** Avera Health, Yankton, SD
Primary Contact: Jeremy Armstrong, Administrator
CFO: Lisa Weisser, Finance Supervisor
CIO: Bernadette Koupal, Business Office Supervisor, Information Systems Coordinator and Administrative Assistant

| 23 | 10 | 20 | 240 | 4 | 3661 | 0 | 1753 | 786 | 44 |

WATERTOWN—Codington County

★ **PRAIRIE LAKES HEALTHCARE SYSTEM**, 401 9th Avenue N.W., Zip 57201–6210, Mailing Address: P.O. Box 1210, Zip 57201–1210; tel. 605/882–7000, (Total facility includes 51 beds in nursing home–type unit) **A**2 9 10 20 **F**2 9 11 12 21 22 23 26 27 28 29 33 34 36 37 45 46 47 48 51 52 53 55 58 59 60 61 62 63 65 66 69 79 81 82 84 85 86 87 88 92 93 94 95 96 97 106 108 109 110 **P**5 **S** Sioux Valley Hospitals and Health System, Sioux Falls, SD
Primary Contact: Paul A. Hanson, Chief Executive Officer
COO: James Lohrman, Chief Operating Officer
CFO: Michael Anderson, Vice President Finance
CMO: Dan Flaherty, Chief of Medical Staff
Web address: www.prairielakes.com

| 23 | 10 | 119 | 3480 | 85 | 67039 | 604 | 38412 | 15631 | 417 |

WEBSTER—Day County

★ **LAKE AREA HOSPITAL**, North First Street, Zip 57274–1816, Mailing Address: P.O. Box 489, Zip 57274–0489; tel. 605/345–3336 **A**9 10 18 **F**11 12 14 21 27 28 29 33 34 36 46 48 50 52 55 59 60 63 65 66 67 68 69 70 81 82 84 88 92 94 95 97 110 **P**6 **S** Sioux Valley Hospitals and Health System, Sioux Falls, SD
Primary Contact: Donald J. Finn, Chief Executive Officer
CFO: Donald J. Finn, Chief Executive Officer
Web address: www.lakeareahospital.org

| 23 | 10 | 25 | 274 | 4 | 6547 | 10 | 4395 | 2211 | 66 |

WESSINGTON SPRINGS—Jerauld County

★ **AVERA WESKOTA MEMORIAL MEDICAL CENTER**, 604 First Street N.E., Zip 57382, Mailing Address: P.O. Box 429, Zip 57382; tel. 605/539–1201 **A**9 10 18 **F**2 9 12 26 27 28 33 34 41 46 48 52 58 60 63 92 94 97 **P**5 **S** Avera Health, Yankton, SD
Primary Contact: Kayleen R. Lee, Chief Executive Officer
COO: Kayleen R. Lee, Chief Executive Officer
CFO: Linda Jager, Director Finance and Reimbursement
CMO: Thomas Dean, Chief of Staff
Web address: www.averaweskota.org

| 23 | 10 | 25 | 248 | 3 | 3024 | 0 | 2272 | 1046 | 31 |

Many Facility Codes have changed. Please refer to the AHA Guide Code Chart. © 2005 AHA Guide

SD

Hospital, Address, Telephone, Approval, Facility, and Physician Codes, Health Care System	Classi-fication Codes		Utilization Data					Expense (thousands) of dollars		
★ American Hospital Association (AHA) membership ☐ Joint Commission on Accreditation of Healthcare Organizations (JCAHO) accreditation ○ American Osteopathic Association (AOA) accreditation △ Commission on Accreditation of Rehabilitation Facilities (CARF) accreditation	Control	Service	Staffed Beds	Admissions	Census	Outpatient Visits	Births	Total	Payroll	Personnel

WINNER—Tripp County

★ **WINNER REGIONAL HEALTHCARE CENTER**, 745 East Eighth Street, Zip 57580–2677; tel. 605/842–7100, (Total facility includes 81 beds in nursing home–type unit) **A**9 10 18 20 **F**9 11 12 14 23 27 28 29 33 37 44 46 47 48 51 52 54 58 59 61 63 81 82 84 88 92 95 96 97 106 **P**5 **S** Sioux Valley Hospitals and Health System, Sioux Falls, SD
Primary Contact: Michael Hall, Chief Executive Officer
CFO: Jim Frank, Chief Financial Officer
CMO: Teresa Martz, M.D., Chief of Staff
CHR: Karleen Flakus, Human Resource Director
Web address: www.winnerregional.org

| 23 | 10 | 106 | 849 | 81 | 6892 | 180 | 6914 | 5261 | 181 |

YANKTON—Yankton County

✉ △ **AVERA SACRED HEART HOSPITAL**, 501 Summit Avenue, Zip 57078–3899; tel. 605/668–8000, (Total facility includes 187 beds in nursing home–type unit) **A**1 2 5 7 9 10 19 20 **F**1 8 9 11 12 17 21 22 23 26 27 28 29 33 36 37 38 40 41 44 46 48 49 51 52 53 54 55 58 59 60 61 62 63 64 66 68 69 70 79 81 82 84 86 87 88 91 92 93 94 95 96 97 106 107 108 **S** Avera Health, Yankton, SD
Primary Contact: Pamela J. Rezac, President and Chief Executive Officer
COO: Douglas R. Ekeren, Vice President Planning and Development
CFO: Michael Healy, Vice President Finance
CMO: Marques Rhoades, M.D., Vice President Medical Service
CIO: Kathy Quinlivan, Management Information Systems Director
CHR: Kim Jensen, Vice President Human Resources
Web address: www.averasacredheart.com

| 21 | 10 | 297 | 4998 | 229 | 32102 | 595 | 55863 | 24758 | 484 |

LEWIS AND CLARK SPECIALTY HOSPITAL, 2601 Fox Run Parkway, Zip 57078; tel. 605/665–5100, (Nonreporting) **A**10

| 33 | 49 | 6 | — | — | — | — | — | — | — |

SD

TENNESSEE

Hospital, Address, Telephone, Approval, Facility, and Physician Codes, Health Care System	Classi-fication Codes		Utilization Data					Expense (thousands) of dollars		
★ American Hospital Association (AHA) membership □ Joint Commission on Accreditation of Healthcare Organizations (JCAHO) accreditation ○ American Osteopathic Association (AOA) accreditation △ Commission on Accreditation of Rehabilitation Facilities (CARF) accreditation	Control	Service	Staffed Beds	Admissions	Census	Outpatient Visits	Births	Total	Payroll	Personnel

ASHLAND CITY—Cheatham County

★ **CENTENNIAL MEDICAL CENTER AT ASHLAND CITY**, 313 North Main Street, Zip 37015–1358; tel. 615/792–3030, (Nonreporting) **A**10 18 **S** HCA, Nashville, TN
Primary Contact: Lawrence Kloess, President
COO: Michael W. Garfield, Chief Operating Officer
CIO: David Archer, Director, Information Systems
Web address: www.centennialmedicalcenter.com
| 33 | 10 | 8 | — | — | — | — | — | — | — |

ATHENS—McMinn County

☒ **ATHENS REGIONAL MEDICAL CENTER**, 1114 West Madison Avenue, Zip 37303–4150, Mailing Address: P.O. Box 250, Zip 37371–0250; tel. 423/745–1411 **A**1 9 10 **F**2 9 11 12 21 22 23 26 27 28 29 33 34 38 39 40 42 46 48 50 52 53 55 58 59 60 61 62 63 64 65 68 69 75 81 82 84 85 86 87 88 93 94 96 97 106 108 110 **P**7 **S** LifePoint Hospitals, Inc., Brentwood, TN
Primary Contact: John R. Workman, Chief Executive Officer
COO: Margie Brusseau, R.N., Chief Nursing Officer
CFO: David Alley, Chief Financial Officer
Web address: www.athensrmc.com
| 33 | 10 | 97 | 3153 | 27 | 70419 | 401 | 25806 | 10447 | 280 |

BARTLETT—Shelby County

☒ **SAINT FRANCIS HOSPITAL–BARTLETT**, 2986 Kate Bond Road, Zip 38133–4003; tel. 901/820–7000 **A**1 10 **F**2 9 11 12 21 22 26 28 29 31 33 35 36 37 39 44 45 46 47 48 49 52 53 55 57 58 59 60 61 62 63 64 65 66 69 75 81 82 84 85 87 88 94 96 106 108 109 110 **P**5 8 **S** TENET Healthcare Corporation, Dallas, TX
Primary Contact: David C. Wilson, Chief Executive Officer
CFO: Emma Canlas, Chief Financial Officer
CIO: Mike Hadley, Director, Information Systems
CHR: Deb Lollar, Director of Human Resources
Web address: www.saintfrancisbartlett.com
| 33 | 10 | 44 | 932 | 19 | 9899 | — | 19726 | 9085 | 287 |

BOLIVAR—Hardeman County

☒ **BOLIVAR GENERAL HOSPITAL**, 650 Nuckolls Road, Zip 38008–1532, Mailing Address: P.O. Box 509, Zip 38008–0509; tel. 731/658–3100 **A**1 9 10 **F**2 12 21 22 26 27 28 29 33 46 48 52 58 63 66 69 71 81 88 94 96 97 108 **S** West Tennessee Healthcare, Jackson, TN
Primary Contact: Ruby Kirby, Administrator
CFO: Terry Swindell, Controller
CMO: Jimmy Komzo Pratt, M.D., Chief of Medical Staff
Web address: www.wth.net
| 16 | 10 | 37 | 972 | 8 | 18395 | 3 | 6814 | 2785 | 94 |

□ **WESTERN MENTAL HEALTH INSTITUTE**, 11100 Old Highway 64, West, Zip 38008; tel. 731/228–2000 **A**1 10 **F**27 71 72 76
Primary Contact: Roger Pursley, Chief Executive Officer
| 12 | 22 | 256 | 2333 | 256 | 0 | 0 | 33281 | 20242 | 637 |

BRISTOL—Sullivan County

□ **SELECT SPECIALTY HOSPITAL–TRICITIES**, One Medical Park Boulevard, 5th Floor, Zip 37620; tel. 423/844–5900, (Nonreporting) **A**1 10
Primary Contact: Christopher E. Anderson, Chief Executive Officer
| 33 | 49 | 25 | — | — | — | — | — | — | — |

☒ **WELLMONT BRISTOL REGIONAL MEDICAL CENTER**, 1 Medical Park Boulevard, Zip 37620–7434; tel. 423/844–1121, (Total facility includes 30 beds in nursing home–type unit) **A**1 2 3 5 9 10 **F**2 9 10 11 12 14 15 17 19 21 22 23 26 27 28 29 31 32 33 34 36 37 38 39 40 41 42 43 44 45 46 47 48 49 50 51 52 55 57 58 59 60 61 62 63 64 65 66 69 70 71 72 73 74 75 76 77 78 79 80 81 82 83 84 85 86 87 88 92 93 94 95 96 106 107 108 109 110 **P**5 **S** Wellmont Health System, Kingsport, TN
Primary Contact: Barton A. Hove, President
COO: Barton A. Hove, President
CFO: Brad H. Price, Vice President Finance and Operations
CMO: Dale Sargent, M.D., Executive Vice President Medical Affairs
CIO: Steve Hill, Chief Information Officer
CHR: Hamlin J. Wilson, Senior Vice President Human Resources
Web address: www.wellmont.org
| 23 | 10 | 348 | 13956 | 181 | 171019 | 901 | 142140 | 52821 | 1195 |

BROWNSVILLE—Haywood County

□ **HAYWOOD PARK COMMUNITY HOSPITAL**, 2545 North Washington Avenue, Zip 38012–1697; tel. 731/772–4110, (Nonreporting) **A**1 9 10 **S** Community Health Systems, Inc., Brentwood, TN
Primary Contact: Thomas Schmitt, Chief Executive Officer
Web address: www.haywoodparkcommunity.com
| 33 | 10 | 44 | — | — | — | — | — | — | — |

CAMDEN—Benton County

☒ **CAMDEN GENERAL HOSPITAL**, 175 Hospital Drive, Zip 38320–1617; tel. 731/584–6135, (Total facility includes 10 beds in nursing home–type unit) **A**1 9 10 **F**2 12 21 22 26 27 28 29 33 46 48 52 58 63 64 66 69 81 88 92 94 96 108 **S** West Tennessee Healthcare, Jackson, TN
Primary Contact: Tina Prescott, Administrator
Web address: www.wth.net
| 16 | 10 | 30 | 444 | 11 | 16641 | 0 | 6044 | 2635 | 91 |

TN

Hospital, Address, Telephone, Approval, Facility, and Physician Codes, Health Care System	Classi-fication Codes		Utilization Data					Expense (thousands) of dollars		
★ American Hospital Association (AHA) membership □ Joint Commission on Accreditation of Healthcare Organizations (JCAHO) accreditation ○ American Osteopathic Association (AOA) accreditation △ Commission on Accreditation of Rehabilitation Facilities (CARF) accreditation	Control	Service	Staffed Beds	Admissions	Census	Outpatient Visits	Births	Total	Payroll	Personnel

CARTHAGE—Smith County

⊠ **CARTHAGE GENERAL HOSPITAL**, 130 Lebanon Highway, Zip 37030–2955, Mailing Address: P.O. Box 319, Zip 37030–0319; tel. 615/735–9815 **A**1 9 10 18 **F**6 27 28 33 58 60 63 65 66 69 81 84 87 88 94 96 97 98 **S** Sumner Regional Health Systems, Gallatin, TN
Primary Contact: Scott Tongate, Administrator
CFO: Nick Swift, Senior Vice President Finance
CIO: David Young, Chief Information Officer
CHR: Amy Overstreet, Human Resources Director
Web address: www.sumner.org

| 23 | 10 | 25 | 792 | 11 | 19364 | 25 | 7890 | 3918 | 195 |

⊠ **SMITH COUNTY MEMORIAL HOSPITAL**, 158 Hospital Drive, Zip 37030–1096; tel. 615/735–1560 **A**1 9 10 **F**21 22 27 28 33 44 46 48 63 71 76 81 84 88 92 97 108 **S** LifePoint Hospitals, Inc., Brentwood, TN
Primary Contact: Ron Walker, Chief Executive Officer
CFO: Danny Warren, Chief Financial Officer
CIO: Valerie Upchurch, Chief Physician Relations

| 33 | 10 | 63 | 1441 | 18 | 21859 | 0 | 12512 | 4707 | 123 |

CELINA—Clay County

□ **CUMBERLAND RIVER HOSPITAL**, 100 Old Jefferson Street, Zip 38551–4040, Mailing Address: P. O. Box 427, Zip 38551–0427; tel. 931/243–3581 **A**1 9 10 **F**12 33 46 51 63 68 71 76 81 88 92 **S** Associated Healthcare Systems, Inc., Brentwood, TN
Primary Contact: Andrea Rich–McLerran, Chief Executive Officer

| 33 | 10 | 34 | 1356 | 14 | 11950 | 0 | 7465 | 3744 | 119 |

CENTERVILLE—Hickman County

⊠ **HICKMAN COMMUNITY HOSPITAL**, 135 East Swan Street, Zip 37033–1446; tel. 931/729–4271, (Total facility includes 40 beds in nursing home–type unit) **A**1 9 10 18 **F**12 21 26 27 28 33 51 52 63 69 77 81 92 94 97 **P**6 **S** Ascension Health, Saint Louis, MO
Primary Contact: Jack M. Keller, Administrator
Web address: www.hickmanhospital.com

| 23 | 10 | 65 | 398 | 42 | 10513 | 0 | 8265 | 4239 | 100 |

CHATTANOOGA—Hamilton County

CUMBERLAND HALL PSYCHIATRIC HOSPITAL, 7351 Standifer Gap Road, Zip 37421; tel. 423/499–9007, (Nonreporting) **A**9 10
Primary Contact: Charles A. Dickens, Regional Administrator and Chief Executive Officer

| 33 | 22 | 64 | — | — | — | — | — | — | — |

⊠ **ERLANGER MEDICAL CENTER**, 975 East Third Street, Zip 37403–2112; tel. 423/778–7000, (Includes ERLANGER NORTH HOSPITAL, 632 Morrison Springs Road, Zip 37415; tel. 615/778–3300; T. C. THOMPSON CHILDREN'S HOSPITAL, 910 Blackford Street, Zip 37403; tel. 615/778–6011; WILLIE D. MILLER EYE CENTER) **A**1 2 3 5 9 10 **F**2 6 9 11 12 13 14 15 16 17 18 19 20 21 22 23 24 28 29 31 32 33 34 35 36 37 41 42 44 45 46 47 48 49 50 51 52 53 55 56 57 58 59 60 61 62 63 65 66 67 69 70 71 76 79 81 82 84 88 89 90 93 94 96 101 107 108 109 110 **P**5 **S** Erlanger Health System, Chattanooga, TN
Primary Contact: James L. Brexler, President and Chief Executive Officer
CFO: Marvin A. Kurtz, Chief Financial Officer
CMO: Mel Twiest, M.D., Senior Vice President Medical Affairs and Chief Medical Officer
CIO: Brad Brown, Senior Vice President, Information Systems
CHR: Gregg Gentry, Senior Vice President Human Resources
Web address: www.erlanger.org

| 16 | 10 | 519 | 28312 | 372 | 354023 | 4590 | 402443 | 177274 | 3860 |

⊠ **HEALTHSOUTH CHATTANOOGA REHABILITATION HOSPITAL**, 2412 McCallie Avenue, Zip 37404–3398; tel. 423/698–0221 **A**1 10 **F**21 45 52 68 69 96 **S** HEALTHSOUTH Corporation, Birmingham, AL
Primary Contact: Donna Bourdon, Administrator
CFO: Julia Smith, Regional Controller
CMO: Sai Oh, M.D., Medical Director
CIO: Denise Smith, Health Information Director
CHR: Julia Doucette, Human Resources Director
Web address: www.healthsouth.com

| 33 | 46 | 54 | 1288 | 54 | 6227 | 0 | 10674 | 6302 | 180 |

□ **KINDRED HOSPITAL–CHATTANOOGA**, 709 Walnut Street, Zip 37402; tel. 423/266–7721, (Nonreporting) **A**1 9 10 **S** Kindred Healthcare, Louisville, KY
Primary Contact: William J. Bryant, Chief Executive Officer
Web address: www.kindredhealthcare.com

| 33 | 80 | 44 | — | — | — | — | — | — | — |

⊠ **MEMORIAL HEALTH CARE SYSTEM**, 2525 De Sales Avenue, Zip 37404–3322; tel. 423/495–8656, (Includes MEMORIAL NORTH PARK HOSPITAL, 2051 Hamill Road, Zip 37343–4096; tel. 423/495–7100), (Total facility includes 15 beds in nursing home–type unit) **A**1 2 9 10 **F**2 6 9 10 12 15 17 19 21 22 23 26 27 28 29 33 35 39 41 42 44 46 47 48 49 50 51 52 57 58 60 61 62 63 64 65 66 69 79 81 82 84 85 86 87 88 90 93 94 96 106 108 109 110 **P**1 3 7 **S** Catholic Health Initiatives, Denver, CO
Primary Contact: Ruth W. Brinkley, President and Chief Executive Officer
COO: Lynn Whisman, R.N., Chief Nursing Executive and Vice President, Operations
CFO: Carol Newton, Chief Financial Officer
CMO: S Gale Fellowes, M.D., Chief Medical Officer
CIO: Alan Bobyarchick, Chief Information Officer
CHR: Lisa Whaley, Vice President, Human Resources
Web address: www.memorial.org

| 21 | 10 | 394 | 22106 | 306 | 321396 | 0 | 290737 | 109180 | 2842 |

Hospital, Address, Telephone, Approval, Facility, and Physician Codes, Health Care System	Classi-fication Codes		Utilization Data					Expense (thousands) of dollars		
★ American Hospital Association (AHA) membership □ Joint Commission on Accreditation of Healthcare Organizations (JCAHO) accreditation ○ American Osteopathic Association (AOA) accreditation △ Commission on Accreditation of Rehabilitation Facilities (CARF) accreditation	Control	Service	Staffed Beds	Admissions	Census	Outpatient Visits	Births	Total	Payroll	Personnel
□ **MOCCASIN BEND MENTAL HEALTH INSTITUTE**, 100 Moccasin Bend Road, Zip 37405–4496; tel. 423/785–3400 **A**1 10 **F**22 26 27 28 39 48 58 66 71 94 108 **P**6 Primary Contact: William L. Ventress, Superintendent Web address: www.state.tn.us/mental/mhs/moc.html	12	22	172	3859	157	0	0	24514	13293	444
⊠ **PARKRIDGE MEDICAL CENTER**, 2333 McCallie Avenue, Zip 37404–3285; tel. 423/698–6061, (Includes EAST RIDGE HOSPITAL, 941 Spring Creek Road, East Ridge, Zip 37412; tel. 423/855–3500; Mark E. Sims, Chief Executive Officer; VALLEY BEHAVIORAL HEALTH SYSTEM, 2200 Morris Hill Road, Zip 37421; tel. 423/499–1204; Philip R. Cook, Chief Executive Officer), (Total facility includes 28 beds in nursing home–type unit) (Nonreporting) **A**1 9 10 **S** HCA, Nashville, TN Primary Contact: Jeff Fee, President and Chief Executive Officer COO: Carlton Ulmer, Chief Operating Officer CFO: Lynne Mitchell, Chief Financial Officer CIO: Paul Marsh, Director Information Systems CHR: Dan Gilbert, Vice President Web address: www.parkridgemedicalcenter.com	33	10	517	—						
⊠ △ **SISKIN HOSPITAL FOR PHYSICAL REHABILITATION**, One Siskin Plaza, Zip 37403–1306; tel. 423/634–1200, (Total facility includes 14 beds in nursing home–type unit) **A**1 7 10 **F**21 22 26 27 28 29 45 52 58 68 69 92 94 96 108 **P**5 Primary Contact: Robert P. Main, President and Chief Executive Officer COO: Linda Knudson Lind, Senior Vice President and Chief Operating Officer CFO: Linda A. Knight, Vice President Finance and Chief Financial Officer CMO: Andrew C. Krouskop, M.D., Medical Director CHR: C Duaine Long, Director Human Resources Web address: www.siskinrehab.org T. C. THOMPSON CHILDREN'S HOSPITAL See Erlanger Medical Center VALLEY BEHAVIORAL HEALTH SYSTEM See Parkridge Medical Center WILLIE D. MILLER EYE CENTER See Erlanger Medical Center	23	46	94	2309	81	30668	0	26215	13337	268
CLARKSVILLE—Montgomery County										
⊠ **GATEWAY HEALTH SYSTEM**, 1771 Madison Street, Zip 37043–4900, Mailing Address: P.O. Box 3160, Zip 37043–3160; tel. 931/552–6622 **A**1 9 10 **F**2 9 10 11 12 14 15 17 19 21 22 23 24 27 28 29 33 35 36 39 40 46 48 50 51 52 55 56 58 59 60 61 62 63 64 65 66 68 69 81 82 84 86 87 88 93 94 96 106 108 109 110 Primary Contact: Randall L. Kelley, President and Chief Executive Officer CFO: Lynn Lambert, Vice President Finance and Chief Financial Officer CMO: Thomas L. Ely, D.O., Vice President Medical Affairs CIO: Stefan Hopper, Chief Information Officer CHR: Margaret Fite, Vice President Human Resources Web address: www.ghsystem.com	23	10	206	10180	111	140266	1614	100595	40748	1061
CLEVELAND—Bradley County										
□ **BRADLEY MEMORIAL HOSPITAL**, 2305 Chambliss Avenue N.W., Zip 37311–3847, Mailing Address: P.O. Box 3060, Zip 37320–3060; tel. 423/559–6000 **A**1 9 10 **F**2 11 12 15 21 22 23 26 27 28 29 33 34 36 37 38 39 40 43 44 46 47 48 49 50 51 52 53 55 58 59 60 61 62 63 64 65 66 69 70 81 82 84 85 86 87 88 93 94 96 108 109 110 Primary Contact: Alan Watson, Chief Executive Officer Web address: www.bradleyhospital.com	13	10	161	6787	72	95804	1031	65427	32670	594
□ **CLEVELAND COMMUNITY HOSPITAL**, 2800 Westside Drive N.W., Zip 37312–3599; tel. 423/339–4100, (Nonreporting) **A**1 9 10 **S** Community Health Systems, Inc., Brentwood, TN Primary Contact: Jim Coleman, Jr, Chief Executive Officer Web address: www.clevelandcommunity.com	33	10	73	—						
COLLIERVILLE—Shelby County										
⊠ **BAPTIST MEMORIAL HOSPITAL–COLLIERVILLE**, 1500 West Poplar Avenue, Zip 38017; tel. 901/861–9400 **A**1 9 10 **F**2 11 12 21 22 23 26 27 28 29 33 40 41 46 48 49 55 58 59 60 62 63 66 81 82 84 87 88 92 93 96 106 108 109 **S** Baptist Memorial Health Care Corporation, Memphis, TN Primary Contact: Glenn Baker, Administrator and Chief Executive Officer CFO: George Oswald, Chief Financial Officer CIO: Jerry Brantley, Vice President and Chief Information Officer CHR: Karen Swanson, Director, Human Resources Web address: www.bmhcc.org	21	10	61	3034	35	34301	172	35685	12992	314
COLUMBIA—Maury County										
⊠ **MAURY REGIONAL HOSPITAL**, 1224 Trotwood Avenue, Zip 38401–4802; tel. 931/381–1111, (Total facility includes 20 beds in nursing home–type unit) (Nonreporting) **A**1 2 9 10 19 Primary Contact: Robert Otwell, Chief Executive Officer COO: C Ron Pope, Chief Operating Officer CFO: Larry E. Moore, Chief Financial Officer CMO: Ensign Roy Harmon, Jr, M.D., Vice President Medical Affairs CIO: Doug Turner, Chief Information Officer CHR: Carolyn Harrison, Director of Human Resources Web address: www.mauryregional.com	13	10	267	—						

TN

Hospital, Address, Telephone, Approval, Facility, and Physician Codes, Health Care System	Classi-fication Codes		Utilization Data					Expense (thousands) of dollars		
★ American Hospital Association (AHA) membership □ Joint Commission on Accreditation of Healthcare Organizations (JCAHO) accreditation ○ American Osteopathic Association (AOA) accreditation △ Commission on Accreditation of Rehabilitation Facilities (CARF) accreditation	Control	Service	Staffed Beds	Admissions	Census	Outpatient Visits	Births	Total	Payroll	Personnel

COOKEVILLE—Putnam County

☒ **COOKEVILLE REGIONAL MEDICAL CENTER**, 142 West Fifth Street, Zip 38501–1760, Mailing Address: P.O. Box 340, Zip 38503–0340; tel. 931/646–2541 **A**1 2 9 10 19 **F**9 11 12 14 15 17 19 21 22 23 26 27 28 29 33 35 39 40 42 46 47 48 51 52 53 55 58 59 60 61 63 65 66 68 69 79 81 82 84 85 87 88 93 94 95 96 106 108 109
Primary Contact: Bernard L. Mattingly, Chief Executive Officer
CFO: Paul Korth, Chief Financial Officer
CIO: Les Bernstein, Director Information Systems
CHR: Angel Lewis, Executive Director Human Resources
Web address: www.crmchealth.org

| | 14 | 10 | 207 | 10684 | 126 | 47469 | 1095 | 107769 | 44978 | 1168 |

COPPERHILL—Polk County

□ **COPPER BASIN MEDICAL CENTER**, 144 Medical Center Drive, Zip 37317, Mailing Address: P.O. Box 990, Zip 37317–0990; tel. 423/496–5511 **A**1 9 10 **F**26 28 33 38 39 46 48 52 58 63 66 70 81 82 88 94
Primary Contact: Brandon W. Jolley, President and Chief Executive Officer

| | 23 | 10 | 44 | 859 | 9 | 12911 | 0 | 7477 | 3124 | 111 |

COVINGTON—Tipton County

☒ **BAPTIST MEMORIAL HOSPITAL–TIPTON**, 1995 Highway 51 South, Zip 38019–3635; tel. 901/476–2621 **A**1 9 10 **F**6 9 11 12 14 21 22 27 28 29 33 36 37 46 47 48 49 51 52 53 55 58 59 60 63 66 69 81 82 84 85 88 93 94 95 96 106 108 110 **S** Baptist Memorial Health Care Corporation, Memphis, TN
Primary Contact: Paul Betz, Administrator and Chief Executive Officer
CFO: Jimmy Robertson, Chief Financial Officer
CMO: Buffy Cook, Chief of Staff
CHR: Myra Cousar, Director of Human Resources
Web address: www.bmhcc.org

| | 23 | 10 | 54 | 2253 | 24 | 33193 | 444 | 25020 | 9602 | 406 |

CROSSVILLE—Cumberland County

☒ **CUMBERLAND MEDICAL CENTER**, 421 South Main Street, Zip 38555–5031; tel. 931/484–9511, (Total facility includes 20 beds in nursing home–type unit) **A**1 9 10 **F**2 11 12 15 21 23 26 27 28 29 33 40 41 46 48 51 53 55 57 58 59 60 61 62 63 66 69 70 81 84 88 92 93 94 95 96 106 108 109
Primary Contact: James L. McMackin, President and Chief Executive Officer
CFO: Kenneth R. Stephens, Executive Vice President
CIO: Joe Lowe, Director Management Information Systems
CHR: Pat Whittenburg, Director, Human Resources and Corporate Compliance Officer
Web address: www.cmchealthcare.org

| | 23 | 10 | 156 | 7602 | 108 | 91510 | 638 | 74672 | 32020 | 998 |

DAYTON—Rhea County

☒ **RHEA MEDICAL CENTER**, 7900 Rhea County Highway, Zip 37321–5912; tel. 423/775–1121, (Total facility includes 89 beds in nursing home–type unit) (Nonreporting) **A**1 9 10 18 **S** Quorum Health Resources, Plano, TX
Primary Contact: Kennedy L. Croom, Jr, Administrator and Chief Executive Officer
CFO: Harv Sanders, Chief Financial Officer
CMO: Christopher Horton, M.D., Chf of Staff
CHR: Peri Meadows, Director, Human Resources
Web address: www.rheamedical.org

| | 13 | 10 | 114 | — | — | — | — | — | — | — |

DICKSON—Dickson County

☒ **HORIZON MEDICAL CENTER**, 111 Highway 70 East, Zip 37055–2033; tel. 615/446–0446 **A**1 10 **F**9 10 11 12 15 21 22 23 27 28 33 37 39 46 48 49 52 55 58 59 60 62 63 64 65 66 68 69 71 76 81 82 84 88 93 94 106 108 109 **S** HCA, Nashville, TN
Primary Contact: John A. Marshall, Chief Executive Officer
COO: Frank Walton, Chief Operating Officer
CFO: Clarence Gray, Chief Financial Officer
CMO: Liisa Ortegon, Chief Nursing Officer
CIO: Robert Hollowell, Director Management Information Systems
CHR: Robbie Miller, Director Human Resources
Web address: www.horizonmedicalcenter.com

| | 33 | 10 | 116 | 4498 | 52 | 62539 | 526 | 48000 | 18578 | 392 |

DYERSBURG—Dyer County

□ **DYERSBURG REGIONAL MEDICAL CENTER**, 400 Tickle Street, Zip 38024–3182; tel. 731/285–2410 **A**1 9 10 20 **F**6 9 11 12 21 22 26 27 28 32 33 46 47 48 49 51 59 62 63 65 66 81 84 88 97 108 110 **P**7 **S** Community Health Systems, Inc., Brentwood, TN
Primary Contact: R. Coleman Foss, Chief Executive Officer
Web address: www.dyersburgregionalmc.com

| | 23 | 10 | 105 | 4456 | 41 | 47570 | 517 | — | — | — |

EAST RIDGE—Hamilton County

EAST RIDGE HOSPITAL See Parkridge Medical Center, Chattanooga

ELIZABETHTON—Carter County

□ **SYCAMORE SHOALS HOSPITAL**, 1501 West Elk Avenue, Zip 37643–2874; tel. 423/542–1300 **A**1 9 10 **F**2 9 11 12 21 22 26 27 28 29 33 35 39 41 44 46 48 51 52 53 55 57 59 60 61 62 63 65 66 69 71 76 81 82 84 85 88 92 94 96 106 108 109 **S** Mountain States Health Alliance, Johnson City, TN
Primary Contact: Dwayne Taylor, Chief Executive Officer
Web address: www.msha.com

| | 23 | 10 | 121 | 3089 | 33 | 70342 | 494 | 30149 | 11588 | 269 |

Hospital, Address, Telephone, Approval, Facility, and Physician Codes, Health Care System	Classi-fication Codes		Utilization Data					Expense (thousands) of dollars		
★ American Hospital Association (AHA) membership □ Joint Commission on Accreditation of Healthcare Organizations (JCAHO) accreditation ○ American Osteopathic Association (AOA) accreditation △ Commission on Accreditation of Rehabilitation Facilities (CARF) accreditation	Control	Service	Staffed Beds	Admissions	Census	Outpatient Visits	Births	Total	Payroll	Personnel

ERIN—Houston County

⊞ **TRINITY HOSPITAL**, 353 Main Street, Zip 37061–0489, Mailing Address: P.O. Box 489, Zip 37061–0489; tel. 931/289–4211 **A**1 9 10 18 **F**12 21 27 28 33 37 41 48 60 62 63 66 69 81 88 97 **P**5 **S** Associated Healthcare Systems, Inc., Brentwood, TN Primary Contact: Yvette Gillespie, Chief Executive Officer CFO: Shannon Allison, Chief Financial Officer CMO: Daniel E. Martin, M.D., Chief Medical Officer CHR: Reta Brady, Administrative Assistant and Human Resource Manager Web address: www.trinityhospitaltn.com	33	10	31	1241	11	23576	0	7287	3089	95

ERWIN—Unicoi County

⊞ **UNICOI COUNTY MEMORIAL HOSPITAL**, 100 Greenway Circle, Zip 37650–2196, Mailing Address: P.O. Box 802, Zip 37650–0802; tel. 423/743–3141, (Total facility includes 46 beds in nursing home–type unit) **A**1 9 10 **F**9 12 21 22 26 27 28 29 33 46 48 51 52 55 58 60 62 63 64 69 81 84 85 88 92 93 94 108 **P**5 Primary Contact: Jim S. Pate, President and Chief Executive Officer CFO: Toni Buchanan, Chief Financial Officer CIO: Don Hembree, Information Systems Director CHR: Susan Broyles, Human Resources Director Web address: www.ucmhnet.org	23	10	94	1025	56	52314	0	6731	5777	190

ETOWAH—McMinn County

⊞ **WOODS MEMORIAL HOSPITAL DISTRICT**, 886 Highway 411 North, Zip 37331–1912; tel. 423/263–3600 **A**1 9 10 **S** Baptist Health System of East Tennessee, Knoxville, TN Primary Contact: David Southerland, Senior Vice President and Administrator CFO: Danny L. Higginbotham, Chief Financial Officer CMO: Nathan Trentham, MC, Chief of Staff CIO: Danny L. Higginbotham, Chief Financial Officer CHR: Pam K. Davis, Director of Human Resources, Compliance Officer Web address: www.woodshospital.org	13	10	46	1598	15	43055	0	15822	7534	224

FAYETTEVILLE—Lincoln County

⊞ **LINCOLN COUNTY HEALTH SYSTEM**, 106 Medical Center Boulevard, Zip 37334–2684; tel. 931/438–1100, (Total facility includes 278 beds in nursing home–type unit) **A**1 9 10 **F**6 8 9 11 12 21 27 29 33 36 41 44 45 46 51 52 55 58 59 60 63 69 76 81 82 84 88 92 93 96 108 **S** Quorum Health Resources, Plano, TX Primary Contact: Gary G. Kendrick, Chief Executive Officer CFO: David Groce, Associate Administrator and Chief Financial Officer CMO: Chris Gafford, Chief of Staff CHR: Pat Marty, Director Web address: www.lchealthsystem.com	13	10	327	2627	301	39984	308	31937	14120	474

FRANKLIN—Williamson County

⊞ **WILLIAMSON MEDICAL CENTER**, 2021 Carothers Road, Zip 37067–8542; tel. 615/791–0500 **A**1 9 10 **F**2 6 9 10 11 12 15 17 23 26 27 28 29 33 34 46 48 52 55 58 59 60 61 62 63 64 65 66 69 70 73 74 75 76 77 78 81 82 84 86 87 88 93 94 95 96 106 108 110 **P**8 Primary Contact: Dennis E. Miller, FACHE, Chief Executive Officer CFO: Donald Webb, Chief Financial Officer CMO: Starling C. Evins, M.D., Chief of Staff CIO: Laura Bustetter, Director of Marketing and Public Relations CHR: Debra Foster, Director of Human Resources Web address: www.williamsonmedicalcntr.org	13	10	131	7071	77	121960	867	90897	39844	918

GALLATIN—Sumner County

⊞ **SUMNER REGIONAL MEDICAL CENTER**, 555 Hartsville Pike, Zip 37066–2449, Mailing Address: P.O. Box 1558, Zip 37066–1558; tel. 615/452–4210, (Total facility includes 10 beds in nursing home–type unit) **A**1 9 10 **F**2 9 11 12 15 21 22 23 26 27 28 29 32 33 35 36 37 39 40 41 45 46 47 48 49 51 52 53 55 57 58 59 60 61 62 63 64 65 66 68 69 75 80 81 82 84 85 88 92 93 94 95 96 106 108 109 **S** Sumner Regional Health Systems, Gallatin, TN Primary Contact: Bruce James, Administrator CFO: Nick Swift, Senior Vice President Finance CIO: David Young, Senior Vice President of Planning and Technology CHR: Jan Hallmark, Senior Vice President of Human Development and Community Outreach Web address: www.sumner.org	23	10	115	5741	93	97285	646	80112	39514	951

GERMANTOWN—Shelby County

⊞ **BAPTIST REHABILITATION–GERMANTOWN**, 2100 Exeter Road, Zip 38138–3978; tel. 901/757–1350 **A**1 9 10 **F**21 27 29 30 31 45 68 69 81 84 88 92 94 95 96 108 **S** Baptist Memorial Health Care Corporation, Memphis, TN Primary Contact: Susan Stralka, Administrator and Chief Executive Officer CFO: Tracy Emery, Chief Financial Officer Web address: www.bmhcc.org METHODIST HEALTHCARE–GERMANTOWN HOSPITAL See Methodist Healthcare–University Hospital, Memphis	23	46	51	1113	40	26071	0	20315	9402	237

TN

Many Facility Codes have changed. Please refer to the AHA Guide Code Chart. © 2005 AHA Guide

Hospital, Address, Telephone, Approval, Facility, and Physician Codes, Health Care System	Classi-fication Codes		Utilization Data					Expense (thousands) of dollars		
★ American Hospital Association (AHA) membership □ Joint Commission on Accreditation of Healthcare Organizations (JCAHO) accreditation ○ American Osteopathic Association (AOA) accreditation △ Commission on Accreditation of Rehabilitation Facilities (CARF) accreditation	Control	Service	Staffed Beds	Admissions	Census	Outpatient Visits	Births	Total	Payroll	Personnel

GREENEVILLE—Greene County

✠ **LAUGHLIN MEMORIAL HOSPITAL**, 1420 Tusculum Boulevard, Zip 37745–5825; tel. 423/787–5000, (Total facility includes 90 beds in nursing home–type unit) **A**1 9 10 **F**2 9 11 12 23 27 28 29 33 39 40 44 46 47 48 51 52 53 55 57 58 59 60 61 62 63 64 65 66 69 81 82 84 85 87 88 92 93 94 95 96 108 109 Primary Contact: Charles H. Whitfield, Jr, President and Chief Executive Officer CFO: Mark Compton, Controller CIO: Burt Ridge, Chief Information Officer CHR: Robert Roark, Director of Human Resources Web address: www.laughlinmemorial.org	23	10	230	5125	147	100200	420	51080	20671	559
✠ **TAKOMA ADVENTIST HOSPITAL**, 401 Takoma Avenue, Zip 37743–4647; tel. 423/639–3151 **A**1 9 10 **F**9 11 12 21 22 26 27 28 29 33 39 44 46 48 51 52 55 58 59 60 61 62 63 65 66 68 69 71 73 74 76 77 81 82 84 88 92 94 96 106 107 108 109 110 **S** Adventist Health System Sunbelt Health Care Corporation, Winter Park, FL Primary Contact: Carlyle L. E. Walton, President CFO: Steve Wilson, Chief Financial Officer CMO: Timothy Fuller, M.D., Chief of Staff Web address: www.takoma.org	21	10	100	2763	41	33613	283	22486	9566	381

HARRIMAN—Roane County

✠ **ROANE MEDICAL CENTER**, 412 Devonia Street, Zip 37748–0489, Mailing Address: P.O. Box 489, Zip 37748–0489; tel. 865/882–1323 **A**1 9 10 **F**2 9 12 15 21 22 26 28 29 33 46 48 55 62 63 71 76 81 84 88 93 94 107 108 109 110 **P**8 Primary Contact: Jim Gann, Administrator CFO: Janice Bardill, Chief Financial Officer CIO: Janice Bardill, Chief Financial Officer CHR: Joyce Marsalis, Human Resource Manager Web address: www.roanemedical.com	16	10	66	4375	42	64690	0	35308	15962	505

HARTSVILLE—Trousdale County

TROUSDALE MEDICAL CENTER, 500 Church Street, Zip 37074, Mailing Address: P.O. Box 319, Carthage, Zip 37030; tel. 615/374–2221 **A**9 10 18 **F**6 27 28 33 58 63 66 69 81 **S** Sumner Regional Health Systems, Gallatin, TN Primary Contact: William D. Mize, Administrator Web address: www.sumner.org	23	10	25	790	7	15644	0	6140	3122	103

HENDERSONVILLE—Sumner County

✠ **HENDERSONVILLE MEDICAL CENTER**, 355 New Shackle Island Road, Zip 37075–2393; tel. 615/338–1000 **A**1 **F**2 9 11 12 15 17 21 26 28 29 33 37 40 44 46 47 48 52 55 57 58 59 60 62 63 64 66 73 81 82 84 88 93 94 95 106 108 109 **S** HCA, Nashville, TN Primary Contact: Mike Esposito, Chief Executive Officer COO: Chad Brown, Chief Operating Officer CFO: Michael Morrison, Chief Financial Officer CIO: Hal Schultheis, Director Information Systems CHR: Kreg Arnold, Director, Human Resources Web address: www.hendersonvillemedicalcenter.com	33	10	70	3597	35	56568	616	49478	17274	—

HERMITAGE—Davidson County

✠ **SUMMIT MEDICAL CENTER**, 5655 Frist Boulevard, Zip 37076–2053; tel. 615/316–3000 **A**1 2 9 10 **F**2 9 10 11 12 14 15 17 21 23 26 27 28 29 31 32 33 37 39 40 41 42 44 46 47 48 50 52 53 55 57 58 59 60 61 62 63 64 65 66 69 70 71 73 74 75 76 79 80 81 82 84 85 87 88 93 94 95 96 106 108 109 110 **S** HCA, Nashville, TN Primary Contact: Jeffrey T. Whitehorn, Chief Executive Officer COO: Wendy Brandon, Chief Operating Officer CFO: Timothy Stanfill, Chief Financial Officer Web address: www.summitmedctr.com	33	10	188	9555	105	107448	1481	91931	35917	782

HUMBOLDT—Gibson County

✠ **HUMBOLDT GENERAL HOSPITAL**, 3525 Chere Carol Road, Zip 38343–3699; tel. 731/784–0301 **A**1 9 10 **F**2 11 12 21 22 26 27 28 29 33 46 48 52 53 58 59 63 64 66 69 81 88 94 96 97 108 **S** West Tennessee Healthcare, Jackson, TN Primary Contact: Bill Kail, Administrator CFO: Terry Swindell, Controller CMO: Cindy Swain, M.D., Chief of Staff Web address: www.wth.net	15	10	42	1284	18	18739	101	8160	3598	116

HUNTINGDON—Carroll County

✠ **BAPTIST MEMORIAL HOSPITAL–HUNTINGDON**, 631 R. B. Wilson Drive, Zip 38344–1675; tel. 731/986–4461, (Nonreporting) **A**1 9 10 **S** Baptist Memorial Health Care Corporation, Memphis, TN Primary Contact: Susan M. Breeden, Administrator and Chief Executive Officer CFO: Sharron Holland, Director Financial Services Web address: www.bmhcc.org	23	10	45	—	—	—	—	—	—	—

Hospital, Address, Telephone, Approval, Facility, and Physician Codes, Health Care System	Classi-fication Codes		Utilization Data					Expense (thousands) of dollars		
	Control	Service	Staffed Beds	Admissions	Census	Outpatient Visits	Births	Total	Payroll	Personnel

★ American Hospital Association (AHA) membership
□ Joint Commission on Accreditation of Healthcare Organizations (JCAHO) accreditation
○ American Osteopathic Association (AOA) accreditation
△ Commission on Accreditation of Rehabilitation Facilities (CARF) accreditation

JACKSON—Madison County

⊠ △ **JACKSON–MADISON COUNTY GENERAL HOSPITAL**, 708 West Forest Avenue, Zip 38301–3956; tel. 731/425–5000, (Total facility includes 85 beds in nursing home–type unit) **A**1 2 3 5 7 9 10 **F**2 6 9 11 12 14 15 17 19 21 22 23 26 27 28 29 33 36 37 38 40 44 46 48 49 52 53 55 56 57 58 59 60 61 62 63 64 65 66 67 68 69 70 81 84 86 88 92 93 94 95 96 106 108 109 110 **P**5 7 8 **S** West Tennessee Healthcare, Jackson, TN
Primary Contact: Jim Dockins, Chief Executive Officer
COO: Bradford J. Baucom, Vice President and Chief Operating Officer
CFO: Bobby Arnold, Vice President and Chief Financial Officer
CMO: Charles Mertz, Chief of Staff
CIO: Jeff Frieling, Chief Information Officer
CHR: Jan Boud, Vice President Communications and Human Resources
Web address: www.wth.org ... 16 10 635 27979 455 173154 3000 334402 135647 3514

★ **PATHWAYS OF TENNESSEE**, 238 Summar Drive, Zip 38301–3982; tel. 731/935–8200 **A**9 10 **F**4 21 26 27 28 29 31 46 48 71 72 73 74 75 76 77 78 92 96 98 106 **S** West Tennessee Healthcare, Jackson, TN
Primary Contact: Kelly R. Yenawine, Executive Director
CFO: Bobby Arnold, Vice President and Chief Financial Officer
CMO: Nat T. Winston, Medical Director
CIO: Jeff Frieling, Chief Information Officer
CHR: Judy Hime, Director Human Resources
Web address: www.wth.net ... 16 22 23 1327 15 152000 0 15878 8567 278

□ **REGIONAL HOSPITAL OF JACKSON**, 367 Hospital Boulevard, Zip 38305–4518; tel. 731/661–2000, (Nonreporting) **A**1 9 10 **S** Community Health Systems, Inc., Brentwood, TN
Primary Contact: Tim Puthoff, Chief Executive Officer
Web address: www.regionalhospital.com ... 33 10 127 — — — — — — —

JAMESTOWN—Fentress County

□ **JAMESTOWN REGIONAL MEDICAL CENTER**, 436 Central Avenue West, Zip 38556–1500, Mailing Address: P.O. Box 1500, Zip 38556–1500; tel. 931/879–8171 **A**1 9 10 20 **F**2 3 9 11 12 13 14 21 22 27 28 29 33 46 48 53 55 56 58 59 60 63 66 67 68 69 71 81 82 88 92 93 94 95 96 106 108 110 **S** Health Management Associates, Naples, FL
Primary Contact: James P. Frazier, III, Chief Executive Officer
Web address: www.jamestownregional.org ... 33 10 71 4352 32 16368 — 15669 8251 281

JASPER—Marion County

⊠ **GRANDVIEW MEDICAL CENTER**, 1000 Highway 28, Zip 37347–3638; tel. 423/837–9500 **A**1 10 **F**4 11 12 21 33 40 42 44 46 48 52 55 58 59 60 63 65 66 69 70 81 82 84 86 87 88 92 94 95 108 109 **S** HCA, Nashville, TN
Primary Contact: George Asbell, Interim President
CFO: Debbie Hennessee, Chief Financial Officer
Web address: www.grandviewhospital.com ... 33 10 68 2289 23 40214 — 21200 7497 202

JEFFERSON CITY—Jefferson County

⊠ **ST. MARY'S JEFFERSON MEMORIAL HOSPITAL**, (Formerly Jefferson Memorial Hospital), 110 Hospital Drive, Zip 37760–5281; tel. 865/471–2500 **A**1 9 10 **F**2 9 11 12 21 22 23 27 28 33 38 55 58 59 62 63 66 69 81 82 84 85 88 94 97 108 **S** Catholic Healthcare Partners, Cincinnati, OH
Primary Contact: Michael C. Hicks, Administrator
COO: Becky Englehardt, R.N., Clinical Operations Leader
Web address: www.jeffersonhealthinc.com ... 23 10 58 2548 25 56107 154 24885 9309 273

JELLICO—Campbell County

⊠ **JELLICO COMMUNITY HOSPITAL**, 188 Hospital Lane, Zip 37762–4432; tel. 423/784–7252 **A**1 9 10 20 **F**2 6 9 11 12 21 22 26 27 28 29 33 34 35 39 45 46 47 48 50 51 52 53 55 58 59 60 62 63 64 65 66 69 70 81 82 85 88 94 95 96 97 98 106 108 110 **S** Adventist Health System Sunbelt Health Care Corporation, Winter Park, FL
Primary Contact: David A. Butler, Chief Executive Officer and President
COO: Robert Opp, Chief Clinical Officer
CFO: Randy Reimer, Chief Financial Officer
CMO: David Bosscher, M.D., Chief of Staff
CIO: Richard Helm, Chief Information Officer
CHR: Brenda Petrey, Director of Human Resources
Web address: www.ahss.org ... 23 10 46 2046 20 86087 225 21764 7855 218

JOHNSON CITY—Washington County

⊠ **JOHNSON CITY MEDICAL CENTER**, 400 North State of Franklin Road, Zip 37604–6094; tel. 423/431–6111, (Total facility includes 13 beds in nursing home–type unit) **A**1 2 3 5 8 9 10 **F**2 6 9 10 11 12 14 15 16 17 18 19 20 21 22 23 24 26 27 28 29 32 33 34 35 36 37 38 39 40 41 42 44 45 46 47 48 49 50 51 52 53 55 56 57 58 59 60 61 62 63 64 65 66 67 68 69 70 73 75 79 80 81 82 84 85 86 87 88 90 92 93 94 95 96 98 101 104 105 106 108 109 110 **S** Mountain States Health Alliance, Johnson City, TN
Primary Contact: John W. Melton, Senior Vice President Operations and Chief Executive Officer
CFO: Marvin Eichorn, Senior Vice President and Chief Financial Officer
CIO: Richard Eshbach, Chief Information Officer
Web address: www.jcmc.com ... 23 10 481 24337 362 221096 1304 272929 95059 1955

TN

Many Facility Codes have changed. Please refer to the AHA Guide Code Chart. © 2005 AHA Guide

Hospital, Address, Telephone, Approval, Facility, and Physician Codes, Health Care System	Classi-fication Codes		Utilization Data					Expense (thousands) of dollars		
★ American Hospital Association (AHA) membership □ Joint Commission on Accreditation of Healthcare Organizations (JCAHO) accreditation ○ American Osteopathic Association (AOA) accreditation △ Commission on Accreditation of Rehabilitation Facilities (CARF) accreditation	Control	Service	Staffed Beds	Admissions	Census	Outpatient Visits	Births	Total	Payroll	Personnel
□ **JOHNSON CITY SPECIALTY HOSPITAL**, 203 East Watauga Avenue, Zip 37601–4651; tel. 423/434–1400 **A**1 9 10 **F**2 11 12 21 22 26 27 28 29 35 39 46 48 53 58 59 63 65 88 92 94 96 109 **S** Mountain States Health Alliance, Johnson City, TN Primary Contact: Rhonda Mann, Director Nursing and Operations Web address: www.msha.com/facilities/jchs.htm	23	44	49	1511	9	9225	1009	9536	4471	108
□ **NORTH SIDE HOSPITAL**, 401 Princeton Road, Zip 37601–2097; tel. 423/854–5600, (Total facility includes 34 beds in nursing home–type unit) **A**1 9 10 **F**2 21 22 26 27 28 33 35 44 45 53 55 57 60 62 65 80 81 82 84 85 87 88 92 94 108 **S** Mountain States Health Alliance, Johnson City, TN Primary Contact: Melanie Stanton, Administrator Web address: www.msha.com	23	10	80	1189	32	37825	0	13686	6358	155
△ **QUILLEN REHABILITATION HOSPITAL**, 2511 Wesley Street, Zip 37601–1723; tel. 423/283–0700 **A**7 10 **F**2 21 22 26 27 28 53 57 62 65 68 69 92 94 96 **S** Mountain States Health Alliance, Johnson City, TN Primary Contact: John Turner, Chief Executive Officer Web address: www.msha.com	23	46	60	1193	39	8085	0	12208	3670	109
□ **WOODRIDGE HOSPITAL**, 403 State of Franklin Road, Zip 37604–6009; tel. 423/928–7111 **A**1 3 5 9 10 **F**3 4 21 26 27 28 31 65 71 72 73 74 75 76 77 78 94 96 **P**6 **S** Mountain States Health Alliance, Johnson City, TN Primary Contact: Ensign Randall E. Jessee, M.D., Administrator Web address: www.frontierhealth.org	23	22	64	3812	64	147	0	—	—	164
KINGSPORT—Sullivan County										
⊠ **HEALTHSOUTH REHABILITATION HOSPITAL**, 113 Cassel Drive, Zip 37660–3775; tel. 423/246–7240 **A**1 10 **F**45 58 60 65 66 68 69 73 96 **S** HEALTHSOUTH Corporation, Birmingham, AL Primary Contact: Terri Alsbrook, Administrator COO: Robert Ley, Director of Marketing CFO: Natalie Tilson, Accounting Manager CMO: James P. Little, M.D., Medical Director CIO: Natalie Tilson, Controller CHR: Heather McMillan, Human Resources Coordinator Web address: www.healthsouth.com	33	46	42	896	42	8277	0	9828	4322	133
□ **INDIAN PATH MEDICAL CENTER**, 2000 Brookside Drive, Zip 37660–4682; tel. 423/857–7000, (Includes INDIAN PATH PAVILION, 2300 Pavilion Drive, Zip 37660–4672; tel. 423/857–5500), (Total facility includes 30 beds in nursing home–type unit) **A**1 9 10 **F**2 3 4 9 11 12 15 21 22 26 27 28 29 31 33 39 40 44 46 48 49 52 53 55 57 58 59 60 61 62 63 65 66 69 70 71 73 74 75 76 77 78 80 81 82 84 85 87 88 92 93 94 95 96 108 109 110 **S** Mountain States Health Alliance, Johnson City, TN Primary Contact: Monty E. McLaurin, President and Chief Executive Officer Web address: www.msha.com	23	10	222	7237	103	140661	647	68723	25649	644
⊠ **WELLMONT HOLSTON VALLEY MEDICAL CENTER**, 130 West Ravine Street, Zip 37660, Mailing Address: P.O. Box 238, Zip 37662–0238; tel. 423/224–4000, (Total facility includes 39 beds in nursing home–type unit) **A**1 2 3 5 9 10 **F**2 9 10 11 12 14 15 17 19 21 22 23 26 27 28 29 30 33 34 35 37 40 42 44 46 48 49 50 51 52 53 55 56 57 58 59 60 61 62 63 66 67 69 79 80 81 82 84 85 86 87 88 92 93 94 95 96 108 109 110 **P**8 **S** Wellmont Health System, Kingsport, TN Primary Contact: E. Berton Whitaker, President and Chief Executive Officer CFO: Alice H. Pope, Vice President, Finance and Operations CMO: J Dale Sargent, M.D., Executive Vice President Medical Affairs CIO: Steve Hill, Chief Information Officer CHR: Hamlin J. Wilson, Senior Vice President Human Resources Web address: www.wellmont.org	23	10	347	16594	222	224956	1203	210351	74173	1926
KNOXVILLE—Knox County										
BAPTIST HOSPITAL FOR WOMEN, 10820 Parkside Drive, Zip 37922–1956; tel. 865/218–7090, (Nonreporting) **A**10 **S** Baptist Health System of East Tennessee, Knoxville, TN Primary Contact: Martha O'Regan Chill, Senior Vice President and Administrator	23	49	16	—	—	—	—	—	—	—
⊠ △ **BAPTIST HOSPITAL OF EAST TENNESSEE**, 137 Blount Avenue S.E., Zip 37920–1643, Mailing Address: P.O. Box 1788, Zip 37901–1788; tel. 865/632–5011 **A**1 2 7 9 10 **F**4 8 9 11 12 14 21 31 32 33 36 37 44 45 46 48 50 51 52 55 58 59 60 61 63 66 68 69 70 71 73 74 75 76 77 78 81 82 84 88 92 94 96 108 109 **S** Baptist Health System of East Tennessee, Knoxville, TN Primary Contact: Brue Chandler, Senior Vice President and Administrator COO: Gregory A. Harb, CHE, Chief Operating Officer CFO: Caryn Hawthorne, Executive Vice President and Chief Financial Officer CIO: Chester Maze, Vice President Information System CHR: Scott Shaffer, Vice President of Human Resources Web address: www.bhset.org	23	10	274	12439	191	142610	0	163108	57742	1656
□ **BAPTIST HOSPITAL WEST**, 10820 Parkside Drive, Zip 37922–1956; tel. 865/218–7011, (Nonreporting) **A**1 10 **S** Baptist Health System of East Tennessee, Knoxville, TN Primary Contact: Martha O'Regan Chill, Senior Vice President and Administrator	23	49	75	—	—	—	—	—	—	—

TN

Hospital, Address, Telephone, Approval, Facility, and Physician Codes, Health Care System	Classi-fication Codes		Utilization Data					Expense (thousands) of dollars		
★ American Hospital Association (AHA) membership □ Joint Commission on Accreditation of Healthcare Organizations (JCAHO) accreditation ○ American Osteopathic Association (AOA) accreditation △ Commission on Accreditation of Rehabilitation Facilities (CARF) accreditation	Control	Service	Staffed Beds	Admissions	Census	Outpatient Visits	Births	Total	Payroll	Personnel
□ **EAST TENNESSEE CHILDREN'S HOSPITAL**, 2018 Clinch Avenue, Zip 37916–2393, Mailing Address: P.O. Box 15010, Zip 37901–5010; tel. 865/541–8000 **A**1 9 10 **F**2 7 9 21 22 23 24 27 28 29 32 33 34 35 37 42 46 48 51 52 53 56 57 58 60 61 62 63 64 65 66 67 69 70 81 84 88 93 94 96 108 **P**8 Primary Contact: Robert F. Koppel, President and Chief Executive Officer Web address: www.etch.com	23	50	122	6335	90	149810	0	92343	43580	991
⊠ △ **FORT SANDERS REGIONAL MEDICAL CENTER**, 1901 Clinch Avenue S.W., Zip 37916–2394; tel. 865/541–1111, (Total facility includes 24 beds in nursing home–type unit) **A**1 2 7 9 10 **F**2 9 11 14 15 17 19 21 22 23 26 27 28 33 37 39 40 41 46 47 48 49 50 52 55 57 58 59 60 61 62 63 64 65 66 68 69 81 82 84 85 87 88 90 92 93 94 95 96 99 104 108 109 110 **S** Covenant Health, Knoxville, TN Primary Contact: Keith Altshuler, Administrator Web address: www.covenanthealth.com	23	10	431	16190	256	150191	2794	178998	64679	1654
□ **LAKESHORE MENTAL HEALTH INSTITUTE**, 5908 Lyons View Drive, Zip 37919–7598; tel. 865/450–5200 **A**1 10 **F**2 22 28 44 48 60 65 66 71 72 73 76 94 108 Primary Contact: Richard Lee Thomas, Superintendent	12	22	184	2894	174	0	0	27867	14958	500
⊠ **PARKWEST MEDICAL CENTER**, 9352 Park West Boulevard, Zip 37923–4387, Mailing Address: P.O. Box 22993, Zip 37933–0993; tel. 865/373–1001, (Nonreporting) **A**1 2 9 10 **S** Covenant Health, Knoxville, TN Primary Contact: Wayne S. Heatherly, President and Chief Administrative Officer COO: Emlyn Cobble, Vice President and Chief Support Officer CFO: Scott Hamilton, Vice President and Chief Financial Officer CHR: Randall Carr, Director Human Resources Web address: www.yesparkwest.com	23	10	277	—	—	—	—	—	—	—
□ **SELECT SPECIALTY HOSPITAL–KNOXVILLE**, 1901 Clinch Avenue, Suite 404, Zip 37916; tel. 865/541–2615 **A**1 10 **F**2 21 44 57 60 62 65 94 110 Primary Contact: Vanda Scott, Chief Executive Officer Web address: www.selectmedicalcorp.com	41	10	25	115	7	0	0	2992	836	47
□ **SELECT SPECIALTY HOSPITAL–NORTH KNOXVILLE**, 900 East Oak Hill Avenue, Zip 37917; tel. 865/541–2615, (Nonreporting) **A**1 10 Primary Contact: Vanda Scott, Chief Executive Officer Web address: www.selectmedicalcorp.com	33	47	33	—	—	—	—	—	—	—
⊠ △ **ST. MARY'S MEDICAL CENTER**, (Formerly St Mary's Health System), 900 East Oak Hill Avenue, Zip 37917–4556; tel. 865/545–8000, (Total facility includes 25 beds in nursing home–type unit) **A**1 2 7 9 10 **F**2 9 11 12 14 15 17 19 21 22 23 26 27 28 29 31 33 35 36 37 38 39 40 44 45 46 47 48 49 51 52 53 55 56 57 58 59 61 62 63 65 66 68 69 70 71 73 74 75 76 77 81 82 84 85 86 88 92 93 94 96 106 108 109 110 **S** Catholic Healthcare Partners, Cincinnati, OH Primary Contact: Debra K. London, President and Chief Executive Officer COO: Jack M. Bryan, Chief Operating Officer CFO: David Nowiski, Chief Financial Officer CMO: Greg Phelps, M.D., Medical Director CIO: John Schlenker, Chief Information Officer CHR: Marty Margetts, Senior Vice President, Human Resource Development Web address: www.stmaryshealth.com	21	10	385	17184	259	181520	1745	186439	65762	1914
□ **UNIVERSITY OF TENNESSEE MEDICAL CENTER**, 1924 Alcoa Highway, Box 81, Zip 37920–6900; tel. 865/544–9000 **A**1 2 9 10 12 13 **F**2 6 9 11 12 14 15 16 17 18 19 20 21 22 23 26 27 28 33 34 36 37 38 39 40 41 49 50 51 52 53 55 56 57 58 59 60 61 62 63 64 66 67 69 70 73 79 80 81 82 83 84 85 86 87 88 90 93 94 95 96 101 105 108 109 **P**6 Primary Contact: Joseph Landsman, President and Chief Executive Officer Web address: www.utmedicalcenter.org	23	10	439	20881	314	169851	2454	353242	123783	2781
LA FOLLETTE—Campbell County										
⊠ **ST. MARY'S MEDICAL CENTER OF CAMPBELL COUNTY**, 923 East Central Avenue, Zip 37766–3106, Mailing Address: P.O. Box 1301, Zip 37766–1301; tel. 423/907–1200, (Total facility includes 98 beds in nursing home–type unit) **A**1 9 10 20 **F**2 21 22 27 28 29 33 37 38 42 46 48 52 55 60 63 64 66 69 70 71 75 76 81 84 92 93 94 97 108 109 110 **S** Catholic Healthcare Partners, Cincinnati, OH Primary Contact: Nicholas P. Lewis, Administrator COO: Tracey Reed, Chief Operating Officer CFO: Marie George, Chief Financial Officer CIO: Doug Kibler, Management Information Systems Specialist Web address: www.stmaryshealth.com	23	10	164	3042	128	96345	0	25324	11711	381
LAFAYETTE—Macon County										
⊠ **MACON COUNTY GENERAL HOSPITAL**, 204 Medical Drive, Zip 37083–1799, Mailing Address: P.O. Box 378, Zip 37083–0378; tel. 615/666–2147 **A**1 9 10 18 **F**6 12 21 22 26 27 28 33 46 48 63 69 70 81 82 92 94 97 108 **S** Quorum Health Resources, Plano, TX Primary Contact: Dennis A. Wolford, FACHE, Chief Executive Officer CFO: Thomas J. Kidd, Assistant Administrator and Chief Financial Officer Web address: www.mcgh.net	23	10	25	1077	10	18315	0	8778	4319	129

TN

Many Facility Codes have changed. Please refer to the AHA Guide Code Chart.

© 2005 AHA Guide

Hospital, Address, Telephone, Approval, Facility, and Physician Codes, Health Care System	Classi-fication Codes		Utilization Data					Expense (thousands) of dollars		
★ American Hospital Association (AHA) membership □ Joint Commission on Accreditation of Healthcare Organizations (JCAHO) accreditation ○ American Osteopathic Association (AOA) accreditation △ Commission on Accreditation of Rehabilitation Facilities (CARF) accreditation	Control	Service	Staffed Beds	Admissions	Census	Outpatient Visits	Births	Total	Payroll	Personnel

LAWRENCEBURG—Lawrence County

☒ **CROCKETT HOSPITAL**, U.S. Highway 43 South, Zip 38464–0847, Mailing Address: P.O. Box 847, Zip 38464–0847; tel. 931/762–6571 **A**1 9 10 **F**2 11 12 21 22 26 27 28 29 31 32 33 37 40 46 47 48 52 53 55 57 58 59 60 62 63 65 66 68 69 81 82 84 87 88 94 95 96 98 109 110 **S** LifePoint Hospitals, Inc., Brentwood, TN
Primary Contact: Jack S. Buck, Chief Executive Officer
CFO: John W. Copeland, Chief Financial Officer
Web address: www.crocketthospital.com
| | 33 | 10 | 98 | 3247 | 35 | 57060 | 315 | 26130 | 8827 | 262 |

LEBANON—Wilson County

☒ △ **UNIVERSITY MEDICAL CENTER/MCFARLAND HOSPITAL**, 1411 Baddour Parkway, Zip 37087–2595; tel. 615/444–8262, (Includes MCFARLAND SPECIALTY HOSPITAL, 500 Park Avenue, Zip 37087–3720; tel. 615/449–0500) **A**1 7 9 10 **F**2 9 11 12 21 27 33 34 37 42 46 48 51 52 53 55 57 59 60 62 63 66 68 69 71 73 74 75 76 77 78 81 82 84 87 88 92 93 94 95 96 108 109 **S** Health Management Associates, Naples, FL
Primary Contact: Mark W. Crawford, Chief Executive Officer
COO: Dean Mazzoni, Chief Operating Officer
CFO: Rhonda Maynard, Chief Financial Officer
CMO: Ken Anderson, M.D., Chief of Staff
CIO: Ann Lee Cockrill, Director of Marketing and Business Development
CHR: Royce Allen, Director Human Resources
Web address: www.universitymedicalcenter.com
| | 33 | 10 | 245 | 8219 | 126 | 61984 | 762 | 82667 | 28621 | 747 |

LENOIR CITY—Loudon County

☒ **FORT LOUDOUN MEDICAL CENTER**, (Formerly Fort Sanders Loudon Medical Center), 550 Fort Loudoun Medical Center Drive, Zip 37772; tel. 865/458–8222 **A**1 9 10 **F**6 9 11 21 28 33 48 55 58 59 60 63 66 69 81 84 87 88 108 **S** Covenant Health, Knoxville, TN
Primary Contact: Jeffrey Feike, President and Chief Administrative Officer
Web address: www.covenanthealth.com
| | 23 | 10 | 30 | 687 | 7 | 36875 | — | 10998 | 4719 | 131 |

LEWISBURG—Marshall County

□ **MARSHALL MEDICAL CENTER**, 1080 North Ellington Parkway, Zip 37091–2227, Mailing Address: P.O. Box 1609, Zip 37091–1609; tel. 931/359–6241 **A**1 9 10 18 **F**9 12 21 22 26 27 28 29 33 46 48 52 55 63 66 69 81 82 84 88 94 95 106 108
Primary Contact: Rick Malone, Interim Chief Executive Officer
Web address: www.mauryregional.com
| | 13 | 10 | 77 | 1073 | 10 | 41113 | 0 | 11938 | 5269 | 145 |

LEXINGTON—Henderson County

□ **HENDERSON COUNTY COMMUNITY HOSPITAL**, 200 West Church Street, Zip 38351–2014; tel. 731/968–3646 **A**1 9 10 **F**6 9 11 12 26 27 28 33 46 48 51 52 58 59 60 63 66 69 81 82 88 94 108 **S** Community Health Systems, Inc., Brentwood, TN
Primary Contact: Holly Fowler, M.D., Administrator
| | 23 | 10 | 36 | 1281 | 11 | 18455 | 75 | 8481 | 4659 | 128 |

LINDEN—Perry County

PERRY COMMUNITY HOSPITAL, 805 Squirrel Hollow Road, Zip 37096; tel. 931/589–2121, (Nonreporting) **A**9 10
Primary Contact: John B. Avery, III, Administrator
| | 23 | 10 | 53 | — | — | — | — | — | — | — |

LIVINGSTON—Overton County

☒ **LIVINGSTON REGIONAL HOSPITAL**, 315 Oak Street, Zip 38570, Mailing Address: P.O. Box 550, Zip 38570–0550; tel. 931/823–5611 **A**1 9 10 **F**2 9 11 12 14 21 22 23 27 28 32 46 48 55 58 59 60 61 62 63 66 68 69 81 84 88 93 94 95 97 108 109 **S** LifePoint Hospitals, Inc., Brentwood, TN
Primary Contact: Timothy W. McGill, Chief Executive Officer
COO: Michelle Watson, Chief Nursing Officer and Chief Operating Officer
CFO: Joseph Ross, Chief Financial Officer
CMO: James Cunningham, Chief Medical Officer
Web address: www.livingston–hospital.com
| | 33 | 10 | 67 | 3341 | 40 | 14829 | 388 | — | — | 0 |

LOUISVILLE—Blount County

□ **PENINSULA HOSPITAL**, 2347 Jones Bend Road, Zip 37777–5213, Mailing Address: P.O. Box 2000, Zip 37777–2000; tel. 865/970–9800 **A**1 9 10 **F**3 4 21 26 27 28 31 44 52 60 71 72 73 74 75 76 77 78
Primary Contact: Barbara S. Blevins, President and Chief Administrative Officer
Web address: www.covenanthealth.com
| | 23 | 22 | 80 | 4452 | 74 | 46349 | 0 | 25478 | 7903 | 261 |

MADISON—Davidson County

☒ △ **TENNESSEE CHRISTIAN MEDICAL CENTER**, 500 Hospital Drive, Zip 37115–5032; tel. 615/865–2373, (Includes TENNESSEE CHRISTIAN MEDICAL CENTER – PORTLAND, 105 Redbud Drive, Portland, Zip 37148) **A**1 7 9 10 **F**3 4 9 10 12 15 21 22 28 29 31 32 33 39 41 44 45 46 47 48 49 51 52 55 57 58 60 62 63 65 66 68 69 70 71 72 73 74 75 76 77 78 81 84 88 93 94 96 106 108 109 110 **P**6 **S** Adventist Health System Sunbelt Health Care Corporation, Winter Park, FL
Primary Contact: Jimm Bunch, President and Chief Executive Officer
COO: Joyce Portela, Chief Operating Officer
CFO: Robert Moon, Chief Financial Officer
CMO: John Wilters, M.D., Chief Medical Officer
CIO: Marie Hoder, Director Information Systems
CHR: Amanda Dobbs, Director of Human Resources
Web address: www.tennesseechristian.com
| | 21 | 10 | 284 | 8819 | 140 | 72572 | 0 | 79064 | 34340 | 823 |

TN

Hospital, Address, Telephone, Approval, Facility, and Physician Codes, Health Care System	Classi-fication Codes		Utilization Data					Expense (thousands) of dollars		
	Control	Service	Staffed Beds	Admissions	Census	Outpatient Visits	Births	Total	Payroll	Personnel

★ American Hospital Association (AHA) membership
☐ Joint Commission on Accreditation of Healthcare Organizations (JCAHO) accreditation
◯ American Osteopathic Association (AOA) accreditation
△ Commission on Accreditation of Rehabilitation Facilities (CARF) accreditation

MANCHESTER—Coffee County

★ ◯ **MEDICAL CENTER OF MANCHESTER**, 481 Interstate Drive, Zip 37355–3108, Mailing Address: P.O. Box 1409, Zip 37349–1409; tel. 931/728–6354 **A**9 10 11 18 **F**21 27 28 33 51 58 63 81 82 84 88 94
Primary Contact: Robert C. Couch, Chief Executive Officer
CFO: James Barnes, Chief Financial Officer
CMO: J D. Sullivan, D.O., Chief of Staff
33 10 49 1420 13 16219 0 6752 4042 143

UNITED REGIONAL MEDICAL CENTER, 1001 McArthur Drive, Zip 37355–2455, Mailing Address: P.O. Box 1079, Zip 37349–1079; tel. 931/728–3586, (Total facility includes 72 beds in nursing home–type unit) (Nonreporting) **A**9 10
Primary Contact: Raymond W. Acker, Jr, Chief Executive Officer
33 10 126 — — — — — — —

MARTIN—Weakley County

⊠ **HEALTHSOUTH CANE CREEK REHABILITATION HOSPITAL**, 180 Mt Pelia Road, Zip 38237; tel. 731/587–4231, (Nonreporting) **A**1 10 **S** HEALTHSOUTH Corporation, Birmingham, AL
Primary Contact: Dayle Unger, Administrator
33 46 40 — — — — — — —

☐ **VOLUNTEER COMMUNITY HOSPITAL**, 161 Mount Pelia Road, Zip 38237–0967; tel. 731/587–4261 **A**1 9 10 **F**11 21 27 28 33 40 41 46 48 55 59 60 63 69 81 84 88 94 95 108 **S** Community Health Systems, Inc., Brentwood, TN
Primary Contact: Steve Westenhofer, Chief Executive Officer
Web address: www.chs.net
23 10 65 2504 25 — — — — —

MARYVILLE—Blount County

⊠ **BLOUNT MEMORIAL HOSPITAL**, 907 East Lamar Alexander Parkway, Zip 37804–5016; tel. 865/983–7211, (Total facility includes 60 beds in nursing home–type unit) **A**1 2 9 10 **F**2 3 4 8 9 10 11 12 14 15 17 21 22 23 24 26 27 28 29 31 32 33 34 36 37 38 41 42 44 46 48 50 51 52 53 54 55 58 59 60 61 62 63 64 65 66 69 70 71 72 73 74 75 76 77 78 79 80 81 82 84 85 86 87 88 92 94 95 96 106 108 109 110 **P**1 7
Primary Contact: Joseph M. Dawson, Administrator
CFO: David E. Arriett, Assistant Administrator
CMO: Samuel D. Evans, M.D., Medical Director
CIO: John Hanks, Director Information Systems
CHR: Patricia Naff, Director, Human Resources
Web address: www.blountmemorial.org
13 10 258 11816 186 191103 834 130415 61055 1769

MCKENZIE—Carroll County

☐ **MCKENZIE REGIONAL HOSPITAL**, 161 Hospital Drive, Zip 38201–1636; tel. 731/352–5344 **A**1 9 10 **F**6 11 12 21 26 33 41 46 51 58 59 63 66 69 81 88 92 94 97 108 **S** Community Health Systems, Inc., Brentwood, TN
Primary Contact: Robert D. Miller, Chief Executive Officer
Web address: www.mckenzieregionalhospital.com
23 10 29 1671 13 14867 363 9639 4221 103

MCMINNVILLE—Warren County

⊠ **RIVER PARK HOSPITAL**, 1559 Sparta Road, Zip 37110–1399; tel. 931/815–4000 **A**1 10 **F**11 12 15 21 22 26 27 28 33 40 46 48 53 55 57 58 59 60 61 62 63 64 65 68 69 81 82 84 88 93 94 108 **S** HCA, Nashville, TN
Primary Contact: George Asbell, Interim President
COO: Nancy Locke, Assistant Administration
CFO: Patrick C. Bolander, Chief Financial Officer
CIO: Hershell Foster, Information Systems Director
CHR: Clair Cochran, Human Resource Director
Web address: www.riverparkhospital.com
33 10 127 4136 46 48496 629 34511 12850 293

MEMPHIS—Shelby County

⊠ **BAPTIST MEMORIAL HOSPITAL – MEMPHIS**, 6019 Walnut Grove Road, Zip 38120–2173; tel. 901/226–5000, (Total facility includes 30 beds in nursing home–type unit) **A**1 2 3 5 9 10 **F**2 14 15 16 17 18 19 20 21 22 23 24 26 27 28 29 33 37 38 40 46 48 49 52 55 57 58 60 61 62 63 64 65 69 79 80 81 82 84 85 86 87 88 90 92 94 96 99 100 103 106 108 **S** Baptist Memorial Health Care Corporation, Memphis, TN
Primary Contact: James VanderSteeg, Administrator and Chief Executive Officer
COO: Sharon Harris, Chief Nursing Officer
CFO: Jeff Nowell, Chief Financial Officer
CMO: C Richard Patterson, M.D., Chief Medical Officer
CIO: Jerry Brantley, Vice President and Chief Information Officer
CHR: Jerry Barbaree, Human Resources Director
Web address: www.baptistonline.org
23 10 625 27309 540 140425 0 399301 133931 2986

⊠ **BAPTIST MEMORIAL HOSPITAL FOR WOMEN**, 6225 Humphreys Boulevard, Zip 38120–2373; tel. 901/227–9000 **A**1 9 10 **F**2 11 12 21 22 27 28 29 39 46 52 53 55 56 59 63 64 65 66 81 82 88 92 94 96 108 109 **S** Baptist Memorial Health Care Corporation, Memphis, TN
Primary Contact: Anita Vaughn, Administrator and Chief Executive Officer
CFO: Kimberly Young, Chief Financial Officer
CMO: Henry Sullivant, President Medical Staff
CHR: Kristie Sutterman, Director of Human Resources
Web address: www.bmhcc.org
23 44 140 7486 78 53225 4748 56877 24581 533

BAPTIST REHABILITATION–GERMANTOWN See Germantown

Many Facility Codes have changed. Please refer to the AHA Guide Code Chart.

TN

Hospital, Address, Telephone, Approval, Facility, and Physician Codes, Health Care System	Classification Codes		Utilization Data					Expense (thousands) of dollars		
★ American Hospital Association (AHA) membership □ Joint Commission on Accreditation of Healthcare Organizations (JCAHO) accreditation ○ American Osteopathic Association (AOA) accreditation △ Commission on Accreditation of Rehabilitation Facilities (CARF) accreditation	Control	Service	Staffed Beds	Admissions	Census	Outpatient Visits	Births	Total	Payroll	Personnel
□ **DELTA MEDICAL CENTER**, 3000 Getwell Road, Zip 38118–2299; tel. 901/369–8500 **A**1 9 10 **F**2 12 21 22 23 26 27 28 29 31 33 39 44 48 49 52 53 55 58 60 61 63 65 66 69 70 71 73 74 75 76 77 78 81 82 84 88 93 94 96 110 Primary Contact: Craig B. Watson, Chief Executive Officer Web address: www.deltamedcenter.com	33	10	170	4412	90	28455	0	32002	14651	395
⊠ **HEALTHSOUTH REHABILITATION HOSPITAL**, 1282 Union Avenue, Zip 38104–3414; tel. 901/722–2000 **A**1 10 **F**7 21 66 68 69 70 94 **S** HEALTHSOUTH Corporation, Birmingham, AL Primary Contact: Mark A. Kelly, Administrator CFO: Tony Richardson, Controller Web address: www.healthsouth.com	32	46	80	1553	67	16694	0	14703	7355	195
⊠ **HEALTHSOUTH REHABILITATION HOSPITAL**, 4100 Austin Peay Highway, Zip 38128; tel. 901/213–5400, (Nonreporting) **A**1 10 **S** HEALTHSOUTH Corporation, Birmingham, AL Primary Contact: Brenda M. Antwine, Administrator	33	46	40	—	—	—	—	—	—	—
□ **LAKESIDE BEHAVIORAL HEALTH SYSTEM**, 2911 Brunswick Road, Zip 38133–4199; tel. 901/377–4700 **A**1 9 10 **F**3 4 6 21 26 27 28 29 31 33 42 44 46 47 48 52 58 60 65 66 71 72 73 74 75 76 77 78 94 96 98 **S** Universal Health Services, Inc., King of Prussia, PA Primary Contact: Robert S. Waggener, Chief Executive Officer Web address: www.lakesidebhs.com	33	22	219	4784	142	15210	0	19243	11813	290
LE BONHEUR CHILDREN'S MEDICAL CENTER See Methodist Healthcare–University Hospital										
□ **MEMPHIS MENTAL HEALTH INSTITUTE**, 865 Poplar Avenue, Zip 38105–4626, Mailing Address: P.O. Box 40966, Zip 38174–0966; tel. 901/524–1201 **A**1 3 5 10 **F**65 66 71 74 76 **P**1 Primary Contact: Lawrence Ventura, Chief Executive Officer	12	22	98	1373	97	0	0	22981	12220	325
□ **METHODIST HEALTHCARE – EXTENDED CARE HOSPITAL**, 225 South Claybrook Street, Zip 38104–3537; tel. 901/726–2113, (Nonreporting) **A**1 9 10 **S** Methodist Healthcare, Memphis, TN Primary Contact: Sandra Bailey, Administrator Web address: www.methodisthealth.org	23	80	36	—	—	—	—	—	—	—
□ **METHODIST HEALTHCARE–UNIVERSITY HOSPITAL**, (Formerly Methodist Healthcare–Memphis Hospital), 1211 Union Avenue, Zip 38104–3499; tel. 901/726–7000, (Includes LE BONHEUR CHILDREN'S MEDICAL CENTER, One Children's Plaza, Zip 38103–2893; tel. 901/572–5952; Peggy N. Troy, President; METHODIST HEALTHCARE–GERMANTOWN HOSPITAL, 7691 Poplar Avenue, Germantown, Zip 38138, Mailing Address: P.O. Box 381588, Zip 38138; tel. 901/516–6967; David G. Baytos, Administrator; METHODIST HEALTHCARE–NORTH HOSPITAL, 3960 New Covington Pike, Zip 38128; tel. 901/384–5389; METHODIST HEALTHCARE–SOUTH HOSPITAL, 1300 Wesley Drive, Zip 38116; tel. 901/516–3081; Joe Webb, Administrator; METHODIST HEALTHCARE–UNIVERSITY HOSPITAL, 1265 Union Avenue, Zip 38104), (Total facility includes 44 beds in nursing home–type unit) **A**1 2 3 5 6 8 9 10 **F**2 4 9 10 11 12 14 15 16 17 18 19 20 21 22 23 24 26 27 28 29 31 33 34 35 36 37 38 39 41 42 44 45 46 47 48 49 50 51 52 53 54 55 56 57 58 59 60 61 62 63 64 65 66 67 69 70 71 72 73 74 75 76 77 78 80 81 82 83 84 85 86 87 88 92 93 94 95 96 97 98 99 101 102 104 105 106 107 108 109 110 **P**5 6 8 **S** Methodist Healthcare, Memphis, TN Primary Contact: Cecelia Sawyer, Administrator Web address: www.methodisthealth.org	23	10	1281	63209	960	532078	6325	703289	306584	8530
⊠ **REGIONAL MEDICAL CENTER AT MEMPHIS**, 877 Jefferson Avenue, Zip 38103–2897; tel. 901/545–7100 **A**1 2 3 5 8 9 10 **F**2 3 6 9 10 11 12 13 14 15 19 21 22 23 26 27 28 29 32 33 34 39 44 45 46 47 48 50 52 53 55 56 57 58 59 60 61 62 63 64 65 66 67 68 69 70 71 73 75 80 81 82 84 88 92 94 96 98 104 105 107 108 109 110 **P**6 Primary Contact: Bruce W. Steinhauer, M.D., President and Chief Executive Officer COO: Brenita Crawford, Chief Operating Officer CFO: Barry Fowler, Chief Financial Officer CMO: Stuart Polly, M.D., Medical Director CIO: Wayne McDaniel, Chief Information Officer CHR: Gloria Thomas, Vice President Human Resources Web address: www.the–med.org	23	10	377	16913	285	295982	4391	266631	107942	2172
★ **SAINT FRANCIS HOSPITAL**, 5959 Park Avenue, Zip 38119–5198, Mailing Address: P.O. Box 171808, Zip 38187–1808; tel. 901/765–1000, (Total facility includes 38 beds in nursing home–type unit) **A**2 3 5 9 10 **F**2 3 4 6 9 10 11 12 14 15 17 19 21 22 23 26 28 29 31 33 35 37 39 42 44 45 46 47 48 49 50 51 52 53 55 56 57 58 59 60 61 62 63 65 66 68 69 71 72 73 74 75 76 77 78 81 82 84 85 87 88 92 93 94 95 96 98 108 109 110 **P**5 8 **S** TENET Healthcare Corporation, Dallas, TX Primary Contact: David L. Archer, Chief Executive Officer COO: Donald E. Laughlin, Chief Operating Officer CFO: Edwin J. Bode, Chief Financial Officer CMO: Paul Getaz, M.D., Chief Medical Officer CIO: Mike Hadley, Chief Information Officer CHR: Laura Adler, Senior Vice President Human Relations Web address: www.saintfrancishosp.com	33	10	562	19989	388	173784	1648	234291	79464	1613

TN

Hospital, Address, Telephone, Approval, Facility, and Physician Codes, Health Care System	Classi-fication Codes		Utilization Data					Expense (thousands) of dollars		
★ American Hospital Association (AHA) membership □ Joint Commission on Accreditation of Healthcare Organizations (JCAHO) accreditation ○ American Osteopathic Association (AOA) accreditation △ Commission on Accreditation of Rehabilitation Facilities (CARF) accreditation	Control	Service	Staffed Beds	Admissions	Census	Outpatient Visits	Births	Total	Payroll	Personnel
□ **SELECT SPECIALTY HOSPITAL–MEMPHIS**, 5959 Park Avenue, 12th Floor, Zip 38119; tel. 901/765–1245, (Nonreporting) **A**1 10 Primary Contact: David Key, Chief Executive Officer	33	80	30	—	—	—	—	—	—	—
⊞ **ST. JUDE CHILDREN'S RESEARCH HOSPITAL**, (Hematology–Oncology), 332 North Lauderdale Street, Zip 38105–2794; tel. 901/495–3300 **A**1 2 3 5 9 10 **F**9 28 31 32 37 50 52 58 61 63 65 66 67 69 73 81 82 84 87 88 94 96 108 Primary Contact: William E. Evans, PharmD, Director COO: John D. Nash, Executive Vice President and Chief Operating Officer CFO: Mike Canarios, Vice President and Chief Financial Officer CMO: Joseph J. Mirro, M.D., Chief Medical Officer and Executive Vice President CIO: Sharon Christian, Vice President and Chief Information Officer CHR: Mary Anna Quinn, Vice President Web address: www.stjude.org	23	59	56	2171	38	47402	0	336904	139710	—
⊞ △ **VETERANS AFFAIRS MEDICAL CENTER**, 1030 Jefferson Avenue, Zip 38104–2193; tel. 901/523–8990 **A**1 2 3 5 7 8 **F**2 3 4 14 15 17 19 21 22 23 26 27 28 29 32 33 36 37 38 39 40 41 42 44 46 48 49 50 51 52 55 57 58 60 61 62 63 66 69 70 71 73 74 75 76 77 78 79 81 82 84 85 87 88 92 93 94 96 106 108 109 110 **S** Department of Veterans Affairs, Washington, DC Primary Contact: Patricia O. Pittman, Director COO: William R. Delamater, Associate Director CFO: Brian P. Fuchs, Chief Fiscal Service CMO: Howard R. Bromley, M.D., Chief of Staff CIO: Charles D. Sternberg, Chief Information Resources Management Service CHR: Bonnie J. Eareckson, Chief, Human Resource Management Services Web address: www.va.gov/sta/guide/home.asp	45	10	263	7554	205	370944	0	224608	95735	1840
MILAN—Gibson County										
⊞ **MILAN GENERAL HOSPITAL**, 4039 South Highland, Zip 38358–3167; tel. 731/686–1591, (Total facility includes 13 beds in nursing home–type unit) **A**1 9 10 **F**2 10 12 21 22 26 27 28 29 33 46 48 52 53 55 63 64 66 69 81 88 92 94 96 97 108 **S** West Tennessee Healthcare, Jackson, TN Primary Contact: John M. Carruth, Administrator CFO: Randy Richardson, Chief Financial Officer Web address: www.wth.net	16	10	41	1062	20	15336	2	8984	3446	94
MORRISTOWN—Hamblen County										
□ △ **LAKEWAY REGIONAL HOSPITAL**, 726 McFarland Street, Zip 37814–3990; tel. 423/586–2302, (Nonreporting) **A**1 7 9 10 19 **S** Community Health Systems, Inc., Brentwood, TN Primary Contact: Priscilla Millis, Chief Executive Officer Web address: www.lakewayregionalhospital.com	33	10	135	—	—	—	—	—	—	—
□ **MORRISTOWN–HAMBLEN HOSPITAL**, 908 West Fourth North Street, Zip 37816–1178, Mailing Address: P.O. Box 1178, Zip 37816–1178; tel. 423/586–4231, (Nonreporting) **A**1 9 10 Primary Contact: Richard L. Clark, Administrator and Chief Executive Officer Web address: www.mhhs1.org	23	10	143	—	—	—	—	—	—	—
MOUNTAIN CITY—Johnson County										
★ **JOHNSON COUNTY HEALTH CENTER**, 1901 South Shady Street, Zip 37683; tel. 423/727–1100 **A**9 10 18 **F**2 12 22 26 27 28 29 33 35 39 53 65 69 70 81 92 **S** Mountain States Health Alliance, Johnson City, TN Primary Contact: Lisa Heaton, Administrator and Chief Nursing Officer Web address: www.msha.com	23	10	2	28	1	40596	0	5765	2477	64
MOUNTAIN HOME—Washington County										
⊞ **JAMES H. QUILLEN VETERANS AFFAIRS MEDICAL CENTER**, Mailing Address: P.O. Box 4000, Zip 37684–4000; tel. 423/926–1171, (Total facility includes 120 beds in nursing home–type unit) (Nonreporting) **A**1 2 3 5 8 **S** Department of Veterans Affairs, Washington, DC Primary Contact: Carl J. Gerber, M.D., Ph.D., Director COO: Rachel Mitchell, Chief Financial Officer CMO: David Reagan, M.D., Ph.D., Chief of Staff CIO: Karen Perry, Chief Information Resource Management Services CHR: Patsy Fish, Chief, Human Resources Management Web address: www.va.gov/621quillen	45	10	603	—	—	—	—	—	—	—
MURFREESBORO—Rutherford County										
ALVIN C. YORK VETERANS AFFAIRS MEDICAL CENTER See Veterans Affairs Tennessee Valley Healthcare System, Nashville										
⊞ **MIDDLE TENNESSEE MEDICAL CENTER**, 400 North Highland Avenue, Zip 37130–3854, Mailing Address: P.O. Box 1178, Zip 37133–1178; tel. 615/396–4100 **A**1 5 9 10 **F**2 11 12 14 15 17 21 22 23 26 27 28 29 33 34 36 37 39 40 41 46 48 49 51 52 53 55 56 58 59 60 61 62 63 64 65 66 69 79 80 81 82 83 84 85 87 88 93 94 95 96 108 109 110 **S** Ascension Health, Saint Louis, MO Primary Contact: Donald R. Gintzig, CHE, Chief Executive Officer COO: Gordon Ferguson, Senior Vice President and Chief Operating Officer CFO: Tom Massey, Chief Financial Officer CMO: Andy Brown, M.D., Vice President of Medical Affairs CIO: Jim Benson, Director Information Systems CHR: Carol Bragdon, Director of Human Resources Web address: www.mtmc.org	21	10	199	12995	139	169882	2173	120628	46352	1119

TN

Many Facility Codes have changed. Please refer to the AHA Guide Code Chart.

© 2005 AHA Guide

Hospital, Address, Telephone, Approval, Facility, and Physician Codes, Health Care System	Classi-fication Codes		Utilization Data					Expense (thousands) of dollars		
★ American Hospital Association (AHA) membership □ Joint Commission on Accreditation of Healthcare Organizations (JCAHO) accreditation ○ American Osteopathic Association (AOA) accreditation △ Commission on Accreditation of Rehabilitation Facilities (CARF) accreditation	Control	Service	Staffed Beds	Admissions	Census	Outpatient Visits	Births	Total	Payroll	Personnel

NASHVILLE—Davidson County

✠ **BAPTIST HOSPITAL**, 2000 Church Street, Zip 37236–0002; tel. 615/284–5555 **A**1 2 3 5 9 10 **F**7 10 11 12 14 15 17 19 21 22 23 26 28 29 33 38 40 41 44 46 48 49 50 51 52 53 55 56 58 59 60 61 62 63 64 65 66 68 69 79 80 81 82 84 86 88 93 94 95 96 108 109 110 **P**3 **S** Ascension Health, Saint Louis, MO Primary Contact: Bernard Sherry, President and Chief Executive Officer COO: Bernard Sherry, President and Chief Executive Officer CFO: Mike Johns, Vice President of Finance CMO: Robert Hardin, M.D., Director Medical Affairs CIO: Chris Young, Chief Information Officer CHR: Martha Underwood, Chief Human Resources Officer Web address: www.baptisthospital.com	21	10	454	27609	336	285901	6247	295466	110676	2479
BAPTIST NORTH TOWER SURGICAL HOSPITAL, 2011 Murphy Avenue, Zip 37203; tel. 615/284–2970, (Nonreporting) **A**10 Primary Contact: Mark Mason, Administrator	32	10	18	—	—	—	—	—	—	—
✠ △ **CENTENNIAL MEDICAL CENTER AND PARTHENON PAVILION**, 2300 Patterson Street, Zip 37203–1528; tel. 615/342–1000 **A**1 2 3 5 7 10 **S** HCA, Nashville, TN Primary Contact: Lawrence Kloess, President and Chief Executive Officer CFO: Micki J. Slingerland, Chief Financial Officer Web address: www.centennialmedctr.com	31	10	556	22722	366	162979	2519	256297	95513	2083
✠ **METROPOLITAN NASHVILLE GENERAL HOSPITAL**, 1818 Albion Street, Zip 37208–2918; tel. 615/341–4000 **A**1 2 3 5 9 10 **F**2 9 11 12 14 15 17 19 21 22 23 26 27 28 29 31 33 35 39 46 47 48 49 50 52 53 55 56 57 58 59 60 61 62 63 65 66 69 70 73 75 81 82 84 85 87 88 94 106 108 109 110 Primary Contact: Reginald W. Coopwood, M.D., Chief Executive Officer COO: Adrianne Black, Chief Operating Officer CFO: Randy B. Pirtle, Chief Financial Officer Web address: www.nashville.org/hosp/general_hospital	15	10	127	6594	78	91675	1080	59031	32308	1110
□ **MIDDLE TENNESSEE MENTAL HEALTH INSTITUTE**, 221 Stewarts Ferry Pike, Zip 37214–3325; tel. 615/902–7535 **A**1 3 5 9 10 **F**22 58 60 71 72 74 75 76 94 96 108 Primary Contact: Lynn McDonald, Chief Executive Officer	12	22	283	4262	276	0	0	47001	25440	763
□ △ **NASHVILLE REHABILITATION HOSPITAL**, 610 Gallatin Avenue, Zip 37206–3238; tel. 615/226–4330 **A**1 7 9 10 **F**21 22 27 33 52 68 69 71 76 94 96 Primary Contact: Barton Huddleston, M.D., Chief Executive Officer Web address: www.nrhcares.com	33	46	46	1030	27	2547	0	10196	5437	69
PSYCHIATRIC HOSPITAL AT VANDERBILT See Vanderbilt University Medical Center										
✠ **SAINT THOMAS HOSPITAL**, 4220 Harding Road, Zip 37205–2095, Mailing Address: P.O. Box 380, Zip 37202–0380; tel. 615/222–2111 **A**1 2 3 5 9 10 **F**2 9 12 14 21 22 23 26 27 28 29 33 35 37 38 39 41 45 46 47 48 49 50 52 53 55 57 58 60 61 62 63 65 66 69 71 73 74 76 79 81 82 84 87 88 93 94 95 96 106 108 **S** Ascension Health, Saint Louis, MO Primary Contact: Dale Batchelor, M.D., Interim President and Chief Executive Officer COO: Cindy Wedel, Chief Operations Officer CFO: Kenneth Venuto, Chief Financial Officer CMO: George Liesmann, M.D., Chief Medical Officer CIO: Chris Young, Chief Information Officer CHR: Glenn Carnathan, Vice President, Chief Resources Officer Web address: www.stthomas.org	21	10	485	24778	357	153655	0	328460	123167	2537
□ **SELECT SPECIALTY HOSPITAL OF NASHVILLE**, 2021 Church Street, Zip 37236; tel. 615/284–4599 **A**1 9 10 **S** Select Medical Corporation, Mechanicsburg, PA Primary Contact: William Bryan Lee, Chief Executive Officer	33	80	35	331	30	0	—	14147	4907	168
✠ **SKYLINE MEDICAL CENTER**, 3441 Dickerson Pike, Zip 37207–2539; tel. 615/769–2000, (Nonreporting) **A**1 2 10 **S** HCA, Nashville, TN Primary Contact: Robert Klein, Chief Executive Officer COO: Regina Bartlett, Chief Operating Officer CFO: Bradley Schultz, Chief Financial Officer CMO: Thomas Taylor, M.D., President Medical Staff CIO: Terry Siemen, Chief Information Officer CHR: Andy Hooper, Director, Human Resources Web address: www.skylinemedicalcenter.com	33	10	202	—	—	—	—	—	—	—
✠ **SOUTHERN HILLS MEDICAL CENTER**, 391 Wallace Road, Zip 37211–4859; tel. 615/781–4000 **A**1 2 10 **F**11 12 17 21 22 26 27 28 29 33 40 46 47 48 52 53 54 55 58 59 60 61 62 63 66 68 69 70 81 82 84 88 92 93 94 106 108 109 110 **P**5 **S** HCA, Nashville, TN Primary Contact: Victor Giovanetti, Chief Executive Officer COO: Travis Capers, Chief Operating Officer CFO: Mark Finkelstein, Chief Financial Officer CIO: Ronnie Gannon, Director Information Services CHR: Dale Beaudoin, Director Human Resources Web address: www.southernhills.com	33	10	120	5936	60	82674	719	63007	26066	410

TN

Hospital, Address, Telephone, Approval, Facility, and Physician Codes, Health Care System	Classi-fication Codes		Utilization Data					Expense (thousands) of dollars		
	Control	Service	Staffed Beds	Admissions	Census	Outpatient Visits	Births	Total	Payroll	Personnel

★ American Hospital Association (AHA) membership
□ Joint Commission on Accreditation of Healthcare Organizations (JCAHO) accreditation
○ American Osteopathic Association (AOA) accreditation
△ Commission on Accreditation of Rehabilitation Facilities (CARF) accreditation

	Control	Service	Staffed Beds	Admissions	Census	Outpatient Visits	Births	Total	Payroll	Personnel
⊠ **VANDERBILT STALLWORTH REHABILITATION HOSPITAL**, 2201 Childrens Way, Zip 37212–3165; tel. 615/320–7600, (Nonreporting) **A**1 5 10 **S** HEALTHSOUTH Corporation, Birmingham, AL Primary Contact: Susan Heath, Administrator CFO: Peggy Belyeu, Controller CMO: Bob Coxe, M.D., Medical Director CHR: Ruth Beasley, Director of Human Resources Web address: www.healthsouth.com	33	10	80	—	—	—	—	—	—	—
⊠ **VANDERBILT UNIVERSITY MEDICAL CENTER**, 1211 22nd Avenue South, Zip 37232–2102; tel. 615/322–5000, (Includes PSYCHIATRIC HOSPITAL AT VANDERBILT, 1601 23rd Avenue South, Zip 37212–3198; tel. 615/320–7770), (Total facility includes 23 beds in nursing home–type unit) **A**1 2 3 5 8 9 10 **F**2 4 7 9 10 11 12 13 14 15 16 17 18 19 20 21 22 23 24 26 27 28 29 31 32 33 34 37 38 41 43 44 45 46 47 48 49 50 52 53 55 56 57 58 59 60 61 62 63 64 65 66 67 69 70 71 72 73 74 75 76 77 78 79 80 81 82 83 84 85 86 87 88 89 90 92 93 94 95 96 98 99 100 101 102 103 104 105 106 107 108 109 110 **P**6 Primary Contact: Larry Goldberg, Executive Director and Chief Executive Officer CFO: Rick Wagers, Chief Financial Officer CMO: C Wright Pinson, Chief Medical Officer CIO: William Stead, M.D., Director Informatics Center CHR: Kevin Myatt, Chief Human Resources Officer Web address: www.vanderbilt.edu	23	10	758	33761	522	900934	1925	792801	292133	5836
⊠ **VETERANS AFFAIRS TENNESSEE VALLEY HEALTHCARE SYSTEM**, 1310 24th Avenue South, Zip 37212–2637; tel. 615/327–4751, (Includes ALVIN C. YORK VETERANS AFFAIRS MEDICAL CENTER, 3400 Lebanon Pike, Murfreesboro, Zip 37129–1236; tel. 615/867–6100; VETERANS AFFAIRS MEDICAL CENTER, 1310 24th Avenue South, tel. 615/327–4751), (Total facility includes 185 beds in nursing home–type unit) **A**1 2 3 5 8 **F**1 2 4 12 15 17 19 21 22 23 28 29 32 33 36 37 38 42 44 45 47 48 49 50 51 52 55 57 58 60 61 62 63 64 65 66 69 70 71 73 74 75 76 77 78 81 82 84 85 88 92 93 94 96 99 101 106 108 109 110 **S** Department of Veterans Affairs, Washington, DC Primary Contact: David N. Pennington, FACHE, Chief Executive Officer COO: Kenyon Dupre, Acting Associate Director CFO: Terry Simmons, Chief Fiscal Services CMO: Samuel Pieper, Jr, Interim Chief of Staff CHR: William Hardwick, Chief Human Resources Web address: www.va.gov/sta/guide/home.asp	45	10	510	9259	406	523990	0	353794	137471	2704
NEWPORT—Cocke County										
□ **BAPTIST HOSPITAL OF COCKE COUNTY**, 435 Second Street, Zip 37821–3799; tel. 423/625–2200, (Total facility includes 56 beds in nursing home–type unit) **A**1 9 10 **F**2 3 11 12 13 14 21 22 27 28 33 44 46 47 48 53 55 56 58 59 60 63 65 66 67 68 69 71 81 82 84 87 88 92 94 97 108 109 **S** Baptist Health System of East Tennessee, Knoxville, TN Primary Contact: James Lee Decker, Senior Vice President and Administrator Web address: www.baptistoneword.org/	21	10	103	2235	74	70441	179	24360	10197	213
OAK RIDGE—Anderson County										
⊠ **METHODIST MEDICAL CENTER OF OAK RIDGE**, 990 Oak Ridge Turnpike, Zip 37830–6976, Mailing Address: P.O. Box 2529, Zip 37831–2529; tel. 865/481–1000, (Nonreporting) **A**1 2 9 10 **S** Covenant Health, Knoxville, TN Primary Contact: Jan McNally, President and Chief Administrative Officer CFO: Susan Hand, Vice President and Chief Financial Officer Web address: www.mccoakridge.com	23	10	219	—	—	—	—	—	—	—
RIDGEVIEW PSYCHIATRIC HOSPITAL AND CENTER, 240 West Tyrone Road, Zip 37830–6571; tel. 865/482–1076 **A**9 10 **F**4 21 28 29 31 71 72 73 74 75 76 77 78 96 **P**6 Primary Contact: Margie Swiney, Administrator and Chief Nursing Officer Web address: www.ridgeviewresources.com	23	22	20	487	5	84554	0	11250	6546	200
ONEIDA—Scott County										
□ **SCOTT COUNTY HOSPITAL**, 18797 Alberta Avenue, Zip 37841–4939, Mailing Address: P.O. Box 4939, Zip 37841–4939; tel. 423/569–8521, (Nonreporting) **A**1 9 10 20 Primary Contact: Larry R. Jeter, Chief Executive Officer Web address: www.scottcountyhospital.com	33	10	77	—	—	—	—	—	—	—
PARIS—Henry County										
⊠ **HENRY COUNTY MEDICAL CENTER**, 301 Tyson Avenue, Zip 38242–4544, Mailing Address: P.O. Box 1030, Zip 38242–1030; tel. 731/642–1220, (Total facility includes 174 beds in nursing home–type unit) **A**1 9 10 **F**2 6 9 11 12 14 22 23 26 27 28 29 32 33 36 40 41 46 48 51 52 53 55 59 60 61 62 63 65 66 69 71 75 76 79 81 84 87 88 92 94 95 96 97 108 110 Primary Contact: Thomas H. Gee, Administrator CFO: Jamie Townsend, Chief Financial Officer CIO: Pam Ridley, Director Information Systems CHR: Edwin L. Ledden, Assistant Administrator Web address: www.hcmc–tn.org	16	10	271	5626	215	85906	381	51980	22580	648
PARSONS—Decatur County										
□ **DECATUR COUNTY GENERAL HOSPITAL**, 969 Tennessee Avenue South, Zip 38363–1649, Mailing Address: P.O. Box 250, Zip 38363–0250; tel. 731/847–3031 **A**1 9 10 **F**6 12 33 46 48 51 52 63 66 69 75 81 88 107 Primary Contact: Larry N. Lindsey, Administrator and Chief Executive Officer Web address: www.dcgh.org	13	10	40	1131	14	18072	—	8198	3944	136

TN

Hospital, Address, Telephone, Approval, Facility, and Physician Codes, Health Care System	Classi-fication Codes		Utilization Data					Expense (thousands) of dollars		
★ American Hospital Association (AHA) membership □ Joint Commission on Accreditation of Healthcare Organizations (JCAHO) accreditation ○ American Osteopathic Association (AOA) accreditation △ Commission on Accreditation of Rehabilitation Facilities (CARF) accreditation	Control	Service	Staffed Beds	Admissions	Census	Outpatient Visits	Births	Total	Payroll	Personnel

PIKEVILLE—Bledsoe County

★ **ERLANGER BLEDSOE HOSPITAL**, 71 Wheeler Avenue, Zip 37367, Mailing Address: P.O. Box 699, Zip 37367–0699; tel. 423/447–2112 **A**9 10 18 **F**2 15 21 28 33 46 48 70 81 88 92 94 97 **P**5 **S** Erlanger Health System, Chattanooga, TN
Primary Contact: Stephanie Boynton, Administrator
Web address: www.erlanger.org

| | 16 | 10 | 28 | 387 | 8 | 11964 | 0 | 6233 | 2608 | 71 |

PORTLAND—Sumner County

TENNESSEE CHRISTIAN MEDICAL CENTER – PORTLAND See Tennessee Christian Medical Center, Madison

PULASKI—Giles County

⊠ **HILLSIDE HOSPITAL**, 1265 East College Street, Zip 38478–4500; tel. 931/363–7531, (Nonreporting) **A**1 9 10 **S** LifePoint Hospitals, Inc., Brentwood, TN
Primary Contact: James H. Edmondson, Chief Executive Officer
CFO: Michael Morrison, Chief Financial Officer
Web address: www.hillsidehospital.com

| | 33 | 10 | 87 | — | — | — | — | — | — | — |

RIPLEY—Lauderdale County

⊠ **BAPTIST MEMORIAL HOSPITAL–LAUDERDALE**, 326 Asbury Avenue, Zip 38063–9701; tel. 731/221–2200 **A**1 9 10 **F**9 11 12 21 22 27 28 29 33 44 46 48 52 58 60 62 63 65 66 69 71 73 74 75 76 77 81 84 88 94 97 104 106 108 **S** Baptist Memorial Health Care Corporation, Memphis, TN
Primary Contact: Keon Falkner, Administrator and Chief Executive Officer
CFO: Jimmy Robertson, Chief Financial Officer
CMO: W Darrell Murray, M.D., Chief Medical Staff
CHR: Gail Anglin, Human Resources Manager
Web address: www.lauderdale.baptistonline.org

| | 21 | 10 | 14 | 938 | 13 | 21200 | 1 | 12267 | 5172 | 152 |

ROGERSVILLE—Hawkins County

□ **WELLMONT HAWKINS COUNTY MEMORIAL HOSPITAL**, 851 Locust Street, Zip 37857–2407, Mailing Address: P.O. Box 130, Zip 37857–0130; tel. 423/921–7000 **A**1 9 10 **F**9 12 21 22 27 28 29 33 46 48 52 60 63 64 69 81 82 85 88 93 94 95 97 108 **P**8 **S** Wellmont Health System, Kingsport, TN
Primary Contact: Fred L. Pelle, President
Web address: www.wellmont.org

| | 23 | 10 | 50 | 1536 | 15 | 28932 | 0 | 11181 | 5152 | 150 |

SAVANNAH—Hardin County

⊠ **HARDIN MEDICAL CENTER**, (Formerly Hardin County General Hospital), 935 Wayne Road, Zip 38372–1937; tel. 731/925–4954, (Total facility includes 73 beds in nursing home–type unit) **A**1 9 10 **F**6 9 11 12 21 22 23 26 27 28 33 46 48 51 52 53 59 60 61 62 63 64 65 66 69 81 82 84 85 88 92 94 97 110 **P**8
Primary Contact: Charlotte Burns, Administrator and Chief Executive Officer
CFO: Joe L. Brown, Chief Financial Officer
CMO: Michael L. Smith, M.D., Chief Medical Staff
CHR: Saundra Pippin, Director of Human Resources
Web address: www.hcgh.cc

| | 13 | 10 | 119 | 1968 | 95 | 61016 | 67 | 17974 | 8924 | 298 |

SELMER—McNairy County

□ **MCNAIRY REGIONAL HOSPITAL**, 705 East Poplar Avenue, Zip 38375–1828; tel. 731/645–3221 **A**1 9 10 **F**2 9 11 12 21 22 27 33 46 48 58 59 60 63 66 69 81 82 88 92 97 108 **S** Community Health Systems, Inc., Brentwood, TN
Primary Contact: Pamela W. Roberts, Administrator
Web address: www.mcnairyregionalhospital.com

| | 23 | 10 | 38 | 1723 | 14 | 21653 | 440 | 12253 | 5153 | 161 |

SEVIERVILLE—Sevier County

⊠ **FORT SANDERS–SEVIER MEDICAL CENTER**, 709 Middle Creek Road, Zip 37862–5016, Mailing Address: P.O. Box 8005, Zip 37864–8005; tel. 865/429–6100, (Total facility includes 54 beds in nursing home–type unit) **A**1 9 10 **F**2 9 11 12 21 22 26 27 28 29 30 33 40 41 44 46 48 50 52 53 55 58 59 62 63 65 66 69 70 81 82 84 85 87 88 92 95 96 97 106 108 109 110 **S** Covenant Health, Knoxville, TN
Primary Contact: Ellen Wilhoit, President and Chief Administrative Officer
COO: Mark Holmstrom, Vice President Operations and Chief Operating Officer
CFO: Karen Patterson, Finance Manager
CMO: Laura Higgins, Chief of Staff
CIO: Misty Brown, Director of Marketing and Public Relations
Web address: www.covenanthealth.com

| | 23 | 10 | 108 | 2827 | 71 | 97964 | 749 | 33896 | 13662 | 413 |

SEWANEE—Franklin County

EMERALD–HODGSON HOSPITAL See Southern Tennessee Medical Center, Winchester

SHELBYVILLE—Bedford County

⊠ **BEDFORD COUNTY MEDICAL CENTER**, 845 Union Street, Zip 37160–2609; tel. 931/685–5433, (Total facility includes 107 beds in nursing home–type unit) **A**1 9 10 **F**2 9 11 12 21 22 26 27 28 29 32 33 39 44 46 47 48 51 52 53 58 59 60 62 63 65 66 69 81 84 85 88 92 93 94 97 108 110 **S** Quorum Health Resources, Plano, TX
Primary Contact: William P. Macri, Chief Executive Officer
CIO: Debbie Sudduth, Director Information Services
Web address: www.bcmctn.com

| | 13 | 10 | 176 | 2821 | 125 | 78005 | 263 | 29968 | 12054 | 373 |

SMITHVILLE—DeKalb County

⊠ **DEKALB HOSPITAL**, 520 West Main Street, Zip 37166–0640, Mailing Address: P.O. Box 640, Zip 37166–0640; tel. 615/597–7171 **A**1 9 10 **F**2 12 21 23 27 33 55 62 63 69 76 81 82 84 88 96 97 **S** Ascension Health, Saint Louis, MO
Primary Contact: Dennis Smock, Chief Executive Officer
CFO: Don Baker, Director Accounting
Web address: www.baptistdekalbhospital.com

| | 21 | 10 | 51 | 1733 | 20 | 20058 | 0 | 13835 | 5975 | 164 |

TN

Hospital, Address, Telephone, Approval, Facility, and Physician Codes, Health Care System	Classi-fication Codes		Utilization Data					Expense (thousands) of dollars		
★ American Hospital Association (AHA) membership □ Joint Commission on Accreditation of Healthcare Organizations (JCAHO) accreditation ○ American Osteopathic Association (AOA) accreditation △ Commission on Accreditation of Rehabilitation Facilities (CARF) accreditation	Control	Service	Staffed Beds	Admissions	Census	Outpatient Visits	Births	Total	Payroll	Personnel

SMYRNA—Rutherford County

☒ **STONECREST MEDICAL CENTER**, 200 StoneCrest Boulevard, Zip 37167; tel. 615/768–2000, (Nonreporting) **A**1 10 **S** HCA, Nashville, TN
Primary Contact: Neil A. Heatherly, CHE, Chief Executive Officer
CFO: Joe E. Bowman, Chief Financial Officer
CMO: Nuson Mangione, M.D., Chief of Staff
CHR: Joe Hill, Director, Human Resources
Web address: www.stonecrestmedical.com

| 33 | 49 | 75 | — | — | — | — | — | — | — |

SOMERVILLE—Fayette County

□ **METHODIST HEALTHCARE–FAYETTE HOSPITAL**, 214 Lakeview Drive, Zip 38068–9737; tel. 901/465–3594 **A**1 9 10 **F**2 9 12 21 26 27 28 29 33 39 44 46 47 52 58 61 62 63 65 66 69 81 82 88 92 94 97 108 **S** Methodist Healthcare, Memphis, TN
Primary Contact: Michael Blome', Administrator
Web address: www.methodisthealth.org

| 23 | 10 | 10 | 765 | 7 | 15532 | 0 | 5903 | 2696 | 68 |

SPARTA—White County

□ **WHITE COUNTY COMMUNITY HOSPITAL**, 401 Sewell Road, Zip 38583–1223; tel. 931/738–9211 **A**1 9 10 **F**12 14 21 33 44 46 55 58 59 63 66 68 69 81 94 95 108 **S** Community Health Systems, Inc., Brentwood, TN
Primary Contact: Mark Cain, Chief Executive Officer
Web address: www.chs.net

| 33 | 10 | 44 | 2108 | 22 | 23683 | 164 | 14688 | 6334 | 181 |

SPRINGFIELD—Robertson County

☒ **NORTHCREST MEDICAL CENTER**, 100 North Crest Drive, Zip 37172–3961; tel. 615/384–2411 **A**1 9 10 **F**2 3 9 11 12 13 14 15 21 22 26 27 28 31 33 34 36 37 42 44 46 48 51 52 53 55 56 58 59 60 62 63 65 66 67 68 69 71 81 82 84 88 92 93 94 95 96 106 107 108 109 110 **P**6
Primary Contact: Scott Raynes, President and Chief Executive Officer
CFO: Steve Sloan, Chief Financial Officer
CIO: Greg Morris, Chief Information Officer
CHR: Phyllis Trevathan, Human Resources Director
Web address: www.northcrest.com

| 23 | 10 | 90 | 4951 | 55 | 80537 | 644 | 46564 | 19674 | 535 |

SWEETWATER—Monroe County

☒ **SWEETWATER HOSPITAL**, 304 Wright Street, Zip 37874–2897; tel. 865/213–8200 **A**1 9 10 **F**2 11 12 26 27 28 33 51 59 63 69 81 88 94 108
Primary Contact: Scott Bowman, Administrator
Web address: www.sweetwaterhospital.org

| 23 | 10 | 59 | 2709 | 31 | 77797 | 262 | 28237 | 8720 | 380 |

TAZEWELL—Claiborne County

☒ **CLAIBORNE COUNTY HOSPITAL**, 1850 Old Knoxville Road, Zip 37879–3625, Mailing Address: P.O. Box 219, Zip 37879–0219; tel. 423/626–4211 **A**1 9 10 20 **F**6 12 21 28 29 33 36 37 45 48 51 52 55 58 60 63 65 66 69 81 84 88 94 108 **S** Baptist Health System of East Tennessee, Knoxville, TN
Primary Contact: Tim S. Brown, Senior Vice President and Administrator
CFO: Tim S. Brown, Chief Financial Officer
CIO: Joe Martin, Director Information Systems
CHR: Susan Stone, Director of Human Resources
Web address: www.claibornehospital.org

| 13 | 10 | 45 | 3104 | 34 | 46758 | 0 | 18483 | 9076 | 390 |

TRENTON—Gibson County

☒ **GIBSON GENERAL HOSPITAL**, 200 Hospital Drive, Zip 38382–3313; tel. 731/855–7900 **A**1 9 10 **F**2 12 21 22 26 27 28 29 33 46 48 52 53 58 63 66 69 81 88 94 108 **S** West Tennessee Healthcare, Jackson, TN
Primary Contact: Sherry Scruggs, Administrator
CFO: Terry Swindell, Controller
CMO: Tom Nelson, Family Practice
CHR: Nancy Riggs, Director Human Resources
Web address: www.wth.net

| 16 | 10 | 34 | 782 | 8 | 17491 | 2 | 6156 | 2338 | 74 |

TULLAHOMA—Coffee County

□ **HARTON REGIONAL MEDICAL CENTER**, 1801 North Jackson Street, Zip 37388–2201; tel. 931/393–3000 **A**1 9 10 **F**9 11 12 15 17 21 22 23 27 28 29 33 39 40 46 48 51 55 57 58 59 60 61 62 63 64 66 83 82 84 85 86 87 88 93 94 106 108 109 110 **S** Health Management Associates, Naples, FL
Primary Contact: Dwayne Blaylock, Chief Executive Officer
Web address: www.hartonmedicalcenter.com

| 33 | 10 | 110 | 5499 | 61 | 48875 | 703 | — | — | 455 |

UNION CITY—Obion County

☒ **BAPTIST MEMORIAL HOSPITAL–UNION CITY**, 1201 Bishop Street, Zip 38261–5403, Mailing Address: P.O. Box 310, Zip 38281–0310; tel. 731/884–8601, (Nonreporting) **A**1 9 10 **S** Baptist Memorial Health Care Corporation, Memphis, TN
Primary Contact: Mike Perryman, Administrator and Chief Executive Officer
COO: Mike Perryman, Administrator
CFO: Joe McWherter, Chief Financial Officer
CIO: David Mercer, Information Systems Coordinator
CHR: Tammy Hall, Human Resources Director
Web address: www.bmhcc.org

| 23 | 10 | 136 | — | — | — | — | — | — | — |

WAVERLY—Humphreys County

□ **THREE RIVERS HOSPITAL**, 451 Highway 13 South, Zip 37185–2149, Mailing Address: P.O. Box 437, Zip 37185–2149; tel. 931/296–4203 **A**1 9 10 18 **F**2 9 12 21 26 27 28 29 33 46 48 60 63 66 68 69 70 81 88 94 97 108 **P**6 **S** Associated Healthcare Systems, Inc., Brentwood, TN
Primary Contact: Kent Koster, Chief Executive Officer

| 32 | 10 | 25 | 668 | 7 | 26180 | 0 | 7108 | 3035 | 90 |

Hospital, Address, Telephone, Approval, Facility, and Physician Codes, Health Care System	Classi-fication Codes		Utilization Data					Expense (thousands) of dollars		
★ American Hospital Association (AHA) membership □ Joint Commission on Accreditation of Healthcare Organizations (JCAHO) accreditation ○ American Osteopathic Association (AOA) accreditation △ Commission on Accreditation of Rehabilitation Facilities (CARF) accreditation	Control	Service	Staffed Beds	Admissions	Census	Outpatient Visits	Births	Total	Payroll	Personnel

WAYNESBORO—Wayne County

□ **WAYNE MEDICAL CENTER**, 103 J. V. Mangubat Drive, Zip 38485, Mailing Address: P.O. Box 580, Zip 38485–0580; tel. 931/722–5411, (Total facility includes 46 beds in nursing home–type unit) **A**1 9 10 20 **F**2 6 12 21 26 27 33 63 69 81 84 88 92 93 94 97
Primary Contact: Byron Quinton, Administrator
Web address: www.mauryregional.com

	23	10	78	1266	56	30313	0	10632	4668	162

WINCHESTER—Franklin County

⊠ **SOUTHERN TENNESSEE MEDICAL CENTER**, 185 Hospital Road, Zip 37398–9504; tel. 931/967–8200, (Includes EMERALD–HODGSON HOSPITAL, 1260 University Avenue, Sewanee, Zip 37375–2303; tel. 615/598–5691; Mike Sherrod, Administrator), (Total facility includes 46 beds in nursing home–type unit) **A**1 9 10 **F**6 9 11 12 15 21 26 28 31 33 37 44 46 47 48 55 58 59 60 61 62 63 65 66 68 69 71 76 81 82 83 84 88 92 93 94 108 109 **S** LifePoint Hospitals, Inc., Brentwood, TN
Primary Contact: William Russell Spray, Chief Executive Officer
CFO: Matthew Tulin, Chief Financial Officer
CIO: Mike Webb, Information Systems Director
Web address: www.southerntennessee.com

	33	10	198	5797	99	66513	458	48978	17427	424

WOODBURY—Cannon County

□ **STONES RIVER HOSPITAL**, 324 Doolittle Road, Zip 37190–1140; tel. 615/563–4001 **A**1 9 10 **F**9 12 21 27 28 33 44 46 52 58 60 63 66 69 71 76 81 82 88 93 97 107 108
Primary Contact: Donald E. Downey, Administrator
Web address: www.stonesriverhospital.com

	33	10	55	1388	21	9508	0	11656	4884	162

TN

TEXAS

Hospital, Address, Telephone, Approval, Facility, and Physician Codes, Health Care System	Classi-fication Codes		Utilization Data					Expense (thousands) of dollars		
★ American Hospital Association (AHA) membership ☐ Joint Commission on Accreditation of Healthcare Organizations (JCAHO) accreditation ○ American Osteopathic Association (AOA) accreditation △ Commission on Accreditation of Rehabilitation Facilities (CARF) accreditation	Control	Service	Staffed Beds	Admissions	Census	Outpatient Visits	Births	Total	Payroll	Personnel

ABILENE—Taylor County

☐ **ABILENE PSYCHIATRIC HOSPITAL**, 4225 Woods Place, Zip 79608; tel. 325/698–6600 **A**1 5 10 **F**3 21 31 71 72 73 74 75 76
Primary Contact: Christopher Kearney, Chief Executive Officer

| | 23 | 22 | 28 | 604 | 19 | 0 | 0 | 3067 | 2050 | 62 |

✣ **ABILENE REGIONAL MEDICAL CENTER**, 6250 Highway 83–84 at Antilley Road, Zip 79606–5299; tel. 325/695–9900, (Total facility includes 25 beds in nursing home–type unit) **A**1 2 9 10 **F**3 9 10 11 12 13 14 15 17 19 21 22 23 26 27 28 29 31 33 34 40 41 44 45 46 47 48 52 53 55 56 58 59 60 61 62 63 64 65 66 67 68 69 71 79 81 82 84 87 88 92 93 94 96 108 109 110 **P**3 **S** Triad Hospitals, Inc., Plano, TX
Primary Contact: Michael D. Murphy, Chief Executive Officer
COO: Xavier Villareal, Chief Operating Officer
CFO: Ron Bennett, Chief Financial Officer
CMO: Charles Thompson, M.D., Chief of Staff
CIO: Dennis Newquist, Director Information Systems
CHR: Emmett Craig, Director Human Resources
Web address: www.abileneregional.com

| | 33 | 10 | 178 | 7062 | 94 | 49278 | 1454 | 84177 | 26313 | 633 |

✣ **HENDRICK HEALTH SYSTEM**, 1900 Pine Street, Zip 79601–2432; tel. 325/670–2000, (Total facility includes 26 beds in nursing home–type unit) **A**1 9 10 **F**2 9 10 11 12 14 15 17 19 21 22 23 27 28 29 30 32 33 34 35 37 39 40 41 42 43 44 45 46 47 48 49 50 51 52 53 55 57 58 59 60 61 62 63 64 65 66 67 68 69 70 75 80 81 82 84 85 87 88 92 93 94 95 96 106 108 109 110
Primary Contact: Tim Lancaster, FACHE, President and Chief Executive Officer
CFO: Stephen Kimmel, Senior Vice President and Chief Financial Officer
CMO: Ted Dyer, M.D., Vice President Medical Affairs
CHR: Mike McBroom, Vice President
Web address: www.ehendrick.org

| | 21 | 10 | 390 | 16955 | 260 | 326640 | 1336 | 187769 | 81445 | 2387 |

ALICE—Jim Wells County

✣ **CHRISTUS SPOHN HOSPITAL ALICE**, 2500 East Main Street, Zip 78332–4794; tel. 361/661–8000 **A**1 9 10 **F**2 9 11 12 15 17 21 22 26 27 28 32 33 34 39 40 42 44 45 46 48 52 53 55 58 59 60 62 63 64 65 66 69 70 71 73 74 75 76 81 84 88 92 94 107 108 110 **P**8 **S** Christus Health, Irving, TX
Primary Contact: Margot Rios, Vice President and Administrator
CMO: Alejandro Lopez, Jr, M.D., Chief of Staff
Web address: www.christusspohn.org/locations_alice.htm

| | 21 | 10 | 73 | 3170 | 40 | 38726 | 148 | 24220 | 10256 | 386 |

ALLEN—Collin County

✣ **PRESBYTERIAN HOSPITAL OF ALLEN**, 1105 Central Expressway North, Zip 75013, Mailing Address: 1105 Central Expressway North, Suite 100, Zip 75013; tel. 972/747–1000 **A**1 9 10 **F**2 11 12 21 22 27 29 31 33 46 48 52 57 58 59 62 63 81 84 88 94 96 106 108 109 **S** Texas Health Resources, Arlington, TX
Primary Contact: Sheila A. McKinney, President
CFO: Dan Rich, Director Finance
CMO: H Lynn Rodgers, M.D., President
CHR: Robert Faircloth, Director Human Resources
Web address: www.texashealth.org

| | 23 | 10 | 29 | 2233 | 15 | 36505 | 1098 | 26668 | 10705 | 207 |

ALPINE—Brewster County

✣ **BIG BEND REGIONAL MEDICAL CENTER**, 2600 Highway 118 North, Zip 79830–2002; tel. 432/837–3447 **A**1 9 10 20 **F**2 9 11 21 22 27 28 29 33 34 39 46 47 48 51 52 53 58 59 60 63 65 69 81 84 88 94 96 108 109 **S** Community Health Systems, Inc., Brentwood, TN
Primary Contact: John Krogness, CHE, Administrator
Web address: www.bigbendhealthcare.com

| | 33 | 10 | 35 | 1483 | 10 | 26139 | 255 | 15477 | 5362 | 127 |

ALVIN—Brazoria County

ALVIN DIAGNOSTIC AND URGENT CARE CENTER See Clear Lake Regional Medical Center, Webster

AMARILLO—Potter County

✣ **AMARILLO VETERANS AFFAIRS HEALTH CARE SYSTEM**, 6010 Amarillo Boulevard West, Zip 79106–1992; tel. 806/355–9703, (Total facility includes 120 beds in nursing home–type unit) (Nonreporting) **A**1 2 3 5 **S** Department of Veterans Affairs, Washington, DC
Primary Contact: Andrew C. Stenhouse, M.D., Acting Director and Chief Executive Officer
CFO: Alton McKinley, Chief Fiscal Services
CMO: Andrew C. Stenhouse, M.D., Chief of Staff
CIO: Toby Dickerson, Acting Chief Information Resource Management
CHR: Ken Creamer, Chief Human Resource
Web address: www.va.gov/sta/guide/home.asp

| | 45 | 10 | 189 | — | — | — | — | — | — | — |

Many Facility Codes have changed. Please refer to the AHA Guide Code Chart.

© 2005 AHA Guide

Hospital, Address, Telephone, Approval, Facility, and Physician Codes, Health Care System	Classi-fication Codes		Utilization Data					Expense (thousands) of dollars		
★ American Hospital Association (AHA) membership □ Joint Commission on Accreditation of Healthcare Organizations (JCAHO) accreditation ○ American Osteopathic Association (AOA) accreditation △ Commission on Accreditation of Rehabilitation Facilities (CARF) accreditation	Control	Service	Staffed Beds	Admissions	Census	Outpatient Visits	Births	Total	Payroll	Personnel

	Control	Service	Staffed Beds	Admissions	Census	Outpatient Visits	Births	Total	Payroll	Personnel
✖ **BAPTIST ST. ANTHONY HEALTH SYSTEM**, 1600 Wallace Boulevard, Zip 79106–1799; tel. 806/212–2000 **A**1 2 5 9 10 **F**2 6 9 11 12 14 15 17 19 21 22 23 26 27 28 29 32 33 36 37 38 40 42 44 45 46 48 51 52 54 55 56 57 58 59 60 61 62 63 64 65 66 67 68 69 70 81 82 84 85 86 87 88 94 95 96 107 108 109 **P**3 Primary Contact: John D. Hicks, FACHE, President and Chief Executive Officer COO: Michael Cruz, Vice President Operations CMO: Kenneth Johnston, M.D., Vice President of Medical Affairs CIO: Don Winschel, Director Information Services CHR: Iris Hicks, Director of Human Resources and Education Web address: www.bsahs.org	21	10	438	22585	279	96115	2294	242374	92383	2288
✖ **NORTHWEST TEXAS HEALTHCARE SYSTEM**, 1501 South Coulter Avenue, Zip 79106–1790; Mailing Address: P.O. Box 1110, Zip 79175–1110; tel. 806/354–1000, (Includes PSYCHIATRIC PAVILION, 7201 Evans, Zip 79106) **A**1 3 5 9 10 **F**2 3 4 6 9 10 11 14 15 17 19 20 21 22 23 24 26 27 28 29 31 32 33 34 35 39 42 44 47 48 49 50 52 53 55 56 57 58 59 60 61 62 63 64 65 66 67 69 70 71 72 73 74 75 76 77 78 81 82 84 85 87 88 93 94 96 108 109 110 **P**6 **S** Universal Health Services, Inc., King of Prussia, PA Primary Contact: Frank Lopez, FACHE, Chief Executive Officer and Managing Director COO: Kyle Sanders, Chief Operating Officer CFO: Raymond Grenier, Chief Financial Officer CMO: Nathan Goldstein, III, M.D., Chief Medical Officer CIO: Sam Mason, Director Management Information Systems CHR: Charlyn Snow, Human Resources Director Web address: www.nwtexashealthcare.com	33	10	433	16576	226	252013	2342	205523	62318	1476
NORTHWEST TEXAS SURGERY CENTER, 3501 Soncy Road, Suite 118, Zip 79109; tel. 805/359–7999 **A**9 10 **F**27 33 63 64 95 110	33	13	4	4682	1	4657	0	8151	2532	41
□ **PLUM CREEK SPECIALTY HOSPITAL**, 5601 Plum Creek Drive, Zip 79124–1801; tel. 806/351–1000 **A**1 9 10 **F**21 27 28 60 69 94 **S** Integrated Health Services, Sparks Glencoe, MD Primary Contact: LeeAnn Griffin, Chief Executive Officer	33	48	32	374	26	0	0	6780	4251	52
✖ **SCCI HOSPITAL OF AMARILLO**, 2828 Southwest 27th Avenue, Zip 79109; tel. 806/351–1600 **A**1 9 10 **F**2 21 28 60 110 **P**5 Primary Contact: Terry Hutton, Chief Executive Officer Web address: www.scci–ltac.com	33	10	62	414	31	0	0	12386	4513	125
ANAHUAC—Chambers County										
★ **BAYSIDE COMMUNITY HOSPITAL**, 200 Hospital Drive, Zip 77514, Mailing Address: P.O. Box 398, Zip 77514; tel. 409/267–3143 **A**10 18 **F**9 21 24 27 28 29 33 34 39 46 47 48 52 53 63 65 66 70 81 88 109 110 **P**7 Primary Contact: Robert Pascasio, Chief Executive Officer COO: Robert Pascasio, Administrator and Chief Executive Officer CFO: Cleo Cable, Chief Financial Officer CMO: Leonidas Andres, M.D., Chief of Staff	16	10	14	259	2	17263	0	3996	1858	57
ANDREWS—Andrews County										
✖ **PERMIAN REGIONAL MEDICAL CENTER**, Northeast By–Pass, Zip 79714, Mailing Address: P.O. Box 2108, Zip 79714–2108; tel. 432/523–2200, (Total facility includes 44 beds in nursing home–type unit) **A**1 9 10 20 **F**2 9 11 12 21 26 27 28 29 30 31 32 33 34 35 37 38 39 41 44 46 47 48 51 52 53 55 58 59 60 63 64 65 66 69 70 81 82 84 88 92 93 94 95 96 97 106 107 108 110 **P**6 7 Primary Contact: Randy R. Richards, Chief Executive Officer CFO: Carol Durham, Chief Financial Officer CIO: Dan Smart, Chief Information Management Web address: www.permianregional.com	16	10	88	1269	52	128831	199	21315	9199	275
ANGLETON—Brazoria County										
✖ **ANGLETON DANBURY MEDICAL CENTER**, 132 East Hospital Drive, Zip 77515–4197; tel. 979/849–7721 **A**1 9 10 **F**2 9 11 12 17 21 22 26 27 28 29 30 33 34 37 41 42 46 47 48 52 53 55 58 59 60 62 63 65 66 69 81 82 84 88 94 96 106 108 **P**1 Primary Contact: David A. Bleakney, Administrator CFO: William D. Garwood, III, Associate Administrator and Chief Financial Officer CHR: Beverly Dahlem, Associate Administrator Web address: www.admc.org	16	10	43	2606	23	47949	423	28238	8661	241
ANSON—Jones County										
★ **ANSON GENERAL HOSPITAL**, 101 Avenue J, Zip 79501–2198; tel. 325/823–3231 **A**9 10 **F**6 9 21 27 29 33 37 39 41 46 48 51 63 69 81 88 92 97 **P**3 8 Primary Contact: Ted D. Matthews, Chief Executive Officer CFO: Pamela Gonzales, Chief Financial Officer	14	10	31	789	16	14294	0	5193	2609	145
ARANSAS PASS—San Patricio County										
□ **NORTH BAY HOSPITAL**, 1711 West Wheeler Avenue, Zip 78336–4536; tel. 361/758–8585 **A**1 9 10 **F**2 3 9 12 21 26 27 28 33 39 44 46 48 52 53 55 58 62 63 64 66 69 70 71 73 75 76 81 82 88 94 97 109 **P**5 **S** AMT Group, Inc., Duluth, GA Primary Contact: Christopher W. Dux, Chief Executive Officer Web address: www.nbhtx.com	33	10	64	2673	32	15176	0	18485	9047	210

TX

Hospital, Address, Telephone, Approval, Facility, and Physician Codes, Health Care System	Classi-fication Codes		Utilization Data					Expense (thousands) of dollars		
★ American Hospital Association (AHA) membership □ Joint Commission on Accreditation of Healthcare Organizations (JCAHO) accreditation ○ American Osteopathic Association (AOA) accreditation △ Commission on Accreditation of Rehabilitation Facilities (CARF) accreditation	Control	Service	Staffed Beds	Admissions	Census	Outpatient Visits	Births	Total	Payroll	Personnel

ARLINGTON—Tarrant County

⊠ **ARLINGTON MEMORIAL HOSPITAL**, 800 West Randol Mill Road, Zip 76012–2503; tel. 817/548–6100 **A**1 9 10 **F**2 9 11 12 14 15 17 19 21 22 23 26 27 28 33 40 41 42 46 48 49 52 53 55 56 57 58 59 60 61 62 63 64 69 81 82 84 88 94 96 99 106 108 110 **P**1 **S** Texas Health Resources, Arlington, TX Primary Contact: Oscar Amparan, President CFO: Joe Tallon, Director Finance Web address: www.arlingtonmemorial.org	23	10	369	19216	266	177663	3304	195463	87730	1935
⊠ **HEALTHSOUTH REHABILITATION HOSPITAL OF ARLINGTON**, 3200 Matlock Road, Zip 76015–2911; tel. 817/468–4000 **A**1 9 10 **F**21 37 42 44 52 60 61 62 68 69 93 94 95 96 **P**5 **S** HEALTHSOUTH Corporation, Birmingham, AL Primary Contact: Bruce Lambdin, Interim Chief Executive Officer CFO: Mike Murray, Controller CMO: Rizwan Shah, M.D., Medical Director CHR: Benet Ford, Director Human Resources Web address: www.healthsouth.com	33	46	65	1399	50	32065	0	14024	7693	182
□ **KINDRED HOSPITAL OF TARRANT COUNTY**, 1000 North Cooper Street, Zip 76011–5540; tel. 817/548–3400 **A**1 9 10 **F**2 21 22 26 28 33 37 44 46 55 60 69 93 94 110 **S** Kindred Healthcare, Louisville, KY Primary Contact: Robert C. Gladney, Chief Executive Officer Web address: www.kindredhealthcare.com	33	80	79	768	74	9	0	24019	10831	251
⊠ △ **MEDICAL CENTER OF ARLINGTON**, 3301 Matlock Road, Zip 76015–2998; tel. 817/465–3241 **A**1 7 9 10 **F**2 9 10 11 12 14 15 17 19 21 23 26 27 28 29 32 33 35 37 39 44 45 46 47 48 49 52 55 56 57 58 59 60 61 62 63 65 66 68 69 81 82 84 88 94 95 106 107 108 109 110 **S** HCA, Nashville, TN Primary Contact: Patrick D. Brilliant, Chief Executive Officer COO: Scott Schmidly, Chief Operating Officer CFO: Marshall Allen, Chief Financial Officer CMO: Bruce Railey, M.D., Chief of Staff CIO: Tammy Phillips, Director Information Services CHR: Donna Coleman, Director Human Resources Web address: www.medicalcenterarlington.com	33	10	271	12621	182	85966	2994	153846	47937	834
□ **MILLWOOD HOSPITAL**, 1011 North Cooper Street, Zip 76011–5517; tel. 817/261–3121 **A**1 10 **F**3 4 26 27 28 31 42 44 71 72 76 77 78 94 96 **S** Psychiatric Solutions, Franklin, TN Primary Contact: Thomas E. Rourke, CHE, Chief Executive Officer Web address: www.millwoodhospital.com	32	22	98	3671	74	25925	0	15498	6725	141
PHYSICIANS' METROPLEX HOSPITAL, 4400 South New York, Zip 76018; tel. 817/395–5100, (Nonreporting) **A**9 10 Primary Contact: Randy B. Bacus, FACHE, Chief Executive Officer Web address: www.lelandmedical.com	33	10	30	—	—	—	—	—	—	—
□ **USMD HOSPITAL AT ARLINGTON**, 801 West Interstate 20, Zip 76017; tel. 817/472–3400 **A**1 9 10 **F**2 12 21 22 28 33 37 40 41 53 58 63 64 66 75 81 82 84 88 94 Primary Contact: Michael C. Zucker, FACHE, President	32	13	18	804	3	46640	2	37433	8334	240

ASPERMONT—Stonewall County

STONEWALL MEMORIAL HOSPITAL, 821 North Broadway, Zip 79502–2913, Mailing Address: P.O. Box C, Zip 79502–2913; tel. 940/989–3551 **A**9 10 18 **F**21 26 27 28 33 46 48 52 70 97 **P**6 Primary Contact: Shalena Hodge, Administrator	16	10	12	165	3	3442	0	2625	1228	56

ATHENS—Henderson County

⊠ **EAST TEXAS MEDICAL CENTER ATHENS**, 2000 South Palestine Street, Zip 75751–5610; tel. 903/676–1000 **A**1 9 10 **F**9 12 15 17 21 33 34 40 42 46 55 57 59 62 63 64 81 82 84 85 88 94 96 108 **P**7 **S** East Texas Medical Center Regional Healthcare System, Tyler, TX Primary Contact: Patrick L. Wallace, Administrator CFO: David A. Travis, Chief Financial Officer Web address: www.etmc.org	23	10	117	8408	89	74057	881	58764	20003	472

ATLANTA—Cass County

★ **ATLANTA MEMORIAL HOSPITAL**, Highway 77 at South William, Zip 75551, Mailing Address: P.O. Box 1049, Zip 75551–1049; tel. 903/799–3000 **A**9 10 **F**9 11 12 21 22 24 27 28 29 33 34 41 46 48 51 52 53 55 58 59 60 63 66 69 71 73 76 81 84 88 93 94 96 97 108 **P**8 Primary Contact: Tom Crow, Administrator COO: Debbie Robison, R.N., Assistant Administrator Nursing CFO: Jodie Harris, Controller and Chief Financial Officer CHR: Debra Embry, Associate Administrator Employee Services Web address: www.atlantamemorial.com	16	10	59	2318	29	23403	141	15010	6985	204

AUSTIN—Travis County

□ **AUSTIN STATE HOSPITAL**, 4110 Guadalupe Street, Zip 78751–4296; tel. 512/452–0381 **A**1 10 **F**22 26 27 28 32 39 53 71 72 74 76 94 108 **P**1 **S** Texas Department of State Health Services, Austin, TX Primary Contact: Carl Schock, Superintendent Web address: www.mhmr.state.tx.us	12	22	297	4318	269	0	0	45955	26994	770

Many Facility Codes have changed. Please refer to the AHA Guide Code Chart.

© 2005 AHA Guide

TX

Hospital, Address, Telephone, Approval, Facility, and Physician Codes, Health Care System	Classi-fication Codes		Utilization Data					Expense (thousands) of dollars		
★ American Hospital Association (AHA) membership □ Joint Commission on Accreditation of Healthcare Organizations (JCAHO) accreditation ○ American Osteopathic Association (AOA) accreditation △ Commission on Accreditation of Rehabilitation Facilities (CARF) accreditation	Control	Service	Staffed Beds	Admissions	Census	Outpatient Visits	Births	Total	Payroll	Personnel
□ **AUSTIN SURGICAL HOSPITAL**, 3003 Bee Caves Road, Zip 78746; tel. 512/314–3800 **A**1 9 10 **F**2 21 22 27 33 37 48 53 55 60 62 63 64 81 84 85 94 **S** Hospital Partners of America, Charlotte, NC Primary Contact: Jess N. Judy, President and Chief Executive Officer Web address: www.austinsurgicalhospital.com	32	47	23	1261	10	5867	0	27691	7330	154
✦ **BRACKENRIDGE HOSPITAL**, 601 East 15th Street, Zip 78701–1996; tel. 512/324–7000, (Includes CHILDREN'S HOSPITAL OF AUSTIN, One Children's Place, tel. 512/324–8000; Bob Bonar, President and Chief Executive Officer) **A**1 9 10 **F**2 9 11 12 14 15 16 17 18 19 20 21 22 23 24 26 27 28 29 32 33 34 35 37 39 46 47 48 50 52 53 55 56 57 58 59 60 61 62 63 64 65 66 67 69 70 73 75 77 80 81 82 84 88 90 92 93 94 96 101 106 107 108 110 **P**8 **S** Ascension Health, Saint Louis, MO Primary Contact: Jesus Garza, President and Chief Executive Officer COO: Bruce Broslat, Vice President and Chief Operating Officer CFO: Douglas D. Waite, Chief Financial Officer CMO: Jim Lindsey, M.D., Senior Vice President Medical Affairs CIO: Mark Barner, Vice President Information Systems Web address: www.seton.net	21	10	382	18129	238	312074	3625	318232	117043	1712
CHRISTOPHER HOUSE, 2820 East Martin Luther King, Zip 78702–1544; tel. 512/322–0747, (Nonreporting) Primary Contact: Marjorie Mulanax, Executive Director	23	49	15	—	—	—	—	—	—	—
□ **CORNERSTONE HOSPITAL OF AUSTIN**, 4207 Burnet Road, Zip 78756–3396; tel. 512/706–1900 **A**1 9 10 **F**2 21 22 27 45 55 60 64 81 84 85 88 94 110 **S** Cornerstone Healthcare Group, Austin, TX Primary Contact: Edward J. Sherwood, M.D., Chief Executive Officer Web address: www.marinerhealthcare.com	33	80	122	1278	93	0	0	27612	11446	298
□ **CORNERSTONE HOSPITAL OF CENTRAL TEXAS**, 8402 Cross Park Drive, Zip 78754; tel. 512/837–6233 **A**1 9 10 **F**2 21 22 27 45 60 64 94 110 **S** Cornerstone Healthcare Group, Austin, TX Primary Contact: Edward J. Sherwood, M.D., Chief Executive Officer Web address: www.cornerstonehealthcaregroup.com	33	80	39	317	21	0	0	6506	2814	60
✦ **HEALTHSOUTH REHABILITATION HOSPITAL OF AUSTIN**, 1215 Red River Street, Zip 78701–1921; tel. 512/474–5700 **A**1 9 10 **F**21 26 27 28 37 44 45 46 48 52 57 58 60 62 65 66 68 69 96 110 **S** HEALTHSOUTH Corporation, Birmingham, AL Primary Contact: Denise Lynch, Administrator CFO: Pamela McLaughlin, Chief Financial Officer CHR: Marilyn Jennings, Director Human Resources Web address: www.healthsouth.com	33	46	83	1306	48	24739	0	16513	8703	205
✦ **HEALTHSOUTH SURGICAL HOSPITAL OF AUSTIN**, 6818 Austin Center Boulevard, Zip 78731–3165; tel. 512/346–1994 **A**1 9 10 **F**33 40 52 63 **S** HEALTHSOUTH Corporation, Birmingham, AL Primary Contact: Diana Zamora, Administrator Web address: www.healthsouth.com	32	13	8	364	1	6853	0	13259	2170	62
□ **HEART HOSPITAL OF AUSTIN**, 3801 North Lamar Boulevard, Zip 78756; tel. 512/407–7000 **A**1 9 10 **F**2 14 15 17 19 21 22 26 27 28 29 33 47 63 65 66 81 82 83 88 94 96 106 108 **S** MedCath, Inc., Charlotte, NC Primary Contact: Roy C. Vinson, President Web address: www.hearthospitalofaustin.com	32	10	58	4849	41	11609	0	53703	16536	295
✦ **NORTH AUSTIN MEDICAL CENTER**, 12221 MoPac Expressway North, Zip 78758–2496; tel. 512/901–1000 **A**1 9 10 **F**2 9 11 12 14 15 17 19 21 22 23 26 27 28 29 32 33 37 41 44 46 47 48 52 55 56 57 58 59 60 61 62 63 64 65 66 69 81 82 84 85 87 88 93 94 96 101 108 109 110 **S** HCA, Nashville, TN Primary Contact: Donald H. Wilkerson, Chief Executive Officer COO: Sheri Wallace, Chief Operating Officer CFO: Cindy Sexton, Chief Financial Officer CMO: Ross Hemphill, M.D., Medical Director CIO: Mike Blom, Director Management Information Systems Web address: www.northaustin.com	23	10	210	11480	145	103228	2999	129447	44114	967
✦ **SETON MEDICAL CENTER**, 1201 West 38th Street, Zip 78705–1056; tel. 512/324–1000, (Includes SETON NORTHWEST HOSPITAL, 11113 Research Boulevard, Zip 78759–7513; tel. 512/324–6000; Charles E. Durant, Jr, FACHE, Administrator; SETON SOUTHWEST HEALTHCARE CENTER, 7900 F. M. 1826, Zip 78737; tel. 412/324–9000; Maria Faria, FACHE, Administrator), (Total facility includes 27 beds in nursing home–type unit) **A**1 2 3 9 10 **F**2 9 11 12 14 15 17 19 21 22 23 26 27 28 29 33 37 38 41 42 46 48 50 52 53 55 56 57 58 59 61 62 63 64 65 66 69 81 82 84 88 92 93 94 95 96 100 106 107 108 110 **P**8 **S** Ascension Health, Saint Louis, MO Primary Contact: John C. Brindley, President and Chief Executive Officer Primary Contact: Charlotte Thrasher, Chief Operating Officer and Administrator COO: Charlotte Thrasher, Chief Operating Officer and Administrator CFO: Douglas D. Waite, Chief Financial Officer CMO: Frank Mazza, M.D., Vice President Medical Affairs CIO: Mark Barner, Vice President Information Systems CHR: Marcia Silverberg, Vice President Human Resources Web address: www.seton.net	21	10	446	21280	309	289591	4577	383849	149190	2765

TX

Hospital, Address, Telephone, Approval, Facility, and Physician Codes, Health Care System	Classification Codes		Utilization Data					Expense (thousands) of dollars		
★ American Hospital Association (AHA) membership □ Joint Commission on Accreditation of Healthcare Organizations (JCAHO) accreditation ○ American Osteopathic Association (AOA) accreditation △ Commission on Accreditation of Rehabilitation Facilities (CARF) accreditation	Control	Service	Staffed Beds	Admissions	Census	Outpatient Visits	Births	Total	Payroll	Personnel
✠ **SETON SHOAL CREEK HOSPITAL**, 3501 Mills Avenue, Zip 78731–6391; tel. 512/324–2040 **A**1 9 10 **F**3 4 21 22 26 27 28 53 65 66 71 72 73 74 75 76 77 92 94 96 **P**8 **S** Ascension Health, Saint Louis, MO Primary Contact: Armin L. Steege, Administrator and Vice President CFO: Douglas D. Waite, Chief Financial Officer CMO: Paul Whitelock, M.D., Medical Director CIO: Mark Barner, Vice President Information Systems CHR: Marcia Silverberg, Vice President Human Resources Web address: www.seton.net	21	22	89	3087	46	22302	0	12662	6629	113
✠ **SOUTH AUSTIN HOSPITAL**, 901 West Ben White Boulevard, Zip 78704–6903; tel. 512/447–2211 **A**1 2 9 10 **F**2 7 9 11 12 14 15 17 19 21 22 23 26 27 28 29 33 37 40 42 44 46 47 48 50 52 55 57 58 59 61 62 63 64 65 66 69 81 82 84 85 87 88 93 94 96 108 109 110 **S** HCA, Nashville, TN Primary Contact: Erol R. Akdamar, Chief Executive Officer COO: Brett Matens, Chief Operating Officer CFO: Dewayne Benefield, Chief Financial Officer CMO: Donald Connell, M.D., Chief Medical Officer CIO: Darron Garza, Director CHR: Kellie Prince, Director Human Resources Web address: www.southaustinhospital.com	23	10	193	11174	134	77780	759	102102	36581	747
✠ **ST. DAVID'S MEDICAL CENTER**, 919 East 32nd Street, Zip 78705–2709, Mailing Address: P.O. Box 4039, Zip 78765–4039; tel. 512/476–7111 **A**1 2 9 10 **F**2 9 10 11 12 14 15 17 19 21 22 23 26 27 28 29 32 33 34 41 44 46 47 48 50 52 55 56 57 58 59 60 61 62 63 64 65 66 68 69 81 82 84 85 88 89 94 96 108 109 110 **S** HCA, Nashville, TN Primary Contact: Cole C. Eslyn, Chief Executive Officer COO: Jeanne Nagy, Chief Operating Officer CFO: Cindy Brouillette, Chief Financial Officer CIO: Paul Klehn, Director Information Systems Web address: www.stdavids.com	23	10	290	16731	231	115422	4778	164046	65666	1174
✠ **ST. DAVID'S PAVILION**, 1025 East 32nd Street, Zip 78765–2705; tel. 512/867–5800 **A**1 10 **F**21 22 26 27 28 29 44 45 52 65 66 71 76 94 **S** HCA, Nashville, TN Primary Contact: Cole C. Eslyn, Chief Executive Officer COO: Caroline Murphy, Chief Operating Officer CFO: Cindy Brouillette, Chief Financial Officer CIO: Paul Klehn, Director Information Systems Web address: www.stdavids.com	23	22	20	422	15	2016	0	5294	1717	26
✠ **ST. DAVID'S REHABILITATION CENTER**, 1005 East 32nd Street, Zip 78705–2705, Mailing Address: P.O. Box 4270, Zip 78765–4270; tel. 512/867–5100 **A**1 9 10 **F**21 22 26 27 28 29 30 37 44 45 46 47 52 57 62 65 66 68 69 94 95 96 **S** HCA, Nashville, TN Primary Contact: Cole C. Eslyn, Chief Executive Officer COO: Caroline Murphy, Chief Operating Officer CFO: Cindy Brouillette, Chief Financial Officer CIO: Paul Klehn, Director Information Systems Web address: www.stdavids.com	23	46	62	1687	50	45458	0	19505	10255	175
□ △ **TEXAS NEURO REHABILITATION CENTER**, 1106 West Dittmar, Zip 78745–6388, Mailing Address: P.O. Box 150459, Zip 78715–0459; tel. 512/444–4835 **A**1 7 9 10 **F**21 28 34 65 66 94 110 **P**4 5 **S** Psychiatric Solutions, Franklin, TN Primary Contact: Edgar F. Prettyman, M.D., Chief Executive Officer Web address: www.psysolutions.com	32	46	31	363	29	—	0	5505	3124	271
AZLE—Tarrant County										
✠ **HARRIS METHODIST NORTHWEST**, 108 Denver Trail, Zip 76020–3697; tel. 817/444–8600 **A**1 9 10 **F**2 12 14 21 22 26 27 28 29 33 34 36 37 39 48 52 53 55 58 60 62 63 64 69 81 88 94 95 106 108 109 110 **S** Texas Health Resources, Arlington, TX Primary Contact: Brett McClung, President CFO: Shelly Miland, Chief Financial Officer Web address: www.hmhs.com	23	10	30	1447	14	23816	2	16337	7138	132
BALLINGER—Runnels County										
BALLINGER MEMORIAL HOSPITAL, 608 Avenue B, Zip 76821–2499; tel. 915/365–2531 **A**9 10 18 **F**6 9 26 27 28 33 34 41 44 46 48 50 52 58 60 62 66 68 69 71 74 77 81 92 94 97 110 Primary Contact: Lance W. Keilers, Administrator	16	10	16	205	2	9217	0	2993	1527	65
BAY CITY—Matagorda County										
✠ **MATAGORDA GENERAL HOSPITAL**, 1115 Avenue G, Zip 77414–3544; tel. 979/245–6383 **A**1 9 10 **F**2 9 11 12 21 22 24 26 27 28 30 31 33 34 37 41 44 46 48 52 55 58 59 62 63 64 68 71 81 82 84 88 91 94 96 106 108 109 110 **S** Quorum Health Resources, Plano, TX Primary Contact: Daryle Voss, Chief Executive Officer CFO: Bryan Prochnow, Chief Financial Officer CMO: George Hanna, M.D., Chief of Staff CIO: Mary Ann Cervantes, District Director Management Information Systems CHR: Cindy Krebs, District Director Human Resources Web address: www.matagordageneral.org	16	10	67	2302	24	34226	331	25993	10406	346

TX

Many Facility Codes have changed. Please refer to the AHA Guide Code Chart. © 2005 AHA Guide

Hospital, Address, Telephone, Approval, Facility, and Physician Codes, Health Care System	Classi-fication Codes		Utilization Data					Expense (thousands) of dollars		
★ American Hospital Association (AHA) membership ☐ Joint Commission on Accreditation of Healthcare Organizations (JCAHO) accreditation ○ American Osteopathic Association (AOA) accreditation △ Commission on Accreditation of Rehabilitation Facilities (CARF) accreditation	Control	Service	Staffed Beds	Admissions	Census	Outpatient Visits	Births	Total	Payroll	Personnel

BAYTOWN—Harris County

✠ **SAN JACINTO METHODIST HOSPITAL**, 4401 Garth Road, Zip 77521–3160; tel. 281/420–8600, (Includes SAN JACINTO METHODIST HOSPITAL – ALEXANDER, 1700 James Bowie Drive, Zip 77520–3386; tel. 281/420–6100), (Total facility includes 30 beds in nursing home–type unit) **A**1 9 10 **F**2 10 11 12 15 17 21 22 23 27 28 29 31 32 33 35 44 46 48 52 55 57 58 59 60 61 62 63 64 65 66 68 69 70 71 73 74 75 76 78 81 82 84 85 87 88 92 94 96 108 **P**3 6 8 **S** The Methodist Hospital System, Houston, TX Primary Contact: S. Jeffrey Ackerman, M.D., President and Chief Executive Officer COO: Christopher Siebenaler, Chief Operating Officer and Chief Financial Officer CFO: Christopher Siebenaler, Chief Operating Officer and Chief Financial Officer CMO: Bruce Kennedy, M.D., Chief Medical Officer CHR: Donald Miller, Director, Human Resources Web address: www.methodisthealth.com	23	10	266	14454	198	163855	1692	143075	71330	1455

BEAUMONT—Jefferson County

✠ **CHRISTUS ST. ELIZABETH HOSPITAL**, 2830 Calder Avenue, Zip 77702–1809, Mailing Address: P.O. Box 5405, Zip 77726–5405; tel. 409/892–7171, (Total facility includes 20 beds in nursing home–type unit) **A**1 2 9 10 **F**2 3 9 11 12 13 14 15 17 19 21 22 26 27 28 29 30 31 33 34 35 39 40 41 42 46 47 48 49 52 55 56 57 58 59 60 62 63 64 65 66 67 68 69 71 81 82 84 85 87 88 92 93 94 96 107 108 109 110 **P**8 **S** Christus Health, Irving, TX Primary Contact: Joel Fagerstrom, Chief Executive Officer CFO: Fred W. Loeb, Chief Financial Officer CIO: Mavis Girlinghouse, Regional Director Information Management CHR: Charles Foster, Regional Director, Human Resources Web address: www.christusste.org	21	10	432	21093	291	188753	2266	220936	83254	2056
✠ **DUBUIS HOSPITAL OF BEAUMONT**, 2830 Calder Avenue, 4th Floor, Zip 77702; tel. 409/899–8154 **A**1 9 10 **F**2 21 22 23 26 27 28 94 110 **P**5 **S** Dubuis Health System, Houston, TX Primary Contact: Stephen Mills, Regional Administrator Web address: www.dubuis.org	21	10	51	512	36	0	—	14363	5757	120
✠ **HEALTHSOUTH REHABILITATION HOSPITAL OF BEAUMONT**, 3340 Plaza 10 Boulevard, Zip 77707–2551; tel. 409/835–0835 **A**1 9 10 **F**2 21 22 26 27 28 52 57 58 62 66 68 69 93 94 95 96 108 110 **S** HEALTHSOUTH Corporation, Birmingham, AL Primary Contact: Bill Klamforth, Administrator CFO: Lynn Webb, Chief Financial Officer Web address: www.healthsouth.com	32	46	61	1408	49	10642	0	11794	5302	146
✠ **MEMORIAL HERMANN BAPTIST BEAUMONT HOSPITAL**, 3080 College Street, Zip 77701–4689, Mailing Address: P.O. Box 1591, Zip 77704–1591; tel. 409/212–5000, (Includes MEMORIAL HERMANN BAPTIST FANNIN BEHAVIORAL HEALTH CENTER, 3250 Fannin Street, Zip 77701; tel. 409/212–7000), (Total facility includes 22 beds in nursing home–type unit) **A**1 9 10 **F**2 3 4 9 11 12 14 15 17 19 21 22 23 27 28 29 32 33 46 48 49 52 55 56 57 58 59 61 62 63 64 65 66 67 68 69 71 72 75 76 77 78 79 81 82 84 85 87 88 92 94 96 107 108 109 **S** Memorial Hermann Healthcare System, Houston, TX Primary Contact: David N. Parmer, President and Chief Executive Officer COO: Wilson J. Weber, Chief Operating Officer CIO: Mark Henderson, Chief Information Officer CHR: Linda Brinkley, Director Human Resources Web address: www.mhbh.org	23	10	365	13437	186	74327	1059	115473	45359	1130

BEDFORD—Tarrant County

✠ **HARRIS METHODIST–HEB**, 1600 Hospital Parkway, Zip 76022–6913, Mailing Address: P.O. Box 669, Zip 76095–0669; tel. 817/685–4000, (Includes HARRIS METHODIST–SPRINGWOOD, 1608 Hospital Parkway, Zip 76022; tel. 817/355–7700) **A**1 9 10 **F**9 11 12 15 17 19 21 22 26 27 28 33 41 44 49 50 52 55 56 58 59 60 61 63 65 66 68 69 81 82 88 93 94 95 96 106 108 109 110 **S** Texas Health Resources, Arlington, TX Primary Contact: Jack McCabe, FACHE, President COO: Alice Landers, Administrative Director Operations CFO: Shelly Miland, Chief Financial Officer and Vice President Finance CMO: Roy Turner, M.D., Chief of Staff CHR: Dale Smith, Director Human Resources Web address: www.texashealth.org	21	10	216	12675	147	101235	1687	161686	68051	1153

BEEVILLE—Bee County

✠ **CHRISTUS SPOHN HOSPITAL BEEVILLE**, 1500 East Houston Street, Zip 78102–5312; tel. 361/354–2000 **A**1 9 10 20 **F**2 9 11 21 22 26 27 28 29 33 34 46 48 52 53 55 58 59 60 62 63 64 65 66 69 81 82 84 88 92 94 96 106 108 109 **P**8 **S** Christus Health, Irving, TX Primary Contact: David S. Wagner, Vice President and Administrator Web address: www.christushealth.org	21	10	63	3485	40	46210	392	25679	11316	256

BELLVILLE—Austin County

✠ **BELLVILLE GENERAL HOSPITAL**, 44 North Cummings Street, Zip 77418–1347; tel. 979/865–3141 **A**1 9 10 **F**2 9 12 21 26 27 28 33 34 39 46 48 52 53 58 63 81 84 88 97 108 Primary Contact: Michael Morris, Administrator CFO: Pat Krupala, Director Financial Services CMO: Christophe Gay, M.D., Chief of Staff Web address: www.bellvillehospital.com	16	10	25	879	8	94262	0	7844	2994	91

TX

Hospital, Address, Telephone, Approval, Facility, and Physician Codes, Health Care System	Classi-fication Codes		Utilization Data					Expense (thousands) of dollars		
★ American Hospital Association (AHA) membership □ Joint Commission on Accreditation of Healthcare Organizations (JCAHO) accreditation ○ American Osteopathic Association (AOA) accreditation △ Commission on Accreditation of Rehabilitation Facilities (CARF) accreditation	Control	Service	Staffed Beds	Admissions	Census	Outpatient Visits	Births	Total	Payroll	Personnel

BIG LAKE—Reagan County

★ **REAGAN MEMORIAL HOSPITAL**, 805 North Main Street, Zip 76932–3999; tel. 325/884–2561 **A**9 10 18 **F**2 33 41 69 97
Primary Contact: Sidney Tucker, Administrator
CMO: Joseph Sudolcan, Medical Director

| | 16 | 10 | 14 | 107 | 1 | 14115 | 1 | 1773 | 667 | 30 |

BIG SPRING—Howard County

□ **BIG SPRING STATE HOSPITAL**, 1901 North Highway 87, Zip 79720; tel. 915/267–8216 **A**1 10 **F**22 26 27 28 33 44 53 58 65 66 71 74 75 76 94 106 108 **P**6 **S** Texas Department of State Health Services, Austin, TX
Primary Contact: Edward Moughon, Superintendent
Web address: www.mhmr.state.tx.us/hospitals/bigspringSH/bigspringsh.html

| | 12 | 22 | 151 | 1187 | 151 | 1187 | 0 | 28851 | 16024 | 500 |

□ **SCENIC MOUNTAIN MEDICAL CENTER**, 1601 West 11th Place, Zip 79720–4198; tel. 432/263–1211 **A**1 9 10 **F**9 11 12 15 21 27 28 33 35 37 44 45 46 48 52 54 55 58 59 60 63 66 69 71 76 81 84 88 94 97 **P**6 **S** Community Health Systems, Inc., Brentwood, TN
Primary Contact: Michael W. Pruitt, Chief Executive Officer
Web address: www.smmccares.com

| | 33 | 10 | 122 | 3316 | 36 | 40556 | 296 | 28817 | 11041 | 310 |

⊠ **WEST TEXAS VA HEALTH CARE SYSTEM**, 300 Veterans Boulevard, Zip 79720–5500; tel. 432/263–7361, (Total facility includes 40 beds in nursing home–type unit) (Nonreporting) **A**1 2 3 5 9 **S** Department of Veterans Affairs, Washington, DC
Primary Contact: Lou Ann Atkins, Director
CFO: Billy Sullivan, Chief Fiscal Service
CMO: Wilfredo Rodriguez, M.D., Chief of Staff
CHR: Cheryl McNeil, Chief Human Resources Management Service
Web address: www.va.gov/sta/guide/home.asp

| | 45 | 10 | 189 | — | — | — | — | — | — | — |

BONHAM—Fannin County

□ **NORTHEAST MEDICAL CENTER**, 504 Lipscomb Boulevard, Zip 75418–4096; Mailing Address: P.O. Drawer C, Zip 75418–4096; tel. 903/583–8585 **A**1 9 10 **F**2 9 12 21 27 28 33 46 48 50 51 52 55 58 63 69 81 82 84 87 88 94 97 108 **P**5
Primary Contact: Jay J. Hodges, Chief Executive Officer
Web address: www.northeastmc.com
SAM RAYBURN MEMORIAL VETERANS CENTER See Veterans Affairs North Texas Health Care System, Dallas

| | 32 | 10 | 39 | 1182 | 9 | 32560 | 0 | 15230 | 6269 | 145 |

BORGER—Hutchinson County

⊠ **GOLDEN PLAINS COMMUNITY HOSPITAL**, 200 South McGee Street, Zip 79007–0495; tel. 806/273–1100 **A**1 9 10 20 **F**6 9 11 12 21 22 24 27 28 29 33 34 37 42 46 47 48 51 52 53 55 58 59 60 62 63 64 65 66 69 70 81 82 88 94 95 97 108 109 110
Primary Contact: Norman Lambert, Chief Executive Officer
COO: Melody Henderson, R.N., Ph.D., CHE, Chief Operating Officer and Chief Nursing Officer
CFO: Charles Powell, Chief Financial Officer
CMO: Wallace Mann, M.D., Chief of Staff
CHR: Kelly McDonald, Human Resource Director
Web address: www.goldenplains.org

| | 16 | 10 | 38 | 1230 | 10 | 33572 | 174 | 14396 | 6207 | 138 |

BOWIE—Montague County

★ **BOWIE MEMORIAL HOSPITAL**, 705 East Greenwood Avenue, Zip 76230–3199; tel. 940/872–1126 **A**9 10 **F**2 8 9 12 21 26 27 28 33 34 36 37 38 41 46 51 52 55 58 60 63 69 81 88 93 94 95 96 97 110
Primary Contact: Joyce Crumpler, R.N., Administrator and Chief Executive Officer
CFO: T Kim Lee, CPA, Chief Financial Officer
CMO: Jay Turk, M.D., Chief of Staff
CIO: Tiffany Browning, Director Data Processing
CHR: Mary Bates, Director of Human Resources

| | 16 | 10 | 44 | 1666 | 19 | 27419 | 0 | 11814 | 5843 | 190 |

BRADY—McCulloch County

★ **HEART OF TEXAS MEMORIAL HOSPITAL**, 2008 Nine Road, Zip 76825–1150; Mailing Address: P.O. Box 1150, Zip 76825–1150; tel. 325/597–2901 **A**9 10 18 20 **F**9 12 33 34 41 63 69 78 81 88 97 **P**4
Primary Contact: Windell M. McCord, Administrator
CFO: Brad Burnett, Chief Financial Officer
CMO: Pete Castro, D.O., Chief of Staff

| | 16 | 10 | 25 | 620 | 7 | 28724 | 0 | 7783 | 2828 | 104 |

BRECKENRIDGE—Stephens County

STEPHENS MEMORIAL HOSPITAL, 200 South Geneva Street, Zip 76424–4799; tel. 254/559–2241 **A**9 10 20 **F**2 6 9 12 26 27 28 30 33 34 36 37 39 41 44 46 47 48 52 53 54 57 60 61 63 69 70 81 84 88 92 94 97 106 108
Primary Contact: Robbie Dewberry, Administrator
Web address: www.smhtx.com

| | 13 | 10 | 33 | 1041 | 12 | 19705 | 4 | 7243 | 3351 | 115 |

BRENHAM—Washington County

⊠ **TRINITY COMMUNITY MEDICAL CENTER OF BRENHAM**, 700 Medical Parkway, Zip 77833–5498; tel. 979/836–6173 **A**1 9 10 **F**2 9 11 21 22 24 26 27 28 29 33 34 35 39 40 44 46 48 52 55 58 59 60 62 63 64 65 66 69 81 82 85 88 92 94 96 97 108 **P**6 **S** Franciscan Services Corporation, Sylvania, OH
Primary Contact: John L. Simms, President and Chief Executive Officer
COO: John L. Simms, President and Chief Executive Officer
CFO: Hank Fender, Chief Financial Officer
CMO: Kenneth Landgraf, M.D., Chief of Staff
CIO: Sharon Schwartz, Medical Records and Information Systems Director
CHR: Debra Makowsky, Human Resources Director
Web address: www.trinitymed.org

| | 21 | 10 | 60 | 2275 | 21 | 42383 | 363 | 22854 | 9556 | 241 |

Many Facility Codes have changed. Please refer to the AHA Guide Code Chart.   © 2005 AHA Guide

Hospital, Address, Telephone, Approval, Facility, and Physician Codes, Health Care System	Classi-fication Codes		Utilization Data					Expense (thousands) of dollars		
★ American Hospital Association (AHA) membership □ Joint Commission on Accreditation of Healthcare Organizations (JCAHO) accreditation ○ American Osteopathic Association (AOA) accreditation △ Commission on Accreditation of Rehabilitation Facilities (CARF) accreditation	Control	Service	Staffed Beds	Admissions	Census	Outpatient Visits	Births	Total	Payroll	Personnel

BROWNFIELD—Terry County

★ **BROWNFIELD REGIONAL MEDICAL CENTER**, 705 East Felt, Zip 79316–3439; tel. 806/637–3551 **A**9 10 20 **F**2 6 11 21 22 26 27 28 33 34 39 41 46 47 48 51 52 53 58 59 63 64 65 66 68 69 70 81 88 94 106 110 **P**4
Primary Contact: Mike Click, Administrator
CFO: Cherie Dale, Chief Financial Officer
Web address: www.brownfield–rmc.org

| | 16 | 10 | 42 | 1027 | 8 | 42179 | 105 | 10373 | 4186 | 148 |

BROWNSVILLE—Cameron County

□ **BROWNSVILLE SURGICAL HOSPITAL**, 4750 North Expressway, Zip 78521; tel. 956/544–2000 **A**1 10 **F**2 12 26 27 28 33 37 45 46 49 52 53 59 62 63 65 66 70 81 84 85 88 110 **P**2

| | 32 | 13 | 8 | 469 | 3 | 11327 | 100 | 12423 | 4525 | 73 |

▣ **VALLEY BAPTIST MEDICAL CENTER–BROWNSVILLE**, (Formerly Brownsville Medical Center), 1040 West Jefferson Street, Zip 78520–5829, Mailing Address: P.O. Box 3590, Zip 78523–3590; tel. 956/544–1400 **A**1 9 10 **F**2 9 11 12 14 15 17 19 21 22 27 28 29 33 34 46 48 52 55 56 57 58 59 60 61 62 63 65 66 69 81 82 84 85 87 88 108 109
Primary Contact: Jim Wesson, Chief Executive Officer
CFO: Glen Boles, Chief Financial Officer
CIO: Carlos Morales, Data Processing Manager
Web address: www.brownsvillemedical.com

| | 23 | 10 | 243 | 6390 | 154 | 28013 | 1629 | 37207 | 22752 | 589 |

▣ **VALLEY REGIONAL MEDICAL CENTER**, 100A Alton Gloor Boulevard, Zip 78526–3346, Mailing Address: P.O. Box 3710, Zip 78521–3710; tel. 956/350–7101 **A**1 9 10 **F**2 9 11 12 17 19 20 21 22 23 24 26 28 29 33 34 35 37 39 41 45 46 47 48 49 52 53 55 56 57 58 59 60 61 62 63 65 66 69 81 82 84 85 88 93 94 95 96 106 108 109 110 **S** HCA, Nashville, TN
Primary Contact: Charles F. Sexton, Chief Executive Officer
COO: Cristina Rivera, Chief Operating Officer
CFO: Jay St Pierre, Chief Financial Officer
CMO: Edward H. McGlynn, M.D., Chief Medical Affairs Officer
CIO: Alfred Pena, Chief Information Officer
CHR: Margie Salazar, Human Resources Director
Web address: www.valleyregionalmedicalcenter.com

| | 32 | 10 | 214 | 10796 | 148 | 52511 | 2932 | 94719 | 36608 | 612 |

BROWNWOOD—Brown County

▣ **BROWNWOOD REGIONAL MEDICAL CENTER**, 1501 Burnet Drive, Zip 76801–5933, Mailing Address: P.O. Box 760, Zip 76804–0760; tel. 325/646–8541, (Total facility includes 20 beds in nursing home–type unit) **A**1 9 10 20 **F**2 9 11 12 21 22 23 26 27 28 29 33 37 39 40 41 42 44 46 48 52 54 55 57 58 59 60 61 62 63 65 66 68 69 70 79 80 81 82 84 86 88 92 93 94 96 108 109 **P**3 8 **S** Triad Hospitals, Inc., Plano, TX
Primary Contact: Matt T. Maxfield, CHE, Chief Executive Officer
COO: Jeff Turner, FACHE, Chief Operating Officer
CFO: John Sharp, Chief Financial Officer
CMO: Stephen Oines, M.D., Chief of Staff
CIO: Margaret L. Martin, Director Information Systems
CHR: Mikeana Bailey, Director Human Resources
Web address: www.brmc–cares.com

| | 32 | 10 | 174 | 7234 | 101 | 116883 | 719 | 59997 | 24901 | 594 |

BRYAN—Brazos County

▣ **ST. JOSEPH REGIONAL HEALTH CENTER**, 2801 Franciscan Drive, Zip 77802–2599; tel. 979/776–3777, (Total facility includes 30 beds in nursing home–type unit) **A**1 2 3 5 9 10 **F**2 6 9 10 11 12 15 17 19 21 22 23 24 26 27 28 29 33 34 35 39 41 42 45 46 47 48 50 51 52 53 55 58 59 60 61 63 64 65 66 68 69 71 73 74 76 77 78 81 82 84 87 88 92 93 94 95 96 106 108 110 **S** Franciscan Services Corporation, Sylvania, OH
Primary Contact: John J. Buckley, Jr, President and Chief Executive Officer
CFO: William F. Hyer, Jr, Senior Vice President and Chief Financial Officer
CMO: Mark Montgomery, M.D., Vice President Quality and Medical Affairs
CIO: John Phillips, Vice President Information Services
CHR: Ray Grossman, Vice President Human Resources
Web address: www.st–joseph.org

| | 21 | 10 | 285 | 16040 | 206 | 225013 | 2456 | 165437 | 65206 | 1835 |

□ **THE PHYSICIANS CENTRE**, 3131 University Drive East, Zip 77802; tel. 979/731–3100, (Nonreporting) **A**1 9 10

| | 33 | 49 | 16 | — | — | — | — | — | — | — |

BURLESON—Tarrant County

HUGULEY MEMORIAL MEDICAL CENTER See Fort Worth

BURNET—Burnet County

▣ **SETON HIGHLAND LAKES**, Highway 281 South, Zip 78611–7219, Mailing Address: P.O. Box 1219, Zip 78611–7219; tel. 512/715–3000 **A**1 9 10 20 **F**2 9 12 21 22 26 27 28 29 33 36 37 38 46 48 50 51 52 53 58 60 61 65 66 69 70 81 84 88 92 93 94 96 97 107 108 110 **P**4 **S** Ascension Health, Saint Louis, MO
Primary Contact: Janna Maturo, R.N., Vice President and Chief Operating Officer
CFO: Douglas D. Waite, Senior Vice President and Chief Financial Officer
CIO: Mark Barner, Vice President Information Systems
Web address: www.seton.net

| | 21 | 10 | 28 | 1173 | 11 | 48008 | 0 | 14327 | 7006 | 140 |

CALDWELL—Burleson County

★ **BURLESON ST. JOSEPH HEALTH CENTER**, 1101 Woodson Drive, Zip 77836–1052, Mailing Address: P.O. Drawer 360, Zip 77836–0360; tel. 979/567–3245 **A**10 18 **F**6 9 24 26 27 28 29 33 34 36 44 46 47 48 52 65 69 81 82 84 88 94 97 **P**6 **S** Franciscan Services Corporation, Sylvania, OH
Primary Contact: Reed Edmundson, Administrator
CFO: William F. Hyer, Jr, Senior Vice President and Chief Financial Officer
Web address: www.st–joseph.org/

| | 21 | 10 | 25 | 308 | 5 | 31121 | 0 | 7078 | — | 77 |

TX

Hospital, Address, Telephone, Approval, Facility, and Physician Codes, Health Care System	Classi-fication Codes		Utilization Data					Expense (thousands) of dollars		
★ American Hospital Association (AHA) membership □ Joint Commission on Accreditation of Healthcare Organizations (JCAHO) accreditation ○ American Osteopathic Association (AOA) accreditation △ Commission on Accreditation of Rehabilitation Facilities (CARF) accreditation	Control	Service	Staffed Beds	Admissions	Census	Outpatient Visits	Births	Total	Payroll	Personnel

CAMERON—Milam County

CENTRAL TEXAS HOSPITAL, 806 North Crockett Avenue, Zip 76520–2599; tel. 254/697–6591 **A**9 10 **F**2 9 21 33 42 48 68 69 81 82 88 92 97 107 108 **P**8
Primary Contact: Tariq Mahmood, Chief Executive Officer

| | 33 | 10 | 34 | 1214 | 10 | 7208 | 1 | — | — | 65 |

CANADIAN—Hemphill County

HEMPHILL COUNTY HOSPITAL, 1020 South Fourth Street, Zip 79014–3315; tel. 806/323–6422 **A**9 10 20 **F**1 6 21 29 33 36 44 46 51 52 53 54 66 69 70 75 81 82 97 108 110
Primary Contact: Robert Ezzell, Administrator
Web address: www.hch.dst.tx.us

| | 16 | 10 | 19 | 147 | 2 | 10849 | 1 | 4272 | 1711 | 60 |

CARRIZO SPRINGS—Dimmit County

DIMMIT COUNTY MEMORIAL HOSPITAL, 704 Hospital Drive, Zip 78834–3836; tel. 830/876–2424 **A**9 10 20 **F**9 11 26 27 28 33 34 46 51 52 55 59 63 66 69 81 88 97
Primary Contact: Ernest Flores, Jr, Administrator

| | 13 | 10 | 35 | 1111 | 11 | 26573 | 206 | 8774 | 3838 | 140 |

CARROLLTON—Denton County

⊞ **TRINITY MEDICAL CENTER**, 4343 North Josey Lane, Zip 75010–4691; tel. 972/492–1010 **A**1 9 10 **F**2 9 10 11 12 15 21 22 23 26 27 28 29 33 37 39 42 44 46 48 52 55 56 57 58 59 61 62 63 65 66 81 82 83 84 85 87 88 89 90 93 94 95 96 108 109 **S** TENET Healthcare Corporation, Dallas, TX
Primary Contact: Ernie Bovio, Chief Executive Officer
COO: Spencer Turner, Chief Operating Officer
CFO: Roger D. Hutchins, Chief Financial Officer
CIO: Paul Ratcliff, Director Information Services
Web address: www.trinitymedicalcenter.com

| | 33 | 10 | 207 | 8244 | 91 | 97084 | 1976 | 97334 | 31774 | 605 |

CARTHAGE—Panola County

⊞ **EAST TEXAS MEDICAL CENTER CARTHAGE**, 409 Cottage Road, Zip 75633–1466, Mailing Address: P.O. Box 549, Zip 75633–0549; tel. 903/693–3841 **A**1 9 10 20 **F**2 9 11 12 15 21 22 23 24 26 28 29 32 33 34 35 37 39 46 48 52 53 55 58 59 62 63 64 65 70 81 82 84 88 94 97 106 108 109 **P**7 **S** East Texas Medical Center Regional Healthcare System, Tyler, TX
Primary Contact: Gary Mikeal Hudson, Administrator
COO: Gary Mikeal Hudson, Administrator
CFO: Jim Holliday, Chief Financial Officer
CMO: Donald Lash, D.O., Chief of Staff
CIO: Renee Lawhorn, Director Medical Records
CHR: Linda Wilkinson, Coordinator Human Resources
Web address: www.etmc.org

| | 23 | 10 | 37 | 1443 | 14 | 40939 | 54 | 14187 | 5878 | 147 |

CENTER—Shelby County

⊞ **SHELBY REGIONAL MEDICAL CENTER**, 602 Hurst Street, Zip 75935–3414, Mailing Address: P.O. Box 1749, Zip 75935–1749; tel. 936/598–2781 **A**1 9 10 **F**2 11 12 21 27 28 33 34 39 46 48 52 58 59 60 63 64 66 69 81 82 88 93 94 **S** TENET Healthcare Corporation, Dallas, TX
Primary Contact: Gary L. Stokes, Chief Executive Officer
Web address: www.shelbyregional.com

| | 33 | 10 | 46 | 1599 | 15 | 23266 | 176 | 11229 | 4549 | 123 |

CHANNELVIEW—Harris County

□ **TRIUMPH HOSPITAL EAST HOUSTON**, 15101 East Freeway, Zip 77530; tel. 832/200–5500, (Nonreporting) **A**1 10 **S** Triumph HealthCare, Houston, TX
Primary Contact: Mike Files, Chief Executive Officer

| | 33 | 49 | 93 | — | — | — | — | — | — | — |

CHILDRESS—Childress County

★ **CHILDRESS REGIONAL MEDICAL CENTER**, Highway 83 North, Zip 79201–5800, Mailing Address: P.O. Box 1030, Zip 79201–1030; tel. 940/937–6371 **A**9 10 20 **F**6 11 12 21 24 26 27 28 29 33 34 36 44 46 47 48 50 51 52 59 62 63 65 66 69 81 88 97
Primary Contact: John Henderson, Administrator
CFO: Kathy McLain, Chief Financial Officer
Web address: www.childresshospital.com

| | 16 | 10 | 38 | 1406 | 12 | 32516 | 217 | 13808 | 5690 | 241 |

CHILLICOTHE—Hardeman County

★ **CHILLICOTHE HOSPITAL DISTRICT**, 303 Avenue I, Zip 79225, Mailing Address: P.O. Box 370, Zip 79225–0370; tel. 940/852–5131 **A**9 10 18 **F**21 26 27 28 33 34 46 48 63 97 **P**5
Primary Contact: Linda Hall, Administrator
Web address: www.chillicothehospital.org

| | 16 | 10 | 21 | 118 | 1 | 5728 | 0 | 1423 | 737 | 26 |

CLARKSVILLE—Red River County

⊞ **EAST TEXAS MEDICAL CENTER CLARKSVILLE**, 3000 West Main Street, Zip 75426, Mailing Address: P.O. Box 1270, Zip 75426–1270; tel. 903/427–3851 **A**1 9 10 **F**9 21 26 27 32 33 34 35 37 42 44 46 47 48 52 53 55 58 63 64 65 66 81 82 85 87 88 93 94 97 106 108 **P**8 **S** East Texas Medical Center Regional Healthcare System, Tyler, TX
Primary Contact: Jack R. Endres, Interim Administrator
CFO: James Hines, Chief Financial Officer
CMO: Angela Tseng, M.D., Chief of Staff
CIO: James Hines, Chief Financial Officer
CHR: Susan Hill, Director Human Resources
Web address: www.etmc.org

| | 23 | 10 | 36 | 1891 | 19 | 19157 | 0 | 10010 | 3772 | 125 |

Many Facility Codes have changed. Please refer to the AHA Guide Code Chart.

© 2005 AHA Guide

Hospital, Address, Telephone, Approval, Facility, and Physician Codes, Health Care System	Classi-fication Codes		Utilization Data					Expense (thousands) of dollars		
★ American Hospital Association (AHA) membership □ Joint Commission on Accreditation of Healthcare Organizations (JCAHO) accreditation ○ American Osteopathic Association (AOA) accreditation △ Commission on Accreditation of Rehabilitation Facilities (CARF) accreditation	Control	Service	Staffed Beds	Admissions	Census	Outpatient Visits	Births	Total	Payroll	Personnel

CLEBURNE—Johnson County

★ **WALLS REGIONAL HOSPITAL**, 201 Walls Drive, Zip 76033–4008; tel. 817/641–2551 **A**1 9 10 **F**2 9 11 12 21 22 26 27 28 29 33 34 35 44 46 47 48 51 52 55 58 59 60 62 63 64 65 66 69 81 82 84 88 93 94 95 96 108 109 110 **S** Texas Health Resources, Arlington, TX
Primary Contact: Brent D. Magers, FACHE, President
CFO: Karen Varnell, Director Finance
CMO: Brent Wallace, M.D., Chief of Staff
CHR: Dianne Mayfield, Director
Web address: www.texashealth.org

	23	10	125	4079	34	51004	606	36279	14609	348

CLEVELAND—Liberty County

□ **CLEVELAND REGIONAL MEDICAL CENTER**, 300 East Crockett Street, Zip 77327–4062, Mailing Address: P.O. Box 1688, Zip 77328–1688; tel. 281/593–1811 **A**1 9 10 **F**2 9 11 12 21 22 26 27 28 29 33 34 39 46 48 52 55 58 59 62 63 64 66 69 81 82 88 94 97 108 **P**6 **S** Community Health Systems, Inc., Brentwood, TN
Primary Contact: Jude Torchia, Chief Executive Officer
Web address: www.clevelandregionalmedicalcenter.com

	32	10	107	3502	33	30055	510	33315	11334	281

CLIFTON—Bosque County

★ **GOODALL–WITCHER HEALTHCARE**, 101 South Avenue T, Zip 76634–1897, Mailing Address: P.O. Box 549, Zip 76634–0549; tel. 254/675–8322 **A**9 10 20 **F**2 9 11 12 14 21 22 26 27 28 29 30 33 34 37 38 46 48 51 52 53 55 59 60 63 69 81 82 88 94 97 108 109 **P**3
Primary Contact: Clarence Fields, Jr, President and Chief Executive Officer
CFO: Vickie Gloff, Accountant
Web address: www.gwhf.org

	23	10	40	1808	18	60958	146	13840	5950	193

COLEMAN—Coleman County

★ **COLEMAN COUNTY MEDICAL CENTER**, 310 South Pecos Street, Zip 76834–4159; tel. 325/625–2135 **A**9 10 18 20 **F**6 9 21 26 27 28 33 41 46 54 55 58 59 60 61 63 69 81 84 88 97 108
Primary Contact: Douglas Langley, Chief Executive Officer

	16	10	25	940	8	4210	47	5882	3468	126

COLLEGE STATION—Brazos County

★ **COLLEGE STATION MEDICAL CENTER**, 1604 Rock Prairie Road, Zip 77845–8345, Mailing Address: P.O. Box 10000, Zip 77842–3500; tel. 979/764–5100 **A**1 2 3 5 9 10 **F**2 9 10 11 12 15 17 19 21 22 23 27 28 29 33 37 40 41 46 48 50 52 55 56 57 59 60 61 62 63 64 66 68 69 81 82 84 86 88 92 93 94 96 106 108 110 **P**7 **S** Triad Hospitals, Inc., Plano, TX
Primary Contact: Thomas W. Jackson, Chief Executive Officer
CFO: Wayne Colson, Chief Financial Officer
Web address: www.csmedcenter.com

	32	10	115	4212	45	23099	1014	49554	16116	365

COLORADO CITY—Mitchell County

★ **MITCHELL COUNTY HOSPITAL**, 997 West Interstate 20, Zip 79512–2685; tel. 325/728–3431 **A**9 10 18 **F**2 6 9 11 21 27 28 33 34 39 48 51 52 53 63 69 81 88 94 97 108 **P**6
Primary Contact: Linda G. Mize, Chief Executive Officer
CFO: Shirley McMahan, Chief Financial Officer
CMO: Dee A. Roach, M.D., Chief of Staff
CIO: Lu Lu Boyd, Information Technology Director
CHR: Sandra Sullivan, Director Human Resources and Payroll
Web address: www.mitchellcountyhospital.com

	16	10	25	659	6	23892	17	10403	4305	200

COLUMBUS—Colorado County

★ **COLUMBUS COMMUNITY HOSPITAL**, 110 Shult Drive, Zip 78934–3010, Mailing Address: P.O. Box 865, Zip 78934–0865; tel. 979/732–2371 **A**9 10 **F**9 11 12 21 23 27 28 33 34 46 51 63 81 82 88 94 97
Primary Contact: Robert Thomas, Administrator
Web address: www.columbusch.com

	23	10	36	1356	14	36529	191	15693	5117	149

COMANCHE—Comanche County

★ **COMANCHE COMMUNITY HOSPITAL**, 211 South Austin Street, Zip 76442–3224; tel. 325/356–5241 **A**9 10 **F**6 9 21 27 28 33 34 36 37 38 39 41 51 52 53 58 59 60 62 63 66 69 75 81 94 96 97 108 110 **P**4
Primary Contact: W. Evan Moore, CHE, District Chief Executive Officer
COO: Michael K. Hare, Administrator
CFO: Pam Rice, Chief Financial Officer
CMO: Howard Dickey, D.O., Chief of Staff
CIO: Bill Moore, Chief Information Officer
CHR: Leisha Hodges, Human Resources

	16	10	19	893	10	33580	1	8868	3760	155

COMMERCE—Hunt County

★ **PRESBYTERIAN HOSPITAL OF COMMERCE**, 2900 Sterling Hart Drive, Zip 75428; tel. 903/886–3161 **A**1 9 10 18 **F**2 9 21 22 26 27 33 46 58 64 66 69 81 88 92 94 97 108
Web address: www.hmhd.org

	16	10	24	574	6	7499	0	5764	2680	45

TX

Hospital, Address, Telephone, Approval, Facility, and Physician Codes, Health Care System	Classi-fication Codes		Utilization Data					Expense (thousands) of dollars		
★ American Hospital Association (AHA) membership □ Joint Commission on Accreditation of Healthcare Organizations (JCAHO) accreditation ○ American Osteopathic Association (AOA) accreditation △ Commission on Accreditation of Rehabilitation Facilities (CARF) accreditation	Control	Service	Staffed Beds	Admissions	Census	Outpatient Visits	Births	Total	Payroll	Personnel

CONROE—Montgomery County

⊠ **CONROE REGIONAL MEDICAL CENTER**, 504 Medical Boulevard, Zip 77304; Mailing Address: P.O. Box 1538, Zip 77305–1538; tel. 936/539–1111 **A**1 9 10 **F**2 9 10 11 12 14 15 17 19 21 23 26 27 28 29 33 34 37 41 46 47 48 52 53 55 56 57 58 59 61 62 63 64 65 69 79 80 81 82 84 85 87 88 93 94 96 106 108 109 110 **S** HCA, Nashville, TN
Primary Contact: Jerry A. Nash, Chief Executive Officer
COO: Russell Pigg, Chief Operating Officer
CFO: Patricia Williams, Chief Financial Officer
CIO: Daniel Andresen, Director Information Services
CHR: Diana Howell, Director Human Resources
Web address: www.conroeregional.com

	33	10	266	13524	187	101326	958	152188	51033	1004

⊠ **HEALTHSOUTH REHABILITATION HOSPITAL OF NORTH HOUSTON**, 18550 I 45 South, Zip 77384; tel. 281/364–2000 **A**1 9 10 **F**2 21 22 26 27 28 29 35 37 44 46 48 52 53 58 60 62 65 66 68 69 93 94 96 110 **S** HEALTHSOUTH Corporation, Birmingham, AL
Primary Contact: Robyne Pack, Administrator
CFO: Rob Tyler, Chief Financial Officer
CMO: Ben Agana, Medical Director
CHR: Becky Guenther, Human Resources Manager
Web address: www.healthsouth.com

	33	46	73	1385	52	9723	0	11650	6893	158

□ **SELECT SPECIALTY HOSPITAL–CONROE**, 506 Medical Center Boulevard, Zip 77304; tel. 936/538–3158 **A**1 10 **F**2 21 27 28 57 65 66 94 110 **P**8
Primary Contact: Vivien Bond, Chief Executive Officer

	33	80	46	451	29	0	0	11807	4582	—

CORPUS CHRISTI—Nueces County

⊠ △ **CHRISTUS SPOHN HOSPITAL CORPUS CHRISTI MEMORIAL**, 2606 Hospital Boulevard, Zip 78405–1818, Mailing Address: P.O. Box 5280, Zip 78465–5280; tel. 361/902–4000, (Includes CHRISTUS SPOHN HOSPITAL CORPUS CHRISTI SHORELINE, 600 Elizabeth Street, Zip 78404–2235; tel. 361/881–3000; CHRISTUS SPOHN HOSPITAL CORPUS CHRISTUS SOUTH, 5950 Saratoga, Zip 78414–4100; tel. 361/985–5000; Michael T. Johnson, Vice President and Administrator), (Total facility includes 24 beds in nursing home–type unit) **A**1 2 3 5 7 9 10 **F**2 4 9 11 12 13 14 15 17 19 21 22 23 26 27 28 29 31 32 33 34 36 39 40 41 44 45 46 47 48 49 52 53 55 57 58 59 60 61 62 63 64 65 66 68 69 70 71 72 73 74 75 76 77 78 81 82 84 85 87 88 92 94 96 108 109 110 **P**8 **S** Christus Health, Irving, TX
Primary Contact: Peter Banko, Vice President and Administrator
CFO: Ferd Gaenzel, Chief Financial Officer
CMO: Richard Davis, M.D., Vice President Medical Affairs
CHR: Sylvia Guzman, Director Human Resources
Web address: www.christusspohn.org

	21	10	784	34792	564	333270	3642	363427	131043	3413

⊠ **CORPUS CHRISTI MEDICAL CENTER**, 3315 South Alameda Street, Zip 78411–1883, Mailing Address: P.O. Box 8991, Zip 78468–8991; tel. 361/761–1400, (Total facility includes 26 beds in nursing home–type unit) (Nonreporting) **A**1 9 **S** HCA, Nashville, TN
Primary Contact: Steve Woerner, Chief Executive Officer
CFO: Chris Nicosia, Chief Financial Officer
CMO: Deborah Carver, M.D., Chief of Staff
CIO: Sharon Orton, Director Information Services and Technology
CHR: Michael Conwill, Director, Human Resources
Web address: www.ccmedicalcenter.com

	32	10	237	—	—	—	—	—	—	—

⊠ **CORPUS CHRISTI MEDICAL CENTER BAY AREA**, 7101 South Padre Island Drive, Zip 78412–4999; tel. 361/985–1200, (Total facility includes 26 beds in nursing home–type unit) **A**1 9 10 12 13 **F**2 9 11 12 14 15 17 19 21 22 23 26 27 28 29 32 33 35 39 41 46 47 48 50 52 53 55 56 57 58 59 60 61 62 63 64 65 66 69 70 79 81 82 84 85 87 88 92 93 94 95 108 109 110 **P**8 **S** HCA, Nashville, TN
Primary Contact: Steve Woerner, Chief Executive Officer
COO: Howard Ainsley, Chief Operating Officer
CFO: Chris Nicosia, Chief Financial Officer
Web address: www.ccmedicalcenter.com

	32	10	325	15755	222	86413	3402	141656	50477	1201

□ **CORPUS CHRISTI SPECIALTY HOSPITAL**, 1310 Third Street, Zip 78404–2208; tel. 361/888–4323 **A**1 9 10 **F**2 21 22 26 27 28 37 38 46 49 53 58 60 65 70 94 106 110 **P**5 **S** Integrated Health Services, Sparks Glencoe, MD
Primary Contact: Sammy E. Davis, Administrator

	33	80	31	300	22	0	0	7669	1528	84

⊠ **DRISCOLL CHILDREN'S HOSPITAL**, 3533 South Alameda Street, Zip 78411–1785, Mailing Address: P.O. Box 6530, Zip 78466–6530; tel. 361/694–5000 **A**1 3 5 9 10 **F**2 6 9 16 18 20 21 22 23 24 26 27 28 29 31 32 33 37 39 41 42 45 46 47 48 49 50 52 53 56 57 58 60 61 62 63 64 65 66 67 69 70 81 82 84 87 88 90 93 94 95 96 98 107 108 110 **P**3
Primary Contact: Rick W. Merrill, President and Chief Executive Officer
COO: Ron Cheadle, Chief Operating Officer
CFO: Bob Martel, Chief Financial Officer
CIO: Tom Schoenig, Director Information Systems
CHR: Bill Larsen, Vice President Human Resources
Web address: www.driscollchildrens.org

	23	50	169	6498	91	122409	0	135954	52993	1496

TX

Many Facility Codes have changed. Please refer to the AHA Guide Code Chart. © 2005 AHA Guide

Hospital, Address, Telephone, Approval, Facility, and Physician Codes, Health Care System	Classi-fication Codes		Utilization Data					Expense (thousands) of dollars		
★ American Hospital Association (AHA) membership □ Joint Commission on Accreditation of Healthcare Organizations (JCAHO) accreditation ○ American Osteopathic Association (AOA) accreditation △ Commission on Accreditation of Rehabilitation Facilities (CARF) accreditation	Control	Service	Staffed Beds	Admissions	Census	Outpatient Visits	Births	Total	Payroll	Personnel
★ **DUBUIS HOSPITAL OF CORPUS CHRISTI**, 600 Elizabeth Street, 3rd Floor, Zip 78404; tel. 361/881–3640 **A**10 **F**2 15 17 19 21 22 23 26 38 49 53 57 58 61 62 64 81 82 84 86 88 94 110 **S** Dubuis Health System, Houston, TX Primary Contact: Tracey S. Richard, Administrator Web address: www.dubuis.org	21	80	12	102	9	0	0	4117	1657	43
★ **NAVAL HOSPITAL**, 10651 E Street, Zip 78419–5131; tel. 361/961–2688, (Nonreporting) **S** Bureau of Medicine and Surgery, Department of the Navy, Washington, DC Primary Contact: Captain James P. Rice, Commanding Officicer COO: Captain Eleanor Valentin, MSN, USN, Executive Officer CFO: Lieutenant Gerald Hall, Comptroller CMO: Captain Laura Omer, Director Medical Services CHR: Earlene Moreno, Human Resources Liaison Web address: www.nhcc.med.navy.mil	43	10	25	—	—	—	—	—	—	—
□ **PADRE BEHAVIORAL HOSPITAL**, 6629 Wooldridge Road, Zip 78414; tel. 361/986–9444 **A**1 10 **F**3 4 21 26 27 28 29 58 65 66 71 72 73 74 77 94 96 Primary Contact: Sharon Medors, Chief Executive Officer	33	22	68	1681	46	3164	0	6853	3642	119
□ △ **WARM SPRINGS REHABILITATION HOSPITAL**, 2606 Hospital Boulevard, Zip 78405–1818; tel. 361/888–4458 **A**1 7 10 **F**21 22 26 27 28 52 68 69 94 96 **S** Warm Springs Rehabilitation System, San Antonio, TX Primary Contact: Patrick Flannery, Administrator Web address: www.warmsprings.org	23	46	22	546	18	3296	0	5883	2546	57
CORSICANA—Navarro County										
⊠ **NAVARRO REGIONAL HOSPITAL**, 3201 West State Highway 22, Zip 75110–2469; tel. 903/654–6800, (Total facility includes 17 beds in nursing home–type unit) **A**1 9 10 19 **F**2 9 11 12 15 21 22 26 27 28 32 33 37 40 46 48 49 50 53 55 57 58 59 61 62 63 64 66 68 69 81 84 88 92 94 108 110 **S** Triad Hospitals, Inc., Plano, TX Primary Contact: Nancy A. Byrnes, Chief Executive Officer CFO: Linda King, Interim Financial Officer CMO: Gary Hart, M.D., Chief Medical Officer CIO: James Fairbanks, Director General Services CHR: Sarah Covert, Director, Human Resources Web address: www.navarrohospital.com	32	10	144	4176	50	36837	514	35003	13797	308
CRANE—Crane County										
★ **CRANE MEMORIAL HOSPITAL**, 1310 South Alford Street, Zip 79731–3899; tel. 432/558–3555 **A**9 10 18 **F**2 24 26 27 28 33 46 47 48 52 63 65 70 **P**6 Primary Contact: David L. Whitaker, Chief Executive Officer	13	10	25	252	1	11184	0	3336	1433	34
CROCKETT—Houston County										
⊠ **EAST TEXAS MEDICAL CENTER CROCKETT**, 1100 Loop 304 East, Zip 75835–1810; tel. 936/546–3862 **A**1 9 10 20 **F**2 9 11 12 15 16 17 18 21 24 26 27 28 29 33 34 39 42 45 46 48 50 52 55 58 59 61 62 63 66 70 81 82 84 87 88 94 96 97 107 108 **P**5 7 **S** East Texas Medical Center Regional Healthcare System, Tyler, TX Primary Contact: Terry Cutler, Administrator and Chief Operating Officer Web address: www.etmc.org	23	10	54	2467	26	28390	170	18626	7043	224
CROSBYTON—Crosby County										
CROSBYTON CLINIC HOSPITAL, 710 West Main Street, Zip 79322–2143; tel. 806/675–2382 **A**9 10 18 20 **F**6 8 21 29 33 37 38 39 41 44 45 46 47 48 50 51 52 66 69 81 84 88 91 94 95 97 **P**6 **S** Covenant Health System, Lubbock, TX Primary Contact: John D. Brock, Chief Executive Officer	23	10	25	944	11	13673	0	6127	2870	73
CUERO—De Witt County										
★ **CUERO COMMUNITY HOSPITAL**, 2550 North Esplanade Street, Zip 77954–4716; tel. 361/275–6191 **A**9 10 **F**2 6 9 11 12 21 22 26 27 28 33 34 39 41 46 48 51 52 55 58 59 60 62 63 64 65 69 76 81 82 84 88 93 94 95 108 Primary Contact: Darryl Stefka, Administrator COO: Dick L. Stout, Chief Operating Officer CFO: Greg Pritchett, Controller CIO: Arthur Mueller, Management Information Systems Director CHR: Wanda Kolodziejcyk, Director Human Resources Web address: www.cuerohosp.org	16	10	60	3348	34	239203	244	30666	13606	403
DALHART—Dallam County										
★ **COON MEMORIAL HOSPITAL AND HOME**, 1411 Denver Avenue, Zip 79022–4809, Mailing Address: P.O. Box 2014, Zip 79022–6014; tel. 806/244–4571, (Total facility includes 81 beds in nursing home–type unit) **A**9 10 18 **F**6 9 11 27 28 33 34 41 48 51 52 54 58 59 60 63 69 81 88 92 94 95 97 Primary Contact: Leroy Schaffner, Chief Executive Officer COO: Mary Beth Willard, Director Nursing CFO: Geoffrey W. Hamilton, Chief Financial Officer CMO: Randy Herring, M.D., Chief of Staff CHR: Dee Dawn McCormick, Director of Personnel and Human Resources Web address: www.coonmemorial.org	16	10	102	613	84	10825	94	10824	4071	270

TX

Hospital, Address, Telephone, Approval, Facility, and Physician Codes, Health Care System	Classi-fication Codes		Utilization Data					Expense (thousands) of dollars		
★ American Hospital Association (AHA) membership □ Joint Commission on Accreditation of Healthcare Organizations (JCAHO) accreditation ○ American Osteopathic Association (AOA) accreditation △ Commission on Accreditation of Rehabilitation Facilities (CARF) accreditation	Control	Service	Staffed Beds	Admissions	Census	Outpatient Visits	Births	Total	Payroll	Personnel

DALLAS—Dallas County

A. WEBB ROBERTS HOSPITAL See Baylor University Medical Center

☒ △ **BAYLOR INSTITUTE FOR REHABILITATION**, 3505 Gaston Avenue, Zip 75246–2018; tel. 214/820–9300 **A**1 7 9 10 **F**2 21 22 26 27 28 29 35 45 51 52 53 57 58 64 65 66 68 69 92 94 95 96 106 110 **P**6 **S** Baylor Health Care System, Dallas, TX
Primary Contact: Luci Neumann, President
CFO: Bruce Bickham, Vice President Financial Services and Controller
Web address: www.bhcs.com

	23	46	92	1705	83	29099	0	33507	14723	297

□ **BAYLOR JACK AND JANE HAMILTON HEART AND VASCULAR HOSPITAL**, 621 North Hall Street, Zip 75226–1337 **A**1 9 10 **F**2 15 16 17 21 22 26 27 28 29 47 53 58 60 63 64 65 66 69 73 81 85 88 92 94
Primary Contact: Michael L. Taylor, President and Chief Executive Officer
Web address: www.baylorhealth.com

	32	42	50	2971	13	18354	0	59604	13821	240

☒ **BAYLOR SPECIALTY HOSPITAL**, 3504 Swiss Avenue, Zip 75204–6224; tel. 214/820–9700 **A**1 9 10 **F**21 26 27 28 37 39 110 **S** Baylor Health Care System, Dallas, TX
Primary Contact: Geraldine Brueckner, R.N., President
COO: Geraldine Brueckner, R.N., President
CFO: Julius Wicke, III, Controller
CMO: Michael Highbaugh, M.D., Medical Director
Web address: www.bhcs.com

	23	80	96	1100	81	846	0	29826	12719	217

☒ **BAYLOR UNIVERSITY MEDICAL CENTER**, 3500 Gaston Avenue, Zip 75246–2088; tel. 214/820–0111, (Includes A. WEBB ROBERTS HOSPITAL; ERIK AND MARGARET JONSSON HOSPITAL; GEORGE W. TRUETT MEMORIAL HOSPITAL; KARL AND ESTHER HOBLITZELLE MEMORIAL HOSPITAL) **A**1 2 3 5 8 9 10 **F**2 3 4 6 9 10 11 12 14 15 17 19 21 22 23 24 26 27 28 29 30 31 32 33 34 35 36 37 38 39 42 44 45 46 47 48 49 50 52 53 55 56 57 58 59 61 62 63 64 65 66 69 70 71 73 74 75 76 77 78 81 82 84 85 86 87 88 90 92 93 94 95 96 99 100 101 102 103 105 106 108 109 110 **S** Baylor Health Care System, Dallas, TX
Primary Contact: John B. McWhorter, III, Interim President
CFO: Lydia Jumonville, Chief Financial Officer
CIO: Robert J. Pickton, Senior Vice President
CHR: Mike Adams, Senior Vice President
Web address: www.baylorhealth.com

	23	10	939	38031	644	393049	4169	681828	234264	4215

☒ **CHILDREN'S MEDICAL CENTER OF DALLAS**, 1935 Motor Street, Zip 75235–7794; tel. 214/456–7000 **A**1 2 3 5 8 9 10 **F**2 6 9 10 14 16 18 20 21 22 23 24 26 27 28 29 31 32 33 34 35 37 38 39 42 45 46 47 48 49 50 52 53 56 57 58 60 61 62 63 64 65 66 67 69 70 71 72 73 74 75 77 78 81 82 84 85 87 88 93 94 95 96 98 99 100 101 102 105 107 108 110
Primary Contact: Christopher J. Durovich, President and Chief Executive Officer
COO: J Mark McLoone, Executive Vice President and Chief Operating Officer
CFO: Mike Fichtel, Senior Vice President and Chief Financial Officer
CMO: Thomas Zellers, M.D., Interim Chief Medical Officer
CIO: Richard Duncan, Vice President Information Systems
CHR: Jim Herring, Vice President Human Resources
Web address: www.childrens.com

	23	50	310	15988	209	316366	0	415973	212300	3710

☒ **DOCTORS HOSPITAL OF DALLAS**, 9440 Poppy Drive, Zip 75218–3694; tel. 214/324–6100 **A**1 9 10 **F**2 10 11 12 15 17 19 21 22 23 33 37 39 46 48 49 52 55 57 58 59 62 63 64 69 81 82 84 85 88 93 94 108 110 **P**5 **S** TENET Healthcare Corporation, Dallas, TX
Primary Contact: Mitch Edgeworth, Chief Executive Officer
COO: Jim Beck Brown, Chief Operating Officer
CFO: Gary Singer, Chief Financial Officer
CIO: Dianne Yarborough, Director Information Systems
CHR: Marlene Urbach, Director Human Resources
Web address: www.doctorshospitaldallas.com

	32	10	156	8082	109	81628	698	79450	31980	651

ERIK AND MARGARET JONSSON HOSPITAL See Baylor University Medical Center

GEORGE W. TRUETT MEMORIAL HOSPITAL See Baylor University Medical Center

☒ **GREEN OAKS HOSPITAL**, 7808 Clodus Fields Drive, Zip 75251–2206; tel. 972/991–9504 **A**1 10 **F**3 4 21 26 27 28 42 66 71 72 75 76 77 78 94 96 **P**5 **S** HCA, Nashville, TN
Primary Contact: Thomas M. Collins, Chief Executive Officer
COO: Pam Whitley, R.N., Chief Operating Officer and Chief Nursing Officer
CFO: Jason Tillman, Chief Financial Officer
CMO: Joel Holiner, M.D., Executive Medical Director
CIO: Chebon Bravo, Director Information Systems
CHR: Alexis Johnson, Director Human Resources
Web address: www.greenoakspsych.com

	32	22	97	5718	91	27744	0	21373	11340	276

☒ **HEALTHSOUTH MEDICAL CENTER**, 2124 Research Row, Zip 75235–2504; tel. 214/904–6100 **A**1 5 10 **F**2 21 28 37 45 46 57 60 62 63 64 68 69 81 94 95 110 **P**8 **S** HEALTHSOUTH Corporation, Birmingham, AL
Primary Contact: Russell Bailey, Administrator
CFO: Stephen Embree, Controller
CMO: George W. Wharton, M.D., Medical Director
CHR: Michelle DiSessa, Director Humaj Resources
Web address: www.healthsouth.com

	33	46	106	1717	57	10849	0	29233	11362	197

KARL AND ESTHER HOBLITZELLE MEMORIAL HOSPITAL See Baylor University Medical Center

Many Facility Codes have changed. Please refer to the AHA Guide Code Chart. © 2005 AHA Guide

Hospital, Address, Telephone, Approval, Facility, and Physician Codes, Health Care System	Classi-fication Codes		Utilization Data					Expense (thousands) of dollars		
★ American Hospital Association (AHA) membership □ Joint Commission on Accreditation of Healthcare Organizations (JCAHO) accreditation ○ American Osteopathic Association (AOA) accreditation △ Commission on Accreditation of Rehabilitation Facilities (CARF) accreditation	Control	Service	Staffed Beds	Admissions	Census	Outpatient Visits	Births	Total	Payroll	Personnel
□ **KINDRED HOSPITAL – DALLAS**, 9525 Greenville Avenue, Zip 75243–4116; tel. 214/355–2600 **A**1 9 10 **F**2 33 55 63 69 94 110 **P**5 **S** Kindred Healthcare, Louisville, KY Primary Contact: Dorothy J. Elford, Chief Executive Officer Web address: www.kindredhealthcare.com	32	80	130	1078	72	630	0	30292	14335	256
□ **KINDRED HOSPITAL–WHITE ROCK**, 9440 Poppy Drive, 4th Floor, Zip 75218; tel. 214/324–6562 **A**1 10 **F**21 64 65 66 94 110 **P**5 Primary Contact: Audra Early, Chief Executive Officer	32	80	23	292	21	0	0	6783	3822	62
□ **LIFECARE HOSPITALS OF NORTH TEXAS–DALLAS**, 6161 Harry Hines Boulevard, Suite 100, Zip 75235–5306; tel. 214/525–6300 **A**1 9 10 **F**2 21 22 37 52 64 69 73 94 96 110 **S** LifeCare Management Services, Plano, TX Primary Contact: Louis Bradley, Chief Executive Officer Web address: www.lifecare–hospitals.com	32	80	64	679	47	126	0	20394	8723	149
⊠ **MARY SHIELS HOSPITAL**, 3515 Howell Street, Zip 75204–2895; tel. 214/443–3000 **A**1 9 10 **F**26 33 63 68 69 81 84 **S** United Surgical Partners International, Addison, TX Primary Contact: Suzanne Greever, Chief Executive Officer Web address: www.maryshiels.com	32	13	14	99	1	3761	0	11173	3584	89
⊠ △ **MEDICAL CITY DALLAS HOSPITAL**, 7777 Forest Lane, Zip 75230–2598; tel. 972/566–7000, (Total facility includes 17 beds in nursing home–type unit) (Nonreporting) **A**1 7 9 10 **S** HCA, Nashville, TN Primary Contact: Britt Berrett, President and Chief Executive Officer COO: John Hill, Vice President and Chief Operating Officer CFO: Tim Burroughs, Vice President and Chief Financial Officer CMO: Richard Snyder, M.D., Chief of Staff CHR: Virginia Rose, Vice President Human Resources Web address: www.medicalcityhospital.com	33	10	537	—	—	—	—	—	—	—
⊠ **METHODIST CHARLTON MEDICAL CENTER**, 3500 West Wheatland Road, Zip 75237–3460, Mailing Address: Box 225357, Zip 75222–5357; tel. 214/947–7777 **A**1 9 10 12 13 **F**2 11 12 15 17 21 22 23 26 27 28 33 35 39 41 46 48 52 53 55 57 58 59 60 61 62 63 64 65 66 69 70 75 81 82 84 85 87 88 94 95 96 106 108 109 **P**1 7 **S** Methodist Health System, Dallas, TX Primary Contact: Kim N. Hollon, FACHE, Executive Vice President, Operations CFO: Michael J. Schaefer, Executive Vice President and Chief Financial Officer CMO: John Hinkle, M.D., President Medical Staff CIO: Pamela McNutt, Vice President Information Systems CHR: Tim Meeks, Vice President Web address: www.mhs.com	23	10	204	12477	154	123101	2314	119500	56345	1178
⊠ △ **METHODIST DALLAS MEDICAL CENTER**, 1441 North Beckley Avenue, Zip 75203–1201, Mailing Address: Box 655999, Zip 75265–5999; tel. 214/947–8181 **A**1 2 3 5 7 8 9 10 **F**2 9 10 11 12 14 15 17 19 21 22 23 26 27 28 29 33 34 35 37 38 41 42 45 47 48 49 50 52 53 55 56 57 58 59 60 61 62 63 64 65 66 68 69 70 80 81 82 84 85 87 88 89 93 94 96 101 102 104 105 106 108 109 110 **P**1 7 **S** Methodist Health System, Dallas, TX Primary Contact: Kim N. Hollon, FACHE, Executive Vice President Operations CFO: Randy Walker, Vice President Web address: www.mhd.com	23	10	394	18292	281	118186	3246	246037	105837	2204
□ **NORTH DALLAS REHABILITATION HOSPITAL**, 8383 Meadow Road, Zip 75231–3798; tel. 214/369–7811 **A**1 9 10 **F**26 27 28 46 58 60 68 69 94 96 **P**6 Primary Contact: Pam Duhon, Administrator and Chief Executive Officer	33	46	34	465	15	468	0	4045	2402	66
★ **OUR CHILDREN'S HOUSE AT BAYLOR**, 3504 Swiss Avenue, Zip 75204–6219; tel. 214/820–9838 **A**9 10 **F**21 24 26 27 28 29 37 39 42 52 61 65 66 94 108 **S** Baylor Health Care System, Dallas, TX Primary Contact: Geraldine Brueckner, R.N., President Web address: www.bhcs.com	23	90	37	298	26	44855	0	15804	8397	123
⊠ **PARKLAND HEALTH & HOSPITAL SYSTEM**, 5201 Harry Hines Boulevard, Zip 75235–7731; tel. 214/590–8000 **A**1 2 3 5 8 9 10 **F**2 7 9 10 11 12 13 14 15 17 19 21 22 23 26 27 28 29 31 32 33 34 37 38 39 40 41 42 44 45 46 47 48 49 50 52 53 55 56 57 58 59 60 61 62 63 65 66 68 69 70 71 73 74 75 76 77 81 82 84 85 87 88 89 90 93 94 96 98 101 104 105 106 107 108 109 110 Primary Contact: Ron J. Anderson, M.D., President and Chief Executive Officer COO: Samuel Ross, M.D., Senior Vice President and Medical Director CFO: John Gates, Senior Vice President and Chief Financial Officer CMO: Samuel Ross, M.D., Senior Vice President and Medical Director CIO: Jack Kowitt, Senior Vice President and Chief Information Officer CHR: Steve Mandle, Vice President Human Resources Web address: www.pmh.org	16	10	796	41425	570	1039248	15938	966918	334138	7246
⊠ △ **PRESBYTERIAN HOSPITAL OF DALLAS**, 8200 Walnut Hill Lane, Zip 75231–4402; tel. 214/345–6789, (Total facility includes 27 beds in nursing home–type unit) **A**1 2 3 5 7 9 10 **F**2 4 7 9 10 11 12 14 15 17 19 21 22 23 24 26 27 28 29 30 31 32 33 35 37 38 39 40 41 42 43 44 45 46 47 48 49 50 51 52 53 55 56 57 58 59 60 61 62 63 64 65 66 68 69 70 71 73 74 75 76 77 78 79 81 82 84 85 86 87 88 89 90 92 93 94 95 96 106 108 109 110 **P**6 **S** Texas Health Resources, Arlington, TX Primary Contact: Mark H. Merrill, President CIO: David Muntz, Senior Vice President and Chief Information Officer Web address: www.texashealth.org	23	10	734	33456	447	423208	5865	436896	172526	3706

TX

Hospital, Address, Telephone, Approval, Facility, and Physician Codes, Health Care System	Classification Codes		Utilization Data					Expense (thousands) of dollars		
	Control	Service	Staffed Beds	Admissions	Census	Outpatient Visits	Births	Total	Payroll	Personnel

★ American Hospital Association (AHA) membership
□ Joint Commission on Accreditation of Healthcare Organizations (JCAHO) accreditation
○ American Osteopathic Association (AOA) accreditation
△ Commission on Accreditation of Rehabilitation Facilities (CARF) accreditation

Hospital	Control	Service	Staffed Beds	Admissions	Census	Outpatient Visits	Births	Total	Payroll	Personnel
⊠ △ **RHD MEMORIAL MEDICAL CENTER**, Seven Medical Parkway, Zip 75381–7829, Mailing Address: P.O. Box 819094, Zip 75381–9094; tel. 972/247–1000 **A**1 7 9 10 **F**2 9 10 11 12 14 15 19 21 23 26 27 28 29 32 33 35 37 39 42 44 46 47 48 52 55 57 59 60 61 62 63 64 65 66 68 69 81 82 84 85 88 94 95 96 108 109 110 **S** TENET Healthcare Corporation, Dallas, TX Primary Contact: Joe Thomason, Chief Executive Officer COO: James Murphy, Chief Operating Officer CFO: Karen Bomersbach, Chief Financial Officer CIO: Jacqueline Miller, Director Health Information Systems CHR: Tony Piazza, Vice President Human Resources Web address: www.rhdmemorial.com	33	10	114	5483	72	64564	816	62818	22058	522
□ **SELECT SPECIALTY HOSPITAL – DALLAS**, 10 Medical Parkway, Suite 205, Zip 75234–7845; tel. 972/488–9167 **A**1 9 10 **F**2 21 29 64 94 110 **P**5 **S** Select Medical Corporation, Mechanicsburg, PA Primary Contact: Joy Dier, R.N., MS, Administrtor and Chief Executive Officer Web address: www.selectmedicalcorp.com	33	80	55	461	34	0	0	14187	5548	117
⊠ **ST. PAUL UNIVERSITY HOSPITAL**, 5909 Harry Hines Boulevard, Zip 75235–6285; tel. 214/879–1000 **A**1 2 3 5 8 9 10 **F**4 7 9 10 11 14 15 17 19 21 22 23 27 28 29 31 33 35 45 49 51 52 53 55 56 57 58 59 60 61 62 63 64 65 66 68 69 70 73 75 77 81 82 84 85 87 88 94 95 96 100 103 108 109 110 **P**5 7 **S** UT Southwestern Medical Center at Dallas, Dallas, TX Primary Contact: Sharon L. Riley, President CFO: Richard E. Rentsch, Senior Vice President and Chief Financial Officer CMO: Michael Jessen, M.D., Medical Director CIO: Bob Kamerman, Chief Information Officer Web address: www.stpauldallas.com	23	10	324	12917	197	49942	2113	176030	78227	1169
⊠ **TEXAS SCOTTISH RITE HOSPITAL FOR CHILDREN**, 2222 Welborn Street, Zip 75219–9982, Mailing Address: P.O. Box 190567, Zip 75219–0567; tel. 214/559–5000 **A**1 3 5 **F**2 7 9 21 22 29 32 35 39 41 45 47 52 53 57 58 60 62 63 64 65 66 81 84 86 88 94 96 108 110 **P**6 Primary Contact: J. C. Montgomery, Jr, President CFO: John T. Schoonmaker, Senior Vice President and Chief Financial Officer CMO: John A. Herring, M.D., Chief of Staff CIO: Hunt Gregg, Director Information Systems Web address: www.tsrh.org	23	57	52	2081	23	101121	0	—	—	761
□ **TEXAS SPECIALTY HOSPITAL AT DALLAS**, 7955 Harry Hines Boulevard, Zip 75235–3395; tel. 214/637–0000 **A**1 9 10 **F**2 21 22 26 37 44 58 60 68 94 110 **S** Integrated Health Services, Sparks Glencoe, MD Primary Contact: Cathy Campbell, Chief Executive Officer Web address: www.thicare.com	33	80	66	598	43	5	0	13977	6228	155
□ **TIMBERLAWN MENTAL HEALTH SYSTEM**, 4600 Samuell Boulevard, Zip 75228–6800; tel. 214/381–7181 **A**1 10 **F**3 4 27 28 42 44 45 46 48 52 66 71 72 73 74 75 76 77 78 94 96 **S** Universal Health Services, Inc., King of Prussia, PA Primary Contact: Craig Nuckles, Chief Executive Officer, Managing Director and Group Director Web address: www.timberlawn.com	33	22	124	4866	94	20048	0	15915	6707	164
⊠ △ **UNIVERSITY OF TEXAS SOUTHWESTERN MEDICAL CENTER**, (Formerly Zale Lipshy University Hospital), 5151 Harry Hines Boulevard, Zip 75390–9265; tel. 214/590–3000 **A**1 2 3 5 7 8 9 10 **F**2 7 9 10 12 21 22 23 26 27 28 29 32 35 37 39 45 51 52 53 55 57 58 60 61 62 63 64 65 66 68 69 71 73 74 75 79 80 81 83 84 85 86 87 88 90 94 95 99 104 108 109 110 **P**6 **S** UT Southwestern Medical Center at Dallas, Dallas, TX Primary Contact: Sharon L. Riley, Chief Executive Officer CFO: Jim Wentz, Associate Vice President and Chief Financial Officer CIO: Suresh Gunasekaran, Chief Information Officer CHR: William Behrendt, Ph.D., Vice President Web address: www.utsouthwestern.edu	12	10	152	6548	114	12604	0	106609	40078	590
⊠ △ **VETERANS AFFAIRS NORTH TEXAS HEALTH CARE SYSTEM**, 4500 South Lancaster Road, Zip 75216–7167; tel. 214/742–8387, (Includes SAM RAYBURN MEMORIAL VETERANS CENTER, 1201 East Ninth Street, Bonham, Zip 75418–4091; tel. 903/583–2111), (Nonreporting) **A**1 2 3 5 7 8 9 **S** Department of Veterans Affairs, Washington, DC Primary Contact: Alan G. Harper, Director CFO: Garry Martin, Chief Fiscal CIO: Lucy Rogers, Chief Information Resource Management Systems Web address: www.va.gov/sta/guide/home.asp	45	10	875	—	—	—	—	—	—	—
DE LEON—Comanche County										
★ **DE LEON HOSPITAL**, 407 South Texas Street, Zip 76444–1947; tel. 254/893–2011 **A**9 10 18 **F**6 9 12 23 26 27 28 33 41 46 48 52 53 55 62 63 66 69 81 88 92 94 97 110 Primary Contact: Michael K. Hare, Administrator CFO: Pam Rice, Chief Financial Officer Web address: www.deleonhospital.com	16	10	14	853	9	24223	0	5267	2186	79
DE SOTO—Dallas County										
□ **CEDARS HOSPITAL**, 2000 North Old Hickory Trail, Zip 75115–2242; tel. 972/298–7323 **A**1 10 **F**3 4 21 26 27 28 31 46 48 52 58 71 73 74 76 77 78 106 **P**5 Primary Contact: Wayne Hallford, Chief Executive Officer Web address: www.cedarshospital.com	33	22	76	691	35	12846	0	3589	2755	105

TX

Hospital, Address, Telephone, Approval, Facility, and Physician Codes, Health Care System	Classi-fication Codes		Utilization Data					Expense (thousands) of dollars		
★ American Hospital Association (AHA) membership □ Joint Commission on Accreditation of Healthcare Organizations (JCAHO) accreditation ○ American Osteopathic Association (AOA) accreditation △ Commission on Accreditation of Rehabilitation Facilities (CARF) accreditation	Control	Service	Staffed Beds	Admissions	Census	Outpatient Visits	Births	Total	Payroll	Personnel
SELECT SPECIALTY HOSPITAL–SOUTH DALLAS, 800 Kirkwood Drive, Zip 75115; tel. 972/780–6500, (Nonreporting) **A**9 10 Primary Contact: Greg Floyd, Chief Executive Officer	33	49	48	—	—	—	—	—	—	—
DECATUR—Wise County										
✚ **WISE REGIONAL HEALTH SYSTEM**, 2000 South FM 51, Zip 76234–9295; tel. 940/627–5921 **A**1 9 10 20 **F**9 10 11 12 15 17 22 26 27 28 33 34 37 41 46 48 49 51 55 58 59 60 63 69 76 81 87 88 94 95 96 106 108 109 110 **P**7 Primary Contact: Stephen M. Summers, CPA, CHE, Chief Executive Officer CFO: Jeanna Adler, Assistant Administrator Fiscal Services CHR: Mike McQuiston, Director Human Resources Web address: www.wiseregional.com	16	10	85	4104	34	101291	628	43712	19382	573
DEL RIO—Val Verde County										
□ **VAL VERDE REGIONAL MEDICAL CENTER**, 801 Bedell Avenue, Zip 78840–4185, Mailing Address: P.O. Box 1527, Zip 78840–1527; tel. 830/775–8566 **A**1 9 10 20 **F**2 6 9 11 12 15 21 22 27 28 29 33 34 36 46 48 49 56 58 59 60 62 63 65 66 69 81 82 84 85 87 88 93 94 97 108 109 **P**5 Primary Contact: Patrick J. Jacobus, Chief Executive Officer Web address: www.vvrmc.org	16	10	72	3617	34	55751	1024	31718	13185	366
DENISON—Grayson County										
✚ **TEXOMA MEDICAL CENTER**, 1000 Memorial Drive, Zip 75020–2035, Mailing Address: P.O. Box 890, Zip 75021–9988; tel. 903/416–4000 **A**1 9 10 **F**2 3 4 9 11 12 15 17 19 21 22 23 26 27 28 33 34 37 39 42 47 48 51 52 53 55 57 58 59 60 62 63 65 66 68 69 71 73 75 76 77 78 79 81 82 84 85 88 93 94 95 96 107 108 109 **P**3 5 Primary Contact: W. Mackey Watkins, M.D., President and Chief Executive Officer CFO: Bobby Pruiett, Chief Financial Officer CMO: Robert Sanders, M.D., Executive Vice President of Medical Staff Affairs CIO: Ty Sweeney, Vice President and Chief Information Officer CHR: Minnie Burkhardt, Vice President and General Counsel Web address: www.thcs.org	23	10	205	10230	150	70765	452	106813	43394	1227
TEXOMA MEDICAL CENTER RESTORATIVE CARE HOSPITAL, 1000 Memorial Drive, 4th Floor, Zip 75020–2035; tel. 903/415–4007, (Total facility includes 13 beds in nursing home–type unit) **A**9 10 **F**2 6 21 22 23 26 27 28 39 44 53 58 60 61 64 92 94 110 **P**8 Primary Contact: Verlinda Cobb, Administrator Web address: www.thcs.org	23	10	29	349	13	0	0	2531	1818	51
DENTON—Denton County										
✚ △ **DENTON REGIONAL MEDICAL CENTER**, 3535 South 1–35 East, Zip 76205; tel. 940/384–3535 **A**1 2 7 9 10 **F**2 10 11 12 15 17 19 21 23 26 27 28 32 33 37 46 48 52 54 55 57 59 60 61 62 63 64 65 66 68 69 81 82 84 88 94 108 109 **S** HCA, Nashville, TN Primary Contact: Bob Haley, Chief Executive Officer CFO: Elia Stokes, Chief Financial Officer CMO: Lesa Ford, M.D., Chief of Staff CHR: Elmo Vinas, Director of Human Resources Web address: www.dentonregional.com	32	10	184	9362	133	110306	1179	96379	36614	791
✚ **PRESBYTERIAN HOSPITAL OF DENTON**, (Formerly Denton Community Hospital), 3000 I. 35 North, Zip 76201–3798; tel. 940/898–7000 **A**1 9 10 **F**2 9 11 12 15 17 19 21 22 23 26 27 29 33 37 46 47 48 55 57 58 59 60 61 62 63 64 65 69 81 82 84 88 93 94 95 96 108 109 110 **S** Triad Hospitals, Inc., Plano, TX Primary Contact: Stan C. Morton, Chief Executive Officer COO: Jeff Reecer, Chief Operating Officer CFO: David B. Meltzer, Chief Financial Officer CIO: Ellen Painter, Director Marketing Web address: www.dentonhospital.com	33	10	112	6472	82	29563	1447	58972	24943	532
DENVER CITY—Yoakum County										
★ **YOAKUM COUNTY HOSPITAL**, 412 Mustang Avenue, Zip 79323–2750, Mailing Address: P.O. Drawer 1130, Zip 79323–1130; tel. 806/592–2121 **A**9 10 18 **F**2 3 9 11 13 14 21 26 27 29 33 34 39 41 46 47 48 49 51 52 55 56 58 59 63 66 67 68 69 71 81 88 92 94 97 108 **P**5 **S** Covenant Health System, Lubbock, TX Primary Contact: Clay Taylor, Chief Executive Officer CFO: Suann Parrish, Chief Financial Officer CMO: Christopher Cotton, M.D., Chief Medical Officer CHR: Joy Goodwin, Business Manager	13	10	24	645	6	54628	90	11324	3416	122
DILLEY—Frio County										
□ **COMMUNITY GENERAL HOSPITAL**, 230 West Miller, Zip 78017; tel. 830/965–2003 **A**1 10 **F**21 33 81 88 **P**5 Primary Contact: Tony Ahmed, Administrator	33	10	18	764	5	5545	0	3027	1412	52
DIMMITT—Castro County										
★ **PLAINS MEMORIAL HOSPITAL**, 310 West Halsell Street, Zip 79027–1846, Mailing Address: P.O. Box 278, Zip 79027–0278; tel. 806/647–2191 **A**9 10 18 **F**6 9 11 21 26 27 28 29 30 33 34 36 38 39 41 46 48 51 53 54 59 60 63 64 68 69 81 88 92 97 110 **P**4 Primary Contact: Linda Rasor, R.N., Chief Executive Officer COO: Nathan Flood, Chief Operating Officer and Chief Financial Officer CFO: Nathan Flood, Chief Operating Officer and Chief Financial Officer CMO: Gary R. Hardee, M.D., Medical Director CHR: Nancy Fuller, Manager Human Resources Web address: www.cchdonline.com	16	10	25	692	7	66414	—	9172	3928	138

TX

Hospital, Address, Telephone, Approval, Facility, and Physician Codes, Health Care System	Classi-fication Codes		Utilization Data					Expense (thousands) of dollars		
★ American Hospital Association (AHA) membership □ Joint Commission on Accreditation of Healthcare Organizations (JCAHO) accreditation ○ American Osteopathic Association (AOA) accreditation △ Commission on Accreditation of Rehabilitation Facilities (CARF) accreditation	Control	Service	Staffed Beds	Admissions	Census	Outpatient Visits	Births	Total	Payroll	Personnel

DUMAS—Moore County

☒ **MOORE COUNTY HOSPITAL DISTRICT**, 224 East Second Street, Zip 79029–3808; tel. 806/935–7171, (Total facility includes 60 beds in nursing home–type unit) **A**1 9 10 20 **F**2 6 9 11 12 26 27 29 32 33 34 36 44 45 46 48 51 53 55 58 59 60 62 63 65 66 69 81 84 88 92 94 95 96 97 107 108 109 110 **P**8
Primary Contact: Theron Park, Chief Executive Officer
CFO: Larry Phillips, Chief Financial Officer
CHR: Eileen Kilsdonk, Director Human Resources
Web address: www.mchd.net
| 16 | 10 | 100 | 1829 | 74 | 28776 | 371 | 19503 | 8118 | 274 |

EAGLE LAKE—Colorado County

☒ **RICE MEDICAL CENTER**, 600 South Austin Road, Zip 77434–3298, Mailing Address: P.O. Box 277, Zip 77434–0277; tel. 979/234–5571 **A**1 9 10 18 **F**9 11 12 21 26 27 28 33 34 46 48 52 55 59 63 81 84 88 97 **P**6 **S** Christus Health, Irving, TX
Primary Contact: Steven L. Henderson, Administrator
COO: Steven L. Henderson, Chief Executive Officer
CFO: Noble Anderson, Director of Fin Services
CMO: R Russell Thomas, D.O., Chief of Staff
Web address: www.ricemedicalcenter.org
| 16 | 10 | 25 | 634 | 6 | 18162 | 58 | 6138 | 2375 | 75 |

EAGLE PASS—Maverick County

□ **FORT DUNCAN MEDICAL CENTER**, 350 South Adams Street, Zip 78852–5110; tel. 830/773–5321 **A**1 9 10 20 **F**9 12 21 22 23 27 28 29 33 34 37 42 46 48 49 52 54 55 57 58 59 60 62 63 65 66 69 81 84 88 93 94 95 108 110 **S** Universal Health Services, Inc., King of Prussia, PA
Primary Contact: Alfredo Ontiveros, Jr, Chief Executive Officer
Web address: www.fortduncanmedicalcenter.com
| 33 | 10 | 73 | 4378 | 40 | 28608 | 1048 | 28845 | 12514 | 255 |

EASTLAND—Eastland County

★ **EASTLAND MEMORIAL HOSPITAL**, 304 South Daugherty Street, Zip 76448–2609, Mailing Address: P.O. Box 897, Zip 76448–0897; tel. 254/629–2601 **A**9 10 20 **F**6 11 12 33 41 44 46 47 48 52 59 60 63 65 66 69 81 84 88 94 95 108 110
Primary Contact: John E. Phillips, Chief Executive Officer
CFO: Mark Thomas, CPA, Chief Financial Officer
Web address: www.eastlandmemorial.com
| 16 | 10 | 40 | 1866 | 18 | 21773 | 99 | 10049 | 4570 | 160 |

EDEN—Concho County

CONCHO COUNTY HOSPITAL, 614 Eaker Street, Zip 76837–0359, Mailing Address: P.O. Box 987, Zip 76837–0359; tel. 325/869–5911 **A**9 10 18 20 **F**2 26 27 28 33 34 46 51 52 69 97 108 **P**5
Primary Contact: Dudley R. White, Administrator and Chief Executive Officer
| 16 | 10 | 16 | 162 | 2 | 3979 | 1 | 1933 | 836 | 25 |

EDINBURG—Hidalgo County

☒ △ **CORNERSTONE REGIONAL HOSPITAL**, 2302 Cornerstone Boulevard, Zip 78539–8471; tel. 956/618–4444 **A**1 7 10 **F**2 3 13 14 21 26 27 28 32 33 34 37 39 40 42 44 46 47 52 55 56 58 62 63 64 65 66 67 68 70 71 88 92 94 95 107 110 **S** Cornerstone Healthcare Group, Austin, TX
Primary Contact: Linda Resendez, R.N., Administrator and Chief Executive Officer
COO: Linda Resendez, R.N., Administrator and Chief Executive Officer
CFO: Jackie Rainey, Accountant
CMO: John G. Orfanos, M.D., Chief of Staff
CIO: Martha Cepeda, Compliance Officer
CHR: Erika Betancourt, Human Resource Coordinator
| 32 | 10 | 14 | 835 | 5 | 3290 | 0 | 9038 | 2622 | 111 |

☒ **DOCTOR'S HOSPITAL AT RENAISSANCE**, 5501 South McColl, Zip 78539; tel. 956/664–0036 **A**1 10 **F**2 10 12 14 15 17 19 21 22 23 28 29 32 33 37 39 40 45 46 49 52 53 55 57 58 61 62 63 64 66 70 81 82 84 86 88 94 96 108 110
Primary Contact: Joseph B. Courtney, Chief Executive Officer
CFO: Joe Beck, Chief Financial Officer
Web address: www.doctorshospitalatrenaissance.com
| 32 | 10 | 110 | 2977 | 24 | 52307 | 0 | 51921 | 15019 | 624 |

□ **EDINBURG REGIONAL MEDICAL CENTER**, 1102 West Trenton Road, Zip 78539–6199; tel. 956/388–6000, (Total facility includes 8 beds in nursing home–type unit) **A**1 10 **F**2 6 9 11 12 21 22 25 27 28 33 34 37 39 44 46 47 48 49 52 55 58 59 62 63 64 65 66 68 69 70 81 82 84 85 87 88 92 94 95 108 109 **P**1 **S** Universal Health Services, Inc., King of Prussia, PA
Primary Contact: Daniel P. McLean, Chief Executive Officer
Web address: www.edinburgregional.com
| 32 | 10 | 151 | 8788 | 99 | 33348 | 2091 | 62948 | 23858 | 398 |

□ **LIFECARE HOSPITALS OF SOUTH TEXAS**, 333 West Freddy Gonzalez Drive, Zip 78539–6132; tel. 956/388–1800 **A**1 9 10 **F**2 9 21 26 27 28 44 46 70 94 110 **P**4 5 **S** LifeCare Management Services, Plano, TX
Primary Contact: David L. Tupper, Administrator and Chief Executive Officer
Web address: www.lifecare-hospitals.com
| 33 | 10 | 39 | 475 | 34 | 0 | 0 | 9998 | 5514 | 191 |

EDNA—Jackson County

JACKSON COUNTY HOSPITAL DISTRICT, 1013 South Wells Street, Zip 77957–4098; tel. 361/782–5241, (Total facility includes 37 beds in nursing home–type unit) **A**9 10 18 **F**1 9 26 27 28 33 34 39 44 45 46 48 51 52 58 63 69 76 81 84 88 92 97 108 **P**4
Primary Contact: Marcella V. Henke, Administrator and Chief Executive Officer
Web address: www.jchd.org
| 16 | 10 | 54 | 454 | 31 | — | 0 | 8145 | 3232 | 107 |

Many Facility Codes have changed. Please refer to the AHA Guide Code Chart. © 2005 AHA Guide

TX

Hospital, Address, Telephone, Approval, Facility, and Physician Codes, Health Care System	Classification Codes		Utilization Data					Expense (thousands) of dollars		
★ American Hospital Association (AHA) membership □ Joint Commission on Accreditation of Healthcare Organizations (JCAHO) accreditation ○ American Osteopathic Association (AOA) accreditation △ Commission on Accreditation of Rehabilitation Facilities (CARF) accreditation	Control	Service	Staffed Beds	Admissions	Census	Outpatient Visits	Births	Total	Payroll	Personnel
EL CAMPO—Wharton County										
EL CAMPO MEMORIAL HOSPITAL, 303 Sandy Corner Road, Zip 77437–9535; tel. 979/543–6251 **A**9 10 **F**2 12 21 27 28 29 30 33 44 46 47 48 51 52 53 55 58 60 62 63 65 69 70 81 82 84 88 93 94 96 97 108 110 **P**1 Primary Contact: Steve Gularte, Administrator Web address: www.ecmh.org	16	10	30	963	10	59068	0	12646	5063	134
EL PASO—El Paso County										
★□ **DEL SOL MEDICAL CENTER**, 10301 Gateway West, Zip 79925–7798; tel. 915/595–9000 **A**1 2 9 10 **F**9 10 11 12 14 15 17 19 21 22 23 27 28 29 30 33 34 37 39 40 41 42 44 46 47 48 50 52 55 56 57 58 59 60 61 62 63 64 65 66 68 69 81 82 83 84 85 87 88 92 93 94 95 96 98 106 108 109 110 **S** HCA, Nashville, TN Primary Contact: Douglas A. Matney, Chief Executive Officer COO: Sally Hurt–Steffen, Chief Operating Officer CFO: Julie Hayes, Chief Financial Officer CMO: Manuel Feliberti, Medical Director CIO: Roman Castaneda, Director Information Services Web address: www.delsolmedicalcenter.com	33	10	293	15283	223	141421	2775	133686	52034	1123
★ △ **DEL SOL REHABILITATION HOSPITAL**, 300 Waymore Drive, Zip 79902–1628; tel. 915/577–2600, (Nonreporting) **A**7 9 **S** HCA, Nashville, TN Primary Contact: Douglas A. Matney, Chief Executive Officer	33	46	40	—	—	—	—	—	—	—
□ **EL PASO PSYCHIATRIC CENTER**, 4615 Alameda Avenue, Zip 79905–2702 **A**1 3 5 10 **F**21 26 28 71 72 76 94 **P**6 **S** Texas Department of State Health Services, Austin, TX Primary Contact: Zulema Carrillo, Chief Executive Officer	12	22	64	1189	50	0	0	9700	5036	167
□ **EL PASO SPECIALTY HOSPITAL**, 1755 Curie Drive, Zip 79902; tel. 915/533–7465 **A**1 9 10 **F**2 21 26 29 33 37 46 48 53 58 62 63 66 94 95 **S** National Surgical Hospitals, Chicago, IL Primary Contact: Mitchell McBeth, Chief Executive Officer Web address: www.elpasospecialtyhospital.com	32	47	31	959	8	9124	0	19095	4787	122
□ △ **HIGHLANDS REGIONAL REHABILITATION HOSPITAL**, 1395 George Dieter Drive, Zip 79936; tel. 915/298–7222, (Nonreporting) **A**1 7 10 Primary Contact: William G. Collins, Chief Executive Officer	33	46	41	—	—	—	—	—	—	—
★□ **LAS PALMAS MEDICAL CENTER**, 1801 North Oregon Street, Zip 79902–3591; tel. 915/521–1200 **A**1 2 9 10 **F**9 11 12 15 17 19 21 22 23 26 27 28 29 30 33 34 39 40 41 42 43 44 46 47 48 50 52 53 55 56 57 58 59 60 61 62 63 65 66 67 68 69 81 82 84 87 88 92 94 95 96 108 109 110 **S** HCA, Nashville, TN Primary Contact: Hank Hernandez, Chief Executive Officer COO: Don Karl, Chief Operating Officer Web address: www.laspalmashealth.com	32	10	266	10226	149	73109	1779	104057	36520	921
□ **MESA HILL SPECIALTY HOSPITAL**, 2311 North Oregon Street, Zip 79902–3216; tel. 915/545–1823 **A**1 9 10 **F**21 27 28 37 38 44 45 46 47 48 50 57 58 60 61 65 66 94 110 **P**5 **S** Integrated Health Services, Sparks Glencoe, MD Primary Contact: Evelyn G. Stewart, Chief Executive Officer Web address: www.ihs–inc.com	33	80	32	391	28	0	0	6281	2649	75
★□ **NCED MENTAL HEALTH CENTER**, 1900 Denver Avenue, Zip 79902–1699; tel. 915/544–4000 **A**1 10 **F**1 3 4 21 27 45 52 58 66 71 72 74 75 77 78 94 96 Primary Contact: Hector R. Morales, Administrator CFO: James Blank, Chief Financial Officer CMO: Rodriguez Chevee, M.D., Medical Director CIO: James Blank, Chief Financial Officer CHR: Elizabeth Rayas, Director of Community Relations Web address: www.nced–mhc.com	23	22	30	561	9	4254	0	3364	1582	40
□ **PHYSICIANS HOSPITAL**, 1416 George Dieter Drive, Zip 79936–7601; tel. 915/598–4240 **A**1 10 **F**2 15 17 19 21 22 27 28 33 62 63 81 82 85 87 88 94 Primary Contact: Sharon H. Peterson, Chief Executive Officer	32	10	40	1564	15	12564	0	26881	8850	215
★□ **PROVIDENCE MEMORIAL HOSPITAL**, 2001 North Oregon Street, Zip 79902–3368; tel. 915/577–6011 **A**1 2 3 5 9 10 **F**2 9 10 11 12 14 15 16 17 18 19 20 21 22 23 24 27 28 29 33 34 35 36 37 38 39 40 42 46 47 48 52 55 56 57 58 59 60 61 62 63 64 65 67 69 81 82 84 85 87 88 89 93 94 96 98 106 108 109 110 **P**8 **S** TENET Healthcare Corporation, Dallas, TX Primary Contact: Thomas E. Casaday, Chief Executive Officer Web address: www.sphn.com/sphn/aboutus/providencememorialhospital.asp	32	10	359	20031	259	241054	4288	202623	77554	1683
□ **R. E. THOMASON GENERAL HOSPITAL**, 4815 Alameda Avenue, Zip 79905–2794, Mailing Address: P.O. Box 20009, Zip 79998–0009; tel. 915/544–1200 **A**1 2 3 5 9 10 **F**2 9 11 12 15 21 22 23 26 27 28 29 32 33 34 39 40 41 42 45 46 48 49 50 52 53 55 56 57 58 59 60 62 63 64 65 66 69 70 73 81 82 84 87 88 94 98 107 108 110 **P**6 Primary Contact: James N. Valenti, FACHE, President and Chief Executive Officer Web address: www.thomasoncares.org	16	10	282	15396	181	482619	5074	258572	75683	1695
★□ △ **RIO VISTA PHYSICAL REHABILITATION HOSPITAL**, 1740 Curie Drive, Zip 79902–2900; tel. 915/544–3399 **A**1 7 9 10 **F**2 21 22 26 27 28 42 45 52 68 69 94 96 106 **S** TENET Healthcare Corporation, Dallas, TX Primary Contact: Thomas E. Casaday, Chief Executive Officer COO: Gene Miller, Senior Vice President and Chief Operating Officer CFO: Kristy Waters, Chief Financial Officer Web address: www.sphn.com/sphn/aboutus/riovistaphysicalrehabilitationhospital.asp	33	46	48	1706	48	49165	0	22430	11415	249

TX

Hospital, Address, Telephone, Approval, Facility, and Physician Codes, Health Care System	Classi-fication Codes		Utilization Data					Expense (thousands) of dollars		
★ American Hospital Association (AHA) membership □ Joint Commission on Accreditation of Healthcare Organizations (JCAHO) accreditation ○ American Osteopathic Association (AOA) accreditation △ Commission on Accreditation of Rehabilitation Facilities (CARF) accreditation	Control	Service	Staffed Beds	Admissions	Census	Outpatient Visits	Births	Total	Payroll	Personnel
□ **SCCI HOSPITAL – EL PASO**, 1740 Curie Drive, Zip 79902; tel. 915/351–9044 **A**1 9 10 **F**2 21 26 27 28 47 60 66 94 107 110 **P**5 Primary Contact: Jay Quintana, Chief Executive Officer	33	80	29	295	18	0	0	8985	3300	128
⊞ **SIERRA MEDICAL CENTER**, 1625 Medical Center Drive, Zip 79902–5044; tel. 915/747–4000 **A**1 2 9 10 **F**2 9 11 12 14 15 17 19 21 22 23 26 27 28 29 33 35 37 38 39 42 43 46 47 48 50 52 53 55 56 57 58 59 60 61 62 63 64 65 66 69 75 81 82 84 85 87 88 93 94 96 98 101 108 109 110 **P**8 **S** TENET Healthcare Corporation, Dallas, TX Primary Contact: Thomas E. Casaday, President and Chief Executive Officer Web address: www.sphn.com	32	10	334	13871	185	119393	2257	167129	52540	1101
□ **SOUTHWESTERN GENERAL HOSPITAL**, 1221 North Cotton, Zip 79902–3096; tel. 915/496–9600, (Nonreporting) **A**1 9 10 Primary Contact: Joseph Wright, Chief Executive Officer	33	10	53	—	—	—	—	—	—	—
⊞ **WILLIAM BEAUMONT ARMY MEDICAL CENTER**, 5005 North Piedras Street, Zip 79920–5001; tel. 915/569–2121, (Nonreporting) **A**1 2 3 5 **S** Department of the Army, Office of the Surgeon General, Falls Church, VA Primary Contact: Colonel James J. Leach, MC, Commander COO: Colonel James J. Leech, Commander CMO: Colonel Homer Lemar, Deputy Commander Clinical Services Web address: www.wbamc.amedd.army.mil	42	10	209	—	—	—	—	—	—	—
ELDORADO—Schleicher County **SCHLEICHER COUNTY MEDICAL CENTER**, 400 West Murchison, Zip 76936, Mailing Address: Box V, Zip 76936; tel. 325/853–2507 **A**9 10 18 **F**9 27 28 33 34 37 38 46 48 52 69 85 88 94 97 **P**6 **S** Preferred Management Corporation, Shawnee, OK Primary Contact: Sharon Dietz, Administrator	16	10	14	164	2	3195	0	1958	1200	31
ELECTRA—Wichita County ★ **ELECTRA MEMORIAL HOSPITAL**, 1207 South Bailey Street, Zip 76360–3221, Mailing Address: P.O. Box 1112, Zip 76360–1112; tel. 940/495–3981 **A**9 10 18 **F**2 6 9 24 27 30 33 34 39 41 44 46 48 51 52 60 63 69 70 81 82 85 88 93 95 97 108 109 110 Primary Contact: Jan A. Reed, CPA, Administrator and Chief Executive Officer CFO: Rebecca McCain, Chief Financial Officer and Assistant Administrator Web address: www.electrahospital.com	16	10	23	647	7	15225	0	6079	3132	106
ENNIS—Ellis County ⊞ **ENNIS REGIONAL MEDICAL CENTER**, 803 West Lampasas Street, Zip 75119; tel. 972/875–0900 **A**1 9 10 **F**11 12 21 26 27 28 33 37 46 52 55 58 59 60 62 63 69 81 84 85 88 108 **P**5 **S** LifePoint Hospitals, Inc., Brentwood, TN Primary Contact: Berney Sweet, Chief Executive Officer CFO: Starsky Bomer, Chief Financial Officer CMO: Michael Jones, Chief of Staff CHR: Vickie Howard, Human Resource Director Web address: www.ennisregional.com	32	10	42	2093	13	30137	449	14875	6429	165
FAIRFIELD—Freestone County ★ **EAST TEXAS MEDICAL CENTER FAIRFIELD**, 125 Newman Street, Zip 75840–1499; tel. 903/389–2121 **A**9 10 **F**12 27 28 33 34 46 48 58 63 81 88 94 96 97 **P**7 **S** East Texas Medical Center Regional Healthcare System, Tyler, TX Primary Contact: Ruth Cook, Administrator CFO: David A. Travis, Chief Financial Officer CHR: Jennifer Rummell, Director Human Resources Web address: www.etmc.org	23	10	44	689	6	19531	0	7488	2671	85
FLORESVILLE—Wilson County **CONNALLY MEDICAL CENTER**, (Formerly Wilson Memorial Hospital), 499 10th Street, Zip 78114–2798; tel. 830/393–1300 **A**9 10 **F**2 9 12 21 26 28 29 33 34 42 46 48 51 52 58 63 65 81 82 88 94 96 97 108 Primary Contact: Frances L. Chilek, R.N., Administrator Web address: www.wilsonhospital.org	16	10	31	872	9	34027	0	13483	5958	175
FORT HOOD—Bell County ⊞ **DARNALL ARMY COMMUNITY HOSPITAL**, 36000 Darnall Loop, Zip 76544–4752; tel. 254/288–8000, (Nonreporting) **A**1 2 3 5 **S** Department of the Army, Office of the Surgeon General, Falls Church, VA Primary Contact: Colonel Bernard DeKoning, Commander COO: Lieutenant Colonel David P. Budinger, Deputy Commander for Administration and Chief of Staff CFO: Lieutenant Colonel Eric Dawson, Chief Resource Management Division CMO: Lieutenant Colonel Eric J. Rubel, Deputy Commander Clinical Services CIO: Major Beverly Beavers, Chief Information Management Division CHR: Major Rick Dixon, Chief, Personnel Division Web address: www.hood-meddac.army.mil	42	10	109	—	—	—	—	—	—	—
FORT SAM HOUSTON—Bexar County ⊞ **BROOKE ARMY MEDICAL CENTER**, 3851 Roger Brookes Drive, Zip 78234–6200; tel. 210/916–4141, (Nonreporting) **A**1 2 3 5 **S** Department of the Army, Office of the Surgeon General, Falls Church, VA Primary Contact: Brigadier General C. William Fox, Jr, Deputy Commander for Administration COO: Colonel John Shero, Deputy Commander for Administration CFO: Lieutenant Colonel Talford Mindingal, Chief Resource Management Division CMO: Colonel Carlos Angueira, Deputy Commander Clinical Services CIO: Lieutenant Colonel Hailey Windham, Chief Information Management Web address: www.gprmc.amedd.army.mil	42	10	226	—	—	—	—	—	—	—

Many Facility Codes have changed. Please refer to the AHA Guide Code Chart. © 2005 AHA Guide

Hospital, Address, Telephone, Approval, Facility, and Physician Codes, Health Care System	Classi-fication Codes		Utilization Data					Expense (thousands) of dollars		
★ American Hospital Association (AHA) membership □ Joint Commission on Accreditation of Healthcare Organizations (JCAHO) accreditation ○ American Osteopathic Association (AOA) accreditation △ Commission on Accreditation of Rehabilitation Facilities (CARF) accreditation	Control	Service	Staffed Beds	Admissions	Census	Outpatient Visits	Births	Total	Payroll	Personnel

FORT STOCKTON—Pecos County

★ **PECOS COUNTY MEMORIAL HOSPITAL**, 387 West I. H–10, Zip 79735–8912,
Mailing Address: P.O. Box 1648, Zip 79735–1648; tel. 432/336–2241 **A**9 10 20
F2 9 11 21 26 27 28 29 33 34 41 46 48 51 58 59 63 69 81 88 94 109 **P**5 6
Primary Contact: Russell Tippin, Administrator and Chief Executive Officer
CFO: Leticia Fox, Chief Financial Officer
CMO: Cecil George, Chief of Staff
Web address: www.pcmhfs.com

| | 13 | 10 | 27 | 1339 | 12 | 44287 | 218 | 14477 | 5927 | 195 |

FORT WORTH—Tarrant County

⊠ **BAYLOR ALL SAINTS MEDICAL CENTER AT FORT WORTH**, 1400 Eighth
Avenue, Zip 76104–4192, Mailing Address: P.O. Box 31, Zip 76101–0031;
tel. 817/926–2544 **A**1 9 10 **F**2 3 4 9 11 12 13 14 15 17 19 21 22 23 26 27
28 29 30 31 33 41 42 43 48 51 52 53 55 56 57 58 59 60 61 62 63 65 66
67 68 69 70 71 73 74 75 76 77 78 81 82 84 85 88 92 94 95 96 101 102
105 106 108 109 110 **P**5 **S** Baylor Health Care System, Dallas, TX
Primary Contact: Steven R. Newton, President and Chief Executive Officer
COO: Sandra Aaron, Chief Operating Officer
CFO: Tod Beasley, Vice President Financial Services
CIO: Sandy Vaughn, Director of Information Services
CHR: Julie Strittmatter, Director Human Resources
Web address: www.baylorhealth.com

| | 23 | 10 | 275 | 12904 | 175 | 95540 | 1543 | 169051 | 62444 | 1338 |

★ **BAYLOR MEDICAL CENTER AT SOUTHWEST FORT WORTH**, (Formerly Baylor
All Saints Medical Center at City View), 7100 Oakmont Boulevard,
Zip 76132–3999; tel. 817/926–2544 **A**9 10 **F**2 9 11 12 21 22 26 27 28 29
32 33 55 59 62 63 64 69 81 82 84 88 94 108 109 **P**5 **S** Baylor Health Care
System, Dallas, TX
Primary Contact: Jon Skinner, Executive Director
COO: Sandra Aaron, Chief Operating Officer
CFO: Tod Beasley, Vice President Financial Services
CIO: Sandy Vaughn, Director Information Technology
CHR: Julie Strittmatter, Director Human Resources
Web address: www.baylorhealth.com

| | 23 | 10 | 59 | 2466 | 21 | 30795 | 992 | 22395 | 9257 | 206 |

□ **COOK CHILDREN'S MEDICAL CENTER**, 801 Seventh Avenue,
Zip 76104–2796; tel. 682/885–4000 **A**1 2 3 9 10 **F**6 16 18 20 21 22 23 24
26 28 29 31 32 33 34 35 37 38 39 42 45 46 47 48 49 50 51 52 53 56 57
58 60 61 62 63 64 65 66 67 68 69 70 71 72 73 74 75 77 78 81 82 84 87
88 90 94 95 96 98 99 101 107 108 110 **P**6
Primary Contact: Nancy C. Cychol, President
Web address: www.cookchildrens.org

| | 23 | 50 | 245 | 9702 | 169 | 245008 | 0 | 271605 | 106430 | 1919 |

⊠ △ **HARRIS CONTINUED CARE HOSPITAL**, 1301 Pennsylvania Avenue, 4th
Floor, Zip 76104–2190; tel. 817/878–5500 **A**1 7 9 10 **F**2 26 27 28 35 66 92
94 110 **S** Texas Health Resources, Arlington, TX
Primary Contact: Louise Baldwin, R.N., President
CFO: Cordel Musch, Chief Financial Officer
CMO: John Pender, M.D., Medical Director
CHR: Lisa Beethe, Senior Human Resources Generalist
Web address: www.texashealth.org

| | 21 | 80 | 10 | 105 | 9 | 0 | 0 | 4984 | 1980 | 40 |

⊠ △ **HARRIS METHODIST FORT WORTH**, 1301 Pennsylvania Avenue,
Zip 76104–2895; tel. 817/882–2000 **A**1 7 9 10 **F**2 9 10 11 12 14 15 17 19
21 22 23 26 27 28 29 33 34 37 38 41 46 47 48 49 53 55 56 57 58 59 60
61 62 63 64 65 66 68 69 73 81 82 84 85 88 94 95 96 101 106 108 109 **P**3
S Texas Health Resources, Arlington, TX
Primary Contact: Barclay E. Berdan, CHE, President
COO: Lillie Biggins, Vice President Operations
CFO: Cordel Musch, Chief Financial Officer
CMO: James Osborn, M.D., Vice President Medical Management
CIO: David Muntz, Senior Vice President and Chief Information Officer
CHR: Bonnie Bell, Executive Vice President, People and Culture
Web address: www.texashealth.org

| | 23 | 10 | 553 | 32287 | 455 | 136816 | 6594 | 399276 | 157014 | 3429 |

⊠ **HARRIS METHODIST SOUTHWEST**, 6100 Harris Parkway, Zip 76132–4199;
tel. 817/433–6550 **A**1 9 10 **F**2 9 11 15 21 22 23 26 27 28 29 33 37 38 39
40 44 46 47 48 52 53 55 56 58 59 61 62 63 64 65 69 75 81 82 84 85 88
92 93 94 108 109 **S** Texas Health Resources, Arlington, TX
Primary Contact: Stansel Harvey, FACHE, President
COO: Allen Tseng, Administrative Director
CFO: Vicki L. Galati, Chief Financial Officer and Director Finance
CMO: Walter Halpenny, M.D., Chief of Staff
CHR: Lee Mulvey, Director, Human Resources
Web address: www.texashealth.org

| | 21 | 10 | 85 | 6591 | 64 | 71192 | 1831 | 62534 | 23739 | 540 |

⊠ **HEALTHSOUTH REHABILITATION HOSPITAL**, 1212 West Lancaster Avenue,
Zip 76102–4510; tel. 817/870–2336 **A**1 9 10 **F**2 21 28 34 45 52 57 58 62
65 68 69 73 93 94 95 110 **S** HEALTHSOUTH Corporation, Birmingham, AL
Primary Contact: Sandra Collins, Administrator
CFO: Mike Murray, Regional Chief Financial Officer
CHR: Dori Hodges, Director of Human Resources
Web address: www.healthsouth.com

| | 33 | 46 | 60 | 1161 | 48 | 18406 | 0 | 11999 | 6731 | 179 |

TX

Hospital, Address, Telephone, Approval, Facility, and Physician Codes, Health Care System	Classi-fication Codes		Utilization Data					Expense (thousands) of dollars		
★ American Hospital Association (AHA) membership □ Joint Commission on Accreditation of Healthcare Organizations (JCAHO) accreditation ○ American Osteopathic Association (AOA) accreditation △ Commission on Accreditation of Rehabilitation Facilities (CARF) accreditation	Control	Service	Staffed Beds	Admissions	Census	Outpatient Visits	Births	Total	Payroll	Personnel
☒ **HEALTHSOUTH REHABILITATION HOSPITAL–CITYVIEW**, 6701 Oakmont Boulevard, Zip 76132–2957; tel. 817/370–4700 **A**1 9 10 **F**2 21 28 37 42 45 52 60 68 69 73 93 94 95 96 **S** HEALTHSOUTH Corporation, Birmingham, AL Primary Contact: Jason Jennings, Administrator CFO: Mike Murray, Controller Web address: www.healthsouth.com	33	46	62	1200	51	31240	0	14273	7824	203
☒ **HUGULEY MEMORIAL MEDICAL CENTER**, 11801 South Freeway, Zip 76134, Mailing Address: P.O. Box 6337, Zip 76115–6337; tel. 817/293–9110 **A**1 9 10 **F**2 4 11 12 14 15 17 19 21 22 23 24 26 27 28 29 31 33 35 40 41 44 46 47 48 49 51 52 53 55 58 59 60 61 62 63 64 65 66 69 71 73 74 75 76 78 81 82 84 85 87 88 91 94 96 108 109 110 **S** Adventist Health System Sunbelt Health Care Corporation, Winter Park, FL Primary Contact: Peter M. Weber, President and Chief Executive Officer CFO: Dan Enderson, Chief Financial Officer CMO: Douglas Toler, M.D., President Medical Staff CIO: David Smith, Data Center Manager CHR: Leah Foley, Director of Human Resources Web address: www.huguley.org	21	10	199	10445	123	95180	1157	99953	37639	1035
☒ **JPS HEALTH NETWORK**, 1500 South Main Street, Zip 76104–4941; tel. 817/921–3431, (Includes JOHN PETER SMITH HOSPITAL), (Total facility includes 15 beds in nursing home–type unit) **A**1 3 5 9 10 12 13 **F**2 9 10 11 12 15 21 22 23 24 26 27 28 29 30 31 32 33 34 35 37 39 42 44 45 46 47 48 49 50 51 52 53 55 56 57 58 59 60 61 62 63 64 65 66 69 70 71 72 73 74 75 76 77 81 82 84 88 90 92 94 95 96 98 105 106 107 108 109 110 **P**3 4 **S** Tarrant County Hospital District, Fort Worth, TX Primary Contact: David M. Cecero, President and Chief Executive Officer CFO: Gale S. Pileggi, Chief Financial Officer CMO: John H. Haynes, Jr, M.D., Senior Vice President and Chief Medical Officer CIO: David Paxton, Vice President Information Systems CHR: Althea Williams, Vice President Human Resources Web address: www.jpshealthnet.org	16	10	378	19453	300	686158	5949	391170	136321	3433
□ **KINDRED HOSPITAL–FORT WORTH**, 715 Eighth Aenue, Zip 76104; tel. 817/332–4812, (Nonreporting) **A**1 9 10 Primary Contact: Carol T. Holguin, Chief Executive Officer	33	49	150	—	—	—	—	—	—	—
□ **KINDRED HOSPITAL–FORT WORTH SOUTHWEST**, 7800 Oakmont Boulevard, Zip 76132–4299; tel. 817/346–0094 **A**1 9 10 **F**2 21 27 28 69 94 110 **S** Kindred Healthcare, Louisville, KY Primary Contact: Robert L. McNew, Chief Executive Officer Web address: www.kindredhealthcare.com	33	10	68	957	63	1192	0	22899	10972	203
LIFECARE HOSPITALS OF FORT WORTH, 6201 Overton Ridge Boulevard, Zip 76132; tel. 817/370–6078 **A**9 10 **F**2 21 33 37 38 50 58 60 94 110 **S** LifeCare Management Services, Plano, TX Primary Contact: Barbara Schmidt, Administrator Web address: www.lifecare–hospitals.com	32	10	68	829	60	0	0	21378	10810	216
□ **MEDICAL CENTRE SURGICAL HOSPITAL**, 750 13th Avenue, Zip 76104; tel. 817/334–5050 **A**1 **F**2 10 21 27 33 40 47 53 58 62 63 65 66 81 84 88 104 108 110 Primary Contact: Brad S. Morse, Chief Executive Officer	32	10	34	388	3	7069	0	13471	3147	80
☒ **PLAZA MEDICAL CENTER OF FORT WORTH**, 900 Eighth Avenue, Zip 76104–3986; tel. 817/336–2100 **A**1 9 10 12 13 **F**2 9 10 14 15 17 19 21 22 23 26 27 28 29 30 32 33 37 39 40 41 42 44 46 47 48 52 53 55 57 58 60 61 62 63 65 68 69 70 81 82 84 87 88 92 94 96 106 108 110 **S** HCA, Nashville, TN Primary Contact: Troy Villarreal, Chief Executive Officer COO: Daniela Wallace, Chief Operating Officer CFO: Wayne Gordon, Chief Financial Officer CIO: Kathie Russell, Director Information Services Web address: www.plazamedicalcenter.com	33	10	264	10847	151	50974	0	131138	44811	880
TRINITY SPRINGS PAVILION, 1500 South Main Street, Zip 76104–4917; tel. 817/927–3636, (Nonreporting) **S** Tarrant County Hospital District, Fort Worth, TX Primary Contact: Lily Wong, Director Psychiatry	16	52	34	—	—	—	—	—	—	—

FREDERICKSBURG—Gillespie County

☒ **HILL COUNTRY MEMORIAL HOSPITAL**, 1020 Highway 16 South, Zip 78624, Mailing Address: P.O. Box 835, Zip 78624–0835; tel. 830/997–4353 **A**1 10 20 **F**2 9 11 12 15 21 22 23 26 27 28 29 33 34 36 37 41 48 51 52 53 55 57 59 60 61 62 63 64 66 69 81 82 84 85 87 88 93 94 95 96 97 108 **P**8 Primary Contact: Jeff A. Bourgeois, Chief Executive Officer COO: Peggy W. Brown, Chief Operating Officer CFO: Thomas R. Letz, Chief Financial Officer CMO: James R. Partin, M.D., Chief of Staff CIO: Don Bonacci, Chief Information Officer CHR: Connie B. Hayes, Director Human Resources Web address: www.hillcountrymemorial.com	23	10	84	4462	42	46846	508	36756	16587	497

FRIONA—Parmer County

PARMER COUNTY COMMUNITY HOSPITAL, 1307 Cleveland Street, Zip 79035–1121; tel. 806/250–2754 **A**9 10 18 **F**9 27 33 34 48 51 52 54 58 69 81 88 94 97 **P**5 **S** Preferred Management Corporation, Shawnee, OK Primary Contact: Brandon L. Gatlin, Administrator	23	10	25	277	3	8612	0	3758	1694	52

Hospital, Address, Telephone, Approval, Facility, and Physician Codes, Health Care System	Classi-fication Codes		Utilization Data					Expense (thousands) of dollars		
★ American Hospital Association (AHA) membership □ Joint Commission on Accreditation of Healthcare Organizations (JCAHO) accreditation ○ American Osteopathic Association (AOA) accreditation △ Commission on Accreditation of Rehabilitation Facilities (CARF) accreditation	Control	Service	Staffed Beds	Admissions	Census	Outpatient Visits	Births	Total	Payroll	Personnel

FRISCO—Collin County

✠ **CENTENNIAL MEDICAL CENTER**, 12505 Lebanon Road, Zip 75035–8298; tel. 972/963–3333 **A**1 10 **F**2 11 15 17 19 21 22 23 28 33 46 48 49 55 56 59 61 62 63 64 66 81 82 84 85 88 94 **S** TENET Healthcare Corporation, Dallas, TX
Primary Contact: Lynn M. Mergen, Chief Executive Officer
Web address: www.centennialmedcenter.com

| | 33 | 10 | 72 | 887 | 17 | 7059 | 77 | 24982 | 9641 | 313 |

□ **FRISCO MEDICAL CENTER**, 5601 Warren Parkway, Zip 75034; tel. 214/618–2000 **A**1 9 10 **F**2 21 27 28 32 33 40 46 52 53 57 58 62 63 64 66 81 84 88 93 **S** United Surgical Partners International, Addison, TX
Primary Contact: William A. Keaton, Chief Executive Officer
Web address: www.friscomedicalcenter.com

| | 32 | 10 | 25 | 872 | 6 | 9357 | 0 | 19305 | 7728 | 125 |

GAINESVILLE—Cooke County

★ **NORTH TEXAS MEDICAL CENTER**, (Formerly Gainesville Memorial Hospital), 1900 Hospital Boulevard, Zip 76240–3539; tel. 940/665–1751 **A**9 10 **F**2 9 11 12 14 22 26 27 28 29 33 34 37 39 42 48 49 51 52 53 55 58 59 60 61 62 63 65 66 69 81 82 84 85 87 88 93 94 96 108 109
Primary Contact: Andrew E. Anderson, Jr, Administrator
COO: Lucy Krahl, Chief Operating Officer
CFO: Jeff Davis, Chief Financial Officer
Web address: www.cookehealthnet.com

| | 16 | 10 | 60 | 2463 | 25 | 210000 | 370 | 20510 | 9780 | 293 |

GALVESTON—Galveston County

□ **SHRINERS HOSPITALS FOR CHILDREN, GALVESTON BURNS HOSPITAL**, (Burn Care), 815 Market Street, Zip 77550–2725; tel. 409/770–6600 **A**1 3 5 **F**9 13 21 52 63 65 73 94 108 **S** Shriners Hospitals for Children, Tampa, FL
Primary Contact: John A. Swartwout, Administrator
Web address: www.shrinershq.org

| | 23 | 59 | 30 | 1783 | 15 | 8385 | 0 | 26867 | 13498 | 378 |

✠ **UNIVERSITY OF TEXAS MEDICAL BRANCH HOSPITALS**, 301 University Boulevard, Zip 77555–0518; tel. 409/772–1011 **A**1 2 5 8 9 10 **F**2 3 4 9 10 11 12 13 14 15 16 17 18 19 20 21 22 23 24 27 28 29 31 33 34 35 37 39 40 41 42 43 44 45 46 47 48 49 50 52 53 55 56 57 58 59 60 61 62 63 64 65 66 67 68 69 70 71 72 73 74 75 76 77 79 81 82 84 85 87 88 89 90 93 94 95 96 98 100 101 103 104 105 107 108 109 110 **P**6 **S** University of Texas System, Austin, TX
Primary Contact: Karen H. Sexton, R.N., Ph.D., Vice President and Chief Executive Officer
CFO: Larry Revill, Chief Financial Officer
CMO: C Joan Richardson, Chief of Medical Staff
CIO: Ralph Farr, Director Clinical and Healthcare Information
CHR: Kathy Shingleton, Chief Human Resources Officer
Web address: www.utmb.edu

| | 12 | 10 | 764 | 33819 | 507 | 845210 | 7096 | 527943 | 228147 | 4593 |

GARLAND—Dallas County

✠ **BAYLOR MEDICAL CENTER AT GARLAND**, 2300 Marie Curie Boulevard, Zip 75042–5706; tel. 972/487–5000 **A**1 9 10 **F**2 9 10 11 12 15 17 19 21 22 23 26 27 28 29 33 34 36 37 39 44 46 48 49 52 55 56 57 58 59 60 61 62 63 66 68 69 81 82 84 85 86 87 88 90 94 96 98 106 108 109 **S** Baylor Health Care System, Dallas, TX
Primary Contact: Stanley D. Tatum, President
CFO: Rhonda Chatham, Vice President and Chief Financial Officer
CMO: Mark Bailey, M.D., Chief of Staff
CIO: Michael Larsen, Director Information Systems
Web address: www.baylorhealth.com

| | 23 | 10 | 205 | 10709 | 133 | 88780 | 1736 | 139966 | 53047 | 895 |

VISTA HOSPITAL OF DALLAS, 2696 West Walnut Street, Zip 75042–6499; tel. 972/487–2401 **A**9 10 **F**33 45 55 62 63 64 81 **S** Dynacq Healthcare, Inc., Houston, TX
Primary Contact: James Bryant, Chief Executive Officer and Chief Nursing Officer
Web address: www.lelandmedical.com

| | 32 | 13 | 14 | 138 | 1 | 2244 | 0 | — | — | 81 |

GATESVILLE—Coryell County

□ **CORYELL MEMORIAL HOSPITAL**, 1507 West Main Street, Zip 76528–1098; tel. 254/248–6300, (Total facility includes 90 beds in nursing home–type unit) **A**1 9 10 **F**2 6 8 9 12 26 27 28 33 34 39 41 46 51 55 63 66 69 70 81 88 91 92 94 97 **P**6
Primary Contact: David Byrom, Chief Executive Officer
Web address: www.cmhos.org

| | 16 | 10 | 138 | 1169 | 99 | 34640 | 0 | 16218 | 8483 | 316 |

GEORGETOWN—Williamson County

✠ △ **GEORGETOWN HEALTHCARE SYSTEM**, 2000 Scenic Drive, Zip 78626–7793; tel. 512/943–3000 **A**1 7 9 10 **F**2 6 9 11 12 21 22 23 26 27 28 29 33 34 37 46 48 51 52 58 59 60 61 62 63 68 69 80 81 82 84 88 93 94 96 108
Primary Contact: Kenneth W. Poteete, President and Chief Executive Officer
CFO: Larry J. Hemenes, Chief Financial Officer
Web address: www.georgetownhealthcare.org

| | 23 | 10 | 96 | 4095 | 41 | 92826 | 1206 | 44576 | 19564 | 460 |

GILMER—Upshur County

★ **EAST TEXAS MEDICAL CENTER–GILMER**, 712 North Wood Street, Zip 75644; tel. 903/841–7100 **A**10 **F**9 21 22 33 39 46 52 53 55 58 62 63 66 70 81 88 94 108 **P**7 **S** East Texas Medical Center Regional Healthcare System, Tyler, TX
Primary Contact: Kenneth May, Chief Executive Officer
Web address: www.etmc.org

| | 23 | 10 | 37 | 411 | 8 | 21090 | 0 | 3770 | 1477 | 115 |

Hospital, Address, Telephone, Approval, Facility, and Physician Codes, Health Care System	Classi-fication Codes		Utilization Data					Expense (thousands) of dollars		
★ American Hospital Association (AHA) membership □ Joint Commission on Accreditation of Healthcare Organizations (JCAHO) accreditation ○ American Osteopathic Association (AOA) accreditation △ Commission on Accreditation of Rehabilitation Facilities (CARF) accreditation	Control	Service	Staffed Beds	Admissions	Census	Outpatient Visits	Births	Total	Payroll	Personnel

GLEN ROSE—Somervell County

⊠ **GLEN ROSE MEDICAL CENTER**, 1021 Holden Street, Zip 76043–4937, Mailing Address: P.O. Box 2099, Zip 76043–2099; tel. 254/897–2215 **A**1 9 10 **F**12 21 26 27 28 33 34 44 45 46 48 63 69 81 88 94 96 97 **P**7
Primary Contact: Gary A. Marks, Executive Director
COO: Mo S. Sheldon, Chief Operating Officer
CFO: Hal Mayo, Chief Financial Officer
CHR: Janice Nickell, Administrative Assistant
Web address: www.glenrosemedicalcenter.com
| | 23 | 10 | 16 | 770 | 7 | 29474 | 0 | 11320 | 4590 | 151 |

GONZALES—Gonzales County

★ **MEMORIAL HOSPITAL**, Highway 90A By–Pass, Zip 78629–2021, Mailing Address: P.O. Box 587, Zip 78629–0587; tel. 830/672–7581 **A**9 10 **F**2 9 11 12 21 26 27 28 29 31 33 34 41 46 47 48 51 52 53 55 58 59 60 63 66 69 70 81 84 88 93 94 96 97 **S** Quorum Health Resources, Plano, TX
Primary Contact: Charles Norris, Chief Executive Officer
CFO: Patty Stewart, Chief Financial Officer
CMO: Commie Hisey, D.O., Chief of Staff
CHR: Joni Leland, Director Human Resources
Web address: www.gonzaleshealthcare.com
| | 16 | 10 | 34 | 1522 | 14 | 64670 | 181 | 16600 | 6564 | 206 |

GRAHAM—Young County

★ **GRAHAM REGIONAL MEDICAL CENTER**, 1301 Montgomery Road, Zip 76450–4224, Mailing Address: P.O. Box 1390, Zip 76450–1390; tel. 940/549–3400 **A**9 10 20 **F**6 9 11 12 21 23 26 27 28 33 34 36 41 46 48 51 58 59 60 61 62 63 69 81 84 88 93 94 95 97 106 **P**5
Primary Contact: Blake Kretz, Administrator
CFO: Bonnie Blevins, Chief Financial Officer
CIO: Jeff Clark, Director of Information Systems
Web address: www.grahamrmc.com
| | 14 | 10 | 37 | 1842 | 17 | 56080 | 289 | 14631 | 6964 | 194 |

GRANBURY—Hood County

□ **LAKE GRANBURY MEDICAL CENTER**, 1310 Paluxy Road, Zip 76048–5699; tel. 817/573–2683 **A**1 9 10 **F**2 9 11 12 21 22 26 27 28 33 37 41 46 48 55 58 59 60 62 63 64 69 81 82 84 87 88 97 108 109 **P**5 **S** Community Health Systems, Inc., Brentwood, TN
Primary Contact: Donnie L. Romine, Chief Executive Officer
Web address: www.lakegranburymedicalcenter.com
| | 33 | 10 | 38 | 1986 | 16 | 30394 | 323 | 25187 | 9234 | 221 |

GRAND SALINE—Van Zandt County

★ **COZBY–GERMANY HOSPITAL**, 707 North Waldrip Street, Zip 75140–1555; tel. 903/962–4242 **A**9 10 20 **F**33 34 44 52 63 77 78 81 88 94 97
Primary Contact: William Rowton, Chief Executive Officer
CFO: Laura Preston, Controller
CMO: Richard L. Ingrim, M.D., Chief of Staff
CIO: Becky Champion, Business Office Manager
Web address: www.cozbygermanyhospital.com
| | 23 | 10 | 24 | 1043 | 11 | 10854 | 0 | 6364 | 3015 | 93 |

GRAPEVINE—Tarrant County

⊠ **BAYLOR REGIONAL MEDICAL CENTER AT GRAPEVINE**, (Formerly Baylor Medical Center at Grapevine), 1650 West College Street, Zip 76051–1650; tel. 817/481–1588, (Nonreporting) **A**1 9 10 **S** Baylor Health Care System, Dallas, TX
Primary Contact: Laura J. Lycan, President
CFO: Tod Beasley, Vice President Finance
CIO: Brian Curnutt, Director Information Systems
Web address: www.bhcs.com
| | 23 | 10 | 102 | — | — | — | — | — | — | — |

GREENVILLE—Hunt County

□ **GLEN OAKS HOSPITAL**, 301 East Division, Zip 75402–4199; tel. 903/454–6000 **A**1 10 **F**3 4 21 29 31 33 35 44 45 46 58 60 71 72 73 74 75 76 78 94 96 **S** Universal Health Services, Inc., King of Prussia, PA
Primary Contact: John Baker, Chief Executive Officer and Managing Director
Web address: www.glenoakshospital.com
| | 33 | 22 | 54 | 1735 | 37 | 3199 | 0 | 6545 | 3351 | 112 |

⊠ **HUNT MEMORIAL HOSPITAL DISTRICT**, 4215 Joe Ramsey Boulevard, Zip 75401–7899, Mailing Address: P.O. Drawer 1059, Zip 75403–1059; tel. 903/408–5000, (Includes PRESBYTERIAN HOSPITAL OF GREENVILLE), (Total facility includes 15 beds in nursing home–type unit) **A**1 9 10 19 **F**2 9 11 12 21 22 23 26 27 33 34 46 47 48 51 57 58 59 60 61 62 63 64 65 66 69 77 81 82 84 87 88 92 93 94 96 97 108 110
Primary Contact: Richard Carter, Chief Executive Officer
COO: Patsy Youngs, Assistant Administrator and Chief Operating Officer
CFO: Jeri Rich, Assistant Administrator and Chief Financial Officer
CMO: David K. Fry, M.D., Chief of Staff
CIO: Ricky Gibson, Director Information Systems
CHR: John Heatherly, Assistant Administrator, Human Support Services
Web address: www.hmhd.org
| | 16 | 10 | 162 | 7680 | 88 | 104041 | 1031 | 66597 | 30087 | 648 |

GROESBECK—Limestone County

LIMESTONE MEDICAL CENTER, 701 McClintic Street, Zip 76642–2105; tel. 254/729–3281 **A**9 10 18 **F**2 6 9 24 27 28 29 33 34 46 52 58 69 70 77 81 94 97 108
Primary Contact: Penny Gray, Administrator and Chief Executive Officer
| | 16 | 10 | 16 | 284 | 3 | 19488 | 1 | 5329 | 2629 | 92 |

Hospital, Address, Telephone, Approval, Facility, and Physician Codes, Health Care System	Classi-fication Codes		Utilization Data					Expense (thousands) of dollars		
★ American Hospital Association (AHA) membership ☐ Joint Commission on Accreditation of Healthcare Organizations (JCAHO) accreditation ○ American Osteopathic Association (AOA) accreditation △ Commission on Accreditation of Rehabilitation Facilities (CARF) accreditation	Control	Service	Staffed Beds	Admissions	Census	Outpatient Visits	Births	Total	Payroll	Personnel

GROVES—Jefferson County

DOCTORS HOSPITAL, 5500 39th Street, Zip 77619–9805; tel. 409/962–5733 **A**10 **F**12 21 26 27 33 52 55 62 63 66 69 71 76 78 81 82 84 87 88 94 108 **P**8
Primary Contact: Ronald E. Hand, Chief Executive Officer
Web address: www.renhealthcare.org

| | 33 | 10 | 77 | 1961 | 31 | 19276 | 0 | 20797 | 8595 | 231 |

HALLETTSVILLE—Lavaca County

LAVACA MEDICAL CENTER, 1400 North Texana Street, Zip 77964–2099; tel. 361/798–3671 **A**9 10 **F**9 12 21 23 26 27 28 33 34 41 44 46 47 48 52 53 60 63 64 65 66 69 70 81 84 88 97 108 110
Primary Contact: James Vanek, Chief Executive Officer

| | 16 | 10 | 36 | 828 | 8 | 16265 | 0 | 8236 | 3006 | 109 |

HAMILTON—Hamilton County

★ **HAMILTON GENERAL HOSPITAL**, 400 North Brown Street, Zip 76531–1598; tel. 254/386–3151 **A**9 10 20 **F**1 2 6 9 26 27 29 33 35 39 44 46 47 48 52 53 58 60 63 65 66 69 70 75 76 77 78 81 94 96 109 **P**4 5
Primary Contact: James R. Shafer, Administrator
CFO: Jason Horton, Chief Financial Officer
Web address: www.hamiltonhospital.org

| | 16 | 10 | 24 | 1603 | 14 | 42510 | 0 | 8907 | 3830 | 129 |

HAMLIN—Jones County

HAMLIN MEMORIAL HOSPITAL, 632 Northwest Second Street, Zip 79520–3831, Mailing Address: P.O. Box 400, Zip 79520–0400; tel. 325/576–3646 **A**9 10 **F**2 6 9 27 28 33 34 52 54 97 108 **P**5
Primary Contact: James L. Barnett, Administrator

| | 16 | 10 | 23 | 315 | 3 | 5999 | 0 | 2527 | 1427 | 87 |

HARLINGEN—Cameron County

☐ **HARLINGEN MEDICAL CENTER**, 5501 South Expressway 77, Zip 78550; tel. 956/365–1000 **A**1 10 **F**2 11 12 14 15 17 19 21 28 33 46 48 52 55 57 58 59 62 63 64 65 81 82 84 85 88 109 110 **S** MedCath, Inc., Charlotte, NC
Primary Contact: Richard L. Gamber, President and Chief Executive Officer
Web address: www.harlingenmedicalcenter.com

| | 32 | 10 | 80 | 5571 | 51 | 25867 | 1179 | 55912 | 16976 | 381 |

☐ **RIO GRANDE STATE CENTER**, 1401 South Rangerville Road, Zip 78552–7638; tel. 956/425–8900 **A**1 10 **F**22 27 28 41 45 46 53 58 66 71 74 94 96 106 108 **P**6 **S** Texas Department of State Health Services, Austin, TX
Primary Contact: Sonia Hernandez–Keeble, Superintendent
Web address: www.dshs.state.tx.us/mentalhealth

| | 12 | 22 | 130 | 1414 | 46 | 0 | 0 | 9532 | 5056 | 324 |

SOUTH TEXAS HEALTH CARE SYSTEM, (Formerly South Texas Hospital), 1301 Rangerville Road, Zip 78552–7609, Mailing Address: P.O. Box 592, Zip 78551–0592; tel. 956/423–3420, (Nonreporting) **A**5 10 **S** Texas Department of State Health Services, Austin, TX
Primary Contact: Sonia Hernandez–Keeble, Superintendent
Web address: www.tdh.texas.gov

| | 12 | 10 | 35 | — | — | — | — | — | — | — |

⊠ △ **VALLEY BAPTIST HEALTH SYSTEM**, 2101 Pease Street, Zip 78550–8307, Mailing Address: P.O. Drawer 2588, Zip 78551–2588; tel. 956/389–1100 **A**1 3 5 7 9 10 **F**2 9 10 11 12 14 15 17 19 21 22 23 26 28 29 30 32 33 34 35 36 37 38 39 40 41 42 44 45 46 47 48 49 51 52 55 56 57 58 59 60 61 62 63 65 66 67 68 69 70 71 72 73 74 76 77 81 82 84 85 87 88 92 94 95 96 106 107 108 109 110 **P**6 8
Primary Contact: James G. Springfield, FACHE, President and Chief Executive Officer
COO: James E. Eastham, FACHE, Chief Operating Officer
CFO: Randy McLelland, Chairman
CMO: Christopher Hansen, M.D., Vice President Medical Affairs and Chief Medical Officer
CIO: Jim Barbaglia, Chief Information Officer
CHR: Irma Pye, Senior Vice President and Chief Human Resource Officer
Web address: www.valleybaptist.net

| | 23 | 10 | 482 | 24957 | 277 | 95166 | 2921 | 256406 | 96103 | 1877 |

HASKELL—Haskell County

HASKELL MEMORIAL HOSPITAL, 1 North Avenue N, Zip 79521–5499, Mailing Address: P.O. Box 1117, Zip 79521–1117; tel. 940/864–2621, (Nonreporting) **A**9 10 18
Primary Contact: Bill Nemir, Administrator

| | 16 | 10 | 25 | — | — | — | — | — | — | — |

HEMPHILL—Sabine County

★ **SABINE COUNTY HOSPITAL**, Highway 83 West, Zip 75948, Mailing Address: P.O. Box 750, Zip 75948–0750; tel. 409/787–3300 **A**9 10 18 20 **F**27 33 34 46 60 63 70 81 88 **P**5
Primary Contact: Edith McCauley, Administrator
CFO: Edith McCauley, Administrator

| | 16 | 10 | 29 | 343 | 3 | 5575 | 0 | 3673 | 1323 | 46 |

HENDERSON—Rusk County

⊠ **HENDERSON MEMORIAL HOSPITAL**, 300 Wilson Street, Zip 75652–5956; tel. 903/657–7541, (Total facility includes 16 beds in nursing home–type unit) **A**1 9 10 **F**2 9 11 12 21 26 27 28 29 33 34 37 39 46 47 48 51 52 53 55 58 59 62 63 64 65 66 69 81 84 88 92 93 94 96 106 108 110 **P**8 **S** Quorum Health Resources, Plano, TX
Primary Contact: David Klein, Interim Chief Executive Officer
COO: Joyce A. Story, R.N., Chief Nursing Officer
CFO: Kevin Storey, Chief Financial Officer
CIO: Kelley Fredrickson, Chief Information Officer
CHR: Maria Stephens, Director of Human Resources
Web address: www.hmhnet.org

| | 23 | 10 | 76 | 3390 | 31 | 39759 | 329 | 23747 | 11686 | 241 |

TX

Hospital, Address, Telephone, Approval, Facility, and Physician Codes, Health Care System	Classi-fication Codes		Utilization Data					Expense (thousands) of dollars		
	Control	Service	Staffed Beds	Admissions	Census	Outpatient Visits	Births	Total	Payroll	Personnel

★ American Hospital Association (AHA) membership
□ Joint Commission on Accreditation of Healthcare Organizations (JCAHO) accreditation
○ American Osteopathic Association (AOA) accreditation
△ Commission on Accreditation of Rehabilitation Facilities (CARF) accreditation

HENRIETTA—Clay County

CLAY COUNTY MEMORIAL HOSPITAL, 310 West South Street, Zip 76365–3346; tel. 940/538–5621 **A**9 10 18 **F**6 9 27 28 33 34 41 46 51 63 68 69 81 84 88 92 97 **P**5
Primary Contact: Jeff Huskey, Chief Executive Officer and Administrator
Web address: www.ccmhospital.com
| 13 | 10 | 25 | 398 | 4 | 21754 | 0 | 2631 | 2570 | 99 |

HEREFORD—Deaf Smith County

HEREFORD REGIONAL MEDICAL CENTER, 801 East Third Street, Zip 79045–5727, Mailing Address: P.O. Box 1858, Zip 79045–1858; tel. 806/364–2141 **A**9 10 **F**2 6 9 12 14 21 26 27 29 33 34 39 46 48 51 52 55 59 60 63 68 69 81 88 92 94 97 109 **P**5
Primary Contact: Ray Mason, Chief Executive Officer
| 16 | 10 | 35 | 1070 | 11 | 65952 | 321 | 9288 | 6460 | 197 |

HILLSBORO—Hill County

□ **HILL REGIONAL HOSPITAL**, 101 Circle Drive, Zip 76645–2670; tel. 254/580–8950, (Total facility includes 21 beds in nursing home–type unit) **A**1 9 10 **F**2 11 12 14 21 27 28 33 34 39 46 48 55 58 59 60 63 65 66 67 69 81 84 87 88 92 108 **S** Community Health Systems, Inc., Brentwood, TN
Primary Contact: Jan McClure, Chief Executive Officer
Web address: www.chs.net
| 33 | 10 | 84 | 2860 | 30 | 21208 | 310 | 15117 | 6782 | 164 |

HONDO—Medina County

MEDINA COMMUNITY HOSPITAL, 3100 Avenue E., Zip 78861–3599; tel. 830/426–7838 **A**9 10 18 **F**2 9 11 12 21 22 26 27 29 33 34 35 39 46 48 52 53 59 62 63 66 69 70 81 88 97 **P**4
Primary Contact: Beverly Gruber, Administrator
| 16 | 10 | 25 | 834 | 7 | 69856 | 148 | 11376 | 4818 | 159 |

HOUSTON—Harris County

BELLAIRE MEDICAL CENTER, 5314 Dashwood Street, Zip 77081–4689; tel. 713/512–1200, (Nonreporting) **A**10 **S** AMT Group, Inc., Duluth, GA
Primary Contact: Stephen R. Selzer, Chief Executive Officer
Web address: www.bellairemedicalcenter.com
| 32 | 10 | 194 | | | | | | | |

BEN TAUB GENERAL HOSPITAL See Harris County Hospital District

✠ **CHRISTUS ST. JOHN HOSPITAL**, 18300 St. John Drive, Zip 77058–6302; tel. 281/333–5503 **A**1 5 9 10 **F**2 9 11 12 15 21 22 23 26 27 28 29 33 35 39 40 41 42 46 47 48 49 51 52 53 54 55 57 58 59 60 61 62 63 64 65 66 68 69 81 82 84 85 87 88 92 94 95 96 108 109 110 **P**8 **S** Christus Health, Irving, TX
Primary Contact: Thomas Permetti, Chief Executive Officer
COO: Paul Generale, Chief Operating Officer and Chief Financial Officer
CFO: Paul Generale, Chief Operating Officer and Chief Financial Officer
Web address: www.christushealth.org
| 23 | 10 | 128 | 6327 | 61 | 145447 | 1050 | 64824 | 27577 | 622 |

✠ △ **CHRISTUS ST. JOSEPH HOSPITAL**, 1401 St. Joseph Parkway, Zip 77002–8321; tel. 713/757–1000, (Total facility includes 14 beds in nursing home–type unit) **A**1 2 3 5 7 9 10 **F**2 3 9 11 12 15 17 19 21 22 23 24 26 27 28 29 33 34 35 36 37 38 39 40 45 46 47 48 49 51 52 55 56 57 58 59 60 61 62 63 64 65 66 68 69 70 71 73 74 75 76 78 79 80 81 82 84 86 87 88 90 92 93 94 95 96 107 108 109 110 **P**8 **S** Christus Health, Irving, TX
Primary Contact: Jeffrey Webster, Administrator
CIO: Tom Shirley, Chief Information Officer
CHR: Pam Rhodes, Vice President, Human Resources
Web address: www.christusstjoseph.org
| 21 | 10 | 433 | 16828 | 223 | 194884 | 4777 | 180991 | 73905 | 1739 |

□ **CORNERSTONE HOSPITAL OF HOUSTON**, 5556 Gasmer Drive, Zip 77035–4598; tel. 713/551–5300 **A**1 9 10 **F**2 21 26 27 28 44 50 55 58 61 65 66 94 110 **S** Cornerstone Healthcare Group, Austin, TX
Primary Contact: Larry F. Wittgan, Executive Director
Web address: www.marinerhealthcare.com
| 33 | 80 | 174 | 1415 | 114 | 0 | 0 | 35391 | 14087 | 349 |

□ **CYPRESS CREEK HOSPITAL**, 17750 Cali Drive, Zip 77090–2700; tel. 281/586–7600 **A**1 10 **F**3 4 26 27 28 48 52 66 71 72 73 74 75 77 78 94 96 **S** Psychiatric Solutions, Franklin, TN
Primary Contact: Ronald Mays, Chief Executive Officer
Web address: www.psysolutions.com
| 33 | 22 | 96 | 4362 | 78 | 8482 | 0 | 15837 | 7911 | — |

✠ **CYPRESS FAIRBANKS MEDICAL CENTER**, 10655 Steepletop Drive, Zip 77065–4297; tel. 281/890–4285 **A**1 9 10 **F**2 9 10 11 12 15 21 23 26 27 28 33 37 41 46 47 48 51 52 55 56 57 58 59 60 62 63 66 69 81 82 84 85 86 87 88 92 94 95 96 108 109 110 **P**8 **S** TENET Healthcare Corporation, Dallas, TX
Primary Contact: Terry J. Wheeler, Chief Executive Officer
COO: Drew Kahn, Chief Operating Officer
CFO: James Wright, Chief Financial Officer
CMO: Stephen Fischer, M.D., Chief of Staff
CIO: Bob Buckey, Director Information Systems
CHR: Lorinnsa Bridges Kee, Human Resource Director
Web address: www.cyfairhospital.com
| 33 | 10 | 146 | 9790 | 112 | 90275 | 1592 | 84184 | 33517 | 821 |

□ **DOCTORS HOSPITAL PARKWAY**, 233 West Parker Road, Zip 77076–2999; tel. 281/765–2600, (Nonreporting) **A**1 9 **S** HealthPlus, Houston, TX
Primary Contact: Alan A. Beauchamp, Chief Executive Officer
| 32 | 10 | 134 | — | — | — | — | — | — | — |

□ **DOCTORS HOSPITAL–TIDWELL**, 510 West Tidwell Road, Zip 77091–4399; tel. 713/691–1111 **A**1 9 10 **F**2 9 10 11 12 21 27 28 33 34 35 39 46 48 49 52 55 58 59 62 63 69 81 82 84 88 94 108 **S** HealthPlus, Houston, TX
Primary Contact: Alan A. Beauchamp, Chief Executive Officer
Web address: www.health–plus.net
| 32 | 10 | 200 | 8639 | 94 | 43967 | 2220 | 69867 | 27454 | 556 |

Many Facility Codes have changed. Please refer to the AHA Guide Code Chart.

TX

Hospital, Address, Telephone, Approval, Facility, and Physician Codes, Health Care System	Classification Codes		Utilization Data					Expense (thousands) of dollars		
★ American Hospital Association (AHA) membership □ Joint Commission on Accreditation of Healthcare Organizations (JCAHO) accreditation ○ American Osteopathic Association (AOA) accreditation △ Commission on Accreditation of Rehabilitation Facilities (CARF) accreditation	Control	Service	Staffed Beds	Admissions	Census	Outpatient Visits	Births	Total	Payroll	Personnel
✦ **DUBUIS HOSPITAL OF HOUSTON**, 1919 Labranch 7GWS Street, Zip 77002; tel. 713/756–8660 **A**1 9 10 **F**21 22 23 26 27 28 53 57 60 61 110 **P**5 **S** Dubuis Health System, Houston, TX Primary Contact: Stephen Mills, Regional Administrator COO: Sam D. Barkman, Vice President Operations CFO: Paul Veillon, CPA, Chief Financial Officer Web address: www.dubuis.org	21	10	30	320	23	0	0	8780	3628	99
✦ **EAST HOUSTON REGIONAL MEDICAL CENTER**, 13111 East Freeway, Zip 77015–5820; tel. 713/393–2000 **A**1 9 10 **F**2 3 9 11 12 13 14 21 22 27 28 29 33 34 37 46 48 55 56 57 59 60 62 63 66 67 68 69 71 81 82 84 87 88 92 93 94 96 107 108 **S** HCA, Nashville, TN Primary Contact: Todd Caliva, Chief Executive Officer CFO: John Armour, Chief Financial Officer Web address: www.easthoustonrmc.com	32	10	131	6896	77	66227	1070	63882	24817	425
GULF POINTE SPECIALTY HOSPITAL, 6160 South Loop East, Zip 77087–1010; tel. 713/640–2400 **A**9 10 **F**2 21 26 27 28 44 52 58 68 69 94 110 **P**5 **S** Integrated Health Services, Sparks Glencoe, MD Primary Contact: Shelley R. Cochran, Executive Director Web address: www.ihsweb.his–inc.com	33	80	59	411	29	0	0	9765	4066	45
□ **HARRIS COUNTY HOSPITAL DISTRICT**, 2525 Holly Hall Street, Zip 77054–4108, Mailing Address: P.O. Box 66769, Zip 77266–6769; tel. 713/566–6403, (Includes BEN TAUB GENERAL HOSPITAL, 1504 Taub Loop, Zip 77030; tel. 713/873–2300; Terence Cunningham, Administrator; LYNDON B JOHNSON GENERAL HOSPITAL, 5656 Kelley, Zip 77026; tel. 713/566–5000; Margo Hilliard, M.D., Administrator; QUENTIN MEASE HOSPITAL, 3601 North MacGregor, Zip 77004; tel. 713/873–3700; Johnnie Stein, Associate Administrator), (Total facility includes 24 beds in nursing home–type unit) **A**1 2 3 5 8 9 10 **F**6 11 12 14 15 16 17 18 19 20 21 22 23 24 26 27 29 32 33 34 37 39 41 42 44 45 46 47 48 49 50 52 53 55 56 57 58 59 60 61 62 63 65 66 67 68 69 71 72 73 74 75 76 77 79 81 82 84 88 90 92 93 94 96 98 106 107 108 109 110 **P**6 Primary Contact: David S. Lopez, FACHE, President and Chief Executive Officer Web address: www.hchdonline.com	16	10	838	41767	654	1037043	11280	786654	300129	6368
✦ **HARRIS COUNTY PSYCHIATRIC CENTER**, 2800 South MacGregor Way, Zip 77021–1000, Mailing Address: P.O. Box 20249, Zip 77225–0249; tel. 713/741–5000 **A**1 3 5 10 **F**21 22 26 27 28 29 42 44 46 47 53 58 65 66 71 72 73 74 76 77 78 94 108 **P**5 **S** University of Texas System, Austin, TX Primary Contact: Robert W. Guynn, M.D., Executive Director COO: Lois Jean Moore, FACHE, Administrator CFO: Ed Williams, Chief Financial Officer CMO: R Andrew Harper, M.D., Medical Director CHR: Sherri Orioli, Director Personnel Systems Web address: www.uth.tmc.edu	12	22	203	6153	184	8001	0	34532	20298	375
□ **HEALTHBRIDGE CHILDREN'S HOSPITAL OF HOUSTON**, 2929 Woodland Park Drive, Zip 77082; tel. 281/293–7774, (Nonreporting) **A**1 10 Primary Contact: Kathy Roberts, Interim Administrator	33	50	24	—	—	—	—	—	—	—
□ **HEALTHSOUTH HOSPITAL FOR SPECIALIZED SURGERY**, 5400 La Branch Street, Zip 77004–6836; tel. 713/528–6800 **A**1 10 **F**2 40 63 Web address: www.healthsouth.com	32	13	7	196	1	2137	0	4639	1469	40
✦ **HEALTHSOUTH HOUSTON REHABILITATION INSTITUTE**, 17506 Red Oak Drive, Zip 77090–7721, Mailing Address: P.O. Box 73684, Zip 77273–3684; tel. 281/580–1212 **A**1 10 **F**2 7 21 26 27 28 37 44 45 52 57 58 60 69 94 95 96 108 110 **S** HEALTHSOUTH Corporation, Birmingham, AL Primary Contact: Edward Downs, Administrator Web address: www.healthsouth.com	32	80	79	541	35	6872	0	13614	5600	126
HOUSTON COMMUNITY HOSPITAL, 2807 Little York Road, Zip 77093–3495; tel. 713/697–7777 **A**10 **F**10 21 25 27 33 37 45 48 52 55 58 60 63 66 69 81 84 88 94 95 **P**8 Primary Contact: Dan De La Garza, Chief Executive Officer Web address: www.houstoncomhospital.com	33	10	39	1569	14	14409	0	20237	7961	189
✦ **HOUSTON NORTHWEST MEDICAL CENTER**, 710 FM 1960 West, Zip 77090–3496; tel. 281/440–1000 **A**1 2 5 9 10 **F**2 6 9 10 11 12 15 17 19 21 22 23 27 28 33 34 37 41 46 47 48 49 50 52 53 55 57 58 59 60 61 62 63 64 65 66 69 81 82 84 86 87 88 93 94 96 106 108 109 110 **P**8 **S** TENET Healthcare Corporation, Dallas, TX Primary Contact: Louis O. Garcia, Chief Executive Officer COO: Susan Jadlowski, Chief Operating Officer CFO: Ronald L. Watson, Chief Financial Officer CIO: Everett Copeland, Director Information System Web address: www.hnmc.com	32	10	378	18980	271	145269	2438	220493	84685	1720
□ **INTRACARE MEDICAL CENTER HOSPITAL**, 7601 Fannin Street, Zip 77054–1905; tel. 713/790–0949 **A**1 10 **F**3 4 27 28 33 71 72 73 74 75 76 77 78 **P**6 **S** Cambridge International, Inc, Houston, TX Primary Contact: Terry Scovill, Chief Executive Officer Web address: www.intracarehospital.com	23	22	120	3549	81	12683	0	16854	9519	362
□ **INTRACARE NORTH HOSPITAL**, 1120 Cypress Station Drive, Zip 77090–3031; tel. 281/893–7200 **A**1 10 **F**3 4 27 28 33 71 72 73 74 75 76 77 78 **P**6 **S** Cambridge International, Inc, Houston, TX Primary Contact: Teisha York, Chief Executive Officer Web address: www.intracarehospital.com	23	22	68	1974	40	1240	0	7711	4297	144

TX

Hospital, Address, Telephone, Approval, Facility, and Physician Codes, Health Care System	Classification Codes		Utilization Data					Expense (thousands) of dollars		
★ American Hospital Association (AHA) membership □ Joint Commission on Accreditation of Healthcare Organizations (JCAHO) accreditation ○ American Osteopathic Association (AOA) accreditation △ Commission on Accreditation of Rehabilitation Facilities (CARF) accreditation	Control	Service	Staffed Beds	Admissions	Census	Outpatient Visits	Births	Total	Payroll	Personnel
□ **KINDRED HOSPITAL–HOUSTON**, 6441 Main Street, Zip 77030–1596; tel. 713/790–0500, (Nonreporting) **A**1 9 10 **S** Kindred Healthcare, Louisville, KY Primary Contact: Bob Stein, Chief Executive Officer Web address: www.kindredhealthcare.com	32	10	92	—	—	—	—	—	—	—
□ **KINDRED HOSPITAL–HOUSTON NORTHWEST**, 11297 Fallbrook Drive, Zip 77065–4292; tel. 281/897–8114 **A**1 9 10 **F**2 21 26 27 28 52 55 81 93 110 **P**5 **S** Kindred Healthcare, Louisville, KY Primary Contact: Mary Anne Craig, Chief Executive Officer Web address: www.kindredhealthcare.com	32	80	84	836	62	0	0	22135	10176	207
LYNDON B JOHNSON GENERAL HOSPITAL See Harris County Hospital District										
MEMORIAL HERMANN CHILDREN'S HOSPITAL See Memorial Hermann Hospital										
⊠ **MEMORIAL HERMANN CONTINUING CARE HOSPITAL**, 3043 Gessner Drive, Zip 77080–2597; tel. 713/462–2515 **A**1 2 9 10 **F**5 21 22 26 27 28 29 58 60 65 66 88 92 94 96 108 110 **S** Memorial Hermann Healthcare System, Houston, TX Primary Contact: Joe G. Baldwin, Chief Executive Officer Web address: www.mhhs.org	23	80	162	1480	104	3668	0	37442	14480	358
⊠ **MEMORIAL HERMANN HOSPITAL**, 6411 Fannin, Zip 77030–1501; tel. 713/704–4000, (Includes MEMORIAL HERMANN CHILDREN'S HOSPITAL, tel. 713/704–5437; MEMORIAL HERMANN THE WOODLANDS HOSPITAL, 9250 Pinecroft Drive, The Woodlands, Zip 77380–3225; tel. 281/364–2300), (Total facility includes 9 beds in nursing home–type unit) **A**1 2 8 9 10 **F**2 6 10 11 12 13 14 15 16 17 18 19 20 21 22 23 24 26 27 28 29 30 32 33 34 35 37 38 39 40 43 44 45 46 47 48 49 50 51 52 53 55 56 58 59 60 61 62 63 65 66 67 68 69 70 73 81 82 83 84 85 86 87 88 89 90 92 93 94 95 96 98 101 102 104 105 107 108 109 110 **S** Memorial Hermann Healthcare System, Houston, TX Primary Contact: Juanita F. Romans, Chief Executive Officer CFO: Barrie Strickland, Chief Financial Officer CMO: William Peruzzi, M.D., Chief Medical Officer CIO: David Bradshaw, Vice President Information Services Web address: www.mhhs.org	23	10	711	29616	522	129753	4083	538564	177332	3799
⊠ **MEMORIAL HERMANN MEMORIAL CITY HOSPITAL**, 920 Frostwood Drive, Zip 77024–9173; tel. 713/932–3000, (Total facility includes 24 beds in nursing home–type unit) **A**1 2 9 10 **F**2 9 10 11 12 15 17 19 21 22 23 26 27 28 29 33 34 40 46 47 48 50 52 55 56 57 58 59 60 61 62 63 64 65 66 69 79 80 81 82 83 84 85 87 88 89 92 94 95 96 107 108 **S** Memorial Hermann Healthcare System, Houston, TX Primary Contact: Wayne M. Voss, Chief Executive Officer COO: Jeff Nowlin, Assistant Vice President Operations CFO: Charles Bumpass, Assistant Vice President CMO: Ronald Zweighaft, M.D., Chief of Staff CHR: Vicki Jones, Director Human Resources Web address: www.mhhs.org	23	10	400	19914	269	112092	3279	223687	69528	1473
⊠ **MEMORIAL HERMANN SOUTHWEST HOSPITAL**, 7600 Beechnut, Zip 77074–1850; tel. 713/776–5000, (Total facility includes 28 beds in nursing home–type unit) **A**1 2 9 10 **F**11 12 15 21 22 23 26 27 28 29 30 31 33 34 35 37 39 40 46 47 48 49 50 51 52 55 56 57 58 59 60 61 63 65 66 68 69 70 79 81 82 84 85 86 87 88 92 93 94 96 106 108 109 110 **P**5 **S** Memorial Hermann Healthcare System, Houston, TX Primary Contact: Chris M. Vasquez, Vice President and Chief Executive Officer CFO: Susan Johnson, Chief Financial Officer CIO: David Bradshaw, Vice President Information Systems Web address: www.mhhs.org	23	10	525	25143	347	151439	4682	282472	102264	2130
□ **MENNINGER CLINIC**, 2801 Gessner, Zip 77080, Mailing Address: P.O. Box 809045, Zip 77280; tel. 713/275–5000 **A**1 **F**22 71 72 94 Primary Contact: Ian Aitken, President and Chief Operating Officer Web address: www.menningerclinic.com	23	22	132	783	97	0	0	28447	13284	288
⊠ **METHODIST WILLOWBROOK HOSPITAL**, 18220 Tomball Parkway, Zip 77070; tel. 281/477–1000 **A**1 9 10 **F**2 11 12 15 21 22 26 27 28 29 30 33 35 37 46 47 48 50 52 55 57 58 59 60 62 63 64 65 66 69 81 82 84 88 92 94 96 106 107 108 **S** The Methodist Hospital System, Houston, TX Primary Contact: Andrew Cochrane, Chief Executive Officer CFO: James Levermann, Chief Financial Officer CHR: Diane Snow, Director Human Resources Web address: www.methodisthealth.com/willowbrook	23	10	110	6319	66	67462	2153	74871	33394	603
⊠ △ **MICHAEL E. DEBAKEY VETERANS AFFAIRS MEDICAL CENTER**, (Formerly Veterans Affairs Medical Center), 2002 Holcombe Boulevard, Zip 77030–4298; tel. 713/791–1414, (Total facility includes 120 beds in nursing home–type unit) (Nonreporting) **A**1 2 3 5 7 8 **S** Department of Veterans Affairs, Washington, DC Primary Contact: Edgar L. Tucker, Director COO: Jim Eddins, Financial Resources Manager CFO: Jim Eddins, Financial Resources Manager CMO: Thomas B. Horvath, Chief of Staff CIO: Derek Drawhorn, Chief Information Officer Web address: www.va.gov/sta/guide/home.asp	45	10	859	—	—	—	—	—	—	—
NORTH CAMPUS See Twelve Oaks Medical Center										

TX

Many Facility Codes have changed. Please refer to the AHA Guide Code Chart.

© 2005 AHA Guide

Hospital, Address, Telephone, Approval, Facility, and Physician Codes, Health Care System	Classi-fication Codes		Utilization Data					Expense (thousands) of dollars		
★ American Hospital Association (AHA) membership □ Joint Commission on Accreditation of Healthcare Organizations (JCAHO) accreditation ○ American Osteopathic Association (AOA) accreditation △ Commission on Accreditation of Rehabilitation Facilities (CARF) accreditation	Control	Service	Staffed Beds	Admissions	Census	Outpatient Visits	Births	Total	Payroll	Personnel
✠ **PARK PLAZA HOSPITAL**, 1313 Hermann Drive, Zip 77004–7092; tel. 713/527–5000, (Total facility includes 15 beds in nursing home–type unit) **A**1 2 3 5 9 10 **F**2 10 11 12 15 17 19 21 22 23 26 27 28 29 33 35 37 39 44 46 47 48 49 50 52 53 55 57 58 59 60 61 62 63 64 65 66 68 69 71 75 76 79 80 81 82 84 85 87 88 92 93 94 95 96 106 108 109 110 **P**5 **S** TENET Healthcare Corporation, Dallas, TX Primary Contact: Lex A. Guinn, Chief Executive Officer COO: Michael Salter, Chief Operating Officer CFO: Charles Handley, Chief Financial Officer CIO: Steve Peacock, Chief Information Officer Director CHR: Bette Matney, Director Human Resources Web address: www.parkplazahospital.com	32	10	373	11025	184	53443	1547	126570	48173	1032
✠ **PLAZA SPECIALTY HOSPITAL**, 1300 Binz, Zip 77004; tel. 713/285–1000 **A**1 9 10 **F**2 21 27 28 44 46 49 50 57 58 61 64 65 66 92 94 110 **S** TENET Healthcare Corporation, Dallas, TX Primary Contact: J. Michael Leger, Interim Chief Executive Officer CFO: Charles R. Handley, Chief Financial Officer CMO: Wasae S. Tabibi, M.D., President of Staff CIO: Steve Peacock, Chief Information Officer Director Web address: www.plazaspecialtyhospital.com	33	80	61	550	38	0	0	19994	6711	118
QUENTIN MEASE HOSPITAL See Harris County Hospital District										
□ **RIVERSIDE GENERAL HOSPITAL**, 3204 Ennis Street, Zip 77004–3299; tel. 713/526–2441 **A**1 9 10 **F**1 3 4 9 21 22 24 26 27 28 29 33 42 44 45 46 47 48 52 55 63 65 66 70 71 72 73 74 75 76 77 78 94 96 108 **P**5 Primary Contact: Earnest Gibson, III, Administrator Web address: www.riversidegeneral.org	23	82	64	753	16	298	0	10111	7131	226
□ **SCCI HOSPITAL**, 105 Drew Avenue, Zip 77006; tel. 713/529–8922 **A**1 10 **F**2 21 22 28 29 35 37 44 50 53 60 64 65 66 76 94 110 Primary Contact: Stan Johnson, Chief Executive Officer Web address: www.sccihospitals.com	33	80	38	317	21	0	0	11554	3043	63
□ **SELECT SPECIALTY HOSPITAL–HOUSTON HEIGHTS**, 1917 Ashland Street, Zip 77008–3994; tel. 713/861–6161 **A**1 9 10 **F**2 21 23 28 33 39 49 52 55 63 66 68 81 85 88 94 110 **P**8 **S** Select Medical Corporation, Mechanicsburg, PA Primary Contact: Teresa L. Davis, Administrator Web address: www.selectmedicalcorp.com	32	80	221	2162	155	5120	0	60399	26867	578
SELECT SPECIALTY HOSPITAL–HOUSTON MEDICAL CENTER, 6447 Main Street, Zip 77030–1502, Mailing Address: 6500 Fannin Street, Suite 907, Zip 77030–1502; tel. 713/363–9393, (Nonreporting) **A**9 10 **S** Select Medical Corporation, Mechanicsburg, PA Primary Contact: Brock Hardaway, Administrator Web address: www.selectmedicalcorp.com	33	49	34	—	—	—	—	—	—	—
□ **SHRINERS HOSPITALS FOR CHILDREN, HOUSTON**, 6977 Main Street, Zip 77030–3701; tel. 713/797–1616 **A**1 3 5 **F**7 21 29 39 46 52 57 58 65 66 69 94 96 108 **P**6 **S** Shriners Hospitals for Children, Tampa, FL Primary Contact: Steven B. Reiter, Administrator Web address: www.shrineshq.org	23	57	40	818	13	9086	0	—	—	185
SOUTH CAMPUS See Twelve Oaks Medical Center										
✠ **SPRING BRANCH MEDICAL CENTER**, 8850 Long Point Road, Zip 77055–3082; tel. 713/467–6555 **A**1 2 9 10 **F**2 9 10 12 19 21 22 23 26 27 28 29 33 37 44 46 48 50 53 55 57 58 60 61 62 63 68 69 79 81 82 84 88 92 93 94 96 97 108 110 **S** HCA, Nashville, TN Primary Contact: Scott Koenig, Chief Executive Officer COO: David Handley, Chief Operating Officer CFO: Stanley K. Nord, Chief Financial Officer Web address: www.springbranchmedical.com	33	10	305	7836	129	62087	—	104531	36075	810
✠ △ **ST. LUKE'S EPISCOPAL HOSPITAL**, 6720 Bertner Avenue, Zip 77030–2697, Mailing Address: Box 20269, Zip 77225–0269; tel. 832/355–1000 **A**1 2 3 5 7 8 9 10 **F**2 9 11 12 14 15 17 19 21 22 23 26 27 28 29 33 35 37 38 39 40 44 46 47 48 49 50 51 52 53 55 57 58 59 60 61 62 63 64 65 66 68 69 73 79 80 81 82 83 84 85 86 87 88 90 93 94 95 96 100 101 102 103 106 107 108 109 110 **P**5 8 **S** St. Luke's Episcopal Health System, Houston, TX Primary Contact: David J. Fine, Chief Executive Officer CFO: Howard K. Schramm, Executive Vice President and Chief Financial Officer CMO: David Pate, M.D., Senior Vice President and Chief Medical Officer CIO: Kay C. Carr, Senior Vice President and Chief Information Officer CHR: Irene Helsinger, Senior Vice President and Chief Human Resource Officer Web address: www.sleh.com	21	10	685	31826	499	203888	2249	586335	229167	4636
✠ **TEXAS CHILDREN'S HOSPITAL**, 6621 Fannin Street, Zip 77030–2399, Mailing Address: Box 300630, Zip 77230–0630; tel. 832/824–1000 **A**1 3 5 8 9 10 **F**2 6 9 14 16 18 21 22 23 24 26 27 28 29 31 32 33 37 39 41 42 45 46 47 48 49 50 51 52 53 56 57 58 60 61 62 63 65 66 67 69 70 73 74 77 81 82 84 85 87 88 90 93 94 95 96 98 99 100 101 102 103 104 107 108 110 **P**7 Primary Contact: Mark A. Wallace, President and Chief Executive Officer COO: Randall P. Wright, Chief Operating Officer CFO: Benjamin B. Melson, CPA, Chief Financial Officer CMO: Ralph D. Feigin, M.D., Physician–in–Chief CIO: David S. Finn, Chief Information Officer CHR: Linda Aldred, Senior Vice President Web address: www.texaschildrenshospital.org	23	50	465	20544	399	959714	0	583189	251023	4454

TX

Hospital, Address, Telephone, Approval, Facility, and Physician Codes, Health Care System	Classi-fication Codes		Utilization Data					Expense (thousands) of dollars		
	Control	Service	Staffed Beds	Admissions	Census	Outpatient Visits	Births	Total	Payroll	Personnel

★ American Hospital Association (AHA) membership
☐ Joint Commission on Accreditation of Healthcare Organizations (JCAHO) accreditation
○ American Osteopathic Association (AOA) accreditation
△ Commission on Accreditation of Rehabilitation Facilities (CARF) accreditation

TX

⊞ **TEXAS ORTHOPEDIC HOSPITAL**, 7401 South Main Street, Zip 77030–4509; tel. 713/799–8600 **A**1 5 9 10 **F**2 21 22 26 28 33 37 53 55 62 63 65 66 69 81 84 88 92 94 95 108 **S** HCA, Nashville, TN
Primary Contact: Jay Woodall, Chief Executive Officer
Web address: www.texasorthopedic.com

	32	47	49	1899	16	38419	0	42546	14510	276

☐ **TEXAS WEST OAKS HOSPITAL**, (Formerly West Oaks Hospital), 6500 Hornwood Drive, Zip 77074–5095; tel. 713/995–0909 **A**1 5 10 **F**3 4 27 28 42 52 53 71 72 73 74 76 77 78 96 **P**6 **S** Psychiatric Solutions, Franklin, TN
Primary Contact: Charlene Arnett, MS, FACHE, Chief Executive Officer
Web address: www.psysolutions.com

	33	22	144	6062	121	11333	0	19835	11361	319

⊞ △ **THE INSTITUTE FOR REHABILITATION AND RESEARCH**, 1333 Moursund, Zip 77030–3405; tel. 713/799–5000 **A**1 3 5 7 10 **F**2 9 21 22 28 32 35 37 39 52 57 62 63 65 66 68 69 89 94 95 96 108 110 **P**5
Primary Contact: John Kajander, President
COO: Jean Herzog, Ph.D., Executive Vice President and Chief Operating Officer
CFO: Virgil Dice, Chief Financial Officer
CMO: William Donovan, M.D., Medical Director
CIO: Satinder Suri, Director Management Information Service
Web address: www.tirr.org

	23	46	96	999	79	32030	0	51076	20570	399

⊞ △ **THE METHODIST HOSPITAL**, 6565 Fannin Street, Zip 77030–2707; tel. 713/790–3311, (Total facility includes 50 beds in nursing home–type unit) **A**1 2 3 5 7 8 9 10 **F**2 9 10 11 12 14 15 17 19 21 22 23 26 27 28 29 30 31 32 33 35 37 38 39 40 41 43 44 46 47 48 49 50 51 52 53 55 57 58 59 60 61 62 63 64 65 66 68 69 71 73 75 76 78 79 80 81 82 84 85 86 87 88 92 93 94 95 96 99 100 101 102 103 105 106 108 109 110 **P**5 6 **S** The Methodist Hospital System, Houston, TX
Primary Contact: Ronald G. Girotto, President and Chief Executive Officer
COO: Marc Boom, M.D., Senior Vice President and Chief Operating Officer
CFO: John E. Hagale, Executive Vice President, Chief Financial Officer and Chief Administrtive Officer
CIO: Jerry Vuchak, Vice President Information Systems
CHR: Fred Pluckhorn, Senior Vice President
Web address: www.methodisthealth.com

	23	10	911	37740	740	342828	1222	783256	265214	5276

⊞ **THE WOMAN'S HOSPITAL OF TEXAS**, 7600 Fannin Street, Zip 77054–1900; tel. 713/790–1234 **A**1 3 5 9 10 **F**2 11 12 21 28 33 41 46 47 48 52 55 56 58 59 60 61 63 64 65 66 69 81 82 87 88 92 94 96 108 109 **S** HCA, Nashville, TN
Primary Contact: Linda B. Russell, Chief Executive Officer
COO: Troy Greer, Chief Operating Officer
CFO: Jeff Sliwinski, Chief Financial Officer
Web address: www.womanshospital.com

	32	44	248	13162	178	56573	8276	103987	52413	855

☐ **TOPS SURGICAL SPECIALTY HOSPITAL**, 17080 Red Oak Drive, Zip 77090; tel. 281/539–2900 **A**1 9 10 **F**2 12 26 27 28 32 40 52 62 63 82 88 105 **P**2 **S** United Surgical Partners International, Addison, TX
Primary Contact: J. L. Flotte', Administrator
Web address: www.unitedsurgical.com

	32	13	18	466	3	6872	0	13919	—	113

☐ **TRIUMPH HOSPITAL NORTH HOUSTON**, 7333 North Freeway, Zip 77076; tel. 832/200–6000, (Nonreporting) **A**1 10 **S** Triumph HealthCare, Houston, TX
Primary Contact: Michael R. Bullard, Chief Executive Officer

	33	49	130	—	—	—	—	—	—	—

☐ **TRIUMPH HOSPITAL NORTHWEST**, 205 Hollow Tree Lane, Zip 77090; tel. 832/249–2700 **A**1 10 **F**2 21 23 28 29 33 46 48 52 55 57 58 60 61 62 66 69 81 88 94 110 **S** Triumph HealthCare, Houston, TX
Primary Contact: Jeffrey Smith, Chief Executive Officer

	32	80	115	1308	87	633	0	34692	14763	237

⊞ **TWELVE OAKS MEDICAL CENTER**, 4200 Twelve Oaks Drive, Zip 77027–6899; tel. 713/623–2500, (Includes NORTH CAMPUS; SOUTH CAMPUS, 6700 Bellaire at Tarnef, Zip 77074–4999, Mailing Address: P.O. Box 740389, Zip 77274–0389; tel. 713/774–7611), (Total facility includes 15 beds in nursing home–type unit) **A**1 9 10 **F**2 9 10 11 12 15 17 19 21 23 26 27 28 29 33 34 37 44 46 47 48 49 50 52 53 55 56 57 58 59 60 61 62 63 69 71 76 81 84 88 92 93 94 96 108 109 **S** Hospital Partners of America, Charlotte, NC
Primary Contact: Kerry Teel, Chief Executive Officer
COO: Todd Mann, System Chief Operating Officer
CFO: Gregg Garrison, Chief Financial Officer
CMO: Timothy Castro, M.D., Chief of Staff
CIO: Stephen Farias, Director Information Services
CHR: Brenda Ray, Director Human Resources
Web address: www.twelveoaksmedicalcenter.com

	32	10	356	8901	98	42624	3152	110970	39597	760

⊞ **UNIVERSITY OF TEXAS M. D. ANDERSON CANCER CENTER**, 1515 Holcombe Boulevard, Box 91, Zip 77030–4095; tel. 713/792–2121 **A**1 2 3 5 8 9 10 **F**9 12 21 22 23 24 26 28 29 30 31 32 33 35 37 38 39 42 46 47 48 49 52 53 55 58 60 61 63 65 66 67 69 70 72 73 74 75 77 79 80 81 82 84 85 86 87 88 94 96 98 99 106 108 **P**6 **S** University of Texas System, Austin, TX
Primary Contact: John Mendelsohn, M.D., President
CMO: Thomas Burke, M.D., Executive Vice President and Physician–in–Chief
CIO: Lynn H. Vogel, Vice President and Chief Information Officer
CHR: Mother Superior Jim Dorn, Vice President Human Resources
Web address: www.mdanderson.org

	12	41	482	20608	412	811982	0	1744154	846696	14550

Many Facility Codes have changed. Please refer to the AHA Guide Code Chart.   © 2005 AHA Guide

Hospital, Address, Telephone, Approval, Facility, and Physician Codes, Health Care System	Classi-fication Codes		Utilization Data					Expense (thousands) of dollars		
★ American Hospital Association (AHA) membership □ Joint Commission on Accreditation of Healthcare Organizations (JCAHO) accreditation ○ American Osteopathic Association (AOA) accreditation △ Commission on Accreditation of Rehabilitation Facilities (CARF) accreditation	Control	Service	Staffed Beds	Admissions	Census	Outpatient Visits	Births	Total	Payroll	Personnel

✦ WEST HOUSTON MEDICAL CENTER, 12141 Richmond Avenue,
Zip 77082–2499; tel. 281/558–3444 **A**1 9 10 **F**2 9 11 12 15 17 19 21 22 26
28 32 33 37 39 40 42 43 44 46 48 52 55 57 58 59 60 61 62 63 65 68 69
71 75 76 79 81 84 86 88 93 94 96 107 108 109 110 **S** HCA, Nashville, TN
Primary Contact: Jeffrey S. Holland, Chief Executive Officer
COO: Jason Cobb, Chief Operating Officer
CFO: Thomas A. Holt, Chief Financial Officer
CMO: Barry Zietz, M.D., Chief of Staff
CIO: Randy Jones, Director Information Systems
CHR: Molly Heath, Director of Human Resources
Web address: www.westhoustonmedical.com
| 32 | 10 | 175 | 10183 | 136 | 93254 | 1882 | 94493 | 42193 | 645 |

HUMBLE—Harris County

✦ HEALTHSOUTH REHABILITATION HOSPITAL, 19002 McKay Drive,
Zip 77338–5701; tel. 281/446–6148 **A**1 10 **F**21 26 27 28 44 45 52 58 60 65
66 68 69 94 96 110 **S** HEALTHSOUTH Corporation, Birmingham, AL
Primary Contact: Robyne Pack, Administrator
CFO: Marsha Ogura, Controller
CHR: Frederica Malone, Human Resources Manager
Web address: www.healthsouth.com
| 33 | 46 | 60 | 926 | 37 | 12634 | 0 | 10100 | 5471 | 118 |

KINGWOOD MEDICAL CENTER See Kingwood

✦ NORTHEAST MEDICAL CENTER HOSPITAL, 18951 Memorial North,
Zip 77338–4297; tel. 281/540–7700 **A**1 2 9 10 **F**2 9 11 12 15 21 22 27 28
29 30 33 36 37 41 44 46 47 48 55 56 58 59 60 61 62 63 64 65 66 69 81
82 84 85 87 88 93 94 96 106 107 108 109
Primary Contact: Syble F. Missildine, Administrator
COO: Alden Vandeveer, Chief Operating Officer
CFO: David Glassburn, Chief Financial Officer
CIO: Carla Maslakowski, Chief Information Officer
CHR: Robert Fontenot, Director Human Resources
Web address: www.nemch.org
| 16 | 10 | 242 | 13374 | 171 | 140439 | 2073 | 112572 | 49621 | 1070 |

HUNT—Kerr County

LA HACIENDA TREATMENT CENTER, FM 1340, Zip 78024, Mailing Address:
P.O. Box 1, Zip 78024–0001; tel. 830/238–4222 **F**3 4 21 22 29 48 58 65 66
73 96 **P**1
Primary Contact: Arthur Van Divier, Executive Director
Web address: www.lahacienda.com
| 32 | 82 | 10 | 433 | 3 | 0 | 0 | 1238 | 898 | 25 |

HUNTSVILLE—Walker County

✦ HUNTSVILLE MEMORIAL HOSPITAL, 110 Memorial Hospital Drive,
Zip 77340–4362, Mailing Address: P.O. Box 4001, Zip 77342–4001;
tel. 936/291–3411, (Total facility includes 10 beds in nursing home–type unit) **A**1
9 10 **F**2 9 11 12 24 26 27 28 29 33 39 40 42 44 46 47 48 51 52 53 55 58
59 60 62 63 65 66 69 70 71 75 76 77 81 82 84 88 92 94 95 96 108 109
110 **P**8
Primary Contact: Ralph E. Beaty, Administrator
CFO: Dorothy Nevill, Assistant Administrator Financial Services
CIO: John Heeman, Director Information Systems
Web address: www.huntsvillememorial.com
| 23 | 10 | 127 | 2885 | 51 | 56237 | 342 | 13009 | 14389 | 450 |

IRAAN—Pecos County

IRAAN GENERAL HOSPITAL, (Formerly Pecos County General Hospital), 305
West Fifth Street, Zip 79744, Mailing Address: P.O. Box 665, Zip 79744–2057;
tel. 432/639–2871 **A**10 18 **F**26 27 28 33 34 44 46 48 52 58 65 69 77 88
94 97
Primary Contact: Teresa Callahan, R.N., MSN, Chief Executive Officer
Web address: www.co.pecos.tx.us/hc.html
| 13 | 10 | 9 | 75 | 2 | 5569 | 0 | 2294 | 1079 | 32 |

IRVING—Dallas County

✦ BAYLOR MEDICAL CENTER AT IRVING, 1901 North MacArthur Boulevard,
Zip 75061–2291; tel. 972/579–8100 **A**1 2 9 10 **F**2 9 12 14 15 17 19 21 22
23 27 28 29 32 33 42 44 45 47 48 50 52 55 57 58 59 60 61 62 63 64 65
66 68 69 73 79 81 82 84 85 87 88 93 94 96 108 109 110 **S** Baylor Health
Care System, Dallas, TX
Primary Contact: James D. Thaxton, President
CFO: Jay Whitfield, Chief Financial Officer
CMO: Larry Schorn, M.D., Vice President Medical Affairs
CIO: David Krejci, Director Information Services
Web address: www.bhcs.com/irving
| 21 | 10 | 222 | 12067 | 145 | 229528 | 2029 | 155558 | 58089 | 1084 |

□ IRVING COPPELL SURGICAL HOSPITAL, 440 West Interstate 635, Zip 75063;
tel. 972/868–4000, (Nonreporting) **A**1 10 **S** United Surgical Partners
International, Addison, TX
Primary Contact: David Yoder, Chief Executive Officer
| 33 | 13 | 20 | — | — | — | — | — | — | — |

✦ LAS COLINAS MEDICAL CENTER, 6800 North MacArthur Boulevard,
Zip 75039–2422; tel. 972/969–2000 **A**1 9 10 **F**3 11 12 13 14 17 21 26 27
28 33 40 46 55 56 59 63 66 67 68 69 71 81 82 84 88 92 93 94 95 108
109 **S** HCA, Nashville, TN
Primary Contact: Douglas Welch, Chief Executive Officer
CFO: Todd Gibson, Chief Financial Officer
Web address: www.lascolinasmedical.com
| 33 | 10 | 70 | 4037 | 32 | 38508 | 1527 | 38421 | 14393 | 257 |

TX

Hospital, Address, Telephone, Approval, Facility, and Physician Codes, Health Care System	Classi-fication Codes		Utilization Data					Expense (thousands) of dollars		
★ American Hospital Association (AHA) membership □ Joint Commission on Accreditation of Healthcare Organizations (JCAHO) accreditation ○ American Osteopathic Association (AOA) accreditation △ Commission on Accreditation of Rehabilitation Facilities (CARF) accreditation	Control	Service	Staffed Beds	Admissions	Census	Outpatient Visits	Births	Total	Payroll	Personnel

JACKSBORO—Jack County

★ **FAITH COMMUNITY HOSPITAL**, 717 Magnolia Street, Zip 76458–1111; tel. 940/567–6633 **A**9 10 **F**6 9 27 33 34 46 51 60 69 81 88 94 97 **P**6 Primary Contact: Donald B. Hopkins, Administrator COO: J D. Hailey, Chief Operating Officer CFO: Margaret Wingo, Chief Financial Officer CMO: S Jamal, M.D., Medical Director Web address: www.faithcommunityhospital.com	16	10	17	449	4	21543	0	4681	2045	65

JACKSONVILLE—Cherokee County

⊞ **EAST TEXAS MEDICAL CENTER JACKSONVILLE**, 501 South Ragsdale Street, Zip 75766–2413; tel. 903/541–5000 **A**1 9 10 **F**2 9 11 12 15 21 23 26 27 29 33 34 40 41 46 48 52 55 58 59 60 61 62 63 64 66 69 81 82 84 87 88 94 95 96 106 108 109 110 **P**8 **S** East Texas Medical Center Regional Healthcare System, Tyler, TX Primary Contact: Steve Bowen, President CFO: Greg Cummings, Chief Operating Officer and Chief Financial Officer CHR: Elysia Epperson, Director Human Resources Web address: www.etmc.org	23	10	58	2679	31	30287	549	30581	11287	265
⊞ **MOTHER FRANCES HOSPITAL – JACKSONVILLE**, 2026 South Jackson, Zip 75766; tel. 903/541–4500 **A**1 9 10 18 **F**2 12 15 21 22 24 26 27 33 37 39 40 46 48 52 53 58 60 62 63 64 69 70 81 82 84 85 88 94 95 109 **P**5 6 8 Primary Contact: Thomas N. Cammack, Jr, Chief Administrative Officer CMO: William Milawski, M.D., President Medical Staff Web address: www.tmfhs.org	23	10	10	1052	9	72060	0	15109	5199	158

JASPER—Jasper County

⊞ **CHRISTUS JASPER MEMORIAL HOSPITAL**, 1275 Marvin Hancock Drive, Zip 75951–4995; tel. 409/384–5461 **A**1 9 10 **F**2 9 11 12 21 22 27 28 33 34 39 40 46 48 52 55 59 60 62 63 68 69 81 84 88 94 97 106 108 **S** Christus Health, Irving, TX Primary Contact: Deborah Wiegand, R.N., Chief Executive Officer CFO: John Breidenthal, Chief Financial Officer CHR: Kay Powell, Director Human Resources Web address: www.christusjasper.org	21	10	50	2254	26	78497	303	23039	7790	216

JOURDANTON—Atascosa County

□ **SOUTH TEXAS REGIONAL MEDICAL CENTER**, 1905 Highway 97 East, Zip 78026–1504; tel. 830/769–3515 **A**1 9 10 20 **F**2 9 11 12 21 22 26 27 28 29 33 35 46 48 51 52 55 58 59 60 62 63 66 68 69 81 82 84 85 87 88 94 96 108 109 110 **P**6 **S** Community Health Systems, Inc., Brentwood, TN Primary Contact: Dennis Barts, Chief Executive Officer Web address: www.strmc.com	33	10	47	3310	33	67337	137	32061	12988	301

JUNCTION—Kimble County

★ **KIMBLE HOSPITAL**, 2101 Main Street, Zip 76849–2101; tel. 325/446–3321 **A**9 10 18 **F**33 34 44 46 51 52 53 60 69 81 88 96 97 106 **P**5 Primary Contact: Marlene Jones, Chief Executive Officer	16	10	15	201	3	85973	0	1847	1937	66

KATY—Fort Bend County

⊞ **CHRISTUS ST. CATHERINE HOSPITAL**, 701 Fry Road, Zip 77450; tel. 281/599–5700 **A**1 9 10 **F**2 9 11 12 21 22 26 27 28 29 33 46 47 48 52 55 58 59 60 62 63 64 65 66 68 69 81 82 84 88 94 96 108 **P**8 **S** Christus Health, Irving, TX Primary Contact: Sheila Fata, Administrator Web address: www.christusstcatherine.org	21	10	58	7189	38	48155	999	45773	17615	350
⊞ **MEMORIAL HERMANN KATY HOSPITAL**, 5602 Medical Center Drive, Zip 77494–6399; tel. 281/392–1111 **A**1 9 10 **F**2 9 11 12 21 22 26 27 28 29 32 33 46 48 50 52 53 54 55 58 59 60 62 63 69 75 81 82 84 88 92 94 96 108 109 **S** Memorial Hermann Healthcare System, Houston, TX Primary Contact: Brian S. Barbe, Chief Executive Officer CFO: Lisa Kendler, Chief Financial Officer Web address: www.mhhs.org	23	10	90	4945	49	46722	1087	42232	18497	410

KAUFMAN—Kaufman County

⊞ **PRESBYTERIAN HOSPITAL OF KAUFMAN**, 850 Highway 243 West, Zip 75142–9998, Mailing Address: P.O. Box 310, Zip 75142–0310; tel. 972/932–7200 **A**1 9 10 **F**2 9 11 12 21 22 27 28 29 33 37 39 46 48 53 55 58 59 62 63 64 65 66 69 75 81 82 84 85 87 88 94 96 98 106 108 110 **S** Texas Health Resources, Arlington, TX Primary Contact: Kirk King, CHE, President CFO: Pattie Ross, Director Finance Web address: www.texashealth.org	23	10	68	1981	23	33881	204	21893	9207	224

KENEDY—Karnes County

OTTO KAISER MEMORIAL HOSPITAL, 3349 South Highway 181, Zip 78119–5240; tel. 830/583–3401 **A**9 10 18 20 **F**9 12 21 28 33 46 48 51 52 55 63 69 81 84 88 96 **P**8 Primary Contact: Nancy Kinkler, Administrator	16	10	30	328	4	18744	0	2536	2443	86

KERMIT—Winkler County

WINKLER COUNTY MEMORIAL HOSPITAL, 821 Jeffee Drive, Zip 79745–4696, Mailing Address: Drawer H, Zip 79745–6008; tel. 915/586–5864 **A**9 10 18 **F**9 24 26 33 54 69 70 81 88 97 Primary Contact: Judene Willhelm, Administrator	13	10	15	230	1	18597	0	4865	1997	63

Many Facility Codes have changed. Please refer to the AHA Guide Code Chart. © 2005 AHA Guide

Hospital, Address, Telephone, Approval, Facility, and Physician Codes, Health Care System	Classi-fication Codes		Utilization Data					Expense (thousands) of dollars		
★ American Hospital Association (AHA) membership □ Joint Commission on Accreditation of Healthcare Organizations (JCAHO) accreditation ○ American Osteopathic Association (AOA) accreditation △ Commission on Accreditation of Rehabilitation Facilities (CARF) accreditation	Control	Service	Staffed Beds	Admissions	Census	Outpatient Visits	Births	Total	Payroll	Personnel

KERRVILLE—Kerr County

KERRVILLE DIVISION See South Texas Veterans Health Care System, San Antonio

□ **KERRVILLE STATE HOSPITAL**, 721 Thompson Drive, Zip 78028–5154; tel. 830/896–2211 **A**1 10 **F**9 22 27 28 32 35 37 39 44 46 47 53 58 65 66 70 71 74 76 94 96 106 108 **S** Texas Department of State Health Services, Austin, TX
Primary Contact: Gloria P. Olsen, Ph.D., Superintendent
Web address: www.dshs.state.tx.us/lmhhospitals/kerrvillesh

| | 12 | 22 | 177 | 669 | 166 | 0 | 0 | 28998 | 15805 | 504 |

✠ **SID PETERSON MEMORIAL HOSPITAL**, 710 Water Street, Zip 78028–5398; tel. 830/896–4200 **A**1 9 10 19 20 **F**2 9 11 12 15 21 22 23 26 27 28 33 37 38 40 46 48 51 52 53 55 58 59 60 61 62 63 64 65 66 68 69 81 82 84 88 93 94 95 96 106 108 109 110 **P**8
Primary Contact: James Patrick Murray, Chief Executive Officer
CFO: Robert H. Walther, Chief Financial Officer
CMO: Brian V. Given, M.D., Chief of Staff
CIO: Richard Cruthirds, Manager Information Systems
CHR: Buddy Volpe, Director, Human Resources
Web address: www.spmh.com

| | 23 | 10 | 105 | 5474 | 71 | 131529 | 482 | 55719 | 23787 | 664 |

KILGORE—Gregg County

★ **LAIRD MEMORIAL HOSPITAL**, 1612 South Henderson Boulevard, Zip 75662–3594; tel. 903/984–3505 **A**9 10 **F**2 9 11 12 21 22 27 28 29 33 34 44 46 48 52 58 59 62 63 66 71 73 74 75 76 77 78 81 84 88 108 109
Primary Contact: Bob Ellzey, Administrator
CFO: Tammy Welch, Chief Financial Officer
CHR: Brandy Richardson, Human Resources Director

| | 23 | 10 | 60 | 2270 | 22 | 30051 | 492 | 15217 | 7716 | 293 |

KILLEEN—Bell County

✠ **METROPLEX ADVENTIST HOSPITAL**, (Formerly Metroplex Hospital), 2201 South Clear Creek Road, Zip 76549–4110; tel. 254/526–7523 **A**1 9 10 **F**2 9 11 12 15 21 22 26 27 28 29 33 37 42 46 47 48 51 53 55 58 59 60 61 62 63 64 65 66 69 71 72 73 74 75 76 77 78 81 82 84 87 88 93 94 95 96 106 108 **P**8 **S** Adventist Health System Sunbelt Health Care Corporation, Winter Park, FL
Primary Contact: Kenneth A. Finch, Chief Executive Officer
CFO: Janice Hagensicker, Chief Financial Officer
CMO: Fredrick Barnett, M.D., Chief of Staff
CIO: Dale Koebnick, Director Management Information Systems and Patient Access
CHR: Brenda Coley, Executive Director
Web address: www.mplex.org

| | 21 | 10 | 177 | 6785 | 74 | 100789 | 958 | 59773 | 24604 | 698 |

KINGSVILLE—Kleberg County

✠ **CHRISTUS SPOHN HOSPITAL KLEBERG**, 1311 General Cavazos Boulevard, Zip 78363–1197, Mailing Address: P.O. Box 1197, Zip 78363–1197; tel. 361/595–9701, (Total facility includes 15 beds in nursing home–type unit) **A**1 9 10 20 **F**2 9 11 12 21 22 26 27 28 33 34 42 46 48 52 55 57 58 59 60 63 64 65 66 69 81 82 84 88 92 94 96 108 **P**8 **S** Christus Health, Irving, TX
Primary Contact: Ernesto M. Flores, Jr, Vice President and Administrator
Web address: www.christusspohn.org

| | 21 | 10 | 100 | 5831 | 79 | 67752 | 341 | 35194 | 16284 | 359 |

KINGWOOD—Harris County

KINGWOOD HEALTH CENTER, 2002 Ladbrook, Zip 77339; tel. 281/358–1495, (Nonreporting) **A**10
Primary Contact: Linda Hodgkins, Chief Executive Officer

| | 33 | 13 | 6 | — | — | — | — | — | — | — |

✠ **KINGWOOD MEDICAL CENTER**, 22999 U.S. Highway 59, Zip 77339; tel. 281/348–8000 **A**1 5 9 10 **F**2 3 9 11 12 13 14 15 21 22 23 26 27 28 29 32 33 37 40 46 48 53 55 56 57 58 59 61 62 63 65 66 67 68 69 71 81 82 83 84 85 86 88 92 94 95 96 108 109 **S** HCA, Nashville, TN
Primary Contact: Gay Nord, Chief Executive Officer
COO: Colin McRae, Chief Operating Officer
CFO: Bryan R. Lee, Chief Financial Officer
CMO: Victor Lugo–Miro, M.D., Chief of Staff
Web address: www.kingwoodmedical.com

| | 33 | 10 | 149 | 6784 | 93 | 60885 | 509 | 62069 | 25401 | 535 |

KNOX CITY—Knox County

KNOX COUNTY HOSPITAL, 701 South Fifth Street, Zip 79529, Mailing Address: P.O. Box 608, Zip 79529–0608; tel. 940/658–3535 **A**9 10 **F**6 9 24 28 33 34 41 42 46 48 51 58 70 97 **P**6
Primary Contact: Stephan Kuehler, Administrator
Web address: www.knoxcountytx.net

| | 16 | 10 | 14 | 309 | 3 | 22377 | 0 | 3341 | 1792 | 76 |

LA GRANGE—Fayette County

✠ **FAYETTE MEMORIAL HOSPITAL**, 543 North Jackson Street, Zip 78945–2040; tel. 979/968–3166 **A**1 9 10 **F**3 9 11 12 13 14 23 27 29 33 39 44 46 48 51 52 55 56 57 59 61 62 63 65 66 67 68 69 71 81 82 85 88 92 93 94 96 97 108
Primary Contact: Kelley Oliphint, Chief Executive Officer and Administrator
CMO: Walter Thomas, M.D., Chief of Staff
Web address: www.fmh–lagrange.org

| | 23 | 10 | 40 | 2143 | 24 | 38605 | 186 | 20575 | 6664 | 186 |

TX

Hospital, Address, Telephone, Approval, Facility, and Physician Codes, Health Care System	Classi-fication Codes		Utilization Data					Expense (thousands) of dollars		
★ American Hospital Association (AHA) membership □ Joint Commission on Accreditation of Healthcare Organizations (JCAHO) accreditation ○ American Osteopathic Association (AOA) accreditation △ Commission on Accreditation of Rehabilitation Facilities (CARF) accreditation	Control	Service	Staffed Beds	Admissions	Census	Outpatient Visits	Births	Total	Payroll	Personnel

LACKLAND AFB—Bexar County

⊠ **WILFORD HALL MEDICAL CENTER**, 2200 Bergquist Drive, Suite 1, Zip 78236–5300; tel. 210/292–7412, (Nonreporting) **A**1 2 3 5 **S** Department of the Air Force, Washington, DC
Primary Contact: Colonel Marc M. Sager, Administrator
COO: Colonel Marc M. Sager, Administrator
CFO: Lieutenant Colonel Joanne McPherson, Director Plans, Programs and Resources
CMO: Colonel Edmund Sabanegh, Chief Medical Staff
CIO: Lieutenant Colonel Gregory Stewart, Commander, Medical Support Squadron
Web address: www.whmc.af.mil

41	10	284	—	—	—	—	—		

LAKE JACKSON—Brazoria County

⊠ △ **BRAZOSPORT MEMORIAL HOSPITAL**, 100 Medical Drive, Zip 77566–9983; tel. 979/297–4411 **A**1 2 7 9 10 **F**2 9 11 12 15 21 22 23 27 28 33 39 40 46 48 49 51 54 55 58 59 60 61 62 63 64 68 69 79 81 82 84 88 92 93 94 96 108 109 110 **P**8 **S** Quorum Health Resources, Plano, TX
Primary Contact: Daniel L. Buche, Chief Executive Officer
CFO: Barbara Brooks, Assistant Administrator Fiscal Services
CMO: Anil Sinha, M.D., President Medical Staff
CIO: Michael Severud, Director Management Information Systems
Web address: www.brazosportmemorial.com

23	10	156	6031	62	106137	770	52569	23956	499

LAMESA—Dawson County

MEDICAL ARTS HOSPITAL, 1600 North Bryan Avenue, Zip 79331–3145; tel. 806/872–2183 **A**9 10 20 **F**2 9 11 12 21 26 27 28 29 33 34 46 48 51 52 59 63 66 69 81 84 88 94 97 108 110 **S** Covenant Health System, Lubbock, TX
Primary Contact: Charles N. Butts, Chief Executive Officer
Web address: www.medicalartshospital.org

13	10	38	696	7	114331	92	9836	5105	163

LAMPASAS—Lampasas County

⊠ **ROLLINS–BROOK COMMUNITY HOSPITAL**, 608 North Key Avenue, Zip 76550, Mailing Address: Box 589, Zip 76550; tel. 512/556–3682 **A**1 9 10 18 **F**2 12 21 22 26 29 33 46 48 50 58 60 63 66 69 81 88 94 96 97 108 **P**8 **S** Adventist Health System Sunbelt Health Care Corporation, Winter Park, FL
Primary Contact: Kenneth A. Finch, Chief Executive Officer
COO: Larry D. Luce, Vice President and Administrator
CFO: Janice Hagensicker, Chief Financial Officer
CHR: Brenda Coley, Executive Director
Web address: www.mplex.org

21	10	25	1079	11	16459	0	8029	2937	81

LANCASTER—Dallas County

□ **MEDICAL CENTER AT LANCASTER**, 2600 West Pleasant Run Road, Zip 75146–1199; tel. 972/223–9600 **A**1 9 10 **F**2 9 12 15 21 27 28 33 35 39 44 46 48 52 53 55 58 62 63 64 65 69 71 76 81 82 84 88 94 96 106 108 **S** AMT Group, Inc., Duluth, GA
Primary Contact: Barry L. Mousa, Chief Executive Officer
Web address: www.medicalcenteratlancaster.com

33	10	90	3920	56	32694	6	31252	15131	327

LAREDO—Webb County

□ **DOCTORS HOSPITAL OF LAREDO**, 10700 McPherson Road, Zip 78045; tel. 956/523–2000, (Total facility includes 19 beds in nursing home–type unit) **A**1 2 9 10 **F**2 9 11 12 15 21 22 23 27 28 33 34 46 48 49 55 56 58 59 60 61 62 63 69 81 82 84 88 92 94 96 **P**5 **S** Universal Health Services, Inc., King of Prussia, PA
Primary Contact: Al Chapa, Chief Executive Officer and Managing Director
Web address: www.doctorshoslaredo.com

32	10	180	8800	105	53898	3448	61209	21817	587

□ △ **LAREDO MEDICAL CENTER**, 1700 East Saunders Avenue, Zip 78041–5401, Mailing Address: Drawer 2068, Zip 78044–2068; tel. 956/796–5000, (Total facility includes 32 beds in nursing home–type unit) **A**1 7 9 10 **F**2 9 11 12 15 17 19 21 22 23 24 26 27 28 29 32 33 34 36 39 40 42 44 46 47 48 49 50 51 52 53 55 56 57 58 59 60 61 62 63 64 65 66 68 69 81 82 84 88 92 93 94 96 108 109 110 **S** Community Health Systems, Inc., Brentwood, TN
Primary Contact: Abraham Martinez, Chief Executive Officer
Web address: www.laredomedical.com

33	10	312	16230	211	165396	2909	153189	49275	1239

PROVIDENCE HOSPITAL, 230 Calle Del Norte, Zip 78041; tel. 956/693–5000 **A**9 10 **F**27 28 63 81 85 88
Primary Contact: Rene Lopez, Chief Executive Officer

32	10	8	51	1	6961	0	6843	1892	48

LEAGUE CITY—Galveston County

□ **DEVEREUX TEXAS TREATMENT NETWORK**, 1150 Devereux Drive, Zip 77573–2043; tel. 281/335–1000 **A**1 10 **F**3 21 24 27 28 29 31 34 41 42 44 48 52 58 65 66 71 72 73 74 75 76 77 78 94 96 98 **S** Devereux, Villanova, PA
Primary Contact: L. Gail Atkinson, Executive Director
Web address: www.devereux.org

23	22	74	406	74	17319	0	11814	3230	103

LEVELLAND—Hockley County

★ **COVENANT HOSPITAL–LEVELLAND**, 1900 South College Avenue, Zip 79336–6508; tel. 806/894–4963 **A**9 10 **F**9 11 12 21 22 26 27 28 33 34 37 39 42 46 47 48 52 59 60 63 64 65 66 69 70 81 84 88 92 94 97 107 108 **P**4 **S** Covenant Health System, Lubbock, TX
Primary Contact: Jerry Osburn, Administrator
CFO: Jared Squires, Chief Financial Officer
CMO: Michael Bailey, M.D., Chief of Staff
CIO: Joe Kenady, Chief Information Officer
CHR: Kathy McDonald, Director Personnel
Web address: www.covenanthealth.org

21	10	22	1627	14	82878	334	13893	5471	166

Many Facility Codes have changed. Please refer to the AHA Guide Code Chart. © 2005 AHA Guide

Hospital, Address, Telephone, Approval, Facility, and Physician Codes, Health Care System	Classi- fication Codes		Utilization Data					Expense (thousands) of dollars		
★ American Hospital Association (AHA) membership □ Joint Commission on Accreditation of Healthcare Organizations (JCAHO) accreditation ○ American Osteopathic Association (AOA) accreditation △ Commission on Accreditation of Rehabilitation Facilities (CARF) accreditation	Control	Service	Staffed Beds	Admissions	Census	Outpatient Visits	Births	Total	Payroll	Personnel

LEWISVILLE—Denton County

| ⊠ **MEDICAL CENTER OF LEWISVILLE**, 500 West Main, Zip 75057–3699; tel. 972/420–1000 **A**1 9 10 **F**2 11 12 23 33 52 55 56 60 61 62 63 64 66 69 82 84 85 87 88 92 93 94 96 108 110 **S** HCA, Nashville, TN
Primary Contact: Raymond M. Dunning, Jr, Chief Executive Officer
COO: Matt Davis, Chief Operating Officer
CFO: Lisa Brodbeck, Chief Financial Officer
CIO: Shirley Archambeault, Chief Information Officer
CHR: Shelly Tyson, Director Human Resources
Web address: www.lewisvillemedical.com | 33 | 10 | 202 | 9476 | 118 | 65336 | 1733 | 81361 | 32766 | 835 |

LIBERTY—Liberty County

| □ **LIBERTY–DAYTON COMMUNITY HOSPITAL**, 1353 North Travis, Zip 77575–1353; tel. 936/336–7316 **A**1 9 10 **F**2 9 12 21 27 28 33 39 42 46 47 48 52 53 63 81 82 108
Primary Contact: Sean Stricker, Administrator
Web address: www.liberty–daytoncommunityhospital.com | 32 | 10 | 29 | 1066 | 8 | 16859 | 0 | 8107 | 3950 | 88 |

LIBERTY HILL—Williamson County

| **MERIDELL ACHIEVEMENT CENTER**, 12550 West Highway 29, Zip 78642, Mailing Address: P.O. Box 87, Zip 78642–0087; tel. 800/366–8656, (Nonreporting) **S** Universal Health Services, Inc., King of Prussia, PA
Primary Contact: Gail M. Oberta, FACHE, Chief Executive Officer and Managing Director
Web address: www.meridell.com | 33 | 52 | 78 | — | — | — | — | — | — | — |

LINDEN—Cass County

| ★ **LINDEN MUNICIPAL HOSPITAL**, 404 North Kaufman Street, Zip 75563–5235; tel. 903/756–5561, (Nonreporting) **A**9 10 18
Primary Contact: Sam DeNunzio, Administrator
CFO: Billy Fitts, Assistant Administrator
CMO: R Bruce LeGrow, M.D., Chief of Medical Staff | 16 | 10 | 25 | — | — | — | — | — | — | — |

LITTLEFIELD—Lamb County

| ★ **LAMB HEALTHCARE CENTER**, 1500 South Sunset, Zip 79339–4899; tel. 806/385–6411 **A**9 10 20 **F**11 21 27 28 29 33 34 46 48 51 52 58 59 63 65 66 81 88 96 97 98 109 **P**6 **S** Covenant Health System, Lubbock, TX
Primary Contact: Randall A. Young, Administrator
CFO: Cindy Klein, Chief Financial Officer
CMO: Tony Hedges, M.D., Chief Medical Officer
CHR: Joan Williams, Administrative Assistant | 13 | 10 | 41 | 885 | 10 | 33695 | 86 | 8749 | 3573 | 128 |

LIVINGSTON—Polk County

| □ **MEMORIAL MEDICAL CENTER – LIVINGSTON**, 1717 Highway 59 Bypass, Zip 77351–1257, Mailing Address: P.O. Box 1257, Zip 77351–1257; tel. 936/327–4381, (Nonreporting) **A**1 9 10 **S** Memorial Health System of East Texas, Lufkin, TX
Primary Contact: James C. Dickson, Administrator
Web address: www.memorialhealth.org | 23 | 10 | 35 | — | — | — | — | — | — | — |

LLANO—Llano County

| ★ **LLANO MEMORIAL HEALTHCARE SYSTEM**, 200 West Ollie Street, Zip 78643–2628; tel. 325/247–5040 **A**9 10 20 **F**6 9 11 12 24 27 28 29 33 34 46 47 59 60 63 69 81 88 94
Primary Contact: Kevin Leeper, Chief Executive Officer
CFO: Michael Choate, Chief Financial Officer
CMO: Jack Franklin, M.D., Chief of Staff
CIO: Rodney Lott, Director Management Information Systems and Facility Operations
CHR: Pearl Oestreic, Human Resource Director
Web address: www.llanomemorial.org | 16 | 10 | 30 | 1749 | 13 | 141968 | 339 | 21048 | 8589 | 273 |

LOCKNEY—Floyd County

| ★ **W. J. MANGOLD MEMORIAL HOSPITAL**, 320 North Main Street, Zip 79241–0037, Mailing Address: Box 37, Zip 79241–0037; tel. 806/652–3373 **A**9 10 18 **F**11 22 26 27 28 29 33 34 41 46 48 51 52 59 60 63 64 69 70 88 94 97 110 **P**4
Primary Contact: Sharon Hunt, Administrator
CFO: Larry Mullins, Controller
Web address: www.mangoldmemorial.org | 16 | 10 | 25 | 654 | 6 | 27870 | 83 | 5548 | 2719 | 90 |

LONGVIEW—Gregg County

| ⊠ △ **GOOD SHEPHERD MEDICAL CENTER**, 700 East Marshall Avenue, Zip 75601–5571; tel. 903/315–2000 **A**1 7 9 10 **F**2 6 9 11 12 14 15 17 19 21 22 23 26 27 28 29 32 33 39 40 42 44 45 47 49 50 51 52 53 55 56 57 58 59 60 61 62 63 64 65 66 68 69 70 75 81 82 84 85 88 93 94 95 96 106 107 108 109 110 **P**2 7 8
Primary Contact: Jerry D. Adair, President and Chief Executive Officer
COO: Judy Brown, Senior Vice President
CFO: Joseph A. Reppert, Vice President and Chief Financial Officer
CIO: Wiley Thomas, Director Information Systems
Web address: www.gsmc.org | 23 | 10 | 373 | 16987 | 219 | 169510 | 1604 | 191286 | 72426 | 1790 |

TX

Hospital, Address, Telephone, Approval, Facility, and Physician Codes, Health Care System	Classi-fication Codes		Utilization Data					Expense (thousands) of dollars		
★ American Hospital Association (AHA) membership □ Joint Commission on Accreditation of Healthcare Organizations (JCAHO) accreditation ○ American Osteopathic Association (AOA) accreditation △ Commission on Accreditation of Rehabilitation Facilities (CARF) accreditation	Control	Service	Staffed Beds	Admissions	Census	Outpatient Visits	Births	Total	Payroll	Personnel
✚ **LONGVIEW REGIONAL MEDICAL CENTER**, 2901 North Fourth Street, Zip 75605–5191, Mailing Address: P.O. Box 14000, Zip 75607–4000; tel. 903/758–1818, (Total facility includes 15 beds in nursing home–type unit) **A**1 9 10 **F**2 9 10 11 12 14 15 17 19 21 22 23 26 27 28 33 39 46 47 48 50 52 55 57 58 59 61 62 63 65 66 68 81 82 84 85 87 88 92 93 94 108 110 **P**8 **S** Triad Hospitals, Inc., Plano, TX Primary Contact: Vicki L. Briggs, Chief Executive Officer COO: Jill Bayless, Chief Nursing Officer and Chief Operating Officer CFO: Martha Carlson, Chief Financial Officer CMO: David R. Witt, II, M.D., Chief of Staff CIO: Keith Jarvis, Director Information Systems CHR: Stella Barrow, Director of Human Resources Web address: www.longviewregional.com	33	10	166	5833	75	48575	931	63029	26456	627
LUBBOCK—Lubbock County										
★ **COVENANT CHILDREN'S HOSPITAL**, 3610 21st Street, Zip 79410–1218; tel. 806/725–1011 **A**9 10 **F**2 22 23 24 26 27 28 33 34 39 48 56 63 67 **S** Covenant Health System, Lubbock, TX Primary Contact: Steven L. Hunter, President and Chief Executive Officer COO: Chris W. Barnette, Executive Vice President and Chief Operating Officer CFO: Craig Rucker, Senior Vice President and Chief Financial Officer CMO: Robert J. Salem, M.D., Chief Medical Officer CIO: John Hoyt, Vice President Chief Information Officer CHR: Jan Campbell, Senior Vice President Human Resources Web address: www.covenanthealth.org	23	50	73	2672	45	26468	0	31917	7410	109
✚ **COVENANT MEDICAL CENTER**, 3615 19th Street, Zip 79410–1201, Mailing Address: P.O. Box 1201, Zip 79408–1201; tel. 806/725–1011, (Includes COVENANT MEDICAL CENTER–LAKESIDE, 4000 24th Street, Zip 79410–1894; tel. 806/725–6000; Steven L. Hunter, President and Chief Executive Officer) **A**1 2 3 5 6 9 10 **F**3 4 9 10 11 12 13 14 15 17 19 21 22 23 26 27 29 32 33 34 37 38 39 40 41 42 45 46 47 48 49 50 51 52 53 55 57 58 59 60 61 62 63 64 65 66 68 69 71 75 78 79 81 82 83 84 85 86 88 92 93 94 95 96 101 106 107 108 109 110 **P**6 **S** Covenant Health System, Lubbock, TX Primary Contact: Steven L. Hunter, President and Chief Executive Officer COO: Chris W. Barnette, Executive Vice President and Chief Operating Officer CFO: Craig Rucker, Senior Vice President and Chief Financial Officer CMO: Robert J. Salem, M.D., Chief Medical Officer CIO: John Hoyt, Vice President Chief Information Officer CHR: Jan Campbell, Senior Vice President Human Resources Web address: www.covenanthealth.org	23	10	868	33379	515	271897	2308	455533	155511	3653
✚ **HIGHLAND MEDICAL CENTER**, 2412 50th Street, Zip 79412–2494; tel. 806/788–4100 **A**1 10 **F**2 9 10 11 21 22 27 28 29 33 34 39 40 46 48 52 53 55 58 59 60 62 63 66 69 81 84 88 94 108 109 110 **S** Community Health Systems, Inc., Brentwood, TN Primary Contact: William W. Weldon, Ph.D., Chief Executive Officer COO: George N. Parsley, Chief Operating Officer CFO: Mark Havins, Chief Financial Officer CIO: Erika Pochybova, Director Management Information Systems CHR: Rick Brown, Director of Human Resources Web address: www.highlandmedcenter.com	33	10	95	1530	15	21935	422	28626	8999	174
LUBBOCK HEART HOSPITAL, 4810 North Loop 289, Zip 79416; tel. 806/687–7777 **A**9 10 **F**2 9 14 15 17 19 21 26 27 28 33 58 63 65 66 81 82 85 88 94 106 Primary Contact: John McGreevy, Chief Executive Officer	32	42	74	3881	27	9760	0	44582	13407	360
□ **SOUTHWEST REGIONAL MEDICAL COMPLEX**, 1409 9th Street, Zip 79401–2601; tel. 806/767–9133 **A**1 9 10 **F**21 27 28 45 52 58 60 69 94 110 **S** Integrated Health Services, Sparks Glencoe, MD Primary Contact: Deanna Graves, Chief Executive Officer Web address: www.ihsoflubbock.com	33	80	30	381	27	29	0	6800	3137	109
□ **SUNRISE CANYON HOSPITAL**, Mailing Address: P.O. Box 2828, Zip 79408–2828; tel. 806/740–1407 **A**1 10 **F**26 27 28 44 45 71 74 76 94 106 **P**8 Primary Contact: Mary Gerlach, Chief Operating Officer Web address: www.lrl.mhmr.state.tx.us	23	22	30	780	23	0	0	3649	1284	43
✚ **UNIVERSITY MEDICAL CENTER**, 602 Indiana Avenue, Zip 79415–3364, Mailing Address: P.O. Box 5980, Zip 79408–5980; tel. 806/775–8200 **A**1 2 3 5 8 9 10 **F**2 6 9 10 11 12 13 14 15 16 17 18 19 20 21 22 23 27 28 29 33 34 37 39 40 44 46 47 48 49 50 51 52 53 55 56 57 58 59 60 61 62 63 64 65 66 67 68 69 79 80 81 82 83 84 85 87 88 94 95 96 99 101 107 108 109 110 **P**6 7 Primary Contact: David G. Allison, Chief Executive Officer COO: Mark Funderburk, Senior Vice President and Chief Operating Officer CFO: Jeff Dane, Vice President and Chief Financial Officer CIO: Bill Eubanks, Vice President Information Systems CHR: Adrienne Cozart, Vice President of Human Resources Web address: www.teamumc.org	16	10	327	19519	240	180458	2089	167795	76165	—

TX

Many Facility Codes have changed. Please refer to the AHA Guide Code Chart. © 2005 AHA Guide

Hospital, Address, Telephone, Approval, Facility, and Physician Codes, Health Care System	Classi-fication Codes		Utilization Data					Expense (thousands) of dollars		
★ American Hospital Association (AHA) membership □ Joint Commission on Accreditation of Healthcare Organizations (JCAHO) accreditation ○ American Osteopathic Association (AOA) accreditation △ Commission on Accreditation of Rehabilitation Facilities (CARF) accreditation	Control	Service	Staffed Beds	Admissions	Census	Outpatient Visits	Births	Total	Payroll	Personnel

LUFKIN—Angelina County

☒ **MEMORIAL HEALTH SYSTEM OF EAST TEXAS**, 1201 West Frank Avenue, Zip 75904–3357, Mailing Address: P.O. Box 1447, Zip 75902–1447; tel. 936/634–8111 **A**1 2 9 10 19 **F**9 11 12 14 15 16 17 18 19 20 21 22 23 26 27 28 29 31 33 35 36 37 38 39 40 44 45 46 47 48 49 50 51 52 53 55 57 58 59 60 61 62 63 64 65 66 68 69 70 73 74 75 81 82 84 85 88 92 93 94 96 106 107 108 109 110 **P**5 7 **S** Memorial Health System of East Texas, Lufkin, TX
Primary Contact: Bryant H. Krenek, Jr, President and Chief Executive Officer
COO: Richard Ahrens, Chief Operating Officer
CFO: Joe Freudenberger, Chief Financial Officer
CHR: Michael H. Taylor, Vice President Human Resources
Web address: www.memorialhealth.org | 23 | 10 | 180 | 9531 | 122 | 97305 | 660 | 84370 | 31164 | 913 |

MEMORIAL SPECIALTY HOSPITAL, 1201 West Frank Avenue, Zip 75904; tel. 936/639–7975 **A**9 10 **F**2 21 26 27 28 **S** Memorial Health System of East Texas, Lufkin, TX
Primary Contact: Les Leach, Administrator
Web address: www.memorialhealth.org | 23 | 80 | 17 | 188 | 14 | 0 | 0 | 5790 | 2557 | 52 |

☒ **WOODLAND HEIGHTS MEDICAL CENTER**, 505 South John Redditt Drive, Zip 75904–3157, Mailing Address: P.O. Box 150610, Zip 75915–0610; tel. 936/634–8311, (Total facility includes 16 beds in nursing home–type unit) **A**1 9 10 19 **F**2 11 12 14 15 17 19 21 22 26 27 28 29 33 37 40 46 48 49 52 53 55 57 58 59 60 61 62 63 64 65 66 68 69 81 82 84 85 87 88 92 93 94 95 108 109 110 **P**5 7 **S** Triad Hospitals, Inc., Plano, TX
Primary Contact: Lance Jones, Chief Executive Officer
COO: Brad D. Holland, Chief Operating Officer
CFO: Terri Wiggers, Chief Financial Officer
CMO: Carlton Lewis, D.O., Chief of Staff
CIO: Terrie Russell–Scott, Director Information System
CHR: Sally McKinney, Director Human Resources
Web address: www.woodlandheights.net | 32 | 10 | 146 | 6799 | 100 | 49938 | 745 | 59173 | 24622 | 569 |

LULING—Caldwell County

☒ **SETON EDGAR B. DAVIS HOSPITAL**, (Formerly Edgar B. Davis Memorial Hospital), 130 Hays Street, Zip 78648–3207; tel. 830/875–7000 **A**1 9 10 **F**2 9 12 21 22 26 27 28 33 37 42 48 50 52 53 57 58 62 63 64 65 66 69 70 76 81 82 84 88 92 94 97 107 108 **P**8 **S** Ascension Health, Saint Louis, MO
Primary Contact: Neal Kelley, Administrator
COO: Michelle Berkhouse, Director Patient Care Services
CFO: Douglas D. Waite, Chief Financial Officer
CMO: Martin E. Weiner, M.D., Chief of Staff
CIO: Mark Barner, Vice President Information Systems
CHR: Cheryl Williams, Human Resource Director
Web address: www.seton.net | 21 | 10 | 27 | 1595 | 18 | 53056 | 0 | 15677 | 6295 | 150 |

□ **WARM SPRINGS SPECIALTY HOSPITAL**, 200 Memorial Drive, Zip 78648; tel. 830/875–8400 **A**1 10 **F**2 21 26 28 41 52 69 94 96 **S** Warm Springs Rehabilitation System, San Antonio, TX
Primary Contact: Brenda Miles, Administrator
Web address: www.warmsprings.org | 23 | 80 | 36 | 443 | 35 | 9636 | 0 | 12981 | 4263 | 120 |

MADISONVILLE—Madison County

☒ **MADISON ST. JOSEPH HEALTH CENTER**, 100 West Cross Street, Zip 77864–0698, Mailing Address: Box 698, Zip 77864–0698; tel. 936/348–2631 **A**1 9 10 18 **F**2 9 12 22 26 27 28 32 33 37 46 48 52 53 63 69 81 82 88 94 97 106 108 **P**6 **S** Franciscan Services Corporation, Sylvania, OH
Primary Contact: Reed Edmundson, Administrator | 21 | 10 | 25 | 642 | 8 | 26688 | 0 | 7959 | 4122 | 103 |

MANSFIELD—Tarrant County

□ **KINDRED HOSPITAL–MANSFIELD**, 1802 Highway 157 North, Zip 76063–9555; tel. 817/473–6101 **A**1 9 10 **F**21 22 28 33 34 37 49 55 58 62 63 69 81 94 110 **S** Kindred Healthcare, Louisville, KY
Primary Contact: Dalton Stewart, Chief Executive Officer
Web address: www.kindredmansfield.com | 33 | 10 | 39 | 289 | 23 | 350 | 0 | 10410 | 5054 | 96 |

MARLIN—Falls County

★ **FALLS COMMUNITY HOSPITAL AND CLINIC**, 322 Coleman Street, Zip 76661–2358, Mailing Address: Box 60, Zip 76661–0060; tel. 254/803–3561 **A**9 10 20 **F**2 9 24 25 27 28 29 33 34 37 41 44 46 47 48 52 53 58 66 69 72 76 77 81 95 106 108 **P**5
Primary Contact: Willis L. Reese, Administrator
CMO: Dileen Bhateley, M.D., Chief of Staff
CIO: Julie Sharp, Director Business Operations
CHR: Peggy Polster, Personnel Manager and Administrative Assistant
Web address: www.fallshospital.org | 23 | 10 | 32 | 1305 | 14 | 64998 | 0 | 10774 | 3122 | 130 |

MARSHALL—Harrison County

☒ **MARSHALL REGIONAL MEDICAL CENTER**, 811 South Washington Avenue, Zip 75670–5336, Mailing Address: P.O. Box 1599, Zip 75671–1599; tel. 903/927–6000 **A**1 9 10 **F**2 9 11 12 21 22 26 27 28 29 33 39 41 42 46 47 48 51 52 53 55 58 60 62 63 65 66 68 69 70 75 81 82 84 88 94 108 109 **P**7 8
Primary Contact: Russell J. Collier, Chief Executive Officer and Chief Financial Officer
CFO: Russell J. Collier, Chief Executive Officer and Chief Financial Officer
Web address: www.mrmc.net | 23 | 10 | 122 | 3914 | 43 | 96985 | 540 | 53851 | 17178 | 442 |

TX

Hospital, Address, Telephone, Approval, Facility, and Physician Codes, Health Care System	Classi-fication Codes		Utilization Data					Expense (thousands) of dollars		
	Control	Service	Staffed Beds	Admissions	Census	Outpatient Visits	Births	Total	Payroll	Personnel

★ American Hospital Association (AHA) membership
□ Joint Commission on Accreditation of Healthcare Organizations (JCAHO) accreditation
○ American Osteopathic Association (AOA) accreditation
△ Commission on Accreditation of Rehabilitation Facilities (CARF) accreditation

MCALLEN—Hidalgo County

□ **MCALLEN MEDICAL CENTER**, 301 West Expressway 83, Zip 78503–3045; tel. 956/632–4000, (Includes MCALLEN HEART HOSPITAL, 1900 South D. Street, Zip 78503; tel. 956/994–2000) **A**1 3 5 10 **F**2 3 9 11 12 14 15 17 18 19 20 21 22 23 26 27 28 33 34 35 37 39 40 44 46 47 48 49 52 55 56 58 59 60 61 62 63 65 66 67 69 70 71 72 73 74 75 76 81 82 84 86 87 88 92 94 96 108 109 **P**1 **S** Universal Health Services, Inc., King of Prussia, PA Primary Contact: Daniel P. McLean, Chief Executive Officer and Managing Director Web address: www.mcallenmedicalcenter.com	32	10	552	27734	438	59393	5245	253335	94422	2183
✸ **RIO GRANDE REGIONAL HOSPITAL**, 101 East Ridge Road, Zip 78503–1299; tel. 956/632–6000 **A**1 9 10 **F**2 9 10 11 12 14 15 17 19 21 22 23 28 29 32 33 39 40 42 44 46 47 48 49 52 53 55 56 57 58 59 61 62 63 64 66 69 81 82 84 85 88 94 96 108 109 110 **P**7 **S** HCA, Nashville, TN Primary Contact: William A. Burns, Chief Executive Officer COO: Anthony S. Sala, Jr, Chief Operating Officer CFO: Susan S. Turley, Chief Financial Officer CIO: Craig Longenecker, Chief Information Officer Web address: www.riohealth.com	33	10	319	16982	217	91971	4923	134941	43938	956

MCCAMEY—Upton County

★ **MCCAMEY HOSPITAL**, Highway 305 South, Zip 79752, Mailing Address: P.O. Box 1200, Zip 79752–1200; tel. 432/652–8626, (Total facility includes 30 beds in nursing home–type unit) **A**9 10 18 **F**9 27 33 52 63 69 92 97 Primary Contact: Bill Boswell, Chief Executive Officer COO: Tana Robertson, Chief Operating Officer CFO: Arnold Wagner, Controller CMO: Ramon Domingo, M.D., Chief of Staff CHR: Judith Gulihur, Chief Financial Officer	16	10	44	94	25	10509	0	4214	2068	75

MCKINNEY—Collin County

✸ **MEDICAL CENTER OF MCKINNEY**, (Formerly North Central Medical Center), 4500 Medical Center Drive, Zip 75069–3499; tel. 972/547–8000, (Includes WESTPARK SURGERY CENTER, 130 South Central Expressway, Zip 75070; tel. 972/548–5300) **A**1 9 10 **F**2 3 4 9 11 12 15 17 19 21 22 23 26 27 28 33 37 42 44 46 48 49 52 55 58 59 60 62 63 66 68 69 70 71 75 76 77 79 81 82 84 88 92 93 94 96 108 109 110 **S** HCA, Nashville, TN Primary Contact: Ernest C. Lynch, III, Chief Executive Officer COO: Shawn Barbarin, Chief Operating Officer CFO: Dwayne Ray, Chief Financial Officer CMO: Father Ernie Carpenter, M.D., Medical Director CIO: Richard Adams, Director Information Systems CHR: Laura Settles, Director Human Resources Web address: www.ncentralmedical.com	32	10	179	9769	119	49429	756	82389	34756	681

MESQUITE—Dallas County

□ **MEDICAL CENTER OF MESQUITE**, 1011 North Galloway Avenue, Zip 75149–2433; tel. 214/320–7000 **A**1 9 10 **F**2 10 11 12 14 15 17 18 19 21 22 27 28 29 33 34 38 39 40 46 47 48 49 52 53 55 57 58 59 60 62 63 65 69 70 73 81 82 84 85 88 93 94 107 108 109 110 **P**8 **S** Health Management Associates, Naples, FL Primary Contact: Raymond P. De Blasi, Chief Executive Officer Web address: www.hma–corp.com	33	10	156	8813	102	52107	679	62009	26879	467
□ **MESQUITE COMMUNITY HOSPITAL**, 3500 Interstate 30, Zip 75150–2696; tel. 972/698–3300 **A**1 9 10 **F**2 10 11 12 15 21 22 26 27 28 32 33 34 45 48 52 53 55 57 58 59 62 63 64 68 69 77 81 82 84 88 94 96 108 **S** Health Management Associates, Naples, FL Primary Contact: Raymond P. De Blasi, Chief Executive Officer Web address: www.mchtx.com	32	10	137	9131	94	76760	2241	66248	31262	611

MEXIA—Limestone County

✸ **PARKVIEW REGIONAL HOSPITAL**, 600 South Bonham, Zip 76667–3608; tel. 254/562–0408 **A**1 9 10 20 **F**2 9 12 21 22 26 27 28 29 33 40 41 44 46 47 48 52 55 58 60 61 62 63 65 66 68 69 70 81 82 84 88 94 95 97 107 108 109 110 **S** LifePoint Hospitals, Inc., Brentwood, TN Primary Contact: Jimmy D. Stuart, Chief Executive Officer CFO: Jeff Casbeer, Chief Financial Officer CMO: Ron Stephens, M.D., Chief of Staff Web address: www.parkviewregional.com	32	10	59	2851	34	66304	54	21636	9998	298

MIDLAND—Midland County

□ **DESERT SPRINGS MEDICAL CENTER**, 3300 South FM 1788, Zip 79706, Mailing Address: P.O. Box 60608, Zip 79711–0608; tel. 915/563–1200 **A**1 10 **F**3 27 28 71 72 73 74 Primary Contact: Tammy Ross, Interim Chief Executive Officer	33	22	64	959	37	1083	0	4811	3003	86
✸ **HEALTHSOUTH REHABILITATION HOSPITAL MIDLAND–ODESSA**, 1800 Heritage Boulevard, Zip 79707–9750; tel. 432/520–1600 **A**1 10 **F**2 21 28 45 46 48 52 68 69 94 95 96 110 **S** HEALTHSOUTH Corporation, Birmingham, AL Primary Contact: William Grey, Administrator Web address: www.healthsouth.com	33	46	30	683	29	10273	0	9357	4429	119
HEART PLACE HOSPITAL, 25 Village Circle, Zip 79701; tel. 432/571–7000 **A**10 **F**2 15 17 19 21 33 55 57 63 73 79 86 87 88 94 **P**8	32	10	16	251	2	1439	0	4960	2237	56

Many Facility Codes have changed. Please refer to the AHA Guide Code Chart. © 2005 AHA Guide

Hospital, Address, Telephone, Approval, Facility, and Physician Codes, Health Care System	Classification Codes		Utilization Data					Expense (thousands) of dollars		
★ American Hospital Association (AHA) membership □ Joint Commission on Accreditation of Healthcare Organizations (JCAHO) accreditation ○ American Osteopathic Association (AOA) accreditation △ Commission on Accreditation of Rehabilitation Facilities (CARF) accreditation	Control	Service	Staffed Beds	Admissions	Census	Outpatient Visits	Births	Total	Payroll	Personnel

★ **MIDLAND MEMORIAL HOSPITAL**, 2200 West Illinois Avenue, Zip 79701–6499; tel. 432/685–1111, (Includes MEMORIAL REHABILITATION HOSPITAL, Zip 79704; tel. 432/520–2333; MIDLAND MEMORIAL HOSPITAL–WEST CAMPUS, Zip 79703; tel. 432/522–3270) **A**2 3 5 9 10 **F**2 6 9 11 12 14 15 17 19 21 22 23 24 26 27 28 29 33 37 39 44 46 47 48 50 52 55 57 58 59 60 61 62 63 64 65 67 68 69 70 81 82 84 85 88 93 94 95 96 108 109 110 **P**8 Primary Contact: Russell Meyers, President and Chief Executive Officer CFO: Lawrence Sanz, Vice President Finance and Chief Financial Officer CIO: David Whiles, Director Health Information Systems CHR: Maria Znamirowski, Vice President Human Resources Web address: www.midland–memorial.com	16	10	246	10714	159	116097	1745	158177	55180	1338
MIDLAND MEMORIAL HOSPITAL, 4214 Andrews Highway, Zip 79703–4861; tel. 432/685–1584, (Nonreporting) **A**9 10 Primary Contact: Russell Meyers, President and Chief Executive Officer Web address: www.midland–memorial.com	33	10	86	—	—	—	—	—	—	—
□ **SELECT SPECIALTY HOSPITAL OF MIDLAND**, 4214 Andrews Highway, Zip 79703; tel. 432/522–3270, (Nonreporting) **A**1 9 10	33	49	29	—	—	—	—	—	—	—
MINERAL WELLS—Palo Pinto County										
⊞ **PALO PINTO GENERAL HOSPITAL**, 400 S.W. 25th Avenue, Zip 76067–9685; tel. 940/328–6403 **A**1 9 10 **F**9 11 12 14 21 24 26 27 28 33 34 36 38 40 41 42 46 47 48 51 52 53 54 58 59 60 61 62 63 65 66 69 81 82 84 88 93 94 95 97 106 108 109 **P**1 Primary Contact: Patricia Dorris, Chief Executive Officer CFO: Dee Waldow, Chief Financial Officer CMO: Alice Ramsey, M.D., Chief of Staff CHR: Barbara Stagner, Human Resources Director Web address: www.ppgh.com	16	10	42	2736	27	86641	400	28994	13722	335
MISSION—Hidalgo County										
⊞ △ **MISSION HOSPITAL**, 900 South Bryan Road, Zip 78572–6613; tel. 956/323–9000 **A**1 7 9 10 **F**2 9 11 12 15 17 21 22 23 24 26 27 28 29 33 34 39 44 46 48 49 52 53 55 57 58 59 60 61 62 63 66 68 69 70 81 82 84 88 94 95 96 108 109 110 **P**8 Primary Contact: Randy Slack, Interim Chief Executive Officer COO: Mario J. Garza, Chief Operating Officer CFO: Randy Slack, Chief Financial Officer CIO: Major Raymond Bruels, Director Management Information Systems CHR: Susan Willars, Human Resource Director Web address: www.missionhospital.com	23	10	148	9361	124	65186	2138	70041	28064	678
MISSOURI CITY—Fort Bend County										
⊞ **MEMORIAL HERMANN FORT BEND HOSPITAL**, 3803 FM 1092 at Highway 6, Zip 77459; tel. 281/499–4800 **A**1 9 10 **F**2 9 11 12 21 22 26 27 28 29 32 35 36 37 38 39 41 42 44 46 48 52 53 55 58 59 62 63 65 66 68 69 81 82 84 85 88 92 93 94 95 108 **P**5 **S** Memorial Hermann Healthcare System, Houston, TX Primary Contact: Rod Brace, Chief Executive Officer CFO: Brian Hamilton, Chief Financial Officer CMO: Humberto A. Lara, M.D., Chief of Staff CHR: Patsy Jones, Director Web address: www.mhhs.org	23	10	65	3488	40	36508	495	46709	14866	301
MONAHANS—Ward County										
WARD MEMORIAL HOSPITAL, 406 South Gary Street, Zip 79756–4798, Mailing Address: P.O. Box 40, Zip 79756–0040; tel. 432/943–2511 **A**9 10 20 **F**6 26 27 28 33 34 51 59 63 81 88 97 **P**5 Primary Contact: Viki Yates, Interim Administrator Web address: www.wardmemorial.org	13	10	25	502	4	17720	2	178	2588	109
MORTON—Cochran County										
★ **COCHRAN MEMORIAL HOSPITAL**, 201 East Grant Street, Zip 79346–3444; tel. 806/266–5565 **A**9 10 20 **F**27 33 34 39 46 47 48 108 **P**5 6 Primary Contact: Larry Turney, Interim Administrator CHR: Niona Tunney, Director Human Resources	16	10	18	186	1	7488	0	2660	1340	38
MOUNT PLEASANT—Titus County										
⊞ **TITUS REGIONAL MEDICAL CENTER**, 2001 North Jefferson Avenue, Zip 75455–2398; tel. 903/577–6000 **A**1 9 10 19 **F**6 9 11 12 15 21 22 27 28 29 33 34 39 40 42 44 46 47 48 51 52 53 55 56 57 58 59 60 61 62 63 68 69 70 76 81 82 84 85 87 88 93 94 95 96 106 108 109 110 **P**8 Primary Contact: Ronald D. Davis, Chief Executive Officer COO: Daniel L. Gideon, CHE, Chief Executive Officer CFO: Joseph Minissale, Chief Financial Officer CMO: Colton Bradshaw, M.D., Chief of Staff CIO: David Jones, Director Information Systems CHR: George Laurin, Interim Director Human Resources Web address: www.titusregional.com	16	10	144	5110	66	287244	943	50172	22546	600
MOUNT VERNON—Franklin County										
★ **EAST TEXAS MEDICAL CENTER–MOUNT VERNON**, 500 Highway 37 South, Zip 75457–3602, Mailing Address: P.O. Box 477, Zip 75457–0477; tel. 903/537–8000 **A**9 10 **F**2 21 28 29 33 34 39 46 52 58 62 63 65 66 75 81 84 85 88 **S** East Texas Medical Center Regional Healthcare System, Tyler, TX Primary Contact: Stephen Pitts, Administrator CFO: Margaret Haak–Muse, Chief Financial Officer and Assistant Administrator CMO: Robert White, Chief of Staff Web address: www.etmc.org	23	10	30	829	7	6844	0	5364	2048	59

TX

Hospital, Address, Telephone, Approval, Facility, and Physician Codes, Health Care System	Classi-fication Codes		Utilization Data					Expense (thousands) of dollars		
★ American Hospital Association (AHA) membership □ Joint Commission on Accreditation of Healthcare Organizations (JCAHO) accreditation ○ American Osteopathic Association (AOA) accreditation △ Commission on Accreditation of Rehabilitation Facilities (CARF) accreditation	Control	Service	Staffed Beds	Admissions	Census	Outpatient Visits	Births	Total	Payroll	Personnel

MUENSTER—Cooke County

MUENSTER MEMORIAL HOSPITAL, 605 North Maple Street, Zip 76252–2424, Mailing Address: P.O. Box 370, Zip 76252–0370; tel. 940/759–2271 **A**9 10 18 **F**9 11 12 29 33 34 37 41 46 48 51 52 58 59 60 63 69 81 82 88 94 97 **P**8
Primary Contact: Lynn Heller, Administrator and Chief Executive Officer

| | 16 | 10 | 18 | 366 | 5 | 16396 | 9 | 6296 | 1806 | 70 |

MULESHOE—Bailey County

★ MULESHOE AREA MEDICAL CENTER, 708 South First Street, Zip 79347; tel. 806/272–4524 **A**9 10 20 **F**9 11 26 28 29 33 34 39 42 46 47 48 51 52 53 59 63 69 81 84 85 88 97 108 **S** Covenant Health System, Lubbock, TX
Primary Contact: Jim G. Bone, Administrator
CFO: Sharon Novak, CPA, Controller
CMO: Bruce Purdy, M.D., Chief of Staff
Web address: www.mahdservices.org

| | 16 | 10 | 25 | 913 | 7 | 90237 | 71 | 7522 | 3123 | 121 |

NACOGDOCHES—Nacogdoches County

⊠ NACOGDOCHES MEDICAL CENTER, 4920 N.E. Stallings, Zip 75965–1200, Mailing Address: P.O. Box 631604, Zip 75963–1604; tel. 936/569–9481 **A**1 9 10 19 **F**9 10 11 12 15 17 19 21 23 27 28 29 32 33 34 37 40 42 44 46 47 48 49 52 55 57 58 59 60 61 62 63 64 65 66 69 80 81 82 84 85 87 88 93 94 95 96 107 108 109 110 **S** TENET Healthcare Corporation, Dallas, TX
Primary Contact: Gary L. Stokes, Chief Executive Officer
CFO: Rhonda Rogers, Chief Financial Officer
Web address: www.nacmedicalcenter.com

| | 32 | 10 | 150 | 6323 | 68 | 54377 | 661 | 47271 | 20542 | 487 |

□ NACOGDOCHES MEMORIAL HOSPITAL, 1204 North Mound Street, Zip 75961–4061; tel. 936/564–4611 **A**1 9 10 19 **F**2 6 9 11 12 15 17 19 21 22 26 27 28 33 34 36 39 40 46 48 49 50 51 52 53 55 57 59 60 61 62 63 64 65 68 69 81 82 84 85 87 88 93 94 96 108 109 110
Primary Contact: Tim Hayward, Administrator
Web address: www.nacmem.org

| | 16 | 10 | 137 | 6778 | 97 | 73655 | 765 | 73643 | 28893 | 772 |

NAVASOTA—Grimes County

⊠ GRIMES ST. JOSEPH HEALTH CENTER, 210 South Judson Street, Zip 77868–3704, Mailing Address: P.O. Box 1390, Zip 77868–1390; tel. 936/825–6585 **A**1 9 10 18 **F**2 21 26 27 28 33 34 46 48 58 60 63 69 81 84 88 94 96 97 106 108 **S** Franciscan Services Corporation, Sylvania, OH
Primary Contact: Molly Hurst, Administrator
CMO: L. P. Scamardo, II, M.D., Chief of Staff
CHR: Leslie Stratta, Director Human Resources
Web address: www.st–joseph.org

| | 21 | 10 | 25 | 746 | 10 | 16667 | 0 | 5749 | 3046 | 89 |

NEW BOSTON—Bowie County

□ LIVING HOPE NEW BOSTON MEDICAL CENTER, (Formerly Doctor's Hospital), 520 Hospital Drive, Zip 75570–2398, Mailing Address: P.O. Box 7, Zip 75570–0007; tel. 903/628–5531 **A**1 9 10 **F**2 3 13 14 21 22 33 48 52 55 56 58 60 63 65 66 67 68 71 81 92
Primary Contact: Keith T. Naples, Administrator
Web address: www.nbgh.edu

| | 31 | 10 | 6 | 93 | 1 | 2328 | 0 | — | — | — |

NEW BRAUNFELS—Comal County

⊠ MCKENNA MEMORIAL HOSPITAL, 600 North Union Avenue, Zip 78130–4191; tel. 830/606–9111 **A**1 9 10 **F**2 3 9 11 12 13 14 15 21 22 23 24 26 27 28 29 31 33 37 38 39 41 42 46 47 48 51 52 55 56 57 58 59 60 61 62 65 66 67 68 69 71 81 84 85 88 89 92 94 95 96 106 108 109 110
Primary Contact: Tim Brierty, Chief Executive Officer
COO: Karl D. Hittle, Chief Operating Officer
CFO: Allen Strickland, Chief Financial Officer
CIO: Kim Deese, Vice President Information Systems
Web address: www.mckenna.org

| | 23 | 10 | 132 | 6457 | 67 | 87304 | 904 | 69569 | 33720 | 772 |

NOCONA—Montague County

★ NOCONA GENERAL HOSPITAL, 100 Park Street, Zip 76255–3616; tel. 940/825–3235 **A**9 10 **F**6 9 11 12 21 22 26 27 28 29 33 34 37 39 46 47 48 51 52 58 63 66 69 70 81 82 88 94 97 108 110 **P**5
Primary Contact: Michael R. Graham, Administrator
CFO: Lance Meekins, Chief Financial Officer

| | 16 | 10 | 33 | 1146 | 11 | 13788 | 101 | 6113 | 3347 | 116 |

NORTH RICHLAND HILLS—Tarrant County

⊠ NORTH HILLS HOSPITAL, 4401 Booth Calloway Road, Zip 76180–7399; tel. 817/255–1000 **A**1 9 10 **F**2 9 10 11 12 14 15 17 19 21 22 23 27 28 33 41 44 46 47 48 52 55 58 59 60 61 62 63 64 65 66 68 69 81 82 84 85 88 94 96 108 109 110 **S** HCA, Nashville, TN
Primary Contact: Randolph Moresi, Chief Executive Officer
COO: Glenn Wallace, Chief Operating Officer
CFO: Kathleen Sweeney, Chief Information Officer
CMO: James McDonald, M.D., Chief of Staff
CIO: Noah Downs, Director Information Systems
Web address: www.northhillshospital.com

| | 32 | 10 | 140 | 7710 | 98 | 90804 | 798 | 95122 | 29587 | 517 |

ODESSA—Ector County

ALLIANCE HOSPITAL, 515 North Adams, Zip 79761, Mailing Address: P.O. Box 1272, Zip 79760; tel. 432/550–1903 **A**9 10 **F**19 21 22 27 28 33 58 62 63 66 81 84 85 88 106 108 **P**8
Primary Contact: William R. Cook, Chief Executive Officer
Web address: www.alliancehospital.com

| | 32 | 13 | 70 | 2113 | 22 | 6137 | 0 | 38011 | 10205 | 195 |

Many Facility Codes have changed. Please refer to the AHA Guide Code Chart.

Hospital, Address, Telephone, Approval, Facility, and Physician Codes, Health Care System	Classi-fication Codes		Utilization Data					Expense (thousands) of dollars		
★ American Hospital Association (AHA) membership ☐ Joint Commission on Accreditation of Healthcare Organizations (JCAHO) accreditation ○ American Osteopathic Association (AOA) accreditation △ Commission on Accreditation of Rehabilitation Facilities (CARF) accreditation	Control	Service	Staffed Beds	Admissions	Census	Outpatient Visits	Births	Total	Payroll	Personnel
✠ **HEALTHSOUTH REHABILITATION HOSPITAL**, 515 North Adams, 3rd Floor, Zip 79760; tel. 432/550–1800 **A**1 10 **F**2 21 26 45 46 48 52 68 69 94 95 96 110 **S** HEALTHSOUTH Corporation, Birmingham, AL Primary Contact: William Grey, Administrator CFO: Angela Ellis, Chief Financial Officer CMO: Mark Fredrickson, M.D., Medical Director CHR: Tina Parker, Director Human Resources Web address: www.healthsouth.com	33	46	28	544	23	691	0	4961	2465	42
✠ **MEDICAL CENTER HOSPITAL**, 500 West Fourth Street, Zip 79761–5059, Mailing Address: P.O. Drawer 7239, Zip 79760–7239; tel. 432/640–4000 **A**1 3 5 9 10 **F**9 10 11 12 14 15 17 19 21 22 23 26 28 29 33 34 39 46 48 52 53 55 56 57 58 59 60 61 62 63 64 66 68 69 75 81 82 84 85 87 88 92 93 94 96 108 109 110 **P**6 8 Primary Contact: William W. Webster, Chief Executive Officer CFO: Robert Abernethy, Chief Financial Officer CMO: Bruce Becker, M.D., Chief Medical Director CIO: Gary Barnes, Chief Information Officer CHR: Harvey Hudspeth, Executive Director Human Resources Web address: www.mchodessa.com	16	10	311	13078	178	175015	1255	167734	60097	1558
☐ **ODESSA REGIONAL HOSPITAL**, 520 East Sixth Street, Zip 79761–4565, Mailing Address: P.O. Box 4859, Zip 79760–4859; tel. 432/334–8200 **A**1 9 10 **F**11 12 21 22 27 28 29 33 34 39 46 47 48 52 55 56 58 59 62 63 65 66 81 85 88 89 90 94 108 109 **P**8 **S** IASIS Healthcare, Franklin, TN Primary Contact: R. Craig Preston, Chief Executive Officer Web address: www.odessaregionalhospital.com	32	10	146	4663	49	42775	2030	34773	16074	374
✠ **REGENCY HOSPITAL OF ODESSA**, 500 West 4th Street, Suite 701, Zip 79761; tel. 432/552–4000 **A**1 10 **F**2 21 22 26 27 28 37 47 48 49 58 65 94 110 **S** Regency Hospital Company, Alpharetta, GA Primary Contact: Patrick A. Auman, Ph.D., Chief Executive Officer	33	80	36	359	22	0	0	9323	3137	78
OLNEY—Young County										
★ **HAMILTON HOSPITAL**, 903 West Hamilton Street, Zip 76374–1725, Mailing Address: P.O. Box 158, Zip 76374–0158; tel. 940/564–5521 **A**9 10 18 20 **F**6 9 11 21 33 41 63 65 81 97 Primary Contact: Ray Harris, Administrator CFO: Cindy Goldsmith, Chief Financial Officer CMO: Mark L. Mankins, M.D., Chief of Staff	16	10	25	913	8	5483	22	1672	—	97
ORANGE—Orange County										
✠ **MEMORIAL HERMANN BAPTIST IN ORANGE**, 608 Strickland Drive, Zip 77630–4717; tel. 409/883–9361 **A**1 10 **F**11 12 21 22 28 29 33 46 48 52 55 58 59 62 63 68 69 81 84 88 94 108 109 110 **S** Memorial Hermann Healthcare System, Houston, TX Primary Contact: Rosanne Akin, Chief Administrative Officer Web address: www.mhhs.org	23	10	154	3125	41	31193	383	29653	10518	237
PALACIOS—Matagorda County										
PALACIOS COMMUNITY MEDICAL CENTER, 311 Green Street, Zip 77465–3214; tel. 361/972–2511 **A**9 10 18 20 **F**26 28 33 46 53 68 69 97 108 110 Primary Contact: Kathy Nichols, Co–Administrator Web address: www.palacioscommunitymedcenter.com	23	10	17	245	2	2804	0	1091	1103	28
PALESTINE—Anderson County										
✠ **PALESTINE REGIONAL MEDICAL CENTER–EAST**, 2900 South Loop 256, Zip 75801–6958; tel. 903/731–1000 **A**1 9 10 19 **F**2 11 12 15 21 22 26 27 28 33 35 37 39 40 45 46 48 53 55 59 62 63 65 66 69 70 71 73 74 75 76 81 82 84 87 88 93 94 95 108 109 110 **S** LifePoint Hospitals, Inc., Brentwood, TN Primary Contact: Randall L. Hoover, Chief Executive Officer CIO: Rebecca Chou, Director Information Systems Web address: www.palestineregional.com	32	10	124	6604	58	68929	859	48940	18981	479
✠ **PALESTINE REGIONAL REHABILITATION CENTER**, 4000 South Loop 256, Zip 75801–8467, Mailing Address: P.O. Box 4070, Zip 75802–4070; tel. 903/731–1000 **A**1 9 10 **F**6 26 27 28 35 65 66 68 69 **S** LifePoint Hospitals, Inc., Brentwood, TN Primary Contact: Randall L. Hoover, Chief Executive Officer CFO: Jeff Van Horn, Chief Financial Officer Web address: www.palestineregional.com	32	46	22	463	13	6349	0	4309	2109	70
PAMPA—Gray County										
✠ **PAMPA REGIONAL MEDICAL CENTER**, (Formerly Columbia Medical Center), One Medical Plaza, Zip 79065; tel. 806/665–3721, (Total facility includes 16 beds in nursing home–type unit) **A**1 9 10 20 **F**2 9 11 12 14 21 28 33 37 40 44 46 47 53 58 59 60 63 64 65 66 69 71 76 81 82 84 88 92 94 108 109 **P**8 **S** Triad Hospitals, Inc., Plano, TX Primary Contact: Alan N. King, Chief Executive Officer COO: Thomas Barton, Chief Operating Officer and Chief Nursing Officer CFO: Steven Smith, Chief Financial Officer CMO: Laxmichand Kamnani, M.D., Chief Medical Staff CIO: Jeff Anderson, Director Information Services CHR: Debbie Dixon, Director, Human Resources Web address: www.triadhospitals.com	32	10	91	3021	44	25850	280	25489	11002	240

TX

Hospital, Address, Telephone, Approval, Facility, and Physician Codes, Health Care System	Classi-fication Codes		Utilization Data					Expense (thousands) of dollars		
★ American Hospital Association (AHA) membership □ Joint Commission on Accreditation of Healthcare Organizations (JCAHO) accreditation ○ American Osteopathic Association (AOA) accreditation △ Commission on Accreditation of Rehabilitation Facilities (CARF) accreditation	Control	Service	Staffed Beds	Admissions	Census	Outpatient Visits	Births	Total	Payroll	Personnel

PARIS—Lamar County

★ **DUBUIS HOSPITAL OF PARIS**, 865 Deshong Drive, 5th Floor, Zip 75462;
tel. 903/782–2960 **A**9 10 **F**2 21 27 28 **S** Dubuis Health System, Houston, TX
Primary Contact: Berry Gilbert, Administrator
Web address: www.dubuis.org

| | 21 | 10 | 25 | 198 | 14 | 0 | 0 | 4663 | 2303 | 40 |

□ **PARIS REGIONAL MEDICAL CENTER**, 820 Clarksville Street, Zip 75460–9070;
tel. 903/785–4521, (Includes PARIS REGIONAL MEDICAL CENTER, 865 Deshong
Drive, Zip 75462–2097; tel. 903/737–1111; PARIS REGIONAL MEDICAL
CENTER–SOUTH CAMPUS, Mailing Address: P.O. Box 9070, Zip 75461–9070;
Andrew Knizley, Chief Executive Officer), (Nonreporting) **A**1 9 10 19 **S** Essent
Healthcare, Nashville, TN
Primary Contact: Andrew Knizley, Chief Executive Officer
Web address: www.parisrmc.com

| | 21 | 10 | 445 | — | — | — | — | — | — | — |

PASADENA—Harris County

⊞ **BAYSHORE MEDICAL CENTER**, 4000 Spencer Highway, Zip 77504–1294;
tel. 713/359–2000 **A**1 9 10 **F**2 10 11 12 14 15 17 19 21 23 27 28 29 33 37
38 40 44 46 47 48 52 55 56 57 58 59 60 61 62 63 65 66 68 69 70 75 79
81 82 84 86 87 88 90 93 94 95 96 97 107 108 109 **S** HCA, Nashville, TN
Primary Contact: Phillip D. Robinson, Chief Executive Officer
COO: Tayo Fichtl, Chief Operating Officer
CFO: Patrick J. Mathews, Chief Financial Officer
CHR: Major Tommy Doss, Director Human Resources
Web address: www.bayshoremedical.com

| | 32 | 10 | 360 | 16360 | 223 | 96254 | 2208 | 127529 | 51244 | 1010 |

KINDRED HOSPITAL–BAY AREA, 1004 Seymour Street, Zip 77506–2699;
tel. 713/473–9700 **A**9 10 **F**2 3 13 14 21 27 28 55 56 64 67 68 69 71 81 92
93 94 110 **P**5 **S** Kindred Healthcare, Louisville, KY
Primary Contact: Randy E. Johnson, Chief Executive Officer
Web address: www.kindredhealthcare.com

| | 33 | 80 | 78 | 778 | 52 | 120 | 0 | 19712 | 8525 | 155 |

VISTA MEDICAL CENTER HOSPITAL, 4301B Vista, Zip 77504;
tel. 713/378–3000 **A**10 **F**2 10 21 22 25 33 37 45 53 55 58 60 62 63 64 66
81 82 84 88 93 94 **P**8 **S** Dynacq Healthcare, Inc., Houston, TX
Primary Contact: Rick Dicapo, Chief Executive Officer
Web address: www.dynacq.com

| | 33 | 10 | 37 | 697 | 5 | 6816 | 0 | 26720 | 5832 | 162 |

PEARSALL—Frio County

★ **FRIO REGIONAL HOSPITAL**, 200 South I. H. 35, Zip 78061–3998;
tel. 830/334–3617 **A**9 10 20 **F**11 12 27 28 33 34 51 52 63 69 81 88
Primary Contact: Alan D. Holmes, Chief Executive Officer
Web address: www.frioregionalhospital.com

| | 23 | 10 | 22 | 778 | 7 | 16431 | 142 | 6941 | 2926 | 88 |

PECOS—Reeves County

★ **REEVES COUNTY HOSPITAL**, 2323 Texas Street, Zip 79772–7338;
tel. 432/447–3551 **A**9 10 20 **F**6 9 11 26 27 29 33 34 46 51 52 55 59 63 66
69 81 85 88 94 95 97 108 109
Primary Contact: Bill Conder, Administrator and Chief Executive Officer
CFO: Frank Seals, Chief Financial Officer
CMO: W J. Bang, Chief of Staff
CHR: Nadine Smith, Director Human Resources
Web address: www.reevescountyhospital.com

| | 16 | 10 | 44 | 789 | 8 | 19365 | 67 | 10546 | 4364 | 147 |

PERRYTON—Ochiltree County

★ **OCHILTREE GENERAL HOSPITAL**, 3101 Garrett Drive, Zip 79070–5393;
tel. 806/435–3606 **A**9 10 18 20 **F**8 9 11 12 27 28 29 33 34 36 45 46 47 48
51 52 54 55 59 60 63 69 81 82 88 94 96 97 108 109 **P**1
Primary Contact: Wallace N. Boyd, Administrator
CIO: Dyan Harrison, Health Information Manager
Web address: www.ochiltreehospital.com

| | 16 | 10 | 25 | 889 | 10 | 23562 | 190 | 8629 | 3816 | 117 |

PITTSBURG—Camp County

⊞ **EAST TEXAS MEDICAL CENTER PITTSBURG**, 414 Quitman Street,
Zip 75686–1032; tel. 903/856–6663 **A**1 9 10 **F**2 9 14 21 26 27 28 33 34 39
42 45 46 48 51 52 63 64 81 82 88 94 **S** East Texas Medical Center Regional
Healthcare System, Tyler, TX
Primary Contact: W. Perry Henderson, Administrator
CFO: Thomas O'Gorman, Jr, Assistant Administrator and Chief Financial Officer
CMO: W R. Christensen, M.D., Chief of Staff
CIO: Paula Anthony, Vice President Information Sevices
Web address: www.etmc.com

| | 23 | 10 | 42 | 1594 | 15 | 60025 | 0 | 17549 | 6597 | 158 |

PLAINVIEW—Hale County

⊞ **COVENANT HOSPITAL PLAINVIEW**, 2601 Dimmitt Road, Zip 79072–1833;
tel. 806/296–5531 **A**1 9 10 **F**2 9 11 12 15 21 22 26 27 28 29 32 33 34 35
37 40 42 44 46 48 50 52 53 55 58 59 60 62 63 65 66 69 70 81 82 84 85
88 93 94 95 96 97 98 108 110 **P**8 **S** Covenant Health System, Lubbock, TX
Primary Contact: Joe S. Langford, Chief Executive Officer
CFO: Kirk Cristy, Chief Financial Officer
CMO: W Hank Landers, M.D., Chief of Staff
CIO: Tim Branch, Information Technology Manager
CHR: Mike McNutt, Director of Human Resources
Web address: www.covenantplainview.org

| | 21 | 10 | 31 | 2312 | 23 | 54034 | 640 | 22965 | 8126 | 253 |

PLANO—Collin County

⊞ **BAYLOR REGIONAL MEDICAL CENTER AT PLANO**, 4700 Alliance Boulevard,
Zip 75093; tel. 469/814–2000, (Nonreporting) **A**1 10 **S** Baylor Health Care
System, Dallas, TX
Primary Contact: Arthur E. Aenchbacher, Jr, President

| | 23 | 10 | 96 | — | — | — | — | — | — | — |

Many Facility Codes have changed. Please refer to the AHA Guide Code Chart. © 2005 AHA Guide

Hospital, Address, Telephone, Approval, Facility, and Physician Codes, Health Care System	Classi-fication Codes		Utilization Data					Expense (thousands) of dollars		
★ American Hospital Association (AHA) membership ☐ Joint Commission on Accreditation of Healthcare Organizations (JCAHO) accreditation ○ American Osteopathic Association (AOA) accreditation △ Commission on Accreditation of Rehabilitation Facilities (CARF) accreditation	Control	Service	Staffed Beds	Admissions	Census	Outpatient Visits	Births	Total	Payroll	Personnel
⊞ **HEALTHSOUTH PLANO REHABILITATION HOSPITAL**, 2800 West 15th Street, Zip 75075–7526; tel. 972/612–9000 **A**1 10 **F**21 22 26 27 37 52 57 58 68 69 76 88 93 95 96 108 110 **S** HEALTHSOUTH Corporation, Birmingham, AL Primary Contact: Chester Crouch, Administrator CFO: Patricia Weigel, Controller CMO: Richard Jones, M.D., Medical Director CHR: April Maldonado, Manager Human Resources Web address: www.healthsouth.com	32	46	65	1605	57	27640	0	17382	9470	179
LIFECARE HOSPITALS OF PLANO, 6800 Preston Road, Zip 75024; tel. 214/473–8822 **A**9 **F**2 21 28 33 37 38 44 49 52 58 60 65 69 88 94 110 **S** LifeCare Management Services, Plano, TX Primary Contact: Kent Ashley, Chief Executive Officer Web address: www.lifecare–hospitals.com	32	80	66	651	48	23	0	20120	8158	201
⊞ **MEDICAL CENTER OF PLANO**, 3901 West 15th Street, Zip 75075–7799; tel. 972/596–6800 **A**1 2 9 10 **F**2 9 11 12 15 17 19 21 22 23 26 27 28 29 32 33 37 40 41 42 44 46 47 48 49 50 52 55 56 57 58 59 61 62 63 64 65 66 67 68 69 81 82 84 85 86 87 88 93 94 96 106 108 109 110 **P**5 **S** HCA, Nashville, TN Primary Contact: Harvey L. Fishero, President and Chief Executive Officer COO: Winston Borland, Chief Operating Officer CFO: Mark Atchley, Vice President and Chief Financial Officer CIO: Michael Gfellerr, Director Information Systems CHR: Jerry McMorrough, Vice President Human Resources Web address: www.medicalcenterplano.com	32	10	348	17605	249	147054	3877	192582	74414	1317
☐ **PLANO SPECIALTY HOSPITAL**, (Formerly IHS Hospital at Plano), 1621 Coit Road, Zip 75075; tel. 972/758–5200 **A**1 9 10 **F**2 21 26 27 33 37 94 110 **P**8 **S** Integrated Health Services, Sparks Glencoe, MD Primary Contact: Terry Kepler, Administrator and Chief Executive Officer	33	80	30	390	26	0	0	7934	4194	112
⊞ **PRESBYTERIAN HOSPITAL OF PLANO**, 6200 West Parker Road, Zip 75093–7914; tel. 972/981–8000, (Includes SEAY BEHAVIORAL HEALTH CENTER, 6200 West Parker Road, Zip 75093–7938; tel. 972/981–8000; Gayle Jensen–Savoie, Director Psychiatric Services) **A**1 9 10 **F**2 4 10 11 12 15 17 19 21 22 24 26 27 28 29 31 33 35 37 46 47 48 49 52 53 55 56 57 58 59 60 61 62 63 65 66 69 72 73 74 81 82 84 87 88 89 90 93 94 96 106 108 109 110 **P**8 **S** Texas Health Resources, Arlington, TX Primary Contact: Philip M. Wentworth, FACHE, President CFO: Ray Cassens, Vice President and Chief Financial Officer CMO: Michael Gross, M.D., Medical Director CHR: Deborah Diehl, Director, Human Resources Web address: www.texashealth.org	23	10	203	14899	175	99629	3407	183617	72167	1288
PORT ARTHUR—Jefferson County										
⊞ **CHRISTUS ST. MARY HOSPITAL**, 3600 Gates Boulevard, Zip 77642–3601, Mailing Address: P.O. Box 3696, Zip 77643–3696; tel. 409/985–7431, (Total facility includes 19 beds in nursing home–type unit) **A**1 9 10 **F**2 9 11 12 14 15 17 19 21 22 23 24 26 27 28 29 30 31 32 33 35 39 40 41 42 46 47 48 52 57 58 59 60 61 62 63 64 65 66 69 70 81 82 84 88 92 94 96 106 107 108 109 **P**8 **S** Christus Health, Irving, TX Primary Contact: Wayne Moore, Administrator CFO: Wayne Moore, Assistant Administrator CHR: Charles Foster, Regional Director Human Resources Web address: www.christusstmary.org	21	10	196	8148	116	110514	442	84270	30750	907
★ **DUBUIS HOSPITAL OF PORT ARTHUR**, 3600 Gates Boulevard, Zip 77642; tel. 409/989–5300, (Nonreporting) **A**9 **S** Dubuis Health System, Houston, TX Primary Contact: Stephen Mills, Administrator	21	49	15	—	—	—	—	—	—	—
☐ **THE MEDICAL CENTER OF SOUTHEAST TEXAS**, 2555 Jimmy Johnson Boulevard, Zip 77640; tel. 409/724–7389, (Nonreporting) **A**1 5 9 10 **S** IASIS Healthcare, Franklin, TN Primary Contact: P. Craig Desmond, Chief Executive Officer Web address: www.medicalcentersetexas.com	33	10	216	—	—	—	—	—	—	—
PORT LAVACA—Calhoun County										
★ **MEMORIAL MEDICAL CENTER**, 815 North Virginia Street, Zip 77979–3025, Mailing Address: P.O. Box 25, Zip 77979–0025; tel. 361/552–6713 **A**9 10 18 **F**2 9 11 12 21 22 23 24 26 27 28 29 33 34 36 37 38 39 42 44 46 48 49 51 52 53 55 58 59 60 61 62 63 64 65 66 69 70 75 81 82 84 85 88 93 94 96 97 98 108 109 110 **P**5 Primary Contact: Elwood E. Currier, Jr, CHE, Administrator CFO: Jamie R. Jacoby, Chief Financial Officer CMO: Richard Arroyo–Diaz, M.D., Chief of Staff CIO: Matthew Torres, Chief Information Officer CHR: Pat Trigg, Direcor of Human Resources and Public Relations Web address: www.mmcportlavaca.com	13	10	25	1363	14	29040	147	17393	7204	180
QUANAH—Hardeman County										
HARDEMAN COUNTY MEMORIAL HOSPITAL, 402 Mercer Street, Zip 79252–4026, Mailing Address: P.O. Box 90, Zip 79252–0090; tel. 940/663–2795 **A**9 10 18 **F**9 21 27 28 29 33 34 39 47 48 51 52 58 66 69 97 109 **P**6 Primary Contact: Scott Nail, Administrator	16	10	24	115	1	26140	0	3161	1478	57

TX

Hospital, Address, Telephone, Approval, Facility, and Physician Codes, Health Care System	Classification Codes		Utilization Data					Expense (thousands) of dollars		
★ American Hospital Association (AHA) membership □ Joint Commission on Accreditation of Healthcare Organizations (JCAHO) accreditation ○ American Osteopathic Association (AOA) accreditation △ Commission on Accreditation of Rehabilitation Facilities (CARF) accreditation	Control	Service	Staffed Beds	Admissions	Census	Outpatient Visits	Births	Total	Payroll	Personnel

QUITMAN—Wood County

⊠ **EAST TEXAS MEDICAL CENTER–QUITMAN**, 117 Winnsboro Street, Zip 75783–2144, Mailing Address: P.O. Box 1000, Zip 75783–1000; tel. 903/763–6300 **A**1 9 10 **F**11 12 15 21 23 26 27 28 33 34 37 39 42 46 48 53 62 63 66 81 88 94 96 97 108 **P**7 **S** East Texas Medical Center Regional Healthcare System, Tyler, TX
Primary Contact: Ernest R. Parisi, CHE, Administrator and Chief Executive Officer
CFO: Judy Callison, Chief Financial Officer
CMO: Beverly Waddelton, D.O., Chief Medical Staff
CHR: Diane Hinds, Human Resources Director
Web address: www.etmc.org

| | 23 | 10 | 28 | 1498 | 15 | 34480 | 99 | 12984 | 5340 | 157 |

RANKIN—Upton County

RANKIN HOSPITAL DISTRICT, 1105 Elizabeth Street, Zip 79778, Mailing Address: P.O. Box 327, Zip 79778–0327; tel. 432/693–2443 **A**9 10 18 **F**26 27 28 33 52
Primary Contact: Juanita Wheeler, Interim Chief Executive Officer

| | 16 | 10 | 5 | 53 | 1 | 1218 | 0 | 1780 | 816 | 22 |

REFUGIO—Refugio County

REFUGIO COUNTY MEMORIAL HOSPITAL, 107 Swift Street, Zip 78377–2425; tel. 361/526–2321 **A**9 10 18 **F**2 6 21 26 27 28 33 34 46 50 52 58 63 65 66 69 70 81 88 97 108 **P**6
Primary Contact: Louis R. Willeke, Administrator

| | 16 | 10 | 20 | 289 | 3 | 32157 | 0 | 8694 | 2746 | 97 |

RICHARDSON—Dallas County

⊠ **RICHARDSON REGIONALMEDICAL CENTER**, 401 West Campbell Road, Zip 75080–3499; tel. 972/498–4000 **A**1 9 10 **F**2 3 4 9 11 12 15 17 19 21 22 23 26 27 28 29 31 32 33 37 38 40 43 44 45 46 47 48 52 53 55 56 57 58 59 60 61 62 63 64 65 66 68 69 70 71 73 74 75 76 77 78 79 80 81 82 83 84 85 86 87 88 90 92 93 94 95 96 106 108 109 110 **P**6
Primary Contact: Ronald L. Boring, President and Chief Executive Officer
CFO: Bob Simpson, Chief Financial Officer
CIO: Ron Franquiz, Director Information Systems
CHR: Connie Wright, Director Human Resources
Web address: www.richardsonregional.com

| | 16 | 10 | 141 | 7756 | 80 | 75785 | 965 | 102239 | 34791 | 700 |

RICHMOND—Fort Bend County

□ **OAKBEND MEDICAL CENTER**, (Formerly Polly Ryon Memorial Hospital), 1705 Jackson Street, Zip 77469–3289; tel. 281/341–3000, (Total facility includes 26 beds in nursing home–type unit) **A**1 9 10 **F**2 9 11 12 21 22 26 27 28 33 34 39 46 48 53 55 57 58 59 61 62 63 64 66 73 75 81 82 84 87 88 92 94 95 96 108 109 110 **P**6 8
Primary Contact: David B. Rowe, Chief Executive Officer
Web address: www.oakbendmedcenter.org

| | 16 | 10 | 122 | 6186 | 76 | 54149 | 1110 | 53517 | 21957 | 532 |

RIO GRANDE CITY—Starr County

★ **STARR COUNTY MEMORIAL HOSPITAL**, 2573 Hospital Court, Zip 78582–9801, Mailing Address: P.O. Box 78, Zip 78582–0078; tel. 956/487–5561 **A**9 10 20 **F**6 9 11 22 26 27 28 33 34 46 48 58 59 63 81 88 94 97 **P**5
Primary Contact: Thalia H. Munoz, Administrator
CFO: Rafael Olivares, Controller
Web address: www.starrcountyhospital.com

| | 16 | 10 | 49 | 2246 | 21 | 80425 | 776 | 17673 | 8177 | 249 |

ROCKDALE—Milam County

RICHARDS MEMORIAL HOSPITAL, 1700 Brazos Street, Zip 76567–2517, Mailing Address: Drawer 1010, Zip 76567–1010; tel. 512/446–2513 **A**9 10 18 **F**8 26 27 28 33 34 63 81 **P**5
Primary Contact: Jeffrey Madison, Administrator
Web address: www.richardsmemorial.com

| | 16 | 10 | 25 | 689 | 6 | 11109 | 0 | 4829 | 2523 | 150 |

ROTAN—Fisher County

FISHER COUNTY HOSPITAL DISTRICT, Roby Highway, Zip 79546–4019, Mailing Address: Drawer F, Zip 79546–4019; tel. 325/735–2256 **A**9 10 18 **F**6 8 24 27 28 29 30 31 33 34 41 45 46 47 48 51 52 58 69 70 88 97 98 106 **P**6
Primary Contact: Ella Raye Helms, Administrator

| | 16 | 10 | 10 | 286 | 3 | 17968 | 0 | 5344 | 2231 | 70 |

ROUND ROCK—Williamson County

⊠ **ROUND ROCK MEDICAL CENTER**, 2400 Round Rock Avenue, Zip 78681–4097; tel. 512/341–1000 **A**1 9 10 **F**2 9 10 11 12 15 17 21 22 23 26 27 28 29 33 44 46 47 48 52 55 57 58 59 60 61 62 63 64 65 66 69 81 82 84 85 88 93 94 96 108 109 110 **S** HCA, Nashville, TN
Primary Contact: Deborah L. Ryle, Administrator and Chief Executive Officer
CFO: Kellie Bolin, Chief Financial Officer
Web address: www.roundrockmc.com

| | 23 | 10 | 114 | 7143 | 72 | 76239 | 1785 | 61922 | 24892 | 476 |

ROWLETT—Rockwall County

⊠ **LAKE POINTE MEDICAL CENTER**, 6800 Scenic Drive, Zip 75088–4552, Mailing Address: P.O. Box 1550, Zip 75030–1550; tel. 972/412–2273 **A**1 9 10 **F**2 9 10 11 12 14 15 21 24 28 32 33 39 41 46 48 57 58 59 60 62 63 64 65 69 81 84 85 87 88 93 94 95 96 106 108 109 **S** TENET Healthcare Corporation, Dallas, TX
Primary Contact: John Harris, Chief Executive Officer
COO: Carolyn Jackson, Chief Operating Officer
CFO: Mike Bierman, Chief Financial Officer
CMO: Paul Zopolsky, M.D., Chief of Staff
CIO: Dianna Miller, Interim Director Medical Records
CHR: Eileen Beasley, Director of Human Resources
Web address: www.lakepointemedical.com

| | 33 | 10 | 99 | 5956 | 58 | 57681 | 882 | 45704 | 20162 | 546 |

Many Facility Codes have changed. Please refer to the AHA Guide Code Chart. © 2005 AHA Guide

TX

Hospital, Address, Telephone, Approval, Facility, and Physician Codes, Health Care System	Classification Codes		Utilization Data					Expense (thousands) of dollars		
	Control	Service	Staffed Beds	Admissions	Census	Outpatient Visits	Births	Total	Payroll	Personnel

★ American Hospital Association (AHA) membership
☐ Joint Commission on Accreditation of Healthcare Organizations (JCAHO) accreditation
○ American Osteopathic Association (AOA) accreditation
△ Commission on Accreditation of Rehabilitation Facilities (CARF) accreditation

RUSK—Cherokee County

☐ **RUSK STATE HOSPITAL**, Jacksonville Highway North, Zip 75785, Mailing Address: P.O. Box 318, Zip 75785–0318; tel. 903/683–3421 **A**1 10 **F**2 22 26 27 28 32 35 39 53 58 65 66 71 76 94 106 108 110 **P**6 **S** Texas Department of State Health Services, Austin, TX
Primary Contact: Ted Debbs, Administrator
Web address: www.mhmr.state.tx.us/hospitals/rusksh/rusksh.html

	12	22	271	1963	267	0	0	42915	23529	787

SAN ANGELO—Tom Green County

☐ **RIVER CREST HOSPITAL**, 1636 Hunters Glen Road, Zip 76901–5016; tel. 325/949–5722 **A**1 10 **F**3 4 21 24 27 28 29 44 45 48 66 71 72 73 74 75 76 77 78 94 96 **S** Universal Health Services, Inc., King of Prussia, PA
Primary Contact: Larry Grimes, Chief Executive Officer and Managing Director
Web address: www.rivercresthospital.com

	33	22	80	1864	37	1067	0	5560	2854	93

⊞ △ **SAN ANGELO COMMUNITY MEDICAL CENTER**, 3501 Knickerbocker Road, Zip 76904–7698; tel. 325/949–9511 **A**1 2 7 9 10 **F**2 9 11 12 14 15 17 19 21 22 23 24 26 27 28 29 32 33 34 35 37 38 39 40 41 42 44 46 47 48 49 50 52 53 55 56 57 58 59 60 61 62 63 64 65 66 67 68 69 70 71 81 82 84 85 87 88 92 93 94 95 96 97 107 108 109 110 **P**7 8 **S** Triad Hospitals, Inc., Plano, TX
Primary Contact: Samuel G. Feazell, Chief Executive Officer
CFO: Ed Romero, Chief Financial Officer
CMO: Cecil Jameson, R.N., Chief Clinical Officer
CHR: Lisa Bibb, Director of Human Resources
Web address: www.sacmc.com

	32	10	127	6905	86	74394	1005	56295	22294	633

☐ **SCCI HOSPITAL–SAN ANGELO**, 2018 Pulliam Street, 3rd Floor, Zip 76905; tel. 325/659–3906 **A**1 9 10 **F**2 21 110
Primary Contact: Steve Grappe, Administrator
Web address: www.scci–ltac.com

	33	80	28	258	18	0	0	6194	2427	64

⊞ △ **SHANNON MEDICAL CENTER**, 120 East Harris Street, Zip 76903–5976; tel. 325/653–6741, (Includes SHANNON MEDICAL CENTER– ST. JOHN'S CAMPUS, 2018 Pulliam Street, Zip 76905–5197; tel. 915/659–7100), (Total facility includes 22 beds in nursing home–type unit) **A**1 2 7 9 10 **F**2 6 9 11 12 15 17 19 21 22 23 26 27 28 29 31 33 34 37 39 40 41 42 44 46 47 48 49 51 52 55 56 57 58 59 60 61 62 63 64 65 66 68 69 71 73 74 75 76 78 81 82 84 85 86 87 88 92 93 94 95 96 107 108 109 110
Primary Contact: Lawrence Leonard, President and Chief Executive Officer
COO: Bryan Horner, Chief Operating Officer
CFO: Daniel E. Davis, Chief Financial Officer
CMO: Irvin Zeitler, D.O., Vice President Medical Affairs
CHR: Teresa Morgan, Assistant Vice President Human Resources
Web address: www.shannonhealth.com

	23	10	258	12306	167	117212	1037	129086	51504	1324

SAN ANTONIO—Bexar County

⊞ **BAPTIST MEDICAL CENTER**, 111 Dallas Street, Zip 78205–1230; tel. 210/297–7000 **A**1 2 6 9 10 **F**2 9 11 12 14 15 17 19 21 22 23 27 28 29 33 34 35 39 46 48 49 52 53 55 56 59 62 63 64 65 66 68 69 70 71 74 75 76 81 82 84 88 93 108 109 **S** Vanguard Health System, Nashville, TN
Primary Contact: Keith L. Swinney, Chief Executive Officer
COO: Philip J. Noel, III, Assistant Administrator and Chief Operating Officer
CFO: Linda Kirks, Chief Financial Officer
CMO: Herman Williams, M.D., Chief Medical Officer
CIO: Gary Davis, Vice President Information Systems
CHR: Sarah Spinharney, Senior Vice President
Web address: www.baptisthealth.com/bmc.asp

	21	10	375	16254	232	49425	1269	122426	51159	1058

★ △ **CHRISTUS SANTA ROSA CHILDREN'S HOSPITAL**, 333 North Santa Rosa Street, Zip 78207; tel. 210/704–2011 **A**7 9 10 **F**2 16 18 20 21 22 24 26 27 28 33 36 37 38 42 49 52 56 57 58 61 62 63 64 65 66 67 77 81 82 84 85 88 90 94 108 **S** Christus Health, Irving, TX
Primary Contact: Richard Wayne, M.D., Vice President and Administrator
COO: Don A. Beeler, President and Chief Executive Officer
CFO: William Pack, Chief Financial Officer
CHR: Carlos V. Torres
Web address: www.christussantarosa.org/childrenshospital.html

	21	50	187	5827	113	111503	0	76628	33981	2233

⊞ △ **CHRISTUS SANTA ROSA HEALTH CARE**, 333 North Santa Rosa, Zip 78207–3108; tel. 210/704–2011 **A**1 3 5 7 9 10 **F**2 9 11 12 14 15 17 19 21 22 26 27 28 29 33 34 49 52 55 57 58 59 60 61 62 63 64 65 66 68 69 81 82 84 85 88 90 93 94 96 100 101 102 103 108 109 110 **S** Christus Health, Irving, TX
Primary Contact: Don A. Beeler, President and Chief Executive Officer
CFO: William Pack, Chief Financial Officer
CHR: Carlos V. Torres, Regional Vice President, Human Resources
Web address: www.christussantarosa.org

	21	10	378	18696	271	98413	2841	199249	76074	2233

☐ **COMPASS HOSPITAL OF SAN ANTONIO**, 14743 Jones Maltsberger Avenue, Zip 78247–3713; tel. 210/402–0029 **A**1 9 10 **F**2 21 22 28 94 110 **P**5 **S** Psychiatric Solutions, Franklin, TN
Primary Contact: Edgar F. Prettyman, M.D., Chief Executive Officer

	33	80	35	361	25	0	0	9148	3963	91

☐ **HEALTHSOUTH INTEGRATED MEDICAL PLAZA**, 4243 East Southcross Boulevard, Zip 78222; tel. 210/368–7400, (Nonreporting) **A**1 10 **S** HEALTHSOUTH Corporation, Birmingham, AL

	33	13	6	—	—	—	—	—	—	—

TX

Hospital, Address, Telephone, Approval, Facility, and Physician Codes, Health Care System	Classi-fication Codes		Utilization Data					Expense (thousands) of dollars		
★ American Hospital Association (AHA) membership □ Joint Commission on Accreditation of Healthcare Organizations (JCAHO) accreditation ○ American Osteopathic Association (AOA) accreditation △ Commission on Accreditation of Rehabilitation Facilities (CARF) accreditation	Control	Service	Staffed Beds	Admissions	Census	Outpatient Visits	Births	Total	Payroll	Personnel
✖ **HEALTHSOUTH REHABILITATION INSTITUTE OF SAN ANTONIO**, 9119 Cinnamon Hill, Zip 78240–5401; tel. 210/691–0737 **A**1 10 **F**7 21 26 27 28 37 42 52 58 68 69 94 96 **P**5 **S** HEALTHSOUTH Corporation, Birmingham, AL Primary Contact: Diane B. Lampe, Administrator CFO: Larry Spriggs, Controller CMO: Richard Senelick, Medical Director Web address: www.healthsouth.com	33	46	96	1607	69	17529	0	17497	8250	240
□ **KINDRED HOSPITAL–SAN ANTONIO**, 3636 Medical Drive, Zip 78229–3184; tel. 210/616–0616 **A**1 9 10 **F**2 26 28 33 34 55 60 94 96 110 **S** Kindred Healthcare, Louisville, KY Primary Contact: John M. Griffes, Chief Executive Officer Web address: www.kindredhealthcare.com	32	10	59	569	47	—	—	14522	8165	176
□ **LAUREL RIDGE HOSPITAL**, 17720 Corporate Woods Drive, Zip 78259–3500, Mailing Address: P.O. Box 700590, Zip 78259–3500; tel. 210/491–9400 **A**1 10 **F**4 21 27 31 71 72 73 74 75 78 94 **S** Psychiatric Solutions, Franklin, TN Primary Contact: Ramona T. Key, Chief Executive Officer Web address: www.brownschools.com	33	22	94	2812	60	5904	0	19586	9428	216
□ **LIFECARE HOSPITALS OF SAN ANTONIO**, (Specialty Hospital), 8026 Floyd Curl Drive, Zip 78229; tel. 210/575–8005 **A**1 9 10 **F**2 21 37 38 57 58 60 61 62 64 65 66 70 88 94 108 110 **P**8 **S** LifeCare Management Services, Plano, TX Primary Contact: Randall G. Stokes, Chief Executive Officer Web address: www.lifecare–hospitals.com	32	49	38	492	38	0	0	12890	—	111
✖ **METHODIST AMBULATORY SURGERY HOSPITAL**, 9150 Huebner Road, Suite 100, Zip 78240–1545; tel. 210/691–8000 **A**1 9 10 **F**2 21 26 27 28 39 53 62 63 64 66 **P**8 **S** HCA, Nashville, TN Primary Contact: Elaine F. Morris, Administrator CFO: Tim Carr, Chief Financial Officer Web address: www.mas.sahealth.com	32	13	27	529	4	10848	0	19308	6445	155
✖ **METHODIST CHILDREN'S HOSPITAL OF SOUTH TEXAS**, 7700 Floyd Curl Drive, Zip 78229–3383; tel. 210/575–7138, (Nonreporting) **A**1 10 **S** HCA, Nashville, TN Primary Contact: Annie Holt, FACHE, Chief Executive Officer COO: Michael E. Duffy, Chief Operating Officer CFO: Nancy Meadows, Chief Financial Officer CMO: Kevin Browne, M.D., Chairman, Medical Board CIO: Eddie Cuellar, Vice President Information Systems CHR: Michele Benoit, Vice President, Human Resources Web address: www.mch.sahealth.com/	32	10	150	—	—	—	—	—	—	—
✖ **METHODIST HOSPITAL**, (Formerly Southwest Texas Methodist Hospital), 7700 Floyd Curl Drive, Zip 78229–3993; tel. 210/575–4000, (Includes METHODIST SPECIALTY AND TRANSPLANT HOSPITAL, 8026 Floyd Curl Drive, Zip 78229–3915; tel. 210/575–4000; John E. Hornbeak, FACHE, Chief Executive Officer; NORTHEAST METHODIST HOSPITAL, 12412 Judson Road, Zip 78233–3255; tel. 210/650–4949; Mark L. Bernard, Chief Executive Officer) **A**1 2 3 5 9 10 **F**2 3 4 9 10 11 12 14 15 16 17 18 19 20 21 22 23 24 26 27 28 29 31 32 33 34 35 37 38 40 41 43 44 45 46 47 48 49 52 53 55 56 57 58 59 60 61 62 63 64 65 66 67 68 69 71 72 73 74 75 76 77 78 79 81 82 84 85 87 88 93 94 96 99 100 101 102 105 106 108 109 110 **S** HCA, Nashville, TN Primary Contact: John E. Hornbeak, FACHE, Chief Executive Officer COO: Michael E. Duffy, Chief Operating Officer CFO: Nancy Meadows, Chief Financial Officer CMO: Roby Joyce, M.D., Chairman, Medical Board CIO: Eddie Cuellar, Vice President Information Systems CHR: Michele Benoit, Vice President, Human Resources Web address: www.sahealth.com	32	10	1338	64227	932	339591	10129	692027	256633	6250
✖ **METROPOLITAN METHODIST HOSPITAL**, 1310 McCullough Avenue, Zip 78212–2617; tel. 210/208–2200, (Total facility includes 16 beds in nursing home–type unit) (Nonreporting) **A**1 3 9 **S** HCA, Nashville, TN Primary Contact: Mark L. Bernard, Chief Executive Officer COO: Donna J. Arpin, Chief Nursing Officer and Chief Operating Officer CFO: John Wisniewski, Chief Financial Officer CIO: Mike Angelico, Director Information Systems Web address: www.metro.sahealth.com	32	10	244	—	—	—	—	—	—	—
□ **MISSION VISTA GERIATRIC PSYCHIATRIC HOSPITAL**, (Formerly Mission Vista Behavioral Health System), 14747 Jones Maltsberger, Zip 78247–3713; tel. 210/490–0000 **A**1 10 **F**21 27 28 29 31 71 73 74 76 94 96 **P**5 **S** Psychiatric Solutions, Franklin, TN Primary Contact: Ramona T. Key, Chief Executive Officer Web address: www.missionvistabhc.com	33	22	34	611	11	248	0	3042	1241	22
□ **NIX HEALTH CARE SYSTEM**, 414 Navarro Street, Zip 78205–2522; tel. 210/271–1800, (Total facility includes 17 beds in nursing home–type unit) **A**1 3 5 9 10 **F**2 4 10 11 12 15 17 19 21 22 23 29 35 37 44 45 46 48 49 51 52 55 57 58 59 61 62 63 64 66 68 69 70 71 72 76 77 78 81 82 84 85 87 88 92 93 94 105 109 **S** Merit Health Systems, Louisville, KY Primary Contact: John F. Strieby, Chief Executive Officer Web address: www.nixhealth.com	32	10	181	7523	122	106146	562	60418	25752	704

TX

Many Facility Codes have changed. Please refer to the AHA Guide Code Chart.   © 2005 AHA Guide

Hospital, Address, Telephone, Approval, Facility, and Physician Codes, Health Care System	Classi-fication Codes		Utilization Data					Expense (thousands) of dollars		
★ American Hospital Association (AHA) membership ☐ Joint Commission on Accreditation of Healthcare Organizations (JCAHO) accreditation ○ American Osteopathic Association (AOA) accreditation △ Commission on Accreditation of Rehabilitation Facilities (CARF) accreditation	Control	Service	Staffed Beds	Admissions	Census	Outpatient Visits	Births	Total	Payroll	Personnel
NORTH CENTRAL BAPTIST HOSPITAL, 520 Madison Oak Drive, Zip 78258–3912; tel. 210/297–4000 **A**9 **F**2 10 11 12 15 16 21 22 26 27 28 29 33 37 46 55 57 59 60 61 62 63 65 66 67 69 81 82 88 92 93 94 106 108 109 110 **S** Vanguard Health System, Nashville, TN Primary Contact: Mark W. Clayton, Chief Executive Officer Web address: www.baptisthealthsystem.com	21	10	126	9735	87	60045	1883	58061	29140	580
NORTHEAST BAPTIST HOSPITAL, 8811 Village Drive, Zip 78217–5440; tel. 210/297–2000 **A**9 **F**11 12 15 17 19 21 22 23 26 27 28 29 32 33 34 44 46 48 55 56 57 58 59 61 62 63 64 65 69 81 82 87 88 94 106 108 110 **S** Vanguard Health System, Nashville, TN Primary Contact: Bruce F. Buchanan, FACHE, Chief Executive Officer Web address: www.baptisthealth.org	21	10	221	12535	144	55253	1989	96176	39948	861
☐ **PROMISE SPECIALTY HOSPITAL OF SAN ANTONIO**, 7400 Barlite Boulevard, 2nd Floor, Zip 78224; tel. 210/921–3550 **A**1 5 10 **F**2 21 22 26 94 110 **S** Promise Healthcare, Lafayette, LA Primary Contact: Karen Pitcher, Chief Executive Officer Web address: www.promise–sanantonio.com	33	80	26	157	10	0	0	5141	1505	46
☐ **SAN ANTONIO STATE HOSPITAL**, 6711 South New Braunfels, Zip 78223–3006, Mailing Address: Box 23991, Highland Hills Station, Zip 78223–3006; tel. 210/531–7711 **A**1 10 **F**22 26 27 28 32 47 48 53 58 60 65 66 71 72 73 74 76 94 96 106 108 **P**6 **S** Texas Department of State Health Services, Austin, TX Primary Contact: Robert C. Arizpe, Superintendent Web address: www.mhmr.state.tx.us	12	22	292	2779	280	0	0	47424	25242	893
☐ **SELECT SPECIALTY HOSPITAL–SAN ANTONIO**, 111 Dallas Street, 4th Floor, Zip 78205; tel. 210/297–7185, (Nonreporting) **A**1 10 Primary Contact: Steven Tucker, Chief Executive Officer	33	49	34	—	—	—	—	—	—	—
⊠ △ **SOUTH TEXAS VETERANS HEALTH CARE SYSTEM**, 7400 Merton Minter Boulevard, Zip 78284–5799; tel. 210/617–5140, (Includes KERRVILLE DIVISION, 3600 Memorial Boulevard, Kerrville, Zip 78028; tel. 210/896–2020; SAN ANTONIO DIVISION), (Total facility includes 274 beds in nursing home–type unit) (Nonreporting) **A**1 2 3 5 7 8 **S** Department of Veterans Affairs, Washington, DC Primary Contact: Jose R. Coronado, FACHE, Director COO: Charles E. Sepich, CHE, Associate Director CFO: I M. Rachal, Chief Fiscal Service CMO: Richard Bauer, M.D., Chief of Staff CIO: Simon Willett, Director Administrative Operations CHR: Creager Brown, Chief, Human Resource Management Service Web address: www.vasthcs.med.va.gov	45	10	1112	—	—	—	—	—	—	—
☐ △ **SOUTHEAST BAPTIST HOSPITAL**, 4214 East Southcross Boulevard, Zip 78222–3740; tel. 210/297–3000 **A**1 7 9 **F**2 11 12 15 21 22 26 27 28 29 33 34 39 46 52 55 57 58 59 60 61 62 63 65 66 68 69 81 82 84 88 93 94 96 108 **S** Vanguard Health System, Nashville, TN Primary Contact: Richard Marsh, Chief Executive officer Web address: www.baptisthealth.org/SBH.asp	21	10	146	6793	78	42127	253	48948	24462	412
☐ △ **SOUTHWEST GENERAL HOSPITAL**, 7400 Barlite Boulevard, Zip 78224–1399; tel. 210/921–2000 **A**1 7 9 10 **F**2 10 11 12 15 21 22 23 26 27 28 29 33 34 39 44 45 46 48 52 55 56 58 59 60 61 62 63 64 66 68 69 71 73 75 76 81 82 84 85 87 88 94 96 108 109 110 **S** IASIS Healthcare, Franklin, TN Primary Contact: Richard D. Gonzalez, Chief Executive Officer Web address: www.swgeneralhospital.com	33	10	266	9271	130	65028	2338	72718	28032	621
☐ **SOUTHWEST MENTAL HEALTH CENTER**, 8535 Tom Slick, Zip 78229–3363; tel. 210/616–0300 **A**1 5 **F**21 27 28 71 72 74 75 77 78 94 Primary Contact: Frederick W. Hines, President Web address: www.smhc.org	23	52	52	1335	36	3824	0	8955	4916	154
SPINE HOSPITAL OF SOUTH TEXAS, 18600 North Hardy Oak, Zip 78258; tel. 210/404–0800, (Nonreporting) **A**10	33	47	30	—	—	—	—	—	—	—
△ **ST. LUKE'S BAPTIST HOSPITAL**, 7930 Floyd Curl Drive, Zip 78229–0100; tel. 210/297–5000 **A**3 5 7 9 **F**2 9 11 12 14 15 17 19 21 22 23 26 27 28 29 31 33 34 37 44 47 52 55 56 57 58 59 60 61 62 63 64 65 66 68 69 71 73 76 81 82 86 87 88 94 95 96 106 108 109 110 **P**8 **S** Vanguard Health System, Nashville, TN Primary Contact: Dominic J. Dominguez, Chief Executive Officer Web address: www.baptisthealthsystem.org	21	10	248	11094	117	25295	2747	89102	35208	662
☐ **TEXAS CENTER FOR INFECTIOUS DISEASE**, 2303 S.E. Military Drive, Zip 78223–3597; tel. 210/534–8857 **A**1 10 **F**2 22 26 27 28 45 50 52 53 58 66 94 96 106 108 **P**4 **S** Texas Department of State Health Services, Austin, TX Primary Contact: James N. Elkins, FACHE, Director Web address: www.dshs.state.tx.us/tcid/default/shtm	12	33	72	97	44	1367	0	8340	4510	170
☐ **TEXAS SPECIALTY HOSPITAL AT SAN ANTONIO**, (Formerly Specialty Hospital of San Antonio), 7310 Oak Manor Drive, Zip 78229–4509; tel. 210/308–0261 **A**1 9 10 **F**2 21 26 27 28 49 58 92 94 110 **S** Integrated Health Services, Sparks Glencoe, MD Primary Contact: Peggy Cliffe, Administrator Web address: www.thicare.com	33	80	24	316	24	0	0	6962	3391	98

Many Facility Codes have changed. Please refer to the AHA Guide Code Chart.

Hospital, Address, Telephone, Approval, Facility, and Physician Codes, Health Care System	Classification Codes		Utilization Data					Expense (thousands) of dollars		
	Control	Service	Staffed Beds	Admissions	Census	Outpatient Visits	Births	Total	Payroll	Personnel

★ American Hospital Association (AHA) membership
□ Joint Commission on Accreditation of Healthcare Organizations (JCAHO) accreditation
○ American Osteopathic Association (AOA) accreditation
△ Commission on Accreditation of Rehabilitation Facilities (CARF) accreditation

⊠ **TEXSAN HEART HOSPITAL**, 6700 IH–10 West, Zip 78201; tel. 210/736–6700, (Nonreporting) **A**1 10 **S** MedCath, Inc., Charlotte, NC Primary Contact: Robert S. Freymuller, Chief Executive Officer Web address: www.texsanhearthospital.com	33	10	60	—	—	—	—	—	—	—
□ **THE SPINE HOSPITAL OF SOUTH TEXAS**, 18600 Hardy Oak Boulevard, Zip 78258; tel. 210/404–0800 **A**1 **F**2 21 22 27 29 33 37 46 47 52 53 58 62 63 64 65 66 73 74 94 96 **S** National Surgical Hospitals, Chicago, IL Primary Contact: Chris Shoup, Chief Executive Officer Web address: www.shst.net	32	13	30	1969	5	833	0	17432	3313	64
⊠ **UNIVERSITY HEALTH SYSTEM**, 4502 Medical Drive, Zip 78229–4493; tel. 210/358–4000, (Includes UNIVERSITY HEALTH CENTER – DOWNTOWN, tel. 210/358–3400; UNIVERSITY HOSPITAL, tel. 210/358–4000) **A**1 2 3 5 8 9 10 **F**2 3 4 6 9 11 12 14 15 16 17 18 19 20 21 22 23 24 26 27 28 29 31 32 33 34 35 37 38 39 40 41 42 44 45 46 47 48 49 50 52 53 55 56 57 58 59 60 61 62 63 64 65 66 67 68 69 70 71 72 73 74 75 76 77 81 82 83 84 87 88 89 90 93 94 95 96 99 101 102 103 104 105 106 107 108 109 110 **P**6 Primary Contact: George B. Hernandez, Jr, President and Chief Executive Officer CFO: Peggy Deming, Executive Vice President and Chief Financial Officer CMO: David Hnatow, M.D., President Medical and Dental Staff CIO: John Blandford, Vice President Information Services CHR: Linda Boyer Owens, Vice President, People and Organizational Development Web address: www.universityhealthsystem.com	16	10	361	21897	342	382029	2864	569846	166328	4663
□ △ **WARM SPRINGS REHABILITATION HOSPITAL**, 5101 Medical Drive, Zip 78229–6098; tel. 210/616–0100 **A**1 3 5 7 10 **F**2 9 21 26 27 28 29 37 45 46 47 48 52 57 62 65 68 69 94 96 108 110 **S** Warm Springs Rehabilitation System, San Antonio, TX Primary Contact: Rick Marek, President and Chief Executive Officer Web address: www.warmsprings.org	23	46	64	1319	49	71048	0	23609	9239	233
SAN AUGUSTINE—San Augustine County										
MEMORIAL MEDICAL CENTER – SAN AUGUSTINE, 511 East Hospital Street, Zip 75972–2121, Mailing Address: P.O. Box 658, Zip 75972–0658; tel. 936/275–3446 **A**9 10 18 **F**2 21 27 28 29 33 46 48 52 75 81 88 96 97 **S** Memorial Health System of East Texas, Lufkin, TX Primary Contact: Darlene Williams, R.N., Administrator Web address: www.memorialhealth.org	23	10	18	499	4	18713	0	4362	2144	44
SAN BENITO—Cameron County										
□ **DOLLY VINSANT MEMORIAL HOSPITAL**, 400 East U.S. Highway 77, Zip 78586–5310, Mailing Address: P.O. Box 42, Zip 78586–0042; tel. 956/365–5200 **A**1 9 10 **F**2 9 12 21 22 27 28 33 39 44 46 52 58 62 63 81 82 88 93 106 **P**5 Primary Contact: Igor Kozlik, Chief Executive Officer Web address: www.dvmh.com	33	10	28	1603	12	13245	1	8636	3860	33
SAN MARCOS—Hays County										
⊠ **CENTRAL TEXAS MEDICAL CENTER**, 1301 Wonder World Drive, Zip 78666–7544; tel. 512/753–3500 **A**1 9 10 **F**11 12 15 17 19 21 22 26 27 28 29 32 33 36 41 42 44 46 47 48 51 53 55 57 58 59 60 62 63 65 66 69 76 81 82 84 86 88 94 95 96 108 110 **P**6 8 **S** Adventist Health System Sunbelt Health Care Corporation, Winter Park, FL Primary Contact: Gary L. Jepson, President and Chief Executive Officer CFO: Fran Crunk, Chief Financial Officer CMO: A Lane Lee, M.D., President Medical Staff CHR: Debbie Cox, Director, Human Resources Web address: www.ctmc.org	21	10	113	5372	51	69013	1076	47599	19326	480
SEGUIN—Guadalupe County										
⊠ **GUADALUPE VALLEY HOSPITAL**, 1215 East Court Street, Zip 78155–5189; tel. 830/379–2411 **A**1 9 10 **F**2 4 9 10 11 12 21 22 23 28 29 31 33 34 36 37 39 40 41 44 45 47 51 52 53 55 57 58 59 60 61 62 63 64 65 66 68 69 70 76 77 81 82 84 85 88 93 94 96 108 110 **P**1 Primary Contact: Robert Haynes, Administrator CFO: Penny Wallace, Chief Financial Officer CMO: Steve White, M.D., Chief of Staff CIO: Chuck McWhorter, Director CHR: Fay Bennett, Director Web address: www.gvh.com	15	10	97	5142	58	104106	672	52835	24243	642
SEMINOLE—Gaines County										
★ **MEMORIAL HOSPITAL**, 209 N.W. Eighth Street, Zip 79360–3447; tel. 432/758–5811 **A**9 10 18 **F**2 8 9 11 21 22 24 26 27 28 29 33 34 36 41 44 45 46 47 48 51 52 58 59 60 63 66 69 70 75 81 88 94 95 96 97 108 109 110 **S** Covenant Health System, Lubbock, TX Primary Contact: Steve Beck, Chief Executive Officer and Administrator CFO: Traci Anderson, Controller CMO: Michael Watson, M.D., Chief of Staff CHR: La Rue Bledsoe, Personnel Director Web address: www.semmem.com	16	10	37	965	12	35392	228	14142	3984	160
SEYMOUR—Baylor County										
SEYMOUR HOSPITAL, 200 Stadium Drive, Zip 76380–2344; tel. 940/889–5572 **A**9 10 20 **F**6 9 11 21 33 34 46 48 51 53 55 58 59 60 63 65 66 69 76 81 88 92 93 94 97 108 Primary Contact: Joseph F. Sloan, CHE, Chief Executive Officer	16	10	38	896	10	26548	42	6590	3063	139

Many Facility Codes have changed. Please refer to the AHA Guide Code Chart. © 2005 AHA Guide

Hospital, Address, Telephone, Approval, Facility, and Physician Codes, Health Care System	Classi-fication Codes		Utilization Data					Expense (thousands) of dollars		
	Control	Service	Staffed Beds	Admissions	Census	Outpatient Visits	Births	Total	Payroll	Personnel

★ American Hospital Association (AHA) membership
□ Joint Commission on Accreditation of Healthcare Organizations (JCAHO) accreditation
○ American Osteopathic Association (AOA) accreditation
△ Commission on Accreditation of Rehabilitation Facilities (CARF) accreditation

SHAMROCK—Wheeler County

SHAMROCK GENERAL HOSPITAL, 1000 South Main Street, Zip 79079–2896; tel. 806/256–2114, (Total facility includes 9 beds in nursing home–type unit) **A**9 10 18 **F**6 9 21 24 33 34 36 53 69 81 88 92 94 97 **P**4
Primary Contact: Wiley M. Fires, Administrator

| 16 | 10 | 25 | 334 | 9 | 30357 | 1 | 3498 | 1673 | 68 |

SHEPPARD AFB—Wichita County

✠ **U. S. AIR FORCE REGIONAL HOSPITAL–SHEPPARD**, 149 Hart Street, Suite 1, Zip 76311–3478; tel. 940/676–5874, (Nonreporting) **A**1 **S** Department of the Air Force, Washington, DC
Primary Contact: Lieutenant Colonel Joseph Kennedy, Administrator
COO: Colonel Robert Lenahan, Commander Medical Support Squadron
CFO: Lieutenant Colonel Scott E. Lawrence, Flight Commander, Business Operations Beneficiary Support
CMO: Colonel Ernest E. Emmerton, Chief of Medical Staff
CIO: Captain Ruben Matos, Chief Medical Information Systems
Web address: www.sheppard.af.mil

| 41 | 10 | 65 | — | — | — | — | — | — | — |

SHERMAN—Grayson County

✠ **WILSON N. JONES MEDICAL CENTER**, 500 North Highland Avenue, Zip 75092–7354; tel. 903/870–4611, (Total facility includes 32 beds in nursing home–type unit) **A**1 9 10 **F**2 9 11 12 14 15 17 19 21 22 23 26 27 29 33 38 41 42 44 46 48 50 52 55 57 58 59 61 63 65 66 68 69 70 81 82 84 87 88 92 93 94 96 108 109 110 **P**6
Primary Contact: Patrick D. Flynn, Chief Executive Officer
CFO: Mitch Mulvehill, Senior Vice President and Chief Financial Officer
CMO: Max Cogswell, M.D., President Medical Staff
CIO: Mel Ostlie, Director Information Services
CHR: Linda Creswell, Director Human Resources
Web address: www.wnj.org

| 23 | 10 | 274 | 11060 | 146 | 87713 | 1274 | 114139 | 45024 | 920 |

SMITHVILLE—Bastrop County

★ **SMITHVILLE REGIONAL HOSPITAL**, 800 East Highway 71, Zip 78957; tel. 512/237–3214, (Total facility includes 114 beds in nursing home–type unit) **A**5 9 10 **F**2 9 11 12 21 26 27 28 33 45 46 51 52 55 59 60 62 63 69 81 82 84 88 92 94 108
Primary Contact: Grady Hooper, Chief Executive Officer
CFO: Noralene Corder, Chief Financial Officer
CIO: Derek McKinley, Chief Information Officer
CHR: Julie Waid, Director Human Resources
Web address: www.srhnet.org

| 16 | 10 | 150 | 1981 | 114 | 44737 | 180 | 22656 | 11404 | 349 |

SNYDER—Scurry County

★ **D. M. COGDELL MEMORIAL HOSPITAL**, 1700 Cogdell Boulevard, Zip 79549–6198; tel. 325/573–6374, (Total facility includes 24 beds in nursing home–type unit) **A**9 10 **F**8 9 11 12 21 27 33 34 41 46 48 51 52 55 58 59 60 63 64 66 69 81 82 85 88 94 97 **P**7
Primary Contact: Carol H. Hanes, Administrator
CFO: Dan Honerbrink, Chief Financial Officer
CMO: Bid Cooper, M.D., Chief Medical Officer
CIO: Betty Woodard, Health Information Management Manager
CHR: Janie Naizer, Director Human Resources
Web address: www.cogdellhospital.com

| 13 | 10 | 73 | 1398 | 29 | 65946 | 149 | 14501 | 6092 | 201 |

SONORA—Sutton County

★ **LILLIAN M. HUDSPETH MEMORIAL HOSPITAL**, 308 Hudspeth Avenue, Zip 76950–3399, Mailing Address: P.O. Box 455, Zip 76950–0455; tel. 325/387–2521 **A**9 10 18 **F**2 4 9 27 29 33 34 46 48 52 53 60 66 69 81 96 98 106 110
Primary Contact: Keith L. Butler, Chief Executive Officer
CFO: Michelle Schaefer, Chief Financial Officer
Web address: www.sonora–hospital.org

| 16 | 10 | 12 | 241 | 2 | 5245 | 0 | 2533 | 1186 | 36 |

SPEARMAN—Hansford County

★ **HANSFORD HOSPITAL**, 707 South Roland Street, Zip 79081–3441; tel. 806/659–2535 **A**9 10 18 20 **F**9 23 24 26 33 34 36 44 46 48 51 52 53 54 61 69 81 94 97 **P**6
Primary Contact: Steve Hartgraves, Chief Executive Officer
CFO: Scott Beedy, Chief Financial Officer
CHR: Jackie Nelson, Director Human Resources
Web address: www.hchd.net

| 16 | 10 | 20 | 261 | 3 | 21210 | 0 | 6306 | 2250 | 71 |

STAMFORD—Jones County

STAMFORD MEMORIAL HOSPITAL, 1601 Columbia Street, Zip 79553, Mailing Address: P.O. Box 911, Zip 79553–0911; tel. 325/773–2725 **A**9 10 **F**9 27 28 33 34 36 37 41 46 51 52 58 63 65 69 95 97 108 110 **P**5
Primary Contact: Paula Bennett, Administrator

| 16 | 10 | 25 | 397 | 7 | 34374 | 1 | 6307 | 3254 | 136 |

STANTON—Martin County

MARTIN COUNTY HOSPITAL DISTRICT, 610 North St. Peter Street, Zip 79782, Mailing Address: P.O. Box 640, Zip 79782–0640; tel. 432/756–3345 **A**9 10 18 **F**6 27 28 33 34 51 59 63 97
Primary Contact: William G. Jones, Administrator

| 16 | 10 | 20 | 295 | 3 | 9805 | 0 | 4660 | 1791 | 63 |

TX

Hospital, Address, Telephone, Approval, Facility, and Physician Codes, Health Care System	Classi-fication Codes		Utilization Data					Expense (thousands) of dollars		
★ American Hospital Association (AHA) membership □ Joint Commission on Accreditation of Healthcare Organizations (JCAHO) accreditation ○ American Osteopathic Association (AOA) accreditation △ Commission on Accreditation of Rehabilitation Facilities (CARF) accreditation	Control	Service	Staffed Beds	Admissions	Census	Outpatient Visits	Births	Total	Payroll	Personnel

STEPHENVILLE—Erath County

☒ **HARRIS METHODIST–ERATH COUNTY**, 411 North Belknap Street, Zip 76401–3415, Mailing Address: P.O. Box 1399, Zip 76401–1399; tel. 254/965–1500 **A**1 9 10 **F**2 9 11 12 15 19 20 21 22 27 28 29 33 34 39 40 46 48 55 58 59 60 61 62 63 65 69 81 82 84 85 87 88 93 94 97 106 108 **S** Texas Health Resources, Arlington, TX
Primary Contact: Deborah Paganelli, CHE, President
CFO: Lorenzo Olivarez, Chief Financial Officer
Web address: www.texashealth.org
| 23 | 10 | 55 | 2827 | 29 | 24455 | 449 | 28991 | 11097 | 242 |

SUGAR LAND—Fort Bend County

☒ **METHODIST SUGAR LAND HOSPITAL**, 16655 S.W. Freeway, Zip 77479–2343; tel. 281/274–8000 **A**1 9 10 **F**2 11 12 15 21 22 27 28 33 48 52 53 55 58 59 60 63 79 80 81 82 84 85 88 94 108 **S** The Methodist Hospital System, Houston, TX
Primary Contact: James F. Heitzenrater, Administrator
CFO: Lowell Stanton, Chief Financial Officer
CMO: Michelle Bowman Howard, M.D., Medical Director
CHR: Luis Garcia, Director
Web address: www.methodisthealth.com
| 23 | 10 | 54 | 4431 | 38 | 76465 | 1463 | 50130 | 21318 | 452 |

□ **SUGAR LAND SURGICAL HOSPITAL**, 1211 Highway 6, Suite 70, Zip 77478; tel. 281/243–1000 **A**1 10 **F**2 21 27 28 33 37 46 48 58 62 63 64 65 66 70 94 **S** United Surgical Partners International, Addison, TX
Primary Contact: Carol Champagne, Chief Executive Officer
| 32 | 13 | 6 | 225 | 2 | 4064 | 0 | 8748 | 1875 | 46 |

□ **TRIUMPH HOSPITAL SOUTHWEST**, 1550 First Colony Boulevard, Zip 77479; tel. 281/275–6000, (Nonreporting) **A**1 10 **S** Triumph HealthCare, Houston, TX
Primary Contact: Joan Damon, Chief Executive Officer
| 33 | 49 | 85 | — | — | — | — | — | — | — |

SULPHUR SPRINGS—Hopkins County

☒ **HOPKINS COUNTY MEMORIAL HOSPITAL**, 115 Airport Road, Zip 75482–0115; tel. 903/885–7671 **A**1 9 10 **F**6 11 12 21 26 27 28 29 33 34 36 37 38 44 48 55 59 63 66 69 81 82 84 87 88 94 108
Primary Contact: Michael McAndrew, Chief Executive Officer
COO: Donna Geiken Wallace, Chief Operating Officer
CFO: Donna Geiken Wallace, Chief Operating Officer and Chief Financial Officer
CMO: Paul Martin, M.D., Chief Medical Staff
CIO: Ken Mikos, Director Information Systems
CHR: Donna Rudzik, Director of Human Resources
Web address: www.hcmh.com
| 16 | 10 | 54 | 4509 | 43 | 32798 | 961 | 30031 | 14020 | 408 |

SWEENY—Brazoria County

SWEENY COMMUNITY HOSPITAL, 305 North McKinney Street, Zip 77480–2895; tel. 979/548–3311 **A**9 10 18 **F**6 9 27 29 33 41 44 45 48 51 54 55 63 69 76 77 81 88 94 96 97
Primary Contact: Herbert A. Turk, FACHE, Administrator
Web address: www.sweenyhospital.org
| 16 | 10 | 14 | 239 | 2 | 15486 | 0 | 8598 | 4327 | 119 |

SWEETWATER—Nolan County

☒ **ROLLING PLAINS MEMORIAL HOSPITAL**, 200 East Arizona Street, Zip 79556–7199, Mailing Address: P.O. Box 690, Zip 79556–0690; tel. 325/235–1701 **A**1 9 10 20 **F**9 11 12 26 27 28 33 34 51 55 59 63 64 69 70 81 88 94 96 97 108
Primary Contact: Thomas F. Kennedy, Administrator
CFO: Fran Tinnin, Controller
CMO: Larry McEachern, M.D., Chief of Staff
CHR: Gay Nell Cherry, Human Resources Director
| 16 | 10 | 54 | 2096 | 24 | 88786 | 257 | 17766 | 8357 | 246 |

TAHOKA—Lynn County

★ **LYNN COUNTY HOSPITAL DISTRICT**, Brownfield Highway, Zip 79373–1310, Mailing Address: Box 1310, Zip 79373–1310; tel. 806/998–4533 **A**9 10 18 **F**6 8 9 11 24 27 29 31 33 34 35 41 42 44 46 48 52 58 59 60 63 65 69 70 81 88 97 107 109 **P**5 8
Primary Contact: Daniell Powers, Chief Executive Officer
COO: Daniell Powers, Chief Executive Officer
CIO: Jimmy Morris, Chief Operations Officer
CHR: Sharon Gandy, Manager Human Resources
Web address: www.lchdhealthcare.org
| 16 | 10 | 24 | 221 | 3 | 21508 | 18 | 4401 | 2119 | 86 |

TAYLOR—Williamson County

□ **JOHNS COMMUNITY HOSPITAL**, 305 Mallard Lane, Zip 76574–1208; tel. 512/352–7611 **A**1 9 10 **F**2 9 12 21 27 28 33 45 48 51 52 55 63 64 65 69 70 81 82 88 94 97 **P**6
Primary Contact: Ernest Balla, R.N., Administrator
Web address: www.johnscommunityhospital.org
| 23 | 10 | 53 | 990 | 34 | 55913 | 1 | 13363 | 6909 | 193 |

TEMPLE—Bell County

☒ △ **CENTRAL TEXAS VETERANS HEALTHCARE SYSTEM**, 1901 South First Street, Zip 76504–7493; tel. 254/778–4811, (Includes OLIN E. TEAGUE VETERANS' CENTER; WACO VETERANS AFFAIRS HOSPITAL, 4800 Memorial Drive, Waco, Zip 76711–1397; tel. 254/752–6581), (Total facility includes 320 beds in nursing home–type unit) (Nonreporting) **A**1 2 3 5 7 **S** Department of Veterans Affairs, Washington, DC
Primary Contact: Robert W. Ratliff, Ph.D., FACHE, Acting Director
COO: Robert W. Ratliff, Ph.D., FACHE, Deputy Director
CFO: Toby Brooks, Chief Financial Services
CMO: Valerie H. Van Wormer, M.D., Chief of Staff
CIO: Alvin Byars, Chief Information Management Service
Web address: www.texvet.com
| 45 | 10 | 1852 | — | — | — | — | — | — | — |

Many Facility Codes have changed. Please refer to the AHA Guide Code Chart.

© 2005 AHA Guide

Hospital, Address, Telephone, Approval, Facility, and Physician Codes, Health Care System	Classi- fication Codes		Utilization Data					Expense (thousands) of dollars		
	Control	Service	Staffed Beds	Admissions	Census	Outpatient Visits	Births	Total	Payroll	Personnel

★   American Hospital Association (AHA) membership
☐   Joint Commission on Accreditation of Healthcare Organizations (JCAHO) accreditation
◯   American Osteopathic Association (AOA) accreditation
△   Commission on Accreditation of Rehabilitation Facilities (CARF) accreditation

	Control	Service	Staffed Beds	Admissions	Census	Outpatient Visits	Births	Total	Payroll	Personnel
✖ **KING'S DAUGHTERS HOSPITAL**, 1901 S.W. H. K. Dodgen Loop, Zip 76502–1896; tel. 254/771–8600, (Total facility includes 12 beds in nursing home–type unit) **A**1 9 10 **F**2 6 9 11 21 22 23 26 27 28 33 37 45 46 48 49 51 52 53 55 57 58 59 61 62 63 64 65 66 69 75 81 82 84 85 87 88 92 93 94 96 106 108 109 110 **P**5 Primary Contact: Tucker Bonner, President CFO: Eric Lashbrook, Vice President Finance CIO: Matt Adams, Director Information Technology CHR: Ben Coldicutt, Vice President Web address: www.kdhosp.org OLIN E. TEAGUE VETERANS' CENTER See Central Texas Veterans Healthcare System	23	10	116	3308	31	36933	677	33973	13778	363
✖ △ **SCOTT AND WHITE MEMORIAL HOSPITAL**, 2401 South 31st Street, Zip 76508–0002; tel. 254/724–2111, (Total facility includes 40 beds in nursing home–type unit) **A**1 2 3 5 7 8 9 10 **F**2 4 6 9 10 11 12 14 21 22 23 26 27 28 29 30 32 33 34 35 36 37 38 39 40 42 44 45 46 47 48 49 50 51 52 53 55 56 57 59 60 61 62 63 64 65 66 67 68 69 70 71 72 73 74 75 76 77 78 81 82 84 85 86 87 88 89 92 93 94 95 96 98 99 101 105 106 107 108 109 110 **P**3 Primary Contact: Patricia M. Currie, FACHE, Executive Director COO: Donny Sequin, Chief Operating Officer CFO: Kenneth Johnson, Chief Financial Officer CIO: William McCombs, M.D., Chief Information Officer Web address: www.sw.org	23	10	517	29864	343	1414515	2297	697287	316117	5804
TERRELL—Kaufman County										
✖ **MEDICAL CENTER AT TERRELL**, 1551 Highway 34 South, Zip 75160–4833; tel. 972/563–7611, (Total facility includes 14 beds in nursing home–type unit) **A**1 9 10 **F**2 11 12 15 21 22 27 28 33 37 40 48 52 53 55 58 59 62 63 64 65 66 68 69 81 82 84 88 92 93 94 108 109 **S** Resurgence Health Group, Sugar Hill, GA Primary Contact: Kenneth Pittman, Interim Chief Executive Officer CFO: Gary Gunder, Chief Financial Officer CMO: Steven Altshuler, M.D., Chief of Staff CIO: Paul Ferguson, Director Information Systems CHR: Kelli Patton, Director Human Resources Web address: www.medcenter–terrell.com	32	10	130	1935	34	22958	225	14132	6671	235
☐ **TERRELL STATE HOSPITAL**, 1200 East Brin Street, Zip 75160–2938; tel. 972/524–6452 **A**1 3 5 10 **F**22 26 27 28 32 46 47 53 58 60 65 66 71 72 73 74 75 76 94 96 106 108 **P**6 **S** Texas Department of State Health Services, Austin, TX Primary Contact: Fred Hale, Superintendent Web address: www.dshs.state.tx.us	12	22	273	2289	273	0	0	44134	23873	764
TEXARKANA—Bowie County										
✖ **CHRISTUS ST. MICHAEL HEALTH SYSTEM**, 2600 St. Michael Drive, Zip 75503–2372; tel. 903/614–1000 **A**1 2 9 10 **F**2 9 11 12 14 15 17 19 21 22 23 24 26 27 28 29 33 37 40 41 42 44 45 46 47 48 49 52 53 55 57 58 59 60 61 62 63 64 66 69 70 79 80 81 82 83 84 85 87 88 94 95 96 106 107 108 109 110 **P**8 **S** Christus Health, Irving, TX Primary Contact: Chris Karam, President and Chief Executive Officer COO: William McDonald, Vice President and Chief Operating Officer CFO: Tommy McGee, Vice President and Chief Financial Officer CMO: Dennis O'Banion, M.D., Chief of Staff CIO: Robert Jacobs, Market Information Officer CHR: Pam Kennedy, Customer Relations Service Line Director Web address: www.christusstmichael.org	21	10	278	14894	190	146411	855	145229	50839	1358
✖ **CHRISTUS ST. MICHAEL REHABILITATION HOSPITAL**, 2400 St. Michael Drive, Zip 75503; tel. 903/614–4000 **A**1 9 10 **F**2 9 21 22 26 27 28 37 45 53 58 64 68 69 93 94 96 110 **S** Christus Health, Irving, TX Primary Contact: Cookie Gender, Administrator CFO: Tommy McGee, Vice President and Chief Financial Officer Web address: www.christusstmichael.org	21	46	80	1221	42	3075	0	13715	4922	121
✖ **DUBUIS HOSPITAL OF TEXARKANA**, 2600 St. Michael Drive, 6th Floor, Zip 75503–2372; tel. 903/899–7168 **A**1 9 10 **F**2 21 27 28 37 38 60 65 66 94 110 **S** Dubuis Health System, Houston, TX Primary Contact: Tim Freeman, Administrator Web address: www.dubuis.org	23	80	34	361	28	0	0	9124	4152	79
✖ **HEALTHSOUTH REHABILITATION HOSPITAL OF TEXARKANA**, 515 West 12th Street, Zip 75501–4416; tel. 903/793–0088 **A**1 10 **F**21 26 27 28 42 45 52 57 60 62 66 68 69 94 95 96 109 110 **S** HEALTHSOUTH Corporation, Birmingham, AL Primary Contact: Joanne Rose, Administrator CFO: Tammy Welch, Controller Web address: www.healthsouth.com	33	46	60	976	40	19195	0	11202	6115	197

TX

Hospital, Address, Telephone, Approval, Facility, and Physician Codes, Health Care System	Classification Codes		Utilization Data					Expense (thousands) of dollars		
★ American Hospital Association (AHA) membership □ Joint Commission on Accreditation of Healthcare Organizations (JCAHO) accreditation ○ American Osteopathic Association (AOA) accreditation △ Commission on Accreditation of Rehabilitation Facilities (CARF) accreditation	Control	Service	Staffed Beds	Admissions	Census	Outpatient Visits	Births	Total	Payroll	Personnel
⊠ **WADLEY REGIONAL MEDICAL CENTER**, 1000 Pine Street, Zip 75501–5170, Mailing Address: Box 1878, Zip 75504–1878; tel. 903/798–8000, (Total facility includes 13 beds in nursing home–type unit) **A**1 2 9 10 **F**2 9 10 11 12 15 17 19 21 22 23 27 28 29 32 33 38 39 40 46 47 48 49 52 53 55 56 57 58 59 60 61 62 63 64 65 66 71 76 79 81 82 83 84 85 87 88 92 93 94 96 106 108 109 110 **P**4 Primary Contact: Michael S. Potter, FACHE, President and Chief Executive Officer CFO: Milton E. Aunan, II, CPA, Chief Financial Officer CMO: Cordell Klein, M.D., Chief of Staff CIO: David Friday, Chief Information Officer CHR: Debby Butler, Director Human Resources Web address: www.wadleyhealth.com	23	10	183	11019	132	184659	1398	100641	39324	863
TEXAS CITY—Galveston County										
⊠ **MAINLAND MEDICAL CENTER**, 6801 E F Lowry Expressway, Zip 77591; tel. 409/938–5000, (Total facility includes 22 beds in nursing home–type unit) **A**1 5 9 10 **F**4 9 11 12 21 27 28 31 32 33 35 36 37 38 39 44 46 48 51 52 53 55 57 59 60 61 62 63 65 66 68 69 70 71 73 74 75 76 77 78 81 82 84 88 92 93 94 95 96 106 107 108 109 110 **S** HCA, Nashville, TN Primary Contact: Dean Alexander, Chief Executive Officer CFO: Scott Bentley, Chief Financial Officer CIO: Mark Tanet, Director Management Information Systems CHR: Jennifer Johnson, Director Human Resources Web address: www.mainlandmedical.com	32	10	206	9378	120	101149	567	71619	35107	650
THE WOODLANDS—Montgomery County										
BEACON SPECIALTY HOSPITAL See Nexus Specialty Hospital MEMORIAL HERMANN THE WOODLANDS HOSPITAL See Memorial Hermann Hospital, Houston										
□ **NEXUS SPECIALTY HOSPITAL**, (Formerly Beacon Specialty Hospital), 9182 Six Pines Drive, Zip 77380; tel. 281/364–0317 **A**1 9 10 **F**2 21 27 28 45 52 94 108 110 Primary Contact: Suzanne Kretschmer, Administrator Web address: www.beaconwoodlands.com	32	80	21	154	17	32	0	4607	2224	56
□ **ST LUKE'S COMMUNITY MEDICAL CENTER–THE WOODLANDS**, 17200 St. Luke's Way, Zip 77384; tel. 936/266–2000 **A**1 10 **F**2 9 11 12 21 22 27 28 29 31 33 39 46 47 48 52 53 55 56 57 58 59 62 63 64 66 81 82 84 85 88 93 94 106 108 109 **S** St. Luke's Episcopal Health System, Houston, TX Primary Contact: Stephen R. Selzer, Chief Executive Officer Web address: www.stlukeswoodlands.com	21	10	76	5013	47	35413	1172	52262	19105	322
THROCKMORTON—Throckmorton County										
THROCKMORTON COUNTY MEMORIAL HOSPITAL, 802 North Minter Street, Zip 76483–5357, Mailing Address: P.O. Box 729, Zip 76483–0729; tel. 940/849–2151 **A**9 10 18 **F**6 26 27 28 33 52 53 58 66 70 92 97 108 **P**5 6 Primary Contact: Kirk Parsons, Administrator	13	10	14	213	1	3568	0	1513	610	26
TOMBALL—Harris County										
⊠ △ **TOMBALL REGIONAL HOSPITAL**, 605 Holderrieth Street, Zip 77375–0889, Mailing Address: P.O. Box 889, Zip 77375–6445; tel. 281/401–7500, (Total facility includes 18 beds in nursing home–type unit) (Nonreporting) **A**1 5 7 9 10 Primary Contact: Robert F. Schaper, President and Chief Executive Officer CFO: Keith Barber, CPA, Chief Financial Officer CIO: Marlene Pezzia, Director CHR: Marcia Moore, Vice President Web address: www.tomballhospital.org	16	10	184	—	—	—	—	—	—	—
TRINITY—Trinity County										
★ **EAST TEXAS MEDICAL CENTER TRINITY**, 317 Prospect Drive, Zip 75862, Mailing Address: P.O. Box 3169, Zip 75862; tel. 936/594–3541 **A**9 10 **F**12 21 27 28 33 34 52 63 81 84 88 108 **P**3 5 7 **S** East Texas Medical Center Regional Healthcare System, Tyler, TX Primary Contact: Terry Cutler, Administrator and Chief Operating Officer COO: Terry Cutler, Administrator and Chief Operating Officer CFO: Ronald Hunt, Chief Financial Officer CMO: Masoud Romezi, M.D., Chief of Staff CHR: Kathy Turner, Human Resources Director Web address: www.etmc.org	23	10	22	731	9	26836	0	6306	2605	61
TULIA—Swisher County										
★ **SWISHER MEMORIAL HOSPITAL DISTRICT**, 539 Southeast Second, Zip 79088–2403, Mailing Address: P.O. Box 808, Zip 79088–0808; tel. 806/995–3581, (Total facility includes 9 beds in nursing home–type unit) **A**9 10 18 20 **F**6 8 9 21 28 29 31 33 41 42 44 46 47 48 51 52 53 60 65 66 68 69 70 92 94 97 108 **P**6 Primary Contact: Jeff Messer, Chief Executive Officer CFO: Mary Lick, Chief Financial Officer	16	10	29	382	14	24627	0	6349	2953	106
TYLER—Smith County										
□ △ **EAST TEXAS MEDICAL CENTER REHABILITATION CENTER**, 701 Olympic Plaza Circle, Zip 75701–1996; tel. 903/596–3000 **A**1 7 10 **F**2 11 22 28 41 46 47 48 58 65 68 69 94 95 96 110 **S** East Texas Medical Center Regional Healthcare System, Tyler, TX Primary Contact: Eddie L. Howard, Vice President and Chief Operating Officer Web address: www.etmc.org	23	46	49	1329	45	57702	0	21888	9452	232

Many Facility Codes have changed. Please refer to the AHA Guide Code Chart. © 2005 AHA Guide

TX

Hospital, Address, Telephone, Approval, Facility, and Physician Codes, Health Care System	Classification Codes		Utilization Data					Expense (thousands) of dollars		
	Control	Service	Staffed Beds	Admissions	Census	Outpatient Visits	Births	Total	Payroll	Personnel

★ American Hospital Association (AHA) membership
□ Joint Commission on Accreditation of Healthcare Organizations (JCAHO) accreditation
○ American Osteopathic Association (AOA) accreditation
△ Commission on Accreditation of Rehabilitation Facilities (CARF) accreditation

□ **EAST TEXAS MEDICAL CENTER SPECIALTY HOSPITAL**, 1000 South Beckham, 5th Floor, Zip 75701; tel. 903/596–3600 **A**1 9 10 **F**2 21 22 27 38 58 94 110 **S** East Texas Medical Center Regional Healthcare System, Tyler, TX
Primary Contact: Eddie L. Howard, Vice President, Chief Operating Officer and Administrator
Web address: www.etmc.org

| | 23 | 80 | 36 | 396 | 29 | 0 | 0 | 10832 | 4090 | 86 |

✦ **EAST TEXAS MEDICAL CENTER TYLER**, 1000 South Beckham Street, Zip 75701–1996, Mailing Address: Box 6400, Zip 75711–6400; tel. 903/597–0351, (Includes EAST TEXAS MEDICAL CENTER BEHAVIORAL HEALTH CENTER, 4101 University Boulevard, Zip 75701–6600; tel. 903/566–8668) **A**1 2 9 10 **F**2 3 4 9 10 11 12 14 15 17 19 21 22 23 27 28 29 31 32 33 34 35 37 38 39 40 43 44 46 48 49 52 53 55 57 58 59 60 61 62 63 64 65 66 71 72 73 74 75 76 77 78 79 80 81 84 85 86 87 88 93 94 101 108 109 110 **S** East Texas Medical Center Regional Healthcare System, Tyler, TX
Primary Contact: Robert B. Evans, Administrator and Chief Executive Officer
CFO: Byron Hale, Vice President Finance
CMO: Bill Moore, M.D., Chief of Staff
CIO: Paula Anthony, Vice President Information Sevices
CHR: Mike Gray, Corporate Vice President Human Resources
Web address: www.etmc.org

| | 23 | 10 | 422 | 21223 | 282 | 137655 | 1275 | 273467 | 94674 | 3317 |

✦ **HEALTHSOUTH REHABILITATION HOSPITAL–TYLER**, 3131 Troup Highway, Zip 75701–8352; tel. 903/510–7000 **A**1 10 **F**7 21 26 27 28 37 44 45 52 57 60 62 66 68 69 94 95 96 109 110 **S** HEALTHSOUTH Corporation, Birmingham, AL
Primary Contact: Sharla Anderson, Administrator
CFO: Michael G. Treadway, Controller
Web address: www.healthsouth.com

| | 32 | 46 | 62 | 1293 | 55 | 10589 | 0 | 12515 | 6582 | 193 |

TEXAS SPINE & JOINT HOSPITAL, 1814 Roseland Boulevard, Suite 100, Zip 75701; tel. 903/526–8754 **A**10 **F**2 21 33 37 60 62 63 64 65 81 84 108
Primary Contact: Tony Wahl, Chief Executive Officer
Web address: www.tsjh.org

| | 32 | 47 | 20 | 1289 | 9 | 13643 | 0 | 22188 | 5778 | 154 |

✦ **TRINITY MOTHER FRANCES HEALTH SYSTEM**, 910 East Houston, Zip 75702–8369; tel. 903/593–8441 **A**1 2 9 10 **F**2 9 10 11 12 14 15 17 19 21 22 23 24 26 27 33 34 37 39 40 41 42 49 52 53 55 57 58 59 60 61 62 63 64 65 66 69 75 81 82 84 85 88 93 94 95 96 98 107 108 109 110 **P**5 6 7 8
Primary Contact: J. Lindsey Bradley, Jr, FACHE, President and Chief Administrative Officer
COO: Ray Thompson, Executive Vice President and Chief Operating Officer
CFO: William L. Bellenfant, Chief Financial Officer
CMO: David Teegarden, M.D., President and Chief Medical Officer
CIO: Lee Portwood, Vice President
CHR: Laura Owen, Senior Vice President
Web address: www.tmfhs.org

| | 23 | 10 | 356 | 20990 | 258 | 223787 | 2873 | 269593 | 96729 | 2889 |

✦ **UNIVERSITY OF TEXAS HEALTH CENTER AT TYLER**, 11937 Highway 271, Zip 75708–3154; tel. 903/877–3451 **A**1 3 5 9 10 **F**2 9 12 15 17 19 21 22 23 24 27 28 29 33 35 39 40 41 42 44 46 47 48 52 53 55 57 58 60 61 63 64 65 66 69 70 72 77 81 82 84 85 86 87 88 93 94 96 106 108 109 110 **P**6 **S** University of Texas System, Austin, TX
Primary Contact: Kirk A. Calhoun, M.D., President
COO: Charles Spicer, Chf Oper Officer
CFO: Rick L. Hefner, Vice President for Finance and Administration
CMO: Steven Brown, M.D., Chief Medical Officer
CIO: Donna Martin, Director Information Technology
CHR: Sharyn Wrinkle, Director Human Resources
Web address: www.uthct.edu

| | 12 | 10 | 109 | 3369 | 68 | 144857 | 0 | 125934 | 60515 | 1203 |

UVALDE—Uvalde County

✦ **UVALDE COUNTY HOSPITAL AUTHORITY**, 1025 Garner Field Road, Zip 78801–1025; tel. 830/278–6251 **A**1 9 10 20 **F**2 9 11 12 14 21 22 27 28 32 33 34 36 39 42 44 46 51 52 55 59 60 62 63 65 66 67 68 69 76 77 81 82 84 87 88 92 94 97 108 109 110 **P**5
Primary Contact: James E. Buckner, Jr, CHE, Administrator
CFO: Valerie Lopez, CPA, Controller
CIO: Carolina Velasquez, Chief Information Officer
CHR: Amber Garcia, Human Resource Director
Web address: www.umhtx.org

| | 16 | 10 | 54 | 2664 | 31 | 61500 | 495 | 27809 | 13120 | 372 |

VAN HORN—Culberson County

★ **CULBERSON HOSPITAL DISTRICT**, (rural acute acess hopsital), Eisenhower–Farm Market Road 2185, Zip 79855, Mailing Address: P.O. Box 609, Zip 79855–0609; tel. 432/283–2760 **A**9 10 18 20 **F**3 6 9 27 33 55 81 88 97 **P**8 **S** Preferred Management Corporation, Shawnee, OK
Primary Contact: Mike Easley, Administrator
CMO: K S. Wong, M.D., Chief Medical Staff
Web address: www.culbersonhospital.com

| | 16 | 49 | 14 | 106 | 3 | 2084 | 0 | 2590 | 838 | 46 |

VERNON—Wilbarger County

□ **WILBARGER GENERAL HOSPITAL**, 920 Hillcrest Drive, Zip 76384–3196; tel. 940/552–9351 **A**1 9 10 **F**2 9 12 21 26 27 28 29 33 37 44 46 47 49 51 55 63 65 66 69 76 81 84 88 94 96 97 106 **P**5
Primary Contact: Larry Parsons, Administrator

| | 16 | 10 | 47 | 1171 | 18 | 23771 | 0 | 13674 | 5760 | 185 |

Hospital, Address, Telephone, Approval, Facility, and Physician Codes, Health Care System	Classi-fication Codes		Utilization Data					Expense (thousands) of dollars		
★ American Hospital Association (AHA) membership □ Joint Commission on Accreditation of Healthcare Organizations (JCAHO) accreditation ○ American Osteopathic Association (AOA) accreditation △ Commission on Accreditation of Rehabilitation Facilities (CARF) accreditation	Control	Service	Staffed Beds	Admissions	Census	Outpatient Visits	Births	Total	Payroll	Personnel

VICTORIA—Victoria County

✠ **CITIZENS MEDICAL CENTER**, 2701 Hospital Drive, Zip 77901–5749; tel. 361/573–9181, (Total facility includes 20 beds in nursing home–type unit) **A**1 2 9 10 **F**2 9 10 11 12 14 15 16 17 18 19 20 21 22 23 26 27 28 29 31 33 39 40 41 42 44 46 47 48 51 52 55 57 58 59 60 61 62 63 64 65 66 67 69 70 71 73 74 75 76 78 81 82 83 84 85 86 87 88 92 94 95 96 106 107 108 109 110 **P**6 8
Primary Contact: David P. Brown, Administrator
CFO: Robert M. Pert, Chief Financial Officer
CHR: Jim Heger, Director Human Resources
Web address: www.citizensmedicalcenter.org
| 13 | 10 | 279 | 10504 | 123 | 89545 | 1034 | 96566 | 38085 | 1083 |

✠ **DETAR HEALTHCARE SYSTEM**, (Formerly DeTar Hospital Navarro), 506 East San Antonio Street, Zip 77901–6060, Mailing Address: P.O. Box 2089, Zip 77902–2089; tel. 361/575–7441, (Includes DETAR HOSPITAL NORTH, 101 Medical Drive, Zip 77904–3198; tel. 361/573–6100; William R. Blanchard, Chief Executive Officer), (Total facility includes 16 beds in nursing home–type unit) **A**1 9 10 **F**2 11 12 15 17 19 21 22 23 26 27 28 29 32 33 34 40 41 53 55 56 57 58 59 60 61 62 63 64 65 66 68 69 75 81 84 85 86 87 88 92 93 94 96 108 109 **P**3 5 7 8 **S** Triad Hospitals, Inc., Plano, TX
Primary Contact: William R. Blanchard, Chief Executive Officer
COO: Charles Darcy, Chief Operating Officer
CFO: Woody White, Chief Financial Officer
CMO: John E. Barber, M.D., Chief of Staff
CIO: Kim Tompkins, Director Information Services
CHR: Penny Benefiel, Director Human Resources
Web address: www.detar.com
| 33 | 10 | 329 | 10198 | 128 | 83858 | 1194 | 84752 | 35167 | 924 |

□ **SCCI HOSPITAL OF VICTORIA**, 506 East San Antonio Street, Zip 77901–6060; tel. 361/575–1445 **A**1 10 **F**2 21 22 23 27 28 32 37 38 44 58 64 65 66 94 110
Primary Contact: Terry F. Robinson, Chief Executive Officer and Administrator
Web address: www.sccihospitals.com
| 33 | 80 | 23 | 225 | 17 | 0 | 0 | 6756 | 2533 | 56 |

□ △ **VICTORIA WARM SPRINGS REHABILITATION HOSPITAL**, 102 Medical Drive, Zip 77904; tel. 210/829–0009 **A**1 7 10 **F**2 21 22 26 27 28 37 58 60 65 68 69 94 96 106 110 **S** Warm Springs Rehabilitation System, San Antonio, TX
Primary Contact: Linda Vaclavik, Administrator
Web address: www.warmsprings.org
| 23 | 46 | 22 | 444 | 14 | 8931 | 0 | 6137 | 2435 | 66 |

WACO—McLennan County

✠ △ **HILLCREST BAPTIST MEDICAL CENTER**, 3000 Herring Avenue, Zip 76708–3299, Mailing Address: P.O. Box 5100, Zip 76708–0100; tel. 254/202–2000 **A**1 3 5 7 9 10 **F**2 7 9 10 11 12 14 15 17 19 21 22 23 26 27 28 29 33 34 36 37 39 40 41 42 44 46 47 48 49 50 51 52 53 55 56 57 58 59 60 61 62 63 64 65 66 68 69 75 81 82 84 85 86 87 88 89 93 94 95 96 107 108 109
Primary Contact: Arthur L. Hohenberger, FACHE, President and Chief Executive Officer
COO: Jim Gebhart, Chief Operating Officer
CFO: Richard Perkins, Chief Financial Officer
CMO: James E. Gray, M.D., Chief Medical Officer
CIO: Richard Warren, Director Information Systems
CHR: Bob Brace, Director Human Resources
Web address: www.hillcrest.net
| 21 | 10 | 274 | 13550 | 170 | 155084 | 2896 | 142233 | 54145 | 1356 |

✠ **PROVIDENCE HEALTH CENTER**, 6901 Medical Parkway, Zip 76712–7998, Mailing Address: P.O. Box 2589, Zip 76702–2589; tel. 254/751–4000, (Total facility includes 341 beds in nursing home–type unit) **A**1 2 3 5 9 10 **F**1 2 3 4 5 8 9 10 11 15 16 17 19 21 22 23 26 27 28 29 31 33 40 41 42 43 44 45 46 47 48 49 50 51 52 53 55 57 58 59 60 61 62 63 65 66 69 70 71 72 73 74 75 76 77 78 81 82 83 84 88 91 92 94 95 96 106 107 108 109 110 **P**6 8 **S** Ascension Health, Saint Louis, MO
Primary Contact: Kent A. Keahey, President and Chief Executive Officer
COO: Odis W. Nichols, Senior Vice President and Chief Operating Officer
CFO: Philip E. Halford, Senior Vice President and Chief Financial Officer
CMO: Joe H. Cunningham, M.D., Senior Vice President Medical Affairs
CIO: Barbara Roscher, Director Information Systems
CHR: Douglas J. Lennier, Vice President Human Resources
Web address: www.providence.net
| 21 | 10 | 549 | 14427 | 486 | 169975 | 689 | 143108 | 55025 | 1621 |

WACO VETERANS AFFAIRS HOSPITAL See Central Texas Veterans Healthcare System, Temple

WAXAHACHIE—Ellis County

✠ **BAYLOR MEDICAL CENTER AT WAXAHACHIE**, 1405 West Jefferson Street, Zip 75165–2275; tel. 972/923–7000 **A**1 9 10 **F**2 9 11 12 21 22 26 27 28 33 37 41 45 55 58 59 60 62 63 69 81 82 84 88 94 96 106 109 **S** Baylor Health Care System, Dallas, TX
Primary Contact: Jerri J. Stuart, R.N., President
CFO: Preshie Wilson, Vice President Finance
CMO: David Morehead, M.D., President Medical Staff
CIO: Gary Beazley, Information Systems Coordinator
CHR: Mike Adams, Vice President Human Resources
Web address: www.bhcs.com
| 23 | 10 | 53 | 3649 | 31 | 64303 | 746 | 42522 | 16415 | 329 |

Many Facility Codes have changed. Please refer to the AHA Guide Code Chart.

© 2005 AHA Guide

Hospital, Address, Telephone, Approval, Facility, and Physician Codes, Health Care System	Classi-fication Codes		Utilization Data					Expense (thousands) of dollars		
★ American Hospital Association (AHA) membership ☐ Joint Commission on Accreditation of Healthcare Organizations (JCAHO) accreditation ○ American Osteopathic Association (AOA) accreditation △ Commission on Accreditation of Rehabilitation Facilities (CARF) accreditation	Control	Service	Staffed Beds	Admissions	Census	Outpatient Visits	Births	Total	Payroll	Personnel

WEATHERFORD—Parker County

☒ **CAMPBELL HEALTH SYSTEM**, 713 East Anderson Street, Zip 76086–9971; tel. 817/596–8751 **A**1 9 10 **F**2 6 9 11 12 14 21 22 23 26 27 28 29 33 34 41 48 51 55 58 59 60 61 63 64 66 69 81 82 84 85 88 94 96 97 108 110 **P**8 **S** Quorum Health Resources, Plano, TX
Primary Contact: Scott M. Landrum, Chief Executive Officer
CFO: Nancy Cooke, Chief Financial Officer
CMO: Donna Boone, Chief Nursing Officer
CHR: Rose Thomason, Administration Director Human Resources
Web address: www.campbellhealth.com

	16	10	78	4579	42	61473	656	47246	18785	492

WEBSTER—Harris County

☒ **CLEAR LAKE REGIONAL MEDICAL CENTER**, 500 Medical Center Boulevard, Zip 77598–4286; tel. 281/332–2511, (Includes ALVIN DIAGNOSTIC AND URGENT CARE CENTER, 301 Medic Lane, Alvin, Zip 77511–5597; tel. 281/331–6141) **A**1 9 10 **F**2 9 11 12 14 15 17 19 21 23 26 27 28 29 33 39 40 42 46 47 48 49 52 55 56 57 58 59 60 61 62 63 64 65 66 68 69 70 75 81 82 84 88 92 93 94 108 109 110 **S** HCA, Nashville, TN
Primary Contact: Donald A. Shaffett, Chief Executive Officer
COO: Melinda Stephenson, Chief Operating Officer
CFO: Galen Russell, Chief Financial Officer
CMO: Richard Marietta, M.D., Medical Director
CIO: Roger Crutchfield, Director Information Systems
CHR: Shibu Varghese, Director Human Resources
Web address: www.clearlakermc.com

	32	10	391	20373	263	131124	3383	147364	68342	1276

☐ **MEADOWBROOK REHABILITATION HOSPITAL CLEAR LAKE**, 655 East Medical Center Boulevard, Zip 77598–4328; tel. 281/286–1500 **A**1 10 **F**2 21 26 27 28 45 52 57 58 62 65 66 68 69 94 95 96 108 110
Primary Contact: Claudia McCready, Administrator and Chief Executive Officer

	33	46	53	884	38	609	0	—	—	—

WEIMAR—Colorado County

★ **COLORADO–FAYETTE MEDICAL CENTER**, 400 Youens Drive, Zip 78962–9561; tel. 979/725–9531 **A**5 9 10 **F**8 9 12 21 26 27 28 33 46 52 62 63 69 81 88 108
Primary Contact: James M. Robinson, Sr, Chief Executive Officer
COO: Betty Wick, Assistant Administrator
CFO: David Austin, Chief Financial Officer
CMO: H James Wall, M.D., Chief of Staff
Web address: www.cfmc–online.com

	23	10	38	1189	13	30447	0	10187	3506	130

WELLINGTON—Collingsworth County

★ **COLLINGSWORTH GENERAL HOSPITAL**, 1014 15th Street, Zip 79095–3704, Mailing Address: P.O. Box 1112, Zip 79095–1112; tel. 806/447–2521 **A**9 10 18 20 **F**24 26 27 28 33 46 51 58 69 81 97 **P**6 **S** Preferred Management Corporation, Shawnee, OK
Primary Contact: Mike Easley, Administrator
COO: S Beth Caison, Administrator
CFO: Wanda Breedlove, Chief Financial Officer
CMO: John H. Thomas, M.D., Chief of Staff

	16	10	16	296	2	12238	0	3842	1454	48

WESLACO—Hidalgo County

☒ **KNAPP MEDICAL CENTER**, 1401 East Eighth Street, Zip 78596–6640, Mailing Address: P.O. Box 1110, Zip 78599–1110; tel. 956/968–8567 **A**1 9 10 **F**2 9 10 11 12 21 22 23 26 27 28 29 32 33 34 35 36 37 38 39 40 44 45 46 48 49 52 53 55 57 58 59 60 61 62 63 64 65 66 69 81 82 84 85 87 88 94 96 98 106 108 109 110 **P**3
Primary Contact: Robert W. Vanderveer, President and Chief Executive Officer
COO: Terry Bergstrom, Chief Operating Officer
CFO: Curtis F. Haley, Jr, Chief Financial Officer
CIO: Noel De Leon, Chief Information Officer
CHR: Joe Vasquez, Chief Human Resource Officer
Web address: www.knappmed.org

	23	10	194	12880	137	65607	1969	78740	37328	950

WHARTON—Wharton County

☒ **GULF COAST MEDICAL CENTER**, 1400 Highway 59, Zip 77488–3004, Mailing Address: P.O. Box 3004, Zip 77488–3004; tel. 979/532–2500, (Total facility includes 20 beds in nursing home–type unit) **A**1 2 9 10 **F**9 15 17 21 26 27 28 33 37 52 55 59 60 61 62 63 68 69 79 81 82 85 88 92 93 94 108 **S** Triad Hospitals, Inc., Plano, TX
Primary Contact: Donald J. Frederic, Chief Executive Officer
CFO: Gary Williams, Chief Financial Officer
CIO: Linda Dornak, Director Information Systems
CHR: Loretta Flynn, Director Human Resources
Web address: www.gulfcoastmedical.com

	32	10	128	3901	51	27960	664	31238	14504	360

WHEELER—Wheeler County

★ **PARKVIEW HOSPITAL**, 1000 Sweetwater Street, Zip 79096, Mailing Address: P.O. Box 1030, Zip 79096–1030; tel. 806/826–5581 **A**9 10 18 **F**2 6 8 12 26 27 28 32 33 46 51 53 69 81 85 88 94 97 110 **P**5
Primary Contact: Ann Fagan–Cook, Administrator and Chief Executive Officer
CIO: Sheryl Lane, Chief Information Officer

	16	10	16	282	4	4163	0	3924	214	61

WHITNEY—Hill County

LAKE WHITNEY MEDICAL CENTER, 200 North San Jacinto Street, Zip 76692–2388, Mailing Address: P.O. Box 458, Zip 76692–0458; tel. 254/694–3165 **A**9 10 **F**2 3 4 6 23 27 28 29 33 45 46 51 52 53 66 68 71 72 73 74 75 76 77 78 81 92 94 97 108 110 **P**5
Primary Contact: Ted Howard, Administrator

	33	10	20	1741	6	14605	0	5389	1809	113

TX

Hospital, Address, Telephone, Approval, Facility, and Physician Codes, Health Care System	Classi-fication Codes		Utilization Data					Expense (thousands) of dollars		
★ American Hospital Association (AHA) membership □ Joint Commission on Accreditation of Healthcare Organizations (JCAHO) accreditation ○ American Osteopathic Association (AOA) accreditation △ Commission on Accreditation of Rehabilitation Facilities (CARF) accreditation	Control	Service	Staffed Beds	Admissions	Census	Outpatient Visits	Births	Total	Payroll	Personnel

WICHITA FALLS—Wichita County

☒ **HEALTHSOUTH REHABILITATION HOSPITAL–WICHITA FALLS**, 3901 Armory Road, Zip 76302–2204; tel. 940/720–5700 **A**1 10 **F**2 21 22 26 27 28 30 35 37 39 45 46 47 48 53 57 58 60 62 65 66 68 69 94 95 96 108 110 **S** HEALTHSOUTH Corporation, Birmingham, AL Primary Contact: Michael L. Bullitt, Administrator COO: Michael L. Bullitt, Chief Executive Officer and Administrator CFO: Karen Fischer, CPA, Controller CMO: Virgil Frardo, M.D., Medical Director CHR: Kathleen Pirtle, Human Resources Manager Web address: www.healthsouth.com	32	46	63	1166	46	13722	0	10910	5481	173
☒ **KELL WEST REGIONAL HOSPITAL**, 5420 Kell West Boulevard, Zip 76310–1610; tel. 940/692–5888 **A**1 9 10 **F**2 21 26 28 33 37 39 40 57 58 61 62 63 64 66 81 88 **P**5 Primary Contact: Jerry Myers, M.D., Interim Chief Executive Officer COO: Diane Stewart, Chief Operating Officer CFO: Fran Lindemann, Chief Financial Officer Web address: www.kellwest.com	32	10	41	1335	15	18881	0	16367	5470	165
□ **NORTH TEXAS STATE HOSPITAL, WICHITA FALLS CAMPUS**, 6515 Lake Road, Zip 76308–5419, Mailing Address: Box 300, Zip 76307–0300; tel. 940/692–1220, (Nonreporting) **A**1 10 Primary Contact: James E. Smith, Superintendent Web address: www.mhmr.state.tx.us	12	22	381	—	—	—	—	—	—	—
□ **RED RIVER HOSPITAL**, 1505 Eighth Street, Zip 76301–3106; tel. 940/322–3171 **A**1 10 **F**3 4 21 22 27 29 58 65 66 71 72 74 75 76 77 78 94 96 Primary Contact: Ricky Powell, Chief Executive Officer Web address: www.redriverhospital.com	32	22	66	1548	42	828	0	4766	2537	—
□ **TEXAS SPECIALTY HOSPITAL AT WICHITA FALLS**, 1103 Grace Street, Zip 76301–4414; tel. 940/720–6633 **A**1 9 10 **F**2 21 26 27 28 44 45 46 47 58 60 64 65 66 94 110 **S** Integrated Health Services, Sparks Glencoe, MD Primary Contact: Billy Blasingame, Administrator Web address: www.thicare.com	33	80	31	297	22	0	0	6006	2631	71
☒ **UNITED REGIONAL HEALTH CARE SYSTEM**, 1600 Tenth Street, Zip 76301–4307; tel. 940/764–7000, (Includes UNITED REGIONAL HEALTH CARE SYSTEM–EIGHTH STREET CAMPUS, 1600 Eighth Street, Zip 76301–3164; UNITED REGIONAL HEALTH CARE SYSTEM–ELEVENTH STREET CAMPUS, 1600 11th Street, Zip 76301–9988; tel. 940/764–0055) **A**1 2 3 5 10 **F**2 9 10 11 12 14 15 16 17 19 21 22 23 24 26 27 28 29 32 33 34 35 37 39 40 41 46 47 48 49 50 52 55 57 58 59 60 61 62 63 64 65 66 69 75 79 80 81 82 84 85 86 87 88 92 93 94 95 96 98 108 109 110 **P**3 Primary Contact: Phyllis A. Cowling, Chief Executive Officer COO: Philip C. Robinson, Executive Vice President and Chief Operating Officer CFO: Gerard Diviney, Vice President Finance and Chief Financial Officer CMO: Leo Mercer, M.D., Vice President Medical Affairs CIO: Jerry Marshall, Information Systems Director CHR: Marshall Jones, Vice President Human Resources Web address: www.urhcs.org	23	10	331	15593	195	106279	2374	173734	63827	1727
□ **WICHITA VALLEY REHABILITATION HOSPITAL**, 302 Loop 11, Zip 76306; tel. 940/397–8200 **A**1 10 **F**2 3 21 27 28 41 52 60 66 73 94 Primary Contact: Delnita Bray, Administrator	32	46	48	869	35	9027	0	9142	4434	131

WINNIE—Chambers County

WINNIE COMMUNITY HOSPITAL, 538 Broadway, Zip 77665–1249, Mailing Address: P.O. Box 1249, Zip 77665–1249; tel. 409/296–6000 **A**9 10 18 **F**2 21 26 29 30 33 46 48 52 63 81 97 108 Primary Contact: Deborah Verret, Administrator Web address: www.winniecommunityhospital.com	32	10	25	611	7	3351	0	5441	2182	55

WINNSBORO—Wood County

☒ **PRESBYTERIAN HOSPITAL OF WINNSBORO**, 719 West Coke Road, Zip 75494–3098, Mailing Address: P.O. Box 628, Zip 75494–0628; tel. 903/342–5227 **A**1 9 10 **F**2 12 21 22 26 27 28 29 33 34 46 48 52 53 55 58 62 63 64 69 81 82 85 94 96 97 108 **S** Texas Health Resources, Arlington, TX Primary Contact: Matthew Troup, President CFO: Gorman Warren, Director Finance CMO: Bart Pruitt, D.O., President Medical Staff Web address: www.texashealth.org	23	10	46	1201	14	16013	0	15475	5884	151

WINTERS—Runnels County

NORTH RUNNELS HOSPITAL, East Highway 53, Zip 79567, Mailing Address: P.O. Box 185, Zip 79567–0185; tel. 915/754–4553 **A**9 10 18 **F**6 9 33 46 48 51 53 70 97 **P**5 Primary Contact: Roland K. Rickard, Administrator	16	10	21	83	1	8980	0	2465	1205	56

WOODVILLE—Tyler County

★ **TYLER COUNTY HOSPITAL**, 1100 West Bluff Street, Zip 75979–4799, Mailing Address: P.O. Box 549, Zip 75979–0549; tel. 409/283–8141 **A**9 10 20 **F**8 9 22 26 33 34 46 51 52 63 81 88 108 **P**5 Primary Contact: Sandra S. Jackson, Ed.D., R.N., Administrator COO: Sandra S. Jackson, Ed.D., R.N., Administrator CFO: David C. Campbell, CPA, Controller, Chief Financial Officer and Assistant Administrator Web address: www.tchospital.us	16	10	25	1188	12	23484	0	9972	4132	131

Hospital, Address, Telephone, Approval, Facility, and Physician Codes, Health Care System	Classi-fication Codes		Utilization Data					Expense (thousands) of dollars		
★ American Hospital Association (AHA) membership ☐ Joint Commission on Accreditation of Healthcare Organizations (JCAHO) accreditation ○ American Osteopathic Association (AOA) accreditation △ Commission on Accreditation of Rehabilitation Facilities (CARF) accreditation	Control	Service	Staffed Beds	Admissions	Census	Outpatient Visits	Births	Total	Payroll	Personnel

WYLIE—Dallas County

☐ **BARIATRIC CARE CENTER OF TEXAS**, (Gastric Bypass Surgery), 801 South Highway 78, Zip 75098; tel. 972/429–8000 **A**1 10 **F**2 10 22 27 28 33 52 53 58 63 64 88 96 **P**6
Primary Contact: Gary Litwin, Administrator

| | 33 | 49 | 32 | 301 | 3 | 210 | 0 | 130700 | 1427 | 43 |

YOAKUM—Lavaca County

YOAKUM COMMUNITY HOSPITAL, 1200 Carl Ramert Drive, Zip 77995–4198, Mailing Address: P.O. Box 753, Zip 77995–0753; tel. 361/293–2321 **A**9 10 18 **F**2 9 11 12 21 26 27 28 29 33 34 44 46 47 48 51 52 55 59 63 65 69 81 84 88 96 97 108
Primary Contact: Wayne L. Ogburn, FACHE, Chief Executive Officer
Web address: www.yoakumhospital.org

| | 23 | 10 | 25 | 1219 | 14 | 17087 | 107 | 10556 | 3783 | 145 |

TX

UTAH

Hospital, Address, Telephone, Approval, Facility, and Physician Codes, Health Care System	Classi-fication Codes		Utilization Data					Expense (thousands) of dollars		
	Control	Service	Staffed Beds	Admissions	Census	Outpatient Visits	Births	Total	Payroll	Personnel

★ American Hospital Association (AHA) membership
□ Joint Commission on Accreditation of Healthcare Organizations (JCAHO) accreditation
○ American Osteopathic Association (AOA) accreditation
△ Commission on Accreditation of Rehabilitation Facilities (CARF) accreditation

AMERICAN FORK—Utah County

⊠ **AMERICAN FORK HOSPITAL**, 170 North 1100 East, Zip 84003–2096; tel. 801/855–3300, (Total facility includes 12 beds in nursing home–type unit) **A**1 9 10 **F**2 9 11 12 21 24 26 27 28 31 32 33 34 35 37 42 46 47 48 51 52 55 58 59 60 63 64 65 66 69 70 80 81 84 88 92 94 95 96 98 107 108 109 110 **S** Intermountain Health Care, Inc., Salt Lake City, UT
Primary Contact: Michael R. Olson, Administrator
CFO: Rodney Lisonbee, Chief Financial Officer
CIO: Diane Rindlisbacher, Information Systems Manager
Web address: www.ihc.com
| 23 | 10 | 81 | 5783 | 41 | 142373 | 2590 | 52139 | 18795 | 446 |

BEAVER—Beaver County

BEAVER VALLEY HOSPITAL, 1109 North 100 West, Zip 84713, Mailing Address: P.O. Box 1670, Zip 84713–1670; tel. 435/438–2531, (Total facility includes 36 beds in nursing home–type unit) (Nonreporting) **A**9 10 20
Primary Contact: Craig Val Davidson, CHE, Administrator
| 14 | 10 | 57 | — | — | — | — | — | — | — |

BOUNTIFUL—Davis County

⊠ **LAKEVIEW HOSPITAL**, 630 East Medical Drive, Zip 84010–4996; tel. 801/292–6231, (Nonreporting) **A**1 9 10 **S** HCA, Nashville, TN
Primary Contact: Steven M. Anderson, CHE, Chief Executive Officer
CFO: Wayne Dalton, Chief Financial Officer
Web address: www.lakeviewhospital.com
| 33 | 10 | 128 | — | — | — | — | — | — | — |

SOUTH DAVIS COMMUNITY HOSPITAL, 401 South 400 East, Zip 84010; tel. 801/295–2361, (Nonreporting) **A**9 10
Primary Contact: Gordon Bennett, Chief Executive Officer
| 33 | 49 | 39 | — | — | — | — | — | — | — |

BRIGHAM CITY—Box Elder County

⊠ **BRIGHAM CITY COMMUNITY HOSPITAL**, 950 South Medical Drive, Zip 84302; tel. 435/734–9471 **A**1 9 10 **F**2 9 11 12 21 26 33 41 46 48 55 58 59 60 63 64 69 81 88 94 108 **S** HCA, Nashville, TN
Primary Contact: Steven B. Bateman, Chief Executive Officer
COO: Richard Spuhler, Chief Financial Officer and Chief Operating Officer
CFO: Richard Spuhler, Chief Financial Officer
CMO: Jan Ashdown, Chief Medical Officer
CIO: Steve Reichard, Manager Information Systems
CHR: Chris Bissenden, Director Human Resources
Web address: www.brighamcityhospital.com
| 33 | 10 | 49 | 1089 | 7 | 17011 | 405 | 12197 | 4535 | 132 |

CEDAR CITY—Iron County

⊠ **VALLEY VIEW MEDICAL CENTER**, 1303 North Main Street, Zip 84720–3462; tel. 435/868–5000 **A**1 9 10 20 **F**2 9 11 12 14 21 22 26 27 28 29 33 34 39 40 42 44 46 47 48 50 52 53 55 57 58 59 60 61 62 63 65 66 67 70 81 82 84 88 94 96 106 107 108 109 110 **S** Intermountain Health Care, Inc., Salt Lake City, UT
Primary Contact: Steven Smoot, Administrator
CFO: Reed Sargent, Assistant Administrator Finance
Web address: www.ihc.com
| 23 | 10 | 42 | 2385 | 18 | 92598 | 760 | 29969 | 10085 | 293 |

DELTA—Millard County

★ **DELTA COMMUNITY MEDICAL CENTER**, 126 South White Sage Avenue, Zip 84624–8928; tel. 435/864–5591 **A**9 10 18 20 **F**2 9 11 12 26 33 36 37 42 44 46 47 48 51 52 53 58 59 63 65 66 79 81 84 88 92 97 108 109 110 **P**5 **S** Intermountain Health Care, Inc., Salt Lake City, UT
Primary Contact: James E. Beckstrand, Administrator
CFO: Chris Thompson, Chief Financial Officer
Web address: www.ihc.com
| 23 | 10 | 20 | 353 | 3 | 8937 | 101 | 4218 | 1591 | 38 |

FILLMORE—Millard County

★ **FILLMORE COMMUNITY MEDICAL CENTER**, 674 South Highway 99, Zip 84631–9701; tel. 435/743–5591 **A**9 10 18 20 **F**2 9 11 12 21 26 27 29 31 33 36 37 39 44 46 47 48 51 52 53 58 59 63 69 81 84 88 92 94 97 108 **S** Intermountain Health Care, Inc., Salt Lake City, UT
Primary Contact: James E. Beckstrand, Administrator
CFO: Chris Thompson, Chief Financial Officer
Web address: www.ihc.com
| 23 | 10 | 20 | 296 | 13 | 18466 | 60 | 4178 | 1606 | 40 |

GUNNISON—Sanpete County

★ **GUNNISON VALLEY HOSPITAL**, 64 East 100 North, Zip 84634, Mailing Address: P.O. Box 759, Zip 84634–0759; tel. 435/528–7246 **A**9 10 20 **F**6 11 12 23 33 36 46 51 52 59 63 81 85 88 93 94 97 108 **P**6
Primary Contact: Greg Rosenvall, Administrator
CFO: Brian Murray, Chief Financial Officer
CHR: Dave Peterson, Manager Human Resources
| 16 | 10 | 29 | 1005 | 10 | 55726 | 190 | 10110 | 4436 | 149 |

HEBER CITY—Wasatch County

★ **HEBER VALLEY MEDICAL CENTER**, 1485 South Highway 40, Zip 84032–3522; tel. 435/654–2500, (Nonreporting) **A**9 10 20 **S** Intermountain Health Care, Inc., Salt Lake City, UT
Primary Contact: Ezra Segura, Administrator
Web address: www.ihc.com
| 23 | 10 | 19 | — | — | — | — | — | — | — |

Many Facility Codes have changed. Please refer to the AHA Guide Code Chart.

UT

Hospital, Address, Telephone, Approval, Facility, and Physician Codes, Health Care System	Classi-fication Codes		Utilization Data					Expense (thousands) of dollars		
	Control	Service	Staffed Beds	Admissions	Census	Outpatient Visits	Births	Total	Payroll	Personnel

★ American Hospital Association (AHA) membership
□ Joint Commission on Accreditation of Healthcare Organizations (JCAHO) accreditation
○ American Osteopathic Association (AOA) accreditation
△ Commission on Accreditation of Rehabilitation Facilities (CARF) accreditation

KANAB—Kane County

KANE COUNTY HOSPITAL, 355 North Main Street, Zip 84741–3238; tel. 435/644–5811, (Nonreporting) **A**9 10 20
Primary Contact: Mike Sinclair, Administrator
| | 16 | 10 | 38 | — | — | — | — | — | — | — |

LAYTON—Davis County

□ DAVIS HOSPITAL AND MEDICAL CENTER, 1600 West Antelope Drive, Zip 84041–1142; tel. 801/825–9561 **A**1 9 10 **F**2 9 11 12 15 17 21 23 27 28 29 33 46 47 48 55 56 58 59 60 62 63 66 81 82 84 85 87 88 94 108 109 **P**6 **S** IASIS Healthcare, Franklin, TN
Primary Contact: Michael E. Jensen, President and Chief Executive Officer
Web address: www.davishospital.com
| | 33 | 10 | 136 | 7001 | 61 | 141836 | 2718 | — | — | 551 |

LOGAN—Cache County

⊞ LOGAN REGIONAL HOSPITAL, 1400 North 500 East, Zip 84341–2499; tel. 435/716–1000, (Total facility includes 14 beds in nursing home–type unit) **A**1 9 10 20 **F**2 11 12 14 15 21 23 26 27 28 29 30 33 36 37 41 46 47 48 49 51 52 53 55 58 59 60 61 62 63 65 69 70 71 72 73 75 76 78 81 82 84 88 92 93 94 95 96 106 107 108 109 110 **P**6 **S** Intermountain Health Care, Inc., Salt Lake City, UT
Primary Contact: Robert C. Cash, CHE, Administrator
CFO: Alan Robinson, Chief Financial Officer
CIO: Dave Felts, Chief Informaiton Systems
CHR: Kim Dority, Director Human Resources
Web address: www.ihc.com
| | 23 | 10 | 127 | 7439 | 64 | 239592 | 2695 | 71144 | 29969 | 801 |

MIDVALE—Salt Lake County

HIGHLAND RIDGE HOSPITAL, 7309 South 180 West, Zip 84047–3769; tel. 801/569–2153, (Nonreporting) **A**9 **S** Pioneer Behavioral Health, Peabody, MA
Primary Contact: David Schroeder, Ph.D., Chief Executive Officer
Web address: www.highlandridgehospital.com
| | 33 | 22 | 32 | — | — | — | — | — | — | — |

MILFORD—Beaver County

★ MILFORD VALLEY MEMORIAL HOSPITAL, 451 North Main Street, Zip 84751–0640, Mailing Address: P.O. Box 640, Beaver, Zip 84713; tel. 435/387–2411 **A**9 10 18 20 **F**2 9 11 21 26 27 33 36 39 44 51 53 63 66 81 88 92 94 96 97 108 **P**5
Primary Contact: Craig Val Davidson, CHE, Administrator
| | 13 | 10 | 57 | 812 | 5 | 10718 | 142 | 7170 | 2915 | 80 |

MOAB—Grand County

★ ALLEN MEMORIAL HOSPITAL, 719 West 400 North Street, Zip 84532–2297, Mailing Address: P.O. Box 998, Zip 84532–0998; tel. 435/259–7191, (Nonreporting) **A**9 10 18 20 **S** Rural Health Management Corporation, Nephi, UT
Primary Contact: Marla Shelby–Drabner, FACHE, Administrator and Chief Executive Officer
COO: Doug Garrett, Chief Financial Officer and Chief Operating Officer
CFO: Doug Garrett, Chief Financial Officer and Chief Operating Officer
CIO: Mike Foster, Management Information Systems
Web address: www.amh–moab.org
| | 23 | 10 | 25 | — | — | — | — | — | — | — |

MONTICELLO—San Juan County

SAN JUAN HOSPITAL, 364 West First North, Zip 84535, Mailing Address: P.O. Box 308, Zip 84535–0308; tel. 435/587–2116, (Nonreporting) **A**9 10 20
Primary Contact: John S. Hart, Chief Executive Officer
| | 13 | 10 | 26 | — | — | — | — | — | — | — |

MOUNT PLEASANT—Sanpete County

★ SANPETE VALLEY HOSPITAL, 1100 South Medical Drive, Zip 84647–2222; tel. 435/462–2441 **A**9 10 18 20 **F**2 11 12 21 26 27 28 30 33 37 40 46 47 48 53 58 59 63 64 65 70 75 81 85 88 93 94 106 108 110 **P**7 **S** Intermountain Health Care, Inc., Salt Lake City, UT
Primary Contact: Ned Hill, Administrator
CFO: Chris Thompson, Chief Financial Officer
CMO: Gary Cole, D.O., Medical Staff President
CIO: Michael Ence, Computer Specialist
CHR: Heidi Kelso, Human Resources Manager
Web address: www.ihc.com
| | 23 | 10 | 20 | 727 | 4 | 25751 | 125 | 7705 | 2419 | 65 |

MURRAY—Salt Lake County

⊞ COTTONWOOD HOSPITAL MEDICAL CENTER, 5770 South 300 East, Zip 84107–6186, Mailing Address: P.O. Box 57800, Salt Lake City, Zip 84107–0800; tel. 801/314–5300, (Nonreporting) **A**1 2 9 10 **S** Intermountain Health Care, Inc., Salt Lake City, UT
Primary Contact: David Grauer, Administrator and Chief Executive Officer
Web address: www.ihc.com
| | 23 | 10 | 172 | — | — | — | — | — | — | — |

□ THE ORTHOPEDIC SPECIALTY HOSPITAL, 5848 South 300 East, Zip 84107; tel. 801/314–4100, (Nonreporting) **A**1 10
Primary Contact: David Grauer, Administrator and Chief Executive Officer
| | 63 | 47 | 1 | — | — | — | — | — | — | — |

NEPHI—Juab County

★ CENTRAL VALLEY MEDICAL CENTER, 48 West 1500 North, Zip 84648; tel. 435/623–3000 **A**9 10 18 20 **F**2 11 12 21 29 33 34 36 46 51 52 59 62 63 65 70 81 88 93 97 **P**6 **S** Rural Health Management Corporation, Nephi, UT
Primary Contact: Mark R. Stoddard, President
COO: Randy Allinson, Chief Operating Officer
CFO: Brent Davis, Chief Financial Officer
CMO: Connie Vail, M.D., Chief of Staff
CIO: Ken Richens, Chief Information Officer
Web address: www.centralvalleymed.com
| | 23 | 10 | 19 | 960 | 10 | 81073 | 147 | 13987 | 4762 | 159 |

Hospital, Address, Telephone, Approval, Facility, and Physician Codes, Health Care System	Classi-fication Codes		Utilization Data					Expense (thousands) of dollars		
★ American Hospital Association (AHA) membership □ Joint Commission on Accreditation of Healthcare Organizations (JCAHO) accreditation ○ American Osteopathic Association (AOA) accreditation △ Commission on Accreditation of Rehabilitation Facilities (CARF) accreditation	Control	Service	Staffed Beds	Admissions	Census	Outpatient Visits	Births	Total	Payroll	Personnel

NORTH LOGAN—Cache County

□ **CACHE VALLEY SPECIALTY HOSPITAL**, 2380 North 400 East, Zip 84341; tel. 435/713–9700, (Nonreporting) **A**1 9 10 **S** National Surgical Hospitals, Chicago, IL
Primary Contact: Michael Staheli, Chief Executive Officer
Web address: www.cvsh.com

| | 33 | 13 | 33 | — | — | — | — | — | — | |

OGDEN—Weber County

⊠ **MCKAY–DEE HOSPITAL CENTER**, 4401 Harrison Boulevard, Zip 84403, Mailing Address: Box 9370, Zip 84409–0370; tel. 801/387–2800 **A**1 2 9 10 **F**1 2 9 11 12 14 21 23 26 27 28 29 31 32 33 34 35 36 37 38 39 41 46 47 48 51 52 53 55 56 57 58 59 60 61 62 63 65 66 67 68 69 70 71 72 73 74 75 76 77 78 79 81 82 84 85 88 92 93 94 95 96 98 107 108 109 **P**6 **S** Intermountain Health Care, Inc., Salt Lake City, UT
Primary Contact: Timothy T. Pehrson, Chief Executive Officer
COO: Timothy T. Pehrson, Assistant Vice President
CFO: Doug Smith, Chief Financial Officer
CMO: Richard Arbogast, M.D., Medical Director
CIO: Joe Boyce, M.D., Director Information Systems
CHR: Karen Burnett, Regional Director Human Resources
Web address: www.ihc.com/xp/ihc/mckaydee

| | 23 | 10 | 299 | 18615 | 194 | 197721 | — | 212528 | 86230 | 2102 |

⊠ **OGDEN REGIONAL MEDICAL CENTER**, 5475 South 500 East, Zip 84405–6978; tel. 801/479–2111 **A**1 9 10 **F**2 3 4 9 11 12 14 15 17 19 21 22 23 24 25 26 27 28 29 31 32 33 34 37 40 41 44 46 47 48 55 56 57 58 59 60 61 62 63 64 65 66 68 75 79 81 82 84 88 92 93 94 96 106 108 109 110 **P**6 **S** HCA, Nashville, TN
Primary Contact: Steven B. Bateman, Chief Executive Officer
COO: Mary Joe Jones, Chief Operating Officer
CFO: Bryan McKinley, Chief Financial Officer
CMO: Neil O. Spencer, President
CIO: Xydell Hobbs, Director
CHR: Chris Bissenden, Director Human Resources
Web address: www.ogdenregional.com

| | 33 | 10 | 167 | 7302 | 78 | 106504 | 2152 | 75923 | 26582 | 609 |

OREM—Utah County

★ **OREM COMMUNITY HOSPITAL**, 331 North 400 West, Zip 84057–1999; tel. 801/224–4080 **A**9 10 **F**9 11 12 21 24 26 27 28 29 31 32 33 35 37 42 48 52 53 58 59 63 65 66 69 70 81 84 88 92 96 106 108 **S** Intermountain Health Care, Inc., Salt Lake City, UT
Primary Contact: Gail McGuill, Administrator and Chief Executive Officer
COO: Gail McGuill, Operations Officer Patient Care Services
CFO: Rodney Lisonbee, Chief Financial Officer
CMO: Neil Whitaker, M.D., Chief Medical Director
CIO: Diane Rindlisbacher, Information Systems Manager
CHR: Ken Walker, Director Human Resources
Web address: www.ihc.com

| | 23 | 10 | 20 | 1509 | 8 | 74929 | 1278 | 17690 | 6940 | 161 |

⊠ **TIMPANOGOS REGIONAL HOSPITAL**, 750 West 800 North, Zip 84059–3660; tel. 801/714–6000 **A**1 9 10 **F**2 11 12 14 15 16 17 18 26 28 33 40 46 55 59 63 66 73 75 81 82 84 88 94 108 **P**8 **S** HCA, Nashville, TN
Primary Contact: Keith D. Tintle, Chief Executive Officer
Web address: www.timpanogosregionalhospital.com

| | 33 | 10 | 51 | 4160 | 33 | 47713 | 1530 | 35003 | 12882 | 259 |

PANGUITCH—Garfield County

★ **GARFIELD MEMORIAL HOSPITAL AND CLINICS**, 200 North 400 East, Zip 84759, Mailing Address: P.O. Box 389, Zip 84759–0389; tel. 435/676–8811 **A**9 10 20 **F**1 11 12 21 24 26 27 28 29 33 37 44 45 46 47 48 50 52 58 59 63 65 66 69 81 88 92 94 95 96 97 106 108 110 **P**6 **S** Intermountain Health Care, Inc., Salt Lake City, UT
Primary Contact: Alberto Vasquez, Administrator
CFO: Reed Sargent, Assistant Administrator Finance
Web address: www.ihc.com/xp/ihc/garfield

| | 23 | 10 | 44 | 408 | 26 | 29290 | 32 | 6257 | 3313 | 85 |

PAYSON—Utah County

⊠ **MOUNTAIN VIEW HOSPITAL**, 1000 East 100 North, Zip 84651–1690; tel. 801/465–7000 **A**1 9 10 **F**2 3 4 9 10 11 12 13 14 15 21 26 28 29 31 33 44 46 47 48 49 52 53 55 56 57 58 59 60 62 63 65 66 67 68 69 71 72 73 74 75 76 77 81 82 84 85 86 87 88 92 93 94 95 96 106 107 108 109 **S** HCA, Nashville, TN
Primary Contact: Kevin Johnson, Chief Executive Officer
COO: Kim Anderson, FACHE, Chief Operating Officer
CFO: Steven R. Schramm, Chief Financial Officer
CMO: Brent Jones, Chief of Medical Staff
Web address: www.mvhpayson.com

| | 33 | 10 | 114 | 4147 | 42 | 47814 | 935 | 38284 | 13710 | 326 |

PRICE—Carbon County

⊠ **CASTLEVIEW HOSPITAL**, 300 North Hospital Drive, Zip 84501–4200; tel. 435/637–4800, (Total facility includes 8 beds in nursing home–type unit) (Nonreporting) **A**1 9 10 20 **S** LifePoint Hospitals, Inc., Brentwood, TN
Primary Contact: Jeffrey J. Manley, Chief Executive Officer
CFO: Craig M. Daniels, Chief Financial Officer
CMO: Leo Hardy, M.D., Chief of Staff
CIO: Harvey Peet, Director Information Systems
CHR: Dave Donaldson, Director Human Resources
Web address: www.castleviewhospital.net

| | 33 | 10 | 57 | — | — | — | — | — | — | |

Many Facility Codes have changed. Please refer to the AHA Guide Code Chart.   © 2005 AHA Guide

Hospital, Address, Telephone, Approval, Facility, and Physician Codes, Health Care System	Classi-fication Codes		Utilization Data					Expense (thousands) of dollars		
★ American Hospital Association (AHA) membership □ Joint Commission on Accreditation of Healthcare Organizations (JCAHO) accreditation ○ American Osteopathic Association (AOA) accreditation △ Commission on Accreditation of Rehabilitation Facilities (CARF) accreditation	Control	Service	Staffed Beds	Admissions	Census	Outpatient Visits	Births	Total	Payroll	Personnel

PROVO—Utah County

□ **UTAH STATE HOSPITAL**, 1300 East Center Street, Zip 84606–3554, Mailing Address: P.O. Box 270, Zip 84603–0270; tel. 801/344–4400, (Nonreporting) **A**1 10
Primary Contact: Mark I. Payne, Superintendent
Web address: www.hsush.state.ut.us
| 12 | 22 | 384 | — | — | — | — | | | |

⊞ △ **UTAH VALLEY REGIONAL MEDICAL CENTER**, 1034 North 500 West, Zip 84604–3337; tel. 801/373–7850, (Total facility includes 16 beds in nursing home–type unit) **A**1 2 7 9 10 **F**2 9 11 12 14 15 16 17 18 19 20 21 22 23 24 26 27 28 29 31 32 33 34 35 36 37 38 39 40 41 42 44 46 47 48 49 50 51 52 53 54 55 56 57 58 59 60 61 63 64 65 66 67 68 69 70 71 72 73 74 75 76 77 78 80 81 82 84 85 86 87 88 92 93 94 95 96 97 98 107 108 109 110 **P**6 **S** Intermountain Health Care, Inc., Salt Lake City, UT
Primary Contact: Mary Ann Young, R.N., Administrator
COO: David Clark, Chief Operating Officer
CFO: Rodney Lisonbee, Chief Financial Officer
CMO: Neil Whitaker, M.D., Medical Director
CIO: Diane Rindlisbacher, Acting Director Information Systems
CHR: Ken Walker, Director Human Resources
Web address: www.ihc.com
| 23 | 10 | 355 | 17880 | 225 | 318011 | 4252 | 253438 | 101625 | 2297 |

RICHFIELD—Sevier County

⊞ **SEVIER VALLEY HOSPITAL**, 1000 North Main Street, Zip 84701–1843; tel. 435/896–8271 **A**1 9 10 20 **F**2 3 11 12 13 14 21 27 28 29 33 46 47 48 51 52 53 55 56 58 59 60 62 63 67 68 69 70 71 81 82 84 87 88 92 93 94 97 108 **P**6 8 **S** Intermountain Health Care, Inc., Salt Lake City, UT
Primary Contact: Gary E. Beck, Administrator
CFO: Chris Thompson, Chief Financial Officer
CHR: Katey Nelson, Director Human Resources
Web address: www.ihc.com
| 23 | 10 | 27 | 1105 | 7 | 46468 | 262 | 13281 | 4068 | 113 |

ROOSEVELT—Duchesne County

★ **UINTAH BASIN MEDICAL CENTER**, 250 West 300 North, 75–2, Zip 84066–2399; tel. 435/722–6163, (Total facility includes 59 beds in nursing home–type unit) **A**9 10 20 **F**6 9 11 12 14 27 28 29 33 36 37 38 39 41 46 48 51 55 59 62 63 66 69 81 84 85 88 89 92 93 94 97 108 109 **P**7
Primary Contact: Bradley D. LeBaron, President and Chief Executive Officer
CFO: Brent Hales, Chief Financial Officer
CHR: Randall Bennett, Assistant Administrator
Web address: www.ubmc.org
| 23 | 10 | 97 | 1795 | 57 | 46313 | 462 | 34461 | 11361 | 427 |

SAINT GEORGE—Washington County

⊞ **DIXIE REGIONAL MEDICAL CENTER**, 544 South 400 East, Zip 84770–3799; tel. 435/634–4000 **A**1 2 9 10 19 20 **F**2 9 11 12 15 17 19 21 23 26 27 28 29 31 33 36 37 38 39 46 47 48 52 53 55 57 58 59 60 61 62 63 64 65 68 69 71 75 80 81 82 84 85 88 92 93 94 95 96 106 108 109 110 **P**5 **S** Intermountain Health Care, Inc., Salt Lake City, UT
Primary Contact: L. Steven Wilson, Administrator
CFO: Mary Hatch, Chief Financial Officer
CMO: Steven Van Norman, M.D., Medical Director
CHR: Vicki Wilson, Chief Human Resources Officer
Web address: www.ihc.com
| 23 | 10 | 212 | 13748 | 144 | 305610 | 2450 | 168657 | 63932 | 1568 |

SALT LAKE CITY—Salt Lake County

⊞ △ **LDS HOSPITAL**, Eighth Avenue and C Street, Zip 84143–0001; tel. 801/408–1100, (Total facility includes 32 beds in nursing home–type unit) (Nonreporting) **A**1 2 3 5 7 9 10 **S** Intermountain Health Care, Inc., Salt Lake City, UT
Primary Contact: Mikelle D. Moore, CHE, Chief Executive Officer
CMO: William L. Hamilton, Chief Medical Officer
CIO: David Baird, Chief Information Officer
CHR: Nancy Adams, Chief Human Resources Officer
Web address: www.ihc.com/xp/ihc/lds
| 23 | 10 | 468 | — | — | — | — | | | |

⊞ **PRIMARY CHILDREN'S MEDICAL CENTER**, 100 North Medical Drive, Zip 84113–1100; tel. 801/588–2000 **A**1 3 5 9 10 **F**2 9 16 18 20 21 22 23 24 26 27 28 29 31 32 33 34 35 36 37 38 39 42 47 48 49 52 53 56 57 58 60 61 62 63 64 65 66 67 69 71 72 73 74 75 77 78 81 82 83 84 85 87 88 92 93 94 96 98 99 100 101 102 103 108 **S** Intermountain Health Care, Inc., Salt Lake City, UT
Primary Contact: Joseph R. Horton, Chief Executive Officer and Administrator
COO: Joe Mott, Chief Operating Officer
CFO: David Thompson, Chief Financial Officer
CMO: Ed Clark, M.D., Medical Director
CIO: Joe Hales, Director of Information Systems
CHR: Albert Bennett Buckworth, Director of Human Resources
Web address: www.ihc.com
| 23 | 50 | 225 | 11223 | 169 | 151934 | 0 | 240905 | 106538 | 2452 |

□ **SALT LAKE REGIONAL MEDICAL CENTER**, 1050 East South Temple, Zip 84102–1599; tel. 801/350–4111 **A**1 3 5 9 10 **F**2 9 10 11 12 14 15 17 19 21 22 23 26 27 28 29 31 33 40 44 46 48 50 52 53 55 56 57 58 59 60 61 62 63 64 66 68 69 70 81 82 84 85 86 87 88 93 94 95 96 107 108 109 110 **S** IASIS Healthcare, Franklin, TN
Primary Contact: Brian E. Dunn, Chief Executive Officer
Web address: www.saltlakeregional.com
| 33 | 10 | 132 | 5902 | 55 | 55000 | 1662 | — | — | 497 |

UT

Hospital, Address, Telephone, Approval, Facility, and Physician Codes, Health Care System	Classi-fication Codes		Utilization Data					Expense (thousands) of dollars		
★ American Hospital Association (AHA) membership □ Joint Commission on Accreditation of Healthcare Organizations (JCAHO) accreditation ○ American Osteopathic Association (AOA) accreditation △ Commission on Accreditation of Rehabilitation Facilities (CARF) accreditation	Control	Service	Staffed Beds	Admissions	Census	Outpatient Visits	Births	Total	Payroll	Personnel
□ **SHRINERS HOSPITALS FOR CHILDREN–INTERMOUNTAIN**, Fairfax Road and Virginia Street, Zip 84103–4399; tel. 801/536–3500, (Nonreporting) **A**1 3 5 **S** Shriners Hospitals for Children, Tampa, FL Primary Contact: J. Craig Patchin, Administrator Web address: www.shriners.com	23	57	40	—	—	—	—	—	—	—
⊠ **ST. MARK'S HOSPITAL**, 1200 East 3900 South, Zip 84124–1390; tel. 801/268–7111 **A**1 2 9 10 **F**2 9 10 11 12 14 15 17 19 21 22 26 27 28 29 30 31 32 33 34 35 37 38 39 40 41 42 44 46 47 48 49 52 53 55 56 57 58 59 61 62 63 64 65 66 73 81 82 84 85 88 92 93 94 96 106 107 108 109 110 **P**5 6 8 **S** HCA, Nashville, TN Primary Contact: John Hanshaw, Chief Executive Officer COO: Rand Kerr, Chief Operating Officer CFO: Mitch Tibbitts, Chief Financial Officer CMO: Craig Carpenter, Medical Staff President CIO: Bruk Kammerman, Director Information Systems CHR: Robyn Opheikens, Assistant Administrator, Human Resources Web address: www.stmarkshospital.com	33	10	293	16598	189	129811	3375	178447	56949	1340
⊠ △ **UNIVERSITY OF UTAH HOSPITALS AND CLINICS**, 50 North Medical Drive, Zip 84132–0002; tel. 801/581–2121 **A**1 2 3 5 7 8 9 10 **F**2 4 6 7 9 11 12 13 14 15 17 19 21 22 23 24 26 27 28 29 30 31 32 33 34 35 37 38 39 40 42 44 46 47 48 49 50 52 53 55 56 57 58 59 60 61 62 63 64 66 68 69 70 71 72 73 75 76 77 78 79 80 81 82 84 85 86 87 88 89 90 93 94 95 96 98 99 100 103 107 108 109 110 **P**1 Primary Contact: Richard A. Fullmer, Executive Director CFO: Gordon Crabtree, Chief Financial Officer CMO: Neil K. Kochenour, M.D., Medical Director CIO: Pierre Pincetl, M.D., Chief Information Officer and Associate Vice President for Health Sciences Information Technology Services CHR: Loretta Harper, Vice President Human Resources Web address: www.uuhsc.utah.edu	12	10	392	19876	308	720085	3524	469501	181922	4791
□ △ **UNIVERSITY OF UTAH NEUROPSYCHIATRIC INSTITUTE**, 501 Chipeta Way, Zip 84108–1225; tel. 801/583–2500 **A**1 3 5 7 9 10 **F**3 4 21 26 27 28 29 44 46 53 65 71 72 73 74 76 77 78 94 96 97 98 108 **P**1 5 6 Primary Contact: Ross Van Vranken, Chief Executive Officer Web address: www.med.utah.edu/uni	12	22	90	3239	75	34132	—	22931	10107	332
⊠ △ **VETERANS AFFAIRS SALT LAKE CITY HEALTH CARE SYSTEM**, 500 Foothill Drive, Zip 84148–0002; tel. 801/582–1565 **A**1 3 5 7 **F**2 4 15 17 19 21 22 26 27 28 29 30 31 32 33 34 35 36 37 38 39 41 42 44 45 46 47 48 49 50 51 52 55 57 58 60 61 62 63 65 66 68 69 70 71 73 74 75 76 77 78 81 82 84 88 97 100 106 107 108 109 110 **P**6 **S** Department of Veterans Affairs, Washington, DC Primary Contact: James R. Floyd, Director COO: Cynthia Abair, Associate Director CFO: W Neil Hardy, Director, Financial Management Service Center CMO: Ronald J. Gebhart, Chief of Staff CIO: Carl Worstell, Chief Information Officer CHR: Robin Korogl, Director, Human Resources, Leadership and Education Web address: www.va.gov/sta/guide/home.asp	45	10	121	5386	99	345280	0	181551	82238	1333
SANDY—Salt Lake County										
⊠ **ALTA VIEW HOSPITAL**, 9660 South 1300 East, Zip 84094–3793; tel. 801/501–2600, (Nonreporting) **A**1 9 10 **S** Intermountain Health Care, Inc., Salt Lake City, UT Primary Contact: Tim Bricker, Administrator and Chief Executive Officer Web address: www.ihc.com	23	10	73	—	—	—	—	—	—	—
⊠ **HEALTHSOUTH REHABILITATION HOSPITAL OF UTAH**, 8074 South 1300 East, Zip 84094–0743; tel. 801/561–3400, (Nonreporting) **A**1 9 10 **S** HEALTHSOUTH Corporation, Birmingham, AL Primary Contact: Tom Almerico, Administrator CMO: Joseph VickRoy, Medical Director CHR: Vauna Allinson, Director Human Resources Web address: www.healthsouth.com	33	46	84	—	—	—	—	—	—	—
TOOELE—Tooele County										
□ **MOUNTAIN WEST MEDICAL CENTER**, 2055 North Main, Zip 84074–2794; tel. 435/843–3600 **A**1 9 10 20 **F**2 6 9 11 12 21 22 27 28 33 39 46 48 51 55 58 59 62 63 69 81 84 88 92 94 96 97 108 109 110 **S** Community Health Systems, Inc., Brentwood, TN Primary Contact: Charles A. Davis, Chief Executive Officer Web address: www.mountainwestmc.com	33	10	35	1832	12	30341	322	—	—	170
TREMONTON—Box Elder County										
★ **BEAR RIVER VALLEY HOSPITAL**, 440 West 600 North, Zip 84337–2497; tel. 435/257–7441, (Total facility includes 38 beds in nursing home–type unit) (Nonreporting) **A**9 10 **S** Intermountain Health Care, Inc., Salt Lake City, UT Primary Contact: Eric Packer, Administrator Web address: www.ihc.com	23	10	58	—	—	—	—	—	—	—

UT

Many Facility Codes have changed. Please refer to the AHA Guide Code Chart.

© 2005 AHA Guide

Hospital, Address, Telephone, Approval, Facility, and Physician Codes, Health Care System	Classi-fication Codes		Utilization Data					Expense (thousands) of dollars		
★ American Hospital Association (AHA) membership ☐ Joint Commission on Accreditation of Healthcare Organizations (JCAHO) accreditation ○ American Osteopathic Association (AOA) accreditation △ Commission on Accreditation of Rehabilitation Facilities (CARF) accreditation	Control	Service	Staffed Beds	Admissions	Census	Outpatient Visits	Births	Total	Payroll	Personnel
VERNAL—Uintah County										
⊞ **ASHLEY VALLEY MEDICAL CENTER**, (Formerly Columbia Ashley Valley Medical Center), 151 West 200 North, Zip 84078–1907; tel. 435/789–3342, (Nonreporting) **A**1 9 10 20 **S** LifePoint Hospitals, Inc., Brentwood, TN Primary Contact: Si Hutt, Chief Executive Officer COO: Mark Holyoak, Chief Clinical Officer CFO: Chad Labrum, Chief Financial Officer CIO: Mark Rich, Director Information Services CHR: Deena Mansfield, Director Human Resources Web address: www.avmc–hospital.com	33	10	31	—	—	—	—	—	—	—
WEST JORDAN—Salt Lake County										
COPPER HILLS YOUTH CENTER, 5899 West Rivendell Drive, Zip 84088–5700; tel. 800/776–7116 **F**26 27 28 71 72 77 78 94 Primary Contact: Michael Rowley, Chief Executive Officer Web address: www.copperhillsyouthcenter.com	33	52	110	230	107	0	0	10273	5754	256
☐ **JORDAN VALLEY HOSPITAL**, 3580 West 9000 South, Zip 84088–8811; tel. 801/561–8888, (Nonreporting) **A**1 9 10 **S** IASIS Healthcare, Franklin, TN Primary Contact: Bryanie W. Swilley, Chief Executive Officer Web address: www.jordanvalleyhospital.com	32	10	50	—	—	—	—	—	—	—
WEST VALLEY CITY—Salt Lake County										
☐ **PIONEER VALLEY HOSPITAL**, 3460 South Pioneer Parkway, Zip 84120–2648; tel. 801/964–3100 **A**1 9 10 **F**10 11 12 15 17 21 22 23 26 27 28 31 33 36 37 41 44 46 48 52 55 59 60 62 63 64 69 75 81 82 84 85 86 88 93 94 96 107 108 109 **S** IASIS Healthcare, Franklin, TN Primary Contact: Iris Simonis, Chief Executive Officer Web address: www.pioneervalleyhospital.com	33	10	100	4091	32	97891	1007	—	—	219
WOODS CROSS—Davis County										
☐ **BENCHMARK BEHAVIORAL HEALTH SYSTEMS**, 592 West 1350 South, Zip 84087–1665; tel. 801/299–5300 **A**1 9 **F**28 71 72 **P**5 **S** Psychiatric Solutions, Franklin, TN Primary Contact: John A. Holter, Chief Executive Officer Web address: www.bbhsnet.com	33	22	104	54	104	27	0	13285	7985	474

UT

VERMONT

Hospital, Address, Telephone, Approval, Facility, and Physician Codes, Health Care System	Classi-fication Codes		Utilization Data					Expense (thousands) of dollars		
★ American Hospital Association (AHA) membership □ Joint Commission on Accreditation of Healthcare Organizations (JCAHO) accreditation ○ American Osteopathic Association (AOA) accreditation △ Commission on Accreditation of Rehabilitation Facilities (CARF) accreditation	Control	Service	Staffed Beds	Admissions	Census	Outpatient Visits	Births	Total	Payroll	Personnel

BARRE—Washington County

✠ **CENTRAL VERMONT MEDICAL CENTER**, Fisher Road, Zip 05641–9060, Mailing Address: P.O. Box 547, Zip 05641–0547; tel. 802/371–4100, (Total facility includes 153 beds in nursing home–type unit) **A**1 9 10 19 20 **F**9 11 12 21 22 23 26 27 28 29 33 35 37 38 39 40 41 43 46 47 48 50 52 53 55 58 59 60 63 65 66 69 71 73 74 75 76 81 82 84 85 87 88 92 93 94 95 96 108 109 110 **P**6
Primary Contact: Daria V. Mason, President and Chief Executive Officer
CFO: Stephen Moss, Chief Financial Officer
CMO: Russell Davignon, M.D., Vice President, Quality and Medical Affairs
CIO: Russell Davignon, M.D., Vice President, Quality and Medical Affairs
CHR: Richard Theken, Vice President Human Resources
Web address: www.cvmc.hitchock.org
| 23 | 10 | 238 | 3751 | 193 | — | 425 | 74594 | 34394 | 681 |

BENNINGTON—Bennington County

✠ **SOUTHWESTERN VERMONT MEDICAL CENTER**, 100 Hospital Drive East, Zip 05201; tel. 802/442–6361 **A**1 2 9 10 19 **F**2 11 12 14 21 23 24 26 27 28 29 30 33 34 36 37 38 45 46 47 48 50 51 52 55 58 59 60 61 62 63 64 65 66 69 70 72 73 74 75 76 77 78 81 82 85 88 92 93 94 95 96 106 107 108 109 **P**1 6
Primary Contact: Harvey M. Yorke, President and Chief Executive Officer
COO: Mary Wicker, Chief Operating Officer
CFO: Tom Lenkowski, Chief Financial Officer and Vice President Finance
CMO: Mark Novotny, M.D., Chief Operating Officer Medical Practice Division
CIO: Richard Ogilvie, Chief Information Officer
CHR: Craig Ghidotti, Vice President Human Resources
Web address: www.svhealthcare.org
| 23 | 10 | 99 | 4470 | 50 | 153111 | 540 | 68357 | 31864 | 630 |

BRATTLEBORO—Windham County

✠ **BRATTLEBORO MEMORIAL HOSPITAL**, 17 Belmont Avenue, Zip 05301–3498; tel. 802/257–0341 **A**1 9 10 **F**2 9 10 11 12 14 15 22 23 26 27 28 29 33 37 38 41 46 48 52 53 54 55 57 59 60 61 62 63 64 65 66 69 81 82 85 87 88 89 94 96 106 108 109 110
Primary Contact: Katherine Anderson, Interim President
CFO: Michael Rogers, Vice President Fiscal Services
CMO: David Albright, M.D., Medical Staff President
CIO: Jonathan Farina, Chief Information Officer
Web address: www.bmhvt.org
| 23 | 10 | 47 | 2042 | 23 | 74488 | 358 | 34221 | 12856 | 290 |

✠ **BRATTLEBORO RETREAT**, Anna Marsh Lane, Zip 05301, Mailing Address: P.O. Box 803, Zip 05302–0803; tel. 802/257–7785 **A**1 3 5 9 10 **F**4 21 26 27 28 29 37 41 42 44 45 48 52 58 71 72 73 74 76 77 78 94 96 **P**6
Primary Contact: Richard T. Palmisano, II, R.N., President and Chief Executive Officer
COO: Robert Soucy, Chief Operating Officer
CFO: John E. Blaha, Vice President Finance and Chief Financial Officer
CMO: Frederick Engstrom, M.D., Senior Vice President Medical Affairs
CIO: Doreen Lincoln, Director Information Services
Web address: www.bratretreat.org
| 23 | 22 | 149 | 2001 | 52 | 21025 | 0 | 32202 | 16592 | 287 |

BURLINGTON—Chittenden County

✠ **FLETCHER ALLEN HEALTH CARE**, 111 Colchester Avenue, Zip 05401–1429; tel. 802/847–0000, (Includes FANNY ALLEN CAMPUS, 101 College Parkway, Colchester, Zip 05446–3035; tel. 802/655–1234; MEDICAL CENTER HOSPITAL CAMPUS, Colchester Avenue, Zip 05401; tel. 802/847–2345) **A**1 2 3 5 8 9 10 **F**2 4 5 6 7 9 10 11 12 14 15 16 17 18 19 20 21 22 23 24 26 27 28 29 30 32 33 34 35 37 38 39 40 42 44 45 46 47 48 49 50 52 53 55 56 57 58 59 60 61 62 63 64 65 66 67 68 69 70 71 72 73 74 75 76 77 78 79 80 81 82 84 85 86 87 88 89 90 93 94 95 96 99 101 104 105 106 107 108 109 110
Primary Contact: Melinda Estes, M.D., President and Chief Executive Officer
COO: Angeline M. Marano, Senior Vice President, Chief Operating Officer
CFO: Richard Magnuson, Chief Financial Officer
CMO: John R. Brumsted, M.D., Chief Medical Officer
CIO: John K. Evans, Senior Vice President and Chief Technology Officer
CHR: Paul Macuga, Chief Human Resources Officer
Web address: www.fahc.org
| 23 | 10 | 519 | 21366 | 317 | 1041494 | 2154 | 547724 | 287020 | 4668 |

COLCHESTER—Chittenden County

FANNY ALLEN CAMPUS See Fletcher Allen Health Care, Burlington

MIDDLEBURY—Addison County

✠ **PORTER MEDICAL CENTER**, 115 Porter Drive, Zip 05753–8606; tel. 802/388–4701 **A**1 9 10 20 **F**2 9 12 15 22 26 27 29 33 38 42 52 58 59 60 62 63 64 69 70 81 82 84 85 88 94 97 106 108 109 110 **P**6
Primary Contact: James L. Daily, President
COO: Patricia Jannene, Vice President Patient Care Services
CFO: Duncan Brines, Vice President Finance
CMO: Allan Curtiss, President Medical Staff
CIO: Ronald Hallman, Vice President Development and Public Relations
CHR: Dan Arseneau, Vice President Human Resources
Web address: www.portermedical.org
| 23 | 10 | 45 | 1328 | 14 | 144263 | 267 | 35395 | 16631 | 327 |

VT

Many Facility Codes have changed. Please refer to the AHA Guide Code Chart. © 2005 AHA Guide

Hospital, Address, Telephone, Approval, Facility, and Physician Codes, Health Care System	Classi-fication Codes		Utilization Data					Expense (thousands) of dollars		
★ American Hospital Association (AHA) membership □ Joint Commission on Accreditation of Healthcare Organizations (JCAHO) accreditation ○ American Osteopathic Association (AOA) accreditation △ Commission on Accreditation of Rehabilitation Facilities (CARF) accreditation	Control	Service	Staffed Beds	Admissions	Census	Outpatient Visits	Births	Total	Payroll	Personnel

MORRISVILLE—Lamoille County

★ **COPLEY HOSPITAL**, 528 Washington Highway, Zip 05661–9209; tel. 802/888–4231 **A**9 10 20 **F**11 12 22 23 26 27 28 29 33 46 47 48 52 53 57 58 59 60 62 63 64 65 68 69 72 77 81 88 94 95 96 97 98 106 108
Primary Contact: Warren K. West, President
CFO: Rassoul Rangaviz, Vice President Finance
CMO: Mark Lichtenstein, M.D., Medical Director
CIO: Conrad Garven, Manager Information Services
CHR: Linda Alderton, Director Human Resources
Web address: www.copleyvt.org

	23	10	42	1402	16	66470	235	29495	11146	331

NEWPORT—Orleans County

★ **NORTH COUNTRY HOSPITAL AND HEALTH CENTER**, 189 Prouty Drive, Zip 05855–9329; tel. 802/334–7331, (Total facility includes 23 beds in nursing home–type unit) **A**9 10 18 20 **F**2 9 11 14 21 22 23 26 27 28 29 30 33 37 38 39 41 44 46 47 48 53 55 57 59 60 61 62 63 64 69 70 75 77 81 82 84 88 92 93 94 96 97 98 106 108 109 **P**6
Primary Contact: Karen A. Weller, Chief Executive Officer
COO: Kim Campbell, R.N., Vice President Professional Services
CFO: Robert L. Fotter, Vice President Finance
CMO: Darius Rhodes Zorovfy, M.D., President Medical Staff
CIO: Ervin Goodwin, Department Manager of Information Services
CHR: Thomas Girard, Vice President Human Resources
Web address: www.nchsi.org

	23	10	48	2011	39	62871	225	41197	20630	376

RANDOLPH—Orange County

★ **GIFFORD MEDICAL CENTER**, 44 South Main Street, Zip 05060–1381, Mailing Address: P.O. Box 2000, Zip 05060–2000; tel. 802/728–7000, (Total facility includes 20 beds in nursing home–type unit) **A**2 9 10 18 **F**1 9 10 11 12 21 22 23 24 26 27 28 29 30 31 33 36 37 38 39 40 44 46 47 48 52 55 57 58 59 60 61 62 63 65 66 69 70 81 82 84 88 92 94 96 97 106 108 109 110 **P**6
Primary Contact: Joseph L. Woodin, President and Chief Executive Officer
CFO: David Sanville, Chief Financial Officer
CMO: Louis DiNicola, M.D., Medical Staff Director
CIO: John Brugger, Director of Information Systems
Web address: www.giffordmed.com

	23	10	45	1394	36	37525	341	29137	14014	310

RUTLAND—Rutland County

✠ **RUTLAND REGIONAL MEDICAL CENTER**, 160 Allen Street, Zip 05701–4595; tel. 802/775–7111 **A**1 2 9 10 19 20 **F**2 9 11 12 15 17 19 21 22 23 26 27 28 29 33 34 40 46 48 50 52 55 58 59 60 61 62 63 65 66 68 69 71 73 74 76 77 79 80 81 84 86 88 93 94 95 96 97 106 107 108 110
Primary Contact: Thomas W. Huebner, President and Chief Executive Officer
CFO: Ed Ogorzalek, Chief Financial Officer
CIO: Kim Kalajainen, Chief Information Officer
CHR: Robert VanHeiningen, Administrative Leader
Web address: www.rrmc.org

	23	10	120	6876	91	161306	510	118282	47533	813

SAINT ALBANS—Franklin County

✠ **NORTHWESTERN MEDICAL CENTER**, 133 Fairfield Street, Zip 05478–1734, Mailing Address: P.O. Box 1370, Zip 05478–1370; tel. 802/524–5911 **A**1 2 10 20 **F**2 9 11 12 14 21 22 26 27 28 29 33 37 38 46 48 52 58 59 60 61 62 63 65 66 69 76 81 88 92 94 96 97 106 107 108 **P**8 **S** Quorum Health Resources, Plano, TX
Primary Contact: Peter A. Hofstetter, Chief Executive Officer
CFO: Dawn Bugbee, Chief Financial Officer
CIO: John Johnston, Manager Information Systems
CHR: Mary Lou Beaulieu, Director of Human Resources and Compliance Officer
Web address: www.nmcinc.org

	23	10	52	2440	23	125217	532	24172	18321	413

SAINT JOHNSBURY—Caledonia County

★ **NORTHEASTERN VERMONT REGIONAL HOSPITAL**, 1315 Hospital Drive, Zip 05819–9962, Mailing Address: P.O. Box 905, Zip 05819–9962; tel. 802/748–8141 **A**9 10 18 20 **F**2 9 11 12 14 21 22 23 26 28 29 33 35 36 37 38 39 40 45 46 47 48 50 52 53 55 58 59 60 61 62 63 65 66 69 81 82 84 88 94 95 96 97 106 108 109 **P**6
Primary Contact: Paul R. Bengtson, Chief Executive Officer
CFO: Robert Hersey, Chief Financial Officer
CIO: Andrea Lott, Vice President Information Services
CHR: Betty Ann Gwatkins, Vice President of Human Resources
Web address: www.nvrh.org

	23	10	25	1538	12	86438	253	30948	12249	280

SPRINGFIELD—Windsor County

✠ **SPRINGFIELD HOSPITAL**, 25 Ridgewood Road, Zip 05156–2003, Mailing Address: P.O. Box 2003, Zip 05156–2003; tel. 802/885–2151 **A**1 9 10 **F**1 2 4 11 12 21 24 26 27 28 29 30 31 33 37 38 39 41 42 44 46 47 48 50 52 55 58 59 60 62 63 64 65 66 69 70 71 73 74 75 76 77 78 81 82 85 88 94 96 106 107 108 109 110 **P**4 7 8
Primary Contact: Glenn D. Cordner, Chief Executive Officer
COO: Tom Crawford, Director General Services and Chief Information Officer
CFO: Laverne Lindamood, Director Finance
CMO: Mark C. Hamilton, M.D., President Medical Staff
CIO: Tom Crawford, Director General Services and Chief Information Officer
Web address: www.springfieldhospital.org

	23	10	69	2916	33	—	203	30081	13388	318

VT

Hospital, Address, Telephone, Approval, Facility, and Physician Codes, Health Care System	Classi-fication Codes		Utilization Data					Expense (thousands) of dollars		
★ American Hospital Association (AHA) membership □ Joint Commission on Accreditation of Healthcare Organizations (JCAHO) accreditation ○ American Osteopathic Association (AOA) accreditation △ Commission on Accreditation of Rehabilitation Facilities (CARF) accreditation	Control	Service	Staffed Beds	Admissions	Census	Outpatient Visits	Births	Total	Payroll	Personnel

TOWNSHEND—Windham County

★ **GRACE COTTAGE HOSPITAL**, Route 35, Zip 05353–0216, Mailing Address: P.O. Box 216, Zip 05353–0216; tel. 802/365–7357, (Total facility includes 14 beds in nursing home–type unit) **A**10 18 **F**1 2 6 9 26 28 33 36 38 44 45 48 52 54 60 63 69 70 77 92 94 95 97 106 108 **P**6
Primary Contact: Albert LaRochelle, Administrator
CFO: Stephen A. Brown, Chief Financial Officer
CIO: Kathleen Stover, Business Manager
Web address: www.gracecottage.org

| | 23 | 10 | 33 | 376 | 24 | 43694 | 0 | 12707 | 5898 | 130 |

WATERBURY—Washington County

VERMONT STATE HOSPITAL, 103 South Main Street, Zip 05671–2501; tel. 802/241–1000 **A**5 9 10 **F**22 48 58 60 65 71 75 76 94 96 108 **P**6
Primary Contact: Bertold Francke, M.D., Interim Executive Director
Web address: www.state.vt.us/dmh/

| | 12 | 22 | 56 | 221 | 47 | 0 | 0 | 13519 | 7904 | 179 |

WHITE RIVER JUNCTION—Windsor County

✠ **VETERANS AFFAIRS MEDICAL CENTER**, 215 North Main Street, Zip 05009–0001; tel. 802/295–9363 **A**1 3 5 8 **F**2 4 9 15 21 22 23 26 27 28 29 30 31 33 35 36 37 38 39 42 44 45 47 48 50 52 55 57 58 61 62 63 64 65 66 69 70 71 73 74 75 76 77 78 81 82 88 94 96 107 108 109 110 **P**1 6
S Department of Veterans Affairs, Washington, DC
Primary Contact: Gary M. De Gasta, Director
CFO: Ryan Lilly, Chief Fiscal Services
CMO: Arthur E. Sauvigne, M.D., Medical Director
CIO: Karen Merrill, Chief Information Officer
CHR: Vickie Grubb, Chief Human Resources Officer
Web address: www.va.gov/sta/guide/home.asp

| | 45 | 10 | 60 | 2613 | 45 | 171397 | 0 | 94284 | 38461 | 667 |

WINDSOR—Windsor County

★ **MT. ASCUTNEY HOSPITAL AND HEALTH CENTER**, 289 County Road, Zip 05089–9702; tel. 802/674–6711, (Total facility includes 58 beds in nursing home–type unit) **A**9 10 18 **F**8 9 12 21 22 23 26 27 28 29 30 32 33 35 36 38 39 44 45 47 48 50 52 53 55 58 60 61 62 63 64 65 66 68 69 70 73 77 81 88 91 92 94 96 97 106 107 108 110 **P**6
Primary Contact: Richard Slusky, Administrator
CFO: Michael Long, Chief Financial Officer
CMO: William S. Palmer, M.D., President Medical Staff
CIO: Tom Sims, Chief Information Officer
CHR: Jean Martaniuk, Personnel Director
Web address: www.mtascutneyhospital.org

| | 23 | 10 | 91 | 943 | 76 | — | 0 | 26741 | 13612 | 324 |

VT

Many Facility Codes have changed. Please refer to the AHA Guide Code Chart. © 2005 AHA Guide

VIRGINIA

Hospital, Address, Telephone, Approval, Facility, and Physician Codes, Health Care System	Classi-fication Codes		Utilization Data					Expense (thousands) of dollars		
	Control	Service	Staffed Beds	Admissions	Census	Outpatient Visits	Births	Total	Payroll	Personnel

★ American Hospital Association (AHA) membership
□ Joint Commission on Accreditation of Healthcare Organizations (JCAHO) accreditation
○ American Osteopathic Association (AOA) accreditation
△ Commission on Accreditation of Rehabilitation Facilities (CARF) accreditation

ABINGDON—Washington County

✖ **JOHNSTON MEMORIAL HOSPITAL**, 351 Court Street N.E., Zip 24210–2955; tel. 276/676–7000 **A**1 2 9 10 **F**2 9 11 12 21 22 23 24 26 29 30 31 33 37 38 39 40 46 47 48 50 51 52 53 55 56 57 58 59 60 61 62 63 64 65 66 69 81 82 84 85 87 88 94 95 96 106 107 108 109 110 **P**8
Primary Contact: Sean S. McMurray, CHE, Chief Executive Officer
COO: Stephen K. Givens, Chief Operating Officer
CFO: Fred W. Wright, Chief Financial Officer
CMO: Richard Buddington, M.D., President, Medical Staff
CIO: George Lewis, Director Management Information Services
CHR: Jackie G. Phipps, Executive Director Human Resources
Web address: www.jmh.org
| 23 | 10 | 135 | 4802 | 54 | 102078 | 600 | 57502 | 21986 | 609 |

ALEXANDRIA—Independent City County

✖ **INOVA ALEXANDRIA HOSPITAL**, 4320 Seminary Road, Zip 22304–1594; tel. 703/504–3000 **A**1 2 3 5 9 10 **F**2 9 11 12 14 15 17 19 21 22 23 26 27 28 29 31 32 33 35 37 38 39 41 46 47 48 49 50 52 53 54 55 56 57 58 59 60 61 62 63 64 65 66 69 73 75 79 80 81 82 84 85 86 87 88 92 93 94 95 96 108 109 110 **P**6 **S** Inova Health System, Falls Church, VA
Primary Contact: Kenneth H. Kozloff, FACHE, Administrator
CFO: Thomas F. Knight, Chief Financial Officer
CMO: Joel Temme, M.D., President, Medical Staff
CIO: Nanci Little Gosnell, Vice President Information Services
Web address: www.inova.org
| 23 | 10 | 330 | 17367 | 244 | 99691 | 3499 | 188945 | 83427 | 1312 |

✖ △ **INOVA MOUNT VERNON HOSPITAL**, 2501 Parker's Lane, Zip 22306; tel. 703/664–7000 **A**1 2 7 9 10 **F**2 9 12 14 21 22 23 26 27 28 29 31 32 33 35 37 38 39 41 46 47 48 49 50 52 53 54 55 57 58 60 61 62 63 64 65 66 68 69 71 73 74 75 76 78 81 82 84 85 86 87 88 92 94 96 108 110 **S** Inova Health System, Falls Church, VA
Primary Contact: Arlen Reynolds, Interim Chief Executive Officer
CFO: Michael A. Barger, Associate Administrator Finance and Chief Financial Officer
CMO: Howard Lando, President Medical Staff
CHR: Bev Sugar, Associate Administrator and Director Human Resources
Web address: www.inova.org
| 23 | 10 | 236 | 9123 | 165 | 69457 | 0 | 115533 | 47688 | 935 |

ARLINGTON—Arlington County

✖ **NORTHERN VIRGINIA COMMUNITY HOSPITAL**, (Formerly Vencor Hospital–Arlington), 601 South Carlin Springs Road, Zip 22204–1096; tel. 703/671–1200 **A**1 9 10 **F**2 10 12 15 21 22 33 55 57 62 63 69 71 81 82 85 87 88 108 **S** HCA, Nashville, TN
Primary Contact: Bryan K. Dearing, Chief Executive Officer
COO: Scott H. Hill, Chief Operating Officer
CFO: Michael Wyers, Chief Financial Officer
CHR: Jerry Clipp, Director Human Resources
Web address: www.nvchospital.com
| 33 | 10 | 100 | 2324 | 49 | 10686 | 0 | 38967 | 18841 | 368 |

✖ **VIRGINIA HOSPITAL CENTER – ARLINGTON**, 1701 North George Mason Drive, Zip 22205–3698; tel. 703/558–5000 **A**1 2 3 5 9 10 **F**2 3 4 9 11 12 14 15 17 19 21 22 23 31 33 38 40 42 47 48 49 52 55 56 57 58 59 61 62 63 64 65 66 68 69 71 74 75 77 79 81 82 84 85 86 87 88 93 94 106 107 108 109 110
Primary Contact: James B. Cole, Chief Executive Officer
COO: Carl Bahnlein, Executive Vice President and Chief Operating Officer
CMO: Archie McPherson, M.D., Vice President and Chief Medical Officer
CIO: David Crutchfield, Vice President and Chief Information Officer
CHR: Michael Malone, Vice President Administrative Services
Web address: www.virginiahospitalcenter.com
| 23 | 10 | 298 | 10512 | 164 | 194808 | 3240 | 189891 | 81736 | 1430 |

BEDFORD—Independent City County

✖ **BEDFORD MEMORIAL HOSPITAL**, 1613 Oakwood Street, Zip 24523–0688, Mailing Address: P.O. Box 688, Zip 24523–0688; tel. 540/586–2441, (Total facility includes 111 beds in nursing home–type unit) **A**1 9 10 **F**1 2 6 9 11 12 21 22 26 27 28 29 31 32 33 36 37 39 40 44 45 46 47 48 51 52 53 55 58 59 63 64 69 77 81 82 84 85 87 88 92 93 94 96 108 109 110 **S** Carilion Health System, Roanoke, VA
Primary Contact: E. W. Tibbs, President and Chief Executive Officer
CFO: Donald E. Lorton, Executive Vice President
CMO: E Allen Joslyn, M.D., Chief Medical Officer
Web address: www.bmhva.com
| 23 | 10 | 161 | 1817 | 121 | 15503 | 190 | 21631 | 9877 | 290 |

BIG STONE GAP—Wise County

✖ **WELLMONT LONESOME PINE HOSPITAL**, 1990 Holton Avenue East, Zip 24219–0230; tel. 276/523–3111, (Nonreporting) **A**1 9 10 **S** Wellmont Health System, Kingsport, TN
Primary Contact: Robert G. Polahar, President
Web address: www.wellmont.org
| 23 | 10 | 60 | — | — | — | — | — | — | — |

VA

Hospital, Address, Telephone, Approval, Facility, and Physician Codes, Health Care System	Classi-fication Codes		Utilization Data					Expense (thousands) of dollars		
★ American Hospital Association (AHA) membership □ Joint Commission on Accreditation of Healthcare Organizations (JCAHO) accreditation ○ American Osteopathic Association (AOA) accreditation △ Commission on Accreditation of Rehabilitation Facilities (CARF) accreditation	Control	Service	Staffed Beds	Admissions	Census	Outpatient Visits	Births	Total	Payroll	Personnel

BLACKSBURG—Montgomery County

⊞ **MONTGOMERY REGIONAL HOSPITAL**, 3700 South Main Street, Zip 24060–7081, Mailing Address: P.O. Box 90004, Zip 24062–9004; tel. 540/951–1111 **A**1 9 10 **F**2 3 11 12 13 14 15 21 22 23 26 27 28 29 30 33 34 37 40 44 46 47 48 52 55 56 57 58 59 60 61 62 63 64 65 66 67 68 69 71 81 82 84 86 87 88 92 94 95 96 108 109 110 **P**8 **S** HCA, Nashville, TN Primary Contact: Ward W. Stevens, III, CHE, Chief Executive Officer COO: Stan Hickson, Chief Operating Officer CFO: Angela D. Hoke, Chief Financial Officer CHR: Mark F. Montgomery, Director Human Resources Web address: www.mrhospital.com	33	10	89	4909	54	70261	655	—		

BURKEVILLE—Nottoway County

□ **PIEDMONT GERIATRIC HOSPITAL**, 5001 East Patrick Henry Highway, Zip 23922–0427, Mailing Address: P.O. Box 427, Zip 23922–0427; tel. 434/767–4401, (Nonreporting) **A**1 10 **S** Virginia Department of Mental Health, Richmond, VA Primary Contact: Stephen M. Herrick, Ph.D., Acting Director Web address: www.pgh.state.va.us	12	49	150	—	—	—	—	—	—	—

CATAWBA—Roanoke County

□ **CATAWBA HOSPITAL**, 5525 Catawba Hospital Drive, Zip 24070–2115, Mailing Address: P.O. Box 200, Zip 24070–0200; tel. 540/375–4200 **A**1 10 **F**21 22 26 27 28 29 30 31 32 35 39 53 58 60 65 66 71 76 94 108 **P**6 **S** Virginia Department of Mental Health, Richmond, VA Primary Contact: Jack L. Wood, Director Web address: www.catawba.state.va.us	12	22	110	561	97	0	0	15970	10607	289

CHARLOTTESVILLE—Independent City County

⊞ **MARTHA JEFFERSON HOSPITAL**, 459 Locust Avenue, Zip 22902–9940; tel. 434/982–7000 **A**1 2 9 10 **F**2 11 12 15 17 21 22 23 26 27 28 29 30 33 37 42 46 47 48 51 52 55 57 58 59 61 62 63 64 65 66 69 70 79 81 82 84 85 86 87 88 93 96 106 107 108 109 110 **P**1 Primary Contact: James E. Haden, President and Chief Executive Officer COO: Elliot H. Kuida, Vice President and Chief Operating Officer CFO: J Michael Burris, Vice President Corporate Services and Chief Financial Officer CMO: William F. Tompkins, III, Vice President and Medical Director CIO: Marijo Lecker, Vice President CHR: Susan M. Cabell, Vice President, Administration Web address: www.marthajefferson.org	23	10	144	9556	87	270014	1772	134153	—	1234
⊞ **UNIVERSITY OF VIRGINIA MEDICAL CENTER**, Jefferson Park Avenue, Zip 22908–0001, Mailing Address: P.O. Box 800809, Zip 22908–0809; tel. 434/924–0211 **A**1 2 3 5 8 9 10 **F**2 4 5 6 7 9 10 11 12 13 14 15 16 17 18 19 20 22 23 24 28 29 30 31 32 33 34 35 36 37 38 39 40 42 43 44 45 46 47 48 49 50 51 52 53 54 55 56 57 58 59 60 61 62 63 64 65 66 67 68 69 70 71 72 73 74 75 76 77 79 80 81 82 84 85 86 87 88 89 90 93 94 95 96 98 99 100 101 102 103 104 105 106 108 109 110 **P**3 Primary Contact: R. Edward Howell, Vice President and Chief Executive Officer COO: Margaret M. Van Bree, Dr.PH, Chief Operations Officer CFO: Larry Fitzgerald, Chief Financial Officer CMO: Thomas A. Massaro, M.D., Ph.D., Associate Dean GME, Dir Performance Improvement CIO: Barbara Baldwin, Chief Information Officer CHR: Jeff Chitester, Human Resources Administrator Web address: www.med.virginia.edu	12	10	556	29207	458	1220373	1503	648529	245945	5584
⊞ **UVA–HEALTHSOUTH REHABILITATION HOSPITAL**, 515 Ray C. Hunt Drive, Zip 22903; tel. 434/244–2000 **A**1 10 **F**26 28 68 69 96 109 110 **S** HEALTHSOUTH Corporation, Birmingham, AL Primary Contact: Thomas J. Cook, Administrator	32	46	50	999	37	9189	0	—	—	—

CHESAPEAKE—Independent City County

⊞ **CHESAPEAKE GENERAL HOSPITAL**, 736 Battlefield Boulevard North, Zip 23320–4941, Mailing Address: P.O. Box 2028, Zip 23327–2028; tel. 757/312–8121 **A**1 2 9 10 **F**1 2 8 9 10 11 12 15 17 21 22 23 28 29 30 33 36 37 38 39 41 42 44 45 46 47 48 50 51 52 53 55 57 58 59 60 61 62 63 64 65 66 68 69 70 71 76 78 79 80 81 82 84 85 88 94 96 106 108 109 110 Primary Contact: Christopehr R. Mosley, President and Chief Executive Officer CFO: Ernest C. Padden, Vice President and Chief Financial Officer CIO: David Niven, Siemens Site Manager CHR: Wynn Dixon, Vice President Human Resources and Quality Web address: www.chesapeakehealth.com	16	10	310	16165	215	191922	3315	171613	69130	1604

CHRISTIANSBURG—Montgomery County

⊞ **CARILION NEW RIVER VALLEY MEDICAL CENTER**, 2900 Lamb Circle, Zip 24073–5041, Mailing Address: P.O. Box 5, Radford, Zip 24143–0005; tel. 540/731–2000, (Total facility includes 27 beds in nursing home–type unit) (Nonreporting) **A**1 9 10 **S** Carilion Health System, Roanoke, VA Primary Contact: Matthew J. Perry, President CFO: Don Halliwill, Director of Finance CMO: Anand Kishore, M.D., Chief of Staff CHR: Jeff Smith, Director Human Resources Web address: www.carilion.com	23	10	97	—	—	—	—	—	—	—

Many Facility Codes have changed. Please refer to the AHA Guide Code Chart. © 2005 AHA Guide

VA

Hospital, Address, Telephone, Approval, Facility, and Physician Codes, Health Care System	Classi-fication Codes		Utilization Data					Expense (thousands) of dollars		
★ American Hospital Association (AHA) membership ☐ Joint Commission on Accreditation of Healthcare Organizations (JCAHO) accreditation ○ American Osteopathic Association (AOA) accreditation △ Commission on Accreditation of Rehabilitation Facilities (CARF) accreditation	Control	Service	Staffed Beds	Admissions	Census	Outpatient Visits	Births	Total	Payroll	Personnel

CLINTWOOD—Dickenson County

★ **DICKENSON COMMUNITY HOSPITAL**, Hospital Drive, Zip 24228, Mailing Address: P.O. Box 1440, Zip 24228–1440; tel. 276/926–0300 **A**9 10 18 **F**2 9 21 22 33 39 46 53 55 58 65 66 70 81 88 94 97 108 **S** Quorum Health Resources, Plano, TX
Primary Contact: Kenneth Boyd, Chief Executive Officer
CFO: Christy Fleming, Chief Financial Officer
CMO: Patricia Vanover, Chief of Medical Staff
CHR: Judy Hall, Administrative Specialist
Web address: www.dchosp.com

	23	10	15	798	8	16505	2	7705	2893	101

CULPEPER—Culpeper County

⊞ **CULPEPER REGIONAL HOSPITAL**, 501 Sunset Lane, Zip 22701–3917, Mailing Address: Box 592, Zip 22701–0592; tel. 540/829–4100 **A**1 9 10 **F**2 6 9 11 12 14 21 22 23 26 27 28 29 32 33 36 37 39 42 46 47 48 49 51 55 57 58 59 60 61 62 63 65 66 69 81 82 84 88 94 97 **P**8
Primary Contact: H. Lee Kirk, Jr, President and Chief Executive Officer
COO: Patricia Mullins, Senior Vice President Hospital Operations
CFO: James C. Rutkowski, Senior Vice President Financial Operations
CMO: Karl Beier, M.D., President Medical Staff
CIO: Rose Gooch, Director Information Systems
CHR: Susan Edwards, Director Human Resources
Web address: www.culpeperhospital.com

	23	10	60	4010	39	48900	428	—	—	503

DANVILLE—Independent City County

⊞ **DANVILLE REGIONAL MEDICAL CENTER**, 142 South Main Street, Zip 24541–2922; tel. 434/799–2100, (Total facility includes 46 beds in nursing home–type unit) **A**1 2 5 6 9 10 **F**2 3 4 8 9 11 12 14 15 17 19 21 22 23 26 27 28 29 33 36 37 39 41 42 45 46 47 48 49 50 51 52 53 55 58 59 60 61 63 64 65 66 68 69 70 71 73 74 75 77 78 81 82 84 86 87 88 91 92 94 96 106 107 108 109 **P**6 8 **S** LifePoint Hospitals, Inc., Brentwood, TN
Primary Contact: Tod N. Lambert, Interim President and Chief Executive Officer
COO: William R. Isemann, Executive Vice President and Chief Operating Officer
CFO: Gilbert R. Collins, Vice President Finance and Chief Financial Officer
CIO: David Cartwright, Director Management Information Systems
Web address: www.danvilleregional.org

	23	10	201	12072	201	98868	1048	135427	57328	1319

☐ **SOUTHERN VIRGINIA MENTAL HEALTH INSTITUTE**, 382 Taylor Drive, Zip 24541–4023; tel. 434/799–6220 **A**1 10 **F**55 71 **P**6 **S** Virginia Department of Mental Health, Richmond, VA
Primary Contact: David M. Lyon, Director
Web address: www.svmhi.dmhmrsas.virginia.gov

	12	22	80	477	75	0	0	10361	6131	—

EMPORIA—Independent City County

☐ **SOUTHERN VIRGINIA REGIONAL MEDICAL CENTER**, 727 North Main Street, Zip 23847–1482; tel. 434/348–4400, (Total facility includes 65 beds in nursing home–type unit) (Nonreporting) **A**1 9 10 **S** Community Health Systems, Inc., Brentwood, TN
Primary Contact: Robert D. Towler, Chief Executive Officer
Web address: www.svrmc.com

	33	10	154	—	—	—	—	—	—	—

FAIRFAX—Independent City County

⊞ **INOVA FAIR OAKS HOSPITAL**, 3600 Joseph Siewick Drive, Zip 22033–1798; tel. 703/391–3600 **A**1 2 3 5 9 10 **F**2 9 10 11 12 21 22 23 26 27 28 29 31 32 33 35 37 38 39 40 41 46 47 48 50 52 53 54 55 56 57 58 59 60 61 62 63 64 65 66 69 73 75 81 82 84 85 87 88 92 93 94 95 96 108 109 110 **S** Inova Health System, Falls Church, VA
Primary Contact: John L. Fitzgerald, Vice President and Administrator
CFO: Henry Schmitt, Assistant Administrator and Director Finance
CIO: Nanci Little Gosnell, Vice President Information Services
Web address: www.inova.org

	23	10	174	13016	128	98679	3621	141585	54996	860

FALLS CHURCH—Independent City County

⊞ **DOMINION HOSPITAL**, 2960 Sleepy Hollow Road, Zip 22044–2001; tel. 703/536–2000 **A**1 10 **F**71 72 78 **P**5 **S** HCA, Nashville, TN
Primary Contact: Bryan K. Dearing, Chief Executive Officer
CFO: Carl S. Chitwood, Chief Financial Officer
CIO: Rob Roy, Hospital Director Information Services
Web address: www.dominionhospital.com

	33	22	100	1703	41	304	0	—	—	144

HOSPICE OF NORTHERN VIRGINIA, 6565 Arlington Boulevard, Suite 500, Zip 22042–3000; tel. 703/538–2065, (Nonreporting) **A**10
Primary Contact: David J. English, President and Chief Executive Officer
Web address: www.hospiceonline.org

	23	49	15							

⊞ **INOVA FAIRFAX HOSPITAL**, 3300 Gallows Road, Zip 22042–3300; tel. 703/776–4001 **A**1 2 3 5 8 9 10 **F**2 3 4 6 9 10 11 12 14 15 16 17 18 19 20 21 22 23 24 26 27 28 29 30 31 32 33 34 35 37 38 39 40 41 42 44 46 47 48 49 50 52 53 54 55 56 57 58 59 60 61 62 63 64 65 66 67 69 70 71 72 73 74 75 76 77 78 79 80 81 82 84 85 86 87 88 90 92 94 95 96 99 100 101 102 103 104 107 108 109 110 **P**6 **S** Inova Health System, Falls Church, VA
Primary Contact: Douglas P. Cropper, Administrator
COO: Toni R. Ardabell, R.N., Chief Operating Officer
CFO: Ronald Ewald, Chief Financial Officer
CMO: Joseph Hallal, M.D., President, Medical Staff
CIO: Geoff Brown, Vice President Information Systems
CHR: Ellen Menard, Senior Vice President Human Resources
Web address: www.inova.com

	23	10	924	51710	717	349443	11183	687714	269070	5837

VA

Hospital, Address, Telephone, Approval, Facility, and Physician Codes, Health Care System	Classi-fication Codes		Utilization Data					Expense (thousands) of dollars		
★ American Hospital Association (AHA) membership □ Joint Commission on Accreditation of Healthcare Organizations (JCAHO) accreditation ○ American Osteopathic Association (AOA) accreditation △ Commission on Accreditation of Rehabilitation Facilities (CARF) accreditation	Control	Service	Staffed Beds	Admissions	Census	Outpatient Visits	Births	Total	Payroll	Personnel
□ **NORTHERN VIRGINIA MENTAL HEALTH INSTITUTE**, 3302 Gallows Road, Zip 22042–3398; tel. 703/207–7110, (Nonreporting) **A**1 9 10 **S** Virginia Department of Mental Health, Richmond, VA Primary Contact: Lynn Delacy, R.N., MS, Facility Director Web address: www.nvmhi.state.va.us	12	22	137	—	—	—	—	—	—	—
FARMVILLE—Prince Edward County										
⊞ **SOUTHSIDE COMMUNITY HOSPITAL**, 800 Oak Street, Zip 23901–1199; tel. 434/392–8811 **A**1 3 5 9 10 20 **F**2 9 11 12 21 22 23 26 27 28 29 33 34 35 39 40 46 47 48 49 51 52 53 54 55 57 58 59 60 61 62 63 65 66 69 81 82 84 85 88 93 94 95 96 97 108 110 **P**6 Primary Contact: Gwen S. Eddleman, R.N., President and Chief Executive Officer CFO: William J. Downes, Vice President Finance Web address: www.sch–farmville.org	23	10	116	4030	42	49029	385	33426	14694	378
FISHERSVILLE—Augusta County										
□ **AUGUSTA HEALTH CARE**, 78 Medical Center Drive, Zip 22939–2332, Mailing Address: P.O. Box 1000, Zip 22939–1000; tel. 540/932–4000 **A**1 2 3 9 10 19 20 **F**1 2 3 4 6 9 11 12 21 22 23 26 27 28 29 30 32 33 34 36 37 40 41 43 44 45 46 47 48 50 51 52 53 55 57 58 59 60 61 62 63 64 65 66 68 69 70 71 72 73 74 75 76 77 78 79 80 81 82 84 86 87 88 92 93 94 95 96 106 107 108 109 110 Primary Contact: Richard H. Graham, President and Chief Executive Officer Web address: www.augustamed.com	23	10	167	11626	142	360571	1094	150520	65707	1663
WOODROW WILSON REHABILITATION CENTER, Mailing Address: P.O. Box 1500, Zip 22939–1500; tel. 540/332–7000, (Nonreporting) Primary Contact: Richard Luck, Facility Director Web address: www.wwrc.net	12	46	30	—	—	—	—	—	—	—
FORT BELVOIR—Fairfax County										
⊞ **DEWITT ARMY COMMUNITY HOSPITAL**, 9501 Farrell Road, Zip 22060–5901, Mailing Address: 9501 Farrell Road, Suite GC11, Zip 22060–5901; tel. 703/805–0510 **A**1 3 5 **F**4 6 9 10 11 12 21 22 23 28 29 31 33 34 39 42 44 45 46 47 48 52 53 57 58 59 60 62 63 64 65 66 69 70 72 73 75 77 78 81 84 88 94 95 96 106 108 109 **P**6 **S** Department of the Army, Office of the Surgeon General, Falls Church, VA Primary Contact: Colonel Patricia Horoho, Commander CFO: Captain Robert Hoerauf, Chief Resources Management CMO: Lieutenant Colonel Alan Janusziewicz, Deputy Commander Clinical Services CIO: Captain Daniel Jetton, Chief Information Management Division Web address: www.dewitt.wramc.amedd.army.mil	42	10	43	2468	15	617828	972	—	—	1399
FORT EUSTIS—Independent City County										
⊞ **MCDONALD ARMY COMMUNITY HOSPITAL**, Jefferson Avenue, Zip 23604–5548; tel. 757/314–7501 **A**1 **F**4 6 9 10 12 21 24 26 27 28 29 31 32 35 39 42 45 46 47 48 52 53 58 60 62 63 65 66 69 70 73 74 88 94 96 106 107 108 109 110 **P**6 **S** Department of the Army, Office of the Surgeon General, Falls Church, VA Primary Contact: Colonel Steven Hunte, Commander Web address: www.narmc.amedd.army.mil/mcdonald/	42	10	30	652	5	207439	0	20000	15000	588
FRANKLIN—Independent City County										
□ **SOUTHAMPTON MEMORIAL HOSPITAL**, 100 Fairview Drive, Zip 23851–1206, Mailing Address: P.O. Box 817, Zip 23851–0817; tel. 757/569–6100, (Total facility includes 131 beds in nursing home–type unit) (Nonreporting) **A**1 9 10 20 **S** Community Health Systems, Inc., Brentwood, TN Primary Contact: Sean T. Dardeau, Chief Executive Officer Web address: www.smhfranklin.com	33	10	203	—	—	—	—	—	—	—
FREDERICKSBURG—Independent City County										
⊞ **MARY WASHINGTON HOSPITAL**, 1001 Sam Perry Boulevard, Zip 22401–3354; tel. 540/741–1100 **A**1 2 9 10 19 20 **F**2 9 11 12 14 15 17 19 21 22 23 26 28 29 30 33 35 37 39 40 44 46 47 48 50 52 53 55 56 57 58 59 60 61 62 63 64 65 66 69 71 72 73 75 81 82 84 85 86 87 88 92 93 94 95 106 108 109 110 **P**8 Primary Contact: Fred M. Rankin, III, President and Chief Executive Officer COO: Walter J. Kiwall, Executive Vice Presidentand Chief Operating Officer CFO: Les Abernathy, Executive Vice President, Corporate Services CMO: J Thomas Ryan, M.D., Executive Vice President, Medical Affairs CIO: Steve Cooley, Vice President Information Services CHR: Kathryn Wall, Executive Vice President Human Resources and Organizational Development Web address: www.medicorp.org	23	10	408	24261	273	134428	3536	272554	106267	1921
□ **SNOWDEN AT FREDERICKSBURG**, 1200 Sam Perry Boulevard, Zip 22401; tel. 540/741–3900, (Nonreporting) **A**1 9 10 Primary Contact: Jim King, Chief Executive Officer	33	49	40	—	—	—	—	—	—	—
FRONT ROYAL—Warren County										
⊞ **WARREN MEMORIAL HOSPITAL**, 1000 Shenandoah Avenue, Zip 22630–3598; tel. 540/636–0300, (Total facility includes 120 beds in nursing home–type unit) **A**1 9 10 **F**2 9 11 12 21 22 26 27 29 30 33 37 39 44 46 48 51 52 53 55 58 59 60 62 63 64 65 66 69 81 84 87 88 92 94 96 106 108 109 110 **S** Valley Health System, Winchester, VA Primary Contact: Patrick B. Nolan, President and Chief Executive Officer CFO: Mark Bower, Vice President Web address: www.valleyhealthlink.com	23	10	166	3098	141	62263	278	41216	19514	380

VA

Many Facility Codes have changed. Please refer to the AHA Guide Code Chart.   © 2005 AHA Guide

Hospital, Address, Telephone, Approval, Facility, and Physician Codes, Health Care System	Classi-fication Codes		Utilization Data					Expense (thousands) of dollars		
★ American Hospital Association (AHA) membership □ Joint Commission on Accreditation of Healthcare Organizations (JCAHO) accreditation ○ American Osteopathic Association (AOA) accreditation △ Commission on Accreditation of Rehabilitation Facilities (CARF) accreditation	Control	Service	Staffed Beds	Admissions	Census	Outpatient Visits	Births	Total	Payroll	Personnel

GALAX—Independent City County

□ **TWIN COUNTY REGIONAL HOSPITAL**, 200 Hospital Drive, Zip 24333–2283; tel. 276/236–8181 **A**1 9 10 20 **F**2 10 11 12 14 21 22 23 26 28 29 33 36 41 42 44 46 47 51 52 59 60 62 63 64 66 69 71 73 74 75 76 77 78 81 82 84 88 94 96 97 106 108 109 110 **P**5 8
Primary Contact: Marcus G. Kuhn, President and Chief Executive Officer
Web address: www.tcrh.org

| | 23 | 10 | 76 | 4357 | 46 | 62688 | 374 | 40909 | 19451 | 570 |

GLOUCESTER—Gloucester County

□ **RIVERSIDE WALTER REED HOSPITAL**, 7519 Hospital Drive, Zip 23061–4178, Mailing Address: P.O. Box 1130, Zip 23061–1130; tel. 804/693–8800 **A**1 9 10 **F**2 9 12 21 27 28 29 33 34 35 36 39 40 46 48 52 55 58 60 62 63 64 65 66 69 81 82 84 87 88 92 94 96 108 **P**6 **S** Riverside Health System, Newport News, VA
Primary Contact: Robert E. Bryant, Vice President and Administrator
Web address: www.riversideonline.com/rwrh/index.html

| | 23 | 10 | 27 | 1948 | 26 | 63565 | 0 | 23254 | 9936 | 256 |

GRUNDY—Buchanan County

✠ **BUCHANAN GENERAL HOSPITAL**, Mailing Address: Route 5, Box 20, Zip 24614–9611; tel. 276/935–1000 **A**1 9 10 20 **F**12 15 22 23 26 27 28 33 34 40 46 48 51 55 61 62 63 64 65 66 69 81 82 87 88 94 96 106 108 109
Primary Contact: Joan Jamison, Interim Chief Executive Officer
CFO: Kim Boyd, Chief Financial Officer
CMO: J G. Patel, M.D., Chief of Staff
CIO: Rita Ramey, Director of Information Systems
CHR: Wanda Stiltner, Director Human Resources
Web address: www.bgh.org

| | 23 | 10 | 134 | 3379 | 38 | 53368 | 115 | 28664 | 11727 | 337 |

HAMPTON—Independent City County

✠ **RIVERSIDE BEHAVIORAL HEALTH CENTER**, 2244 Executive Drive, Zip 23666–2430; tel. 757/827–1001, (Nonreporting) **A**1 9 10 **S** Riverside Health System, Newport News, VA
Primary Contact: Debora S. Tanner, Vice President and Administrator
CFO: Mike Boggs, Director of Finance, Business Services
CMO: Linda M. Sabonya, M.D., Executive Medical Director
Web address: www.riversideonline.com

| | 23 | 22 | 125 | — | — | — | — | — | — | — |

✠ **SENTARA CAREPLEX HOSPITAL**, 3000 Coliseum Drive, Zip 23666–5963; tel. 757/736–2656 **A**1 2 9 10 **F**2 9 10 11 12 15 17 21 22 23 26 27 28 29 30 32 33 35 37 38 39 40 41 42 46 47 48 49 50 52 53 55 57 58 59 60 61 62 63 64 65 66 69 73 75 79 80 81 82 84 85 86 87 88 92 93 94 95 96 107 108 109 110 **S** Sentara Healthcare, Norfolk, VA
Primary Contact: Megan R. Perry, Senior Vice President and Administrator
CMO: Gary R. Yates, M.D., Vice President and Executive Medical Director, Clinical Effectiveness
Web address: www.sentara.com

| | 23 | 10 | 194 | 10687 | 146 | 160575 | 1009 | 150690 | 61492 | 1367 |

✠ **U. S. AIR FORCE HOSPITAL**, 45 Pine Street, Zip 23665–2080; tel. 757/764–6969, (Nonreporting) **A**1 **S** Department of the Air Force, Washington, DC
Primary Contact: Colonel David C. Houglum, MC, Administrator
COO: Colonel Paul Ziaya, Commander
CFO: Captain Wendy Barnes, Chief Medical Resource Management
CMO: Colonel June Carraher, Chief Hospital Services
CIO: Major Charles Chapdelaine, Chief of Information Management and Technology

| | 41 | 10 | 59 | — | — | — | — | — | — | — |

✠ **VETERANS AFFAIRS MEDICAL CENTER**, 100 Emancipation Drive, Zip 23667–0001; tel. 757/722–9961, (Total facility includes 120 beds in nursing home–type unit) (Nonreporting) **A**1 2 3 5 **S** Department of Veterans Affairs, Washington, DC
Primary Contact: Joseph Williams, Director
COO: Lorraine B. Price, Associate Director
CFO: Terry Grew, Chief Business Office
CMO: Val Gibberman, Acting Chief of Staff
CIO: Cary Parks, Chief Information Resource Management
Web address: www.va.gov/sta/guide/home.asp

| | 45 | 10 | 485 | — | — | — | — | — | — | — |

HARRISONBURG—Independent City County

✠ **ROCKINGHAM MEMORIAL HOSPITAL**, 235 Cantrell Avenue, Zip 22801–3293; tel. 540/433–4100 **A**1 2 9 10 19 20 **F**2 3 4 9 11 12 15 17 21 22 23 24 26 27 28 29 31 33 36 37 41 42 46 47 48 51 55 57 58 59 60 61 62 63 65 66 69 71 75 77 78 79 81 82 84 86 87 88 93 94 95 98 108 109 110 **P**6 8
Primary Contact: T. Carter Melton, Jr, President
COO: James D. Krauss, Chief Operating Officer
CFO: Richard L. Haushalter, Vice President Finance and Chief Financial Officer
CMO: Dale Carroll, M.D., Senior Vice President Medical Affairs & Perform Improvement
CIO: Mike Rozmus, Director of Information Systems
CHR: Mark Zimmerman, Vice President Human Resources
Web address: www.rmhonline.com

| | 23 | 10 | 270 | 13729 | 149 | 472849 | 1867 | 167037 | 75963 | 1641 |

VA

Hospital, Address, Telephone, Approval, Facility, and Physician Codes, Health Care System	Classi-fication Codes		Utilization Data					Expense (thousands) of dollars		
★ American Hospital Association (AHA) membership □ Joint Commission on Accreditation of Healthcare Organizations (JCAHO) accreditation ○ American Osteopathic Association (AOA) accreditation △ Commission on Accreditation of Rehabilitation Facilities (CARF) accreditation	Control	Service	Staffed Beds	Admissions	Census	Outpatient Visits	Births	Total	Payroll	Personnel

HOPEWELL—Independent City County

⊠ **JOHN RANDOLPH MEDICAL CENTER**, 411 West Randolph Road, Zip 23860–2938; tel. 804/541–1600, (Total facility includes 124 beds in nursing home–type unit) **A**1 9 10 **F**2 4 9 11 12 15 17 21 22 23 26 27 28 31 32 33 35 39 44 46 47 48 50 52 53 54 55 57 58 59 60 61 62 63 64 65 66 69 71 73 74 75 76 77 78 81 82 84 85 87 88 92 94 95 96 106 108 109 110 **S** HCA, Nashville, TN
Primary Contact: Elwood Bernard Boone, III, Chief Executive Officer
COO: Dia Nichols, Chief Operating Officer
CFO: Chigger Bynum, Chief Financial Officer
Web address: www.johnrandolphmed.com
33	10	264	6774	221	97111	519	—	—	—

HOT SPRINGS—Bath County

⊠ **BATH COUNTY COMMUNITY HOSPITAL**, Route 220, Zip 24445, Mailing Address: Drawer Z, Zip 24445; tel. 540/839–7000 **A**1 9 10 18 **F**92
Primary Contact: Deborah Lipes, R.N., Chief Executive Officer
CFO: James A. Greer, Chief Financial Officer
CHR: Patricia Foutz, Human Resources Director
Web address: www.bcchospital.org
23	10	25	463	6	9624	0	—	—	104

KILMARNOCK—Lancaster County

⊠ **RAPPAHANNOCK GENERAL HOSPITAL**, 101 Harris Drive, Zip 22482, Mailing Address: P.O. Box 1449, Zip 22482–1449; tel. 804/435–8000 **A**1 9 10 20 **F**2 9 12 21 22 23 24 26 27 28 32 33 37 38 44 46 48 50 51 52 53 55 58 59 60 61 62 63 65 66 69 71 73 75 76 78 81 82 84 88 94 95 96 97 108 110 **P**3 4
Primary Contact: James M. Holmes, Jr, President and Chief Executive Officer
Web address: www.rgh–hospital.com
23	10	63	2301	26	49082	225	28044	12664	331

LEBANON—Russell County

□ **RUSSELL COUNTY MEDICAL CENTER**, Carroll and Tate Streets, Zip 24266–4510, Mailing Address: P.O. Box 3600, Zip 24266–3600; tel. 276/889–1224 **A**1 9 10 **F**2 9 10 12 21 22 26 27 28 31 33 34 36 37 38 39 42 44 46 48 51 52 53 55 58 62 63 64 69 70 71 73 75 76 77 81 82 84 85 88 94 96 97 108 **P**6 **S** Community Health Systems, Inc., Brentwood, TN
Primary Contact: David L. Brash, Chief Executive Officer
Web address: www.rcmc.net
33	10	78	3449	39	86829	0	22982	10325	281

LEESBURG—Loudoun County

GRAYDON MANOR, 801 Children's Center Road S.W., Zip 20175–2598; tel. 703/777–3485, (Nonreporting)
Primary Contact: Bernard J. Haberlein, President
Web address: www.graydonmanor.org
23	52	51							

□ **INOVA LOUDOUN HOSPITAL**, (Formerly Loudoun Hospital Center), 44045 Riverside Parkway, Zip 20176–2799, Mailing Address: P.O. Box 6000, Zip 20176–6000; tel. 703/858–6000, (Nonreporting) **A**1 2 9 10 **S** Inova Health System, Falls Church, VA
Primary Contact: Rodney N. Huebbers, President and Chief Executive Officer
Web address: www.loudounhospital.org
23	10	92							

LOUDOUN HOSPITAL CENTER See Inova Loudoun Hospital

WHISPER RIDGE AT LEESBURG, (Formerly Piedmont Behavioral Health Center), 42009 Victory Lane, Zip 20176–6269; tel. 703/777–0800, (Nonreporting) **S** Psychiatric Solutions, Franklin, TN
Primary Contact: Bill Bailey, Chief Executive Officer
33	22	77	—	—					

LEXINGTON—Independent City County

⊠ **STONEWALL JACKSON HOSPITAL**, 1 Health Circle, Zip 24450–2492; tel. 540/458–3300, (Nonreporting) **A**1 9 10 18 20
Primary Contact: Chad E. Boore, Interim President and Chief Executive Officer
CFO: Gary W. Swink, Chief Financial Officer
CMO: Steven Arcangeli, M.D., Chief of Staff
Web address: www.sjhospital.com
23	10	45	—	—					

LOW MOOR—Alleghany County

⊠ **ALLEGHANY REGIONAL HOSPITAL**, One ARH Lane, Zip 24457, Mailing Address: P.O. Box 7, Zip 24457–0007; tel. 540/862–6011 **A**1 9 10 20 **F**2 9 10 11 12 21 22 26 28 32 36 46 48 52 55 58 59 62 63 64 66 69 81 82 87 88 93 94 95 96 108 110 **S** HCA, Nashville, TN
Primary Contact: Timothy C. Tobin, President and Chief Executive Officer
COO: Chip Peal, Associate Administrator
CFO: Joe Jeans, Chief Financial Officer
CMO: Hassan Honainy, M.D., President Medical Staff
CIO: Jeffrey Steelman, Director Information Systems
Web address: www.alleghanyregional.com
33	10	89	3886	55	41790	50	31754	12778	343

LURAY—Page County

⊠ **PAGE MEMORIAL HOSPITAL**, 200 Memorial Drive, Zip 22835–1005; tel. 540/743–4561 **A**1 9 10 **F**2 6 9 12 21 22 26 27 33 44 45 51 58 60 62 63 64 66 69 81 86 88 94 97 108
Primary Contact: John E. Barrett, III, President and Chief Executive Officer
CFO: Travis Clark, Chief Financial Officer
Web address: www.pagememorialhospital.org
23	10	15	1057	9	43946	0	—	—	—

Many Facility Codes have changed. Please refer to the AHA Guide Code Chart.

Hospital, Address, Telephone, Approval, Facility, and Physician Codes, Health Care System	Classi-fication Codes		Utilization Data					Expense (thousands) of dollars		
	Control	Service	Staffed Beds	Admissions	Census	Outpatient Visits	Births	Total	Payroll	Personnel

★ American Hospital Association (AHA) membership
□ Joint Commission on Accreditation of Healthcare Organizations (JCAHO) accreditation
○ American Osteopathic Association (AOA) accreditation
△ Commission on Accreditation of Rehabilitation Facilities (CARF) accreditation

LYNCHBURG—Independent City County

✠ **CENTRA HEALTH**, 1920 Atherholt Road, Zip 24501–1104; tel. 434/947–4700, (Includes LYNCHBURG GENERAL HOSPITAL, 1901 Tate Springs Road, Zip 24501–1167; tel. 434/947–3000; Ronald J. Galonsky, Jr, Senior Vice President; VIRGINIA BAPTIST HOSPITAL, 3300 Rivermont Avenue, Zip 24503–9989; tel. 434/947–4000; William W. Semones, Vice President), (Total facility includes 295 beds in nursing home–type unit) **A**1 2 3 5 6 9 10 **F**2 3 9 14 15 17 19 26 27 28 30 33 34 37 55 56 59 63 68 71 92 93 110 **P**6 7 8 Primary Contact: George W. Dawson, President and Chief Executive Officer CFO: Lewis C. Addison, Chief Financial Officer and Senior Vice President CIO: Ben Clark, Chief Information Officer and Vice President CHR: Glenn E. McGarth, Vice President and Human Resources Web address: www.centrahealth.com	23	10	823	26394	676	147361	2273	306025	145459	4354

MADISON HEIGHTS—Amherst County

CENTRAL VIRGINIA TRAINING CENTER, 210 East Colony Road, Zip 24572–2005, Mailing Address: P.O. Box 1098, Lynchburg, Zip 24505–1098; tel. 434/947–6326, (Total facility includes 104 beds in nursing home–type unit) (Nonreporting) **A**10 **S** Virginia Department of Mental Health, Richmond, VA Primary Contact: Denise D. Micheletti, Acting Director Web address: www.cvtc.state.va.us	12	62	1112	—	—	—	—	—	—	—

MANASSAS—Independent City County

✠ **PRINCE WILLIAM HOSPITAL**, 8700 Sudley Road, Zip 20110–4418, Mailing Address: P.O. Box 2610, Zip 20108–0867; tel. 703/369–8000 **A**1 2 9 10 **F**2 4 8 9 11 12 19 21 22 23 24 25 26 27 28 29 30 31 32 33 35 37 38 39 41 42 46 47 48 51 52 53 55 56 57 58 59 60 61 62 63 64 65 66 69 71 72 73 74 75 76 77 78 81 82 83 84 85 87 88 93 94 96 98 106 107 108 109 110 Primary Contact: Michael J. Schwartz, President and Chief Executive Officer COO: Gary J. Herbek, Chief Operating Officer CFO: Robert Riley, Chief Financial Officer CMO: Richard D. Travers, M.D. Web address: www.pwhs.org	23	10	163	9888	106	200164	2479	125973	59267	839

MARION—Smyth County

✠ **SMYTH COUNTY COMMUNITY HOSPITAL**, 565 Radio Hill Road, Zip 24354–3526, Mailing Address: P.O. Box 880, Zip 24354–0880; tel. 276/782–1234, (Total facility includes 125 beds in nursing home–type unit) (Nonreporting) **A**1 9 10 20 **S** Carilion Health System, Roanoke, VA Primary Contact: William Mahone, V, President and Chief Executive Officer CFO: Lindy White, Chief Financial Officer CHR: Paul Morlock, Vice President Human Resources Web address: www.scchosp.org	23	10	285	—	—	—	—	—	—	—
□ **SOUTHWESTERN VIRGINIA MENTAL HEALTH INSTITUTE**, 340 Bagley Circle, Zip 24354–3390; tel. 276/783–1200, (Nonreporting) **A**1 10 **S** Virginia Department of Mental Health, Richmond, VA Primary Contact: Cynthia McClure, Ph.D., Director	12	22	266	—	—	—	—	—	—	—

MARTINSVILLE—Independent City County

✠ **MEMORIAL HOSPITAL**, 320 Hospital Drive, Zip 24112–1981, Mailing Address: P.O. Box 4788, Zip 24115–4788; tel. 276/666–7200, (Nonreporting) **A**1 2 9 10 19 **S** LifePoint Hospitals, Inc., Brentwood, TN Primary Contact: Joseph Roach, Chief Executive Officer CFO: Mark Anderson, Chief Financial Officer CMO: J G. Cargill, III, M.D., President, Medical Staff CIO: Jeff Butker, Chief Information Officer CHR: Sherry Schofield, Director Human Resources Web address: www.martinsvillehospital.com	33	10	152	—	—	—	—	—	—	—

MECHANICSVILLE—Hanover County

✠ **MEMORIAL REGIONAL MEDICAL CENTER**, 8260 Atlee Road, Zip 23116–1844; tel. 804/764–6000 **A**1 2 5 9 10 **F**2 8 9 11 12 14 15 17 19 21 22 23 24 25 26 27 28 29 30 31 33 34 36 37 38 39 42 44 46 47 48 49 50 51 52 53 55 56 57 58 59 60 61 62 63 64 65 66 69 70 73 75 81 82 84 85 86 87 88 94 95 96 106 108 109 110 **P**7 **S** Bon Secours Health System, Inc., Marriottsville, MD Primary Contact: Michael Robinson, Executive Vice President and Administrator COO: Charles Malloy, Vice President of Operations CFO: Pete Gallagher, Vice President and Chief Financial Officer CIO: Jeff Burke, Chief Information Officer CHR: Bonnie Shelor, Vice President Human Resources Web address: www.bonsecours.com	23	10	225	11095	151	98540	1341	126931	42432	1178
✠ **SHELTERING ARMS REHABILITATION HOSPITAL**, 8254 Atlee Road, Zip 23116–1844; tel. 804/764–6000 **A**1 5 10 **F**26 27 28 30 41 42 45 46 47 48 60 65 66 68 69 94 95 **P**6 Primary Contact: Jack A. Carroll, Ph.D., President and Chief Executive Officer COO: Michael J. McDonnell, Vice President and Chief Operating Officer CFO: Richard Beckler, Vice President and Chief Financial Officer CMO: Albert Jones, M.D., Director Medical CHR: Kelly Lewis, Associate Vice President Human Resources Web address: www.shelteringarms.com	23	46	40	1037	34	64796	—	25299	13858	304

VA

Hospital, Address, Telephone, Approval, Facility, and Physician Codes, Health Care System	Classi-fication Codes		Utilization Data					Expense (thousands) of dollars		
★ American Hospital Association (AHA) membership □ Joint Commission on Accreditation of Healthcare Organizations (JCAHO) accreditation ○ American Osteopathic Association (AOA) accreditation △ Commission on Accreditation of Rehabilitation Facilities (CARF) accreditation	Control	Service	Staffed Beds	Admissions	Census	Outpatient Visits	Births	Total	Payroll	Personnel

NASSAWADOX—Northampton County

⊠ **SHORE MEMORIAL HOSPITAL**, 9507 Hospital Avenue, Zip 23413–1821, Mailing Address: P.O. Box 17, Zip 23413–0017; tel. 757/414–8000, (Total facility includes 149 beds in nursing home–type unit) (Nonreporting) **A**1 2 9 10 20
Primary Contact: Joseph P. Zager, President and Chief Executive Officer
COO: Gene Erb, Senior Vice President and Chief Operating Officer
CFO: Wilson Patteson, Senior Vice President Fiscal Services
CMO: David Jones, M.D., Medical Staff President
CIO: Rob Gayman, Director of Information Systems
CHR: Charles Waters, Director Human Resources
Web address: www.shorehealthservices.org
23 10 256 — — — — — — —

NEW KENT—New Kent County

□ **CUMBERLAND HOSPITAL FOR CHILDREN AND ADOLESCENTS**, 9407 Cumberland Road, Zip 23124–0150; tel. 804/966–2242 **A**1 10 **F**68 92 **P**5 **S** Psychiatric Solutions, Franklin, TN
Primary Contact: Patrice Gay Brooks, Chief Operating Officer
Web address: www.cumberlandhospital.com
33 56 132 201 112 0 0 21083 11309 277

NEWPORT NEWS—Independent City County

KEYSTONE NEWPORT NEWS, 17579 Warwick Boulevard, Zip 23603–1343; tel. 757/888–0400, (Nonreporting) **A**10
Primary Contact: Robert J. Lehmann, Chief Executive Officer
33 22 68 — — — — — — —

⊠ **MARY IMMACULATE HOSPITAL**, 2 Bernardine Drive, Zip 23602–4499; tel. 757/886–6000, (Includes ST. FRANCIS NURSING CENTER), (Total facility includes 115 beds in nursing home–type unit) **A**1 9 10 **F**2 9 11 12 21 22 26 27 28 29 32 33 35 38 39 42 46 47 48 49 50 52 55 57 58 59 60 61 62 63 65 66 69 75 81 82 84 85 87 88 92 94 96 107 108 109 110 **S** Bon Secours Health System, Inc., Marriottsville, MD
Primary Contact: Patricia L. Robertson, Executive Vice President and Administrator
CMO: Ron Rejzer, Medical Director
CIO: Laishy Williams Carlson, Chief Information Officer
Web address: www.bonsecourshamptonroads.com
23 10 225 6769 181 — — 75769 29448

⊠ **RIVERSIDE REGIONAL MEDICAL CENTER**, 500 J. Clyde Morris Boulevard, Zip 23601–1976; tel. 757/594–2000, (Includes RIVERSIDE PSYCHIATRIC INSTITUTE) **A**1 2 3 5 6 9 10 **F**2 4 9 10 11 12 14 15 17 19 21 22 23 24 27 28 29 31 32 33 34 35 36 37 39 40 42 44 46 48 49 50 51 52 55 57 58 59 60 61 62 63 64 65 66 69 70 71 72 73 74 75 76 77 78 79 81 82 84 86 87 88 92 93 94 96 107 108 109 110 **P**6 **S** Riverside Health System, Newport News, VA
Primary Contact: William B. Downey, Executive Vice President and Administrator
COO: William B. Downey, Executive Vice President and Administrator
CFO: Wade Broughman, Executive Vice President and Chief Financial Officer
CMO: Barry L. Gross, M.D., Executive Vice President and Chief Medical Officer
CIO: John T. Stanley, Vice President Planning and Information Systems
CHR: Larry Boyles, Senior Vice President
Web address: www.riverside–online.com
23 10 237 17450 220 338750 2938 254467 103414 1574

□ **RIVERSIDE REHABILITATION INSTITUTE**, 245 Chesapeake Avenue, Zip 23607–6038; tel. 757/928–8000 **A**1 5 7 10 **F**9 21 22 27 28 29 35 46 48 52 57 58 60 62 64 65 66 68 69 92 94 96 108 **P**6 **S** Riverside Health System, Newport News, VA
Primary Contact: Renee K. Rountree, Vice President and Administrator
Web address: www.riverside–online.com
23 46 41 1270 40 8990 0 11875 6147 170

NORFOLK—Independent City County

⊠ △ **BON SECOURS–DEPAUL MEDICAL CENTER**, 150 Kingsley Lane, Zip 23505–4650; tel. 757/889–5000 **A**1 2 3 5 7 9 10 **F**2 9 11 12 14 15 17 19 21 22 23 26 27 28 29 31 32 33 35 37 38 40 44 45 46 47 48 49 50 52 55 57 59 61 62 63 65 66 68 69 70 75 76 77 78 79 81 82 84 85 87 88 92 93 94 96 108 109 110 **S** Bon Secours Health System, Inc., Marriottsville, MD
Primary Contact: Susan A. Erickson, Executive Vice President and Administrator
Web address: www.bonsecourshamptonroads.com
23 10 238 8760 137 — 1113 99762 37835 —

⊠ **CHILDREN'S HOSPITAL OF THE KING'S DAUGHTERS**, 601 Children's Lane, Zip 23507–1969; tel. 757/668–7000 **A**1 2 3 5 9 10 **F**2 6 9 10 16 18 20 21 22 23 24 28 29 33 37 39 42 45 46 48 49 50 52 56 57 58 60 61 62 63 65 66 67 68 69 70 81 82 84 85 88 93 94 96 98 106 107 108 110 **P**1
Primary Contact: James D. Dahling, President and Chief Executive Officer
CFO: Dennis Ryan, Senior Vice President and Chief Financial Officer
CMO: Al Finch, M.D., Executive Medical Director
CIO: Debbie Barnes, Vice President and Chief Information Officer
CHR: David Bowers, Vice President Support Services
Web address: www.chkd.org
23 50 157 6497 128 153234 0 149161 68386 1562

★ **LAKE TAYLOR TRANSITIONAL CARE HOSPITAL**, 1309 Kempsville Road, Zip 23502–2286; tel. 757/461–5001, (Total facility includes 192 beds in nursing home–type unit) **A**10 **F**2 9 21 22 26 32 36 37 38 49 50 58 62 64 92 94 108 110
Primary Contact: Thomas J. Orsini, President and Chief Executive Officer
CFO: Robert W. Fogg, Director Finance
CMO: Antoine A. Arrage, M.D., Director Medical Services
CIO: Mark Davis, Director Information Systems
CHR: LeeAnn Allen, Director Human Resources
Web address: www.laketaylor.org
16 46 289 982 253 0 0 23961 10694 386

Many Facility Codes have changed. Please refer to the AHA Guide Code Chart.

© 2005 AHA Guide

VA

Hospital, Address, Telephone, Approval, Facility, and Physician Codes, Health Care System	Classi-fication Codes		Utilization Data					Expense (thousands) of dollars		
★ American Hospital Association (AHA) membership □ Joint Commission on Accreditation of Healthcare Organizations (JCAHO) accreditation ○ American Osteopathic Association (AOA) accreditation △ Commission on Accreditation of Rehabilitation Facilities (CARF) accreditation	Control	Service	Staffed Beds	Admissions	Census	Outpatient Visits	Births	Total	Payroll	Personnel
NORFOLK PSYCHIATRIC CENTER, 860 Kempsville Road, Zip 23502–3980; tel. 757/461–4565, (Nonreporting) **A**10 Primary Contact: Arlene Manzella, Administrator	33	22	77	—	—	—	—	—	—	—
✠ **SENTARA LEIGH HOSPITAL**, 830 Kempsville Road, Zip 23502–3920; tel. 757/466–6000 **A**1 3 5 9 10 **F**2 7 9 10 11 12 15 17 21 22 23 26 27 28 29 31 32 33 35 37 38 39 42 46 47 48 49 50 52 53 55 57 58 59 60 61 62 63 64 65 66 69 73 75 81 82 83 84 85 86 87 88 92 94 95 96 104 108 109 110 **S** Sentara Healthcare, Norfolk, VA Primary Contact: Mark A. Szalwinski, Vice President and Administrator CIO: Bert Reese, Vice President Information Systems Web address: www.sentara.com	23	10	223	13615	176	122594	2289	146872	53166	1175
✠ **SENTARA NORFOLK GENERAL HOSPITAL**, 600 Gresham Drive, Zip 23507; tel. 757/668–3000 **A**1 2 3 5 6 8 9 10 **F**1 2 6 7 9 10 11 12 13 14 15 17 18 19 20 21 22 23 26 27 28 29 30 31 32 33 34 35 37 38 39 40 42 43 44 46 47 48 49 50 52 53 55 56 57 58 59 60 61 62 63 64 65 66 68 69 70 71 73 75 76 77 78 79 80 81 82 83 84 85 86 87 88 92 93 94 95 96 99 100 101 103 104 105 106 107 108 109 110 **S** Sentara Healthcare, Norfolk, VA Primary Contact: Bruce E. Holstien, Senior Vice President and Administrator CMO: Gene Burke, M.D., Vice President Medical Affairs CIO: Bert Reese, Vice President Information Technology Web address: www.sentara.com	23	10	461	23760	400	410385	2789	408445	163793	3278
NORTON—Independent City County										
✠ **MOUNTAIN VIEW REGIONAL MEDICAL CENTER**, (Formerly Bon Secours St. Mary's Hospital), Third Street N.E., Zip 24273–1131, Mailing Address: P.O. Box 620, Zip 24273–0620; tel. 276/679–9100, (Total facility includes 43 beds in nursing home–type unit) (Nonreporting) **A**1 9 10 **S** Health Management Associates, Naples, FL Primary Contact: Jamie Guin, Chief Executive Officer CFO: Stephen Hardy, Chief Financial Officer CMO: Kenneth Kiser, M.D., Chief of Staff CIO: Teresa Stough, Chief Information Officer CHR: Barbara Stanley, Human Resources Director Web address: www.smhnorton.org	23	10	133	—	—	—	—	—	—	—
✠ ○ **NORTON COMMUNITY HOSPITAL**, 100 15th Street N.W., Zip 24273–1699; tel. 276/679–9600 **A**1 9 10 11 12 13 **F**2 9 10 11 12 15 21 22 24 26 27 28 29 30 31 33 36 37 38 39 40 41 42 44 46 47 48 50 51 52 53 55 58 59 60 62 63 64 65 66 68 69 70 81 82 84 85 87 88 93 94 95 96 97 98 106 107 108 109 110 **S** Quorum Health Resources, Plano, TX Primary Contact: David G. Fuqua, Chief Executive Officer CFO: Brenda Quales, Chief Financial Officer CMO: Maurice Nida, D.O., Chief of Staff CIO: Judy Lawson, Director Information Services CHR: Valeri Colyer, Director of Human Resources Web address: www.nchosp.org	23	10	129	5740	55	83836	451	44020	18219	446
PEARISBURG—Giles County										
✠ **CARILION GILES MEMORIAL HOSPITAL**, 1 Taylor Avenue, Zip 24134–1932; tel. 540/921–6000 **A**1 9 10 18 **F**1 2 9 12 21 22 26 27 28 29 30 32 33 39 45 46 48 52 53 55 58 60 62 63 65 66 69 81 84 88 92 94 97 106 108 **P**6 **S** Carilion Health System, Roanoke, VA Primary Contact: James E. Tyler, Administrator and Chief Executive Officer CMO: John Tamminen, M.D., President, Medical Staff CHR: Becky Fritz, Director of Human Resources Web address: www.carilion.com	23	10	33	1353	33	21659	0	16201	6419	161
PENNINGTON GAP—Lee County										
✠ **LEE REGIONAL MEDICAL CENTER**, West Morgan Avenue, Zip 24277–0070, Mailing Address: P.O. Box 70, Zip 24277–0070; tel. 276/546–1440 **A**1 9 10 20 **F**2 9 12 15 21 22 28 33 35 39 48 51 52 53 55 57 60 62 63 64 66 68 69 81 82 84 85 88 93 95 96 97 108 110 **P**6 **S** Health Management Associates, Naples, FL Primary Contact: S. Scott McIntyre, Chief Executive Officer CFO: Michael Ackley, Administrator Web address: www.leeregional.com	33	10	52	2710	31	35968	0	15464	7518	227
PETERSBURG—Independent City County										
□ **CENTRAL STATE HOSPITAL**, 26317 West Washington Street, Zip 23803, Mailing Address: P.O. Box 4030, Zip 23803–4030; tel. 804/524–7000 **A**1 5 9 10 **F**26 71 72 73 74 75 76 77 78 **P**6 **S** Virginia Department of Mental Health, Richmond, VA Primary Contact: Charles S. Davis, M.D., Ph.D., Director Web address: www.csh.state.va.us	12	22	277	600	245	0	0	—	—	781
✠ **POPLAR SPRINGS HOSPITAL**, 350 Poplar Drive, Zip 23805–4657, Mailing Address: P.O. Box 3060, Zip 23805–3060; tel. 804/733–6874 **A**1 9 10 **F**4 21 26 71 72 73 74 75 76 77 78 **P**1 **S** Horizon Health Corporation, Lewisville, TX Primary Contact: Anthony J. Vadella, President and Chief Executive Officer CFO: Matt Lisagor, Vice President and Chief Financial Officer CHR: Charles Story, Director Human Resources Web address: www.poplarsprings.com	33	22	161	2018	126	—	0	—	—	—

VA

Hospital, Address, Telephone, Approval, Facility, and Physician Codes, Health Care System	Classification Codes		Utilization Data					Expense (thousands) of dollars		
★ American Hospital Association (AHA) membership □ Joint Commission on Accreditation of Healthcare Organizations (JCAHO) accreditation ○ American Osteopathic Association (AOA) accreditation △ Commission on Accreditation of Rehabilitation Facilities (CARF) accreditation	Control	Service	Staffed Beds	Admissions	Census	Outpatient Visits	Births	Total	Payroll	Personnel

□ **SOUTHSIDE REGIONAL MEDICAL CENTER**, 801 South Adams Street, Zip 23803–5133; tel. 804/862–5000, (Total facility includes 20 beds in nursing home–type unit) (Nonreporting) **A**1 6 9 10 **S** Community Health Systems, Inc., Brentwood, TN Primary Contact: David J. Fikse, Chief Executive Officer Web address: www.srmconline.com	33	10	283	—	—	—	—	—	—	—

PORTSMOUTH—Independent City County

★ △ **MARYVIEW MEDICAL CENTER**, 3636 High Street, Zip 23707–3270; tel. 757/398–2200, (Total facility includes 120 beds in nursing home–type unit) **A**1 2 3 5 7 9 10 **F**2 3 4 9 10 11 12 14 21 22 23 26 27 28 29 30 31 32 33 35 36 37 38 39 40 42 46 47 48 49 50 51 52 55 57 58 59 60 61 62 63 65 66 68 69 70 71 72 73 74 75 77 78 81 82 84 85 87 88 92 93 94 96 106 107 108 109 **P**6 **S** Bon Secours Health System, Inc., Marriottsville, MD Primary Contact: Jack McNamara, Interim Executive Vice President and Administrator CFO: Alan Chapman, Chief Financial Officer CMO: Ronald Rejzer, M.D., Chief Medical Officer CIO: Laishy Williams Carlson, Chief Information Officer Web address: www.bonsecourshamptonroads.com	23	10	466	16003	333	—	1065	170404	65203	—
★ **NAVAL MEDICAL CENTER**, 620 John Paul Jones Circle, Zip 23708–2197; tel. 757/953–7424, (Nonreporting) **A**1 2 3 5 **S** Bureau of Medicine and Surgery, Department of the Navy, Washington, DC Primary Contact: Admiral Thomas Burkhard, Commander CFO: Captain Mark Munson, Director Business Operations CMO: Captain Kevin Knoop, Director Medical Education CIO: Lieutenant James W. Martin, Chief Information Officer	43	10	274	—	—	—	—	—	—	—

PULASKI—Independent City County

★ **PULASKI COMMUNITY HOSPITAL**, 2400 Lee Highway, Zip 24301–0759, Mailing Address: P.O. Box 759, Zip 24301–0759; tel. 540/994–8100, (Total facility includes 12 beds in nursing home–type unit) **A**1 9 10 **F**2 26 28 33 46 48 53 55 59 60 61 62 63 65 66 69 81 82 84 85 86 87 88 92 94 95 96 108 **S** HCA, Nashville, TN Primary Contact: Jackson Nunley, Chief Executive Officer COO: Kathleen Kirk, Chief Operating Officer CFO: Tom Lawhorne, Vice President Finance CMO: Paul J. D'Amico, Chief of Staff CIO: Donald Stuart, Information Systems Director Web address: www.pch–va.com	33	10	72	3309	43	51410	139	—	—	304

RESTON—Fairfax County

★ **RESTON HOSPITAL CENTER**, 1850 Town Center Parkway, Zip 20190–3210; tel. 703/689–9000 **A**1 2 9 10 **F**2 10 11 12 21 22 23 26 27 28 29 30 32 33 35 37 38 40 41 46 47 48 52 54 55 57 58 59 60 61 62 63 64 65 66 69 79 81 82 84 85 87 88 94 95 96 106 108 109 110 **S** HCA, Nashville, TN Primary Contact: William A. Adams, President and Chief Executive Officer COO: Jane Raymond, Vice President and Chief Operating Officer CFO: Edward R. Stojakovich, Chief Financial Officer CMO: Walter R. Zolkiwsky, M.D., Vice President Medical Affairs CIO: Paresh Shah, Director Hospital Information Systems Web address: www.restonhospital.com	33	10	160	10504	108	131519	2836	134085	46354	729

RICHLANDS—Tazewell County

★ **CLINCH VALLEY MEDICAL CENTER**, 2949 West Front Street, Zip 24641–2099; tel. 276/596–6000, (Total facility includes 14 beds in nursing home–type unit) **A**1 9 10 **F**2 11 12 14 15 21 22 23 26 27 28 29 32 33 40 46 47 48 49 50 52 55 57 58 59 60 61 62 63 64 65 66 68 69 70 79 81 82 84 85 86 87 88 92 93 94 96 108 109 **S** HCA, Nashville, TN Primary Contact: Timothy C. Tobin, President and Chief Executive Officer COO: John Berry, Chief Operating Officer CFO: Bob Haralson, Chief Financial Officer CMO: M R. Patel, M.D., Chief of Staff CIO: Jeanine Harris, Director of Information Services CHR: John Knowles, Director Human Resources Web address: www.clinchvalleymedicalcenter.com	33	10	140	6333	80	51519	435	—	—	483

RICHMOND—Independent City County

★ **BON SECOURS ST. MARY'S HOSPITAL**, 5801 Bremo Road, Zip 23226–1907; tel. 804/285–2011 **A**1 2 3 5 9 10 **F**2 3 9 10 11 12 13 14 15 17 19 21 22 23 26 27 28 30 33 35 36 37 38 39 40 44 46 47 48 49 52 53 55 56 57 58 59 61 62 63 64 65 66 67 68 71 75 76 81 82 84 85 86 87 88 92 94 95 96 108 P7 8 **S** Bon Secours Health System, Inc., Marriottsville, MD Contact: Michael K. Kerner, Executive Vice President and Administrator Gallagher, Chief Financial Officer www.bonsecours.com	21	10	320	20962	302	242508	2591	245355	81065	1589
RICHMOND COMMUNITY HOSPITAL, 1500 North 28th ...96, Mailing Address: Box 27184, Zip 23261–7184; ... 9 10 **F**12 21 22 23 27 28 29 31 33 35 36 39 45 46 ...4 65 66 69 71 73 74 75 76 77 81 82 84 87 ... Health System, Inc., Marriottsville, MD ...y, Executive Vice President and Administrator ...nancial Officer ...tion Officer ...luman Resources ...urs.com	21	10	88	3105	56	33253	0	25545	10582	208

VA

Many Facility Codes have changed. Please refer to the AHA Guide Code Chart.

© 2005 AHA Guide

Hospital, Address, Telephone, Approval, Facility, and Physician Codes, Health Care System	Classi-fication Codes		Utilization Data					Expense (thousands) of dollars		
★ American Hospital Association (AHA) membership □ Joint Commission on Accreditation of Healthcare Organizations (JCAHO) accreditation ○ American Osteopathic Association (AOA) accreditation △ Commission on Accreditation of Rehabilitation Facilities (CARF) accreditation	Control	Service	Staffed Beds	Admissions	Census	Outpatient Visits	Births	Total	Payroll	Personnel

Hospital	Control	Service	Staffed Beds	Admissions	Census	Outpatient Visits	Births	Total	Payroll	Personnel
✠ △ **CHILDREN'S HOSPITAL**, 2924 Brook Road, Zip 23220–1298; tel. 804/321–7474, (Nonreporting) **A**1 3 5 7 9 10 Primary Contact: Leslie G. Wyatt, President and Chief Executive Officer COO: Leslie G. Wyatt, President and Chief Executive Officer CFO: Samuel G. Weidman, Vice President and Chief Financial Officer CMO: Donald A. Taylor, M.D., Medical Director CIO: George Masiello, Director Information Technology Web address: www.childrenshosp–richmond.org	23	56	36	—	—	—	—	—	—	—
✠ **CJW MEDICAL CENTER**, 7101 Jahnke Road, Zip 23225–4044; tel. 804/320–3911, (Includes CHIPPENHAM MEDICAL CENTER; JOHNSTON–WILLIS HOSPITAL, 1401 Johnston–Willis Drive, Zip 23235; tel. 804/330–2000) **A**1 2 3 5 9 10 **F**2 4 9 11 12 14 15 17 19 21 22 23 26 27 28 29 31 33 34 39 41 42 43 44 46 47 48 49 52 55 56 57 58 59 60 61 62 63 64 65 66 67 68 69 70 71 72 74 75 76 77 78 79 80 81 82 84 85 86 87 88 90 93 94 95 96 106 108 109 110 **S** HCA, Nashville, TN Primary Contact: Peter A. Marmerstein, Chief Executive Officer COO: Clay Franklin, Chief Operating Officer CFO: David McClurg, Chief Financial Officer CMO: Jeffrey Hull, Chairman of the Medical Staff CIO: Steven Smith, Healthcare Director Information Services CHR: Mike Cassity, Human Resources Officer Web address: www.cjwmedical.com	33	10	758	32852	524	195216	3987	—	—	2924
HALLMARK YOUTHCARE – RICHMOND, 12800 West Creek Parkway, Zip 23238–1116; tel. 804/784–2200, (Nonreporting) **A**10 Primary Contact: Wanda H. Sadler, Chief Executive Officer	33	22	84	—	—	—	—	—	—	—
✠ **HEALTHSOUTH REHABILITATION HOSPITAL OF VIRGINIA**, 5700 Fitzhugh Avenue, Zip 23226–1877; tel. 804/288–5700, (Nonreporting) **A**1 10 **S** HEALTHSOUTH Corporation, Birmingham, AL Primary Contact: Jeff Ruskan, Administrator CFO: Chuck Fraley, Controller CIO: Marjorie Morris, Director Information Management Web address: www.healthsouth.com	33	46	40	—	—	—	—	—	—	—
✠ **HENRICO DOCTORS' HOSPITAL**, 1602 Skipwith Road, Zip 23229–5205; tel. 804/289–4500, (Includes HENRICO DOCTORS' HOSPITAL – FOREST, 1602 Skipwith Road, Zip 23229–5298; tel. 804/289–4500; HENRICO DOCTORS' HOSPITAL – PARHAM, 7700 East Parham Road, Zip 23294–4301; tel. 804/747–5600; Patrick W. Farrell, Chief Executive Officer) **A**1 2 9 10 **F**2 4 6 10 11 12 15 17 19 21 22 23 26 27 28 29 33 35 37 39 46 47 48 50 52 53 55 56 57 58 59 60 61 62 63 64 65 66 68 69 70 79 80 81 82 84 85 86 88 89 92 93 94 95 96 100 101 106 108 109 110 **S** HCA, Nashville, TN Primary Contact: Patrick W. Farrell, Chief Executive Officer COO: Lisa R. Valentine, Chief Operating Officer CFO: Roy J. Ward, Jr, Chief Financial Officer CIO: Daniel Patton, Director Information Systems CHR: Steve Burgess, Human Resources Administrator Web address: www.henricodoctorshospital.com	33	10	496	20355	315	149827	3695	—	—	1763
✠ △ **HUNTER HOLMES MCGUIRE VETERANS AFFAIRS MEDICAL CENTER**, 1201 Broad Rock Boulevard, Zip 23249–0002; tel. 804/675–5000, (Total facility includes 98 beds in nursing home–type unit) **A**1 2 3 5 7 8 **F**1 2 3 4 12 14 15 17 19 21 22 23 28 29 30 32 33 36 37 40 42 44 47 48 49 50 51 52 53 55 57 58 60 61 62 63 64 65 66 68 69 70 71 73 75 77 79 80 81 82 84 85 88 92 93 94 96 97 100 103 106 107 108 109 110 **P**1 **S** Department of Veterans Affairs, Washington, DC Primary Contact: Michael B. Phaup, Director COO: Charlene Ehret, FACHE, Associate Director CFO: Roger T. Vergne, Chief, Fiscal Service CMO: Judy Brannen, M.D., Interim Chief of Staff CIO: Katherine Gianola, M.D., Associate Chief of Staff for Information Technology CHR: Ted Knicely, Chief, Human Resource Management Web address: www.va.gov/sta/guide/home.asp	45	10	427	7098	200	385463	0	262372	142541	1956
JOHNSTON–WILLIS HOSPITAL See CJW Medical Center										
✠ **RETREAT HOSPITAL**, 2621 Grove Avenue, Zip 23220–4308; tel. 804/254–5100 **A**1 2 9 10 **F**2 12 13 15 21 22 23 26 27 28 29 33 39 46 48 50 53 55 57 58 60 61 62 63 64 65 66 69 81 82 84 88 92 93 94 108 110 **S** HCA, Nashville, TN Primary Contact: Paul L. Baldwin, Chief Executive Officer CFO: Ronald P. Powell, Jr, Chief Financial Officer Web address: www.retreathospital.com	33	10	116	4258	85	52638	0	—	—	—
STONY POINT SURGERY CENTER, (Formerly Richmond Eye and Ear Surgical Specialty Center), 8700 Stony Point Parkway, Zip 23235–1962; tel. 804/775–4500, (Nonreporting) Primary Contact: Bruce P. Kupper, FACHE, Chief Executive Officer Web address: www.stonypointsc.com	23	45	60	—	—	—	—	—	—	—

VA

Hospital, Address, Telephone, Approval, Facility, and Physician Codes, Health Care System	Classi-fication Codes		Utilization Data					Expense (thousands) of dollars		
	Control	Service	Staffed Beds	Admissions	Census	Outpatient Visits	Births	Total	Payroll	Personnel

★ American Hospital Association (AHA) membership
□ Joint Commission on Accreditation of Healthcare Organizations (JCAHO) accreditation
○ American Osteopathic Association (AOA) accreditation
△ Commission on Accreditation of Rehabilitation Facilities (CARF) accreditation

★ △ **VCU HEALTH SYSTEM**, 1250 East Marshall Street, Zip 23219, Mailing Address: P.O. Box 980510, Zip 23298–0510; tel. 804/828–9000 **A**1 2 3 5 7 8 9 10 **F**2 4 5 6 7 9 10 11 12 13 14 15 16 17 18 19 20 21 22 23 24 26 27 28 29 30 31 32 33 34 35 37 38 39 40 41 42 44 45 46 47 48 49 50 51 52 53 55 56 57 58 59 60 61 62 63 64 65 66 67 68 69 70 71 72 73 74 75 76 77 78 79 80 81 82 83 84 85 86 87 88 89 90 93 94 95 96 98 99 100 101 102 103 104 105 106 107 108 109 110 **P**6
Primary Contact: John Duval, Chief Executive Officer
CFO: Dominic J. Puleo, Executive Vice President Finance and Chief Financial Officer
CMO: Ron Clark, M.D., Vice President Clinical Activities and Chief Medical Officer
CHR: Maria Curran, Vice President Human Resources
Web address: www.vcuhealth.org
— 16 10 703 27690 481 406892 2186 542370 214741 5127

ROANOKE—Independent City County

★ △ **CARILION MEDICAL CENTER**, (Formerly Carilion Roanoke Memorial Hospital), Belleview at Jefferson Street, Zip 24014, Mailing Address: P.O. Box 13367, Zip 24033–3367; tel. 540/981–7000, (Includes CARILION ROANOKE COMMUNITY HOSPITAL, 101 Elm Avenue S.E., Zip 24013–2230, Mailing Address: P.O. Box 12946, Zip 24029–2946; tel. 540/985–8000; ROANOKE MEMORIAL REHABILITATION CENTER, South Jefferson and McClanahan Streets, Mailing Address: P.O. Box 13367, Zip 24033) **A**1 2 3 5 7 9 10 12 13 **F**2 3 4 7 9 10 11 12 13 14 15 17 19 21 22 23 24 26 27 28 29 30 31 32 33 34 35 36 37 38 39 40 41 42 44 45 46 47 48 49 50 51 52 53 55 56 57 58 59 60 61 62 63 64 65 66 67 68 69 70 71 72 73 74 75 76 77 78 79 80 81 82 84 85 86 87 88 89 90 92 93 94 95 96 98 106 107 108 109 110 **P**6 **S** Carilion Health System, Roanoke, VA
Primary Contact: Edward G. Murphy, M.D., Chief Executive Officer
COO: Nancy H. Agee, Chief Operating Officer
CFO: Donald E. Lorton, Executive Vice President and Chief Financial Officer
CIO: Greg Walton, Senior Vice President and Chief Information Officer
CHR: Bruce Boggs, Senior Vice President and Director Human Resources
Web address: www.carilion.com
— 23 10 723 33060 471 747285 3085 468326 175316 4416

ROCKY MOUNT—Franklin County

★ **CARILION FRANKLIN MEMORIAL HOSPITAL**, 180 Floyd Avenue, Zip 24151–1389; tel. 540/483–5277 **A**1 9 10 **F**9 11 12 22 27 28 29 33 36 37 38 39 48 49 51 53 55 58 59 60 63 66 69 81 88 94 96 97 106 108 **S** Carilion Health System, Roanoke, VA
Primary Contact: Chad E. Boore, Vice President and Administrator
Web address: www.carilion.com
— 23 10 37 2343 23 40678 238 23054 9215 228

SALEM—Independent City County

★ △ **LEWIS–GALE MEDICAL CENTER**, 1900 Electric Road, Zip 24153–7494; tel. 540/776–4000, (Includes LEWIS–GALE PAVILION, 1902 Braeburn Drive, Zip 24153–7391; tel. 703/772–2800), (Nonreporting) **A**1 2 7 9 10 **S** HCA, Nashville, TN
Primary Contact: James W. Thweatt, Jr, Chief Executive Officer
COO: Mark Rader, Chief Operating Officer
CFO: William S. Bainter, Chief Financial Officer
CMO: Steven Harris, President Medical Staff
CIO: Beth Cole, Director Information Services
Web address: www.lewis–gale.com
— 33 10 521 — — — — — — —

MOUNT REGIS CENTER, 405 Kimball Avenue, Zip 24153–6299; tel. 540/389–4761, (Nonreporting) **A**9 **S** Pioneer Behavioral Health, Peabody, MA
Primary Contact: Gail S. Basham, Chief Executive Officer
Web address: www.mtregis.com
— 33 82 25 — — — — — — —

★ **VETERANS AFFAIRS MEDICAL CENTER**, 1970 Roanoke Boulevard, Zip 24153–6478; tel. 540/982–2463, (Total facility includes 90 beds in nursing home–type unit) **A**1 2 3 5 8 **F**2 3 4 12 14 15 17 19 21 22 23 28 29 32 33 36 37 38 39 40 41 42 44 45 46 47 48 49 50 52 55 57 58 60 61 62 63 64 65 66 69 70 71 73 74 75 76 77 78 81 84 85 87 88 92 93 94 96 106 107 108 109 110 **S** Department of Veterans Affairs, Washington, DC
Primary Contact: Stephen L. Lemons, Ed.D., Director
CFO: Richard J. Schroeder, Chief Financial Officer
Web address: www.va.gov/sta/guide/home.asp
— 45 10 298 4650 262 293028 0 157866 63587 1389

SOUTH BOSTON—Independent City County

★ **HALIFAX REGIONAL HEALTH SYSTEM**, 2204 Wilborn Avenue, Zip 24592–1638; tel. 434/517–3100, (Total facility includes 19 beds in nursing home–type unit) **A**1 9 10 19 20 **F**3 4 5 8 9 11 12 14 21 22 26 27 28 29 31 33 34 36 44 46 47 48 49 50 51 57 58 59 60 61 62 63 65 66 69 70 73 74 75 76 77 81 82 84 86 87 88 92 93 94 95 96 106 108 110 **P**8
Primary Contact: Chris A. Lumsden, Chief Executive Officer
COO: Thomas S. Kluge, Chief Operating Officer
CFO: Stewart R. Nelson, Chief Financial Officer
CMO: Richard D. Goulah, M.D., Board of Director
CIO: William Zirkle, Information Systems Manager
CHR: Catherine Howard, Director of Human Resources
Web address: www.hrhs.org
— 23 10 144 5591 77 101656 477 51451 20036 586

VA

Many Facility Codes have changed. Please refer to the AHA Guide Code Chart.

© 2005 AHA Guide

Hospital, Address, Telephone, Approval, Facility, and Physician Codes, Health Care System	Classi-fication Codes		Utilization Data					Expense (thousands) of dollars		
	Control	Service	Staffed Beds	Admissions	Census	Outpatient Visits	Births	Total	Payroll	Personnel

★ American Hospital Association (AHA) membership
□ Joint Commission on Accreditation of Healthcare Organizations (JCAHO) accreditation
○ American Osteopathic Association (AOA) accreditation
△ Commission on Accreditation of Rehabilitation Facilities (CARF) accreditation

SOUTH HILL—Mecklenburg County

⊞ **COMMUNITY MEMORIAL HEALTHCENTER**, 125 Buena Vista Circle, Zip 23970–0090, Mailing Address: P.O. Box 90, Zip 23970–0090; tel. 434/447–3151, (Total facility includes 161 beds in nursing home–type unit) **A**1 9 10 20 **F**2 3 4 9 11 12 21 22 23 24 26 27 28 29 30 31 32 33 34 36 37 38 39 41 44 45 46 47 48 49 50 51 52 53 55 57 58 59 60 61 62 63 64 65 66 69 70 71 75 76 77 81 82 84 85 87 88 94 95 96 97 106 108 109 110 **P**8
Primary Contact: W. Scott Burnette, President and Chief Executive Officer
COO: Edward Brandenburg, Vice President Operations and Human Resources
CFO: Ronald E. Tatum, Jr, Vice President Finance
CMO: Wallace J. Horne, M.D., Vice President Medical Affairs
CIO: Mark Clemmons, Director of Information Systems
CHR: Edward Brandenburg, Vice President Operations and Human Resources
Web address: www.cmh–sh.org

| | 23 | 10 | 284 | 5402 | 213 | 90517 | 368 | 52886 | 21982 | 624 |

STAUNTON—Independent City County

COMMONWEALTH CENTER FOR CHILDREN AND ADOLESCENTS, 1355 Richmond Road, Zip 24401–1091, Mailing Address: Box 4000, Zip 24402–4000; tel. 540/332–2100, (Nonreporting) **A**9 **S** Virginia Department of Mental Health, Richmond, VA
Primary Contact: William J. Tuell, MSN, Facility Director
Web address: www.ccca.state.va.us

| | 12 | 59 | 60 | — | — | — | — | — | — | — |

□ **WESTERN STATE HOSPITAL**, 1301 Richmond Avenue, Zip 24401–9146, Mailing Address: P.O. Box 2500, Zip 24402–2500; tel. 540/332–8000, (Nonreporting) **A**1 3 9 10 **S** Virginia Department of Mental Health, Richmond, VA
Primary Contact: Jack W. Barber, M.D., Director
Web address: www.wsh.state.va.us

| | 12 | 22 | 488 | — | — | — | — | — | — | — |

STUART—Patrick County

⊞ **R. J. REYNOLDS–PATRICK COUNTY MEMORIAL HOSPITAL**, 18688 Jeb Stuart Highway, Zip 24171–1559; tel. 276/694–3151, (Total facility includes 25 beds in nursing home–type unit) **A**1 9 10 18 **F**2 6 9 12 21 22 27 28 29 33 36 37 38 39 44 46 48 52 58 63 66 69 81 88 92 94 97 108
Primary Contact: Janice F. Wilkins, Administrator
COO: Janice F. Wilkins, Administrator
CFO: Alvin C. Arrowood, Director Information Systems
CMO: Ralph Kramer, M.D., Chief Medical Staff
CIO: Douglas Whorley, Director Information Systems
CHR: Judy Poindexter, Executive Assistant and Human Resources Coordinator
Web address: www.rjrhospital.org

| | 33 | 10 | 50 | 660 | 30 | 24316 | 0 | 8563 | 3269 | 125 |

SUFFOLK—Independent City County

⊞ **LOUISE OBICI MEMORIAL HOSPITAL**, 2800 Godwin Boulevard, Zip 23434–4323, Mailing Address: P.O. Box 1100, Zip 23439–1100; tel. 757/934–4000 **A**1 5 9 10 **F**2 9 10 11 12 15 17 21 22 23 26 29 33 37 38 39 40 42 46 47 48 52 54 55 57 58 59 60 61 62 63 64 65 69 71 72 78 79 80 81 82 84 85 87 88 93 94 96 107 108 109 110 **P**6
Primary Contact: Rosemary C. Check, President and Chief Executive Officer
COO: Chet M. Hart, Senior Vice President and Chief Operating Officer
CFO: William A. Carpenter, Senior Vice President and Chief Financial Officer
CMO: Brian Gruber, M.D., President of the Medical Staff
CIO: Chip Mills, Director, Information Technology
CHR: Sandra Lane, Vice President Human Resources
Web address: www.obici.com

| | 23 | 10 | 138 | 8238 | 106 | 124108 | 1090 | 92317 | 35482 | 807 |

TAPPAHANNOCK—Essex County

□ **RIVERSIDE TAPPAHANNOCK HOSPITAL**, 618 Hospital Road, Zip 22560–5000; tel. 804/443–3311, (Total facility includes 11 beds in nursing home–type unit) **A**1 9 10 20 **F**2 9 12 21 23 27 28 29 31 33 34 35 36 37 39 40 44 46 47 48 49 51 52 55 58 60 61 62 63 64 65 66 69 70 81 82 84 87 88 92 94 95 96 97 106 108 110 **P**6 **S** Riverside Health System, Newport News, VA
Primary Contact: Elizabeth J. Martin, Vice President and Administrator
Web address: www.riverside–online.com

| | 23 | 10 | 28 | 2095 | 27 | 48296 | 0 | 23149 | 9261 | 214 |

TAZEWELL—Tazewell County

⊞ **TAZEWELL COMMUNITY HOSPITAL**, 141 Ben Bolt Avenue, Zip 24651–9700; tel. 276/988–8700 **A**1 9 10 **F**2 9 12 21 22 27 32 33 46 48 51 52 53 55 58 62 63 64 66 69 81 84 85 88 97 106 108 **S** Carilion Health System, Roanoke, VA
Primary Contact: Christopher L. Wearmouth, President and Chief Executive Officer
CFO: Melinda Fanning, Director Financial Services
CMO: Pablo Carpio, M.D., Chief of Staff
CHR: Shelley Keene Hicks, Director of Human Resources
Web address: www.tazecommhospital.org

| | 23 | 10 | 34 | 1423 | 15 | 35222 | 0 | 10556 | 4520 | 142 |

VIRGINIA BEACH—Independent City County

⊞ **SENTARA BAYSIDE HOSPITAL**, 800 Independence Boulevard, Zip 23455–6076; tel. 757/363–6100 **A**1 9 10 **F**2 9 10 12 21 22 23 26 27 28 29 31 32 33 35 37 38 39 46 48 49 50 52 53 55 57 58 61 62 63 64 65 66 69 73 75 81 82 84 85 86 87 88 92 93 94 95 96 108 109 110 **S** Sentara Healthcare, Norfolk, VA
Primary Contact: Larry T. DePriest, Vice President and Administrator
COO: Howard P. Kern, Chief Operating Officer
CMO: Irving Pike, M.D., Vice President Medical Affairs
CIO: Bert Reese, Chief Information Officer
CHR: Michael V. Taylor, Vice President Human Resources
Web address: www.sentara.com

| | 23 | 10 | 99 | 5248 | 61 | 82822 | 0 | 64699 | 24140 | 508 |

VA

Hospital, Address, Telephone, Approval, Facility, and Physician Codes, Health Care System	Classi-fication Codes		Utilization Data					Expense (thousands) of dollars		
	Control	Service	Staffed Beds	Admissions	Census	Outpatient Visits	Births	Total	Payroll	Personnel

★ American Hospital Association (AHA) membership
□ Joint Commission on Accreditation of Healthcare Organizations (JCAHO) accreditation
○ American Osteopathic Association (AOA) accreditation
△ Commission on Accreditation of Rehabilitation Facilities (CARF) accreditation

✷ **SENTARA VIRGINIA BEACH GENERAL HOSPITAL**, (Formerly Virginia Beach General Hospital), 1060 First Colonial Road, Zip 23454–3002; tel. 757/395–8000 **A**1 2 3 5 9 10 **F**2 9 10 11 12 14 15 17 19 21 22 23 26 27 28 29 31 32 33 34 35 37 38 39 40 41 46 47 48 49 50 52 53 55 56 57 58 59 61 62 63 64 65 66 69 73 75 79 80 81 82 83 84 85 86 87 88 92 93 94 95 96 104 105 107 108 109 110 **S** Sentara Healthcare, Norfolk, VA Primary Contact: Les A. Donahue, Vice President and Administrator CFO: Ronald Vinson, Director Finance Web address: www.sentara.com	23	10	240	13384	191	136380	2030	172229	64004	1428
□ **VIRGINIA BEACH PSYCHIATRIC CENTER**, 1100 First Colonial Road, Zip 23454; tel. 757/496–6000, (Nonreporting) **A**1 9 10 Primary Contact: Denise Webb, Administrator	33	22	100	—	—	—	—	—	—	—
WARRENTON—Fauquier County										
✷ **FAUQUIER HOSPITAL**, 500 Hospital Drive, Zip 20186–3099; tel. 540/349–0531 **A**1 9 10 **F**2 9 11 12 21 22 23 26 27 28 29 30 33 40 46 47 48 51 52 55 57 58 59 60 61 62 63 64 65 66 69 81 82 84 85 87 88 92 93 94 95 96 108 110 Primary Contact: Rodger H. Baker, President and Chief Executive Officer COO: Barbara K. Overton, R.N., Vice President Patient Services CFO: Lionel J. Phillips, Vice President Financial Services CMO: Thomas Sherman, President Medical Staff CIO: William Johnson, Chief Information Officer CHR: David Tatro, Vice President Human Resources Web address: www.fauquierhospital.org	23	10	83	4683	50	74256	583	80079	35798	722
WILLIAMSBURG—Independent City County										
□ **EASTERN STATE HOSPITAL**, 4601 Ironbound Road, Zip 23187–8791, Mailing Address: P.O. Box 8791, Zip 23187–8791; tel. 757/253–5161, (Total facility includes 230 beds in nursing home–type unit) **A**1 5 9 10 **F**2 5 6 10 22 26 27 28 32 37 38 44 45 46 47 48 50 53 58 60 65 66 69 70 71 73 74 76 94 96 97 107 108 109 110 **P**5 6 **S** Virginia Department of Mental Health, Richmond, VA Primary Contact: John M. Favret, Director Web address: www.esh.state.va.us	12	22	488	670	443	0	0	65432	39312	1069
✷ **SENTARA WILLIAMSBURG COMMUNITY HOSPITAL**, 301 Monticello Avenue, Zip 23185, Mailing Address: P.O. Box 8700, Zip 23187–8700; tel. 757/259–6000 **A**1 2 9 10 **F**2 4 8 9 11 12 15 21 22 23 26 27 28 29 31 32 33 35 36 37 38 40 42 44 46 47 48 49 50 52 53 54 55 57 58 59 60 61 62 63 64 65 69 73 75 81 82 84 85 87 88 92 93 94 95 96 106 107 108 109 110 **S** Sentara Healthcare, Norfolk, VA Primary Contact: Robert L. Graves, Vice President and Administrator CFO: Andreas Roehrl, Chief Financial Officer CMO: Robert Hamilton, M.D., Vice President for Medical Affairs CIO: Thomas Ewing, Director Information Technology CHR: Lois Demrich, Senior Director Human Resources Web address: www.sentara.com	23	10	110	6835	66	106370	880	90664	34502	617
WINCHESTER—Independent City County										
✷ △ **WINCHESTER MEDICAL CENTER**, 1840 Amherst Street, Zip 22601–2540, Mailing Address: P.O. Box 3340, Zip 22604–3340; tel. 540/536–8000 **A**1 2 7 9 10 19 **F**2 4 5 6 9 11 12 14 15 17 19 21 22 23 27 28 29 30 31 33 34 37 38 39 40 43 46 47 48 49 51 52 53 55 56 57 58 59 60 61 62 63 64 65 66 68 69 71 72 73 74 75 76 77 78 79 81 82 84 85 86 87 88 92 93 94 96 98 106 107 108 109 110 **P**5 **S** Valley Health System, Winchester, VA Primary Contact: James L. Woodward, President and Chief Administrative Officer CFO: J Craig Lewis, Senior Vice President and Chief Financial Officer CMO: Terry Sinclair, M.D., Senior Vice President Medical Staff Affairs CIO: Joan Roscoe, Chief Information Officer CHR: Adrienne McKenna, Vice President and Human Resources Officer Web address: www.valleyhealthlink.com	23	10	411	23997	281	248804	2153	275484	101525	2646
WOODBRIDGE—Prince William County										
✷ **POTOMAC HOSPITAL**, 2300 Opitz Boulevard, Zip 22191–3399; tel. 703/670–1313 **A**1 2 9 10 **F**2 9 10 11 12 15 17 21 22 23 26 27 28 29 33 36 37 38 46 48 49 53 55 56 57 58 59 61 62 63 64 66 75 81 82 84 85 87 88 94 96 106 108 109 Primary Contact: William Mason Moss, President CFO: Paula Brown, Senior Vice President Corporate Finance Web address: www.potomachospital.com	23	10	153	10549	112	142372	2279	109500	46772	998
WOODSTOCK—Shenandoah County										
✷ **SHENANDOAH MEMORIAL HOSPITAL**, 759 South Main Street, Zip 22664–1127; tel. 540/459–1100 **A**1 9 10 18 **F**2 9 11 12 21 22 28 29 33 37 39 41 46 47 48 51 52 53 55 58 59 62 63 65 66 69 70 81 82 84 85 87 88 94 96 97 106 108 109 110 **S** Valley Health System, Winchester, VA Primary Contact: Floyd Heater, Chief Executive Officer CFO: Virginia Kilmer, Chief Financial Officer CIO: Donna Brill, Director, Informatimon Systems Web address: www.shenmemhosp.com	23	10	23	1573	15	101230	236	28234	12106	276

VA

Many Facility Codes have changed. Please refer to the AHA Guide Code Chart.

© 2005 AHA Guide

Hospital, Address, Telephone, Approval, Facility, and Physician Codes, Health Care System	Classi-fication Codes		Utilization Data					Expense (thousands) of dollars		
★ American Hospital Association (AHA) membership □ Joint Commission on Accreditation of Healthcare Organizations (JCAHO) accreditation ○ American Osteopathic Association (AOA) accreditation △ Commission on Accreditation of Rehabilitation Facilities (CARF) accreditation	Control	Service	Staffed Beds	Admissions	Census	Outpatient Visits	Births	Total	Payroll	Personnel

WYTHEVILLE—Wythe County

⊠ **WYTHE COUNTY COMMUNITY HOSPITAL**, 600 West Ridge Road, Zip 24382–1099; tel. 276/228–0200, (Total facility includes 8 beds in nursing home–type unit) **A**1 2 9 10 20 **F**2 9 11 12 14 21 22 24 26 29 33 36 37 38 39 42 44 46 47 48 50 51 52 53 55 58 59 61 62 63 65 66 69 70 73 75 81 85 88 92 94 96 97 108 109 110 **P**6 **S** LifePoint Hospitals, Inc., Brentwood, TN
Primary Contact: John R. McLain, Administrator
CMO: William Deal, Chief of Staff
CIO: Andrea Harless, Director Information Services
CHR: Michael D. Cole, Vice President Support Services and Human Resources
Web address: www.wcch.org

23	10	90	3588	40	34833	250	35672	14378	374

VA

WASHINGTON

Hospital, Address, Telephone, Approval, Facility, and Physician Codes, Health Care System	Classi-fication Codes		Utilization Data					Expense (thousands) of dollars		
★ American Hospital Association (AHA) membership □ Joint Commission on Accreditation of Healthcare Organizations (JCAHO) accreditation ○ American Osteopathic Association (AOA) accreditation △ Commission on Accreditation of Rehabilitation Facilities (CARF) accreditation	Control	Service	Staffed Beds	Admissions	Census	Outpatient Visits	Births	Total	Payroll	Personnel

ABERDEEN—Grays Harbor County

□ **GRAYS HARBOR COMMUNITY HOSPITAL**, 915 Anderson Drive, Zip 98520–1097; tel. 360/532–8330 **A**1 9 10 **F**2 3 4 9 11 22 27 28 29 33 34 51 55 58 59 63 82 85 88 94 96 107 108
Primary Contact: Thomas Hightower, Vice President Operations
Web address: www.ghchwa.org

| | 23 | 10 | 112 | 4504 | 50 | — | 487 | 55761 | 23074 | 459 |

ANACORTES—Skagit County

✠ **ISLAND HOSPITAL**, 1211 24th Street, Zip 98221–2590; tel. 360/299–1300 **A**1 2 5 9 10 **F**2 9 11 12 21 22 23 26 27 28 29 33 34 41 44 46 47 48 51 52 55 58 59 60 61 62 63 65 66 69 70 81 82 84 88 93 94 96 98 106 108 109 110 **P**6 8
Primary Contact: Vincent Oliver, Administrator
CFO: Peter Swanson, Assistant Administrator Fiscal Services
CMO: Bob Prins, M.D., Chief of Staff
CIO: Tom Bluhm, Director Information Systems
CHR: Kit Maris, Director Human Resources
Web address: www.islandhospital.org

| | 16 | 10 | 43 | 2338 | 25 | 113822 | 316 | 41986 | 17745 | 321 |

ARLINGTON—Snohomish County

✠ **CASCADE VALLEY HOSPITAL AND CLINICS**, (Formerly Cascade Valley Hospital), 330 South Stillaguamish Avenue, Zip 98223–1642; tel. 360/435–2133 **A**1 9 10 **F**11 12 21 22 23 33 42 47 52 55 59 61 62 63 66 81 82 88 93 108 110 **P**6 8
Primary Contact: W. Clark Jones, Administrator
CFO: W Clark Jones, Administrator and Chief Fiancial Officer
CMO: Ross Hartling, M.D., Medical Staff President
CIO: Heather Logan, Information Process Coordinator
CHR: Connie DiGregorio, Resource Process Coordinator
Web address: www.cascadevalley.org

| | 16 | 10 | 32 | 1991 | 16 | 62304 | 317 | — | — | 332 |

AUBURN—King County

□ **AUBURN REGIONAL MEDICAL CENTER**, 202 North Division, Plaza One, Zip 98001–4908; tel. 253/833–7711 **A**1 2 9 10 **F**6 7 10 11 12 15 17 21 22 23 29 31 33 34 37 38 39 44 46 47 48 52 53 55 56 57 58 59 60 61 62 63 65 66 71 76 78 79 84 88 89 90 91 93 94 99 100 101 102 103 104 107 108 109 **S** Universal Health Services, Inc., King of Prussia, PA
Primary Contact: Leonard Freehof, Chief Executive Officer and Managing Director
Web address: www.auburnregional.com

| | 33 | 10 | 120 | 6209 | 70 | 78763 | 1009 | 74705 | 30819 | 543 |

BELLEVUE—King County

✠ **OVERLAKE HOSPITAL MEDICAL CENTER**, 1035 116th Avenue N.E., Zip 98004–4686; tel. 425/688–5000 **A**1 2 5 9 10 **F**2 9 10 11 12 14 15 17 19 21 22 23 29 30 31 33 34 36 37 38 40 41 44 46 47 48 50 52 53 55 56 57 58 59 60 61 62 63 64 65 66 68 69 70 71 72 73 74 75 76 77 78 79 81 82 85 87 88 89 90 93 94 95 96 98 107 108 109 110 **P**6
Primary Contact: Kenneth D. Graham, FACHE, President and Chief Executive Officer
COO: Craig L. Hendrickson, Chief Operating Officer
CFO: Gary McLaughlin, Vice President Finance and Chief Financial Officer
CIO: Kent Hargrave, Chief Information Officer
CHR: Lisa Brock, Vice President Human Resources
Web address: www.overlakehospital.org

| | 23 | 10 | 251 | 17198 | 168 | 228686 | 3844 | 222986 | 98283 | 1604 |

BELLINGHAM—Whatcom County

✠ △ **ST. JOSEPH HOSPITAL**, 2901 Squalicum Parkway, Zip 98225–1898; tel. 360/734–5400 **A**1 2 7 9 10 **F**1 2 3 4 6 9 11 12 14 15 17 19 21 22 23 26 27 28 29 31 33 34 36 37 38 39 40 44 45 46 47 48 49 50 52 53 55 57 58 59 60 61 62 63 65 66 68 69 70 71 73 74 75 77 81 82 83 84 85 86 88 94 96 106 107 108 **P**4 5 6 **S** PeaceHealth, Bellevue, WA
Primary Contact: Nancy J. Bitting, Regional Chief Executive Officer
COO: Stephen R. Omta, Chief Operating Officer
CFO: Dale Zender, Regional Vice President Finance and Chief Financial Officer
CMO: Ione Adams, M.D., Chief of Staff
CIO: Kelly Lundy, Director Information Services
CHR: Terry Brennan, Vice President Human Resources
Web address: www.peacehealth.org

| | 23 | 10 | 235 | 13460 | 158 | 109356 | 1932 | 188791 | 81038 | 1381 |

BREMERTON—Kitsap County

✠ **HARRISON MEMORIAL HOSPITAL**, 2520 Cherry Avenue, Zip 98310–4270; tel. 360/377–3911 **A**1 2 9 10 **F**2 9 11 12 13 14 15 17 19 21 22 23 26 27 28 29 31 32 33 34 35 37 38 39 42 44 46 47 48 49 50 51 52 53 55 57 58 59 60 61 62 63 65 66 67 68 69 71 72 73 74 75 76 81 82 86 88 93 94 96 106 107 108 109 110 **P**1
Primary Contact: Scott W. Bosch, President and Chief Executive Officer
CFO: James S. Rowson, Vice President Operations and Chief Financial Officer
CMO: Mel Belding, M.D., Vice President Operations and Chief Medical Officer
CIO: Adar Palis, Chief Information Officer
CHR: Peter J. Denis, Vice President Human Resources
Web address: www.harrisonhospital.org

| | 23 | 10 | 255 | 14096 | 150 | 129471 | 1874 | 167669 | 74176 | 1172 |

Many Facility Codes have changed. Please refer to the AHA Guide Code Chart.   © 2005 AHA Guide

Hospital, Address, Telephone, Approval, Facility, and Physician Codes, Health Care System	Classi-fication Codes		Utilization Data					Expense (thousands) of dollars		
★ American Hospital Association (AHA) membership □ Joint Commission on Accreditation of Healthcare Organizations (JCAHO) accreditation ○ American Osteopathic Association (AOA) accreditation △ Commission on Accreditation of Rehabilitation Facilities (CARF) accreditation	Control	Service	Staffed Beds	Admissions	Census	Outpatient Visits	Births	Total	Payroll	Personnel

<table>
<tr><td colspan="11">✠ NAVAL HOSPITAL, One Boone Road, Zip 98312–1898; tel. 360/475–4000, (Nonreporting) A1 3 5 9 S Bureau of Medicine and Surgery, Department of the Navy, Washington, DC
Primary Contact: Captain William Roberts, Commanding Officer
COO: Lieutenant Colonel Reginald B. McNeil, Director for Administration
CFO: Judith Hogan, Controller
CIO: Patrick Flaherty, Director Management Information
Web address: www.nh_bremerton.med.navy.mil</td></tr>
</table>

	Control	Service	Staffed Beds	Admissions	Census	Outpatient Visits	Births	Total	Payroll	Personnel
✠ NAVAL HOSPITAL ...	43	10	51	—	—	—	—	—	—	—

BREWSTER—Okanogan County

	Control	Service	Staffed Beds	Admissions	Census	Outpatient Visits	Births	Total	Payroll	Personnel
OKANOGAN DOUGLAS DISTRICT HOSPITAL	16	10	20	—	—	—	—	—	—	—

OKANOGAN DOUGLAS DISTRICT HOSPITAL, 507 Hospital Way, Zip 98812–0577, Mailing Address: P.O. Box 577, Zip 98812–0577; tel. 509/689–2517, (Nonreporting) **A**9 10 18 20
Primary Contact: Dale E. Polla, Administrator
Web address: www.oddh.org

CENTRALIA—Lewis County

	Control	Service	Staffed Beds	Admissions	Census	Outpatient Visits	Births	Total	Payroll	Personnel
✠ **PROVIDENCE CENTRALIA HOSPITAL**	21	10	114	5278	74	176261	525	63252	28987	596

PROVIDENCE CENTRALIA HOSPITAL, 914 South Scheuber Road, Zip 98531–9027; tel. 360/736–2803, (Total facility includes 35 beds in nursing home–type unit) **A**1 2 9 10 20 **F**4 9 11 12 22 26 27 28 33 34 46 47 48 52 53 55 58 59 60 62 63 65 66 68 69 70 75 81 82 85 88 92 94 95 96 107 108 109 110 **P**6 **S** Providence Health System, Seattle, WA
Primary Contact: Steven A. Burdick, Administrator
CFO: Thomas Risse, Chief Financial Officer
CIO: Stacy Steck, Chief Information Officer
Web address: www.providence.org

CHELAN—Chelan County

	Control	Service	Staffed Beds	Admissions	Census	Outpatient Visits	Births	Total	Payroll	Personnel
★ **LAKE CHELAN COMMUNITY HOSPITAL**	16	10	34	895	14	2976	84	11730	6593	161

LAKE CHELAN COMMUNITY HOSPITAL, 503 East Highland Avenue, Zip 98816–0908, Mailing Address: P.O. Box 908, Zip 98816–0908; tel. 509/682–2531 **A**9 10 18 20 **F**3 4 6 8 11 12 26 27 28 29 33 34 36 39 51 52 53 54 58 59 60 63 66 71 77 81 84 88 94 97 108
Primary Contact: Larry Peterson, Chief Executive Officer
CFO: MaLisa Mudgett, Chief Financial Officer
CMO: William Cagle, M.D., Medical Director
CIO: MaLisa Mudgett, Chief Financial Officer
CHR: Nancy Young, Director Human Resources
Web address: www.lakechelancommunityhospital.com

CHEWELAH—Stevens County

	Control	Service	Staffed Beds	Admissions	Census	Outpatient Visits	Births	Total	Payroll	Personnel
★ **ST. JOSEPH'S HOSPITAL**	21	10	65	813	46	20364	60	12364	5553	160

ST. JOSEPH'S HOSPITAL, 500 East Webster Street, Zip 99109–0197, Mailing Address: P.O. Box 197, Zip 99109–0197; tel. 509/935–8211, (Total facility includes 40 beds in nursing home–type unit) **A**9 10 18 **F**9 11 12 21 22 27 29 33 34 48 52 58 60 63 69 81 88 92 94 97 108 **S** Providence Services, Spokane, WA
Primary Contact: Gary V. Peck, Administrator
CFO: Sean Douglas, Chief Financial Officer
Web address: www.sjhospital.org

CLARKSTON—Asotin County

	Control	Service	Staffed Beds	Admissions	Census	Outpatient Visits	Births	Total	Payroll	Personnel
✠ **TRI–STATE MEMORIAL HOSPITAL**	23	10	25	1594	18	69172	0	27153	9807	255

TRI–STATE MEMORIAL HOSPITAL, 1221 Highland Avenue, Zip 99403–0189, Mailing Address: P.O. Box 189, Zip 99403–0189; tel. 509/758–5511 **A**1 9 10 18 **F**2 9 12 22 26 27 28 29 33 34 36 37 48 49 51 52 55 58 63 66 81 84 85 88 94 97 107 110
Primary Contact: Christopher Noland, Chief Executive Officer and Administrator
CFO: Alex Town, Chief Financial Officer
Web address: www.tristatehospital.org

COLFAX—Whitman County

	Control	Service	Staffed Beds	Admissions	Census	Outpatient Visits	Births	Total	Payroll	Personnel
★ **WHITMAN HOSPITAL AND MEDICAL CENTER**	16	10	33	732	6	16144	54	14073	5532	154

WHITMAN HOSPITAL AND MEDICAL CENTER, 1200 West Fairview, Zip 99111–9579; tel. 509/397–3435 **A**9 10 18 **F**9 11 12 22 28 29 33 34 36 51 52 54 58 59 62 63 64 66 75 77 81 88 94 97 110 **S** Providence Services, Spokane, WA
Primary Contact: Jon R. Davis, FACHE, Chief Executive Officer
COO: Jim Heilsberg, Chief Operating Officer and Chief Financial Officer
CFO: Jim Heilsberg, Chief Operating Officer and Chief Financial Officer
CMO: Anthony Lundberg, M.D., Chief Medical Officer
CIO: Jon R. Davis, FACHE, Chief Executive Officer
CHR: Linda Ledgerwood, Director Human Resources
Web address: www.whitmanhospital.com

COLVILLE—Stevens County

	Control	Service	Staffed Beds	Admissions	Census	Outpatient Visits	Births	Total	Payroll	Personnel
★ **MOUNT CARMEL HOSPITAL**	21	10	25	1183	12	32811	210	21769	9292	160

MOUNT CARMEL HOSPITAL, 982 East Columbia Street, Zip 99114–3352; tel. 509/684–2561 **A**9 10 18 20 **F**9 11 12 21 22 26 27 28 33 34 46 47 48 52 55 58 59 60 62 63 64 65 66 69 81 82 88 94 96 97 105 106 108 **P**6 **S** Providence Services, Spokane, WA
Primary Contact: Gordon C. McLean, President
CFO: Sean Douglas, Chief Financial Officer
CMO: Angela Ball, M.D., Chief of Staff
CIO: Theron DePaulo, Information Systems Manager
Web address: www.mtcarmelhospital.org

WA

Hospital, Address, Telephone, Approval, Facility, and Physician Codes, Health Care System	Classi-fication Codes		Utilization Data					Expense (thousands) of dollars		
★ American Hospital Association (AHA) membership ☐ Joint Commission on Accreditation of Healthcare Organizations (JCAHO) accreditation ○ American Osteopathic Association (AOA) accreditation △ Commission on Accreditation of Rehabilitation Facilities (CARF) accreditation	Control	Service	Staffed Beds	Admissions	Census	Outpatient Visits	Births	Total	Payroll	Personnel

COUPEVILLE—Island County

⊠ **WHIDBEY GENERAL HOSPITAL**, 101 North Main Street, Zip 98239; tel. 360/678–5151, (Nonreporting) **A**1 2 9 10
Primary Contact: Scott Rhine, Administrator and Chief Executive Officer
CFO: Doug Bishop, Chief Financial Officer
CMO: Terry Lee, M.D., Chief of Staff
CIO: Tom Tomasino, Chief Information Officer
CHR: Carolyn Pape, Manager Human Resources
Web address: www.whidbeygen.org

| | 16 | 10 | 49 | — | — | — | — | — | — | |

DAVENPORT—Lincoln County

★ **LINCOLN HOSPITAL**, 10 Nicholls Street, Zip 99122–9729; tel. 509/725–7101, (Total facility includes 68 beds in nursing home–type unit) **A**9 10 18 **F**6 8 9 12 21 27 28 29 33 34 39 41 46 48 52 53 62 63 69 70 81 88 92 96 97 109 **P**6
Primary Contact: Thomas J. Martin, Administrator
CFO: Ron Gleason, Chief Financial Officer
CMO: Rolf Panke, D.O., Chief of Staff
CIO: Elliott Donson, Chief Information Specialist
CHR: Janelle Hiccox, Director Human Resources
Web address: www.lincolnhospital.org

| | 16 | 10 | 92 | 647 | 70 | 12669 | 0 | — | — | 160 |

DAYTON—Columbia County

★ **DAYTON GENERAL HOSPITAL**, 1012 South Third Street, Zip 99328–1696; tel. 509/382–2531, (Nonreporting) **A**9 10 18
Primary Contact: Bruce P. Grimshaw, Chief Executive Officer
COO: John Burns, Chief Operating Officer
Web address: www.cchd–wa.org

| | 13 | 10 | 25 | — | — | — | — | — | — | |

DEER PARK—Spokane County

★ **DEER PARK HOSPITAL**, 1015 East D Street, Zip 99006–0742, Mailing Address: P.O. Box 742, Zip 99006–0742; tel. 509/276–3500, (Nonreporting) **A**9 10 18 **S** Providence Services, Spokane, WA
Primary Contact: M. Colleen Febach, Administrator
CFO: Janis H. Simpson, Chief Financial Officer
CMO: Julie A. Moran, M.D., President Medical Staff
CIO: Margaret Ryan, Director Health Information
CHR: Jill Breitkreutz, Manager Human Resources

| | 21 | 10 | 25 | — | — | — | — | — | — | |

EDMONDS—Snohomish County

⊠ **STEVENS HEALTHCARE**, 21601 76th Avenue West, Zip 98026–7506; tel. 425/640–4000 **A**1 2 9 10 **F**1 2 9 10 11 12 21 22 26 27 28 29 30 31 32 33 34 36 37 38 39 40 44 46 47 48 52 55 56 57 58 59 60 61 62 63 65 66 69 70 71 73 74 75 76 78 81 82 84 88 93 94 97 106 107 108 109 **P**6 7
Primary Contact: John Todd, M.D., President and Chief Executive Officer
CFO: Gary L. Wangsmo, President, Board of Commissioner
CIO: Fred Grannen, Vice President Information Management
CHR: Robert Lowy, Vice President Human Resources
Web address: www.stevenshealthcare.org

| | 16 | 10 | 156 | 7215 | 93 | 214250 | 1144 | 135666 | 56126 | 1049 |

ELLENSBURG—Kittitas County

★ **KITTITAS VALLEY COMMUNITY HOSPITAL**, 603 South Chestnut Street, Zip 98926–3875; tel. 509/962–7302, (Nonreporting) **A**9 10 18 20
Primary Contact: Eric Jensen, Administrator
COO: Eric Jensen, Administrator
CFO: Harold Brockman, Chief Financial Officer
CMO: Craig Wilson, Assistant Administrator Patient Care Services
CIO: Eric Jensen, Administrator
CHR: Lisa McDaniel, Assistant Administrator Human Resources
Web address: www.kvch.com

| | 16 | 10 | 25 | — | — | — | — | — | — | |

ENUMCLAW—King County

ENUMCLAW COMMUNITY HOSPITAL, 1450 Battersby Avenue, Zip 98022–0218, Mailing Address: P.O. Box 218, Zip 98022–0218; tel. 360/825–2505 **A**9 10 18 **F**2 3 11 12 13 14 26 27 28 33 34 45 52 55 56 58 59 62 63 64 66 67 68 71 75 81 88 92 96 108
Primary Contact: Dennis A. Popp, Administrator and Chief Executive Officer
Web address: www.enumclawhospital.org

| | 23 | 10 | 25 | 1216 | 9 | 16068 | 234 | 17173 | 7107 | 168 |

EPHRATA—Grant County

★ **COLUMBIA BASIN HOSPITAL**, 200 Southeast Boulevard, Zip 98823–1973; tel. 509/754–4631, (Total facility includes 29 beds in nursing home–type unit) **A**9 10 18 **F**8 9 12 21 27 28 29 33 34 44 45 46 48 52 58 60 69 70 88 92 94 95 108 **P**6
Primary Contact: Donald W. James, Ph.D., Administrator
CFO: Rhonda Handley, Chief Financial Officer
CMO: Ravinder S. Nijjar, M.D., Chief of Staff
CHR: Bonnie Polhamus, Director Human Resources

| | 16 | 10 | 86 | 356 | 68 | 0 | 0 | 9206 | 4751 | 129 |

Many Facility Codes have changed. Please refer to the AHA Guide Code Chart. © 2005 AHA Guide

Hospital, Address, Telephone, Approval, Facility, and Physician Codes, Health Care System	Classi-fication Codes		Utilization Data					Expense (thousands) of dollars		
★ American Hospital Association (AHA) membership □ Joint Commission on Accreditation of Healthcare Organizations (JCAHO) accreditation ○ American Osteopathic Association (AOA) accreditation △ Commission on Accreditation of Rehabilitation Facilities (CARF) accreditation	Control	Service	Staffed Beds	Admissions	Census	Outpatient Visits	Births	Total	Payroll	Personnel

EVERETT—Snohomish County

☒ △ **PROVIDENCE EVERETT MEDICAL CENTER**, 1321 Colby Street,
Zip 98206–1147, Mailing Address: P.O. Box 1147, Zip 98206–1147;
tel. 425/261–2000, (Includes PROVIDENCE EVERETT MEDICAL CENTER – COLBY
CAMPUS, 14th and Colby Avenue, Zip 98206; tel. 206/261–2000; PROVIDENCE
EVERETT MEDICAL CENTER – PACIFIC CAMPUS, Pacific and Nassau Streets,
Zip 98201) **A**1 2 7 9 10 **F**2 3 4 9 11 12 14 15 17 19 21 22 23 24 26 27 28
29 30 31 33 34 35 37 38 39 41 42 46 47 48 49 52 53 55 56 57 58 59 60
61 62 63 64 65 66 68 69 70 79 80 81 82 83 84 85 86 87 88 92 93 94 96
106 108 109 110 **P**6 8 **S** Providence Health System, Seattle, WA
Primary Contact: Gail C. Larson, Chief Executive Officer
COO: David Brooks, Chief Operating Officer
CFO: Dave Mast, Chief Financial Officer
CMO: Lawrence Schecter, M.D., Chief Medical Officer
Web address: www.providence.org

| | 21 | 10 | 325 | 21876 | 229 | 212731 | 3748 | 329794 | 142143 | 2503 |

FEDERAL WAY—King County

★ **ST. FRANCIS HOSPITAL**, 34515 Ninth Avenue South, Zip 98003–6799;
tel. 253/927–9700 **A**2 9 10 **F**2 9 10 11 12 15 17 21 22 23 27 28 29 30 31
33 35 39 40 42 46 48 52 55 57 58 59 60 61 62 63 64 65 66 69 71 75 79
80 81 82 84 85 87 88 92 93 94 96 106 108 109 **P**6 **S** Catholic Health
Initiatives, Denver, CO
Primary Contact: Syd Bersante, Chief Operating Officer
COO: Syd Bersante, Chief Operating Officer
CMO: Everett Newcomb, D.O., Senior Vice President Medical Affairs
CIO: Keith Stauffer, Regional Information Technology Director
CHR: David Lawson, Vice President Human Resources
Web address: www.fhshealth.org

| | 21 | 10 | 108 | 7319 | 67 | 81002 | 1241 | 92864 | 43558 | 610 |

FORKS—Clallam County

FORKS COMMUNITY HOSPITAL, 530 Bogachiel Way, Zip 98331–9120;
tel. 360/374–6271, (Total facility includes 20 beds in nursing home–type unit) **A**9
10 18 20 **F**4 6 9 11 12 21 22 23 26 27 28 29 33 34 37 44 46 47 48 50 53
58 59 62 63 65 66 68 69 70 77 81 84 88 92 94 96 97 106 107 108 109 **P**6
Primary Contact: Camille Scott, Administrator
Web address: www.forkshospital.org

| | 16 | 10 | 45 | 479 | 23 | 22300 | 106 | 14838 | 7366 | 138 |

GOLDENDALE—Klickitat County

★ **KLICKITAT VALLEY HEALTH SERVICES**, 310 South Roosevelt,
Zip 98620–9201, Mailing Address: P.O. Box 5, Zip 98620–0005;
tel. 509/773–4022 **A**9 10 18 **F**6 11 12 21 26 27 33 37 51 52 53 58 59 60
61 62 63 69 70 75 81 82 88 92 97 107 110 **P**3 5 **S** Brim Healthcare, Inc.,
Brentwood, TN
Primary Contact: Sharon Cox, Chief Executive Officer
CFO: Wade Sturgeon, Chief Financial Officer
CMO: Michael Garnett, Chief of Staff
CHR: Gwyn Miller, Manager Human Resources
Web address: www.kvhs.net

| | 13 | 10 | 18 | 541 | 4 | 52542 | 61 | 9479 | 5378 | 135 |

GRAND COULEE—Grant County

★ **COULEE COMMUNITY HOSPITAL**, 411 Fortuyn Road, Zip 99133–8718;
tel. 509/633–1753, (Total facility includes 29 beds in nursing home–type unit) **A**9
10 18 **F**9 11 12 21 23 24 27 28 29 33 34 42 44 48 58 59 60 63 70 81 85
88 91 92 97 **P**6
Primary Contact: Jerry Lane, Chief Executive Officer
CFO: Debbie Bigelow, Chief Financial Officer

| | 16 | 10 | 48 | 375 | 18 | — | 91 | — | — | 134 |

ILWACO—Pacific County

★ **OCEAN BEACH HOSPITAL**, 174 First Avenue North, Zip 98624–0258, Mailing
Address: P.O. Drawer H, Zip 98624–0258; tel. 360/642–3181 **A**9 10 18 **F**9 12
21 23 29 33 46 48 60 61 63 66 69 81 88 96 97 106
Primary Contact: James E. Robertson, Jr, Chief Executive Officer
CFO: Edward A. Norris, Chief Financial Officer
CMO: Michael Sthay, M.D., Chief Medical Officer
CIO: Julie Oakes, R.N., Director Information Systems
CHR: Mary Ward–Riggs, Director Human Resources
Web address: www.oceanbeachhospital.com

| | 16 | 10 | 15 | 635 | 5 | 13219 | 0 | 13113 | 4795 | 107 |

KENNEWICK—Benton County

☒ **KENNEWICK GENERAL HOSPITAL**, 900 South Auburn Street,
Zip 99336–6128, Mailing Address: P.O. Box 6128, Zip 99336–6128;
tel. 509/586–6111 **A**1 2 9 10 **F**1 2 6 9 11 12 15 16 17 18 21 22 23 27 28
32 33 34 37 42 46 47 48 51 52 53 55 58 59 63 65 69 81 82 83 84 86 87
88 107 108 **P**6 7
Primary Contact: Glen Marshall, Chief Executive Officer
CFO: Tom Birmingham, Chief Financial Officer
CHR: Esther Schmidt, Supervisor Human Resources
Web address: www.kennewickgeneral.com

| | 16 | 10 | 101 | 4157 | 36 | 44249 | 1217 | 62166 | 23885 | 624 |

KIRKLAND—King County

☒ **EVERGREEN HEALTHCARE**, 12040 N.E. 128th Street, Zip 98034–9917;
tel. 425/899–1000, (Nonreporting) **A**1 2 5 9 10
Primary Contact: Steven E. Brown, FACHE, Chief Executive Officer
CFO: David R. Kiehn, Senior Vice President Finance and Chief Financial Officer
CMO: Mitch Weinberg, M.D., Chief of Staff
Web address: www.evergreenhealthcare.org

| | 16 | 10 | 230 | — | — | — | — | — | — | — |

WA

Hospital, Address, Telephone, Approval, Facility, and Physician Codes, Health Care System	Classi-fication Codes		Utilization Data					Expense (thousands) of dollars		
	Control	Service	Staffed Beds	Admissions	Census	Outpatient Visits	Births	Total	Payroll	Personnel

★ American Hospital Association (AHA) membership
□ Joint Commission on Accreditation of Healthcare Organizations (JCAHO) accreditation
○ American Osteopathic Association (AOA) accreditation
△ Commission on Accreditation of Rehabilitation Facilities (CARF) accreditation

Hospital	Control	Service	Staffed Beds	Admissions	Census	Outpatient Visits	Births	Total	Payroll	Personnel
□ **FAIRFAX HOSPITAL**, 10200 N.E. 132nd Street, Zip 98034–2899; tel. 425/821–2000, (Nonreporting) **A**1 9 10 **S** Psychiatric Solutions, Franklin, TN Primary Contact: Ron Escarda, Chief Executive Officer Web address: www.fairfaxhospital.com	33	22	65	—	—	—	—	—	—	—
LEAVENWORTH—Chelan County **CASCADE MEDICAL CENTER**, 817 Commercial Street, Zip 98826, Mailing Address: P.O. Box 330, Zip 98826; tel. 509/548–5815 **A**9 10 18 **F**6 12 33 97 Primary Contact: Douglas Williams, Administrator	16	10	7	121	1	33180	—	5245	3068	—
LONGVIEW—Cowlitz County ⊠ **ST. JOHN MEDICAL CENTER**, 1615 Delaware Street, Zip 98632–2310, Mailing Address: P.O. Box 3002, Zip 98632–3002; tel. 360/414–2000, (Nonreporting) **A**1 2 9 10 19 20 **S** PeaceHealth, Bellevue, WA Primary Contact: Medrice Coluccio, Chief Executive Officer COO: James Meskew, Chief Operating Officer CFO: Sy Johnson, Chief Financial Officer Web address: www.peacehealth.org	21	10	202	—	—	—	—	—	—	—
MCCLEARY—Grays Harbor County ★ **MARK REED HOSPITAL**, 322 South Birch Street, Zip 98557–9522; tel. 360/495–3244 **A**9 10 18 **F**12 33 34 48 70 Primary Contact: Jean E. Roberts, Administrator CFO: Georgette Hiles, Accountant CMO: R Samantha Ritchie, M.D., President Medical Staff CIO: David Gibson, Chief Information Officer CHR: Mindy Portchy, Manager Human Resources Web address: www.markreedhospital.com	16	10	4	21	1	13570	0	4934	2720	71
MEDICAL LAKE—Spokane County □ **EASTERN STATE HOSPITAL**, Maple Street, Zip 99022–0045, Mailing Address: P.O. Box 800, Zip 99022–0800; tel. 509/299–3121, (Nonreporting) **A**1 9 10 Primary Contact: Harold E. Wilson, Chief Executive Officer	12	22	319	—	—	—	—	—	—	—
MONROE—Snohomish County ⊠ **VALLEY GENERAL HOSPITAL**, 14701 179th S.E., Zip 98272–1108, Mailing Address: P.O. Box 646, Zip 98272–0646; tel. 360/794–7497, (Nonreporting) **A**1 9 10 Primary Contact: Mark D. Judy, Chief Executive Officer COO: Sherry Stoll, Chief Operating Officer CIO: Kathy Nelson, Director Marketing CHR: Deborah Martin, Director Human Resources Web address: www.valleygeneral.com	16	10	72	—	—	—	—	—	—	—
MORTON—Lewis County ★ **MORTON GENERAL HOSPITAL**, 521 Adams Street, Zip 98356, Mailing Address: Drawer C, Zip 98356–0019; tel. 360/496–5112, (Total facility includes 6 beds in nursing home–type unit) **A**9 10 18 20 **F**2 9 11 12 33 34 47 59 63 69 70 81 84 88 92 94 97 107 **P**6 Primary Contact: Ron DeArth, Interim Superintendent CFO: Ron DeArth, Chief Financial Officer Web address: www.lewiscountyhelp.com	13	10	31	370	19	—	—	—	—	113
MOSES LAKE—Grant County ★ **SAMARITAN HEALTHCARE**, 801 East Wheeler Road, Zip 98837–1899; tel. 509/765–5606 **A**9 10 **F**11 12 22 28 29 33 34 42 46 47 48 52 53 55 58 59 60 62 63 65 66 69 70 82 85 88 94 96 107 108 **P**6 Primary Contact: John R. White, Chief Executive Officer and Superintendent COO: Lynn Bales, Assistant Administrator Clinical and Support Servicess CFO: Terry Litke, Chief Financial Officer CIO: Michael Cloutier, Information Systems Director CHR: Kim Garza, Director Human Resources Web address: www.samaritanhealthcare.com	16	10	50	3212	27	81168	966	42610	19346	395
MOUNT VERNON—Skagit County ⊠ **SKAGIT VALLEY HOSPITAL**, 1415 East Kincaid Street, Zip 98273, Mailing Address: P.O. Box 1376, Zip 98273–1376; tel. 360/424–4111 **A**1 9 10 **F**2 5 7 9 11 15 17 21 22 23 26 27 28 29 30 32 33 34 35 37 38 39 42 46 47 48 49 52 53 55 57 58 59 60 61 62 63 64 65 66 69 71 78 82 93 94 96 106 108 109 110 **P**6 Primary Contact: Gregg A. Davidson, Chief Executive Officer COO: Lori Daisley, Chief Operating Officer CFO: Thomas Litaker, Chief Financial Officer CMO: Richard Abbott, M.D., Quality Improvement Medical Advisor CIO: Doug Riley, Director Information Services CHR: Elizabeth Feingold, Interim Director Human Resources Web address: www.skagitvalleyhospital.org	16	10	115	7821	73	71878	1193	92089	36887	702
NEWPORT—Pend Oreille County **NEWPORT COMMUNITY HOSPITAL**, 714 West Pine Street, Zip 99156–9046; tel. 509/447–2441, (Total facility includes 50 beds in nursing home–type unit) (Nonreporting) **A**9 10 18 Primary Contact: Thomas W. Wilbur, Chief Executive Officer and Superintendent Web address: www.phd1.org	16	10	74	—	—	—	—	—	—	—
OAK HARBOR—Island County ⊠ **NAVAL HOSPITAL**, 3475 North Saratoga Street, Zip 98278–8800; tel. 360/257–9500 **A**1 9 **F**4 6 10 11 12 21 24 27 28 33 39 48 52 58 59 60 62 63 66 69 73 77 81 88 92 94 106 108 109 **P**1 **S** Bureau of Medicine and Surgery, Department of the Navy, Washington, DC Primary Contact: Captain Susan Herrold, Commanding Officer Web address: www.nhoh.med.navy.mil/	43	10	25	1084	6	144824	461	—	—	318

WA

Many Facility Codes have changed. Please refer to the AHA Guide Code Chart. © 2005 AHA Guide

Hospital, Address, Telephone, Approval, Facility, and Physician Codes, Health Care System	Classi-fication Codes		Utilization Data					Expense (thousands) of dollars		
	Control	Service	Staffed Beds	Admissions	Census	Outpatient Visits	Births	Total	Payroll	Personnel

★ American Hospital Association (AHA) membership
□ Joint Commission on Accreditation of Healthcare Organizations (JCAHO) accreditation
○ American Osteopathic Association (AOA) accreditation
△ Commission on Accreditation of Rehabilitation Facilities (CARF) accreditation

ODESSA—Lincoln County

★ **ODESSA MEMORIAL HEALTHCARE CENTER**, (CAH), 502 East Amende Drive, Zip 99159–0368, Mailing Address: P.O. Box 368, Zip 99159–0368; tel. 509/982–2611, (Total facility includes 11 beds in nursing home–type unit) **A**9 10 18 **F**6 8 9 26 27 28 29 33 39 44 45 46 48 52 58 63 69 92 94 95 96 97 **P**6
Primary Contact: Mark Barglof, Administrator
CFO: Carol Schott, Chief Financial Officer and Assistant Administrator
CMO: Linda J. Powel, M.D., Medical Director
Web address: www.odessahealth.org

	16	49	36	97	11	—	0	—	—	—

OLYMPIA—Thurston County

✠ **CAPITAL MEDICAL CENTER**, 3900 Capital Mall Drive S.W., Zip 98502–5026, Mailing Address: P.O. Box 19002, Zip 98507–9002; tel. 360/754–5858, (Total facility includes 9 beds in nursing home–type unit) **A**1 2 9 10 **F**2 9 10 11 12 15 17 21 22 23 26 27 28 29 33 34 37 48 52 53 59 60 61 62 63 64 65 66 69 81 82 84 85 88 92 96 108 109 **S** HCA, Nashville, TN
Primary Contact: Joseph Sharp, Chief Executive Officer
COO: Ann Pelissier Neeld, Chief Operating Officer
CFO: Michael Motte, Chief Financial Officer
CMO: Robert Nipp, M.D., Chief of Staff
CIO: Susan G. Kent, Director of Marketing and Public Relations
CHR: Joe Schmier, Director Human Resources
Web address: www.capitalmedical.com

	32	10	105	3923	41	85413	719	53236	21266	324

✠ △ **PROVIDENCE ST. PETER HOSPITAL**, 413 Lilly Road N.E., Zip 98506–5166; tel. 360/491–9480 **A**1 2 3 5 7 9 10 **F**2 3 4 9 10 11 12 14 15 17 19 21 22 26 28 29 30 31 33 34 35 40 41 42 46 47 48 50 52 55 57 58 59 60 61 62 63 64 65 66 68 69 70 71 72 73 74 75 77 78 81 82 83 85 86 87 88 93 94 95 96 97 98 106 107 108 109 **S** Providence Health System, Seattle, WA
Primary Contact: C. Scott Bond, Administrator and Chief Executive Officer
COO: Jim Leonard, Chief Operating Officer
CFO: Thomas Risse, Chief Financial Officer
CMO: Mike Matlock, M.D., Chief Medical Officer
CIO: Stacey Steck, Chief Information Officer
CHR: Susan Meenk, Administrator Human Resources
Web address: www.providence.org/swsa/facilities/st_peter_hospital

	21	10	317	17776	205	306461	2054	235980	100318	1788

OMAK—Okanogan County

★ **MID–VALLEY HOSPITAL**, 810 Jasmine, Zip 98841–0793, Mailing Address: P.O. Box 793, Zip 98841–0793; tel. 509/826–1760 **A**3 5 9 10 18 20 **F**9 11 12 21 33 34 37 52 55 59 63 66 69 81 82 88
Primary Contact: Michael D. Billing, Administrator
CFO: Scott Attridge, Controller
CMO: Grace Yelland, M.D., Physician
CIO: Kelly Cariker, Manager
CHR: Norene Van Brunt, Manager Human Resources
Web address: www.mvhealth.org

	16	10	32	1495	10	—	267	18696	7516	189

OTHELLO—Adams County

★ **OTHELLO COMMUNITY HOSPITAL**, 315 North 14th Street, Zip 99344–1297; tel. 509/488–2636 **A**9 10 18 **F**2 6 9 11 12 22 33 34 53 59 63 69 81 85 88 97 110
Primary Contact: Harold S. Geller, Administrator
CFO: Leon Walsh, Director Finance
CHR: Kurt Richter, Chief Human Resources Officer
Web address: www.othellocommunityhospital.org

	16	10	25	1239	7	—	—	—	—	124

PASCO—Franklin County

✠ △ **LOURDES MEDICAL CENTER**, 520 North Fourth Avenue, Zip 99301–2568, Mailing Address: P.O. Box 2568, Zip 99302–2568; tel. 509/547–7704, (Total facility includes 17 beds in nursing home–type unit) (Nonreporting) **A**1 2 7 9 10 18 **S** Ascension Health, Saint Louis, MO
Primary Contact: John Serle, President and Chief Executive Officer
CFO: Frank Becker, Chief Financial Officer
CIO: Dotty Jolley, Supervisor Information Systems
CHR: Sally Ann Peters, Director Human Resources
Web address: www.lourdesonline.org

	21	10	52	—	—	—	—	—	—	—

POMEROY—Garfield County

GARFIELD COUNTY PUBLIC HOSPITAL DISTRICT, 66th North Sixth Street, Zip 99347–0880, Mailing Address: P.O. Box 880, Zip 99347–0880; tel. 509/843–1591, (Total facility includes 20 beds in nursing home–type unit) **A**9 10 18 **F**1 2 5 9 21 22 24 27 28 29 33 34 35 36 37 38 39 44 45 46 47 48 52 53 60 63 66 69 70 92 94 96 97 106 108 109 110 **P**6
Primary Contact: Andrew Craigie, Administrator
Web address: www.garfieldcountyphd.org

	16	80	45	133	39	8310	0	4622	2493	83

WA

Hospital, Address, Telephone, Approval, Facility, and Physician Codes, Health Care System	Classi-fication Codes		Utilization Data					Expense (thousands) of dollars		
	Control	Service	Staffed Beds	Admissions	Census	Outpatient Visits	Births	Total	Payroll	Personnel

★ American Hospital Association (AHA) membership
□ Joint Commission on Accreditation of Healthcare Organizations (JCAHO) accreditation
○ American Osteopathic Association (AOA) accreditation
△ Commission on Accreditation of Rehabilitation Facilities (CARF) accreditation

PORT ANGELES—Clallam County

⊠ OLYMPIC MEDICAL CENTER, 939 Caroline Street, Zip 98362–3997;
tel. 360/417–7000, (Total facility includes 125 beds in nursing home–type unit)
A1 2 9 10 19 20 **F**9 11 12 14 23 26 27 28 33 34 37 46 48 51 52 55 58 59
60 61 63 64 65 66 68 69 79 81 82 85 88 92 93 94 106 108 110
Primary Contact: Michael Glenn, Chief Executive Officer
COO: Joyce Cardinal, Assistant Administrator, Chf Operating Officer and Chief Nursing Officer
CFO: Eric Lewis, Assistant Administrator Finance and Chief Financial Officer
CMO: R Scott Kennedy, M.D., Chief Medical Officer
CIO: Evan Boyd, Director Information Technology
CHR: Richard Neuman, Assistant Administrator
Web address: www.olympicmedical.org

| 16 | 10 | 211 | 5896 | 158 | 153038 | 448 | 83948 | 36148 | 718 |

PORT TOWNSEND—Jefferson County

★ JEFFERSON HEALTHCARE, (Formerly Jefferson General Hospital), 834 Sheridan
Street, Zip 98368–2443; tel. 360/385–2200 **A**9 10 18 20 **F**2 9 11 12 21 22
23 26 27 28 29 33 34 36 37 41 46 47 48 50 51 53 55 58 59 60 62 63 64
65 66 69 70 81 82 84 88 93 94 95 96 97 106 108 110 **P**6
Primary Contact: Victor J. Dirksen, Administrator
COO: Paul Dowdle, Chief Operating Officer
CFO: James Chaney, Chief Financial Officer
CMO: Frank Magill, M.D., Chief Medical Officer
CIO: John Nowak, Information Systems Director
CHR: Beki Lischalk, Director Human Resources
Web address: www.jeffersonhealthcare.org

| 16 | 10 | 25 | 1235 | 11 | 54310 | 119 | — | — | 301 |

PROSSER—Benton County

★ PROSSER MEMORIAL HOSPITAL, 723 Memorial Street, Zip 99350–1593;
tel. 509/786–2222, (Total facility includes 36 beds in nursing home–type unit) **A**9
10 18 **F**6 9 11 12 29 33 34 42 44 45 46 51 52 53 58 59 63 64 66 81 88 92
94 97 108 110
Primary Contact: James Tavary, Administrator
CFO: Julie Petersen, Director Financial Services
CIO: Greg Belkle, Information Systems Manager
CHR: Sharon Cloos, Manager Human Resources
Web address: www.prossermemorialhospital.com

| 16 | 10 | 62 | 800 | 36 | 32165 | 356 | 17440 | 8723 | 184 |

PULLMAN—Whitman County

□ PULLMAN REGIONAL HOSPITAL, (Formerly Pullman Memorial Hospital), 835
S.E. Bishop Boulevard, Zip 99163–4742; tel. 509/332–2541 **A**1 9 10 18 **F**2 11
12 21 22 26 27 28 29 30 31 33 34 35 40 41 46 48 52 53 55 58 59 60 61
62 63 65 66 69 71 74 75 77 78 81 82 84 88 93 94 95 96 97 107 108 **P**4
Primary Contact: Scott K. Adams, Administrator
Web address: www.pullmanhospital.org

| 16 | 10 | 26 | 1095 | 9 | 46513 | 290 | 22738 | 10637 | 240 |

PUYALLUP—Pierce County

⊠ △ GOOD SAMARITAN COMMUNITY HEALTHCARE, 407 14th Avenue S.E.,
Zip 98372–0118, Mailing Address: P.O. Box 1247, Zip 98371–1247;
tel. 253/848–6661, (Nonreporting) **A**1 2 7 9 10
Primary Contact: George A. Govier, President and Chief Executive Officer
CIO: Scott Quigley, Director Management Information Systems
Web address: www.goodsamhealth.org

| 23 | 10 | 201 | — | — | — | — | — | — | — |

QUINCY—Grant County

★ QUINCY VALLEY MEDICAL CENTER, 908 10th Avenue S.W., Zip 98848–1376;
tel. 509/787–3531, (Total facility includes 4 beds in nursing home–type unit) **A**9
10 18 **F**6 33 46 48 52 53 81 88 91 92 94 97
Primary Contact: John R. Perushek, Administrator
CFO: John L. Howrey, Chief Financial Officer
CMO: Mark Vance, M.D., Chief Medical Officer
CIO: Ruth Vance, Director Information Systems
CHR: Alene Adams, Director Human Resources
Web address: www.quincyhospital.org

| 16 | 10 | 29 | 160 | 22 | 2870 | 0 | — | — | — |

REDMOND—King County

□ GROUP HEALTH COOPERATIVE, 2700 152nd Avenue N.E., Zip 98052–5560;
tel. 425/883–5151, (Nonreporting) **A**1 3 9 10
Primary Contact: Susan Kropelnicki, Administrator
Web address: www.ghc.org

| 23 | 10 | 125 | — | — | — | — | — | — | — |

RENTON—King County

⊠ VALLEY MEDICAL CENTER, 400 South 43rd Street, Zip 98055–5784;
tel. 425/228–3450 **A**1 2 3 5 9 10 **F**2 4 10 11 12 17 21 22 23 26 27 28 29
31 33 34 37 39 40 41 42 44 46 47 48 49 52 53 55 56 57 58 59 60 61 62
63 65 66 68 69 70 73 74 75 76 77 79 81 82 84 85 87 88 90 93 94 95 96
107 108 109 110 **P**8
Primary Contact: Richard D. Roodman, Chief Executive Officer
COO: Paul Hayes, R.N., Chief Operating Officer
CFO: Michael Bernstein, Chief Financial Officer
CMO: Terence Block, M.D., Chief Medical Officer
CIO: Phil Perry, Chief Information Officer
CHR: Barbara Mitchell, Administrator Organizational Development
Web address: www.valleymed.org

| 16 | 10 | 168 | 14373 | 123 | 476233 | 2856 | 226579 | 96492 | 1581 |

WA

Many Facility Codes have changed. Please refer to the AHA Guide Code Chart. © 2005 AHA Guide

Hospital, Address, Telephone, Approval, Facility, and Physician Codes, Health Care System	Classi-fication Codes		Utilization Data					Expense (thousands) of dollars		
★ American Hospital Association (AHA) membership □ Joint Commission on Accreditation of Healthcare Organizations (JCAHO) accreditation ○ American Osteopathic Association (AOA) accreditation △ Commission on Accreditation of Rehabilitation Facilities (CARF) accreditation	Control	Service	Staffed Beds	Admissions	Census	Outpatient Visits	Births	Total	Payroll	Personnel

REPUBLIC—Ferry County

★ **FERRY COUNTY MEMORIAL HOSPITAL**, 36 Klondike Road, Zip 99166–9701; tel. 509/775–3333 **A**9 10 18 20 **F**2 11 21 26 27 28 29 30 31 33 41 44 46 47 48 52 54 58 59 60 63 64 65 66 69 70 81 88 92 94 96 97 107 **P**6
Primary Contact: Ronald O'Halloran, Administrator
CFO: Marvel Brenner, Chief Financial Officer
CHR: Kelly Leslie, Human Resources Officer
Web address: www.fcphd.org

| 16 | 10 | 25 | 280 | 17 | 19644 | 1 | 5631 | 3236 | 96 |

RICHLAND—Benton County

⊠ △ **KADLEC MEDICAL CENTER**, 888 Swift Boulevard, Zip 99352–3542; tel. 509/946–4611 **A**1 2 7 9 10 **F**2 9 11 12 15 17 19 21 22 23 26 27 28 30 33 34 37 39 40 46 52 53 55 56 58 59 60 61 62 63 65 66 68 69 70 81 82 84 85 86 87 88 94 107 108 110 **P**6 **S** Quorum Health Resources, Plano, TX
Primary Contact: Rand J. Wortman, President and Chief Executive Officer
COO: Suzanne Richins, Chief Operating Officer
CFO: Julie Meek, Vice President Finance
CMO: Thomas Rado, M.D., Chief of Staff
CIO: David Roach, Vice President Information System
CHR: Jeff Clark, Vice President Human Resources
Web address: www.kadlecmed.org

| 23 | 10 | 166 | 9002 | 103 | 105296 | 1702 | 145922 | 54413 | 920 |

★ **LOURDES COUNSELING CENTER**, 1175 Carondelet Drive, Zip 99352–3396; tel. 509/943–9104 **A**10 **F**4 21 26 27 28 31 42 52 71 72 73 74 76 77 78 92 94 96 98 106 **P**6 **S** Ascension Health, Saint Louis, MO
Primary Contact: Barbara Mead, Executive Director
CFO: Frank Becker, Chief Financial Officer
Web address: www.lourdesonline.org

| 21 | 22 | 32 | 739 | 22 | 47929 | 0 | 12018 | 6855 | 126 |

RITZVILLE—Adams County

EAST ADAMS RURAL HOSPITAL, 903 South Adams Street, Zip 99169–2298; tel. 509/659–1200 **A**9 10 18 **F**6 27 28 33 34 46 48 52 63 69 81 97 107 **P**6
Primary Contact: Larry Hutcheson, Interim Administrator
Web address: www.earh.com

| 16 | 10 | 9 | 154 | 1 | 7462 | 1 | 2439 | 1409 | 45 |

SEATTLE—King County

⊠ △ **CHILDREN'S HOSPITAL AND REGIONAL MEDICAL CENTER**, 4800 Sand Point Way N.E., Zip 98105–0371, Mailing Address: Box 5371, Zip 98105–0371; tel. 206/987–2000 **A**1 2 3 5 7 8 9 10 **F**2 7 16 18 20 21 22 23 24 26 27 28 29 31 32 33 34 37 38 42 46 47 49 50 52 53 56 57 58 60 61 62 63 64 65 66 67 68 69 70 71 72 73 74 75 77 78 81 82 84 88 90 93 94 95 96 98 99 100 101 102 104 105 107 108 110
Primary Contact: Treuman Katz, President and Chief Executive Officer
CFO: Kelly Wallace, Vice President and Chief Financial Officer
CMO: Richard Molteni, M.D., Vice President and Medical Director
CIO: John Dwight, Chief Information Officer
CHR: Charles Sims, Director Human Resources
Web address: www.seattlechildrens.org

| 23 | 50 | 237 | 11415 | 165 | 197926 | 0 | 297647 | 122507 | 2009 |

⊠ △ **HARBORVIEW MEDICAL CENTER**, (Level I/Trauma Center/Burn Cen), 325 Ninth Avenue, Box 359717, Zip 98104–2499; tel. 206/731–3000 **A**1 3 5 7 8 9 10 **F**2 4 12 13 14 15 17 21 22 23 27 28 29 31 32 33 34 37 38 39 43 44 47 48 50 52 53 55 57 58 60 61 62 63 64 65 66 67 68 69 70 71 72 73 74 75 76 77 78 81 82 84 85 87 88 93 94 95 96 106 107 108 109 110 **P**6
Primary Contact: David E. Jaffe, Executive Director
COO: Johnese Spisso, Chief Operating Officer
CFO: Lori J. Mitchell, Chief Financial Officer
CMO: Scott Barnhart, M.D., Medical Director
CIO: Tom Martin, Director Systems Development and Medical Information Services
CHR: Janelle Browne, Executive Director Health Sciences and Human Resources
Web address: www.washington.edu/medical/hmc/index.html

| 13 | 49 | 367 | 19087 | 359 | 355669 | 0 | 477407 | 226653 | 4195 |

⊠ **HIGHLINE MEDICAL CENTER**, (Formerly Highline Community Hospital), 16251 Sylvester Road S.W., Zip 98166–3052; tel. 206/244–9970, (Includes HIGHLINE SPECIALTY CENTER, 12844 MILITARY ROAD FORK, TUKWILA, ZIP 98168; MARK BENEDUM, ADMINISTRATOR), (Total facility includes 30 beds in nursing home-type unit) **A**1 2 9 10 **F**3 11 33 34 36 51 55 58 59 60 63 68 71 81 82 84 92 93 108
Primary Contact: Paul Tucker, Administrator
CFO: Don Halterman, Administrator Finance and Chief Financial Officer

| 23 | 10 | 177 | 8982 | 129 | 235554 | 1379 | — | — | 958 |

⊠ **KINDRED HOSPITAL SEATTLE**, 10560 Fifth Avenue N.E., Zip 98125–0977; tel. 206/364–2050, (Nonreporting) **A**1 9 10 **S** Kindred Healthcare, Louisville, KY
Primary Contact: Cheryl Payseno, Chief Executive Officer
CFO: Gregg Terreson, Assistant Administrator Finance and Chief Financial Officer
Web address: www.kindredhealthcare.com

| 33 | 10 | 42 | — | — | — | — | — | — | — |

⊠ △ **NORTHWEST HOSPITAL**, 1550 North 115th Street, Zip 98133–0806; tel. 206/364–0500 **A**1 2 3 5 7 9 10 **F**2 9 11 12 14 21 22 23 26 27 28 29 30 31 33 34 37 38 41 42 43 44 46 47 48 52 55 56 57 58 59 60 61 62 63 65 68 69 70 71 76 78 81 82 84 88 94 95 96 108 109 110 **P**6 7
Primary Contact: C. W. Schneider, President and Chief Executive Officer
COO: Chris Roth, Vice President Operations
CFO: Robert Steigmeyer, Chief Financial Officer
CMO: Greg Schroedl, M.D., Vice President Medical and Chief Quality Officer
CIO: Michael Krouse, Vice President Administrative Services
Web address: www.nwhospital.org

| 23 | 10 | 187 | 9478 | 111 | — | — | — | — | 1594 |

WA

Hospital, Address, Telephone, Approval, Facility, and Physician Codes, Health Care System	Classi-fication Codes		Utilization Data					Expense (thousands) of dollars		
★ American Hospital Association (AHA) membership □ Joint Commission on Accreditation of Healthcare Organizations (JCAHO) accreditation ○ American Osteopathic Association (AOA) accreditation △ Commission on Accreditation of Rehabilitation Facilities (CARF) accreditation	Control	Service	Staffed Beds	Admissions	Census	Outpatient Visits	Births	Total	Payroll	Personnel
□ **REGIONAL HOSPITAL FOR RESPIRATORY AND COMPLEX CARE**, 12844 Military Road South, Zip 98168–9981; tel. 206/248–4548, (Nonreporting) **A**1 10 Primary Contact: James C. Cannon, Administrator and Chief Executive Officer Web address: www.regionalhospital.org	23	80	27	—	—	—	—	—	—	—
□ **SCHICK SHADEL HOSPITAL**, 12101 Ambaum Boulevard S.W., Zip 98146–2699, Mailing Address: Box 48149, Zip 98148–0149; tel. 206/244–8100, (Nonreporting) **A**1 9 10 Primary Contact: Thomas B. Bullen, Administrator Web address: www.schick–shadel.com	33	82	48	—	—	—	—	—	—	—
□ **SEATTLE CANCER CARE ALLIANCE**, 825 Eastlake Avenue East, Zip 98109, Mailing Address: P.O. Box 19023, Zip 98109–1023; tel. 206/288–1400 **A**1 2 9 10 **F**12 22 23 61 79 94 Primary Contact: Fred R. Appelbaum, M.D., Executive Director Web address: www.seattlecca.org	23	10	18	368	13	38149	0	127096	26155	530
⊠ **SWEDISH HEALTH SERVICES**, 747 Broadway Avenue, Zip 98122–4307; tel. 206/386–6000, (Includes SWEDISH MEDICAL CENTER–BALLARD, 5300 Tallman Avenue N.W., Zip 98107–3932; tel. 206/782–2700; SWEDISH MEDICAL CENTER–FIRST HILL, 747 Broadway Avenue, tel. 206/386–6000), (Total facility includes 30 beds in nursing home–type unit) **A**1 2 3 5 9 10 **F**2 3 4 6 9 10 11 12 14 15 16 17 18 19 20 21 22 23 29 30 31 32 33 35 36 37 38 39 40 43 44 45 46 47 48 49 50 51 52 53 55 56 57 58 59 60 61 62 63 64 65 66 67 68 69 70 73 79 80 81 82 83 84 85 86 87 88 89 90 92 93 94 95 96 98 99 101 104 105 106 108 110 **P**6 Primary Contact: Richard H. Peterson, President and Chief Executive Officer COO: Calvin K. Knight, Chief Operating Officer CFO: Ronald K. Sperling, Chief Financial Officer CMO: Nancy Auer, M.D., Chief Medical Officer CIO: Chris Leininger, M.D., Chief Information Officer Web address: www.swedish.org	23	10	688	34075	430	439975	7344	622368	251893	5226
⊠ △ **SWEDISH MEDICAL CENTER–PROVIDENCE CAMPUS**, 500 17th Avenue, Zip 98122–5711; tel. 206/320–2000 **A**1 2 3 5 7 9 10 **F**9 10 12 14 15 17 19 21 22 23 29 33 37 38 39 45 46 47 48 49 50 52 57 58 60 61 62 63 64 65 66 68 69 70 71 73 74 75 76 77 78 81 82 83 84 88 92 93 96 108 110 Primary Contact: Marcel C. Loh, Chief Operating Officer CFO: Ronald K. Sperling, Chief Financial Officer Web address: www.swedish.org	23	10	202	8162	117	109345	0	156865	67062	1043
⊠ △ **UNIVERSITY OF WASHINGTON MEDICAL CENTER**, 1959 Northeast Pacific Street, Box 356151, Zip 98195–6151; tel. 206/598–3300 **A**1 2 3 5 7 8 9 10 **F**2 7 9 10 11 12 14 15 17 19 22 23 29 32 33 35 37 38 39 40 42 44 45 46 47 48 49 50 52 53 55 56 57 58 59 60 61 62 63 64 65 66 68 69 70 71 73 74 75 76 77 79 80 81 82 84 85 86 87 88 90 92 94 95 96 99 100 101 102 103 104 105 107 108 109 110 **P**6 Primary Contact: Kathleen Sellick, Executive Director COO: Preston M. Simmons, Senior Operations Officer CFO: Paul Ishizuka, Associate Executive Director and Chief Financial Officer CMO: Ed Walker, M.D., Medical Director CIO: Tom Martin, Director Medical Information Systems CHR: Mason Hudson, Assistant Director Human Resources Web address: www.washington.edu/medical	12	10	390	17919	323	392709	1703	516963	207480	3726
⊠ △ **VETERANS AFFAIRS PUGET SOUND HEALTH CARE SYSTEM**, 1660 South Columbian Way, Zip 98108–1597; tel. 206/762–1010, (Includes VETERANS AFFAIRS PUGET SOUND HEALTH CARE SYSTEM–AMERICAN LAKE DIVISION, Tacoma, Zip 98493; tel. 253/582–8440), (Total facility includes 131 beds in nursing home–type unit) (Nonreporting) **A**1 2 3 5 7 8 **S** Department of Veterans Affairs, Washington, DC Primary Contact: Timothy B. Williams, Director CFO: Kenneth J. Hudson, Chief Financial Officer CMO: Gordon Starkebaum, M.D., Chief of Staff CIO: Glenn Zwinger, Manager Information Systems Services Web address: www.va.gov/sta/guide/home.asp	45	10	512	—	—	—	—	—	—	—
⊠ △ **VIRGINIA MASON MEDICAL CENTER**, 1100 Ninth Avenue, Zip 98101–2756, Mailing Address: P.O. Box 900, Zip 98111–0900; tel. 206/223–6600, (Total facility includes 35 beds in nursing home–type unit) **A**1 2 3 5 7 9 10 **F**1 2 10 12 15 16 17 18 19 20 21 22 23 26 27 28 29 30 33 37 40 42 44 48 49 50 51 52 53 55 57 58 60 61 62 63 65 68 69 70 73 76 77 79 80 81 82 83 84 85 86 87 88 89 90 92 93 94 95 96 99 101 104 105 106 107 108 109 110 **P**6 Primary Contact: J. Michael Rona, President CFO: Ned Bongstrom, Chief Financial Officer Web address: www.vmmc.org	23	10	307	16412	226	933969	0	572495	290203	4072
□ **WEST SEATTLE PSYCHIATRIC HOSPITAL**, 2600 S.W. Holden Street, Zip 98126; tel. 206/933–7199, (Nonreporting) **A**1 10 Primary Contact: David Johnson, Chief Executive Officer	23	22	40	—	—	—	—	—	—	—
SEDRO–WOOLLEY—Skagit County										
⊠ **UNITED GENERAL HOSPITAL**, 2000 Hospital Drive, Zip 98284; tel. 360/856–6021, (Nonreporting) **A**1 9 10 18 Primary Contact: Greg Reed, Chief Executive Officer CFO: Michael W. Bonthuis, Chief Financial Officer CMO: Daryl Vogel, M.D., Chief Medical Officer CHR: Tracie Skrinde, Director Human Resources Web address: www.unitedgeneral.org	16	10	20	—	—	—	—	—	—	—

WA

Hospital, Address, Telephone, Approval, Facility, and Physician Codes, Health Care System	Classi-fication Codes		Utilization Data					Expense (thousands) of dollars		
	Control	Service	Staffed Beds	Admissions	Census	Outpatient Visits	Births	Total	Payroll	Personnel

★ American Hospital Association (AHA) membership
□ Joint Commission on Accreditation of Healthcare Organizations (JCAHO) accreditation
○ American Osteopathic Association (AOA) accreditation
△ Commission on Accreditation of Rehabilitation Facilities (CARF) accreditation

SHELTON—Mason County

☒ **MASON GENERAL HOSPITAL**, 901 Mountain View Drive, Building 1, Zip 98584–1668, Mailing Address: P.O. Box 1668, Zip 98584–1668; tel. 360/426–1611, (Nonreporting) **A**1 9 10 18
Primary Contact: G. Robert Appel, Chief Executive Officer
COO: Diane Stillman, Chief Operating Officer
CFO: Eric Moll, Financial Director
CIO: Brian Conklin, Information Systems Director
CHR: Claudia Hawley, Director Human Resources
Web address: www.masongeneral.com

| | 16 | 10 | 56 | — | — | — | — | — | — | — |

SOUTH BEND—Pacific County

WILLAPA HARBOR HOSPITAL, 800 Alder Street, Zip 98586–0438, Mailing Address: P.O. Box 438, Zip 98586–0438; tel. 360/875–4502 **A**9 10 18 **F**27 28 33 34 63 81 84 85 88 97
Primary Contact: Carole Halsan, Chief Executive Officer
Web address: www.willapaharborhospital.com

| | 13 | 10 | 12 | 438 | 4 | 20253 | 0 | 8478 | 4318 | — |

SPOKANE—Spokane County

☒ **DEACONESS MEDICAL CENTER–SPOKANE**, 800 West Fifth Avenue, Zip 99204–2803, Mailing Address: P.O. Box 248, Zip 99210–0248; tel. 509/458–5800, (Nonreporting) **A**1 2 3 5 9 10 12 **S** Empire Health Services, Spokane, WA
Primary Contact: Michael T. Liepman, Chief Operating Officer
CFO: Garman E. Lutz, Chief Financial Officer
CIO: Paul Fitzpatrick, Manager Information Technology
Web address: www.deaconess–spokane.org

| | 23 | 10 | 287 | | | | | | | |

☒ **HOLY FAMILY HOSPITAL**, North 5633 Lidgerwood Avenue, Zip 99208–2533; tel. 509/482–0111 **A**1 2 9 10 **F**2 9 11 12 14 15 17 21 22 23 26 27 28 29 31 32 33 34 36 37 38 39 41 44 45 46 47 48 49 50 52 53 55 57 58 59 60 61 62 63 64 65 66 69 70 73 79 80 81 82 84 85 88 92 93 94 95 96 106 107 108 109 110 **P**7 **S** Providence Services, Spokane, WA
Primary Contact: Thomas Corley, President
CFO: Kevin Walstrom, Chief Financial Officer
CMO: Kathleen Meyer, M.D., President
CIO: Mark Vogelsang, Director Information Services
CHR: Kellie Sheldon, Vice President Human Resources
Web address: www.holy–family.org

| | 21 | 10 | 198 | 9060 | 93 | 112930 | 1075 | 102092 | 41484 | 787 |

☒ **SACRED HEART MEDICAL CENTER**, 101 West Eighth Avenue, Zip 99204–2364, Mailing Address: P.O. Box 2555, Zip 99220–2555; tel. 509/474–3040 **A**1 2 3 5 9 10 **F**2 9 11 12 14 15 16 17 18 19 20 21 22 23 26 27 33 34 37 40 41 44 46 52 53 55 56 57 58 59 61 62 63 64 65 67 71 72 73 75 76 77 78 81 82 83 84 85 86 87 88 94 100 101 102 103 108 109 110 **P**6 **S** Providence Services, Spokane, WA
Primary Contact: Ryland P. Davis, Chief Executive Officer
CFO: Michael A. Banks, Chief Financial Officer
CMO: G Thomas Miller, M.D., Vice President Medical Affairs
CHR: Patrick Clary, Director Human Resources
Web address: www.shmc.org

| | 21 | 10 | 610 | 25641 | 364 | 112733 | 2148 | 402929 | 168667 | 2411 |

□ **SHRINERS HOSPITALS FOR CHILDREN–SPOKANE**, 911 West Fifth Avenue, Zip 99204–2901, Mailing Address: P.O. Box 2472, Zip 99210–2472; tel. 509/455–7844 **A**1 **F**37 45 52 53 57 58 62 63 64 65 69 94 95 108 **S** Shriners Hospitals for Children, Tampa, FL
Primary Contact: Charles R. Young, Administrator
Web address: www.shrinershq.org

| | 23 | 57 | 30 | 778 | 9 | 4923 | 0 | — | — | 156 |

☒ △ **ST. LUKE'S REHABILITATION INSTITUTE**, 711 South Cowley Street, Zip 99202–1388; tel. 509/838–4771 **A**1 7 9 10 **F**21 22 26 27 28 34 37 45 46 47 52 53 57 58 60 62 65 66 68 69 90 94 95 96 108
Primary Contact: Thomas M. Fritz, Administrator
COO: Gary J. Smith, Ph.D., Chief Operating Officer
CFO: John D. Craig, Chief Financial Officer
CMO: Vivian Moise, M.D., Interim Chief Medical Director
CIO: Fred Galusha, Chief Information Officer
CHR: Alan Wagner, Director Human Resources
Web address: www.stlukesrehab.org

| | 23 | 46 | 80 | 1460 | 55 | 66500 | 0 | 27543 | 15491 | 426 |

☒ **VALLEY HOSPITAL AND MEDICAL CENTER**, 12606 East Mission Avenue, Zip 99216–1090; tel. 509/924–6650, (Nonreporting) **A**1 2 9 10 12 13 **S** Empire Health Services, Spokane, WA
Primary Contact: Keith J. Baldwin, Chief Operating Officer
Web address: www.valleyhospital.org

| | 23 | 10 | 93 | — | — | — | — | — | — | — |

☒ **VETERANS AFFAIRS MEDICAL CENTER**, North 4815 Assembly Street, Zip 99205–6197; tel. 509/434–7000, (Total facility includes 40 beds in nursing home–type unit) (Nonreporting) **A**1 **S** Department of Veterans Affairs, Washington, DC
Primary Contact: Joseph M. Manley, Director
COO: Ken Eigen, Chief Engineering and Technology
CFO: Mark Morrissey, Chief Financial Officer
CMO: Jacy Ryan, M.D., Chief Medical Service
CHR: Thomas Williams, Chief Human Resources Management Service
Web address: www.spokane.med.va.gov

| | 45 | 10 | 92 | — | — | — | — | — | — | — |

WA

Hospital, Address, Telephone, Approval, Facility, and Physician Codes, Health Care System	Classi-fication Codes		Utilization Data					Expense (thousands) of dollars		
★ American Hospital Association (AHA) membership □ Joint Commission on Accreditation of Healthcare Organizations (JCAHO) accreditation ○ American Osteopathic Association (AOA) accreditation △ Commission on Accreditation of Rehabilitation Facilities (CARF) accreditation	Control	Service	Staffed Beds	Admissions	Census	Outpatient Visits	Births	Total	Payroll	Personnel

SUNNYSIDE—Yakima County

★ ○ **SUNNYSIDE COMMUNITY HOSPITAL**, 1016 Tacoma Avenue, Zip 98944–0719, Mailing Address: P.O. Box 719, Zip 98944–0719; tel. 509/837–1500, (Nonreporting) **A**2 9 10 11 18 **S** Brim Healthcare, Inc., Brentwood, TN
Primary Contact: Jon D. Smiley, Chief Executive Officer
CFO: Jim Schlenker, Chief Financial Officer
CMO: Coke R. Smith, M.D., Chief of Staff
CIO: Salvador Betancourt, Information Systems Manager
CHR: Lisa Gray, Director Human Resources
Web address: www.sunnysidehospital.com
→ 33 10 25 — — — — — — — —

TACOMA—Pierce County

ALLENMORE HOSPITAL See Tacoma General Hospital

☒ **MADIGAN ARMY MEDICAL CENTER**, Fitzsimmons Drive, Building 9040, Zip 98431–1100; tel. 253/968–1110, (Nonreporting) **A**1 2 3 5 9 **S** Department of the Army, Office of the Surgeon General, Falls Church, VA
Primary Contact: Brigadier General Michael A. Dunn, M.D., Commanding General
CFO: Lieutenant Colonel Michael R. Cook, Chief Resource Management
CMO: Colonel George McClure, Deputy Commander for Clinical Services
CIO: Lieutenant Colonel Craig Anderson, Chief Information Management
CHR: David Aiken, Chief Human Resources Officer
Web address: www.mamc.amedd.army.mil
→ 42 10 169 — — — — — — — —

□ **MARY BRIDGE CHILDREN'S HOSPITAL AND HEALTH CENTER**, 317 Martin Luther King Jr. Way, Zip 98405–0299, Mailing Address: Box 5299, Zip 98405–0299; tel. 253/403–1400, (Nonreporting) **A**1 3 5 9 10 **S** MultiCare Health System, Tacoma, WA
Primary Contact: Diane Cecchettini, President and Chief Executive Officer
Web address: www.multicare.org
→ 23 50 68 — — — — — — — —

★ **ST. CLARE HOSPITAL**, 11315 Bridgeport Way S.W., Zip 98499–3004, Mailing Address: P.O. Box 99998, Lakewood, Zip 98499–0998; tel. 253/588–1711 **A**2 9 10 **F**2 10 12 14 21 22 23 24 27 28 29 31 33 35 37 38 39 46 48 52 55 58 60 61 62 63 64 65 66 69 81 82 84 87 88 92 93 94 96 98 108 **P**6 **S** Catholic Health Initiatives, Denver, CO
Primary Contact: Brooks Sutton, R.N., Chief Operating Officer
COO: Brooks Sutton, R.N., Chief Operating Officer
CFO: Mike Fitzgerald, Chief Financial Officer
CMO: Everett Newcomb, D.O., Senior Vice President Medical Affairs
CIO: Bruce Elkington, Vice President Information Technology
CHR: David Lawson, Vice President Human Resources
Web address: www.fhshealth.org
→ 21 10 106 5779 63 59519 0 65657 31574 486

☒ △ **ST. JOSEPH MEDICAL CENTER**, 1717 South J Street, Zip 98405–3004, Mailing Address: P.O. Box 2197, Zip 98401–2197; tel. 253/426–4101 **A**1 2 7 9 10 **F**2 10 11 12 13 14 15 17 19 21 22 23 24 27 28 29 30 31 33 34 35 36 37 38 39 46 47 48 49 52 53 55 56 57 58 59 60 61 62 63 64 65 66 68 69 71 72 75 77 81 82 84 85 87 88 92 94 96 98 99 106 108 109 **P**6 **S** Catholic Health Initiatives, Denver, CO
Primary Contact: June C. Bowman, R.N., Chief Operating Officer and Nurse Executive
COO: June C. Bowman, R.N., Chief Operating Officer and Nurse Executive
CFO: Mike Fitzgerald, Chief Financial Officer
CMO: Everett Newcomb, D.O., Senior Vice President Medical Affairs
CIO: Bruce Elkington, Vice President Information Technology
CHR: David Lawson, Vice President Human Resources
Web address: www.fhshealth.org
→ 21 10 290 20445 231 351465 3557 298402 127905 2481

☒ **TACOMA GENERAL HOSPITAL**, 315 Martin Luther King Jr. Way, Zip 98405–0299, Mailing Address: P.O. Box 5299, Zip 98415–0299; tel. 253/403–1000, (Includes ALLENMORE HOSPITAL, South 19th and Union Avenue, Zip 98405, Mailing Address: P.O. Box 11414, Zip 98411–0414; tel. 253/403–2323), (Nonreporting) **A**1 3 5 9 10 **S** MultiCare Health System, Tacoma, WA
Primary Contact: Diane Cecchettini, President and Chief Executive Officer
COO: George J. Brown, M.D., Vice President Acute Care Service and Facilities
CFO: Vince Schmitz, Vice President and Chief Financial Officer
CMO: W Richard Stubbs, M.D., Vice President Medical Affairs
CIO: Carroll Wilt, Vice President and Chief Information Officer
CHR: Sarah Horsman, ViceHuman Resources
Web address: www.multicare.org
→ 23 10 308 — — — — — — — —

VETERANS AFFAIRS PUGET SOUND HEALTH CARE SYSTEM–AMERICAN LAKE DIVISION See Veterans Affairs Puget Sound Health Care System, Seattle

□ **WESTERN STATE HOSPITAL**, 9601 Steilacoom Boulevard S.W., Zip 98498–7213; tel. 253/582–8900 **A**1 9 10 **F**22 29 32 44 45 48 57 58 65 66 71 74 76 94 96 108 110
Primary Contact: Andrew J. Phillips, Ed.D., Chief Executive Officer
Web address: www.dshs.wa.gov/mentalhealth/wsh.shtml
→ 12 22 776 1335 775 0 0 — — — —

Many Facility Codes have changed. Please refer to the AHA Guide Code Chart. © 2005 AHA Guide

Hospital, Address, Telephone, Approval, Facility, and Physician Codes, Health Care System	Classi-fication Codes		Utilization Data					Expense (thousands) of dollars		
★ American Hospital Association (AHA) membership □ Joint Commission on Accreditation of Healthcare Organizations (JCAHO) accreditation ○ American Osteopathic Association (AOA) accreditation △ Commission on Accreditation of Rehabilitation Facilities (CARF) accreditation	Control	Service	Staffed Beds	Admissions	Census	Outpatient Visits	Births	Total	Payroll	Personnel

TONASKET—Okanogan County

★ **NORTH VALLEY HOSPITAL**, 203 South Western Avenue, Zip 98855–8803; tel. 509/486–2151, (Total facility includes 70 beds in nursing home–type unit) (Nonreporting) **A**9 10 18 20
Primary Contact: Warner H. Bartleson, Administrator
CFO: Bomi Bharucha, Chief Financial Officer
CMO: Navin Paucholy, M.D., Chief Medical Staff
CIO: Peggy Weddle, Information Systems Manager
CHR: Jan Gonzales, Director Human Resources
Web address: www.nvhospital.org

| 16 | 10 | 95 | — | — | — | — | — | — | — |

TOPPENISH—Yakima County

✠ **TOPPENISH COMMUNITY HOSPITAL**, 502 West Fourth Avenue, Zip 98948–0672, Mailing Address: P.O. Box 672, Zip 98948–0672; tel. 509/865–3105 **A**1 9 10 **F**9 33 34 52 55 59 63 66 81 88 96 109 **S** Health Management Associates, Naples, FL
Primary Contact: Monte Bostwick, Administrator and Chief Operating Officer
COO: Monte Bostwick, Administrator and Chief Operating Officer
CFO: Caroline Wong, Chief Financial Officer
CHR: Stefanie Durand, Director Human Resources
Web address: www.hma–corp.com

| 33 | 10 | 50 | 2079 | 14 | 0 | 547 | 13535 | 6791 | 139 |

VANCOUVER—Clark County

✠ △ **SOUTHWEST WASHINGTON MEDICAL CENTER**, 400 N.E. Mother Joseph Place, Zip 98664–3200, Mailing Address: P.O. Box 1600, Zip 98668–1600; tel. 360/256–2000, (Includes VANCOUVER MEMORIAL CAMPUS, 3400 Main Street, Zip 98663; tel. 206/696–5000) **A**1 2 3 5 7 9 10 **F**2 9 10 11 12 14 15 17 19 21 22 23 26 27 28 29 33 34 35 36 37 38 40 42 46 47 48 49 50 51 52 53 55 57 58 59 60 61 62 63 64 65 66 68 69 70 71 72 73 74 75 76 77 78 79 81 82 83 84 85 86 88 94 95 96 106 107 108 109 110 **P**5 6
Primary Contact: Joseph M. Kortum, President and Chief Executive Officer
COO: Rainy Atkins, Chief Operating Officer
CFO: Eugene G. Johnson, Chief Financial Officer
CMO: Gilbert Rodriguez, M.D., Chief Medical Officer
CIO: Kerry Craig, Chief Information Officer
CHR: Cheri Meyerhofer, vice President Human Resources
Web address: www.swmedctr.com

| 23 | 10 | 356 | 22104 | 237 | 245772 | 4870 | 313818 | 135234 | 2583 |

WALLA WALLA—Walla Walla County

✠ **JONATHAN M. WAINWRIGHT MEMORIAL VA MEDICAL CENTER**, 77 Wainwright Drive, Zip 99362–3994; tel. 509/525–5200, (Total facility includes 30 beds in nursing home–type unit) **A**1 **F**2 3 4 9 12 22 28 32 36 38 39 48 50 52 55 58 66 70 71 72 77 88 92 93 94 96 108 109 **P**6 **S** Department of Veterans Affairs, Washington, DC
Primary Contact: Bruce E. Stewart, Acting Director
COO: Bruce E. Stewart, Acting Director
CFO: Ron Preszler, Business Officer Manager
CMO: Donald L. Rowberg, Chief of Staff
CIO: Gary Ramer, Information Management Manager
Web address: www.va.gov/sta/guide/home.asp

| 45 | 10 | 66 | 914 | 28 | 91101 | 0 | — | — | 344 |

✠ △ **ST. MARY MEDICAL CENTER**, 401 West Poplar Street, Zip 99362–1477, Mailing Address: Box 1477, Zip 99362–1477; tel. 509/525–3320 **A**1 2 7 9 10 19 **F**2 9 11 12 14 15 21 22 23 27 33 34 37 38 44 49 50 51 52 55 59 60 61 62 63 64 68 69 79 81 84 86 88 93 94 107 108 109 110 **P**6 **S** Providence Services, Spokane, WA
Primary Contact: John A. Isely, President
CFO: Michael Parenteau, Vice President Finance
Web address: www.smmc.com

| 21 | 10 | 103 | 4628 | 54 | 104974 | 628 | 77001 | 35807 | 806 |

STATE PENITENTIARY HOSPITAL, Mailing Address: Box 520, Zip 99362; tel. 509/525–3610, (Nonreporting)
Primary Contact: Pat Rima, Health Care Manager

| 12 | 11 | 36 | — | — | — | — | — | — | — |

✠ **WALLA WALLA GENERAL HOSPITAL**, 1025 South Second Avenue, Zip 99362–1398, Mailing Address: P.O. Box 1398, Zip 99362–1398; tel. 509/525–0480, (Nonreporting) **A**1 2 9 10 **S** Adventist Health, Roseville, CA
Primary Contact: Morre Dean, President and Chief Executive Officer
CFO: Duane Meidinger, Vice President Finance
CIO: Gary Dietz, Director Information Systems
Web address: www.wwgh.com

| 23 | 10 | 72 | — | — | — | — | — | — | — |

WENATCHEE—Chelan County

✠ **CENTRAL WASHINGTON HOSPITAL**, 1201 South Miller Street, Zip 98801–1948, Mailing Address: P.O. Box 1887, Zip 98807–1887; tel. 509/662–1511 **A**1 9 10 19 **F**2 11 12 14 15 17 19 21 23 27 28 29 32 33 34 36 37 40 46 47 48 49 51 52 53 54 55 57 58 59 60 61 62 63 64 65 66 69 70 81 84 85 88 90 92 94 108 109 110 **P**6
Primary Contact: John T. Evans, Jr, President and Chief Executive Officer
CFO: Steven R. Jacobs, Chief Financial Officer
CIO: Darryl Higa, Chief Information Officer
CHR: Jack Powers, Director Human Resources
Web address: www.cwhs.com

| 23 | 10 | 159 | 8857 | 86 | 152578 | 1236 | 126040 | 56309 | 998 |

WA

Hospital, Address, Telephone, Approval, Facility, and Physician Codes, Health Care System	Classi-fication Codes		Utilization Data					Expense (thousands) of dollars		
★ American Hospital Association (AHA) membership □ Joint Commission on Accreditation of Healthcare Organizations (JCAHO) accreditation ○ American Osteopathic Association (AOA) accreditation △ Commission on Accreditation of Rehabilitation Facilities (CARF) accreditation	Control	Service	Staffed Beds	Admissions	Census	Outpatient Visits	Births	Total	Payroll	Personnel

△ **WENATCHEE VALLEY HOSPITAL**, 820 North Chelan Street, Zip 98807; tel. 509/663–8711, (Nonreporting) **A**7 10 Primary Contact: David Weber, Chief Executive Officer	33	49	21	—	—	—	—	—	—	—
WHITE SALMON—Klickitat County										
SKYLINE HOSPITAL, 211 Skyline Drive, Zip 98672–0099, Mailing Address: P.O. Box 99, Zip 98672–0099; tel. 509/493–1101 **A**9 10 18 **F**6 11 12 21 29 33 46 55 58 59 63 69 82 95 Primary Contact: Michael J. Madden, Superintendent and Chief Executive Officer Web address: www.skylinehospital.com	15	10	32	592	5	17888	—		—	111
YAKIMA—Yakima County										
□ △ **YAKIMA REGIONAL MEDICAL AND HEART CENTER**, 110 South Ninth Avenue, Zip 98902–3397; tel. 509/575–5000, (Total facility includes 12 beds in nursing home–type unit) **A**1 2 7 9 10 **F**12 14 21 22 26 27 28 29 30 33 34 36 37 38 39 41 46 47 48 49 50 51 52 55 57 58 60 61 62 63 65 66 68 69 70 81 82 84 86 87 88 92 93 94 96 107 108 109 110 **P**6 **S** Health Management Associates, Naples, FL Primary Contact: Timothy Trottier, Chief Executive Officer	33	10	169	6514	76	—	0	82610	35799	708
⊠ **YAKIMA VALLEY MEMORIAL HOSPITAL**, 2811 Tieton Drive, Zip 98902–3761; tel. 509/575–8000 **A**1 2 9 10 **F**2 9 11 12 21 22 23 24 26 27 28 29 33 34 36 46 47 48 49 51 52 53 55 56 57 58 59 60 61 62 63 65 66 69 71 73 74 75 76 77 81 82 87 88 90 94 95 96 106 108 109 110 **P**7 Primary Contact: Richard W. Linneweh, Jr, President and Chief Executive Officer COO: Russ Myers, Vice President and Chief Operating Officer CFO: John G. Vornbrock, Senior Vice President and Chief Financial Officer CMO: Jan Lange, M.D., Medical Director Performance Improvement CIO: James Aberle, Vice President and Chief Information Officer and Support Services CHR: Kathy Franz, Director Human Resources Web address: www.yakimamemorialhospital.org	23	10	218	10487	118	260497	2912		—	1285

WA

WEST VIRGINIA

Hospital, Address, Telephone, Approval, Facility, and Physician Codes, Health Care System	Classi-fication Codes		Utilization Data					Expense (thousands) of dollars		
★ American Hospital Association (AHA) membership □ Joint Commission on Accreditation of Healthcare Organizations (JCAHO) accreditation ○ American Osteopathic Association (AOA) accreditation △ Commission on Accreditation of Rehabilitation Facilities (CARF) accreditation	Control	Service	Staffed Beds	Admissions	Census	Outpatient Visits	Births	Total	Payroll	Personnel

BECKLEY—Raleigh County

⊠ **BECKLEY APPALACHIAN REGIONAL HOSPITAL**, 306 Stanaford Road, Zip 25801–3142; tel. 304/255–3000 **A**1 9 10 **F**2 9 12 14 15 21 22 23 26 27 28 29 31 32 33 35 37 39 46 47 48 50 51 52 55 57 58 60 61 62 63 64 65 66 68 69 70 71 72 73 74 75 76 81 82 85 87 88 92 93 94 108 **P**6 **S** Appalachian Regional Healthcare, Lexington, KY Primary Contact: Rocco K. Massey, Community Chief Executive Officer CFO: Dave Jones, Chief Financial Officer CMO: Syed Siddiqi, M.D., Chief of Staff CHR: Sue Thomas, Human Resource Manager Web address: www.arh.org	23	10	173	7901	116	75435	0	55862	22334	651
⊠ **RALEIGH GENERAL HOSPITAL**, 1710 Harper Road, Zip 25801–3397; tel. 304/256–4100 **A**1 9 10 13 19 **F**2 11 12 14 15 21 22 27 28 29 33 34 38 46 48 49 52 55 56 58 59 61 62 63 64 66 69 81 82 87 88 94 95 96 108 109 **S** HCA, Nashville, TN Primary Contact: Karen L. Bowling, Chief Executive Officer COO: Joseph G. Koch, Vice President and Chief Operating Officer CFO: Renee Cross, Vice President and Chief Financial Officer CIO: Lou Worrell, Director Information Systems CHR: Debbie Christian, Director Human Resources Web address: www.raleighgeneral.com	33	10	225	11537	141	104256	1662	87193	35666	875
⊠ **VETERANS AFFAIRS MEDICAL CENTER**, 200 Veterans Avenue, Zip 25801–6499; tel. 304/255–2121 **A**1 **F**2 4 6 21 22 23 29 31 32 36 37 38 40 41 44 45 47 48 50 51 52 55 58 61 62 63 65 66 69 70 73 74 75 76 77 81 82 87 88 92 94 96 106 107 108 109 110 **P**6 **S** Department of Veterans Affairs, Washington, DC Primary Contact: Gerard P. Husson, Director CFO: G Darrell Harvey, Chief Fiscal Services Web address: www.va.gov/sta/guide/home.asp	45	10	90	1630	68	126828	0	62862	30135	530

BERKELEY SPRINGS—Morgan County

★ **MORGAN COUNTY WAR MEMORIAL HOSPITAL**, 109 War Memorial Drive, Zip 25411–1718; tel. 304/258–1234, (Total facility includes 16 beds in nursing home–type unit) **A**9 10 18 **F**2 12 21 27 28 29 33 37 46 47 48 51 52 60 63 65 69 81 84 85 88 92 94 96 97 106 108 110 **P**6 **S** Valley Health System, Winchester, VA Primary Contact: John H. Borg, Administrator CFO: David Applewood, Chief Financial Officer and Compliance Officer CIO: Janet Fagan, Data Processing Director CHR: Helen Miller, Human Resources Department Manager Web address: www.warmemorialhospital.com	13	10	41	634	26	20013	0	11564	4569	127

BLUEFIELD—Mercer County

⊠ **BLUEFIELD REGIONAL MEDICAL CENTER**, 500 Cherry Street, Zip 24701–3390; tel. 304/327–1100, (Total facility includes 25 beds in nursing home–type unit) **A**1 9 10 19 **F**11 12 14 15 21 22 23 26 27 28 29 33 34 38 44 45 46 48 49 51 52 53 55 57 58 59 60 61 62 63 65 66 69 81 82 87 88 92 93 94 96 98 106 107 108 109 110 **P**8 Primary Contact: Steven A. Caywood, Interim Chief Executive Officer CFO: Lynn Whitteker, Vice President CIO: Dinah Farmer, Director Information Services CHR: Sandee Cheynet, Vice President Administrative Services Web address: www.bluefield.org	23	10	265	7315	106	138895	734	93327	39003	942
⊠ **ST. LUKE'S HOSPITAL**, 1333 Southview Drive, Zip 24701–4399, Mailing Address: P.O. Box 1190, Zip 24701–1190; tel. 304/327–2900 **A**1 9 10 **F**9 12 21 26 27 28 33 40 46 48 55 58 62 63 64 69 81 82 84 87 88 94 96 97 108 Primary Contact: James F. Valeyko, Interim Chief Executive Officer CFO: Keith St John, Controller Web address: www.slhonline.org	23	10	52	2012	24	32198	0	27325	11160	277

BUCKEYE—Pocahontas County

★ **POCAHONTAS MEMORIAL HOSPITAL**, Mailing Address: Rural Route 2, Box 52 W, Zip 24924; tel. 304/799–7400 **A**9 10 18 20 **F**2 9 22 26 27 28 33 44 46 47 48 51 52 65 66 69 81 88 94 96 97 107 Primary Contact: Donald Muhlenthaler, FACHE, Administrator and Chief Executive Officer CFO: Greg Curry, Chief Accountant CHR: Jane Gordon, Executive Secretary Web address: www.wvha.com/web/pmh/index.htm	13	10	25	910	15	20675	0	5355	2267	80

Hospital, Address, Telephone, Approval, Facility, and Physician Codes, Health Care System	Classi-fication Codes		Utilization Data					Expense (thousands) of dollars		
	Control	Service	Staffed Beds	Admissions	Census	Outpatient Visits	Births	Total	Payroll	Personnel

★ American Hospital Association (AHA) membership
□ Joint Commission on Accreditation of Healthcare Organizations (JCAHO) accreditation
○ American Osteopathic Association (AOA) accreditation
△ Commission on Accreditation of Rehabilitation Facilities (CARF) accreditation

BUCKHANNON—Upshur County

✠ **ST. JOSEPH'S HOSPITAL OF BUCKHANNON**, 1 Amalia Drive, Zip 26201–2222; tel. 304/473–2000, (Total facility includes 16 beds in nursing home–type unit) **A**1 9 10 **F**2 9 11 12 21 22 23 26 27 28 29 32 33 34 35 36 37 38 39 46 47 48 51 52 55 58 59 61 62 63 64 66 81 82 84 85 87 88 92 94 96 107 108 **P**6 Primary Contact: Tony E. Atkins, Chief Executive Officer CFO: Renee Hofer, Vice President Fiscal Services CMO: Jose Reed, M.D., Chief of Staff CHR: Allen Wilson, Director Human Resources Web address: www.stj.net	23	10	69	2097	34	67001	356	23443	9597	300

CHARLESTON—Kanawha County

✠ △ **CHARLESTON AREA MEDICAL CENTER**, 501 Morris Street, Zip 25301–1300, Mailing Address: P.O. Box 1547, Zip 25326–1547; tel. 304/388–5432, (Includes GENERAL HOSPITAL, 501 Morris Street, Zip 25301, Mailing Address: Box 1393, Zip 25325; tel. 304/388–6203; MEMORIAL HOSPITAL, 3200 MacCorkle Avenue S.E., Zip 25304; tel. 304/388–5432; WOMEN AND CHILDREN'S HOSPITAL, 800 Pennsylvania Avenue, Zip 25302; tel. 304/388–2286; Sarah Llewellyn, Vice President and Administrator) **A**1 2 3 5 7 8 9 10 12 13 **F**2 7 9 10 11 12 14 15 17 19 21 22 23 24 27 28 29 31 32 33 34 35 37 38 39 40 42 44 45 46 47 48 49 50 52 53 55 56 57 58 59 60 61 62 63 64 65 66 67 68 69 70 71 72 73 74 75 76 81 82 83 84 85 86 87 88 89 90 92 93 94 95 96 98 101 104 106 107 108 109 110 **P**7 **S** Charleston Area Medical Center Health System, Inc., Charleston, WV Primary Contact: David L. Ramsey, President and Chief Executive Officer COO: Glenn Crotty, Jr, M.D., Executive Vice President and Chief Operating Officer CFO: Larry C. Hudson, Executive Vice President and Chief Financial Officer CMO: Elizabeth Spangler, M.D., Vice President Medical Affairs CIO: Lynn Brookshire, Vice President Information Services and Chief Information Officer; Privacy Officer CHR: Leslie W. Melton, Vice President for Human Resources and Support Services Web address: www.camc.org	23	10	793	36216	522	514849	3183	541327	194710	4715
□ **EYE AND EAR CLINIC OF CHARLESTON**, 1306 Kanawha Boulevard East, Zip 25301–3001, Mailing Address: P.O. Box 2271, Zip 25328–2271; tel. 304/343–4371 **A**1 9 10 **F**3 13 14 55 56 63 67 68 71 92 105 Primary Contact: Christina Arvon, Acting Administrator and Chief Executive Officer Web address: www.eyeandearclinicwv.com	33	45	21	7	1	3682	0	3769	1420	75
GENERAL HOSPITAL See Charleston Area Medical Center										
✠ **HIGHLAND HOSPITAL**, 300 56th Street S.E., Zip 25304–2361, Mailing Address: P.O. Box 4107, Zip 25364–4107; tel. 304/926–1600 **A**1 9 10 **F**21 27 28 29 46 58 71 72 74 78 94 **P**6 Primary Contact: David M. McWatters, Administrator CFO: Lisa Layden, Director of Finance CMO: Charles Weise, M.D., Medical Director CIO: Pearl McWatters, Director of Information Services Web address: www.highlandhosp.com	23	22	58	1141	29	4179	0	9073	4776	169
MEMORIAL HOSPITAL See Charleston Area Medical Center										
✠ **SAINT FRANCIS HOSPITAL**, 333 Laidley Street, Zip 25301–1628, Mailing Address: P.O. Box 471, Zip 25322–0471; tel. 304/347–6500, (Total facility includes 10 beds in nursing home–type unit) **A**1 9 10 **F**10 12 21 22 26 27 28 33 37 38 40 45 46 47 48 52 53 54 55 57 58 60 62 63 65 66 69 70 81 82 84 86 88 92 93 94 95 106 108 109 110 **P**6 **S** HCA, Nashville, TN Primary Contact: Dan Lauffer, FACHE, Chief Executive Officer COO: Tim Bess, Chief Operating Officer CFO: Bradley Owens, Chief Financial Officer CMO: Mallinath Kayi, M.D., Medical Staff President CIO: Jane Harless, Director of Information Services CHR: Terri McCormick, Director Human Resources Web address: www.stfrancishospital.com	33	10	114	4780	67	87573	0	—	—	644
□ **SELECT SPECIALTY HOSPITAL–CHARLESTON**, 501 Morris Street, 3rd Floor, Zip 25301; tel. 304/388–6600 **A**1 9 10 **F**2 21 28 57 58 62 64 94 110 Primary Contact: Luis Roe, Chief Executive Officer	33	80	32	309	23	0	0	9830	4048	100
WOMEN AND CHILDREN'S HOSPITAL See Charleston Area Medical Center										

CLARKSBURG—Harrison County

✠ **LOUIS A. JOHNSON VETERANS AFFAIRS MEDICAL CENTER**, 1 Medical Center Drive, Zip 26301–4199; tel. 304/623–3461, (Total facility includes 27 beds in nursing home–type unit) **A**1 2 3 5 9 **F**2 3 4 6 15 21 22 23 26 28 29 31 32 33 36 37 38 39 42 44 46 47 48 52 55 58 60 61 63 65 66 69 70 71 73 74 75 76 77 78 81 82 85 87 88 92 94 96 106 107 108 109 110 **P**6 **S** Department of Veterans Affairs, Washington, DC Primary Contact: Cheryl Welch, Acting Director CFO: Brian Besten, Program Leader Business Officer CIO: Randy Ledsome, Program Leader Information Management Web address: www.va.gov/sta/guide/home.asp	45	10	98	3255	70	195327	0	82231	34829	619

WV

Many Facility Codes have changed. Please refer to the AHA Guide Code Chart. © 2005 AHA Guide

Hospital, Address, Telephone, Approval, Facility, and Physician Codes, Health Care System	Classi-fication Codes		Utilization Data						Expense (thousands) of dollars		
★ American Hospital Association (AHA) membership □ Joint Commission on Accreditation of Healthcare Organizations (JCAHO) accreditation ○ American Osteopathic Association (AOA) accreditation △ Commission on Accreditation of Rehabilitation Facilities (CARF) accreditation	Control	Service	Staffed Beds	Admissions	Census	Outpatient Visits	Births	Total	Payroll	Personnel
⊞ **UNITED HOSPITAL CENTER**, Route 19 South, Zip 26301, Mailing Address: P.O. Box 1680, Zip 26302–1680; tel. 304/624–2121, (Total facility includes 51 beds in nursing home–type unit) **A**1 2 3 5 9 10 12 13 19 20 **F**2 4 8 9 10 11 12 14 15 17 21 22 23 26 28 30 31 32 33 36 37 38 40 42 46 48 49 51 52 53 55 57 58 59 60 61 62 63 64 65 66 69 70 71 72 73 74 75 76 77 79 80 81 82 83 84 85 86 87 88 91 92 93 94 96 108 110 **P**6 8 **S** West Virginia United Health System, Fairmont, WV Primary Contact: Bruce C. Carter, President COO: Michael Tillman, Vice President Patient Servies and Chief Operating Officer CFO: Douglas Coffman, Vice President and Chief Financial Officer CMO: Eric Radcliffe, M.D., Medical Director CIO: Ed Collins, Chief Information Officer CHR: Tim Allen, Vice President Human Resources Web address: www.uhcwv.org	23	10	369	15438	265	374518	911	147830	63085	1486
ELKINS—Randolph County										
⊞ **DAVIS MEMORIAL HOSPITAL**, Gorman Avenue and Reed Street, Zip 26241, Mailing Address: P.O. Box 1484, Zip 26241–1484; tel. 304/636–3300 **A**1 9 10 20 **F**9 11 12 15 21 22 23 26 28 29 33 37 40 42 44 46 47 48 51 52 53 54 55 57 58 59 60 61 62 63 65 66 69 81 84 86 88 93 94 96 97 106 107 108 109 110 **P**8 Primary Contact: Mark Doak, President and Chief Executive Officer COO: D Parker Haddix, Chief Operating Officer CFO: Rebecca Hammer, Chief Financial Officer CMO: Steven Toney, M.D., Chief Medical Officer CIO: Steve Crowl, Acting Chief Information Officer Web address: www.davishealthcare.com	23	10	90	5269	54	148857	490	62659	26140	598
FAIRMONT—Marion County										
⊞ **FAIRMONT GENERAL HOSPITAL**, 1325 Locust Avenue, Zip 26554–1435; tel. 304/367–7100, (Total facility includes 12 beds in nursing home–type unit) **A**1 2 9 10 19 **F**2 4 9 11 12 14 15 17 21 22 23 26 27 28 29 31 33 35 37 38 39 40 41 45 46 47 48 51 52 53 54 57 58 60 61 62 63 65 66 69 71 72 73 74 75 76 77 81 82 84 85 86 88 92 94 95 96 98 106 108 109 110 **P**7 Primary Contact: Albert Pilkington, III, Chief Executive Officer CFO: Mike Sengewalt, Senior Vice President and Chief Financial Officer CMO: Pat Bonasso, M.D., Chief of Staff Web address: www.fghi.com	23	10	167	6706	102	176999	425	60379	21400	604
GASSAWAY—Braxton County										
★ **BRAXTON COUNTY MEMORIAL HOSPITAL**, 100 Hoylman Drive, Zip 26624–9320; tel. 304/364–5156 **A**9 10 18 **F**2 9 12 24 27 28 29 33 46 47 48 51 52 58 63 70 81 94 97 108 109 **P**6 **S** Charleston Area Medical Center Health System, Inc., Charleston, WV Primary Contact: Benjamin Vincent, Administrator CFO: Annette Keenan, Chief Financial Officer CMO: Russell L. Stewart, M.D., D.O., Chief Medical Officer CHR: Craig Madden, Director Human Resources Web address: www.braxmh.org	23	10	25	681	7	26007	0	8511	4319	133
GLEN DALE—Marshall County										
⊞ **REYNOLDS MEMORIAL HOSPITAL**, 800 Wheeling Avenue, Zip 26038–1697; tel. 304/845–3211, (Total facility includes 20 beds in nursing home–type unit) **A**1 9 10 **F**2 9 11 12 22 26 27 28 32 33 34 38 39 41 44 48 51 52 55 57 58 59 60 61 62 63 64 65 69 81 82 84 87 88 92 94 96 106 108 110 **P**8 Primary Contact: John Sicurella, Chief Executive Officer COO: Jay E. Prager, Chief Operating Officer CFO: William Robert Hunt, Chief Financial Officer CMO: Robert B. Wade, M.D., President Medical Staff CIO: Warren Kelley, Chief Information Officer Web address: www.reynoldsmemorial.com	23	10	127	2699	51	74351	192	33618	14550	373
GRAFTON—Taylor County										
GRAFTON CITY HOSPITAL, 500 Market Street, Zip 26354–1187; tel. 304/265–0400, (Total facility includes 76 beds in nursing home–type unit) **A**9 10 18 **F**9 12 21 22 24 26 27 28 29 32 33 38 41 42 44 45 46 47 48 50 52 58 60 61 62 63 65 66 69 70 73 74 75 76 77 78 81 82 84 88 92 94 95 96 97 107 108 109 110 **P**6 Primary Contact: Gary R. Willmon, Administrator Web address: www.graftonhospital.com	14	10	101	1250	84	44027	0	15704	7294	303
GRANTSVILLE—Calhoun County										
MINNIE HAMILTON HEALTHCARE CENTER, Hospital Hill, Zip 26147, Mailing Address: 186 Hospital Drive, Zip 26147; tel. 304/354–9244, (Total facility includes 24 beds in nursing home–type unit) **A**9 10 18 **F**2 6 9 12 21 22 24 26 27 28 29 30 32 33 35 39 41 44 45 46 48 50 53 58 65 66 69 70 72 74 81 88 92 93 94 96 97 98 106 108 109 110 **P**6 Primary Contact: Barbara Lay, Administrator Web address: www.mhhcc.com	23	10	43	466	28	61709	0	11807	6950	204

WV

Hospital, Address, Telephone, Approval, Facility, and Physician Codes, Health Care System	Classi-fication Codes		Utilization Data					Expense (thousands) of dollars		
★ American Hospital Association (AHA) membership □ Joint Commission on Accreditation of Healthcare Organizations (JCAHO) accreditation ○ American Osteopathic Association (AOA) accreditation △ Commission on Accreditation of Rehabilitation Facilities (CARF) accreditation	Control	Service	Staffed Beds	Admissions	Census	Outpatient Visits	Births	Total	Payroll	Personnel

HINTON—Summers County

☒ **SUMMERS COUNTY APPALACHIAN REGIONAL HOSPITAL**, Terrace Street, Zip 25951–2407, Mailing Address: Drawer 940, Zip 25951–0940; tel. 304/466–1000, (Total facility includes 36 beds in nursing home–type unit) **A**1 9 10 18 **F**9 12 21 22 24 26 27 28 29 30 33 35 37 39 42 44 46 47 48 51 52 63 65 66 68 69 70 81 88 92 94 97 108 109 110 **S** Appalachian Regional Healthcare, Lexington, KY
Primary Contact: Chris Vaught, Community Chief Executive Officer
CMO: Amarinder Chhabra, M.D., President Medical Staff
Web address: www.arh.org

| | 23 | 10 | 61 | 785 | 40 | 24877 | 0 | 11195 | 4699 | 138 |

HUNTINGTON—Cabell County

☒ △ **CABELL HUNTINGTON HOSPITAL**, 1340 Hal Greer Boulevard, Zip 25701–0195; tel. 304/526–2000, (Total facility includes 15 beds in nursing home–type unit) **A**1 2 3 5 7 9 10 **F**2 6 9 10 11 12 13 15 21 22 23 24 26 27 28 29 30 32 33 34 35 36 37 38 39 40 42 44 46 47 48 49 50 51 52 55 56 57 58 59 60 61 62 63 64 65 66 67 69 70 81 82 84 85 86 87 88 89 90 92 93 94 95 96 106 108 109 110 **P**8
Primary Contact: Brent A. Marsteller, President and Chief Executive Officer
COO: T Douglas Lawson, Senior Vice President and Chief Operating Officer
CFO: David M. Ward, Senior Vice President and Chief Financial Officer
CMO: Hoyt J. Burdick, M.D., Vice President Medical Affairs
CIO: Sanjay Shah, Vice President and Chief Information Officer
Web address: www.cabellhuntington.org

| | 23 | 10 | 268 | 17235 | 191 | 287743 | 2591 | 175573 | 68037 | 1554 |

☒ **HEALTHSOUTH HUNTINGTON REHABILITATION HOSPITAL**, 6900 West Country Club Drive, Zip 25705–2000; tel. 304/733–1060 **A**1 9 10 **F**21 26 27 28 29 48 68 69 96 108 **S** HEALTHSOUTH Corporation, Birmingham, AL
Primary Contact: Frank Weber, Administrator
Web address: www.healthsouth.com

| | 33 | 46 | 52 | 947 | 41 | 6902 | 0 | 8253 | 4604 | 132 |

□ **MILDRED MITCHELL–BATEMAN HOSPITAL**, 1530 Norway Avenue, Zip 25705–1358, Mailing Address: P.O. Box 448, Zip 25709–0448; tel. 304/525–7801 **A**1 9 10 **F**2 22 71 94 108 **P**6
Primary Contact: Mary Beth Carlisle, Chief Executive Officer
Web address: www.state.wv.us/newhh

| | 12 | 22 | 90 | 1813 | 88 | 0 | 0 | 21597 | 10202 | 320 |

☒ **RIVER PARK HOSPITAL**, 1230 Sixth Avenue, Zip 25701–2312, Mailing Address: P.O. Box 1875, Zip 25719–1875; tel. 304/526–9111 **A**1 9 10 **F**28 29 31 33 46 48 71 72 73 74 75 76 77 94
Primary Contact: Scott C. Stamm, Chief Executive Officer
CFO: Patrick D. Burrows, CPA, Chief Financial Officer
CMO: David J. Humphreys, M.D., Medical Director
CIO: Emily Cornwell, Operations Manager
Web address: www.riverparkhospital.net/home.htm

| | 32 | 22 | 147 | 1691 | 103 | 51 | 0 | 17146 | 8520 | 259 |

☒ **ST. MARY'S MEDICAL CENTER**, 2900 First Avenue, Zip 25702–1272; tel. 304/526–1234, (Total facility includes 19 beds in nursing home–type unit) **A**1 2 3 5 9 10 **F**2 9 10 11 12 14 15 17 19 21 22 23 24 27 28 29 32 33 34 37 38 39 41 46 47 48 49 51 52 53 55 57 58 59 61 62 63 65 66 69 70 71 73 74 75 76 79 80 81 82 84 85 87 88 92 93 94 96 97 106 108 109 110 **P**8
Primary Contact: Michael G. Sellards, President and Chief Executive Officer
CFO: Todd Campbell, Vice President Financial Affairs and Chief Financial Officer
CMO: Vera Rose, M.D., Vice President Medical Affairs
CIO: James Jordan, Director Information Systems
CHR: Susan Beth McKenzie, Vice President of Human Resources
Web address: www.st-marys.org

| | 21 | 10 | 369 | 17704 | 280 | 205968 | 478 | 221986 | 80939 | 1929 |

☒ **VETERANS AFFAIRS MEDICAL CENTER**, 1540 Spring Valley Drive, Zip 25704–9300; tel. 304/429–6741, (Nonreporting) **A**1 3 5 **S** Department of Veterans Affairs, Washington, DC
Primary Contact: Betty Bolin Brown, Ed.D., Chief Executive Officer
CMO: Joseph Pellecchia, M.D., Chief of Staff
CIO: Gary Henderson, Chief Information Resources Management Services
Web address: www.va.gov/sta/guide/home.asp

| | 45 | 10 | 80 | — | — | — | — | — | — | — |

HURRICANE—Putnam County

☒ **PUTNAM GENERAL HOSPITAL**, 1400 Hospital Drive, Zip 25526–9210; tel. 304/757–1700 **A**1 9 10 **F**9 10 12 21 26 27 28 29 33 46 48 52 55 57 58 61 62 63 64 66 69 70 73 75 81 82 88 94 95 96 106 108 110 **S** HCA, Nashville, TN
Primary Contact: Dan Lauffer, FACHE, Chief Executive Officer
COO: Ronda Moore, Chief Operating Officer and Chief Financial Officer
CFO: Ronda Moore, Chief Financial Officer
CMO: Gregory Kelly, D.O., Medical Staff President
CIO: Jackie Scott, Risk Manager and Director of Information Services and Safety
Web address: www.putnamgeneralhospital.com

| | 33 | 10 | 68 | 3451 | 50 | 65615 | 0 | 43949 | 14389 | 348 |

INSTITUTE—Kanawha County

△ **WEST VIRGINIA REHABILITATION CENTER**, Barron Drive, Zip 25112 **A**7 9 10 **F**2 9 21 26 27 28 35 39 41 46 47 48 52 58 60 65 66 68 69 70 73 94 108 **P**6
Primary Contact: Sonja Scholl, Administrator
Web address: www.wvdrs.org

| | 12 | 46 | 40 | 98 | 5 | 12124 | 0 | 12577 | 6673 | 232 |

Many Facility Codes have changed. Please refer to the AHA Guide Code Chart.

WV

Hospital, Address, Telephone, Approval, Facility, and Physician Codes, Health Care System	Classi-fication Codes		Utilization Data					Expense (thousands) of dollars		
★ American Hospital Association (AHA) membership □ Joint Commission on Accreditation of Healthcare Organizations (JCAHO) accreditation ○ American Osteopathic Association (AOA) accreditation △ Commission on Accreditation of Rehabilitation Facilities (CARF) accreditation	Control	Service	Staffed Beds	Admissions	Census	Outpatient Visits	Births	Total	Payroll	Personnel

KEYSER—Mineral County

□ **POTOMAC VALLEY HOSPITAL**, 167 South Mineral Street, Zip 26726–2699; tel. 304/788–3141 **A**1 9 10 18 **F**2 12 22 26 27 28 33 36 38 39 42 46 51 52 55 58 63 64 66 69 81 82 85 87 88 94 96 106 108 **S** Mid Atlantic Health Management, Inc., Stevensville, MD
Primary Contact: Michael Makosky, Administrator

| | 33 | 10 | 30 | 1205 | 11 | 44463 | 0 | 14387 | 5358 | 186 |

KINGWOOD—Preston County

★ **PRESTON MEMORIAL HOSPITAL**, 300 South Price Street, Zip 26537–1495; tel. 304/329–1400 **A**9 10 18 20 **F**9 11 12 21 22 29 33 34 38 41 46 48 51 52 58 59 60 62 63 69 81 82 84 87 88 93 94 96 97 108 **P**5
Primary Contact: Michael S. Thompson, Chief Executive Officer
CFO: Melissa Lockwood, Chief Financial Officer
CIO: Beth Horne, Controller
CHR: Ryan Dineen, Director Human Resources
Web address: www.prestonmemorial.org

| | 23 | 10 | 25 | 1080 | 11 | 53875 | 135 | 13837 | 5728 | 210 |

LOGAN—Logan County

★ **GUYAN VALLEY HOSPITAL**, 396 Dingess Street, Zip 25601–3695; tel. 304/831–1700 **A**10 18 **F**26 27 28 33 52 60 94 97 **P**7 **S** LifePoint Hospitals, Inc., Brentwood, TN
Primary Contact: Kevin N. Fowler, Chief Executive Officer
COO: Michael Meadows, Chief Operating Officer
CFO: Jim Giest, Chief Financial Officer
CMO: Ernesto Manuel, M.D., Medical Director
CIO: Fred Langva, Director Information Systems
CHR: Michael Ohea, Director of Human Resources
Web address: www.loganregionalmedicalcenter.com/gvh.shtml

| | 33 | 10 | 15 | 190 | 7 | 5821 | 0 | 3030 | 1412 | 54 |

⊞ **LOGAN REGIONAL MEDICAL CENTER**, 20 Hospital Drive, Zip 25601–3473; tel. 304/831–1101 **A**1 9 10 12 13 20 **F**2 9 11 12 21 23 26 27 28 29 33 34 42 46 48 52 55 57 58 59 60 61 62 63 65 66 68 69 70 81 82 84 88 93 94 106 108 **P**6 **S** LifePoint Hospitals, Inc., Brentwood, TN
Primary Contact: Kevin N. Fowler, Chief Executive Officer
CFO: John May, Chief Financial Officer
Web address: www.loganregionalmedicalcenter.com

| | 33 | 10 | 129 | 7175 | 80 | 91004 | 352 | 57226 | 18210 | 575 |

MADISON—Boone County

⊞ **BOONE MEMORIAL HOSPITAL**, 701 Madison Avenue, Zip 25130–1699; tel. 304/369–1230 **A**1 9 10 18 20 **F**9 12 26 27 28 33 34 46 51 63 81 82 88 94 95 97 **P**6
Primary Contact: Tommy H. Mullins, Administrator
CFO: Randy Foxx, Chief Financial Officer
CMO: Shane Bowen, M.D., Chief of Staff
CIO: Susan Shreve, Executive Director Information Technology
Web address: www.bmh.org

| | 13 | 10 | 25 | 967 | 16 | 55309 | 0 | 11235 | 3964 | 146 |

MARTINSBURG—Berkeley County

⊞ **CITY HOSPITAL**, Dry Run Road, Zip 25401, Mailing Address: P.O. Box 1418, Zip 25402–1418; tel. 304/264–1000, (Total facility includes 19 beds in nursing home–type unit) **A**1 2 3 9 10 **F**2 9 11 12 21 22 23 27 28 29 33 40 41 46 48 52 55 57 58 59 60 61 62 63 65 66 69 71 73 75 77 81 82 84 87 88 92 93 94 95 96 106 108 109 **P**8 **S** West Virginia United Health System, Fairmont, WV
Primary Contact: Jon D. Applebaum, Chief Executive Officer
CFO: Gary W. Broadwater, Chief Financial Officer
Web address: www.cityhospital.org

| | 23 | 10 | 143 | 7291 | 96 | 141399 | 862 | 74560 | 33040 | 819 |

⊞ **VETERANS AFFAIRS MEDICAL CENTER**, 510 Butler Avenue, Zip 25401–0205; tel. 304/263–0811, (Nonreporting) **A**1 3 5 9 **S** Department of Veterans Affairs, Washington, DC
Primary Contact: Guy B. Richardson, Acting Director
CFO: Jody Slonaker, Chief, Fiscal Section
CIO: Debe Gantt, Chief Information Resource Management
CHR: Steve Childs, Chief, Business Programs and Operations
Web address: www.va.gov/sta/guide/home.asp

| | 45 | 10 | 559 | — | — | — | — | — | — | — |

MONTGOMERY—Fayette County

⊞ **MONTGOMERY GENERAL HOSPITAL**, 401 Sixth Avenue, Zip 25136–0270, Mailing Address: P.O. Box 270, Zip 25136–0270; tel. 304/442–5151, (Total facility includes 44 beds in nursing home–type unit) **A**1 9 10 18 20 **F**9 12 21 22 27 28 29 33 45 46 52 55 60 62 63 66 69 70 81 84 88 92 93 94 95 106 108 **P**6 8
Primary Contact: Vickie Gay, Chief Executive Officer
COO: Jack Case, Chief Operating Officer
CFO: Sherri Murray, Chief Financial Officer
CMO: Traci Acklin, M.D., Chief of Staff
CHR: LeeAnn Snyder, Vice President Human Resources
Web address: www.montgomeryhealth.com

| | 23 | 10 | 99 | 1657 | 50 | 40211 | 0 | 23353 | 7437 | 237 |

MORGANTOWN—Monongalia County

CHESTNUT RIDGE HOSPITAL See West Virginia University Hospitals

WV

Hospital, Address, Telephone, Approval, Facility, and Physician Codes, Health Care System	Classi-fication Codes		Utilization Data					Expense (thousands) of dollars		
★ American Hospital Association (AHA) membership □ Joint Commission on Accreditation of Healthcare Organizations (JCAHO) accreditation ○ American Osteopathic Association (AOA) accreditation △ Commission on Accreditation of Rehabilitation Facilities (CARF) accreditation	Control	Service	Staffed Beds	Admissions	Census	Outpatient Visits	Births	Total	Payroll	Personnel
✠ HEALTHSOUTH MOUNTAINVIEW REGIONAL REHABILITATION HOSPITAL, 1160 Van Voorhis Road, Zip 26505–3435; tel. 304/598–1100 **A**1 9 10 **F**2 7 10 21 22 28 37 42 44 46 48 52 57 58 60 61 62 65 66 68 69 72 73 76 77 93 94 95 96 108 110 **P**6 **S** HEALTHSOUTH Corporation, Birmingham, AL Primary Contact: John C. Forester, Administrator CFO: Jason Gizzi, Controller CMO: Russell Biundo, M.D., Medical Director CIO: Rita D' Aurora, R.N., Risk Manager & Quality Assurance – Health Information Management Director CHR: Trish Plevich, Human Resource Director Web address: www.healthsouth.com	33	46	96	1540	85	18696	—	23529	11390	307
✠ MONONGALIA GENERAL HOSPITAL, 1200 J. D. Anderson Drive, Zip 26505–3486; tel. 304/598–1200 **A**1 2 9 10 19 **F**2 10 11 12 14 15 17 19 21 22 23 24 26 27 28 29 30 33 36 37 38 39 40 41 42 46 47 48 52 55 57 58 59 60 61 62 63 65 66 81 82 84 86 87 88 92 93 94 96 106 107 108 109 110 **P**8 Primary Contact: David J. Robertson, Chief Executive Officer CFO: Nicholas Grubbs, Chief Financial Officer Web address: www.monhealthsys.org	23	10	175	8525	105	125227	502	111619	41783	977
✠ WEST VIRGINIA UNIVERSITY HOSPITALS, Medical Center Drive, Zip 26506–4749; tel. 304/598–4000, (Includes CHESTNUT RIDGE HOSPITAL, 930 Chestnut Ridge Road, Zip 26505–2854; tel. 304/293–4000), (Total facility includes 20 beds in nursing home–type unit) **A**1 2 3 5 8 9 10 12 13 19 **F**2 3 4 9 10 11 12 14 15 16 17 18 19 20 21 22 23 29 30 31 32 33 34 37 38 39 40 43 46 48 49 50 52 53 55 56 57 58 59 60 61 62 63 64 65 66 67 71 72 73 74 75 76 78 79 80 81 82 85 87 88 92 93 94 96 99 101 108 109 **S** West Virginia United Health System, Fairmont, WV Primary Contact: Bruce McClymonds, President COO: John H. Yoder, Chief Operating Officer CFO: David Salsberry, Vice President and Chief Financial Officer CMO: Kevin Halbritter, M.D., Vice President Medical Staff Affairs CIO: Michael Balassone, Vice President Information Technology CHR: Cindy Klein, Vice President Human Resources Web address: www.health.wvu.edu	23	10	440	20285	345	472398	1585	343907	126623	3320
NEW MARTINSVILLE—Wetzel County										
✠ WETZEL COUNTY HOSPITAL, 3 East Benjamin Drive, Zip 26155–2758; tel. 304/455–8000, (Total facility includes 10 beds in nursing home–type unit) **A**1 9 10 **F**2 12 23 27 28 33 46 48 51 52 55 59 60 62 63 69 81 82 84 87 88 92 94 96 108 **P**6 Primary Contact: Joseph F. Turner, Jr, Chief Executive Officer CFO: David K. McCartney, CPA, Chief Financial Officer CIO: Amy Fraizer, Management Information Systems Supervisor CHR: Sarah Boley, Director of Human Resources Web address: www.wetzelhealth.org	13	10	53	1779	23	102058	92	21625	10499	242
OAK HILL—Fayette County										
PLATEAU MEDICAL CENTER, INC., 430 Main Street, Zip 25901–3455; tel. 304/469–8600 **A**9 10 18 **F**2 9 12 21 22 25 26 27 28 29 32 33 39 41 44 46 48 52 53 55 57 58 60 62 63 65 66 70 73 81 82 85 88 94 97 108 **P**6 **S** Community Health Systems, Inc., Brentwood, TN Primary Contact: David V. Bunch, Chief Executive Officer Web address: www.camc.org	33	10	25	2013	18	24282	0	14653	6256	160
PARKERSBURG—Wood County										
✠ CAMDEN–CLARK MEMORIAL HOSPITAL, 800 Garfield Avenue, Zip 26101–5378, Mailing Address: P.O. Box 718, Zip 26102–0718; tel. 304/424–2111, (Total facility includes 25 beds in nursing home–type unit) **A**1 2 9 10 **F**2 9 11 12 14 15 21 22 23 26 27 28 29 33 36 37 38 40 41 45 46 47 48 51 52 53 55 57 58 59 60 61 62 63 64 65 66 69 79 81 82 84 85 86 87 88 92 94 95 96 106 108 109 110 **P**6 Primary Contact: Thomas J. Corder, President and Chief Executive Officer COO: Michael A. King, Chief Operating Officer CFO: Allen R. Butcher, Vice President Finance CMO: Judith Kemp, M.D., President Medical Staff CIO: Josh Woods, Director Information Systems CHR: Tom Heller, Vice President Human Resources Web address: www.ccmh.org	23	10	313	13397	175	294437	1306	125072	49260	1290
✠ HEALTHSOUTH WESTERN HILLS REHABILITATION CENTER, 3 Western Hills Drive, Zip 26101–8122; tel. 304/420–1300 **A**1 9 10 **F**21 26 27 28 42 52 58 68 69 95 108 **S** HEALTHSOUTH Corporation, Birmingham, AL Primary Contact: Dean Hatcher, Administrator Web address: www.healthsouth.com	33	46	40	936	38	20947	0	10604	5348	137
✠ ST. JOSEPH'S HOSPITAL, 1824 Murdoch Avenue, Zip 26101–3246, Mailing Address: P.O. Box 327, Zip 26102–0327; tel. 304/424–4111 **A**1 9 10 **F**2 11 12 14 15 17 19 21 22 23 26 27 28 29 33 34 37 38 39 40 46 47 48 50 52 53 55 57 58 59 61 62 63 64 65 66 71 75 76 81 82 84 85 86 87 88 90 93 94 96 98 108 109 **S** HCA, Nashville, TN Primary Contact: Patsy A. Hardy, Chief Executive Officer COO: Jon McDowell, Chief Operating Officer CFO: H. H. Thompson, Chief Financial Officer CIO: Brandon Holbert, Director Information Systems CHR: Allyson Mason, Vice President Human Resources Web address: www.stjosephs–hospital.com	32	10	194	7394	97	90048	304	—	—	578

WV

Many Facility Codes have changed. Please refer to the AHA Guide Code Chart.

© 2005 AHA Guide

Hospital, Address, Telephone, Approval, Facility, and Physician Codes, Health Care System	Classi-fication Codes		Utilization Data					Expense (thousands) of dollars		
★ American Hospital Association (AHA) membership □ Joint Commission on Accreditation of Healthcare Organizations (JCAHO) accreditation ○ American Osteopathic Association (AOA) accreditation △ Commission on Accreditation of Rehabilitation Facilities (CARF) accreditation	Control	Service	Staffed Beds	Admissions	Census	Outpatient Visits	Births	Total	Payroll	Personnel

PETERSBURG—Grant County

★ **GRANT MEMORIAL HOSPITAL**, Route 55 West, Zip 26847, Mailing Address: P.O. Box 1019, Zip 26847–1019; tel. 304/257–1026, (Total facility includes 10 beds in nursing home–type unit) **A**9 10 20 **F**2 6 11 12 21 24 28 29 30 32 33 34 35 36 39 41 46 47 48 51 52 55 58 59 60 62 63 64 65 69 81 82 84 85 87 88 92 94 96 97 109 **P**6
Primary Contact: Robert L. Harman, Chief Executive Officer
COO: Mary Beth Barr, R.N., Chief Operating Officer
CFO: Sandy Michaels, Chief Financial Officer
CMO: Fernando Indacochea, M.D., Chief of Staff
CIO: Jinny McKinney, Director Information Systems
CHR: Roanie Arbaugh, Director Human Resources
Web address: www.grantmemorial.com
| | 13 | 10 | 57 | 2163 | 29 | 90152 | 273 | 20960 | 9891 | 284 |

PHILIPPI—Barbour County

★ **BROADDUS HOSPITAL**, Mansfield Hill, Zip 26416–1051; tel. 304/457–1760, (Total facility includes 60 beds in nursing home–type unit) **A**9 10 18 **F**12 21 24 26 27 28 29 33 46 48 52 58 60 69 70 81 88 92 94 97 107 108 109 110
Primary Contact: Jeffrey A. Powelson, Chief Executive Officer
CHR: Penny Brown, Human Resources Representative
Web address: www.davishealthcare.com
| | 23 | 10 | 72 | 405 | 64 | 34541 | 0 | 9767 | 4283 | 174 |

POINT PLEASANT—Mason County

⊠ **PLEASANT VALLEY HOSPITAL**, 2520 Valley Drive, Zip 25550–2083; tel. 304/675–4340, (Total facility includes 100 beds in nursing home–type unit) **A**1 9 10 **F**2 9 11 12 14 21 22 23 26 27 28 29 30 32 33 35 36 39 40 41 44 45 46 47 48 50 51 52 53 55 57 58 59 60 61 62 63 65 66 69 70 81 82 84 85 87 88 92 94 95 96 106 108 109 **P**8
Primary Contact: Alvin R. Lawson, JD, FACHE, Chief Executive Officer
CFO: Thomas Schauer, Assistant Executive Director and Chief Financial Officer
CMO: Shrikart Vaidya, President Medical Staff
CIO: Paula Brooker, Director Information Services
CHR: Brenda McKenzie, Director Human Resources
Web address: www.pvalley.org
| | 23 | 10 | 201 | 5881 | 149 | 123260 | 197 | 52336 | 22833 | 701 |

PRINCETON—Mercer County

⊠ **HEALTHSOUTH SOUTHERN HILLS REHABILITATION HOSPITAL**, 120 Twelfth Street, Zip 24740–2312; tel. 304/487–8000 **A**1 9 10 **F**7 21 26 27 28 42 44 45 46 47 48 52 58 65 66 68 69 73 74 76 77 94 95 96 108 109 **S** HEALTHSOUTH Corporation, Birmingham, AL
Primary Contact: Marion Houser, Administrator
CFO: Hasan Baig, CPA, Assistant Controller
CMO: Carl Shelton, M.D., Medical Director
CHR: Sharon Boggess, Human Resource Director
Web address: www.healthsouth.com
| | 33 | 46 | 60 | 1166 | 44 | 12836 | 0 | 6955 | 5347 | 129 |

⊠ **PRINCETON COMMUNITY HOSPITAL**, 122 12th Street, Zip 24740–1369, Mailing Address: P.O. Box 1369, Zip 24740–1369; tel. 304/487–7000 **A**1 2 9 10 12 13 19 **F**2 9 11 12 14 21 23 24 26 27 28 29 32 33 34 35 38 39 40 41 44 46 47 48 50 51 52 55 57 58 59 60 61 62 63 64 65 66 69 70 71 73 74 75 76 81 82 84 85 86 87 88 93 94 95 96 98 106 108 109 110 **P**1
Primary Contact: Clinton Matthews, Chief Executive Officer
COO: James F. Valeyko, Vice President Operations
CFO: Frank J. Sinicrope, Jr, Vice President Financial Services
CIO: Danny Farley, Director Information Services
CHR: D Darlene Huffman, Director Human Resources
Web address: www.pchonline.org
| | 14 | 10 | 160 | 8378 | 128 | 165071 | 409 | 94225 | 34204 | 892 |

RANSON—Jefferson County

⊠ **JEFFERSON MEMORIAL HOSPITAL**, 300 South Preston Street, Zip 25438–1699; tel. 304/728–1600, (Total facility includes 10 beds in nursing home–type unit) **A**1 3 5 9 10 **F**9 11 12 21 22 26 27 28 29 33 34 46 48 51 52 55 58 59 60 62 63 65 66 69 81 88 92 93 94 96 106 107 108 **P**8 **S** West Virginia United Health System, Fairmont, WV
Primary Contact: John M. Sherwood, FACHE, Chief Executive Officer
CFO: John Sella, Chief Financial Officer
CMO: Jan Kletter, M.D., Medical Staff President
CIO: Todd Smoot, Chief Information Officer
CHR: Becky Nucilli, Director of Human Resources
Web address: www.jeffmem.com
| | 23 | 10 | 60 | 2290 | 23 | 65773 | 270 | 30881 | 14784 | 381 |

RICHWOOD—Nicholas County

RICHWOOD AREA COMMUNITY HOSPITAL, 75 Avenue B., Zip 26261; tel. 304/846–2573, (Total facility includes 25 beds in nursing home–type unit) **A**9 10 18 **F**9 27 31 33 39 46 48 52 60 63 69 70 81 92 94 97 108 **P**6
Primary Contact: Elaine Butler, Chief Executive Officer
Web address: www.pihn.org
| | 23 | 10 | 38 | 415 | 27 | 21991 | 0 | 5701 | 2729 | 92 |

RIPLEY—Jackson County

⊠ **JACKSON GENERAL HOSPITAL**, Pinnell Street, Zip 25271–1009, Mailing Address: P.O. Box 720, Zip 25271–0720; tel. 304/372–2731 **A**1 9 10 20 **F**2 9 11 12 14 21 22 26 27 28 29 33 39 46 48 52 53 55 58 59 63 69 81 82 84 85 88 97 106 **P**6
Primary Contact: Sandra Elza, Chief Executive Officer
CFO: Angela Frame, Chief Financial Officer
CIO: Jim Bentley, Director Information Systems
CHR: Kimberli Lanham, Director of Human Resources
Web address: www.jacksongeneral.com
| | 23 | 10 | 60 | 2220 | 20 | 44044 | 96 | 21378 | 9811 | 412 |

WV

Hospital, Address, Telephone, Approval, Facility, and Physician Codes, Health Care System	Classi-fication Codes		Utilization Data					Expense (thousands) of dollars		
★ American Hospital Association (AHA) membership ☐ Joint Commission on Accreditation of Healthcare Organizations (JCAHO) accreditation ○ American Osteopathic Association (AOA) accreditation △ Commission on Accreditation of Rehabilitation Facilities (CARF) accreditation	Control	Service	Staffed Beds	Admissions	Census	Outpatient Visits	Births	Total	Payroll	Personnel

ROMNEY—Hampshire County

☐ **HAMPSHIRE MEMORIAL HOSPITAL**, 549 Center Avenue, Zip 26757–1199; tel. 304/822–4561, (Total facility includes 30 beds in nursing home–type unit) **A**1 9 10 18 **F**26 27 28 33 44 48 50 51 63 69 81 88 92 94 96 97 **P**4 **S** Mid Atlantic Health Management, Inc., Stevensville, MD
Primary Contact: Roberta D. McCauley, Chief Executive Officer

	33	10	44	444	33	30631	0	8503	3271	120

RONCEVERTE—Greenbrier County

⊠ ○ **GREENBRIER VALLEY MEDICAL CENTER**, 202 Maplewood Avenue, Zip 24970–0497, Mailing Address: P.O. Box 497, Zip 24970–0497; tel. 304/647–4411 **A**1 9 10 11 12 13 19 20 **F**11 12 21 27 28 32 33 40 46 47 48 52 55 58 59 61 62 63 65 66 81 82 84 86 87 88 94 96 97 106 108 109 **P**2 6 **S** Triad Hospitals, Inc., Plano, TX
Primary Contact: Mark Nosacka, Chief Executive Officer
Web address: www.gvmc.com

	33	10	101	4735	54	54517	504	37618	17645	386

SISTERSVILLE—Tyler County

SISTERSVILLE GENERAL HOSPITAL, 314 South Wells Street, Zip 26175–1098; tel. 304/652–2611 **A**10 18 **F**6 12 27 28 29 33 36 41 45 51 62 63 70 81 88 93 94 97 106 108
Primary Contact: Michael Hall, Interim Chief Executive Officer
Web address: www.wvha.com/web/sgh

	14	10	12	198	2	24132	0	5707	3024	112

SOUTH CHARLESTON—Kanawha County

⊠ **THOMAS MEMORIAL HOSPITAL**, 4605 MacCorkle Avenue S.W., Zip 25309–1398; tel. 304/766–3600, (Total facility includes 19 beds in nursing home–type unit) **A**1 3 5 9 10 **F**2 3 4 9 11 12 14 22 23 24 26 27 28 29 31 33 37 38 39 41 46 47 48 49 51 52 53 54 55 56 57 58 59 60 61 62 63 64 65 69 71 72 73 74 75 76 77 78 81 82 84 85 86 87 88 92 93 94 95 96 107 108 110
Primary Contact: Stephen P. Dexter, President and Chief Executive Officer
CFO: Charles O. Covert, Vice President Finance
Web address: www.thomaswv.org

	23	10	216	11014	156	193494	879	117829	44924	1138

SPENCER—Roane County

⊠ **ROANE GENERAL HOSPITAL**, 200 Hospital Drive, Zip 25276–1060; tel. 304/927–4444, (Total facility includes 35 beds in nursing home–type unit) **A**1 9 10 18 **F**2 9 11 12 21 24 27 28 29 33 34 37 39 41 46 48 51 52 59 63 65 66 69 70 81 82 88 92 94 95 97 106 110 **P**6
Primary Contact: Doug Bentz, Chief Executive Officer
COO: Ann Kendall, R.N., Chief Operating Officer
Web address: www.roanegeneralhospital.com

	23	10	60	939	40	57254	121	17752	9165	249

SUMMERSVILLE—Nicholas County

★ **SUMMERSVILLE MEMORIAL HOSPITAL**, 400 Fairview Heights Road, Zip 26651–0400; tel. 304/872–2891, (Total facility includes 52 beds in nursing home–type unit) **A**9 10 20 **F**2 11 12 22 23 27 28 29 33 34 37 38 39 42 44 46 48 52 53 55 58 59 61 62 63 65 66 69 70 81 82 84 85 88 89 92 93 94 95 97 106 108 109 **P**6
Primary Contact: Deborah A. Hill, R.N., Chief Executive Officer
CFO: Dora Douglas, Chief Financial Officer
CMO: Mark Wantz, M.D., Chief of Staff
CHR: David Henderson, Director Human Resources
Web address: www.summersvillememorial.org

	14	10	105	2163	75	103758	249	28595	12493	380

WEBSTER SPRINGS—Webster County

★ **WEBSTER COUNTY MEMORIAL HOSPITAL**, 324 Miller Mountain Drive, Zip 26288–1087, Mailing Address: P.O. Box 312, Zip 26288–0312; tel. 304/847–5682 **A**9 10 18 **F**6 12 22 24 26 27 28 29 33 41 46 47 48 58 63 69 70 81 88 94 **P**6
Primary Contact: Stephen M. Gavalchik, Administrator
CFO: Deborah Bragg, Chief Financial Officer
CMO: Robert Mace, M.D., Chief of Staff
CIO: Margaret W. Short, Chief Information Officer
Web address: www.wcmhwv.com

	13	10	15	401	3	46210	0	7993	4406	108

WEIRTON—Brooke County

⊠ **WEIRTON MEDICAL CENTER**, 601 Colliers Way, Zip 26062–5091; tel. 304/797–6000, (Total facility includes 33 beds in nursing home–type unit) **A**1 9 10 **F**2 4 7 9 11 12 14 15 17 21 22 24 26 27 28 29 32 33 34 37 40 41 42 44 45 46 47 48 49 50 51 52 53 55 57 58 59 60 62 63 64 65 69 70 71 72 73 74 75 76 77 78 81 82 84 85 87 88 92 94 95 96 106 108 109 110 **P**6
Primary Contact: Joseph Endrich, M.D., President and Chief Executive Officer
COO: Cynthia R. Nixon, Executive Vice President
CIO: Carol Karpa, Director Information Services
CHR: Jennifer Anderson, Director
Web address: www.weirtonmedical.com

	23	10	238	7870	90	178635	379	75452	32103	840

WELCH—McDowell County

WELCH COMMUNITY HOSPITAL, 454 McDowell Street, Zip 24801–2097; tel. 304/436–8461, (Total facility includes 59 beds in nursing home–type unit) **A**9 10 **F**2 11 12 21 27 28 29 33 39 46 48 52 53 55 58 59 63 65 66 70 81 88 92 94 108 109 **P**6
Primary Contact: Walter Garrett, Administrator

	12	10	108	1073	62	37046	96	36033	9039	307

WV

Hospital, Address, Telephone, Approval, Facility, and Physician Codes, Health Care System	Classi-fication Codes		Utilization Data					Expense (thousands) of dollars		
★ American Hospital Association (AHA) membership □ Joint Commission on Accreditation of Healthcare Organizations (JCAHO) accreditation ○ American Osteopathic Association (AOA) accreditation △ Commission on Accreditation of Rehabilitation Facilities (CARF) accreditation	Control	Service	Staffed Beds	Admissions	Census	Outpatient Visits	Births	Total	Payroll	Personnel

WESTON—Lewis County

⊠ **STONEWALL JACKSON MEMORIAL HOSPITAL**, 230 Hospital Plaza, Zip 26452–8558; tel. 304/269–8000 **A**1 9 10 20 **F**9 11 12 21 22 23 26 27 28 33 34 39 44 46 48 51 52 55 58 59 61 62 63 65 69 81 82 84 85 87 88 93 94 96 97 106 108 **P**8
Primary Contact: David D. Shaffer, Chief Executive Officer
CFO: Dodie Albogest, Controller
CIO: Harriett Williams, Director Management Information
Web address: www.stonewallhospital.com

| | 23 | 10 | 70 | 3350 | 37 | 65293 | 204 | 22693 | 12214 | 313 |

□ **WILLIAM R. SHARPE, JR. HOSPITAL**, 936 Sharpe Hospital Road, Zip 26452–8550; tel. 304/269–1210 **A**1 5 9 10 **F**26 27 28 44 45 65 66 71 73 74 75 76 94 96 108 **P**6
Primary Contact: Jack C. Clohan, Jr, Chief Executive Officer
Web address: www.wvdhhr.org/sharpe

| | 12 | 22 | 156 | 746 | 156 | 0 | 0 | 26466 | 11562 | 434 |

WHEELING—Ohio County

⊠ **OHIO VALLEY MEDICAL CENTER**, 2000 Eoff Street, Zip 26003–3870; tel. 304/234–0123 **A**1 2 9 10 12 13 **F**2 4 7 9 11 12 14 15 21 22 23 26 27 28 29 30 31 32 33 34 35 37 38 39 40 41 44 45 46 47 48 49 50 52 53 55 57 58 59 60 61 62 63 64 65 66 67 69 70 71 72 73 74 77 78 81 82 84 86 87 88 90 93 94 95 96 98 106 108 109 **P**6 **S** Ohio Valley Health Services and Education Corporation, Wheeling, WV
Primary Contact: Brian K. Felici, President and Chief Executive Officer
CFO: David T. Baranik, Senior Vice President and Chief Financial Officer
CIO: Robert Panichi, Chief Information Officer
CHR: James R. Stultz, Senior Vice President, Human Resources
Web address: www.ohiovalleymedicalcenter.com

| | 23 | 10 | 171 | 6594 | 91 | 169699 | 383 | 74668 | 29770 | 757 |

⊠ **WHEELING HOSPITAL**, 1 Medical Park, Zip 26003–0708; tel. 304/243–3000, (Total facility includes 24 beds in nursing home–type unit) **A**1 2 9 10 12 13 **F**2 9 11 12 14 15 17 19 21 22 23 24 27 28 29 30 33 34 35 38 39 41 42 45 46 47 48 49 50 51 52 55 57 58 59 60 61 62 63 64 65 66 69 70 79 80 81 82 85 87 88 92 93 94 95 96 106 108 109 110 **P**5
Primary Contact: Donald H. Hofreuter, M.D., Administrator and Chief Executive Officer
CFO: M Christina Koch, Chief Financial Officer and Associate Administrator
CMO: John Dudich, M.D., President Medical and Dental Staff
CIO: Bob Travis, Director Information Systems
CHR: Dan McGee, Director Human Resources and Asistant Administrator
Web address: www.wheelinghospital.com

| | 23 | 10 | 276 | 12772 | 166 | 374960 | 939 | 169816 | 70335 | 1798 |

WILLIAMSON—Mingo County

□ **WILLIAMSON MEMORIAL HOSPITAL**, 859 Alderson Street, Zip 25661–3215, Mailing Address: P.O. Box 1980, Zip 25661–1980; tel. 304/235–2500 **A**1 9 10 **F**2 11 12 15 21 22 23 27 28 33 39 40 46 48 50 53 55 58 60 61 62 63 66 69 81 82 84 88 93 94 95 108 110 **P**6 **S** Health Management Associates, Naples, FL
Primary Contact: Jeffrey Rains, Interim Chief Executive Officer
Web address: www.hmawmh.com

| | 33 | 10 | 76 | 3085 | 35 | 46775 | 101 | 30919 | 11211 | 300 |

WV

WISCONSIN

Hospital, Address, Telephone, Approval, Facility, and Physician Codes, Health Care System	Classi-fication Codes		Utilization Data					Expense (thousands) of dollars		
★ American Hospital Association (AHA) membership □ Joint Commission on Accreditation of Healthcare Organizations (JCAHO) accreditation ○ American Osteopathic Association (AOA) accreditation △ Commission on Accreditation of Rehabilitation Facilities (CARF) accreditation	Control	Service	Staffed Beds	Admissions	Census	Outpatient Visits	Births	Total	Payroll	Personnel

AMERY—Polk County

★ **AMERY REGIONAL MEDICAL CENTER**, 225 Scholl Court, Zip 54001–1292; tel. 715/268–8000 **A**9 10 18 **F**9 11 12 27 28 30 33 42 47 52 58 59 60 61 63 65 69 81 88 94 **P**6 **S** Quorum Health Resources, Plano, TX
Primary Contact: Michael Karuschak, Jr, Chief Executive Officer
CFO: Scott D. Edin, Chief Financial Officer
CMO: Craig Johnson, M.D., Chief Medical Officer
CIO: Bill Lehner, Director Management Information Systems
CHR: Joanne Jackson, Administrator Human Resources and Community Relations
Web address: www.amerymedicalcenter.org

| | 23 | 10 | 13 | 1181 | 11 | 75876 | 155 | 21258 | 7142 | — |

ANTIGO—Langlade County

□ **LANGLADE MEMORIAL HOSPITAL**, 112 East Fifth Avenue, Zip 54409–2796; tel. 715/623–2331 **A**1 3 5 9 10 18 20 **F**1 8 9 11 12 13 14 21 27 28 33 36 37 41 44 47 52 54 55 58 59 60 61 63 65 66 69 81 82 84 87 88 94 95 107 109
Primary Contact: David R. Schneider, Executive Director
Web address: www.langlademorial.org

| | 21 | 10 | 42 | 1495 | 18 | 52128 | 205 | 36905 | 15628 | — |

APPLETON—Outagamie County

★ **APPLETON MEDICAL CENTER**, 1818 North Meade Street, Zip 54911–3496; tel. 920/731–4101 **A**2 3 5 10 **F**3 9 11 12 14 21 26 27 28 33 34 37 41 44 47 49 52 54 55 58 59 60 61 63 65 66 69 81 82 84 86 88 89 90 94 95 107 109 **P**6 8 **S** ThedaCare, Inc., Appleton, WI
Primary Contact: Kathryn Correia, Senior Vice President
COO: Matthew Furlan, Chief Operating Officer
CFO: Jacqueline Klein, Vice President Finance
CMO: Kevin Garrett, M.D., Senior Medical Director
CIO: Keith Livingston, Senior Vice President and Chief Information Officer
CHR: Nancy Gurnee, Director, Human Resources
Web address: www.thedacare.org

| | 23 | 10 | 156 | 8465 | 90 | 99427 | 1199 | 125175 | 52339 | — |

⊠ △ **ST. ELIZABETH HOSPITAL**, 1506 South Oneida Street, Zip 54915–1397; tel. 920/738–2000 **A**1 2 3 5 7 9 10 **F**2 3 4 7 9 11 12 14 15 17 19 21 22 23 26 27 28 30 33 34 35 37 39 44 47 52 54 55 56 57 58 59 60 61 62 63 64 65 66 67 68 69 71 72 73 75 76 77 78 79 80 81 82 84 85 87 88 92 93 94 95 96 98 107 108 109 110 **S** Wheaton Franciscan Services, Inc., Wheaton, IL
Primary Contact: Robert J. Turner, Chief Operating Officer
COO: Robert J. Turner, Chief Operating Officer
CFO: Jeff Badger, Chief Financial Officer
CMO: Ronald Molony, M.D., Vice President, Medical Affairs
CIO: Will Weider, Chief Information Officer
CHR: Vince Gallucci, Senior Vice President, Human Resources
Web address: www.affinityhealth.org

| | 21 | 10 | 191 | 7868 | 93 | 77729 | 1288 | 101762 | 42634 | 729 |

ARCADIA—Trempealeau County

□ **FRANCISCAN SKEMP HEALTHCARE–ARCADIA CAMPUS**, 464 South St. Joseph Avenue, Zip 54612–1401; tel. 608/323–3341, (Total facility includes 75 beds in nursing home–type unit) **A**1 9 10 18 **F**3 9 11 26 27 28 33 37 44 47 52 59 60 63 65 66 69 81 92 94 95 **S** Mayo Foundation, Rochester, MN
Primary Contact: Robert M. Tracey, Administrator, Regional Hospitals
Web address: www.mayo.edu/fsh/

| | 21 | 10 | 100 | 395 | 76 | 17456 | 50 | 3827 | 2058 | 53 |

ASHLAND—Ashland County

⊠ **MEMORIAL MEDICAL CENTER**, 1615 Maple Lane, Zip 54806–3689; tel. 715/685–5500 **A**1 9 10 20 **F**2 3 4 9 11 12 14 22 26 27 32 33 39 44 46 47 52 53 55 57 58 59 60 61 62 63 64 65 68 69 71 72 73 74 75 76 77 78 81 82 84 87 88 94 95 96 106 107 108 110 **P**6
Primary Contact: Daniel J. Hymans, President
CFO: Les Whiteaker, Vice President for Finance and Information
CMO: Craig Florine, M.D., President Medical Staff
CIO: Todd Reynolds, Chief Information Officer
Web address: www.ashlandmmc.com

| | 23 | 10 | 100 | 3367 | 39 | 35113 | 275 | 37195 | 17777 | 388 |

BALDWIN—St. Croix County

★ **BALDWIN AREA MEDICAL CENTER**, 730 10th Avenue, Zip 54002–0300, Mailing Address: P.O. Box 300, Zip 54002–0300; tel. 715/684–3311 **A**9 10 18 **F**2 9 11 12 14 21 22 23 24 27 29 30 33 34 37 41 46 47 48 52 55 58 59 60 61 63 64 65 66 68 69 70 81 82 88 94 95 96 97 106 110
Primary Contact: Richard L. Range, Chief Executive Officer
CFO: Karen Traynor, Chief Financial Officer
CMO: Clemma Nash, M.D., Chief of Staff
CIO: Scott Swedien, Information Services Director
CHR: Trudy Acterhof, Human Resources Director
Web address: www.baldwinhospital.com

| | 23 | 10 | 25 | 1127 | 9 | 39000 | 94 | 19429 | 7624 | 168 |

Many Facility Codes have changed. Please refer to the AHA Guide Code Chart. © 2005 AHA Guide

Hospital, Address, Telephone, Approval, Facility, and Physician Codes, Health Care System	Classi- fication Codes		Utilization Data					Expense (thousands) of dollars		
★ American Hospital Association (AHA) membership □ Joint Commission on Accreditation of Healthcare Organizations (JCAHO) accreditation ○ American Osteopathic Association (AOA) accreditation △ Commission on Accreditation of Rehabilitation Facilities (CARF) accreditation	Control	Service	Staffed Beds	Admissions	Census	Outpatient Visits	Births	Total	Payroll	Personnel

BARABOO—Sauk County

✠ **ST. CLARE HOSPITAL AND HEALTH SERVICES**, 707 14th Street, Zip 53913–1597; tel. 608/356–1400 **A**1 3 5 9 10 **F**2 3 4 9 11 12 21 22 26 27 28 29 31 33 37 41 44 47 49 52 54 58 59 61 62 63 65 69 70 71 75 76 77 80 81 88 93 94 95 106 107 108 110 **S** SSM Health Care, Saint Louis, MO
Primary Contact: Sandra L. Anderson, President
CFO: Troy Walker, Director Finance
CIO: Alan Steevens, Director Management Information
CHR: Marilyn Forbush, Director Human Resources
Web address: www.stclare.com

| 21 | 10 | 84 | 3082 | 31 | 39643 | 309 | 35317 | 16077 | 363 |

BARRON—Barron County

□ **BARRON MEDICAL CENTER–MAYO HEALTH SYSTEM**, 1222 Woodland Avenue, Zip 54812–1798; tel. 715/537–3186, (Total facility includes 50 beds in nursing home–type unit) (Nonreporting) **A**1 9 10 18 **S** Mayo Foundation, Rochester, MN
Primary Contact: Bradley D. Groseth, Administrator
Web address: www.barronmedicalcenter.org

| 23 | 10 | 75 | — | — | — | — | — | — | — |

BEAVER DAM—Dodge County

✠ **BEAVER DAM COMMUNITY HOSPITALS**, 707 South University Avenue, Zip 53916–3089; tel. 920/887–7181, (Total facility includes 123 beds in nursing home–type unit) **A**1 9 10 19 **F**3 8 9 12 14 21 26 27 28 33 41 44 47 52 54 55 58 59 60 61 63 65 66 68 69 71 81 88 92 94 95 107 109
Primary Contact: John R. Landdeck, President
CFO: Scott Abrams, Vice President Finance
CIO: Carol Ciancio, Health Information Systems Director
CHR: Tam Cohen, Director, Employee Services
Web address: www.bdch.org

| 23 | 10 | 216 | 2884 | 143 | 78953 | 383 | 44279 | 18765 | 545 |

BELOIT—Rock County

□ △ **BELOIT MEMORIAL HOSPITAL**, 1969 West Hart Road, Zip 53511–2299; tel. 608/364–5011 **A**1 7 9 10 **F**4 7 9 11 12 14 15 21 23 26 27 28 29 30 33 34 37 40 41 42 44 46 47 48 49 51 52 53 55 57 58 59 60 61 62 63 64 65 66 68 69 70 72 73 74 75 76 77 79 80 81 82 84 85 87 88 93 94 95 96 106 107 108 109 110 **P**1
Primary Contact: Gregory K. Britton, President and Chief Executive Officer
Web address: www.beloitmemorialhospital.org

| 23 | 10 | 124 | 5109 | 63 | 153106 | 712 | 77928 | 32905 | 813 |

BERLIN—Green Lake County

□ **BERLIN MEMORIAL HOSPITAL**, 225 Memorial Drive, Zip 54923–1295; tel. 920/361–1313, (Includes JULIETTE MANOR NURSING HOME, COMMUNITY CLINICS), (Total facility includes 86 beds in nursing home–type unit) **A**1 9 10 **F**8 9 11 12 14 21 26 27 28 33 34 37 41 42 44 47 51 52 54 55 58 59 60 61 63 65 67 69 81 82 84 87 88 91 92 94 95 107 109
Primary Contact: Craig W. C. Schmidt, President and Chief Executive Officer
Web address: www.communityhealthnetwork.org

| 23 | 10 | 135 | 2197 | 90 | 65401 | 235 | 38765 | 19956 | 261 |

BLACK RIVER FALLS—Jackson County

BLACK RIVER MEMORIAL HOSPITAL, 711 West Adams Street, Zip 54615–9113; tel. 715/284–5361 **A**9 10 18 **F**3 26 27 28 33 36 44 47 52 54 58 59 60 63 65 68 69 81 84 88 94 95 107
Primary Contact: Stanley J. Gaynor, Chief Executive Officer
Web address: www.blackriverhospital.com

| 23 | 10 | 25 | 1201 | 11 | 31920 | 151 | 15303 | 6452 | 158 |

BLOOMER—Chippewa County

□ **BLOOMER MEMORIAL MEDICAL CENTER**, 1501 Thompson Street, Zip 54724–1299; tel. 715/568–2000, (Total facility includes 45 beds in nursing home–type unit) **A**1 9 10 18 **F**3 12 22 24 27 28 29 33 44 45 46 47 48 52 53 58 60 63 65 68 69 81 92 94 96 97 106 107 108 110 **P**6 **S** Mayo Foundation, Rochester, MN
Primary Contact: Colleen Skold, Administrator
Web address: www.bloomermedicalcenter.org

| 23 | 10 | 70 | 632 | 51 | 16406 | 0 | 6796 | 3227 | — |

BOSCOBEL—Grant County

BOSCOBEL AREA HEALTH CARE, 205 Parker Street, Zip 53805–1698; tel. 608/375–4112, (Total facility includes 66 beds in nursing home–type unit) **A**9 10 18 **F**1 2 3 4 9 11 12 22 23 29 31 33 34 35 37 42 44 46 47 48 52 53 55 58 59 60 61 62 63 65 66 68 69 70 71 72 73 74 76 77 81 84 87 88 92 93 94 96 97 98 106 107 108 110 **P**6
Primary Contact: Gary Bezucha, Administrator
Web address: www.boscobelhealth.com

| 23 | 10 | 110 | 1442 | 77 | 3875 | 64 | 13108 | 6340 | 179 |

BROOKFIELD—Waukesha County

✠ △ **ELMBROOK MEMORIAL HOSPITAL**, 19333 West North Avenue, Zip 53045–4198; tel. 262/785–2000 **A**1 7 9 10 **F**2 3 9 11 12 14 21 22 23 26 27 28 29 30 33 34 44 45 46 47 48 52 54 55 56 57 58 59 60 61 62 63 64 65 66 68 69 70 73 79 80 81 82 83 84 85 87 88 93 94 95 96 106 108 109 **S** Wheaton Franciscan Services, Inc., Wheaton, IL
Primary Contact: Kimry A. Johnsrud, President
CFO: Annette Schiebel, Controller
Web address: www.covhealth.org

| 21 | 10 | 92 | 6434 | 70 | 83987 | 752 | 89820 | 31877 | 644 |

WI

Hospital, Address, Telephone, Approval, Facility, and Physician Codes, Health Care System	Classi-fication Codes		Utilization Data					Expense (thousands) of dollars		
★ American Hospital Association (AHA) membership □ Joint Commission on Accreditation of Healthcare Organizations (JCAHO) accreditation ○ American Osteopathic Association (AOA) accreditation △ Commission on Accreditation of Rehabilitation Facilities (CARF) accreditation	Control	Service	Staffed Beds	Admissions	Census	Outpatient Visits	Births	Total	Payroll	Personnel

BURLINGTON—Racine County

✚ **MEMORIAL HOSPITAL CORPORATION OF BURLINGTON**, 252 McHenry Street, Zip 53105–1828; tel. 262/767–6000 **A**1 9 10 **F**2 9 11 12 14 15 21 22 26 27 28 29 33 35 37 39 40 41 44 45 46 47 48 49 52 53 55 57 58 59 62 63 65 66 69 73 81 82 84 85 87 88 94 95 96 106 108 110 **S** Aurora Health Care, Milwaukee, WI
Primary Contact: Ann R. Navera, R.N., Administrator and Chief Nurse Executive
COO: Loren J. Anderson, Executive Vice President
CFO: E Stuart Arnett, Vice President Finance and Chief Financial Officer
CMO: Arthur Rein, M.D., Chief of Staff
CIO: Jean Chase, Regional Manager Information Services
CHR: Gene Krauklis, Regional Vice President Human Resources
Web address: www.aurorahealthcare.org

	23	10	65	3475	36	59188	408	52751	18663	472

CHILTON—Calumet County

□ **CALUMET MEDICAL CENTER**, 614 Memorial Drive, Zip 53014–1597; tel. 920/849–2386 **A**1 9 10 18 **F**2 6 9 12 21 28 29 33 34 37 39 44 47 48 52 54 58 61 62 63 65 69 75 81 85 88 94 95 97 107
Primary Contact: Lea Whitby, President and Chief Executive Officer
Web address: www.affinityhealth.org

	23	10	25	659	8	37308	0	13176	5819	152

CHIPPEWA FALLS—Chippewa County

✚ **ST. JOSEPH'S HOSPITAL**, 2661 County Highway I, Zip 54729–1498; tel. 715/723–1811 **A**1 9 10 **F**2 3 4 9 11 12 14 21 22 23 26 27 28 29 30 33 36 37 39 44 46 47 48 51 52 55 58 59 60 61 62 63 65 66 67 75 81 82 84 85 93 94 96 98 106 108 110 **S** Hospital Sisters Health System, Springfield, IL
Primary Contact: David B. Fish, Executive Vice President and Administrator
CFO: Robert Koehler, Financial Service Manager
CMO: Michael Walton, M.D., Chief of Staff
CIO: Kevin Groskreutz, Information Systems Coordinator
CHR: Carolyn Craft, Human Resources Director
Web address: www.stjoeschipfalls.com

	21	10	127	3788	42	60824	460	43476	20481	438

COLUMBUS—Columbia County

✚ **COLUMBUS COMMUNITY HOSPITAL**, 1515 Park Avenue, Zip 53925–1618; tel. 920/623–2200 **A**1 9 10 18 **F**2 11 12 13 14 21 22 26 27 28 29 33 35 44 46 47 48 52 55 58 59 60 61 63 65 67 69 70 81 88 94 96 97 106 107 108 109
Primary Contact: Edward A. Harding, FACHE, President and Chief Executive Officer
CFO: Roger Sneath, Vice President and Chief Financial Officer
CMO: Bruce A. Kraus, M.D., Chief of Staff
CIO: Lori Cherrier, Director Health Information
CHR: Ann Roundy, Director of Employee Services
Web address: www.cch–inc.com

	23	10	25	1593	13	24898	134	17533	9011	180

CUBA CITY—Grant County

SOUTHWEST HEALTH CENTER NURSING HOME See Southwest Health Center, Platteville

CUDAHY—Milwaukee County

ST. LUKE'S SOUTH SHORE See St. Luke's Medical Center, Milwaukee

CUMBERLAND—Barron County

□ **CUMBERLAND MEMORIAL HOSPITAL**, 1110 Seventh Avenue, Zip 54829–9133; tel. 715/822–2741, (Total facility includes 50 beds in nursing home–type unit) **A**1 9 10 **F**3 6 9 11 12 21 27 28 33 34 41 44 47 52 58 59 60 63 65 66 71 75 76 77 91 92 94 95 **P**6
Primary Contact: Robert J. Hansen, Chief Executive Officer and Administrator
Web address: www.cumberlandhealthcare.com

	23	10	90	1816	67	8748	84	11423	5883	160

DARLINGTON—Lafayette County

MEMORIAL HOSPITAL OF LAFAYETTE COUNTY, 800 Clay Street, Zip 53530–1228, Mailing Address: P.O. Box 70, Zip 53530–0070; tel. 608/776–4466 **A**9 10 18 **F**2 3 9 11 12 21 23 26 27 28 29 33 34 46 47 52 53 57 58 59 61 62 63 65 66 68 69 70 71 75 81 84 88 94 97 106
Primary Contact: Sherry Kudronowicz, Administrator
Web address: www.mhlc–mhf.org

	13	10	25	665	5	25137	38	6730	2076	70

DODGEVILLE—Iowa County

✚ **UPLAND HILLS HEALTH**, 800 Compassion Way, Zip 53533–0800, Mailing Address: P.O. Box 800, Zip 53533–0800; tel. 608/930–8000, (Total facility includes 44 beds in nursing home–type unit) **A**1 9 10 18 **F**1 9 11 12 14 21 26 27 28 33 36 37 41 42 44 47 51 52 55 58 59 60 61 63 65 66 67 68 69 81 84 86 88 92 94 95 107 109
Primary Contact: Phyllis Fritsch, Interim Administrator
COO: Steve McCarthy, Assistant Administrator and Strategic Business Operations
CFO: Karl Pustina, Assistant Administrator for Finance
CIO: Phyllis Fritsch, Health Information Management Director
CHR: Troy Marx, Human Resources Director
Web address: www.uplandhillshealth.org

	23	10	84	1277	53	45440	280	19006	8070	200

DURAND—Pepin County

★ **CHIPPEWA VALLEY HOSPITAL AND OAKVIEW CARE CENTER**, 1220 Third Avenue West, Zip 54736–1600, Mailing Address: P.O. Box 224, Zip 54736–0224; tel. 715/672–4211, (Total facility includes 58 beds in nursing home–type unit) **A**9 10 18 **F**3 12 21 27 28 33 44 47 52 54 58 63 65 66 81 92 94 **S** Adventist Health System Sunbelt Health Care Corporation, Winter Park, FL
Primary Contact: Douglas R. Peterson, President and Chief Executive Officer

	21	10	83	588	62	7838	0	8584	3869	75

WI

Many Facility Codes have changed. Please refer to the AHA Guide Code Chart.   © 2005 AHA Guide

Hospital, Address, Telephone, Approval, Facility, and Physician Codes, Health Care System	Classi-fication Codes		Utilization Data					Expense (thousands) of dollars		
	Control	Service	Staffed Beds	Admissions	Census	Outpatient Visits	Births	Total	Payroll	Personnel

★ American Hospital Association (AHA) membership
□ Joint Commission on Accreditation of Healthcare Organizations (JCAHO) accreditation
○ American Osteopathic Association (AOA) accreditation
△ Commission on Accreditation of Rehabilitation Facilities (CARF) accreditation

EAGLE RIVER—Vilas County

★ **EAGLE RIVER MEMORIAL HOSPITAL**, 201 Hospital Road, Zip 54521–8835; tel. 715/479–7411 **A**9 10 18 **F**2 6 9 12 22 26 27 28 29 33 41 44 45 46 47 48 52 54 58 63 64 65 70 79 81 88 93 96 97 107 108 **S** Marian Health System, Tulsa, OK
Primary Contact: Patricia Van Acker, R.N., Administrator
CFO: Jack P. Sutliff, Vice President and Chief Financial Officer
CHR: Karen Tart, Vice President Human Resources
Web address: www.ministryhealth.org
| 23 | 10 | 8 | 700 | 6 | 32222 | 0 | 12341 | 4362 | 86 |

EAU CLAIRE—Eau Claire County

□ **LUTHER HOSPITAL**, 1221 Whipple Street, Zip 54702–4105, Mailing Address: P.O. Box 5, Zip 54702–0005; tel. 715/838–3311 **A**1 3 5 9 10 **F**3 4 9 11 12 14 26 27 28 33 34 37 41 47 49 52 55 56 58 59 60 61 63 65 66 71 72 73 74 75 76 77 78 81 82 84 87 88 94 109 **S** Mayo Foundation, Rochester, MN
Primary Contact: Randall Linton, M.D., President and Chief Executive Officer
Web address: www.mhs.mayo.edu
| 23 | 10 | 172 | 8932 | 96 | 143373 | 706 | 118845 | 51234 | — |

□ **OAK LEAF SURGICAL CENTER**, 3802 West Oakwood Mall Drive, Zip 54701; tel. 715/831–8130 **A**1 9 10 **F**37 40 52 58 63 88 94
Primary Contact: Dale Larson, Administrator
| 32 | 10 | 13 | 411 | 3 | 4539 | 0 | 13795 | 3906 | — |

⊞ △ **SACRED HEART HOSPITAL**, 900 West Clairemont Avenue, Zip 54701–6122; tel. 715/839–4121 **A**1 2 3 5 7 9 10 **F**9 11 12 14 21 26 27 28 31 33 34 37 41 42 44 47 49 52 54 55 56 58 59 60 61 63 65 66 67 68 69 71 72 73 74 76 81 82 84 86 87 88 94 109 **S** Hospital Sisters Health System, Springfield, IL
Primary Contact: Stephen F. Ronstrom, Executive Vice President and Administrator
CFO: Patricia Huettl, Assistant Administrator Financial Services
CMO: James Geraghty, M.D., President Medical Staff
CIO: Robert Hassemer, Division Director Human Resources
CHR: Robert Hassemer, Division Director Human Resources
Web address: www.sacredhearthospital–ec.org
| 21 | 10 | 194 | 8991 | 121 | 121638 | 1154 | 107480 | 44989 | 999 |

EDGERTON—Rock County

★ **MEMORIAL COMMUNITY HOSPITAL**, 313 Stoughton Road, Zip 53534–1198; tel. 608/884–3441, (Total facility includes 61 beds in nursing home–type unit) **A**9 10 18 **F**2 12 33 34 44 47 48 51 52 54 63 64 65 68 69 70 81 85 92 94 97 107 108 **S** Brim Healthcare, Inc., Brentwood, TN
Primary Contact: Ronald V. Wolff, Interim Chief Executive Officer
CFO: Charles Roader, Vice President Finance
CMO: Thomas Berentsen, M.D., Chief of Staff
CIO: Sheryl Rucker
CHR: Brad Young, Human Resources Director
Web address: www.edgertonhospital.com
| 23 | 10 | 86 | 650 | 68 | 1405 | 0 | 13582 | 6465 | 127 |

ELKHORN—Walworth County

⊞ △ **AURORA LAKELAND MEDICAL CENTER**, W3985 County Road NN, Zip 53121–4389; tel. 262/741–2000 **A**1 7 9 10 **F**2 9 11 12 14 21 22 23 26 27 28 29 33 35 37 39 40 44 45 46 47 48 49 52 53 55 57 58 59 61 62 63 65 66 68 69 73 81 82 84 85 87 88 93 94 95 96 106 108 110 **S** Aurora Health Care, Milwaukee, WI
Primary Contact: Kathleen Skowlund, R.N., MS, Administrator and Chief Nurse Executive
COO: Loren J. Anderson, Executive Vice President
CFO: E Stuart Arnett, Regional Vice President Finance
CMO: Chad Kort, M.D., Medical Staff President
CIO: Jean Chase, Regional Manager Information Services
CHR: Gene Krauklis, Regional Vice President Human Resources
Web address: www.aurorahealthcare.org
| 23 | 10 | 75 | 4565 | 42 | 55850 | 636 | 50753 | 18599 | 421 |

FOND DU LAC—Fond Du Lac County

⊞ △ **AGNESIAN HEALTHCARE**, 430 East Division Street, Zip 54935–0385, Mailing Address: P.O. Box 385, Zip 54936–0385; tel. 920/929–2300 **A**1 2 7 9 10 20 **F**1 2 3 4 9 11 12 14 15 19 21 22 23 26 27 28 29 31 33 34 35 36 37 39 40 43 44 45 46 47 48 49 51 52 53 54 55 57 58 59 60 61 62 63 64 65 66 67 68 69 71 72 73 74 75 76 77 78 79 81 82 84 85 87 88 92 93 94 95 96 106 107 108 109 110 **P**3
Primary Contact: Robert A. Fale, President and Chief Executive Officer
CFO: Steven N. Little, Chief Financial Officer
CMO: Kirk Veit, M.D., Medical Director
CHR: Norma Tirado, Vice President Employee Relations and Staff Organizational Development
Web address: www.agnesian.com
| 21 | 10 | 176 | 7380 | 90 | 173828 | 990 | 168246 | 55685 | 782 |

FOND DU LAC COUNTY MENTAL HEALTH CENTER, 459 East First Street, Zip 54935–4599; tel. 920/929–3571 **A**10 **F**3 26 27 28 31 71 72 75 76 94 **P**6
Primary Contact: Don Stout, Administrator
| 13 | 22 | 25 | 1002 | 15 | 371 | 0 | 2943 | 1636 | — |

FORT ATKINSON—Jefferson County

⊞ **FORT HEALTHCARE**, 611 East Sherman Avenue, Zip 53538–1998; tel. 920/568–5000, (Total facility includes 28 beds in nursing home–type unit) **A**1 9 10 **F**2 4 9 11 12 13 14 21 26 27 28 29 33 37 41 42 44 46 47 48 51 52 53 55 58 59 60 61 62 63 65 66 67 68 69 81 82 84 87 88 92 93 94 95 96 106 107 108 109 **P**5 7
Primary Contact: Gregory A. Banaszynski, President and Chief Executive Officer
CFO: James J. Nelson, Vice President Fiscal Services
CIO: James E. Dahl, Manager Information Systems
Web address: www.forthealthsource.com
| 23 | 10 | 100 | 3672 | 51 | 159297 | 471 | 61700 | 26679 | 556 |

WI

Many Facility Codes have changed. Please refer to the AHA Guide Code Chart.

Hospital, Address, Telephone, Approval, Facility, and Physician Codes, Health Care System	Classi- fication Codes		Utilization Data					Expense (thousands) of dollars		
★ American Hospital Association (AHA) membership □ Joint Commission on Accreditation of Healthcare Organizations (JCAHO) accreditation ○ American Osteopathic Association (AOA) accreditation △ Commission on Accreditation of Rehabilitation Facilities (CARF) accreditation	Control	Service	Staffed Beds	Admissions	Census	Outpatient Visits	Births	Total	Payroll	Personnel

FRIENDSHIP—Adams County

MOUNDVIEW MEMORIAL HOSPITAL & CLINICS, 402 West Lake Street, Zip 53934–0040, Mailing Address: P.O. Box 40, Zip 53934–0040; tel. 608/339–3331, (Total facility includes 18 beds in nursing home–type unit) **A**9 10 18 **F**1 6 8 9 12 21 27 31 33 42 44 47 51 52 58 60 63 65 66 68 69 81 87 88 92 94 95 **P**5 6
Primary Contact: Janet M. Herrell, Chief Executive Officer
Web address: www.moundview.org

| | 23 | 10 | 43 | 677 | 26 | 33210 | 0 | 11883 | 5592 | 149 |

GLENDALE—Milwaukee County

ORTHOPAEDIC HOSPITAL OF WISCONSIN – GLENDALE, 575 West River Woods Parkway, Zip 53212; tel. 414/961–6800 **A**9 10 **F**3 26 37 41 47 52 63 65 69 84 95 **P**2
Primary Contact: Susan Henckel, Chief Executive Officer

| | 32 | 10 | 7 | 274 | 1 | 31169 | 0 | 10501 | 3580 | — |

GRANTSBURG—Burnett County

★ **BURNETT MEDICAL CENTER**, 257 West St. George Avenue, Zip 54840–7827; tel. 715/463–5353, (Total facility includes 53 beds in nursing home–type unit) **A**9 10 18 **F**1 2 11 12 21 23 26 27 28 29 33 44 46 47 48 52 53 58 59 60 61 63 64 65 66 68 69 70 81 92 94 95 97 107 **P**6 **S** Brim Healthcare, Inc., Brentwood, TN
Primary Contact: Timothy J. Wick, Chief Executive Officer
CFO: Charles J. Faught, Chief Financial Officer
CHR: Linda Price, Human Resources Director
Web address: www.burnettmedicalcenter.com

| | 23 | 10 | 70 | 626 | 56 | 31130 | 48 | 9224 | 4079 | 85 |

GREEN BAY—Brown County

⊠ △ **AURORA BAYCARE MEDICAL CENTER**, 2845 Greenbrier Road, Zip 54311, Mailing Address: P.O. Box 8900, Zip 54308; tel. 920/288–8000 **A**1 7 9 10 **F**2 11 12 14 15 17 19 21 22 23 26 27 28 29 30 33 34 35 37 39 41 42 46 47 48 52 55 56 57 58 59 61 62 63 64 65 66 68 69 79 80 81 82 83 84 85 87 88 93 94 95 106 107 108 109 110 **S** Aurora Health Care, Milwaukee, WI
Primary Contact: Linda Smith, Administrator
CFO: Sandra Ewald, Vice President Finance
CMO: Lane Goolsby, M.D., Chief of Staff
CIO: Chuck Geurts, Manager Information Services
CHR: Gwen Baumel, Vice President, Human Resources
Web address: www.aurorabaycare.com

| | 32 | 10 | 126 | 6863 | 72 | 64168 | 1126 | 120111 | 38789 | 915 |

⊠ **BELLIN MEMORIAL HOSPITAL**, 744 South Webster Avenue, Zip 54301–3581, Mailing Address: P.O. Box 23400, Zip 54305–3400; tel. 920/433–3500 **A**1 9 10 **F**9 11 12 14 21 26 27 28 30 33 37 40 41 42 44 47 51 52 58 59 60 61 63 65 66 82 87 88 94 95 107 **P**6 8
Primary Contact: George Kerwin, President
COO: Robert W. Fry, Operations Leader
CFO: David Albrecht, Executive Vice President and Chief Financial Officer
CMO: Christopher Watson, M.D., Chief Medical Officer
Web address: www.bellin.org

| | 21 | 10 | 167 | 7355 | 77 | 299601 | 1269 | 191879 | 84330 | 1719 |

□ **BELLIN PSYCHIATRIC CENTER**, 301 East St. Joseph Street, Zip 54301–2241, Mailing Address: P.O. Box 23725, Zip 54305–3725; tel. 920/433–3630 **A**1 9 10 **F**3 4 21 26 27 31 42 44 47 61 65 66 71 72 73 74 75 76 77 78 94 **P**6
Primary Contact: Linda Roethle, President
Web address: www.bellin.org

| | 21 | 22 | 53 | 1609 | 22 | 50242 | 0 | — | — | 125 |

BROWN COUNTY HUMAN SERVICES MENTAL HEALTH CENTER, 2900 St. Anthony Drive, Zip 54311–5899; tel. 920/468–1136 **A**10 **F**3 4 52 58 71 72 74 75 76 77 94
Primary Contact: Earlene Ronk, Administrator

| | 13 | 22 | 37 | 1675 | 26 | 4807 | 0 | 6897 | 3434 | — |

⊠ **ST. MARY'S HOSPITAL MEDICAL CENTER**, 1726 Shawano Avenue, Zip 54303–3282; tel. 920/498–4200 **A**1 9 10 **F**2 11 12 14 21 22 23 24 26 27 28 29 33 34 35 37 39 40 41 45 46 47 48 52 53 54 55 57 58 59 61 62 63 65 66 67 70 81 82 83 85 87 88 90 94 96 98 106 107 108 109 110 **P**2 **S** Hospital Sisters Health System, Springfield, IL
Primary Contact: James G. Coller, Executive Vice President and Administrator
CFO: John Miller, Chief Financial Officer
Web address: www.stmgb.org

| | 21 | 10 | 94 | 5437 | 51 | 89983 | 566 | 75000 | 32518 | 589 |

⊠ △ **ST. VINCENT HOSPITAL**, 835 South Van Buren Street, Zip 54307–3508, Mailing Address: P.O. Box 13508, Zip 54307–3508; tel. 920/433–0111 **A**1 2 7 9 10 **F**2 7 9 11 12 14 15 21 22 23 24 26 27 28 29 30 32 33 34 37 40 44 46 47 48 49 51 52 53 54 55 56 57 58 59 60 61 62 63 64 65 66 67 68 69 79 80 81 82 83 85 86 87 88 93 94 96 98 106 108 109 110 **P**2 **S** Hospital Sisters Health System, Springfield, IL
Primary Contact: Joseph J. Neidenbach, Executive Vice President and Administrator
CFO: Karl Appleton, Assistant Administrator and Chief Financial Officer
CMO: James McGovern, M.D., President Medical Staff
CIO: Rohan Corea, Director Information Services
CHR: Jean Marsch, Director Human Resources
Web address: www.stvgb.org

| | 21 | 10 | 275 | 12618 | 168 | 115044 | 1364 | 192618 | 86366 | 1796 |

WI

Many Facility Codes have changed. Please refer to the AHA Guide Code Chart.

© 2005 AHA Guide

Hospital, Address, Telephone, Approval, Facility, and Physician Codes, Health Care System	Classification Codes		Utilization Data					Expense (thousands) of dollars		
	Control	Service	Staffed Beds	Admissions	Census	Outpatient Visits	Births	Total	Payroll	Personnel

★ American Hospital Association (AHA) membership
□ Joint Commission on Accreditation of Healthcare Organizations (JCAHO) accreditation
○ American Osteopathic Association (AOA) accreditation
△ Commission on Accreditation of Rehabilitation Facilities (CARF) accreditation

HARTFORD—Washington County

⊞ **AURORA MEDICAL CENTER OF WASHINGTON COUNTY**, 1032 East Sumner Street, Zip 53027–1698; tel. 262/673–2300 **A**1 9 10 **F**1 2 9 11 12 14 21 22 27 28 29 30 33 34 35 37 39 41 44 45 46 47 48 52 53 54 55 57 58 59 62 63 64 65 69 70 81 82 85 87 88 92 93 94 95 96 97 98 106 108 110 **S** Aurora Health Care, Milwaukee, WI
Primary Contact: Mark Schwartz, Administrator
CMO: William T. Erbes, D.D.S., Chief of Staff
Web address: www.aurorahealthcare.org

	23	10	55	2238	31	55492	319	38016	14313	312

HAYWARD—Sawyer County

★ **HAYWARD AREA MEMORIAL HOSPITAL AND NURSING HOME**, 11040 North State Road 77, Zip 54843–6391; tel. 715/934–4321, (Total facility includes 76 beds in nursing home–type unit) **A**9 10 18 **F**2 9 11 12 23 26 27 28 29 33 47 52 58 59 63 65 70 75 81 85 88 92 94 97 106 108
Primary Contact: Barbara A. Peickert, R.N., Chief Executive Officer
Web address: www.hamhnh.com

	23	10	117	1477	81	18511	160	16088	7694	133

HILLSBORO—Vernon County

★ **ST. JOSEPH'S COMMUNITY HEALTH SERVICES**, 400 Water Avenue, Zip 54634–0527, Mailing Address: P.O. Box 527, Zip 54634–0527; tel. 608/489–8000, (Total facility includes 65 beds in nursing home–type unit) **A**9 10 18 **F**9 11 12 21 27 28 33 34 41 44 47 58 59 60 63 65 68 69 81 92 94 95 107 **P**6
Primary Contact: Billy J. Bruce, Jr, Chief Executive Officer and President
CFO: Nick Bottom, Chief Financial Officer and Vice President Finance
CHR: Kristie McCoil, Human Resources Director
Web address: www.stjhealthcare.org

	21	10	74	596	67	19447	18	10713	4792	105

HUDSON—St. Croix County

□ **HUDSON HOSPITAL**, 405 Stageline Road, Zip 54016–1600; tel. 715/531–6000 **A**1 9 10 18 **F**2 4 9 11 12 23 26 27 28 29 32 33 35 39 41 44 45 46 47 52 54 58 59 62 63 64 65 66 69 70 81 84 88 94 96 97 106 108 110
Primary Contact: Marian M. Furlong, R.N., Chief Executive Officer
Web address: www.hudsonhospital.org

	23	10	28	1832	15	20512	308	22344	8207	244

JANESVILLE—Rock County

⊞ **MERCY HEALTH SYSTEM**, 1000 Mineral Point Avenue, Zip 53547–2982, Mailing Address: P.O. Box 5003, Zip 53547–5003; tel. 608/756–6000, (Total facility includes 24 beds in nursing home–type unit) **A**1 2 9 10 **F**3 4 7 9 11 12 14 21 26 28 30 31 33 34 37 40 41 42 44 47 49 52 58 59 60 61 63 65 66 67 68 69 71 72 73 74 75 76 77 78 81 82 84 86 87 88 90 92 94 95 107 109 **P**5 6
Primary Contact: Javon R. Bea, President and Chief Executive Officer
CFO: Joseph D. Nemeth, Vice President and Chief Financial Officer
Web address: www.mercyhealthsystem.org

	23	10	191	9137	120	872195	1262	254911	59093	1915

KENOSHA—Kenosha County

⊞ **AURORA MEDICAL CENTER**, 10400 South 75th Street, Zip 53142; tel. 262/948–5600 **A**1 9 10 **F**2 9 11 12 14 21 22 23 26 27 28 29 33 35 37 39 40 42 44 45 46 47 48 49 52 53 55 57 58 59 62 63 65 66 69 73 79 80 81 82 84 87 88 93 94 95 96 106 108 110 **S** Aurora Health Care, Milwaukee, WI
Primary Contact: Christine Olson, Administrator
CFO: Stuart Arnett, Vice President of Finance
CMO: Alfred J. Capelli, M.D., President Medical Staff
CIO: Jean Chase, Regional Manager Information Services
CHR: Gene Krauklis, Regional Vice President Human Resources
Web address: www.aurorahealthcare.org

	23	10	72	4905	56	77918	1039	67183	23376	526

□ **CHILDREN'S HOSPITAL OF WISCONSIN**, 6308 Eighth Avenue, 6th Floor, Zip 53143–5082; tel. 262/656–2261 **A**1 9 10 **F**2 21 26 27 28 29 31 39 47 52 53 58 65 66 94 **P**1 5
Primary Contact: Ron Benner, Chief Executive Officer

	23	10	23	912	4	1058	0	3743	968	15

□ **UNITED HEALTH SYSTEM—KENOSHA CAMPUS**, 6308 Eighth Avenue, Zip 53143–5082; tel. 262/656–2011, (Nonreporting) **A**1 9 10
Primary Contact: Richard O. Schmidt, Jr, President and Chief Executive Officer

	23	10	151	—	—	—	—	—	—	—

LA CROSSE—La Crosse County

□ **FRANCISCAN SKEMP HEALTHCARE–LA CROSSE CAMPUS**, 700 West Avenue South, Zip 54601–4783; tel. 608/785–0940, (Total facility includes 17 beds in nursing home–type unit) **A**1 2 9 10 **F**3 7 8 9 11 14 21 26 28 31 33 34 37 41 44 52 54 55 56 58 59 61 63 66 67 68 69 71 73 74 75 76 78 81 82 84 87 88 92 94 95 **P**6 **S** Mayo Foundation, Rochester, MN
Primary Contact: Robert Nesse, M.D., President and Chief Executive Officer
Web address: www.franciscanskemp.org

	21	10	226	7279	91	63182	722	90673	43530	

⊞ △ **GUNDERSEN LUTHERAN MEDICAL CENTER**, (Formerly Gundersen Lutheran), 1910 South Avenue, Zip 54601–9980; tel. 608/785–0530 **A**1 2 3 5 7 8 9 10 **F**3 4 7 9 11 14 21 26 27 28 30 31 33 34 36 37 40 42 44 47 49 50 51 52 54 55 56 59 60 61 63 65 66 67 68 69 71 72 73 74 75 76 77 94 109
Primary Contact: Jeffrey E. Thompson, M.D., Chief Executive Officer
CMO: Julio J. Bird, M.D., Chief Medical Officer
CIO: Deb Rislow, Director Information Systems
Web address: www.gundluth.org

	23	10	256	15379	174	148330	1585	207532	64961	

WI

Hospital, Address, Telephone, Approval, Facility, and Physician Codes, Health Care System	Classi-fication Codes		Utilization Data					Expense (thousands) of dollars		
★ American Hospital Association (AHA) membership □ Joint Commission on Accreditation of Healthcare Organizations (JCAHO) accreditation ○ American Osteopathic Association (AOA) accreditation △ Commission on Accreditation of Rehabilitation Facilities (CARF) accreditation	Control	Service	Staffed Beds	Admissions	Census	Outpatient Visits	Births	Total	Payroll	Personnel

LADYSMITH—Rusk County

★ **RUSK COUNTY MEMORIAL HOSPITAL AND NURSING HOME**, 900 College Avenue West, Zip 54848–2116; tel. 715/532–5561, (Total facility includes 93 beds in nursing home–type unit) **A**9 10 18 20 **F**2 9 11 12 14 21 22 33 34 37 44 52 55 59 60 63 66 68 70 81 84 85 92 94 97 108
Primary Contact: J. Michael Shaw, Administrator
CFO: Judith Strop, Director Finance
CMO: Cecilia Placencia, M.D., Chief of Staff

13	10	122	1201	99	37678	82	12130	4549	127

LANCASTER—Grant County

✠ **GRANT REGIONAL HEALTH CENTER**, 507 South Monroe Street, Zip 53813–2099; tel. 608/723–2143 **A**1 9 10 18 **F**2 9 11 12 13 27 28 29 30 33 37 44 46 47 48 52 54 55 57 59 60 61 62 63 65 66 68 69 70 81 82 85 88 93 94 95 96 97 106 107 108 110 **P**6 **S** Brim Healthcare, Inc., Brentwood, TN
Primary Contact: Larry D. Rentfro, FACHE, President and Chief Executive Officer
CFO: David R. Pitman, Chief Financial Officer
CMO: Robert J. Smith, Chief of Staff
CIO: David Chitwood, Information Systems Coordinator
CHR: Sheri Fischer, Human Resources Manager
Web address: www.grantregional.com

23	10	29	817	6	28319	93	12094	5308	129

MADISON—Dane County

□ **MENDOTA MENTAL HEALTH INSTITUTE**, 301 Troy Drive, Zip 53704–1599; tel. 608/301–1000 **A**1 3 5 10 **F**3 21 31 32 37 44 47 53 58 65 66 71 72 73 74 76 77 78 94 **P**6
Primary Contact: Greg Van Rybroek, Chief Executive Officer
Web address: www.dhfs.state.wi.us

12	22	249	1325	224	27298	0	53388	31271	698

✠ △ **MERITER HOSPITAL**, 202 South Park Street, Zip 53715–1599; tel. 608/267–6000 **A**1 3 5 7 9 10 **F**2 3 4 7 9 11 12 14 15 22 23 27 28 30 32 33 34 35 37 41 42 44 46 47 48 52 53 55 56 57 58 59 61 62 63 64 65 66 67 68 69 71 72 73 74 75 76 78 81 82 84 85 87 88 90 93 94 96 106 107 108 109 110 **P**6
Primary Contact: Terri L. Potter, President and Chief Executive Officer
COO: Robert L. Coats, Senior Vice President and Chief Operating Officer
CFO: Tom Fuss, Chief Financial Officer
CMO: Geoff Priest, M.D., Senior Vice President Medical Affairs
CIO: Peter Strombom, Vice President Information System
CHR: Mary Nick, Vice President Human Resources
Web address: www.meriter.com

23	10	360	17299	205	151514	3442	212004	95049	1959

✠ **ST. MARYS HOSPITAL MEDICAL CENTER**, 707 South Mills Street, Zip 53715–0450; tel. 608/251–6100 **A**1 3 5 9 10 **F**1 2 6 9 11 12 14 15 17 19 21 22 23 26 27 28 29 31 33 34 37 39 41 44 47 48 49 52 53 55 56 57 58 59 61 62 63 64 65 66 67 69 70 71 73 74 75 76 81 82 85 87 88 93 94 96 98 106 108 110 **S** SSM Health Care, Saint Louis, MO
Primary Contact: Frank D. Byrne, M.D., President
CFO: Charlie Johnson, Vice President Finance and Chief Financial Officer
CMO: Richard Hendricks, M.D., Vice President Medical Affairs
CIO: John Ries, Director Information Systems
CHR: Karen Wolfram, Director of Human Resources
Web address: www.stmarysmadison.com

23	10	307	20150	239	82800	3374	214192	82382	1708

✠ △ **UNIVERSITY OF WISCONSIN HOSPITAL AND CLINICS**, 600 Highland Avenue, Zip 53792–0002; tel. 608/263–6400, (Includes UNIVERSITY OF WISCONSIN CHILDREN'S HOSPITAL) **A**1 3 5 7 8 9 10 12 13 **F**2 4 6 7 12 13 14 15 16 17 18 19 20 21 22 23 24 26 27 28 29 32 33 34 37 39 40 41 42 44 46 47 48 49 50 51 52 53 55 57 58 60 61 62 63 64 65 66 67 68 69 70 71 72 73 74 75 76 77 79 81 82 84 85 86 87 88 89 90 93 94 95 96 98 99 100 101 103 104 106 107 108 109 110 **P**3
Primary Contact: Donna K. Sollenberger, President and Chief Executive Officer
COO: David Entwistle, Senior Vice President and Chief Operating Officer
CFO: Gary Eiler, Chief Financial Officer
CMO: Carl J. Getto, M.D., Senior Vice President Medical Affairs and Associate Dean Hospital Affairs
CIO: Dennis Dassenko, Vice President and Chief Information Officer
CHR: Jan Bultema, Vice President, Human Resources
Web address: www.uwhospital.org

23	10	465	20617	350	690761	0	574130	228848	5230

✠ **WILLIAM S. MIDDLETON MEMORIAL VETERANS HOSPITAL**, 2500 Overlook Terrace, Zip 53705–2286; tel. 608/256–1901, (Nonreporting) **A**1 3 5 **S** Department of Veterans Affairs, Washington, DC
Primary Contact: Nathan L. Geraths, Director
CFO: James E. Michael, Chief Fiscal Services
CMO: Jeffrey M. Jones, M.D., Ph.D., Chief of Staff
CIO: Randall Margenau, Chief Information Officer
CHR: Angela Rickard, Ph.D., Human Resources Coordinator
Web address: www.madison.med.va.gov

45	10	87	—	—	—	—	—	—	—

WI

Many Facility Codes have changed. Please refer to the AHA Guide Code Chart. © 2005 AHA Guide

Hospital, Address, Telephone, Approval, Facility, and Physician Codes, Health Care System	Classification Codes		Utilization Data					Expense (thousands) of dollars		
	Control	Service	Staffed Beds	Admissions	Census	Outpatient Visits	Births	Total	Payroll	Personnel

★ American Hospital Association (AHA) membership
□ Joint Commission on Accreditation of Healthcare Organizations (JCAHO) accreditation
○ American Osteopathic Association (AOA) accreditation
△ Commission on Accreditation of Rehabilitation Facilities (CARF) accreditation

MANITOWOC—Manitowoc County

☒ △ **HOLY FAMILY MEMORIAL MEDICAL CENTER**, 2300 Western Avenue, Zip 54220, Mailing Address: P.O. Box 1450, Zip 54221–1450; tel. 920/684–2011 **A**1 2 7 9 10 **F**1 2 3 4 9 11 12 14 15 21 22 23 24 25 26 27 28 29 33 35 36 37 39 40 41 42 44 45 46 47 48 49 51 52 55 58 59 60 61 62 63 64 65 68 69 70 71 72 73 74 75 76 77 80 81 82 84 86 88 93 94 95 96 98 106 107 108 110 **S** Franciscan Sisters of Christian Charity HealthCare Ministry, Inc, Manitowoc, WI
Primary Contact: Mark P. Herzog, President and Chief Executive Officer
COO: Terri Malandro, Chief Operating Officer
CFO: Patrick J. Brandel, Chief Financial Officer
CMO: Steve D. Driggers, M.D., Chief Medical Officer
CIO: Ed Bauknecht, Director Management Information Systems
Web address: www.hfmhealth.org
| | | | | | | | | | |
| 21 | 10 | 148 | 4910 | 53 | 170645 | 431 | 92981 | 48890 | 828 |

MARINETTE—Marinette County

☒ **BAY AREA MEDICAL CENTER**, 3100 Shore Drive, Zip 54143–4297; tel. 715/735–6621 **A**1 9 10 20 **F**2 6 9 11 12 14 15 21 22 23 26 28 31 33 37 40 42 44 46 47 49 52 55 58 59 60 61 63 65 66 69 73 74 76 77 81 82 84 85 87 88 93 94 95 107 108 109
Primary Contact: David Olson, President and Chief Executive Officer
COO: Bernie VanCourt, Chief Operating Officer
CFO: Dan Carlson, Assistant Administrator Finance and Chief Financial Officer
CIO: Pete Eisenzoph, Director Information Technology
CHR: Curt Oberholtzer, Assistant Administrator of Human Resources and Organizational Development
Web address: www.bamc.org
| | | | | | | | | | |
| 23 | 10 | 99 | 4781 | 45 | 74574 | 440 | 71719 | 29642 | 516 |

MARSHFIELD—Wood County

NORWOOD HEALTH CENTER, 1600 North Chestnut Avenue, Zip 54449–1499; tel. 715/384–2188, (Total facility includes 45 beds in nursing home–type unit) **A**10 **F**2 3 29 35 37 39 53 64 71 72 73 74 75 76 78 92 96 **P**6
Primary Contact: Rhonda Kozik, Administrator
| | | | | | | | | | |
| 13 | 22 | 67 | 702 | 53 | 0 | 0 | 2442 | 1415 | 128 |

☒ △ **SAINT JOSEPH'S HOSPITAL**, 611 St. Joseph Avenue, Zip 54449–1898; tel. 715/387–1713 **A**1 2 3 5 7 9 10 20 **F**2 3 4 6 7 9 11 13 14 15 16 17 19 20 21 22 23 26 27 28 29 30 33 34 37 39 41 42 43 44 46 47 48 49 52 53 54 55 56 57 58 59 60 61 62 63 65 66 67 68 69 71 73 74 75 76 79 80 82 86 87 93 94 95 96 99 108 109 **P**3 **S** Marian Health System, Tulsa, OK
Primary Contact: Michael A. Schmidt, President
CFO: John Skaden, Chief Financial Officer
CIO: Steve Pelton, Chief Information Officer
Web address: www.stjosephs–marshfield.org
| | | | | | | | | | |
| 33 | 10 | 319 | 18230 | 258 | 91031 | 1225 | 249664 | 86233 | 2033 |

MAUSTON—Juneau County

□ **MILE BLUFF MEDICAL CENTER**, 1050 Division Street, Zip 53948–1997; tel. 608/847–6161, (Total facility includes 132 beds in nursing home–type unit) **A**1 10 20 **F**8 9 11 12 27 28 33 37 42 44 47 49 51 52 58 59 60 61 63 65 66 69 73 77 81 82 84 86 87 88 91 92 94 95 107 **P**5 6
Primary Contact: Daniel N. Manders, President and Chief Executive Officer
Web address: www.milebluff.com
| | | | | | | | | | |
| 23 | 10 | 157 | 2394 | 150 | 108643 | 220 | 34894 | 18216 | 383 |

MEDFORD—Taylor County

☒ **MEMORIAL HEALTH CENTER**, (Formerly Memorial Hospital of Taylor County), 135 South Gibson Street, Zip 54451–1696; tel. 715/748–8100, (Includes MEMORIAL NURSING HOME), (Total facility includes 97 beds in nursing home–type unit) **A**1 9 10 18 20 **F**1 8 9 11 12 21 23 26 27 28 29 30 33 37 39 44 46 47 48 52 53 58 59 60 61 63 65 66 68 69 70 81 88 91 92 93 94 95 96 97 106 107 108 109 **P**4
Primary Contact: Greg Roraff, President and Chief Executive Officer
CFO: Mike Gutsch, Vice President Finance
CMO: Cathy Reuter, M.D., Medical Director
CIO: Dave Zoromski, Director Information Systems
CHR: Angela Hupf, Vice President Human Resources and Marketing
Web address: www.memhc.org
| | | | | | | | | | |
| 23 | 10 | 122 | 1301 | 106 | 42056 | 183 | 17546 | 8587 | 211 |

MENOMONEE FALLS—Waukesha County

☒ △ **COMMUNITY MEMORIAL HOSPITAL**, W180 N8085 Town Hall Road, Zip 53051–3518, Mailing Address: P.O. Box 408, Zip 53052–0408; tel. 262/251–1000 **A**1 2 3 5 7 9 10 **F**2 3 4 9 11 12 14 15 19 21 22 23 26 27 28 29 30 31 32 33 34 35 37 39 40 41 44 46 47 48 49 52 53 54 55 56 57 58 59 60 61 62 63 64 65 67 68 69 70 71 73 74 75 76 77 78 79 80 81 82 84 88 93 94 95 96 106 108 109 110
Primary Contact: William E. Bestor, President and Chief Executive Officer
CFO: Lisa A. Heider, Vice President Finance
CMO: Michael Unger, Vice President Medical Affairs
CIO: Rodney Dykehouse, Vice President, Chief Information Officer
Web address: www.communitymemorial.com
| | | | | | | | | | |
| 23 | 10 | 183 | 8325 | 104 | 87289 | 934 | 111887 | 45468 | 993 |

MENOMONIE—Dunn County

□ **MYRTLE WERTH HOSPITAL–MAYO HEALTH SYSTEM**, 2321 Stout Road, Zip 54751–2397; tel. 715/235–5531 **A**1 3 5 9 10 18 **F**9 11 12 14 28 30 33 34 37 44 47 52 55 58 59 60 63 65 66 68 69 81 94 95 109 **S** Mayo Foundation, Rochester, MN
Primary Contact: Hank Simpson, M.D., Chief Executive Officer
Web address: www.rcmc–mhs.org
| | | | | | | | | | |
| 23 | 10 | 43 | 1263 | 10 | 37153 | 272 | 21166 | 9671 | — |

Hospital, Address, Telephone, Approval, Facility, and Physician Codes, Health Care System	Classi-fication Codes		Utilization Data					Expense (thousands) of dollars		
★ American Hospital Association (AHA) membership □ Joint Commission on Accreditation of Healthcare Organizations (JCAHO) accreditation ○ American Osteopathic Association (AOA) accreditation △ Commission on Accreditation of Rehabilitation Facilities (CARF) accreditation	Control	Service	Staffed Beds	Admissions	Census	Outpatient Visits	Births	Total	Payroll	Personnel

MEQUON—Ozaukee County

☒ **COLUMBIA ST. MARY'S OZAUKEE CAMPUS**, 13111 North Port Washington Road, Zip 53097–2416; tel. 262/243–7300 **A**1 9 10 **F**2 3 4 11 12 14 21 22 23 26 27 28 29 30 31 34 35 39 40 41 42 44 46 47 48 52 53 55 57 58 59 60 61 62 63 65 70 71 72 73 74 75 76 77 78 79 81 82 84 85 87 88 94 95 96 107 108 109 110 **P**6 **S** Ascension Health, Saint Louis, MO
Primary Contact: Leo P. Brideau, President and Chief Executive Officer
COO: Therese B. Pandl, Executive Vice President for Hospital Operations
CMO: James P. Ketterhagen, M.D., Vice President Medical Affairs and Chief Quality Officer
CIO: Mary Paul, Chief Information Officer
Web address: www.columbia–stmarys.com

| | 21 | 10 | 106 | 6115 | 67 | 224319 | 809 | 101902 | 39795 | 788 |

MERRILL—Lincoln County

☒ **GOOD SAMARITAN HEALTH CENTER OF MERRILL**, 601 Center Avenue South, Zip 54452–3404; tel. 715/536–5511 **A**1 9 10 18 **F**1 2 9 11 12 14 22 23 27 29 30 33 37 41 44 46 47 48 52 54 55 58 59 60 61 62 63 65 66 68 69 70 81 82 84 87 88 94 96 97 106 107 108 109 **S** Marian Health System, Tulsa, OK
Primary Contact: Michael Hammer, President and Chief Operating Officer
CFO: Cathy Burkowski, Vice President Finance
Web address: www.gshc.org

| | 21 | 10 | 14 | 1352 | 14 | 40459 | 133 | 18044 | 7683 | 172 |

MILWAUKEE—Milwaukee County

☒ △ **AURORA SINAI MEDICAL CENTER**, 945 North 12th Street, Zip 53233–1337, Mailing Address: P.O. Box 342, Zip 53201–0342; tel. 414/219–2000 **A**1 2 3 5 7 8 9 10 **F**2 3 4 7 9 11 12 14 15 17 19 21 22 23 26 27 28 29 30 31 33 34 35 37 39 41 42 44 45 47 48 49 50 52 53 55 56 57 58 59 60 61 62 63 65 66 67 68 69 70 71 75 79 81 82 83 85 87 88 89 90 93 94 95 96 106 107 108 109 110 **S** Aurora Health Care, Milwaukee, WI
Primary Contact: Leonard E. Wilk, Administrator
CFO: Kevin Jones, Director Financial
Web address: www.aurorahealthcare.org

| | 23 | 10 | 236 | 13494 | 161 | 276904 | 2638 | 213001 | 73454 | 1656 |

☒ **CHILDREN'S HOSPITAL OF WISCONSIN**, 9000 West Wisconsin Avenue, Zip 53226–4810, Mailing Address: P.O. Box 1997, Zip 53201–1997; tel. 414/266–2000 **A**1 3 5 8 9 10 **F**2 7 15 16 17 18 19 20 21 22 23 24 25 26 27 28 29 30 31 32 33 34 35 37 40 42 46 47 48 49 50 52 53 56 57 58 60 61 62 63 64 65 66 67 68 69 70 72 73 75 77 81 82 84 85 87 88 93 94 95 96 98 99 100 101 103 104 107 108 110 **P**4
Primary Contact: Jon E. Vice, President and Chief Executive Officer
COO: Cinthia S. Christensen, Executive Vice President and Chief Operating Officer
CFO: Timothy L. Birkenstock, Treasurer and Chief Financial Officer
CMO: Michael Gutzeit, M.D., Chief Medical Officer
CIO: Michael L. Jones, Ph.D., Corporate Vice President and Chief Information Officer
CHR: Peggy Niemer, Vice President, Human Resources
Web address: www.chw.org

| | 23 | 50 | 222 | 21090 | 189 | 265595 | 0 | 270306 | 91253 | 2178 |

☒ △ **CLEMENT J. ZABLOCKI VETERANS AFFAIRS MEDICAL CENTER**, 5000 West National Avenue, Zip 53295; tel. 414/384–2000, (Total facility includes 196 beds in nursing home–type unit) (Nonreporting) **A**1 2 3 5 7 **S** Department of Veterans Affairs, Washington, DC
Primary Contact: Glen W. Grippen, Director
COO: Larry L. Berkeley, Associate Director
CFO: Lynn Bemann, Chief Fiscal Service
CMO: Michael Erdmann, M.D., Chief of Staff
CIO: Chris Houterman, Chief Information Officer
CHR: Wayne Davis, Chief, Human Resources
Web address: www.va.gov/sta/guide/home.asp

| | 45 | 10 | 566 | — | — | — | — | — | — | — |

COLUMBIA CENTER, 2025 East Newport Avenue, Suite 3000, Zip 53211; tel. 414/961–3590 **A**9 10 **F**11 21 26 27 28 37 47 52 59 65 66 88 90 **P**6
Primary Contact: Karen J. Casey, President and Chief Executive Officer
Web address: www.columbiacenteronline.org

| | 23 | 44 | 45 | 818 | 6 | 539 | 798 | — | — | 55 |

☒ **COLUMBIA ST. MARY'S—COLUMBIA CAMPUS**, 2025 East Newport Avenue, Zip 53211–2990; tel. 414/961–3300 **A**1 9 10 **F**2 4 12 14 22 23 25 26 27 28 29 30 31 32 33 34 35 37 39 40 41 42 44 45 46 47 48 49 52 53 55 57 58 61 62 63 65 69 70 71 72 73 74 75 76 77 78 79 81 82 84 85 86 87 88 90 93 94 96 106 108 109 110 **P**6 **S** Ascension Health, Saint Louis, MO
Primary Contact: Leo P. Brideau, President and Chief Executive Officer
COO: Therese B. Pandl, Executive Vice President for Hospital Operations
CIO: Mary Paul, Chief Information Officer
Web address: www.columbia–stmarys.com

| | 23 | 10 | 287 | 8231 | 99 | 246103 | 0 | 162093 | 68058 | 1355 |

☒ **COLUMBIA ST. MARY'S—MILWAUKEE CAMPUS**, 2323 North Lake Drive, Zip 53211–9682, Mailing Address: P.O. Box 503, Zip 53201–0503; tel. 414/291–1000 **A**1 2 9 10 **F**2 4 7 11 12 13 14 21 22 23 25 26 27 28 29 30 31 32 33 35 39 40 42 44 45 46 47 48 49 52 53 55 56 57 58 59 60 61 62 63 65 66 69 70 72 73 74 75 76 77 78 79 81 82 84 85 87 88 90 94 96 104 106 107 108 109 110 **P**6 **S** Ascension Health, Saint Louis, MO
Primary Contact: Leo P. Brideau, President and Chief Executive Officer
COO: Therese B. Pandl, Executive Vice President for Hospital Operations
CFO: Charles J. Dreher, Vice President Finance and Chief Financial Officer
CMO: James P. Ketterhagen, M.D., Vice President Medical Affairs and Chief Quality Officer
CIO: Mary Paul, Chief Information Officer
Web address: www.columbia–stmarys.com

| | 21 | 10 | 237 | 10828 | 153 | 395242 | 2998 | 208341 | 98621 | 1932 |

WI

Many Facility Codes have changed. Please refer to the AHA Guide Code Chart.

© 2005 AHA Guide

Hospital, Address, Telephone, Approval, Facility, and Physician Codes, Health Care System	Classi-fication Codes		Utilization Data					Expense (thousands) of dollars		
★ American Hospital Association (AHA) membership □ Joint Commission on Accreditation of Healthcare Organizations (JCAHO) accreditation ○ American Osteopathic Association (AOA) accreditation △ Commission on Accreditation of Rehabilitation Facilities (CARF) accreditation	Control	Service	Staffed Beds	Admissions	Census	Outpatient Visits	Births	Total	Payroll	Personnel
⊠ △ **FROEDTERT MEMORIAL LUTHERAN HOSPITAL**, 9200 West Wisconsin Avenue, Zip 53226–3596, Mailing Address: P.O. Box 26099, Zip 53226–3596; tel. 414/805–3000 **A**1 2 3 5 7 8 9 10 **F**9 11 12 14 21 26 27 28 31 33 34 37 40 42 44 47 49 52 55 58 59 60 61 63 65 66 68 69 73 74 75 76 77 81 82 84 86 87 88 89 90 94 95 99 100 101 103 104 107 109 Primary Contact: William D. Petasnick, President and Chief Executive Officer COO: Catherine Buck, Executive Vice President Operations CFO: Blaine J. O'Connell, Senior Vice President Finance CMO: Andrew J. Norton, M.D., Senior Vice President Medical Affairs CIO: Rodney Dykehouse, Vice President Information Systems CHR: Elizabeth J. Forman, Vice President, Human Resources Web address: www.froedtert.com	23	10	414	21012	320	417302	1352	451879	144509	—
⊠ **KINDRED HOSPITAL–MILWAUKEE**, 5017 South 110th Street, Zip 53228–3131; tel. 414/427–8282 **A**1 9 10 **F**21 28 33 44 47 52 55 58 65 66 68 69 73 94 **S** Kindred Healthcare, Louisville, KY Primary Contact: Linda Newberry–Ferguson, Chief Executive Officer COO: Christine Ninu, Chief Operating Officer CFO: Sharon Rand, Chief Financial Officer CMO: Scott Fenske, M.D., Medical Director Web address: www.kindredhealthcare.com	33	90	56	318	35	4	0	13383	6067	—
□ **LIFECARE HOSPITALS OF MILWAUKEE**, 5000 West Chambers Street, 8th FL, Zip 53210; tel. 414/447–3600 **A**1 9 10 **F**2 21 26 58 94 110 **S** LifeCare Management Services, Plano, TX Primary Contact: Steven J. Schultz, Chief Executive Officer Web address: www.lifecare–hospitals.com	33	90	35	223	16	0	0	7490	3312	—
LIFECARE HOSPITALS OF MILWAUKEE, 2400 West Villard Avenue, 3rd Floor, Zip 53209; tel. 414/527–5825 **A**9 10 **F**21 26 58 94 Primary Contact: William Fox, Chief Executive Officer	33	90	17	137	10	0	0	4994	2208	—
★ **MILWAUKEE COUNTY BEHAVIORAL HEALTH DIVISION**, 9455 Watertown Plank Road, Zip 53226–3559; tel. 414/257–6995, (Total facility includes 165 beds in nursing home–type unit) **A**3 5 10 **F**2 21 22 26 27 28 31 54 58 66 71 72 75 92 94 96 Primary Contact: James M. Hill, Administrator CFO: Michael Kreuser, Director Fiscal Support CMO: Thomas Harding, M.D., Acting Medical Director CIO: William Borja, Chief Information Officer CHR: Charles McDowell, Corporate Vice President Human Resources Web address: www.milwaukeecounty.org	13	22	285	3487	272	13735	0	143475	38234	864
⊠ △ **SACRED HEART REHABILITATION INSTITUTE**, 2025 East Newport Avenue, Zip 53211–2906; tel. 414/298–6700 **A**1 7 9 10 **F**7 21 22 24 26 27 28 29 35 39 45 46 47 48 52 58 65 68 69 94 95 96 98 **P**6 **S** Ascension Health, Saint Louis, MO Primary Contact: Jack Burke, Administrator CFO: Charles J. Dreher, Vice President Finance and Chief Financial Officer CIO: Mary Paul, Chief Information Officer CHR: Cheryl Hill Web address: www.columbia–stmarys.com	21	46	49	783	22	9357	0	14964	5869	117
□ **SELECT SPECIALTY HOSPITAL**, 8901 West Lincoln Avenue, 6th Floor, Zip 53227; tel. 414/328–7700 **A**1 9 10 **F**14 21 30 31 37 44 47 55 58 60 61 65 66 68 73 76 94 Primary Contact: Dennis Mattes, Chief Executive Officer	33	90	34	304	28	0	0	11172	3574	—
⊠ △ **ST. FRANCIS HOSPITAL**, 3237 South 16th Street, Zip 53215–4592; tel. 414/647–5000 **A**1 2 7 9 10 **F**2 7 11 12 14 15 19 21 22 23 26 27 28 29 30 31 33 35 37 42 44 45 46 47 48 52 53 55 56 57 58 59 60 61 62 63 64 65 66 69 73 74 81 82 84 85 87 88 93 94 95 96 97 98 108 109 110 **S** Wheaton Franciscan Services, Inc., Wheaton, IL Primary Contact: Debra Standridge, President COO: Debra Standridge, President CFO: Michael Petitt, Director Finance CMO: Parmod Kumar, M.D., Chief of Staff CHR: Robert F. Scott, Director, Human Resources Web address: www.stfrancishospital.net	23	10	212	10357	125	160731	1379	165181	53085	1062
⊠ △ **ST. JOSEPH'S REGIONAL MEDICAL CENTER**, 5000 West Chambers Street, Zip 53210–9988; tel. 414/447–2000, (Includes ST. JOSEPH'S REGIONAL MEDICAL CENTER), (Nonreporting) **A**1 2 3 5 7 9 10 **S** Wheaton Franciscan Services, Inc., Wheaton, IL Primary Contact: Ron Groepper, President CFO: Patty Allen, Finance Director CMO: Rita Hanson, M.D., Vice President Medical Affairs CIO: Alan Grant, Regional Director Information Services CHR: Shakila Shimp, Director, Human Resources Web address: www.covhealth.org	21	10	396	—	—	—	—	—	—	—

WI

Hospital, Address, Telephone, Approval, Facility, and Physician Codes, Health Care System	Classi-fication Codes		Utilization Data					Expense (thousands) of dollars		
	Control	Service	Staffed Beds	Admissions	Census	Outpatient Visits	Births	Total	Payroll	Personnel

★ American Hospital Association (AHA) membership
□ Joint Commission on Accreditation of Healthcare Organizations (JCAHO) accreditation
○ American Osteopathic Association (AOA) accreditation
△ Commission on Accreditation of Rehabilitation Facilities (CARF) accreditation

�х △ **ST. LUKE'S MEDICAL CENTER**, 2900 West Oklahoma Avenue, Zip 53215–4330, Mailing Address: P.O. Box 2901, Zip 53201–2901; tel. 414/649–6000, (Includes ST. LUKE'S SOUTH SHORE, 5900 South Lake Drive, Cudahy, Zip 53110–8903; tel. 414/769–9000) **A**1 3 5 7 8 9 10 12 **F**2 3 4 7 12 14 15 17 19 21 22 23 26 27 28 29 30 31 32 33 34 35 36 37 39 40 41 42 43 44 45 47 50 51 52 53 55 57 58 60 61 62 63 64 65 66 68 69 70 71 72 73 74 75 76 77 78 79 80 81 82 84 85 86 87 88 89 90 93 94 95 96 99 100 101 103 104 106 107 108 109 110 **S** Aurora Health Care, Milwaukee, WI Primary Contact: Mark R. Ambrosius, Administrator Web address: www.aurorahealthcare.org	23	10	752	36404	533	500201	0	661425	208120	—
✕ △ **ST. MICHAEL HOSPITAL**, 2400 West Villard Avenue, Zip 53209–4999; tel. 414/527–8000 **A**1 2 3 5 7 9 10 **F**2 3 4 9 12 14 15 19 21 22 23 24 26 27 28 29 30 31 33 34 35 37 39 40 41 43 44 45 46 47 48 49 52 55 57 58 60 61 62 63 64 65 66 69 70 71 72 73 74 75 76 77 81 82 84 85 87 88 93 94 95 96 98 106 108 109 110 **P**7 **S** Wheaton Franciscan Services, Inc., Wheaton, IL Primary Contact: Alicia Modjeska, President COO: Janet Pangborn, Vice President Operations CFO: Dan Pfannenstiel, Manager Finance CMO: Marvin O. Kolb, M.D., Chief Medical Officer CHR: Sherri Du Charme White, Director Human Resources Web address: www.stmichaelhospital.net	21	10	121	7414	95	189416	611	130228	44036	727
MONROE—Green County										
□ **THE MONROE CLINIC**, 515 22nd Avenue, Zip 53566–1598; tel. 608/324–1000 **A**1 9 10 **F**2 3 4 7 9 11 12 14 22 23 24 26 27 28 29 30 31 33 35 36 37 39 41 42 44 46 47 48 51 52 55 57 58 59 60 61 62 63 65 66 67 68 69 70 72 73 75 76 77 81 82 85 87 88 90 93 94 95 96 107 108 109 **P**6 Primary Contact: Michael B. Sanders, President and Chief Executive Officer Web address: www.monroeclinic.org	21	10	100	3371	29	200681	383	83621	43114	787
NEENAH—Winnebago County										
□ **CHILDREN'S HOSPITAL OF WISCONSIN–FOX VALLEY**, 130 Second Avenue, 3rd Floor S., Zip 54956; tel. 920/969–7900 **A**1 9 10 **F**2 21 26 27 28 47 52 56 65 66 94 108 109 110 **P**1 5 Primary Contact: Tim Klunk, Executive Director	23	10	38	744	15	2358	0	9633	4028	56
✕ △ **THEDA CLARK MEDICAL CENTER**, 130 Second Street, Zip 54956–2883, Mailing Address: P.O. Box 2021, Zip 54957–2021; tel. 920/729–3100 **A**1 2 7 10 **F**3 4 7 9 11 12 14 21 26 27 28 33 34 37 41 44 47 49 52 54 55 58 59 60 61 63 65 66 68 69 71 72 74 75 76 77 78 81 82 84 88 90 94 95 107 109 **P**6 8 **S** ThedaCare, Inc., Appleton, WI Primary Contact: Kathryn Correia, Senior Vice President COO: Matthew Furlan, Chief Operating Officer CFO: Jacqueline Klein, Vice President Finance CMO: Kevin Garrett, M.D., Senior Medical Director CIO: Keith Livingston, Senior Vice President and Chief Information Officer CHR: Michael N. Speer, Senior Vice President, Human Resources Web address: www.thedacare.org	23	10	166	7788	83	67327	1195	103765	46321	—
NEILLSVILLE—Clark County										
MEMORIAL MEDICAL CENTER, 216 Sunset Place, Zip 54456–1799; tel. 715/743–3101, (Includes NEILLSVILLE MEMORIAL HOME), (Total facility includes 114 beds in nursing home–type unit) **A**9 10 18 **F**2 9 11 12 27 28 29 33 37 39 42 44 46 47 48 51 52 53 58 59 60 62 63 65 66 69 70 81 82 88 91 92 94 95 96 97 106 107 108 **P**6 Primary Contact: Glen E. Grady, Administrator Web address: www.mmcneillsville.com	23	10	141	1039	113	80609	51	9355	4579	127
NEW LONDON—Outagamie County										
✕ **NEW LONDON FAMILY MEDICAL CENTER**, 1405 Mill Street, Zip 54961–2155, Mailing Address: P.O. Box 307, Zip 54961–0307; tel. 920/982–5330 **A**1 9 10 18 **F**2 3 6 9 11 12 21 22 26 27 28 33 35 37 39 46 47 48 52 53 58 59 60 62 63 65 68 69 70 81 82 88 95 96 97 106 108 110 **S** ThedaCare, Inc., Appleton, WI Primary Contact: William Schmidt, President and Chief Executive Officer CFO: Cindy Mischler, Vice President Finance CIO: Christal Engel, Information Systems Analyst Web address: www.newlondon.thedacare.org	23	10	15	1314	12	39353	112	16729	7262	169
NEW RICHMOND—St. Croix County										
★ **HOLY FAMILY HOSPITAL**, 535 Hospital Road, Zip 54017–1495; tel. 715/246–2101 **A**9 10 18 **F**3 9 12 21 26 27 28 31 33 37 41 44 47 52 54 58 59 60 61 63 65 66 68 69 71 81 84 88 90 94 95 104 **P**6 Primary Contact: Jean M. Needham, President CFO: David Kuehn, Chief Financial Officer CIO: Kim Rosario, Chief Information Officer CHR: Chris Riba, Human Resource Manager Web address: www.holyfamilyhospital.org	21	10	22	1102	10	21616	146	16454	6536	—

WI

Many Facility Codes have changed. Please refer to the AHA Guide Code Chart.   © 2005 AHA Guide

Hospital, Address, Telephone, Approval, Facility, and Physician Codes, Health Care System	Classification Codes		Utilization Data					Expense (thousands) of dollars		
★ American Hospital Association (AHA) membership □ Joint Commission on Accreditation of Healthcare Organizations (JCAHO) accreditation ○ American Osteopathic Association (AOA) accreditation △ Commission on Accreditation of Rehabilitation Facilities (CARF) accreditation	Control	Service	Staffed Beds	Admissions	Census	Outpatient Visits	Births	Total	Payroll	Personnel

OCONOMOWOC—Waukesha County

⊠ **OCONOMOWOC MEMORIAL HOSPITAL**, 791 Summit Avenue, Zip 53066–3896; tel. 262/569–9400 **A**1 9 10 **F**1 9 11 12 14 21 26 27 28 33 34 36 37 44 47 51 52 55 58 59 60 61 63 65 66 68 69 75 81 82 84 87 88 94 107 109 **S** ProHealth Care, Waukesha, WI Primary Contact: John R. Robertstad, FACHE, President and Chief Executive Officer COO: Janet Schulz, Executive Vice President CFO: Robert W. Mlynarek, Vice President Finance CMO: Brian Lipman, M.D., Chief of Staff CIO: William Miller, Vice President Information Services CHR: Tom Constable, Senior Vice President Human Resources Web address: www.oconomowocmemorial.org	23	10	74	4630	39	94660	777	80043	26669	615
□ **ROGERS MEMORIAL HOSPITAL**, 34700 Valley Road, Zip 53066–4599; tel. 262/646–4411 **A**1 9 10 **F**4 21 22 27 28 29 31 47 52 53 58 65 66 71 72 73 74 76 77 78 94 96 Primary Contact: David L. Moulthrop, Ph.D., President and Chief Executive Officer Web address: www.rogershospital.org	23	22	90	1402	27	26593	0	18380	11089	239

OCONTO FALLS—Oconto County

★ **COMMUNITY MEMORIAL HOSPITAL**, 855 South Main Street, Zip 54154–1296; tel. 920/846–3444 **A**9 10 18 **F**2 9 11 12 21 27 28 33 34 37 42 44 46 47 48 52 57 58 59 60 62 63 64 65 66 67 69 70 81 82 85 88 94 96 97 108 109 110 **P**6 **S** Brim Healthcare, Inc., Brentwood, TN Primary Contact: James Van Dornick, Administrator COO: Judy Sytsma, Chief Nursing Officer CFO: Bill Beaston, Chief Financial Officer CMO: James Wallace, D.O., Chief of Staff CIO: Andy Miller, Chief Information Officer CHR: Trisha Brown, Human Resources Manager Web address: www.cmhospital.org	23	10	25	1347	13	51796	78	18641	7504	164

OSCEOLA—Polk County

OSCEOLA MEDICAL CENTER, 301 River Street, Zip 54020, Mailing Address: P.O. Box 218, Zip 54020–0218; tel. 715/294–2111 **A**9 10 18 **F**2 11 21 26 33 37 44 47 52 59 60 63 65 66 68 69 71 81 82 84 88 91 92 94 **P**4 Primary Contact: Jeffrey K. Meyer, Chief Executive Officer Web address: www.osceolamedicalcenter.com	23	10	55	796	46	30351	0	7589	3730	—

OSHKOSH—Winnebago County

⊠ **AURORA MEDICAL CENTER OF OSHKOSH**, 855 North Westhaven Drive, Zip 54904; tel. 920/456–6000, (Nonreporting) **A**1 9 10 **S** Aurora Health Care, Milwaukee, WI Primary Contact: Frances R. Finley, Administrator CHR: Linda Mingus, Director, Human Resources Web address: www.aurorahealthcare.com	23	10	84	—	—	—	—	—	—	—
□ △ **MERCY MEDICAL CENTER**, 500 South Oakwood, Zip 54903–3370, Mailing Address: P.O. Box 3370, Zip 54903–3370; tel. 920/223–2000 **A**1 2 7 9 10 **F**3 4 9 11 12 13 14 21 26 27 28 31 33 34 37 40 41 44 47 52 55 58 59 61 63 65 66 67 68 69 71 76 77 81 82 84 87 88 92 94 95 107 109 Primary Contact: Clifford R. Lehman, Chief Operating Officer Web address: www.affinityhealth.org	21	10	172	7160	84	76698	740	103753	40954	624

OSSEO—Trempealeau County

OSSEO MEDICAL CENTER, (Formerly Osseo Area Hospital and Nursing Home), 13025 Eighth Street, Zip 54758–7673, Mailing Address: P.O. Box 70, Zip 54758–0070; tel. 715/597–3121, (Total facility includes 54 beds in nursing home–type unit) **A**9 10 18 **F**1 6 8 9 13 21 28 33 44 47 52 54 58 65 66 68 69 91 92 94 **S** Mayo Foundation, Rochester, MN Primary Contact: Michael Ryan, Administrator Web address: www.osseomedicalcenter.org	23	10	72	177	43	8763	0	3605	1946	63

PARK FALLS—Price County

⊠ **FLAMBEAU HOSPITAL**, 98 Sherry Avenue, Zip 54552–1467, Mailing Address: P.O. Box 310, Zip 54552–0310; tel. 715/762–2484 **A**1 9 10 18 20 **F**9 11 12 14 21 26 27 28 33 36 37 41 44 47 51 52 54 55 58 59 60 63 65 66 68 69 81 82 88 94 95 107 **S** Marian Health System, Tulsa, OK Primary Contact: David A. Grundstrom, Administrator CFO: James R. Braun, Chief Financial Officer Web address: www.flambeauhospital.org	23	10	25	1149	12	31741	56	15135	6018	168

PLATTEVILLE—Grant County

⊠ **SOUTHWEST HEALTH CENTER**, 1400 Eastside Road, Zip 53818–9800; tel. 608/348–2331, (Includes SOUTHWEST HEALTH CENTER NURSING HOME, 808 South Washington Street, Cuba City, Zip 53807; tel. 608/744–2161), (Total facility includes 94 beds in nursing home–type unit) **A**1 9 10 **F**2 9 11 12 23 26 27 28 29 33 39 44 45 46 47 48 52 54 57 58 59 61 62 63 65 66 68 69 70 71 75 76 77 81 84 85 86 88 92 93 94 96 97 106 107 108 **S** Brim Healthcare, Inc., Brentwood, TN Primary Contact: Anne K. Klawiter, President and Chief Executive Officer CFO: James Ehasz, Chief Financial Officer Web address: www.southwesthealth.org	23	10	132	1535	91	27220	176	16699	5174	148

WI

Hospital, Address, Telephone, Approval, Facility, and Physician Codes, Health Care System	Classi-fication Codes		Utilization Data					Expense (thousands) of dollars		
★ American Hospital Association (AHA) membership □ Joint Commission on Accreditation of Healthcare Organizations (JCAHO) accreditation ○ American Osteopathic Association (AOA) accreditation △ Commission on Accreditation of Rehabilitation Facilities (CARF) accreditation	Control	Service	Staffed Beds	Admissions	Census	Outpatient Visits	Births	Total	Payroll	Personnel

PLEASANT PRAIRIE—Kenosha County

⊠ **UNITED HOSPITAL SYSTEM, ST. CATHERINE'S MEDICAL CENTER CAMPUS**, 9555 76th Street, Zip 53158; tel. 262/656–2011, (Nonreporting) **A**1 2 9 10 **S** Wheaton Franciscan Services, Inc., Wheaton, IL
Primary Contact: Richard O. Schmidt, Jr, President and Chief Executive Officer

| 21 | 10 | 114 | — | — | — | — | — | — | — |

PORTAGE—Columbia County

□ **DIVINE SAVIOR HEALTHCARE**, 2817 New Pinery Road, Zip 53901–0387, Mailing Address: P.O. Box 387, Zip 53901–0387; tel. 608/742–4131, (Total facility includes 124 beds in nursing home–type unit) **A**1 9 10 **F**3 6 9 11 12 26 27 28 30 33 34 42 44 47 49 51 52 54 55 58 59 60 61 63 65 66 68 69 75 81 82 84 87 88 92 94 95 109 **P**6
Primary Contact: Michael Decker, President and Chief Executive Officer
Web address: www.dshealthcare.com

| 23 | 10 | 176 | 2453 | 116 | 126180 | 282 | 37092 | 17508 | 443 |

PRAIRIE DU CHIEN—Crawford County

⊠ **PRAIRIE DU CHIEN MEMORIAL HOSPITAL**, 705 East Taylor Street, Zip 53821–2196; tel. 608/357–2000 **A**1 9 10 18 20 **F**1 3 4 8 9 11 12 14 21 26 27 28 33 36 44 47 51 52 54 55 58 59 60 61 63 65 66 69 75 78 81 94 95 107
Primary Contact: Harold W. Brown, Chief Executive Officer
COO: M Connie Achenbach, Assistant Administrator and Chief Operating Officer
CFO: Dave Breitbach, Chief Financial Officer
CHR: Laurie Hampton, Human Resources Director
Web address: www.pdchospital.org

| 23 | 10 | 24 | 1574 | 21 | 27678 | 161 | 17827 | 8849 | 229 |

PRAIRIE DU SAC—Sauk County

⊠ **SAUK PRAIRIE MEMORIAL HOSPITAL**, 80 First Street, Zip 53578–1550; tel. 608/643–7166 **A**1 9 10 **F**3 9 11 12 14 21 22 24 26 27 28 29 30 33 34 39 41 42 44 47 52 53 54 55 58 59 61 62 63 64 65 68 69 70 73 81 82 84 87 88 93 94 95 96 97 107 108 **P**6
Primary Contact: Richard L. Palagi, Chief Executive Officer
COO: Larry Schroeder, Chief Operating Officer
CFO: Stephen Plaisance, Chief Financial Officer
CMO: John McAuliffe, M.D., Medical Director
CIO: Mike Bartman, Chief Information Officer
CHR: Sandy Niemi, Human Resources Director
Web address: www.spmh.org

| 23 | 10 | 36 | 2382 | 20 | 48936 | 248 | 33350 | 15936 | 328 |

RACINE—Racine County

⊠ △ **ALL SAINTS HEALTHCARE**, 3801 Spring Street, Zip 53405–1690; tel. 262/687–4011, (Nonreporting) **A**1 2 3 5 7 9 10 **S** Wheaton Franciscan Services, Inc., Wheaton, IL
Primary Contact: Kenneth R. Buser, President and Chief Executive Officer
CFO: James D. Beck, Senior Vice Persident Finance and Chief Financial Officer
CIO: Joanne Bisterfeldt, Vice President Information Systems
Web address: www.allsaintshealthcare.org

| 21 | 10 | 200 | — | — | — | — | — | — | — |

★ **ST. LUKE'S HOSPITAL**, (Formerly St. Luke's Memorial Hospital), 1320 Wisconsin Avenue, Zip 53403–1987; tel. 262/687–2011, (Total facility includes 50 beds in nursing home–type unit) (Nonreporting) **A**9 10 **S** Wheaton Franciscan Services, Inc., Wheaton, IL
Primary Contact: Kenneth R. Buser, President and Chief Executive Officer
COO: Michael McAvoy, Vice President, Operations
CFO: James D. Beck, Senior Vice Persident Finance and Chief Financial Officer
CHR: Shelly Olejniczak, Director Human Resources
Web address: www.allsaintshealth.com

| 23 | 10 | 175 | — | — | — | — | — | — | — |

REEDSBURG—Sauk County

⊠ **REEDSBURG AREA MEDICAL CENTER**, 2000 North Dewey Street, Zip 53959–1097; tel. 608/524–6487, (Total facility includes 50 beds in nursing home–type unit) **A**1 9 10 18 **F**2 9 11 12 14 15 21 23 26 27 28 29 30 31 33 34 37 41 46 47 48 52 53 55 59 60 61 62 63 64 65 67 68 69 81 82 85 87 92 93 94 96 97 106 107 108 110 **P**6
Primary Contact: George L. Johnson, President
Web address: www.ramchealth.org

| 23 | 10 | 88 | 1910 | 68 | 63993 | 221 | 25080 | 10927 | 262 |

RHINELANDER—Oneida County

⊠ **SACRED HEART–ST. MARY'S HOSPITALS**, 2251 North Shore Drive, Zip 54501–3998; tel. 715/361–2000, (Includes SACRED HEART HOSPITAL, 401 West Mohawk Drive, Tomahawk, Zip 54487; tel. 715/453–7700; ST. MARY'S HOSPITAL), (Nonreporting) **A**1 9 10 **S** Marian Health System, Tulsa, OK
Primary Contact: Kevin J. O'Donnell, President and Chief Executive Officer
COO: William A. Erickson, Vice President and Chief Operating Officer
CFO: Jack P. Sutliff, Vice President and Chief Financial Officer
CIO: Monica Hilt, Assistant Vice President Quality Improvement and Information Services
Web address: www.ministryhealth.org

| 21 | 10 | 44 | — | — | — | — | — | — | — |

RICE LAKE—Barron County

⊠ **LAKEVIEW MEDICAL CENTER**, 1100 North Main Street, Zip 54868–1238; tel. 715/234–1515 **A**1 9 10 **F**2 6 9 11 14 27 28 29 33 36 37 41 44 46 47 48 49 51 52 54 55 58 59 62 63 64 65 69 85 88 94 95 96 106 107 108 110
Primary Contact: Edward H. Wolf, President and Chief Executive Officer
COO: Howard P. Johnson, MS, Vice President and Chief Operating Officer
CFO: Scott Moebius, Vice President Finance
CMO: Brad Bekkum, M.D., Medical Director
CIO: Brad Gerrits, Director Information Systems
CHR: Howard P. Johnson, MS, Vice President and Chief Operating Officer
Web address: www.lakeviewmedical.com

| 23 | 10 | 69 | 3397 | 36 | 45560 | 448 | 31893 | 16145 | 321 |

WI

Many Facility Codes have changed. Please refer to the AHA Guide Code Chart.
© 2005 AHA Guide

Hospital, Address, Telephone, Approval, Facility, and Physician Codes, Health Care System	Classi-fication Codes		Utilization Data					Expense (thousands) of dollars		
	Control	Service	Staffed Beds	Admissions	Census	Outpatient Visits	Births	Total	Payroll	Personnel

★ American Hospital Association (AHA) membership
□ Joint Commission on Accreditation of Healthcare Organizations (JCAHO) accreditation
○ American Osteopathic Association (AOA) accreditation
△ Commission on Accreditation of Rehabilitation Facilities (CARF) accreditation

RICHLAND CENTER—Richland County

□ **RICHLAND HOSPITAL**, 333 East Second Street, Zip 53581–1899; tel. 608/647–6321, (Nonreporting) **A**1 9 10 18
Primary Contact: Steven R. Nockerts, Chief Executive Officer
Web address: www.richlandhospital.com

| | 23 | 10 | 25 | — | — | — | — | — | — | — |

RIPON—Fond Du Lac County

⊠ **RIPON MEDICAL CENTER**, 933 Newbury Street, Zip 54971–1798, Mailing Address: P.O. Box 390, Zip 54971–0390; tel. 920/748–3101 **A**1 9 10 18 **F**2 9 12 14 21 23 24 27 28 29 32 33 34 35 37 39 41 42 44 46 47 48 52 53 54 55 58 60 61 62 63 65 66 67 69 70 73 77 81 82 88 94 95 96 97 98 106 107 108 109 110 **P**6 **S** Brim Healthcare, Inc., Brentwood, TN
Primary Contact: Tommy Hobbs, Chief Executive Officer
CFO: Bobbie Pollesch, Chief Financial Officer
CIO: Andy Miller, Director of Information Systems
CHR: George Truell, Director Human Resources
Web address: www.riponmedicalcenter.com

| | 23 | 10 | 19 | 841 | 9 | 36556 | 0 | 14570 | 5804 | 135 |

RIVER FALLS—St. Croix County

⊠ **RIVER FALLS AREA HOSPITAL**, 1629 East Division Street, Zip 54022–1571; tel. 715/425–6155 **A**1 9 10 18 **F**11 12 14 21 27 28 30 33 37 41 47 52 55 59 60 63 65 66 67 68 69 81 88 94 95 107 109 **S** Allina Hospitals & Clinics, Minneapolis, MN
Primary Contact: Randy Farrow, President
CFO: Tom Halada, Director Finance
Web address: www.allina.com

| | 23 | 10 | 27 | 1377 | 10 | 14712 | 245 | — | — | — |

SAINT CROIX FALLS—Polk County

ST. CROIX REGIONAL MEDICAL CENTER, 204 South Adams Street, Zip 54024–9400; tel. 715/483–3261 **A**9 10 18 **F**9 11 12 21 27 31 33 34 37 42 44 47 52 55 58 59 60 61 63 65 66 69 72 73 74 77 81 82 88 94 95 107 109 **P**6 7
Primary Contact: Leonard B. Libis, Chief Executive Officer
Web address: www.scrmc.org

| | 23 | 10 | 25 | 2090 | 13 | 19047 | 254 | 33877 | 11522 | 310 |

SHAWANO—Shawano County

⊠ **SHAWANO MEDICAL CENTER**, 309 North Bartlette Street, Zip 54166–0477; tel. 715/526–2111 **A**1 9 10 18 20 **F**11 12 14 26 27 28 33 36 37 41 44 47 51 52 55 58 59 63 65 66 68 69 75 81 88 95 **P**5 **S** Brim Healthcare, Inc., Brentwood, TN
Primary Contact: James E. Baer, FACHE, Chief Executive Officer
CFO: Vince Studer, Chief Financial Officer
CMO: Peter Keenan, President Medical Staff
CIO: Ken Zade, Information Technology Manager
CHR: Mark Gabavics, Director Human Resources
Web address: www.shawanomed.org

| | 23 | 10 | 39 | 1902 | 16 | 56990 | 340 | 24719 | 10752 | 232 |

SHEBOYGAN—Sheboygan County

⊠ △ **AURORA SHEBOYGAN MEMORIAL MEDICAL CENTER**, 2629 North Seventh Street, Zip 53083–4998; tel. 920/451–5000, (Total facility includes 60 beds in nursing home–type unit) **A**1 2 7 9 10 **F**2 3 4 9 11 12 14 15 21 22 23 26 27 28 29 33 35 39 44 45 47 48 52 54 55 57 58 59 60 61 62 63 64 65 66 68 69 71 72 73 74 75 76 77 81 82 84 88 91 92 93 94 95 96 97 106 107 108 109 **S** Aurora Health Care, Milwaukee, WI
Primary Contact: Daniel Meyer, Administrator
CFO: Brad Hahn, Chief Financial Officer
CIO: Jim Gisch, Manager Client Services
Web address: www.aurorahealthcare.org

| | 23 | 10 | 233 | 7633 | 126 | 50303 | 1199 | 73603 | 32279 | 878 |

⊠ △ **ST. NICHOLAS HOSPITAL**, 3100 Superior Avenue, Zip 53081; tel. 920/459–8300, (Total facility includes 15 beds in nursing home–type unit) **A**1 2 7 9 10 **F**9 11 12 13 14 21 26 27 28 31 33 34 36 37 41 42 44 47 49 51 52 55 58 59 60 61 63 65 66 68 69 81 82 84 86 87 88 92 94 95 107 109 **P**5 **S** Hospital Sisters Health System, Springfield, IL
Primary Contact: Mary T. Brasseaux, Executive Vice President and Administrator
CFO: Donald R. Pieters, Asst Administrator Financial and Support Services
CMO: Warren A. Brauer, President Medical Staff
CHR: Christine F. Jensema, Administrative Director Human Resources
Web address: www.stnicholashospital.org

| | 21 | 10 | 78 | 3525 | 44 | 91696 | 328 | 48991 | 18557 | 350 |

SHELL LAKE—Washburn County

INDIANHEAD MEDICAL CENTER, 113 Fourth Avenue, Zip 54871, Mailing Address: P.O. Box 300, Zip 54871–0300; tel. 715/468–7833 **A**9 10 18 **F**9 11 12 14 27 28 33 34 44 47 51 52 55 59 61 63 65 66 81 88 94 **S** Mid Atlantic Health Management, Inc., Stevensville, MD
Primary Contact: Paul Naglosky, Administrator

| | 33 | 10 | 49 | 571 | 5 | 8160 | 25 | 4691 | 2009 | — |

SPARTA—Monroe County

□ **FRANCISCAN SKEMP HEALTHCARE–SPARTA CAMPUS**, 310 West Main Street, Zip 54656–2171; tel. 608/269–2132, (Total facility includes 30 beds in nursing home–type unit) **A**1 9 10 18 **F**3 9 11 12 21 26 27 28 33 34 42 44 47 52 58 59 60 61 63 65 66 69 81 88 92 94 95 109 **S** Mayo Foundation, Rochester, MN
Primary Contact: Robert M. Tracey, Administrator
Web address: www.mayo.edu/fsh

| | 21 | 10 | 55 | 573 | 34 | 34823 | 75 | 8083 | 4454 | — |

WI

Hospital, Address, Telephone, Approval, Facility, and Physician Codes, Health Care System	Classification Codes		Utilization Data					Expense (thousands) of dollars		
★ American Hospital Association (AHA) membership ☐ Joint Commission on Accreditation of Healthcare Organizations (JCAHO) accreditation ◯ American Osteopathic Association (AOA) accreditation △ Commission on Accreditation of Rehabilitation Facilities (CARF) accreditation	Control	Service	Staffed Beds	Admissions	Census	Outpatient Visits	Births	Total	Payroll	Personnel

SPOONER—Washburn County

★ **SPOONER HEALTH SYSTEM**, 819 Ash Street, Zip 54801–1299;
tel. 715/635–2111, (Total facility includes 90 beds in nursing home–type unit) **A**9
10 18 **F**2 12 14 21 23 26 27 28 29 33 44 46 47 48 51 52 53 54 55 58 59
63 64 65 66 68 69 70 81 85 92 94 96 97 106 107 108 110 **S** Brim
Healthcare, Inc., Brentwood, TN
Primary Contact: Michael Schafer, Chief Executive Officer and Administrator
CFO: Rebecca Busch, Chief Financial Officer
CHR: Cindy Rouzer, Human Resources Director
Web address: www.spoonerhealthsystem.com

| | | 23 | 10 | 115 | 890 | 91 | 13429 | 79 | 9884 | 4035 | 131 |

STANLEY—Chippewa County

★ **OUR LADY OF VICTORY HOSPITAL**, 1120 Pine Street, Zip 54768–0220,
Mailing Address: P.O. Box 220, Zip 54768–0220; tel. 715/644–5571 **A**9 10 18
F2 12 14 22 24 27 29 33 34 39 46 47 48 53 55 58 60 63 65 66 69 70 81
94 95 96 97 106 107 108 **P**6 **S** Marian Health System, Tulsa, OK
Primary Contact: Cynthia Eichman, Chief Executive Officer and Administrator
CFO: Linda Klapperich, Director of Financial Services
CIO: Eric Haglund, Director Information Systems
Web address: www.ministryhealth.org

| | | 23 | 10 | 24 | 658 | 8 | 23826 | 0 | 17503 | 6434 | 129 |

STEVENS POINT—Portage County

⊠ **SAINT MICHAEL'S HOSPITAL**, 900 Illinois Avenue, Zip 54481–3196;
tel. 715/346–5000 **A**1 9 10 19 **F**2 3 4 11 14 21 22 23 26 27 28 29 32 33 35
37 40 44 46 47 48 49 52 53 55 56 58 59 60 61 62 63 64 65 66 67 69 71
72 73 74 75 76 78 79 80 81 82 84 86 87 88 90 93 94 95 96 98 106 107
108 110 **S** Marian Health System, Tulsa, OK
Primary Contact: Bradley Neet, President and Chief Operating Officer
COO: Bradley Neet, President and Chief Operating Officer
CFO: William J. Hinner, Vice President Fiscal Services and Chief Financial Officer
CIO: Mark Erdman, Manager Information Services
Web address: www.saintmichaelshospital.org

| | | 21 | 10 | 122 | 4252 | 43 | 160924 | 651 | 86652 | 34541 | 755 |

STOUGHTON—Dane County

☐ **STOUGHTON HOSPITAL ASSOCIATION**, 900 Ridge Street, Zip 53589–1896;
tel. 608/873–6611 **A**1 9 10 18 **F**2 3 9 12 14 21 22 26 28 29 30 33 37 42 44
46 47 48 52 53 55 60 62 63 65 66 68 69 71 76 81 88 93 94 95 96 97 107
108 109 110
Primary Contact: Terrence Brenny, President and Chief Executive Officer
Web address: www.stoughtonhospital.com

| | | 23 | 10 | 34 | 1355 | 17 | 35417 | 0 | 22304 | 9523 | 1208 |

STURGEON BAY—Door County

⊠ **DOOR COUNTY MEMORIAL HOSPITAL**, 323 South 18th Avenue,
Zip 54235–1495; tel. 920/743–5566, (Total facility includes 30 beds in nursing
home–type unit) **A**1 9 10 20 **F**1 2 9 11 12 14 22 23 24 26 27 28 29 32 33 34
37 44 46 47 48 50 52 53 55 58 59 60 62 63 65 66 68 69 70 77 81 82 84
88 90 92 93 94 95 96 97 106 107 108 110 **P**1 **S** Marian Health System,
Tulsa, OK
Primary Contact: Gerald M. Worrick, President and Chief Executive Officer
CFO: Robert C. Scieszinski, Vice President Finance
CIO: Mary Lopas, Chief Information Officer
CHR: Sandy McKuen, Vice President Human Resources
Web address: www.dcmh.org

| | | 21 | 10 | 73 | 2337 | 53 | 67256 | 173 | 39007 | 20274 | 360 |

SUPERIOR—Douglas County

☐ **ST. MARY'S HOSPITAL OF SUPERIOR**, 3500 Tower Avenue, Zip 54880–5395;
tel. 715/392–8281 **A**1 9 10 18 **F**4 9 12 14 21 26 27 28 33 44 47 52 55 58
60 61 63 65 66 68 69 81 88 94 95 **S** St. Mary's/Duluth Clinic Health System,
Duluth, MN
Primary Contact: Maribeth Olson, Interim Administrator
Web address: www.smdc.org

| | | 23 | 10 | 24 | 768 | 9 | 60021 | 0 | 14854 | 6558 | 138 |

TOMAH—Monroe County

⊠ **TOMAH MEMORIAL HOSPITAL**, 321 Butts Avenue, Zip 54660–1412;
tel. 608/372–2181 **A**1 9 10 18 **F**2 9 11 26 33 36 37 44 47 52 54 58 59 60
63 65 66 81 84 88 94 107 **S** Brim Healthcare, Inc., Brentwood, TN
Primary Contact: Philip Stuart, Administrator and Chief Executive Officer
CFO: Toby Freier, Vice President Finance
Web address: www.tomahhospital.org

| | | 23 | 10 | 25 | 1066 | 10 | 16856 | 251 | 15105 | 6404 | 149 |

⊠ **VETERANS AFFAIRS MEDICAL CENTER**, 500 East Veterans Street, Zip 54660;
tel. 608/372–3971, (Total facility includes 200 beds in nursing home–type unit)
(Nonreporting) **A**1 **S** Department of Veterans Affairs, Washington, DC
Primary Contact: Stan Johnson, Medical Center Director
COO: Stan Johnson, Medical Center Director
CFO: Donna Welch, Resources Service Line Manager
CMO: David Houlihan, M.D., Chief of Staff
CIO: John Hina, Information Technology Services Line Manager
Web address: www.va.gov/tomahvamc

| | | 45 | 22 | 331 | — | — | — | — | — | — | — |

TOMAHAWK—Lincoln County

SACRED HEART HOSPITAL See Sacred Heart–St. Mary's Hospitals, Rhinelander

WI

Many Facility Codes have changed. Please refer to the AHA Guide Code Chart.

© 2005 AHA Guide

Hospital, Address, Telephone, Approval, Facility, and Physician Codes, Health Care System	Classi-fication Codes		Utilization Data					Expense (thousands) of dollars		
	Control	Service	Staffed Beds	Admissions	Census	Outpatient Visits	Births	Total	Payroll	Personnel

TWO RIVERS—Manitowoc County

✠ **AURORA MEDICAL CENTER – MANITOWOC**, 5000 Memorial Drive, Zip 54241–2399; tel. 920/794–5000 **A**1 9 10 **F**2 9 11 12 21 22 23 26 27 28 29 30 33 34 35 37 39 44 45 46 47 48 52 58 59 61 62 63 64 65 66 69 81 82 88 93 94 95 96 97 106 107 108 109 110 **S** Aurora Health Care, Milwaukee, WI
Primary Contact: Bobbe Teigen, Administrator
CFO: Sandra Ewald, Vice President Finance
Web address: www.aurorahealthcare.org

| | 23 | 10 | 69 | 2763 | 31 | 33397 | 271 | 34300 | 12704 | 334 |

VIROQUA—Vernon County

VERNON MEMORIAL HEALTHCARE, (Formerly Vernon Memorial Hospital), 507 South Main Street, Zip 54665–2096; tel. 608/637–2101 **A**9 10 18 **F**2 4 9 11 12 21 23 24 27 28 29 30 33 34 36 37 39 41 44 46 47 48 51 52 58 59 60 61 62 63 64 65 66 69 81 84 88 94 95 96 97 98 106 107 108 109 **P**6
Primary Contact: Garith W. Steiner, Chief Executive Officer and Administrator
Web address: www.vmh.org

| | 23 | 10 | 14 | 1594 | 13 | 67250 | 182 | 25472 | 12550 | 214 |

WATERTOWN—Dodge County

✠ △ **WATERTOWN MEMORIAL HOSPITAL**, 125 Hospital Drive, Zip 53098–3384; tel. 920/261–4210 **A**1 7 9 10 **F**1 2 4 8 9 11 12 14 21 27 28 29 30 33 34 37 42 44 45 46 47 48 51 52 53 54 55 58 59 60 61 62 63 65 66 67 69 70 77 81 82 84 87 88 91 93 94 95 96 97 106 107 108 109 110 **P**6 8
Primary Contact: John P. Kosanovich, President
CFO: John Graf, Senior Vice President
CIO: Tim Strauch, Director Information Services
CHR: Duane Floyd, Vice President Human Resources and Support Services
Web address: www.wahs.com

| | 23 | 10 | 51 | 2778 | 30 | 116818 | 353 | 48279 | 22705 | 457 |

WAUKESHA—Waukesha County

WAUKESHA COUNTY MENTAL HEALTH CENTER, 25042 West Northview Road, Zip 53186; tel. 262/548–7950 **A**10 **F**3 26 27 28 60 71
Primary Contact: William T. Pratt, Administrator

| | 13 | 22 | 28 | 1159 | 21 | 0 | 0 | 4582 | 2206 | — |

★ △ **WAUKESHA MEMORIAL HOSPITAL**, 725 American Avenue, Zip 53188–5099; tel. 262/928–1000 **A**3 5 7 9 10 **F**2 3 9 11 12 14 15 17 19 21 22 23 24 27 28 29 32 33 34 35 37 39 42 44 46 47 48 52 53 54 55 56 57 58 59 60 61 62 63 64 65 68 69 70 71 72 73 74 75 76 78 79 80 81 82 84 85 86 87 88 93 94 95 96 106 107 108 109 110 **S** ProHealth Care, Waukesha, WI
Primary Contact: Edward A. Olson, President and Chief Executive Officer
CFO: Robert W. Mlynarek, Vice President Finance
CMO: James D. Gardner, M.D., Vice President Medical Staff
CIO: William Miller, Vice President Information Services
Web address: www.waukeshamemorial.org

| | 23 | 10 | 319 | 16257 | 198 | 294068 | 2381 | 276784 | 94428 | 1804 |

WAUPACA—Waupaca County

✠ **RIVERSIDE MEDICAL CENTER**, 800 Riverside Drive, Zip 54981–1999; tel. 715/258–1000 **A**1 9 10 18 **F**9 11 12 14 21 33 37 44 47 52 55 59 60 61 63 65 66 67 68 81 88 94 107 109 **S** Quorum Health Resources, Plano, TX
Primary Contact: Craig A. Kantos, Chief Executive Officer
CFO: Kerry Lee Blanke, Director Financial Services
CMO: Matthew Oetken, Chief of Staff
CIO: Cathy Reynertson, Management Information Systems Manager
CHR: Kevin Gossens, Human Resources Director
Web address: www.riversidemedical.org

| | 23 | 10 | 25 | 1602 | 13 | 49382 | 242 | 23177 | 10768 | 252 |

WAUPUN—Fond Du Lac County

✠ **WAUPUN MEMORIAL HOSPITAL**, 620 West Brown Street, Zip 53963–1799; tel. 920/324–5581 **A**1 9 10 18 **F**9 11 12 21 26 27 28 30 33 37 40 42 47 49 52 54 55 58 59 63 65 81 82 88 94 107
Primary Contact: DeAnn Thurmer, Interim President and Chief Executive Officer
CFO: William Fenske, Vice President Finance
Web address: www.agnesian.com

| | 21 | 10 | 25 | 1097 | 11 | 45782 | 107 | 17229 | 6741 | 108 |

WAUSAU—Marathon County

✠ △ **ASPIRUS WAUSAU HOSPITAL**, (Formerly Wausau Hospital), 333 Pine Ridge Boulevard, Zip 54401–4187, Mailing Address: P.O. Box 1847, Zip 54402–1847; tel. 715/847–2121 **A**1 2 3 5 7 9 10 **F**2 6 9 11 12 13 14 15 19 22 23 26 27 28 33 34 36 37 40 42 44 46 47 48 49 52 53 58 59 60 61 63 64 65 66 67 68 69 71 72 73 75 76 77 78 79 80 81 82 85 86 87 88 93 94 96 108 110
Primary Contact: Charles L. Shabino, M.D., President and Chief Executive Officer
COO: Diane Postler–Slattery, Ph.D., President and Chief Operating Officer
CFO: Sidney C. Sczygelski, Senior Vice President Finance and Chief Financial Officer
CMO: James E. Casanova, M.D., Senior Vice President Medical Affairs
CIO: Alan Wyman, Vice President Information Technology
CHR: Roger Lucas, Vice President Human Resources
Web address: www.chcsys.org/wausau_hospital

| | 23 | 10 | 253 | 16271 | 180 | 91918 | 1473 | 204947 | 77005 | 1558 |

NORTH CENTRAL HEALTH CARE FACILITIES, 1100 Lakeview Drive, Zip 54403–6799; tel. 715/848–4600, (Total facility includes 320 beds in nursing home–type unit) **A**10 **F**3 4 21 27 29 31 42 44 47 52 58 65 69 71 72 73 74 75 76 77 78 92 94 96 108 110
Primary Contact: Tim Steller, Chief Executive Officer
Web address: www.norcen.org
WAUSAU HOSPITAL See Aspirus Wausau Hospital

| | 13 | 22 | 363 | 1523 | 363 | 167234 | 0 | 35549 | 15697 | 282 |

WI

Hospital, Address, Telephone, Approval, Facility, and Physician Codes, Health Care System	Classi-fication Codes		Utilization Data					Expense (thousands) of dollars		
★ American Hospital Association (AHA) membership □ Joint Commission on Accreditation of Healthcare Organizations (JCAHO) accreditation ○ American Osteopathic Association (AOA) accreditation △ Commission on Accreditation of Rehabilitation Facilities (CARF) accreditation	Control	Service	Staffed Beds	Admissions	Census	Outpatient Visits	Births	Total	Payroll	Personnel

WAUWATOSA—Milwaukee County

✠ **AURORA PSYCHIATRIC HOSPITAL**, 1220 Dewey Avenue, Zip 53213–2598; tel. 414/454–6600 **A**1 3 5 10 **F**3 4 21 22 24 26 27 28 29 39 42 45 46 47 48 52 53 57 58 65 66 71 72 73 74 77 78 94 96 98 106 108 **S** Aurora Health Care, Milwaukee, WI
Primary Contact: Peter Carlson, Executive Director
Web address: www.aurorahealthcare.org

| 23 | 22 | 105 | 2505 | 64 | 76321 | 0 | — | — | 269 |

✠ **THE WISCONSIN HEART HOSPITAL**, 10000 West Bluemound Road, Zip 53226; tel. 414/778–7800, (Nonreporting) **A**1 10 **S** Wheaton Franciscan Services, Inc., Wheaton, IL
Primary Contact: Norma J. McCutcheon, President
CHR: Mark Farrell, Manager, Human Resources
Web address: www.twhh.org

| 33 | 42 | 40 | — | — | — | — | | | |

WEST ALLIS—Milwaukee County

✠ △ **WEST ALLIS MEMORIAL HOSPITAL**, 8901 West Lincoln Avenue, Zip 53227–0901, Mailing Address: P.O. Box 27901, Zip 53227–0901; tel. 414/328–6000 **A**1 7 9 10 **F**2 7 11 12 21 22 23 26 27 28 29 30 33 35 37 39 40 42 44 45 47 48 52 53 55 56 57 58 59 61 62 63 64 65 68 69 70 79 80 81 82 83 84 85 87 88 93 94 95 96 98 106 108 109 110 **S** Aurora Health Care, Milwaukee, WI
Primary Contact: Richard A. Kellar, Administrator
CFO: David Eager, Vice President Finance
Web address: www.aurora.org

| 23 | 10 | 227 | 11579 | 154 | 85639 | 2475 | — | — | 955 |

WEST BEND—Washington County

✠ **ST. JOSEPH'S COMMUNITY HOSPITAL OF WEST BEND**, 551 South Silverbrook Drive, Zip 53095–3898; tel. 262/334–5533 **A**1 9 10 **F**3 11 12 14 21 26 27 28 30 31 33 34 40 42 44 47 52 54 55 58 59 60 61 63 65 67 69 71 73 76 81 82 84 88 94
Primary Contact: John Reiling, President and Chief Executive Officer
CFO: Mike Malzewski, Chief Financial Officer
CIO: Kim Penble, Chief Information Officer
CHR: Deb Lavenstein, Vice President Human Resources and Marketing
Web address: www.synergyhealth.org

| 23 | 10 | 103 | 4706 | 49 | 48619 | 625 | — | — | 460 |

WHITEHALL—Trempealeau County

TRI–COUNTY MEMORIAL HOSPITAL, 18601 Lincoln Street, Zip 54773–0065; tel. 715/538–4361, (Total facility includes 75 beds in nursing home–type unit) **A**9 10 18 **F**2 6 8 9 12 14 23 26 27 28 29 33 44 46 47 48 49 52 54 55 58 60 61 63 65 66 68 69 81 84 91 92 94 96 97 98 106 107 108 110
Primary Contact: Curtis A. Johnson, President and Chief Executive Officer
Web address: www.gundluth.org

| 23 | 10 | 100 | 668 | 75 | 14806 | 0 | | | 95 |

WILD ROSE—Waushara County

WILD ROSE COMMUNITY MEMORIAL HOSPITAL, 601 Grove Avenue, Zip 54984, Mailing Address: P.O. Box 243, Zip 54984–0243; tel. 920/622–3257 **A**9 10 18 **F**8 9 12 21 27 28 33 41 44 47 52 58 63 65 68 69 81 88 107 **P**6
Primary Contact: Donald Caves, Chief Executive Officer
Web address: www.wildrosehospital.org

| 23 | 10 | 27 | 387 | 7 | 16611 | 0 | 2919 | 2436 | — |

WINNEBAGO—Winnebago County

□ **WINNEBAGO MENTAL HEALTH INSTITUTE**, Mailing Address: Box 9, Zip 54985–0009; tel. 920/235–4910 **A**1 10 **F**3 37 47 65 66 71 72 73 74 76 94 **P**6
Primary Contact: Joann B. O'Connor, Director and Chief Executive Officer
Web address: www.dhfs.state.wi.us/mh_winnebago

| 12 | 22 | 280 | 1209 | 266 | 0 | 0 | — | — | 713 |

WISCONSIN RAPIDS—Wood County

✠ **RIVERVIEW HOSPITAL ASSOCIATION**, 410 Dewey Street, Zip 54494–4715, Mailing Address: P.O. Box 8080, Zip 54494–8080; tel. 715/423–6060, (Total facility includes 114 beds in nursing home–type unit) **A**1 9 10 **F**2 3 11 12 14 23 27 28 29 33 34 44 47 48 52 53 54 55 57 58 59 60 61 62 63 64 65 67 68 69 70 71 73 79 81 82 84 87 88 92 93 94 95 96 107
Primary Contact: Celse A. Berard, President
CFO: Michael Bovee, Vice President Finance
CIO: Marge Tell, Director Information Services
CHR: Tom Hunsberger, Vice President Human Resources
Web address: www.rhahealthcare.org

| 23 | 10 | 183 | 3443 | 129 | 40994 | 515 | — | — | 447 |

WOODRUFF—Oneida County

✠ **HOWARD YOUNG MEDICAL CENTER**, 240 Maple Street, Zip 54568, Mailing Address: P.O. Box 470, Zip 54568–0470; tel. 715/356–8000 **A**1 9 10 **F**2 4 6 9 11 12 13 14 22 26 27 28 29 30 33 37 39 41 44 45 46 47 48 49 52 55 58 59 60 61 62 63 65 66 67 68 69 75 77 81 82 84 85 87 88 93 94 95 96 97 106 108 109 110 **S** Marian Health System, Tulsa, OK
Primary Contact: Brian Kief, President and Chief Executive Officer
CFO: Jack P. Sutliff, Vice President and Chief Financial Officer
CIO: Laurie Oungst, Assistant Vice President
CHR: Karen Tait, Vice President
Web address: www.hyhc.com

| 23 | 10 | 65 | 4407 | 47 | 80776 | 325 | — | — | 425 |

WI

WYOMING

Hospital, Address, Telephone, Approval, Facility, and Physician Codes, Health Care System	Classi-fication Codes		Utilization Data					Expense (thousands) of dollars		
★ American Hospital Association (AHA) membership □ Joint Commission on Accreditation of Healthcare Organizations (JCAHO) accreditation ○ American Osteopathic Association (AOA) accreditation △ Commission on Accreditation of Rehabilitation Facilities (CARF) accreditation	Control	Service	Staffed Beds	Admissions	Census	Outpatient Visits	Births	Total	Payroll	Personnel

AFTON—Lincoln County

★ **STAR VALLEY MEDICAL CENTER**, 901 Adams Street, Zip 83110–0579, Mailing Address: P.O. Box 579, Zip 83110–0579; tel. 307/885–5800, (Total facility includes 24 beds in nursing home–type unit) **A**9 10 18 20 **F**2 9 11 12 21 23 27 33 34 44 46 52 59 62 63 66 70 81 84 88 92 94 97 107 108 109 **P**6 Primary Contact: J. Steve Perry, Chief Executive Officer CFO: Ken Brough, Chief Financial Officer CMO: D Scott Bender, M.D., Chief of Staff CIO: Marty Ashton, Chief Information Officer CHR: Len Gross, Director Human Resources Web address: www.svmcwy.info	16	10	40	647	28	13949	98	11742	5063	130

BASIN—Big Horn County

SOUTH BIG HORN COUNTY HOSPITAL, 388 South U.S. Highway 20, Zip 82410; tel. 307/568–3311, (Total facility includes 37 beds in nursing home–type unit) **A**9 10 18 **F**33 37 38 39 45 46 48 88 92 94 **P**6 Primary Contact: Jackie Claudson, Administrator Web address: www.midwayclinic.com	16	10	43	178	37	1078	0	2987	1849	65

BUFFALO—Johnson County

⊠ **JOHNSON COUNTY HEALTHCARE CENTER**, 497 West Lott Street, Zip 82834–1691; tel. 307/684–5521, (Total facility includes 50 beds in nursing home–type unit) **A**1 9 10 18 20 **F**5 9 11 12 23 33 36 44 46 51 55 59 61 62 63 65 81 88 92 94 97 Primary Contact: Sandy Ward, Administrator CFO: Sandy Ward, Administrator CMO: Doziier Tabb, M.D., Chief of Staff CIO: Laurie Hansen, Director Administrative Services CHR: Karen Ferguson, Director Human Resources	16	10	75	583	55	11284	55	11390	5147	161

CASPER—Natrona County

□ **WYOMING BEHAVIORAL INSTITUTE**, 2521 East 15th Street, Zip 82609–4126; tel. 800/457–9312 **A**1 10 **F**3 4 21 27 28 29 30 71 72 73 74 75 76 77 78 94 **P**7 Primary Contact: Bill Sexton, Chief Executive Officer Web address: www.wbihelp.com	32	22	67	944	50	1235	0	8930	4689	141
⊠ △ **WYOMING MEDICAL CENTER**, 1233 East Second Street, Zip 82601–2988; tel. 307/577–7201, (Total facility includes 15 beds in nursing home–type unit) **A**1 7 9 10 20 **F**2 4 6 9 11 15 17 19 21 22 23 26 27 28 29 33 34 39 40 43 45 46 47 48 49 50 55 57 59 60 61 62 63 64 65 66 68 70 75 81 82 84 85 86 87 88 92 93 94 96 107 108 109 110 **P**6 Primary Contact: Pam Fulks, President and Chief Executive Officer COO: Vickie Diamond, Senior Vice President and Chief Operating Officer CFO: Edmond R. Renemans, Vice President and Chief Financial Officer CIO: Don Claunch, Chief Information Officer Web address: www.wmcnet.org	23	10	205	9781	115	66830	985	125644	44754	1088

CHEYENNE—Laramie County

⊠ **UNITED MEDICAL CENTER**, 214 East 23rd Street, Zip 82001–3790; tel. 307/634–2273, (Total facility includes 12 beds in nursing home–type unit) **A**1 9 10 20 **F**2 4 9 11 12 15 17 19 21 22 23 24 27 28 29 33 34 36 37 39 40 41 46 48 49 51 53 55 57 58 59 60 61 62 63 66 68 69 71 72 73 74 75 76 77 79 81 82 84 85 87 88 92 93 94 108 109 110 Primary Contact: Charles F. Harms, Chief Executive Officer CFO: Bruce Anderson, Vice President Fiscal Services CMO: Robert J. Stuart, M.D., Vice President for Medical Affairs CIO: David Squires, Chief Information Officer CHR: Phyllis Bell, Vice President Human Resources Web address: www.umcwy.info	13	10	210	9738	113	134062	1189	118537	47942	1177
⊠ **VETERANS AFFAIRS MEDICAL CENTER**, 2360 East Pershing Boulevard, Zip 82001–5392; tel. 307/778–7550, (Total facility includes 50 beds in nursing home–type unit) **A**1 9 **F**2 4 9 21 22 23 26 28 29 31 32 33 36 37 38 39 44 45 46 50 52 53 55 58 60 61 62 63 64 65 66 68 69 70 73 74 75 76 77 81 82 88 92 93 94 96 106 108 109 110 **P**6 **S** Department of Veterans Affairs, Washington, DC Primary Contact: David M. Kilpatrick, M.D., Director COO: Robert Anselmi, Director Environment of Care CFO: Melvin Cranford, Acting Chief Fiscal Services CMO: Roger Johnson, M.D., Chief of Staff CIO: Chad Cartwright, Chief Information Resource Management Systems CHR: Sandra Willoughby, Chief Human Resources Web address: www.va.gov/sta/guide/home.asp	45	10	71	1115	43	125705	0	58904	—	438

Hospital, Address, Telephone, Approval, Facility, and Physician Codes, Health Care System	Classi-fication Codes		Utilization Data					Expense (thousands) of dollars		
★ American Hospital Association (AHA) membership □ Joint Commission on Accreditation of Healthcare Organizations (JCAHO) accreditation ○ American Osteopathic Association (AOA) accreditation △ Commission on Accreditation of Rehabilitation Facilities (CARF) accreditation	Control	Service	Staffed Beds	Admissions	Census	Outpatient Visits	Births	Total	Payroll	Personnel

CODY—Park County

★ **WEST PARK HOSPITAL**, 707 Sheridan Avenue, Zip 82414–3409; tel. 307/527–7501, (Total facility includes 128 beds in nursing home–type unit) **A**9 10 18 20 **F**2 4 6 9 11 12 21 22 23 27 28 29 32 33 34 36 37 38 44 45 46 48 49 51 52 53 55 58 59 60 62 63 64 65 66 69 70 81 82 84 88 92 94 95 96 97 98 106 107 108 109 110 **S** Quorum Health Resources, Plano, TX
Primary Contact: Douglas A. McMillan, Administrator and Chief Executive Officer
CFO: Patrick G. McConnell, Chief Financial Officer
Web address: www.westparkhospital.org

| | 16 | 10 | 153 | 1780 | 95 | 49559 | 178 | 26974 | 12921 | 352 |

DOUGLAS—Converse County

★ **MEMORIAL HOSPITAL OF CONVERSE COUNTY**, 111 South Fifth Street, Zip 82633–1450, Mailing Address: P.O. Box 1450, Zip 82633–1450; tel. 307/358–2122 **A**9 10 18 **F**2 11 12 21 24 26 27 28 29 33 34 39 47 48 52 55 58 59 62 63 64 65 66 81 82 88 92 97 98 106 108 109 110 **P**6
Primary Contact: Thomas Nordwick, President and Chief Executive Officer
CFO: Curtis R. Dugger, Chief Financial Officer
CMO: Dennis Yutani, M.D., Chief of Staff
CIO: Dave Patterson, Director
CHR: Linda York, Manager Human Resources
Web address: www.conversehospital.com

| | 13 | 10 | 25 | 769 | 8 | 26185 | 115 | 19269 | 7905 | 211 |

EVANSTON—Uinta County

✚ **EVANSTON REGIONAL HOSPITAL**, 190 Arrowhead Drive, Zip 82930–9266; tel. 307/789–3636 **A**1 9 10 20 **F**12 21 27 28 33 34 47 49 52 55 59 60 63 66 69 81 85 88 93 97 106 **S** Community Health Systems, Inc., Brentwood, TN
Primary Contact: R. Clifford Park, Chief Executive Officer
CFO: Greg Hexem, Chief Financial Officer
Web address: www.evanstonregionalhospital.com

| | 33 | 10 | 42 | 1454 | 8 | 43506 | 255 | 14774 | 6770 | 166 |

WYOMING STATE HOSPITAL, 830 Highway 150 South, Zip 82931–5341, Mailing Address: P.O. Box 177, Zip 82931–0177; tel. 307/789–3464 **A**10 **F**4 21 22 26 27 28 31 35 39 45 47 52 58 60 71 72 73 74 75 76 77 94 96 106 **P**6
Primary Contact: Pablo Hernandez, M.D., Administrator
Web address: www.mentalhealth.state.wy.us/hospital/index.html

| | 12 | 22 | 166 | 438 | 74 | 0 | 0 | 20973 | 12127 | 426 |

GILLETTE—Campbell County

✚ **CAMPBELL COUNTY MEMORIAL HOSPITAL**, 501 South Burma Avenue, Zip 82716–3426, Mailing Address: P.O. Box 3011, Zip 82717–3011; tel. 307/682–8811, (Total facility includes 125 beds in nursing home–type unit) **A**1 9 10 20 **F**4 5 6 8 9 11 12 21 22 23 26 27 28 29 31 33 34 36 40 41 42 44 45 46 48 49 51 52 53 54 55 58 59 60 61 62 63 64 65 66 67 69 70 71 72 73 74 75 76 77 78 79 80 81 82 83 84 85 88 91 92 93 94 95 96 97 106 108 109 110 **P**6
Primary Contact: Gene Balzer, Administrator
CFO: Bart Hansen, Chief Financial Officer
CMO: Lawrence Long, M.D., Chief of Staff
CIO: Ron King, Information Systems Manager
Web address: www.ccmh.net

| | 16 | 10 | 201 | 3600 | 85 | 115590 | 602 | 57762 | 25405 | 811 |

JACKSON—Teton County

✚ **ST. JOHN'S MEDICAL CENTER AND LIVING CENTER**, 625 East Broadway Street, Zip 83001, Mailing Address: P.O. Box 428, Zip 83001–0428; tel. 307/733–3636, (Total facility includes 60 beds in nursing home–type unit) **A**1 9 10 20 **F**2 6 9 10 11 12 21 22 23 26 27 28 29 30 31 32 33 34 36 37 39 40 41 42 44 45 46 47 48 51 52 53 55 58 59 60 61 62 63 64 65 66 69 70 73 75 81 82 84 85 88 92 93 94 96 97 108 109 110
Primary Contact: Ronald A. Ommen, Chief Executive Officer and Administrator
CFO: Robert Flake, Chief Financial Officer
CIO: David Witton, Manager
CHR: Glenda Bernhardt, Manager
Web address: www.tetonhospital.org

| | 16 | 10 | 108 | 2984 | 74 | 29839 | 366 | 46011 | 18362 | 416 |

KEMMERER—Lincoln County

★ **SOUTH LINCOLN MEDICAL CENTER**, 711 Onyx Street, Zip 83101–3214, Mailing Address: P.O. Box 390, Zip 83101–0390; tel. 307/877–4401, (Total facility includes 24 beds in nursing home–type unit) **A**9 10 20 **F**2 6 11 12 24 32 33 46 48 53 58 59 60 62 63 69 70 81 84 88 92 97 108 **P**6
Primary Contact: Eric Boley, Administrator and Chief Executive Officer
CFO: Curtis Nielson, Chief Financial Officer
CMO: G Christopher Krell, M.D., Chief of Staff
CIO: Kristin Housley, Chief Management Information Systems
Web address: www.southlincolnmedical.com

| | 16 | 10 | 40 | 326 | 23 | 32902 | 27 | 10180 | 4701 | 144 |

LANDER—Fremont County

✚ **LANDER VALLEY MEDICAL CENTER**, 1320 Bishop Randall Drive, Zip 82520–3996; tel. 307/332–4420 **A**1 9 10 **F**2 3 4 9 11 12 17 21 27 28 29 33 34 52 55 57 58 59 60 62 63 66 68 69 72 73 74 75 76 77 81 82 84 85 87 88 94 96 97 108 109 110 **P**5 **S** LifePoint Hospitals, Inc., Brentwood, TN
Primary Contact: Phil Eaton, Chief Executive Officer
CFO: Ann Huhnke, Chief Financial Officer
CMO: Greg Clifford, M.D., Emergency Services Director
CIO: Keith Blair, M.D., Information Systems Manager
CHR: Carolyn Livingston, Manager
Web address: www.landerhospital.com

| | 33 | 10 | 89 | 2225 | 27 | 41816 | 299 | 17778 | 8532 | 221 |

Many Facility Codes have changed. Please refer to the AHA Guide Code Chart.
© 2005 AHA Guide

Hospital, Address, Telephone, Approval, Facility, and Physician Codes, Health Care System	Classi-fication Codes		Utilization Data					Expense (thousands) of dollars		
★ American Hospital Association (AHA) membership □ Joint Commission on Accreditation of Healthcare Organizations (JCAHO) accreditation ○ American Osteopathic Association (AOA) accreditation △ Commission on Accreditation of Rehabilitation Facilities (CARF) accreditation	Control	Service	Staffed Beds	Admissions	Census	Outpatient Visits	Births	Total	Payroll	Personnel

LARAMIE—Albany County

⊞ **IVINSON MEMORIAL HOSPITAL**, 255 North 30th Street, Zip 82072–5195; tel. 307/742–2141, (Total facility includes 8 beds in nursing home–type unit) **A**1 9 10 12 20 **F**9 11 12 21 22 23 26 27 28 29 30 31 33 39 40 44 46 47 48 49 55 58 59 60 61 62 63 64 65 69 71 72 73 74 76 77 79 80 81 82 83 84 85 87 88 92 93 94 96 97 106 108 109 **P**6 8 **S** Quorum Health Resources, Plano, TX
Primary Contact: Nelson Toebbe, Chief Executive Officer
CFO: Paul Zuidema, Chief Financial Officer
CMO: Thomas Bienz, M.D., Chief of Staff
CHR: John Ysebaert, Director Human Resources
Web address: www.ivinsonhospital.org

| | 16 | 10 | 99 | 2828 | 27 | 46259 | 423 | 45818 | 18252 | 406 |

LOVELL—Big Horn County

★ **NORTH BIG HORN HOSPITAL DISTRICT**, (Formerly North Big Horn Hospital), 1115 Lane 12, Zip 82431–9537; tel. 307/548–5200, (Total facility includes 85 beds in nursing home–type unit) **A**9 10 18 20 **F**5 6 17 21 26 33 36 41 44 45 46 48 52 58 60 63 65 66 69 70 81 88 92 94 95 96 97 108
Primary Contact: Grant M. Winn, Interim Chief Executive Officer
COO: Grant M. Winn, Interim Chief Executive Officer
CFO: Daphne Hartman, Chief Financial Officer
CMO: David E. Hoffman, M.D., Chief of Staff
CIO: Eileen Fink, Health Information Officer
CHR: Barbara Shumway, Human Resources Officer
Web address: www.nbhh.com

| | 16 | 10 | 100 | 447 | 72 | 8517 | 0 | 8546 | 4837 | 145 |

NEWCASTLE—Weston County

★ **WESTON COUNTY HEALTH SERVICES**, 1124 Washington Boulevard, Zip 82701–2996; tel. 307/746–4491, (Total facility includes 51 beds in nursing home–type unit) **A**9 10 18 20 **F**2 14 23 26 29 33 34 46 51 52 55 59 63 81 88 92 96 97 **S** Regional Health, Rapid City, SD
Primary Contact: George Minder, Chief Executive Officer
CFO: Bob Tipton, Chief Financial Officer
CIO: Clara Varner, Business Office Manager
CHR: Shirley Parks, Coordinator Human Resources
Web address: www.wchs–wy.org

| | 16 | 10 | 69 | 405 | 52 | 1711 | 3 | 6909 | 3287 | 99 |

POWELL—Park County

★ **POWELL VALLEY HEALTHCARE**, 777 Avenue H, Zip 82435–2296; tel. 307/754–2267, (Total facility includes 100 beds in nursing home–type unit) **A**9 10 18 20 **F**6 8 9 11 12 21 23 26 27 28 29 33 34 36 37 44 46 48 51 52 55 58 59 61 62 63 64 81 82 84 88 92 94 95 96 97 106 107 108 110 **P**1 **S** Brim Healthcare, Inc., Brentwood, TN
Primary Contact: Rod Barton, Chief Executive Officer
CFO: Steve Ramsey, Chief Financial Officer
CMO: Hugh Fraser, M.D., Chief of Staff
CHR: Terry Bradford, Director Human Resources
Web address: www.pvhc.org

| | 23 | 10 | 125 | 1110 | 107 | 22979 | 196 | 20736 | 10946 | 281 |

RAWLINS—Carbon County

MEMORIAL HOSPITAL OF CARBON COUNTY, 2221 West Elm Street, Zip 82301–0460, Mailing Address: P.O. Box 460, Zip 82301–0460; tel. 307/324–8213, (Total facility includes 10 beds in nursing home–type unit) **A**9 10 20 **F**6 9 11 12 21 23 26 27 28 29 33 34 44 45 46 51 52 53 55 59 60 61 62 63 64 66 69 81 82 84 87 88 92 94 96 97 106 108
Primary Contact: Patricia L. Carter, Chief Executive Officer
Web address: www.imhcc.com

| | 13 | 10 | 45 | 1544 | 22 | 22122 | 113 | 18740 | 7895 | 187 |

RIVERTON—Fremont County

⊞ **RIVERTON MEMORIAL HOSPITAL**, 2100 West Sunset Drive, Zip 82501–2274; tel. 307/856–4161 **A**1 9 10 20 **F**2 9 11 12 23 26 27 28 33 40 46 53 55 58 59 60 62 63 64 69 81 82 88 93 94 97 106 110 **P**7 **S** LifePoint Hospitals, Inc., Brentwood, TN
Primary Contact: Robert M. Peterson, Chief Executive Officer
CFO: Susan Goetzinger, Chief Financial Officer
CIO: Tim Foley, Director Information Systems
Web address: www.riverton–hospital.com

| | 33 | 10 | 70 | 1619 | 14 | 29907 | 215 | 15365 | 6250 | 156 |

ROCK SPRINGS—Sweetwater County

⊞ **MEMORIAL HOSPITAL OF SWEETWATER COUNTY**, 1200 College Drive, Zip 82901–5868, Mailing Address: Box 1359, Zip 82902–1359; tel. 307/362–3711 **A**1 9 10 20 **F**2 9 12 21 22 23 28 29 32 33 34 37 46 48 49 53 55 58 59 61 62 63 64 65 69 81 84 88 93 94 95 96 106 108
Primary Contact: Stuart J. Thomas, Interim Executive Director
CFO: Mark Hamilton, Interim Assistant Executive Director Finance
CMO: Alan Richardson, M.D., Medical Staff President
Web address: www.minershospital.com

| | 13 | 10 | 99 | 2517 | 19 | 93575 | 519 | 35197 | 14030 | 339 |

SHERIDAN—Sheridan County

□ **MEMORIAL HOSPITAL OF SHERIDAN COUNTY**, 1401 West Fifth Street, Zip 82801–2799; tel. 307/672–1000 **A**1 9 10 20 **F**2 9 11 12 14 21 26 27 29 30 31 33 34 35 36 38 46 47 48 51 52 55 57 58 59 60 61 62 63 64 65 66 72 73 74 75 77 80 81 82 84 85 88 93 94 95 96 106 108 110
Primary Contact: Kenneth R. Huey, Administrator
Web address: www.sheridanhospital.org

| | 13 | 10 | 62 | 2792 | 32 | 40296 | 339 | 35343 | 16063 | 390 |

WY

Hospital, Address, Telephone, Approval, Facility, and Physician Codes, Health Care System	Classi-fication Codes		Utilization Data					Expense (thousands) of dollars		
★ American Hospital Association (AHA) membership □ Joint Commission on Accreditation of Healthcare Organizations (JCAHO) accreditation ○ American Osteopathic Association (AOA) accreditation △ Commission on Accreditation of Rehabilitation Facilities (CARF) accreditation	Control	Service	Staffed Beds	Admissions	Census	Outpatient Visits	Births	Total	Payroll	Personnel
☒ **VETERANS AFFAIRS MEDICAL CENTER**, 1898 Fort Road, Zip 82801–8320; tel. 307/672–3473, (Total facility includes 50 beds in nursing home–type unit) (Nonreporting) **A**1 5 9 **S** Department of Veterans Affairs, Washington, DC Primary Contact: Maureen Humphrys, Director CFO: William Brayton, Financial Manager CMO: Wendell Robison, M.D., Chief of Staff CIO: Kaylene Zimmer, Chief Information Officer CHR: Jeanne Wood, Manager Human Resources Web address: www.va.gov/sta/guide/home.asp	45	22	149	—	—	—	—	—	—	—
SUNDANCE—Crook County										
★ **CROOK COUNTY MEDICAL SERVICES DISTRICT**, 713 Oak Street, Zip 82729; Mailing Address: P.O. Box 517, Zip 82729–0517; tel. 307/283–3501, (Total facility includes 32 beds in nursing home–type unit) **A**9 10 18 20 **F**1 6 26 27 28 33 36 44 46 47 48 51 65 69 88 92 94 97 **P**6 Primary Contact: Larry Potter, Chief Executive Officer CMO: Cynthia Casey, M.D., Chief of Staff CHR: Patricia Feist, Manager Human Resources Web address: www.crookcountymedical.com	16	10	48	222	31	5669	0	4416	3894	90
THERMOPOLIS—Hot Springs County										
★ **HOT SPRINGS COUNTY MEMORIAL HOSPITAL**, 150 East Arapahoe Street, Zip 82443–2498; tel. 307/864–3121 **A**9 10 18 20 **F**9 11 12 26 28 33 34 46 47 51 58 63 65 81 82 84 87 88 94 97 **S** Brim Healthcare, Inc., Brentwood, TN Primary Contact: Trudy Chittick, Chief Executive Officer CFO: Ken Knight, Chief Financial Officer CIO: Tim Knight, Director of Information Technology CHR: Patti Jeunehomme, Director Human Resources Web address: www.hscmh.com	13	10	25	549	6	26287	42	9579	3421	94
TORRINGTON—Goshen County										
★ **COMMUNITY HOSPITAL**, 2000 Campbell Drive, Zip 82240–1597; tel. 307/532–4181 **A**9 10 18 20 **F**2 9 11 12 21 22 26 27 28 29 30 33 34 38 46 48 51 52 53 54 55 58 62 63 66 81 88 92 93 94 95 96 97 106 107 108 **P**5 6 **S** Banner Health, Phoenix, AZ Primary Contact: Gordon Lewis, Chief Executive Officer CFO: Debra Cummings, Chief Financial Officer CMO: Richard Campbell, D.O., Chief of Staff CIO: Rod Miller, Chief Information Technology CHR: Sandy Dugger, Director Human Resources Web address: www.torringtonhealth.com	23	10	25	987	6	20446	79	10020	4456	120
WHEATLAND—Platte County										
☒ **PLATTE COUNTY MEMORIAL HOSPITAL**, 201 14th Street, Zip 82201–3201, Mailing Address: P.O. Box 848, Zip 82201–0848; tel. 307/322–3636, (Total facility includes 43 beds in nursing home–type unit) **A**1 9 10 18 20 **F**11 12 21 25 26 27 28 33 34 46 48 52 58 59 62 63 81 88 92 94 96 97 **S** Banner Health, Phoenix, AZ Primary Contact: Kenneth W. Leisher, Chief Executive Officer CFO: Ed Johlman, Director Finance CIO: Robin Wood, Director Information Systems CHR: Mark Winger, Director People Resources and Organizational Planning Web address: www.plattecountyhospital.com	13	10	68	718	50	13605	57	10603	5049	146
WORLAND—Washakie County										
☒ **WASHAKIE MEDICAL CENTER**, 400 South 15th Street, Zip 82401–3531, Mailing Address: P.O. Box 700, Zip 82401–0700; tel. 307/347–3221 **A**1 9 10 18 20 **F**2 9 11 12 21 27 33 34 37 46 51 52 53 55 58 59 60 63 64 65 66 69 81 84 88 92 94 97 110 **P**6 8 **S** Banner Health, Phoenix, AZ Primary Contact: George A. Rohrich, Chief Executive Officer CFO: Joe Devin, Chief Financial Officer CMO: James Randolph, M.D., Chief of Staff CHR: Beverly Walton, Manager Human Resources Web address: www.washakiemedicalcenter.com	23	10	25	884	9	23163	65	12266	5279	116

Many Facility Codes have changed. Please refer to the AHA Guide Code Chart.

© 2005 AHA Guide

Hospitals in Areas Associated with the Undited States by Area

Hospital, Address, Telephone, Approval, Facility, and Physician Codes, Health Care System	Classi-fication Codes		Utilization Data					Expense (thousands) of dollars		
★ American Hospital Association (AHA) membership □ Joint Commission on Accreditation of Healthcare Organizations (JCAHO) accreditation ○ American Osteopathic Association (AOA) accreditation △ Commission on Accreditation of Rehabilitation Facilities (CARF) accreditation	Control	Service	Staffed Beds	Admissions	Census	Outpatient Visits	Births	Total	Payroll	Personnel

AMERICAN SAMOA

PAGO PAGO—American Samoa County
LYNDON B. JOHNSON TROPICAL MEDICAL CENTER, Zip 96799; tel. 684/633–1222, (Nonreporting) **A**10
Primary Contact: Iotamo T. Saleapaga, M.D., Director Health

| | 12 | 10 | 125 | — | — | — | — | — | — | — |

GUAM

AGANA—Guam County
★ **U. S. NAVAL HOSPITAL**, Mailing Address: PSC 490, Box 7607, FPO, AP, Zip 96538–1600; tel. 671/344–9340, (Nonreporting) **S** Bureau of Medicine and Surgery, Department of the Navy, Washington, DC
Primary Contact: Captain Kathleen A. Rief, Commanding Officer
Web address: www.usnhgvam.med.navy.mil

| | 43 | 10 | 55 | — | — | — | — | — | — | — |

TAMUNING—Guam County
★ **GUAM MEMORIAL HOSPITAL AUTHORITY**, 850 Governor Carlos G. Camacho Road, Zip 96911; tel. 671/647–2108, (Total facility includes 29 beds in nursing home–type unit) **A**10 **F**11 12 22 28 33 45 49 50 52 55 56 58 59 63 65 66 67 69 81 82 88 92 94 108
Primary Contact: William I. McMillan, Administrator
CFO: Austin Swett, Chief Financial Officer
CIO: Vince Quichocho, Managerment Information Systems
Web address: www.gmha.org

| | 12 | 10 | 201 | 10558 | 118 | 162823 | 2563 | 16580 | — | 792 |

MARSHALL ISLANDS

KWAJALEIN ISLAND—Marshall Islands County
KWAJALEIN HOSPITAL, U.S. Army Kwajalein Atoll, Zip 96960, Mailing Address: Box 1702, APO, AP, Zip 96555–5000; tel. 805/355–2225 **S** Department of the Army, Office of the Surgeon General, Falls Church, VA
Primary Contact: Elaine McMahon, Administrator

| | 23 | 10 | 100 | 100 | 997 | 0 | 0 | — | — | 20 |

PUERTO RICO

AGUADILLA—Aguadilla County
⊠ **HOSPITAL BUEN SAMARITANO**, Carr Aguadilla San Juan, Zip 00605; tel. 787/819–0844, (Nonreporting) **A**1 10
Primary Contact: Marco Reyes, Executive Director

| | 12 | 10 | 110 | — | — | — | — | ⊠ | — | — |

AIBONITO—Aibonito County
★ **MENNONITE GENERAL HOSPITAL**, Calle Jose C. Vasquez, Zip 00705, Mailing Address: P.O. Box 373130, Cayey, Zip 00737–3130; tel. 787/535–1001, (Nonreporting) **A**9 10
Primary Contact: Pedro Melendez, Administrator
CFO: Ruben Norat Roig, Chief Financial Officer
CIO: Daniza Morales, Manager Information System

| | 23 | 10 | 131 | — | — | — | — | — | — | — |

ARECIBO—Arecibo County
⊠ **HOSPITAL DR. CAYETANO COLL Y TOSTE**, 129 San Luis Avenue, Zip 00612, Mailing Address: P.O. Box 659, Zip 00613; tel. 787/650–7272, (Nonreporting) **A**1 10
Primary Contact: Homar Perez, Chief Executive Officer and Vice President Administration
COO: Maritza Rodriguez, Chief Financial Officer
CFO: Luis Curbelo, Finance Director
CMO: Ada S. Miranda, M.D., Vice President Medical Affairs
CIO: Alex Ortiz, Billing Manager
CHR: Carmen Sanchez, Director Human Resources
Web address: www.cayetano@xsn.net

| | 33 | 10 | 188 | — | — | — | — | — | — | — |

Other Associated Areas

Hospital, Address, Telephone, Approval, Facility, and Physician Codes, Health Care System	Classi-fication Codes		Utilization Data					Expense (thousands) of dollars		
	Control	Service	Staffed Beds	Admissions	Census	Outpatient Visits	Births	Total	Payroll	Personnel

★ American Hospital Association (AHA) membership
□ Joint Commission on Accreditation of Healthcare Organizations (JCAHO) accreditation
○ American Osteopathic Association (AOA) accreditation
△ Commission on Accreditation of Rehabilitation Facilities (CARF) accreditation

Hospital	Control	Service	Staffed Beds	Admissions	Census	Outpatient Visits	Births	Total	Payroll	Personnel
HOSPITAL DR. SUSONI, 55 Nicomedes Rivera Street, Zip 00612, Mailing Address: P.O. Box 145200, Zip 00614; tel. 787/878–1010, (Nonreporting) **A**9 10 Primary Contact: Homar Perez, Administrator	12	10	131	—	—	—	—	—	—	—
HOSPITAL EL BUEN PASTOR, 52 De Diego, Zip 00612–4503, Mailing Address: P.O. Box 413, Zip 00612–0413; tel. 787/878–2730, (Nonreporting) **A**9 Primary Contact: Hector Mercado, Executive Director	33	10	48	—	—	—	—	—	—	—
ARROYO—Arroyo County										
★ **LAFAYETTE HOSPITAL**, Central Lafayette, Zip 00714, Mailing Address: P.O. Box 207, Zip 00714; tel. 787/839–3232, (Nonreporting) **A**9 10 Primary Contact: Francisco Santiago–Vega, Consultor CFO: Francisco Vazquez, General Manager and Executive Director CIO: Francisco Vazquez, General Manager and Executive Director	33	10	34	—	—	—	—	—	—	—
BAYAMON—Bayamon County										
⊠ **HOSPITAL HERMANOS MELENDEZ**, Route 2, KM 11–7, Zip 00960, Mailing Address: P.O. Box 306, Zip 00960; tel. 787/620–8181, (Nonreporting) **A**1 9 10 Primary Contact: Maria Machado, Administrator CFO: Luz D. Medina, Controller CIO: Brenda Guerrios, Administrator Medical Records	33	10	211	—	—	—	—	—	—	—
HOSPITAL MATILDE BRENES, Extension Hermanas Davila, Zip 00960, Mailing Address: P.O. Box 2957, Zip 00960; tel. 787/786–0050, (Nonreporting) **A**9 10 Primary Contact: Manuel J. Vazquez, Administrator	33	10	91	—	—	—	—	—	—	—
⊠ **HOSPITAL SAN PABLO**, Calle Santa Cruz 70, Zip 00961–7020, Mailing Address: P.O. Box 236, Zip 00960–0236; tel. 787/740–4747 **A**1 3 5 9 10 **F**10 11 14 15 17 19 23 28 33 49 55 56 57 58 59 61 62 63 64 66 81 88 94 108 Primary Contact: Jorge Matta, Chief Executive Officer and Managing Director Web address: www.sanpablo.com	33	10	341	19694	325	170335	2861	100586	37299	1393
⊠ **HOSPITAL UNIVERSITARIO DR. RAMON RUIZ ARNAU**, Avenue Laurel, Santa Juanita, Zip 00956; tel. 787/787–5151 **A**1 9 10 **F**2 6 9 11 12 22 27 28 33 45 50 52 55 56 59 67 69 72 75 81 88 94 108 **P**1 5 6 **S** Puerto Rico Department of Health, San Juan, PR Primary Contact: Rafael Garcia, Chief Executive Officer COO: Arturo Geigel Bunker, Director of Operations Services CFO: Elsie Morales, Chief Financial Officer CMO: Cesar Ortiz Sorrentini, Director CIO: Irma Duprey, Administrator of Medical Records	12	10	148	769	49	28080	477	—	—	593
⊠ **MEPSI CENTER**, Carretera Numero 2 K 8–2, Zip 00959–6089, Mailing Address: P.O. Box 600089, Zip 00960–0089; tel. 787/793–3030, (Nonreporting) **A**1 10 Primary Contact: Wilfredo Rafelo, Administrator CFO: Noel Ortiz, Finance Director and Controller	33	22	450	—	—	—	—	—	—	—
CAGUAS—Caguas County										
□ **HOSPITAL INTERAMERICANO DE MEDICINA AVANZADA**, Avenida Luis Munoz Marin, Zip 00726, Mailing Address: Apartado 4980, Zip 00726; tel. 787/743–3434, (Nonreporting) **A**1 9 10 Primary Contact: Carlos M. Pineiro, President	32	10	300	—	—	—	—	—	—	—
⊠ **SAN JUAN BAUTISTA MEDICAL CENTER**, Carretera Caguas A Cidra, Zip 00725, Mailing Address: Call Box 4964, Zip 00726–4964; tel. 787/744–2500, (Nonreporting) **A**1 9 10 **S** Puerto Rico Department of Health, San Juan, PR Primary Contact: Rosita Esteras, Executive Director	12	10	195	—	—	—	—	—	—	—
CAROLINA—Carolina County										
⊠ **HOSPITAL DE LA UNIVERSIDAD DE PUERTO RICO/DR. FEDERICO TRILLA**, 65th Infanteria, KM 8 3, Zip 00984, Mailing Address: P.O. Box 6021, Zip 00984; tel. 787/757–1800, (Nonreporting) **A**1 9 10 Primary Contact: Domingo Nevarez, Administrator COO: Domingo Nevarez, Administrator CFO: Leslie Resto, Chief Financial Officer CMO: Marina Roman, M.D., Medical Director CIO: Francisco Perez, Management Informatio Systems CHR: Sonia Bonilla, Director Human Resources	33	10	199	—	—	—	—	—	—	—
CASTANER—Lares County										
★ **CASTANER GENERAL HOSPITAL**, KM 64–2, Route 135, Zip 00631, Mailing Address: P.O. Box 1003, Zip 00631; tel. 787/829–5010, (Nonreporting) **A**9 10 Primary Contact: Domingo Monroig, Administrator CFO: Ernesto Montes, Finance Director CMO: Jose O. Rodriguez, M.D., Medical Director CIO: Domingo Monroig, Administrator CHR: Domingo Monroig, Administrator	23	10	24	—	—	—	—	—	—	—
CAYEY—Cayey County										
HOSPITAL MENONITA DE CAYEY, 4 H. Mendoza Street, Zip 00736–3801, Mailing Address: P.O. Box 373130, Zip 00737–3130; tel. 787/263–1001, (Nonreporting) **A**9 10 Primary Contact: Pedro Melendez, Administrator	23	10	71	—	—	—	—	—	—	—
CIDRA—Cidra County										
□ **FIRST HOSPITAL PANAMERICANO**, State Road 787 KM 1 5, Zip 00739, Mailing Address: P.O. Box 1400, Zip 00739; tel. 787/739–5555 **A**1 3 5 9 10 **F**3 4 21 27 28 31 58 60 69 70 71 72 73 74 75 76 77 78 **P**1 Primary Contact: Marta Rivera, Executive Director Web address: www.firsthospitalpr.org	33	22	190	6670	147	22461	0	20359	9229	420

Many Facility Codes have changed. Please refer to the AHA Guide Code Chart.

© 2005 AHA Guide

Hospital, Address, Telephone, Approval, Facility, and Physician Codes, Health Care System	Classi-fication Codes		Utilization Data					Expense (thousands) of dollars		
	Control	Service	Staffed Beds	Admissions	Census	Outpatient Visits	Births	Total	Payroll	Personnel

★ American Hospital Association (AHA) membership
□ Joint Commission on Accreditation of Healthcare Organizations (JCAHO) accreditation
○ American Osteopathic Association (AOA) accreditation
△ Commission on Accreditation of Rehabilitation Facilities (CARF) accreditation

COTO LAUREL—Ponce County

HOSPITAL SAN CRISTOBAL, 506 Carr Road, Zip 00780; tel. 787/848–2100, (Nonreporting) **A**9 10 — *Control* 33 *Service* 49 *Staffed Beds* 103
Primary Contact: Pedro L. Benete, Administrator

FAJARDO—Fajardo County

✠ **HOSPITAL SAN PABLO DEL ESTE**, Avenida General Valero, 404, Zip 00738, Mailing Address: P.O. Box 1028, Zip 00738–1028; tel. 787/863–0505 **A**1 9 10 **F**2 12 21 26 27 28 33 55 59 63 81 88 94 108 — *Control* 33 *Service* 10 *Staffed Beds* 137 *Admissions* 7666 *Census* 111 *Outpatient Visits* 33798 *Births* 951 *Personnel* 403
Primary Contact: Humberto M. Monserrate, Executive Administrator
COO: Maria Elena Rodriguez, Patient Relations Director
CFO: Luis Arroyo, Chief Financial Officer
CMO: Manuel Navas, M.D., Medical Director
CHR: Vilma Rodriguez, Human Resources Director
Web address: www.sanpablo.com

GUAYAMA—Guayama County

✠ **HOSPITAL EPISCOPAL CRISTO REDENTOR**, Avenue Pedro Albesus, Zip 00784, Mailing Address: PO Box 10011, Zip 00785–1006; tel. 787/864–4300, (Nonreporting) **A**1 5 9 10 — *Control* 21 *Service* 10 *Staffed Beds* 124
Primary Contact: Guillermo J. Martin, Executive Director
COO: Wilfredo Rabelo Millan, Chief Operating Officer
CMO: Gerson Jimenez, M.D., Medical Director
CHR: Ivette Ramos, Human Resources

★ **HOSPITAL SANTA ROSA**, Veterans Avenue, Zip 00784, Mailing Address: P.O. Box 10008, Zip 00785; tel. 787/864–0101 **A**9 10 **F**6 11 15 33 49 55 58 59 63 69 81 84 88 94 — *Control* 23 *Service* 10 *Staffed Beds* 87 *Admissions* 4217 *Census* 50 *Outpatient Visits* 23037 *Births* 472 *Total* 11749 *Payroll* 4151 *Personnel* 252
Primary Contact: Herson E. Morales, Executive Director
CFO: Edwin De Jesus, Comptroller
CMO: Joaquin Pales, President
CIO: Waleska Rolon, Manager

HUMACAO—Humacao County

□ **FONT MARTELO HOSPITAL**, 3 Font Martelo Street, Zip 00791–3342, Mailing Address: P.O. Box 639, Zip 00792–0639; tel. 787/852–2424, (Nonreporting) **A**1 9 10 — *Control* 33 *Service* 10 *Staffed Beds* 64
Primary Contact: Julio A. Ortiz, M.D., Chairman

HOSPITAL DR. DOMINGUEZ, 300 Font Martelo Street, Zip 00791–3230, Mailing Address: P.O. Box 699, Zip 00792–0699; tel. 787/852–0505, (Nonreporting) **A**9 10 — *Control* 33 *Service* 10 *Staffed Beds* 60
Primary Contact: Gilberto Gonzalez, Administrator

★ **RYDER MEMORIAL HOSPITAL**, 355 Font Martelo Street, Zip 00791–3249, Mailing Address: P.O. Box 859, Zip 00792–0859; tel. 787/852–0768, (Total facility includes 62 beds in nursing home–type unit) **A**9 10 **F**1 5 6 8 11 12 14 15 22 23 29 32 33 36 44 45 49 50 51 52 55 56 57 58 59 60 61 62 63 65 66 69 70 75 81 84 87 88 92 94 108 **P**8 — *Control* 23 *Service* 10 *Staffed Beds* 235 *Admissions* 9686 *Census* 134 *Outpatient Visits* 53507 *Births* 1573 *Total* 52325 *Payroll* 22485 *Personnel* 1185
Primary Contact: Jose R. Feliciano, Chief Executive Officer
CFO: Jose O. Ortiz, Chief Financial Officer
CMO: Juan F. Gonzalez–Diaz, M.D., Medical Director
CIO: Joseph V. Cruz, Chief Information Officer
CHR: Maria Figueroa, Director Human Resources
Web address: www.hryder@prtc.net

MANATI—Manati County

□ **ALEJANDRO OTERO LOPEZ HOSPITAL**, Mailing Address: P.O. Box 1142, Zip 00674–1142; tel. 787/621–3700, (Nonreporting) **A**1 3 5 9 10 — *Control* 33 *Service* 49 *Staffed Beds* 178
Primary Contact: Justo Lugo, Executive Director

CLINICA SAN AGUSTIN, Route 2, KM 49–5, Zip 00674–9801, Mailing Address: P.O. Box 991, Zip 00674–0991; tel. 787/854–2091, (Nonreporting) **A**10 — *Control* 33 *Service* 10 *Staffed Beds* 12
Primary Contact: Astrid Abreu, Administrator

DOCTORS CENTER, KM 47–7, Zip 00674, Mailing Address: P.O. Box 30532, Zip 00674; tel. 787/854–3322, (Nonreporting) **A**9 10 — *Control* 33 *Service* 10 *Staffed Beds* 150
Primary Contact: Pedro Rivera, Administrator

MAYAGUEZ—Mayaguez County

✠ **BELLA VISTA HOSPITAL**, State Road 349, Zip 00680, Mailing Address: P.O. Box 1750, Zip 00681; tel. 787/834–6000, (Nonreporting) **A**1 9 10 — *Control* 21 *Service* 10 *Staffed Beds* 157
Primary Contact: Jesus Nieves, Chief Executive Officer
CFO: Enrique Rivera, Chief Financial Officer
CMO: Miguel Cruz, M.D., Medical Director
CHR: Benjamin Astacio, Director Human Resources
Web address: www.bvhpr.com

CLINICA ESPANOLA, Barrio La Quinta, Zip 00680, Mailing Address: P.O. Box 490, Zip 00681–0490; tel. 787/832–0442, (Nonreporting) **A**10 — *Control* 33 *Service* 10 *Staffed Beds* 89
Primary Contact: Emigdio Inigo–Agostini, M.D., Board President

✠ **DR. RAMON E. BETANCES HOSPITAL–MAYAGUEZ MEDICAL CENTER BRANCH**, 410 Hostos Avenue, Zip 00680–1501; tel. 787/834–8656, (Nonreporting) **A**1 3 5 10 — *Control* 12 *Service* 10 *Staffed Beds* 144
Primary Contact: Julio Andino Rodriguez, Chief Executive Officer
CFO: Carlos Muniz, Director Finance

★ **HOSPITAL PEREA**, 15 Basora Street, Zip 00681, Mailing Address: P.O. Box 170, Zip 00681; tel. 787/834–0101, (Nonreporting) **A**9 10 **S** United Medical Corporation, Windermere, FL — *Control* 33 *Service* 10 *Staffed Beds* 103
Primary Contact: Rafael Alvarado, Chief Executive Officer
CFO: Joannie Garcia, CPA, Finance Director
CMO: Humberto Olivencia, M.D., Medical Director
Web address: www.paviahealth.com/perea_hospital.htm

Other Associated Areas

Hospital, Address, Telephone, Approval, Facility, and Physician Codes, Health Care System	Classi-fication Codes		Utilization Data					Expense (thousands) of dollars		
	Control	Service	Staffed Beds	Admissions	Census	Outpatient Visits	Births	Total	Payroll	Personnel

★ American Hospital Association (AHA) membership
□ Joint Commission on Accreditation of Healthcare Organizations (JCAHO) accreditation
○ American Osteopathic Association (AOA) accreditation
△ Commission on Accreditation of Rehabilitation Facilities (CARF) accreditation

MOCA—Moca County

HOSPITAL SAN CARLOS BORROMEO, 550 Concepcion Bera Ayala, Zip 00676; tel. 787/877–8000, (Nonreporting) **A**10
Primary Contact: Malave Javier, Administrator
| | 33 | 49 | 64 | — | — | — | — | — | — | — |

PONCE—Ponce County

✠ **DR. PILA'S HOSPITAL**, Avenida Las Americas, Zip 00731, Mailing Address: P.O. Box 1910, Zip 00733–1910; tel. 787/848–5600 **A**1 3 5 9 10 **F**2 11 21 22 26 27 28 33 51 52 55 56 58 59 63 69 81 84 85 88 94 108 **P**8
Primary Contact: Malben Lambog, Chief Executive Officer
Web address: www.dr.pila.com
| | 23 | 10 | 177 | 8224 | 116 | 72654 | 883 | 37658 | 12243 | 527 |

✠ **HOSPITAL DE DAMAS**, Ponce by Pass, Zip 00731; tel. 787/840–8686, (Nonreporting) **A**1 3 5 9 10
Primary Contact: Roberto A. Rentas, Administrator
COO: Enrique A. Vicens, Jr, Corporate Vice President and Legal Counsel
CFO: Nayda Cintron, Vice President Finance
CIO: Ramon Rios, Information Systems Manager
CHR: Gilberto Cuevas, Human Resources Vice President
Web address: www.hospitaldamas.com
| | 23 | 10 | 267 | — | — | — | — | — | — | — |

✠ **HOSPITAL EPISCOPAL SAN LUCAS**, Guadalupe Street, Zip 00731, Mailing Address: P.O. Box 2027, Zip 00733; tel. 787/840–4545 **A**1 3 5 9 10 **F**14 15 17 19 22 23 26 27 28 33 34 55 58 59 71 72 81 82 87 88 94 108 **P**5
Primary Contact: Guillermo J. Martin, Executive Director
Web address: www.ssepr.com/sl_bienvenido1.htm
| | 21 | 10 | 130 | 6829 | 115 | 36576 | 0 | 43721 | 11587 | 522 |

✠ **HOSPITAL ONCOLOGICO ANDRES GRILLASCA**, Centro Medico De Ponce, Zip 00733, Mailing Address: P.O. Box 1324, Zip 00733; tel. 787/848–0800, (Nonreporting) **A**1 2 3 5 9 10
Primary Contact: Santiago Rivera, Executive Administrator
CIO: Jackeline Baez Martinez, Public Relations Director
| | 23 | 41 | 49 | — | — | — | — | — | — | — |

★ **ST. LUKE'S EPISCOPAL HOSPITAL**, 917 Tito Castro Avenue, Zip 00731–4717; tel. 787/844–2080, (Nonreporting) **A**9 10
Primary Contact: Guillermo J. Martin, Executive Director
COO: Ramon Lopez Maldonado, Chief Operating Officer
CFO: Aristides Castro, Chief Financial Officer
CMO: Gilberto Rodriguez, M.D., Chief Medical Officer
CIO: Mike Cintron, Chief Information Officer
| | 12 | 10 | 324 | — | — | — | — | — | — | — |

SAN GERMAN—San German County

✠ **HOSPITAL DE LA CONCEPCION**, Avenida Universidad Interamericana, 41, Zip 00683–3920, Mailing Address: P.O. Box 285, Zip 00683–0285; tel. 787/892–1860, (Nonreporting) **A**1 3 5 9 10
Primary Contact: Jaime F. Maestre Grau, Executive Director
CFO: Gustavo Almodovar, Finance Director
CIO: Aaron Mendez, Management Information Systems
CHR: Jorge Rodriguez Diaz, Human Resources Director
Web address: www.hospitalconcepcion.org
| | 21 | 10 | 140 | — | — | — | — | — | — | — |

HOSPITAL METROPOLITANO SAN GERMAN, Calle Javilla Al Costado Parque de Bombas, Zip 00683; tel. 787/892–5300, (Nonreporting) **A**10
Primary Contact: Rafael Alvarado, Chief Executive Officer
| | 33 | 49 | 40 | — | — | — | — | — | — | — |

SAN JUAN—San Juan County

✠ **ASHFORD PRESBYTERIAN COMMUNITY HOSPITAL**, 1451 Ashford Avenue Condado, Zip 00907, Mailing Address: P.O. Box 9020032, Zip 00902–0032; tel. 787/721–2160 **A**1 9 10 **F**2 10 11 12 14 21 22 24 26 27 28 29 33 40 41 48 52 53 55 56 58 59 62 63 65 66 67 69 70 81 82 85 88 94 95 106 108
Primary Contact: Pedro J. Gonzalez, Executive Director
CFO: Milagros Ortiz, CPA, Finance Director
CMO: Francisco de Torres, M.D., Medical Director
CHR: Irma Carrillo, Human Resources Director
Web address: www.presbypr.com
| | 23 | 10 | 198 | 12109 | 155 | 88903 | 233 | 51583 | 16222 | 717 |

✠ **AUXILIO MUTUO HOSPITAL**, Ponce De Leon Avenue, Zip 00918–1000, Mailing Address: P.O. Box 191227, Zip 00919–1227; tel. 787/758–2000, (Nonreporting) **A**1 5 9 10
Primary Contact: Jorge L. Matta Serrano, Administrator
COO: Carmen Martin, Associate Administrator
CFO: Angela Varona, Administrator Fiscal Services
CMO: Jose Isado, M.D., Medical Director
CIO: Edgardo Rodriguez, Management Information Systems Director
CHR: Maria Vega, Human Resources Director
Web address: www.auxiliopr.com
| | 23 | 10 | 510 | — | — | — | — | — | — | — |

✠ **CARDIOVASCULAR CENTER OF PUERTO RICO AND THE CARIBBEAN**, Americo Miranda Centro Medico, Zip 00936, Mailing Address: P.O. Box 366528, Zip 00936–6528; tel. 787/754–8500 **A**1 9 10 **F**14 15 17 19 20 21 27 37 55 63 67 94 100 108 **S** Puerto Rico Department of Health, San Juan, PR
Primary Contact: Carlos G. Melendez, Executive Director
COO: Sonia E Malave Hernandez, Associate Administrator
CFO: Maria de Lourdes Alegria, Comptroller
CMO: Jose E. Novoa, M.D., Medical Director
CIO: Eugenio Torres Ayala, Director Information Systems
CHR: Hector Troche Garcia, Director Human Resources
Web address: www.cardiovascularpr.com
| | 12 | 42 | 122 | 4199 | 84 | 18560 | 0 | 61158 | 16013 | 595 |

Many Facility Codes have changed. Please refer to the AHA Guide Code Chart.
© 2005 AHA Guide

Hospital, Address, Telephone, Approval, Facility, and Physician Codes, Health Care System	Classi-fication Codes		Utilization Data					Expense (thousands) of dollars		
★ American Hospital Association (AHA) membership □ Joint Commission on Accreditation of Healthcare Organizations (JCAHO) accreditation ○ American Osteopathic Association (AOA) accreditation △ Commission on Accreditation of Rehabilitation Facilities (CARF) accreditation	Control	Service	Staffed Beds	Admissions	Census	Outpatient Visits	Births	Total	Payroll	Personnel
✚ **CARIBBEAN PEDIATRIC AND SURGERY HOSPITAL**, 371 Avenida De Diego, Zip 00923–1711, Mailing Address: P.O. Box 29025, Zip 00929–0025; tel. 787/767–2528, (Nonreporting) **A**1 9 10 Primary Contact: Henry Ruberte, Chief Executive Officer and Managing Director COO: Juan C Benitez Chacon, Associate Executive Administrastor CFO: Glorimar Alejandro, Finance Director CMO: Hector L. Cotto, M.D., Medical Director CIO: Deborah Nieves, Management Information Systems Director Web address: www.sanpablo.com	33	10	160	—	—	—	—	—	—	—
DOCTORS HOSPITAL, 1395 San Rafael Street, Zip 00909–2518, Mailing Address: Box 11338, Santurce Station, Zip 00910–1338; tel. 787/723–2950, (Nonreporting) **A**9 10 Primary Contact: Roberto Ruiz, Administrator	33	10	89	—	—	—	—	—	—	—
★ **HEALTHSOUTH REHABILITATION HOSPITAL**, University Hospital, 3rd Floor, Zip 00923, Mailing Address: P.O. Box 70344, Zip 00923; tel. 787/274–5100, (Nonreporting) **A**10 **S** HEALTHSOUTH Corporation, Birmingham, AL Primary Contact: Edwin Sueiro, Administrator	33	46	32	—	—	—	—	—	—	—
✚ **HOSPITAL DEL MAESTRO**, 550 Sergio Cuevas, Zip 00918–3741, Mailing Address: P.O. Box 364708, Zip 00936–4708; tel. 787/758–8383, (Nonreporting) **A**1 9 10 Primary Contact: Milton Maldonado, Administrator COO: Milton Maldonado, Administrator CFO: Marisol Vargas, Finance Director CMO: Jose Montalvo, M.D., Medical Director CIO: Myrna Rivera, Director Medical Records CHR: Orlando Santiago, HumanResources Officer	23	10	247	—	—	—	—	—	—	—
✚ **HOSPITAL METROPOLITAN**, (Formerly Fundacion Hospital Metropolitan), 1785 Route 21, Zip 00922, Mailing Address: P.O. Box 11981, Zip 00922; tel. 787/782–9999, (Nonreporting) **A**1 10 Primary Contact: Gilberto Gonzalez, Chief Executive Officer CFO: Maritza Rodriguez, Chief Financial Officer CMO: Jadmmal Torres Castro, M.D., Medical Director CIO: Abel Velez, Chief Information Officer	33	10	130	—	—	—	—	—	—	—
✚ **HOSPITAL PAVIA–HATO REY**, (Formerly Hato Rey Community Hospital), Mailing Address: 435 Ponce De Leon, Hato Rey, Zip 00917–3428; tel. 787/754–0909, (Nonreporting) **A**1 3 5 **S** United Medical Corporation, Windermere, FL Primary Contact: Alfredo E. Volckers, Executive Vice President Web address: www.paviahealth.com	33	10	180	—	—	—	—	—	—	—
✚ **HOSPITAL PAVIA–SANTURCE**, 1462 Asia Street, Zip 00909–2143, Mailing Address: Box 11137, Santurce Station, Zip 00910–1137; tel. 787/727–6060, (Nonreporting) **A**1 9 10 **S** United Medical Corporation, Windermere, FL Primary Contact: Alfredo E. Volckers, Executive Director CFO: Francisco Espina, Finance Director Web address: www.paviahealth.com	33	10	309	—	—	—	—	—	—	—
HOSPITAL SAN GERARDO, 844 Cupey Bajo, Rio Piedras, Zip 00926; tel. 787/761–8383, (Nonreporting) **A**9 10 Primary Contact: Bradalic Rosario, Administrator	33	49	60	—	—	—	—	—	—	—
✚ **I. GONZALEZ MARTINEZ ONCOLOGIC HOSPITAL**, Puerto Rico Medical Center, Hato Rey, Zip 00935, Mailing Address: P.O. Box 191811, Zip 00919–1811; tel. 787/765–2382, (Nonreporting) **A**1 2 3 5 10 Primary Contact: Milagros Vargas, Executive Director COO: Felix Ortiz, Administrator CFO: Yolanda Quinonez, Director Finance CMO: Carlos Chevere, M.D., Medical Director CHR: Luz Maria Hernandez, Director Human Resources	23	49	42	—	—	—	—	—	—	—
★ **INDUSTRIAL HOSPITAL**, Puerto Rico Medical Center, Zip 00936, Mailing Address: P.O. Box 365028, Zip 00936; tel. 787/764–3660 **A**9 **F**2 13 15 21 30 33 45 52 57 58 60 62 63 66 68 69 70 94 110 **P**5 6 Primary Contact: Lisette Diaz, Administrator COO: Neffer E. Carrillo, Administrator CFO: Robert Berniev Casanova, Chief Financial Officer CMO: Carmen Carrasquillo, M.D., Medical Director CHR: Alba Nydia Llamas, Specialist Human Administrative Resources	12	10	125	3844	80	140237	0	—	—	696
SAN CARLOS GENERAL HOSPITAL, 1822 Ponce De Leon Avenue, Zip 00909–1906, Mailing Address: Call Box 8410, Zip 00910–8410; tel. 787/727–5858, (Nonreporting) **A**9 10 Primary Contact: Pedro J. Gonzalez, Executive Director	33	10	66	—	—	—	—	—	—	—
✚ **SAN JORGE CHILDREN'S HOSPITAL**, 258 San Jorge Avenue, Zip 00912–3310; tel. 787/727–1000 **A**1 5 9 **F**22 23 33 34 46 58 61 62 63 66 67 81 85 88 99 108 **S** United Medical Corporation, Windermere, FL Primary Contact: Domingo Cruz Vivaldi, Administrator CFO: Jose Marrero, Finance Director CMO: Luis Clavell, M.D., Medical Director CIO: Jorge Calderon, Chief Information Systems CHR: Ana Acevedo, Supervisor Human Resources Web address: www.sanjorgechildrenhospital.com	33	50	125	7375	106	—	0	27654	9434	400

Other Associated Areas

Hospital, Address, Telephone, Approval, Facility, and Physician Codes, Health Care System	Classi-fication Codes		Utilization Data					Expense (thousands) of dollars		
★ American Hospital Association (AHA) membership □ Joint Commission on Accreditation of Healthcare Organizations (JCAHO) accreditation ○ American Osteopathic Association (AOA) accreditation △ Commission on Accreditation of Rehabilitation Facilities (CARF) accreditation	Control	Service	Staffed Beds	Admissions	Census	Outpatient Visits	Births	Total	Payroll	Personnel
⊠ **SAN JUAN CAPESTRANO HOSPITAL**, Mailing Address: Rural Route 2, Box 11, Zip 00926; tel. 787/760–0222 **A**1 9 10 **F**1 4 8 21 22 26 27 28 31 52 71 72 73 74 75 76 77 78 94 96 **S** Universal Health Services, Inc., King of Prussia, PA Primary Contact: Laura Vargas, Chief Executive Officer and Managing Director CFO: Julia Cruz, Chief Financial Officer CMO: Luis Dorta, M.D., Medical Director CIO: Ana Morandeira, Marketing Director CHR: Luis Perez Rivera, Administrator Web address: www.sjcapestrano.com	33	22	108	4087	88	20080	0	12179	4895	227
⊠ **SAN JUAN CITY HOSPITAL**, Puerto Rico Medical Center, Zip 00928, Mailing Address: PMB 79, P.O. Box 70344, Zip 00936–8344; tel. 787/766–2222, (Nonreporting) **A**1 3 10 Primary Contact: Samuel Monroig, Executive Director COO: Fernando Sosa, Chief Operating Officer CFO: Juan Gonzalez, Chief Financial Officer CMO: Ana Barletta, M.D., Medical Director CIO: Julio Motta, Chief Information Officer CHR: Mildred Oritz, Chief Human Resources Officer Web address: www.massalud.com	14	10	267	—	—	—	—	—	—	—
⊠ **STATE PSYCHIATRIC HOSPITAL**, Monacillos Avenue, Zip 00936, Mailing Address: Call Box 2100, Caparra Heights Station, Zip 00922–2100; tel. 787/766–4646, (Nonreporting) **A**1 10 **S** Puerto Rico Department of Health, San Juan, PR Primary Contact: Rafael Garcia Alvarez, Executive Director CFO: Juan Gomez, Controller CMO: Reynaldo Rodriguez, M.D., Medical Director	12	22	153	—	—	—	—	—	—	—
★ **U. S. NAVAL HOSPITAL**, Roosevelt Roads, Mailing Address: P.O. Box 3007, FPO, AA, Zip 34051–8100; tel. 787/865–5762, (Nonreporting) **S** Bureau of Medicine and Surgery, Department of the Navy, Washington, DC Primary Contact: Captain Patricia H. Netzer, Commanding Officer CFO: David L. Tullison, Comptroller CMO: Captain Raymond Pumarejo, M.D., Head Information Resources Management CIO: Lieutenant Charles Redmond, Head Information Resources Management Web address: www.rooseyroads.med.navy.mil	43	10	36	—	—	—	—	—	—	—
⊠ **UNIVERSITY HOSPITAL**, Mailing Address: P.O. Box 2116, Zip 00922; tel. 787/754–0101 **A**1 2 3 5 10 **F**2 11 23 49 55 57 58 59 61 62 63 69 90 93 94 99 108 110 **P**5 **S** Puerto Rico Department of Health, San Juan, PR Primary Contact: Roberto Burgos, Executive Director CFO: Janet Baez, Director CMO: Donald Dexter, M.D., President CIO: Angel Hernandez, Information Systems Coordinator CHR: Wanda Maldonado, Director Human Resources	12	10	260	10157	213	—	1775	—	—	—
⊠ **UNIVERSITY PEDIATRIC HOSPITAL**, Mailing Address: Call Box 191079, Zip 00910–1079; tel. 787/777–3535, (Nonreporting) **A**1 3 5 9 10 **S** Puerto Rico Department of Health, San Juan, PR Primary Contact: Sylvette Llovet, Executive Director COO: Sylvette Llovet, Executive Director CFO: Blanca Olmo, Director of Finance CMO: Concepcion Q. De Longo, M.D., Medical Director CIO: Alberto Medina, Director of Information System	12	50	145	—	—	—	—	—	—	—
⊠ △ **VETERANS AFFAIRS MEDICAL CENTER**, 10 Casia Street, Zip 00921–3201; tel. 787/641–7582, (Total facility includes 149 beds in nursing home–type unit) **A**1 2 3 5 7 8 9 **F**2 4 14 15 17 21 22 23 28 31 32 33 36 37 38 39 42 44 45 47 48 49 50 51 52 55 57 58 60 61 62 63 64 65 66 68 69 70 71 73 74 75 76 77 78 81 82 84 85 86 87 88 92 94 106 107 108 109 110 **S** Department of Veterans Affairs, Washington, DC Primary Contact: Rafael E. Ramirez, M.D., Center Director CFO: Abraham Colon, Chief Fiscal Officer CMO: Sandra C. Gracia, M.D., Chief of Staff CIO: Manuel Negron, Information Technology Service Chief CHR: Helen Nunci, Manager Human Resources Web address: www.va.gov/visn8/sanjuan	45	10	468	7904	401	759682	0	353113	194031	3226
VEGA BAJA—Vega Baja County										
★ **WILMA N. VAZQUEZ MEDICAL CENTER**, KM 391/2 Road 2, Call Box 7001, Zip 00694; tel. 787/858–1580, (Total facility includes 20 beds in nursing home–type unit) (Nonreporting) **A**9 10 Primary Contact: Ramon J. Vilar, Administrator COO: Jose O. Pabon, Operating Director CFO: Luis Rosa, Controller CMO: Jaime Rodriguez Solis, M.D., President Medical Staff CIO: Miguel Aponte, Supervisor Management Information Systems CHR: Eugenia Martinez, Director Human Resources	33	10	130	—	—	—	—	—	—	—

Many Facility Codes have changed. Please refer to the AHA Guide Code Chart.

© 2005 AHA Guide

Hospital, Address, Telephone, Approval, Facility, and Physician Codes, Health Care System	Classi-fication Codes		Utilization Data					Expense (thousands) of dollars		
★ American Hospital Association (AHA) membership □ Joint Commission on Accreditation of Healthcare Organizations (JCAHO) accreditation ○ American Osteopathic Association (AOA) accreditation △ Commission on Accreditation of Rehabilitation Facilities (CARF) accreditation	Control	Service	Staffed Beds	Admissions	Census	Outpatient Visits	Births	Total	Payroll	Personnel

YAUCO—Yauco County

☒ **HOSPITAL METROPOLITANO DR. TITO MATTEI**, Carretera 128 KM 1, Zip 00698, Mailing Address: P.O. Box 68, Zip 00698; tel. 787/856–1000, (Nonreporting) **A**1 5 9 10 **S** Adventist Health System Sunbelt Health Care Corporation, Winter Park, FL
Primary Contact: Pedro Barez, Chief Executive Officer
CFO: Elizabeth Gonzalez, Controller
CMO: Juan Carlos Velazco, M.D., Director Staff Medicine
CIO: Edson Ortiz, Chief Information Officer
CHR: Nannete Acosta, Director Human Resources
Web address: www.hmyauco.com

| 23 | 10 | 106 | — | — | — | — | — | — | — |

VIRGIN ISLANDS

CHRISTIANSTED—St. Croix County

☒ **GOVERNOR JUAN F. LOUIS HOSPITAL**, 4007 Estate Diamond Ruby, Zip 00820–4421; tel. 340/778–6311 **A**1 10 **F**2 9 11 15 17 22 26 27 28 29 30 33 34 37 46 48 49 52 53 55 56 57 58 59 62 63 64 66 69 70 71 72 75 76 77 88 94 **P**6
Primary Contact: Michael P. Potts, M.D., Interim Chief Executive Officer
CFO: Nellon Bowery, Chief Financial Officer
CMO: Lloyd N. Henry, M.D., Medical Director
CIO: Reuben D. Molloy, Chief Information Officer
Web address: www.jflusvi.org

| 16 | 10 | 113 | 3839 | 94 | 44353 | 770 | 42116 | 18469 | — |

SAINT THOMAS—St. Thomas County

☒ **ROY LESTER SCHNEIDER HOSPITAL**, 9048 Sugar Estate, Charlotte Amalie, Zip 00802; tel. 340/776–8311 **A**1 10 **F**2 3 11 12 13 14 22 23 26 27 33 34 49 52 55 56 57 58 59 60 61 62 63 67 68 69 71 75 81 86 88 92 94 109 110 **P**6
Primary Contact: Rodney E. Miller, Sr, Chief Executive Officer
COO: Amos W. Carty, Jr, Chief Operating Officer and General Counsel
CFO: Peter R. Najawicz, Chief Financial Officer
CMO: Thelma Ruth Watson, M.D., Medical Director
CIO: J C. Creque, Director Management Information Systems
CHR: Marlene J. Adams, Director Human Resources
Web address: www.rlshospital.org

| 16 | 10 | 123 | 4763 | 65 | 49526 | 870 | 65456 | 21530 | 436 |

U.S. Government Hospitals
Outside the United States, by Area

GERMANY
Heidelberg: ★ U. S. Army Hospital, APO, USAMEDDAC HEIDELBERG, AE 09042

Landstuhl: ★ Landstuhl Army Regional Medical Center, APO, CMR 402, AE 09180

Wurzburg: ★ U. S. Army Hospital, APO, USAMEDDAC Wurzburg, AE 09244

ICELAND
Keflavilk: ★ U. S. Naval Hospital–Keflavilk, FPO, PSC 1003, Box 8, AE 09728–0308

ITALY
Naples: ★ U. S. Naval Hospital, FPO, AE 09619

JAPAN
Yokosuka: ★ U. S. Naval Hospital, FPO, Box 1487, AP 96350

KOREA
Seoul: ★ U. S. Army Community Hospital Seoul, APO, 121st General Hospital, AP 96205

Yongsan: Medcom 18th Commander, Facilities Division Eamc L EM, APO, AP 96205

SPAIN
Rota: ★ U. S. Naval Hospital, Rota, FPO, PSC 819, Box 18, AE 09645–2500

TAIWAN
Taipei: U. S. Naval Hospital Taipei, Taipei, No 300 Shin–Pai Road, Sec 2

Many Facility Codes have changed. Please refer to the AHA Guide Code Chart. © 2005 AHA Guide

Notes

Notes

Notes

Notes

Notes

Notes

Index of Hospitals

This section is an index of all hospitals in alphabetical order by hospital name, followed by the city, state, Medicare Provider Number (where available), and page reference to the hospital's listing in Section A.

B

BAPTIST HOSPITAL, PENSACOLA, FL, 100093, p. A142

BAPTIST HOSPITAL, NASHVILLE, TN, 440133, p. A615

BAPTIST HOSPITAL EAST, LOUISVILLE, KY, 180130, p. A268

BAPTIST HOSPITAL FOR WOMEN, KNOXVILLE, TN, 440225, p. A609

BAPTIST HOSPITAL NORTHEAST, LA GRANGE, KY, 180138, p. A267

BAPTIST HOSPITAL OF COCKE COUNTY, NEWPORT, TN, 440153, p. A616

BAPTIST HOSPITAL OF EAST TENNESSEE, KNOXVILLE, TN, 440019, p. A609

BAPTIST HOSPITAL OF MIAMI, MIAMI, FL, 100008, p. A136

BAPTIST HOSPITAL WEST, KNOXVILLE, TN, 440226, p. A609

BAPTIST MEDICAL CENTER, JACKSONVILLE, FL, 100088, p. A132

BAPTIST MEDICAL CENTER, SAN ANTONIO, TX, 450058, p. A663

BAPTIST MEDICAL CENTER EAST, MONTGOMERY, AL, 010149, p. A21

BAPTIST MEDICAL CENTER NASSAU, FERNANDINA BEACH, FL, 100140, p. A128

BAPTIST MEDICAL CENTER SOUTH, MONTGOMERY, AL, 010023, p. A22

BAPTIST MEDICAL CENTER–BEACHES, JACKSONVILLE BEACH, FL, 100117, p. A133

BAPTIST MEMORIAL HOSPITAL – MEMPHIS, MEMPHIS, TN, 440048, p. A612

BAPTIST MEMORIAL HOSPITAL FOR WOMEN, MEMPHIS, TN, 440222, p. A612

BAPTIST MEMORIAL HOSPITAL–BOONEVILLE, BOONEVILLE, MS, 250044, p. A367

BAPTIST MEMORIAL HOSPITAL–COLLIERVILLE, COLLIERVILLE, TN, 440217, p. A604

BAPTIST MEMORIAL HOSPITAL–DESOTO, SOUTHAVEN, MS, 250141, p. A375

BAPTIST MEMORIAL HOSPITAL–FORREST CITY, FORREST CITY, AR, 040019, p. A43

BAPTIST MEMORIAL HOSPITAL–GOLDEN TRIANGLE, COLUMBUS, MS, 250100, p. A368

BAPTIST MEMORIAL HOSPITAL–HUNTINGDON, HUNTINGDON, TN, 440016, p. A607

BAPTIST MEMORIAL HOSPITAL–LAUDERDALE, RIPLEY, TN, 440114, p. A617

BAPTIST MEMORIAL HOSPITAL–NORTH MISSISSIPPI, OXFORD, MS, 250034, p. A374

BAPTIST MEMORIAL HOSPITAL–TIPTON, COVINGTON, TN, 440131, p. A605

BAPTIST MEMORIAL HOSPITAL–UNION CITY, UNION CITY, TN, 440130, p. A618

BAPTIST MEMORIAL HOSPITAL–UNION COUNTY, NEW ALBANY, MS, 250006, p. A374

BAPTIST MONTCLAIR, BIRMINGHAM, AL, 010104, p. A14

BAPTIST NORTH TOWER SURGICAL HOSPITAL, NASHVILLE, TN, 440218, p. A615

BAPTIST PRINCETON, BIRMINGHAM, AL, 010103, p. A14

BAPTIST REGIONAL MEDICAL CENTER, CORBIN, KY, 180080, p. A263

BAPTIST REHABILITATION–GERMANTOWN, GERMANTOWN, TN, 440147, p. A606

BAPTIST ST. ANTHONY HEALTH SYSTEM, AMARILLO, TX, 450231, p. A621

BAPTIST–LUTHERAN MEDICAL CENTER, KANSAS CITY, MO, 260107, p. A384

BARAGA COUNTY MEMORIAL HOSPITAL, L'ANSE, MI, 231307, p. A338

BARBERTON CITIZENS HOSPITAL, BARBERTON, OH, 360019, p. A503

BARIATRIC CARE CENTER OF TEXAS, WYLIE, TX, 450849, p. A675

BARLOW RESPIRATORY HOSPITAL, LOS ANGELES, CA, 052031, p. A69

BARNERT HOSPITAL, PATERSON, NJ, 310026, p. A434

BARNES–JEWISH HOSPITAL, SAINT LOUIS, MO, 260032, p. A390

BARNES–JEWISH ST. PETERS HOSPITAL, SAINT PETERS, MO, 260191, p. A393

BARNES–JEWISH WEST COUNTY HOSPITAL, SAINT LOUIS, MO, 260162, p. A390

BARNES–KASSON COUNTY HOSPITAL, SUSQUEHANNA, PA, 390224, p. A576

BARNESVILLE HOSPITAL ASSOCIATION, BARNESVILLE, OH, 361321, p. A503

BARNWELL COUNTY HOSPITAL, BARNWELL, SC, 420016, p. A583

BARRETT HOSPITAL & HEALTHCARE, DILLON, MT, 271318, p. A398

BARRON MEDICAL CENTER–MAYO HEALTH SYSTEM, BARRON, WI, 521315, p. A723

BARROW COMMUNITY HOSPITAL, WINDER, GA, 110045, p. A172

BARSTOW COMMUNITY HOSPITAL, BARSTOW, CA, 050298, p. A54

BARTLETT REGIONAL HOSPITAL, JUNEAU, AK, 020008, p. A27

BARTON COUNTY MEMORIAL HOSPITAL, LAMAR, MO, 260073, p. A386

BARTON MEMORIAL HOSPITAL, SOUTH LAKE TAHOE, CA, 050352, p. A94

BARTOW REGIONAL MEDICAL CENTER, BARTOW, FL, 100121, p. A123

BASCOM PALMER EYE INSTITUTE–ANNE BATES LEACH EYE HOSPITAL, MIAMI, FL, 100240, p. A136

BASSETT ARMY COMMUNITY HOSPITAL, FORT WAINWRIGHT, AK, p. A27

BASSETT HOSPITAL OF SCHOHARIE COUNTY, COBLESKILL, NY, 330268, p. A450

BASTROP REHABILITATION HOSPITAL, BASTROP, LA, 193058, p. A277

BATES COUNTY MEMORIAL HOSPITAL, BUTLER, MO, 260034, p. A379

BATH COUNTY COMMUNITY HOSPITAL, HOT SPRINGS, VA, 491300, p. A690

BATON ROUGE GENERAL MEDICAL CENTER, BATON ROUGE, LA, 190065, p. A277

BATON ROUGE GENERAL MEDICAL CENTER–BLUEBONNET, BATON ROUGE, LOUISIANA (see BATON ROUGE GENERAL MEDICAL CENTER), p. A277

BATTLE CREEK HEALTH SYSTEM, BATTLE CREEK, MI, 230075, p. A328

BATTLE MOUNTAIN GENERAL HOSPITAL, BATTLE MOUNTAIN, NV, 291303, p. A415

BAUM HARMON MERCY HOSPITAL, PRIMGHAR, IA, 161300, p. A240

BAXTER REGIONAL MEDICAL CENTER, MOUNTAIN HOME, AR, 040027, p. A48

BAY AREA HOSPITAL, COOS BAY, OR, 380090, p. A543

BAY AREA MEDICAL CENTER, MARINETTE, WI, 520113, p. A729

BAY MEDICAL CENTER, PANAMA CITY, FL, 100026, p. A142

BAY PARK COMMUNITY HOSPITAL, OREGON, OH, 360259, p. A520

BAY REGIONAL MEDICAL CENTER, BAY CITY, MI, 230041, p. A328

BAY REGIONAL MEDICAL CENTER–WEST CAMPUS, BAY CITY, MICHIGAN (see BAY REGIONAL MEDICAL CENTER), p. A328

BAY SPECIAL CARE HOSPITAL, BAY CITY, MI, 232020, p. A328

BAYFRONT MEDICAL CENTER, SAINT PETERSBURG, FL, 100032, p. A145

BAYHEALTH MEDICAL CENTER, DOVER, DE, 080004, p. A119

BAYHEALTH MEDICAL CENTER AT KENT GENERAL, DOVER, DELAWARE (see BAYHEALTH MEDICAL CENTER), p. A119

BAYHEALTH MEDICAL CENTER, MILFORD MEMORIAL HOSPITAL, MILFORD, DELAWARE (see BAYHEALTH MEDICAL CENTER), p. A119

BAYLEY SETON CAMPUS, NEW YORK, NEW YORK (see ST. VINCENT'S HOSPITAL), p. A465

BAYLEY SETON CAMPUS, STATEN ISLAND, NEW YORK (see (see ST. VINCENT'S HOSPITAL)), p. A465

BAYLOR ALL SAINTS MEDICAL CENTER AT FORT WORTH, FORT WORTH, TX, 450137, p. A639

BAYLOR INSTITUTE FOR REHABILITATION, DALLAS, TX, 453036, p. A632

BAYLOR JACK AND JANE HAMILTON HEART AND VASCULAR HOSPITAL, DALLAS, TX, 450851, p. A632

BAYLOR MEDICAL CENTER AT GARLAND, GARLAND, TX, 450280, p. A641

BAYLOR MEDICAL CENTER AT IRVING, IRVING, TX, 450079, p. A649

BAYLOR MEDICAL CENTER AT SOUTHWEST FORT WORTH, FORT WORTH, TX, 450137, p. A639

BAYLOR MEDICAL CENTER AT WAXAHACHIE, WAXAHACHIE, TX, 450372, p. A672

BAYLOR REGIONAL MEDICAL CENTER AT GRAPEVINE, GRAPEVINE, TX, 450563, p. A642

BAYLOR REGIONAL MEDICAL CENTER AT PLANO, PLANO, TX, 450890, p. A660

BAYLOR SPECIALTY HOSPITAL, DALLAS, TX, 452017, p. A632

BAYLOR UNIVERSITY MEDICAL CENTER, DALLAS, TX, 450021, p. A632

BAYNE–JONES ARMY COMMUNITY HOSPITAL, FORT POLK, LA, p. A281

BAYONNE MEDICAL CENTER, BAYONNE, NJ, 310025, p. A425

BAYSHORE COMMUNITY HOSPITAL, HOLMDEL, NJ, 310112, p. A429

BAYSHORE MEDICAL CENTER, PASADENA, TX, 450097, p. A660

BAYSIDE COMMUNITY HOSPITAL, ANAHUAC, TX, 451320, p. A621

BAYSTATE MEDICAL CENTER, SPRINGFIELD, MA, 220077, p. A323

BAYVIEW HOSPITAL AND MENTAL HEALTH SYSTEM, CHULA VISTA, CA, p. A56

BEACHAM MEMORIAL HOSPITAL, MAGNOLIA, MS, 250049, p. A372

BEAR LAKE MEMORIAL HOSPITAL, MONTPELIER, ID, 131316, p. A180

BEAR RIVER VALLEY HOSPITAL, TREMONTON, UT, 460039, p. A680

BEAR VALLEY COMMUNITY HOSPITAL, BIG BEAR LAKE, CA, 050618, p. A55

BEARTOOTH HOSPITAL AND HEALTH CENTER, RED LODGE, MT, 271326, p. A401

BEATRICE COMMUNITY HOSPITAL AND HEALTH CENTER, BEATRICE, NE, 280054, p. A405

BEAUFORT COUNTY HOSPITAL, WASHINGTON, NC, 340038, p. A493

BEAUFORT MEMORIAL HOSPITAL, BEAUFORT, SC, 420067, p. A583

BEAUREGARD MEMORIAL HOSPITAL, DE RIDDER, LA, 190050, p. A280

BEAVER COUNTY MEMORIAL HOSPITAL, BEAVER, OK, 371322, p. A528

BEAVER DAM COMMUNITY HOSPITALS, BEAVER DAM, WI, 520076, p. A723

BEAVER VALLEY HOSPITAL, BEAVER, UT, 460035, p. A676

BECKLEY APPALACHIAN REGIONAL HOSPITAL, BECKLEY, WV, 510062, p. A713

BEDFORD COUNTY MEDICAL CENTER, SHELBYVILLE, TN, 440137, p. A617

BEDFORD MEMORIAL HOSPITAL, BEDFORD, VA, 490088, p. A685

BEDFORD REGIONAL MEDICAL CENTER, BEDFORD, IN, 150124, p. A211

BEEBE MEDICAL CENTER, LEWES, DE, 080007, p. A119

BEHAVIORAL HEALTH CARE OF CAPE FEAR VALLEY HEALTH SYSTEM, FAYETTEVILLE, NC, 344010, p. A482

BEHAVIORAL HEALTH CENTER, GREENSBORO, NC, p. A483

BEHAVIORAL HEALTH CENTER, WINFIELD, ILLINOIS (see CENTRAL DUPAGE HOSPITAL), p. A210

BELL HOSPITAL, ISHPEMING, MI, 231301, p. A337

BELLA VISTA HOSPITAL, MAYAGUEZ, PR, 400014, p. A745

BELLAIRE MEDICAL CENTER, HOUSTON, TX, 450418, p. A644

BELLEVUE COMPREHENSIVE GENERAL CARE, BELLEVUE PHYSICAL MEDICINE AND REHABILITATION SERVICES, BELLEVUE PSYCHIATRIC SERVICES, BELLEVUE TUBERCULOSIS SERVICES, COMPREHENSIVE AMBULATORY CARE SERVICES: LEVEL I TRAUMA CENTER (see BELLEVUE HOSPITAL CENTER), p. A458

BELLEVUE HOSPITAL, BELLEVUE, OH, 360107, p. A504

BELLEVUE HOSPITAL CENTER, NEW YORK, NY, 330204, p. A458

BELLEVUE WOMAN'S HOSPITAL, SCHENECTADY, NY, 330339, p. A472

BELLFLOWER MEDICAL CENTER, BELLFLOWER, CA, 050531, p. A54

BELLIN MEMORIAL HOSPITAL, GREEN BAY, WI, 520049, p. A726

BELLIN PSYCHIATRIC CENTER, GREEN BAY, WI, 524038, p. A726

BELLVILLE GENERAL HOSPITAL, BELLVILLE, TX, 450253, p. A625

BELMOND MEDICAL CENTER, BELMOND, IA, 161301, p. A228

BELMONT CENTER FOR COMPREHENSIVE TREATMENT, PHILADELPHIA, PA, 394023, p. A567

BELMONT COMMUNITY HOSPITAL, BELLAIRE, OH, 360153, p. A504

BELMONT PINES HOSPITAL, YOUNGSTOWN, OH, 364038, p. A525

BELOIT MEMORIAL HOSPITAL, BELOIT, WI, 520100, p. A723

BEN TAUB GENERAL HOSPITAL, HOUSTON, TEXAS (see HARRIS COUNTY HOSPITAL DISTRICT), p. A645

BENCHMARK BEHAVIORAL HEALTH SYSTEMS, WOODS CROSS, UT, p. A681

BENEDICTINE HOSPITAL, KINGSTON, NY, 330224, p. A455

BENEFIS HEALTH CARE–EAST CAMPUS, GREAT FALLS, MONTANA (see BENEFIS HEALTHCARE), p. A399

BENEFIS HEALTH CARE–WEST CAMPUS, GREAT FALLS, MONTANA (see BENEFIS HEALTHCARE), p. A399

BENEFIS HEALTHCARE, GREAT FALLS, MT, 270012, p. A399

BENEWAH COMMUNITY HOSPITAL, SAINT MARIES, ID, 131317, p. A181

BENNETT COUNTY HEALTHCARE CENTER, MARTIN, SD, 431314, p. A597

BENSON HOSPITAL, BENSON, AZ, 031301, p. A30

BENTON REHABILITATION HOSPITAL, BATON ROUGE, LA, 193070, p. A277

BEREA HOSPITAL, BEREA, KY, 180055, p. A261

BERGEN REGIONAL MEDICAL CENTER, PARAMUS, NJ, 310058, p. A433

BERGER HEALTH SYSTEM, CIRCLEVILLE, OH, 360170, p. A508

BERKSHIRE MEDICAL CENTER, PITTSFIELD, MA, 220046, p. A322

BERLIN MEMORIAL HOSPITAL, BERLIN, WI, 520060, p. A723

BERNARD MITCHELL HOSPITAL, CHICAGO, ILLINOIS (see UNIVERSITY OF CHICAGO HOSPITALS), p. A191

BERNICE COMMUNITY REHABILITATION HOSPITAL – MINDEN, MINDEN, LA, 192026, p. A286

BERRIEN COUNTY HOSPITAL, NASHVILLE, GA, 110112, p. A166

BERT FISH MEDICAL CENTER, NEW SMYRNA BEACH, FL, 100014, p. A139

BERTIE MEMORIAL HOSPITAL, WINDSOR, NC, 341304, p. A494

BERTRAND CHAFFEE HOSPITAL, SPRINGVILLE, NY, 330111, p. A472

BERWICK HOSPITAL CENTER, BERWICK, PA, 390072, p. A552

BETH ISRAEL DEACONESS HOSPITAL–NEEDHAM CAMPUS, NEEDHAM, MASSACHUSETTS (see BETH ISRAEL DEACONESS MEDICAL CENTER), p. A313

BETH ISRAEL DEACONESS MEDICAL CENTER, BOSTON, MA, 220086, p. A313

BETH ISRAEL MEDICAL CENTER, NEW YORK, NY, 330169, p. A458

BETH ISRAEL MEDICAL CENTER–KINGS HIGHWAY DIVISION, NEW YORK, NEW YORK (see BETH ISRAEL MEDICAL CENTER), p. A458

BETHESDA HOSPITAL, ZANESVILLE, OHIO (see GENESIS HEALTHCARE SYSTEM), p. A526

BETHESDA MEMORIAL HOSPITAL, BOYNTON BEACH, FL, 100002, p. A124

BETHESDA NORTH HOSPITAL, CINCINNATI, OH, 360179, p. A506

BETHESDA REHABILITATION HOSPITAL, SAINT PAUL, MN, 242004, p. A361

BETSY JOHNSON REGIONAL HOSPITAL, DUNN, NC, 340071, p. A481

BEVERLY HOSPITAL, MONTEBELLO, CA, 050350, p. A76

BEVERLY HOSPITAL, BEVERLY, MA, 220033, p. A312

BIBB MEDICAL CENTER, CENTREVILLE, AL, 010058, p. A16

BIG BEND REGIONAL MEDICAL CENTER, ALPINE, TX, 450830, p. A620

BIG FORK VALLEY HOSPITAL, BIGFORK, MN, 241316, p. A350

BIG HORN COUNTY MEMORIAL HOSPITAL, HARDIN, MT, 271338, p. A399

BIG SANDY MEDICAL CENTER, BIG SANDY, MT, 271311, p. A396

BIG SPRING STATE HOSPITAL, BIG SPRING, TX, 454000, p. A626

BIGGS–GRIDLEY MEMORIAL HOSPITAL, GRIDLEY, CA, 051311, p. A63

BILOXI REGIONAL MEDICAL CENTER, BILOXI, MS, 250007, p. A366

BINGHAM MEMORIAL HOSPITAL, BLACKFOOT, ID, 131325, p. A177

BINGHAMTON GENERAL HOSPITAL, BINGHAMTON, NEW YORK (see UNITED HEALTH SERVICES HOSPITALS–BINGHAMTON), p. A448

BISHOP CLARKSON MEMORIAL HOSPITAL, OMAHA, NEBRASKA (see NEBRASKA MEDICAL CENTER), p. A411

BJC MEDICAL CENTER, COMMERCE, GA, 110040, p. A159

BLACK HILLS SURGERY CENTER, RAPID CITY, SD, 430091, p. A598

BLACK RIVER MEMORIAL HOSPITAL, BLACK RIVER FALLS, WI, 521333, p. A723

BLACKFORD COMMUNITY HOSPITAL, HARTFORD CITY, IN, 151302, p. A217

BLADEN COUNTY HOSPITAL, ELIZABETHTOWN, NC, 341315, p. A482

BLAKE MEDICAL CENTER, BRADENTON, FL, 100213, p. A124

BLANCHARD VALLEY HEALTH ASSOCIATION, FINDLAY, OH, 360095, p. A513

BLANCHARD VALLEY REGIONAL HEALTH CENTER–BLUFFTON CAMPUS, BLUFFTON, OHIO (see BLANCHARD VALLEY HEALTH ASSOCIATION), p. A513

BLANCHARD VALLEY REGIONAL HEALTH CENTER–FINDLAY CAMPUS, FINDLAY, OHIO (see BLANCHARD VALLEY HEALTH ASSOCIATION), p. A513

BLECKLEY MEMORIAL HOSPITAL, COCHRAN, GA, 111302, p. A158

BLESSING HOSPITAL, QUINCY, IL, 140015, p. A206

BLESSING HOSPITAL, QUINCY, ILLINOIS (see BLESSING HOSPITAL), p. A206

BLOOMER MEMORIAL MEDICAL CENTER, BLOOMER, WI, 521314, p. A723

BLOOMINGTON HOSPITAL, BLOOMINGTON, IN, 150051, p. A212

BLOOMINGTON HOSPITAL OF ORANGE COUNTY, PAOLI, IN, 151306, p. A223

BLOOMSBURG HOSPITAL, BLOOMSBURG, PA, 390003, p. A553

BLOUNT MEMORIAL HOSPITAL, MARYVILLE, TN, 440011, p. A612

BLOWING ROCK HOSPITAL, BLOWING ROCK, NC, 341321, p. A478

BLUE HILL MEMORIAL HOSPITAL, BLUE HILL, ME, 201300, p. A297

BLUE MOUNTAIN HOSPITAL, JOHN DAY, OR, 381305, p. A545

BLUEFIELD REGIONAL MEDICAL CENTER, BLUEFIELD, WV, 510071, p. A713

BLUEGRASS COMMUNITY HOSPITAL, VERSAILLES, KY, 181308, p. A275

BLUFFTON REGIONAL MEDICAL CENTER, BLUFFTON, IN, 150075, p. A212

BLYTHEDALE CHILDREN'S HOSPITAL, VALHALLA, NY, 333301, p. A475

BOB WILSON MEMORIAL GRANT COUNTY HOSPITAL, ULYSSES, KS, 170110, p. A258

BOCA RATON COMMUNITY HOSPITAL, BOCA RATON, FL, 100168, p. A124

BOGALUSA COMMUNITY MEDICAL CENTER, BOGALUSA, LOUISIANA (see BOGALUSA MEDICAL CENTER), p. A278

BOGALUSA MEDICAL CENTER, BOGALUSA, LA, 190095, p. A278

BOLIVAR GENERAL HOSPITAL, BOLIVAR, TN, 440181, p. A602

BOLIVAR MEDICAL CENTER, CLEVELAND, MS, 250093, p. A368

BON SECOURS BALTIMORE HEALTH SYSTEM, BALTIMORE, MD, 210013, p. A302

BON SECOURS COMMUNITY HOSPITAL, PORT JERVIS, NY, 330135, p. A470

BON SECOURS HOSPITAL, GROSSE POINTE, MI, 230089, p. A335

BON SECOURS HOSPITAL CAMPUS, ALTOONA, PA, 390121, p. A552

BON SECOURS ST. FRANCIS HEALTH SYSTEM, GREENVILLE, SC, 420023, p. A588

BON SECOURS ST. MARY'S HOSPITAL, RICHMOND, VA, 490059, p. A694

BON SECOURS–DEPAUL MEDICAL CENTER, NORFOLK, VA, 490011, p. A692

BON SECOURS–RICHMOND COMMUNITY HOSPITAL, RICHMOND, VA, 490094, p. A694

BON SECOURS–ST. FRANCIS XAVIER HOSPITAL, CHARLESTON, SC, 420065, p. A584

BONE AND JOINT HOSPITAL, OKLAHOMA CITY, OK, 370105, p. A535

BONNER GENERAL HOSPITAL, SANDPOINT, ID, 130024, p. A181

BOONE COUNTY HEALTH CENTER, ALBION, NE, 281334, p. A404

BOONE COUNTY HOSPITAL, BOONE, IA, 160026, p. A229

BOONE HOSPITAL CENTER, COLUMBIA, MO, 260068, p. A380

BOONE MEMORIAL HOSPITAL, MADISON, WV, 510015, p. A717

BOONEVILLE COMMUNITY HOSPITAL, BOONEVILLE, AR, 041318, p. A41

BORGESS MEDICAL CENTER, KALAMAZOO, MI, 230117, p. A338

BORGESS–LEE MEMORIAL HOSPITAL, DOWAGIAC, MI, 231315, p. A332

BORGESS–PIPP HOSPITAL, PLAINWELL, MICHIGAN (see BORGESS MEDICAL CENTER), p. A338

BOSCOBEL AREA HEALTH CARE, BOSCOBEL, WI, 521344, p. A723

BOSTON MEDICAL CENTER, BOSTON, MA, 220031, p. A313

BOTHWELL REGIONAL HEALTH CENTER, SEDALIA, MO, 260009, p. A393

BOTSFORD GENERAL HOSPITAL, FARMINGTON HILLS, MI, 230151, p. A333

BOULDER CITY HOSPITAL, BOULDER CITY, NV, 290010, p. A415

BOULDER COMMUNITY HOSPITAL, BOULDER, CO, 060027, p. A101

BOUNDARY COMMUNITY HOSPITAL, BONNERS FERRY, ID, 131301, p. A178

BOUNDARY COUNTY NURSING HOME (see BOUNDARY COMMUNITY HOSPITAL), p. A178

BOURBON COMMUNITY HOSPITAL, PARIS, KY, 180046, p. A273

BOURNEWOOD HEALTH SYSTEM, BROOKLINE, MA, 224022, p. A316

BOWDLE HOSPITAL, BOWDLE, SD, 431318, p. A594

BOWIE MEMORIAL HOSPITAL, BOWIE, TX, 450497, p. A626

BOX BUTTE GENERAL HOSPITAL, ALLIANCE, NE, 281360, p. A404

BOYS TOWN NATIONAL RESEARCH HOSPITAL, OMAHA, NE, 283300, p. A411

BOZEMAN DEACONESS HOSPITAL, BOZEMAN, MT, 270057, p. A396

BRACKENRIDGE HOSPITAL, AUSTIN, TX, 450124, p. A623

BRADFORD HEALTH SERVICES AT HUNTSVILLE, MADISON, AL, p. A21

BRADFORD REGIONAL MEDICAL CENTER, BRADFORD, PA, 390118, p. A553

BRADLEY CENTER OF ST. FRANCIS, COLUMBUS, GEORGIA (see ST. FRANCIS HOSPITAL, INC.), p. A158

BRADLEY COUNTY MEDICAL CENTER, WARREN, AR, 040077, p. A51

BRADLEY MEMORIAL HOSPITAL, CLEVELAND, TN, 440024, p. A604

BRADLEY MEMORIAL HOSPITAL AND HEALTH CENTER, SOUTHINGTON, CT, 070009, p. A116

BRAINERD REGIONAL HUMAN SERVICES CENTER, BRAINERD, MN, 244008, p. A350

BRANDON REGIONAL HOSPITAL, BRANDON, FL, 100243, p. A124

BRANDYWINE HOSPITAL, COATESVILLE, PA, 390076, p. A555

BRATTLEBORO MEMORIAL HOSPITAL, BRATTLEBORO, VT, 470011, p. A682

BRATTLEBORO RETREAT, BRATTLEBORO, VT, 474001, p. A682

BRAXTON COUNTY MEMORIAL HOSPITAL, GASSAWAY, WV, 511308, p. A715

BRAZOSPORT MEMORIAL HOSPITAL, LAKE JACKSON, TX, 450072, p. A652

BRECKINRIDGE MEMORIAL HOSPITAL, HARDINSBURG, KY, 181319, p. A265

BRENTWOOD BEHAVIORAL HEALTH COMPANY, SHREVEPORT, LA, 194020, p. A292

BRENTWOOD BEHAVIORAL HEALTHCARE OF MISSISSIPPI, JACKSON, MS, 254007, p. A370

BRIDGEPORT HOSPITAL, BRIDGEPORT, CT, 070010, p. A112

BRIDGES MEDICAL SERVICES, ADA, MN, 241313, p. A349

BRIDGETON HEALTH CENTER, BRIDGETON, NEW JERSEY (see SOUTH JERSEY HEALTHCARE), p. A426

BRIDGEWATER STATE HOSPITAL, BRIDGEWATER, MA, p. A315

BRIDGEWAY, NORTH LITTLE ROCK, AR, 044005, p. A48

BRIDGTON HOSPITAL, BRIDGTON, ME, 201310, p. A297

BRIGHAM AND WOMEN'S HOSPITAL, BOSTON, MA, 220110, p. A313

BRIGHAM CITY COMMUNITY HOSPITAL, BRIGHAM CITY, UT, 460017, p. A676

BRIGHTON HOSPITAL, BRIGHTON, MI, 230279, p. A329

BRISTOL BAY AREA HEALTH CORPORATION, DILLINGHAM, AK, 021309, p. A27

BRISTOL HOSPITAL, BRISTOL, CT, 070029, p. A112

BRISTOW MEMORIAL HOSPITAL, BRISTOW, OK, 370041, p. A528

BROADDUS HOSPITAL, PHILIPPI, WV, 511300, p. A719

BROADLAWNS MEDICAL CENTER, DES MOINES, IA, 160101, p. A232

BROADWATER HEALTH CENTER, TOWNSEND, MT, 271333, p. A402

BROCKTON HOSPITAL, BROCKTON, MA, 220052, p. A315

BROCKTON VETERANS AFFAIRS MEDICAL CENTER, BROCKTON, MA, p. A315

BRODSTONE MEMORIAL HOSPITAL, SUPERIOR, NE, 281315, p. A413

BROMENN HEALTHCARE SYSTEM, NORMAL, IL, 140127, p. A202

BROMENN REGIONAL MEDICAL CENTER, NORMAL, ILLINOIS (see BROMENN HEALTHCARE SYSTEM), p. A202

BRONSON METHODIST HOSPITAL, KALAMAZOO, MI, 230017, p. A338

BRONSON VICKSBURG HOSPITAL, VICKSBURG, MI, 230190, p. A347

BRONX CHILDREN'S PSYCHIATRIC CENTER, NEW YORK, NY, p. A458

BRONX PSYCHIATRIC CENTER, NEW YORK, NY, 334053, p. A458

BRONX–LEBANON HOSPITAL CENTER, NEW YORK, NY, 330009, p. A458

BROOK LANE HEALTH SERVICES, HAGERSTOWN, MD, 214003, p. A308

BROOKDALE HOSPITAL MEDICAL CENTER, NEW YORK, NY, 330233, p. A458

BROOKE ARMY MEDICAL CENTER, FORT SAM HOUSTON, TX, p. A638

BROOKE GLEN BEHAVIORAL HOSPITAL, FORT WASHINGTON, PA, 394049, p. A559

BROOKHAVEN HOSPITAL, TULSA, OK, 374012, p. A539

BROOKHAVEN MEMORIAL HOSPITAL MEDICAL CENTER, PATCHOGUE, NY, 330141, p. A469

BROOKINGS HEALTH SYSTEM, BROOKINGS, SD, 430008, p. A594

BROOKLYN HOSPITAL CENTER, NEW YORK, NY, 330056, p. A459

BROOKS COUNTY HOSPITAL, QUITMAN, GA, 111332, p. A167

BROOKS MEMORIAL HOSPITAL, DUNKIRK, NY, 330229, p. A451

BROOKS REHABILITATION HOSPITAL, JACKSONVILLE, FL, 103039, p. A132

BROOKSVILLE REGIONAL HOSPITAL, BROOKSVILLE, FL, 100071, p. A125

BROOKVILLE HOSPITAL, BROOKVILLE, PA, 390191, p. A553

BROOKWOOD MEDICAL CENTER, BIRMINGHAM, AL, 010139, p. A14

BROTMAN MEDICAL CENTER, CULVER CITY, CA, 050144, p. A58

BROUGHTON HOSPITAL, MORGANTON, NC, 340137, p. A488

BROWARD GENERAL MEDICAL CENTER, FORT LAUDERDALE, FL, 100039, p. A128

BROWN COUNTY GENERAL HOSPITAL, GEORGETOWN, OH, 360116, p. A514

BROWN COUNTY HOSPITAL, AINSWORTH, NE, 281325, p. A404

BROWN COUNTY HUMAN SERVICES MENTAL HEALTH CENTER, GREEN BAY, WI, 524014, p. A726

BROWN MEMORIAL CONVALESCENT CENTER, COBB HEALTH CARE CENTER AND THE GABLES (see COBB MEMORIAL HOSPITAL), p. A168

BROWNFIELD REGIONAL MEDICAL CENTER, BROWNFIELD, TX, 450399, p. A627

BROWNSVILLE GENERAL HOSPITAL, BROWNSVILLE, PA, 390166, p. A553

BROWNSVILLE SURGICAL HOSPITAL, BROWNSVILLE, TX, 450841, p. A627

BROWNWOOD REGIONAL MEDICAL CENTER, BROWNWOOD, TX, 450587, p. A627

BRUNSWICK COMMUNITY HOSPITAL, SUPPLY, NC, 340158, p. A492

BRUNSWICK GENERAL HOSPITAL, AMITYVILLE, NY, 330314, p. A446

BRUNSWICK HALL, AMITYVILLE, NEW YORK (see BRUNSWICK GENERAL HOSPITAL), p. A446

BRUNSWICK PHYSICAL MEDICINE AND REHABILITATION HOSPITAL, AMITYVILLE, NEW YORK (see BRUNSWICK GENERAL HOSPITAL), p. A446

BRYAN HOSPITAL, BRYAN, OHIO (see COMMUNITY HOSPITALS AND WELLNESS CENTERS), p. A504

BRYAN W. WHITFIELD MEMORIAL HOSPITAL, DEMOPOLIS, AL, 010112, p. A17

BRYANLGH MEDICAL CENTER, LINCOLN, NE, 280003, p. A408

BRYANLGH MEDICAL CENTER–EAST, LINCOLN, NEBRASKA (see BRYANLGH MEDICAL CENTER), p. A408

BRYANLGH MEDICAL CENTER–WEST, LINCOLN, NEBRASKA (see BRYANLGH MEDICAL CENTER), p. A408

BRYCE HOSPITAL, TUSCALOOSA, AL, 014007, p. A24

BRYLIN HOSPITALS, BUFFALO, NY, 334022, p. A448

BRYN MAWR HOSPITAL, BRYN MAWR, PA, 390139, p. A553

BRYN MAWR REHABILITATION HOSPITAL, MALVERN, PA, 393025, p. A564

BRYNN MARR BEHAVIORAL HEALTHCARE SYSTEM, JACKSONVILLE, NC, 344016, p. A485

BUCHANAN COUNTY HEALTH CENTER, INDEPENDENCE, IA, 161335, p. A235

BUCHANAN GENERAL HOSPITAL, GRUNDY, VA, 490127, p. A689

BUCKS COUNTY CAMPUS, LANGHORNE, PENNSYLVANIA (see FRANKFORD HOSPITAL OF THE CITY OF PHILADELPHIA), p. A568

BUCKTAIL MEDICAL CENTER, RENOVO, PA, 391304, p. A574

BUCYRUS COMMUNITY HOSPITAL, BUCYRUS, OH, 361316, p. A504

BUENA VISTA REGIONAL MEDICAL CENTER, STORM LAKE, IA, 160066, p. A242

BUFFALO GENERAL HOSPITAL, BUFFALO, NY, 330005, p. A448

BUFFALO HOSPITAL, BUFFALO, MN, 240076, p. A351

BUFFALO PSYCHIATRIC CENTER, BUFFALO, NY, 334052, p. A449

BULLOCK COUNTY HOSPITAL, UNION SPRINGS, AL, 010110, p. A25

BUNKIE GENERAL HOSPITAL, BUNKIE, LA, 191311, p. A278

BURDETTE TOMLIN MEMORIAL HOSPITAL, CAPE MAY COURT HOUSE, NJ, 310011, p. A427

BURGESS HEALTH CENTER, ONAWA, IA, 161359, p. A239

BURKE MEDICAL CENTER, WAYNESBORO, GA, 110113, p. A172

BURKE REHABILITATION HOSPITAL, WHITE PLAINS, NY, 333028, p. A476

BURLESON ST. JOSEPH HEALTH CENTER, CALDWELL, TX, 451305, p. A627

BURNETT MEDICAL CENTER, GRANTSBURG, WI, 521331, p. A726

BUTLER COUNTY HEALTH CARE CENTER, DAVID CITY, NE, 281332, p. A406

BUTLER HEALTH SYSTEM, BUTLER, PA, 390168, p. A554

BUTLER HOSPITAL, PROVIDENCE, RI, 414000, p. A581

BYRD REGIONAL HOSPITAL, LEESVILLE, LA, 190164, p. A285

BYWATER HOSPITAL, NEW ORLEANS, LA, 190253, p. A288

C

CABELL HUNTINGTON HOSPITAL, HUNTINGTON, WV, 510055, p. A716

CABRINI MEDICAL CENTER, NEW YORK, NY, 330133, p. A459

CACHE VALLEY SPECIALTY HOSPITAL, NORTH LOGAN, UT, 460054, p. A678

CALAIS REGIONAL HOSPITAL, CALAIS, ME, 201305, p. A297

CALDWELL COUNTY HOSPITAL, PRINCETON, KY, 181322, p. A274

CALDWELL MEMORIAL HOSPITAL, COLUMBIA, LA, 190190, p. A279

CALDWELL MEMORIAL HOSPITAL, LENOIR, NC, 340041, p. A486

CALHOUN HEALTH SERVICES, CALHOUN CITY, MS, 250112, p. A367

CALHOUN MEMORIAL HOSPITAL, ARLINGTON, GA, 111309, p. A152

CALHOUN–LIBERTY HOSPITAL, BLOUNTSTOWN, FL, 101304, p. A124

CALIFORNIA HOSPITAL MEDICAL CENTER, LOS ANGELES, CA, 050149, p. A69

CALIFORNIA MEDICAL FACILITY, VACAVILLE, CA, p. A97

CALIFORNIA MENS COLONY HOSPITAL, SAN LUIS OBISPO, CA, p. A91

CALIFORNIA PACIFIC MEDICAL CENTER, SAN FRANCISCO, CA, 050047, p. A88

CALIFORNIA PACIFIC MEDICAL CENTER–DAVIES CAMPUS, SAN FRANCISCO, CALIFORNIA (see CALIFORNIA PACIFIC MEDICAL CENTER), p. A88

CALLAHAN EYE FOUNDATION HOSPITAL, BIRMINGHAM, AL, 010018, p. A14

CALLAWAY COMMUNITY HOSPITAL, FULTON, MO, 260209, p. A382

CALLAWAY DISTRICT HOSPITAL, CALLAWAY, NE, 281335, p. A405

CALUMET MEDICAL CENTER, CHILTON, WI, 521317, p. A724

CALVARY HOSPITAL, NEW YORK, NY, 332006, p. A459

CALVERT MEMORIAL HOSPITAL, PRINCE FREDERICK, MD, 210039, p. A309

CAMBRIDGE HEALTH ALLIANCE, CAMBRIDGE, MA, 220011, p. A316

CAMBRIDGE HOSPITAL, CAMBRIDGE, MASSACHUSETTS (see CAMBRIDGE HEALTH ALLIANCE), p. A316

CAMBRIDGE MEDICAL CENTER, CAMBRIDGE, MN, 240020, p. A351

CAMDEN COUNTY HEALTH SERVICES CENTER, BLACKWOOD, NJ, 314018, p. A426

CAMDEN GENERAL HOSPITAL, CAMDEN, TN, 440145, p. A602

CAMDEN–CLARK MEMORIAL HOSPITAL, PARKERSBURG, WV, 510058, p. A718

CAMERON MEMORIAL COMMUNITY HOSPITAL, ANGOLA, IN, 151315, p. A211

CAMERON REGIONAL MEDICAL CENTER, CAMERON, MO, 260057, p. A379

CAMPBELL COUNTY MEMORIAL HOSPITAL, GILLETTE, WY, 530002, p. A740

CAMPBELL HEALTH SYSTEM, WEATHERFORD, TX, 450203, p. A673

CAMPBELLTON GRACEVILLE HOSPITAL, GRACEVILLE, FL, 101302, p. A130

CANDLER COUNTY HOSPITAL, METTER, GA, 111334, p. A166

CANNON FALLS COMMUNITY HOSPITAL, CANNON FALLS, MN, 241346, p. A351

CANNON MEMORIAL HOSPITAL, PICKENS, SC, 420011, p. A591

CANONSBURG GENERAL HOSPITAL, CANONSBURG, PA, 390160, p. A554

CANTON–INWOOD MEMORIAL HOSPITAL, CANTON, SD, 431333, p. A594

CANTON–POTSDAM HOSPITAL, POTSDAM, NY, 330197, p. A470

CANYON RIDGE HOSPITAL, CHINO, CA, 054111, p. A56

CAPE CANAVERAL HOSPITAL/HEALTH FIRST, COCOA BEACH, FL, 100177, p. A126

CAPE COD HOSPITAL, HYANNIS, MA, 220012, p. A319

CAPE CORAL HOSPITAL, CAPE CORAL, FL, 100244, p. A125

CAPE FEAR HOSPITAL, WILMINGTON, NORTH CAROLINA (see NEW HANOVER REGIONAL MEDICAL CENTER), p. A494

CAPE FEAR VALLEY HEALTH SYSTEM, FAYETTEVILLE, NC, 340028, p. A482

CAPITAL DISTRICT PSYCHIATRIC CENTER, ALBANY, NY, 334046, p. A446

CAPITAL HEALTH SYSTEM AT FULD, TRENTON, NJ, 310092, p. A437

CAPITAL HEALTH SYSTEM AT MERCER, TRENTON, NJ, 310044, p. A437

CAPITAL MEDICAL CENTER, OLYMPIA, WA, 500139, p. A705

CAPITAL REGION MEDICAL CENTER, JEFFERSON CITY, MO, 260047, p. A383

CAPITAL REGIONAL MEDICAL CENTER, TALLAHASSEE, FL, 100254, p. A147

CARDINAL HILL REHABILITATION HOSPITAL, LEXINGTON, KY, 183026, p. A267

CARDINAL HILL SPECIALTY HOSPITAL, FORT THOMAS, KY, 182004, p. A264

CARDIOVASCULAR CENTER OF PUERTO RICO AND THE CARIBBEAN, SAN JUAN, PR, 400124, p. A746

CARIBBEAN PEDIATRIC AND SURGERY HOSPITAL, SAN JUAN, PR, 400098, p. A747

CARIBOU MEMORIAL HOSPITAL AND LIVING CENTER, SODA SPRINGS, ID, 131309, p. A182

CARILION FRANKLIN MEMORIAL HOSPITAL, ROCKY MOUNT, VA, 490089, p. A696

CARILION GILES MEMORIAL HOSPITAL, PEARISBURG, VA, 491302, p. A693

CARILION MEDICAL CENTER, ROANOKE, VA, 490024, p. A696

CARILION NEW RIVER VALLEY MEDICAL CENTER, CHRISTIANSBURG, VA, 490042, p. A686

CARILION ROANOKE COMMUNITY HOSPITAL, ROANOKE, VIRGINIA (see CARILION MEDICAL CENTER), p. A696

CARITAS CARNEY HOSPITAL, DORCHESTER, MA, 220017, p. A317

CARITAS GOOD SAMARITAN MEDICAL CENTER, BROCKTON, MA, 220111, p. A315

CARITAS HOLY FAMILY HOSPITAL AND MEDICAL CENTER, METHUEN, MA, 220080, p. A320

CARITAS MEDICAL CENTER, LOUISVILLE, KY, 180037, p. A269

CARITAS NORWOOD HOSPITAL, NORWOOD, MA, 220126, p. A321

CARITAS PEACE CENTER, LOUISVILLE, KY, p. A269

CARITAS ST. ELIZABETH'S MEDICAL CENTER, BRIGHTON, MA, 220036, p. A315

CARL ALBERT COMMUNITY MENTAL HEALTH CENTER, MCALESTER, OK, 374006, p. A533

CARL T. HAYDEN VETERANS AFFAIRS MEDICAL CENTER, PHOENIX, AZ, p. A33

CARL VINSON VETERANS AFFAIRS MEDICAL CENTER, DUBLIN, GA, p. A161

CARLE FOUNDATION HOSPITAL, URBANA, IL, 140091, p. A209

CARLINVILLE AREA HOSPITAL, CARLINVILLE, IL, 140141, p. A185

CARLISLE REGIONAL MEDICAL CENTER, CARLISLE, PA, 390058, p. A554

CARLSBAD MEDICAL CENTER, CARLSBAD, NM, 320063, p. A441

CARNEGIE TRI–COUNTY MUNICIPAL HOSPITAL, CARNEGIE, OK, 370064, p. A528

CARO CENTER, CARO, MI, 234025, p. A329

CARO COMMUNITY HOSPITAL, CARO, MI, 230235, p. A329

CAROLINA CENTER FOR BEHAVIORAL HEALTH, GREER, SC, 424010, p. A589

CAROLINA PINES REGIONAL MEDICAL CENTER, HARTSVILLE, SC, 420010, p. A589

CAROLINAS HOSPITAL SYSTEM, FLORENCE, SC, 420091, p. A587

CAROLINAS MEDICAL CENTER, CHARLOTTE, NC, 340113, p. A479

CAROLINAS MEDICAL CENTER– PINEVILLE, CHARLOTTE, NORTH CAROLINA (see CAROLINAS MEDICAL CENTER–MERCY), p. A479

CAROLINAS MEDICAL CENTER–MERCY, CHARLOTTE, NC, 340098, p. A479

CAROLINAS MEDICAL CENTER–PINEVILLE, CHARLOTTE, NC, 340098, p. A479

CAROLINAS MEDICAL CENTER–UNIVERSITY, CHARLOTTE, NC, 340166, p. A480

CARONDELET HOLY CROSS HOSPITAL, NOGALES, AZ, 030040, p. A32

CARONDELET ST. JOSEPH'S HOSPITAL–TUCSON, TUCSON, AZ, 030011, p. A37

CARONDELET ST. MARY'S HOSPITAL–TUCSON, TUCSON, AZ, 030010, p. A37

CARRAWAY METHODIST MEDICAL CENTER, BIRMINGHAM, AL, 010064, p. A14

CARRIE TINGLEY HOSPITAL, ALBUQUERQUE, NM, 323307, p. A440

CARRIER CLINIC, BELLE MEAD, NJ, 314012, p. A425

CARRINGTON HEALTH CENTER, CARRINGTON, ND, 351318, p. A497

CARROLL COUNTY HOSPITAL, CARROLLTON, KY, 181310, p. A262

CARROLL COUNTY MEMORIAL HOSPITAL, CARROLLTON, MO, 260067, p. A379

CARROLL HOSPITAL CENTER, WESTMINSTER, MD, 210033, p. A311

CARSON CITY HOSPITAL, CARSON CITY, MI, 230208, p. A329

COLLEGE STATION MEDICAL CENTER, COLLEGE STATION, TX, 450299, p. A629

COLLETON MEDICAL CENTER, WALTERBORO, SC, 420030, p. A593

COLLINGSWORTH GENERAL HOSPITAL, WELLINGTON, TX, 451355, p. A673

COLMERY-O'NEIL VETERANS AFFAIRS MEDICAL CENTER, TOPEKA, KANSAS (see VETERANS AFFAIRS EASTERN KANSAS HEALTH CARE SYSTEM), p. A258

COLONEL FLORENCE A. BLANCHFIELD ARMY COMMUNITY HOSPITAL, FORT CAMPBELL, KY, p. A264

COLORADO ACUTE SPECIALTY CARE HOSPITAL, DENVER, CO, 062012, p. A103

COLORADO MENTAL HEALTH INSTITUTE AT FORT LOGAN, DENVER, CO, 064003, p. A103

COLORADO MENTAL HEALTH INSTITUTE AT PUEBLO, PUEBLO, CO, 062008, p. A109

COLORADO PLAINS MEDICAL CENTER, FORT MORGAN, CO, 060044, p. A105

COLORADO RIVER MEDICAL CENTER, NEEDLES, CA, 050469, p. A77

COLORADO-FAYETTE MEDICAL CENTER, WEIMAR, TX, 450438, p. A673

COLQUITT REGIONAL MEDICAL CENTER, MOULTRIE, GA, 110105, p. A166

COLUMBIA BASIN HOSPITAL, EPHRATA, WA, 501317, p. A702

COLUMBIA CENTER, MILWAUKEE, WI, 520195, p. A730

COLUMBIA HOSPITAL, WEST PALM BEACH, FL, 100234, p. A150

COLUMBIA MEMORIAL HOSPITAL, HUDSON, NY, 330094, p. A454

COLUMBIA MEMORIAL HOSPITAL, ASTORIA, OR, 381320, p. A542

COLUMBIA REGIONAL HOSPITAL, COLUMBIA, MO, 260178, p. A380

COLUMBIA REGIONAL MEDICAL CENTER-SOUTH CAMPUS, AURORA, COLORADO (see MEDICAL CENTER OF AURORA), p. A101

COLUMBIA ST. MARY'S OZAUKEE CAMPUS, MEQUON, WI, 520027, p. A730

COLUMBIA ST. MARY'S-COLUMBIA CAMPUS, MILWAUKEE, WI, 520140, p. A730

COLUMBIA ST. MARY'S-MILWAUKEE CAMPUS, MILWAUKEE, WI, 520051, p. A730

COLUMBIA-GREENE LONG TERM CARE, CATSKILL, NEW YORK (see COLUMBIA MEMORIAL HOSPITAL), p. A454

COLUMBUS COMMUNITY HOSPITAL, COLUMBUS, NE, 280111, p. A406

COLUMBUS COMMUNITY HOSPITAL, COLUMBUS, TX, 450370, p. A629

COLUMBUS COMMUNITY HOSPITAL, COLUMBUS, WI, 521338, p. A724

COLUMBUS COUNTY HOSPITAL, WHITEVILLE, NC, 340068, p. A493

COLUMBUS HOSPITAL, NEWARK, NJ, 310093, p. A432

COLUMBUS REGIONAL HOSPITAL, COLUMBUS, IN, 150112, p. A213

COLUMBUS SPECIALTY HOSPITAL, COLUMBUS, GA, 112012, p. A158

COLUSA REGIONAL MEDICAL CENTER, COLUSA, CA, 050434, p. A57

COMANCHE COMMUNITY HOSPITAL, COMANCHE, TX, 450234, p. A629

COMANCHE COUNTY HOSPITAL, COLDWATER, KS, 171312, p. A245

COMANCHE COUNTY MEMORIAL HOSPITAL, LAWTON, OK, 370056, p. A532

COMMMUNITY HOSPITAL OF SAN BERNARDINO, SAN BERNARDINO, CA, 050089, p. A86

COMMONWEALTH CENTER FOR CHILDREN AND ADOLESCENTS, STAUNTON, VA, p. A697

COMMONWEALTH REGIONAL SPECIALTY HOSPITAL, BOWLING GREEN, KY, 180147, p. A261

COMMUNITY AND MISSION HOSPITALS OF HUNTINGTON PARK, HUNTINGTON PARK, CA, 050091, p. A64

COMMUNITY BEHAVIORAL HEALTH CENTER, FRESNO, CA, 054091, p. A61

COMMUNITY CARE HOSPITAL, NEW ORLEANS, LA, 194056, p. A288

COMMUNITY GENERAL HEALTH CENTER, FORT FAIRFIELD, MAINE (see AROOSTOOK MEDICAL CENTER), p. A300

COMMUNITY GENERAL HOSPITAL, DILLEY, TX, 450813, p. A635

COMMUNITY HEALTH CENTER, VISALIA, CALIFORNIA (see KAWEAH DELTA HEALTH CARE DISTRICT), p. A98

COMMUNITY HEALTH CENTER OF BRANCH COUNTY, COLDWATER, MI, 230022, p. A330

COMMUNITY HEALTH NETWORK, INDIANAPOLIS, IN, 150074, p. A218

COMMUNITY HEALTH PARTNERS REGIONAL MEDICAL CENTER, LORAIN, OH, 360172, p. A516

COMMUNITY HOSPITAL, TALLASSEE, AL, 010034, p. A24

COMMUNITY HOSPITAL, GRAND JUNCTION, CO, 060054, p. A106

COMMUNITY HOSPITAL, NEW PORT RICHEY, FL, 100191, p. A139

COMMUNITY HOSPITAL, MUNSTER, IN, 150125, p. A222

COMMUNITY HOSPITAL, WATERVLIET, MI, 230078, p. A347

COMMUNITY HOSPITAL, MCCOOK, NE, 280021, p. A409

COMMUNITY HOSPITAL, MONTPELIER, OH, 361327, p. A519

COMMUNITY HOSPITAL, SPRINGFIELD, OH, 360187, p. A522

COMMUNITY HOSPITAL, TORRINGTON, WY, 531307, p. A742

COMMUNITY HOSPITAL ASSOCIATION, FAIRFAX, MO, 261303, p. A381

COMMUNITY HOSPITAL AT DOBBS FERRY, DOBBS FERRY, NY, 330036, p. A451

COMMUNITY HOSPITAL EAST, INDIANAPOLIS, INDIANA (see COMMUNITY HEALTH NETWORK), p. A218

COMMUNITY HOSPITAL NORTH, INDIANAPOLIS, INDIANA (see COMMUNITY HEALTH NETWORK), p. A218

COMMUNITY HOSPITAL OF ANACONDA, ANACONDA, MT, 271335, p. A396

COMMUNITY HOSPITAL OF ANDERSON AND MADISON COUNTY, ANDERSON, INDIANA (see COMMUNITY HEALTH NETWORK), p. A218

COMMUNITY HOSPITAL OF BREMEN, BREMEN, IN, 151300, p. A212

COMMUNITY HOSPITAL OF GARDENA, GARDENA, CA, 050456, p. A62

COMMUNITY HOSPITAL OF LONG BEACH, LONG BEACH, CA, 050727, p. A68

COMMUNITY HOSPITAL OF LOS GATOS, LOS GATOS, CA, 050188, p. A74

COMMUNITY HOSPITAL OF OTTAWA, OTTAWA, IL, 140110, p. A204

COMMUNITY HOSPITAL OF THE MONTEREY PENINSULA, MONTEREY, CA, 050145, p. A76

COMMUNITY HOSPITAL ONAGA, ONAGA, KS, 171354, p. A254

COMMUNITY HOSPITAL SOUTH, INDIANAPOLIS, INDIANA (see COMMUNITY HEALTH NETWORK), p. A218

COMMUNITY HOSPITAL-LAKEVIEW, EUFAULA, OK, 370169, p. A530

COMMUNITY HOSPITALS AND WELLNESS CENTERS, BRYAN, OH, 360121, p. A504

COMMUNITY MEDICAL CENTER, MISSOULA, MT, 270023, p. A400

COMMUNITY MEDICAL CENTER, FALLS CITY, NE, 281352, p. A406

COMMUNITY MEDICAL CENTER, TOMS RIVER, NJ, 310041, p. A437

COMMUNITY MEDICAL CENTER, SCRANTON, PA, 390001, p. A575

COMMUNITY MEDICAL CENTER AT WESTERN ILLINOIS, MONMOUTH, IL, 141318, p. A201

COMMUNITY MEDICAL CENTER OF IZARD COUNTY, CALICO ROCK, AR, 041306, p. A41

COMMUNITY MEDICAL CENTER-CLOVIS, CLOVIS, CA, 050492, p. A57

COMMUNITY MEDICAL CENTER-FRESNO, FRESNO, CA, 050060, p. A61

COMMUNITY MEMORIAL HEALTHCARE, MARYSVILLE, KS, 171363, p. A252

COMMUNITY MEMORIAL HEALTHCENTER, SOUTH HILL, VA, 490098, p. A697

COMMUNITY MEMORIAL HOSPITAL, STAUNTON, IL, 141306, p. A208

COMMUNITY MEMORIAL HOSPITAL, SUMNER, IA, 161320, p. A242

COMMUNITY MEMORIAL HOSPITAL, SYRACUSE, NE, 281309, p. A413

COMMUNITY MEMORIAL HOSPITAL, HAMILTON, NY, 330249, p. A453

COMMUNITY MEMORIAL HOSPITAL, TURTLE LAKE, ND, 351304, p. A500

COMMUNITY MEMORIAL HOSPITAL, HICKSVILLE, OH, 361301, p. A515

COMMUNITY MEMORIAL HOSPITAL, BURKE, SD, 431309, p. A594

COMMUNITY MEMORIAL HOSPITAL, REDFIELD, SD, 431316, p. A598

COMMUNITY MEMORIAL HOSPITAL, MENOMONEE FALLS, WI, 520103, p. A729

COMMUNITY MEMORIAL HOSPITAL, OCONTO FALLS, WI, 521310, p. A733

COMMUNITY MEMORIAL HOSPITAL OF SAN BUENAVENTURA, VENTURA, CA, 050394, p. A98

COMMUNITY REHABILITATION HOSPITAL OF COUSHATTA, COUSHATTA, LA, 193080, p. A279

COMMUNITY REHABILITATION HOSPITAL OF LAFAYETTE, LAFAYETTE, LA, 192020, p. A283

COMMUNITY SITE, BATTLE CREEK, MICHIGAN (see BATTLE CREEK HEALTH SYSTEM), p. A328

COMMUNITY-GENERAL HOSPITAL OF GREATER SYRACUSE, SYRACUSE, NY, 330159, p. A473

COMPASS HOSPITAL OF SAN ANTONIO, SAN ANTONIO, TX, 452045, p. A663

CONCHO COUNTY HOSPITAL, EDEN, TX, 451325, p. A636

CONCORD HOSPITAL, CONCORD, NH, 300001, p. A420

CONCOURSE DIVISION, NEW YORK, NEW YORK (see BRONX-LEBANON HOSPITAL CENTER), p. A458

CONCOURSE DIVISION, BRONX, NEW YORK (see (see BRONX-LEBANON HOSPITAL CENTER)), p. A458

CONDELL MEDICAL CENTER, LIBERTYVILLE, IL, 140202, p. A199

CONEJOS COUNTY HOSPITAL, LA JARA, CO, 061308, p. A107

CONEY ISLAND HOSPITAL, NEW YORK, NY, 330196, p. A459

CONIFER PARK, SCHENECTADY, NY, p. A472

CONNALLY MEDICAL CENTER, FLORESVILLE, TX, 450108, p. A638

CONNECTICUT CHILDREN'S MEDICAL CENTER, HARTFORD, CT, 073300, p. A113

CONNECTICUT DEPARTMENT OF CORRECTION'S HOSPITAL, SOMERS, CT, p. A116

CONNECTICUT MENTAL HEALTH CENTER, NEW HAVEN, CT, 074011, p. A115

CONNECTICUT VALLEY HOSPITAL, MIDDLETOWN, CT, 074003, p. A114

CONROE REGIONAL MEDICAL CENTER, CONROE, TX, 450222, p. A630

CONTINENTAL REHABILITATION HOSPITAL, SAN DIEGO, CA, 052044, p. A87

CONTINUING CARE HOSPITAL, LEXINGTON, KY, 182002, p. A267

CONTINUOUS CARE CENTER OF TULSA, TULSA, OK, 372011, p. A539

CONTINUOUS CARE CENTERS OF BARTLESVILLE, BARTLESVILLE, OK, 372014, p. A528

CONTRA COSTA REGIONAL MEDICAL CENTER, MARTINEZ, CA, 050276, p. A75

CONWAY MEDICAL CENTER, CONWAY, SC, 420049, p. A587

CONWAY REGIONAL MEDICAL CENTER, CONWAY, AR, 040029, p. A41

COOK CHILDREN'S MEDICAL CENTER, FORT WORTH, TX, 453300, p. A639

COOK COUNTY NORTH SHORE HOSPITAL, GRAND MARAIS, MN, 241317, p. A354

COOK HOSPITAL AND CONVALESCENT NURSING CARE UNIT, COOK, MN, 241312, p. A351

COOKEVILLE REGIONAL MEDICAL CENTER, COOKEVILLE, TN, 440059, p. A605

COOLEY DICKINSON HOSPITAL, NORTHAMPTON, MA, 220015, p. A321

COON MEMORIAL HOSPITAL AND HOME, DALHART, TX, 451331, p. A631

COOPER COUNTY MEMORIAL HOSPITAL, BOONVILLE, MO, 260004, p. A379

COOPER GREEN HOSPITAL, BIRMINGHAM, AL, 010137, p. A14

COOPER HEALTH SYSTEM, CAMDEN, NJ, 310014, p. A426

COOPERSTOWN MEDICAL CENTER, COOPERSTOWN, ND, 351306, p. A497

COOSA VALLEY MEDICAL CENTER, SYLACAUGA, AL, 010164, p. A24

COPLEY HOSPITAL, MORRISVILLE, VT, 471305, p. A683

COPPER BASIN MEDICAL CENTER, COPPERHILL, TN, 440041, p. A605

COPPER HILLS YOUTH CENTER, WEST JORDAN, UT, p. A681

COPPER QUEEN COMMUNITY HOSPITAL, BISBEE, AZ, 030027, p. A30

COQUILLE VALLEY HOSPITAL, COQUILLE, OR, 381312, p. A543

CORAL GABLES HOSPITAL, CORAL GABLES, FL, 100183, p. A126

CORAL SPRINGS MEDICAL CENTER, CORAL SPRINGS, FL, 100276, p. A126

CORCORAN DISTRICT HOSPITAL, CORCORAN, CA, 050349, p. A57

CORDELL MEMORIAL HOSPITAL, CORDELL, OK, 371325, p. A529

CORDOVA COMMUNITY MEDICAL CENTER, CORDOVA, AK, 021307, p. A26

CORNERSTONE HOSPITAL OF AUSTIN, AUSTIN, TX, 452034, p. A623

CORNERSTONE HOSPITAL OF BOSSIER CITY, BOSSIER CITY, LA, 192006, p. A278

CORNERSTONE HOSPITAL OF CENTRAL TEXAS, AUSTIN, TX, 452053, p. A623

CORNERSTONE HOSPITAL OF HOUSTON, HOUSTON, TX, 452032, p. A644

CORNERSTONE HOSPITAL OF SOUTHEAST ARIZONA, TUCSON, AZ, 032004, p. A37

CORNERSTONE HOSPITAL OF SOUTHWEST LOUISIANA, SULPHUR, LA, 192013, p. A293

CORNERSTONE HOSPITAL–WEST MONROE, WEST MONROE, LA, 192031, p. A294

CORNERSTONE OF MEDICAL ARTS CENTER HOSPITAL, NEW YORK, NY, p. A459

CORNERSTONE REGIONAL HOSPITAL, EDINBURG, TX, 450825, p. A636

CORNING HOSPITAL, CORNING, NY, 330277, p. A451

CORONA REGIONAL MEDICAL CENTER, CORONA, CA, 050329, p. A57

CORONA REGIONAL MEDICAL CENTER–REHABILITATION, CORONA, CALIFORNIA (see CORONA REGIONAL MEDICAL CENTER), p. A57

CORPUS CHRISTI MEDICAL CENTER, CORPUS CHRISTI, TX, p. A630

CORPUS CHRISTI MEDICAL CENTER BAY AREA, CORPUS CHRISTI, TX, 450788, p. A630

CORPUS CHRISTI SPECIALTY HOSPITAL, CORPUS CHRISTI, TX, 452036, p. A630

CORRY MEMORIAL HOSPITAL, CORRY, PA, 391308, p. A556

CORTLAND MEMORIAL HOSPITAL, CORTLAND, NY, 330175, p. A451

CORYELL MEMORIAL HOSPITAL, GATESVILLE, TX, 450239, p. A641

COSHOCTON COUNTY MEMORIAL HOSPITAL, COSHOCTON, OH, 360109, p. A511

COTEAU DES PRAIRIES HOSPITAL, SISSETON, SD, 430064, p. A599

COTTAGE GROVE COMMUNITY HOSPITAL, COTTAGE GROVE, OR, 381301, p. A543

COTTAGE HOSPITAL, GROSSE POINTE FARMS, MI, 230135, p. A336

COTTAGE HOSPITAL, WOODSVILLE, NH, 301301, p. A424

COTTONWOOD HOSPITAL MEDICAL CENTER, MURRAY, UT, 460006, p. A677

COULEE COMMUNITY HOSPITAL, GRAND COULEE, WA, 501308, p. A703

COVE FORGE BEHAVIORAL HEALTH SYSTEM, WILLIAMSBURG, PA, p. A579

COVENANT CHILDREN'S HOSPITAL, LUBBOCK, TX, 453306, p. A654

COVENANT HOSPITAL PLAINVIEW, PLAINVIEW, TX, 450539, p. A660

COVENANT HOSPITAL–LEVELLAND, LEVELLAND, TX, 450755, p. A652

COVENANT MEDICAL CENTER, WATERLOO, IA, 160067, p. A243

COVENANT MEDICAL CENTER, SAGINAW, MI, 230070, p. A344

COVENANT MEDICAL CENTER, LUBBOCK, TX, 450040, p. A654

COVENANT MEDICAL CENTER–COOPER, SAGINAW, MICHIGAN (see COVENANT MEDICAL CENTER), p. A344

COVENANT MEDICAL CENTER–HARRISON, SAGINAW, MICHIGAN (see COVENANT MEDICAL CENTER), p. A344

COVENANT MEDICAL CENTER–LAKESIDE, LUBBOCK, TEXAS (see COVENANT MEDICAL CENTER), p. A654

COVINGTON COUNTY HOSPITAL, COLLINS, MS, 250105, p. A368

COX MONETT HOSPITAL, MONETT, MO, 260012, p. A388

COZAD COMMUNITY HOSPITAL, COZAD, NE, 281327, p. A406

COZBY–GERMANY HOSPITAL, GRAND SALINE, TX, 450283, p. A642

CRAIG GENERAL HOSPITAL, VINITA, OK, 370065, p. A540

CRAIG HOSPITAL, ENGLEWOOD, CO, 062011, p. A105

CRANE MEMORIAL HOSPITAL, CRANE, TX, 451353, p. A631

CRAVEN REGIONAL MEDICAL CENTER, NEW BERN, NC, 340131, p. A488

CRAWFORD COUNTY MEMORIAL HOSPITAL, DENISON, IA, 161369, p. A232

CRAWFORD MEMORIAL HOSPITAL, VAN BUREN, AR, 040018, p. A51

CRAWFORD MEMORIAL HOSPITAL, ROBINSON, IL, 141343, p. A206

CRAWLEY MEMORIAL HOSPITAL, BOILING SPRINGS, NC, 340104, p. A478

CREEDMOOR PSYCHIATRIC CENTER, NEW YORK, NY, 334004, p. A459

CREEK NATION COMMUNITY HOSPITAL, OKEMAH, OK, 370179, p. A534

CREIGHTON AREA HEALTH SERVICES, CREIGHTON, NE, 281331, p. A406

CREIGHTON UNIVERSITY MEDICAL CENTER, OMAHA, NE, 280030, p. A411

CRENSHAW COMMUNITY HOSPITAL, LUVERNE, AL, 010008, p. A20

CRESTWOOD MEDICAL CENTER, HUNTSVILLE, AL, 010131, p. A20

CRETE AREA MEDICAL CENTER, CRETE, NE, 281354, p. A406

CRISP REGIONAL HOSPITAL, CORDELE, GA, 110104, p. A159

CRITTENDEN COUNTY HOSPITAL, MARION, KY, 180095, p. A271

CRITTENDEN MEMORIAL HOSPITAL, WEST MEMPHIS, AR, 040042, p. A51

CRITTENTON CHILDREN'S CENTER, KANSAS CITY, MO, 264018, p. A384

CRITTENTON HOSPITAL MEDICAL CENTER, ROCHESTER, MI, 230254, p. A343

CROCKETT HOSPITAL, LAWRENCEBURG, TN, 440175, p. A611

CROOK COUNTY MEDICAL SERVICES DISTRICT, SUNDANCE, WY, 531311, p. A742

CROSBY MEMORIAL HOSPITAL, PICAYUNE, MS, 250117, p. A374

CROSBYTON CLINIC HOSPITAL, CROSBYTON, TX, 451345, p. A631

CROSSRIDGE COMMUNITY HOSPITAL, WYNNE, AR, 041307, p. A51

CROSSROADS COMMUNITY HOSPITAL, MOUNT VERNON, IL, 140294, p. A202

CROSSROADS REGIONAL HOSPITAL, ALEXANDRIA, LA, 194022, p. A276

CROSSROADS REGIONAL MEDICAL CENTER, WENTZVILLE, MO, 260198, p. A395

CROTCHED MOUNTAIN REHABILITATION CENTER, GREENFIELD, NH, p. A421

CROUSE HOSPITAL, SYRACUSE, NY, 330203, p. A473

CROW/NORTHERN CHEYENNE HOSPITAL, CROW AGENCY, MT, 271339, p. A397

CROWLEY REHABILITATION HOSPITAL, CROWLEY, LA, 192050, p. A280

CROZER–CHESTER MEDICAL CENTER, UPLAND, PA, 390180, p. A577

CUBA MEMORIAL HOSPITAL, CUBA, NY, 331301, p. A451

CUERO COMMUNITY HOSPITAL, CUERO, TX, 450597, p. A631

CULBERSON HOSPITAL DISTRICT, VAN HORN, TX, 451338, p. A671

CULLMAN REGIONAL MEDICAL CENTER, CULLMAN, AL, 010035, p. A16

CULPEPER REGIONAL HOSPITAL, CULPEPER, VA, 490019, p. A687

CUMBERLAND COUNTY HOSPITAL, BURKESVILLE, KY, 181317, p. A262

CUMBERLAND HALL HOSPITAL, HOPKINSVILLE, KY, 184014, p. A266

CUMBERLAND HALL PSYCHIATRIC HOSPITAL, CHATTANOOGA, TN, 444016, p. A603

CUMBERLAND HOSPITAL FOR CHILDREN AND ADOLESCENTS, NEW KENT, VA, 493300, p. A692

CUMBERLAND MEDICAL CENTER, CROSSVILLE, TN, 440009, p. A605

CUMBERLAND MEMORIAL HOSPITAL, CUMBERLAND, WI, 520068, p. A724

CUMBERLAND RIVER HOSPITAL, CELINA, TN, 440141, p. A603

CURRY GENERAL HOSPITAL, GOLD BEACH, OR, 381322, p. A544

CUSHING MEMORIAL HOSPITAL, LEAVENWORTH, KS, 170133, p. A251

CUSHING REGIONAL HOSPITAL, CUSHING, OK, 370099, p. A529

CUSTER COMMUNITY HOSPITAL, CUSTER, SD, 431323, p. A595

CUYAHOGA FALLS GENERAL HOSPITAL, CUYAHOGA FALLS, OH, 360150, p. A511

CUYUNA REGIONAL MEDICAL CENTER, CROSBY, MN, 241353, p. A352

CYPRESS CREEK HOSPITAL, HOUSTON, TX, 454063, p. A644

CYPRESS FAIRBANKS MEDICAL CENTER, HOUSTON, TX, 450716, p. A644

CYPRESS PSYCHIATRIC HOSPITAL, BATON ROUGE, LA, 194071, p. A277

CYPRESS REHABILITATION HOSPITAL, BATON ROUGE, LA, 192045, p. A277

D

D. M. COGDELL MEMORIAL HOSPITAL, SNYDER, TX, 450073, p. A667

D. W. MCMILLAN MEMORIAL HOSPITAL, BREWTON, AL, 010099, p. A16

DAHL MEMORIAL MEDICAL ASSISTANCE FACILITY, EKALAKA, MT, 271302, p. A398

DAKOTA PLAINS SURGICAL CENTER, ABERDEEN, SD, 430092, p. A594

DALE MEDICAL CENTER, OZARK, AL, 010021, p. A23

DALLAS COUNTY HOSPITAL, PERRY, IA, 161322, p. A240

DALLAS COUNTY MEDICAL CENTER, FORDYCE, AR, 041317, p. A43

DAMERON HOSPITAL, STOCKTON, CA, 050122, p. A94

DANA–FARBER CANCER INSTITUTE, BOSTON, MA, 220162, p. A313

DANBURY HOSPITAL, DANBURY, CT, 070033, p. A112

DANIELS MEMORIAL HOSPITAL, SCOBEY, MT, 271342, p. A402

DANVILLE REGIONAL MEDICAL CENTER, DANVILLE, VA, 490075, p. A687

DANVILLE STATE HOSPITAL, DANVILLE, PA, 394004, p. A556

DARDANELLE HOSPITAL, DARDANELLE, AR, 041302, p. A42

DARNALL ARMY COMMUNITY HOSPITAL, FORT HOOD, TX, p. A638

DAUTERIVE HOSPITAL, NEW IBERIA, LA, 190003, p. A288

DAVANT REHABILITATION AND EXTENDED CARE CENTER (see BLOWING ROCK HOSPITAL), p. A478

DAVID GRANT MEDICAL CENTER, TRAVIS AFB, CA, p. A96

DAVIE COUNTY HOSPITAL, MOCKSVILLE, NC, 341313, p. A487

DAVIESS COMMUNITY HOSPITAL, WASHINGTON, IN, 150061, p. A227

DAVIS COUNTY HOSPITAL, BLOOMFIELD, IA, 161327, p. A229

DAVIS HOSPITAL AND MEDICAL CENTER, LAYTON, UT, 460041, p. A677

DAVIS MEMORIAL HOSPITAL, ELKINS, WV, 510030, p. A715

DAVIS REGIONAL MEDICAL CENTER, STATESVILLE, NC, 340144, p. A492

DAY KIMBALL HOSPITAL, PUTNAM, CT, 070003, p. A116

DAYTON CAMPUS, DAYTON, OH, 364023, p. A511

DAYTON GENERAL HOSPITAL, DAYTON, WA, 501302, p. A702

DAYTON HEART HOSPITAL, DAYTON, OH, 360253, p. A511

DCH REGIONAL MEDICAL CENTER, TUSCALOOSA, AL, 010092, p. A24

DE GRAFF MEMORIAL HOSPITAL, NORTH TONAWANDA, NEW YORK (see BUFFALO GENERAL HOSPITAL), p. A448

DE LEON HOSPITAL, DE LEON, TX, 451336, p. A634

DE POO HOSPITAL, KEY WEST, FLORIDA (see LOWER KEYS MEDICAL CENTER), p. A133

DE QUEEN REGIONAL MEDICAL CENTER, DE QUEEN, AR, 041319, p. A42

DE SMET MEMORIAL HOSPITAL, DE SMET, SD, 431332, p. A595

DE SOTO REGIONAL HEALTH SYSTEM, MANSFIELD, LA, 190118, p. A286

DEACONESS BILLINGS CLINIC, BILLINGS, MT, 270004, p. A396

DEACONESS CROSS POINTE CENTER, EVANSVILLE, IN, 154042, p. A214

DEACONESS HOSPITAL, EVANSVILLE, IN, 150082, p. A214

DEACONESS HOSPITAL, CINCINNATI, OH, 360038, p. A506

DEACONESS HOSPITAL, OKLAHOMA CITY, OK, 370032, p. A535

DEACONESS MEDICAL CENTER–SPOKANE, SPOKANE, WA, 500044, p. A709

DEARBORN COUNTY HOSPITAL, LAWRENCEBURG, IN, 150086, p. A221

DEBORAH HEART AND LUNG CENTER, BROWNS MILLS, NJ, 310031, p. A426

DECATUR COUNTY GENERAL HOSPITAL, PARSONS, TN, 440070, p. A616

DECATUR COUNTY HOSPITAL, LEON, IA, 161340, p. A237

DECATUR COUNTY HOSPITAL AND CEDAR LIVING CENTER, OBERLIN, KS, 171352, p. A253

DECATUR COUNTY MEMORIAL HOSPITAL, GREENSBURG, IN, 150062, p. A217

DECATUR GENERAL HOSPITAL, DECATUR, AL, 010085, p. A17

DECATUR GENERAL HOSPITAL–WEST, DECATUR, ALABAMA (see DECATUR GENERAL HOSPITAL), p. A17

DECATUR MEMORIAL HOSPITAL, DECATUR, IL, 140135, p. A192

DECKERVILLE COMMUNITY HOSPITAL, DECKERVILLE, MI, 231311, p. A330

DEER PARK HOSPITAL, DEER PARK, WA, 501306, p. A702

DEER RIVER HEALTHCARE CENTER, DEER RIVER, MN, 240154, p. A352

DEER'S HEAD HOSPITAL CENTER, SALISBURY, MD, 212003, p. A310

DEFIANCE REGIONAL MEDICAL CENTER, DEFIANCE, OH, 360093, p. A512

DEKALB HOSPITAL, SMITHVILLE, TN, 440148, p. A617

DEKALB MEDICAL CENTER, DECATUR, GA, 110076, p. A160

DEKALB MEDICAL CENTER AT DECATUR, DECATUR, GA, 112006, p. A160

DEKALB MEMORIAL HOSPITAL, AUBURN, IN, 150045, p. A211

DEL AMO HOSPITAL, TORRANCE, CA, 054053, p. A95

DEL E. WEBB MEMORIAL HOSPITAL, SUN CITY WEST, AZ, 030093, p. A37

DEL SOL MEDICAL CENTER, EL PASO, TX, 450646, p. A637

DEL SOL REHABILITATION HOSPITAL, EL PASO, TX, p. A637

DELANO REGIONAL MEDICAL CENTER, DELANO, CA, 050608, p. A58

DELAWARE COUNTY MEMORIAL HOSPITAL, DREXEL HILL, PA, 390081, p. A557
DELAWARE PSYCHIATRIC CENTER, NEW CASTLE, DE, 084001, p. A119
DELAWARE VALLEY HOSPITAL, WALTON, NY, 331312, p. A475
DELLS AREA HEALTH CENTER, DELL RAPIDS, SD, 431331, p. A595
DELNOR–COMMUNITY HOSPITAL, GENEVA, IL, 140211, p. A195
DELRAY MEDICAL CENTER, DELRAY BEACH, FL, 100258, p. A127
DELTA COMMUNITY MEDICAL CENTER, DELTA, UT, 461300, p. A676
DELTA COUNTY MEMORIAL HOSPITAL, DELTA, CO, 060071, p. A103
DELTA MEDICAL CENTER, MEMPHIS, TN, 440159, p. A613
DELTA MEMORIAL HOSPITAL, DUMAS, AR, 040053, p. A42
DELTA REGIONAL MEDICAL CENTER, GREENVILLE, MS, 250082, p. A368
DENTON REGIONAL MEDICAL CENTER, DENTON, TX, 450634, p. A635
DENVER HEALTH MEDICAL CENTER, DENVER, CO, 060011, p. A103
DEPAUL/TULANE BEHAVIORAL HEALTH CENTER, NEW ORLEANS, LOUISIANA (see TULANE UNIVERSITY HOSPITAL AND CLINIC), p. A290
DEQUINCY MEMORIAL HOSPITAL, DEQUINCY, LA, 191307, p. A280
DES MOINES DIVISION, DES MOINES, IOWA (see VETERANS AFFAIRS CENTRAL IOWA HEALTH CARE SYSTEM), p. A233
DES PERES HOSPITAL, SAINT LOUIS, MO, 260176, p. A390
DESERT HILLS HOSPITAL, ALBUQUERQUE, NM, p. A440
DESERT REGIONAL MEDICAL CENTER, PALM SPRINGS, CA, 050243, p. A80
DESERT SPRINGS HOSPITAL, LAS VEGAS, NV, 290022, p. A416
DESERT SPRINGS MEDICAL CENTER, MIDLAND, TX, 454049, p. A656
DESERT VALLEY HOSPITAL, WILDOMAR, CA, 050709, p. A99
DESOTO MEMORIAL HOSPITAL, ARCADIA, FL, 100175, p. A123
DETAR HEALTHCARE SYSTEM, VICTORIA, TX, 450147, p. A672
DETAR HOSPITAL NORTH, VICTORIA, TEXAS (see DETAR HEALTHCARE SYSTEM), p. A672
DETROIT RECEIVING HOSPITAL AND UNIVERSITY HEALTH CENTER, DETROIT, MI, 230273, p. A331
DETTMER HOSPITAL, TROY, OHIO (see UPPER VALLEY MEDICAL CENTER), p. A523
DEUEL COUNTY MEMORIAL HOSPITAL, CLEAR LAKE, SD, 431307, p. A595
DEVEREUX CHILDREN'S BEHAVIORAL HEALTH CENTER, MALVERN, PA, p. A564
DEVEREUX GEORGIA TREATMENT NETWORK, KENNESAW, GA, p. A164
DEVEREUX HOSPITAL AND CHILDREN'S CENTER OF FLORIDA, MELBOURNE, FL, p. A136
DEVEREUX TEXAS TREATMENT NETWORK, LEAGUE CITY, TX, 454085, p. A652
DEWITT ARMY COMMUNITY HOSPITAL, FORT BELVOIR, VA, p. A688
DEWITT HOSPITAL, DE WITT, AR, 041314, p. A42
DICKENSON COMMUNITY HOSPITAL, CLINTWOOD, VA, 491303, p. A687
DICKINSON COUNTY HEALTHCARE SYSTEM, IRON MOUNTAIN, MI, 230055, p. A337
DIMMIT COUNTY MEMORIAL HOSPITAL, CARRIZO SPRINGS, TX, 450620, p. A628
DISTRICT ONE HOSPITAL, FARIBAULT, MN, 240071, p. A353
DIVINE PROVIDENCE HEALTH CENTER/AVERA HEALTH, IVANHOE, MN, 241324, p. A355
DIVINE PROVIDENCE HOSPITAL, WILLIAMSPORT, PENNSYLVANIA (see SUSQUEHANNA HEALTH SYSTEM), p. A580
DIVINE SAVIOR HEALTHCARE, PORTAGE, WI, 520041, p. A734
DIVISION OF ADOLESCENT MEDICINE, CINCINNATI CENTER FOR DEVELOPMENTAL DISORDERS, AND CONVALESCENT HOSPITAL FOR CHILDREN, CHILDREN'S HOSPITAL, CINCINNATI, OHIO (see CHILDREN'S HOSPITAL MEDICAL CENTER), p. A506
DIXIE REGIONAL MEDICAL CENTER, SAINT GEORGE, UT, 460021, p. A679
DOCTOR ROBERT L. YEAGER HEALTH CENTER, POMONA, NY, 332014, p. A469
DOCTOR'S HOSPITAL, LEAWOOD, KS, p. A251
DOCTOR'S HOSPITAL AT RENAISSANCE, EDINBURG, TX, 450869, p. A636
DOCTOR'S HOSPITAL OF OPELOUSAS, OPELOUSAS, LA, 190191, p. A290
DOCTOR'S MEMORIAL HOSPITAL, PERRY, FL, 100106, p. A143
DOCTORS CENTER, MANATI, PR, 400118, p. A745

DOCTORS COMMUNITY HOSPITAL, LANHAM, MD, 210051, p. A309
DOCTORS HOSPITAL, CORAL GABLES, FL, 100296, p. A126
DOCTORS HOSPITAL, AUGUSTA, GA, 110177, p. A155
DOCTORS HOSPITAL, JACKSON, MI, 232036, p. A337
DOCTORS HOSPITAL, COLUMBUS, OH, 360152, p. A510
DOCTORS HOSPITAL, SAN JUAN, PR, 400006, p. A747
DOCTORS HOSPITAL, GROVES, TX, 450123, p. A643
DOCTORS HOSPITAL MEDICAL CENTER OF MONTCLAIR, MONTCLAIR, CA, 050584, p. A76
DOCTORS HOSPITAL NELSONVILLE, NELSONVILLE, OH, 361305, p. A519
DOCTORS HOSPITAL OF COLUMBUS, COLUMBUS, GA, 110186, p. A158
DOCTORS HOSPITAL OF DALLAS, DALLAS, TX, 450678, p. A632
DOCTORS HOSPITAL OF JEFFERSON, METAIRIE, LOUISIANA (see EAST JEFFERSON GENERAL HOSPITAL), p. A286
DOCTORS HOSPITAL OF LAREDO, LAREDO, TX, 450643, p. A652
DOCTORS HOSPITAL OF MANTECA, MANTECA, CA, 050118, p. A74
DOCTORS HOSPITAL OF SARASOTA, SARASOTA, FL, 100166, p. A146
DOCTORS HOSPITAL OF SLIDELL, SLIDELL, LA, 190256, p. A293
DOCTORS HOSPITAL OF SPRINGFIELD, SPRINGFIELD, MO, 260207, p. A393
DOCTORS HOSPITAL OF STARK COUNTY, MASSILLON, OH, 360151, p. A518
DOCTORS HOSPITAL OF WEST COVINA, WEST COVINA, CA, 050096, p. A99
DOCTORS HOSPITAL PARKWAY, HOUSTON, TX, p. A644
DOCTORS HOSPITAL–TIDWELL, HOUSTON, TX, 450803, p. A644
DOCTORS MEDICAL CENTER, MODESTO, CA, 050464, p. A76
DOCTORS MEDICAL CENTER–SAN PABLO CAMPUS, SAN PABLO, CA, 050079, p. A91
DOCTORS MEMORIAL HOSPITAL, BONIFAY, FL, 101307, p. A124
DOCTORS SPECIALTY HOSPITAL, SHAWNEE MISSION, KS, 170194, p. A257
DOCTORS' HOSPITAL OF SHREVEPORT, SHREVEPORT, LA, 190115, p. A292
DODGE COUNTY HOSPITAL, EASTMAN, GA, 110092, p. A161
DOERNBECHER CHILDREN'S HOSPITAL, PORTLAND, OREGON (see OHSU HOSPITAL), p. A547
DOLLY VINSANT MEMORIAL HOSPITAL, SAN BENITO, TX, 450047, p. A666
DOMINICAN HOSPITAL, SANTA CRUZ, CA, 050242, p. A92
DOMINION HOSPITAL, FALLS CHURCH, VA, 494023, p. A687
DONALSONVILLE HOSPITAL, DONALSONVILLE, GA, 110194, p. A160
DOOR COUNTY MEMORIAL HOSPITAL, STURGEON BAY, WI, 520152, p. A736
DORCHESTER GENERAL HOSPITAL, CAMBRIDGE, MD, 210010, p. A306
DORMINY MEDICAL CENTER, FITZGERALD, GA, 110073, p. A162
DOROTHEA DIX HOSPITAL, RALEIGH, NC, 340138, p. A489
DOUGLAS COUNTY HEALTH CENTER, OMAHA, NE, 284009, p. A411
DOUGLAS COUNTY HOSPITAL, ALEXANDRIA, MN, 240030, p. A349
DOUGLAS COUNTY MEMORIAL HOSPITAL, ARMOUR, SD, 431305, p. A594
DOWN EAST COMMUNITY HOSPITAL, MACHIAS, ME, 200027, p. A299
DOWNEY REGIONAL MEDICAL CENTER, DOWNEY, CA, 050393, p. A58
DOYLESTOWN HOSPITAL, DOYLESTOWN, PA, 390203, p. A557
DR. DAN C. TRIGG MEMORIAL HOSPITAL, TUCUMCARI, NM, 321302, p. A445
DR. J. CORRIGAN MENTAL HEALTH CENTER, FALL RIVER, MA, 224028, p. A317
DR. JOHN WARNER HOSPITAL, CLINTON, IL, 141303, p. A191
DR. PILA'S HOSPITAL, PONCE, PR, 400003, p. A746
DR. RAMON E. BETANCES HOSPITAL–MAYAGUEZ MEDICAL CENTER BRANCH, MAYAGUEZ, PR, 400103, p. A745
DRAKE CENTER, CINCINNATI, OH, 362004, p. A506
DRAKE PAVILION, CINCINNATI, OH, 362030, p. A506
DREW MEMORIAL HOSPITAL, MONTICELLO, AR, 040051, p. A48
DRISCOLL CHILDREN'S HOSPITAL, CORPUS CHRISTI, TX, 453301, p. A630
DRUMRIGHT REGIONAL HOSPITAL, DRUMRIGHT, OK, 371331, p. A529
DU BOIS REGIONAL MEDICAL CENTER, DU BOIS, PA, 390086, p. A557
DUANE L. WATERS HOSPITAL, JACKSON, MI, p. A337

DUBUIS HOSPITAL OF ALEXANDRIA, ALEXANDRIA, LA, 192012, p. A276
DUBUIS HOSPITAL OF BEAUMONT, BEAUMONT, TX, 452042, p. A625
DUBUIS HOSPITAL OF CORPUS CHRISTI, CORPUS CHRISTI, TX, 452086, p. A631
DUBUIS HOSPITAL OF HOUSTON, HOUSTON, TX, 452055, p. A645
DUBUIS HOSPITAL OF LAKE CHARLES, LAKE CHARLES, LA, 192024, p. A284
DUBUIS HOSPITAL OF PARIS, PARIS, TX, 452082, p. A660
DUBUIS HOSPITAL OF PORT ARTHUR, PORT ARTHUR, TX, p. A661
DUBUIS HOSPITAL OF SHREVEPORT, SHREVEPORT, LA, 192025, p. A292
DUBUIS HOSPITAL OF TEXARKANA, TEXARKANA, TX, 452061, p. A669
DUKE HEALTH RALEIGH HOSPITAL, RALEIGH, NC, 340073, p. A489
DUKE UNIVERSITY HOSPITAL, DURHAM, NC, 340030, p. A481
DUKE UNIVERSITY HOSPITAL, DURHAM, NORTH CAROLINA (see DUKE UNIVERSITY HOSPITAL), p. A481
DUKES MEMORIAL HOSPITAL, PERU, IN, 151318, p. A223
DUNCAN REGIONAL HOSPITAL, DUNCAN, OK, 370023, p. A529
DUNDY COUNTY HOSPITAL, BENKELMAN, NE, 281340, p. A405
DUNLAP MEMORIAL HOSPITAL, ORRVILLE, OH, 361323, p. A520
DUNN MEMORIAL HOSPITAL, BEDFORD, IN, 150049, p. A211
DUPLIN GENERAL HOSPITAL, KENANSVILLE, NC, 340120, p. A485
DUPONT HOSPITAL, FORT WAYNE, IN, 150150, p. A215
DURHAM REGIONAL HOSPITAL, DURHAM, NC, 340155, p. A481
DURHAM VETERANS AFFAIRS MEDICAL CENTER, DURHAM, NC, p. A481
DWIGHT D. EISENHOWER VETERANS AFFAIRS MEDICAL CENTER, LEAVENWORTH, KANSAS (see VETERANS AFFAIRS EASTERN KANSAS HEALTH CARE SYSTEM), p. A258
DWIGHT DAVID EISENHOWER ARMY MEDICAL CENTER, FORT GORDON, GA, p. A162
DYERSBURG REGIONAL MEDICAL CENTER, DYERSBURG, TN, 440072, p. A605

E

E. A. CONWAY MEDICAL CENTER, MONROE, LA, 190011, p. A287
EAGLE RIVER MEMORIAL HOSPITAL, EAGLE RIVER, WI, 521300, p. A725
EAGLEVILLE HOSPITAL, EAGLEVILLE, PA, 390278, p. A557
EARL K. LONG MEDICAL CENTER, BATON ROUGE, LA, 190122, p. A277
EARLY MEMORIAL HOSPITAL, BLAKELY, GA, 111314, p. A156
EAST ADAMS RURAL HOSPITAL, RITZVILLE, WA, 501311, p. A707
EAST ALABAMA MEDICAL CENTER, OPELIKA, AL, 010029, p. A23
EAST CAMPUS, NORFOLK, NEBRASKA (see FAITH REGIONAL HEALTH SERVICES), p. A410
EAST CAMPUS, MERIDEN, CONNECTICUT (see MIDSTATE MEDICAL CENTER), p. A114
EAST CARROLL PARISH HOSPITAL, LAKE PROVIDENCE, LA, 190208, p. A285
EAST CENTRAL REGIONAL HOSPITAL, AUGUSTA, GA, 114029, p. A155
EAST CENTRAL REGIONAL HOSPITAL, GRACEWOOD, GEORGIA (see EAST CENTRAL REGIONAL HOSPITAL), p. A155
EAST COOPER REGIONAL MEDICAL CENTER, MOUNT PLEASANT, SC, 420089, p. A590
EAST GEORGIA REGIONAL MEDICAL CENTER, STATESBORO, GA, 110075, p. A169
EAST HOUSTON REGIONAL MEDICAL CENTER, HOUSTON, TX, 450126, p. A645
EAST JEFFERSON GENERAL HOSPITAL, METAIRIE, LA, 190146, p. A286
EAST LIVERPOOL CITY HOSPITAL, EAST LIVERPOOL, OH, 360096, p. A513
EAST LOS ANGELES DOCTORS HOSPITAL, LOS ANGELES, CA, 050641, p. A70
EAST MISSISSIPPI STATE HOSPITAL, MERIDIAN, MS, p. A373
EAST MORGAN COUNTY HOSPITAL, BRUSH, CO, 061303, p. A101
EAST MOUNTAIN HOSPITAL, BELLE MEAD, NJ, 314026, p. A425
EAST OHIO REGIONAL HOSPITAL, MARTINS FERRY, OH, 360080, p. A517

EAST ORANGE DIVISION, EAST ORANGE, NEW JERSEY (see VETERANS AFFAIRS NEW JERSEY HEALTH CARE SYSTEM), p. A427

EAST ORANGE FACILITY, WEST ORANGE FACILITY, SADDLE BROOK FACILITY AND CHESTER FACILITY (see KESSLER INSTITUTE FOR REHABILITATION), p. A438

EAST ORANGE GENERAL HOSPITAL, EAST ORANGE, NJ, 310083, p. A427

EAST PASCO MEDICAL CENTER, ZEPHYRHILLS, FL, 100046, p. A151

EAST RIDGE HOSPITAL, EAST RIDGE, TENNESSEE (see PARKRIDGE MEDICAL CENTER), p. A604

EAST TENNESSEE CHILDREN'S HOSPITAL, KNOXVILLE, TN, 443303, p. A610

EAST TEXAS MEDICAL CENTER ATHENS, ATHENS, TX, 450389, p. A622

EAST TEXAS MEDICAL CENTER BEHAVIORAL HEALTH CENTER, TYLER, TEXAS (see EAST TEXAS MEDICAL CENTER TYLER), p. A671

EAST TEXAS MEDICAL CENTER CARTHAGE, CARTHAGE, TX, 450210, p. A628

EAST TEXAS MEDICAL CENTER CLARKSVILLE, CLARKSVILLE, TX, 450188, p. A628

EAST TEXAS MEDICAL CENTER CROCKETT, CROCKETT, TX, 450580, p. A631

EAST TEXAS MEDICAL CENTER FAIRFIELD, FAIRFIELD, TX, 450658, p. A638

EAST TEXAS MEDICAL CENTER JACKSONVILLE, JACKSONVILLE, TX, 450194, p. A650

EAST TEXAS MEDICAL CENTER PITTSBURG, PITTSBURG, TX, 450098, p. A660

EAST TEXAS MEDICAL CENTER REHABILITATION CENTER, TYLER, TX, 453072, p. A670

EAST TEXAS MEDICAL CENTER SPECIALTY HOSPITAL, TYLER, TX, 452051, p. A671

EAST TEXAS MEDICAL CENTER TRINITY, TRINITY, TX, 450749, p. A670

EAST TEXAS MEDICAL CENTER TYLER, TYLER, TX, 450083, p. A671

EAST TEXAS MEDICAL CENTER–GILMER, GILMER, TX, 450884, p. A641

EAST TEXAS MEDICAL CENTER–MOUNT VERNON, MOUNT VERNON, TX, 450373, p. A657

EAST TEXAS MEDICAL CENTER–QUITMAN, QUITMAN, TX, 450547, p. A662

EAST VALLEY HOSPITAL MEDICAL CENTER, GLENDORA, CA, 050205, p. A63

EASTERN IDAHO REGIONAL MEDICAL CENTER, IDAHO FALLS, ID, 130018, p. A179

EASTERN LONG ISLAND HOSPITAL, GREENPORT, NY, 330088, p. A453

EASTERN LOUISIANA MENTAL HEALTH SYSTEM, JACKSON, LA, 194008, p. A282

EASTERN MAINE MEDICAL CENTER, BANGOR, ME, 200033, p. A296

EASTERN NEW MEXICO MEDICAL CENTER, ROSWELL, NM, 320006, p. A444

EASTERN OKLAHOMA MEDICAL CENTER, POTEAU, OK, 370040, p. A537

EASTERN OREGON PSYCHIATRIC CENTER, PENDLETON, OR, 384011, p. A547

EASTERN PLUMAS DISTRICT HOSPITAL, PORTOLA, CA, 051300, p. A82

EASTERN SHORE HOSPITAL CENTER, CAMBRIDGE, MD, 214002, p. A306

EASTERN STATE HOSPITAL, LEXINGTON, KY, 184004, p. A267

EASTERN STATE HOSPITAL, WILLIAMSBURG, VA, 490109, p. A698

EASTERN STATE HOSPITAL, MEDICAL LAKE, WA, 504004, p. A704

EASTLAND MEMORIAL HOSPITAL, EASTLAND, TX, 450411, p. A636

EASTON HOSPITAL, EASTON, PA, 390162, p. A558

EATON RAPIDS MEDICAL CENTER, EATON RAPIDS, MI, 230153, p. A332

ED FRASER MEMORIAL HOSPITAL AND BAKER COMMUNITY HEALTH CENTER, MACCLENNY, FL, 100134, p. A135

EDEN MEDICAL CENTER, CASTRO VALLEY, CALIFORNIA (see SAN LEANDRO HOSPITAL), p. A91

EDGEFIELD COUNTY HOSPITAL, EDGEFIELD, SC, 421304, p. A587

EDGEWOOD HOSPITAL, MARION, LA, 194067, p. A286

EDINBURG REGIONAL MEDICAL CENTER, EDINBURG, TX, 450119, p. A636

EDITH NOURSE ROGERS MEMORIAL VETERANS HOSPITAL, BEDFORD, MA, p. A312

EDMOND MEDICAL CENTER, EDMOND, OK, 370148, p. A530

EDMOND SPECIALTY HOSPITAL, EDMOND, OK, 372005, p. A530

EDWARD HOSPITAL, NAPERVILLE, IL, 140231, p. A202

EDWARD JOHN NOBLE HOSPITAL OF GOUVERNEUR, GOUVERNEUR, NY, 330177, p. A453

EDWARD WHITE HOSPITAL, SAINT PETERSBURG, FL, 100239, p. A145

EDWARDS COUNTY HOSPITAL AND HEALTHCARE CENTER, KINSLEY, KS, 171317, p. A250

EDWIN SHAW HOSPITAL FOR REHABILITATION, AKRON, OH, 360241, p. A502

EFFINGHAM HOSPITAL, SPRINGFIELD, GA, 111306, p. A169

EISENHOWER MEMORIAL HOSPITAL AND BETTY FORD CENTER AT EISENHOWER, RANCHO MIRAGE, CA, 050573, p. A83

EL CAMINO HOSPITAL, MOUNTAIN VIEW, CA, 050308, p. A77

EL CAMPO MEMORIAL HOSPITAL, EL CAMPO, TX, 450694, p. A637

EL CENTRO REGIONAL MEDICAL CENTER, EL CENTRO, CA, 050045, p. A59

EL DORADO HOSPITAL, TUCSON, AZ, 030080, p. A38

EL PASO PSYCHIATRIC CENTER, EL PASO, TX, 454100, p. A637

EL PASO SPECIALTY HOSPITAL, EL PASO, TX, 450845, p. A637

ELBA GENERAL HOSPITAL, ELBA, AL, 010027, p. A18

ELBERT MEMORIAL HOSPITAL, ELBERTON, GA, 110026, p. A161

ELEAH MEDICAL CENTER, ELBOW LAKE, MN, 240109, p. A353

ELEANOR SLATER HOSPITAL, CRANSTON, RI, 412001, p. A581

ELECTRA MEMORIAL HOSPITAL, ELECTRA, TX, 451343, p. A638

ELGIN MENTAL HEALTH CENTER, ELGIN, IL, 144037, p. A193

ELIZA COFFEE MEMORIAL HOSPITAL, FLORENCE, AL, 010006, p. A18

ELIZABETHTOWN COMMUNITY HOSPITAL, ELIZABETHTOWN, NY, 331302, p. A452

ELK REGIONAL HEALTH CENTER, SAINT MARYS, PA, 390154, p. A574

ELKHART GENERAL HOSPITAL, ELKHART, IN, 150018, p. A214

ELKVIEW GENERAL HOSPITAL, HOBART, OK, 370153, p. A531

ELLENVILLE REGIONAL HOSPITAL, ELLENVILLE, NY, 331310, p. A452

ELLETT MEMORIAL HOSPITAL, APPLETON CITY, MO, 261301, p. A378

ELLINWOOD DISTRICT HOSPITAL, ELLINWOOD, KS, 171301, p. A246

ELLIOT HOSPITAL, MANCHESTER, NH, 300012, p. A422

ELLIS FISCHEL CANCER CENTER, COLUMBIA, MISSOURI (see UNIVERSITY OF MISSOURI HOSPITALS AND CLINICS), p. A381

ELLIS HOSPITAL, SCHENECTADY, NY, 330153, p. A472

ELLSWORTH COUNTY MEDICAL CENTER, ELLSWORTH, KS, 171327, p. A246

ELLSWORTH MUNICIPAL HOSPITAL, IOWA FALLS, IA, 160034, p. A236

ELLWOOD CITY HOSPITAL, ELLWOOD CITY, PA, 390008, p. A558

ELMBROOK MEMORIAL HOSPITAL, BROOKFIELD, WI, 520170, p. A723

ELMER HOSPITAL, ELMER, NEW JERSEY (see SOUTH JERSEY HEALTHCARE), p. A426

ELMHURST HOSPITAL CENTER, NEW YORK, NY, 330128, p. A459

ELMHURST MEMORIAL HOSPITAL, NEW YORK, IL, 140200, p. A193

ELMIRA PSYCHIATRIC CENTER, ELMIRA, NY, 334045, p. A452

ELMORE COMMUNITY HOSPITAL, WETUMPKA, AL, 010097, p. A25

ELMORE MEDICAL CENTER, MOUNTAIN HOME, ID, 131311, p. A180

ELY–BLOOMENSON COMMUNITY HOSPITAL, ELY, MN, 241318, p. A353

EMANUEL MEDICAL CENTER, TURLOCK, CA, 050179, p. A96

EMANUEL MEDICAL HOSPITAL, SWAINSBORO, GA, 110109, p. A170

EMERALD–HODGSON HOSPITAL, SEWANEE, TENNESSEE (see SOUTHERN TENNESSEE MEDICAL CENTER), p. A619

EMERSON HOSPITAL, CONCORD, MA, 220084, p. A317

EMH REGIONAL MEDICAL CENTER, ELYRIA, OH, 360145, p. A513

EMMA PENDLETON BRADLEY HOSPITAL, EAST PROVIDENCE, RI, 414003, p. A581

EMORY CARTERSVILLE MEDICAL CENTER, CARTERSVILLE, GA, 110030, p. A157

EMORY CRAWFORD LONG HOSPITAL, ATLANTA, GA, 110078, p. A153

EMORY DUNWOODY MEDICAL CENTER, ATLANTA, GA, 110172, p. A153

EMORY EASTSIDE MEDICAL CENTER, SNELLVILLE, GA, 110192, p. A169

EMORY PEACHTREE REGIONAL HOSPITAL, NEWNAN, GEORGIA (see NEWNAN HOSPITAL EAST), p. A167

EMORY UNIVERSITY HOSPITAL, ATLANTA, GA, 110010, p. A153

EMORY–ADVENTIST HOSPITAL, SMYRNA, GA, 110183, p. A169

EMPORIA SURGICAL HOSPITAL, EMPORIA, KS, 170193, p. A246

ENCINO–TARZANA REGIONAL MEDICAL CENTER ENCINO CAMPUS, LOS ANGELES, CA, 050158, p. A70

ENCINO–TARZANA REGIONAL MEDICAL CENTER TARZANA CAMPUS, LOS ANGELES, CA, 050601, p. A70

ENDLESS MOUNTAIN HEALTH SYSTEMS, MONTROSE, PA, 391306, p. A565

ENGLEWOOD COMMUNITY HOSPITAL, ENGLEWOOD, FL, 100267, p. A128

ENGLEWOOD HOSPITAL AND MEDICAL CENTER, ENGLEWOOD, NJ, 310045, p. A428

ENLOE MEDICAL CENTER, CHICO, CA, 050039, p. A56

ENLOE MEDICAL CENTER–COHASSET, CHICO, CALIFORNIA (see ENLOE MEDICAL CENTER), p. A56

ENNIS REGIONAL MEDICAL CENTER, ENNIS, TX, 450833, p. A638

ENUMCLAW COMMUNITY HOSPITAL, ENUMCLAW, WA, 501335, p. A702

EPHRAIM MCDOWELL REGIONAL MEDICAL CENTER, DANVILLE, KY, 180048, p. A263

EPHRATA COMMUNITY HOSPITAL, EPHRATA, PA, 390225, p. A558

ERIE COUNTY MEDICAL CENTER, BUFFALO, NY, 330219, p. A449

ERIK AND MARGARET JONSSON HOSPITAL, DALLAS, TEXAS (see BAYLOR UNIVERSITY MEDICAL CENTER), p. A632

ERLANGER BLEDSOE HOSPITAL, PIKEVILLE, TN, 441306, p. A617

ERLANGER MEDICAL CENTER, CHATTANOOGA, TN, 440104, p. A603

ERLANGER NORTH HOSPITAL, CHATTANOOGA, TENNESSEE (see ERLANGER MEDICAL CENTER), p. A603

ESPANOLA HOSPITAL, ESPANOLA, NM, 320011, p. A442

ESSEX COUNTY HOSPITAL CENTER, CEDAR GROVE, NJ, 314020, p. A427

ESTES PARK MEDICAL CENTER, ESTES PARK, CO, 061312, p. A105

EUCLID HOSPITAL, EUCLID, OH, 360082, p. A513

EUGENIA HOSPITAL, LAFAYETTE HILL, PA, 394031, p. A562

EUNICE COMMUNITY MEDICAL CENTER, EUNICE, LA, 190078, p. A280

EUREKA COMMUNITY HEALTH SERVICES/AVERA HEALTH, EUREKA, SD, 431308, p. A595

EUREKA COMMUNITY HOSPITAL, EUREKA, IL, 141309, p. A193

EUREKA SPRINGS HOSPITAL, EUREKA SPRINGS, AR, 041304, p. A42

EVANGELICAL COMMUNITY HOSPITAL, LEWISBURG, PA, 390013, p. A563

EVANS MEMORIAL HOSPITAL, CLAXTON, GA, 110142, p. A158

EVANS U. S. ARMY COMMUNITY HOSPITAL, FORT CARSON, CO, p. A105

EVANSTON HOSPITAL, EVANSTON, ILLINOIS (see EVANSTON NORTHWESTERN HEALTHCARE), p. A194

EVANSTON NORTHWESTERN HEALTHCARE, EVANSTON, IL, 140010, p. A194

EVANSTON REGIONAL HOSPITAL, EVANSTON, WY, 530032, p. A740

EVANSVILLE STATE HOSPITAL, EVANSVILLE, IN, p. A214

EVERETT TOWER, OKLAHOMA CITY, OKLAHOMA (see OU MEDICAL CENTER), p. A536

EVERGREEN HEALTHCARE, KIRKLAND, WA, 500124, p. A703

EVERGREEN MEDICAL CENTER, EVERGREEN, AL, 010148, p. A18

EXCELA FRICK HOSPITAL, MOUNT PLEASANT, PA, 390217, p. A565

EXCELA LATROBE AREA HOSPITAL, LATROBE, PA, 390219, p. A563

EXCELA WESTMORELAND REGIONAL HOSPITAL, GREENSBURG, PA, 390145, p. A559

EXCELSIOR SPRINGS MEDICAL CENTER, EXCELSIOR SPRINGS, MO, 261322, p. A381

EXEMPLA GOOD SAMARITAN MEDICAL CENTER, LAFAYETTE, CO, 060116, p. A107

EXEMPLA LUTHERAN MEDICAL CENTER, WHEAT RIDGE, CO, 060009, p. A110

EXEMPLA SAINT JOSEPH HOSPITAL, DENVER, CO, 060028, p. A103

EXEMPLA WEST PINES, WHEAT RIDGE, COLORADO (see EXEMPLA LUTHERAN MEDICAL CENTER), p. A110

EXETER HOSPITAL, EXETER, NH, 300023, p. A421

EXTENDED CARE OF SOUTHWEST LOUIASIANA, LAKE CHARLES, LA, 192019, p. A285

EYE AND EAR CLINIC OF CHARLESTON, CHARLESTON, WV, 510059, p. A714

EYE AND EAR HOSPITAL OF PITTSBURGH, PITTSBURGH, PENNSYLVANIA (see UPMC PRESBYTERIAN), p. A572

F

G

GOOD SAMARITAN MEDICAL AND REHABILITATION CENTER, ZANESVILLE, OHIO (see GENESIS HEALTHCARE SYSTEM), p. A526

GOOD SAMARITAN MEDICAL CENTER, WEST PALM BEACH, FL, 100287, p. A150

GOOD SAMARITAN MEDICAL CENTER, JOHNSTOWN, PENNSYLVANIA (see MEMORIAL MEDICAL CENTER), p. A561

GOOD SAMARITAN MEDICAL CENTER – CUSHING CAMPUS, BROCKTON, MASSACHUSETTS (see CARITAS GOOD SAMARITAN MEDICAL CENTER), p. A315

GOOD SAMARITAN REGIONAL HEALTH CENTER, MOUNT VERNON, IL, 140046, p. A202

GOOD SAMARITAN REGIONAL MEDICAL CENTER, CORVALLIS, OR, 380014, p. A543

GOOD SAMARITAN REGIONAL MEDICAL CENTER, POTTSVILLE, PA, 390031, p. A573

GOOD SHEPHERD HEALTHCARE SYSTEM, HERMISTON, OR, 380023, p. A544

GOOD SHEPHERD MEDICAL CENTER, LONGVIEW, TX, 450037, p. A653

GOOD SHEPHERD REHABILITATION HOSPITAL, ALLENTOWN, PA, 393035, p. A551

GOOD SHEPHERD SPECIALTY HOSPITAL, ALLENTOWN, PA, 392033, p. A551

GOODALL–WITCHER HEALTHCARE, CLIFTON, TX, 450052, p. A629

GOODING COUNTY MEMORIAL HOSPITAL, GOODING, ID, 131302, p. A179

GOODLAND REGIONAL MEDICAL CENTER, GOODLAND, KS, 171370, p. A247

GORDON HOSPITAL, CALHOUN, GA, 110023, p. A157

GORDON MEMORIAL HOSPITAL, GORDON, NE, 281358, p. A407

GOSHEN GENERAL HOSPITAL, GOSHEN, IN, 150026, p. A216

GOTHENBURG MEMORIAL HOSPITAL, GOTHENBURG, NE, 281313, p. A407

GOTTLIEB MEMORIAL HOSPITAL, MELROSE PARK, IL, 140008, p. A201

GOVE COUNTY MEDICAL CENTER, QUINTER, KS, 171367, p. A256

GOVERNOR JUAN F. LUIS HOSPITAL, CHRISTIANSTED, VI, 480002, p. A749

GRACE COTTAGE HOSPITAL, TOWNSHEND, VT, 471300, p. A684

GRACE HOSPITAL, MORGANTON, NC, 340075, p. A488

GRACE HOSPITAL, CLEVELAND, OH, 362015, p. A508

GRACEVILLE HEALTH CENTER, GRACEVILLE, MN, 241321, p. A354

GRACIE SQUARE HOSPITAL, NEW YORK, NY, 334048, p. A459

GRADUATE HOSPITAL, PHILADELPHIA, PA, 390285, p. A568

GRADY GENERAL HOSPITAL, CAIRO, GA, 110121, p. A157

GRADY MEMORIAL HOSPITAL, ATLANTA, GA, 110079, p. A154

GRADY MEMORIAL HOSPITAL, DELAWARE, OH, 360210, p. A512

GRADY MEMORIAL HOSPITAL, CHICKASHA, OK, 370054, p. A528

GRAFTON CITY HOSPITAL, GRAFTON, WV, 511307, p. A715

GRAHAM COUNTY HOSPITAL, HILL CITY, KS, 171325, p. A248

GRAHAM HOSPITAL, CANTON, IL, 140001, p. A185

GRAHAM REGIONAL MEDICAL CENTER, GRAHAM, TX, 450085, p. A642

GRAND ITASCA CLINIC AND HOSPITAL, GRAND RAPIDS, MN, 240064, p. A354

GRAND RIVER HOSPITAL DISTRICT, RIFLE, CO, 061317, p. A109

GRAND STRAND REGIONAL MEDICAL CENTER, MYRTLE BEACH, SC, 420085, p. A590

GRAND VIEW HOSPITAL, IRONWOOD, MI, 230143, p. A337

GRAND VIEW HOSPITAL, SELLERSVILLE, PA, 390057, p. A575

GRANDE RONDE HOSPITAL, LA GRANDE, OR, 381321, p. A545

GRANDVIEW HOSPITAL AND MEDICAL CENTER, DAYTON, OH, 360133, p. A512

GRANDVIEW MEDICAL CENTER, JASPER, TN, 440064, p. A608

GRANITE COUNTY MEDICAL CENTER, PHILIPSBURG, MT, 271303, p. A401

GRANITE FALLS MUNICIPAL HOSPITAL AND MANOR, GRANITE FALLS, MN, 241343, p. A354

GRANT MEDICAL CENTER, COLUMBUS, OH, 360017, p. A510

GRANT MEMORIAL HOSPITAL, PETERSBURG, WV, 510026, p. A719

GRANT REGIONAL HEALTH CENTER, LANCASTER, WI, 521322, p. A728

GRANVILLE MEDICAL CENTER, OXFORD, NC, 340127, p. A489

GRAPE COMMUNITY HOSPITAL, HAMBURG, IA, 161324, p. A234

GRATIOT MEDICAL CENTER, ALMA, MI, 230030, p. A327

GRAVETTE MEDICAL CENTER HOSPITAL, GRAVETTE, AR, 040075, p. A44

GRAYDON MANOR, LEESBURG, VA, p. A690

GRAYS HARBOR COMMUNITY HOSPITAL, ABERDEEN, WA, 500031, p. A700

GREAT PLAINS REGIONAL MEDICAL CENTER, NORTH PLATTE, NE, 280065, p. A410

GREAT PLAINS REGIONAL MEDICAL CENTER, ELK CITY, OK, 370019, p. A530

GREAT RIVER MEDICAL CENTER, BLYTHEVILLE, AR, 040069, p. A41

GREAT RIVER MEDICAL CENTER, WEST BURLINGTON, IA, 160057, p. A243

GREATER BALTIMORE MEDICAL CENTER, BALTIMORE, MD, 210044, p. A302

GREATER BINGHAMTON HEALTH CENTER, BINGHAMTON, NY, 334012, p. A448

GREATER COMMUNITY HOSPITAL, CRESTON, IA, 161365, p. A231

GREATER EL MONTE COMMUNITY HOSPITAL, EL MONTE, CA, 050615, p. A59

GREATER LAFAYETTE HEALTH SERVICES, LAFAYETTE, IN, 150109, p. A220

GREATER SOUTHEAST COMMUNITY HOSPITAL, WASHINGTON, DC, 090008, p. A121

GREELEY COUNTY HEALTH SERVICES, TRIBUNE, KS, 171359, p. A258

GREEN CLINIC SURGICAL HOSPITAL, RUSTON, LA, 190257, p. A291

GREEN OAKS HOSPITAL, DALLAS, TX, 454094, p. A632

GREENBRIAR REHABILITATION HOSPITAL, BOARDMAN, OH, 363032, p. A504

GREENBRIER VALLEY MEDICAL CENTER, RONCEVERTE, WV, 510002, p. A720

GREENE COUNTY GENERAL HOSPITAL, LINTON, IN, 151317, p. A221

GREENE COUNTY HOSPITAL, EUTAW, AL, 010051, p. A18

GREENE COUNTY MEDICAL CENTER, JEFFERSON, IA, 161325, p. A236

GREENE COUNTY MEMORIAL HOSPITAL, WAYNESBURG, PA, 390150, p. A578

GREENE MEMORIAL HOSPITAL, XENIA, OH, 360026, p. A525

GREENFIELD AREA MEDICAL CENTER, GREENFIELD, OH, 361304, p. A514

GREENLEAF CENTER, VALDOSTA, GEORGIA (see SOUTH GEORGIA MEDICAL CENTER), p. A171

GREENVIEW REGIONAL HOSPITAL, BOWLING GREEN, KY, 180124, p. A262

GREENVILLE CAMPUS, GREENVILLE, PENNSYLVANIA (see UPMC HORIZON), p. A559

GREENVILLE MEMORIAL HOSPITAL, GREENVILLE, SC, 420078, p. A588

GREENVILLE REGIONAL HOSPITAL, GREENVILLE, IL, 140137, p. A196

GREENWICH HOSPITAL, GREENWICH, CT, 070018, p. A113

GREENWOOD COUNTY HOSPITAL, EUREKA, KS, 171339, p. A247

GREENWOOD LEFLORE HOSPITAL, GREENWOOD, MS, 250099, p. A369

GREENWOOD SPECIALTY HOSPITAL, GREENWOOD, MS, 250156, p. A369

GREIL MEMORIAL PSYCHIATRIC HOSPITAL, MONTGOMERY, AL, 014005, p. A22

GRENADA LAKE MEDICAL CENTER, GRENADA, MS, 250015, p. A369

GREYSTONE PARK PSYCHIATRIC HOSPITAL, MORRIS PLAINS, NJ, 314016, p. A431

GRIFFIN HOSPITAL, DERBY, CT, 070031, p. A112

GRIFFIN MEMORIAL HOSPITAL, NORMAN, OK, 374000, p. A534

GRIMES ST. JOSEPH HEALTH CENTER, NAVASOTA, TX, 451322, p. A658

GRINNELL REGIONAL MEDICAL CENTER, GRINNELL, IA, 160147, p. A234

GRISELL MEMORIAL HOSPITAL DISTRICT ONE, RANSOM, KS, 171300, p. A256

GRITMAN MEDICAL CENTER, MOSCOW, ID, 131327, p. A180

GROUP HEALTH COOPERATIVE, REDMOND, WA, 500052, p. A706

GROVE HILL MEMORIAL HOSPITAL, GROVE HILL, AL, 010091, p. A19

GROVER C. DILS MEDICAL CENTER, CALIENTE, NV, 290027, p. A415

GRUNDY COUNTY MEMORIAL HOSPITAL, GRUNDY CENTER, IA, 161303, p. A234

GUADALUPE COUNTY HOSPITAL, SANTA ROSA, NM, 320067, p. A444

GUADALUPE VALLEY HOSPITAL, SEGUIN, TX, 450104, p. A666

GUAM MEMORIAL HOSPITAL AUTHORITY, TAMUNING, GU, 650001, p. A743

GULF BREEZE HOSPITAL, GULF BREEZE, FL, 100266, p. A130

GULF COAST HOSPITAL, FORT MYERS, FL, 100279, p. A129

GULF COAST MEDICAL CENTER, PANAMA CITY, FL, 100242, p. A142

GULF COAST MEDICAL CENTER, BILOXI, MS, 250125, p. A366

GULF COAST MEDICAL CENTER, WHARTON, TX, 450214, p. A673

GULF OAKS HOSPITAL, BILOXI, MISSISSIPPI (see GULF COAST MEDICAL CENTER), p. A366

GULF PINES HOSPITAL, PORT SAINT JOE, FL, 100027, p. A144

GULF POINTE SPECIALTY HOSPITAL, HOUSTON, TX, 452043, p. A645

GULF STATE LONG TERM ACUTE CARE OF COVINGTON, COVINGTON, LA, 192048, p. A279

GULF STATES LTAC OF DENHAM SPRINGS, DENHAM SPRINGS, LA, 192008, p. A280

GUNDERSEN LUTHERAN MEDICAL CENTER, LA CROSSE, WI, 520087, p. A727

GUNNISON VALLEY HOSPITAL, GUNNISON, CO, 061320, p. A106

GUNNISON VALLEY HOSPITAL, GUNNISON, UT, 460037, p. A676

GUTHRIE COUNTY HOSPITAL, GUTHRIE CENTER, IA, 161314, p. A234

GUTTENBERG MUNICIPAL HOSPITAL, GUTTENBERG, IA, 161312, p. A234

GUYAN VALLEY HOSPITAL, LOGAN, WV, 511302, p. A717

GWINNETT HOSPITAL SYSTEM, LAWRENCEVILLE, GA, 110087, p. A164

GWINNETT MEDICAL CENTER, LAWRENCEVILLE, GEORGIA (see GWINNETT HOSPITAL SYSTEM), p. A164

H

H. B. MAGRUDER MEMORIAL HOSPITAL, PORT CLINTON, OH, 361314, p. A521

H. C. WATKINS MEMORIAL HOSPITAL, QUITMAN, MS, 251316, p. A375

H. DOUGLAS SINGER MENTAL HEALTH AND DEVELOPMENTAL CENTER, ROCKFORD, IL, 144023, p. A206

H. LEE MOFFITT CANCER CENTER AND RESEARCH INSTITUTE, TAMPA, FL, 100271, p. A148

H.S.C. MEDICAL CENTER, MALVERN, AR, 040076, p. A47

HABERSHAM COUNTY MEDICAL CENTER, DEMOREST, GA, 110041, p. A160

HACKENSACK UNIVERSITY MEDICAL CENTER, HACKENSACK, NJ, 310001, p. A429

HACKETTSTOWN COMMUNITY HOSPITAL, HACKETTSTOWN, NJ, 310115, p. A429

HACKLEY HEALTH, MUSKEGON, MI, 230066, p. A341

HACKLEY LAKESHORE HOSPITAL, SHELBY, MI, 231320, p. A345

HADLEY MEMORIAL HOSPITAL, WASHINGTON, DC, 092003, p. A121

HAHNEMANN CAMPUS, WORCESTER, MASSACHUSETTS (see UMASS MEMORIAL MEDICAL CENTER), p. A326

HAHNEMANN UNIVERSITY HOSPITAL, PHILADELPHIA, PA, 390290, p. A568

HALE COUNTY HOSPITAL, GREENSBORO, AL, 010095, p. A19

HALE HO'OLA HAMAKUA, HONOKAA, HI, 120016, p. A173

HALIFAX BEHAVIORAL SERVICES, DAYTONA BEACH, FLORIDA (see HALIFAX FISH COMMUNITY HEALTH), p. A127

HALIFAX FISH COMMUNITY HEALTH, DAYTONA BEACH, FL, 100017, p. A127

HALIFAX MEDICAL CENTER, DAYTONA BEACH, FLORIDA (see HALIFAX FISH COMMUNITY HEALTH), p. A127

HALIFAX REGIONAL HEALTH SYSTEM, SOUTH BOSTON, VA, 490013, p. A696

HALIFAX REGIONAL MEDICAL CENTER, ROANOKE RAPIDS, NC, 340151, p. A490

HALL–BROOKE HOSPITAL, A DIVISION OF HALL–BROOKE BEHAVIORAL HEALTH SERVICES, WESTPORT, CONNECTICUT (see ST. VINCENT'S MEDICAL CENTER), p. A112

HALLMARK HEALTH SYSTEM, MELROSE, MA, 220070, p. A320

HALLMARK YOUTHCARE – RICHMOND, RICHMOND, VA, 494026, p. A695

HAMILTON CENTER, TERRE HAUTE, IN, 154009, p. A226

HAMILTON COUNTY HOSPITAL, SYRACUSE, KS, 171322, p. A257

HAMILTON GENERAL HOSPITAL, HAMILTON, TX, 450754, p. A643

HAMILTON HOSPITAL, WEBSTER CITY, IA, 161361, p. A243

HAMILTON HOSPITAL, OLNEY, TX, 451354, p. A659

HAMILTON MEDICAL CENTER, DALTON, GA, 110001, p. A160

HAMILTON MEMORIAL HOSPITAL DISTRICT, MCLEANSBORO, IL, 141326, p. A200

HAMLIN MEMORIAL HOSPITAL, HAMLIN, TX, 450243, p. A643

HAMMOND REHABILITATION HOSPITAL, HAMMOND, LA, 192036, p. A281

HAMMOND–HENRY HOSPITAL, GENESEO, IL, 141319, p. A195

HAMOT MEDICAL CENTER, ERIE, PA, 390063, p. A558

HOLLYWOOD MEDICAL CENTER, HOLLYWOOD, FL, 100225, p. A131

HOLLYWOOD PAVILION, HOLLYWOOD, FL, 104015, p. A131

HOLLYWOOD PRESBYTERIAN MEDICAL CENTER, LOS ANGELES, CA, 050063, p. A70

HOLMES REGIONAL MEDICAL CENTER, MELBOURNE, FL, 100019, p. A136

HOLTON COMMUNITY HOSPITAL, HOLTON, KS, 171319, p. A249

HOLY CROSS HOSPITAL, FORT LAUDERDALE, FL, 100073, p. A128

HOLY CROSS HOSPITAL, CHICAGO, IL, 140133, p. A187

HOLY CROSS HOSPITAL, SILVER SPRING, MD, 210004, p. A311

HOLY CROSS HOSPITAL, TAOS, NM, 320013, p. A445

HOLY FAMILY HOME, NEW YORK, NEW YORK (see SAINT VINCENTS CATHOLIC MEDICAL CENTERS OF NEW YORK), p. A465

HOLY FAMILY HOME, BROOKLYN, NEW YORK (see (see SAINT VINCENTS CATHOLIC MEDICAL CENTERS OF NEW YORK)), p. A465

HOLY FAMILY HOSPITAL, SPOKANE, WA, 500077, p. A709

HOLY FAMILY HOSPITAL, NEW RICHMOND, WI, 521345, p. A732

HOLY FAMILY MEDICAL CENTER, DES PLAINES, IL, 140105, p. A192

HOLY FAMILY MEMORIAL MEDICAL CENTER, MANITOWOC, WI, 520107, p. A729

HOLY INFANT HOSPITAL, HOVEN, SD, 430060, p. A596

HOLY NAME HOSPITAL, TEANECK, NJ, 310008, p. A436

HOLY REDEEMER HOSPITAL AND MEDICAL CENTER, JENKINTOWN, PA, 390097, p. A561

HOLY ROSARY HEALTHCARE, MILES CITY, MT, 270002, p. A400

HOLY ROSARY MEDICAL CENTER, ONTARIO, OR, 380052, p. A546

HOLY SPIRIT HOSPITAL, CAMP HILL, PA, 390004, p. A554

HOLYOKE MEDICAL CENTER, HOLYOKE, MA, 220024, p. A318

HOLZER MEDICAL CENTER, GALLIPOLIS, OH, 360054, p. A514

HOLZER MEDICAL CENTER – JACKSON, JACKSON, OH, 361320, p. A515

HOMER MEMORIAL HOSPITAL, HOMER, LA, 190114, p. A282

HOMESTEAD HOSPITAL, HOMESTEAD, FL, 100125, p. A131

HOOD MEMORIAL HOSPITAL, AMITE, LA, 191309, p. A276

HOOPESTON COMMUNITY MEMORIAL HOSPITAL, HOOPESTON, IL, 141316, p. A197

HOOTS MEMORIAL HOSPITAL, YADKINVILLE, NC, 341308, p. A495

HOPEDALE MEDICAL COMPLEX, HOPEDALE, IL, 141330, p. A197

HOPI HEALTH CARE CENTER, KEAMS CANYON, AZ, 031305, p. A31

HOPKINS COUNTY MEMORIAL HOSPITAL, SULPHUR SPRINGS, TX, 450236, p. A668

HORIZON MEDICAL CENTER, DICKSON, TN, 440046, p. A605

HORIZON SPECIALTY HOSPITAL, LAS VEGAS, NV, 292003, p. A416

HORN MEMORIAL HOSPITAL, IDA GROVE, IA, 161354, p. A235

HORSHAM CLINIC, AMBLER, PA, 394034, p. A552

HOSPICE OF NORTHERN VIRGINIA, FALLS CHURCH, VA, 490129, p. A687

HOSPICE OF PALM BEACH COUNTY, WEST PALM BEACH, FL, p. A150

HOSPITAL BUEN SAMARITANO, AGUADILLA, PR, 400079, p. A743

HOSPITAL DE DAMAS, PONCE, PR, 400022, p. A746

HOSPITAL DE LA CONCEPCION, SAN GERMAN, PR, 400021, p. A746

HOSPITAL DE LA UNIVERSIDAD DE PUERTO RICO/DR. FEDERICO TRILLA, CAROLINA, PR, 400112, p. A744

HOSPITAL DEL MAESTRO, SAN JUAN, PR, 400004, p. A747

HOSPITAL DISTRICT NUMBER 1 OF CRAWFORD COUNTY, GIRARD, KS, 170098, p. A247

HOSPITAL DISTRICT NUMBER FIVE OF HARPER COUNTY, HARPER, KS, 171366, p. A248

HOSPITAL DISTRICT NUMBER SIX OF HARPER COUNTY, ANTHONY, KS, 171346, p. A244

HOSPITAL DR. CAYETANO COLL Y TOSTE, ARECIBO, PR, 400087, p. A743

HOSPITAL DR. DOMINGUEZ, HUMACAO, PR, 400011, p. A745

HOSPITAL DR. SUSONI, ARECIBO, PR, 400117, p. A744

HOSPITAL EL BUEN PASTOR, ARECIBO, PR, p. A744

HOSPITAL EPISCOPAL CRISTO REDENTOR, GUAYAMA, PR, 400048, p. A745

HOSPITAL EPISCOPAL SAN LUCAS, PONCE, PR, 400044, p. A746

HOSPITAL FOR JOINT DISEASES ORTHOPAEDIC INSTITUTE, NEW YORK, NY, 330389, p. A460

HOSPITAL FOR SICK CHILDREN, WASHINGTON, DC, p. A121

HOSPITAL FOR SPECIAL CARE, NEW BRITAIN, CT, 072004, p. A114

HOSPITAL FOR SPECIAL SURGERY, NEW YORK, NY, 330270, p. A460

HOSPITAL HERMANOS MELENDEZ, BAYAMON, PR, 400032, p. A744

HOSPITAL INTERAMERICANO DE MEDICINA AVANZADA, CAGUAS, PR, 400120, p. A744

HOSPITAL MATILDE BRENES, BAYAMON, PR, 400102, p. A744

HOSPITAL MENONITA DE CAYEY, CAYEY, PR, 400013, p. A744

HOSPITAL METROPOLITAN, SAN JUAN, PR, 400106, p. A747

HOSPITAL METROPOLITANO DR. TITO MATTEI, YAUCO, PR, 400110, p. A749

HOSPITAL METROPOLITANO SAN GERMAN, SAN GERMAN, PR, 400126, p. A746

HOSPITAL OF SAINT RAPHAEL, NEW HAVEN, CT, 070001, p. A115

HOSPITAL OF THE UNIVERSITY OF PENNSYLVANIA, PHILADELPHIA, PA, 390111, p. A568

HOSPITAL ONCOLOGICO ANDRES GRILLASCA, PONCE, PR, 400028, p. A746

HOSPITAL PAVIA–HATO REY, SAN JUAN, PR, p. A747

HOSPITAL PAVIA–SANTURCE, SAN JUAN, PR, 400019, p. A747

HOSPITAL PEREA, MAYAGUEZ, PR, 400123, p. A745

HOSPITAL SAN CARLOS BORROMEO, MOCA, PR, 400111, p. A746

HOSPITAL SAN CRISTOBAL, COTO LAUREL, PR, 400113, p. A745

HOSPITAL SAN GERARDO, RIO PIEDRAS, PR, 400121, p. A747

HOSPITAL SAN PABLO, BAYAMON, PR, 400109, p. A744

HOSPITAL SAN PABLO DEL ESTE, FAJARDO, PR, 400125, p. A745

HOSPITAL SANTA ROSA, GUAYAMA, PR, 400009, p. A745

HOSPITAL UNIVERSITARIO DR. RAMON RUIZ ARNAU, BAYAMON, PR, 400105, p. A744

HOT SPRINGS COUNTY MEMORIAL HOSPITAL, THERMOPOLIS, WY, 531304, p. A742

HOT SPRINGS REHABILITATION CENTER, HOT SPRINGS NATIONAL, AR, 043027, p. A44

HOULTON REGIONAL HOSPITAL, HOULTON, ME, 201308, p. A299

HOUSTON COMMUNITY HOSPITAL, HOUSTON, TX, 450795, p. A645

HOUSTON MEDICAL CENTER, WARNER ROBINS, GA, 110069, p. A172

HOUSTON NORTHWEST MEDICAL CENTER, HOUSTON, TX, 450638, p. A645

HOWARD A. RUSK REHABILITATION CENTER, COLUMBIA, MO, 263027, p. A381

HOWARD COUNTY COMMUNITY HOSPITAL, SAINT PAUL, NE, 281338, p. A412

HOWARD COUNTY GENERAL HOSPITAL, COLUMBIA, MD, 210048, p. A307

HOWARD MEMORIAL HOSPITAL, NASHVILLE, AR, 041311, p. A48

HOWARD REGIONAL HEALTH SYSTEM, KOKOMO, IN, 150007, p. A220

HOWARD REGIONAL HEALTH SYSTEM WEST CAMPUS SPECIALTY HOSPITAL, KOKOMO, IN, 153039, p. A220

HOWARD UNIVERSITY HOSPITAL, WASHINGTON, DC, 090003, p. A121

HOWARD YOUNG MEDICAL CENTER, WOODRUFF, WI, 520091, p. A738

HUBBARD REGIONAL HOSPITAL, WEBSTER, MA, 220025, p. A324

HUDSON HOSPITAL, HUDSON, WI, 521335, p. A727

HUDSON RIVER PSYCHIATRIC CENTER, POUGHKEEPSIE, NY, 334010, p. A470

HUDSON VALLEY HOSPITAL CENTER, CORTLANDT MANOR, NY, 330267, p. A451

HUEY P. LONG MEDICAL CENTER, PINEVILLE, LA, 190009, p. A291

HUGGINS HOSPITAL, WOLFEBORO, NH, 301312, p. A424

HUGH CHATHAM MEMORIAL HOSPITAL, ELKIN, NC, 340097, p. A482

HUGHSTON ORTHOPEDIC HOSPITAL, COLUMBUS, GA, 110200, p. A158

HUGULEY MEMORIAL MEDICAL CENTER, FORT WORTH, TX, 450677, p. A640

HUHUKAM MEMORIAL HOSPITAL, SACATON, AZ, 031308, p. A35

HUMBOLDT COUNTY MEMORIAL HOSPITAL, HUMBOLDT, IA, 161334, p. A235

HUMBOLDT GENERAL HOSPITAL, WINNEMUCCA, NV, 290016, p. A419

HUMBOLDT GENERAL HOSPITAL, HUMBOLDT, TN, 440115, p. A607

HUMPHREYS COUNTY MEMORIAL HOSPITAL, BELZONI, MS, 251311, p. A366

HUNT MEMORIAL HOSPITAL DISTRICT, GREENVILLE, TX, 450352, p. A642

HUNTER HOLMES MCGUIRE VETERANS AFFAIRS MEDICAL CENTER, RICHMOND, VA, p. A695

HUNTERDON MEDICAL CENTER, FLEMINGTON, NJ, 310005, p. A428

HUNTINGTON BEACH HOSPITAL, HUNTINGTON BEACH, CA, 050526, p. A64

HUNTINGTON HOSPITAL, HUNTINGTON, NY, 330045, p. A454

HUNTINGTON MEMORIAL HOSPITAL, PASADENA, CA, 050438, p. A81

HUNTSVILLE HOSPITAL, HUNTSVILLE, AL, 010039, p. A20

HUNTSVILLE HOSPITAL FOR WOMEN AND CHILDREN, HUNTSVILLE, ALABAMA (see HUNTSVILLE HOSPITAL), p. A20

HUNTSVILLE MEMORIAL HOSPITAL, HUNTSVILLE, TX, 450347, p. A649

HURLEY MEDICAL CENTER, FLINT, MI, 230132, p. A333

HURON HOSPITAL, CLEVELAND, OH, 360101, p. A508

HURON MEDICAL CENTER, BAD AXE, MI, 230118, p. A328

HURON REGIONAL MEDICAL CENTER, HURON, SD, 431335, p. A596

HURON VALLEY–SINAI HOSPITAL, COMMERCE TOWNSHIP, MI, 230277, p. A330

HUTCHESON MEDICAL CENTER, FORT OGLETHORPE, GA, 110004, p. A162

HUTCHINSON AREA HEALTH CARE, HUTCHINSON, MN, 240187, p. A355

HUTCHINSON HOSPITAL CORPORATION, HUTCHINSON, KS, 170020, p. A249

HUTZEL HOSPITAL, DETROIT, MICHIGAN (see HARPER UNIVERSITY HOSPITAL), p. A331

I

I. GONZALEZ MARTINEZ ONCOLOGIC HOSPITAL, HATO REY, PR, 400012, p. A747

IBERIA MEDICAL CENTER, NEW IBERIA, LA, 190054, p. A288

IDAHO ELKS REHABILITATION HOSPITAL, BOISE, ID, 133025, p. A177

IDAHO FALLS RECOVERY CENTER, IDAHO FALLS, ID, 130062, p. A179

ILLIANA SURGERY AND MEDICAL CENTER, MUNSTER, IN, 150147, p. A222

ILLINI COMMUNITY HOSPITAL, PITTSFIELD, IL, 141315, p. A205

ILLINOIS VALLEY COMMUNITY HOSPITAL, PERU, IL, 140234, p. A205

IMMANUEL ST. JOSEPH'S–MAYO HEALTH SYSTEM, MANKATO, MN, 240093, p. A356

IMPACT DRUG AND ALCOHOL TREATMENT CENTER, PASADENA, CA, p. A81

IMPERIAL POINT MEDICAL CENTER, FORT LAUDERDALE, FL, 100200, p. A128

INCLINE VILLAGE COMMUNITY HOSPITAL, INCLINE VILLAGE, NV, 291301, p. A416

INCLUDES SUNRISE CHILDREN'S HOSPITAL (see SUNRISE HOSPITAL AND MEDICAL CENTER), p. A417

INDEPENDENCE REGIONAL HEALTH CENTER, INDEPENDENCE, MO, 260095, p. A383

INDIAN HEALTH SERVICE HOSPITAL, RAPID CITY, SD, 430082, p. A598

INDIAN PATH MEDICAL CENTER, KINGSPORT, TN, 440176, p. A609

INDIAN PATH PAVILION, KINGSPORT, TENNESSEE (see INDIAN PATH MEDICAL CENTER), p. A609

INDIAN RIVER MEMORIAL HOSPITAL, VERO BEACH, FL, 100105, p. A150

INDIAN VALLEY HEALTH CARE DISTRICT, GREENVILLE, CA, 050433, p. A63

INDIANA HEART HOSPITAL, INDIANAPOLIS, IN, 150154, p. A218

INDIANA REGIONAL MEDICAL CENTER, INDIANA, PA, 390173, p. A561

INDIANA UNIVERSITY MEDICAL CENTER, INDIANAPOLIS, INDIANA (see CLARIAN HEALTH PARTNERS), p. A218

INDIANHEAD MEDICAL CENTER, SHELL LAKE, WI, 521342, p. A735

INDUSTRIAL HOSPITAL, SAN JUAN, PR, p. A747

INGALLS MEMORIAL HOSPITAL, HARVEY, IL, 140191, p. A196

INGHAM REGIONAL MEDICAL CENTER, LANSING, MI, 230167, p. A338

INGHAM REGIONAL MEDICAL CENTER, GREENLAWN CAMPUS, LANSING, MICHIGAN (see INGHAM REGIONAL MEDICAL CENTER), p. A338

INGHAM REGIONAL MEDICAL CENTER, PENNSYLVANIA CAMPUS, LANSING, MICHIGAN (see INGHAM REGIONAL MEDICAL CENTER), p. A338

INLAND HOSPITAL, WATERVILLE, ME, 200041, p. A301

INLAND VALLEY MEDICAL CENTER, WILDOMAR, CA, p. A99

J

JOHN UMSTEAD HOSPITAL, BUTNER, NC, 344004, p. A479
JOHNS COMMUNITY HOSPITAL, TAYLOR, TX, 450020, p. A668
JOHNS HOPKINS BAYVIEW MEDICAL CENTER, BALTIMORE, MD, 210029, p. A303
JOHNS HOPKINS HOSPITAL, BALTIMORE, MD, 210009, p. A303
JOHNSON CITY MEDICAL CENTER, JOHNSON CITY, TN, 440063, p. A608
JOHNSON CITY SPECIALTY HOSPITAL, JOHNSON CITY, TN, 440105, p. A609
JOHNSON COUNTY HEALTH CENTER, MOUNTAIN CITY, TN, 441304, p. A614
JOHNSON COUNTY HEALTHCARE CENTER, BUFFALO, WY, 531308, p. A739
JOHNSON COUNTY HOSPITAL, TECUMSEH, NE, 281350, p. A413
JOHNSON MEMORIAL HEALTH SERVICES, DAWSON, MN, 241314, p. A352
JOHNSON MEMORIAL HOSPITAL, STAFFORD SPRINGS, CT, 070008, p. A116
JOHNSON MEMORIAL HOSPITAL, FRANKLIN, IN, 150001, p. A216
JOHNSON REGIONAL MEDICAL CENTER, CLARKSVILLE, AR, 040002, p. A41
JOHNSON–MATHERS NURSING HOME (see NICHOLAS COUNTY HOSPITAL), p. A262
JOHNSTON MEMORIAL HOSPITAL, SMITHFIELD, NC, 340090, p. A491
JOHNSTON MEMORIAL HOSPITAL, TISHOMINGO, OK, 371304, p. A539
JOHNSTON MEMORIAL HOSPITAL, ABINGDON, VA, 490053, p. A685
JOHNSTON R. BOWMAN HEALTH CENTER, CHICAGO, ILLINOIS (see RUSH UNIVERSITY MEDICAL CENTER), p. A189
JOHNSTON–WILLIS HOSPITAL, RICHMOND, VIRGINIA (see CJW MEDICAL CENTER), p. A695
JOINT TOWNSHIP DISTRICT MEMORIAL HOSPITAL, SAINT MARYS, OH, 360032, p. A521
JONATHAN M. WAINWRIGHT MEMORIAL VA MEDICAL CENTER, WALLA WALLA, WA, p. A711
JONES MEMORIAL HOSPITAL, WELLSVILLE, NY, 330096, p. A475
JONES REGIONAL MEDICAL CENTER, ANAMOSA, IA, 161306, p. A228
JORDAN HOSPITAL, PLYMOUTH, MA, 220060, p. A322
JORDAN VALLEY HOSPITAL, WEST JORDAN, UT, 460051, p. A681
JPS HEALTH NETWORK, FORT WORTH, TX, 450039, p. A640
JULIAN F. KEITH ALCOHOL AND DRUG ABUSE TREATMENT CENTER, BLACK MOUNTAIN, NC, 344023, p. A478
JULIETTE MANOR NURSING HOME, COMMUNITY CLINICS (see BERLIN MEMORIAL HOSPITAL), p. A723
JUPITER MEDICAL CENTER, JUPITER, FL, 100253, p. A133

K

KADLEC MEDICAL CENTER, RICHLAND, WA, 500058, p. A707
KAHI MOHALA BEHAVIORAL HEALTH, EWA BEACH, HI, 124001, p. A173
KAHUKU HOSPITAL, KAHUKU, HI, 121304, p. A174
KAISER FOUNDATION HOSPITAL, FONTANA, CA, 050140, p. A60
KAISER FOUNDATION HOSPITAL, FRESNO, CA, 050710, p. A61
KAISER FOUNDATION HOSPITAL, HAYWARD, CA, 050512, p. A64
KAISER FOUNDATION HOSPITAL, LOS ANGELES, CA, 050138, p. A70
KAISER FOUNDATION HOSPITAL, LOS ANGELES, CA, 050411, p. A70
KAISER FOUNDATION HOSPITAL, LOS ANGELES, CA, 050137, p. A70
KAISER FOUNDATION HOSPITAL, LOS ANGELES, CA, 050677, p. A71
KAISER FOUNDATION HOSPITAL, OAKLAND, CA, 050075, p. A79
KAISER FOUNDATION HOSPITAL, REDWOOD CITY, CA, 050541, p. A83
KAISER FOUNDATION HOSPITAL, SACRAMENTO, CA, 050425, p. A84
KAISER FOUNDATION HOSPITAL, SACRAMENTO, CA, 050674, p. A84
KAISER FOUNDATION HOSPITAL, SAN DIEGO, CA, 050515, p. A87
KAISER FOUNDATION HOSPITAL, SAN FRANCISCO, CA, 050076, p. A89
KAISER FOUNDATION HOSPITAL, SAN RAFAEL, CA, 050510, p. A91

KAISER FOUNDATION HOSPITAL, SANTA CLARA, CA, 050071, p. A92
KAISER FOUNDATION HOSPITAL, SANTA ROSA, CA, 050690, p. A93
KAISER FOUNDATION HOSPITAL, SOUTH SAN FRANCISCO, CA, 050070, p. A94
KAISER FOUNDATION HOSPITAL, WALNUT CREEK, CA, 050072, p. A98
KAISER FOUNDATION HOSPITAL, MARTINEZ, CALIFORNIA (see KAISER FOUNDATION HOSPITAL), p. A98
KAISER FOUNDATION HOSPITAL – ORANGE COUNTY, ANAHEIM, CA, 050609, p. A52
KAISER FOUNDATION HOSPITAL – SANTA TERESA, SAN JOSE, CA, 050604, p. A90
KAISER FOUNDATION HOSPITAL AND REHABILITATION CENTER, VALLEJO, CA, 050073, p. A97
KAISER FOUNDATION HOSPITAL–BALDWIN PARK, BALDWIN PARK, CA, 050723, p. A54
KAISER FOUNDATION HOSPITAL–BELLFLOWER, BELLFLOWER, CA, 050139, p. A54
KAISER FOUNDATION HOSPITAL–RIVERSIDE, RIVERSIDE, CA, 050686, p. A84
KAISER FOUNDATION HOSPITAL–WEST LOS ANGELES, LOS ANGELES, CA, 050561, p. A71
KAISER FOUNDATION MENTAL HEALTH CENTER, LOS ANGELES, CALIFORNIA (see KAISER FOUNDATION HOSPITAL), p. A70
KAISER PERMANENTE MEDICAL CENTER, HONOLULU, HI, 120011, p. A173
KAISER SUNNYSIDE MEDICAL CENTER, CLACKAMAS, OR, 380091, p. A542
KALAMAZOO PSYCHIATRIC HOSPITAL, KALAMAZOO, MI, 234026, p. A338
KALISPELL REGIONAL MEDICAL CENTER, KALISPELL, MT, 270051, p. A400
KALKASKA MEMORIAL HEALTH CENTER, KALKASKA, MI, 231301, p. A338
KANABEC HOSPITAL, MORA, MN, 240152, p. A358
KANE COMMUNITY HOSPITAL, KANE, PA, 390104, p. A562
KANE COUNTY HOSPITAL, KANAB, UT, 460018, p. A677
KANSAS CITY ORTHOPAEDIC INSTITUTE, SHAWNEE MISSION, KS, 170188, p. A257
KANSAS HEART HOSPITAL, WICHITA, KS, 170186, p. A259
KANSAS NEUROLOGICAL INSTITUTE, TOPEKA, KS, p. A257
KANSAS REHABILITATION HOSPITAL, TOPEKA, KS, 173025, p. A257
KANSAS SPINE HOSPITAL, WICHITA, KS, 170196, p. A259
KANSAS SURGERY AND RECOVERY CENTER, WICHITA, KS, 170183, p. A259
KAPIOLANI MEDICAL CENTER AT PALI MOMI, AIEA, HI, 120026, p. A173
KAPIOLANI MEDICAL CENTER FOR WOMEN & CHILDREN, HONOLULU, HI, 123300, p. A173
KAPLAN REHABILITATION HOSPITAL, KAPLAN, LA, 193057, p. A283
KARL AND ESTHER HOBLITZELLE MEMORIAL HOSPITAL, DALLAS, TEXAS (see BAYLOR UNIVERSITY MEDICAL CENTER), p. A632
KATHERINE SHAW BETHEA HOSPITAL, DIXON, IL, 140012, p. A192
KAU HOSPITAL, PAHALA, HI, 121301, p. A176
KAUAI VETERANS MEMORIAL HOSPITAL, WAIMEA, HI, 121300, p. A176
KAWEAH DELTA HEALTH CARE DISTRICT, VISALIA, CA, 050057, p. A98
KEARNEY COUNTY HEALTH SERVICES, MINDEN, NE, 281306, p. A409
KEARNY COUNTY HOSPITAL, LAKIN, KS, 171313, p. A251
KEEFE MEMORIAL HOSPITAL, CHEYENNE WELLS, CO, 060043, p. A102
KELL WEST REGIONAL HOSPITAL, WICHITA FALLS, TX, 450827, p. A674
KELLER ARMY COMMUNITY HOSPITAL, WEST POINT, NY, p. A476
KENDALL REGIONAL MEDICAL CENTER, MIAMI, FL, 100209, p. A137
KENMARE COMMUNITY HOSPITAL, KENMARE, ND, 351305, p. A499
KENMORE MERCY HOSPITAL, KENMORE, NY, 330102, p. A455
KENNEDY KRIEGER INSTITUTE, BALTIMORE, MD, 213301, p. A303
KENNEDY MEMORIAL HOSPITAL, STRATFORD, NEW JERSEY (see KENNEDY MEMORIAL HOSPITALS–UNIVERSITY MEDICAL CENTER), p. A427
KENNEDY MEMORIAL HOSPITAL, TURNERSVILLE, NEW JERSEY (see KENNEDY MEMORIAL HOSPITALS–UNIVERSITY MEDICAL CENTER), p. A427
KENNEDY MEMORIAL HOSPITALS–UNIVERSITY MEDICAL CENTER, CHERRY HILL, NJ, 310086, p. A427

KENNER REGIONAL MEDICAL CENTER, KENNER, LA, 190206, p. A283
KENNETH HALL REGIONAL HOSPITAL, EAST ST. LOUIS, IL, 140066, p. A192
KENNEWICK GENERAL HOSPITAL, KENNEWICK, WA, 500053, p. A703
KENSINGTON HOSPITAL, PHILADELPHIA, PA, 390025, p. A568
KENT COUNTY MEMORIAL HOSPITAL, WARWICK, RI, 410009, p. A582
KENTFIELD REHABILITATION HOSPITAL, SAN RAFAEL, CA, 052043, p. A91
KENTUCKY RIVER MEDICAL CENTER, JACKSON, KY, 180139, p. A266
KEOKUK AREA HOSPITAL, KEOKUK, IA, 160008, p. A236
KEOKUK COUNTY HEALTH CENTER, SIGOURNEY, IA, 161315, p. A241
KERN MEDICAL CENTER, BAKERSFIELD, CA, 050315, p. A54
KERN VALLEY HEALTHCARE DISTRICT, LAKE ISABELLA, CA, 051314, p. A66
KERRVILLE DIVISION, KERRVILLE, TEXAS (see SOUTH TEXAS VETERANS HEALTH CARE SYSTEM), p. A665
KERRVILLE STATE HOSPITAL, KERRVILLE, TX, 454014, p. A651
KERSHAW COUNTY MEDICAL CENTER, CAMDEN, SC, 420048, p. A584
KESSLER INSTITUTE FOR REHABILITATION, WEST ORANGE, NJ, 313025, p. A438
KETCHIKAN GENERAL HOSPITAL, KETCHIKAN, AK, 020004, p. A27
KETTERING YOUTH SERVICES, DAYTON, OHIO (see SYCAMORE HOSPITAL), p. A518
KEWANEE HOSPITAL, KEWANEE, IL, 141325, p. A199
KEWEENAW MEMORIAL MEDICAL CENTER, LAURIUM, MI, 231319, p. A339
KEYSTONE CENTER, CHESTER, PA, p. A555
KEYSTONE NEWPORT NEWS, NEWPORT NEWS, VA, 494031, p. A692
KIDSPEACE CHILDREN'S HOSPITAL, OREFIELD, PA, 394047, p. A567
KILMICHAEL HOSPITAL, KILMICHAEL, MS, 250051, p. A371
KIMBALL HEALTH SERVICES, KIMBALL, NE, 281305, p. A408
KIMBALL MEDICAL CENTER, LAKEWOOD, NJ, 310084, p. A430
KIMBALL–RIDGE CENTER, WATERLOO, IOWA (see COVENANT MEDICAL CENTER), p. A243
KIMBLE HOSPITAL, JUNCTION, TX, 451306, p. A650
KINDRED CHICAGO CENTRAL HOSPITAL, CHICAGO, IL, 142009, p. A187
KINDRED HOSPITAL – ALBUQUERQUE, ALBUQUERQUE, NM, 322002, p. A440
KINDRED HOSPITAL – CENTRAL TAMPA, TAMPA, FL, 102013, p. A148
KINDRED HOSPITAL – DALLAS, DALLAS, TX, 452015, p. A633
KINDRED HOSPITAL – DELAWARE COUNTY, DARBY, PA, 392032, p. A556
KINDRED HOSPITAL – LA MIRADA, LA MIRADA, CA, p. A66
KINDRED HOSPITAL – NEW ORLEANS, NEW ORLEANS, LA, 192009, p. A288
KINDRED HOSPITAL – PHOENIX, PHOENIX, AZ, 032000, p. A34
KINDRED HOSPITAL – TUCSON, TUCSON, AZ, 032002, p. A38
KINDRED HOSPITAL BAY AREA –TAMPA, TAMPA, FL, 102009, p. A148
KINDRED HOSPITAL BOSTON NORTH SHORE, PEABODY, MA, 222044, p. A322
KINDRED HOSPITAL INDIANAPOLIS SOUTH, GREENWOOD, IN, 152008, p. A217
KINDRED HOSPITAL KANSAS CITY, KANSAS CITY, MO, 262011, p. A384
KINDRED HOSPITAL NORTH FLORIDA, GREEN COVE SPRINGS, FL, 102015, p. A130
KINDRED HOSPITAL OF TARRANT COUNTY, ARLINGTON, TX, 452028, p. A622
KINDRED HOSPITAL SEATTLE, SEATTLE, WA, 502002, p. A707
KINDRED HOSPITAL– OKLAHOMA CITY, OKLAHOMA CITY, OK, 372004, p. A535
KINDRED HOSPITAL–ATLANTA, ATLANTA, GA, 112004, p. A154
KINDRED HOSPITAL–BAY AREA, PASADENA, TX, 452039, p. A660
KINDRED HOSPITAL–BOSTON, BOSTON, MA, 222045, p. A314
KINDRED HOSPITAL–BREA, BREA, CA, 052039, p. A55
KINDRED HOSPITAL–CHARLESTON, CHARLESTON, SC, 422005, p. A584
KINDRED HOSPITAL–CHATTANOOGA, CHATTANOOGA, TN, 442007, p. A603
KINDRED HOSPITAL–CHICAGO NORTH, CHICAGO, IL, p. A187
KINDRED HOSPITAL–CHICAGO NORTHLAKE, NORTHLAKE, IL, 142008, p. A203
KINDRED HOSPITAL–CLEVELAND, CLEVELAND, OH, 362026, p. A509
KINDRED HOSPITAL–DAYTON, DAYTON, OH, 360268, p. A512
KINDRED HOSPITAL–DENVER, DENVER, CO, 062009, p. A103

KINDRED HOSPITAL–DETROIT, LINCOLN PARK, MI, 232019, p. A339

KINDRED HOSPITAL–FLAMINGO, LAS VEGAS, NEVADA (*see* KINDRED HOSPITAL–LAS VEGAS), p. A416

KINDRED HOSPITAL–FORT LAUDERDALE, FORT LAUDERDALE, FL, 102010, p. A128

KINDRED HOSPITAL–FORT WORTH, FORT WORTH, TX, 452088, p. A640

KINDRED HOSPITAL–FORT WORTH SOUTHWEST, FORT WORTH, TX, 452088, p. A640

KINDRED HOSPITAL–GREENSBORO, GREENSBORO, NC, 342012, p. A484

KINDRED HOSPITAL–HERITAGE VALLEY, BEAVER, PA, 392043, p. A552

KINDRED HOSPITAL–HOUSTON, HOUSTON, TX, 452023, p. A646

KINDRED HOSPITAL–HOUSTON NORTHWEST, HOUSTON, TX, 452039, p. A646

KINDRED HOSPITAL–INDIANAPOLIS, INDIANAPOLIS, IN, 152007, p. A218

KINDRED HOSPITAL–LAS VEGAS, LAS VEGAS, NV, 292002, p. A416

KINDRED HOSPITAL–LOS ANGELES, LOS ANGELES, CA, 052032, p. A71

KINDRED HOSPITAL–LOUISVILLE, LOUISVILLE, KY, 182001, p. A269

KINDRED HOSPITAL–MANSFIELD, MANSFIELD, TX, 452019, p. A655

KINDRED HOSPITAL–MILWAUKEE, MILWAUKEE, WI, 522004, p. A731

KINDRED HOSPITAL–NEW JERSEY MORRIS COUNTY, DOVER, NJ, 310125, p. A427

KINDRED HOSPITAL–ONTARIO, ONTARIO, CA, 052037, p. A79

KINDRED HOSPITAL–PHILADELPHIA, PHILADELPHIA, PA, 392027, p. A568

KINDRED HOSPITAL–PITTSBURGH, OAKDALE, PA, 392028, p. A566

KINDRED HOSPITAL–SACRAMENTO, FOLSOM, CA, 052033, p. A60

KINDRED HOSPITAL–SAN ANTONIO, SAN ANTONIO, TX, 452016, p. A664

KINDRED HOSPITAL–SAN DIEGO, SAN DIEGO, CA, 052036, p. A87

KINDRED HOSPITAL–SAN FRANCISCO BAY AREA, SAN LEANDRO, CA, 052034, p. A91

KINDRED HOSPITAL–SOUTH FLORIDA/CORAL GABLES, CORAL GABLES, FL, p. A126

KINDRED HOSPITAL–ST. LOUIS, SAINT LOUIS, MO, 262010, p. A391

KINDRED HOSPITAL–ST. PETERSBURG, SAINT PETERSBURG, FL, p. A145

KINDRED HOSPITAL–SYCAMORE, SYCAMORE, IL, 142006, p. A209

KINDRED HOSPITAL–WESTMINSTER, WESTMINSTER, CA, 052035, p. A99

KINDRED HOSPITAL–WHITE ROCK, DALLAS, TX, 452071, p. A633

KINDRED HOSPITAL–WOMING VALLEY, WILKES–BARRE, PA, 392042, p. A579

KING'S DAUGHTERS HOSPITAL, YAZOO CITY, MS, 251313, p. A377

KING'S DAUGHTERS HOSPITAL, TEMPLE, TX, 450008, p. A669

KING'S DAUGHTERS MEDICAL CENTER, ASHLAND, KY, 180009, p. A261

KING'S DAUGHTERS MEDICAL CENTER, BROOKHAVEN, MS, 250057, p. A367

KING'S DAUGHTERS' HOSPITAL AND HEALTH SERVICES, MADISON, IN, 150069, p. A221

KINGFISHER REGIONAL HOSPITAL, KINGFISHER, OK, 371313, p. A532

KINGMAN REGIONAL MEDICAL CENTER, KINGMAN, AZ, 030055, p. A31

KINGS COUNTY HOSPITAL CENTER, NEW YORK, NY, 330202, p. A460

KINGS MOUNTAIN HOSPITAL, KINGS MOUNTAIN, NC, 340037, p. A486

KINGS PARK PSYCHIATRIC CENTER, BRENTWOOD, NEW YORK (*see* PILGRIM PSYCHIATRIC CENTER), p. A448

KINGSBORO PSYCHIATRIC CENTER, NEW YORK, NY, 334058, p. A461

KINGSBROOK JEWISH MEDICAL CENTER, NEW YORK, NY, 330201, p. A461

KINGSBURG MEDICAL CENTER, KINGSBURG, CA, 050682, p. A65

KINGSTON HOSPITAL, KINGSTON, NY, 330004, p. A455

KINGWOOD HEALTH CENTER, KINGWOOD, TX, 454099, p. A651

KINGWOOD MEDICAL CENTER, KINGWOOD, TX, 450775, p. A651

KIOWA COUNTY MEMORIAL HOSPITAL, GREENSBURG, KS, 171332, p. A248

KIOWA DISTRICT HOSPITAL AND MANOR, KIOWA, KS, 171331, p. A250

KISHWAUKEE COMMUNITY HOSPITAL, DE KALB, IL, 140286, p. A191

KIT CARSON COUNTY MEMORIAL HOSPITAL, BURLINGTON, CO, 061313, p. A101

KITTITAS VALLEY COMMUNITY HOSPITAL, ELLENSBURG, WA, 501333, p. A702

KITTSON MEMORIAL HEALTHCARE CENTER, HALLOCK, MN, 241336, p. A354

KLICKITAT VALLEY HEALTH SERVICES, GOLDENDALE, WA, 501316, p. A703

KNAPP MEDICAL CENTER, WESLACO, TX, 450128, p. A673

KNOX COMMUNITY HOSPITAL, MOUNT VERNON, OH, 360040, p. A519

KNOX COUNTY HOSPITAL, BARBOURVILLE, KY, 180063, p. A261

KNOX COUNTY HOSPITAL, KNOX CITY, TX, 450746, p. A651

KNOXVILLE AREA COMMUNITY HOSPITAL AND CLINIC, KNOXVILLE, IA, 161355, p. A236

KNOXVILLE DIVISION, KNOXVILLE, IOWA (*see* VETERANS AFFAIRS CENTRAL IOWA HEALTH CARE SYSTEM), p. A233

KOHALA HOSPITAL, KOHALA, HI, 121302, p. A175

KONA COMMUNITY HOSPITAL, KEALAKEKUA, HI, 120019, p. A175

KOOTENAI MEDICAL CENTER, COEUR D'ALENE, ID, 130049, p. A178

KOSAIR CHILDREN'S HOSPITAL, LOUISVILLE, KENTUCKY (*see* NORTON HOSPITAL), p. A270

KOSCIUSKO COMMUNITY HOSPITAL, WARSAW, IN, 150133, p. A227

KOSSUTH REGIONAL HEALTH CENTER, ALGONA, IA, 161353, p. A228

KREMMLING MEMORIAL HOSPITAL, KREMMLING, CO, 061318, p. A107

KUAKINI MEDICAL CENTER, HONOLULU, HI, 120007, p. A173

KULA HOSPITAL, KULA, HI, 120024, p. A175

KWAJALEIN HOSPITAL, KWAJALEIN ISLAND, MH, p. A743

L

L. V. STABLER MEMORIAL HOSPITAL, GREENVILLE, AL, 010150, p. A19

LA HACIENDA TREATMENT CENTER, HUNT, TX, p. A649

LA PALMA INTERCOMMUNITY HOSPITAL, LA PALMA, CA, 050580, p. A66

LA PAZ REGIONAL HOSPITAL, PARKER, AZ, 030067, p. A33

LA PLACE REHABILITATION HOSPITAL, LA PLACE, LA, 193064, p. A283

LA PORTE REGIONAL HEALTH SYSTEM, LA PORTE, IN, 150006, p. A220

LA RABIDA CHILDREN'S HOSPITAL, CHICAGO, IL, 143301, p. A187

LABETTE COUNTY MEDICAL CENTER, PARSONS, KS, 170120, p. A255

LAC–HARBOR–UNIVERSITY OF CALIFORNIA AT LOS ANGELES MEDICAL CENTER, TORRANCE, CA, 050376, p. A96

LAC–KING–DREW MEDICAL CENTER, LOS ANGELES, CA, 050578, p. A71

LAC–OLIVE VIEW–UCLA MEDICAL CENTER, LOS ANGELES, CA, 050040, p. A71

LAC/UNIVERSITY OF SOUTHERN CALIFORNIA MEDICAL CENTER, LOS ANGELES, CA, 050373, p. A71

LADY OF THE SEA GENERAL HOSPITAL, CUT OFF, LA, 190048, p. A280

LAFAYETTE GENERAL MEDICAL CENTER, LAFAYETTE, LA, 190002, p. A283

LAFAYETTE HOME HOSPITAL, LAFAYETTE, INDIANA (*see* GREATER LAFAYETTE HEALTH SERVICES), p. A220

LAFAYETTE HOSPITAL, ARROYO, PR, 400026, p. A744

LAFAYETTE REGIONAL HEALTH CENTER, LEXINGTON, MO, 261320, p. A386

LAFAYETTE SURGICAL SPECICALTY HOSPITAL, LAFAYETTE, LA, 190259, p. A283

LAGUNA HONDA HOSPITAL AND REHABILITATION CENTER, SAN FRANCISCO, CA, 050668, p. A89

LAHEY CLINIC HOSPITAL, BURLINGTON, MA, 220171, p. A316

LAIRD HOSPITAL, UNION, MS, 251321, p. A376

LAIRD MEMORIAL HOSPITAL, KILGORE, TX, 450488, p. A651

LAKE AREA HOSPITAL, WEBSTER, SD, 431311, p. A600

LAKE BUTLER HOSPITAL HAND SURGERY CENTER, LAKE BUTLER, FL, 101303, p. A134

LAKE CHARLES MEMORIAL HOSPITAL, LAKE CHARLES, LA, 190060, p. A285

LAKE CHELAN COMMUNITY HOSPITAL, CHELAN, WA, 501334, p. A701

LAKE CITY COMMUNITY HOSPITAL, LAKE CITY, SC, 420066, p. A589

LAKE CITY MEDICAL CENTER, LAKE CITY, FL, 100156, p. A134

LAKE CITY MEDICAL CENTER–MAYO, LAKE CITY, MN, 241338, p. A355

LAKE CUMBERLAND REGIONAL HOSPITAL, SOMERSET, KY, 180132, p. A274

LAKE DISTRICT HOSPITAL, LAKEVIEW, OR, 381309, p. A545

LAKE FOREST HOSPITAL, LAKE FOREST, IL, 140130, p. A199

LAKE GRANBURY MEDICAL CENTER, GRANBURY, TX, 450596, p. A642

LAKE HOSPITAL SYSTEM, PAINESVILLE, OH, 360098, p. A520

LAKE MARTIN COMMUNITY HOSPITAL, DADEVILLE, AL, 010052, p. A16

LAKE NORMAN REGIONAL MEDICAL CENTER, MOORESVILLE, NC, 340129, p. A487

LAKE POINTE MEDICAL CENTER, ROWLETT, TX, 450742, p. A662

LAKE REGION HEALTHCARE CORPORATION, FERGUS FALLS, MN, 240052, p. A353

LAKE REGIONAL HEALTH SYSTEM, OSAGE BEACH, MO, 260186, p. A388

LAKE SHORE HEALTH CARE CENTER, IRVING, NY, 330293, p. A454

LAKE TAYLOR TRANSITIONAL CARE HOSPITAL, NORFOLK, VA, 492001, p. A692

LAKE VIEW MEMORIAL HOSPITAL AND HOME, TWO HARBORS, MN, 241308, p. A364

LAKE WALES MEDICAL CENTERS, LAKE WALES, FL, 100099, p. A134

LAKE WHITNEY MEDICAL CENTER, WHITNEY, TX, 450270, p. A673

LAKELAND COMMUNITY HOSPITAL, HALEYVILLE, AL, 010125, p. A20

LAKELAND HOSPITAL–NILES, NILES, MICHIGAN (*see* LAKELAND HOSPITAL–ST. JOSEPH), p. A344

LAKELAND HOSPITAL–ST. JOSEPH, SAINT JOSEPH, MI, 230021, p. A344

LAKELAND MEDICAL CENTER, NEW ORLEANS, LOUISIANA (*see* METHODIST HOSPITAL), p. A289

LAKELAND REGIONAL HOSPITAL, SPRINGFIELD, MO, 264024, p. A394

LAKELAND REGIONAL MEDICAL CENTER, LAKELAND, FL, 100157, p. A134

LAKELAND SPECIALTY HOSPITAL, BERRIEN CENTER, BERRIEN CENTER, MICHIGAN (*see* LAKELAND HOSPITAL–ST. JOSEPH), p. A344

LAKES REGION GENERAL HOSPITAL, LACONIA, NH, 300005, p. A421

LAKES REGIONAL HEALTHCARE, SPIRIT LAKE, IA, 160124, p. A242

LAKESHORE MENTAL HEALTH INSTITUTE, KNOXVILLE, TN, 444000, p. A610

LAKESIDE BEHAVIORAL HEALTH SYSTEM, MEMPHIS, TN, 444004, p. A613

LAKESIDE HOSPITAL, METAIRIE, LA, 190182, p. A286

LAKESIDE MEDICAL CENTER, PINE CITY, MN, 240211, p. A359

LAKESIDE MEMORIAL HOSPITAL, BROCKPORT, NY, 330037, p. A448

LAKESIDE WOMEN'S HOSPITAL, OKLAHOMA CITY, OK, 370199, p. A535

LAKEVIEW COMMUNITY HOSPITAL, EUFAULA, AL, 010069, p. A18

LAKEVIEW COMMUNITY HOSPITAL, PAW PAW, MI, 230172, p. A342

LAKEVIEW HOSPITAL, STILLWATER, MN, 240066, p. A363

LAKEVIEW HOSPITAL, BOUNTIFUL, UT, 460042, p. A676

LAKEVIEW MEDICAL CENTER, RICE LAKE, WI, 520011, p. A734

LAKEVIEW REGIONAL MEDICAL CENTER, COVINGTON, LA, 190177, p. A279

LAKEWAY REGIONAL HOSPITAL, MORRISTOWN, TN, 440067, p. A614

LAKEWOOD HEALTH CENTER, BAUDETTE, MN, 241301, p. A350

LAKEWOOD HEALTH SYSTEM, STAPLES, MN, 241329, p. A363

LAKEWOOD HOSPITAL, LAKEWOOD, OH, 360212, p. A515

LAKEWOOD RANCH MEDICAL CENTER, BRADENTON, FL, 100299, p. A124

LAKEWOOD REGIONAL MEDICAL CENTER, LAKEWOOD, CA, 050581, p. A67

LALLIE KEMP MEDICAL CENTER, INDEPENDENCE, LA, 190010, p. A282

LAMB HEALTHCARE CENTER, LITTLEFIELD, TX, 450698, p. A653

LANAI COMMUNITY HOSPITAL, LANAI CITY, HI, 121305, p. A175

LANCASTER COMMUNITY HOSPITAL, LANCASTER, CA, 050204, p. A67

LODI MEMORIAL HOSPITAL WEST, LODI, CALIFORNIA (*see* LODI MEMORIAL HOSPITAL), p. A67
LOEB CENTER NURSING REHABILITATION, NEW YORK, NEW YORK (*see* MONTEFIORE MEDICAL CENTER), p. A462
LOEB CENTER NURSING REHABILITATION, BRONX, NEW YORK (*see* (*see* MONTEFIORE MEDICAL CENTER)), p. A462
LOGAN COUNTY HOSPITAL, OAKLEY, KS, 171326, p. A253
LOGAN MEDICAL CENTER, GUTHRIE, OK, 371317, p. A531
LOGAN MEMORIAL HOSPITAL, RUSSELLVILLE, KY, 180066, p. A274
LOGAN REGIONAL HOSPITAL, LOGAN, UT, 460015, p. A677
LOGAN REGIONAL MEDICAL CENTER, LOGAN, WV, 510048, p. A717
LOGANSPORT STATE HOSPITAL, LOGANSPORT, IN, p. A221
LOMA LINDA UNIVERSITY BEHAVIORAL MEDICINE CENTER, REDLANDS, CA, 054093, p. A83
LOMA LINDA UNIVERSITY COMMUNITY MEDICAL CENTER, LOMA LINDA, CALIFORNIA (*see* LOMA LINDA UNIVERSITY MEDICAL CENTER), p. A68
LOMA LINDA UNIVERSITY MEDICAL CENTER, LOMA LINDA, CA, 050327, p. A68
LOMPOC HEALTHCARE DISTRICT, LOMPOC, CA, 050110, p. A68
LONG BEACH MEDICAL CENTER, LONG BEACH, NY, 330225, p. A455
LONG BEACH MEMORIAL MEDICAL CENTER, LONG BEACH, CA, 050485, p. A68
LONG ISLAND COLLEGE HOSPITAL, NEW YORK, NY, 330152, p. A461
LONG ISLAND JEWISH MEDICAL CENTER, NEW YORK, NY, 330195, p. A461
LONG PRAIRIE MEMORIAL HOSPITAL AND HOME, LONG PRAIRIE, MN, 241326, p. A356
LONG TERM CARE CENTER (*see* NORTHFIELD HOSPITAL), p. A359
LONG TERM CARE HOSPITAL, BIRMINGHAM, AL, 012009, p. A15
LONG TERM HOSPITAL OF ANNISTON, ANNISTON, AL, 010165, p. A13
LONG TERM HOSPITAL OF DOTHAN, DOTHAN, AL, 012010, p. A17
LONG TERM HOSPITAL OF MONTGOMERY, MONTGOMERY, AL, 012007, p. A22
LONG TERM HOSPITAL OF TUSCALOOSA, TUSCALOOSA, AL, 010166, p. A24
LONGMONT UNITED HOSPITAL, LONGMONT, CO, 060003, p. A108
LONGVIEW REGIONAL MEDICAL CENTER, LONGVIEW, TX, 450702, p. A654
LOOKOUT MEMORIAL HOSPITAL, SPEARFISH, SD, 430048, p. A599
LORETTO HOSPITAL, CHICAGO, IL, 140083, p. A188
LORING HOSPITAL, SAC CITY, IA, 161370, p. A241
LORIS COMMUNITY HOSPITAL, LORIS, SC, 420064, p. A590
LOS ALAMITOS MEDICAL CENTER, LOS ALAMITOS, CA, 050551, p. A69
LOS ALAMOS MEDICAL CENTER, LOS ALAMOS, NM, 320033, p. A443
LOS ANGELES COMMUNITY HOSPITAL, LOS ANGELES, CA, 050663, p. A71
LOS ANGELES COMMUNITY HOSPITAL OF NORWALK, LOS ANGELES, CALIFORNIA (*see* LOS ANGELES COMMUNITY HOSPITAL), p. A71
LOS ANGELES COUNTY CENTRAL JAIL HOSPITAL, LOS ANGELES, CA, p. A71
LOS ANGELES METROPOLITAN MEDICAL CENTER, LOS ANGELES, CA, 050644, p. A71
LOS NINOS HOSPITAL, PHOENIX, AZ, 033301, p. A34
LOS ROBLES HOSPITAL AND MEDICAL CENTER, THOUSAND OAKS, CA, 050549, p. A95
LOST RIVERS DISTRICT HOSPITAL, ARCO, ID, 131324, p. A177
LOUIS A. JOHNSON VETERANS AFFAIRS MEDICAL CENTER, CLARKSBURG, WV, p. A714
LOUIS A. WEISS MEMORIAL HOSPITAL, CHICAGO, IL, 140082, p. A188
LOUIS SMITH MEMORIAL HOSPITAL, LAKELAND, GA, 111326, p. A164
LOUISE OBICI MEMORIAL HOSPITAL, SUFFOLK, VA, 490044, p. A697
LOUISIANA EXTENDED CARE HOSPITAL OF LAFAYETTE, LAFAYETTE, LA, 192032, p. A283
LOUISIANA EXTENDED CARE HOSPITAL OF NATCHITOCHES, NATCHITOCHES, LA, 192035, p. A288
LOUISIANA EXTENDED CARE HOSPITAL WEST MONROE, WEST MONROE, LA, 190265, p. A294
LOUISIANA HEART HOSPITAL, LACOMBE, LA, 190250, p. A283
LOUISIANA REHABILITATION HOSPITAL OF MORGAN CITY, MORGAN CITY, LA, 193084, p. A287
LOURDES COUNSELING CENTER, RICHLAND, WA, 504008, p. A707

LOURDES HOSPITAL, PADUCAH, KY, 180102, p. A273
LOURDES MEDICAL CENTER, PASCO, WA, 501337, p. A705
LOURDES MEDICAL CENTER OF BURLINGTON COUNTY, WILLINGBORO, NJ, 310061, p. A438
LOVELACE MEDICAL CENTER, ALBUQUERQUE, NM, 320019, p. A440
LOWELL GENERAL HOSPITAL, LOWELL, MA, 220063, p. A319
LOWER BUCKS HOSPITAL, BRISTOL, PA, 390070, p. A553
LOWER KEYS MEDICAL CENTER, KEY WEST, FL, 100150, p. A133
LOWER UMPQUA HOSPITAL DISTRICT, REEDSPORT, OR, 381311, p. A548
LOYOLA UNIVERSITY MEDICAL CENTER, MAYWOOD, IL, 140276, p. A200
LSU MEDICAL CENTER–UNIVERSITY HOSPITAL, SHREVEPORT, LA, 190098, p. A292
LUBBOCK HEART HOSPITAL, LUBBOCK, TX, 450876, p. A654
LUCAS COUNTY HEALTH CENTER, CHARITON, IA, 161341, p. A230
LUCILE SALTER PACKARD CHILDREN'S HOSPITAL AT STANFORD, PALO ALTO, CA, 053305, p. A80
LULING REHABILITATION HOSPITAL, LULING, LA, 193060, p. A285
LUTHER HOSPITAL, EAU CLAIRE, WI, 520070, p. A725
LUTHERAN HOSPITAL, CLEVELAND, OH, 360087, p. A509
LUTHERAN HOSPITAL OF INDIANA, FORT WAYNE, IN, 150017, p. A215
LUTHERAN MEDICAL CENTER, NEW YORK, NY, 330306, p. A461
LUTZ WING CONVALESCENT AND NURSING CARE UNIT (*see* FAIRMONT MEDICAL CENTER–MAYO HEALTH SYSTEM), p. A353
LYNCHBURG GENERAL HOSPITAL, LYNCHBURG, VIRGINIA (*see* CENTRA HEALTH), p. A691
LYNDON B JOHNSON GENERAL HOSPITAL, HOUSTON, TEXAS (*see* HARRIS COUNTY HOSPITAL DISTRICT), p. A645
LYNDON B. JOHNSON TROPICAL MEDICAL CENTER, PAGO PAGO, AS, 640001, p. A743
LYNN COUNTY HOSPITAL DISTRICT, TAHOKA, TX, 451351, p. A668
LYONS DIVISION, LYONS, NEW JERSEY (*see* VETERANS AFFAIRS NEW JERSEY HEALTH CARE SYSTEM), p. A427
LYSTER U. S. ARMY COMMUNITY HOSPITAL, FORT RUCKER, AL, p. A19

M

M. I. T. MEDICAL DEPARTMENT, CAMBRIDGE, MA, p. A316
MACKINAC STRAITS HOSPITAL AND HEALTH CENTER, SAINT IGNACE, MI, 231306, p. A344
MACNEAL HOSPITAL, BERWYN, IL, 140054, p. A184
MACON COUNTY GENERAL HOSPITAL, LAFAYETTE, TN, 441305, p. A610
MACON NORTHSIDE HOSPITAL, MACON, GA, 110201, p. A165
MAD RIVER COMMUNITY HOSPITAL, ARCATA, CA, 050028, p. A53
MADELIA COMMUNITY HOSPITAL, MADELIA, MN, 241323, p. A356
MADERA COMMUNITY HOSPITAL, MADERA, CA, 050568, p. A74
MADIGAN ARMY MEDICAL CENTER, TACOMA, WA, p. A710
MADISON CENTER AND HOSPITAL, SOUTH BEND, IN, 154040, p. A225
MADISON COMMUNITY HOSPITAL, MADISON, SD, 431300, p. A596
MADISON COUNTY HEALTH CARE SYSTEM, WINTERSET, IA, 161326, p. A243
MADISON COUNTY HOSPITAL, LONDON, OH, 360189, p. A516
MADISON COUNTY MEDICAL CENTER, CANTON, MS, 250038, p. A367
MADISON COUNTY MEMORIAL HOSPITAL, MADISON, FL, 100004, p. A135
MADISON HOSPITAL, MADISON, MN, 240143, p. A356
MADISON MEDICAL CENTER, FREDERICKTOWN, MO, 261302, p. A382
MADISON MEMORIAL HOSPITAL, REXBURG, ID, 130025, p. A181
MADISON PARISH HOSPITAL, TALLULAH, LA, 191314, p. A293
MADISON ST. JOSEPH HEALTH CENTER, MADISONVILLE, TX, 451316, p. A655
MADISON STATE HOSPITAL, MADISON, IN, 152005, p. A221
MADISON VALLEY HOSPITAL, ENNIS, MT, 271329, p. A398
MADONNA REHABILITATION HOSPITAL, LINCOLN, NE, 283025, p. A409
MAGEE GENERAL HOSPITAL, MAGEE, MS, 250124, p. A372
MAGEE REHABILITATION HOSPITAL, PHILADELPHIA, PA, 393038, p. A568

MAGEE–WOMENS HOSPITAL OF UPMC, PITTSBURGH, PA, 390114, p. A571
MAGIC VALLEY REGIONAL MEDICAL CENTER, TWIN FALLS, ID, 130002, p. A182
MAGNOLIA HOSPITAL, MAGNOLIA, AR, 040067, p. A47
MAGNOLIA REGIONAL HEALTH CENTER, CORINTH, MS, 250009, p. A368
MAHASKA HEALTH PARTNERSHIP, OSKALOOSA, IA, 160050, p. A239
MAHNOMEN HEALTH CENTER, MAHNOMEN, MN, 241300, p. A356
MAHONING VALLEY HOSPITAL, YOUNGSTOWN, OH, 362023, p. A525
MAIMONIDES MEDICAL CENTER, NEW YORK, NY, 330194, p. A461
MAIN CAMPUS, BATTLE CREEK, MICHIGAN (*see* BATTLE CREEK HEALTH SYSTEM), p. A328
MAINE COAST MEMORIAL HOSPITAL, ELLSWORTH, ME, 200050, p. A298
MAINE MEDICAL CENTER, PORTLAND, ME, 200009, p. A300
MAINE MEDICAL CENTER, BRIGHTON CAMPUS, PORTLAND, MAINE (*see* MAINE MEDICAL CENTER), p. A300
MAINEGENERAL MEDICAL CENTER–AUGUSTA CAMPUS, AUGUSTA, MAINE (*see* MAINEGENERAL MEDICAL CENTER–WATERVILLE CAMPUS), p. A301
MAINEGENERAL MEDICAL CENTER–WATERVILLE CAMPUS, WATERVILLE, ME, 200039, p. A301
MAINLAND MEDICAL CENTER, TEXAS CITY, TX, 450530, p. A670
MAJOR HOSPITAL, SHELBYVILLE, IN, 150097, p. A225
MALCOLM GROW MEDICAL CENTER, ANDREWS AFB, MD, p. A302
MALCOM RANDALL VETERANS AFFAIRS MEDICAL CENTER, GAINESVILLE, FL, p. A129
MALVERN INSTITUTE, MALVERN, PA, p. A564
MAMMOTH HOSPITAL, MAMMOTH LAKES, CA, 051303, p. A74
MANATEE GLEN HOSPITAL, BRADENTON, FL, 104040, p. A124
MANATEE MEMORIAL HOSPITAL, BRADENTON, FL, 100035, p. A124
MANCHESTER MEMORIAL HOSPITAL, MANCHESTER, CT, 070027, p. A113
MANGUM CITY HOSPITAL, MANGUM, OK, 371330, p. A533
MANHASSET AMBULATORY CARE PAVILION, MANHASSET, NEW YORK (*see* LONG ISLAND JEWISH MEDICAL CENTER), p. A461
MANHATTAN EYE, EAR AND THROAT HOSPITAL, NEW YORK, NY, 330247, p. A462
MANHATTAN PSYCHIATRIC CENTER–WARD'S ISLAND, NEW YORK, NY, 334054, p. A462
MANHATTAN SURGICAL CENTER, NEW YORK, KS, 170190, p. A252
MANIILAQ HEALTH CENTER, KOTZEBUE, AK, 021310, p. A28
MANNING REGIONAL HEALTHCARE CENTER, MANNING, IA, 161332, p. A237
MANSFIELD HOSPITAL, MANSFIELD, OHIO (*see* MEDCENTRAL HEALTH SYSTEM), p. A517
MARCUM AND WALLACE MEMORIAL HOSPITAL, IRVINE, KY, 181301, p. A266
MARCUS DALY MEMORIAL HOSPITAL, HAMILTON, MT, 271340, p. A399
MARENGO MEMORIAL HOSPITAL, MARENGO, IA, 161317, p. A237
MARGARET MARY COMMUNITY HOSPITAL, BATESVILLE, IN, 150122, p. A211
MARGARET R. PARDEE MEMORIAL HOSPITAL, HENDERSONVILLE, NC, 340017, p. A484
MARGARETVILLE MEMORIAL HOSPITAL, MARGARETVILLE, NY, 331304, p. A456
MARIA PARHAM MEDICAL CENTER, HENDERSON, NC, 340132, p. A484
MARIAN COMMUNITY HOSPITAL, CARBONDALE, PA, 390095, p. A554
MARIAN MEDICAL CENTER, SANTA MARIA, CA, 050107, p. A93
MARIANJOY REHABILITATION HOSPITAL, WHEATON, IL, 143027, p. A210
MARIAS MEDICAL CENTER, SHELBY, MT, 271328, p. A402
MARICOPA INTEGRATED HEALTH SYSTEM, PHOENIX, AZ, 030022, p. A34
MARIETTA MEMORIAL HOSPITAL, MARIETTA, OH, 360147, p. A517
MARIN GENERAL HOSPITAL, GREENBRAE, CA, 050360, p. A63
MARINERS HOSPITAL, TAVERNIER, FL, 100160, p. A149
MARION COUNTY MEDICAL CENTER, MULLINS, SC, 420055, p. A590
MARION GENERAL HOSPITAL, MARION, IN, 150011, p. A221
MARION GENERAL HOSPITAL, COLUMBIA, MS, 250085, p. A368
MARION GENERAL HOSPITAL, MARION, OH, 360011, p. A517
MARK REED HOSPITAL, MCCLEARY, WA, 501304, p. A704

MERCY HOSPITAL–NORTH SHORE CAMPUS, PITTSBURGH, PA, 390136, p. A572

MERCY HOSPITAL–TURNER MEMORIAL, OZARK, AR, 041303, p. A49

MERCY JEANNETTE HOSPITAL, JEANNETTE, PA, 390010, p. A561

MERCY MEDICAL, DAPHNE, AL, 013027, p. A17

MERCY MEDICAL CENTER, DURANGO, CO, 060013, p. A104

MERCY MEDICAL CENTER, NAMPA, ID, 130013, p. A180

MERCY MEDICAL CENTER, CEDAR RAPIDS, IA, 160079, p. A229

MERCY MEDICAL CENTER, BALTIMORE, MD, 210008, p. A304

MERCY MEDICAL CENTER, SPRINGFIELD, MA, 220066, p. A323

MERCY MEDICAL CENTER, ROCKVILLE CENTRE, NY, 330259, p. A471

MERCY MEDICAL CENTER, WILLISTON, ND, 350017, p. A501

MERCY MEDICAL CENTER, CANTON, OH, 360070, p. A505

MERCY MEDICAL CENTER, SPRINGFIELD, OH, 360086, p. A522

MERCY MEDICAL CENTER, ROSEBURG, OR, 380027, p. A548

MERCY MEDICAL CENTER, OSHKOSH, WI, 520048, p. A733

MERCY MEDICAL CENTER – NORTH IOWA, MASON CITY, IA, 160064, p. A238

MERCY MEDICAL CENTER MERCED–COMMUNITY CAMPUS, MERCED, CA, 050444, p. A75

MERCY MEDICAL CENTER MERCED–DOMINICAN CAMPUS, MERCED, CA, 050117, p. A75

MERCY MEDICAL CENTER MOUNT SHASTA, MOUNT SHASTA, CA, 050419, p. A77

MERCY MEDICAL CENTER REDDING, REDDING, CA, 050280, p. A83

MERCY MEDICAL CENTER–CENTERVILLE, CENTERVILLE, IA, 160020, p. A230

MERCY MEDICAL CENTER–CLINTON, CLINTON, IA, 160080, p. A230

MERCY MEDICAL CENTER–DES MOINES, DES MOINES, IA, 160083, p. A233

MERCY MEDICAL CENTER–DUBUQUE, DUBUQUE, IA, 160069, p. A233

MERCY MEDICAL CENTER–DYERSVILLE, DYERSVILLE, IOWA (see MERCY MEDICAL CENTER–DUBUQUE), p. A233

MERCY MEDICAL CENTER–NEW HAMPTON, NEW HAMPTON, IA, 161331, p. A238

MERCY MEDICAL CENTER–SIOUX CITY, SIOUX CITY, IA, 160153, p. A241

MERCY MEMORIAL HEALTH CENTER, ARDMORE, OK, 370047, p. A527

MERCY MEMORIAL HOSPITAL, URBANA, OH, 361312, p. A523

MERCY MEMORIAL HOSPITAL SYSTEM, MONROE, MI, 230099, p. A340

MERCY REGIONAL HEALTH CENTER, NEW YORK, KS, 170142, p. A252

MERCY SAN JUAN HOSPITAL, CARMICHAEL, CALIFORNIA (see MERCY SAN JUAN MEDICAL CENTER), p. A56

MERCY SAN JUAN MEDICAL CENTER, CARMICHAEL, CA, 050516, p. A56

MERCY SERVICES FOR AGING, CLINTON, IOWA (see MERCY MEDICAL CENTER–CLINTON), p. A230

MERCY SOUTHWEST HOSPITAL, BAKERSFIELD, CALIFORNIA (see MERCY HOSPITAL), p. A54

MERCY SPECIAL CARE HOSPITAL, NANTICOKE, PA, 392025, p. A566

MERCY SUBURBAN HOSPITAL, NORRISTOWN, PA, 390116, p. A566

MERIDELL ACHIEVEMENT CENTER, LIBERTY HILL, TX, p. A653

MERITCARE MEDICAL CENTER, FARGO, ND, 350011, p. A497

MERITCARE SOUTH UNIVERSITY, FARGO, NORTH DAKOTA (see MERITCARE MEDICAL CENTER), p. A497

MERITER HOSPITAL, MADISON, WI, 520089, p. A728

MERLE WEST MEDICAL CENTER, KLAMATH FALLS, OR, 380050, p. A545

MERRILL PIONEER COMMUNITY HOSPITAL, ROCK RAPIDS, IA, 161321, p. A240

MERRIMACK VALLEY HOSPITAL, HAVERHILL, MA, 220174, p. A318

MESA GENERAL HOSPITAL MEDICAL CENTER, MESA, AZ, 030017, p. A32

MESA HILL SPECIALTY HOSPITAL, EL PASO, TX, 452035, p. A637

MESA VIEW REGIONAL HOSPITAL, MESQUITE, NV, 291307, p. A417

MESILLA VALLEY HOSPITAL, LAS CRUCES, NM, 324010, p. A443

MESQUITE COMMUNITY HOSPITAL, MESQUITE, TX, 450688, p. A656

METHODIST AMBULATORY SURGERY HOSPITAL, SAN ANTONIO, TX, 450780, p. A664

METHODIST BEHAVIORAL HOSPITAL OF ARKANSAS, MAUMELLE, AR, 044017, p. A47

METHODIST CHARLTON MEDICAL CENTER, DALLAS, TX, 450723, p. A633

METHODIST CHILDREN'S HOSPITAL OF SOUTH TEXAS, SAN ANTONIO, TX, 450388, p. A664

METHODIST DALLAS MEDICAL CENTER, DALLAS, TX, 450051, p. A633

METHODIST HEALTHCARE – EXTENDED CARE HOSPITAL, MEMPHIS, TN, 442013, p. A613

METHODIST HEALTHCARE–FAYETTE HOSPITAL, SOMERVILLE, TN, 440168, p. A618

METHODIST HEALTHCARE–GERMANTOWN HOSPITAL, GERMANTOWN, TENNESSEE (see METHODIST HEALTHCARE–UNIVERSITY HOSPITAL), p. A613

METHODIST HEALTHCARE–NORTH HOSPITAL, MEMPHIS, TENNESSEE (see METHODIST HEALTHCARE–UNIVERSITY HOSPITAL), p. A613

METHODIST HEALTHCARE–SOUTH HOSPITAL, MEMPHIS, TENNESSEE (see METHODIST HEALTHCARE–UNIVERSITY HOSPITAL), p. A613

METHODIST HEALTHCARE–UNIVERSITY HOSPITAL, MEMPHIS, TN, 440049, p. A613

METHODIST HEALTHCARE–UNIVERSITY HOSPITAL, MEMPHIS, TENNESSEE (see METHODIST HEALTHCARE–UNIVERSITY HOSPITAL), p. A613

METHODIST HOSPITAL, HENDERSON, KY, 180056, p. A266

METHODIST HOSPITAL, NEW ORLEANS, LA, 190124, p. A289

METHODIST HOSPITAL, SAINT LOUIS PARK, MN, 240053, p. A361

METHODIST HOSPITAL, SAN ANTONIO, TX, 450388, p. A664

METHODIST HOSPITAL, PHILADELPHIA, PENNSYLVANIA (see THOMAS JEFFERSON UNIVERSITY HOSPITAL), p. A570

METHODIST HOSPITAL OF CHICAGO, CHICAGO, IL, 140197, p. A188

METHODIST HOSPITAL OF INDIANA, INDIANAPOLIS, INDIANA (see CLARIAN HEALTH PARTNERS), p. A218

METHODIST HOSPITAL OF SACRAMENTO, SACRAMENTO, CA, 050590, p. A85

METHODIST HOSPITAL OF SOUTHERN CALIFORNIA, ARCADIA, CA, 050238, p. A53

METHODIST HOSPITAL UNION COUNTY, MORGANFIELD, KY, 181306, p. A272

METHODIST HOSPITALS, GARY, IN, 150002, p. A216

METHODIST MEDICAL CENTER OF ILLINOIS, PEORIA, IL, 140209, p. A205

METHODIST MEDICAL CENTER OF OAK RIDGE, OAK RIDGE, TN, 440034, p. A616

METHODIST REHABILITATION CENTER, JACKSON, MS, 250152, p. A370

METHODIST SPECIALTY AND TRANSPLANT HOSPITAL, SAN ANTONIO, TEXAS (see METHODIST HOSPITAL), p. A664

METHODIST SUGAR LAND HOSPITAL, SUGAR LAND, TX, 450820, p. A668

METHODIST WILLOWBROOK HOSPITAL, HOUSTON, TX, 450844, p. A646

METROHEALTH MEDICAL CENTER, CLEVELAND, OH, 360059, p. A509

METROPLEX ADVENTIST HOSPITAL, KILLEEN, TX, 450152, p. A651

METROPOLITAN GENERAL CARE UNIT, METROPOLITAN DRUG DETOXIFICATION AND METROPOLITAN PSYCHIATRIC UNIT (see METROPOLITAN HOSPITAL CENTER), p. A462

METROPOLITAN HOSPITAL, GRAND RAPIDS, MI, 230236, p. A334

METROPOLITAN HOSPITAL CENTER, NEW YORK, NY, 330199, p. A462

METROPOLITAN METHODIST HOSPITAL, SAN ANTONIO, TX, p. A664

METROPOLITAN NASHVILLE GENERAL HOSPITAL, NASHVILLE, TN, 440111, p. A615

METROPOLITAN ST. LOUIS PSYCHIATRIC CENTER, SAINT LOUIS, MO, 264025, p. A391

METROPOLITAN STATE HOSPITAL, NORWALK, CA, 054133, p. A78

METROWEST MEDICAL CENTER, FRAMINGHAM, MA, 220089, p. A318

MEYERSDALE MEDICAL CENTER, MEYERSDALE, PA, 391302, p. A565

MIAMI CHILDREN'S HOSPITAL, MIAMI, FL, 103301, p. A137

MIAMI COUNTY MEDICAL CENTER, PAOLA, KS, 170109, p. A255

MIAMI HEART INSTITUTE AND MEDICAL CENTER, MIAMI, FLORIDA (see MOUNT SINAI MEDICAL CENTER), p. A138

MIAMI JEWISH HOME AND HOSPITAL FOR AGED, MIAMI, FL, 100277, p. A137

MIAMI VALLEY HOSPITAL, DAYTON, OH, 360051, p. A512

MICHAEL E. DEBAKEY VETERANS AFFAIRS MEDICAL CENTER, HOUSTON, TX, p. A646

MICHAEL REESE HOSPITAL AND MEDICAL CENTER, CHICAGO, IL, 140075, p. A188

MICHIANA BEHAVIORAL HEALTH CENTER, PLYMOUTH, IN, 154047, p. A223

MICHIGAN ORTHOPAEDIC SPECIATY HOSPITAL, MADISON HEIGHTS, MI, 230186, p. A339

MID COAST HOSPITAL, BRUNSWICK, ME, 200021, p. A297

MID DAKOTA MEDICAL CENTER, CHAMBERLAIN, SD, 431329, p. A594

MID MISSOURI MENTAL HEALTH CENTER, COLUMBIA, MO, 264011, p. A381

MID–AMERICA REHABILITATION HOSPITAL, SHAWNEE MISSION, KS, 173026, p. A257

MID–COLUMBIA MEDICAL CENTER, THE DALLES, OR, 380001, p. A549

MID–HUDSON FORENSIC PSYCHIATRIC CENTER, NEW HAMPTON, NY, 334061, p. A457

MID–VALLEY HOSPITAL, PECKVILLE, PA, 390109, p. A567

MID–VALLEY HOSPITAL, OMAK, WA, 501328, p. A705

MIDDLE TENNESSEE MEDICAL CENTER, MURFREESBORO, TN, 440053, p. A614

MIDDLE TENNESSEE MENTAL HEALTH INSTITUTE, NASHVILLE, TN, 444014, p. A615

MIDDLESBORO APPALACHIAN REGIONAL HOSPITAL, MIDDLESBORO, KY, 180020, p. A271

MIDDLESEX HOSPITAL, MIDDLETOWN, CT, 070020, p. A114

MIDDLETOWN PSYCHIATRIC CENTER, MIDDLETOWN, NY, 334017, p. A456

MIDDLETOWN REGIONAL HOSPITAL, MIDDLETOWN, OH, 360076, p. A519

MIDLAND MEMORIAL HOSPITAL, MIDLAND, TX, 450133, p. A657

MIDLAND MEMORIAL HOSPITAL, MIDLAND, TX, 450545, p. A657

MIDLAND MEMORIAL HOSPITAL–WEST CAMPUS, MIDLAND, TEXAS (see MIDLAND MEMORIAL HOSPITAL), p. A657

MIDLANDS CENTER, COLUMBIA, SC, p. A586

MIDMICHIGAN MEDICAL CENTER–CLARE, CLARE, MI, 230180, p. A330

MIDMICHIGAN MEDICAL CENTER–GLADWIN, GLADWIN, MI, 230189, p. A334

MIDMICHIGAN MEDICAL CENTER–MIDLAND, MIDLAND, MI, 230222, p. A340

MIDSTATE MEDICAL CENTER, MERIDEN, CT, 070017, p. A114

MIDWEST REGIONAL MEDICAL CENTER, MIDWEST CITY, OK, 370094, p. A533

MIDWESTERN REGIONAL MEDICAL CENTER, ZION, IL, 140100, p. A210

MIKE O'CALLAGHAN FEDERAL HOSPITAL, NELLIS AFB, NV, p. A417

MILAN GENERAL HOSPITAL, MILAN, TN, 440060, p. A614

MILBANK AREA HOSPITAL/AVERA HEALTH, MILBANK, SD, 431326, p. A597

MILDRED MITCHELL–BATEMAN HOSPITAL, HUNTINGTON, WV, 514009, p. A716

MILE BLUFF MEDICAL CENTER, MAUSTON, WI, 520109, p. A729

MILES MEMORIAL HOSPITAL, DAMARISCOTTA, ME, 200002, p. A298

MILFORD HOSPITAL, MILFORD, CT, 070019, p. A114

MILFORD REGIONAL MEDICAL CENTER, MILFORD, MA, 220090, p. A320

MILFORD VALLEY MEMORIAL HOSPITAL, MILFORD, UT, 461305, p. A677

MILLARD FILLMORE GATES CIRCLE HOSPITAL, BUFFALO, NEW YORK (see BUFFALO GENERAL HOSPITAL), p. A448

MILLARD FILLMORE SUBURBAN HOSPITAL, WILLIAMSVILLE, NEW YORK (see BUFFALO GENERAL HOSPITAL), p. A448

MILLCREEK COMMUNITY HOSPITAL, ERIE, PA, 390198, p. A558

MILLE LACS HEALTH SYSTEM, ONAMIA, MN, 241356, p. A359

MILLER CHILDREN'S HOSPITAL, LONG BEACH, CA, 053309, p. A68

MILLER COUNTY HOSPITAL, COLQUITT, GA, 111305, p. A158

MILLER–DWAN MEDICAL CENTER, DULUTH, MN, 240019, p. A352

MILLINOCKET REGIONAL HOSPITAL, MILLINOCKET, ME, 201307, p. A299

MILLS HOSPITAL, SAN MATEO, CALIFORNIA (see MILLS–PENINSULA HEALTH SERVICES), p. A55

MILLS–PENINSULA HEALTH SERVICES, BURLINGAME, CA, 050007, p. A55

MILLWOOD HOSPITAL, ARLINGTON, TX, 454012, p. A622

MILTON HOSPITAL, MILTON, MA, 220108, p. A320

MILWAUKEE COUNTY BEHAVIORAL HEALTH DIVISION, MILWAUKEE, WI, 524001, p. A731

MIMBRES MEMORIAL HOSPITAL, DEMING, NM, 320014, p. A442

MINDEN MEDICAL CENTER, MINDEN, LA, 190144, p. A287

MINERAL AREA REGIONAL MEDICAL CENTER, FARMINGTON, MO, 260116, p. A382

MINERAL COMMUNITY HOSPITAL, SUPERIOR, MT, 271331, p. A402

MINERS MEDICAL CENTER, HASTINGS, PA, 390130, p. A560

MINERS' COLFAX MEDICAL CENTER, RATON, NM, 320069, p. A444

MINERS' HOSPITAL OF NEW MEXICO, RATON, NEW MEXICO (see MINERS' COLFAX MEDICAL CENTER), p. A444

MINIDOKA MEMORIAL HOSPITAL AND EXTENDED CARE FACILITY, RUPERT, ID, 131319, p. A181

MINNEOLA DISTRICT HOSPITAL, MINNEOLA, KS, 171368, p. A253

MINNESOTA VALLEY HEALTH CENTER, LE SUEUR, MN, 240021, p. A355

MINNEWASKA DISTRICT HOSPITAL, STARBUCK, MN, 241310, p. A363

MINNIE G. BOSWELL MEMORIAL HOSPITAL, GREENSBORO, GA, 111329, p. A163

MINNIE HAMILTON HEALTHCARE CENTER, GRANTSVILLE, WV, 511303, p. A715

MIRIAM HOSPITAL, PROVIDENCE, RI, 410012, p. A581

MISSION COMMUNITY HOSPITAL–PANORAMA CITY CAMPUS, LOS ANGELES, CALIFORNIA (see MISSION COMMUNITY HOSPITAL–SAN FERNANDO CAMPUS), p. A88

MISSION COMMUNITY HOSPITAL–PANORAMA CITY CAMPUS, PANORAMA CITY, CALIFORNIA (see (see MISSION COMMUNITY HOSPITAL–SAN FERNANDO CAMPUS)), p. A88

MISSION COMMUNITY HOSPITAL–SAN FERNANDO CAMPUS, SAN FERNANDO, CA, 050704, p. A88

MISSION HOSPITAL, MISSION VIEJO, CA, 050567, p. A75

MISSION HOSPITAL, MISSION, TX, 450176, p. A657

MISSION HOSPITAL OF HUNTINGTON PARK, HUNTINGTON PARK, CALIFORNIA (see COMMUNITY AND MISSION HOSPITALS OF HUNTINGTON PARK), p. A64

MISSION HOSPITALS, ASHEVILLE, NC, 340002, p. A477

MISSION VISTA GERIATRIC PSYCHIATRIC HOSPITAL, SAN ANTONIO, TX, 454078, p. A664

MISSISSIPPI BAPTIST HEALTH SYSTEMS, JACKSON, MS, 250102, p. A370

MISSISSIPPI HOSPITAL FOR RESTORATIVE CARE, JACKSON, MS, 252003, p. A371

MISSISSIPPI STATE HOSPITAL, WHITFIELD, MS, p. A377

MISSOURI BAPTIST HOSPITAL–SULLIVAN, SULLIVAN, MO, 260115, p. A394

MISSOURI BAPTIST MEDICAL CENTER, TOWN AND COUNTRY, MO, 260108, p. A394

MISSOURI DELTA MEDICAL CENTER, SIKESTON, MO, 260113, p. A393

MISSOURI REHABILITATION CENTER, MOUNT VERNON, MO, 262001, p. A388

MISSOURI RIVER MEDICAL CENTER, FORT BENTON, MT, 271304, p. A398

MISSOURI SOUTHERN HEALTHCARE, DEXTER, MO, 260160, p. A381

MITCHELL COUNTY HOSPITAL, CAMILLA, GA, 111331, p. A157

MITCHELL COUNTY HOSPITAL, BELOIT, KS, 171375, p. A244

MITCHELL COUNTY HOSPITAL, COLORADO CITY, TX, 451342, p. A629

MITCHELL COUNTY REGIONAL HEALTH CENTER, OSAGE, IA, 161323, p. A239

MIZELL MEMORIAL HOSPITAL, OPP, AL, 010007, p. A23

MOBERLY REGIONAL MEDICAL CENTER, MOBERLY, MO, 260074, p. A388

MOBILE INFIRMARY MEDICAL CENTER, MOBILE, AL, 010113, p. A21

MOBRIDGE REGIONAL HOSPITAL, MOBRIDGE, SD, 431325, p. A597

MOCCASIN BEND MENTAL HEALTH INSTITUTE, CHATTANOOGA, TN, 444002, p. A604

MODOC MEDICAL CENTER, ALTURAS, CA, 050430, p. A52

MOHAWK VALLEY PSYCHIATRIC CENTER, UTICA, NY, 334021, p. A474

MOLOKAI GENERAL HOSPITAL, KAUNAKAKAI, HI, 121303, p. A175

MONADNOCK COMMUNITY HOSPITAL, PETERBOROUGH, NH, 301309, p. A423

MONCRIEF ARMY COMMUNITY HOSPITAL, FORT JACKSON, SC, p. A588

MONMOUTH MEDICAL CENTER, LONG BRANCH, NJ, 310075, p. A430

MONONGAHELA VALLEY HOSPITAL, MONONGAHELA, PA, 390147, p. A565

MONONGALIA GENERAL HOSPITAL, MORGANTOWN, WV, 510024, p. A718

MONROE COUNTY HOSPITAL, MONROEVILLE, AL, 010120, p. A21

MONROE COUNTY HOSPITAL, FORSYTH, GA, 111318, p. A162

MONROE COUNTY HOSPITAL, ALBIA, IA, 161342, p. A228

MONROE COUNTY MEDICAL CENTER, TOMPKINSVILLE, KY, 180105, p. A275

MONROE SURGICAL HOSPITAL, MONROE, LA, 190245, p. A287

MONSIGNOR JAMES H FITZPATRICK PAVILION FOR SKILLED NURSING CARE, NEW YORK, NEW YORK (see SAINT

VINCENTS CATHOLIC MEDICAL CENTERS OF NEW YORK), p. A465

MONSIGNOR JAMES H FITZPATRICK PAVILION FOR SKILLED NURSING CARE, JAMAICA, NEW YORK (see (see SAINT VINCENTS CATHOLIC MEDICAL CENTERS OF NEW YORK)), p. A465

MONSOUR MEDICAL CENTER, JEANNETTE, PA, 390103, p. A561

MONTANA STATE HOSPITAL, WARM SPRINGS, MT, 274086, p. A402

MONTEFIORE HOSPITAL, PITTSBURGH, PENNSYLVANIA (see UPMC PRESBYTERIAN), p. A572

MONTEFIORE MEDICAL CENTER, NEW YORK, NY, 330059, p. A462

MONTEREY PARK HOSPITAL, MONTEREY PARK, CA, 050591, p. A76

MONTEVISTA HOSPITAL, LAS VEGAS, NV, p. A416

MONTFORT JONES MEMORIAL HOSPITAL, KOSCIUSKO, MS, 250059, p. A371

MONTGOMERY COUNTY EMERGENCY SERVICE, NORRISTOWN, PA, 394033, p. A566

MONTGOMERY COUNTY MEMORIAL HOSPITAL, RED OAK, IA, 161363, p. A240

MONTGOMERY DIVISION, MONTGOMERY, ALABAMA (see CENTRAL ALABAMA VETERANS HEALTH CARE SYSTEM), p. A22

MONTGOMERY GENERAL HOSPITAL, OLNEY, MD, 210018, p. A309

MONTGOMERY GENERAL HOSPITAL, MONTGOMERY, WV, 511318, p. A717

MONTGOMERY HOSPITAL MEDICAL CENTER, NORRISTOWN, PA, 390108, p. A566

MONTGOMERY REGIONAL HOSPITAL, BLACKSBURG, VA, 490110, p. A686

MONTICELLO BIG LAKE HOSPITAL, MONTICELLO, MN, 241362, p. A358

MONTPELIER HOSPITAL, MONTPELIER, OHIO (see COMMUNITY HOSPITALS AND WELLNESS CENTERS), p. A504

MONTROSE MEMORIAL HOSPITAL, MONTROSE, CO, 060006, p. A108

MOORE COUNTY HOSPITAL DISTRICT, DUMAS, TX, 450221, p. A636

MOREHEAD MEMORIAL HOSPITAL, EDEN, NC, 340060, p. A481

MOREHOUSE GENERAL HOSPITAL, BASTROP, LA, 190116, p. A277

MORENO VALLEY COMMUNITY HOSPITAL, MORENO VALLEY, CA, 050694, p. A77

MORGAN COUNTY APPALACHIAN REGIONAL HOSPITAL, WEST LIBERTY, KY, 181307, p. A275

MORGAN COUNTY WAR MEMORIAL HOSPITAL, BERKELEY SPRINGS, WV, 511309, p. A713

MORGAN HOSPITAL AND MEDICAL CENTER, MARTINSVILLE, IN, 150038, p. A222

MORGAN MEMORIAL HOSPITAL, MADISON, GA, 111304, p. A165

MORGAN STANLEY CHILDREN'S HOSPITAL OF NEW YORK–PRESBYTERIAN, NEW YORK, NEW YORK (see NEW YORK–PRESBYTERIAN HOSPITAL), p. A463

MORRILL COUNTY COMMUNITY HOSPITAL, BRIDGEPORT, NE, 281318, p. A405

MORRIS COUNTY HOSPITAL, COUNCIL GROVE, KS, 170070, p. A246

MORRIS HOSPITAL & HEALTHCARE CENTERS, MORRIS, IL, 140101, p. A201

MORRISON COMMUNITY HOSPITAL, MORRISON, IL, 141329, p. A201

MORRISTOWN MEMORIAL HOSPITAL, MORRISTOWN, NJ, 310015, p. A431

MORRISTOWN–HAMBLEN HOSPITAL, MORRISTOWN, TN, 440030, p. A614

MORROW COUNTY HOSPITAL, MOUNT GILEAD, OH, 361313, p. A519

MORTON COUNTY HEALTH SYSTEM, ELKHART, KS, 170166, p. A246

MORTON GENERAL HOSPITAL, MORTON, WA, 501319, p. A704

MORTON HOSPITAL AND MEDICAL CENTER, TAUNTON, MA, 220073, p. A324

MORTON PLANT HOSPITAL, CLEARWATER, FL, 100127, p. A125

MORTON PLANT NORTH BAY HOSPITAL, NEW PORT RICHEY, FL, 100063, p. A139

MOSES CONE HEALTH SYSTEM, GREENSBORO, NC, 340091, p. A484

MOSES H. CONE MEMORIAL HOSPITAL, GREENSBORO, NORTH CAROLINA (see MOSES CONE HEALTH SYSTEM), p. A484

MOSES LUDINGTON HOSPITAL, TICONDEROGA, NY, 331306, p. A474

MOSES TAYLOR HOSPITAL, SCRANTON, PA, 390119, p. A575

MOSS REHAB, PHILADELPHIA, PENNSYLVANIA (see ALBERT EINSTEIN MEDICAL CENTER), p. A567

MOSS REHAB, EINSTEIN AT ELKINS PARK, ELKINS PARK, PA, 390289, p. A558

MOTHER FRANCES HOSPITAL – JACKSONVILLE, JACKSONVILLE, TX, 451319, p. A650

MOTION PICTURE AND TELEVISION FUND HOSPITAL AND RESIDENTIAL SERVICES, LOS ANGELES, CA, 050552, p. A71

MOUNDVIEW MEMORIAL HOSPITAL & CLINICS, FRIENDSHIP, WI, 521309, p. A726

MOUNT AUBURN HOSPITAL, CAMBRIDGE, MA, 220002, p. A316

MOUNT CARMEL, COLUMBUS, OH, 360035, p. A510

MOUNT CARMEL EAST HOSPITAL, COLUMBUS, OHIO (see MOUNT CARMEL), p. A510

MOUNT CARMEL HOSPITAL, COLVILLE, WA, 501326, p. A701

MOUNT CARMEL ST. ANN'S, WESTERVILLE, OH, 360012, p. A524

MOUNT CARMEL WEST HOSPITAL, COLUMBUS, OHIO (see MOUNT CARMEL), p. A510

MOUNT CLEMENS GENERAL HOSPITAL, MOUNT CLEMENS, MI, 230227, p. A340

MOUNT DESERT ISLAND HOSPITAL, BAR HARBOR, ME, 201304, p. A296

MOUNT DIABLO MEDICAL CENTER, CONCORD, CA, 050496, p. A57

MOUNT GRANT GENERAL HOSPITAL, HAWTHORNE, NV, 291300, p. A415

MOUNT NITTANY MEDICAL CENTER, STATE COLLEGE, PA, 390268, p. A576

MOUNT REGIS CENTER, SALEM, VA, p. A696

MOUNT SINAI HOSPITAL MEDICAL CENTER OF CHICAGO, CHICAGO, IL, 140018, p. A188

MOUNT SINAI HOSPTIAL, NEW YORK, NY, 330024, p. A462

MOUNT SINAI MEDICAL CENTER, MIAMI BEACH, FL, 100034, p. A138

MOUNT ST. MARY'S HOSPITAL AND HEALTH CENTER, LEWISTON, NY, 330188, p. A455

MOUNT VERNON HOSPITAL, MOUNT VERNON, NY, 330086, p. A457

MOUNTAIN CREST HOSPITAL, FORT COLLINS, COLORADO (see POUDRE VALLEY HOSPITAL), p. A105

MOUNTAIN MANOR TREATMENT CENTER, EMMITSBURG, MD, p. A308

MOUNTAIN VIEW HOSPITAL, GADSDEN, AL, 014006, p. A19

MOUNTAIN VIEW HOSPITAL, IDAHO FALLS, ID, 130065, p. A179

MOUNTAIN VIEW HOSPITAL, PAYSON, UT, 460013, p. A678

MOUNTAIN VIEW HOSPITAL DISTRICT, MADRAS, OR, 380081, p. A545

MOUNTAIN VIEW REGIONAL MEDICAL CENTER, NORTON, VA, 490027, p. A693

MOUNTAIN WEST MEDICAL CENTER, TOOELE, UT, 460014, p. A680

MOUNTAINS COMMUNITY HOSPITAL, LAKE ARROWHEAD, CA, 051312, p. A66

MOUNTAINSIDE HOSPITAL, MONTCLAIR, NJ, 310054, p. A431

MOUNTAINVIEW HOSPITAL, LAS VEGAS, NV, 290039, p. A416

MOUNTAINVIEW MEDICAL CENTER, WHITE SULPHUR SPRINGS, MT, 271306, p. A402

MOUNTAINVIEW REGIONAL MEDICAL CENTER, LAS CRUCES, NM, 320085, p. A443

MOUNTRAIL COUNTY MEDICAL CENTER, STANLEY, ND, 351301, p. A500

MT. ASCUTNEY HOSPITAL AND HEALTH CENTER, WINDSOR, VT, 471302, p. A684

MT. CARMEL BEHAVIORAL HEALTHCARE SYSTEM, NEWARK, NJ, 314010, p. A432

MT. CARMEL REGIONAL MEDICAL CENTER, PITTSBURG, KS, 170006, p. A255

MT. DIABLO MEDICAL PAVILION, CONCORD, CA, 054131, p. A57

MT. GRAHAM REGIONAL MEDICAL CENTER, SAFFORD, AZ, 030068, p. A36

MT. SAN RAFAEL HOSPITAL, TRINIDAD, CO, 061321, p. A110

MT. WASHINGTON PEDIATRIC HOSPITAL, BALTIMORE, MD, 213300, p. A304

MUENSTER MEMORIAL HOSPITAL, MUENSTER, TX, 451335, p. A658

MUHLENBERG COMMUNITY HOSPITAL, GREENVILLE, KY, 180004, p. A265

MUHLENBERG REGIONAL MEDICAL CENTER, NORTH PLAINFIELD, NJ, 310063, p. A433

MULESHOE AREA MEDICAL CENTER, MULESHOE, TX, 450761, p. A658

MUNCY VALLEY HOSPITAL, MUNCY, PENNSYLVANIA (see SUSQUEHANNA HEALTH SYSTEM), p. A580

MUNISING MEMORIAL HOSPITAL, MUNISING, MI, 231308, p. A341

MUNROE REGIONAL MEDICAL CENTER, OCALA, FL, 100062, p. A140

MUNSON MEDICAL CENTER, TRAVERSE CITY, MI, 230097, p. A346

MURPHY MEDICAL CENTER, MURPHY, NC, 340160, p. A488
MURRAY COUNTY MEMORIAL HOSPITAL, SLAYTON, MN, 241319, p. A363
MURRAY MEDICAL CENTER, CHATSWORTH, GA, 110050, p. A158
MURRAY–CALLOWAY COUNTY HOSPITAL, MURRAY, KY, 180027, p. A272
MUSC MEDICAL CENTER OF MEDICAL UNIVERSITY OF SOUTH CAROLINA, CHARLESTON, SC, 420004, p. A584
MUSKOGEE REGIONAL MEDICAL CENTER, MUSKOGEE, OK, 370025, p. A534
MYRTLE WERTH HOSPITAL–MAYO HEALTH SYSTEM, MENOMONIE, WI, 521340, p. A729

N

NACOGDOCHES MEDICAL CENTER, NACOGDOCHES, TX, 450656, p. A658
NACOGDOCHES MEMORIAL HOSPITAL, NACOGDOCHES, TX, 450508, p. A658
NANTICOKE MEMORIAL HOSPITAL, SEAFORD, DE, 080006, p. A119
NANTUCKET COTTAGE HOSPITAL, NANTUCKET, MA, 221301, p. A321
NAPA STATE HOSPITAL, NAPA, CA, 054122, p. A77
NAPLES COMMUNITY HOSPITAL, NAPLES, FL, 100018, p. A139
NASH HEALTH CARE SYSTEMS, ROCKY MOUNT, NC, 340147, p. A490
NASHOBA VALLEY MEDICAL CENTER, AYER, MA, 220098, p. A312
NASHVILLE REHABILITATION HOSPITAL, NASHVILLE, TN, 440026, p. A615
NASON HOSPITAL, ROARING SPRING, PA, 390062, p. A574
NASSAU UNIVERSITY MEDICAL CENTER, EAST MEADOW, NY, 330027, p. A451
NATCHAUG HOSPITAL, MANSFIELD CENTER, CT, 074008, p. A114
NATCHEZ COMMUNITY HOSPITAL, NATCHEZ, MS, 250122, p. A373
NATCHEZ REGIONAL MEDICAL CENTER, NATCHEZ, MS, 250084, p. A373
NATCHITOCHES PARISH HOSPITAL, NATCHITOCHES, LA, 190007, p. A288
NATHAN LITTAUER HOSPITAL AND NURSING HOME, GLOVERSVILLE, NY, 330276, p. A453
NATIONAL JEWISH MEDICAL AND RESEARCH CENTER, DENVER, CO, 060107, p. A103
NATIONAL NAVAL MEDICAL CENTER, BETHESDA, MD, p. A305
NATIONAL PARK MEDICAL CENTER, HOT SPRINGS, AR, 040078, p. A44
NATIONAL REHABILITATION HOSPITAL, WASHINGTON, DC, 093025, p. A122
NATIVIDAD MEDICAL CENTER, SALINAS, CA, 050248, p. A86
NATURE COAST REGIONAL HOSPITAL, WILLISTON, FL, 100139, p. A151
NAVAL HOSPITAL, CAMP PENDLETON, CA, p. A56
NAVAL HOSPITAL, LEMOORE, CA, p. A67
NAVAL HOSPITAL, TWENTYNINE PALMS, CA, p. A97
NAVAL HOSPITAL, JACKSONVILLE, FL, p. A132
NAVAL HOSPITAL, PENSACOLA, FL, p. A143
NAVAL HOSPITAL, GREAT LAKES, IL, p. A195
NAVAL HOSPITAL, CAMP LEJEUNE, NC, p. A479
NAVAL HOSPITAL, CHERRY POINT, NC, p. A480
NAVAL HOSPITAL, BEAUFORT, SC, p. A584
NAVAL HOSPITAL, NORTH CHARLESTON, SC, p. A591
NAVAL HOSPITAL, CORPUS CHRISTI, TX, p. A631
NAVAL HOSPITAL, BREMERTON, WA, p. A701
NAVAL HOSPITAL, OAK HARBOR, WA, p. A704
NAVAL MEDICAL CENTER, SAN DIEGO, CA, p. A87
NAVAL MEDICAL CENTER, PORTSMOUTH, VA, p. A694
NAVAPACHE REGIONAL MEDICAL CENTER, SHOW LOW, AZ, 030062, p. A36
NAVARRO REGIONAL HOSPITAL, CORSICANA, TX, 450447, p. A631
NAZARETH HOSPITAL, PHILADELPHIA, PA, 390204, p. A569
NCED MENTAL HEALTH CENTER, EL PASO, TX, 454097, p. A637
NEA MEDICAL CENTER, JONESBORO, AR, 040118, p. A45
NEBRASKA HEART INSTITUTE, LINCOLN, NE, 280128, p. A409
NEBRASKA MEDICAL CENTER, OMAHA, NE, 280013, p. A411
NEBRASKA METHODIST HOSPITAL, OMAHA, NE, 280040, p. A411
NEBRASKA ORTHOPAEDIC HOSPITAL, OMAHA, NE, 280129, p. A411
NEILLSVILLE MEMORIAL HOME (see MEMORIAL MEDICAL CENTER), p. A732

NELSON COUNTY HEALTH SYSTEM, MCVILLE, ND, 351308, p. A499
NEMAHA COUNTY HOSPITAL, AUBURN, NE, 281324, p. A404
NEMAHA VALLEY COMMUNITY HOSPITAL, SENECA, KS, 171315, p. A257
NEOSHO MEMORIAL REGIONAL MEDICAL CENTER, CHANUTE, KS, 170143, p. A245
NESHOBA COUNTY GENERAL HOSPITAL, PHILADELPHIA, MS, 250043, p. A374
NESS COUNTY HOSPITAL, NESS CITY, KS, 171336, p. A253
NEURO MEDICAL CENTER HOSPITAL, BATON ROUGE, LA, 190266, p. A277
NEVADA REGIONAL MEDICAL CENTER, NEVADA, MO, 260061, p. A388
NEW ALBANY SURGICAL HOSPITAL, NEW ALBANY, OH, 360266, p. A519
NEW BEDFORD REHABILITATION HOSPITAL, NEW BEDFORD, MA, p. A321
NEW BRITAIN GENERAL HOSPITAL, NEW BRITAIN, CT, 070035, p. A114
NEW ENGLAND BAPTIST HOSPITAL, BOSTON, MA, 220088, p. A314
NEW ENGLAND REHABILITATION HOSPITAL OF PORTLAND, PORTLAND, ME, 203025, p. A300
NEW ENGLAND SINAI HOSPITAL AND REHABILITATION CENTER, STOUGHTON, MA, 222027, p. A324
NEW HAMPSHIRE HOSPITAL, CONCORD, NH, 304000, p. A420
NEW HANOVER REGIONAL MEDICAL CENTER, WILMINGTON, NC, 340141, p. A494
NEW HORIZONS HEALTH SYSTEMS, INC., OWENTON, KY, 181312, p. A273
NEW ISLAND HOSPITAL, BETHPAGE, NY, 330332, p. A448
NEW LONDON FAMILY MEDICAL CENTER, NEW LONDON, WI, 521326, p. A732
NEW LONDON HOSPITAL, NEW LONDON, NH, 301304, p. A423
NEW MEXICO REHABILITATION CENTER, ROSWELL, NM, 323026, p. A444
NEW MILFORD HOSPITAL, NEW MILFORD, CT, 070015, p. A115
NEW ORLEANS ADOLESCENT HOSPITAL, NEW ORLEANS, LA, 194012, p. A289
NEW ORLEANS EAST REHABILITATION HOSPITAL, NEW ORLEANS, LA, 193089, p. A289
NEW ULM MEDICAL CENTER, NEW ULM, MN, 240083, p. A358
NEW YORK COMMUNITY HOSPITAL, NEW YORK, NY, 330019, p. A462
NEW YORK EYE AND EAR INFIRMARY, NEW YORK, NY, 330100, p. A463
NEW YORK HOSPITAL MEDICAL CENTER OF QUEENS, NEW YORK, NY, 330055, p. A463
NEW YORK METHODIST HOSPITAL, NEW YORK, NY, 330236, p. A463
NEW YORK STATE PSYCHIATRIC INSTITUTE, NEW YORK, NY, 334009, p. A463
NEW YORK UNITED HOSPITAL MEDICAL CENTER, PORT CHESTER, NY, 330171, p. A469
NEW YORK UNIVERSITY MEDICAL CENTER, NEW YORK, NY, 330214, p. A463
NEW YORK WESTCHESTER SQUARE MEDICAL CENTER, NEW YORK, NY, 330316, p. A463
NEW YORK–PRESBYTERIAN HOSPITAL, NEW YORK, NY, 330101, p. A463
NEW YORK–PRESBYTERIAN HOSPITAL, WESTCHESTER DIVISION, NEW YORK, NEW YORK (see NEW YORK–PRESBYTERIAN HOSPITAL), p. A463
NEW YORK–PRESBYTERIAN HOSPITAL/WEILL CORNELL MEDICAL CENTER, NEW YORK, NEW YORK (see NEW YORK–PRESBYTERIAN HOSPITAL), p. A463
NEW YORK–PRESBYTERIAN/COLUMBIA UNIVERSITY MEDICAL CENTER, NEW YORK, NEW YORK (see NEW YORK–PRESBYTERIAN HOSPITAL), p. A463
NEWARK BETH ISRAEL MEDICAL CENTER, NEWARK, NJ, 310002, p. A432
NEWARK–WAYNE COMMUNITY HOSPITAL, NEWARK, NY, 330030, p. A467
NEWBERRY COUNTY MEMORIAL HOSPITAL, NEWBERRY, SC, 420053, p. A590
NEWMAN MEMORIAL HOSPITAL, SHATTUCK, OK, 370007, p. A538
NEWMAN REGIONAL HEALTH, EMPORIA, KS, 170001, p. A246
NEWNAN HOSPITAL, NEWNAN, GEORGIA (see NEWNAN HOSPITAL EAST), p. A167
NEWNAN HOSPITAL EAST, NEWNAN, GA, 110193, p. A167
NEWPORT COMMUNITY HOSPITAL, NEWPORT, WA, 501310, p. A704
NEWPORT HOSPITAL, NEWPORT, RI, 410006, p. A581
NEWPORT HOSPITAL AND CLINIC, NEWPORT, AR, 040054, p. A48
NEWTON MEDICAL CENTER, COVINGTON, GA, 110018, p. A159
NEWTON MEDICAL CENTER, NEWTON, KS, 170103, p. A253

NEWTON MEMORIAL HOSPITAL, NEWTON, NJ, 310028, p. A433
NEWTON REGIONAL HOSPITAL, NEWTON, MS, 250149, p. A374
NEWTON–WELLESLEY HOSPITAL, NEWTON LOWER FALLS, MA, 220101, p. A321
NEXUS SPECIALTY HOSPITAL, THE WOODLANDS, TX, 452057, p. A670
NIAGARA FALLS MEMORIAL MEDICAL CENTER, NIAGARA FALLS, NY, 330065, p. A467
NICHOLAS COUNTY HOSPITAL, CARLISLE, KY, 181303, p. A262
NICHOLAS H. NOYES MEMORIAL HOSPITAL, DANSVILLE, NY, 330238, p. A451
NINNESCAH VALLEY HEALTH SYSTEM, KINGMAN, KS, 170052, p. A250
NIOBRARA VALLEY HOSPITAL, LYNCH, NE, 281303, p. A409
NIX HEALTH CARE SYSTEM, SAN ANTONIO, TX, 450130, p. A664
NOBLE HOSPITAL, WESTFIELD, MA, 220065, p. A325
NOCONA GENERAL HOSPITAL, NOCONA, TX, 450641, p. A658
NOR–LEA GENERAL HOSPITAL, LOVINGTON, NM, 321305, p. A443
NORFOLK PSYCHIATRIC CENTER, NORFOLK, VA, 494011, p. A693
NORFOLK REGIONAL CENTER, NORFOLK, NE, 284004, p. A410
NORMAN AND IDA STONE INSTITUTE OF PSYCHIATRY, CHICAGO, ILLINOIS (see NORTHWESTERN MEMORIAL HOSPITAL), p. A188
NORMAN REGIONAL HOSPITAL, NORMAN, OK, 370008, p. A534
NORRISTOWN STATE HOSPITAL, NORRISTOWN, PA, 394001, p. A566
NORTH ADAMS REGIONAL HOSPITAL, NORTH ADAMS, MA, 220051, p. A321
NORTH ALABAMA REGIONAL HOSPITAL, DECATUR, AL, 014009, p. A17
NORTH ARKANSAS REGIONAL MEDICAL CENTER, HARRISON, AR, 040017, p. A44
NORTH AUSTIN MEDICAL CENTER, AUSTIN, TX, 450809, p. A623
NORTH BALDWIN INFIRMARY, BAY MINETTE, AL, 010129, p. A14
NORTH BAY HOSPITAL, ARANSAS PASS, TX, 450605, p. A621
NORTH BIG HORN HOSPITAL DISTRICT, LOVELL, WY, 531309, p. A741
NORTH BROWARD MEDICAL CENTER, POMPANO BEACH, FL, 100086, p. A144
NORTH CADDO MEDICAL CENTER, VIVIAN, LA, 191304, p. A294
NORTH CAMPUS, HOUSTON, TEXAS (see TWELVE OAKS MEDICAL CENTER), p. A648
NORTH CAROLINA BAPTIST HOSPITAL (WAKE FOREST UNIVERSITY BAPTIST MEDICAL CENTER), WINSTON–SALEM, NC, 340047, p. A494
NORTH CAROLINA CHILDREN'S AND WOMEN'S HOSPITAL, NORTH CAROLINA NEUROSCIENCES HOSPITAL, CHAPEL HILL, NORTH CAROLINA (see UNIVERSITY OF NORTH CAROLINA HOSPITALS), p. A479
NORTH CAROLINA EYE AND EAR HOSPITAL, DURHAM, NC, 340049, p. A481
NORTH CAROLINA SPECIALTY HOSPITAL, DURHAM, NC, 340049, p. A481
NORTH CENTRAL BAPTIST HOSPITAL, SAN ANTONIO, TX, p. A665
NORTH CENTRAL BRONX HOSPITAL, NEW YORK, NY, 330385, p. A464
NORTH CENTRAL HEALTH CARE FACILITIES, WAUSAU, WI, 524017, p. A737
NORTH COLORADO MEDICAL CENTER, GREELEY, CO, 060001, p. A106
NORTH COUNTRY HOSPITAL AND HEALTH CENTER, NEWPORT, VT, 471304, p. A683
NORTH COUNTRY REGIONAL HOSPITAL, BEMIDJI, MN, 240100, p. A350
NORTH DAKOTA STATE HOSPITAL, JAMESTOWN, ND, 354003, p. A499
NORTH DALLAS REHABILITATION HOSPITAL, DALLAS, TX, 453032, p. A633
NORTH FLORIDA RECEPTION CENTER HOSPITAL, LAKE BUTLER, FL, p. A134
NORTH FLORIDA REGIONAL MEDICAL CENTER, GAINESVILLE, FL, 100204, p. A130
NORTH FULTON REGIONAL HOSPITAL, ROSWELL, GA, 110198, p. A168
NORTH GENERAL HOSPITAL, NEW YORK, NY, 330390, p. A464
NORTH GEORGIA MEDICAL CENTER, ELLIJAY, GA, 110205, p. A162
NORTH GREENVILLE HOSPITAL, TRAVELERS REST, SC, 422008, p. A592

NORTH HAWAII COMMUNITY HOSPITAL, KAMUELA, HI, 120028, p. A175

NORTH HILLS HOSPITAL, NORTH RICHLAND HILLS, TX, 450087, p. A658

NORTH IDAHO BEHAVIORAL HEALTH, DIVISION OF KOOTENAI MEDICAL CENTER, COEUR D'ALENE, IDAHO (see KOOTENAI MEDICAL CENTER), p. A178

NORTH KANSAS CITY HOSPITAL, KANSAS CITY, MO, 260096, p. A384

NORTH LITTLE ROCK DIVISION, NORTH LITTLE ROCK, ARKANSAS (see CENTRAL ARKANSAS VETERANS HEALTHCARE SYSTEM), p. A46

NORTH LOGAN MERCY HOSPITAL, PARIS, AR, 041300, p. A49

NORTH MEMORIAL HEALTH CARE, ROBBINSDALE, MN, 240001, p. A360

NORTH MISSISSIPPI MEDICAL CENTER – TUPELO, TUPELO, MS, 250004, p. A376

NORTH MISSISSIPPI MEDICAL CENTER–EUPORA, EUPORA, MS, 250020, p. A368

NORTH MISSISSIPPI MEDICAL CENTER–HAMILTON, HAMILTON, AL, 010044, p. A20

NORTH MISSISSIPPI MEDICAL CENTER–IUKA, IUKA, MS, 250002, p. A370

NORTH MISSISSIPPI MEDICAL CENTER–PONTOTOC HOSPITAL AND NURSING HOME, PONTOTOC, MS, 251308, p. A374

NORTH MISSISSIPPI MEDICAL CENTER–WEST POINT, WEST POINT, MS, 250067, p. A376

NORTH MISSISSIPPI STATE HOSPITAL, TUPELO, MS, 254009, p. A376

NORTH MONROE MEDICAL CENTER, MONROE, LA, 190197, p. A287

NORTH OAK REGIONAL MEDICAL CENTER, SENATOBIA, MS, 250126, p. A375

NORTH OAKLAND MEDICAL CENTERS, PONTIAC, MI, 230013, p. A342

NORTH OAKS MEDICAL CENTER, HAMMOND, LA, 190015, p. A281

NORTH OAKS REHABILITATION HOSPITAL, HAMMOND, LA, 193044, p. A282

NORTH OKALOOSA MEDICAL CENTER, CRESTVIEW, FL, 100122, p. A126

NORTH OTTAWA COMMUNITY HOSPITAL, GRAND HAVEN, MI, 230174, p. A334

NORTH PHILADELPHIA HEALTH SYSTEM, PHILADELPHIA, PA, 390132, p. A569

NORTH RIDGE MEDICAL CENTER, FORT LAUDERDALE, FL, 100237, p. A129

NORTH RUNNELS HOSPITAL, WINTERS, TX, 451315, p. A674

NORTH SHORE CHILDREN'S HOSPITAL, SALEM, MASSACHUSETTS (see NORTH SHORE MEDICAL CENTER), p. A323

NORTH SHORE MEDICAL CENTER, MIAMI, FL, 100029, p. A138

NORTH SHORE MEDICAL CENTER, SALEM, MA, 220035, p. A323

NORTH SHORE UNIVERSITY HOSPITAL, MANHASSET, NY, 330106, p. A456

NORTH SHORE UNIVERSITY HOSPITAL AT PLAINVIEW, PLAINVIEW, NY, 330331, p. A469

NORTH SHORE UNIVERSITY HOSPITAL AT SYOSSET, SYOSSET, NY, 330106, p. A473

NORTH SHORE UNIVERSITY HOSPITAL–FOREST HILLS, NEW YORK, NY, 330353, p. A464

NORTH SIDE HOSPITAL, JOHNSON CITY, TN, 440184, p. A609

NORTH STAR BEHAVIORAL HEALTH SYSTEM, ANCHORAGE, AK, 024001, p. A26

NORTH STAR BEHAVIORAL HEALTH SYSTEM, ANCHORAGE, ALASKA (see NORTH STAR BEHAVIORAL HEALTH SYSTEM), p. A26

NORTH SUBURBAN MEDICAL CENTER, THORNTON, CO, 060065, p. A110

NORTH SUNFLOWER MEDICAL CENTER, RULEVILLE, MS, 251318, p. A375

NORTH TEXAS MEDICAL CENTER, GAINESVILLE, TX, 450090, p. A641

NORTH TEXAS STATE HOSPITAL, WICHITA FALLS CAMPUS, WICHITA FALLS, TX, 454008, p. A674

NORTH VALLEY HEALTH CENTER, WARREN, MN, 241337, p. A364

NORTH VALLEY HOSPITAL, WHITEFISH, MT, 271336, p. A403

NORTH VALLEY HOSPITAL, TONASKET, WA, 501321, p. A711

NORTH VALLEY REHABILITATION HOSPITAL, THORNTON, CO, 064018, p. A110

NORTH VISTA HOSPITAL, NORTH LAS VEGAS, NV, 290005, p. A417

NORTHBAY MEDICAL CENTER, FAIRFIELD, CA, 050367, p. A60

NORTHBAY VACAVALLEY HOSPITAL, VACAVILLE, CA, 050680, p. A97

NORTHCOAST BEHAVIORAL HEALTHCARE SYSTEM, NORTHFIELD, OH, 364011, p. A519

NORTHCREST MEDICAL CENTER, SPRINGFIELD, TN, 440065, p. A618

NORTHEAST ALABAMA REGIONAL MEDICAL CENTER, ANNISTON, AL, 010078, p. A13

NORTHEAST BAPTIST HOSPITAL, SAN ANTONIO, TX, p. A665

NORTHEAST GEORGIA MEDICAL CENTER, GAINESVILLE, GA, 110029, p. A163

NORTHEAST KANSAS CENTER FOR HEALTH AND WELLNESS, HORTON, KS, 171320, p. A249

NORTHEAST MEDICAL CENTER, CONCORD, NC, 340001, p. A481

NORTHEAST MEDICAL CENTER, BONHAM, TX, 450623, p. A626

NORTHEAST MEDICAL CENTER HOSPITAL, HUMBLE, TX, 450684, p. A649

NORTHEAST METHODIST HOSPITAL, SAN ANTONIO, TEXAS (see METHODIST HOSPITAL), p. A664

NORTHEAST REGIONAL MEDICAL CENTER, KIRKSVILLE, MO, 260022, p. A386

NORTHEAST REHABILITATION HOSPITAL, SALEM, NH, 303026, p. A423

NORTHEAST SPECIALTY HOSPITAL, BRAINTREE, MA, 222002, p. A315

NORTHEASTERN NEVADA REGIONAL HOSPITAL, ELKO, NV, 290008, p. A415

NORTHEASTERN VERMONT REGIONAL HOSPITAL, SAINT JOHNSBURY, VT, 471303, p. A683

NORTHERN ARIZONA VA HEALTH CARE SYSTEM, PRESCOTT, AZ, p. A35

NORTHERN CALIFORNIA REHABILITATION HOSPITAL, REDDING, CA, 050699, p. A83

NORTHERN COCHISE COMMUNITY HOSPITAL, WILLCOX, AZ, 031302, p. A39

NORTHERN DUTCHESS HOSPITAL, RHINEBECK, NY, 330049, p. A470

NORTHERN HILLS GENERAL HOSPITAL, DEADWOOD, SD, 431320, p. A595

NORTHERN HOSPITAL OF SURRY COUNTY, MOUNT AIRY, NC, 340003, p. A488

NORTHERN INYO HOSPITAL, BISHOP, CA, 050015, p. A55

NORTHERN MAINE MEDICAL CENTER, FORT KENT, ME, 200052, p. A298

NORTHERN MICHIGAN REGIONAL HEALTH SYSTEM, PETOSKEY, MI, 230105, p. A342

NORTHERN MONTANA HOSPITAL, HAVRE, MT, 270032, p. A399

NORTHERN NAVAJO MEDICAL CENTER, SHIPROCK, NM, 320059, p. A445

NORTHERN NEVADA ADULT MENTAL HEALTH SERVICES, SPARKS, NV, 294000, p. A419

NORTHERN NEVADA MEDICAL CENTER, SPARKS, NV, 290032, p. A419

NORTHERN ROCKIES MEDICAL CENTER, CUT BANK, MT, 271337, p. A397

NORTHERN VIRGINIA COMMUNITY HOSPITAL, ARLINGTON, VA, 490073, p. A685

NORTHERN VIRGINIA MENTAL HEALTH INSTITUTE, FALLS CHURCH, VA, 494010, p. A688

NORTHERN WESTCHESTER HOSPITAL, MOUNT KISCO, NY, 330162, p. A457

NORTHFIELD CAMPUS, NORTHFIELD, OHIO (see NORTHCOAST BEHAVIORAL HEALTHCARE SYSTEM), p. A519

NORTHFIELD HOSPITAL, NORTHFIELD, MN, 240014, p. A359

NORTHKEY COMMUNITY CARE, COVINGTON, KY, 184006, p. A263

NORTHLAKE CAMPUS, GARY, INDIANA (see METHODIST HOSPITALS), p. A216

NORTHLAKE MEDICAL CENTER, TUCKER, GA, 110033, p. A171

NORTHPORT MEDICAL CENTER, NORTHPORT, AL, 010145, p. A22

NORTHRIDGE HOSPITAL MEDICAL CENTER–ROSCOE BOULEVARD CAMPUS, LOS ANGELES, CA, 050116, p. A72

NORTHSHORE REGIONAL MEDICAL CENTER, SLIDELL, LA, 190204, p. A293

NORTHSIDE HOSPITAL, ATLANTA, GA, 110161, p. A154

NORTHSIDE HOSPITAL – CHEROKEE, CANTON, GA, 110008, p. A157

NORTHSIDE HOSPITAL AND HEART INSTITUTE, SAINT PETERSBURG, FL, 100238, p. A145

NORTHSIDE HOSPITAL FORSYTH, CUMMING, GA, 110005, p. A159

NORTHSIDE MEDICAL CENTER, YOUNGSTOWN, OHIO (see WESTERN RESERVE CARE SYSTEM), p. A526

NORTHWEST COMMUNITY HEALTHCARE, ARLINGTON HEIGHTS, IL, 140252, p. A183

NORTHWEST FLORIDA COMMUNITY HOSPITAL, CHIPLEY, FL, 101308, p. A125

NORTHWEST GEORGIA REGIONAL HOSPITAL, ROME, GA, 114014, p. A168

NORTHWEST HOSPITAL, SEATTLE, WA, 500001, p. A707

NORTHWEST HOSPITAL CENTER, RANDALLSTOWN, MD, 210040, p. A310

NORTHWEST IOWA HEALTH CENTER, SHELDON, IA, 160126, p. A241

NORTHWEST MEDICAL CENTER, WINFIELD, AL, 010086, p. A25

NORTHWEST MEDICAL CENTER, TUCSON, AZ, 030085, p. A38

NORTHWEST MEDICAL CENTER, MARGATE, FL, 100189, p. A136

NORTHWEST MEDICAL CENTER, THIEF RIVER FALLS, MN, 240017, p. A363

NORTHWEST MEDICAL CENTER, ALBANY, MO, 260086, p. A378

NORTHWEST MEDICAL CENTER OF BENTON COUNTY, BENTONVILLE, AR, 040138, p. A40

NORTHWEST MEDICAL CENTER OF WASHINGTON COUNTY, SPRINGDALE, AR, 040022, p. A50

NORTHWEST MEDICAL CENTER, ORO VALLEY, ORO VALLEY, AZ, p. A33

NORTHWEST MISSISSIPPI REGIONAL MEDICAL CENTER, CLARKSDALE, MS, 250042, p. A367

NORTHWEST MISSOURI PSYCHIATRIC REHABILITATION CENTER, SAINT JOSEPH, MO, 264007, p. A390

NORTHWEST SPECIALTY HOSPITAL, POST FALLS, ID, 130066, p. A181

NORTHWEST SUBURBAN COMMUNITY HOSPITAL, BELVIDERE, IL, 140205, p. A184

NORTHWEST SURGICAL HOSPITAL, OKLAHOMA CITY, OK, 370192, p. A535

NORTHWEST TEXAS HEALTHCARE SYSTEM, AMARILLO, TX, 450209, p. A621

NORTHWEST TEXAS SURGERY CENTER, AMARILLO, TX, 450796, p. A621

NORTHWESTERN CENTER FOR BEHAVIORAL HEALTH, WOODWARD, OK, 374001, p. A541

NORTHWESTERN MEDICAL CENTER, SAINT ALBANS, VT, 470024, p. A683

NORTHWESTERN MEMORIAL HOSPITAL, CHICAGO, IL, 140281, p. A188

NORTHWOOD DEACONESS HEALTH CENTER, NORTHWOOD, ND, 351312, p. A500

NORTON AUDUBON HOSPITAL, LOUISVILLE, KY, p. A269

NORTON COMMUNITY HOSPITAL, NORTON, VA, 490001, p. A693

NORTON COUNTY HOSPITAL, NORTON, KS, 171348, p. A253

NORTON HEALTHCARE PAVILION, LOUISVILLE, KENTUCKY (see NORTON HOSPITAL), p. A270

NORTON HOSPITAL, LOUISVILLE, KY, 180088, p. A270

NORTON SOUND REGIONAL HOSPITAL, NOME, AK, 021308, p. A28

NORTON SOUTHWEST HOSPITAL, LOUISVILLE, KY, 180133, p. A270

NORTON SUBURBAN HOSPITAL, LOUISVILLE, KY, 180123, p. A270

NORWALK HOSPITAL, NORWALK, CT, 070034, p. A115

NORWEGIAN–AMERICAN HOSPITAL, CHICAGO, IL, 140206, p. A188

NORWOOD HEALTH CENTER, MARSHFIELD, WI, 524019, p. A729

NOVATO COMMUNITY HOSPITAL, NOVATO, CA, 050131, p. A78

NOXUBEE GENERAL HOSPITAL, MACON, MS, 251307, p. A372

NYACK HOSPITAL, NYACK, NY, 330104, p. A467

NYE REGIONAL MEDICAL CENTER, TONOPAH, NV, 290020, p. A419

NYU DOWNTOWN HOSPITAL, NEW YORK, NY, 330064, p. A464

O

O'BLENESS MEMORIAL HOSPITAL, ATHENS, OH, 360014, p. A503

O'CONNOR HOSPITAL, SAN JOSE, CA, 050153, p. A90

O'CONNOR HOSPITAL, DELHI, NY, 331305, p. A451

OAK FOREST HOSPITAL OF COOK COUNTY, OAK FOREST, IL, 140301, p. A203

OAK HILL HOSPITAL, BROOKSVILLE, FL, 100264, p. A125

OAK LEAF SURGICAL CENTER, EAU CLAIRE, WI, 520196, p. A725

OAK TREE HOSPITAL, CORBIN, KY, 180148, p. A263

OAK VALLEY DISTRICT HOSPITAL, OAKDALE, CA, 050067, p. A78

OAKBEND MEDICAL CENTER, RICHMOND, TX, 450330, p. A662

OAKDALE COMMUNITY HOSPITAL, OAKDALE, LA, 190106, p. A290

OAKES COMMUNITY HOSPITAL, OAKES, ND, 351315, p. A500

OAKLAND MEMORIAL HOSPITAL, OAKLAND, NE, 281321, p. A410

OAKLAND REGIONAL HOSPITAL, SOUTHFIELD, MI, 233028, p. A345

OAKLAWN HOSPITAL, MARSHALL, MI, 230217, p. A340

OAKLAWN PSYCHIATRIC CENTER, GOSHEN, IN, 154031, p. A216

OAKWOOD ANNAPOLIS HOSPITAL, WAYNE, MI, 230142, p. A348

OAKWOOD CENTER OF THE PALM BEACHES, INC., WEST PALM BEACH, FL, 104008, p. A150

OAKWOOD CORRECTIONAL FACILITY, LIMA, OH, p. A516

OAKWOOD HERITAGE HOSPITAL, TAYLOR, MI, 230270, p. A346

OAKWOOD HOSPITAL AND MEDICAL CENTER–DEARBORN, DEARBORN, MI, 230020, p. A330

OAKWOOD SOUTHSHORE MEDICAL CENTER, TRENTON, MI, 230176, p. A347

OASIS LONG TERM CARE ACUTE HOSPITAL, NEW ORLEANS, LA, 192039, p. A289

OCALA REGIONAL MEDICAL CENTER, OCALA, FL, 100212, p. A140

OCEAN BEACH HOSPITAL, ILWACO, WA, 501314, p. A703

OCEAN MEDICAL CENTER, BRICK TOWNSHIP, NJ, 310052, p. A426

OCEAN SPRINGS HOSPITAL, OCEAN SPRINGS, MISSISSIPPI (see SINGING RIVER HOSPITAL SYSTEM), p. A374

OCHILTREE GENERAL HOSPITAL, PERRYTON, TX, 451359, p. A660

OCHSNER CLINIC FOUNDATION, NEW ORLEANS, LA, 190036, p. A289

OCONEE MEMORIAL HOSPITAL, SENECA, SC, 420009, p. A591

OCONEE REGIONAL MEDICAL CENTER, MILLEDGEVILLE, GA, 110150, p. A166

OCONOMOWOC MEMORIAL HOSPITAL, OCONOMOWOC, WI, 520062, p. A733

ODESSA MEMORIAL HEALTHCARE CENTER, ODESSA, WA, 501307, p. A705

ODESSA REGIONAL HOSPITAL, ODESSA, TX, 450661, p. A659

OGALLALA COMMUNITY HOSPITAL, OGALLALA, NE, 281355, p. A410

OGDEN REGIONAL MEDICAL CENTER, OGDEN, UT, 460005, p. A678

OHIO COUNTY HOSPITAL, HARTFORD, KY, 181323, p. A266

OHIO STATE UNIVERSITY HOSPITALS EAST, COLUMBUS, OH, 360062, p. A510

OHIO STATE UNIVERSITY JAMES CANCER HOSPITAL, COLUMBUS, OH, 360242, p. A510

OHIO STATE UNIVERSITY MEDICAL CENTER, COLUMBUS, OH, 360085, p. A511

OHIO VALLEY GENERAL HOSPITAL, MCKEES ROCKS, PA, 390157, p. A564

OHIO VALLEY MEDICAL CENTER, WHEELING, WV, 510039, p. A721

OHSU HOSPITAL, PORTLAND, OR, 380009, p. A547

OJAI VALLEY COMMUNITY HOSPITAL, OJAI, CA, 050046, p. A79

OKANOGAN DOUGLAS DISTRICT HOSPITAL, BREWSTER, WA, 501324, p. A701

OKEENE MUNICIPAL HOSPITAL, OKEENE, OK, 371327, p. A534

OKLAHOMA CENTER FOR ORTHOPEDIC AND MULTI–SPECIALTY SURGERY, OKLAHOMA CITY, OK, 370212, p. A535

OKLAHOMA FORENSIC CENTER, VINITA, OK, p. A541

OKLAHOMA HEART HOSPITAL, OKLAHOMA CITY, OK, 370215, p. A536

OKLAHOMA SPINE HOSPITAL, OKLAHOMA CITY, OK, 370206, p. A536

OKMULGEE MEMORIAL HOSPITAL, OKMULGEE, OK, 370057, p. A536

OKTIBBEHA COUNTY HOSPITAL, STARKVILLE, MS, 250050, p. A376

OLATHE MEDICAL CENTER, OLATHE, KS, 170049, p. A254

OLD BRIDGE DIVISION, OLD BRIDGE, NEW JERSEY (see RARITAN BAY MEDICAL CENTER), p. A434

OLD VINEYARD YOUTH SERVICES, WINSTON–SALEM, NC, p. A494

OLEAN GENERAL HOSPITAL, OLEAN, NY, 330103, p. A468

OLIN E. TEAGUE VETERANS' CENTER, TEMPLE, TEXAS (see CENTRAL TEXAS VETERANS HEALTHCARE SYSTEM), p. A668

OLMSTED MEDICAL CENTER, ROCHESTER, MN, 240006, p. A360

OLYMPIA MEDICAL CENTER, LOS ANGELES, CA, 050477, p. A72

OLYMPIC MEDICAL CENTER, PORT ANGELES, WA, 500072, p. A706

ONEIDA COUNTY HOSPITAL, MALAD CITY, ID, 131303, p. A180

ONEIDA HEALTHCARE CENTER, ONEIDA, NY, 330115, p. A468

ONSLOW MEMORIAL HOSPITAL, JACKSONVILLE, NC, 340042, p. A485

ONTONAGON MEMORIAL HOSPITAL, ONTONAGON, MI, 231309, p. A342

OPELOUSAS GENERAL HEALTH SYSTEM, OPELOUSAS, LA, 190017, p. A291

ORANGE CITY HEALTH SYSTEM, ORANGE CITY, IA, 161360, p. A239

ORANGE COAST MEMORIAL MEDICAL CENTER, FOUNTAIN VALLEY, CA, 050678, p. A61

ORANGE PARK MEDICAL CENTER, ORANGE PARK, FL, 100226, p. A140

ORANGE REGIONAL MEDICAL CENTER, MIDDLETOWN, NY, 330126, p. A457

ORANGE REGIONAL MEDICAL CENTER–ARDEN HILL CAMPUS, GOSHEN, NEW YORK (see ORANGE REGIONAL MEDICAL CENTER), p. A457

OREGON STATE HOSPITAL, SALEM, OR, 384008, p. A548

OREM COMMUNITY HOSPITAL, OREM, UT, 460043, p. A678

ORLANDO REGIONAL MEDICAL CENTER, ORLANDO, FL, 100006, p. A141

ORLANDO REGIONAL SOUTH SEMINOLE HOSPITAL, LONGWOOD, FL, p. A135

OROVILLE HOSPITAL, OROVILLE, CA, 050030, p. A80

ORTHOPAEDIC HOSPITAL, LOS ANGELES, CA, 050256, p. A72

ORTHOPAEDIC HOSPITAL AT PARKVIEW NORTH, FORT WAYNE, INDIANA (see PARKVIEW HOSPITAL), p. A215

ORTHOPAEDIC HOSPITAL OF WISCONSIN – GLENDALE, GLENDALE, WI, 520194, p. A726

ORTHOPEDIC HOSPITAL OF OKLAHOMA, TULSA, OK, 370210, p. A539

ORTONVILLE AREA HEALTH SERVICES, ORTONVILLE, MN, 241342, p. A359

OSAWATOMIE STATE HOSPITAL, OSAWATOMIE, KS, 174004, p. A254

OSBORNE COUNTY MEMORIAL HOSPITAL, OSBORNE, KS, 171364, p. A254

OSCEOLA COMMUNITY HOSPITAL, SIBLEY, IA, 161345, p. A241

OSCEOLA MEDICAL CENTER, OSCEOLA, WI, 521318, p. A733

OSCEOLA REGIONAL MEDICAL CENTER, KISSIMMEE, FL, 100110, p. A133

OSF SAINT ANTHONY MEDICAL CENTER, ROCKFORD, IL, 140233, p. A206

OSF SAINT FRANCIS MEDICAL CENTER, PEORIA, IL, 140067, p. A205

OSF SAINT JAMES – JOHN W. ALBRECHT MEDICAL CENTER, PONTIAC, IL, 140161, p. A205

OSF ST. FRANCIS HOSPITAL, ESCANABA, MI, 230101, p. A332

OSF ST. JOSEPH MEDICAL CENTER, BLOOMINGTON, IL, 140162, p. A185

OSF ST. MARY MEDICAL CENTER, GALESBURG, IL, 140064, p. A195

OSMOND GENERAL HOSPITAL, OSMOND, NE, 281347, p. A412

OSSEO MEDICAL CENTER, OSSEO, WI, 521302, p. A733

OSSINING CORRECTIONAL FACILITIES HOSPITAL, OSSINING, NY, p. A468

OSWEGO HOSPITAL, OSWEGO, NY, 330218, p. A468

OSWEGO MEDICAL CENTER, OSWEGO, KS, 171302, p. A254

OTHELLO COMMUNITY HOSPITAL, OTHELLO, WA, 501318, p. A705

OTSEGO MEMORIAL HOSPITAL, GAYLORD, MI, 230133, p. A334

OTTAWA COUNTY HEALTH CENTER, MINNEAPOLIS, KS, 171328, p. A253

OTTO KAISER MEMORIAL HOSPITAL, KENEDY, TX, 451364, p. A650

OTTUMWA REGIONAL HEALTH CENTER, OTTUMWA, IA, 160089, p. A240

OU MEDICAL CENTER, OKLAHOMA CITY, OK, 370093, p. A536

OUACHITA MEDICAL CENTER, CAMDEN, AR, 040050, p. A41

OUACHITA SURGICAL HOSPITAL, WEST MONROE, LA, 190261, p. A294

OUR CHILDREN'S HOUSE AT BAYLOR, DALLAS, TX, 453308, p. A633

OUR COMMUNITY HOSPITAL, SCOTLAND NECK, NC, 341302, p. A491

OUR LADY OF BELLEFONTE HOSPITAL, ASHLAND, KY, 180036, p. A261

OUR LADY OF FATIMA HOSPITAL, NORTH PROVIDENCE, RHODE ISLAND (see ST. JOSEPH HEALTH SERVICES OF RHODE ISLAND), p. A581

OUR LADY OF LOURDES MEDICAL CENTER, CAMDEN, NJ, 310029, p. A426

OUR LADY OF LOURDES MEMORIAL HOSPITAL, BINGHAMTON, NY, 330011, p. A448

OUR LADY OF LOURDES REGIONAL MEDICAL CENTER, LAFAYETTE, LA, 190102, p. A284

OUR LADY OF MERCY MEDICAL CENTER, NEW YORK, NY, 330072, p. A464

OUR LADY OF PEACE HOSPITAL, SOUTH BEND, IN, 152018, p. A225

OUR LADY OF THE LAKE REGIONAL MEDICAL CENTER, BATON ROUGE, LA, 190064, p. A277

OUR LADY OF THE RESURRECTION MEDICAL CENTER, CHICAGO, IL, 140251, p. A188

OUR LADY OF THE WAY HOSPITAL, MARTIN, KY, 181305, p. A271

OUR LADY OF VICTORY HOSPITAL, STANLEY, WI, 521311, p. A736

OVERLAKE HOSPITAL MEDICAL CENTER, BELLEVUE, WA, 500051, p. A700

OVERLAND PARK REGIONAL MEDICAL CENTER, OVERLAND PARK, KS, 170176, p. A254

OVERLOOK HOSPITAL, SUMMIT, NJ, 310051, p. A436

OVERTON BROOKS VETERANS AFFAIRS MEDICAL CENTER, SHREVEPORT, LA, p. A292

OWATONNA HOSPITAL, OWATONNA, MN, 240069, p. A359

OWENSBORO MEDICAL HEALTH SYSTEM, OWENSBORO, KY, 180038, p. A272

OZARK HEALTH MEDICAL CENTER, CLINTON, AR, 041313, p. A41

OZARKS MEDICAL CENTER, WEST PLAINS, MO, 260078, p. A395

P

P & S SURGICAL HOSPITAL, MONROE, LA, 190246, p. A287

PACIFIC ALLIANCE MEDICAL CENTER, LOS ANGELES, CA, 050018, p. A72

PACIFIC HOSPITAL OF LONG BEACH, LONG BEACH, CA, 050277, p. A68

PACIFICA HOSPITAL OF THE VALLEY, LOS ANGELES, CA, 050378, p. A72

PADRE BEHAVIORAL HOSPITAL, CORPUS CHRISTI, TX, 454096, p. A631

PAGE HOSPITAL, PAGE, AZ, 031304, p. A33

PAGE MEMORIAL HOSPITAL, LURAY, VA, 490047, p. A690

PALACIOS COMMUNITY MEDICAL CENTER, PALACIOS, TX, 451332, p. A659

PALESTINE REGIONAL MEDICAL CENTER–EAST, PALESTINE, TX, 450747, p. A659

PALESTINE REGIONAL REHABILITATION CENTER, PALESTINE, TX, 450113, p. A659

PALISADES MEDICAL CENTER, NORTH BERGEN, NJ, 310003, p. A433

PALM BEACH GARDENS MEDICAL CENTER, PALM BEACH GARDENS, FL, 100176, p. A141

PALM DRIVE HOSPITAL, SEBASTOPOL, CA, 050385, p. A93

PALM SPRINGS GENERAL HOSPITAL, HIALEAH, FL, 100050, p. A130

PALMER LUTHERAN HEALTH CENTER, WEST UNION, IA, 161316, p. A243

PALMERTON HOSPITAL, PALMERTON, PA, 390019, p. A567

PALMETTO GENERAL HOSPITAL, HIALEAH, FL, 100187, p. A131

PALMETTO HEALTH BAPTIST EASLEY, EASLEY, SC, 420015, p. A587

PALMETTO HEALTH BAPTIST/COLUMBIA, COLUMBIA, SC, 420086, p. A586

PALMETTO HEALTH RICHLAND, COLUMBIA, SC, 420018, p. A586

PALMETTO LOWCOUNTRY BEHAVIORAL HEALTH SYSTEM, CHARLESTON, SC, 424006, p. A584

PALMS OF PASADENA HOSPITAL, SAINT PETERSBURG, FL, 100126, p. A145

PALMS WEST HOSPITAL, LOXAHATCHEE, FL, 100269, p. A135

PALMYRA MEDICAL CENTERS, ALBANY, GA, 110163, p. A152

PALO ALTO COUNTY HEALTH SYSTEM, EMMETSBURG, IA, 161357, p. A233

PALO ALTO DIVISION, PALO ALTO, CALIFORNIA (see VETERANS AFFAIRS PALO ALTO HEALTH CARE SYSTEM), p. A80

PALO PINTO GENERAL HOSPITAL, MINERAL WELLS, TX, 450565, p. A657

PALO VERDE HOSPITAL, BLYTHE, CA, 050423, p. A55

PALO VERDE MENTAL HEALTH SERVICES, TUCSON, ARIZONA (see TUCSON MEDICAL CENTER), p. A38

PALOMAR MEDICAL CENTER, ESCONDIDO, CA, 050115, p. A59

PALOS COMMUNITY HOSPITAL, PALOS HEIGHTS, IL, 140062, p. A204

PAMPA REGIONAL MEDICAL CENTER, PAMPA, TX, 450099, p. A659

PAN AMERICAN HOSPITAL, MIAMI, FL, 100076, p. A138

PANA COMMUNITY HOSPITAL, PANA, IL, 141341, p. A204

PAOLI HOSPITAL, PAOLI, PA, 390153, p. A567

PARADISE VALLEY HOSPITAL, PHOENIX, AZ, 030083, p. A34

PARADISE VALLEY HOSPITAL, NATIONAL CITY, CA, 050024, p. A77

PARIS COMMUNITY HOSPITAL, PARIS, IL, 141320, p. A204

PARIS REGIONAL MEDICAL CENTER, PARIS, TX, 450196, p. A660

PARIS REGIONAL MEDICAL CENTER, PARIS, TEXAS (see PARIS REGIONAL MEDICAL CENTER), p. A660

PARIS REGIONAL MEDICAL CENTER–SOUTH CAMPUS, PARIS, TEXAS (see PARIS REGIONAL MEDICAL CENTER), p. A660

PARK PLACE SURGERY CENTER, LAFAYETTE, LA, 190255, p. A284
PARK PLAZA HOSPITAL, HOUSTON, TX, 450659, p. A647
PARK RIDGE HOSPITAL, ROCHESTER, NY, 330226, p. A471
PARK RIDGE HOSPITAL, FLETCHER, NC, 340023, p. A483
PARK VIEW SPECIALTY HOSPITAL, SPRINGFIELD, MA, 222046, p. A324
PARKCARE PAVILION, YONKERS, NEW YORK (see ST. JOHN'S RIVERSIDE HOSPTIAL), p. A476
PARKER ADVENTIST HOSPITAL, PARKER, CO, 060114, p. A109
PARKLAND HEALTH & HOSPITAL SYSTEM, DALLAS, TX, 450015, p. A633
PARKLAND HEALTH CENTER, FARMINGTON, MO, 260163, p. A382
PARKLAND HEALTH CENTER–BONNE TERRE, BONNE TERRE, MO, 261315, p. A378
PARKLAND MEDICAL CENTER, DERRY, NH, 300017, p. A420
PARKRIDGE MEDICAL CENTER, CHATTANOOGA, TN, 440156, p. A604
PARKSIDE HOSPITAL, TULSA, OK, 374021, p. A539
PARKVIEW ADVENTIST MEDICAL CENTER, BRUNSWICK, ME, 200025, p. A297
PARKVIEW COMMUNITY HOSPITAL MEDICAL CENTER, RIVERSIDE, CA, 050102, p. A84
PARKVIEW HOSPITAL, FORT WAYNE, IN, 150021, p. A215
PARKVIEW HOSPITAL, EL RENO, OK, 370011, p. A530
PARKVIEW HOSPITAL, WHEELER, TX, 450258, p. A673
PARKVIEW HUNTINGTON HOSPITAL, HUNTINGTON, IN, 150091, p. A218
PARKVIEW LAGRANGE HOSPITAL, LAGRANGE, IN, 151323, p. A221
PARKVIEW MEDICAL CENTER, PUEBLO, CO, 060020, p. A109
PARKVIEW NOBLE HOSPITAL, KENDALLVILLE, IN, 150146, p. A220
PARKVIEW NORTH HOSPITAL, FORT WAYNE, INDIANA (see PARKVIEW HOSPITAL), p. A215
PARKVIEW REGIONAL HOSPITAL, MEXIA, TX, 450400, p. A656
PARKVIEW WHITLEY HOSPITAL, COLUMBIA CITY, IN, 150101, p. A213
PARKWAY HOSPITAL, NEW YORK, NY, 330041, p. A464
PARKWAY MEDICAL CENTER, DECATUR, AL, 010054, p. A17
PARKWAY REGIONAL HOSPITAL, FULTON, KY, 180117, p. A265
PARKWAY REGIONAL MEDICAL CENTER, NORTH MIAMI BEACH, FL, 100114, p. A139
PARKWEST MEDICAL CENTER, KNOXVILLE, TN, 440173, p. A610
PARKWOOD BEHAVIORAL HEALTH SYSTEM, OLIVE BRANCH, MS, 254005, p. A374
PARMA COMMUNITY GENERAL HOSPITAL, PARMA, OH, 360041, p. A520
PARMER COUNTY COMMUNITY HOSPITAL, FRIONA, TX, 451300, p. A640
PARRISH MEDICAL CENTER, TITUSVILLE, FL, 100028, p. A149
PARSONS STATE HOSPITAL AND TRAINING CENTER, PARSONS, KS, p. A255
PASCACK VALLEY HOSPITAL, WESTWOOD, NJ, 310037, p. A438
PASCO REGIONAL MEDICAL CENTER, DADE CITY, FL, 100211, p. A126
PASSAVANT AREA HOSPITAL, JACKSONVILLE, IL, 140058, p. A198
PATHWAYS OF TENNESSEE, JACKSON, TN, 444010, p. A608
PATHWAYS TREATMENT CENTER, KALISPELL, MONTANA (see KALISPELL REGIONAL MEDICAL CENTER), p. A400
PATIENT'S HOSPITAL OF REDDING, REDDING, CA, 050697, p. A83
PATRICK B. HARRIS PSYCHIATRIC HOSPITAL, ANDERSON, SC, 424011, p. A583
PATTIE A. CLAY REGIONAL MEDICAL CENTER, RICHMOND, KY, 180049, p. A274
PATTON STATE HOSPITAL, PATTON, CA, p. A81
PAUL B. HALL REGIONAL MEDICAL CENTER, PAINTSVILLE, KY, 180078, p. A273
PAUL OLIVER MEMORIAL HOSPITAL, FRANKFORT, MI, 231300, p. A333
PAULDING COUNTY HOSPITAL, PAULDING, OH, 361300, p. A520
PAULS VALLEY GENERAL HOSPITAL, PAULS VALLEY, OK, 370156, p. A537
PAWHUSKA HOSPITAL, PAWHUSKA, OK, 371309, p. A537
PAWNEE COUNTY MEMORIAL HOSPITAL, PAWNEE CITY, NE, 281302, p. A412
PAWNEE MUNICIPAL HOSPITAL, PAWNEE, OK, 370060, p. A537
PAYNE WHITNEY PSYCHIATRIC CLINIC, NEW YORK, NEW YORK (see NEW YORK–PRESBYTERIAN HOSPITAL), p. A463
PAYNESVILLE AREA HEALTH CARE SYSTEM, PAYNESVILLE, MN, 241349, p. A359
PAYSON REGIONAL MEDICAL CENTER, PAYSON, AZ, 030033, p. A33

PBI REGIONAL MEDICAL CENTER, PASSAIC, NJ, 310020, p. A434
PEACE HARBOR HOSPITAL, FLORENCE, OR, 381316, p. A543
PEACE RIVER REGIONAL MEDICAL CENTER, PORT CHARLOTTE, FL, 100077, p. A144
PEACH REGIONAL MEDICAL CENTER, FORT VALLEY, GA, 111310, p. A162
PEACHFORD BEHAVIORAL HEALTH SYSTEM, ATLANTA, GA, 114010, p. A154
PEAK BEHAVIORAL HEALTH SERVICES, SANTA TERESA, NM, 324012, p. A444
PEARL RIVER COUNTY HOSPITAL, POPLARVILLE, MS, 250023, p. A375
PECOS COUNTY MEMORIAL HOSPITAL, FORT STOCKTON, TX, 450178, p. A639
PECOS VALLEY LODGE, ROSWELL, NEW MEXICO (see NEW MEXICO REHABILITATION CENTER), p. A444
PEKIN HOSPITAL, PEKIN, IL, 140120, p. A204
PELLA REGIONAL HEALTH CENTER, PELLA, IA, 161367, p. A240
PEMBINA COUNTY MEMORIAL HOSPITAL AND WEDGEWOOD MANOR, CAVALIER, ND, 351319, p. A497
PEMBROKE HOSPITAL, PEMBROKE, MA, p. A322
PEMISCOT MEMORIAL HEALTH SYSTEM, HAYTI, MO, 260070, p. A382
PENDER COMMUNITY HOSPITAL, PENDER, NE, 281349, p. A412
PENDER MEMORIAL HOSPITAL, BURGAW, NC, 341307, p. A478
PENINSULA HOSPITAL, BURLINGAME, CALIFORNIA (see MILLS–PENINSULA HEALTH SERVICES), p. A55
PENINSULA HOSPITAL, LOUISVILLE, TN, 444017, p. A611
PENINSULA HOSPITAL CENTER, NEW YORK, NY, 330002, p. A464
PENINSULA REGIONAL HEALTH SYSTEM, SALISBURY, MD, 210019, p. A310
PENN STATE MILTON S. HERSHEY MEDICAL CENTER, HERSHEY, PA, 390256, p. A560
PENNOCK HOSPITAL, HASTINGS, MI, 230040, p. A336
PENNSYLVANIA HOSPITAL, PHILADELPHIA, PA, 390226, p. A569
PENOBSCOT BAY MEDICAL CENTER, ROCKPORT, ME, 200063, p. A300
PENOBSCOT VALLEY HOSPITAL, LINCOLN, ME, 201303, p. A299
PENROSE COMMUNITY HOSPITAL, COLORADO SPRINGS, COLORADO (see PENROSE–ST. FRANCIS HEALTH SERVICES), p. A102
PENROSE HOSPITAL, COLORADO SPRINGS, COLORADO (see PENROSE–ST. FRANCIS HEALTH SERVICES), p. A102
PENROSE–ST. FRANCIS HEALTH SERVICES, COLORADO SPRINGS, CO, 060031, p. A102
PERHAM MEMORIAL HOSPITAL AND HOME, PERHAM, MN, 240103, p. A359
PERKINS COUNTY HEALTH SERVICES, GRANT, NE, 281356, p. A407
PERMIAN REGIONAL MEDICAL CENTER, ANDREWS, TX, 450144, p. A621
PERRY COMMUNITY HOSPITAL, LINDEN, TN, 440040, p. A611
PERRY COUNTY GENERAL HOSPITAL, RICHTON, MS, 251306, p. A375
PERRY COUNTY MEMORIAL HOSPITAL, TELL CITY, IN, 151322, p. A226
PERRY COUNTY MEMORIAL HOSPITAL, PERRYVILLE, MO, 261311, p. A389
PERRY HOSPITAL, PERRY, GA, 110153, p. A167
PERRY MEMORIAL HOSPITAL, PRINCETON, IL, 141337, p. A205
PERRY MEMORIAL HOSPITAL, PERRY, OK, 370139, p. A537
PERSHING GENERAL HOSPITAL, LOVELOCK, NV, 291304, p. A417
PERSON MEMORIAL HOSPITAL, ROXBORO, NC, 340159, p. A490
PERTH AMBOY DIVISION, PERTH AMBOY, NEW JERSEY (see RARITAN BAY MEDICAL CENTER), p. A434
PETALUMA VALLEY HOSPITAL, PETALUMA, CA, 050136, p. A81
PETERSBURG MEDICAL CENTER, PETERSBURG, AK, 021304, p. A28
PHELPS COUNTY REGIONAL MEDICAL CENTER, ROLLA, MO, 260017, p. A389
PHELPS MEMORIAL HEALTH CENTER, HOLDREGE, NE, 280108, p. A408
PHELPS MEMORIAL HOSPITAL CENTER, SLEEPY HOLLOW, NY, 330261, p. A472
PHILHAVEN, BEHAVIORAL HEALTHCARE SERVICES, MOUNT GRETNA, PA, 394020, p. A565
PHILIPSBURG AREA HOSPITAL, PHILIPSBURG, PA, 390279, p. A570
PHILLIPS COUNTY HOSPITAL, PHILLIPSBURG, KS, 171353, p. A255
PHILLIPS COUNTY MEDICAL CENTER, MALTA, MT, 271312, p. A400

PHILLIPS EYE INSTITUTE, MINNEAPOLIS, MN, 240196, p. A357
PHOEBE PUTNEY MEMORIAL HOSPITAL, ALBANY, GA, 110007, p. A152
PHOEBE WORTH MEDICAL CENTER, SYLVESTER, GA, 111328, p. A170
PHOENIX BAPTIST HOSPITAL, PHOENIX, AZ, 030030, p. A34
PHOENIX CHILDREN'S HOSPITAL, PHOENIX, AZ, 033302, p. A34
PHOENIX MEMORIAL HOSPITAL, PHOENIX, AZ, 030106, p. A34
PHOENIXVILLE HOSPITAL, PHOENIXVILLE, PA, 390127, p. A571
PHS SANTA FE INDIAN HOSPITAL, SANTA FE, NM, 320057, p. A444
PHYSICIANS HOSPITAL, OKLAHOMA CITY, OK, 370203, p. A536
PHYSICIANS HOSPITAL, EL PASO, TX, 450877, p. A637
PHYSICIANS SURGICAL SPECIALTY HOSPITAL, HOUMA, LA, 190241, p. A282
PHYSICIANS' HOSPITAL IN ANADARKO, ANADARKO, OK, 371314, p. A527
PHYSICIANS' METROPLEX HOSPITAL, ARLINGTON, TX, 450858, p. A622
PICKENS COUNTY MEDICAL CENTER, CARROLLTON, AL, 010109, p. A16
PIEDMONT FAYETTE HOSPITAL, FAYETTEVILLE, GA, 110215, p. A162
PIEDMONT GERIATRIC HOSPITAL, BURKEVILLE, VA, 490134, p. A686
PIEDMONT HEALTHCARE SYSTEM, ROCK HILL, SC, 420002, p. A591
PIEDMONT HOSPITAL, ATLANTA, GA, 110083, p. A154
PIEDMONT MOUNTAINSIDE HOSPITAL, JASPER, GA, 110225, p. A164
PIGGOTT COMMUNITY HOSPITAL, PIGGOTT, AR, 040045, p. A49
PIKE COMMUNITY HOSPITAL, WAVERLY, OH, 360047, p. A524
PIKE COUNTY MEMORIAL HOSPITAL, MURFREESBORO, AR, 040081, p. A48
PIKE COUNTY MEMORIAL HOSPITAL, LOUISIANA, MO, 260127, p. A387
PIKEVILLE MEDICAL CENTER, PIKEVILLE, KY, 180044, p. A273
PILGRIM PSYCHIATRIC CENTER, BRENTWOOD, NY, 334013, p. A448
PINCKNEYVILLE COMMUNITY HOSPITAL, PINCKNEYVILLE, IL, 141307, p. A205
PINE MEDICAL CENTER, SANDSTONE, MN, 241309, p. A362
PINE REST CHRISTIAN MENTAL HEALTH SERVICES, GRAND RAPIDS, MI, 234006, p. A334
PINECREST REHABILITATION HOSPITAL, DELRAY BEACH, FL, 103030, p. A127
PINEVILLE COMMUNITY HOSPITAL ASSOCIATION, PINEVILLE, KY, 180021, p. A273
PINNACLE POINTE HOSPITAL, LITTLE ROCK, AR, 044013, p. A46
PINNACLEHEALTH AT COMMUNITY GENERAL OSTEOPATHIC HOSPITAL, HARRISBURG, PENNSYLVANIA (see PINNACLEHEALTH SYSTEM), p. A560
PINNACLEHEALTH AT HARRISBURG HOSPITAL, HARRISBURG, PENNSYLVANIA (see PINNACLEHEALTH SYSTEM), p. A560
PINNACLEHEALTH AT POLYCLINIC HOSPITAL, HARRISBURG, PENNSYLVANIA (see PINNACLEHEALTH SYSTEM), p. A560
PINNACLEHEALTH AT SEIDLE MEMORIAL HOSPITAL, MECHANICSBURG, PENNSYLVANIA (see PINNACLEHEALTH SYSTEM), p. A560
PINNACLEHEALTH SYSTEM, HARRISBURG, PA, 390067, p. A560
PIONEER COMMUNITY HOSPITAL OF ABERDEEN, ABERDEEN, MS, 251302, p. A366
PIONEER MEDICAL CENTER, BIG TIMBER, MT, 271313, p. A396
PIONEER MEMORIAL HOSPITAL, HEPPNER, OR, 381310, p. A544
PIONEER MEMORIAL HOSPITAL, PRINEVILLE, OR, 381313, p. A548
PIONEER MEMORIAL HOSPITAL AND HEALTH SERVICES, VIBORG, SD, 431328, p. A600
PIONEER VALLEY HOSPITAL, WEST VALLEY CITY, UT, 460008, p. A681
PIONEERS HOSPITAL OF RIO BLANCO COUNTY, MEEKER, CO, 060041, p. A108
PIONEERS MEMORIAL HEALTHCARE DISTRICT, BRAWLEY, CA, 050342, p. A55
PIPESTONE COUNTY MEDICAL CENTER/AVERA HEALTH, PIPESTONE, MN, 240123, p. A359
PITT COUNTY MEMORIAL HOSPITAL, GREENVILLE, NC, 340040, p. A484
PLACENTIA LINDA HOSPITAL, PLACENTIA, CA, 050589, p. A81
PLAINS MEMORIAL HOSPITAL, DIMMITT, TX, 451350, p. A635
PLAINS REGIONAL MEDICAL CENTER, CLOVIS, NM, 320022, p. A442
PLAINVIEW AREA HEALTH SYSTEM, PLAINVIEW, NE, 281346, p. A412
PLANO SPECIALTY HOSPITAL, PLANO, TX, 452054, p. A661

PLANTATION GENERAL HOSPITAL, PLANTATION, FL, 100167, p. A143

PLATEAU MEDICAL CENTER, INC., OAK HILL, WV, 510088, p. A718

PLATTE COUNTY MEMORIAL HOSPITAL, WHEATLAND, WY, 531305, p. A742

PLATTE HEALTH CENTER/AVERA HEALTH, PLATTE, SD, 431306, p. A598

PLATTE VALLEY MEDICAL CENTER, BRIGHTON, CO, 060004, p. A101

PLAZA MEDICAL CENTER OF FORT WORTH, FORT WORTH, TX, 450672, p. A640

PLAZA SPECIALTY HOSPITAL, HOUSTON, TX, 452046, p. A647

PLEASANT VALLEY HOSPITAL, POINT PLEASANT, WV, 510012, p. A719

PLUM CREEK SPECIALTY HOSPITAL, AMARILLO, TX, 452066, p. A621

PLUMAS DISTRICT HOSPITAL, QUINCY, CA, 050148, p. A82

POCAHONTAS COMMUNITY HOSPITAL, POCAHONTAS, IA, 161305, p. A240

POCAHONTAS MEMORIAL HOSPITAL, BUCKEYE, WV, 511314, p. A713

POCONO MEDICAL CENTER, EAST STROUDSBURG, PA, 390201, p. A557

POH MEDICAL CENTER, PONTIAC, MI, 230207, p. A342

POINTE COUPEE GENERAL HOSPITAL, NEW ROADS, LA, 191316, p. A290

POLK MEDICAL CENTER, CEDARTOWN, GA, 111330, p. A157

POMERADO HOSPITAL, POWAY, CA, 050636, p. A82

POMERENE HOSPITAL, MILLERSBURG, OH, 360148, p. A519

POMONA VALLEY HOSPITAL MEDICAL CENTER, POMONA, CA, 050231, p. A82

PONDERA MEDICAL CENTER, CONRAD, MT, 271324, p. A397

POPLAR BLUFF REGIONAL MEDICAL CENTER, POPLAR BLUFF, MO, 260119, p. A389

POPLAR COMMUNITY HOSPITAL, POPLAR, MT, 271300, p. A401

POPLAR SPRINGS HOSPITAL, PETERSBURG, VA, 494022, p. A693

PORT HURON HOSPITAL, PORT HURON, MI, 230216, p. A343

PORTAGE HEALTH SYSTEM, HANCOCK, MI, 230108, p. A336

PORTER ADVENTIST HOSPITAL, DENVER, CO, 060064, p. A104

PORTER MEDICAL CENTER, MIDDLEBURY, VT, 470006, p. A682

PORTER–VALPARAISO HOSPITAL CAMPUS, VALPARAISO, IN, 150035, p. A226

PORTERVILLE DEVELOPMENTAL CENTER, PORTERVILLE, CA, 050546, p. A82

PORTNEUF MEDICAL CENTER, POCATELLO, ID, 130028, p. A181

PORTSMOUTH REGIONAL HOSPITAL, PORTSMOUTH, NH, 300029, p. A423

POTOMAC HOSPITAL, WOODBRIDGE, VA, 490113, p. A698

POTOMAC RIDGE BEHAVIORAL HEALTH SYSTEM, ROCKVILLE, MD, 214013, p. A310

POTOMAC VALLEY HOSPITAL, KEYSER, WV, 510061, p. A717

POTTSTOWN MEMORIAL MEDICAL CENTER, POTTSTOWN, PA, 390123, p. A573

POTTSVILLE HOSPITAL AND WARNE CLINIC, POTTSVILLE, PA, 390030, p. A573

POUDRE VALLEY HOSPITAL, FORT COLLINS, CO, 060010, p. A105

POWELL CONVALESCENT CENTER, DES MOINES, IOWA (see IOWA METHODIST MEDICAL CENTER), p. A232

POWELL COUNTY MEMORIAL HOSPITAL, DEER LODGE, MT, 271314, p. A397

POWELL VALLEY HEALTHCARE, POWELL, WY, 531310, p. A741

PRAGUE MUNICIPAL HOSPITAL, PRAGUE, OK, 371301, p. A537

PRAIRIE AT ST. JOHN'S, FARGO, ND, 354004, p. A498

PRAIRIE COMMUNITY HEALTH CENTER, TERRY, MT, 271309, p. A402

PRAIRIE DU CHIEN MEMORIAL HOSPITAL, PRAIRIE DU CHIEN, WI, 521330, p. A734

PRAIRIE LAKES HEALTHCARE SYSTEM, WATERTOWN, SD, 430005, p. A600

PRAIRIE VIEW, NEWTON, KS, 174016, p. A253

PRATT REGIONAL MEDICAL CENTER, PRATT, KS, 170027, p. A255

PRATTVILLE BAPTIST HOSPITAL, PRATTVILLE, AL, 010108, p. A23

PREMIER REHABILITATION HOSPITAL, MONROE, LA, 193082, p. A287

PRENTICE WOMEN'S HOSPITAL, CHICAGO, ILLINOIS (see NORTHWESTERN MEMORIAL HOSPITAL), p. A188

PRESBYTERIAN HOSPITAL, ALBUQUERQUE, NM, 320021, p. A440

PRESBYTERIAN HOSPITAL, CHARLOTTE, NC, 340053, p. A480

PRESBYTERIAN HOSPITAL HUNTERSVILLE, HUNTERSVILLE, NC, 340183, p. A485

PRESBYTERIAN HOSPITAL OF ALLEN, ALLEN, TX, 450840, p. A620

PRESBYTERIAN HOSPITAL OF COMMERCE, COMMERCE, TX, 451321, p. A629

PRESBYTERIAN HOSPITAL OF DALLAS, DALLAS, TX, 450462, p. A633

PRESBYTERIAN HOSPITAL OF DENTON, DENTON, TX, 450743, p. A635

PRESBYTERIAN HOSPITAL OF GREENVILLE, GREENVILLE, TEXAS (see HUNT MEMORIAL HOSPITAL DISTRICT), p. A642

PRESBYTERIAN HOSPITAL OF KAUFMAN, KAUFMAN, TX, 450292, p. A650

PRESBYTERIAN HOSPITAL OF PLANO, PLANO, TX, 450771, p. A661

PRESBYTERIAN HOSPITAL OF WINNSBORO, WINNSBORO, TX, 450224, p. A674

PRESBYTERIAN HOSPITAL–MATTHEWS, MATTHEWS, NC, 340171, p. A487

PRESBYTERIAN INTERCOMMUNITY HOSPITAL, WHITTIER, CA, 050169, p. A99

PRESBYTERIAN KASEMAN HOSPITAL, ALBUQUERQUE, NM, 320079, p. A441

PRESBYTERIAN MEDICAL CENTER OF THE UNIVERSITY OF PENNSYLVANIA HEALTH SYSTEM, PHILADELPHIA, PA, 390223, p. A569

PRESBYTERIAN TOWER, OKLAHOMA CITY, OKLAHOMA (see OU MEDICAL CENTER), p. A536

PRESBYTERIAN–DENVER HOSPITAL, DENVER, COLORADO (see PRESBYTERIAN–ST. LUKE'S MEDICAL CENTER), p. A104

PRESBYTERIAN–ORTHOPAEDIC HOSPITAL, CHARLOTTE, NC, 340153, p. A480

PRESBYTERIAN–ST. LUKE'S MEDICAL CENTER, DENVER, CO, 060014, p. A104

PRESENTATION MEDICAL CENTER, ROLLA, ND, 351316, p. A500

PRESTON MEMORIAL HOSPITAL, KINGWOOD, WV, 511312, p. A717

PREVOST MEMORIAL HOSPITAL, DONALDSONVILLE, LA, 191308, p. A280

PRIMARY CHILDREN'S MEDICAL CENTER, SALT LAKE CITY, UT, 463301, p. A679

PRINCE GEORGE'S HOSPITAL CENTER, CHEVERLY, MD, 210003, p. A306

PRINCE WILLIAM HOSPITAL, MANASSAS, VA, 490045, p. A691

PRINCETON COMMUNITY HOSPITAL, PRINCETON, WV, 510046, p. A719

PROCTOR HOSPITAL, PEORIA, IL, 140013, p. A205

PROGRESSIVE HOSPITAL, LAS VEGAS, NV, 290044, p. A416

PROMISE HOSPITAL OF EAST LOS ANGELES, LOS ANGELES, CA, 052046, p. A72

PROMISE HOSPITAL OF EAST LOS ANGELES, SUBURBAN MEDICAL CENTER CAMPUS, PARAMOUNT, CA, 050571, p. A81

PROMISE SPECIALTY HOSPITAL OF FERRIDAY, FERRIDAY, LA, 192028, p. A280

PROMISE SPECIALTY HOSPITAL OF PHOENIX, PHOENIX, AZ, 030109, p. A35

PROMISE SPECIALTY HOSPITAL OF SAN ANTONIO, SAN ANTONIO, TX, 450873, p. A665

PROMISE SPECIALTY HOSPITAL OF SHREVEPORT, SHREVEPORT, LA, 192010, p. A293

PROMISE SPECIALTY HOSPITAL OF VICKSBURG, VICKSBURG, MS, 252008, p. A376

PROSSER MEMORIAL HOSPITAL, PROSSER, WA, 501312, p. A706

PROVENA COVENANT MEDICAL CENTER, URBANA, IL, 140113, p. A209

PROVENA MERCY CENTER, AURORA, IL, 140174, p. A183

PROVENA SAINT JOSEPH HOSPITAL, ELGIN, IL, 140217, p. A193

PROVENA SAINT JOSEPH MEDICAL CENTER, JOLIET, IL, 140007, p. A198

PROVENA ST. MARY'S HOSPITAL, KANKAKEE, IL, 140155, p. A198

PROVENA UNITED SAMARITANS MEDICAL CENTER, DANVILLE, IL, 140093, p. A191

PROVIDENCE ALASKA MEDICAL CENTER, ANCHORAGE, AK, 020001, p. A26

PROVIDENCE CENTRALIA HOSPITAL, CENTRALIA, WA, 500019, p. A701

PROVIDENCE EVERETT MEDICAL CENTER, EVERETT, WA, 500014, p. A703

PROVIDENCE EVERETT MEDICAL CENTER – COLBY CAMPUS, EVERETT, WASHINGTON (see PROVIDENCE EVERETT MEDICAL CENTER), p. A703

PROVIDENCE EVERETT MEDICAL CENTER – PACIFIC CAMPUS, EVERETT, WASHINGTON (see PROVIDENCE EVERETT MEDICAL CENTER), p. A703

PROVIDENCE HEALTH CENTER, WACO, TX, 450042, p. A672

PROVIDENCE HOLY CROSS MEDICAL CENTER, SAN FERNANDO, CA, 050278, p. A88

PROVIDENCE HOOD RIVER MEMORIAL HOSPITAL, HOOD RIVER, OR, 381318, p. A544

PROVIDENCE HOSPITAL, MOBILE, AL, 010090, p. A21

PROVIDENCE HOSPITAL, WASHINGTON, DC, 090006, p. A122

PROVIDENCE HOSPITAL, LAREDO, TX, 450879, p. A652

PROVIDENCE HOSPITAL AND MEDICAL CENTER, SOUTHFIELD, MI, 230019, p. A345

PROVIDENCE HOSPITAL NORTHEAST, COLUMBIA, SOUTH CAROLINA (see SISTERS OF CHARITY PROVIDENCE HOSPITALS), p. A586

PROVIDENCE KODIAK ISLAND MEDICAL CENTER, KODIAK, AK, 021306, p. A27

PROVIDENCE MEDFORD MEDICAL CENTER, MEDFORD, OR, 380075, p. A546

PROVIDENCE MEDICAL CENTER, KANSAS CITY, KS, 170146, p. A250

PROVIDENCE MEDICAL CENTER, WAYNE, NE, 281345, p. A414

PROVIDENCE MEMORIAL HOSPITAL, EL PASO, TX, 450002, p. A637

PROVIDENCE MILWAUKIE HOSPITAL, MILWAUKIE, OR, 380082, p. A546

PROVIDENCE NEWBERG HOSPITAL, NEWBERG, OR, 380037, p. A546

PROVIDENCE PORTLAND MEDICAL CENTER, PORTLAND, OR, 380061, p. A547

PROVIDENCE SAINT JOSEPH MEDICAL CENTER, BURBANK, CA, 050235, p. A55

PROVIDENCE SEASIDE HOSPITAL, SEASIDE, OR, 381303, p. A549

PROVIDENCE SEWARD MEDICAL CENTER, SEWARD, AK, 021302, p. A28

PROVIDENCE ST. PETER HOSPITAL, OLYMPIA, WA, 500024, p. A705

PROVIDENCE ST. VINCENT MEDICAL CENTER, PORTLAND, OR, 380004, p. A548

PROVIDENCE VALDEZ MEDICAL CENTER, VALDEZ, AK, 021301, p. A29

PROVIDENCE–LITTLE COMPANY OF MARY SERVICE AREA, TORRANCE, CA, 050353, p. A96

PROVIDENT HOSPITAL OF COOK COUNTY, CHICAGO, IL, 140300, p. A189

PROWERS MEDICAL CENTER, LAMAR, CO, 061323, p. A107

PSYCHIATRIC HOSPITAL AT VANDERBILT, NASHVILLE, TENNESSEE (see VANDERBILT UNIVERSITY MEDICAL CENTER), p. A616

PSYCHIATRIC INSTITUTE OF WASHINGTON, WASHINGTON, DC, 094004, p. A122

PSYCHIATRIC MEDICINE CENTER, SALEM, OREGON (see SALEM HOSPITAL), p. A549

PSYCHIATRIC PAVILION, AMARILLO, TEXAS (see NORTHWEST TEXAS HEALTHCARE SYSTEM), p. A621

PUBLIC HEALTH SERVICE INDIAN HOSPITAL, ALBUQUERQUE, NM, 320056, p. A441

PULASKI COMMUNITY HOSPITAL, PULASKI, VA, 490116, p. A694

PULASKI MEMORIAL HOSPITAL, WINAMAC, IN, 151305, p. A227

PULLMAN REGIONAL HOSPITAL, PULLMAN, WA, 501331, p. A706

PUNGO DISTRICT HOSPITAL, BELHAVEN, NC, 341310, p. A478

PUNXSUTAWNEY AREA HOSPITAL, PUNXSUTAWNEY, PA, 390199, p. A574

PURCELL MUNICIPAL HOSPITAL, PURCELL, OK, 370158, p. A537

PUSHMATAHA COUNTY–TOWN OF ANTLERS HOSPITAL AUTHORITY, ANTLERS, OK, 370083, p. A527

PUTNAM COMMUNITY MEDICAL CENTER, PALATKA, FL, 100232, p. A141

PUTNAM COUNTY HOSPITAL, GREENCASTLE, IN, 150027, p. A217

PUTNAM COUNTY MEMORIAL HOSPITAL, UNIONVILLE, MO, 261305, p. A395

PUTNAM GENERAL HOSPITAL, EATONTON, GA, 111313, p. A161

PUTNAM GENERAL HOSPITAL, HURRICANE, WV, 510085, p. A716

PUTNAM HOSPITAL CENTER, CARMEL, NY, 330273, p. A450

Q

QUEEN OF PEACE HOSPITAL, NEW PRAGUE, MN, 241361, p. A358

QUEEN OF THE VALLEY HOSPITAL, NAPA, CA, 050009, p. A77

QUEEN'S MEDICAL CENTER, HONOLULU, HI, 120001, p. A174

QUEENS CHILDREN'S PSYCHIATRIC CENTER, NEW YORK, NY, p. A464

QUEENS HOSPITAL CENTER, NEW YORK, NY, 330231, p. A464
QUENTIN MEASE HOSPITAL, HOUSTON, TEXAS (see HARRIS COUNTY HOSPITAL DISTRICT), p. A645
QUILLEN REHABILITATION HOSPITAL, JOHNSON CITY, TN, p. A609
QUINCY MEDICAL CENTER, QUINCY, MA, 220067, p. A322
QUINCY VALLEY MEDICAL CENTER, QUINCY, WA, 501320, p. A706
QUITMAN COUNTY HOSPITAL, MARKS, MS, 251314, p. A372

R

R M L SPECIALTY HOSPITAL, HINSDALE, IL, 142010, p. A197
R. E. THOMASON GENERAL HOSPITAL, EL PASO, TX, 450024, p. A637
R. J. REYNOLDS–PATRICK COUNTY MEMORIAL HOSPITAL, STUART, VA, 491306, p. A697
RABUN COUNTY HOSPITAL, CLAYTON, GA, 111336, p. A158
RAINBOW MENTAL HEALTH FACILITY, KANSAS CITY, KS, 174010, p. A250
RALEIGH GENERAL HOSPITAL, BECKLEY, WV, 510070, p. A713
RALPH H. JOHNSON VETERANS AFFAIRS MEDICAL CENTER, CHARLESTON, SC, p. A585
RANCHO LOS AMIGOS NATIONAL REHABILITATION CENTER, DOWNEY, CA, 050717, p. A59
RANCHO SPRINGS MEDICAL CENTER, MURRIETA, CA, 050701, p. A77
RANDOLPH COUNTY MEDICAL CENTER, POCAHONTAS, AR, 040047, p. A49
RANDOLPH HOSPITAL, ASHEBORO, NC, 340123, p. A477
RANDOLPH MEDICAL CENTER, ROANOKE, AL, 010098, p. A23
RANGELY DISTRICT HOSPITAL, RANGELY, CO, 061307, p. A109
RANKEN JORDAN, MARYLAND HEIGHTS, MO, 263303, p. A387
RANKIN HOSPITAL DISTRICT, RANKIN, TX, 451329, p. A662
RANKIN MEDICAL CENTER, BRANDON, MS, 250096, p. A367
RANSOM MEMORIAL HOSPITAL, OTTAWA, KS, 170014, p. A254
RAPID CITY REGIONAL HOSPITAL SYSTEM OF CARE, RAPID CITY, SD, 430077, p. A598
RAPIDES REGIONAL MEDICAL CENTER, ALEXANDRIA, LA, 190026, p. A276
RAPPAHANNOCK GENERAL HOSPITAL, KILMARNOCK, VA, 490123, p. A690
RARITAN BAY MEDICAL CENTER, PERTH AMBOY, NJ, 310039, p. A434
RAULERSON HOSPITAL, OKEECHOBEE, FL, 100252, p. A140
RAWLINS COUNTY HEALTH CENTER, ATWOOD, KS, 171307, p. A244
RAY COUNTY MEMORIAL HOSPITAL, RICHMOND, MO, 260122, p. A389
RAYMOND BLANK MEMORIAL HOSPITAL FOR CHILDREN, DES MOINES, IOWA (see IOWA METHODIST MEDICAL CENTER), p. A232
READING HOSPITAL AND MEDICAL CENTER, WEST READING, PA, 390044, p. A579
REAGAN MEMORIAL HOSPITAL, BIG LAKE, TX, 451301, p. A626
REBSAMEN MEDICAL CENTER, JACKSONVILLE, AR, 040074, p. A45
RED BAY HOSPITAL, RED BAY, AL, 010115, p. A23
RED BUD REGIONAL HOSPITAL, RED BUD, IL, 140061, p. A206
RED RIVER HOSPITAL, WICHITA FALLS, TX, 454018, p. A674
REDBUD COMMUNITY HOSPITAL, CLEARLAKE, CA, 051317, p. A57
REDGATE MEMORIAL HOSPITAL, LONG BEACH, CA, p. A68
REDINGTON–FAIRVIEW GENERAL HOSPITAL, SKOWHEGAN, ME, 200012, p. A301
REDLANDS COMMUNITY HOSPITAL, REDLANDS, CA, 050272, p. A83
REDMOND REGIONAL MEDICAL CENTER, ROME, GA, 110168, p. A168
REDWOOD AREA HOSPITAL, REDWOOD FALLS, MN, 241351, p. A360
REDWOOD MEMORIAL HOSPITAL, FORTUNA, CA, 050172, p. A60
REEDSBURG AREA MEDICAL CENTER, REEDSBURG, WI, 521351, p. A734
REEVES COUNTY HOSPITAL, PECOS, TX, 450201, p. A660
REFUGIO COUNTY MEMORIAL HOSPITAL, REFUGIO, TX, 451317, p. A662
REGENCY HOSPITAL OF AKRON, BARBERTON, OH, 362029, p. A503
REGENCY HOSPITAL OF CENTRAL GEORGIA, MACON, GA, 110224, p. A165
REGENCY HOSPITAL OF COVINGTON, COVINGTON, LA, 190262, p. A279
REGENCY HOSPITAL OF FLORENCE, FLORENCE, SC, 422007, p. A588

REGENCY HOSPITAL OF HATTIESBURG, HATTIESBURG, MS, 252009, p. A369
REGENCY HOSPITAL OF MERIDIAN, MERIDIAN, MS, 250155, p. A373
REGENCY HOSPITAL OF MINNEAPOLIS, GOLDEN VALLEY, MN, p. A354
REGENCY HOSPITAL OF NORTHWEST ARKANSAS, FAYETTEVILLE, AR, 042009, p. A42
REGENCY HOSPITAL OF NORTHWEST INDIANA, EAST CHICAGO, IN, 152024, p. A214
REGENCY HOSPITAL OF ODESSA, ODESSA, TX, 452085, p. A659
REGENCY HOSPITAL OF RAVENNA, RAVENNA, OH, p. A521
REGENCY HOSPITAL OF SOUTH ATLANTA, EAST POINT, GA, 112014, p. A161
REGENCY HOSPITAL OF SPRINGDALE, SPRINGDALE, AR, p. A51
REGINA MEDICAL CENTER, HASTINGS, MN, 240059, p. A354
REGIONAL HEALTH SERVICES OF HOWARD COUNTY, CRESCO, IA, 161328, p. A231
REGIONAL HOSPITAL FOR RESPIRATORY AND COMPLEX CARE, SEATTLE, WA, 502001, p. A708
REGIONAL HOSPITAL OF JACKSON, JACKSON, TN, 440189, p. A608
REGIONAL MEDICAL CENTER, MANCHESTER, IA, 161343, p. A237
REGIONAL MEDICAL CENTER, VINELAND, NEW JERSEY (see SOUTH JERSEY HEALTHCARE), p. A426
REGIONAL MEDICAL CENTER AT MEMPHIS, MEMPHIS, TN, 440152, p. A613
REGIONAL MEDICAL CENTER OF HOPKINS COUNTY, MADISONVILLE, KY, 180093, p. A270
REGIONAL MEDICAL CENTER OF ORANGEBURG AND CALHOUN COUNTIES, ORANGEBURG, SC, 420068, p. A591
REGIONAL MEDICAL CENTER OF SAN JOSE, SAN JOSE, CA, 050125, p. A90
REGIONAL MEDICAL CENTER–BAYONET POINT, HUDSON, FL, 100256, p. A131
REGIONAL REHABILITATION CENTER, SALEM, OREGON (see SALEM HOSPITAL), p. A549
REGIONAL REHABILITATION HOSPITAL, PHENIX CITY, AL, 013033, p. A23
REGIONAL WEST MEDICAL CENTER, SCOTTSBLUFF, NE, 280061, p. A413
REGIONS HOSPITAL, SAINT PAUL, MN, 240106, p. A362
REHABILITATION HOSPITAL OF ACADIANA, LAFAYETTE, LA, 192029, p. A284
REHABILITATION HOSPITAL OF FORT WAYNE, FORT WAYNE, IN, 153030, p. A215
REHABILITATION HOSPITAL OF INDIANA, INDIANAPOLIS, IN, 153028, p. A218
REHABILITATION HOSPITAL OF NEW MEXICO, ALBUQUERQUE, NM, 323028, p. A441
REHABILITATION HOSPITAL OF RHODE ISLAND, NORTH SMITHFIELD, RI, 413025, p. A581
REHABILITATION HOSPITAL OF SOUTH JERSEY, VINELAND, NJ, 313036, p. A438
REHABILITATION HOSPITAL OF THE CAPE AND ISLANDS, EAST SANDWICH, MA, 223032, p. A317
REHABILITATION HOSPITAL OF THE PACIFIC, HONOLULU, HI, 123025, p. A174
REHABILITATION HOSPITAL OF TINTON FALLS, EATONTOWN, NJ, 313035, p. A427
REHABILITATION INSTITUTE AT SANTA BARBARA, SANTA BARBARA, CA, 053028, p. A92
REHABILITATION INSTITUTE AT THE MOUNT KEMBLE DIVISION (see MORRISTOWN MEMORIAL HOSPITAL), p. A431
REHABILITATION INSTITUTE OF CHICAGO, CHICAGO, IL, 143026, p. A189
REHABILITATION INSTITUTE OF MICHIGAN, DETROIT, MI, 233027, p. A331
REHABILITATION INSTITUTE OF OREGON, PORTLAND, OREGON (see LEGACY GOOD SAMARITAN HOSPITAL AND MEDICAL CENTER), p. A547
REHABILITATION INSTITUTE OF WEST FLORIDA, PENSACOLA, FLORIDA (see WEST FLORIDA HOSPITAL), p. A143
REHOBOTH MCKINLEY CHRISTIAN HOSPITAL, GALLUP, NM, 320038, p. A442
REID HOSPITAL AND HEALTH CARE SERVICES, RICHMOND, IN, 150048, p. A224
REISCH MEMORIAL NURSING HOME (see THOMAS H. BOYD MEMORIAL HOSPITAL), p. A185
RENAISSANCE WOMEN'S HOSPITAL OF EDMOND, EDMOND, OK, 370196, p. A530
RENVILLE COUNTY HOSPITAL, OLIVIA, MN, 241306, p. A359
REPUBLIC COUNTY HOSPITAL, BELLEVILLE, KS, 171361, p. A244
RESEARCH BELTON HOSPITAL, BELTON, MO, 260214, p. A378
RESEARCH MEDICAL CENTER, KANSAS CITY, MO, 260027, p. A384

RESEARCH PSYCHIATRIC CENTER, KANSAS CITY, MO, 264016, p. A384
RESTON HOSPITAL CENTER, RESTON, VA, 490107, p. A694
RESURRECTION MEDICAL CENTER, CHICAGO, IL, 140117, p. A189
RETREAT HOSPITAL, RICHMOND, VA, 490071, p. A695
REX HEALTHCARE, RALEIGH, NC, 340114, p. A489
REYNOLDS ARMY COMMUNITY HOSPITAL, FORT SILL, OK, p. A531
REYNOLDS MEMORIAL HOSPITAL, GLEN DALE, WV, 510013, p. A715
RHD MEMORIAL MEDICAL CENTER, DALLAS, TX, 450379, p. A634
RHEA MEDICAL CENTER, DAYTON, TN, 441310, p. A605
RHODE ISLAND HOSPITAL, PROVIDENCE, RI, 410007, p. A582
RICE COUNTY HOSPITAL DISTRICT NUMBER ONE, LYONS, KS, 171330, p. A252
RICE MEDICAL CENTER, EAGLE LAKE, TX, 451312, p. A636
RICE MEMORIAL HOSPITAL, WILLMAR, MN, 240088, p. A365
RICHARD H. HUTCHINGS PSYCHIATRIC CENTER, SYRACUSE, NY, 334001, p. A473
RICHARD H. YOUNG PSYCHIATRIC HOSPITAL, KEARNEY, NE, 284007, p. A408
RICHARD L. ROUDEBUSH VETERANS AFFAIRS MEDICAL CENTER, INDIANAPOLIS, IN, p. A218
RICHARD P. STADTER PSYCHIATRIC CENTER, GRAND FORKS, ND, 354005, p. A498
RICHARDS MEMORIAL HOSPITAL, ROCKDALE, TX, 450648, p. A662
RICHARDSON MEDICAL CENTER, RAYVILLE, LA, 190151, p. A291
RICHARDSON REGIONALMEDICAL CENTER, RICHARDSON, TX, 450537, p. A662
RICHARDTON HEALTH CENTER, RICHARDTON, ND, 351317, p. A500
RICHLAND HOSPITAL, RICHLAND CENTER, WI, 521341, p. A735
RICHLAND MEMORIAL HOSPITAL, OLNEY, IL, 140147, p. A203
RICHLAND PARISH HOSPITAL, DELHI, LA, 190149, p. A280
RICHLAND PARISH REHABILITATION HOSPITAL, RAYVILLE, LA, 193075, p. A291
RICHMOND STATE HOSPITAL, RICHMOND, IN, 154018, p. A224
RICHWOOD AREA COMMUNITY HOSPITAL, RICHWOOD, WV, 511305, p. A719
RIDDLE MEMORIAL HOSPITAL, MEDIA, PA, 390222, p. A565
RIDEOUT MEMORIAL HOSPITAL, MARYSVILLE, CA, 050133, p. A75
RIDGE BEHAVIORAL HEALTH SYSTEM, LEXINGTON, KY, 184009, p. A267
RIDGECREST REGIONAL HOSPITAL, RIDGECREST, CA, 050448, p. A84
RIDGEVIEW INSTITUTE, SMYRNA, GA, 114012, p. A169
RIDGEVIEW MEDICAL CENTER, WACONIA, MN, 240056, p. A364
RIDGEVIEW PSYCHIATRIC HOSPITAL AND CENTER, OAK RIDGE, TN, 444003, p. A616
RILEY HOSPITAL, MERIDIAN, MS, 250081, p. A373
RILEY HOSPITAL FOR CHILDREN, INDIANAPOLIS, INDIANA (see CLARIAN HEALTH PARTNERS), p. A218
RINGGOLD COUNTY HOSPITAL, MOUNT AYR, IA, 160048, p. A238
RIO GRANDE HOSPITAL, DEL NORTE, CO, 061301, p. A103
RIO GRANDE REGIONAL HOSPITAL, MCALLEN, TX, 450711, p. A656
RIO GRANDE STATE CENTER, HARLINGEN, TX, 454088, p. A643
RIO VISTA PHYSICAL REHABILITATION HOSPITAL, EL PASO, TX, 453033, p. A637
RIPLEY COUNTY MEMORIAL HOSPITAL, DONIPHAN, MO, 260080, p. A381
RIPON MEDICAL CENTER, RIPON, WI, 521321, p. A735
RIVENDELL BEHAVIORAL HEALTH, BOWLING GREEN, KY, 184017, p. A262
RIVENDELL BEHAVIORAL HEALTH SERVICES, BENTON, AR, 044007, p. A40
RIVER CREST HOSPITAL, SAN ANGELO, TX, 454064, p. A663
RIVER FALLS AREA HOSPITAL, RIVER FALLS, WI, 521349, p. A735
RIVER HOSPITAL, ALEXANDRIA BAY, NY, 331309, p. A446
RIVER OAKS CHILD AND ADOLESCENT HOSPITAL, NEW ORLEANS, LA, 194042, p. A289
RIVER OAKS HOSPITAL, NEW ORLEANS, LA, 194031, p. A289
RIVER OAKS HOSPITAL, JACKSON, MS, 250138, p. A371
RIVER PARISHES HOSPITAL, LA PLACE, LA, 190175, p. A283
RIVER PARK HOSPITAL, MCMINNVILLE, TN, 440151, p. A612
RIVER PARK HOSPITAL, HUNTINGTON, WV, 514008, p. A716
RIVER REGION HEALTH SYSTEM, VICKSBURG, MS, 250031, p. A376
RIVER REGION MEDICAL CENTER, VICKSBURG, MISSISSIPPI (see RIVER REGION HEALTH SYSTEM), p. A376

S

SAINT FRANCIS HOSPITAL–BARTLETT, BARTLETT, TN, 440228, p. A602

SAINT FRANCIS MEDICAL CENTER, CAPE GIRARDEAU, MO, 260183, p. A379

SAINT FRANCIS MEDICAL CENTER, GRAND ISLAND, NE, 280023, p. A407

SAINT FRANCIS MEMORIAL HEALTH CENTER, GRAND ISLAND, NEBRASKA (see SAINT FRANCIS MEDICAL CENTER), p. A407

SAINT FRANCIS MEMORIAL HOSPITAL, SAN FRANCISCO, CA, 050152, p. A89

SAINT JAMES HOSPITAL OF NEWARK, NEWARK, NJ, 310018, p. A433

SAINT JOHN HOSPITAL, LEAVENWORTH, KS, 170009, p. A251

SAINT JOHN'S HEALTH CENTER, SANTA MONICA, CA, 050290, p. A93

SAINT JOHN'S HEALTH SYSTEM, ANDERSON, IN, 150088, p. A211

SAINT JOSEPH HOSPITAL, CHICAGO, IL, 140224, p. A190

SAINT JOSEPH HOSPITAL, LEXINGTON, KY, 180010, p. A267

SAINT JOSEPH HOSPITAL EAST, LEXINGTON, KY, 180143, p. A268

SAINT JOSEPH MEDICAL CENTER, KANSAS CITY, MO, 260085, p. A385

SAINT JOSEPH MERCY HEALTH SYSTEM, YPSILANTI, MI, 230156, p. A348

SAINT JOSEPH MERCY LIVINGSTON HOSPITAL, HOWELL, MI, 230069, p. A336

SAINT JOSEPH MERCY SALINE HOSPITAL, SALINE, MI, 230212, p. A345

SAINT JOSEPH REGIONAL MEDICAL CENTER, SOUTH BEND, IN, 150012, p. A225

SAINT JOSEPH REGIONAL MEDICAL CENTER–MISHAWAKA CAMPUS, MISHAWAKA, IN, 150029, p. A222

SAINT JOSEPH REGIONAL MEDICAL CENTER–PLYMOUTH CAMPUS, PLYMOUTH, IN, 150076, p. A224

SAINT JOSEPH'S HOSPITAL, MARSHFIELD, WI, 520037, p. A729

SAINT JOSEPH'S HOSPITAL OF ATLANTA, ATLANTA, GA, 110082, p. A154

SAINT LOUIS UNIVERSITY HOSPITAL, SAINT LOUIS, MO, 260105, p. A391

SAINT LUKE INSTITUTE, SILVER SPRING, MD, p. A311

SAINT LUKE'S HOSPITAL OF KANSAS CITY, KANSAS CITY, MO, 260138, p. A385

SAINT LUKE'S MEDICAL CENTER, CLEVELAND, OHIO (see ST. VINCENT CHARITY HOSPITAL), p. A509

SAINT LUKE'S NORTHLAND HOSPITAL, KANSAS CITY, MO, p. A385

SAINT LUKE'S NORTHLAND HOSPITAL–SMITHVILLE CAMPUS, SMITHVILLE, MO, 260062, p. A393

SAINT LUKE'S SOUTH HOSPITAL, OVERLAND PARK, KS, 170185, p. A255

SAINT MARGARET MERCY HEALTHCARE CENTERS, HAMMOND, IN, 150004, p. A217

SAINT MARGARET MERCY HEALTHCARE CENTERS–NORTH CAMPUS, HAMMOND, INDIANA (see SAINT MARGARET MERCY HEALTHCARE CENTERS), p. A217

SAINT MARGARET MERCY HEALTHCARE CENTERS–SOUTH CAMPUS, DYER, INDIANA (see SAINT MARGARET MERCY HEALTHCARE CENTERS), p. A217

SAINT MARY HOSPITAL, NEW YORK, KANSAS (see MERCY REGIONAL HEALTH CENTER), p. A252

SAINT MARY HOSPITAL, MANHATTAN, KANSAS (see (see MERCY REGIONAL HEALTH CENTER)), p. A252

SAINT MARY'S HEALTH CARE, GRAND RAPIDS, MI, 230059, p. A335

SAINT MARY'S HOSPITAL, WATERBURY, CT, 070016, p. A117

SAINT MARY'S MEDICAL CENTER, SAGINAW, MI, 230077, p. A344

SAINT MARY'S REGIONAL MEDICAL CENTER, RUSSELLVILLE, AR, 040041, p. A50

SAINT MARY'S REGIONAL MEDICAL CENTER, RENO, NV, 290009, p. A418

SAINT MARY'S STANDISH COMMUNITY HOSPITAL, STANDISH, MI, 231305, p. A345

SAINT MARYS HOSPITAL, ROCHESTER, MN, 240010, p. A360

SAINT MICHAEL'S HOSPITAL, STEVENS POINT, WI, 520002, p. A736

SAINT MICHAEL'S MEDICAL CENTER, NEWARK, NJ, 310096, p. A433

SAINT PETER'S UNIVERSITY HOSPITAL, NEW BRUNSWICK, NJ, 310070, p. A432

SAINT THOMAS HOSPITAL, NASHVILLE, TN, 440082, p. A615

SAINT THOMAS HOSPITAL, AKRON, OHIO (see SUMMA HEALTH SYSTEM), p. A502

SAINT VINCENT HEALTH CENTER, ERIE, PA, 390009, p. A558

SAINT VINCENT HOSPITAL AT WORCESTER MEDICAL CENTER, WORCESTER, MA, 220028, p. A325

SAINT VINCENT'S HOSPITAL – MANHATTAN, NEW YORK, NY, 330290, p. A464

SAINT VINCENTS CATHOLIC MEDICAL CENTERS OF NEW YORK, NEW YORK, NY, 330357, p. A465

SAINT'S MARY & ELIZABETH MEDICAL CENTER, CLAREMONT AVENUE, CHICAGO, IL, 140094, p. A190

SAINT'S MARY & ELIZABETH MEDICAL CENTER, DIVISION STREET, CHICAGO, IL, 140180, p. A190

SAINTS MEMORIAL MEDICAL CENTER, LOWELL, MA, 220082, p. A319

SAKAKAWEA MEDICAL CENTER, HAZEN, ND, 351310, p. A498

SALEM COMMUNITY HOSPITAL, SALEM, OH, 360185, p. A521

SALEM HOSPITAL, SALEM, MASSACHUSETTS (see NORTH SHORE MEDICAL CENTER), p. A323

SALEM HOSPITAL, SALEM, OR, 380051, p. A549

SALEM MEMORIAL DISTRICT HOSPITAL, SALEM, MO, 261318, p. A393

SALEM TOWNSHIP HOSPITAL, SALEM, IL, 141345, p. A207

SALINA REGIONAL HEALTH CENTER, SALINA, KS, 170012, p. A256

SALINA REGIONAL HEALTH CENTER– PENN CAMPUS, SALINA, KANSAS (see SALINA REGIONAL HEALTH CENTER), p. A256

SALINA REGIONAL HEALTH CENTER–SANTA FE CAMPUS, SALINA, KANSAS (see SALINA REGIONAL HEALTH CENTER), p. A256

SALINA SURGICAL HOSPITAL, SALINA, KS, 170187, p. A256

SALINAS VALLEY MEMORIAL HEALTHCARE SYSTEM, SALINAS, CA, 050334, p. A86

SALINE MEMORIAL HOSPITAL, BENTON, AR, 040084, p. A40

SALT LAKE REGIONAL MEDICAL CENTER, SALT LAKE CITY, UT, 460003, p. A679

SAM RAYBURN MEMORIAL VETERANS CENTER, BONHAM, TEXAS (see VETERANS AFFAIRS NORTH TEXAS HEALTH CARE SYSTEM), p. A634

SAMARITAN ALBANY GENERAL HOSPITAL, ALBANY, OR, 380022, p. A542

SAMARITAN BEHAVIORAL HEALTH CENTER–DESERT SAMARITAN MEDICAL CENTER, MESA, ARIZONA (see BANNER DESERT MEDICAL CENTER), p. A32

SAMARITAN HEALTHCARE, MOSES LAKE, WA, 500033, p. A704

SAMARITAN HOSPITAL, LEXINGTON, KY, 180007, p. A268

SAMARITAN HOSPITAL, TROY, NY, 330180, p. A474

SAMARITAN LEBANON COMMUNITY HOSPITAL, LEBANON, OR, 380008, p. A545

SAMARITAN MEDICAL CENTER, WATERTOWN, NY, 330157, p. A475

SAMARITAN MEMORIAL HOSPITAL, MACON, MO, 261313, p. A387

SAMARITAN NORTH LINCOLN HOSPITAL, LINCOLN CITY, OR, 381302, p. A545

SAMARITAN PACIFIC COMMUNITIES HOSPITAL, NEWPORT, OR, 381314, p. A546

SAMARITAN REGIONAL HEALTH SYSTEM, ASHLAND, OH, 360002, p. A502

SAME DAY SURGERY CENTER, RAPID CITY, SD, 430093, p. A598

SAMPSON REGIONAL MEDICAL CENTER, CLINTON, NC, 340024, p. A480

SAMUEL MAHELONA MEMORIAL HOSPITAL, KAPAA, HI, 120025, p. A175

SAMUEL SIMMONDS MEMORIAL HOSPITAL, BARROW, AK, 020019, p. A26

SAN ANGELO COMMUNITY MEDICAL CENTER, SAN ANGELO, TX, 450340, p. A663

SAN ANTONIO COMMUNITY HOSPITAL, UPLAND, CA, 050099, p. A97

SAN ANTONIO DIVISION, SAN ANTONIO, TEXAS (see SOUTH TEXAS VETERANS HEALTH CARE SYSTEM), p. A665

SAN ANTONIO STATE HOSPITAL, SAN ANTONIO, TX, 454011, p. A665

SAN CARLOS GENERAL HOSPITAL, SAN JUAN, PR, 400017, p. A747

SAN DIEGO COUNTY PSYCHIATRIC HOSPITAL, SAN DIEGO, CA, 054114, p. A87

SAN DIEGO HOSPICE & PALLIATIVE CARE, SAN DIEGO, CA, 050698, p. A87

SAN DIEGO REHABILITATION INSTITUTE, SAN DIEGO, CALIFORNIA (see ALVARADO HOSPITAL MEDICAL CENTER), p. A86

SAN DIMAS COMMUNITY HOSPITAL, SAN DIMAS, CA, 050588, p. A88

SAN FRANCISCO GENERAL HOSPITAL MEDICAL CENTER, SAN FRANCISCO, CA, 050228, p. A89

SAN GABRIEL VALLEY MEDICAL CENTER, SAN GABRIEL, CA, 050132, p. A90

SAN GORGONIO MEMORIAL HOSPITAL, BANNING, CA, 050054, p. A54

SAN JACINTO METHODIST HOSPITAL, BAYTOWN, TX, 450424, p. A625

SAN JACINTO METHODIST HOSPITAL – ALEXANDER, BAYTOWN, TEXAS (see SAN JACINTO METHODIST HOSPITAL), p. A625

SAN JOAQUIN COMMUNITY HOSPITAL, BAKERSFIELD, CA, 050455, p. A54

SAN JOAQUIN GENERAL HOSPITAL, FRENCH CAMP, CA, 050167, p. A61

SAN JOAQUIN VALLEY REHABILITATION HOSPITAL, FRESNO, CA, 053032, p. A61

SAN JORGE CHILDREN'S HOSPITAL, SAN JUAN, PR, p. A747

SAN JUAN BAUTISTA MEDICAL CENTER, CAGUAS, PR, 400104, p. A744

SAN JUAN CAPESTRANO HOSPITAL, SAN JUAN, PR, 404005, p. A748

SAN JUAN CITY HOSPITAL, SAN JUAN, PR, 400015, p. A748

SAN JUAN HOSPITAL, MONTICELLO, UT, 460020, p. A677

SAN JUAN REGIONAL MEDICAL CENTER, FARMINGTON, NM, 320005, p. A442

SAN JUAN REGIONAL MEDICAL CENTER REHABILITATION HOSPITAL, FARMINGTON, NEW MEXICO (see SAN JUAN REGIONAL MEDICAL CENTER), p. A442

SAN LEANDRO HOSPITAL, SAN LEANDRO, CA, 050264, p. A91

SAN LUIS VALLEY REGIONAL MEDICAL CENTER, ALAMOSA, CO, 060008, p. A101

SAN MATEO MEDICAL CENTER, SAN MATEO, CA, 050113, p. A91

SAN PEDRO PENINSULA HOSPITAL, LOS ANGELES, CA, 050078, p. A72

SAN RAMON REGIONAL MEDICAL CENTER, SAN RAMON, CA, 050689, p. A91

SAN VICENTE HOSPITAL, LOS ANGELES, CA, 050681, p. A72

SANDHILLS REGIONAL MEDICAL CENTER, HAMLET, NC, 340106, p. A484

SANDYPINES, TEQUESTA, FL, p. A149

SANGER GENERAL HOSPITAL, SANGER, CA, 050410, p. A92

SANPETE VALLEY HOSPITAL, MOUNT PLEASANT, UT, 461303, p. A677

SANTA BARBARA COTTAGE HOSPITAL, SANTA BARBARA, CA, 050396, p. A92

SANTA CLARA VALLEY MEDICAL CENTER, SAN JOSE, CA, 050038, p. A90

SANTA MONICA–UCLA MEDICAL CENTER, SANTA MONICA, CA, 050112, p. A93

SANTA ROSA MEDICAL CENTER, MILTON, FL, 100124, p. A138

SANTA ROSA MEMORIAL HOSPITAL, SANTA ROSA, CA, 050174, p. A93

SANTA YNEZ VALLEY COTTAGE HOSPITAL, SOLVANG, CA, 050478, p. A94

SANTIAM MEMORIAL HOSPITAL, STAYTON, OR, 380056, p. A549

SARAH BUSH LINCOLN HEALTH CENTER, MATTOON, IL, 140189, p. A200

SARAH D. CULBERTSON MEMORIAL HOSPITAL, RUSHVILLE, IL, 141333, p. A207

SARASOTA MEMORIAL HOSPITAL, SARASOTA, FL, 100087, p. A146

SARATOGA HOSPITAL, SARATOGA SPRINGS, NY, 330222, p. A472

SARTORI MEMORIAL HOSPITAL, CEDAR FALLS, IA, 160040, p. A229

SATANTA DISTRICT HOSPITAL, SATANTA, KS, 171324, p. A256

SATILLA REGIONAL MEDICAL CENTER, WAYCROSS, GA, 110003, p. A172

SAUK PRAIRIE MEMORIAL HOSPITAL, PRAIRIE DU SAC, WI, 520095, p. A734

SAUNDERS COUNTY HEALTH SERVICE, WAHOO, NE, 281307, p. A413

SAVANNAS HOSPITAL, PORT ST. LUCIE, FL, 104036, p. A144

SAVOY MEDICAL CENTER, MAMOU, LA, 190025, p. A285

SAYRE MEMORIAL HOSPITAL, SAYRE, OK, 370103, p. A538

SCCI – MANSFIELD, MANSFIELD, OH, 362021, p. A517

SCCI HOSPITAL, HOUSTON, TX, 452027, p. A647

SCCI HOSPITAL – AURORA, AURORA, CO, 062013, p. A101

SCCI HOSPITAL – EASTON, EASTON, PA, 392034, p. A558

SCCI HOSPITAL – EL PASO, EL PASO, TX, 450846, p. A638

SCCI HOSPITAL – FARGO, FARGO, ND, 352004, p. A498

SCCI HOSPITAL – HARRISBURG, HARRISBURG, PA, 392035, p. A560

SCCI HOSPITAL – LIMA, LIMA, OH, 362020, p. A516

SCCI HOSPITAL OF AMARILLO, AMARILLO, TX, 452060, p. A621

SCCI HOSPITAL OF DETROIT, DETROIT, MI, 232027, p. A331

SCCI HOSPITAL OF VICTORIA, VICTORIA, TX, 452056, p. A672

SCCI HOSPITAL–SAN ANGELO, SAN ANGELO, TX, 452064, p. A663

SCENIC MOUNTAIN MEDICAL CENTER, BIG SPRING, TX, 450653, p. A626

SCHEURER HOSPITAL, PIGEON, MI, 231310, p. A342

SCHICK SHADEL HOSPITAL, SEATTLE, WA, 500134, p. A708

SCHLEICHER COUNTY MEDICAL CENTER, ELDORADO, TX, 451304, p. A638

SCHNECK MEDICAL CENTER, SEYMOUR, IN, 150065, p. A225

SHAMROCK GENERAL HOSPITAL, SHAMROCK, TX, 451340, p. A667

SHANDS AT AGH, GAINESVILLE, FL, p. A130

SHANDS AT LAKE SHORE, LAKE CITY, FL, 100102, p. A134

SHANDS AT LIVE OAK, LIVE OAK, FL, 101301, p. A135

SHANDS AT STARKE, STARKE, FL, 101310, p. A146

SHANDS AT THE UNIVERSITY OF FLORIDA, GAINESVILLE, FL, 100113, p. A130

SHANDS JACKSONVILLE MEDICAL CENTER, JACKSONVILLE, FL, 100001, p. A132

SHANDS REHAB HOSPITAL, GAINESVILLE, FL, p. A130

SHANNON MEDICAL CENTER, SAN ANGELO, TX, 450571, p. A663

SHANNON MEDICAL CENTER– ST. JOHN'S CAMPUS, SAN ANGELO, TEXAS (see SHANNON MEDICAL CENTER), p. A663

SHARE MEDICAL CENTER, ALVA, OK, 370080, p. A527

SHARKEY–ISSAQUENA COMMUNITY HOSPITAL, ROLLING FORK, MS, 250079, p. A375

SHARON HOSPITAL, SHARON, CT, 070004, p. A116

SHARON REGIONAL HEALTH SYSTEM, SHARON, PA, 390211, p. A576

SHARP CHULA VISTA MEDICAL CENTER, CHULA VISTA, CA, 050222, p. A57

SHARP CORONADO HOSPITAL AND HEALTH CENTER, CORONADO, CA, 050234, p. A58

SHARP GROSSMONT HOSPITAL, LA MESA, CA, 050026, p. A66

SHARP MARY BIRCH HOSPITAL FOR WOMEN, SAN DIEGO, CA, 050722, p. A87

SHARP MEMORIAL HOSPITAL, SAN DIEGO, CA, 050100, p. A87

SHARP MESA VISTA HOSPITAL, SAN DIEGO, CALIFORNIA (see SHARP MEMORIAL HOSPITAL), p. A87

SHASTA REGIONAL MEDICAL CENTER, REDDING, CA, 050733, p. A83

SHAUGHNESSY–KAPLAN REHABILITATION HOSPITAL, SALEM, MA, 222026, p. A323

SHAWANO MEDICAL CENTER, SHAWANO, WI, 521346, p. A735

SHAWNEE MISSION MEDICAL CENTER, SHAWNEE MISSION, KS, 170104, p. A257

SHEEHAN MEMORIAL HOSPITAL, BUFFALO, NY, 330029, p. A449

SHELBY BAPTIST MEDICAL CENTER, ALABASTER, AL, 010016, p. A13

SHELBY COUNTY MYRTUE MEMORIAL HOSPITAL, HARLAN, IA, 160031, p. A235

SHELBY HOSPITAL, SHELBY, OHIO (see MEDCENTRAL HEALTH SYSTEM), p. A517

SHELBY MEMORIAL HOSPITAL, SHELBYVILLE, IL, 140019, p. A207

SHELBY REGIONAL MEDICAL CENTER, CENTER, TX, 450839, p. A628

SHELTERING ARMS REHABILITATION HOSPITAL, MECHANICSVILLE, VA, 493025, p. A691

SHENANDOAH MEDICAL CENTER, SHENANDOAH, IA, 161366, p. A241

SHENANDOAH MEMORIAL HOSPITAL, WOODSTOCK, VA, 160092, p. A698

SHENANGO VALLEY CAMPUS, FARRELL, PENNSYLVANIA (see UPMC HORIZON), p. A559

SHEPHERD CENTER, ATLANTA, GA, 112003, p. A154

SHEPPARD AND ENOCH PRATT HOSPITAL, BALTIMORE, MD, 214000, p. A304

SHERIDAN COMMUNITY HOSPITAL, SHERIDAN, MI, 231312, p. A345

SHERIDAN COUNTY HEALTH COMPLEX, HOXIE, KS, 171347, p. A249

SHERIDAN MEMORIAL HOSPITAL, PLENTYWOOD, MT, 271322, p. A401

SHERMAN HOSPITAL, ELGIN, IL, 140030, p. A193

SHERMAN OAKS HOSPITAL AND HEALTH CENTER, LOS ANGELES, CA, 050114, p. A72

SHOALS HOSPITAL, MUSCLE SHOALS, AL, 010157, p. A22

SHODAIR CHILDREN'S HOSPITAL, HELENA, MT, 274004, p. A399

SHORE MEMORIAL HOSPITAL, SOMERS POINT, NJ, 310047, p. A436

SHORE MEMORIAL HOSPITAL, NASSAWADOX, VA, 490037, p. A692

SHOSHONE MEDICAL CENTER, KELLOGG, ID, 131314, p. A179

SHREVEPORT REHABILITATION HOSPITAL, SHREVEPORT, LA, 193083, p. A293

SHRINERS HOSPITALS FOR CHILDREN, ERIE, ERIE, PA, p. A558

SHRINERS HOSPITALS FOR CHILDREN, GALVESTON BURNS HOSPITAL, GALVESTON, TX, p. A641

SHRINERS HOSPITALS FOR CHILDREN, GREENVILLE, GREENVILLE, SC, p. A588

SHRINERS HOSPITALS FOR CHILDREN, HONOLULU, HONOLULU, HI, p. A174

SHRINERS HOSPITALS FOR CHILDREN, HOUSTON, HOUSTON, TX, p. A647

SHRINERS HOSPITALS FOR CHILDREN, LOS ANGELES, LOS ANGELES, CA, p. A72

SHRINERS HOSPITALS FOR CHILDREN, NORTHERN CALIFORNIA, SACRAMENTO, CA, p. A85

SHRINERS HOSPITALS FOR CHILDREN, PHILADELPHIA, PHILADELPHIA, PA, p. A569

SHRINERS HOSPITALS FOR CHILDREN, PORTLAND, PORTLAND, OR, p. A548

SHRINERS HOSPITALS FOR CHILDREN, SHREVEPORT, SHREVEPORT, LA, p. A293

SHRINERS HOSPITALS FOR CHILDREN, SHRINERS BURNS HOSPITAL, CINCINNATI, CINCINNATI, OH, p. A507

SHRINERS HOSPITALS FOR CHILDREN, SHRINERS BURNS HOSPITAL–BOSTON, BOSTON, MA, p. A314

SHRINERS HOSPITALS FOR CHILDREN, SPRINGFIELD, SPRINGFIELD, MA, p. A324

SHRINERS HOSPITALS FOR CHILDREN, ST. LOUIS, SAINT LOUIS, MO, p. A391

SHRINERS HOSPITALS FOR CHILDREN, TAMPA, TAMPA, FL, p. A148

SHRINERS HOSPITALS FOR CHILDREN, TWIN CITIES, MINNEAPOLIS, MN, p. A357

SHRINERS HOSPITALS FOR CHILDREN–CHICAGO, CHICAGO, IL, p. A190

SHRINERS HOSPITALS FOR CHILDREN–INTERMOUNTAIN, SALT LAKE CITY, UT, p. A680

SHRINERS HOSPITALS FOR CHILDREN–LEXINGTON, LEXINGTON, KY, p. A268

SHRINERS HOSPITALS FOR CHILDREN–SPOKANE, SPOKANE, WA, p. A709

SIBLEY MEDICAL CENTER, ARLINGTON, MN, 241311, p. A349

SIBLEY MEMORIAL HOSPITAL, WASHINGTON, DC, 090005, p. A122

SID PETERSON MEMORIAL HOSPITAL, KERRVILLE, TX, 450007, p. A651

SIDNEY HEALTH CENTER, SIDNEY, MT, 270021, p. A402

SIERRA MEDICAL CENTER, EL PASO, TX, 450668, p. A638

SIERRA NEVADA MEMORIAL HOSPITAL, GRASS VALLEY, CA, 050150, p. A63

SIERRA TUCSON, TUCSON, AZ, p. A38

SIERRA VALLEY DISTRICT HOSPITAL, LOYALTON, CA, 050355, p. A74

SIERRA VIEW DISTRICT HOSPITAL, PORTERVILLE, CA, 050261, p. A82

SIERRA VISTA HOSPITAL, SACRAMENTO, CA, 054087, p. A85

SIERRA VISTA HOSPITAL, TRUTH OR CONSEQUENCES, NM, 321300, p. A445

SIERRA VISTA REGIONAL HEALTH CENTER, SIERRA VISTA, AZ, 030043, p. A37

SIERRA VISTA REGIONAL MEDICAL CENTER, SAN LUIS OBISPO, CA, 050506, p. A91

SIERRA–KINGS DISTRICT HOSPITAL, REEDLEY, CA, 050192, p. A84

SILOAM SPRINGS MEMORIAL HOSPITAL, SILOAM SPRINGS, AR, 040001, p. A50

SILVER CROSS HOSPITAL, JOLIET, IL, 140213, p. A198

SILVER HILL HOSPITAL, NEW CANAAN, CT, 074014, p. A115

SILVERTON HOSPITAL, SILVERTON, OR, 380029, p. A549

SIMI VALLEY HOSPITAL AND HEALTH CARE SERVICES, SIMI VALLEY, CA, 050236, p. A94

SIMI VALLEY HOSPITAL AND HEALTH CARE SERVICES–SOUTH CAMPUS, SIMI VALLEY, CALIFORNIA (see SIMI VALLEY HOSPITAL AND HEALTH CARE SERVICES), p. A94

SIMPSON GENERAL HOSPITAL, MENDENHALL, MS, 250065, p. A372

SIMPSON INFIRMARY, WELLESLEY COLLEGE, WELLESLEY, MA, p. A324

SINAI HOSPITAL OF BALTIMORE, BALTIMORE, MD, 210012, p. A304

SINAI–GRACE HOSPITAL, DETROIT, MI, 230024, p. A332

SINGING RIVER HOSPITAL, PASCAGOULA, MISSISSIPPI (see SINGING RIVER HOSPITAL SYSTEM), p. A374

SINGING RIVER HOSPITAL SYSTEM, PASCAGOULA, MS, 250040, p. A374

SIOUX CENTER COMMUNITY HOSPITAL AND HEALTH CENTER/AVERA HEALTH, SIOUX CENTER, IA, 161346, p. A241

SIOUX FALLS SURGICAL CENTER, SIOUX FALLS, SD, 430090, p. A599

SIOUX VALLEY CANBY CAMPUS, CANBY, MN, 241347, p. A351

SIOUX VALLEY HOSPITAL UNIVERSITY MEDICAL CENTER, SIOUX FALLS, SD, 430027, p. A599

SIOUX VALLEY LUVERNE MEDICAL CENTER, LUVERNE, MN, 240128, p. A356

SIOUX VALLEY VERMILLION MEDICAL CENTER, VERMILLION, SD, 431336, p. A600

SIOUXLAND SURGERY CENTER, DAKOTA DUNES, SD, 430089, p. A595

SISKIN HOSPITAL FOR PHYSICAL REHABILITATION, CHATTANOOGA, TN, 443025, p. A604

SISTER EMMANUEL HOSPITAL FOR CONTINUING CARE, MIAMI, FL, 102016, p. A138

SISTER KENNY REHABILITATION INSTITUTE, MINNEAPOLIS, MINNESOTA (see ABBOTT NORTHWESTERN HOSPITAL), p. A357

SISTERS OF CHARITY HOSPITAL OF BUFFALO, BUFFALO, NY, 330078, p. A449

SISTERS OF CHARITY PROVIDENCE HOSPITALS, COLUMBIA, SC, 420026, p. A586

SISTERSVILLE GENERAL HOSPITAL, SISTERSVILLE, WV, 511304, p. A720

SITKA COMMUNITY HOSPITAL, SITKA, AK, 021303, p. A28

SKAGGS COMMUNITY HEALTH CENTER, BRANSON, MO, 260094, p. A379

SKAGIT VALLEY HOSPITAL, MOUNT VERNON, WA, 500003, p. A704

SKIFF MEDICAL CENTER, NEWTON, IA, 160032, p. A239

SKY RIDGE MEDICAL CENTER, LONE TREE, CO, 060112, p. A108

SKYLINE HOSPITAL, WHITE SALMON, WA, 501315, p. A712

SKYLINE MEDICAL CENTER, NASHVILLE, TN, 440006, p. A615

SLEEPY EYE MEDICAL CENTER, SLEEPY EYE, MN, 241327, p. A363

SLIDELL MEMORIAL HOSPITAL AND MEDICAL CENTER, SLIDELL, LA, 190040, p. A293

SMITH COUNTY MEMORIAL HOSPITAL, SMITH CENTER, KS, 170093, p. A257

SMITH COUNTY MEMORIAL HOSPITAL, CARTHAGE, TN, 440186, p. A603

SMITH NORTHVIEW HOSPITAL, VALDOSTA, GA, 110212, p. A171

SMITHVILLE REGIONAL HOSPITAL, SMITHVILLE, TX, 450143, p. A667

SMYTH COUNTY COMMUNITY HOSPITAL, MARION, VA, 490038, p. A691

SNOWDEN AT FREDERICKSBURG, FREDERICKSBURG, VA, 494028, p. A688

SOCORRO GENERAL HOSPITAL, SOCORRO, NM, 321301, p. A445

SOLDIERS AND SAILORS MEMORIAL HOSPITAL, WELLSBORO, PA, 390043, p. A578

SOLDIERS AND SAILORS MEMORIAL HOSPITAL OF YATES COUNTY, PENN YAN, NY, 330097, p. A469

SOLDIERS' HOME IN HOLYOKE, HOLYOKE, MA, 220153, p. A319

SOMERSET HOSPITAL CENTER FOR HEALTH, SOMERSET, PA, 390039, p. A576

SOMERSET MEDICAL CENTER, SOMERVILLE, NJ, 310048, p. A436

SOMERVILLE HOSPITAL, SOMERVILLE, MASSACHUSETTS (see CAMBRIDGE HEALTH ALLIANCE), p. A316

SONOMA DEVELOPMENTAL CENTER, ELDRIDGE, CA, 050547, p. A59

SONOMA VALLEY HOSPITAL, SONOMA, CA, 050090, p. A94

SONORA REGIONAL MEDICAL CENTER, SONORA, CA, 050335, p. A94

SOUND SHORE MEDICAL CENTER OF WESTCHESTER, NEW ROCHELLE, NY, 330184, p. A458

SOUTH AUSTIN HOSPITAL, AUSTIN, TX, 450713, p. A624

SOUTH BALDWIN REGIONAL MEDICAL CENTER, FOLEY, AL, 010083, p. A18

SOUTH BAY HOSPITAL, SUN CITY CENTER, FL, 100259, p. A147

SOUTH BEACH PSYCHIATRIC CENTER, NEW YORK, NY, 334043, p. A465

SOUTH BIG HORN COUNTY HOSPITAL, BASIN, WY, 531301, p. A739

SOUTH CAMERON MEMORIAL HOSPITAL, CAMERON, LA, 190037, p. A278

SOUTH CAMPUS, HOUSTON, TEXAS (see TWELVE OAKS MEDICAL CENTER), p. A648

SOUTH CAROLINA STATE HOSPITAL, COLUMBIA, SC, p. A586

SOUTH CENTRAL EXTENDED CARE, ELLISVILLE, MISSISSIPPI (see SOUTH CENTRAL REGIONAL MEDICAL CENTER), p. A372

SOUTH CENTRAL KANSAS REGIONAL MEDICAL CENTER, ARKANSAS CITY, KS, 170150, p. A244

SOUTH CENTRAL REGIONAL MEDICAL CENTER, LAUREL, MS, 250058, p. A372

SOUTH COAST MEDICAL CENTER, LAGUNA BEACH, CA, 050193, p. A66

SOUTH COUNTY HOSPITAL, WAKEFIELD, RI, 410008, p. A582

SOUTH DAVIS COMMUNITY HOSPITAL, BOUNTIFUL, UT, 462003, p. A676

SOUTH FLORIDA BAPTIST HOSPITAL, PLANT CITY, FL, 100132, p. A143

SOUTH FLORIDA STATE HOSPITAL, LOS ANGELES, FL, 104001, p. A131

SOUTH FULTON MEDICAL CENTER, ATLANTA, GA, 110219, p. A154

ST. PETER'S HOSPITAL, HELENA, MT, 270003, p. A399
ST. PETER'S HOSPITAL, ALBANY, NY, 330057, p. A446
ST. PETERSBURG GENERAL HOSPITAL, SAINT PETERSBURG, FL, 100180, p. A145
ST. RITA'S MEDICAL CENTER, LIMA, OH, 360066, p. A516
ST. ROSE DOMINICAN HOSPITALS – ROSE DE LIMA CAMPUS, HENDERSON, NV, 290012, p. A416
ST. ROSE DOMINICAN HOSPITALS – SIENA CAMPUS, HENDERSON, NV, 290045, p. A416
ST. ROSE HOSPITAL, HAYWARD, CA, 050002, p. A64
ST. TAMMANY PARISH HOSPITAL, COVINGTON, LA, 190045, p. A279
ST. THOMAS MORE HOSPITAL, CANON CITY, CO, 060016, p. A102
ST. VINCENT CHARITY HOSPITAL, CLEVELAND, OH, 360037, p. A509
ST. VINCENT CLAY HOSPITAL, BRAZIL, IN, 151309, p. A212
ST. VINCENT DOCTORS HOSPITAL, LITTLE ROCK, ARKANSAS (see ST. VINCENT INFIRMARY MEDICAL CENTER), p. A47
ST. VINCENT FRANKFORT HOSPITAL, FRANKFORT, IN, 151316, p. A216
ST. VINCENT GENERAL HOSPITAL DISTRICT, LEADVILLE, CO, 061319, p. A107
ST. VINCENT HEALTHCARE, BILLINGS, MT, 270049, p. A396
ST. VINCENT HOSPITAL, SANTA FE, NM, 320002, p. A444
ST. VINCENT HOSPITAL, GREEN BAY, WI, 520075, p. A726
ST. VINCENT HOSPITALS AND HEALTH SERVICES, INDIANAPOLIS, IN, 150084, p. A219
ST. VINCENT INFIRMARY MEDICAL CENTER, LITTLE ROCK, AR, 040007, p. A47
ST. VINCENT JENNINGS HOSPITAL, NORTH VERNON, IN, 151303, p. A223
ST. VINCENT MEDICAL CENTER, LOS ANGELES, CA, 050502, p. A72
ST. VINCENT MEDICAL CENTER–NORTH, SHERWOOD, AR, 040137, p. A50
ST. VINCENT MEMORIAL HOSPITAL, TAYLORVILLE, IL, 141339, p. A209
ST. VINCENT MERCY HOSPITAL, ELWOOD, IN, 151308, p. A214
ST. VINCENT MERCY MEDICAL CENTER, TOLEDO, OH, 360112, p. A523
ST. VINCENT RANDOLPH HOSPITAL, WINCHESTER, IN, 151301, p. A227
ST. VINCENT REHABILITATION HOSPITAL, SHERWOOD, AR, 043031, p. A50
ST. VINCENT STRESS CENTER, INDIANAPOLIS, INDIANA (see ST. VINCENT HOSPITALS AND HEALTH SERVICES), p. A219
ST. VINCENT WILLIAMSPORT HOSPITAL, WILLIAMSPORT, IN, 151307, p. A227
ST. VINCENT WOMEN'S HOSPITAL, INDIANAPOLIS, IN, 150084, p. A219
ST. VINCENT'S HOSPITAL, BIRMINGHAM, AL, 010056, p. A15
ST. VINCENT'S HOSPITAL, NEW YORK, NY, 330028, p. A465
ST. VINCENT'S MEDICAL CENTER, BRIDGEPORT, CT, 070028, p. A112
ST. VINCENT'S MEDICAL CENTER, JACKSONVILLE, FL, 100040, p. A133
ST. VINCENT'S MIDTOWN HOSPITAL, NEW YORK, NY, 330230, p. A465
ST. WILLIAM HOME FOR THE AGED (see MILBANK AREA HOSPITAL/AVERA HEALTH), p. A597
STAFFORD DISTRICT HOSPITAL, STAFFORD, KS, 171323, p. A257
STAMFORD HEALTH SYSTEM, STAMFORD, CT, 070006, p. A116
STAMFORD MEMORIAL HOSPITAL, STAMFORD, TX, 450306, p. A667
STANFORD HOSPITAL AND CLINICS, PALO ALTO, CA, 050441, p. A80
STANISLAUS SURGICAL HOSPITAL, MODESTO, CA, 050726, p. A76
STANLY MEMORIAL HOSPITAL, ALBEMARLE, NC, 340119, p. A477
STANTON COUNTY HEALTH CARE FACILITY, JOHNSON, KS, 171343, p. A249
STAR VALLEY MEDICAL CENTER, AFTON, WY, 531313, p. A739
STARKE MEMORIAL HOSPITAL, KNOX, IN, 150102, p. A220
STARR COUNTY MEMORIAL HOSPITAL, RIO GRANDE CITY, TX, 450654, p. A662
STATE CORRECTIONAL INSTITUTION AT CAMP HILL, CAMP HILL, PA, p. A554
STATE CORRECTIONAL INSTITUTION HOSPITAL, PITTSBURGH, PA, p. A572
STATE HOSPITAL NORTH, OROFINO, ID, p. A180
STATE HOSPITAL SOUTH, BLACKFOOT, ID, 134010, p. A177
STATE PENITENTIARY HOSPITAL, WALLA WALLA, WA, p. A711
STATE PSYCHIATRIC HOSPITAL, SAN JUAN, PR, 404006, p. A748
STATE PSYCHIATRIC HOSPITAL, IOWA CITY, IOWA (see UNIVERSITY OF IOWA HOSPITALS AND CLINICS), p. A236

STATEN ISLAND UNIVERSITY HOSPITAL, NEW YORK, NY, 330160, p. A465
STATEN ISLAND UNIVERSITY HOSPITAL–CONCORD, NEW YORK, NY, 330212, p. A466
STE. GENEVIEVE COUNTY MEMORIAL HOSPITAL, STE. GENEVIEVE, MO, 260164, p. A394
STEELE MEMORIAL HOSPITAL, SALMON, ID, 131305, p. A181
STEPHENS COUNTY HOSPITAL, TOCCOA, GA, 110032, p. A171
STEPHENS MEMORIAL HOSPITAL, NORWAY, ME, 200032, p. A299
STEPHENS MEMORIAL HOSPITAL, BRECKENRIDGE, TX, 450498, p. A626
STERLING REGIONAL MEDCENTER, STERLING, CO, 060076, p. A109
STERLINGTON REHABILITATION HOSPITAL, STERLINGTON, LA, 193069, p. A293
STEVENS COMMUNITY MEDICAL CENTER, MORRIS, MN, 241363, p. A358
STEVENS COUNTY HOSPITAL, HUGOTON, KS, 171335, p. A249
STEVENS HEALTHCARE, EDMONDS, WA, 500026, p. A702
STEWART MEMORIAL COMMUNITY HOSPITAL, LAKE CITY, IA, 161350, p. A237
STEWART–WEBSTER HOSPITAL, RICHLAND, GA, 111322, p. A167
STILLMAN INFIRMARY, HARVARD UNIVERSITY HEALTH SERVICES, CAMBRIDGE, MA, 220133, p. A316
STILLWATER COMMUNITY HOSPITAL, COLUMBUS, MT, 271330, p. A397
STILLWATER MEDICAL CENTER, STILLWATER, OK, 370049, p. A538
STOKES–REYNOLDS MEMORIAL HOSPITAL, DANBURY, NC, 341317, p. A481
STONE COUNTY HOSPITAL, WIGGINS, MS, 251303, p. A377
STONE COUNTY MEDICAL CENTER, MOUNTAIN VIEW, AR, 041310, p. A48
STONECREST MEDICAL CENTER, SMYRNA, TN, 440227, p. A618
STONES RIVER HOSPITAL, WOODBURY, TN, 440200, p. A619
STONEWALL JACKSON HOSPITAL, LEXINGTON, VA, 491304, p. A690
STONEWALL JACKSON MEMORIAL HOSPITAL, WESTON, WV, 510038, p. A721
STONEWALL MEMORIAL HOSPITAL, ASPERMONT, TX, 451318, p. A622
STONY BROOK UNIVERSITY HOSPITAL, STONY BROOK, NY, 330393, p. A473
STONY LODGE HOSPITAL, OSSINING, NY, 334059, p. A468
STONY POINT SURGERY CENTER, RICHMOND, VA, p. A695
STORMONT–VAIL HEALTHCARE, TOPEKA, KS, 170086, p. A258
STORY COUNTY MEDICAL CENTER, NEVADA, IA, 161333, p. A238
STOUGHTON HOSPITAL ASSOCIATION, STOUGHTON, WI, 521343, p. A736
STRAITH HOSPITAL FOR SPECIAL SURGERY, SOUTHFIELD, MI, 230071, p. A345
STRAUB CLINIC & HOSPITAL, HONOLULU, HI, 120022, p. A174
STREAMWOOD BEHAVIORAL HEALTH CENTER, STREAMWOOD, IL, 144034, p. A209
STRINGFELLOW MEMORIAL HOSPITAL, ANNISTON, AL, 010038, p. A13
STRONG MEMORIAL HOSPITAL OF THE UNIVERSITY OF ROCHESTER, ROCHESTER, NY, 330285, p. A471
STROUD REGIONAL MEDICAL CENTER, STROUD, OK, 371316, p. A538
STURDY MEMORIAL HOSPITAL, ATTLEBORO, MA, 220008, p. A312
STURGIS COMMUNITY HEALTH CARE CENTER, STURGIS, SD, 431321, p. A600
STURGIS HOSPITAL, STURGIS, MI, 230096, p. A346
STUTTGART REGIONAL MEDICAL CENTER, STUTTGART, AR, 040072, p. A51
SUBURBAN GENERAL HOSPITAL, PITTSBURGH, PENNSYLVANIA (see ALLEGHENY GENERAL HOSPITAL), p. A571
SUBURBAN HOSPITAL HEALTHCARE SYSTEM, BETHESDA, MD, 210022, p. A305
SUGAR LAND SURGICAL HOSPITAL, SUGAR LAND, TX, 450860, p. A668
SULLIVAN COUNTY COMMUNITY HOSPITAL, SULLIVAN, IN, 151327, p. A225
SULLIVAN COUNTY MEMORIAL HOSPITAL, MILAN, MO, 261306, p. A387
SUMMA HEALTH SYSTEM, AKRON, OH, 360020, p. A502
SUMMERLIN HOSPITAL MEDICAL CENTER, LAS VEGAS, NV, 290041, p. A417
SUMMERS COUNTY APPALACHIAN REGIONAL HOSPITAL, HINTON, WV, 511310, p. A716
SUMMERSVILLE MEMORIAL HOSPITAL, SUMMERSVILLE, WV, 510082, p. A720
SUMMERVILLE MEDICAL CENTER, SUMMERVILLE, SC, p. A592

SUMMIT BEHAVIORAL HEALTHCARE, CINCINNATI, OH, 364035, p. A507
SUMMIT HOSPITAL, BATON ROUGE, LA, 190202, p. A278
SUMMIT HOSPITAL, SUMMIT, NJ, 314001, p. A436
SUMMIT MEDICAL CENTER, HERMITAGE, TN, 440150, p. A607
SUMMIT PARK HOSPITAL–ROCKLAND COUNTY INFIRMARY (see DOCTOR ROBERT L. YEAGER HEALTH CENTER), p. A469
SUMNER COUNTY HOSPITAL DISTRICT ONE, CALDWELL, KS, 171329, p. A245
SUMNER REGIONAL MEDICAL CENTER, WELLINGTON, KS, 170039, p. A259
SUMNER REGIONAL MEDICAL CENTER, GALLATIN, TN, 440003, p. A606
SUMTER REGIONAL HOSPITAL, AMERICUS, GA, 110044, p. A152
SUN COAST HOSPITAL, LARGO, FL, 100015, p. A135
SUNBURY COMMUNITY HOSPITAL, SUNBURY, PA, 390084, p. A576
SUNNYSIDE COMMUNITY HOSPITAL, SUNNYSIDE, WA, 501330, p. A710
SUNNYVIEW REHABILITATION HOSPITAL, SCHENECTADY, NY, 333025, p. A472
SUNRISE CANYON HOSPITAL, LUBBOCK, TX, 454093, p. A654
SUNRISE HOSPITAL AND MEDICAL CENTER, LAS VEGAS, NV, 290003, p. A417
SUNY DOWNSTATE MEDICAL CENTER UNIVERSITY HOSPITAL, NEW YORK, NY, 330350, p. A466
SURGICAL AND DIAGNOSTIC CENTER OF GREAT BEND, GREAT BEND, KS, 170191, p. A248
SURGICAL HOSPITAL OF JONESBORO, JONESBORO, AR, 040145, p. A46
SURGICAL HOSPITAL OF OKLAHOMA, OKLAHOMA CITY, OK, 370201, p. A536
SURGICAL SPECIALTY CENTRE, BATON ROUGE, LA, 190251, p. A278
SURGICAL SPECIALTY HOSPITAL OF ARIZONA, PHOENIX, AZ, 030108, p. A35
SURPRISE VALLEY HEALTHCARE DISTRICT, CEDARVILLE, CA, 051308, p. A56
SUSAN B. ALLEN MEMORIAL HOSPITAL, EL DORADO, KS, 170017, p. A246
SUSQUEHANNA HEALTH SYSTEM, WILLIAMSPORT, PA, 390045, p. A580
SUTTER AMADOR HOSPITAL, JACKSON, CA, 050014, p. A65
SUTTER AUBURN FAITH HOSPITAL, AUBURN, CA, 050498, p. A53
SUTTER CENTER FOR PSYCHIATRY, SACRAMENTO, CA, 054096, p. A85
SUTTER COAST HOSPITAL, CRESCENT CITY, CA, 050417, p. A58
SUTTER DAVIS HOSPITAL, DAVIS, CA, 050537, p. A58
SUTTER DELTA MEDICAL CENTER, ANTIOCH, CA, 050523, p. A52
SUTTER GENERAL HOSPITAL, SACRAMENTO, CALIFORNIA (see SUTTER MEDICAL CENTER, SACRAMENTO), p. A85
SUTTER LAKESIDE HOSPITAL, LAKEPORT, CA, 050476, p. A67
SUTTER MATERNITY AND SURGERY CENTER OF SANTA CRUZ, SANTA CRUZ, CA, 050714, p. A93
SUTTER MEDICAL CENTER OF SANTA ROSA, SANTA ROSA, CA, 050291, p. A93
SUTTER MEDICAL CENTER, SACRAMENTO, SACRAMENTO, CA, 050108, p. A85
SUTTER MEMORIAL HOSPITAL, SACRAMENTO, CALIFORNIA (see SUTTER MEDICAL CENTER, SACRAMENTO), p. A85
SUTTER ROSEVILLE MEDICAL CENTER, ROSEVILLE, CA, 050309, p. A84
SUTTER SOLANO MEDICAL CENTER, VALLEJO, CA, 050101, p. A98
SUTTER TRACY COMMUNITY HOSPITAL, TRACY, CA, 050313, p. A96
SUTTER WARRACK HOSPITAL, SANTA ROSA, CALIFORNIA (see SUTTER MEDICAL CENTER OF SANTA ROSA), p. A93
SWAIN COUNTY HOSPITAL, BRYSON CITY, NC, 341305, p. A478
SWEDISH COVENANT HOSPITAL, CHICAGO, IL, 140114, p. A190
SWEDISH HEALTH SERVICES, SEATTLE, WA, 500027, p. A708
SWEDISH MEDICAL CENTER, ENGLEWOOD, CO, 060034, p. A105
SWEDISH MEDICAL CENTER–BALLARD, SEATTLE, WASHINGTON (see SWEDISH HEALTH SERVICES), p. A708
SWEDISH MEDICAL CENTER–FIRST HILL, SEATTLE, WASHINGTON (see SWEDISH HEALTH SERVICES), p. A708
SWEDISH MEDICAL CENTER–PROVIDENCE CAMPUS, SEATTLE, WA, 500025, p. A708
SWEDISHAMERICAN HOSPITAL, ROCKFORD, IL, 140228, p. A207
SWEENY COMMUNITY HOSPITAL, SWEENY, TX, 451311, p. A668
SWEETWATER HOSPITAL, SWEETWATER, TN, 440084, p. A618

SWIFT COUNTY–BENSON HOSPITAL, BENSON, MN, 241365, p. A350

SWISHER MEMORIAL HOSPITAL DISTRICT, TULIA, TX, 451349, p. A670

SYCAMORE HOSPITAL, MIAMISBURG, OH, 360239, p. A518

SYCAMORE SHOALS HOSPITAL, ELIZABETHTON, TN, 440018, p. A605

SYLVAN GROVE HOSPITAL, JACKSON, GA, 111319, p. A164

SYRINGA GENERAL HOSPITAL, GRANGEVILLE, ID, 131315, p. A179

T

T. C. THOMPSON CHILDREN'S HOSPITAL, CHATTANOOGA, TENNESSEE (see ERLANGER MEDICAL CENTER), p. A603

T. J. SAMSON COMMUNITY HOSPITAL, GLASGOW, KY, 180017, p. A265

TACOMA GENERAL HOSPITAL, TACOMA, WA, 500129, p. A710

TAHLEQUAH CITY HOSPITAL, TAHLEQUAH, OK, 370089, p. A539

TAHOE FOREST HOSPITAL DISTRICT, TRUCKEE, CA, 050494, p. A96

TAHOE PACIFIC HOSPITALS, RENO, NV, 292004, p. A418

TAKOMA ADVENTIST HOSPITAL, GREENEVILLE, TN, 440050, p. A607

TALLAHASSEE MEMORIAL HEALTHCARE, TALLAHASSEE, FL, 100135, p. A147

TALLAHATCHIE GENERAL HOSPITAL, CHARLESTON, MS, 251304, p. A367

TAMPA GENERAL HOSPITAL, TAMPA, FL, 100128, p. A148

TANNER MEDICAL CENTER, CARROLLTON, GA, 110011, p. A157

TANNER MEDICAL CENTER–VILLA RICA, VILLA RICA, GA, 110015, p. A171

TATTNALL COMMUNITY HOSPITAL, REIDSVILLE, GA, 111323, p. A167

TAUNTON STATE HOSPITAL, TAUNTON, MA, 224001, p. A324

TAYLOR HARDIN SECURE MEDICAL FACILITY, TUSCALOOSA, AL, 014011, p. A24

TAYLOR HOSPITAL, RIDLEY PARK, PENNSYLVANIA (see CROZER–CHESTER MEDICAL CENTER), p. A577

TAYLOR MANOR HOSPITAL, ELLICOTT CITY, MARYLAND (see SHEPPARD AND ENOCH PRATT HOSPITAL), p. A304

TAYLOR REGIONAL HOSPITAL, HAWKINSVILLE, GA, 110135, p. A163

TAYLOR REGIONAL HOSPITAL, CAMPBELLSVILLE, KY, 180087, p. A262

TAYLOR–TELFAIR REGIONAL HOSPITAL, MCRAE, GA, 111301, p. A166

TAZEWELL COMMUNITY HOSPITAL, TAZEWELL, VA, 490117, p. A697

TECHE REGIONAL MEDICAL CENTER, MORGAN CITY, LA, 190014, p. A287

TEHACHAPI VALLEY HEALTHCARE DISTRICT, TEHACHAPI, CA, 051301, p. A95

TEMPE ST. LUKE'S HOSPITAL, TEMPE, AZ, 030019, p. A37

TEMPLE COMMUNITY HOSPITAL, LOS ANGELES, CA, 050111, p. A72

TEMPLE EAST, NORTHEASTERN HOSPITAL, PHILADELPHIA, PA, 390023, p. A570

TEMPLE UNIVERSITY CHILDREN'S MEDICAL CENTER, PHILADELPHIA, PA, 393306, p. A570

TEMPLE UNIVERSITY HOSPITAL, PHILADELPHIA, PA, 390027, p. A570

TEMPLE UNIVERSITY HOSPITAL – EPISCOPAL DIVISION, PHILADELPHIA, PENNSYLVANIA (see TEMPLE UNIVERSITY HOSPITAL), p. A570

TEN BROECK HOSPITAL, LOUISVILLE, KY, 184008, p. A270

TEN BROECK HOSPITAL JACKSONVILLE, JACKSONVILLE, FL, 104016, p. A133

TENNESSEE CHRISTIAN MEDICAL CENTER, MADISON, TN, 440135, p. A611

TENNESSEE CHRISTIAN MEDICAL CENTER – PORTLAND, PORTLAND, TENNESSEE (see TENNESSEE CHRISTIAN MEDICAL CENTER), p. A611

TERRE HAUTE REGIONAL HOSPITAL, TERRE HAUTE, IN, 150046, p. A226

TERREBONNE GENERAL MEDICAL CENTER, HOUMA, LA, 190008, p. A282

TERRELL STATE HOSPITAL, TERRELL, TX, 454006, p. A669

TETON MEDICAL CENTER, CHOTEAU, MT, 271307, p. A397

TETON VALLEY HOSPITAL AND SURGICENTER, DRIGGS, ID, 131313, p. A179

TEWKSBURY HOSPITAL, TEWKSBURY, MA, 222003, p. A324

TEXAS CENTER FOR INFECTIOUS DISEASE, SAN ANTONIO, TX, 452033, p. A665

TEXAS CHILDREN'S HOSPITAL, HOUSTON, TX, 453304, p. A647

TEXAS COUNTY MEMORIAL HOSPITAL, HOUSTON, MO, 260024, p. A383

TEXAS NEURO REHABILITATION CENTER, AUSTIN, TX, 452038, p. A624

TEXAS ORTHOPEDIC HOSPITAL, HOUSTON, TX, 450804, p. A648

TEXAS SCOTTISH RITE HOSPITAL FOR CHILDREN, DALLAS, TX, p. A634

TEXAS SPECIALTY HOSPITAL AT DALLAS, DALLAS, TX, 452067, p. A634

TEXAS SPECIALTY HOSPITAL AT SAN ANTONIO, SAN ANTONIO, TX, 452040, p. A665

TEXAS SPECIALTY HOSPITAL AT WICHITA FALLS, WICHITA FALLS, TX, 452068, p. A674

TEXAS SPINE & JOINT HOSPITAL, TYLER, TX, 450864, p. A671

TEXAS WEST OAKS HOSPITAL, HOUSTON, TX, 454026, p. A648

TEXOMA MEDICAL CENTER, DENISON, TX, 450324, p. A635

TEXOMA MEDICAL CENTER RESTORATIVE CARE HOSPITAL, DENISON, TX, 452041, p. A635

TEXSAN HEART HOSPITAL, SAN ANTONIO, TX, 450878, p. A666

THAYER COUNTY HEALTH SERVICES, HEBRON, NE, 281304, p. A407

THE ALLEN PAVILION, NEW YORK, NEW YORK (see NEW YORK–PRESBYTERIAN HOSPITAL), p. A463

THE CANCER INSTITUTE, KANSAS CITY, MO, 260211, p. A385

THE CHARLOTTE HUNGERFORD HOSPITAL, TORRINGTON, CT, 070011, p. A117

THE CHILDREN'S HOSPITAL OF ALABAMA, BIRMINGHAM, AL, 013030, p. A15

THE CHILDREN'S INSTITUTE OF PITTSBURGH, PITTSBURGH, PA, 393308, p. A572

THE CONNECTICUT HOSPICE, BRANFORD, CT, 070038, p. A112

THE FRIARY OF BAPTIST HEALTH CENTER, GULF BREEZE, FL, p. A130

THE GOOD SAMARITAN HOSPITAL, LEBANON, PA, 390066, p. A563

THE HEART CENTER OF INDIANA, INDIANAPOLIS, IN, 150153, p. A219

THE HOSPITAL FOR ORTHOPAEDIC AND SPECIALTY SERVICES, AMHERST, OH, 360130, p. A502

THE INSTITUTE FOR REHABILITATION AND RESEARCH, HOUSTON, TX, 453025, p. A648

THE JAMES B. HAGGIN MEMORIAL HOSPITAL, HARRODSBURG, KY, 181302, p. A265

THE KING'S DAUGHTERS HOSPITAL, GREENVILLE, MS, 250120, p. A369

THE MEDICAL CENTER, COLUMBUS, GA, 110064, p. A159

THE MEDICAL CENTER AT BOWLING GREEN, BOWLING GREEN, KY, 180013, p. A262

THE MEDICAL CENTER AT FRANKLIN, FRANKLIN, KY, 181318, p. A265

THE MEDICAL CENTER OF SOUTHEAST TEXAS, PORT ARTHUR, TX, 450518, p. A661

THE MEDICAL CENTER, BEAVER, BEAVER, PA, 390036, p. A552

THE METHODIST HOSPITAL, HOUSTON, TX, 450358, p. A648

THE MONROE CLINIC, MONROE, WI, 520028, p. A732

THE MOUNT SINAI HOSPITAL OF QUEENS, NEW YORK, NY, 330258, p. A466

THE NEUROLOGIC AND ORTHOPEDIC INSTITUTE OF CHICAGO, CHICAGO, IL, 140303, p. A191

THE ORTHOPEDIC SPECIALTY HOSPITAL, MURRAY, UT, 460049, p. A677

THE OUTER BANKS HOSPITAL, NAGS HEAD, NC, 340177, p. A488

THE PAVILION, CHAMPAIGN, IL, 144029, p. A186

THE PAVILION, PENSACOLA, FLORIDA (see WEST FLORIDA HOSPITAL), p. A143

THE PHYSICIANS CENTRE, BRYAN, TX, 450834, p. A627

THE REHABILITATION HOSPITAL OF CONNECTICUT, HARTFORD, CT, 073025, p. A113

THE REHABILITATION INSTITUTE OF ST. LOUIS, SAINT LOUIS, MO, 263028, p. A393

THE SPINE HOSPITAL OF SOUTH TEXAS, SAN ANTONIO, TX, p. A666

THE TOLEDO HOSPITAL, TOLEDO, OH, 360068, p. A523

THE UNIVERSITY OF CHICAGO COMER CHILDREN'S HOSPITAL, CHICAGO, ILLINOIS (see UNIVERSITY OF CHICAGO HOSPITALS), p. A191

THE VILLAGES REGIONAL HOSPITAL, THE VILLAGES, FL, 100290, p. A149

THE WILLIAM W. BACKUS HOSPITAL, NORWICH, CT, 070024, p. A116

THE WISCONSIN HEART HOSPITAL, WAUWATOSA, WI, 520199, p. A738

THE WOMAN'S HOSPITAL OF TEXAS, HOUSTON, TX, 450674, p. A648

THE WOMEN'S HOSPITAL, NEWBURGH, IN, 150149, p. A223

THEDA CLARK MEDICAL CENTER, NEENAH, WI, 520045, p. A732

THIBODAUX REGIONAL MEDICAL CENTER, THIBODAUX, LA, 190004, p. A294

THOMAS B. FINAN CENTER, CUMBERLAND, MD, 214012, p. A307

THOMAS H. BOYD MEMORIAL HOSPITAL, CARROLLTON, IL, 141300, p. A185

THOMAS HOSPITAL, FAIRHOPE, AL, 010100, p. A18

THOMAS JEFFERSON UNIVERSITY HOSPITAL, PHILADELPHIA, PA, 390174, p. A570

THOMAS JEFFERSON UNIVERSITY HOSPITAL–FORD ROAD CAMPUS, PHILADELPHIA, PENNSYLVANIA (see THOMAS JEFFERSON UNIVERSITY HOSPITAL), p. A570

THOMAS MEMORIAL HOSPITAL, SOUTH CHARLESTON, WV, 510029, p. A720

THOMASVILLE MEDICAL CENTER, THOMASVILLE, NC, 340085, p. A493

THOMPSON HEALTH, CANANDAIGUA, NY, 330074, p. A449

THOMS REHABILITATION HOSPITAL, ASHEVILLE, NC, 343025, p. A477

THOREK HOSPITAL AND MEDICAL CENTER, CHICAGO, IL, 140115, p. A191

THREE RIVERS CENTER FOR BEHAVIORAL HEALTH, WEST COLUMBIA, SC, 424008, p. A593

THREE RIVERS COMMUNITY HOSPITAL AND HEALTH CENTER, GRANTS PASS, OR, 380002, p. A544

THREE RIVERS HEALTH, THREE RIVERS, MI, 230015, p. A346

THREE RIVERS HEALTHCARE–NORTH CAMPUS, POPLAR BLUFF, MISSOURI (see POPLAR BLUFF REGIONAL MEDICAL CENTER), p. A389

THREE RIVERS HEALTHCARE–SOUTH CAMPUS, POPLAR BLUFF, MISSOURI (see POPLAR BLUFF REGIONAL MEDICAL CENTER), p. A389

THREE RIVERS HOSPITAL, WAVERLY, TN, 441303, p. A618

THREE RIVERS MEDICAL CENTER, LOUISA, KY, 180128, p. A268

THROCKMORTON COUNTY MEMORIAL HOSPITAL, THROCKMORTON, TX, 451339, p. A670

TIFT REGIONAL MEDICAL CENTER, TIFTON, GA, 110095, p. A171

TILDEN COMMUNITY HOSPITAL, TILDEN, NE, 281317, p. A413

TILLAMOOK COUNTY GENERAL HOSPITAL, TILLAMOOK, OR, 381317, p. A549

TIMBERLAWN MENTAL HEALTH SYSTEM, DALLAS, TX, 454081, p. A634

TIMPANOGOS REGIONAL HOSPITAL, OREM, UT, 460052, p. A678

TINLEY PARK MENTAL HEALTH CENTER, TINLEY PARK, IL, 144019, p. A209

TIOGA MEDICAL CENTER, TIOGA, ND, 351300, p. A500

TIPPAH COUNTY HOSPITAL, RIPLEY, MS, 250010, p. A375

TIPTON COUNTY MEMORIAL HOSPITAL, TIPTON, IN, 151311, p. A226

TITUS REGIONAL MEDICAL CENTER, MOUNT PLEASANT, TX, 450080, p. A657

TITUSVILLE AREA HOSPITAL, TITUSVILLE, PA, 390122, p. A576

TOBEY HOSPITAL, WAREHAM, MASSACHUSETTS (see SOUTHCOAST HEALTH SYSTEM GROUP), p. A317

TOD CHILDREN'S HOSPITAL, YOUNGSTOWN, OHIO (see WESTERN RESERVE CARE SYSTEM), p. A526

TOLEDO CAMPUS, TOLEDO, OHIO (see NORTHCOAST BEHAVIORAL HEALTHCARE SYSTEM), p. A519

TOLEDO CHILDREN'S HOSPITAL, TOLEDO, OHIO (see THE TOLEDO HOSPITAL), p. A523

TOMAH MEMORIAL HOSPITAL, TOMAH, WI, 521320, p. A736

TOMBALL REGIONAL HOSPITAL, TOMBALL, TX, 450670, p. A670

TOPPENISH COMMUNITY HOSPITAL, TOPPENISH, WA, 500037, p. A711

TOPS SURGICAL SPECIALTY HOSPITAL, HOUSTON, TX, 450774, p. A648

TORRANCE MEMORIAL MEDICAL CENTER, TORRANCE, CA, 050351, p. A96

TORRANCE STATE HOSPITAL, TORRANCE, PA, 394026, p. A576

TOUCHETTE REGIONAL HOSPITAL, EAST ST. LOUIS, IL, 140077, p. A192

TOURO INFIRMARY, NEW ORLEANS, LA, 190046, p. A290

TOURO REHABILITATION CENTER, NEW ORLEANS, LA, 193034, p. A290

TOWN AND COUNTRY HOSPITAL, TAMPA, FL, 100255, p. A148

TOWNER COUNTY MEDICAL CENTER, CANDO, ND, 350014, p. A496

TRACE REGIONAL HOSPITAL, HOUSTON, MS, 250017, p. A370

TRACY AREA MEDICAL SERVICES, TRACY, MN, 241303, p. A364

U

UNITED HOSPITAL DISTRICT, BLUE EARTH, MN, 240162, p. A350

UNITED HOSPITAL SYSTEM, ST. CATHERINE'S MEDICAL CENTER CAMPUS, PLEASANT PRAIRIE, WI, 520021, p. A734

UNITED MEDICAL CENTER, CHEYENNE, WY, 530014, p. A739

UNITED MEDICAL REHABILITATION HOSPITAL, NEW ORLEANS, LA, 193079, p. A290

UNITED MEMORIAL MEDICAL CENTER, BATAVIA, NY, 330073, p. A447

UNITED MEMORIAL MEDICAL CENTER–BANK STREET, BATAVIA, NEW YORK (see UNITED MEMORIAL MEDICAL CENTER), p. A447

UNITED MEMORIAL MEDICAL CENTER–NORTH STREET, BATAVIA, NEW YORK (see UNITED MEMORIAL MEDICAL CENTER), p. A447

UNITED REGIONAL HEALTH CARE SYSTEM, WICHITA FALLS, TX, 450010, p. A674

UNITED REGIONAL HEALTH CARE SYSTEM–EIGHTH STREET CAMPUS, WICHITA FALLS, TEXAS (see UNITED REGIONAL HEALTH CARE SYSTEM), p. A674

UNITED REGIONAL HEALTH CARE SYSTEM–ELEVENTH STREET CAMPUS, WICHITA FALLS, TEXAS (see UNITED REGIONAL HEALTH CARE SYSTEM), p. A674

UNITED REGIONAL MEDICAL CENTER, MANCHESTER, TN, 440007, p. A612

UNITED SAMARITANS MEDICAL CENTER, DANVILLE, ILLINOIS (see PROVENA UNITED SAMARITANS MEDICAL CENTER), p. A191

UNITY HEALTH CENTER, SHAWNEE, OK, 370149, p. A538

UNITY HOSPITAL, MUSCATINE, IA, 160013, p. A238

UNITY HOSPITAL, FRIDLEY, MN, 240132, p. A354

UNITY MEDICAL CENTER, GRAFTON, ND, 351320, p. A498

UNIVERSITY CAMPUS, NEW ORLEANS, LOUISIANA (see MEDICAL CENTER OF LOUISIANA AT NEW ORLEANS), p. A289

UNIVERSITY CAMPUS, WORCESTER, MASSACHUSETTS (see UMASS MEMORIAL MEDICAL CENTER), p. A326

UNIVERSITY COMMUNITY HOSPITAL, SAN DIEGO, CA, 050447, p. A87

UNIVERSITY COMMUNITY HOSPITAL, TAMPA, FL, 100173, p. A149

UNIVERSITY COMMUNITY HOSPITAL–CARROLLWOOD, TAMPA, FL, 100069, p. A149

UNIVERSITY HEALTH CARE SYSTEM, AUGUSTA, GA, 110028, p. A155

UNIVERSITY HEALTH CENTER – DOWNTOWN, SAN ANTONIO, TEXAS (see UNIVERSITY HEALTH SYSTEM), p. A666

UNIVERSITY HEALTH SERVICES, AMHERST, MA, 220172, p. A312

UNIVERSITY HEALTH SYSTEM, SAN ANTONIO, TX, 450213, p. A666

UNIVERSITY HOSPITAL, SAN ANTONIO, TEXAS (see UNIVERSITY HEALTH SYSTEM), p. A666

UNIVERSITY HOSPITAL, ALBUQUERQUE, NM, 320001, p. A441

UNIVERSITY HOSPITAL, CINCINNATI, OH, 360003, p. A507

UNIVERSITY HOSPITAL, SAN JUAN, PR, 400061, p. A748

UNIVERSITY HOSPITAL AND CLINICS – HOLMES COUNTY, LEXINGTON, MS, 251319, p. A372

UNIVERSITY HOSPITAL AND MEDICAL CENTER, TAMARAC, FL, 100224, p. A147

UNIVERSITY HOSPITAL SCHOOL, IOWA CITY, IOWA (see UNIVERSITY OF IOWA HOSPITALS AND CLINICS), p. A236

UNIVERSITY HOSPITAL, UNIVERSITY OF NEBRASKA MEDICAL CENTER, OMAHA, NEBRASKA (see NEBRASKA MEDICAL CENTER), p. A411

UNIVERSITY HOSPITALS AND CLINICS, UNIVERSITY OF MISSISSIPPI MEDICAL CENTER, JACKSON, MS, 250001, p. A371

UNIVERSITY HOSPITALS OF CLEVELAND, CLEVELAND, OH, 360137, p. A509

UNIVERSITY MEDICAL CENTER, TUCSON, AZ, 030064, p. A38

UNIVERSITY MEDICAL CENTER, FRESNO, CA, p. A62

UNIVERSITY MEDICAL CENTER, LAFAYETTE, LA, 190006, p. A284

UNIVERSITY MEDICAL CENTER, LAS VEGAS, NV, 290007, p. A417

UNIVERSITY MEDICAL CENTER, LUBBOCK, TX, 450686, p. A654

UNIVERSITY MEDICAL CENTER AT PRINCETON, PRINCETON, NJ, 310010, p. A435

UNIVERSITY MEDICAL CENTER/MCFARLAND HOSPITAL, LEBANON, TN, 440193, p. A611

UNIVERSITY OF ALABAMA HOSPITAL, BIRMINGHAM, AL, 010033, p. A15

UNIVERSITY OF CALIFORNIA LOS ANGELES MEDICAL CENTER, LOS ANGELES, CA, 050262, p. A73

UNIVERSITY OF CALIFORNIA LOS ANGELES NEUROPSYCHIATRIC HOSPITAL, LOS ANGELES, CA, 054009, p. A73

UNIVERSITY OF CALIFORNIA SAN DIEGO MEDICAL CENTER, SAN DIEGO, CA, 050025, p. A88

UNIVERSITY OF CALIFORNIA, DAVIS MEDICAL CENTER, SACRAMENTO, CA, 050599, p. A85

UNIVERSITY OF CALIFORNIA, IRVINE MEDICAL CENTER, ORANGE, CA, 050348, p. A79

UNIVERSITY OF CHICAGO HOSPITALS, CHICAGO, IL, 140088, p. A191

UNIVERSITY OF COLORADO HOSPITAL, DENVER, CO, 060024, p. A104

UNIVERSITY OF CONNECTICUT HEALTH CENTER, JOHN DEMPSEY HOSPITAL, FARMINGTON, CT, 070036, p. A113

UNIVERSITY OF ILLINOIS MEDICAL CENTER AT CHICAGO, CHICAGO, IL, 140150, p. A191

UNIVERSITY OF IOWA HOSPITALS AND CLINICS, IOWA CITY, IA, 160058, p. A236

UNIVERSITY OF KANSAS HOSPITAL, KANSAS CITY, KS, 170040, p. A250

UNIVERSITY OF KENTUCKY HOSPITAL, LEXINGTON, KY, 180067, p. A268

UNIVERSITY OF LOUISVILLE HOSPITAL, LOUISVILLE, KY, 180141, p. A270

UNIVERSITY OF MARYLAND MEDICAL CENTER, BALTIMORE, MD, 210002, p. A304

UNIVERSITY OF MEDICINE AND DENTISTRY OF NEW JERSEY, UNIVERSITY BEHAVIORAL HEALTHCARE, PISCATAWAY, NJ, 314011, p. A434

UNIVERSITY OF MEDICINE AND DENTISTRY OF NEW JERSEY–UNIVERSITY HOSPITAL, NEWARK, NJ, 310119, p. A433

UNIVERSITY OF MIAMI HOSPITAL AND CLINICS, MIAMI, FL, 100079, p. A138

UNIVERSITY OF MICHIGAN HOSPITALS AND HEALTH CENTERS, ANN ARBOR, MI, 230046, p. A327

UNIVERSITY OF MINNESOTA HOSPITAL AND CLINIC, MINNEAPOLIS, MINNESOTA (see UNIVERSITY OF MINNESOTA MEDICAL CENTER), p. A357

UNIVERSITY OF MINNESOTA MEDICAL CENTER, MINNEAPOLIS, MN, 240080, p. A357

UNIVERSITY OF MISSOURI HOSPITALS AND CLINICS, COLUMBIA, MO, 260141, p. A381

UNIVERSITY OF NEW MEXICO CHILDREN'S PSYCHIATRIC HOSPITAL, ALBUQUERQUE, NEW MEXICO (see UNIVERSITY HOSPITAL), p. A441

UNIVERSITY OF NORTH CAROLINA HOSPITALS, CHAPEL HILL, NC, 340061, p. A479

UNIVERSITY OF SOUTH ALABAMA KNOLLWOOD PARK HOSPITAL, MOBILE, AL, 012006, p. A21

UNIVERSITY OF SOUTH ALABAMA MEDICAL CENTER, MOBILE, AL, 010087, p. A21

UNIVERSITY OF SOUTHERN CALIFORNIA–NORRIS COMPREHENSIVE CANCER CENTER AND HOSPITAL, LOS ANGELES, CA, 050660, p. A73

UNIVERSITY OF TENNESSEE MEDICAL CENTER, KNOXVILLE, TN, 440015, p. A610

UNIVERSITY OF TEXAS HEALTH CENTER AT TYLER, TYLER, TX, 450690, p. A671

UNIVERSITY OF TEXAS M. D. ANDERSON CANCER CENTER, HOUSTON, TX, 450076, p. A648

UNIVERSITY OF TEXAS MEDICAL BRANCH HOSPITALS, GALVESTON, TX, 450018, p. A641

UNIVERSITY OF TEXAS SOUTHWESTERN MEDICAL CENTER, DALLAS, TX, 450766, p. A634

UNIVERSITY OF UTAH HOSPITALS AND CLINICS, SALT LAKE CITY, UT, 460009, p. A680

UNIVERSITY OF UTAH NEUROPSYCHIATRIC INSTITUTE, SALT LAKE CITY, UT, 464009, p. A680

UNIVERSITY OF VIRGINIA MEDICAL CENTER, CHARLOTTESVILLE, VA, 490009, p. A686

UNIVERSITY OF WASHINGTON MEDICAL CENTER, SEATTLE, WA, 500008, p. A708

UNIVERSITY OF WISCONSIN CHILDREN'S HOSPITAL (see UNIVERSITY OF WISCONSIN HOSPITAL AND CLINICS), p. A728

UNIVERSITY OF WISCONSIN HOSPITAL AND CLINICS, MADISON, WI, 520098, p. A728

UNIVERSITY PAVILION, TAMARAC, FLORIDA (see UNIVERSITY HOSPITAL AND MEDICAL CENTER), p. A147

UNIVERSITY PEDIATRIC HOSPITAL, SAN JUAN, PR, 403301, p. A748

UNIVERSITY PHYSICIANS HEALTHCARE HOSPITAL AT KINO CAMPUS, TUCSON, AZ, 030111, p. A39

UNIVERSITY SPECIALTY HOSPITAL, BALTIMORE, MD, 212007, p. A305

UPLAND HILLS HEALTH, DODGEVILLE, WI, 521352, p. A724

UPMC BEDFORD MEMORIAL, EVERETT, PA, 390117, p. A559

UPMC BRADDOCK, BRADDOCK, PA, 390128, p. A553

UPMC HORIZON, GREENVILLE, PA, 390178, p. A559

UPMC LEE REGIONAL, JOHNSTOWN, PA, 390011, p. A562

UPMC MCKEESPORT, MCKEESPORT, PA, 390002, p. A564

UPMC NORTHWEST, SENECA, PA, 390091, p. A575

UPMC PASSAVANT, PITTSBURGH, PA, 390107, p. A572

UPMC PASSAVANT CRANBERRY, CRANBERRY, PA, 390291, p. A556

UPMC PRESBYTERIAN, PITTSBURGH, PA, 390164, p. A572

UPMC PRESBYTERIAN HOSPITAL, PITTSBURGH, PENNSYLVANIA (see UPMC PRESBYTERIAN), p. A572

UPMC SHADYSIDE, PITTSBURGH, PENNSYLVANIA (see UPMC PRESBYTERIAN), p. A572

UPMC SOUTH SIDE, PITTSBURGH, PA, 390131, p. A572

UPMC ST. MARGARET, PITTSBURGH, PA, 390102, p. A573

UPPER CHESAPEAKE MEDICAL CENTER, BEL AIR, MD, 210049, p. A305

UPPER CONNECTICUT VALLEY HOSPITAL, COLEBROOK, NH, 301300, p. A420

UPPER SHORE COMMUNITY MENTAL HEALTH CENTER, CHESTERTOWN, MD, 214019, p. A306

UPPER VALLEY MEDICAL CENTER, TROY, OH, 360174, p. A523

UPSON REGIONAL MEDICAL CENTER, THOMASTON, GA, 110002, p. A170

UPSTATE CAROLINA MEDICAL CENTER, GAFFNEY, SC, 420043, p. A588

UPSTATE MEDICAL UNIVERSITY, SYRACUSE, NY, 330241, p. A474

USA CHILDREN'S AND WOMEN'S HOSPITAL, MOBILE, AL, 013301, p. A21

USC UNIVERSITY HOSPITAL, LOS ANGELES, CA, 050696, p. A73

USMD HOSPITAL AT ARLINGTON, ARLINGTON, TX, 450872, p. A622

UTAH STATE HOSPITAL, PROVO, UT, 464001, p. A679

UTAH VALLEY REGIONAL MEDICAL CENTER, PROVO, UT, 460001, p. A679

UVA–HEALTHSOUTH REHABILITATION HOSPITAL, CHARLOTTESVILLE, VA, 493029, p. A686

UVALDE COUNTY HOSPITAL AUTHORITY, UVALDE, TX, 450177, p. A671

V

VAIL VALLEY MEDICAL CENTER, VAIL, CO, 060096, p. A110

VAL VERDE REGIONAL MEDICAL CENTER, DEL RIO, TX, 450154, p. A635

VALDESE GENERAL HOSPITAL, VALDESE, NC, 340055, p. A493

VALIR REHABILITATION HOSPITAL, OKLAHOMA CITY, OK, 373025, p. A536

VALLE VISTA HEALTH SYSTEM, GREENWOOD, IN, 154024, p. A217

VALLEY BAPTIST HEALTH SYSTEM, HARLINGEN, TX, 450033, p. A643

VALLEY BAPTIST MEDICAL CENTER–BROWNSVILLE, BROWNSVILLE, TX, 450028, p. A627

VALLEY BEHAVIORAL HEALTH SYSTEM, CHATTANOOGA, TENNESSEE (see PARKRIDGE MEDICAL CENTER), p. A604

VALLEY COUNTY HOSPITAL, ORD, NE, 281353, p. A411

VALLEY FORGE MEDICAL CENTER AND HOSPITAL, NORRISTOWN, PA, 390272, p. A566

VALLEY GENERAL HOSPITAL, MONROE, WA, 500084, p. A704

VALLEY HOSPITAL, PALMER, AK, 020006, p. A28

VALLEY HOSPITAL, RIDGEWOOD, NJ, 310012, p. A435

VALLEY HOSPITAL AND MEDICAL CENTER, SPOKANE, WA, 500119, p. A709

VALLEY HOSPITAL MEDICAL CENTER, LAS VEGAS, NV, 290021, p. A417

VALLEY MEDICAL CENTER, RENTON, WA, 500088, p. A706

VALLEY MEMORIAL, LIVERMORE, CALIFORNIA (see VALLEYCARE MEDICAL CENTER), p. A82

VALLEY PRESBYTERIAN HOSPITAL, LOS ANGELES, CA, 050126, p. A73

VALLEY REGIONAL HOSPITAL, CLAREMONT, NH, 300024, p. A420

VALLEY REGIONAL MEDICAL CENTER, BROWNSVILLE, TX, 450662, p. A627

VALLEY VIEW HOSPITAL, GLENWOOD SPRINGS, CO, 060075, p. A106

VALLEY VIEW MEDICAL CENTER, CEDAR CITY, UT, 460007, p. A676

VALLEY VIEW REGIONAL HOSPITAL, ADA, OK, 370020, p. A527

VALLEY WEST COMMUNITY HOSPITAL, SANDWICH, IL, 141340, p. A207

VALLEYCARE MEDICAL CENTER, PLEASANTON, CA, 050283, p. A82

VAN BUREN COUNTY HOSPITAL, KEOSAUQUA, IA, 161337, p. A236

VAN MATRE HEALTHSOUTH REHABILITATION HOSPITAL, ROCKFORD, IL, 143028, p. A207

VAN WERT COUNTY HOSPITAL, VAN WERT, OH, 360071, p. A523

VICTORY MEMORIAL HOSPITAL, NEW YORK, NY, 330242, p. A466

VILLA FELICIANA MEDICAL COMPLEX, JACKSON, LA, 190199, p. A282

VILLE PLATTE MEDICAL CENTER, VILLE PLATTE, LA, 190167, p. A294

VINELAND HEALTH CENTER, VINELAND, NEW JERSEY (see SOUTH JERSEY HEALTHCARE), p. A426

VIRGINIA BAPTIST HOSPITAL, LYNCHBURG, VIRGINIA (see CENTRA HEALTH), p. A691

VIRGINIA BEACH PSYCHIATRIC CENTER, VIRGINIA BEACH, VA, 494025, p. A698

VIRGINIA GAY HOSPITAL, VINTON, IA, 161349, p. A242

VIRGINIA HOSPITAL CENTER – ARLINGTON, ARLINGTON, VA, 490050, p. A685

VIRGINIA MASON MEDICAL CENTER, SEATTLE, WA, 500005, p. A708

VIRGINIA REGIONAL MEDICAL CENTER, VIRGINIA, MN, 240084, p. A364

VIRTUA MEMORIAL HOSPITAL BURLINGTON COUNTY, MOUNT HOLLY, NJ, 310057, p. A432

VIRTUA WEST JERSEY HOSPITAL–BERLIN, BERLIN, NJ, p. A426

VIRTUA WEST JERSEY HOSPITAL–MARLTON, MARLTON, NJ, 313032, p. A431

VIRTUA WEST JERSEY HOSPITAL–VOORHEES, VOORHEES, NJ, 310022, p. A438

VIRTUE STREET MEDICAL PAVILION, CHALMETTE, LOUISIANA (see CHALMETTE MEDICAL CENTER), p. A279

VISTA HEALTH, FAYETTEVILLE, AR, 044004, p. A43

VISTA HEALTH OF FORT SMITH, BARLING, AR, 044006, p. A40

VISTA HEALTH–PROVENA SAINT THERESE MEDICAL CENTER, WAUKEGAN, IL, 140033, p. A210

VISTA HEALTH–VICTORY MEMORIAL HOSPITAL, WAUKEGAN, IL, 140084, p. A210

VISTA HOSPITAL OF DALLAS, GARLAND, TX, 450315, p. A641

VISTA MEDICAL CENTER HOSPITAL, PASADENA, TX, 450831, p. A660

VISTA SURGICAL HOSPITAL OF BATON ROUGE, BATON ROUGE, LA, 190249, p. A278

VOLUNTEER COMMUNITY HOSPITAL, MARTIN, TN, 440061, p. A612

W

W. J. BARGE MEMORIAL HOSPITAL, GREENVILLE, SC, p. A588

W. J. MANGOLD MEMORIAL HOSPITAL, LOCKNEY, TX, 451337, p. A653

WABASH COUNTY HOSPITAL, WABASH, IN, 151310, p. A227

WABASH GENERAL HOSPITAL DISTRICT, MOUNT CARMEL, IL, 141327, p. A201

WABASH VALLEY HOSPITAL, WEST LAFAYETTE, IN, 154005, p. A227

WACCAMAW COMMUNITY HOSPITAL, MURRELLS INLET, SC, 420098, p. A590

WACO VETERANS AFFAIRS HOSPITAL, WACO, TEXAS (see CENTRAL TEXAS VETERANS HEALTHCARE SYSTEM), p. A668

WADLEY REGIONAL MEDICAL CENTER, TEXARKANA, TX, 450200, p. A670

WADSWORTH–RITTMAN HOSPITAL, WADSWORTH, OH, 360195, p. A524

WAGNER COMMUNITY MEMORIAL HOSPITAL, WAGNER, SD, 431315, p. A600

WAGONER COMMUNITY HOSPITAL, WAGONER, OK, 370166, p. A541

WAHIAWA GENERAL HOSPITAL, WAHIAWA, HI, 120004, p. A176

WAKEMED CARY HOSPITAL, CARY, NC, 340173, p. A479

WAKEMED RALEIGH CAMPUS, RALEIGH, NC, 340069, p. A490

WALBRIDGE MEMORIAL CONVALESCENT WING (see PIONEERS HOSPITAL OF RIO BLANCO COUNTY), p. A108

WALDO COUNTY GENERAL HOSPITAL, BELFAST, ME, 200013, p. A296

WALKER BAPTIST MEDICAL CENTER, JASPER, AL, 010089, p. A20

WALLA WALLA GENERAL HOSPITAL, WALLA WALLA, WA, 500049, p. A711

WALLACE THOMSON HOSPITAL, UNION, SC, 420039, p. A592

WALLOWA MEMORIAL HOSPITAL, ENTERPRISE, OR, 381306, p. A543

WALLS REGIONAL HOSPITAL, CLEBURNE, TX, 450148, p. A629

WALTER B. JONES ALCOHOL AND DRUG ABUSE TREATMENT CENTER, GREENVILLE, NC, 344024, p. A484

WALTER KNOX MEMORIAL HOSPITAL, EMMETT, ID, 131318, p. A179

WALTER O. BOSWELL MEMORIAL HOSPITAL, SUN CITY, AZ, 030061, p. A37

WALTER OLIN MOSS REGIONAL MEDICAL CENTER, LAKE CHARLES, LA, 190161, p. A285

WALTER P. REUTHER PSYCHIATRIC HOSPITAL, WESTLAND, MI, 234035, p. A348

WALTER REED ARMY MEDICAL CENTER, WASHINGTON, DC, p. A122

WALTHALL COUNTY GENERAL HOSPITAL, TYLERTOWN, MS, 250107, p. A376

WALTON REGIONAL MEDICAL CENTER, MONROE, GA, 110046, p. A166

WALTON REHABILITATION HOSPITAL, AUGUSTA, GA, 113026, p. A156

WAMEGO CITY HOSPITAL, WAMEGO, KS, 171337, p. A258

WAR MEMORIAL HOSPITAL, SAULT STE. MARIE, MI, 230239, p. A345

WARD MEMORIAL HOSPITAL, MONAHANS, TX, 450050, p. A657

WARM SPRINGS MEDICAL CENTER, WARM SPRINGS, GA, 111316, p. A171

WARM SPRINGS REHABILITATION HOSPITAL, CORPUS CHRISTI, TX, 453055, p. A631

WARM SPRINGS REHABILITATION HOSPITAL, SAN ANTONIO, TX, 453035, p. A666

WARM SPRINGS SPECIALTY HOSPITAL, LULING, TX, 452062, p. A655

WARMINSTER HOSPITAL, WARMINSTER, PA, 390286, p. A577

WARREN G. MAGNUSON CLINICAL CENTER, NATIONAL INSTITUTES OF HEALTH, BETHESDA, MD, p. A306

WARREN GENERAL HOSPITAL, WARREN, PA, 390146, p. A578

WARREN HOSPITAL, PHILLIPSBURG, NJ, 310060, p. A434

WARREN MEMORIAL HOSPITAL, FRIEND, NE, 281330, p. A406

WARREN MEMORIAL HOSPITAL, FRONT ROYAL, VA, 490033, p. A688

WARREN STATE HOSPITAL, WARREN, PA, 394016, p. A578

WARWICK MANOR BEHAVIORAL HEALTH, EAST NEW MARKET, MD, p. A307

WASECA MEDICAL CENTER, WASECA, MN, 241345, p. A364

WASHAKIE MEDICAL CENTER, WORLAND, WY, 531306, p. A742

WASHINGTON ADVENTIST HOSPITAL, TAKOMA PARK, MD, 210016, p. A311

WASHINGTON COUNTY HEALTH SYSTEM, HAGERSTOWN, MD, 210001, p. A308

WASHINGTON COUNTY HOSPITAL, NASHVILLE, IL, 141308, p. A202

WASHINGTON COUNTY HOSPITAL, WASHINGTON, IA, 161344, p. A242

WASHINGTON COUNTY HOSPITAL, WASHINGTON, KS, 171351, p. A259

WASHINGTON COUNTY HOSPITAL, PLYMOUTH, NC, 341314, p. A489

WASHINGTON COUNTY HOSPITAL AND NURSING HOME, CHATOM, AL, 011300, p. A16

WASHINGTON COUNTY HOSPITAL DISTRICT 1, HANOVER, KS, 171365, p. A248

WASHINGTON COUNTY MEMORIAL HOSPITAL, SALEM, IN, 151314, p. A224

WASHINGTON COUNTY MEMORIAL HOSPITAL, POTOSI, MO, 261308, p. A389

WASHINGTON COUNTY REGIONAL MEDICAL CENTER, SANDERSVILLE, GA, 110086, p. A168

WASHINGTON HOSPITAL, WASHINGTON, PA, 390042, p. A578

WASHINGTON HOSPITAL CENTER, WASHINGTON, DC, 090011, p. A122

WASHINGTON REGIONAL MEDICAL CENTER, FAYETTEVILLE, AR, 040004, p. A43

WASHINGTON TOWNSHIP HEALTH CARE DISTRICT, FREMONT, CA, 050195, p. A61

WASHINGTON–ST. TAMMANY REGIONAL MEDICAL CENTER, BOGALUSA, LOUISIANA (see BOGALUSA MEDICAL CENTER), p. A278

WASHOE MEDICAL CENTER, RENO, NV, 290001, p. A418

WASHOE MEDICAL CENTER REHABILITATION HOSPITAL, RENO, NV, 293027, p. A418

WASHOE MEDICAL CENTER SOUTH MEADOWS, RENO, NV, 290049, p. A418

WATAUGA MEDICAL CENTER, BOONE, NC, 340051, p. A478

WATERBURY HOSPITAL, WATERBURY, CT, 070005, p. A117

WATERTOWN MEMORIAL HOSPITAL, WATERTOWN, WI, 520116, p. A737

WATONGA MUNICIPAL HOSPITAL, WATONGA, OK, 371302, p. A541

WATSONVILLE COMMUNITY HOSPITAL, WATSONVILLE, CA, 050194, p. A98

WAUKESHA COUNTY MENTAL HEALTH CENTER, WAUKESHA, WI, 524026, p. A737

WAUKESHA MEMORIAL HOSPITAL, WAUKESHA, WI, 520008, p. A737

WAUPUN MEMORIAL HOSPITAL, WAUPUN, WI, 521327, p. A737

WAVERLY HEALTH CENTER, WAVERLY, IA, 161339, p. A243

WAYNE COUNTY HOSPITAL, CORYDON, IA, 161358, p. A231

WAYNE COUNTY HOSPITAL, MONTICELLO, KY, 181321, p. A271

WAYNE GENERAL HOSPITAL, WAYNESBORO, MS, 250077, p. A376

WAYNE HOSPITAL, GREENVILLE, OH, 360044, p. A515

WAYNE MEDICAL CENTER, WAYNESBORO, TN, 440010, p. A619

WAYNE MEMORIAL HOSPITAL, JESUP, GA, 110124, p. A164

WAYNE MEMORIAL HOSPITAL, GOLDSBORO, NC, 340010, p. A483

WAYNE MEMORIAL HOSPITAL, HONESDALE, PA, 390125, p. A560

WAYNESBORO HOSPITAL, WAYNESBORO, PA, 390138, p. A578

WEBSTER COUNTY COMMUNITY HOSPITAL, RED CLOUD, NE, 281316, p. A412

WEBSTER COUNTY MEMORIAL HOSPITAL, WEBSTER SPRINGS, WV, 511301, p. A720

WEDOWEE HOSPITAL, WEDOWEE, AL, 010032, p. A25

WEED ARMY COMMUNITY HOSPITAL, FORT IRWIN, CA, p. A60

WEEKS MEDICAL CENTER, LANCASTER, NH, 301303, p. A421

WEIRTON MEDICAL CENTER, WEIRTON, WV, 510023, p. A720

WEISBROD MEMORIAL COUNTY HOSPITAL, EADS, CO, 061300, p. A105

WEISER MEMORIAL HOSPITAL, WEISER, ID, 131307, p. A182

WEISMAN CHILDREN'S REHABILITATION HOSPITAL, MARLTON, NJ, 313034, p. A431

WELCH COMMUNITY HOSPITAL, WELCH, WV, 510086, p. A720

WELLINGTON REGIONAL MEDICAL CENTER, WEST PALM BEACH, FL, 100275, p. A150

WELLMONT BRISTOL REGIONAL MEDICAL CENTER, BRISTOL, TN, 440012, p. A602

WELLMONT HAWKINS COUNTY MEMORIAL HOSPITAL, ROGERSVILLE, TN, 440032, p. A617

WELLMONT HOLSTON VALLEY MEDICAL CENTER, KINGSPORT, TN, 440017, p. A609

WELLMONT LONESOME PINE HOSPITAL, BIG STONE GAP, VA, 490114, p. A685

WELLSPRING FOUNDATION, BETHLEHEM, CT, p. A112

WELLSTAR COBB HOSPITAL, AUSTELL, GA, 110143, p. A156

WELLSTAR DOUGLAS HOSPITAL, DOUGLASVILLE, GA, 110184, p. A161

WELLSTAR KENNESTONE HOSPITAL, MARIETTA, GA, 110035, p. A165

WELLSTAR PAULDING HOSPITAL, DALLAS, GA, 110042, p. A160

WELLSTAR WINDY HILL HOSPITAL, MARIETTA, GA, 112007, p. A165

WELLSTONE REGIONAL HOSPITAL, JEFFERSONVILLE, IN, 144051, p. A219

WENATCHEE VALLEY HOSPITAL, WENATCHEE, WA, 500148, p. A712

WENTWORTH–DOUGLASS HOSPITAL, DOVER, NH, 300018, p. A420

WERNERSVILLE STATE HOSPITAL, WERNERSVILLE, PA, 394014, p. A578

WESLEY LONG COMMUNITY HOSPITAL, GREENSBORO, NORTH CAROLINA (see MOSES CONE HEALTH SYSTEM), p. A484

WESLEY MEDICAL CENTER, WICHITA, KS, 170123, p. A260

WESLEY MEDICAL CENTER, HATTIESBURG, MS, 250094, p. A369

WESLEY REHABILITATION HOSPITAL, WICHITA, KS, 173027, p. A260

WESLEY WOODS CENTER OF EMORY UNIVERSITY, ATLANTA, GA, 110203, p. A155

WEST ALLIS MEMORIAL HOSPITAL, WEST ALLIS, WI, 520139, p. A738

WEST ANAHEIM MEDICAL CENTER, ANAHEIM, CA, 050426, p. A52

WEST BOCA MEDICAL CENTER, BOCA RATON, FL, 100268, p. A124

WEST BRANCH REGIONAL MEDICAL CENTER, WEST BRANCH, MI, 230095, p. A348

WEST CALCASIEU CAMERON HOSPITAL, SULPHUR, LA, 190013, p. A293

WEST CAMPUS, NORFOLK, NEBRASKA (see FAITH REGIONAL HEALTH SERVICES), p. A410

WEST CARROLL MEMORIAL HOSPITAL, OAK GROVE, LA, 190081, p. A290

WEST CENTRAL COMMUNITY HOSPITAL, CLINTON, IN, 151326, p. A213

WEST CENTRAL GEORGIA REGIONAL HOSPITAL, COLUMBUS, GA, 114013, p. A159

WEST FELICIANA PARISH HOSPITAL, SAINT FRANCISVILLE, LA, 191306, p. A292

WEST FLORIDA HOSPITAL, PENSACOLA, FL, 100231, p. A143

WEST GEORGIA HEALTH SYSTEM, LA GRANGE, GA, 110016, p. A164

WEST HAVEN DIVISION, WEST HAVEN, CONNECTICUT (see VETERANS AFFAIRS CONNECTICUT HEALTHCARE SYSTEM–NEW HAVEN DIVISION), p. A117

WEST HILLS HOSPITAL, RENO, NV, 294003, p. A418

WEST HILLS HOSPITAL AND MEDICAL CENTER, LOS ANGELES, CA, 050481, p.73

WEST HOLT MEMORIAL HOSPITAL, ATKINSON, NE, 281343, p. A404

WEST HOUSTON MEDICAL CENTER, HOUSTON, TX, 450644, p. A649

WEST JEFFERSON MEDICAL CENTER, MARRERO, LA, 190039, p. A286

WEST MESA MEDICAL CENTER, ALBUQUERQUE, NM, 320074, p. A441

WEST PARK HOSPITAL, CODY, WY, 531312, p. A740

WEST RIVER REGIONAL MEDICAL CENTER, HETTINGER, ND, 351330, p. A498

WEST SEATTLE PSYCHIATRIC HOSPITAL, SEATTLE, WA, 504009, p. A708

WEST SHORE MEDICAL CENTER, MANISTEE, MI, 230060, p. A339

WEST SUBURBAN MEDICAL CENTER, OAK PARK, IL, 140049, p. A203

WEST TEXAS VA HEALTH CARE SYSTEM, BIG SPRING, TX, p. A626

WEST VALLEY HOSPITAL, GOODYEAR, AZ, 030110, p. A31

WEST VALLEY HOSPITAL, DALLAS, OR, 381308, p. A543

WEST VALLEY MEDICAL CENTER, CALDWELL, ID, 130014, p. A178

WEST VIRGINIA REHABILITATION CENTER, INSTITUTE, WV, 513029, p. A716

WEST VIRGINIA UNIVERSITY HOSPITALS, MORGANTOWN, WV, 510001, p. A718

WESTBOROUGH STATE HOSPITAL, WESTBOROUGH, MA, 224026, p. A325

WESTBROOK HEALTH CENTER, WESTBROOK, MN, 241302, p. A365

WESTCHESTER GENERAL HOSPITAL, MIAMI, FL, 100284, p. A138

WESTCHESTER MEDICAL CENTER, VALHALLA, NY, 330234, p. A475

WESTERLY HOSPITAL, WESTERLY, RI, 410013, p. A582

WESTERN ARIZONA REGIONAL MEDICAL CENTER, BULLHEAD CITY, AZ, 030101, p. A30

WESTERN BAPTIST HOSPITAL, PADUCAH, KY, 180104, p. A273

WESTERN MARYLAND CENTER, HAGERSTOWN, MD, 212002, p. A308

WESTERN MASSACHUSETTS HOSPITAL, WESTFIELD, MA, 222023, p. A325

WESTERN MEDICAL CENTER ANAHEIM, ANAHEIM, CA, 050594, p. A52

WESTERN MEDICAL CENTER–SANTA ANA, SANTA ANA, CA, 050065, p. A92

WESTERN MENTAL HEALTH INSTITUTE, BOLIVAR, TN, 444008, p. A602

WESTERN MISSOURI MEDICAL CENTER, WARRENSBURG, MO, 260097, p. A395

WESTERN MISSOURI MENTAL HEALTH CENTER, KANSAS CITY, MO, 264008, p. A386

WESTERN NEW YORK CHILDREN'S PSYCHIATRIC CENTER, BUFFALO, NY, p. A449

WESTERN PENNSYLVANIA HOSPITAL, PITTSBURGH, PA, 390090, p. A573

WESTERN PLAINS MEDICAL COMPLEX, DODGE CITY, KS, 170175, p. A246

WESTERN PSYCHIATRIC INSTITUTE AND CLINIC, PITTSBURGH, PENNSYLVANIA (see UPMC PRESBYTERIAN), p. A572

WESTERN RESERVE CARE SYSTEM, YOUNGSTOWN, OH, 360141, p. A526

WESTERN STATE HOSPITAL, HOPKINSVILLE, KY, 184002, p. A266

WESTERN STATE HOSPITAL, STAUNTON, VA, 494021, p. A697

WESTERN STATE HOSPITAL, TACOMA, WA, 504003, p. A710

WESTFIELD MEMORIAL HOSPITAL, WESTFIELD, NY, 330166, p. A476

WESTLAKE HOSPITAL, MELROSE PARK, IL, 140240, p. A201

WESTLAKE REGIONAL HOSPITAL, COLUMBIA, KY, 181313, p. A263

WESTON COUNTY HEALTH SERVICES, NEWCASTLE, WY, 531303, p. A741

WESTPARK SURGERY CENTER, MCKINNEY, TEXAS (see MEDICAL CENTER OF MCKINNEY), p. A656

WESTSIDE REGIONAL MEDICAL CENTER, PLANTATION, FL, 100228, p. A143

WESTVIEW HOSPITAL, INDIANAPOLIS, IN, 150129, p. A219

WESTWOOD LODGE HOSPITAL, WESTWOOD, MA, 224023, p. A325

WETZEL COUNTY HOSPITAL, NEW MARTINSVILLE, WV, 510072, p. A718

WHEATLAND MEMORIAL HOSPITAL, HARLOWTON, MT, 271321, p. A399

WHEATON COMMUNITY HOSPITAL, WHEATON, MN, 241304, p. A365

WHEELER COUNTY HOSPITAL, GLENWOOD, GA, 111321, p. A163

WHEELING HOSPITAL, WHEELING, WV, 510050, p. A721

WHIDBEY GENERAL HOSPITAL, COUPEVILLE, WA, 500122, p. A702

WHIDDEN MEMORIAL HOSPITAL, EVERETT, MASSACHUSETTS (see CAMBRIDGE HEALTH ALLIANCE), p. A316

WHISPER RIDGE AT LEESBURG, LEESBURG, VA, p. A690

WHITE COMMUNITY HOSPITAL, AURORA, MN, 241340, p. A349

WHITE COUNTY COMMUNITY HOSPITAL, SPARTA, TN, 440192, p. A618

WHITE COUNTY MEDICAL CENTER, SEARCY, AR, 040100, p. A50

WHITE COUNTY MEDICAL CENTER, CARMI, IL, 141314, p. A185

WHITE COUNTY MEMORIAL HOSPITAL, MONTICELLO, IN, 151312, p. A222

WHITE MEMORIAL MEDICAL CENTER, LOS ANGELES, CA, 050103, p. A73

WHITE MOUNTAIN REGIONAL MEDICAL CENTER, SPRINGERVILLE, AZ, 030099, p. A37

WHITE PLAINS HOSPITAL CENTER, WHITE PLAINS, NY, 330304, p. A476

WHITE RIVER MEDICAL CENTER, BATESVILLE, AR, 040119, p. A40

WHITESBURG APPALACHIAN REGIONAL HOSPITAL, WHITESBURG, KY, 180002, p. A275

WHITFIELD MEDICAL SURGICAL HOSPITAL, WHITFIELD, MISSISSIPPI (see MISSISSIPPI STATE HOSPITAL), p. A377

WHITING FORENSIC DIVISION OF CONNECTICUT VALLEY HOSPITAL, MIDDLETOWN, CONNECTICUT (see CONNECTICUT VALLEY HOSPITAL), p. A114

WHITINSVILLE MEDICAL CENTER, WHITINSVILLE, MASSACHUSETTS (see MILFORD REGIONAL MEDICAL CENTER), p. A320

WHITMAN HOSPITAL AND MEDICAL CENTER, COLFAX, WA, 501327, p. A701

WHITTEN CENTER, CLINTON, SC, p. A585

WHITTIER HOSPITAL MEDICAL CENTER, WHITTIER, CA, 050175, p. A99

WHITTIER REHABILITATION HOSPITAL, HAVERHILL, MA, 223028, p. A318

WHITTIER REHABILITATION HOSPITAL, WESTBOROUGH, MA, 223033, p. A325

WICHITA COUNTY HEALTH CENTER, LEOTI, KS, 171306, p. A251

WICHITA COUNTY HOSPITAL LONG TERM CARE, LEOTI, KANSAS (see WICHITA COUNTY HEALTH CENTER), p. A251

WICHITA SPECIALTY HOSPITAL, WICHITA, KS, 172003, p. A260

WICHITA VALLEY REHABILITATION HOSPITAL, WICHITA FALLS, TX, 453088, p. A674

WICKENBURG REGIONAL MEDICAL CENTER, WICKENBURG, AZ, 031300, p. A39

WILBARGER GENERAL HOSPITAL, VERNON, TX, 450584, p. A671

WILCOX MEMORIAL HOSPITAL, LIHUE, HI, 120014, p. A175

WILD ROSE COMMUNITY MEMORIAL HOSPITAL, WILD ROSE, WI, 521303, p. A738

WILDWOOD LIFESTYLE CENTER AND HOSPITAL, WILDWOOD, GA, p. A172

WILFORD HALL MEDICAL CENTER, LACKLAND AFB, TX, p. A652

WILKES REGIONAL MEDICAL CENTER, NORTH WILKESBORO, NC, 340064, p. A488

WILKES–BARRE GENERAL HOSPITAL, WILKES–BARRE, PENNSYLVANIA (see WYOMING VALLEY HEALTH CARE SYSTEM), p. A579

WILLAMETTE FALLS HOSPITAL, OREGON CITY, OR, 380038, p. A546

WILLAMETTE VALLEY MEDICAL CENTER, MCMINNVILLE, OR, 380071, p. A546

WILLAPA HARBOR HOSPITAL, SOUTH BEND, WA, 501303, p. A709

WILLIAM B. KESSLER MEMORIAL HOSPITAL, HAMMONTON, NJ, 310088, p. A429

WILLIAM BEAUMONT ARMY MEDICAL CENTER, EL PASO, TX, p. A638

WILLIAM BEAUMONT HOSPITAL–ROYAL OAK, ROYAL OAK, MI, 230130, p. A343

WILLIAM BEAUMONT HOSPITAL–TROY, TROY, MI, 230269, p. A347

WILLIAM BEE RIRIE HOSPITAL, ELY, NV, 291302, p. A415

WILLIAM NEWTON HOSPITAL, WINFIELD, KS, 170019, p. A260

WILLIAM R. SHARPE, JR. HOSPITAL, WESTON, WV, 514010, p. A721

WILLIAM S. HALL PSYCHIATRIC INSTITUTE, COLUMBIA, SC, 424003, p. A586

WILLIAM S. MIDDLETON MEMORIAL VETERANS HOSPITAL, MADISON, WI, p. A728

WILLIAM W. HASTINGS INDIAN HOSPITAL, TAHLEQUAH, OK, 370171, p. A539

WILLIAMSBURG REGIONAL HOSPITAL, KINGSTREE, SC, 421303, p. A589

WILLIAMSON ARH HOSPITAL, SOUTH WILLIAMSON, KY, 180069, p. A275

WILLIAMSON MEDICAL CENTER, FRANKLIN, TN, 440029, p. A606

WILLIAMSON MEMORIAL HOSPITAL, WILLIAMSON, WV, 510077, p. A721

WILLIAMSPORT HOSPITAL AND MEDICAL CENTER, WILLIAMSPORT, PENNSYLVANIA (see SUSQUEHANNA HEALTH SYSTEM), p. A580

WILLIE D. MILLER EYE CENTER, CHATTANOOGA, TENNESSEE (see ERLANGER MEDICAL CENTER), p. A603

WILLINGWAY HOSPITAL, STATESBORO, GA, p. A170

WILLIS–KNIGHTON BOSSIER HEALTH CENTER, BOSSIER CITY, LA, 190236, p. A278

WILLIS–KNIGHTON MEDICAL CENTER, SHREVEPORT, LA, 190111, p. A293

WILLMAR REGIONAL TREATMENT CENTER, WILLMAR, MN, 244005, p. A365

WILLOUGH HEALTHCARE SYSTEM, NAPLES, FL, 104063, p. A139

WILLOW CREEK WOMEN'S HOSPITAL, JOHNSON, AR, 040141, p. A45

WILLOW CREST HOSPITAL, MIAMI, OK, 374017, p. A533

WILLOW SPRINGS RESIDENTIAL TREATMENT CENTER, RENO, NV, p. A418

WILLS EYE HOSPITAL, PHILADELPHIA, PA, 390024, p. A570

WILLS MEMORIAL HOSPITAL, WASHINGTON, GA, 111325, p. A172

WILMA N. VAZQUEZ MEDICAL CENTER, VEGA BAJA, PR, 400115, p. A748

WILMINGTON HOSPITAL, WILMINGTON, DELAWARE (see CHRISTIANA CARE HEALTH SYSTEM), p. A120

WILMINGTON TREATMENT CENTER, WILMINGTON, NC, 340168, p. A494

WILSON COUNTY HOSPITAL, NEODESHA, KS, 171344, p. A253

WILSON MEDICAL CENTER, WILSON, NC, 340126, p. A494

WILSON MEMORIAL HOSPITAL, SIDNEY, OH, 360013, p. A522

WILSON MEMORIAL REGIONAL MEDICAL CENTER, JOHNSON CITY, NEW YORK (see UNITED HEALTH SERVICES HOSPITALS–BINGHAMTON), p. A448

WILSON N. JONES MEDICAL CENTER, SHERMAN, TX, 450469, p. A667

WINCHESTER HOSPITAL, WINCHESTER, MA, 220105, p. A325

WINCHESTER MEDICAL CENTER, WINCHESTER, VA, 490005, p. A698

WINDBER MEDICAL CENTER, WINDBER, PA, 390112, p. A580

WINDHAM COMMUNITY MEMORIAL HOSPITAL, WILLIMANTIC, CT, 070021, p. A118

WINDMOOR HEALTHCARE OF CLEARWATER, CLEARWATER, FL, 104017, p. A125

WINDOM AREA HOSPITAL, WINDOM, MN, 241332, p. A365

WINDSOR HOSPITAL, CHAGRIN FALLS, OH, 364017, p. A505

WING MEMORIAL HOSPITAL AND MEDICAL CENTERS, PALMER, MA, 220030, p. A322

WINKLER COUNTY MEMORIAL HOSPITAL, KERMIT, TX, 451314, p. A650

WINN ARMY COMMUNITY HOSPITAL, HINESVILLE, GA, p. A163

WINN PARISH MEDICAL CENTER, WINNFIELD, LA, 190090, p. A294

WINNEBAGO MENTAL HEALTH INSTITUTE, WINNEBAGO, WI, 524002, p. A738

WINNER REGIONAL HEALTHCARE CENTER, WINNER, SD, 431334, p. A601

WINNESHIEK MEDICAL CENTER, DECORAH, IA, 161371, p. A232

WINNIE COMMUNITY HOSPITAL, WINNIE, TX, 451328, p. A674

WINONA HEALTH, WINONA, MN, 240044, p. A365

WINSLOW MEMORIAL HOSPITAL, WINSLOW, AZ, 031311, p. A39

WINSTON MEDICAL CENTER, LOUISVILLE, MS, 250027, p. A372

WINTER HAVEN HOSPITAL, WINTER HAVEN, FL, 100052, p. A151

WINTER PARK MEMORIAL HOSPITAL, WINTER PARK, FLORIDA (see FLORIDA HOSPITAL), p. A141

WINTHROP–UNIVERSITY HOSPITAL, MINEOLA, NY, 330167, p. A457

WIREGRASS MEDICAL CENTER, GENEVA, AL, 010062, p. A19

WISE REGIONAL HEALTH SYSTEM, DECATUR, TX, 450271, p. A635

WISHARD HEALTH SERVICES, INDIANAPOLIS, IN, 150024, p. A219

WISHEK COMMUNITY HOSPITAL AND CLINICS, WISHEK, ND, 351321, p. A501

WITHAM MEMORIAL HOSPITAL, LEBANON, IN, 150104, p. A221

WM. JENNINGS BRYAN DORN VETERANS AFFAIRS MEDICAL CENTER, COLUMBIA, SC, p. A586

WOMACK ARMY MEDICAL CENTER, FORT BRAGG, NC, p. A483

WOMAN'S CHRISTIAN ASSOCIATION HOSPITAL, JAMESTOWN, NY, 330239, p. A454
WOMAN'S HOSPITAL, BATON ROUGE, LA, 190128, p. A278
WOMAN'S HOSPITAL AT RIVER OAKS, JACKSON, MS, 250136, p. A371
WOMEN AND CHILDREN'S HOSPITAL, CHARLESTON, WEST VIRGINIA (see CHARLESTON AREA MEDICAL CENTER), p. A714
WOMEN AND CHILDREN'S HOSPITAL, LAKE CHARLES, LA, 190201, p. A285
WOMEN AND CHILDREN'S HOSPITAL, BUFFALO, NY, p. A449
WOMEN AND INFANTS HOSPITAL OF RHODE ISLAND, PROVIDENCE, RI, 410010, p. A582
WOMEN'S AND CHILDREN'S HOSPITAL, LOS ANGELES, CALIFORNIA (see LAC/UNIVERSITY OF SOUTHERN CALIFORNIA MEDICAL CENTER), p. A71
WOMEN'S AND CHILDREN'S HOSPITAL, LAFAYETTE, LA, 190196, p. A284
WOMEN'S HOSPITAL, ALBUQUERQUE, NM, 320017, p. A441
WOMEN'S HOSPITAL OF GREENSBORO, GREENSBORO, NORTH CAROLINA (see MOSES CONE HEALTH SYSTEM), p. A484
WOOD COUNTY HOSPITAL, BOWLING GREEN, OH, 360029, p. A504
WOODBRIDGE DEVELOPMENT CENTER, WOODBRIDGE, NJ, p. A439
WOODHULL MEDICAL AND MENTAL HEALTH CENTER, NEW YORK, NY, 330396, p. A466
WOODLAND HEALTHCARE, WOODLAND, CA, 050127, p. A99
WOODLAND HEIGHTS MEDICAL CENTER, LUFKIN, TX, 450484, p. A655
WOODLAND MEDICAL CENTER, CULLMAN, AL, 010143, p. A16
WOODLAWN HOSPITAL, ROCHESTER, IN, 151313, p. A224
WOODRIDGE HOSPITAL, JOHNSON CITY, TN, 444006, p. A609
WOODROW WILSON REHABILITATION CENTER, FISHERSVILLE, VA, p. A688
WOODS MEMORIAL HOSPITAL DISTRICT, ETOWAH, TN, 440054, p. A606
WOODWARD REGIONAL HOSPITAL, WOODWARD, OK, 370002, p. A541
WOODWARD RESOURCE CENTER, WOODWARD, IA, p. A243
WOODWINDS HEALTH CAMPUS, WOODBURY, MN, 240213, p. A365
WOOSTER COMMUNITY HOSPITAL, WOOSTER, OH, 360036, p. A525

WORCESTER STATE HOSPITAL, WORCESTER, MA, 224032, p. A326
WORTHINGTON REGIONAL HOSPITAL, WORTHINGTON, MN, 240022, p. A365
WRANGELL MEDICAL CENTER, WRANGELL, AK, 021305, p. A29
WRAY COMMUNITY DISTRICT HOSPITAL, WRAY, CO, 061309, p. A111
WRIGHT MEDICAL CENTER, CLARION, IA, 161302, p. A230
WRIGHT MEMORIAL HOSPITAL, TRENTON, MO, 261309, p. A394
WRIGHT PATTERSON MEDICAL CENTER, WRIGHT–PATTERSON AFB, OH, p. A525
WUESTHOFF MEDICAL CENTER – MELBOURNE, MELBOURNE, FL, 100291, p. A136
WUESTHOFF MEDICAL CENTER – ROCKLEDGE, ROCKLEDGE, FL, 100092, p. A144
WYANDOT MEMORIAL HOSPITAL, UPPER SANDUSKY, OH, 361329, p. A523
WYCKOFF HEIGHTS MEDICAL CENTER, NEW YORK, NY, 330221, p. A466
WYOMING BEHAVIORAL INSTITUTE, CASPER, WY, 534004, p. A739
WYOMING COUNTY COMMUNITY HOSPITAL, WARSAW, NY, 330008, p. A475
WYOMING MEDICAL CENTER, CASPER, WY, 530012, p. A739
WYOMING STATE HOSPITAL, EVANSTON, WY, 532002, p. A740
WYOMING VALLEY HEALTH CARE SYSTEM, WILKES–BARRE, PA, 390137, p. A579
WYTHE COUNTY COMMUNITY HOSPITAL, WYTHEVILLE, VA, 490111, p. A699

Y

YAKIMA REGIONAL MEDICAL AND HEART CENTER, YAKIMA, WA, 500012, p. A712
YAKIMA VALLEY MEMORIAL HOSPITAL, YAKIMA, WA, 500036, p. A712
YALE–NEW HAVEN CHILDREN'S HOSPITAL, NEW HAVEN, CONNECTICUT (see YALE–NEW HAVEN HOSPITAL), p. A115

YALE–NEW HAVEN HOSPITAL, NEW HAVEN, CT, 070022, p. A115
YALE–NEW HAVEN PSYCHIATRIC HOSPITAL, NEW HAVEN, CONNECTICUT (see YALE–NEW HAVEN HOSPITAL), p. A115
YALOBUSHA GENERAL HOSPITAL, WATER VALLEY, MS, 250061, p. A376
YAMPA VALLEY MEDICAL CENTER, STEAMBOAT SPRINGS, CO, 060049, p. A109
YANCEY COMMUNITY MEDICAL CENTER, BURNSVILLE, NC, 341301, p. A479
YAVAPAI REGIONAL MEDICAL CENTER, PRESCOTT, AZ, 030012, p. A35
YOAKUM COMMUNITY HOSPITAL, YOAKUM, TX, 451346, p. A675
YOAKUM COUNTY HOSPITAL, DENVER CITY, TX, 451308, p. A635
YORK GENERAL HEALTH CARE SERVICES, YORK, NE, 281336, p. A414
YORK HOSPITAL, YORK, ME, 200020, p. A301
YORK HOSPITAL, YORK, PA, 390046, p. A580
YOUNKER MEMORIAL REHABILITATION CENTER, DES MOINES, IOWA (see IOWA METHODIST MEDICAL CENTER), p. A232
YOUVILLE HOSPITAL AND REHABILITATION CENTER, CAMBRIDGE, MA, 222000, p. A316
YUKON–KUSKOKWIM DELTA REGIONAL HOSPITAL, BETHEL, AK, 020018, p. A26
YUMA DISTRICT HOSPITAL, YUMA, CO, 061315, p. A111
YUMA REGIONAL MEDICAL CENTER, YUMA, AZ, 030013, p. A39
YUMA REHABILITATION HOSPITAL, YUMA, AZ, 033034, p. A39

Z

ZEELAND COMMUNITY HOSPITAL, ZEELAND, MI, 230003, p. A348
ZUCKER HILLSIDE HOSPITAL, NEW YORK, NEW YORK (see LONG ISLAND JEWISH MEDICAL CENTER), p. A461
ZUCKER HILLSIDE HOSPITAL, GLEN OAKS, NEW YORK (see (see LONG ISLAND JEWISH MEDICAL CENTER)), p. A461

This section is an index of the key health care professionals for the hospitals and/or health care systems listed in this publication. The index is in alphabetical order, by individual, followed by the title, institutional affiliation, city, state and page reference to the hospital and/or health care system listing in section A and/or B.

A

AANONSON, Mark, Executive Director, St. Cloud Hospital, Saint Cloud, FL, p. A145

AARON, Carol
Senior Vice President Human Resources, Petaluma Valley Hospital, Petaluma, CA, p. A81
Senior Vice President Human Resources, Santa Rosa Memorial Hospital, Santa Rosa, CA, p. A93

AARON, M.D., Mike, Chief of Staff, Southwestern Memorial Hospital, Weatherford, OK, p. A541

AARON, Sandra
Chief Operating Officer, Baylor All Saints Medical Center at Fort Worth, Fort Worth, TX, p. A639
Chief Operating Officer, Baylor Medical Center at Southwest Fort Worth, Fort Worth, TX, p. A639

AASVED, Craig E., Chief Executive Officer, North Valley Hospital, Whitefish, MT, p. A403

ABAIR, Cynthia, Associate Director, Veterans Affairs Salt Lake City Health Care System, Salt Lake City, UT, p. A680

ABAUNZA, M.D., Alfred E., Chief Medical Officer, West Jefferson Medical Center, Marrero, LA, p. A286

ABAY, Eustaquio, M.D., Chief Executive Officer, Kansas Spine Hospital, Wichita, KS, p. A259

ABBOTT, Jody, Chief Operating Officer, Hillcrest Medical Center, Tulsa, OK, p. A539

ABBOTT, M.D., Richard, Quality Improvement Medical Advisor, Skagit Valley Hospital, Mount Vernon, WA, p. A704

ABBOTT, Stephen L., President and Chief Executive Officer, Cape Cod Healthcare, Inc., Hyannis, MA, p. B21

ABDAI, Joe, Chief Human Resources, Banner Behavioral Health Hospital, Scottsdale, AZ, p. A36

ABEL, Barbara, Vice President of Human Resources, Heart of the Rockies Regional Medical Center, Salida, CO, p. A109

ABELY, Susan Cerrone, Vice President and Chief Information Officer, Roger Williams Medical Center, Providence, RI, p. A582

ABENDROTH, M.D., Thomas, Chief Information Officer, Penn State Milton S. Hershey Medical Center, Hershey, PA, p. A560

ABERCROMBIE, David, Chief Executive Officer, Fairview Hospital, Fairview, OK, p. A531

ABERLE, James, Vice President and Chief Information Officer and Support Services, Yakima Valley Memorial Hospital, Yakima, WA, p. A712

ABERNATHY, Les, Executive Vice President, Corporate Services, Mary Washington Hospital, Fredericksburg, VA, p. A688

ABERNETHY, Robert, Chief Financial Officer, Medical Center Hospital, Odessa, TX, p. A659

ABRAHAM, M.D., Kamel, Chief of Staff, Community Hospital, Springfield, OH, p. A522

ABRAHAM, Mathew, President and Chief Executive Officer, Saint Agnes Medical Center, Fresno, CA, p. A61

ABRAHAMSEN, Lynn, Chief Operating Officer, Hennepin County Medical Center, Minneapolis, MN, p. A357

ABRAMOVITZ, Alan, Senior Director Human Resources, Saint Luke's Northland Hospital–Smithville Campus, Smithville, MO, p. A393

ABRAMS, R.N., MS, Catherine H., Vice President Nursing, Mercy Hospital, Iowa City, IA, p. A235

ABRAMS, Scott, Vice President Finance, Beaver Dam Community Hospitals, Beaver Dam, WI, p. A723

ABREU, Astrid, Administrator, Clinica San Agustin, Manati, PR, p. A745

ABREU, John, Chief Financial Officer, Valley Hospital, Palmer, AK, p. A28

ABRUTZ Jr, Joseph F., Administrator, Cameron Regional Medical Center, Cameron, MO, p. A379

ABSHER, M.D., Denise, Chief Medical Staff, Alleghany Memorial Hospital, Sparta, NC, p. A492

ABSHIRE, Allen, Director Information Services, Christus St. Patrick Hospital of Lake Charles, Lake Charles, LA, p. A284

ACEVEDO, Ana, Supervisor Human Resources, San Jorge Children's Hospital, San Juan, PR, p. A747

ACEVEDO, M.D., Jose
Vice President Medical Affairs and Chief Medical Officer, Geneva General Hospital, Geneva, NY, p. A452
Vice President Medical Affairs and Chief Medical Officer, Soldiers and Sailors Memorial Hospital of Yates County, Penn Yan, NY, p. A469

ACHENBACH, M Connie, Assistant Administrator and Chief Operating Officer, Prairie du Chien Memorial Hospital, Prairie Du Chien, WI, p. A734

ACHTER, Dick
Chief Operating Officer and Chief Financial Officer, Barrett Hospital & HealthCare, Dillon, MT, p. A398
Chief Operating Officer and Chief Financial Officer, Barrett Hospital & HealthCare, Dillon, MT, p. A398

ACKELSON, Rocky, Director Information Services, Arkansas Valley Regional Medical Center, La Junta, CO, p. A107

ACKER, David B., FACHE, Chief Executive Officer, Charles Cole Memorial Hospital, Coudersport, PA, p. A556

ACKER, Emily, Administrator, Inner Harbour Hospitals, Douglasville, GA, p. A161

ACKER, Peter W., President and Chief Executive Officer, Lincoln Medical Center, Lincolnton, NC, p. A486

ACKER Jr, Raymond W., Chief Executive Officer, United Regional Medical Center, Manchester, TN, p. A612

ACKERMAN, S. Jeffrey, M.D., President and Chief Executive Officer, San Jacinto Methodist Hospital, Baytown, TX, p. A625

ACKERMAN, Sigurd H., M.D., President and Chief Executive Officer, Silver Hill Hospital, New Canaan, CT, p. A115

ACKLEY, Michael, Administrator, Lee Regional Medical Center, Pennington Gap, VA, p. A693

ACKLIN, M.D., Traci, Chief of Staff, Montgomery General Hospital, Montgomery, WV, p. A717

ACOSTA, Nannete, Director Human Resources, Hospital Metropolitano Dr. Tito Mattei, Yauco, PR, p. A749

ACOSTA CARLSON, M.D., Fran, Chief of Staff, Tri-County Area Hospital, Lexington, NE, p. A408

ACREE, Charis, Senior Vice President, West Georgia Health System, La Grange, GA, p. A164

ACTERHOF, Trudy, Human Resources Director, Baldwin Area Medical Center, Baldwin, WI, p. A722

ADAIR, Jerry D., President and Chief Executive Officer, Good Shepherd Medical Center, Longview, TX, p. A653

ADAMS, Alan L., President, Memorial Hospital, Stilwell, OK, p. A538

ADAMS, Alene, Director Human Resources, Quincy Valley Medical Center, Quincy, WA, p. A706

ADAMS, Andy, Director of Information Systems, Murray–Calloway County Hospital, Murray, KY, p. A272

ADAMS, Bob, Information Services Manager, Bay Area Hospital, Coos Bay, OR, p. A543

ADAMS, Charles T., Chief Executive Officer, Ty Cobb Healthcare System, Inc., Royston, GA, p. B111

ADAMS, Gini, Director of Human Resources, Yuma District Hospital, Yuma, CO, p. A111

ADAMS, Gregory, Senior Vice President and Chief Financial Officer, Holy Name Hospital, Teaneck, NJ, p. A436

ADAMS, Gregory A., Chief Operating Officer, Kaiser Foundation Hospital – Orange County, Anaheim, CA, p. A52

ADAMS, M.D., Ione, Chief of Staff, St. Joseph Hospital, Bellingham, WA, p. A700

ADAMS, Janice, Director Human Resources, St. Elizabeth Hospital, Gonzales, LA, p. A281

ADAMS, Jay, Chief Information Officer, North Valley Hospital, Whitefish, MT, p. A403

ADAMS, Jennifer B., Chief Financial Officer, Lake City Medical Center, Lake City, FL, p. A134

ADAMS, Jerry W., Chief Executive Officer, Greenwood Leflore Hospital, Greenwood, MS, p. A369

ADAMS, Karen L., Chief Executive Officer, Southeast Missouri Mental Health Center, Farmington, MO, p. A382

ADAMS, Liz, Informatics Manager, The Women's Hospital, Newburgh, IN, p. A223

ADAMS, Mark A., President and Chief Executive Officer, Methodist Rehabilitation Center, Jackson, MS, p. A370

ADAMS, Mark B., Chief Executive Officer, West Valley Medical Center, Caldwell, ID, p. A178

ADAMS, Marlene J., Director Human Resources, Roy Lester Schneider Hospital, Saint Thomas, VI, p. A749

ADAMS, Matt, Director Information Technology, King's Daughters Hospital, Temple, TX, p. A669

ADAMS, Mike
Vice President Human Resources, Baylor Medical Center at Waxahachie, Waxahachie, TX, p. A672
Senior Vice President, Baylor University Medical Center, Dallas, TX, p. A632

ADAMS, Nancy, Chief Human Resources Officer, LDS Hospital, Salt Lake City, UT, p. A679

ADAMS, M.D., Patricia L., Chief Professional Services, North Carolina Baptist Hospital (Wake Forest University Baptist Medical Center), Winston–Salem, NC, p. A494

ADAMS, Patsy, Director Human Resources, Redmond Regional Medical Center, Rome, GA, p. A168

ADAMS, Richard, Director Information Systems, Medical Center of McKinney, McKinney, TX, p. A656

ADAMS, M.D., Richard, Vice President Medical Affairs, Falmouth Hospital, Falmouth, MA, p. A317

ADAMS, Richard L., Chief Executive Officer, Regency Hospital of Akron, Barberton, OH, p. A503

ADAMS, Scott K., Administrator, Pullman Regional Hospital, Pullman, WA, p. A706

ADAMS, Shannon, Chief Financial Officer, Saunders County Health Service, Wahoo, NE, p. A413

ADAMS, Stephen D.
Executive Vice President and Chief Executive Officer, Mercy Hospital of Pittsburgh, Pittsburgh, PA, p. A572
Chief Information Officer, Mercy Hospital–North Shore Campus, Pittsburgh, PA, p. A572

ADAMS, William A., President and Chief Executive Officer, Reston Hospital Center, Reston, VA, p. A694

ADCOCK, M.D., D W., Medical Director, Colquitt Regional Medical Center, Moultrie, GA, p. A166

ADCOCK, David L., Administrator, All Saints Special Care Hospital, Bridgeton, MO, p. A379

ADCOCK, Robert S., Chief Operating Officer, St. Alexius Hospital, Saint Louis, MO, p. A392

ADDISON, Lewis C., Chief Financial Officer and Senior Vice President, Centra Health, Lynchburg, VA, p. A691

ADELMAN, Michael, M.D., Acting Director, Veterans Affairs Medical Center, Erie, PA, p. A558

ADELMAN, M.D., Michael, Chief of Staff, Veterans Affairs Medical Center, Erie, PA, p. A558

ADEMA, Carolyn, Human Resources Officer, North Oaks Medical Center, Hammond, LA, p. A281

ADERHOLDT, Elizabeth, President, St. Marys Health Center, Jefferson City, MO, p. A383

ADKINS, Gary W., Chief Executive Officer, Paulding County Hospital, Paulding, OH, p. A520

ADKINS, Jo, Chief Executive Officer, Del E. Webb Memorial Hospital, Sun City West, AZ, p. A37

ADKINS, John, Vice President and Chief Information Officer, St. Joseph's/Candler, Candler Hospital, Savannah, GA, p. A169

ADKINS, Raymond, Chief Information Officer, Peninsula Regional Health System, Salisbury, MD, p. A310

ADLER, Jeanna, Assistant Administrator Fiscal Services, Wise Regional Health System, Decatur, TX, p. A635

ADLER, Laura, Senior Vice President Human Relations, Saint Francis Hospital, Memphis, TN, p. A613

ADLER, Maurita, Director Information Services, Gottlieb Memorial Hospital, Melrose Park, IL, p. A201

ADLER, Paula, Human Resources Director, Oswego Medical Center, Oswego, KS, p. A254

ADLER, Ronald M., Chief Executive Officer, Alaska Psychiatric Institute, Anchorage, AK, p. A26

ADRIAANSE, Steve, Chief Human Resources Officer and Vice President, Tallahassee Memorial HealthCare, Tallahassee, FL, p. A147

AEA, Richard, Human Resources Director, Wahiawa General Hospital, Wahiawa, HI, p. A176

AENCHBACHER Jr, Arthur E., President, Baylor Regional Medical Center at Plano, Plano, TX, p. A660

AFSARIFARD, Farshid, CHE, President and Chief Executive Officer, Laurelwood Hospital, Willoughby, OH, p. A525

AGANA, Ben, Medical Director, HEALTHSOUTH Rehabilitation Hospital of North Houston, Conroe, TX, p. A630

AGARWAL, M.D., Ravinder, Medical Director, Claxton–Hepburn Medical Center, Ogdensburg, NY, p. A468

AGEE, Nancy H., Chief Operating Officer, Carilion Medical Center, Roanoke, VA, p. A696

AGNEW, R.N., Nettie L., Senior Vice President and Chief Operating Officer, North Kansas City Hospital, Kansas City, MO, p. A384

AGRESTI, D.O., James, Vice President Medical Affairs, Union Hospital, Union, NJ, p. A438

AGWUNOBI, Andrew, M.D., President and Chief Executive Officer, Grady Memorial Hospital, Atlanta, GA, p. A154

AHEARN, Patrick
Senior Vice President Finance and Administrative Services, Saint Barnabas Medical Center, Livingston, NJ, p. A430
Senior Vice President Finance and Administrative Services, Union Hospital, Union, NJ, p. A438

AHERN, G. Sam, President and Chief Executive Officer, Henry Medical Center, Stockbridge, GA, p. A170

AHERN, Steve, Chief Information Officer, Windber Medical Center, Windber, PA, p. A580

AHLE, John M., Corporate Senior Vice President and Chief Financial Officer, St. Vincent's Medical Center, Bridgeport, CT, p. A112

AHMAD, Asif, Chief Information Officer, Duke University Hospital, Durham, NC, p. A481

AHMED, M.D., Altaf, Medical Director, HEALTHSOUTH Rehabilitation Center, Albuquerque, NM, p. A440

AHMED, M.D., Sameena, Medical Staff President, Genesis Medical Center, Illini Campus, Silvis, IL, p. A208

AHMED, Tony, Administrator, Community General Hospital, Dilley, TX, p. A635

AHRENDSEN, M.D., Jon, Chief of Staff, Wright Medical Center, Clarion, IA, p. A230

AHRENS, Richard, Chief Operating Officer, Memorial Health System of East Texas, Lufkin, TX, p. A655

AHSAN, M.D., Arshad, Chief of Staff, St. James Health Services, Saint James, MN, p. A361

AIELLO, Louis, Chief Financial Officer, St. Elizabeth Medical Center, Utica, NY, p. A475

AIKEN, David, Chief Human Resources Officer, Madigan Army Medical Center, Tacoma, WA, p. A710

AINSLEY, Howard, Chief Operating Officer, Corpus Christi Medical Center Bay Area, Corpus Christi, TX, p. A630

AINSWORTH, Larry K., President and Chief Executive Officer, St. Joseph Hospital, Orange, CA, p. A79

AIRHART, Steven, Chief Executive Officer, Hartgrove Hospital, Chicago, IL, p. A187

AITKEN, Ian, President and Chief Operating Officer, Menninger Clinic, Houston, TX, p. A646

AJAMY, Louis
Vice President and Chief Information Officer, Lenox Hill Hospital, New York, NY, p. A461
Vice President and Chief Information Officer, Manhattan Eye, Ear and Throat Hospital, New York, NY, p. A462

AKDAMAR, Erol R., Chief Executive Officer, South Austin Hospital, Austin, TX, p. A624

AKIN, Rosanne, Chief Administrative Officer, Memorial Hermann Baptist in Orange, Orange, TX, p. A659

AKINS, M.D., Carlton, Medical Director, Massachusetts Hospital School, Canton, MA, p. A316

AL–IBRAHIM, M.D., Muhamed, Executive Chief of Staff, Veterans Affairs Maryland Health Care System–Baltimore Division, Baltimore, MD, p. A305

ALAND, Kent, Chief Executive Officer, Memorial Health Center, Sidney, NE, p. A413

ALBANESE, Joseph
Chief Financial Officer, Veterans Affairs Medical Center, Decatur, GA, p. A160
Chief Fiscal Services, Veterans Affairs Medical Center, Fayetteville, NC, p. A483

ALBARANO, Francis G., Chief Executive Officer, Fayette County Memorial Hospital, Washington Court House, OH, p. A524

ALBERT, James, Director Information Services, Masonic Healthcare Center, Wallingford, CT, p. A117

ALBERTO, Carl M., Vice Prersident Finance, Warren Hospital, Phillipsburg, NJ, p. A434

ALBERTS, Patrick J., Senior Vice President and Chief Operating Officer, Monongahela Valley Hospital, Monongahela, PA, p. A565

ALBERTS, M.D., W Michael, Associate Center Director Clinical Affairs/Chief Medical Officer, H. Lee Moffitt Cancer Center and Research Institute, Tampa, FL, p. A148

ALBERY, Linda, Vice President and Chief Operating Officer, Borgess Medical Center, Kalamazoo, MI, p. A338

ALBIN, James
Regional Vice President and Chief Information Officer, St. Anne Mercy Hospital, Toledo, OH, p. A523
Regional Vice President and Chief Information Officer, St. Charles Mercy Hospital, Oregon, OH, p. A520
Regional Vice President and Chief Information Officer, St. Vincent Mercy Medical Center, Toledo, OH, p. A523

ALBOGEST, Dodie, Controller, Stonewall Jackson Memorial Hospital, Weston, WV, p. A721

ALBRECHT, David, Executive Vice President and Chief Financial Officer, Bellin Memorial Hospital, Green Bay, WI, p. A726

ALBRIGHT, Colleen, Vice President Administration and Human Relations, Sunbury Community Hospital, Sunbury, PA, p. A576

ALBRIGHT, David, Vice President Operations, Abbott Northwestern Hospital, Minneapolis, MN, p. A357

ALBRIGHT, M.D., David, Medical Staff President, Brattleboro Memorial Hospital, Brattleboro, VT, p. A682

ALBRIGHT, Mark, Director Information Services, Platte Valley Medical Center, Brighton, CO, p. A101

ALCALA, Paul
Vice President and Chief Information Officer, NorthBay Medical Center, Fairfield, CA, p. A60
Vice President and Chief Information Officer, Northbay VacaValley Hospital, Vacaville, CA, p. A97

ALDERSON, Pam, Chief Financial Officer, Fountain Valley Regional Hospital and Medical Center, Fountain Valley, CA, p. A60

ALDERTON, Linda, Director Human Resources, Copley Hospital, Morrisville, VT, p. A683

ALDRED, Linda, Senior Vice President, Texas Children's Hospital, Houston, TX, p. A647

ALDRICH, Alan, Chief Financial Officer, Central Montana Medical Center, Lewistown, MT, p. A400

ALDRIDGE, Karen, Director Human Resources, Rehabilitation Institute at Santa Barbara, Santa Barbara, CA, p. A92

ALDRIDGE, Mark, Chief Executive Officer, Wamego City Hospital, Wamego, KS, p. A258

ALEJANDRO, Glorimar, Finance Director, Caribbean Pediatric and Surgery Hospital, San Juan, PR, p. A747

ALEMAN, Dianne, Senior Vice President and Chief Operating Officer, Boca Raton Community Hospital, Boca Raton, FL, p. A124

ALEMAN, Ralph A., Chief Executive Officer, Palmetto General Hospital, Hialeah, FL, p. A131

ALENDER, James P., President and Chief Executive Officer, Howard Regional Health System, Kokomo, IN, p. A220

ALEXANDER, Alan B., Chief Executive Officer, Caverna Memorial Hospital, Horse Cave, KY, p. A266

ALEXANDER, Albert, Chief Human Resources Officer, Halifax Fish Community Health, Daytona Beach, FL, p. A127

ALEXANDER, Dean, Chief Executive Officer, Mainland Medical Center, Texas City, TX, p. A670

ALEXANDER, M.D., Fred, Medical Director, Kaiser Foundation Hospital–West Los Angeles, Los Angeles, CA, p. A71

ALEXANDER, Georgette, Director Human Resources, St. Joseph Health System, Tawas City, MI, p. A346

ALEXANDER, Gordon L., President, University of Minnesota Medical Center, Minneapolis, MN, p. A357

ALEXANDER, M.D., Jack, Chief Medical Officer, Fairview Red Wing Medical Center, Red Wing, MN, p. A360

ALEXANDER, Kenneth E., Administrator, HEALTHSOUTH Rehabilitation Hospital of Baton Rouge, Baton Rouge, LA, p. A277

ALEXANDER, Melvin, Vice President and Chief Financial Officer, Norman Regional Hospital, Norman, OK, p. A534

ALEXANDER, Michael, President and Chief Executive Officer, Candler County Hospital, Metter, GA, p. A166

ALEXANDER, Peter H.
Administrator, St Elizabeth Ann Seton Hospital of Kokomo, Kokomo, IN, p. A220
Administrator, St. Elizabeth Ann Seton Hospital of Carmel, Carmel, IN, p. A212
Administrator, St. Elizabeth Ann Seton Hospital of Indianapolis, Indianapolis, IN, p. A219

ALEXANDER, R. Michael, Senior Vice President and Area Manager, Kaiser Foundation Hospital, San Francisco, CA, p. A89

ALEXANDER, M.D., Richmond, President and Medical Staff, Specialty Hospital of Meridian, Meridian, MS, p. A373

ALEXANDER, M.D., Teresa, President Medical Staff, Starke Memorial Hospital, Knox, IN, p. A220

ALEXANDER, Trudi, Director Human Resources, Jersey Shore Hospital, Jersey Shore, PA, p. A561

ALEXANDER, Victoria A.
Chief Executive Officer, Ojai Valley Community Hospital, Ojai, CA, p. A79
Chief Executive Officer, Steele Memorial Hospital, Salmon, ID, p. A181

ALFARO, M.D., Samuel, Vice President Medical Affairs, St. Joseph Medical Center, Reading, PA, p. A574

ALFORD, Charles, Vice President Financial Services, Heritage Hospital, Tarboro, NC, p. A492

ALFORD, Larry D., Chief Financial Officer, St. Joseph's Mercy Health Center, Hot Springs National Park, AR, p. A45

ALFORD, D.O., Tony
Executive Director of Medical Affairs, Houston Medical Center, Warner Robins, GA, p. A172
Executive Director of Medical Affairs, Perry Hospital, Perry, GA, p. A167

ALFORD, Wendell, Administrator, Madison Parish Hospital, Tallulah, LA, p. A293

ALHAND, Liz, Senior Vice President Finance, Presbyterian Kaseman Hospital, Albuquerque, NM, p. A441

ALLAN, M.D., Christian, Chief Medical Officer, Central Michigan Community Hospital, Mount Pleasant, MI, p. A341

ALLARD, Margaret, Commanding Officer, Naval Hospital, North Charleston, SC, p. A591

ALLATT, M.D., Richard, Medical Director, HEALTHSOUTH Nittany Valley Rehabilitation Hospital, Pleasant Gap, PA, p. A573

ALLBRITTON, Jim, Chief Financial Officer, Lincoln General Hospital, Ruston, LA, p. A292

ALLEE, Al, Chief Executive Officer, Memorial Hospital and Physician Group, Frederick, OK, p. A531

ALLEN, Al, Information Administrator, Community Memorial Hospital, Syracuse, NE, p. A413

ALLEN, Bill, Chief Executive Officer, Rabun County Hospital, Clayton, GA, p. A158

ALLEN, Carol, Chief Financial Officer, Clark Regional Medical Center, Winchester, KY, p. A275

ALLEN, Charlie, President and Chief Executive, Triumph HealthCare, Houston, TX, p. B111

ALLEN, Claudia, Chief Information Officer, St. John Hospital and Medical Center, Detroit, MI, p. A332

ALLEN, Dennis, Chief Financial Officer, Mayo Regional Hospital, Dover–Foxcroft, ME, p. A298

ALLEN, Douglas, Chief Human Resources Officer, Hahnemann University Hospital, Philadelphia, PA, p. A568

ALLEN, M.D., Elms, Senior Vice President Medical Affairs, Forsyth Medical Center, Winston–Salem, NC, p. A494

ALLEN, George, Chief Financial Officer, Catholic Medical Center, Manchester, NH, p. A422

ALLEN, John
President and Chief Executive Officer, Good Samaritan Health Systems, Kearney, NE, p. A408
Chief Information Officer, Memorial Hospital, Fremont, OH, p. A514

ALLEN, Julie, Chief Financial Officer, Allendale County Hospital, Fairfax, SC, p. A587

ALLEN, Kay B., R.N., Administrator, Dubuis Hospital of Shreveport, Shreveport, LA, p. A292

ALLEN, LeeAnn, Director Human Resources, Lake Taylor Transitional Care Hospital, Norfolk, VA, p. A692

ALLEN, Marshall, Chief Financial Officer, Medical Center of Arlington, Arlington, TX, p. A622

ALLEN, Michael, Chief Financial Officer, Winona Health, Winona, MN, p. A365

ALLEN, Pam, Chief Financial Officer, Wamego City Hospital, Wamego, KS, p. A258

ALLEN, Patty, Finance Director, St. Joseph's Regional Medical Center, Milwaukee, WI, p. A731

ALLEN, Peggy, Chief Financial Officer, Carraway Methodist Medical Center, Birmingham, AL, p. A14

ALLEN II, Percy, FACHE, Chief Executive Officer, Bon Secours Baltimore Health System, Baltimore, MD, p. A302

ALLEN, R Keith, Senior Vice President Human Resources, University of Maryland Medical Center, Baltimore, MD, p. A304

ALLEN, M.D., Raymond K., Chief of Medical Staff, Williamsburg Regional Hospital, Kingstree, SC, p. A589

ALLEN, Richard L., President and Chief Executive Officer, Mercy Regional Health Center, New York, KS, p. A252

ALLEN, Robert, Director Communications, Crouse Hospital, Syracuse, NY, p. A473

ALLEN, M.D., Robert, Medical Staff Liaison Officer, Rapid City Regional Hospital System of Care, Rapid City, SD, p. A598

ALLEN, Robert W., Chief Executive Officer, Memorial Hospital of Salem County, Salem, NJ, p. A435

ALLEN, Roger, Director Management Information Systems, McAlester Regional Health Center, McAlester, OK, p. A533

ALLEN, Royce, Director Human Resources, University Medical Center/McFarland Hospital, Lebanon, TN, p. A611

ALLEN, Sam J., Chief Executive Officer, Broadwater Health Center, Townsend, MT, p. A402

ALLEN, Terry, Vice President, Human Resources, Ball Memorial Hospital, Muncie, IN, p. A222

ALLEN, Tim, Vice President Human Resources, United Hospital Center, Clarksburg, WV, p. A715

ALLENSWORTH, M.D., Ed, Medical Director, Craig General Hospital, Vinita, OK, p. A540

ALLEY, USAF, MS, Carl M., Administrator, U. S. Air Force Academy Hospital, USAF Academy, CO, p. A110

ALLEY, David, Chief Financial Officer, Athens Regional Medical Center, Athens, TN, p. A602

ALLEY, John L., Director Finance, Woodlawn Hospital, Rochester, IN, p. A224

ALLIES, Karla, Director Human Resources, Rosebud Health Care Center, Forsyth, MT, p. A398

ALLINSON, Randy, Chief Operating Officer, Central Valley Medical Center, Nephi, UT, p. A677

ALLINSON, Vauna, Director Human Resources, HEALTHSOUTH Rehabilitation Hospital of Utah, Sandy, UT, p. A680

ALLISON, David G., Chief Executive Officer, University Medical Center, Lubbock, TX, p. A654

ALLISON, Della, Chief Financial Officer, Bristow Memorial Hospital, Bristow, OK, p. A528

ALLISON, M.D., E Jackson, Chief of Staff, Veterans Affairs Medical Center, Syracuse, NY, p. A474

ALLISON, Elaine, Director Human Resources, Iredell Memorial Hospital, Statesville, NC, p. A492

ALLISON, Jay, President Medical Staff, Avera St. Anthony's Hospital, O'Neill, NE, p. A410

ALLISON, Joel T., President and Chief Executive Officer, Baylor Health Care System, Dallas, TX, p. B16

ALLISON, Neal, Chief Financial Officer, Doctors Hospital Nelsonville, Nelsonville, OH, p. A519

ALLISON, Shannon, Chief Financial Officer, Trinity Hospital, Erin, TN, p. A606

ALLMAN, Roger J., Chief Executive Officer, King's Daughters' Hospital and Health Services, Madison, IN, p. A221

ALLORE, Gary
Vice President Financial Services, Gerber Memorial Health Services, Fremont, MI, p. A333
Vice President Financial Services, Gerber Memorial Health Services, Fremont, MI, p. A333
Chief Financial Officer, Mercy General Health Partners, Muskegon, MI, p. A341

ALLOWAY, Cindy, R.N., Vice President and Chief Operating Officer, Alegent Health Lakeside Hospital, Omaha, NE, p. A411

ALLOY, William R., Chief Executive Officer, Perry County Memorial Hospital, Perryville, MO, p. A389

ALLRED, Al W., Chief Executive Officer, Wiregrass Medical Center, Geneva, AL, p. A19

ALLRED, M.D., William, Vice President of Medical Affairs, St. John Medical Center, Tulsa, OK, p. A540

ALLVIN, Patricia, Information Specialist, Galena–Stauss Hospital and Healthcare Center, Galena, IL, p. A195

ALLYN, Sue, Vice President Human Resources, Iowa Methodist Medical Center, Des Moines, IA, p. A232

ALMERICO, Tom, Administrator, HEALTHSOUTH Rehabilitation Hospital of Utah, Sandy, UT, p. A680

ALMODOVAR, Gustavo, Finance Director, Hospital De La Concepcion, San German, PR, p. A746

ALSBROOK, Terri, Administrator, HEALTHSOUTH Rehabilitation Hospital, Kingsport, TN, p. A609

ALSEVER, M.D., Robert, Vice President Medical Affairs, Parkview Medical Center, Pueblo, CO, p. A109

ALSHEIMER, Bob, Chief Financial Officer, Veterans Affairs Medical Center, Syracuse, NY, p. A474

ALSTER, M.D., Howard, President, Medical Staff, Carlisle Regional Medical Center, Carlisle, PA, p. A554

ALSTON, Shawanza L., Administrator, Benton Rehabilitation Hospital, Baton Rouge, LA, p. A277

ALTAFULLAH, M.D., Irfan, Chief of Staff, North Memorial Health Care, Robbinsdale, MN, p. A360

ALTEBARMAKIAN, M.D., Varouj, Physician in Chief, Kaiser Foundation Hospital, Fresno, CA, p. A61

ALTMILLER, Steve, President and Chief Executive Officer, San Juan Regional Medical Center, Farmington, NM, p. A442

ALTOE, Ann, Senior Information Systems Director and Security Officer, Alfred I. duPont Hospital for Children, Wilmington, DE, p. A119

ALTON, Aaron, President and Chief Executive Officer, Sisters of Mary of the Presentation Health System, Fargo, ND, p. B99

ALTSCHULER, Steven M., President and Chief Executive Officer, Children's Hospital of Philadelphia, Philadelphia, PA, p. A567

ALTSHULER, Keith, Administrator, Fort Sanders Regional Medical Center, Knoxville, TN, p. A610

ALTSHULER, M.D., Steven, Chief of Staff, Medical Center at Terrell, Terrell, TX, p. A669

ALULI, M.D., N Emmett, Medical Executive Director, Molokai General Hospital, Kaunakakai, HI, p. A175

ALVARADO, Gloria, Associate Director Human Resources, University of California, Davis Medical Center, Sacramento, CA, p. A85

ALVARADO, Rafael
Chief Executive Officer, Hospital Metropolitano San German, San German, PR, p. A746
Chief Executive Officer, Hospital Perea, Mayaguez, PR, p. A745

ALVAREZ, M.D., Faust M., Chief of Staff, Veterans Affairs Montana Healthcare System, Fort Harrison, MT, p. A398

ALVAREZ, Frank D.
President and Chief Executive Officer, TMC HealthCare, Tucson, AZ, p. B108
President and Chief Executive Officer, Tucson Medical Center, Tucson, AZ, p. A38

ALVAREZ, M Raymond, Vice President Ancillary, Barnert Hospital, Paterson, NJ, p. A434

ALVAREZ, M.D., Mike, Chief Medical Officer, Dauterive Hospital, New Iberia, LA, p. A288

ALVAREZ, Rafael Garcia, Executive Director, State Psychiatric Hospital, San Juan, PR, p. A748

ALVES, Richard, Chief Financial Officer, Kaiser Foundation Hospital, Fresno, CA, p. A61

ALVEY, Raymond, Chief Financial Officer, Saint Louis University Hospital, Saint Louis, MO, p. A391

ALWINE, Steven, Controller, HEALTHSOUTH Nittany Valley Rehabilitation Hospital, Pleasant Gap, PA, p. A573

AMAR, Jr, Eugene, Chief Financial Officer, Kohala Hospital, Kohala, HI, p. A175

AMARAL, Joseph F., M.D., President and Chief Executive Officer, Rhode Island Hospital, Providence, RI, p. A582

AMARIA, M.D., Yazdi, Medical Staff President, Sturgis Hospital, Sturgis, MI, p. A346

AMAROL, Michael, Chief, Directorate of Medical Administration, Walter Reed Army Medical Center, Washington, DC, p. A122

AMATO, Jerry
Administrator, HEALTHSOUTH Hospital of Tenaya, Las Vegas, NV, p. A416
Chief Operating Officer and Administrator, HEALTHSOUTH Hospital of Tenaya, Las Vegas, NV, p. A416

AMATO, Joe, Chief Financial Officer, University Hospitals and Clinics, University of Mississippi Medical Center, Jackson, MS, p. A371

AMBERG, Ed, Administrator, Montana State Hospital, Warm Springs, MT, p. A402

AMBERSON, Rose, Vice President Human Resources, Boca Raton Community Hospital, Boca Raton, FL, p. A124

AMBROSIANI, Craig, Vice President of Finance, Yukon–Kuskokwim Delta Regional Hospital, Bethel, AK, p. A26

AMBROSINI, M.D., Virginia, Area Medical Director, Kaiser Foundation Hospital, Los Angeles, CA, p. A70

AMBROSIUS, Mark R., Administrator, St. Luke's Medical Center, Milwaukee, WI, p. A732

AMEEN, David J., President and Chief Executive Officer, St. Charles Mercy Hospital, Oregon, OH, p. A520

AMEER, Adil M., Chief Executive Officer, Health Quest, Poughkeepsie, NY, p. B56

AMENT, Rick, President and Chief Executive Officer, LakeView Community Hospital, Paw Paw, MI, p. A342

AMERSON, Jeff, Director Information System, West Florida Hospital, Pensacola, FL, p. A143

AMES, Craig M., President and Chief Operating Officer, BryanLGH Medical Center, Lincoln, NE, p. A408

AMES, Elise, Director Information Services, Cooley Dickinson Hospital, Northampton, MA, p. A321

AMEY, Mark, Chief Information Officer, White Memorial Medical Center, Los Angeles, CA, p. A73

AMIGO, D.O., Isidro, Chief of Staff, Selby General Hospital, Marietta, OH, p. A517

AMIGONE, Daniel K., Director, Dr. J. Corrigan Mental Health Center, Fall River, MA, p. A317

AMMON, Donald R., President and Chief Executive Officer, Adventist Health, Roseville, CA, p. B4

AMODO, Mitch, Executive Vice President and Chief Financial Officer, Orange Regional Medical Center, Middletown, NY, p. A457

AMON, R.N., Jeannine F., Vice President and Chief Operating Officer, Riverview Healthcare Association, Crookston, MN, p. A352

AMON, Robert, Interim Chief Financial Officer, Graduate Hospital, Philadelphia, PA, p. A568

AMOROSE, Carl, Associate Vice President, Finance, Norton Hospital, Louisville, KY, p. A270

AMOROSO, Henry, President and Chief Executive Officer, Cathedral Healthcare System, Inc., Newark, NJ, p. B22

AMOS, Bob, Director Fiscal Services, Genesis Medical Center, DeWitt, De Witt, IA, p. A232

AMOS, James L., President, Margaret Mary Community Hospital, Batesville, IN, p. A211

AMPARAN, Oscar, President, Arlington Memorial Hospital, Arlington, TX, p. A622

AMROM, M.D., George, Vice President Medical Affairs, Hahnemann University Hospital, Philadelphia, PA, p. A568

AMSTUTZ, Terry L., CHE,
Chief Executive Officer, Magnolia Hospital, Magnolia, AR, p. A47
Administrator, Morrison Community Hospital, Morrison, IL, p. A201

AMUNDSON, David H.
Chief Financial Officer, Miller–Dwan Medical Center, Duluth, MN, p. A352
Chief Financial Officer, St. Mary's Medical Center, Duluth, MN, p. A352

AMYX, Maleigha, Chief Informatio Officer, Rockcastle Hospital and Respiratory Care Center, Mount Vernon, KY, p. A272

ANAEBONAM, Nneka, Administrator, Isham Health Center, Andover, MA, p. A312

ANASTASI, Frank, Director Finance, Pennsylvania Hospital, Philadelphia, PA, p. A569

ANASTASIO, Lance W., President, Winter Haven Hospital, Winter Haven, FL, p. A151

ANAYA Sr, Michael A., FACHE, Chief Executive Officer, Colorado Plains Medical Center, Fort Morgan, CO, p. A105

ANCELL, Charles D., President, Missouri Delta Medical Center, Sikeston, MO, p. A393

ANCHO, Kathy, Administrator, Battle Mountain General Hospital, Battle Mountain, NV, p. A415

ANDERLE, Wolfgang, Chief Information Officer, Advocate Good Shepherd Hospital, Barrington, IL, p. A184

ANDERMAN, Steven
Senior Vice President and Chief Operating Officer, Bronx–Lebanon Hospital Center, New York, NY, p. A458
Senior Vice President and Chief Operating Officer, Bronx–Lebanon Hospital Center, New York, NY, p. A458

ANDERS, Jr, James M., Administrator and Chief Operating Officer, Kennedy Krieger Institute, Baltimore, MD, p. A303

ANDERS, Robert, Chief Financial Officer, Ouachita Medical Center, Camden, AR, p. A41

ANDERSEN, David, President and Chief Executive Officer, Saratoga Hospital, Saratoga Springs, NY, p. A472

ANDERSEN, Edward, President and Chief Executive Officer, CGH Medical Center, Sterling, IL, p. A209

ANDERSEN, Mark, Senior Vice President, Information Systems and Chief Information Officer, Yale–New Haven Hospital, New Haven, CT, p. A115

ANDERSEN, Susan, Chief Financial Officer, French Hospital Medical Center, San Luis Obispo, CA, p. A91

ANDERSON, Allyson, Vice President and Administrator, Legacy Meridian Park Hospital, Tualatin, OR, p. A550

ANDERSON Jr, Andrew E., Administrator, North Texas Medical Center, Gainesville, TX, p. A641

ANDERSON, Angela
Human Resources Manager, Murray County Memorial Hospital, Slayton, MN, p. A363
Human Resources Manager, Tracy Area Medical Services, Tracy, MN, p. A364
Human Resources Manager, Westbrook Health Center, Westbrook, MN, p. A365

ANDERSON, Beth, Administrator, University of South Alabama Medical Center, Mobile, AL, p. A21

ANDERSON, Brad, Chief Financial Officer, Cloquet Community Memorial Hospital, Cloquet, MN, p. A351

ANDERSON, Bruce, Vice President Fiscal Services, United Medical Center, Cheyenne, WY, p. A739

ANDERSON, Cecelia A., Clinical Director, Northern Navajo Medical Center, Shiprock, NM, p. A445

ANDERSON, Christopher E., Chief Executive Officer, Select Specialty Hospital–Tricities, Bristol, TN, p. A602

ANDERSON, Craig, Chief Information Management, Madigan Army Medical Center, Tacoma, WA, p. A710

ANDERSON, Daniel K., President, Fairview Lakes Regional Health Care, Wyoming, MN, p. A365

ANDERSON, M.D., Danny, Chief of Staff, Sonora Regional Medical Center, Sonora, CA, p. A94

ANDERSON, Dave, Vice President Operations, Union Regional Medical Center, Monroe, NC, p. A487

ANDERSON, David, Vice President Human Resources, WellStar Kennestone Hospital, Marietta, GA, p. A165

ANDERSON, David E., Ph.D., Chief Executive Officer, Sierra Tucson, Tucson, AZ, p. A38

ANDERSON, David S., FACHE, Chief Executive Officer, Banner Lassen Medical Center, Susanville, CA, p. A95

ANDERSON, Donald, Vice President Human Resources, Lester E. Cox Medical Centers, Springfield, MO, p. A394

ANDERSON, Donna, Director of Human Resources, HEALTHSOUTH Sea Pines Rehabilitation Hospital, Melbourne, FL, p. A136

ANDERSON, M.D., Doug, President Medical Staff, Saint Luke's South Hospital, Overland Park, KS, p. A255

ANDERSON, Edward, Chief Financial Officer, Johnson Regional Medical Center, Clarksville, AR, p. A41

ANDERSON, Harold, Vice President Human Resources, St. Vincent Healthcare, Billings, MT, p. A396

ANDERSON, Harold E., Chief Executive Officer, Moses Taylor Hospital, Scranton, PA, p. A575

ANDERSON, J. Bryant, Administrator and Chief Executive Officer, Hospital District Number Six of Harper County, Anthony, KS, p. A244

ANDERSON, James M., President and Chief Executive Officer, Children's Hospital Medical Center, Cincinnati, OH, p. A506

ANDERSON, Jana, Director Information Services, Holy Rosary Healthcare, Miles City, MT, p. A400

ANDERSON, JaNelle, Director, Mary Greeley Medical Center, Ames, IA, p. A228

ANDERSON, Jason, Chief Financial Officer, Mackinac Straits Hospital and Health Center, Saint Ignace, MI, p. A344

ANDERSON, Jeff, Director Information Services, Pampa Regional Medical Center, Pampa, TX, p. A659

ANDERSON, Jennifer, Director, Weirton Medical Center, Weirton, WV, p. A720

ANDERSON, M.D., Jerome, President Medical Staff, McDonough District Hospital, Macomb, IL, p. A200

ANDERSON, Jimmy, Director Information Systems, Great Plains Regional Medical Center, North Platte, NE, p. A410

ANDERSON, Joann, Chief Executive Officer, Pikeville Medical Center, Pikeville, KY, p. A273

ANDERSON, John D., Administrator, Marshall Medical Center South, Boaz, AL, p. A16

ANDERSON, Katherine, Interim President, Brattleboro Memorial Hospital, Brattleboro, VT, p. A682

ANDERSON, M.D., Ken, Chief of Staff, University Medical Center/McFarland Hospital, Lebanon, TN, p. A611

ANDERSON, M.D., Kent, Chief of Staff, St. Joseph Regional Medical Center, Lewiston, ID, p. A180

ANDERSON, FACHE, Kim, Chief Operating Officer, Mountain View Hospital, Payson, UT, p. A678

ANDERSON, M.D., Leigh, Chief of Staff, Veterans Affairs Eastern Colorado Health Care System, Denver, CO, p. A104

ANDERSON, Lex S., Executive Vice President, St. John Medical Center, Tulsa, OK, p. A540

ANDERSON, Loren J.
Executive Vice President, Aurora Lakeland Medical Center, Elkhorn, WI, p. A725
Executive Vice President, Memorial Hospital Corporation of Burlington, Burlington, WI, p. A724

ANDERSON, MC, USN, M H., Executive Officer, Naval Hospital, Cherry Point, NC, p. A480

ANDERSON, M.D., Malcolm, Acting Chief of Staff, Veterans Affairs Medical Center, Fresno, CA, p. A62

ANDERSON, Mark, Chief Financial Officer, Memorial Hospital, Martinsville, VA, p. A691

ANDERSON, Matthew, Administrator, U. S. Public Health Service Indian Hospital, Mescalero, NM, p. A444

ANDERSON, Melinda, Chief Executive Officer, LAC–Olive View–UCLA Medical Center, Los Angeles, CA, p. A71

ANDERSON, Michael
Commanding Officer, Naval Hospital, Great Lakes, IL, p. A195
Chief Financial Officer, Benewah Community Hospital, Saint Maries, ID, p. A181
Vice President Finance, Prairie Lakes Healthcare System, Watertown, SD, p. A600

ANDERSON, Monica, Director Information Systems, Newton–Wellesley Hospital, Newton Lower Falls, MA, p. A321

ANDERSON, Noble, Director of Fin Services, Rice Medical Center, Eagle Lake, TX, p. A636

ANDERSON, Nora, Director, Human Resources, Presbyterian–St. Luke's Medical Center, Denver, CO, p. A104

ANDERSON, Randal, Chief Financial Officer, Wallowa Memorial Hospital, Enterprise, OR, p. A543

ANDERSON, Randy, Administrator and Chief Executive Officer, Flandreau Medical Center/Avera Health, Flandreau, SD, p. A595

ANDERSON, Rhonda, Chief Financial Officer, St. Agnes HealthCare, Baltimore, MD, p. A304

ANDERSON, Richard A., President and Chief Executive Officer, St. Luke's Hospital – Bethlehem Campus, Bethlehem, PA, p. A553

ANDERSON, Ron J., M.D., President and Chief Executive Officer, Parkland Health & Hospital System, Dallas, TX, p. A633

ANDERSON, Sandra, Chief Financial Officer, De Soto Regional Health System, Mansfield, LA, p. A286

ANDERSON, Sandra L., President, St. Clare Hospital and Health Services, Baraboo, WI, p. A723

ANDERSON, Scott R., Chief Executive Officer, North Memorial Health Care, Robbinsdale, MN, p. A360

ANDERSON, Sharla, Administrator, HEALTHSOUTH Rehabilitation Hospital–Tyler, Tyler, TX, p. A671

ANDERSON, Shawn, Chief Operating Officer, Cary Medical Center, Caribou, ME, p. A298

ANDERSON, Steven M., CHE, Chief Executive Officer, Lakeview Hospital, Bountiful, UT, p. A676

ANDERSON, Ted, Chief Financial Officer, Fayette County Hospital, Vandalia, IL, p. A209

ANDERSON, Thomas E., Administrator, St. Mary–Corwin Medical Center, Pueblo, CO, p. A109

ANDERSON, Traci, Controller, Memorial Hospital, Seminole, TX, p. A666

ANDERSON, M.D., William, Chief of Staff, South Coast Medical Center, Laguna Beach, CA, p. A66

ANDERSON, William H., President, Helen Keller Hospital, Sheffield, AL, p. A24

ANDERSSON, M.D., Ph, Gunnar B J, Senior Vice President Medical Affairs, Rush University Medical Center, Chicago, IL, p. A189

ANDERTON, Beth, Director Human Resources, Ferrell Hospital, Eldorado, IL, p. A193

ANDRADA, Sally, Chief Information Officer, Los Alamitos Medical Center, Los Alamitos, CA, p. A69

ANDRADE, Don, Area Director Information Technology, HEALTHSOUTH Braintree Rehabilitation Hospital, Braintree, MA, p. A315

ANDRES, M.D., Leonidas, Chief of Staff, Bayside Community Hospital, Anahuac, TX, p. A621

ANDRESEN, Daniel, Director Information Services, Conroe Regional Medical Center, Conroe, TX, p. A630

ANDREW, Sarah H., Ph.D., Administrator, Choate Mental Health Center, Anna, IL, p. A183

ANDREWS, Lawrence, Chief Fiscal Services, Veterans Affairs Medical Center, Dayton, OH, p. A512

ANDREWS, Mike
Assistant Administrator and Chief Operating Officer, Oktibbeha County Hospital, Starkville, MS, p. A376
Assistant Administrator and Chief Operating Officer, Oktibbeha County Hospital, Starkville, MS, p. A376

ANDREWS, Paul, Chief Executive Officer, Ten Broeck Hospital Jacksonville, Jacksonville, FL, p. A133

ANDREWS, Steve, Chief Financial Officer, Three Rivers Health, Three Rivers, MI, p. A346

ANDREWS, William J., President, Licking Memorial Hospital, Newark, OH, p. A519

ANDRUS, Michael G., Administrator and Chief Executive Officer, Franklin County Medical Center, Preston, ID, p. A181

ANDRUS, Terry W., President, East Alabama Medical Center, Opelika, AL, p. A23

ANEN, Trish, Vice President, Operations, Edward Hospital, Naperville, IL, p. A202

ANFINSON, Julie, Director Human Resources, Mercy Medical Center–Sioux City, Sioux City, IA, p. A241

ANGELI, D.O., Daniel, Vice President Medical Affairs, Port Huron Hospital, Port Huron, MI, p. A343

ANGELICO, Mike, Director Information Systems, Metropolitan Methodist Hospital, San Antonio, TX, p. A664

ANGELO, M.D., C K., Chief Medical Staff, Prevost Memorial Hospital, Donaldsonville, LA, p. A280

ANGELO, Gregory, Chief Fiscal Program, Veterans Affairs Medical Center, New York, NY, p. A466

ANGELO, Ralph R., Associate Director for Operations, Veterans Affairs Medical Center, Augusta, GA, p. A155

ANGERMEIER, Ingo, FACHE,
President and Chief Executive Officer, Spartanburg Regional Healthcare System, Spartanburg, SC, p. B101
President and Chief Executive Officer, Spartanburg Regional Medical Center, Spartanburg, SC, p. A592

ANGIUS, Barbara, Chief Financial Officer, Veterans Affairs San Diego Healthcare System, San Diego, CA, p. A88

ANGLE, Gregory R., Chief Executive Officer, Carondelet St. Mary's Hospital–Tucson, Tucson, AZ, p. A37

ANGLE, Toni, Administrator, Fresno Surgery Center–The Hospital for Surgery, Fresno, CA, p. A61

ANGLIN, Gail, Human Resources Manager, Baptist Memorial Hospital–Lauderdale, Ripley, TN, p. A617

ANGLIN, Jason, Chief Executive Officer, Atoka Memorial Hospital, Atoka, OK, p. A527

ANGLIN, Marilyn, Director of Human Resources, BJC Medical Center, Commerce, GA, p. A159

ANGUEIRA, Carlos, Deputy Commander Clinical Services, Brooke Army Medical Center, Fort Sam Houston, TX, p. A638

ANGUIANO, M.D., Francisco, Chief of Staff, Sharp Chula Vista Medical Center, Chula Vista, CA, p. A57

ANKERSEN, Susan
Manager Information Services, University of South Alabama Medical Center, Mobile, AL, p. A21
Manager Information Services, USA Children's and Women's Hospital, Mobile, AL, p. A21

ANMUTH, M.D., Craig, Medical Director, Bacharach Institute for Rehabilitation, Pomona, NJ, p. A435

ANNESSER, Sue
Director Information Technology, Freeman Health System, Joplin, MO, p. A383
Director Information Systems, Freeman Neosho Hospital, Neosho, MO, p. A388

ANNIS, Donald D., Service Unit Director, U. S. Public Health Service Indian Hospital, Eagle Butte, SD, p. A595

ANNIS, Donald E., Chief Executive Officer, Good Hope Hospital, Erwin, NC, p. A482

ANNIS, Rick, Senior Vice President and Chief Financial Officer, St. Joseph's Regional Medical Center, Paterson, NJ, p. A434

ANOTHAYANONTHA, Aaron, Chief Executive Officer, Select Specialty Hospital–Jackson, Jackson, MS, p. A371

ANSARI, M.D., Asif, Chief Medical Staff, Northern Maine Medical Center, Fort Kent, ME, p. A298

ANSEDE, Scott, Chief Operating Officer, Central Carolina Hospital, Sanford, NC, p. A491

ANSELMI, Robert, Director Environment of Care, Veterans Affairs Medical Center, Cheyenne, WY, p. A739

ANSORGE, John, Chief Financial Officer, Ephraim McDowell Regional Medical Center, Danville, KY, p. A263

ANTHONY, Anne G., Administrator and Chief Executive Officer, Willow Crest Hospital, Miami, OK, p. A533

ANTHONY, Jean, Chief Operating Officer, Hills and Dales General Hospital, Cass City, MI, p. A329

ANTHONY, Paula
Vice President Information Sevices, East Texas Medical Center Pittsburg, Pittsburg, TX, p. A660
Vice President Information Sevices, East Texas Medical Center Tyler, Tyler, TX, p. A671

ANTINELLI, Mark, Human Resources Manager, Veterans Affairs Medical Center, Syracuse, NY, p. A474

ANTON, III, M.D., Manuel P., Senior Vice President and Medical Director, Mercy Hospital, Miami, FL, p. A137

ANTONSON, Pete, Chief Executive Officer, Northwood Deaconess Health Center, Northwood, ND, p. A500

ANTONYUK, Ivan, Director Information Technology, Amsterdam Memorial Hospital, Amsterdam, NY, p. A446

ANTTZAK, Kenneth, Vice President, St. Mary Mercy Hospital, Livonia, MI, p. A339

ANTWINE, Brenda M., Administrator, HEALTHSOUTH Rehabilitation Hospital, Memphis, TN, p. A613

ANZEVENO, Jim, Chief Information Officer, Faulkner Hospital, Boston, MA, p. A313

APODACA, Mark, Vice President Operations, Focus by–the–Sea, Saint Simons Island, GA, p. A168

APONTE, Miguel, Supervisor Management Information Systems, Wilma N. Vazquez Medical Center, Vega Baja, PR, p. A748

APPEL, G. Robert, Chief Executive Officer, Mason General Hospital, Shelton, WA, p. A709

APPELBAUM, Fred R., M.D., Executive Director, Seattle Cancer Care Alliance, Seattle, WA, p. A708

APPLE, Donald L., Chief Financial Officer, Saint John's Health System, Anderson, IN, p. A211

APPLEBAUM, Jon D., Chief Executive Officer, City Hospital, Martinsburg, WV, p. A717

APPLETON, Karl, Assistant Administrator and Chief Financial Officer, St. Vincent Hospital, Green Bay, WI, p. A726

APPLEWOOD, David, Chief Financial Officer and Compliance Officer, Morgan County War Memorial Hospital, Berkeley Springs, WV, p. A713

AQUILANTE, Joe, Vice President Finance, PBI Regional Medical Center, Passaic, NJ, p. A434

AQUINO, M.D., Adelo, Chief of Staff, North Sunflower Medical Center, Ruleville, MS, p. A375

ARANDA, Dan, Chief Executive Officer, Glades General Hospital, Belle Glade, FL, p. A123

ARANIO, S Lani, Regional Human Resources Director, Kauai Veterans Memorial Hospital, Waimea, HI, p. A176

ARANOW, Meg, Chief Information Officer, Boston Medical Center, Boston, MA, p. A313

ARATA, Nancy, Chief Financial Officer, Laguna Honda Hospital and Rehabilitation Center, San Francisco, CA, p. A89

ARBAUGH, Cindy, Chief Executive Officer, Nebraska Orthopaedic Hospital, Omaha, NE, p. A411

ARBAUGH, Roanie, Director Human Resources, Grant Memorial Hospital, Petersburg, WV, p. A719

ARBOGAST, M.D., Richard, Medical Director, McKay–Dee Hospital Center, Ogden, UT, p. A678

ARBONEAUX, Jane, Chief Financial Officer, Prevost Memorial Hospital, Donaldsonville, LA, p. A280

ARBONEAUX, Wayne M., Administrator, Assumption Community Hospital, Napoleonville, LA, p. A288

ARBOUR, Doug, Assistant Administrator, River West Medical Center, Plaquemine, LA, p. A291

ARBUCKLE, Barry S., Ph.D., President and Chief Executive Officer, Memorial Health Services, Long Beach, CA, p. B73

ARCANGELI, M.D., Steven, Chief of Staff, Stonewall Jackson Hospital, Lexington, VA, p. A690

ARCENEAUX, R.N., Susan, Information Technology Coordinator, Leonard J. Chabert Medical Center, Houma, LA, p. A282

ARCH, John K., Administrator, Boys Town National Research Hospital, Omaha, NE, p. A411

ARCHAMBEAULT, Shirley, Chief Information Officer, Medical Center of Lewisville, Lewisville, TX, p. A653

ARCHBELL, Larry J., Chief Executive Officer, Sun Coast Hospital, Largo, FL, p. A135

ARCHER, David, Director, Information Systems, Centennial Medical Center at Ashland City, Ashland City, TN, p. A602

ARCHER, David L., Chief Executive Officer, Saint Francis Hospital, Memphis, TN, p. A613

ARCHER, Kenneth W., Chief Executive Officer, Ortonville Area Health Services, Ortonville, MN, p. A359

ARCHER, Lorne J., Vice President finance and Chief Financial Officer, Atchison Hospital, Atchison, KS, p. A244

ARCHER, Martha, Director Human Resources, St. Francis Hospital and Health Services, Maryville, MO, p. A387

ARCHER, Stuart, Administrator, Louisiana Extended CAre Hospital of Lafayette, Lafayette, LA, p. A283

ARCHIBALD, Colin, Chief Information Officer, Naval Hospital, Camp Pendleton, CA, p. A56

ARCHIE, M.D., Thomas, Chief of Staff, Seneca Healthcare District, Chester, CA, p. A56

ARCIDI, Alfred J., M.D.,
Senior Vice President, Whittier Rehabilitation Hospital, Haverhill, MA, p. A318
Senior Vice President, Whittier Rehabilitation Hospital, Westborough, MA, p. A325

ARDABELL, R.N., Toni R., Chief Operating Officer, Inova Fairfax Hospital, Falls Church, VA, p. A687

ARELLANO, M.D., Andres, Chief of Staff, Oak Valley District Hospital, Oakdale, CA, p. A78

AREND SINCLAIR, Deb, Human Resource Director, DeKalb Memorial Hospital, Auburn, IN, p. A211

ARGYS, Dick, Executive Vice President and Chief Operating Officer, Women and Infants Hospital of Rhode Island, Providence, RI, p. A582

ARISMENDI, Christopher, M.D., Chief Executive Officer, Dameron Hospital, Stockton, CA, p. A94

ARIZPE, Robert C., Superintendent, San Antonio State Hospital, San Antonio, TX, p. A665

ARKENS, James, Human Resource Director, Holy Cross Hospital, Taos, NM, p. A445

ARMADA, Anthony A., President and Chief Executive Officer, Henry Ford Hospital, Detroit, MI, p. A331

ARMATO, Carl, President, Presbyterian Hospital, Charlotte, NC, p. A480

ARMICA, M.D., Michael, Vice President, Allied Services Rehabilitation Hospital, Scranton, PA, p. A575

ARMINGTON, Dennis, Chief Executive Officer, Rehabilitation Hospital of Indiana, Indianapolis, IN, p. A218

ARMOUR, John, Chief Financial Officer, East Houston Regional Medical Center, Houston, TX, p. A645

ARMSTRONG, Anthony W., Chief Executive Officer and President, Muskogee Regional Medical Center, Muskogee, OK, p. A534

ARMSTRONG, MC, USN, C R., Director Outpatient Care, Naval Hospital, Cherry Point, NC, p. A480

ARMSTRONG, Dale, Chief Executive Officer, Central Carolina Hospital, Sanford, NC, p. A491

ARMSTRONG, Gary
Executive Vice President, Methodist Rehabilitation Center, Jackson, MS, p. A370
Executive Vice President, Methodist Rehabilitation Center, Jackson, MS, p. A370

ARMSTRONG, Jeremy, Administrator, Wagner Community Memorial Hospital, Wagner, SD, p. A600

ARMSTRONG, Justin, Chief Information Officer, HEALTHSOUTH Hospital of Pittsburgh, Monroeville, PA, p. A565

ARMSTRONG, Kim, Chief Financial Officer, Windom Area Hospital, Windom, MN, p. A365

ARMSTRONG, Marcus, Director Finance, Sutter Center for Psychiatry, Sacramento, CA, p. A85

ARMSTRONG, M.D., Richard, Chief of Staff, Helen Newberry Joy Hospital, Newberry, MI, p. A341

ARMSTRONG, Robert, Senior Vice President and Chief Operating Officer, Lima Memorial Health System, Lima, OH, p. A516

ARMSTRONG, Sandra, Vice Chancellor Information Technology, University of Connecticut Health Center, John Dempsey Hospital, Farmington, CT, p. A113

ARMSTRONG, William C., Vice President and Chief Financial Officer, St. Francis Hospital, Roslyn, NY, p. A471

ARNDELL, Scott, Chief Financial Officer, Twin Lakes Regional Medical Center, Leitchfield, KY, p. A267

ARNETT, Charlene, FACHE, Chief Executive Officer, Texas West Oaks Hospital, Houston, TX, p. A648

ARNETT, E Stuart
  Regional Vice President Finance, Aurora Lakeland Medical Center, Elkhorn, WI, p. A725
  Vice President Finance and Chief Financial Officer, Memorial Hospital Corporation of Burlington, Burlington, WI, p. A724

ARNETT, Gayle, Vice President and Chief Financial Officer, Susan B. Allen Memorial Hospital, El Dorado, KS, p. A246

ARNETT, Randal M., President and Chief Executive Officer, Southern Ohio Medical Center, Portsmouth, OH, p. A521

ARNETT, Stuart, Vice President of Finance, Aurora Medical Center, Kenosha, WI, p. A727

ARNETTE, Mary F., Chief Financial Officer, Cannon Memorial Hospital, Pickens, SC, p. A591

ARNO, Michael J., Chief Executive Officer, Pasco Regional Medical Center, Dade City, FL, p. A126

ARNOLD, Bobby
  Vice President and Chief Financial Officer, Jackson–Madison County General Hospital, Jackson, TN, p. A608
  Vice President and Chief Financial Officer, Pathways of Tennessee, Jackson, TN, p. A608

ARNOLD, Douglas, Chief Executive Officer, Northwest Mississippi Regional Medical Center, Clarksdale, MS, p. A367

ARNOLD, Kreg, Director, Human Resources, Hendersonville Medical Center, Hendersonville, TN, p. A607

ARNOLD, Nancy, R.N., Director, John J. Pershing Veterans Affairs Medical Center, Poplar Bluff, MO, p. A389

ARNOLD, Sandi, Director Human Resources, Mercy Medical Center, Canton, OH, p. A505

ARNOLD, Sherry, Risk Management, Schoolcraft Memorial Hospital, Manistique, MI, p. A340

AROCHO, Jacqueline, Administrator, HEALTHSOUTH Rehabilitation Hospital, Miami, FL, p. A137

ARONZON, Daniel Z., M.D., Acting President and Chief Executive Officer, Vassar Brothers Medical Center, Poughkeepsie, NY, p. A470

ARORA, Pamela, Chief Information Officer, UMass Memorial Medical Center, Worcester, MA, p. A326

AROSE, David, Director Management Information Systems, Greene Memorial Hospital, Xenia, OH, p. A525

ARP, James, Chief Executive Officer, Providence Hood River Memorial Hospital, Hood River, OR, p. A544

ARPIN, Donna J., Chief Nursing Officer and Chief Operating Officer, Metropolitan Methodist Hospital, San Antonio, TX, p. A664

ARRAGE, M.D., Antoine A., Director Medical Services, Lake Taylor Transitional Care Hospital, Norfolk, VA, p. A692

ARRIETT, David E., Assistant Administrator, Blount Memorial Hospital, Maryville, TN, p. A612

ARRINGTON, Gary, Director Human Resources, Haywood Regional Medical Center, Clyde, NC, p. A480

ARRIOLA, Buddy, Information Services Manager, Carrier Clinic, Belle Mead, NJ, p. A425

ARROWOOD, Alvin C., Director Information Systems, R. J. Reynolds–Patrick County Memorial Hospital, Stuart, VA, p. A697

ARROYO, Luis, Chief Financial Officer, Hospital San Pablo Del Este, Fajardo, PR, p. A745

ARROYO–DIAZ, M.D., Richard, Chief of Staff, Memorial Medical Center, Port Lavaca, TX, p. A661

ARSENAULT, Donna, Manager Human Resources, Mary Lane Hospital, Ware, MA, p. A324

ARSENAULT, Lisa, Human Resources Director, Millinocket Regional Hospital, Millinocket, ME, p. A299

ARSENEAU, Dan, Vice President Human Resources, Porter Medical Center, Middlebury, VT, p. A682

ART, Steve, Senior Vice President and Chief Information Officer, Lutheran Medical Center, New York, NY, p. A461

ARTENSTEIN, Andrew, Physician in Chief, Medicine, Memorial Hospital of Rhode Island, Pawtucket, RI, p. A581

ARTHUR, Donald C., USN, Commander, National Naval Medical Center, Bethesda, MD, p. A305

ARTHUR, Sarah, Director Human Resources, HEALTHSOUTH Rehabilitation Hospital of York, York, PA, p. A580

ARVON, Christina, Acting Administrator and Chief Executive Officer, Eye and Ear Clinic of Charleston, Charleston, WV, p. A714

ASAY, Grant
  Chief Executive Officer, Select Specialty Hospital–Ann Arbor, Ypsilanti, MI, p. A348
  Chief Executive Officer, Select Specialty Hospital–Flint, Flint, MI, p. A333

ASBECK, Lynn, Business Office Manager, Missouri River Medical Center, Fort Benton, MT, p. A398

ASBELL, George
  Interim President, Grandview Medical Center, Jasper, TN, p. A608
  Interim President, River Park Hospital, McMinnville, TN, p. A612

ASCHI, D.O., Philip C., Chief of Staff, Clinton Memorial Hospital, Wilmington, OH, p. A525

ASCHOFF, Jodi, Chief Financial Officer, Osmond General Hospital, Osmond, NE, p. A412

ASH, Beverly, Administrator, Stroud Regional Medical Center, Stroud, OK, p. A538

ASH, M.D., Eric, Chief of Staff, Dallas County Hospital, Perry, IA, p. A240

ASH, Richard M.
  Chief Executive Officer, Conejos County Hospital, La Jara, CO, p. A107
  Chief Executive Officer, Conejos County Hospital, La Jara, CO, p. A107

ASH, Sharon, Vice President Finance, St. John's Hospital–Berryville, Berryville, AR, p. A40

ASHAMALLA, M.D., Medhat, Vice President Medical Affairs, Mercy Memorial Hospital System, Monroe, MI, p. A340

ASHBAUGH, James L., Chief Executive Officer, Long Term Hospital of Tuscaloosa, Tuscaloosa, AL, p. A24

ASHBRIDGE, Donna M., Chief Executive Officer, Danville State Hospital, Danville, PA, p. A556

ASHBY, Pamela, Associate Vice President, Human Resources, Union Memorial Hospital, Baltimore, MD, p. A304

ASHCOM, Thomas L., Ph.D., Chief Executive Officer, Kansas Heart Hospital, Wichita, KS, p. A259

ASHDOWN, Jan, Chief Medical Officer, Brigham City Community Hospital, Brigham City, UT, p. A676

ASHENFELTER, Kathy, Chief Financial Officer, Swedish Medical Center, Englewood, CO, p. A105

ASHIN, Jeffrey A., Interim President and Chief Executive Officer, Mercy Hospital Fairfield, Fairfield, OH, p. A513

ASHKIN, David, M.D., Medical Executive Director, A. G. Holley State Hospital, Lantana, FL, p. A134

ASHLEY, Dennis, Vice President Human Resources, Sound Shore Medical Center of Westchester, New Rochelle, NY, p. A458

ASHLEY, Kent, Chief Executive Officer, LifeCare Hospitals of Plano, Plano, TX, p. A661

ASHLEY, Vincent, Chief Executive Officer, Cibola General Hospital, Grants, NM, p. A443

ASHMADPOUR, M.D., Saeid, Chief of Staff, Keefe Memorial Hospital, Cheyenne Wells, CO, p. A102

ASHTON, Becky, Administrator, Herrin Hospital, Herrin, IL, p. A196

ASHTON, Marty, Chief Information Officer, Star Valley Medical Center, Afton, WY, p. A739

ASHWORTH, Ronald B., Chief Executive Officer, Sisters of Mercy Health System, Chesterfield, MO, p. B100

ASKEY, Raymond C., Vice President Fiscal Services, Nason Hospital, Roaring Spring, PA, p. A574

ASKINAZI, Murray, Vice President Finance, Lawrence Hospital Center, Bronxville, NY, p. A448

ASPAAS, Ken, Chief Medical Officer, Sioux Valley Hospital University Medical Center, Sioux Falls, SD, p. A599

ASPLING, Deborah, Vice President and Chief Operating Officer, Lodi Memorial Hospital, Lodi, CA, p. A67

ASTACIO, Benjamin, Director Human Resources, Bella Vista Hospital, Mayaguez, PR, p. A745

ASUNCION, Flora, Area Finance Officer, Kaiser Foundation Hospital – Santa Teresa, San Jose, CA, p. A90

ATCHLEY, Mark, Vice President and Chief Financial Officer, Medical Center of Plano, Plano, TX, p. A661

ATCITTY, Josie, Finance Officer, Northern Navajo Medical Center, Shiprock, NM, p. A445

ATHA, Shannon, Human Resource and Compliance Director, Doctors Hospital Nelsonville, Nelsonville, OH, p. A519

ATKIN, M.D., Suzanne, Chief of Staff and Associate Dean Clinical Affairs, University of Medicine and Dentistry of New Jersey–University Hospital, Newark, NJ, p. A433

ATKINS, Barbara, Director Human Resources, Northwest Hospital Center, Randallstown, MD, p. A310

ATKINS, Jim, Employee Services Director, Idaho Elks Rehabilitation Hospital, Boise, ID, p. A177

ATKINS, M.D., John, Chief Medical Officer, Allen County Hospital, Iola, KS, p. A249

ATKINS, Lou Ann, Director, West Texas VA Health Care System, Big Spring, TX, p. A626

ATKINS, Rainy, Chief Operating Officer, Southwest Washington Medical Center, Vancouver, WA, p. A711

ATKINS, Tony E., Chief Executive Officer, St. Joseph's Hospital of Buckhannon, Buckhannon, WV, p. A714

ATKINSON, Allan, Chief Administrative Officer, Winneshiek Medical Center, Decorah, IA, p. A232

ATKINSON, Jodi, President and Chief Executive Officer, St. Andrew's Health Center, Bottineau, ND, p. A496

ATKINSON, L. Gail, Executive Director, Devereux Texas Treatment Network, League City, TX, p. A652

ATKINSON, Lannie, Chf Information Officer, Chester County Hospital and Nursing Center, Chester, SC, p. A585

ATKINSON, Robert P., President and Chief Executive Officer, Jefferson Regional Medical Center, Pine Bluff, AR, p. A49

ATKINSON II, William K., Ph.D.,
  President and Chief Executive Officer, WakeMed, Raleigh, NC, p. B121
  President and Chief Executive Officer, WakeMed Raleigh Campus, Raleigh, NC, p. A490

ATLURI, M.D., Seetha, President Medical Staff, Parkview Hospital, Fort Wayne, IN, p. A215

ATTRIDGE, Scott, Controller, Mid–Valley Hospital, Omak, WA, p. A705

ATWOOD, Julie, Director Human Resources, Mountains Community Hospital, Lake Arrowhead, CA, p. A66

ATZROTT, Allan E., President and Chief Executive Officer, St. Luke's Cornwall Hospital – Newburgh Campus, Newburgh, NY, p. A467

AU, M.D., Thomas, Senior Vice President Clinical Operations and Medical Director, Rehabilitation Hospital of the Pacific, Honolulu, HI, p. A174

AUBEL, James
  Chief Financial Officer, Jameson Hospital, New Castle, PA, p. A566
  Director Fiscal Services and Information Management Services, Jameson Hospital, New Castle, PA, p. A566

AUBRY, Michael, Director Information Systems, Hanford Community Medical Center, Hanford, CA, p. A63

AUBUT, Richard, President and Chief Executive Officer, South Shore Hospital, South Weymouth, MA, p. A323

AUCOIN, Rita, Director Human Resources, Ville Platte Medical Center, Ville Platte, LA, p. A294

AUDETT, M.D., John R., Vice President, Medical Director, Kent County Memorial Hospital, Warwick, RI, p. A582

AUER, M.D., Nancy, Chief Medical Officer, Swedish Health Services, Seattle, WA, p. A708

AUERBACH, D.O., Jeffrey, Medical Director, Bon Secours Community Hospital, Port Jervis, NY, p. A470

AUGSBURGER, Tod, Senior Vice President and Chief Operating Officer, Lexington Medical Center, West Columbia, SC, p. A593

AULT, Daryl, Director Information Services, HEALTHSOUTH Rehabilitation Hospital, Sewickley, PA, p. A575

AUMAN, Patrick A., Ph.D., Chief Executive Officer, Regency Hospital of Odessa, Odessa, TX, p. A659

AUNAN, II, CPA, Milton E., Chief Financial Officer, Wadley Regional Medical Center, Texarkana, TX, p. A670

AUSLANDER, Joseph, Chief Medical Officer, Wesley Woods Center of Emory University, Atlanta, GA, p. A155

AUSMAN, Dan F., Chief Executive Officer, Irvine Regional Hospital and Medical Center, Irvine, CA, p. A65

AUSTEN, Terry L.
Senior Vice President and Area Manager, Kaiser Foundation Hospital – Santa Teresa, San Jose, CA, p. A90
Director Operations, Kaiser Foundation Hospital – Santa Teresa, San Jose, CA, p. A90

AUSTIN, Aaron
Vice President Human Resources, Saint Joseph Regional Medical Center, South Bend, IN, p. A225
Vice President Human Resources, Saint Joseph Regional Medical Center–Plymouth Campus, Plymouth, IN, p. A224

AUSTIN, Barbara, Director Public Affairs, University Hospitals and Clinics, University of Mississippi Medical Center, Jackson, MS, p. A371

AUSTIN, Dan, Data Processing Manager, Ashley County Medical Center, Crossett, AR, p. A41

AUSTIN, David, Chief Financial Officer, Colorado–Fayette Medical Center, Weimar, TX, p. A673

AUSTIN, James D., FACHE,
Administrator, Kalkaska Memorial Health Center, Kalkaska, MI, p. A338
Administrator, Paul Oliver Memorial Hospital, Frankfort, MI, p. A333

AUSTIN, Judy, Human Resources Director, Campbellton Graceville Hospital, Graceville, FL, p. A130

AUSTIN, L. Joe, Chief Executive Officer, Huntsville Hospital, Huntsville, AL, p. A20

AUSTIN, Laura
Chief Financial Officer, Community Hospital of Anaconda, Anaconda, MT, p. A396
Chief Financial Officer, Community Hospital of Anaconda, Anaconda, MT, p. A396

AUSTIN, M.D., Robert, President Medical Staff, Union Regional Medical Center, Monroe, NC, p. A487

AUTH, Jeanette
Human Resources Director, Garfield Medical Center, Monterey Park, CA, p. A76
Human Resources Director, Monterey Park Hospital, Monterey Park, CA, p. A76

AUTRY, Paula R., Executive Vice President and Administrator, Bon Secours–Richmond Community Hospital, Richmond, VA, p. A694

AUYANG, Rod, Director Human Resources, San Francisco General Hospital Medical Center, San Francisco, CA, p. A89

AVANT, Donna, Chief Financial Officer, Southwestern Memorial Hospital, Weatherford, OK, p. A541

AVATO, Rich, Director, St. Mary's Medical Center, West Palm Beach, FL, p. A150

AVENEL, William, Vice President Information Systems and Chief Information Officer, Cape Fear Valley Health System, Fayetteville, NC, p. A482

AVERETT, Elaine, Chief Financial Officer, Grove Hill Memorial Hospital, Grove Hill, AL, p. A19

AVERILL, Clark, Director Information Technology, St. Luke's Hospital, Duluth, MN, p. A352

AVERNA, Russell, Vice President Clinical and Support Services, Jordan Hospital, Plymouth, MA, p. A322

AVERY, Donald R., FACHE, President and Chief Executive Officer, Hughston Orthopedic Hospital, Columbus, GA, p. A158

AVERY III, John B., Administrator, Perry Community Hospital, Linden, TN, p. A611

AVILES, Alan D., Acting President, New York City Health and Hospitals Corporation, New York, NY, p. B78

AVVISATO, Michael, Vice President and Chief Financial Officer, Allied Services Rehabilitation Hospital, Scranton, PA, p. A575

AVVISATO, Mike, Vice President and Chief Financial Officer, John Heinz Institute of Rehabilitation Medicine, Wilkes–Barre, PA, p. A579

AYALA, R.N., Lisa, Human Resources Manager, Specialty Hospital Jacksonville, Jacksonville, FL, p. A132

AYCOCK, Mark, Chief Financial Officer, Emory Crawford Long Hospital, Atlanta, GA, p. A153

AYCOCK, M.D., Susan, President Medical Staff, Bladen County Hospital, Elizabethtown, NC, p. A482

AYERS, M.D., John, Vice President Medical Affairs, St. Joseph Hospital, Kokomo, IN, p. A220

AYERSMAN, Jim, Chief Financial Officer, Specialty Hospital Jacksonville, Jacksonville, FL, p. A132

AYRES, Doreen, Human Resources Director, Seneca Healthcare District, Chester, CA, p. A56

AYRES, Larry J., Administrator and Chief Executive Officer, Pointe Coupee General Hospital, New Roads, LA, p. A290

AYRES, Michael D., Senior Vice President and Chief Financial Officer, Christ Hospital, Jersey City, NJ, p. A430

AZBIK, Ginger, Director Human Resources, Baptist Montclair, Birmingham, AL, p. A14

B

BAACKE, M.D., George, Clinical Director, Northern Navajo Medical Center, Shiprock, NM, p. A445

BAADE, Leigh, Director Human Resources, New England Rehabilitation Hospital of Portland, Portland, ME, p. A300

BAAS, Dina, Director Financial Services, Orange City Health System, Orange City, IA, p. A239

BABAKANIAN, Ed, Chief Information Officer, University of California San Diego Medical Center, San Diego, CA, p. A88

BABB, Cindy, Director Human Resources, St. Joseph Hospital, Kokomo, IN, p. A220

BABB, Donald J., Chief Executive Officer, Citizens Memorial Hospital, Bolivar, MO, p. A378

BABB, Mary, Director Information Technology, St. Joseph Medical Center, Reading, PA, p. A574

BABCOCK, Daniel
Chief Financial Officer, Marlette Community Hospital, Marlette, MI, p. A340
Chief Financial Officer, Marlette Community Hospital, Marlette, MI, p. A340

BABCOCK, Matthew D., Chief Operating Officer, St. Elizabeth Medical Center, Utica, NY, p. A475

BABCOCK, M.D., Robert, Chief of Staff, Veterans Affairs Medical Center, Canandaigua, NY, p. A450

BABIN, Robert, Acting Chief Information Officer, Saint Peter's University Hospital, New Brunswick, NJ, p. A432

BACA, James, Chief Executive Officer, Peak Behavioral Health Services, Santa Teresa, NM, p. A444

BACH, Debbie, Chief Financial Officer, Corcoran District Hospital, Corcoran, CA, p. A57

BACH, M.D., Terry, Director Medical Affairs, Bay Area Hospital, Coos Bay, OR, p. A543

BACHARACH, Paul, President and Chief Executive Officer, Uniontown Hospital, Uniontown, PA, p. A577

BACHELDOR, D.O., H Lee, Medical Director, St. John River District Hospital, East China, MI, p. A332

BACHER, Beth
Administrator, HEALTHSOUTH Valley of the Sun Rehabilitation Hospital, Glendale, AZ, p. A31
Chief Operating Officer, HEALTHSOUTH Valley of the Sun Rehabilitation Hospital, Glendale, AZ, p. A31

BACHMAN, David T., Vice President of Medical Affairs, Mercy Hospital of Portland, Portland, ME, p. A300

BACHMAN, Robert J., Chief Operating Officer, Emory University Hospital, Atlanta, GA, p. A153

BACHMAN, Ronald J., President and Chief Executive Officer, Marion General Hospital, Marion, OH, p. A517

BACIARELLI, Renato V., President, St. Rose Dominican Hospitals – Rose de Lima Campus, Henderson, NV, p. A416

BACKELMAN, Paul, Associate Director, Veterans Affairs Central Iowa Health Care System, Des Moines, IA, p. A233

BACKSTROM, M.D., Dean, Vice President Medical Affairs, St. John's Regional Medical Center, Joplin, MO, p. A384

BACON, Ken, President, Parker Adventist Hospital, Parker, CO, p. A109

BACUS, Randy B., FACHE, Chief Executive Officer, Physicians' Metroplex Hospital, Arlington, TX, p. A622

BADGER, Jeff, Chief Financial Officer, St. Elizabeth Hospital, Appleton, WI, p. A722

BADGER Jr, Theodore J., CHE, Chief Executive Officer, Beauregard Memorial Hospital, De Ridder, LA, p. A280

BAECKER, William E., Vice President and Chief Financial Officer, Clinton Memorial Hospital, Wilmington, OH, p. A525

BAER, Douglas, President and Chief Operating Officer, Brooks Rehabilitation Hospital, Jacksonville, FL, p. A132

BAER, James E., FACHE, Chief Executive Officer, Shawano Medical Center, Shawano, WI, p. A735

BAEZ, Janet, Director, University Hospital, San Juan, PR, p. A748

BAGBY, Philip D., President and Chief Executive Officer, Ozarks Medical Center, West Plains, MO, p. A395

BAGLEY, Douglas D., Chief Executive Officer, Riverside County Regional Medical Center, Moreno Valley, CA, p. A77

BAGLEY, Norb, Executive Vice President and Chief Operating Officer, Lester E. Cox Medical Centers, Springfield, MO, p. A394

BAGLEY, M.D., Peter, Medical Director, Fairlawn Rehabilitation Hospital, Worcester, MA, p. A325

BAHA–ALCHESAY, Carla, Chief Executive Officer, Northern Navajo Medical Center, Shiprock, NM, p. A445

BAHL, Barry I.
Director, Veterans Affairs Medical Center, Saint Cloud, MN, p. A361
Director, Veterans Affairs Medical Center, Saint Cloud, MN, p. A361

BAHNLEIN, Carl, Executive Vice President and Chief Operating Officer, Virginia Hospital Center – Arlington, Arlington, VA, p. A685

BAICKER, Martin W., CHE, Senior Vice President and Administrator, LibertyHealth–Meadowlands Hospital Medical Center, Secaucus, NJ, p. A436

BAIER, Roger, Chief Executive Officer, Union Hospital, Mayville, ND, p. A499

BAIG, CPA, Hasan, Assistant Controller, HEALTHSOUTH Southern Hills Rehabilitation Hospital, Princeton, WV, p. A719

BAILEY, Bill, Chief Executive Officer, Whisper Ridge at Leesburg, Leesburg, VA, p. A690

BAILEY, Bruce P., Chief Executive Officer, Georgetown Memorial Hospital, Georgetown, SC, p. A588

BAILEY, Carl W.
President and Chief Executive Officer, Coffee Health Group, Florence, AL, p. B30
Administrator, Eliza Coffee Memorial Hospital, Florence, AL, p. A18

BAILEY, David, Chief Executive Officer, Community Memorial Healthcare, Marysville, KS, p. A252

BAILEY, G. Owen, President and Chief Executive Officer, Thomas Hospital, Fairhope, AL, p. A18

BAILEY, K. Michael, Ph.D., Administrator, North Mississippi Medical Center–Eupora, Eupora, MS, p. A368

BAILEY, Larry, Vice President and Chief Operating Officer, Bloomington Hospital, Bloomington, IN, p. A212

BAILEY, Loretta, Administrator, Wright Patterson Medical Center, Wright–Patterson AFB, OH, p. A525

BAILEY, M.D., Mark, Chief of Staff, Baylor Medical Center at Garland, Garland, TX, p. A641

BAILEY, Marvin, Chief Executive Officer, Central State Hospital, Milledgeville, GA, p. A166

BAILEY, Matthew D., President and Chief Executive Officer, Good Samaritan Hospital, Vincennes, IN, p. A226

BAILEY, M.D., Michael, Chief of Staff, Covenant Hospital–Levelland, Levelland, TX, p. A652

BAILEY, Mikeana, Director Human Resources, Brownwood Regional Medical Center, Brownwood, TX, p. A627

BAILEY, Russell, Administrator, HEALTHSOUTH Medical Center, Dallas, TX, p. A632

BAILEY, Sally, Chief Financial Officer, HEALTHSOUTH Rehabilitation Hospital of Sarasota, Sarasota, FL, p. A146

BAILEY, Sandra, Administrator, Methodist Healthcare – Extended Care Hospital, Memphis, TN, p. A613

BAILEY, Susan, Chief Executive Officer, Kindred Hospital–San Diego, San Diego, CA, p. A87

BAILEY, Ted, Vice President Information Systems, Peace River Regional Medical Center, Port Charlotte, FL, p. A144

BAILEY, Travis, Vice President, St. Claire Regional Medical Center, Morehead, KY, p. A272

BAILON, Amy R., M.D., Medical Director, Woodbridge Development Center, Woodbridge, NJ, p. A439

BAILY, Ted, Vice President Information Systems, Venice Regional Medical Center, Venice, FL, p. A149

BAIN, Brad, Information Systems Leader, Kaiser Foundation Hospital, Fresno, CA, p. A61

BAINTER, William S., Chief Financial Officer, Lewis–Gale Medical Center, Salem, VA, p. A696

BAIOCCHI, Angelo, Vice President Information Management, Veterans Affairs Pittsburgh Healthcare System, Pittsburgh, PA, p. A573

BAIOCCO, Jeffrey D., Chief Financial Officer, Ocala Regional Medical Center, Ocala, FL, p. A140

BAIR, Ada, Chief Executive Officer, Memorial Hospital, Carthage, IL, p. A186

BAIR, Jon L., Administrator, Royal Oaks Hospital, Windsor, MO, p. A395

BAIRCH, M.D., Bruce, President Medical Staff, Swedish Medical Center, Englewood, CO, p. A105

BAIRD, David, Chief Information Officer, LDS Hospital, Salt Lake City, UT, p. A679

BAIRD, M.D., Eric, Medical Staff President, Eastern Idaho Regional Medical Center, Idaho Falls, ID, p. A179

BAIRD, Jan, Chief Financial Officer, Petersburg Medical Center, Petersburg, AK, p. A28

BAIRD, Jim, Chief Executive Officer, Select Specialty Hospital–Birmingham, Birmingham, AL, p. A15

BAIRD, John, Administrtor and Chief Executive Officer, Select Specialty Hospital, Cincinnati, OH, p. A507

BAIRD, Marvin L., Executive Director, Adams Memorial Hospital, Decatur, IN, p. A214

BAJERSKI, Beverly, Regional Administrator, Southwestern State Hospital, Thomasville, GA, p. A170

BAKER, Angela C., Manager Human Resources, Adventist Rehabilitation Hospital of Maryland, Rockville, MD, p. A310

BAKER, Bonnie, Vice President Finance and Chief Financial Officer, Butler Hospital, Providence, RI, p. A581

BAKER, M.D., Bonnie, Chief Medical Services, Veterans Affairs Medical Center, Fayetteville, AR, p. A43

BAKER, Denis, Chief Information Officer, Sarasota Memorial Hospital, Sarasota, FL, p. A146

BAKER, Don, Director Accounting, DeKalb Hospital, Smithville, TN, p. A617

BAKER, Donald, Vice President Finance, Hillcrest Medical Center, Tulsa, OK, p. A539

BAKER, Gary A., President, Memorial Hospital, Towanda, PA, p. A577

BAKER, Gary E., Vice President, Scottsdale Healthcare–Osborn, Scottsdale, AZ, p. A36

BAKER, Glenn, Administrator and Chief Executive Officer, Baptist Memorial Hospital–Collierville, Collierville, TN, p. A604

BAKER, Harlan T., Director Information Systems, McDonough District Hospital, Macomb, IL, p. A200

BAKER, James, Vice President Business Support Services, Veterans Affairs Pittsburgh Healthcare System, Pittsburgh, PA, p. A573

BAKER, Jeannie, Administrator, Shands at Starke, Starke, FL, p. A146

BAKER, John, Chief Executive Officer and Managing Director, Glen Oaks Hospital, Greenville, TX, p. A642

BAKER, M.D., Lee, Vice President Medical Affairs, Rutherford Hospital, Rutherfordton, NC, p. A491

BAKER, Linda, Director Human Resources, St. Alexius Medical Center, Hoffman Estates, IL, p. A197

BAKER, Maribel, Human Resource Director, Johnson Regional Medical Center, Clarksville, AR, p. A41

BAKER, Michael E., Director Information Systems, Underwood–Memorial Hospital, Woodbury, NJ, p. A439

BAKER, Michele, Director Human Resources, Good Hope Hospital, Erwin, NC, p. A482

BAKER, D.O., Nancy, Vice Chair, Pershing General Hospital, Lovelock, NV, p. A417

BAKER, Reese, Chief Information Technology, Crittenden County Hospital, Marion, KY, p. A271

BAKER, Reta
Chief Operating Officer, Mercy Health System of Kansas, Fort Scott, KS, p. A247
Vice President Operations, Mercy Health System of Kansas, Independence, KS, p. A249

BAKER, Rodger H., President and Chief Executive Officer, Fauquier Hospital, Warrenton, VA, p. A698

BAKER, Ronald D., Chief Executive Officer, Franklin General Hospital, Hampton, IA, p. A235

BAKER Jr, Wendell H., President, Heritage Hospital, Tarboro, NC, p. A492

BAKKEN, Mary, Senior Vice President and Chief Operating Officer, Fairview Southdale Hospital, Edina, MN, p. A353

BAKKER, Victor, Chief Financial Officer, Lincoln Medical and Mental Health Center, New York, NY, p. A461

BAKOS, Martha, Chief Financial Officer, South Bay Hospital, Sun City Center, FL, p. A147

BALASSONE, Michael, Vice President Information Technology, West Virginia University Hospitals, Morgantown, WV, p. A718

BALDWIN, Barbara, Chief Information Officer, University of Virginia Medical Center, Charlottesville, VA, p. A686

BALDWIN, Bruce A., Chief Executive Officer, Putnam Community Medical Center, Palatka, FL, p. A141

BALDWIN, Gilda, Chief Executive Officer, Westchester General Hospital, Miami, FL, p. A138

BALDWIN, Joe G., Chief Executive Officer, Memorial Hermann Continuing Care Hospital, Houston, TX, p. A646

BALDWIN, Keith J., Chief Operating Officer, Valley Hospital and Medical Center, Spokane, WA, p. A709

BALDWIN, Louise, R.N., President, Harris Continued Care Hospital, Fort Worth, TX, p. A639

BALDWIN, Paul L., Chief Executive Officer, Retreat Hospital, Richmond, VA, p. A695

BALDWIN, William, Chief Information Officer, Ashe Memorial Hospital, Jefferson, NC, p. A485

BALES, Avary, Director Information Systems, Emory Dunwoody Medical Center, Atlanta, GA, p. A153

BALES, Correen, Director Human Resources, Navapache Regional Medical Center, Show Low, AZ, p. A36

BALES, Lynn, Assistant Administrator Clinical and Support Servicess, Samaritan Healthcare, Moses Lake, WA, p. A704

BALGROSKY, Jean
Senior Vice President and Chief Information Officer, Scripps Green Hospital, La Jolla, CA, p. A65
Vice President and Chief Information Officer, Scripps Memorial Hospital–Encinitas, Encinitas, CA, p. A59
Vice President and Chief Information Offiecer, Scripps Memorial Hospital–La Jolla, La Jolla, CA, p. A66
Vice President and Chief Information Officer, Scripps Mercy Hospital, San Diego, CA, p. A87

BALL, M.D., Angela, Chief of Staff, Mount Carmel Hospital, Colville, WA, p. A701

BALL, Craig, President and Chief Executive Officer, Tri Parish Rehabilitation Hospital, Rosepine, LA, p. A291

BALL, Debra A., Vice President Human Resources, St. Luke's Hospital, Maumee, OH, p. A518

BALLA, Ernest, R.N., Administrator, Johns Community Hospital, Taylor, TX, p. A668

BALLARD, Bryan M., Chief Executive Officer, Mendocino Coast District Hospital, Fort Bragg, CA, p. A60

BALLARD, Susan, Chief Executive Officer, Valley Health System, Hemet, CA, p. B118

BALLI, Donald, Human Resources Director, South Coast Medical Center, Laguna Beach, CA, p. A66

BALLOCK, Steve, Chief Financial Officer, St. Vincent Healthcare, Billings, MT, p. A396

BALOGA, Marie, Public Relations Director, William Beaumont Hospital–Troy, Troy, MI, p. A347

BALONIS, Marcia
Chief Financial Officer, Ralph H. Johnson Veterans Affairs Medical Center, Charleston, SC, p. A585
Comptroller, Veterans Affairs Medical Center, Leeds, MA, p. A319

BALSANO, Tony, Vice President Finance, Saint Francis Medical Center, Cape Girardeau, MO, p. A379

BALTZ, Richard J., Director, G.V. Montgomery Veterans Affairs Medical Center, Jackson, MS, p. A370

BALTZER, David J., President, Rehoboth McKinley Christian Hospital, Gallup, NM, p. A442

BALZER, Gene, Administrator, Campbell County Memorial Hospital, Gillette, WY, p. A740

BAMESBARGER, Matt, Information Services Director, Tri–Valley Health System, Cambridge, NE, p. A405

BANASZYNSKI, Gregory A., President and Chief Executive Officer, Fort HealthCare, Fort Atkinson, WI, p. A725

BANBURY, Brian, Information Technology Site Manager, Advocate Christ Medical Center, Oak Lawn, IL, p. A203

BANCROFT, Kenneth H., President and Chief Executive Officer, St. Agnes HealthCare, Baltimore, MD, p. A304

BANDY, M.D., P Ross, Chief Medical Officer and Chief of Staff, Levi Hospital, Hot Springs National Park, AR, p. A45

BANG, W J., Chief of Staff, Reeves County Hospital, Pecos, TX, p. A660

BANK, Kendall C., President, Northfield Hospital, Northfield, MN, p. A359

BANKO, Peter, Vice President and Administrator, Christus Spohn Hospital Corpus Christi Memorial, Corpus Christi, TX, p. A630

BANKS, Elizabeth, Chief Executive Officer, Summit Behavioral Healthcare, Cincinnati, OH, p. A507

BANKS, Michael A., Chief Financial Officer, Sacred Heart Medical Center, Spokane, WA, p. A709

BANKS, Walter, Director Human Resources, Baptist Memorial Hospital–Desoto, Southaven, MS, p. A375

BANKTSON, Julie, Human Resources Manager, Paul Oliver Memorial Hospital, Frankfort, MI, p. A333

BANOS, Edward D., Chief Executive Officer, North Shore Medical Center, Miami, FL, p. A138

BANSEMER, Donald, Vice President Information Systems, Silver Cross Hospital, Joliet, IL, p. A198

BAPTISTE, Ernest, Chief Operating Officer, Durham Regional Hospital, Durham, NC, p. A481

BARABAS, Mark C., President and Chief Executive Officer, Mercy Suburban Hospital, Norristown, PA, p. A566

BARANEK, Richard, Director Human Resources, Midwest Regional Medical Center, Midwest City, OK, p. A533

BARANIK, David T.
Senior Vice President and Chief Financial Officer, East Ohio Regional Hospital, Martins Ferry, OH, p. A517
Senior Vice President and Chief Financial Officer, Ohio Valley Medical Center, Wheeling, WV, p. A721

BARB, Thomas D., Executive Director, Brooksville Regional Hospital, Brooksville, FL, p. A125

BARBA, James J., President and Chief Executive Officer, Albany Medical Center, Albany, NY, p. A446

BARBAGLIA, J Joseph
Vice President Financial Services, Columbus Community Hospital, Columbus, NE, p. A406
Vice President Financial Services, Columbus Community Hospital, Columbus, NE, p. A406

BARBAGLIA, Jim, Chief Information Officer, Valley Baptist Health System, Harlingen, TX, p. A643

BARBANEL, Lori, Resource Management Center Leader, Veterans Affairs Medical Center, Wilmington, DE, p. A120

BARBAREE, Jerry, Human Resources Director, Baptist Memorial Hospital – Memphis, Memphis, TN, p. A612

BARBARIN, Shawn, Chief Operating Officer, Medical Center of McKinney, McKinney, TX, p. A656

BARBATO, Anthony L., M.D., President and Chief Executive Officer, Loyola University Medical Center, Maywood, IL, p. A200

BARBE, Brian S., Chief Executive Officer, Memorial Hermann Katy Hospital, Katy, TX, p. A650

BARBEE, Sue, Director Human Resources, Stanly Memorial Hospital, Albemarle, NC, p. A477

BARBER, Chris, Administrator, St. Bernards Medical Center, Jonesboro, AR, p. A45

BARBER, Jack W., M.D., Director, Western State Hospital, Staunton, VA, p. A697

BARBER, Jeffrey B., Dr.PH, President and Chief Executive Officer, Owensboro Medical Health System, Owensboro, KY, p. A272

BARBER, M.D., John E., Chief of Staff, DeTar Healthcare System, Victoria, TX, p. A672

BARBER, CPA, Keith, Chief Financial Officer, Tomball Regional Hospital, Tomball, TX, p. A670

BARBER, Michael, Senior Vice President Operations, Chester County Hospital, West Chester, PA, p. A578

BARBER, Jr, Paul M., Vice President for Finance, St. Mary's Hospital, Leonardtown, MD, p. A309

BARBER, M.D., Tom, Chief Medical Officer, Quincy Medical Center, Quincy, MA, p. A322

BARBERA, Sal A., FACHE, Administrator, South Florida State Hospital, Hollywood, FL, p. A131

BARBIER, Robert P., Chief Financial Officer, University of Louisville Hospital, Louisville, KY, p. A270

BARBINI, Gerald J., President and Chief Executive Officer, Allegan General Hospital, Allegan, MI, p. A327

BARBO, Steve, R.N., Administrator, Citizens Medical Center, Columbia, LA, p. A279

BARBUAT, James P., Vice President Financial Services, Opelousas General Health System, Opelousas, LA, p. A291

BARCA, Robin
  Senior Vice President and Chief Operating Officer, Baptist Medical Center East, Montgomery, AL, p. A21
  Senior Vice President and Chief Operating Officer, Baptist Medical Center South, Montgomery, AL, p. A22

BARCIA, M.D., Thomas C., Chief of Staff, Veterans Affairs Sierra Nevada Health Care System, Reno, NV, p. A418

BARCLAY, M.D., Duane, Vice President Physician Support Services, DeKalb Medical Center, Decatur, GA, p. A160

BARCLAY, Emily, Vice President Human Resources, Dana–Farber Cancer Institute, Boston, MA, p. A313

BARCLAY, Rick, Vice President Human Resources, St. Mary–Rogers Memorial Hospital, Rogers, AR, p. A49

BARCLAY, Robin M., President, United Community Hospital, Detroit, MI, p. A332

BARCO, Lawrence F., President, MidMichigan Medical Center–Clare, Clare, MI, p. A330

BARDILL, Janice
  Chief Financial Officer, Roane Medical Center, Harriman, TN, p. A607
  Chief Financial Officer, Roane Medical Center, Harriman, TN, p. A607

BARDWELL, Jean
  Vice President and Chief Financial Officer, Ranken Jordan, Maryland Heights, MO, p. A387
  Vice President and Chief Financial Officer, Ranken Jordan, Maryland Heights, MO, p. A387

BARDWELL, Sheila, Director Information Systems, Baptist Memorial Hospital–Golden Triangle, Columbus, MS, p. A368

BARDWELL, Tom, Director Human Resources, Hills and Dales General Hospital, Cass City, MI, p. A329

BAREA, Al
  Vice President Information Services, Baptist Hospital East, Louisville, KY, p. A268
  Chief Information Officer and Vice President, Baptist Hospital Northeast, La Grange, KY, p. A267

BARELA, Barbara, Human Resources Director, Gila Regional Medical Center, Silver City, NM, p. A445

BAREZ, Pedro, Chief Executive Officer, Hospital Metropolitano Dr. Tito Mattei, Yauco, PR, p. A749

BARG, Guy A., Executive Vice President and Chief Operating Officer, Bergen Regional Medical Center, Paramus, NJ, p. A433

BARGER, Michael A., Associate Administrator Finance and Chief Financial Officer, Inova Mount Vernon Hospital, Alexandria, VA, p. A685

BARGLOF, Mark, Administrator, Odessa Memorial Healthcare Center, Odessa, WA, p. A705

BARKER, Deb, Communications and Information Specialist, Davis County Hospital, Bloomfield, IA, p. A229

BARKER, Karen
  Vice President and Chief Information Officer, Levindale Hebrew Geriatric Center and Hospital, Baltimore, MD, p. A303
  Vice President and Chief Information Officer, Northwest Hospital Center, Randallstown, MD, p. A310
  Vice President and Chief Information Officer, Sinai Hospital of Baltimore, Baltimore, MD, p. A304

BARKER, Richard, Administrator, Mercy Health Love County, Marietta, OK, p. A533

BARKER, Russel, Chief Executive Officer, McDowell ARH Hospital, McDowell, KY, p. A271

BARKER, Russell, Chief Information Officer, U. S. Public Health Service Indian Hospital–Whiteriver, Whiteriver, AZ, p. A39

BARKMAN, M.D., H William, Chief of Staff, University of Kansas Hospital, Kansas City, KS, p. A250

BARKMAN, Sam D., Vice President Operations, Dubuis Hospital of Houston, Houston, TX, p. A645

BARLETTA, M.D., Ana, Medical Director, San Juan City Hospital, San Juan, PR, p. A748

BARLEY, Tammy, Manager Human Resources, HEALTHSOUTH Rehabilitation Hospital of Jonesboro, Jonesboro, AR, p. A45

BARLOW, Walt
  Interim Chief Financial Officer, Natchez Regional Medical Center, Natchez, MS, p. A373
  Interim Chief Financial Officer, Neshoba County General Hospital, Philadelphia, MS, p. A374

BARNARD, M.D., David, Medical Director, Huey P. Long Medical Center, Pineville, LA, p. A291

BARNER, James W., President and Chief Executive Officer, Altoona Hospital Campus, Altoona, PA, p. A551

BARNER, Mark
  Vice President Information Systems, Brackenridge Hospital, Austin, TX, p. A623
  Vice President Information Systems, Seton Edgar B. Davis Hospital, Luling, TX, p. A655
  Vice President Information Systems, Seton Highland Lakes, Burnet, TX, p. A627
  Vice President Information Systems, Seton Medical Center, Austin, TX, p. A623
  Vice President Information Systems, Seton Shoal Creek Hospital, Austin, TX, p. A624

BARNES, Debbie, Vice President and Chief Information Officer, Children's Hospital of The King's Daughters, Norfolk, VA, p. A692

BARNES, Gary, Chief Information Officer, Medical Center Hospital, Odessa, TX, p. A659

BARNES, M.D., George, Medical Director, Lakeview Regional Medical Center, Covington, LA, p. A279

BARNES, James, Chief Financial Officer, Medical Center of Manchester, Manchester, TN, p. A612

BARNES, Larry, Vice President Information Technology, Salina Regional Health Center, Salina, KS, p. A256

BARNES, Peter, Senior Vice President Human Resources, University of North Carolina Hospitals, Chapel Hill, NC, p. A479

BARNES, M.D., Roy M., President Medical Staff, Valley Regional Hospital, Claremont, NH, p. A420

BARNES, Shirley, Senior Vice President Human Resources, Mission Hospital, Mission Viejo, CA, p. A75

BARNES, Wendy, Chief Medical Resource Management, U. S. Air Force Hospital, Hampton, VA, p. A689

BARNETT, M.D., Fredrick, Chief of Staff, Metroplex Adventist Hospital, Killeen, TX, p. A651

BARNETT, Gary L., President and Chief Executive Officer, Sarah Bush Lincoln Health Center, Mattoon, IL, p. A200

BARNETT, James L., Administrator, Hamlin Memorial Hospital, Hamlin, TX, p. A643

BARNETT, Jeffrey, Chief Executive Officer, Clarion Psychiatric Center, Clarion, PA, p. A555

BARNETT, Richard J., President, Mercy Medical Center Redding, Redding, CA, p. A83

BARNETT, Shawn, Chief Financial Officer, Northwest Medical Center of Washington County, Springdale, AR, p. A50

BARNETT, Steve, Chief Executive Officer, Harbor Beach Community Hospital, Harbor Beach, MI, p. A336

BARNETT, Timothy, Chief Executive Officer, Yavapai Regional Medical Center, Prescott, AZ, p. A35

BARNETTE, Burt, Chief Financial Officer, Chatham Hospital, Siler City, NC, p. A491

BARNETTE, Chris W.
  Executive Vice President and Chief Operating Officer, Covenant Children's Hospital, Lubbock, TX, p. A654
  Executive Vice President and Chief Operating Officer, Covenant Medical Center, Lubbock, TX, p. A654

BARNETTE, Larry, Senior Vice President Finance, Spartanburg Regional Medical Center, Spartanburg, SC, p. A592

BARNHART, Ann, Chief Executive Officer, Heart of Florida Regional Medical Center, Davenport, FL, p. A127

BARNHART, James R., Chief Executive Officer, Peace Harbor Hospital, Florence, OR, p. A543

BARNHART, M.D., Scott, Medical Director, Harborview Medical Center, Seattle, WA, p. A707

BARNHILL, Steve, Chief Financial Officer, St. Lucie Medical Center, Port St. Lucie, FL, p. A144

BARNUM, M.D., Grant, Chief of Staff, Lake Regional Health System, Osage Beach, MO, p. A388

BAROCO, Paul T., Senior Vice President, Medical Affairs, Sacred Heart Hospital of Pensacola, Pensacola, FL, p. A143

BARONE, John, Vice President Finance and Chief Financial Officer, St. Mary Hospital, Hoboken, NJ, p. A429

BAROUGHS, Burt, Chief of Staff, Monroe County Hospital, Monroeville, AL, p. A21

BARR, Bret, Vice President Fiscal Services, Conway Medical Center, Conway, SC, p. A587

BARR, R.N., Mary Beth, Chief Operating Officer, Grant Memorial Hospital, Petersburg, WV, p. A719

BARR, Nancy, Manager/Information Systems, Cheboygan Memorial Hospital, Cheboygan, MI, p. A329

BARR, Vivian, Director Human Resources, Tanner Medical Center, Carrollton, GA, p. A157

BARRETT, Anne, Director Human Resources, Southside Hospital, Bay Shore, NY, p. A447

BARRETT, Bill, Director Human Resources, Great Plains Regional Medical Center, Elk City, OK, p. A530

BARRETT, David M., M.D., Chief Executive Officer, Lahey Clinic Hospital, Burlington, MA, p. A316

BARRETT, Frank, Executive Vice President Corporate Affairs and Chief Financial Officer, Jackson Memorial Hospital, Miami, FL, p. A137

BARRETT, Gina, Chief Financial Officer, Greene County Memorial Hospital, Waynesburg, PA, p. A578

BARRETT, Jack, Director Data Processing, MedCentral Health System, Mansfield, OH, p. A517

BARRETT III, John E., President and Chief Executive Officer, Page Memorial Hospital, Luray, VA, p. A690

BARRETT, M.D., Leonard, Acting Medical Director, Nassau University Medical Center, East Meadow, NY, p. A451

BARRETT, Linda, Director Information Systems, St. James Healthcare, Butte, MT, p. A397

BARRETT, Susan, President and Chief Executive Officer, St. Mary–Rogers Memorial Hospital, Rogers, AR, p. A49

BARRETTO, M.D., Roberto, Vice President of Medical Affairs, St. John Macomb Hospital, Warren, MI, p. A347

BARRILLEAUX, Scott, Chief Executive Officer and Administrator, Allen Parish Hospital, Kinder, LA, p. A283

BARRIOS, Frankie, Department Head Information Systems, St. Tammany Parish Hospital, Covington, LA, p. A279

BARRON, Steven R., President, St. Bernardine Medical Center, San Bernardino, CA, p. A86

BARROW, Stella, Director of Human Resources, Longview Regional Medical Center, Longview, TX, p. A654

BARROW II, William F., Chief Executive Officer, Opelousas General Health System, Opelousas, LA, p. A291

BARROWS, Bonne, Director, Florida Hospital Fish Memorial, Orange City, FL, p. A140

BARRY, Amy, Vice President Human Resources, Martin Memorial Health Systems, Stuart, FL, p. A147

BARRY, Cindy, Coordinator Human Resources, Saunders County Health Service, Wahoo, NE, p. A413

BARRY, R. Michael, Chief Executive Officer, Jupiter Medical Center, Jupiter, FL, p. A133

BARRY, Jr, Thomas F., Vice President, Johnson Memorial Hospital, Franklin, IN, p. A216

BARSANTI, Bill, Operations Services Director, Humboldt General Hospital, Winnemucca, NV, p. A419

BARSE, Steve, Chief Information Officer, U. S. Public Health Service Indian Hospital, Lawton, OK, p. A532

BARSTAD, M.D., Brian, Chief of Staff, Pine Medical Center, Sandstone, MN, p. A362

BARSTAD, Stacy
Chief Financial Officer, Tracy Area Medical Services, Tracy, MN, p. A364
Chief Financial Officer, Westbrook Health Center, Westbrook, MN, p. A365

BARTAL, Ely, M.D., Administrator and Chief Executive Officer, Kansas Surgery and Recovery Center, Wichita, KS, p. A259

BARTELL III, Frank J., President and Chief Executive Officer, St. Luke's Hospital, Maumee, OH, p. A518

BARTELS, Bruce M., President, WellSpan Health, York, PA, p. B121

BARTH, M.D., Brad, Chief of Staff, Colorado River Medical Center, Needles, CA, p. A77

BARTH, Kenneth, Vice President Finance, Battle Creek Health System, Battle Creek, MI, p. A328

BARTLE, James W., Vice President Finance, Beebe Medical Center, Lewes, DE, p. A119

BARTLESON, Warner H., Administrator, North Valley Hospital, Tonasket, WA, p. A711

BARTLETT, Jerry, Chief Financial Officer, Sarah D. Culbertson Memorial Hospital, Rushville, IL, p. A207

BARTLETT, Jonathan W., Chief Executive Officer, Arrowhead Community Hospital and Medical Center, Glendale, AZ, p. A31

BARTLETT, Regina, Chief Operating Officer, Skyline Medical Center, Nashville, TN, p. A615

BARTLETT, Ronald E., Chief Financial Officer, Boston Medical Center, Boston, MA, p. A313

BARTLETT III, Thomas G., M.D., Administrator, Laird Hospital, Union, MS, p. A376

BARTMAN, Mike, Chief Information Officer, Sauk Prairie Memorial Hospital, Prairie Du Sac, WI, p. A734

BARTO, Albert A.
Vice President Operations, St. Joseph's Hospital, Elmira, NY, p. A452
Vice President Operations, St. Joseph's Hospital, Elmira, NY, p. A452

BARTO Jr, John K.
Chief Executive Officer, New Hanover Health Network, Wilmington, NC, p. B77
Chief Executive Officer, New Hanover Regional Medical Center, Wilmington, NC, p. A494

BARTON, Dave, Leader Business Office, Veterans Affairs Medical Center, North Chicago, IL, p. A203

BARTON, Gratia, Chief Financial Officer, Sequoia Hospital, Redwood City, CA, p. A83

BARTON, Larry O., President, Western Baptist Hospital, Paducah, KY, p. A273

BARTON, Rod, Chief Executive Officer, Powell Valley Healthcare, Powell, WY, p. A741

BARTON, Thomas, Chief Operating Officer and Chief Nursing Officer, Pampa Regional Medical Center, Pampa, TX, p. A659

BARTOS, John M., Chief Executive Officer, Marcus Daly Memorial Hospital, Hamilton, MT, p. A399

BARTS, Dennis, Chief Executive Officer, South Texas Regional Medical Center, Jourdanton, TX, p. A650

BARTZ, Daniel R., Administrator, Trego County–Lemke Memorial Hospital, Wakeeney, KS, p. A258

BARWIS, Kurt, Senior Vice President and Chief Operating Officer, St. Mary's Hospital, Leonardtown, MD, p. A309

BARZILAI, Jack, Chief Financial Officer, Riveredge Hospital, Forest Park, IL, p. A194

BASAVAPPA, Kash, Senior Vice President and Chief Information Officer, MaineGeneral Medical Center–Waterville Campus, Waterville, ME, p. A301

BASHAM, Gail S., Chief Executive Officer, Mount Regis Center, Salem, VA, p. A696

BASHAM, Virginia, Human Resources Director, Southeast Colorado Hospital and Long Term Care, Springfield, CO, p. A109

BASLER, Peter A., Chief Operating Officer, Wesley Woods Center of Emory University, Atlanta, GA, p. A155

BASS, Gordon B., Chief Operating Officer, Children's Memorial Hospital, Chicago, IL, p. A187

BASS, Michael, Chief Operating Officer, Northwest Medical Center, Margate, FL, p. A136

BASS, M.D., Sharon, Chief of Staff, Teche Regional Medical Center, Morgan City, LA, p. A287

BASSETT, Eugene
Chief Administrative Officer, Mercy Hospital of Wilkes–Barre, Wilkes–Barre, PA, p. A579
Chief Administrative Officer, Mercy Hospital of Wilkes–Barre, Wilkes–Barre, PA, p. A579

BASTIAN, Helena G., Director Human Resource Services, Charleston Memorial Hospital, Charleston, SC, p. A584

BASTIANELLI, Italo, Deputy Commander for Clinical Services, Keller Army Community Hospital, West Point, NY, p. A476

BASTONE, Peter F., President and Chief Executive Officer, Mission Hospital, Mission Viejo, CA, p. A75

BATAL, Lucille M., Administrator, Baldpate Hospital, Haverhill, MA, p. A318

BATCHELDER, Chester G., Superintendent, New Hampshire Hospital, Concord, NH, p. A420

BATCHELOR, Dale, M.D., Interim President and Chief Executive Officer, Saint Thomas Hospital, Nashville, TN, p. A615

BATCHELOR, Susan G., President, Clay County Hospital, Flora, IL, p. A194

BATCHLER, Betty, Director Human Resources, Kings Mountain Hospital, Kings Mountain, NC, p. A486

BATEMAN, Kenneth, President and Chief Executive Officer, Somerset Medical Center, Somerville, NJ, p. A436

BATEMAN, Mark T., Chief Administrative Officer, Our Lady of Lourdes Medical Center, Camden, NJ, p. A426

BATEMAN, Steven B.
Chief Executive Officer, Brigham City Community Hospital, Brigham City, UT, p. A676
Chief Executive Officer, Ogden Regional Medical Center, Ogden, UT, p. A678

BATES, M.D., Barbara, Chief Medical Oficer, Veterans Affairs Medical Center, Albany, NY, p. A446

BATES, M.D., Bob, Chief Medical Officer, Holland Hospital, Holland, MI, p. A336

BATES, Jonathan R., M.D., President and Chief Executive Officer, Arkansas Children's Hospital, Little Rock, AR, p. A46

BATES, Juanita, Administrator, Luling Rehabilitation Hospital, Luling, LA, p. A285

BATES, Mary, Director of Human Resources, Bowie Memorial Hospital, Bowie, TX, p. A626

BATISTA, David, Chief Operating Officer, San Dimas Community Hospital, San Dimas, CA, p. A88

BATMAN, Brent L., President, Ball Memorial Hospital, Muncie, IN, p. A222

BATORY, Robert J., Vice President Human Resources, York Hospital, York, PA, p. A580

BATT, Richard A., President and Chief Executive Officer, Franklin Memorial Hospital, Farmington, ME, p. A298

BATTERTON, M.D., Owen A., Chief of Staff, Greene County General Hospital, Linton, IN, p. A221

BATTIN, Anne, Administrator, Palmetto Lowcountry Behavioral Health System, Charleston, SC, p. A584

BATTISTA, Donald P., President and Chief Executive Officer, Garrett County Memorial Hospital, Oakland, MD, p. A309

BATTLE, Arenda, Director Human Resources, Heritage Hospital, Tarboro, NC, p. A492

BATTLE, Arthur, Senior Vice President Human Resources, Cambridge Health Alliance, Cambridge, MA, p. A316

BATTLES, M.D., Paul, Chief Medical Staff, Integris Mayes County Medical Center, Pryor, OK, p. A537

BATTLES, Rita, President and Chief Executive Officer, Long Island College Hospital, New York, NY, p. A461

BATTS, M.D., Mark, Chief of Staff, Caldwell Memorial Hospital, Lenoir, NC, p. A486

BATTY, Jill I., Chief Financial Officer, Cheshire Medical Center, Keene, NH, p. A421

BATULIS, Scott, Chief Executive Officer, St. Joseph's Hospital, Saint Paul, MN, p. A362

BAUCOM, Bradford J., Vice President and Chief Operating Officer, Jackson–Madison County General Hospital, Jackson, TN, p. A608

BAUER, Anne, Chief Financial Officer, Hollywood Medical Center, Hollywood, FL, p. A131

BAUER, Clifford J., Chief Executive Officer, Kindred Hospital–Fort Lauderdale, Fort Lauderdale, FL, p. A128

BAUER, Janice, Administrator, Cardinal Hill Specialty Hospital, Fort Thomas, KY, p. A264

BAUER, Kyle, Chief Financial Officer, Cuyuna Regional Medical Center, Crosby, MN, p. A352

BAUER, M.D., Richard, Chief of Staff, South Texas Veterans Health Care System, San Antonio, TX, p. A665

BAUER, Robert
Chief Executive Officer, Smith Northview Hospital, Valdosta, GA, p. A171
Vice President Finance and Chief Financial Officer, Doylestown Hospital, Doylestown, PA, p. A557

BAUER, William
Vice President Finance and Chief Financial Officer, Hazleton General Hospital, Hazleton, PA, p. A560
Vice President Finance and Chief Financial Officer, Hazleton–St. Joseph Medical Center, Hazleton, PA, p. A560

BAUGHAN, Jeffrey
Vice President Information Technology, Kenmore Mercy Hospital, Kenmore, NY, p. A455
Vice President Information Technology, Sisters of Charity Hospital of Buffalo, Buffalo, NY, p. A449
Chief Information Officer, St. Joseph Hospital, Cheektowaga, NY, p. A450

BAUGHMAN, Sally, Director Human Resources, Acadia Hospital, Bangor, ME, p. A296

BAUKNECHT, Ed, Director Management Information Systems, Holy Family Memorial Medical Center, Manitowoc, WI, p. A729

BAUMAN, Jonathan, Medical Director, Four Winds Hospital, Katonah, NY, p. A455

BAUMAN, Stephen, Director of Human Resources, Buffalo Hospital, Buffalo, MN, p. A351

BAUMEL, Gwen, Vice President, Human Resources, Aurora BayCare Medical Center, Green Bay, WI, p. A726

BAUMEL, M.D., MS, Mark J., Chief Medical Officer and Senior Vice President Medical Management, Mercy Catholic Medical Center, Darby, PA, p. A557

BAUMERT, Steven P., Senior Vice President Operations, Jennie Edmundson Memorial Hospital, Council Bluffs, IA, p. A231

BAUMGARDNER, Brian P., Chief Executive Officer, Lawnwood Regional Medical Center, Fort Pierce, FL, p. A129

BAUMGARDNER, David, Director Information Services, Union Hospital, Dover, OH, p. A513

BAUMGART, Kris, Chief Executive Officer, Stewart Memorial Community Hospital, Lake City, IA, p. A237

BAUMGARTNER, M.D., David, Vice President Medical Affairs, Saint Mary's Health Care, Grand Rapids, MI, p. A335

BAUMGARTNER, Michael, President, St. Francis Hospital and Health Services, Maryville, MO, p. A387

BAUNCHALK, James M., Commander, Moncrief Army Community Hospital, Fort Jackson, SC, p. A588

BAUTE, Robert E., M.D., President and Chief Executive Officer, Kent County Memorial Hospital, Warwick, RI, p. A582

BAVA, Michele, Director Human Resources, Doctors Hospital of Manteca, Manteca, CA, p. A74

BAWDEN, David, Executive Medical Director, Riveredge Hospital, Forest Park, IL, p. A194

BAXTER, M.D., Brian, President Medical Staff, The Outer Banks Hospital, Nags Head, NC, p. A488

BAXTER, Mike, Chief Operating Officer, Parkview Medical Center, Pueblo, CO, p. A109

BAYDUZA, Ronnie, Administrator, San Leandro Hospital, San Leandro, CA, p. A91

BAYLESS, Jill, Chief Nursing Officer and Chief Operating Officer, Longview Regional Medical Center, Longview, TX, p. A654

BAYLY, M.D., Robert, Vice President Medical Affairs, Muhlenberg Regional Medical Center, North Plainfield, NJ, p. A433

BAYNTON, Kim, Chief Financial Officer, Crouse Hospital, Syracuse, NY, p. A473

BAZEMORE, Wendi, Senior Operations Manager Human Resources, Mercy Hospital, Buffalo, NY, p. A449

BAZZICALUPO, Mary T., Chief Operating Officer, Good Samaritan Medical Center, West Palm Beach, FL, p. A150

BEA, Javon R., President and Chief Executive Officer, Mercy Health System, Janesville, WI, p. A727

BEACH, Orville, Director Information Systems, Simi Valley Hospital and Health Care Services, Simi Valley, CA, p. A94

BEADMAN, Cindi, Director Medical Records, Hospital District Number Five of Harper County, Harper, KS, p. A248

BEALE, Robert, Chief of Staff, Marshall County Hospital, Benton, KY, p. A261

BEALL, T. David, Chief Executive Officer, Methodist Behavioral Hospital of Arkansas, Maumelle, AR, p. A47

BEAMAN Jr, Charles D., President, Palmetto Health Alliance, Columbia, SC, p. B82

BEAMAN, Gale, Chief Fiscal Service, Veterans Affairs Medical Center–Lexington, Lexington, KY, p. A268

BEAMES, Bo, Administrator, Dr. Dan C. Trigg Memorial Hospital, Tucumcari, NM, p. A445

BEAN, Amy A., Human Resources Director, Pulaski Memorial Hospital, Winamac, IN, p. A227

BEAN, Robert H., Ph.D., President and Chief Executive Officer, Sumner Regional Medical Center, Wellington, KS, p. A259

BEAR, Lawrence P.
Administrator, Jersey Community Hospital, Jerseyville, IL, p. A198
Administrator, Jersey Community Hospital, Jerseyville, IL, p. A198

BEARB, April, Administrator, Acadia Rehabilitation Hospital, Crowley, LA, p. A279

BEARD, Les, Chief Executive Officer, Emory Eastside Medical Center, Snellville, GA, p. A169

BEARD, Raleigh, Chief Fiscal Services, Veterans Affairs Edward Hines, Jr. Hospital, Hines, IL, p. A197

BEARDSLEY, Douglas, Administrator, Regency Hospital of Minneapolis, Golden Valley, MN, p. A354

BEASLEY, Eileen, Director of Human Resources, Lake Pointe Medical Center, Rowlett, TX, p. A662

BEASLEY, Jerry, Chief Executive Officer, St. Joseph Hospital, Fort Wayne, IN, p. A216

BEASLEY, Lynn W., President and Chief Executive Officer, Newberry County Memorial Hospital, Newberry, SC, p. A590

BEASLEY, M.D., Michael, President Medical Staff, West Branch Regional Medical Center, West Branch, MI, p. A348

BEASLEY, Ruth, Director of Human Resources, Vanderbilt Stallworth Rehabilitation Hospital, Nashville, TN, p. A616

BEASLEY, Tod
Vice President Financial Services, Baylor All Saints Medical Center at Fort Worth, Fort Worth, TX, p. A639
Vice President Financial Services, Baylor Medical Center at Southwest Fort Worth, Fort Worth, TX, p. A639
Vice President Finance, Baylor Regional Medical Center at Grapevine, Grapevine, TX, p. A642

BEASTON, Bill, Chief Financial Officer, Community Memorial Hospital, Oconto Falls, WI, p. A733

BEATTY, Alan, Vice President Human Resources, Shore Memorial Hospital, Somers Point, NJ, p. A436

BEATTY, James R., Executive Director, Spring Hill Regional Hospital, Brooksville, FL, p. A125

BEATTY, Kemp, Director Information Management, Carlisle Regional Medical Center, Carlisle, PA, p. A554

BEATY, M.D., David, Chief of Staff, Habersham County Medical Center, Demorest, GA, p. A160

BEATY, Ralph E., Administrator, Huntsville Memorial Hospital, Huntsville, TX, p. A649

BEATY, Ryan D., President and Chief Executive Officer, Citrus Memorial Hospital, Inverness, FL, p. A131

BEAUBOUEF, Annette, Human Resources Officer, Savoy Medical Center, Mamou, LA, p. A285

BEAUCHAMP, Alan A.
Chief Executive Officer, Doctors Hospital Parkway, Houston, TX, p. A644
Chief Executive Officer, Doctors Hospital–Tidwell, Houston, TX, p. A644

BEAUCHAMP, Philip K., FACHE,
President and Chief Executive Officer, Morton Plant Hospital, Clearwater, FL, p. A125
President and Chief Executive Officer, Morton Plant Mease Health Care, Dunedin, FL, p. B76

BEAUDOIN, Dale, Director Human Resources, Southern Hills Medical Center, Nashville, TN, p. A615

BEAUDOIN, Paul, Vice President Finance and Chief Financial Officer, Kent County Memorial Hospital, Warwick, RI, p. A582

BEAULAC, Gary, Chief Operating Officer, St. Joseph's Mercy of Macomb, Clinton Township, MI, p. A330

BEAULIEU, Mary Lou, Director of Human Resources and Compliance Officer, Northwestern Medical Center, Saint Albans, VT, p. A683

BEAUVAIS, Richard E., Ph.D., Chief Executive Officer, Wellspring Foundation, Bethlehem, CT, p. A112

BEAVER, Michael, Chief Operating Officer, Meadowcrest Hospital, Gretna, LA, p. A281

BEAVERS, Beverly, Chief Information Management Division, Darnall Army Community Hospital, Fort Hood, TX, p. A638

BEAZLEY, Gary, Information Systems Coordinator, Baylor Medical Center at Waxahachie, Waxahachie, TX, p. A672

BEBOW, Gary, Administrator and Chief Executive Officer, White River Medical Center, Batesville, AR, p. A40

BECHTOLD, Gregg A., President and Chief Executive Officer, Johnson Memorial Hospital, Franklin, IN, p. A216

BECK, Bob, Vice President Medical Affairs, St. Joseph's Hospital, Saint Paul, MN, p. A362

BECK, Brian, Human Resources Director, Providence Kodiak Island Medical Center, Kodiak, AK, p. A27

BECK, David, Chief Administrative Officer and Director Human Resources, Lane Memorial Hospital, Zachary, LA, p. A295

BECK, E. Dean, Administrator, Fulton County Health Center, Wauseon, OH, p. A524

BECK, Gary E., Administrator, Sevier Valley Hospital, Richfield, UT, p. A679

BECK, Harvey, Director Information Systems, Annie Penn Hospital, Reidsville, NC, p. A490

BECK, M.D., J Robert, Vice President Information Services and Chief Information Officer, Fox Chase Cancer Center–American Oncologic Hospital, Philadelphia, PA, p. A567

BECK, James D.
Senior Vice Persident Finance and Chief Financial Officer, All Saints Healthcare, Racine, WI, p. A734
Senior Vice President Finance and Chief Financial Officer, St. Luke's Hospital, Racine, WI, p. A734

BECK, Joe, Chief Financial Officer, Doctor's Hospital at Renaissance, Edinburg, TX, p. A636

BECK, Joyce, Administrator, Thayer County Health Services, Hebron, NE, p. A407

BECK, Lawrence M., President, Good Samaritan Hospital of Maryland, Baltimore, MD, p. A302

BECK, M.D., Robert, Vice President Medical Affairs, Bethesda Rehabilitation Hospital, Saint Paul, MN, p. A361

BECK, Steve, Chief Executive Officer and Administrator, Memorial Hospital, Seminole, TX, p. A666

BECK, Walter G., Chief Executive Officer, George L. Mee Memorial Hospital, King City, CA, p. A65

BECKEMEYER, M.D., Shawn, Chief Medical Staff, Sparta Community Hospital, Sparta, IL, p. A208

BECKER, Bernard, Vice President and Chief Human Resources Officer, Stormont–Vail HealthCare, Topeka, KS, p. A258

BECKER, M.D., Bruce, Chief Medical Director, Medical Center Hospital, Odessa, TX, p. A659

BECKER, Charles T., Manager Resources, James E. Van Zandt Veterans Affairs Medical Center, Altoona, PA, p. A552

BECKER, Cindy, Vice President and Chief Operating Officer, Highland Hospital of Rochester, Rochester, NY, p. A470

BECKER, Frank
Chief Financial Officer, Lourdes Counseling Center, Richland, WA, p. A707
Chief Financial Officer, Lourdes Medical Center, Pasco, WA, p. A705

BECKER, Ralph W., Chief Financial Officer, MidState Medical Center, Meriden, CT, p. A114

BECKER, Richard B., M.D., Chief Executive Officer, George Washington University Hospital, Washington, DC, p. A121

BECKER, Scott A., Chief Executive Officer, Memorial Medical Center, Johnstown, PA, p. A561

BECKER, Sue, Area Technology Director, Kaiser Foundation Hospital – Santa Teresa, San Jose, CA, p. A90

BECKER, Walter S., Chief Executive Officer, Carthage Area Hospital, Carthage, NY, p. A450

BECKER, M.D., William K., Chief of Staff and Medical Director, Veterans Affairs Medical and Regional Office Center, Fargo, ND, p. A498

BECKLER, Richard, Vice President and Chief Financial Officer, Sheltering Arms Rehabilitation Hospital, Mechanicsville, VA, p. A691

BECKMAN, Jill, Vice President Human Resources, Via Christi Regional Medical Center, Wichita, KS, p. A259

BECKSTRAND, James E.
Administrator, Delta Community Medical Center, Delta, UT, p. A676
Administrator, Fillmore Community Medical Center, Fillmore, UT, p. A676

BECKSTROM, Mike, Chief Financial Officer, Marquette General Health System, Marquette, MI, p. A340

BEDAR, Jeanne, Interim Vice President Human Resources, UMass Memorial Medical Center, Worcester, MA, p. A326

BEDFORD, Jeff, Executive Vice President and Chief Financial Officer, River Oaks Hospital, Jackson, MS, p. A371

BEDNAREK, Robert J., President and Chief Executive Officer, Transylvania Community Hospital, Brevard, NC, p. A478

BEDSOLE, Bill R., Chief Executive Officer, Beaufort County Hospital, Washington, NC, p. A493

BEEBY, Lori, Director Information Systems, Community Hospital, McCook, NE, p. A409

BEEDY, Scott, Chief Financial Officer, Hansford Hospital, Spearman, TX, p. A667

BEEG, Gregg
Vice President Finance and Operations, Central Michigan Community Hospital, Mount Pleasant, MI, p. A341
Vice President Finance and Operations, Central Michigan Community Hospital, Mount Pleasant, MI, p. A341

BEEHLER, Robert J., President and Chief Executive Officer, San Joaquin Community Hospital, Bakersfield, CA, p. A54

BEELER, Don A.
President and Chief Executive Officer, Christus Santa Rosa Health Care, San Antonio, TX, p. A663
President and Chief Executive Officer, Christus Santa Rosa Children's Hospital, San Antonio, TX, p. A663

BEEMAN, Barry G., President and Chief Executive Officer, Atlantic General Hospital, Berlin, MD, p. A305

BEEMAN, Thomas E., President and Chief Executive Officer, Lancaster General Hospital, Lancaster, PA, p. A562

BEESON, M.D., John C., Vice President Medical Affairs, St. Mary's Hospital and Medical Center, Grand Junction, CO, p. A106

BEETHE, Lisa, Senior Human Resources Generalist, Harris Continued Care Hospital, Fort Worth, TX, p. A639

BEGAY, R. C., Chief Executive Officer, Acoma–Canoncito–Laguna Hospital, San Fidel, NM, p. A444

BEGBIE, Alan K.
Acting Director, Durham Veterans Affairs Medical Center, Durham, NC, p. A481
Associate Director, Durham Veterans Affairs Medical Center, Durham, NC, p. A481

BEGGS, Shaun
Interim Chief Executive Officer, McAlester Regional Health Center, McAlester, OK, p. A533
Controller, McAlester Regional Health Center, McAlester, OK, p. A533

BEGIN, Jim, Director Information Systems, Casa Grande Regional Medical Center, Casa Grande, AZ, p. A30

BEGLEY, Bruce D., Executive Director, Methodist Hospital, Henderson, KY, p. A266

BEHR, Alan, Chief Financial Officer, Bartow Regional Medical Center, Bartow, FL, p. A123

BEHRENDT, Ph.D., William, Vice President, University of Texas Southwestern Medical Center, Dallas, TX, p. A634

BEHRENS, B. Lyn, President and Chief Executive Officer, Loma Linda University Adventist Health Sciences Center, Loma Linda, CA, p. B70

BEIER, Gregory J., President, Forsyth Medical Center, Winston–Salem, NC, p. A494

BEIER, M.D., Karl, President Medical Staff, Culpeper Regional Hospital, Culpeper, VA, p. A687

BEIERMAN, Jennifer, Director Human Resources, Boone County Health Center, Albion, NE, p. A404

BEILER, Jeffrey, Financial Manager, Veterans Affairs Medical Center, Lebanon, PA, p. A563

BEIRNE, Frank, Chief Executive Officer, Samaritan Hospital, Lexington, KY, p. A268

BEISWENGER, Joel, Director Financial Services, Tri–County Hospital, Wadena, MN, p. A364

BEITING, Mark, Vice President Human Resources, Alta Bates Summit Medical Center – Summit Campus, Oakland, CA, p. A78

BEKKUM, M.D., Brad, Medical Director, Lakeview Medical Center, Rice Lake, WI, p. A734

BELAIR, Lisa, Director Human Resources, Austen Riggs Center, Stockbridge, MA, p. A324

BELDING, M.D., Mel, Vice President Operations and Chief Medical Officer, Harrison Memorial Hospital, Bremerton, WA, p. A700

BELKE, Ken, Interim Administrator, St. Benedicts Family Medical Center, Jerome, ID, p. A179

BELKLE, Greg, Information Systems Manager, Prosser Memorial Hospital, Prosser, WA, p. A706

BELL, Bonnie, Executive Vice President, People and Culture, Harris Methodist Fort Worth, Fort Worth, TX, p. A639

BELL, Cindy, Director Finance, Willow Crest Hospital, Miami, OK, p. A533

BELL, David, Chief Executive Officer, Valle Vista Health System, Greenwood, IN, p. A217

BELL, Deidra S.
Senior Vice President and Chief Financial Officer, Dorchester General Hospital, Cambridge, MD, p. A306
Senior Vice President and Chief Financial Officer, Memorial Hospital at Easton Maryland, Easton, MD, p. A307

BELL, Dorene, Human Resources Coordinator, Leelanau Memorial Health Center, Northport, MI, p. A341

BELL, Heath, VicePresident and Chief Information Officer, Broadlawns Medical Center, Des Moines, IA, p. A232

BELL, Jack, Executive Vice Persident and Chief Operating Officer, St. Vincent Healthcare, Billings, MT, p. A396

BELL, Kristen, Director Human Resources, Mercy Hospital of Pittsburgh, Pittsburgh, PA, p. A572

BELL, Phyllis, Vice President Human Resources, United Medical Center, Cheyenne, WY, p. A739

BELL, Sheryl, Director Information Technology, St. Luke's Regional Medical Center, Boise, ID, p. A178

BELL, M.D., Stuart, Vice President Medical Affairs, Union Memorial Hospital, Baltimore, MD, p. A304

BELL, Talana, Chief Financial Officer, Flowers Hospital, Dothan, AL, p. A17

BELL, Tanya, Public Information Officer, Penrose–St. Francis Health Services, Colorado Springs, CO, p. A102

BELL–SHAMBLEY, Beverly, Ph.D., Facility Director, Mary S Harper Geriatric Psychiatric Center, Tuscaloosa, AL, p. A24

BELLAMY, Cameron, Director Information Technology and Systems, Southern Hills Hospital and Medical Center, Las Vegas, NV, p. A417

BELLAR, M.D., Ralph, Chief of Staff, Hospital District Number Five of Harper County, Harper, KS, p. A248

BELLENFANT, William L., Chief Financial Officer, Trinity Mother Frances Health System, Tyler, TX, p. A671

BELLER, Robert H.
Acting Director, Veterans Affairs Northern Indiana Health Care System, Fort Wayne, IN, p. A216
Associate Director and Chief Operating Officer, Veterans Affairs Northern Indiana Health Care System, Fort Wayne, IN, p. A216

BELMONT, M.D., H Michael, Medical Director, Hospital for Joint Diseases Orthopaedic Institute, New York, NY, p. A460

BELMONT, Terry A.
Senior Vice President and Administrator, Kaiser Foundation Hospital, Fontana, CA, p. A60
Senior Vice President and Administrator, Kaiser Foundation Hospital–Riverside, Riverside, CA, p. A84

BELSKY, M.D., Murray, Vice President Medical Affairs, Newark Beth Israel Medical Center, Newark, NJ, p. A432

BELTER, Paul E., Vice President Finance and Chief Financial Officer, Mount St. Mary's Hospital and Health Center, Lewiston, NY, p. A455

BELYEU, Peggy, Controller, Vanderbilt Stallworth Rehabilitation Hospital, Nashville, TN, p. A616

BELZER, Michael, Medical Director, Hennepin County Medical Center, Minneapolis, MN, p. A357

BEMANN, Lynn, Chief Fiscal Service, Clement J. Zablocki Veterans Affairs Medical Center, Milwaukee, WI, p. A730

BEMENT, Doug, Chief Financial Officer, Bluffton Regional Medical Center, Bluffton, IN, p. A212

BEN, Nella J.
Chief Executive Officer, U. S. Public Health Service Indian Hospital, San Carlos, AZ, p. A36
Chief Executive Officer, U. S. Public Health Service Indian Hospital, San Carlos, AZ, p. A36

BENCOMO, Dionisio, Chief Executive Officer, Select Specialty Hospital of Miami, Miami, FL, p. A138

BENDER, Austin, Director Human Resources, Hospital for Joint Diseases Orthopaedic Institute, New York, NY, p. A460

BENDER, M.D., Brad, Chief of Staff, Malcom Randall Veterans Affairs Medical Center, Gainesville, FL, p. A129

BENDER, M.D., D Scott, Chief of Staff, Star Valley Medical Center, Afton, WY, p. A739

BENDER, Douglas, Human Resource Manager, Veterans Affairs Medical Center, Albany, NY, p. A446

BENDER, Robert, Director Information Technology Services, St. Mary's Medical Center, Duluth, MN, p. A352

BENDER, Ronald, Chief Executive Officer, Clay County Medical Center, Clay Center, KS, p. A245

BENDER, Sally, Director Information Services, Ingham Regional Medical Center, Lansing, MI, p. A338

BENEDICT, Joy, Director Human Resources, Pattie A. Clay Regional Medical Center, Richmond, KY, p. A274

BENEDICT, William, Executive Director, Elmira Psychiatric Center, Elmira, NY, p. A452

BENEFIEL, Penny, Director Human Resources, DeTar Healthcare System, Victoria, TX, p. A672

BENEFIELD, Beth, Executive Director of Hospital Information Systems, Houston Medical Center, Warner Robins, GA, p. A172

BENEFIELD, Dewayne, Chief Financial Officer, South Austin Hospital, Austin, TX, p. A624

BENEFIELD, Micki, Chief Financial Officer, Baptist Memorial Hospital–Desoto, Southaven, MS, p. A375

BENETE, Pedro L., Administrator, Hospital San Cristobal, Coto Laurel, PR, p. A745

BENFER, David W., FACHE, President and Chief Executive Officer, Hospital of Saint Raphael, New Haven, CT, p. A115

BENFIELD, Ronald K., Chief Financial Officer and Vice President, Florida Hospital Waterman, Tavares, FL, p. A149

BENFORD, Barry C., Director, Altoona Center, Altoona, PA, p. A551

BENGALI, Abdul
Chairman Information Systems, Rochester Methodist Hospital, Rochester, MN, p. A360
Chairman Foundation Information Technology, Saint Marys Hospital, Rochester, MN, p. A360

BENGE, M.D., Eddie
Vice President Medical Staff Affairs, Presbyterian Hospital, Albuquerque, NM, p. A440
Vice President Medical Staff Affairs, Presbyterian Kaseman Hospital, Albuquerque, NM, p. A441

BENGTSON, Paul R., Chief Executive Officer, Northeastern Vermont Regional Hospital, Saint Johnsbury, VT, p. A683

BENINCOSA, Warren
Chief Executive Officer, Seneca Healthcare District, Chester, CA, p. A56
Chief Executive Officer, Seneca Healthcare District, Chester, CA, p. A56

BENJAMIN, Richard, Chief Fiscal Services, Veterans Affairs Medical Center, Cincinnati, OH, p. A508

BENJAMIN, Sunny, Director Human Resources, Continuous Care Center of Tulsa, Tulsa, OK, p. A539

BENN, David P., Chief Executive Officer, Memorial Hospitals Association, Modesto, CA, p. A76

BENNER, Ron, Chief Executive Officer, Children's Hospital of Wisconsin, Kenosha, WI, p. A727

BENNETT, Barbara, Controller, HEALTHSOUTH Reading Rehabilitation Hospital, Reading, PA, p. A574

BENNETT, Bruce A., Chief Executive Officer, Brown County General Hospital, Georgetown, OH, p. A514

BENNETT, David
Director, Bryce Hospital, Tuscaloosa, AL, p. A24
Chief Executive Officer, Select Specialty Hospital – Tulsa, Tulsa, OK, p. A540

BENNETT, E Kyle, Executive Vice President, Memorial Hospital and Health Care Center, Jasper, IN, p. A219

BENNETT, Ellie, Chief Operating Officer, Riverside County Regional Medical Center, Moreno Valley, CA, p. A77

BENNETT, Fay, Director, Guadalupe Valley Hospital, Seguin, TX, p. A666

BENNETT, Gloria
Corporate Director Human Resources, Mercy Health System of Kansas, Fort Scott, KS, p. A247
Corporate Director Human Resources, Mercy Health System of Kansas, Independence, KS, p. A249

BENNETT, Gordon, Chief Executive Officer, South Davis Community Hospital, Bountiful, UT, p. A676

BENNETT, Joan, Vice President, Human Resources, Lawrence & Memorial Hospital, New London, CT, p. A115

BENNETT, John, President and Chief Executive Officer, Shelby Memorial Hospital, Shelbyville, IL, p. A207

BENNETT, Kris, Finance Director, UHHS Richmond Heights Hospital, Richmond Heights, OH, p. A521

BENNETT, Laurie, Director Human Resources, Sarasota Memorial Hospital, Sarasota, FL, p. A146

BENNETT, Lee, Interim Administrator, Sitka Community Hospital, Sitka, AK, p. A28

BENNETT, CPA, Lisa, Director Financial Services, Waverly Health Center, Waverly, IA, p. A243

BENNETT, Paula, Administrator, Stamford Memorial Hospital, Stamford, TX, p. A667

BENNETT, Randall, Assistant Administrator, Uintah Basin Medical Center, Roosevelt, UT, p. A679

BENNETT, M.D., Richard G., Senior Vice President Medical Affairs, Johns Hopkins Bayview Medical Center, Baltimore, MD, p. A303

BENNETT, Richard I.
Senior Vice President and Chief Financial Officer, Crozer–Chester Medical Center, Upland, PA, p. A577
Senior Vice President and Chief Financial Officer, Delaware County Memorial Hospital, Drexel Hill, PA, p. A557

BENNETT, Ron, Chief Financial Officer, Abilene Regional Medical Center, Abilene, TX, p. A620

BENNETT, Sharon, Information Systems Manager, Cobre Valley Community Hospital, Globe, AZ, p. A31

BENNETT, Tony N., Administrator, HEALTHSOUTH Emerald Coast Rehabilitation Hospital, Panama City, FL, p. A142

BENNETT, William, Chief Financial Officer, Riverview Healthcare Association, Crookston, MN, p. A352

BENOIT, Michele
Vice President, Human Resources, Methodist Children's Hospital of South Texas, San Antonio, TX, p. A664
Vice President, Human Resources, Methodist Hospital, San Antonio, TX, p. A664

BENOIT, Rebecca, Chief Operating Officer, OU Medical Center, Oklahoma City, OK, p. A536

BENSING, Gary, Vice President, University of Louisville Hospital, Louisville, KY, p. A270

BENSON, Damon, Chief Executive Officer, Kingfisher Regional Hospital, Kingfisher, OK, p. A532

BENSON, Eric, Vice President Human Resources, Sarah Bush Lincoln Health Center, Mattoon, IL, p. A200

BENSON, Jim, Director Information Systems, Middle Tennessee Medical Center, Murfreesboro, TN, p. A614

BENSON, Peggy, Assistant Administrator Human Resources, Jackson Hospital and Clinic, Montgomery, AL, p. A22

BENSON, Sheena, Director Human Resources, Havasu Regional Medical Center, Lake Havasu City, AZ, p. A32

BENTE, Julie
Vice President Human and Facility Resources, Regional Medical Center, Manchester, IA, p. A237
Vice President Human and Facility Resources, Regional Medical Center, Manchester, IA, p. A237

BENTELMANN, Delsa, Human Resources Leader, North Hawaii Community Hospital, Kamuela, HI, p. A175

BENTLAGE, M.D., Charles H., Chief Medical Officer, Freeman Health System, Joplin, MO, p. A383

BENTLEY, Brian S., Administrator, Plains Regional Medical Center, Clovis, NM, p. A442

BENTLEY, Jim, Director Information Systems, Jackson General Hospital, Ripley, WV, p. A719

BENTLEY, Nancy, Director Human Resources, Good Samaritan Medical Center, West Palm Beach, FL, p. A150

BENTLEY, Scott, Chief Financial Officer, Mainland Medical Center, Texas City, TX, p. A670

BENTON, Dennis
Business Strategy and Finance Leader, Kaiser Foundation Hospital, Los Angeles, CA, p. A70
Business Strategy and Finance Leader, Kaiser Foundation Hospital, Los Angeles, CA, p. A71

BENTZ, Doug, Chief Executive Officer, Roane General Hospital, Spencer, WV, p. A720

BENTZINGER, Rick, Vice President of Human Resources, OHSU Hospital, Portland, OR, p. A547

BENYA, Susan, Vice President, Memorial Medical Center, Johnstown, PA, p. A561

BENZ, Blake, Director Data Processing, Eastern Long Island Hospital, Greenport, NY, p. A453

BENZ Jr, Edward J., M.D., President and Chief Executive Officer, Dana–Farber Cancer Institute, Boston, MA, p. A313

BERARD, Celse A., President, Riverview Hospital Association, Wisconsin Rapids, WI, p. A738

BERDAN, Barclay E., CHE, President, Harris Methodist Fort Worth, Fort Worth, TX, p. A639

BERDISCHEWSKY, M.D., Myron
Regional Chief Medical Officer, Providence Holy Cross Medical Center, San Fernando, CA, p. A88
Chief Medical Officer, Providence Saint Joseph Medical Center, Burbank, CA, p. A55

BERENTSEN, M.D., Thomas, Chief of Staff, Memorial Community Hospital, Edgerton, WI, p. A725

BERG, D.O., Gary, Vice President Medical Affairs, St. John Oakland Hospital, Madison Heights, MI, p. A339

BERG, James A., President, Methodist Hospitals, Gary, IN, p. A216

BERG, M.D., John, Chief of Staff, Queen of Peace Hospital, New Prague, MN, p. A358

BERG, M.D., Jon, Chief of Staff, Northwood Deaconess Health Center, Northwood, ND, p. A500

BERG, Odin, Vice President Finance and Chief Financial Officer, Provena Saint Joseph Hospital, Elgin, IL, p. A193

BERG, William, Financial Manager, Veterans Affairs Medical Center, Erie, PA, p. A558

BERGEN, Sharon A., Chief Operating Officer, Belmont Center for Comprehensive Treatment, Philadelphia, PA, p. A567

BERGER, George, Chief Financial Officer, Tyrone Hospital, Tyrone, PA, p. A577

BERGER, Susan, Prioress, Benedictine Sisters of the Annunciation, Bismarck, ND, p. B17

BERGER, Warren, Chief Fiscal Service, Edith Nourse Rogers Memorial Veterans Hospital, Bedford, MA, p. A312

BERGERSEN, M.D., Dean, Chief Medical Officer, Sibley Medical Center, Arlington, MN, p. A349

BERGH, Roger, Director Human Resources, Helen Newberry Joy Hospital, Newberry, MI, p. A341

BERGLIN, Sally, Vice President Patient Care Services, LakeView Community Hospital, Paw Paw, MI, p. A342

BERGLING, Richard Q., Administrator and Chief Executive Officer, Ness County Hospital, Ness City, KS, p. A253

BERGLUND, Kay, Vice President Finance and Chief Financial Officer, Methodist Hospital of Southern California, Arcadia, CA, p. A53

BERGMAN, Sonya, Chief Human Resources Officer, Hazard ARH Regional Medical Center, Hazard, KY, p. A266

BERGMANN, Peter, President and Chief Executive Officer, Good Samaritan Regional Medical Center, Pottsville, PA, p. A573

BERGREN, Jeff, Regional Chief Executive Officer, Streamwood Behavioral Health Center, Streamwood, IL, p. A209

BERGSENG, M.D., D., John H., Vice President Medical Affairs, Glencoe Regional Health Services, Glencoe, MN, p. A354

BERGSTROM, Terry, Chief Operating Officer, Knapp Medical Center, Weslaco, TX, p. A673

BERKELEY, Larry L., Associate Director, Clement J. Zablocki Veterans Affairs Medical Center, Milwaukee, WI, p. A730

BERKHOUSE, Michelle, Director Patient Care Services, Seton Edgar B. Davis Hospital, Luling, TX, p. A655

BERLUCCHI, Scott A., President and Chief Executive Officer, Elk Regional Health Center, Saint Marys, PA, p. A574

BERMAN, Manuel S., Chief Operating Officer, Tuality Healthcare, Hillsboro, OR, p. A544

BERNALES, M.D., Nannette, Medical Staff President, St. Luke Hospital East, Fort Thomas, KY, p. A264

BERNARD, Mark L., Chief Executive Officer, Metropolitan Methodist Hospital, San Antonio, TX, p. A664

BERND, David L., Chief Executive Officer, Sentara Healthcare, Norfolk, VA, p. B96

BERNDT, Carol, Administrator Human Resources, Innovis Health, Fargo, ND, p. A497

BERNER, Tom, Vice President and Chief Financial Officer, Bristol Bay Area Health Corporation, Dillingham, AK, p. A27

BERNHARDT, Glenda, Manager, St. John's Medical Center and Living Center, Jackson, WY, p. A740

BERNSTEIN, Les, Director Information Systems, Cookeville Regional Medical Center, Cookeville, TN, p. A605

BERNSTEIN, Lori, Manager Human Resources, Clinton Memorial Hospital, Saint Johns, MI, p. A344

BERNSTEIN, Martin B., Chief Executive Officer, Northern Maine Medical Center, Fort Kent, ME, p. A298

BERNSTEIN, Michael, Chief Financial Officer, Valley Medical Center, Renton, WA, p. A706

BERNSTEIN, Ronald T., President and Chief Executive Officer, Foundations Behavioral Health, Doylestown, PA, p. A557

BERRETT, Britt, President and Chief Executive Officer, Medical City Dallas Hospital, Dallas, TX, p. A633

BERRIDGE, Linda, Chief Executive Officer, Two Rivers Psychiatric Hospital, Kansas City, MO, p. A385

BERRIGAN, M.D., Michael, Interim Medical Director, George Washington University Hospital, Washington, DC, p. A121

BERRY, Clement, Chief Executive Officer, Upper Connecticut Valley Hospital, Colebrook, NH, p. A420

BERRY, David, Information Systems Director, Morehouse General Hospital, Bastrop, LA, p. A277

BERRY, Diane, Controller, HEALTHSOUTH Rehabilitation Hospital of Jonesboro, Jonesboro, AR, p. A45

BERRY, Greg, Chief Financial Officer, Doctors Hospital of Manteca, Manteca, CA, p. A74

BERRY, Joe, Chief Information Officer, Pekin Hospital, Pekin, IL, p. A204

BERRY, John, Chief Operating Officer, Clinch Valley Medical Center, Richlands, VA, p. A694

BERRY, Kevin G., Deputy Commander for Clinical Services, Tripler Army Medical Center, Honolulu, HI, p. A174

BERRY, Linda, Vice President Human Resources, Memorial Hospital, Towanda, PA, p. A577

BERRY, Stan B., FACHE, Chief Executive Officer, North Hawaii Community Hospital, Kamuela, HI, p. A175

BERRYMAN, Joanne, Senior Vice President, Frazier Rehab Institute, Louisville, KY, p. A269

BERRYMAN, William R., M.D., Acting Director, Veterans Affairs Medical Center, Grand Junction, CO, p. A106

BERSANTE, Syd
Chief Operating Officer, St. Francis Hospital, Federal Way, WA, p. A703
Chief Operating Officer, St. Francis Hospital, Federal Way, WA, p. A703

BERT, Alisa, Chief Financial Officer, University Hospital and Medical Center, Tamarac, FL, p. A147

BERTHA, M.D., Ernest G., Chief Medical Officer, Temple University Children's Medical Center, Philadelphia, PA, p. A570

BERTIN–EPP, Denise
Chief Executive Officer, Brighton Hospital, Brighton, MI, p. A329
Chief Executive Officer, Brighton Hospital, Brighton, MI, p. A329

BERTKE, Brad, Vice President Support Services, Mercy Hospital Clermont, Batavia, OH, p. A503

BERTRAND, Neil W., Chief Financial Officer, Longmont United Hospital, Longmont, CO, p. A108

BERTSCH, Darrold, Administrator, Southwest Healthcare Services, Bowman, ND, p. A496

BERTY, Donna, Chief Executive Officer, Select Specialty Hospital of Colorado Springs, Colorado Springs, CO, p. A102

BESKE, Timothy, Information Systems Manager, Redwood Area Hospital, Redwood Falls, MN, p. A360

BESS, Tim, Chief Operating Officer, Saint Francis Hospital, Charleston, WV, p. A714

BESSON, M.D., Stephen, Chief of Medical Staff, Nicholas County Hospital, Carlisle, KY, p. A262

BESST, Kara, Chief Financial Officer, Gritman Medical Center, Moscow, ID, p. A180

BEST, Candis
Chief Information Officer and Chief Operating Officer, Woodhull Medical and Mental Health Center, New York, NY, p. A466
Chief Information Officer and Chief Operating Officer, Woodhull Medical and Mental Health Center, New York, NY, p. A466

BESTEN, Brian, Program Leader Business Officer, Louis A. Johnson Veterans Affairs Medical Center, Clarksburg, WV, p. A714

BESTOR, William E., President and Chief Executive Officer, Community Memorial Hospital, Menomonee Falls, WI, p. A729

BESWICK, Elizabeth, Vice President Human Resources, Carteret General Hospital, Morehead City, NC, p. A488

BESWICK, Melinda D., Chief Executive Officer, Anaheim Memorial Medical Center, Anaheim, CA, p. A52

BETANCOURT, Erika, Human Resource Coordinator, Cornerstone Regional Hospital, Edinburg, TX, p. A636

BETANCOURT, Salvador, Information Systems Manager, Sunnyside Community Hospital, Sunnyside, WA, p. A710

BETHELL, Mark, Chief Operating Officer, North Monroe Medical Center, Monroe, LA, p. A287

BETSCH, Jeff, Director, Fairfield Memorial Hospital, Winnsboro, SC, p. A593

BETTS, Brooks, Director Information Systems, St. Andrews Hospital and Healthcare Center, Boothbay Harbor, ME, p. A297

BETZ, Paul, Administrator and Chief Executive Officer, Baptist Memorial Hospital–Tipton, Covington, TN, p. A605

BEVERLY, Douglas H., CHE, Administrator, HEALTHSOUTH Rehabilitation Hospital of North Alabama, Huntsville, AL, p. A20

BEVERLY, Ken B., President and Chief Executive Officer, Archbold Medical Center, Thomasville, GA, p. B9

BEVINS, O. David, Chief Executive Officer, Kentucky River Medical Center, Jackson, KY, p. A266

BEYUKA, Harriett, Management Informatom Systems Manager, Gallup Indian Medical Center, Gallup, NM, p. A442

BEZANSON, Robert H.
President and Chief Executive Officer, CoxHealth, Springfield, MO, p. B34
President and Chief Executive Officer, Lester E. Cox Medical Centers, Springfield, MO, p. A394

BEZUCHA, Gary, Administrator, Boscobel Area Health Care, Boscobel, WI, p. A723

BHANDARI, M.D., Raj, Physician–in–Chief, Kaiser Foundation Hospital – Santa Teresa, San Jose, CA, p. A90

BHARDWAJ, Neelam, Chief Executive Officer and Administrator, Valley County Hospital, Ord, NE, p. A411

BHARUCHA, Bomi, Chief Financial Officer, North Valley Hospital, Tonasket, WA, p. A711

BHATELEY, M.D., Dileen, Chief of Staff, Falls Community Hospital and Clinic, Marlin, TX, p. A655

BHATIA, Krishin L., Administrator, Victory Memorial Hospital, New York, NY, p. A466

BHATTACHARYYA, Anjan, Commissioner, Doctor Robert L. Yeager Health Center, Pomona, NY, p. A469

BIALORVCKI, Tom, Chief Information Officer, Bay Medical Center, Panama City, FL, p. A142

BIANCAMANO, John, Vice President Finance, Hartford Hospital, Hartford, CT, p. A113

BIANCANIELLO, Thomas, Chief Medical Officer, Stony Brook University Hospital, Stony Brook, NY, p. A473

BIANCARELLI, M.D., Joseph, President Medical Staff, Memorial Hospital, Towanda, PA, p. A577

BIANCHI, Charles A., President and Chief Executive Officer, Hillsdale Community Health Center, Hillsdale, MI, p. A336

BIBB, Lisa, Director of Human Resources, San Angelo Community Medical Center, San Angelo, TX, p. A663

BIBI, John, Director Human Resources, St. John's Regional Medical Center, Oxnard, CA, p. A80

BICKEL, Brian E., President and Chief Executive Officer, Howard Memorial Hospital, Nashville, AR, p. A48

BICKELMAN, Carol, President and Chief Executive Officer, Desert Hills Hospital, Albuquerque, NM, p. A440

BICKERT, Ron, Director Human Resources, ValleyCare Medical Center, Pleasanton, CA, p. A82

BICKHAM, Bruce, Vice President Financial Services and Controller, Baylor Institute for Rehabilitation, Dallas, TX, p. A632

BIDERMAN, Chris, Director Information Systems, Parrish Medical Center, Titusville, FL, p. A149

BIE, Gary, Senior Vice President for Finance and Administration and Chief Financial Officer, Nassau University Medical Center, East Meadow, NY, p. A451

BIEBER, Courtney, Director Information Systems, Ville Platte Medical Center, Ville Platte, LA, p. A294

BIEBER, Martin A., President and Chief Executive Officer, Mercy Medical Center, Rockville Centre, NY, p. A471

BIEDIGER, Dan, Vice President Human Resources, FirstHealth Moore Regional Hospital, Pinehurst, NC, p. A489

BIEDIGER, Michael J., President and Chief Executive Officer, Lexington Medical Center, West Columbia, SC, p. A593

BIEGANSKI, Gary, CHE, President, Community Hospital, McCook, NE, p. A409

BIEHL, M.D., Albert, Vice President Medical Affairs, Bethesda Memorial Hospital, Boynton Beach, FL, p. A124

BIELECKI, Thomas A., Chief Financial Officer, Temple East, Northeastern Hospital, Philadelphia, PA, p. A570

BIEN, John, Vice President Finance, United Hospital, Saint Paul, MN, p. A362

BIENSTOCK, Mark D., Executive Director, Bronx Children's Psychiatric Center, New York, NY, p. A458

BIENVENU, Russel, Administrator, Louisiana Extended Care Hospital of Natchitoches, Natchitoches, LA, p. A288

BIENZ, M.D., Thomas, Chief of Staff, Ivinson Memorial Hospital, Laramie, WY, p. A741

BIERMAN, Joan, Controller, Cherokee Regional Medical Center, Cherokee, IA, p. A230

BIERMAN, Mike, Chief Financial Officer, Lake Pointe Medical Center, Rowlett, TX, p. A662

BIERSCHENK, Kevin
Chief Executive Officer, Southwest Alabama Medical Center, Thomasville, AL, p. A24
Chief Executive Officer, Southwest Alabama Medical Center, Thomasville, AL, p. A24

BIESTER, Dori J., R.N., President and Chief Executive Officer, Children's Hospital, Denver, CO, p. A103

BIGA, Thomas A., Executive Director, Clara Maass Medical Center, Belleville, NJ, p. A425

BIGBY, Walter O., Administrator and Owner, Bastrop Rehabilitation Hospital, Bastrop, LA, p. A277

BIGELOW, David C., Chief Executive Officer, Samaritan Pacific Communities Hospital, Newport, OR, p. A546

BIGELOW, Debbie, Chief Financial Officer, Coulee Community Hospital, Grand Coulee, WA, p. A703

BIGELOW, Timothy, Director of Human Resources, Butler Hospital, Providence, RI, p. A581

BIGGINS, Karen, Chief Financial Officer, St. Dominic's Hospital, Manteca, CA, p. A74

BIGGINS, Lillie, Vice President Operations, Harris Methodist Fort Worth, Fort Worth, TX, p. A639

BIGGS, Alan W.
Chief Financial and Operating Officer, Memorial Hospital, Logansport, IN, p. A221
Chief Financial and Operating Officer, Memorial Hospital, Logansport, IN, p. A221

BIGLEY, Robert F., Executive Director, East Georgia Regional Medical Center, Statesboro, GA, p. A169

BIGNOTTI, M.D., Donald, Vice President Medical Affairs, St. Joseph Mercy Oakland, Pontiac, MI, p. A343

BIGOTT, Albert L., Chief Financial Officer, Metropolitan Hospital Center, New York, NY, p. A462

BIHUNIAK, Peter, Vice President Finance, Robert Wood Johnson University Hospital at Rahway, Rahway, NJ, p. A435

BILBO, Dorothy C., Administrator, Pearl River County Hospital, Poplarville, MS, p. A375

BILBREY, M.D., George M., Chief of Staff, Mission Hospitals, Asheville, NC, p. A477

BILL, Charles E., CHE, Chief Executive Officer, Southwest Memorial Hospital, Cortez, CO, p. A102

BILLERBECK, M.D., Robert, Vice President Medical Affairs, Good Samaritan Health Systems, Kearney, NE, p. A408

BILLING, Michael D., Administrator, Mid–Valley Hospital, Omak, WA, p. A705

BILLING, Tommye
Vice President and Chief Information Officer, St. Vincent Infirmary Medical Center, Little Rock, AR, p. A47
Vice President and Chief Information Officer, St. Vincent Medical Center–North, Sherwood, AR, p. A50

BILLINGS, Charlotte, Interim Chief Executive Officer, Seiling Hospital, Seiling, OK, p. A538

BILLINGS, Robert E., Chief Financial Officer, Largo Medical Center, Largo, FL, p. A134

BILLINGSLEY, Linn P., Chief Executive Officer, Kindred Hospital–Las Vegas, Las Vegas, NV, p. A416

BILLS, Robert C., President, Valley Presbyterian Hospital, Los Angeles, CA, p. A73

BINDER, Forest, Vice President Finance, St. Mary's Hospital and Medical Center, Grand Junction, CO, p. A106

BING, William W.
Administrator, Morehouse General Hospital, Bastrop, LA, p. A277
Administrator, Morehouse General Hospital, Bastrop, LA, p. A277

BINGHAM, Sharon L., Administrator, Meadowbrook Rehabilitation Hospital, Gardner, KS, p. A247

BIRCHELL, Bruce K., Administrator and Chief Executive Officer, Greenwood County Hospital, Eureka, KS, p. A247

BIRD, Alan, Administrator, Nature Coast Regional Hospital, Williston, FL, p. A151

BIRD, M.D., Julio J., Chief Medical Officer, Gundersen Lutheran Medical Center, La Crosse, WI, p. A727

BIRDZELL, JoAnn, President and Chief Executive Officer, St. Catherine Hospital, East Chicago, IN, p. A214

BIRKENSTOCK, Timothy L., Treasurer and Chief Financial Officer, Children's Hospital of Wisconsin, Milwaukee, WI, p. A730

BIRKHOLTZ, Marlene, Chief of Staff, Ogallala Community Hospital, Ogallala, NE, p. A410

BIRLEW, Ron, Director Human Resources, Des Peres Hospital, Saint Louis, MO, p. A390

BIRMINGHAM, Tom, Chief Financial Officer, Kennewick General Hospital, Kennewick, WA, p. A703

BISCONE, Mark A., Executive Director, Waldo County General Hospital, Belfast, ME, p. A296

BISHARA, M.D., Nagi, Chief of Staff, St. Charles Mercy Hospital, Oregon, OH, p. A520

BISHOP, Doug, Chief Financial Officer, Whidbey General Hospital, Coupeville, WA, p. A702

BISHOP, Harry, Director Human Resources, Mercy Medical, Daphne, AL, p. A17

BISHOP, James, Director Medical Affairs, Fairview Southdale Hospital, Edina, MN, p. A353

BISHOP, Jim, Interim Administrator, Harney District Hospital, Burns, OR, p. A542

BISHOP, Timothy B., Administrator Financial Services, Estes Park Medical Center, Estes Park, CO, p. A105

BISKUP, Bernadette
Interim Chief Operating Officer, University of Illinois Medical Center at Chicago, Chicago, IL, p. A191
Interim Chief Operating Officer, University of Illinois Medical Center at Chicago, Chicago, IL, p. A191

BISSEL, Jane
Chief Financial Officer, Carrington Health Center, Carrington, ND, p. A497
Chief Financial Officer, Mercy Hospital, Valley City, ND, p. A500

BISSENDEN, Chris
Director Human Resources, Brigham City Community Hospital, Brigham City, UT, p. A676
Director Human Resources, Ogden Regional Medical Center, Ogden, UT, p. A678

BISTERFELDT, Joanne, Vice President Information Systems, All Saints Healthcare, Racine, WI, p. A734

BISTKO, Laurel, Director Information Systems, Mercy Jeannette Hospital, Jeannette, PA, p. A561

BISWELL, Vic, Administrator, Sierra Valley District Hospital, Loyalton, CA, p. A74

BITAR, Carlos, Assistant Administrator, Kendall Regional Medical Center, Miami, FL, p. A137

BITHER, Dean, Chief Financial Officer, Valley Regional Hospital, Claremont, NH, p. A420

BITTING, Nancy J., Regional Chief Executive Officer, St. Joseph Hospital, Bellingham, WA, p. A700

BITTNER, Augustine, Chief Information Officer, Veterans Affairs Medical Center–Louisville, Louisville, KY, p. A270

BITTNER, Ben, Director Human Resources, Plantation General Hospital, Plantation, FL, p. A143

BIUNDO, M.D., Russell, Medical Director, HEALTHSOUTH MountainView Regional Rehabilitation Hospital, Morgantown, WV, p. A718

BIXEL, Kenneth, Senior Vice President and Chief Information Officer, Mount Nittany Medical Center, State College, PA, p. A576

BIXLER, David, Senior Vice President, Regional Medical Center of Orangeburg and Calhoun Counties, Orangeburg, SC, p. A591

BIZZLE, Ben, Information Systems Manager, Great River Medical Center, Blytheville, AR, p. A41

BJELICH, Steven C., President and Chief Executive Officer, Saint Francis Medical Center, Cape Girardeau, MO, p. A379

BJELLA, Karmon T., Chief Executive Officer, Unity Hospital, Muscatine, IA, p. A238

BJERKE, Carolyn, Human Resources Director, Kingfisher Regional Hospital, Kingfisher, OK, p. A532

BJORGUM, Deb, Data Processing Manager, Johnson Regional Medical Center, Clarksville, AR, p. A41

BJORK, M.D., David, Chief of Staff, Lake Region Healthcare Corporation, Fergus Falls, MN, p. A353

BLACH, Ed, Director Information Systems, Clarinda Regional Health Center, Clarinda, IA, p. A230

BLACK, Adrianne, Chief Operating Officer, Metropolitan Nashville General Hospital, Nashville, TN, p. A615

BLACK, Jr, Albert, Chief Operating Officer, Hospital of the University of Pennsylvania, Philadelphia, PA, p. A568

BLACK, Bob, Vice President, University Medical Center, Tucson, AZ, p. A38

BLACK, IV, Charles, Chief Financial Officer, Rockcastle Hospital and Respiratory Care Center, Mount Vernon, KY, p. A272

BLACK, Diane, Human Resources Director, Marlette Community Hospital, Marlette, MI, p. A340

BLACK, Gary E., President and Chief Executive Officer, Lenoir Memorial Hospital, Kinston, NC, p. A486

BLACK, Marilynn
   Chief Information Officer, Carroll County Hospital, Carrollton, KY, p. A262
   Vice President Systems Integration, Norton Audubon Hospital, Louisville, KY, p. A269
   Chief Information Officer, Norton Hospital, Louisville, KY, p. A270
   Vice President Systems Integration, Norton Southwest Hospital, Louisville, KY, p. A270
   Vice President Systems Integration, Norton Suburban Hospital, Louisville, KY, p. A270

BLACK, Michael, Vice President Human Resources, Grady Memorial Hospital, Atlanta, GA, p. A154

BLACK, Randall, Chief of Staff, St. Mary–Rogers Memorial Hospital, Rogers, AR, p. A49

BLACKBURN, Gloria
   Director Operations and Chief Nursing Executive, Kaiser Foundation Hospital–West Los Angeles, Los Angeles, CA, p. A71
   Director Operations, Kaiser Foundation Hospital–West Los Angeles, Los Angeles, CA, p. A71

BLACKBURN, Joslyn, Administrator, Oasis Long Term Care Acute Hospital, New Orleans, LA, p. A289

BLACKMON, David, Chief Financial Officer, Comanche County Memorial Hospital, Lawton, OK, p. A532

BLACKMON, Millie, Administrative Officer, U. S. Public Health Service Indian Hospital, Clinton, OK, p. A529

BLACKMON, Tanya, Executive Director Orthopaedic Services, Presbyterian–Orthopaedic Hospital, Charlotte, NC, p. A480

BLACKWELDER, FACHE, Albert K., Chief Operating Officer, Emory Crawford Long Hospital, Atlanta, GA, p. A153

BLACKWELL, David, Vice President of Human Resources, Vail Valley Medical Center, Vail, CO, p. A110

BLACKWELL, Jack, Chief Financial Officer, Highlands Regional Medical Center, Prestonsburg, KY, p. A273

BLACKWOOD, M.D., Don, Chief Medical Staff, Bolivar Medical Center, Cleveland, MS, p. A368

BLACKWOOD, Terry W., Senior Vice President and Chief Financial Officer, City of Hope National Medical Center, Duarte, CA, p. A59

BLAHA, Bill, Management Information Systems Manager, Tri–County Hospital, Wadena, MN, p. A364

BLAHA, John E., Vice President Finance and Chief Financial Officer, Brattleboro Retreat, Brattleboro, VT, p. A682

BLAIR, Betty, Director Information Systems, Andalusia Regional Hospital, Andalusia, AL, p. A13

BLAIR, Jr, George A., Chief Financial Officer, Bon Secours Baltimore Health System, Baltimore, MD, p. A302

BLAIR, Jan, Vice President Human Resources, Foote Health System, Jackson, MI, p. A337

BLAIR, Jim, Senior Vice President, Chief Financial Officer, Muskogee Regional Medical Center, Muskogee, OK, p. A534

BLAIR, M.D., Keith, Information Systems Manager, Lander Valley Medical Center, Lander, WY, p. A740

BLAIR, Michael, Chief Information Officer, Carson Tahoe Hospital, Carson City, NV, p. A415

BLAIR, Robert D., Chief Executive Officer, Kindred Hospital – La Mirada, La Mirada, CA, p. A66

BLAKE, Ph.D., J, David, Vice President, Saint John's Health Center, Santa Monica, CA, p. A93

BLAKE, M.D., Robert A L, Chief Medical Officer, Hospital for Sick Children, Washington, DC, p. A121

BLALOCK, Cam, Senior Vice President Corporate Services, Nash Health Care Systems, Rocky Mount, NC, p. A490

BLANCHARD, Tim, Vice President Finance, Willamette Falls Hospital, Oregon City, OR, p. A546

BLANCHARD, Todd, Chief Executive Officer, Springhill Medical Center, Springhill, LA, p. A293

BLANCHARD, William R., Chief Executive Officer, DeTar Healthcare System, Victoria, TX, p. A672

BLANCHETTE, Edward A., M.D., Director, Connecticut Department of Correction's Hospital, Somers, CT, p. A116

BLAND, Douglas, Manager Information Services, Spring View Hospital, Lebanon, KY, p. A267

BLAND, M.D., James G., Chief of Staff, Jane Todd Crawford Hospital, Greensburg, KY, p. A265

BLAND, Mary, Chief Information Officer and Vice President, Tallahassee Memorial HealthCare, Tallahassee, FL, p. A147

BLANDFORD, John, Vice President Information Services, University Health System, San Antonio, TX, p. A666

BLANDFORD, Kirk, Vice President Finance, Calvert Memorial Hospital, Prince Frederick, MD, p. A309

BLANFORD, M.D., Donald, Chief Medical Officer, Community Health Partners Regional Medical Center, Lorain, OH, p. A516

BLANK, Arthur J., President and Chief Executive Officer, Mount Desert Island Hospital, Bar Harbor, ME, p. A296

BLANK, James
   Chief Financial Officer, NCED Mental Health Center, El Paso, TX, p. A637
   Chief Financial Officer, NCED Mental Health Center, El Paso, TX, p. A637

BLANKE, Kerry Lee, Director Financial Services, Riverside Medical Center, Waupaca, WI, p. A737

BLANKENSHIP, Bruce, Vice President Human Resources, Flagstaff Medical Center, Flagstaff, AZ, p. A30

BLANKS, Debra, Human Resources Manager, Regional Rehabilitation Hospital, Phenix City, AL, p. A23

BLANTON, Forest, Administrator Management Systems, Memorial Regional Hospital, Hollywood, FL, p. A131

BLANTON, Ron, Chief Fiscal Services, Veterans Affairs Medical Center, Boise, ID, p. A178

BLASINGAME, Billy, Administrator, Texas Specialty Hospital at Wichita Falls, Wichita Falls, TX, p. A674

BLAUFUSS, Max, Administrator and Chief Executive Officer, Lakeside Medical Center, Pine City, MN, p. A359

BLAYLOCK, Dwayne, Chief Executive Officer, Harton Regional Medical Center, Tullahoma, TN, p. A618

BLAYLOCK, Kevin, Chief Executive Officer, Oklahoma Spine Hospital, Oklahoma City, OK, p. A536

BLEAKNEY, David A., Administrator, Angleton Danbury Medical Center, Angleton, TX, p. A621

BLECHA, M.D., Timothy, Medical Director, Brodstone Memorial Hospital, Superior, NE, p. A413

BLEDSOE, La Rue, Personnel Director, Memorial Hospital, Seminole, TX, p. A666

BLESSING, William H., President, Mary Free Bed Rehabilitation Hospital, Grand Rapids, MI, p. A334

BLESSITT, H. J., Administrator, South Sunflower County Hospital, Indianola, MS, p. A370

BLEVINS, Barbara S., President and Chief Administrative Officer, Peninsula Hospital, Louisville, TN, p. A611

BLEVINS, Bonnie, Chief Financial Officer, Graham Regional Medical Center, Graham, TX, p. A642

BLEVINS, Gary, Director Human Resources, Mercy Medical Center Mount Shasta, Mount Shasta, CA, p. A77

BLEVINS, Maggie, Administrator, Jane Phillips Nowata Health Center, Nowata, OK, p. A534

BLEYER, Alan J.
   President and Chief Executive Officer, Akron General Health System, Akron, OH, p. B6
   President, Akron General Medical Center, Akron, OH, p. A502

BLOCK, Donna, Director Human Resources, Massac Memorial Hospital, Metropolis, IL, p. A201

BLOCK, M.D., Terence, Chief Medical Officer, Valley Medical Center, Renton, WA, p. A706

BLOEMER, Brad, Vice President Finance, Murray–Calloway County Hospital, Murray, KY, p. A272

BLOM, David P., President and Chief Executive Officer, OhioHealth, Columbus, OH, p. B81

BLOM, Mike, Director Management Information Systems, North Austin Medical Center, Austin, TX, p. A623

BLOME', Michael, Administrator, Methodist Healthcare–Fayette Hospital, Somerville, TN, p. A618

BLOMSTEDT, M.D., Jeffrey, Director Medical Affairs, Franklin Medical Center, Greenfield, MA, p. A318

BLONDIN, Robert, Vice President Finance, Noble Hospital, Westfield, MA, p. A325

BLOOD, Michael, Vice President Human Resources, Monadnock Community Hospital, Peterborough, NH, p. A423

BLOODWORTH, Donna, Administrator, HEALTHSOUTH Rehabilitation Hospital of Jonesboro, Jonesboro, AR, p. A45

BLOOM, Stephanie L., Chief Operating Officer, Southern Ocean County Hospital, Manahawkin, NJ, p. A431

BLOOMQUIST, Margaret A.
   Chief Human Resources, Emory Crawford Long Hospital, Atlanta, GA, p. A153
   Assistant Administrator Human Resources, Emory University Hospital, Atlanta, GA, p. A153
   Associate Administrator, Wesley Woods Center of Emory University, Atlanta, GA, p. A155

BLOUGH Jr, Daniel D., Chief Executive Officer, Punxsutawney Area Hospital, Punxsutawney, PA, p. A574

BLUA, Gayla, Human Resources Director, Northern Inyo Hospital, Bishop, CA, p. A55

BLUE, David, Chief Executive Officer, Hawthorn Children Psychiatric Hospital, Saint Louis, MO, p. A391

BLUE, M.D., Glen, Chief of Staff, Central Arkansas Hospital, Searcy, AR, p. A50

BLUE, Lawrence
   Administrator and Chief Executive Officer, Cavalier County Memorial Hospital, Langdon, ND, p. A499
   Administrator and Chief Executive Officer, Cavalier County Memorial Hospital, Langdon, ND, p. A499

BLUFORD, John W.
   Chief Executive Officer, Truman Medical Center–Hospital Hill, Kansas City, MO, p. A385
   President and Chief Executive Officer, Truman Medical Centers, Kansas City, MO, p. B111

BLUHM, Tom, Director Information Systems, Island Hospital, Anacortes, WA, p. A700

BLUMBERG, M.D., Bruce, Physician in Chief, Kaiser Foundation Hospital, San Francisco, CA, p. A89

BLUNK, D.O., Jim, Chief Medical Officer, Sumner County Hospital District One, Caldwell, KS, p. A245

BOARD, Patricia, Vice President Human Resources, Community Hospital of Bremen, Bremen, IN, p. A212

BOARDMAN, Debra K., President and Chief Executive Officer, Riverview Healthcare Association, Crookston, MN, p. A352

BOBBS, Kathy J., Chief Executive Officer, Women's and Children's Hospital, Lafayette, LA, p. A284

BOBYARCHICK, Alan
   Director Information Services, Good Samaritan Health Systems, Kearney, NE, p. A408
   Chief Information Officer, Memorial Health Care System, Chattanooga, TN, p. A603

BOCK, Brooks, M.D., President, Harper University Hospital, Detroit, MI, p. A331

BODE, Edwin J., Chief Financial Officer, Saint Francis Hospital, Memphis, TN, p. A613

BODENMANN, Linda, Chief Operating Officer, Southcoast Hospitals Group, Fall River, MA, p. A317

BODENSTEINER, Kim, Chief Financial Officer, First Care Medical Services, Fosston, MN, p. A353

BODIE, M.D., Barry, Chief of Staff, Transylvania Community Hospital, Brevard, NC, p. A478

BODINE, Robert, Director Human Resources, St. Luke's Medical Center, Phoenix, AZ, p. A35

BODNAR, Tony, Assistant Controller, HEALTHSOUTH Rehabilitation Hospital, Sewickley, PA, p. A575

BOECKER, Thomas J., President and Chief Executive Officer, Wilson Memorial Hospital, Sidney, OH, p. A522

BOEHLER, Richard, Vice President Medical Affairs, St. Joseph Medical Center, Towson, MD, p. A311

BOEHM, Scott, vice President Human Resources, MedCenter One, Bismarck, ND, p. A496

BOEHMER, Peggy, Chief Financial Officer, Belmond Medical Center, Belmond, IA, p. A228

BOEKELOO, Larry, Chief Information Officer, Allegan General Hospital, Allegan, MI, p. A327

BOERBOOM, Jerry J., Chief Executive Officer and Administrator, Minnesota Valley Health Center, Le Sueur, MN, p. A355

BOERNER, David, Medical Director, Rex Healthcare, Raleigh, NC, p. A489

BOERUM, George, Vice President for Human Resources, Nassau University Medical Center, East Meadow, NY, p. A451

BOETTCHER, D.O., Greg, Chief of Staff, Minidoka Memorial Hospital and Extended Care Facility, Rupert, ID, p. A181

BOEVERS, Jennifer, Medical Staff President, Palo Alto County Health System, Emmetsburg, IA, p. A233

BOGAN, James, President and Chief Executive Officer, Portage Health System, Hancock, MI, p. A336

BOGGESS, Richard, Chief Financial Officer, Memorial Hospital, Manchester, KY, p. A271

BOGGESS, Sharon, Human Resource Director, HEALTHSOUTH Southern Hills Rehabilitation Hospital, Princeton, WV, p. A719

BOGGS, Bruce, Senior Vice President and Director Human Resources, Carilion Medical Center, Roanoke, VA, p. A696

BOGGS, Danny L., President and Chief Executive Officer, Samaritan Regional Health System, Ashland, OH, p. A502

BOGGS, Lynn Ingram
Executive Vice President and Chief Operating Officer, Presbyterian Hospital, Charlotte, NC, p. A480
Executive Vice President and Chief Operating Officer, Presbyterian Hospital–Matthews, Matthews, NC, p. A487

BOGGS, Mike, Director of Finance, Business Services, Riverside Behavioral Health Center, Hampton, VA, p. A689

BOHART, Andrew, Vice President of Medical Affairs, Madonna Rehabilitation Hospital, Lincoln, NE, p. A409

BOHN, Anthony, Vice President Human Resources, Baptist Hospital East, Louisville, KY, p. A268

BOHN, Brian, Vice President Human Resources, Avera Marshall Regional Medical Center, Marshall, MN, p. A356

BOHNENKAMP, Russ, Director Finance, Chadron Community Hospital and Health Services, Chadron, NE, p. A405

BOICE, Sheila, Director Human Resources, Barton County Memorial Hospital, Lamar, MO, p. A386

BOIKE, Darlene, Business Office Manager, Chippewa County–Montevideo Hospital, Montevideo, MN, p. A358

BOISVERT, Gerald J., Vice President and Chief Financial Officer, Connecticut Children's Medical Center, Hartford, CT, p. A113

BOLAND, Marie, Chief Human Resource Management Service, Veterans Affairs Medical Center, San Francisco, CA, p. A90

BOLANDER, Patrick C., Chief Financial Officer, River Park Hospital, McMinnville, TN, p. A612

BOLCAVAGE, Ted, Regiional Controller, Kessler Institute for Rehabilitation, West Orange, NJ, p. A438

BOLD, Harry, Administrator, Big Sandy Medical Center, Big Sandy, MT, p. A396

BOLDEN, Charles, Human Resources Director, Hilo Medical Center, Hilo, HI, p. A173

BOLDS, Kevin, Director Information Technology, Earl K. Long Medical Center, Baton Rouge, LA, p. A277

BOLDUC, Tiana, Chief Information Officer, Mercy Hospital–Turner Memorial, Ozark, AR, p. A49

BOLES, Becki, Director of Health and Information Services, Jewish Hospital–Shelbyville, Shelbyville, KY, p. A274

BOLES, Glen, Chief Financial Officer, Valley Baptist Medical Center–Brownsville, Brownsville, TX, p. A627

BOLES, Lee, Chief Financial Officer, Halifax Regional Medical Center, Roanoke Rapids, NC, p. A490

BOLEY, Eric, Administrator and Chief Executive Officer, South Lincoln Medical Center, Kemmerer, WY, p. A740

BOLEY, Sarah, Director of Human Resources, Wetzel County Hospital, New Martinsville, WV, p. A718

BOLGER, Allison
Chief Financial Officer, Dells Area Health Center, Dell Rapids, SD, p. A595
Chief Financial Officer, Milbank Area Hospital/Avera Health, Milbank, SD, p. A597

BOLGER, Thomas, Chief Financial Officer, Chinese Hospital, San Francisco, CA, p. A88

BOLICK, Diann, Chief Financial Officer, Thoms Rehabilitation Hospital, Asheville, NC, p. A477

BOLIN, Kellie, Chief Financial Officer, Round Rock Medical Center, Round Rock, TX, p. A662

BOLIVAR, Mario, Executive Director, Devereux Georgia Treatment Network, Kennesaw, GA, p. A164

BOLLIG, Bill, Chief Information Officer, Martin Memorial Health Systems, Stuart, FL, p. A147

BOLLINGER, Kathy, Chief Executive Officer, Banner Baywood Heart Hospital, Mesa, AZ, p. A32

BOLLONE, Ann, Vice President Organizational Effectiveness and Human Resources, St. Marys Health Center, Jefferson City, MO, p. A383

BOLOGNA, Therese, Director Human Resources, Providence Hospital and Medical Center, Southfield, MI, p. A345

BOLOGNANI, Lauri, Human Resources Officer, Speare Memorial Hospital, Plymouth, NH, p. A423

BOLTON, Keith, Manager, Barnes–Jewish St. Peters Hospital, Saint Peters, MO, p. A393

BOMAR, Betsy, Chief Operating Officer, Northside Hospital and Heart Institute, Saint Petersburg, FL, p. A145

BOMBA, Douglas, Vice President Finance, Wilson Memorial Hospital, Sidney, OH, p. A522

BOMER, Starsky, Chief Financial Officer, Ennis Regional Medical Center, Ennis, TX, p. A638

BOMERSBACH, Karen, Chief Financial Officer, RHD Memorial Medical Center, Dallas, TX, p. A634

BONACCI, Don, Chief Information Officer, Hill Country Memorial Hospital, Fredericksburg, TX, p. A640

BONAMO, John F., M.D., Executive Director, Saint Barnabas Medical Center, Livingston, NJ, p. A430

BONANNO, Joseph S., Interim President and Chief Executive Officer, Pocono Medical Center, East Stroudsburg, PA, p. A557

BONASSO, M.D., Pat, Chief of Staff, Fairmont General Hospital, Fairmont, WV, p. A715

BONBRISCO, D.O., Daniel, Vice President and Chief Medical Officer, Botsford General Hospital, Farmington Hills, MI, p. A333

BOND, C. Scott, Administrator and Chief Executive Officer, Providence St. Peter Hospital, Olympia, WA, p. A705

BOND, Troy, Chief Human Resources Officer, Atlanta Medical Center, Atlanta, GA, p. A153

BOND, Vivien, Chief Executive Officer, Select Specialty Hospital–Conroe, Conroe, TX, p. A630

BONDI, Blaise, Chief Financial Officer, St. Charles Specialty Hospital, New Orleans, LA, p. A289

BONDI, Joseph A., Chairman and Chief Executive Officer, Integrated Health Services, Sparks Glencoe, MD, p. B61

BONE, Jim G., Administrator, Muleshoe Area Medical Center, Muleshoe, TX, p. A658

BONECUTTER, Bruce E., Ph.D., Executive Director, Elgin Mental Health Center, Elgin, IL, p. A193

BONETTI, Juan, Chief of Staff, Abbeville County Memorial Hospital, Abbeville, SC, p. A583

BONGIOVANNI, Tony, Vice President Human Resources, St. Peter's Hospital, Albany, NY, p. A446

BONGSTROM, Ned, Chief Financial Officer, Virginia Mason Medical Center, Seattle, WA, p. A708

BONHAM, Chris, Chief Executive Officer, Morgan Memorial Hospital, Madison, GA, p. A165

BONI, Shirley M.
Administrative Officer, U. S. Public Health Service Indian Hospital, San Carlos, AZ, p. A36
Administrative Officer, U. S. Public Health Service Indian Hospital, San Carlos, AZ, p. A36
Administrative Officer, U. S. Public Health Service Indian Hospital, San Carlos, AZ, p. A36

BONILLA, Sonia, Director Human Resources, Hospital de la Universidad de Puerto Rico/Dr. Federico Trilla, Carolina, PR, p. A744

BONIN, M.D., Tom, Medical Director, Choctaw Nation Health Care Center, Talihina, OK, p. A539

BONIS, Paul, Chief Executive Officer, Spectrum Health–United Memorial, Greenville, MI, p. A335

BONITO, Raymond J., Senior Vice President and Chief Operating Officer, Catholic Medical Center, Manchester, NH, p. A422

BONN, Edward J., President and Chief Executive Officer, Southern Regional Medical Center, Riverdale, GA, p. A167

BONNER, Daphne, Administrator, Greenbriar Rehabilitation Hospital, Boardman, OH, p. A504

BONNER, Frank, M.D., Chief Executive Officer, Rehabilitation Hospital of South Jersey, Vineland, NJ, p. A438

BONNER, Stephen B., President and Chief Executive Officer, Cancer Treatment Centers of America, Arlington Heights, IL, p. B20

BONNER, Tucker, President, King's Daughters Hospital, Temple, TX, p. A669

BONNESS, Jackie, Chief Financial Officer, Kindred Hospital–St. Louis, Saint Louis, MO, p. A391

BONNETT, Melonie
Financial Analyst, Banner Behavioral Health Hospital, Scottsdale, AZ, p. A36
Financial Analyst, Banner Behavioral Health Hospital, Scottsdale, AZ, p. A36

BONTEMPO, C. Angela
President and Chief Executive Officer, Saint Vincent Health Center, Erie, PA, p. A558
President and Chief Executive Officer, St. Vincent Health System, Erie, PA, p. B103

BONTHUIS, Michael W., Chief Financial Officer, United General Hospital, Sedro–Woolley, WA, p. A708

BONTREGER, Sheldon, Chief Financial Officer, Abbeville County Memorial Hospital, Abbeville, SC, p. A583

BOOHER, Pamela, Area Finance Officer, Kaiser Foundation Hospital and Rehabilitation Center, Vallejo, CA, p. A97

BOOKER, Oliver J., Chief Executive Officer, Monroe County Hospital, Forsyth, GA, p. A162

BOOKMYER, John L., Executive Vice President and Chief Operating Officer, Blanchard Valley Health Association, Findlay, OH, p. A513

BOOM, M.D., Marc, Senior Vice President and Chief Operating Officer, The Methodist Hospital, Houston, TX, p. A648

BOOMSMA, M.D., Joan, Vice President Medical Affairs, St. Francis Hospital & Health Center, Blue Island, IL, p. A185

BOONE, Donna, Chief Nursing Officer, Campbell Health System, Weatherford, TX, p. A673

BOONE III, Elwood Bernard, Chief Executive Officer, John Randolph Medical Center, Hopewell, VA, p. A690

BOORE, Chad E.
Vice President and Administrator, Carilion Franklin Memorial Hospital, Rocky Mount, VA, p. A696
Interim President and Chief Executive Officer, Stonewall Jackson Hospital, Lexington, VA, p. A690

BOORNAZIAN, M.D., John, Chief Medical Officer, Huggins Hospital, Wolfeboro, NH, p. A424

BOOS, Shari, Director Human Resources, Atchison Hospital, Atchison, KS, p. A244

BOOSALIS, Mary H., Executive Vice President and Chief Operating Officer, Miami Valley Hospital, Dayton, OH, p. A512

BOOTE, Jim, Executive Vice President and Chief Operating Officer, Holy Cross Hospital, Fort Lauderdale, FL, p. A128

BOOTH, Daniel, Vice President Human Resources and Facilities, Inland Hospital, Waterville, ME, p. A301

BOOTH, M.D., David, Chairman Medical Staff, North Mississippi Medical Center–Eupora, Eupora, MS, p. A368

BOOTH, M.D., Randy, President Medical Staff, Nevada Regional Medical Center, Nevada, MO, p. A388

BOOTHE, Dwaine, Chief Engineer, Franklin Medical Center, Winnsboro, LA, p. A294

BOPP, James H.
Executive Director, Middletown Psychiatric Center, Middletown, NY, p. A456
Executive Director, Rockland Psychiatric Center, Orangeburg, NY, p. A468

BORAN, Patrick, Chief Financial Officer, North Memorial Health Care, Robbinsdale, MN, p. A360

BORDEN, Sandy, Chief Financial Officer, Brodstone Memorial Hospital, Superior, NE, p. A413

BORDENKIRCHER, Kimberly, Chief Executive Officer, Henry County Hospital, Napoleon, OH, p. A519

BOREN, Shed, Administrator, Sister Emmanuel Hospital for Continuing Care, Miami, FL, p. A138

BORENSTEIN, Jeffrey, M.D., Chief Executive Officer and Medical Director, Holliswood Hospital, New York, NY, p. A460

BORENSTEIN-LEVY, Ronna, Director Marketing and Communications, Suburban Hospital Healthcare System, Bethesda, MD, p. A305

BORG, John H., Administrator, Morgan County War Memorial Hospital, Berkeley Springs, WV, p. A713

BORG, Randy, USAF, Administrator, U. S. Air Force Medical Center Keesler, Keesler AFB, MS, p. A371

BORGSTROM, Marna P., Executive Vice President and Chief Operating Officer, Yale–New Haven Hospital, New Haven, CT, p. A115

BORIA, M.D., Maria E., Vice President Medical Staff, Palisades Medical Center, North Bergen, NJ, p. A433

BORING, Ronald L., President and Chief Executive Officer, Richardson RegionalMedical Center, Richardson, TX, p. A662

BORJA, William, Chief Information Officer, Milwaukee County Behavioral Health Division, Milwaukee, WI, p. A731

BORLAND, Winston, Chief Operating Officer, Medical Center of Plano, Plano, TX, p. A661

BORNSTEIN, M.D., Ph, William A., Chief Quality and Medical Officer, Emory Crawford Long Hospital, Atlanta, GA, p. A153

BOROWSKI, Thomas, Director Information Systems, Immanuel St. Joseph's–Mayo Health System, Mankato, MN, p. A356

BORR, Robert, Chief Information Officer, Quincy Medical Center, Quincy, MA, p. A322

BORTEL, Karol, Vice President Financial Services, Wood County Hospital, Bowling Green, OH, p. A504

BORTNEM, Mark, Director of Finance, Phillips Eye Institute, Minneapolis, MN, p. A357

BORUFF, Roger S.
Vice President Fiscal Services, Morgan Hospital and Medical Center, Martinsville, IN, p. A222
Vice President Fiscal Services, Morgan Hospital and Medical Center, Martinsville, IN, p. A222

BOSCH, Scott W., President and Chief Executive Officer, Harrison Memorial Hospital, Bremerton, WA, p. A700

BOSER, Andrew, Chief Executive Officer, Cuba Memorial Hospital, Cuba, NY, p. A451

BOSICA, Jr, Thomas A., Vice President Human Resources, Penobscot Bay Medical Center, Rockport, ME, p. A300

BOSS, Janice M., CHE, Director, Veterans Affairs Medical Center, Iron Mountain, MI, p. A337

BOSSARD, Karen L., Administrator and Chief Executive Officer, Greene County Medical Center, Jefferson, IA, p. A236

BOSSCHER, M.D., David, Chief of Staff, Jellico Community Hospital, Jellico, TN, p. A608

BOST, R.N., Donna, Vice President and Cape Fear Hospital Administrator, New Hanover Regional Medical Center, Wilmington, NC, p. A494

BOSTON, Martha, Ph.D., Director, Delaware Psychiatric Center, New Castle, DE, p. A119

BOSTON III, Ward, Chief Executive Officer, Northside Hospital and Heart Institute, Saint Petersburg, FL, p. A145

BOSTROM, Gary, Chief Financial Officer, Roundup Memorial Healthcare, Roundup, MT, p. A402

BOSTWICK, Monte
Administrator and Chief Operating Officer, Toppenish Community Hospital, Toppenish, WA, p. A711
Administrator and Chief Operating Officer, Toppenish Community Hospital, Toppenish, WA, p. A711

BOSWELL, Bill, Chief Executive Officer, McCamey Hospital, McCamey, TX, p. A656

BOSWELL, Diane, Director Human Resources and Marketing, Salem Township Hospital, Salem, IL, p. A207

BOTAK, Geoff, Chief Executive Officer, Fairmount Behavioral Health System, Philadelphia, PA, p. A567

BOTSFORD, Norm, Chief Executive Officer, University Physicians Healthcare Hospital at Kino Campus, Tucson, AZ, p. A39

BOTTICELLA, Mary, Chief Executive Officer, Huntington Beach Hospital, Huntington Beach, CA, p. A64

BOTTOM, Nick, Chief Financial Officer and Vice President Finance, St. Joseph's Community Health Services, Hillsboro, WI, p. A727

BOTTOMS, Amber, Director Medical Records, Chambers Memorial Hospital, Danville, AR, p. A42

BOUCHARD, Lorraine, Director Human Resources, Southern Maine Medical Center, Biddeford, ME, p. A297

BOUCK, Nancy, Director Human Resources, Huron Medical Center, Bad Axe, MI, p. A328

BOUD, Jan, Vice President Communications and Human Resources, Jackson–Madison County General Hospital, Jackson, TN, p. A608

BOUDREAUX, Scott, Chief Executive Officer, River Parishes Hospital, La Place, LA, p. A283

BOUDROW, Gordon, Chief Financial Officer, Cambridge Health Alliance, Cambridge, MA, p. A316

BOUE, Lourdes, Chief Financial Officer, Miami Jewish Home and Hospital for Aged, Miami, FL, p. A137

BOUGHAL, Ginni, Health Information Manager, Peace Harbor Hospital, Florence, OR, p. A543

BOUILLION, Bobby, Chief Financial Officer, HEALTHSOUTH Rehabilitation Hospital of Alexandria, Alexandria, LA, p. A276

BOULA, Rodney C., Administrator, Elizabethtown Community Hospital, Elizabethtown, NY, p. A452

BOULENGER, Bo, Chief Executive Officer, Homestead Hospital, Homestead, FL, p. A131

BOULWARE, Jet, Director Information and Technology Services, Oak Forest Hospital of Cook County, Oak Forest, IL, p. A203

BOUNDS, Floyd D., Chief Executive Officer, Minnie G. Boswell Memorial Hospital, Greensboro, GA, p. A163

BOUR, Thomas C., Administrator, Mayo Clinic Hospital, Phoenix, AZ, p. A34

BOURDON, Donna, Administrator, HEALTHSOUTH Chattanooga Rehabilitation Hospital, Chattanooga, TN, p. A603

BOURGASSER, M.D., Gene, Chief of Staff, Sullivan County Community Hospital, Sullivan, IN, p. A225

BOURGAULT, Catherine, Director Human Resources, Providence Hood River Memorial Hospital, Hood River, OR, p. A544

BOURGEOIS, Jeff A., Chief Executive Officer, Hill Country Memorial Hospital, Fredericksburg, TX, p. A640

BOURGEOIS Jr, Milton D., Chief Executive Officer, St. Anne General Hospital, Raceland, LA, p. A291

BOURLAND, Don, Vice President, Human Resources, Peace Harbor Hospital, Florence, OR, p. A543

BOUTIN, M.D., Geosges, Chief Medical Officer, Imperial Point Medical Center, Fort Lauderdale, FL, p. A128

BOUTROS, M.D., Akram
Executive Vice President and Chief Medical Officer, South Nassau Communities Hospital, Oceanside, NY, p. A467
Executive Vice President and Chief Medical Officer, South Nassau Communities Hospital, Oceanside, NY, p. A467

BOUTTELLE, M.D., William E., Chief of Staff and Service Line Manager Mental Health, Veterans Affairs Medical Center, Leeds, MA, p. A319

BOUYEA, Janine, Human Resources Director, Natividad Medical Center, Salinas, CA, p. A86

BOVEE, Michael, Vice President Finance, Riverview Hospital Association, Wisconsin Rapids, WI, p. A738

BOVENDER Jr, Jack O., Chairman and Chief Executive Officer, HCA, Nashville, TN, p. B48

BOVIO, Ernie, Chief Executive Officer, Trinity Medical Center, Carrollton, TX, p. A628

BOW, Beverly, Vice President Human Resources, Salem Hospital, Salem, OR, p. A549

BOWDLE, M.D., Richard, Medical Director Service Line, Sutter Center for Psychiatry, Sacramento, CA, p. A85

BOWE, Larry, Chief Executive, Yamhill Service Area, Providence Newberg Hospital, Newberg, OR, p. A546

BOWEN, Chris, Director Information Services, Union Regional Medical Center, Monroe, NC, p. A487

BOWEN, Claire L., Chief Executive Officer, Valley Regional Hospital, Claremont, NH, p. A420

BOWEN, Don, Executive Director, Griffin Memorial Hospital, Norman, OK, p. A534

BOWEN, Lynn, Vice President Information Services, Caritas St. Elizabeth's Medical Center, Brighton, MA, p. A315

BOWEN, M.D., Shane, Chief of Staff, Boone Memorial Hospital, Madison, WV, p. A717

BOWEN, Steve, President, East Texas Medical Center Jacksonville, Jacksonville, TX, p. A650

BOWEN, Theresa, Administrative Director, Lima Memorial Health System, Lima, OH, p. A516

BOWEN, M.D., Thomas, Chief of Staff, James A. Haley Veterans Hospital, Tampa, FL, p. A148

BOWER, M.D., David, Chief of Staff, Veterans Affairs Medical Center, Decatur, GA, p. A160

BOWER, Mark, Vice President, Warren Memorial Hospital, Front Royal, VA, p. A688

BOWERMAN, CPA, Paul, Chief Financial Officer, Sumner County Hospital District One, Caldwell, KS, p. A245

BOWERS, Dan, Chief Executive Officer, San Dimas Community Hospital, San Dimas, CA, p. A88

BOWERS, David, Vice President Support Services, Children's Hospital of The King's Daughters, Norfolk, VA, p. A692

BOWERS, Gregory, Chief Financial Officer, Spring Harbor Hospital, Westbrook, ME, p. A301

BOWERS, Susan P., Director, Richard L. Roudebush Veterans Affairs Medical Center, Indianapolis, IN, p. A218

BOWERSOX, Bruce D., Administrator, Hillsboro Medical Center, Hillsboro, ND, p. A499

BOWERY, Nellon, Chief Financial Officer, Governor Juan F. Louis Hospital, Christiansted, VI, p. A749

BOWES, Arthur, Senior Vice President Human Resources, North Shore Medical Center, Salem, MA, p. A323

BOWHAY, M.D., Thomas, Chief of Staff, Sutter Amador Hospital, Jackson, CA, p. A65

BOWIE, M.D., Constance, Chief Medical Staff, O'Connor Hospital, San Jose, CA, p. A90

BOWLIN–NORRIS, TinaMarie, Assistant Vice President Human Resources, St. Joseph Hospital, Bangor, ME, p. A296

BOWLING, John S., President and Chief Executive Officer, Hamilton Medical Center, Dalton, GA, p. A160

BOWLING, Karen L., Chief Executive Officer, Raleigh General Hospital, Beckley, WV, p. A713

BOWMAN, Barbara, Chief Human Resource Officer, Children's Memorial Hospital, Chicago, IL, p. A187

BOWMAN, Brian, Vice President, Chester River Hospital Center, Chestertown, MD, p. A306

BOWMAN, Clarence W., Chief Executive Officer, Lake City Community Hospital, Lake City, SC, p. A589

BOWMAN, Hoye A., Chief Financial Officer, Magnolia Hospital, Magnolia, AR, p. A47

BOWMAN, Joe E., Chief Financial Officer, StoneCrest Medical Center, Smyrna, TN, p. A618

BOWMAN, June C., R.N., Chief Operating Officer and Nurse Executive, St. Joseph Medical Center, Tacoma, WA, p. A710

BOWMAN, R.N., June C., Chief Operating Officer and Nurse Executive, St. Joseph Medical Center, Tacoma, WA, p. A710

BOWMAN, Michael R., Administrator, Litzenberg Memorial County Hospital, Central City, NE, p. A405

BOWMAN, Scott, Administrator, Sweetwater Hospital, Sweetwater, TN, p. A618

BOWMAN, Steve, Interim Administrator, North Caddo Medical Center, Vivian, LA, p. A294

BOWMAN, Terry, Vice President Human Resources, Our Lady of the Lake Regional Medical Center, Baton Rouge, LA, p. A277

BOWMAN, Terry R., Chief Financial Officer, Davie County Hospital, Mocksville, NC, p. A487

BOWMER, Carolyn, Vice President Human Resources, Providence Medical Center, Kansas City, KS, p. A250

BOYCE, M.D., Joe, Director Information Systems, McKay–Dee Hospital Center, Ogden, UT, p. A678

BOYCE, M.D., William, President Medical Staff, SSM St. Joseph Hospital of Kirkwood, Saint Louis, MO, p. A392

BOYD, Amy, Manager Information Systems, Beaufort County Hospital, Washington, NC, p. A493

BOYD, Christopher L., Chief Executive Officer, Sharp Chula Vista Medical Center, Chula Vista, CA, p. A57

BOYD, Evan, Director Information Technology, Olympic Medical Center, Port Angeles, WA, p. A706

BOYD, M.D., John A K, Executive Director Mission and Chief Medical Officer, Mercy Medical Center, Durango, CO, p. A104

BOYD, Kenneth, Chief Executive Officer, Dickenson Community Hospital, Clintwood, VA, p. A687

BOYD, Kim, Chief Financial Officer, Buchanan General Hospital, Grundy, VA, p. A689

BOYD, Lu Lu, Information Technology Director, Mitchell County Hospital, Colorado City, TX, p. A629

BOYD, Roy, Chief Financial Officer, Phoenixville Hospital, Phoenixville, PA, p. A571

BOYD, Wallace N., Administrator, Ochiltree General Hospital, Perryton, TX, p. A660

BOYER, Aurelia, Senior Vice President and Chief Information Officer, New York–Presbyterian Hospital, New York, NY, p. A463

BOYER, David, Vice President Finance and Chief Financial Officer, Samaritan Regional Health System, Ashland, OH, p. A502

BOYER, Gregory E., Chief Executive Officer, Valley Hospital Medical Center, Las Vegas, NV, p. A417

BOYER, Jim, Management Information Systems Manager, Rush Memorial Hospital, Rushville, IN, p. A224

BOYER OWENS, Linda, Vice President, People and Organizational Development, University Health System, San Antonio, TX, p. A666

BOYETTE, R.N., Wanda L., Senior Vice President and Chief Operating Officer, Sampson Regional Medical Center, Clinton, NC, p. A480

BOYKIN, Alfred, Chief Medical Officer, Wm. Jennings Bryan Dorn Veterans Affairs Medical Center, Columbia, SC, p. A586

BOYLE, Angie, Director Human Resources, Doctors Hospital of Stark County, Massillon, OH, p. A518

BOYLE, Donna, Director, Columbia Hospital, West Palm Beach, FL, p. A150

BOYLE, James W., Chief Executive Officer, Porter Adventist Hospital, Denver, CO, p. A104

BOYLE, Patrick, Director Human Resources, Hunterdon Medical Center, Flemington, NJ, p. A428

BOYLE, Steven P., President and Chief Executive Officer, St. Peter's Hospital, Albany, NY, p. A446

BOYLE, Thomas W., Chief Financial Officer, St. Lawrence Rehabilitation Center, Trenton, NJ, p. A437

BOYLES, Jackie, Administrator, Cedar County Memorial Hospital, El Dorado Springs, MO, p. A381

BOYLES, Larry, Senior Vice President, Riverside Regional Medical Center, Newport News, VA, p. A692

BOYLES, Michael E., Chief Executive Officer, Rangely District Hospital, Rangely, CO, p. A109

BOYLES, M.D., Richard E., Chief of Medical Staff, Barnwell County Hospital, Barnwell, SC, p. A583

BOYNTON, Stephanie, Administrator, Erlanger Bledsoe Hospital, Pikeville, TN, p. A617

BOYSEN, Robert, Vice President Inforamtion Systems, Providence Medical Center, Kansas City, KS, p. A250

BOZEMAN, Larry C., Chief Executive Officer, Lea Regional Medical Center, Hobbs, NM, p. A443

BRABAND, Jon D., President and Chief Executive Officer, Glencoe Regional Health Services, Glencoe, MN, p. A354

BRACCINO, Nick, Chief Financial Officer, Hendry Regional Medical Center, Clewiston, FL, p. A126

BRACE, Bob, Director Human Resources, Hillcrest Baptist Medical Center, Waco, TX, p. A672

BRACE, Rod, Chief Executive Officer, Memorial Hermann Fort Bend Hospital, Missouri City, TX, p. A657

BRACHT, Gerald E.
Chief Administrative Officer, Palomar Medical Center, Escondido, CA, p. A59
Chief Administrative Officer, Palomar Medical Center, Escondido, CA, p. A59

BRACKEN, Thomas H., Chief of Staff, Mille Lacs Health System, Onamia, MN, p. A359

BRACKIN, D. Wayne, Chief Executive Officer, South Miami Hospital, Miami, FL, p. A138

BRADBURY, Kent, Human Resources Coordinator, Sutter Center for Psychiatry, Sacramento, CA, p. A85

BRADEL, William T., Executive Director and Chief Operating Officer, St. Agnes HealthCare, Baltimore, MD, p. A304

BRADEN, III, D.O., Terence, Medical Director, HEALTHSOUTH Rehabilitation Hospital of Jonesboro, Jonesboro, AR, p. A45

BRADFORD, Alan, Vice President Human Resources, Saint Joseph's Hospital of Atlanta, Atlanta, GA, p. A154

BRADFORD, John, Chief Financial Officer, Flaget Memorial Hospital, Bardstown, KY, p. A261

BRADFORD, Roberta J., President and Chief Executive Officer, Drake Center, Cincinnati, OH, p. A506

BRADFORD, R.N., Sue E., Chief Operating Officer, Memorial Hospital West, Pembroke Pines, FL, p. A142

BRADFORD, Terry, Director Human Resources, Powell Valley Healthcare, Powell, WY, p. A741

BRADHAM, James E., Administrator, Villa Feliciana Medical Complex, Jackson, LA, p. A282

BRADLEY, David, Chief Executive Officer, Marin General Hospital, Greenbrae, CA, p. A63

BRADLEY, David K., CHE, Chief Executive Officer, Geary Community Hospital, Junction City, KS, p. A250

BRADLEY Jr, J. Lindsey, FACHE, President and Chief Administrative Officer, Trinity Mother Frances Health System, Tyler, TX, p. A671

BRADLEY, M.D., James, Medical Staff President, St. Francis Hospital and Health Services, Maryville, MO, p. A387

BRADLEY, Linda
Chief Executive Officer, Inland Valley Medical Center, Wildomar, CA, p. A99
Chief Executive Officer, Rancho Springs Medical Center, Murrieta, CA, p. A77

BRADLEY, Louis, Chief Executive Officer, Lifecare Hospitals of North Texas–Dallas, Dallas, TX, p. A633

BRADLEY, Lucinda A., Chief Executive Officer, Great Plains Regional Medical Center, North Platte, NE, p. A410

BRADLEY, William L., President and Chief Executive Officer, Washington Regional Medical Center, Fayetteville, AR, p. A43

BRADSHAW, M.D., Colton, Chief of Staff, Titus Regional Medical Center, Mount Pleasant, TX, p. A657

BRADSHAW, David
Vice President Information Services, Memorial Hermann Hospital, Houston, TX, p. A646
Vice President Information Systems, Memorial Hermann Southwest Hospital, Houston, TX, p. A646

BRADSHAW, Donald M., Commander, Dwight David Eisenhower Army Medical Center, Fort Gordon, GA, p. A162

BRADSHAW, Thomas A., Vice President Operations, Wayne Memorial Hospital, Goldsboro, NC, p. A483

BRADY, James L., President, Allied Services Rehabilitation Hospital, Scranton, PA, p. A575

BRADY, Jeff
Director Information Systems, Hazard ARH Regional Medical Center, Hazard, KY, p. A266
Director Information Systems, McDowell ARH Hospital, McDowell, KY, p. A271
Director Information Systems, Morgan County Appalachian Regional Hospital, West Liberty, KY, p. A275
Chief Information Officer, Williamson ARH Hospital, South Williamson, KY, p. A275

BRADY, John, Director Human Resources, Franklin Medical Center, Greenfield, MA, p. A318

BRADY, Kevin, Director Human Resources, Lallie Kemp Medical Center, Independence, LA, p. A282

BRADY, Linda, M.D., President and Chief Executive Officer, Kingsbrook Jewish Medical Center, New York, NY, p. A461

BRADY, Noreen, Vice President of Human Resources, Champlain Valley Physicians Hospital Medical Center, Plattsburgh, NY, p. A469

BRADY, Patrick R., Chief Executive Officer, Sutter Roseville Medical Center, Roseville, CA, p. A84

BRADY, Reta, Administrative Assistant and Human Resource Manager, Trinity Hospital, Erin, TN, p. A606

BRADY, Tim, Director Information Systems, Mt. Washington Pediatric Hospital, Baltimore, MD, p. A304

BRADY, Timothy F., FACHE, Administrator, St. Elizabeth's Hospital, Belleville, IL, p. A184

BRAENDEL, Lynn, Director Health Information Management Systems, HEALTHSOUTH Rehabilitation Hospital of Erie, Erie, PA, p. A558

BRAGDON, Carol, Director of Human Resources, Middle Tennessee Medical Center, Murfreesboro, TN, p. A614

BRAGG, Deborah, Chief Financial Officer, Webster County Memorial Hospital, Webster Springs, WV, p. A720

BRAGG, Melissa, Chief Human Resources Management, Veterans Affairs Medical Center, Asheville, NC, p. A477

BRAID, George, Director of Human Resources, Mercer County Joint Township Community Hospital, Coldwater, OH, p. A510

BRAIMSTEIN, M.D., Peter, Director Medical Affairs, Saint Mary's Regional Medical Center, Reno, NV, p. A418

BRAMLETT Jr, E. Chandler
President and Chief Executive Officer, Gulf Health Hospitals, Mobile, AL, p. B47
President and Chief Executive Officer, Mobile Infirmary Medical Center, Mobile, AL, p. A21

BRAMMER, Randy, Director Finance, Hedrick Medical Center, Chillicothe, MO, p. A380

BRANCATO, Joyce, Chief Executive Officer, Seven Rivers Regional Medical Center, Crystal River, FL, p. A126

BRANCH, Rich, Director Information Systems, Mercer County Joint Township Community Hospital, Coldwater, OH, p. A510

BRANCH, Tim, Information Technology Manager, Covenant Hospital Plainview, Plainview, TX, p. A660

BRANCO, Patrick J., Chief Executive Officer, Ketchikan General Hospital, Ketchikan, AK, p. A27

BRANDEL, Patrick J., Chief Financial Officer, Holy Family Memorial Medical Center, Manitowoc, WI, p. A729

BRANDENBURG, Edward
Vice President Operations and Human Resources, Community Memorial Healthcenter, South Hill, VA, p. A697
Vice President Operations and Human Resources, Community Memorial Healthcenter, South Hill, VA, p. A697

BRANDON, David R., Chief Executive Officer, Fayette Memorial Hospital, Connersville, IN, p. A213

BRANDON, Wendy, Chief Operating Officer, Summit Medical Center, Hermitage, TN, p. A607

BRANDT, Lowell, Warden, Iowa Medical and Classification Center, Oakdale, IA, p. A239

BRANDT, Nancy
Chief Financial Officer, Carrie Tingley Hospital, Albuquerque, NM, p. A440
Chief Financial Officer, University Hospital, Albuquerque, NM, p. A441

BRANISH, Ron, Vice President Finance, Craig Hospital, Englewood, CO, p. A105

BRANNEN, Charles C., Senior Vice President and Chief Operating Officer, Southeast Alabama Medical Center, Dothan, AL, p. A17

BRANNEN, M.D., Judy, Interim Chief of Staff, Hunter Holmes McGuire Veterans Affairs Medical Center, Richmond, VA, p. A695

BRANNIGAN, Laurie, Administrator, New Mexico Rehabilitation Center, Roswell, NM, p. A444

BRANNIGAN, Robert C., VicePresident, Chief Operating Officer and Chief Nursing Officer, Redwood Memorial Hospital, Fortuna, CA, p. A60

BRANNON, M.D., David, Chief of Staff, Gordon Hospital, Calhoun, GA, p. A157

BRANNON, Jeffrey M., Chief Executive Officer, Medical Center Enterprise, Enterprise, AL, p. A18

BRANNON, Jim, Vice President, Human Resources, Atlantic General Hospital, Berlin, MD, p. A305

BRANT, James R., Senior Vice President Finance and Chief Financial Officer, Underwood–Memorial Hospital, Woodbury, NJ, p. A439

BRANT, Karen, Senior Vice President and Chief Operating Officer, Foote Health System, Jackson, MI, p. A337

BRANT, Mick, Vice President of Information Systems, Yuma District Hospital, Yuma, CO, p. A111

BRANTLEY, M.D., Ph, Alton, Senior Vice President and Chief Information Officer, MedStar–Georgetown Medical Center, Washington, DC, p. A121

BRANTLEY, Jerry
  Vice President and Chief Information Officer, Baptist Memorial Hospital – Memphis, Memphis, TN, p. A612
  Vice President and Chief Information Officer, Baptist Memorial Hospital–Collierville, Collierville, TN, p. A604

BRANTZ, Jerry, Chief Financial Officer, Shoshone Medical Center, Kellogg, ID, p. A179

BRANZELL, Russ, Chief Information Officer, Poudre Valley Hospital, Fort Collins, CO, p. A105

BRASH, David L., Chief Executive Officer, Russell County Medical Center, Lebanon, VA, p. A690

BRASHEAR, Denise, Director Human Resources, Daviess Community Hospital, Washington, IN, p. A227

BRASS, Alan W., FACHE, Chief Executive Officer and President, ProMedica Health System, Toledo, OH, p. B85

BRASSEAUX, Mary T., Executive Vice President and Administrator, St. Nicholas Hospital, Sheboygan, WI, p. A735

BRASWELL, John
  Vice President and Chief Information Officer, Carondelet Holy Cross Hospital, Nogales, AZ, p. A32
  Chief Information Officer, Carondelet St. Joseph's Hospital–Tucson, Tucson, AZ, p. A37
  Chief Information Officer, Carondelet St. Mary's Hospital–Tucson, Tucson, AZ, p. A37

BRAUER, Warren A., President Medical Staff, St. Nicholas Hospital, Sheboygan, WI, p. A735

BRAUN, James R., Chief Financial Officer, Flambeau Hospital, Park Falls, WI, p. A733

BRAUN, Norma, Director Human Resources, Brotman Medical Center, Culver City, CA, p. A58

BRAUTIGAN, Emery
  Chief Executive Officer, Fairfax Memorial Hospital, Fairfax, OK, p. A531
  Chief Executive Officer, Fairfax Memorial Hospital, Fairfax, OK, p. A531

BRAVO, Chebon, Director Information Systems, Green Oaks Hospital, Dallas, TX, p. A632

BRAWLEY, Harry, Information Services Director, Lincoln General Hospital, Ruston, LA, p. A292

BRAY, Bob, Chief Information Officer, Jersey Community Hospital, Jerseyville, IL, p. A198

BRAY, Delnita, Administrator, Wichita Valley Rehabilitation Hospital, Wichita Falls, TX, p. A674

BRAYTON, Jackie, Vice President, Human Resources, Portsmouth Regional Hospital, Portsmouth, NH, p. A423

BRAYTON, William, Financial Manager, Veterans Affairs Medical Center, Sheridan, WY, p. A742

BRAZASKI, Karrie, Chief Nursing Officer, Bourbon Community Hospital, Paris, KY, p. A273

BRAZEL, M.D., Gary, Vice President Physician and Clinical Services, Saint John's Health System, Anderson, IN, p. A211

BRAZIL, Robert, Chief Operating Officer, Memorial Hospital, Abilene, KS, p. A244

BREEDEN, Susan M., Administrator and Chief Executive Officer, Baptist Memorial Hospital–Huntingdon, Huntingdon, TN, p. A607

BREEDLOVE, Jean Ann, Chief Information Officer, Children's Mercy Hospital, Kansas City, MO, p. A384

BREEDLOVE, Nelson, Vice President Support Services, Gilmore Memorial Hospital, Amory, MS, p. A366

BREEDLOVE, Wanda, Chief Financial Officer, Collingsworth General Hospital, Wellington, TX, p. A673

BREEDVELD, Stacey, Executive Director, Saint Joseph Mercy Saline Hospital, Saline, MI, p. A345

BREEN, Thomas, Vice President Finance, Norwalk Hospital, Norwalk, CT, p. A115

BREGIN, Susan, Controller, HEALTHSOUTH Rehabilitation Hospital, Columbia, SC, p. A585

BREHM, Robert, President, Kessler Institute for Rehabilitation, West Orange, NJ, p. A438

BREIDENTHAL, John, Chief Financial Officer, Christus Jasper Memorial Hospital, Jasper, TX, p. A650

BREIER, Dave, Comptroller, Naval Hospital, Jacksonville, FL, p. A132

BREITBACH, Dave, Chief Financial Officer, Prairie du Chien Memorial Hospital, Prairie Du Chien, WI, p. A734

BREITKREUTZ, Jill, Manager Human Resources, Deer Park Hospital, Deer Park, WA, p. A702

BREITLING, Bryan, Administrator, Hand County Memorial Hospital/Avera Health, Miller, SD, p. A597

BREKHUS, Pete, Chief Executive Officer, Madison Valley Hospital, Ennis, MT, p. A398

BREMER Jr, Louis H., Interim Chief Executive Officer, Leesburg Regional Medical Center, Leesburg, FL, p. A135

BRENCKLE, Ph.D., George M., Chief Information Officer, Hospital of the University of Pennsylvania, Philadelphia, PA, p. A568

BRENDLER, Stephen, Director Information Systems, Hilton Head Regional Medical Center, Hilton Head Island, SC, p. A589

BRENN, Jonathan, Chief Executive Officer, St. Joseph's Hospital, Huntingburg, IN, p. A217

BRENNAN, Charles L., President and Chief Executive Officer, St. Lawrence Rehabilitation Center, Trenton, NJ, p. A437

BRENNAN, Kevin F., Executive Vice President and Chief Financial Officer, Geisinger Medical Center, Danville, PA, p. A556

BRENNAN, Terry, Vice President Human Resources, St. Joseph Hospital, Bellingham, WA, p. A700

BRENNER, Marvel, Chief Financial Officer, Ferry County Memorial Hospital, Republic, WA, p. A707

BRENNY, Terrence, President and Chief Executive Officer, Stoughton Hospital Association, Stoughton, WI, p. A736

BREON, Richard C., President and Chief Executive Officer, Spectrum Health, Grand Rapids, MI, p. B101

BRESCIA, Michael J., Executive Medical Director, Calvary Hospital, New York, NY, p. A459

BRESETTE, Elwin, Vice President and Chief Financial Officer, Lawrence & Memorial Hospital, New London, CT, p. A115

BRESLIN, Tim, Chief Financial Officer, Lakeview Regional Medical Center, Covington, LA, p. A279

BRESSANELLI, Leo A., FACHE,
  President and Chief Executive Officer, Genesis Health System, Davenport, IA, p. B46
  Chief Executive Officer, Genesis Medical Center, Davenport, Davenport, IA, p. A231

BRETT, C. William, Ph.D., President and Owner, Windmoor Healthcare of Clearwater, Clearwater, FL, p. A125

BRETZ, Joe, Director Human Resources, St. John's Hospital, Springfield, IL, p. A208

BREUER, Rick, Chief Executive Officer and Administrator, Cloquet Community Memorial Hospital, Cloquet, MN, p. A351

BREWER, Gary L., Chief Executive Officer, Valley View Hospital, Glenwood Springs, CO, p. A106

BREWER, Kelley, Chief Executive Officer, Lakeside Women's Hospital, Oklahoma City, OK, p. A535

BREWER, Rebecca T., FACHE, Chief Executive Officer, Colleton Medical Center, Walterboro, SC, p. A593

BREWER, Ted, Chief Executive Officer, Old Vineyard Youth Services, Winston–Salem, NC, p. A494

BREXLER, James L.
  President, Erlanger Health System, Chattanooga, TN, p. B44
  President and Chief Executive Officer, Erlanger Medical Center, Chattanooga, TN, p. A603

BREZENOFF, Stanley, President and Chief Executive Officer, Continuum Health Partners, New York, NY, p. B33

BRIAN, M.D., Francis, Senior Vice President Medical Affairs, Rapides Regional Medical Center, Alexandria, LA, p. A276

BRICHER, Joan, Senior Vice President Finance, Santa Barbara Cottage Hospital, Santa Barbara, CA, p. A92

BRICKER, Steve, Chief Financial Officer, Sparta Community Hospital, Sparta, IL, p. A208

BRICKER, Tim, Administrator and Chief Executive Officer, Alta View Hospital, Sandy, UT, p. A680

BRICKMAN, Jeffrey, President and Chief Executive Officer, Provena Saint Joseph Medical Center, Joliet, IL, p. A198

BRIDEAU, Leo P.
  President and Chief Executive Officer, Columbia St. Mary's Ozaukee Campus, Mequon, WI, p. A730
  President and Chief Executive Officer, Columbia St. Mary's–Columbia Campus, Milwaukee, WI, p. A730
  President and Chief Executive Officer, Columbia St. Mary's–Milwaukee Campus, Milwaukee, WI, p. A730

BRIDEN, David, Chief Information Officer, Exeter Hospital, Exeter, NH, p. A421

BRIDGE, James B., Vice President Finance, Port Huron Hospital, Port Huron, MI, p. A343

BRIDGES, James M.
  Executive Vice President and Chief Operating Officer, Palmetto Health Baptist/Columbia, Columbia, SC, p. A586
  Executive Vice President and Chief Operating Officer, Palmetto Health Baptist/Columbia, Columbia, SC, p. A586

BRIDGES, Mary, Director Human Resources, Ouachita Medical Center, Camden, AR, p. A41

BRIDGES, Terry, Chief Executive Officer, Fremont Hospital, Fremont, CA, p. A61

BRIDGES, Vince, Controller, Specialty Hospital of Midwest City, Midwest City, OK, p. A533

BRIDGES KEE, Lorinnsa, Human Resource Director, Cypress Fairbanks Medical Center, Houston, TX, p. A644

BRIDON, Daniel, Chief Information Management Division, Bayne–Jones Army Community Hospital, Fort Polk, LA, p. A281

BRIEN, Arthur L., President and Chief Executive Officer, Catskill Regional Medical Center, Harris, NY, p. A453

BRIEN, Curtis, Administrative Officer, Crow/Northern Cheyenne Hospital, Crow Agency, MT, p. A397

BRIER, Pamela S., President and Chief Executive Officer, Maimonides Medical Center, New York, NY, p. A461

BRIERTY, Tim, Chief Executive Officer, McKenna Memorial Hospital, New Braunfels, TX, p. A658

BRIGGS, Paul, Senior Vice President and Chief Financial Officer, Presbyterian Hospital, Albuquerque, NM, p. A440

BRIGGS, M.D., Paul, Chief of Staff, Integris Blackwell Regional Hospital, Blackwell, OK, p. A528

BRIGGS, Ronald O., FACHE, President and Chief Executive Officer, St. Francis Memorial Hospital, West Point, NE, p. A414

BRIGGS, Vicki L., Chief Executive Officer, Longview Regional Medical Center, Longview, TX, p. A654

BRIGHT, John, Associate Director, Veterans Affairs Southern Nevada Healthcare System, North Las Vegas, NV, p. A418

BRILEY, Ellen C., Administrator and Chief Executive Officer, Elba General Hospital, Elba, AL, p. A18

BRILL, Beth, Director Human Resources, Barnesville Hospital Association, Barnesville, OH, p. A503

BRILL, Cheryl, Vice President, Chief Nursing Officer and Chief Operating Officer, Somerset Hospital Center for Health, Somerset, PA, p. A576

BRILL, Donna, Director, Informatimon Systems, Shenandoah Memorial Hospital, Woodstock, VA, p. A698

BRILL, M.D., John, Acting Chief Information Officer, Rush University Medical Center, Chicago, IL, p. A189

BRILLIANT, Patrick D., Chief Executive Officer, Medical Center of Arlington, Arlington, TX, p. A622

BRIMHALL, Dennis C., President and Chief Executive Officer, University of Colorado Hospital, Denver, CO, p. A104

BRINDLEY, John C., President and Chief Executive Officer, Seton Medical Center, Austin, TX, p. A623

BRINES, Duncan, Vice President Finance, Porter Medical Center, Middlebury, VT, p. A682

BRINGHURST, John F., Administrator, Petersburg Medical Center, Petersburg, AK, p. A28

BRINK, Greg, Director Finance, Franklin Medical Center, Greenfield, MA, p. A318

BRINKERHOFF, Cindy, Human Resources Director, South Peninsula Hospital, Homer, AK, p. A27

BRINKLEY, Linda, Director Human Resources, Memorial Hermann Baptist Beaumont Hospital, Beaumont, TX, p. A625

BRINKLEY, Ruth W., President and Chief Executive Officer, Memorial Health Care System, Chattanooga, TN, p. A603

BRINKLEY, Terry, Vice President Finance, Paris Community Hospital, Paris, IL, p. A204

BRINKMAN, Jim, Chief Financial Officer, Clay County Medical Center, Clay Center, KS, p. A245

BRINSON, Patricia, Administrator, Wayne County Hospital, Monticello, KY, p. A271

BRISSON, George, Chief Financial Officer, St. Mary's Hospital, Decatur, IL, p. A192

BRISTER, Shirley, Chief Executive Officer, Meadowbrook Rehabilitation Hospital of Tulsa, Tulsa, OK, p. A539

BRISTOL, Doug, Chief Financial Officer, Yavapai Regional Medical Center, Prescott, AZ, p. A35

BRITSON, Lindsay, Director Human Resources, Belmond Medical Center, Belmond, IA, p. A228

BRITT, Key, Associate Director, Greenwood Leflore Hospital, Greenwood, MS, p. A369

BRITT, Rose, Executive Director, Saint Vincents Catholic Medical Centers of New York, New York, NY, p. A465

BRITT-BOYETTE, Patricia, Vice President Human Resources, Sampson Regional Medical Center, Clinton, NC, p. A480

BRITTO, Vanessa M., MSC, Director Health Service, Simpson Infirmary, Wellesley College, Wellesley, MA, p. A324

BRITTON, Gregory K., President and Chief Executive Officer, Beloit Memorial Hospital, Beloit, WI, p. A723

BRITTON, John, Director of Information Services, Fisher-Titus Medical Center, Norwalk, OH, p. A520

BRITTON, Ted, Director Human Resources, Gerber Memorial Health Services, Fremont, MI, p. A333

BRITTON, William N., Associate Administrator for Finance, Alfred I. duPont Hospital for Children, Wilmington, DE, p. A119

BROADUS, Ronald, Assistant Administrator Human Resources, Medical Center of Louisiana at New Orleans, New Orleans, LA, p. A289

BROADWATER, Gary W., Chief Financial Officer, City Hospital, Martinsburg, WV, p. A717

BROCCOLINO, Victor A., President and Chief Executive Officer, Howard County General Hospital, Columbia, MD, p. A307

BROCK, John D., Chief Executive Officer, Crosbyton Clinic Hospital, Crosbyton, TX, p. A631

BROCK, Lisa, Vice President Human Resources, Overlake Hospital Medical Center, Bellevue, WA, p. A700

BROCK, Mark, Human Resources Manager, Northwest Florida Community Hospital, Chipley, FL, p. A125

BROCK, Robert
　Chief Financial Officer, Marymount Medical Center, London, KY, p. A268
　Chief Financial Officer, Our Lady of the Way Hospital, Martin, KY, p. A271

BROCKIE, Daryl A., Director, U. S. Public Health Service Indian Hospital, Harlem, MT, p. A399

BROCKMAN, Harold, Chief Financial Officer, Kittitas Valley Community Hospital, Ellensburg, WA, p. A702

BRODAR, David, Associate Director Human Resources, Temple East, Northeastern Hospital, Philadelphia, PA, p. A570

BRODBECK, Lisa, Chief Financial Officer, Medical Center of Lewisville, Lewisville, TX, p. A653

BRODERICK, D.O., Paul, Chief of Staff, Morgan Hospital and Medical Center, Martinsville, IN, p. A222

BRODEUR, Mark S., Chief Executive Officer, Jefferson Memorial Hospital, Crystal City, MO, p. A381

BRODHEAD, Robert T., President, St. John's Hospital, Springfield, MO, p. A394

BRODIAN, Craig, Vice President Human Resources, Johns Hopkins Bayview Medical Center, Baltimore, MD, p. A303

BRODIE, Patricia, Chief Executive Officer, Central State Hospital, Louisville, KY, p. A269

BRODY, Jeff, Chief Information Officer, Whitesburg Appalachian Regional Hospital, Whitesburg, KY, p. A275

BRODY, M.D., Robert, Chief Information Officer, San Francisco General Hospital Medical Center, San Francisco, CA, p. A89

BRODY, Robert J., President and Chief Executive Officer, St. Francis Hospital and Health Centers – North Campus, Beech Grove, IN, p. A212

BRODY, Sue G., President and Chief Executive Officer, Bayfront Medical Center, Saint Petersburg, FL, p. A145

BROEKHUIS, Arlyn, Director Information Systems, Sioux Valley Hospital University Medical Center, Sioux Falls, SD, p. A599

BROKAW, Dave, Chief Financial Officer, Greater Community Hospital, Creston, IA, p. A231

BROMAN, Craig J., President and Chief Executive Officer, St. Cloud Hospital, Saint Cloud, MN, p. A361

BROMLEY, M.D., Howard R., Chief of Staff, Veterans Affairs Medical Center, Memphis, TN, p. A614

BROOKER, Paula, Director Information Services, Pleasant Valley Hospital, Point Pleasant, WV, p. A719

BROOKMAN, Mark, Director Information Systems, Hardin Memorial Hospital, Elizabethtown, KY, p. A263

BROOKS, Barbara, Assistant Administrator Fiscal Services, Brazosport Memorial Hospital, Lake Jackson, TX, p. A652

BROOKS, Bruce, Chief Financial Officer, Bladen County Hospital, Elizabethtown, NC, p. A482

BROOKS, David, Chief Operating Officer, Providence Everett Medical Center, Everett, WA, p. A703

BROOKS, Elliot, Senior Vice President Human Resources, Englewood Hospital and Medical Center, Englewood, NJ, p. A428

BROOKS, M.D., H Belk, Chief of Staff, St. Francis Hospital, Inc., Columbus, GA, p. A158

BROOKS III, J. Milton, Administrator, Pineville Community Hospital Association, Pineville, KY, p. A273

BROOKS, Keith, Director Information and Technology Services, Southwest Florida Regional Medical Center, Fort Myers, FL, p. A129

BROOKS, Lynn, Assistant Vice President Human Resources, St. Patrick Hospital, Missoula, MT, p. A401

BROOKS, Marilyn, Commander, Irwin Army Community Hospital, Junction City, KS, p. A250

BROOKS, M.D., Michael, Medical Director, Brighton Hospital, Brighton, MI, p. A329

BROOKS, Patrice Gay, Chief Operating Officer, Cumberland Hospital for Children and Adolescents, New Kent, VA, p. A692

BROOKS, Patti, Director Information Systems, Avera Queen of Peace, Mitchell, SD, p. A597

BROOKS, M.D., Robert L., Vice President Medical Affairs, Washington County Health System, Hagerstown, MD, p. A308

BROOKS, Ronald, Vice President Human Resources, LibertyHealth–Greenville Hospital, Jersey City, NJ, p. A430

BROOKS, Toby, Chief Financial Services, Central Texas Veterans Healthcare System, Temple, TX, p. A668

BROOKS, Troy, Assistant Administrator Fiscal Services, Newton Medical Center, Covington, GA, p. A159

BROOKSHIRE, Lynn, Vice President Information Services and Chief Information Officer; Privacy Officer, Charleston Area Medical Center, Charleston, WV, p. A714

BROOS, Timothy W., Vice President Support Services, Katherine Shaw Bethea Hospital, Dixon, IL, p. A192

BROSLAT, Bruce, Vice President and Chief Operating Officer, Brackenridge Hospital, Austin, TX, p. A623

BROSS, James B., Vice President and Chief Financial Officer, Rutherford Hospital, Rutherfordton, NC, p. A491

BROSS, Mary Ann, Vice President Human Resources, Somerset Medical Center, Somerville, NJ, p. A436

BROTHERS, R Andrew
　Senior Vice President Finance and Chief Financial Officer, St. Elizabeth Health Center, Youngstown, OH, p. A526
　Senior Vice President Finance, St. Joseph Health Center, Warren, OH, p. A524

BROTHMAN, Daniel, Chief Executive Officer, Western Medical Center–Santa Ana, Santa Ana, CA, p. A92

BROTMAN, Martin, M.D., President and Chief Executive Officer, California Pacific Medical Center, San Francisco, CA, p. A88

BROUDE, Alan L., Senior Vice President and Chief Financial Officer, Jewish Hospital, Louisville, KY, p. A269

BROUGH, Ken, Chief Financial Officer, Star Valley Medical Center, Afton, WY, p. A739

BROUGHMAN, Wade, Executive Vice President and Chief Financial Officer, Riverside Regional Medical Center, Newport News, VA, p. A692

BROUGHTON, CPA, Sue, Vice President and Chief Financial Officer, Rangely District Hospital, Rangely, CO, p. A109

BROUHARD, M.D., Ben H., Executive Vice President and Chief of Staff, MetroHealth Medical Center, Cleveland, OH, p. A509

BROUILLETTE, Cindy
　Chief Financial Officer, St. David's Medical Center, Austin, TX, p. A624
　Chief Financial Officer, St. David's Pavilion, Austin, TX, p. A624
　Chief Financial Officer, St. David's Rehabilitation Center, Austin, TX, p. A624

BROUSSARD, Diane, Director Human Resources, Lafayette General Medical Center, Lafayette, LA, p. A283

BROUSSARD, Tammy, Controller, West Calcasieu Cameron Hospital, Sulphur, LA, p. A293

BROUSSARD, Timothy, CHE, Chief Executive Officer, West Calcasieu Cameron Hospital, Sulphur, LA, p. A293

BROUWER, Heath, Administrator, Douglas County Memorial Hospital, Armour, SD, p. A594

BROWER, Fred B., President and Chief Executive Officer, Trinity Health System, Steubenville, OH, p. A522

BROWN, M.D., Albert, Chief of Staff, Kalkaska Memorial Health Center, Kalkaska, MI, p. A338

BROWN, M.D., Andy, Vice President of Medical Affairs, Middle Tennessee Medical Center, Murfreesboro, TN, p. A614

BROWN, B Blaine, General Counsel, Prattville Baptist Hospital, Prattville, AL, p. A23

BROWN, D.O., Barbara, Chief of Staff, Osborne County Memorial Hospital, Osborne, KS, p. A254

BROWN, Betty Bolin, Ed.D., Chief Executive Officer, Veterans Affairs Medical Center, Huntington, WV, p. A716

BROWN, Bill, Chief Operating Officer, Saint Mary's Regional Medical Center, Russellville, AR, p. A50

BROWN, Bob, Director Human Resources, The Children's Institute of Pittsburgh, Pittsburgh, PA, p. A572

BROWN, Brad, Senior Vice President, Information Systems, Erlanger Medical Center, Chattanooga, TN, p. A603

BROWN, Brooke, Human Resources Coordinator, Tulare Local Health Care District, Tulare, CA, p. A96

BROWN, Cathy, Information Systems Manager, Bucyrus Community Hospital, Bucyrus, OH, p. A504

BROWN, Chad, Chief Operating Officer, Hendersonville Medical Center, Hendersonville, TN, p. A607

BROWN, Creager, Chief, Human Resource Management Service, South Texas Veterans Health Care System, San Antonio, TX, p. A665

BROWN, M.D., Crystal, Medical Director, Peach Regional Medical Center, Fort Valley, GA, p. A162

BROWN, M.D., Curtis, Chief of Staff, INTEGRIS Canadian Valley Regional Hospital, Yukon, OK, p. A541

BROWN, David E., President and Chief Executive Officer, Beaufort Memorial Hospital, Beaufort, SC, p. A583

BROWN, David P., Administrator, Citizens Medical Center, Victoria, TX, p. A672

BROWN, M.D., Deborah, Chief of Staff, Grand River Hospital District, Rifle, CO, p. A109

BROWN, Denise, Vice President Human Resources, Saint Joseph Hospital, Chicago, IL, p. A190

BROWN, Donald C., Director Corporate Operations, Fort Washington Medical Center, Fort Washington, MD, p. A308

BROWN, Donald G., Chief Executive Officer, Community Medical Center at Western Illinois, Monmouth, IL, p. A201

BROWN, Doris, Assistant Administrator and Director Human Resources, McCurtain Memorial Hospital, Idabel, OK, p. A532

BROWN, Ed
Chief Financial Officer, Effingham Hospital, Springfield, GA, p. A169
Chief Information Officer, Gwinnett Hospital System, Lawrenceville, GA, p. A164

BROWN, Geoff, Vice President Information Systems, Inova Fairfax Hospital, Falls Church, VA, p. A687

BROWN, M.D., George J., Vice President Acute Care Service and Facilities, Tacoma General Hospital, Tacoma, WA, p. A710

BROWN, Gordon, Chief Information Resources Management, Veterans Affairs Edward Hines, Jr. Hospital, Hines, IL, p. A197

BROWN, H. Thomas, Chief Executive Officer, Washington County Regional Medical Center, Sandersville, GA, p. A168

BROWN, Harold W., Chief Executive Officer, Prairie du Chien Memorial Hospital, Prairie Du Chien, WI, p. A734

BROWN, Hugh, Chief Executive Officer, Brunswick Community Hospital, Supply, NC, p. A492

BROWN, James H.
Chief Financial Officer, Baptist–Lutheran Medical Center, Kansas City, MO, p. A384
Chief Financial Officer, Research Psychiatric Center, Kansas City, MO, p. A384

BROWN, Jim Beck, Chief Operating Officer, Doctors Hospital of Dallas, Dallas, TX, p. A632

BROWN, Joe L., Chief Financial Officer, Hardin Medical Center, Savannah, TN, p. A617

BROWN, Joetta, Director Human Resources, Walter Olin Moss Regional Medical Center, Lake Charles, LA, p. A285

BROWN, Johnny C., Chief Operating Officer, John H. Stroger Jr. Hospital of Cook County, Chicago, IL, p. A187

BROWN, Judy, Senior Vice President, Good Shepherd Medical Center, Longview, TX, p. A653

BROWN, Julie, Human Resources Assistant, Alegent Health Community Memorial Hospital, Missouri Valley, IA, p. A238

BROWN, Karen, Director Information Systems, Memorial Hospital, Towanda, PA, p. A577

BROWN, Karen C., Assistant Director for Strategic Human Resources, OSF Saint Anthony Medical Center, Rockford, IL, p. A206

BROWN, Ken, Vice President Human Services, Pratt Regional Medical Center, Pratt, KS, p. A255

BROWN, M.D., Kenneth, Medical Director, Woman's Hospital, Baton Rouge, LA, p. A278

BROWN, Kent L., Chief Operating Officer, Holmes Regional Medical Center, Melbourne, FL, p. A136

BROWN, Kirstin, Director Human Resources, HEALTHSOUTH Nittany Valley Rehabilitation Hospital, Pleasant Gap, PA, p. A573

BROWN, Larry
Chief Financial Officer, Crawford County Memorial Hospital, Denison, IA, p. A232
Assistant Vice President Information Systems, Phoebe Putney Memorial Hospital, Albany, GA, p. A152

BROWN, D.O., Lawrence, Medical Director, Carson City Hospital, Carson City, MI, p. A329

BROWN, R.N., Linda E., Vice President Clinical Support, Unity Health Center, Shawnee, OK, p. A538

BROWN, Mark, Assistant Administrator and Chief Financial Officer, Northwest Iowa Health Center, Sheldon, IA, p. A241

BROWN, M.D., Maurice, Chief of Staff, St. Joseph Hospital, Polson, MT, p. A401

BROWN, Michael, Vice President Finance and Chief Financial Officer, Children's Hospital, Omaha, NE, p. A411

BROWN, Michael J., Chief Financial Officer, Fairfield Memorial Hospital, Fairfield, IL, p. A194

BROWN, Michael L., Chief Executive Officer, Hoopeston Community Memorial Hospital, Hoopeston, IL, p. A197

BROWN, Misty, Director of Marketing and Public Relations, Fort Sanders–Sevier Medical Center, Sevierville, TN, p. A617

BROWN, Murray L., Chief Executive Officer, Neosho Memorial Regional Medical Center, Chanute, KS, p. A245

BROWN, Patti, Medical Director, HEALTHSOUTH Reading Rehabilitation Hospital, Reading, PA, p. A574

BROWN, Paula, Senior Vice President Corporate Finance, Potomac Hospital, Woodbridge, VA, p. A698

BROWN, Peggy W., Chief Operating Officer, Hill Country Memorial Hospital, Fredericksburg, TX, p. A640

BROWN, Penny, Human Resources Representative, Broaddus Hospital, Philippi, WV, p. A719

BROWN, Rex H., Chief Executive Officer, Hillsboro Area Hospital, Hillsboro, IL, p. A197

BROWN, Rick, Director of Human Resources, Highland Medical Center, Lubbock, TX, p. A654

BROWN, Rickie F., Chief Financial Officer, Monroe County Medical Center, Tompkinsville, KY, p. A275

BROWN, Rita, Personnel Director, Franklin Medical Center, Winnsboro, LA, p. A294

BROWN, Robert, Director Human Resources, Southern Hills Hospital and Medical Center, Las Vegas, NV, p. A417

BROWN, Robert A., President, Forest Health Medical Center, Ypsilanti, MI, p. A348

BROWN, Robin, Chief Executive Officer, Scripps Green Hospital, La Jolla, CA, p. A65

BROWN, Samuel L., Vice President Financial Services, Jennie Stuart Medical Center, Hopkinsville, KY, p. A266

BROWN, Sherri, Director Human Resources, Lawrence Memorial Hospital, Walnut Ridge, AR, p. A51

BROWN, Stephen A., Chief Financial Officer, Grace Cottage Hospital, Townshend, VT, p. A684

BROWN, Steve, Information Officer, Sylvan Grove Hospital, Jackson, GA, p. A164

BROWN, M.D., Steven, Chief Medical Officer, University of Texas Health Center at Tyler, Tyler, TX, p. A671

BROWN, Steven E., FACHE, Chief Executive Officer, Evergreen Healthcare, Kirkland, WA, p. A703

BROWN, Steven E., Director Information Systems, Spalding Regional Medical Center, Griffin, GA, p. A163

BROWN, Susan, Chief Human Resources Officer, North Fulton Regional Hospital, Roswell, GA, p. A168

BROWN, Terry, Administrator and Chief Executive Officer, HEALTHSOUTH Lakeshore Rehabilitation Hospital, Birmingham, AL, p. A15

BROWN, M.D., Terry N., Medical Director, Stillwater Medical Center, Stillwater, OK, p. A538

BROWN, Theodore, Chief Operating Officer, Howard Regional Health System, Kokomo, IN, p. A220

BROWN, Tim S.
Senior Vice President and Administrator, Claiborne County Hospital, Tazewell, TN, p. A618
Chief Financial Officer, Claiborne County Hospital, Tazewell, TN, p. A618

BROWN, Trisha, Human Resources Manager, Community Memorial Hospital, Oconto Falls, WI, p. A733

BROWN, William A., CHE, President and Chief Executive Officer, Provena Saint Joseph Hospital, Elgin, IL, p. A193

BROWN, William K., Vice President and Administrator, Carolinas Medical Center–Pineville, Charlotte, NC, p. A479

BROWN, Zigrida, Vice President Human Resources, Blessing Hospital, Quincy, IL, p. A206

BROWNE, J. Timothy, President and Chief Executive Officer, Loris Community Hospital, Loris, SC, p. A590

BROWNE, Janelle, Executive Director Health Sciences and Human Resources, Harborview Medical Center, Seattle, WA, p. A707

BROWNE, M.D., Kevin, Chairman, Medical Board, Methodist Children's Hospital of South Texas, San Antonio, TX, p. A664

BROWNE, M.D., Mark, Vice President Medical Affairs, Regional Medical Center of Hopkins County, Madisonville, KY, p. A270

BROWNELL, Jamie, Clinic Chief Executive Officer, Marias Medical Center, Shelby, MT, p. A402

BROWNING, Chris, Regional Vice President Human Resources, Mercy Franciscan Hospital Mount Airy, Cincinnati, OH, p. A507

BROWNING, Christine, Regional Vice President Human Resources, Mercy Hospital Fairfield, Fairfield, OH, p. A513

BROWNING, Michael, Senior Vice President and Chief Financial Officer, McLeod Health, Florence, SC, p. A588

BROWNING, Tiffany, Director Data Processing, Bowie Memorial Hospital, Bowie, TX, p. A626

BROWNLOW, William R., Senior Vice Preisdent Finance, Silver Cross Hospital, Joliet, IL, p. A198

BROYLES, Susan, Human Resources Director, Unicoi County Memorial Hospital, Erwin, TN, p. A606

BROZOST, Brian A., M.D., Executive Director and Administrator, Las Vegas Medical Center, Las Vegas, NM, p. A443

BRUCE Jr, Billy J., Chief Executive Officer and President, St. Joseph's Community Health Services, Hillsboro, WI, p. A727

BRUCE, Michael D., Administrator, Lake Martin Community Hospital, Dadeville, AL, p. A16

BRUCE, Sandra B., President and Chief Executive Officer, Saint Alphonsus Regional Medical Center, Boise, ID, p. A177

BRUCE, Scott, Vice President of Operations, St. Mary's Hospital, Amsterdam, NY, p. A447

BRUCKMAN, M.D., Joseph A., Medical Director, Floyd Memorial Hospital and Health Services, New Albany, IN, p. A222

BRUECKNER, Geraldine, R.N.,
President, Baylor Specialty Hospital, Dallas, TX, p. A632
President, Our Children's House at Baylor, Dallas, TX, p. A633

BRUECKNER, R.N., Geraldine, President, Baylor Specialty Hospital, Dallas, TX, p. A632

BRUEHL, Edna
Vice President and Chief Information Officer, Potomac Ridge Behavioral Health System, Rockville, MD, p. A310
Vice President and Chief Information Officer, Shady Grove Adventist Hospital, Rockville, MD, p. A310

BRUELS, Raymond, Director Management Information Systems, Mission Hospital, Mission, TX, p. A657

BRUEMMER, Michael, Controller, Glacial Ridge Health System, Glenwood, MN, p. A354

BRUER, James H., President and Chief Executive Officer, Southwestern Regional Medical Center, Tulsa, OK, p. A540

BRUGGER, John, Director of Information Systems, Gifford Medical Center, Randolph, VT, p. A683

BRUHN, Charles E., Chief Executive Officer, Genesis Medical Center, Illini Campus, Silvis, IL, p. A208

BRUMBAUGH, David, Vice President Human Resources, Children's Hospital and Clinics, Saint Paul, MN, p. A362

BRUMMOND, Bob, Administrator, Harms Memorial Hospital District, American Falls, ID, p. A177

BRUMMUND, Calvin J., Operations Leader Financial Services, Alegent–Health Midlands Community Hospital, Papillion, NE, p. A412

BRUMSTED, M.D., John R., Chief Medical Officer, Fletcher Allen Health Care, Burlington, VT, p. A682

BRUNELLE, Thomas R., Executive Vice President and Administrator, Bon Secours Community Hospital, Port Jervis, NY, p. A470

BRUNER, Debra, Director Quality, Accreditation, and Information Technology, Dunn Memorial Hospital, Bedford, IN, p. A211

BRUNES, Suzan
Administrator and Director of Nursing, Belmond Medical Center, Belmond, IA, p. A228
Administrator and Director of Nursing, Belmond Medical Center, Belmond, IA, p. A228

BRUNICARDI, Rusty O., President, Community Hospital, Montpelier, OH, p. A519

BRUNNWORTH, Donald, Chief Financial Officer, Community Memorial Hospital, Staunton, IL, p. A208

BRUNO, Catherine
  Chief Information Officer, Aroostook Medical Center, Presque Isle, ME, p. A300
  Chief Information Officer, Eastern Maine Medical Center, Bangor, ME, p. A296
BRUNO, Frank, Chief Executive Officer, Gracie Square Hospital, New York, NY, p. A459
BRUNO, M.D., Yolanda, Medical Director, Coler–Goldwater Specialty Hospital and Nursing Facility, New York, NY, p. A459
BRUNS, Dennis Ray, Chief Executive Officer, Frye Regional Medical Center, Hickory, NC, p. A485
BRUNSON Jr, Bobby J., Chief Executive Officer, Tallahatchie General Hospital, Charleston, MS, p. A367
BRUNTZ, Troy, Chief Financial Officer, Community Hospital, McCook, NE, p. A409
BRUSS, Jonathan R., Interim President, Advocate Christ Medical Center, Oak Lawn, IL, p. A203
BRUSSEAU, R.N., Margie, Chief Nursing Officer, Athens Regional Medical Center, Athens, TN, p. A602
BRUSTMAN, Patricia, Chief Financial Officer, HEALTHSOUTH Rehabilitation Hospital of New Jersey, Toms River, NJ, p. A437
BRUTICO, M.D., Carmen A., Chief Medical Officer, Moses Taylor Hospital, Scranton, PA, p. A575
BRUTON, Jeff, Director, Human Resources, Fairview Park Hospital, Dublin, GA, p. A161
BRUUN, Edward, Chief Executive Officer, Clinton Memorial Hospital, Saint Johns, MI, p. A344
BRVENIK, Richard A., FACHE, President and Chief Executive Officer, Windham Community Memorial Hospital, Willimantic, CT, p. A118
BRYAN, Jack M., Chief Operating Officer, St. Mary's Medical Center, Knoxville, TN, p. A610
BRYAN, Jay, Chief Executive Officer, Hackley Lakeshore Hospital, Shelby, MI, p. A345
BRYAN, Kenneth E., Chief Operating Officer, Adena Health System, Chillicothe, OH, p. A506
BRYAN, Margaret, Administrator, Shriners Hospitals for Children, Northern California, Sacramento, CA, p. A85
BRYAN, Marilyn, Administrator, Roger Mills Memorial Hospital, Cheyenne, OK, p. A528
BRYAN, Peter K., Chief Executive Officer, Kern Medical Center, Bakersfield, CA, p. A54
BRYAN–SMITH, Lissa, Chief Administrative Officer, Geisinger Wyoming Valley Medical Center, Wilkes–Barre, PA, p. A579
BRYANT, Dawn
  Vice President Organizational Development, Saint Joseph Medical Center, Kansas City, MO, p. A385
  Vice President Organizational Development, St. Mary's Medical Center, Blue Springs, MO, p. A378
BRYANT, James, Chief Executive Officer and Chief Nursing Officer, Vista Hospital of Dallas, Garland, TX, p. A641
BRYANT, Karen, Chief Officer Support Services, Prowers Medical Center, Lamar, CO, p. A107
BRYANT, Kevin, Vice President Information, Southern Ocean County Hospital, Manahawkin, NJ, p. A431
BRYANT, Lisa G., Director of Human Resources, Cannon Memorial Hospital, Pickens, SC, p. A591
BRYANT, Maureen A., Executive Vice President, Morton Hospital and Medical Center, Taunton, MA, p. A324
BRYANT, Robert E., Vice President and Administrator, Riverside Walter Reed Hospital, Gloucester, VA, p. A689
BRYANT, Ron, Chief Financial Officer, Martha's Vineyard Hospital, Oak Bluffs, MA, p. A322
BRYANT, Rusty, Information Technology Director, Drew Memorial Hospital, Monticello, AR, p. A48
BRYANT, M.D., Thomas, Chief of Staff, Midwest Regional Medical Center, Midwest City, OK, p. A533
BRYANT, W. Michael, President and Chief Executive Officer, Methodist Medical Center of Illinois, Peoria, IL, p. A205
BRYANT, William, Controller, Clinton Hospital, Clinton, MA, p. A317
BRYANT, William J., Chief Executive Officer, Kindred Hospital–Chattanooga, Chattanooga, TN, p. A603
BRYSON, Ron, Director Human Resources, Riveredge Hospital, Forest Park, IL, p. A194
BRZUZ, Richard W., FACHE, Administrator, Shriners Hospitals for Children, Erie, Erie, PA, p. A558

BUBACZ, Joe, Director Information Resources, Soldiers and Sailors Memorial Hospital, Wellsboro, PA, p. A578
BUCCELLATO, Brenda, Information Technology Manager, Sutter Delta Medical Center, Antioch, CA, p. A52
BUCHALTER, M.D., Scott, Chief of Staff, University of Alabama Hospital, Birmingham, AL, p. A15
BUCHANAN, A. C., President and Chief Executive Officer, Rapides Regional Medical Center, Alexandria, LA, p. A276
BUCHANAN, Bruce F., FACHE, Chief Executive Officer, Northeast Baptist Hospital, San Antonio, TX, p. A665
BUCHANAN, David, Director Information Systems, El Centro Regional Medical Center, El Centro, CA, p. A59
BUCHANAN, Donna, Ph.D., Chief Operating Officer, Northwest Missouri Psychiatric Rehabilitation Center, Saint Joseph, MO, p. A390
BUCHANAN, M.D., James, Chief Medical Officer, DeKalb Memorial Hospital, Auburn, IN, p. A211
BUCHANAN, Kevin, Director Management Information Systems, Lexington Memorial Hospital, Lexington, NC, p. A486
BUCHANAN, Pam
  Chief Financial Officer, Harris Regional Hospital, Sylva, NC, p. A492
  Chief Financial Officer, Swain County Hospital, Bryson City, NC, p. A478
BUCHANAN, M.D., Robert, Chief Information Officer, Anna Jaques Hospital, Newburyport, MA, p. A321
BUCHANAN, CPA, Teena, Chief Financial Officer, Louis Smith Memorial Hospital, Lakeland, GA, p. A164
BUCHANAN, Toni, Chief Financial Officer, Unicoi County Memorial Hospital, Erwin, TN, p. A606
BUCHANAN, Tracy, Chief Operating Officer, Thoms Rehabilitation Hospital, Asheville, NC, p. A477
BUCHART, Phyllis, Chief Operating Officer, Centinela Freeman Regional Medical Center, Marina Campus, Marina Del Rey, CA, p. A74
BUCHE, Daniel L., Chief Executive Officer, Brazosport Memorial Hospital, Lake Jackson, TX, p. A652
BUCHHOLZ, Curt, Chief of Staff, Central Peninsula General Hospital, Soldotna, AK, p. A28
BUCK, Catherine, Executive Vice President Operations, Froedtert Memorial Lutheran Hospital, Milwaukee, WI, p. A731
BUCK, Cheryl, Human Resource Manager, Lake Region Healthcare Corporation, Fergus Falls, MN, p. A353
BUCK, Cindy D., Vice President Business Office Group and Chief Financial Officer, Nevada Regional Medical Center, Nevada, MO, p. A388
BUCK, Jack S., Chief Executive Officer, Crockett Hospital, Lawrenceburg, TN, p. A611
BUCKEY, Bob, Director Information Systems, Cypress Fairbanks Medical Center, Houston, TX, p. A644
BUCKINGHAM, R.N., Deborah, Director Human Resources, Redington–Fairview General Hospital, Skowhegan, ME, p. A301
BUCKINGHAM, M.D., John, Chief Medical Staff, Keokuk County Health Center, Sigourney, IA, p. A241
BUCKLAND, Eric, CHE, Site Administrator, West Valley Hospital, Dallas, OR, p. A543
BUCKLEY, M.D., Charles, Chief of Staff, Morrison Community Hospital, Morrison, IL, p. A201
BUCKLEY, Jeffrey L.
  President and Chief Executive Officer, Wabash County Hospital, Wabash, IN, p. A227
  President and Chief Executive Officer, Wabash County Hospital, Wabash, IN, p. A227
BUCKLEY, John J., Executive Director and Chief Executive Officer, Temple East, Northeastern Hospital, Philadelphia, PA, p. A570
BUCKLEY Jr, John J., President and Chief Executive Officer, St. Joseph Regional Health Center, Bryan, TX, p. A627
BUCKLEY, Mary, Vice President Information Technology, Chester County Hospital, West Chester, PA, p. A578
BUCKLEY, Patrick, Director of Human Resources, St. Elizabeth Medical Center, Utica, NY, p. A475
BUCKLEY, Peg, Information Services Coordinator, Littleton Regional Hospital, Littleton, NH, p. A422
BUCKLEY, M.D., R Michael, Chief Medical Officer, Pennsylvania Hospital, Philadelphia, PA, p. A569

BUCKNER, Dan, Chief Executive Officer, Lehigh Regional Medical Center, Lehigh Acres, FL, p. A135
BUCKNER Jr, James E., CHE, Administrator, Uvalde County Hospital Authority, Uvalde, TX, p. A671
BUCKNER, M.D., Randy, President of Medical Staff, Decatur General Hospital, Decatur, AL, p. A17
BUCKNER, Terry, Chief Executive Officer, Eastern Oklahoma Medical Center, Poteau, OK, p. A537
BUCKWORTH, Albert Bennett, Director of Human Resources, Primary Children's Medical Center, Salt Lake City, UT, p. A679
BUDDE, Rex P.
  Senior Vice President and Chief Financial Officer, Franklin Hospital, Benton, IL, p. A184
  Senior Vice President and Chief Financial Officer, St. Joseph Memorial Hospital, Murphysboro, IL, p. A202
BUDDINGTON, M.D., Richard, President, Medical Staff, Johnston Memorial Hospital, Abingdon, VA, p. A685
BUDINGER, David P., Deputy Commander for Administration and Chief of Staff, Darnall Army Community Hospital, Fort Hood, TX, p. A638
BUDNICK, Michael J., FACHE, Chief Executive Officer, Gibson General Hospital, Princeton, IN, p. A224
BUDRYS, Raymond, Chief Executive Officer, Craven Regional Medical Center, New Bern, NC, p. A488
BUDZINSKI, A James, Vice President Finance and Chief Financial Officer, Sparrow Health System, Lansing, MI, p. A338
BUE, Scott, Health Information Systems Manager, Ridgecrest Regional Hospital, Ridgecrest, CA, p. A84
BUELL, Jack, Chief Information Officer, Sutter Lakeside Hospital, Lakeport, CA, p. A67
BUGBEE, Dawn, Chief Financial Officer, Northwestern Medical Center, Saint Albans, VT, p. A683
BUGBEE, M.D., Thomas, Chief of Staff, Blue Hill Memorial Hospital, Blue Hill, ME, p. A297
BUGG, Robert, Chief Financial Officer, Imperial Point Medical Center, Fort Lauderdale, FL, p. A128
BUGIN, Timothy, Chief Operating Officer, HEALTHSOUTH Hospital of Pittsburgh, Monroeville, PA, p. A565
BUKHARI, Kim, Human Resources Manager, Oak Valley District Hospital, Oakdale, CA, p. A78
BUKOVAC, John, Chief Executive Officer, Monsour Medical Center, Jeannette, PA, p. A561
BULINSKI, Chuck, Chief Financial Officer, Ontonagon Memorial Hospital, Ontonagon, MI, p. A342
BULKLEY, M.D., William, Chief of Staff, Arkansas Methodist Medical Center, Paragould, AR, p. A49
BULL, Oneida, Controller, Integris Marshall County Medical Center, Madill, OK, p. A533
BULLARD, Michael R., Chief Executive Officer, Triumph Hospital North Houston, Houston, TX, p. A648
BULLARD, M.D., Timothy, Chief of Staff, Orlando Regional Medical Center, Orlando, FL, p. A141
BULLEN, Thomas B., Administrator, Schick Shadel Hospital, Seattle, WA, p. A708
BULLITT, Michael L.
  Administrator, HEALTHSOUTH Rehabilitation Hospital–Wichita Falls, Wichita Falls, TX, p. A674
  Chief Executive Officer and Administrator, HEALTHSOUTH Rehabilitation Hospital–Wichita Falls, Wichita Falls, TX, p. A674
BULLOCK, Renee, Vice President for Human Resources, Berea Hospital, Berea, KY, p. A261
BULLOCK, Scott B., President, MaineGeneral Medical Center–Waterville Campus, Waterville, ME, p. A301
BULMAN, Jr, Cornelius P., Senior Vice President and Chief Operating Officer, Caritas Carney Hospital, Dorchester, MA, p. A317
BULS, Karen, Director Human Resources, Waverly Health Center, Waverly, IA, p. A243
BULTEMA, Jan, Vice President, Human Resources, University of Wisconsin Hospital and Clinics, Madison, WI, p. A728
BULTEMA, Robert J., Chief Executive Officer, Sheridan Community Hospital, Sheridan, MI, p. A345
BUMGARDNER, Chuck, Director Information Systems, Southeast Georgia Health System Brunswick Campus, Brunswick, GA, p. A157
BUMGARNER, William, Chief Executive Officer, Avera Holy Family Hospital, Estherville, IA, p. A233

© 2005 AHA Guide

BUMPASS, Charles, Assistant Vice President, Memorial Hermann Memorial City Hospital, Houston, TX, p. A646

BUNCH, Brian A.
Vice President Financial Services, Bertie Memorial Hospital, Windsor, NC, p. A494
Vice President Financial Services, Chowan Hospital, Edenton, NC, p. A482

BUNCH, David V., Chief Executive Officer, Plateau Medical Center, Inc., Oak Hill, WV, p. A718

BUNCH, Jimm, President and Chief Executive Officer, Tennessee Christian Medical Center, Madison, TN, p. A611

BUND, Linda, Chief Information Officer, Director of Education, Veterans Affairs Medical Center, New York, NY, p. A466

BUNDY, William H., Chief Executive Officer, Chester County Hospital and Nursing Center, Chester, SC, p. A585

BUNKER, Arturo Geigel, Director of Operations Services, Hospital Universitario Dr. Ramon Ruiz Arnau, Bayamon, PR, p. A744

BUNN, M.D., Barry, Chief of Staff, Heritage Hospital, Tarboro, NC, p. A492

BUNT, M.D., Clayton, Chief Medical Officer, Crow/Northern Cheyenne Hospital, Crow Agency, MT, p. A397

BUNTING, Katherine, Chief Nurse Executive, Fairfield Memorial Hospital, Fairfield, IL, p. A194

BUNTYN, Jacqueline, Head Management Information, Naval Hospital, Cherry Point, NC, p. A480

BURANDT, D.O., Timothy, Chief of Staff, Cheboygan Memorial Hospital, Cheboygan, MI, p. A329

BURCH, Eric, Chief Financial Officer, Lewis County General Hospital, Lowville, NY, p. A456

BURCH, Todd, Administrator and Chief Executive Officer, Greeley County Health Services, Tribune, KS, p. A258

BURCHAM, Jim, Chief Executive Officer, Gateway Rehabilitation Hospital, Florence, KY, p. A264

BURCHELL, Pam, Director of Human Resources, Lawnwood Regional Medical Center, Fort Pierce, FL, p. A129

BURCHETT, Claudia, Vice President Patient Services, Southern Ohio Medical Center, Portsmouth, OH, p. A521

BURCHILL, Kevin R., Chief Operating Officer, Saint Vincent Hospital at Worcester Medical Center, Worcester, MA, p. A325

BURD, Gene, Management Information Systems Director, Indiana Regional Medical Center, Indiana, PA, p. A561

BURDETT, Gregg, Vice President Human Resources, Valley Regional Hospital, Claremont, NH, p. A420

BURDETT, Stephanie, Coordinator Human Resources, Kansas Rehabilitation Hospital, Topeka, KS, p. A257

BURDICK, M.D., Hoyt J., Vice President Medical Affairs, Cabell Huntington Hospital, Huntington, WV, p. A716

BURDICK, Mindy, Administrator, Baptist Medical Center East, Montgomery, AL, p. A21

BURDICK, Steven A., Administrator, Providence Centralia Hospital, Centralia, WA, p. A701

BURETTA, Nancy, Business Office Manager, Mahnomen Health Center, Mahnomen, MN, p. A356

BURGE, Billy, Chief Executive Officer, Harmon Memorial Hospital, Hollis, OK, p. A532

BURGER, Brent, Administrator, HEALTHSOUTH Regional Specialty Hospital, Mechanicsburg, PA, p. A564

BURGESS, Alan J., FAAMA, Administrator, U. S. Public Health Service Owyhee Community Health Facility, Owyhee, NV, p. A418

BURGESS, CHE, FAA, Alan J., Administrator, U. S. Public Health Service Owyhee Community Health Facility, Owyhee, NV, p. A418

BURGESS, M.D., Charles, Chief of Staff, South Peninsula Hospital, Homer, AK, p. A27

BURGESS, Kelly, Medical Staff President, Georgetown Community Hospital, Georgetown, KY, p. A265

BURGESS, Linda, Director Human Resources, Regions Hospital, Saint Paul, MN, p. A362

BURGESS, Mike, Chief Financial Officer, The Children's Hospital of Alabama, Birmingham, AL, p. A15

BURGESS, Shawn, Director Information Systems, Kingman Regional Medical Center, Kingman, AZ, p. A31

BURGESS, Steve, Human Resources Administrator, Henrico Doctors' Hospital, Richmond, VA, p. A695

BURGETT, John, Team Leader, Baptist Regional Medical Center, Corbin, KY, p. A263

BURGETT, D.O., Monica, Chief Medical Staff, Community Memorial Hospital, Sumner, IA, p. A242

BURGOS, Roberto, Executive Director, University Hospital, San Juan, PR, p. A748

BURK, Scott, Chief of Staff, Share Medical Center, Alva, OK, p. A527

BURKE, M.D., Brian, Chief Medical Officer, Fairview Hospital, Great Barrington, MA, p. A318

BURKE, Dennis E., President, Good Shepherd Healthcare System, Hermiston, OR, p. A544

BURKE, Ed, Chief Financial Officer, Medical Center of Louisiana at New Orleans, New Orleans, LA, p. A289

BURKE, M.D., Gene, Vice President Medical Affairs, Sentara Norfolk General Hospital, Norfolk, VA, p. A693

BURKE, Hugh, Director Human Resources, Shaughnessy–Kaplan Rehabilitation Hospital, Salem, MA, p. A323

BURKE, Jack, Administrator, Sacred Heart Rehabilitation Institute, Milwaukee, WI, p. A731

BURKE, M.D., James
Senior Vice President and Chief Medical Officer, Scottsdale Healthcare–Osborn, Scottsdale, AZ, p. A36
Senior Vice President and Chief Medical Officer, Scottsdale Healthcare–Shea, Scottsdale, AZ, p. A36

BURKE, Jeff
Chief Information Officer, Bon Secours St. Francis Health System, Greenville, SC, p. A588
Chief Information Officer, Bon Secours–Richmond Community Hospital, Richmond, VA, p. A694
Chief Information Officer, Memorial Regional Medical Center, Mechanicsville, VA, p. A691

BURKE, John P., Chief Information Officer, Richard L. Roudebush Veterans Affairs Medical Center, Indianapolis, IN, p. A218

BURKE, Kathy A., Chief Executive Officer, Sebastian River Medical Center, Sebastian, FL, p. A146

BURKE, Kaye, Administrator, Long Term Hospital of Dothan, Dothan, AL, p. A17

BURKE, Marsha
Senior Vice President and Chief Financial Officer, WellStar Cobb Hospital, Austell, GA, p. A156
Senior Vice President and Chief Financial Officer, WellStar Douglas Hospital, Douglasville, GA, p. A161
Senior Vice President and Chief Financial Officer, WellStar Kennestone Hospital, Marietta, GA, p. A165
Senior Vice President Financial Services, WellStar Paulding Hospital, Dallas, GA, p. A160
Senior Vice President and Chief Financial Officer, WellStar Windy Hill Hospital, Marietta, GA, p. A165

BURKE, M.D., Thomas, Executive Vice President and Physician–in–Chief, University of Texas M. D. Anderson Cancer Center, Houston, TX, p. A648

BURKE, Tim
Chief Executive Officer, LifeCare Hospitals of New Orleans–Baptist Campus, New Orleans, LA, p. A288
Chief Executive Officer, LifeCare Hospitals–Kenner Campus, Kenner, LA, p. A283

BURKEL, Gregory, Chief Financial Officer, Immanuel St. Joseph's–Mayo Health System, Mankato, MN, p. A356

BURKET, Mark, Chief Executive Officer, Platte Health Center/Avera Health, Platte, SD, p. A598

BURKETT, M.D., Eric, Vice President Medical Affairs, Monmouth Medical Center, Long Branch, NJ, p. A430

BURKETT, Evan, Chief Human Resource Officer, Sioux Valley Hospital University Medical Center, Sioux Falls, SD, p. A599

BURKETT, William T., Chief Executive Officer, Oklahoma Forensic Center, Vinita, OK, p. A541

BURKHARD, Thomas, Commander, Naval Medical Center, Portsmouth, VA, p. A694

BURKHARDT, Minnie, Vice President and General Counsel, Texoma Medical Center, Denison, TX, p. A635

BURKHART, James R., FACHE, President and Administrator, Shands Jacksonville Medical Center, Jacksonville, FL, p. A132

BURKHART, FACHE, James R., President and Chief Executive Officer, Shands Jacksonville Medical Center, Jacksonville, FL, p. A132

BURKOWSKI, Cathy, Vice President Finance, Good Samaritan Health Center of Merrill, Merrill, WI, p. A730

BURLESON, M.D., Stan, Chief Medical Staff, DeWitt Hospital, De Witt, AR, p. A42

BURMAN, Don, Chief Executive Officer, Orthopedic Hospital of Oklahoma, Tulsa, OK, p. A539

BURMEISTER, Geraldine, Chief Executive Officer and Administrator, Windom Area Hospital, Windom, MN, p. A365

BURNETT, Brad, Chief Financial Officer, Heart of Texas Memorial Hospital, Brady, TX, p. A626

BURNETT, Karen, Regional Director Human Resources, McKay–Dee Hospital Center, Ogden, UT, p. A678

BURNETTE, W. Scott, President and Chief Executive Officer, Community Memorial Healthcenter, South Hill, VA, p. A697

BURNHAM, Ben, Administrator, Calhoun–Liberty Hospital, Blountstown, FL, p. A124

BURNS, Bernard, Vice President Finance, St. Mary's Hospital, Amsterdam, NY, p. A447

BURNS, Bruce R., Chief Financial Officer, Concord Hospital, Concord, NH, p. A420

BURNS, Charlotte, Administrator and Chief Executive Officer, Hardin Medical Center, Savannah, TN, p. A617

BURNS, Darlene A., R.N., President and Chief Executive Officer, Rome Memorial Hospital, Rome, NY, p. A471

BURNS, Dennis R., FACHE, Administrator, Hillcrest Hospital, Simpsonville, SC, p. A591

BURNS, James P., Vice President and Chief Financial Officer, Fawcett Memorial Hospital, Port Charlotte, FL, p. A144

BURNS, John, Chief Operating Officer, Dayton General Hospital, Dayton, WA, p. A702

BURNS, Kevin J., Chief Financial Officer, University Medical Center, Tucson, AZ, p. A38

BURNS, Steve
Driector Information Services, Summerville Medical Center, Summerville, SC, p. A592
Driector Information Services, Trident Medical Center, Charleston, SC, p. A585

BURNS, Terry
Chief Operating Officer, Charles F. Kettering Memorial Hospital, Kettering, OH, p. A515
Vice President Finance and Operations, Sycamore Hospital, Miamisburg, OH, p. A518

BURNS, William A., Chief Executive Officer, Rio Grande Regional Hospital, McAllen, TX, p. A656

BURNSIDE, Brian, Administrator, Wayne County Hospital, Corydon, IA, p. A231

BURNSIDE, Ron, Chief Human Resources Officer, Memorial Hospital, Colorado Springs, CO, p. A102

BURNWORTH, Rex, Director Information Systems, Wilson Medical Center, Wilson, NC, p. A494

BURRELL, Carol H., Executive Vice President and Chief Operating Officer, Northeast Georgia Medical Center, Gainesville, GA, p. A163

BURRIS, Bradley D.
President and Chief Executive Officer, Lisbon Area Health Services, Lisbon, ND, p. A499
President and Chief Executive Officer, Oakes Community Hospital, Oakes, ND, p. A500

BURRIS, J Michael, Vice President Corporate Services and Chief Financial Officer, Martha Jefferson Hospital, Charlottesville, VA, p. A686

BURRIS, Lisa, Manager Human Resources, Frazier Rehab Institute, Louisville, KY, p. A269

BURRIS, Stephen W., Vice President Human Resources, Rex Healthcare, Raleigh, NC, p. A489

BURRISS, Jessica, Chief Financial Officer, Barnwell County Hospital, Barnwell, SC, p. A583

BURROUGHS, Tim, Vice President and Chief Financial Officer, Medical City Dallas Hospital, Dallas, TX, p. A633

BURROUGHS, M.D., Valentine, Medical Director, North General Hospital, New York, NY, p. A464

BURROWS, CPA, Patrick D., Chief Financial Officer, River Park Hospital, Huntington, WV, p. A716

BURRUSS, Cheryl, Human Resources Director, Corcoran District Hospital, Corcoran, CA, p. A57

BURRY, M.D., V Fred, Executive Medical Director, Children's Mercy Hospital, Kansas City, MO, p. A384

BURT, Mac, President and Chief Executive Officer, HealthPlus, Houston, TX, p. B56

BURT, Ph.D., Noel, Vice President Human Resources, Moses Cone Health System, Greensboro, NC, p. A484

BURTCH, Sue, Director of Management Information Systems, Burgess Health Center, Onawa, IA, p. A239

BURTHAY, Darcy K., R.N., Interim President and Chief Nursing Officer, St. Joseph Hospital, Kokomo, IN, p. A220

BURTON, Larry, Chief Operating Officer, Great River Medical Center, Blytheville, AR, p. A41

BURY, John, Vice President and Chief Financial Officer, Passavant Area Hospital, Jacksonville, IL, p. A198

BURY, Peter, Vice President Finance, Advocate Good Samaritan Hospital, Downers Grove, IL, p. A192

BURZYNSKI, Cheryl A., President, Bay Special Care Hospital, Bay City, MI, p. A328

BUSATTI, David, Chief Financial Officer, Wesley Medical Center, Wichita, KS, p. A260

BUSBEE, Benton L., Chief Executive Officer, Troy Regional Medical Center, Troy, AL, p. A24

BUSBY, Lisa, Information Systems Manager, Moses Ludington Hospital, Ticonderoga, NY, p. A474

BUSCH, Rebecca, Chief Financial Officer, Spooner Health System, Spooner, WI, p. A736

BUSCH, Walter S., Chief Executive Officer, Liberty County Hospital and Nursing Home, Chester, MT, p. A397

BUSER, Kenneth R.
President and Chief Executive Officer, All Saints Healthcare, Racine, WI, p. A734
President and Chief Executive Officer, St. Luke's Hospital, Racine, WI, p. A734

BUSH, M.D., Bruce A., Vice President Medical Affairs, Indiana Regional Medical Center, Indiana, PA, p. A561

BUSH, M.D., David, Vice Presisdent Medical Affairs, Our Lady of Bellefonte Hospital, Ashland, KY, p. A261

BUSH, Debbie, Director Information Services, North Florida Regional Medical Center, Gainesville, FL, p. A130

BUSH, M.D., E C., Medical Staff President, Henry Ford Wyandotte Hospital, Wyandotte, MI, p. A348

BUSH, Linda, Chief Operating Officer, Franklin County Memorial Hospital, Franklin, NE, p. A406

BUSH, Mark E., Executive Vice President, MidMichigan Medical Center–Gladwin, Gladwin, MI, p. A334

BUSH, Ray, Manager Information Management, Veterans Affairs Medical Center, Lebanon, PA, p. A563

BUSH, William B.
Assistant Administrator Finance, University of South Alabama Knollwood Park Hospital, Mobile, AL, p. A21
Assistant Administrator Finance, University of South Alabama Medical Center, Mobile, AL, p. A21
Assistant Administrator Finance, USA Children's and Women's Hospital, Mobile, AL, p. A21

BUSH, M.D., William G., Chief of Staff, River Oaks Hospital, Jackson, MS, p. A371

BUSKO, Laura, Interim Chief Information Officer, Phoenix Children's Hospital, Phoenix, AZ, p. A34

BUSSELL, Walter, Chief Financial Officer, Memorial Hospital West, Pembroke Pines, FL, p. A142

BUSSEY, M.D., George, Chief Medical Officer, FirstHealth Richmond Memorial Hospital, Rockingham, NC, p. A490

BUSSEY, Starling, Director Human Resources, Miller County Hospital, Colquitt, GA, p. A158

BUSTETTER, Laura, Director of Marketing and Public Relations, Williamson Medical Center, Franklin, TN, p. A606

BUTCHER, Allen R., Vice President Finance, Camden–Clark Memorial Hospital, Parkersburg, WV, p. A718

BUTCHER, D.O., Steven, Director Medical Affairs, Citizens Memorial Hospital, Bolivar, MO, p. A378

BUTIKOFER, Lon D., Ph.D., Chief Executive Officer, Regional Medical Center, Manchester, IA, p. A237

BUTKER, Jeff, Chief Information Officer, Memorial Hospital, Martinsville, VA, p. A691

BUTLER, Anita M., Chief Executive Officer, Spartanburg Hospital for Restorative Care, Spartanburg, SC, p. A592

BUTLER, Barbara, Administrator, HEALTHSOUTH Deaconess Rehabilitation Hospital, Evansville, IN, p. A214

BUTLER, Brad, Network Administrator, Barton County Memorial Hospital, Lamar, MO, p. A386

BUTLER, M.D., Carol, President Medical Staff, Bluffton Regional Medical Center, Bluffton, IN, p. A212

BUTLER, David A., Chief Executive Officer and President, Jellico Community Hospital, Jellico, TN, p. A608

BUTLER, Debby, Director Human Resources, Wadley Regional Medical Center, Texarkana, TX, p. A670

BUTLER, Elaine, Chief Executive Officer, Richwood Area Community Hospital, Richwood, WV, p. A719

BUTLER, Everett A., Chief Executive Officer, Unity Medical Center, Grafton, ND, p. A498

BUTLER, Jan, Administrator, Frye Regional Medical Center–Alexander Campus, Taylorsville, NC, p. A493

BUTLER, Jeffrey, Superintendent, Richmond State Hospital, Richmond, IN, p. A224

BUTLER, Keith L., Chief Executive Officer, Lillian M. Hudspeth Memorial Hospital, Sonora, TX, p. A667

BUTLER, Peter W., Executive Vice President and Chief Operating Officer, Rush University Medical Center, Chicago, IL, p. A189

BUTLER, Randy, Chief Financial Officer, West Florida Hospital, Pensacola, FL, p. A143

BUTLER, Raymond, President, Callahan Eye Foundation Hospital, Birmingham, AL, p. A14

BUTLER, Sandra, Vice President Human Resources, Union Regional Medical Center, Monroe, NC, p. A487

BUTLER, Susan, Chief Financial Officer, North Valley Health Center, Warren, MN, p. A364

BUTROS, M.D., Rezkalla, Medical Staff President, Gateway Regional Health System, Mount Sterling, KY, p. A272

BUTTERFIELD, Don, Marketing and Public Relations Specialist, St. Vincent Hospital, Santa Fe, NM, p. A444

BUTTERICK, M.D., John, Medical Advisor, Brandon Regional Hospital, Brandon, FL, p. A124

BUTTON, Charlie, Chief Financial Officer, Bingham Memorial Hospital, Blackfoot, ID, p. A177

BUTTS, Charles N., Chief Executive Officer, Medical Arts Hospital, Lamesa, TX, p. A652

BUTTS, Christine, Human Resources Director, HEALTHSOUTH Rehabilitation Hospital, Columbia, SC, p. A585

BUTTURFF, Sandra J., Site Director, Willmar Regional Treatment Center, Willmar, MN, p. A365

BUTZ, M.D., William, Chief of Staff, Montgomery County Memorial Hospital, Red Oak, IA, p. A240

BUTZER, M.D., John, Medical Director, Mary Free Bed Rehabilitation Hospital, Grand Rapids, MI, p. A334

BUURMAN, Rita K., Chief Executive Officer, Sabetha Community Hospital, Sabetha, KS, p. A256

BUXTON, Barton, Chief Executive Officer, Lapeer Regional Medical Center, Lapeer, MI, p. A339

BUZACHERO, Vic
Vice President Human Resources, Scripps Green Hospital, La Jolla, CA, p. A65
Vice President Human Resources, Scripps Memorial Hospital–La Jolla, La Jolla, CA, p. A66

BYARS, Alvin, Chief Information Management Service, Central Texas Veterans Healthcare System, Temple, TX, p. A668

BYERLY, Carolyn, Chief Information Officer, Stanford Hospital and Clinics, Palo Alto, CA, p. A80

BYERS, Alton T., Chief Operating Officer, Haywood Regional Medical Center, Clyde, NC, p. A480

BYHAM, James, Vice President Financial Services, Elk Regional Health Center, Saint Marys, PA, p. A574

BYLANCIK, Robert J., CHE, President and Chief Executive Officer, Sunnyview Rehabilitation Hospital, Schenectady, NY, p. A472

BYNUM, Chigger, Chief Financial Officer, John Randolph Medical Center, Hopewell, VA, p. A690

BYNUM, M.D., Glenn, Vice Persident Medical Management, Advocate Bethany Hospital, Chicago, IL, p. A186

BYORICK, F Joseph, Senior Vice President Finance, Lancaster General Hospital, Lancaster, PA, p. A562

BYRD, M.D., Becky, Vice President Medical Affairs, Baptist Montclair, Birmingham, AL, p. A14

BYRD, Jeffrey, Administrator, Atlantic Shores Hospital, Fort Lauderdale, FL, p. A128

BYRD, Sue, Vice President Human Resources, Sacred Heart Hospital of Pensacola, Pensacola, FL, p. A143

BYRD, Sylvia, Director Human Resources, Edgefield County Hospital, Edgefield, SC, p. A587

BYRNE, Frank D., M.D., President, St. Marys Hospital Medical Center, Madison, WI, p. A728

BYRNE, Kevin T., Vice President Human Resources, Phelps Memorial Hospital Center, Sleepy Hollow, NY, p. A472

BYRNES, Nancy A., Chief Executive Officer, Navarro Regional Hospital, Corsicana, TX, p. A631

BYRNS, David, Chief Executive Officer, South Cameron Memorial Hospital, Cameron, LA, p. A278

BYROM, David, Chief Executive Officer, Coryell Memorial Hospital, Gatesville, TX, p. A641

C

CABE, Joan, Vice President Operations, Highlands–Cashiers Hospital, Highlands, NC, p. A485

CABELL, Susan M., Vice President, Administration, Martha Jefferson Hospital, Charlottesville, VA, p. A686

CABLE, Cleo, Chief Financial Officer, Bayside Community Hospital, Anahuac, TX, p. A621

CABONOR, Regis, Administrator, Bloomsburg Hospital, Bloomsburg, PA, p. A553

CABOOR, Pete, Manager Information Systems, Advocate Good Samaritan Hospital, Downers Grove, IL, p. A192

CACKLER, Ron, President and Chief Executive Officer, Cushing Regional Hospital, Cushing, OK, p. A529

CADWELL, Maureen, Chief Executive Officer, Mid Dakota Medical Center, Chamberlain, SD, p. A594

CADY, Thomas, Vice President Human Resources, UMass Memorial–Marlborough Hospital, Marlborough, MA, p. A320

CAESAR, Diane, Director, Englewood Hospital and Medical Center, Englewood, NJ, p. A428

CAFASSO, Larry, Senior Vice President and Chief Operating Officer, Catskill Regional Medical Center, Harris, NY, p. A453

CAGLE, Mary Jo, Acting Chief Medical Officer, Bon Secours St. Francis Health System, Greenville, SC, p. A588

CAGLE, M.D., William, Medical Director, Lake Chelan Community Hospital, Chelan, WA, p. A701

CAHILL, Donna, Director Human Resources, Palisades Medical Center, North Bergen, NJ, p. A433

CAHILL, Joseph, Executive Vice President and Chief Operating Officer, South Shore Hospital, South Weymouth, MA, p. A323

CAHO–MOONEY, Linda, Chief Financial Officer, Claiborne County Hospital, Port Gibson, MS, p. A375

CAIN, Kathleen, Chief Financial Officer, San Leandro Hospital, San Leandro, CA, p. A91

CAIN, Mark, Chief Executive Officer, White County Community Hospital, Sparta, TN, p. A618

CAIN, Roxie, Chief Financial Officer, Big Horn County Memorial Hospital, Hardin, MT, p. A399

CAINE, Claudia, Executive Vice President and Chief Operating Officer, Lutheran Medical Center, New York, NY, p. A461

CAISON, S Beth, Administrator, Collingsworth General Hospital, Wellington, TX, p. A673

CALABRESE, M.D., Jamie, Medical Director, The Children's Institute of Pittsburgh, Pittsburgh, PA, p. A572

CALABRESI, Joseph, Chief Information Service, Edith Nourse Rogers Memorial Veterans Hospital, Bedford, MA, p. A312

CALAIS, C Matthew
Senior Vice President and Chief Information Officer, Legacy Good Samaritan Hospital and Medical Center, Portland, OR, p. A547
Senior Vice President and Chief Information Officer, Legacy Meridian Park Hospital, Tualatin, OR, p. A550
CALAMARI, Frank A., President and Chief Executive Officer, Calvary Hospital, New York, NY, p. A459
CALANDRIELLO, John, Chief Financial Officer, Saint Peter's University Hospital, New Brunswick, NJ, p. A432
CALBONE, Angelo G., President and Chief Executive Officer, Mount St. Mary's Hospital and Health Center, Lewiston, NY, p. A455
CALCUTT, Andrew, Chief of Medical Staff, Colleton Medical Center, Walterboro, SC, p. A593
CALDAS, James F., President, Washington Hospital Center, Washington, DC, p. A122
CALDERON, Jorge, Chief Information Systems, San Jorge Children's Hospital, San Juan, PR, p. A747
CALDERONE, John A., Ph.D., Chief Executive Officer, Corona Regional Medical Center, Corona, CA, p. A57
CALDWELL, Carolyn W., Chief Executive Officer, Lee's Summit Hospital, Lees Summit, MO, p. A386
CALDWELL, Dari, Executive Vice President and Chief Operating Officer, NorthEast Medical Center, Concord, NC, p. A481
CALDWELL, Darren, Chief Executive Officer, DeWitt Hospital, De Witt, AR, p. A42
CALDWELL, Harvey G., Administrator and Chief Executive Officer, Brainerd Regional Human Services Center, Brainerd, MN, p. A350
CALDWELL, Richard E., Chief Information Officer, Jackson Hospital and Clinic, Montgomery, AL, p. A22
CALHOUN, Kevin P., Chief Executive Officer, Selby General Hospital, Marietta, OH, p. A517
CALHOUN, Kirk A., M.D., President, University of Texas Health Center at Tyler, Tyler, TX, p. A671
CALHOUN, Royce
Fiscal Officer, Veterans Affairs Medical Center, Albany, NY, p. A446
Business Manager, Veterans Affairs Western New York Healthcare System–Buffalo Division, Buffalo, NY, p. A449
CALIA, M.D., Frank M., Acting Chief Medical Officer, University of Maryland Medical Center, Baltimore, MD, p. A304
CALIVA, Todd, Chief Executive Officer, East Houston Regional Medical Center, Houston, TX, p. A645
CALKIN, Pitt R., Interim Chief Financial Officer, Bon Secours Hospital, Grosse Pointe, MI, p. A335
CALKINS, Andrew, Chief Executive Officer, Park View Specialty Hospital, Springfield, MA, p. A324
CALL, Carie, Chief Computer Support, Cassia Regional Medical Center, Burley, ID, p. A178
CALLAHAN, Deanna, Director Information Systems, Titusville Area Hospital, Titusville, PA, p. A576
CALLAHAN, Kevin J., President and Chief Executive Officer, Exeter Hospital, Exeter, NH, p. A421
CALLAHAN, Michael A., Chief Executive Officer, Andalusia Regional Hospital, Andalusia, AL, p. A13
CALLAHAN, Teresa, MSN, Chief Executive Officer, Iraan General Hospital, Iraan, TX, p. A649
CALLAIS, Elizabeth, Chief Fiscal Officer, Leonard J. Chabert Medical Center, Houma, LA, p. A282
CALLARI, M.D., Richard, Chief of Staff, Broward General Medical Center, Fort Lauderdale, FL, p. A128
CALLAS, Elaine, Chief Information Officer, St. Anthony Central Hospital, Denver, CO, p. A104
CALLAWAY, Warren E., FACHE, Chief Executive Officer, Brandywine Hospital, Coatesville, PA, p. A555
CALLECOD, David L., FACHE, President and Chief Executive Officer, Marion General Hospital, Marion, IN, p. A221
CALLENDER, David L., M.D., Director, University of California Los Angeles Medical Center, Los Angeles, CA, p. A73
CALLENS, Paul A., Ph.D., Director, North Mississippi State Hospital, Tupelo, MS, p. A376
CALLISON, Judy, Chief Financial Officer, East Texas Medical Center–Quitman, Quitman, TX, p. A662
CALMAN, Richard, Director Information Systems Technology and Health Management Information

Systems, University of Medicine and Dentistry of New Jersey–University Hospital, Newark, NJ, p. A433
CALVARUSO, Joseph T.
President and Chief Executive Officer, Mount Carmel, Columbus, OH, p. A510
Chief Executive Officer, Mount Carmel St. Ann's, Westerville, OH, p. A524
CALVERT, Doug, Director Information Systems, Bolivar Medical Center, Cleveland, MS, p. A368
CAMELLERI, Mary Ann, Senior Vice President, Chief Operating Officer and General Counsel, Hospital for Special Care, New Britain, CT, p. A114
CAMERON, M.D., Ph, Ray, Chief of Staff, Dickinson County Healthcare System, Iron Mountain, MI, p. A337
CAMERON, Sandra A., Chief Executive Officer, Kearny County Hospital, Lakin, KS, p. A251
CAMMACK Jr, Thomas N., Chief Administrative Officer, Mother Frances Hospital – Jacksonville, Jacksonville, TX, p. A650
CAMMARATA, Ph.D., S, Jerry, Associate Executive Director, Coney Island Hospital, New York, NY, p. A459
CAMP III, Claude E., Chief Executive Officer, Artesia General Hospital, Artesia, NM, p. A441
CAMP, Daniel, Vice President Human Resources, Good Samaritan Hospital, San Jose, CA, p. A90
CAMP, James, Chief Operating Officer, Select Specialty Hospital–Mesa, Mesa, AZ, p. A32
CAMPANA, Barb, Director Information Systems, Missouri Baptist Medical Center, Town and Country, MO, p. A394
CAMPAS, Janice, Chief Financial Officer, Wichita County Health Center, Leoti, KS, p. A251
CAMPBELL, Bruce C., President, Advocate Lutheran General Hospital, Park Ridge, IL, p. A204
CAMPBELL, Carole
Director Finance, SSM St. Joseph Health Center, Saint Charles, MO, p. A390
Director Finance, SSM St. Joseph Hospital West, Lake Saint Louis, MO, p. A386
CAMPBELL, Cathy, Chief Executive Officer, Texas Specialty Hospital at Dallas, Dallas, TX, p. A634
CAMPBELL, Charlotte, Director Human Resources, Beatrice Community Hospital and Health Center, Beatrice, NE, p. A405
CAMPBELL, M.D., Darrell, Chief of Clinical Affairs, University of Michigan Hospitals and Health Centers, Ann Arbor, MI, p. A327
CAMPBELL, CPA, David C., Controller, Chief Financial Officer and Assistant Administrator, Tyler County Hospital, Woodville, TX, p. A674
CAMPBELL, Deborah, Administrator, Thomas H. Boyd Memorial Hospital, Carrollton, IL, p. A185
CAMPBELL, Gary L., CHE, Director, Harry S. Truman Memorial Veterans Hospital, Columbia, MO, p. A380
CAMPBELL, Gayla, Executive Director, Edmond Specialty Hospital, Edmond, OK, p. A530
CAMPBELL, Jan
Senior Vice President Human Resources, Covenant Children's Hospital, Lubbock, TX, p. A654
Senior Vice President Human Resources, Covenant Medical Center, Lubbock, TX, p. A654
CAMPBELL, John, Director Management Information Systems, Spaulding Rehabilitation Hospital, Boston, MA, p. A314
CAMPBELL, Katharine Ann, Chief Executive Officer and Administrator, Mountainview Medical Center, White Sulphur Springs, MT, p. A402
CAMPBELL, R.N., Kim, Vice President Professional Services, North Country Hospital and Health Center, Newport, VT, p. A683
CAMPBELL, Lou, Acting Executive Director, Capital District Psychiatric Center, Albany, NY, p. A446
CAMPBELL, Mary Pat, Director Human Resources, SSM Cardinal Glennon Children's Hospital, Saint Louis, MO, p. A391
CAMPBELL, D.O., Richard, Chief of Staff, Community Hospital, Torrington, WY, p. A742
CAMPBELL, Sharon, Director Human Resources, Florida Hospital – Deland, De Land, FL, p. A127
CAMPBELL, Stephen J., Administrator, Union County General Hospital, Clayton, NM, p. A442

CAMPBELL, Sue, Vice President Human Resources, Lincoln General Hospital, Ruston, LA, p. A292
CAMPBELL, Susie, Director Human Resources, Community Memorial Hospital, Staunton, IL, p. A208
CAMPBELL, Terri, Director Information Systems, Baptist Memorial Hospital–North Mississippi, Oxford, MS, p. A374
CAMPBELL, Todd, Vice President Financial Affairs and Chief Financial Officer, St. Mary's Medical Center, Huntington, WV, p. A716
CAMPBELL, Trish, Director Management Information Systems, Westside Regional Medical Center, Plantation, FL, p. A143
CAMPBELL, Val, Director of Human Resources, St. Peter Community Hospital, Saint Peter, MN, p. A362
CAMPBELL, Wayne, Chief Executive Officer, Fort Walton Beach Medical Center, Fort Walton Beach, FL, p. A129
CAMPEAU, Benjamin
Interim Director, Veterans Affairs Medical Center, Muskogee, OK, p. A534
Associate Director, Veterans Affairs Medical Center, Muskogee, OK, p. A534
CAMPO, Linda, Regional Director of Human Resources, HEALTHSOUTH Rehabilitation Hospital of Spring Hill, Brooksville, FL, p. A125
CAMPOS, Ariel, Director Human Resources, Women's and Children's Hospital, Lafayette, LA, p. A284
CAMPOS, Christina, Administrator, Guadalupe County Hospital, Santa Rosa, NM, p. A444
CANALES, Deb, Senior Vice President Human Resources, Littleton Adventist Hospital, Littleton, CO, p. A107
CANARIOS, Mike, Vice President and Chief Financial Officer, St. Jude Children's Research Hospital, Memphis, TN, p. A614
CANDIO, Christine, Executive Vice President, Hallmark Health System, Melrose, MA, p. A320
CANDULLO, Carl, Chief Information Officer, Munroe Regional Medical Center, Ocala, FL, p. A140
CANFIELD, Brian, Deputy Chief for Administration, Dwight David Eisenhower Army Medical Center, Fort Gordon, GA, p. A162
CANIZARO, Tom, Associate Executive Director, South Central Regional Medical Center, Laurel, MS, p. A372
CANLAS, Emma, Chief Financial Officer, Saint Francis Hospital–Bartlett, Bartlett, TN, p. A602
CANNON, David, Chief of Staff, Northwest Medical Center of Washington County, Springdale, AR, p. A50
CANNON, James C., Administrator and Chief Executive Officer, Regional Hospital for Respiratory and Complex Care, Seattle, WA, p. A708
CANNON, M.D., Nass, Chief of Staff, Cooper Green Hospital, Birmingham, AL, p. A14
CANOVA, Jr, Frank, Chief Financial Officer, Medical Center of South Arkansas, El Dorado, AR, p. A42
CANTELOPE, Marlena, Director Management Information Systems, St. Luke's Medical Center, Phoenix, AZ, p. A35
CANTLEY, J Scott, Vice President and Chief Operating Officer, Marietta Memorial Hospital, Marietta, OH, p. A517
CANTRELL, Debra, Chief Information Officer, Emory Crawford Long Hospital, Atlanta, GA, p. A153
CANTRELL, Dedra
Chief Information Officer, Emory University Hospital, Atlanta, GA, p. A153
Chief Information Officer, Wesley Woods Center of Emory University, Atlanta, GA, p. A155
CANTRELL, Gary, President and Chief Executive Officer, St. Lucie Medical Center, Port St. Lucie, FL, p. A144
CANTU, Nick, Chief of Stafff, Ville Platte Medical Center, Ville Platte, LA, p. A294
CANUPP, M.D., Tony, Chief of Staff, Hugh Chatham Memorial Hospital, Elkin, NC, p. A482
CAPECE, Vincent, Vice President Finance and Treasurer, Middlesex Hospital, Middletown, CT, p. A114
CAPELLI, M.D., Alfred J., President Medical Staff, Aurora Medical Center, Kenosha, WI, p. A727
CAPELLI, M.D., John P., Vice President Medical Affairs, Our Lady of Lourdes Medical Center, Camden, NJ, p. A426
CAPERS, Travis, Chief Operating Officer, Southern Hills Medical Center, Nashville, TN, p. A615

CAPITELLI, M.D., Robert, Senior Vice President and Chief Medical Officer, St. Tammany Parish Hospital, Covington, LA, p. A279

CAPLES, Greg, Chief Financial Officer, Emory Eastside Medical Center, Snellville, GA, p. A169

CAPOBIANCO, Peter E., President and Chief Executive Officer, St. Clare's Hospital of Schenectady, Schenectady, NY, p. A472

CAPOBIANCO, Thomas, Executive Vice President Finance, Resurrection Medical Center, Chicago, IL, p. A189

CAPONE, David, Senior Vice President Finance and Chief Financial Officer, St. James Mercy Hospital, Hornell, NY, p. A454

CAPPELLO, Thomas A., Director, Veterans Affairs Medical Center, Decatur, GA, p. A160

CAPPETTA, Wende, Administrator, Santa Ynez Valley Cottage Hospital, Solvang, CA, p. A94

CAPPS, Kim
Chief Financial Officer, Hayes–Green–Beach Memorial Hospital, Charlotte, MI, p. A329
Chief Financial Officer, Hayes–Green–Beach Memorial Hospital, Charlotte, MI, p. A329

CARACCI, Jeff, Information Systems Manager, Pella Regional Health Center, Pella, IA, p. A240

CARACCIOLA, Kevin, Vice President, Human Resources, Peninsula Regional Health System, Salisbury, MD, p. A310

CARBARY, Janet, Chief Financial Officer, Carlsbad Medical Center, Carlsbad, NM, p. A441

CARBEN, Tammy, Interim Chief Executive Officer, SCCI Hospital – Harrisburg, Harrisburg, PA, p. A560

CARBONE, Davide M., Chief Executive Officer, Aventura Hospital and Medical Center, Aventura, FL, p. A123

CARDA, Vern, Administrator and Chief Executive Officer, Brookings Health System, Brookings, SD, p. A594

CARDAMONE, M.D., Stephen
Vice President Medical Affairs, Covenant Medical Center, Waterloo, IA, p. A243
Senior Vice President and Chief Medical Officer, Mercy Hospital of Franciscan Sisters, Oelwein, IA, p. A239

CARDAMONE, D.O., Steven, Chief Medical Officer, Sartori Memorial Hospital, Cedar Falls, IA, p. A229

CARDELLO, Deborah, Chief Operating Officer, Robert Wood Johnson University Hospital at Hamilton, Hamilton, NJ, p. A429

CARDILE, Eileen K., Executive Vice President and Chief Operating Officer, Underwood–Memorial Hospital, Woodbury, NJ, p. A439

CARDINAL, Joyce, Assistant Administrator, Chf Operating Officer and Chief Nursing Officer, Olympic Medical Center, Port Angeles, WA, p. A706

CARDWELL, Paul, Chief Executive Officer, White County Memorial Hospital, Monticello, IN, p. A222

CAREY, Calvin, Assistant Administrator and Chief Financial Officer, Madison Memorial Hospital, Rexburg, ID, p. A181

CAREY, Debra D.
Associate Executive Director and Chief Operating Officer, Howard University Hospital, Washington, DC, p. A121
Chief Administrative Officer, SUNY Downstate Medical Center University Hospital, New York, NY, p. A466

CAREY, Lavaughn, Chief Financial Officer, Edmond Medical Center, Edmond, OK, p. A530

CARGILL, III, M.D., J G., President, Medical Staff, Memorial Hospital, Martinsville, VA, p. A691

CARIKER, Ann, Chief Operating Officer, Northeastern Nevada Regional Hospital, Elko, NV, p. A415

CARIKER, Kelly, Manager, Mid–Valley Hospital, Omak, WA, p. A705

CARISSIMI, Derek, Vice President Human Resources and Support Services, Saint Alphonsus Regional Medical Center, Boise, ID, p. A177

CARL, Gerald E., Chief Executive Officer, Sioux Valley Luverne Medical Center, Luverne, MN, p. A356

CARLE, Chris, Administrator, St. Elizabeth Medical Center–Grant County, Williamstown, KY, p. A275

CARLIN, Martin E., President, Park Ridge Hospital, Rochester, NY, p. A471

CARLISLE, Charles, Director, East Mississippi State Hospital, Meridian, MS, p. A373

CARLISLE, M.D., Jack, Chief of Staff, Grand Itasca Clinic and Hospital, Grand Rapids, MN, p. A354

CARLISLE, Mary Beth, Chief Executive Officer, Mildred Mitchell–Bateman Hospital, Huntington, WV, p. A716

CARLISLE, Robert, Senior Vice President and Chief Financial Officer, Parkview Hospital, Fort Wayne, IN, p. A215

CARLSON, Bev, Chief Financial Officer, Delta County Memorial Hospital, Delta, CO, p. A103

CARLSON, Brian J., FACHE, President and Chief Executive Officer, Lake View Memorial Hospital and Home, Two Harbors, MN, p. A364

CARLSON, Carol, Director Marketing, Memorial Health Care Systems, Seward, NE, p. A413

CARLSON, Dan, Assistant Administrator Finance and Chief Financial Officer, Bay Area Medical Center, Marinette, WI, p. A729

CARLSON, M.D., Daniel, Senior Vice President Medical Affairs, Community–General Hospital of Greater Syracuse, Syracuse, NY, p. A473

CARLSON, D.O., David J., Vice President Medical Affairs, Chambersburg Hospital, Chambersburg, PA, p. A555

CARLSON, Edward B., Vice President and Chief Financial Officer, Munson Medical Center, Traverse City, MI, p. A346

CARLSON, John M., President and Chief Executive Officer, Bridgton Hospital, Bridgton, ME, p. A297

CARLSON, Kathy, Vice President Patient Care and Support Services, Osborne County Memorial Hospital, Osborne, KS, p. A254

CARLSON, Lisa, Chief Financial Officer, MeritCare Medical Center, Fargo, ND, p. A497

CARLSON, Martha, Chief Financial Officer, Longview Regional Medical Center, Longview, TX, p. A654

CARLSON, Nancy
Administrator, San Pedro Peninsula Hospital, Los Angeles, CA, p. A72
Director Finance, Sioux Center Community Hospital and Health Center/Avera Health, Sioux Center, IA, p. A241

CARLSON, Peter, Executive Director, Aurora Psychiatric Hospital, Wauwatosa, WI, p. A738

CARLSON, Richard, Chief Financial Officer, Crawford Memorial Hospital, Robinson, IL, p. A206

CARLSON, Richard J., Executive Vice President and Administrator, St. John's Hospital, Springfield, IL, p. A208

CARLSON, Roland R., Chief Executive Officer, Pana Community Hospital, Pana, IL, p. A204

CARLSON, M.D., Sam, Executive Vice President and Chief Medical Officer, Methodist Hospital, Saint Louis Park, MN, p. A361

CARLSON, Stephen G., President, Flagstaff Medical Center, Flagstaff, AZ, p. A30

CARLTON, Brian, Chief Financial Officer, Norton County Hospital, Norton, KS, p. A253

CARMAIN, Jim, Vice President Financial and Information Services, Western Baptist Hospital, Paducah, KY, p. A273

CARMAN, Angela, President and Chief Executive Officer, Berea Hospital, Berea, KY, p. A261

CARMAN, Thomas H., President and Chief Executive Officer, Samaritan Medical Center, Watertown, NY, p. A475

CARMEN, Lee, Director Health Care Information Systems, University of Iowa Hospitals and Clinics, Iowa City, IA, p. A236

CARMICHAEL, Craig, Vice President Operations, Saint Mary's Medical Center, Saginaw, MI, p. A344

CARMICHAEL, LeRoy, Executive Director, Bronx Psychiatric Center, New York, NY, p. A458

CARMIN, Ron, Vice President Fiscal Affairs, Mary Rutan Hospital, Bellefontaine, OH, p. A504

CARMODY, Kerry, Administrator, Providence Holy Cross Medical Center, San Fernando, CA, p. A88

CARNATHAN, Glenn, Vice President, Chief Resources Officer, Saint Thomas Hospital, Nashville, TN, p. A615

CARNES, Gary, President and Chief Executive Officer, All Children's Hospital, Saint Petersburg, FL, p. A145

CARNEY, Michael J., Chief Executive Officer, Brentwood Behavioral HealthCare of Mississippi, Jackson, MS, p. A370

CARNEY, Patrick, Chief Information Officer, Long Island Jewish Medical Center, New York, NY, p. A461

CAROSELLI, Joseph P., Administrator, Idaho Elks Rehabilitation Hospital, Boise, ID, p. A177

CARP, Steven, Director of Rehabilitation Services, Chestnut Hill Rehabilitation Hospital, Glenside, PA, p. A559

CARPENTER, Beverly, Chief Executive Officer, Surgical Specialty Hospital of Arizona, Phoenix, AZ, p. A35

CARPENTER, Chad, President and Chief Executive Officer, Dayton Heart Hospital, Dayton, OH, p. A511

CARPENTER, Craig, Medical Staff President, St. Mark's Hospital, Salt Lake City, UT, p. A680

CARPENTER, David R., FACHE, President and Chief Executive Officer, North Kansas City Hospital, Kansas City, MO, p. A384

CARPENTER, M.D., Ernie, Medical Director, Medical Center of McKinney, McKinney, TX, p. A656

CARPENTER, Jon, Vice President Finance and Chief Financial Officer, Maria Parham Medical Center, Henderson, NC, p. A484

CARPENTER, M.D., Kim, Vice President Medical Management, St. Francis Hospital, Wilmington, DE, p. A120

CARPENTER, Tom, Vice President Human Resources and Public Relations, Community Hospital, McCook, NE, p. A409

CARPENTER, William A., Senior Vice President and Chief Financial Officer, Louise Obici Memorial Hospital, Suffolk, VA, p. A697

CARPINELLO, Sharon E., Ph.D., Commissioner, New York State Office of Mental Health, Albany, NY, p. B78

CARPIO, M.D., Pablo, Chief of Staff, Tazewell Community Hospital, Tazewell, VA, p. A697

CARR, Deborah, Vice President Human Resources, Orange Regional Medical Center, Middletown, NY, p. A457

CARR, Kay C., Senior Vice President and Chief Information Officer, St. Luke's Episcopal Hospital, Houston, TX, p. A647

CARR, Randall, Director Human Resources, Parkwest Medical Center, Knoxville, TN, p. A610

CARR, Tim, Chief Financial Officer, Methodist Ambulatory Surgery Hospital, San Antonio, TX, p. A664

CARRAHER, June, Chief Hospital Services, U. S. Air Force Hospital, Hampton, VA, p. A689

CARRASQUILLO, M.D., Carmen, Medical Director, Industrial Hospital, San Juan, PR, p. A747

CARREL, Robert F.
Chief Financial Officer, Gulf Coast Hospital, Fort Myers, FL, p. A129
Chief Financial Officer, Southwest Florida Regional Medical Center, Fort Myers, FL, p. A129

CARREN, Donald, Information Technology Leader, Kaiser Foundation Hospital – Orange County, Anaheim, CA, p. A52

CARRICO, Tom, Chief Information Officer, Central Baptist Hospital, Lexington, KY, p. A267

CARRIER, Karl
Vice President Corporate Finance, Providence–Little Company of Mary Service Area, Torrance, CA, p. A96
Chief Financial Officer, San Pedro Peninsula Hospital, Los Angeles, CA, p. A72

CARRIGAN, Lisa, Director Information Systems, Canonsburg General Hospital, Canonsburg, PA, p. A554

CARRILLO, Irma, Human Resources Director, Ashford Presbyterian Community Hospital, San Juan, PR, p. A746

CARRILLO, Neffer E., Administrator, Industrial Hospital, San Juan, PR, p. A747

CARRILLO, Zulema, Chief Executive Officer, El Paso Psychiatric Center, El Paso, TX, p. A637

CARROCINO, Joanne, FACHE, President and Chief Executive Officer, Burdette Tomlin Memorial Hospital, Cape May Court House, NJ, p. A427

CARROLL, Allen P., Chief Executive Officer, Bon Secours–St. Francis Xavier Hospital, Charleston, SC, p. A584

CARROLL, M.D., Dale, Senior Vice President Medical Affairs & Perform Improvement, Rockingham Memorial Hospital, Harrisonburg, VA, p. A689

CARROLL, Jack A., Ph.D., President and Chief Executive Officer, Sheltering Arms Rehabilitation Hospital, Mechanicsville, VA, p. A691

CARROLL, Jacqueline, Director Human Resources, Los Alamos Medical Center, Los Alamos, NM, p. A443

CARROLL, James H.
Manager Information Systems, Mercy Medical Center, Canton, OH, p. A505
Manager Information Systems, St. Vincent Charity Hospital, Cleveland, OH, p. A509

CARROLL, Marsha, Director Financial Services, Screven County Hospital, Sylvania, GA, p. A170

CARROLL, Michael W., Administrator, Richland Parish Hospital, Delhi, LA, p. A280

CARROLL, Patricia, Executive Director, Irvington General Hospital, Irvington, NJ, p. A430

CARROLL, Peggy, Chief Information Officer, Palos Community Hospital, Palos Heights, IL, p. A204

CARROLL, Stephen
Senior Vice President and Chief Financial Officer, Lutheran Hospital of Indiana, Fort Wayne, IN, p. A215
Senior Vice President and Chief Financial Officer, Rehabilitation Hospital of Fort Wayne, Fort Wayne, IN, p. A215

CARROLL, Terri L., Vice President Financial Services, Hillsboro Area Hospital, Hillsboro, IL, p. A197

CARRON, CHE, Patrick E., Vice President Operations, Perry County Memorial Hospital, Perryville, MO, p. A389

CARRUTH, Claude, Vice President and Chief Financial Officer, Henry Medical Center, Stockbridge, GA, p. A170

CARRUTH, John M., Administrator, Milan General Hospital, Milan, TN, p. A614

CARSON, Christine, Director Human Resources, St. Mary Medical Center, Long Beach, CA, p. A68

CARSON, Jim, Human Resources Manager, Henry County Health Center, Mount Pleasant, IA, p. A238

CARSON, Kara Jo
Chief Financial Officer, Pinckneyville Community Hospital, Pinckneyville, IL, p. A205
Chief Financial Officer, Pinckneyville Community Hospital, Pinckneyville, IL, p. A205

CARSON, Mitchell C., President and Chief Executive Officer, Longmont United Hospital, Longmont, CO, p. A108

CARSON, Terry M., Chief Executive Officer, Harrison Community Hospital, Cadiz, OH, p. A504

CARTER, Benjamin R., Executive Vice President and Chief Operating Officer, Harper University Hospital, Detroit, MI, p. A331

CARTER, Bruce C., President, United Hospital Center, Clarksburg, WV, p. A715

CARTER, M.D., David, Chief of Staff, Albemarle Hospital, Elizabeth City, NC, p. A482

CARTER, Doug, Chief Financial Officer, Brookwood Medical Center, Birmingham, AL, p. A14

CARTER Jr, James R., Administrator, North Mississippi Medical Center–Iuka, Iuka, MS, p. A370

CARTER, Len, Vice President Human Resources, FHN Memorial Hospital, Freeport, IL, p. A194

CARTER, Leslie J., Senior Vice President Finance, Maryland General Hospital, Baltimore, MD, p. A303

CARTER, Michael C., Interim Chief Executive Officer, Allen County Hospital, Iola, KS, p. A249

CARTER, Michael J., Chief Executive Officer, Southeast Arizona Medical Center, Douglas, AZ, p. A30

CARTER, Patricia L., Chief Executive Officer, Memorial Hospital of Carbon County, Rawlins, WY, p. A741

CARTER, MSN, Rebecca W., Chief Operating Officer, Transylvania Community Hospital, Brevard, NC, p. A478

CARTER, Richard, Chief Executive Officer, Hunt Memorial Hospital District, Greenville, TX, p. A642

CARTER, Ed.D., Suzanne
Chief Information Officer, Lincoln Medical and Mental Health Center, New York, NY, p. A461
Chief Information Officer, Metropolitan Hospital Center, New York, NY, p. A462

CARTER, Trey, Chief Executive Officer, Anchor Hospital, Atlanta, GA, p. A153

CARTON, Daniel, Vice President Human Resources, Jewish Memorial Hospital and Rehabilitation Center, Boston, MA, p. A314

CARTWRIGHT, Chad, Chief Information Resource Management Systems, Veterans Affairs Medical Center, Cheyenne, WY, p. A739

CARTWRIGHT, Christina, Director Human Resources, Labette County Medical Center, Parsons, KS, p. A255

CARTWRIGHT, David, Director Management Information Systems, Danville Regional Medical Center, Danville, VA, p. A687

CARTY, Jr, Amos W., Chief Operating Officer and General Counsel, Roy Lester Schneider Hospital, Saint Thomas, VI, p. A749

CARUANA, M.D., Ralph, Senior Vice President and Chief Medical Officer, Medical College of Georgia Hospital and Clinics, Augusta, GA, p. A155

CARUSO, M.D., Patrick, President Medical Staff, Hackettstown Community Hospital, Hackettstown, NJ, p. A429

CARUSO, Richard, Vice President Finance, Excela Frick Hospital, Mount Pleasant, PA, p. A565

CARVER, M.D., Deborah, Chief of Staff, Corpus Christi Medical Center, Corpus Christi, TX, p. A630

CARVER, Leota, Finance Manager, Caribou Memorial Hospital and Living Center, Soda Springs, ID, p. A182

CARY, Roger C., President and Chief Executive Officer, Midwestern Regional Medical Center, Zion, IL, p. A210

CASABONA, Nicholas, Director Management Information Services, Winthrop–University Hospital, Mineola, NY, p. A457

CASADAY, Thomas E.
Chief Executive Officer, Providence Memorial Hospital, El Paso, TX, p. A637
Chief Executive Officer, Rio Vista Physical Rehabilitation Hospital, El Paso, TX, p. A637
President and Chief Executive Officer, Sierra Medical Center, El Paso, TX, p. A638

CASADY, M.D., W Stephen, Chief of Staff, Putnam County Memorial Hospital, Unionville, MO, p. A395

CASALOU, Robert F., President, Providence Hospital and Medical Center, Southfield, MI, p. A345

CASANOVA, M.D., James E., Senior Vice President Medical Affairs, Aspirus Wausau Hospital, Wausau, WI, p. A737

CASANOVA, Robert Berniev, Chief Financial Officer, Industrial Hospital, San Juan, PR, p. A747

CASARELLA, Joseph, Director Human Resources, Marian Community Hospital, Carbondale, PA, p. A554

CASBEER, Jeff, Chief Financial Officer, Parkview Regional Hospital, Mexia, TX, p. A656

CASE, Cliff, Chief Financial Officer, Mineral Community Hospital, Superior, MT, p. A402

CASE, Jack, Chief Operating Officer, Montgomery General Hospital, Montgomery, WV, p. A717

CASEY, M.D., Cynthia, Chief of Staff, Crook County Medical Services District, Sundance, WY, p. A742

CASEY, Dennis A., Executive Director, Albert Lindley Lee Memorial Hospital, Fulton, NY, p. A452

CASEY, John P., Administrator, Shodair Children's Hospital, Helena, MT, p. A399

CASEY, Joseph, Chief Financial Officer, Sturdy Memorial Hospital, Attleboro, MA, p. A312

CASEY, Karen J., President and Chief Executive Officer, Columbia Center, Milwaukee, WI, p. A730

CASEY, Peter, Acting Director, East Mountain Hospital, Belle Mead, NJ, p. A425

CASEY, Richard J., Assistant Vice President Operations, Rush North Shore Medical Center, Skokie, IL, p. A208

CASEY, Timothy M., President and Chief Executive Officer, Montgomery Hospital Medical Center, Norristown, PA, p. A566

CASH, Jeff, Vice President and Chief Information Officer, Mercy Medical Center, Cedar Rapids, IA, p. A229

CASH, Robert C., CHE, Administrator, Logan Regional Hospital, Logan, UT, p. A677

CASH, Steve, Director Information Systems, Massachusetts Hospital School, Canton, MA, p. A316

CASHIO, David, Chief Financial Officer, Decatur General Hospital, Decatur, AL, p. A17

CASHION, John A., FACHE, President, Lexington Memorial Hospital, Lexington, NC, p. A486

CASHMAN, Tim, Chief Financial Officer, Gunnison Valley Hospital, Gunnison, CO, p. A106

CASIMIR, M.D., Georges J., Vice President Medical Affairs, Kingsbrook Jewish Medical Center, New York, NY, p. A461

CASKEY, Pam, Director Information Systems, St. James Mercy Hospital, Hornell, NY, p. A454

CASNER, Trina, Chief Financial Officer, Pana Community Hospital, Pana, IL, p. A204

CASON, Randall R., Administrator and Chief Executive Officer, St. Vincent Medical Center–North, Sherwood, AR, p. A50

CASON, Will, Vice President, Human Resources, St. Rita's Medical Center, Lima, OH, p. A516

CASPERSON, M.D., William, Medical Director, St. Elizabeth's Hospital, Belleville, IL, p. A184

CASS, Scott F., Deputy Commander of Administration, Keller Army Community Hospital, West Point, NY, p. A476

CASSARD, Wayne
Service Area Director Human Resources, Providence Holy Cross Medical Center, San Fernando, CA, p. A88
Service Area Director Human Resources, Providence Saint Joseph Medical Center, Burbank, CA, p. A55

CASSEL, Kari, Director Clinical Information Systems, UAMS Medical Center, Little Rock, AR, p. A47

CASSELS, William H., Administrator, DCH Regional Medical Center, Tuscaloosa, AL, p. A24

CASSENS, Ray, Vice President and Chief Financial Officer, Presbyterian Hospital of Plano, Plano, TX, p. A661

CASSIDY, Doris B., Associate Director, Veterans Affairs Medical Center, Fayetteville, AR, p. A43

CASSIDY, James E., President and Chief Executive Officer, St. Mary's Regional Medical Center, Lewiston, ME, p. A299

CASSIDY, R.N., Joseph J., Interim Vice President, Holy Redeemer Hospital and Medical Center, Jenkintown, PA, p. A561

CASSIDY, Louise, Chief Executive Officer, Cornerstone Hospital of SouthEast Arizona, Tucson, AZ, p. A37

CASSITY, Mike, Human Resources Officer, CJW Medical Center, Richmond, VA, p. A695

CASTAGNARO, Marie, President and Chief Executive Officer, St. Joseph's Hospital, Elmira, NY, p. A452

CASTANEDA, Edmundo, Chief Operating Officer, MountainView Regional Medical Center, Las Cruces, NM, p. A443

CASTANEDA, Roman, Director Information Services, Del Sol Medical Center, El Paso, TX, p. A637

CASTEEL, Karen, Director Human Resources, Brandon Regional Hospital, Brandon, FL, p. A124

CASTEEL, Rick
Vice President Management Information Systems and Chief Information Officer, Harford Memorial Hospital, Havre De Grace, MD, p. A308
Vice President Management Information Systems and Chief Information Officer, Upper Chesapeake Medical Center, Bel Air, MD, p. A305

CASTERLINE, Carolyn, Financial Director, Roosevelt Memorial Medical Center, Culbertson, MT, p. A397

CASTILLO, Ralph, Chief Financial Officer, Alleghany Memorial Hospital, Sparta, NC, p. A492

CASTLE, Dorothy, Manager, North Mississippi Medical Center–Eupora, Eupora, MS, p. A368

CASTLE, Eric, Director Information Services, Lawnwood Regional Medical Center, Fort Pierce, FL, p. A129

CASTLE, Janice, Vice President and Chief Information Officer, McLeod Health, Florence, SC, p. A588

CASTLEBERRY, David L., Chief Executive Officer, Carolina Pines Regional Medical Center, Hartsville, SC, p. A589

CASTON, David, Assistant Vice President Administrative Services, Lincoln General Hospital, Ruston, LA, p. A292

CASTRO, Aristides, Chief Financial Officer, St. Luke's Episcopal Hospital, Ponce, PR, p. A746

CASTRO, D.O., Pete, Chief of Staff, Heart of Texas Memorial Hospital, Brady, TX, p. A626

CASTRO, M.D., Rafael, Chief of Staff, Silver Cross Hospital, Joliet, IL, p. A198

CASTRO, Rick, President and Chief Executive Officer, Arroyo Grande Community Hospital, Arroyo Grande, CA, p. A53

CASTRO, M.D., Timothy, Chief of Staff, Twelve Oaks Medical Center, Houston, TX, p. A648

CASTROP, Richard F., President, O'Bleness Memorial Hospital, Athens, OH, p. A503

CATALDO, Linda, Human Resources Secretary, Prevost Memorial Hospital, Donaldsonville, LA, p. A280

CATALDO, Vincent A., Administrator, Prevost Memorial Hospital, Donaldsonville, LA, p. A280

CATANIA, Joe, Chief Executive Officer, St. Anthony's Rehabilitation Hospital, Lauderdale Lakes, FL, p. A135

CATE, Maurine, Chief Executive Officer, Brotman Medical Center, Culver City, CA, p. A58

CATELLIER, Julie A., Director, Veterans Affairs Gulf Coast Veterans Health Care System, Biloxi, MS, p. A367

CATENA, Cornelio R., President and Chief Executive Officer, Easton Hospital, Easton, PA, p. A558

CATHEY Jr, James E., Chief Executive Officer, North Oaks Medical Center, Hammond, LA, p. A281

CATIEL, Mary, Acting Administrator, Lanai Community Hospital, Lanai City, HI, p. A175

CATLIN, Rex, Administrator, Endless Mountain Health Systems, Montrose, PA, p. A565

CATLIN, D.O., Sharon F., Regional Medical Director, Peace Harbor Hospital, Florence, OR, p. A543

CATON, Mark W., Chief Executive Officer, Doctor's Hospital of Opelousas, Opelousas, LA, p. A290

CATTON, R.N., Carolyn, Chief Operating Officer, Greater El Monte Community Hospital, El Monte, CA, p. A59

CAUBLE, David, Chief Financial Officer, Regional Medical Center of Hopkins County, Madisonville, KY, p. A270

CAUDEL, Debbie, Director Information System, T. J. Samson Community Hospital, Glasgow, KY, p. A265

CAUSBY, Gabrielle K., President, Thomasville Medical Center, Thomasville, NC, p. A493

CAUSEY, Cynthia, Associate Administrator Human and Mission Services, McLeod Medical Center–Dillon, Dillon, SC, p. A587

CAUSEY, Jack, Administrator, Leesville Rehabilitation Hospital, Leesville, LA, p. A285

CAUSIN, M.D., Pastor, Medical Director, Wesley Rehabilitation Hospital, Wichita, KS, p. A260

CAVA, Tony, Vice President Operations, Kimball Medical Center, Lakewood, NJ, p. A430

CAVACINI, Pam, Chief Financial Officer, Dukes Memorial Hospital, Peru, IN, p. A223

CAVAGNARO, Charles E., M.D., President and Chief Executive Officer, Wing Memorial Hospital and Medical Centers, Palmer, MA, p. A322

CAVALLO, M.D., Charles, Vice President Medical Affairs, Provena Saint Joseph Hospital, Elgin, IL, p. A193

CAVANAGH, James, Chief Information Officer, St. Joseph's Regional Medical Center, Paterson, NJ, p. A434

CAVANAUGH, James, Chief Fiscal Officer, Wm. Jennings Bryan Dorn Veterans Affairs Medical Center, Columbia, SC, p. A586

CAVANAUGH, Paul, Director Human Resources, Chestnut Hill Rehabilitation Hospital, Glenside, PA, p. A559

CAVE, M.D., Rogelio, Medical Director, Roseland Community Hospital, Chicago, IL, p. A189

CAVE, M.D., William T., Vice President for Medical Affairs, Lakeside Memorial Hospital, Brockport, NY, p. A448

CAVENEY, Timothy, Chief Financial Officer, South Shore Hospital, Chicago, IL, p. A190

CAVES, Donald, Chief Executive Officer, Wild Rose Community Memorial Hospital, Wild Rose, WI, p. A738

CAYER, Jerry, Vice President and Chief Operating Officer, Franklin Memorial Hospital, Farmington, ME, p. A298

CAYWOOD, Karen
Chief Executive Officer, SCCI – Mansfield, Mansfield, OH, p. A517
Chief Executive Officer, SCCI Hospital – Lima, Lima, OH, p. A516

CAYWOOD, Steven A., Interim Chief Executive Officer, Bluefield Regional Medical Center, Bluefield, WV, p. A713

CECCHETTINI, Diane
President and Chief Executive Officer, Mary Bridge Children's Hospital and Health Center, Tacoma, WA, p. A710
President and Chief Executive Officer, MultiCare Health System, Tacoma, WA, p. B77
President and Chief Executive Officer, Tacoma General Hospital, Tacoma, WA, p. A710

CECCHINI, Marina T., Administrator, Shands Rehab Hospital, Gainesville, FL, p. A130

CECCIO, Cathy M., MSN, Executive Director, Edwin Shaw Hospital for Rehabilitation, Akron, OH, p. A502

CECCIO, M.D., Cathy M., Executive Vice President and Chief Operating Officer, Akron General Medical Center, Akron, OH, p. A502

CECCONI, Thomas E., President and Chief Executive, Mercy Medical Center, Canton, OH, p. A505

CECERO, David M.
President and Chief Executive Officer, JPS Health Network, Fort Worth, TX, p. A640
President and Chief Executive Officer, Tarrant County Hospital District, Fort Worth, TX, p. B104

CECIL, Jon C., Chief Human Resource Officer, Lee Memorial Health System, Fort Myers, FL, p. A129

CEDENO, M.D., Douglas A., Medical Director, Alice Peck Day Memorial Hospital, Lebanon, NH, p. A421

CELESTIN, Joel, Assistant Executive Director and Chief Financial Officer, Howard University Hospital, Washington, DC, p. A121

CELIBERTI, Richard, President and Chief Executive Officer, Our Lady of Mercy Medical Center, New York, NY, p. A464

CELLA, M.D., Robert, Vice President Medical Affairs, Berkshire Medical Center, Pittsfield, MA, p. A322

CEMATE, David, Executive Vice President and Chief Operating Officer, St. Francis Hospital & Health Center, Blue Island, IL, p. A185

CEPEDA, Martha, Compliance Officer, Cornerstone Regional Hospital, Edinburg, TX, p. A636

CERCEO, Richard, Executive Vice President and Chief Operating Officer, Mercy Hospital and Medical Center, Chicago, IL, p. A188

CERDA, Greg, Chief Executive Officer, Advanced Healthcare Medical Center, Ellington, MO, p. A381

CERKVENIK, Leah, Executive Vice President, Administrator and Chief Executive Officer, St. Anthony Community Hospital, Warwick, NY, p. A475

CERLETTY, Susan, Executive Vice President, Rehabilitation Institute of Chicago, Chicago, IL, p. A189

CERMAK, Penny, Vice President and Chief Financial Officer, BroMenn Healthcare System, Normal, IL, p. A202

CERULLO, Timothy J., Chief Financial Officer, St. Petersburg General Hospital, Saint Petersburg, FL, p. A145

CERVANTES, Mary Ann, District Director Management Information Systems, Matagorda General Hospital, Bay City, TX, p. A624

CESCA, Ken, Director Human Resources, MidState Medical Center, Meriden, CT, p. A114

CETTI, Janet E., President and Chief Executive Officer, San Diego Hospice & Palliative Care, San Diego, CA, p. A87

CHABALOWSKI, Edward, Chief Financial Officer, Temple University Hospital, Philadelphia, PA, p. A570

CHABNER, David, Director Information Services, Merle West Medical Center, Klamath Falls, OR, p. A545

CHACON, Juan C Benitez, Associate Executive Administrastor, Caribbean Pediatric and Surgery Hospital, San Juan, PR, p. A747

CHADHA, Beenu, Chief Financial Officer, San Ramon Regional Medical Center, San Ramon, CA, p. A91

CHADWICK, Lionel K., Chief Executive Officer, Natividad Medical Center, Salinas, CA, p. A86

CHAFFIN, Linda, Director Quality, Baptist Memorial Hospital–Booneville, Booneville, MS, p. A367

CHAFFIN, Robert A., President and Chief Executive Officer, Community Hospital of Ottawa, Ottawa, IL, p. A204

CHAGNON, Tamara, Human Resource Coordinator, Moses Ludington Hospital, Ticonderoga, NY, p. A474

CHAILDIN, Roberta, Manager Human Resources, Parrish Medical Center, Titusville, FL, p. A149

CHALKE, Peter E., President and Chief Executive Officer, Central Maine Medical Center, Lewiston, ME, p. A299

CHALONER, Robert S., President and Chief Executive Officer, Cabrini Medical Center, New York, NY, p. A459

CHAMBERLAIN, Joe, Chief Financial Officer, CGH Medical Center, Sterling, IL, p. A209

CHAMBERLIN, William, Chief Medical Officer, University of Illinois Medical Center at Chicago, Chicago, IL, p. A191

CHAMBERS, Bradley, Senior Vice President, Union Memorial Hospital, Baltimore, MD, p. A304

CHAMBERS, Gina, Human Resource Manager, Rome Memorial Hospital, Rome, NY, p. A471

CHAMBERS, Gwen, Director Human Resources, Western Medical Center–Santa Ana, Santa Ana, CA, p. A92

CHAMBERS, M.D., Jodi, Chief Medical Officer, St. Anthony North Hospital, Westminster, CO, p. A110

CHAMBERS, Matthew, Chief Executive Officer, Three Rivers Health, Three Rivers, MI, p. A346

CHAMBERS, Nita, Chief Financial Officer, Huey P. Long Medical Center, Pineville, LA, p. A291

CHAMBERS, Pamela, Chief Executive Officer, Surgical and Diagnostic Center of Great Bend, Great Bend, KS, p. A248

CHAMBERS, Susan, Administrator, Greil Memorial Psychiatric Hospital, Montgomery, AL, p. A22

CHAMBLESS, Marcy, Business Office Service Line Manager, Carl Vinson Veterans Affairs Medical Center, Dublin, GA, p. A161

CHAMNES, M.D., Mattie, Medical Staff President, St. Joseph Memorial Hospital, Murphysboro, IL, p. A202

CHAMPAGNE, Carol, Chief Executive Officer, Sugar Land Surgical Hospital, Sugar Land, TX, p. A668

CHAMPAGNE, Charles, Chief Financial Officer, Spaulding Rehabilitation Hospital, Boston, MA, p. A314

CHAMPION, Becky, Business Office Manager, Cozby–Germany Hospital, Grand Saline, TX, p. A642

CHAMPOUX, Cheryl, Vice President Human Resource Management and Development, St. Francis Hospital & Health Center, Blue Island, IL, p. A185

CHAN, Chiu Moon, Chairman, President and Chief Executive Officer, Dynacq Healthcare, Inc., Houston, TX, p. B42

CHAN, M.D., Dennis, Chief of Staff, Garfield Medical Center, Monterey Park, CA, p. A76

CHANCE, Jr, M.D., Alfred B., Chief Medical Director, Mercy Medical, Daphne, AL, p. A17

CHANCE, D.O., Tammara, Medical Director, Skiff Medical Center, Newton, IA, p. A239

CHANDLER, Brue, Senior Vice President and Administrator, Baptist Hospital of East Tennessee, Knoxville, TN, p. A609

CHANDLER, Loren F., Vice President Finance and Chief Financial Officer, Missouri Baptist Medical Center, Town and Country, MO, p. A394

CHANDLER, Warren L., Senior Vice President and Chief Information Officer, St. Vincent's Medical Center, Jacksonville, FL, p. A133

CHANDLER, Zachary, Administrator and Chief Executive Officer, Baptist Memorial Hospital–North Mississippi, Oxford, MS, p. A374

CHANEY, James, Chief Financial Officer, Jefferson Healthcare, Port Townsend, WA, p. A706

CHANEY, Roy, Chief Information Management Service, Veterans Affairs Medical Center, San Francisco, CA, p. A90

CHANG, Alex, Chief Operating Officer, South Bay Hospital, Sun City Center, FL, p. A147

CHANG, C. Joseph, President and Chief Executive Officer, East Valley Hospital Medical Center, Glendora, CA, p. A63

CHANG, M.D., Clifford, Medical Director, Leahi Hospital, Honolulu, HI, p. A174

CHANG, M.D., Sylvia, Chief Medical Staff, Marengo Memorial Hospital, Marengo, IA, p. A237

CHANNING, Alan H., President and Chief Executive Officer, Sinai Health System, Chicago, IL, p. B98

CHAPA, Al, Chief Executive Officer and Managing Director, Doctors Hospital of Laredo, Laredo, TX, p. A652

CHAPDELAINE, Charles, Chief of Information Management and Technology, U. S. Air Force Hospital, Hampton, VA, p. A689

CHAPIN, Rocklon B., Chief Operating Officer and Administrator, Miller–Dwan Medical Center, Duluth, MN, p. A352

CHAPIN, Ted G., Chief Executive Officer, Wilkes Regional Medical Center, North Wilkesboro, NC, p. A488

CHAPLIN, Pamela, Data Processing Director, Marcus Daly Memorial Hospital, Hamilton, MT, p. A399

CHAPMAN, Alan, Chief Financial Officer, Maryview Medical Center, Portsmouth, VA, p. A694

CHAPMAN, Alan G., Chief Executive Officer, Cumberland Hall Hospital, Hopkinsville, KY, p. A266

CHAPMAN, Brenda, Director Human Resources, Bellevue Hospital Center, New York, NY, p. A458

CHAPMAN, Janet, Vice President Human Resources, Habersham County Medical Center, Demorest, GA, p. A160

CHAPMAN, Kathleen, Vice President and Chief Financial Officer, Shamokin Area Community Hospital, Coal Township, PA, p. A555

CHAPMAN, Robert C., FACHE, President and Chief Executive Officer, Eastern Health System, Inc., Birmingham, AL, p. B43

CHAPMAN, Roland, Chief Information Officer, Northern Navajo Medical Center, Shiprock, NM, p. A445

CHAPMAN, Scott, Administrator, Manhattan Surgical Center, New York, KS, p. A252

CHARBONNEAU, D.O., Elissa, Medical Director, New England Rehabilitation Hospital of Portland, Portland, ME, p. A300

CHARBONNEAU, Robert, Senior Vice President and Chief Information Officer, Seton Health System, Troy, NY, p. A474

CHARLES, Timothy, Executive Vice President and Chief Operating Officer, Mercy Medical Center, Cedar Rapids, IA, p. A229

CHARLEY, Linda J., Chief Financial Officer, Provena Saint Joseph Medical Center, Joliet, IL, p. A198

CHARMEL, Patrick, President and Chief Executive Officer, Griffin Hospital, Derby, CT, p. A112

CHARTRAND, Gregg, Chief Financial Officer, Pine Medical Center, Sandstone, MN, p. A362

CHASE, Howard M., FACHE, President and Chief Executive Officer, Methodist Health System, Dallas, TX, p. B75

CHASE, Jean
  Regional Manager Information Services, Aurora Lakeland Medical Center, Elkhorn, WI, p. A725
  Regional Manager Information Services, Aurora Medical Center, Kenosha, WI, p. A727
  Regional Manager Information Services, Memorial Hospital Corporation of Burlington, Burlington, WI, p. A724

CHASE, Kyle, Chief Financial Officer, Appleton Municipal Hospital and Nursing Home, Appleton, MN, p. A349

CHASKA, M.D., Benjamin, Chief Medical Staff, St. Peter Community Hospital, Saint Peter, MN, p. A362

CHASON, Robert E., Chief Executive Officer, University of California, Davis Medical Center, Sacramento, CA, p. A85

CHASSE, Tony, Computer Systems Coordinator, Northern Maine Medical Center, Fort Kent, ME, p. A298

CHASSEY, Patricia, Director Information Services, Saint Vincent Hospital at Worcester Medical Center, Worcester, MA, p. A325

CHASTAIN, James G., CHE, Director, Mississippi State Hospital, Whitfield, MS, p. A377

CHATHAM, Rhonda, Vice President and Chief Financial Officer, Baylor Medical Center at Garland, Garland, TX, p. A641

CHATMAN, Jim
  Chief Financial Officer, Hoots Memorial Hospital, Yadkinville, NC, p. A495
  Chief Financial Officer, Stokes–Reynolds Memorial Hospital, Danbury, NC, p. A481

CHATTERTON, Claude, Administrator and Chief Executive Officer, Harrisburg Medical Center, Harrisburg, IL, p. A196

CHAUARRIA, Ami, Director Human Resources, Arroyo Grande Community Hospital, Arroyo Grande, CA, p. A53

CHAUDOIN, Becky, Director Finance, Brooks Rehabilitation Hospital, Jacksonville, FL, p. A132

CHAUNDY, Kimberly, Information Systems Manager, Shamokin Area Community Hospital, Coal Township, PA, p. A555

CHAUS, Tim, Chief Information Officer, Bon Secours Hospital, Grosse Pointe, MI, p. A335

CHAUSSARD, David, Chief Executive Officer, Claremore Regional Hospital, Claremore, OK, p. A529

CHAVA, M.D., N Rao, Chief of Staff, Central Alabama Veterans Health Care System, Montgomery, AL, p. A22

CHAVA, N. Rao, M.D., Director, Central Alabama Veterans Health Care System, Montgomery, AL, p. A22

CHAVEZ, Adolfo, Chief Financial Officer, St. Mary Medical Center, Long Beach, CA, p. A68

CHAVEZ, Margaret, Manager Human Resources, Hammond–Henry Hospital, Geneseo, IL, p. A195

CHAWBLESS, Lesley, Assistant Vice President Human Resources, Lincoln Medical Center, Lincolnton, NC, p. A486

CHAWK, Gary W., Chief Financial Officer, Saint Mary's Medical Center, Saginaw, MI, p. A344

CHAWLA, M.D., Satish, Vice President Medical Affairs, War Memorial Hospital, Sault Ste. Marie, MI, p. A345

CHAYKIN, Lee, Chief Operating Officer, Cedars Medical Center, Miami, FL, p. A137

CHEADLE, Ron, Chief Operating Officer, Driscoll Children's Hospital, Corpus Christi, TX, p. A630

CHECK, Rosemary C., President and Chief Executive Officer, Louise Obici Memorial Hospital, Suffolk, VA, p. A697

CHECKETTS, B Lannie, Vice President Finance, Mercy Medical Center, Nampa, ID, p. A180

CHEEK, James R., Administrator, White County Medical Center, Carmi, IL, p. A185

CHEEK, Thomas M., Chief Executive Officer, Northcoast Behavioral Healthcare System, Northfield, OH, p. A519

CHEEMA, M.D., Imran, Chief Medical Officer, Ellett Memorial Hospital, Appleton City, MO, p. A378

CHEEMA, Linde, Director Human Resources, Seton Medical Center, Daly City, CA, p. A58

CHEESEMAN, Karen, Director Human Resources, Mackinac Straits Hospital and Health Center, Saint Ignace, MI, p. A344

CHELF, Alan, Chief Information Officer, Baptist Regional Medical Center, Corbin, KY, p. A263

CHEN, Steve, Chief Financial Officer, Hinsdale Hospital, Hinsdale, IL, p. A197

CHENSVOLD, Debrah, President and Chief Executive Officer, Palmer Lutheran Health Center, West Union, IA, p. A243

CHERRIER, Lori, Director Health Information, Columbus Community Hospital, Columbus, WI, p. A724

CHERRY, Cindy, Chief Financial Officer, Butler County Health Care Center, David City, NE, p. A406

CHERRY, Gay Nell, Human Resources Director, Rolling Plains Memorial Hospital, Sweetwater, TX, p. A668

CHERRY Jr, Vincent T., Chief Executive Director, Davis Regional Medical Center, Statesville, NC, p. A492

CHESHER, Pamela, Chief Financial Officer, Meadowview Regional Medical Center, Maysville, KY, p. A271

CHESLEY, Jeanine, Controller, New England Rehabilitation Hospital of Portland, Portland, ME, p. A300

CHESNEY, Jim
  Chief Information Officer, Baptist Medical Center East, Montgomery, AL, p. A21
  Chief Information Officer, Baptist Medical Center South, Montgomery, AL, p. A22

CHESNOS, Richard C.
  Vice President Operations and Chief Financial Officer, Forbes Regional Hospital, Monroeville, PA, p. A565
  Vice President Operations and Director Finance, Western Pennsylvania Hospital, Pittsburgh, PA, p. A573

CHESSARE, M.D., John, Chief Medical Officer, Boston Medical Center, Boston, MA, p. A313

CHESSIN, Neil A., Vice President, Jameson Hospital, New Castle, PA, p. A566

CHESSUM, George
  Senior Vice President Information Systems and Chief Information Officer, Resurrection Medical Center, Chicago, IL, p. A189
  Senior Vice President Information Systems and Chief Information Officer, Saint Joseph Hospital, Chicago, IL, p. A190

CHESTER, Kate, Senior Public Relations Coordinator, Providence St. Vincent Medical Center, Portland, OR, p. A548

CHESTER, William, Manager Human Resources, Veterans Affairs Medical Center, Grand Junction, CO, p. A106

CHESTNUT, Jeffrey, Director Finance, Owatonna Hospital, Owatonna, MN, p. A359

CHEUNG, Francis, Chief Information Officer, Methodist Hospital, Saint Louis Park, MN, p. A361

CHEVEE, M.D., Rodriguez, Medical Director, NCED Mental Health Center, El Paso, TX, p. A637

CHEVERE, M.D., Carlos, Medical Director, I. Gonzalez Martinez Oncologic Hospital, Hato Rey, PR, p. A747

CHEW, Roy G., Ph.D., President, Grandview Hospital and Medical Center, Dayton, OH, p. A512

CHEWNING III, Larry H., Chief Executive Officer, Sampson Regional Medical Center, Clinton, NC, p. A480

CHEYNET, Sandee, Vice President Administrative Services, Bluefield Regional Medical Center, Bluefield, WV, p. A713

CHHABRA, M.D., Amarinder, President Medical Staff, Summers County Appalachian Regional Hospital, Hinton, WV, p. A716

CHIANESE, Robert, Vice President Human Resources, Newton Memorial Hospital, Newton, NJ, p. A433

CHIANTELLO, Charmaine, Chief Financial Officer, Grand View Hospital, Ironwood, MI, p. A337

CHIARAMONTE, Francis P., M.D., President, Southern Maryland Hospital Center, Clinton, MD, p. A306

CHIARCHIARO, Martha, Vice President Human Resources, Clinton Hospital, Clinton, MA, p. A317

CHICK, James R., President, Joint Township District Memorial Hospital, Saint Marys, OH, p. A521

CHICKEN, Kurt, Director Support Services, Palmer Lutheran Health Center, West Union, IA, p. A243

CHILDERS Jr, Leo F., FACHE, President, Good Samaritan Regional Health Center, Mount Vernon, IL, p. A202

CHILDS, Deborah, Chief Human Resources Officer, University of Michigan Hospitals and Health Centers, Ann Arbor, MI, p. A327

CHILDS, Elizabeth, Human Resources Manager, San Juan Regional Medical Center, Farmington, NM, p. A442

CHILDS, Robb, Chief Operating Officer, Willamette Valley Medical Center, McMinnville, OR, p. A546

CHILDS, Ronald P., FACHE, Health Services Administrator, Midlands Center, Columbia, SC, p. A586

CHILDS, Steve, Chief, Business Programs and Operations, Veterans Affairs Medical Center, Martinsburg, WV, p. A717

CHILEK, Frances L., R.N., Administrator, Connally Medical Center, Floresville, TX, p. A638

CHILESKI, Andy, Corporate Vice President Management Information Systems, Berger Health System, Circleville, OH, p. A508

CHILL, Martha O'Regan
  Senior Vice President and Administrator, Baptist Hospital for Women, Knoxville, TN, p. A609
  Senior Vice President and Administrator, Baptist Hospital West, Knoxville, TN, p. A609

CHILSON, Jeffrey, Chief Financial Officer, Ashland Regional Medical Center, Ashland, PA, p. A552

CHIN, David, Controller, HEALTHSOUTH Rehabilitation Hospital, Concord, NH, p. A420

CHINBURG, M.D., Paul, Medical Director, Lane County Hospital, Dighton, KS, p. A246

CHINN, Colin, Executive Officer, Naval Hospital, Lemoore, CA, p. A67

CHIODO, Deborah
Director Human Resources, Freeman Health System, Joplin, MO, p. A383
Director Human Resourcesw, Freeman Neosho Hospital, Neosho, MO, p. A388

CHIPLOCK, Jerry, Vice President Human Resources, Saint Mary's Medical Center, Saginaw, MI, p. A344

CHITESTER, Jeff, Human Resources Administrator, University of Virginia Medical Center, Charlottesville, VA, p. A686

CHITLURI, M.D., Murali K., Chief of Staff, Veterans Affairs Medical Center, Chillicothe, OH, p. A506

CHITTICK, Trudy, Chief Executive Officer, Hot Springs County Memorial Hospital, Thermopolis, WY, p. A742

CHITTOM, Tommy, Assistant Vice President Information Services, East Alabama Medical Center, Opelika, AL, p. A23

CHITWOOD, Carl S., Chief Financial Officer, Dominion Hospital, Falls Church, VA, p. A687

CHITWOOD, David, Information Systems Coordinator, Grant Regional Health Center, Lancaster, WI, p. A728

CHOATE, Charlotte, Director Information Systems, St. Joseph Hospital, Augusta, GA, p. A155

CHOATE, Julie, Chief Human Resources, Veterans Affairs Medical Center, Augusta, GA, p. A155

CHOATE, Michael, Chief Financial Officer, Llano Memorial Healthcare System, Llano, TX, p. A653

CHOI, Wing, Vice President Finance and Chief Financial Officer, Parkview Adventist Medical Center, Brunswick, ME, p. A297

CHOINIERE, Leon, Vice President, Antelope Valley Hospital, Lancaster, CA, p. A67

CHOINKA, Keith A., Vice President Information Systems and Chief Information Officer, St. Joseph Hospital, Nashua, NH, p. A423

CHOKSHI, M.D., Hitesh, Chief of Staff, Henry Medical Center, Stockbridge, GA, p. A170

CHOO, Michael O., Chief Executive Officer, Promise Specialty Hospital of Shreveport, Shreveport, LA, p. A293

CHOPP, Robin, Vice President and Chief Financial Officer, St. Alexius Medical Center, Hoffman Estates, IL, p. A197

CHOREY, Raymond, Chief Operating Officer, Southeastern Ohio Regional Medical Center, Cambridge, OH, p. A505

CHOU, Rebecca, Director Information Systems, Palestine Regional Medical Center–East, Palestine, TX, p. A659

CHOW, M.D., Hubert, Chief of Staff, San Gabriel Valley Medical Center, San Gabriel, CA, p. A90

CHOW, Karen, Director Human Resources, Chinese Hospital, San Francisco, CA, p. A88

CHRISMAN, Carol, Chief Executive Officer, Select Specialty Hospital Wilmington, Wilmington, DE, p. A120

CHRISTENSEN, C. James, Chief Executive Officer, Pondera Medical Center, Conrad, MT, p. A397

CHRISTENSEN, Cinthia S., Executive Vice President and Chief Operating Officer, Children's Hospital of Wisconsin, Milwaukee, WI, p. A730

CHRISTENSEN, Earlean, Director Human Resources, Highland District Hospital, Hillsboro, OH, p. A515

CHRISTENSEN, M.D., James, Chief of Staff, St. Mary's Regional Health Center, Detroit Lakes, MN, p. A352

CHRISTENSEN, Jay, Administrator, Mahaska Health Partnership, Oskaloosa, IA, p. A239

CHRISTENSEN, Mark
Director Finance, Samaritan North Lincoln Hospital, Lincoln City, OR, p. A545
Director Finance, Samaritan Pacific Communities Hospital, Newport, OR, p. A546

CHRISTENSEN, Sandra, Chief Financial Officer, Dallas County Hospital, Perry, IA, p. A240

CHRISTENSEN, M.D., W R., Chief of Staff, East Texas Medical Center Pittsburg, Pittsburg, TX, p. A660

CHRISTENSON, Lee, Chief Executive Officer, Heart of Lancaster Regional Medical Center, Lititz, PA, p. A563

CHRISTIAN, Charles, Director Information Systems, Good Samaritan Hospital, Vincennes, IN, p. A226

CHRISTIAN, Debbie, Director Human Resources, Raleigh General Hospital, Beckley, WV, p. A713

CHRISTIAN, Glenn, Interim Chief Executive Officer and Administrator, Cannon Falls Community Hospital, Cannon Falls, MN, p. A351

CHRISTIAN, James A., Director, Veterans Affairs Medical Center, Asheville, NC, p. A477

CHRISTIAN, Patricia L., R.N., Chief Executive Officer, John Umstead Hospital, Butner, NC, p. A479

CHRISTIAN, Sharon, Vice President and Chief Information Officer, St. Jude Children's Research Hospital, Memphis, TN, p. A614

CHRISTIANO, Nicholas, Chief Information Officer, Vassar Brothers Medical Center, Poughkeepsie, NY, p. A470

CHRISTIANSEN, Anne, Chief Financial Officer, Pioneer Memorial Hospital and Health Services, Viborg, SD, p. A600

CHRISTIANSEN, Cathy, Director Information Systems, Delray Medical Center, Delray Beach, FL, p. A127

CHRISTIANSEN, Lance, Chief Information Officer, West Valley Medical Center, Caldwell, ID, p. A178

CHRISTIANSON, Clark P., President and Chief Executive Officer, Providence Hospital, Mobile, AL, p. A21

CHRISTIANSON, Clinton J., Chief Executive Officer, Mercy Medical Center–Centerville, Centerville, IA, p. A230

CHRISTIANSON, Delano, Administrator, St. Michael's Hospital and Nursing Home, Sauk Centre, MN, p. A363

CHRISTIE, Arthur P., Administrator, Houston Medical Center, Warner Robins, GA, p. A172

CHRISTIE, James, Chief Information Officer, St. Alexius Medical Center, Hoffman Estates, IL, p. A197

CHRISTIE, Janet L.
Vice President Human Resources, Shands at AGH, Gainesville, FL, p. A130
Senior Vice President Human Resources, Shands at the University of Florida, Gainesville, FL, p. A130

CHRISTIE, Theresa, Chief of Staff, St. Joseph Hospital, Augusta, GA, p. A155

CHRISTMAN, Jerri, Chief Financial Officer, Davis County Hospital, Bloomfield, IA, p. A229

CHRISTMAN, Marlene, Administrator, Bennett County Healthcare Center, Martin, SD, p. A597

CHRISTMAS, Robert, Chief Operating Officer, Laguna Honda Hospital and Rehabilitation Center, San Francisco, CA, p. A89

CHRISTOPHEL, Randal, Executive Vice President and Chief Financial Officer, Goshen General Hospital, Goshen, IN, p. A216

CHRISTOPHER, William T., President and Chief Executive Officer, Lawrence & Memorial Hospital, New London, CT, p. A115

CHROMIK, James R., President, DeSoto Memorial Hospital, Arcadia, FL, p. A123

CHRONISTER, James, Human Resources Director, Integris Mayes County Medical Center, Pryor, OK, p. A537

CHU, David, Chief Executive Officer, Doctors Hospital Medical Center of Montclair, Montclair, CA, p. A76

CHUBB, John M., Chief Executive Officer, Coastal Communities Hospital, Santa Ana, CA, p. A92

CHUMLEY, Michael, Vice President Human Resources, Union Hospital, Terre Haute, IN, p. A226

CHUNN, Nellie, Chief Financial Officer, Monroe County Hospital, Monroeville, AL, p. A21

CHURCH Jr, John D., FACHE, Director, Veterans Affairs Medical Center, New Orleans, LA, p. A290

CHURCHILL, Beverly, Vice President Human Resources, Chester River Hospital Center, Chestertown, MD, p. A306

CHURCHILL, Stephen W., M.D., Chief Executive Officer and Medical Director, Crittenton Children's Center, Kansas City, MO, p. A384

CHURCHILL, Timothy A., President, Stephens Memorial Hospital, Norway, ME, p. A299

CHUSTZ, Mark, Administrator, West Feliciana Parish Hospital, Saint Francisville, LA, p. A292

CIANCIO, Carol, Health Information Systems Director, Beaver Dam Community Hospitals, Beaver Dam, WI, p. A723

CIBRONE, Connie M., President and Chief Executive Officer, Allegheny General Hospital, Pittsburgh, PA, p. A571

CICERO, David, President, Ouachita Medical Center, Camden, AR, p. A41

CICERO, Rick, Vice President Business Development, St. John West Shore Hospital, Cleveland, OH, p. A509

CIERLIK, Gregory A., President and Chief Executive Officer, Lincoln Park Hospital, Chicago, IL, p. A187

CIHAK, Scott A., Chief Operating Officer, Westside Regional Medical Center, Plantation, FL, p. A143

CINELLI, Kim, Administrator and Chief Executive Officer, Hospital District Number Five of Harper County, Harper, KS, p. A248

CINTRON, Mike, Chief Information Officer, St. Luke's Episcopal Hospital, Ponce, PR, p. A746

CINTRON, Nayda, Vice President Finance, Hospital De Damas, Ponce, PR, p. A746

CIOTA, Mark, M.D., Chief Executive Officer, Albert Lea Medical Center, Albert Lea, MN, p. A349

CIRALDO, Lou, Community Hospitals Representative Information Services, UHHS Geauga Regional Hospital, Chardon, OH, p. A505

CIRNE–NEVES, Ceu, Administrator, Saint James Hospital of Newark, Newark, NJ, p. A433

CITA, Bob, Director Information Services, SEARHC MT. Edgecumbe Hospital, Sitka, AK, p. A28

CITERONE, Bernard P., Chief Financial Officer, St. Francis Hospital, Wilmington, DE, p. A120

CITRON, Richard S., Director, Veterans Affairs Medical Center, Wilmington, DE, p. A120

CIVIC, Dave, Associate Director Clinical Services, U. S. Public Health Service Phoenix Indian Medical Center, Phoenix, AZ, p. A35

CLABAUGH, Jodene, Human Resources Clerk, Brodstone Memorial Hospital, Superior, NE, p. A413

CLAFFEY, Patricia, Executive Director, Saint Joseph Mercy Livingston Hospital, Howell, MI, p. A336

CLAIRMONT, Thomas
President, Franklin Regional Hospital, Franklin, NH, p. A421
President, Lakes Region General Hospital, Laconia, NH, p. A421
President, LRG Healthcare, Laconia, NH, p. B70

CLANCY, Mikki
Vice President and Chief Information Officer, Good Samaritan Hospital, Dayton, OH, p. A512
Vice President and Chief Information Officer, Miami Valley Hospital, Dayton, OH, p. A512

CLAPP, Mary, Controller, Henry County Hospital, Napoleon, OH, p. A519

CLARK, Ben, Chief Information Officer and Vice President, Centra Health, Lynchburg, VA, p. A691

CLARK, Cindy, Director Human Resources, Gateway Regional Health System, Mount Sterling, KY, p. A272

CLARK, David
Vice President Human Resources, Monongahela Valley Hospital, Monongahela, PA, p. A565
Chief Operating Officer, Utah Valley Regional Medical Center, Provo, UT, p. A679

CLARK, Douglas A., FACHE, President, Excela Latrobe Area Hospital, Latrobe, PA, p. A563

CLARK, M.D., Ed, Medical Director, Primary Children's Medical Center, Salt Lake City, UT, p. A679

CLARK, Ellen, Community Relations Officer, Northern Cochise Community Hospital, Willcox, AZ, p. A39

CLARK, Frank
Chief Information Officer, MUSC Medical Center of Medical University of South Carolina, Charleston, SC, p. A584
Chief Financial Officer, St. Benedicts Family Medical Center, Jerome, ID, p. A179

CLARK, Hal, Interim Chief Financial Officer, Hazard ARH Regional Medical Center, Hazard, KY, p. A266

CLARK, M.D., James, Medical Director, Banner Behavioral Health Hospital, Scottsdale, AZ, p. A36

CLARK, Jeff
Director of Information Systems, Graham Regional Medical Center, Graham, TX, p. A642
Vice President Human Resources, Kadlec Medical Center, Richland, WA, p. A707

CLARK, John, Vice President and Chief Financial Officer, Queen of the Valley Hospital, Napa, CA, p. A77

CLARK, Karen S., Chief Financial Officer, St. Mary's Hospital, Streator, IL, p. A209

CLARK, Laura E., Director of Human Resources, Inter–Community Memorial Hospital, Newfane, NY, p. A467

CLARK, Linda A., Senior Vice President and Administrator, WellStar Kennestone Hospital, Marietta, GA, p. A165

CLARK, M. Victoria, Chief Executive Officer, La Paz Regional Hospital, Parker, AZ, p. A33

CLARK, Mark
Director Networks, Good Samaritan Regional Health Center, Mount Vernon, IL, p. A202
Director Information Systems, St. Mary's Hospital, Centralia, IL, p. A186

CLARK, Melinda, FACHE, President and Chief Executive Officer, SSM DePaul Health Center, Saint Louis, MO, p. A391

CLARK, Michael
Chief Executive Officer, Georgetown Community Hospital, Georgetown, KY, p. A265
Vice President Finance, FHN Memorial Hospital, Freeport, IL, p. A194

CLARK Jr, Murray B., Associate Vice President Operations, University of Kentucky Hospital, Lexington, KY, p. A268

CLARK, Patrick
Senior Vice President Finance and Support Services, Avera Queen of Peace, Mitchell, SD, p. A597
Manager Information Technology, Sunnyview Rehabilitation Hospital, Schenectady, NY, p. A472

CLARK, Paul, President and Chief Executive Officer, Munroe Regional Medical Center, Ocala, FL, p. A140

CLARK, Raimonda, President and Chief Executive Officer, Bayshore Community Hospital, Holmdel, NJ, p. A429

CLARK, Randall, Vice President Finance, Sebasticook Valley Hospital, Pittsfield, ME, p. A300

CLARK, Richard L., Administrator and Chief Executive Officer, Morristown–Hamblen Hospital, Morristown, TN, p. A614

CLARK, Robert J., FACHE,
President and Chief Executive Officer, Blue Mountain Health System, Lehighton, PA, p. B18
President and Chief Executive Officer, Gnaden Huetten Memorial Hospital, Lehighton, PA, p. A563
President and Chief Executive Officer, Palmerton Hospital, Palmerton, PA, p. A567

CLARK, M.D., Ron, Vice President Clinical Activities and Chief Medical Officer, VCU Health System, Richmond, VA, p. A696

CLARK, Shannon, Chief Financial Officer, Ashley County Medical Center, Crossett, AR, p. A41

CLARK, Sharon, Director Human Resources, Hillsboro Area Hospital, Hillsboro, IL, p. A197

CLARK, Terry, Chief Information Officer, Chickasaw Nation Health System, Ada, OK, p. A527

CLARK, Thomas, President and Chief Executive Officer, Saints Memorial Medical Center, Lowell, MA, p. A319

CLARK, Thomas A., Chief Executive Officer, Bluffton Regional Medical Center, Bluffton, IN, p. A212

CLARK, Travis, Chief Financial Officer, Page Memorial Hospital, Luray, VA, p. A690

CLARK, Troy E., Chief Executive Officer, Heartland Spine & Specialty Hospital, Overland Park, KS, p. A254

CLARK, Weldon, Chief Information Officer, Menifee Valley Medical Center, Sun City, CA, p. A95

CLARK, William S., Chief Executive Officer, Columbus County Hospital, Whiteville, NC, p. A493

CLARKE, Gloria, Vice President Human Resources, Bon Secours Baltimore Health System, Baltimore, MD, p. A302

CLARKE, Robert T.
President and Chief Executive Officer, Memorial Health System, Springfield, IL, p. B74
President and Chief Executive Officer, Memorial Medical Center, Springfield, IL, p. A208

CLARY, Patrick, Director Human Resources, Sacred Heart Medical Center, Spokane, WA, p. A709

CLAUDSON, Jackie, Administrator, South Big Horn County Hospital, Basin, WY, p. A739

CLAUDY, M.D., Frank, Vice Persident Medical Staff Affairs, Genesis Medical Center, Davenport, Davenport, IA, p. A231

CLAUNCH, Don, Chief Information Officer, Wyoming Medical Center, Casper, WY, p. A739

CLAUSEN, Mary, Chief Financial Officer, Veterans Affairs Medical Center, Saint Cloud, MN, p. A361

CLAVELL, M.D., Luis, Medical Director, San Jorge Children's Hospital, San Juan, PR, p. A747

CLAWSON, Tonya, Manager Human Resources, Mercy Medical Center–Centerville, Centerville, IA, p. A230

CLAYPOOL, Blain, Chief Operating Officer, University Medical Center, Las Vegas, NV, p. A417

CLAYTON, Kent G., President and Chief Executive Officer, Placentia Linda Hospital, Placentia, CA, p. A81

CLAYTON, Mark W., Chief Executive Officer, North Central Baptist Hospital, San Antonio, TX, p. A665

CLAYTON, Philip A., President and Chief Executive Officer, Conway Medical Center, Conway, SC, p. A587

CLEARY, John J., President and Chief Executive Officer, River Oaks Hospital, Jackson, MS, p. A371

CLEARY, Margaret S., Chief Executive Officer, Northern Nevada Medical Center, Sparks, NV, p. A419

CLEM, Sandra, Manager Information Management Service Line, Carl Vinson Veterans Affairs Medical Center, Dublin, GA, p. A161

CLEMENS, Brian L., Chief Executive Officer, Midwest Regional Medical Center, Midwest City, OK, p. A533

CLEMENS, Holly, Director Human Resources, St. Vincent Randolph Hospital, Winchester, IN, p. A227

CLEMENT, Kevin, Chief Executive Officer, Crawford Memorial Hospital, Van Buren, AR, p. A51

CLEMENTE, Jerry, Controller, Molokai General Hospital, Kaunakakai, HI, p. A175

CLEMENTS, Dan A., Chief Executive Officer, Coal County General Hospital, Coalgate, OK, p. A529

CLEMENTS, Jill, Associate Director and Chief Human Resources Officer, Excela Latrobe Area Hospital, Latrobe, PA, p. A563

CLEMENTS, Larry E., Administrator, Wildwood Lifestyle Center and Hospital, Wildwood, GA, p. A172

CLEMMENSEN, Scott
Vice President Human Resources and Leadership Enhancement, Capital Health System at Fuld, Trenton, NJ, p. A437
Vice President Human Resources and Leadership Enhancement, Capital Health System at Mercer, Trenton, NJ, p. A437

CLEMMER, Deb, Vice President Human Resources, Bothwell Regional Health Center, Sedalia, MO, p. A393

CLEMMON, M.D., James A., Chief of Staff, Northwest Florida Community Hospital, Chipley, FL, p. A125

CLEMMONS, Mark, Director of Information Systems, Community Memorial Healthcenter, South Hill, VA, p. A697

CLEMONS, Deneace, Director Human Resources, Twin Lakes Regional Medical Center, Leitchfield, KY, p. A267

CLENDENIN, Phillip A., Chief Executive Officer, River Region Health System, Vicksburg, MS, p. A376

CLEVELAND, Austin B., President and Chief Executive Officer, Lower Bucks Hospital, Bristol, PA, p. A553

CLEVENGER, Jerry, Vice President Human Resources, Rowan Regional Medical Center, Salisbury, NC, p. A491

CLEVENGER, Phyllis, Manager Human Resources, Keweenaw Memorial Medical Center, Laurium, MI, p. A339

CLIBORNE Jr, James J., Chief Executive Officer and Administrator, Sierra Vista Hospital, Truth or Consequences, NM, p. A445

CLICK, Mike, Administrator, Brownfield Regional Medical Center, Brownfield, TX, p. A627

CLIFFE, Peggy, Administrator, Texas Specialty Hospital at San Antonio, San Antonio, TX, p. A665

CLIFFORD, M.D., Greg, Emergency Services Director, Lander Valley Medical Center, Lander, WY, p. A740

CLIFFORD, Michael J., Director Finance, Wayne Memorial Hospital, Honesdale, PA, p. A560

CLIFTON, Gary
Executive Vice President, Finance, Saint Joseph Medical Center, Kansas City, MO, p. A385
Executive Vice President, Finance, St. Mary's Medical Center, Blue Springs, MO, p. A378

CLINE, Terry, Ph.D., Commissioner, Oklahoma State Department of Mental Health and Substance Abuse Services, Oklahoma City, OK, p. B81

CLINE, William H., Vice President Human Resources, Washington Hospital, Washington, PA, p. A578

CLINGENPEEL, Jeremy, Business Office Manager, Greeley County Health Services, Tribune, KS, p. A258

CLIPP, Jerry, Director Human Resources, Northern Virginia Community Hospital, Arlington, VA, p. A685

CLISTER, Martha L., Director Human Resources, Canonsburg General Hospital, Canonsburg, PA, p. A554

CLOER, Carl, Director Information Systems, Singing River Hospital System, Pascagoula, MS, p. A374

CLOHAN Jr, Jack C., Chief Executive Officer, William R. Sharpe, Jr. Hospital, Weston, WV, p. A721

CLOOS, Sharon, Manager Human Resources, Prosser Memorial Hospital, Prosser, WA, p. A706

CLOPTON, Melody, Director Human Resources, The Outer Banks Hospital, Nags Head, NC, p. A488

CLOSE, Debra, Interim Chief Executive Officer, Parkview LaGrange Hospital, LaGrange, IN, p. A221

CLOSE, M.D., Jan, Chief Medical Officer, Alice Hyde Medical Center, Malone, NY, p. A456

CLOSSON, Angela, Director Human Resources, Huggins Hospital, Wolfeboro, NH, p. A424

CLOUD, Avery, Vice President and Chief Information Officer, New Hanover Regional Medical Center, Wilmington, NC, p. A494

CLOUGH, James L., Administrator and Chief Executive Officer, Grape Community Hospital, Hamburg, IA, p. A234

CLOUGH, Jeanette G., President and Chief Executive Officer, Mount Auburn Hospital, Cambridge, MA, p. A316

CLOUTIER, Michael, Information Systems Director, Samaritan Healthcare, Moses Lake, WA, p. A704

CLUTE, Jerry, Senior Vice President and Chief Operating Officer, St. Vincent Medical Center, Los Angeles, CA, p. A72

CLYDE, M.D., Mark, Chief of Staff, Valley Hospital, Palmer, AK, p. A28

CLYMER, Mike, Chief Financial Officer, Oakland Memorial Hospital, Oakland, NE, p. A410

CLYNE, Eileen, Director Human Resources, Christ Hospital, Jersey City, NJ, p. A430

COAKLEY, Tim, Human Resources Director, Estes Park Medical Center, Estes Park, CO, p. A105

COALTER, Barbara, Director Human Resources, Greene Memorial Hospital, Xenia, OH, p. A525

COATES, M.D., Joann, Chief of Staff, Choctaw Health Center, Philadelphia, MS, p. A374

COATS, Robert L., Senior Vice President and Chief Operating Officer, Meriter Hospital, Madison, WI, p. A728

COBB, Carolyn J., Director, Human Resources, Oconee Memorial Hospital, Seneca, SC, p. A591

COBB, Jason, Chief Operating Officer, West Houston Medical Center, Houston, TX, p. A649

COBB, Verlinda, Administrator, Texoma Medical Center Restorative Care Hospital, Denison, TX, p. A635

COBBLE, Emlyn, Vice President and Chief Support Officer, Parkwest Medical Center, Knoxville, TN, p. A610

COCHENNET, Brad, Chief Operating Officer, Mercy Medical Center, Durango, CO, p. A104

COCHRAN, Barry S., FACHE, President, Cullman Regional Medical Center, Cullman, AL, p. A16

COCHRAN, Clair, Human Resource Director, River Park Hospital, McMinnville, TN, p. A612

COCHRAN, Dan, Chief Operating Officer, Bingham Memorial Hospital, Blackfoot, ID, p. A177

COCHRAN, Shelley R., Executive Director, Gulf Pointe Specialty Hospital, Houston, TX, p. A645

COCHRANE, Andrew, Chief Executive Officer, Methodist Willowbrook Hospital, Houston, TX, p. A646

COCKER, Robert, Director Human Resources, Fairview Southdale Hospital, Edina, MN, p. A353

COCKERHAM, Mary Ellen, Vice President Human Resources, Nazareth Hospital, Philadelphia, PA, p. A569

COCKRELL, Dennis, Director Human Resources, Gritman Medical Center, Moscow, ID, p. A180

COCKRILL, Ann Lee, Director of Marketing and Business Development, University Medical Center/McFarland Hospital, Lebanon, TN, p. A611

COCORULLO, Mark, Senior Vice President and Chief Financial Officer, Martin Memorial Health Systems, Stuart, FL, p. A147

CODY, James, Director, Veterans Affairs Medical Center, Syracuse, NY, p. A474

COE, Jason, Chief Operating Officer, Hackettstown Community Hospital, Hackettstown, NJ, p. A429

COFFEY, Daniel B., Senior Vice President and Chief Financial Officer, Eastern Maine Medical Center, Bangor, ME, p. A296

COFFEY, Jerry, Hardware Specialist, Speare Memorial Hospital, Plymouth, NH, p. A423

COFFEY, Kevin, Chief Financial Officer, Brookings Health System, Brookings, SD, p. A594

COFFIELD, Daniel, Executive Vice President and Chief Financial Officer, Hurley Medical Center, Flint, MI, p. A333

COFFMAN, Douglas, Vice President and Chief Financial Officer, United Hospital Center, Clarksburg, WV, p. A715

COFFMAN, Stephen, Chief Information Officer, Meadowcrest Hospital, Gretna, LA, p. A281

COFONE, Michael
  Chief Financial Officer, Franciscan Hospital for Children and Rehabilitation Center, Boston, MA, p. A314
  Chief Financial Officer, Health Alliance Hospitals, Leominster, MA, p. A319

COGLEY, M.D., Richard, Senior Vice President Medical Affairs, Saint Vincent Health Center, Erie, PA, p. A558

COGSWELL, M.D., Max, President Medical Staff, Wilson N. Jones Medical Center, Sherman, TX, p. A667

COHEE, Jon, Chief Executive Officer, Select Specialty Hospital–Saginaw, Saginaw, MI, p. A344

COHEN, Aaron, Chief Financial Officer, Bellevue Hospital Center, New York, NY, p. A458

COHEN, Bruce M., Ph.D., President and Psychiatrist–in–Chief, McLean Hospital, Belmont, MA, p. A312

COHEN, Cindy, Director Human Resources, University of California Los Angeles Neuropsychiatric Hospital, Los Angeles, CA, p. A73

COHEN, M.D., Howard A., Medical Staff President, Doctors Hospital, Augusta, GA, p. A155

COHEN, M.D., Jon R., Chief Medical Officer, Long Island Jewish Medical Center, New York, NY, p. A461

COHEN, M.D., Joseph, Director Medical Services, Lemuel Shattuck Hospital, Jamaica Plain, MA, p. A319

COHEN, Kenneth B.
  Chief Executive Officer, Alameda County Medical Center–Highland Campus, Oakland, CA, p. A78
  Chief Executive Officer, San Joaquin General Hospital, French Camp, CA, p. A61

COHEN, M.D., Max M., Chief Medical Officer, New York University Medical Center, New York, NY, p. A463

COHEN, Philip A.
  Chief Executive Officer, Garfield Medical Center, Monterey Park, CA, p. A76
  Chief Executive Officer, Greater El Monte Community Hospital, El Monte, CA, p. A59
  Chief Executive Officer, Monterey Park Hospital, Monterey Park, CA, p. A76

COHEN, Steven M., M.D., Director, Veterans Affairs Medical Center, Dayton, OH, p. A512

COHEN, Tam, Director, Employee Services, Beaver Dam Community Hospitals, Beaver Dam, WI, p. A723

COHILL, Michael J., Chief Executive Officer, Sutter Medical Center of Santa Rosa, Santa Rosa, CA, p. A93

COHN, M.D., Charles J., Chief of Staff, Georgetown Memorial Hospital, Georgetown, SC, p. A588

COHN, Jr, Lewis Z., Chief Financial Officer, Long Beach Medical Center, Long Beach, NY, p. A455

COKER, John, Director, Human Resource, Carolinas Hospital System, Florence, SC, p. A587

COKER, Raymond, Chief of Staff, Stuttgart Regional Medical Center, Stuttgart, AR, p. A51

COKER Jr, Robert J., Administrator, Greene County Hospital, Eutaw, AL, p. A18

COLANGELO, Nicholas, Chief Executive Officer, Clear Brook Lodge, Shickshinny, PA, p. A576

COLBERG, Gary R., CHE,
  President and Chief Executive Officer, Southeast Georgia Health System, Brunswick, GA, p. B101
  President and Chief Executive Officer, Southeast Georgia Health System Brunswick Campus, Brunswick, GA, p. A157

COLBERT, William, Chief Information Officer, University Health Care System, Augusta, GA, p. A155

COLBURN, Tim, Corporate Vice President Finance, Berger Health System, Circleville, OH, p. A508

COLBY, M.D., Dennis, Chief of Staff, Regional Health Services of Howard County, Cresco, IA, p. A231

COLCHER, Marian W., President, Valley Forge Medical Center and Hospital, Norristown, PA, p. A566

COLCHER, M.D., Robert E., Medical Director, Valley Forge Medical Center and Hospital, Norristown, PA, p. A566

COLCLAZIER, Mary, Administrator, Kiowa County Memorial Hospital, Greensburg, KS, p. A248

COLDICUTT, Ben, Vice President, King's Daughters Hospital, Temple, TX, p. A669

COLE, Beth, Director Information Services, Lewis–Gale Medical Center, Salem, VA, p. A696

COLE, D.O., Gary, Medical Staff President, Sanpete Valley Hospital, Mount Pleasant, UT, p. A677

COLE, Geoffrey F., President and Chief Executive Officer, Norwalk Hospital, Norwalk, CT, p. A115

COLE Jr, Harry, Administrator, Georgiana Hospital, Georgiana, AL, p. A19

COLE, James B., Chief Executive Officer, Virginia Hospital Center – Arlington, Arlington, VA, p. A685

COLE, Lori, Director Information Management, Wayne Memorial Hospital, Goldsboro, NC, p. A483

COLE, Michael D., Vice President Support Services and Human Resources, Wythe County Community Hospital, Wytheville, VA, p. A699

COLE, Valerie, Director Information Systems, Community Medical Center, Missoula, MT, p. A400

COLECCHI, Stephen, President and Chief Executive Officer, Robinson Memorial Hospital, Ravenna, OH, p. A521

COLEMAN, Andrea C., Chief Operating Officer, Penrose–St. Francis Health Services, Colorado Springs, CO, p. A102

COLEMAN, Curt, CHE, Chief Executive Officer, Jackson County Public Hospital, Maquoketa, IA, p. A237

COLEMAN, Dan C., President and Chief Executive Officer, John C. Lincoln Health Network, Phoenix, AZ, p. B64

COLEMAN, Deanna J., Senior Vice President Finance and Chief Financial Officer, Saint Joseph Regional Medical Center–Mishawaka Campus, Mishawaka, IN, p. A222

COLEMAN, Donna, Director Human Resources, Medical Center of Arlington, Arlington, TX, p. A622

COLEMAN, James
  Director, Kalamazoo Psychiatric Hospital, Kalamazoo, MI, p. A338
  Vice President Human Resources, Johnston Memorial Hospital, Smithfield, NC, p. A491

COLEMAN Jr, Jim, Chief Executive Officer, Cleveland Community Hospital, Cleveland, TN, p. A604

COLEMAN, Mitzi, Director Human Resources, Gilmore Memorial Hospital, Amory, MS, p. A366

COLEMAN, Jr, M.D., Wyche, Christus Coushatta Health Care Center, Coushatta, LA, p. A279

COLEMAN–HALL, Ann, Chief Executive Officer, White Mountain Regional Medical Center, Springerville, AZ, p. A37

COLES, Bettie L., R.N., Senior Vice President and Administrator, Kaiser Foundation Hospital, Oakland, CA, p. A79

COLEY, Brenda
  Executive Director, Metroplex Adventist Hospital, Killeen, TX, p. A651
  Executive Director, Rollins–Brook Community Hospital, Lampasas, TX, p. A652

COLLAMORE, M.D., Beth, President Medical Staff, Cary Medical Center, Caribou, ME, p. A298

COLLER, James G., Executive Vice President and Administrator, St. Mary's Hospital Medical Center, Green Bay, WI, p. A726

COLLETTE, Dennis H., President and Chief Executive Officer, Newton Memorial Hospital, Newton, NJ, p. A433

COLLIER, C. Thomas, President and Chief Executive Officer, Sierra Nevada Memorial Hospital, Grass Valley, CA, p. A63

COLLIER, M.D., Gary, Vice President and Chief Medical Officer, Medical Affairs, Miami Valley Hospital, Dayton, OH, p. A512

COLLIER, Laura, Data Processing Coordinator, Bellevue Hospital, Bellevue, OH, p. A504

COLLIER, Russell J.
  Chief Executive Officer and Chief Financial Officer, Marshall Regional Medical Center, Marshall, TX, p. A655
  Chief Executive Officer and Chief Financial Officer, Marshall Regional Medical Center, Marshall, TX, p. A655

COLLIER, Shari, Chief Financial Officer, Overland Park Regional Medical Center, Overland Park, KS, p. A254

COLLINS, D.O., Brian, Medical Staff President, York Hospital, York, ME, p. A301

COLLINS, Chauncey, Director Operations, Austen Riggs Center, Stockbridge, MA, p. A324

COLLINS, Dale, President and Chief Executive Officer, Baptist Health System of East Tennessee, Knoxville, TN, p. B15

COLLINS, Ed, Chief Information Officer, United Hospital Center, Clarksburg, WV, p. A715

COLLINS, Gilbert R., Vice President Finance and Chief Financial Officer, Danville Regional Medical Center, Danville, VA, p. A687

COLLINS, Greg, Information Systems Director, Bothwell Regional Health Center, Sedalia, MO, p. A393

COLLINS, JD, Harold E., Chief Financial Officer, Illiana Surgery and Medical Center, Munster, IN, p. A222

COLLINS, Hugh, Assistant Administrator Finance, St. John's Hospital, Springfield, IL, p. A208

COLLINS, James M., President and Chief Executive Officer, Western Pennsylvania Hospital, Pittsburgh, PA, p. A573

COLLINS, Jeffrey A.
  Interim Chief Executive Officer, Bon Secours Hospital, Grosse Pointe, MI, p. A335
  Chief Operating Officer, Bon Secours Hospital, Grosse Pointe, MI, p. A335
  Chief Operating Officer, Cottage Hospital, Grosse Pointe Farms, MI, p. A336

COLLINS, Kathryn, Vice President Information Systems, Kimball Medical Center, Lakewood, NJ, p. A430

COLLINS, Michael, Assistant Administrator and Chief Financial Officere, Cass County Memorial Hospital, Atlantic, IA, p. A228

COLLINS, Michael L., President and Chief Executive Officer, Jewish Hospital–Shelbyville, Shelbyville, KY, p. A274

COLLINS, Roger, Chief Executive Officer, Jacksonville Medical Center, Jacksonville, AL, p. A20

COLLINS, Sandra, Administrator, HEALTHSOUTH Rehabilitation Hospital, Fort Worth, TX, p. A639

COLLINS, Sharon, Human Resources Director, Russell Regional Hospital, Russell, KS, p. A256

COLLINS, Thomas M., Chief Executive Officer, Green Oaks Hospital, Dallas, TX, p. A632

COLLINS, William G., Chief Executive Officer, Highlands Regional Rehabilitation Hospital, El Paso, TX, p. A637

COLON, Abraham, Chief Fiscal Officer, Veterans Affairs Medical Center, San Juan, PR, p. A748

COLON, Daniel A., Vice President Operations, Wood County Hospital, Bowling Green, OH, p. A504

COLONES, Robert L., President and Chief Executive Officer, McLeod Health, Florence, SC, p. A588

COLPO, Susan
  Chief Executive Officer, Kindred Hospital–Heritage Valley, Beaver, PA, p. A552
  Chief Operating Officer, Kindred Hospital–Pittsburgh, Oakdale, PA, p. A566

COLSON, Curt, Administrator, Satanta District Hospital, Satanta, KS, p. A256

COLSON, Wayne, Chief Financial Officer, College Station Medical Center, College Station, TX, p. A629

COLTHARP, Missy, Director, Baptist Memorial Hospital–Union County, New Albany, MS, p. A374

COLUCCI, Eugene, Vice President Finance, Greenwich Hospital, Greenwich, CT, p. A113

COLUCCIO, Medrice, Chief Executive Officer, St. John Medical Center, Longview, WA, p. A704

COLVERT, Charles C., President, Shelby Baptist Medical Center, Alabaster, AL, p. A13

COLVIN, Garren, Senior Vice President and Chief Financial Officer, St. Elizabeth Medical Center–South, Covington, KY, p. A263

COLVIN, Robert A., President and Chief Executive Officer, Memorial Health, Savannah, GA, p. A169

COLVIN, M.D., Thomas, Chief Medical Staff, Franklin Medical Center, Winnsboro, LA, p. A294

COLVIN, Wesley E., Chief Executive Officer, Carondelet St. Joseph's Hospital–Tucson, Tucson, AZ, p. A37

COLWELL, Loretto Marie, President and Chief Executive Officer, St. Francis Health Center, Topeka, KS, p. A258

COLYER, Valeri, Director of Human Resources, Norton Community Hospital, Norton, VA, p. A693

COMBS, Randy, Chief Financial Officer, St. John's Mercy Medical Center, Saint Louis, MO, p. A392

COMEAUX, M.D., Paul, Medical Staff Director, Lake Charles Memorial Hospital, Lake Charles, LA, p. A285

COMER Sr, W. Jefferson, FACHE, Chief Executive Officer, Northwest Medical Center, Tucson, AZ, p. A38

COMERFORD, Jennifer, Information Services Manager, MidState Medical Center, Meriden, CT, p. A114

COMERFORD Jr, Thomas P., Superintendent, Clarks Summit State Hospital, Clarks Summit, PA, p. A555

COMITTO, Judy, Vice President Information Services and Chief Information Officer, Trinitas Hospital–Williamson Street Campus, Elizabeth, NJ, p. A428

COMO, James, Chief Information Officer, Veterans Affairs Medical Center, Leeds, MA, p. A319

COMPAGNA, Margo, Vice President Human Resources, Catholic Medical Center, Manchester, NH, p. A422

COMPTON, Catherine, Vice President, Ridgeview Medical Center, Waconia, MN, p. A364

COMPTON, Mark, Controller, Laughlin Memorial Hospital, Greeneville, TN, p. A607

COMSTOCK, John M., Chief Executive Officer, Cherokee Regional Medical Center, Cherokee, IA, p. A230

CONANT, Cathy, Chief Human Resources and Personnel, Eastern Plumas District Hospital, Portola, CA, p. A82

CONARY, Sally
President and Chief Executive Officer, Inland Hospital, Waterville, ME, p. A301
President and Chief Executive Officer, Inland Hospital, Waterville, ME, p. A301

CONATY, Robert B., Executive Vice President Operations, Montefiore Medical Center, New York, NY, p. A462

CONCANNON, Margaret, Acting Administrator, Veterans Home and Hospital, Rocky Hill, CT, p. A116

CONCORDIA, Elizabeth B., President, UPMC Presbyterian, Pittsburgh, PA, p. A572

CONDER, Bill, Administrator and Chief Executive Officer, Reeves County Hospital, Pecos, TX, p. A660

CONDINO, Debbie, Vice President Customer Service, St. John Hospital and Medical Center, Detroit, MI, p. A332

CONDON, William, Deputy Administrative Officer, U. S. Public Health Service Indian Hospital, Fort Yates, ND, p. A498

CONDRASKY, Louis M., Administrator, HEALTHSOUTH Rehabilitation Hospital of Erie, Erie, PA, p. A558

CONE, Jr, T William, Executive Vice President, East Cooper Regional Medical Center, Mount Pleasant, SC, p. A590

CONGER, Rex D., President and Chief Executive Officer, Iroquois Memorial Hospital and Resident Home, Watseka, IL, p. A210

CONKLIN, Brian, Information Systems Director, Mason General Hospital, Shelton, WA, p. A709

CONKLIN, Jr, Michael E., Senior Vice President Finance, Faulkner Hospital, Boston, MA, p. A313

CONKLIN, Richard L.
President, Parkland Health Center, Farmington, MO, p. A382
President, Parkland Health Center–Bonne Terre, Bonne Terre, MO, p. A378

CONKLIN, Todd A., Vice President and Chief Financial Officer, Saint Anthony Hospital, Chicago, IL, p. A189

CONLEY, Andrea, Chief Executive Officer, South Mississippi County Regional Medical Center, Osceola, AR, p. A49

CONLEY, Eric, Senior Vice President and Chief Operating Officer, Franklin Square Hospital Center, Baltimore, MD, p. A302

CONLEY, Gerald, Administrator, Carson Valley Medical Center, Gardnerville, NV, p. A415

CONLEY, Joseph M., Chief Operating Officer, Concord Hospital, Concord, NH, p. A420

CONLEY, Marguerite M., Chief Executive Officer, Norristown State Hospital, Norristown, PA, p. A566

CONLEY, Sue, Chief Executive Officer, Mesa View Regional Hospital, Mesquite, NV, p. A417

CONLEY, Teressa, Chief Operating Officer, St. Rose Dominican Hospitals – Siena Campus, Henderson, NV, p. A416

CONLEY, Thomas C., Vice President, Human Resources, St. Agnes HealthCare, Baltimore, MD, p. A304

CONLIN, Kevin P., President and Chief Executive Officer, Via Christi Health System, Wichita, KS, p. B119

CONLIN, Thomas, Vice President Human Resources, Bloomsburg Hospital, Bloomsburg, PA, p. A553

CONN, Kevin R., Administrator, HEALTHSOUTH Sunrise Rehabilitation Hospital, Fort Lauderdale, FL, p. A128

CONNEL, Lorene, Chief Human Resources Management Service, Veterans Affairs Sierra Nevada Health Care System, Reno, NV, p. A418

CONNELL, M.D., Donald, Chief Medical Officer, South Austin Hospital, Austin, TX, p. A624

CONNELL, J Douglas, Chief Financial Officer, Nanticoke Memorial Hospital, Seaford, DE, p. A119

CONNELLY, Harrell L., Interim Chief Executive Officer, Fleming County Hospital, Flemingsburg, KY, p. A264

CONNELLY, Jack, Chief Financial Officer, Rose Medical Center, Denver, CO, p. A104

CONNELLY, Michael D., President and Chief Executive Officer, Catholic Healthcare Partners, Cincinnati, OH, p. B25

CONNER, Laurie A., Chief Executive Officer, Dallas County Hospital, Perry, IA, p. A240

CONNERTON, Kathy, Chief Operating Officer, Venice Regional Medical Center, Venice, FL, p. A149

CONNERY Jr, W. Hudson, President and Chief Executive Officer, Essent Healthcare, Nashville, TN, p. B44

CONNETT, M.D., David, Chief Medical Officer, Garden City Hospital, Garden City, MI, p. A333

CONNOLLY, Brian M.
President and Chief Executive Officer, Blue Water Health Services Corporation, Port Huron, MI, p. B18
President and Chief Executive Officer, Port Huron Hospital, Port Huron, MI, p. A343

CONNOLLY, Dan
Chief Information Officer, Alegent Health Bergan Mercy Medical Center, Omaha, NE, p. A410
Chief Information Officer, Alegent–Health Midlands Community Hospital, Papillion, NE, p. A412

CONNOLLY, James W., Executive Vice President and Chief Operating Officer, Glens Falls Hospital, Glens Falls, NY, p. A453

CONNOR III, Paul J., President and Chief Executive Officer, Eastern Long Island Hospital, Greenport, NY, p. A453

CONNORS, Dennis, Executive Director, Glen Cove Hospital, Glen Cove, NY, p. A453

CONNORS, Karen H., President and Chief Executive Officer, St. Anne Mercy Hospital, Toledo, OH, p. A523

CONNORS, Michael, Vice President and Chief Financial Officer, Brockton Hospital, Brockton, MA, p. A315

CONOLE, Charles P., FACHE, Chief Executive Officer, Edward John Noble Hospital of Gouverneur, Gouverneur, NY, p. A453

CONOVER, Jevne, Administrator, LifeCare Hospitals of West Michigan, Muskegon, MI, p. A341

CONOWAY, Robert, Chief Executive Officer, Arizona Orthopedic Surgical Hospital, Chandler, AZ, p. A30

CONRAD, M.D., Alan, Chief of Staff, Pomerado Hospital, Poway, CA, p. A82

CONRAD, M.D., Stephen, President Medical Staff, Seton Medical Center, Daly City, CA, p. A58

CONRAD, Stephen J., Director Information Systems, Memorial Hospital and Medical Center of Cumberland, Cumberland, MD, p. A307

CONRAD, Steve, Director Information Services, Sacred Heart Hospital, Cumberland, MD, p. A307

CONROY, M.D., Joanne M.
Executive Vice President and Chief Operating Officer, Morristown Memorial Hospital, Morristown, NJ, p. A431
Executive Vice President and Chief Operating Officer, Morristown Memorial Hospital, Morristown, NJ, p. A431
Executive Vice President and Chief Operating Officer, Mountainside Hospital, Montclair, NJ, p. A431
Executive Vice President and Chief Operating Officer, Mountainside Hospital, Montclair, NJ, p. A431
Executive Vice President and Chief Operating Officer, Overlook Hospital, Summit, NJ, p. A436

CONROY, Joseph, Administrator, Emporia Surgical Hospital, Emporia, KS, p. A246

CONROY, M.D., Joseph, Vice President Medical Affairs, St. Mary Medical Center, Langhorne, PA, p. A562

CONROY, Jr, Robert B., Chief Operating Officer, Regional Medical Center–Bayonet Point, Hudson, FL, p. A131

CONROY, Tracy, Chief Executive Officer, Select Specialty Hospital of Evansville, Evansville, IN, p. A215

CONSIDINE, William H., President, Akron Children's Hospital, Akron, OH, p. A502

CONSILVIO, Eileen, MS, Executive Director, Manhattan Psychiatric Center–Ward's Island, New York, NY, p. A462

CONSTABLE, Tom, Senior Vice President Human Resources, Oconomowoc Memorial Hospital, Oconomowoc, WI, p. A733

CONSTANTINO, Chris D., Executive Director, Elmhurst Hospital Center, New York, NY, p. A459

CONTE, John, Director Facility Services, Wayne Memorial Hospital, Honesdale, PA, p. A560

CONTE, Michael, Financial Consultant, Brownsville General Hospital, Brownsville, PA, p. A553

CONTE, William A., Director, Edith Nourse Rogers Memorial Veterans Hospital, Bedford, MA, p. A312

CONTI, Vincent S., President and Chief Executive Officer, Maine Medical Center, Portland, ME, p. A300

CONTRATTO, Blair, Chief Executive Officer, Providence–Little Company of Mary Service Area, Torrance, CA, p. A96

CONTRERAS–SOTO, Alex, Chief Operating Officer, Palmetto General Hospital, Hialeah, FL, p. A131

CONVERY, Paul, M.D.,
Interim President and Chief Executive Officer, SSM St. Joseph Health Center, Saint Charles, MO, p. A390
Interim President and Chief Executive Officer, SSM St. Joseph Hospital West, Lake Saint Louis, MO, p. A386

CONWAY, James B., Chief Operations Officer, Dana–Farber Cancer Institute, Boston, MA, p. A313

CONWAY, Mary M., Director Nursing and Clinical Services, Waverly Health Center, Waverly, IA, p. A243

CONWAY, M.D., William F., Senior Vice President, Medical Staff Affairs, St. Peter's Hospital, Albany, NY, p. A446

CONWILL, Michael, Director, Human Resources, Corpus Christi Medical Center, Corpus Christi, TX, p. A630

CONYERS, Lois, Senior Vice President and Chief Financial Officer, Foothill Presbyterian Hospital–Morris L. Johnston Memorial, Glendora, CA, p. A63

COOK, Buffy, Chief of Staff, Baptist Memorial Hospital–Tipton, Covington, TN, p. A605

COOK, Dave, Vice President and Chief Financial Officer, EMH Regional Medical Center, Elyria, OH, p. A513

COOK, E. Tim, Chief Executive Officer, Osceola Regional Medical Center, Kissimmee, FL, p. A133

COOK, Elizabeth, Chief Information Officer, Mizell Memorial Hospital, Opp, AL, p. A23

COOK, Harold G., Agency Director, Northern Nevada Adult Mental Health Services, Sparks, NV, p. A419

COOK, Jack, Chief Executive Officer and Administrator, Cornerstone Hospital of Bossier City, Bossier City, LA, p. A278

COOK, John, Chief Financial Officer, Mercy Harvard Hospital, Harvard, IL, p. A196

COOK, LaMont, Administrator, Oswego Medical Center, Oswego, KS, p. A254

COOK, Lorene, Vice President Financial and Information Services, Cushing Regional Hospital, Cushing, OK, p. A529

COOK, Michael R., Chief Resource Management, Madigan Army Medical Center, Tacoma, WA, p. A710

COOK, Randy, Vice President and Administrator, WellStar Cobb Hospital, Austell, GA, p. A156

COOK, Ruth, Administrator, East Texas Medical Center Fairfield, Fairfield, TX, p. A638

COOK, Shelia, Director Information Systems, Presbyterian–Orthopaedic Hospital, Charlotte, NC, p. A480

COOK, Thom, Chief Financial Officer, Howard Regional Health System, Kokomo, IN, p. A220

COOK, Thomas J., Administrator, UVA–HEALTHSOUTH Rehabilitation Hospital, Charlottesville, VA, p. A686

COOK, Timothy W., Chief Executive Officer, Adventist La Grange Memorial Hospital, La Grange, IL, p. A199

COOK, William R., Chief Executive Officer, Alliance Hospital, Odessa, TX, p. A658

COOKE, David J., Senior Vice President and Chief Financial Officer, Methodist Hospital, Saint Louis Park, MN, p. A361

COOKE, Nancy, Chief Financial Officer, Campbell Health System, Weatherford, TX, p. A673

COOLEY, Steve, Vice President Information Services, Mary Washington Hospital, Fredericksburg, VA, p. A688

COOMAN, M.D., Lynn
Vice President Medical Affairs, Mercy Medical Center Merced–Community Campus, Merced, CA, p. A75
Vice President Medical Affairs, Mercy Medical Center Merced–Dominican Campus, Merced, CA, p. A75

COOMBES, Rob, Network Administrator, Kewanee Hospital, Kewanee, IL, p. A199

COONE, Dave, Chief Financial Officer, Kenmore Mercy Hospital, Kenmore, NY, p. A455

COONER, Suzanne, Vice President Operations, Grinnell Regional Medical Center, Grinnell, IA, p. A234

COONS, Margaret, Controller, Lucas County Health Center, Chariton, IA, p. A230

COOPER, Allison, Administrator, Community Rehabilitation Hospital of Coushatta, Coushatta, LA, p. A279

COOPER, Anthony J., FACHE, President and Chief Executive Officer, Arnot Ogden Medical Center, Elmira, NY, p. A452

COOPER, M.D., Bid, Chief Medical Officer, D. M. Cogdell Memorial Hospital, Snyder, TX, p. A667

COOPER, Cathy, Director Human Resources, Richardson Medical Center, Rayville, LA, p. A291

COOPER, Chad, Chief Executive Officer, United Hospital District, Blue Earth, MN, p. A350

COOPER, Cliff, Chief Financial Officer, Wills Memorial Hospital, Washington, GA, p. A172

COOPER, Dennis, Director Human Resources, Arkansas Methodist Medical Center, Paragould, AR, p. A49

COOPER, Donald C., Director, Veterans Affairs Central Iowa Health Care System, Des Moines, IA, p. A233

COOPER, Ed, Chief Financial Officer, Lawrence County Memorial Hospital, Lawrenceville, IL, p. A199

COOPER, James C., President and Chief Executive Officer, MedCenter One, Bismarck, ND, p. A496

COOPER, Jeffrey M., President and Chief Executive Officer, Genesis Medical Center, DeWitt, De Witt, IA, p. A232

COOPER, John C., Chief Executive Officer, Arizona State Hospital, Phoenix, AZ, p. A33

COOPER, Kevin S., R.N., Chief Executive Officer and Administrator, Lifecare Hospitals of North Carolina, Rocky Mount, NC, p. A490

COOPER, Maxine T., Chief Executive Officer, Garden Grove Hospital and Medical Center, Garden Grove, CA, p. A62

COOPER, Michael W., Chief Executive Officer, Dunn Memorial Hospital, Bedford, IN, p. A211

COOPER, Pamela, Director Finance, Providence Seaside Hospital, Seaside, OR, p. A549

COOPER, Pat, Comptroller, Conejos County Hospital, La Jara, CO, p. A107

COOPER, Robert, Chief Executive Officer, Marshalltown Medical and Surgical Center, Marshalltown, IA, p. A237

COOPER, Thomas W., Chief Executive Officer, Lafayette Surgical Specialty Hospital, Lafayette, LA, p. A283

COOPER, M.D., Tina, Medical Director, Chickasaw Nation Health System, Ada, OK, p. A527

COOPER–LOHR, Willie, Chief Financial Officer, Barnesville Hospital Association, Barnesville, OH, p. A503

COOPER–WEIDNER, Cathy, Vice President Information Systems, Memorial Hospital of South Bend, South Bend, IN, p. A225

COOPERMAN, Todd, Medical Director, Rehabilitation Hospital of Tinton Falls, Eatontown, NJ, p. A427

COOPERSMITH, M.D., Norman
Vice President Medical Affairs, Capital Health System at Fuld, Trenton, NJ, p. A437
Vice President Medical Affairs, Capital Health System at Mercer, Trenton, NJ, p. A437

COOPWOOD, Reginald W., M.D., Chief Executive Officer, Metropolitan Nashville General Hospital, Nashville, TN, p. A615

COORPENDER, William, Assistant Vice President Human Resources, North Florida Regional Medical Center, Gainesville, FL, p. A130

COOVERT, Beckie, Director Information Systems, Rush–Copley Medical Center, Aurora, IL, p. A184

COPE, Donald, Director Information Systems, Faith Regional Health Services, Norfolk, NE, p. A410

COPE, M.D., Kevin P., Chief Medical Director, Amsterdam Memorial Hospital, Amsterdam, NY, p. A446

COPELAND, Everett, Director Information System, Houston Northwest Medical Center, Houston, TX, p. A645

COPELAND, Gail, Director Management Information Systems, CrossRidge Community Hospital, Wynne, AR, p. A51

COPELAND, John W., Chief Financial Officer, Crockett Hospital, Lawrenceburg, TN, p. A611

COPELAND Jr, Robert Y., FACHE, Chief Executive Officer, McCune–Brooks Hospital, Carthage, MO, p. A380

COPENHAVER, C. Curtis, President, Carolinas Medical Center–Mercy, Charlotte, NC, p. A479

COPPING, DruAnn, Director Public Affairs, St. Jude Medical Center, Fullerton, CA, p. A62

COPPLE, Brad
Administrator, Kishwaukee Community Hospital, De Kalb, IL, p. A191
Administrator, Valley West Community Hospital, Sandwich, IL, p. A207

COPPLE, Sandra, Human Resources Manager, Jay Hospital, Jay, FL, p. A133

COPPOCK, Alan, Administrator, Oak Tree Hospital, Corbin, KY, p. A263

CORAPI, Gene A., Senior Vice President Operations, Suburban Hospital Healthcare System, Bethesda, MD, p. A305

CORBETT, Clifford L., President and Chief Executive Officer, Morris Hospital & Healthcare Centers, Morris, IL, p. A201

CORBETT, Gregory
Senior Vice President, Lenawee Health Alliance – Bixby Campus, Adrian, MI, p. A327
Senior Vice President, Lenawee Health Alliance–Herrick Campus, Tecumseh, MI, p. A346

CORBY, M.D., Gary, Medical Director, HEALTHSOUTH Hospital of Terre Haute, Terre Haute, IN, p. A226

CORCORAN, Joseph P., President and Chief Executive Officer, New York Eye and Ear Infirmary, New York, NY, p. A463

CORDER, Noralene, Chief Financial Officer, Smithville Regional Hospital, Smithville, TX, p. A667

CORDER, Thomas J., President and Chief Executive Officer, Camden–Clark Memorial Hospital, Parkersburg, WV, p. A718

CORDI, Mike, Director Information Systems, Burdette Tomlin Memorial Hospital, Cape May Court House, NJ, p. A427

CORDNER, Glenn D., Chief Executive Officer, Springfield Hospital, Springfield, VT, p. A683

CORE, Carolyn, Vice President Corporate Services, Civista Health, La Plata, MD, p. A309

COREA, Rohan, Director Information Services, St. Vincent Hospital, Green Bay, WI, p. A726

COREY, Jack M., President, DeKalb Memorial Hospital, Auburn, IN, p. A211

CORFITS, Joseph, Senior Vice President Finance, Iowa Methodist Medical Center, Des Moines, IA, p. A232

CORICA, Tony, Director Human Resources, Alameda Hospital, Alameda, CA, p. A52

CORK, Ronald J., President and Chief Executive Officer, Avera St. Anthony's Hospital, O'Neill, NE, p. A410

CORKERN, Robert, M.D., Chief Executive Officer, Tri–Lakes Medical Center, Batesville, MS, p. A366

CORLEY, Thomas, President, Holy Family Hospital, Spokane, WA, p. A709

CORLEY, William E., President, Community Health Network, Indianapolis, IN, p. A218

CORMIER, Kasey, Director Human Resources, Women and Children's Hospital, Lake Charles, LA, p. A285

CORMIER, Philip M., Chief Operating Officer and Executive Vice President, Beverly Hospital, Beverly, MA, p. A312

CORNEJO, Steve, Chief Operating Officer, Promise Hospital of East Los Angeles, Suburban Medical Center Campus, Paramount, CA, p. A81

CORNELI, Cindy, Accountant, Hermann Area District Hospital, Hermann, MO, p. A383

CORNELIUS, David, Director Information Services, Doctors Hospital of Columbus, Columbus, GA, p. A158

CORNELL, John, Chief Operating Officer, Oconee Regional Medical Center, Milledgeville, GA, p. A166

CORNELL, Leon, Vice President Human Resources, Concord Hospital, Concord, NH, p. A420

CORNELL, Michael, Employee and Community Relations Director, Walter Knox Memorial Hospital, Emmett, ID, p. A179

CORNELL, Richard, Commander Resource Management, U. S. Air Force Hospital Dover, Dover, DE, p. A119

CORNETT, Joyce, Human Resources Officer, Ralph H. Johnson Veterans Affairs Medical Center, Charleston, SC, p. A585

CORNICELLI, Kari, Chief Financial Officer, Sharp Grossmont Hospital, La Mesa, CA, p. A66

CORNISH, Kenneth D., Chief Financial Officer, St. Peter Community Hospital, Saint Peter, MN, p. A362

CORNWELL, Emily, Operations Manager, River Park Hospital, Huntington, WV, p. A716

CORNWELL, Shelli, Administrator, Genoa Community Hospital, Genoa, NE, p. A407

CORONADO, Jose R., FACHE, Director, South Texas Veterans Health Care System, San Antonio, TX, p. A665

CORRADINO, Richard L., Chief Finance Officer, Spanish Peaks Regional Health Center, Walsenburg, CO, p. A110

CORREA, Jerry, Vice President Information Services, St. Francis Medical Center–West, Ewa Beach, HI, p. A173

CORREIA, Antonio, Chief Financial Officer, Holyoke Medical Center, Holyoke, MA, p. A318

CORREIA, Kathryn
Senior Vice President, Appleton Medical Center, Appleton, WI, p. A722
Senior Vice President, Theda Clark Medical Center, Neenah, WI, p. A732

CORRELL, Edana, Manager Human Resources, Community Hospital Onaga, Onaga, KS, p. A254

CORRIGAN, James M., Chief Financial Officer, St. Vincent's Medical Center, Jacksonville, FL, p. A133

CORRIGAN, Paula, Assistant Administrator Information and Financial Services, OSF Saint James – John W. Albrecht Medical Center, Pontiac, IL, p. A205

CORS, M.D., William, Senior Vice President Medical Affairs, Somerset Medical Center, Somerville, NJ, p. A436

CORSENTINO, Lori, Director Human Resources, Mt. San Rafael Hospital, Trinidad, CO, p. A110

CORSINI, M.D., William, Chief of Staff, Huron Medical Center, Bad Axe, MI, p. A328

CORSO, Michael, Chief Information Officer, Bon Secours Hospital Campus, Altoona, PA, p. A552

CORTESE, Denis A., M.D., President and Chief Executive Officer, Mayo Foundation, Rochester, MN, p. B72

CORTEZ, Regina, Administrative Assistant and Human Resource Director, Dallas County Medical Center, Fordyce, AR, p. A43

CORTI, Ronald, President and Chief Executive Officer, Community Hospital at Dobbs Ferry, Dobbs Ferry, NY, p. A451

CORTRIGHT, Michael, Chief Information Officer, Ralph H. Johnson Veterans Affairs Medical Center, Charleston, SC, p. A585

CORVINO, Frank A., President and Chief Executive Officer, Greenwich Hospital, Greenwich, CT, p. A113

CORWIN, Julie, Director Public Affairs and Marketing, Hallmark Health System, Melrose, MA, p. A320

COSCO, John A., FACHE, Chief Executive Officer, Powell County Memorial Hospital, Deer Lodge, MT, p. A397

COSGROVE, Delos, M.D., President and Chief Executive Officer, Cleveland Clinic Foundation, Cleveland, OH, p. A508

COSLETT, John, Administrator, Via Christi Riverside Medical Center, Wichita, KS, p. A259

COSTA, M.D., Gerald, Vice President Medical Affairs, Bayshore Community Hospital, Holmdel, NJ, p. A429

COSTA, Joe, Acting Chief Fiscal Officer, Brockton Veterans Affairs Medical Center, Brockton, MA, p. A315

COSTA, Joseph R., Chief Financial Officer, Veterans Affairs Boston Healthcare System, Boston, MA, p. A315

COSTANTINO, Vincent, Vice President Human Resources, Raritan Bay Medical Center, Perth Amboy, NJ, p. A434

COSTELLO, Benny, Chief Executive Officer, Regency Hospital of Meridian, Meridian, MS, p. A373

COSTELLO, Bud, Administrator and Chief Executive Officer, Macon Northside Hospital, Macon, GA, p. A165

COSTELLO, Jack, Senior Vice President Finance and Chief Financial Officer, Staten Island University Hospital, New York, NY, p. A465

COSTELLO, Jeff, Chief Financial Officer, Memorial Hospital of South Bend, South Bend, IN, p. A225

COSTIC, Andrew, Regional Chief Financial Officer, Abraham Lincoln Memorial Hospital, Lincoln, IL, p. A199

COTTER, Richard W., Chief Operating Officer, Veterans Affairs Medical Center, Butler, PA, p. A554

COTTLE, Gil, Chief Financial Officer, St. Christopher's Hospital for Children, Philadelphia, PA, p. A570

COTTO, M.D., Hector L., Medical Director, Caribbean Pediatric and Surgery Hospital, San Juan, PR, p. A747

COTTON, C. Gerald, Executive Director, Mississippi Hospital for Restorative Care, Jackson, MS, p. A371

COTTON, M.D., Christopher, Chief Medical Officer, Yoakum County Hospital, Denver City, TX, p. A635

COTTRELL, Tonya, Senior Financial Analyst, Missouri Baptist Hospital–Sullivan, Sullivan, MO, p. A394

COUCH, Robert C., Chief Executive Officer, Medical Center of Manchester, Manchester, TN, p. A612

COUGHLIN, Jean, President and Chief Executive Officer, Marian Community Hospital, Carbondale, PA, p. A554

COULTER, M.D., James, Vice President Medical Affairs, Lester E. Cox Medical Centers, Springfield, MO, p. A394

COUNTS, Angie, Director Public Relations, Alamance Regional Medical Center, Burlington, NC, p. A478

COUNTY, Vickie, Coordinator Human Resources, Mitchell County Hospital, Camilla, GA, p. A157

COUNTZLER, John, Senior Vice President Finance and Chief Financial Officer, Owensboro Medical Health System, Owensboro, KY, p. A272

COURAGE, Kenneth F., Chief Executive Officer and Chairman of the Board, Psychiatric Institute of Washington, Washington, DC, p. A122

COUROUNIS, Glen, Vice President Human Resources, Manhattan Eye, Ear and Throat Hospital, New York, NY, p. A462

COURTNEY, M.D., Donald L., Acting Chief of Staff, Veterans Affairs Eastern Kansas Health Care System, Topeka, KS, p. A258

COURTNEY, Gayle, Director Human Resources, HEALTHSOUTH Rehabilitation Hospital of Baton Rouge, Baton Rouge, LA, p. A277

COURTNEY, Joseph B., Chief Executive Officer, Doctor's Hospital at Renaissance, Edinburg, TX, p. A636

COURTNEY, Linda, Director Health Information, Northwest Medical Center, Albany, MO, p. A378

COURTWAY, Peter, Chief Information Officer, Danbury Hospital, Danbury, CT, p. A112

COUSAR, Myra, Director of Human Resources, Baptist Memorial Hospital–Tipton, Covington, TN, p. A605

COVA, Charles J., President, Marian Medical Center, Santa Maria, CA, p. A93

COVERDALE, Miles, Chief Financial Officer, Caritas Carney Hospital, Dorchester, MA, p. A317

COVERT, Charles O., Vice President Finance, Thomas Memorial Hospital, South Charleston, WV, p. A720

COVERT, David G., President and Chief Administrative Officer, Chandler Regional Hospital, Chandler, AZ, p. A30

COVERT, Michael H., FACHE, Chief Executive Officer, Palomar Pomerado Health, San Diego, CA, p. B82

COVERT, Rob, President and Chief Executive Officer, Oaklawn Hospital, Marshall, MI, p. A340

COVERT, Sarah, Director, Human Resources, Navarro Regional Hospital, Corsicana, TX, p. A631

COVEY, Laird P., Exec Vice President and Chief Operating Officer, Central Maine Medical Center, Lewiston, ME, p. A299

COVEY, Staci, Administrator, Troy Community Hospital, Troy, PA, p. A577

COVIN, Charles
Chief Information Officer, Manchester Memorial Hospital, Manchester, CT, p. A113
Chief Information Officer, Rockville General Hospital, Vernon Rockville, CT, p. A117

COWAN, Ron, Chief Information Officer, Lewistown Hospital, Lewistown, PA, p. A563

COWLES, Deborah, Vice President Human Resources, Flaget Memorial Hospital, Bardstown, KY, p. A261

COWLEY, Markie, Executive Vice President and Chief Operating Officer, Mission Hospital, Mission Viejo, CA, p. A75

COWLING, Michael, President, Baptist Montclair, Birmingham, AL, p. A14

COWLING, Phyllis A., Chief Executive Officer, United Regional Health Care System, Wichita Falls, TX, p. A674

COX, Amy, Director Health Information Services, Pratt Regional Medical Center, Pratt, KS, p. A255

COX, M.D., Bob, Medical Director, Hays Medical Center, Hays, KS, p. A248

COX, Darlene L., President and Chief Executive Officer, University of Medicine and Dentistry of New Jersey–University Hospital, Newark, NJ, p. A433

COX, Debbie, Director, Human Resources, Central Texas Medical Center, San Marcos, TX, p. A666

COX, Dorothy, Manager Information Systems, Hackettstown Community Hospital, Hackettstown, NJ, p. A429

COX, Gray, President, Unity Health Center, Shawnee, OK, p. A538

COX, Jay, President and Chief Executive Officer, Tuomey Healthcare System, Sumter, SC, p. A592

COX, John, Assistant Vice President and Chief Information Officer, Hospital for Special Surgery, New York, NY, p. A460

COX, Kenneth, Chief Medical Officer, Lucile Salter Packard Children's Hospital at Stanford, Palo Alto, CA, p. A80

COX, Kevin, Chief Financial Officer, Integris Grove General Hospital, Grove, OK, p. A531

COX, Leigh
Chief Executive Officer, Navapache Regional Medical Center, Show Low, AZ, p. A36
Chief Information Officer, WellStar Cobb Hospital, Austell, GA, p. A156
Chief Information Officer, WellStar Douglas Hospital, Douglasville, GA, p. A161
Chief Information Officer, WellStar Kennestone Hospital, Marietta, GA, p. A165
Chief Information Officer, WellStar Windy Hill Hospital, Marietta, GA, p. A165

COX, Randy, Chief Information Officer, Riverview Hospital, Noblesville, IN, p. A223

COX, Russ, Executive Vice President, Norton Audubon Hospital, Louisville, KY, p. A269

COX, Sharon, Chief Executive Officer, Klickitat Valley Health Services, Goldendale, WA, p. A703

COX, Sherry, Chief Human Resources Officer, Ashe Memorial Hospital, Jefferson, NC, p. A485

COX, Todd
Interim Chief Financial Officer, Phoebe Worth Medical Center, Sylvester, GA, p. A170
Chief Financial Officer, Southwest Georgia Regional Medical Center, Cuthbert, GA, p. A159

COXE, M.D., Bob, Medical Director, Vanderbilt Stallworth Rehabilitation Hospital, Nashville, TN, p. A616

COYLE, Joseph P., President and Chief Executive Officer, Southern Ocean County Hospital, Manahawkin, NJ, p. A431

COYNE, Kathryn W.
Executive Director, Union Hospital, Union, NJ, p. A438
Executive Director, Union Hospital, Union, NJ, p. A438

COYNE, Rose, Vice President and Chief Financial Officer, Cleveland Regional Medical Center, Shelby, NC, p. A491

COZART, Adrienne, Vice President of Human Resources, University Medical Center, Lubbock, TX, p. A654

CRABLE, Trent, Chief Operating Officer, George Washington University Hospital, Washington, DC, p. A121

CRABTREE, Douglas, Chief Executive Officer, Eastern Idaho Regional Medical Center, Idaho Falls, ID, p. A179

CRABTREE, Gordon, Chief Financial Officer, University of Utah Hospitals and Clinics, Salt Lake City, UT, p. A680

CRACROFT, M.D., Davis, Medical Director, Scripps Mercy Hospital, San Diego, CA, p. A87

CRAFA, Regina, Vice President Human Resources, Bethesda Memorial Hospital, Boynton Beach, FL, p. A124

CRAFT, Carolyn, Human Resources Director, St. Joseph's Hospital, Chippewa Falls, WI, p. A724

CRAFT, M.D., Chuck, Chief of Staff, Hanford Community Medical Center, Hanford, CA, p. A63

CRAFT, Karen, Administrator, Stone County Medical Center, Mountain View, AR, p. A48

CRAIG, Celine, Manager Human Resources, King's Daughters Medical Center, Brookhaven, MS, p. A367

CRAIG, Deb, Chief Financial Officer, Thayer County Health Services, Hebron, NE, p. A407

CRAIG, Donnette, Director of Human Resources, Christus Coushatta Health Care Center, Coushatta, LA, p. A279

CRAIG, Emmett, Director Human Resources, Abilene Regional Medical Center, Abilene, TX, p. A620

CRAIG, John D., Chief Financial Officer, St. Luke's Rehabilitation Institute, Spokane, WA, p. A709

CRAIG, Kerry, Chief Information Officer, Southwest Washington Medical Center, Vancouver, WA, p. A711

CRAIG, Mary Anne, Chief Executive Officer, Kindred Hospital–Houston Northwest, Houston, TX, p. A646

CRAIG, Patrice, Chief Human Resources Management Division, Veterans Affairs Medical Center, Portland, OR, p. A548

CRAIG, Rebecca W., Vice President and Chief Financial Officer, Wayne Memorial Hospital, Goldsboro, NC, p. A483

CRAIGHTON, Michelle, Finance Manager, Franklin General Hospital, Hampton, IA, p. A235

CRAIGIE, Andrew, Administrator, Garfield County Public Hospital District, Pomeroy, WA, p. A705

CRAIGIN, Jane, Chief Executive Officer, St. Vincent Williamsport Hospital, Williamsport, IN, p. A227

CRAIN, Allen, Director Human Resources, Rapides Regional Medical Center, Alexandria, LA, p. A276

CRAIN, Doris, Vice President Information Services, Holy Cross Hospital, Fort Lauderdale, FL, p. A128

CRAIN, Greg, Vice President, Baptist Health Rehabilitation Institute, Little Rock, AR, p. A46

CRAIN, Stephen L., President and Chief Executive Officer, Mineral Area Regional Medical Center, Farmington, MO, p. A382

CRALL, Carlene, Executive Director Human Resources, Deaconess Billings Clinic, Billings, MT, p. A396

CRALL, Ron, Chief Information Officer, St. Joseph Hospital, Bangor, ME, p. A296

CRAM, Suzanne, Chief Operating Officer, Sunrise Hospital and Medical Center, Las Vegas, NV, p. A417

CRAMER, Donna, Director Human Resources, Alice Peck Day Memorial Hospital, Lebanon, NH, p. A421

CRAMER, James R.
Vice President and Chief Information Officer, Scottsdale Healthcare–Osborn, Scottsdale, AZ, p. A36
Vice President and Chief Information Officer, Scottsdale Healthcare–Shea, Scottsdale, AZ, p. A36

CRANDALL, David, FACHE, President and Chief Executive Officer, Hospital for Special Care, New Britain, CT, p. A114

CRANDALL, M.D., Jeff, Chief Medical Officer, Allen Memorial Hospital, Waterloo, IA, p. A242

CRANDELL, Kim O., Chief Executive Officer and Administrator, Boulder City Hospital, Boulder City, NV, p. A415

CRANE, Aaron, Chief Financial Officer, Salem Hospital, Salem, OR, p. A549

CRANE, David, Chief Executive Officer, Littleton Adventist Hospital, Littleton, CO, p. A107

CRANE, M.D., John, Chief of Staff, St. Vincent Frankfort Hospital, Frankfort, IN, p. A216

CRANE, K David, Chief Financial Officer, Sisters of Charity Hospital of Buffalo, Buffalo, NY, p. A449

CRANE, Margaret W., Chief Executive Officer, Barlow Respiratory Hospital, Los Angeles, CA, p. A69

CRANE, M.D., Michael, Chief of Staff, Memorial Hospital, Craig, CO, p. A103

CRANFORD, David, Chief Financial Officer, Hutcheson Medical Center, Fort Oglethorpe, GA, p. A162

CRANFORD, Melvin, Acting Chief Fiscal Services, Veterans Affairs Medical Center, Cheyenne, WY, p. A739

CRANSTON, M.D., David C., Vice President Medical Staff Affairs, Grinnell Regional Medical Center, Grinnell, IA, p. A234

CRATON, M.D., Deborah, Chief Medical Staff, Dunn Memorial Hospital, Bedford, IN, p. A211

CRAVEN, Nicole, Acting Chief, Human Resources, Veterans Affairs Medical Center, Oklahoma City, OK, p. A536

CRAWFORD, Brenda, Process Leader Management of Information, SouthCrest Hospital, Tulsa, OK, p. A540

CRAWFORD, Brenita, Chief Operating Officer, Regional Medical Center at Memphis, Memphis, TN, p. A613

CRAWFORD, Jim, Chief Executive Officer, Missouri Southern Healthcare, Dexter, MO, p. A381

CRAWFORD, Jo Beth, Vice President Human Resources, Chandler Regional Hospital, Chandler, AZ, p. A30

CRAWFORD, John W., Chief Executive Officer, Wagoner Community Hospital, Wagoner, OK, p. A541

CRAWFORD, Johnny, Chief Financial Officer, Rapides Regional Medical Center, Alexandria, LA, p. A276

CRAWFORD, Mark W., Chief Executive Officer, University Medical Center/McFarland Hospital, Lebanon, TN, p. A611

CRAWFORD, Samantha D., Director, Human Resources, Carraway Methodist Medical Center, Birmingham, AL, p. A14

CRAWFORD, Thomas, Chief Executive Officer, St. Vincent Frankfort Hospital, Frankfort, IN, p. A216

CRAWFORD, Tom
Vice President Human Resources, DeKalb Medical Center, Decatur, GA, p. A160
Director General Services and Chief Information Officer, Springfield Hospital, Springfield, VT, p. A683
Director General Services and Chief Information Officer, Springfield Hospital, Springfield, VT, p. A683

CRAWLEY, Rick, Administrator and Chief Executive Officer, Wabash Valley Hospital, West Lafayette, IN, p. A227

CREAMER, Ken, Chief Human Resource, Amarillo Veterans Affairs Health Care System, Amarillo, TX, p. A620

CREARY, Michael, Chief Financial Officer, Knoxville Area Community Hospital and Clinic, Knoxville, IA, p. A236

CREELEY, Melvin R., President, East Liverpool City Hospital, East Liverpool, OH, p. A513

CREELMAN, M.D., Wayne L., Executive Vice President and Chief Medical Officer, Pine Rest Christian Mental Health Services, Grand Rapids, MI, p. A334

CREEM, Mitchell, Senior Vice President Finance and Chief Financial Officer, Beth Israel Deaconess Medical Center, Boston, MA, p. A313

CRELLY, Rick, Vice President Employee Services, Zeeland Community Hospital, Zeeland, MI, p. A348

CREQUE, J C., Director Management Information Systems, Roy Lester Schneider Hospital, Saint Thomas, VI, p. A749

CRESS, David W., Vice President and Chief Operating Officer, North Memorial Health Care, Robbinsdale, MN, p. A360

CRESS, Michael D., President, Cornerstone Healthcare Group, Austin, TX, p. B33

CRESSIONNIE, Vicki, Executive Director, Healthwest Rehabilitation Hospital, Gretna, LA, p. A281

CRESWELL, Linda, Director Human Resources, Wilson N. Jones Medical Center, Sherman, TX, p. A667

CRIGER, Sara, President and Chief Executive Officer, Fairview Ridges Hospital, Burnsville, MN, p. A351

CRIPE, Kimberly C.
President and Chief Executive Officer, Children's Hospital at Mission, Mission Viejo, CA, p. A75
President and Chief Executive Officer, Children's Hospital of Orange County, Orange, CA, p. A79

CRIPPEN, Angela, Director of Health Information Services, HEALTHSOUTH Sunrise Rehabilitation Hospital, Fort Lauderdale, FL, p. A128

CRIPPIN, M.D., David, Chief Medical Staff, Buena Vista Regional Medical Center, Storm Lake, IA, p. A242

CRISANTI, M.D., John, Vice President Medical Affairs, Community Medical Center, Toms River, NJ, p. A437

CRISTY, Kirk, Chief Financial Officer, Covenant Hospital Plainview, Plainview, TX, p. A660

CRITCHLEY, James, Chief Information Management, Veterans Affairs Medical Center–Lexington, Lexington, KY, p. A268

CRITTLE, Marsha, Human Resource Director, Huey P. Long Medical Center, Pineville, LA, p. A291

CRITZ, M.D., Carl, Chief of Staff, San Ramon Regional Medical Center, San Ramon, CA, p. A91

CROFFORD, Patricia, Vice President Employee Services, Valley Hospital, Palmer, AK, p. A28

CROFITS, Joe, Chief Financial Officer, Iowa Lutheran Hospital, Des Moines, IA, p. A232

CROFT, Cheryl, Chairman, Information Services, St. Luke's Hospital, Jacksonville, FL, p. A132

CROKER, James, Director Information Services, Central Arkansas Hospital, Searcy, AR, p. A50

CROLY, Jennifer, Vice President Technology, Rockdale Medical Center, Conyers, GA, p. A159

CRONBERG, Chris, Chief Executive Officer, Northern Cochise Community Hospital, Willcox, AZ, p. A39

CRONKLETON, Kevin, Chief Financial Officer, St. Luke Hospital and Living Center, Marion, KS, p. A252

CROOM Jr, Kennedy L., Administrator and Chief Executive Officer, Rhea Medical Center, Dayton, TN, p. A605

CROPPER, Douglas P., Administrator, Inova Fairfax Hospital, Falls Church, VA, p. A687

CROSBIE, John, Director Support Services, Blackford Community Hospital, Hartford City, IN, p. A217

CROSBY, Marilu
Director of Human Resources, Houston Medical Center, Warner Robins, GA, p. A172
Director of Human Resources, Perry Hospital, Perry, GA, p. A167

CROSBY, Robert, Chief Financial Officer, UMass Memorial–Marlborough Hospital, Marlborough, MA, p. A320

CROSHAW, Diane, Vice President Human Resources, Bacharach Institute for Rehabilitation, Pomona, NJ, p. A435

CROSS, David, Chief Executive Officer, Select Specialty Hospital of Wichita, Wichita, KS, p. A259

CROSS, Helene M., President and Chief Executive Officer, Fairbanks, Indianapolis, IN, p. A218

CROSS, Janice, Controller, Tippah County Hospital, Ripley, MS, p. A375

CROSS, Mark A., Chief Executive Officer, Marias Medical Center, Shelby, MT, p. A402

CROSS, Renee, Vice President and Chief Financial Officer, Raleigh General Hospital, Beckley, WV, p. A713

CROSSER, Roxanna, Senior Assistant Administrator Staff Services, OSF St. Mary Medical Center, Galesburg, IL, p. A195

CROSSETT, Joseph W., Administrator, Liberty Hospital, Liberty, MO, p. A386

CROSSIN, William J., President and Chief Executive Officer, St. Luke's Miner's Memorial Hospital, Coaldale, PA, p. A555

CROTEAU, Gary, Chief Information Officer, South County Hospital, Wakefield, RI, p. A582

CROTTY, Jr, M.D., Glenn, Executive Vice President and Chief Operating Officer, Charleston Area Medical Center, Charleston, WV, p. A714

CROTWELL, Lori, Human Resources Manager, P & S Surgical Hospital, Monroe, LA, p. A287

CROUCH, Chester, Administrator, HEALTHSOUTH Plano Rehabilitation Hospital, Plano, TX, p. A661

CROUCH, Mary, Director Information Technologies, Phelps County Regional Medical Center, Rolla, MO, p. A389

CROUCH, Matthew, Chief Executive Officer, Peachford Behavioral Health System, Atlanta, GA, p. A154

CROUCH, M.D., Richard, Chief Medical Officer, Murray–Calloway County Hospital, Murray, KY, p. A272

CROUSHORE, Susan, Executive Director and Senior Vice President, Christ Hospital, Cincinnati, OH, p. A506

CROW, Barbra, Chief Financial Officer, Little River Memorial Hospital, Ashdown, AR, p. A40

CROW, Jack, Vice President Health Services, Yukon–Kuskokwim Delta Regional Hospital, Bethel, AK, p. A26

CROW, Tom, Administrator, Atlanta Memorial Hospital, Atlanta, TX, p. A622

CROWDER, Jerry W., President and Chief Executive Officer, Bradford Health Services, Birmingham, AL, p. B18

CROWE, Danny, Chief Financial Officer, Lawrence Medical Center, Moulton, AL, p. A22

CROWE, William R., Chief Financial Officer, Providence Hospital and Medical Center, Southfield, MI, p. A345

CROWELL, Alan L., Senior Vice President and Chief Financial Officer, Health Central, Ocoee, FL, p. A140

CROWELL, Eric T.
President and Chief Executive Officer, Iowa Lutheran Hospital, Des Moines, IA, p. A232
President and Chief Executive Officer, Iowa Methodist Medical Center, Des Moines, IA, p. A232

CROWELL, Lynn, Chief Executive Officer, Arkansas Valley Regional Medical Center, La Junta, CO, p. A107

CROWL, Heather, Executive Director Human Resources, Kingman Regional Medical Center, Kingman, AZ, p. A31

CROWL, Steve, Acting Chief Information Officer, Davis Memorial Hospital, Elkins, WV, p. A715

CROWLEY, Gary, Administrator, HEALTHSOUTH Chesapeake Rehabilitation Hospital, Salisbury, MD, p. A310

CROWLEY, Sheryl, Chief Information Officer, Jordan Hospital, Plymouth, MA, p. A322

CROWLEY, Thomas, President, Saint Elizabeth's Medical Center, Wabasha, MN, p. A364

CROWLEY, Jr, Thomas J., Executive Vice President, Doctors Community Hospital, Lanham, MD, p. A309

CROWLEY, Timothy J., President and Chief Executive Officer, Clinton Memorial Hospital, Wilmington, OH, p. A525

CROWTHER, Bruce K., President and Chief Executive Officer, Northwest Community Healthcare, Arlington Heights, IL, p. A183

CROZIER, Jon, Director, Community Memorial Hospital of San Buenaventura, Ventura, CA, p. A98

CRUICKSHANK, James A., Chief Executive Officer, University Hospital and Medical Center, Tamarac, FL, p. A147

CRUICKSHANK, Roland, Chief Operating Officer, South Fulton Medical Center, Atlanta, GA, p. A154

CRUM, Dennis L., Chief Financial Officer and Vice President, Tift Regional Medical Center, Tifton, GA, p. A171

CRUM, Jr, Herbert, Chief Financial Officer, St. Anthony's Healthcare Center, Morrilton, AR, p. A48

CRUMMEY, Charlotte, Director Information Services, St. Elizabeth Hospital, Gonzales, LA, p. A281

CRUMP, M.D., Jay, Director Medical Staff, Phelps County Regional Medical Center, Rolla, MO, p. A389

CRUMPLER, Joyce, R.N., Administrator and Chief Executive Officer, Bowie Memorial Hospital, Bowie, TX, p. A626

CRUMPTON, Althea H., Administrator, Magee General Hospital, Magee, MS, p. A372

CRUNK, Fran, Chief Financial Officer, Central Texas Medical Center, San Marcos, TX, p. A666

CRUTCHFIELD, David, Vice President and Chief Information Officer, Virginia Hospital Center – Arlington, Arlington, VA, p. A685

CRUTCHFIELD, Roger, Director Information Systems, Clear Lake Regional Medical Center, Webster, TX, p. A673

CRUTHIRDS, Richard, Manager Information Systems, Sid Peterson Memorial Hospital, Kerrville, TX, p. A651

CRUZ, M.D., Francisco P., Chief Medical Officer, Pioneer Memorial Hospital and Health Services, Viborg, SD, p. A600

CRUZ, Joseph V., Chief Information Officer, Ryder Memorial Hospital, Humacao, PR, p. A745

CRUZ, Julia, Chief Financial Officer, San Juan Capestrano Hospital, San Juan, PR, p. A748

CRUZ, Michael, Vice President Operations, Baptist St. Anthony Health System, Amarillo, TX, p. A621

CRUZ, M.D., Miguel, Medical Director, Bella Vista Hospital, Mayaguez, PR, p. A745

CSANADI, M.D., Mary Ellen, Chief of Staff, Los Alamos Medical Center, Los Alamos, NM, p. A443

CUDWORTH, Craig R., Chief Executive Officer, Hendry Regional Medical Center, Clewiston, FL, p. A126

CUELLAR, Eddie
Vice President Information Systems, Methodist Children's Hospital of South Texas, San Antonio, TX, p. A664
Vice President Information Systems, Methodist Hospital, San Antonio, TX, p. A664

CUEVAS, Gilberto, Human Resources Vice President, Hospital De Damas, Ponce, PR, p. A746

CULBERSON, David K., Chief Executive Officer, West Anaheim Medical Center, Anaheim, CA, p. A52

CULLEN, James J., President and Chief Executive Officer, Gaylord Hospital, Wallingford, CT, p. A117

CULLEN, M.D., John, Chief of Stf and Long Term Care Medical Director, Providence Valdez Medical Center, Valdez, AK, p. A29

CULLEN, Mark, Chief Executive Officer, Kaplan Rehabilitation Hospital, Kaplan, LA, p. A283

CULLEN, Michael E.
Vice President Fiscal Services, Berkshire Medical Center, Pittsfield, MA, p. A322
Vice President Fin, Fairview Hospital, Great Barrington, MA, p. A318

CULLEN, Sheila M., Director, Veterans Affairs Medical Center, San Francisco, CA, p. A90

CULLER, Angela, Chief Human Resources Officer, High Point Regional Health System, High Point, NC, p. A485

CULLISON, Mark, Director Facility Services, Wilkes Regional Medical Center, North Wilkesboro, NC, p. A488

CULLIVER, Sandra, Director, Human Resources, National Park Medical Center, Hot Springs, AR, p. A44

CULVER, M.D., Donald, Chief of Staff, Park Ridge Hospital, Fletcher, NC, p. A483

CULVER, Shawna, Head Information Systems, Western Plains Medical Complex, Dodge City, KS, p. A246

CULVERN, Rita, Administrator, Jefferson Hospital, Louisville, GA, p. A164

CUMBEE, Lib, Director Information Systems, Sisters of Charity Providence Hospitals, Columbia, SC, p. A586

CUMBERLEDGE, Brad, Director Information Services, Greene County Memorial Hospital, Waynesburg, PA, p. A578

CUMMING, Irene M., Chief Executive Officer, University of Kansas Hospital, Kansas City, KS, p. A250

CUMMINGS, Bruce D., President and Chief Executive Officer, Olean General Hospital, Olean, NY, p. A468

CUMMINGS, Debra, Chief Financial Officer, Community Hospital, Torrington, WY, p. A742

CUMMINGS, Elmer, Vice President Financial Services, Hardin Memorial Hospital, Elizabethtown, KY, p. A263

CUMMINGS, Greg, Chief Operating Officer and Chief Financial Officer, East Texas Medical Center Jacksonville, Jacksonville, TX, p. A650

CUMMINGS, James J., Administrative Director, Human Resources, Corning Hospital, Corning, NY, p. A451

CUMMINS, Bill, Vice President System Resources, Porter–Valparaiso Hospital Campus, Valparaiso, IN, p. A226

CUMMINS, Frank, Vice President Human Resources, Walter O. Boswell Memorial Hospital, Sun City, AZ, p. A37

CUMMINS, Steve
Chief Financial Officer, Russell County Hospital, Russell Springs, KY, p. A274
Chief Financial Officer, Russell County Hospital, Russell Springs, KY, p. A274

CUMP, D.O., Paul, Medical Director, Kremmling Memorial Hospital, Kremmling, CO, p. A107

CUNNINGHAM, James, Chief Medical Officer, Livingston Regional Hospital, Livingston, TN, p. A611

CUNNINGHAM, M.D., Joe H., Senior Vice President Medical Affairs, Providence Health Center, Waco, TX, p. A672

CUNNINGHAM, Leslie
Chief Human Resources Officer, HEALTHSOUTH Hospital of Pittsburgh, Monroeville, PA, p. A565
Director Human Resources, HEALTHSOUTH Rehabilitation Hospital, Sewickley, PA, p. A575

CUNNINGHAM, Mark Edward, Chief Executive Officer, Greenwood Specialty Hospital, Greenwood, MS, p. A369

CUNNINGHAM, Michelle P., Chief Executive Officer, Highlands Hospital, Connellsville, PA, p. A556

CUNNINGHAM, Richard, President, Caritas Norwood Hospital, Norwood, MA, p. A321

CUNNINGHAM, Tom, Flight Commander Resource Management Officer, Mike O'Callaghan Federal Hospital, Nellis AFB, NV, p. A417

CUPP, Roy, Director Management Information Systems, Fayette Memorial Hospital, Connersville, IN, p. A213

CURBELO, Luis, Finance Director, Hospital Dr. Cayetano Coll Y Toste, Arecibo, PR, p. A743

CURCURUTO, James J., Senior Vice President Finance, St. Joseph's Medical Center, Yonkers, NY, p. A476

CUREE, Robert, Chief Information Management, Dwight David Eisenhower Army Medical Center, Fort Gordon, GA, p. A162

CURLEE, Robbin, Chief Financial Officer, Jacksonville Medical Center, Jacksonville, AL, p. A20

CURLEY, Jacqueline
Supervisory Accountant, U. S. Public Health Service Indian Hospital, Lawton, OK, p. A532
Supervisory Accountant, U. S. Public Health Service Indian Hospital, Lawton, OK, p. A532

CURNUTT, Brian, Director Information Systems, Baylor Regional Medical Center at Grapevine, Grapevine, TX, p. A642

CURRAN, Bob, Driector Health Information Management, SSM St. Mary's Health Center, Saint Louis, MO, p. A392

CURRAN, Maria, Vice President Human Resources, VCU Health System, Richmond, VA, p. A696

CURRANS, Sheila, Chief Operating Officer, Harrison Memorial Hospital, Cynthiana, KY, p. A263

CURRIE, Patricia M., FACHE, Executive Director, Scott and White Memorial Hospital, Temple, TX, p. A669

CURRIER Jr, Elwood E., CHE, Administrator, Memorial Medical Center, Port Lavaca, TX, p. A661

CURRY, M.D., C Richard, Chief of Staff, Cannon Memorial Hospital, Pickens, SC, p. A591

CURRY, Cheryl, Vice President Finance, Ukiah Valley Medical Center, Ukiah, CA, p. A97

CURRY, Greg, Chief Accountant, Pocahontas Memorial Hospital, Buckeye, WV, p. A713

CURRY, Robert H., President and Chief Executive Officer, O'Connor Hospital, San Jose, CA, p. A90

CURRY, Steve, Human Resources Director, Leonard J. Chabert Medical Center, Houma, LA, p. A282

CURTIS, R.N., Edgar J., Executive Vice President and Chief Operating Officer, Memorial Medical Center, Springfield, IL, p. A208

CURTIS, Jeff, Chief Operating Officer, Greenwood Leflore Hospital, Greenwood, MS, p. A369

CURTIS, Keri, Director Human Resources, HEALTHSOUTH Rehabilitation Hospital of Montgomery, Montgomery, AL, p. A22

CURTIS, Linda, Acting Executive Director, Bellevue Hospital Center, New York, NY, p. A458

CURTIS, Lorna, Assistant Administrator Finance, Kaiser Foundation Hospital, San Diego, CA, p. A87

CURTIS, Lynda D., Executive Director, Woodhull Medical and Mental Health Center, New York, NY, p. A466

CURTIS, Mary, Administrator, Jefferson Davis Community Hospital, Prentiss, MS, p. A375

CURTIS, Robert S., President and Chief Executive Officer, Cardinal Health System, Muncie, IN, p. B21

CURTIS, Scott, Administrator, Kossuth Regional Health Center, Algona, IA, p. A228

CURTISS, Allan, President Medical Staff, Porter Medical Center, Middlebury, VT, p. A682

CUSA, Philip L., Senior Vice President and Chief Financial Officer, Thomas Hospital, Fairhope, AL, p. A18

CUSHING, Jeffrey, Executive Vice President Operations, Salem Hospital, Salem, OR, p. A549

CUSSEN, James F., Director, U. S. Public Health Service Comprehensive Indian Health Facility, Claremore, OK, p. A529

CUSTER–MITCHELL, Marilyn J.
Chief Operating Officer, Corning Hospital, Corning, NY, p. A451
President and Chief Executive Officer, Corning Hospital, Corning, NY, p. A451

CUTLER, Terry
Administrator and Chief Operating Officer, East Texas Medical Center Crockett, Crockett, TX, p. A631
Administrator and Chief Operating Officer, East Texas Medical Center Trinity, Trinity, TX, p. A670
Administrator and Chief Operating Officer, East Texas Medical Center Trinity, Trinity, TX, p. A670

CUTRIGHT, Bruce, Vice President Human Resources, Mary Lanning Memorial Hospital, Hastings, NE, p. A407

CUTSPEC, Jay, President and Chief Executive Officer, Asheville Specialty Hospital, Asheville, NC, p. A477

CUTTS, Charles, Director, North Alabama Regional Hospital, Decatur, AL, p. A17

CUTTS, W. Darrell, President and Chief Executive Officer, Piedmont Fayette Hospital, Fayetteville, GA, p. A162

CUZZOLA, Anthony, Vice President Rehabilitation Services, JFK Johnson Rehabilitation Institute, Edison, NJ, p. A428

CYCHOL, Nancy C., President, Cook Children's Medical Center, Fort Worth, TX, p. A639

CYGAN, Ralph, M.D., Chief Executive Officer, University of California, Irvine Medical Center, Orange, CA, p. A79

CYMERMAN, Andrew J., Chief Information Officer, Temple East, Northeastern Hospital, Philadelphia, PA, p. A570

CZAHOR, John, Chief Information Officer, Botsford General Hospital, Farmington Hills, MI, p. A333

CZAPLA, Steve, Vice President Information Technical Technology, Mercy Catholic Medical Center, Darby, PA, p. A557

CZIPO, Kevin F., Executive Director, Stony Lodge Hospital, Ossining, NY, p. A468

D

D' AURORA, R.N., Rita, Risk Manager & Quality Assurance – Health Information Management

Director, HEALTHSOUTH MountainView Regional Rehabilitation Hospital, Morgantown, WV, p. A718

D'ACCURZIO, Albert, Medical Director, St. Elizabeth Medical Center, Utica, NY, p. A475

D'AGNES, Michael R., President and Chief Executive Officer, Raritan Bay Medical Center, Perth Amboy, NJ, p. A434

D'AGOSTINO, James P., Chief Executive Officer, Roosevelt General Hospital, Portales, NM, p. A444

D'ALBERTO, Richard E., FACHE, Chief Executive Officer, Laurens County Healthcare System, Clinton, SC, p. A585

D'AMBROSIO, Tovah, Manager Human Resources, HEALTHSOUTH Hospital of Tenaya, Las Vegas, NV, p. A416

D'AMICO, Ken, Chief Executive Officer, LifeCare Hospital of Dayton, Miamisburg, OH, p. A518

D'AMICO, Paul J., Chief of Staff, Pulaski Community Hospital, Pulaski, VA, p. A694

D'ENBEAU, Richard, President and Chief Executive Officer, New Albany Surgical Hospital, New Albany, OH, p. A519

D'ESMOND, C. Thomas, Administrator, Shriners Hospitals for Children, Portland, Portland, OR, p. A548

D'ETTORRE, Joseph A., Chief Executive Officer, Wyandot Memorial Hospital, Upper Sandusky, OH, p. A523

DAAM, William
Chief Operating Officer, Borgess–Lee Memorial Hospital, Dowagiac, MI, p. A332
Chief Operating Officer, Borgess–Lee Memorial Hospital, Dowagiac, MI, p. A332

DABNEY, Ann, Manager, Human Resources, Spring View Hospital, Lebanon, KY, p. A267

DABROWSKI, Paul C., Senior Vice President and Chief Financial Officer, Trinitas Hospital–Williamson Street Campus, Elizabeth, NJ, p. A428

DACEY, Michael, Vice President Human Resources, Kent County Memorial Hospital, Warwick, RI, p. A582

DADLEZ, Christopher M.
President and Chief Executive Officer, Saint Francis Care, Inc., Hartford, CT, p. B95
President and Chief Executive Officer, Saint Francis Hospital and Medical Center, Hartford, CT, p. A113
President and Chief Executive Officer, The Rehabilitation Hospital of Connecticut, Hartford, CT, p. A113

DADO, Joseph
Associate Director and Chief Information Officer, Excela Frick Hospital, Mount Pleasant, PA, p. A565
Associate Director and Chief Information Officer, Excela Latrobe Area Hospital, Latrobe, PA, p. A563

DAEGER, Brian, Vice President Financial Services, Margaret Mary Community Hospital, Batesville, IN, p. A211

DAGHER, M.D., Michel, Chief Medical Officer, Orange Park Medical Center, Orange Park, FL, p. A140

DAGUE, James O., President and Chief Executive Officer, Goshen General Hospital, Goshen, IN, p. A216

DAHDUL, M.D., Adnan, Medical Director, HEALTHSOUTH Rehabilitation Hospital of Western Massachusetts, Ludlow, MA, p. A320

DAHL, James E., Manager Information Systems, Fort HealthCare, Fort Atkinson, WI, p. A725

DAHLBERG, Edwin E., President and Chief Executive Officer, St. Luke's Regional Medical Center, Boise, ID, p. A178

DAHLEM, Beverly, Associate Administrator, Angleton Danbury Medical Center, Angleton, TX, p. A621

DAHLING, James D., President and Chief Executive Officer, Children's Hospital of The King's Daughters, Norfolk, VA, p. A692

DAHLMAN, Kim, Administrator, Lost Rivers District Hospital, Arco, ID, p. A177

DAIGLE, Anthony A., Administrator, Southwest Medical Center, Liberal, KS, p. A251

DAIGLE, J Barry, Manager Information Systems, University Medical Center, Lafayette, LA, p. A284

DAIKER, David, Chief Information Resource Management, Veterans Affairs Nebraska–Western Iowa Health Care System, Lincoln, NE, p. A409

DAILY, James L., President, Porter Medical Center, Middlebury, VT, p. A682

DAINES, Richard F., M.D., President and Chief Executive Officer, St. Luke's–Roosevelt Hospital Center, New York, NY, p. A465

DAISLEY, Lori, Chief Operating Officer, Skagit Valley Hospital, Mount Vernon, WA, p. A704

DALE, Cherie, Chief Financial Officer, Brownfield Regional Medical Center, Brownfield, TX, p. A627

DALEY, R.N., Kimberlee H., Chief Operating Officer, Upper Connecticut Valley Hospital, Colebrook, NH, p. A420

DALLEY, Mark F., President and Chief Executive Officer, Holy Rosary Medical Center, Ontario, OR, p. A546

DALLY, Kris, Business Office Manager, First Care Medical Services, Fosston, MN, p. A353

DALPIAZ, Joseph M., Director, Royal C. Johnson Veterans Memorial Hospital, Sioux Falls, SD, p. A599

DALTON, Dayle, Vice President Human Resources, Los Robles Hospital and Medical Center, Thousand Oaks, CA, p. A95

DALTON, Eric, Chief Financial Officer, Sutter Tracy Community Hospital, Tracy, CA, p. A96

DALTON, Ray, Superintendent, Kansas Neurological Institute, Topeka, KS, p. A257

DALTON, Wayne, Chief Financial Officer, Lakeview Hospital, Bountiful, UT, p. A676

DALTON, William S., Ph.D., Chief Executive Officer and Director, H. Lee Moffitt Cancer Center and Research Institute, Tampa, FL, p. A148

DALVA, Joel, Chief Financial Officer, St. Mary's Medical Center, West Palm Beach, FL, p. A150

DALY, James, Director, Information Management Service Line, Veterans Affairs Medical Center, Saint Louis, MO, p. A393

DALY, Paul
Director Information Systems, Garfield Medical Center, Monterey Park, CA, p. A76
Director Information Systems, Greater El Monte Community Hospital, El Monte, CA, p. A59
Director Information Systems, Monterey Park Hospital, Monterey Park, CA, p. A76

DALY, Sheila, Chief Executive Officer, Clinton Hospital, Clinton, MA, p. A317

DAMBOISE, Robin, Director Human Resources, Northern Maine Medical Center, Fort Kent, ME, p. A298

DAMM, Julie
Chief Financial Officer, Hancock County Memorial Hospital, Britt, IA, p. A229
Chief Financial Officer, Hancock County Memorial Hospital, Britt, IA, p. A229

DAMON, Joan, Chief Executive Officer, Triumph Hospital Southwest, Sugar Land, TX, p. A668

DAMORE, Joseph F., President and Chief Executive Officer, Mission Hospitals, Asheville, NC, p. A477

DAMRON, G Gregory, Chief Financial Officer, Durham Regional Hospital, Durham, NC, p. A481

DANDLIKER, Nancy N., Executive Director, Willow Springs Residential Treatment Center, Reno, NV, p. A418

DANDRIDGE, Thomas C., President, Regional Medical Center of Orangeburg and Calhoun Counties, Orangeburg, SC, p. A591

DANE, Jeff, Vice President and Chief Financial Officer, University Medical Center, Lubbock, TX, p. A654

DANG, Minh, Vice President Finance, Robert Packer Hospital, Sayre, PA, p. A574

DANGERFIELD, Wesley, Community Chief Executive Officer, Williamson ARH Hospital, South Williamson, KY, p. A275

DANIEL, Christopher W., Chief Financial Officer, Meadowcrest Hospital, Gretna, LA, p. A281

DANIEL, Colene, President and Chief Executive Officer, Maryland General Hospital, Baltimore, MD, p. A303

DANIEL, Samuel J., M.D., President and Chief Executive Officer, North General Hospital, New York, NY, p. A464

DANIEL, Steven G., President and Chief Executive Officer, Western Plains Medical Complex, Dodge City, KS, p. A246

DANIEL, M.D., William, Chief of Staff, Booneville Community Hospital, Booneville, AR, p. A41

DANIEL, William W., Chief Executive Officer, Mission Community Hospital–San Fernando Campus, San Fernando, CA, p. A88

DANIELS, Craig M., Chief Financial Officer, Castleview Hospital, Price, UT, p. A678

DANIELS, Jeff, Vice President Finance and Chief Financial Officer, St. Elizabeth Health Services, Baker City, OR, p. A542

DANIELS, Richard A., President and Chief Executive Officer, McCullough–Hyde Memorial Hospital, Oxford, OH, p. A520

DANIELS, Val, Vice President and Chief Financial Officer, Mercy Medical, Daphne, AL, p. A17

DANIELS, W. Peter, President, Ocean Medical Center, Brick Township, NJ, p. A426

DANN, R.N., Doreen, Executive Vice President and Chief Operating Officer, St. Jude Medical Center, Fullerton, CA, p. A62

DANTIS, Gerry, Assistant Vice President Finance, SUNY Downstate Medical Center University Hospital, New York, NY, p. A466

DANULOFF, Rose Mary, Manager Medical Records, HEALTHSOUTH Hospital of Tenaya, Las Vegas, NV, p. A416

DANUSER, M.D., Carol, Chief Medical Officer, Boone Hospital Center, Columbia, MO, p. A380

DANZI, M.D., Joseph Thomas, Senior Vice President and Chief Medical Officer, Tampa General Hospital, Tampa, FL, p. A148

DAR, M.D., Akram, Medical Director, Regency Hospital of Akron, Barberton, OH, p. A503

DARCY, Charles, Chief Operating Officer, DeTar Healthcare System, Victoria, TX, p. A672

DARCY, Martin, Acting Executive Director, Kingsboro Psychiatric Center, New York, NY, p. A461

DARDEAU, Sean T., Chief Executive Officer, Southampton Memorial Hospital, Franklin, VA, p. A688

DARDEN, David B., Chief Executive Officer, Memorial Medical Center, Las Cruces, NM, p. A443

DARENBOURG, Lyndon, Administrator, Cypress Rehabilitation Hospital, Baton Rouge, LA, p. A277

DARNELL, Linda, Director Management Information Systems, King's Daughters' Hospital and Health Services, Madison, IN, p. A221

DAROFF, M.D., Robert B., Chief of Staff and Senior Vice President Academic Affairs, St. John West Shore Hospital, Cleveland, OH, p. A509

DARR, Joan, Chief Operating Officer, Kosciusko Community Hospital, Warsaw, IN, p. A227

DARVISH, Adam, M.P.H., Chief Executive Officer, Kindred Hospital–Los Angeles, Los Angeles, CA, p. A71

DASCHER Jr, Norman E., Chief Executive Officer, Albany Memorial Hospital, Albany, NY, p. A446

DASCHER, Phillip, Chief of Staff, Florida Hospital Waterman, Tavares, FL, p. A149

DASHNER, George H., FACHE, Administrator, Advance Care Hospital of Oklahoma City, Oklahoma City, OK, p. A534

DASSENKO, Dennis, Vice President and Chief Information Officer, University of Wisconsin Hospital and Clinics, Madison, WI, p. A728

DAUBY, Randall W., Chief Executive Officer, Hamilton Memorial Hospital District, McLeansboro, IL, p. A200

DAUGHERTY, Alan, Administrator, Monroe Surgical Hospital, Monroe, LA, p. A287

DAUGHERTY, Charles R., Chief Executive Officer, Select Specialty Hospital of Lexington, Lexington, KY, p. A268

DAUGHERTY, Thomas E., Administrator, Mecosta County Medical Center, Big Rapids, MI, p. A328

DAUSTER, William, Vice President Public Affairs, LibertyHealth–Greenville Hospital, Jersey City, NJ, p. A430

DAVANT, III, M.D, Charles, Chief Medical Officer, Blowing Rock Hospital, Blowing Rock, NC, p. A478

DAVANZO, John P., President and Chief Executive Officer, Mercy Hospital, Buffalo, NY, p. A449

DAVE, Bhasker J., M.D., Superintendent, Mental Health Institute, Independence, IA, p. A235

DAVENPORT, Michael, Vice President Medical Management, Advocate Trinity Hospital, Chicago, IL, p. A186

DAVID, M.D., Gerard R., Clinical Director, U. S. Public Health Service Owyhee Community Health Facility, Owyhee, NV, p. A418

DAVID, Myers M., Chief Information Officer, Iredell Memorial Hospital, Statesville, NC, p. A492

DAVID, Rob
Director Finance Services, UHHS Brown Memorial Hospital, Conneaut, OH, p. A511
Director Finance Services, UHHS–Memorial Hospital of Geneva, Geneva, OH, p. A514

DAVID, M.D., Thomas, Senior Vice President and Chief Medical Officer, Saint Francis Hospital, Tulsa, OK, p. A540

DAVIDGE, Robert C., Chief Executive Officer, Our Lady of the Lake Regional Medical Center, Baton Rouge, LA, p. A277

DAVIDOW, Bruce B., Senior Vice President and Chief Operating Officer, Phelps Memorial Hospital Center, Sleepy Hollow, NY, p. A472

DAVIDSON, Craig Val, CHE,
Administrator, Beaver Valley Hospital, Beaver, UT, p. A676
Administrator, Milford Valley Memorial Hospital, Milford, UT, p. A677

DAVIDSON, Daniel R., Deputy Commander for Clinical Services, Moncrief Army Community Hospital, Fort Jackson, SC, p. A588

DAVIDSON, Eugene, Chief of Staff, Saint Joseph's Hospital of Atlanta, Atlanta, GA, p. A154

DAVIDSON, Gary, Vice President and Chief Information Officer, Hospital of Saint Raphael, New Haven, CT, p. A115

DAVIDSON, Gregg A., Chief Executive Officer, Skagit Valley Hospital, Mount Vernon, WA, p. A704

DAVIDSON, James, Chief Financial Officer, Cheboygan Memorial Hospital, Cheboygan, MI, p. A329

DAVIDSON, Janet, Director of Human Resources, Arkansas Valley Regional Medical Center, La Junta, CO, p. A107

DAVIDSON, John, Vice President Human Resources, Sharon Regional Health System, Sharon, PA, p. A576

DAVIDSON, Nancy, Senior Vice President and Chief Financial Officer, Jackson County Memorial Hospital, Altus, OK, p. A527

DAVIGNON, M.D., Russell
Vice President, Quality and Medical Affairs, Central Vermont Medical Center, Barre, VT, p. A682
Vice President, Quality and Medical Affairs, Central Vermont Medical Center, Barre, VT, p. A682

DAVIN, Joni, Director Information–Business Management Service Line, Veterans Affairs Eastern Kansas Health Care System, Topeka, KS, p. A258

DAVIS, Andrew, Chief Financial Officer, Crawford Memorial Hospital, Van Buren, AR, p. A51

DAVIS, Barry L., Vice President Operations, Arkansas Methodist Medical Center, Paragould, AR, p. A49

DAVIS, Brent, Chief Financial Officer, Central Valley Medical Center, Nephi, UT, p. A677

DAVIS, Brian
Chief Executive Officer, Select Specialty Hospital, Augusta, GA, p. A155
Chief Executive Officer, Select Specialty Hospital of Augusta, Augusta, GA, p. A155

DAVIS, Carol, Vice President Financial Services, Union Regional Medical Center, Monroe, NC, p. A487

DAVIS, Charles A., Chief Executive Officer, Mountain West Medical Center, Tooele, UT, p. A680

DAVIS, Charles S., Ph.D., Director, Central State Hospital, Petersburg, VA, p. A693

DAVIS, Curtis, Manager Finance, Mary Lane Hospital, Ware, MA, p. A324

DAVIS, Cynthia, Chief Information Officer, DeKalb Medical Center, Decatur, GA, p. A160

DAVIS, Daniel E., Chief Financial Officer, Shannon Medical Center, San Angelo, TX, p. A663

DAVIS, David, Information Technology Director, Sibley Medical Center, Arlington, MN, p. A349

DAVIS, Deb, Director Support Services, Palo Alto County Health System, Emmetsburg, IA, p. A233

DAVIS, Deborah W., President, Pitt County Memorial Hospital, Greenville, NC, p. A484

DAVIS, Diane, Business Office Manager, HEALTHSOUTH Rehabilitation Hospital of Montgomery, Montgomery, AL, p. A22

DAVIS, Eddy D.
Chf Financial Officer and Administrative Service Director, Humboldt General Hospital, Winnemucca, NV, p. A419
Chf Financial Officer and Administrative Service Director, Humboldt General Hospital, Winnemucca, NV, p. A419

DAVIS, Gary
Vice President Information Systems, Baptist Medical Center, San Antonio, TX, p. A663
Director Information Systems, Great River Medical Center, West Burlington, IA, p. A243

DAVIS, Greg, Chief Executive Officer, Continental Rehabilitation Hospital, San Diego, CA, p. A87

DAVIS, Hervey E., Chief Executive Officer, Franklin Hospital, Benton, IL, p. A184

DAVIS, Jack L., Vice President Information Systems, St. John's Regional Medical Center, Joplin, MO, p. A384

DAVIS, James R., Executive Vice President and Chief Operating Officer, St. Elizabeth Health Center, Youngstown, OH, p. A526

DAVIS, Jeff
Chief Financial Officer, Harrison County Hospital, Corydon, IN, p. A213
Senior Vice President Human Resources, Massachusetts General Hospital, Boston, MA, p. A314
Chief Financial Officer, North Texas Medical Center, Gainesville, TX, p. A641

DAVIS, Jeryl, Vice President Marketing and Public Affairs, Valdese General Hospital, Valdese, NC, p. A493

DAVIS, Joan, Human Resources Director, Gallup Indian Medical Center, Gallup, NM, p. A442

DAVIS, Jon R., FACHE, Chief Executive Officer, Whitman Hospital and Medical Center, Colfax, WA, p. A701

DAVIS, FACHE, Jon R., Chief Executive Officer, Whitman Hospital and Medical Center, Colfax, WA, p. A701

DAVIS, Jonathan S., Chief Executive Officer and Administrator, St. Anthony's Healthcare Center, Morrilton, AR, p. A48

DAVIS, Justin, Chief Executive Officer, Bartow Regional Medical Center, Bartow, FL, p. A123

DAVIS, Kathleen, Vice President and Chief Information Officer, BroMenn Healthcare System, Normal, IL, p. A202

DAVIS, M.D., Keith, Chief of Staff, Gooding County Memorial Hospital, Gooding, ID, p. A179

DAVIS, Kenneth, Assistant Vice President Information Systems, Kennedy Krieger Institute, Baltimore, MD, p. A303

DAVIS, Lary, President and Chief Executive Officer, Sonora Regional Medical Center, Sonora, CA, p. A94

DAVIS, Leslie C., President, Magee–Womens Hospital of UPMC, Pittsburgh, PA, p. A571

DAVIS, Lora, Administrator, Perry Hospital, Perry, GA, p. A167

DAVIS, Lyle E., Administrator, Cozad Community Hospital, Cozad, NE, p. A406

DAVIS, Lynn, Chief Financial Officer, U. S. Public Health Service Indian Hospital, Belcourt, ND, p. A496

DAVIS, Mark
Chief Executive Officer, Select Specialty Hospital – Topeka, Topeka, KS, p. A258
Director Information Systems, Lake Taylor Transitional Care Hospital, Norfolk, VA, p. A692

DAVIS, Mary, Vice President, Avera St. Luke's, Aberdeen, SD, p. A594

DAVIS, Matt, Chief Operating Officer, Medical Center of Lewisville, Lewisville, TX, p. A653

DAVIS, Michael J., Ph.D., Superintendent, Woodward Resource Center, Woodward, IA, p. A243

DAVIS, Milena, Chief Financial Officer, Perry Memorial Hospital, Perry, OK, p. A537

DAVIS, P Susan, Director Communications and Public Affairs, Johns Hopkins Bayview Medical Center, Baltimore, MD, p. A303

DAVIS, Pam K., Director of Human Resources, Compliance Officer, Woods Memorial Hospital District, Etowah, TN, p. A606

DAVIS, Pamela Meyer, President and Chief Executive Officer, Edward Hospital, Naperville, IL, p. A202

DAVIS, Paul, Administrator, Gove County Medical Center, Quinter, KS, p. A256

DAVIS, M.D., Peggy Miller, Chief Medical Officer, University Hospitals and Clinics, University of Mississippi Medical Center, Jackson, MS, p. A371

DAVIS, Peter B., President and Chief Executive Officer, St. Joseph Hospital, Nashua, NH, p. A423

DAVIS Jr, Ray H., Chief Executive Officer, Calais Regional Hospital, Calais, ME, p. A297

DAVIS, Richard, Chief Financial Officer, George Washington University Hospital, Washington, DC, p. A121

DAVIS, M.D., Richard, Vice President Medical Affairs, Christus Spohn Hospital Corpus Christi Memorial, Corpus Christi, TX, p. A630

DAVIS, M.D., Richard F., Chief of Staff, Veterans Affairs Medical Center, Portland, OR, p. A548

DAVIS, Robert L., President and Chief Executive Officer, North Oakland Medical Centers, Pontiac, MI, p. A342

DAVIS, Rod A., President and Chief Executive Officer, St. Rose Dominican Hospitals – Siena Campus, Henderson, NV, p. A416

DAVIS, M.D., Ron, Chief Medical Officer, Providence Alaska Medical Center, Anchorage, AK, p. A26

DAVIS, Ronald D., Chief Executive Officer, Titus Regional Medical Center, Mount Pleasant, TX, p. A657

DAVIS, Rosemari, Chief Executive Officer, Willamette Valley Medical Center, McMinnville, OR, p. A546

DAVIS, Ryland P., Chief Executive Officer, Sacred Heart Medical Center, Spokane, WA, p. A709

DAVIS, Sammy E., Administrator, Corpus Christi Specialty Hospital, Corpus Christi, TX, p. A630

DAVIS, Shirley, Director Information Services, White River Medical Center, Batesville, AR, p. A40

DAVIS, Steve, Chief Financial Officer, St. Vincent Frankfort Hospital, Frankfort, IN, p. A216

DAVIS, D.O., Steven, Chief Medical Staff, San Dimas Community Hospital, San Dimas, CA, p. A88

DAVIS, Susan L., Ed.D., President and Chief Executive Officer, St. Vincent's Medical Center, Bridgeport, CT, p. A112

DAVIS, Susan R., Administrator, HEALTHSOUTH Specialty Hospital of New Orleans, New Orleans, LA, p. A288

DAVIS, Teresa L., Administrator, Select Specialty Hospital–Houston Heights, Houston, TX, p. A647

DAVIS, Terry, Chief Information Officer, Great Plains Regional Medical Center, Elk City, OK, p. A530

DAVIS, Texas, Controller, Union County General Hospital, Clayton, NM, p. A442

DAVIS, Thomas L., Chief Executive Officer, Central Louisiana State Hospital, Pineville, LA, p. A291

DAVIS, Verlene, Human Resources Director, Blue Mountain Hospital, John Day, OR, p. A545

DAVIS, Wayne, Chief, Human Resources, Clement J. Zablocki Veterans Affairs Medical Center, Milwaukee, WI, p. A730

DAVIS, Wilmont, Vice President Human Resources, Heywood Hospital, Gardner, MA, p. A318

DAVISON, M.D., William, President Medical Staff, Resurrection Medical Center, Chicago, IL, p. A189

DAVY, Larry, Administrator and Chief Executive Officer, Wallowa Memorial Hospital, Enterprise, OR, p. A543

DAVY, M.D., Timothy, Vice President Medical Affairs, Faith Regional Health Services, Norfolk, NE, p. A410

DAWDY, David, Director Information Systems, Memorial Hospital, Belleville, IL, p. A184

DAWES, Christopher G., President and Chief Executive Officer, Lucile Salter Packard Children's Hospital at Stanford, Palo Alto, CA, p. A80

DAWES, Dennis W., FACHE, President, Hendricks Regional Health, Danville, IN, p. A213

DAWES, John M., Chief Executive Officer, Bothwell Regional Health Center, Sedalia, MO, p. A393

DAWKINS, Stephen, Chief Operating Officer, Fairfield Memorial Hospital, Fairfield, IL, p. A194

DAWSON, Eric, Chief Resource Management Division, Darnall Army Community Hospital, Fort Hood, TX, p. A638

DAWSON, George W., President and Chief Executive Officer, Centra Health, Lynchburg, VA, p. A691

DAWSON, M.D., John, Chief of Staff, North Hawaii Community Hospital, Kamuela, HI, p. A175

DAWSON, Joseph M., Administrator, Blount Memorial Hospital, Maryville, TN, p. A612

DAWSON, Lynn, Chief Executive Officer, Select Specialty Hospital, Denver, CO, p. A104

DAY, Bryan, Administrator, HEALTHSOUTH Riverside Hospital of Alexandria, Alexandria, LA, p. A276

DAY, Frank, Vice President Patient Services, Wood County Hospital, Bowling Green, OH, p. A504

DAY, Georgia, Finance Director, Virginia Regional Medical Center, Virginia, MN, p. A364

DAY, Jackie
Chief Financial Officer, Bob Wilson Memorial Grant County Hospital, Ulysses, KS, p. A258
Chief Financial Officer, Bob Wilson Memorial Grant County Hospital, Ulysses, KS, p. A258

DAY, John B., Administrator, United Medical Rehabilitation Hospital, New Orleans, LA, p. A290

DAY, Kim, Chief Financial Officer, St. John's Hospital, Springfield, MO, p. A394

DAY, Lenore
Interim President, Buffalo Hospital, Buffalo, MN, p. A351
Director Operations and Clinical Support, Buffalo Hospital, Buffalo, MN, p. A351

DAY, Mark, Chief Financial Officer, Twin Cities Hospital, Niceville, FL, p. A139

DAY, Scott, Vice President Human Resources, Exempla Lutheran Medical Center, Wheat Ridge, CO, p. A110

DAY, CPA, Sherry C., Chief Financial Officer, Skaggs Community Health Center, Branson, MO, p. A379

DAY, Stephen, Director Management Information Systems, Southwest Memorial Hospital, Cortez, CO, p. A102

DAY, William J., Vice President Finance, Ohio Valley General Hospital, McKees Rocks, PA, p. A564

DAY, Zed, Chief Information Officer, University of Kentucky Hospital, Lexington, KY, p. A268

DAYHOFF, John D., Interim Chief Information Officer, Washington Hospital Center, Washington, DC, p. A122

DE BLASI, Raymond P.
Chief Executive Officer, Medical Center of Mesquite, Mesquite, TX, p. A656
Chief Executive Officer, Mesquite Community Hospital, Mesquite, TX, p. A656

DE FUR, Kyle, FACHE, President, Saint John's Health System, Anderson, IN, p. A211

DE GASTA, Gary M., Director, Veterans Affairs Medical Center, White River Junction, VT, p. A684

DE HART, Kristen, Administrator, Mid–America Rehabilitation Hospital, Shawnee Mission, KS, p. A257

DE JESUS, M.D., Alexander, Medical Director, HEALTHSOUTH Rehabilitation Hospital of Sarasota, Sarasota, FL, p. A146

DE JESUS, Edwin, Comptroller, Hospital Santa Rosa, Guayama, PR, p. A745

DE LA CRUZ, M.D., Jose, Chief of Staff, Wayne Memorial Hospital, Jesup, GA, p. A164

DE LA CRUZ, Manny, Controller, Maniilaq Health Center, Kotzebue, AK, p. A28

DE LA GARZA, Dan, Chief Executive Officer, Houston Community Hospital, Houston, TX, p. A645

DE LA PENA, Will, Vice President and Chief Financial Officer, Shady Grove Adventist Hospital, Rockville, MD, p. A310

DE LEON, M.D., Ernest, Chief of Medicine, Lake City Medical Center, Lake City, FL, p. A134

DE LEON, Noel, Chief Information Officer, Knapp Medical Center, Weslaco, TX, p. A673

DE LONGO, M.D., Concepcion Q., Medical Director, University Pediatric Hospital, San Juan, PR, p. A748

DE LOURDES ALEGRIA, Maria, Comptroller, Cardiovascular Center of Puerto Rico and the Caribbean, San Juan, PR, p. A746

DE MARTINI, Thomas J., Chief Executive Officer, Springbrook Behavioral Health System, Travelers Rest, SC, p. A592

DE PASQUALE, Edward, Chief Financial Officer, Memorial Medical Center, Johnstown, PA, p. A561

DE PIANO, Linda, Ph.D., Chief Executive Officer and Executive Director, Oakwood Center of the Palm Beaches, Inc., West Palm Beach, FL, p. A150

DE ROBERTIS, M.D., Nicholas, Medical Director, St. Joseph's Medical Center, Yonkers, NY, p. A476

DE VOSS, Gerald, Acting Administrator, Duane L. Waters Hospital, Jackson, MI, p. A337

DEACON, R.N., Kathleen M., Chief Operating Officer, McKenzie–Willamette Medical Center, Springfield, OR, p. A549

DEAKYNE, John, Chief Financial Officer, Mark Twain St. Joseph's Hospital, San Andreas, CA, p. A86

DEAL, D.O., Eric A., Chief of Staff, Northlake Medical Center, Tucker, GA, p. A171

DEAL, Lisa, Budget Analyst, U. S. Public Health Service Indian Hospital, Eagle Butte, SD, p. A595

DEAL, Mark, Chief Executive Officer, Delta Memorial Hospital, Dumas, AR, p. A42

DEAL, Wayne I., Chief Financial Officer, Veterans Affairs Gulf Coast Veterans Health Care System, Biloxi, MS, p. A367

DEAL, William, Chief of Staff, Wythe County Community Hospital, Wytheville, VA, p. A699

DEAM, M.D., David, Chief of Staff, Oak Hill Hospital, Brooksville, FL, p. A125

DEAN, Doug, Chief Human Resources Officer, The Children's Hospital of Alabama, Birmingham, AL, p. A15

DEAN Jr, Douglas F., President and Chief Executive Officer, Elliot Hospital, Manchester, NH, p. A422

DEAN, Harrison M., Senior Vice President and Administrator, Baptist Health Medical Center – North Little Rock, North Little Rock, AR, p. A48

DEAN, Lloyd H., President and Chief Executive Officer, Catholic Healthcare West, San Francisco, CA, p. B26

DEAN, Morre, President and Chief Executive Officer, Walla Walla General Hospital, Walla Walla, WA, p. A711

DEAN, Rhonda, Chief Executive Officer, El Dorado Hospital, Tucson, AZ, p. A38

DEAN, Thomas, Chief of Staff, Avera Weskota Memorial Medical Center, Wessington Springs, SD, p. A600

DEANGELIS, Gene, Chief Fiscal Service, Veterans Affairs Medical Center, Cleveland, OH, p. A509

DEANGELIS, Patricia B., President and Chief Executive Officer, Nazareth Hospital, Philadelphia, PA, p. A569

DEANS, Jr, Kenneth R., Vice President Information Services and Chief Information Officer, Mary Imogene Bassett Hospital, Cooperstown, NY, p. A450

DEARING, Bryan K.
Chief Executive Officer, Dominion Hospital, Falls Church, VA, p. A687
Chief Executive Officer, Northern Virginia Community Hospital, Arlington, VA, p. A685

DEARTH, Jim, M.D., Chief Executive Officer, The Children's Hospital of Alabama, Birmingham, AL, p. A15

DEARTH, Ron
Interim Superintendent, Morton General Hospital, Morton, WA, p. A704
Chief Financial Officer, Morton General Hospital, Morton, WA, p. A704

DEASY, Scott, M.D., Acting Chief Executive Officer, Tuba City Indian Medical Center, Tuba City, AZ, p. A37

DEATON, David, Administrator and Chief Executive Officer, Little River Memorial Hospital, Ashdown, AR, p. A40

DEATON, Eric, Chief Executive Officer, Coastal Carolina Medical Center, Hardeeville, SC, p. A589

DEAUSTIN, Ellen, Administrator, HEALTHSOUTH Rehabilitation Hospital of Colorado Springs, Colorado Springs, CO, p. A102

DEBARTOLO, Anthony, Director Human Resources, Underwood–Memorial Hospital, Woodbury, NJ, p. A439

DEBBS, Ted, Administrator, Rusk State Hospital, Rusk, TX, p. A663

DEBOER, K C., Vice President Hospital Division, Avera St. Luke's, Aberdeen, SD, p. A594

DEBORD, Thomas, Chief Operating Officer, Barberton Citizens Hospital, Barberton, OH, p. A503

DEBRUCE, Lucinda, Chief Executive Officer, Pinnacle Pointe Hospital, Little Rock, AR, p. A46

DECASTRO, Helio, Director Information Systems, Ninnescah Valley Health System, Kingman, KS, p. A250

DECERBO, Ralph, Chief Financial Officer, Delray Medical Center, Delray Beach, FL, p. A127

DECKARD, Rick, Chief, Fiscal Service, Veterans Affairs Medical Center, Chillicothe, OH, p. A506

DECKARD, Steven, Vice President Human Resources, Bloomington Hospital, Bloomington, IN, p. A212

DECKER, Dale A., Administrator, Wickenburg Regional Medical Center, Wickenburg, AZ, p. A39

DECKER, James Lee, Senior Vice President and Administrator, Baptist Hospital of Cocke County, Newport, TN, p. A616

DECKER, Michael, President and Chief Executive Officer, Divine Savior Healthcare, Portage, WI, p. A734

DECREMER, Dean, Chief Information Officer, Dickinson County Healthcare System, Iron Mountain, MI, p. A337

DEDMAN, M.D., Thomas, Medical Director, Baptist Hospital East, Louisville, KY, p. A268

DEE, Thomas A., President and Chief Executive Officer, Benedictine Hospital, Kingston, NY, p. A455

DEERFIELD, Della, Vice President Finance, Berea Hospital, Berea, KY, p. A261

DEERING, M.D., Ronald, Medical Director, St. John's Hospital, Springfield, IL, p. A208

DEERY, Libba, Human Resource Manager, Abbeville County Memorial Hospital, Abbeville, SC, p. A583

DEES, Kim, Chief Executive Officer, Carroll County Hospital, Carrollton, KY, p. A262

DEESE, Kim, Vice President Information Systems, McKenna Memorial Hospital, New Braunfels, TX, p. A658

DEETS, Daniel J., Chief Financial Officer, Hunterdon Medical Center, Flemington, NJ, p. A428

DEFAIL, Anthony J., FACHE, President and Chief Executive Officer, Meadville Medical Center, Meadville, PA, p. A564

DEFAUW, Thomas D., President and Chief Executive Officer, Gratiot Medical Center, Alma, MI, p. A327

DEFURIO, Anthony C., Associate Director and Chief Financial Officer, University of Iowa Hospitals and Clinics, Iowa City, IA, p. A236

DEGA, Vanessa, Human Resources Manager, Sutter Tracy Community Hospital, Tracy, CA, p. A96

DEGEN, Tom, Vice President Administrative Services, South Haven Community Hospital, South Haven, MI, p. A345

DEGENER, Darlene
Chief Operating Officer, Rehabilitation Hospital of Fort Wayne, Fort Wayne, IN, p. A215
Chief Operating Officer, Rehabilitation Hospital of Fort Wayne, Fort Wayne, IN, p. A215

DEGINA Jr, Anthony M., Chief Executive Officer, Plantation General Hospital, Plantation, FL, p. A143

DEGRAAF, Douglas P., Chief Executive Officer, Gadsden Regional Medical Center, Gadsden, AL, p. A19

DEGRANDIS, Fred M., Chief Executive Officer, Fairview Hospital, Cleveland, OH, p. A508

DEGROOT, Randy, Chief Executive Officer, Community Health Center of Branch County, Coldwater, MI, p. A330

DEGROOT, Sandra, Commanding Officer, Naval Hospital, Lemoore, CA, p. A67

DEHEY, Arthur, Senior Vice President and Chief Financial Officer, Clifton Springs Hospital and Clinic, Clifton Springs, NY, p. A450

DEHMER, Joyce, Director Finance, Buffalo Hospital, Buffalo, MN, p. A351

DEIKER, Tom, Ph.D., Superintendent, Mental Health Institute, Cherokee, IA, p. A230

DEIS, Terry, Vice President General Services and Chief Information Officer, Parma Community General Hospital, Parma, OH, p. A520

DEJACO, Lynn S., Senior Vice President and Chief Financial Officer, FirstHealth Moore Regional Hospital, Pinehurst, NC, p. A489

DEJESUS, David, Vice President Human Resources, Southcoast Hospitals Group, Fall River, MA, p. A317

DEJONG, Terry, Chief Executive Officer, Community Memorial Hospital, Redfield, SD, p. A598

DEKEYZER, Ron, Chief Information Officer and Vice President Planning, Christus St. Frances Cabrini Hospital, Alexandria, LA, p. A276

DEKOFF, John, Interim Vice President Fiscal Services, North Adams Regional Hospital, North Adams, MA, p. A321

DEKONING, Bernard, Commander, Darnall Army Community Hospital, Fort Hood, TX, p. A638

DEVANEY, Chris, Finance Director, White Community Hospital, Aurora, MN, p. A349

DEVANSKY, Gary W., Director, Veterans Affairs Medical Center, Coatesville, PA, p. A556

DEVAULT, Jennifer, Director Associate Services, Thompson Health, Canandaigua, NY, p. A449

DEVEREAUX, M.D., Michael, Medical Director and Vice President Clinical Integration, UHHS Richmond Heights Hospital, Richmond Heights, OH, p. A521

DEVEY, Robert, Senior Vice President and Chief Financial Officer, Mercy Medical Center, Springfield, MA, p. A323

DEVILLIER, Becky, Administrator, USA Children's and Women's Hospital, Mobile, AL, p. A21

DEVIN, Joe, Chief Financial Officer, Washakie Medical Center, Worland, WY, p. A742

DEVINE, Joseph W., Vice President, Hospital Services, Kennedy Memorial Hospitals–University Medical Center, Cherry Hill, NJ, p. A427

DEVINE, Kathleen K., Chief Executive Officer, Saint Anthony Hospital, Chicago, IL, p. A189

DEVITO, Joseph M., Chief Financial Officer, Bloomsburg Hospital, Bloomsburg, PA, p. A553

DEVLIN, Karl
    Chief, Resource Management Division, Bayne–Jones Army Community Hospital, Fort Polk, LA, p. A281
    Chief, Resource Management Division, Bayne–Jones Army Community Hospital, Fort Polk, LA, p. A281

DEVOCELLE, Frank H., President and Chief Executive Officer, Olathe Medical Center, Olathe, KS, p. A254

DEVOE, Andrew
    Senior Vice President and Chief Financial Officer, Hospital of the University of Pennsylvania, Philadelphia, PA, p. A568
    Chief Financial Officer, Presbyterian Medical Center of the University of Pennsylvania Health System, Philadelphia, PA, p. A569

DEVONEY, William, Senior Vice President and Chief Financial Officer, Edward Hospital, Naperville, IL, p. A202

DEVORE, Michael
    Chief Information Officer, Louis A. Weiss Memorial Hospital, Chicago, IL, p. A188
    Chief Information Officer, MacNeal Hospital, Berwyn, IL, p. A184

DEVORE, Pam, Financial Manager, Hillcrest Hospital, Simpsonville, SC, p. A591

DEWALSCHE, R.N., Diane, Chief Operating Officer, Community Hospital of Long Beach, Long Beach, CA, p. A68

DEWBERRY, Robbie, Administrator, Stephens Memorial Hospital, Breckenridge, TX, p. A626

DEWERFF, Mike, Chief Financial Officer, Buena Vista Regional Medical Center, Storm Lake, IA, p. A242

DEWITT, Jocelyn, Chief Information Officer, University of Michigan Hospitals and Health Centers, Ann Arbor, MI, p. A327

DEWS, M.D., Peter, Medical Director, Alliance HealthCare System, Holly Springs, MS, p. A370

DEXTER, M.D., Donald, President, University Hospital, San Juan, PR, p. A748

DEXTER, R.N., Marianne, Chief Operating Officer, Spalding Rehabilitation Hospital, Aurora, CO, p. A101

DEXTER, Stephen P., President and Chief Executive Officer, Thomas Memorial Hospital, South Charleston, WV, p. A720

DEXTER, Sue, Administrative Director Human Resources, McDonough District Hospital, Macomb, IL, p. A200

DEXTROM, Nancy, Executive Director, Rogers City Rehabilitation Hospital, Rogers City, MI, p. A343

DHINGRA, Ashok, Executive Medical Director, HEALTHSOUTH Deaconess Rehabilitation Hospital, Evansville, IN, p. A214

DHOLAKIA, M.D., Gautami, Chief of Staff, Middlesboro Appalachian Regional Hospital, Middlesboro, KY, p. A271

DHULIPALA, M.D., Vasudeva, Medical Director, HEALTHSOUTH Rehabilitation Hospital of Alexandria, Alexandria, LA, p. A276

DI BACCO, David J., Chief Operating Officer, Inter–Community Memorial Hospital, Newfane, NY, p. A467

DI BERNARDO, Deborah, Chief Information Officer, St. Joseph's Medical Center, Yonkers, NY, p. A476

DI LORENZO, Anthony, Vice President Operations, Rush North Shore Medical Center, Skokie, IL, p. A208

DI MARIA, M.D., Anthony, Chief Medical Officer, Jamaica Hospital Medical Center, New York, NY, p. A460

DI SANZO, Frank, Vice President and Chief Information Officer, Staten Island University Hospital, New York, NY, p. A465

DI TARANTO, Michael, Associate Executive Director, North Shore University Hospital, Manhasset, NY, p. A456

DIAL, Karen, Chief Systems Officer, Scott Medical Center, Scott AFB, IL, p. A207

DIAL, Marcia R., Chief Executive Officer, Scotland County Memorial Hospital, Memphis, MO, p. A387

DIALTO, Margaret, Vice President Human Resources, Staten Island University Hospital, New York, NY, p. A465

DIAMANDI, M.D., Mike, Chief of Staff, Bridges Medical Services, Ada, MN, p. A349

DIAMOND, Robert, Vice President Information Technology and Chief Information Officer, Orange Regional Medical Center, Middletown, NY, p. A457

DIAMOND, Timothy, Chief Information Officer, La Rabida Children's Hospital, Chicago, IL, p. A187

DIAMOND, Vickie, Senior Vice President and Chief Operating Officer, Wyoming Medical Center, Casper, WY, p. A739

DIANGELO, John A., Senior Vice President Finance and Chief Financial Officer, South Jersey Healthcare, Bridgeton, NJ, p. A426

DIANO, Robert, Director Human Resources, University Hospital and Medical Center, Tamarac, FL, p. A147

DIAS, Paula, Vice President and Chief Operating Officer, Wilcox Memorial Hospital, Lihue, HI, p. A175

DIAS, Walter, Vice President and Chief Operating Officer, Butler Hospital, Providence, RI, p. A581

DIASIO, Anthony, Vice President Finance and Chief Financial Officer, Fox Chase Cancer Center–American Oncologic Hospital, Philadelphia, PA, p. A567

DIAZ, M.D., Al, Medical Director, Redmond Regional Medical Center, Rome, GA, p. A168

DIAZ, M.D., Ph, Fernando, Senior Vice President and Chief Medical Officer, Detroit Receiving Hospital and University Health Center, Detroit, MI, p. A331

DIAZ, Georgina, Chief Operating Officer, Kendall Regional Medical Center, Miami, FL, p. A137

DIAZ, Jorge Rodriguez, Human Resources Director, Hospital De La Concepcion, San German, PR, p. A746

DIAZ, Lisette, Administrator, Industrial Hospital, San Juan, PR, p. A747

DIAZ, Paul J., President and Chief Operating Officer, Kindred Healthcare, Louisville, KY, p. B66

DIBNER, David A., FACHE, Chief Executive Officer, Hospital for Joint Diseases Orthopaedic Institute, New York, NY, p. A460

DICAPO, Rick, Chief Executive Officer, Vista Medical Center Hospital, Pasadena, TX, p. A660

DICE, Virgil, Chief Financial Officer, The Institute for Rehabilitation and Research, Houston, TX, p. A648

DICESARE, Gayle, President and Chief Officer, RiverValley Behavioral Health Hospital, Owensboro, KY, p. A272

DICESARE, Jan, Chief Financial Officer, HEALTHSOUTH Medical Center, Birmingham, AL, p. A15

DICICCO, Christopher, Chief Executive Officer, St. Mary Medical Center, Long Beach, CA, p. A68

DICK, C Lynn, Chief Financial Officer, Northwest Medical Center, Margate, FL, p. A136

DICK, David, Chief Executive Officer, Hans P. Peterson Memorial Hospital, Philip, SD, p. A597

DICKENS, Charles A., Regional Administrator and Chief Executive Officer, Cumberland Hall Psychiatric Hospital, Chattanooga, TN, p. A603

DICKERSON, M.D., Gene, Vice President of Medical Affairs, Tuomey Healthcare System, Sumter, SC, p. A592

DICKERSON, Taylor
    Chief Information Officer, Lake City Medical Center, Lake City, FL, p. A134
    Director Information Services, Ocala Regional Medical Center, Ocala, FL, p. A140

DICKERSON, Toby, Acting Chief Information Resource Management, Amarillo Veterans Affairs Health Care System, Amarillo, TX, p. A620

DICKEY, D.O., Howard, Chief of Staff, Comanche Community Hospital, Comanche, TX, p. A629

DICKEY, Janelle
    Information Technology Director, Sutter Medical Center, Sacramento, Sacramento, CA, p. A85
    Director Information Systems, Sutter Roseville Medical Center, Roseville, CA, p. A84

DICKEY, Sarah, Personnel Manager, Marshall Browning Hospital, Du Quoin, IL, p. A192

DICKEY MELTON, Linda, Vice President Human Resources, North Arkansas Regional Medical Center, Harrison, AR, p. A44

DICKINSON, Galen, Chief Financial Officer, Cary Medical Center, Caribou, ME, p. A298

DICKSON, James C., Administrator, Memorial Medical Center – Livingston, Livingston, TX, p. A653

DICKSON, James J., Administrator and Chief Executive Officer, Copper Queen Community Hospital, Bisbee, AZ, p. A30

DICKSON, Thomas C., Chief Executive Officer, Walter O. Boswell Memorial Hospital, Sun City, AZ, p. A37

DIEDERICH, J Joseph
    Executive Vice President and Chief Operating Officer, Oakwood Heritage Hospital, Taylor, MI, p. A346
    Executive Vice President and Chief Operating Officer, Oakwood Hospital and Medical Center–Dearborn, Dearborn, MI, p. A330
    Executive Vice President and Chief Operating Officer, Oakwood Southshore Medical Center, Trenton, MI, p. A347

DIEDERICH, Thomas, Vice President Human Resources, Phoenix Children's Hospital, Phoenix, AZ, p. A34

DIEHL, Deborah, Director, Human Resources, Presbyterian Hospital of Plano, Plano, TX, p. A661

DIEHL, John, Vice President, Methodist Hospitals, Gary, IN, p. A216

DIER, Joy, MS, Administrtor and Chief Executive Officer, Select Specialty Hospital – Dallas, Dallas, TX, p. A634

DIERCKS, Sue, Chief Financial Officer, Lake City Medical Center–Mayo, Lake City, MN, p. A355

DIERKER, Anne, Vice President Human Resources, Mary Free Bed Rehabilitation Hospital, Grand Rapids, MI, p. A334

DIETER, Brian, Vice President and Chief Financial Officer, Mary Greeley Medical Center, Ames, IA, p. A228

DIETERICH, Kevin, Manager Information Services, Inland Hospital, Waterville, ME, p. A301

DIETZ, Francis R., President, Memorial Hospital of Rhode Island, Pawtucket, RI, p. A581

DIETZ, Gary, Director Information Systems, Walla Walla General Hospital, Walla Walla, WA, p. A711

DIETZ, Sharon, Administrator, Schleicher County Medical Center, Eldorado, TX, p. A638

DIETZE, Fred, Director Human Resources and Community Relations, Crawford County Memorial Hospital, Denison, IA, p. A232

DIFABBIO, Marc, Director Information System, McLean Hospital, Belmont, MA, p. A312

DIFRANCO, Vince, Chief Executive Officer, Mena Medical Center, Mena, AR, p. A47

DIGGINS, Dana P., Senior Vice President and Chief Financial Officer, Emerson Hospital, Concord, MA, p. A317

DIGNUM, Kirk, Ph.D., President and Chief Executive Officer, Mercy Medical Center, Durango, CO, p. A104

DIGREGORIO, Connie, Resource Process Coordinator, Cascade Valley Hospital and Clinics, Arlington, WA, p. A700

DIIESO, R.N., Nicholas T., Chief Operating Officer, Mount Auburn Hospital, Cambridge, MA, p. A316

DILALLO, Kevin, Chief Executive Officer, Wellington Regional Medical Center, West Palm Beach, FL, p. A150

DILEO, Micheal, Chief of Staff, River West Medical Center, Plaquemine, LA, p. A291

DILJAK, Dan, Chief Information Officer, Tyler Memorial Hospital, Tunkhannock, PA, p. A577

DILL, Nancy, Human Resources Director, Chicot Memorial Hospital, Lake Village, AR, p. A46

DILLARD, Evan S., Chief Operating Officer and Vice President, Tallahassee Memorial HealthCare, Tallahassee, FL, p. A147

DILLARD, Leigh, Chief of Staff, De Soto Regional Health System, Mansfield, LA, p. A286

DILLEHUNT, David B., Vice President Information Systems and Chief Information Officer, FirstHealth Moore Regional Hospital, Pinehurst, NC, p. A489

DILLENSCHNEIDER, Grace Anne, Assistant General Minister, Sisters of Saint Francis, Syracuse, NY, p. B100

DILLER, Carrie, Information Systems Coordinator, Saunders County Health Service, Wahoo, NE, p. A413

DILLON, Lorie, Administrator, Geisinger HEALTHSOUTH Rehabilitation Hospital, Danville, PA, p. A556

DILLON, M.D., Michael, Chief of Staff, Northern Inyo Hospital, Bishop, CA, p. A55

DIMARE, M.D., John, Medical Director, Foothill Presbyterian Hospital–Morris L. Johnston Memorial, Glendora, CA, p. A63

DIMENSTEIN, Michael, Vice President Human Resources, Norwalk Hospital, Norwalk, CT, p. A115

DIMEOLA, M.D., Herbert J., Vice President Medical Affairs, Johnson Memorial Hospital, Stafford Springs, CT, p. A116

DINAN, Edward M., President and Chief Executive Officer, Lawrence Hospital Center, Bronxville, NY, p. A448

DINDAL, Ed, Information Services Manager, Sierra Vista Regional Health Center, Sierra Vista, AZ, p. A37

DINEEN, Ryan, Director Human Resources, Preston Memorial Hospital, Kingwood, WV, p. A717

DINGES, Larry, Human Resources Director, Skaggs Community Health Center, Branson, MO, p. A379

DINICOLA, M.D., Louis, Medical Staff Director, Gifford Medical Center, Randolph, VT, p. A683

DINKINS, Vicki, Human Resources Director, Louis Smith Memorial Hospital, Lakeland, GA, p. A164

DINON, Nancy, Chief Human Resources, Orlando Regional Medical Center, Orlando, FL, p. A141

DINSLAGE, Dennis, Vice President Finance and Chief Financial Officer, St. Francis Memorial Hospital, West Point, NE, p. A414

DINSMOOR, William S., Senior Vice President and Chief Financial Officer, Nebraska Medical Center, Omaha, NE, p. A411

DINTER, M.D., Richard W., Chief Operating Officer, Fairview University Medical Center–Mesabi, Hibbing, MN, p. A355

DIONISIO, Joseph D., President and Chief Executive Officer, New England Baptist Hospital, Boston, MA, p. A314

DIONNE, Michele, Chief Executive Officer, Kindred Hospital–Chicago Northlake, Northlake, IL, p. A203

DIONNE, Philip G., President and Chief Executive Officer, New York United Hospital Medical Center, Port Chester, NY, p. A469

DIPALO, Joseph A., Chief Executive Officer, Margaretville Memorial Hospital, Margaretville, NY, p. A456

DIPILLA, Victor, Vice President, Christ Hospital, Cincinnati, OH, p. A506

DIRKES, M.D., William, President, Medical Staff, Christ Hospital, Cincinnati, OH, p. A506

DIRKSEN, Victor J., Administrator, Jefferson Healthcare, Port Townsend, WA, p. A706

DIRUBBIO, Vincent, President and Chief Executive Officer, St. Catherine of Siena Medical Center, Smithtown, NY, p. A472

DISANTO, Larry
Executive Vice President and Chief Operating Officer, Capital Health System at Fuld, Trenton, NJ, p. A437
Executive Vice President and Chief Operating Officer, Capital Health System at Mercer, Trenton, NJ, p. A437

DISCH, Catherine D., Chief Operating Officer, Truman Medical Center–Hospital Hill, Kansas City, MO, p. A385

DISESSA, Michelle, Director Humaj Resources, HEALTHSOUTH Medical Center, Dallas, TX, p. A632

DISTASIO, Stephen R., Associate Director for Operations, Veterans Affairs Black Hills Health Care System, Fort Meade, SD, p. A596

DITCH, Donna M., MS, President, Chief Executive Officer and Chief Nursing Officer, Athol Memorial Hospital, Athol, MA, p. A312

DITTMAN, Adam, Vice President Professional and Support Services, Mercy Hospital Anderson, Cincinnati, OH, p. A507

DITTMANN, Jerry, Vice President Human Resources, Mount Nittany Medical Center, State College, PA, p. A576

DITTMEYER, Terrie, Chief Executive Officer, Select Specialty Hospital–Lancaster, Lancaster, PA, p. A562

DITTRICH, Lisa, Manager, Employee Relations, Auburn Memorial Hospital, Auburn, NY, p. A447

DITZEL Jr, Louis A., President and Chief Executive Officer, Jersey Shore Hospital, Jersey Shore, PA, p. A561

DIVINE, Linda, Manager Human Resources, St. John's St. Francis Hospital, Mountain View, MO, p. A388

DIVINEY, Gerard, Vice President Finance and Chief Financial Officer, United Regional Health Care System, Wichita Falls, TX, p. A674

DIX, Roger J., Senior Vice President and Chief Financial Officer, Hannibal Regional Hospital, Hannibal, MO, p. A382

DIXON, M.D., Darrell, Vice President Medical Affairs, Christus St. Patrick Hospital of Lake Charles, Lake Charles, LA, p. A284

DIXON, Debbie, Director, Human Resources, Pampa Regional Medical Center, Pampa, TX, p. A659

DIXON, Del, Chief Information Officer, South Shore Hospital, South Weymouth, MA, p. A323

DIXON, Jon L., Chief Executive Officer, Warm Springs Medical Center, Warm Springs, GA, p. A171

DIXON, Rick, Chief, Personnel Division, Darnall Army Community Hospital, Fort Hood, TX, p. A638

DIXON, Sally J., President and Chief Executive Officer, Memorial Hospital, York, PA, p. A580

DIXON, Shannon, Human Resources Executive Secretary, Weisbrod Memorial County Hospital, Eads, CO, p. A105

DIXON, Stephen E., Chief Executive Officer, Southern Hills Hospital and Medical Center, Las Vegas, NV, p. A417

DIXON, Wynn, Vice President Human Resources and Quality, Chesapeake General Hospital, Chesapeake, VA, p. A686

DIZNEY, Donald R., Chairman and Chief Executive Officer, United Medical Corporation, Windermere, FL, p. B113

DOAK, Mark, President and Chief Executive Officer, Davis Memorial Hospital, Elkins, WV, p. A715

DOAN, Angela, Chief Financial Officer, Scott Memorial Hospital, Scottsburg, IN, p. A225

DOAN, Richard L., CHE, Chief Executive Officer, Barnesville Hospital Association, Barnesville, OH, p. A503

DOBBINS, Jim, Vice President Human Resources, Lenoir Memorial Hospital, Kinston, NC, p. A486

DOBBINS, M.D., Tom, President Medical Staff, Beauregard Memorial Hospital, De Ridder, LA, p. A280

DOBBS, Amanda, Director of Human Resources, Tennessee Christian Medical Center, Madison, TN, p. A611

DOBBS, Steve, Chief Executive Officer, Hillcrest Medical Center, Tulsa, OK, p. A539

DOBBS–JOHNSON, Lena, President, Advocate Bethany Hospital, Chicago, IL, p. A186

DOBSON, Glenn
Interim Chief Executive Officer, Iron County Community Hospital, Iron River, MI, p. A337
Chief Financial Officer, Iron County Community Hospital, Iron River, MI, p. A337

DOCKING, Gordon, Chief Executive Officer, St. Mary's Medical Center, Blue Springs, MO, p. A378

DOCKINS, Jim, Chief Executive Officer, Jackson–Madison County General Hospital, Jackson, TN, p. A608

DOCKTER, Robert A., Administrator, Eureka Community Health Services/Avera Health, Eureka, SD, p. A595

DODD, James L., Ph.D., Superintendent, West Central Georgia Regional Hospital, Columbus, GA, p. A159

DODD, John, Corporate Director Human Resources, Conway Regional Medical Center, Conway, AR, p. A41

DODDS, Sheryl D., Chief Executive Officer, Nebraska Heart Institute, Lincoln, NE, p. A409

DODGE, Wayne, Administrator, Clinton Rehabilitation Hospital, Clinton, LA, p. A279

DODSON, James, Chief Medical Staff, Logan Memorial Hospital, Russellville, KY, p. A274

DODSON, Stanley D., Director for Psychiatric Services, Behavioral Health Care of Cape Fear Valley Health System, Fayetteville, NC, p. A482

DODSON, Thomas, Executive Director, Buffalo Psychiatric Center, Buffalo, NY, p. A449

DODWELL, Wayne, Chief Executive Officer, Down East Community Hospital, Machias, ME, p. A299

DOE, Jr, Brian J., Chief Financial Officer, Tehachapi Valley Healthcare District, Tehachapi, CA, p. A95

DOEDEN, Lynn, Chief Executive Officer, Decatur County Hospital and Cedar Living Center, Oberlin, KS, p. A253

DOELE, Harry, Chief Executive Officer, Pennock Hospital, Hastings, MI, p. A336

DOERR, David R., Chief Executive Officer, Union Hospital, Terre Haute, IN, p. A226

DOHERTY, John, Chief Operating Officer, MeritCare Medical Center, Fargo, ND, p. A497

DOHERTY, Randy, Administrator, HEALTHSOUTH Braintree Rehabilitation Hospital, Braintree, MA, p. A315

DOHN, William, Chief Financial Officer, Northlake Medical Center, Tucker, GA, p. A171

DOLAN, M.D., Paul, Vice President Medical Affairs, Benefis Healthcare, Great Falls, MT, p. A399

DOLAN, Paula, Vice President Human Resources, Park Ridge Hospital, Rochester, NY, p. A471

DOLAN, Robert S., Chief Executive Officer, Saint Francis Heart Hospital, Tulsa, OK, p. A539

DOLES, Patty, Chief Financial Officer, Minden Medical Center, Minden, LA, p. A287

DOMANICO, Lee, Chief Executive Officer, El Camino Hospital, Mountain View, CA, p. A77

DOMINGO, M.D., Ramon, Chief of Staff, McCamey Hospital, McCamey, TX, p. A656

DOMINGUE, Kevin, Director, Human Resources, Our Lady of Lourdes Regional Medical Center, Lafayette, LA, p. A284

DOMINGUEZ, Dominic J., Chief Executive Officer, St. Luke's Baptist Hospital, San Antonio, TX, p. A665

DONAHEY, Kenneth C., Chairman and Chief Executive Officer, LifePoint Hospitals, Inc., Brentwood, TN, p. B68

DONAHUE, Brian, Chief Financial Officer, Portage Health System, Hancock, MI, p. A336

DONAHUE, Les A., Vice President and Administrator, Sentara Virginia Beach General Hospital, Virginia Beach, VA, p. A698

DONAHUE, Patrick, Administrator, Methodist Hospital Union County, Morganfield, KY, p. A272

DONALDSON, Brooke, Assistant Administrator, Human Resources, Jackson Hospital, Marianna, FL, p. A136

DONALDSON, Dave, Director Human Resources, Castleview Hospital, Price, UT, p. A678

DONALDSON, Duane, Chief Financial Officer, Blanchard Valley Health Association, Findlay, OH, p. A513

DONALDSON, Sherry, Director of Human Resources, Barnwell County Hospital, Barnwell, SC, p. A583

DONHAM, Rick, Human Resources Director, Drew Memorial Hospital, Monticello, AR, p. A48

DONKER, Susan, Vice President Human Resources, Memorial Hospitals Association, Modesto, CA, p. A76

DONLIN, John, Vice President Human Resources, MetroWest Medical Center, Framingham, MA, p. A318

DONLIN, Michael T., Administrator, Floyd Valley Hospital/Avera Health, Le Mars, IA, p. A237

DONNARD, Rene, Director Marketing and Public Relations, Presbyterian Medical Center of the University of Pennsylvania Health System, Philadelphia, PA, p. A569

DONNELL, Vern F., Service Unit Director, U. S. Public Health Service Indian Hospital, Pine Ridge, SD, p. A598

DONNELLAN Jr, John J., Director, Veterans Administration New York Harbor Healthcare System, New York, NY, p. A466

DONNELLY Jr, John J., Chief Executive Officer, Roxborough Memorial Hospital, Philadelphia, PA, p. A569

DONNELLY, Leo J., Executive Director, The Friary of Baptist Health Center, Gulf Breeze, FL, p. A130

DONNELLY, M.D., Mark, President Medical Staff, Samaritan Lebanon Community Hospital, Lebanon, OR, p. A545

DONO, D.O., Francis V., Vice President Medical Affairs, Doctors Hospital, Columbus, OH, p. A510

DONOHOO, William M., FACHE, Chief Executive Officer, Washington County Hospital, Plymouth, NC, p. A489

DONOVAN, Janise, Chief Information Officer, Thoms Rehabilitation Hospital, Asheville, NC, p. A477

DONOVAN, Mary
    Controller, HEALTHSOUTH Rehabilitation Institute of Tucson, Tucson, AZ, p. A38
    Controller, HEALTHSOUTH Rehabilitation Institute of Tucson, Tucson, AZ, p. A38

DONOVAN, Mike, Chief Financial Officer, Lemuel Shattuck Hospital, Jamaica Plain, MA, p. A319

DONOVAN, Tom, Chief Financial Officer, Upstate Medical University, Syracuse, NY, p. A474

DONOVAN, M.D., William, Medical Director, The Institute for Rehabilitation and Research, Houston, TX, p. A648

DONSON, Elliott, Chief Information Specialist, Lincoln Hospital, Davenport, WA, p. A702

DONZE, D.O., Richard D., Senior Vice President Medical Affairs, Chester County Hospital, West Chester, PA, p. A578

DOODY–CHABRE, Kris, Chief Executive Officer, Cary Medical Center, Caribou, ME, p. A298

DOOLEY, Chuck, Vice President Information Services, St. Cloud Hospital, Saint Cloud, MN, p. A361

DOOLEY, James J.
    President and Chief Executive Officer, Geneva General Hospital, Geneva, NY, p. A452
    President and Chief Executive Officer, Soldiers and Sailors Memorial Hospital of Yates County, Penn Yan, NY, p. A469

DOOLEY, Mark, Executive Vice President and Administrator, St. Mary's Warrick Hospital, Boonville, IN, p. A212

DOOLING, Noncy J., Vice President, Saint Anthony's Health Center, Alton, IL, p. A183

DOORDAN, Martin L., President, Anne Arundel Medical Center, Annapolis, MD, p. A302

DOORN, Douglas, Chief Executive Officer, Spencer Hospital, Spencer, IA, p. A242

DORAM, M.D., Keith R., Chief Medical Officer, Christiana Care Health System, Wilmington, DE, p. A120

DORAN, Dennis J., President, Cambridge Medical Center, Cambridge, MN, p. A351

DORIA, Eugene, Chief Information Officer, Veterans Affairs Medical Center, Coatesville, PA, p. A556

DORIS, Doug, Chief Executive Officer, St. Alexius Hospital, Saint Louis, MO, p. A392

DORITY, Kim, Director Human Resources, Logan Regional Hospital, Logan, UT, p. A677

DORKO, Joseph M., Vice President Operations, Lutheran Hospital of Indiana, Fort Wayne, IN, p. A215

DORMAN, Charles M., Acting Director, Veterans Affairs Greater Los Angeles Healthcare System, Los Angeles, CA, p. A73

DORMAN III, Harry G., President and Chief Executive Officer, Alice Peck Day Memorial Hospital, Lebanon, NH, p. A421

DORN, Jim, Vice President Human Resources, University of Texas M. D. Anderson Cancer Center, Houston, TX, p. A648

DORNAK, Linda, Director Information Systems, Gulf Coast Medical Center, Wharton, TX, p. A673

DOROGY, Sharon, Director Information Systems, The Children's Institute of Pittsburgh, Pittsburgh, PA, p. A572

DORRIS, Patricia, Chief Executive Officer, Palo Pinto General Hospital, Mineral Wells, TX, p. A657

DORSEY, Lawrence T., Administrator and Chief Executive Officer, University Medical Center, Lafayette, LA, p. A284

DORSEY, Michael A., Chief Operating Officer, St. Francis Health Center, Topeka, KS, p. A258

DORTA, M.D., Luis, Medical Director, San Juan Capestrano Hospital, San Juan, PR, p. A748

DORWART, M.D., Clint, Chief of Staff, Memorial Health Center, Sidney, NE, p. A413

DOSE, Mark, Director Marketing, Crisp Regional Hospital, Cordele, GA, p. A159

DOSS, Lynne T., Administrator, Davie County Hospital, Mocksville, NC, p. A487

DOSS, Mounir F., Executive Vice President and Chief Financial Officer, Jamaica Hospital Medical Center, New York, NY, p. A460

DOSS, Tommy, Director Human Resources, Bayshore Medical Center, Pasadena, TX, p. A660

DOTEN, Charles, Chief Executive Officer, Kindred Hospital–South Florida/Coral Gables, Coral Gables, FL, p. A126

DOTSON, Gina, Director of Human Resources, Coral Springs Medical Center, Coral Springs, FL, p. A126

DOTSON, Philip E., Chief Executive Officer, Athens–Limestone Hospital, Athens, AL, p. A13

DOTY, Elizabeth A., Chief Executive Officer, Regional Health Services of Howard County, Cresco, IA, p. A231

DOUCETTE, Elmer, Vice President Fiscal Services, Penobscot Bay Medical Center, Rockport, ME, p. A300

DOUCETTE, Julia, Human Resources Director, HEALTHSOUTH Chattanooga Rehabilitation Hospital, Chattanooga, TN, p. A603

DOUD, Tony, Controller, Saint Mary's Standish Community Hospital, Standish, MI, p. A345

DOUGHERTY, Paul, President and Chief Executive Officer, Deaconess Hospital, Oklahoma City, OK, p. A535

DOUGHERTY, Peter, Director Information Services, Touro Infirmary, New Orleans, LA, p. A290

DOUGHERTY, Thomas, Chief Financial Officer, Tyler Memorial Hospital, Tunkhannock, PA, p. A577

DOUGHTY, Stephanie, Chief Financial Officer, Poudre Valley Hospital, Fort Collins, CO, p. A105

DOUGLAS, Bill, Chief Financial Officer, Riverside Medical Center, Kankakee, IL, p. A198

DOUGLAS, Dora, Chief Financial Officer, Summersville Memorial Hospital, Summersville, WV, p. A720

DOUGLAS, Doug, Vice President Human Resources, AnMED Health Medical Center, Anderson, SC, p. A583

DOUGLAS, Ernest, Treasurer, Akron Children's Hospital, Akron, OH, p. A502

DOUGLAS, Jason, Administrator, Sibley Medical Center, Arlington, MN, p. A349

DOUGLAS, Paul, Vice President, Human Resources, Baton Rouge General Medical Center, Baton Rouge, LA, p. A277

DOUGLAS, Sean
    Chief Financial Officer, Mount Carmel Hospital, Colville, WA, p. A701
    Chief Financial Officer, St. Joseph's Hospital, Chewelah, WA, p. A701

DOULD, Philip E., Chief Operating Officer, Massachusetts Hospital School, Canton, MA, p. A316

DOULTER, Doc, Interim Chief Financial Officer, Good Samaritan Health Systems, Kearney, NE, p. A408

DOVER, CPA, Chris, Chief Financial Officer, Holdenville General Hospital, Holdenville, OK, p. A532

DOVER, James F., FACHE, Administrator, St. Anthony North Hospital, Westminster, CO, p. A110

DOVER, Jerry, Administrator and Chief Executive Officer, Carroll County Memorial Hospital, Carrollton, MO, p. A379

DOVER, Jim, Vice President Human Resources, St. Charles Medical Center – Bend, Bend, OR, p. A542

DOW, Amanda, Director Community Relations, Cannon Memorial Hospital, Pickens, SC, p. A591

DOWDELL, Thomas C., Executive Director and Senior Vice President, Memorial Hospital and Medical Center of Cumberland, Cumberland, MD, p. A307

DOWDLE, Paul, Chief Operating Officer, Jefferson Healthcare, Port Townsend, WA, p. A706

DOWELL Jr, Floyd B., Administrator, Lincoln County Medical Center, Troy, MO, p. A395

DOWGUN, Richard, Chief Information Officer, St. Francis Medical Center, Trenton, NJ, p. A437

DOWLING, Dennis
    Executive Director, Long Island Jewish Medical Center, New York, NY, p. A461
    Executive Director, North Shore University Hospital, Manhasset, NY, p. A456

DOWLING, Edward J., Senior Vice President Human Resources, Yale–New Haven Hospital, New Haven, CT, p. A115

DOWLING, Kathy, Vice President Operations, Fountain Valley Regional Hospital and Medical Center, Fountain Valley, CA, p. A60

DOWLING, Mary A., Director, Veterans Affairs Medical Center, Albuquerque, NM, p. A441

DOWLING, Michael J., President and Chief Executive Officer, North Shore–LIJ Health System, Great Neck, NY, p. B80

DOWN, Melanie Falls, Site Manager, Crow/Northern Cheyenne Hospital, Crow Agency, MT, p. A397

DOWN, Philip B., President and Chief Executive Officer, Doctors Community Hospital, Lanham, MD, p. A309

DOWNES, William J., Vice President Finance, Southside Community Hospital, Farmville, VA, p. A688

DOWNEY, Daniel, Chief Fiscal Service, Veterans Administration New York Harbor Healthcare System, New York, NY, p. A466

DOWNEY, Donald E., Administrator, Stones River Hospital, Woodbury, TN, p. A619

DOWNEY, Helen
    Chief Operating Officer, Berkshire Medical Center, Pittsfield, MA, p. A322
    Chief Operating Officer, Berkshire Medical Center, Pittsfield, MA, p. A322

DOWNEY, Patti, Assistant Administrator, Liberty Hospital, Liberty, MO, p. A386

DOWNEY, Robert
    Vice President Finance, Marshalltown Medical and Surgical Center, Marshalltown, IA, p. A237
    Vice President Finance, Marshalltown Medical and Surgical Center, Marshalltown, IA, p. A237

DOWNEY, William B.
    Executive Vice President and Administrator, Riverside Regional Medical Center, Newport News, VA, p. A692
    Executive Vice President and Administrator, Riverside Regional Medical Center, Newport News, VA, p. A692

DOWNING, Samuel W., President and Chief Executive Officer, Salinas Valley Memorial Healthcare System, Salinas, CA, p. A86

DOWNS, Bryan, Director, Information Services, Central Peninsula General Hospital, Soldotna, AK, p. A28

DOWNS, Connie, Chief Financial Officer, Sturgis Hospital, Sturgis, MI, p. A346

DOWNS, Edward, Administrator, HEALTHSOUTH Houston Rehabilitation Institute, Houston, TX, p. A645

DOWNS, Noah, Director Information Systems, North Hills Hospital, North Richland Hills, TX, p. A658

DOWNS, Stephen, Chief Financial Officer, Doctor's Hospital of Opelousas, Opelousas, LA, p. A290

DOWNS, Steven, Chief Executive Officer and Administrator, Ville Platte Medical Center, Ville Platte, LA, p. A294

DOXTATOR, Rick, Chief Financial Officer, St. Vincent Hospital, Santa Fe, NM, p. A444

DOYEL, Brenda K.
    Chief Executive Officer, Watonga Municipal Hospital, Watonga, OK, p. A541
    Chief Executive Officer, Watonga Municipal Hospital, Watonga, OK, p. A541

DOYLE, Bev, Chief Information Resource Management, Aleda E. Lutz Veterans Affairs Medical Center, Saginaw, MI, p. A344

DOYLE, James F., Senior Vice President Finance, Elmhurst Memorial Hospital, New York, IL, p. A193

DOZIER Jr, J. Larry, FACHE, Chief Executive Officer, Fairfield Memorial Hospital, Winnsboro, SC, p. A593

DRAPEAU, Thomas, Information Systems Manager, Holyoke Medical Center, Holyoke, MA, p. A318

DRASS, Joy, M.D., President, MedStar–Georgetown Medical Center, Washington, DC, p. A121

DRAWHORN, Derek, Chief Information Officer, Michael E. Debakey Veterans Affairs Medical Center, Houston, TX, p. A646

DRAYER, Burton P., M.D., President, Mount Sinai Hosptial, New York, NY, p. A462

DREHER, Charles J.
Vice President Finance and Chief Financial Officer, Columbia St. Mary's–Milwaukee Campus, Milwaukee, WI, p. A730
Vice President Finance and Chief Financial Officer, Sacred Heart Rehabilitation Institute, Milwaukee, WI, p. A731

DREIMILLER, Marcy, Vice President Human Resources and Support Services, Glens Falls Hospital, Glens Falls, NY, p. A453

DRESCICH, Patrick
Vice President Human Resources, Mercy Hospital, Coon Rapids, MN, p. A351
Vice President Human Resources, Unity Hospital, Fridley, MN, p. A354

DREW, John A., President and Chief Executive Officer, Athens Regional Medical Center, Athens, GA, p. A152

DREW, Michael R., Assistant Administrator and Director of Pharmacy, Ontonagon Memorial Hospital, Ontonagon, MI, p. A342

DREWETTE, Frederick J., Chief Financial Officer, San Dimas Community Hospital, San Dimas, CA, p. A88

DREWNIAK, Robert, Senior Vice President Clinical Resources, Glendale Memorial Hospital and Health Center, Glendale, CA, p. A62

DRIEWER, Robert L., CHE, Chief Executive Officer, Faith Regional Health Services, Norfolk, NE, p. A410

DRIGGERS, M.D., Steve D., Chief Medical Officer, Holy Family Memorial Medical Center, Manitowoc, WI, p. A729

DRISCOLL, Angie, Director Human Resources, Los Alamitos Medical Center, Los Alamitos, CA, p. A69

DRISCOLL, Larry, Director Human Resources, Keokuk County Health Center, Sigourney, IA, p. A241

DRISKILL Jr, Thomas M., President and Chief Executive Officer, Hawaii Health Systems Corporation, Honolulu, HI, p. B48

DRIVER, Kevin, Human Resource Director, Mimbres Memorial Hospital, Deming, NM, p. A442

DROBOT, Michael D., Chairman and Chief Executive Officer, Pacific Hospital of Long Beach, Long Beach, CA, p. A68

DROEGE, Marie T., Executive Vice President Operations, St. Mary Hospital, Hoboken, NJ, p. A429

DROP, Jeffrey S., President and Chief Executive Officer, St. Anthony Hospital, Pendleton, OR, p. A547

DROPPERS, Larry, Chief Financial Officer, Walter Knox Memorial Hospital, Emmett, ID, p. A179

DROZD, Lori C., Director Public Affairs, Kaiser Foundation Hospital, Fontana, CA, p. A60

DRUCKER, M.D., Jack, Chief of Staff, Veterans Affairs Medical Center, Minneapolis, MN, p. A358

DRUCKER, Steve C., President and Chief Executive Officer, Loretto Hospital, Chicago, IL, p. A188

DRUMMOND, Frank J., M.D., Chief Executive Officer, Georgia Regional Hospital at Savannah, Savannah, GA, p. A168

DRUMMOND, Michael, Chief Financial Officer, Runnells Specialized Hospital of Union County, Berkeley Heights, NJ, p. A425

DRUMWRIGHT, Douglas, Chief Executive Officer, Parkview Community Hospital Medical Center, Riverside, CA, p. A84

DRURY, Tim, Chief Financial Officer, Bert Fish Medical Center, New Smyrna Beach, FL, p. A139

DRYBURGH, Louise, Administrator, First Care Health Center, Park River, ND, p. A500

DRYDEN, D.O., Jeffrey L., Vice President, Ozarks Medical Center, West Plains, MO, p. A395

DRYE, Theresa, Manager Human Resources, Mercy Jeannette Hospital, Jeannette, PA, p. A561

DRYER, Len, Chief Financial Officer, Children's Hospital, Denver, CO, p. A103

DRYNAN, Eric C., Deputy Commander Information Management, Moncrief Army Community Hospital, Fort Jackson, SC, p. A588

DU CHARME WHITE, Sherri, Director Human Resources, St. Michael Hospital, Milwaukee, WI, p. A732

DU RALL, Marty, Executive Director Human Resources, St. Vincent Hospitals and Health Services, Indianapolis, IN, p. A219

DUANE, M.D., Larry, Medical Staff Director, Satilla Regional Medical Center, Waycross, GA, p. A172

DUANE, Paul K.
Executive Vice President and Chief Financial Officer, Palmetto Health Baptist/Columbia, Columbia, SC, p. A586
Executive Vice President and Chief Financial Officer, Palmetto Health Richland, Columbia, SC, p. A586

DUBBS, M.D., William F., Chief of Staff, Veterans Affairs Medical Center, Muskogee, OK, p. A534

DUBE, Rose, Human Resource Manager, District One Hospital, Faribault, MN, p. A353

DUBEY, Dennis, Ph.D., Executive Director, Sagamore Children's Psychiatric Center, Huntington Station, NY, p. A454

DUBIS, John S., Executive Vice President, SSM Cardinal Glennon Children's Hospital, Saint Louis, MO, p. A391

DUBORD, Jerri, Human Resources Manager, St. Elizabeth Ann Seton Specialty Care Hospital, Evansville, IN, p. A215

DUCHAK, Douglas A., President and Chief Executive Officer, Englewood Hospital and Medical Center, Englewood, NJ, p. A428

DUCHENE, R.N., Pam, Vice President Patient Care Services, St. Joseph Hospital, Nashua, NH, p. A423

DUCKWORTH, Ken, Interim Commissioner, Massachusetts Department of Mental Health, Boston, MA, p. B71

DUDA, Thomas J., Chief Financial Officer, Hi–Desert Medical Center, Joshua Tree, CA, p. A65

DUDICH, M.D., John, President Medical and Dental Staff, Wheeling Hospital, Wheeling, WV, p. A721

DUDLEY, M.D., Gatewood, Vice Pres of Med Stf Servs, Sumter Regional Hospital, Americus, GA, p. A152

DUDLEY, Patrick, Director, St. James Healthcare, Butte, MT, p. A397

DUDZIK, M.D., Mary, President Medical Staff, Mount Desert Island Hospital, Bar Harbor, ME, p. A296

DUENWALD, Jay, Interim Administrator, Holy Infant Hospital, Hoven, SD, p. A596

DUERR, Joe, Chief Executive Officer, Perry Memorial Hospital, Perry, OK, p. A537

DUFF, M.D., John, Vice President Support Services and Chief Information Officer, Lester E. Cox Medical Centers, Springfield, MO, p. A394

DUFFY, Charles, Chief Financial Officer, Harrison Memorial Hospital, Cynthiana, KY, p. A263

DUFFY, Jack, Executive Director, Conifer Park, Schenectady, NY, p. A472

DUFFY, Mary Elizabeth, Vice President and Chief Financial Officer, St. Luke's Cornwall Hospital – Newburgh Campus, Newburgh, NY, p. A467

DUFFY, Michael E.
Chief Operating Officer, Methodist Children's Hospital of South Texas, San Antonio, TX, p. A664
Chief Operating Officer, Methodist Hospital, San Antonio, TX, p. A664

DUFOUR, Lonnie, Human Resource Manager, Bunkie General Hospital, Bunkie, LA, p. A278

DUGAN, Margaret R., Executive Director, Greater Binghamton Health Center, Binghamton, NY, p. A448

DUGAN, Thomas F., Administrator, St. John Vianney Hospital, Downingtown, PA, p. A557

DUGAS, Denise S., Administrator, Premier Rehabilitation Hospital, Monroe, LA, p. A287

DUGGAN, Michael, President and Chief Executive Officer, Detroit Medical Center, Detroit, MI, p. B41

DUGGER, Curtis R., Chief Financial Officer, Memorial Hospital of Converse County, Douglas, WY, p. A740

DUGGER, Sandy, Director Human Resources, Community Hospital, Torrington, WY, p. A742

DUHON, Pam, Administrator and Chief Executive Officer, North Dallas Rehabilitation Hospital, Dallas, TX, p. A633

DUKE, Gail, Director of Human Resources, Clarendon Memorial Hospital, Manning, SC, p. A590

DUKE, Kelly O., Associate Director, Carl Vinson Veterans Affairs Medical Center, Dublin, GA, p. A161

DUKE, Lance B., FACHE, President and Chief Executive Officer, The Medical Center, Columbus, GA, p. A159

DUKE, Paige, Chief Human Resources and Marketing, Montfort Jones Memorial Hospital, Kosciusko, MS, p. A371

DUKE, Scott, Chief Executive Officer, Glendive Medical Center, Glendive, MT, p. A398

DULLEA, Robert, Chief Information Officer, Wentworth–Douglass Hospital, Dover, NH, p. A420

DUMAL, Jennifer H., Vice President Patient Care Services, Memorial Hospital at Gulfport, Gulfport, MS, p. A369

DUNAWAY, Clay, Administrator, Earl K. Long Medical Center, Baton Rouge, LA, p. A277

DUNAWAY, James, Director Information Management, Mississippi State Hospital, Whitfield, MS, p. A377

DUNCAN, Bob, Vice President Finance, High Point Regional Health System, High Point, NC, p. A485

DUNCAN, Cindy, Director Human Resources, Memorial Hospital and Physician Group, Frederick, OK, p. A531

DUNCAN, Darryl L., Chief Operating Officer, Provena Saint Joseph Hospital, Elgin, IL, p. A193

DUNCAN, Ph.D., F, David J., Senior Vice President, Altoona Hospital Campus, Altoona, PA, p. A551

DUNCAN, Erika, Chief Human Resources Officer, Spectrum Health–Reed City Campus, Reed City, MI, p. A343

DUNCAN, Gary D.
President and Chief Executive Officer, Freeman Health System, Joplin, MO, p. B46
President and Chief Executive Officer, Freeman Health System, Joplin, MO, p. A383

DUNCAN, Jr, H Clark, Administrator, Washington County Memorial Hospital, Potosi, MO, p. A389

DUNCAN Jr, H. Clark, Administrator, Washington County Memorial Hospital, Potosi, MO, p. A389

DUNCAN, Jeremy, Director of Information Systems, Lawrence Medical Center, Moulton, AL, p. A22

DUNCAN, Richard, Vice President Information Systems, Children's Medical Center of Dallas, Dallas, TX, p. A632

DUNCAN, Thomas, Vice President and Chief Financial Officer, Good Samaritan Hospital, Dayton, OH, p. A512

DUNHAM, Ann, Director Human Resources, Memorial Hospital, Carthage, IL, p. A186

DUNHAM, David S.
President, Mercy Medical Center Merced–Community Campus, Merced, CA, p. A75
President, Mercy Medical Center Merced–Dominican Campus, Merced, CA, p. A75

DUNHAM, Shelly, Administrator, Okeene Municipal Hospital, Okeene, OK, p. A534

DUNKIEL, Barbara, Human Resources Director, HEALTHSOUTH Sunrise Rehabilitation Hospital, Fort Lauderdale, FL, p. A128

DUNKLE, Ron
Administrator, Pawhuska Hospital, Pawhuska, OK, p. A537
Administrator, Sedan City Hospital, Sedan, KS, p. A257

DUNMYER, Daniel C., Chief Executive Officer, Regency Hospital of Florence, Florence, SC, p. A588

DUNN, Brian E., Chief Executive Officer, Salt Lake Regional Medical Center, Salt Lake City, UT, p. A679

DUNN, Daniel N., Vice President Operations, Wentworth–Douglass Hospital, Dover, NH, p. A420

DUNN, M.D., George, Senior Vice President Medical Affairs, Glen Cove Hospital, Glen Cove, NY, p. A453

DUNN, Jeffrey, Chief Executive Officer, North Georgia Medical Center, Ellijay, GA, p. A162

DUNN, Michael A., M.D., Commanding General, Madigan Army Medical Center, Tacoma, WA, p. A710

DUNN, M.D., Thaddeus, President Medical Staff, New Hanover Regional Medical Center, Wilmington, NC, p. A494

DUNN, Wayne, Vice President Finance, Benefis Healthcare, Great Falls, MT, p. A399

DUNNE, Liz, Chief Operating Officer, Anaheim Memorial Medical Center, Anaheim, CA, p. A52

DUNNE, R.N., Penny
Human Resource Director, Samaritan North Lincoln Hospital, Lincoln City, OR, p. A545
Human Resource Director, Samaritan Pacific Communities Hospital, Newport, OR, p. A546

DUNNING Jr, Raymond M., Chief Executive Officer, Medical Center of Lewisville, Lewisville, TX, p. A653

DUNNING, Shane, Administrator, Carnegie Tri–County Municipal Hospital, Carnegie, OK, p. A528

DUNNING, Thomas, Executive Director, Franklin Regional Medical Center, Louisburg, NC, p. A487

DUNOP, Jim, Vice President Finance, Mercy Hospital, Buffalo, NY, p. A449

DUNWOODY, Robert, Chief Financial Officer, Lawnwood Regional Medical Center, Fort Pierce, FL, p. A129

DUPLESSIS, Andre, Chief Operating Officer, Women's and Children's Hospital, Lafayette, LA, p. A284

DUPPER, Harold, Chief Financial Officer, Platte Valley Medical Center, Brighton, CO, p. A101

DUPPER, Larry L., Chief Financial Officer, Valley View Hospital, Glenwood Springs, CO, p. A106

DUPRE, Charlotte, Chief Executive Officer, Eunice Community Medical Center, Eunice, LA, p. A280

DUPRE, Kenyon, Acting Associate Director, Veterans Affairs Tennessee Valley Healthcare System, Nashville, TN, p. A616

DUPREY, Irma, Administrator of Medical Records, Hospital Universitario Dr. Ramon Ruiz Arnau, Bayamon, PR, p. A744

DUPUIS, Burton, Chief Executive Officer, St. Martin Hospital, Breaux Bridge, LA, p. A278

DUQUETTE, Bill, Vice President Operations, Homestead Hospital, Homestead, FL, p. A131

DURAIRAJ, S. K., M.D., Chief Executive Officer, Pacifica Hospital of the Valley, Los Angeles, CA, p. A72

DURAND, Crista, Senior Vice President Finance and Chief Financial Officer, Day Kimball Hospital, Putnam, CT, p. A116

DURAND, Pierre, Administrator, Ventura County Medical Center, Ventura, CA, p. A98

DURAND, Stefanie, Director Human Resources, Toppenish Community Hospital, Toppenish, WA, p. A711

DURBIN, Steven, Vice President Human Resources, Tampa General Hospital, Tampa, FL, p. A148

DURETT, William, Director Human Resources, Warren Hospital, Phillipsburg, NJ, p. A434

DURHAM, Barbara, Director Human Resources, Carson Tahoe Hospital, Carson City, NV, p. A415

DURHAM, Carol, Chief Financial Officer, Permian Regional Medical Center, Andrews, TX, p. A621

DURHAM, Dennis, Chief Operating Officerf, Palmyra Medical Centers, Albany, GA, p. A152

DURHAM, Donald E., Vice President Finance and Chief Financial Officer, Peninsula Regional Health System, Salisbury, MD, p. A310

DURHAM, Jeffrey L., Chief Executive Officer, Massac Memorial Hospital, Metropolis, IL, p. A201

DURHAM, M.D., Joseph R., Medical Director, Oak Forest Hospital of Cook County, Oak Forest, IL, p. A203

DUROVICH, Christopher J., President and Chief Executive Officer, Children's Medical Center of Dallas, Dallas, TX, p. A632

DURR, Michael, Controller, South Miami Hospital, Miami, FL, p. A138

DURRER, Christopher T., President and Chief Executive Officer, Wilson Medical Center, Wilson, NC, p. A494

DURST, Geoff, Vice President Finance, Avera St. Luke's, Aberdeen, SD, p. A594

DURST, Jennifer, Director Information Services, Washington County Hospital, Washington, IA, p. A242

DUSENBERY, Jack, President and Chief Executive Officer, Covenant Medical Center, Waterloo, IA, p. A243

DUTHE, Robert J., Director Information Services, United Memorial Medical Center, Batavia, NY, p. A447

DUTMERS, David, Team Leader Information and Technology Management, Spectrum Health–United Memorial, Greenville, MI, p. A335

DUTTON, Stephanie, Chief Operating Officer, Mid–America Rehabilitation Hospital, Shawnee Mission, KS, p. A257

DUVAL, John, Chief Executive Officer, VCU Health System, Richmond, VA, p. A696

DUVALL, Gary, Chief Information Resource Management, Veterans Affairs Medical Center, Muskogee, OK, p. A534

DUVALL, Wendy, Accountant, Barton County Memorial Hospital, Lamar, MO, p. A386

DUVENDACK, Chris, Vice President Ancil Services, Graham Hospital, Canton, IL, p. A185

DUX, Christopher W., Chief Executive Officer, North Bay Hospital, Aransas Pass, TX, p. A621

DVORAK, Robert M., Interim Chief Financial Officer, Providence Alaska Medical Center, Anchorage, AK, p. A26

DWIGHT, John, Chief Information Officer, Children's Hospital and Regional Medical Center, Seattle, WA, p. A707

DWORKIN, M.D., Paul, Physician–in–Chief, Connecticut Children's Medical Center, Hartford, CT, p. A113

DWOZAN, C. Richard, Chief Executive Officer, Habersham County Medical Center, Demorest, GA, p. A160

DYE, Blake A., President and Chief Executive Officer, Henry County Memorial Hospital, New Castle, IN, p. A223

DYE, Chris, Information Systems Director, Our Lady of the Way Hospital, Martin, KY, p. A271

DYE, M.D., David, Chief of Staff, Great River Medical Center, Blytheville, AR, p. A41

DYE, David L., Chief Financial Officer, North Florida Regional Medical Center, Gainesville, FL, p. A130

DYER, Dave, Vice President and Chief Information Officer, Somerset Medical Center, Somerville, NJ, p. A436

DYER, Debra, Chief Information Officer, Veterans Affairs San Diego Healthcare System, San Diego, CA, p. A88

DYER, Eddie, Chief Executive Officer, Select Specialty Hospital of Northwest Indiana, Hammond, IN, p. A217

DYER, Rebecca T., Administrator, Union General Hospital, Blairsville, GA, p. A156

DYER, M.D., Ted, Vice President Medical Affairs, Hendrick Health System, Abilene, TX, p. A620

DYESS, M.D., Lance K., Chief Medical Officer, Elba General Hospital, Elba, AL, p. A18

DYKEHOUSE, Rodney
Vice President, Chief Information Officer, Community Memorial Hospital, Menomonee Falls, WI, p. A729
Vice President Information Systems, Froedtert Memorial Lutheran Hospital, Milwaukee, WI, p. A731

DYKES, Barry, President and Chief Executive Officer, Desert Regional Medical Center, Palm Springs, CA, p. A80

DYKES, Bradford W., President and Chief Executive Officer, Bedford Regional Medical Center, Bedford, IN, p. A211

DYKES, C. Barry, Chief Executive Officer, Saint Vincent Hospital at Worcester Medical Center, Worcester, MA, p. A325

DYKES, Greg, Chief Operating Officer, Wiregrass Medical Center, Geneva, AL, p. A19

DYKSTRA, Janet, Administrator, Osceola Community Hospital, Sibley, IA, p. A241

DYNES, M.D., Gerrald, Medical Director, HEALTHSOUTH Rehabilitation Hospital of Baton Rouge, Baton Rouge, LA, p. A277

DZAU, Victor J., M.D., President and Chief Executive Officer, Duke University Health System, Durham, NC, p. B42

DZIESINSKI, Ray R., Senior Vice President Fiscal Services and Chief Financial Officer, Southern Regional Medical Center, Riverdale, GA, p. A167

E

EADS, John S., Administrator, North Baldwin Infirmary, Bay Minette, AL, p. A14

EAGER, David, Vice President Finance, West Allis Memorial Hospital, West Allis, WI, p. A738

EAKIN, M.D., K Max, President Medical Staff, Anderson Hospital, Maryville, IL, p. A200

EAKS, C. Alan, Chief Executive Officer, Chicago Lakeshore Hospital, Chicago, IL, p. A186

EARECKSON, Bonnie J., Chief, Human Resource Management Services, Veterans Affairs Medical Center, Memphis, TN, p. A614

EARL, M.D., Anna, Chief of Staff, Liberty County Hospital and Nursing Home, Chester, MT, p. A397

EARL, Mindy, Administrator, Health Information Systems, Harms Memorial Hospital District, American Falls, ID, p. A177

EARLY, Audra, Chief Executive Officer, Kindred Hospital–White Rock, Dallas, TX, p. A633

EASLEY, Marsha A., Chief Operating Officer, Orange Park Medical Center, Orange Park, FL, p. A140

EASLEY, Mike
Administrator, Collingsworth General Hospital, Wellington, TX, p. A673
Administrator, Culberson Hospital District, Van Horn, TX, p. A671

EAST, Stephen, Controller, River Parishes Hospital, La Place, LA, p. A283

EAST, Ph.D., Thomas, Chief Information Officer, Alaska Native Medical Center, Anchorage, AK, p. A26

EASTERLING, Patrick, Vice President and Chief Financial Officer, Presbyterian Hospital, Charlotte, NC, p. A480

EASTHAM, FACHE, James E., Chief Operating Officer, Valley Baptist Health System, Harlingen, TX, p. A643

EASTMAN, M.D., Brent, Chief Medical Officer, Scripps Green Hospital, La Jolla, CA, p. A65

EASTMAN, David, Regional Chief Information Officer, Adventist Medical Center, Portland, OR, p. A547

EASTMAN, Joseph, Director Human Resources, Roger Williams Medical Center, Providence, RI, p. A582

EASTMAN, Kim, R.N., Administrator, Menifee Valley Medical Center, Sun City, CA, p. A95

EASTMAN III, Philip H., President, Resurgence Health Group, Sugar Hill, GA, p. B93

EASTON, Laura J., President and Chief Executive Officer, Caldwell Memorial Hospital, Lenoir, NC, p. A486

EATON, Ellen, Director Human Resources, Tift Regional Medical Center, Tifton, GA, p. A171

EATON, Phil, Chief Executive Officer, Lander Valley Medical Center, Lander, WY, p. A740

EATON, R. Philip, M.D., Vice President Health Sciences, University of New Mexico, Albuquerque, NM, p. B117

EBAUGH, Elaine D., Administrator, HEALTHSOUTH Rehabilitation Hospital, Largo, FL, p. A134

EBAUGH, Matt, Chief Information Officer, The Medical Center at Bowling Green, Bowling Green, KY, p. A262

EBELING, Toni, Administrator, Hancock County Memorial Hospital, Britt, IA, p. A229

EBERS, Layne, Director Human Resources, Pike County Memorial Hospital, Louisiana, MO, p. A387

EBKEN, M.D., Richard, Central Carolina Hospital, Sanford, NC, p. A491

ECHELARD, Paul D., Chief Executive Officer, Good Samaritan Medical Center, West Palm Beach, FL, p. A150

ECHELBERGER, Scott, Vice President Operations, Catawba Valley Medical Center, Hickory, NC, p. A484

ECHOLS, III, Leon F., Executive Vice President and Chief Operating Officer, Henry Medical Center, Stockbridge, GA, p. A170

ECKELS, Dan, Chief Financial Officer, Washington Regional Medical Center, Fayetteville, AR, p. A43

ECKENFELS, Susan, Director Finance, Ste. Genevieve County Memorial Hospital, Ste. Genevieve, MO, p. A394

ECKENHOFF, Edward A., President and Chief Executive Officer, National Rehabilitation Hospital, Washington, DC, p. A122

ECKENRODE, Dean, Chief Executive Officer, UPMC Horizon, Greenville, PA, p. A559

ECKENRODE, M.D., James
Chief Operating Officer and Chief Medical Officer, Windber Medical Center, Windber, PA, p. A580
Chief Operating Officer and Chief Medical Officer, Windber Medical Center, Windber, PA, p. A580

ECKER, G. T. Dunlop
President and Chief Executive Officer, Dimensions Healthcare System, Cheverly, MD, p. B41
President and Chief Executive Officer, Prince George's Hospital Center, Cheverly, MD, p. A306

ECKERT, Bruce, Director Information Systems, Pine Rest Christian Mental Health Services, Grand Rapids, MI, p. A334

ECKERT, Mark, Chief Financial Officer, Kenner Regional Medical Center, Kenner, LA, p. A283

ECKERT, Mary L., President and Chief Executive Officer, Millcreek Community Hospital, Erie, PA, p. A558

ECKERT, Tim, Vice President Finance and Chief Operations Officer, Rochelle Community Hospital, Rochelle, IL, p. A206

ECTON, Doris, Administrator and Chief Executive Officer, Nicholas County Hospital, Carlisle, KY, p. A262

EDDINS, Jim
Financial Resources Manager, Michael E. Debakey Veterans Affairs Medical Center, Houston, TX, p. A646
Financial Resources Manager, Michael E. Debakey Veterans Affairs Medical Center, Houston, TX, p. A646

EDDLEMAN, Gwen S., R.N., President and Chief Executive Officer, Southside Community Hospital, Farmville, VA, p. A688

EDELSTEIN, Mark S., Assistant Chief of Staff for Medicine, John D. Dingell Veterans Affairs Medical Center, Detroit, MI, p. A331

EDEMA, M.D., Douglas A., Vice President and Chief Operating Officer, Saint Joseph Mercy Livingston Hospital, Howell, MI, p. A336

EDGAR, Joseph H., Senior Vice President Operations, Gettysburg Hospital, Gettysburg, PA, p. A559

EDGE, David, Fiscal Officer, Veterans Affairs Central Iowa Health Care System, Des Moines, IA, p. A233

EDGEWORTH, Mitch, Chief Executive Officer, Doctors Hospital of Dallas, Dallas, TX, p. A632

EDIN, Scott D., Chief Financial Officer, Amery Regional Medical Center, Amery, WI, p. A722

EDMONDSON, Bobby, Accounting Supervisor, Regional Rehabilitation Hospital, Phenix City, AL, p. A23

EDMONDSON, James H., Chief Executive Officer, Hillside Hospital, Pulaski, TN, p. A617

EDMONDSON, Theresa, Director, Walter B. Jones Alcohol and Drug Abuse Treatment Center, Greenville, NC, p. A484

EDMUNDSON, Reed
Administrator, Burleson St. Joseph Health Center, Caldwell, TX, p. A627
Administrator, Madison St. Joseph Health Center, Madisonville, TX, p. A655

EDUSADA, M, Head Staff Administration, Naval Hospital, Camp Pendleton, CA, p. A56

EDWARDS, Becky, Human Resource Manager, Irwin County Hospital, Ocilla, GA, p. A167

EDWARDS Jr, Bob S., Chief Executive Officer, Cushing Memorial Hospital, Leavenworth, KS, p. A251

EDWARDS, Carol, Vice President and Chief Information Officer, Legacy Emanuel Hospital and Health Center, Portland, OR, p. A547

EDWARDS, Cathy, Director Human Resources, Battle Creek Health System, Battle Creek, MI, p. A328

EDWARDS, Dana, Controller, HEALTHSOUTH Sea Pines Rehabilitation Hospital, Melbourne, FL, p. A136

EDWARDS, Danny R., Chief Executive Officer, Kindred Hospital – Central Tampa, Tampa, FL, p. A148

EDWARDS, James
President, Hazleton General Hospital, Hazleton, PA, p. A560
President, Hazleton–St. Joseph Medical Center, Hazleton, PA, p. A560

EDWARDS, James D., President, Greater Hazleton Health Alliance, Hazleton, PA, p. B47

EDWARDS, Jim, Director Information Systems, Decatur Memorial Hospital, Decatur, IL, p. A192

EDWARDS, John R., Administrator and Chief Executive Officer, Pacific Alliance Medical Center, Los Angeles, CA, p. A72

EDWARDS, Liston G., Director, Cherry Hospital, Goldsboro, NC, p. A483

EDWARDS, Michael R., Chief Executive Officer, Scott Regional Hospital, Morton, MS, p. A373

EDWARDS, Rick
Vice President Finance and Business Services, Hancock Memorial Hospital and Health Services, Greenfield, IN, p. A217
Director Information Systems, Howard County General Hospital, Columbia, MD, p. A307

EDWARDS, Sandra, Director Human Resources, St. Petersburg General Hospital, Saint Petersburg, FL, p. A145

EDWARDS, Susan, Director Human Resources, Culpeper Regional Hospital, Culpeper, VA, p. A687

EDWARDS, Sylvia, Acting Chief Operating Officer, Oak Forest Hospital of Cook County, Oak Forest, IL, p. A203

EDWARDS, Tanya, Chief Financial Officer, Schoolcraft Memorial Hospital, Manistique, MI, p. A340

EDWARDS, Terry, Controller, Kings Mountain Hospital, Kings Mountain, NC, p. A486

EDWARDS, Vicky B., Director Human Resources, Effingham Hospital, Springfield, GA, p. A169

EESLEY, Michael S.
President and Chief Executive Officer, Centegra Health System, Woodstock, IL, p. B27
President and Chief Executive Officer, Centegra Memorial Medical Center, Woodstock, IL, p. A210
President and Chief Executive Officer, Centegra Northern Illinois Medical Center, McHenry, IL, p. A200

EFFERSON, Douglas P., Administrator, Homer Memorial Hospital, Homer, LA, p. A282

EGAN, Gail A., President, Lankenau Hospital, Wynnewood, PA, p. A580

EGBERT, Jeff R., Chief Executive Officer, Tempe St. Luke's Hospital, Tempe, AZ, p. A37

EGGEBRECHT, Kurt, Information Systems Supervisor, Mackinac Straits Hospital and Health Center, Saint Ignace, MI, p. A344

EGGLETON, Peter, Human Resources Director, Sutter Solano Medical Center, Vallejo, CA, p. A98

EHASZ, James, Chief Financial Officer, Southwest Health Center, Platteville, WI, p. A733

EHLER, Phyllis, Human Resource Director, Avera St. Benedict Health Center, Parkston, SD, p. A597

EHLERS, Bob, Director Human Resources, Doctors Hospital of Sarasota, Sarasota, FL, p. A146

EHLERS, Jeffrey, Vice President Finance and Information Services, Memorial Hospital of Union County, Marysville, OH, p. A517

EHLERT, Marilyn, Director Human Resources, Fitzgibbon Hospital, Marshall, MO, p. A387

EHLKE, Ranae, Administrative Secretary and Risk Management and Human Resources Coordinator, Kenmare Community Hospital, Kenmare, ND, p. A499

EHRET, FACHE, Charlene, Associate Director, Hunter Holmes McGuire Veterans Affairs Medical Center, Richmond, VA, p. A695

EHRLICH, Jane, President and Chief Executive Officer, Columbia Memorial Hospital, Hudson, NY, p. A454

EICHELBERGER, Larry, Administrator, Fillmore County Hospital, Geneva, NE, p. A407

EICHER, Kim D., Chief Executive Officer, St. Francis Health Care Centre, Green Springs, OH, p. A514

EICHMAN, Cynthia, Chief Executive Officer and Administrator, Our Lady of Victory Hospital, Stanley, WI, p. A736

EICHORN, Marvin, Senior Vice President and Chief Financial Officer, Johnson City Medical Center, Johnson City, TN, p. A608

EIG, M.D., Blair, Senior Vice President Medical Affairs, Holy Cross Hospital, Silver Spring, MD, p. A311

EIGEN, Ken, Chief Engineering and Technology, Veterans Affairs Medical Center, Spokane, WA, p. A709

EIKELBOOM, Richard, Network Manager, Lucas County Health Center, Chariton, IA, p. A230

EILER, Gary, Chief Financial Officer, University of Wisconsin Hospital and Clinics, Madison, WI, p. A728

EISEMAN, Cynthia, Chief Operating Officer, HEALTHSOUTH Harmarville Rehabilitation Hospital, Pittsburgh, PA, p. A571

EISENMAN, Edward
Vice President Finance, Sunnyview Rehabilitation Hospital, Schenectady, NY, p. A472
Vice President Finance, Sunnyview Rehabilitation Hospital, Schenectady, NY, p. A472

EISENMANN, Claudia Ann, Chief Executive Officer, Crittenden County Hospital, Marion, KY, p. A271

EISENRING, Richard, Chief Financial Officer, Holy Cross Hospital, Taos, NM, p. A445

EISENZOPH, Pete, Director Information Technology, Bay Area Medical Center, Marinette, WI, p. A729

EISGRUB, Fred, Vice President, Human Resources, Wyckoff Heights Medical Center, New York, NY, p. A466

EISNER, Nina W., Chief Executive Officer and Managing Director, Ridge Behavioral Health System, Lexington, KY, p. A267

EITEL, Richard, Chief Executive Officer, Memorial Hospital, Colorado Springs, CO, p. A102

EKDAHL, Patricia, R.N., President and Chief Executive Officer, Russell County Hospital, Russell Springs, KY, p. A274

EKENGREN, M.D., Francie H., Chief Medical Officer, Wesley Medical Center, Wichita, KS, p. A260

EKEREN, Douglas R., Vice President Planning and Development, Avera Sacred Heart Hospital, Yankton, SD, p. A601

EL–ASMAR, M.D., Hoda, Chief Medical Officer, St. Joseph's Mercy of Macomb, Clinton Township, MI, p. A330

ELCHERT, Annette, Director Information Services, Blanchard Valley Health Association, Findlay, OH, p. A513

ELDER, Becky, Assistant Administrator Clinical Services, Perry County Memorial Hospital, Tell City, IN, p. A226

ELDRED, Mary Ann
Executive Vice President and Chief Operating Officer, Geneva General Hospital, Geneva, NY, p. A452
Executive Vice President and Chief Operating Officer, Soldiers and Sailors Memorial Hospital of Yates County, Penn Yan, NY, p. A469

ELDRIDGE, Jim
Business, Strategy and Finance Leader, Kaiser Foundation Hospital, Sacramento, CA, p. A84
Business, Strategy and Financial Leader, Kaiser Foundation Hospital, Sacramento, CA, p. A84

ELEGANT, Bruce M., President and Chief Executive Officer, Rush Oak Park Hospital, Oak Park, IL, p. A203

ELFERT, Mike, Director Information Services, Lourdes Medical Center of Burlington County, Willingboro, NJ, p. A438

ELFORD, Dorothy J., Chief Executive Officer, Kindred Hospital – Dallas, Dallas, TX, p. A633

ELFRINK, M.D., Roy, Chief of Staff, Fitzgibbon Hospital, Marshall, MO, p. A387

ELING, Patsy, Director Human Resources, Wheatland Memorial Hospital, Harlowton, MT, p. A399

ELJAIEK, Lester, Chief Financial Officer, Aventura Hospital and Medical Center, Aventura, FL, p. A123

ELKAIR, M.D., Mervet, Chief of Medicine, Hospital for Special Care, New Britain, CT, p. A114

ELKINGTON, Bruce
Vice President Information Technology, St. Clare Hospital, Tacoma, WA, p. A710
Vice President Information Technology, St. Joseph Medical Center, Tacoma, WA, p. A710

ELKINGTON, M.D., Mark, Chief Medical Officer, Willow Crest Hospital, Miami, OK, p. A533

ELKINS, James N., FACHE, Director, Texas Center for Infectious Disease, San Antonio, TX, p. A665

ELKINS, Wendy, Director Operations, Dundy County Hospital, Benkelman, NE, p. A405

ELLERBE, F Dana, Assistant Administrator, Sutter Medical Center of Santa Rosa, Santa Rosa, CA, p. A93

ELLERTON, M.D., John, Chief of Staff, University Medical Center, Las Vegas, NV, p. A417

ELLERY, Loren, M.P.H., Chief Executive Officer, Huhukam Memorial Hospital, Sacaton, AZ, p. A35

ELLINGTON, Chris
Chief Financial Officer, McDowell ARH Hospital, McDowell, KY, p. A271
Chief Financial Officer and Vice President for Fiscal Affairs, Morgan County Appalachian Regional Hospital, West Liberty, KY, p. A275
Vice President for Fiscal Affairs, Whitesburg Appalachian Regional Hospital, Whitesburg, KY, p. A275
Chief Financial Officer, Williamson ARH Hospital, South Williamson, KY, p. A275

ELLIOT, Anna, Head Information Technology, Dundy County Hospital, Benkelman, NE, p. A405

ELLIOTT, M.D., Charles M., Chief of Staff, Tippah County Hospital, Ripley, MS, p. A375

ELLIOTT Jr, Charles W., Chief Executive Officer, Rowan Regional Medical Center, Salisbury, NC, p. A491

ELLIOTT, R James, Vice President Human Resources, The Charlotte Hungerford Hospital, Torrington, CT, p. A117

ELLIOTT, Robin, Personnel Officer, Community Memorial Hospital, Sumner, IA, p. A242

ELLIOTT, Shane, Chief Information Technology Service, Jerry L. Pettis Memorial Veterans Medical Center, Loma Linda, CA, p. A67

ELLIS, Angela, Chief Financial Officer, HEALTHSOUTH Rehabilitation Hospital, Odessa, TX, p. A659

ELLIS, M.D., Avery, Chief of Staff, Veterans Affairs Western New York Healthcare System–Buffalo Division, Buffalo, NY, p. A449

ELLIS, Betts, Administrator, Institutional Relations, MUSC Medical Center of Medical University of South Carolina, Charleston, SC, p. A584

ELLIS, M.D., Cheryl, Vice President Medical Services and Medical Director, Rehabilitation Institute at Santa Barbara, Santa Barbara, CA, p. A92

ELLIS, Dan, Administrator, Horn Memorial Hospital, Ida Grove, IA, p. A235

ELLIS, Jr, Edwin, Executive Vice President and Chief Financial Officer, Mercy Hospital–North Shore Campus, Pittsburgh, PA, p. A572

ELLIS, Elmer G., FACHE, President and Chief Executive Officer, East Texas Medical Center Regional Healthcare System, Tyler, TX, p. B42

ELLIS, Lynn, Chief Financial Officer, LakeWood Health Center, Baudette, MN, p. A350

ELLIS, Michael J., Administrator and Chief Executive Officer, Community Medical Center, Falls City, NE, p. A406

ELLIS, R.N., Susan, Vice President of Human Resources, Highlands Regional Medical Center, Prestonsburg, KY, p. A273

ELLISH, Patti M., R.N., President and Chief Executive Officer, St. Tammany Parish Hospital, Covington, LA, p. A279

ELLISON, M.D., Edward, Area Associate Medical Director, Kaiser Foundation Hospital – Orange County, Anaheim, CA, p. A52

ELLZEY, Bob, Administrator, Laird Memorial Hospital, Kilgore, TX, p. A651

ELMER, Dan, Chief Financial Officer, Laurens County Healthcare System, Clinton, SC, p. A585

ELMORE, Buddy, Senior Vice President Finance and Managed Care, and Chief Financial Officer, Christiana Care Health System, Wilmington, DE, p. A120

ELMORE, Nadine, Chief Executive Officer, Dahl Memorial Medical Assistance Facility, Ekalaka, MT, p. A398

ELMORE, Paul, Vice President Human Resources, St. John's Hospital, Springfield, MO, p. A394

ELMORE, Thomas, Information System Director, National Park Medical Center, Hot Springs, AR, p. A44

ELRABIE, M.D., Nazmi, President Medical Staff, Barnert Hospital, Paterson, NJ, p. A434

ELROD, James K., President and Chief Executive Officer, Willis–Knighton Health System, Shreveport, LA, p. B123

ELSOM, Donald, Administrator, Providence St. Vincent Medical Center, Portland, OR, p. A548

ELWELL, Richard, Senior Vice President and Chief Financial Officer, Elliot Hospital, Manchester, NH, p. A422

ELWELL, M.D., Russell, Medical Director, Westfield Memorial Hospital, Westfield, NY, p. A476

ELY, D.O., Thomas L., Vice President Medical Affairs, Gateway Health System, Clarksville, TN, p. A604

ELZA, Sandra, Chief Executive Officer, Jackson General Hospital, Ripley, WV, p. A719

EMANUEL, Kate, Human Resources Director, Clarke County Hospital, Osceola, IA, p. A239

EMBREE, Stephen, Controller, HEALTHSOUTH Medical Center, Dallas, TX, p. A632

EMBRY, Debra, Associate Administrator Employee Services, Atlanta Memorial Hospital, Atlanta, TX, p. A622

EMBURY, Stuart
　　Medical Staff Director, Phelps Memorial Health Center, Holdrege, NE, p. A408
　　Medical Staff Director, Thayer County Health Services, Hebron, NE, p. A407

EMERSON, Marsha, Administrator for Support Services, Craig General Hospital, Vinita, OK, p. A540

EMERY, Betty, Chief Financial Officer, Santiam Memorial Hospital, Stayton, OR, p. A549

EMERY, Tracy, Chief Financial Officer, Baptist Rehabilitation–Germantown, Germantown, TN, p. A606

EMGE, Joann
　　Chief Executive Officer, Sparta Community Hospital, Sparta, IL, p. A208
　　Chief Executive Officer, Sparta Community Hospital, Sparta, IL, p. A208

EMMERTON, Ernest E., Chief of Medical Staff, U. S. Air Force Regional Hospital–Sheppard, Sheppard AFB, TX, p. A667

EMPEY, Dennis, Chief Financial Officer, St. Luke's Hospital, Duluth, MN, p. A352

ENCE, Michael, Computer Specialist, Sanpete Valley Hospital, Mount Pleasant, UT, p. A677

ENDERLE, Joseph, Chief Information Officer, Veterans Affairs Medical Center, Chillicothe, OH, p. A506

ENDERS, Robert, President, Morehead Memorial Hospital, Eden, NC, p. A481

ENDERSON, Dan, Chief Financial Officer, Huguley Memorial Medical Center, Fort Worth, TX, p. A640

ENDO, Karl, Director Information Services, Portneuf Medical Center, Pocatello, ID, p. A181

ENDRES, Jack R., Interim Administrator, East Texas Medical Center Clarksville, Clarksville, TX, p. A628

ENDRICH, Joseph, M.D., President and Chief Executive Officer, Weirton Medical Center, Weirton, WV, p. A720

ENG, Bland, Chief Operating Officer, Central Florida Regional Hospital, Sanford, FL, p. A146

ENG, M.D., Jeffrey, Medical Director, HEALTHSOUTH Rehabilitation Hospital of Montgomery, Montgomery, AL, p. A22

ENGEL, Christal, Information Systems Analyst, New London Family Medical Center, New London, WI, p. A732

ENGEL, Terry, Information Technology Manager, Oakes Community Hospital, Oakes, ND, p. A500

ENGELHART, Robert, Commanding Officer, Naval Hospital, Twentynine Palms, CA, p. A97

ENGELKEN, Joseph T., Chief Executive Officer, Community Hospital Onaga, Onaga, KS, p. A254

ENGLE, Bruce, Vice President Human Resources, MedCentral Health System, Mansfield, OH, p. A517

ENGLE, Dana E., Vice President Finance, Community Hospital, Springfield, OH, p. A522

ENGLEHARDT, R.N., Becky, Clinical Operations Leader, St. Mary's Jefferson Memorial Hospital, Jefferson City, TN, p. A608

ENGLER, Jr, Frank R., Director Administrative Services, Grandview Hospital and Medical Center, Dayton, OH, p. A512

ENGLERTH, Ladonna, Administrator, East Carroll Parish Hospital, Lake Providence, LA, p. A285

ENGLISH, David J., President and Chief Executive Officer, Hospice of Northern Virginia, Falls Church, VA, p. A687

ENGLISH, M.D., Dennis, Director Health Management, Magee–Womens Hospital of UPMC, Pittsburgh, PA, p. A571

ENGLISH, Jeff, Vice President Human Resources, St. Mary's Health Care System, Athens, GA, p. A153

ENGLISH, R.N., Kathy L., Senior Vice President and Chief Operating Officer, Children's Hospital, Omaha, NE, p. A411

ENGLISH, M.D., Scott, Chief Medical Officer, Parkway Regional Medical Center, North Miami Beach, FL, p. A139

ENGSTROM, M.D., Frederick, Senior Vice President Medical Affairs, Brattleboro Retreat, Brattleboro, VT, p. A682

ENICKS, Charles, Vice President and Chief Information Officer, Children's Hospital of Philadelphia, Philadelphia, PA, p. A567

ENNEN, Philip L., Vice President and Chief Executive Officer, Community Hospitals and Wellness Centers, Bryan, OH, p. A504

ENOKA, Christina, Director Human Resources, Kahi Mohala Behavioral Health, Ewa Beach, HI, p. A173

ENSLEY, Gordon, Chief Executive Officer, Lake District Hospital, Lakeview, OR, p. A545

ENSMINGER, M.D., Bobby, Chief of Staff, Winn Parish Medical Center, Winnfield, LA, p. A294

ENSRUDE, Layne, Chief Financial Officer, First Care Health Center, Park River, ND, p. A500

ENTWISTLE, David, Senior Vice President and Chief Operating Officer, University of Wisconsin Hospital and Clinics, Madison, WI, p. A728

ENTZMINGER, Julie, Manager Human Resources, Oakes Community Hospital, Oakes, ND, p. A500

EPLEY, Dan, Chief Executive Officer, Select Specialty Hospital of Winston–Salem, Winston–Salem, NC, p. A495

EPP, Kathy, Assistant Administrator Fiscal Services, Beatrice Community Hospital and Health Center, Beatrice, NE, p. A405

EPPERSON, Edward L.
　　Chief Executive Officer, Carson Rehabilitation Center, Carson City, NV, p. A415
　　Chief Executive Officer, Carson Tahoe Hospital, Carson City, NV, p. A415

EPPERSON, Elysia, Director Human Resources, East Texas Medical Center Jacksonville, Jacksonville, TX, p. A650

EPSTEIN, M.D., Michael
　　Chief Operating Officer, Beth Israel Deaconess Medical Center, Boston, MA, p. A313
　　Chief of Staff, Children's Hospital of Michigan, Detroit, MI, p. A331

EPSTEIN, Norman B., CHE,
　　President, Chambersburg Hospital, Chambersburg, PA, p. A555
　　President, Summit Health, Chambersburg, PA, p. B103

EPSTEIN, Richard, Vice President Operations, Ocean Medical Center, Brick Township, NJ, p. A426

ERB, Gene, Senior Vice President and Chief Operationg Officer, Shore Memorial Hospital, Nassawadox, VA, p. A692

ERB–GUNDEL, Myrna, Administrator, Adair County Memorial Hospital, Greenfield, IA, p. A234

ERBES, D.D.S., William T., Chief of Staff, Aurora Medical Center of Washington County, Hartford, WI, p. A727

ERCANBRACK, M.D., Lance, Chief of Staff, St. John's Lutheran Hospital, Libby, MT, p. A400

ERDMAN, Donja, Chief Financial Officer, Marcus Daly Memorial Hospital, Hamilton, MT, p. A399

ERDMAN, Mark, Manager Information Services, Saint Michael's Hospital, Stevens Point, WI, p. A736

ERDMANN, Dorothy, President, Owatonna Hospital, Owatonna, MN, p. A359

ERDMANN, M.D., Michael, Chief of Staff, Clement J. Zablocki Veterans Affairs Medical Center, Milwaukee, WI, p. A730

ERDOS, M.D., Joseph, Chief Information Officer, Veterans Affairs Connecticut Healthcare System–New Haven Division, West Haven, CT, p. A117

ERGLE, Jeanine, Chief Financial Officer, Veterans Affairs Medical Center, Bay Pines, FL, p. A123

ERHARDT, Beverly, Chief Information Management Services, Veterans Affairs New Jersey Health Care System, East Orange, NJ, p. A427

ERICH, Kevin R., President and Chief Executive Officer, Frank R. Howard Memorial Hospital, Willits, CA, p. A99

ERICKSON, Doug, Chief Financial Officer, Prague Municipal Hospital, Prague, OK, p. A537

ERICKSON, Douglas, Associate Director, Veterans Affairs Medical Center, Albany, NY, p. A446

ERICKSON, Nancy, Administrator Information Systems, Kossuth Regional Health Center, Algona, IA, p. A228

ERICKSON, Robyn, Division Director Support Services, Hutchinson Area Health Care, Hutchinson, MN, p. A355

ERICKSON, Susan A., Executive Vice President and Administrator, Bon Secours–DePaul Medical Center, Norfolk, VA, p. A692

ERICKSON, Thomas W., Board Chairman and Chief Executive Officer, LifeCare Management Services, Plano, TX, p. B68

ERICKSON, Ty W., Chief Executive Officer, Falls Memorial Hospital, International Falls, MN, p. A355

ERICKSON, William A., Vice President and Chief Operating Officer, Sacred Heart–St. Mary's Hospitals, Rhinelander, WI, p. A734

F

FAGAN–COOK, Ann, Administrator and Chief Executive Officer, Parkview Hospital, Wheeler, TX, p. A673

FAGERBERG, Lesley, Vice President of Fiscal Services, Heart of the Rockies Regional Medical Center, Salida, CO, p. A109

FAGERSTROM, Joel, Chief Executive Officer, Christus St. Elizabeth Hospital, Beaumont, TX, p. A625

FAHD II, Charles F., Chief Executive Officer, Massena Memorial Hospital, Massena, NY, p. A456

FAHERTY, Shawn, Chief Information Management Division, Martin Army Community Hospital, Fort Benning, GA, p. A162

FAHEY, Walter, Acting Chief Information Officer, Maimonides Medical Center, New York, NY, p. A461

FAHRENBACHER, Fritz, Interim President and Chief Executive Officer, Community Hospital, Watervliet, MI, p. A347

FAHS, Melvin H., Chief Executive Officer, Community Memorial Hospital, Hicksville, OH, p. A515

FAIL, M.D., Peter, Chief of Staff, Terrebonne General Medical Center, Houma, LA, p. A282

FAILE, J. Gene, Community Chief Executive Officer, Middlesboro Appalachian Regional Hospital, Middlesboro, KY, p. A271

FAILING, Richard J., Chief Executive Officer, Kittson Memorial Healthcare Center, Hallock, MN, p. A354

FAILLA, Richard, Chief Executive Officer, Intermountain Hospital, Boise, ID, p. A177

FAIRBANKS, James, Director General Services, Navarro Regional Hospital, Corsicana, TX, p. A631

FAIRCHILD, James W., Chief Executive Officer, Holton Community Hospital, Holton, KS, p. A249

FAIRCLOTH, Robert, Director Human Resources, Presbyterian Hospital of Allen, Allen, TX, p. A620

FAISON, Linda, Director Human Resources, St. Mary's Hospital, Passaic, NJ, p. A434

FAJA, Garry C., President and Chief Executive Officer, Saint Joseph Mercy Health System, Ypsilanti, MI, p. A348

FAJT, John D., FACHE, President and Chief Executive Officer, Paris Community Hospital, Paris, IL, p. A204

FAKHAR, Shahzad, Chief Information Officer, Research Belton Hospital, Belton, MO, p. A378

FALCONE, Robert, M.D., President, Grant Medical Center, Columbus, OH, p. A510

FALCONE, M.D., Robert, Senior Operations Officer, Grant Medical Center, Columbus, OH, p. A510

FALE, Randall J., FACHE, President and Chief Executive Officer, St. Joseph's Mercy Health Center, Hot Springs National Park, AR, p. A45

FALE, Robert A., President and Chief Executive Officer, Agnesian HealthCare, Fond Du Lac, WI, p. A725

FALKNER, Keon, Administrator and Chief Executive Officer, Baptist Memorial Hospital–Lauderdale, Ripley, TN, p. A617

FALKNER, Neil, Director Human Resources Services, Veterans Affairs Medical Center, Minneapolis, MN, p. A358

FALKOWSKI, William R., Chief financial Officer, Hubbard Regional Hospital, Webster, MA, p. A324

FALL, Mark, Chief Executive Officer, Specialty Hospital, Rome, GA, p. A168

FALTERMAN, Jr, M.D., James, Medical Director, University Medical Center, Lafayette, LA, p. A284

FALTZ, M.D., Lawrence L., Senior Vice President for Medical Affairs and Medical Director, Phelps Memorial Hospital Center, Sleepy Hollow, NY, p. A472

FAMA, Cheryl A., President and Chief Executive Officer, Saint Francis Memorial Hospital, San Francisco, CA, p. A89

FANALE, M.D., James
Chief Operating Officer, Mercy Medical Center, Springfield, MA, p. A323
Chief Operating Officer, Mercy Medical Center, Springfield, MA, p. A323

FANALE, Linda, Principal Partner, Windber Medical Center, Windber, PA, p. A580

FANGMEIER, M.D., Angela, Chief of Staff, Siloam Springs Memorial Hospital, Siloam Springs, AR, p. A50

FANNIN, CPA, Allyson, Chief Financial Officer, LaSalle General Hospital, Jena, LA, p. A282

FANNING, Melinda, Director Financial Services, Tazewell Community Hospital, Tazewell, VA, p. A697

FANTUZZO, D.O., Alan, Chief of Staff, Veterans Affairs Medical Center, Bath, NY, p. A447

FARBER, Nancy D., Chief Executive Officer, Washington Township Health Care District, Fremont, CA, p. A61

FARBER, Shannan, Director Human Resources, Norton County Hospital, Norton, KS, p. A253

FARGASON, M.D., Crayton A., Medical Director, The Children's Hospital of Alabama, Birmingham, AL, p. A15

FARHOOD, Janet, Executive Vice President and Chief Operating Officer, Bone and Joint Hospital, Oklahoma City, OK, p. A535

FARIAS, Stephen, Director Information Services, Twelve Oaks Medical Center, Houston, TX, p. A648

FARINA, Jonathan, Chief Information Officer, Brattleboro Memorial Hospital, Brattleboro, VT, p. A682

FARLEY, Danny, Director Information Services, Princeton Community Hospital, Princeton, WV, p. A719

FARLEY, Forest
Director, James A. Haley Veterans Hospital, Tampa, FL, p. A148
Director, Veterans Affairs Medical Center–Lexington, Lexington, KY, p. A268

FARLEY, FACHE, P, H Fred, Chief Operating Officer, Arnot Ogden Medical Center, Elmira, NY, p. A452

FARLEY, Timothy
Vice President Human Resources, Hazleton General Hospital, Hazleton, PA, p. A560
Vice President Human Resources, Hazleton–St. Joseph Medical Center, Hazleton, PA, p. A560

FARMER, Dennis, Controller, HEALTHSOUTH Rehabilitation Hospital, Dothan, AL, p. A17

FARMER, Dinah, Director Information Services, Bluefield Regional Medical Center, Bluefield, WV, p. A713

FARMER, Kathleen, Assistant Administrator Finance and Chief Financial Officer, El Centro Regional Medical Center, El Centro, CA, p. A59

FARNAND, Lawrence J.
Treasurer and Chief Financial Officer, Geneva General Hospital, Geneva, NY, p. A452
Treasurer and Chief Financial Officer, Soldiers and Sailors Memorial Hospital of Yates County, Penn Yan, NY, p. A469

FARNELL, Leland E., President, Johnston Memorial Hospital, Smithfield, NC, p. A491

FARNSWORTH, Edward F., FACHE, President, Capital Region Medical Center, Jefferson City, MO, p. A383

FARR, Ralph, Director Clinical and Healthcare Information, University of Texas Medical Branch Hospitals, Galveston, TX, p. A641

FARR, Ron, Senior Vice President Finance, Avera McKennan Hospital and University Health Center, Sioux Falls, SD, p. A599

FARR, M.D., William L., Chief Medical Officer, University Health Care System, Augusta, GA, p. A155

FARRELL, Darin, Chief Executive Officer, Arbuckle Memorial Hospital, Sulphur, OK, p. A538

FARRELL, Mark, Manager, Human Resources, The Wisconsin Heart Hospital, Wauwatosa, WI, p. A738

FARRELL, Michael J., CHE, Chief Executive Officer, Somerset Hospital Center for Health, Somerset, PA, p. A576

FARRELL, Mike, Executive Vice President, Chief Operating Officer, Children's Hospital, Denver, CO, p. A103

FARRELL, Patrick W., Chief Executive Officer, Henrico Doctors' Hospital, Richmond, VA, p. A695

FARRELL, Vernon, Vice President Finance, Katherine Shaw Bethea Hospital, Dixon, IL, p. A192

FARRER, Deborah, Human Resources Manager, Advance Care Hospital, Hot Springs National Park, AR, p. A44

FARRIS, Bain J., President and Chief Executive Officer, Daughters of Charity Health System, Los Altos Hills, CA, p. B35

FARRIS, James R., CHE, Chief Executive Officer, Union County Hospital District, Anna, IL, p. A183

FARRIS, Randy, Chief Fiscal Service, Overton Brooks Veterans Affairs Medical Center, Shreveport, LA, p. A292

FARROW, Randy, President, River Falls Area Hospital, River Falls, WI, p. A735

FATA, Sheila, Administrator, Christus St. Catherine Hospital, Katy, TX, p. A650

FATCH, Casey, Chief Executive Officer, Hollywood Community Hospital, Los Angeles, CA, p. A70

FATTIG, Marty, Administrator and Chief Executive Officer, Nemaha County Hospital, Auburn, NE, p. A404

FAUCHEUX, Lisa, Director Human Resources, St. James Parish Hospital, Lutcher, LA, p. A285

FAUGHT, Charles J., Chief Financial Officer, Burnett Medical Center, Grantsburg, WI, p. A726

FAULK, A. Donald, FACHE, President, Medical Center of Central Georgia, Macon, GA, p. A165

FAULK, Gordon, Administrator, Elmore Community Hospital, Wetumpka, AL, p. A25

FAULKNER, Charlie, President, Baptist Princeton, Birmingham, AL, p. A14

FAULKNER, David M., Chief Executive Officer, Central Montana Medical Center, Lewistown, MT, p. A400

FAULKNER, Nancy, Chief Executive Officer, Heritage Oaks Hospital, Sacramento, CA, p. A84

FAULKNER, Robert, Administrator, Leake Memorial Hospital, Carthage, MS, p. A367

FAULWELL, James A., Chief Executive Officer and Administrator, Dells Area Health Center, Dell Rapids, SD, p. A595

FAUQUIER, Tom, Senior Vice President Support Services, Broadlawns Medical Center, Des Moines, IA, p. A232

FAUS, Douglas, Chief Executive Officer, Estes Park Medical Center, Estes Park, CO, p. A105

FAUST, Bill D., Administrator, Floyd County Memorial Hospital, Charles City, IA, p. A230

FAUX, M.D., Nelson, Chief of Staff, John C. Lincoln Hospital – North Mountain, Phoenix, AZ, p. A34

FAVRET, John M., Director, Eastern State Hospital, Williamsburg, VA, p. A698

FAWELL, Tom, Chief Medical Officer, Littleton Adventist Hospital, Littleton, CO, p. A107

FAWKES, DeLany, Vice President and Chief Financial Officer, Southwest Medical Center, Liberal, KS, p. A251

FAWZY, Fawzy I., M.D., Chief Executive Officer, University of California Los Angeles Neuropsychiatric Hospital, Los Angeles, CA, p. A73

FAYEN, Edward J., Chief of Operations and Support, Washington Township Health Care District, Fremont, CA, p. A61

FEARS, John R.
Director, Carl T. Hayden Veterans Affairs Medical Center, Phoenix, AZ, p. A33
Director, Carl T. Hayden Veterans Affairs Medical Center, Phoenix, AZ, p. A33

FEASEL, Jeff, Chief Executive Officer, Halifax Fish Community Health, Daytona Beach, FL, p. A127

FEASELMAN, Linda, Chief Information Officer, Veterans Affairs Medical Center, Decatur, GA, p. A160

FEAVER, Ann, Administrator, HEALTHSOUTH Bakersfield Rehabilitation Hospital, Bakersfield, CA, p. A54

FEAZELL, Samuel G., Chief Executive Officer, San Angelo Community Medical Center, San Angelo, TX, p. A663

FEBACH, M. Colleen, Administrator, Deer Park Hospital, Deer Park, WA, p. A702

FEDELE, Jerry J., President and Chief Executive Officer, West Penn Allegheny Health System, Pittsburgh, PA, p. B122

FEDER, Eric, Chief Operating Officer, Bayfront Medical Center, Saint Petersburg, FL, p. A145

FEDERSPIEL, John C., President and Chief Executive Officer, Hudson Valley Hospital Center, Cortlandt Manor, NY, p. A451

FEE, Jeff, President and Chief Executive Officer, Parkridge Medical Center, Chattanooga, TN, p. A604

FEE, M.D., Maureen, Chief Medical Officer, St. Christopher's Hospital for Children, Philadelphia, PA, p. A570

FEEMAN, Kimberly, Vice President Human Resources, The Good Samaritan Hospital, Lebanon, PA, p. A563

FEENEY, Jeffrey A., Interim Chief Executive Officer, North Ridge Medical Center, Fort Lauderdale, FL, p. A129

FEENEY, Keith, Director Human Resources, Southern Maryland Hospital Center, Clinton, MD, p. A306

FEGAN, M.D., Jeffrey, Chief of Staff, Valley View Hospital, Glenwood Springs, CO, p. A106

FEHR, Mike, Director Information System, Jupiter Medical Center, Jupiter, FL, p. A133

FEIGIN, M.D., Ralph D., Physician–in–Chief, Texas Children's Hospital, Houston, TX, p. A647

FEIKE, Jeffrey, President and Chief Administrative Officer, Fort Loudoun Medical Center, Lenoir City, TN, p. A611

FEIL, Julie, Accountant, Cavalier County Memorial Hospital, Langdon, ND, p. A499

FEILER, Kenneth H., President and Chief Executive Officer, Rose Medical Center, Denver, CO, p. A104

FEILNER, Marge
 Director Information Services, SSM St. Joseph Health Center, Saint Charles, MO, p. A390
 Manager Information Systems, SSM St. Joseph Hospital West, Lake Saint Louis, MO, p. A386

FEINBERG, M.D., David, Medical Director, University of California Los Angeles Neuropsychiatric Hospital, Los Angeles, CA, p. A73

FEINER, M.D., David, Chief of Staff, Calais Regional Hospital, Calais, ME, p. A297

FEINGOLD, Elizabeth, Interim Director Human Resources, Skagit Valley Hospital, Mount Vernon, WA, p. A704

FEINOUR, Terry, Senior Vice President and Corporate Services, Bayhealth Medical Center, Dover, DE, p. A119

FEISAL, Phil, Administrator, Allen Bennett Hospital, Greer, SC, p. A589

FEIST, Patricia, Manager Human Resources, Crook County Medical Services District, Sundance, WY, p. A742

FEISTMAN, Charles H., Chief Resources Health Care Group, Veterans Affairs Long Beach Healthcare System, Long Beach, CA, p. A69

FEIT, Marcy L., President and Chief Executive Officer, ValleyCare Medical Center, Pleasanton, CA, p. A82

FELBER, M.D., Matt, Medical Director, Pender Community Hospital, Pender, NE, p. A412

FELBINGER, Richard, Interim Chief Financial Officer, Borgess Medical Center, Kalamazoo, MI, p. A338

FELDMAN, Mitchell S.
 Chief Executive Officer, Delray Medical Center, Delray Beach, FL, p. A127
 Chief Executive Officer, Pinecrest Rehabilitation Hospital, Delray Beach, FL, p. A127

FELDT, Roger D., FACHE, Interim President and Chief Executive Officer, J. C. Blair Memorial Hospital, Huntingdon, PA, p. A561

FELEGE, Lester, Controller, HEALTHSOUTH New England Rehabilitation Hospital, Woburn, MA, p. A325

FELGAR, Alvin D., President and Chief Executive Officer, Frisbie Memorial Hospital, Rochester, NH, p. A423

FELIBERTI, Manuel, Medical Director, Del Sol Medical Center, El Paso, TX, p. A637

FELICI, Brian K.
 President and Chief Executive Officer, East Ohio Regional Hospital, Martins Ferry, OH, p. A517
 President and Chief Executive Officer, Ohio Valley Health Services and Education Corporation, Wheeling, WV, p. B81
 President and Chief Executive Officer, Ohio Valley Medical Center, Wheeling, WV, p. A721

FELICIANO, Jose R., Chief Executive Officer, Ryder Memorial Hospital, Humacao, PR, p. A745

FELIX, Larry A., CHE, Administrator, Ransom Memorial Hospital, Ottawa, KS, p. A254

FELKNER, Joseph, Chief Financial Officer and Senior Vice President Finance, Baptist Hospital, Pensacola, FL, p. A142

FELLOWES, M.D., S Gale, Chief Medical Officer, Memorial Health Care System, Chattanooga, TN, p. A603

FELLOWS, Steven A., Executive Vice President and Chief Operating Officer, Santa Barbara Cottage Hospital, Santa Barbara, CA, p. A92

FELS, R Jeffrey, Vice President Finance and Support Services, Brown County General Hospital, Georgetown, OH, p. A514

FELTMAN, Steven, Chief Financial Officer, Grand Itasca Clinic and Hospital, Grand Rapids, MN, p. A354

FELTON, David, President and Chief Executive Officer, Community Memorial Hospital, Hamilton, NY, p. A453

FELTON, Debby, Chief Financial Officer, Central Arkansas Veterans Healthcare System, Little Rock, AR, p. A46

FELTS, Dave, Chief Informaiton Systems, Logan Regional Hospital, Logan, UT, p. A677

FENCEL, Michael M., Chief Executive Officer, Brandon Regional Hospital, Brandon, FL, p. A124

FENDER, Hank, Chief Financial Officer, Trinity Community Medical Center of Brenham, Brenham, TX, p. A626

FENDT, Phil, Chief Financial Officer, Memorial Hospital, Aurora, NE, p. A404

FENER, Michael, Associate Executive Director Finance, North Shore University Hospital at Plainview, Plainview, NY, p. A469

FENNELL, Jennifer, Chief Financial Officer, St. John Oakland Hospital, Madison Heights, MI, p. A339

FENSKE, Candace, Administrator, Madelia Community Hospital, Madelia, MN, p. A356

FENSKE, M.D., Scott, Medical Director, Kindred Hospital–Milwaukee, Milwaukee, WI, p. A731

FENSKE, William, Vice President Finance, Waupun Memorial Hospital, Waupun, WI, p. A737

FENSTEMACHER, Keith A., President and Chief Executive Officer, Faxton–St. Luke's Healthcare, Utica, NY, p. A474

FENTON, John V., Chief Executive Officer, Los Angeles Metropolitan Medical Center, Los Angeles, CA, p. A71

FENWICK, Sandra, Chief Operating Officer, Children's Hospital Boston, Boston, MA, p. A313

FERAUDO, Mary, Chief Executive Officer, Trinity Community Hospital, Jasper, FL, p. A133

FERCH, A. Wayne, President and Chief Executive Officer, Feather River Hospital, Paradise, CA, p. A80

FERGUS, Linda, Director Information Systems, Alle–Kiski Medical Center, Natrona Heights, PA, p. A566

FERGUSON, Cheryl, Associate Administrator, Sioux Valley Canby Campus, Canby, MN, p. A351

FERGUSON, Christine C., Commissioner, Massschusetts Department of Public Health, Boston, MA, p. B72

FERGUSON, M.D., Dan, Chief Medical Officer, Mercy General Hospital, Sacramento, CA, p. A85

FERGUSON, Gary W., Executive Vice President and Chief Operating Officer, Christiana Care Health System, Wilmington, DE, p. A120

FERGUSON, Gordon, Senior Vice President and Chief Operating Officer, Middle Tennessee Medical Center, Murfreesboro, TN, p. A614

FERGUSON, John P., FACHE, President and Chief Executive Officer, Hackensack University Medical Center, Hackensack, NJ, p. A429

FERGUSON, Karen, Director Human Resources, Johnson County Healthcare Center, Buffalo, WY, p. A739

FERGUSON, Paul, Director Information Systems, Medical Center at Terrell, Terrell, TX, p. A669

FERGUSON, Thomas, Senior Vice President and Chief Human Resources Officer, New York–Presbyterian Hospital, New York, NY, p. A463

FERGUSON, M.D., William, Chief of Staff, Ridgecrest Regional Hospital, Ridgecrest, CA, p. A84

FERLISI, Gerald R., Vice President Finance, Hospital for Joint Diseases Orthopaedic Institute, New York, NY, p. A460

FERNANDEZ, Aurelio, Chief Executive Officer, Florida Medical Center, Fort Lauderdale, FL, p. A128

FERNANDEZ, Gregory, Chief Financial Officer, Albert Lindley Lee Memorial Hospital, Fulton, NY, p. A452

FERNANDEZ, John, Director, Human Resources, Mariners Hospital, Tavernier, FL, p. A149

FERNANDEZ, Oscar J., Chief Financial Officer, Good Samaritan Medical Center, West Palm Beach, FL, p. A150

FERRANTE, Fritz, Information Services Manager, Providence Kodiak Island Medical Center, Kodiak, AK, p. A27

FERRANTO, Carmen N., Chief Executive Officer, Warren State Hospital, Warren, PA, p. A578

FERRAUIOLA, Lex, Vice President Information Technology and Chief Information Officer, Hackensack University Medical Center, Hackensack, NJ, p. A429

FERRELLI, John J., Chief Executive Officer, John F. Kennedy Memorial Hospital, Indio, CA, p. A64

FERREN, Alison, Director Information Services, Abington Memorial Hospital, Abington, PA, p. A551

FERRERI, Anthony C.
 President and Chief Executive Officer, Staten Island University Hospital, New York, NY, p. A465
 President and Chief Executive Officer, Staten Island University Hospital–Concord, New York, NY, p. A466

FERRIGNO, Sandie, Human Resouces Director, Mercy Hospital Anderson, Cincinnati, OH, p. A507

FERRONI, M.D., Karen, Medical Director, Holyoke Medical Center, Holyoke, MA, p. A318

FERRY, Thomas P., Administrator and Chief Executive Officer, Alfred I. duPont Hospital for Children, Wilmington, DE, p. A119

FERULLO, Andre J., Senior Vice President Human Resources, Hackensack University Medical Center, Hackensack, NJ, p. A429

FESKE, Barbara, Administrator Management and Support, Our Lady of Lourdes Regional Medical Center, Lafayette, LA, p. A284

FETTER, Alfred R., Vice President Finance, Barnert Hospital, Paterson, NJ, p. A434

FETTER, Lee F., President and Senior Executive Officer, St. Louis Children's Hospital, Saint Louis, MO, p. A392

FETTER, Trevor, President and Chief Executive Officer, TENET Healthcare Corporation, Dallas, TX, p. B105

FETTERS, Larry S., Administrator, Foothill Presbyterian Hospital–Morris L. Johnston Memorial, Glendora, CA, p. A63

FETTERS, Valerie, Chief Financial Officer, Hillsdale Community Health Center, Hillsdale, MI, p. A336

FEUQUAY, Judith K., Chief Executive Officer, Nevada Regional Medical Center, Nevada, MO, p. A388

FEYH, Jerry G., Vice President Financial Services, Marion General Hospital, Marion, OH, p. A517

FIAMINGO, Nancy A.
 Senior Vice President and Chief Operating Officer, Muhlenberg Regional Medical Center, North Plainfield, NJ, p. A433
 Senior Vice President and Chief Operating Officer, Muhlenberg Regional Medical Center, North Plainfield, NJ, p. A433

FICCHI, Adrienne, Vice President Information Management, Veterans Affairs Medical Center, Philadelphia, PA, p. A570

FICHTEL, Mike, Senior Vice President and Chief Financial Officer, Children's Medical Center of Dallas, Dallas, TX, p. A632

FICHTL, Tayo, Chief Operating Officer, Bayshore Medical Center, Pasadena, TX, p. A660

FICKEN, Robert A., Vice President Finance, Touro Infirmary, New Orleans, LA, p. A290

FICKLE, Marvin D., M.D., Superintendent, Oregon State Hospital, Salem, OR, p. A548

FICKLIN, Dennis E., Chief Executive Officer, Family Health West, Fruita, CO, p. A105

FICKLIN, Terry, Director Information Systems, St. Bernardine Medical Center, San Bernardino, CA, p. A86

FIDUCIA, Karen A., Interim Chief Executive Officer, Wallace Thomson Hospital, Union, SC, p. A592

FIEKER, Dan
 Chief Executive Officer, Tulsa Regional Medical Center, Tulsa, OK, p. A540
 Chief Executive Officer, Tulsa Regional Medical Center, Tulsa, OK, p. A540

FIELDER, Barbara, Unit Financial Director, Saint Joseph Mercy Saline Hospital, Saline, MI, p. A345

FIELDER, Jaf, Director Human Resources, Willis–Knighton Medical Center, Shreveport, LA, p. A293

FIELDING, David, Chief Executive Officer, Hospice of Palm Beach County, West Palm Beach, FL, p. A150

FIELDING, Mindra, Director Information Services, South Coast Medical Center, Laguna Beach, CA, p. A66

FIELDING, Wendy, Vice President Finance and Support Services, Mount Desert Island Hospital, Bar Harbor, ME, p. A296

FIELDS Jr, Clarence, President and Chief Executive Officer, Goodall–Witcher Healthcare, Clifton, TX, p. A629

FIELDS, Donald, Community Chief Executive Officer, Whitesburg Appalachian Regional Hospital, Whitesburg, KY, p. A275

FIELDS, Duane, Controller, Russell Regional Hospital, Russell, KS, p. A256

FIELDS, Glenn, Vice President, Human Resources, Saint John's Health System, Anderson, IN, p. A211

FIELDS, Lexi M., Vice President, Finance, North Hawaii Community Hospital, Kamuela, HI, p. A175

FIFE, Bill, Vice President Operations, Carson City Hospital, Carson City, MI, p. A329

FIFER, Joseph J., Senior Vice President Corporate Services and Chief Financial Officer, Spectrum Health, Grand Rapids, MI, p. A335

FIGUEROA, Barbara, Controller, Kern Valley Healthcare District, Lake Isabella, CA, p. A66

FIGUEROA, Maria, Director Human Resources, Ryder Memorial Hospital, Humacao, PR, p. A745

FIGURA, Elizabeth, Vice President, Human Resources, Brooks Rehabilitation Hospital, Jacksonville, FL, p. A132

FIKE, Ruthita J.
President, Loma Linda University Behavioral Medicine Center, Redlands, CA, p. A83
Chief Executive Officer, Loma Linda University Medical Center, Loma Linda, CA, p. A68
Chief Executive Officer, Loma Linda University Medical Center, Loma Linda, CA, p. A68

FIKES, Jerald, Administrator and Chief Executive Officer, Mayers Memorial Hospital District, Fall River Mills, CA, p. A60

FIKSE, David J., Chief Executive Officer, Southside Regional Medical Center, Petersburg, VA, p. A694

FILER, Christine, Director Human Resources, HEALTHSOUTH Rehabilitation Hospital of Altoona, Altoona, PA, p. A552

FILES, Mike, Chief Executive Officer, Triumph Hospital East Houston, Channelview, TX, p. A628

FILLER, Scott, Administrator, HEALTHSOUTH Rehabilitation Hospital of Altoona, Altoona, PA, p. A552

FILOSA, Frank, Fiscal Manager, Veterans Affairs Medical Center, Washington, DC, p. A122

FILSON, Debbie, Office Manager, Ashland Health Center, Ashland, KS, p. A244

FINAN Jr, John J., President and Chief Executive Officer, Franciscan Missionaries of Our Lady Health System, Inc., Baton Rouge, LA, p. B45

FINCH, M.D., Al, Executive Medical Director, Children's Hospital of The King's Daughters, Norfolk, VA, p. A692

FINCH Jr, J. W., Administrator, Elkview General Hospital, Hobart, OK, p. A531

FINCH, John, Vice President Corporate Development, Benedictine Hospital, Kingston, NY, p. A455

FINCH, Kenneth A.
Chief Executive Officer, Metroplex Adventist Hospital, Killeen, TX, p. A651
Chief Executive Officer, Rollins–Brook Community Hospital, Lampasas, TX, p. A652

FINCH, Ronald A., Ed.D., Director Healthcare, Mt. Carmel Behavioral Healthcare System, Newark, NJ, p. A432

FINCH, Teresa, Chief Financial Officer, Grady Memorial Hospital, Atlanta, GA, p. A154

FINCK–BOYLE, Janine, Administrator, Hadley Memorial Hospital, Washington, DC, p. A121

FINDO, Charles
Chief Financial Officer, HEALTHSOUTH Rehabilitation Hospital, Miami, FL, p. A137
Controller, HEALTHSOUTH Rehabilitation Hospital of Tallahassee, Tallahassee, FL, p. A147

FINE, David J.
Chief Executive Officer, St. Luke's Episcopal Health System, Houston, TX, p. B102
Chief Executive Officer, St. Luke's Episcopal Hospital, Houston, TX, p. A647

FINE, Peter S., FACHE, President and Chief Executive Officer, Banner Health, Phoenix, AZ, p. B13

FINE, Stuart H., Chief Executive Officer, Grand View Hospital, Sellersville, PA, p. A575

FINE, Vicky, Vice President and Chief Financial Officer, Unity Health Center, Shawnee, OK, p. A538

FINEGAN, Michael S.
Director, Veterans Affairs Western New York Healthcare System–Batavia Division, Batavia, NY, p. A447
Director, Veterans Affairs Western New York Healthcare System–Buffalo Division, Buffalo, NY, p. A449

FINESTEIN, Brian, President, Graduate Hospital, Philadelphia, PA, p. A568

FINK, Eileen, Health Information Officer, North Big Horn Hospital District, Lovell, WY, p. A741

FINK, Robert M., Chief Executive Officer, Ridgeview Institute, Smyrna, GA, p. A169

FINKEL, Steven, Vice President and Treasurer, Reading Hospital and Medical Center, West Reading, PA, p. A579

FINKELSTEIN, Mark, Chief Financial Officer, Southern Hills Medical Center, Nashville, TN, p. A615

FINKLEIN, Terry O., Chief Executive Officer, Columbia Memorial Hospital, Astoria, OR, p. A542

FINLEY, Edward, Administrator, Wray Community District Hospital, Wray, CO, p. A111

FINLEY, Frances R., Administrator, Aurora Medical Center of Oshkosh, Oshkosh, WI, p. A733

FINLEY, Jane
Interim Service Area Manager, Kaiser Foundation Hospital, Los Angeles, CA, p. A70
Interim Service Area Manager, Kaiser Foundation Hospital, Los Angeles, CA, p. A71
Interim Service Area Manager, Kaiser Foundation Hospital, Los Angeles, CA, p. A70
Interim Service Area Manager, Kaiser Foundation Hospital, Los Angeles, CA, p. A71

FINLEY, Tommy, Chief Information Officer, Rutherford Hospital, Rutherfordton, NC, p. A491

FINLON, Anne H., Chief Financial Officer, Rockdale Medical Center, Conyers, GA, p. A159

FINN, Barry C., President and Chief Executive Officer, Rush–Copley Medical Center, Aurora, IL, p. A184

FINN, David S., Chief Information Officer, Texas Children's Hospital, Houston, TX, p. A647

FINN, Donald J.
Chief Executive Officer, Lake Area Hospital, Webster, SD, p. A600
Chief Executive Officer, Lake Area Hospital, Webster, SD, p. A600

FINN, Patti, Assistant Administrator, Fulton County Health Center, Wauseon, OH, p. A524

FINNEGAN, John R., Chief Executive Officer, Central Mississippi Medical Center, Jackson, MS, p. A370

FINNEN, Wendy, Director Human Resources, Parkview Hospital, El Reno, OK, p. A530

FINNEY, Michele, Chief Executive Officer, Los Alamitos Medical Center, Los Alamitos, CA, p. A69

FINSTAD, M.D., Gary A., Chief of Staff, Kern Valley Healthcare District, Lake Isabella, CA, p. A66

FINTON, M.D., Chris, Senior Vice President Medical Staff Services, Holmes Regional Medical Center, Melbourne, FL, p. A136

FIORET, M.D., Phil, Vice President Medical Affairs, King's Daughters Medical Center, Ashland, KY, p. A261

FIRES, Wiley M., Administrator, Shamrock General Hospital, Shamrock, TX, p. A667

FIRESTONE, Thomas J., M.D., President and Chief Executive Officer, Southern Illinois Hospital Services, Carbondale, IL, p. B101

FISCHELS, Diane, Vice President Organizational Development, Mercy Medical Center – North Iowa, Mason City, IA, p. A238

FISCHER, Angie, Chief Financial Officer, Loring Hospital, Sac City, IA, p. A241

FISCHER, CPA, Karen, Controller, HEALTHSOUTH Rehabilitation Hospital–Wichita Falls, Wichita Falls, TX, p. A674

FISCHER, Orvie E., Senior Vice President and Chief Financial Officer, Marietta Memorial Hospital, Marietta, OH, p. A517

FISCHER, Sheri, Human Resources Manager, Grant Regional Health Center, Lancaster, WI, p. A728

FISCHER, M.D., Stephen, Chief of Staff, Cypress Fairbanks Medical Center, Houston, TX, p. A644

FISH, Amy, Administrator, Warren Memorial Hospital, Friend, NE, p. A406

FISH, Carrie, Vice President and Chief Operating Officer, Florida Hospital Waterman, Tavares, FL, p. A149

FISH, David B., Executive Vice President and Administrator, St. Joseph's Hospital, Chippewa Falls, WI, p. A724

FISH, Patsy, Chief, Human Resources Management, James H. Quillen Veterans Affairs Medical Center, Mountain Home, TN, p. A614

FISHBERG, M.D., Alex, Chief Medical Officer, Wabash County Hospital, Wabash, IN, p. A227

FISHER, Angela, Director Human Resources, Franklin Hospital Medical Center, Valley Stream, NY, p. A475

FISHER, M.D., David J., Medical Director, Children's Hospital, Columbus, OH, p. A510

FISHER, Diana D., President and Chief Executive Officer, Morrow County Hospital, Mount Gilead, OH, p. A519

FISHER, Edward L., President and Chief Information Officer, The William W. Backus Hospital, Norwich, CT, p. A116

FISHER, Jan E., President and Chief Executive Officer, Soldiers and Sailors Memorial Hospital, Wellsboro, PA, p. A578

FISHER, Jennifer, Manager Human Resources, Henry County Hospital, Napoleon, OH, p. A519

FISHER, Joey, Chief Executive Officer, Kindred Hospital–Charleston, Charleston, SC, p. A584

FISHER, Ken, Interim Chief Financial Officer, Glenwood Regional Medical Center, West Monroe, LA, p. A294

FISHER, Linda, Director Information Services, Huntington Hospital, Huntington, NY, p. A454

FISHER, Michael W., Chief Financial Officer, Veterans Affairs Medical Center, New Orleans, LA, p. A290

FISHER, Robert E., President and Chief Executive Officer, Brookville Hospital, Brookville, PA, p. A553

FISHER CRUM, Nancy, Chief Financial Officer, MetroHealth Medical Center, Cleveland, OH, p. A509

FISHERO, Harvey L., President and Chief Executive Officer, Medical Center of Plano, Plano, TX, p. A661

FISHKIN, M.D., Edward, Medical Director, Woodhull Medical and Mental Health Center, New York, NY, p. A466

FISHMAN, Len, President and Chief Executive Officer, Hebrew Rehabilitation Center for Aged, Boston, MA, p. A314

FISK, Art, Chief Information Officer, North Kansas City Hospital, Kansas City, MO, p. A384

FISNE, Joseph, Chief Information Officer, Community Medical Center, Scranton, PA, p. A575

FISSEL, Bryan, Director of Finance, Hillcrest Specialty Hospital, Tulsa, OK, p. A539

FISSORI, Michele, Chief Financial Officer, North Star Behavioral Health System, Anchorage, AK, p. A26

FITE, Margaret, Vice President Human Resources, Gateway Health System, Clarksville, TN, p. A604

FITTS, Billy, Assistant Administrator, Linden Municipal Hospital, Linden, TX, p. A653

FITZ Jr, Thomas E., FACHE, President and Chief Executive Officer, St. Mary's Health Care System, Athens, GA, p. A153

FITZ–PATRICK, R.N., Christina, Chief Operating Officer, Nazareth Hospital, Philadelphia, PA, p. A569

FITZGERALD, Gerald D., President and Chief Executive Officer, Oakwood Healthcare, Inc., Dearborn, MI, p. B81

FITZGERALD, John L., Vice President and Administrator, Inova Fair Oaks Hospital, Fairfax, VA, p. A687

FITZGERALD, John R., Interim Chief Financial Officer, Nantucket Cottage Hospital, Nantucket, MA, p. A321

FITZGERALD, Larry, Chief Financial Officer, University of Virginia Medical Center, Charlottesville, VA, p. A686

FITZGERALD, Mike
Chief Financial Officer, St. Clare Hospital, Tacoma, WA, p. A710
Chief Financial Officer, St. Joseph Medical Center, Tacoma, WA, p. A710

FITZGERALD, Rhonda, Vice President Patient Care Services, Queen of the Valley Hospital, Napa, CA, p. A77

FITZGIBBON, Susan H.
President and Executive Vice President, Annie Penn Hospital, Reidsville, NC, p. A490
President, Annie Penn Hospital, Reidsville, NC, p. A490

FITZHUGH, Clayton, Vice President of Human Resources, Holy Cross Hospital, Fort Lauderdale, FL, p. A128

FITZPATRICK, James G., President and Chief Executive Officer, Mercy Medical Center – North Iowa, Mason City, IA, p. A238

FITZPATRICK, Paul, Manager Information Technology, Deaconess Medical Center–Spokane, Spokane, WA, p. A709

FITZPATRICK, Thomas, Chief Medical Staff, Walter Reed Army Medical Center, Washington, DC, p. A122

FLAHERTY, Dan, Chief of Medical Staff, Prairie Lakes Healthcare System, Watertown, SD, p. A600

FLAHERTY, John, Controller, Fairlawn Rehabilitation Hospital, Worcester, MA, p. A325

FLAHERTY, Patrick, Director Management Information, Naval Hospital, Bremerton, WA, p. A701

FLAHERTY, Tom, Assistant Administrator, Los Angeles County Central Jail Hospital, Los Angeles, CA, p. A71

FLAIG, Jack T., Chief Executive Officer, Samaritan North Lincoln Hospital, Lincoln City, OR, p. A545

FLAIG, William G., Administrator, Douglas County Hospital, Alexandria, MN, p. A349

FLAKE, Glenn M., Executive Director, Newnan Hospital East, Newnan, GA, p. A167

FLAKE, Robert, Chief Financial Officer, St. John's Medical Center and Living Center, Jackson, WY, p. A740

FLAKS, Jeffrey A., Executive Vice President and Chief Operating Officer, MidState Medical Center, Meriden, CT, p. A114

FLAKUS, Karleen, Human Resource Director, Winner Regional Healthcare Center, Winner, SD, p. A601

FLAMINI, Joseph, Vice President Operations, St. Francis Medical Center, Trenton, NJ, p. A437

FLANAGAN, Susan, Chief Operating Officer, Lucile Salter Packard Children's Hospital at Stanford, Palo Alto, CA, p. A80

FLANNERY, Patrick, Administrator, Warm Springs Rehabilitation Hospital, Corpus Christi, TX, p. A631

FLANSBURG, Gary, Chief Financial Officer, Memorial Hospital, Colorado Springs, CO, p. A102

FLAUM, M.D., Morris, Vice President Medical Affairs, California Pacific Medical Center, San Francisco, CA, p. A88

FLEECE, Monica M., Director Human Resources, Emory Dunwoody Medical Center, Atlanta, GA, p. A153

FLEEGLER, M.D., Bruce, Chief Medical Officer, Sarasota Memorial Hospital, Sarasota, FL, p. A146

FLEISCHMANN, Larry, M.D., President, Children's Hospital of Michigan, Detroit, MI, p. A331

FLEISCHMANN, Tim, Chief Financial Officer, Tuality Healthcare, Hillsboro, OR, p. A544

FLEITES, Fernando, Vice President Human Resources, Holy Cross Hospital, Silver Spring, MD, p. A311

FLEMING, Cheryl, Administrator, HEALTHSOUTH Rehabilitation Hospital of York, York, PA, p. A580

FLEMING, Christy, Chief Financial Officer, Dickenson Community Hospital, Clintwood, VA, p. A687

FLEMING, Donald, Chief Information Officer, Brookhaven Memorial Hospital Medical Center, Patchogue, NY, p. A469

FLEMING Jr, Pearce W., CHE, Chief Executive Officer, Summerville Medical Center, Summerville, SC, p. A592

FLEMING, Robert, Administrator, Brooke Glen Behavioral Hospital, Fort Washington, PA, p. A559

FLEMING, Wanda C., Administrator and Chief Executive Officer, Claiborne County Hospital, Port Gibson, MS, p. A375

FLESCH, Timothy A., President and Chief Executive Officer, St. Mary's Medical Center of Evansville, Evansville, IN, p. A215

FLETCHALL, Loretta, Director Human Resources, Hutchinson Hospital Corporation, Hutchinson, KS, p. A249

FLETCHALL, Terry L., Administrator, Santiam Memorial Hospital, Stayton, OR, p. A549

FLETCHER, Allen P., President and Chief Executive Officer, Northeast Alabama Regional Medical Center, Anniston, AL, p. A13

FLETCHER, Gary, Executive Vice President, St. Luke's Regional Medical Center, Boise, ID, p. A178

FLETCHER, John
Chief Executive Officer, Patrick B. Harris Psychiatric Hospital, Anderson, SC, p. A583
Senior Vice President Finance, Salinas Valley Memorial Healthcare System, Salinas, CA, p. A86

FLETCHER, Marvella, Vice President Fiscal Services, Wayne Hospital, Greenville, OH, p. A515

FLICKINGER, Kenneth E., Corporate Vice President Finance, Chester County Hospital, West Chester, PA, p. A578

FLINN, James T.
Chief Administrative Officer, Pomerado Hospital, Poway, CA, p. A82
Chief Administrative Officer, Pomerado Hospital, Poway, CA, p. A82

FLINT, Jr, M.D., Loring S., Senior Vice President Medical Affairs, Baystate Medical Center, Springfield, MA, p. A323

FLIPPIN, Arthur, M.D., Administrator, Kaiser Foundation Hospital, San Diego, CA, p. A87

FLODEN, Scott, Chief Executive Officer, Kindred Hospital–Ontario, Ontario, CA, p. A79

FLOOD, Nathan
Chief Operating Officer and Chief Financial Officer, Plains Memorial Hospital, Dimmitt, TX, p. A635
Chief Operating Officer and Chief Financial Officer, Plains Memorial Hospital, Dimmitt, TX, p. A635

FLORENCE, Jared, Financial Coordinator, St. Elizabeth Ann Seton Specialty Care Hospital, Evansville, IN, p. A215

FLORENTINE, Erich, Vice President Human Resources and Organizational Effectiveness, South Jersey Healthcare, Bridgeton, NJ, p. A426

FLORES, Cathy, R.N., Administrator and Controller, Chowchilla District Memorial Hospital, Chowchilla, CA, p. A56

FLORES Jr, Ernest, Administrator, Dimmit County Memorial Hospital, Carrizo Springs, TX, p. A628

FLORES Jr, Ernesto M., Vice President and Administrator, Christus Spohn Hospital Kleberg, Kingsville, TX, p. A651

FLORES, Jeanne, Senior Vice President Human Resources and Organizational Development, Cedars–Sinai Medical Center, Los Angeles, CA, p. A69

FLORINE, M.D., Craig, President Medical Staff, Memorial Medical Center, Ashland, WI, p. A722

FLORO, Mark K., Chief Executive Officer, Kindred Hospital–Dayton, Dayton, OH, p. A512

FLOTTE', J. L., Administrator, TOPS Surgical Specialty Hospital, Houston, TX, p. A648

FLOWERS, Conrad G., Chief Executive Officer, Riverside Medical Center, Franklinton, LA, p. A281

FLOWERS, James J., D.O., President and Chief Executive Officer, St. Agnes Continuing Care Center, Philadelphia, PA, p. A569

FLOWERS, Randel, Ph.D., Administrator, Clinton County Hospital, Albany, KY, p. A261

FLOYD, Duane, Vice President Human Resources and Support Services, Watertown Memorial Hospital, Watertown, WI, p. A737

FLOYD, Greg, Chief Executive Officer, Select Specialty Hospital–South Dallas, De Soto, TX, p. A635

FLOYD, James R., Director, Veterans Affairs Salt Lake City Health Care System, Salt Lake City, UT, p. A680

FLOYD, Kiley, Administrator, Osborne County Memorial Hospital, Osborne, KS, p. A254

FLOYD, Richard B., President and Chief Executive Officer, Sherman Hospital, Elgin, IL, p. A193

FLOYD, Tonya, Manager Human Resources, Veterans Affairs Medical Center, Marion, IL, p. A200

FLYER, Jerrold, Deputy Commander, U. S. Air Force Hospital Luke, Glendale, AZ, p. A31

FLYNN, Brian T., Chief Executive Officer, Manatee Memorial Hospital, Bradenton, FL, p. A124

FLYNN, M.D., James P G.
Vice President Medical Affairs, James Lawrence Kernan Hospital, Baltimore, MD, p. A303
Vice President Medical Affairs, University Specialty Hospital, Baltimore, MD, p. A305

FLYNN, Kerry, Vice President Human Resources, Northern Westchester Hospital, Mount Kisco, NY, p. A457

FLYNN, Loretta, Director Human Resources, Gulf Coast Medical Center, Wharton, TX, p. A673

FLYNN, Matthew, Vice President and Chief Financial Officer, St. Joseph Hospital, Bangor, ME, p. A296

FLYNN, Patrick D., Chief Executive Officer, Wilson N. Jones Medical Center, Sherman, TX, p. A667

FLYNN, Rick, Vice President Human Resources, Shamokin Area Community Hospital, Coal Township, PA, p. A555

FOCHT, M.D., Glenn, Vice President Medical Affairs, Cooley Dickinson Hospital, Northampton, MA, p. A321

FODI, Nancy C., R.N., Chief Executive Officer, Southwest Regional Medical Center, Little Rock, AR, p. A47

FOELSCH, Paul, Chief Information Officer, Mercy Hospital, Iowa City, IA, p. A235

FOELSKE, Loren
Vice President Finance, Kishwaukee Community Hospital, De Kalb, IL, p. A191
Vice President Finance, Valley West Community Hospital, Sandwich, IL, p. A207

FOGARTY, MS, Kathleen, Associate Director, Veterans Affairs Medical Center, Oklahoma City, OK, p. A536

FOGG, Robert W., Director Finance, Lake Taylor Transitional Care Hospital, Norfolk, VA, p. A692

FOGLER, Joyce, Chief Executive Officer, Select Specialty Hospital of Indianapolis, Indianapolis, IN, p. A219

FOJTASEK, Georgia R., President and Chief Executive Officer, Foote Health System, Jackson, MI, p. A337

FOLEY, James T., Vice President and Chief Financial Officer, Shore Memorial Hospital, Somers Point, NJ, p. A436

FOLEY, Leah, Director of Human Resources, Huguley Memorial Medical Center, Fort Worth, TX, p. A640

FOLEY, Mary Anne, Aministrator, Mercy Hospital–North Shore Campus, Pittsburgh, PA, p. A572

FOLEY, M.D., Sean, Medical Director, St. Vincent Rehabilitation Hospital, Sherwood, AR, p. A50

FOLEY, Tim, Director Information Systems, Riverton Memorial Hospital, Riverton, WY, p. A741

FOLEY, William T., Chief Executive Officer, Provena Health, Mokena, IL, p. B85

FOLK, M.D., Jeffrey R., Medical Director, Geisinger Wyoming Valley Medical Center, Wilkes–Barre, PA, p. A579

FOLKWEIN, Charles
Senior Vice President Ancillary Services and Information Technology, St. Elizabeth Health Center, Youngstown, OH, p. A526
Vice President Ancillary Services and Information Technology, St. Joseph Health Center, Warren, OH, p. A524

FOLL, Gary R., Vice President Finance and Chief Financial Officer, Paradise Valley Hospital, National City, CA, p. A77

FOLLETT, Richard, Director Information Services, The Good Samaritan Hospital, Lebanon, PA, p. A563

FOLLOWELL, Rob, Chief Executive Officer, Chestatee Regional Hospital, Dahlonega, GA, p. A159

FOLTS, Patricia, Assistant Vice President and Human Resources, Our Lady of Lourdes Memorial Hospital, Binghamton, NY, p. A448

FONTAINE, Steven M., Administrator, Pioneer Community Hospital of Aberdeen, Aberdeen, MS, p. A366

FONTENOT, M.D., Cathi E., Medical Director, Medical Center of Louisiana at New Orleans, New Orleans, LA, p. A289

FONTENOT, Robert, Director Human Resources, Northeast Medical Center Hospital, Humble, TX, p. A649

FONTENOT, Teri G., CHE, President and Chief Executive Officer, Woman's Hospital, Baton Rouge, LA, p. A278

FONTS, Phillip, Chief Financial Officer, Warm Springs Medical Center, Warm Springs, GA, p. A171

FOOS, Robert, Senior Vice President and Chief Information Officer, Saint Agnes Medical Center, Fresno, CA, p. A61

FOOTE, Donald E., Fiscal Officer, Veterans Affairs Medical Center, Wilkes–Barre, PA, p. A579

FORBES, Bill, Administrator, Clinch Memorial Hospital, Homerville, GA, p. A163

FORBES, James, Chief Medical Director, Hendry Regional Medical Center, Clewiston, FL, p. A126

FORBES, M.D., Kathleen, Senior Vice President Medical Affairs, Chief Quality Officer, Good Samaritan Hospital, Cincinnati, OH, p. A507

FORBORT, Gordy, Chief Financial Officer, Kanabec Hospital, Mora, MN, p. A358

FORBUSH, Marilyn, Director Human Resources, St. Clare Hospital and Health Services, Baraboo, WI, p. A723

FORD, Benet, Director Human Resources, HEALTHSOUTH Rehabilitation Hospital of Arlington, Arlington, TX, p. A622

FORD, Connie, Vice President Human Resources, La Porte Regional Health System, La Porte, IN, p. A220

FORD, Fred, Assistant Administrator, Sutter Tracy Community Hospital, Tracy, CA, p. A96

FORD, John, Director of Human Resources, Terrebonne General Medical Center, Houma, LA, p. A282

FORD, M.D., Lesa, Chief of Staff, Denton Regional Medical Center, Denton, TX, p. A635

FORD, Lloyd, Chief Executive Officer, Muhlenberg Community Hospital, Greenville, KY, p. A265

FORD, Mary, Vice President and Chief Information Officer, Faxton–St. Luke's Healthcare, Utica, NY, p. A474

FORD, Mike, Director, Human Resources, Floyd Memorial Hospital and Health Services, New Albany, IN, p. A222

FORD, Raymond L., FACHE, Chief Executive Officer, Lady of the Sea General Hospital, Cut Off, LA, p. A280

FORD, Tim, Senior Vice President Operations, Watauga Medical Center, Boone, NC, p. A478

FORD, W Raymond C, Chief Executive Officer, Specialty Hospital Jacksonville, Jacksonville, FL, p. A132

FORD, W. Raymond C., Chief Executive Officer, Specialty Hospital Jacksonville, Jacksonville, FL, p. A132

FORDE, Terry
Vice President and Chief Financial Officer, Avista Adventist Hospital, Louisville, CO, p. A108
Chief Financial Officer, Porter Adventist Hospital, Denver, CO, p. A104

FORDHAM, Lorraine, Chief Information Officer, Sibley Memorial Hospital, Washington, DC, p. A122

FOREHAND, Jerry, R.N., Chief Executive Officer, Northwest Surgical Hospital, Oklahoma City, OK, p. A535

FOREMAN, Spencer, M.D., President, Montefiore Medical Center, New York, NY, p. A462

FORESE, Laura, Senior Vice President and Chief Medical Officer, New York–Presbyterian Hospital, New York, NY, p. A463

FORESTER, John C., Administrator, HEALTHSOUTH MountainView Regional Rehabilitation Hospital, Morgantown, WV, p. A718

FORGE, Brenda, Director of Human Resources, St. Joseph Regional Medical Center, Lewiston, ID, p. A180

FORGEY, Warren, Vice President Fiscal Services, Schneck Medical Center, Seymour, IN, p. A225

FORKNER, Christine, Chief Financial Officer, National Jewish Medical and Research Center, Denver, CO, p. A103

FORMAN, Christine, Vice President and Chief Information Officer, Nassau University Medical Center, East Meadow, NY, p. A451

FORMAN, Elizabeth J., Vice President, Human Resources, Froedtert Memorial Lutheran Hospital, Milwaukee, WI, p. A731

FORMBY–RENGER, Diane, Human Resources Manager, St. Dominic's Hospital, Manteca, CA, p. A74

FORMICA, Vince N., Senior Vice President Finance and Chief Financial Officer, Providence Hospital, Mobile, AL, p. A21

FORMIGONI, Ugo, Metro–West Network Manager, John J. Madden Mental Health Center, Hines, IL, p. A197

FORNAL, Christine, Chief Nursing Executive, St. John Oakland Hospital, Madison Heights, MI, p. A339

FORNOFF, Gerald A., Chief Executive Officer, Savoy Medical Center, Mamou, LA, p. A285

FORREST, Brian, Director of Human Resources, Arnot Ogden Medical Center, Elmira, NY, p. A452

FORREST, Carrie, Vice President Human Resources, Calvert Memorial Hospital, Prince Frederick, MD, p. A309

FORREST, Jr, James L., Controller, Southeast Colorado Hospital and Long Term Care, Springfield, CO, p. A109

FORRESTER, John M., Director, Hamilton Medical Center, Dalton, GA, p. A160

FORSMAN, Mark, Director Management Information Systems, Harrington Memorial Hospital, Southbridge, MA, p. A323

FORSYTH, Larry, Director Information Services, OU Medical Center, Oklahoma City, OK, p. A536

FORSYTH, Rhonda
Executive Vice President and Chief Executive Officer, John C. Lincoln Hospital – North Mountain, Phoenix, AZ, p. A34
Executive Vice President and Chief Executive Officer, John C. Lincoln Hospital – North Mountain, Phoenix, AZ, p. A34

FORT, Claudio, Executive Vice President and Administrator, St. Joseph's Hospital, Highland, IL, p. A196

FORTENBERRY, Doris, Human Resources Coordinator, Delta Memorial Hospital, Dumas, AR, p. A42

FORTENBERRY, Larry, Controller, Jeff Anderson Regional Medical Center, Meridian, MS, p. A373

FORTHMAN, Gary S., USAF, Commander, U. S. Air Force Regional Hospital, Eglin AFB, FL, p. A127

FORTNER, Gary, Systems Support Manager, BJC Medical Center, Commerce, GA, p. A159

FORTNER, Randy, Chief Operating Officer, St. Joseph's Mercy Health Center, Hot Springs National Park, AR, p. A45

FOSDICK, Glenn A., FACHE, President and Chief Executive Officer, Nebraska Medical Center, Omaha, NE, p. A411

FOSS, Kay
System Director Human Resources, Baptist Medical Center East, Montgomery, AL, p. A21
System Director Human Resources, Baptist Medical Center South, Montgomery, AL, p. A22

FOSS, Marilyn, Director Management Information Systems, Ridgeview Medical Center, Waconia, MN, p. A364

FOSS, R. Coleman, Chief Executive Officer, Dyersburg Regional Medical Center, Dyersburg, TN, p. A605

FOSS, Taylor, Vice President Human Resources, Sinai Hospital of Baltimore, Baltimore, MD, p. A304

FOSSUM, John, Chief Executive Officer and Administrator, Ely–Bloomenson Community Hospital, Ely, MN, p. A353

FOSTER, Allen, Chief Executive Officer, Mizell Memorial Hospital, Opp, AL, p. A23

FOSTER, Charles
Regional Director, Human Resources, Christus St. Elizabeth Hospital, Beaumont, TX, p. A625
Regional Director Human Resources, Christus St. Mary Hospital, Port Arthur, TX, p. A661

FOSTER, Chris, Director Health Information Management, Powell County Memorial Hospital, Deer Lodge, MT, p. A397

FOSTER, Debra, Director of Human Resources, Williamson Medical Center, Franklin, TN, p. A606

FOSTER, Hershell, Information Systems Director, River Park Hospital, McMinnville, TN, p. A612

FOSTER, James, Finance Administrator, Ortonville Area Health Services, Ortonville, MN, p. A359

FOSTER, M.D., James, Medical Director, Marcum and Wallace Memorial Hospital, Irvine, KY, p. A266

FOSTER, James R., Chief Executive Officer, Select Specialty Hospital – Biloxi, Biloxi, MS, p. A366

FOSTER, Larry, Chief Executive Officer, Kindred Chicago Central Hospital, Chicago, IL, p. A187

FOSTER, Mike, Management Information Systems, Allen Memorial Hospital, Moab, UT, p. A677

FOSTER, CHE, Richard, Chief Financial Officer, Integris Clinton Regional Hospital, Clinton, OK, p. A529

FOSTER, Sandra J., Chief Patient Services Officer, Memorial Hospital, Fremont, OH, p. A514

FOSTER, Shirley J., Executive Vice President and Chief Operations Officer, Madonna Rehabilitation Hospital, Lincoln, NE, p. A409

FOSTER, Steven, Chief of Staff, Northwest Medical Center, Margate, FL, p. A136

FOTHERGILL, M.D., John, Medical Director, Upper Connecticut Valley Hospital, Colebrook, NH, p. A420

FOTTER, Robert L., Vice President Finance, North Country Hospital and Health Center, Newport, VT, p. A683

FOULKE, Elvia, Executive Vice President and Chief Operating Officer, Foothill Presbyterian Hospital–Morris L. Johnston Memorial, Glendora, CA, p. A63

FOULKES, Rhys, Chief Information Management Service, Veterans Affairs Medical Center, Battle Creek, MI, p. A328

FOUNTAIN, Wesley, Chief Financial Officer, Gulf Coast Medical Center, Panama City, FL, p. A142

FOURAKER, Jason, Director of Human Resources, Baptist Medical Center Nassau, Fernandina Beach, FL, p. A128

FOUST, Lisa, Senior Vice President Human Resources, Foothill Presbyterian Hospital–Morris L. Johnston Memorial, Glendora, CA, p. A63

FOUTZ, Patricia, Human Resources Director, Bath County Community Hospital, Hot Springs, VA, p. A690

FOWLER, Barry, Chief Financial Officer, Regional Medical Center at Memphis, Memphis, TN, p. A613

FOWLER, Holly, M.D., Administrator, Henderson County Community Hospital, Lexington, TN, p. A611

FOWLER, Kevin, Director Finance, Putnam County Hospital, Greencastle, IN, p. A217

FOWLER, Kevin N.
Chief Executive Officer, Guyan Valley Hospital, Logan, WV, p. A717
Chief Executive Officer, Logan Regional Medical Center, Logan, WV, p. A717

FOWLER, Lynan, Director Patient Financial Services, Wheeler County Hospital, Glenwood, GA, p. A163

FOWLER, Mark, Executive Director Human Resources, St. Helena Hospital, Saint Helena, CA, p. A85

FOWLER, Maureen, Director, Human Resources, Amsterdam Memorial Hospital, Amsterdam, NY, p. A446

FOWLER, Sean S., Chief Executive Officer, St. Charles Specialty Hospital, New Orleans, LA, p. A289

FOX, Alan, Chief Financial Officer, Saint Francis Memorial Hospital, San Francisco, CA, p. A89

FOX Jr, C. William, Deputy Commander for Administration, Brooke Army Medical Center, Fort Sam Houston, TX, p. A638

FOX, David S., President, Advocate Good Samaritan Hospital, Downers Grove, IL, p. A192

FOX, Erik, Chief Executive Officer, Benewah Community Hospital, Saint Maries, ID, p. A181

FOX, Geraldine, Chief Human Resources, U. S. Public Health Service Phoenix Indian Medical Center, Phoenix, AZ, p. A35

FOX, M.D., John E., Chief of Staff, Lincoln Community Hospital and Nursing Home, Hugo, CO, p. A107

FOX, John T.
Chief Executive Officer, Emory Crawford Long Hospital, Atlanta, GA, p. A153
Chief Executive Officer, Emory Healthcare, Atlanta, GA, p. B43
Chief Executive Officer, Emory University Hospital, Atlanta, GA, p. A153
Chief Executive Officer, Wesley Woods Center of Emory University, Atlanta, GA, p. A155

FOX, Leticia, Chief Financial Officer, Pecos County Memorial Hospital, Fort Stockton, TX, p. A639

FOX, Lorna, Director Human Resources, Mountainview Medical Center, White Sulphur Springs, MT, p. A402

FOX, Mary, Director Information Systems, Oneida Healthcare Center, Oneida, NY, p. A468

FOX, Patricia K., President and Chief Executive Officer, Riverview Hospital, Noblesville, IN, p. A223

FOX, M.D., Richard, Medical Staff President, Passavant Area Hospital, Jacksonville, IL, p. A198

FOX, Theodore P., President and Chief Operating Officer, St. Louise Regional Hospital, Gilroy, CA, p. A62

FOX, Tom, Chief Financial Officer, St. Joseph Hospital, Fort Wayne, IN, p. A216

FOX, William
Interim Chief Executive Officer, Colorado Acute Specialty Care Hospital, Denver, CO, p. A103
Chief Executive Officer, LifeCare Hospitals of Milwaukee, Milwaukee, WI, p. A731

FOXX, Randy, Chief Financial Officer, Boone Memorial Hospital, Madison, WV, p. A717

FOY, Greg, Human Resources System Leader, Scheurer Hospital, Pigeon, MI, p. A342

FOY, James, President and Chief Executive Officer, St. John's Riverside Hosptial, Yonkers, NY, p. A476

FRABLE, Arthur H., Chief Executive Officer, Howard County Community Hospital, Saint Paul, NE, p. A412

FRAIZE, Larry, Director Management Information Systems, Milford Regional Medical Center, Milford, MA, p. A320

FRAIZER, Amy, Management Information Systems Supervisor, Wetzel County Hospital, New Martinsville, WV, p. A718

FRAKER, Steven, Chief Financial Officer, Banner Churchill Community Hospital, Fallon, NV, p. A415

FRALEY, Chuck, Controller, HEALTHSOUTH Rehabilitation Hospital of Virginia, Richmond, VA, p. A695

FRALEY, Gary F., Administrator, Shriners Hospitals for Children, Greenville, Greenville, SC, p. A588

FRAME, Angela, Chief Financial Officer, Jackson General Hospital, Ripley, WV, p. A719

FRANCETICH, Kane, Chief Information Officer, Gritman Medical Center, Moscow, ID, p. A180

FRANCIS, Duane, President, Mid–Columbia Medical Center, The Dalles, OR, p. A549

FRANCIS, Karen, Vice President Finance, McKenzie–Willamette Medical Center, Springfield, OR, p. A549

FRANCIS, Mark J., President and Chief Executive Officer, Community Hospital, Grand Junction, CO, p. A106

FRANCKE, Bertold, M.D., Interim Executive Director, Vermont State Hospital, Waterbury, VT, p. A684

FRANCO, Ralph A., Chief Information Management Division, Tripler Army Medical Center, Honolulu, HI, p. A174

FRANEY, Hank, Chief Financial Officer, University Specialty Hospital, Baltimore, MD, p. A305

FRANEY, Henry J., Senior Vice President Finance and Chief Financial Officer, University of Maryland Medical Center, Baltimore, MD, p. A304

FRANGESCH, Wayne
Vice President Human Resources, St. Rose Dominican Hospitals – Rose de Lima Campus, Henderson, NV, p. A416
Vice President Human Resources, St. Rose Dominican Hospitals – Siena Campus, Henderson, NV, p. A416

FRANK, Ben, Chief Executive Officer, Central Arkansas Hospital, Searcy, AR, p. A50

FRANK, M.D., Gary, Chief Medical Officer, St. Vincent Hospital, Santa Fe, NM, p. A444

FRANK, Jeff, Human Resource Director, Queen of Peace Hospital, New Prague, MN, p. A358

FRANK, Jim
Chief Financial Officer, Community Memorial Hospital, Burke, SD, p. A594
Chief Financial Officer, Winner Regional Healthcare Center, Winner, SD, p. A601

FRANK, Kim, Chief Human Resources Officer, Virginia Gay Hospital, Vinton, IA, p. A242

FRANKENBACH, James T., President and Chief Executive Officer, Rush North Shore Medical Center, Skokie, IL, p. A208

FRANKLIN, Barry L., Executive Vice President and Chief Financial Officer, Parma Community General Hospital, Parma, OH, p. A520

FRANKLIN, Clay, Chief Operating Officer, CJW Medical Center, Richmond, VA, p. A695

FRANKLIN, M.D., Jack, Chief of Staff, Llano Memorial Healthcare System, Llano, TX, p. A653

FRANKLIN, James P., Administrator, Calhoun Health Services, Calhoun City, MS, p. A367

FRANKLIN, Michael, Vice President Operations, Shady Grove Adventist Hospital, Rockville, MD, p. A310

FRANKLIN, Vicki L., Senior Vice President Operations, Lake Regional Health System, Osage Beach, MO, p. A388

FRANKO, Connie, Chief Operating Officer and Chief Nursing Executive, Huron Valley–Sinai Hospital, Commerce Township, MI, p. A330

FRANKO, Stephen
Vice President Finance and Chief Financial Officer, Mercy Hospital of Scranton, Scranton, PA, p. A575
Vice President Finance and Chief Financial Officer, Mercy Hospital of Wilkes–Barre, Wilkes–Barre, PA, p. A579
Chief Financial Officer, Mercy Special Care Hospital, Nanticoke, PA, p. A566

FRANKS, Dennis, Chief Executive Officer, Pushmataha County–Town of Antlers Hospital Authority, Antlers, OK, p. A527

FRANKS, Sandra, Chief Financial Officer, Shenandoah Medical Center, Shenandoah, IA, p. A241

FRANQUIZ, Ron, Director Information Systems, Richardson RegionalMedical Center, Richardson, TX, p. A662

FRANZ, Charles C., CHE, Chief Executive Officer, South Peninsula Hospital, Homer, AK, p. A27

FRANZ, Kathy, Director Human Resources, Yakima Valley Memorial Hospital, Yakima, WA, p. A712

FRANZBLAU, M.D., David R., Chief Medical Officer, St. Vincent Mercy Medical Center, Toledo, OH, p. A523

FRARACCIO, Robert D., Chief Executive Officer, Clark Regional Medical Center, Winchester, KY, p. A275

FRARDO, M.D., Virgil, Medical Director, HEALTHSOUTH Rehabilitation Hospital–Wichita Falls, Wichita Falls, TX, p. A674

FRASCHETTI, Robert J., President and Chief Executive Officer, St. Jude Medical Center, Fullerton, CA, p. A62

FRASER, M.D., Hugh, Chief of Staff, Powell Valley Healthcare, Powell, WY, p. A741

FRASER, James, Chief Financial Officer, Ferrell Hospital, Eldorado, IL, p. A193

FRASER, John M., President and Chief Executive Officer, Nebraska Methodist Hospital, Omaha, NE, p. A411

FRAYNE, Laurence J., Chief Executive Officer, Regency Hospital of Covington, Covington, LA, p. A279

FRAZIER III, James P., Chief Executive Officer, Jamestown Regional Medical Center, Jamestown, TN, p. A608

FRAZIER, Karen, Director, George Washington University Hospital, Washington, DC, p. A121

FRAZIER, Sandy, Vice President Human Resources and Medical Staff Services, Mt. Graham Regional Medical Center, Safford, AZ, p. A36

FRECH, Terry, Chief Executive Officer, Chilton Medical Center, Clanton, AL, p. A16

FRECHETTE, Beth, Vice President Human Resources, Saint Francis Hospital and Medical Center, Hartford, CT, p. A113

FREDERIC, Donald J., Chief Executive Officer, Gulf Coast Medical Center, Wharton, TX, p. A673

FREDERICK, Kathy, Senior Director Human Resources, Scripps Mercy Hospital, San Diego, CA, p. A87

FREDERICK, Lynn
Administrator, Rochester Methodist Hospital, Rochester, MN, p. A360
Administrator, Saint Marys Hospital, Rochester, MN, p. A360

FREDERICKS, Raymond F.
Senior Vice President and Chief Financial Officer, JFK Johnson Rehabilitation Institute, Edison, NJ, p. A428
Executive Vice President and Chief Financial Officer, JFK Medical Center, Edison, NJ, p. A428
Executive Vice President and Chief Financial Officer, Muhlenberg Regional Medical Center, North Plainfield, NJ, p. A433

FREDRICKSON, Kelley, Chief Information Officer, Henderson Memorial Hospital, Henderson, TX, p. A643

FREDRICKSON, M.D., Mark, Medical Director, HEALTHSOUTH Rehabilitation Hospital, Odessa, TX, p. A659

FREEBURG, Eric, Administrator, Memorial Hospital, Chester, IL, p. A186

FREED, David H., President and Chief Executive Officer, Nyack Hospital, Nyack, NY, p. A467

FREEDMAN, Barry R.
President and Chief Executive Officer, Albert Einstein Healthcare Network, Philadelphia, PA, p. B6
President and Chief Executive Officer, Albert Einstein Medical Center, Philadelphia, PA, p. A567

FREEHOF, Leonard, Chief Executive Officer and Managing Director, Auburn Regional Medical Center, Auburn, WA, p. A700

FREEL, Lynne, Finance Manager, Rehabilitation Hospital of Tinton Falls, Eatontown, NJ, p. A427

FREEL, M.D., Paul D., Chief of Staff, McLeod Medical Center–Dillon, Dillon, SC, p. A587

FREELAND, Franklin R., Ed.D., Chief Executive Officer, Fort Defiance Indian Health Service Hospital, Fort Defiance, AZ, p. A31

FREELAND, Mike
Regional Director, Florida Hospital – Deland, De Land, FL, p. A127
Regional Manager, Florida Hospital Waterman, Tavares, FL, p. A149

FREEMAN, Amy E., Executive Vice President, Mercy Medical Center, Baltimore, MD, p. A304

FREEMAN, Brian, Director Management Information Systems, Stanly Memorial Hospital, Albemarle, NC, p. A477

FREEMAN, Charles Ray, Chief Executive Officer, Ripley County Memorial Hospital, Doniphan, MO, p. A381

FREEMAN, Deanna, Administrator, Jewell County Hospital, Mankato, KS, p. A252

FREEMAN, Donald, President and Chief Executive Officer, Preferred Management Corporation, Shawnee, OK, p. B84

FREEMAN, Elizabeth Joyce, Director, Veterans Affairs Palo Alto Health Care System, Palo Alto, CA, p. A80

FREEMAN, M.D., James
Vice President Medical Affairs, SSM St. Joseph Health Center, Saint Charles, MO, p. A390
Vice President Medical Affairs, SSM St. Joseph Hospital West, Lake Saint Louis, MO, p. A386

FREEMAN, Michael, Human Resources Director, Huhukam Memorial Hospital, Sacaton, AZ, p. A35

FREEMAN, M.D., Richard, Chief Medical Officer, SUNY Downstate Medical Center University Hospital, New York, NY, p. A466

FREEMAN, Richard H., Chief Executive Officer, Eleanor Slater Hospital, Cranston, RI, p. A581

FREEMAN, Suzanne H., R.N., President, Carolinas Medical Center, Charlotte, NC, p. A479

FREEMAN, Tim, Administrator, Dubuis Hospital of Texarkana, Texarkana, TX, p. A669

FREIDERS, Wayne, Vice President Human Resources, St. Luke's Regional Medical Center, Boise, ID, p. A178

FREIER, Toby, Vice President Finance, Tomah Memorial Hospital, Tomah, WI, p. A736

FRENCH, M.D., Charles, Medical Director, St. Vincent Clay Hospital, Brazil, IN, p. A212

FRENCH, M.D., Dean O., Chief of Staff, Clark Fork Valley Hospital, Plains, MT, p. A401

FRENCH, Ed, Vice President, Memorial Hospital, Belleville, IL, p. A184

FRENCH III, George E., CHE, Chief Executive Officer, Minden Medical Center, Minden, LA, p. A287

FRENCH, Holly, Interim Chief Financial Officer, Newman Regional Health, Emporia, KS, p. A246

FRENCH, Jennifer, Director of Organizational Quality, St. Vincent Clay Hospital, Brazil, IN, p. A212

FRENCH, Robert
Vice President Information Services, Good Samaritan Regional Medical Center, Corvallis, OR, p. A543
Vice President Information Services, Samaritan Lebanon Community Hospital, Lebanon, OR, p. A545
Director Information Services, Samaritan North Lincoln Hospital, Lincoln City, OR, p. A545

FRENCHIE, Richard J.
President and Chief Executive Officer, Heather Hill Hospital and Health Partnership, Chardon, OH, p. A505
President and Chief Executive Officer, UHHS Geauga Regional Hospital, Chardon, OH, p. A505

FRERICHS, Craig, Chief Information Technology Service, Veterans Affairs Medical Center, Grand Junction, CO, p. A106

FRESHOUR, David, Chief Financial Officer, San Luis Valley Regional Medical Center, Alamosa, CO, p. A101

FRESOLONE, Victor J., FACHE, President and Chief Executive Officer, Mercy Medical Center, Roseburg, OR, p. A548

FREUDENBERGER, Joe, Chief Financial Officer, Memorial Health System of East Texas, Lufkin, TX, p. A655

FREW, Anne, Chief Executive Officer, Select Specialty Hospital–Erie, Erie, PA, p. A558

FREY, Mark A., President and Chief Executive Officer, Alexian Brothers Behavioral Health Hospital, Hoffman Estates, IL, p. A197

FREY, Mary Ellen, Chief Operating Officer, Jamestown Hospital, Jamestown, ND, p. A499

FREY, Rachel, Director Human Resources, Athens–Limestone Hospital, Athens, AL, p. A13

FREYMULLER, Robert S., Chief Executive Officer, Texsan Heart Hospital, San Antonio, TX, p. A666

FRICK, Mark P., Vice President Human Resources, Excela Frick Hospital, Mount Pleasant, PA, p. A565

FRIDAY, David, Chief Information Officer, Wadley Regional Medical Center, Texarkana, TX, p. A670

FRIED, Jeffrey M., FACHE, President and Chief Executive Officer, Beebe Medical Center, Lewes, DE, p. A119

FRIEDEN, Robert
Vice President Information Systems, Genesis Medical Center, Davenport, Davenport, IA, p. A231
Vice President Information Systems, Genesis Medical Center, Illini Campus, Silvis, IL, p. A208

FRIEDENBACH, Daryl, Director Fiscal Services, Floyd Valley Hospital/Avera Health, Le Mars, IA, p. A237

FRIEDMAN, Larry, Director Information Services, Grand Itasca Clinic and Hospital, Grand Rapids, MN, p. A354

FRIEDMAN, Michael A., M.D., Chief Executive Officer, City of Hope National Medical Center, Duarte, CA, p. A59

FRIEDMAN, M.D., Richard, Vice President Medical Affairs, Queen's Medical Center, Honolulu, HI, p. A174

FRIEDMAN, M.D., Robert, Medical Director, Idaho Elks Rehabilitation Hospital, Boise, ID, p. A177

FRIEDMAN, Steven H., Ph.D., Executive Vice President, Methodist Hospital of Chicago, Chicago, IL, p. A188

FRIEDRICH, III, Daniel J., President and Chief Executive Officer, Blake Medical Center, Bradenton, FL, p. A124

FRIEDRICH III, Daniel J., Chief Executive Officer, Blake Medical Center, Bradenton, FL, p. A124

FRIEL, John P., Chief Executive Officer, Oak Valley District Hospital, Oakdale, CA, p. A78

FRIELING, Jeff
Chief Information Officer, Jackson–Madison County General Hospital, Jackson, TN, p. A608
Chief Information Officer, Pathways of Tennessee, Jackson, TN, p. A608

FRIER, Nancy, Chief Financial Officer, Eastern Oklahoma Medical Center, Poteau, OK, p. A537

FRIESEN, Carol, Chief Financial Officer, Boone County Health Center, Albion, NE, p. A404

FRIESEN, Nancy, Chief Financial Officer, Monticello Big Lake Hospital, Monticello, MN, p. A358

FRIESEN, Quinton J., Executive Vice President and Chief Operating Officer, Greenwich Hospital, Greenwich, CT, p. A113

FRISBY, CPA, Nancy L., Senior Vice President and Chief Financial Officer, DeSoto Memorial Hospital, Arcadia, FL, p. A123

FRITSCH, Frank, Chief Human Resources Officer, Kessler Institute for Rehabilitation, West Orange, NJ, p. A438

FRITSCH, Phyllis
Interim Administrator, Upland Hills Health, Dodgeville, WI, p. A724
Health Information Management Director, Upland Hills Health, Dodgeville, WI, p. A724

FRITSCHE, Jeff, Chief Financial Officer, Silverton Hospital, Silverton, OR, p. A549

FRITTS, Doris, Director, Same Day Surgery Center, Rapid City, SD, p. A598

FRITTS, Robert
Chief Financial Officer, Grace Hospital, Morganton, NC, p. A488
Chief Financial Officer, Valdese General Hospital, Valdese, NC, p. A493

FRITTS, Rosemary, Administrator, Pike County Memorial Hospital, Murfreesboro, AR, p. A48

FRITZ, Becky, Director of Human Resources, Carilion Giles Memorial Hospital, Pearisburg, VA, p. A693

FRITZ, Chris, Chief Financial Officer, Scripps Green Hospital, La Jolla, CA, p. A65

FRITZ, D.O., John, Vice President Outreach and Referral Services, Avera St. Luke's, Aberdeen, SD, p. A594

FRITZ, Thomas M., Administrator, St. Luke's Rehabilitation Institute, Spokane, WA, p. A709

FRITZ, Timothy, Director Accounting and Taxation, Leelanau Memorial Health Center, Northport, MI, p. A341

FRIZZELL, Neil, Chief Financial Officer, Murray County Memorial Hospital, Slayton, MN, p. A363

FROCK, Charles T., President and Chief Executive Officer, FirstHealth of the Carolinas, Pinehurst, NC, p. B45

FROEBE, Tim, Vice President Human Resources, Mary Rutan Hospital, Bellefontaine, OH, p. A504

FROHRIP, Jay, Director Management Information Systems, Cloquet Community Memorial Hospital, Cloquet, MN, p. A351

FRONZA Jr, Leo F., President and Chief Executive Officer, Elmhurst Memorial Hospital, New York, IL, p. A193

FROTHINGHAM, M.D., Rodney, Chief Medical Officer, Delta Regional Medical Center, Greenville, MS, p. A368

FRY, M.D., David K., Chief of Staff, Hunt Memorial Hospital District, Greenville, TX, p. A642

FRY, Kenneth, Chief Financial Officer, Saint Alphonsus Regional Medical Center, Boise, ID, p. A177

FRY, Patrick E., Chief Executive Officer, Sutter Health, Sacramento, CA, p. B104

FRY, Richard W., Director, Carl Vinson Veterans Affairs Medical Center, Dublin, GA, p. A161

FRY, Robert W., Operations Leader, Bellin Memorial Hospital, Green Bay, WI, p. A726

FRYE Jr, Edward R., Chief Executive Officer, Clarendon Memorial Hospital, Manning, SC, p. A590

FUCHS, Brian P., Chief Fiscal Service, Veterans Affairs Medical Center, Memphis, TN, p. A614

FUENTES Jr, Miguel A., President and Chief Executive Officer, Bronx–Lebanon Hospital Center, New York, NY, p. A458

FUERSTENBERG, Donna, Chief Fiscal Services, Veterans Affairs Medical Center, Muskogee, OK, p. A534

FUGATE, Shawn, Chief Medical Officer, Pineville Community Hospital Association, Pineville, KY, p. A273

FUHRHOP, Teresa, Chief Financial Officer, Salem Township Hospital, Salem, IL, p. A207

FUHRMAN, Wayne J., Chief Financial Officer, St. Joseph's Hospital and Health Center, Dickinson, ND, p. A497

FULBRIGHT, Rob, Administrator, Florida Hospital – Deland, De Land, FL, p. A127

FULCHER, M.D., William, Chief of Staff, Keokuk Area Hospital, Keokuk, IA, p. A236

FULGHAM, Janet, Director Information Services, North Sunflower Medical Center, Ruleville, MS, p. A375

FULKERSON, Judy, Director Human Resources, Greenview Regional Hospital, Bowling Green, KY, p. A262

FULKERSON, William J., M.D., Chief Executive Officer, Duke University Hospital, Durham, NC, p. A481

FULKERSON, M.D., William J., Chief Executive Officer, Duke University Hospital, Durham, NC, p. A481

FULKS, Chris, Interim Chief Financial Officer, Huron Medical Center, Bad Axe, MI, p. A344

FULKS, Gerald N., President and Chief Executive Officer, West Georgia Health System, La Grange, GA, p. A164

FULKS, Pam, President and Chief Executive Officer, Wyoming Medical Center, Casper, WY, p. A739

FULLBRIGHT, Gary D., Comptroller, Citizens Memorial Hospital, Bolivar, MO, p. A378

FULLER, David, Director Radiology and Information Systems, Lake City Community Hospital, Lake City, SC, p. A589

FULLER, David W.
Chief Executive Officer, The King's Daughters Hospital, Greenville, MS, p. A369
Chief Executive Officer, Woodland Medical Center, Cullman, AL, p. A16

FULLER, Debbie, Director Health Information Systems and Chief Information Officer, Doctors Medical Center, Modesto, CA, p. A76

FULLER, M.D., Greg, Chief Of Staff, Doctors Hospital, Jackson, MI, p. A337

FULLER, D.O., Gregory, Vice President Medical Affairs, Lenawee Health Alliance – Bixby Campus, Adrian, MI, p. A327

FULLER, Lexie, Controller, Specialty Hospital of Meridian, Meridian, MS, p. A373

FULLER, Nancy, Manager Human Resources, Plains Memorial Hospital, Dimmitt, TX, p. A635

FULLER, M.D., Timothy, Chief of Staff, Takoma Adventist Hospital, Greeneville, TN, p. A607

FULLMER, Richard A., Executive Director, University of Utah Hospitals and Clinics, Salt Lake City, UT, p. A680

FULTON, Lynn, Chief Operating Officer, Kewanee Hospital, Kewanee, IL, p. A199

FULTS, Kendall R., President and Chief Executive Officer, Redbud Community Hospital, Clearlake, CA, p. A57

FULTZ, D.O., Clark, Chief Medical Staff, Northern Rockies Medical Center, Cut Bank, MT, p. A397

FUNDERBURK, Mark, Senior Vice President and Chief Operating Officer, University Medical Center, Lubbock, TX, p. A654

FUNK, Michael J., President and Chief Executive Officer, Dukes Memorial Hospital, Peru, IN, p. A223

FUQUA, David G., Chief Executive Officer, Norton Community Hospital, Norton, VA, p. A693

FUREY, M.D., Warren, Chairman, Department of Medicine, Mercy Hospital and Medical Center, Chicago, IL, p. A188

FURLAN, Matthew
Chief Operating Officer, Appleton Medical Center, Appleton, WI, p. A722
Chief Operating Officer, Theda Clark Medical Center, Neenah, WI, p. A732

FURLONG, Marian M., R.N., Chief Executive Officer, Hudson Hospital, Hudson, WI, p. A727

FURMAN, John, Executive Vice President Human Resources, Oakwood Hospital and Medical Center–Dearborn, Dearborn, MI, p. A330

FURNER, Kristine, Director Management Information Systems, O'Bleness Memorial Hospital, Athens, OH, p. A503

FURST, David, Information Officer, Sequoia Hospital, Redwood City, CA, p. A83

FURY, Dianna, Chief Medical Officer, Southwest Memorial Hospital, Cortez, CO, p. A102

FUSCO, Kevin, Chief Operating Officer, North Broward Medical Center, Pompano Beach, FL, p. A144

FUSELIER, Michael M., FACHE, Administrator, Dubuis Hospital of Lake Charles, Lake Charles, LA, p. A284

FUSS, Tom, Chief Financial Officer, Meriter Hospital, Madison, WI, p. A728

FUSSELL, Eugene, Vice President Medical Affairs and Clinical Operations, St. John's Regional Medical Center, Oxnard, CA, p. A80

FUTCH, Margaret
Chief Operating Officer and Administrator, HEALTHSOUTH Rehabilitation Hospital, Dothan, AL, p. A17
Chief Operating Officer and Administrator, HEALTHSOUTH Rehabilitation Hospital, Dothan, AL, p. A17

FYBEL, Gary G., Chief Executive Officer, Scripps Memorial Hospital–La Jolla, La Jolla, CA, p. A66

G

GAAL, M.D., Peter, Medical Director, Community Memorial Hospital of San Buenaventura, Ventura, CA, p. A98

GABALDON, Karen, Chief Management Information Systems, Veterans Affairs Medical Center, West Palm Beach, FL, p. A150

GABARRO, Ralph, Chief Executive Officer, Mayo Regional Hospital, Dover-Foxcroft, ME, p. A298

GABAVICS, Mark, Director Human Resources, Shawano Medical Center, Shawano, WI, p. A735

GABIS, M.D., John, Medical Director, Adena Health System, Chillicothe, OH, p. A506

GABOW, Patricia A., M.D., Chief Executive Officer and Medical Director, Denver Health Medical Center, Denver, CO, p. A103

GABRIAL, Brenda, Director Human Resources, Harrison County Community Hospital, Bethany, MO, p. A378

GABRIEL, John, Director, Ellsworth Municipal Hospital, Iowa Falls, IA, p. A236

GABRIEL, R.N., Kay, Assistant Administrator and Chief Nursing Officer, Mitchell County Regional Health Center, Osage, IA, p. A239

GABRIELE, Gary, Director Budget and Finance, Miners' Colfax Medical Center, Raton, NM, p. A444

GADE, Ronald, M.D., President, St. Barnabas Hospital, New York, NY, p. A465

GAENZEL, Ferd, Chief Financial Officer, Christus Spohn Hospital Corpus Christi Memorial, Corpus Christi, TX, p. A630

GAENZLE, Jack, Senior Vice President Finance and Administration, Mercy Hospital of Pittsburgh, Pittsburgh, PA, p. A572

GAFFORD, Chris, Chief of Staff, Lincoln County Health System, Fayetteville, TN, p. A606

GAFFORD, Deborah, Chief Financial Officer, Menorah Medical Center, Overland Park, KS, p. A254

GAGEN, Thomas C., Chief Executive Officer, Sutter Medical Center, Sacramento, Sacramento, CA, p. A85

GAGNON, Andy, Director Information Systems, Mercy Regional Health Center, New York, KS, p. A252

GAGNON, Nelson R., Chief Information Officer, Lahey Clinic Hospital, Burlington, MA, p. A316

GAIKOWSKI, Dixie, Acting Chief Executive Officer, U. S. Public Health Service Indian Hospital, Rosebud, SD, p. A598

GAINDH, M.D., Ramesh, President Medical Staff, Bridgton Hospital, Bridgton, ME, p. A297

GAINER, Rolf B., Chief Executive Officer and Administrator, Brookhaven Hospital, Tulsa, OK, p. A539

GAINES, M.D., David C., Chief of Staff, Clarendon Memorial Hospital, Manning, SC, p. A590

GAINES, Jacquelyn, Administrator, Providence Milwaukie Hospital, Milwaukie, OR, p. A546

GALATI, John P., President and Chief Executive Officer, Clifton Springs Hospital and Clinic, Clifton Springs, NY, p. A450

GALATI, Vicki L., Chief Financial Officer and Director Finance, Harris Methodist Southwest, Fort Worth, TX, p. A639

GALGERUD, Linda, Chief Financial Officer, Ottawa County Health Center, Minneapolis, KS, p. A253

GALINDO, Dan, Director Information Systems, Irvine Regional Hospital and Medical Center, Irvine, CA, p. A65

GALLAGHER, James P., Chief Executive Officer, Hampton Hospital, Mount Holly, NJ, p. A432

GALLAGHER, Joseph, President and Chief Executive Officer, Bergen Regional Medical Center, Paramus, NJ, p. A433

GALLAGHER, Pete
    Chief Financial Officer, Bon Secours St. Mary's Hospital, Richmond, VA, p. A694
    Chief Financial Officer, Bon Secours–Richmond Community Hospital, Richmond, VA, p. A694
    Vice President and Chief Financial Officer, Memorial Regional Medical Center, Mechanicsville, VA, p. A691

GALLAGHER, Sean, Vice President Finance, University Hospital, Cincinnati, OH, p. A507

GALLAGHER, M.D., Timothy, Chief of Staff, Lake District Hospital, Lakeview, OR, p. A545

GALLARDO, Laura, Interim Public Affairs Leader, Kaiser Foundation Hospital, Los Angeles, CA, p. A70

GALLATI, Todd, Chief Executive Officer, Gulf Coast Medical Center, Panama City, FL, p. A142

GALLATIN, David S.
    Chief Executive Officer, Excela Frick Hospital, Mount Pleasant, PA, p. A565
    Chief Executive Officer, Excela Health, Greensburg, PA, p. B44
    Chief Executive Officer, Excela Westmoreland Regional Hospital, Greensburg, PA, p. A559

GALLERIZZO, Steven, Acting Associate Director, Veterans Affairs Medical Center, Lebanon, PA, p. A563

GALLIMORE, Lynne, Vice President, Wilson Medical Center, Wilson, NC, p. A494

GALLIN, John I., M.D., Director, Warren G. Magnuson Clinical Center, National Institutes of Health, Bethesda, MD, p. A306

GALLOWAY, Glenn, Director Information Technology, Children's Hospital and Clinics, Saint Paul, MN, p. A362

GALLOWAY, Robert
    Senior Vice President Finance and Chief Financial Officer, Cape Canaveral Hospital/Health First, Cocoa Beach, FL, p. A126
    Senior Vice President Finance and Chief Financial Officer, Holmes Regional Medical Center, Melbourne, FL, p. A136

GALLUCCI, Vince, Senior Vice President, Human Resources, St. Elizabeth Hospital, Appleton, WI, p. A722

GALUSHA, Fred, Chief Information Officer, St. Luke's Rehabilitation Institute, Spokane, WA, p. A709

GALVIN, Kathleen, Executive Director, Saint Vincent's Hospital – Manhattan, New York, NY, p. A464

GALYON, Darlene, Administrator Human Resources, Choctaw Memorial Hospital, Hugo, OK, p. A532

GAMACHE, Edward L., Administrator, Deckerville Community Hospital, Deckerville, MI, p. A330

GAMBAROTA, Jim, Vice President Finance, Advocate Bethany Hospital, Chicago, IL, p. A186

GAMBER, Richard L., President and Chief Executive Officer, Harlingen Medical Center, Harlingen, TX, p. A643

GAMBILL, Bill, Chief Financial Officer, Veterans Affairs Black Hills Health Care System, Fort Meade, SD, p. A596

GAMBLE, Allen J., Administrator, Crenshaw Community Hospital, Luverne, AL, p. A20

GAMBOA, Rafael, Information Systems Manager, Community Hospital of Long Beach, Long Beach, CA, p. A68

GAMBRELL Jr, Edward C., Administrator, Stephens County Hospital, Toccoa, GA, p. A171

GAMEL, Richard B., Chief Executive Officer, Norfolk Regional Center, Norfolk, NE, p. A410

GAMEZ, Jesse M., Administrator, Kaiser Sunnyside Medical Center, Clackamas, OR, p. A542

GAMMIERE, Thomas A., Chief Executive, Scripps Mercy Hospital, San Diego, CA, p. A87

GAMMON, Diane, Director Information Systems, Saint Francis Medical Center, Cape Girardeau, MO, p. A379

GAMMON, Sally, President and Chief Executive Officer, Good Shepherd Rehabilitation Hospital, Allentown, PA, p. A551

GANCI, Alan, Executive Vice President, Bellevue Hospital, Bellevue, OH, p. A504

GANCI, Deborah, Vice President Human Resources, Bellevue Hospital, Bellevue, OH, p. A504

GANDERSMAN, Richard, Chief Executive Officer, Deaconess Hospital, Cincinnati, OH, p. A506

GANDY Jr, M. P., Chief Executive Officer, Santa Rosa Medical Center, Milton, FL, p. A138

GANDY, Patrick W., Chief Executive Officer, Sabine Medical Center, Many, LA, p. A286

GANDY, Sharon, Manager Human Resources, Lynn County Hospital District, Tahoka, TX, p. A668

GANGULY, Indranil, Vice President and Chief Information Officer, CentraState Healthcare System, Freehold, NJ, p. A428

GANN, Jim, Administrator, Roane Medical Center, Harriman, TN, p. A607

GANNON, Ronnie, Director Information Services, Southern Hills Medical Center, Nashville, TN, p. A615

GANONG, Harvey, Chief Information Officer, Slidell Memorial Hospital and Medical Center, Slidell, LA, p. A293

GANS, M.D., Bruce M., Executive Vice President and Chief Medical Officer, Kessler Institute for Rehabilitation, West Orange, NJ, p. A438

GANSERT, M.D., Guy, Chief of Staff, Washoe Medical Center, Reno, NV, p. A418

GANTNER, John, Treasurer, Robert Wood Johnson University Hospital, New Brunswick, NJ, p. A432

GANTT, Debe, Chief Information Resource Management, Veterans Affairs Medical Center, Martinsburg, WV, p. A717

GARBER, Gena, Director Human Resources, Skiff Medical Center, Newton, IA, p. A239

GARCES MILANES, M.D., Dagoberto, Chief and President of the Medical Staff, Cedars Medical Center, Miami, FL, p. A137

GARCIA, Amber, Human Resource Director, Uvalde County Hospital Authority, Uvalde, TX, p. A671

GARCIA, M.D., Dolly R., Clinical Director, U. S. Public Health Service Indian Hospital, Clinton, OK, p. A529

GARCIA, Hector Troche, Director Human Resources, Cardiovascular Center of Puerto Rico and the Caribbean, San Juan, PR, p. A746

GARCIA, M.D., Hugo, Chief of Staff, Kendall Regional Medical Center, Miami, FL, p. A137

GARCIA, CPA, Joannie, Finance Director, Hospital Perea, Mayaguez, PR, p. A745

GARCIA, Kay, Administrator, Cascade Medical Center, Cascade, ID, p. A178

GARCIA, Louis O., Chief Executive Officer, Houston Northwest Medical Center, Houston, TX, p. A645

GARCIA, Luis, Director, Methodist Sugar Land Hospital, Sugar Land, TX, p. A668

GARCIA, Martha, Administrator, Memorial Hospital Pembroke, Pembroke Pines, FL, p. A142

GARCIA, M.D., Michael, Medical Director, Leonard J. Chabert Medical Center, Houma, LA, p. A282

GARCIA, Michelle, Human Resources, Heart Hospital of New Mexico, Albuquerque, NM, p. A440

GARCIA, Rafael, Chief Executive Officer, Hospital Universitario Dr. Ramon Ruiz Arnau, Bayamon, PR, p. A744

GARCIA, Robert A., Administrative Director, Presbyterian Kaseman Hospital, Albuquerque, NM, p. A441

GARCIA, D.O., Roger, Medical Staff President, Bellevue Hospital, Bellevue, OH, p. A504

GARCIA, Roland
    Chief Information Officer, Baptist Medical Center, Jacksonville, FL, p. A132
    Senior Vice President and Chief Information Officer, Baptist Medical Center–Beaches, Jacksonville Beach, FL, p. A133

GARDENIER, Michael, Chief Financial Officer, Saint Joseph's Hospital of Atlanta, Atlanta, GA, p. A154

GARDINER, Karen, Director Fiscal Services, University Medical Center, Lafayette, LA, p. A284

GARDINER, M.D., Thomas K., Executive Vice President Clinical Development, Ball Memorial Hospital, Muncie, IN, p. A222

GARDNER, Donald F., Vice President Fiscal Services, Caldwell Memorial Hospital, Lenoir, NC, p. A486

GARDNER, Gary, Director, Business Service Line, Veterans Affairs Medical Center, Saint Louis, MO, p. A393

GARDNER, Greg, Senior Vice President and Chief Financial Officer, Indian River Memorial Hospital, Vero Beach, FL, p. A150

GARDNER, M.D., James D., Vice President Medical Staff, Waukesha Memorial Hospital, Waukesha, WI, p. A737

GARDNER, Jim, President and Chief Executive Officer, Northeast Georgia Medical Center, Gainesville, GA, p. A163

GARDNER, Jonathan H., Chief Executive Officer, Southern Arizona Veterans Affairs Health Care System, Tucson, AZ, p. A38

GARDNER, Paul A., CPA, Administrator, George County Hospital, Lucedale, MS, p. A372

GARDNER, Phil, Director Human Resources, St. Luke's Hospital, San Francisco, CA, p. A89

GARDNER, Russell W., Chief Financial Officer, Mount Carmel, Columbus, OH, p. A510

GARDNER, M.D., Samuel, Chief of Staff, Steele Memorial Hospital, Salmon, ID, p. A181

GARDNER, Sharon, Vice President Human Resources, Yuma Regional Medical Center, Yuma, AZ, p. A39

GARDNER, Zoe, Manager Human Resources, Sharp Chula Vista Medical Center, Chula Vista, CA, p. A57

GARFIELD, Michael W., Chief Operating Officer, Centennial Medical Center at Ashland City, Ashland City, TN, p. A602

GARFUNKEL, Sanford M., Director, Veterans Affairs Medical Center, Washington, DC, p. A122

GARG, Parmod
    Chief Financial Officer, St. Rose Dominican Hospitals – Rose de Lima Campus, Henderson, NV, p. A416
    Chief Financial Officer, St. Rose Dominican Hospitals – Siena Campus, Henderson, NV, p. A416

GARGIULO, Frederick J., Administrator, Tripler Army Medical Center, Honolulu, HI, p. A174

GARKO, Michael
    Chief Financial Officer, Hemet Valley Medical Center, Hemet, CA, p. A64
    Chief Financial Officer, Menifee Valley Medical Center, Sun City, CA, p. A95

GARLICK, May, Chief Information Officer, Irwin Army Community Hospital, Junction City, KS, p. A250

GARMAN, Michael
    Chief Financial Officer, Avera St. Anthony's Hospital, O'Neill, NE, p. A410
    Chief Financial Officer, Avera St. Anthony's Hospital, O'Neill, NE, p. A410

GARNAS, David, Chief Executive Officer, Sedgwick County Health Center, Julesburg, CO, p. A107

GARNER, Craig B., Chief Executive Officer, Coast Plaza Doctors Hospital, Norwalk, CA, p. A78

GARNER, Douglas, Vice President, Thomas Hospital, Fairhope, AL, p. A18

GARNER, Harvey, Chief Operating Officer, Coast Plaza Doctors Hospital, Norwalk, CA, p. A78

GARNER, Manlia, Chief Financial Officer, Doctors Hospital, Coral Gables, FL, p. A126

GARNETT, Elaine, Director Human Resources, USC University Hospital, Los Angeles, CA, p. A73

GARNETT, Michael, Chief of Staff, Klickitat Valley Health Services, Goldendale, WA, p. A703

GARONE, M.D., Marlene, Vice President Medical Affairs and Medical Director, Woman's Christian Association Hospital, Jamestown, NY, p. A454

GARRED, Sr, M.D., John, Chief Medical Officer, Burgess Health Center, Onawa, IA, p. A239

GARRETT, Alan
    Vice President and Chief Financial Officer, St. Joseph Hospital, Orange, CA, p. A79
    Vice President and Chief Financial Officer, St. Joseph Hospital, Orange, CA, p. A79

GARRETT, Christine, Cheif Human Resoruces Management Service, Veterans Affairs Medical Center, Bay Pines, FL, p. A123

GARRETT, Darlene, Chief Operating Officer, Parkview Huntington Hospital, Huntington, IN, p. A218

GARRETT, David
    Executive Vice President for Information Technology, Palmetto Health Baptist/Columbia, Columbia, SC, p. A586
    Executive Vice President for Information Technology, Palmetto Health Richland, Columbia, SC, p. A586

GARRETT, Doug
    Chief Financial Officer and Chief Operating Officer, Allen Memorial Hospital, Moab, UT, p. A677
    Chief Financial Officer and Chief Operating Officer, Allen Memorial Hospital, Moab, UT, p. A677

GARRETT, Henry, Chairman, Prairie Community Health Center, Terry, MT, p. A402

GARRETT, M.D., Kevin
    Senior Medical Director, Appleton Medical Center, Appleton, WI, p. A722
    Senior Medical Director, Theda Clark Medical Center, Neenah, WI, p. A732

GARRETT, Patrick R., President and Chief Executive Officer, Battle Creek Health System, Battle Creek, MI, p. A328

GARRETT, Robert C., Executive Vice President and Chief Operating Officer, Hackensack University Medical Center, Hackensack, NJ, p. A429

GARRETT, Walter, Administrator, Welch Community Hospital, Welch, WV, p. A720

GARRIGAN, Kerry A., Vice President Human Resources, North Carolina Baptist Hospital (Wake Forest University Baptist Medical Center), Winston–Salem, NC, p. A494

GARRIN, Paul, Vice President Information Systems and Chief Information Officer, Holy Name Hospital, Teaneck, NJ, p. A436

GARRISON, Gregg, Chief Financial Officer, Twelve Oaks Medical Center, Houston, TX, p. A648

GARRISON, Robert
    Administrator and Chief Executive Officer, Rawlins County Health Center, Atwood, KS, p. A244
    Administrator and Chief Executive Officer, Rawlins County Health Center, Atwood, KS, p. A244

GARRITY, Timothy, Chief Executive Officer, Blue Hill Memorial Hospital, Blue Hill, ME, p. A297

GARSKE, Tom, Director Information Systems, Wiregrass Medical Center, Geneva, AL, p. A19

GARTHE, Kathrine, Administrator, Leelanau Memorial Health Center, Northport, MI, p. A341

GARTHWAITE, Thomas L., M.D., Director and Chief Medical Officer, Los Angeles County–Department of Health Services, Los Angeles, CA, p. B70

GARVEN, Conrad, Manager Information Services, Copley Hospital, Morrisville, VT, p. A683

GARVEY, Thomas J.
    Chief Financial Officer, Mercy Hospital and Medical Center, Chicago, IL, p. A188
    Chief Financial Officer, Mercy Hospital and Medical Center, Chicago, IL, p. A188

GARVIN, Henry, Chief Operating Officer, San Luis Valley Regional Medical Center, Alamosa, CO, p. A101

GARWOOD, III, William D., Associate Administrator and Chief Financial Officer, Angleton Danbury Medical Center, Angleton, TX, p. A621

GARZA, Darron, Director, South Austin Hospital, Austin, TX, p. A624

GARZA, Jesus, President and Chief Executive Officer, Brackenridge Hospital, Austin, TX, p. A623

GARZA, Kim, Director Human Resources, Samaritan Healthcare, Moses Lake, WA, p. A704

GARZA, Mario J., Chief Operating Officer, Mission Hospital, Mission, TX, p. A657

GASCHO, Dwight, President and Chief Executive Officer, Scheurer Hospital, Pigeon, MI, p. A342

GASPARD, H. J., Chief Executive Officer, Oakdale Community Hospital, Oakdale, LA, p. A290

GAST, Edwin A., Chief Executive Officer and Administrator, Crawford County Memorial Hospital, Denison, IA, p. A232

GATES, John, Senior Vice President and Chief Financial Officer, Parkland Health & Hospital System, Dallas, TX, p. A633

GATES, Mark, Director Human Resources, Decatur Memorial Hospital, Decatur, IL, p. A192

GATES, M.D., Thomas, Chief of Staff, St. Mary Medical Center, Long Beach, CA, p. A68

GATHRIGHT, Dan, Senior Vice President and Administrator, Baptist Health Medical Center–Arkadelphia, Arkadelphia, AR, p. A40

GATHRIGHT, Marsha, Human Resources Manager, Bucyrus Community Hospital, Bucyrus, OH, p. A504

GATLIN, Brandon L., Administrator, Parmer County Community Hospital, Friona, TX, p. A640

GATMAITAN, Alfonso W., Chief Executive Officer, Clarian West Medical Center, Avon, IN, p. A211

GATTIS, Jacqueline D.
    Senior Vice President Human Resources, Forsyth Medical Center, Winston–Salem, NC, p. A494
    Senior Vice President Human Resources, Presbyterian Hospital, Charlotte, NC, p. A480

GAU, Kimberley, Chief Executive Officer, Guttenberg Municipal Hospital, Guttenberg, IA, p. A234

GAUBE, Gary J., President, Landmark Medical Center, Woonsocket, RI, p. A582

GAUBERT, Steve C., Chief Financial Officer, Thibodaux Regional Medical Center, Thibodaux, LA, p. A294

GAUDREAULT, J. Ronald, President and Chief Executive Officer, Huntington Hospital, Huntington, NY, p. A454

GAUSE, Garry L., Chief Executive Officer, Brookwood Medical Center, Birmingham, AL, p. A14

GAUTHIER, Bonnie B., President and Chief Executive Officer, Hebrew Health Care, West Hartford, CT, p. A117

GAUTHIER, Paul, Chief Information Resources Management, Veterans Affairs Montana Healthcare System, Fort Harrison, MT, p. A398

GAUTIER, Doug, Chief Operating Officer, St. Edward Mercy Medical Center, Fort Smith, AR, p. A44

GAUTNEY, Steven, President, Citizens Baptist Medical Center, Talladega, AL, p. A24

GAVALCHIK, Stephen M., Administrator, Webster County Memorial Hospital, Webster Springs, WV, p. A720

GAVENS, Mark R., Chief Operating Officer and Senior Vice President Clinical Care Services, Cedars–Sinai Medical Center, Los Angeles, CA, p. A69

GAVIN, James M., Vice President and Chief Financial Officer, Saratoga Hospital, Saratoga Springs, NY, p. A472

GAVIN, Linda, Associate Executive Director Marketing and Physician Recruitment, South Central Regional Medical Center, Laurel, MS, p. A372

GAVIN, Patrick, Chief Operating Officer, Chilton Memorial Hospital, Pompton Plains, NJ, p. A435

GAVIN, Tammy, Assistant Administrator and Chief Operating Officer, White River Medical Center, Batesville, AR, p. A40

GAWNE, M.D., Bernard B., Chief Medical Officer, Provena Covenant Medical Center, Urbana, IL, p. A209

GAY, M.D., Christophe, Chief of Staff, Bellville General Hospital, Bellville, TX, p. A625

GAY, Vickie, Chief Executive Officer, Montgomery General Hospital, Montgomery, WV, p. A717

GAYMAN, Rob, Director of Information Systems, Shore Memorial Hospital, Nassawadox, VA, p. A692

GAYNOR, Stanley J., Chief Executive Officer, Black River Memorial Hospital, Black River Falls, WI, p. A723

GEARIG, W Allan, Vice President Finance, Allegan General Hospital, Allegan, MI, p. A327

GEARING, Nicola, Chief Executive Officer, Sage Rehabilitation Institute, Baton Rouge, LA, p. A277

GEBHARD, Scott, Executive Vice President and Chief Executive Officer, JFK Medical Center, Edison, NJ, p. A428

GEBHART, Cheryl, Human Resources Director, Willamette Valley Medical Center, McMinnville, OR, p. A546

GEBHART, Jim, Chief Operating Officer, Hillcrest Baptist Medical Center, Waco, TX, p. A672

GEBHART, Ronald J., Chief of Staff, Veterans Affairs Salt Lake City Health Care System, Salt Lake City, UT, p. A680

GEE, Kyle
    Chief Financial Officer, Beartooth Hospital and Health Center, Red Lodge, MT, p. A401
    Chief Financial Officer, Rosebud Health Care Center, Forsyth, MT, p. A398

GEE, Roland D., Interim Chief Executive Officer, Gooding County Memorial Hospital, Gooding, ID, p. A179

GEE, Thomas H., Administrator, Henry County Medical Center, Paris, TN, p. A616

GEFFRARD, M.D., Antoine, Chief of Staff, Rehabilitation Institute of Michigan, Detroit, MI, p. A331

GEHANT, David P., President and Chief Executive Officer, Boulder Community Hospital, Boulder, CO, p. A101

GEHLAUF, Dee Ann, Administrative Director, Human Resources, Marietta Memorial Hospital, Marietta, OH, p. A517

GEHRIG, Ryan, Chief Executive Officer, Bristow Memorial Hospital, Bristow, OK, p. A528

GEHRING, M.D., Samuel, Chief of Staff, Fleming County Hospital, Flemingsburg, KY, p. A264

GEHRING, Terri, Vice President Operations, Memorial Hospital, McPherson, KS, p. A252

GEHRINGER, Dave, Chief Executive Officer, Select Specialty Hospital–Battle Creek, Battle Creek, MI, p. A328

GEHRKE, John, Vice President, Prince George's Hospital Center, Cheverly, MD, p. A306

GEIDT, Steve, Chief Executive Officer, Saddleback Memorial Medical Center, Laguna Hills, CA, p. A66

GEIER, Peter E.
Chief Executive Officer, Ohio State University Health System, Columbus, OH, p. B81
Chief Executive Officer, Ohio State University Medical Center, Columbus, OH, p. A511

GEIGER, Cathy, Director Information Services, Mercy Hospital, Port Huron, MI, p. A343

GEISSLER, Curt, Assistant Administrator and Chief Operating Officer, Lakeview Hospital, Stillwater, MN, p. A363

GEISSLER, Michael E., Chief Executive Officer, Crossroads Regional Hospital, Alexandria, LA, p. A276

GEIST, Tammy, Chief Financial Officer, Presbyterian–Orthopaedic Hospital, Charlotte, NC, p. A480

GEITZ, Cheri, Human Resources Director, Ellsworth Municipal Hospital, Iowa Falls, IA, p. A236

GEIVER, Betsy, Chief Human Resources, Royal C. Johnson Veterans Memorial Hospital, Sioux Falls, SD, p. A599

GELDHOF, Jay, Director Information Systems, Whittier Hospital Medical Center, Whittier, CA, p. A99

GELLER, Guy, Administrator and Chief Executive Officer, Beacham Memorial Hospital, Magnolia, MS, p. A372

GELLER, Harold S., Administrator, Othello Community Hospital, Othello, WA, p. A705

GELLER, M.D., Robert D., Vice President Medical Affairs, FHN Memorial Hospital, Freeport, IL, p. A194

GELLER, Schuyler K., Commander, U. S. Air Force Hospital Luke, Glendale, AZ, p. A31

GELLER, Warren, Senior Vice President, Administration, Northern Westchester Hospital, Mount Kisco, NY, p. A457

GELORMINI, Frank, Vice President Support Services, Community Medical Center, Toms River, NJ, p. A437

GENDER, Cookie, Administrator, Christus St. Michael Rehabilitation Hospital, Texarkana, TX, p. A669

GENERALE, Paul
Chief Operating Officer and Chief Financial Officer, Christus St. John Hospital, Houston, TX, p. A644
Chief Operating Officer and Chief Financial Officer, Christus St. John Hospital, Houston, TX, p. A644

GENGLER, Laraine, Chief Financial Officer, Lindsborg Community Hospital, Lindsborg, KS, p. A252

GENNA, Nick, Chief Executive Officer, Northwest Specialty Hospital, Post Falls, ID, p. A181

GENOVA, Peter, Chief Information Officer, Long Beach Medical Center, Long Beach, NY, p. A455

GENTILE, Barbara, Assistant Vice President Patient Care Services, Newton Memorial Hospital, Newton, NJ, p. A433

GENTILE, M.D., John, Vice President Medical Affairs, Alta Bates Summit Medical Center – Summit Campus, Oakland, CA, p. A78

GENTILE, Lawrence, President and Chief Executive Officer, Redgate Memorial Hospital, Long Beach, CA, p. A68

GENTLING, Steven J., FACHE, Director, Veterans Affairs Medical Center, Oklahoma City, OK, p. A536

GENTRY, Carl, Chief Information Officer and Vice President Management Information Systems, Day Kimball Hospital, Putnam, CT, p. A116

GENTRY, Gregg, Senior Vice President Human Resources, Erlanger Medical Center, Chattanooga, TN, p. A603

GENTRY, Jeanie, Director Support Services, St. John's Lutheran Hospital, Libby, MT, p. A400

GENTRY, Michael V., President, Florida Hospital–Ormond Memorial, Ormond Beach, FL, p. A141

GEORGE, Alan E., Chief Executive Officer, Walton Regional Medical Center, Monroe, GA, p. A166

GEORGE, Brad, Director of Information Systems, Parkland Medical Center, Derry, NH, p. A420

GEORGE, C. Shayne, President and Chief Executive Officer, Doctors Hospital, Augusta, GA, p. A155

GEORGE, Cecil, Chief of Staff, Pecos County Memorial Hospital, Fort Stockton, TX, p. A639

GEORGE, Dennis L., Chief Executive Officer, Coffey County Hospital, Burlington, KS, p. A245

GEORGE, Doug, Financial Manager, Veterans Affairs Medical Center, Butler, PA, p. A554

GEORGE, Elnora, Administrator, Chief Executive Officer and Chief Financial Officer, John C. Fremont Healthcare District, Mariposa, CA, p. A75

GEORGE, Gary
Regional Vice President Human Resources, St. Anne Mercy Hospital, Toledo, OH, p. A523
Regional Vice President Human Resources, St. Charles Mercy Hospital, Oregon, OH, p. A520
Regional Vice President Human Resources, St. Vincent Mercy Medical Center, Toledo, OH, p. A523

GEORGE, Gladys, President and Chief Executive Officer, Lenox Hill Hospital, New York, NY, p. A461

GEORGE, Joseph, Director Information Services, Russell Medical Center, Alexander City, AL, p. A13

GEORGE, Marie, Chief Financial Officer, St. Mary's Medical Center of Campbell County, La Follette, TN, p. A610

GEORGE, Tracy L., Chief Financial Officer, St. James Parish Hospital, Lutcher, LA, p. A285

GERAGHTY, M.D., James, President Medical Staff, Sacred Heart Hospital, Eau Claire, WI, p. A725

GERAGHTY, William, Vice President Human Resources, Mary Hitchcock Memorial Hospital, Lebanon, NH, p. A422

GERARD, Greg D., Administrator and Chief Executive Officer, Prowers Medical Center, Lamar, CO, p. A107

GERARD, Jeff, Chief Operating Officer, Mills–Peninsula Health Services, Burlingame, CA, p. A55

GERARD, Susan, Assistant Administrator, Beaufort County Hospital, Washington, NC, p. A493

GERATHS, Nathan L., Director, William S. Middleton Memorial Veterans Hospital, Madison, WI, p. A728

GERBER, Carl J., Ph.D., Director, James H. Quillen Veterans Affairs Medical Center, Mountain Home, TN, p. A614

GERDES, Jerrell F., FACHE, Administrator, Franklin County Memorial Hospital, Franklin, NE, p. A406

GERDES, Kathy, Administrator, Bowdle Hospital, Bowdle, SD, p. A594

GERDES, Trisha, Health Information Director, Nemaha County Hospital, Auburn, NE, p. A404

GERHART, Paul, Chief Financial Off, Canton–Inwood Memorial Hospital, Canton, SD, p. A594

GERICK, Robert, Vice President Strategic Operations, La Porte Regional Health System, La Porte, IN, p. A220

GERIGK, Terry M., Director, Veterans Affairs Medical Center, Lebanon, PA, p. A563

GERING, Richard, Interim Chief Executive Officer, Southern Inyo Healthcare District, Lone Pine, CA, p. A68

GERLACH, George, Administrator, Granite Falls Municipal Hospital and Manor, Granite Falls, MN, p. A354

GERLACH, Mary, Chief Operating Officer, Sunrise Canyon Hospital, Lubbock, TX, p. A654

GERLOFF, Greg, Chief Executive Officer, Altru Health System, Grand Forks, ND, p. A498

GERMANN, William, Commanding Officer, Malcolm Grow Medical Center, Andrews AFB, MD, p. A302

GERRICK, Arthur J., President and Chief Executive Officer, Tri–City Regional Medical Center, Hawaiian Gardens, CA, p. A64

GERRITS, Brad, Director Information Systems, Lakeview Medical Center, Rice Lake, WI, p. A734

GERSDORF, Chuck, President, Mercy Medical Center Mount Shasta, Mount Shasta, CA, p. A77

GERSTEIN, M.D., Richard, Director Medical Staff, Mary Lane Hospital, Ware, MA, p. A324

GERVAIN, Edward, Chief Operating Officer, Adventist La Grange Memorial Hospital, La Grange, IL, p. A199

GERVELER, Patrick M., Vice President Finance and Chief Financial Officer, Blessing Hospital, Quincy, IL, p. A206

GESSEL, Thomas, Chief Operating Officer, CARITAS Medical Center, Louisville, KY, p. A269

GETAZ, M.D., Paul, Chief Medical Officer, Saint Francis Hospital, Memphis, TN, p. A613

GETMAN, Sylvia, Chief Executive Officer, Mitchell County Regional Health Center, Osage, IA, p. A239

GETMAN, M.D., Thomas, Chief of Staff, Smith Northview Hospital, Valdosta, GA, p. A171

GETTLER, Rand G., Chief Operating Officer, Winona Health, Winona, MN, p. A365

GETTO, M.D., Carl J., Senior Vice President Medical Affairs and Associate Dean Hospital Affairs, University of Wisconsin Hospital and Clinics, Madison, WI, p. A728

GETTYS III, Roddey E., Executive Vice President and Chief Operating Officer, Palmetto Health Baptist Easley, Easley, SC, p. A587

GETTYS, Sky, Vice President Finance, Fairfield Medical Center, Lancaster, OH, p. A515

GETZ, Peter, Administrator, South Carolina State Hospital, Columbia, SC, p. A586

GEURTS, Chuck, Manager Information Services, Aurora BayCare Medical Center, Green Bay, WI, p. A726

GEVEDON, Rhonda, Human Resources Representative, Morgan County Appalachian Regional Hospital, West Liberty, KY, p. A275

GFELLERR, Michael, Director Information Systems, Medical Center of Plano, Plano, TX, p. A661

GHARGHOURY, M.D., Ayad, Chief Medical Staff, Hi–Desert Medical Center, Joshua Tree, CA, p. A65

GHERKE, John, Chief Information Officer, Laurel Regional Hospital, Laurel, MD, p. A309

GHIDOTTI, Craig, Vice President Human Resources, Southwestern Vermont Medical Center, Bennington, VT, p. A682

GIANCOLA, Louis R., President and Chief Executive Officer, South County Hospital, Wakefield, RI, p. A582

GIANG, M.D., Daniel, Vice President for Medical Administration, Loma Linda University Medical Center, Loma Linda, CA, p. A68

GIANGARDELLA, Mike, Vice President Finance and Administration, Salem Community Hospital, Salem, OH, p. A521

GIANNUNZIO, Diane D.
President and Chief Executive Officer, Southwest Regional Rehabilitation Center, Battle Creek, MI, p. A328
President and Chief Executive Officer, Southwest Regional Rehabilitation Center, Battle Creek, MI, p. A328

GIANOLA, M.D., Katherine, Associate Chief of Staff for Information Technology, Hunter Holmes McGuire Veterans Affairs Medical Center, Richmond, VA, p. A695

GIARDINA, Deborah, Chief Human Resource Officer, Rehabilitation Hospital of Fort Wayne, Fort Wayne, IN, p. A215

GIBBEN, Lori, Assistant Controller, HEALTHSOUTH Rehabilitation Hospital of Erie, Erie, PA, p. A558

GIBBERMAN, Val, Acting Chief of Staff, Veterans Affairs Medical Center, Hampton, VA, p. A689

GIBBONS, Eileen, Administrator, HEALTHSOUTH New England Rehabilitation Hospital, Woburn, MA, p. A325

GIBBONS, Gary, M.D., Interim President and Chief Executive Officer, Quincy Medical Center, Quincy, MA, p. A322

GIBBONS, H. Ray, FACHE, Chief Executive Officer, Teton Medical Center, Choteau, MT, p. A397

GIBSON, David, Chief Information Officer, Mark Reed Hospital, McCleary, WA, p. A704

GIBSON III, Earnest, Administrator, Riverside General Hospital, Houston, TX, p. A647

GIBSON, James P., Administrator, Lincoln County Medical Center, Ruidoso, NM, p. A444

GIBSON, Joel, Vice President Human Resources, St. Joseph's Mercy of Macomb, Clinton Township, MI, p. A330

GIBSON, Michael, Director Information Systems, Northlake Medical Center, Tucker, GA, p. A171

GIBSON, Ricky, Director Information Systems, Hunt Memorial Hospital District, Greenville, TX, p. A642

GIBSON, Robert, Senior Director Operating Services, Community Hospital of Ottawa, Ottawa, IL, p. A204

GIBSON, M.D., Ronald, Chief of Staff, Community Health Center of Branch County, Coldwater, MI, p. A330

GIBSON, Thomas J., Administrator, University of South Alabama Knollwood Park Hospital, Mobile, AL, p. A21

GIBSON, Todd, Chief Financial Officer, Las Colinas Medical Center, Irving, TX, p. A649

GIBSON, William, Chief Executive Officer, Hastings Regional Center, Hastings, NE, p. A407

GIDDINGS, Lucille C., CHE, President and Chief Executive Officer, Nantucket Cottage Hospital, Nantucket, MA, p. A321

GIDDINGS, Robert, Chief Financial Officer, Garden City Hospital, Garden City, MI, p. A333

GIDEON, CHE, Daniel L., Chief Executive Officer, Titus Regional Medical Center, Mount Pleasant, TX, p. A657

GIDEON, Dawn M., Executive Director, St. Vincent's Hospital, New York, NY, p. A465

GIENGER, Del, Director of Financial Services, Frances Mahon Deaconess Hospital, Glasgow, MT, p. A398

GIERKE, M.D., Peter, Chief of Staff, Mark Twain St. Joseph's Hospital, San Andreas, CA, p. A86

GIEST, Jim, Chief Financial Officer, Guyan Valley Hospital, Logan, WV, p. A717

GIGLIOTTI, Ralph F., Associate Director, Veterans Affairs Eastern Colorado Health Care System, Denver, CO, p. A104

GIJANTO, Charles, Executive Vice President and Chief Operating Officer, Champlain Valley Physicians Hospital Medical Center, Plattsburgh, NY, p. A469

GIL, Julio, Manager Information Services, Hazel Hawkins Memorial Hospital, Hollister, CA, p. A64

GILBERT, Andrea F., CHE, President, Bryn Mawr Hospital, Bryn Mawr, PA, p. A553

GILBERT, Berry, Administrator, Dubuis Hospital of Paris, Paris, TX, p. A660

GILBERT, Brian D., Chief Executive Officer, Wrangell Medical Center, Wrangell, AK, p. A29

GILBERT, Dan, Vice President, Parkridge Medical Center, Chattanooga, TN, p. A604

GILBERT, Jack, Vice President Finance, Advocate Illinois Masonic Medical Center, Chicago, IL, p. A186

GILBERT, Jr, Ronald, Chief Financial Officer, Soldiers and Sailors Memorial Hospital, Wellsboro, PA, p. A578

GILBERT, Thomas D., President and Chief Executive Officer, Emory Dunwoody Medical Center, Atlanta, GA, p. A153

GILBERT, William L., Chief Executive Officer, Regional Medical Center of San Jose, San Jose, CA, p. A90

GILBERTI, Gary M., Regional Vice President, Arbour–Fuller Hospital, Attleboro, MA, p. A312

GILBERTSON, Dennis, Chief Information Resource Management, Veterans Affairs Medical and Regional Office Center, Fargo, ND, p. A498

GILBERTSON, Doris White, Administrator, Granite County Medical Center, Philipsburg, MT, p. A401

GILBERTSON, Roger L., M.D.,
President and Chief Executive Officer, MeritCare Health System, Fargo, ND, p. B75
President, MeritCare Medical Center, Fargo, ND, p. A497

GILBREATH, David D., President and Chief Executive Officer, Central Peninsula General Hospital, Soldotna, AK, p. A28

GILDEA, Steve
Director Management Information Systems, J. C. Blair Memorial Hospital, Huntingdon, PA, p. A561
Director Management Information Systems, Tyrone Hospital, Tyrone, PA, p. A577

GILDERSLEEVE, Robert E., Executive Vice President and Chief Financial Officer, Ball Memorial Hospital, Muncie, IN, p. A222

GILES, Alyson Pitman, President and Chief Executive Officer, Catholic Medical Center, Manchester, NH, p. A422

GILES, Kent, Director Finance, Wabash County Hospital, Wabash, IN, p. A227

GILES–LUICK, Glenda, Director Human Resources, Fountain Valley Regional Hospital and Medical Center, Fountain Valley, CA, p. A60

GILGEN, Steve, Assistant Administrator Fiscal Services, Murphy Medical Center, Murphy, NC, p. A488

GILKEY, M.D., Edward, Chief Physician Executive, Alaska Native Medical Center, Anchorage, AK, p. A26

GILL, Dorothy, Vice President Human Resources, Parkview Medical Center, Pueblo, CO, p. A109

GILL, Maggie, Chief Financial Officer, Coral Gables Hospital, Coral Gables, FL, p. A126

GILL, Mark, Vice President Finance and Chief Financial Officer, Burdette Tomlin Memorial Hospital, Cape May Court House, NJ, p. A427

GILL, Robert D., Vice President and Chief Financial Officer, St. Joseph's Hospital, Saint Paul, MN, p. A362

GILLELAND, Jr, M.D., William, Medical Staff President, Jameson Hospital, New Castle, PA, p. A566

GILLEN, Michael J., Chief Executive Officer, Sterling Regional MedCenter, Sterling, CO, p. A109

GILLENWATERS, Gail, Chief Operating Officer, Broward General Medical Center, Fort Lauderdale, FL, p. A128

GILLES, Ken, Director of Information Systems, Innovis Health, Fargo, ND, p. A497

GILLESBY, M.D., Robert J., Executive Vice President Clinical Services and Chief Medical Officer, Chestnut Hill Health System, Philadelphia, PA, p. A567

GILLESPIE, Christina, Chief Financial Officer, Harrison County Community Hospital, Bethany, MO, p. A378

GILLESPIE, M.D., John, Chief of Staff, Pattie A. Clay Regional Medical Center, Richmond, KY, p. A274

GILLESPIE, Lynn, Assistant Administrator, OSF Saint Francis Medical Center, Peoria, IL, p. A205

GILLESPIE, Tom, Vice President Finance, Morehead Memorial Hospital, Eden, NC, p. A481

GILLESPIE, William J., Vice President and Chief Information Officer, York Hospital, York, PA, p. A580

GILLESPIE, Yvette, Chief Executive Officer, Trinity Hospital, Erin, TN, p. A606

GILLETTE, Kathryn, Chief Executive Officer, Community Hospital, New Port Richey, FL, p. A139

GILLETTE, Robert, Chief Information Officer, St. Elizabeth Medical Center, Utica, NY, p. A475

GILLIAM, Eric, Administrator, Continuing Care Hospital, Lexington, KY, p. A267

GILLIARD, Ronald M., FACHE, Chief Executive Officer, Evans Memorial Hospital, Claxton, GA, p. A158

GILLIES, Christopher, Chief Executive Officer, Marlton Rehabilitation Hospital, Marlton, NJ, p. A431

GILLIHAN, Kerry G., FACHE,
President and Chief Executive Officer, Cardinal Hill Healthcare System, Lexington, KY, p. B21
President and Chief Executive Officer, Cardinal Hill Rehabilitation Hospital, Lexington, KY, p. A267

GILLS, Karl B., Chief Executive Officer, Yampa Valley Medical Center, Steamboat Springs, CO, p. A109

GILLY, M.D., Frank, Vice President Medical Affairs, Warren Hospital, Phillipsburg, NJ, p. A434

GILMAN, Howard, Medical Executive, Christian Health Care Center, Wyckoff, NJ, p. A439

GILMAN, James K., Commander, Walter Reed Army Medical Center, Washington, DC, p. A122

GILMORE, Beverly, President and Chief Executive Officer, West Hills Hospital and Medical Center, Los Angeles, CA, p. A73

GILMORE, Joshua, Chief Financial Officer, Marias Medical Center, Shelby, MT, p. A402

GILMORE, Phillip K., Chief Executive Officer, H.S.C. Medical Center, Malvern, AR, p. A47

GILMORE, Stephen, Chief Financial Officer, Saint Vincent Hospital at Worcester Medical Center, Worcester, MA, p. A325

GILPIN, Ann C., President and Chief Executive Officer, Jones Memorial Hospital, Wellsville, NY, p. A475

GILSTON, Jennifer, Chief Operating Officer and Corporate Compliance Officer, Amsterdam Memorial Hospital, Amsterdam, NY, p. A446

GILSTRAP, M. E., President and Chief Executive Officer, Halifax Regional Medical Center, Roanoke Rapids, NC, p. A490

GILSTRAP, Mike, Chief Operating Officer, Medical Center of Central Georgia, Macon, GA, p. A165

GILTNER, Michelle, Director Patient Care Services, UHHS Bedford Medical Center, Bedford, OH, p. A503

GINGERICH, James H., Chief Executive Officer, Cobre Valley Community Hospital, Globe, AZ, p. A31

GINN, Bobby, Chief Executive Officer, Marlboro Park Hospital, Bennettsville, SC, p. A584

GINSBERG, Ronald L., Vice President Medical Affairs, Northwest Hospital Center, Randallstown, MD, p. A310

GINTY, Jr, John J., Senior Vice President, Patient Services, Aroostook Medical Center, Presque Isle, ME, p. A300

GINTY, Neil W., Administrator, Louis Smith Memorial Hospital, Lakeland, GA, p. A164

GINTZIG, Donald R., CHE, Chief Executive Officer, Middle Tennessee Medical Center, Murfreesboro, TN, p. A614

GIO, Dominick J., President and Chief Executive Officer, Wyckoff Heights Medical Center, New York, NY, p. A466

GIONFRIDDO, Paul, Vice President Human Resources, Moses Taylor Hospital, Scranton, PA, p. A575

GIORDANO, James V., Interim President and Chief Executive Officer, St. Francis Hospital, Inc., Columbus, GA, p. A158

GIORDANO, Paul, Vice President and Human Resources, South Nassau Communities Hospital, Oceanside, NY, p. A467

GIORGINO, Richard, Administrator, Columbus Hospital, Newark, NJ, p. A432

GIOVANETTI, Victor, Chief Executive Officer, Southern Hills Medical Center, Nashville, TN, p. A615

GIRARD, Thomas, Vice President Human Resources, North Country Hospital and Health Center, Newport, VT, p. A683

GIRARDOT, Angie, Director Human Resources, Ridgecrest Regional Hospital, Ridgecrest, CA, p. A84

GIRAULO, Ronald A., Vice President Finance and Administration, Brookhaven Memorial Hospital Medical Center, Patchogue, NY, p. A469

GIRLINGHOUSE, Mavis, Regional Director Information Management, Christus St. Elizabeth Hospital, Beaumont, TX, p. A625

GIROTTO, Ronald G.
President and Chief Executive Officer, The Methodist Hospital, Houston, TX, p. A648
President and Chief Executive Officer, The Methodist Hospital System, Houston, TX, p. B108

GIRTEN, David M., Corporate Director Financial Services, St. Elizabeth Ann Seton Hospital of Carmel, Carmel, IN, p. A212

GIRTY, Tara, Director Human Resources, Kiowa District Hospital and Manor, Kiowa, KS, p. A250

GISCH, Jim, Manager Client Services, Aurora Sheboygan Memorial Medical Center, Sheboygan, WI, p. A735

GISLESON, Joni, Financial Director, Palmer Lutheran Health Center, West Union, IA, p. A243

GITMAN, M.D., Paul, Medical Director, North Shore University Hospital, Manhasset, NY, p. A456

GITTELMAN, Michael B.
Administrator, Bascom Palmer Eye Institute–Anne Bates Leach Eye Hospital, Miami, FL, p. A136
Administrator, Bascom Palmer Eye Institute–Anne Bates Leach Eye Hospital, Miami, FL, p. A136

GIUDICE, William A., Chief Financial Officer and Vice President, Tallahassee Memorial HealthCare, Tallahassee, FL, p. A147

GIULIANELLI, Victor, President and Chief Executive Officer, St. Mary's Hospital, Amsterdam, NY, p. A447

GIVEN, M.D., Brian V., Chief of Staff, Sid Peterson Memorial Hospital, Kerrville, TX, p. A651

GIVENS, Birdge, Associate Administrator and Director Human Resources, John H. Stroger Jr. Hospital of Cook County, Chicago, IL, p. A187

GIVENS, M.D., Jerry, Chief Medical Officer, Skaggs Community Health Center, Branson, MO, p. A379

GIVENS, Stephen K., Chief Operating Officer, Johnston Memorial Hospital, Abingdon, VA, p. A685

GIZZI, Jason, Controller, HEALTHSOUTH MountainView Regional Rehabilitation Hospital, Morgantown, WV, p. A718

GJERVOLD, Sandra, Chief Financial Officer, Kittson Memorial Healthcare Center, Hallock, MN, p. A354

GLADNEY, Robert C., Chief Executive Officer, Kindred Hospital of Tarrant County, Arlington, TX, p. A622

GLANVILLE, Charles T., Interim Chief Financial Officer, J. C. Blair Memorial Hospital, Huntingdon, PA, p. A561

GLANZER, Elgin, Chief Financial Officer, Memorial Hospital, Abilene, KS, p. A244

GLASBERG, Michael
Chief Operating Officer, Petaluma Valley Hospital, Petaluma, CA, p. A81
Chief Operating Officer, Santa Rosa Memorial Hospital, Santa Rosa, CA, p. A93

GLASGOW, M.D., John, Chief of Staff, Jackson County Memorial Hospital, Altus, OK, p. A527

GLASRUD, Scott, Senior Vice President and Chief Financial Officer, University of Kansas Hospital, Kansas City, KS, p. A250

GLASS, Steven, Interim Chief Financial Officer, Cleveland Clinic Foundation, Cleveland, OH, p. A508

GLASSBURN, David, Chief Financial Officer, Northeast Medical Center Hospital, Humble, TX, p. A649

GLASSMAN, Scott, Information Systems Director, Russell Regional Hospital, Russell, KS, p. A256

GLASSMAN, M.D., Stuart, Medical Director, HEALTHSOUTH Rehabilitation Hospital, Concord, NH, p. A420

GLAZIER, Stephen M., Executive Director, Orlando Regional South Seminole Hospital, Longwood, FL, p. A135

GLEASON, Larry, Chief Administrative Officer, Fairmont Medical Center–Mayo Health System, Fairmont, MN, p. A353

GLEASON, Ron, Chief Financial Officer, Lincoln Hospital, Davenport, WA, p. A702

GLEASON, Tracy, Assistant Administrator, Sutter Lakeside Hospital, Lakeport, CA, p. A67

GLEIM, Kathi, Chief Executive Officer, Integrated Specialty Hospital of Albuquerque, Albuquerque, NM, p. A440

GLEN, Diane M., Chief Financial Officer, Barnes–Jewish West County Hospital, Saint Louis, MO, p. A390

GLENN, Jeannette, Vice President, Human Resources and Education and Training, McLeod Health, Florence, SC, p. A588

GLENN, Michael, Chief Executive Officer, Olympic Medical Center, Port Angeles, WA, p. A706

GLENNING, Robert, Executive Vice President and Chief Financial Officer, Buffalo General Hospital, Buffalo, NY, p. A448

GLEZEN, Joseph W., Director Human Resources, Southeastern Regional Medical Center, Lumberton, NC, p. A487

GLICKSMAN, Edward J., Chief Executive Officer, Interfaith Medical Center, New York, NY, p. A460

GLIDDEN, Nancy, Chief Financial Officer, Millinocket Regional Hospital, Millinocket, ME, p. A299

GLIDEWELL, Calvin, Chief Executive Officer, University Community Hospital, Tampa, FL, p. A149

GLOFF, Vickie, Accountant, Goodall–Witcher Healthcare, Clifton, TX, p. A629

GLOGGNER, Peter, Vice President Human Resources, Union Hospital, Elkton, MD, p. A307

GLONER, James, Senior Vice President, North Philadelphia Health System, Philadelphia, PA, p. A569

GLOOR, Michael R., FACHE, President and Chief Executive Officer, Saint Francis Medical Center, Grand Island, NE, p. A407

GLOTZBACK, Lee, Director of Human Resources, Citrus Memorial Hospital, Inverness, FL, p. A131

GLOVER, Al, Chief Operating Officer, Staten Island University Hospital, New York, NY, p. A465

GLOVER, Sharon, Director Human Resources, Somerset Hospital Center for Health, Somerset, PA, p. A576

GLUBKA, Theresa, Chief Executive Officer, Sutter Solano Medical Center, Vallejo, CA, p. A98

GLUECKERT, John W., President, St. Joseph Hospital, Polson, MT, p. A401

GLYER, David, Director Financial Services, Community Memorial Hospital of San Buenaventura, Ventura, CA, p. A98

GLYNN, M.D., Russell, Chief of Staff, Veterans Affairs Central Iowa Health Care System, Des Moines, IA, p. A233

GOAD, Pat, Human Resources Director, Claremore Regional Hospital, Claremore, OK, p. A529

GOBEL, John, Director Information Services, Alice Peck Day Memorial Hospital, Lebanon, NH, p. A421

GOBLE, Mandy C., President & Chief Executive Officer, Mary Rutan Hospital, Bellefontaine, OH, p. A504

GOCHE, Jeanne, Chief Executive Officer and Administrator, Manning Regional Healthcare Center, Manning, IA, p. A237

GODAR, Neil, Administrator Director Personnel, Anderson Hospital, Maryville, IL, p. A200

GODDARD, Richard L., Chief Executive Officer, Drew Memorial Hospital, Monticello, AR, p. A48

GODFREY, M.D., David, Vice President Medical Affairs, Bradford Regional Medical Center, Bradford, PA, p. A553

GODFREY, Larry, Deputy Commander Clinical Services, Reynolds Army Community Hospital, Fort Sill, OK, p. A531

GODFREY, M.D., Thomas, Medical Director, Kaiser Foundation Hospital, Los Angeles, CA, p. A70

GODSEY, Carol, Chief Executive Officer, St. Elizabeth Ann Seton Specialty Care Hospital, Evansville, IN, p. A215

GODSOE, Al, Director Information Systems, Johnson Memorial Hospital, Franklin, IN, p. A216

GOEBEL, Dennis
Administrator, Community Memorial Hospital, Turtle Lake, ND, p. A500
President and Chief Executive Officer, Garrison Memorial Hospital, Garrison, ND, p. A498

GOEBEL, Michael, Chief Financial Officer, Regional West Medical Center, Scottsbluff, NE, p. A413

GOEHRING, David, Interim Vice President Financial Services, Rapid City Regional Hospital System of Care, Rapid City, SD, p. A598

GOETZINGER, Susan, Chief Financial Officer, Riverton Memorial Hospital, Riverton, WY, p. A741

GOFF, Kerry, Director of Operations and Personnel Services, Washington County Hospital and Nursing Home, Chatom, AL, p. A16

GOGLIETTINO, Deborah, Vice President Human Resources, Lawrence Hospital Center, Bronxville, NY, p. A448

GOGOLA, Michael, Chief Information Officer, Satilla Regional Medical Center, Waycross, GA, p. A172

GOH, Jonathan, Chief Financial Officer, San Gorgonio Memorial Hospital, Banning, CA, p. A54

GOHL, Daryl, Director Human Resources, Tuality Healthcare, Hillsboro, OR, p. A544

GOIN, Mel, Chief Financial Officer, Mt. Carmel Regional Medical Center, Pittsburg, KS, p. A255

GOKLI, M.D., Asit, Vice President Medical Affairs, St. Mary Mercy Hospital, Livonia, MI, p. A339

GOLAN, J Marc, Chief Financial Officer, Seton Medical Center, Daly City, CA, p. A58

GOLD, Larry M., President and Chief Executive Officer, Connecticut Children's Medical Center, Hartford, CT, p. A113

GOLDAMMER, Kyle, Chief Financial Officer, Sioux Falls Surgical Center, Sioux Falls, SD, p. A599

GOLDAMMER, Shellie, Information Systems, Avera St. Benedict Health Center, Parkston, SD, p. A597

GOLDBERG, M.D., David, Medical Director, Greene Memorial Hospital, Xenia, OH, p. A525

GOLDBERG, Edward M., President and Chief Executive Officer, St. Alexius Medical Center, Hoffman Estates, IL, p. A197

GOLDBERG, M.D., Frederick, Senior Vice President and Medical Director, Faxton–St. Luke's Healthcare, Utica, NY, p. A474

GOLDBERG, Jonathan, Chief Information Officer, St. Peter's Hospital, Albany, NY, p. A446

GOLDBERG, Larry, Executive Director and Chief Executive Officer, Vanderbilt University Medical Center, Nashville, TN, p. A616

GOLDBERG, M.D., Lawrence, Chief Medical Officer, CARITAS Medical Center, Louisville, KY, p. A269

GOLDBLOOM, Alan L., M.D.,
President and Chief Executive Officer, Children's Hospital and Clinics, Saint Paul, MN, p. A362
President and Chief Executive Officer, Children's Hospitals and Clinics, Minneapolis, MN, p. A357
President and Chief Executive Officer, Children's Hospitals and Clinics of Minnesota, Minneapolis, MN, p. B28

GOLDENBOGEN, Tom, Chief Financial Officer, Mercy Hospital, Port Huron, MI, p. A343

GOLDFARB, Timothy J., Chief Executive Officer, Shands at the University of Florida, Gainesville, FL, p. A130

GOLDFARB, Timothy M., Chief Executive Officer, Shands HealthCare, Gainesville, FL, p. B97

GOLDFEIN, M.D., Michael, Chief Medical Staff, Martha's Vineyard Hospital, Oak Bluffs, MA, p. A322

GOLDHAHN KOWEN, Laura, Chief Operating Officer and Senior Vice President, Benefis Healthcare, Great Falls, MT, p. A399

GOLDMAN, David, Vice President Medical Affairs and Education, Prince George's Hospital Center, Cheverly, MD, p. A306

GOLDMAN, Eric, Chief Operating Officer, Columbia Hospital, West Palm Beach, FL, p. A150

GOLDMAN, T. Marvin, Chief Executive Officer, Wills Memorial Hospital, Washington, GA, p. A172

GOLDSCHMIDT, Diane, Manager Human Resources, HEALTHSOUTH Northern Kentucky Rehabilitation Hospital, Edgewood, KY, p. A263

GOLDSMITH, Cindy, Chief Financial Officer, Hamilton Hospital, Olney, TX, p. A659

GOLDSMITH, M.D., Dana L., Vice President Medical Affairs, Penobscot Bay Medical Center, Rockport, ME, p. A300

GOLDSTEIN, M.D., Brian, Chief of Staff, University of North Carolina Hospitals, Chapel Hill, NC, p. A479

GOLDSTEIN, Gary W., M.D., President and Chief Executive Officer, Kennedy Krieger Institute, Baltimore, MD, p. A303

GOLDSTEIN, M.D., Leonard, President Medical Staff, Potomac Ridge Behavioral Health System, Rockville, MD, p. A310

GOLDSTEIN, Lisa, Vice President and Chief Operating Officer, Hospital for Special Surgery, New York, NY, p. A460

GOLDSTEIN, III, M.D, Nathan, Chief Medical Officer, Northwest Texas Healthcare System, Amarillo, TX, p. A621

GOLDSTEIN, Paul, Vice President Finance and Chief Financial Officer, Orlando Regional Medical Center, Orlando, FL, p. A141

GOLDSTEIN, Stephen, Director Information Systems, Regional Medical Center–Bayonet Point, Hudson, FL, p. A131

GOLDSTEIN, Steven I.
President and Chief Executive Officer, Highland Hospital of Rochester, Rochester, NY, p. A470
General Director and Chief Executive Officer, Strong Memorial Hospital, Rochester, NY, p. B103
General Director and Chief Executive Officer, Strong Memorial Hospital of the University of Rochester, Rochester, NY, p. A471

GOLDSTEIN, Wendy Z., President and Chief Executive Officer, Lutheran Medical Center, New York, NY, p. A461

GOLLAHER, Jeff, Vice President Fiscal Servs, Holy Rosary Healthcare, Miles City, MT, p. A400

GOLSON, Allen, Chief Executive Officer, Coliseum Medical Centers, Macon, GA, p. A165

GOMBAR, Greg A., Chief Financial Officer, Carolinas Medical Center, Charlotte, NC, p. A479

GOMEZ, Juan, Controller, State Psychiatric Hospital, San Juan, PR, p. A748

GOMPF, Shelly
Vice President Human Resources, Central Kansas Medical Center, Great Bend, KS, p. A247
Vice President Human Resources, St. Joseph Memorial Hospital, Larned, KS, p. A251

GONNELLA, Michael J., President and Chief Executive Officer, William B. Kessler Memorial Hospital, Hammonton, NJ, p. A429

GONYEA, Sonja, Director of Human Resources, United Memorial Medical Center, Batavia, NY, p. A447

GONZALES, Jan, Director Human Resources, North Valley Hospital, Tonasket, WA, p. A711

GONZALES, Pamela, Chief Financial Officer, Anson General Hospital, Anson, TX, p. A621

GONZALES, Ray, Manager Information Systems, Saint Anthony Hospital, Chicago, IL, p. A189

GONZALES, M.D., Ruben, President Medical Staff, Terre Haute Regional Hospital, Terre Haute, IN, p. A226

GONZALEZ, Arthur A., FACHE, President and Chief Executive Officer, Tri–City Medical Center, Oceanside, CA, p. A79

GONZALEZ, Aurelio, Chief Financial Officer, Hialeah Hospital, Hialeah, FL, p. A130

GONZALEZ, Elizabeth, Controller, Hospital Metropolitano Dr. Tito Mattei, Yauco, PR, p. A749

GONZALEZ, Gilberto
Administrator, Hospital Dr. Dominguez, Humacao, PR, p. A745
Chief Executive Officer, Hospital Metropolitan, San Juan, PR, p. A747

GONZALEZ, Juan, Chief Financial Officer, San Juan City Hospital, San Juan, PR, p. A748

GONZALEZ, Pedro J.
Executive Director, Ashford Presbyterian Community Hospital, San Juan, PR, p. A746
Executive Director, San Carlos General Hospital, San Juan, PR, p. A747

GONZALEZ, Richard D., Chief Executive Officer, Southwest General Hospital, San Antonio, TX, p. A665

GONZALEZ, R.N., Sonia I., Chief Operating Officer, Oak Hill Hospital, Brooksville, FL, p. A125

GONZALEZ–DIAZ, M.D., Juan F., Medical Director, Ryder Memorial Hospital, Humacao, PR, p. A745

GOOCH, M.D., Matthew, Chief of Staff, Whitesburg Appalachian Regional Hospital, Whitesburg, KY, p. A275

GOOCH, Rose, Director Information Systems, Culpeper Regional Hospital, Culpeper, VA, p. A687

GOOD, M.D., Vance A., Chief Medical Staff, Troy Community Hospital, Troy, PA, p. A577

GOODALL, M.D., David, Chief Medical Staff, Deer River HealthCare Center, Deer River, MN, p. A352

GOODE, Galen, Chief Executive Officer, Hamilton Center, Terre Haute, IN, p. A226

GOODE, Lori, Director Human Resources, Baptist Memorial Hospital–Union County, New Albany, MS, p. A374

GOODLETT, Lisa, Vice President Finance, Regional Medical Center of Orangeburg and Calhoun Counties, Orangeburg, SC, p. A591

GOODMAN, Ph.D., David M., Chief Information Officer, Veterans Affairs Boston Healthcare System, Boston, MA, p. A315

GOODMAN, Doug, Director Human Resources, Oak Hill Hospital, Brooksville, FL, p. A125

GOODMAN, Larry J., M.D.,
President, Rush University Medical Center, Chicago, IL, p. B94
President and Chief Executive Officer, Rush University Medical Center, Chicago, IL, p. A189

GOODMAN, Norman B., President and Chief Executive Officer, Brockton Hospital, Brockton, MA, p. A315

GOODMAN, Steven, Chief Information Officer, Willow Crest Hospital, Miami, OK, p. A533

GOODMAN, Todd, Vice President and Chief Financial Officer, Florida Hospital Heartland Medical Center, Sebring, FL, p. A146

GOODNO, Janell, Chief Financial Officer, Stafford District Hospital, Stafford, KS, p. A257

GOODNOW, John H., President and Chief Executive Officer, Benefis Healthcare, Great Falls, MT, p. A399

GOODRICH, Barbara K., R.N., Vice President and Chief Operating Officer, Alegent Health Immanuel Medical Center, Omaha, NE, p. A410

GOODRICH, C Harlan, Vice President & Chief Information Officer, MidMichigan Medical Center–Midland, Midland, MI, p. A340

GOODRICH, Rosemarie, Director, Information Services, Bert Fish Medical Center, New Smyrna Beach, FL, p. A139

GOODRICH, Scott, Commander, Winn Army Community Hospital, Hinesville, GA, p. A163

GOODSPEED, Ronald B., M.P.H., Chief Executive Officer, Southcoast Hospitals Group, Fall River, MA, p. A317

GOODSTEIN, M.D., Jordan, Chief of Staff, Brotman Medical Center, Culver City, CA, p. A58

GOODWIN, David, Chief of Staff, Cuyuna Regional Medical Center, Crosby, MN, p. A352

GOODWIN, Ervin, Department Manager of Information Services, North Country Hospital and Health Center, Newport, VT, p. A683

GOODWIN, M.D., James O., Vice President Medical Affairs, Maria Parham Medical Center, Henderson, NC, p. A484

GOODWIN, Jeffrey C., President and Chief Executive Officer, Warren Hospital, Phillipsburg, NJ, p. A434

GOODWIN, Joy, Business Manager, Yoakum County Hospital, Denver City, TX, p. A635

GOODWIN, Keith D., Chief Operating Officer, Children's Hospital, Columbus, OH, p. A510

GOODWIN, Robert P., President and Chief Executive Officer, Margaret R. Pardee Memorial Hospital, Hendersonville, NC, p. A484

GOODWIN, M.D., W Jarrad, Director, University of Miami Hospital and Clinics, Miami, FL, p. A138

GOODYEAR, R.N., Penny, Vice President Applications, Mercy Hospital of Franciscan Sisters, Oelwein, IA, p. A239

GOOLSBY, M.D., Lane, Chief of Staff, Aurora BayCare Medical Center, Green Bay, WI, p. A726

GOOLSBY, M.D., Louis, Senior Vice President Medical Affairs, Medical Center of Central Georgia, Macon, GA, p. A165

GORBY, R.N., MS, Cherie, Chief Operating Officer, Memorial Hospital, Colorado Springs, CO, p. A102

GORCHYNSKY, M.D., Andrew, President Medical Staff, Saint Joseph Hospital, Chicago, IL, p. A190

GORDON, Bruce A., Director, Veterans Affairs Medical Center, Leeds, MA, p. A319

GORDON, Dan, Chief Financial Officer, Feather River Hospital, Paradise, CA, p. A80

GORDON, Ed, Director Information Services, Tehachapi Valley Healthcare District, Tehachapi, CA, p. A95

GORDON, Jane, Executive Secretary, Pocahontas Memorial Hospital, Buckeye, WV, p. A713

GORDON, Joseph R., Chief Executive Officer, Select Specialty Hospital–Wyandotte, Wyandotte, MI, p. A348

GORDON, Mark M., Chief Executive Officer, Our Lady of Bellefonte Hospital, Ashland, KY, p. A261

GORDON, M.D., Randolph, Interim Vice President Medical Affairs, Bon Secours Hospital, Grosse Pointe, MI, p. A335

GORDON, Scott, Executive Vice President and Chief Operating Officer, Arkansas Children's Hospital, Little Rock, AR, p. A46

GORDON, Tonia, Principal Partner, Windber Medical Center, Windber, PA, p. A580

GORDON, Wayne, Chief Financial Officer, Plaza Medical Center of Fort Worth, Fort Worth, TX, p. A640

GORDON, William G., Chief Executive Officer, Barton Memorial Hospital, South Lake Tahoe, CA, p. A94

GORDY, Joseph S., President, Flagler Hospital, Saint Augustine, FL, p. A145

GORE, Gary R., Chief Executive Officer, Marshall County Health Care Authority, Guntersville, AL, p. B71

GORMAN, Galen, Chief Financial Officer, St. Joseph Hospital, Eureka, CA, p. A59

GORMAN, John A., Chief Executive Officer, Memorial Hospital, Fremont, OH, p. A514

GORMLEY, Maureen, Chief Operating Officer, Warren G. Magnuson Clinical Center, National Institutes of Health, Bethesda, MD, p. A306

GORMSEN, D.O., David, Chief Medical Officer, Mercy Medical Center, Canton, OH, p. A505

GORN, Angela, Vice President, Norton Sound Regional Hospital, Nome, AK, p. A28

GORR, Cindy, Chief Executive Officer, Ashland Regional Medical Center, Ashland, PA, p. A552

GORRELL, Karl E.
Chief Financial Officer, Summerville Medical Center, Summerville, SC, p. A592
Chief Financial Officer, Trident Medical Center, Charleston, SC, p. A585

GORRELL, Mark, Vice President Information Services, Baystate Medical Center, Springfield, MA, p. A323

GORS, Ann, Chief Executive Officer, Kentfield Rehabilitation Hospital, San Rafael, CA, p. A91

GORSKI, John, Interim Administrator, Community Hospital, Munster, IN, p. A222

GOSLINE, Peter L., Chief Executive Officer, Monadnock Community Hospital, Peterborough, NH, p. A423

GOSNELL, Nanci Little
Vice President Information Services, Inova Alexandria Hospital, Alexandria, VA, p. A685
Vice President Information Services, Inova Fair Oaks Hospital, Fairfax, VA, p. A687

GOSNEY, Brenda, Administrator, HEALTHSOUTH Northern Kentucky Rehabilitation Hospital, Edgewood, KY, p. A263

GOSNEY, Brett, Chief Executive Officer, Animas Surgical Hospital, Durango, CO, p. A104

GOSPODAREK, Robert E., President and Chief Executive Officer, Mercy Hospital of Willard, Willard, OH, p. A525

GOSSENS, Kevin, Human Resources Director, Riverside Medical Center, Waupaca, WI, p. A737

GOTSCHLICH, Emil, M.D., Vice President Medical Sciences, Rockefeller University Hospital, New York, NY, p. A464

GOTSIS, M.D., Perry, Executive Vice President and Medical Director, Naples Community Hospital, Naples, FL, p. A139

GOTTLIEB, Gary L., M.D., Chief Executive Officer, Brigham and Women's Hospital, Boston, MA, p. A313

GOTTLIEB, M.D., Michael, Chief Medical Officer, MetroWest Medical Center, Framingham, MA, p. A318

GOTTSCHALK, M. Therese, President, Marian Health System, Tulsa, OK, p. B71

GOUGE, Victor, Information Systems Leader, North Hawaii Community Hospital, Kamuela, HI, p. A175

GOUGEON, Michele L., Executive Vice President and Chief Operating Officer, McLean Hospital, Belmont, MA, p. A312

GOUGH, M.D., Galal S., Chief of Staff, Coast Plaza Doctors Hospital, Norwalk, CA, p. A78

GOUGH, Michael W., Chief Financial Officer, Norton Audubon Hospital, Louisville, KY, p. A269

GOULAH, M.D., Richard D., Board of Director, Halifax Regional Health System, South Boston, VA, p. A696

GOULD, Bill, Chief People Resource Officer, Winona Health, Winona, MN, p. A365

GOULD, Gary R., FACHE, Chief Executive Officer, Belmont Community Hospital, Bellaire, OH, p. A504

GOULD, Robert, Associate Administrator and Chief Financial Officer, Fairbanks Memorial Hospital, Fairbanks, AK, p. A27

GOULET, James P., Vice President Operations, Columbus Community Hospital, Columbus, NE, p. A406

GOUX, L. Rene', Chief Executive Officer, Memorial Medical Center, New Orleans, LA, p. A289

GOVIER, George A., President and Chief Executive Officer, Good Samaritan Community Healthcare, Puyallup, WA, p. A706

GOWDER, Mike, Assistant Administrator, Union General Hospital, Blairsville, GA, p. A156

GOWER, Vaughn C.
Senior Vice President and Chief Financial Officer, Lehigh Valley Hospital, Allentown, PA, p. A551
Senior Vice President Finance and Chief Financial Officer, Lehigh Valley Hospital–Muhlenberg, Bethlehem, PA, p. A552

GOWING, Robert E., Administrator, Atmore Community Hospital, Atmore, AL, p. A14

GOYNES, Jack, Director Information Resources, East Cooper Regional Medical Center, Mount Pleasant, SC, p. A590

GOZIA, M.D., Penny, President Medical Staff, St. Joseph's Hospital, Breese, IL, p. A185

GRABER, Jerald, Senior Manager Finance, Greenville Regional Hospital, Greenville, IL, p. A196

GRABILL, II, L Kenneth, Vice President Finance, Johns Hopkins Bayview Medical Center, Baltimore, MD, p. A303

GRACE, Robert, Chief Financial Officer, Oak Hill Hospital, Brooksville, FL, p. A125

GRACIA, Judy, Vice President Human Resources, St. Tammany Parish Hospital, Covington, LA, p. A279

GRACIA, M.D., Sandra C., Chief of Staff, Veterans Affairs Medical Center, San Juan, PR, p. A748

GRADDY, Steve W.
Chief Financial Officer, Freeman Health System, Joplin, MO, p. A383
Chief Financial Officer, Freeman Neosho Hospital, Neosho, MO, p. A388

GRADY, Glen E., Administrator, Memorial Medical Center, Neillsville, WI, p. A732

GRADY, Phillip L., Chief Executive Officer, King's Daughters Medical Center, Brookhaven, MS, p. A367

GRAEBER, Lawrence, Chief Executive Officer, Neshoba County General Hospital, Philadelphia, MS, p. A374

GRAEBER, Tod, Controller, Garrison Memorial Hospital, Garrison, ND, p. A498

GRAEBNER, M.D., Margaret, Chief of Staff, Virginia Regional Medical Center, Virginia, MN, p. A364

GRAECA, Raymond A., President and Chief Executive Officer, Du Bois Regional Medical Center, Du Bois, PA, p. A557

GRAEFF, Les, Chief Financial Officer, Burgess Health Center, Onawa, IA, p. A239

GRAF, John, Senior Vice President, Watertown Memorial Hospital, Watertown, WI, p. A737

GRAFFIS, M.D., Richard, Executive Vice President Medical Operations, Clarian Health Partners, Indianapolis, IN, p. A218

GRAGG, Connie, Director Human Resources, Saint Mary's Regional Medical Center, Russellville, AR, p. A50

GRAGG, Martha, MSN, Chief Executive Officer, Sullivan County Memorial Hospital, Milan, MO, p. A387

GRAGNOLATI, Brian A., President and Chief Executive Officer, Suburban Hospital Healthcare System, Bethesda, MD, p. A305

GRAHAM, Esmeralda, Human Resources and People Services, Sierra Vista Hospital, Truth or Consequences, NM, p. A445

GRAHAM, George W., President and Chief Executive Officer, Torrance Memorial Medical Center, Torrance, CA, p. A96

GRAHAM, H. James, Administrator, Highlands–Cashiers Hospital, Highlands, NC, p. A485

GRAHAM, Jeff, Chief Executive Officer, Greenfield Area Medical Center, Greenfield, OH, p. A514

GRAHAM, Joe B., Chief Operating Officer, Nebraska Medical Center, Omaha, NE, p. A411

GRAHAM, John R., Vice President of Operations, William Beaumont Hospital–Royal Oak, Royal Oak, MI, p. A343

GRAHAM, Karen, Chief Information Officer, Cooper Health System, Camden, NJ, p. A426

GRAHAM, Kathryn, Director Communications and Community Relations, Novato Community Hospital, Novato, CA, p. A78

GRAHAM, Kenneth D., FACHE, President and Chief Executive Officer, Overlake Hospital Medical Center, Bellevue, WA, p. A700

GRAHAM, Michael R., Administrator, Nocona General Hospital, Nocona, TX, p. A658

GRAHAM, Paul, Chief Financial Officer, Baptist Montclair, Birmingham, AL, p. A14

GRAHAM, Richard H., President and Chief Executive Officer, Augusta Health Care, Fishersville, VA, p. A688

GRAHAM, Richard W., Chief Executive Officer, Regency Hospital of Central Georgia, Macon, GA, p. A165

GRAHAM, Sheri S., Director Human Resources and Administrative Services, Parkland Health Center, Farmington, MO, p. A382

GRAHAM, Susan, MSN, Chief Executive Officer, Cedarcrest Hospital, Newington, CT, p. A115

GRAHE, Raymond A., Vice President Finance, Washington County Health System, Hagerstown, MD, p. A308

GRAHM, Peg, Chief Information Officer, Veterans Affairs Palo Alto Health Care System, Palo Alto, CA, p. A80

GRAMBY, Tiffany, Director Health Information Management and Privacy Officer, Barnesville Hospital Association, Barnesville, OH, p. A503

GRAN, Daniel, Chief Executive Officer, Freeman Regional Health Services, Freeman, SD, p. A596

GRAND, Lawrence N., Vice President and Chief Operating Officer, Hunterdon Medical Center, Flemington, NJ, p. A428

GRANDBOIS, Ray, M.P.H., Director, Indian Health Service Hospital, Rapid City, SD, p. A598

GRANGE, Russell, Chief Human Resources Officer, Providence Alaska Medical Center, Anchorage, AK, p. A26

GRANGEIA, John, Senior Vice President Operations, Saint Peter's University Hospital, New Brunswick, NJ, p. A432

GRANGER, Keith, President and Chief Executive Officer, Flowers Hospital, Dothan, AL, p. A17

GRANGER, Robert P., Senior Vice President and Chief Financial Officer, Sacred Heart Hospital of Pensacola, Pensacola, FL, p. A143

GRANNEN, Fred, Vice President Information Management, Stevens Healthcare, Edmonds, WA, p. A702

GRANT, Alan, Regional Director Information Services, St. Joseph's Regional Medical Center, Milwaukee, WI, p. A731

GRANT, M.D., Howard, Chief Medical Officer, Temple University Hospital, Philadelphia, PA, p. A570

GRANT, Joe, Information Systems Manager, Millinocket Regional Hospital, Millinocket, ME, p. A299

GRANT, Pauline, Chief Executive Officer, North Broward Medical Center, Pompano Beach, FL, p. A144

GRANT, Stewant, Chief Information Officer, St. Mary's Medical Center, Blue Springs, MO, p. A378

GRANT, Stewart, Vice President and Chief Information Officer, Saint Joseph Medical Center, Kansas City, MO, p. A385

GRANT, Will, Senior Vice President Finance, Watauga Medical Center, Boone, NC, p. A478

GRANVILLE, Sabrina M., Vice President Human Resources, Caritas Holy Family Hospital and Medical Center, Methuen, MA, p. A320

GRAPPE, Steve, Administrator, SCCI Hospital–San Angelo, San Angelo, TX, p. A663

GRASER, David, Chief Information Officer, West Jefferson Medical Center, Marrero, LA, p. A286

GRASS, Linda J., Executive Director and Chief Executive Officer, Jeanes Hospital, Philadelphia, PA, p. A568

GRASSE, A. Meryl, M.D., Chief Executive Officer, Community Medical Center of Izard County, Calico Rock, AR, p. A41

GRATTAN, M.D., William, Chief Medical Officer, Seton Health System, Troy, NY, p. A474

GRAUER, David
    Administrator and Chief Executive Officer, Cottonwood Hospital Medical Center, Murray, UT, p. A677
    Administrator and Chief Executive Officer, The Orthopedic Specialty Hospital, Murray, UT, p. A677

GRAVELL, James
    President and Chief Executive Officer, Mercy Franciscan Hospital Mount Airy, Cincinnati, OH, p. A507
    Executive Vice President, Mercy Franciscan Hospital Mount Airy, Cincinnati, OH, p. A507

GRAVENDER, Dave, Vice President and Chief Information Officer, Kaweah Delta Health Care District, Visalia, CA, p. A98

GRAVES, Amanda, Chief Information Systems, Veterans Affairs Medical Center, Washington, DC, p. A122

GRAVES, Deanna, Chief Executive Officer, Southwest Regional Medical Complex, Lubbock, TX, p. A654

GRAVES, Jimmy, Administrator, Walthall County General Hospital, Tylertown, MS, p. A376

GRAVES, John T., Chief Executive Officer, Callaway Community Hospital, Fulton, MO, p. A382

GRAVES, Philip G., President, Hutchinson Area Health Care, Hutchinson, MN, p. A355

GRAVES, Robert L., Vice President and Administrator, Sentara Williamsburg Community Hospital, Williamsburg, VA, p. A698

GRAVITT, Keith, Information Systems Manager, Person Memorial Hospital, Roxboro, NC, p. A490

GRAY, Carolyn, Chief Human Resources Management, Overton Brooks Veterans Affairs Medical Center, Shreveport, LA, p. A292

GRAY, Carolyn S., Chief Executive Officer, Regency Hospital of South Atlanta, East Point, GA, p. A161

GRAY, Clarence, Chief Financial Officer, Horizon Medical Center, Dickson, TN, p. A605

GRAY, David L., President, Hardin Memorial Hospital, Elizabethtown, KY, p. A263

GRAY, Ed, Chief Executive Officer, Edmond Medical Center, Edmond, OK, p. A530

GRAY, Edward, Chief Operating Officer, Memorial Medical Center, New Orleans, LA, p. A289

GRAY, M.D., Herman B., Chief Operating Officer, Children's Hospital of Michigan, Detroit, MI, p. A331

GRAY, M.D., James E., Chief Medical Officer, Hillcrest Baptist Medical Center, Waco, TX, p. A672

GRAY, Janice, Director Human Resources, Sierra–Kings District Hospital, Reedley, CA, p. A84

GRAY, Lisa, Director Human Resources, Sunnyside Community Hospital, Sunnyside, WA, p. A710

GRAY, Mike, Corporate Vice President Human Resources, East Texas Medical Center Tyler, Tyler, TX, p. A671

GRAY, Penny, Administrator and Chief Executive Officer, Limestone Medical Center, Groesbeck, TX, p. A642

GRAY, Riley, Vice President Fiscal Services, Carteret General Hospital, Morehead City, NC, p. A488

GRAY, Tami, Chief Financial Officer, Irwin County Hospital, Ocilla, GA, p. A167

GRAY, Terry, Vice President Human Resources, Emanuel Medical Center, Turlock, CA, p. A96

GRAYBILL, Scott R., President and Chief Executive Officer, Community Hospital of Bremen, Bremen, IN, p. A212

GRAZIANI, Dave, Executive Director, Napa State Hospital, Napa, CA, p. A77

GRAZIO, Marilyn, Clinical Administrator, Henry Ford Kingswood Hospital, Ferndale, MI, p. A333

GREASOM, Linda, Vice President Human Resources, Milford Regional Medical Center, Milford, MA, p. A320

GRECK, Sonya, Chief Executive Officer, McDowell Hospital, Marion, NC, p. A487

GREEN, Brenda, R.N., Correctional Health Services Administrator II, California Medical Facility, Vacaville, CA, p. A97

GREEN, M.D., David, Medical Staff President, Concord Hospital, Concord, NH, p. A420

GREEN, David R., Administrator and Chief Executive Officer, El Centro Regional Medical Center, El Centro, CA, p. A59

GREEN, Garry K., Administrator, Shriners Hospitals for Children, Shreveport, Shreveport, LA, p. A293

GREEN, J. Calvin, Chief Executive Officer, Franklin Foundation Hospital, Franklin, LA, p. A281

GREEN, Jack W.
    Administrator, Antelope Memorial Hospital, Neligh, NE, p. A409
    Administrator, Antelope Memorial Hospital, Neligh, NE, p. A409

GREEN, James S., Senior Vice President and Chief Financial Officer, Sisters of Charity Providence Hospitals, Columbia, SC, p. A586

GREEN, Jerry, Administrator, Tippah County Hospital, Ripley, MS, p. A375

GREEN, Jill Hoggard, Ph.D., Administrator, Sacred Heart Medical Center, Eugene, OR, p. A543

GREEN, R.N., Ph, Jill Hoggard, Assistant Vice President, Sacred Heart Medical Center, Eugene, OR, p. A543

GREEN, Judy, Director Human Resources, Putnam County Memorial Hospital, Unionville, MO, p. A395

GREEN, Julie, Vice President Human Resources, Cheshire Medical Center, Keene, NH, p. A421

GREEN, Karen, Chief Information Officer, Brooks Rehabilitation Hospital, Jacksonville, FL, p. A132

GREEN, Katherine, Chief Financial Officer, Sutter Medical Center, Sacramento, Sacramento, CA, p. A85

GREEN, CHE, Kaye, Asociate Director, Veterans Affairs Medical Center, Bay Pines, FL, p. A123

GREEN, Leo, Vice President, Medical Affairs, Alton Memorial Hospital, Alton, IL, p. A183

GREEN, Jr., M.D., Louis, Vice President Medical Affairs, United Memorial Medical Center, Batavia, NY, p. A447

GREEN, Michael B., President and Chief Executive Officer, Concord Hospital, Concord, NH, p. A420

GREEN, Raymond, Vice President Human Resources, Southern Ocean County Hospital, Manahawkin, NJ, p. A431

GREEN, Rose Marie, Director Human Resources, Humboldt General Hospital, Winnemucca, NV, p. A419

GREEN, Sam, Chief of Staff, MountainView Hospital, Las Vegas, NV, p. A416

GREEN, Susan
    Interim President and Chief Executive Officer, Anna Jaques Hospital, Newburyport, MA, p. A321
    Vice President Finance, Anna Jaques Hospital, Newburyport, MA, p. A321

GREEN, Warren A., President and Chief Executive Officer, LifeBridge Health, Baltimore, MD, p. B68

GREENBAUM, M.D., Maurice, Medical Director, Shaughnessy–Kaplan Rehabilitation Hospital, Salem, MA, p. A323

GREENDALE, Jim, Information Technology Leader, Kaiser Foundation Hospital, Walnut Creek, CA, p. A98

GREENE, Albert L., Chief Executive Officer, Hollywood Presbyterian Medical Center, Los Angeles, CA, p. A70

GREENE, Carolyn, Chief Financial Officer, Slidell Memorial Hospital and Medical Center, Slidell, LA, p. A293

GREENE Jr, Charles H., Administrator, Cordell Memorial Hospital, Cordell, OK, p. A529

GREENE Jr, Edward C., President, Charles E. Cannon Jr. Memorial Hospital, Linville, NC, p. A486

GREENE, Hugh, Chief Executive Officer, Baptist Health, Jacksonville, FL, p. B14

GREENE, Michael, Chief Operating Officer, North General Hospital, New York, NY, p. A464

GREENE, Steve, Chief Financial Officer, Northside Hospital – Cherokee, Canton, GA, p. A157

GREENE, Steven J., Chief Executive Officer, Palms of Pasadena Hospital, Saint Petersburg, FL, p. A145

GREENE, William M., FACHE, Chief Executive Officer, Catalina Island Medical Center, Avalon, CA, p. A53

GREENHILL, Phil, Chief Executive Officer, Select Specialty Hospital–Atlanta, Atlanta, GA, p. A154

GREENMAN, Sharon, Human Resources Director, Melissa Memorial Hospital, Holyoke, CO, p. A107

GREENSHER, M.D., Joseph, Medical Director, Winthrop–University Hospital, Mineola, NY, p. A457

GREENSPAN, M.D., David, Medical Director, Carrier Clinic, Belle Mead, NJ, p. A425

GREENSWEIG, D.O., Gary
Chief Medical Officer, Petaluma Valley Hospital, Petaluma, CA, p. A81
Chief Medical Officer, Santa Rosa Memorial Hospital, Santa Rosa, CA, p. A93

GREENWALD, M.D., Richard A., Vice President Medical Affairs, Boca Raton Community Hospital, Boca Raton, FL, p. A124

GREENWOOD, Gail, Chief Operating Officer, Oswego Hospital, Oswego, NY, p. A468

GREENWOOD, Kay, MS, Administrator, Alton Mental Health Center, Alton, IL, p. A183

GREENWOOD, Sherri, Administrator, Sartori Memorial Hospital, Cedar Falls, IA, p. A229

GREENYER, Janice, Vice President Planning and Information Technology, Monadnock Community Hospital, Peterborough, NH, p. A423

GREER, M.D., Anthony, Vice President Medical Affairs, Cayuga Medical Center at Ithaca, Ithaca, NY, p. A454

GREER, Claude, Director Information Technology, Arkansas Methodist Medical Center, Paragould, AR, p. A49

GREER, James A., Chief Financial Officer, Bath County Community Hospital, Hot Springs, VA, p. A690

GREER, Troy, Chief Operating Officer, The Woman's Hospital of Texas, Houston, TX, p. A648

GREER, M.D., W Anthony, Vice President Medical Affairs, St. John Detroit Riverview Hospital – Northeast Campus, Detroit, MI, p. A332

GREER, William, Acting Chief Information Officer, Central Alabama Veterans Health Care System, Montgomery, AL, p. A22

GREEVER, Suzanne, Chief Executive Officer, Mary Shiels Hospital, Dallas, TX, p. A633

GREGG, Hunt, Director Information Systems, Texas Scottish Rite Hospital for Children, Dallas, TX, p. A634

GREGORE, Jacky, Chief Executive Officer, Patient's Hospital of Redding, Redding, CA, p. A83

GREGORIO, Lou, Vice President Human Resources, Chambersburg Hospital, Chambersburg, PA, p. A555

GREGORY, Jan, Vice President Human Resources, Crittenden County Hospital, Marion, KY, p. A271

GREGORY, Lynda, Human Resources Director, Mercy General Hospital, Sacramento, CA, p. A85

GREGORY, Mary Jo, Chief Executive Officer, Palm Beach Gardens Medical Center, Palm Beach Gardens, FL, p. A141

GREGORY, Samuel S., Chief Executive Officer, Edgefield County Hospital, Edgefield, SC, p. A587

GREGORY, Trip
Senior Vice President of Human Resources, Palmetto Health Baptist/Columbia, Columbia, SC, p. A586
Senior Vice President of Human Resources, Palmetto Health Richland, Columbia, SC, p. A586

GREGORY, M.D., Winn, Medical Staff President, Good Shepherd Healthcare System, Hermiston, OR, p. A544

GREGSON, C. Mark, Chief Executive Officer, Mesa General Hospital Medical Center, Mesa, AZ, p. A32

GREINER, Stan, Director Finance, Douglas County Hospital, Alexandria, MN, p. A349

GREMILLION, Kenneth, Director Human Resources, Avoyelles Hospital, Marksville, LA, p. A286

GRENIER, Raymond, Chief Financial Officer, Northwest Texas Healthcare System, Amarillo, TX, p. A621

GRENNAN, M.D., Joseph, Medical Director and Vice President Clinical Quality and Resource Management, Forbes Regional Hospital, Monroeville, PA, p. A565

GRESKO, Teresa A., Chief Financial Officer, St. Agnes Continuing Care Center, Philadelphia, PA, p. A569

GRESKOVICH, William, Chief Information Officer, St. Agnes HealthCare, Baltimore, MD, p. A304

GRESS, Jr, Harold M., Manager Management Information Systems, Fulton County Medical Center, McConnellsburg, PA, p. A564

GREW, Terry, Chief Business Office, Veterans Affairs Medical Center, Hampton, VA, p. A689

GREY, William
Administrator, HEALTHSOUTH Rehabilitation Hospital, Odessa, TX, p. A659
Administrator, HEALTHSOUTH Rehabilitation Hospital Midland–Odessa, Midland, TX, p. A656

GRIBBIN, Diane, Communications and Marketing Manager, Riverview Medical Center, Red Bank, NJ, p. A435

GRIBBIN, John T., President and Chief Executive Officer, CentraState Healthcare System, Freehold, NJ, p. A428

GRIEF, M.D., Mark, Chief of Staff, Kapiolani Medical Center at Pali Momi, Aiea, HI, p. A173

GRIESBAUM, M.D., Robert V., Vice President Patient Care Quality, St. Anthony's Medical Center, Saint Louis, MO, p. A392

GRIESS, Dan, Chief Executive Officer, Box Butte General Hospital, Alliance, NE, p. A404

GRIFFES, John M., Chief Executive Officer, Kindred Hospital–San Antonio, San Antonio, TX, p. A664

GRIFFIN, Brad, Associate Administrator, Fairview Park Hospital, Dublin, GA, p. A161

GRIFFIN, M.D., Brian, Chief of Staff, Charles A. Dean Memorial Hospital and Nursing Home, Greenville, ME, p. A299

GRIFFIN, M.D., Christopher P., President Medical Staff, Wayne Memorial Hospital, Goldsboro, NC, p. A483

GRIFFIN, Dean A., Vice President Human Resources, Decatur General Hospital, Decatur, AL, p. A17

GRIFFIN, Debra L., Administrator, Humphreys County Memorial Hospital, Belzoni, MS, p. A366

GRIFFIN, LeeAnn, Chief Executive Officer, Plum Creek Specialty Hospital, Amarillo, TX, p. A621

GRIFFIN, Shirley, Manager, North Mississippi Medical Center–Eupora, Eupora, MS, p. A368

GRIFFIN, Tanya, Senior Director, Human Resources, Massena Memorial Hospital, Massena, NY, p. A456

GRIFFITH, Dena, Information Systems Manager, Kern Valley Healthcare District, Lake Isabella, CA, p. A66

GRIFFITH, Greg, Chief Executive Officer, Memorial Health Services, Adel, GA, p. B74

GRIFFITH, Wayne B., FACHE, Regional Chief Executive Officer, Hazard ARH Regional Medical Center, Hazard, KY, p. A266

GRIFFITH–COLLISON, June, Chief Executive Officer, Arrowhead Regional Medical Center, Colton, CA, p. A57

GRIFFITHS, Eileen, Director Information Technology, Newton Memorial Hospital, Newton, NJ, p. A433

GRIFFITHS, Kathleen S., President and Chief Executive Officer, Chelsea Community Hospital, Chelsea, MI, p. A330

GRIGG, William, Chief Financial Officer, Southcoast Hospitals Group, Fall River, MA, p. A317

GRIM, Charles, D.D.S., Acting Director, U. S. Indian Health Service, Rockville, MD, p. B112

GRIM, Mary Kay
Senior Vice President Human Resources, Lehigh Valley Hospital, Allentown, PA, p. A551
Senior Vice President Human Resources, Lehigh Valley Hospital–Muhlenberg, Bethlehem, PA, p. A552

GRIMES, Larry, Chief Executive Officer and Managing Director, River Crest Hospital, San Angelo, TX, p. A663

GRIMES, Teresa F., Administrator, Jackson Medical Center, Jackson, AL, p. A20

GRIMM, Bill, Director Support Services, Henry County Health Center, Mount Pleasant, IA, p. A238

GRIMM, Steve, CHE, Chief Executive Officer, Crosby Memorial Hospital, Picayune, MS, p. A374

GRIMSHAW, Bruce P., Chief Executive Officer, Dayton General Hospital, Dayton, WA, p. A702

GRIMSLEY, Jack, Interim Chief Executive Officer, Jane Todd Crawford Hospital, Greensburg, KY, p. A265

GRINIER, Walter, Chief Financial Officer, Atlanticare Regional Medical Center, Atlantic City, NJ, p. A425

GRINNEY, Jay, President, HEALTHSOUTH Corporation, Birmingham, AL, p. B56

GRIPP, Mary Jo, Human Resources Director, Down East Community Hospital, Machias, ME, p. A299

GRIPPEN, Glen W., Director, Clement J. Zablocki Veterans Affairs Medical Center, Milwaukee, WI, p. A730

GRISDELA, Michael, Vice President Administration and Chief Financial Officer, Memorial Healthcare, Owosso, MI, p. A342

GRISSLER, Brian G., President and Chief Executive Officer, Stamford Health System, Stamford, CT, p. A116

GRIX, M.D., Gary J., Chief of Staff, Parkland Health Center, Farmington, MO, p. A382

GROAH, Linda, Chief Operating Officer, Kaiser Foundation Hospital, San Francisco, CA, p. A89

GROCE, David, Associate Administrator and Chief Financial Officer, Lincoln County Health System, Fayetteville, TN, p. A606

GROCHALA, Gene
Vice President Information Systems, Capital Health System at Fuld, Trenton, NJ, p. A437
Vice President Information Systems, Capital Health System at Mercer, Trenton, NJ, p. A437

GROEBER, M.D., David, Chief of Staff, Veterans Affairs Medical Center, Albuquerque, NM, p. A441

GROEPPER, Ron, President, St. Joseph's Regional Medical Center, Milwaukee, WI, p. A731

GROESBECK, John, Chief Financial Officer, Magic Valley Regional Medical Center, Twin Falls, ID, p. A182

GROFF, M.D., Gerald D., Vice President Medical Affairs, Mary Imogene Bassett Hospital, Cooperstown, NY, p. A450

GROGAN, Ed, Vice President, Calvert Memorial Hospital, Prince Frederick, MD, p. A309

GROH, Charles, Flight Commander, Medical Information Management, Malcolm Grow Medical Center, Andrews AFB, MD, p. A302

GRONBACH, Sue, Director, St. John Macomb Hospital, Warren, MI, p. A347

GRONBERG, Mark, Chief Financial Officer, Quincy Medical Center, Quincy, MA, p. A322

GRONO, Walter J., Executive Director, Devereux Children's Behavioral Health Center, Malvern, PA, p. A564

GRONSETH, Tim, Vice President Finance, Ridgeview Medical Center, Waconia, MN, p. A364

GROOMS, Richard, Vice President, Human Resources, Sisters of Charity Providence Hospitals, Columbia, SC, p. A586

GROSE, Jana, Director Management Information Systems, Massena Memorial Hospital, Massena, NY, p. A456

GROSETH, Bradley D., Administrator, Barron Medical Center–Mayo Health System, Barron, WI, p. A723

GROSKREUTZ, Kevin, Information Systems Coordinator, St. Joseph's Hospital, Chippewa Falls, WI, p. A724

GROSS, Arther, Interim Chief Information Officer, Henry Ford Hospital, Detroit, MI, p. A331

GROSS, FACHE, Arthur K., Executive Vice President and Chief Information Officer, Henry Ford Wyandotte Hospital, Wyandotte, MI, p. A348

GROSS, M.D., Barry L., Executive Vice President and Chief Medical Officer, Riverside Regional Medical Center, Newport News, VA, p. A692

GROSS, Chris, Chief Financial Officer, Mille Lacs Health System, Onamia, MN, p. A359

GROSS, Cindy, Assistant Administrator, Finance, Barnes-Jewish St. Peters Hospital, Saint Peters, MO, p. A393

GROSS, Daniel
Chief Executive Officer, Sharp Memorial Hospital, San Diego, CA, p. A87
Senior Vice President Finance and Chief Financial Officer, Newton-Wellesley Hospital, Newton Lower Falls, MA, p. A321

GROSS, Joseph W., President and Chief Executive Officer, St. Elizabeth Medical Center-South, Covington, KY, p. A263

GROSS, Kevin J., President and Chief Executive Officer, Hillcrest HealthCare System, Tulsa, OK, p. B59

GROSS, Kristin, Director Information Technology Center, Avera McKennan Hospital and University Health Center, Sioux Falls, SD, p. A599

GROSS, Len, Director Human Resources, Star Valley Medical Center, Afton, WY, p. A739

GROSS, Michael, Vice President Finance, Ozarks Medical Center, West Plains, MO, p. A395

GROSS, M.D., Michael, Medical Director, Presbyterian Hospital of Plano, Plano, TX, p. A661

GROSS, Randy, Director Fiscal Services, Osceola Regional Medical Center, Kissimmee, FL, p. A133

GROSS, Rodney D., Administrator, Madison Medical Center, Fredericktown, MO, p. A382

GROSSER, Joy, Chief Information Officer, University of California, Irvine Medical Center, Orange, CA, p. A79

GROSSMAN, Marty, Director Information Technology, Christ Hospital, Jersey City, NJ, p. A430

GROSSMAN, Ray, Vice President Human Resources, St. Joseph Regional Health Center, Bryan, TX, p. A627

GROSSMAN, M.D., William K., Chief of Staff, Veterans Affairs Medical Center, Wilkes-Barre, PA, p. A579

GROSSMEIER, John C., President and Chief Executive Officer, Hannibal Regional Hospital, Hannibal, MO, p. A382

GROSSO, M.D., Michael, Vice President Medical Affairs, Huntington Hospital, Huntington, NY, p. A454

GROTE, M.D., James, Medical Staff President, Illini Community Hospital, Pittsfield, IL, p. A205

GROTE, Wayne, Vice President Administrative Services, Good Samaritan Regional Health Center, Mount Vernon, IL, p. A202

GROTJOHN, Dean, Director of Human Resources, Northfield Hospital, Northfield, MN, p. A359

GROVES, Glen, Chief Financial Officer, Sutter Maternity and Surgery Center of Santa Cruz, Santa Cruz, CA, p. A93

GRUBA, M.D., Stephen, Medical Staff President, Alegent Health Mercy Hospital, Corning, IA, p. A231

GRUBB, Vickie, Chief Human Resources Officer, Veterans Affairs Medical Center, White River Junction, VT, p. A684

GRUBBS, Nicholas, Chief Financial Officer, Monongalia General Hospital, Morgantown, WV, p. A718

GRUBBS, Patricia, Human Resources Director, Southeastern Ohio Regional Medical Center, Cambridge, OH, p. A505

GRUBER, Beverly, Administrator, Medina Community Hospital, Hondo, TX, p. A644

GRUBER, M.D., Brian, President of the Medical Staff, Louise Obici Memorial Hospital, Suffolk, VA, p. A697

GRUBER, Kreg, President, Doctors Hospital, Columbus, OH, p. A510

GRUBER, Norman F., President and Chief Executive Officer, Salem Hospital, Salem, OR, p. A549

GRUEBER, Cynthia M., Director, University of Missouri Hospitals and Clinics, Columbia, MO, p. A381

GRUNDSTROM, David A., Administrator, Flambeau Hospital, Park Falls, WI, p. A733

GRYZBEK, Thomas J., President, Saint Margaret Mercy Healthcare Centers, Hammond, IN, p. A217

GUACCIO, Anthony, Senior Vice President Operations and Chief Human Resource Officer, Swedish Covenant Hospital, Chicago, IL, p. A190

GUARINI, Lucia A., Administrator, Essex County Hospital Center, Cedar Grove, NJ, p. A427

GUARINO, M.D., Rick, Senior Vice President and Chief Medical Officer, Nash Health Care Systems, Rocky Mount, NC, p. A490

GUARNIERI, Ellen
Vice President and Chief Operating Officer, Virtua West Jersey Hospital-Marlton, Marlton, NJ, p. A431
Vice President and Chief Operating Officer, Virtua West Jersey Hospital-Marlton, Marlton, NJ, p. A431

GUBA, Greg, Director Human Resources, Lemuel Shattuck Hospital, Jamaica Plain, MA, p. A319

GUCKIAN, James C., M.D., Executive Vice Chancellor, University of Texas System, Austin, TX, p. B118

GUENTHER, Becky, Human Resources Manager, HEALTHSOUTH Rehabilitation Hospital of North Houston, Conroe, TX, p. A630

GUENTHER, Charles R., Chief Executive Officer, Eastern Plumas District Hospital, Portola, CA, p. A82

GUERCI, Alan D., M.D., Chief Executive Officer, St. Francis Hospital, Roslyn, NY, p. A471

GUERRA, Tony, Chief Financial Officer, Sharp Coronado Hospital and Health Center, Coronado, CA, p. A58

GUERRERO, M.D., Levi, Chief of Staff, Deckerville Community Hospital, Deckerville, MI, p. A330

GUERRIOS, Brenda, Administrator Medical Records, Hospital Hermanos Melendez, Bayamon, PR, p. A744

GUEST, John A., Chief Executive Officer, Sparks Regional Medical Center, Fort Smith, AR, p. A43

GUETZKO, Gary, Vice President Finance, Mercy Medical Center-Dubuque, Dubuque, IA, p. A233

GUEVARA, Jesse, Senior Vice President and Chief Financial Officer, St. Francis Medical Center, Lynwood, CA, p. A74

GUEZ, Roberta H., Administrator and Chief Operating Officer, Taunton State Hospital, Taunton, MA, p. A324

GUFFEY, Kerra, Senior Vice President and Chief Information Officer, Memorial Medical Center, Springfield, IL, p. A208

GUGGENHEIM, Paul A., Administrator, Hawaii State Hospital, Kaneohe, HI, p. A175

GUGIN, Alan, Director Human Resources, Mercy Medical Center Redding, Redding, CA, p. A83

GUIDRY, M.D., Floyd, Medical Director, Women and Children's Hospital, Lake Charles, LA, p. A285

GUIDRY, Gary, Chief Executive Officer, Vista Surgical Hospital of Baton Rouge, Baton Rouge, LA, p. A278

GUIDRY, Randy, Administrator, Vermilion Rehabilitation Hospital, Abbeville, LA, p. A276

GUIGNIER, Liz, Vice President Human Resources, Eisenhower Memorial Hospital and Betty Ford Center at Eisenhower, Rancho Mirage, CA, p. A83

GUILD, D.O., Gordon, Vice President Medical Affairs, Lenawee Health Alliance-Herrick Campus, Tecumseh, MI, p. A346

GUILD, Samuel T.
Chief Executive Officer, Cleveland Area Hospital, Cleveland, OK, p. A529
Chief Executive Officer, Pawnee Municipal Hospital, Pawnee, OK, p. A537

GUILLORY, Jr, M.D., Robert K., Chief Medical Staff, Eunice Community Medical Center, Eunice, LA, p. A280

GUIMOND, Stephen J.
Senior Vice President and Chief Financial Officer, Cape Cod Hospital, Hyannis, MA, p. A319
Senior Vice President and Chief Financial Officer, Falmouth Hospital, Falmouth, MA, p. A317

GUIN, Jamie, Chief Executive Officer, Mountain View Regional Medical Center, Norton, VA, p. A693

GUINN, Lex A., Chief Executive Officer, Park Plaza Hospital, Houston, TX, p. A647

GULARTE, Steve, Administrator, El Campo Memorial Hospital, El Campo, TX, p. A637

GULBENKIAN, Karen, Chief Operating Officer, Garden Grove Hospital and Medical Center, Garden Grove, CA, p. A62

GULIHUR, Judith, Chief Financial Officer, McCamey Hospital, McCamey, TX, p. A656

GULLEKSON, M.D., Edwin H., Vice President Medical Affairs, McLaren Regional Medical Center, Flint, MI, p. A333

GULLETT, M.D., Robert, Medical Director, Jefferson Regional Medical Center, Pine Bluff, AR, p. A49

GULLIFORD, Deryl E., Ph.D., Chief Executive Officer, Holdenville General Hospital, Holdenville, OK, p. A532

GUMBS, M.D., Milton A., Vice President Medical Affairs and Medical Director, Bronx-Lebanon Hospital Center, New York, NY, p. A458

GUNASEKARAN, Suresh, Chief Information Officer, University of Texas Southwestern Medical Center, Dallas, TX, p. A634

GUNDER, Gary, Chief Financial Officer, Medical Center at Terrell, Terrell, TX, p. A669

GUNDY, Keith, Chief Financial Officer, Lucile Salter Packard Children's Hospital at Stanford, Palo Alto, CA, p. A80

GUNN, B. Joe, FACHE, Administrator and Chief Executive Officer, Craig General Hospital, Vinita, OK, p. A540

GUNN, Terry J., President and Chief Executive Officer, Trident Medical Center, Charleston, SC, p. A585

GUNNELS, M.D., Wheeler, Medical Director, Mizell Memorial Hospital, Opp, AL, p. A23

GUNTHER, Mary, Director Human Resources, Wayne Memorial Hospital, Jesup, GA, p. A164

GUPTA, M.D., Ashok K., Chief of Staff, Eaton Rapids Medical Center, Eaton Rapids, MI, p. A332

GUPTA, Vijay D., M.D., President and Chief Executive Officer, Illiana Surgery and Medical Center, Munster, IN, p. A222

GUPTA, M.D., Vijay D., President and Chief Executive Officer, Illiana Surgery and Medical Center, Munster, IN, p. A222

GURNEE, Nancy, Director, Human Resources, Appleton Medical Center, Appleton, WI, p. A722

GURTNER, William, Vice President Clinical Services, University of California-Systemwide Administration, Oakland, CA, p. B116

GUSHO, Michael, Vice President and Chief Financial Officer, St. Mary Mercy Hospital, Livonia, MI, p. A339

GUSMER, Peter B., Chief of Staff, Stanly Memorial Hospital, Albemarle, NC, p. A477

GUSSERT, Jeff, Director Operations, Dickinson County Healthcare System, Iron Mountain, MI, p. A337

GUSTAFSON, Brian, Chief Financial Officer, Veterans Affairs Montana Healthcare System, Fort Harrison, MT, p. A398

GUSTAFSON, Carl, Vice President, Baptist Hospital of Miami, Miami, FL, p. A136

GUSTAFSON, Margaret, Chief Executive Officer, Kewanee Hospital, Kewanee, IL, p. A199

GUSTAFSON, Philip P., Chief Executive Officer, Creighton University Medical Center, Omaha, NE, p. A411

GUSTAFSON, Sarah S., Director Finance, Pembina County Memorial Hospital and Wedgewood Manor, Cavalier, ND, p. A497

GUSTIN, Jack D., Chief Administrative Officer, Lakewood Hospital, Lakewood, OH, p. A515

GUTH, Ron, Chief Financial Officer, Providence Hood River Memorial Hospital, Hood River, OR, p. A544

GUTHMILLER, Martin W., Administrator and Chief Executive Officer, Orange City Health System, Orange City, IA, p. A239

GUTIERREZ, Albert, President and Chief Executive Officer, Shore Memorial Hospital, Somers Point, NJ, p. A436

GUTJAHR, Susan, Reimbursement Specialist, Sparta Community Hospital, Sparta, IL, p. A208

GUTNICK, Michael, Senior Vice President Finance, Memorial Sloan-Kettering Cancer Center, New York, NY, p. A462

GUTSCH, Mike, Vice President Finance, Memorial Health Center, Medford, WI, p. A729

GUTSCHENRITTER, John, Chief Financial Officer, Wilson County Hospital, Neodesha, KS, p. A253

GUTTENBERG, Ellen, Chief Operating Officer, Frances Mahon Deaconess Hospital, Glasgow, MT, p. A398

GUTZEIT, M.D., Michael, Chief Medical Officer, Children's Hospital of Wisconsin, Milwaukee, WI, p. A730

GUY, Ronald J.
Chief Financial Officer, Capital Health System at Fuld, Trenton, NJ, p. A437
Chief Financial Officer, Capital Health System at Mercer, Trenton, NJ, p. A437

GUYNN, Robert W., M.D., Executive Director, Harris County Psychiatric Center, Houston, TX, p. A645

GUYON, Robert, Chief Financial Officer and Vice President of Finance, Caritas Norwood Hospital, Norwood, MA, p. A321

GUZEWSKI, Rita, Director Human Resources, Chestnut Hill Health System, Philadelphia, PA, p. A567

GUZMAN, Nancy
Chief Financial Officer, Jacobi Medical Center, New York, NY, p. A460
Chief Financial Officer, North Central Bronx Hospital, New York, NY, p. A464

GUZMAN, Sylvia, Director Human Resources, Christus Spohn Hospital Corpus Christi Memorial, Corpus Christi, TX, p. A630

GWATKINS, Betty Ann, Vice President of Human Resources, Northeastern Vermont Regional Hospital, Saint Johnsbury, VT, p. A683

GYCZYNSKI, Carl, Vice President Operations, Bladen County Hospital, Elizabethtown, NC, p. A482

H

HAAG, M.D., Stanley W., Medical Director, Oswego Medical Center, Oswego, KS, p. A254

HAAK–MUSE, Margaret, Chief Financial Officer and Assistant Administrator, East Texas Medical Center–Mount Vernon, Mount Vernon, TX, p. A657

HAAR, Clare A.
Chief Executive Officer, Inter–Community Memorial Hospital, Newfane, NY, p. A467
Chief Executive Officer, Lockport Memorial Hospital, Lockport, NY, p. A455

HAAS, Gerard, Senior Vice President and Chief Financial Officer, South Nassau Communities Hospital, Oceanside, NY, p. A467

HAAS, Juanita, Human Resources Director, Meadowcrest Hospital, Gretna, LA, p. A281

HAAS, Marvin
Senior Vice President, Administration and Finance, Rogue Valley Medical Center, Medford, OR, p. A546
Senior Vice President Finance, Three Rivers Community Hospital and Health Center, Grants Pass, OR, p. A544

HAAS, Richard
Senior Executive Officer, Sycamore Hospital, Miamisburg, OH, p. A518
Senior Executive Officer, Sycamore Hospital, Miamisburg, OH, p. A518

HABERLEIN, Bernard J., President, Graydon Manor, Leesburg, VA, p. A690

HABIB, M.D., Noel, Chief Medical Officer, Huhukam Memorial Hospital, Sacaton, AZ, p. A35

HACHENBERG, Dennis A., CHE, Chief Executive Officer, Anderson County Hospital, Garnett, KS, p. A247

HACHEY, Michael, Chief Financial Officer, Mercy Hospital of Portland, Portland, ME, p. A300

HACKBARTH, CPA, CHE, John, Vice President Finance, Deaconess Hospital, Oklahoma City, OK, p. A535

HACKER, Jo, Director Nursing, Thayer County Health Services, Hebron, NE, p. A407

HACKETT Jr, James P., Administrator and Chief Executive Officer, Four Winds Syracuse, Syracuse, NY, p. A473

HACKMAN, Paul, Chief Operating Officer, Ridgeview Institute, Smyrna, GA, p. A169

HADDAD, Robert M., M.D.
President, Caritas Christi Health Care, Boston, MA, p. B22
President, Caritas St. Elizabeth's Medical Center, Brighton, MA, p. A315

HADDIX, D Parker, Chief Operating Officer, Davis Memorial Hospital, Elkins, WV, p. A715

HADEN, James E., President and Chief Executive Officer, Martha Jefferson Hospital, Charlottesville, VA, p. A686

HADLEY, M.D., John, Chief of Staff, Weisbrod Memorial County Hospital, Eads, CO, p. A105

HADLEY, Mike
Chief Information Officer, Saint Francis Hospital, Memphis, TN, p. A613
Director, Information Systems, Saint Francis Hospital–Bartlett, Bartlett, TN, p. A602

HAFFORD, Juliet, Director Human Resources, Oakwood Southshore Medical Center, Trenton, MI, p. A347

HAGALE, John E., Executive Vice President, Chief Financial Officer and Chief Administrtive Officer, The Methodist Hospital, Houston, TX, p. A648

HAGAN, Dolores, Director Information Systems, Twin Lakes Regional Medical Center, Leitchfield, KY, p. A267

HAGAN, Donald E., Chief Financial Officer, Crestwood Medical Center, Huntsville, AL, p. A20

HAGAN, Francis, Chief Financial Officer, North General Hospital, New York, NY, p. A464

HAGEL, Sonja, Vice President Operations and Chief Executive Officer, Phoenix Memorial Hospital, Phoenix, AZ, p. A34

HAGEMANN, M.D., Margarethe, Chief of Staff, Veterans Affairs Medical Center, Saint Louis, MO, p. A393

HAGEN, Bruce P.
President, Riverside Methodist Hospital, Columbus, OH, p. A511
President, Riverside Methodist Hospital, Columbus, OH, p. A511

HAGEN, Michael, Chief Executive Officer, Riverwood HealthCare Center, Aitkin, MN, p. A349

HAGEN, Paulette, Human Resource Director, Paynesville Area Health Care System, Paynesville, MN, p. A359

HAGENOW, Norma R., R.N., President and Chief Executive Officer, Genesys Regional Medical Center, Grand Blanc, MI, p. A334

HAGENS, Gary, Vice President Medical Affairs, BroMenn Healthcare System, Normal, IL, p. A202

HAGENSICKER, Janice
Chief Financial Officer, Metroplex Adventist Hospital, Killeen, TX, p. A651
Chief Financial Officer, Rollins–Brook Community Hospital, Lampasas, TX, p. A652

HAGER, Richard J., Senior Vice President and Chief Financial Officer, Gnaden Huetten Memorial Hospital, Lehighton, PA, p. A563

HAGERSTROM, Tom, Director Human Resources, Franklin Memorial Hospital, Farmington, ME, p. A298

HAGGARD, R.N., Ann, Chief Operating Officer, Bear Valley Community Hospital, Big Bear Lake, CA, p. A55

HAGLE, Julie, Director Information Systems, Maine Coast Memorial Hospital, Ellsworth, ME, p. A298

HAGLUND, Eric, Director Information Systems, Our Lady of Victory Hospital, Stanley, WI, p. A736

HAGSTROM, Vic, Vice President Finance, North Country Regional Hospital, Bemidji, MN, p. A350

HAGWELL, Michael, Chief Financial Officer, Keweenaw Memorial Medical Center, Laurium, MI, p. A339

HAHN, Brad, Chief Financial Officer, Aurora Sheboygan Memorial Medical Center, Sheboygan, WI, p. A735

HAHN, James W., Administrator, Decatur General Hospital, Decatur, AL, p. A17

HAHN, Kyle, Administrator, Logan County Hospital, Oakley, KS, p. A253

HAHN, Victoria J., Administrator and Chief Executive Officer, Wichita County Health Center, Leoti, KS, p. A251

HAIK, Louise, Information Services Manager, West Shore Medical Center, Manistee, MI, p. A339

HAILE, Michael, Senior Vice President Finance, Faxton–St. Luke's Healthcare, Utica, NY, p. A474

HAILEY, J D., Chief Operating Officer, Faith Community Hospital, Jacksboro, TX, p. A650

HAILSTONE, Sherlyn, Chief Executive Officer, Saint Francis Hospital, Evanston, IL, p. A194

HAINES, Cynthia, Vice President Strategic Planning and Business Development, Lucile Salter Packard Children's Hospital at Stanford, Palo Alto, CA, p. A80

HAIR, Troy, Chief Financial Officer, Abbeville General Hospital, Abbeville, LA, p. A276

HAKES, Charlee, Director Human Resources, St. Joseph Hospital, Fort Wayne, IN, p. A216

HALADA, Tom, Director Finance, River Falls Area Hospital, River Falls, WI, p. A735

HALAMKA, M.D., John, Chief Information Officer, Beth Israel Deaconess Medical Center, Boston, MA, p. A313

HALBRITTER, M.D., Kevin, Vice President Medical Staff Affairs, West Virginia University Hospitals, Morgantown, WV, p. A718

HALCROW, Douglas, Vice President Medical Affairs, St. Joseph Hospital, Orange, CA, p. A79

HALDEMAN, M.D., Larry
Executive Vice President and Chief Medical Officer, WellStar Cobb Hospital, Austell, GA, p. A156
Executive Vice President and Chief Medical Officer, WellStar Kennestone Hospital, Marietta, GA, p. A165
Executive Vice President and Chief Medical Officer, WellStar Windy Hill Hospital, Marietta, GA, p. A165

HALDERMAN, M.D., Larry
Executive Vice President and Chief Medical Officer, WellStar Douglas Hospital, Douglasville, GA, p. A161
Executive Vice President and Chief Medical Officer, WellStar Paulding Hospital, Dallas, GA, p. A160

HALE, Byron, Vice President Finance, East Texas Medical Center Tyler, Tyler, TX, p. A671

HALE, Edna, Director Information System, McLeod Medical Center–Dillon, Dillon, SC, p. A587

HALE, Fred, Superintendent, Terrell State Hospital, Terrell, TX, p. A669

HALE, Jeffrey, Vice President Information Services, Akron Children's Hospital, Akron, OH, p. A502

HALE, Steven, Deputy Commander for Administration, Bayne–Jones Army Community Hospital, Fort Polk, LA, p. A281

HALEN, Catherine, Vice President Human Resources, Beebe Medical Center, Lewes, DE, p. A119

HALES, Brent, Chief Financial Officer, Uintah Basin Medical Center, Roosevelt, UT, p. A679

HALES, Joe, Director of Information Systems, Primary Children's Medical Center, Salt Lake City, UT, p. A679

HALES Jr, John C., FACHE, Chief Executive Officer, Williamsburg Regional Hospital, Kingstree, SC, p. A589

HALES, Thomas M., Vice President Finance, Lourdes Hospital, Paducah, KY, p. A273

HALEY, Bob, Chief Executive Officer, Denton Regional Medical Center, Denton, TX, p. A635

HALEY, Jr, Curtis F., Chief Financial Officer, Knapp Medical Center, Weslaco, TX, p. A673

HALEY, Kevin, Interim Chief Financial Officer, Penn State Milton S. Hershey Medical Center, Hershey, PA, p. A560

HALEY, Michael E., President and Chief Executive Officer, La Porte Regional Health System, La Porte, IN, p. A220

HALFEN, John
Administrator, Chief Executive Officer and Chief Financial Officer, Northern Inyo Hospital, Bishop, CA, p. A55
Corporate Finance Officer, Northern Inyo Hospital, Bishop, CA, p. A55

HALFHIDE, Jon W., President, St. Elizabeth Community Hospital, Red Bluff, CA, p. A83

HALFORD, Philip E., Senior Vice President and Chief Financial Officer, Providence Health Center, Waco, TX, p. A672

HALL, Charlene, Vice President, Human Resources and Guest Support Services, Morgan Hospital and Medical Center, Martinsville, IN, p. A222

HALL, Clara Cordelia, Chief Human Resources Officer, Breckinridge Memorial Hospital, Hardinsburg, KY, p. A265

HALL, Daniel, Administrator, Bullock County Hospital, Union Springs, AL, p. A25

HALL, David, Chief Information Officer, Pineville Community Hospital Association, Pineville, KY, p. A273

HALL, M.D., David
 Senior Vice Presdient and Chief Medical Affairs, St. Vincent Infirmary Medical Center, Little Rock, AR, p. A47
 Senior Vice Presdient and Chief Medical Affairs, St. Vincent Medical Center–North, Sherwood, AR, p. A50

HALL, Gerald, Comptroller, Naval Hospital, Corpus Christi, TX, p. A631

HALL, Jeff, Director Information Services, St. Francis Health Center, Topeka, KS, p. A258

HALL, Joan S., R.N., Administrator, South Lyon Medical Center, Yerington, NV, p. A419

HALL, Judy, Administrative Specialist, Dickenson Community Hospital, Clintwood, VA, p. A687

HALL, M.D., Kim, Chief Medical Officer, St. Luke Hospital and Living Center, Marion, KS, p. A252

HALL, Leslie Kelly, Vice President Information Technology, Saint Alphonsus Regional Medical Center, Boise, ID, p. A177

HALL, Linda, Administrator, Chillicothe Hospital District, Chillicothe, TX, p. A628

HALL, Marcia K., Chief Executive Officer, Sharp Coronado Hospital and Health Center, Coronado, CA, p. A58

HALL, Mary A., Chief of Medical Staff, McDowell ARH Hospital, McDowell, KY, p. A271

HALL, Michael
 Interim Chief Executive Officer, Sistersville General Hospital, Sistersville, WV, p. A720
 Chief Executive Officer, Winner Regional Healthcare Center, Winner, SD, p. A601

HALL, Roger L., Chief Executive Officer, Sacred Heart Hospital on the Emerald Coast, Destin, FL, p. A127

HALL, Roy, Chief of Staff, Holton Community Hospital, Holton, KS, p. A249

HALL, Scott F., Comptroller, Naval Hospital, North Charleston, SC, p. A591

HALL, Tammy, Human Resources Director, Baptist Memorial Hospital–Union City, Union City, TN, p. A618

HALL, Trena F., Community Chief Executive Officer, Hazard ARH Regional Medical Center, Hazard, KY, p. A266

HALLADAY, Mark, Director Information Services, Thompson Health, Canandaigua, NY, p. A449

HALLAL, M.D., Joseph, President, Medical Staff, Inova Fairfax Hospital, Falls Church, VA, p. A687

HALLBERG, Colleen, Chief Executive Officer, Banner Thunderbird Medical Center, Glendale, AZ, p. A31

HALLER, M.D., Fred, Chief of Staff, Shoshone Medical Center, Kellogg, ID, p. A179

HALLFORD, Wayne, Chief Executive Officer, Cedars Hospital, De Soto, TX, p. A634

HALLGREN, Hugh R., Administrator, Maniilaq Health Center, Kotzebue, AK, p. A28

HALLIGAN, Ron, Vice President Human Resources, Great River Medical Center, West Burlington, IA, p. A243

HALLISEY, Thomas, Vice President Information Management, Cortland Memorial Hospital, Cortland, NY, p. A451

HALLIWILL, Don, Director of Finance, Carilion New River Valley Medical Center, Christiansburg, VA, p. A686

HALLMAN, Gary D., President and Chief Executive Officer, Medina General Hospital, Medina, OH, p. A518

HALLMAN, Ronald, Vice President Development and Public Relations, Porter Medical Center, Middlebury, VT, p. A682

HALLMARK, Jan, Senior Vice President of Human Development and Community Outreach, Sumner Regional Medical Center, Gallatin, TN, p. A606

HALLMARK, Todd, Chief Operating Officer, Choctaw Nation Health Care Center, Talihina, OK, p. A539

HALONEN, Ph.D., Robert, Senior Vice President and Chief Financial Officer, Good Samaritan Hospital, Cincinnati, OH, p. A507

HALPENNY, M.D., Walter, Chief of Staff, Harris Methodist Southwest, Fort Worth, TX, p. A639

HALPERN, Kevin G., Chief Executive Officer, Camden County Health Services Center, Blackwood, NJ, p. A426

HALSAN, Carole, Chief Executive Officer, Willapa Harbor Hospital, South Bend, WA, p. A709

HALSELL, David, Chief Financial Officer, Bothwell Regional Health Center, Sedalia, MO, p. A393

HALSETH, Michael J., President and Chief Executive Officer, Valley Health System, Winchester, VA, p. B119

HALTER, Michael P., Chief Executive Officer, Hahnemann University Hospital, Philadelphia, PA, p. A568

HALTERMAN, Don, Administrator Finance and Chief Financial Officer, Highline Medical Center, Seattle, WA, p. A707

HALVORSON, George C., M.D., Chairman and Chief Executive Officer, Kaiser Foundation Hospitals, Oakland, CA, p. B64

HAM, Mike, Chief Executive Officer, Heartland Behavioral Health Services, Nevada, MO, p. A388

HAMB, M.D., Aaron, Chief Medical Officer, Provident Hospital of Cook County, Chicago, IL, p. A189

HAMBLEN, Jeffrey J., Administrator, Winslow Memorial Hospital, Winslow, AZ, p. A39

HAMBLIN, M.D., David, Vice President of Medical Affairs, Mercy Memorial Health Center, Ardmore, OK, p. A527

HAMBLIN, Garth, Chief Financial Officer, Bartlett Regional Hospital, Juneau, AK, p. A27

HAMBUCHEN, Bob, Director Information Systems, Conway Regional Medical Center, Conway, AR, p. A41

HAMBURGER, Stephen, Senior Vice President, Academic Affairs and Medical Staff Affairs, Carraway Methodist Medical Center, Birmingham, AL, p. A14

HAMBY, R.N., Amy, Chief Clinical Officer, Good Hope Hospital, Erwin, NC, p. A482

HAMILL, Dave H., President and Chief Executive Officer, Hampton Regional Medical Center, Varnville, SC, p. A592

HAMILL, James P., President and Chief Executive Officer, Washington County Health System, Hagerstown, MD, p. A308

HAMILTON, Aggie, Chief Human Resources, Veterans Affairs Montana Healthcare System, Fort Harrison, MT, p. A398

HAMILTON, Brian, Chief Financial Officer, Memorial Hermann Fort Bend Hospital, Missouri City, TX, p. A657

HAMILTON, Bruce, Vice President Human Resources, Lutheran Hospital of Indiana, Fort Wayne, IN, p. A215

HAMILTON, Dennis L., Chief Executive Officer, FHN Memorial Hospital, Freeport, IL, p. A194

HAMILTON, Geoffrey W., Chief Financial Officer, Coon Memorial Hospital and Home, Dalhart, TX, p. A631

HAMILTON, Mark, Interim Assistant Executive Director Finance, Memorial Hospital of Sweetwater County, Rock Springs, WY, p. A741

HAMILTON, M.D., Mark C., President Medical Staff, Springfield Hospital, Springfield, VT, p. A683

HAMILTON, M.D., Michael, Chief Medical Officer, Rockcastle Hospital and Respiratory Care Center, Mount Vernon, KY, p. A272

HAMILTON, Phil, R.N., Chief Executive Officer, General John J. Pershing Memorial Hospital, Brookfield, MO, p. A379

HAMILTON, Richard C., Administrator, Harrison County Community Hospital, Bethany, MO, p. A378

HAMILTON, M.D., Robert, Vice President for Medical Affairs, Sentara Williamsburg Community Hospital, Williamsburg, VA, p. A698

HAMILTON, Scott, Vice President and Chief Financial Officer, Parkwest Medical Center, Knoxville, TN, p. A610

HAMILTON, Steve, Chief Information Officer, Seneca Healthcare District, Chester, CA, p. A56

HAMILTON, M.D., Stewart, Vice President Medical Affairs, Yuma Regional Medical Center, Yuma, AZ, p. A39

HAMILTON, Terry, Executive Director Finance, St. Vincent Hospitals and Health Services, Indianapolis, IN, p. A219

HAMILTON, William L., Chief Medical Officer, LDS Hospital, Salt Lake City, UT, p. A679

HAMILTON–BEYER, Maggie, Interim Chief Financial Officer, Story County Medical Center, Nevada, IA, p. A238

HAMLIN, Scott J., Chief Financial Officer, Children's Hospital Medical Center, Cincinnati, OH, p. A506

HAMM, David, President and Chief Executive Officer, Exempla Good Samaritan Medical Center, Lafayette, CO, p. A107

HAMMACK, Kathy, Chief Financial Officer, Western Medical Center–Santa Ana, Santa Ana, CA, p. A92

HAMMACK, Stanley K., Associate Vice President Hospital Affairs/Chief Executive Officer, University of South Alabama Hospitals, Mobile, AL, p. B118

HAMMAN, Dan, Chief Financial Officer, Sparks Regional Medical Center, Fort Smith, AR, p. A43

HAMMEKE, Paul, Chief Executive Officer, Sheridan County Health Complex, Hoxie, KS, p. A249

HAMMER, Michael, President and Chief Operating Officer, Good Samaritan Health Center of Merrill, Merrill, WI, p. A730

HAMMER, Patrick T., President and Chief Executive Officer, Wellstone Regional Hospital, Jeffersonville, IN, p. A219

HAMMER, Rebecca, Chief Financial Officer, Davis Memorial Hospital, Elkins, WV, p. A715

HAMMER, Rosemary, Information System Director, Holy Cross Hospital, Taos, NM, p. A445

HAMMES, Chris, Administrator, Integris Southwest Medical Center, Oklahoma City, OK, p. A535

HAMMETT, Doran, Chief Financial Officer, Kingfisher Regional Hospital, Kingfisher, OK, p. A532

HAMMETT, Troy, Vice President Finance and Chief Financial Officer, Sumter Regional Hospital, Americus, GA, p. A152

HAMMETT, Warren E., Administrator, Bamberg County Memorial Hospital and Nursing Center, Bamberg, SC, p. A583

HAMMON, David, Director Information Services, Advance Care Hospital, Hot Springs National Park, AR, p. A44

HAMMOND, Thomas H., Chief Information Officer, St. Francis Medical Center, Monroe, LA, p. A287

HAMMONDS, Laura, Controller, Jasper Memorial Hospital, Monticello, GA, p. A166

HAMORY, M.D., Bruce H., Executive Vice President and Chief Medical Officer, Geisinger Medical Center, Danville, PA, p. A556

HAMP, Matthew, Chief Operating Officer, Sisters of Charity Hospital of Buffalo, Buffalo, NY, p. A449

HAMPLE, David L., Chief Executive Officer, Jackson Hospital, Marianna, FL, p. A136

HAMPTON, Brenda, Network Manager, Tinley Park Mental Health Center, Tinley Park, IL, p. A209

HAMPTON, Laurie, Human Resources Director, Prairie du Chien Memorial Hospital, Prairie Du Chien, WI, p. A734

HAMPTON, Lynn, Director Information Systems, Via Christi Oklahoma Regional Medical Center, Ponca City, OK, p. A537

HANBY, Greg, Director Ancillary Services, Hills and Dales General Hospital, Cass City, MI, p. A329

HANCKEL, Elizabeth, Human Resources Director, Valley View Hospital, Glenwood Springs, CO, p. A106

HANCOCK, Bill, Director Human Resources, Northern Hospital of Surry County, Mount Airy, NC, p. A488

HANCOCK, Michael, Interim Vice President Human Resources, Rogue Valley Medical Center, Medford, OR, p. A546

HAND, Richard A., Vice President Information and Chief Financial Officer, Southern Ocean County Hospital, Manahawkin, NJ, p. A431

HAND, Ronald E., Chief Executive Officer, Doctors Hospital, Groves, TX, p. A643

HAND, Susan, Vice President and Chief Financial Officer, Methodist Medical Center of Oak Ridge, Oak Ridge, TN, p. A616

HANDLEY, Charles, Chief Financial Officer, Park Plaza Hospital, Houston, TX, p. A647

HANDLEY, Charles R., Chief Financial Officer, Plaza Specialty Hospital, Houston, TX, p. A647

HANDLEY, David, Chief Operating Officer, Spring Branch Medical Center, Houston, TX, p. A647

HANDLEY, Rhonda, Chief Financial Officer, Columbia Basin Hospital, Ephrata, WA, p. A702

HANDY, CPA, Steven P.
Senior Vice President, Chief Financial Officer and Chief Information Officer, Uniontown Hospital, Uniontown, PA, p. A577
Senior Vice President, Chief Financial Officer and Chief Information Officer, Uniontown Hospital, Uniontown, PA, p. A577
HANEKE, David, Administrator, Ellinwood District Hospital, Ellinwood, KS, p. A246
HANEN, David G., Vice President Fiscal Services and Chief Financial Officer, Fremont Area Medical Center, Fremont, NE, p. A406
HANENBURG, Thomas, Vice President and Chief Operating Officer, Duke Health Raleigh Hospital, Raleigh, NC, p. A489
HANES, Brenda, Flight Commander Resource Management, Wright Patterson Medical Center, Wright–Patterson AFB, OH, p. A525
HANES, Carol H., Administrator, D. M. Cogdell Memorial Hospital, Snyder, TX, p. A667
HANG, R.N., Martha, Vice President Patient Care Services, St. Joseph Health System, Tawas City, MI, p. A346
HANKINS, Debbie, Director Human Resources, San Joaquin Community Hospital, Bakersfield, CA, p. A54
HANKO, James F., President and Chief Executive Officer, North Country Regional Hospital, Bemidji, MN, p. A350
HANKS, John, Director Information Systems, Blount Memorial Hospital, Maryville, TN, p. A612
HANKS, M.D., Steven D., Senior Vice President Medical Affairs and Chief Medical Officer, New Britain General Hospital, New Britain, CT, p. A114
HANKS, Tammy, Director Human Resources, Minidoka Memorial Hospital and Extended Care Facility, Rupert, ID, p. A181
HANLEY, Richard, Chief Operating Officer, Spring Harbor Hospital, Westbrook, ME, p. A301
HANNA, David, Chief Financial Officer, Savoy Medical Center, Mamou, LA, p. A285
HANNA, M.D., George, Chief of Staff, Matagorda General Hospital, Bay City, TX, p. A624
HANNA, Mitchell J., Chief Administrative Officer, Sutter Auburn Faith Hospital, Auburn, CA, p. A53
HANNAH, Brian D., Chief Operating Officer, North Oaks Medical Center, Hammond, LA, p. A281
HANNAH, Steven, Interim President and Chief Executive Officer, Carlinville Area Hospital, Carlinville, IL, p. A185
HANNAH, M.D., JD, Wayne, Vice President Medical Affairs, Southeast Alabama Medical Center, Dothan, AL, p. A17
HANNER, R. Andy, Chief Executive Officer, Three Rivers Center for Behavioral Health, West Columbia, SC, p. A593
HANNERS, Rodney, Director Operations, Kaiser Foundation Hospital, Los Angeles, CA, p. A70
HANNIFAN, Kevin R., Executive Vice President and Chief Executive Officer, Hartford Hospital, Hartford, CT, p. A113
HANNIGAN, Terrence, Chief Operating Officer, Wm. Jennings Bryan Dorn Veterans Affairs Medical Center, Columbia, SC, p. A586
HANNON, Edward J., President and Chief Executive Officer, Clarion Hospital, Clarion, PA, p. A555
HANNON, Kay, Facility Information Systems Director, Des Peres Hospital, Saint Louis, MO, p. A390
HANNON, Trish, Senior Vice President and Chief Operating Officer, Baystate Medical Center, Springfield, MA, p. A323
HANOLD, Gary, Director Management Information Systems, Angel Medical Center, Franklin, NC, p. A483
HANOVER, Kenneth, President and Chief Executive Officer, Health Alliance of Greater Cincinnati, Cincinnati, OH, p. B54
HANOVER, Peggy, Vice President Human Resources, Southwest Florida Regional Medical Center, Fort Myers, FL, p. A129
HANOVER, Van A., Executive Vice President, Condell Medical Center, Libertyville, IL, p. A199

HANSELMAN, Vicki
Chief Operating Officer, Bluffton Regional Medical Center, Bluffton, IN, p. A212
Chief Operating Officer, Bluffton Regional Medical Center, Bluffton, IN, p. A212
HANSEN, Amy, Chief Operating Officer, Patient Care, Pine Medical Center, Sandstone, MN, p. A362
HANSEN, Bart, Chief Financial Officer, Campbell County Memorial Hospital, Gillette, WY, p. A740
HANSEN, M.D., Christopher, Vice President Medical Affairs and Chief Medical Officer, Valley Baptist Health System, Harlingen, TX, p. A643
HANSEN, Curtis J., Senior Financial Officer, Adventist Rehabilitation Hospital of Maryland, Rockville, MD, p. A310
HANSEN, Dennis, Vice President Operations, Littleton Adventist Hospital, Littleton, CO, p. A107
HANSEN, Edwin L., Chief Executive Officer, Sunbury Community Hospital, Sunbury, PA, p. A576
HANSEN, Irwin C., Chief Executive Officer, Doctors Medical Center–San Pablo Campus, San Pablo, CA, p. A91
HANSEN, Jay, Director Information Services, Oconee Memorial Hospital, Seneca, SC, p. A591
HANSEN, Justin, Information Systems Director, Bingham Memorial Hospital, Blackfoot, ID, p. A177
HANSEN, Laurie, Director Administrative Services, Johnson County Healthcare Center, Buffalo, WY, p. A739
HANSEN, M.D., Mark, Chief of Staff, Estes Park Medical Center, Estes Park, CO, p. A105
HANSEN, Nancy, Administrator, McCone County Health Center, Circle, MT, p. A397
HANSEN, Robert J., Chief Executive Officer and Administrator, Cumberland Memorial Hospital, Cumberland, WI, p. A724
HANSEN, Thomas N., M.D., Chief Executive Officer, Children's Hospital, Columbus, OH, p. A510
HANSEN–BAYLESS, Genanne, Administrator, U. S. Air Force Hospital Dover, Dover, DE, p. A119
HANSHAW, John, Chief Executive Officer, St. Mark's Hospital, Salt Lake City, UT, p. A680
HANSON, Bryant R., President and Chief Executive Officer, Floyd Memorial Hospital and Health Services, New Albany, IN, p. A222
HANSON, Carl, Administrator, Minidoka Memorial Hospital and Extended Care Facility, Rupert, ID, p. A181
HANSON, Lisa, Human Resources Officer, Greater Community Hospital, Creston, IA, p. A231
HANSON, Margaret, Chief Administrative Officer, Cape Cod Hospital, Hyannis, MA, p. A319
HANSON, Mark
Director Information Systems, Central Kansas Medical Center, Great Bend, KS, p. A247
Director Information Systems, St. Joseph Memorial Hospital, Larned, KS, p. A251
HANSON, Paul A., Chief Executive Officer, Prairie Lakes Healthcare System, Watertown, SD, p. A600
HANSON, Polly, Chief Financial Officer, Mountainview Medical Center, White Sulphur Springs, MT, p. A402
HANSON, Rhonda, Director Human Resources, Huron Regional Medical Center, Huron, SD, p. A596
HANSON, M.D., Rita, Vice President Medical Affairs, St. Joseph's Regional Medical Center, Milwaukee, WI, p. A731
HANSON, Timothy H., President and Chief Executive Officer, HealthEast Care System, Saint Paul, MN, p. B56
HAPPEL, M.D., Terry J., Medical Director, Medical Staff Affairs, Chandler Regional Hospital, Chandler, AZ, p. A30
HARALDSON, Richard, Chief Executive Officer, Sidney Health Center, Sidney, MT, p. A402
HARALSON, Bob, Chief Financial Officer, Clinch Valley Medical Center, Richlands, VA, p. A694
HARATI, M.D., Nibal A., Chief of Staff, Landmann–Jungman Memorial Hospital, Scotland, SD, p. A598
HARB, CHE, Gregory A., Chief Operating Officer, Baptist Hospital of East Tennessee, Knoxville, TN, p. A609
HARBARGER, Claude W., President, St. Dominic–Jackson Memorial Hospital, Jackson, MS, p. A371

HARBAUGH, Ken, Chief Financial Officer, OSF Saint Francis Medical Center, Peoria, IL, p. A205
HARBIN, Jim, Director Information Systems, National Jewish Medical and Research Center, Denver, CO, p. A103
HARCOMBE, Douglas, Director Human Resources, Florida Hospital Heartland Medical Center, Sebring, FL, p. A146
HARDAWAY, Brock, Administrator, Select Specialty Hospital–Houston Medical Center, Houston, TX, p. A647
HARDCASTLE, Brad, Chief Financial Officer, Daviess Community Hospital, Washington, IN, p. A227
HARDEE, M.D., Gary R., Medical Director, Plains Memorial Hospital, Dimmitt, TX, p. A635
HARDEMAN, Diane, Personnel Director, Stephens County Hospital, Toccoa, GA, p. A171
HARDEN, James, President and Chief Executive Officer, Catholic Health Services of Long Island, Rockville Centre, NY, p. B25
HARDEN, Jean, Executive Director of Human Resources, Baptist Hospital Northeast, La Grange, KY, p. A267
HARDEN, M.D., V Anthony, Chief of Staff, Saint Mary's Regional Medical Center, Russellville, AR, p. A50
HARDIN, M.D., Robert, Director Medical Affairs, Baptist Hospital, Nashville, TN, p. A615
HARDIN, R.N., Toma G., Chief Nursing Officer, Chicot Memorial Hospital, Lake Village, AR, p. A46
HARDING, Edward A., FACHE, President and Chief Executive Officer, Columbus Community Hospital, Columbus, WI, p. A724
HARDING, John R., President and Chief Executive Officer, Florida Hospital Heartland Medical Center, Sebring, FL, p. A146
HARDING, M.D., Thomas, Acting Medical Director, Milwaukee County Behavioral Health Division, Milwaukee, WI, p. A731
HARDING, William W., President and Chief Executive Officer, Union Hospital, Dover, OH, p. A513
HARDWICK, William, Chief Human Resources, Veterans Affairs Tennessee Valley Healthcare System, Nashville, TN, p. A616
HARDY, David, Senior Vice President Operations and Chief Financial Officer, Cortland Memorial Hospital, Cortland, NY, p. A451
HARDY, Kevin, Chief Financial Officer, HEALTHSOUTH Treasure Coast Rehabilitation Hospital, Vero Beach, FL, p. A150
HARDY, M.D., Leo, Chief of Staff, Castleview Hospital, Price, UT, p. A678
HARDY, Patsy A., Chief Executive Officer, St. Joseph's Hospital, Parkersburg, WV, p. A718
HARDY, Stephen, Chief Financial Officer, Mountain View Regional Medical Center, Norton, VA, p. A693
HARDY, D.O., Tom, Vice President Medical Affairs, Grandview Hospital and Medical Center, Dayton, OH, p. A512
HARDY, W Neil, Director, Financial Management Service Center, Veterans Affairs Salt Lake City Health Care System, Salt Lake City, UT, p. A680
HARE, Michael K.
Administrator, De Leon Hospital, De Leon, TX, p. A634
Administrator, Comanche Community Hospital, Comanche, TX, p. A629
HARFF, Chris, Chief Operating Officer, Monticello Big Lake Hospital, Monticello, MN, p. A358
HARFF, Christine K., Chief Executive Officer, Northwest Medical Center, Thief River Falls, MN, p. A363
HARGETT, Stephen A., Senior Vice President and Chief Financial Officer, Centinela Freeman Regional Medical Center, Marina Campus, Marina Del Rey, CA, p. A74
HARGIS, Bryan J., President and Chief Executive Officer, Jennersville Regional Hospital, West Grove, PA, p. A578
HARGRAVE, Kent, Chief Information Officer, Overlake Hospital Medical Center, Bellevue, WA, p. A700
HARGREAVES, Chris, Director Human Resources, Ingalls Memorial Hospital, Harvey, IL, p. A196
HARGREAVES, Diane, Vice President Human Resources, Provena Saint Joseph Hospital, Elgin, IL, p. A193
HARING, Don, Vice President Finance and Treasurer, SwedishAmerican Hospital, Rockford, IL, p. A207

HARKER, Sandra, Director, Community Development, Livingston Memorial Hospital, Livingston, MT, p. A400

HARKLEROAD, Lisa, Director Human Resources, Logan Memorial Hospital, Russellville, KY, p. A274

HARLAN, Kevin, Chief Executive Officer, Alleghany Memorial Hospital, Sparta, NC, p. A492

HARLAN, Sandra, Chief Financial Officer, Christus Coushatta Health Care Center, Coushatta, LA, p. A279

HARLAN, Thomas M., President and Chief Administrative Officer, Mount Diablo Medical Center, Concord, CA, p. A57

HARLESS, Andrea, Director Information Services, Wythe County Community Hospital, Wytheville, VA, p. A699

HARLESS, Jane, Director of Information Services, Saint Francis Hospital, Charleston, WV, p. A714

HARLEY, Richard A., Senior Vice President Finance and Chief Financial Officer, Gettysburg Hospital, Gettysburg, PA, p. A559

HARLOW, Tom, Vice President Operations, Memorial Hospital, York, PA, p. A580

HARLOWE, Michael, President and Chief Executive Officer, Tipton County Memorial Hospital, Tipton, IN, p. A226

HARMAN, Ken, Administrator, Cassia Regional Medical Center, Burley, ID, p. A178

HARMAN, Richmond M., President and Chief Executive Officer, Martin Memorial Health Systems, Stuart, FL, p. A147

HARMAN, Robert L., Chief Executive Officer, Grant Memorial Hospital, Petersburg, WV, p. A719

HARMON, Cheryl A.
Chief Financial Officer, Provena Covenant Medical Center, Urbana, IL, p. A209
Vice President Finance, Provena United Samaritans Medical Center, Danville, IL, p. A191

HARMON, Clifford K., President, Hocking Valley Community Hospital, Logan, OH, p. A516

HARMON, Jr., M.D., Roy, Vice President Medical Affairs, Maury Regional Hospital, Columbia, TN, p. A604

HARMS, Arlene, Administrator, Melissa Memorial Hospital, Holyoke, CO, p. A107

HARMS, Charles F., Chief Executive Officer, United Medical Center, Cheyenne, WY, p. A739

HARMS, George, Chief Financial Officer, Columbus County Hospital, Whiteville, NC, p. A493

HARMS, Jacquelyn, R.N., Executive Director, Medical Center of Southeastern Oklahoma, Durant, OK, p. A530

HARMSEN, Constance, R.N., Chief Executive Officer, Banner Estrella Medical, Phoenix, AZ, p. A33

HARNESS, Lorraine L., Administrator, Pike County Memorial Hospital, Louisiana, MO, p. A387

HARNESS, Phil, Chief Executive Officer, Doctor's Hospital, Leawood, KS, p. A251

HARNEY, Geraldine, Chief Financial Officer, U. S. Public Health Service Phoenix Indian Medical Center, Phoenix, AZ, p. A35

HARNING, Richard, Vice President Finance and Treasurer, Sinai-Grace Hospital, Detroit, MI, p. A332

HARNS, James F., Director Human Resources, Eaton Rapids Medical Center, Eaton Rapids, MI, p. A332

HARPER, Alan G., Director, Veterans Affairs North Texas Health Care System, Dallas, TX, p. A634

HARPER, Cindy, Director Information Systems, Westfield Memorial Hospital, Westfield, NY, p. A476

HARPER, Corwin, Vice President and Administrator, Kaiser Foundation Hospital, Fresno, CA, p. A61

HARPER, M.D., Greta, Chief of Staff, Palmetto Health Richland, Columbia, SC, p. A586

HARPER, James, Chief Human Resources Officer, Jupiter Medical Center, Jupiter, FL, p. A133

HARPER, Loretta, Vice President Human Resources, University of Utah Hospitals and Clinics, Salt Lake City, UT, p. A680

HARPER, M.D., R Andrew, Medical Director, Harris County Psychiatric Center, Houston, TX, p. A645

HARR, M.D., Charles, President Medical Staff, Carolinas Medical Center-Mercy, Charlotte, NC, p. A479

HARR, M.D., Virginia, Chief of Staff, Grady Memorial Hospital, Chickasha, OK, p. A528

HARREL, Mark, Chief Executive Officer, Haskell County Healthcare System, Stigler, OK, p. A538

HARRIER, Margie, Chief Operating Officer, Western Medical Center Anaheim, Anaheim, CA, p. A52

HARRIGAN, Robert, President and Chief Operating Officer, Summa Health System, Akron, OH, p. A502

HARRIMAN, Robert, Administrator, Gulf Breeze Hospital, Gulf Breeze, FL, p. A130

HARRINGTON, Dan, Chief Operating Officer and Human Resources Director, Williamsburg Regional Hospital, Kingstree, SC, p. A589

HARRINGTON Jr, John L., FACHE, President and Chief Executive Officer, Paradise Valley Hospital, Phoenix, AZ, p. A34

HARRINGTON, Joseph P., Chief Executive Officer, Lodi Memorial Hospital, Lodi, CA, p. A67

HARRINGTON, Ron, Chief Financial Officer, Fleming County Hospital, Flemingsburg, KY, p. A264

HARRINGTON Jr, Russell D., President and Chief Executive Officer, Baptist Health, Little Rock, AR, p. B14

HARRINGTON, Timothy J., President and Chief Executive Officer, Vista Health-Provena Saint Therese Medical Center, Waukegan, IL, p. A210

HARRIS, Andrew E., Chief Executive Officer, Warminster Hospital, Warminster, PA, p. A577

HARRIS, M.D., C Martin, Chief Information Officer, Cleveland Clinic Foundation, Cleveland, OH, p. A508

HARRIS, Frank W., President and Chief Executive Officer, Russell Medical Center, Alexander City, AL, p. A13

HARRIS, Gregory R., Acting Associate Director, Veterans Affairs Medical Center, Battle Creek, MI, p. A328

HARRIS, Howard, Vice President Human Resources, Regional Medical Center of Orangeburg and Calhoun Counties, Orangeburg, SC, p. A591

HARRIS, Jeanine, Director of Information Services, Clinch Valley Medical Center, Richlands, VA, p. A694

HARRIS, Jodie, Controller and Chief Financial Officer, Atlanta Memorial Hospital, Atlanta, TX, p. A622

HARRIS, John, Chief Executive Officer, Lake Pointe Medical Center, Rowlett, TX, p. A662

HARRIS, Lee, Assistant Administrator Support Services, Memorial Hospital and Manor, Bainbridge, GA, p. A156

HARRIS, Lisa E., M.D., Chief Executive Officer and Medical Director, Wishard Health Services, Indianapolis, IN, p. A219

HARRIS, Marcia, Chief Executive Officer, Madison County Health Care System, Winterset, IA, p. A243

HARRIS, Merilyn, Administrator, Kau Hospital, Pahala, HI, p. A176

HARRIS, Mike, Chief Operating Officer, Continuous Care Center of Tulsa, Tulsa, OK, p. A539

HARRIS, Nancy, Chief Financial Officer, Fitzgibbon Hospital, Marshall, MO, p. A387

HARRIS, M.D., Norman, Chief of Staff, Chapman Medical Center, Orange, CA, p. A79

HARRIS, Ray, Administrator, Hamilton Hospital, Olney, TX, p. A659

HARRIS, M.D., Robert M., President Medical and Dental Staff, Bergen Regional Medical Center, Paramus, NJ, p. A433

HARRIS, Sharon, Chief Nursing Officer, Baptist Memorial Hospital – Memphis, Memphis, TN, p. A612

HARRIS, Steven, President Medical Staff, Lewis-Gale Medical Center, Salem, VA, p. A696

HARRIS, Vena, Director Human Resources, Minneola District Hospital, Minneola, KS, p. A253

HARRISON, Bomar, Interim Chief Financial Officer, Cooper Green Hospital, Birmingham, AL, p. A14

HARRISON, Carolyn, Director of Human Resources, Maury Regional Hospital, Columbia, TN, p. A604

HARRISON, Chris, Director Information Services, St. Mary's Healthcare Center, Pierre, SD, p. A597

HARRISON, Dean M., President and Chief Executive Officer, Northwestern Memorial Hospital, Chicago, IL, p. A188

HARRISON, Denise, Site Manager, Veterans Affairs Nebraska-Western Iowa Health Care System, Lincoln, NE, p. A409

HARRISON, Doug, Vice President Human Resources, Bon Secours-St. Francis Xavier Hospital, Charleston, SC, p. A584

HARRISON, Douglas, Vice President for Human Resources, Roper Hospital, Charleston, SC, p. A585

HARRISON, Dyan, Health Information Manager, Ochiltree General Hospital, Perryton, TX, p. A660

HARRISON, Janice, Administrator, Southern Crescent Hospital for Specialty Care, Riverdale, GA, p. A167

HARRISON, Linda, Chief Executive Officer, Highlands Regional Medical Center, Sebring, FL, p. A146

HARROLD, Robin, Senior Vice President and Chief Operating Officer, Shawnee Mission Medical Center, Shawnee Mission, KS, p. A257

HARRON, Rick, Chief Financial Officer, Dominican Hospital, Santa Cruz, CA, p. A92

HARRYMAN, John D., President and Administrator, Norton Suburban Hospital, Louisville, KY, p. A270

HARSY, Brice, Chief Financial Officer, Marshall Browning Hospital, Du Quoin, IL, p. A192

HART, Charles, M.D., President and Chief Executive Officer, Regional Health, Rapid City, SD, p. B93

HART, Chet M., Senior Vice President and Chief Operating Officer, Louise Obici Memorial Hospital, Suffolk, VA, p. A697

HART, Diane M.
Interim Chief Executive Officer, Moses Ludington Hospital, Ticonderoga, NY, p. A474
Interim Chief Executive Officer, Moses Ludington Hospital, Ticonderoga, NY, p. A474

HART, Donna, Chief Information Officer, Provident Hospital of Cook County, Chicago, IL, p. A189

HART, M.D., Gary, Chief Medical Officer, Navarro Regional Hospital, Corsicana, TX, p. A631

HART, Joel A., FACHE, Chief Executive Officer, Integris Baptist Regional Health Center, Miami, OK, p. A533

HART, John S., Chief Executive Officer, San Juan Hospital, Monticello, UT, p. A677

HART, Joseph, Controller and Chief Financial Officer, New Milford Hospital, New Milford, CT, p. A115

HART, Linda, Vice President Finance, Grady Memorial Hospital, Chickasha, OK, p. A528

HART, Lisa, Controller, Memorial Hospital and Physician Group, Frederick, OK, p. A531

HART, Noel W., Administrator, King's Daughters Hospital, Yazoo City, MS, p. A377

HARTBERG, David, Chief Executive Officer, Grand View Hospital, Ironwood, MI, p. A337

HARTEL, M.D., Kelly, Chief of Staff, Washington County Memorial Hospital, Potosi, MO, p. A389

HARTGRAVES, Steve, Chief Executive Officer, Hansford Hospital, Spearman, TX, p. A667

HARTIGAN, William J., President and Chief Executive Officer, Liberty Management Group, Inc., Ramsey, NJ, p. B67

HARTLEY, Joan, Chief Executive Officer, Taylor-Telfair Regional Hospital, McRae, GA, p. A166

HARTLEY, Norma, Director Human Resources, Harms Memorial Hospital District, American Falls, ID, p. A177

HARTLEY, William, FACHE, President and Chief Executive Officer, Ferrell Hospital, Eldorado, IL, p. A193

HARTLING, M.D., Ross, Medical Staff President, Cascade Valley Hospital and Clinics, Arlington, WA, p. A700

HARTMAN, C. Richard, M.D., President and Chief Executive Officer, Community Medical Center, Scranton, PA, p. A575

HARTMAN, Daphne, Chief Financial Officer, North Big Horn Hospital District, Lovell, WY, p. A741

HARTMAN, R. Michael, Chief Executive Officer, Tustin Hospital and Medical Center, Tustin, CA, p. A97

HARTMAN, Susan, Administrator, HEALTHSOUTH Nittany Valley Rehabilitation Hospital, Pleasant Gap, PA, p. A573

HARTMANN, Doreen
Vice President and Chief Financial Officer, Mercy Medical Center Merced-Community Campus, Merced, CA, p. A75
Vice President and Chief Financial Officer, Mercy Medical Center Merced-Dominican Campus, Merced, CA, p. A75

HARTMANN, M.D., Peter M., Vice President Medical Affairs, York Hospital, York, PA, p. A580

HARTSFIELD, M.D., Melvin
  Vice President Medical Affairs, John D. Archbold Memorial Hospital, Thomasville, GA, p. A170
  Vice President Medical Affairs, Mitchell County Hospital, Camilla, GA, p. A157
HARVEL, Norilina, Chief Financial Officer, Bonner General Hospital, Sandpoint, ID, p. A181
HARVEY, Bruce
  Interim Chief Executive Officer, Minnewaska District Hospital, Starbuck, MN, p. A363
  Controller, Minnewaska District Hospital, Starbuck, MN, p. A363
HARVEY, Dana, Director Human Resources and Public Relations, Marshall County Hospital, Benton, KY, p. A261
HARVEY, G Darrell, Chief Fiscal Services, Veterans Affairs Medical Center, Beckley, WV, p. A713
HARVEY, Keith D., Chief Executive Officer, Virginia Regional Medical Center, Virginia, MN, p. A364
HARVEY, Linda, Chief Financial Officer, West Feliciana Parish Hospital, Saint Francisville, LA, p. A292
HARVEY, Sally, R.N., Regional Administrator, Memorial Community Hospital and Health System, Blair, NE, p. A405
HARVEY, Stansel, FACHE, President, Harris Methodist Southwest, Fort Worth, TX, p. A639
HARYASZ, Sandy, R.N., Chief Executive Officer, Page Hospital, Page, AZ, p. A33
HASBROUCK, Merritt J., President, Jackson Park Hospital and Medical Center, Chicago, IL, p. A187
HASKELL, Jean, Vice President Human Resources, Kaweah Delta Health Care District, Visalia, CA, p. A98
HASKELL, Lynnette
  Chief Financial Officer, Down East Community Hospital, Machias, ME, p. A299
  Chief Financial Officer, Down East Community Hospital, Machias, ME, p. A299
HASKINS, Randy, Director Information Systems, Mercy Medical Center – North Iowa, Mason City, IA, p. A238
HASS, M.D., Brian, Chief of Staff, St. Francis Memorial Hospital, West Point, NE, p. A414
HASSEMER, Robert
  Division Director Human Resources, Sacred Heart Hospital, Eau Claire, WI, p. A725
  Division Director Human Resources, Sacred Heart Hospital, Eau Claire, WI, p. A725
HASSETT, Thomas E., Vice President, Carolinas Medical Center–Mercy, Charlotte, NC, p. A479
HASSLER, M.D., Robert, Director Medical Affairs, Brunswick Community Hospital, Supply, NC, p. A492
HASTINGS, David, Chief Informatio Officer, Baton Rouge General Medical Center, Baton Rouge, LA, p. A277
HASTINGS, G. Richard
  President and Chief Executive Officer, Saint Luke's Health System, Kansas City, MO, p. B95
  Chief Executive Officer, Saint Luke's Hospital of Kansas City, Kansas City, MO, p. A385
HASTINGS, Jeff, Information Technology Manager, Mayo Regional Hospital, Dover-Foxcroft, ME, p. A298
HATCH, Mary, Chief Financial Officer, Dixie Regional Medical Center, Saint George, UT, p. A679
HATCHER, Dean, Administrator, HEALTHSOUTH Western Hills Rehabilitation Center, Parkersburg, WV, p. A718
HATCHER, James T.
  Chief Financial Officer, Emory University Hospital, Atlanta, GA, p. A153
  Chief Financial Officer, Wesley Woods Center of Emory University, Atlanta, GA, p. A155
HATCHER, Robert, Chief Financial Officer, Tulane University Hospital and Clinic, New Orleans, LA, p. A290
HATHARASINGHE, M.D., Roger, President Medical Staff, Iredell Memorial Hospital, Statesville, NC, p. A492
HATHAWAY, Richard D., Chief Executive Officer, Plumas District Hospital, Quincy, CA, p. A82
HATHAWAY, Steve, Vice President Finance and Chief Financial Officer, St. Joseph's Mercy of Macomb, Clinton Township, MI, p. A330
HATHAWAY Jr, Woodrow W., Chief Executive Officer, Chatham Hospital, Siler City, NC, p. A491
HATHCOAT, Rinda, Associate Director Fiscal and Administrative Services, U. S. Public Health Service Phoenix Indian Medical Center, Phoenix, AZ, p. A35

HATHORN, Mike, Chief Financial Officer, Lallie Kemp Medical Center, Independence, LA, p. A282
HATKIN, Steve
  Director Finance, New Ulm Medical Center, New Ulm, MN, p. A358
  Director Finance, New Ulm Medical Center, New Ulm, MN, p. A358
HATLESTAD, Jill, Vice President Human Resources and Organizational Support, Glencoe Regional Health Services, Glencoe, MN, p. A354
HAUCK, Cindy, Administrator, Institute for Orthopaedic Surgery, Lima, OH, p. A516
HAUER, Thomas, Director Human Resources, Phoenix Memorial Hospital, Phoenix, AZ, p. A34
HAUG, Norman, M.D., Administrator, Rio Grande Hospital, Del Norte, CO, p. A103
HAUG, William F., FACHE, President and Chief Executive Officer, Children's Hospital Central California, Madera, CA, p. A74
HAUGO, Glenn, Administrator, Johnson Memorial Health Services, Dawson, MN, p. A352
HAUN, Carol, Director Human Resources, Sky Ridge Medical Center, Lone Tree, CO, p. A108
HAUSE, Eileen, Chief Executive Officer, Kensington Hospital, Philadelphia, PA, p. A568
HAUSE, Roxann, Administrator Ancillary and Support Services, Estes Park Medical Center, Estes Park, CO, p. A105
HAUSER, M.D., Mark J., Chief Medical Officer, Baptist Hospital of Miami, Miami, FL, p. A136
HAUSHALTER, Richard L., Vice President Finance and Chief Financial Officer, Rockingham Memorial Hospital, Harrisonburg, VA, p. A689
HAUSMANN, Sherry, President, SSM St. Joseph Hospital of Kirkwood, Saint Louis, MO, p. A392
HAUSWIRTH, Renay, Chief Financial Officer, Palo Alto County Health System, Emmetsburg, IA, p. A233
HAVARD, Diane, Information Systems Specialist, Hedrick Medical Center, Chillicothe, MO, p. A380
HAVE, M.D., Christopher Tom, Chief of Staff, Howard County Community Hospital, Saint Paul, NE, p. A412
HAVILAND, Bruce, Chief Information Officer, Magee–Womens Hospital of UPMC, Pittsburgh, PA, p. A571
HAVILL, Nancy, Director Employee Services, Dunn Memorial Hospital, Bedford, IN, p. A211
HAVINS, Mark, Chief Financial Officer, Highland Medical Center, Lubbock, TX, p. A654
HAWK, Tricia, Director Development and Human Resources, Lindsborg Community Hospital, Lindsborg, KS, p. A252
HAWKINS, M.D., D., James, Chief of Staff, Valley West Community Hospital, Sandwich, IL, p. A207
HAWKINS, Jason F.
  Interim President and Chief Executive, Fulton County Medical Center, McConnellsburg, PA, p. A564
  Chief Financial Officer, Fulton County Medical Center, McConnellsburg, PA, p. A564
HAWKINS, M.D., Randy, Chief of Staff, Evans Memorial Hospital, Claxton, GA, p. A158
HAWKINS, Thomas J., Hospital Services Administrator, Central Prison Hospital, Raleigh, NC, p. A489
HAWKINS, Victor, Executive Director Marketing, St. Catherine Hospital, Garden City, KS, p. A247
HAWKINSON, Curtis, Chief Executive Officer, Keefe Memorial Hospital, Cheyenne Wells, CO, p. A102
HAWLEY, Claudia, Director Human Resources, Mason General Hospital, Shelton, WA, p. A709
HAWLEY, Jess
  Administrator, Syringa General Hospital, Grangeville, ID, p. A179
  Administrator, Syringa General Hospital, Grangeville, ID, p. A179
HAWLEY Jr, Robert L., Chief Executive Officer, Slidell Memorial Hospital and Medical Center, Slidell, LA, p. A293
HAWLEY, William, Chief Executive Officer, Memorial Hospital of Adel, Adel, GA, p. A152
HAWTHORNE, Caryn, Executive Vice President and Chief Financial Officer, Baptist Hospital of East Tennessee, Knoxville, TN, p. A609
HAWTHORNE, Douglas D., FACHE, President and Chief Executive Officer, Texas Health Resources, Arlington, TX, p. B107

HAYES, Bridget, Chief Operating Officer, Lincoln Park Hospital, Chicago, IL, p. A187
HAYES, Connie B., Director Human Resources, Hill Country Memorial Hospital, Fredericksburg, TX, p. A640
HAYES, David R., Vice President and Chief Financial Officer, Breckinridge Memorial Hospital, Hardinsburg, KY, p. A265
HAYES, Debbie, Vice President, Christ Hospital, Cincinnati, OH, p. A506
HAYES, Howard A., President and Chief Executive Officer, St. Joseph Regional Medical Center, Lewiston, ID, p. A180
HAYES, J. Matthew, Executive Director, Riverview Regional Medical Center, Gadsden, AL, p. A19
HAYES, James M., President and Chief Executive Officer, Greenville Regional Hospital, Greenville, IL, p. A196
HAYES, Julie, Chief Financial Officer, Del Sol Medical Center, El Paso, TX, p. A637
HAYES, R.N., Paul, Chief Operating Officer, Valley Medical Center, Renton, WA, p. A706
HAYES, Steven A., Administrator, Illinois Valley Community Hospital, Peru, IL, p. A205
HAYES, Thomas P.
  Chief Executive Officer, Biggs–Gridley Memorial Hospital, Gridley, CA, p. A63
  Chief Executive Officer, Fremont Medical Center, Yuba City, CA, p. A100
  Chief Executive Officer, Fremont–Rideout Health Group, Yuba City, CA, p. B46
  Chief Executive Officer, Rideout Memorial Hospital, Marysville, CA, p. A75
HAYES, IV, William G., Vice President Human Resources, Medical College of Georgia Hospital and Clinics, Augusta, GA, p. A155
HAYES, William M., Chief Executive Officer, Northside Hospital – Cherokee, Canton, GA, p. A157
HAYMAN, Alex L., Chief Human Resources, Keller Army Community Hospital, West Point, NY, p. A476
HAYMAN, Dannette, Chief Operating Officer, Mercy Hospital, Port Huron, MI, p. A343
HAYMON, Beverly
  Chief Financial Officer, Baptist Cherokee, Centre, AL, p. A16
  Vice President Finance, Baptist DeKalb Medical Center, Fort Payne, AL, p. A18
HAYNES, Crystal L., Chief Executive Officer, Saint Louis University Hospital, Saint Louis, MO, p. A391
HAYNES, Freida Nan, Chief, Veterans Affairs Medical Center, Muskogee, OK, p. A534
HAYNES, Jerry, Interim President and Chief Executive Officer, Appalachian Regional Healthcare, Lexington, KY, p. B9
HAYNES, Jill, Financial Coach, Veterans Affairs Medical Center, Bath, NY, p. A447
HAYNES, Jr, M.D., John H., Senior Vice President and Chief Medical Officer, JPS Health Network, Fort Worth, TX, p. A640
HAYNES, Ken
  Senior Vice President and Chief Operating Officer, St. Vincent Infirmary Medical Center, Little Rock, AR, p. A47
  Senior Vice President and Chief Operating Officer, St. Vincent Medical Center–North, Sherwood, AR, p. A50
HAYNES, Robert, Administrator, Guadalupe Valley Hospital, Seguin, TX, p. A666
HAYNES, Susanne, Executive Director Finance, Baptist Hospital Northeast, La Grange, KY, p. A267
HAYRYNEN, D.O., Terry, Chief of Staff, Bell Hospital, Ishpeming, MI, p. A337
HAYS, Cheryl M., FACHE, Administrator, Marshall Medical Center North, Guntersville, AL, p. A19
HAYS, FACHE, Cheryl M., Administrator, Marshall Medical Center North, Guntersville, AL, p. A19
HAYS, Chuck, Chief Operating Officer, MaineGeneral Medical Center–Waterville Campus, Waterville, ME, p. A301
HAYS, Marilyn, Chief Financial Officer, North Valley Hospital, Whitefish, MT, p. A403
HAYS, Timothy A., Vice President Human Resources, Bradford Regional Medical Center, Bradford, PA, p. A553

HAYTAIAN, Mike, Head Director, Information Resources Management Department, Naval Hospital, Jacksonville, FL, p. A132

HAYWARD, John, President and Chief Executive Officer, PeaceHealth, Bellevue, WA, p. B83

HAYWARD, Tim, Administrator, Nacogdoches Memorial Hospital, Nacogdoches, TX, p. A658

HAYWOOD III, Edgar, Administrator, J. Arthur Dosher Memorial Hospital, Southport, NC, p. A492

HAYWOOD, D.O., James, Medical Director, Hocking Valley Community Hospital, Logan, OH, p. A516

HAZEL, James, M.D., Chief Executive Officer, Murray Medical Center, Chatsworth, GA, p. A158

HAZELETT, Marybess, Human Resources Director, Ira Davenport Memorial Hospital, Bath, NY, p. A447

HAZEN, Carol, Vice President Finance, Emory–Adventist Hospital, Smyrna, GA, p. A169

HAZZARD, Aaron R., Vice President and Chief Operating Officer, Jewish Hospital, Louisville, KY, p. A269

HEAD, M.D., David, Chief Medical Staff, Norton Sound Regional Hospital, Nome, AK, p. A28

HEAFNER, Dwayne, Chief Information Officer, Fall River Hospital, Hot Springs, SD, p. A596

HEALEY, Kevin, Vice President Human Resources, St. Mary's Regional Medical Center, Lewiston, ME, p. A299

HEALTH, M.D., Karen, Clinical Director, U. S. Public Health Service Indian Hospital, San Carlos, AZ, p. A36

HEALTON, M.D., Edward B., Senior Vice President and Medical Director, National Rehabilitation Hospital, Washington, DC, p. A122

HEALY, Michael, Vice President Finance, Avera Sacred Heart Hospital, Yankton, SD, p. A601

HEALY, Victoria, Controller, HEALTHSOUTH Rehabilitation Hospital of Western Massachusetts, Ludlow, MA, p. A320

HEANEY, M.D., Susan, Vice President Medical Affairs, SSM Cardinal Glennon Children's Hospital, Saint Louis, MO, p. A391

HEARD, John E., Chief Executive Officer, McGehee–Desha County Hospital, McGehee, AR, p. A47

HEARD, M Denise, Director Business Services, North Mississippi Medical Center–Pontotoc Hospital and Nursing Home, Pontotoc, MS, p. A374

HEARN, Stephanie, Administrator, Spectrum Health–Kent Community Campus, Grand Rapids, MI, p. A335

HEARTSILL, Keith, Chief Financial Officer, Grenada Lake Medical Center, Grenada, MS, p. A369

HEATER, Floyd, Chief Executive Officer, Shenandoah Memorial Hospital, Woodstock, VA, p. A698

HEATH, Molly, Director of Human Resources, West Houston Medical Center, Houston, TX, p. A649

HEATH, Susan, Administrator, Vanderbilt Stallworth Rehabilitation Hospital, Nashville, TN, p. A616

HEATHERLY, John, Assistant Administrator, Human Support Services, Hunt Memorial Hospital District, Greenville, TX, p. A642

HEATHERLY, Neil A., CHE, Chief Executive Officer, StoneCrest Medical Center, Smyrna, TN, p. A618

HEATHERLY, Wayne S., President and Chief Administrative Officer, Parkwest Medical Center, Knoxville, TN, p. A610

HEATON, Linda, Chief Financial Officer, Blowing Rock Hospital, Blowing Rock, NC, p. A478

HEATON, Lisa, Administrator and Chief Nursing Officer, Johnson County Health Center, Mountain City, TN, p. A614

HEAUKULANI, Ed, Information Technology Manager, Kona Community Hospital, Kealakekua, HI, p. A175

HEBEL, Barbara, Director Human Resources, Doylestown Hospital, Doylestown, PA, p. A557

HEBELA, CPA, Mohamed, Vice President Finance and Chief Financial Officer, Kingsbrook Jewish Medical Center, New York, NY, p. A461

HEBERT, Donald R., FACHE, Administrator, Willis–Knighton Bossier Health Center, Bossier City, LA, p. A278

HEBERT, Jr, FACH, Erie J., Senior Vice President, West Jefferson Medical Center, Marrero, LA, p. A286

HEBERT, Gerard, Chief Financial Officer, Natchitoches Parish Hospital, Natchitoches, LA, p. A288

HEBERT, Michael, Director Management Information Systems, MetroWest Medical Center, Framingham, MA, p. A318

HEBERT, Roddy, Administrator, St. Landry Extended Care Hospital, Opelousas, LA, p. A291

HEBERT, Tim, Director Human Resources, Teche Regional Medical Center, Morgan City, LA, p. A287

HECHT, Bill, Chief Operating Officer, Christus St. Patrick Hospital of Lake Charles, Lake Charles, LA, p. A284

HECHT, Lee
Chief Financial Officer, Rochester Methodist Hospital, Rochester, MN, p. A360
Chief Financial Officer, Saint Marys Hospital, Rochester, MN, p. A360

HECK, III, George L., President and Chief Executive Officer, Coffee Regional Medical Center, Douglas, GA, p. A161

HECK III, George L., President and Chief Executive Officer, Coffee Regional Medical Center, Douglas, GA, p. A161

HECK, M.D., Michael, Chief Medical Officer, Fairview University Medical Center–Mesabi, Hibbing, MN, p. A355

HECK, Suzanne, Vice President and Interim Chief Financial Officer, Memorial Health, Savannah, GA, p. A169

HECK, Terry
Vice President Finance and Chief Financial Officer, Saint Joseph Regional Medical Center, South Bend, IN, p. A225
Vice President Finance and Chief Financial Officer, Saint Joseph Regional Medical Center–Plymouth Campus, Plymouth, IN, p. A224

HECKER, Lisa, Director Human Resources, Hedrick Medical Center, Chillicothe, MO, p. A380

HECKERMAN, Ray, Chief Executive Officer, Coastal Harbor Treatment Center, Savannah, GA, p. A168

HECKERT, Brian, Chief Executive Officer, Wm. Jennings Bryan Dorn Veterans Affairs Medical Center, Columbia, SC, p. A586

HECKERT Jr, Robert J., Chief Executive Officer, Daviess Community Hospital, Washington, IN, p. A227

HECKMAN, Katie, Community Relations Director, Berea Hospital, Berea, KY, p. A261

HEDDE, M.D., Charles C., Vice President Medical Affairs, Good Samaritan Hospital, Vincennes, IN, p. A226

HEDDERMAN, Michael, Senior Vice President Finance and Chief Financial Officer, Marianjoy Rehabilitation Hospital, Wheaton, IL, p. A210

HEDGES, M.D., Robert, Chief Medical Staff, Hancock County Memorial Hospital, Britt, IA, p. A229

HEDGES, M.D., Tony, Chief Medical Officer, Lamb Healthcare Center, Littlefield, TX, p. A653

HEDRICK, Bill, Warden, U. S. Medical Center for Federal Prisoners, Springfield, MO, p. A394

HEDRICK, William, Chief Medical Officer, Rehabilitation Hospital of Fort Wayne, Fort Wayne, IN, p. A215

HEEMAN, John, Director Information Systems, Huntsville Memorial Hospital, Huntsville, TX, p. A649

HEER, John R.
President and Chief Executive Officer, North Mississippi Health Services, Inc., Tupelo, MS, p. B79
President and Chief Executive Officer, North Mississippi Medical Center – Tupelo, Tupelo, MS, p. A376

HEFFERS, Margaret, Assistant Vice President Human Resources, Geisinger Wyoming Valley Medical Center, Wilkes-Barre, PA, p. A579

HEFFLER, David, Ph.D., Executive Director, Western New York Children's Psychiatric Center, Buffalo, NY, p. A449

HEFFNER, John
Chief Executive Officer, Select Specialty Hospital of Savannah, Savannah, GA, p. A169
Executive Medical Director, Charleston Memorial Hospital, Charleston, SC, p. A584
Medical Director, MUSC Medical Center of Medical University of South Carolina, Charleston, SC, p. A584

HEFNER, David, Executive Director and Chief Operating Officer, Penn State Milton S. Hershey Medical Center, Hershey, PA, p. A560

HEFNER, Rick L., Vice President for Finance and Administration, University of Texas Health Center at Tyler, Tyler, TX, p. A671

HEGER, Jim, Director Human Resources, Citizens Medical Center, Victoria, TX, p. A672

HEGGEM, M.D., Mark, Medical Director, Riverwood HealthCare Center, Aitkin, MN, p. A349

HEIDEN, Stacie, Chief Financial Officer, Innovis Health, Fargo, ND, p. A497

HEIDER, Lisa A., Vice President Finance, Community Memorial Hospital, Menomonee Falls, WI, p. A729

HEIDER, Susan, Vice President and Chief Information Officer, Regional West Medical Center, Scottsbluff, NE, p. A413

HEIDT, Robert, Director Information Systems, Pembina County Memorial Hospital and Wedgewood Manor, Cavalier, ND, p. A497

HEILSBERG, Jim
Chief Operating Officer and Chief Financial Officer, Whitman Hospital and Medical Center, Colfax, WA, p. A701
Chief Operating Officer and Chief Financial Officer, Whitman Hospital and Medical Center, Colfax, WA, p. A701

HEIMAN, Cathy, Senior Vice President Human Resources, Genesys Regional Medical Center, Grand Blanc, MI, p. A334

HEIMAN, Thomas, Assistant Vice President of Information Services, John T. Mather Memorial Hospital, Port Jefferson, NY, p. A469

HEIN, Joyce Grove, Administrator and Chief Executive Officer, Phelps Memorial Health Center, Holdrege, NE, p. A408

HEINE, M.D., David, Chief Medical Officer, Winneshiek Medical Center, Decorah, IA, p. A232

HEINRICH, Michael G., Vice President Finance, Mercy Hospital, Iowa City, IA, p. A235

HEINRICHS, CPA, Alice, Chief Financial Officer, Hamilton Hospital, Webster City, IA, p. A243

HEINZ, M.D., Stephen, President, Medicl Staff, Sky Ridge Medical Center, Lone Tree, CO, p. A108

HEINZMAN, Jerry, Senior Vice President and Chief Financial Officer, Sampson Regional Medical Center, Clinton, NC, p. A480

HEISE, Patrick B., Chief Executive Officer, Community Memorial Hospital, Staunton, IL, p. A208

HEISE, Teresa, Management Information Systems Coordinator, Pender Community Hospital, Pender, NE, p. A412

HEITHOLD, M.D., Daniel, Chief of Staff, Hutcheson Medical Center, Fort Oglethorpe, GA, p. A162

HEITZENRATER, James F., Administrator, Methodist Sugar Land Hospital, Sugar Land, TX, p. A668

HELLA, Timothy, Director Information Management, Otsego Memorial Hospital, Gaylord, MI, p. A334

HELLER, Lisa, Manager Human Resources and Payroll, Mercy Medical Center–New Hampton, New Hampton, IA, p. A238

HELLER, Lynn, Administrator and Chief Executive Officer, Muenster Memorial Hospital, Muenster, TX, p. A658

HELLER, Tom, Vice President Human Resources, Camden–Clark Memorial Hospital, Parkersburg, WV, p. A718

HELLERSTEDT, Wayne P., Chief Executive Officer, Helen Newberry Joy Hospital, Newberry, MI, p. A341

HELLSTERN, Anne, Associate Administrator and Chief Operating Officer, East Ohio Regional Hospital, Martins Ferry, OH, p. A517

HELM, Ben, Chief Financial Officer, Memorial Hospital of Texas County, Guymon, OK, p. A531

HELM, Richard, Chief Information Officer, Jellico Community Hospital, Jellico, TN, p. A608

HELMER, M.D., Lynn, Senior Vice President Medical Affairs, Riverview Medical Center, Red Bank, NJ, p. A435

HELMINIAK, Clare, Clinical Director, U. S. Public Health Service Indian Hospital, Parker, AZ, p. A33

HELMS, Candace, Director Information Services, Good Samaritan Medical Center, West Palm Beach, FL, p. A150

HELMS, Ella Raye, Administrator, Fisher County Hospital District, Rotan, TX, p. A662

HELMUTH, Robin, President Medical Staff, Hancock Memorial Hospital and Health Services, Greenfield, IN, p. A217

HELSEL, David S., M.D., Superintendent, Spring Grove Hospital Center, Baltimore, MD, p. A304

HELSINGER, Irene, Senior Vice President and Chief Human Resource Officer, St. Luke's Episcopal Hospital, Houston, TX, p. A647

HELTON, Stephanie, Director Health Information Management, Southwestern Memorial Hospital, Weatherford, OK, p. A541

HELWIG, Ann M.
Chief Executive Officer, Knoxville Area Community Hospital and Clinic, Knoxville, IA, p. A236
Chief Executive Officer, Knoxville Area Community Hospital and Clinic, Knoxville, IA, p. A236

HEMBREE, Don, Information Systems Director, Unicoi County Memorial Hospital, Erwin, TN, p. A606

HEMBREE, Greg, Chief Financial Officer, South Georgia Medical Center, Valdosta, GA, p. A171

HEMENES, Larry J., Chief Financial Officer, Georgetown Healthcare System, Georgetown, TX, p. A641

HEMEON, Frank, Vice President Financial Administration, Kaiser Sunnyside Medical Center, Clackamas, OR, p. A542

HEMETER, Donald, Administrator, Wayne General Hospital, Waynesboro, MS, p. A376

HEMKER, Robert
Chief Financial Officer, Palomar Medical Center, Escondido, CA, p. A59
Chief Financial Officer, Pomerado Hospital, Poway, CA, p. A82

HEMMING, Stuart, Chief Operating Officer, Portsmouth Regional Hospital, Portsmouth, NH, p. A423

HEMPEL, John, Director, Veterans Affairs Southern Nevada Healthcare System, North Las Vegas, NV, p. A418

HEMPHILL, M.D., Ross, Medical Director, North Austin Medical Center, Austin, TX, p. A623

HEMPLING, Randall, Chief Executive Officer, Barstow Community Hospital, Barstow, CA, p. A54

HEMSCHOOT, Ed, Director Information Systems, Montgomery Hospital Medical Center, Norristown, PA, p. A566

HENA, John, Chief Information Management, Veterans Affairs Medical Center, Albuquerque, NM, p. A441

HENCKEL, Susan, Chief Executive Officer, Orthopaedic Hospital of Wisconsin – Glendale, Glendale, WI, p. A726

HENDEL, Diana, PharmD, Administrator, Saddleback Memorial Medical Center – San Clemente Campus, San Clemente, CA, p. A86

HENDERSON, Bob, Vice President Human Resources, Gaston Memorial Hospital, Gastonia, NC, p. A483

HENDERSON, Carol, Vice President Human Resources, Scottsdale Healthcare–Shea, Scottsdale, AZ, p. A36

HENDERSON, David, Director Human Resources, Summersville Memorial Hospital, Summersville, WV, p. A720

HENDERSON, M.D., David K., Deputy Director Clinical Care, Warren G. Magnuson Clinical Center, National Institutes of Health, Bethesda, MD, p. A306

HENDERSON, Donald G., President and Chief Executive Officer, Jackson Hospital and Clinic, Montgomery, AL, p. A22

HENDERSON, Gary, Chief Information Resources Management Services, Veterans Affairs Medical Center, Huntington, WV, p. A716

HENDERSON, John, Administrator, Childress Regional Medical Center, Childress, TX, p. A628

HENDERSON, Kathy, Director Human Resources, Willow Crest Hospital, Miami, OK, p. A533

HENDERSON, Mark, Chief Information Officer, Memorial Hermann Baptist Beaumont Hospital, Beaumont, TX, p. A625

HENDERSON, R.N., Ph, Melody, Chief Operating Officer and Chief Nursing Officer, Golden Plains Community Hospital, Borger, TX, p. A626

HENDERSON, Pamela, Assistant Vice President, USA Children's and Women's Hospital, Mobile, AL, p. A21

HENDERSON, Sharon, Director Human Resources, Sequoia Hospital, Redwood City, CA, p. A83

HENDERSON, Steven L.
Administrator, Rice Medical Center, Eagle Lake, TX, p. A636
Chief Executive Officer, Rice Medical Center, Eagle Lake, TX, p. A636

HENDERSON, W. Perry, Administrator, East Texas Medical Center Pittsburg, Pittsburg, TX, p. A660

HENDRICK, Kirk, Director, Community Hospital, New Port Richey, FL, p. A139

HENDRICK, Patricia, Human Resources Director, Colleton Medical Center, Walterboro, SC, p. A593

HENDRICKS, M.D., Richard, Vice President Medical Affairs, St. Marys Hospital Medical Center, Madison, WI, p. A728

HENDRICKS, Vickie, Director Human Resources, Good Shepherd Healthcare System, Hermiston, OR, p. A544

HENDRICKSON, Craig L., Chief Operating Officer, Overlake Hospital Medical Center, Bellevue, WA, p. A700

HENELT, D.O., Ann, Chief of Staff, Allegan General Hospital, Allegan, MI, p. A327

HENINGER, Bev, Director Nursing, Kenmare Community Hospital, Kenmare, ND, p. A499

HENKE, Marcella V., Administrator and Chief Executive Officer, Jackson County Hospital District, Edna, TX, p. A636

HENKE, Mark, Chief Operating Officer, Winneshiek Medical Center, Decorah, IA, p. A232

HENKENIUS, Jim, Chief Financial Officer, Stewart Memorial Community Hospital, Lake City, IA, p. A237

HENLEY, George, Human Resources Director, HEALTHSOUTH Hospital of Terre Haute, Terre Haute, IN, p. A226

HENNEKEN, Maureen, Chief Executive Officer, Select Specialty Hospital–Little Rock, Little Rock, AR, p. A46

HENNESSEE, Debbie, Chief Financial Officer, Grandview Medical Center, Jasper, TN, p. A608

HENNESSEY, Ruth, Senior Vice President and Chief Operating Officer, St. Francis Hospital, Roslyn, NY, p. A471

HENNIGAN, M.D., Michael, Medical Director, HEALTHSOUTH Emerald Coast Rehabilitation Hospital, Panama City, FL, p. A142

HENNING, Charles, Program Director Business, Veterans Affairs Medical Center, Kansas City, MO, p. A385

HENOCH, M.D., Malcolm S.
Chief Medical Officer, Oakwood Heritage Hospital, Taylor, MI, p. A346
Chief Medical Officer, Oakwood Hospital and Medical Center–Dearborn, Dearborn, MI, p. A330

HENRI, William, Executive Director, South Beach Psychiatric Center, New York, NY, p. A465

HENRIKSON, Mary, Chief Operating Officer, Sharp Mary Birch Hospital for Women, San Diego, CA, p. A87

HENRY, David, President and Chief Executive Officer, Northern Montana Hospital, Havre, MT, p. A399

HENRY, Debbie, Vice President Financial Services, North Arkansas Regional Medical Center, Harrison, AR, p. A44

HENRY, Elizabeth, Mission and Quality Coordinator, Marcum and Wallace Memorial Hospital, Irvine, KY, p. A266

HENRY, Heather, Information Systems Manager, Hammond–Henry Hospital, Geneseo, IL, p. A195

HENRY Jr, Jake, President and Chief Executive Officer, Saint Francis Health System, Tulsa, OK, p. B95

HENRY, Sr, FACH, John D., Chief Operating Officer, Grady Memorial Hospital, Atlanta, GA, p. A154

HENRY, M.D., Lloyd N., Medical Director, Governor Juan F. Louis Hospital, Christiansted, VI, p. A749

HENRY, Peter P., CHE, Director, Veterans Affairs Black Hills Health Care System, Fort Meade, SD, p. A596

HENRY, Tim, Chief Financial Officer, Union General Hospital, Blairsville, GA, p. A156

HENSHAW, James P., Chief Executive Officer, Mineral Community Hospital, Superior, MT, p. A402

HENSHAW, Robert, Chief Financial Officer, Arkansas Valley Regional Medical Center, La Junta, CO, p. A107

HENSLEY, Connie, Acting Chief Operating Officer, Knox County Hospital, Barbourville, KY, p. A261

HENSLEY, Dena, Administrator, Yancey Community Medical Center, Burnsville, NC, p. A479

HENSLEY, Emery, Chief Financial Officer, Citrus Memorial Hospital, Inverness, FL, p. A131

HENSLEY, Kerry A., R.N., Vice President Operations, FirstHealth Montgomery Memorial Hospital, Troy, NC, p. A493

HENSON, Blair W., Administrator, Florala Memorial Hospital, Florala, AL, p. A18

HENSON, David L., Chief Executive Officer, Northeastern Nevada Regional Hospital, Elko, NV, p. A415

HENSON, John S., President, Baptist Regional Medical Center, Corbin, KY, p. A263

HENTON, Kathie, Information Management Manager, Sumner Regional Medical Center, Wellington, KS, p. A259

HENZE, Michael E., Chief Executive Officer, Lake Regional Health System, Osage Beach, MO, p. A388

HEPBURN, Margaret
President and Chief Executive Officer, Sierra Vista Regional Health Center, Sierra Vista, AZ, p. A37
President, St. Dominic's Hospital, Manteca, CA, p. A74

HEPLER, Mark, Chief Financial Officer, Paul Oliver Memorial Hospital, Frankfort, MI, p. A333

HERBEK, Gary J., Chief Operating Officer, Prince William Hospital, Manassas, VA, p. A691

HERBERT, Annie, Chief Human Resources Management Services, Richard L. Roudebush Veterans Affairs Medical Center, Indianapolis, IN, p. A218

HERBERT, M.D., Daniel, Medical Administrative Officer, Millinocket Regional Hospital, Millinocket, ME, p. A299

HERBERT, M.D., Peter N., Senior Vice President Medical Affairs and Chief of Staff, Yale–New Haven Hospital, New Haven, CT, p. A115

HERBERT, D.O., Richard, Senior Vice President and Medical Director, William Beaumont Hospital–Troy, Troy, MI, p. A347

HERBST, Gary, Senior Vice President and Chief Financial Officer, Kaweah Delta Health Care District, Visalia, CA, p. A98

HERBST, Laurel, Vice President, Medical Affairs, San Diego Hospice & Palliative Care, San Diego, CA, p. A87

HERDENER, Tony, Vice President Systems and Finance, Northeast Georgia Medical Center, Gainesville, GA, p. A163

HERGERT, Richard, Chief Information Officer, Loma Linda University Medical Center, Loma Linda, CA, p. A68

HERIOT, James H., Chief Medical Staff, Scott Medical Center, Scott AFB, IL, p. A207

HERMAN, John W., Chief Administrative Officer, Methodist Hospital, Saint Louis Park, MN, p. A361

HERMAN, M.D., Joseph, Chief of Staff, Veterans Affairs Medical Center, Marion, IL, p. A200

HERMAN, Linda, Vice President and Chief Financial Officer, Saint Mary's Regional Medical Center, Reno, NV, p. A418

HERMANS, Louis H.
Vice President Information Systems, JFK Johnson Rehabilitation Institute, Edison, NJ, p. A428
Vice President Information Systems, JFK Medical Center, Edison, NJ, p. A428
Vice President Information Systems and Chief Information Officer, Muhlenberg Regional Medical Center, North Plainfield, NJ, p. A433

HERMANSON, Patrick M., FACHE, President and Chief Executive Officer, Portneuf Medical Center, Pocatello, ID, p. A181

HERMISTON, Jennet, Medical Director, Providence Seward Medical Center, Seward, AK, p. A28

HERMONSTYNE, Dennis, Interim Director Management Information Systems, Howard University Hospital, Washington, DC, p. A121

HERMSEN, Kevin, Prioress, Missionary Benedictine Sisters American Province, Norfolk, NE, p. B76

HERN, Warren, Executive Vice President and Chief Financial Officer, Park Ridge Hospital, Rochester, NY, p. A471

HERNANDEZ, M.D., Ana, Chief of Staff, DeSoto Memorial Hospital, Arcadia, FL, p. A123

HERNANDEZ, Angel, Information Systems Coordinator, University Hospital, San Juan, PR, p. A748

HERNANDEZ Jr, George B., President and Chief Executive Officer, University Health System, San Antonio, TX, p. A666

HERNANDEZ, Hank, Chief Executive Officer, Las Palmas Medical Center, El Paso, TX, p. A637

HERNANDEZ, Leonard, Chief Executive Officer, Morton County Health System, Elkhart, KS, p. A246

HERNANDEZ, Luis, Chief Executive Officer, St. John's Episcopal Hospital–South Shore, New York, NY, p. A465

HERNANDEZ, Luz Maria, Director Human Resources, I. Gonzalez Martinez Oncologic Hospital, Hato Rey, PR, p. A747

HERNANDEZ, Pablo, M.D., Administrator, Wyoming State Hospital, Evanston, WY, p. A740

HERNANDEZ, Sonia E Malave, Associate Administrator, Cardiovascular Center of Puerto Rico and the Caribbean, San Juan, PR, p. A746

HERNANDEZ–KEEBLE, Sonia
Superintendent, Rio Grande State Center, Harlingen, TX, p. A643
Superintendent, South Texas Health Care System, Harlingen, TX, p. A643

HERON, Thomas, Chief Financial Officer, Marian Community Hospital, Carbondale, PA, p. A554

HERR, Sandra, Administrator Human Resources, Banner Good Samaritan Medical Center, Phoenix, AZ, p. A33

HERRELL, Janet M., Chief Executive Officer, Moundview Memorial Hospital & Clinics, Friendship, WI, p. A726

HERRERA, Jocelyn, Director Human Resources, Whittier Hospital Medical Center, Whittier, CA, p. A99

HERRERO, M.D., Frank, Director Medical Affairs and Medical Staff, Halifax Fish Community Health, Daytona Beach, FL, p. A127

HERRICK, Robert, Chief Executive Officer, Robert H. Ballard Rehabilitation Hospital, San Bernardino, CA, p. A86

HERRICK, Stephen M., Ph.D., Acting Director, Piedmont Geriatric Hospital, Burkeville, VA, p. A686

HERRIN, Billy, Information Technology Director, Marshall Medical Center North, Guntersville, AL, p. A19

HERRIN, M.D., Tom, Medical Director, St. Dominic–Jackson Memorial Hospital, Jackson, MS, p. A371

HERRING, Jim, Vice President Human Resources, Children's Medical Center of Dallas, Dallas, TX, p. A632

HERRING, M.D., John A., Chief of Staff, Texas Scottish Rite Hospital for Children, Dallas, TX, p. A634

HERRING, Michael S., Administrator, Samuel Simmonds Memorial Hospital, Barrow, AK, p. A26

HERRING, M.D., Randy, Chief of Staff, Coon Memorial Hospital and Home, Dalhart, TX, p. A631

HERRINGTON, Bruce, Chief Medical Officer, Louis Smith Memorial Hospital, Lakeland, GA, p. A164

HERRMANN, Lee, Chief Information Officer, Washington Township Health Care District, Fremont, CA, p. A61

HERRMANN, Tim, Administrator, Cottage Grove Community Hospital, Cottage Grove, OR, p. A543

HERROLD, Susan, Commanding Officer, Naval Hospital, Oak Harbor, WA, p. A704

HERRON, John M., Administrator, Cobb Memorial Hospital, Royston, GA, p. A168

HERRON, Kathy, Interim Chief Financial Officer, St. John Detroit Riverview Hospital – Northeast Campus, Detroit, MI, p. A332

HERRON, Thomas L., FACHE, President and Chief Executive Officer, Largo Medical Center, Largo, FL, p. A134

HERSCHER, M.D., Mark, Chief of Staff, Mercy Medical Center, Roseburg, OR, p. A548

HERSEY, Robert, Chief Financial Officer, Northeastern Vermont Regional Hospital, Saint Johnsbury, VT, p. A683

HERTZAK, Peter, M.D., Administrator, Doctors Hospital of Slidell, Slidell, LA, p. A293

HERTZLER, Barbara, Chief Operating Officer, St. Joseph Mercy Oakland, Pontiac, MI, p. A343

HERWALDT, Debra J., Chief Financial Officer, Los Robles Hospital and Medical Center, Thousand Oaks, CA, p. A95

HERWIG, Karen, Director Human Resources, Ashland Community Hospital, Ashland, OR, p. A542

HERZBERG, Deborah
Chief Operating Officer, Clarinda Regional Health Center, Clarinda, IA, p. A230
Chief Operating Officer, Clarinda Regional Health Center, Clarinda, IA, p. A230

HERZBERG, Joseph W., Vice President Human Resources, Piedmont Hospital, Atlanta, GA, p. A154

HERZIG, Dennis G.
Director Finance, St. Joseph's Hospital, Breese, IL, p. A185
Chief Financial Officer, St. Joseph's Hospital, Breese, IL, p. A185

HERZOG, M.D., Alfred, Vice President, Medical Affairs, Hartford Hospital, Hartford, CT, p. A113

HERZOG, Ph.D., Jean, Executive Vice President and Chief Operating Officer, The Institute for Rehabilitation and Research, Houston, TX, p. A648

HERZOG, Mark P., President and Chief Executive Officer, Holy Family Memorial Medical Center, Manitowoc, WI, p. A729

HERZOG, Paul F., Chief Executive Officer, Memorial Medical Center, Las Cruces, NM, p. A443

HESS, Bob, Chief Information Officer, Bonner General Hospital, Sandpoint, ID, p. A181

HESS, Carolyn K., R.N., Administrator, Smith County Memorial Hospital, Smith Center, KS, p. A257

HESS, Steve, Chief Information Officer, Christiana Care Health System, Wilmington, DE, p. A120

HESS, Steven, Director of Information Systems, Hendry Regional Medical Center, Clewiston, FL, p. A126

HESSELTINE, Wendell, President and Chief Executive Officer, Tillamook County General Hospital, Tillamook, OR, p. A549

HESSING, M.D., Jeffrey, Medical Director, HEALTHSOUTH Treasure Valley Hospital, Boise, ID, p. A177

HESTER, Forrest G., President and Chief Executive Officer, Abraham Lincoln Memorial Hospital, Lincoln, IL, p. A199

HESTER, John C., Chief Financial Officer, Coffeyville Regional Medical Center, Coffeyville, KS, p. A245

HESTER, Julie A., Administrator, Mercy Jeannette Hospital, Jeannette, PA, p. A561

HESTER, Sharon
Information Technology Site Manager, St. Rose Dominican Hospitals – Rose de Lima Campus, Henderson, NV, p. A416
Information Technology Site Manager, St. Rose Dominican Hospitals – Siena Campus, Henderson, NV, p. A416

HETLAGE, C. Kennon, Administrator, Memorial Hospital Miramar, Miramar, FL, p. A139

HETRICK, Jack G.
Director, Veterans Affairs Edward Hines, Jr. Hospital, Hines, IL, p. A197
Associate Director, Veterans Affairs Edward Hines, Jr. Hospital, Hines, IL, p. A197

HETRICK, Robert G., Chief Financial Officer, Northern Hospital of Surry County, Mount Airy, NC, p. A488

HETTENBACH, Robert T., Executive Director, North Shore University Hospital–Forest Hills, New York, NY, p. A464

HETTINGER, Jeanne, Chief Financial Officer, Foote Health System, Jackson, MI, p. A337

HETU, Maureen, Administrator, Information Services, Our Lady of Lourdes Medical Center, Camden, NJ, p. A426

HETZ, Mark
Chief Information Officer, Rogue Valley Medical Center, Medford, OR, p. A546
Chief Information Officer, Three Rivers Community Hospital and Health Center, Grants Pass, OR, p. A544

HEUBLEIN, Susan P., Associate Director for Financial Services, Veterans Affairs Medical Center, Portland, OR, p. A548

HEURING, Ron, Director Information Systems, Perry County Memorial Hospital, Perryville, MO, p. A389

HEUSER, Keith E., Chief Executive Officer, Clarinda Regional Health Center, Clarinda, IA, p. A230

HEWIT, Craig, Executive Partner Information Management, MeritCare Medical Center, Fargo, ND, p. A497

HEXEM, Greg, Chief Financial Officer, Evanston Regional Hospital, Evanston, WY, p. A740

HEYBOER Jr, Lester, President and Chief Executive Officer, HealthSource Saginaw, Saginaw, MI, p. A344

HEYDEL, M. John, President and Chief Executive Officer, Self Regional Healthcare, Greenwood, SC, p. A589

HEYDON, Larry, Chief Financial Officer, Johnson Memorial Hospital, Franklin, IN, p. A216

HEYE, John E., Chief Financial Officer, Maine Medical Center, Portland, ME, p. A300

HEYWOD, Matt, Chief Operating Officer, Delray Medical Center, Delray Beach, FL, p. A127

HEYWORTH, M.D., Martin F., Chief of Staff, Veterans Affairs Medical Center, Philadelphia, PA, p. A570

HIATT, M. K., Administrator, Allendale County Hospital, Fairfax, SC, p. A587

HICCOX, Janelle, Director Human Resources, Lincoln Hospital, Davenport, WA, p. A702

HICKENLOOPER, Brian, Assistant Administrator Finance and Chief Financial Officer, Cassia Regional Medical Center, Burley, ID, p. A178

HICKERSON, Jerome, Director Information Systems, Mary Rutan Hospital, Bellefontaine, OH, p. A504

HICKEY, M.D., Michael, Medical Director, Gerald Champion Regional Medical Center, Alamogordo, NM, p. A440

HICKMAN, Darrell, Director Information Services, AnMED Health Medical Center, Anderson, SC, p. A583

HICKMAN, Michael, Chief Information Resource Management, Veterans Affairs Medical Center, Cleveland, OH, p. A509

HICKS, Albert, Director, Methodist Hospital of Southern California, Arcadia, CA, p. A53

HICKS, M.D., Charles, Chief of Staff, Chicot Memorial Hospital, Lake Village, AR, p. A46

HICKS, Iris, Director of Human Resources and Education, Baptist St. Anthony Health System, Amarillo, TX, p. A621

HICKS, Joan, Interim Chief Information Officer, University of Alabama Hospital, Birmingham, AL, p. A15

HICKS, Joe, Executive Director, Kimball Medical Center, Lakewood, NJ, p. A430

HICKS, John D., FACHE, President and Chief Executive Officer, Baptist St. Anthony Health System, Amarillo, TX, p. A621

HICKS, John R., President and Chief Executive Officer, Platte Valley Medical Center, Brighton, CO, p. A101

HICKS, Kevin J., Chief Executive Officer, Overland Park Regional Medical Center, Overland Park, KS, p. A254

HICKS, Michael, Director Information Systems, Beverly Hospital, Beverly, MA, p. A312

HICKS, Michael C., Administrator, St. Mary's Jefferson Memorial Hospital, Jefferson City, TN, p. A608

HICKS, Susan, Chief Operating Officer, Sky Ridge Medical Center, Lone Tree, CO, p. A108

HICKS, Terri, Chief Operating Officer and Chief Financial Officer, P & S Surgical Hospital, Monroe, LA, p. A287

HICKS, Tommy L., Administrator, Ray County Memorial Hospital, Richmond, MO, p. A389

HICKS, M.D., W E., Chief Medical Staff, Osceola Community Hospital, Sibley, IA, p. A241

HICKSON, Stan, Chief Operating Officer, Montgomery Regional Medical Center, Blacksburg, VA, p. A686

HIEB, Dotty, Human Resource Director, Mid Dakota Medical Center, Chamberlain, SD, p. A594

HIERS, Mitch, Director Information Services, Colquitt Regional Medical Center, Moultrie, GA, p. A166

HIERS, Susan, Director of Human Resources, Bamberg County Memorial Hospital and Nursing Center, Bamberg, SC, p. A583

HIGA, Darryl, Chief Information Officer, Central Washington Hospital, Wenatchee, WA, p. A711

HIGDON, Kevin, Vice President Finance, Elkhart General Hospital, Elkhart, IN, p. A214

HIGGINBOTHAM, Danny L.
Chief Financial Officer, Woods Memorial Hospital District, Etowah, TN, p. A606
Chief Financial Officer, Woods Memorial Hospital District, Etowah, TN, p. A606

HIGGINBOTHAM, G. Douglas, Executive Director, South Central Regional Medical Center, Laurel, MS, p. A372

HIGGINS, John, Chief Financial Officer, St. Peter's Hospital, Helena, MT, p. A399

HIGGINS, Kristi, Vice President for Human Resources, Legal and Compliance Services, Goshen General Hospital, Goshen, IN, p. A216

HIGGINS, Larry, Vice President of Human Resources, King's Daughters Medical Center, Ashland, KY, p. A261

HIGGINS, Laura, Chief of Staff, Fort Sanders–Sevier Medical Center, Sevierville, TN, p. A617

HIGGINS, Myron, Director Operations, Mercer County Hospital, Aledo, IL, p. A183

HIGGINS, Patrick, Director Human Resources, North Star Behavioral Health System, Anchorage, AK, p. A26

HIGGINS, Sheila, Interim Director, Newton Medical Center, Covington, GA, p. A159

HIGGINS–BOWERS, Shirley, Vice President Human Resources, Muhlenberg Regional Medical Center, North Plainfield, NJ, p. A433

HIGH, Kim, Controller, Baptist Memorial Hospital–Union County, New Albany, MS, p. A374

HIGHBAUGH, M.D., Michael, Medical Director, Baylor Specialty Hospital, Dallas, TX, p. A632

HIGHSMITH, C. Cameron, President and Chief Executive Officer, St. Luke's Hospital, Columbus, NC, p. A480

HIGHTOWER, George W., CHE, President and Chief Executive Officer, St. Francis Specialty Hospital, Monroe, LA, p. A287

HIGHTOWER, Thomas, Vice President Operations, Grays Harbor Community Hospital, Aberdeen, WA, p. A700

HILAL, M.D., Marwan, Chief of Staff, UHHS Bedford Medical Center, Bedford, OH, p. A503

HILAMAN, M.D., Brad L., Chief of Staff, J. Arthur Dosher Memorial Hospital, Southport, NC, p. A492

HILBURN, Diana, Vice President Information Management Services, Via Christi Regional Medical Center, Wichita, KS, p. A259

HILDWEIN, Robin, Chief Information Officer, Boca Raton Community Hospital, Boca Raton, FL, p. A124

HILES, Georgette, Accountant, Mark Reed Hospital, McCleary, WA, p. A704

HILL, C. David, Chief Executive Officer, Integris Marshall County Medical Center, Madill, OK, p. A533

HILL, Cheryl,Sacred Heart Rehabilitation Institute, Milwaukee, WI, p. A731

HILL, Deborah A., R.N., Chief Executive Officer, Summersville Memorial Hospital, Summersville, WV, p. A720

HILL, Dorothy E., Chief Executive Officer and Chief Nursing Officer, Acadia Hospital, Bangor, ME, p. A296

HILL, M.D., Douglas, Medical Director, Cascade Medical Center, Cascade, ID, p. A178

HILL, Dwight, Vice President Human Resources, Northside Hospital, Atlanta, GA, p. A154

HILL, Herbert, Director, Human Resources, Adventist Medical Center, Portland, OR, p. A547

HILL, Jackie, Manager Finance, Children's Hospital of Michigan, Detroit, MI, p. A331

HILL, James M., Administrator, Milwaukee County Behavioral Health Division, Milwaukee, WI, p. A731

HILL, James P., Executive Vice President, Administrative Services, Resurrection Medical Center, Chicago, IL, p. A189

HILL, Jeff, Chief Executive Officer, Galena–Stauss Hospital and Healthcare Center, Galena, IL, p. A195

HILL, Joe, Director, Human Resources, StoneCrest Medical Center, Smyrna, TN, p. A618

HILL, John, Vice President and Chief Operating Officer, Medical City Dallas Hospital, Dallas, TX, p. A633

HILL, Kent D., Director, Veterans Affairs Medical Center, Kansas City, MO, p. A385

HILL, Ned, Administrator, Sanpete Valley Hospital, Mount Pleasant, UT, p. A677

HILL, Robert B.
   President and Chief Executive Officer, Bethesda Memorial Hospital, Boynton Beach, FL, p. A124
   President and Chief Executive Officer, Bethesda Memorial Hospital, Boynton Beach, FL, p. A124

HILL, Scott H., Chief Operating Officer, Northern Virginia Community Hospital, Arlington, VA, p. A685

HILL, Steve
   Chief Information Officer, Wellmont Bristol Regional Medical Center, Bristol, TN, p. A602
   Chief Information Officer, Wellmont Holston Valley Medical Center, Kingsport, TN, p. A609

HILL, Steven, Vice President Finance, University of Minnesota Medical Center, Minneapolis, MN, p. A357

HILL, Stuart, Vice President and Treasurer, White County Medical Center, Searcy, AR, p. A50

HILL, Sue, Director Finance, St. Vincent Memorial Hospital, Taylorville, IL, p. A209

HILL, Susan, Director Human Resources, East Texas Medical Center Clarksville, Clarksville, TX, p. A628

HILL, Terri L., Administrator, West Central Community Hospital, Clinton, IN, p. A213

HILL, Timothy E., President and Chief Executive Officer, North Arkansas Regional Medical Center, Harrison, AR, p. A44

HILL–DAVIS, Nancy L., Chief Human Resources Officer, Mercy Hospital and Medical Center, Chicago, IL, p. A188

HILLBOM, Richard, Division President, Oakwood Heritage Hospital, Taylor, MI, p. A346

HILLEBRAND, Jeffrey H., Chief Operating Officer, Evanston Northwestern Healthcare, Evanston, IL, p. A194

HILLENMEYER, John, President and Chief Executive Officer, Orlando Regional Healthcare, Orlando, FL, p. B82

HILLIARD, D.O., David J., Chief of Staff, Barnesville Hospital Association, Barnesville, OH, p. A503

HILLIARD, John, Vice President Information Systems, Piedmont Hospital, Atlanta, GA, p. A154

HILLIS, David W., President and Chief Executive Officer, Adcare Hospital of Worcester, Worcester, MA, p. A325

HILMO, Betty, Director Human Resources, Community Medical Center, Missoula, MT, p. A400

HILMOE, Eric, Chief Executive Officer, Canton–Inwood Memorial Hospital, Canton, SD, p. A594

HILT, Monica, Assistant Vice President Quality Improvement and Information Services, Sacred Heart–St. Mary's Hospitals, Rhinelander, WI, p. A734

HILTON, Dave, Director Financial Services, Providence Portland Medical Center, Portland, OR, p. A547

HILTON, Lois, Director Human Resources, DeSoto Memorial Hospital, Arcadia, FL, p. A123

HILTON, Neil, Chief Executive Officer, Brown County Hospital, Ainsworth, NE, p. A404

HILTON, Richard G., Associate Administrator and Chief Financial Officer, Oktibbeha County Hospital, Starkville, MS, p. A376

HILTON, Shirley, Budget Analyst, Cherokee Indian Hospital Authority, Cherokee, NC, p. A480

HILTON–SIEBERT, Stephanie, Chief Operating Officer, Salem Township Hospital, Salem, IL, p. A207

HILTUNEN, Terrie, Director Information Systems, Phoenixville Hospital, Phoenixville, PA, p. A571

HIME, Judy, Director Human Resources, Pathways of Tennessee, Jackson, TN, p. A608

HINA, John, Information Technology Services Line Manager, Veterans Affairs Medical Center, Tomah, WI, p. A736

HINCH, Nick, Chief Financial Officer, Northern Rockies Medical Center, Cut Bank, MT, p. A397

HINCHEY, Paul P.
   President and Chief Executive Officer, St. Joseph's/Candler, Candler Hospital, Savannah, GA, p. A169
   President and Chief Executive Officer, St. Joseph's/Candler, St. Joseph's Hospital, Savannah, GA, p. A169
   President and Chief Executive Officer, St. Joseph's/Candler, Candler Hospital, Savannah, GA, p. A169

HINDS, Bob, Executive Director, Bradford Health Services at Huntsville, Madison, AL, p. A21

HINDS, Diane, Human Resources Director, East Texas Medical Center–Quitman, Quitman, TX, p. A662

HINDS, Rick, Vice President and Chief Financial Officer, Fort Hamilton Hospital, Hamilton, OH, p. A515

HINDT, Ron, Chief Information Officer, St. Alexius Medical Center, Bismarck, ND, p. A496

HINER Jr, Calvin A., Administrator, Tri–County Area Hospital, Lexington, NE, p. A408

HINES, Frederick W., President, Southwest Mental Health Center, San Antonio, TX, p. A665

HINES, James
   Chief Financial Officer, East Texas Medical Center Clarksville, Clarksville, TX, p. A628
   Chief Financial Officer, East Texas Medical Center Clarksville, Clarksville, TX, p. A628

HINES, Ron, Information Technology Director, Valley View Hospital, Glenwood Springs, CO, p. A106

HINGTGEN, Tim, Chief Executive Officer and Managing Director, Summerlin Hospital Medical Center, Las Vegas, NV, p. A417

HINKLE, David, Vice President and Chief Information Officer, Nash Health Care Systems, Rocky Mount, NC, p. A490

HINKLE, M.D., John, President Medical Staff, Methodist Charlton Medical Center, Dallas, TX, p. A633

HINNER, William J., Vice President Fiscal Services and Chief Financial Officer, Saint Michael's Hospital, Stevens Point, WI, p. A736

HINO, Raymond T., Chief Executive Officer, Tehachapi Valley Healthcare District, Tehachapi, CA, p. A95

HINRICHS, James, Vice President and Chief Financial Officer, Shawnee Mission Medical Center, Shawnee Mission, KS, p. A257

HINSDALE, Laurence C., President and Chief Executive Officer, NorthEast Medical Center, Concord, NC, p. A481

HINSHAW, M.D., Steve, Chief of Staff, Jefferson County Hospital, Waurika, OK, p. A541

HINSON, Roy M., FACHE, President and Chief Executive Officer, Stanly Memorial Hospital, Albemarle, NC, p. A477

HINTON, James H., President and Chief Executive Officer, Presbyterian Healthcare Services, Albuquerque, NM, p. B84

HINTZE, M.D., Paul, Vice President Medical Affairs, St. John's Mercy Medical Center, Saint Louis, MO, p. A392

HINTZE, Sheila, Manager, Riverview Medical Center, Red Bank, NJ, p. A435

HIOTT, Jimmy, Chief Financial Officer, Colleton Medical Center, Walterboro, SC, p. A593

HIPPE, Jeanne, Director, St. Francis Health Center, Topeka, KS, p. A258

HIRE, Stan, Vice President Human Resources, Fisher–Titus Medical Center, Norwalk, OH, p. A520

HIRKALER, Kim, Director of Human Resources, Bon Secours Community Hospital, Port Jervis, NY, p. A470

HIRSCH, Jeffrey D., President and Chief Executive Officer, Orange Regional Medical Center, Middletown, NY, p. A457

HIRSCH, John D., M.D., President and Chief Executive Officer, Forest Park Hospital, Saint Louis, MO, p. A391

HIRSCH, Leslie D., President and Chief Executive Officer, Touro Infirmary, New Orleans, LA, p. A290

HIRSCH, Ted W., Chief Executive Officer, Kalispell Regional Medical Center, Kalispell, MT, p. A400

HIRSCHMAN, Debra, Chief Operating Officer, Patient Support Services, Southern Arizona Veterans Affairs Health Care System, Tucson, AZ, p. A38

HIRSHBERG, Mark I., Chief Operating Officer, Bothwell Regional Health Center, Sedalia, MO, p. A393

HIRT, Joe, Chief Financial Officer, Memorial Hospitals Association, Modesto, CA, p. A76

HISEY, D.O., Commie, Chief of Staff, Memorial Hospital, Gonzales, TX, p. A642

HITCH, Walter, Chief Fiscal, Veterans Affairs Medical Center, Augusta, GA, p. A155

HITCHINGS Jr, Roy A., FACHE, President and Chief Executive Officer, Penobscot Bay Medical Center, Rockport, ME, p. A300

HITE, Roger, Chief Operating Officer, Dominican Hospital, Santa Cruz, CA, p. A92

HITT, Patricia A., Associate Director, Veterans Affairs Medical Center, Grand Junction, CO, p. A106

HITTLE, Karl D., Chief Operating Officer, McKenna Memorial Hospital, New Braunfels, TX, p. A658

HITTNER, Kathleen C., M.D., President and Chief Executive Officer, Miriam Hospital, Providence, RI, p. A581

HITZLER, Ronald R., Administrator, Shriners Hospitals for Children, Shriners Burns Hospital, Cincinnati, Cincinnati, OH, p. A507

HITZMAN, M.D., Jonathan, Chief of Staff, St. Anthony Hospital, Pendleton, OR, p. A547

HIXSON, Lynne M., Manager Human Resources, Fulton County Medical Center, McConnellsburg, PA, p. A564

HLAVENKA, Richard, Director Management Information Systems, Jamaica Hospital Medical Center, New York, NY, p. A460

HNATOW, M.D., David, President Medical and Dental Staff, University Health System, San Antonio, TX, p. A666

HO, Stuart, President and Chief Executive Officer, Rehabilitation Hospital of the Pacific, Honolulu, HI, p. A174

HO, Sylvia, Director Information Services, Grady Memorial Hospital, Chickasha, OK, p. A528

HOBACK, Kim, Supervisor Information Systems, Athens–Limestone Hospital, Athens, AL, p. A13

HOBAN, Douglas, Chief Financial Officer, St. John's Hospital – Cassville, Cassville, MO, p. A380

HOBBS, Ed, Director Information Services, DeKalb Memorial Hospital, Auburn, IN, p. A211

HOBBS, Jim R.
President and Chief Executive Officer, Cascade Healthcare Community, Bend, OR, p. B22
President and Chief Executive Officer, St. Charles Medical Center – Bend, Bend, OR, p. A542
President and Chief Executive Officer, St. Charles Medical Center – Redmond, Redmond, OR, p. A548

HOBBS, Tommy, Chief Executive Officer, Ripon Medical Center, Ripon, WI, p. A735

HOBBS, Xydell, Director, Ogden Regional Medical Center, Ogden, UT, p. A678

HOBSON, Jim, Chief Operating Officer, Phoebe Putney Memorial Hospital, Albany, GA, p. A152

HOBSON–PANICO, Paul, Chief Information Officer, North Colorado Medical Center, Greeley, CO, p. A106

HOCE, N. Kristopher
President and Chief Executive Officer, Forum Health, Youngstown, OH, p. B45
President and Chief Executive Officer, Forum Health Trumbull Memorial Hospital, Warren, OH, p. A524
President and Chief Executive Officer, Western Reserve Care System, Youngstown, OH, p. A526

HOCH, Marcia, Interim Chief Executive Officer, Arbour H. R. I. Hospital, Brookline, MA, p. A315

HOCHBERG, Ginny, Chief Executive Officer and Clinical Administrator, Curry General Hospital, Gold Beach, OR, p. A544

HOCKADAY, Marilyn, Chief Financial Officer, Howard Memorial Hospital, Nashville, AR, p. A48

HOCKING, Dale E.
Chief Financial Officer, Leesburg Regional Medical Center, Leesburg, FL, p. A135
Chief Financial Officer, The Villages Regional Hospital, The Villages, FL, p. A149

HOCUM, Timothy, Chief Financial Officer, Providence Kodiak Island Medical Center, Kodiak, AK, p. A27

HODER, Marie, Director Information Systems, Tennessee Christian Medical Center, Madison, TN, p. A611

HODGE, Shalena, Administrator, Stonewall Memorial Hospital, Aspermont, TX, p. A622

HODGES, Audra, Human Resources Coordinator, Trigg County Hospital, Cadiz, KY, p. A262

HODGES, Dori, Director of Human Resources, HEALTHSOUTH Rehabilitation Hospital, Fort Worth, TX, p. A639

HODGES, M.D., James, Chief of Staff, Frye Regional Medical Center, Hickory, NC, p. A485

HODGES, Jay J., Chief Executive Officer, Northeast Medical Center, Bonham, TX, p. A626

HODGES, Joe, President, St. Anthony Hospital, Oklahoma City, OK, p. A536

HODGES, Leisha, Human Resources, Comanche Community Hospital, Comanche, TX, p. A629

HODGES, Teresa, Assistant Administrator, De Queen Regional Medical Center, De Queen, AR, p. A42

HODGES, Thomas, Executive Vice President Finance and Treasurer, Evanston Northwestern Healthcare, Evanston, IL, p. A194

HODGKINS, Linda, Chief Executive Officer, Kingwood Health Center, Kingwood, TX, p. A651

HODSON, Tom, Acting Chief Executive Officer, The Neurologic and Orthopedic Institute of Chicago, Chicago, IL, p. A191

HOE, Adele, Director Human Resources, Castle Medical Center, Kailua, HI, p. A174

HOEFLE, Brian, Chief Financial Officer, Navapache Regional Medical Center, Show Low, AZ, p. A36

HOEFT, Kathleen, Administrator and Chief Executive Officer, Ashley Medical Center, Ashley, ND, p. A496

HOELSCHER, Steve C., Chief Executive Officer, Polk Medical Center, Cedartown, GA, p. A157

HOERAUF, Robert, Chief Resources Management, DeWitt Army Community Hospital, Fort Belvoir, VA, p. A688

HOERNER, Nancie, Information Management Coordinator, Riverview Healthcare Association, Crookston, MN, p. A352

HOFER, Renee, Vice President Fiscal Services, St. Joseph's Hospital of Buckhannon, Buckhannon, WV, p. A714

HOFF, David L., Executive Director, Wayne Memorial Hospital, Honesdale, PA, p. A560

HOFF, Terry G., President, Trinity Health, Minot, ND, p. A499

HOFFA, Jeff, Chief Information Management Division, Evans U. S. Army Community Hospital, Fort Carson, CO, p. A105

HOFFART, Terry L., Administrator, Annie Jeffrey Memorial County Health Center, Osceola, NE, p. A412

HOFFERBER, Scott, Chief Operating Officer, University of California San Diego Medical Center, San Diego, CA, p. A88

HOFFMAN, Brad, Administrative Director, Shawnee Mission Medical Center, Shawnee Mission, KS, p. A257

HOFFMAN, M.D., Brian, Chief Medical Services, Veterans Affairs Boston Healthcare System, Boston, MA, p. A315

HOFFMAN, Charles
Chief Financial Officer, Saint Joseph Mercy Health System, Ypsilanti, MI, p. A348
Vice President Financial Services and Chief Financial Officer, Saint Joseph Mercy Livingston Hospital, Howell, MI, p. A336

HOFFMAN, Chris, Chief Operating Officer, Highlands Regional Medical Center, Prestonsburg, KY, p. A273

HOFFMAN, M.D., Daniel, Administrative Medical Director, Good Samaritan Regional Health Center, Mount Vernon, IL, p. A202

HOFFMAN, M.D., David E., Chief of Staff, North Big Horn Hospital District, Lovell, WY, p. A741

HOFFMAN, Grant, Director Human Resources, Phoenixville Hospital, Phoenixville, PA, p. A571

HOFFMAN, Jerry, Chief Financial Officer, Platte Health Center/Avera Health, Platte, SD, p. A598

HOFFMAN, III, Joseph
Senior Vice President and Chief Financial Officer, Harford Memorial Hospital, Havre De Grace, MD, p. A308
Senior Vice President and Chief Financial Officer, Upper Chesapeake Medical Center, Bel Air, MD, p. A305

HOFFMAN, Mary
President and Senior Administrative Officer, Kenmore Mercy Hospital, Kenmore, NY, p. A455
Chief Financial Officer, St. Luke's Hospital, Jacksonville, FL, p. A132

HOFFMAN, Tom, Information Systems Manager, Wayne Memorial Hospital, Honesdale, PA, p. A560

HOFFMANN, Sally, Chief Executive Officer, Kindred Hospital Bay Area –Tampa, Tampa, FL, p. A148

HOFFOWER, James, Commanding Officer, Naval Hospital, Beaufort, SC, p. A584

HOFIUS, Chuck, Administrator, Perham Memorial Hospital and Home, Perham, MN, p. A359

HOFREUTER, Donald H., M.D., Administrator and Chief Executive Officer, Wheeling Hospital, Wheeling, WV, p. A721

HOFSTETTER, Peter A., Chief Executive Officer, Northwestern Medical Center, Saint Albans, VT, p. A683

HOGAN, Dan
Vice President Finance, Mercy Hospital Cadillac, Cadillac, MI, p. A329
Vice President Finance, Mercy Hospital Grayling, Grayling, MI, p. A335

HOGAN, Judith, Controller, Naval Hospital, Bremerton, WA, p. A701

HOGAN, Karen C., Administrator and Chief Executive Officer, San Diego County Psychiatric Hospital, San Diego, CA, p. A87

HOGAN, Robert, Chief Financial Officer, University of California San Diego Medical Center, San Diego, CA, p. A88

HOGAN, Ronald C., Chief Executive Officer, Georgia Regional Hospital at Atlanta, Decatur, GA, p. A160

HOGAN, Ronald E., Senior Vice President and Chief Financial Officer, St. Francis Medical Center, Monroe, LA, p. A287

HOGAN, Sean, Vice President and Chief Operating Officer, SSM DePaul Health Center, Saint Louis, MO, p. A391

HOGAN, Timothy J., President, Riverview Medical Center, Red Bank, NJ, p. A435

HOGARTY, John F., Chief Financial Officer, Montgomery General Hospital, Olney, MD, p. A309

HOGSTROM, CPA, Harold P., Executive Vice President Finance and Chief Financial Officer, Hackensack University Medical Center, Hackensack, NJ, p. A429

HOHENBERGER, Arthur L., FACHE, President and Chief Executive Officer, Hillcrest Baptist Medical Center, Waco, TX, p. A672

HOHENBERGER, Joseph W., Chief Financial Officer, Mahaska Health Partnership, Oskaloosa, IA, p. A239

HOHN, David C., M.D., President and Chief Executive Officer, Roswell Park Cancer Institute, Buffalo, NY, p. A449

HOIDAL, David E.
Chief Executive Officer, UAB Health System, Birmingham, AL, p. B113
Chief Executive Officer, University of Alabama Hospital, Birmingham, AL, p. A15

HOJNACKI, Bruce, Chief Information Officer, Waccamaw Community Hospital, Murrells Inlet, SC, p. A590

HOKE, Angela D., Chief Financial Officer, Montgomery Regional Hospital, Blacksburg, VA, p. A686

HOLANCHOCK, Howard, Executive Director, Mid–Hudson Forensic Psychiatric Center, New Hampton, NY, p. A457

HOLBERT, Brandon, Director Information Systems, St. Joseph's Hospital, Parkersburg, WV, p. A718

HOLBROOK, M.D., Peter, Chief Medical Officer, Children's National Medical Center, Washington, DC, p. A121

HOLBROOK, Timothy, Vice President Human Resourc, Our Lady of Bellefonte Hospital, Ashland, KY, p. A261

HOLCOMB, Bertha, Director Human Resources, Fairview Hospital, Great Barrington, MA, p. A318

HOLCOMB, David M., President and Chief Executive Officer, Jennie Edmundson Memorial Hospital, Council Bluffs, IA, p. A231

HOLCOMB, M.D., Sheila, Medical Staff President, Floyd Valley Hospital/Avera Health, Le Mars, IA, p. A237

HOLDEN, James, Chief Financial Officer, Belmont Community Hospital, Bellaire, OH, p. A504

HOLDEN, Jay, Director Human Resources, William Beaumont Hospital–Royal Oak, Royal Oak, MI, p. A343

HOLDEN, Patricia, Chief Executive Officer, Sullivan County Community Hospital, Sullivan, IN, p. A225

HOLDEN, Peter J., President and Chief Executive Officer, Caritas Holy Family Hospital and Medical Center, Methuen, MA, p. A320

HOLDER, Harold C., Vice President Financial Services, Genesis Medical Center, Illini Campus, Silvis, IL, p. A208

HOLDERMAN, Clay, Chief Executive Officer, Bourbon Community Hospital, Paris, KY, p. A273

HOLDERMAN, Wanda, Chief Operating Officer, Doctors Medical Center, Modesto, CA, p. A76

HOLDSWORTH, Michael P., Vice President Finance and Chief Financial Officer, California Pacific Medical Center, San Francisco, CA, p. A88

HOLEKAMP, M.D., Nicholas, Medical Director, Ranken Jordan, Maryland Heights, MO, p. A387

HOLGUIN, Carol T., Chief Executive Officer, Kindred Hospital–Fort Worth, Fort Worth, TX, p. A640

HOLINER, M.D., Joel, Executive Medical Director, Green Oaks Hospital, Dallas, TX, p. A632

HOLIVER, John J., President, Caritas Good Samaritan Medical Center, Brockton, MA, p. A315

HOLL, Donald R., Chief Executive Officer, Miners' Colfax Medical Center, Raton, NM, p. A444

HOLLADAY, M.D., Clinton, Chief of Staff, Newton Medical Center, Covington, GA, p. A159

HOLLAND, Brad D., Chief Operating Officer, Woodland Heights Medical Center, Lufkin, TX, p. A655

HOLLAND, David, Vice President and Chief Information Officer, Genesys Regional Medical Center, Grand Blanc, MI, p. A334

HOLLAND, Helen, Chief Financial Officer, Van Buren County Hospital, Keosauqua, IA, p. A236

HOLLAND, Jeffrey S., Chief Executive Officer, West Houston Medical Center, Houston, TX, p. A649

HOLLAND, John F., Chief Executive Officer, North Fulton Regional Hospital, Roswell, GA, p. A168

HOLLAND, Joy, Chief Executive Officer, St. Elizabeths Hospital, Washington, DC, p. A122

HOLLAND, Kwi, Director Information Services, Knox Community Hospital, Mount Vernon, OH, p. A519

HOLLAND, Larry, Chief Financial Officer, Gulf Coast Medical Center, Biloxi, MS, p. A366

HOLLAND, Sharron, Director Financial Services, Baptist Memorial Hospital–Huntingdon, Huntingdon, TN, p. A607

HOLLEMAN, Ivan, Chief Financial Officer, Baxter Regional Medical Center, Mountain Home, AR, p. A48

HOLLIDAY, Jim, Chief Financial Officer, East Texas Medical Center Carthage, Carthage, TX, p. A628

HOLLIDAY, Michael T., Vice President Fiscal and Administrative Services, Van Wert County Hospital, Van Wert, OH, p. A523

HOLLINGER, Brad, Chairman and Chief Executive Officer, VIBRA Healthcare, Mechanicsburg, PA, p. B120

HOLLINGSWORTH, Barbara, Administrator and Chief Executive Officer, DeQuincy Memorial Hospital, DeQuincy, LA, p. A280

HOLLINGSWORTH, Carl, Chief Financial Officer, St. Luke's Wood River Medical Center, Ketchum, ID, p. A179

HOLLINGSWORTH, Karen, Chief Information Officer, Saint Mary's Medical Center, Saginaw, MI, p. A344

HOLLINGSWORTH, Sherri, Vice President Human Resources, Hoag Memorial Hospital Presbyterian, Newport Beach, CA, p. A78

HOLLINSWORTH, John, Executive Director, Ten Broeck Hospital, Louisville, KY, p. A270

HOLLON, Kim N., FACHE,
Executive Vice President, Operations, Methodist Charlton Medical Center, Dallas, TX, p. A633
Executive Vice President Operations, Methodist Dallas Medical Center, Dallas, TX, p. A633

HOLLOWAY, M.D., James, President Medical Staff, Northern Hills General Hospital, Deadwood, SD, p. A595

HOLLOWAY, Margaret, Administrator, HEALTHSOUTH Rehabilitation Hospital of Sarasota, Sarasota, FL, p. A146

HOLLOWAY, Mary Ann, Manager Human Resources, Hospital District Number 1 of Crawford County, Girard, KS, p. A247

HOLLOWELL, M.D., Melvin L., Vice President Medical Affairs, Sinai–Grace Hospital, Detroit, MI, p. A332

HOLLOWELL, Robert, Director Management Information Systems, Horizon Medical Center, Dickson, TN, p. A605

HOLMAN, William R., CHE, President and Chief Executive Officer, Baton Rouge General Medical Center, Baton Rouge, LA, p. A277

HOLMES, Alan D., Chief Executive Officer, Frio Regional Hospital, Pearsall, TX, p. A660

HOLMES, M.D., Brian, Chairman, Memorial Hospital, Abilene, KS, p. A244

HOLMES, Dave, Vice President Support Services, Hancock Memorial Hospital and Health Services, Greenfield, IN, p. A217

HOLMES Jr, James M., President and Chief Executive Officer, Rappahannock General Hospital, Kilmarnock, VA, p. A690

HOLMES, James R., President and Chief Executive Officer, Redlands Community Hospital, Redlands, CA, p. A83

HOLMES, Jim, Chief Information Officer, San Juan Regional Medical Center, Farmington, NM, p. A442

HOLMES, Mike, Chief Financial Officer, Cook Hospital and Convalescent Nursing Care Unit, Cook, MN, p. A351

HOLMES, William E., Chief Executive Officer, Littleton Regional Hospital, Littleton, NH, p. A422

HOLMGREN, Linda, Chief Operating Officer, Anne Arundel Medical Center, Annapolis, MD, p. A302

HOLMSTROM, Mark, Vice President Operations and Chief Operating Officer, Fort Sanders–Sevier Medical Center, Sevierville, TN, p. A617

HOLOM, Randall G., Chief Executive Officer, Frances Mahon Deaconess Hospital, Glasgow, MT, p. A398

HOLSINGER, M.D., Donald, Chief Medical Officer, Mt. Carmel Regional Medical Center, Pittsburg, KS, p. A255

HOLST, Ken, Chief Financial Officer, Borgess–Lee Memorial Hospital, Dowagiac, MI, p. A332

HOLSTEN, Jack W., Chief Financial Officer, Pitt County Memorial Hospital, Greenville, NC, p. A484

HOLSTIEN, Bruce E., Senior Vice President and Administrator, Sentara Norfolk General Hospital, Norfolk, VA, p. A693

HOLT, Annie, FACHE, Chief Executive Officer, Methodist Children's Hospital of South Texas, San Antonio, TX, p. A664

HOLT, Brian, Chief Executive Officer, Promise Specialty Hospital of Phoenix, Phoenix, AZ, p. A35

HOLT, Pat, Chief Information Officer, Hospital District Number 1 of Crawford County, Girard, KS, p. A247

HOLT, Thomas A., Chief Financial Officer, West Houston Medical Center, Houston, TX, p. A649

HOLTER, John A., Chief Executive Officer, Benchmark Behavioral Health Systems, Woods Cross, UT, p. A681

HOLTER, Lee H., Chief Financial Officer, Winslow Memorial Hospital, Winslow, AZ, p. A39

HOLTERMAN, M.D., Robert, Medical Director, Moses Ludington Hospital, Ticonderoga, NY, p. A474

HOLTSCLAW, Keith S., Chief Executive Officer, Spruce Pine Community Hospital, Spruce Pine, NC, p. A492

HOLTVOIGT, Donald, Director Human Resources, Blanchard Valley Health Association, Findlay, OH, p. A513

HOLTZ, Josephine B., R.N., Interim Administrator, Shriners Hospitals for Children, St. Louis, Saint Louis, MO, p. A391

HOLWAY, Mike, Administrator, Red Bay Hospital, Red Bay, AL, p. A23

HOLWERDA, Daniel L., President and Chief Executive Officer, Pine Rest Christian Mental Health Services, Grand Rapids, MI, p. A334

HOLYFIELD, Linda, Chief Executive Officer and Administrator, P & S Surgical Hospital, Monroe, LA, p. A287

HOLYOAK, Mark, Chief Clinical Officer, Ashley Valley Medical Center, Vernal, UT, p. A681

HOLZBERG, Harvey A., President and Chief Executive Officer, Robert Wood Johnson University Hospital, New Brunswick, NJ, p. A432

HOLZMANN, Bill, Director Human Resources, River Region Health System, Vicksburg, MS, p. A376

HOMAN, Cheryl, Administrative Director, Lima Memorial Health System, Lima, OH, p. A516

HOMYK, David A., Vice President Human Resources, Ellis Hospital, Schenectady, NY, p. A472

HONAINY, M.D., Hassan, President Medical Staff, Alleghany Regional Hospital, Low Moor, VA, p. A690

HONAKER, C. Ray, President and Chief Executive Officer, St. Thomas More Hospital, Canon City, CO, p. A102

HONAKER, Linda, Director Financial Services, Scripps Memorial Hospital–Encinitas, Encinitas, CA, p. A59

HONEA, M.D., Bert, Medical Director, McKee Medical Center, Loveland, CO, p. A108

HONEA, Bruce, Director Information Services, Christus Coushatta Health Care Center, Coushatta, LA, p. A279

HONELLS, John, Chief Information Officer, Mercy Hospital of Scranton, Scranton, PA, p. A575

HONER, Debi, Vice President Human Resources, Central Peninsula General Hospital, Soldotna, AK, p. A28

HONERBRINK, Dan, Chief Financial Officer, D. M. Cogdell Memorial Hospital, Snyder, TX, p. A667

HONEYCUTT, Steven, Chief Executive Officer, Lakeview Community Hospital, Eufaula, AL, p. A18

HONSTEAD, Mari, Human Resources Manager, Bob Wilson Memorial Grant County Hospital, Ulysses, KS, p. A258

HONTS, Gary, Chief Executive Officer, Community Hospital of Los Gatos, Los Gatos, CA, p. A74

HOOD, Fred B., Administrator, North Mississippi Medical Center–Pontotoc Hospital and Nursing Home, Pontotoc, MS, p. A374

HOOD, Kathy, Administrative Assistant, Union General Hospital, Blairsville, GA, p. A156

HOOD, M. Michelle, President and Chief Executive Officer, St. Vincent Healthcare, Billings, MT, p. A396

HOOFMAN, Kevin, Director Management Information, White County Medical Center, Searcy, AR, p. A50

HOOGENDOORN, Kari, Chief Financial Officer, Hegg Memorial Health Center/Avera Health, Rock Valley, IA, p. A240

HOOGESTRAAT, Tom, Superintendent, Glenwood Resource Center, Glenwood, IA, p. A234

HOOKFIN, Sherre P., Associate Administrator, Lallie Kemp Medical Center, Independence, LA, p. A282

HOOKS, Al, Senior Vice President and Chief Financial Officer, Nash Health Care Systems, Rocky Mount, NC, p. A490

HOOPER, Andy, Director, Human Resources, Skyline Medical Center, Nashville, TN, p. A615

HOOPER, Grady, Chief Executive Officer, Smithville Regional Hospital, Smithville, TX, p. A667

HOOPER, Helen, Director Human Resources, Southwestern Medical Center, Lawton, OK, p. A532

HOOPER, Ross, Chief Executive Officer, Crittenden Memorial Hospital, West Memphis, AR, p. A51

HOOPES, John L., Chief Executive Officer, Caribou Memorial Hospital and Living Center, Soda Springs, ID, p. A182

HOOSE, Gregory R., Chief Executive Officer, Straith Hospital for Special Surgery, Southfield, MI, p. A345

HOOVER, Alvin, CHE, Chief Executive Officer, Abbeville County Memorial Hospital, Abbeville, SC, p. A583

HOOVER, Craig, Chief Executive Officer, Kindred Hospital–Atlanta, Atlanta, GA, p. A154

HOOVER, Dennis, Vice President Human Resources, Port Huron Hospital, Port Huron, MI, p. A343

HOOVER, Garrett W., President and Chief Executive Officer, Nason Hospital, Roaring Spring, PA, p. A574

HOOVER, Jeremy, Chief Information Officer, Kiowa County Memorial Hospital, Greensburg, KS, p. A248

HOOVER, Randall L.
Chief Executive Officer, Palestine Regional Medical Center–East, Palestine, TX, p. A659
Chief Executive Officer, Palestine Regional Rehabilitation Center, Palestine, TX, p. A659

HOPE, Lisa R., Director, Human Resources, Muhlenberg Community Hospital, Greenville, KY, p. A265

HOPE, Steve, Vice President Corporate Services, Methodist Rehabilitation Center, Jackson, MS, p. A370

HOPKINS, Donald B., Administrator, Faith Community Hospital, Jacksboro, TX, p. A650

HOPKINS, James, Finance Officer, Tuba City Indian Medical Center, Tuba City, AZ, p. A37

HOPKINS, D.O., Ronald, Chief of Staff, Nor–Lea General Hospital, Lovington, NM, p. A443

HOPKINS, Wallace M., FACHE, Director, Veterans Affairs Medical Center, Bay Pines, FL, p. A123

HOPKINS, William, Director Finance, Charlotte Institute of Rehabilitation, Charlotte, NC, p. A480

HOPPE, M.D., Wayne, Chief Medical Officer, Kit Carson County Memorial Hospital, Burlington, CO, p. A101

HOPPER, Stefan, Chief Information Officer, Gateway Health System, Clarksville, TN, p. A604

HOPPER, Stephen R., President and Chief Executive Officer, McDonough District Hospital, Macomb, IL, p. A200

HOPSON, M.D., W Briggs, Clinical Medical Director, River Region Health System, Vicksburg, MS, p. A376

HORAN, Gary S., FACHE, President and Chief Executive Officer, Trinitas Hospital–Williamson Street Campus, Elizabeth, NJ, p. A428

HORGAN, Debbie, Director, La Palma Intercommunity Hospital, La Palma, CA, p. A66

HORLANDER, Fred, Vice President, Clark Memorial Hospital, Jeffersonville, IN, p. A219

HORN, Linda, Chief Executive Officer, Sutter Delta Medical Center, Antioch, CA, p. A52

HORN, Syndi, Director Information Systems, Memorial Hospital, Carthage, IL, p. A186

HORNBEAK, John E., FACHE, Chief Executive Officer, Methodist Hospital, San Antonio, TX, p. A664

HORNE, Beth, Controller, Preston Memorial Hospital, Kingwood, WV, p. A717

HORNE, M.D., Wallace J., Vice President Medical Affairs, Community Memorial Healthcenter, South Hill, VA, p. A697

HORNER, Bryan, Chief Operating Officer, Shannon Medical Center, San Angelo, TX, p. A663

HORNER, Cheryl, Data Processing Supervisor, Community Memorial Hospital, Staunton, IL, p. A208

HORNER, John M., Vice President and Chief Information Officer, Major Hospital, Shelbyville, IN, p. A225

HORNER, Lynn V., President and Chief Executive Officer, Dunlap Memorial Hospital, Orrville, OH, p. A520

HORNS, John E., President, Defiance Regional Medical Center, Defiance, OH, p. A512

HORNUNG, Kurt, Chief Information Officer, Oak Hill Hospital, Brooksville, FL, p. A125

HOROHO, Patricia, Commander, DeWitt Army Community Hospital, Fort Belvoir, VA, p. A688

HORRIGAN, M.D., Francis D., Medical Director, Noble Hospital, Westfield, MA, p. A325

HORRY, Malcolm, Director Medical Services, Naval Hospital, Jacksonville, FL, p. A132

HORSMAN, Sarah, ViceHuman Resources, Tacoma General Hospital, Tacoma, WA, p. A710

HORSTMANN, Debbie S., Director Human Resources, St. Francis Medical Center, Monroe, LA, p. A287

HORTON, M.D., Christopher, Chf of Staff, Rhea Medical Center, Dayton, TN, p. A605

HORTON, Holly, Director Human Resources, Pender Memorial Hospital, Burgaw, NC, p. A478

HORTON, Jason, Chief Financial Officer, Hamilton General Hospital, Hamilton, TX, p. A643

HORTON, Joseph R., Chief Executive Officer and Administrator, Primary Children's Medical Center, Salt Lake City, UT, p. A679

HORTON, Kenny, Director Information Systems, Walker Baptist Medical Center, Jasper, AL, p. A20

HORTON, Warren, Information and Technology Support Services Officer, Stuttgart Regional Medical Center, Stuttgart, AR, p. A51

HORVATH, Alex, Vice President Human Resources, BroMenn Healthcare System, Normal, IL, p. A202

HORVATH, Thomas B., Chief of Staff, Michael E. Debakey Veterans Affairs Medical Center, Houston, TX, p. A646

HOSFELD, Anne L., Chief Administrative Officer, Novato Community Hospital, Novato, CA, p. A78

HOSKINS, M.D., Donald, Chief Medical Officer, Beth Israel Medical Center, New York, NY, p. A458

HOSLER, M.D., Fred, Senior Vice President for Medical Affairs, Methodist Medical Center of Illinois, Peoria, IL, p. A205

HOSS, James R., Executive Director, Mountains Community Hospital, Lake Arrowhead, CA, p. A66

HOST, William R., M.D., President and Chief Executive Officer, Wyoming Valley Health Care System, Wilkes–Barre, PA, p. A579

HOSTETTER, Lynne, Director Human Resources, Hospital for Sick Children, Washington, DC, p. A121

HOTES, M.D., Lawrence S., Physician–in–Chief, New England Sinai Hospital and Rehabilitation Center, Stoughton, MA, p. A324

HOUCK, Randy, Information Technology Manager, Highland District Hospital, Hillsboro, OH, p. A515

HOUGHTON, Dan, Chief Financial Officer, Alaska Regional Hospital, Anchorage, AK, p. A26

HOUGHTON, Jack F., Chief Executive Officer, Natchez Regional Medical Center, Natchez, MS, p. A373

HOUGLUM, David C., MC, Administrator, U. S. Air Force Hospital, Hampton, VA, p. A689

HOULE, David, Senior Vice President and Chief Financial Officer, Hebrew Health Care, West Hartford, CT, p. A117

HOULIHAN, M.D., David, Chief of Staff, Veterans Affairs Medical Center, Tomah, WI, p. A736

HOUSE, Alan, Interim Vice President Finance and Accounting, Akron General Medical Center, Akron, OH, p. A502

HOUSE, M.D., Daniel, Chief of Staff, Henry County Memorial Hospital, New Castle, IN, p. A223

HOUSE, David
  Vice President and Chief Information Officer, Baptist Health Medical Center – North Little Rock, North Little Rock, AR, p. A48
  Vice President and Chief Information Officer, Baptist Health Medical Center–Little Rock, Little Rock, AR, p. A46
  Vice President and Chief Information Officer, Baptist Health Rehabilitation Institute, Little Rock, AR, p. A46

HOUSE, Michael, Director Information Services, Cheshire Medical Center, Keene, NH, p. A421

HOUSER, Marion, Administrator, HEALTHSOUTH Southern Hills Rehabilitation Hospital, Princeton, WV, p. A719

HOUSER, Robert, Chief Executive Officer, Blue Mountain Hospital, John Day, OR, p. A545

HOUSLEY, Kristin, Chief Management Information Systems, South Lincoln Medical Center, Kemmerer, WY, p. A740

HOUSTON, Michael, Chief Financial Officer, Westside Regional Medical Center, Plantation, FL, p. A143

HOUSTON, Robin, Director, Banner Mesa Medical Center, Mesa, AZ, p. A32

HOUTERMAN, Chris, Chief Information Officer, Clement J. Zablocki Veterans Affairs Medical Center, Milwaukee, WI, p. A730

HOVE, Barton A.
  President, Wellmont Bristol Regional Medical Center, Bristol, TN, p. A602
  President, Wellmont Bristol Regional Medical Center, Bristol, TN, p. A602

HOVHANESIAN, Joan, Vice President and Chief Information Officer, Shands at the University of Florida, Gainesville, FL, p. A130

HOWARD, Catherine, Director of Human Resources, Halifax Regional Health System, South Boston, VA, p. A696

HOWARD, Craig, Chief Operating Officer, Veterans Affairs Eastern Kansas Health Care System, Topeka, KS, p. A258

HOWARD, Dallis, Senior Vice President Human Resources, Methodist Medical Center of Illinois, Peoria, IL, p. A205

HOWARD, Dan, Chief Information Officer, John H. Stroger Jr. Hospital of Cook County, Chicago, IL, p. A187

HOWARD, Daniel, Chief Financial Officer, Veterans Affairs Medical Center, Togus, ME, p. A301

HOWARD, Eddie L.
  Vice President and Chief Operating Officer, East Texas Medical Center Rehabilitation Center, Tyler, TX, p. A670
  Vice President, Chief Operating Officer and Administrator, East Texas Medical Center Specialty Hospital, Tyler, TX, p. A671

HOWARD, Gary L., Chief Financial Officer, Hamilton Medical Center, Dalton, GA, p. A160

HOWARD, Loy M., Chief Executive Officer, Tanner Medical Center, Carrollton, GA, p. A157

HOWARD, Mark J., President and Chief Executive Officer, MountainView Hospital, Las Vegas, NV, p. A416

HOWARD, M.D., Michelle Bowman, Medical Director, Methodist Sugar Land Hospital, Sugar Land, TX, p. A668

HOWARD, Pamela, Administrator, Lake Butler Hospital Hand Surgery Center, Lake Butler, FL, p. A134

HOWARD, Sabra, Manager Human Resources, Harlan ARH Hospital, Harlan, KY, p. A265

HOWARD, Ted, Administrator, Lake Whitney Medical Center, Whitney, TX, p. A673

HOWARD, Tim, Regional Director Human Resources, La Palma Intercommunity Hospital, La Palma, CA, p. A66

HOWARD, Vickie, Human Resource Director, Ennis Regional Medical Center, Ennis, TX, p. A638

HOWE Jr, Bruce, Chief Executive Officer, Richardton Health Center, Richardton, ND, p. A500

HOWE, Debbie, Chief Executive Officer, Southwestern Memorial Hospital, Weatherford, OK, p. A541

HOWE, G. Edwin, President, Aurora Health Care, Milwaukee, WI, p. B12

HOWE, Scott W., Chief Executive Officer, Weeks Medical Center, Lancaster, NH, p. A421

HOWE, Vicki, Chief Information Officer, Ness County Hospital, Ness City, KS, p. A253

HOWE, CPA, Ward, Vice President Finance, O'Bleness Memorial Hospital, Athens, OH, p. A503

HOWELL, Brad, Chief Operating Officer, Madison Memorial Hospital, Rexburg, ID, p. A181

HOWELL, Diana, Director Human Resources, Conroe Regional Medical Center, Conroe, TX, p. A630

HOWELL, Doug
  Senior Vice President Organization and Performance, Norton Audubon Hospital, Louisville, KY, p. A269
  Senior Vice President Organization and Performance, Norton Hospital, Louisville, KY, p. A270
  Senior Vice President Organization and Performance, Norton Southwest Hospital, Louisville, KY, p. A270
  Senior Vice President Organization and Performance, Norton Suburban Hospital, Louisville, KY, p. A270

HOWELL, Jerry M., Chief Operating Officer, Marion General Hospital, Columbia, MS, p. A368

HOWELL, Joe D., Executive Director, Upstate Carolina Medical Center, Gaffney, SC, p. A588

HOWELL, Kenneth, President and Chief Executive Officer, Arizona Heart Hospital, Phoenix, AZ, p. A33

HOWELL, R. Edward, Vice President and Chief Executive Officer, University of Virginia Medical Center, Charlottesville, VA, p. A686

HOWES, Constance A., President and Chief Executive Officer, Women and Infants Hospital of Rhode Island, Providence, RI, p. A582

HOWREY, John L., Chief Financial Officer, Quincy Valley Medical Center, Quincy, WA, p. A706

HOYOS, Kent, Director of Information, Pomona Valley Hospital Medical Center, Pomona, CA, p. A82

HOYT, John
  Vice President Chief Information Officer, Covenant Children's Hospital, Lubbock, TX, p. A654
  Vice President Chief Information Officer, Covenant Medical Center, Lubbock, TX, p. A654

HOYT, M.D., John, Chief Medical Officer, Greater Community Hospital, Creston, IA, p. A231

HREHOROVICH, M.D., Victor R., Executive Vice President and Medical Director, Lutheran Medical Center, New York, NY, p. A461

HSING, Shirley, Chief Financial Officer, North Oaks Medical Center, Hammond, LA, p. A281

HUBBARD, F. David, Superintendent, McCain Correctional Hospital, McCain, NC, p. A487

HUBBARD, Gene, Director, Information Technology and Systems, Sky Ridge Medical Center, Lone Tree, CO, p. A108

HUBBARD, M.D., James, Chief Medical Staff, Grand View Hospital, Ironwood, MI, p. A337

HUBBS III, Olas A., President and Chief Executive Officer, Memorial Hospital of Union County, Marysville, OH, p. A517

HUBER, Dalton, Vice President Fiscal Services, St. Mary's Healthcare Center, Pierre, SD, p. A597

HUBER, David, Chief Executive Officer, Rockdale Medical Center, Conyers, GA, p. A159

HUBER, M.D., Joel, Chief of Staff, Hand County Memorial Hospital/Avera Health, Miller, SD, p. A597

HUBER, Thomas A., Vice President Finance, Unity Hospital, Muscatine, IA, p. A238

HUBER, Timothy, Manager Financial Support, Mercy Hospital of Franciscan Sisters, Oelwein, IA, p. A239

HUBERT, Michael, Vice President Human Resources, J. C. Blair Memorial Hospital, Huntingdon, PA, p. A561

HUCK, Richard, Vice President of Human Resources, Marymount Medical Center, London, KY, p. A268

HUCKABY, Don, Chief, Information Management Service, Veterans Affairs Eastern Colorado Health Care System, Denver, CO, p. A104

HUCKABY, Lee
Chief Executive Officer, Promise Specialty Hospital of Ferriday, Ferriday, LA, p. A280
Chief Executive Officer, Promise Specialty Hospital of Vicksburg, Vicksburg, MS, p. A376

HUDDLESTON, Barton, M.D., Chief Executive Officer, Nashville Rehabilitation Hospital, Nashville, TN, p. A615

HUDDLESTON, M.D., Lisa, Chief of Staff, Providence Seaside Hospital, Seaside, OR, p. A549

HUDGINS, Paul
Associate Vice President Human Resources, Bascom Palmer Eye Institute–Anne Bates Leach Eye Hospital, Miami, FL, p. A136
Associate Vice President Human Resources, University of Miami Hospital and Clinics, Miami, FL, p. A138

HUDGINS, Thomas J., FACHE, Administrator and Chief Executive Officer, Pinckneyville Community Hospital, Pinckneyville, IL, p. A205

HUDSON, M.D., Cecil, Chief Medical Officer, Athens Regional Medical Center, Athens, GA, p. A152

HUDSON, Donald C., President, Mercy Hospital of Folsom, Folsom, CA, p. A60

HUDSON, Gary Mikeal
Administrator, East Texas Medical Center Carthage, Carthage, TX, p. A628
Administrator, East Texas Medical Center Carthage, Carthage, TX, p. A628

HUDSON, James, Assistant Chief IRM, Veterans Affairs Medical Center, Lake City, FL, p. A134

HUDSON, Joan, Director Human Resources, Twin Cities Hospital, Niceville, FL, p. A139

HUDSON, Kenneth J., Chief Financial Officer, Veterans Affairs Puget Sound Health Care System, Seattle, WA, p. A708

HUDSON, Kim, Chief Information Officer, Harper County Community Hospital, Buffalo, OK, p. A528

HUDSON, Larry C., Executive Vice President and Chief Financial Officer, Charleston Area Medical Center, Charleston, WV, p. A714

HUDSON, Maggie, Director Operations and Financial Services, Santiam Memorial Hospital, Stayton, OR, p. A549

HUDSON, Mason, Assistant Director Human Resources, University of Washington Medical Center, Seattle, WA, p. A708

HUDSON, Norma, Chief Financial Officer, Palo Verde Hospital, Blythe, CA, p. A55

HUDSON, M.D., Pamela, Chief Operating Officer, Crestwood Medical Center, Huntsville, AL, p. A20

HUDSON, Paula, Chief Information Officer, Hahnemann University Hospital, Philadelphia, PA, p. A568

HUDSON, Robert J.
Chief Executive Officer and President, Pattie A. Clay Regional Medical Center, Richmond, KY, p. A274
Chief Executive Officer and President, Pattie A. Clay Regional Medical Center, Richmond, KY, p. A274
Vice President Fiscal Services, Pattie A. Clay Regional Medical Center, Richmond, KY, p. A274

HUDSPETH, Harvey, Executive Director Human Resources, Medical Center Hospital, Odessa, TX, p. A659

HUDSPETH, Todd, Chief Executive Officer, Buena Vista Regional Medical Center, Storm Lake, IA, p. A242

HUEBBERS, Rodney N., President and Chief Executive Officer, Inova Loudoun Hospital, Leesburg, VA, p. A690

HUEBNER, Thomas W., President and Chief Executive Officer, Rutland Regional Medical Center, Rutland, VT, p. A683

HUELSKAMP, Donald P., Vice President Finance and Chief Financial Officer, Southeastern Ohio Regional Medical Center, Cambridge, OH, p. A505

HUERTER, Holly, Vice President Human Resources, Nebraska Methodist Hospital, Omaha, NE, p. A411

HUETTL, Patricia, Assistant Administrator Financial Services, Sacred Heart Hospital, Eau Claire, WI, p. A725

HUEY, Kenneth R., Administrator, Memorial Hospital of Sheridan County, Sheridan, WY, p. A741

HUFF, David A., President, Good Samaritan Hospital, Bakersfield, CA, p. A53

HUFF, Jeffrey
Administrator, HEALTHSOUTH Rehabilitation Hospital, Fayetteville, AR, p. A42
Controller, HEALTHSOUTH Rehabilitation Hospital, Fayetteville, AR, p. A42

HUFF, Michael H., Interim Chief Executive Officer, Fannin Regional Hospital, Blue Ridge, GA, p. A156

HUFF, Richard, Administrator, U. S. Public Health Service Indian Hospital, Sisseton, SD, p. A599

HUFF, Sally, Controller, Harrison Community Hospital, Cadiz, OH, p. A504

HUFF, M.D., W Alexander, President Medical Staff, Sampson Regional Medical Center, Clinton, NC, p. A480

HUFF, William J., Chief Executive Officer, Marshall Browning Hospital, Du Quoin, IL, p. A192

HUFFMAN, D Darlene, Director Human Resources, Princeton Community Hospital, Princeton, WV, p. A719

HUFFMAN, James
Chief Operating Officer and Chief Financial Officer, Baptist Memorial Hospital–Golden Triangle, Columbus, MS, p. A368
Chief Operating Officer and Chief Financial Officer, Baptist Memorial Hospital–Golden Triangle, Columbus, MS, p. A368

HUFFMAN, Sherry, Director Human Resources, Oakwood Heritage Hospital, Taylor, MI, p. A346

HUFNAGEL, Keith, Director Human Resources, Via Christi Oklahoma Regional Medical Center, Ponca City, OK, p. A537

HUGGINS, Beth, Controller, Lake City Community Hospital, Lake City, SC, p. A589

HUGGINS, Michael C., Network System Administrator, Eastern Oklahoma Medical Center, Poteau, OK, p. A537

HUGHES, Beth, Executive Vice President and Chief Operating Officer, Elliot Hospital, Manchester, NH, p. A422

HUGHES, David, Chief Financial Officer, Plantation General Hospital, Plantation, FL, p. A143

HUGHES, FACHE, David T., Senior Vice President Operations, Good Shepherd Healthcare System, Hermiston, OR, p. A544

HUGHES, Edith M., Division President, Oakwood Southshore Medical Center, Trenton, MI, p. A347

HUGHES, Faye, Chief Nursing Officer and Chief Operating Officer, Medical Park Hospital, Hope, AR, p. A44

HUGHES, James, Information Systems Flight Commander, U. S. Air Force Academy Hospital, USAF Academy, CO, p. A110

HUGHES Jr, Ned B., President, Gerber Memorial Health Services, Fremont, MI, p. A333

HUGHES, Robert, Chief Operating Officer, Coler–Goldwater Specialty Hospital and Nursing Facility, New York, NY, p. A459

HUGHES, Sandra, Chief Financial Officer, Clinch Memorial Hospital, Homerville, GA, p. A163

HUGHES, Terry, Management Information Systems Coordinator, Nantucket Cottage Hospital, Nantucket, MA, p. A321

HUGHES, Thomas, Director Information Systems, Baptist Memorial Hospital–Forrest City, Forrest City, AR, p. A43

HUGHES, W. Russell, Ph.D.,
Director, G. Werber Bryan Psychiatric Hospital, Columbia, SC, p. A585
Director, William S. Hall Psychiatric Institute, Columbia, SC, p. A586

HUGHES, William L., Chief Financial Officer and Vice President of Business Development, Anne Arundel Medical Center, Annapolis, MD, p. A302

HUHNKE, Ann, Chief Financial Officer, Lander Valley Medical Center, Lander, WY, p. A740

HUIE, Robert, Executive Vice President and Chief Financial Officer, Willis–Knighton Medical Center, Shreveport, LA, p. A293

HULL, Jeffrey, Chairman of the Medical Staff, CJW Medical Center, Richmond, VA, p. A695

HULLETT, Sandral, M.D., Chief Executive Officer and Medical Director, Cooper Green Hospital, Birmingham, AL, p. A14

HULSE, Mark, Vice President Information Services, North Shore Medical Center, Salem, MA, p. A323

HUMMEL, John, Vice President and Chief Information Officer, Sutter Center for Psychiatry, Sacramento, CA, p. A85

HUMMER, Christopher, Chief Executive Officer, South Fulton Medical Center, Atlanta, GA, p. A154

HUMMER, John L., Chief Executive Officer, MountainView Regional Medical Center, Las Cruces, NM, p. A443

HUMPHREY, James
Chief Medical Officer, Community Hospital Association, Fairfax, MO, p. A381
Director, Human Resource and Educational Resources, Penrose–St. Francis Health Services, Colorado Springs, CO, p. A102

HUMPHREY, Randy, Chief Financial Officer, NorthShore Regional Medical Center, Slidell, LA, p. A293

HUMPHREY, Robert J., Chief Executive Officer and Administrator, Lanier Health Services, Valley, AL, p. A25

HUMPHREYS, Carl, Senior Vice President Finance, Howard County General Hospital, Columbia, MD, p. A307

HUMPHREYS, M.D., David J., Medical Director, River Park Hospital, Huntington, WV, p. A716

HUMPHREYS, L. Ray, Chief Executive Officer, Delta Regional Medical Center, Greenville, MS, p. A368

HUMPHRYS, Maureen, Director, Veterans Affairs Medical Center, Sheridan, WY, p. A742

HUNN, Michael, Chief Executive Officer, Lakewood Regional Medical Center, Lakewood, CA, p. A67

HUNSAKER, Susan L., CHE, President and Chief Executive Officer, Broadlawns Medical Center, Des Moines, IA, p. A232

HUNSBERGER, Tom, Vice President Human Resources, Riverview Hospital Association, Wisconsin Rapids, WI, p. A738

HUNSTOCK, R.N., Leanne M., Chief Operating Officer, Scripps Mercy Hospital, San Diego, CA, p. A87

HUNT, Craig P., Vice President Operations and Finance, Pottsville Hospital and Warne Clinic, Pottsville, PA, p. A573

HUNT, Deloris, Corporate Vice President Human Resources, Harper University Hospital, Detroit, MI, p. A331

HUNT, Kathy, Chief of Human Resources, Washington Township Health Care District, Fremont, CA, p. A61

HUNT, Linda A., President, St. Joseph's Hospital and Medical Center, Phoenix, AZ, p. A35

HUNT, Roger S., Chief Executive Officer, BroMenn Healthcare System, Normal, IL, p. A202

HUNT, Ronald, Chief Financial Officer, East Texas Medical Center Trinity, Trinity, TX, p. A670

HUNT Jr, Seth P., Director and Chief Executive Officer, Broughton Hospital, Morganton, NC, p. A488

HUNT, Sharon, Administrator, W. J. Mangold Memorial Hospital, Lockney, TX, p. A653

HUNT, William Robert, Chief Financial Officer, Reynolds Memorial Hospital, Glen Dale, WV, p. A715

HUNTE, Steven, Commander, McDonald Army Community Hospital, Fort Eustis, VA, p. A688

HUNTER, Byron, Vice President Human Resources, Burdette Tomlin Memorial Hospital, Cape May Court House, NJ, p. A427

HUNTER, David C.
Chief Operating Officer, Parkview Noble Hospital, Kendallville, IN, p. A220
Chief Operating Officer, Parkview Noble Hospital, Kendallville, IN, p. A220

HUNTER, George, Vice President Administration and Human Resoruces, Mid Coast Hospital, Brunswick, ME, p. A297

HUNTER, Karen, Director Human Resources, Integris Clinton Regional Hospital, Clinton, OK, p. A529

HUNTER, Melvin, Executive Director, Atascadero State Hospital, Atascadero, CA, p. A53

HUNTER, Steven L.
President and Chief Executive Officer, Covenant Children's Hospital, Lubbock, TX, p. A654
President and Chief Executive Officer, Covenant Health System, Lubbock, TX, p. B34
President and Chief Executive Officer, Covenant Medical Center, Lubbock, TX, p. A654

HUNTINGTON, M.D., Mark, Medical Director, Ortonville Area Health Services, Ortonville, MN, p. A359

HUNTINGTON, Vince, Administrator and Chief Operating Officer, Providence Alaska Medical Center, Anchorage, AK, p. A26

HUNTLEY, Lee S., Chief Executive Officer, Baptist Hospital of Miami, Miami, FL, p. A136

HUNTSMAN, Kim, Accounting Manager, Trigg County Hospital, Cadiz, KY, p. A262

HUONKER, George, Assistant Administrator Human Resources, OSF St. Joseph Medical Center, Bloomington, IL, p. A185

HUPF, Angela, Vice President Human Resources and Marketing, Memorial Health Center, Medford, WI, p. A729

HUPFELD, Stanley F., President and Chief Executive Officer, INTEGRIS Health, Oklahoma City, OK, p. B62

HURD, Paul, CHE, Chief Executive Officer, Creighton Area Health Services, Creighton, NE, p. A406

HURLBUTT, IV, M.D., Robert H., Chief Medical Staff, Northeast Alabama Regional Medical Center, Anniston, AL, p. A13

HURLEY, Phillip D., Chief Executive Officer, SemperCare Hospital of Little Rock, Little Rock, AR, p. A47

HUROWITZ, D.O., Marc P., Chief Medical Officer, Temple East, Northeastern Hospital, Philadelphia, PA, p. A570

HURRAY, Joan, Regional Director Information Services, Saint Joseph Mercy Health System, Ypsilanti, MI, p. A348

HURSEY, Will, Controller, Macon Northside Hospital, Macon, GA, p. A165

HURSH, John, Vice President Human Resources, Southern Regional Medical Center, Riverdale, GA, p. A167

HURST, Gregory A., Executive Vice President and Chief Financial Officer, Piedmont Hospital, Atlanta, GA, p. A154

HURST, James, Chief Fiscal Service, Veterans Affairs Medical Center, Fayetteville, AR, p. A43

HURST, Molly, Administrator, Grimes St. Joseph Health Center, Navasota, TX, p. A658

HURST, Patty, Administrator, Devereux Hospital and Children's Center of Florida, Melbourne, FL, p. A136

HURT–STEFFEN, Sally, Chief Operating Officer, Del Sol Medical Center, El Paso, TX, p. A637

HURYSZ, Edwin E., Administrator, Hamilton County Hospital, Syracuse, KS, p. A257

HURZELER, Rosemary Johnson, President and Chief Executive Officer, The Connecticut Hospice, Branford, CT, p. A112

HUSEBY, Custer, Chief Executive Officer, SCCI Hospital – Fargo, Fargo, ND, p. A498

HUSHKA, Richard, Chief Financial Officer, Ellinwood District Hospital, Ellinwood, KS, p. A246

HUSKEY, Jeff, Chief Executive Officer and Administrator, Clay County Memorial Hospital, Henrietta, TX, p. A644

HUSMANN, Torrey, Chief Executive Officer, Select Specialty Hospital of Western Michigan, Muskegon, MI, p. A341

HUSS, Cathy, Chief Financial Officer, Roseau Area Hospital and Homes, Roseau, MN, p. A361

HUSSAIN, Iftikhar, Chief Financial Officer, Mills–Peninsula Health Services, Burlingame, CA, p. A55

HUSSON, Gerard P., Director, Veterans Affairs Medical Center, Beckley, WV, p. A713

HUSTON, D.O., Gary, Director Medical Affairs, UHHS Brown Memorial Hospital, Conneaut, OH, p. A511

HUSTON, Joye H., Chief Executive Officer, Jefferson County Memorial Hospital, Winchester, KS, p. A260

HUSTON, Samuel R.
President and Chief Executive Officer, Rochester General Hospital, Rochester, NY, p. A471
President and Chief Executive Officer, ViaHealth, Rochester, NY, p. B120

HUTCHENRIDER, E. Kenneth, Chief Executive Officer, Terre Haute Regional Hospital, Terre Haute, IN, p. A226

HUTCHENS, Steve, Vice President General Services, Grady Memorial Hospital, Chickasha, OK, p. A528

HUTCHERSON, James, Accounting Supervisor, HEALTHSOUTH Rehabilitation Hospital of Central Kentucky, Elizabethtown, KY, p. A264

HUTCHESON, Larry, Interim Administrator, East Adams Rural Hospital, Ritzville, WA, p. A707

HUTCHESON, M.D., Lou Ellen, Chief of Staff, Bacon County Hospital and Health System, Alma, GA, p. A152

HUTCHINS, M.D., J F., Chief of Staff, Gordon Memorial Hospital, Gordon, NE, p. A407

HUTCHINS, Michael T., Administrator, Jay Hospital, Jay, FL, p. A133

HUTCHINS, Roger D., Chief Financial Officer, Trinity Medical Center, Carrollton, TX, p. A628

HUTCHINSON, Leann Moren, Chief Executive Officer, Meadows Hospital, Bloomington, IN, p. A212

HUTCHISON, Dee, R.N., Administrator, Alaska Native Medical Center, Anchorage, AK, p. A26

HUTCHISON, Dennis L., Chief Executive Officer, Fayette County Hospital, Vandalia, IL, p. A209

HUTCHISON, M.D., Florence N., Chief of Staff, Ralph H. Johnson Veterans Affairs Medical Center, Charleston, SC, p. A585

HUTCHISON, Harry, Vice President Fiscal Services, St. Bernards Medical Center, Jonesboro, AR, p. A45

HUTH, Richard, Chief Operating Officer, Capital Regional Medical Center, Tallahassee, FL, p. A147

HUTSELL, Dick, Vice President Information Technology Services, St. Louise Regional Hospital, Gilroy, CA, p. A62

HUTSELL, Linda, Assistant Vice President of Human Resources, Carroll Hospital Center, Westminster, MD, p. A311

HUTSELL, Richard
Vice President and Chief Information Officer, O'Connor Hospital, San Jose, CA, p. A90
Vice President, Chief Information Officer, Seton Medical Center, Daly City, CA, p. A58

HUTSON, Mark S., Chief Information Officer, Greenwood Leflore Hospital, Greenwood, MS, p. A369

HUTSON, Penny, Chief Financial Officer, Southwest Medical Center, Lafayette, LA, p. A284

HUTSON, Wayne, Chief Financial Officer, Union Hospital, Terre Haute, IN, p. A226

HUTT, Si, Chief Executive Officer, Ashley Valley Medical Center, Vernal, UT, p. A681

HUTTON, Terry, Chief Executive Officer, SCCI Hospital of Amarillo, Amarillo, TX, p. A621

HYATT, Ronnie, Vice Pres Finance, Bon Secours St. Francis Health System, Greenville, SC, p. A588

HYBARGER, Margaret, Vice President Finance, Ionia County Memorial Hospital, Ionia, MI, p. A337

HYDE, Cynthia, Director Information Systems, Providence Hospital, Mobile, AL, p. A21

HYDE, Dwight, Executive Vice President and Chief Financial Officer, Children's Mercy Hospital, Kansas City, MO, p. A384

HYDE, James A., Administrator, Bone and Joint Hospital, Oklahoma City, OK, p. A535

HYDE, Van, Chief Executive Officer, Sturgis Community Health Care Center, Sturgis, SD, p. A600

HYDER, M.D., Shiraz, Director Medical Affairs, St. Alexius Medical Center, Bismarck, ND, p. A496

HYER, Julie, President, Dominican Hospital, Santa Cruz, CA, p. A92

HYER, Jr, William F.
Senior Vice President and Chief Financial Officer, Burleson St. Joseph Health Center, Caldwell, TX, p. A627
Senior Vice President and Chief Financial Officer, St. Joseph Regional Health Center, Bryan, TX, p. A627

HYMAN, Craig, Vice President Human Resources, Conway Medical Center, Conway, SC, p. A587

HYMANS, Daniel J., President, Memorial Medical Center, Ashland, WI, p. A722

HYNES, John J., President and Chief Executive Officer, Care New England Health System, Providence, RI, p. B21

HYNSON, David, Director Information Systems, St. Joseph Medical Center, Towson, MD, p. A311

HYTOFF, Ronald A., President and Chief Executive Officer, Tampa General Hospital, Tampa, FL, p. A148

I

IACOBELL, Frank P., President, Michigan Orthopaedic Specialty Hospital, Madison Heights, MI, p. A339

IANNOLO, M.D., Patsy, Director of Medical Affairs, Oswego Hospital, Oswego, NY, p. A468

IANNONI, Joseph
Chief Financial Officer, Caritas St. Elizabeth's Medical Center, Brighton, MA, p. A315
Chief Financial Officer, Roger Williams Medical Center, Providence, RI, p. A582

IERO, Tony, Director Management Information Systems, North Philadelphia Health System, Philadelphia, PA, p. A569

IFTINIUK, Alan, President, French Hospital Medical Center, San Luis Obispo, CA, p. A91

IGNELZI, James
Chief Executive Officer, Dayton Campus, Dayton, OH, p. A511
Chief Executive Officer, Twin Valley Behavioral Healthcare–Columbus Campus, Columbus, OH, p. A511

IKNER, Don, Chief Financial Officer, Vaughan Regional Medical Center, Selma, AL, p. A24

ILTIS, Michael T., Vice President Professional Services, Emanuel Medical Center, Turlock, CA, p. A96

IMBIMBO, Richard, Chief Financial Officer, Memorial Hospital, York, PA, p. A580

IMERMAN, Pat, Director Human Resources, Samaritan Hospital, Lexington, KY, p. A268

IMLER, James, Director Human Resources, Regional West Medical Center, Scottsbluff, NE, p. A413

IMSEIS, M.D., Mikhail, Chief of Staff, Ness County Hospital, Ness City, KS, p. A253

INCARNATI, Philip A., President and Chief Executive Officer, McLaren Health Care Corporation, Flint, MI, p. B72

INDACOCHEA, M.D., Fernando, Chief of Staff, Grant Memorial Hospital, Petersburg, WV, p. A719

INDIHAR, Frank, M.D., Chief Executive Officer, Bethesda Rehabilitation Hospital, Saint Paul, MN, p. A361

INGALLS, Dawn, Human Resources Regional Representative, Dells Area Health Center, Dell Rapids, SD, p. A595

INGHAM, Raymond V., Ph.D., President and Chief Executive Officer, Witham Memorial Hospital, Lebanon, IN, p. A221

INGLE, M.D., Richard M., Chief of Staff, Humboldt General Hospital, Winnemucca, NV, p. A419

INGLEDUE, M.D., Vickie, Chief of Staff, Ashe Memorial Hospital, Jefferson, NC, p. A485

INGLES, Kimberly, Director Human Resources, Winn Parish Medical Center, Winnfield, LA, p. A294

INGRAM, Herman, Director, Riverside Medical Center, Franklinton, LA, p. A281

INGRAM, Peter, Vice President and Chief Information Officer, Mount Sinai Hospital Medical Center of Chicago, Chicago, IL, p. A188

INGRIM, M.D., Richard L., Chief of Staff, Cozby–Germany Hospital, Grand Saline, TX, p. A642

INIGO–AGOSTINI, Emigdio, M.D., Board President, Clinica Espanola, Mayaguez, PR, p. A745

INMAN, M.D., Charles C., Medical Staff President, Winter Haven Hospital, Winter Haven, FL, p. A151

INSLEY, William, Chief Human Resources Management, Veterans Affairs Medical Center, New Orleans, LA, p. A290

INZANA, Lou, Vice President Finance and Chief Financial Officer, Olean General Hospital, Olean, NY, p. A468

IRANI, M.D., Glenn
Medical Chief of Staff, Encino–Tarzana Regional Medical Center Encino Campus, Los Angeles, CA, p. A70
Medical Chief of Staff, Encino–Tarzana Regional Medical Center Tarzana Campus, Los Angeles, CA, p. A70

IRIEL, Shannon, Director, Human Resources, East Cooper Regional Medical Center, Mount Pleasant, SC, p. A590

IRION, Denise, Controller, Socorro General Hospital, Socorro, NM, p. A445

IRISH, Gary G., President and Chief Executive Officer, South Coast Medical Center, Laguna Beach, CA, p. A66

IRSIK, Ginger, Administrator, Prattville Baptist Hospital, Prattville, AL, p. A23

IRVINE, William, Vice President Human Resources, Wentworth–Douglass Hospital, Dover, NH, p. A420

IRVING, Ginger, Administrator, St. Catherine's Rehabilitation Hospital, North Miami, FL, p. A139

IRVING, Mark, Manager Management Information Systems, OSF St. Francis Hospital, Escanaba, MI, p. A332

IRWIN, Gene, Chief Financial Officer, Jefferson County Hospital, Fairfield, IA, p. A234

IRWIN Jr, Richard M., President and Chief Executive Officer, Health Central, Ocoee, FL, p. A140

ISAAC, Wendy, Director Management Information, Lincoln Medical Center, Lincolnton, NC, p. A486

ISAACS, Linda, Vice President Human Resources, California Pacific Medical Center, San Francisco, CA, p. A88

ISADO, M.D., Jose, Medical Director, Auxilio Mutuo Hospital, San Juan, PR, p. A746

ISAIAH, Marlin, Director Management Information Services, Kenneth Hall Regional Hospital, East St. Louis, IL, p. A192

ISELY, John A., President, St. Mary Medical Center, Walla Walla, WA, p. A711

ISELY, M.D., William A., Chief of Staff, Chambers Memorial Hospital, Danville, AR, p. A42

ISEMANN, William R., Executive Vice President and Chief Operating Officer, Danville Regional Medical Center, Danville, VA, p. A687

ISHIZUKA, Paul, Associate Executive Director and Chief Financial Officer, University of Washington Medical Center, Seattle, WA, p. A708

ISKANDER, M.D., Henein, Chief of Staff, Baptist Memorial Hospital–Forrest City, Forrest City, AR, p. A43

ISQUIERDO, Maria, Director, Human Resources, Swedish Medical Center, Englewood, CO, p. A105

ISRAEL, Robert
  network Administrator Information Systems, John C. Lincoln Hospital – North Mountain, Phoenix, AZ, p. A34
  Network Administrator Information Systems, John C. Lincoln Hospital–Deer Valley, Phoenix, AZ, p. A34

ISSAI, Alice H.
  Business Strategy and Finance Leader, Kaiser Foundation Hospital, Los Angeles, CA, p. A70
  Business Strategy and Finance Leader, Kaiser Foundation Hospital–West Los Angeles, Los Angeles, CA, p. A71

ISSAI, Robert
  Executive Vice President and Chief Financial Officer, O'Connor Hospital, San Jose, CA, p. A90
  Chief Financial Officer, St. Louise Regional Hospital, Gilroy, CA, p. A62

IVERSEN, Dale E., Chief Executive Officer, Healdsburg District Hospital, Healdsburg, CA, p. A64

IVERSON, Charles, Vice President Finance and Chief Financial Officer, Woman's Christian Association Hospital, Jamestown, NY, p. A454

IVES, Karen, Interim Administrator, Harper County Community Hospital, Buffalo, OK, p. A528

IVES, Matt
  Chief Financial Officer, Keokuk County Health Center, Sigourney, IA, p. A241
  Chief Financial Officer, Keokuk County Health Center, Sigourney, IA, p. A241

IVES, R. Wayne, Administrator, San Vicente Hospital, Los Angeles, CA, p. A72

IVESON, Sara C., Executive Director, Barnes–Kasson County Hospital, Susquehanna, PA, p. A576

IVESTER, Roger, Information Systems Manager, Habersham County Medical Center, Demorest, GA, p. A160

IVIE, Jack, Executive Vice President and Chief Operating Officer, St. Bernardine Medical Center, San Bernardino, CA, p. A86

IZES, M.D., Jay, Vice President Medical Affairs, St. John's Riverside Hosptial, Yonkers, NY, p. A476

IZQUIERDO, Elizabeth, Chief Financial Officer, Cedars Medical Center, Miami, FL, p. A137

J

JABEL, M.D., Juvenal, Chief Medical Officer, Satanta District Hospital, Satanta, KS, p. A256

JABLONOWSKI, Gerald J., President and Chief Executive Officer, St. Francis Medical Center, Trenton, NJ, p. A437

JACKMUFF, Steven W., President and Chief Executive Officer, Underwood–Memorial Hospital, Woodbury, NJ, p. A439

JACKSON, Anthony W., Administrator, HEALTHSOUTH Rehabilitation Hospital, Rock Hill, SC, p. A591

JACKSON, Bryan, Vice President Finance, Arkansas Methodist Medical Center, Paragould, AR, p. A49

JACKSON, Carolyn, Chief Operating Officer, Lake Pointe Medical Center, Rowlett, TX, p. A662

JACKSON, Cindy, Director Human Resources, Phelps Memorial Health Center, Holdrege, NE, p. A408

JACKSON, Claudia, Director Human Resources, Upson Regional Medical Center, Thomaston, GA, p. A170

JACKSON, Daniel W., Chief Executive Officer, Northlake Medical Center, Tucker, GA, p. A171

JACKSON, Dennis, Director Management Information Systems, Valley View Regional Hospital, Ada, OK, p. A527

JACKSON, Doreen, Chief Executive Officer, Drake Pavilion, Cincinnati, OH, p. A506

JACKSON, Fred L., Chief Executive Officer, King's Daughters Medical Center, Ashland, KY, p. A261

JACKSON, Gail C., M.D., Chief Executive Officer, East Central Regional Hospital, Augusta, GA, p. A155

JACKSON, J D., Chief Information Officer, Highlands Regional Medical Center, Prestonsburg, KY, p. A273

JACKSON, M.D., Jack, Chief of Staff, Blue Mountain Hospital, John Day, OR, p. A545

JACKSON, M.D., James, Vice President Medical Affairs, St. Joseph's/Candler, Candler Hospital, Savannah, GA, p. A169

JACKSON, Jr, James H., Chief Financial Officer, Greenwood Leflore Hospital, Greenwood, MS, p. A369

JACKSON, Janice, Director Human Resources, Shands at Lake Shore, Lake City, FL, p. A134

JACKSON, Joan, Administrator, Melrose Area Hospital – Centra Care, Melrose, MN, p. A357

JACKSON, Joanne, Administrator Human Resources and Community Relations, Amery Regional Medical Center, Amery, WI, p. A722

JACKSON, John J., Vice President Operations, FirstHealth Richmond Memorial Hospital, Rockingham, NC, p. A490

JACKSON, Lee J., Vice President of Nursing Services, Central Peninsula General Hospital, Soldotna, AK, p. A28

JACKSON, Lynn, Administrator, Northside Hospital Forsyth, Cumming, GA, p. A159

JACKSON, Mary, Chief Executive Officer, Select Specialty Hospital – Fort Smith, Fort Smith, AR, p. A43

JACKSON, Mary Lane, Administrator, St. Vincent Women's Hospital, Indianapolis, IN, p. A219

JACKSON, Max G., Vice President Medical Affairs, Research Belton Hospital, Belton, MO, p. A378

JACKSON, Meg, Director Biomedical Management Information Systems, Beauregard Memorial Hospital, De Ridder, LA, p. A280

JACKSON, Melinda, Director Human Resources, Bates County Memorial Hospital, Butler, MO, p. A379

JACKSON, Mike, President and Chief Executive Officer, Fort Logan Hospital, Stanford, KY, p. A275

JACKSON, CPA, Pam, Chief Financial Officer, South Central Kansas Regional Medical Center, Arkansas City, KS, p. A244

JACKSON, Reese
  Senior Vice President and Administrator, Laureate Psychiatric Clinic and Hospital, Tulsa, OK, p. A539
  Senior Vice President and Administrator, Saint Francis Hospital, Tulsa, OK, p. A540
  Chief Operating Officer, Saint Francis Hospital, Tulsa, OK, p. A540

JACKSON Jr, Robert, Interim Chief Executive Officer, United Community Hospital, Grove City, PA, p. A559

JACKSON, Robert, Chief Financial Officer, Eunice Community Medical Center, Eunice, LA, p. A280

JACKSON, Sandra S., R.N., Administrator, Tyler County Hospital, Woodville, TX, p. A674

JACKSON, Ed.D., R, Sandra S., Administrator, Tyler County Hospital, Woodville, TX, p. A674

JACKSON, Sarah, Director, Saint Anne's Hospital, Fall River, MA, p. A317

JACKSON, Teresa, Chief Financial Officer, Choctaw Nation Health Care Center, Talihina, OK, p. A539

JACKSON, Terry, Director Information System, Regional Medical Center of Hopkins County, Madisonville, KY, p. A270

JACKSON, Thomas W., Chief Executive Officer, College Station Medical Center, College Station, TX, p. A629

JACKSON, Timothy D., Executive Vice President and Chief Financial Officer, Miami Valley Hospital, Dayton, OH, p. A512

JACKSON, Tony, Information Technology Director, Sutter Amador Hospital, Jackson, CA, p. A65

JACKSON, Valerie A., Chief Executive Officer, Columbia Hospital, West Palm Beach, FL, p. A150

JACKSON, M.D., Vaughn, Chief of Staff, Conejos County Hospital, La Jara, CO, p. A107

JACKSON, William, President, Charlevoix Area Hospital, Charlevoix, MI, p. A329

JACOBS, JD, M.D., Fred M., President Medical Staff, Elmhurst Memorial Hospital, New York, IL, p. A193

JACOBS, Joey, President and Chief Executive Officer, Psychiatric Solutions, Franklin, TN, p. B87

JACOBS, Lloyd A., M.D., President, Medical College of Ohio Hospitals, Toledo, OH, p. A523

JACOBS, Nicholas, FACHE, President, Windber Medical Center, Windber, PA, p. A580

JACOBS, Robert, Market Information Officer, Christus St. Michael Health System, Texarkana, TX, p. A669

JACOBS, Robert P., M.D., Chief Executive Officer, SUNY Downstate Medical Center University Hospital, New York, NY, p. A466

JACOBS, Selby, M.D., Chief Executive Officer, Connecticut Mental Health Center, New Haven, CT, p. A115

JACOBS, Steven R., Chief Financial Officer, Central Washington Hospital, Wenatchee, WA, p. A711

JACOBS, Terri, Administrator, SouthCrest Hospital, Tulsa, OK, p. A540

JACOBSEN, Barry, Chief Financial Officer, Shelby County Myrtue Memorial Hospital, Harlan, IA, p. A235

JACOBSMEYER, Barb, Chief Operating Officer, Des Peres Hospital, Saint Louis, MO, p. A390

JACOBSON, Becky, Manager Business Office and Human Resources, Community Memorial Hospital, Burke, SD, p. A594

JACOBSON, Carlton, Vice President Finance, Frank R. Howard Memorial Hospital, Willits, CA, p. A99

JACOBSON, John L., President and Chief Executive Officer, Atchison Hospital, Atchison, KS, p. A244

JACOBSON, Loren, Vice President and Chief Financial Officer, St. Patrick Hospital, Missoula, MT, p. A401

JACOBSON, D.O., Mark, Vice President Medical Affairs, The Good Samaritan Hospital, Lebanon, PA, p. A563

JACOBSON, Peter, President and Chief Executive Officer, St. Joseph's Area Health Services, Park Rapids, MN, p. A359

JACOBSON, Randolph, Chief Financial Officer, Carrier Clinic, Belle Mead, NJ, p. A425

JACOBSON, Rod, Administrator, Bear Lake Memorial Hospital, Montpelier, ID, p. A180

JACOBSON, Ronald L., President and Chief Executive Officer, Avera St. Luke's, Aberdeen, SD, p. A594

JACOBSON, Steven K., Chief Executive Officer and Administrator, Choctaw Memorial Hospital, Hugo, OK, p. A532

JACOBSON, Teresa, Director Human Resources, Riverwood HealthCare Center, Aitkin, MN, p. A349

JACOBUS, Patrick J., Chief Executive Officer, Val Verde Regional Medical Center, Del Rio, TX, p. A635

JACOBY, Jamie R., Chief Financial Officer, Memorial Medical Center, Port Lavaca, TX, p. A661

JACQUES, Teresa, Chief Executive Officer, Modoc Medical Center, Alturas, CA, p. A52

JADLOWSKI, Susan, Chief Operating Officer, Houston Northwest Medical Center, Houston, TX, p. A645

JAEGER, CHE, Mark J., Executive Vice President and Chief Operating Officer, Saint Anthony's Health Center, Alton, IL, p. A183

JAFFE, David E., Executive Director, Harborview Medical Center, Seattle, WA, p. A707

JAFFE, M.D., Gabriel, Vice President Medical Affairs, Doctors Community Hospital, Lanham, MD, p. A309

JAGER, Linda, Director Finance and Reimbursement, Avera Weskota Memorial Medical Center, Wessington Springs, SD, p. A600

JAHN, Francie, Senior Vice President Clinical Services, Broadlawns Medical Center, Des Moines, IA, p. A232

JAHNIG, Jay, Chief Executive Officer, Faulk County Memorial Hospital, Faulkton, SD, p. A595

JAIN, M.D., Rajiv, Chief of Staff, Veterans Affairs Pittsburgh Healthcare System, Pittsburgh, PA, p. A573

JAKACKI, Timothy, President, Fostoria Community Hospital, Fostoria, OH, p. A514

JAKOUBECK, Denise, Director Human Resources, Hancock County Memorial Hospital, Britt, IA, p. A229

JAMAL, M.D., S, Medical Director, Faith Community Hospital, Jacksboro, TX, p. A650

JAMERSON, Carlene, President and Chief Executive Officer, Gordon Hospital, Calhoun, GA, p. A157

JAMES, Bruce, Administrator, Sumner Regional Medical Center, Gallatin, TN, p. A606

JAMES, Craig B., Chief Executive Officer, Person Memorial Hospital, Roxboro, NC, p. A490

JAMES, Curtis, President and Chief Executive Officer, St. Vincent's Hospital, Birmingham, AL, p. A15

JAMES, Diane R., Administrator, Florida State Hospital, Chattahoochee, FL, p. A125

JAMES, Donald W., Ph.D., Administrator, Columbia Basin Hospital, Ephrata, WA, p. A702

JAMES, M.D., Jeanne, Chief Medical Officer, Tulane University Hospital and Clinic, New Orleans, LA, p. A290

JAMES, Laura, Director Human Resources, St. Francis Medical Center, Trenton, NJ, p. A437

JAMES, Marilyn, Chief Financial Officer, Lane County Hospital, Dighton, KS, p. A246

JAMES, Pat, Chief Operating Officer, Great Plains Regional Medical Center, Elk City, OK, p. A530

JAMES, Taya, Director, St. John's Hospital–Berryville, Berryville, AR, p. A40

JAMES, William B., Chief Executive Officer, Northern Hospital of Surry County, Mount Airy, NC, p. A488

JAMESON, R.N., Cecil, Chief Clinical Officer, San Angelo Community Medical Center, San Angelo, TX, p. A663

JAMIESON, Anne, Chief Executive Officer, Parkland Medical Center, Derry, NH, p. A420

JAMIN, David, Administrative Director Finance, Tulsa Regional Medical Center, Tulsa, OK, p. A540

JAMINET, Robert, Director Fiscal Services, Hawarden Community Hospital, Hawarden, IA, p. A235

JAMISON, Joan, Interim Chief Executive Officer, Buchanan General Hospital, Grundy, VA, p. A689

JAMISON, Richard, Chief Financial Officer, Royal C. Johnson Veterans Memorial Hospital, Sioux Falls, SD, p. A599

JAMNADAS, M.D., Brij B., Medical Staff President, OSF St. Mary Medical Center, Galesburg, IL, p. A195

JAN, M.D., Abdali, Chief of Staff, Parkview Noble Hospital, Kendallville, IN, p. A220

JANATKA, Lucille A., President and Chief Executive Officer, MidState Medical Center, Meriden, CT, p. A114

JANCZAK, Linda M., President and Chief Executive Officer, Thompson Health, Canandaigua, NY, p. A449

JANELL, Joseph, Senior Vice President Human Resources, Bridgeport Hospital, Bridgeport, CT, p. A112

JANEWAY, M.D., Mike, Executive Director Information Systems, Glendive Medical Center, Glendive, MT, p. A398

JANICAK, Dan, Chief Financial Officer, Littleton Adventist Hospital, Littleton, CO, p. A107

JANKE, Paul, Senior Vice President, Three Rivers Community Hospital and Health Center, Grants Pass, OR, p. A544

JANKOWSKI, Raymond M., President and Chief Executive Officer, Community Hospital of Long Beach, Long Beach, CA, p. A68

JANKOWSKI, Stan, Corporate Manager Information Technology, Hospital for Special Care, New Britain, CT, p. A114

JANNENE, Patricia, Vice President Patient Care Services, Porter Medical Center, Middlebury, VT, p. A682

JANOSO, Jack, Chief Information Officer, Sharon Regional Health System, Sharon, PA, p. A576

JANSSEN, Jerry, Chief Executive Officer, Select Specialty Hospital – Western Missouri, Kansas City, MO, p. A385

JANSSEN, Paul, Chief Financial Officer/Senior Vice President, Henry County Memorial Hospital, New Castle, IN, p. A223

JANUSZIEWICZ, Alan, Deputy Commander Clinical Services, DeWitt Army Community Hospital, Fort Belvoir, VA, p. A688

JANVRIN, Susan, R.N., Senior Vice President and Administrator, Kaiser Foundation Hospital, Santa Rosa, CA, p. A93

JARAMILLO, M.D., Andrew, Chief of Staff, St. Dominic's Hospital, Manteca, CA, p. A74

JARM, Timothy L., President, Jewish Hospital, Louisville, KY, p. A269

JARRETT, M.D., Mark, Chief Medical Officer, Staten Island University Hospital, New York, NY, p. A465

JARVIS, Keith, Director Information Systems, Longview Regional Medical Center, Longview, TX, p. A654

JARVIS, Patrick, Vice President Finance, Citizens Baptist Medical Center, Talladega, AL, p. A24

JASPERS, Anthony, President of the Medical Staff, Immanuel St. Joseph's–Mayo Health System, Mankato, MN, p. A356

JASPERSON, Steven W.
Chief Executive Officer, Good Samaritan Regional Medical Center, Corvallis, OR, p. A543
Executive Vice President Operations and Chief Operating Officer, Good Samaritan Regional Medical Center, Corvallis, OR, p. A543

JASTREMSKI, M.D., Michael S., Vice President Medical Affairs and Director Emergency Services, Community Memorial Hospital, Hamilton, NY, p. A453

JATCZAK, CPA, Tracy E., Chief Operating Officer, Box Butte General Hospital, Alliance, NE, p. A404

JAUDES, Paula Kienberger, M.D., President and Chief Executive Officer, La Rabida Children's Hospital, Chicago, IL, p. A187

JAVERSACK, Dawn, Vice President and Chief Financial Officer, Allegheny General Hospital, Pittsburgh, PA, p. A571

JAVIER, Malave, Administrator, Hospital San Carlos Borromeo, Moca, PR, p. A746

JEANS, Joe, Chief Financial Officer, Alleghany Regional Hospital, Low Moor, VA, p. A690

JED, Stuart A., Chief Executive Officer, Alameda Hospital, Alameda, CA, p. A52

JEFFCOTE, Richard, Chief Financial Officer, Lowell General Hospital, Lowell, MA, p. A319

JEFFREY, Paul A., Vice President, Behavioral Health Center, Greensboro, NC, p. A483

JEFFRIES, Larry, Senior Director Human Resources, Parma Community General Hospital, Parma, OH, p. A520

JEFFRIES, Richard, Commanding Officer, Naval Hospital, Camp Pendleton, CA, p. A56

JELALIAN, M.D., Christine, Medical Director, St. Luke's Cornwall Hospital – Newburgh Campus, Newburgh, NY, p. A467

JELLINEK, Michael, M.D., President, Newton–Wellesley Hospital, Newton Lower Falls, MA, p. A321

JENEY, Jeffrey S., President and Chief Executive Officer, St. Vincent Charity Hospital, Cleveland, OH, p. A509

JENKINS, Bonnie, Chief Financial Officer, Methodist Hospital of Sacramento, Sacramento, CA, p. A85

JENKINS, Jennifer, Service Unit Director, U. S. Public Health Service Indian Hospital, Cass Lake, MN, p. A351

JENKINS, Jim
Director Human Resources, Truman Medical Center–Hospital Hill, Kansas City, MO, p. A385
Director Human Resources, Truman Medical Center–Lakewood, Kansas City, MO, p. A385

JENKINS, John, Vice President and Chief Information Officer, Moses Cone Health System, Greensboro, NC, p. A484

JENKINS, Maynard, Director Human Resources, St. Mary's Medical Center, San Francisco, CA, p. A89

JENNER, Jody, Chief Executive Officer and Administrator, Pipestone County Medical Center/Avera Health, Pipestone, MN, p. A359

JENNER, Pam, Director Information Systems, Robert Wood Johnson University Hospital at Hamilton, Hamilton, NJ, p. A429

JENNEY, Karol A., Director Business Operations, Southwest Regional Rehabilitation Center, Battle Creek, MI, p. A328

JENNINGS, Barbara, Chief Financial Officer, Sierra–Kings District Hospital, Reedley, CA, p. A84

JENNINGS, D Arlo, Chief Information Officer, Mission Hospitals, Asheville, NC, p. A477

JENNINGS, Jason, Administrator, HEALTHSOUTH Rehabilitation Hospital–Cityview, Fort Worth, TX, p. A640

JENNINGS, Marilyn, Director Human Resources, HEALTHSOUTH Rehabilitation Hospital of Austin, Austin, TX, p. A623

JENNINGS, Mark, Director Information Systems, Northeast Georgia Medical Center, Gainesville, GA, p. A163

JENNINGS, Peter G., Chief Executive Officer, OSF St. Francis Hospital, Escanaba, MI, p. A332

JENNINGS, William M., Administrator and Chief Operating Officer, Morton Plant North Bay Hospital, New Port Richey, FL, p. A139

JENSEMA, Christine F., Administrative Director Human Resources, St. Nicholas Hospital, Sheboygan, WI, p. A735

JENSEN, Amy, Director Human Resources, Community Health Center of Branch County, Coldwater, MI, p. A330

JENSEN, Bruce C., Chief Executive Officer, St. Luke's Wood River Medical Center, Ketchum, ID, p. A179

JENSEN, David M A, Chief Financial Officer and Treasurer, Rush University Medical Center, Chicago, IL, p. A189

JENSEN, M.D., Donald, Chief Medical Officer, Broadlawns Medical Center, Des Moines, IA, p. A232

JENSEN, Eric
Administrator, Kittitas Valley Community Hospital, Ellensburg, WA, p. A702
Administrator, Kittitas Valley Community Hospital, Ellensburg, WA, p. A702
Administrator, Kittitas Valley Community Hospital, Ellensburg, WA, p. A702

JENSEN, Kayleen, Nursing Services Administrator, Gothenburg Memorial Hospital, Gothenburg, NE, p. A407

JENSEN, Ken, Chief Financial Officer, ValleyCare Medical Center, Pleasanton, CA, p. A82

JENSEN, Keri, Chief Financial Officer, Pioneers Hospital of Rio Blanco County, Meeker, CO, p. A108

JENSEN, Kim, Vice President Human Resources, Avera Sacred Heart Hospital, Yankton, SD, p. A601

JENSEN, Linda
Senior Vice President and Area Manager, Kaiser Foundation Hospital, Redwood City, CA, p. A83
Senior Vice President and Administrator, Kaiser Foundation Hospital, South San Francisco, CA, p. A94

JENSEN, Michael E., President and Chief Executive Officer, Davis Hospital and Medical Center, Layton, UT, p. A679

JENSEN, Neal, Chief Financial Officer, Cobre Valley Community Hospital, Globe, AZ, p. A31

JENSEN, Sherry, Chief Financial Officer, Granville Medical Center, Oxford, NC, p. A489

JENSEN, Twyla, Director Human Resources, Pioneers Hospital of Rio Blanco County, Meeker, CO, p. A108

JENSEN, Vicki, Chief Human Resources Officer, Spectrum Health–United Memorial, Greenville, MI, p. A335

JENSON, Paul M.
Chief Executive Officer, St. Luke's Behavioral Health Center, Phoenix, AZ, p. A35
Chief Executive Officer, St. Luke's Medical Center, Phoenix, AZ, p. A35

JENTES, Marge, Interim Chief Executive Officer, Twin City Hospital, Dennison, OH, p. A513

JEPSEN, Don, Director Information Systems, SwedishAmerican Hospital, Rockford, IL, p. A207

JEPSON, Brian, Chief Operating Officer, Morris Hospital & Healthcare Centers, Morris, IL, p. A201

JEPSON, Gary L., President and Chief Executive Officer, Central Texas Medical Center, San Marcos, TX, p. A666

JEPSON, Jeanne, Director Human Resources, Hackettstown Community Hospital, Hackettstown, NJ, p. A429

JEPSON, Mark, Associate Vice President, Silver Cross Hospital, Joliet, IL, p. A198

JERGENSON, Teresa, Director of Human Resources, Minnewaska District Hospital, Starbuck, MN, p. A363

JERGER, Greg, Chief Financial Officer, Memorial Health Care Systems, Seward, NE, p. A413

JERNIGAN, Donald L., Ph.D., President, Florida Hospital, Orlando, FL, p. A141

JERNIGAN Jr, Robert F., Chief Executive Officer, Summit Hospital, Baton Rouge, LA, p. A278

JESSEE, Randall E., M.D., Administrator, Woodridge Hospital, Johnson City, TN, p. A609

JESSEN, M.D., Michael, Medical Director, St. Paul University Hospital, Dallas, TX, p. A634

JESSON, M.D., Mark, Chief of Staff, Greenview Regional Hospital, Bowling Green, KY, p. A262

JESSOP, Daniel E., Executive Vice President and Chief Operating Officer, Queen's Medical Center, Honolulu, HI, p. A174

JESSUP, Daniel L., Chief Financial Officer, Southwest Memorial Hospital, Cortez, CO, p. A102

JETER, John H., M.D., President and Chief Executive Officer, Hays Medical Center, Hays, KS, p. A248

JETER, Larry R., Chief Executive Officer, Scott County Hospital, Oneida, TN, p. A616

JETTON, Dana, Chief Information Officer, Continuous Care Center of Tulsa, Tulsa, OK, p. A539

JETTON, Daniel, Chief Information Management Division, DeWitt Army Community Hospital, Fort Belvoir, VA, p. A688

JEUNEHOMME, Patti, Director Human Resources, Hot Springs County Memorial Hospital, Thermopolis, WY, p. A742

JEWELL, D. Keith, President and Executive Officer, St. Francis Hospital–Mooresville, Mooresville, IN, p. A222

JILANI, M.D., Sohail M., Chief of Staff, Hills and Dales General Hospital, Cass City, MI, p. A329

JIMBOY, Twylla, Supervisor Human Resources, U. S. Public Health Service Indian Hospital, Lawton, OK, p. A532

JIMENEZ, Daniel, Deputy Commander for Clinical Services, Moncrief Army Community Hospital, Fort Jackson, SC, p. A588

JIMENEZ, M.D., Gerson, Medical Director, Hospital Episcopal Cristo Redentor, Guayama, PR, p. A745

JINRIGHT, Nicki, Chief Financial Officer, Elba General Hospital, Elba, AL, p. A18

JIRINEC, Joe, Chief Executive Officer, South Central Kansas Regional Medical Center, Arkansas City, KS, p. A244

JOHANSSON, Sharon, Chief Financial Officer, Carson Tahoe Hospital, Carson City, NV, p. A415

JOHLMAN, Ed, Director Finance, Platte County Memorial Hospital, Wheatland, WY, p. A742

JOHN, Roger S., President and Chief Executive Officer, Great Plains Health Alliance, Inc., Phillipsburg, KS, p. B46

JOHNS, Chris, Chief Executive Officer, Monroe County Hospital, Monroeville, AL, p. A21

JOHNS, Mike, Vice President of Finance, Baptist Hospital, Nashville, TN, p. A615

JOHNS, Robert, Director Human Resources, Rochelle Community Hospital, Rochelle, IL, p. A206

JOHNSEN, Timothy J., President, St. John's Hospital – Lebanon, Lebanon, MO, p. A386

JOHNSON, Al, Vice President Human Resources, Abbott Northwestern Hospital, Minneapolis, MN, p. A357

JOHNSON, Alan, Director Information Systems, Doctors Community Hospital, Lanham, MD, p. A309

JOHNSON, Alexis, Director Human Resources, Green Oaks Hospital, Dallas, TX, p. A632

JOHNSON, Allen, Chief Financial Officer, Truman Medical Center–Hospital Hill, Kansas City, MO, p. A385

JOHNSON, Ashley F., Chief Financial Officer, Central Florida Regional Hospital, Sanford, FL, p. A146

JOHNSON, Barbara Jo
Senior Vice President Human Resources, Centegra Memorial Medical Center, Woodstock, IL, p. A210
Senior Vice President Human Resources, Centegra Northern Illinois Medical Center, McHenry, IL, p. A200

JOHNSON, Becky, Director Management Information Systems, Bedford Regional Medical Center, Bedford, IN, p. A211

JOHNSON, Betsey, Director Human Resources, Washington County Memorial Hospital, Salem, IN, p. A224

JOHNSON, Beverly, Vice President Human Resources, North Kansas City Hospital, Kansas City, MO, p. A384

JOHNSON, Bret
Chief Financial Officer, Bon Secours–St. Francis Xavier Hospital, Charleston, SC, p. A584
Chief Financial Officer, Roper Hospital, Charleston, SC, p. A585

JOHNSON, Brian, Chief Financial Officer, Bethesda Rehabilitation Hospital, Saint Paul, MN, p. A361

JOHNSON, Bridget, Interim Chief Operating Officer, Parkview Whitley Hospital, Columbia City, IN, p. A213

JOHNSON, III, C Thomas, Vice President Finance, Southeastern Regional Medical Center, Lumberton, NC, p. A487

JOHNSON, Calvin D., Chief Executive Officer, Kilmichael Hospital, Kilmichael, MS, p. A371

JOHNSON, Carrie H., Chief Nursing Officer, Georgetown Community Hospital, Georgetown, KY, p. A265

JOHNSON, Cassandra L., Vice President Human Resources, Memorial Health, Savannah, GA, p. A169

JOHNSON, Charles, Vice President Information Technology, Nebraska Methodist Hospital, Omaha, NE, p. A411

JOHNSON, Charlie, Vice President Finance and Chief Financial Officer, St. Marys Hospital Medical Center, Madison, WI, p. A728

JOHNSON, Chris, Information Services Manager, Dr. John Warner Hospital, Clinton, IL, p. A191

JOHNSON, Cindy, Vice President Human Resources, Lucile Salter Packard Children's Hospital at Stanford, Palo Alto, CA, p. A80

JOHNSON, M.D., Craig, Chief Medical Officer, Amery Regional Medical Center, Amery, WI, p. A722

JOHNSON, Craig A.
Chief Executive Officer and Chief Financial Officer, Boundary Community Hospital, Bonners Ferry, ID, p. A178
Chief Executive Officer and Chief Financial Officer, Boundary Community Hospital, Bonners Ferry, ID, p. A178

JOHNSON, Curtis A., President and Chief Executive Officer, Tri–County Memorial Hospital, Whitehall, WI, p. A738

JOHNSON, Danielle, Administrator, St. Joseph Memorial Hospital, Larned, KS, p. A251

JOHNSON, David, Chief Executive Officer, West Seattle Psychiatric Hospital, Seattle, WA, p. A708

JOHNSON, David L., Director, Medical Resource Management & Chief Financial Officer, U. S. Air Force Medical Center Keesler, Keesler AFB, MS, p. A371

JOHNSON, Debi, Chief Financial Officer, Minneola District Hospital, Minneola, KS, p. A253

JOHNSON, Deborah Carey, R.N., President and Chief Executive Officer, Eastern Maine Medical Center, Bangor, ME, p. A296

JOHNSON, Dennis, Director Human Resources, Baptist–Lutheran Medical Center, Kansas City, MO, p. A384

JOHNSON, Dennis B., Administrator, Baptist Hospital Northeast, La Grange, KY, p. A267

JOHNSON, Derrick, Vice President Operations, University of Medicine and Dentistry of New Jersey–University Hospital, Newark, NJ, p. A433

JOHNSON, Diana G., Acting Chief Human Resources Officer, Novato Community Hospital, Novato, CA, p. A78

JOHNSON, M.D., Donald, Chief Medical Officer, Mercy Medical Center, Springfield, OH, p. A522

JOHNSON, Donald D., Assistant Administrator Human Resources, Cass County Memorial Hospital, Atlantic, IA, p. A228

JOHNSON, Doug, Chief Financial Officer, Lakeview Hospital, Stillwater, MN, p. A363

JOHNSON, Douglas C., Associate Administrator and Chief Financial Officer, St. Joseph Regional Medical Center, Lewiston, ID, p. A180

JOHNSON, Douglas V., Executive Director, Sioux Falls Surgical Center, Sioux Falls, SD, p. A599

JOHNSON, Doyle K., Administrator, Mercy Hospital, Moundridge, KS, p. A253

JOHNSON, E D., Vice President Employee Development, South Haven Community Hospital, South Haven, MI, p. A345

JOHNSON, Earle, Site Manager, St. Mary Medical Center, Long Beach, CA, p. A68

JOHNSON, Eugene G., Chief Financial Officer, Southwest Washington Medical Center, Vancouver, WA, p. A711

JOHNSON, Gary, Director Human Resources, St. Luke's Regional Medical Center, Sioux City, IA, p. A242

JOHNSON, George, Administrator, David Grant Medical Center, Travis AFB, CA, p. A96

JOHNSON, George L., President, Reedsburg Area Medical Center, Reedsburg, WI, p. A734

JOHNSON, Gregory D., Administrator and Chief Executive Officer, Cox Monett Hospital, Monett, MO, p. A388

JOHNSON, MS, Howard P.
Vice President and Chief Operating Officer, Lakeview Medical Center, Rice Lake, WI, p. A734
Vice President and Chief Operating Officer, Lakeview Medical Center, Rice Lake, WI, p. A734

JOHNSON, Jama, Chief Financial Officer, Saint Luke's Hospital of Kansas City, Kansas City, MO, p. A385

JOHNSON, James, Chief Financial Officer, St. Joseph's Hospital, Highland, IL, p. A196

JOHNSON, James K., Chief Executive Officer, Hedrick Medical Center, Chillicothe, MO, p. A380

JOHNSON, Jana R., Associate Director, Veterans Affairs Sierra Nevada Health Care System, Reno, NV, p. A418

JOHNSON, Jay R., Chief Operating Officer, Mary Black Health System, Spartanburg, SC, p. A592

JOHNSON, Jeff
Vice President Human Resources and Community Services, LakeView Community Hospital, Paw Paw, MI, p. A342
Information Systems Director, Women's and Children's Hospital, Lafayette, LA, p. A284

JOHNSON, Jennifer, Director Human Resources, Mainland Medical Center, Texas City, TX, p. A670

JOHNSON, Jess, Director Information Services, North Star Behavioral Health System, Anchorage, AK, p. A26

JOHNSON, Jim, Director Information Systems, Ozarks Medical Center, West Plains, MO, p. A395

JOHNSON, Joe, President and Chief Executive Officer, Florida Hospital Fish Memorial, Orange City, FL, p. A140

JOHNSON, John C., Chief Executive Officer, Holy Cross Hospital, Fort Lauderdale, FL, p. A128

JOHNSON, John H.
Chief Executive Officer, Gothenburg Memorial Hospital, Gothenburg, NE, p. A407
Chief Executive Officer, Gothenburg Memorial Hospital, Gothenburg, NE, p. A407

JOHNSON, John W., President and Chief Executive Officer, Alice Hyde Medical Center, Malone, NY, p. A456

JOHNSON, Joy, R.N., Administrator, Ottawa County Health Center, Minneapolis, KS, p. A253

JOHNSON, R.N., Joyce E., Senior Vice President Operations, MedStar–Georgetown Medical Center, Washington, DC, p. A121

JOHNSON, Judith, Controller, HEALTHSOUTH Rehabilitation Hospital, Largo, FL, p. A134

JOHNSON, Kathryn, Manager Human Resources, St. Vincent Jennings Hospital, North Vernon, IN, p. A223

JOHNSON, Kathy, Chief Operating Officer, Mille Lacs Health System, Onamia, MN, p. A359

JOHNSON, Kenneth, Chief Financial Officer, Scott and White Memorial Hospital, Temple, TX, p. A669

JOHNSON, Kevin, Chief Executive Officer, Mountain View Hospital, Payson, UT, p. A678

JOHNSON, M.D., Kevin, Vice President Medical Affairs, SSM DePaul Health Center, Saint Louis, MO, p. A391

JOHNSON, Kirk, Chief Financial Officer, Paynesville Area Health Care System, Paynesville, MN, p. A359

JOHNSON, Kurt E., President and Chief Executive Officer, Ingalls Memorial Hospital, Harvey, IL, p. A196

JOHNSON, Laurence E., Administrator, Shriners Hospitals for Children, Twin Cities, Minneapolis, MN, p. A357

JOHNSON, Lori, Chief Financial Officer, Jackson Medical Center, Jackson, MN, p. A355

JOHNSON, Lowell W.
Senior Vice President and Chief Operating Officer, Hazleton General Hospital, Hazleton, PA, p. A560
Senior Vice President and Chief Operating Officer, Hazleton–St. Joseph Medical Center, Hazleton, PA, p. A560

JOHNSON, Ludwig, Vice President Information Technology, Middlesex Hospital, Middletown, CT, p. A114

JOHNSON, Lynn, Medical Information Systems Flight Commander, U. S. Air Force Regional Hospital, Elmendorf AFB, AK, p. A27

JOHNSON, Mark
Vice President Operations, St. John Detroit Riverview Hospital – Northeast Campus, Detroit, MI, p. A332
Vice President and Chief Financial Officer, St. Luke's Regional Medical Center, Sioux City, IA, p. A242
Vice President and Chief Financial Officer, St. Luke's Regional Medical Center, Sioux City, IA, p. A242

JOHNSON, M.D., Mark, Chief Medical Officer, Mercy Health Center, Oklahoma City, OK, p. A535

JOHNSON, M.D., Michael A., Chief of Staff, Bucyrus Community Hospital, Bucyrus, OH, p. A504

JOHNSON, Mike, Director Information Systems, Gaston Memorial Hospital, Gastonia, NC, p. A483

JOHNSON, Mitchell, Administrator and Chief Executive Officer, Baptist Memorial Hospital–Union County, New Albany, MS, p. A374

JOHNSON, Pamela, Corporate Vice President and Chief Financial Officer, Community–General Hospital of Greater Syracuse, Syracuse, NY, p. A473

JOHNSON, Paul
Director, Information Systems, Adirondack Medical Center, Saranac Lake, NY, p. A471
Executive Vice President Operations, WellStar Cobb Hospital, Austell, GA, p. A156
Executive Vice President Operations, WellStar Douglas Hospital, Douglasville, GA, p. A161
Executive Vice President Operations, WellStar Kennestone Hospital, Marietta, GA, p. A165
Executive Vice President Operations, WellStar Windy Hill Hospital, Marietta, GA, p. A165

JOHNSON, Peter A., Vice President Information Services, Mary Hitchcock Memorial Hospital, Lebanon, NH, p. A422

JOHNSON, Philip B., Vice President, Human Resources, Saint Mary's Hospital, Waterbury, CT, p. A117

JOHNSON, Phyllis, Chief Executive Officer, Select Specialty Hospital of Panama City, Panama City, FL, p. A142

JOHNSON, Randy E., Chief Executive Officer, Kindred Hospital–Bay Area, Pasadena, TX, p. A660

JOHNSON, Richard, Director Information Services, Connecticut Children's Medical Center, Hartford, CT, p. A113

JOHNSON, Richard E., Vice President Fiscal Services, New England Sinai Hospital and Rehabilitation Center, Stoughton, MA, p. A324

JOHNSON, Richard F., Senior Vice President and Chief Information Officer, Clarian Health Partners, Indianapolis, IN, p. A218

JOHNSON, Robert C., Chief Business Practices, John D. Dingell Veterans Affairs Medical Center, Detroit, MI, p. A331

JOHNSON, Roger, President and Chief Executive Officer, Alexian Brothers Medical Center, Elk Grove Village, IL, p. A193

JOHNSON, M.D., Roger, Chief of Staff, Veterans Affairs Medical Center, Cheyenne, WY, p. A739

JOHNSON, Roger L., Director, Veterans Affairs Connecticut Healthcare System–New Haven Division, West Haven, CT, p. A117

JOHNSON, Ronald
Vice President Operations and Chief Operating Officer, Shore Memorial Hospital, Somers Point, NJ, p. A436
Vice President Operations and Chief Operating Officer, Shore Memorial Hospital, Somers Point, NJ, p. A436

JOHNSON, Russell, Chief Executive Officer, San Luis Valley Regional Medical Center, Alamosa, CO, p. A101

JOHNSON, Samuel, Information Systems Manager, Halifax Regional Medical Center, Roanoke Rapids, NC, p. A490

JOHNSON, Sean, Administrator, Quitman County Hospital, Marks, MS, p. A372

JOHNSON, Stan
Acting Director, Jesse Brown Veterans Affairs Chicago Health Care System, Chicago, IL, p. A187
Chief Executive Officer, SCCI Hospital, Houston, TX, p. A647
Medical Center Director, Veterans Affairs Medical Center, Tomah, WI, p. A736
Medical Center Director, Veterans Affairs Medical Center, Tomah, WI, p. A736

JOHNSON, Steven M., President and Chief Executive Officer, Bay Medical Center, Panama City, FL, p. A142

JOHNSON, Steven P., Ph.D., President, SSM Rehab, Saint Louis, MO, p. A391

JOHNSON, Steven P.
President and Chief Executive Officer, Susquehanna Health System, Williamsport, PA, p. A580
Senior Vice President and Chief Operating Officer, Susquehanna Health System, Williamsport, PA, p. A580

JOHNSON, Susan, Chief Financial Officer, Memorial Hermann Southwest Hospital, Houston, TX, p. A646

JOHNSON, Sy, Chief Financial Officer, St. John Medical Center, Longview, WA, p. A704

JOHNSON, Tim, Chief Financial Officer, Eaton Rapids Medical Center, Eaton Rapids, MI, p. A332

JOHNSON, Timothy, M.D., President, Austin Medical Center, Austin, MN, p. A349

JOHNSON, Todd, President and Chief Executive Officer, Hospital Partners of America, Charlotte, NC, p. B60

JOHNSON, Jr, Torrey M., Chief Financial Officer, Cape Fear Valley Health System, Fayetteville, NC, p. A482

JOHNSON, Vernon, Administrator, Dale Medical Center, Ozark, AL, p. A23

JOHNSON, Jr, Walter E., Senior Vice President Operations, Jefferson Regional Medical Center, Pine Bluff, AR, p. A49

JOHNSON, William
Chief Information Officer, Fauquier Hospital, Warrenton, VA, p. A698
Vice President and Chief Financial Officer, Tuomey Healthcare System, Sumter, SC, p. A592

JOHNSON–BROWN, Pamela, Human Resources Director, North Ridge Medical Center, Fort Lauderdale, FL, p. A129

JOHNSRUD, Kimry A., President, Elmbrook Memorial Hospital, Brookfield, WI, p. A723

JOHNSTON, Charles, Administrator, Pauls Valley General Hospital, Pauls Valley, OK, p. A537

JOHNSTON, M.D., Charles B., Chief of Staff, Alegent Health Community Memorial Hospital, Missouri Valley, IA, p. A238

JOHNSTON, Clay, Administrator, Covington County Hospital, Collins, MS, p. A368

JOHNSTON, Greg, Chief Financial Officer, Baptist Princeton, Birmingham, AL, p. A14

JOHNSTON, Jeff, Chief Operating Officer, Mercy Health Center, Oklahoma City, OK, p. A535

JOHNSTON, Joe, Chief Executive Officer, Jay County Hospital, Portland, IN, p. A224

JOHNSTON, John, Manager Information Systems, Northwestern Medical Center, Saint Albans, VT, p. A683

JOHNSTON, M.D., Kenneth, Vice President of Medical Affairs, Baptist St. Anthony Health System, Amarillo, TX, p. A621

JOHNSTON, Lori, Vice President Finance, The Toledo Hospital, Toledo, OH, p. A523

JOHNSTON, M.D., Michael V., Chief Medical Officer and Senior Vice President Medical Programs, Kennedy Krieger Institute, Baltimore, MD, p. A303

JOHNSTON, Phyllis, Director, Catawba Valley Medical Center, Hickory, NC, p. A484

JOHNSTON, Wayne W., President and Chief Executive Officer, Sharon Regional Health System, Sharon, PA, p. A576

JOINER, Wayne, Vice President Human Resources, The Medical Center, Columbus, GA, p. A159

JOLET, Peter, Administrator, La Place Rehabilitation Hospital, La Place, LA, p. A283

JOLLEY, Brandon W., President and Chief Executive Officer, Copper Basin Medical Center, Copperhill, TN, p. A605

JOLLEY, Dotty, Supervisor Information Systems, Lourdes Medical Center, Pasco, WA, p. A705

JOLLY, Jay P., Chief Executive Officer, Goodland Regional Medical Center, Goodland, KS, p. A247

JONAS, Stanley W., Chief Executive Officer, Alliance Community Hospital, Alliance, OH, p. A502

JONES, Alan, Director, Christ Hospital, Cincinnati, OH, p. A506

JONES, M.D., Albert, Director Medical, Sheltering Arms Rehabilitation Hospital, Mechanicsville, VA, p. A691

JONES, Alma, Administrator, Gadsden Community Hospital, Quincy, FL, p. A144

JONES, Bradley E., Chief Executive Officer, Crestwood Medical Center, Huntsville, AL, p. A20

JONES, Brent, Chief of Medical Staff, Mountain View Hospital, Payson, UT, p. A678

JONES, Chris, Administrator, Northern California Rehabilitation Hospital, Redding, CA, p. A83

JONES, Christiane J., Associate Director, Veterans Affairs Gulf Coast Veterans Health Care System, Biloxi, MS, p. A367

JONES, Dale, Administrator, Long Term Care Hospital, Birmingham, AL, p. A15

JONES, Dallas, Head Management Information / Naval Hospital, Beaufort, SC, p. A584

JONES Jr, Dan L.
Chief Executive Officer, Independence Regional Health Center, Independence, MO, p. A383
Chief Executive Officer, Medical Center of Independence, Independence, MO, p. A383

JONES, Dave, Chief Financial Officer, Beckley Appalachian Regional Hospital, Beckley, WV, p. A713

JONES, David, Director Information Systems, Titus Regional Medical Center, Mount Pleasant, TX, p. A657

JONES, M.D., David, Medical Staff President, Shore Memorial Hospital, Nassawadox, VA, p. A692

JONES, David R., Chief Executive Officer, Hartselle Medical Center, Hartselle, AL, p. A20

JONES, Deron, Acting Chief Information Resource Management, Veterans Affairs Illiana Health Care System, Danville, IL, p. A191

JONES, Derrick A., Administrator, Wishek Community Hospital and Clinics, Wishek, ND, p. A501

JONES, Deryl L., President and Chief Executive Officer, Adventist Medical Center, Portland, OR, p. A547

JONES, Donald J., Administrator, North Mississippi Medical Center–Hamilton, Hamilton, AL, p. A20

JONES, Douglas T., Chief Executive Officer, Maine Coast Memorial Hospital, Ellsworth, ME, p. A298

JONES, Dwayne, Chief Executive Officer, Fairchild Medical Center, Yreka, CA, p. A100

JONES, Ellen M., President and Chief Executive Officer, Christus St. Patrick Hospital of Lake Charles, Lake Charles, LA, p. A284

JONES, Evelyn, Director Human Resources, Choctaw Nation Health Care Center, Talihina, OK, p. A539

JONES, Gary, Vice President Human Resources, St. Anthony Central Hospital, Denver, CO, p. A104

JONES, George R., Director, Carl Albert Community Mental Health Center, McAlester, OK, p. A533

JONES, Greg
 Chief Financial Officer, Appling Healthcare System, Baxley, GA, p. A156
 Interim Chief Information Officer, St. Vincent Hospitals and Health Services, Indianapolis, IN, p. A219

JONES, H Roger, Chief Financial Officer, Straith Hospital for Special Surgery, Southfield, MI, p. A345

JONES, J. Thomas, President and Chief Executive Officer, West Virginia United Health System, Fairmont, WV, p. B122

JONES, Jeff, Director Human Resources, Florida Hospital–Ormond Memorial, Ormond Beach, FL, p. A141

JONES, M.D., Ph, Jeffrey M., Chief of Staff, William S. Middleton Memorial Veterans Hospital, Madison, WI, p. A728

JONES, Jerry, Administrator, Integris Clinton Regional Hospital, Clinton, OK, p. A529

JONES, John M., Administrator, Richland Parish Rehabilitation Hospital, Rayville, LA, p. A291

JONES, Kathleen, Vice President Finance and Chief Financial Officer, San Diego Hospice & Palliative Care, San Diego, CA, p. A87

JONES, Ken M., Chief Financial Officer, UCSF Medical Center, San Francisco, CA, p. A89

JONES, Kevin, Director Financial, Aurora Sinai Medical Center, Milwaukee, WI, p. A730

JONES, Lance
 Chief Executive Officer, Woodland Heights Medical Center, Lufkin, TX, p. A655
 Chief Operating Officer, Carolinas Hospital System, Florence, SC, p. A587

JONES, Lola, R.N., Administrator, Chase County Community Hospital, Imperial, NE, p. A408

JONES, Mark T., Executive Vice President and System Chief Executive Officer, Holy Redeemer Hospital and Medical Center, Jenkintown, PA, p. A561

JONES, Marlene, Chief Executive Officer, Kimble Hospital, Junction, TX, p. A650

JONES, Marshall, Vice President Human Resources, United Regional Health Care System, Wichita Falls, TX, p. A674

JONES, Mary, Director Human Resources, Beauregard Memorial Hospital, De Ridder, LA, p. A280

JONES, Mary Anne, Chief Financial Officer, Spectrum Health–United Memorial, Greenville, MI, p. A335

JONES, Mary Joe, Chief Operating Officer, Ogden Regional Medical Center, Ogden, UT, p. A678

JONES, Meg, Vice President Human Resources, Children's Hospital of Philadelphia, Philadelphia, PA, p. A567

JONES, Melissa, Director of Health Information, Flandreau Medical Center/Avera Health, Flandreau, SD, p. A595

JONES, Michael, Chief of Staff, Ennis Regional Medical Center, Ennis, TX, p. A638

JONES, M.D., Michael, Chief of Staff, Atchison Hospital, Atchison, KS, p. A244

JONES, Ph.D., Michael L., Corporate Vice President and Chief Information Officer, Children's Hospital of Wisconsin, Milwaukee, WI, p. A730

JONES, Nancy, Chief Information Officer, Akron General Medical Center, Akron, OH, p. A502

JONES, Pat, Director Information Systems, River Oaks Hospital, Jackson, MS, p. A371

JONES, Patsy, Director, Memorial Hermann Fort Bend Hospital, Missouri City, TX, p. A657

JONES, Randy, Director Information Systems, West Houston Medical Center, Houston, TX, p. A649

JONES, Rex
 Interim Chief Executive Officer, Okmulgee Memorial Hospital, Okmulgee, OK, p. A536
 Chief Executive Officer, Sayre Memorial Hospital, Sayre, OK, p. A538

JONES, Richard, Chief Financial Officer, Louis A. Weiss Memorial Hospital, Chicago, IL, p. A188

JONES, M.D., Richard, Medical Director, HEALTHSOUTH Plano Rehabilitation Hospital, Plano, TX, p. A661

JONES, Jr, CPA, Richard L., Senior Vice President Finance and Chief Financial Officer, Stamford Health System, Stamford, CT, p. A116

JONES Jr, Richard L., FACHE, President and Chief Executive Officer, Abington Memorial Hospital, Abington, PA, p. A551

JONES, Rita, Chief Executive Officer, Dundy County Hospital, Benkelman, NE, p. A405

JONES, Robert
 Director Management Information Systems, St. Joseph Mercy Oakland, Pontiac, MI, p. A343
 Director, Trinity Information Systems, St. Joseph's Mercy of Macomb, Clinton Township, MI, p. A330

JONES, Robert D., President, Rutherford Hospital, Rutherfordton, NC, p. A491

JONES, Rodney, Chief Operating Officer, Forum Hillside Rehabilitation Hospital, Warren, OH, p. A524

JONES, Ruth, Comptroller, Dr. Dan C. Trigg Memorial Hospital, Tucumcari, NM, p. A445

JONES, Scott R., Chief Executive Officer, North Greenville Hospital, Travelers Rest, SC, p. A592

JONES, Shana, Ph.D., Administrator, Shriners Hospitals for Children–Chicago, Chicago, IL, p. A190

JONES, Sonny, Vice President Finance, St. Claire Regional Medical Center, Morehead, KY, p. A272

JONES, M.D., Stephen K.
 Vice President Medical Staff Affairs, St. Rose Dominican Hospitals – Rose de Lima Campus, Henderson, NV, p. A416
 Vice President Medical Staff Affairs, St. Rose Dominican Hospitals – Siena Campus, Henderson, NV, p. A416

JONES Jr, Stephen K., FACHE, Chief Executive Officer, Southwest Medical Center, Lafayette, LA, p. A284

JONES, Susan, Vice President of Human Resources, Self Regional Healthcare, Greenwood, SC, p. A589

JONES, Tami, Administrator, Choctaw County Medical Center, Ackerman, MS, p. A366

JONES, Terry L., Executive Vice President and Chief Operating Officer, Gaston Memorial Hospital, Gastonia, NC, p. A483

JONES, M.D., Terry R., Medical Director, Lallie Kemp Medical Center, Independence, LA, p. A282

JONES, Theresa, Manager Human Resources, St. Luke Community Hospital, Ronan, MT, p. A401

JONES, Tonya, Director Human Resourceds, Granville Medical Center, Oxford, NC, p. A489

JONES, Vernita, Site Manager, PHS Santa Fe Indian Hospital, Santa Fe, NM, p. A444

JONES, Vicki, Director Human Resources, Memorial Hermann Memorial City Hospital, Houston, TX, p. A646

JONES, Vivian, Senior Vice President Operations, Bon Secours Baltimore Health System, Baltimore, MD, p. A302

JONES, W Clark, Administrator and Chief Fiancial Officer, Cascade Valley Hospital and Clinics, Arlington, WA, p. A700

JONES, W. Clark, Administrator, Cascade Valley Hospital and Clinics, Arlington, WA, p. A700

JONES, William G., Administrator, Martin County Hospital District, Stanton, TX, p. A667

JORDAN, Bobby, Chief Executive Officer, Winn Parish Medical Center, Winnfield, LA, p. A294

JORDAN, David, Vice President Human Resources, Valley View Regional Hospital, Ada, OK, p. A527

JORDAN, Gary W.
 President, St. John's Hospital – Aurora, Aurora, MO, p. A378
 President, St. John's Hospital – Cassville, Cassville, MO, p. A380

JORDAN, James
 Chief Executive Officer, Kit Carson County Memorial Hospital, Burlington, CO, p. A101
 Director Information Systems, St. Mary's Medical Center, Huntington, WV, p. A716

JORDAN, Jill, Administrator, Regional Rehabilitation Hospital, Phenix City, AL, p. A23

JORDAN, Kathy, Administrator, Hill Hospital of Sumter County, York, AL, p. A25

JORDAN, Linda U., Administrator, Clay County Hospital, Ashland, AL, p. A13

JORDAN, Lori, Director Human Resources Services, Oak Forest Hospital of Cook County, Oak Forest, IL, p. A203

JORDAN, Patrick, Senior Vice President for Administration, Newton–Wellesley Hospital, Newton Lower Falls, MA, p. A321

JORDAN, M.D., Paul, Chief of Staff, Placentia Linda Hospital, Placentia, CA, p. A81

JORDAN, Randall, Budget Analyst, U. S. Public Health Service Indian Hospital, Cass Lake, MN, p. A351

JORDAN, W. Charles, Administrator, Integris Mayes County Medical Center, Pryor, OK, p. A537

JORVE, Helen, Chief Executive Officer, Graceville Health Center, Graceville, MN, p. A354

JORY, M.D., Carl, Chief of Staff, Bunkie General Hospital, Bunkie, LA, p. A278

JOSEF, Norma C., M.D., Director, Walter P. Reuther Psychiatric Hospital, Westland, MI, p. A348

JOSEHART, Carl
 Chief Operating Officer, Mount Sinai Hospital Medical Center of Chicago, Chicago, IL, p. A188
 Senior Vice President and Chief Operating Officer, Schwab Rehabilitation Hospital, Chicago, IL, p. A190

JOSEPH, Gloria, Superintendent, Western Missouri Mental Health Center, Kansas City, MO, p. A386

JOSEPH, Michael G., Administrator, Cedars Medical Center, Miami, FL, p. A137

JOSEPH, Vincent D., Executive Vice President and Chief Operating Officer, Greater Baltimore Medical Center, Baltimore, MD, p. A302

JOSEY, Brenda, Administrator, Wheeler County Hospital, Glenwood, GA, p. A163

JOSHI, Shobhana, M.D., Facility Director, Hawthorn Center, Northville, MI, p. A342

JOSLIN, Tim A., President and Chief Executive Officer, Community Medical Centers, Fresno, CA, p. B32

JOSLYN, M.D., E Allen, Chief Medical Officer, Bedford Memorial Hospital, Bedford, VA, p. A685

JOUBERT, James A., Chief Executive Officer, Premier Rehabilitation Hospital, Monroe, LA, p. A287

JOYAL, Shirley, Director Information Systems, Regional Medical Center of San Jose, San Jose, CA, p. A90

JOYCE, Christopher, Director Human Resources, Methodist Hospital of Sacramento, Sacramento, CA, p. A85

JOYCE, M.D., Roby, Chairman, Medical Board, Methodist Hospital, San Antonio, TX, p. A664

JOYNER, M.D., Lee Roy, Medical Director, Bogalusa Medical Center, Bogalusa, LA, p. A278

JUAREZ, Jay, Director Information Systems, San Ramon Regional Medical Center, San Ramon, CA, p. A91

JUDD, Russell V., President, Mercy Hospital, Bakersfield, CA, p. A54

JUDY, Jess N., President and Chief Executive Officer, Austin Surgical Hospital, Austin, TX, p. A623

JUDY, Mark D., Chief Executive Officer, Valley General Hospital, Monroe, WA, p. A704

JUENGLING, Craig S., President, Potomac Ridge Behavioral Health System, Rockville, MD, p. A310

JULIAN, Bell, Administrator Fiscal Services, Ohio State University James Cancer Hospital, Columbus, OH, p. A510

JULIAN, Marcus, Chief Operating Officer and Vice President Mission, St. Francis Regional Medical Center, Shakopee, MN, p. A363

JULIAN, Paul J., Vice President, Chief Information Officer, Muskogee Regional Medical Center, Muskogee, OK, p. A534

JULIUS, John D., Chief Executive Officer, Wahiawa General Hospital, Wahiawa, HI, p. A176

JUMONVILLE III, John E., Administrator, Community Rehabilitation Hospital of Lafayette, Lafayette, LA, p. A283

JUMONVILLE, Lydia, Chief Financial Officer, Baylor University Medical Center, Dallas, TX, p. A632

JUMP, Beth, Chief Information Officer, Memorial Hospital, Logansport, IN, p. A221

JUMP, Gary, Vice President Information and Materials Systems, Our Lady of the Lake Regional Medical Center, Baton Rouge, LA, p. A277

JUNGBLUT, M.D., Peter R., Vice President Medical Affairs and Chief Medical Officer, Shore Memorial Hospital, Somers Point, NJ, p. A436

JUNK, Stacy, Human Resources Team Specialist, Dupont Hospital, Fort Wayne, IN, p. A215

JURENA, Jerry E., Executive Director, Heart of America Medical Center, Rugby, ND, p. A500

JURGENS, Chad, Chief Financial Officer, Jefferson Community Health Center, Fairbury, NE, p. A406

JURICA, M.D., John, Vice President Medical Affairs, Riverside Medical Center, Kankakee, IL, p. A198

JUST, Paula, Director Human Resources, Saint Louis University Hospital, Saint Louis, MO, p. A391

JUSTIN, Patrick A.
Chief Financial Officer, District One Hospital, Faribault, MN, p. A353
Chief Financial Officer, District One Hospital, Faribault, MN, p. A353

JUSTUS, M.D., Michael, Chief of Staff, White County Medical Center, Searcy, AR, p. A50

JUSTYN, Kathryn D., Chief Executive Officer, Aiken Regional Medical Centers, Aiken, SC, p. A583

JUZDOWSKI, Kimberly, Manager, Human Resources, St. Joseph Hospital, Cheektowaga, NY, p. A450

K

KAATZ, Gary E., President and Chief Executive Officer, Rockford Memorial Hospital, Rockford, IL, p. A206

KADISH, M.D., Lawrence J., Executive Vice President and Medical Director, White Plains Hospital Center, White Plains, NY, p. A476

KAHN, Drew, Chief Operating Officer, Cypress Fairbanks Medical Center, Houston, TX, p. A644

KAHN, Maureen A., President and Chief Executive Officer, Blessing Hospital, Quincy, IL, p. A206

KAHN, Robert C., Chief of Staff, Roanoke–Chowan Hospital, Ahoskie, NC, p. A477

KAHN, Russell, Administrator, Vermilion Hospital, Lafayette, LA, p. A284

KAI, Celeese, Director Foundation and Communications, Sierra–Kings District Hospital, Reedley, CA, p. A84

KAIGLER, James S., FACHE, Chief Executive Officer, Regency Hospital of Hattiesburg, Hattiesburg, MS, p. A369

KAIL, Bill, Administrator, Humboldt General Hospital, Humboldt, TN, p. A607

KAISER, Brenda, Director Human Resources, McCune–Brooks Hospital, Carthage, MO, p. A380

KAISER, M.D., Gerard A., Senior Vice President, Jackson Memorial Hospital, Miami, FL, p. A137

KAISER, Melissa, Human Resources Director, Galena–Stauss Hospital and Healthcare Center, Galena, IL, p. A195

KAJANDER, John, President, The Institute for Rehabilitation and Research, Houston, TX, p. A648

KAJIWARA, Gary K., President and Chief Executive Officer, Kuakini Medical Center, Honolulu, HI, p. A173

KALAJAINEN, Kim, Chief Information Officer, Rutland Regional Medical Center, Rutland, VT, p. A683

KALANIHUIA, Janice, Administrator, Molokai General Hospital, Kaunakakai, HI, p. A175

KALBERER, Kenneth, Information System Manager, Veterans Affairs Medical Center, Butler, PA, p. A554

KALCHIK, Kevin, Chief Financial Officer, War Memorial Hospital, Sault Ste. Marie, MI, p. A345

KALE, Debbie, Assistant Vice President Human Resources, Cleveland Regional Medical Center, Shelby, NC, p. A491

KALETKOWSKI, Chester B., President and Chief Executive Officer, South Jersey Healthcare, Bridgeton, NJ, p. A426

KALGAARD, Jan, Chief Financial Officer, Shodair Children's Hospital, Helena, MT, p. A399

KALLEN–ZURY, Karen, Chief Executive Officer, Hollywood Pavilion, Hollywood, FL, p. A131

KALLENBERGER, Dianna, Chief Manpower Branch, Irwin Army Community Hospital, Junction City, KS, p. A250

KALMAN, M.D., Alfred, Chief of Staff, University Hospital and Medical Center, Tamarac, FL, p. A147

KALTHOFF, Stella, Quality Improvement Coordinator, Swift County–Benson Hospital, Benson, MN, p. A350

KALVAITIS, Christiana, Manager Management Information Systems, Claxton–Hepburn Medical Center, Ogdensburg, NY, p. A468

KAMBIC, Phillip, Senior Vice President and Chief Operating Officer, Riverside Medical Center, Kankakee, IL, p. A198

KAMERMAN, Bob, Chief Information Officer, St. Paul University Hospital, Dallas, TX, p. A634

KAMINSKI, Michael S., President and Chief Executive Officer, Kingston Hospital, Kingston, NY, p. A455

KAMMERMAN, Bruk, Director Information Systems, St. Mark's Hospital, Salt Lake City, UT, p. A680

KAMNANI, M.D., Laxmichand, Chief Medical Staff, Pampa Regional Medical Center, Pampa, TX, p. A659

KAMP, Pam Renne, Human Resources Director, Rush Memorial Hospital, Rushville, IN, p. A224

KAMPS, Mary Jane, Chief Information Officer, Union Hospital, Elkton, MD, p. A307

KANALEY, John, Chief Executive Officer, Laguna Honda Hospital and Rehabilitation Center, San Francisco, CA, p. A89

KANE, Cynthia B., Executive Vice President and Chief Operating Officer, Lawrence & Memorial Hospital, New London, CT, p. A115

KANE, Daniel A., Acting President and Chief Executive Officer, Nassau University Medical Center, East Meadow, NY, p. A451

KANKEL, LeAnne, Director Human Resources, Barton Memorial Hospital, South Lake Tahoe, CA, p. A94

KANNADAY, Colleen, President, St. Francis Hospital & Health Center, Blue Island, IL, p. A185

KANNADY, Donald L., Chief Executive Officer, Bunkie General Hospital, Bunkie, LA, p. A278

KANSGEN, Mike, Director Information Services, Community Hospital, Grand Junction, CO, p. A106

KANTOS, Craig A., Chief Executive Officer, Riverside Medical Center, Waupaca, WI, p. A737

KAPASKA, D.O., David, Senior Vice President Medical Affairs, Avera McKennan Hospital and University Health Center, Sioux Falls, SD, p. A599

KAPFER, Don, Chief Financial Officer, Oakes Community Hospital, Oakes, ND, p. A500

KAPFER, Donald, Finance Director, Lisbon Area Health Services, Lisbon, ND, p. A499

KAPHINES, Mary, Human Resource Manager, Fairview Red Wing Medical Center, Red Wing, MN, p. A360

KAPLAN, M.D., Alan, Vice President and Chief Medical Officer, Edward Hospital, Naperville, IL, p. A202

KAPLAN, Ronald, Chief Financial Officer, North Philadelphia Health System, Philadelphia, PA, p. A569

KAPPELMAN, Paul, Chief Executive Officer, Northwest Medical Center, Oro Valley, Oro Valley, AZ, p. A33

KARADJOFF, Peter, President and Chief Executive Officer, Mercy Hospital, Port Huron, MI, p. A343

KARAM, Chris, President and Chief Executive Officer, Christus St. Michael Health System, Texarkana, TX, p. A669

KARAM, Judith Ann, President and Chief Executive Officer, Sisters of Charity of St. Augustine Health System, Cleveland, OH, p. B99

KARBER, M.D., Steven, Medical Director, Greene County Medical Center, Jefferson, IA, p. A236

KAREL, Thomas, Director Human Resources, Saint Mary's Health Care, Grand Rapids, MI, p. A335

KARGBO, Mary, Chief Operating Officer, Medina Memorial Hospital, Medina, NY, p. A456

KARL, Don, Chief Operating Officer, Las Palmas Medical Center, El Paso, TX, p. A637

KARL, Peter J.
President and Chief Executive Officer, Eastern Connecticut Health Network, Manchester, CT, p. B43
President and Chief Executive Officer, Manchester Memorial Hospital, Manchester, CT, p. A113
President and Chief Executive Officer, Rockville General Hospital, Vernon Rockville, CT, p. A117

KARL, Thomas P., Assistant Administrator Finance, Parkland Health Center, Farmington, MO, p. A382

KARLIN, Jane, Director Human Resources, Southwestern Memorial Hospital, Weatherford, OK, p. A541

KARNAP, Fred W., Vice President Finance, Iredell Memorial Hospital, Statesville, NC, p. A492

KARPA, Carol, Director Information Services, Weirton Medical Center, Weirton, WV, p. A720

KARSH, Sheri, Director Human Resources, Siloam Springs Memorial Hospital, Siloam Springs, AR, p. A50

KARSNER, Garry L., Chief Executive Officer, Lake City Medical Center, Lake City, FL, p. A134

KARSON, Bryan E., Acting Vice President Finance and Chief Financial Officer, Medical Center East, Birmingham, AL, p. A15

KARSOS, Felicia, Acting Administrator, Saint Michael's Medical Center, Newark, NJ, p. A433

KARSTEN, Margo A., Chief Executive Officer and President, Poudre Valley Hospital, Fort Collins, CO, p. A105

KARSTEN, Paul H., Vice President Finance and Chief Financial Officer, Pine Rest Christian Mental Health Services, Grand Rapids, MI, p. A334

KARTTUNEN, Pam, Administrative Assistant, Ontonagon Memorial Hospital, Ontonagon, MI, p. A342

KARUSCHAK Jr, Michael, Chief Executive Officer, Amery Regional Medical Center, Amery, WI, p. A722

KASABIAN, Carolyn, Chief Financial Officer, St. Mary's Regional Medical Center, Lewiston, ME, p. A299

KASBERGER, John, Vice President, Chief Financial Officer and Corporate Responsibility Officer, Mercy Medical Center, Roseburg, OR, p. A548

KASEY, Jay D., Interim Chief Operating Officer, University of California Los Angeles Medical Center, Los Angeles, CA, p. A73

KASINATHAN, Chitra, Finance Site Manager, Riverview Medical Center, Red Bank, NJ, p. A435

KASKIE, James R., President and Chief Operating Officer, Buffalo General Hospital, Buffalo, NY, p. A448

KASPERBAUER, Dwight, Vice President Human Resources, University of Kansas Hospital, Kansas City, KS, p. A250

KASS, Christine, Vice President Human Resources, Advocate Good Shepherd Hospital, Barrington, IL, p. A184

KASS, Stephan, Vice President for Human Resources, SUNY Downstate Medical Center University Hospital, New York, NY, p. A466

KASTELIC, John, Vice President Finance, MedCentral Health System, Mansfield, OH, p. A517

KASTER, Laura, Chief Information Officer, Yampa Valley Medical Center, Steamboat Springs, CO, p. A109

KATEN–BAHENSKY, Donna, Director and Chief Executive Officer, University of Iowa Hospitals and Clinics, Iowa City, IA, p. A236

KATES, Kenneth P., Executive Vice President and Chief Operating Officer, University of Chicago Hospitals, Chicago, IL, p. A191

KATHAHN, Laura, Associate Administrator, St. John's Hospital, Saint Paul, MN, p. A362

KATHRINS, Richard J., Administrator and Chief Executive Officer, Bacharach Institute for Rehabilitation, Pomona, NJ, p. A435

KATO, Laura, Vice President Human Resources, St. Francis Medical Center, Lynwood, CA, p. A74

KATOVICH, Jr, J R., Chief of Staff, Benewah Community Hospital, Saint Maries, ID, p. A181

KATSIANIS, John
Chief Financial Officer, CARITAS Medical Center, Louisville, KY, p. A269
Chief Financial Officer, CARITAS Peace Center, Louisville, KY, p. A269

KATZ, M.D., Richard, Senior Vice President Medical Affairs, Mt. Washington Pediatric Hospital, Baltimore, MD, p. A304

KATZ, Treuman, President and Chief Executive Officer, Children's Hospital and Regional Medical Center, Seattle, WA, p. A707

KATZ, M.D., Vern, Chief of Staff, Sacred Heart Medical Center, Eugene, OR, p. A543

KAUFFMAN, M.D., Clint, Medical Staff President, Pulaski Memorial Hospital, Winamac, IN, p. A227

KAUFMAN, Alan G., Director, Division of Mental Health Services, Department of Human Services, State of New Jersey, Trenton, NJ, p. B41

KAUFMAN, Lawrence W., Administrator and Chief Operating Officer, Largo Medical Center, Largo, FL, p. A134

KAUFMAN, M.D., Ronald, Chief Medical Officer, Lakewood Regional Medical Center, Lakewood, CA, p. A67

KAUFMAN, Samuel, Chief Executive Officer and Managing Director, Desert Springs Hospital, Las Vegas, NV, p. A416

KAUFMAN, Thomas D., President and Chief Executive Officer, Spectrum Health–Reed City Campus, Reed City, MI, p. A343

KAUL, Sid, Chief Information Officer, Wyckoff Heights Medical Center, New York, NY, p. A466

KAULEY, Nadine K., Chief Financial Officer, U. S. Public Health Service Indian Hospital, Sells, AZ, p. A36

KAUSCH, Mary, Interim Director Human Resources, SSM St. Mary's Health Center, Saint Louis, MO, p. A392

KAUTZER, Kenneth A., Senior Vice President Finance and Treasurer, Saint's Mary & Elizabeth Medical Center, Division Street, Chicago, IL, p. A190

KAVANAUGH, Paul B., President and Chief Executive Officer, Community Care Hospital, New Orleans, LA, p. A288

KAWABATA, Lloyd, Chief Financial Officer, Kula Hospital, Kula, HI, p. A175

KAY, Brian, Chief Financial Officer, Bay Regional Medical Center, Bay City, MI, p. A328

KAY, M.D., Robert, Chief of Staff, Cleveland Clinic Foundation, Cleveland, OH, p. A508

KAY, Robert W., Senior Vice President and Chief Financial Officer, Memorial Medical Center, Springfield, IL, p. A208

KAYE, Jane, Vice President Finance, Bayshore Community Hospital, Holmdel, NJ, p. A429

KAYE, Jessie, Chief Executive Officer, Prairie View, Newton, KS, p. A253

KAYI, M.D., Mallinath, Medical Staff President, Saint Francis Hospital, Charleston, WV, p. A714

KAZALSKI, M.D., John J., President Medical Staff, St. Andrews Hospital and Healthcare Center, Boothbay Harbor, ME, p. A297

KEAHEY, Kent A., President and Chief Executive Officer, Providence Health Center, Waco, TX, p. A672

KEANE, Fran, Vice President Human Resources, CentraState Healthcare System, Freehold, NJ, p. A428

KEARL, Kirk, Chief Financial Officer, Banner Mesa Medical Center, Mesa, AZ, p. A32

KEARNEY, Christopher, Chief Executive Officer, Abilene Psychiatric Hospital, Abilene, TX, p. A620

KEARNEY, M Clark, Vice President Human Resources, Johnson Memorial Hospital, Stafford Springs, CT, p. A116

KEARNEY, W. Michael, President and Chief Executive Officer, Mary Lanning Memorial Hospital, Hastings, NE, p. A407

KEARSCHNER, Cale, Manager Information Systems, Washington County Memorial Hospital, Salem, IN, p. A224

KEATHLEY, M.P.H., Wayne, Chief Operating Officer, Mount Sinai Hosptial, New York, NY, p. A462

KEATING, Matthew, Chief Financial Officer, Irvine Regional Hospital and Medical Center, Irvine, CA, p. A65

KEATING, Todd, Chief Financial Officer, UMass Memorial Medical Center, Worcester, MA, p. A326

KEATON, William A., Chief Executive Officer, Frisco Medical Center, Frisco, TX, p. A641

KEE, John, Chief Executive Officer, Magic Valley Regional Medical Center, Twin Falls, ID, p. A182

KEE, Sheila, President and Chief Executive Officer, Sheehan Memorial Hospital, Buffalo, NY, p. A449

KEEF, Shaun, Administrator, Edwards County Hospital and Healthcare Center, Kinsley, KS, p. A250

KEEFE, Dennis D., Chief Executive Officer, Cambridge Health Alliance, Cambridge, MA, p. A316

KEEFE, Tom, Director Human Resources, Shady Grove Adventist Hospital, Rockville, MD, p. A310

KEEL, Barry L.
Administrator, Lawrence Medical Center, Moulton, AL, p. A22
Chief Executive Officer, Northwest Medical Center, Winfield, AL, p. A25

KEELAN, John E., Administrator and Chief Executive Officer, Brodstone Memorial Hospital, Superior, NE, p. A413

KEELEY, Brian E., President and Chief Executive Officer, Baptist Health South Florida, Coral Gables, FL, p. B15

KEELING, Gary, Chief Information Officer, Brodstone Memorial Hospital, Superior, NE, p. A413

KEEN, Robert C., FACHE, President and Chief Executive Officer, Hancock Memorial Hospital and Health Services, Greenfield, IN, p. A217

KEENAN, Annette, Chief Financial Officer, Braxton County Memorial Hospital, Gassaway, WV, p. A715

KEENAN, Peter, President Medical Staff, Shawano Medical Center, Shawano, WI, p. A735

KEENAN, Richard, Senior Vice President Finance, Valley Hospital, Ridgewood, NJ, p. A435

KEENE, Russell G., Chief Executive Officer, Androscoggin Valley Hospital, Berlin, NH, p. A420

KEENE HICKS, Shelley, Director of Human Resources, Tazewell Community Hospital, Tazewell, VA, p. A697

KEEVER, Jerry, Administrator, Sharkey–Issaquena Community Hospital, Rolling Fork, MS, p. A375

KEEVIL, M.D., Jean, Chief Medical Staff, Ashland Community Hospital, Ashland, OR, p. A542

KEFFER, Russ, Senior Vice President, Robert Packer Hospital, Sayre, PA, p. A574

KEGEL, Cheryl, Manager Human Resources, Clark Fork Valley Hospital, Plains, MT, p. A401

KEIGHRON, Kevin, Chief Operating Officer, Yavapai Regional Medical Center, Prescott, AZ, p. A35

KEILERS, Lance W., Administrator, Ballinger Memorial Hospital, Ballinger, TX, p. A624

KEIMIG, H. John, President and Chief Executive Officer, St. Joseph Health Services of Rhode Island, North Providence, RI, p. A581

KEIR, Douglas C., Chief Executive Officer, McDuffie Regional Medical Center, Thomson, GA, p. A170

KEISER, Trish, Comptroller, Avera Gregory Healthcare Center, Gregory, SD, p. A596

KEITH, Darlene, Chief Information Systems, Alleghany Memorial Hospital, Sparta, NC, p. A492

KEITH, James, Director Information Systems, Emory Eastside Medical Center, Snellville, GA, p. A169

KELBLY, Kevin, Senior Vice President Finance and Corporate Fiscal Affairs, Carroll Hospital Center, Westminster, MD, p. A311

KELCH, Charles, Administrator, Humboldt County Memorial Hospital, Humboldt, IA, p. A235

KELLAR, Richard A., Administrator, West Allis Memorial Hospital, West Allis, WI, p. A738

KELLER, Allen, Director Human Resources, Sumner Regional Medical Center, Wellington, KS, p. A259

KELLER, Diane R., Administrator, Memorial Hospital, Aurora, NE, p. A404

KELLER, J Michael, Vice President Operations, Newton Medical Center, Newton, KS, p. A253

KELLER, Jack M., Administrator, Hickman Community Hospital, Centerville, TN, p. A603

KELLER, James W., M.D., President, Chief Executive Officer and Chief Medical Officer, Southeastern Ohio Regional Medical Center, Cambridge, OH, p. A505

KELLER, M.D., James W., President, Chief Executive Officer and Chief Medical Officer, Southeastern Ohio Regional Medical Center, Cambridge, OH, p. A505

KELLER, Jim, Information Systems Site Director, Battle Creek Health System, Battle Creek, MI, p. A328

KELLERMAN, Daniel, Chief Operating Officer, Veterans Affairs Medical Center, Iowa City, IA, p. A236

KELLERMAN, Scott, Chief Financial Officer, Ely–Bloomenson Community Hospital, Ely, MN, p. A353

KELLEY, Connie, Human Resources Manager, St. Vincent Rehabilitation Hospital, Sherwood, AR, p. A50

KELLEY, Edie, Hum Res Representative, Middlesboro Appalachian Regional Hospital, Middlesboro, KY, p. A271

KELLEY, Jalinda, Director, Chickasaw Nation Health System, Ada, OK, p. A527

KELLEY, Janice, Chief Financial Officer, Marshall County Hospital, Benton, KY, p. A261

KELLEY, Lewis, Administrator, Chatuge Regional Hospital and Nursing Home, Hiawassee, GA, p. A163

KELLEY, M.D., Mark A., Executive Vice President and Chief Medical Officer, Henry Ford Hospital, Detroit, MI, p. A331

KELLEY, Neal, Administrator, Seton Edgar B. Davis Hospital, Luling, TX, p. A655

KELLEY, Randall L., President and Chief Executive Officer, Gateway Health System, Clarksville, TN, p. A604

KELLEY, Robert C., President and Chief Executive Officer, Madera Community Hospital, Madera, CA, p. A74

KELLEY, Steven L., President and Chief Executive Officer, Ellenville Regional Hospital, Ellenville, NY, p. A452

KELLEY, Sue, Chief Financial Officer, Cordell Memorial Hospital, Cordell, OK, p. A529

KELLEY, Warren, Chief Information Officer, Reynolds Memorial Hospital, Glen Dale, WV, p. A715

KELLIE, Karen J., President and Administrator, McCall Memorial Hospital, McCall, ID, p. A180

KELLY, Arthur C., Administrator and Chief Executive Officer, Oktibbeha County Hospital, Starkville, MS, p. A376

KELLY, Brian, Vice President Finance, Advocate South Suburban Hospital, Hazel Crest, IL, p. A196

KELLY, D.O., Charles, Chief of Staff, Saint Joseph Mercy Livingston Hospital, Howell, MI, p. A336

KELLY, Colan, Chief Financial Officer, Pineville Community Hospital Association, Pineville, KY, p. A273

KELLY, Daniel J., President and Chief Executive Officer, St. Mary's Hospital, Nebraska City, NE, p. A409

KELLY, Daniel R., Chief Executive Officer, Sharon Hospital, Sharon, CT, p. A116

KELLY, Edward, Vice President Finance, Milford Regional Medical Center, Milford, MA, p. A320

KELLY, Frank J., President and Chief Executive Officer, Danbury Hospital, Danbury, CT, p. A112

KELLY, D.O., Gregory, Medical Staff President, Putnam General Hospital, Hurricane, WV, p. A716

KELLY, Jeffrey W., Senior Vice President Administration, Warren Hospital, Phillipsburg, NJ, p. A434

KELLY, M.D., John J., Chief of Staff, Abington Memorial Hospital, Abington, PA, p. A551

KELLY, M.D., Johnson, Vice President and Chief Medical Officer, Cleveland Regional Medical Center, Shelby, NC, p. A491

KELLY, M.D., Kathleen, Chief Medical Officer and Chief Quality Officer, SwedishAmerican Hospital, Rockford, IL, p. A207

KELLY, Laurence E., President and Chief Executive Officer, Nathan Littauer Hospital and Nursing Home, Gloversville, NY, p. A453

KELLY, Lynn, Vice President Human Resources, San Antonio Community Hospital, Upland, CA, p. A97

KELLY, Mark A., Administrator, HEALTHSOUTH Rehabilitation Hospital, Memphis, TN, p. A613

KELLY, Mary, Director of Human Resources, Calvary Hospital, New York, NY, p. A459

KELLY, Patricia, Chief Fiscal Section, John D. Dingell Veterans Affairs Medical Center, Detroit, MI, p. A331

KELLY, Patrick
Chief Executive Officer, Vista Health, Fayetteville, AR, p. A43
Chief Executive Officer, Vista Health of Fort Smith, Barling, AR, p. A40

KELLY, Peter A., President and Chief Executive Officer, Christ Hospital, Jersey City, NJ, p. A430

KELLY, Robert C., Senior Vice President Finance and Chief Financial Officer, St. Francis Hospital, Inc., Columbus, GA, p. A158

KELLY, Steven G., President and Chief Executive Officer, Newton Medical Center, Newton, KS, p. A253

KELLY, Sylvia K., Administrator, HEALTHSOUTH Rehabilitation Center, Albuquerque, NM, p. A440

KELLY, Thomas, Chief Financial Officer, Selby General Hospital, Marietta, OH, p. A517

KELLY, Jr, Thomas, Senior Vice President and Chief Financial Officer, Medical College of Georgia Hospital and Clinics, Augusta, GA, p. A155

KELLY, M.P.H., , Thomas J., Vice President Medical Affairs, Union Hospital, Dover, OH, p. A513

KELSO, Don, Vice President Professional Services, Daviess Community Hospital, Washington, IN, p. A227

KELSO, Heidi, Human Resources Manager, Sanpete Valley Hospital, Mount Pleasant, UT, p. A677

KELSO, M.D., Scott A., Vice President Medical Affairs, Southern Maryland Hospital Center, Clinton, MD, p. A306

KEM, Mark, Vice President Finance, Chandler Regional Hospital, Chandler, AZ, p. A30

KEMMERLY, M.D., J Robert, Medical Director, Minden Medical Center, Minden, LA, p. A287

KEMP, M.D., Judith, President Medical Staff, Camden–Clark Memorial Hospital, Parkersburg, WV, p. A718

KEMP, Kenneth, Director Information Systems, Carlsbad Medical Center, Carlsbad, NM, p. A441

KEMPF, M.D., John, Chief of Staff, Opelousas General Health System, Opelousas, LA, p. A291

KEMPIAK, Matthew, Human Resources Director, Coast Plaza Doctors Hospital, Norwalk, CA, p. A78

KEMPINSKI, Paul D., Chief Operating Officer, Alfred I. duPont Hospital for Children, Wilmington, DE, p. A119

KEMPTON, Dana, Associate Director and Chief Financial Officer, Redington–Fairview General Hospital, Skowhegan, ME, p. A301

KEMSKE, Gary, Chief Financial Officer, Coral Springs Medical Center, Coral Springs, FL, p. A126

KENADY, Joe, Chief Information Officer, Covenant Hospital–Levelland, Levelland, TX, p. A652

KENAGY, John, Chief Information Officer, OHSU Hospital, Portland, OR, p. A547

KENDALL, R.N., Ann, Chief Operating Officer, Roane General Hospital, Spencer, WV, p. A720

KENDALL, Anthony, Vice President Human Resources, Baptist Health Medical Center–Little Rock, Little Rock, AR, p. A46

KENDALL, Frank, Director Information Systems, Saint Mary's Standish Community Hospital, Standish, MI, p. A345

KENDALL, Kim, Director Human Resources, Lawrence County Memorial Hospital, Lawrenceville, IL, p. A199

KENDLER, Lisa, Chief Financial Officer, Memorial Hermann Katy Hospital, Katy, TX, p. A650

KENDRICK, Gary G., Chief Executive Officer, Lincoln County Health System, Fayetteville, TN, p. A606

KENDRICK, Jim R., Chief Operating Officer, Wesley Medical Center, Hattiesburg, MS, p. A369

KENDRICK, Michael, Chief Financial Officer, Des Peres Hospital, Saint Louis, MO, p. A390

KENEALY, Michael, Director Information Technology, California Hospital Medical Center, Los Angeles, CA, p. A69

KENKELEN, Maryann, Vice President Human Resources and Tenant Services, St. Agnes Continuing Care Center, Philadelphia, PA, p. A569

KENNA, Tim, Administrator, Fort Lauderdale Hospital, Fort Lauderdale, FL, p. A128

KENNEDY, M.D., Bruce, Chief Medical Officer, San Jacinto Methodist Hospital, Baytown, TX, p. A625

KENNEDY, Christopher S., President and Chief Executive Officer, Holmes Regional Medical Center, Melbourne, FL, p. A136

KENNEDY, Daniel E., President and Chief Executive Officer, Riddle Memorial Hospital, Media, PA, p. A565

KENNEDY, Elizabeth M., Administrator, J. Paul Jones Hospital, Camden, AL, p. A16

KENNEDY, Jerry, Administrator, Jefferson County Hospital, Fayette, MS, p. A368

KENNEDY, Joseph, Administrator, U. S. Air Force Regional Hospital–Sheppard, Sheppard AFB, TX, p. A667

KENNEDY, Pam, Customer Relations Service Line Director, Christus St. Michael Health System, Texarkana, TX, p. A669

KENNEDY, M.D., R Scott, Chief Medical Officer, Olympic Medical Center, Port Angeles, WA, p. A706

KENNEDY, Richard S., Chief Operating Officer, Aventura Hospital and Medical Center, Aventura, FL, p. A123

KENNEDY, Rochelle, Chief Financial Officer, Sheridan County Health Complex, Hoxie, KS, p. A249

KENNEDY III, Thomas D., President and Chief Executive Officer, Bristol Hospital, Bristol, CT, p. A112

KENNEDY, Thomas F., Administrator, Rolling Plains Memorial Hospital, Sweetwater, TX, p. A668

KENNEDY, Tori, Business Entity Management Information Systems Manager, OSF St. Mary Medical Center, Galesburg, IL, p. A195

KENNETT, David, Chief Financial Officer, Jersey Community Hospital, Jerseyville, IL, p. A198

KENNIFF, CPA, Peter B., Chief Financial Officer, Mercy Suburban Hospital, Norristown, PA, p. A566

KENNY, Richard, Vice President Human Resources, Hallmark Health System, Melrose, MA, p. A320

KENOGY, David, M.D., Medical Director, Cleveland Clinic Children's Hospital for Rehabilitation, Cleveland, OH, p. A508

KENT, Alan, Chief Executive Officer, Meadows Regional Medical Center, Vidalia, GA, p. A171

KENT, Ray, Human Resources Manager, Veterans Affairs Medical Center, Lebanon, PA, p. A563

KENT, Susan G., Director of Marketing and Public Relations, Capital Medical Center, Olympia, WA, p. A705

KENYON, Douglas M., Director, Veterans Affairs Medical and Regional Office Center, Fargo, ND, p. A498

KEPLER, Terry, Administrator and Chief Executive Officer, Plano Specialty Hospital, Plano, TX, p. A661

KEPLINGER, Chelle, Chief Financial Officer, Massac Memorial Hospital, Metropolis, IL, p. A201

KEPNER, Donald L., Chief Financial Officer, Inter–Community Memorial Hospital, Newfane, NY, p. A467

KEPPLINGER, Darcy, Business Office Manager, Landmann–Jungman Memorial Hospital, Scotland, SD, p. A598

KERBY, M.D., Clifford, Chief of Medical Staff, Berea Hospital, Berea, KY, p. A261

KERCORIAN, Robert A., Chief Executive Officer, Havenwyck Hospital, Auburn Hills, MI, p. A327

KERLIN, Kerry, Vice President Information Technology, Saint Vincent Health Center, Erie, PA, p. A558

KERN, Howard P., Chief Operating Officer, Sentara Bayside Hospital, Virginia Beach, VA, p. A697

KERN, Stephen V., Chief Operating Officer, St. Mary's Medical Center of Evansville, Evansville, IN, p. A215

KERNER, Kevin, Vice President Human Resources, Saint Peter's University Hospital, New Brunswick, NJ, p. A432

KERNER, Michael K., Executive Vice President and Administrator, Bon Secours St. Mary's Hospital, Richmond, VA, p. A694

KERNES, Paul, Administrator, Kansas City Orthopaedic Institute, Shawnee Mission, KS, p. A257

KERNS, Debbie, Human Resources Director, Steele Memorial Hospital, Salmon, ID, p. A181

KERR, Gavin R., Executive Vice President and Chief Operating Officer, Children's Hospital of Philadelphia, Philadelphia, PA, p. A567

KERR, Joseph F., Chief Financial Officer, Gadsden Regional Medical Center, Gadsden, AL, p. A19

KERR, Rand, Chief Operating Officer, St. Mark's Hospital, Salt Lake City, UT, p. A680

KERR, Robert, Chief Financial Officer, Highland District Hospital, Hillsboro, OH, p. A515

KERR, Roger, President and Chief Executive Officer, Central Michigan Community Hospital, Mount Pleasant, MI, p. A341

KERRWOOD, Patrick, Director Human Resources, South Bay Hospital, Sun City Center, FL, p. A147

KERSTEIN, M.D., Morris D., Chief of Staff, Veterans Affairs Medical Center, Wilmington, DE, p. A120

KERWIN, Dale, Information Director, Regional Medical Center of Orangeburg and Calhoun Counties, Orangeburg, SC, p. A591

KERWIN, George, President, Bellin Memorial Hospital, Green Bay, WI, p. A726

KERWIN, Thomas, Administrator Information Systems and Chief Information Officer, Memorial Hospital, Colorado Springs, CO, p. A102

KESSEN, Donald J., Administrator and Chief Executive Officer, Minneola District Hospital, Minneola, KS, p. A253

KESSINGER, A. Jay, Administrative Director, State Hospital North, Orofino, ID, p. A180

KESSLER, David, Clinical Director, U. S. Public Health Service Indian Hospital, Zuni, NM, p. A445

KESSLER, Jeffrey R., Vice President Information Services, Dana–Farber Cancer Institute, Boston, MA, p. A313

KESSLER, William E., FACHE, President, Saint Anthony's Health Center, Alton, IL, p. A183

KETCH, Lynn, Manager Human Resources and Volunteer Services, INTEGRIS Canadian Valley Regional Hospital, Yukon, OK, p. A541

KETCHAM, Michael S., President and Chief Executive Officer, Loring Hospital, Sac City, IA, p. A241

KETCHAM, Richard H., President, Brooks Memorial Hospital, Dunkirk, NY, p. A451

KETNER, J B., Medical Director, Memorial Health Care Systems, Seward, NE, p. A413

KETTERHAGEN, M.D., James P.
Vice President Medical Affairs and Chief Quality Officer, Columbia St. Mary's Ozaukee Campus, Mequon, WI, p. A730
Vice President Medical Affairs and Chief Quality Officer, Columbia St. Mary's–Milwaukee Campus, Milwaukee, WI, p. A730

KETTLER, Carl, Human Resources Business Partner, Kaiser Foundation Hospital – Santa Teresa, San Jose, CA, p. A90

KEUSENKOTHEN, Thomas, President and Chief Executive Officer, Alexian Brothers Health System, Arlington Heights, IL, p. B7

KEUTEN, John, Senior Vice President and Chief Financial Officer, Genesys Regional Medical Center, Grand Blanc, MI, p. A334

KEY, David, Chief Executive Officer, Select Specialty Hospital–Memphis, Memphis, TN, p. A614

KEY, Ramona T.
Chief Executive Officer, Laurel Ridge Hospital, San Antonio, TX, p. A664
Chief Executive Officer, Mission Vista Geriatric Psychiatric Hospital, San Antonio, TX, p. A664

KEY, Sean, Director Information Technology, Mercy Medical Center, Williston, ND, p. A501

KEYSER, Gail, Director Information Technology Services, St. Joseph's Wayne Hospital, Wayne, NJ, p. A438

KHALID, Ahsan, Medical Director, Cavalier County Memorial Hospital, Langdon, ND, p. A499

KHAN, Nasir A., M.D., Chief Executive Officer, Bournewood Health System, Brookline, MA, p. A316

KHAN, Sharaz, Director, Rush Oak Park Hospital, Oak Park, IL, p. A203

KHAN, M.D., Waseem, President Medical Staff, Shands at Lake Shore, Lake City, FL, p. A134

KHANNA, Rajive
Chief Executive Officer, Grace Hospital, Cleveland, OH, p. A508
Chief Operating Officer, Grace Hospital, Cleveland, OH, p. A508

KHARMA, M.D., Bassam K., Chairman, Department of Medicine, Mercy Jeannette Hospital, Jeannette, PA, p. A561

KHOUDEIR, M.D., Yasser, Medical Staff President, Ashland Regional Medical Center, Ashland, PA, p. A552

KHOUDOUD, M.D., Hassan, Chief of Staff, Pembina County Memorial Hospital and Wedgewood Manor, Cavalier, ND, p. A497

KIBAR, M.D., Nizar, Chief Medical Staff, Kiowa County Memorial Hospital, Greensburg, KS, p. A248

KIBBY, Kevin, Manager Information Systems, Greene County Medical Center, Jefferson, IA, p. A236

KIBILOSKI, M.D., Leinard, Chief of Staff, Elkhart General Hospital, Elkhart, IN, p. A214

KIBLER, Doug, Management Information Systems Specialist, St. Mary's Medical Center of Campbell County, La Follette, TN, p. A610

KIBORT, M.D., Phillip M., Vice President Medical Affairs and Chief Medical Officer, Children's Hospital and Clinics, Saint Paul, MN, p. A362

KICHAK, J P., Vice President Information Services, University of North Carolina Hospitals, Chapel Hill, NC, p. A479

KICK, M.D., Kimberly, Chief of Staff, Margaret Mary Community Hospital, Batesville, IN, p. A211

KIDD, Thomas J., Assistant Administrator and Chief Financial Officer, Macon County General Hospital, Lafayette, TN, p. A610

KIDDER, Suzanne, Director Human Resources, Opelousas General Health System, Opelousas, LA, p. A291

KIDO, Bert, Vice President Human Resources, Queen's Medical Center, Honolulu, HI, p. A174

KIE, Katrina, Chief Financial Officer, Logan Memorial Hospital, Russellville, KY, p. A274

KIEF, Brian, President and Chief Executive Officer, Howard Young Medical Center, Woodruff, WI, p. A738

KIEHN, David R., Senior Vice President Finance and Chief Financial Officer, Evergreen Healthcare, Kirkland, WA, p. A703

KIELMAN, Richard C., President and Chief Executive Officer, Lakes Regional Healthcare, Spirit Lake, IA, p. A242

KIELY, Robert Gerard, President and Chief Executive Officer, Middlesex Hospital, Middletown, CT, p. A114

KIERNAN, M.D., Thomas, Chief of Staff, Veterans Affairs Medical Center, Augusta, GA, p. A155

KIESLING, Mary Kay, Senior Vice President Operations and Chief Operating Officer, Southern Regional Medical Center, Riverdale, GA, p. A167

KIESSLING, Kristin, Vice President Finance and Chief Financial Officer, Bayonne Medical Center, Bayonne, NJ, p. A425

KIFF, Gary V., President and Chief Executive Officer, Beverly Hospital, Montebello, CA, p. A76

KIGER, Tom, Director Information Systems, Trinity Health System, Steubenville, OH, p. A522

KILARSKI, David J., President and Chief Executive Officer, Marymount Hospital, Garfield Heights, OH, p. A514

KILBURN, Richard L., Chief Executive Officer and Administrator, Nye Regional Medical Center, Tonopah, NV, p. A419

KILEY, Dennis, President, Emory–Adventist Hospital, Smyrna, GA, p. A169

KILEY, Kevin C., M.D., Surgeon General, Department of the Army, Office of the Surgeon General, Falls Church, VA, p. B36

KILEY, Tracy, Chief Financial Officer, Galena–Stauss Hospital and Healthcare Center, Galena, IL, p. A195

KILLIAN, Steve, Chief Financial Officer, Southern Hills Hospital and Medical Center, Las Vegas, NV, p. A417

KILLION, William, Chief Executive Officer, Whitten Center, Clinton, SC, p. A585

KILMER, Virginia, Chief Financial Officer, Shenandoah Memorial Hospital, Woodstock, VA, p. A698

KILPATRICK, David M., M.D., Director, Veterans Affairs Medical Center, Cheyenne, WY, p. A739

KILROY, John E.
Vice President and Chief Information Officer, Cape Cod Hospital, Hyannis, MA, p. A319
Vice President and Chief Information Officer, Falmouth Hospital, Falmouth, MA, p. A317

KILSDONK, Eileen, Director Human Resources, Moore County Hospital District, Dumas, TX, p. A636

KIMBALL, D.O., Catherine M., Chief of Staff, Inland Hospital, Waterville, ME, p. A301

KIMBALL, Sheila, Director of Human Resources, Emory–Adventist Hospital, Smyrna, GA, p. A169

KIMBLE, Gay, Director Human Resources, Susan B. Allen Memorial Hospital, El Dorado, KS, p. A246

KIMBLER, R.N., Christine M., Chief Operating Officer, Kanabec Hospital, Mora, MN, p. A358

KIMES, Kent, Director Information Systems, North Arkansas Regional Medical Center, Harrison, AR, p. A44

KIMMEL, Stephen, Senior Vice President and Chief Financial Officer, Hendrick Health System, Abilene, TX, p. A620

KIMMES, Robb, Director of Human Resources and Operations, Grand View Hospital, Ironwood, MI, p. A337

KIMMEY, Susan, Associate Director, Veterans Affairs Medical Center, Manchester, NH, p. A422

KIMPLE, Robin, Director Information Services, Gettysburg Hospital, Gettysburg, PA, p. A559

KIMSAL, Ken, Chief Financial Officer, Cumberland County Hospital, Burkesville, KY, p. A262

KINDER, Bruce, R.N., Chief Operating Officer, University Medical Center, Fresno, CA, p. A62

KINDRED, Bryan N., President and Chief Executive Officer, DCH Health System, Tuscaloosa, AL, p. B35

KING, Abner, Information Systems Director, Steele Memorial Hospital, Salmon, ID, p. A181

KING, Alan N., Chief Executive Officer, Pampa Regional Medical Center, Pampa, TX, p. A659

KING, Brad, Vice President and Chief Financial Officer, OHSU Hospital, Portland, OR, p. A547

KING, Bruce, President and Chief Executive Officer, New London Hospital, New London, NH, p. A423

KING, Cynthia, Administrative Director Human Resources, Parkland Medical Center, Derry, NH, p. A420

KING, Dennis P., Chief Executive Officer, Spring Harbor Hospital, Westbrook, ME, p. A301

KING, George, Controller, Wayne Memorial Hospital, Jesup, GA, p. A164

KING, Gordon A., Interim Vice President Financial Services, Ellis Hospital, Schenectady, NY, p. A472

KING, Grace, Regional Director, North Broward Medical Center, Pompano Beach, FL, p. A144

KING, Jim
Chief Executive Officer, Snowden at Fredericksburg, Fredericksburg, VA, p. A688
Executive Vice President and Chief Operating Officer, Jackson County Memorial Hospital, Altus, OK, p. A527

KING, Kirk, CHE, President, Presbyterian Hospital of Kaufman, Kaufman, TX, p. A650

KING, Linda
Chief Human Resources Management Service, Central Alabama Veterans Health Care System, Montgomery, AL, p. A22
Interim Financial Officer, Navarro Regional Hospital, Corsicana, TX, p. A631

KING, Lindsie, Finance Manager, Providence Valdez Medical Center, Valdez, AK, p. A29

KING, Michael A., Chief Operating Officer, Camden–Clark Memorial Hospital, Parkersburg, WV, p. A718

KING, Mike, Chief Financial Officer, Doctors Medical Center, Modesto, CA, p. A76

KING, Peter J., Senior Vice President and Chief Financial Officer, Grandview Hospital and Medical Center, Dayton, OH, p. A512

KING, Randy, Administrator and Chief Executive Officer, Baptist Memorial Hospital–Desoto, Southaven, MS, p. A375

KING, Ron
Information Systems Manager, Campbell County Memorial Hospital, Gillette, WY, p. A740
Chief Financial Officer, University of California, Irvine Medical Center, Orange, CA, p. A79

KING, Stewart, Vice President Human Resources, Coffee Regional Medical Center, Douglas, GA, p. A161

KING, Victoria, Chief Nursing Officer, Phoenix Memorial Hospital, Phoenix, AZ, p. A34

KINGHAM, CPA, Darrell L., Vice President Finance, Beauregard Memorial Hospital, De Ridder, LA, p. A280

KINGSBURY, James A., Executive Director and Senior Vice President, University Hospital, Cincinnati, OH, p. A507

KINGSLEY, Christi, Director Human Resources, West Calcasieu Cameron Hospital, Sulphur, LA, p. A293

KINGSTON, Peggy, Chief Executive Officer and Administrator, Select Specialty Hospital–Pontiac, Pontiac, MI, p. A342

KINKAID, Steve, Director Information Systems, Helen Newberry Joy Hospital, Newberry, MI, p. A341

KINKLER, Nancy, Administrator, Otto Kaiser Memorial Hospital, Kenedy, TX, p. A650

KINNEBREW, Tom, Chief Executive Officer, Helena Regional Medical Center, Helena, AR, p. A44

KINNEY, Charles S., President and Chief Executive Officer, Westerly Hospital, Westerly, RI, p. A582

KINNEY, Jean, Controller, Pender Community Hospital, Pender, NE, p. A412

KINNEY, Kristen, Administrative Operations Manager and Patient Advocate, Hebrew Health Care, West Hartford, CT, p. A117

KINNEY–SMITH, Deanna, Director Employee and Labor Relations, St. Joseph Mercy Oakland, Pontiac, MI, p. A343

KINSAUL, David, President and Chief Executive Officer, Children's Medical Center, Dayton, OH, p. A511

KINSLOW, Kathleen, Chief Operating Officer, Pennsylvania Hospital, Philadelphia, PA, p. A569

KINTZ, Ronald J., Vice President and Treasurer, Arnot Ogden Medical Center, Elmira, NY, p. A452

KINYON, Craig, Vice President Finance and Chief Financial Officer, Reid Hospital and Health Care Services, Richmond, IN, p. A224

KIOUS, A. Gus, M.D., Chief Administrative Officer, Huron Hospital, Cleveland, OH, p. A508

KIPFER, Deborah, Chief Financial Officer, Community Hospital of Bremen, Bremen, IN, p. A212

KIPP, Christine T., Vice President Patient Care Services, St. Francis Medical Center, Monroe, LA, p. A287

KIRBY, Dale A., Chief Executive Officer, Colusa Regional Medical Center, Colusa, CA, p. A57

KIRBY, E Stephen
Chief Operating Officer, LibertyHealth–Greenville Hospital, Jersey City, NJ, p. A430
Senior Vice President Finance, Chief Financial Officer and Chief Operating Officer, LibertyHealth–Greenville Hospital, Jersey City, NJ, p. A430

KIRBY, Mick, President and Chief Executive Officer, Centennial Peaks Hospital, Louisville, CO, p. A108

KIRBY, Richard S., Executive Vice President and Chief Financial Officer, Community Memorial Hospital, Hamilton, NY, p. A453

KIRBY, Ruby, Administrator, Bolivar General Hospital, Bolivar, TN, p. A602

KIRCH, Darrell G., M.D., Chief Executive Officer, Penn State Milton S. Hershey Medical Center, Hershey, PA, p. A560

KIRCHER, Mark, Associate Vice President, Hospital Finance, Norton Suburban Hospital, Louisville, KY, p. A270

KIRCHNER, M.D., Kent, Chief of Staff, G.V. Montgomery Veterans Affairs Medical Center, Jackson, MS, p. A370

KIRK, David J., Chief Human Resources Management Service, Veterans Affairs Medical and Regional Office Center, Fargo, ND, p. A498

KIRK Jr, H. Lee, President and Chief Executive Officer, Culpeper Regional Hospital, Culpeper, VA, p. A687

KIRK, Kathleen, Chief Operating Officer, Pulaski Community Hospital, Pulaski, VA, p. A694

KIRK, Jr, Lee Roy, Senior Vice President and Chief Operating Officer, Rowan Regional Medical Center, Salisbury, NC, p. A491

KIRK, Paul, Director, Woman's Hospital, Baton Rouge, LA, p. A278

KIRK, Shirley, Vice President Human Resources, Memorial Medical Center, Springfield, IL, p. A208

KIRK Jr, Thomas A., Ph.D., Commissioner, Connecticut Department of Mental Health and Addiction Services, Hartford, CT, p. B33

KIRK, Tim, Chief Information Officer, Huntington Memorial Hospital, Pasadena, CA, p. A81

KIRK, Warren J.
Chief Executive Officer, Alta Bates Summit Medical Center, Berkeley, CA, p. A54
President and Chief Executive Officer, Alta Bates Summit Medical Center – Summit Campus, Oakland, CA, p. A78

KIRK Jr, William R., President and Chief Executive Officer, Chester River Hospital Center, Chestertown, MD, p. A306

KIRKS, Linda, Chief Financial Officer, Baptist Medical Center, San Antonio, TX, p. A663

KIRKWOOD, Ph.D., William, Vice President Human Resources, Caritas Good Samaritan Medical Center, Brockton, MA, p. A315

KIRN, Galen, Administrator, California Mens Colony Hospital, San Luis Obispo, CA, p. A91

KIROUSIS, Theodore E., Area Director, Westborough State Hospital, Westborough, MA, p. A325

KIRSHMAN, John, Chief Information Officer, South Haven Community Hospital, South Haven, MI, p. A345

KIRSHNER, Arthur, Director Information System, Crestwood Medical Center, Huntsville, AL, p. A20

KIRSHNER, David, Senior Vice President and Chief Financial Officer, Children's Hospital Boston, Boston, MA, p. A313

KISER, Greg, Chief Executive Officer, Three Rivers Medical Center, Louisa, KY, p. A268

KISER II, James, Chief Administrative Officer, St. James Healthcare, Butte, MT, p. A397

KISER, M.D., Kenneth, Chief of Staff, Mountain View Regional Medical Center, Norton, VA, p. A693

KISER, Terry L.
Chief Financial Officer, Georgetown Memorial Hospital, Georgetown, SC, p. A588
Chief Financial Officer, Waccamaw Community Hospital, Murrells Inlet, SC, p. A590

KISHNER, Janice, Chief Operating Officer and Nurse Executive, East Jefferson General Hospital, Metairie, LA, p. A286

KISHORE, M.D., Anand, Chief of Staff, Carilion New River Valley Medical Center, Christiansburg, VA, p. A686

KISSNER, Michael, Chief Executive Officer, Fishermen's Hospital, Marathon, FL, p. A135

KISYLIA, Peter, Executive Vice President and Chief Financial Officer, Saint Clare's Hospital, Dover, NJ, p. A427

KITAKULE, M.D., Moses, Chief of Staff, Franklin Foundation Hospital, Franklin, LA, p. A281

KIWALL, Walter J., Executive Vice Presidentand Chief Operating Officer, Mary Washington Hospital, Fredericksburg, VA, p. A688

KJENTVET, Lisa
Vice President Finance, Mercy Hospital, Coon Rapids, MN, p. A351
Vice President Finance, Unity Hospital, Fridley, MN, p. A354

KJOSA, R.N., MS, AnnMarie, Vice President & Chief Nursing Officer, Community Hospital, Grand Junction, CO, p. A106

KLAASMEYER, Al, Administrator, Community Memorial Hospital, Syracuse, NE, p. A413

KLAASSEN, M.D., Paul A., Chief Medical Staff, South Central Kansas Regional Medical Center, Arkansas City, KS, p. A244

KLABO, Sue, Administrator, Mahnomen Health Center, Mahnomen, MN, p. A356

KLAGSBRUN, Samuel C., M.D., Executive Medical Director, Four Winds Hospital, Katonah, NY, p. A455

KLAMAN, Edward M., Senior Vice President and Chief Operating Officer, Western Pennsylvania Hospital, Pittsburgh, PA, p. A573

KLAMET, Frank, Chief of Staff, Fayette County Memorial Hospital, Washington Court House, OH, p. A524

KLAMFORTH, Bill, Administrator, HEALTHSOUTH Rehabilitation Hospital of Beaumont, Beaumont, TX, p. A625

KLAMFOTH, William E., Administrator, Richardson Medical Center, Rayville, LA, p. A291

KLAMKE, Alexis, Chief Financial Officer, Newnan Hospital East, Newnan, GA, p. A167

KLAPPERICH, Linda, Director of Financial Services, Our Lady of Victory Hospital, Stanley, WI, p. A736

KLASS, Cheryl, President, Women and Children's Hospital, Buffalo, NY, p. A449

KLASSEN, Thomas H., Executive Vice Persident and Chief Operating Officer, Miller–Dwan Medical Center, Duluth, MN, p. A352

KLAWITER, Anne K., President and Chief Executive Officer, Southwest Health Center, Platteville, WI, p. A733

KLAWITTER, Kyle, Vice President Human Resources, Summa Health System, Akron, OH, p. A502

KLEBE, Douglas, Chief Financial Officer, Torrance Memorial Medical Center, Torrance, CA, p. A96

KLEHN, Paul
Director Information Systems, St. David's Medical Center, Austin, TX, p. A624
Director Information Systems, St. David's Pavilion, Austin, TX, p. A624
Director Information Systems, St. David's Rehabilitation Center, Austin, TX, p. A624

KLEIN, M.D., Bernard
Chief Operating Officer and Medical Director, Los Robles Hospital and Medical Center, Thousand Oaks, CA, p. A95
Chief Operating Officer and Medical Director, Los Robles Hospital and Medical Center, Thousand Oaks, CA, p. A95

KLEIN, Cindy
Chief Financial Officer, Lamb Healthcare Center, Littlefield, TX, p. A653
Vice President Human Resources, West Virginia University Hospitals, Morgantown, WV, p. A718

KLEIN, M.D., Cordell, Chief of Staff, Wadley Regional Medical Center, Texarkana, TX, p. A670

KLEIN, David, Interim Chief Executive Officer, Henderson Memorial Hospital, Henderson, TX, p. A643

KLEIN, Ed, Chief Financial Officer, Gordon Hospital, Calhoun, GA, p. A157

KLEIN, Gerald H., Vice President Finance, Bucyrus Community Hospital, Bucyrus, OH, p. A504

KLEIN, Gerard D., President and Chief Executive Officer, Bucyrus Community Hospital, Bucyrus, OH, p. A504

KLEIN, Greg, Director Finance, Presbyterian Hospital–Matthews, Matthews, NC, p. A487

KLEIN, Jacqueline
Vice President Finance, Appleton Medical Center, Appleton, WI, p. A722
Vice President Finance, Theda Clark Medical Center, Neenah, WI, p. A732

KLEIN, Joel, Chief Executive Officer and Managing Director, BridgeWay, North Little Rock, AR, p. A48

KLEIN, Lynn E., Director Human Resources, Mendota Community Hospital, Mendota, IL, p. A201

KLEIN, Robert, Chief Executive Officer, Skyline Medical Center, Nashville, TN, p. A615

KLEIN, Steve, Assistant Administrator and Chief Financial Officer, Cass Medical Center, Harrisonville, MO, p. A382

KLEIN, Steven M., Executive Vice President and Chief Operating Officer, Jackson Memorial Hospital, Miami, FL, p. A137

KLEINGLASS, Steven, Director, Veterans Affairs Medical Center, Minneapolis, MN, p. A358

KLEINHANZL, Thomas A., President and Chief Executive Officer, Frederick Memorial Hospital, Frederick, MD, p. A308

KLEINHOLZ, Jr, M.D., Emil, Vice President Medical Management, St. Francis Health Center, Topeka, KS, p. A258

KLEINSCHMIDT, Mark, Vice President Finance and Chief Financial Officer, Genesis Medical Center, Davenport, Davenport, IA, p. A231

KLEPIN, Michael R., Administrator, Washoe Medical Center Rehabilitation Hospital, Reno, NV, p. A418

KLETTER, M.D., Jan, Medical Staff President, Jefferson Memorial Hospital, Ranson, WV, p. A719

KLICKSTEIN, Judith K., Chief Information Officer, Cambridge Health Alliance, Cambridge, MA, p. A316

KLIMA, Dennis E., President and Chief Executive Officer, Bayhealth Medical Center, Dover, DE, p. A119

KLIMP, Mary, Chief Executive Officer, Queen of Peace Hospital, New Prague, MN, p. A358

KLINE, David, Chief Financial Officer, Fairfield Memorial Hospital, Winnsboro, SC, p. A593

KLINEFELTER, Robin E., Vice President Support and Administrative Services, Chester River Hospital Center, Chestertown, MD, p. A306

KLINGENBERG, Pat, Director Human Resources, Towner County Medical Center, Cando, ND, p. A496

KLINGER, David, Vice President Human Resources, Mount Clemens General Hospital, Mount Clemens, MI, p. A340

KLINK, Sheryl, Chief Financial Officer, Piedmont Mountainside Hospital, Jasper, GA, p. A164

KLINKNER, Donna M., Business Manager, Madelia Community Hospital, Madelia, MN, p. A356

KLITGAARD, M.D., Don, Chief of Staff, Shelby County Myrtue Memorial Hospital, Harlan, IA, p. A235

KLOCK, Sally J., Chief Operating Officer, UHHS Geauga Regional Hospital, Chardon, OH, p. A505

KLOCKARS, Bruce A., President and Chief Executive Officer, Flaget Memorial Hospital, Bardstown, KY, p. A261

KLOCKMAN, Dena, Operations Administrator, Ogallala Community Hospital, Ogallala, NE, p. A410

KLOESS, Lawrence
President and Chief Executive Officer, Centennial Medical Center and Parthenon Pavilion, Nashville, TN, p. A615
President, Centennial Medical Center at Ashland City, Ashland City, TN, p. A602

KLOEWER, Ron, Chief Information Officer, Montgomery County Memorial Hospital, Red Oak, IA, p. A240

KLONSKY, M.D., Ira, Medical Director, Franklin Hospital Medical Center, Valley Stream, NY, p. A475

KLOOSTERMAN, James, Information Technology Site Manager – Perot Systems, St. John's Regional Medical Center, Oxnard, CA, p. A80

KLOSTER, Kathy, Administrator, Providence Seward Medical Center, Seward, AK, p. A28

KLOSTERMAN, Mark, Chief Executive Officer, Avera Gregory Healthcare Center, Gregory, SD, p. A596

KLOTZ, M.D., Ken, Chief of Staff, Richard L. Roudebush Veterans Affairs Medical Center, Indianapolis, IN, p. A218

KLUGE, Thomas S., Chief Operating Officer, Halifax Regional Health System, South Boston, VA, p. A696

KLUGHERZ, Greg, Vice President and Chief Financial Officer, Regions Hospital, Saint Paul, MN, p. A362

KLUNK, Tim, Executive Director, Children's Hospital of Wisconsin–Fox Valley, Neenah, WI, p. A732

KLUSKY, Jerome, Chief Financial Officer, Mount Diablo Medical Center, Concord, CA, p. A57

KLUSKY, Jerry, Chief Financial Officer, Mt. Diablo Medical Pavilion, Concord, CA, p. A57

KLUTTS, Robert, Chief Executive Officer, Touchette Regional Hospital, East St. Louis, IL, p. A192

KMETZ, Thomas D., President, Norton Audubon Hospital, Louisville, KY, p. A269

KNAK, Roger, R.N., Administrator and Chief Executive Officer, Russell Regional Hospital, Russell, KS, p. A256

KNAPKE, Bill, Director Information Technology and Systems, Frankfort Regional Medical Center, Frankfort, KY, p. A264

KNAPP, Dennis L., President and Chief Executive Officer, Cameron Memorial Community Hospital, Angola, IN, p. A211

KNAUF, Andrew, Vice President Finance, Gottlieb Memorial Hospital, Melrose Park, IL, p. A201

KNECHT, Brian, Chief Operating Officer, Good Samaritan Hospital, San Jose, CA, p. A90

KNECHT, Joseph H., Chief Executive Officer, First Hospital Wyoming Valley, Kingston, PA, p. A562

KNEDLER, Marie E., R.N., Vice President and Chief Operating Officer, Alegent Health Mercy Hospital, Council Bluffs, IA, p. A231

KNETZER, Larry, Chief Executive Officer, Victor Valley Community Hospital, Wildomar, CA, p. A99

KNICELY, Ted, Chief, Human Resource Management, Hunter Holmes McGuire Veterans Affairs Medical Center, Richmond, VA, p. A695

KNIGHT, Alan D., President and Chief Executive Officer, Jordan Hospital, Plymouth, MA, p. A322

KNIGHT, Bo, Management Information Department Head, Naval Hospital, North Charleston, SC, p. A591

KNIGHT, Calvin K., Chief Operating Officer, Swedish Health Services, Seattle, WA, p. A708

KNIGHT, James P., Chief Executive Officer, Duke Health Raleigh Hospital, Raleigh, NC, p. A489

KNIGHT, Ken, Chief Financial Officer, Hot Springs County Memorial Hospital, Thermopolis, WY, p. A742

KNIGHT, Kim, Chief Executive Officer, SCCI Hospital of Detroit, Detroit, MI, p. A331

KNIGHT, Linda A., Vice President Finance and Chief Financial Officer, Siskin Hospital for Physical Rehabilitation, Chattanooga, TN, p. A604

KNIGHT, M.D., Napoleon, Vice President Medical Affairs, Carle Foundation Hospital, Urbana, IL, p. A209

KNIGHT, Russell M., President and Chief Executive Officer, Mercy Medical Center–Dubuque, Dubuque, IA, p. A233

KNIGHT, Sue, Controller, St. Elizabeth Hospital, Gonzales, LA, p. A281

KNIGHT, Thomas F., Chief Financial Officer, Inova Alexandria Hospital, Alexandria, VA, p. A685

KNIGHT, Tim, Director of Information Technology, Hot Springs County Memorial Hospital, Thermopolis, WY, p. A742

KNIGHT, Warren, Chief Financial Officer, Potomac Ridge Behavioral Health System, Rockville, MD, p. A310

KNIZLEY, Andrew, Chief Executive Officer, Paris Regional Medical Center, Paris, TX, p. A660

KNOBLOCH, Stan, Chief Financial Officer, Sioux Valley Luverne Medical Center, Luverne, MN, p. A356

KNOBLOCH, Stanley, Finance Director, Merrill Pioneer Community Hospital, Rock Rapids, IA, p. A240

KNOCKE, CHE, David L., Senior Vice President and Chief Operating Officer, Stormont–Vail HealthCare, Topeka, KS, p. A258

KNOERL, Thomas, Chief Financial Officer, Spectrum Health–Reed City Campus, Reed City, MI, p. A343

KNOLL, M.D., Rolf W., Senior Vice President Medical Affairs, Saint Francis Hospital and Medical Center, Hartford, CT, p. A113

KNOOP, Kevin, Director Medical Education, Naval Medical Center, Portsmouth, VA, p. A694

KNOWLES, Candy, Senior Vice President Human Resources, Parkview Hospital, Fort Wayne, IN, p. A215

KNOWLES, Christy, Director Human Resources, Coosa Valley Medical Center, Sylacauga, AL, p. A24

KNOWLES, John, Director Human Resources, Clinch Valley Medical Center, Richlands, VA, p. A694

KNOWLES, Petra, Chief Information Officr, Bradley Memorial Hospital and Health Center, Southington, CT, p. A116

KNOWLES, Shanna, Chief Financial Officer, Drew Memorial Hospital, Monticello, AR, p. A48

KNOX, Candace, Administrator, HEALTHSOUTH Rehabilitation Hospital, Columbia, SC, p. A585

KNOX, Dennis M., Chief Executive Officer, Phoenix Baptist Hospital, Phoenix, AZ, p. A34

KNOX, John E., President and Chief Executive Officer, Finley Hospital, Dubuque, IA, p. A233

KNOX, III, John J., Vice President and Chief Information Officer, Carolinas Medical Center, Charlotte, NC, p. A479

KNOX, Jud, President, York Hospital, York, ME, p. A301

KNOX, Myrna, Budget Analyst, U. S. Public Health Service Indian Hospital, Rosebud, SD, p. A598

KNOX, Roland
Vice President and Chief Operating Officer, Mt. Graham Regional Medical Center, Safford, AZ, p. A36
Vice President and Chief Operating Officer, Mt. Graham Regional Medical Center, Safford, AZ, p. A36

KNOX, Stacey, Administrator, Rock County Hospital, Bassett, NE, p. A404

KNUDSON LIND, Linda, Senior Vice President and Chief Operating Officer, Siskin Hospital for Physical Rehabilitation, Chattanooga, TN, p. A604

KNUTSON, Larry, Finance Director, Long Prairie Memorial Hospital and Home, Long Prairie, MN, p. A356

KOBI, Kristin, Comptroller, Naval Hospital, Twentynine Palms, CA, p. A97

KOBJOHN, Vicky, Director Human Resources, Keokuk Area Hospital, Keokuk, IA, p. A236

KOCH, Charles S., Chief Operating Officer, Kaiser Foundation Hospital, Santa Clara, CA, p. A92

KOCH, David, Director, Information Systems, Saint Joseph Mercy Livingston Hospital, Howell, MI, p. A336

KOCH, Joseph G., Vice President and Chief Operating Officer, Raleigh General Hospital, Beckley, WV, p. A713

KOCH, M Christina, Chief Financial Officer and Associate Administrator, Wheeling Hospital, Wheeling, WV, p. A721

KOCHANOWSKI, Mark, Vice President Human Resources, Vassar Brothers Medical Center, Poughkeepsie, NY, p. A470

KOCHENOUR, M.D., Neil K., Medical Director, University of Utah Hospitals and Clinics, Salt Lake City, UT, p. A680

KOCHIE, CPA, Daniel A., Senior Vice President and Chief Financial Officer, Good Samaritan Regional Medical Center, Pottsville, PA, p. A573

KOCHIS, Thomas, Division President, Oakwood Annapolis Hospital, Wayne, MI, p. A348

KOCZENT, Trisha, Controller, Clifton Springs Hospital and Clinic, Clifton Springs, NY, p. A450

KOEBNICK, Dale, Director Management Information Systems and Patient Access, Metroplex Adventist Hospital, Killeen, TX, p. A651

KOEHLER, Amy, Director Human Resources, Shelby Memorial Hospital, Shelbyville, IL, p. A207

KOEHLER, Duane G., Chief of Staff, Integris Baptist Regional Health Center, Miami, OK, p. A533

KOEHLER, Robert, Financial Service Manager, St. Joseph's Hospital, Chippewa Falls, WI, p. A724

KOEHLER, Theresa M., Vice President Finance, Alice Peck Day Memorial Hospital, Lebanon, NH, p. A421

KOELBL, Tom, Vice President Human Resources, SwedishAmerican Hospital, Rockford, IL, p. A207

KOENEN, LaVonne, Business Office Manager, Granite Falls Municipal Hospital and Manor, Granite Falls, MN, p. A354

KOENIG, Ann, Director Human Resources, Madonna Rehabilitation Hospital, Lincoln, NE, p. A409

KOENIG, M.D., C Scott, Director Medical Staff, Harrington Memorial Hospital, Southbridge, MA, p. A323

KOENIG, Harris, Chief Executive Officer, Centinela Freeman Regional Medical Center, Memorial Campus, Inglewood, CA, p. A65

KOENIG, Scott, Chief Executive Officer, Spring Branch Medical Center, Houston, TX, p. A647

KOEPKE, Eldon
Chief Financial Officer, Kearney County Health Services, Minden, NE, p. A409
Chief Financial Officer, Mitchell County Hospital, Beloit, KS, p. A244

KOESTER, Barb, Director Human Resources, York General Health Care Services, York, NE, p. A414

KOGAN, M.D., Mark, President, Medical Staff, Doctors Medical Center–San Pablo Campus, San Pablo, CA, p. A91

KOHANSKI, Mary, Senior Vice President Human Resources, Rockville General Hospital, Vernon Rockville, CT, p. A117

KOHLRUSS, Chuck, Vice President Human Resources and Operations Support, Holland Hospital, Holland, MI, p. A336

KOLB, Fred L., Chief Executive Officer, Madison County Hospital, London, OH, p. A516

KOLB, M.D., Marvin O., Chief Medical Officer, St. Michael Hospital, Milwaukee, WI, p. A732

KOLESK, Stephen, M.D., Vice President and Chief Operating Officer, Virtua Memorial Hospital Burlington County, Mount Holly, NJ, p. A432

KOLHEDE, Deborah
Vice President Operations, Mercy Medical Center Merced–Community Campus, Merced, CA, p. A75
Vice President Operations, Mercy Medical Center Merced–Dominican Campus, Merced, CA, p. A75

KOLLASCH, Albert J., Chief Medical Staff, Belmond Medical Center, Belmond, IA, p. A228

KOLLER, George J., President and Chief Executive Officer, Noble Hospital, Westfield, MA, p. A325

KOLMAN, Bret, CPA, Chief Executive Officer, Lafayette Regional Health Center, Lexington, MO, p. A386

KOLODZIEJCYK, Wanda, Director Human Resources, Cuero Community Hospital, Cuero, TX, p. A631

KOLOSKY, John A., Executive Vice President Planning, Finance and Chief Financial Officer, H. Lee Moffitt Cancer Center and Research Institute, Tampa, FL, p. A148

KOMANDURI, M.D., Ramanujam, Chief of Staff, Veterans Affairs Southern Nevada Healthcare System, North Las Vegas, NV, p. A418

KOMAREK, Allan G., Ph.D., Executive Director, Delano Regional Medical Center, Delano, CA, p. A58

KOMENDA, John, Vice President Finance, Hendricks Regional Health, Danville, IN, p. A213

KOMOROSKI, MSN, R.N, Pat, Executive Vice President, SSM St. Joseph Hospital West, Lake Saint Louis, MO, p. A386

KOMZO PRATT, M.D., Jimmy, Chief of Medical Staff, Bolivar General Hospital, Bolivar, TN, p. A602

KONGS, Mike, Vice President Finance and Information Services, St. Francis Health Center, Topeka, KS, p. A258

KONIECZEK, Raymond, Human Resource Business Partner, Kaiser Foundation Hospital, Walnut Creek, CA, p. A98

KONTOR, M.D., John, Chief Medical Officer, Venice Regional Medical Center, Venice, FL, p. A149

KOOBATIAN, M.D., Thomas, President Medical Staff, New Milford Hospital, New Milford, CT, p. A115

KOOIMAN, Thomas, Chief Operating Officer, Paynesville Area Health Care System, Paynesville, MN, p. A359

KOOY, Donald C., President and Chief Executive Officer, McLaren Regional Medical Center, Flint, MI, p. A333

KOPEL, M.D., Samuel, Medical Director, Maimonides Medical Center, New York, NY, p. A461

KOPHAMER, Amy
Chief Financial Officer, Morrison Community Hospital, Morrison, IL, p. A201
Chief Financial Officer, Morrison Community Hospital, Morrison, IL, p. A201

KOPMAN, Alan, President and Chief Executive Officer, New York Westchester Square Medical Center, New York, NY, p. A463

KOPPEL, Guy, Chief Information Officer, University of California, Davis Medical Center, Sacramento, CA, p. A85

KOPPEL, Robert F., President and Chief Executive Officer, East Tennessee Children's Hospital, Knoxville, TN, p. A610

KOPPELMAN, Benjamin, Administrator, Albany Area Hospital and Medical Center, Albany, MN, p. A349

KOPPENHAVER, Colleen, Chief Financial Officer, Oaklawn Hospital, Marshall, MI, p. A340

KORDUCKI, Stanley R., President, Wood County Hospital, Bowling Green, OH, p. A504

KORLASKE, John, MSC, Administrator, Mike O'Callaghan Federal Hospital, Nellis AFB, NV, p. A417

KORMAN, Marshall, Chief Executive Officer, Prairie at St. John's, Fargo, ND, p. A498

KORN, Larry, Financial Manager, Southern Arizona Veterans Affairs Health Care System, Tucson, AZ, p. A38

KORNEFF, Allen R., President and Chief Executive Officer, Downey Regional Medical Center, Downey, CA, p. A58

KORNRUMPF, Rod, Regional Administrator, Anoka–Metropolitan Regional Treatment Center, Anoka, MN, p. A349

KOROGL, Robin, Director, Human Resources, Leadership and Education, Veterans Affairs Salt Lake City Health Care System, Salt Lake City, UT, p. A680

KOROLY, Marla, Chief Medical Officer and Senior Vice President Medical Affairs, Northern Westchester Hospital, Mount Kisco, NY, p. A457

KORSMO, Jeffrey
Administrator, Rochester Methodist Hospital, Rochester, MN, p. A360
Administrator, Saint Marys Hospital, Rochester, MN, p. A360

KORSVOLD, R.N., Regina, Chief Operating Officer, Kit Carson County Memorial Hospital, Burlington, CO, p. A101

KORT, M.D., Chad, Medical Staff President, Aurora Lakeland Medical Center, Elkhorn, WI, p. A725

KORTEN, Robert, Manager, Cardinal Hill Rehabilitation Hospital, Lexington, KY, p. A267

KORTH, Mark, Chief Operating Officer, Los Alamitos Medical Center, Los Alamitos, CA, p. A69

KORTH, Paul, Chief Financial Officer, Cookeville Regional Medical Center, Cookeville, TN, p. A605

KORTH–WHITE, Kirsten, Chief Human Resources Officer, Mercy Hospital Grayling, Grayling, MI, p. A335

KORTUM, Joseph M., President and Chief Executive Officer, Southwest Washington Medical Center, Vancouver, WA, p. A711

KORZEN, R.N., Joyce P., Senior Vice President and Chief Operating Officer, Cape Fear Valley Health System, Fayetteville, NC, p. A482

KOSANOVICH, John P., President, Watertown Memorial Hospital, Watertown, WI, p. A737

KOSE, M.D., Bill, Senior Vice President Medical Affairs, Blanchard Valley Health Association, Findlay, OH, p. A513

KOSLOW, Howard B., President and Chief Executive Officer, Promise Healthcare, Lafayette, LA, p. B85

KOSOWAN, Karen, Vice President, Human Resources, Holy Rosary Medical Center, Ontario, OR, p. A546

KOSSEFF, Christopher O., President and Chief Executive Officer, University of Medicine and Dentistry of New Jersey, University Behavioral Healthcare, Piscataway, NJ, p. A434

KOSTER, John, M.D., President and Chief Executive Officer, Providence Health System, Seattle, WA, p. B86

KOSTER, Kent, Chief Executive Officer, Three Rivers Hospital, Waverly, TN, p. A618

KOSTOK, Barbara, Manager Human Resources, Punxsutawney Area Hospital, Punxsutawney, PA, p. A574

KOSYLA, Gail, Vice President Finance and Chief Financial Officer, St. Francis Medical Center, Trenton, NJ, p. A437

KOTCHICK, M.D., E Donald, Vice President Medical Affairs, Mercy Hospital of Scranton, Scranton, PA, p. A575

KOTIN, Kathy, Chief Financial Officer, Banner Good Samaritan Medical Center, Phoenix, AZ, p. A33

KOTZEN, Michael S., Vice President and Chief Operating Officer, Virtua West Jersey Hospital–Voorhees, Voorhees, NJ, p. A438

KOUDSI, M.D., Nabil, President Medical Staff, San Antonio Community Hospital, Upland, CA, p. A97

KOULOVATOS, James E., Chief Executive Officer, Lindsay Municipal Hospital, Lindsay, OK, p. A533

KOUPAL, Bernadette, Business Office Supervisor, Information Systems Coordinator and Administrative Assistant, Wagner Community Memorial Hospital, Wagner, SD, p. A600

KOUPAL SMITH, Nanette, Medical Records Director, Northeastern Nevada Regional Hospital, Elko, NV, p. A415

KOURY, Peter G., Executive Vice President Fiscal Services, St. Dominic–Jackson Memorial Hospital, Jackson, MS, p. A371

KOVACH, Andrew
   Vice President Human Resources and Shared Services, Morristown Memorial Hospital, Morristown, NJ, p. A431
   Vice President Human Resources and Shared Services, Mountainside Hospital, Montclair, NJ, p. A431
   Vice President Human Resources and Shared Services, Overlook Hospital, Summit, NJ, p. A436

KOWAL, Robert P., President and Chief Executive Officer, Sonoma Valley Hospital, Sonoma, CA, p. A94

KOWALOFF, Harvey, Chief Medical Officer, Saint Vincent Hospital at Worcester Medical Center, Worcester, MA, p. A325

KOWALSKI, Patrick, Chief Financial Officer, Mercy Franciscan Hospital–Western Hills, Cincinnati, OH, p. A507

KOWALSKI, Richard S., Administrator and Chief Executive Officer, OSF St. Mary Medical Center, Galesburg, IL, p. A195

KOWITT, Jack, Senior Vice President and Chief Information Officer, Parkland Health & Hospital System, Dallas, TX, p. A633

KOZAI, Gerald T., President, St. Francis Medical Center, Lynwood, CA, p. A74

KOZEL, Kenneth
   Senior Vice President and Chief Operating Officer, Harford Memorial Hospital, Havre De Grace, MD, p. A308
   Senior Vice President and Chief Operating Officer, Upper Chesapeake Medical Center, Bel Air, MD, p. A305

KOZIK, Rhonda, Administrator, Norwood Health Center, Marshfield, WI, p. A729

KOZIOL, Michael J., Vice President and Chief Financial Officer, South County Hospital, Wakefield, RI, p. A582

KOZLIK, Igor, Chief Executive Officer, Dolly Vinsant Memorial Hospital, San Benito, TX, p. A666

KOZLOFF, Kenneth H., FACHE, Administrator, Inova Alexandria Hospital, Alexandria, VA, p. A685

KRABBENHOFT, Kelby K., President and Chief Executive Officer, Sioux Valley Hospitals and Health System, Sioux Falls, SD, p. B98

KRAGER, Dan, Information Systems Manager, Richland Memorial Hospital, Olney, IL, p. A203

KRAHL, Lucy, Chief Operating Officer, North Texas Medical Center, Gainesville, TX, p. A641

KRAJEWSKI, David, Vice President Finance, Northwest Hospital Center, Randallstown, MD, p. A310

KRALIK, M.D., Michael, Chief of Staff, Phoenix Memorial Hospital, Phoenix, AZ, p. A34

KRAMER, Danette, Vice President Finance and Chief Financial Officer, Regional Medical Center, Manchester, IA, p. A237

KRAMER, M.D., Ralph, Chief Medical Staff, R. J. Reynolds–Patrick County Memorial Hospital, Stuart, VA, p. A697

KRAML, Louis D., CHE, Chief Executive Officer, Bingham Memorial Hospital, Blackfoot, ID, p. A177

KRANZ, Marlene, Chief Financial Officer, Holton Community Hospital, Holton, KS, p. A249

KRASNAUSKAS, Richard J., President and Chief Executive Officer, Canton–Potsdam Hospital, Potsdam, NY, p. A470

KRASON, Jane E., R.N., Chief Executive Officer, Appalachian Behavioral Healthcare, Cambridge, OH, p. A505

KRASOVEC, Emro, Vice President Human Resources, Bayshore Community Hospital, Holmdel, NJ, p. A429

KRASS, Todd
   President and Chief Executive Officer, Research Belton Hospital, Belton, MO, p. A378
   President and Chief Executive Officer, Research Psychiatric Center, Kansas City, MO, p. A384

KRAUKLIS, Gene
   Regional Vice President Human Resources, Aurora Lakeland Medical Center, Elkhorn, WI, p. A725
   Regional Vice President Human Resources, Aurora Medical Center, Kenosha, WI, p. A727
   Regional Vice President Human Resources, Memorial Hospital Corporation of Burlington, Burlington, WI, p. A724

KRAUS, M.D., Bruce A., Chief of Staff, Columbus Community Hospital, Columbus, WI, p. A724

KRAUS, Carol A., Administrator and Chief Executive Officer, Perkins County Health Services, Grant, NE, p. A407

KRAUSE, Allen A.
   Chief Financial Officer, Caritas Good Samaritan Medical Center, Brockton, MA, p. A315
   Chief Financial Officer, Caritas Holy Family Hospital and Medical Center, Methuen, MA, p. A320
   Vice President Finance and Chief Financial Officer, Saint Anne's Hospital, Fall River, MA, p. A317

KRAUSE, Lisa, Chief Financial Officer, Richardson Medical Center, Rayville, LA, p. A291

KRAUSE, Steven, Manager Information Technology, Illiana Surgery and Medical Center, Munster, IN, p. A222

KRAUSS, James D., Chief Operating Officer, Rockingham Memorial Hospital, Harrisonburg, VA, p. A689

KRAVITZ, John, Chief Information Officer, Allied Services Rehabilitation Hospital, Scranton, PA, p. A575

KRAWIEC, Ronald J.
   President and Chief Executive Officer, Lake Shore Health Care Center, Irving, NY, p. A454
   President and Chief Executive Officer, Tri–County Memorial Hospital, Gowanda, NY, p. A453

KREBS, Anne, Chief Financial Officer, Butler Health System, Butler, PA, p. A554

KREBS, Cindy, District Director Human Resources, Matagorda General Hospital, Bay City, TX, p. A624

KREBSBACH, Mayla, Chief Executive Officer, Aurora Vista Del Mar Hospital, Ventura, CA, p. A98

KREHBILL, M.D., Todd, Chief of Staff, Logan Medical Center, Guthrie, OK, p. A531

KREHBREL, Beth, Chief Operating Officer, Fairview Red Wing Medical Center, Red Wing, MN, p. A360

KREHO, Kelvin, Vice President Finance, Bristol Hospital, Bristol, CT, p. A112

KREIDER, Robert Q., President and Chief Executive, Devereux, Villanova, PA, p. B41

KREIN, Marlene J., President and Chief Executive Officer, Mercy Hospital, Devils Lake, ND, p. A497

KREITZ, Don, Chief Operating Officer, Encino–Tarzana Regional Medical Center Encino Campus, Los Angeles, CA, p. A70

KREITZER, Teri, Director Human Resources, Saint Francis Medical Center, Cape Girardeau, MO, p. A379

KREJCI, David, Director Information Services, Baylor Medical Center at Irving, Irving, TX, p. A649

KRELL, M.D., G Christopher, Chief of Staff, South Lincoln Medical Center, Kemmerer, WY, p. A740

KREMER, Nancy
   Senior Vice President, St. Luke Hospital East, Fort Thomas, KY, p. A264
   Senior Vice President, St. Luke Hospital West, Florence, KY, p. A264
   Senior Vice President, St. Luke Hospital East, Fort Thomas, KY, p. A264
   Senior Vice President, St. Luke Hospital West, Florence, KY, p. A264

KRENEK Jr, Bryant H.
   President and Chief Executive Officer, Memorial Health System of East Texas, Lufkin, TX, p. B74
   President and Chief Executive Officer, Memorial Health System of East Texas, Lufkin, TX, p. A655

KRETSCHMER, Suzanne, Administrator, Nexus Specialty Hospital, The Woodlands, TX, p. A670

KRETTEK, M.D., John, Vice President Medical Affairs and Chief Medical Officer, Missouri Baptist Medical Center, Town and Country, MO, p. A394

KRETZ, Blake, Administrator, Graham Regional Medical Center, Graham, TX, p. A642

KRETZ, Karen, Chief Financial Officer, Western Medical Center Anaheim, Anaheim, CA, p. A52

KRETZCHMER, Deborah, Commander, U. S. Air Force Regional Hospital, Elmendorf AFB, AK, p. A27

KRETZINGER, Curt, Chief Operating Officer, Heartland Regional Medical Center, Saint Joseph, MO, p. A390

KREUSER, Michael, Director Fiscal Support, Milwaukee County Behavioral Health Division, Milwaukee, WI, p. A731

KREUTNER, Ron, Chief Financial Officer, Lodi Memorial Hospital, Lodi, CA, p. A67

KREUZER, Jay E., FACHE, President and Chief Executive Officer, West Suburban Medical Center, Oak Park, IL, p. A203

KRIEGER, Robert M., Chief Executive Officer, Orange Park Medical Center, Orange Park, FL, p. A140

KRIKAVA, M.D., Joan, Director Medical Affairs, New Ulm Medical Center, New Ulm, MN, p. A358

KRISHNA, M.D., Doddanna, Chief of Staff, Antelope Valley Hospital, Lancaster, CA, p. A67

KRISIAK, Steve, Chief Executive Officer, Bertrand Chaffee Hospital, Springville, NY, p. A472

KRISTEL, John, Chief Operating Officer, Graduate Hospital, Philadelphia, PA, p. A568

KRITIKOS, Peter, Chief Financial Officer, Speare Memorial Hospital, Plymouth, NH, p. A423

KRITZ, Howard, Director, Coler–Goldwater Specialty Hospital and Nursing Facility, New York, NY, p. A459

KRITZ, John D., Regional Financial Officer, Fairview University Medical Center–Mesabi, Hibbing, MN, p. A355

KRIVENKO, M.D., Chuck, Chief Medical Officer Clinical and Quality Services, Lee Memorial Health System, Fort Myers, FL, p. A129

KROELL Jr, H. Scott, Chief Executive Officer, Liberty Regional Medical Center, Hinesville, GA, p. A163

KROESE, Robert D.
   Chief Executive Officer, Pella Regional Health Center, Pella, IA, p. A240
   Chief Executive Officer, Pella Regional Health Center, Pella, IA, p. A240

KROGNESS, John, CHE, Administrator, Big Bend Regional Medical Center, Alpine, TX, p. A620

KROK, Stan, Chief Information Officer, Children's Memorial Hospital, Chicago, IL, p. A187

KROLL, Ronald, Chief Financial Officer, Mercy General Hospital, Sacramento, CA, p. A85

KRONENBERG, Paul J., M.D., President and Chief Executive Officer, Crouse Hospital, Syracuse, NY, p. A473

KRONENBERGER, M.D., Brett, Medical Staff President, St. James Healthcare, Butte, MT, p. A397

KROPELNICKI, Susan, Administrator, Group Health Cooperative, Redmond, WA, p. A706

KROUSE, Michael, Vice President Administrative Services, Northwest Hospital, Seattle, WA, p. A707

KROUSKOP, M.D., Andrew C., Medical Director, Siskin Hospital for Physical Rehabilitation, Chattanooga, TN, p. A604

KROUTH, M.D., Gary, Vice President Professional Relations, St. Luke's Regional Medical Center, Boise, ID, p. A178

L

LADEW, Lisa, Chief Executive Officer, Rehabilitation Hospital of Rhode Island, North Smithfield, RI, p. A581

LADNIER, Dennis, Manager, Information Systems, Centinela Freeman Regional Medical Center, Memorial Campus, Inglewood, CA, p. A65

LAFACE, Nicholas, Executive Director Fiscal and Support Services, Richland Memorial Hospital, Olney, IL, p. A203

LAFFERTY, Aline, Vice President Human Resources, Bon Secours Hospital, Grosse Pointe, MI, p. A335

LAFFERTY, Douglas L.
Administrator, Central Valley General Hospital, Hanford, CA, p. A63
President and Chief Executive Officer, Hanford Community Medical Center, Hanford, CA, p. A63

LAFLEUR, M.D., Dan, Chief of Staff, Richardson Medical Center, Rayville, LA, p. A291

LAFRANCE, Pam, Vice President of Human Resources, St. John's Riverside Hosptial, Yonkers, NY, p. A476

LAGASSE, David A., Senior Vice President Fiscal Affairs, McLean Hospital, Belmont, MA, p. A312

LAGASSE, Roger, Chief Financial Officer, Northern Maine Medical Center, Fort Kent, ME, p. A298

LAGATTUTA, Joseph, Assistant Director of Medical Affairs, Adventist GlenOaks Hospital, Glendale Heights, IL, p. A195

LAHAYE, Bryan, Chief Financial Officer, Bogalusa Medical Center, Bogalusa, LA, p. A278

LAHAYE, Daniel, Manager, Savoy Medical Center, Mamou, LA, p. A285

LAI, Iris, Acting Chief Executive Officer, Alhambra Hospital Medical Center, Alhambra, CA, p. A52

LAIBLE, Ray, Administrator, State Hospital South, Blackfoot, ID, p. A177

LAIGN, Michael B., President and Chief Executive Officer, Holy Redeemer Hospital and Medical Center, Jenkintown, PA, p. A561

LAIN, M.D., Richard F., Vice President Medical Affairs, Pocono Medical Center, East Stroudsburg, PA, p. A557

LAIRD, Jeff, Controller, Stephens County Hospital, Toccoa, GA, p. A171

LAIRD, Michael J., FACHE, Chief Executive Officer, Ste. Genevieve County Memorial Hospital, Ste. Genevieve, MO, p. A394

LAKE, Jane, Director, Information Technology, St. Luke's Cornwall Hospital – Newburgh Campus, Newburgh, NY, p. A467

LAKE, Lana, Assistant Administrator Human Resources, Christus St. Patrick Hospital of Lake Charles, Lake Charles, LA, p. A284

LAKE, Michael C.
Chief Executive Officer, DasSee Community Health System, Quincy, FL, p. B35
Chief Executive Officer, George E. Weems Memorial Hospital, Apalachicola, FL, p. A123

LAKE, Nathan, Director of Human Resources, Sibley Medical Center, Arlington, MN, p. A349

LAKE, Robin E., Chief Executive Officer, Great Plains Regional Medical Center, Elk City, OK, p. A530

LALIBERTE, John, Director Information Services, Our Lady of Lourdes Memorial Hospital, Binghamton, NY, p. A448

LALLY, Jr, Robert P., Vice President Finance, Franklin Square Hospital Center, Baltimore, MD, p. A302

LALO, Gil
Interim Chief Executive Officer Informtion Services, Central Michigan Community Hospital, Mount Pleasant, MI, p. A341
Information Systems Manager, Zeeland Community Hospital, Zeeland, MI, p. A348

LAMANTIA, Joseph, Executive Director, Franklin Hospital Medical Center, Valley Stream, NY, p. A478

LAMAR, Paula, Chief Financial Officer, San Gabriel Valley Medical Center, San Gabriel, CA, p. A90

LAMAY, M.D., Edward N., Chief Medical Officer, Durham Regional Hospital, Durham, NC, p. A481

LAMB, Edward H., FACHE, President and Chief Executive Officer, Alaska Regional Hospital, Anchorage, AK, p. A26

LAMBDIN, Bruce, Interim Chief Executive Officer, HEALTHSOUTH Rehabilitation Hospital of Arlington, Arlington, TX, p. A622

LAMBERT, James M., Chief Operating Officer, Conway Regional Medical Center, Conway, AR, p. A41

LAMBERT, Karen A., President, Advocate Good Shepherd Hospital, Barrington, IL, p. A184

LAMBERT, Lynn, Vice President Finance and Chief Financial Officer, Gateway Health System, Clarksville, TN, p. A604

LAMBERT, M. Aurora, Senior Vice President, Jewish Hospital, Cincinnati, OH, p. A507

LAMBERT, Norman, Chief Executive Officer, Golden Plains Community Hospital, Borger, TX, p. A626

LAMBERT, Terry R., CHE, Chief Executive Officer, Newman Regional Health, Emporia, KS, p. A246

LAMBERT, Timothy, Controller, HEALTHSOUTH Hospital of Terre Haute, Terre Haute, IN, p. A226

LAMBERT, Tod N., Interim President and Chief Executive Officer, Danville Regional Medical Center, Danville, VA, p. A687

LAMBERTI, Patrick, Chief Executive Officer, POH Medical Center, Pontiac, MI, p. A342

LAMBETH, Donny C., Senior Vice President and Chief Operating Officer, North Carolina Baptist Hospital (Wake Forest University Baptist Medical Center), Winston–Salem, NC, p. A494

LAMBIOTTE, M.D., Charles, Medical Staff President, Punxsutawney Area Hospital, Punxsutawney, PA, p. A574

LAMBOG, Malben, Chief Executive Officer, Dr. Pila's Hospital, Ponce, PR, p. A746

LAMBRECHT, Becky, Administrator, Plainview Area Health System, Plainview, NE, p. A412

LAMBRECHT, M.D., Craig, Medical Director, MedCenter One, Bismarck, ND, p. A496

LAMBRECHT, Sandra, Chief Financial Officer, Haxtun Hospital District, Haxtun, CO, p. A106

LAMEY, Rebecca, Vice President Human Resources, MaineGeneral Medical Center–Waterville Campus, Waterville, ME, p. A301

LAMHORN, Cheryl, Director Human Resources, Mercy Medical Center, Springfield, OH, p. A522

LAMKIN, Elizabeth, President and Chief Executive Officer, Hilton Head Regional Medical Center, Hilton Head Island, SC, p. A589

LAMMERS, Sandra, Human Resources and Finance Coordinator, Alegent Health Mercy Hospital, Corning, IA, p. A231

LAMMERTSE, M.D., Daniel P., Medical Director, Craig Hospital, Englewood, CO, p. A105

LAMORELLA, Vincent M., Chief Financial Officer, Clarion Hospital, Clarion, PA, p. A555

LAMORGESE, M.D., James, Vice President and Chief Medical Officer, St. Luke's Hospital, Cedar Rapids, IA, p. A229

LAMPARTER, David
Chief Financial Officer, John C. Lincoln Hospital – North Mountain, Phoenix, AZ, p. A34
Chief Financial Officer, John C. Lincoln Hospital–Deer Valley, Phoenix, AZ, p. A34

LAMPE, Diane B., Administrator, HEALTHSOUTH Rehabilitation Institute of San Antonio, San Antonio, TX, p. A664

LAMPERT, Vickie, Director Information Systems and Data Center, Doctors Medical Center–San Pablo Campus, San Pablo, CA, p. A91

LANCASTER, Tim, FACHE, President and Chief Executive Officer, Hendrick Health System, Abilene, TX, p. A620

LANCE, Bill, Administrator, Chickasaw Nation Health System, Ada, OK, p. A527

LAND, Laura, Chief Human Resources Officer, OU Medical Center, Oklahoma City, OK, p. A536

LANDAU, Ken, Chief Financial Officer, Lake District Hospital, Lakeview, OR, p. A545

LANDDECK, John R., President, Beaver Dam Community Hospitals, Beaver Dam, WI, p. A723

LANDERS, Alice, Administrative Director Operations, Harris Methodist–HEB, Bedford, TX, p. A625

LANDERS, M.D., W Hank, Chief of Staff, Covenant Hospital Plainview, Plainview, TX, p. A660

LANDGARTEN, M.D., Steven, Senior Vice President Medical Staff Affairs, Hillcrest Medical Center, Tulsa, OK, p. A539

LANDGRAF, M.D., Kenneth, Chief of Staff, Trinity Community Medical Center of Brenham, Brenham, TX, p. A626

LANDIS, Steve, Director Information Services, St. Christopher's Hospital for Children, Philadelphia, PA, p. A570

LANDO, Howard, President Medical Staff, Inova Mount Vernon Hospital, Alexandria, VA, p. A685

LANDOLL, Therese, Chief Financial Officer, Community Memorial Healthcare, Marysville, KS, p. A252

LANDRETH, Shannan, Chief Information Technology, Livingston Hospital and Healthcare Services, Salem, KY, p. A274

LANDRUM, Scott M., Chief Executive Officer, Campbell Health System, Weatherford, TX, p. A673

LANDRY, Chad, Information Systems Director, Swedish Medical Center, Englewood, CO, p. A105

LANDRY, Donna, Chief Operating Officer, Lafayette General Medical Center, Lafayette, LA, p. A283

LANDRY, Michael J., Chief Executive Officer, Teche Regional Medical Center, Morgan City, LA, p. A287

LANDRY, Ray A., Chief Executive Officer, Abbeville General Hospital, Abbeville, LA, p. A276

LANDSMAN, Joseph, President and Chief Executive Officer, University of Tennessee Medical Center, Knoxville, TN, p. A610

LANDY, Douglas O., Executive Vice President and Chief Operating Officer, Sound Shore Medical Center of Westchester, New Rochelle, NY, p. A458

LANE, Jerry, Chief Executive Officer, Coulee Community Hospital, Grand Coulee, WA, p. A703

LANE, Peter, Director Human Resources, Mercy Hospital Cadillac, Cadillac, MI, p. A329

LANE, Richard, Chief Financial Officer, Mid–America Rehabilitation Hospital, Shawnee Mission, KS, p. A257

LANE, Sandra, Vice President Human Resources, Louise Obici Memorial Hospital, Suffolk, VA, p. A697

LANE, Sheryl, Chief Information Officer, Parkview Hospital, Wheeler, TX, p. A673

LANE, Stacey, Executive Assistant Human Resources, Chambers Memorial Hospital, Danville, AR, p. A42

LANE MYERS, Amy, Human Resources Manager, Deer River HealthCare Center, Deer River, MN, p. A352

LANEAUX, Eleanor, Director Information Systems, Lakewood Regional Medical Center, Lakewood, CA, p. A67

LANER, Jr, Richard, Information Systems Manager, Miners' Colfax Medical Center, Raton, NM, p. A444

LANFORD, Alice Reed, R.N., Administrator, Shriners Hospitals for Children, Tampa, Tampa, FL, p. A148

LANG, Barbara,Warren G. Magnuson Clinical Center, National Institutes of Health, Bethesda, MD, p. A306

LANG, Cyndi
Director Information Services, Arroyo Grande Community Hospital, Arroyo Grande, CA, p. A53
Director Information Services, French Hospital Medical Center, San Luis Obispo, CA, p. A91

LANG, David, Vice President Human Resources, Regional Medical Center of Hopkins County, Madisonville, KY, p. A270

LANG, Gary, Chief Financial Officer, St. Peter's Hospital, Albany, NY, p. A446

LANG, Jeffrey M., Administrator, Milbank Area Hospital/Avera Health, Milbank, SD, p. A597

LANG, John Christopher, Chief Executive Officer, Cass Medical Center, Harrisonville, MO, p. A382

LANG, Nicholas P., M.D., Interim Director, Central Arkansas Veterans Healthcare System, Little Rock, AR, p. A46

LANG, M.D., Nicholas P., Chief of Staff, Central Arkansas Veterans Healthcare System, Little Rock, AR, p. A46

LANGBEHN, Cody, Chief Executive Officer, Pioneer Medical Center, Big Timber, MT, p. A396

LANGBERG, M.D., Michael, Senior Vice President Medical Affairs and Chief Medical Officer, Cedars–Sinai Medical Center, Los Angeles, CA, p. A69

LANGE, M.D., Jan, Medical Director Performance Improvement, Yakima Valley Memorial Hospital, Yakima, WA, p. A712

LANGER, M.D., Bradley, Interim Medical Director, John H. Stroger Jr. Hospital of Cook County, Chicago, IL, p. A187

LANGFELDER, Richard, Executive Vice President and Chief Financial Officer, Lutheran Medical Center, New York, NY, p. A461

LANGFORD, Joe S., Chief Executive Officer, Covenant Hospital Plainview, Plainview, TX, p. A660

LANGLEY, Douglas, Chief Executive Officer, Coleman County Medical Center, Coleman, TX, p. A629

LANGLOTZ, Karla, Director, Human Resources, Central Florida Regional Hospital, Sanford, FL, p. A146

LANGMEAD, Paula A., Chief Executive Officer, Springfield Hospital Center, Sykesville, MD, p. A311

LANGOSCH, Rick, Interim Chief Executive Officer, Berrien County Hospital, Nashville, GA, p. A166

LANGVA, Fred, Director Information Systems, Guyan Valley Hospital, Logan, WV, p. A717

LANHAM, Kimberli, Director of Human Resources, Jackson General Hospital, Ripley, WV, p. A719

LANIER, Lynn T., Vice President Finance and Chief Financial Officer, Roanoke–Chowan Hospital, Ahoskie, NC, p. A477

LANIK, Robert J., President and Chief Executive Officer, Saint Elizabeth Regional Medical Center, Lincoln, NE, p. A409

LANIUS, Joe, Vice President Finance, Memorial Hospital, Belleville, IL, p. A184

LANSPA, M.D., Stephen, Vice President Medical Affairs, Creighton University Medical Center, Omaha, NE, p. A411

LANTOS, Phyllis R., Senior Vice President, Chief Financial Officer and Treasurer, New York–Presbyterian Hospital, New York, NY, p. A463

LANTZ, M.D., Gordon, Medical Director, Continuous Care Center of Tulsa, Tulsa, OK, p. A539

LANTZY, William, Vice President of Finance, Huron Valley–Sinai Hospital, Commerce Township, MI, p. A330

LANZA, Nicholas, Interim Chief Financial Officer, Catskill Regional Medical Center, Harris, NY, p. A453

LANZA, D.O., Raymond, Medical Director, Runnells Specialized Hospital of Union County, Berkeley Heights, NJ, p. A425

LAPRAD, Guy J., Interim Chief Financial Officer, Baptist Medical Center East, Montgomery, AL, p. A21

LAQUINTA, Fred J., Vice President, Corporate Human Resources, Atlanticare Regional Medical Center, Atlantic City, NJ, p. A425

LARA, M.D., Humberto A., Chief of Staff, Memorial Hermann Fort Bend Hospital, Missouri City, TX, p. A657

LARA, M.D., Rolando, Medical Director, Saint Anthony Hospital, Chicago, IL, p. A189

LARAWAY, Dennis, Chief Financial Officer, St. Joseph's Hospital and Medical Center, Phoenix, AZ, p. A35

LARCEN, Stephen W., Ph.D., President and Chief Executive Officer, Natchaug Hospital, Mansfield Center, CT, p. A114

LAREAU, Kim, Vice President and Chief Information Officer, Regions Hospital, Saint Paul, MN, p. A362

LARET, Mark R., Chief Executive Officer, UCSF Medical Center, San Francisco, CA, p. A89

LAREY, D.O., Mark, Vice President Medical Affairs, St. Joseph's Mercy Health Center, Hot Springs National Park, AR, p. A45

LARIA, Tony, Director Management Information Systems, Rome Memorial Hospital, Rome, NY, p. A471

LARIO, Joseph, Senior Vice President Management Support Services, Kennedy Memorial Hospitals–University Medical Center, Cherry Hill, NJ, p. A427

LARKIN, Carol, Chief Financial Officer, Rush County Memorial Hospital, La Crosse, KS, p. A250

LARKIN, Donald N., Chief Executive Officer, San Gorgonio Memorial Hospital, Banning, CA, p. A54

LARKIN, Kim, Chief Information Officer, Washington County Hospital, Nashville, IL, p. A202

LAROCHELLE, Albert, Administrator, Grace Cottage Hospital, Townshend, VT, p. A684

LAROSE, Mark, President and Chief Executive Officer, Ukiah Valley Medical Center, Ukiah, CA, p. A97

LARSEN, Bill, Vice President Human Resources, Driscoll Children's Hospital, Corpus Christi, TX, p. A630

LARSEN, David, Vice President Finance, Sonora Regional Medical Center, Sonora, CA, p. A94

LARSEN, Michael, Director Information Systems, Baylor Medical Center at Garland, Garland, TX, p. A641

LARSEN, Rod, Chief Financial Officer, Wray Community District Hospital, Wray, CO, p. A111

LARSEN, Ryan, Chief Financial Officer, Memorial Hospital, Carthage, IL, p. A186

LARSON, Dale, Administrator, Oak Leaf Surgical Center, Eau Claire, WI, p. A725

LARSON, Gail C., Chief Executive Officer, Providence Everett Medical Center, Everett, WA, p. A703

LARSON, Jon, Medical Director, HEALTHSOUTH Rehabilitation Institute of Tucson, Tucson, AZ, p. A38

LARSON, Karl, Human Res Director, Stevens Community Medical Center, Morris, MN, p. A358

LARSON, Mike, Chief Financial Officer, Fairview Red Wing Medical Center, Red Wing, MN, p. A360

LARSON, Pamela, Chief Financial Officer, Hutchinson Area Health Care, Hutchinson, MN, p. A355

LARSON, R. Alan, Chief Executive Officer, Mercy Catholic Medical Center, Darby, PA, p. A557

LARSON, Rodney, Human Resource Director, Hendry Regional Medical Center, Clewiston, FL, p. A126

LARSON, M.D., Scott
Vice President Medical Affairs and Chief Medical Officer, Bronson Methodist Hospital, Kalamazoo, MI, p. A338
Vice President Medical Affairs and Chief Medical Officer, Bronson Vicksburg Hospital, Vicksburg, MI, p. A347

LARSON, Shelly, Chief Financial Officer, Melissa Memorial Hospital, Holyoke, CO, p. A107

LARSON, Steve, Director Information Systems, Mercy Medical Center–Sioux City, Sioux City, IA, p. A241

LARSON, Steven, Chief Financial Officer, Deer River HealthCare Center, Deer River, MN, p. A352

LARSON, M.D., Valorie, Chief of Staff, Dells Area Health Center, Dell Rapids, SD, p. A595

LASH, C Patrick, Chief Financial Officer, Glendale Memorial Hospital and Health Center, Glendale, CA, p. A62

LASH, D.O., Donald, Chief of Staff, East Texas Medical Center Carthage, Carthage, TX, p. A628

LASHBROOK, Eric, Vice President Finance, King's Daughters Hospital, Temple, TX, p. A669

LASHMETT, Gordon, Chief Information Officer, St. Anthony's Medical Center, Saint Louis, MO, p. A392

LASKOWSKI, Robert J., M.D.,
President and Chief Executive Officer, Christiana Care Health System, Wilmington, DE, p. B28
President and Chief Executive Officer, Christiana Care Health System, Wilmington, DE, p. A120

LASKOWSKI, Rose, R.N., Hospital Director, Caro Center, Caro, MI, p. A329

LASSER, Andrew A., Dr.PH, President and Chief Executive Officer, St. Joseph Hospital, Augusta, GA, p. A155

LASSITER, Susan S., President, Roanoke–Chowan Hospital, Ahoskie, NC, p. A477

LASTER, Charles, Director Information Management, Willis–Knighton Medical Center, Shreveport, LA, p. A293

LASTUFKA, Kjerstin, Director Marketing and Public Relations, Alaska Regional Hospital, Anchorage, AK, p. A26

LATHAM, Fred L., Executive Vice President and Chief Operating Officer, Self Regional Healthcare, Greenwood, SC, p. A589

LATHREN, James E.
Executive Vice President and Chief Operating Officer, Palmetto Health Richland, Columbia, SC, p. A586
Executive Vice President and Chief Operating Officer, Palmetto Health Richland, Columbia, SC, p. A586

LATHROP, Amy, Director Information Technology, McKenzie–Willamette Medical Center, Springfield, OR, p. A549

LATTA, Priscilla, Chief Financial Officer, Bunkie General Hospital, Bunkie, LA, p. A278

LATTA, Ron, Director Information Technology, North Ottawa Community Hospital, Grand Haven, MI, p. A334

LATUCHIE, Richard, Vice President Business Development, Rapid City Regional Hospital System of Care, Rapid City, SD, p. A598

LAUDERDALE, Max, Chief Executive Officer, Lakeview Regional Medical Center, Covington, LA, p. A279

LAUDON, Larry, Chief Executive Officer, Clearwater Health Services, Bagley, MN, p. A350

LAUE, Jerry, Administrator, St. Vincent Clay Hospital, Brazil, IN, p. A212

LAUER, Christopher, Chief Financial Officer, Littleton Regional Hospital, Littleton, NH, p. A422

LAUF, Michael K., President, Miners Medical Center, Hastings, PA, p. A560

LAUFFER, Dan, FACHE,
Chief Executive Officer, Putnam General Hospital, Hurricane, WV, p. A716
Chief Executive Officer, Saint Francis Hospital, Charleston, WV, p. A714

LAUGHLIN, Donald E., Chief Operating Officer, Saint Francis Hospital, Memphis, TN, p. A613

LAUGHLIN Jr, Raymond E., President and Chief Executive Officer, Wayne Hospital, Greenville, OH, p. A515

LAUGHLIN, Rod, President and Chief Executive Officer, Regency Hospital Company, Alpharetta, GA, p. B92

LAUGHLIN, M.D., Ted, Medical Director, Banner Thunderbird Medical Center, Glendale, AZ, p. A31

LAUGHLIN, Warren, Director of Human Resources, Longmont United Hospital, Longmont, CO, p. A108

LAUGHNAN Jr, Woody J., Administrator, Glenn Medical Center, Willows, CA, p. A99

LAUREIJS, M.D., Peter, Medical Staff President, Genesis Medical Center, DeWitt, De Witt, IA, p. A232

LAURIN, George, Interim Director Human Resources, Titus Regional Medical Center, Mount Pleasant, TX, p. A657

LAUX, Thomas W., President and Chief Executive Officer, Morgan Hospital and Medical Center, Martinsville, IN, p. A222

LAVAN, Paul, Chief Information Management Division, Walter Reed Army Medical Center, Washington, DC, p. A122

LAVATER, Ronald, Chief Operating Officer, Research Medical Center, Kansas City, MO, p. A384

LAVELLE, Thomas F.
Chief Medical Officer, Saint Joseph Regional Medical Center, South Bend, IN, p. A225
Chief Medical Officer, Saint Joseph Regional Medical Center–Plymouth Campus, Plymouth, IN, p. A224

LAVENDER, Paul, Vice President Finance, Newton Medical Center, Newton, KS, p. A253

LAVENSTEIN, Deb, Vice President Human Resources and Marketing, St. Joseph's Community Hospital of West Bend, West Bend, WI, p. A738

LAVERTY, Stephen R., President and Chief Executive Officer, Beverly Hospital, Beverly, MA, p. A312

LAVNIUS, Billie, Business Finance Director, Dallas County Medical Center, Fordyce, AR, p. A43

LAVOIE, Reginald J., Administrator, Cottage Hospital, Woodsville, NH, p. A424

LAW, John, Site Administrator, WellStar Paulding Hospital, Dallas, GA, p. A160

LAW, Johnny, Information Technology Leader, Kaiser Foundation Hospital, Oakland, CA, p. A79

LAWATSCH, Frank, Chief Executive Officer, Swift County–Benson Hospital, Benson, MN, p. A350

LAWHORN, Renee, Director Medical Records, East Texas Medical Center Carthage, Carthage, TX, p. A628

LAWHORNE, Tom, Vice President Finance, Pulaski Community Hospital, Pulaski, VA, p. A694

LAWLER, CPA, James P., Vice President Finance, University of Medicine and Dentistry of New Jersey–University Hospital, Newark, NJ, p. A433

LAWLOR, Kevin, Senior Vice President and Chief Financial Officer, Huntington Hospital, Huntington, NY, p. A454

LAWONN, Ken, Vice President, Information Technology, Alegent Health Immanuel Medical Center, Omaha, NE, p. A410

LAWRENCE, C Bruce, President and Chief Operating Officer, Integris Baptist Medical Center, Oklahoma City, OK, p. A535

LAWRENCE, C. Bruce
President and Chief Operating Officer, Integris Baptist Medical Center, Oklahoma City, OK, p. A535
President and Chief Operating Officer, Integris Southwest Medical Center, Oklahoma City, OK, p. A535
LAWRENCE, Jonathan I., President and Chief Executive Offier, Little Falls Hospital, Little Falls, NY, p. A455
LAWRENCE, Scott E., Flight Commander, Business Operations Beneficiary Support, U. S. Air Force Regional Hospital–Sheppard, Sheppard AFB, TX, p. A667
LAWRENCE, William P.
President, UHHS Brown Memorial Hospital, Conneaut, OH, p. A511
President, UHHS Richmond Heights Hospital, Richmond Heights, OH, p. A521
LAWS, M.D., G L., Medical Staff President, Carlinville Area Hospital, Carlinville, IL, p. A185
LAWSON, Alvin R., FACHE, Chief Executive Officer, Pleasant Valley Hospital, Point Pleasant, WV, p. A719
LAWSON, David
Vice President Human Resources, St. Clare Hospital, Tacoma, WA, p. A710
Vice President Human Resources, St. Francis Hospital, Federal Way, WA, p. A703
Vice President Human Resources, St. Joseph Medical Center, Tacoma, WA, p. A710
LAWSON, Judy, Director Information Services, Norton Community Hospital, Norton, VA, p. A693
LAWSON, Michael E., Director, Brockton Veterans Affairs Medical Center, Brockton, MA, p. A315
LAWSON, Michael M., Director, Veterans Affairs Boston Healthcare System, Boston, MA, p. A315
LAWSON, Michael P., President, Mark Twain St. Joseph's Hospital, San Andreas, CA, p. A86
LAWSON, M.D., Noel, Vice President Medical Affairs, St. John Hospital and Medical Center, Detroit, MI, p. A332
LAWSON, Ralph E., Executive Vice President and Chief Financial Officer, Baptist Hospital of Miami, Miami, FL, p. A136
LAWSON, T Douglas, Senior Vice President and Chief Operating Officer, Cabell Huntington Hospital, Huntington, WV, p. A716
LAY, Barbara, Administrator, Minnie Hamilton HealthCare Center, Grantsville, WV, p. A715
LAYDEN, Lisa, Director of Finance, Highland Hospital, Charleston, WV, p. A714
LAYFIELD, Michael G., Community Chief Executive Officer, Harlan ARH Hospital, Harlan, KY, p. A265
LAZATIN, Lou, Interim President, Saint John's Health Center, Santa Monica, CA, p. A93
LAZO, Nelson, Chief Operating Officer, MacNeal Hospital, Berwyn, IL, p. A184
LAZORITZ, M.D., Steve, Vice President Medical Affairs, Children's Hospital, Omaha, NE, p. A411
LAZROFF, Gary
Vice President Human Resources, St. John West Shore Hospital, Cleveland, OH, p. A509
Vice President Human Resources, St. Vincent Charity Hospital, Cleveland, OH, p. A509
LAZZARO, Frank, Administrative Director, Phelps County Regional Medical Center, Rolla, MO, p. A389
LE, Vu, M.D., Chief Executive Officer, Specialty Hospital of Santa Ana, Santa Ana, CA, p. A92
LE BLANC BOLAND, Sandra, Human Resources Representative, Big Fork Valley Hospital, Bigfork, MN, p. A350
LEACH, Craig, Executive Vice President and Chief Operating Officer, Torrance Memorial Medical Center, Torrance, CA, p. A96
LEACH, James J., MC, Commander, William Beaumont Army Medical Center, El Paso, TX, p. A638
LEACH, Les, Administrator, Memorial Specialty Hospital, Lufkin, TX, p. A655
LEACH, M.D., Ronald, Medical Director, Union Hospital, Terre Haute, IN, p. A226
LEADER, Skip, Chief Information Officer, Choctaw Nation Health Care Center, Talihina, OK, p. A539
LEAHEY, Daniel P., President and Chief Executive Officer, Youville Hospital and Rehabilitation Center, Cambridge, MA, p. A316

LEAHY, Annette B., President and Chief Executive Officer, Southampton Hospital, Southampton, NY, p. A472
LEAHY, Kevin D., President and Chief Executive Officer, Sisters of St. Francis Health Services, Inc., Mishawaka, IN, p. B100
LEAHY, Rosanne, Vice President Nursing Services, Craven Regional Medical Center, New Bern, NC, p. A488
LEAL, Jr, M.D., Joseph M., Medical Director, Prairie Community Health Center, Terry, MT, p. A402
LEAMING, Larry E.
Chief Executive Officer, East Morgan County Hospital, Brush, CO, p. A101
Chief Executive Officer, St. Vincent General Hospital District, Leadville, CO, p. A107
LEARY, Edward B., Chief Executive Officer, New Bedford Rehabilitation Hospital, New Bedford, MA, p. A321
LEARY, Matthew, Chief Financial Officer, Lee's Summit Hospital, Lees Summit, MO, p. A386
LEASURE, Sandie, Senior Vice President Human Resources, O'Bleness Memorial Hospital, Athens, OH, p. A503
LEAVER, William B.
President and Chief Executive Officer, Trinity at Terrace Park, Bettendorf, IA, p. A228
President and Chief Executive Officer, Trinity Medical Center–West, Rock Island, IL, p. A206
LEBARON, Bradley D., President and Chief Executive Officer, Uintah Basin Medical Center, Roosevelt, UT, p. A679
LEBLANC, David B., Interim Chief Executive Officer, Doctors' Hospital of Shreveport, Shreveport, LA, p. A292
LEBLANC, Pete, Information Systems Director, Abbeville General Hospital, Abbeville, LA, p. A276
LECKER, Marijo, Vice President, Martha Jefferson Hospital, Charlottesville, VA, p. A686
LECKEY, Scott, Chief Financial Officer, John F. Kennedy Memorial Hospital, Indio, CA, p. A64
LECONTE, Chantal
Chief Operating Officer, Cleveland Clinic Hospital, Weston, FL, p. A151
Chief Operating Officer, Coral Springs Medical Center, Coral Springs, FL, p. A126
LEDBETTER, D.O., Carl E., President Medical Staff, Excelsior Springs Medical Center, Excelsior Springs, MO, p. A381
LEDBETTER, Hardy, Chief Operating Officer, Columbus County Hospital, Whiteville, NC, p. A493
LEDBETTER, James E., Ph.D., Chief Executive Officer, Summit Hospital, Summit, NJ, p. A436
LEDDEN, Edwin L., Assistant Administrator, Henry County Medical Center, Paris, TN, p. A616
LEDFORD, Maribeth, Director Human Resources, Henry Medical Center, Stockbridge, GA, p. A170
LEDGERWOOD, Linda, Director Human Resources, Whitman Hospital and Medical Center, Colfax, WA, p. A701
LEDOUX, Roger C., Chief Executive Officer, Byrd Regional Hospital, Leesville, LA, p. A285
LEDSOME, Randy, Program Leader Information Management, Louis A. Johnson Veterans Affairs Medical Center, Clarksburg, WV, p. A714
LEDWIN, Norman A., President and Chief Executive Officer, Eastern Maine Healthcare, Bangor, ME, p. B43
LEE, M.D., A Lane, President Medical Staff, Central Texas Medical Center, San Marcos, TX, p. A666
LEE, M.D., Bobbilynn, Chief Medical Officer, Irwin Army Community Hospital, Junction City, KS, p. A250
LEE, M.D., Brian, Medical Staff President, Dupont Hospital, Fort Wayne, IN, p. A215
LEE, Bryan R., Chief Financial Officer, Kingwood Medical Center, Kingwood, TX, p. A651
LEE, Dennis M., President and Chief Executive Officer, Methodist Hospital of Southern California, Arcadia, CA, p. A53
LEE, Donald, Service Unit Director, U. S. Public Health Service Indian Hospital, Winnebago, NE, p. A414
LEE, Helen, Manager Information Systems, Chinese Hospital, San Francisco, CA, p. A88

LEE, John, Director Finance, Dickinson County Healthcare System, Iron Mountain, MI, p. A337
LEE, Karen, Human Resources Director, Hopi Health Care Center, Keams Canyon, AZ, p. A31
LEE, Kayleen R.
Chief Executive Officer, Avera Weskota Memorial Medical Center, Wessington Springs, SD, p. A600
Chief Executive Officer, Avera Weskota Memorial Medical Center, Wessington Springs, SD, p. A600
LEE, Larry, Chief Financial Officer, Minidoka Memorial Hospital and Extended Care Facility, Rupert, ID, p. A181
LEE, M.D., Laurance C., Medical Director, Little Falls Hospital, Little Falls, NY, p. A455
LEE, MaryEllen, Director Management Information Systems, Plantation General Hospital, Plantation, FL, p. A143
LEE, Mihi, Chief Financial Officer, Coast Plaza Doctors Hospital, Norwalk, CA, p. A78
LEE, Nancy, Chief Operating Officer, Centinela Freeman Regional Medical Center, Memorial Campus, Inglewood, CA, p. A65
LEE, Patrick N., CHE, Administrator, Howard A. Rusk Rehabilitation Center, Columbia, MO, p. A381
LEE, Robert H., President, Raulerson Hospital, Okeechobee, FL, p. A140
LEE, CPA, T Kim, Chief Financial Officer, Bowie Memorial Hospital, Bowie, TX, p. A626
LEE, M.D., Terry, Chief of Staff, Whidbey General Hospital, Coupeville, WA, p. A702
LEE, Thomas J., Chief Executive Officer, Palo Alto County Health System, Emmetsburg, IA, p. A233
LEE, Victor, FACHE, President and Chief Executive Officer, Boone County Health Center, Albion, NE, p. A404
LEE, Vincent H. S., FACHE, Administrator, Leahi Hospital, Honolulu, HI, p. A174
LEE, William Bryan, Chief Executive Officer, Select Specialty Hospital of Nashville, Nashville, TN, p. A615
LEECH, James J., Commander, William Beaumont Army Medical Center, El Paso, TX, p. A638
LEEDY, R Donald, Chief Operating Officer, Fox Chase Cancer Center–American Oncologic Hospital, Philadelphia, PA, p. A567
LEEKA, Andrew B., President and Chief Executive Officer, Good Samaritan Hospital, Los Angeles, CA, p. A70
LEEPER, Kevin, Chief Executive Officer, Llano Memorial Healthcare System, Llano, TX, p. A653
LEESER, M.D., Robert, Director Medical Affairs, Hayes–Green–Beach Memorial Hospital, Charlotte, MI, p. A329
LEESON, M.D., Peter, Chief Medical Officer, Natividad Medical Center, Salinas, CA, p. A86
LEFEBVRE, Jean, Vice President Fiscal Services, Harrington Memorial Hospital, Southbridge, MA, p. A323
LEFF, Marc, Vice President, Human Resources, Maimonides Medical Center, New York, NY, p. A461
LEFTON, Ruth, Chief Operating Officer, Moss Rehab, Einstein at Elkins Park, Elkins Park, PA, p. A558
LEFTWICH, Hal W., FACHE, Administrator, Hancock Medical Center, Bay Saint Louis, MS, p. A366
LEGA, M.D., Mark, Medical Director, Kindred Hospital–Pittsburgh, Oakdale, PA, p. A566
LEGEL, Tom
Vice President and Chief Financial Officer, Kootenai Medical Center, Coeur D'Alene, ID, p. A178
Vice President and Chief Financial Officer, Kootenai Medical Center, Coeur D'Alene, ID, p. A178
LEGENOS, Tracey, Vice President, Information Systems, Bethesda Memorial Hospital, Boynton Beach, FL, p. A124
LEGER, J. Michael, Interim Chief Executive Officer, Plaza Specialty Hospital, Houston, TX, p. A647
LEGER, Lynn, Director Information Systems, Ridgeview Institute, Smyrna, GA, p. A169
LEGER, Tracy, Information Systems Director, Women and Children's Hospital, Lake Charles, LA, p. A285
LEGG, Alyce, Vice President Human Resources, Samaritan Regional Health System, Ashland, OH, p. A502

LEGGETT, G Raymond, Vice President, Administration, Craven Regional Medical Center, New Bern, NC, p. A488

LEGGETT, Penny, Manager Human Resources, Beaufort County Hospital, Washington, NC, p. A493

LEGGETT, Vi, Vice President, Aultman Hospital, Canton, OH, p. A505

LEGROW, M.D., R Bruce, Chief of Medical Staff, Linden Municipal Hospital, Linden, TX, p. A653

LEHMAN, Clifford R., Chief Operating Officer, Mercy Medical Center, Oshkosh, WI, p. A733

LEHMAN, Sandi, Chief Financial Officer, Harms Memorial Hospital District, American Falls, ID, p. A177

LEHMANN, Robert J., Chief Executive Officer, Keystone Newport News, Newport News, VA, p. A692

LEHNER, Bill, Director Management Information Systems, Amery Regional Medical Center, Amery, WI, p. A722

LEHR, M.D., Gary S., Chief of Staff, North Broward Medical Center, Pompano Beach, FL, p. A144

LEHRFELD, Samuel, President and Chief Executive Officer, Brooklyn Hospital Center, New York, NY, p. A459

LEIBERT, D. Michael, FACHE, President and Chief Executive Officer, Fremont Area Medical Center, Fremont, NE, p. A406

LEIN, Brian C., Commander, Evans U. S. Army Community Hospital, Fort Carson, CO, p. A105

LEINEN, Rick, Chief Financial Officer, Montgomery County Memorial Hospital, Red Oak, IA, p. A240

LEININGER, M.D., Chris, Chief Information Officer, Swedish Health Services, Seattle, WA, p. A708

LEIS, Jr, James L., Chief Financial Officer, Person Memorial Hospital, Roxboro, NC, p. A490

LEISHER, George, Chief Human Resources Officer, Hemet Valley Medical Center, Hemet, CA, p. A64

LEISHER, Kenneth W., Chief Executive Officer, Platte County Memorial Hospital, Wheatland, WY, p. A742

LEITE, Dolores
 Chief Human Resource Exec, Jacobi Medical Center, New York, NY, p. A460
 Chief Human Resource Exec, North Central Bronx Hospital, New York, NY, p. A464

LEITNER, M.D., William A., Vice President Medical Affairs, St. Vincent's Hospital, Birmingham, AL, p. A15

LEITZ, Arlene, Chief Financial Officer, Community Hospital, Watervliet, MI, p. A347

LEJEUNE, Dee, Chief Executive Officer, St. Elizabeth Hospital, Gonzales, LA, p. A281

LELAND, Joni, Director Human Resources, Memorial Hospital, Gonzales, TX, p. A642

LELEUX, Ross, Chief Information Officer, Iberia Medical Center, New Iberia, LA, p. A288

LEM, Alan, Vice President Finance, St. Francis Regional Medical Center, Shakopee, MN, p. A363

LEMAIRE, Suzanne, Health Information Management Services Manager, Scheurer Hospital, Pigeon, MI, p. A342

LEMAR, Homer, Deputy Commander Clinical Services, William Beaumont Army Medical Center, El Paso, TX, p. A638

LEMIEUX, Kandie, Administrative Assistant for Human Resources, Northern Rockies Medical Center, Cut Bank, MT, p. A397

LEMKE, Jodi, Director of Human Resources, Mobridge Regional Hospital, Mobridge, SD, p. A597

LEMMER, Donn J., Vice President Finance, West Shore Medical Center, Manistee, MI, p. A339

LEMON, Brian J., President and Chief Executive Officer, Holy Cross Hospital, Chicago, IL, p. A187

LEMON, Jeffrey, Chief Executive Officer, Select Specialty Hospital–Northwest Detroit, Detroit, MI, p. A332

LEMON, Thomas R., Chief Executive Officer, Otsego Memorial Hospital, Gaylord, MI, p. A334

LEMONS, Stephen L., Ed.D., Director, Veterans Affairs Medical Center, Salem, VA, p. A696

LEMONTE, David, Chief Operating Officer, St. Joseph Hospital, Fort Wayne, IN, p. A216

LENAHAN, Robert, Commander Medical Support Squadron, U. S. Air Force Regional Hospital–Sheppard, Sheppard AFB, TX, p. A667

LENARD, Gary, Director Human Resources, Hendricks Regional Health, Danville, IN, p. A213

LENCH, Robert, Director, Saint Elizabeth Regional Medical Center, Lincoln, NE, p. A409

LENEAVE, Mark, Chief Executive Officer, Elbert Memorial Hospital, Elberton, GA, p. A161

LENKOWSKI, Tom, Chief Financial Officer and Vice President Finance, Southwestern Vermont Medical Center, Bennington, VT, p. A682

LENNEN, Anthony B., President and Chief Executive Officer, Major Hospital, Shelbyville, IN, p. A225

LENNIER, Douglas J., Vice President Human Resources, Providence Health Center, Waco, TX, p. A672

LENTENBRINK, Laura, Vice President Human Resources, Borgess Medical Center, Kalamazoo, MI, p. A338

LENZ, Judy, Chief Financial Officer, Blue Mountain Hospital, John Day, OR, p. A545

LEON, Jean G., R.N., Senior Vice President, Kings County Hospital Center, New York, NY, p. A460

LEONARD, Douglas J., Chief Executive Officer, Columbus Regional Hospital, Columbus, IN, p. A213

LEONARD, George C., Vice President and Treasurer, Wing Memorial Hospital and Medical Centers, Palmer, MA, p. A322

LEONARD, James, M.D., President and Chief Executive Officer, Carle Foundation Hospital, Urbana, IL, p. A209

LEONARD, Jim
 Chief Information Officer, Mary Black Health System, Spartanburg, SC, p. A592
 Chief Operating Officer, Providence St. Peter Hospital, Olympia, WA, p. A705

LEONARD, Lawrence, President and Chief Executive Officer, Shannon Medical Center, San Angelo, TX, p. A663

LEONARD, Mark T.
 Chief Executive Officer, Harris Regional Hospital, Sylva, NC, p. A492
 Chief Executive Officer, WestCare Health System, Sylva, NC, p. B122
 Chief Executive Officer, Swain County Hospital, Bryson City, NC, p. A478

LEONARD, Robert, Director Information Services, Sierra Vista Regional Medical Center, San Luis Obispo, CA, p. A91

LEONARD, M.D., Roger, Vice President Medical Affairs, Montgomery General Hospital, Olney, MD, p. A309

LEONARD, Steven, Vice President, Human Resources, Memorial Hospital of South Bend, South Bend, IN, p. A225

LEONARD, William H., Chief Executive Officer, Sandhills Regional Medical Center, Hamlet, NC, p. A484

LEONHARD Jr, Robert A., Chief Executive Officer, Regency Hospital of Ravenna, Ravenna, OH, p. A521

LEONHARDT, Darrell, Senior Vice President Information Systems, Arkansas Children's Hospital, Little Rock, AR, p. A46

LEONHARDT, George E., CHE, President and Chief Executive Officer, Bradford Regional Medical Center, Bradford, PA, p. A553

LEOPARD, Jimmy, Chief Executive Officer, Medical Park Hospital, Hope, AR, p. A44

LEPORE, FACS, M., Timothy J., Medical Director, Nantucket Cottage Hospital, Nantucket, MA, p. A321

LEPP, Jerry, Chief Financial Officer, Ashley Medical Center, Ashley, ND, p. A496

LEPPER, Dale, Director Information Services, St. Mary Medical Center, Apple Valley, CA, p. A53

LEQUE, Veronica, Director, Human Resources, Delray Medical Center, Delray Beach, FL, p. A127

LERA, Margaret, Chief Financial Officer, Emanuel Medical Center, Turlock, CA, p. A96

LERNER, Wayne M., DPH, President and Chief Executive Officer, Rehabilitation Institute of Chicago, Chicago, IL, p. A189

LEROY, Michael
 Chief Information Officer, Detroit Receiving Hospital and University Health Center, Detroit, MI, p. A331
 Executive Vice President and Chief Information Officer, Harper University Hospital, Detroit, MI, p. A331

LEROY, Mike, Information Resource Manager, Veterans Affairs Medical Center, Syracuse, NY, p. A474

LERZ, Alfred A., President and Chief Executive Officer, Johnson Memorial Hospital, Stafford Springs, CT, p. A116

LESCHKE, Gwenn, Vice President Human Resources, Condell Medical Center, Libertyville, IL, p. A199

LESLIE, Desdemona, Finance Officer, U. S. Public Health Service Indian Hospital–Whiteriver, Whiteriver, AZ, p. A39

LESLIE, Frank, Corporate Compliance Officer, Highlands–Cashiers Hospital, Highlands, NC, p. A485

LESLIE, Kelly, Human Resources Officer, Ferry County Memorial Hospital, Republic, WA, p. A707

LESOING LUCS, Jennifer, Vice President and Chief Financial Officer, BryanLGH Medical Center, Lincoln, NE, p. A408

LESSING, Tim
 Chief Financial Officer, Parkview Huntington Hospital, Huntington, IN, p. A218
 Chief Financial Officer, Parkview Noble Hospital, Kendallville, IN, p. A220

LESTER, Wade K., Chief Executive Officer, Cornerstone Hospital of Southwest Louisiana, Sulphur, LA, p. A293

LESTER, M.D., William, Vice President of Medical Affairs, Cardinal Hill Rehabilitation Hospital, Lexington, KY, p. A267

LETSON, Robert F., Chief Executive Officer, Southwest Georgia Regional Medical Center, Cuthbert, GA, p. A159

LETT, Bryan W., Chief Executive Officer, Michiana Behavioral Health Center, Plymouth, IN, p. A223

LETTERA, Frank, Vice President Finance, John T. Mather Memorial Hospital, Port Jefferson, NY, p. A469

LETZ, Thomas R., Chief Financial Officer, Hill Country Memorial Hospital, Fredericksburg, TX, p. A640

LEU, M.D., Jerry, Vice President Medical Affairs, Norman Regional Hospital, Norman, OK, p. A534

LEUPP, Mitch, Administrator, Mountrail County Medical Center, Stanley, ND, p. A500

LEVENSON, Adam, Information Systems Manager, Glades General Hospital, Belle Glade, FL, p. A123

LEVENSON, Marc, Administrator, Veterans Affairs Medical Center, Manchester, NH, p. A422

LEVENTRY, Diana, Director Human Resources, University of Iowa Hospitals and Clinics, Iowa City, IA, p. A236

LEVERETT, Carey O., Vice President for Information Services, Washington County Health System, Hagerstown, MD, p. A308

LEVERMANN, James, Chief Financial Officer, Methodist Willowbrook Hospital, Houston, TX, p. A646

LEVEY, M.D., Michael B., Chief Medical Staff, West Hills Hospital and Medical Center, Los Angeles, CA, p. A73

LEVI, Allen, Director Information Services, Ephraim McDowell Regional Medical Center, Danville, KY, p. A263

LEVINE, Alexandra, Medical Director, University of Southern California–Norris Comprehensive Cancer Center and Hospital, Los Angeles, CA, p. A73

LEVINE, M.D., Jack M., President Medical Staff, Shelby Memorial Hospital, Shelbyville, IL, p. A207

LEVINE, Larry L., President and Chief Executive Officer, Blythedale Children's Hospital, Valhalla, NY, p. A475

LEVINE, Marty, Vice President Human Resources, Windham Community Memorial Hospital, Willimantic, CT, p. A118

LEVINE, Robert V., President and Chief Executive Officer, Peninsula Hospital Center, New York, NY, p. A464

LEVINSOHN, David, President and Chief Executive Officer, Sherman Oaks Hospital and Health Center, Los Angeles, CA, p. A72

LEVITAN, M.D., Nathan, Chief Medical Officer and Senior Vice President Academic Affairs, University Hospitals of Cleveland, Cleveland, OH, p. A509

LEVY, Becky, Chief Financial Officer, Sutter Delta Medical Center, Antioch, CA, p. A52

LEVY, Glenn, Chief Administrative Officer, Hillcrest Hospital, Cleveland, OH, p. A508

LEVY, Paul F., Chief Executive Officer, Beth Israel Deaconess Medical Center, Boston, MA, p. A313

LEVY, M.D., Scott S., Vice President and Chief Medical Officer, Doylestown Hospital, Doylestown, PA, p. A557

LEVY, Shari E., President, Phillips Eye Institute, Minneapolis, MN, p. A357

LEVY, M.D., Susan M., Vice President Medical Affairs, Levindale Hebrew Geriatric Center and Hospital, Baltimore, MD, p. A303

LEWGOOD, Tony, Administrator, Shriners Hospitals for Children–Lexington, Lexington, KY, p. A268

LEWIS, Angel, Executive Director Human Resources, Cookeville Regional Medical Center, Cookeville, TN, p. A605

LEWIS, Brinsley B., Chief Executive Officer, Adventist GlenOaks Hospital, Glendale Heights, IL, p. A195

LEWIS, Candy, Administrator, St. James Psychiatric Hospital, Lutcher, LA, p. A285

LEWIS, D.O., Carlton, Chief of Staff, Woodland Heights Medical Center, Lufkin, TX, p. A655

LEWIS, D.O., Chuck, Chief of Staff, Sturgis Community Health Care Center, Sturgis, SD, p. A600

LEWIS, M.D., Curtis, Chief of Staff, Grady Memorial Hospital, Atlanta, GA, p. A154

LEWIS, Dave, Information Services Director, St. Francis Hospital and Health Services, Maryville, MO, p. A387

LEWIS, Del, Chief Fiscal Services, Veterans Affairs Medical Center, San Francisco, CA, p. A90

LEWIS, Donald C., President and Chief Executive Officer, Schuyler Hospital, Montour Falls, NY, p. A457

LEWIS, Jr, Donald C., Vice President and Chief Financial Officer, Coffee Regional Medical Center, Douglas, GA, p. A161

LEWIS, Doug, Chief Financial Officer, Perry County Memorial Hospital, Tell City, IN, p. A226

LEWIS, Eric, Assistant Administrator Finance and Chief Financial Officer, Olympic Medical Center, Port Angeles, WA, p. A706

LEWIS, George, Director Management Information Services, Johnston Memorial Hospital, Abingdon, VA, p. A685

LEWIS, Gordon, Chief Executive Officer, Community Hospital, Torrington, WY, p. A742

LEWIS, Harriett, Interim Chief Information Officer, Cooper Green Hospital, Birmingham, AL, p. A14

LEWIS, J Craig, Senior Vice President and Chief Financial Officer, Winchester Medical Center, Winchester, VA, p. A698

LEWIS, Jackie, Human Resources Director, Bacon County Hospital and Health System, Alma, GA, p. A152

LEWIS, Jo
    Director Human Resources, Encino–Tarzana Regional Medical Center Encino Campus, Los Angeles, CA, p. A70
    Director Human Resources, Encino–Tarzana Regional Medical Center Tarzana Campus, Los Angeles, CA, p. A70

LEWIS, John I., Chief Executive Officer, Armstrong County Memorial Hospital, Kittanning, PA, p. A562

LEWIS, John P., Vice President Finance and Chief Financial Officer, Rex Healthcare, Raleigh, NC, p. A489

LEWIS, Kathy, Director Information Management Services, Public Health Service Indian Hospital, Albuquerque, NM, p. A441

LEWIS, Kelly, Associate Vice President Human Resources, Sheltering Arms Rehabilitation Hospital, Mechanicsville, VA, p. A691

LEWIS, Kenneth S., JD, President and Chief Executive Officer, Union Hospital, Elkton, MD, p. A307

LEWIS, Lawrence E.
    Chief Operating Officer and Chief Financial Officer, Kingman Regional Medical Center, Kingman, AZ, p. A31
    Chief Operating Officer and Chief Financial Officer, Kingman Regional Medical Center, Kingman, AZ, p. A31

LEWIS, Luther J., FACHE, Chief Executive Officer, Medical Center of South Arkansas, El Dorado, AR, p. A42

LEWIS, Marie, Human Resources Liaison, Veterans Affairs Medical Center, Saint Louis, MO, p. A393

LEWIS, Mary Jo, Chief Executive Officer, Jackson Purchase Medical Center, Mayfield, KY, p. A271

LEWIS, Nicholas P., Administrator, St. Mary's Medical Center of Campbell County, La Follette, TN, p. A610

LEWIS, Robert, Chief Financial Officer, Singing River Hospital System, Pascagoula, MS, p. A374

LEWIS, M.D., Ron, Medical Director, Dubuis Hospital of Lake Charles, Lake Charles, LA, p. A284

LEWIS, Sam, Chairman and Chief Executive Officer, Ameris Health Systems, Nashville, TN, p. B8

LEWIS, Sharon, Client Service Manager, Forbes Regional Hospital, Monroeville, PA, p. A565

LEWIS, M.D., Stacy, Chief Medical Staff, Granville Medical Center, Oxford, NC, p. A489

LEWIS, Steve, Director Administrative Services, Tri–County Area Hospital, Lexington, NE, p. A408

LEWIS, Theodore M., President and Chief Executive Officer, Parkview Adventist Medical Center, Brunswick, ME, p. A297

LEWIS, Thomas J., CHE, President and Chief Executive Officer, Thomas Jefferson University Hospital, Philadelphia, PA, p. A570

LEWIS, William, Vice President Human Resources, Schneck Medical Center, Seymour, IN, p. A225

LEWIS, M.D., William, Chief of Staff, Good Samaritan Hospital, San Jose, CA, p. A90

LEWIS–BLAKE, Sheryl, Executive Vice President and Chief Operating Officer, Goshen General Hospital, Goshen, IN, p. A216

LEY, Gary R., President and Chief Executive Officer, Garden City Hospital, Garden City, MI, p. A333

LEY, Robert, Director of Marketing, HEALTHSOUTH Rehabilitation Hospital, Kingsport, TN, p. A609

LI, Ronald, Vice President Management Information Systems, Bergen Regional Medical Center, Paramus, NJ, p. A433

LIBENGOOD, Mary L., President, Meyersdale Medical Center, Meyersdale, PA, p. A565

LIBERATORE, Kristi, Chief Financial Officer, Placentia Linda Hospital, Placentia, CA, p. A81

LIBIS, Leonard B., Chief Executive Officer, St. Croix Regional Medical Center, Saint Croix Falls, WI, p. A735

LICHTENSTEIN, M.D., Mark, Medical Director, Copley Hospital, Morrisville, VT, p. A683

LICINA, Leonard, Chief Financial Officer, Kahi Mohala Behavioral Health, Ewa Beach, HI, p. A173

LICK, Mary, Chief Financial Officer, Swisher Memorial Hospital District, Tulia, TX, p. A670

LIDHOLM, Helen, Chief Operting Officer, California Hospital Medical Center, Los Angeles, CA, p. A69

LIDIAK, Brian, Chief Operating Officer, Baptist–Lutheran Medical Center, Kansas City, MO, p. A384

LIEB, M.D., George, President Medical Executive Committee, Riddle Memorial Hospital, Media, PA, p. A565

LIEBER, Alan R., Chief Operating Officer, Overlook Hospital, Summit, NJ, p. A436

LIEBERMAN, Jeffrey A., M.D., Executive Director, New York State Psychiatric Institute, New York, NY, p. A463

LIEBERMAN, M.D., Lawrence, Medical Director, Blake Medical Center, Bradenton, FL, p. A124

LIEBERS, M.D., David, Interim Chief Medical Officer, Ellis Hospital, Schenectady, NY, p. A472

LIEBHABER, Louis L.
    Chief Operating Officer, Lehigh Valley Hospital, Allentown, PA, p. A551
    Chief Operating Officer, Lehigh Valley Hospital–Muhlenberg, Bethlehem, PA, p. A552

LIEKWEG, Richard, Director, University of California San Diego Medical Center, San Diego, CA, p. A88

LIEPMAN, Michael T., Chief Operating Officer, Deaconess Medical Center–Spokane, Spokane, WA, p. A709

LIES, Bob, Director Information Systems, Hutchinson Hospital Corporation, Hutchinson, KS, p. A249

LIESMANN, M.D., George, Chief Medical Officer, Saint Thomas Hospital, Nashville, TN, p. A615

LIEVENSE, William C., Chief Executive Officer, NEA Medical Center, Jonesboro, AR, p. A45

LIGHTBODY, Harvey, Vice President Human Resources, Vista Health–Victory Memorial Hospital, Waukegan, IL, p. A210

LIGHTCAP, Deb, Director Human Resources, Mercy Medical Center, Roseburg, OR, p. A548

LIGHTFOOT, M.D., William M., Vice President Medical Services, Providence Hospital, Mobile, AL, p. A21

LIIMATTA, Connie, Medical Records and Business Office Director, Meeker County Memorial Hospital, Litchfield, MN, p. A355

LILES, M.D., Richard A., Medical Director, HEALTHSOUTH Rehabilitation Hospital, Largo, FL, p. A134

LILLY, Brian, Director Information Systems, Nason Hospital, Roaring Spring, PA, p. A574

LILLY, Don, Interim Administrator, HEALTHSOUTH Medical Center, Birmingham, AL, p. A15

LILLY, Ryan, Chief Fiscal Services, Veterans Affairs Medical Center, White River Junction, VT, p. A684

LILLY, W. Spencer, Administrator, Carolinas Medical Center–University, Charlotte, NC, p. A480

LIMBOCKER, Jeff, Chief Financial Officer, Our Lady of Lourdes Regional Medical Center, Lafayette, LA, p. A284

LINAFELTER, Robb, Chief Executive Officer, Lincoln Surgical Hospital, Lincoln, NE, p. A409

LINARES, Manny, Chief Operating Officer, North Shore Medical Center, Miami, FL, p. A138

LINCOLN, David R., President and Chief Executive Officer, Covenant Health Systems, Inc., Lexington, MA, p. B34

LINCOLN, Doreen, Director Information Services, Brattleboro Retreat, Brattleboro, VT, p. A682

LIND, R Trent, Associate Administrator, Fawcett Memorial Hospital, Port Charlotte, FL, p. A144

LIND, Sharon, Chief Financial Officer, Memorial Health Center, Sidney, NE, p. A413

LINDA, M.D., Lawrence, Senior Vice President and Chief Medical Officer, Baltimore Washington Medical Center, Glen Burnie, MD, p. A308

LINDAMOOD, Laverne, Director Finance, Springfield Hospital, Springfield, VT, p. A683

LINDBERG, Robert A., Chief Clinical Officer, Southwest Memorial Hospital, Cortez, CO, p. A102

LINDELL, Jerry S., Senior Vice President, Mercy Hospital, Devils Lake, ND, p. A497

LINDEMAN, Barry, Director of Human Resources, Clark Regional Medical Center, Winchester, KY, p. A275

LINDEMAN, Gretchen, Director Human Resources, Chapman Medical Center, Orange, CA, p. A79

LINDEMANN, Fran, Chief Financial Officer, Kell West Regional Hospital, Wichita Falls, TX, p. A674

LINDEN, Todd C., President and Chief Executive Officer, Grinnell Regional Medical Center, Grinnell, IA, p. A234

LINDENBAUM, Jerry, Administrator, Specialty Hospital of Mid–America, Overland Park, KS, p. A255

LINDER, Lori, Chief Financial Officer, Banner Desert Medical Center, Mesa, AZ, p. A32

LINDQUIST, Gina, Director Human Resources, Schoolcraft Memorial Hospital, Manistique, MI, p. A340

LINDSAY, Diane, Chief Financial Officer, St. Francis Hospital, Litchfield, IL, p. A199

LINDSEY, M.D., Jim, Senior Vice President Medical Affairs, Brackenridge Hospital, Austin, TX, p. A623

LINDSEY, Larry N., Administrator and Chief Executive Officer, Decatur County General Hospital, Parsons, TN, p. A616

LINDSEY, Teresa L., Human Resources Supervisor, Carl Vinson Veterans Affairs Medical Center, Dublin, GA, p. A161

LINER, Sallye A., Executive Vice President and Chief Operating Officer, Forsyth Medical Center, Winston–Salem, NC, p. A494

LINES, John, Chief Financial Officer, St. Vincent Jennings Hospital, North Vernon, IN, p. A223

LINESCH, William
    Vice President Human Resources, Good Samaritan Hospital, Dayton, OH, p. A512
    Vice President Human Resources, Miami Valley Hospital, Dayton, OH, p. A512

LINGENFELTER, Wayne M., Ed.D., Chief Executive Officer, College Hospital Costa Mesa, Costa Mesa, CA, p. A58

LINGOR, John Daniel, President and Chief Executive Officer, Mt. Carmel Regional Medical Center, Pittsburg, KS, p. A255

LINHARES, James, Chief Executive Officer, Bellflower Medical Center, Bellflower, CA, p. A54

LINHARES, Jim, Chief Executive Officer, Kindred Hospital–San Francisco Bay Area, San Leandro, CA, p. A91

LINN, M.D., Steven C., Vice President for Medical Affairs, South Jersey Healthcare, Bridgeton, NJ, p. A426

LINNA, Gina, Administrative Assistant, Ontonagon Memorial Hospital, Ontonagon, MI, p. A342

LINNEBUR, Carlene, Chief Financial Officer, Satanta District Hospital, Satanta, KS, p. A256

LINNELL, Jon E., Chief Executive Officer, North Valley Health Center, Warren, MN, p. A364

LINNES, Debra, Chief Operating Officer, St. John's Regional Medical Center, Joplin, MO, p. A384

LINNEWEH Jr, Richard W., President and Chief Executive Officer, Yakima Valley Memorial Hospital, Yakima, WA, p. A712

LINSCHEID, Carol, Vice President Human Resources, Enloe Medical Center, Chico, CA, p. A56

LINSKY, Jack
Vice President, Human Resources, Geneva General Hospital, Geneva, NY, p. A452
Vice President, Human Resources, Soldiers and Sailors Memorial Hospital of Yates County, Penn Yan, NY, p. A469

LINTJER, Gregory W., President, Elkhart General Hospital, Elkhart, IN, p. A214

LINTON, Randall, M.D., President and Chief Executive Officer, Luther Hospital, Eau Claire, WI, p. A725

LINZ, M.D., Geoffrey, Chief Medical Officer, Ingham Regional Medical Center, Lansing, MI, p. A338

LIPAN, Kenneth, Vice President Finance, Henry Ford Bi-County Hospital, Warren, MI, p. A347

LIPARI, Cheryl, Manager Information Systems, Teche Regional Medical Center, Morgan City, LA, p. A287

LIPE, Curt, Chief Financial Officer, OSF St. Mary Medical Center, Galesburg, IL, p. A195

LIPES, Deborah, R.N., Chief Executive Officer, Bath County Community Hospital, Hot Springs, VA, p. A690

LIPMAN, M.D., Brian, Chief of Staff, Oconomowoc Memorial Hospital, Oconomowoc, WI, p. A733

LIPMAN, Henry D.
Executive Vice President and Chief Financial Officer, Franklin Regional Hospital, Franklin, NH, p. A421
Executive Vice President and Chief Financial Officer, Lakes Region General Hospital, Laconia, NH, p. A421

LIPNER, Zach, Vice President Human Resources, Newark Beth Israel Medical Center, Newark, NJ, p. A432

LIPOMI, Michael, Chief Executive Officer, Stanislaus Surgical Hospital, Modesto, CA, p. A76

LIPPERT, Brandt, Vice President Human Resources, Adena Health System, Chillicothe, OH, p. A506

LIPSCOMB, Balfour, Administrative Director Human Resources, Southwest Mississippi Regional Medical Center, McComb, MS, p. A372

LIPSKY, Jan, Vice President Organizational Effectiveness, St. Vincent's Medical Center, Jacksonville, FL, p. A133

LIPSON, Robert A., M.D., President and Chief Executive Officer, WellStar Health System, Marietta, GA, p. B121

LIPSTEIN, Steven H., President and Chief Executive Officer, BJC HealthCare, Saint Louis, MO, p. B17

LIRETTE, M.D., Aaron, Chief of Staff, Oakdale Community Hospital, Oakdale, LA, p. A290

LISAGOR, Matt, Vice President and Chief Financial Officer, Poplar Springs Hospital, Petersburg, VA, p. A693

LISCHALK, Beki, Director Human Resources, Jefferson Healthcare, Port Townsend, WA, p. A706

LISELL, Susan C., Senior Leader Patient Services, Roseau Area Hospital and Homes, Roseau, MN, p. A361

LISONBEE, Rodney
Chief Financial Officer, American Fork Hospital, American Fork, UT, p. A676
Chief Financial Officer, Orem Community Hospital, Orem, UT, p. A678
Chief Financial Officer, Utah Valley Regional Medical Center, Provo, UT, p. A679

LISS, Barry, Vice President and Chief Financial Officer, Carlinville Area Hospital, Carlinville, IL, p. A185

LISTON, Denise R., Vice President of Clinical Services, Garrett County Memorial Hospital, Oakland, MD, p. A309

LISTOPADZKI, M.D., Dariusz, Chief of Staff, Kimball Health Services, Kimball, NE, p. A408

LISZEWSKI, CHE, Richard S., Chief Operating Officer, Marin General Hospital, Greenbrae, CA, p. A63

LITAKER, Thomas, Chief Financial Officer, Skagit Valley Hospital, Mount Vernon, WA, p. A704

LITCHFORD, Jim, Administrator, Barrow Community Hospital, Winder, GA, p. A172

LITE, Randy, Chief Information Officer, Molokai General Hospital, Kaunakakai, HI, p. A175

LITKE, Terry, Chief Financial Officer, Samaritan Healthcare, Moses Lake, WA, p. A704

LITOS, Dennis M., President and Chief Executive Officer, Ingham Regional Medical Center, Lansing, MI, p. A338

LITTLE, Gary, Vice President Human Resources, St. John's Regional Medical Center, Joplin, MO, p. A384

LITTLE, James E., Chief Financial Officer, Siloam Springs Memorial Hospital, Siloam Springs, AR, p. A50

LITTLE, M.D., James P., Medical Director, HEALTHSOUTH Rehabilitation Hospital, Kingsport, TN, p. A609

LITTLE, Jason, Administrator and Chief Executive Officer, Baptist Memorial Hospital–Golden Triangle, Columbus, MS, p. A368

LITTLE, Keith, Acting Executive Director, Queens Children's Psychiatric Center, New York, NY, p. A464

LITTLE, Lou, Vice President and Administrator, WellStar Windy Hill Hospital, Marietta, GA, p. A165

LITTLE, Raymond, Site Manager, U. S. Public Health Service Indian Hospital, Mescalero, NM, p. A444

LITTLE, Shari, Inforamtion System Manager, Johnson County Hospital, Tecumseh, NE, p. A413

LITTLE, Steven N., Chief Financial Officer, Agnesian HealthCare, Fond Du Lac, WI, p. A725

LITTLE–UPAH, Patricia A., Chief Executive Officer, Banner Behavioral Health Hospital, Scottsdale, AZ, p. A36

LITTLESON, Steven G., President, Jersey Shore University Medical Center, Neptune, NJ, p. A432

LITTLETON, Kim, Director, Phoebe Worth Medical Center, Sylvester, GA, p. A170

LITWIN, Gary, Administrator, Bariatric Care Center of Texas, Wylie, TX, p. A675

LITZ, Thomas H., FACHE, Chief Executive Officer, Carraway Methodist Medical Center, Birmingham, AL, p. A14

LIVANOS, Chris
Chief Information Officer, Encino–Tarzana Regional Medical Center Encino Campus, Los Angeles, CA, p. A70
Chief Information Officer, Encino–Tarzana Regional Medical Center Tarzana Campus, Los Angeles, CA, p. A70

LIVELY, Julia, Vice President Finance, Woman's Hospital, Baton Rouge, LA, p. A278

LIVERMORE, Craig A., President and Chief Executive Officer, Delnor–Community Hospital, Geneva, IL, p. A195

LIVINGSTON, Carolyn, Manager, Lander Valley Medical Center, Lander, WY, p. A740

LIVINGSTON, Charles, Administrator, Dakota Plains Surgical Center, Aberdeen, SD, p. A594

LIVINGSTON, Keith
Senior Vice President and Chief Information Officer, Appleton Medical Center, Appleton, WI, p. A722
Senior Vice President and Chief Information Officer, Theda Clark Medical Center, Neenah, WI, p. A732

LIVINGSTON, Paul, Administrator, Kansas Rehabilitation Hospital, Topeka, KS, p. A257

LLAMAS, Alba Nydia, Specialist Human Administrative Resources, Industrial Hospital, San Juan, PR, p. A747

LLAMAS, Roberto, Chief Human Resources Officer, Cleveland Clinic Foundation, Cleveland, OH, p. A508

LLOVET, Sylvette
Executive Director, University Pediatric Hospital, San Juan, PR, p. A748
Executive Director, University Pediatric Hospital, San Juan, PR, p. A748

LLOYD, John K., President and Chief Executive Officer, Meridian Health, Neptune, NJ, p. B75

LLOYD, Russell
Chief Financial Officer, Veterans Affairs Medical Center, Omaha, NE, p. A411
Chief Financial Officer, Veterans Affairs Nebraska–Western Iowa Health Care System, Lincoln, NE, p. A409

LLOYD, Susan, Chief Health Information Management and Revenue Administration, Veterans Affairs Medical Center, Augusta, GA, p. A155

LO, Wesley, Chief Executive Officer, Maui Memorial Medical Center, Wailuku, HI, p. A176

LOBERG, S, Director Resource Support Services, Naval Hospital, Camp Pendleton, CA, p. A56

LOCAPARRA, Frank J., Chief Financial Officer, Calvary Hospital, New York, NY, p. A459

LOCHNER, Lisa, Assistant Administrator, Missouri Baptist Hospital–Sullivan, Sullivan, MO, p. A394

LOCKCUFF, Todd, Chief Financial Officer, Hilton Head Regional Medical Center, Hilton Head Island, SC, p. A589

LOCKE, Nancy, Assistant Administration, River Park Hospital, McMinnville, TN, p. A612

LOCKLEAR, Ann, Director Human Resources, Scotland Memorial Hospital, Laurinburg, NC, p. A486

LOCKRIDGE, Anita, Senior Vice President and Chief Financial Officer, Self Regional Healthcare, Greenwood, SC, p. A589

LOCKWOOD, Jason, Information Systems Manager, U. S. Public Health Service Indian Hospital, Sells, AZ, p. A36

LOCKWOOD, Melissa, Chief Financial Officer, Preston Memorial Hospital, Kingwood, WV, p. A717

LOCOCO, Mary, Director Finance, SSM St. Mary's Health Center, Saint Louis, MO, p. A392

LODGE, Dale M., President and Chief Executive Officer, Winchester Hospital, Winchester, MA, p. A325

LOEB, Fred W., Chief Financial Officer, Christus St. Elizabeth Hospital, Beaumont, TX, p. A625

LOEHRKE, Lawrence C., Chief Information Officer, St. Luke's Hospital, Maumee, OH, p. A518

LOERA, M.D., Arnold, Vice President and Medical Director, Bristol Bay Area Health Corporation, Dillingham, AK, p. A27

LOEWEN, Harold C., President, Oaklawn Psychiatric Center, Goshen, IN, p. A216

LOFF, Michael, Vice President Finance, Mercy Hospital, Devils Lake, ND, p. A497

LOFGREN, Richard, Chief Medical Officer, University of Kentucky Hospital, Lexington, KY, p. A268

LOFTON, Kevin E., President and Chief Executive Officer, Catholic Health Initiatives, Denver, CO, p. B23

LOFURNO, Justin, Director Human Resources, Nanticoke Memorial Hospital, Seaford, DE, p. A119

LOGAN, Bruce D., M.D., President and Chief Executive Officer, NYU Downtown Hospital, New York, NY, p. A464

LOGAN, Heather, Information Process Coordinator, Cascade Valley Hospital and Clinics, Arlington, WA, p. A700

LOGAN, Mitch, Director Finance, Northside Hospital Forsyth, Cumming, GA, p. A159

LOGAN, Rebekah, Chief Operating Officer, Spalding Regional Medical Center, Griffin, GA, p. A163

LOGSDON, Terri, Chief Financial Officer, River West Medical Center, Plaquemine, LA, p. A291

LOH, Marcel C., Chief Operating Officer, Swedish Medical Center–Providence Campus, Seattle, WA, p. A708

LOHR, Daniel E., Senior Vice President and Chief Financial Officer, The William W. Backus Hospital, Norwich, CT, p. A116

LOHRMAN, James, Chief Operating Officer, Prairie Lakes Healthcare System, Watertown, SD, p. A600

LOHRMAN, Joseph W., Administrator, Crete Area Medical Center, Crete, NE, p. A406

LOISEL, Margaret, Vice President, Saint Anthony Hospital, Chicago, IL, p. A189

LOLLAR, Deb, Director of Human Resources, Saint Francis Hospital–Bartlett, Bartlett, TN, p. A602

LOLLIS, Sylvia, Director Human Resources, Osceola Regional Medical Center, Kissimmee, FL, p. A133

LOMBARDI, Joe, Vice President Human Resources, Mercy Medical Center Merced–Community Campus, Merced, CA, p. A75

LOMBARDINO, Tony, Vice President Medical Affairs, Kimball Medical Center, Lakewood, NJ, p. A430

LOMMEL, Marsha, President and Chief Executive Officer, Madonna Rehabilitation Hospital, Lincoln, NE, p. A409

LONDE, M.D., Alan, Chief of Staff, Barnes–Jewish West County Hospital, Saint Louis, MO, p. A390

LONDENE, Jolanta, Vice President Finance and Chief Financial Officer, St. Mary's Hospital, Passaic, NJ, p. A434

LONDEWILK, Kerry, Senior Vice President and Chief Financial Officer, Phoebe Putney Memorial Hospital, Albany, GA, p. A152

LONDON, Debra K., President and Chief Executive Officer, St. Mary's Medical Center, Knoxville, TN, p. A610

LONERGAN, Araceli, Administrator and Chief Executive Officer, East Los Angeles Doctors Hospital, Los Angeles, CA, p. A70

LONG, Adrian, Executive Vice President and Chief Medical Officer, St. Agnes HealthCare, Baltimore, MD, p. A304

LONG, C Duaine, Director Human Resources, Siskin Hospital for Physical Rehabilitation, Chattanooga, TN, p. A604

LONG, Charles H., Chief Operating Officer, Medical Center of South Arkansas, El Dorado, AR, p. A42

LONG, Don, Director Human Resources, Gulf Coast Medical Center, Biloxi, MS, p. A366

LONG, Erik
Controller, Homestead Hospital, Homestead, FL, p. A131
Controller, Mariners Hospital, Tavernier, FL, p. A149

LONG, Faye, Administrator, Caldwell Memorial Hospital, Columbia, LA, p. A279

LONG, Gary L., Vice President and Chief Operating Officer, Virtua West Jersey Hospital–Berlin, Berlin, NJ, p. A426

LONG, Hosea, Director Human Resources, UAMS Medical Center, Little Rock, AR, p. A47

LONG, James K., CPA, Administrator and Chief Executive Officer, West River Regional Medical Center, Hettinger, ND, p. A498

LONG, Kathy, Chief Executive Officer, Marshall County Hospital, Benton, KY, p. A261

LONG, Kirk, Chief Executive Officer, Neuro Medical Center Hospital, Baton Rouge, LA, p. A277

LONG, M.D., Lawrence, Chief of Staff, Campbell County Memorial Hospital, Gillette, WY, p. A740

LONG, Max, Chief Executive Officer, Walter Knox Memorial Hospital, Emmett, ID, p. A179

LONG, Michael, Chief Financial Officer, Mt. Ascutney Hospital and Health Center, Windsor, VT, p. A684

LONG, M.D., Michael, Executive Medical Staff, Sharp Grossmont Hospital, La Mesa, CA, p. A66

LONG, Michael L., Administrator, HEALTHSOUTH Treasure Valley Hospital, Boise, ID, p. A177

LONG, Mike, Chief Financial Officer, Northeastern Nevada Regional Hospital, Elko, NV, p. A415

LONG, Patrick, Chief Financial Officer, Regional Medical Center–Bayonet Point, Hudson, FL, p. A131

LONG, Richard A., President and Chief Executive Officer, St. Francis Hospital, Wilmington, DE, p. A120

LONG, Ronald, Chief Financial Officer, Jewish Hospital, Cincinnati, OH, p. A507

LONG, Stephen D., President and Executive Officer, Nebraska Methodist Health System, Inc., Omaha, NE, p. B77

LONG, Terry L., Chief Financial Officer, St. Francis Medical Center–West, Ewa Beach, HI, p. A173

LONG, Vernon, Vice President and Chief Financial Officer, Stormont–Vail HealthCare, Topeka, KS, p. A258

LONGACRE, Leslie, Executive Director and Chief Executive Officer, South Lake Hospital, Clermont, FL, p. A125

LONGBINE, Vicki, Director Human Resources, Hospital District Number Five of Harper County, Harper, KS, p. A248

LONGENDERFER, Roger, M.D., President and Chief Executive Officer, PinnacleHealth System, Harrisburg, PA, p. A560

LONGENECKER, Craig, Chief Information Officer, Rio Grande Regional Hospital, McAllen, TX, p. A656

LONGEST, Sarah, Chief Information Officer, Grenada Lake Medical Center, Grenada, MS, p. A369

LONGNECKER, M.D., David E., Senior Vice President and Chief Medical Officer, Hospital of the University of Pennsylvania, Philadelphia, PA, p. A568

LONGO, Robert J., CHE, President and Chief Executive Officer, The Good Samaritan Hospital, Lebanon, PA, p. A563

LOOMIS, Greg, Chief Operation Officer, Mercy General Health Partners, Muskegon, MI, p. A341

LOOMIS, Michael, Chief Executive Officer, Philipsburg Area Hospital, Philipsburg, PA, p. A570

LOOPER, Gary N.
Chief Executive Officer, Northwest Medical Center of Benton County, Bentonville, AR, p. A40
Chief Executive Officer, Northwest Medical Center of Washington County, Springdale, AR, p. A50
Chief Executive Officer, Willow Creek Women's Hospital, Johnson, AR, p. A45

LOOSLE, Kent, Chief Operating Officer, Magic Valley Regional Medical Center, Twin Falls, ID, p. A182

LOPAS, Mary, Chief Information Officer, Door County Memorial Hospital, Sturgeon Bay, WI, p. A736

LOPEZ, Jr, M.D., Alejandro, Chief of Staff, Christus Spohn Hospital Alice, Alice, TX, p. A620

LOPEZ, Augustine, Chief Financial Officer, Alvarado Hospital Medical Center, San Diego, CA, p. A86

LOPEZ, David S., FACHE, President and Chief Executive Officer, Harris County Hospital District, Houston, TX, p. A645

LOPEZ, Frank, FACHE, Chief Executive Officer and Managing Director, Northwest Texas Healthcare System, Amarillo, TX, p. A621

LOPEZ, M.D., Maritza, Chief of Staff, Sioux Valley Canby Campus, Canby, MN, p. A351

LOPEZ, Rene, Chief Executive Officer, Providence Hospital, Laredo, TX, p. A652

LOPEZ, M.D., Rosalio J., Vice President of Medical Affairs, White Memorial Medical Center, Los Angeles, CA, p. A73

LOPEZ, Susan Nordstrom, President, Advocate Illinois Masonic Medical Center, Chicago, IL, p. A186

LOPEZ, Tony
Chief Financial Officer, West Hills Hospital and Medical Center, Los Angeles, CA, p. A73
Chief Financial Officer, West Hills Hospital and Medical Center, Los Angeles, CA, p. A73

LOPEZ, CPA, Valerie, Controller, Uvalde County Hospital Authority, Uvalde, TX, p. A671

LOPPE, Lyndia
Interim Administrator, Yuma District Hospital, Yuma, CO, p. A111
Vice President Administrative Services and Chief Operating Officer, Yuma District Hospital, Yuma, CO, p. A111

LORENZ, Jeffrey D., Chief Operating Officer, Silverton Hospital, Silverton, OR, p. A549

LORENZ, Pat, Assistant Administrator, Okeene Municipal Hospital, Okeene, OK, p. A534

LORMAND, Jared, Vice President Information Technology, Opelousas General Health System, Opelousas, LA, p. A291

LORTON, Donald E.
Executive Vice President, Bedford Memorial Hospital, Bedford, VA, p. A685
Executive Vice President and Chief Financial Officer, Carilion Medical Center, Roanoke, VA, p. A696

LORUSSO, Paul M., Vice President Information Services, Chief Information Officer, North Carolina Baptist Hospital (Wake Forest University Baptist Medical Center), Winston-Salem, NC, p. A494

LOSEY, M.D., Larry, President Medical Staff, Parkview Adventist Medical Center, Brunswick, ME, p. A297

LOTENERO, Larry, Chief Information Officer, UCSF Medical Center, San Francisco, CA, p. A89

LOTHE, Eric L., President and Chief Executive Officer, Skiff Medical Center, Newton, IA, p. A239

LOTT, Andrea, Vice President Information Services, Northeastern Vermont Regional Hospital, Saint Johnsbury, VT, p. A683

LOTT Jr, Carlos B., Director, Veterans Affairs Medical Center, Cincinnati, OH, p. A508

LOTT, Rodney, Director Management Information Systems and Facility Operations, Llano Memorial Healthcare System, Llano, TX, p. A653

LOTURCO, D.O., Frank P., Medical Director, Auburn Memorial Hospital, Auburn, NY, p. A447

LOUGE, Michael, Senior Vice President and Chief Financial Officer, Grant Medical Center, Columbus, OH, p. A510

LOUGHLIN, Brendan
Senior Vice President, Beth Israel Medical Center, New York, NY, p. A458
Executive Vice President and Chief Financial Officer, St. Luke's–Roosevelt Hospital Center, New York, NY, p. A465

LOUGHLIN, Patricia, Director, Human Resources, Baltimore Washington Medical Center, Glen Burnie, MD, p. A308

LOUGHRAN, Michael, Vice President Human Resources, Kennedy Krieger Institute, Baltimore, MD, p. A303

LOUIE, M.D., Milton, Chief of Staff, Glendale Memorial Hospital and Health Center, Glendale, CA, p. A62

LOUK, Rodney, Vice President Information Systems, Washington Hospital, Washington, PA, p. A578

LOVE, M.D., David, Chief Medical Officer, Haywood Regional Medical Center, Clyde, NC, p. A480

LOVE, Gregory, Business Manager, Trenton Psychiatric Hospital, Trenton, NJ, p. A438

LOVE, Jud, Director Finance, Twin City Hospital, Dennison, OH, p. A513

LOVELACE, Alan
Chief Financial Officer, Great River Medical Center, Blytheville, AR, p. A41
Chief Financial Officer, South Mississippi County Regional Medical Center, Osceola, AR, p. A49

LOVELESS, Jane Doll, Vice President Information Services, Grand View Hospital, Sellersville, PA, p. A575

LOVELL Jr, Charles D., President and Chief Executive Officer, Caldwell County Hospital, Princeton, KY, p. A274

LOVELL, Robert M.
Interim President and Chief Executive Officer, CARITAS Medical Center, Louisville, KY, p. A269
Interim President and Chief Executive Officer, CARITAS Peace Center, Louisville, KY, p. A269

LOVERING, Keith, Information Technician, Miller County Hospital, Colquitt, GA, p. A158

LOVERING, Richard, Senior Vice President Human Resources and Health Promotion, Robert Wood Johnson University Hospital at Hamilton, Hamilton, NJ, p. A429

LOVERN, Ed, President and Chief Executive Officer, Piedmont Mountainside Hospital, Jasper, GA, p. A164

LOVERSO, Felice, Ph.D., President and Chief Executive Officer, Casa Colina Hospital for Rehabilitative Medicine, Pomona, CA, p. A82

LOVESINK, Kay, Chief Medical Staff, Delta County Memorial Hospital, Delta, CO, p. A103

LOVING, David E., Chief Executive Officer, Meadowview Regional Medical Center, Maysville, KY, p. A271

LOVSTAD, Corliss, Director Human Resources, Children's Hospital, Omaha, NE, p. A411

LOWE, Joe, Director Management Information Systems, Cumberland Medical Center, Crossville, TN, p. A605

LOWE, Phil, Controller, HEALTHSOUTH Rehabilitation Center, Albuquerque, NM, p. A440

LOWE, Phillip W., Chief Executive Officer, Hodgeman County Health Center, Jetmore, KS, p. A249

LOWE, Raymond, information Technology Leader, Kaiser Foundation Hospital, Los Angeles, CA, p. A70

LOWE, Scott, Director of Human Resources, Emory Eastside Medical Center, Snellville, GA, p. A169

LOWE, M.D., Vickie, Medical Director, HEALTHSOUTH Rehabilitation Hospital of Central Kentucky, Elizabethtown, KY, p. A264

LOWERY, Gaylon C., CHE, Chief Executive Officer, Bates County Memorial Hospital, Butler, MO, p. A379

LOWRY, James R., FACHE, Chief Executive Officer, Colquitt Regional Medical Center, Moultrie, GA, p. A166

LOWY, Robert, Vice President Human Resources, Stevens Healthcare, Edmonds, WA, p. A702

LOYD, M.D., Robert, Chief of Staff, Wray Community District Hospital, Wray, CO, p. A111

LOZAR, Beverly, Chief Administrative Officer, South Pointe Hospital, Warrensville Heights, OH, p. A524

LOZIER, Tina, Director Human Resources, Perry County Memorial Hospital, Perryville, MO, p. A389

LU, M.D., Jin-Jou, Chief of Staff, Fountain Valley Regional Hospital and Medical Center, Fountain Valley, CA, p. A60

LUBITSKY, John, Director Human Resources, Trenton Psychiatric Hospital, Trenton, NJ, p. A438

LUCAS, Bob, Vice President Operations, King's Daughters Medical Center, Ashland, KY, p. A261

LUCAS, Kasey, Controller, Salem Memorial District Hospital, Salem, MO, p. A393

LUCAS, Richard M., Chief Financial Officer, Russell Medical Center, Alexander City, AL, p. A13

LUCAS, Roger, Vice President Human Resources, Aspirus Wausau Hospital, Wausau, WI, p. A737

LUCAS, Stephen M., FACHE, Director, Veterans Affairs Medical Center, Miami, FL, p. A138

LUCAS-HELBER, LeeAnn, Vice President Finance, Hocking Valley Community Hospital, Logan, OH, p. A516

LUCCI, Betty, Vice President Human Resources, Knox Community Hospital, Mount Vernon, OH, p. A519

LUCE, Larry D., Vice President and Administrator, Rollins-Brook Community Hospital, Lampasas, TX, p. A652

LUCIA, Dave, Director Human Resources, St. Luke's Hospital, Duluth, MN, p. A352

LUCIANO, M.D., James, Vice President Medical Affairs, Good Samaritan Hospital, Suffern, NY, p. A473

LUCIO, D.O., John, President of Medical Staff, St. Marys Health Center, Jefferson City, MO, p. A383

LUCK Jr, James V., M.D., Chief Executive Officer and Medical Director, Orthopaedic Hospital, Los Angeles, CA, p. A72

LUCK, Richard, Facility Director, Woodrow Wilson Rehabilitation Center, Fishersville, VA, p. A688

LUDEWIG, M.D., Robert M., Vice President Medical Affairs, Sibley Memorial Hospital, Washington, DC, p. A122

LUDFORD, Brad, Vice President Finance, Exempla Lutheran Medical Center, Wheat Ridge, CO, p. A110

LUDINGTON, Gail, Chief Financial Officer, Coquille Valley Hospital, Coquille, OR, p. A543

LUDWIG, Julie, Data Coordinator, Van Buren County Hospital, Keosauqua, IA, p. A236

LUEBBERING, Tom, Vice President Finance, St. Marys Health Center, Jefferson City, MO, p. A383

LUECKEN, Gladys, Chief Financial Officer, Clearwater Health Services, Bagley, MN, p. A350

LUETMER, M.D., Stacey, Chief Medical Officer, Minnewaska District Hospital, Starbuck, MN, p. A363

LUFKIN, M.D., Kirk, Medical Director, Portage Health System, Hancock, MI, p. A336

LUGO, Justo, Executive Director, Alejandro Otero Lopez Hospital, Manati, PR, p. A745

LUGO-MIRO, M.D., Victor, Chief of Staff, Kingwood Medical Center, Kingwood, TX, p. A651

LUJAN, Raul, Vice President Finance, Levindale Hebrew Geriatric Center and Hospital, Baltimore, MD, p. A303

LUKACH, M.D., James, Chief of Staff, Veterans Affairs Medical Center, Saint Cloud, MN, p. A361

LUKASZEWSKI, Mike, Chief Financial Officer, Baptist Medical Center, Jacksonville, FL, p. A132

LUKE, Josh, Chief Executive Officer, Anaheim General Hospital, Anaheim, CA, p. A52

LUKE, Ronald E., Chief Financial Officer, Mountains Community Hospital, Lake Arrowhead, CA, p. A66

LUKE, Sheila, Vice President Finance, Northwest Medical Center, Albany, MO, p. A378

LUKENS, Harry
  Senior Vice President and Chief Information Officer, Lehigh Valley Hospital, Allentown, PA, p. A551
  Senior Vice President and Chief Information Officer, Lehigh Valley Hospital-Muhlenberg, Bethlehem, PA, p. A552

LUKER, Patricia, Chief Executive Officer and Administrator, Dr. John Warner Hospital, Clinton, IL, p. A191

LUKHARD, Kenneth W., President, SSM St. Mary's Health Center, Saint Louis, MO, p. A392

LUMSDEN, Chris A., Chief Executive Officer, Halifax Regional Health System, South Boston, VA, p. A696

LUND, Maggie, Vice President Human Resources, Mercy Hospital of Wilkes-Barre, Wilkes-Barre, PA, p. A579

LUND, Mark, Superintendent, Mental Health Institute, Clarinda, IA, p. A230

LUNDBERG, M.D., Anthony, Chief Medical Officer, Whitman Hospital and Medical Center, Colfax, WA, p. A701

LUNDBLAD, M.D., Nancy, Medical Director, Hilo Medical Center, Hilo, HI, p. A173

LUNDEEN, M.D., Peter, Vice President Medical Affairs, Spectrum Health, Grand Rapids, MI, p. A335

LUNDGREN, Charlene, Vice President, Doctors Community Hospital, Lanham, MD, p. A309

LUNDGREN, Patricia, Administrator, Henderson Health Care Services, Henderson, NE, p. A408

LUNDQUIST, David, President and Chief Executive Officer, Saint Clare's Hospital, Dover, NJ, p. A427

LUNDSTEN, M.D., Thomas, Medical Director, St. John's Hospital, Saint Paul, MN, p. A362

LUNDSTROM, Greg, Administrator and Chief Executive Officer, Lindsborg Community Hospital, Lindsborg, KS, p. A252

LUNDY, Kelly, Director Information Services, St. Joseph Hospital, Bellingham, WA, p. A700

LUPINACCI, M.D., Michael, Medical Director, HEALTHSOUTH Rehabilitation of Mechanicsburg, Mechanicsburg, PA, p. A564

LUPTON, Todd, Chief Financial Officer, Dupont Hospital, Fort Wayne, IN, p. A215

LUSE, Robert H., Chief Executive Officer, Mariners Hospital, Tavernier, FL, p. A149

LUSSON, Mark, Vice President Human Resources, Northwest Community Healthcare, Arlington Heights, IL, p. A183

LUSTER, Randy B.
  Senior Vice President and Chief Financial Officer, Scottsdale Healthcare-Osborn, Scottsdale, AZ, p. A36
  Senior Vice President and Chief Financial Officer, Scottsdale Healthcare-Shea, Scottsdale, AZ, p. A36

LUSTICK, M.D., Martin, Senior Vice President Medical Services, Thompson Health, Canandaigua, NY, p. A449

LUTES, Michael, Chief Operating Officer, Mary Black Health System, Spartanburg, SC, p. A592

LUTHER, Linda, Chief Executive Officer, SCCI Hospital - Easton, Easton, PA, p. A558

LUTJEMEIER, Everett, Administrator, Washington County Hospital, Washington, KS, p. A259

LUTTJOHANN, Debra, Chief Information Officer, Veterans Affairs Medical Center, Cincinnati, OH, p. A508

LUTTRELL, Pat, Director Human Resources, Macon Northside Hospital, Macon, GA, p. A165

LUTZ, Garman E., Chief Financial Officer, Deaconess Medical Center-Spokane, Spokane, WA, p. A709

LUTZ, Terry, Chief Financial Officer, Scheurer Hospital, Pigeon, MI, p. A342

LYCAN, Laura J., President, Baylor Regional Medical Center at Grapevine, Grapevine, TX, p. A642

LYDA, Charlotte, Director Human Resources, Park Ridge Hospital, Fletcher, NC, p. A483

LYMBEROPOULOS, Nick
  Chief Financial Officer, Community and Mission Hospitals of Huntington Park, Huntington Park, CA, p. A64
  Chief Financial Officer, Encino-Tarzana Regional Medical Center Encino Campus, Los Angeles, CA, p. A70
  Chief Financial Officer, Encino-Tarzana Regional Medical Center Tarzana Campus, Los Angeles, CA, p. A70

LYNAM, Gene
  Chief Operating Officer and Teasurer, Camden County Health Services Center, Blackwood, NJ, p. A426
  Chief Operating Officer and Teasurer, Camden County Health Services Center, Blackwood, NJ, p. A426

LYNCH, Christine, Associate Vice President Human Resources, Presbyterian Medical Center of the University of Pennsylvania Health System, Philadelphia, PA, p. A569

LYNCH, David, Director Information Systems, Barberton Citizens Hospital, Barberton, OH, p. A503

LYNCH, Denise, Administrator, HEALTHSOUTH Rehabilitation Hospital of Austin, Austin, TX, p. A623

LYNCH, Elizabeth A., Vice President Human Resources, New Britain General Hospital, New Britain, CT, p. A114

LYNCH III, Ernest C., Chief Executive Officer, Medical Center of McKinney, McKinney, TX, p. A656

LYNCH, James F., Vice President, Hospital Administration, Fox Chase Cancer Center-American Oncologic Hospital, Philadelphia, PA, p. A567

LYNCH, Jim, Director People Resources, Fairbanks Memorial Hospital, Fairbanks, AK, p. A27

LYNCH, Kevin, Director Information Systems, North Ridge Medical Center, Fort Lauderdale, FL, p. A129

LYNE, Sheila, President and Chief Executive Officer, Mercy Hospital and Medical Center, Chicago, IL, p. A188

LYNN, George F., President, AtlantiCare, Egg Harbor City, NJ, p. B12

LYON, David M., Director, Southern Virginia Mental Health Institute, Danville, VA, p. A687

LYON, Jonathan, Chief Information Officer, Central Maine Medical Center, Lewiston, ME, p. A299

LYONS, Althea C., Vice President Human Resources, Beverly Hospital, Beverly, MA, p. A312

LYONS, Joseph, Vice President Human Resources, Bay Regional Medical Center, Bay City, MI, p. A328

LYONS, Linda, Director Human Resources, Garden Grove Hospital and Medical Center, Garden Grove, CA, p. A62

LYONS, Richard D., Chief Executive Officer, Twin Cities Community Hospital, Templeton, CA, p. A95

LYSAGHT, William, Chief Financial Officer, Jerry L. Pettis Memorial Veterans Medical Center, Loma Linda, CA, p. A67

LYTHGOE, Derek, Chief Financial Officer, Eastern Idaho Regional Medical Center, Idaho Falls, ID, p. A179

M

MA, M.D., Jose, Vice President Medical Affairs, Union Hospital, Elkton, MD, p. A307

MABE, David L., Senior Vice President and Chief Financial Officer, St. Tammany Parish Hospital, Covington, LA, p. A279

MABRY, Jerry D., Chief Executive Officer, National Park Medical Center, Hot Springs, AR, p. A44

MACAFEE, Francis M., Vice President Finance, Corning Hospital, Corning, NY, p. A451

MACARONAS, Thomas, Chief Financial Officer, Labette County Medical Center, Parsons, KS, p. A255

MACCARINI, Christoper, Manager Information Services, Shaughnessy-Kaplan Rehabilitation Hospital, Salem, MA, p. A323

MACDONALD, R.N., Julie, Senior Vice President Patient Care Services and Chief Operating Officer, Saint Joseph Mercy Health System, Ypsilanti, MI, p. A348

MACDONALD, Sandra, Acting Vice President of Finance, Alice Hyde Medical Center, Malone, NY, p. A456

MACDONALD, R.N., Shelley, Senior Vice President Operations, Memorial Hospital of Rhode Island, Pawtucket, RI, p. A581

MACDOUGALL, David, Vice President Finance, Winter Haven Hospital, Winter Haven, FL, p. A151

MACDOWELL, Barry S., President, Reid Hospital and Health Care Services, Richmond, IN, p. A224

MACE, M.D., Robert, Chief of Staff, Webster County Memorial Hospital, Webster Springs, WV, p. A720

MACEK, Paul E., President, Christian Hospital, Saint Louis, MO, p. A390

MACHADO, Maria, Administrator, Hospital Hermanos Melendez, Bayamon, PR, p. A744

MACHEN, Stephen J., Senior Vice President and Chief Operations Officer, Sumter Regional Hospital, Americus, GA, p. A152

MACIAS, Lois, Vice President Ancillary Services, Maine Coast Memorial Hospital, Ellsworth, ME, p. A298

MACINNES, M.D., Robert, Medical Director, Marin General Hospital, Greenbrae, CA, p. A63

MACK, M.D., Edward, Chief of Staff, Veterans Affairs Medical Center, Northport, NY, p. A467

MACK, Wilhelmina, Vice President and Chief Human Resources Officer, Broward General Medical Center, Fort Lauderdale, FL, p. A128

MACK, Winnie, Vice President, Southside Hospital, Bay Shore, NY, p. A447

MACKAY, Calvin R., Chief Financial Officer, Methodist Medical Center of Illinois, Peoria, IL, p. A205

MACKENZIE, D. Rob, M.D., President and Chief Executive Officer, Cayuga Medical Center at Ithaca, Ithaca, NY, p. A454

MACKENZIE, Gwen, R.N., Chief Executive Officer, Sarasota Memorial Hospital, Sarasota, FL, p. A146

MACKENZIE, Ph.D., Susan A., Associate Director, Veterans Affairs Boston Healthcare System, Boston, MA, p. A315

MACKETT, Charles W., Commander, U. S. Air Force Hospital, MacDill AFB, FL, p. A135

MACKLIN, M.D., Ph, Martin, Vice President Medical Affairs, UHHS Geauga Regional Hospital, Chardon, OH, p. A505

MACLAUCHLAN, Steven, Chief Executive Officer, Helen Ellis Memorial Hospital, Tarpon Springs, FL, p. A149

MACLEOD, John L., Chief Executive Officer, Mercy Hospital Cadillac, Cadillac, MI, p. A329

MACLEOD, Leslie N. H., President, Huggins Hospital, Wolfeboro, NH, p. A424

MACLER, M.D., Henry H., Vice President Medical Affairs, St. Francis Medical Center, Monroe, LA, p. A287

MACRI, William P., Chief Executive Officer, Bedford County Medical Center, Shelbyville, TN, p. A617

MACUGA, Paul, Chief Human Resources Officer, Fletcher Allen Health Care, Burlington, VT, p. A682

MADALA, M.D., Srinivasa, Physician, Kenmare Community Hospital, Kenmare, ND, p. A499

MADDAMMA, Mark, Executive Director Information Systems, Butler Health System, Butler, PA, p. A554

MADDEN, Craig, Director Human Resources, Braxton County Memorial Hospital, Gassaway, WV, p. A715

MADDEN, Lynn M., Vice President & Chief Operating Officer, Acadia Hospital, Bangor, ME, p. A296

MADDEN, Mary, Director Information Services, OSF Saint Anthony Medical Center, Rockford, IL, p. A206

MADDEN, Michael J., Superintendent and Chief Executive Officer, Skyline Hospital, White Salmon, WA, p. A712

MADDISON, Brenda, Human Resources Director, Knoxville Area Community Hospital and Clinic, Knoxville, IA, p. A236

MADDOCK, Dan S., President, Taylor Regional Hospital, Hawkinsville, GA, p. A163

MADDOX, Jim L.
Administrator, Mercy Hospital of Scott County, Waldron, AR, p. A51
Administrator, Mercy Hospital–Turner Memorial, Ozark, AR, p. A49
Administrator, North Logan Mercy Hospital, Paris, AR, p. A49
Administrator, Mercy Hospital–Turner Memorial, Ozark, AR, p. A49

MADDOX, M.D., Truett, Chief of Staff, Lea Regional Medical Center, Hobbs, NM, p. A443

MADDUX, Yvonne, Chief Executive Officer, Livingston Hospital and Healthcare Services, Salem, KY, p. A274

MADER, Frank, Director Information Services, East Liverpool City Hospital, East Liverpool, OH, p. A513

MADI, M.D., Amed, Chief Medical Officer, Roundup Memorial Healthcare, Roundup, MT, p. A402

MADISON, Jeffrey, Administrator, Richards Memorial Hospital, Rockdale, TX, p. A662

MADSEN, Greg, Vice President and Administrator, Saint John Hospital, Leavenworth, KS, p. A251

MAEKAWA, Steve, Chief Financial Officer, Olympia Medical Center, Los Angeles, CA, p. A72

MAERTENS, Mary, Interim Administrator, Divine Providence Health Center/Avera Health, Ivanhoe, MN, p. A355

MAESTRE GRAU, Jaime F., Executive Director, Hospital De La Concepcion, San German, PR, p. A746

MAFFETT, Sheila, Chief Human Resources and Public Relations Officer, Brookings Health System, Brookings, SD, p. A594

MAGEE, Becky, Chief Information Officer, Washington Regional Medical Center, Fayetteville, AR, p. A43

MAGEE, James L., Executive Director, Piggott Community Hospital, Piggott, AR, p. A49

MAGEE, M.D., Kyle, Chief of Staff, Riverside Medical Center, Franklinton, LA, p. A281

MAGEE, Nancy, President, UPMC South Side, Pittsburgh, PA, p. A572

MAGERS, Brent D., FACHE, President, Walls Regional Hospital, Cleburne, TX, p. A629

MAGERS, Larry, Chief Financial Officer, Elbert Memorial Hospital, Elberton, GA, p. A161

MAGERS, Ray, Chief Executive Officer, Putnam County Memorial Hospital, Unionville, MO, p. A395

MAGHAZEHE, Al
President and Chief Executive Officer, Capital Health System, Trenton, NJ, p. B21
Chief Executive Officer, Capital Health System at Fuld, Trenton, NJ, p. A437
Chief Executive Officer, Capital Health System at Mercer, Trenton, NJ, p. A437

MAGID, Philip, Director Fiscal Services, Shriners Hospitals for Children–Chicago, Chicago, IL, p. A190

MAGILL, M.D., Frank, Chief Medical Officer, Jefferson Healthcare, Port Townsend, WA, p. A706

MAGNUSON, Richard, Chief Financial Officer, Fletcher Allen Health Care, Burlington, VT, p. A682

MAGNUSSON, M.D., A Roy, Chief Medical Officer, OHSU Hospital, Portland, OR, p. A547

MAGOON, Patrick M., President and Chief Executive Officer, Children's Memorial Hospital, Chicago, IL, p. A187

MAGRI, Jill, Senior Vice President and Administrator, Kaiser Foundation Hospital, San Rafael, CA, p. A91

MAGUIRE, M.D., David L., Vice President Medical Affairs, Wing Memorial Hospital and Medical Centers, Palmer, MA, p. A322

MAHADEVAN, Dev, Chief Financial Officer, Doctors Medical Center–San Pablo Campus, San Pablo, CA, p. A91

MAHAN, Michelle, Executive Vice President Finance and Administration, St. Joseph Medical Center, Towson, MD, p. A311

MAHAN, Stephen, Chief Executive Officer, Vaughan Regional Medical Center, Selma, AL, p. A24

MAHAR, Priscillia, ChiefOperating Officer, Spectrum Health–United Memorial, Greenville, MI, p. A335

MAHER, Edward, Chief Financial Officer and Vice President Finance, St. Mary Medical Center, Langhorne, PA, p. A562

MAHER, Thomas, Administrator, HEALTHSOUTH Rehabilitation Hospital – Henderson, Henderson, NV, p. A415

MAHMOOD, Tariq, Chief Executive Officer, Central Texas Hospital, Cameron, TX, p. A628

MAHONE V, William, President and Chief Executive Officer, Smyth County Community Hospital, Marion, VA, p. A691

MAHONEY, M.D., Gerard, Chief of Staff, Paul Oliver Memorial Hospital, Frankfort, MI, p. A333

MAHONEY, M.D., John P., Chief Medical Officer, Tallahassee Memorial HealthCare, Tallahassee, FL, p. A147

MAHONEY, Mark, Manager Information Systems, Meadville Medical Center, Meadville, PA, p. A564

MAHONEY, D.O., Michael, Chief of Staff, Hermann Area District Hospital, Hermann, MO, p. A383

MAHONEY, Michael P., President and Chief Executive Officer, St. Rose Hospital, Hayward, CA, p. A64

MAHONEY, William K., Chief Executive Officer, Labette County Medical Center, Parsons, KS, p. A255

MAHOVICH, Pat, Chief Executive Officer, Select Specialty Hospital–Northeast Ohio, Akron, OH, p. A502

MAIDLOW, Spencer, President and Chief Executive Officer, Covenant Medical Center, Saginaw, MI, p. A344

MAIER, Farrell, Ethics and Compliance and Chief Information, Edmond Medical Center, Edmond, OK, p. A530

MAIER, Gerald J., FACHE, Chief Executive Officer, OU Medical Center, Oklahoma City, OK, p. A536

MAIER, Harry R., President, Memorial Hospital, Belleville, IL, p. A184

MAILEN, Janice, Chief Resource Management Division, Irwin Army Community Hospital, Junction City, KS, p. A250

MAIN, Robert P., President and Chief Executive Officer, Siskin Hospital for Physical Rehabilitation, Chattanooga, TN, p. A604

MAINIERI, John J., Chief Executive Officer, Memorial Hospital of Tampa, Tampa, FL, p. A148

MAITLEN, M.D., Robert, Medical Staff President, Memorial Hospital and Health Care Center, Jasper, IN, p. A219

MAJURE, Thomas K., Administrator, Our Community Hospital, Scotland Neck, NC, p. A491

MAKI, M.D., Eric, Director Medical Staff, Ontonagon Memorial Hospital, Ontonagon, MI, p. A342

MAKI, James W., Chief Operating Officer, Garfield Medical Center, Monterey Park, CA, p. A76

MAKOSKY, Michael, Administrator, Potomac Valley Hospital, Keyser, WV, p. A717

MAKOWSKI, Frederick J., Chief Executive Officer, Schoolcraft Memorial Hospital, Manistique, MI, p. A340

MAKOWSKI, Peter E., President and Chief Executive Officer, Mercy Medical Center–Sioux City, Sioux City, IA, p. A241

MAKOWSKY, Debra, Human Resources Director, Trinity Community Medical Center of Brenham, Brenham, TX, p. A626

MAKSOUD, Jane, Director, Human Resources, Mount Sinai Hosptial, New York, NY, p. A462

MALAKOFF, Stacey, Chief Financial Officer, Hospital for Special Surgery, New York, NY, p. A460

MALANDRO, Terri, Chief Operating Officer, Holy Family Memorial Medical Center, Manitowoc, WI, p. A729

MALANEY, Scott C., President and Chief Executive Officer, Blanchard Valley Health Association, Findlay, OH, p. A513

MALCOLM, M.D., Douglas, Chief Medical Staff, Tulare Local Health Care District, Tulare, CA, p. A96

MALCOLM, Stacey, Director Information Systems, Massillon Community Hospital, Massillon, OH, p. A518

MALCOLMSON, M.D., James F., Chief of Staff, Sierra Vista Hospital, Truth or Consequences, NM, p. A445

MALDONADO, Abby, Chief Financial Officer, Hollywood Presbyterian Medical Center, Los Angeles, CA, p. A70

MALDONADO, April, Manager Human Resources, HEALTHSOUTH Plano Rehabilitation Hospital, Plano, TX, p. A661

MALDONADO, Milton
Administrator, Hospital Del Maestro, San Juan, PR, p. A747
Administrator, Hospital Del Maestro, San Juan, PR, p. A747

MALDONADO, Ramon Lopez, Chief Operating Officer, St. Luke's Episcopal Hospital, Ponce, PR, p. A746

MALDONADO, Wanda, Director Human Resources, University Hospital, San Juan, PR, p. A748

MALERBA, Michael, Chief Information Officer, Mercy Medical Center, Springfield, MA, p. A323

MALICK, M.D., Gerald, Vice President and Medical Director, Reading Hospital and Medical Center, West Reading, PA, p. A579

MALIK, Rizwan, Acting Associate Director Medical Affairs, St. Elizabeths Hospital, Washington, DC, p. A122

MALIK, Tariq F., CPA, Chief Executive Officer, CenterPointe Hospital, Saint Charles, MO, p. A389

MALIN, M.D., Seth, President Medical and Dental Staff, Delaware County Memorial Hospital, Drexel Hill, PA, p. A557

MALINKY, Kim, President and Chief Executive Officer, Canonsburg General Hospital, Canonsburg, PA, p. A554

MALINOWSKA, M.D., Dorota, Medical Staff Chairman, Deuel County Memorial Hospital, Clear Lake, SD, p. A595

MALINOWSKI, Mary Norberta, President, St. Joseph Hospital, Bangor, ME, p. A296

MALLAH, Isaac, President and Chief Executive Officer, St. Joseph's Hospital, Tampa, FL, p. A148

MALLEK, Brent, Vice President Human Resources, Riverside Medical Center, Kankakee, IL, p. A198

MALLETT Jr, Conrad L., President, Sinai–Grace Hospital, Detroit, MI, p. A332

MALLING, M.D., Timothy, Chief of Staff, Paynesville Area Health Care System, Paynesville, MN, p. A359

MALLOY, Charles, Vice President of Operations, Memorial Regional Medical Center, Mechanicsville, VA, p. A691

MALON, Kathryn, Chief Fiscal Officer, Blythedale Children's Hospital, Valhalla, NY, p. A475

MALONE, Brian, Director Finance, Virtua West Jersey Hospital–Marlton, Marlton, NJ, p. A431

MALONE, Frederica, Human Resources Manager, HEALTHSOUTH Rehabilitation Hospital, Humble, TX, p. A649

MALONE, John T., President and Chief Executive Officer, Hamot Medical Center, Erie, PA, p. A558

MALONE, Maureen A.
Chief Operating Officer, St. John's Pleasant Valley Hospital, Camarillo, CA, p. A55
Chief Operating Officer, St. John's Regional Medical Center, Oxnard, CA, p. A80

MALONE, Michael, Vice President Administrative Services, Virginia Hospital Center – Arlington, Arlington, VA, p. A685

MALONE, Rick, Interim Chief Executive Officer, Marshall Medical Center, Lewisburg, TN, p. A611

MALONE Jr, Robert M., Director, Veterans Affairs Eastern Kansas Health Care System, Topeka, KS, p. A258

MALONE, M.D., Thomas, Executive Vice President and Chief Medical Officer, Harper University Hospital, Detroit, MI, p. A331

MALONEY, D.O., Gerald, Chief Medical Officer, Mercy Hospital of Wilkes–Barre, Wilkes–Barre, PA, p. A579

MALONEY, M.D., Lisabeth L., Medical Director, Mary Hitchcock Memorial Hospital, Lebanon, NH, p. A422

MALPHURS, Frederick L.
Director, Malcom Randall Veterans Affairs Medical Center, Gainesville, FL, p. A129
Director, Veterans Affairs Medical Center, Lake City, FL, p. A134

MALSAM, Stacey, Chief Financial Officer, Trego County–Lemke Memorial Hospital, Wakeeney, KS, p. A258

MALTE, Robert H., President and Chief Executive Officer, Exempla Lutheran Medical Center, Wheat Ridge, CO, p. A110

MALZAHN, Carolyn, Director Human Resources, Tri–County Area Hospital, Lexington, NE, p. A408

MALZEWSKI, Mike, Chief Financial Officer, St. Joseph's Community Hospital of West Bend, West Bend, WI, p. A738

MAMARY, Glenn, Chief Information Officer, Hunterdon Medical Center, Flemington, NJ, p. A428

MAMBOURG, M.D., Rolland, Vice President Physician Services, Saint Joseph Mercy Health System, Ypsilanti, MI, p. A348

MAMBRINO, Lawrence, President Medical Staff, Mount Auburn Hospital, Cambridge, MA, p. A316

MAMMEN, M.D., Joshua P., Chief of Staff, American Legion Hospital, Crowley, LA, p. A279

MANCE, Bill, Vice President Human Resources, Mission Hospitals, Asheville, NC, p. A477

MANCHESTER, M.D., George, Senior Vice President Medical Affairs, Susquehanna Health System, Williamsport, PA, p. A580

MANCHUR, Fred M., President, Charles F. Kettering Memorial Hospital, Kettering, OH, p. A515

MANCINI, Dorothy J., R.N., Chief Executive Officer, Imperial Point Medical Center, Fort Lauderdale, FL, p. A128

MANDEL, M.D., Dale, Chief Medical Officer, Nazareth Hospital, Philadelphia, PA, p. A569

MANDELL, James, M.D., President and Chief Executive Officer, Children's Hospital Boston, Boston, MA, p. A313

MANDERINO, Michelle, Chief Human Resources, Malcom Randall Veterans Affairs Medical Center, Gainesville, FL, p. A129

MANDERS, Daniel N., President and Chief Executive Officer, Mile Bluff Medical Center, Mauston, WI, p. A729

MANDLE, Steve, Vice President Human Resources, Parkland Health & Hospital System, Dallas, TX, p. A633

MANEEN, Vincent S., Chief Financial Officer, Oneida Healthcare Center, Oneida, NY, p. A468

MANGANO, Richard, Administrator and Chief Executive Officer, Malvern Institute, Malvern, PA, p. A564

MANGIN, Paul, Vice President Finance, Mercy Medical Center–Clinton, Clinton, IA, p. A230

MANGION, Richard M., President and Chief Executive Officer, Harrington Memorial Hospital, Southbridge, MA, p. A323

MANGIONE, M.D., Nuson, Chief of Staff, StoneCrest Medical Center, Smyrna, TN, p. A618

MANGONA, John, Chief Information Officer, Saratoga Hospital, Saratoga Springs, NY, p. A472

MANHEIMER, Dean, Senior Vice President, Human Resources, Northwestern Memorial Hospital, Chicago, IL, p. A188

MANHEIMER, M.D., Eric, Medical Director, Bellevue Hospital Center, New York, NY, p. A458

MANINT, M.D., James E., President, Medical Stafff, John and Mary Kirby Hospital, Monticello, IL, p. A201

MANION, Gary, Chief Financial Officer, Children's National Medical Center, Washington, DC, p. A121

MANIS, Jonathan L., System Vice President Information Services and Chief Information Officer, Provena Covenant Medical Center, Urbana, IL, p. A209

MANKER, Marcia, Chief Executive Officer, Orange Coast Memorial Medical Center, Fountain Valley, CA, p. A61

MANKINS, M.D., Mark L., Chief of Staff, Hamilton Hospital, Olney, TX, p. A659

MANLEY, Jeffrey J., Chief Executive Officer, Castleview Hospital, Price, UT, p. A678

MANLEY, Joseph M., Director, Veterans Affairs Medical Center, Spokane, WA, p. A709

MANN, Julie, Director Human Resources, Katherine Shaw Bethea Hospital, Dixon, IL, p. A192

MANN, Lindsay K., Chief Executive Officer, Kaweah Delta Health Care District, Visalia, CA, p. A98

MANN, Loretta, Director Information Services, Mission Hospital, Mission Viejo, CA, p. A75

MANN, Lucile, Chief Information Officer, Louis Smith Memorial Hospital, Lakeland, GA, p. A164

MANN, Rhonda, Director Nursing and Operations, Johnson City Specialty Hospital, Johnson City, TN, p. A609

MANN, Terry, Director Management Information Services, Marin General Hospital, Greenbrae, CA, p. A63

MANN, Todd, System Chief Operating Officer, Twelve Oaks Medical Center, Houston, TX, p. A648

MANN, M.D., Wallace, Chief of Staff, Golden Plains Community Hospital, Borger, TX, p. A626

MANNING, M.D., Donald, Chief Medical Officer, Alegent Health Immanuel Medical Center, Omaha, NE, p. A410

MANNING, Floss, Director Human Resources, Alvarado Hospital Medical Center, San Diego, CA, p. A86

MANNING, JoAnn, Chief Financial Officer, Emory Dunwoody Medical Center, Atlanta, GA, p. A153

MANNING, Noni, Chief Financial Officer, U. S. Public Health Service Owyhee Community Health Facility, Owyhee, NV, p. A418

MANNING, Richard W., Administrator, Montfort Jones Memorial Hospital, Kosciusko, MS, p. A371

MANNIX, Mary N.
Senior Vice President and Chief Information Officer, Robert Packer Hospital, Sayre, PA, p. A574
Senior Vice President and Chief Operating Officer, Robert Packer Hospital, Sayre, PA, p. A574

MANOR UNDERWOOD, Lori, Administrator, HEALTHSOUTH Rehabilitation Hospital, Concord, NH, p. A420

MANOS, D.O., Andrew, Chief Medical Staff, Community Hospital of Long Beach, Long Beach, CA, p. A68

MANSFIELD, Al, Chief Financial Officer, Prince George's Hospital Center, Cheverly, MD, p. A306

MANSFIELD, Deena, Director Human Resources, Ashley Valley Medical Center, Vernal, UT, p. A681

MANSFIELD, Jodi J.
Executive Vice President and Chief Operating Officer, Shands at AGH, Gainesville, FL, p. A130
Executive Vice President and Chief Operating Officer, Shands at the University of Florida, Gainesville, FL, p. A130

MANSFIELD, Robert, Chief Executive Officer, Mesilla Valley Hospital, Las Cruces, NM, p. A443

MANSFIELD, Stephen L., President and Chief Executive Officer, St. Vincent Infirmary Medical Center, Little Rock, AR, p. A47

MANSFIELD, Steve, Vice President Support Services, Penobscot Bay Medical Center, Rockport, ME, p. A300

MANSON, Lisa, Chief Financial Officer, Central Community Hospital, Elkader, IA, p. A233

MANSON, III, William T., Executive Vice President, AnMED Health Medical Center, Anderson, SC, p. A583

MANSUE, Amy B., President and Chief Executive Officer, Children's Specialized Hospital, Mountainside, NJ, p. A432

MANTEGAZZA, Peter M., Chief Executive Officer, Fairlawn Rehabilitation Hospital, Worcester, MA, p. A325

MANTELL, Amy, Director Human Resources, Mercy Hospital of Folsom, Folsom, CA, p. A60

MANTEY, Carl W., Chief Executive Officer, Gerald Champion Regional Medical Center, Alamogordo, NM, p. A440

MANUEL, M.D., Ernesto, Medical Director, Guyan Valley Hospital, Logan, WV, p. A717

MANUEL, Katherine, Vice President Foundation Affairs and Chief Operating Officer, Sutter Maternity and Surgery Center of Santa Cruz, Santa Cruz, CA, p. A93

MANZELLA, Arlene, Administrator, Norfolk Psychiatric Center, Norfolk, VA, p. A693

MANZO, Arnie, Vice President Human Resources, Saint Barnabas Medical Center, Livingston, NJ, p. A430

MAPES, Dale, Vice President Human Resources and Support Services, Portneuf Medical Center, Pocatello, ID, p. A181

MAPLES, M.D., Belinda, Chief of Staff, Athens–Limestone Hospital, Athens, AL, p. A13

MARABELLA, M.D., Patrick, Chief Medical Officer, Saint Agnes Medical Center, Fresno, CA, p. A61

MARANO, Angeline M., Senior Vice President, Chief Operating Officer, Fletcher Allen Health Care, Burlington, VT, p. A682

MARCELLINO, David, Vice President Finance and Chief Financial Officer, Botsford General Hospital, Farmington Hills, MI, p. A333

MARCHAND, Gary G., President and Chief Executive Officer, Memorial Hospital at Gulfport, Gulfport, MS, p. A369

MARCHANTE, Lazara, Director Human Resources, Kendall Regional Medical Center, Miami, FL, p. A137

MARCHETTI, M.D., Carl M., Senior Vice President Medical Affairs, Jersey Shore University Medical Center, Neptune, NJ, p. A432

MARCHETTI, Mark E., President and Chief Executive Officer, Ashland Community Hospital, Ashland, OR, p. A542

MARCHI, Angela M., Chief Executive Officer, West Mesa Medical Center, Albuquerque, NM, p. A441

MARCO, Jr, James E., Vice President, Chief Human Resources Officer, Saratoga Hospital, Saratoga Springs, NY, p. A472

MARCOGLIESE, John, Vice President for Financial Operations, Rye Hospital Center, Rye, NY, p. A471

MARCUS, Christopher, Resource Management Flight Commander, U. S. Air Force Regional Hospital, Elmendorf AFB, AK, p. A27

MARDONES, M.D., Daniel, Medical Director, North Star Behavioral Health System, Anchorage, AK, p. A26

MAREADY, Lucinda
Chief Financial Officer, Duplin General Hospital, Kenansville, NC, p. A485
Chief Financial Officer, Duplin General Hospital, Kenansville, NC, p. A485

MAREK, Rick, President and Chief Executive Officer, Warm Springs Rehabilitation Hospital, San Antonio, TX, p. A666

MARGENAU, Randall, Chief Information Officer, William S. Middleton Memorial Veterans Hospital, Madison, WI, p. A728

MARGETTS, Marty, Senior Vice President, Human Resource Development, St. Mary's Medical Center, Knoxville, TN, p. A610

MARGO, John G., Human Resources Director, Oneida Healthcare Center, Oneida, NY, p. A468

MARGOLIS, Ron
Chief Information Officer, Carrie Tingley Hospital, Albuquerque, NM, p. A440
Chief Information Officer, University Hospital, Albuquerque, NM, p. A441

MARGOLIS, M.D., Sandy, President Professional Staff, Sequoia Hospital, Redwood City, CA, p. A83

MARIETTA, M.D., Richard, Medical Director, Clear Lake Regional Medical Center, Webster, TX, p. A673

MARIHUGH, Mark, Information Technology Director, Mitchell County Hospital, Beloit, KS, p. A244

MARIN, Chris, Vice President Human Resources, Sparrow Health System, Lansing, MI, p. A338

MARIN, M.D., Derborah, Chief Medical Officer, Mount Sinai Hosptial, New York, NY, p. A462

MARINELLO, Anthony, Chief Executive Officer, North Vista Hospital, North Las Vegas, NV, p. A417

MARINGER, R.N., Michalene D., Executive Vice President and Chief Hospital Officer, St. Anthony's Medical Center, Saint Louis, MO, p. A392

MARINI, Frank R., Director Information Services, Tucson Medical Center, Tucson, AZ, p. A38

MARINO, M.D., A Michael, Senior Vice President Medical Administration, Greenwich Hospital, Greenwich, CT, p. A113

MARINO, Alfred
Chief Information Officer, Elmhurst Hospital Center, New York, NY, p. A459
Chief Information Officer, Queens Hospital Center, New York, NY, p. A464

MARION, Ben, Chief Executive Officer, Turning Point Hospital, Moultrie, GA, p. A166

MARIS, Kit, Director Human Resources, Island Hospital, Anacortes, WA, p. A700

MARKANT, David, Information Systems Manager, Albert Lindley Lee Memorial Hospital, Fulton, NY, p. A452

MARKER, M.D., Jason, President Medical Staff, Community Hospital of Bremen, Bremen, IN, p. A212

MARKEY, M.D., William, Medical Staff President, Lincoln Park Hospital, Chicago, IL, p. A187

MARKHAM, Barbara, Chief Financial Officer, Glendive Medical Center, Glendive, MT, p. A398

MARKHAM, Marlin, Vice President and Chief Financial Officer, Rowan Regional Medical Center, Salisbury, NC, p. A491

MARKHAM, Patricia, Administrator, Cass County Memorial Hospital, Atlantic, IA, p. A228

MARKOS, Dennis R., Chief Executive Officer, Ed Fraser Memorial Hospital and Baker Community Health Center, MacClenny, FL, p. A135

MARKOV, M.D., Peter, Chief of Staff, BJC Medical Center, Commerce, GA, p. A159

MARKOWITZ, Bruce J., President and Chief Executive Officer, Palisades Medical Center, North Bergen, NJ, p. A433

MARKS, Craig J., President and Chief Executive Officer, South Haven Community Hospital, South Haven, MI, p. A345

MARKS, Gary A., Executive Director, Glen Rose Medical Center, Glen Rose, TX, p. A642

MARKS, Mary, Director Medical Records, Beartooth Hospital and Health Center, Red Lodge, MT, p. A401

MARKS, Melvin, M.D., Administrator, Miller Children's Hospital, Long Beach, CA, p. A68

MARKS, M.D., Stanley, Chief Medical Officer, Memorial Hospital Pembroke, Pembroke Pines, FL, p. A142

MARKSTROM, Scott, Chief Financial Officer, Premier Rehabilitation Hospital, Monroe, LA, p. A287

MARKWITH, Candace L., Chief Executive Officer, Sierra Vista Regional Medical Center, San Luis Obispo, CA, p. A91

MARLEY, Mark E., CHE, Administrator, Natchitoches Parish Hospital, Natchitoches, LA, p. A288

MARLOW, Billy, Administrator, North Sunflower Medical Center, Ruleville, MS, p. A375

MARLOW, Gary P., Senior Vice President Finance and Chief Financial Officer, Southern New Hampshire Medical Center, Nashua, NH, p. A422

MARMERSTEIN, Peter A., Chief Executive Officer, CJW Medical Center, Richmond, VA, p. A695

MARNELL, George, Director, Veterans Affairs Roseburg Healthcare System, Roseburg, OR, p. A548

MAROC, Genice, Chief Executive Officer, Marengo Memorial Hospital, Marengo, IA, p. A237

MARON, Michael, President and Chief Executive Officer, Holy Name Hospital, Teaneck, NJ, p. A436

MARONEY, George, Senior Vice President and Administrator, Memorial Hospital of Carbondale, Carbondale, IL, p. A185

MAROSTICA, L Anthony, Human Resources Director, Spanish Peaks Regional Health Center, Walsenburg, CO, p. A110

MAROTTA, Diane, Vice President for Human Resources, John T. Mather Memorial Hospital, Port Jefferson, NY, p. A469

MARPLE, Anthony, Executive Vice President and Treasurer, MaineGeneral Medical Center-Waterville Campus, Waterville, ME, p. A301

MARQUARDT, Robert C., FACHE, President and Chief Executive Officer, Memorial Medical Center of West Michigan, Ludington, MI, p. A339

MARQUETTE, Jr, Gerald J., Chief Executive Officer, Coffeyville Regional Medical Center, Coffeyville, KS, p. A245

MARQUETTE Jr, Gerald J., Chief Executive Officer, Coffeyville Regional Medical Center, Coffeyville, KS, p. A245

MARQUINO, M.D., Rey, Chief of Staff, Twin City Hospital, Dennison, OH, p. A513

MARR, Debbie, Director Human Resources, Fredonia Regional Hospital, Fredonia, KS, p. A247

MARR, Larry, Chief Executive Officer, Select Specialty Hospital-Pine Bluff, Pine Bluff, AR, p. A49

MARRERO, Jose, Finance Director, San Jorge Children's Hospital, San Juan, PR, p. A747

MARS, William J., Vice President and Chief Information Officer, Doctors Hospital of Stark County, Massillon, OH, p. A518

MARSALA, Theresa, Administrator, Louisiana Extended Care Hospital West Monroe, West Monroe, LA, p. A294

MARSALIS, Joyce, Human Resource Manager, Roane Medical Center, Harriman, TN, p. A607

MARSCH, Jean, Director Human Resources, St. Vincent Hospital, Green Bay, WI, p. A726

MARSCHKE, Dennis L., Chief Information Officer, Porter-Valparaiso Hospital Campus, Valparaiso, IN, p. A226

MARSEE, DeWayne, Director Information Systems, Joint Township District Memorial Hospital, Saint Marys, OH, p. A521

MARSH, James W., Chief of Staff, Bradley County Medical Center, Warren, AR, p. A51

MARSH, Janet, Director, Hillsdale Community Health Center, Hillsdale, MI, p. A336

MARSH, Mark A., Chief Executive Officer, Greenview Regional Hospital, Bowling Green, KY, p. A262

MARSH, Martha H.
President and Chief Executive Officer, Stanford Health Care, Palo Alto, CA, p. B103
President and Chief Executive Officer, Stanford Hospital and Clinics, Palo Alto, CA, p. A80

MARSH, Paul, Director Information Systems, Parkridge Medical Center, Chattanooga, TN, p. A604

MARSH, Richard, Chief Executive officer, Southeast Baptist Hospital, San Antonio, TX, p. A665

MARSHALL, Daryl, Administrator, Ashland Health Center, Ashland, KS, p. A244

MARSHALL, Debra, Human Resources Director, Bradley County Medical Center, Warren, AR, p. A51

MARSHALL, Dolores, Chief Nursing Officer, St. Luke's Medical Center, Phoenix, AZ, p. A35

MARSHALL, Glen, Chief Executive Officer, Kennewick General Hospital, Kennewick, WA, p. A703

MARSHALL, Jerry, Information Systems Director, United Regional Health Care System, Wichita Falls, TX, p. A674

MARSHALL, John A., Chief Executive Officer, Horizon Medical Center, Dickson, TN, p. A605

MARSHALL, M.D., John B., Vice President Clinical Integration, St. Vincent Charity Hospital, Cleveland, OH, p. A509

MARSHALL III, Joseph W., Chairman and Chief Executive Officer, Temple University Health System, Philadelphia, PA, p. B105

MARSHALL, CPA, Larry J., Senior Vice President Finance, Indiana Regional Medical Center, Indiana, PA, p. A561

MARSHALL, Michael, Vice President Finance and Chief Financial Officer, Anderson Hospital, Maryville, IL, p. A200

MARSHALL, Michael D., Administrator and Chief Executive Officer, Bryan W. Whitfield Memorial Hospital, Demopolis, AL, p. A17

MARSHALL, M.D., Robert, Vice President Medical Affairs, Bakersfield Memorial Hospital, Bakersfield, CA, p. A53

MARSHALL, Robert E., Chief Executive Officer, Cedar Springs Hospital, Colorado Springs, CO, p. A102

MARSHALL, Jr, Robert L., Chief Operating Officer, Baxter Regional Medical Center, Mountain Home, AR, p. A48

MARSHALL, M.D., William H., Corporate Director Medical Services, OSF Saint James – John W. Albrecht Medical Center, Pontiac, IL, p. A205

MARSICOVETE, Joseph, Vice President Administrative and Regulatory Services, Saint Clare's Hospital, Dover, NJ, p. A427

MARSO, Paul, Vice President Human Resources, St. Mary's Healthcare Center, Pierre, SD, p. A597

MARSTELLER, Brent A., President and Chief Executive Officer, Cabell Huntington Hospital, Huntington, WV, p. A716

MARTANIUK, Jean, Personnel Director, Mt. Ascutney Hospital and Health Center, Windsor, VT, p. A684

MARTEL, Bob, Chief Financial Officer, Driscoll Children's Hospital, Corpus Christi, TX, p. A630

MARTI, Gary, Chief Financial Officer, Franklin Foundation Hospital, Franklin, LA, p. A281

MARTIN, Amy, Human Resources Director, Jacksonville Medical Center, Jacksonville, AL, p. A20

MARTIN, Antonio D., Executive Director, Queens Hospital Center, New York, NY, p. A464

MARTIN, B J., Director Information Services, San Leandro Hospital, San Leandro, CA, p. A91

MARTIN, Barbara J., R.N., Interim President and Chief Executive Officer, Vista Health–Victory Memorial Hospital, Waukegan, IL, p. A210

MARTIN, Bruce A., Vice President Human Resources, Craven Regional Medical Center, New Bern, NC, p. A488

MARTIN, Carmen, Associate Administrator, Auxilio Mutuo Hospital, San Juan, PR, p. A746

MARTIN, Cary, Administrator, Bleckley Memorial Hospital, Cochran, GA, p. A158

MARTIN Jr, Charles N., Chairman and Chief Executive Officer, Vanguard Health System, Nashville, TN, p. B119

MARTIN, Christine, Chief Financial Officer, Knox Community Hospital, Mount Vernon, OH, p. A519

MARTIN, Connie, Administrator, Physicians Surgical Specialty Hospital, Houma, LA, p. A282

MARTIN, D. Wayne, President and Chief Executive Officer, Crisp Regional Hospital, Cordele, GA, p. A159

MARTIN, M.D., Daniel E., Chief Medical Officer, Trinity Hospital, Erin, TN, p. A606

MARTIN, David T., President, UPMC St. Margaret, Pittsburgh, PA, p. A573

MARTIN, MSN, Deanna, Chief Nursing Officer and Chief Operating Officer, West Valley Medical Center, Caldwell, ID, p. A178

MARTIN, Deborah, Director Human Resources, Valley General Hospital, Monroe, WA, p. A704

MARTIN, Donna, Director Information Technology, University of Texas Health Center at Tyler, Tyler, TX, p. A671

MARTIN, Elizabeth J., Vice President and Administrator, Riverside Tappahannock Hospital, Tappahannock, VA, p. A697

MARTIN, M.D., Eva, Chief of Staff, Carl Vinson Veterans Affairs Medical Center, Dublin, GA, p. A161

MARTIN, Garry, Chief Fiscal, Veterans Affairs North Texas Health Care System, Dallas, TX, p. A634

MARTIN, Greg, Administrator and Chief Executive Officer, Integris Grove General Hospital, Grove, OK, p. A531

MARTIN, Gregg, Manager Management Information Systems, Arnot Ogden Medical Center, Elmira, NY, p. A452

MARTIN, Guillermo J.
Executive Director, Hospital Episcopal Cristo Redentor, Guayama, PR, p. A745
Executive Director, Hospital Episcopal San Lucas, Ponce, PR, p. A746
Executive Director, St. Luke's Episcopal Hospital, Ponce, PR, p. A746

MARTIN, James W., Chief Information Officer, Naval Medical Center, Portsmouth, VA, p. A694

MARTIN, D.D.S., James W., Interim Chief of Staff, Veterans Affairs Medical Center, Asheville, NC, p. A477

MARTIN, Jeffrey W., Chief Executive Officer, Gritman Medical Center, Moscow, ID, p. A180

MARTIN, Joe, Director Information Systems, Claiborne County Hospital, Tazewell, TN, p. A618

MARTIN, Kathleen L., Deputy Surgeon General, Bureau of Medicine and Surgery, Department of the Navy, Washington, DC, p. B20

MARTIN, Kathryn, Senior Vice President, Hospital Administrator, Memorial Sloan–Kettering Cancer Center, New York, NY, p. A462

MARTIN, Kevin C.
President and Chief Executive Officer, EMH Regional Medical Center, Elyria, OH, p. A513
President and Chief Executive Officer, The Hospital for Orthopaedic and Specialty Services, Amherst, OH, p. A502

MARTIN, Leonard, Vice President Information Services, Lancaster General Hospital, Lancaster, PA, p. A562

MARTIN, Margaret L., Director Information Systems, Brownwood Regional Medical Center, Brownwood, TX, p. A627

MARTIN, Patricia A., President, Advocate South Suburban Hospital, Hazel Crest, IL, p. A196

MARTIN, Patrick, Director of Information Systems, Calvary Hospital, New York, NY, p. A459

MARTIN, Patrick J., President and Chief Executive Officer, Fisher–Titus Medical Center, Norwalk, OH, p. A520

MARTIN, M.D., Paul, Chief Medical Staff, Hopkins County Memorial Hospital, Sulphur Springs, TX, p. A668

MARTIN, Rick, Senior Vice President Operations, St. Charles Medical Center – Bend, Bend, OR, p. A542

MARTIN, Thomas J., Administrator, Lincoln Hospital, Davenport, WA, p. A702

MARTIN, Tom
Director Systems Development and Medical Information Services, Harborview Medical Center, Seattle, WA, p. A707
Director Medical Information Systems, University of Washington Medical Center, Seattle, WA, p. A708

MARTIN, W Carl, Senior Vice President and Chief Operating Officer, Indian River Memorial Hospital, Vero Beach, FL, p. A150

MARTIN LYDE, Shawn, Human Resources Director, Lexington Medical Center, West Columbia, SC, p. A593

MARTIN LYDE, Shawna, Director, Fairfield Memorial Hospital, Winnsboro, SC, p. A593

MARTIN–SHAW, Carolyn, Chief Executive Officer, Mercy Medical Center–New Hampton, New Hampton, IA, p. A238

MARTINEZ, Abraham, Chief Executive Officer, Laredo Medical Center, Laredo, TX, p. A652

MARTINEZ, Edward, Vice President Information Technology and Chief Information Officer, H. Lee Moffitt Cancer Center and Research Institute, Tampa, FL, p. A148

MARTINEZ, Eugenia, Director Human Resources, Wilma N. Vazquez Medical Center, Vega Baja, PR, p. A748

MARTINEZ, Fernando, Chief Information Officer, Mercy Hospital, Miami, FL, p. A137

MARTINEZ Jr, Fred, Chief Executive Officer, St. Charles Parish Hospital, Luling, LA, p. A285

MARTINEZ, Jackeline Baez, Public Relations Director, Hospital Oncologico Andres Grillasca, Ponce, PR, p. A746

MARTINEZ, Rafael, Human Resources Officer, Carl T. Hayden Veterans Affairs Medical Center, Phoenix, AZ, p. A33

MARTINO, Anthony, Chief Executive Officer, Select Specialty Hospital of Greensburg, Greensburg, PA, p. A559

MARTINSEN, Eric, Vice President Finance, Franklin Memorial Hospital, Farmington, ME, p. A298

MARTINSON, M.D., Terry, Medical Director, Fairview Lakes Regional Health Care, Wyoming, MN, p. A365

MARTIR, Louis, Executive Director, Metropolitan Hospital Center, New York, NY, p. A462

MARTON, M.D., Judit, Chief of Staff, Southeast Colorado Hospital and Long Term Care, Springfield, CO, p. A109

MARTON, M.D., Keith I.
Senior Vice President and Chief Medical Officer, Legacy Emanuel Hospital and Health Center, Portland, OR, p. A547
Senior Vice President and Chief Medical Officer, Legacy Good Samaritan Hospital and Medical Center, Portland, OR, p. A547
Senior Vice President and Chief Medical Officer, Legacy Meridian Park Hospital, Tualatin, OR, p. A550

MARTS, M.D., Teresa, Chief of Medical Staff, Community Memorial Hospital, Burke, SD, p. A594

MARTY, Pat, Director, Lincoln County Health System, Fayetteville, TN, p. A606

MARTYAK, M.D., JD, Stephen, Interim Vice President Medical Affairs, Arnot Ogden Medical Center, Elmira, NY, p. A452

MARTZ, M.D., Teresa, Chief of Staff, Winner Regional Healthcare Center, Winner, SD, p. A601

MARVIN, Catherine, Manager of Application Services, Mercy Hospital of Tiffin, Tiffin, OH, p. A522

MARX, Edward, Vice President and Chief Information Officer, University Hospitals of Cleveland, Cleveland, OH, p. A509

MARX, Tomasine, Vice President Finance, St. John Hospital and Medical Center, Detroit, MI, p. A332

MARX, Troy, Human Resources Director, Upland Hills Health, Dodgeville, WI, p. A724

MARYLAND, Patricia A., Dr.PH, President, St. Vincent Hospitals and Health Services, Indianapolis, IN, p. A219

MARZINZIK, John A., Vice President Finance, Frisbie Memorial Hospital, Rochester, NH, p. A423

MARZOLF, M.D., Mark, Chief of Staff, Spectrum Health–Reed City Campus, Reed City, MI, p. A343

MASHBURN, Jerry, Senior Vice President and Chief Financial Officer, Mercy Hospital, Miami, FL, p. A137

MASI, Anthony, Medical Director, All Saints Special Care Hospital, Bridgeton, MO, p. A379

MASIELLO, George, Director Information Technology, Children's Hospital, Richmond, VA, p. A695

MASLAKOWSKI, Carla, Chief Information Officer, Northeast Medical Center Hospital, Humble, TX, p. A649

MASLYN, Jay T., Chief Financial Officer, Nicholas H. Noyes Memorial Hospital, Dansville, NY, p. A451

MASON, Allyson, Vice President Human Resources, St. Joseph's Hospital, Parkersburg, WV, p. A718

MASON, Bill A., President and Chief Executive Officer, Springhill Memorial Hospital, Mobile, AL, p. A21

MASON Jr, Charles H., President and Chief Executive Officer, Parkview Health, Fort Wayne, IN, p. B83

MASON, Daria V., President and Chief Executive Officer, Central Vermont Medical Center, Barre, VT, p. A682

MASON, M.D., H F., Chief of Staf, Baptist Memorial Hospital–Union County, New Albany, MS, p. A374

MASON, Lisa, Human Resources Director, Hubbard Regional Hospital, Webster, MA, p. A324

MASON, Mark, Administrator, Baptist North Tower Surgical Hospital, Nashville, TN, p. A615

MASON, III, M.D., Miles H., President, Medical Staff, Gwinnett Hospital System, Lawrenceville, GA, p. A164

MASON, Ray, Chief Executive Officer, Hereford Regional Medical Center, Hereford, TX, p. A644

MASON, Robert, Interim Administrator, Shelby County Myrtue Memorial Hospital, Harlan, IA, p. A235

MASON, Sam, Director Management Information Systems, Northwest Texas Healthcare System, Amarillo, TX, p. A621

MASSA, Lawrence J., Chief Executive Officer, Rice Memorial Hospital, Willmar, MN, p. A365

MASSARO, M.D., Ph, Thomas A., Associate Dean GME, Dir Performance Improvement, University of Virginia Medical Center, Charlottesville, VA, p. A686

MASSE, Roger A., Chief Executive Officer, Clifton–Fine Hospital, Star Lake, NY, p. A473

MASSENGALE, David, Chief Financial Officer, Taylor Regional Hospital, Campbellsville, KY, p. A262

MASSENGILL, Leigh, Chief Administrative Officer, Jackson South Community Hospital, Miami, FL, p. A137

MASSEY, Donald W., President and Chief Executive Officer, Amsterdam Memorial Hospital, Amsterdam, NY, p. A446

MASSEY, Rocco K., Community Chief Executive Officer, Beckley Appalachian Regional Hospital, Beckley, WV, p. A713

MASSEY, Tom, Chief Financial Officer, Middle Tennessee Medical Center, Murfreesboro, TN, p. A614

MASSIE, Jamie, Chief Financial Officer, Coal County General Hospital, Coalgate, OK, p. A529

MASSIMILLA, John P., Vice President Administration, Chambersburg Hospital, Chambersburg, PA, p. A555

MASSMANN, Jerry, Chief Financial Officer, Children's Hospital and Clinics, Saint Paul, MN, p. A362

MAST, Dave, Chief Financial Officer, Providence Everett Medical Center, Everett, WA, p. A703

MASTER, Maryann, Vice President Human Resources, University of Medicine and Dentistry of New Jersey–University Hospital, Newark, NJ, p. A433

MASTERS, Mona, Chief Financial Officer, Kit Carson County Memorial Hospital, Burlington, CO, p. A101

MASTERSON, David J., Chief Executive Officer, Bladen County Hospital, Elizabethtown, NC, p. A482

MASTERSON, James, Vice President Human Resources, Union Hospital, Union, NJ, p. A438

MASTERSON, Paul, Chief Financial Officer, Genesis HealthCare System, Zanesville, OH, p. A526

MASTERTON, William J., Chief Financial Officer, Atlanta Medical Center, Atlanta, GA, p. A153

MASTRO, Mary Lou, Chief Executive Officer, Linden Oaks Hospital at Edward, Naperville, IL, p. A202

MATECZUN, John M., USN, Commander, Naval Medical Center, San Diego, CA, p. A87

MATEJKA, Cheryl, Chief Financial Officer, Christian Hospital, Saint Louis, MO, p. A390

MATEN, Joan, Vice President Nursing Services, McLaren Regional Medical Center, Flint, MI, p. A333

MATENS, Brett, Chief Operating Officer, South Austin Hospital, Austin, TX, p. A624

MATHER, Kelly, Chief Executive Officer, Sutter Lakeside Hospital, Lakeport, CA, p. A67

MATHESON, Ruthie, Chief Financial Officer, Harmon Memorial Hospital, Hollis, OK, p. A532

MATHEWS, Hilary G., Administrator, St. Luke's Hospital, Jacksonville, FL, p. A132

MATHEWS, Patrick J., Chief Financial Officer, Bayshore Medical Center, Pasadena, TX, p. A660

MATHEWS, Paul G., Administrator, Hardtner Medical Center, Olla, LA, p. A290

MATHEWSON, M.D., Herbert, Chief Medical Officer, Cape Cod Hospital, Hyannis, MA, p. A319

MATHIASEN, Bill, Director Information Systems, Fountain Valley Regional Hospital and Medical Center, Fountain Valley, CA, p. A60

MATHUR, M.D., Manish, President Medical Staff, Community Memorial Hospital, Staunton, IL, p. A208

MATIAS, Cheryl, Chief Financial Officer, Centinela Freeman Regional Medical Center, Memorial Campus, Inglewood, CA, p. A65

MATICH, Ann, Vice President Marketing, Riverside Community Hospital, Riverside, CA, p. A84

MATLACK, Ross, President and Chief Executive Officer, Holzer Medical Center – Jackson, Jackson, OH, p. A515

MATLOCK, M.D., Mike, Chief Medical Officer, Providence St. Peter Hospital, Olympia, WA, p. A705

MATLOCK, Ph.D., Mildred, Chief Operating Officer, Rehabilitation Institute of Michigan, Detroit, MI, p. A331

MATNEY, Bette, Director Human Resources, Park Plaza Hospital, Houston, TX, p. A647

MATNEY, Douglas A.
Chief Executive Officer, Del Sol Medical Center, El Paso, TX, p. A637
Chief Executive Officer, Del Sol Rehabilitation Hospital, El Paso, TX, p. A637

MATOS, Ruben, Chief Medical Information Systems, U. S. Air Force Regional Hospital–Sheppard, Sheppard AFB, TX, p. A667

MATSON, Tracie, Chief Financial Officer, Pike County Memorial Hospital, Louisiana, MO, p. A387

MATSUSHIMA, Paul, Information Systems Director, Wahiawa General Hospital, Wahiawa, HI, p. A176

MATTA, Jorge, Chief Executive Officer and Managing Director, Hospital San Pablo, Bayamon, PR, p. A744

MATTA SERRANO, Jorge L., Administrator, Auxilio Mutuo Hospital, San Juan, PR, p. A746

MATTES, Bryan, Associate Administrator, CrossRidge Community Hospital, Wynne, AR, p. A51

MATTES, Dennis, Chief Executive Officer, Select Specialty Hospital, Milwaukee, WI, p. A731

MATTES, James A., President, Grande Ronde Hospital, La Grande, OR, p. A545

MATTHEWS, M.D., Adora, Medical Director, HEALTHSOUTH Rehabilitation Hospital, Florence, SC, p. A587

MATTHEWS, Clinton, Chief Executive Officer, Princeton Community Hospital, Princeton, WV, p. A719

MATTHEWS, Ed, Chief Financial Officer, St. John's Pleasant Valley Hospital, Camarillo, CA, p. A55

MATTHEWS, Elizabeth, Director Finance, Shands at AGH, Gainesville, FL, p. A130

MATTHEWS, Sharyn, Vice President Human Resources, Irvington General Hospital, Irvington, NJ, p. A430

MATTHEWS, Ted D., Chief Executive Officer, Anson General Hospital, Anson, TX, p. A621

MATTICE, Thomas, Associate Director, Richard L. Roudebush Veterans Affairs Medical Center, Indianapolis, IN, p. A218

MATTINGLY, Bernard L., Chief Executive Officer, Cookeville Regional Medical Center, Cookeville, TN, p. A605

MATTIS, Paul, Vice President Finance, Titusville Area Hospital, Titusville, PA, p. A576

MATTISON, Kenneth R., President and Chief Executive Officer, Florida Hospital Waterman, Tavares, FL, p. A149

MATTKE, Roger, Chief Financial Officer, Lafayette General Medical Center, Lafayette, LA, p. A283

MATTOO, M.D., Nirmal K., Senior Vice President and Medical Director, Wyckoff Heights Medical Center, New York, NY, p. A466

MATURO, Janna, R.N., Vice President and Chief Operating Officer, Seton Highland Lakes, Burnet, TX, p. A627

MATUSKA, John E., President and Chief Executive Officer, Mercy Hospital, Miami, FL, p. A137

MATZ, Rhonda, Chief Financial Officer, Sibley Medical Center, Arlington, MN, p. A349

MATZICK, Kenneth J., President and Chief Executive Officer, William Beaumont Hospitals, Royal Oak, MI, p. B123

MATZKE, Mary, Chief Information Officer, Community Hospital Onaga, Onaga, KS, p. A254

MATZKIN, D.D.S., Michael, Chief of Staff, Saint Mary's Hospital, Waterbury, CT, p. A117

MAUCK, Dorothea, Chief Financial Officer, Nemaha Valley Community Hospital, Seneca, KS, p. A257

MAUL, Ronald, Commander, Womack Army Medical Center, Fort Bragg, NC, p. A483

MAURER, Gregory L., Administrator, Elmore Medical Center, Mountain Home, ID, p. A180

MAURER, III, Rix, Vice President Finance and Chief Financial Officer, Queen's Medical Center, Honolulu, HI, p. A174

MAUST, Richard, Chief Information Officer, Jacksonville Medical Center, Jacksonville, AL, p. A20

MAVROMATIS, Lou, Director Data Processing, Southern Maryland Hospital Center, Clinton, MD, p. A306

MAXFIELD, Matt T., CHE, Chief Executive Officer, Brownwood Regional Medical Center, Brownwood, TX, p. A627

MAXWELL, Jody, Business Office Manager, Smith County Memorial Hospital, Smith Center, KS, p. A257

MAXWELL, D.O., Jon, Chief of Staff, McCurtain Memorial Hospital, Idabel, OK, p. A532

MAXWELL, Karen, Chief Executive Officer, Fox Run Hospital, Saint Clairsville, OH, p. A521

MAXWELL, Ronnie, Director Information Systems, Glenwood Regional Medical Center, West Monroe, LA, p. A294

MAXWELL, Steve, Chief Financial Officer, Venice Regional Medical Center, Venice, FL, p. A149

MAY, Frank, Chief Financial Officer, Yampa Valley Medical Center, Steamboat Springs, CO, p. A109

MAY, John, Chief Financial Officer, Logan Regional Medical Center, Logan, WV, p. A717

MAY, John C., Chief Executive Officer, Sebasticook Valley Hospital, Pittsfield, ME, p. A300

MAY, Kenneth, Chief Executive Officer, East Texas Medical Center–Gilmer, Gilmer, TX, p. A641

MAY, Kevin B., Executie Director Finance, Mercy Jeannette Hospital, Jeannette, PA, p. A561

MAY, M.D., Richard, Chairman Medical Staff, Decatur County Hospital and Cedar Living Center, Oberlin, KS, p. A253

MAY, Ronald B., Vice President, Medical Affairs, Craven Regional Medical Center, New Bern, NC, p. A488

MAY, Sonja, Director Human Resources, Morton County Health System, Elkhart, KS, p. A246

MAY, Stuart, Vice President Finance and Chief Financial Officer, St. Joseph's Wayne Hospital, Wayne, NJ, p. A438

MAY, Troy, Chief Information Officer, University of Louisville Hospital, Louisville, KY, p. A270

MAY, William J., Deputy Chief Executive Officer, Trenton Psychiatric Hospital, Trenton, NJ, p. A438

MAYA, Victor, Chief Executive Officer, Kendall Regional Medical Center, Miami, FL, p. A137

MAYBERRY, Patty, Director Applications System and Support, Providence Saint Joseph Medical Center, Burbank, CA, p. A55

MAYERCHAK, Dolly, Director Human Resources, Lexington Memorial Hospital, Lexington, NC, p. A486

MAYEUX, Michael, Chief Financial Officer, Dauterive Hospital, New Iberia, LA, p. A288

MAYEWSKI, M.D., Raymond, Chief Medical Officer, Highland Hospital of Rochester, Rochester, NY, p. A470

MAYFIELD, Dianne, Director, Walls Regional Hospital, Cleburne, TX, p. A629

MAYFIELD, Jana, Vice President Human Resources, Good Samaritan Regional Health Center, Mount Vernon, IL, p. A202

MAYFIELD HOWE, Huberta, Director Human Resources, Cooper Green Hospital, Birmingham, AL, p. A14

MAYHEW, Nick, Vice President and Chief Financial Officer, Rome Memorial Hospital, Rome, NY, p. A471

MAYHLE, M.D., Douglas, Medical Director, Nicholas H. Noyes Memorial Hospital, Dansville, NY, p. A451

MAYNARD, John, Information Systems Director, Community Hospital of Ottawa, Ottawa, IL, p. A204

MAYNARD, Rhonda, Chief Financial Officer, University Medical Center/McFarland Hospital, Lebanon, TN, p. A611

MAYNARD, Robert W., President and Chief Executive Officer, Piedmont Hospital, Atlanta, GA, p. A154

MAYO, Hal, Chief Financial Officer, Glen Rose Medical Center, Glen Rose, TX, p. A642

MAYO, Jim L., Administrator, Baptist Medical Center Nassau, Fernandina Beach, FL, p. A128

MAYO, M. Andrew, Ph.D., Chief Executive Officer, Parkwood Behavioral Health System, Olive Branch, MS, p. A374

MAYO, Michael A., FACHE, Chief Executive Officer, Frankfort Regional Medical Center, Frankfort, KY, p. A264

MAYO, Randy, Director Information Technology, William Newton Hospital, Winfield, KS, p. A260

MAYO, Sarah, Vice President Financial and Information Services, Lenoir Memorial Hospital, Kinston, NC, p. A486

MAYS, Ronald, Chief Executive Officer, Cypress Creek Hospital, Houston, TX, p. A644

MAYSON, M.D., Mark James, Chief of Staff, Palmetto Health Baptist/Columbia, Columbia, SC, p. A586

MAZE, Chester, Vice President Information System, Baptist Hospital of East Tennessee, Knoxville, TN, p. A609

MAZIKOWSKI, Jeff, Information Technology Site Manager, St. Dominic's Hospital, Manteca, CA, p. A74

MAZO, Scott, Vice President Human Resources, Northwest Medical Center, Margate, FL, p. A136

MAZOUR, M.D., Linda, President, Franklin County Memorial Hospital, Franklin, NE, p. A406

MAZZA, M.D., Frank, Vice President Medical Affairs, Seton Medical Center, Austin, TX, p. A623

MAZZA, Mary, Director Human Resources, HEALTHSOUTH Rehabilitation Hospital of Western Massachusetts, Ludlow, MA, p. A320

MAZZARELLA, M.D., Frank, Vice President Medical Affairs, Clara Maass Medical Center, Belleville, NJ, p. A425

MAZZONE, Joan, Associate Vice President, University of Connecticut Health Center, John Dempsey Hospital, Farmington, CT, p. A113

MAZZONI, Dean, Chief Operating Officer, University Medical Center/McFarland Hospital, Lebanon, TN, p. A611

MCADAM, P Bernard, Chief Financial Officer, Calais Regional Hospital, Calais, ME, p. A297

MCAFEE, M.D., Thomas V., Physician–in–Chief, University of California San Diego Medical Center, San Diego, CA, p. A88

MCALEER, A. Gordon, FACHE, President and Chief Executive Officer, Lewistown Hospital, Lewistown, PA, p. A563

MCALHANEY, M.D., Danette, Chief of Staff, Bamberg County Memorial Hospital and Nursing Center, Bamberg, SC, p. A583

MCALLISTER, Ph.D., David, Chief Information Officer, Northern Arizona VA Health Care System, Prescott, AZ, p. A35

MCALOON, Richard, Vice President, Human Resources, Hartford Hospital, Hartford, CT, p. A113

MCALVAIN, LaDonna, R.N., Administrator, Seminole Medical Center, Seminole, OK, p. A538

MCANDREW, Michael, Chief Executive Officer, Hopkins County Memorial Hospital, Sulphur Springs, TX, p. A668

MCANDREW, D.O., Patrick, President Medical Staff, Marian Community Hospital, Carbondale, PA, p. A554

MCAULIFFE, M.D., John, Medical Director, Sauk Prairie Memorial Hospital, Prairie Du Sac, WI, p. A734

MCAVOY, Michael, Vice President, Operations, St. Luke's Hospital, Racine, WI, p. A734

MCBEE, Gala, Administrator, George Nigh Rehabilitation Center, Okmulgee, OK, p. A536

MCBEE Jr, Harold A., President, Mid Atlantic Health Management, Inc., Stevensville, MD, p. B75

MCBEE, Marie, Chief Executive Officer, Warwick Manor Behavioral Health, East New Market, MD, p. A307

MCBEE, D.O., Marty, Chief of Staff, Integris Southwest Medical Center, Oklahoma City, OK, p. A535

MCBETH, Mitchell, Chief Executive Officer, El Paso Specialty Hospital, El Paso, TX, p. A637

MCBRADY, Peter M., Interim Director, Veterans Affairs Medical Center, Saint Louis, MO, p. A393

MCBREARTY, M.D., Michael, Vice President Medical Affairs, Thomas Hospital, Fairhope, AL, p. A18

MCBRIDE, Dan, Information Systems and Security Officer, Newman Regional Health, Emporia, KS, p. A246

MCBRIDE, Joyce, Director Information System, Wesley Medical Center, Wichita, KS, p. A260

MCBRIDE, Norman L.
Regional Director Human Resources, Adventist GlenOaks Hospital, Glendale Heights, IL, p. A195
Regional Director Human Resources, Hinsdale Hospital, Hinsdale, IL, p. A197

MCBRIDE, III, Thomas Y., Vice President and Chief Financial Officer, Gwinnett Hospital System, Lawrenceville, GA, p. A164

MCBROOM, Mike, Vice President, Hendrick Health System, Abilene, TX, p. A620

MCCABE, Jack, FACHE, President, Harris Methodist–HEB, Bedford, TX, p. A625

MCCABE, Mary, Chief Financial Officer, McKee Medical Center, Loveland, CO, p. A108

MCCABE, Patrick, Senior Vice President Finance and Chief Financial Officer, Bridgeport Hospital, Bridgeport, CT, p. A112

MCCABE Jr, Patrick G., President and Chief Executive Officer, Levi Hospital, Hot Springs National Park, AR, p. A45

MCCABE, Steve, Chief Executive Officer, Hill Crest Behavioral Health Services, Birmingham, AL, p. A15

MCCAFFREE, M.D., Robert, Chief of Staff, Veterans Affairs Medical Center, Oklahoma City, OK, p. A536

MCCAIG, Douglas, Controller, Weeks Medical Center, Lancaster, NH, p. A421

MCCAIN, Rebecca, Chief Financial Officer and Assistant Administrator, Electra Memorial Hospital, Electra, TX, p. A638

MCCALL, Gerald A.
Senior Vice President and Administrator, Kaiser Foundation Hospital, Los Angeles, CA, p. A70
Senior Vice President and Administrator, Kaiser Foundation Hospital–Baldwin Park, Baldwin Park, CA, p. A54
Senior Vice President and Administrator, Kaiser Foundation Hospital–Bellflower, Bellflower, CA, p. A54

MCCALL, Marybeth, Chief Medical Officer, Rome Memorial Hospital, Rome, NY, p. A471

MCCALLISTER, Bob, Director Human Resources, Baptist Memorial Hospital–Golden Triangle, Columbus, MS, p. A368

MCCANCE, D.O., Dan, Chief of Staff, Hillsdale Community Health Center, Hillsdale, MI, p. A336

MCCANN, M.D., David, Chief of Staff, Miller County Hospital, Colquitt, GA, p. A158

MCCANNA, Pete, Senior Vice President, Northwestern Memorial Hospital, Chicago, IL, p. A188

MCCARROLL, David, Nursing Home Administrator, Medina Memorial Hospital, Medina, NY, p. A456

MCCART, Janice, Chief Executive Officer, Citizens Medical Center, Colby, KS, p. A245

MCCARTAN, Mary Beth, Human Resources Manager, Veterans Affairs Long Beach Healthcare System, Long Beach, CA, p. A69

MCCARTHY, Richard
Chief Executive Officer, Promise Hospital of East Los Angeles, Los Angeles, CA, p. A72
Chief Executive Officer, Promise Hospital of East Los Angeles, Suburban Medical Center Campus, Paramount, CA, p. A81

MCCARTHY, Sean P., Chief Executive Officer, Menlo Park Surgical Hospital, Menlo Park, CA, p. A75

MCCARTHY, Steve, Assistant Administrator and Strategic Business Operations, Upland Hills Health, Dodgeville, WI, p. A724

MCCARTHY, Sue, Chief Financial Officer, Magee–Womens Hospital of UPMC, Pittsburgh, PA, p. A571

MCCARTNEY, CPA, David K., Chief Financial Officer, Wetzel County Hospital, New Martinsville, WV, p. A718

MCCARTY, Daniel P., Chief Operating Officer, Orange City Health System, Orange City, IA, p. A239

MCCARTY, Maryland, Director Information Systems, Atlanta Medical Center, Atlanta, GA, p. A153

MCCARTY, Terry, Human Resources Director, Alaska Regional Hospital, Anchorage, AK, p. A26

MCCARTY, Wendy, Director Human Resources, Hillsboro Community Medical Center, Hillsboro, KS, p. A248

MCCASKEY, Bill, Director Human Resources, Wilson Memorial Hospital, Sidney, OH, p. A522

MCCAUL, Harriette, Executive Partner Human Resources, MeritCare Medical Center, Fargo, ND, p. A497

MCCAULEY, Brian, Chief Financial Officer, North Monroe Medical Center, Monroe, LA, p. A287

MCCAULEY, Cynthia, Chief Financial Officer, West Boca Medical Center, Boca Raton, FL, p. A124

MCCAULEY, Dudley, Chief Financial Officer, Lincoln County Medical Center, Ruidoso, NM, p. A444

MCCAULEY, Edith
Administrator, Sabine County Hospital, Hemphill, TX, p. A643
Administrator, Sabine County Hospital, Hemphill, TX, p. A643

MCCAULEY, Roberta D., Chief Executive Officer, Hampshire Memorial Hospital, Romney, WV, p. A720

MCCAULEY, Sue E., Director Finance, Baum Harmon Mercy Hospital, Primghar, IA, p. A240

MCCAWLEY, Tom, Manager Human Resources, CGH Medical Center, Sterling, IL, p. A209

MCCLAIN, Martha, Controller, The Women's Hospital, Newburgh, IN, p. A223

MCCLAIN, Penny, Chief Executive Officer, Siloam Springs Memorial Hospital, Siloam Springs, AR, p. A50

MCCLATCHY, Tina, Director Human Resources, Onslow Memorial Hospital, Jacksonville, NC, p. A485

MCCLEESE, Randy, Chief Information Services, St. Claire Regional Medical Center, Morehead, KY, p. A272

MCCLELLAN, John W., Chief Executive Officer, Twin Rivers Regional Medical Center, Kennett, MO, p. A386

MCCLELLAND, Bill, Director Information Systems, Montrose Memorial Hospital, Montrose, CO, p. A108

MCCLEMENTS, Rich, Administrator, Jeff Davis Hospital, Hazlehurst, GA, p. A163

MCCLERNON, Susan E.
Chief Operating Officer, St. Mary's Medical Center, Duluth, MN, p. A352
Chief Operating Officer, St. Mary's Medical Center, Duluth, MN, p. A352

MCCLOSKEY, Jack, Director Information Systems, Floyd Memorial Hospital and Health Services, New Albany, IN, p. A222

MCCLOUD, Charles J., Director, Medical Resource Management Flight, Malcolm Grow Medical Center, Andrews AFB, MD, p. A302

MCCLUNG, Brett, President, Harris Methodist Northwest, Azle, TX, p. A624

MCCLUNG, David, Chief Financial Officer, Presbyterian–St. Luke's Medical Center, Denver, CO, p. A104

MCCLUNG, Eric, Chief Information Management Division, Lyster U. S. Army Community Hospital, Fort Rucker, AL, p. A19

MCCLURE, Cynthia, Ph.D., Director, Southwestern Virginia Mental Health Institute, Marion, VA, p. A691

MCCLURE, Dan, Director Information Services, Hi–Desert Medical Center, Joshua Tree, CA, p. A65

MCCLURE, Deborah, Director Human Resources, Catskill Regional Medical Center, Harris, NY, p. A453

MCCLURE, George, Deputy Commander for Clinical Services, Madigan Army Medical Center, Tacoma, WA, p. A710

MCCLURE, Jan, Chief Executive Officer, Hill Regional Hospital, Hillsboro, TX, p. A644

MCCLURE, Joy, Chief Financial Officer, Ashe Memorial Hospital, Jefferson, NC, p. A485

MCCLURE, Mike, Human Resources Director, Kaiser Foundation Hospital and Rehabilitation Center, Vallejo, CA, p. A97

MCCLURG, Cathy, Director Human Resources, William Newton Hospital, Winfield, KS, p. A260

MCCLURG, David, Chief Financial Officer, CJW Medical Center, Richmond, VA, p. A695

MCCLURG, Eric, Chief Information Management Division, Reynolds Army Community Hospital, Fort Sill, OK, p. A531

MCCLURKAN, Mac, Vice President Information Technology, Bronson Vicksburg Hospital, Vicksburg, MI, p. A347

MCCLUSKEY, Diane, Human Resources Director, Placentia Linda Hospital, Placentia, CA, p. A81

MCCLUSKIE, Lisa, Director Marketing and Planning, Sturdy Memorial Hospital, Attleboro, MA, p. A312

MCCLYMONDS, Bruce, President, West Virginia University Hospitals, Morgantown, WV, p. A718

MCCOBB, David, Chief Information Officer, Foothill Presbyterian Hospital–Morris L. Johnston Memorial, Glendora, CA, p. A63

MCCOIL, Kristie, Human Resources Director, St. Joseph's Community Health Services, Hillsboro, WI, p. A727

MCCOLLOUGH, Kristy, Assistant Administrator and Chief Financial Officer, Integris Mayes County Medical Center, Pryor, OK, p. A537

MCCOLM, Denni, Chief Information Officer, Citizens Memorial Hospital, Bolivar, MO, p. A378

MCCOMBS, M.D., William, Chief Information Officer, Scott and White Memorial Hospital, Temple, TX, p. A669

MCCONAHY, Richard L., Chief Operating Officer, Tanner Medical Center, Carrollton, GA, p. A157

MCCONNELL, Cheryl, Director Human Resources, Bone and Joint Hospital, Oklahoma City, OK, p. A535

MCCONNELL, David J., Chief Financial Officer, Bon Secours Hospital Campus, Altoona, PA, p. A552

MCCONNELL, Patrick G., Chief Financial Officer, West Park Hospital, Cody, WY, p. A740

MCCORD, Windell M., Administrator, Heart of Texas Memorial Hospital, Brady, TX, p. A626

MCCORKLE Jr, Philip H., President and Chief Executive Officer, Saint Mary's Health Care, Grand Rapids, MI, p. A335

MCCORKLE, Vincent J., President and Chief Executive Officer, Mercy Medical Center, Springfield, MA, p. A323

MCCORMACK, David, Chief Executive Officer, Peace River Regional Medical Center, Port Charlotte, FL, p. A144

MCCORMACK, Marcella M., Administrator, Veterans Home of California, Yountville, CA, p. A100

MCCORMICK, Brad, Chief Financial Officer, Morehouse General Hospital, Bastrop, LA, p. A277

MCCORMICK, Dan, President and Chief Executive Officer, Grand Itasca Clinic and Hospital, Grand Rapids, MN, p. A354

MCCORMICK, Darryl, Senior Vice President Human Resources, Stamford Health System, Stamford, CT, p. A116

MCCORMICK, Dee Dawn, Director of Personnel and Human Resources, Coon Memorial Hospital and Home, Dalhart, TX, p. A631

MCCORMICK, Taylor, Chief Financial Officer, Mercy Catholic Medical Center, Darby, PA, p. A557

MCCORMICK, Terri, Director Human Resources, Saint Francis Hospital, Charleston, WV, p. A714

MCCOY, Andy, Vice President Finance, Fairview Lakes Regional Health Care, Wyoming, MN, p. A365

MCCOY, M.D., James, Chief Medical Officer, Advocate Lutheran General Hospital, Park Ridge, IL, p. A204

MCCOY, M.D., Michael
Senior Associate Director, Chief Information Officer, Santa Monica–UCLA Medical Center, Santa Monica, CA, p. A93
Chief Information Officer, University of California Los Angeles Medical Center, Los Angeles, CA, p. A73

MCCOY, Mike, Chief Executive Officer, Saint Mary's Regional Medical Center, Russellville, AR, p. A50

MCCOY, Shawn W., Vice President Operations, Deaconess Hospital, Evansville, IN, p. A214

MCCOY, Sherman P., Executive Director and Chief Executive Officer, Howard University Hospital, Washington, DC, p. A121

MCCRACKEN, M.D., Rachel, Acting Chief of Staff, Royal C. Johnson Veterans Memorial Hospital, Sioux Falls, SD, p. A599

MCCREA, Mary Anne, Vice President and Chief Operating Officer, St. Joseph Hospital, Eureka, CA, p. A59

MCCREADY, Claudia, Administrator and Chief Executive Officer, Meadowbrook Rehabilitation Hospital Clear Lake, Webster, TX, p. A673

MCCRORY, Melinda, Vice President and Chief Financial Officer, Gilmore Memorial Hospital, Amory, MS, p. A366

MCCUE, Robert N., Vice President Finance, Mid Coast Hospital, Brunswick, ME, p. A297

MCCULLOCH, Andrew R.
President and Chief Executive Officer, Community Hospital, Springfield, OH, p. A522
President and Chief Executive Officer, Mercy Medical Center, Springfield, OH, p. A522

MCCULLOCH, Colin, Chief Financial Officer, Dunn Memorial Hospital, Bedford, IN, p. A211

MCCULLUM, Joe, Financial Manager, Carroll County Hospital, Carrollton, KY, p. A262

MCCUNE, Anne, Chief Operating Officer, City of Hope National Medical Center, Duarte, CA, p. A59

MCCUNE, Connie, Vice President Human Resources, Mt. Carmel Regional Medical Center, Pittsburg, KS, p. A255

MCCUNE, William, Chief Operating Officer, Delaware County Memorial Hospital, Drexel Hill, PA, p. A557

MCCURRY, M.D., Mark, Chief of Staff, Haskell County Healthcare System, Stigler, OK, p. A538

MCCUTCHEON, Edna I., Chief Executive Officer, Torrance State Hospital, Torrance, PA, p. A576

MCCUTCHEON, Norma J., President, The Wisconsin Heart Hospital, Wauwatosa, WI, p. A738

MCDANEL, Joyce, Chief Operating Officer, Wayne County Hospital, Corydon, IA, p. A231

MCDANEL, Stuart, Vice President and Chief Financial Officer, Mercy Medical Center–Centerville, Centerville, IA, p. A230

MCDANIEL, Amy, Controller, Wright Medical Center, Clarion, IA, p. A230

MCDANIEL, Dana, Director of Human Resources, Oakdale Community Hospital, Oakdale, LA, p. A290

MCDANIEL, III, Donald E., Chief Financial Officer, Ville Platte Medical Center, Ville Platte, LA, p. A294

MCDANIEL, Lisa, Assistant Administrator Human Resources, Kittitas Valley Community Hospital, Ellensburg, WA, p. A702

MCDANIEL, Ruth A., Chief Executive Officer, Bolivar Medical Center, Cleveland, MS, p. A368

MCDANIEL, Wayne, Chief Information Officer, Regional Medical Center at Memphis, Memphis, TN, p. A613

MCDEAVITT, M.D., James, Chief Medical Staff, Charlotte Institute of Rehabilitation, Charlotte, NC, p. A480

MCDERMOTT, Margaret
Chief Executive Officer, Saint's Mary & Elizabeth Medical Center, Claremont Avenue, Chicago, IL, p. A190
Chief Executive Officer, Saint's Mary & Elizabeth Medical Center, Division Street, Chicago, IL, p. A190

MCDEWITT, Mike, Chief Information Officer, The Children's Hospital of Alabama, Birmingham, AL, p. A15

MCDONALD, M.D., Bruce M., Senior Vice President Medical Affairs, Bridgeport Hospital, Bridgeport, CT, p. A112

MCDONALD, Buck, Chief Financial Officer, Redbud Community Hospital, Clearlake, CA, p. A57

MCDONALD, Cindy McNeill, Chief Operating Officer and Chief Nursing Officer, FirstHealth Richmond Memorial Hospital, Rockingham, NC, p. A490

MCDONALD, Debbie, Manager Accounting, University Hospital and Clinics – Holmes County, Lexington, MS, p. A372

MCDONALD, Edward A.
Chief Financial Officer, St Helena Hospital–Center for Behavioral Health, Vallejo, CA, p. A97
Chief Financial Officer, St. Helena Hospital, Saint Helena, CA, p. A85

MCDONALD, Elizabeth, Director Human Resources, Wayne Memorial Hospital, Honesdale, PA, p. A560

MCDONALD, Gregory, Vice President of Finance and Chief Financial Officer, Roswell Park Cancer Institute, Buffalo, NY, p. A449

MCDONALD, Harold E., Executive Vice President and Chief Operating Officer, Wyckoff Heights Medical Center, New York, NY, p. A466

MCDONALD, M.D., James, Chief of Staff, North Hills Hospital, North Richland Hills, TX, p. A658

MCDONALD, Jeff, Chief Executive Officer, Canyon Ridge Hospital, Chino, CA, p. A56

MCDONALD, Joe, Vice President Finance, Boulder Community Hospital, Boulder, CO, p. A101

MCDONALD, Joseph D., President and Chief Executive Officer, Catholic Health System, Buffalo, NY, p. B25

MCDONALD, Kathy, Director Personnel, Covenant Hospital–Levelland, Levelland, TX, p. A652

MCDONALD, Kelly, Human Resource Director, Golden Plains Community Hospital, Borger, TX, p. A626

MCDONALD, Larry, Director Human Resources, Miami Jewish Home and Hospital for Aged, Miami, FL, p. A137

MCDONALD, Lynn, Chief Executive Officer, Middle Tennessee Mental Health Institute, Nashville, TN, p. A615

MCDONALD, Steve, Director, Information Systems, Northside Hospital and Heart Institute, Saint Petersburg, FL, p. A145

MCDONALD, William, Vice President and Chief Operating Officer, Christus St. Michael Health System, Texarkana, TX, p. A669

MCDONALD, William A.
Interim Chief Executive Officer, St. Joseph's Healthcare System, Paterson, NJ, p. B102
Interim Chief Executive Officer, St. Joseph's Regional Medical Center, Paterson, NJ, p. A434
Interim Chief Executive Officer, St. Joseph's Wayne Hospital, Wayne, NJ, p. A438

MCDONNELL, D.O., Bernard C., Vice President Medical Affairs, Mercy Suburban Hospital, Norristown, PA, p. A566

MCDONNELL, Michael J., Vice President and Chief Operating Officer, Sheltering Arms Rehabilitation Hospital, Mechanicsville, VA, p. A691

MCDONNELL, Stephen C., Senior Vice President and Chief Financial Officer, Sibley Memorial Hospital, Washington, DC, p. A122

MCDONOUGH, Lawrence J., Interim Administrator, Trinity Hospital, Weaverville, CA, p. A98

MCDOUGAL, Haze, Chief Fiscal Service, Veterans Affairs Medical Center, Oklahoma City, OK, p. A536

MCDOUGAL Jr, Tom R., Chief Executive Officer, Parkway Medical Center, Decatur, AL, p. A17

MCDOUGLE, Mark, Executive Vice President and Chief Operating Officer, Maimonides Medical Center, New York, NY, p. A461

MCDOWELL, Charles
Corporate Vice President Human Resources, Milwaukee County Behavioral Health Division, Milwaukee, WI, p. A731
Corporate Vice President Human Resources, The Toledo Hospital, Toledo, OH, p. A523

MCDOWELL, Jane, Administrator, Jefferson County Hospital, Waurika, OK, p. A541

MCDOWELL, Jon
Vice President, Bayhealth Medical Center, Dover, DE, p. A119
Chief Operating Officer, St. Joseph's Hospital, Parkersburg, WV, p. A718

MCDOWELL, Paul L., Vice President Finance & Chief Financial Officer, King's Daughters Medical Center, Ashland, KY, p. A261

MCDRURY, R.N., Martha M., Senior Vice President and Chief Operating Officer, Caritas Holy Family Hospital and Medical Center, Methuen, MA, p. A320

MCEACHERN, M.D., Larry, Chief of Staff, Rolling Plains Memorial Hospital, Sweetwater, TX, p. A668

MCEACHERN, Michael L.
Senior Vice President and Chief Operating Officer, Sisters of Charity Providence Hospitals, Columbia, SC, p. A586
Chief Operating Officer and Senior Vice President, St. Vincent's Hospital, Birmingham, AL, p. A15

MCELDOWNEY, Michael, Director Information Services, Delta Regional Medical Center, Greenville, MS, p. A368

MCELLIGOTT, Dan, Chief Operating Officer, Saint Francis Medical Center, Grand Island, NE, p. A407

MCELROY, q, Administrator, Pickens County Medical Center, Carrollton, AL, p. A16

MCELROY, Sherry, Health Information Management Director, Osceola Community Hospital, Sibley, IA, p. A241

MCELVEEN, Larry, Chief Information Officer, Carolinas Hospital System, Florence, SC, p. A587

MCENROY, Karolyn, Business Office Manager, Oakland Memorial Hospital, Oakland, NE, p. A410

MCEWEN, David S., Chief Executive Officer, Marlette Community Hospital, Marlette, MI, p. A340

MCEWEN, James, Administrator, Hammond Rehabilitation Hospital, Hammond, LA, p. A281

MCEWEN, Mary Louise, Superintendent, Bangor Mental Health Institute, Bangor, ME, p. A296

MCEWEN, Michelle, President and Chief Executive Officer, Speare Memorial Hospital, Plymouth, NH, p. A423

MCFALL, Edward, Chief Information Officer, Pitt County Memorial Hospital, Greenville, NC, p. A484

MCFALL, Vicky
Chief Executive Officer, Monroe County Medical Center, Tompkinsville, KY, p. A275
Chief Clinical Officer, Monroe County Medical Center, Tompkinsville, KY, p. A275

MCFARLAND, Kenneth, Chief Financial Officr and Vice President Finance, Mission Hospital, Mission Viejo, CA, p. A75

MCFARLAND, M.D., Rodney, Medical Director, Freeman Neosho Hospital, Neosho, MO, p. A388

MCFERRIN, Christy, Chief Information Officer, DeWitt Hospital, De Witt, AR, p. A42

MCGAHEE, James, Administrator and Chief Executive Officer, South Georgia Medical Center, Valdosta, GA, p. A171

MCGAHEY, Nikki, Information Officer, Jefferson County Hospital, Waurika, OK, p. A541

MCGARTH, Glenn E., Vice President and Human Resources, Centra Health, Lynchburg, VA, p. A691

MCGARY, Stephanie, Regional Director Human Resources, Carolinas Medical Center–Mercy, Charlotte, NC, p. A479

MCGEACHEY, Edward J., President and Chief Executive Officer, Southern Maine Medical Center, Biddeford, ME, p. A297

MCGEE, Dan, Director Human Resources and Asistant Administrator, Wheeling Hospital, Wheeling, WV, p. A721

MCGEE, Donna, Director Human Resources, Belmont Community Hospital, Bellaire, OH, p. A504

MCGEE, John, Chief Executive Officer, Bywater Hospital, New Orleans, LA, p. A288

MCGEE, John P., President and Chief Executive Officer, Solaris Health System, Edison, NJ, p. B101

MCGEE, Tommy
Vice President and Chief Financial Officer, Christus St. Michael Health System, Texarkana, TX, p. A669
Vice President and Chief Financial Officer, Christus St. Michael Rehabilitation Hospital, Texarkana, TX, p. A669

MCGILL, Richard M., Administrator, Hale County Hospital, Greensboro, AL, p. A19

MCGILL, Steve, Chief Financial Officer, Wabash General Hospital District, Mount Carmel, IL, p. A201

MCGILL, Timothy W., Chief Executive Officer, Livingston Regional Hospital, Livingston, TN, p. A611

MCGILVRAY, Greg, Chief Financial Officer, Medical Center Enterprise, Enterprise, AL, p. A18

MCGINNIS, Mark J., Senior Vice President, West Jefferson Medical Center, Marrero, LA, p. A286

MCGLONE, Robert, Vice President of Human Resources, Rapid City Regional Hospital System of Care, Rapid City, SD, p. A598

MCGLYNN, M.D., Edward H., Chief Medical Affairs Officer, Valley Regional Medical Center, Brownsville, TX, p. A627

MCGOLDRICK, Margaret M., Executive Vice President and Administrator, Abington Memorial Hospital, Abington, PA, p. A551

MCGONNELL, James, Chief Financial Officer, Putnam Community Medical Center, Palatka, FL, p. A141

MCGOUGH, Susan, Administrator, Mountain View Hospital District, Madras, OR, p. A545

MCGOVERN, M.D., James, President Medical Staff, St. Vincent Hospital, Green Bay, WI, p. A726

MCGOVERN, Julia, Vice President Human Resources, Chilton Memorial Hospital, Pompton Plains, NJ, p. A435

MCGOVERN, Sandra, Executive Director Human Resources, Glendive Medical Center, Glendive, MT, p. A398

MCGOWAN, Donna, Administrator, Lane County Hospital, Dighton, KS, p. A246

MCGOWAN, George, FACHE, Chief Executive Officer, Medical Center East, Birmingham, AL, p. A15

MCGOWAN, Michael, Director Human Resources, HEALTHSOUTH Rehabilitation Hospital of New Jersey, Toms River, NJ, p. A437

MCGOWAN, Sharon, Director Finance, UHHS Geauga Regional Hospital, Chardon, OH, p. A505

MCGOWAN, William, Chief Financial Officer, University of California, Davis Medical Center, Sacramento, CA, p. A85

MCGRAIL, Robert, Chief Financial Officer, West Branch Regional Medical Center, West Branch, MI, p. A348

MCGRATH, Bradley, Chief Operating Officer, Carlsbad Medical Center, Carlsbad, NM, p. A441

MCGRATH, Brendan P., Administrator, Auburn Memorial Hospital, Auburn, NY, p. A447

MCGRATH, Denise B., Administrator, HEALTHSOUTH Sea Pines Rehabilitation Hospital, Melbourne, FL, p. A136

MCGRAW, Patricia, Director Human Resources, Nason Hospital, Roaring Spring, PA, p. A574

MCGREAHAM, David S., Vice President Medical Affairs, Munson Medical Center, Traverse City, MI, p. A346

MCGREEVY, John, Chief Executive Officer, Lubbock Heart Hospital, Lubbock, TX, p. A654

MCGREGOR, Donna, Chief Financial Officer, Vassar Brothers Medical Center, Poughkeepsie, NY, p. A470

MCGREGOR, Julie, Director of Human Resources, CARITAS Medical Center, Louisville, KY, p. A269

MCGUE, Lisa, Accounting Manager, HEALTHSOUTH Northern Kentucky Rehabilitation Hospital, Edgewood, KY, p. A263

MCGUIGAN, Timothy, Chief Human Resources Management Service, Veterans Affairs Black Hills Health Care System, Fort Meade, SD, p. A596

MCGUILL, Gail
Administrator and Chief Executive Officer, Orem Community Hospital, Orem, UT, p. A678
Operations Officer Patient Care Services, Orem Community Hospital, Orem, UT, p. A678

MCGUINNESS, Luke, President, Central DuPage Hospital, Winfield, IL, p. A210

MCGUINNESS, Patrick, Chief Information Management, Keller Army Community Hospital, West Point, NY, p. A476

MCGUIRE, H. Aryon, Administrator, E. A. Conway Medical Center, Monroe, LA, p. A287

MCGUIRE, Jay, Director Information Systems, Southeast Missouri Hospital, Cape Girardeau, MO, p. A379

MCGUIRE, John, Executive Vice President and Chief Financial Officer, St. Anthony's Medical Center, Saint Louis, MO, p. A392

MCGUIRE, William D.
Chief Executive Officer, Buffalo General Hospital, Buffalo, NY, p. A448
President and Chief Executive Officer, KALEIDA Health, Buffalo, NY, p. B65

MCHUGH, M.D., John, Medical Director, Soldiers' Home in Holyoke, Holyoke, MA, p. A319

MCHUGH, M.D., William, Chief Medical Officer, Trinitas Hospital–Williamson Street Campus, Elizabeth, NJ, p. A428

MCILWAIN, Lisa, Vice President Human Resources, Miles Memorial Hospital, Damariscotta, ME, p. A298

MCINDOE, Brian, Senior Vice President Finance, Pascack Valley Hospital, Westwood, NJ, p. A438

MCINTOSH, Charles, Senior Director Human Resources, University of Minnesota Medical Center, Minneapolis, MN, p. A357

MCINTYRE, Daniel J., President and Chief Executive Officer, The Charlotte Hungerford Hospital, Torrington, CT, p. A117

MCINTYRE, S. Scott, Chief Executive Officer, Lee Regional Medical Center, Pennington Gap, VA, p. A693

MCKAGUE, Kirby, Chief Financial Officer, Hanford Community Medical Center, Hanford, CA, p. A63

MCKAY, Daniel E., Chief Executive Officer, Springs Memorial Hospital, Lancaster, SC, p. A589

MCKAY, Sharon, Director Human Resources, Irvine Regional Hospital and Medical Center, Irvine, CA, p. A65

MCKEEN, John, Information Technology Director, Marias Medical Center, Shelby, MT, p. A402

MCKENNA, Adrienne, Vice President and Human Resources Officer, Winchester Medical Center, Winchester, VA, p. A698

MCKENNA, Ph.D., Bertine C., Executive Vice President and Chief Operating Officer, Mary Imogene Bassett Hospital, Cooperstown, NY, p. A450

MCKENNA, Donald, Administrator, Wuesthoff Medical Center – Melbourne, Melbourne, FL, p. A136

MCKENNA, John F., Chief Executive Officer, Rockford Center, Newark, DE, p. A119

MCKENNA, Kathleen
Public Affairs Leader, Kaiser Foundation Hospital, Sacramento, CA, p. A84
Public Affairs Leader, Kaiser Foundation Hospital, Sacramento, CA, p. A84

MCKENNA, Mary, Chief Information Officer, Bellevue Hospital Center, New York, NY, p. A458

MCKENNA, M.D., Michael, Vice President Medical Management, Advocate Good Samaritan Hospital, Downers Grove, IL, p. A192

MCKENZIE, Brenda, Director Human Resources, Pleasant Valley Hospital, Point Pleasant, WV, p. A719

MCKENZIE, Susan Beth, Vice President of Human Resources, St. Mary's Medical Center, Huntington, WV, p. A716

MCKENZIE, Taylor, M.D., Chief Executive Officer, Sage Memorial Hospital, Ganado, AZ, p. A31

MCKENZIE, William G., President and Chief Executive Officer, Gilliard Health Services, Montgomery, AL, p. B46

MCKEON, John, Vice President Human Resources, Kingsbrook Jewish Medical Center, New York, NY, p. A461

MCKERNAN, Stephen W., Chief Executive Officer, University Hospital, Albuquerque, NM, p. A441

MCKIBBEN, Sean, President, UHHS Bedford Medical Center, Bedford, OH, p. A503

MCKIERNAN, Jay, Director, Information Systems, St. Vincent Healthcare, Billings, MT, p. A396

MCKILLOP, Gail, President, Crawley Memorial Hospital, Boiling Springs, NC, p. A478

MCKINLEY, Alton, Chief Fiscal Services, Amarillo Veterans Affairs Health Care System, Amarillo, TX, p. A620

MCKINLEY, Bryan, Chief Financial Officer, Ogden Regional Medical Center, Ogden, UT, p. A678

MCKINLEY, Derek, Chief Information Officer, Smithville Regional Hospital, Smithville, TX, p. A667

MCKINLEY, Johnetta, Associate Director, Ralph H. Johnson Veterans Affairs Medical Center, Charleston, SC, p. A585

MCKINLEY, Ph.D., Ronald, Vice President Human Resources, Children's Hospital Medical Center, Cincinnati, OH, p. A506

MCKINNEY, Dan, Administrator, Hermann Area District Hospital, Hermann, MO, p. A383

MCKINNEY, Gary, Chief of Staff, St. Thomas More Hospital, Canon City, CO, p. A102

MCKINNEY, Jinny, Director Information Systems, Grant Memorial Hospital, Petersburg, WV, p. A719

MCKINNEY, Sally, Director Human Resources, Woodland Heights Medical Center, Lufkin, TX, p. A655

MCKINNEY, Sheila A., President, Presbyterian Hospital of Allen, Allen, TX, p. A620

MCKINNON, Ronald A., Chief Executive Officer, Benson Hospital, Benson, AZ, p. A30

MCKNIGHT, Rich B., Interim Senior Vice President Information Technology, Presbyterian Hospital, Charlotte, NC, p. A480

MCKROW, Dee, Chief Executive Officer, Hills and Dales General Hospital, Cass City, MI, p. A329

MCKUEN, Sandy, Vice President Human Resources, Door County Memorial Hospital, Sturgeon Bay, WI, p. A736

MCKULA, Tim, Vice President Information Systems and Chief Information Officer, Rehabilitation Institute of Chicago, Chicago, IL, p. A189

MCLAIN, M.D., Allen, Chief of Staff, Grisell Memorial Hospital District One, Ransom, KS, p. A256

MCLAIN, John R., Administrator, Wythe County Community Hospital, Wytheville, VA, p. A699

MCLAIN, Kathy, Chief Financial Officer, Childress Regional Medical Center, Childress, TX, p. A628

MCLAIN, Terri L., CHE, President, Bay Park Community Hospital, Oregon, OH, p. A520

MCLANE, Kerry, Chief Executive Officer, Select Specialty Hospital of Baton Rouge, Baton Rouge, LA, p. A278

MCLAREN, Roseanne, Administrator, Rogue Valley Medical Center, Medford, OR, p. A546

MCLARTY, Walter, Vice President Human Resources, Good Samaritan Hospital, Cincinnati, OH, p. A507

MCLAUGHLIN, Gary, Vice President Finance and Chief Financial Officer, Overlake Hospital Medical Center, Bellevue, WA, p. A700

MCLAUGHLIN, Jason
Chief Financial Officer, Chapman Medical Center, Orange, CA, p. A79
Chief Financial Officer, Coastal Communities Hospital, Santa Ana, CA, p. A92

MCLAUGHLIN, Kevin, Chief Information Officer, Medical Center of Southern Indiana, Charlestown, IN, p. A213

MCLAUGHLIN, Mederic D., Chief Executive Officer, Massachusetts Hospital School, Canton, MA, p. A316

MCLAUGHLIN, Michael, Director Information Systems, Southern Maine Medical Center, Biddeford, ME, p. A297

MCLAUGHLIN, Pamela, Chief Financial Officer, HEALTHSOUTH Rehabilitation Hospital of Austin, Austin, TX, p. A623

MCLAUGHLIN, M.D., Thomas, Chief Medical Officer, Good Samaritan Regional Medical Center, Pottsville, PA, p. A573

MCLAUGHLIN, William R., President, Sacred Heart Hospital of Pensacola, Pensacola, FL, p. A143

MCLAURIN, Monty E., President and Chief Executive Officer, Indian Path Medical Center, Kingsport, TN, p. A609

MCLEAN, Beatrice J., Facility Director, Searcy Hospital, Mount Vernon, AL, p. A22

MCLEAN, Bill, Senior Vice President Human Resources, Avera McKennan Hospital and University Health Center, Sioux Falls, SD, p. A599

MCLEAN, Daniel P.
Chief Executive Officer, Edinburg Regional Medical Center, Edinburg, TX, p. A636
Chief Executive Officer and Managing Director, McAllen Medical Center, McAllen, TX, p. A656

MCLEAN, Gordon C., President, Mount Carmel Hospital, Colville, WA, p. A701

MCLEAN, Michael A., Chief Executive Officer, Regency Hospital of Northwest Arkansas, Fayetteville, AR, p. A42

MCLEAN, Michael J., Chief Executive Officer, River Hospital, Alexandria Bay, NY, p. A446

MCLELLAND, Randy, Chairman, Valley Baptist Health System, Harlingen, TX, p. A643

MCLEMORE, M.D., William, Chief of Staff, Memorial Hospital of Union County, Marysville, OH, p. A517

MCLENDON, Carla, Director Information Resource Management Services, Veterans Affairs Medical Center, Asheville, NC, p. A477

MCLENDON, John, Chief Information Officer, Bayfront Medical Center, Saint Petersburg, FL, p. A145

MCLIN, Robert, Vice President Finance, Good Samaritan Hospital, Vincennes, IN, p. A226

MCLOONE, J Mark, Executive Vice President and Chief Operating Officer, Children's Medical Center of Dallas, Dallas, TX, p. A632

MCMACKIN, James L., President and Chief Executive Officer, Cumberland Medical Center, Crossville, TN, p. A605

MCMAHAN, Debbie, Director Information Technology, Wesley Medical Center, Hattiesburg, MS, p. A369

MCMAHAN, Shirley, Chief Financial Officer, Mitchell County Hospital, Colorado City, TX, p. A629

MCMAHON, M.D., Daniel, President Medical Staff, Akron Children's Hospital, Akron, OH, p. A502

MCMAHON, Elaine, Administrator, Kwajalein Hospital, Kwajalein Island, MH, p. A743

MCMAHON, Sid, Assistant Administrator Information Management, Charleston Memorial Hospital, Charleston, SC, p. A584

MCMANUS, James, Chief Financial Officer, St. Mary Medical Center, Apple Valley, CA, p. A53

MCMANUS, Joseph S., President and Chief Executive Officer, Lawrence General Hospital, Lawrence, MA, p. A319

MCMANUS, Michael T.
Chief Operating Officer, Kenneth Hall Regional Hospital, East St. Louis, IL, p. A192
Chief Operating Officer, Kenneth Hall Regional Hospital, East St. Louis, IL, p. A192

MCMANUS, Tim, Administrator and Chief Operating Officer, River Region Health System, Vicksburg, MS, p. A376

MCMASTER, Sandra
Regional Chief Information Officer, Kauai Veterans Memorial Hospital, Waimea, HI, p. A176
Regional Chief Information Officer, Samuel Mahelona Memorial Hospital, Kapaa, HI, p. A175

MCMATH, Mark W., Chief Information Officer, Bloomington Hospital, Bloomington, IN, p. A212

MCMICHAN, Diane, Director of Human Resources, Baptist Cherokee, Centre, AL, p. A16

MCMICHEN, Diane, Director Human Resources, Baptist DeKalb Medical Center, Fort Payne, AL, p. A18

MCMILLAN, Don, Chief Information Officer, Sacred Heart Medical Center, Eugene, OR, p. A543

MCMILLAN, Douglas A., Administrator and Chief Executive Officer, West Park Hospital, Cody, WY, p. A740

MCMILLAN, Heather, Human Resources Coordinator, HEALTHSOUTH Rehabilitation Hospital, Kingsport, TN, p. A609

MCMILLAN, Jon, Controller, St. Vincent Randolph Hospital, Winchester, IN, p. A227

MCMILLAN, Linda, Patient Relations and Personnel Specialist, Choctaw Health Center, Philadelphia, MS, p. A374

MCMILLAN, William I., Administrator, Guam Memorial Hospital Authority, Tamuning, GU, p. A743

MCMILLEN, Dan, Director, Shawnee Mission Medical Center, Shawnee Mission, KS, p. A257

MCMORROUGH, Jerry, Vice President Human Resources, Medical Center of Plano, Plano, TX, p. A661

MCMULLEN, Ronald B., President, Alton Memorial Hospital, Alton, IL, p. A183

MCMURRAY, R.N., Jean Ann, Chief Nursing Officer, Jacksonville Medical Center, Jacksonville, AL, p. A20

MCMURRAY, Mary, Director Human Resources, Mercy Hospital, Iowa City, IA, p. A235

MCMURRAY, D.O., R Kelly, Chief of Staff, Memorial Hospital of Texas County, Guymon, OK, p. A531

MCMURRAY, Sean S., CHE, Chief Executive Officer, Johnston Memorial Hospital, Abingdon, VA, p. A685

MCMURTRY, Roger, Chief Mental Health Bureau, Mississippi State Department of Mental Health, Jackson, MS, p. B76

MCNALLY, Jan, President and Chief Administrative Officer, Methodist Medical Center of Oak Ridge, Oak Ridge, TN, p. A616

MCNALLY, Meg, Chief Executive Officer, Select Specialty Hospital–Jefferson Parish, Metairie, LA, p. A286

MCNAMARA, M.D., David, Medical Director, Meadville Medical Center, Meadville, PA, p. A564

MCNAMARA, Jack, Interim Executive Vice President and Administrator, Maryview Medical Center, Portsmouth, VA, p. A694

MCNAMARA, M.D., John, Chief of Staff, Torrance Memorial Medical Center, Torrance, CA, p. A96

MCNAMARA, Robert, Vice President Finance, St. Joseph's Hospital, Elmira, NY, p. A452

MCNAMARA, Steve, Chief Financial Officer, Anaheim Memorial Medical Center, Anaheim, CA, p. A52

MCNAMARA, Tom, Director Information Technology, Community Hospital of the Monterey Peninsula, Monterey, CA, p. A76

MCNAUGHTON, Neil H., Executive Director and Administrator, Serenity Lane, Eugene, OR, p. A543

MCNAUGHTON, Richard, Chief Information Management Service, Veterans Affairs Medical Center, Togus, ME, p. A301

MCNAULL, Thomas E., President and Chief Executive Officer, AMT Group, Inc., Duluth, GA, p. B8

MCNEA, Mel, Vice President Operations, Great Plains Regional Medical Center, North Platte, NE, p. A410

MCNEECE, Steve, Chief Executive Officer, Community Hospital of Anaconda, Anaconda, MT, p. A396

MCNEICE, Keith, Vice President and Chief Information Officer, NorthEast Medical Center, Concord, NC, p. A481

MCNEIL, Cheryl, Chief Human Resources Management Service, West Texas VA Health Care System, Big Spring, TX, p. A626

MCNEIL, Greg R., Chief Executive Officer, Lincoln County Hospital, Lincoln, KS, p. A251

MCNEIL, Hal, Vice President and Chief Financial Officer, Wyckoff Heights Medical Center, New York, NY, p. A466

MCNEIL, Reginald B., Director for Administration, Naval Hospital, Bremerton, WA, p. A701

MCNEILL, Douglas W., FACHE, President and Chief Executive Officer, Middletown Regional Hospital, Middletown, OH, p. A519

MCNEILL, Michael, Chief Fiscal Service, Veterans Affairs Medical Center, Albuquerque, NM, p. A441

MCNELLY, Robert, Information Services Director, Somerset Hospital Center for Health, Somerset, PA, p. A576

MCNEW, Robert L., Chief Executive Officer, Kindred Hospital–Fort Worth Southwest, Fort Worth, TX, p. A640

MCNEY, Jim, Vice President Finance and Chief Financial Officer, North Kansas City Hospital, Kansas City, MO, p. A384

MCNICHOLS, James P., Vice President Finance and Chief Financial Officer, Vista Health–Provena Saint Therese Medical Center, Waukegan, IL, p. A210

MCNICHOLS, Jim, Chief Financial Officer, Vista Health–Victory Memorial Hospital, Waukegan, IL, p. A210

MCNULTY, Joseph S., President and Chief Executive Officer, Pioneer Health Services, Magee, MS, p. B84

MCNUTT, Mike, Director of Human Resources, Covenant Hospital Plainview, Plainview, TX, p. A660

MCNUTT, Pamela, Vice President Information Systems, Methodist Charlton Medical Center, Dallas, TX, p. A633

MCPHAIL, Mark D., Chief Executive Officer, Jeff Anderson Regional Medical Center, Meridian, MS, p. A373

MCPHEE, M.D., Mark, Chief Operating Officer, Saint Luke's Hospital of Kansas City, Kansas City, MO, p. A385

MCPHERSON, M.D., Archie, Vice President and Chief Medical Officer, Virginia Hospital Center – Arlington, Arlington, VA, p. A685

MCPHERSON, Joanne, Director Plans, Programs and Resources, Wilford Hall Medical Center, Lackland AFB, TX, p. A652

MCPHERSON, M.D., Lon, Vice President Medical Affairs, Provena Saint Joseph Medical Center, Joliet, IL, p. A198

MCPHERSON, Stephen B.
Chief Financial Officer, Masonic Healthcare Center, Wallingford, CT, p. A117
Chief Financial Officer, Masonic Healthcare Center, Wallingford, CT, p. A117

MCQUAID, Bill, Director Information Systems, Parkview Adventist Medical Center, Brunswick, ME, p. A297

MCQUAID, David P., Chief Executive Officer, Durham Regional Hospital, Durham, NC, p. A481

MCQUEEN, Elbert T., Administrator, HEALTHSOUTH Central Georgia Rehabilitation Hospital, Macon, GA, p. A165

MCQUEEN, Harry, Vice President and Chief Information Officer, Integris Baptist Medical Center, Oklahoma City, OK, p. A535

MCQUILLAN, Kent, Chief Information Officer, Navapache Regional Medical Center, Show Low, AZ, p. A36

MCQUISTAN, Bob, Vice President Finance, York General Health Care Services, York, NE, p. A414

MCQUISTON, Mike, Director Human Resources, Wise Regional Health System, Decatur, TX, p. A635

MCQUISTON, William
Chief Information Officer, Truman Medical Center–Hospital Hill, Kansas City, MO, p. A385
Chief Information Officer, Truman Medical Center–Lakewood, Kansas City, MO, p. A385

MCRAE, Colin, Chief Operating Officer, Kingwood Medical Center, Kingwood, TX, p. A651

MCRAE, Dave C., Chief Executive Officer, University Health Systems of Eastern Carolina, Greenville, NC, p. B116

MCRAY, Kathy, Chief Financial Officer, HEALTHSOUTH Rehabilitation Hospital of Fort Smith, Fort Smith, AR, p. A43

MCREYNOLDS, Adrienne, Chief Information Officer, San Joaquin Community Hospital, Bakersfield, CA, p. A54

MCSPERITT, Linda, Accounting Supervisor, Watonga Municipal Hospital, Watonga, OK, p. A541

MCTIERNAN, Judyth, Chief Executive Officer, Northeast Specialty Hospital, Braintree, MA, p. A315

MCTIGUE, Michael, Chief Information Officer, Clara Maass Medical Center, Belleville, NJ, p. A425

MCVEETY, John A., Chief Executive Officer, Alpena Regional Medical Center, Alpena, MI, p. A327

MCVEY, Eric A., Vice President and Chief Medical Officer, Mississippi Baptist Health Systems, Jackson, MS, p. A370

MCWATTERS, David M., Administrator, Highland Hospital, Charleston, WV, p. A714

MCWATTERS, Pearl, Director of Information Services, Highland Hospital, Charleston, WV, p. A714

MCWAY, Jacob, Senior Vice President and Chief Financial Officer, Lester E. Cox Medical Centers, Springfield, MO, p. A394

MCWHERTER, Joe, Chief Financial Officer, Baptist Memorial Hospital–Union City, Union City, TN, p. A618

MCWHORTER, Chuck, Director, Guadalupe Valley Hospital, Seguin, TX, p. A666

MCWHORTER III, John B., Interim President, Baylor University Medical Center, Dallas, TX, p. A632

MCWILLIAMS, Kendria, Chief Executive Officer, Eagleville Hospital, Eagleville, PA, p. A557

MEACHAM, Steve, Vice President Finance, King's Daughters' Hospital and Health Services, Madison, IN, p. A221

MEAD, Barbara, Executive Director, Lourdes Counseling Center, Richland, WA, p. A707

MEAD, Richard, Senior Director Human Resources, Saint Francis Memorial Hospital, San Francisco, CA, p. A89

MEADE, M.D., R, Executive Director Primary Care, Naval Hospital, Camp Pendleton, CA, p. A56

MEADE, Robert C.
Chief Executive Officer, Doctors Hospital of Sarasota, Sarasota, FL, p. A146
Chief Executive Officer, Englewood Community Hospital, Englewood, FL, p. A128

MEADES, LeVern S.
Administrator, Bogalusa Medical Center, Bogalusa, LA, p. A278
Administrator, Lallie Kemp Medical Center, Independence, LA, p. A282

MEADOWS, Julia, Chief Financial Officer, Virginia Gay Hospital, Vinton, IA, p. A242

MEADOWS, Michael, Chief Operating Officer, Guyan Valley Hospital, Logan, WV, p. A717

MEADOWS, Nancy
Chief Financial Officer, Methodist Children's Hospital of South Texas, San Antonio, TX, p. A664
Chief Financial Officer, Methodist Hospital, San Antonio, TX, p. A664

MEADOWS, Peri, Director, Human Resources, Rhea Medical Center, Dayton, TN, p. A605

MEADOWS, Tom, Consulting Controller, Campbellton Graceville Hospital, Graceville, FL, p. A130

MEANS, Michael D., President and Chief Executive Officer, First Health, Inc., Rockledge, FL, p. B45

MEARS, Terry, Director Information Systems, Durham Regional Hospital, Durham, NC, p. A481

MECHTENBERG, David A., Chief Executive Officer, Ridgecrest Regional Hospital, Ridgecrest, CA, p. A84

MECKSTROTH, David J., President and Chief Executive Officer, Upper Valley Medical Center, Troy, OH, p. A523

MEDEIROS, Alan H., Executive Director, Lanterman Developmental Center, Pomona, CA, p. A82

MEDEIROS, Katherine
Chief Executive Officer, Doctors Hospital of Manteca, Manteca, CA, p. A74
Interim Chief Executive Officer, Doctors Medical Center, Modesto, CA, p. A76

MEDEROS, Ana J., Chief Executive Officer, Hialeah Hospital, Hialeah, FL, p. A130

MEDINA, Alberto, Director of Information System, University Pediatric Hospital, San Juan, PR, p. A748

MEDINA, M.D., Juan, Chief of Staff, Corcoran District Hospital, Corcoran, CA, p. A57

MEDINA, Luz D., Controller, Hospital Hermanos Melendez, Bayamon, PR, p. A744

MEDIRATTA, M.D., Ravinder P., Chief of Staff, LakeView Community Hospital, Paw Paw, MI, p. A342

MEDLEY, Lena, Director Financial Services, Annie Penn Hospital, Reidsville, NC, p. A490

MEDLIN, Marcia, Chief Executive Officer, Select Specialty Hospital–Camp Hill, Camp Hill, PA, p. A554

MEDLIN, Randy, Vice President Fiscal Services, Stanly Memorial Hospital, Albemarle, NC, p. A477

MEDORS, Sharon, Chief Executive Officer, Padre Behavioral Hospital, Corpus Christi, TX, p. A631

MEDUNA, M.D., Leo, Chief Medical Officer, Saunders County Health Service, Wahoo, NE, p. A413

MEEHAN, Donald, Chief Information Officer, Southern Arizona Veterans Affairs Health Care System, Tucson, AZ, p. A38

MEEHAN, John J., President and Chief Executive Officer, Hartford Hospital, Hartford, CT, p. A113

MEEHAN, Kenneth L., President and Chief Administrative Officer, John Muir Medical Center, Walnut Creek, CA, p. A98

MEEK, Julie, Vice President Finance, Kadlec Medical Center, Richland, WA, p. A707

MEEKER, D.O., Brian, Medical Staff President, Virginia Gay Hospital, Vinton, IA, p. A242

MEEKINS, Lance, Chief Financial Officer, Nocona General Hospital, Nocona, TX, p. A658

MEEKS, Julia M., President and Chief Executive Officer, Specialty Hospital of Lorain, Lorain, OH, p. A517

MEEKS, Mike, Vice President Human Resources, St. Francis Hospital, Inc., Columbus, GA, p. A158

MEEKS, Tim, Vice President, Methodist Charlton Medical Center, Dallas, TX, p. A633

MEENK, Susan, Administrator Human Resources, Providence St. Peter Hospital, Olympia, WA, p. A705

MEETH, John, M.D., Acting Chief Executive Officer, U. S. Public Health Service Phoenix Indian Medical Center, Phoenix, AZ, p. A35

MEFFERT, Karen, Chief Financial Officer, Veterans Affairs Connecticut Healthcare System–New Haven Division, West Haven, CT, p. A117

MEGEHEE, Mark, Vice President and Chief Information Officer, Decatur General Hospital, Decatur, AL, p. A17

MEHAFFEY, Beth, Administrative Director Human Resources, Baptist Medical Center, Jacksonville, FL, p. A132

MEHL, Edward J., Chief Executive Officer, Lake Region Healthcare Corporation, Fergus Falls, MN, p. A353

MEHLHAUS, M.D., Brian, Chief of Staff, Boone County Hospital, Boone, IA, p. A229

MEHRINGER, Todd, Director Information Systems, Memorial Hospital and Health Care Center, Jasper, IN, p. A219

MEHTA, Raj, Chief Financial Officer, Medina Memorial Hospital, Medina, NY, p. A456

MEHTA, M.D., Varsha, Chief of Staff, Veterans Affairs Medical Center, Butler, PA, p. A554

MEIDINGER, Duane, Vice President Finance, Walla Walla General Hospital, Walla Walla, WA, p. A711

MEIER, Marv, Administrative Director Information Services, Altru Health System, Grand Forks, ND, p. A498

MEIERGERD, Jean, Director Information Systems, St. Francis Memorial Hospital, West Point, NE, p. A414

MEIGS, Jeffrey L., Chief Financial Officer, Wesley Medical Center, Hattiesburg, MS, p. A369

MEINKE, Kenneth, Vice President and Chief Financial Officer, Boca Raton Community Hospital, Boca Raton, FL, p. A124

MEINKE, Terry, Faiclity Accountant, Crete Area Medical Center, Crete, NE, p. A406

MEIS, Fred J., Administrator and Chief Executive Officer, Graham County Hospital, Hill City, KS, p. A248

MEISTER, James, Director of Information Systems, Our Lady of Bellefonte Hospital, Ashland, KY, p. A261

MEITZ, Mary
Vice President Finance, Bronson Methodist Hospital, Kalamazoo, MI, p. A338
Vice President Finance, Bronson Vicksburg Hospital, Vicksburg, MI, p. A347

MEJIA, M.D., Jorge, Chief of Staff, Homestead Hospital, Homestead, FL, p. A131

MEKALA, M.D., Bhavani P., President Medical Staff, LibertyHealth–Greenville Hospital, Jersey City, NJ, p. A430

MEKHJIAN, M.D., Hagop, Medical Director, Ohio State University Medical Center, Columbus, OH, p. A511

MELARAGNO, Robert V., Vice President and Chief Financial Officer, Galion Community Hospital, Galion, OH, p. A514

MELBY, Bernette A., Executive Director, University Health Services, Amherst, MA, p. A312

MELBY, Gina, Chief Executive Officer, J. F. K. Medical Center, Atlantis, FL, p. A123

MELBY, Larry, Chief Executive Officer, Hollywood Medical Center, Hollywood, FL, p. A131

MELCHING, CPA, Wendy, Vice President Finance, Fisher–Titus Medical Center, Norwalk, OH, p. A520

MELCHIONE, Joseph, Chief Operating Officer, University Hospital and Medical Center, Tamarac, FL, p. A147

MELCHIOR, Eric L., Executive Vice President and Chief Financial Officer, Greater Baltimore Medical Center, Baltimore, MD, p. A302

MELCHIORRE Jr, Joseph E., CHE, Executive Administrator, Shriners Hospitals for Children, Tampa, FL, p. B97

MELENDEZ, Carlos G., Executive Director, Cardiovascular Center of Puerto Rico and the Caribbean, San Juan, PR, p. A746

MELENDEZ, Pedro
Administrator, Hospital Menonita De Cayey, Cayey, PR, p. A744
Administrator, Mennonite General Hospital, Aibonito, PR, p. A743

MELGAR, Sergio L.
Chief Financial Officer, Santa Monica–UCLA Medical Center, Santa Monica, CA, p. A93
Chief Financial Officer, University of Kentucky Hospital, Lexington, KY, p. A268

MELIN, Craig N., President and Chief Executive Officer, Cooley Dickinson Hospital, Northampton, MA, p. A321

MELL, Kevin, Vice President, Human Resources, Montgomery General Hospital, Olney, MD, p. A309

MELL, Vicki, Vice President Human Resources, Ohio Valley General Hospital, McKees Rocks, PA, p. A564

MELLETT, David, Chief Financial Officer, Boone County Hospital, Boone, IA, p. A229

MELLMAN, M.D., Donald, Chief Medical Officer, North Colorado Medical Center, Greeley, CO, p. A106

MELLO, M.D., Ana, Chief of Staff, Veterans Affairs Medical Center, Lebanon, PA, p. A563

MELNIKOFF, Jean, Human Resources Leader, Kaiser Foundation Hospital – Orange County, Anaheim, CA, p. A52

MELONIO, Donald E., Executive Vice President and Chief Operating Officer, Jameson Hospital, New Castle, PA, p. A566

MELSON, CPA, Benjamin B., Chief Financial Officer, Texas Children's Hospital, Houston, TX, p. A647

MELTON, John W., Senior Vice President Operations and Chief Executive Officer, Johnson City Medical Center, Johnson City, TN, p. A608

MELTON, Leslie W., Vice President for Human Resources and Support Services, Charleston Area Medical Center, Charleston, WV, p. A714

MELTON Jr, T. Carter, President, Rockingham Memorial Hospital, Harrisonburg, VA, p. A689

MELTZ, David J., Vice President Medical Affairs, Newton Memorial Hospital, Newton, NJ, p. A433

MELTZER, David B., Chief Financial Officer, Presbyterian Hospital of Denton, Denton, TX, p. A635

MELTZER, Neil M.
President and Chief Operating Officer, Sinai Hospital of Baltimore, Baltimore, MD, p. A304
President and Chief Operating Officer, Sinai Hospital of Baltimore, Baltimore, MD, p. A304

MELVIN, Daryl, Chief Executive Officer, Hopi Health Care Center, Keams Canyon, AZ, p. A31

MELZER, Douglas L., Chief Executive Officer, Long Beach Medical Center, Long Beach, NY, p. A455

MENARD, Ellen, Senior Vice President Human Resources, Inova Fairfax Hospital, Falls Church, VA, p. A687

MENAUGH, John E., Chief Executive Officer, Sutter Coast Hospital, Crescent City, CA, p. A58

MENDELOWITZ, Paul, Senior Vice President for Medical Affairs, Holy Name Hospital, Teaneck, NJ, p. A436

MENDELSOHN, John, M.D., President, University of Texas M. D. Anderson Cancer Center, Houston, TX, p. A648

MENDEZ, Aaron, Management Information Systems, Hospital De La Concepcion, San German, PR, p. A746

MENDEZ, Lincoln S., Chief Executive Officer, Doctors Hospital, Coral Gables, FL, p. A126

MENDEZ, Matthew, Administrator, Pender Memorial Hospital, Burgaw, NC, p. A478

MENDOZA, Dana, Chief Information Officer, Maui Memorial Medical Center, Wailuku, HI, p. A176

MENDOZA, Richard L., Chief Executive Officer, Pioneers Memorial Healthcare District, Brawley, CA, p. A55

MENENDEZ, Deborah, Director Human Resources, Bayfront Medical Center, Saint Petersburg, FL, p. A145

MENGLE, Scott, Vice President Human Resources, St. Joseph Medical Center, Reading, PA, p. A574

MENKES, Jeffrey, Executive Vice President and Chief Operating Officer, Beth Israel Medical Center, New York, NY, p. A458

MENTON, Timothy P., Chief Executive Officer, The Villages Regional Hospital, The Villages, FL, p. A149

MEQUIAR, Ramon V., Senior Vice President and Chief Medical Officer, Memorial Health, Savannah, GA, p. A169

MERCADO, Hector, Executive Director, Hospital El Buen Pastor, Arecibo, PR, p. A744

MERCER, Barbara, Information Systems Director, Fleming County Hospital, Flemingsburg, KY, p. A264

MERCER, David, Information Systems Coordinator, Baptist Memorial Hospital–Union City, Union City, TN, p. A618

MERCER, M.D., Leo, Vice President Medical Affairs, United Regional Health Care System, Wichita Falls, TX, p. A674

MERCER, Peter, Chief Financial Officer, North Ridge Medical Center, Fort Lauderdale, FL, p. A129

MERCHANT, Robert, Chief Information Management, Veterans Affairs Medical Center, Saint Cloud, MN, p. A361

MERCURI, Ralph, Vice President Finance and Chief Financial Officer, Floyd Memorial Hospital and Health Services, New Albany, IN, p. A222

MEREDITH, Stephen L., Chief Executive Officer, Twin Lakes Regional Medical Center, Leitchfield, KY, p. A267

MERGEN, Lynn M.
Chief Executive Officer, Centennial Medical Center, Frisco, TX, p. A641
Interim Chief Executive Officer and Managing Director, Lakewood Ranch Medical Center, Bradenton, FL, p. A124

MERKEL, M.D., Earl, Chief of Staff, Russell Regional Hospital, Russell, KS, p. A256

MERKLE, Richard E., Chief Human Resources Officer, Geisinger Medical Center, Danville, PA, p. A556

MERLIS, Laurence M., President and Chief Executive Officer, Greater Baltimore Medical Center, Baltimore, MD, p. A302

MERRED, Mehdi, Chief Executive Officer, Gordon Memorial Hospital, Gordon, NE, p. A407

MERRELL, Bruce, President, St. Mary's Hospital, Centralia, IL, p. A186

MERRILL, Karen, Chief Information Officer, Veterans Affairs Medical Center, White River Junction, VT, p. A684

MERRILL, Mark H., President, Presbyterian Hospital of Dallas, Dallas, TX, p. A633

MERRILL, Rick W., President and Chief Executive Officer, Driscoll Children's Hospital, Corpus Christi, TX, p. A630

MERRITT, Janet, Chief Financial Officer, St. Vincent Williamsport Hospital, Williamsport, IN, p. A227

MERRYMAN, Scott, Chief Financial Officer, Christus St. Frances Cabrini Hospital, Alexandria, LA, p. A276

MERRYWELL, Paul, Vice President Information Services, St. John's Mercy Medical Center, Saint Louis, MO, p. A392

MERSON, Brent, Administrator, North Florida Reception Center Hospital, Lake Butler, FL, p. A134

MERTZ, Charles, Chief of Staff, Jackson–Madison County General Hospital, Jackson, TN, p. A608

MERTZ, John, Director Information Services, South Nassau Communities Hospital, Oceanside, NY, p. A467

MERTZ, Linda, Administrator, Select Specialty Hospital–Omaha, Papillion, NE, p. A412

MERTZ, Mary Ann, Vice President Human Resources, Good Samaritan Health Systems, Kearney, NE, p. A408

MERTZ, Paul A., Executive Director, Newark Beth Israel Medical Center, Newark, NJ, p. A432

MERWIN, Robert W., Chief Executive Officer, Mills–Peninsula Health Services, Burlingame, CA, p. A55

MESIC, M.D., John, Chief Medical Officer, Sutter Auburn Faith Hospital, Auburn, CA, p. A53

MESKEW, James, Chief Operating Officer, St. John Medical Center, Longview, WA, p. A704

MESSELT, Mary Jo, Director Human Resources, Logan Medical Center, Guthrie, OK, p. A531

MESSER, Bristol, Chief Executive Officer, McCurtain Memorial Hospital, Idabel, OK, p. A532

MESSER, Jeff, Chief Executive Officer, Swisher Memorial Hospital District, Tulia, TX, p. A670

MESSINA, Daniel J., Senior Vice President and Chief Operating Officer, CentraState Healthcare System, Freehold, NJ, p. A428

MESSMER, Joseph, President and Chief Executive Officer, Mercy Medical Center, Nampa, ID, p. A180

METCALF, MSC, USN, Edward, Associate Director Information, Technology and Communications, National Naval Medical Center, Bethesda, MD, p. A305

METCALF, Milissa, Human Resources Director, Graham County Hospital, Hill City, KS, p. A248

METHUEN, Jeff, Information Technology Manager, St. Luke Hospital and Living Center, Marion, KS, p. A252

METIVIER, Roland, Chief Executive Officer, Edward White Hospital, Saint Petersburg, FL, p. A145

METSCH, Jonathan M., Dr.PH,
President and Chief Executive Officer, LibertyHealth, Jersey City, NJ, p. B67
President and Chief Executive Officer, LibertyHealth–Jersey City Medical Center, Jersey City, NJ, p. A430

METTS, Michael, Chief Financial Officer, Roxborough Memorial Hospital, Philadelphia, PA, p. A569

METZ, Carl, Director Human Resources Officer, Ephraim McDowell Regional Medical Center, Danville, KY, p. A263

METZER, Lori, Chief Executive Officer, Select Specialty Hospital–Danville, Danville, PA, p. A556

METZGER, Bart
Vice President Human Resources, Beth Israel Medical Center, New York, NY, p. A458
Vice President Human Resources, St. Luke's–Roosevelt Hospital Center, New York, NY, p. A465

METZLER, Michael W., President, Saint Anne's Hospital, Fall River, MA, p. A317

METZNER, Kurt W., President and Chief Executive Officer, Mississippi Baptist Health Systems, Jackson, MS, p. A370

MEYER, CPA, Becky, Chief Financial Officer, Community Hospital Onaga, Onaga, KS, p. A254

MEYER, M.D., Chad, Medical Director, Kula Hospital, Kula, HI, p. A175

MEYER, Cheryl, Director Human Resources, Palmer Lutheran Health Center, West Union, IA, p. A243

MEYER, Daniel, Administrator, Aurora Sheboygan Memorial Medical Center, Sheboygan, WI, p. A735

MEYER, Eugene W., President and Chief Executive Officer, Lawrence Memorial Hospital, Lawrence, KS, p. A251

MEYER, Francis, Vice President Information Systems Technology, Buffalo General Hospital, Buffalo, NY, p. A448

MEYER, Fred, Chief Operating Officer, Huron Medical Center, Bad Axe, MI, p. A328

MEYER, Gary A., President and Chief Executive Officer, Schneck Medical Center, Seymour, IN, p. A225

MEYER, James E., President and Chief Executive Officer, MedCentral Health System, Mansfield, OH, p. A517

MEYER, Jeffrey K., Chief Executive Officer, Osceola Medical Center, Osceola, WI, p. A733

MEYER, M.D., Kathleen, President, Holy Family Hospital, Spokane, WA, p. A709

MEYER, Ken, Head Information Systems, St. Vincent Women's Hospital, Indianapolis, IN, p. A219

MEYER, Kurt, Chief Executive Officer, Rebsamen Medical Center, Jacksonville, AR, p. A45

MEYER, Kurt A., Vice President, Human Resources, Elkhart General Hospital, Elkhart, IN, p. A214

MEYER, Lori, Vice President and Chief Financial Officer, Mt. Graham Regional Medical Center, Safford, AZ, p. A36

MEYER, Luz, Director Information Services, Edward White Hospital, Saint Petersburg, FL, p. A145

MEYER, Michele C., Chief Executive Officer, Des Peres Hospital, Saint Louis, MO, p. A390

MEYER, Nate, Chief Financial Officer, St. Mary's Regional Health Center, Detroit Lakes, MN, p. A352

MEYER, M.D., Paul F., Chief of Staff, Lexington Memorial Hospital, Lexington, NC, p. A486

MEYER, Philip A., Director Finance, Dearborn County Hospital, Lawrenceburg, IN, p. A221

MEYER, Robert L., M.D., President and Chief Executive Officer, Phoenix Children's Hospital, Phoenix, AZ, p. A34

MEYER, Tom, Vice President Finance, Morris Hospital & Healthcare Centers, Morris, IL, p. A201

MEYERHOFER, Cheri, vice President Human Resources, Southwest Washington Medical Center, Vancouver, WA, p. A711

MEYERING, LeRoy, Associate Administrator Financial and Information Services, Rice Memorial Hospital, Willmar, MN, p. A365

MEYERS, Audrey, President and Chief Executive Officer, Valley Hospital, Ridgewood, NJ, p. A435

MEYERS, Brent, Administrator, Beaver County Memorial Hospital, Beaver, OK, p. A528

MEYERS, Dennis, President and Chief Executive Officer, Memorial Hospital, Manchester, KY, p. A271

MEYERS, Karen, Chief Financial Officer, Rush Memorial Hospital, Rushville, IN, p. A224

MEYERS, Mark A., President, California Hospital Medical Center, Los Angeles, CA, p. A69

MEYERS, Robert, Chief Executive Officer, Select Specialty Hospital–Belleville, Belleville, NJ, p. A425

MEYERS, Russell
President and Chief Executive Officer, Midland Memorial Hospital, Midland, TX, p. A657
President and Chief Executive Officer, Midland Memorial Hospital, Midland, TX, p. A657

MEZA, Casey
Chief Executive Officer, Clearwater Valley Hospital and Clinics, Orofino, ID, p. A180
Chief Executive Officer, St. Mary's Hospital, Cottonwood, ID, p. A178

MICHAEL, Amy, Chief Financial Officer, Sullivan County Memorial Hospital, Milan, MO, p. A387

MICHAEL, Barry, President, Ephraim McDowell Regional Medical Center, Danville, KY, p. A263

MICHAEL, James E., Chief Fiscal Services, William S. Middleton Memorial Veterans Hospital, Madison, WI, p. A728

MICHAEL, Lois, Vice President Human Resources, Torrance Memorial Medical Center, Torrance, CA, p. A96

MICHAELS, Sandy, Chief Financial Officer, Grant Memorial Hospital, Petersburg, WV, p. A719

MICHAELSON, Linda, Director Human Resources, Lake District Hospital, Lakeview, OR, p. A545

MICHAELSON, M.D., Stephen P., Chief of Staff, Norwalk Hospital, Norwalk, CT, p. A115

MICHALIK, M.D., Jaroslaw, Chief of Staff, Missouri Baptist Hospital–Sullivan, Sullivan, MO, p. A394

MICHALSKI, Eugene F.
Senior Vice President and Director, William Beaumont Hospital–Troy, Troy, MI, p. A347
Senior Vice President and Director, William Beaumont Hospital–Troy, Troy, MI, p. A347

MICHAUD, Dan, Vice President Human Resources, Caritas Carney Hospital, Dorchester, MA, p. A317

MICHEL, Jack J., M.D., President and Chief Executive Officer, Larkin Community Hospital, South Miami, FL, p. A146

MICHEL–OGBORN, Deborah, Chief Information Resource Management, Malcom Randall Veterans Affairs Medical Center, Gainesville, FL, p. A129

MICHELETTI, Denise D., Acting Director, Central Virginia Training Center, Madison Heights, VA, p. A691

MICHELETTI, Susan C., Chief Operating Officer, San Ramon Regional Medical Center, San Ramon, CA, p. A91

MICHELL, Dyer T., President, Munroe Regional Medical Center, Ocala, FL, p. A140

MICIOTTO, Joseph M., Administrator, LSU Medical Center–University Hospital, Shreveport, LA, p. A292

MICKENS, Walt
Chief Executive Officer, West Boca Medical Center, Boca Raton, FL, p. A124
Chief Operating Officer, Parkway Regional Medical Center, North Miami Beach, FL, p. A139

MICKIEWICZ, M.D., Nanette, Chief Medical Officer, Dominican Hospital, Santa Cruz, CA, p. A92

MICKOSEFF, Tecla A., Chief Executive Officer, LAC–Harbor–University of California at Los Angeles Medical Center, Torrance, CA, p. A96

MIDDENDORF, Tim, Administrator, Renville County Hospital, Olivia, MN, p. A359

MIDDLEMISS, Christine B., Senior Director Information Services, Western Pennsylvania Hospital, Pittsburgh, PA, p. A573

MIDDLETON, M.D., John, Chief Medical Officer, Raritan Bay Medical Center, Perth Amboy, NJ, p. A434

MIDGARDEN, M.D., K J., Chief Medical Staff, First Care Health Center, Park River, ND, p. A500

MIELAK, Gary, Chief Technology Officer, Edward Hospital, Naperville, IL, p. A202

MIGALA, Geoff, Director Human Resources, Coastal Communities Hospital, Santa Ana, CA, p. A92

MIGUEL, Francine, Director of Human Resources, West Jefferson Medical Center, Marrero, LA, p. A286

MIGUEL, Hortense, R.N., Service Unit Director, U. S. Public Health Service Indian Hospital, Winterhaven, CA, p. A99

MIHAL, Denise B., R.N., Chief Executive Officer, Presbyterian Hospital Huntersville, Huntersville, NC, p. A485

MIHAL, M.D., Victor, Chief of Staff, Pioneers Hospital of Rio Blanco County, Meeker, CO, p. A108

MIHALSKY, Stephen, Chief of Staff, Edmond Medical Center, Edmond, OK, p. A530

MIHORA, Michael J., President and Chief Executive Officer, Cheboygan Memorial Hospital, Cheboygan, MI, p. A329

MIKES, James, Administrator and Chief Executive Officer, Select Specialty Hospital, Saint Louis, MO, p. A391

MIKI, M.D., Nobuyuki, Vice President Medical Affairs, Kuakini Medical Center, Honolulu, HI, p. A173

MIKITARIAN Jr, George, Chief Executive Officer, Parrish Medical Center, Titusville, FL, p. A149

MIKLOS, Maggie, Director Human Resources, Northside Hospital and Heart Institute, Saint Petersburg, FL, p. A145

MIKOLS, Mary Beth, Interim Director Information Systems, Port Huron Hospital, Port Huron, MI, p. A343

MIKOS, Ken, Director Information Systems, Hopkins County Memorial Hospital, Sulphur Springs, TX, p. A668

MIKUTIC, Joannia, Director Human Resources, Providence Newberg Hospital, Newberg, OR, p. A546

MILAND, Shelly
Chief Financial Officer, Harris Methodist Northwest, Azle, TX, p. A624
Chief Financial Officer and Vice President Finance, Harris Methodist–HEB, Bedford, TX, p. A625

MILANO, Arthur, Vice President Human Resources, Berkshire Medical Center, Pittsfield, MA, p. A322

MILANO, Rosemarie, Chief Human Resources Director, North Shore University Hospital at Syosset, Syosset, NY, p. A473

MILAS, Sue, Chief Operating Officer and Chief Nursing Officer, Dukes Memorial Hospital, Peru, IN, p. A223

MILAWSKI, M.D., William, President Medical Staff, Mother Frances Hospital – Jacksonville, Jacksonville, TX, p. A650

MILBRATH, Michael, Executive Vice President, Waseca Medical Center, Waseca, MN, p. A364

MILES, Brenda, Administrator, Warm Springs Specialty Hospital, Luling, TX, p. A655

MILES, David K., President and Chief Executive Officer, The Children's Institute of Pittsburgh, Pittsburgh, PA, p. A572

MILES, Pam, Administrator, Good Shepherd Specialty Hospital, Allentown, PA, p. A551

MILEWSKI, Robert, President and Chief Executive Officer, Mount Clemens General Hospital, Mount Clemens, MI, p. A340

MILEY, Dennis C., Administrator, Tri–County Hospital, Wadena, MN, p. A364

MILLAN, Wilfredo Rabelo, Chief Operating Officer, Hospital Episcopal Cristo Redentor, Guayama, PR, p. A745

MILLARD, James M.
President and Senior Administrative Officer, St. Joseph Hospital, Cheektowaga, NY, p. A450
President and Senior Administrative Officer, St. Joseph Hospital, Cheektowaga, NY, p. A450

MILLBURG, Charles L., CHE, Chief Executive Officer, Shenandoah Medical Center, Shenandoah, IA, p. A241

MILLER, Alan B., President and Chief Executive Officer, Universal Health Services, Inc., King of Prussia, PA, p. B114

MILLER, Amy, Chief Financial Officer, Norton Sound Regional Hospital, Nome, AK, p. A28

MILLER, Andy
Chief Information Officer, Community Memorial Hospital, Oconto Falls, WI, p. A733
Director of Information Systems, Ripon Medical Center, Ripon, WI, p. A735

MILLER, Blaine K., Administrator, Republic County Hospital, Belleville, KS, p. A244

MILLER, Bob, Administrative Director Human Resources, St. Elizabeth's Hospital, Belleville, IL, p. A184

MILLER, Charles F., President and Chief Executive Officer, Piedmont Healthcare System, Rock Hill, SC, p. A591

MILLER, Charles R., Chief Executive Officer, Northwest Iowa Health Center, Sheldon, IA, p. A241

MILLER, Cindy, Director Health Information Management, West Branch Regional Medical Center, West Branch, MI, p. A348

MILLER, Connie, Director Human Resources, Overland Park Regional Medical Center, Overland Park, KS, p. A254

MILLER, M.D., Craig, Senior Vice President Medical Affairs, Baptist Hospital, Pensacola, FL, p. A142

MILLER, Daniel, Vice President Human Resources, EMH Regional Medical Center, Elyria, OH, p. A513

MILLER, Dennis E., FACHE, Chief Executive Officer, Williamson Medical Center, Franklin, TN, p. A606

MILLER, Derek, Senior Vice President and Chief Financial Officer, Southeast Alabama Medical Center, Dothan, AL, p. A17

MILLER, Dianna, Interim Director Medical Records, Lake Pointe Medical Center, Rowlett, TX, p. A662

MILLER, Donald
Chief Financial Officer, Petaluma Valley Hospital, Petaluma, CA, p. A81
Director, Human Resources, San Jacinto Methodist Hospital, Baytown, TX, p. A625
Chief Financial Officer, Santa Rosa Memorial Hospital, Santa Rosa, CA, p. A93

MILLER, Duane, Vice President Finance, Carson City Hospital, Carson City, MI, p. A329

MILLER, Emil P.
President and Chief Executive Officer, Wuesthoff Health System, Rockledge, FL, p. B123
President and Chief Executive Officer, Wuesthoff Medical Center – Rockledge, Rockledge, FL, p. A144

MILLER, M.D., G Thomas, Vice President Medical Affairs, Sacred Heart Medical Center, Spokane, WA, p. A709

MILLER, Gary, Senior Vice President and Chief Financial Officer, St. Alexius Medical Center, Bismarck, ND, p. A496

MILLER, Gary L.
Regional Information Systems Director, Saint Joseph Regional Medical Center, South Bend, IN, p. A225
Regional Information Systems Director, Saint Joseph Regional Medical Center–Plymouth Campus, Plymouth, IN, p. A224

MILLER, Gene, Senior Vice President and Chief Operating Officer, Rio Vista Physical Rehabilitation Hospital, El Paso, TX, p. A637

MILLER, M.D., George, Vice President Medical Affairs, Salem Hospital, Salem, OR, p. A549

MILLER, George E., Chief Executive Officer, Central Montgomery Medical Center, Lansdale, PA, p. A562

MILLER Jr, George N., President and Chief Executive Officer, Provena St. Mary's Hospital, Kankakee, IL, p. A198

MILLER, Gerald, President and Chief Executive Officer, Crozer–Keystone Health System, Springfield, PA, p. B35

MILLER, Gwyn, Manager Human Resources, Klickitat Valley Health Services, Goldendale, WA, p. A703

MILLER, Helen, Human Resources Department Manager, Morgan County War Memorial Hospital, Berkeley Springs, WV, p. A713

MILLER, M.D., Howard J., Medical Staff President, Charles Cole Memorial Hospital, Coudersport, PA, p. A556

MILLER, M.D., J D.
Chief Medical Officer, Hazard ARH Regional Medical Center, Hazard, KY, p. A266
Vice President Medical Affairs, Morgan County Appalachian Regional Hospital, West Liberty, KY, p. A275
Vice President Medical Affairs, Williamson ARH Hospital, South Williamson, KY, p. A275

MILLER, Jacqueline, Director Health Information Systems, RHD Memorial Medical Center, Dallas, TX, p. A634

MILLER, James, Chief Financial Officer, Women's and Children's Hospital, Lafayette, LA, p. A284

MILLER, James I., President and Chief Executive Officer, Washoe Medical Center, Reno, NV, p. A418

MILLER, Jamie D.,Doctor's Hospital of Opelousas, Opelousas, LA, p. A290

MILLER, Jeffrey S., President and Chief Executive Officer, High Point Regional Health System, High Point, NC, p. A485

MILLER, M.D., Jeri, President Medical Staff, Fairview Park Hospital, Dublin, GA, p. A161

MILLER, Jim
President and Chief Executive Officer, Washoe Health System, Reno, NV, p. B121
Assistant Vice President Human Resources, Cullman Regional Medical Center, Cullman, AL, p. A16
Chief Operating Officer, Saint Mary's Health Care, Grand Rapids, MI, p. A335

MILLER, John
Vice President Information Services, MedCenter One, Bismarck, ND, p. A496
Chief Financial Officer, St. Mary's Hospital Medical Center, Green Bay, WI, p. A726

MILLER Jr, John A., FACHE, President, AnMED Health Medical Center, Anderson, SC, p. A583

MILLER, John B., Administrator, Fall River Hospital, Hot Springs, SD, p. A596

MILLER, Jon, Team leader Accounting and Information Services, Hancock Memorial Hospital and Health Services, Greenfield, IN, p. A217

MILLER, Joseph, Chief Financial Officer, Amsterdam Memorial Hospital, Amsterdam, NY, p. A446

MILLER, Katherine, Vice President Human Resources, Munroe Regional Medical Center, Ocala, FL, p. A140

MILLER, Kevin J., FACHE, President and Chief Executive Officer, Ashtabula County Medical Center, Ashtabula, OH, p. A503

MILLER, Kim, Director Information Services, North Suburban Medical Center, Thornton, CO, p. A110

MILLER, Kimberly J., CHE, President and Chief Executive Officer, Mercy Medical Center, Williston, ND, p. A501

MILLER, Ph.D., Laban, Vice President Human Resources, Cardinal Hill Rehabilitation Hospital, Lexington, KY, p. A267

MILLER, Leighton, Chief Information Officer, Meade District Hospital, Meade, KS, p. A252

MILLER, Mark, Chief Financial Officer, Brighton Hospital, Brighton, MI, p. A329

MILLER, Mark A., Chief Executive Officer, Memorial Hospital, Abilene, KS, p. A244

MILLER, Mark F., Chief Financial Officer, Duke University Hospital, Durham, NC, p. A481

MILLER, M.D., Matthew, Vice President Medical Affairs, Danbury Hospital, Danbury, CT, p. A112

MILLER, Melody, Director Human Resources, Capital Regional Medical Center, Tallahassee, FL, p. A147

MILLER, Nate, Chief Executive Officer, Surgical Hospital of Jonesboro, Jonesboro, AR, p. A46

MILLER, Paul, Interim Chief Executive Officer, Cimarron Memorial Hospital, Boise City, OK, p. A528

MILLER, Paul C., Chief Executive Officer, Tahoe Pacific Hospitals, Reno, NV, p. A418

MILLER, Reginald A., Director Resource Management, Walter Reed Army Medical Center, Washington, DC, p. A122

MILLER, Richard
Administrator and Chief Executive Officer, Norton County Hospital, Norton, KS, p. A253
Administrator Finance, Banner Thunderbird Medical Center, Glendale, AZ, p. A31
Senior Vice President Finance, New York University Medical Center, New York, NY, p. A463

MILLER, Richard P., President and Chief Executive Officer, Virtua Health, Marlton, NJ, p. B120

MILLER, Rick
Corporate Director Human Resources and Information Services, Children's Hospital, Columbus, OH, p. A510
Corporate Director Human Resources and Information Services, Children's Hospital, Columbus, OH, p. A510

MILLER, Robbie, Director Human Resources, Horizon Medical Center, Dickson, TN, p. A605

MILLER, Robert, Chief Financial Officer, Ridgecrest Regional Hospital, Ridgecrest, CA, p. A84

MILLER, Robert D., Chief Executive Officer, McKenzie Regional Hospital, McKenzie, TN, p. A612

MILLER, Rod, Chief Information Technology, Community Hospital, Torrington, WY, p. A742

MILLER Sr, Rodney E., Chief Executive Officer, Roy Lester Schneider Hospital, Saint Thomas, VI, p. A749

MILLER, Rosemary, Associate Vice President Information Systems Services, Champlain Valley Physicians Hospital Medical Center, Plattsburgh, NY, p. A469

MILLER, Sam
Chief Operating Officer, North Sunflower Medical Center, Ruleville, MS, p. A375
Chief Information Officer, University Medical Center, Tucson, AZ, p. A38

MILLER, Sharon, Chief Information Officer, Howard Regional Health System, Kokomo, IN, p. A220

MILLER, Stan, Vice President Human Resources, St. Thomas More Hospital, Canon City, CO, p. A102

MILLER, Steve, Chief Financial Officer, Kosciusko Community Hospital, Warsaw, IN, p. A227

MILLER, M.D., Stuart P., Medical Director, HEALTHSOUTH Sea Pines Rehabilitation Hospital, Melbourne, FL, p. A136

MILLER, Tamara, Administrator, Madison Community Hospital, Madison, SD, p. A596

MILLER, Thomas D., Chief Executive Officer, Lutheran Hospital of Indiana, Fort Wayne, IN, p. A215

MILLER, M.D., Tim C., Director Medical Affairs, OSF Saint Francis Medical Center, Peoria, IL, p. A205

MILLER, Tom, Administrative Director Human Resources, Community Hospital of Long Beach, Long Beach, CA, p. A68

MILLER, Wayne T., Chief Executive Officer, Forest View Psychiatric Hospital, Grand Rapids, MI, p. A334

MILLER, Jr, Wentz J., Managing Director and Chief Financial Officer, Integris Baptist Medical Center, Oklahoma City, OK, p. A535

MILLER, William
  Vice President Information Services, Oconomowoc Memorial Hospital, Oconomowoc, WI, p. A733
  Vice President Information Services, Waukesha Memorial Hospital, Waukesha, WI, p. A737

MILLER, William P., President and Chief Executive Officer, Caro Community Hospital, Caro, MI, p. A329

MILLER–PHIPPS, Julie K., Senior Vice President and Service Area Manager, Kaiser Foundation Hospital – Orange County, Anaheim, CA, p. A52

MILLIGAN Jr, William M., President and Chief Executive Officer, Tyler Memorial Hospital, Tunkhannock, PA, p. A577

MILLINGTON, Mary
  Chief Financial Officer, Northwest Medical Center of Benton County, Bentonville, AR, p. A40
  Chief Financial Officer, Willow Creek Women's Hospital, Johnson, AR, p. A45

MILLIRONS, Dennis C., President and Chief Executive Officer, Riverside Medical Center, Kankakee, IL, p. A198

MILLIS, Priscilla, Chief Executive Officer, Lakeway Regional Hospital, Morristown, TN, p. A614

MILLNER, Jane, Director Community Relations and Development, St. Lawrence Rehabilitation Center, Trenton, NJ, p. A437

MILLS, Barbara, Chief Information Officer, Sherman Hospital, Elgin, IL, p. A193

MILLS, Chip, Director, Information Technology, Louise Obici Memorial Hospital, Suffolk, VA, p. A697

MILLS, Craig, Vice President Human Resources, St. Anthony's Medical Center, Saint Louis, MO, p. A392

MILLS, Deborah, Chief Nursing Officer, Lake City Community Hospital, Lake City, SC, p. A589

MILLS, Dennis, Director Human Resources, Regional Medical Center of San Jose, San Jose, CA, p. A90

MILLS, Ken, Chief Medical Staff, St. Mary's Medical Center, San Francisco, CA, p. A89

MILLS, Pete, Chief Executive Officer, Jenkins County Hospital, Millen, GA, p. A166

MILLS, M.D., Scott, Director Medical Staff Affairs, Mid Coast Hospital, Brunswick, ME, p. A297

MILLS, Stephen
  Regional Administrator, Dubuis Hospital of Beaumont, Beaumont, TX, p. A625
  Regional Administrator, Dubuis Hospital of Houston, Houston, TX, p. A645
  Administrator, Dubuis Hospital of Port Arthur, Port Arthur, TX, p. A661

MILLS, Stephen S., President and Chief Executive Officer, New York Hospital Medical Center of Queens, New York, NY, p. A463

MILLS, Tina, Personnel Director and Administrative Assistant, Gordon Memorial Hospital, Gordon, NE, p. A407

MILLS, Wayne, Chief Financial Officer, Oak Valley District Hospital, Oakdale, CA, p. A78

MILLS, William, Program Manager Human Resources, Veterans Affairs Pittsburgh Healthcare System, Pittsburgh, PA, p. A573

MILLSAPS, Janet, Staff Services Manager, Harris Regional Hospital, Sylva, NC, p. A492

MILNE, D.O., C Dean, Medical Director, HEALTHSOUTH Hospital of Tenaya, Las Vegas, NV, p. A416

MILNES, Lynn, Chief Executive Officer, Tri–Valley Health System, Cambridge, NE, p. A405

MILONE, Sheri, Chief Executive Officer and Administrator, Women's Hospital, Albuquerque, NM, p. A441

MILOVICH, David, Senior Vice President Human Resources, California Hospital Medical Center, Los Angeles, CA, p. A69

MILSTEIN, Marc
  Vice President and Chief Information Systems, Beth Israel Medical Center, New York, NY, p. A458
  Chief Information Officer, St. Luke's–Roosevelt Hospital Center, New York, NY, p. A465

MILTENBERGER, Cynthia, Director Organizational Effectiveness, Cass Medical Center, Harrisonville, MO, p. A382

MILTNER, James, Vice President, Finance, Massillon Community Hospital, Massillon, OH, p. A518

MILTON, Gene C., President and Chief Executive Officer, Hackettstown Community Hospital, Hackettstown, NJ, p. A429

MILTON, Paul A., Chief Operating Officer, Samaritan Hospital, Troy, NY, p. A474

MIMOSO, Michael, President and Chief Executive Officer, Northern Dutchess Hospital, Rhinebeck, NY, p. A470

MIMS, Wanda, Associate Director, Veterans Affairs Medical Center–Louisville, Louisville, KY, p. A270

MINCY, Lowney, Director Information Systems, Southside Hospital, Bay Shore, NY, p. A447

MINDER, George, Chief Executive Officer, Weston County Health Services, Newcastle, WY, p. A741

MINDINGAL, Talford, Chief Resource Management Division, Brooke Army Medical Center, Fort Sam Houston, TX, p. A638

MINEAR, Michael N., Senior Vice President Information Technology, University of Maryland Medical Center, Baltimore, MD, p. A304

MINER, Greg, Administrator, Siouxland Surgery Center, Dakota Dunes, SD, p. A595

MINER, Robert C., Chief Executive Officer, North Carolina Eye and Ear Hospital, Durham, NC, p. A481

MINES, Kathryn, Director Human Resources, St. Joseph's Hospital, Breese, IL, p. A185

MINGEN, Tom, Chief Executive Officer, Delta County Memorial Hospital, Delta, CO, p. A103

MINGS, M. Sue, Administrator, Latimer County General Hospital, Wilburton, OK, p. A541

MINGUS, Linda, Director, Human Resources, Aurora Medical Center of Oshkosh, Oshkosh, WI, p. A733

MINICK, Mark J., President and Chief Executive Officer, Van Wert County Hospital, Van Wert, OH, p. A523

MINICUS, Raymond, Vice President and Chief Operating Officer, New York Eye and Ear Infirmary, New York, NY, p. A463

MINISSALE, M.D., Anthony, Vice President Medical Affairs, Memorial Hospital, York, PA, p. A580

MINISSALE, Joseph, Chief Financial Officer, Titus Regional Medical Center, Mount Pleasant, TX, p. A657

MINKIN, CHE, Robert A., Executive Vice President and Chief Operating Officer, St. Joseph Hospital, Orange, CA, p. A79

MINKOFF, Dan, Chief Executive Officer, Lucas County Health Center, Chariton, IA, p. A230

MINNICK, D.O., Paul David, Chief Medical Staff, Clinton Memorial Hospital, Saint Johns, MI, p. A344

MINNICK, Peggy, R.N., Chief Executive Officer, Alhambra Hospital, Rosemead, CA, p. A84

MINNIS, Vernon, Administrator and Chief Executive Officer, Stafford District Hospital, Stafford, KS, p. A257

MINOR, Allen C., Vice President Operations, Community Medical Center, Scranton, PA, p. A575

MINOR, Suzanne, Director of Human Resources, Dauterive Hospital, New Iberia, LA, p. A288

MINTON, Vaughn, Director for Information Systems, Saint Francis Medical Center, Grand Island, NE, p. A407

MIRABITO, Frank W., President, Chenango Memorial Hospital, Norwich, NY, p. A467

MIRANDA, A Greg, President Medical Staff, St. Joseph's Hospital, Highland, IL, p. A196

MIRANDA, M.D., Ada S., Vice President Medical Affairs, Hospital Dr. Cayetano Coll Y Toste, Arecibo, PR, p. A743

MIRANDA, Jay S., Chief Executive Officer, Coral Gables Hospital, Coral Gables, FL, p. A126

MIRANDA, Raoul, Chief Financial Officer, Banner Lassen Medical Center, Susanville, CA, p. A95

MIRANDA, Vicki, Director Human Resources, Dominican Hospital, Santa Cruz, CA, p. A92

MIRE, Nona, Director Information Systems, Our Lady of Lourdes Regional Medical Center, Lafayette, LA, p. A284

MIRONE, Nancy, Business Manager, Veterans Affairs Medical Center, Northport, NY, p. A467

MIRRO, M.D., Joseph J., Chief Medical Officer and Executive Vice President, St. Jude Children's Research Hospital, Memphis, TN, p. A614

MIRZABEGIAN, Edward, Executive Vice President and Chief Operating Officer, St. Mary–Rogers Memorial Hospital, Rogers, AR, p. A49

MISCHLER, Cindy, Vice President Finance, New London Family Medical Center, New London, WI, p. A732

MISER, M.D., James, Chief Executive Officer, City of Hope National Medical Center, Duarte, CA, p. A59

MISHEK, Mark G., President, United Hospital, Saint Paul, MN, p. A362

MISHRICK, M.D., Abdallah
  Senior Vice President Medical Affairs, North Shore University Hospital at Plainview, Plainview, NY, p. A469
  Senior Vice President Medical Affairs, North Shore University Hospital at Syosset, Syosset, NY, p. A473

MISSILDINE, Syble F., Administrator, Northeast Medical Center Hospital, Humble, TX, p. A649

MITCHAM, Debbie, Chief Financial Officer, Northside Hospital, Atlanta, GA, p. A154

MITCHEL, David M., Chief Executive Officer, Avoyelles Hospital, Marksville, LA, p. A286

MITCHEL, M.D., Pat, Medical Director, Fall River Hospital, Hot Springs, SD, p. A596

MITCHELL, Adonna, Business Services Manager, North Mississippi Medical Center–Eupora, Eupora, MS, p. A368

MITCHELL, Andrew J., President and Chief Executive Officer, Central Suffolk Hospital, Riverhead, NY, p. A470

MITCHELL, Barbara, Administrator Organizational Development, Valley Medical Center, Renton, WA, p. A706

MITCHELL, Betty, Director of Human Resources, Lake Charles Memorial Hospital, Lake Charles, LA, p. A285

MITCHELL, Brenda, Director Human Resources, Roseland Community Hospital, Chicago, IL, p. A189

MITCHELL, Dennis, Acting Chief Financial Officer, Stony Brook University Hospital, Stony Brook, NY, p. A473

MITCHELL, Errol, Vice President, Integris Southwest Medical Center, Oklahoma City, OK, p. A535

MITCHELL, Gary W., Chief Executive Officer, Newman Memorial Hospital, Shattuck, OK, p. A538

MITCHELL, Harold, Chief Financial Officer, Bradley County Medical Center, Warren, AR, p. A51

MITCHELL, M.D., Jeffrey, Vice President Medical Affairs, Battle Creek Health System, Battle Creek, MI, p. A328

MITCHELL, Jodie, Facility Financial Director, Sturgis Community Health Care Center, Sturgis, SD, p. A600

MITCHELL, Kerlene, Administrator, Wedowee Hospital, Wedowee, AL, p. A25

MITCHELL, Lori J., Chief Financial Officer, Harborview Medical Center, Seattle, WA, p. A707

MITCHELL, Lynne, Chief Financial Officer, Parkridge Medical Center, Chattanooga, TN, p. A604

MITCHELL, Mark R., Ph.D., Chief Executive Officer, Kahi Mohala Behavioral Health, Ewa Beach, HI, p. A173

MITCHELL, Marsha, Director Human Resources, Fleming County Hospital, Flemingsburg, KY, p. A264

MITCHELL, Mary S., Chief Resource Management Services, Veterans Affairs Medical Center, Birmingham, AL, p. A15

MITCHELL, Michael, Chief Information Management, Veterans Affairs Long Beach Healthcare System, Long Beach, CA, p. A69

MITCHELL, Michael A., Chief Financial Officer, Greenview Regional Hospital, Bowling Green, KY, p. A262

MITCHELL, M.D., Perry, Chief of Staff, Winslow Memorial Hospital, Winslow, AZ, p. A39

MITCHELL, Rachel, Chief Financial Officer, James H. Quillen Veterans Affairs Medical Center, Mountain Home, TN, p. A614

MITCHELL, Richard R., Network Administrator, Eagleville Hospital, Eagleville, PA, p. A557

MITCHELL, Scot, CHE, Chief Executive Officer, Wheatland Memorial Hospital, Harlowton, MT, p. A399

MITCHELL, Sidney E., President and Chief Executive Officer, Pascack Valley Hospital, Westwood, NJ, p. A438

MITCHELL, Stan, Vice President Finance, Salina Regional Health Center, Salina, KS, p. A256

MITCHELL, Steve, Chief Operating Officer, Memorial Hospitals Association, Modesto, CA, p. A76

MITCHELL, Timothy W., Chief Executive Officer, Biloxi Regional Medical Center, Biloxi, MS, p. A366

MITCHENER Jr, Charles, President, Arkansas Heart Hospital, Little Rock, AR, p. A46

MITCHUM, Jerry, Chief Financial Officer, Creek Nation Community Hospital, Okemah, OK, p. A534

MITRICK, Joseph, Administrator, Baptist Medical Center, Jacksonville, FL, p. A132

MITROS, M.D., Mark, Medical Director, HEALTHSOUTH Rehabilitation Hospital, Sewickley, PA, p. A575

MITRY, Norman F.
President and Chief Executive Officer, Heritage Valley Health System, Beaver, PA, p. B59
President and Chief Executive Officer, Sewickley Valley Hospital, (A Division of Valley Medical Facilities), Sewickley, PA, p. A575
President and Chief Executive Officer, The Medical Center, Beaver, Beaver, PA, p. A552

MITTEER, Brian R., Chief Executive Officer, Cortland Memorial Hospital, Cortland, NY, p. A451

MITZNER, Jennifer C., Vice President Finance and Chief Financial Officer, Hoag Memorial Hospital Presbyterian, Newport Beach, CA, p. A78

MIXON, Karen, Interim Administrator, Christus Coushatta Health Care Center, Coushatta, LA, p. A279

MIYAMOTO, Faye, Vice President Human Resources, Rehabilitation Hospital of the Pacific, Honolulu, HI, p. A174

MIYAMOTO, Gene K., Chief Operating Officer, Battle Creek Health System, Battle Creek, MI, p. A328

MIZE, Linda G., Chief Executive Officer, Mitchell County Hospital, Colorado City, TX, p. A629

MIZE, William D., Administrator, Trousdale Medical Center, Hartsville, TN, p. A607

MIZELL, Patricia A., Chief Financial Officer, Riverside Medical Center, Franklinton, LA, p. A281

MIZELL, M.D., Philip L., Vice President Clinical Affairs, Baptist Health Medical Center–Little Rock, Little Rock, AR, p. A46

MIZRACH, Kenneth H.
Director, Veterans Affairs New Jersey Health Care System, East Orange, NJ, p. A427
Director, Veterans Affairs New Jersey Health Care System, East Orange, NJ, p. A427

MLADY, Celine M., Chief Executive Officer, Osmond General Hospital, Osmond, NE, p. A412

MLAWSKY, Karen, Executive Director, Ohio State University Hospitals East, Columbus, OH, p. A510

MLYNAREK, Robert W.
Vice President Finance, Oconomowoc Memorial Hospital, Oconomowoc, WI, p. A733
Vice President Finance, Waukesha Memorial Hospital, Waukesha, WI, p. A737

MO, Lin H., President and Chief Executive Officer, New York Community Hospital, New York, NY, p. A462

MOAK, Lance, Administrator, Franklin County Memorial Hospital, Meadville, MS, p. A372

MOAKLER, Thomas J., Chief Executive Officer, Houlton Regional Hospital, Houlton, ME, p. A299

MOALLEMIAN, Patrick, Chief Executive Officer, Harbor Oaks Hospital, New Baltimore, MI, p. A341

MOBLEY, D.O., Paul, Clinical Director, U. S. Public Health Service Comprehensive Indian Health Facility, Claremore, OK, p. A529

MOBLEY, Robert L., Vice President, Medical Affairs, Sisters of Charity Providence Hospitals, Columbia, SC, p. A586

MOBURG, Steven T., Chief Executive Officer, Paynesville Area Health Care System, Paynesville, MN, p. A359

MOCERI, Carmelo J., President, Missouri Baptist Medical Center, Town and Country, MO, p. A394

MOCK, Madison, Vice President Information Services, Medical Center of Central Georgia, Macon, GA, p. A165

MODJESKA, Alicia, President, St. Michael Hospital, Milwaukee, WI, p. A732

MODY, M.D., Amit, Executive Vice President and Chief Operating Officer, Saint Francis Hospital and Medical Center, Hartford, CT, p. A113

MOEBIUS, Geoffrey D., Administrator, Cleveland Clinic Hospital–Naples, Naples, FL, p. A139

MOEBIUS, Scott, Vice President Finance, Lakeview Medical Center, Rice Lake, WI, p. A734

MOEDE, Terry, Chief Information Officer, Brotman Medical Center, Culver City, CA, p. A58

MOELLER, Jerry G., President and Chief Executive Officer, Stillwater Medical Center, Stillwater, OK, p. A538

MOEN, Daniel P., President and Chief Executive Officer, Heywood Hospital, Gardner, MA, p. A318

MOFFATT, Daniel, Chief Information Officer, Anne Arundel Medical Center, Annapolis, MD, p. A302

MOFFETT, Mary B., CPA, Administrator, LaSalle General Hospital, Jena, LA, p. A282

MOFFITT, Grace B., Vice President Human Resources and Support Services, Annie Penn Hospital, Reidsville, NC, p. A490

MOFFITT, Scott, Information Systems Director, Northwest Iowa Health Center, Sheldon, IA, p. A241

MOFFLE, M.D., Lisa, Chief of Staff, Hamilton Hospital, Webster City, IA, p. A243

MOGHISSI, M.D., Etie, Chief Medical Staf, Centinela Freeman Regional Medical Center, Centinela Campus, Inglewood, CA, p. A65

MOGLER, Rick, Director Human Resources, Passavant Area Hospital, Jacksonville, IL, p. A198

MOHNEN, Rita, Assistant Administrator and Chief Financial Officer, Avera St. Benedict Health Center, Parkston, SD, p. A597

MOHR, Steve, Senior Vice President Finance and Chief Financial Officer, Loma Linda University Medical Center, Loma Linda, CA, p. A68

MOHRMAN, Mary Patricia, MSN, President, Barnes–Jewish West County Hospital, Saint Louis, MO, p. A390

MOISE, M.D., Vivian, Interim Chief Medical Director, St. Luke's Rehabilitation Institute, Spokane, WA, p. A709

MOLINARO, Frank L., Chief Operating Officer, Louis A. Weiss Memorial Hospital, Chicago, IL, p. A188

MOLINO, C Gene, Acting Chief Operating Officer, Veterans Affairs Medical Center, Wilkes–Barre, PA, p. A579

MOLITOR, Margie, R.N., Chief Executive Officer, Ogallala Community Hospital, Ogallala, NE, p. A410

MOLL, Eric, Financial Director, Mason General Hospital, Shelton, WA, p. A709

MOLL, Jeffrey S., President and Chief Executive Officer, PBI Regional Medical Center, Passaic, NJ, p. A434

MOLLEUR, Blake M., Executive Director, Western Massachusetts Hospital, Westfield, MA, p. A325

MOLLOHAN, Joan, Vice President Human Resources, Ochsner Clinic Foundation, New Orleans, LA, p. A289

MOLLOY, Reuben D., Chief Information Officer, Governor Juan F. Louis Hospital, Christiansted, VI, p. A749

MOLMEN, David, Chief Operating Officer, Altru Health System, Grand Forks, ND, p. A498

MOLNAR, Troy, Commander, U. S. Air Force Hospital Shaw, Shaw AFB, SC, p. A591

MOLONY, M.D., Ronald, Vice President, Medical Affairs, St. Elizabeth Hospital, Appleton, WI, p. A722

MOLOTSKY, David, Associate Director Human Resources, Temple University Children's Medical Center, Philadelphia, PA, p. A570

MOLT, M.D., Patrick, President Medical Staff, Fairfield Memorial Hospital, Fairfield, IL, p. A194

MOLTENI, M.D., Richard, Vice President and Medical Director, Children's Hospital and Regional Medical Center, Seattle, WA, p. A707

MOMEYER, Deborah, Director Human Resources, Brookville Hospital, Brookville, PA, p. A553

MONAHAN, Paul, General Manager, Labor Relations and Employment, MetroHealth Medical Center, Cleveland, OH, p. A509

MONARCH, Beth, Executive Vice President and Chief Operating Officer, Cardinal Hill Rehabilitation Hospital, Lexington, KY, p. A267

MONCMAN, D.O., Michael Gerard, President, Medical Staff, Altoona Hospital Campus, Altoona, PA, p. A551

MONCRIEF, Bill, Director of Information Systems, Garden City Hospital, Garden City, MI, p. A333

MONDEJAR, Oswald, Vice President Human Resources, Spaulding Rehabilitation Hospital, Boston, MA, p. A314

MONGAN, James J., M.D., President and Chief Executive Officer, Partners HealthCare System, Inc., Boston, MA, p. B83

MONGE, A John, Vice President Operations, Castle Medical Center, Kailua, HI, p. A174

MONGE, Peter W., President and Chief Executive Officer, Montgomery General Hospital, Olney, MD, p. A309

MONGOVEN, Pat, Director Information Systems, Winter Haven Hospital, Winter Haven, FL, p. A151

MONHK, Richard, Chief Information Officer, Health Alliance Hospitals, Leominster, MA, p. A319

MONICAL, Robert, Chief Executive Officer and Administrator, Baum Harmon Mercy Hospital, Primghar, IA, p. A240

MONJE, Mary Anne, Chief Financial Officer, Whittier Hospital Medical Center, Whittier, CA, p. A99

MONNAHAN, John E., Chief Executive Officer, Davis County Hospital, Bloomfield, IA, p. A229

MONROE, Janet, Chief Executive Officer, Greystone Park Psychiatric Hospital, Morris Plains, NJ, p. A431

MONROIG, Domingo
Administrator, Castaner General Hospital, Castaner, PR, p. A744
Administrator, Castaner General Hospital, Castaner, PR, p. A744
Administrator, Castaner General Hospital, Castaner, PR, p. A744

MONROIG, Samuel, Executive Director, San Juan City Hospital, San Juan, PR, p. A748

MONSERRATE, Humberto M., Executive Administrator, Hospital San Pablo Del Este, Fajardo, PR, p. A745

MONSMA, Brian, Chief Executive Officer, Hawarden Community Hospital, Hawarden, IA, p. A235

MONSON, Kerry, Vice President Finance and Chief Financial Officer, Mercy Medical Center, Williston, ND, p. A501

MONTAG, Kathy, Administrator Health Care, State Correctional Institution at Camp Hill, Camp Hill, PA, p. A554

MONTAGUE, William D., Director, Veterans Affairs Medical Center, Cleveland, OH, p. A509

MONTALVO, M.D., Jose, Medical Director, Hospital Del Maestro, San Juan, PR, p. A747

MONTEL, Janet, Chief Financial Officer, Colorado Plains Medical Center, Fort Morgan, CO, p. A105

MONTELLA, Alan J., Assistant Administrator Finance, Sullivan County Community Hospital, Sullivan, IN, p. A225

MONTES, Ernesto, Finance Director, Castaner General Hospital, Castaner, PR, p. A744

MONTES, Lisa K., Chief Executive Officer, Del Amo Hospital, Torrance, CA, p. A95

MONTESI, M.D., Michael W., Chief of Staff, South Sunflower County Hospital, Indianola, MS, p. A370

MONTGOMERY, M.D., Carole, Medical Director, Spectrum Health–Kent Community Campus, Grand Rapids, MI, p. A335

MONTGOMERY, M.D., Charles, Medical Director, Memorial Hospital, Logansport, IN, p. A221

MONTGOMERY Jr, J. C., President, Texas Scottish Rite Hospital for Children, Dallas, TX, p. A634

MONTGOMERY, James T., CHE, President and Chief Executive Officer, Tulane University Hospital and Clinic, New Orleans, LA, p. A290

MONTGOMERY, Jay, Chief of Staff, Laurens County Healthcare System, Clinton, SC, p. A585

MONTGOMERY, Lisa P., Administrator Finance, MUSC Medical Center of Medical University of South Carolina, Charleston, SC, p. A584

MONTGOMERY, M.D., Mark, Vice President Quality and Medical Affairs, St. Joseph Regional Health Center, Bryan, TX, p. A627

MONTGOMERY, Mark F., Director Human Resources, Montgomery Regional Hospital, Blacksburg, VA, p. A686

MONTGOMERY, Mary J., Chief Operating Officer, Bay Medical Center, Panama City, FL, p. A142

MONTGOMERY, Michael J., President and Chief Executive Officer, Cleo Wallace Centers Hospital, Westminster, CO, p. A110

MONTGOMERY II, Raymond W., President and Chief Executive Officer, White County Medical Center, Searcy, AR, p. A50

MONTGOMERY, Scott, Vice President Operations, Lee's Summit Hospital, Lees Summit, MO, p. A386

MONTGOMERY, William L., Senior Vice President and Chief Information Officer, Shands at AGH, Gainesville, FL, p. A130

MONTION, Robert M., Chief Executive Officer, Tulare Local Health Care District, Tulare, CA, p. A96

MONTOUR, Vina, Director, Information Technology, U. S. Public Health Service Phoenix Indian Medical Center, Phoenix, AZ, p. A35

MONTOYA, Leonard, Administrative Officer, PHS Santa Fe Indian Hospital, Santa Fe, NM, p. A444

MOODY, David, Vice President Human Resources, Salina Regional Health Center, Salina, KS, p. A256

MOODY, Michael, Interim Chief Executive Officer, Kindred Hospital–St. Louis, Saint Louis, MO, p. A391

MOOG, Rich, Chief Financial Officer, Liberty County Hospital and Nursing Home, Chester, MT, p. A397

MOON, Lori, Vice President of Clinical Operations, McDonough District Hospital, Macomb, IL, p. A200

MOON, Robert, Chief Financial Officer, Tennessee Christian Medical Center, Madison, TN, p. A611

MOONEY, Jimmy, Chief Executive Officer, Willingway Hospital, Statesboro, GA, p. A170

MOONEY, Melissa, Information Systems Director and Data Processor, Dallas County Medical Center, Fordyce, AR, p. A43

MOOR, Gary, Director Human Resources, St. John's Hospital – Lebanon, Lebanon, MO, p. A386

MOORE, Amanda, Director Human Resources, Spalding Regional Medical Center, Griffin, GA, p. A163

MOORE, Betty, Business Manager, North Mississippi Medical Center–Iuka, Iuka, MS, p. A370

MOORE, Bill, Chief Information Officer, Comanche Community Hospital, Comanche, TX, p. A629

MOORE, M.D., Bill, Chief of Staff, East Texas Medical Center Tyler, Tyler, TX, p. A671

MOORE, Brandon, CHE, Administrator and Chief Executive Officer, Park Place Surgery Center, Lafayette, LA, p. A284

MOORE, Chris, Controller, Saint Joseph Hospital East, Lexington, KY, p. A268

MOORE, M.D., Danny, Chief Medical Officer, Gilmore Memorial Hospital, Amory, MS, p. A366

MOORE, Darrell W., President and Chief Executive Officer, Baptist–Lutheran Medical Center, Kansas City, MO, p. A384

MOORE, Debra, Chief Executive Officer, Parkside Hospital, Tulsa, OK, p. A539

MOORE, Ed, Chief Operating Officer, MetroWest Medical Center, Framingham, MA, p. A318

MOORE, M.D., Ethel L., Chief Medical Officer, U. S. Public Health Service Indian Hospital, Harlem, MT, p. A399

MOORE, Gary
Chief Executive Officer, Shoshone Medical Center, Kellogg, ID, p. A179
Vice President Human Resources, BryanLGH Medical Center, Lincoln, NE, p. A408

MOORE Jr, George M., Director, Overton Brooks Veterans Affairs Medical Center, Shreveport, LA, p. A292

MOORE, M.D., Gerald, Medical Director, CARITAS Peace Center, Louisville, KY, p. A269

MOORE, Greg, Chief Executive Officer, Logan Memorial Hospital, Russellville, KY, p. A274

MOORE, James D., FACHE, Chief Executive Officer and Administrator, INTEGRIS Canadian Valley Regional Hospital, Yukon, OK, p. A541

MOORE, James M., Chief Executive Officer, OSF HealthCare System, Peoria, IL, p. B82

MOORE, Jason H., Chief Operating Officer, University Health Care System, Augusta, GA, p. A155

MOORE, John, Administrator, Hiawatha Community Hospital, Hiawatha, KS, p. A248

MOORE, R.N., MS, Karen O., Vice President, Franklin Medical Center, Greenfield, MA, p. A318

MOORE, Kathy D., Chief Operating Officer, North Suburban Medical Center, Thornton, CO, p. A110

MOORE, Larry E., Chief Financial Officer, Maury Regional Hospital, Columbia, TN, p. A604

MOORE, FACHE, Lois Jean, Administrator, Harris County Psychiatric Center, Houston, TX, p. A645

MOORE, Lori, Director Information Services, Meadowview Regional Medical Center, Maysville, KY, p. A271

MOORE, Marcia, Vice President, Tomball Regional Hospital, Tomball, TX, p. A670

MOORE, Mark E., President and Chief Executive Officer, Bloomington Hospital, Bloomington, IN, p. A212

MOORE, Matthew, Interim Chief Financial Officer, Broward General Medical Center, Fort Lauderdale, FL, p. A128

MOORE, Mike, Chief Financial Officer, Jane Phillips Medical Center, Bartlesville, OK, p. A528

MOORE, Mikelle D., CHE, Chief Executive Officer, LDS Hospital, Salt Lake City, UT, p. A679

MOORE, Nelda, Data Processing Director, Memorial Hospital and Manor, Bainbridge, GA, p. A156

MOORE, Paul David, Administrator, Atoka Memorial Hospital, Atoka, OK, p. A527

MOORE, Rick, Vice President and Chief Information Officer, Good Samaritan Hospital, Cincinnati, OH, p. A507

MOORE, Robbin M., Chief Operating Officer, J. F. K. Medical Center, Atlantis, FL, p. A123

MOORE, Robert J., FACHE, Chief Executive Officer, Red Bud Regional Hospital, Red Bud, IL, p. A206

MOORE, Robin A., Vice President Human Resources, Mary Imogene Bassett Hospital, Cooperstown, NY, p. A450

MOORE, M.D., Rodney, Vice President Medical Affairs, Cape Canaveral Hospital/Health First, Cocoa Beach, FL, p. A126

MOORE, Roland E., Director, Veterans Affairs Medical Center, Wilkes–Barre, PA, p. A579

MOORE, Ronda
Chief Operating Officer and Chief Financial Officer, Putnam General Hospital, Hurricane, WV, p. A716
Chief Financial Officer, Putnam General Hospital, Hurricane, WV, p. A716

MOORE, Sherman, Director Information Systems, Margaret R. Pardee Memorial Hospital, Hendersonville, NC, p. A484

MOORE, M.D., Stephen L., Vice President, Medical Management & Medical Director, Carolinas Medical Center, Charlotte, NC, p. A479

MOORE, Sylvia, Executive Vice President and Chief Operating Officer, St. Joseph Medical Center, Towson, MD, p. A311

MOORE, Terence F., President, MidMichigan Health, Midland, MI, p. B75

MOORE, Thomas F., Administrator, Charleston Memorial Hospital, Charleston, SC, p. A584

MOORE, Timothy H., Administrator, North Mississippi Medical Center–West Point, West Point, MS, p. A376

MOORE, Tom, Chief Operating Officer, Gadsden Regional Medical Center, Gadsden, AL, p. A19

MOORE, W. Evan, CHE, District Chief Executive Officer, Comanche Community Hospital, Comanche, TX, p. A629

MOORE, Wayne
Administrator, Christus St. Mary Hospital, Port Arthur, TX, p. A661
Assistant Administrator, Christus St. Mary Hospital, Port Arthur, TX, p. A661

MOORE, William R., Vice President Human Resources, Mercy Hospital, Bakersfield, CA, p. A54

MOORE, William T., Chief Executive Officer, Atlanta Medical Center, Atlanta, GA, p. A153

MOORE–HARDY, Cynthia Ann, President and Chief Executive Officer, Lake Hospital System, Painesville, OH, p. A520

MOORMAN, Douglas A., Medical Center Director, Veterans Affairs Medical Center, Chillicothe, OH, p. A506

MOORMAN, Julie, Chief Financial Officer, Saint Luke's Northland Hospital–Smithville Campus, Smithville, MO, p. A393

MOORMAN, Kristi, Supervisor Human Resources, Share Medical Center, Alva, OK, p. A527

MOORMANN, Jim, Chief Information Officer, Iowa Methodist Medical Center, Des Moines, IA, p. A232

MOOSA, M.D., M, Chief of Staff, LaSalle General Hospital, Jena, LA, p. A282

MOOTRY, John M.
Chief Executive Officer, Barrett Hospital & HealthCare, Dillon, MT, p. A398
Interim Chief Executive Officer, Ruby Valley Hospital, Sheridan, MT, p. A402

MORAHAN, John R., President and Chief Executive Officer, St. Joseph Medical Center, Reading, PA, p. A574

MORALES, Carlos, Data Processing Manager, Valley Baptist Medical Center–Brownsville, Brownsville, TX, p. A627

MORALES, Daniza, Manager Information System, Mennonite General Hospital, Aibonito, PR, p. A743

MORALES, Elsie, Chief Financial Officer, Hospital Universitario Dr. Ramon Ruiz Arnau, Bayamon, PR, p. A744

MORALES, Hector R., Administrator, NCED Mental Health Center, El Paso, TX, p. A637

MORALES, Herson E., Executive Director, Hospital Santa Rosa, Guayama, PR, p. A745

MORALES, Steve, Chief Human Resources Officer, Sutter Lakeside Hospital, Lakeport, CA, p. A67

MORAN, Janet
Vice President Human Resources, Lourdes Medical Center of Burlington County, Willingboro, NJ, p. A438
Vice President Human Resources, Our Lady of Lourdes Medical Center, Camden, NJ, p. A426

MORAN, John, Chief Executive Officer, Sac–Osage Hospital, Osceola, MO, p. A388

MORAN, Julie, Director Information Services, St. Mary Mercy Hospital, Livonia, MI, p. A339

MORAN, M.D., Julie A., President Medical Staff, Deer Park Hospital, Deer Park, WA, p. A702

MORAN, Marian, Vice President and Chief Information Officer, Pocono Medical Center, East Stroudsburg, PA, p. A557

MORAN, Mark, Director Information Systems, Alameda Hospital, Alameda, CA, p. A52

MORAN, Timothy M., President, Methodist Hospital of Sacramento, Sacramento, CA, p. A85

MORANDEIRA, Ana, Marketing Director, San Juan Capestrano Hospital, San Juan, PR, p. A748

MORASKO, Jerome, President and Chief Executive Officer, Bell Hospital, Ishpeming, MI, p. A337

MORASKO, Robert A., Chief Executive Officer, William Bee Ririe Hospital, Ely, NV, p. A415

MORATH, Julie, Chief Operating Officer, Children's Hospital and Clinics, Saint Paul, MN, p. A362

MOREAU, Gregg
Chief Operating Officer and Chief Financial Officer, Northwest Florida Community Hospital, Chipley, FL, p. A125
Chief Operating Officer and Chief Financial Officer, Northwest Florida Community Hospital, Chipley, FL, p. A125

MOREAU, Steven C., President and Chief Executive Officer, San Antonio Community Hospital, Upland, CA, p. A97

MOREHEAD, M.D., David, President Medical Staff, Baylor Medical Center at Waxahachie, Waxahachie, TX, p. A672

MORELAND, Michael E., Director, Veterans Affairs Pittsburgh Healthcare System, Pittsburgh, PA, p. A573

MORELLI, Gerald, Director Human Resources, Veterans Affairs Medical Center, Philadelphia, PA, p. A570

MORENO, Earlene, Human Resources Liaison, Naval Hospital, Corpus Christi, TX, p. A631

MORENO, M.D., Raymond, Vice President Medical Affairs, Tift Regional Medical Center, Tifton, GA, p. A171

MORESI, Randolph, Chief Executive Officer, North Hills Hospital, North Richland Hills, TX, p. A658

MORETTE, Joseph M., Executive Vice President, Methodist Rehabilitation Center, Jackson, MS, p. A370

MOREY, Frederick, Chief Financial Officer, Claxton–Hepburn Medical Center, Ogdensburg, NY, p. A468

MORGAN, Charles, Director Information Technology, Marietta Memorial Hospital, Marietta, OH, p. A517

MORGAN, Charles R., Chief Executive Officer, Wayne Memorial Hospital, Jesup, GA, p. A164

MORGAN, Daniel R., Chief Financial Officer, Bay Medical Center, Panama City, FL, p. A142

MORGAN, Dirk, Chief Financial Officer, Jackson Purchase Medical Center, Mayfield, KY, p. A271

MORGAN, Gretchen, Human Resources Director, Harbor Beach Community Hospital, Harbor Beach, MI, p. A336

MORGAN, James E., Administrator, Huey P. Long Medical Center, Pineville, LA, p. A291

MORGAN, James H., Chief Executive Officer, Rehabilitation Hospital of Acadiana, Lafayette, LA, p. A284

MORGAN, Jeff
Associate Executive Director and Chief Financial Officer, Carlisle Regional Medical Center, Carlisle, PA, p. A554
Information Systems Director, Northeastern Nevada Regional Hospital, Elko, NV, p. A415

MORGAN, Jeffrey, Chief Financial Officer, Southside Hospital, Bay Shore, NY, p. A447

MORGAN, John, President, Gottlieb Memorial Hospital, Melrose Park, IL, p. A201

MORGAN, Kelly C., President and Chief Executive Officer, Sierra View District Hospital, Porterville, CA, p. A82

MORGAN, Larry, Controller, T. J. Samson Community Hospital, Glasgow, KY, p. A265

MORGAN, M.D., Mallan G., Chief of Staff, Natchez Regional Medical Center, Natchez, MS, p. A373

MORGAN, Margaret, Director Human Resources, Centinela Freeman Regional Medical Center, Centinela Campus, Inglewood, CA, p. A65

MORGAN, Nyle, Director Information Systems, Sycamore Hospital, Miamisburg, OH, p. A518

MORGAN, Richard, Chief Information Officer, Oswego Hospital, Oswego, NY, p. A468

MORGAN, R.N., Shirley H., Vice President and Chief Nursing Officer, Prince George's Hospital Center, Cheverly, MD, p. A306

MORGAN, Teresa, Assistant Vice President Human Resources, Shannon Medical Center, San Angelo, TX, p. A663

MORGAN, Timothy O., Executive Director, Pennsylvania Hospital, Philadelphia, PA, p. A569

MORGAN, Vicky, Director Information Services, Centinela Freeman Regional Medical Center, Centinela Campus, Inglewood, CA, p. A65

MORGANTE, Sally, Controller, Geisinger HEALTHSOUTH Rehabilitation Hospital, Danville, PA, p. A556

MORGESE, M.D., Vincent, Vice President Medical Affairs, Queen of the Valley Hospital, Napa, CA, p. A77

MORIN, Cindy, Chief Financial Officer, Houlton Regional Hospital, Houlton, ME, p. A299

MORIN, Paul A., Superintendent, Soldiers' Home in Holyoke, Holyoke, MA, p. A319

MORIN, M.D., Richard A., Vice President Medical Affairs, BryanLGH Medical Center, Lincoln, NE, p. A408

MORINAGA, Russell, Accountant, Kau Hospital, Pahala, HI, p. A176

MORISSETTE, Robert, Management Information Systems Coordinator, Soldiers' Home in Holyoke, Holyoke, MA, p. A319

MORLEY, Jr, M.D., Andrew P., Senior Vice President and Chief Medical Officer, The Medical Center, Columbus, GA, p. A159

MORLEY, Denise, Director of Human Resources, Nicholas H. Noyes Memorial Hospital, Dansville, NY, p. A451

MORLEY, Tad A., Chief Operating Officer, MountainView Hospital, Las Vegas, NV, p. A416

MORLOCK, Paul, Vice President Human Resources, Smyth County Community Hospital, Marion, VA, p. A691

MORNEAU, Stephen, Director Operations, Soldiers' Home in Holyoke, Holyoke, MA, p. A319

MORREALE, Daniel
Chief Information Officer, Jacobi Medical Center, New York, NY, p. A460
Chief Information Officer, North Central Bronx Hospital, New York, NY, p. A464

MORREL, Robert D., Director, Veterans Affairs Medical Center, Marion, IL, p. A200

MORRELL, Dan, Information System Manager, Sierra Vista Hospital, Truth or Consequences, NM, p. A445

MORRELL, M.D., Douglas, Chief Medical Officer and Chief of Staff, Rush Memorial Hospital, Rushville, IN, p. A224

MORRELL, Nikki C., Superintendent, Madison State Hospital, Madison, IN, p. A221

MORRIS, Angela, Fiscal Officer, Aleda E. Lutz Veterans Affairs Medical Center, Saginaw, MI, p. A344

MORRIS, Beverly, Vice President Human Resources, Sycamore Hospital, Miamisburg, OH, p. A518

MORRIS, David W., Chief Executive Officer, Deaconess Cross Pointe Center, Evansville, IN, p. A214

MORRIS, Debbie, Director Human Resources, Marcus Daly Memorial Hospital, Hamilton, MT, p. A399

MORRIS, Dennis, Vice President and Chief Financial Officer, St. Mary's Medical Center, San Francisco, CA, p. A89

MORRIS, Don, Vice President Human Resources, Wesley Medical Center, Wichita, KS, p. A260

MORRIS, Douglas, Chief Financial Officer, St. Francis Health Care Centre, Green Springs, OH, p. A514

MORRIS, Elaine F., Administrator, Methodist Ambulatory Surgery Hospital, San Antonio, TX, p. A664

MORRIS, George, Vice President Information Technology and Chief Information Officer, Northwest Community Healthcare, Arlington Heights, IL, p. A183

MORRIS, Greg, Chief Information Officer, Northcrest Medical Center, Springfield, TN, p. A618

MORRIS, Janet, Coordinator Human Resources, HEALTHSOUTH Rehabilitation Hospital of Central Kentucky, Elizabethtown, KY, p. A264

MORRIS, Janice, Accountant, CrossRidge Community Hospital, Wynne, AR, p. A51

MORRIS, Jimmy, Chief Operations Officer, Lynn County Hospital District, Tahoka, TX, p. A668

MORRIS, Joseph E., Chief Executive Officer, Kootenai Medical Center, Coeur D'Alene, ID, p. A178

MORRIS, Lois, Chief Financial Officer, Spencer Hospital, Spencer, IA, p. A242

MORRIS, Marjorie, Director Information Management, HEALTHSOUTH Rehabilitation Hospital of Virginia, Richmond, VA, p. A695

MORRIS, Marsha, Manager Information Services, Fairview Park Hospital, Dublin, GA, p. A161

MORRIS, Michael, Administrator, Bellville General Hospital, Bellville, TX, p. A625

MORRIS, Paul, Chief Financial Officer, Carolinas Hospital System, Florence, SC, p. A587

MORRIS, R. Randall, Administrator, West Carroll Memorial Hospital, Oak Grove, LA, p. A290

MORRIS, Randy B., Chief Financial Officer, Sunbury Community Hospital, Sunbury, PA, p. A576

MORRIS, Wayne, Chief Financial Officer, Veterans Affairs Medical Center, Marion, IL, p. A200

MORRISON, Christopher, Director Information Technology, Trenton Psychiatric Hospital, Trenton, NJ, p. A438

MORRISON, Deane, Chief Information Officer, Concord Hospital, Concord, NH, p. A420

MORRISON, Maureen, Vice President Financial Services, Advocate Trinity Hospital, Chicago, IL, p. A186

MORRISON, Michael
Chief Financial Officer, Hendersonville Medical Center, Hendersonville, TN, p. A607
Chief Financial Officer, Hillside Hospital, Pulaski, TN, p. A617

MORRISON, Robert E., President, Randolph Hospital, Asheboro, NC, p. A477

MORRISON, Scott, Director of Information Systems, Brandon Regional Hospital, Brandon, FL, p. A124

MORRISS, III, Edwin, Medical Director, HEALTHSOUTH Rehabilitation Hospital, Dothan, AL, p. A17

MORRISSEY, Joseph V., President, Milton Hospital, Milton, MA, p. A320

MORRISSEY, Mark, Chief Financial Officer, Veterans Affairs Medical Center, Spokane, WA, p. A709

MORRISSEY, Tom, Chief Financial Officer, Sierra Nevada Memorial Hospital, Grass Valley, CA, p. A63

MORROW, Gregory, President Medical Staff, Bay Medical Center, Panama City, FL, p. A142

MORROW, Jeff, Chief Operating Officer, Lady of the Sea General Hospital, Cut Off, LA, p. A280

MORROW, Julia, Administrator, Morrill County Community Hospital, Bridgeport, NE, p. A405

MORROW, Pat, Director Human Resources, Walker Baptist Medical Center, Jasper, AL, p. A20

MORROW, Randy
Vice President and Chief Operating Officer, Boone Hospital Center, Columbia, MO, p. A380
Vice President and Chief Operating Officer, Boone Hospital Center, Columbia, MO, p. A380

MORROW, Shawn, Chief Executive Officer, Logan Medical Center, Guthrie, OK, p. A531

MORSE, Amy, Administrator, New England Rehabilitation Hospital of Portland, Portland, ME, p. A300

MORSE, Brad S., Chief Executive Officer, Medical Centre Surgical Hospital, Fort Worth, TX, p. A640

MORSE, Larry, Chief Executive Officer and Administrator, Johnson Regional Medical Center, Clarksville, AR, p. A41

MORSTAD, Joan, Director Information Systems, Coliseum Medical Centers, Macon, GA, p. A165

MORTENSEN, Margaret
Interim Executive Vice President and Chief Operating Officer, St. Vincent's Medical Center, Jacksonville, FL, p. A133
Interim Executive Vice President and Chief Executive Officer, St. Vincent's Medical Center, Jacksonville, FL, p. A133

MORTH, Paul, Vice President Finance, MedCenter One, Bismarck, ND, p. A496

MORTON, Denise, Chief Financial Officer, Veterans Affairs Medical Center, Alexandria, LA, p. A276

MORTON, Edward A., Chief Executive Officer, Naples Community Hospital, Naples, FL, p. A139

MORTON, Stan C., Chief Executive Officer, Presbyterian Hospital of Denton, Denton, TX, p. A635

MORTON, Stephanie, Chief Information Officer, Providence Alaska Medical Center, Anchorage, AK, p. A26

MOSELEY, Michael, Director, Caswell Center, Kinston, NC, p. A486

MOSER, Brenda, Chief Financial Officer, Regional Health Services of Howard County, Cresco, IA, p. A231

MOSER, M.D., Joseph, Vice President Medical Staff Affairs, Anne Arundel Medical Center, Annapolis, MD, p. A302

MOSER, M.D., Neal, Medical Director, HEALTHSOUTH Northern Kentucky Rehabilitation Hospital, Edgewood, KY, p. A263

MOSER, M.D., Robert, Chief Medical Staff, Greeley County Health Services, Tribune, KS, p. A258

MOSER, Stan P., Chief Financial Officer, Deaconess Billings Clinic, Billings, MT, p. A396

MOSER, Thomas A., President and Chief Executive Officer, Community Medical Center, Missoula, MT, p. A400

MOSESIAN, Robert, Assistant Controller, HEALTHSOUTH Bakersfield Rehabilitation Hospital, Bakersfield, CA, p. A54

MOSHIRPUR, Jasmin, Dean and Medical Director, Elmhurst Hospital Center, New York, NY, p. A459

MOSKALEWICZ, M.D., Thomas, Chief of Staff, Sebasticook Valley Hospital, Pittsfield, ME, p. A300

MOSLEY, Christophr R., President and Chief Executive Officer, Chesapeake General Hospital, Chesapeake, VA, p. A686

MOSS, Austin, Vice President Human Resources, Jennie Stuart Medical Center, Hopkinsville, KY, p. A266

MOSS, Dwayne, Chief Executive Officer, T. J. Samson Community Hospital, Glasgow, KY, p. A265

MOSS, Ira L., Vice President and Administrator, Willis–Knighton Medical Center, Shreveport, LA, p. A293

MOSS, James T., President, West Tennessee Healthcare, Jackson, TN, p. B122

MOSS, John, Assistant Administrator Human Resources, Illinois Valley Community Hospital, Peru, IL, p. A205

MOSS, Paul E., President, Milford Hospital, Milford, CT, p. A114

MOSS, Stephen, Chief Financial Officer, Central Vermont Medical Center, Barre, VT, p. A682

MOSS, Stuart
Vice President Finance and Chief Financial Officer, Chestnut Hill Health System, Philadelphia, PA, p. A567
Executive Vice President and Chief Financial Officer, Chestnut Hill Rehabilitation Hospital, Glenside, PA, p. A559

MOSS, William Mason, President, Potomac Hospital, Woodbridge, VA, p. A698

MOSSER, Kevin H., M.D., Chief Executive Officer, Gettysburg Hospital, Gettysburg, PA, p. A559

MOTEJZIK, Tom, Director of Information Services, Lea Regional Medical Center, Hobbs, NM, p. A443

MOTT, Joe, Chief Operating Officer, Primary Children's Medical Center, Salt Lake City, UT, p. A679

MOTT, Susan, Vice President Finance, St. John's Hospital – Lebanon, Lebanon, MO, p. A386

MOTTA, Julio, Chief Information Officer, San Juan City Hospital, San Juan, PR, p. A748

MOTTE, Michael, Chief Financial Officer, Capital Medical Center, Olympia, WA, p. A705

MOTZER, Earl James, FACHE, Chief Executive Officer, The James B. Haggin Memorial Hospital, Harrodsburg, KY, p. A265

MOUGHON, Edward, Superintendent, Big Spring State Hospital, Big Spring, TX, p. A626

MOULTHROP, David L., Ph.D., President and Chief Executive Officer, Rogers Memorial Hospital, Oconomowoc, WI, p. A733

MOUNT, Mary H., Administrative Officer, U. S. Public Health Service Indian Hospital, Harlem, MT, p. A399

MOUNTCASTLE, William A., CHE, Director, Ralph H. Johnson Veterans Affairs Medical Center, Charleston, SC, p. A585

MOUSA, Barry L., Chief Executive Officer, Medical Center at Lancaster, Lancaster, TX, p. A652

MOUSER, Emily, Vice President Human Resources and Organizational Development, McAlester Regional Health Center, McAlester, OK, p. A533

MOUSTAKAKIS, John, Chief Information Officer, Saint Barnabas Medical Center, Livingston, NJ, p. A430

MOUTON, Lori, Director Public Relations and Marketing, Children's Hospital of Michigan, Detroit, MI, p. A331

MOYLAN, James J., Vice President Finance, Griffin Hospital, Derby, CT, p. A112

MOZINGO, M.D., George W., Chief Medical Staff, Southeastern Regional Medical Center, Lumberton, NC, p. A487

MROCZKOWSKI, Thomas C., President and Chief Executive Officer, Northern Michigan Regional Health System, Petoskey, MI, p. A342

MUCCILLI, Pamela, Vice President and Chief Information Officer, Emerson Hospital, Concord, MA, p. A317

MUCEK, Brad, Vice President and Chief Financial Officer, MacNeal Hospital, Berwyn, IL, p. A184

MUDANO, Mario A., Administrator, HEALTHSOUTH Rehabilitation Hospital of Spring Hill, Brooksville, FL, p. A125

MUDD, Karen, Director Marketing and Public Affairs, Sutter Tracy Community Hospital, Tracy, CA, p. A96

MUDGETT, MaLisa
Chief Financial Officer, Lake Chelan Community Hospital, Chelan, WA, p. A701
Chief Financial Officer, Lake Chelan Community Hospital, Chelan, WA, p. A701

MUDLER, Gordon A.
President and Chief Executive Officer, Hackley Health, Muskegon, MI, p. A341
President and Chief Executive Officer, Hackley Health System, Muskegon, MI, p. B48

MUELLER, Arthur, Management Information Systems Director, Cuero Community Hospital, Cuero, TX, p. A631

MUETZEL, Hal, Chief Operating Oficer, Brandon Regional Hospital, Brandon, FL, p. A124

MUHLENTHALER, Donald, FACHE, Administrator and Chief Executive Officer, Pocahontas Memorial Hospital, Buckeye, WV, p. A713

MULANAX, Leigh, Chief Information Management Services, Veterans Affairs Medical Center, Oklahoma City, OK, p. A536

MULANAX, Marjorie, Executive Director, Christopher House, Austin, TX, p. A623

MULCAHY, Cindi, Business Office Manager, Community Memorial Hospital, Syracuse, NE, p. A413

MULDER, Dale R., Chief Executive Officer, Palo Verde Hospital, Blythe, CA, p. A55

MULDER, M.D., Steven, Director Medical Affairs, Hutchinson Area Health Care, Hutchinson, MN, p. A355

MULDER, M.D., Timothy S., Chief of Staff, Sioux Valley Luverne Medical Center, Luverne, MN, p. A356

MULDOON, Patrick L., President and Chief Executive Officer, Health Alliance Hospitals, Leominster, MA, p. A319

MULFORD, Pete, Director Information Systems, Gerber Memorial Health Services, Fremont, MI, p. A333

MULLAHEY, Mike, Operations Manager, Veterans Affairs Medical Center, Albany, NY, p. A446

MULLANEY, Garrell S., Chief Executive Officer, Connecticut Valley Hospital, Middletown, CT, p. A114

MULLEN, R'Nee, Chief Information Officer, Magic Valley Regional Medical Center, Twin Falls, ID, p. A182

MULLEN, Robert L., Chief Executive Officer, Rice County Hospital District Number One, Lyons, KS, p. A252

MULLEN, Thomas R., President and Chief Executive Officer, Mercy Medical Center, Baltimore, MD, p. A304

MULLER, A. Gary, FACHE, President and Chief Executive Officer, West Jefferson Medical Center, Marrero, LA, p. A286

MULLER, Dwight, Vice President Information Systems and Chief Information Officer, Southern New Hampshire Medical Center, Nashua, NH, p. A422

MULLER, Ralph W.
President and Chief Executive Officer, Hospital of the University of Pennsylvania, Philadelphia, PA, p. A568
President and Chief Executive Officer, University of Pennsylvania Health System, Philadelphia, PA, p. B117

MULLER, M.D., Steven, Senior Vice President Medical Affairs, Southern Regional Medical Center, Riverdale, GA, p. A167

MULLER, M.D., William
Vice President Medical Affairs, Milford Regional Medical Center, Milford, MA, p. A320
President Medical Staff, North Country Regional Hospital, Bemidji, MN, p. A350

MULLICAN, M.D., Charles, Chief Medical Officer, Heartland Regional Medical Center, Saint Joseph, MO, p. A390

MULLIGAN, Janet L., MS, Administrator, Shriners Hospitals for Children, Shriners Burns Hospital–Boston, Boston, MA, p. A314

MULLINGS, Paul, FACHE, Chief Executive Officer, Banner Good Samaritan Medical Center, Phoenix, AZ, p. A33

MULLINS, Kem, Chief Operating Officer, Atlanta Medical Center, Atlanta, GA, p. A153

MULLINS, Larry, Controller, W. J. Mangold Memorial Hospital, Lockney, TX, p. A653

MULLINS, Larry A., FACHE, President and Chief Executive Officer, Samaritan Health Services, Corvallis, OR, p. B95

MULLINS, Michael L., Chief Executive Officer, Kosciusko Community Hospital, Warsaw, IN, p. A227

MULLINS, Patricia, Senior Vice President Hospital Operations, Culpeper Regional Hospital, Culpeper, VA, p. A687

MULLINS, Tommy H., Administrator, Boone Memorial Hospital, Madison, WV, p. A717

MULLNER, Darla, Director Human Resources, Rush–Copley Medical Center, Aurora, IL, p. A184

MULVANEY, M.D., Thomas, Vice President Medical Affairs, Winchester Hospital, Winchester, MA, p. A325

MULVEHILL, Mitch, Senior Vice President and Chief Financial Officer, Wilson N. Jones Medical Center, Sherman, TX, p. A667

MULVEY, Lee, Director, Human Resources, Harris Methodist Southwest, Fort Worth, TX, p. A639

MULVIHILL, Deborah, Chief Executive Officer, Coral Springs Medical Center, Coral Springs, FL, p. A126

MULVIHILL, James J., Chief Executive Officer, Wills Eye Hospital, Philadelphia, PA, p. A570

MULVIHILL, Jody, Assistant Controller, The Children's Institute of Pittsburgh, Pittsburgh, PA, p. A572

MUMBY, Dawn, Chief Financial Officer, Marengo Memorial Hospital, Marengo, IA, p. A237

MUMFORD, Bill, Corporate Director Information Systems, University of Kansas Hospital, Kansas City, KS, p. A250

MUNCH, M.D., David, Vice President and Chief Clinical and Quality Officer, Exempla Lutheran Medical Center, Wheat Ridge, CO, p. A110

MUNDAY, Kathy, Chief Business Service, Veterans Affairs Sierra Nevada Health Care System, Reno, NV, p. A418

MUNDY, Mark J., President and Chief Executive Officer, New York Methodist Hospital, New York, NY, p. A463

MUNDY, Stephens M., President and Chief Executive Officer, Champlain Valley Physicians Hospital Medical Center, Plattsburgh, NY, p. A469

MUNEIO, Paul
Vice President Support Services, Lenawee Health Alliance – Bixby Campus, Adrian, MI, p. A327
Administrative Director, Information Resources, Lenawee Health Alliance–Herrick Campus, Tecumseh, MI, p. A346

MUNETA, Anita
Chief Executive Officer, U. S. Public Health Service Indian Hospital, Crownpoint, NM, p. A442
Chief Executive Officer, U. S. Public Health Service Indian Hospital, Crownpoint, NM, p. A442

MUNGER, Peter L., Chief Financial Officer, MedStar–Georgetown Medical Center, Washington, DC, p. A121

MUNGER, Richard, Administrator, Mount Grant General Hospital, Hawthorne, NV, p. A415

MUNIZ, Carlos, Director Finance, Dr. Ramon E. Betances Hospital–Mayaguez Medical Center Branch, Mayaguez, PR, p. A745

MUNOZ, Thalia H., Administrator, Starr County Memorial Hospital, Rio Grande City, TX, p. A662

MUNROE, Anthony E., President and Chief Executive Officer, St. John Detroit Riverview Hospital – Northeast Campus, Detroit, MI, p. A332

MUNSON, Bill, Chief Financial Officer, North Colorado Medical Center, Greeley, CO, p. A106

MUNSON, Mark, Director Business Operations, Naval Medical Center, Portsmouth, VA, p. A694

MUNTEL, Edward G., Ph.D., President and Chief Executive Officer, NorthKey Community Care, Covington, KY, p. A263

MUNTZ, David
Senior Vice President and Chief Information Officer, Harris Methodist Fort Worth, Fort Worth, TX, p. A639
Senior Vice President and Chief Information Officer, Presbyterian Hospital of Dallas, Dallas, TX, p. A633

MUNTZ, Tim, President and Chief Executive Officer, St. Margaret's Hospital, Spring Valley, IL, p. A208

MURCHISON, Sandra, Director Medical Records, Coosa Valley Medical Center, Sylacauga, AL, p. A24

MURDOCK, Bill, Vice President Fiscal Services, Hammond–Henry Hospital, Geneseo, IL, p. A195

MURDOCK, Judy, Director of Information Systems, Placentia Linda Hospital, Placentia, CA, p. A81

MURGUIA, James
Chief Operating Officer and Chief Financial Officer, Mercy Regional Health Center, New York, KS, p. A252
Chief Operating Officer and Chief Financial Officer, Mercy Regional Health Center, New York, KS, p. A252

MURILLO, Debbie, Vice President Human Resources, St. Joseph's Medical Center, Stockton, CA, p. A95

MURILLO, George, Director Information Services, USC University Hospital, Los Angeles, CA, p. A73

MURIN, William J., Senior Vice President Operations, Huntington Memorial Hospital, Pasadena, CA, p. A81

MURPHY, Caroline
Chief Operating Officer, St. David's Pavilion, Austin, TX, p. A624
Chief Operating Officer, St. David's Rehabilitation Center, Austin, TX, p. A624

MURPHY, M.D., Dale, Vice President Medical Affairs, Summa Health System, Akron, OH, p. A502

MURPHY, Edward G., M.D.,
President and Chief Executvie Officer, Carilion Health System, Roanoke, VA, p. B21
Chief Executive Officer, Carilion Medical Center, Roanoke, VA, p. A696

MURPHY, James, Chief Operating Officer, RHD Memorial Medical Center, Dallas, TX, p. A634

MURPHY, Joyce A., President, Caritas Carney Hospital, Dorchester, MA, p. A317

MURPHY, Kathleen M., Chief Operating Officer, Spaulding Rehabilitation Hospital, Boston, MA, p. A314

MURPHY, Kevin G.
Senior Vice President Finance and Chief Financial Officer, Manchester Memorial Hospital, Manchester, CT, p. A113
Senior Vice President Finance and Chief Financial Officer, Rockville General Hospital, Vernon Rockville, CT, p. A117

MURPHY, Linda, Chief Financial Officer, Osborne County Memorial Hospital, Osborne, KS, p. A254

MURPHY, Lionel, Chief Executive Officer, Southeast Regional Medical Center, Kentwood, LA, p. A283

MURPHY, Margaret M., Chief Executive Officer, Kindred Hospital–Philadelphia, Philadelphia, PA, p. A568

MURPHY, Maureen, Director Information Systems, Rose Medical Center, Denver, CO, p. A104

MURPHY, Michael, President and Chief Executive Officer, Sharp Healthcare, San Diego, CA, p. B97

MURPHY, Michael D., Chief Executive Officer, Abilene Regional Medical Center, Abilene, TX, p. A620

MURPHY, Michelle
Chief Executive Officer, Community Memorial Hospital, Burke, SD, p. A594
Chief Executive Officer, Community Memorial Hospital, Burke, SD, p. A594

MURPHY, Peter J., President and Chief Executive Officer, St. James Hospitals and Health Centers, Olympia Fields, IL, p. A204

MURPHY, Richard J., President and Chief Executive Officer, Good Samaritan Hospital Medical Center, West Islip, NY, p. A476

MURPHY, Rita, Human Resources Manager, Cobre Valley Community Hospital, Globe, AZ, p. A31

MURPHY, Robert, JD, Administrator, Baptist Hospital, Pensacola, FL, p. A142

MURPHY, Susan G., Director, Santa Clara Valley Medical Center, San Jose, CA, p. A90

MURPHY, Terry, Executive Vice President and Chief Operating Officer, Bayhealth Medical Center, Dover, DE, p. A119

MURPHY, Terry Ann, Chief Nursing Officer, Twin Cities Community Hospital, Templeton, CA, p. A95

MURPHY, M.D., Timothy, Chief of Staff, Novato Community Hospital, Novato, CA, p. A78

MURRAY, Brian, Chief Financial Officer, Gunnison Valley Hospital, Gunnison, UT, p. A676

MURRAY, Geno, President and Chief Executive Officer, Charles A. Dean Memorial Hospital and Nursing Home, Greenville, ME, p. A299

MURRAY, James Patrick, Chief Executive Officer, Sid Peterson Memorial Hospital, Kerrville, TX, p. A651

MURRAY, Jean A., Administrator and Senior Vice President of Operations, LibertyHealth–Greenville Hospital, Jersey City, NJ, p. A430

MURRAY, Joan Z., R.N., Administrator and Chief Executive Officer, St. James Parish Hospital, Lutcher, LA, p. A285

MURRAY, M.D., Kent, Chief of Staff, Robert J. Dole Veterans Affairs Medical Center, Wichita, KS, p. A259

MURRAY, Malcolm, Vice President Information Services, Saint Vincents Catholic Medical Centers of New York, New York, NY, p. A465

MURRAY, Mike
Regional Chief Financial Officer, HEALTHSOUTH Rehabilitation Hospital, Fort Worth, TX, p. A639
Controller, HEALTHSOUTH Rehabilitation Hospital of Arlington, Arlington, TX, p. A622
Controller, HEALTHSOUTH Rehabilitation Hospital–Cityview, Fort Worth, TX, p. A640

MURRAY III, Robert B., CHE, President and Chief Executive Officer, Clearfield Hospital, Clearfield, PA, p. A555

MURRAY, Sandi, Director Human Resources, Cheyenne County Hospital, Saint Francis, KS, p. A256

MURRAY, Sherri, Chief Financial Officer, Montgomery General Hospital, Montgomery, WV, p. A717

MURRAY, Susan R., Administrator, Kaiser Permanente Medical Center, Honolulu, HI, p. A173

MURRAY, T. Michael
President, St. John's Pleasant Valley Hospital, Camarillo, CA, p. A55
President, St. John's Regional Medical Center, Oxnard, CA, p. A80

MURRAY, M.D., Thomas, President Medical Staff, Mayo Regional Hospital, Dover–Foxcroft, ME, p. A298

MURRAY, Thomas F., Vice President Human Resources, Middlesex Hospital, Middletown, CT, p. A114

MURRAY, Thomas J., FACHE, President and Chief Executive Officer, Mount Nittany Medical Center, State College, PA, p. A576

MURRAY, M.D., W Darrell, Chief Medical Staff, Baptist Memorial Hospital–Lauderdale, Ripley, TN, p. A617

MURRAY, Wesley E., Chief Executive Officer, Texas County Memorial Hospital, Houston, MO, p. A383

MURRAY, William M., President, Sisters of Charity of Leavenworth Health System, Lenexa, KS, p. B99

MURTHA, Patrick, President and Chief Executive Officer, St. Joseph Health System, Tawas City, MI, p. A346

MUSCH, Cordel
Chief Financial Officer, Harris Continued Care Hospital, Fort Worth, TX, p. A639
Chief Financial Officer, Harris Methodist Fort Worth, Fort Worth, TX, p. A639

MUSGRAVE, M.D., Michael, Chief Medical Officer, Lutheran Hospital of Indiana, Fort Wayne, IN, p. A215

MUSSELMAN, Lynda, Vice President Human Resources, Memorial Hospital, Logansport, IN, p. A221

MUSSI, Natalie, Cheif Operating Officer, Independence Regional Health Center, Independence, MO, p. A383

MUSTIAN, J Perry, Executive Senior Vice President and Chief Operating Officer, John D. Archbold Memorial Hospital, Thomasville, GA, p. A170

MUSTIAN, Perry, Chief Operating Officer, Mitchell County Hospital, Camilla, GA, p. A157

MUSUMECI, Maryann, Director, Veterans Affairs Medical Center, New York, NY, p. A466

MUTARELLI, Richard, Chief Financial Officer, Munroe Regional Medical Center, Ocala, FL, p. A140

MUTCH, Patrick F., Chief Executive Officer, MetroWest Medical Center, Framingham, MA, p. A318

MUZZILLO, Michael, Assistant Administrator, Valley West Community Hospital, Sandwich, IL, p. A207

MYATT, Kevin, Chief Human Resources Officer, Vanderbilt University Medical Center, Nashville, TN, p. A616

MYERS, April, Chief Executive Officer, Kindred Hospital–Denver, Denver, CO, p. A103

MYERS, Charles, Chief Executive Officer, Banner Churchill Community Hospital, Fallon, NV, p. A415

MYERS, Dan, Controller, Kossuth Regional Health Center, Algona, IA, p. A228

MYERS, Gary, Chief Executive Officer, Mammoth Hospital, Mammoth Lakes, CA, p. A74

MYERS, Jerry, M.D., Interim Chief Executive Officer, Kell West Regional Hospital, Wichita Falls, TX, p. A674

MYERS, Jim, Chief Financial Officer, Bloomington Hospital, Bloomington, IN, p. A212

MYERS, Julie, Chief Financial Officer, Kiowa District Hospital and Manor, Kiowa, KS, p. A250

MYERS, Lora, Associate Executive Director, Long Island Jewish Medical Center, New York, NY, p. A461

MYERS, Marie, Director of Patient Care Services, Flandreau Medical Center/Avera Health, Flandreau, SD, p. A595

MYERS, Michael D., Administrator, Veterans Memorial Hospital, Waukon, IA, p. A243

MYERS, Russ, Vice President and Chief Operating Officer, Yakima Valley Memorial Hospital, Yakima, WA, p. A712

MYERS, Sandy, Human Resource Director, Delta County Memorial Hospital, Delta, CO, p. A103

MYERS, R.N., Shane P., Chief Operating Officer, Iberia Medical Center, New Iberia, LA, p. A288

MYERS, Stephanie, Business Office Lead, Alegent Health Community Memorial Hospital, Missouri Valley, IA, p. A238

MYLES, Lee T., Chief Operating Officer, St. Mary's Regional Medical Center, Lewiston, ME, p. A299

MYNARK, Richard H., Chief Executive Officer, Pulaski Memorial Hospital, Winamac, IN, p. A227

MYNHIER, Brent, Chief Financial Officer, Pauls Valley General Hospital, Pauls Valley, OK, p. A537

MYROM, M.D., Ronald, Chief of Staff, Palmer Lutheran Health Center, West Union, IA, p. A243

MYSBURGH, Ronelo, Administrator, Healthbridge Childrens Rehabilitation Hospital, Orange, CA, p. A79

N

NACE, M.D., R Nicholas, Chief Medical Officer, Jewish Memorial Hospital and Rehabilitation Center, Boston, MA, p. A314

NACHTIGAL, Amy, Chief Financial Officer, Saint Luke's South Hospital, Overland Park, KS, p. A255

NACION, Glenn, Vice President Human Resources, Trinitas Hospital–Williamson Street Campus, Elizabeth, NJ, p. A428

NACY, Kevin C., Executive Vice President, Lakeside Memorial Hospital, Brockport, NY, p. A448

NADEAU, Steve, Vice President Human Resources, Gwinnett Hospital System, Lawrenceville, GA, p. A164

NADER, Keoni, Director Human Resources, Louis A. Weiss Memorial Hospital, Chicago, IL, p. A188

NADER, Rick Lee, Chief Financial Officer, Mountain View Hospital District, Madras, OR, p. A545

NADKARNI, M.D., Manasi, Chief of Staff, Kossuth Regional Health Center, Algona, IA, p. A228

NADLE, R.N., Patricia, Chief Operating Officer and Chief Nursing Officer, Cape Cod Hospital, Hyannis, MA, p. A319

NADONE, John, Vice President and Chief Financial Officer, St. Joseph Hospital, Polson, MT, p. A401

NAFF, Harold F., Chief Financial Officer, Franklin Medical Center, Winnsboro, LA, p. A294

NAFF, Patricia, Director, Human Resources, Blount Memorial Hospital, Maryville, TN, p. A612

NAFZIGER, Mark A., Senior Vice President and Chief Financial Officer, Mercy Health Center, Oklahoma City, OK, p. A535

NAGALA, M.D., Vani, Chief Medical Officer, Oakes Community Hospital, Oakes, ND, p. A500

NAGEL, Donna, Senior Director Operations, St. John Sapulpa, Sapulpa, OK, p. A538

NAGLE, M.D., Roy, Medical Director, Kona Community Hospital, Kealakekua, HI, p. A175

NAGLOSKY, Paul, Administrator, Indianhead Medical Center, Shell Lake, WI, p. A735

NAGULA, M.D., Seetaramayya, Chief of Staff, Civista Health, La Plata, MD, p. A309

NAGY, Jeanne, Chief Operating Officer, St. David's Medical Center, Austin, TX, p. A624

NAIBERK, Donald T., Administrator, Butler County Health Care Center, David City, NE, p. A406

NAIL, Scott, Administrator, Hardeman County Memorial Hospital, Quanah, TX, p. A661

NAIMIE, Tina, Chief Financial Officer and Vice President Fiscal Services, New London Hospital, New London, NH, p. A423

NAIZER, Janie, Director Human Resources, D. M. Cogdell Memorial Hospital, Snyder, TX, p. A667

NAJAWICZ, Peter R., Chief Financial Officer, Roy Lester Schneider Hospital, Saint Thomas, VI, p. A749

NAKAYAMA, Makoto, President, San Gabriel Valley Medical Center, San Gabriel, CA, p. A90

NALDI, Robert, Chief Financial Officer, Maimonides Medical Center, New York, NY, p. A461

NALEPPA, Peggy, Executive Vice President and Chief Operating Officer, Peninsula Regional Health System, Salisbury, MD, p. A310

NALL, Brian, Chief Financial Officer, Steele Memorial Hospital, Salmon, ID, p. A181

NALL, M.D., Kenny, Chief of Staff, Beaufort County Hospital, Washington, NC, p. A493

NAMBISAN, M.D., Raman, Chief of Staff, ValleyCare Medical Center, Pleasanton, CA, p. A82

NANCE, Raymon, Director Information Systems, St. Mary–Rogers Memorial Hospital, Rogers, AR, p. A49

NANCE, Sally S., Chief Executive Officer, Excelsior Springs Medical Center, Excelsior Springs, MO, p. A381

NANIA, James A., Executive Vice President and Chief Financial Officer, Hallmark Health System, Melrose, MA, p. A320

NANTZ, Mark, Chief Financial Officer, NorthEast Medical Center, Concord, NC, p. A481

NAPIER, Randy L., President and Chief Executive Officer, Southern Indiana Rehabilitation Hospital, New Albany, IN, p. A223

NAPIER–EVANS, Lisa
Chief Financial Officer, Spalding Regional Medical Center, Griffin, GA, p. A163
Chief Financial Officer, Sylvan Grove Hospital, Jackson, GA, p. A164

NAPIERALA, Edward A., Chief Operating Officer, West Branch Regional Medical Center, West Branch, MI, p. A348

NAPLES, Keith T., Administrator, Living Hope New Boston Medical Center, New Boston, TX, p. A658

NAPP, M.D., Marc, Vice President Medical Staff, Hudson Valley Hospital Center, Cortlandt Manor, NY, p. A451

NAPPER, Ricky D., Chief Executive Officer, Magnolia Regional Health Center, Corinth, MS, p. A368

NARAIN, M.D., Prakash, Chief of Staff, Los Alamitos Medical Center, Los Alamitos, CA, p. A69

NARANJO, Maria, Director Human Resources, Aventura Hospital and Medical Center, Aventura, FL, p. A123

NARBUTAS, Virgis, Chief Executive Officer, Kindred Hospital–Westminster, Westminster, CA, p. A99

NARDUZZI, M.D., Joanne V., Vice President Academic Affairs, Mercy Hospital–North Shore Campus, Pittsburgh, PA, p. A572

NAREMORE, Bruce, Chief Financial Officer, East Jefferson General Hospital, Metairie, LA, p. A286

NASH, Bruce, M.D., President, North Adams Regional Hospital, North Adams, MA, p. A321

NASH, M.D., Clemma, Chief of Staff, Baldwin Area Medical Center, Baldwin, WI, p. A722

NASH, Jack
Interim Director Information Systems, Chestnut Hill Health System, Philadelphia, PA, p. A567
Vice President and Chief Information Officer, Chestnut Hill Rehabilitation Hospital, Glenside, PA, p. A559

NASH, Jerry A., Chief Executive Officer, Conroe Regional Medical Center, Conroe, TX, p. A630

NASH, John D., Executive Vice President and Chief Operating Officer, St. Jude Children's Research Hospital, Memphis, TN, p. A614

NASIR, M.D., Iqbal, Chief of Staff, Oakwood Southshore Medical Center, Trenton, MI, p. A347

NASRALLA, Anthony J., FACHE, President and Chief Executive Officer, Titusville Area Hospital, Titusville, PA, p. A576

NASRALLAH, M.D., Naseem, Chief of Staff, Pender Memorial Hospital, Burgaw, NC, p. A478

NATEMAN, Barry, Director Human Resources, Woman's Christian Association Hospital, Jamestown, NY, p. A454

NATHAN, James R.
Chief Executive Officer, Cape Coral Hospital, Cape Coral, FL, p. A125
Chief Executive Officer, Lee Memorial Health System, Fort Myers, FL, p. A129

NATHAN, Matthew L., Commanding Officer, Naval Hospital, Pensacola, FL, p. A143

NATZKE, Kenneth J., Administrator, OSF St. Joseph Medical Center, Bloomington, IL, p. A185

NAUGLE, Gary, Vice President Human Resources, Altoona Hospital Campus, Altoona, PA, p. A551

NAVARRO, R.N., Danielle, Chief Nursing Officer, Guthrie County Hospital, Guthrie Center, IA, p. A234

NAVAS, M.D., Manuel, Medical Director, Hospital San Pablo Del Este, Fajardo, PR, p. A745

NAVERA, Ann R., R.N., Administrator and Chief Nurse Executive, Memorial Hospital Corporation of Burlington, Burlington, WI, p. A724

NAWROCKI, Bernie, Director Fiscal Services, Defiance Regional Medical Center, Defiance, OH, p. A512

NAWROCKI, Edward, President, St. Luke's Quakertown Hospital, Quakertown, PA, p. A574

NAY, Clifford D., Executive Director, Scott Memorial Hospital, Scottsburg, IN, p. A225

NAYLOR III, George F., FACHE, Chief Executive Officer, Harris Hospital, Newport, AR, p. A48

NEAL, David, Information Systems Coordinator, Artesia General Hospital, Artesia, NM, p. A441

NEAL, Gerald D., Chief Executive Officer, Guthrie County Hospital, Guthrie Center, IA, p. A234

NEAL, John C., Chief Executive Officer, Stuttgart Regional Medical Center, Stuttgart, AR, p. A51

NEAL, Jr., M.D., Ralph D., Chief Medical Staff, Grove Hill Memorial Hospital, Grove Hill, AL, p. A19

NEAL, Roger, Director Information Technology, Duncan Regional Hospital, Duncan, OK, p. A529

NEALE, Ada, Associate Director, Veterans Affairs Long Beach Healthcare System, Long Beach, CA, p. A69

NEALON, Patricia, Acting Associate Director, Veterans Affairs Pittsburgh Healthcare System, Pittsburgh, PA, p. A573

NEAMAN, Mark R., President and Chief Executive Officer, Evanston Northwestern Healthcare, Evanston, IL, p. A194

NEEDHAM, Jean M., President, Holy Family Hospital, New Richmond, WI, p. A732

NEEDMAN, Herbert G., Administrator and Chief Executive Officer, Temple Community Hospital, Los Angeles, CA, p. A72

NEELD, Ann Pelissier, Chief Operating Officer, Capital Medical Center, Olympia, WA, p. A705

NEELEY, Michael, Chief Informaiton Officer, Deaconess Hospital, Evansville, IN, p. A214

NEELY, Cindy, Administrator, St. John's Maude Norton Memorial Hospital, Columbus, KS, p. A245

NEELY, Joseph H.
Senior Vice President and Administrator, Saint Francis Hospital at Broken Arrow, Broken Arrow, OK, p. A528
Senior Vice President and Administrator, Saint Francis Hospital, Tulsa, OK, p. A540

NEELY, Kathy E., Chief Operating Officer, Michael Reese Hospital and Medical Center, Chicago, IL, p. A188

NEESE, Kevin, Chief Financial Officer, St. Mary's Medical Center of Evansville, Evansville, IN, p. A215

NEET, Bradley
President and Chief Operating Officer, Saint Michael's Hospital, Stevens Point, WI, p. A736
President and Chief Operating Officer, Saint Michael's Hospital, Stevens Point, WI, p. A736

NEFF, Mark J., President and Chief Executive Officer, St. Claire Regional Medical Center, Morehead, KY, p. A272

NEFF, Stephen, Chief Financial Officer, Union Hospital, Elkton, MD, p. A307

NEGOSHIAN, Carol, Administrator, Lake Wales Medical Centers, Lake Wales, FL, p. A134

NEGRO, Frank, Vice President Information Services, St. Mary's Hospital, Amsterdam, NY, p. A447

NEGRON, Manuel, Information Technology Service Chief, Veterans Affairs Medical Center, San Juan, PR, p. A748

NEHLS, Dennis E., Administrator and Chief Executive Officer, Hospital District Number 1 of Crawford County, Girard, KS, p. A247

NEIDENBACH, Joseph J., Executive Vice President and Administrator, St. Vincent Hospital, Green Bay, WI, p. A726

NEIMAN, Carla
Chief Financial Officer, Clark Fork Valley Hospital, Plains, MT, p. A401
Chief Financial Officer, Clark Fork Valley Hospital, Plains, MT, p. A401

NEITZEL, Monte, Administrator and Chief Executive Officer, Greater Community Hospital, Creston, IA, p. A231

NEIWEEN, Joseph, Medical Director, CGH Medical Center, Sterling, IL, p. A209

NELL, Rocio, M.D., Chief Executive Officer and Medical Director, Montgomery County Emergency Service, Norristown, PA, p. A566

NELLIS, Mark D., Chief Financial Officer, Sitka Community Hospital, Sitka, AK, p. A28

NELSON, Allison
Chief Financial Officer, Deuel County Memorial Hospital, Clear Lake, SD, p. A595
Controller, Sioux Valley Canby Campus, Canby, MN, p. A351

NELSON, Becky, President, Sioux Valley Hospital University Medical Center, Sioux Falls, SD, p. A599

NELSON, Bill, Administrator and Chief Executive Officer, Coteau Des Prairies Hospital, Sisseton, SD, p. A599

NELSON, Brock D., President and Chief Executive Officer, Regions Hospital, Saint Paul, MN, p. A362

NELSON, Charles, Chief Executive Officer, Keweenaw Memorial Medical Center, Laurium, MI, p. A339

NELSON, Chris, Director Human Resources, Avera Queen of Peace, Mitchell, SD, p. A597

NELSON, Dale, Chief Information Officer, Veterans Affairs Medical Center, Fayetteville, AR, p. A43

NELSON, David, Vice President Finance and Chief Financial Officer, St. Francis Hospital & Health Center, Blue Island, IL, p. A185

NELSON, David A., President and Chief Executive Officer, St. Francis Medical Center, Breckenridge, MN, p. A350

NELSON, Don A., Chief Executive Officer, Northern Hills General Hospital, Deadwood, SD, p. A595

NELSON, Eileen, Administrator, HEALTHSOUTH Rehabilitation Hospital of Central Kentucky, Elizabethtown, KY, p. A264

NELSON, Ellen, Director Human Resources, Emerson Hospital, Concord, MA, p. A317

NELSON, Fred, Administrator, Ontonagon Memorial Hospital, Ontonagon, MI, p. A342

NELSON, Frederick H., Chief Executive Officer, Genesis Specialty Hospital – New Orleans, New Orleans, LA, p. A288

NELSON, Jack, Senior Vice President and Chief Information Officer, Mount Sinai Hosptial, New York, NY, p. A462

NELSON, Jackie, Director Human Resources, Hansford Hospital, Spearman, TX, p. A667

NELSON, M.D., James, Chief Medical Officer, North Oaks Medical Center, Hammond, LA, p. A281

NELSON, James J., Vice President Fiscal Services, Fort HealthCare, Fort Atkinson, WI, p. A725

NELSON, Jeffrey, Interim President and Chief Executive Officer, Empire Health Services, Spokane, WA, p. B44

NELSON, Jeri, Chief Financial Officer, Eastern Plumas District Hospital, Portola, CA, p. A82

NELSON, Katey, Director Human Resources, Sevier Valley Hospital, Richfield, UT, p. A679

NELSON, Kathy
Chief Financial Officer, Marshall Medical Center North, Guntersville, AL, p. A19
Chief Financial Officer, Marshall Medical Center South, Boaz, AL, p. A16
Director Marketing, Valley General Hospital, Monroe, WA, p. A704

NELSON, Kenneth W., Superintendent, Bridgewater State Hospital, Bridgewater, MA, p. A315

NELSON, R.N., Lynn M., Chief Operating Officer, St. John's Riverside Hosptial, Yonkers, NY, p. A476

NELSON, Martha, Chief Financial Officer, Antelope Memorial Hospital, Neligh, NE, p. A409

NELSON, Michael, Executive Vice President and Chief Executive Officer, Pomona Valley Hospital Medical Center, Pomona, CA, p. A82

NELSON, Mike, Executive Vice President and Chief Financial Officer, Saint Anthony's Health Center, Alton, IL, p. A183

NELSON, Mindi, Director Human Resources, Jackson County Public Hospital, Maquoketa, IA, p. A237

NELSON, Paula, Chief Financial Officer and Associate Administrator, Queen of Peace Hospital, New Prague, MN, p. A358

NELSON, Rodney M., President and Chief Executive Officer, Mackinac Straits Hospital and Health Center, Saint Ignace, MI, p. A344

NELSON, Shelia, Process Leader Human Resources, SouthCrest Hospital, Tulsa, OK, p. A540

NELSON, Siri, Chief Financial Officer, Sutter Amador Hospital, Jackson, CA, p. A65

NELSON, Stewart R., Chief Financial Officer, Halifax Regional Health System, South Boston, VA, p. A696

NELSON, M.D., Timothy, Chief of Staff, Keweenaw Memorial Medical Center, Laurium, MI, p. A339

NELSON, Todd, Vice President Finance, Grinnell Regional Medical Center, Grinnell, IA, p. A234

NELSON, Tom, Family Practice, Gibson General Hospital, Trenton, TN, p. A618

NELSON, Wayne, Chief Executive Officer, Sheridan Memorial Hospital, Plentywood, MT, p. A401

NELSON, William H., President and Chief Executive Officer, Intermountain Health Care, Inc., Salt Lake City, UT, p. B62

NEMACHECK, William, Chief Executive Officer, Marquette General Health System, Marquette, MI, p. A340

NEMETH, Joseph D., Vice President and Chief Financial Officer, Mercy Health System, Janesville, WI, p. A727

NEMIR, Bill, Administrator, Haskell Memorial Hospital, Haskell, TX, p. A643

NENABER, Pamela, Chief Operating Officer, Banner Mesa Medical Center, Mesa, AZ, p. A32

NESBIT, Lamar, Senior Vice President Human Resources and Customer Services, St. Dominic–Jackson Memorial Hospital, Jackson, MS, p. A371

NESPOLI, John L., Chief Administrative Officer, Lourdes Medical Center of Burlington County, Willingboro, NJ, p. A438

NESS, Edwin, President and Chief Executive Officer, Munson Medical Center, Traverse City, MI, p. A346

NESSE, Robert, M.D., President and Chief Executive Officer, Franciscan Skemp Healthcare–La Crosse Campus, La Crosse, WI, p. A727

NESTER Jr, Arthur, Administrator, Noxubee General Hospital, Macon, MS, p. A372

NESTER, Michael, Administrator, Simpson General Hospital, Mendenhall, MS, p. A372

NESTER, Tom, Chief Executive Officer, Galichia Heart Hospital, Wichita, KS, p. A259

NETH, Marvin, Administrator, Callaway District Hospital, Callaway, NE, p. A405

NETTERVILLE, Chad, Assistant Administrator Finance, Field Memorial Community Hospital, Centreville, MS, p. A367

NETTLES, Robert, Director Human Resources, MountainView Hospital, Las Vegas, NV, p. A416

NETZER, Patricia H., Commanding Officer, U. S. Naval Hospital, Roosevelt Roads, PR, p. A748

NEUENDORF, David A., President and Chief Executive Officer, Audrain Medical Center, Mexico, MO, p. A387

NEUENSCHWANDER, Darrel, Chief Financial Officer, Good Samaritan Hospital, San Jose, CA, p. A90

NEUMAN, Jeff, Human Resources Director, Henry County Memorial Hospital, New Castle, IN, p. A223

NEUMAN, Michael J., Vice President Finance, Kennedy Krieger Institute, Baltimore, MD, p. A303

NEUMAN, Richard, Assistant Administrator, Olympic Medical Center, Port Angeles, WA, p. A706

NEUMANN, Luci, President, Baylor Institute for Rehabilitation, Dallas, TX, p. A632

NEUMEISTER, CHE, Daniel P., Chief Operations Officer, Enloe Medical Center, Chico, CA, p. A56

NEURA, Sharon, Vice President Marketing and Public Relations, Samaritan Regional Health System, Ashland, OH, p. A502

NEUREITHER, George, Chief Human Resources Management Service, Veterans Affairs Medical Center–Louisville, Louisville, KY, p. A270

NEVAREZ, Domingo
Administrator, Hospital de la Universidad de Puerto Rico/Dr. Federico Trilla, Carolina, PR, p. A744
Administrator, Hospital de la Universidad de Puerto Rico/Dr. Federico Trilla, Carolina, PR, p. A744

NEVILL, David S., President and Chief Executive Officer, Wesley Medical Center, Wichita, KS, p. A260

NEVILL, Dorothy, Assistant Administrator Financial Services, Huntsville Memorial Hospital, Huntsville, TX, p. A649

NEVIN, M.D., Lynn, Chief of Staff, Gerber Memorial Health Services, Fremont, MI, p. A333

NEW, Cathy, Vice President Clinical Services, St. Francis Hospital and Health Services, Maryville, MO, p. A387

NEWBERRY, R. Alan, President and Chief Executive Officer, Peninsula Regional Health System, Salisbury, MD, p. A310

NEWBERRY–FERGUSON, Linda, Chief Executive Officer, Kindred Hospital–Milwaukee, Milwaukee, WI, p. A731

NEWBOLD, Philip A., President and Chief Executive Officer, Memorial Hospital of South Bend, South Bend, IN, p. A225

NEWBY, Nancy M., Ph.D., President and Chief Executive Officer, Washington County Hospital, Nashville, IL, p. A202

NEWCOMB, D.O., Everett
Senior Vice President Medical Affairs, St. Clare Hospital, Tacoma, WA, p. A710
Senior Vice President Medical Affairs, St. Francis Hospital, Federal Way, WA, p. A703
Senior Vice President Medical Affairs, St. Joseph Medical Center, Tacoma, WA, p. A710

NEWCOMB, Sherrie, Administrator, Jenkins Community Hospital, Jenkins, KY, p. A266

NEWELL, Peter, Senior Vice President Finance and Chief Financial Officer, Robert Wood Johnson University Hospital at Hamilton, Hamilton, NJ, p. A429

NEWLAND, Kathie, Accounting Manager, Wheatland Memorial Hospital, Harlowton, MT, p. A399

NEWMAN, Cynthia, Human Resources Manager, Petersburg Medical Center, Petersburg, AK, p. A28

NEWMAN, Diane, Administrator, Johnson County Hospital, Tecumseh, NE, p. A413

NEWMAN, James
Senior Vice President and Chief Financial Officer, Mercy Hospital of Scott County, Waldron, AR, p. A51
Vice President and Chief Financial Officer, Mercy Hospital–Turner Memorial, Ozark, AR, p. A49
Vice President and Chief Financial Officer, St. Edward Mercy Medical Center, Fort Smith, AR, p. A44

NEWMAN, Ken, President and Chief Executive Officer, Horizon Health Corporation, Lewisville, TX, p. B60

NEWMAN, Marti, Acting Manager Human Resources, UHHS Richmond Heights Hospital, Richmond Heights, OH, p. A521

NEWQUIST, Dennis, Director Information Systems, Abilene Regional Medical Center, Abilene, TX, p. A620

NEWSOM, Jamie, Director of Information Systems, Williamsburg Regional Hospital, Kingstree, SC, p. A589

NEWSOM, Terri, Vice President and Chief Financial Officer, Duke Health Raleigh Hospital, Raleigh, NC, p. A489

NEWSOME, M.D., Samuel C., President, Medical Staff, Stokes–Reynolds Memorial Hospital, Danbury, NC, p. A481

NEWTON, Carol, Chief Financial Officer, Memorial Health Care System, Chattanooga, TN, p. A603

NEWTON, David R., Senior Vice President Finance and Chief Financial Officer, New Britain General Hospital, New Britain, CT, p. A114

NEWTON, M.D., E Douglas, President Medical Staff, Western Pennsylvania Hospital, Pittsburgh, PA, p. A573

NEWTON, Mark, President and Chief Executive Officer, Swedish Covenant Hospital, Chicago, IL, p. A190

NEWTON, Steven R., President and Chief Executive Officer, Baylor All Saints Medical Center at Fort Worth, Fort Worth, TX, p. A639

NG, Vincent, Director, Veterans Affairs Medical Center, Providence, RI, p. A582

NGUYEN, Bach, Information Systems Director, North Oaks Medical Center, Hammond, LA, p. A281

NGUYEN, Tim, Chief Financial Officer, Natividad Medical Center, Salinas, CA, p. A86

NIBBE, Susan, Vice President Finance, Advocate Lutheran General Hospital, Park Ridge, IL, p. A204

NICASTRO, Pam, Director Human Resources, Kenmore Mercy Hospital, Kenmore, NY, p. A455

NICELY, Dennis, Director, Missouri Rehabilitation Center, Mount Vernon, MO, p. A388

NICHOLDS, Gary A., FACHE, Chief Executive Officer, Los Alamos Medical Center, Los Alamos, NM, p. A443

NICHOLS, Arthur W., President and Chief Executive Officer, Cheshire Medical Center, Keene, NH, p. A421

NICHOLS, Barbara, R.N., President and Chief Executive Officer, Corry Memorial Hospital, Corry, PA, p. A556

NICHOLS, Bryan, Chief Financial Officer, Stuttgart Regional Medical Center, Stuttgart, AR, p. A51

NICHOLS, Dave, Finance Manager, Decatur County Hospital and Cedar Living Center, Oberlin, KS, p. A253

NICHOLS, Dia, Chief Operating Officer, John Randolph Medical Center, Hopewell, VA, p. A690

NICHOLS, Kathy, Co–Administrator, Palacios Community Medical Center, Palacios, TX, p. A659

NICHOLS, Mark, FACHE, Chief Executive Officer, Coliseum Psychiatric Center, Coliseum Psychiatric Center, Macon, GA, p. A165

NICHOLS, Odis W., Senior Vice President and Chief Operating Officer, Providence Health Center, Waco, TX, p. A672

NICHOLS, Richard, Administrator, Sutter Maternity and Surgery Center of Santa Cruz, Santa Cruz, CA, p. A93

NICHOLS, Robin, Vice President and Chief Financial Officer, Major Hospital, Shelbyville, IN, p. A225

NICHOLS, Stephen, Chief Executive Officer, Riley Hospital, Meridian, MS, p. A373

NICHOLS, M.D., Theodore, Senior Vice President Medical Affairs, Lake Hospital System, Painesville, OH, p. A520

NICHOLSON, M.D., Britain, Chief Medical Officer, Massachusetts General Hospital, Boston, MA, p. A314

NICHOLSON, Cindy, Director Human Resources, Shelby Baptist Medical Center, Alabaster, AL, p. A13

NICHOLSON, Paul, Director Financial Services, James Lawrence Kernan Hospital, Baltimore, MD, p. A303

NICK, Mary, Vice President Human Resources, Meriter Hospital, Madison, WI, p. A728

NICKEL, M.D., Craig, Chief of Staff, Lindsborg Community Hospital, Lindsborg, KS, p. A252

NICKEL, Kathleen, Director Communications, Mercy Medical Center, Roseburg, OR, p. A548

NICKELL, Janice, Administrative Assistant, Glen Rose Medical Center, Glen Rose, TX, p. A642

NICKELL, Jerry, Vice President Human Resource and Mission, St. Elizabeth Health Services, Baker City, OR, p. A542

NICKELL Jr, Roy C., Director Substance Abuse Services, Larry B. Zieverink, Sr. Alcoholism Treatment Center, Raleigh, NC, p. A489

NICKELL, Sarah, Administrative Director Human Resources, Marion General Hospital, Marion, IN, p. A221

NICKELS, M.D., John, President Medical Staff, Grace Hospital, Cleveland, OH, p. A508

NICKRAND, Tami, Chief Information Officer, Harbor Beach Community Hospital, Harbor Beach, MI, p. A336

NICODEMUS, Eileen, Director Information Systems, Garden Grove Hospital and Medical Center, Garden Grove, CA, p. A62

NICODEMUS, Lowell, Director Information Systems, Hendricks Regional Health, Danville, IN, p. A213

NICODEMUS, Robert, Vice President Human Resources, Sparks Regional Medical Center, Fort Smith, AR, p. A43

NICOL, Susan, Director of Human Resources, Jones Memorial Hospital, Wellsville, NY, p. A475

NICOLETTA, Nicholas, Vice President Finance and Chief Financial Officer, Mary Imogene Bassett Hospital, Cooperstown, NY, p. A450

NICOSIA, Chris
Chief Financial Officer, Corpus Christi Medical Center, Corpus Christi, TX, p. A630
Chief Financial Officer, Corpus Christi Medical Center Bay Area, Corpus Christi, TX, p. A630

NIDA, D.O., Maurice, Chief of Staff, Norton Community Hospital, Norton, VA, p. A693

NIEDERPRUEM, Mark L., Administrator, Shriners Hospitals for Children, Springfield, Springfield, MA, p. A324

NIELSEN, Greg, Chief Administrative Officer, Holy Rosary Healthcare, Miles City, MT, p. A400

NIELSEN, Wayne, Director Human Resources, Ocala Regional Medical Center, Ocala, FL, p. A140

NIELSON, Curtis, Chief Financial Officer, South Lincoln Medical Center, Kemmerer, WY, p. A740

NIEMANN, M.D., Shawn, Medical Director, Naval Hospital, North Charleston, SC, p. A591

NIEMANN, Starla, Director Human Resources, Columbia Memorial Hospital, Astoria, OR, p. A542

NIEMER, Peggy, Vice President, Human Resources, Children's Hospital of Wisconsin, Milwaukee, WI, p. A730

NIEMEYER, Romaine, President and Chief Executive Officer, Holy Spirit Hospital, Camp Hill, PA, p. A554

NIEMI, Sandy, Human Resources Director, Sauk Prairie Memorial Hospital, Prairie Du Sac, WI, p. A734

NIES, Lynn, Human Resources Officer, Veterans Affairs Medical Center, Erie, PA, p. A558

NIESE, Mel, Chief, Fiscal Service, Veterans Affairs Palo Alto Health Care System, Palo Alto, CA, p. A80

NIESSINK, Henry
Regional Director Information Technology Services, Mercy Medical Center Redding, Redding, CA, p. A83
Senior Manager Information Technology Systems Perot, St. Elizabeth Community Hospital, Red Bluff, CA, p. A83

NIEVES, Caridad, Chief Nursing Officer and Chief Operating Officer, Coral Gables Hospital, Coral Gables, FL, p. A126

NIEVES, Deborah, Management Information Systems Director, Caribbean Pediatric and Surgery Hospital, San Juan, PR, p. A747

NIEVES, Jesus, Chief Executive Officer, Bella Vista Hospital, Mayaguez, PR, p. A745

NIEWIADOMSKI, M.D., Edward, Vice President Medical Affairs, Southern Ocean County Hospital, Manahawkin, NJ, p. A431

NIGRIN, M.D., Daniel, Interim Vice President Information Services and Chief Information Officer, Children's Hospital Boston, Boston, MA, p. A313

NIJJAR, M.D., Ravinder S., Chief of Staff, Columbia Basin Hospital, Ephrata, WA, p. A702

NILES, D Michael, Vice President Finance, Glens Falls Hospital, Glens Falls, NY, p. A453

NILES, Linda, Chief Executive Officer, Adams County Hospital, West Union, OH, p. A524

NIMMICH, Todd, Fiscal Services Manager, Charleston Memorial Hospital, Charleston, SC, p. A584

NIMMO, Mary Jo, Director Management Information Systems, Lenoir Memorial Hospital, Kinston, NC, p. A486

NIMMOOR, Mitchell, Vice President Human Resources, Garden City Hospital, Garden City, MI, p. A333

NIMTZ, Shawndra, Chief Executive Officer, Palm Drive Hospital, Sebastopol, CA, p. A93

NINU, Christine, Chief Operating Officer, Kindred Hospital–Milwaukee, Milwaukee, WI, p. A731

NIPP, M.D., Robert, Chief of Staff, Capital Medical Center, Olympia, WA, p. A705

NISHIMURA, Koji, Commander, Bassett Army Community Hospital, Fort Wainwright, AK, p. A27

NITZSCHKE, Mary Helen, Director Human Resources, Floyd Valley Hospital/Avera Health, Le Mars, IA, p. A237

NIVEN, David, Siemens Site Manager, Chesapeake General Hospital, Chesapeake, VA, p. A686

NIXON, Cynthia R., Executive Vice President, Weirton Medical Center, Weirton, WV, p. A720

NIXON, Maria, Executive Director, Savannas Hospital, Port St. Lucie, FL, p. A144

NOBLE, James S., Vice President Finance and Chief Financial Officer, Huntington Memorial Hospital, Pasadena, CA, p. A81

NOBLE, Kerry L., Administrator, Pemiscot Memorial Health System, Hayti, MO, p. A382

NOBLE, Mallie S., Administrator, Mary Breckinridge Hospital, Hyden, KY, p. A266

NOBLE, M.D., Melynda, Chief Medical Staff, Greenwood Leflore Hospital, Greenwood, MS, p. A369

NOBLE, Paula, Chief Financial Officer and Treasurer, Children's Memorial Hospital, Chicago, IL, p. A187

NOBLE, Risa, Director Human Resources, HEALTHSOUTH Rehabilitation Institute of Tucson, Tucson, AZ, p. A38

NOBLE, Stephen H.
President, Accord Health Care Corporation, Clearwater, FL, p. B4
President, Stewart–Webster Hospital, Richland, GA, p. A167

NOCE Jr, Walter W., President and Chief Executive Officer, Childrens Hospital Los Angeles, Los Angeles, CA, p. A69

NOCELLA, Al, Vice President Human Resources, Sutter Maternity and Surgery Center of Santa Cruz, Santa Cruz, CA, p. A93

NOCKERTS, Steven R., Chief Executive Officer, Richland Hospital, Richland Center, WI, p. A735

NOE, J Thomas, Director Human Resources, Charles Cole Memorial Hospital, Coudersport, PA, p. A556

NOE, R.N., Kathi, Chief Operating Officer, Holton Community Hospital, Holton, KS, p. A249

NOEL, III, Philip J., Assistant Administrator and Chief Operating Officer, Baptist Medical Center, San Antonio, TX, p. A663

NOFFSINGER, Sandy, Executive Assistant, Dundy County Hospital, Benkelman, NE, p. A405

NOGA, James W., Chief Information Officer, Massachusetts General Hospital, Boston, MA, p. A314

NOJUNAS, Thomas M., Vice President and Administrator, Charlotte Institute of Rehabilitation, Charlotte, NC, p. A480

NOKELS, Kevin
Vice President and Chief Operating Officer, Alegent–Health Midlands Community Hospital, Papillion, NE, p. A412
Vice President and Chief Operating Officer, Alegent–Health Midlands Community Hospital, Papillion, NE, p. A412

NOLAN, Jennifer
Chief Executive Officer, River Oaks Child and Adolescent Hospital, New Orleans, LA, p. A289
Chief Executive Officer, River Oaks Hospital, New Orleans, LA, p. A289

NOLAN, Michael J., Chief Executive Officer, Ascension Hospital, Gonzales, LA, p. A281

NOLAN, Michael L., Prseident and Chief Executive Officer, Southside Hospital, Bay Shore, NY, p. A447

NOLAN, Patrick B., President and Chief Executive Officer, Warren Memorial Hospital, Front Royal, VA, p. A688

NOLAN, Robert, Vice President and General Counsel, Buffalo General Hospital, Buffalo, NY, p. A448

NOLAND, Christopher, Chief Executive Officer and Administrator, Tri–State Memorial Hospital, Clarkston, WA, p. A701

NOLTE, Sue, Director of Human Resources, HEALTHSOUTH Deaconess Rehabilitation Hospital, Evansville, IN, p. A214

NOONAN, Kathleen, Vice President Information, Lemuel Shattuck Hospital, Jamaica Plain, MA, p. A319

NORBY, Ronald, Director, Veterans Affairs Long Beach Healthcare System, Long Beach, CA, p. A69

NORD, Gay, Chief Executive Officer, Kingwood Medical Center, Kingwood, TX, p. A651

NORD, Stanley K., Chief Financial Officer, Spring Branch Medical Center, Houston, TX, p. A647

NORDAHL, Rick
Administrator and Chief Executive Officer, Murray County Memorial Hospital, Slayton, MN, p. A363
Administrator and Chief Executive Officer, Tracy Area Medical Services, Tracy, MN, p. A364
Administrator and Chief Executive Officer, Westbrook Health Center, Westbrook, MN, p. A365
Chief Operating Officer, Westbrook Health Center, Westbrook, MN, p. A365

NORDAN, Clint, Chief Information Resource Management, Veterans Affairs Medical Center, Fayetteville, NC, p. A483

NORDWICK, John A., President and Chief Executive Officer, Bozeman Deaconess Hospital, Bozeman, MT, p. A396

NORDWICK, Thomas, President and Chief Executive Officer, Memorial Hospital of Converse County, Douglas, WY, p. A740

NOREN, Mary Kay
Superintendent, Eastern Shore Hospital Center, Cambridge, MD, p. A306
Chief Executive Officer, Upper Shore Community Mental Health Center, Chestertown, MD, p. A306

NORGAARD, Margaret B.
Chief Executive Officer, Poplar Community Hospital, Poplar, MT, p. A401
Chief Executive Officer, Trinity Hospital, Wolf Point, MT, p. A403

NORMAN, Anna, Director Human Resources, Wills Memorial Hospital, Washington, GA, p. A172

NORMAN, Jeffrey K., Chief Operating Officer, Scottsdale Healthcare–Shea, Scottsdale, AZ, p. A36

NORMAN, Mary, Administrator and Chief Executive Officer, Bear Valley Community Hospital, Big Bear Lake, CA, p. A55

NORMAN, D.O., Mike, Chief Medical Staff, Bear Valley Community Hospital, Big Bear Lake, CA, p. A55

NORO, Sharon
Administrator, HEALTHSOUTH Harmarville Rehabilitation Hospital, Pittsburgh, PA, p. A571
Administrator, HEALTHSOUTH Rehabilitation Hospital, Sewickley, PA, p. A575

NORONHA, Tony, Chief Financial Officer, St. John's Regional Medical Center, Joplin, MO, p. A384

NORRIS, Celeste, Vice President Human Resources, Baptist Hospital, Pensacola, FL, p. A142

NORRIS, Charles, Chief Executive Officer, Memorial Hospital, Gonzales, TX, p. A642

NORRIS, Doug, Chief Executive Officer, Chapman Medical Center, Orange, CA, p. A79

NORRIS, Edward A., Chief Financial Officer, Ocean Beach Hospital, Ilwaco, WA, p. A703

NORRIS, M.D., John G., Chief of Staff, Johnson Memorial Hospital, Franklin, IN, p. A216

NORRIS, Marsha, Director Information Systems, Ste. Genevieve County Memorial Hospital, Ste. Genevieve, MO, p. A394

NORRIS, Timothy
Chief Financial Officer, Greene County General Hospital, Linton, IN, p. A221
Chief Financial Officer, Greene County General Hospital, Linton, IN, p. A221

NORTH, Marilyn, Health Information Management Coordinator, Premier Rehabilitation Hospital, Monroe, LA, p. A287

NORTH, Scott, Chief Executive Officer, St. John's Hospital, Saint Paul, MN, p. A362

NORTHAM, Callen, Executive Vice President and Chief Operating Officer, Portneuf Medical Center, Pocatello, ID, p. A181

NORTHCUTT, Doug, Chief Information Officer, University Medical Center, Las Vegas, NV, p. A417

NORTHROP, Dale, Vice President Finance, Castle Medical Center, Kailua, HI, p. A174

NORTOM, M.D., Mark, President Medical Staff, South Central Regional Medical Center, Laurel, MS, p. A372

NORTON, M.D., Andrew J., Senior Vice President Medical Affairs, Froedtert Memorial Lutheran Hospital, Milwaukee, WI, p. A731

NORTON, Bruce J., Vice President Finance and Chief Financial Officer, Sierra Vista Regional Health Center, Sierra Vista, AZ, p. A37

NORTON, Janet, Human Resources Manager, West Branch Regional Medical Center, West Branch, MI, p. A348

NORTON, Lizette, Executive Director Human Resources Management, Loma Linda University Medical Center, Loma Linda, CA, p. A68

NORTON, Robert G., President and Chief Executive Officer, North Shore Medical Center, Salem, MA, p. A323

NORTON, Sandra, Vice President Human Resources, Advocate Good Samaritan Hospital, Downers Grove, IL, p. A192

NORVELL, Charles D., President and Chief Executive Officer, Thoms Rehabilitation Hospital, Asheville, NC, p. A477

NORWINE, David R., FACHE, President and Chief Executive Officer, H. B. Magruder Memorial Hospital, Port Clinton, OH, p. A521

NORWOOD, Eric P.
President and Chief Executive Officer, DeKalb Medical Center, Decatur, GA, p. B35
President and Chief Executive Officer, DeKalb Medical Center, Decatur, GA, p. A160

NORWOOD, Steve, Executive Director, Northwestern Center for Behavioral Health, Woodward, OK, p. A541

NOSACKA, Mark, Chief Executive Officer, Greenbrier Valley Medical Center, Ronceverte, WV, p. A720

NOTEBAERT, Edmond F., President and Chief Executive Officer, University of Maryland Medical System, Baltimore, MD, p. B117

NOTEBOOM, Kenneth, Chief Executive Officer, Hillcrest Specialty Hospital, Tulsa, OK, p. A539

NOTTIGE, Andrew, Vice President Human Resources, Cortland Memorial Hospital, Cortland, NY, p. A451

NOTTINGHAM, Cheryl, Chief Financial Officer, Atlantic General Hospital, Berlin, MD, p. A305

NOVAK, Edward, President and Chief Executive Officer, Sacred Heart Hospital, Chicago, IL, p. A189

NOVAK, Georgene, Director Human Resources, Littleton Regional Hospital, Littleton, NH, p. A422

NOVAK, CPA, Sharon, Controller, Muleshoe Area Medical Center, Muleshoe, TX, p. A658

NOVAKOSKE, Larry, Vice President Finance, St. Gabriel's Hospital, Little Falls, MN, p. A356

NOVAKOVICH, Kris, Vice President Human Resources, Washoe Medical Center, Reno, NV, p. A418

NOVOA, M.D., Jose E., Medical Director, Cardiovascular Center of Puerto Rico and the Caribbean, San Juan, PR, p. A746

NOVOTNY, M.D., Mark, Chief Operating Officer Medical Practice Division, Southwestern Vermont Medical Center, Bennington, VT, p. A682

NOWAK, Gregory M., Administrator and Chief Executive Officer, Coshocton County Memorial Hospital, Coshocton, OH, p. A511

NOWAK, John, Information Systems Director, Jefferson Healthcare, Port Townsend, WA, p. A706

NOWELL, Jeff, Chief Financial Officer, Baptist Memorial Hospital – Memphis, Memphis, TN, p. A612

NOWICKI, Joseph M., Chief Financial Officer, USC University Hospital, Los Angeles, CA, p. A73

NOWISKI, David, Chief Financial Officer, St. Mary's Medical Center, Knoxville, TN, p. A610

NOWLIN, Jeff, Assistant Vice President Operations, Memorial Hermann Memorial City Hospital, Houston, TX, p. A646

NOWLINS, Tara, Director of Human Resources, Monroe County Hospital, Monroeville, AL, p. A21

NOYES, Debra, Chief Financial Officer, Orange Park Medical Center, Orange Park, FL, p. A140

NUBER, M.D., Tom, Chief of Staff, St. Mary's Healthcare Center, Pierre, SD, p. A597

NUCILLI, Becky, Director of Human Resources, Jefferson Memorial Hospital, Ranson, WV, p. A719

NUCKLES, Craig, Chief Executive Officer, Managing Director and Group Director, Timberlawn Mental Health System, Dallas, TX, p. A634

NUGENT, Joan, Assistant Administrator Human Resources, Ketchikan General Hospital, Ketchikan, AK, p. A27

NULLMAN, Andrew, Chief of Staff, North Shore Medical Center, Miami, FL, p. A138

NUNAMAKER, E. Michael, Chief Executive Officer, Grady Memorial Hospital, Chickasha, OK, p. A528

NUNAMALAER, Gail, Vice President Human Resources, Hayes–Green–Beach Memorial Hospital, Charlotte, MI, p. A329

NUNCI, Helen, Manager Human Resources, Veterans Affairs Medical Center, San Juan, PR, p. A748

NUNELLEY, M.D., Preston, Chief Medical Officer, Central Baptist Hospital, Lexington, KY, p. A267

NUNEZ, Milton, Chief Financial Officer, Woodhull Medical and Mental Health Center, New York, NY, p. A466

NUNLEY, Jackson, Chief Executive Officer, Pulaski Community Hospital, Pulaski, VA, p. A694

NUNLEY, Penny, Vice President Human Resources, Hannibal Regional Hospital, Hannibal, MO, p. A382

NUNN, John, Manager Information Systems, Atchison Hospital, Atchison, KS, p. A244

NUNNELLEY, Greg, Director Human Resources, Pineville Community Hospital Association, Pineville, KY, p. A273

NUNNERY, Reece, Chief Financial Officer, Southwest Mississippi Regional Medical Center, McComb, MS, p. A372

NURICK, Paul E., Senior Vice President & Chief Operating Officer, Norwalk Hospital, Norwalk, CT, p. A115

NURKIN, Brad K., Chief Executive Officer, Lancaster Regional Medical Center, Lancaster, PA, p. A562

NUSSBAUM, M.D., Michael, Chief of Staff, University Hospital, Cincinnati, OH, p. A507

NUTT, M.D., Hugh A., Chief of Staff, Dallas County Medical Center, Fordyce, AR, p. A43

NUTTER, Robert, Vice President Human Resources and Support Services, Mercy Hospital of Portland, Portland, ME, p. A300

NWAOBASI, M.D., Samuel, President Medical Staff, Kenneth Hall Regional Hospital, East St. Louis, IL, p. A192

NYBAKKEN, Kirk, Finance Director, Cambridge Medical Center, Cambridge, MN, p. A351

NYSTROM, Bradford P., Chief Informatics Program, Veterans Affairs Medical Center, North Chicago, IL, p. A203

NYSTROM, M.D., Joseph W., Chief of Staff, East Pasco Medical Center, Zephyrhills, FL, p. A151

O

O'BANION, M.D., Dennis, Chief of Staff, Christus St. Michael Health System, Texarkana, TX, p. A669

O'BOYLE, Michael P., Chief Operating Officer, Cleveland Clinic Foundation, Cleveland, OH, p. A508

O'BRIEN, John, Administrator, Ellsworth Municipal Hospital, Iowa Falls, IA, p. A236

O'BRIEN, John G., President and Chief Executive Officer, UMass Memorial Health Care, Inc., Worcester, MA, p. B113

O'BRIEN, Kevin, Chief Operating Officer, Newman Memorial Hospital, Shattuck, OK, p. A538

O'BRIEN, Lawrence F., Chief Executive Officer, Saint Mary's Regional Medical Center, Reno, NV, p. A418

O'BRIEN, Mary Elizabeth, President and Chief Executive Officer, Baptist Health System, Birmingham, AL, p. B15

O'BRIEN, Patrick, Chief Executive Officer, Mt. Graham Regional Medical Center, Safford, AZ, p. A36

O'BRIEN, Sharon, Director Administration, Dundy County Hospital, Benkelman, NE, p. A405

O'BRIEN, Terence M.
Executive Vice President and Chief Operating Officer, Lenox Hill Hospital, New York, NY, p. A461
Executive Vice President and Chief Operating Officer, Manhattan Eye, Ear and Throat Hospital, New York, NY, p. A462

O'BRYAN, Michael, M.D., Chief Executive Officer, NorthShore Regional Medical Center, Slidell, LA, p. A293

O'BRYANT, G. Mark, Chief Executive Officer, Tallahassee Memorial HealthCare, Tallahassee, FL, p. A147

O'CONNELL, Barbara
Director Information Systems, Centegra Memorial Medical Center, Woodstock, IL, p. A210
Director Information Systems, Rush North Shore Medical Center, Skokie, IL, p. A208

O'CONNELL, Blaine J., Senior Vice President Finance, Froedtert Memorial Lutheran Hospital, Milwaukee, WI, p. A731

O'CONNELL, Gene Marie, Executive Administrator, San Francisco General Hospital Medical Center, San Francisco, CA, p. A89

O'CONNELL, John W., President, Franciscan Services Corporation, Sylvania, OH, p. B45

O'CONNELL, Kathleen, Site Manager Information Systems, Robert Wood Johnson University Hospital at Rahway, Rahway, NJ, p. A435

O'CONNELL, Rick, President and Chief Executive Officer, Penrose–St. Francis Health Services, Colorado Springs, CO, p. A102

O'CONNOR, David, Chief Financial Officer, Frye Regional Medical Center, Hickory, NC, p. A485

O'CONNOR, M.D., Dennis, Medical Director, Ira Davenport Memorial Hospital, Bath, NY, p. A447

O'CONNOR, James, President and Chief Executive Officer, St. Charles Hospital, Port Jefferson, NY, p. A469

O'CONNOR, Joann B., Director and Chief Executive Officer, Winnebago Mental Health Institute, Winnebago, WI, p. A738

O'CONNOR, Mark, Chief Financial Officer, SSM DePaul Health Center, Saint Louis, MO, p. A391

O'CONNOR, Michael F., Senior Vice President Finance, York Hospital, York, PA, p. A580

O'CONNOR, Nick, Vice President and Chief Information Officer, North Shore University Hospital at Plainview, Plainview, NY, p. A469

O'CONNOR, Steve, Director of Information Services, Southwestern Medical Center, Lawton, OK, p. A532

O'CONNOR, Thomas, President, St. Francis Regional Medical Center, Shakopee, MN, p. A363

O'CONNOR, Timothy, Chief Financial Officer, Lahey Clinic Hospital, Burlington, MA, p. A316

O'DONNELL, Barbara, Director Information Systems, Centegra Northern Illinois Medical Center, McHenry, IL, p. A200

O'DONNELL, Charles Thomas, President and Chief Executive Officer, KidsPeace Children's Hospital, Orefield, PA, p. A567

O'DONNELL, Kevin J., President and Chief Executive Officer, Sacred Heart–St. Mary's Hospitals, Rhinelander, WI, p. A734

O'DONNELL, CPA, Patrick W.
Vice President Finance, Chambersburg Hospital, Chambersburg, PA, p. A555
Vice President Finance, Waynesboro Hospital, Waynesboro, PA, p. A578

O'DONNELL, Randall L., Ph.D.,
President and Chief Executive Officer, Children's Mercy Hospital, Kansas City, MO, p. A384
President and Chief Executive Officer, Children's Mercy South, Overland Park, KS, p. A254

O'DONNELL, Thomas J., Director Hospital Services, U. S. Air Force Medical Center Keesler, Keesler AFB, MS, p. A371

O'GORMAN, Jr, Thomas, Assistant Administrator and Chief Financial Officer, East Texas Medical Center Pittsburg, Pittsburg, TX, p. A660

O'GRADY Jr, Michael J., President and Chief Executive Officer, Norwegian–American Hospital, Chicago, IL, p. A188

O'HALLA, Mark S., Executive Vice President and Administrator, St. Mary's Hospital, Streator, IL, p. A209

O'HALLORAN, Ronald, Administrator, Ferry County Memorial Hospital, Republic, WA, p. A707

O'HARA, Gene L., Chief Executive Officer, North Colorado Medical Center, Greeley, CO, p. A106

O'HARE, M.D., Dennis
Vice President Medical Affairs, Mercy Hospital, Coon Rapids, MN, p. A351
Vice President Medical Affairs, Unity Hospital, Fridley, MN, p. A354

O'HARE, Patrick, Corporate Chief Information Officer, Spectrum Health, Grand Rapids, MI, p. A335

O'KEEFE, James M., President and Chief Executive Officer, Woodlawn Hospital, Rochester, IN, p. A224

O'KEEFE, Michael F., FACHE, Chief Executive Officer, Albuquerque Regional Medical Center, Albuquerque, NM, p. A440

O'KEEFE, Michael N., President and Chief Executive Officer, Evangelical Community Hospital, Lewisburg, PA, p. A563

O'KEEFE, R.N., Sharon, Chief Operating Officer, Barnes–Jewish Hospital, Saint Louis, MO, p. A390

O'LAUGHLIN, James, Chief Executive Officer, Carolinas Hospital System, Florence, SC, p. A587

O'LEARY, Kevin J., Senior Vice President and Chief Financial Officer, Exeter Hospital, Exeter, NH, p. A421

O'LEARY, Regina, Human Resources Leader, Kaiser Foundation Hospital, Los Angeles, CA, p. A70

O'MALLEY, Dennis, President, Craig Hospital, Englewood, CO, p. A105

O'MALLEY, Trevor, Site Manager, Provena Saint Joseph Hospital, Elgin, IL, p. A193

O'NEAL, Karen, Chief Executive Officer, Tattnall Community Hospital, Reidsville, GA, p. A167

O'NEAL, Mary Ann, Administrative Officer, U. S. Public Health Service Indian Hospital, Crownpoint, NM, p. A442

O'NEIL, Dan
Director Maqnagement Information Systems, Caritas Holy Family Hospital and Medical Center, Methuen, MA, p. A320
Director Maqnagement Information Systems, Saint Anne's Hospital, Fall River, MA, p. A317

O'NEIL, Daniel, Vice President Information Technology, Caritas Good Samaritan Medical Center, Brockton, MA, p. A315

O'NEIL, David J., Vice President and Chief Financial Officer, Morton Plant Hospital, Clearwater, FL, p. A125

O'NEIL, John D., President and Chief Executive Officer, Our Lady of Lourdes Memorial Hospital, Binghamton, NY, p. A448

O'NEIL, Michael, Administrator, Four Winds Hospital, Saratoga Springs, NY, p. A472

O'NEIL, Rose, Chief Executive Officer, Select Specialty Hospital of Orlando, Orlando, FL, p. A141

O'NEILL, Brian, Vice President Finance, Somerset Medical Center, Somerville, NJ, p. A436

O'NEILL, Daniel R., Vice President Finance, Huggins Hospital, Wolfeboro, NH, p. A424

O'NEILL, Joseph J., Vice President, Medical Affairs, South County Hospital, Wakefield, RI, p. A582

O'NEILL, Mark A., Senior Vice President and Chief Financial Officer, Jersey Shore Hospital, Jersey Shore, PA, p. A561

O'NEILL, Stephan, Vice President Information Services, Hartford Hospital, Hartford, CT, p. A113

O'QUINN, Marvin
President and Chief Executive Officer, Jackson Health System, Miami, FL, p. B63
President and Chief Executive Officer, Jackson Memorial Hospital, Miami, FL, p. A137

O'RIELLY, Robert
Deputy Chief Executive Officer, U. S. Public Health Service Indian Hospital, Parker, AZ, p. A33
Deputy Chief Executive Officer, U. S. Public Health Service Indian Hospital, Parker, AZ, p. A33

O'ROURKE, Kenneth, Administrator, Cypress Psychiatric Hospital, Baton Rouge, LA, p. A277

O'SHAUGHNESSY, Jon C., Chief Executive Officer, Murray–Calloway County Hospital, Murray, KY, p. A272

O'SHEA, James E.
Administrator, Springbrook Hospital, Brooksville, FL, p. A125
Administrator, Willough Healthcare System, Naples, FL, p. A139

O'SHIELDS, Brent, Human Resources Director, Laurens County Healthcare System, Clinton, SC, p. A585

OAKES, R.N., Julie, Director Information Systems, Ocean Beach Hospital, Ilwaco, WA, p. A703

OBER, Tammy L., Administrator, HEALTHSOUTH Reading Rehabilitation Hospital, Reading, PA, p. A574

OBERG, Roger, Administrator, Long Prairie Memorial Hospital and Home, Long Prairie, MN, p. A356

OBERHOLTZER, Curt, Assistant Administrator of Human Resources and Organizational Development, Bay Area Medical Center, Marinette, WI, p. A729

OBERMILLER, Cynthia, Chief Information Officer, Veterans Affairs Medical Center, Manchester, NH, p. A422

OBERSCHLAKE, Tim, Associate Vice President Information Systems, Aultman Hospital, Canton, OH, p. A505

OBERTA, Gail M., FACHE, Chief Executive Officer and Managing Director, Meridell Achievement Center, Liberty Hill, TX, p. A653

OBOMA ASEMOTA, Steve, Chief of Staff, Delta Memorial Hospital, Dumas, AR, p. A42

OCASIO, Manuel, Vice President Information Systems, Holy Cross Hospital, Silver Spring, MD, p. A311

OCCHIOGROSSO, Kathleen, Vice President Human Resources, Seton Health System, Troy, NY, p. A474

OCHS, David T., Administrator, OSF Saint James – John W. Albrecht Medical Center, Pontiac, IL, p. A205

OCHS, Kristine, R.N., Administrator, Grisell Memorial Hospital District One, Ransom, KS, p. A256

OCKER, MSC, USN, Kenneth, Director Resource Management, National Naval Medical Center, Bethesda, MD, p. A305

OCKERS, Thomas, President and Chief Executive Officer, Brookhaven Memorial Hospital Medical Center, Patchogue, NY, p. A469

OCKRYMIEK, M.D., Steven, Senior Vice President, Holy Redeemer Hospital and Medical Center, Jenkintown, PA, p. A561

ODATO, David, Executive Driector Human Resources, UCSF Medical Center, San Francisco, CA, p. A89

ODDIS, Joseph M., President and Chief Executive Officer, Harbor Hospital Center, Baltimore, MD, p. A303

ODEGAARD, Daniel, Chief Executive Officer, Big Fork Valley Hospital, Bigfork, MN, p. A350

ODELL III, Frederick A., FACHE, President, Carteret General Hospital, Morehead City, NC, p. A488

ODLAND, M.D., David, Chief of Staff, Avera Marshall Regional Medical Center, Marshall, MN, p. A356

ODOM, M.D., John, Chief of Medical Staff, Marion County Medical Center, Mullins, SC, p. A590

ODOM, Terry, Vice President Clinical Services, Heart Hospital of New Mexico, Albuquerque, NM, p. A440

OEHLERS, Randi, Management Information Systems Site Director, Mercy Hospital Cadillac, Cadillac, MI, p. A329

OEHRING, David J., Chief Financial Officer, Hills and Dales General Hospital, Cass City, MI, p. A329

OESTMANN, Barbara, Chief Executive Officer, Share Medical Center, Alva, OK, p. A527

OESTREIC, Pearl, Human Resource Director, Llano Memorial Healthcare System, Llano, TX, p. A653

OETKEN, Matthew, Chief of Staff, Riverside Medical Center, Waupaca, WI, p. A737

OETTING, Phyllis, Director Human Resources, Mitchell County Hospital, Beloit, KS, p. A244

OETZEL, Gerald P., Chief Financial Officer, Jeanes Hospital, Philadelphia, PA, p. A568

OFOMA, M.D., Celestine, Chief of Staff, Sheridan County Health Complex, Hoxie, KS, p. A249

OGATA, M.D., Edward S., Chief Medical Officer, Children's Memorial Hospital, Chicago, IL, p. A187

OGAWA, Quin, Vice President and Chief Financial Officer, Kuakini Medical Center, Honolulu, HI, p. A173

OGBURN, Wayne L., FACHE, Chief Executive Officer, Yoakum Community Hospital, Yoakum, TX, p. A675

OGDEN, Janice, Director Human Resource Management, Harrison Memorial Hospital, Cynthiana, KY, p. A263

OGG, Tom, Vice President Information, Support Services and Chief Information Officer, Memorial Healthcare, Owosso, MI, p. A342

OGILVIE, Richard, Chief Information Officer, Southwestern Vermont Medical Center, Bennington, VT, p. A682

OGLESBY, Darrell M., Administrator, Putnam General Hospital, Eatonton, GA, p. A161

OGLESBY, Michele, Human Resources Manager, Eastern Oklahoma Medical Center, Poteau, OK, p. A537

OGLEVIE, Anne, Administrator, Weiser Memorial Hospital, Weiser, ID, p. A182

OGORZALEK, Ed, Chief Financial Officer, Rutland Regional Medical Center, Rutland, VT, p. A683

OGURA, Marsha, Controller, HEALTHSOUTH Rehabilitation Hospital, Humble, TX, p. A649

OH, M.D., Sai, Medical Director, HEALTHSOUTH Chattanooga Rehabilitation Hospital, Chattanooga, TN, p. A603

OHEA, Michael, Director of Human Resources, Guyan Valley Hospital, Logan, WV, p. A717

OHLEN, Robert B., Chief Executive Officer, Bob Wilson Memorial Grant County Hospital, Ulysses, KS, p. A258

OHM, Barbara, Executive Director, Carrie Tingley Hospital, Albuquerque, NM, p. A440

OHMART, Dean, Chief Financial Officer, Ransom Memorial Hospital, Ottawa, KS, p. A254

OINES, M.D., Stephen, Chief of Staff, Brownwood Regional Medical Center, Brownwood, TX, p. A627

OJEDA, Tito, Quality Assurance and Information Systems Director, Greenwood County Hospital, Eureka, KS, p. A247

OKAMOTO, Gary, President and Chief Executive Officer, Queen's Health Systems, Honolulu, HI, p. B88

OKERSON, Alan, Information Technology Director, Kenmare Community Hospital, Kenmare, ND, p. A499

OKESON, Keith, Chief Executive Officer, Roseau Area Hospital and Homes, Roseau, MN, p. A361

OKUHARA, Mary
Director Human Resources, Lakewood Regional Medical Center, Lakewood, CA, p. A67
Director Human Resources, Promise Hospital of East Los Angeles, Suburban Medical Center Campus, Paramount, CA, p. A81

OKUMA, William, Director, Management Systems, South Georgia Medical Center, Valdosta, GA, p. A171

OLAND, Charisse S., President and Chief Executive Officer, Childrens Care Hospital and School, Sioux Falls, SD, p. A599

OLASIN, Regina, Senior Vice President Director of Medical Affairs, Catskill Regional Medical Center, Harris, NY, p. A453

OLAZAGASTI, M.D., Rafael, Vice President Medical Affairs and Network Development, Benedictine Hospital, Kingston, NY, p. A455

OLDEN, R. Don, Chief Executive Officer, Kahuku Hospital, Kahuku, HI, p. A174

OLEJNICZAK, David, Chief Operating Officer, Sartori Memorial Hospital, Cedar Falls, IA, p. A229

OLEJNICZAK, Shelly, Director Human Resources, St. Luke's Hospital, Racine, WI, p. A734

OLEY, Edwin M., President and Chief Executive Officer, Allen Medical Center, Oberlin, OH, p. A520

OLINDE, Chad, Assistant Administrator and Chief Financial Officer, Pointe Coupee General Hospital, New Roads, LA, p. A290

OLINGER, Terry, Vice President Human Resources, Benefis Healthcare, Great Falls, MT, p. A399

OLIPHINT, Kelley, Chief Executive Officer and Administrator, Fayette Memorial Hospital, La Grange, TX, p. A651

OLIVARES, Rafael, Controller, Starr County Memorial Hospital, Rio Grande City, TX, p. A662

OLIVAREZ, Lorenzo, Chief Financial Officer, Harris Methodist–Erath County, Stephenville, TX, p. A668

OLIVE, Alan C., Chief Executive Officer, Washoe Medical Center South Meadows, Reno, NV, p. A418

OLIVENCIA, M.D., Humberto, Medical Director, Hospital Perea, Mayaguez, PR, p. A745

OLIVER, David, Director Information Systems, King's Daughters Medical Center, Ashland, KY, p. A261

OLIVER, Donna M., Chief Executive Officer, Mercy Medical Center–Clinton, Clinton, IA, p. A230

OLIVER, Ginger, Vice President Information Systems, Tampa General Hospital, Tampa, FL, p. A148

OLIVER, Julie, Chief Human Resources Officer, Immanuel St. Joseph's–Mayo Health System, Mankato, MN, p. A356

OLIVER, Karen, Vice President Human Resources, West Florida Hospital, Pensacola, FL, p. A143

OLIVER, M.D., Kerry, Chief Medical Officer, San Joaquin Community Hospital, Bakersfield, CA, p. A54

OLIVER, Vincent, Administrator, Island Hospital, Anacortes, WA, p. A700

OLIVER, William C., President, Forrest General Hospital, Hattiesburg, MS, p. A369

OLIVERIO, John D., President and Chief Executive Officer, Wheaton Franciscan Services, Inc., Wheaton, IL, p. B122

OLIVERIUS, Maynard F., President and Chief Executive Officer, Stormont–Vail HealthCare, Topeka, KS, p. A258

OLIVIA, Christopher, M.D., President and Chief Executive Officer, Cooper Health System, Camden, NJ, p. A426

OLIVIER, John, Director Information Systems, Haywood Regional Medical Center, Clyde, NC, p. A480

OLLIE, Edwin J., Senior Vice President and Chief Financial Officer, New Hanover Regional Medical Center, Wilmington, NC, p. A494

OLLIGES, Janet, Director Human Resources, SSM DePaul Health Center, Saint Louis, MO, p. A391

OLLIS, Linda Neu, Vice President, Christus Schumpert Health System, Shreveport, LA, p. A292

OLMO, Blanca, Director of Finance, University Pediatric Hospital, San Juan, PR, p. A748

OLS, Timothy, Vice President and Chief Operating Officer, Greene Memorial Hospital, Xenia, OH, p. A525

OLSCAMP, Karen, Chief Operating Officer, Baltimore Washington Medical Center, Glen Burnie, MD, p. A308

OLSEN, Gloria P., Ph.D., Superintendent, Kerrville State Hospital, Kerrville, TX, p. A651

OLSEN, Robert T., FACHE, President and Chief Executive Officer, Yuma Regional Medical Center, Yuma, AZ, p. A39

OLSEN–NAKADA, Susan, Chief Operating Officer and Chief Nursing Officer, Sharp Coronado Hospital and Health Center, Coronado, CA, p. A58

OLSON, Bonnie, Director Human Resources, HEALTHSOUTH Braintree Rehabilitation Hospital, Braintree, MA, p. A315

OLSON, Christine, Administrator, Aurora Medical Center, Kenosha, WI, p. A727

OLSON, Dale, Chief Executive Officer, Rehabilitation Hospital of New Mexico, Albuquerque, NM, p. A441

OLSON, David, President and Chief Executive Officer, Bay Area Medical Center, Marinette, WI, p. A729

OLSON, Diana
    Chief Human Resources Officer, Mercy Hospital of Tiffin, Tiffin, OH, p. A522
    Chief Human Resources Officer, Mercy Hospital of Willard, Willard, OH, p. A525

OLSON, Edward A., President and Chief Executive Officer, Waukesha Memorial Hospital, Waukesha, WI, p. A737

OLSON, Gary R., President and Chief Executive Officer, St. Luke's Hospital, Chesterfield, MO, p. A380

OLSON, Gregg, Chief Executive Officer, Rochelle Community Hospital, Rochelle, IL, p. A206

OLSON, James, Chief Information Officer, Waterbury Hospital, Waterbury, CT, p. A117

OLSON, JoAline, R.N.,
    President and Chief Executive Officer, St Helena Hospital–Center for Behavioral Health, Vallejo, CA, p. A97
    President and Chief Executive Officer, St. Helena Hospital, Saint Helena, CA, p. A85

OLSON, Kent
    Chief Financial Officer, Fairmont Medical Center–Mayo Health System, Fairmont, MN, p. A353
    Assistant Administrator and Chief Financial Officer, Riverwood HealthCare Center, Aitkin, MN, p. A349

OLSON, Kevin, Director of Information Systems, Bone and Joint Hospital, Oklahoma City, OK, p. A535

OLSON, Lynn W., President and Chief Executive Officer, Ottumwa Regional Health Center, Ottumwa, IA, p. A240

OLSON, Maribeth, Interim Administrator, St. Mary's Hospital of Superior, Superior, WI, p. A736

OLSON, Michael R., Administrator, American Fork Hospital, American Fork, UT, p. A676

OLSON, Nathan C., Chief Executive Officer, Heart of the Rockies Regional Medical Center, Salida, CO, p. A109

OLSON, Randall M., Chief Executive Officer, Lane Memorial Hospital, Zachary, LA, p. A295

OLSON, Rick, Chief of Staff, Kaiser Sunnyside Medical Center, Clackamas, OR, p. A542

OLSON, Sharon, Director Fiscal Services, Harlan County Health System, Alma, NE, p. A404

OLSON, Susie, Director Human Resources, Wilson County Hospital, Neodesha, KS, p. A253

OLSON, M.D., Theodore, Chief of Staff, Riverview Healthcare Association, Crookston, MN, p. A352

OLSON, M.D., Thomas, Chief of Staff, Sioux Valley Vermillion Medical Center, Vermillion, SD, p. A600

OLSON, William, Director Finance, Providence St. Vincent Medical Center, Portland, OR, p. A548

OLSSON, Clifford Lee, Chief Financial Officer, Gila Regional Medical Center, Silver City, NM, p. A445

OMEL, John, Interim Vice President Human Resources, Provena Saint Joseph Medical Center, Joliet, IL, p. A198

OMER, Laura, Director Medical Services, Naval Hospital, Corpus Christi, TX, p. A631

OMER, Robert W., FACHE, Chief Executive Officer, Pioneers Hospital of Rio Blanco County, Meeker, CO, p. A108

OMMEN, Ronald A., Chief Executive Officer and Administrator, St. John's Medical Center and Living Center, Jackson, WY, p. A740

OMTA, Stephen R., Chief Operating Officer, St. Joseph Hospital, Bellingham, WA, p. A700

ONA, M.D., Celia M., Medical Director, Kahi Mohala Behavioral Health, Ewa Beach, HI, p. A173

ONG, Jesus M., President, South Shore Hospital, Chicago, IL, p. A190

ONTIVEROS Jr, Alfredo, Chief Executive Officer, Fort Duncan Medical Center, Eagle Pass, TX, p. A636

OOSTRA, Randall D., FACHE,
    President, Lenawee Health Alliance – Bixby Campus, Adrian, MI, p. A327
    President, Lenawee Health Alliance–Herrick Campus, Tecumseh, MI, p. A346

OPHEIKENS, Robyn, Assistant Administrator, Human Resources, St. Mark's Hospital, Salt Lake City, UT, p. A680

OPP, Robert, Chief Clinical Officer, Jellico Community Hospital, Jellico, TN, p. A608

OPPENLANDER, David M., Vice President and Treasurer, St. Luke's Hospital, Maumee, OH, p. A518

OQUENDO, Tanja, Vice President Human Resources, Spectrum Health, Grand Rapids, MI, p. A335

ORAM–SMITH, M.D., Jeffrey C., Chief Medical Officer, Penrose–St. Francis Health Services, Colorado Springs, CO, p. A102

ORANGE, Valerie, Chief Executive Officer, Rancho Los Amigos National Rehabilitation Center, Downey, CA, p. A59

ORAVEC, Jon, Vice President Human Resources, St. Anthony Hospital, Pendleton, OR, p. A547

ORCUTT, David, Chief Executive Officer, Stringfellow Memorial Hospital, Anniston, AL, p. A13

OREAR, Kathy, Director Human Resources, Newman Regional Health, Emporia, KS, p. A246

ORFANAKIS, M.D., Nicholas, Chief of Staff, Tuality Healthcare, Hillsboro, OR, p. A544

ORFANOS, M.D., John G., Chief of Staff, Cornerstone Regional Hospital, Edinburg, TX, p. A636

ORFGEN, Lynn C., President and Chief Executive Officer, Crittenton Hospital Medical Center, Rochester, MI, p. A343

ORIOLI, Sherri, Director Personnel Systems, Harris County Psychiatric Center, Houston, TX, p. A645

ORITZ, Mildred, Chief Human Resources Officer, San Juan City Hospital, San Juan, PR, p. A748

ORLANDO, Anthony T., Senior Vice President Finance, Englewood Hospital and Medical Center, Englewood, NJ, p. A428

ORLANDO, Charles, Senior Vice President and Chief Financial Officer, Sinai Hospital of Baltimore, Baltimore, MD, p. A304

ORLANDO, Joseph S., Interim Chief Executive Officer, Barnert Hospital, Paterson, NJ, p. A434

ORLANG, M.D., Vern, Medical Director, East Liverpool City Hospital, East Liverpool, OH, p. A513

ORLOWSKI, M.D., Janis M., Senior Vice President Medical Affairs and Chief Medical Officer, Washington Hospital Center, Washington, DC, p. A122

ORMAN Jr, Bernard A., Administrator, Samaritan Memorial Hospital, Macon, MO, p. A387

ORME, Clifton Neal, FACHE, Administrator and Chief Executive Officer, LifeCare Hospitals of Pittsburgh, Pittsburgh, PA, p. A571

ORME, Dave, Chief Information Officer, Rehabilitation Hospital of the Pacific, Honolulu, HI, p. A174

ORMOND, Evalyn, Administrator, Union General Hospital, Farmerville, LA, p. A280

ORMS, M.D., James M., Medical Director, Maniilaq Health Center, Kotzebue, AK, p. A28

ORNE, Charles T., Executive Vice President Finance and Chief Financial Officer, Central Maine Medical Center, Lewiston, ME, p. A299

ORR, Roy J., Chief Executive Officer, McKenzie–Willamette Medical Center, Springfield, OR, p. A549

ORRICK, Charles H., Administrator, Donalsonville Hospital, Donalsonville, GA, p. A160

ORRIS, Lisa, Director Laboratory, Cardiopulmonary and Information Systems, Brownsville General Hospital, Brownsville, PA, p. A553

ORRISON, Pat, Director Information Services, Marianjoy Rehabilitation Hospital, Wheaton, IL, p. A210

ORSINI, Thomas J., President and Chief Executive Officer, Lake Taylor Transitional Care Hospital, Norfolk, VA, p. A692

ORT, Linda, Chief Financial Officer, Piggott Community Hospital, Piggott, AR, p. A49

ORTEGA, Debra, Vice President Human Resources, Huntington Memorial Hospital, Pasadena, CA, p. A81

ORTEGO, Craig A., Administrator and Chief Executive Officer, Dallas County Medical Center, Fordyce, AR, p. A43

ORTEGON, Liisa, Chief Nursing Officer, Horizon Medical Center, Dickson, TN, p. A605

ORTELT, Raymond, Director Information Systems, Memorial Hospital of Rhode Island, Pawtucket, RI, p. A581

ORTENZIO, Robert, Chief Executive Officer, Select Medical Corporation, Mechanicsburg, PA, p. B96

ORTHAUS, Denis, Director Human Resources, Good Samaritan Regional Medical Center, Pottsville, PA, p. A573

ORTINAU, M.D., Eric T., Medical Staff President, Community Hospital of Ottawa, Ottawa, IL, p. A204

ORTIZ, Alex, Billing Manager, Hospital Dr. Cayetano Coll Y Toste, Arecibo, PR, p. A743

ORTIZ, Edson, Chief Information Officer, Hospital Metropolitano Dr. Tito Mattei, Yauco, PR, p. A749

ORTIZ, Felix, Administrator, I. Gonzalez Martinez Oncologic Hospital, Hato Rey, PR, p. A747

ORTIZ, Jose O., Chief Financial Officer, Ryder Memorial Hospital, Humacao, PR, p. A745

ORTIZ, Julio A., M.D., Chairman, Font Martelo Hospital, Humacao, PR, p. A745

ORTIZ, CPA, Milagros, Finance Director, Ashford Presbyterian Community Hospital, San Juan, PR, p. A746

ORTIZ, Noel, Finance Director and Controller, Mepsi Center, Bayamon, PR, p. A744

ORTMANN, Karen, Senior Vice President Patient Care and Operations, Marianjoy Rehabilitation Hospital, Wheaton, IL, p. A210

ORTON, Sharon, Director Information Services and Technology, Corpus Christi Medical Center, Corpus Christi, TX, p. A630

ORTSMAN, Sheldon, Vice President, Operations and Human Resources, Bronx–Lebanon Hospital Center, New York, NY, p. A458

OSBAHR, Leah, President, Lawrence Memorial Hospital, Walnut Ridge, AR, p. A51

OSBORN, M.D., James, Vice President Medical Management, Harris Methodist Fort Worth, Fort Worth, TX, p. A639

OSBORNE, Jr, Barney E., Chief Financial Officer, Bamberg County Memorial Hospital and Nursing Center, Bamberg, SC, p. A583

OSBORNE, Brad, Chief Information Officer, Providence–Little Company of Mary Service Area, Torrance, CA, p. A96

OSBORNE, Matt, Medical Information Systems Flight Chief, Wright Patterson Medical Center, Wright–Patterson AFB, OH, p. A525

OSBORNE, Sandra, Director Information Systems, Monongahela Valley Hospital, Monongahela, PA, p. A565

OSBORNE, Terry W., CPA, Chief Executive Officer, American Legion Hospital, Crowley, LA, p. A279

OSBOURNE, Pauline, Senior Vice President and Chief Financial Officer, Rehabilitation Hospital of the Pacific, Honolulu, HI, p. A174

OSBURN, Jerry, Administrator, Covenant Hospital–Levelland, Levelland, TX, p. A652

OSCADAL, Martin, Vice President Human Resources, Saint Vincent Hospital at Worcester Medical Center, Worcester, MA, p. A325

OSER, M.D., JD, William F., Senior Vice President and Chief Medical Officer, JFK Medical Center, Edison, NJ, p. A428

OSMUS, Richard D., Chief Executive Officer, Hugh Chatham Memorial Hospital, Elkin, NC, p. A482

OSSE, John M., Administrator, Mitchell County Hospital, Beloit, KS, p. A244

OSTASZEWSKI, Patricia, Administrator, HEALTHSOUTH Rehabilitation Hospital of New Jersey, Toms River, NJ, p. A437

OSTERBERG, Valerie, Chief Financial Officer, Sioux Valley Vermillion Medical Center, Vermillion, SD, p. A600

OSTERLAND, Linda, Director Information Services, St. John River District Hospital, East China, MI, p. A332

OSTLIE, Mel, Director Information Services, Wilson N. Jones Medical Center, Sherman, TX, p. A667

OSTRANDER, Thomas, Vice President Human Resources, Henry Ford Wyandotte Hospital, Wyandotte, MI, p. A348

OSTREM, Jill, Vice President Operations, Jersey Shore University Medical Center, Neptune, NJ, p. A432

OSWALD, George, Chief Financial Officer, Baptist Memorial Hospital–Collierville, Collierville, TN, p. A604

OSWALD, Lynn M., R.N., Senior Vice President, Fort Hamilton Hospital, Hamilton, OH, p. A515

OSWALD, Wesley, Chief Operating Officer, Sparks Regional Medical Center, Fort Smith, AR, p. A43

OSWALT, Charles, Vice President and Chief Financial Officer, Levi Hospital, Hot Springs National Park, AR, p. A45

OTANI, M.D., Eric, President Medical Staff, Alameda Hospital, Alameda, CA, p. A52

OTEY, Barbara, Vice President Human Resources, Doctors Hospital, Columbus, OH, p. A510

OTEY, Dean, Interim Administrator and Chief Executive Officer, Cordova Community Medical Center, Cordova, AK, p. A26

OTHOLE, Jean, Service Unit Director, U. S. Public Health Service Indian Hospital, Zuni, NM, p. A445

OTRADOVEC, Cindy, Director Health Information Systems, Lake Regional Health System, Osage Beach, MO, p. A388

OTT, Pamela, R.N., Chief Executive Officer, Kern Valley Healthcare District, Lake Isabella, CA, p. A66

OTT, Ronald A., Chief Executive Officer, Fitzgibbon Hospital, Marshall, MO, p. A387

OTT, Ronald H., President, UPMC McKeesport, McKeesport, PA, p. A564

OTTATI, David, Administrator, Florida Hospital Wauchula, Wauchula, FL, p. A150

OTTER, Carol, Chief Information Officer, U. S. Public Health Service Indian Hospital, Parker, AZ, p. A33

OTWELL, Robert, Chief Executive Officer, Maury Regional Hospital, Columbia, TN, p. A604

OUNGST, Laurie, Assistant Vice President, Howard Young Medical Center, Woodruff, WI, p. A738

OUSEY, Tracy, Director Human Resources, Washington County Hospital, Washington, IA, p. A242

OUTLER, Jean
    Director Human Resources, Children's Hospital of Michigan, Detroit, MI, p. A331
    Director Human Resources, Huron Valley–Sinai Hospital, Commerce Township, MI, p. A330

OVERACKER, Kymberlee S., Chief Financial Officer, Weiser Memorial Hospital, Weiser, ID, p. A182

OVERBEY, Bill
    Chief Financial Officer and Chief Information Officer, Hays Medical Center, Hays, KS, p. A248
    Chief Financial Officer and Chief Information Officer, Hays Medical Center, Hays, KS, p. A248

OVERBY, Bill, Information Systems Manager, Lakeview Hospital, Stillwater, MN, p. A363

OVERMAN, Pat, Vice President Human Resources, St. Bernards Medical Center, Jonesboro, AR, p. A45

OVERSTREET, Alyson, Chief Financial Officer, Washington County Hospital and Nursing Home, Chatom, AL, p. A16

OVERSTREET, Amy, Human Resources Director, Carthage General Hospital, Carthage, TN, p. A603

OVERTON, R.N., Barbara K., Vice President Patient Services, Fauquier Hospital, Warrenton, VA, p. A698

OWEN, Chris, Director, Mount Desert Island Hospital, Bar Harbor, ME, p. A296

OWEN, Laura, Senior Vice President, Trinity Mother Frances Health System, Tyler, TX, p. A671

OWEN, Mary, R.N., Interim Administrator, Johnston Memorial Hospital, Tishomingo, OK, p. A539

OWEN, Ramona, Administrative Officer, U. S. Public Health Service Indian Hospital, Sisseton, SD, p. A599

OWEN, Ronald S., Chief Executive Officer, Southeast Alabama Medical Center, Dothan, AL, p. A17

OWEN, Sandra, Director Fiscal and Accounting, Hospital District Number Five of Harper County, Harper, KS, p. A248

OWENS, Betina, Chief Information Officer, Bogalusa Medical Center, Bogalusa, LA, p. A278

OWENS, Beverly, Controller, HEALTHSOUTH Central Georgia Rehabilitation Hospital, Macon, GA, p. A165

OWENS, Bradley, Chief Financial Officer, Saint Francis Hospital, Charleston, WV, p. A714

OWENS, Craig A., Senior Vice President and Chief Operating Officer, Eisenhower Memorial Hospital and Betty Ford Center at Eisenhower, Rancho Mirage, CA, p. A83

OWENS, David J., Chief Executive Officer, Jasper Memorial Hospital, Monticello, GA, p. A166

OWENS, Max, Chief Financial Officer, NEA Medical Center, Jonesboro, AR, p. A45

OWENS, Ray, Administrator and Chief Executive Officer, Dubuis Hospital of Alexandria, Alexandria, LA, p. A276

OWERS, Robert, Associate Administrator, Jackson South Community Hospital, Miami, FL, p. A137

OWINGS, David C., Director Information Management Service Line, Wm. Jennings Bryan Dorn Veterans Affairs Medical Center, Columbia, SC, p. A586

OWINGS, Raymond, Chief Financial Officer, St. Joseph Hospital, Augusta, GA, p. A155

OWZCARZAK, Margaret, Chief Information Systems, Veterans Affairs Western New York Healthcare System–Buffalo Division, Buffalo, NY, p. A449

OXENDALE, Roger A., President and Chief Executive Officer, Children's Hospital of Pittsburgh of UPMC, Pittsburgh, PA, p. A571

OXFORD, Janet, Chief Human Resources Officer, Banner Desert Medical Center, Mesa, AZ, p. A32

OXFORD, Tammy, Manager Human Resources, Satanta District Hospital, Satanta, KS, p. A256

OZBURN, Tom, Chief Operating Officer, Greenview Regional Hospital, Bowling Green, KY, p. A262

OZOLS, Ph.D., Robert F., Senior Vice President Medical Sciences, Fox Chase Cancer Center–American Oncologic Hospital, Philadelphia, PA, p. A567

P

PABLO, Victoria, Human Resource Specialist, U. S. Public Health Service Indian Hospital, Crownpoint, NM, p. A442

PABON, Jose O., Operating Director, Wilma N. Vazquez Medical Center, Vega Baja, PR, p. A748

PACCAPANICCIA, Dominic, Senior Vice President Operations, Indiana Regional Medical Center, Indiana, PA, p. A561

PACES, Amy, Director Human Resources, Westside Regional Medical Center, Plantation, FL, p. A143

PACHECO, Kris, Chief Executive Officer, McKenzie County Healthcare System, Watford City, ND, p. A500

PACINI, Carol, Provincialate Superior, American Province of Little Company of Mary Sisters, Evergreen Park, IL, p. B8

PACK, Robyne
    Administrator, HEALTHSOUTH Rehabilitation Hospital, Humble, TX, p. A649
    Administrator, HEALTHSOUTH Rehabilitation Hospital of North Houston, Conroe, TX, p. A630

PACK, William
    Chief Financial Officer, Christus Santa Rosa Children's Hospital, San Antonio, TX, p. A663
    Chief Financial Officer, Christus Santa Rosa Health Care, San Antonio, TX, p. A663

PACKER, Eric, Administrator, Bear River Valley Hospital, Tremonton, UT, p. A680

PACKER, M.D., Michael, Chief Medical Staff, Madison Memorial Hospital, Rexburg, ID, p. A181

PACKER, Steven J., M.D., Chief Executive Officer, Community Hospital of the Monterey Peninsula, Monterey, CA, p. A76

PACKNETT, Michael J.
    President and Chief Executive Officer, Mercy Health Center, Oklahoma City, OK, p. A535
    President and Chief Executive Officer, Oklahoma Heart Hospital, Oklahoma City, OK, p. A536

PADAVANO, Jerry, Chief Information Officer, California Pacific Medical Center, San Francisco, CA, p. A88

PADDEN, Ernest C., Vice President and Chief Financial Officer, Chesapeake General Hospital, Chesapeake, VA, p. A686

PADDEN, Terrance J., Chief Executive Officer, Mercer County Joint Township Community Hospital, Coldwater, OH, p. A510

PADGETT, Audrey, Administrator, Cedar Vale Community Hospital, Cedar Vale, KS, p. A245

PADGETT, Martin, President and Chief Executive Officer, Clark Memorial Hospital, Jeffersonville, IN, p. A219

PADGETT, Randal, Information Systems Manager, Barnwell County Hospital, Barnwell, SC, p. A583

PADILLA, Gregory, Chief Executive Officer, Maryvale Hospital Medical Center, Phoenix, AZ, p. A34

PADRO, Silvia, Director Information Services, Largo Medical Center, Largo, FL, p. A134

PAGANELLI, Deborah, CHE, President, Harris Methodist–Erath County, Stephenville, TX, p. A668

PAGANO, Tom, Chief Information Officer, Lawrence Memorial Hospital, Lawrence, KS, p. A251

PAGE, Bob, Senior Vice President and Chief Operating Officer, University of Kansas Hospital, Kansas City, KS, p. A250

PAGE, David R., President and Chief Executive Officer, Fairview Health Services, Minneapolis, MN, p. B44

PAGE, Keith Allen, President and Chief Executive Officer, Anderson Hospital, Maryville, IL, p. A200

PAGE, M.D., Michael J., Chief Medical Officer, Carrington Health Center, Carrington, ND, p. A497

PAGE, Susan M., President and Chief Executive Officer, Pratt Regional Medical Center, Pratt, KS, p. A255

PAGELS, M.D., George A., Senior Vice President and Chief Medical Officer, Saint Luke's Northland Hospital–Smithville Campus, Smithville, MO, p. A393

PAGLIARO, Michael, Vice President for Human Resources, White Plains Hospital Center, White Plains, NY, p. A476

PAGLIUZZA, Greg
    Senior Vice President and Chief Financial Officer, Centegra Memorial Medical Center, Woodstock, IL, p. A210
    Senior Vice President and Chief Financial Officer, Centegra Northern Illinois Medical Center, McHenry, IL, p. A200

PAINE, Charles J., M.D., President and Chief Executive Officer, Christus Schumpert Health System, Shreveport, LA, p. A292

PAINE, M.D., Charles J., Chief Medical Officer, Christus Schumpert Health System, Shreveport, LA, p. A292

PAINTER, Ellen, Director Marketing, Presbyterian Hospital of Denton, Denton, TX, p. A635

PAKUTZ, Stanley, Manager Business Office, Veterans Affairs Medical Center, Butler, PA, p. A554

PALACIOS, Edward C., R.N., Chief Executive Officer, San Joaquin Valley Rehabilitation Hospital, Fresno, CA, p. A61

PALAGI, Richard L., Chief Executive Officer, Sauk Prairie Memorial Hospital, Prairie Du Sac, WI, p. A734

PALAIA, Jane, Vice President Human Resources, Community Medical Center, Toms River, NJ, p. A437

PALAZZOLO, Christopher, Executive Vice President and Chief Financial Officer, Harper University Hospital, Detroit, MI, p. A331

PALEKA, Chrisey, Human Resources Coordinator, Molokai General Hospital, Kaunakakai, HI, p. A175

PALES, Joaquin, President, Hospital Santa Rosa, Guayama, PR, p. A745

PALIGO, Terry, Chief Financial Officer, Hoopeston Community Memorial Hospital, Hoopeston, IL, p. A197

PALIS, Adar, Chief Information Officer, Harrison Memorial Hospital, Bremerton, WA, p. A700

PALLARI, Robert
President and Chief Executive Officer, Legacy Good Samaritan Hospital and Medical Center, Portland, OR, p. A547
President and Chief Executive Officer, Legacy Health System, Portland, OR, p. B67
President and Chief Executive Officer, Legacy Good Samaritan Hospital and Medical Center, Portland, OR, p. A547

PALLAS, Drew, Vice President Finance, Eastern Long Island Hospital, Greenport, NY, p. A453

PALLETTE, M.D., Edward M., Acting Chief of Staff, Mountains Community Hospital, Lake Arrowhead, CA, p. A66

PALM, SharRay, President and Chief Executive Officer, LakeWood Health Center, Baudette, MN, p. A350

PALMBERG, M.D., Kent, Senior Vice President and Chief Medical Officer, Stormont–Vail HealthCare, Topeka, KS, p. A258

PALMER, Barbara, Director Corporate Human Resources, Botsford General Hospital, Farmington Hills, MI, p. A333

PALMER, Cass, Vice President Human Resources, Blake Medical Center, Bradenton, FL, p. A124

PALMER, Don, Chief of Staff, Kaiser Foundation Hospital, Walnut Creek, CA, p. A98

PALMER, M.D., H Schubert, Chief of Staff, Monterey Park Hospital, Monterey Park, CA, p. A76

PALMER, Janel, Chief Financial Officer, Greenwood County Hospital, Eureka, KS, p. A247

PALMER, John M., Ph.D., Executive Director, Harlem Hospital Center, New York, NY, p. A460

PALMER, Mark R., Chief Executive Officer, Alvarado Hospital Medical Center, San Diego, CA, p. A86

PALMER, Terry, Chief Informaiton Officer, Bradford Regional Medical Center, Bradford, PA, p. A553

PALMER, Tim, Director Information Systems, Caldwell Memorial Hospital, Lenoir, NC, p. A486

PALMER, M.D., William S., President Medical Staff, Mt. Ascutney Hospital and Health Center, Windsor, VT, p. A684

PALMIER, Michael L., Chief Human Resources and Staff Development, Veterans Affairs Illiana Health Care System, Danville, IL, p. A191

PALMISANO II, Richard T., R.N., President and Chief Executive Officer, Brattleboro Retreat, Brattleboro, VT, p. A682

PALO, Alan, Chief Financial Officer, Clarinda Regional Health Center, Clarinda, IA, p. A230

PALSROK, Jerri, Business Office Manager, Osceola Community Hospital, Sibley, IA, p. A241

PALZER, Douglas C., Administrator, Doctors Specialty Hospital, Shawnee Mission, KS, p. A257

PANCOAST, James R., President and Chief Executive Officer, Good Samaritan Hospital, Dayton, OH, p. A512

PANDL, Therese B.
Executive Vice President for Hospital Operations, Columbia St. Mary's Ozaukee Campus, Mequon, WI, p. A730
Executive Vice President for Hospital Operations, Columbia St. Mary's–Columbia Campus, Milwaukee, WI, p. A730
Executive Vice President for Hospital Operations, Columbia St. Mary's–Milwaukee Campus, Milwaukee, WI, p. A730

PANDOLPH, Philip, Chief Operating Officer, Southwest Mississippi Regional Medical Center, McComb, MS, p. A372

PANGBORN, Janet, Vice President Operations, St. Michael Hospital, Milwaukee, WI, p. A732

PANGLE, Brian, Vice President Finance, Spectrum Health–Kent Community Campus, Grand Rapids, MI, p. A335

PANICHI, Bob, Chief Information Officer, East Ohio Regional Hospital, Martins Ferry, OH, p. A517

PANICHI, Robert, Chief Information Officer, Ohio Valley Medical Center, Wheeling, WV, p. A721

PANICUCCI, Michele, Senior Vice President and Chief Financial Officer, Covenant Medical Center, Waterloo, IA, p. A243

PANICUCCI, Shelli, Chief Financial Officer, Sartori Memorial Hospital, Cedar Falls, IA, p. A229

PANKE, D.O., Rolf, Chief of Staff, Lincoln Hospital, Davenport, WA, p. A702

PANKS, Tim
Regional Vice President Finance and Chief Financial Officer, Mercy Medical Center Redding, Redding, CA, p. A83
Chief Financial Officer, St. Elizabeth Community Hospital, Red Bluff, CA, p. A83

PANNELL, Ken, Chief Financial Officer, Southwestern Medical Center, Lawton, OK, p. A532

PANSA, Leonard F., Vice President Human Resources, Mercy Medical Center, Springfield, MA, p. A323

PANZA Jr, Louis J., President and Chief Executive Officer, Monongahela Valley Hospital, Monongahela, PA, p. A565

PAPA, Gregory, Vice President Human Resources, Mercy Catholic Medical Center, Darby, PA, p. A557

PAPACOSTAS, M.D., Arthur, Vice President and Chief Information Officer, Temple University Hospital, Philadelphia, PA, p. A570

PAPADAKOS, James, Vice President Finance and Chief Financial Officer, Windham Community Memorial Hospital, Willimantic, CT, p. A118

PAPALIA, John P., CHE, Chief Executive Officer, Warren General Hospital, Warren, PA, p. A578

PAPANIA, Barry A., Chief Executive Officer, Spring View Hospital, Lebanon, KY, p. A267

PAPE, Becky A., R.N., Chief Executive Officer, Samaritan Lebanon Community Hospital, Lebanon, OR, p. A545

PAPE, Carolyn, Manager Human Resources, Whidbey General Hospital, Coupeville, WA, p. A702

PAPP, Ed, Chief Information Officer, Riverside County Regional Medical Center, Moreno Valley, CA, p. A77

PAPPAS, Nick, Manager Information Systems, Community Memorial Hospital of San Buenaventura, Ventura, CA, p. A98

PAPPAS, Sharon, Chief Operating Officer, Porter Adventist Hospital, Denver, CO, p. A104

PAQUETTE, James T., President and Chief Executive Officer, Providence Medical Center, Kansas City, KS, p. A250

PARADIS, J Brian, Chief Financial Officer, Florida Hospital, Orlando, FL, p. A141

PARADIS, Jeanne, Director Information Systems, Acadia Hospital, Bangor, ME, p. A296

PARDES, Herbert, M.D.,
Chief Executive Officer, New York Presbyterian Healthcare System, New York, NY, p. B78
President and Chief Executive Officer, New York–Presbyterian Hospital, New York, NY, p. A463

PARDINI–KEILY, Kim, Chief Operating Officer, Kaiser Foundation Hospital, Hayward, CA, p. A64

PARDO, Bruce, Vice President Human Resources, Monmouth Medical Center, Long Branch, NJ, p. A430

PARE, M.D., Jean Louis, Chief Medical Staff, Community Memorial Hospital, Syracuse, NE, p. A413

PARENT, Paula, Director Human Resources, Cary Medical Center, Caribou, ME, p. A298

PARENTEAU, Doris, Manager Business and Medical Records, Virginia Regional Medical Center, Virginia, MN, p. A364

PARENTEAU, Michael, Vice President Finance, St. Mary Medical Center, Walla Walla, WA, p. A711

PARETI, Donna, Controller, Saint Joseph Hospital, Chicago, IL, p. A190

PARIKH, M.D., Ajay, Medical Staff President, Advocate South Suburban Hospital, Hazel Crest, IL, p. A196

PARIS, David, Chief Executive Officer, Perry County General Hospital, Richton, MS, p. A375

PARIS, Gregory A., Chief Executive Officer, Monroe County Hospital, Albia, IA, p. A228

PARIS, Herbert, President, Mid Coast Hospital, Brunswick, ME, p. A297

PARIS, M.D., John, Chief Medical Officer, Riverview Hospital, Noblesville, IN, p. A223

PARIS, Phyllis, Director, Hannibal Regional Hospital, Hannibal, MO, p. A382

PARIS, Rick, Vice President, Human Resources, Roswell Park Cancer Institute, Buffalo, NY, p. A449

PARISI, Ernest R., CHE, Administrator and Chief Executive Officer, East Texas Medical Center–Quitman, Quitman, TX, p. A662

PARK, Gary L., President and Chief Executive Officer, University of North Carolina Hospitals, Chapel Hill, NC, p. A479

PARK, R. Clifford, Chief Executive Officer, Evanston Regional Hospital, Evanston, WY, p. A740

PARK, Ron, Chief Financial Officer, Somerset Hospital Center for Health, Somerset, PA, p. A576

PARK, Theron, Chief Executive Officer, Moore County Hospital District, Dumas, TX, p. A636

PARK, M.D., Yong Ho, Medical Director, Mineral Community Hospital, Superior, MT, p. A402

PARKER, Audrey, Budget Analyst, U. S. Public Health Service Indian Hospital, Winnebago, NE, p. A414

PARKER, David, Director Information Systems, Jackson County Memorial Hospital, Altus, OK, p. A527

PARKER, Douglas, Chief Executive Officer, Lifecare Hospitals of Shreveport, Shreveport, LA, p. A292

PARKER, M.D., Gregg S., Chief of Staff, Veterans Affairs Gulf Coast Veterans Health Care System, Biloxi, MS, p. A367

PARKER, Janie E., Director Fiscal Services, Hardin County General Hospital, Rosiclare, IL, p. A207

PARKER, Lynne, Administrator, Baptist Medical Center South, Montgomery, AL, p. A22

PARKER, M.D., Mark, Medical Director, Barberton Citizens Hospital, Barberton, OH, p. A503

PARKER, Michael, Human Resource Director, Northwest Medical Center, Thief River Falls, MN, p. A363

PARKER, Phillip L., Administrator, D. W. McMillan Memorial Hospital, Brewton, AL, p. A16

PARKER, M.D., Robert, Chief Medical Officer, Mount Sinai Hospital Medical Center of Chicago, Chicago, IL, p. A188

PARKER, Teresa, Administrator, Norton Southwest Hospital, Louisville, KY, p. A270

PARKER, Theresa, Chief Financial Officer, Transylvania Community Hospital, Brevard, NC, p. A478

PARKER, Thomas S., Site Administrator, Legacy Mount Hood Medical Center, Gresham, OR, p. A544

PARKER, Tina, Director Human Resources, HEALTHSOUTH Rehabilitation Hospital, Odessa, TX, p. A659

PARKS III, Burton O., President, West Shore Medical Center, Manistee, MI, p. A339

PARKS, Cary, Chief Information Resource Management, Veterans Affairs Medical Center, Hampton, VA, p. A689

PARKS, Dave, Three Rivers Health, Three Rivers, MI, p. A346

PARKS, Jim, Vice President Support Services, Box Butte General Hospital, Alliance, NE, p. A404

PARKS, Richard H., FACHE,
Chief Executive Officer, Cape Fear Valley Health System, Fayetteville, NC, p. A482
Chief Executive Officer, Cumberland County Hospital System, Fayetteville, NC, p. B35

PARKS, Shirley, Coordinator Human Resources, Weston County Health Services, Newcastle, WY, p. A741

PARMAR, M.D., Surinder K., President, Medical Staff, South Shore Hospital, Chicago, IL, p. A190

PARMER, David N., President and Chief Executive Officer, Memorial Hermann Baptist Beaumont Hospital, Beaumont, TX, p. A625

PARNELL, Brenda, Chief Financial Officer, South Peninsula Hospital, Homer, AK, p. A27

PARNELL, Dennis, Senior Vice President Human Resources, Suburban Hospital Healthcare System, Bethesda, MD, p. A305

PAROBEK, James, Chief Executive Officer, Gateway Rehabilitation Hospital, Louisville, KY, p. A269

PAROD, Dan, Vice President Human Resources, Rockford Memorial Hospital, Rockford, IL, p. A206

PAROSKI, M.D., Margaret, Executive Vice President and Chief Medical Officer, Buffalo General Hospital, Buffalo, NY, p. A448

PARRIS, Pat, Chief Financial Officer, McDuffie Regional Medical Center, Thomson, GA, p. A170

PARRIS, Y. C., Director, Veterans Affairs Medical Center, Birmingham, AL, p. A15

PARRISH, E. Al, Vice President and Chief Executive Officer, Providence Alaska Medical Center, Anchorage, AK, p. A26

PARRISH, James G., FACHE, Chief Executive Officer, Humboldt General Hospital, Winnemucca, NV, p. A419

PARRISH, Jerry A., Vice President, AnMED Health Medical Center, Anderson, SC, p. A583

PARRISH, Pamela, Information Systems Director, Brunswick Community Hospital, Supply, NC, p. A492

PARRISH, Priscilla, Chief Financial Officer, Blake Medical Center, Bradenton, FL, p. A124

PARRISH, Suann, Chief Financial Officer, Yoakum County Hospital, Denver City, TX, p. A635

PARRY, David, Chief Information Officer, Methodist Hospitals, Gary, IN, p. A216

PARSLEY, George N., Chief Operating Officer, Highland Medical Center, Lubbock, TX, p. A654

PARSONS, Kirk, Administrator, Throckmorton County Memorial Hospital, Throckmorton, TX, p. A670

PARSONS, Larry, Administrator, Wilbarger General Hospital, Vernon, TX, p. A671

PARSONS, Penny, Vice President, MidMichigan Medical Center–Clare, Clare, MI, p. A330

PARSONS, Roger, Senior Vice President Finance, San Antonio Community Hospital, Upland, CA, p. A97

PARTEE, Jeff, Chief Information Officer, Wilson Memorial Hospital, Sidney, OH, p. A522

PARTENZA, John, Vice President and Treasurer, Northern Westchester Hospital, Mount Kisco, NY, p. A457

PARTHEMORE, M.D., Jacqueline G., Chief of Staff, Veterans Affairs San Diego Healthcare System, San Diego, CA, p. A88

PARTIN, M.D., James R., Chief of Staff, Hill Country Memorial Hospital, Fredericksburg, TX, p. A640

PARTON, Scott, Director Human Resources, Lake City Medical Center, Lake City, FL, p. A134

PASCASIO, Robert
Chief Executive Officer, Bayside Community Hospital, Anahuac, TX, p. A621
Administrator and Chief Executive Officer, Bayside Community Hospital, Anahuac, TX, p. A621

PASCHALL, David, Vice President and Chief Information Officer, Flagstaff Medical Center, Flagstaff, AZ, p. A30

PASCO, Dave, Vice President Human Resources, University Hospitals of Cleveland, Cleveland, OH, p. A509

PASCUA, M.D., Leo, Chief of Staff, Wahiawa General Hospital, Wahiawa, HI, p. A176

PASCUZZI, Mark, President of the Medical Staff, Clark Regional Medical Center, Winchester, KY, p. A275

PASCUZZI, Robert, Controller, Sutter Davis Hospital, Davis, CA, p. A58

PASINSKI, Theodore M., President, St. Joseph's Hospital Health Center, Syracuse, NY, p. A474

PASQUALE, Mark, Vice President Information Systems, St. John's Hospital, Springfield, MO, p. A394

PASQUALE, Richard A., Administrator Resources and Financial Management Services, Carl T. Hayden Veterans Affairs Medical Center, Phoenix, AZ, p. A33

PASSAMA, Gary J., President and Chief Executive Officer, NorthBay Healthcare System, Fairfield, CA, p. B80

PASSAMANI, M.D., Eugene R., Senior Vice President Medical Affairs, Suburban Hospital Healthcare System, Bethesda, MD, p. A305

PATANKAR, M.D., Jayant L., President Medical Staff, Elk Regional Health Center, Saint Marys, PA, p. A574

PATASHNICK, Melvyn, Chief Executive Officer, Sierra–Kings District Hospital, Reedley, CA, p. A84

PATCHIN, J. Craig, Administrator, Shriners Hospitals for Children–Intermountain, Salt Lake City, UT, p. A680

PATE, M.D., David, Senior Vice President and Chief Medical Officer, St. Luke's Episcopal Hospital, Houston, TX, p. A647

PATE, Jim S., President and Chief Executive Officer, Unicoi County Memorial Hospital, Erwin, TN, p. A606

PATE, Linda, Director Human Resources, Davie County Hospital, Mocksville, NC, p. A487

PATEL, M.D., C N., Chief of Staff, Belmont Community Hospital, Bellaire, OH, p. A504

PATEL, M.D., Hasmukh, Chief of Staff, Howard Memorial Hospital, Nashville, AR, p. A48

PATEL, M.D., J G., Chief of Staff, Buchanan General Hospital, Grundy, VA, p. A689

PATEL, M.D., Jayanti, Chief Medical Officer, Western Medical Center Anaheim, Anaheim, CA, p. A52

PATEL, M.D., M R., Chief of Staff, Clinch Valley Medical Center, Richlands, VA, p. A694

PATEL, M.D., Mahendra, Chief of Staff, La Palma Intercommunity Hospital, La Palma, CA, p. A66

PATEL, M.D., Mitesh, Chief Medical Officer, Mercy Hospital, Bakersfield, CA, p. A54

PATEL, M.D., Mukesh, Chief of Staff, Tioga Medical Center, Tioga, ND, p. A500

PATEL, M.D., Natu M., Chief of Staf, Phoebe Worth Medical Center, Sylvester, GA, p. A170

PATEL, D.O., Rakesh, Medical Director, HEALTHSOUTH Rehabilitation Hospital of Altoona, Altoona, PA, p. A552

PATEY, Tommy, Chief Financial Officer, Middlesboro Appalachian Regional Hospital, Middlesboro, KY, p. A271

PATONAI, Steven D., Chief Executive Officer, Galesburg Cottage Hospital, Galesburg, IL, p. A195

PATRICIO, Jr, Marciano, Chief Financial Officer, HEALTHSOUTH Hospital of Tenaya, Las Vegas, NV, p. A416

PATRICK, Beckie, Director Information System Technology, Saint Louis University Hospital, Saint Louis, MO, p. A391

PATRICK, Deborah, Vice President Human Resources, St. Joseph Medical Center, Towson, MD, p. A311

PATRICK, James Chadwick, President and Chief Executive Officer, Mercy Franciscan Hospital–Western Hills, Cincinnati, OH, p. A507

PATRICK, Ronald, Chief Financial Officer, Northwest Medical Center, Tucson, AZ, p. A38

PATRICK, Wade, Director Information Systems, Elkhart General Hospital, Elkhart, IN, p. A214

PATTEN, Bill, Chief Executive Officer, St. John's Lutheran Hospital, Libby, MT, p. A400

PATTERSON, Barbara, Chief Financial Officer, Provident Hospital of Cook County, Chicago, IL, p. A189

PATTERSON, M.D., C Richard, Chief Medical Officer, Baptist Memorial Hospital – Memphis, Memphis, TN, p. A612

PATTERSON, R.N., Carole H., Chief Nursing Officer, Bert Fish Medical Center, New Smyrna Beach, FL, p. A139

PATTERSON, Cheryl, Chief Financial Officer, Claremore Regional Hospital, Claremore, OK, p. A529

PATTERSON, Christina, Chief Financial Officer, Medical Center of Southern Indiana, Charlestown, IN, p. A213

PATTERSON, Dave, Director, Memorial Hospital of Converse County, Douglas, WY, p. A740

PATTERSON, Debbie, Director Health Information Management, Wesley Rehabilitation Hospital, Wichita, KS, p. A260

PATTERSON, Donald E., Chief Executive Officer, Washington County Hospital, Washington, IA, p. A242

PATTERSON, Jennifer, Information Technology Coordinator, Purcell Municipal Hospital, Purcell, OK, p. A537

PATTERSON, Karen, Finance Manager, Fort Sanders–Sevier Medical Center, Sevierville, TN, p. A617

PATTERSON, Lisa, Director Human Resources, Pointe Coupee General Hospital, New Roads, LA, p. A290

PATTERSON, Michael, Chief Executive Officer, Parkway Regional Hospital, Fulton, KY, p. A265

PATTERSON, Paul
Director Information Technology and Services, Doctors Hospital, Augusta, GA, p. A155
Director Information Technology and Services, Upson Regional Medical Center, Thomaston, GA, p. A170

PATTERSON, Richard, Chief Financial Officer, Frankfort Regional Medical Center, Frankfort, KY, p. A264

PATTERSON, Thomas J., Manager Human Resources, Harry S. Truman Memorial Veterans Hospital, Columbia, MO, p. A380

PATTERSON, Tony, Chief Financial Officer, The James B. Haggin Memorial Hospital, Harrodsburg, KY, p. A265

PATTERSON, W. Benjamin, Administrator, Ouachita Surgical Hospital, West Monroe, LA, p. A294

PATTERSON, William, Chief Financial Officer, Parkview Medical Center, Pueblo, CO, p. A109

PATTERSON, M.D., William, Chief of Staff, Harry S. Truman Memorial Veterans Hospital, Columbia, MO, p. A380

PATTERSON, William M., Chief Executive Officer, Alliance Health Center, Meridian, MS, p. A373

PATTESON, Wilson, Senior Vice President Fiscal Services, Shore Memorial Hospital, Nassawadox, VA, p. A692

PATTON, Daniel, Director Information Systems, Henrico Doctors' Hospital, Richmond, VA, p. A695

PATTON, Frank, Chief of Staff, Rockdale Medical Center, Conyers, GA, p. A159

PATTON, Kelli, Director Human Resources, Medical Center at Terrell, Terrell, TX, p. A669

PATTON, Meghan, Vice President Human Resources, Abington Memorial Hospital, Abington, PA, p. A551

PATTON, Paul N., Vice President Human Resources, Riverside Methodist Hospital, Columbus, OH, p. A511

PATTULLO, Douglas E., Chief Executive Officer, West Branch Regional Medical Center, West Branch, MI, p. A348

PAUCHOLY, M.D., Navin, Chief Medical Staff, North Valley Hospital, Tonasket, WA, p. A711

PAUG, Jeffrey, President of Medical Staff, Saratoga Hospital, Saratoga Springs, NY, p. A472

PAUGH, J. William, President and Chief Executive Officer, Wayne Memorial Hospital, Goldsboro, NC, p. A483

PAUL, Mary
Chief Information Officer, Columbia St. Mary's Ozaukee Campus, Mequon, WI, p. A730
Chief Information Officer, Columbia St. Mary's–Columbia Campus, Milwaukee, WI, p. A730
Chief Information Officer, Columbia St. Mary's–Milwaukee Campus, Milwaukee, WI, p. A730
Chief Information Officer, Sacred Heart Rehabilitation Institute, Milwaukee, WI, p. A731

PAULDING, Ralph, President and Chief Executive Officer, Jefferson County Hospital, Fairfield, IA, p. A234

PAULE, Gerald, Chief Financial Officer, Phelps County Regional Medical Center, Rolla, MO, p. A389

PAULK, Pamela, Vice President Resources, Johns Hopkins Hospital, Baltimore, MD, p. A303

PAULSON, Glenda, Human Resources Director, Mahaska Health Partnership, Oskaloosa, IA, p. A239

PAULSON, Gordon, Personnel Manager, Glacial Ridge Health System, Glenwood, MN, p. A354

PAULSON, Mark E., Administrator, Chippewa County–Montevideo Hospital, Montevideo, MN, p. A358

PAULSON, Sybil, R.N., Administrator, North Oaks Rehabilitation Hospital, Hammond, LA, p. A282

PAULUS, M.D., Leslie, Medical Director, Banner Mesa Medical Center, Mesa, AZ, p. A32

PAUNOVICH, Thomas J., Chief Human Resources Officer, John D. Dingell Veterans Affairs Medical Center, Detroit, MI, p. A331

PAUTLER, Stephen, FACHE, Administrator, St. Joseph Memorial Hospital, Murphysboro, IL, p. A202

PAVLOVSKY, Charles, Director Human Resources, Ste. Genevieve County Memorial Hospital, Ste. Genevieve, MO, p. A394

PAVON, Ricardo, Chief Financial Officer, Raulerson Hospital, Okeechobee, FL, p. A140

PAWLAK, Paul, President and Chief Executive Officer, Silver Cross Hospital, Joliet, IL, p. A198

PAWLIKOWSKI, Mary, Vice President, Carrier Clinic, Belle Mead, NJ, p. A425

PAWLOWICZ, James E., Director Human Resources, Shriners Hospitals for Children–Chicago, Chicago, IL, p. A190

PAXTON, David, Vice President Information Systems, JPS Health Network, Fort Worth, TX, p. A640

PAYLOR, Mary, Director Human Resources, Person Memorial Hospital, Roxboro, NC, p. A490

PAYNE, M.D., Brent R., Medical Director, Cassia Regional Medical Center, Burley, ID, p. A178

PAYNE, Cary J., Chief Operating Officer, Athens–Limestone Hospital, Athens, AL, p. A13

PAYNE, Janet S., Vice President Human Resources, Provena Covenant Medical Center, Urbana, IL, p. A209

PAYNE, Judy, Health Information Officer, Grove Hill Memorial Hospital, Grove Hill, AL, p. A19

PAYNE, Mark I., Superintendent, Utah State Hospital, Provo, UT, p. A679

PAYNE, Mary Kay, Vice President and Chief Information Officer, Hoag Memorial Hospital Presbyterian, Newport Beach, CA, p. A78

PAYNE, Michael, Chief Informaton Officer, Grady Memorial Hospital, Atlanta, GA, p. A154

PAYNE, Michael E., President, North Ottawa Community Hospital, Grand Haven, MI, p. A334

PAYNE, Steven, Chief Financial Officer, Lakewood Regional Medical Center, Lakewood, CA, p. A67

PAYSENO, Cheryl, Chief Executive Officer, Kindred Hospital Seattle, Seattle, WA, p. A707

PAYTON, Larry W., Chief Executive Officer, Fallbrook Hospital, Fallbrook, CA, p. A60

PAZZAGLINI, Gino J., FACHE, President and Chief Executive Officer, Seton Health System, Troy, NY, p. A474

PEA, Gary, Chief Financial Officer, Northern Cochise Community Hospital, Willcox, AZ, p. A39

PEABODY, Paul, Vice President and Chief Information Officer, William Beaumont Hospital–Royal Oak, Royal Oak, MI, p. A343

PEACE III, L. E., Administrator, Evergreen Medical Center, Evergreen, AL, p. A18

PEACH, Larry, Assistant Administrator and Chief Financial Officer, Mendota Community Hospital, Mendota, IL, p. A201

PEACOCK, Gary, Senior Vice President and Chief Financial Officer, Decatur Memorial Hospital, Decatur, IL, p. A192

PEACOCK, Steve
   Chief Information Officer Director, Park Plaza Hospital, Houston, TX, p. A647
   Chief Information Officer Director, Plaza Specialty Hospital, Houston, TX, p. A647

PEAK, James G., Chief Executive Officer, Memorial Hospital and Manor, Bainbridge, GA, p. A156

PEAKS, William E., Chief Executive Officer, Garden Park Medical Center, Gulfport, MS, p. A369

PEAL, Chip, Associate Administrator, Alleghany Regional Hospital, Low Moor, VA, p. A690

PEARCE, Charles T., Chief Financial and Information Officer, Kalispell Regional Medical Center, Kalispell, MT, p. A400

PEARCE, M.D., Larry W., Vice President Medical Affairs, St. Edward Mercy Medical Center, Fort Smith, AR, p. A44

PEARCE, Richard J., President and Chief Executive Officer, Riverside Health System, Newport News, VA, p. B94

PEARCH, Bill, Chief Information Officer, Bristol Bay Area Health Corporation, Dillingham, AK, p. A27

PEARSON, Bruce E., Chief Executive Officer, Banner Desert Medical Center, Mesa, AZ, p. A32

PEARSON, Diane L., Administrator, Cook County North Shore Hospital, Grand Marais, MN, p. A354

PEARSON, George, Director Human Resources Management Service, Veterans Affairs Medical Center, Coatesville, PA, p. A556

PEARSON, M.D., Richard, Chief of Staff, Ste. Genevieve County Memorial Hospital, Ste. Genevieve, MO, p. A394

PEARSON, Roger W., Administrator, Ellsworth County Medical Center, Ellsworth, KS, p. A246

PEARSON, M.D., William P., Vice President Medical Affairs, Washington Hospital, Washington, PA, p. A578

PEASLEY, M.D., Gary, Medical Staff President, Marshalltown Medical and Surgical Center, Marshalltown, IA, p. A237

PECK, Bob, Accounting Supervisor, Wesley Rehabilitation Hospital, Wichita, KS, p. A260

PECK, Gary V., Administrator, St. Joseph's Hospital, Chewelah, WA, p. A701

PECK, Kay, Chief Executive Officer, Kindred Hospital–New Jersey Morris County, Dover, NJ, p. A427

PECORARO, David C.
   Vice President and Chief Information Officer, Frazier Rehab Institute, Louisville, KY, p. A269
   Vice President and Chief Information Officer, Jewish Hospital, Louisville, KY, p. A269

PECOT, L. J., Administrator, Jackson Parish Hospital, Jonesboro, LA, p. A282

PEDEN, M.D., Kirby, Chief of Staff, Pioneer Medical Center, Big Timber, MT, p. A396

PEDERSEN, Alan, Vice President Human Resources, Cayuga Medical Center at Ithaca, Ithaca, NY, p. A454

PEDERSEN, M.D., Paul E., Medical Director, OSF St. Joseph Medical Center, Bloomington, IL, p. A185

PEDERSON, Randall K., Chief Executive Officer, Tioga Medical Center, Tioga, ND, p. A500

PEEBLES, Robert, President and Chief Executive Officer, Our Lady of Lourdes Regional Medical Center, Lafayette, LA, p. A284

PEED, Nancy, Administrator and Chief Executive Officer, Peach Regional Medical Center, Fort Valley, GA, p. A162

PEEK, Scott
   Chief Executive Officer, Chambers Memorial Hospital, Danville, AR, p. A42
   Chief Executive Officer and Chief Financial Officer, Chambers Memorial Hospital, Danville, AR, p. A42

PEEPLES, Lewis T., Chief Executive Officer, Jennie Stuart Medical Center, Hopkinsville, KY, p. A266

PEER, Julie, Vice President Finance, Brookville Hospital, Brookville, PA, p. A553

PEET, Harvey, Director Information Systems, Castleview Hospital, Price, UT, p. A678

PEGE, M.D., Diane, Medical Director, Sutter Lakeside Hospital, Lakeport, CA, p. A67

PEHRSON, Timothy T.
   Chief Executive Officer, McKay–Dee Hospital Center, Ogden, UT, p. A678
   Assistant Vice President, McKay–Dee Hospital Center, Ogden, UT, p. A678

PEICKERT, Barbara A., R.N., Chief Executive Officer, Hayward Area Memorial Hospital and Nursing Home, Hayward, WI, p. A727

PEKAREK, Jean, Director Human Resources, Burgess Health Center, Onawa, IA, p. A239

PEKOFSKE, Robert, Vice President Finance, Advocate Christ Medical Center, Oak Lawn, IL, p. A203

PELACCIA, Joseph, Vice President Finance, Milford Hospital, Milford, CT, p. A114

PELLE, Fred L., President, Wellmont Hawkins County Memorial Hospital, Rogersville, TN, p. A617

PELLECCHIA, M.D., Joseph, Chief of Staff, Veterans Affairs Medical Center, Huntington, WV, p. A716

PELLEGRINO, Cynthia Miller, Director and Chief Executive Officer, Western Maryland Center, Hagerstown, MD, p. A308

PELLETIER, Nancy, Director Human Resources, Charles A. Dean Memorial Hospital and Nursing Home, Greenville, ME, p. A299

PELLETIER, Stephen, Leader, Guest Services, York Hospital, York, ME, p. A301

PELLEY, Catherine M., President, Glendale Memorial Hospital and Health Center, Glendale, CA, p. A62

PELLICANO, Anthony, Vice President Human Resources, Holy Name Hospital, Teaneck, NJ, p. A436

PELLINI, Deborah, Administrator and Chief Executive Officer, Kremmling Memorial Hospital, Kremmling, CO, p. A107

PELSMAN, Mara, Chief Executive Officer, Gateways Hospital and Mental Health Center, Los Angeles, CA, p. A70

PELTON, Ray, Vice President Human Resources, St. Joseph's Mercy Health Center, Hot Springs National Park, AR, p. A45

PELTON, Steve, Chief Information Officer, Saint Joseph's Hospital, Marshfield, WI, p. A729

PELTZ, Brian J., Chief Executive Office, Southeast Michigan Surgical Hospital, Warren, MI, p. A347

PEMBER, Marvin G., Executive Vice President and Chief Financial Officer, Clarian Health Partners, Indianapolis, IN, p. A218

PENA, Alfred, Chief Information Officer, Valley Regional Medical Center, Brownsville, TX, p. A627

PENBLE, Kim, Chief Information Officer, St. Joseph's Community Hospital of West Bend, West Bend, WI, p. A738

PENDER, M.D., John, Medical Director, Harris Continued Care Hospital, Fort Worth, TX, p. A639

PENDERGAST, Jim
   Human Resources Administrator, Carrie Tingley Hospital, Albuquerque, NM, p. A440
   Human Resources Administrator, University Hospital, Albuquerque, NM, p. A441

PENDLETON, Judy, Manager Human Resources, Blue Hill Memorial Hospital, Blue Hill, ME, p. A297

PENNING, Tim, Chief Information Officer, Athens Regional Medical Center, Athens, GA, p. A152

PENNINGTON, David N., FACHE, Chief Executive Officer, Veterans Affairs Tennessee Valley Healthcare System, Nashville, TN, p. A616

PENNINGTON, Jamey, Director Information Systems, Grace Hospital, Morganton, NC, p. A488

PENNINGTON, Stephen, Chief Executive Officer, South Baldwin Regional Medical Center, Foley, AL, p. A18

PENROSE, Lee, Vice President Fiscal Services and Chief Financial Officer, St. Jude Medical Center, Fullerton, CA, p. A62

PENTON, Kelly, Chief Financial Officer, Doctors Hospital, Augusta, GA, p. A155

PENTZ, Thomas R., President and Chief Executive Officer, Lawnwood Regional Medical Center, Fort Pierce, FL, p. A129

PEOPLES, Phyllis, R.N., President and Chief Executive Officer, Terrebonne General Medical Center, Houma, LA, p. A282

PEOPLES, Terry, Director Human Resources, West Valley Medical Center, Caldwell, ID, p. A178

PEPE, M.D., Joseph, Medical Director, Catholic Medical Center, Manchester, NH, p. A422

PEPPER, H. L. Perry, FACHE, President, Chester County Hospital, West Chester, PA, p. A578

PEPPERWORTH, Lisa, Director Human Resources, Terre Haute Regional Hospital, Terre Haute, IN, p. A226

PEPPING, Tom
   Senior Vice President and Chief Financial Officer, Carondelet Holy Cross Hospital, Nogales, AZ, p. A32
   Chief Financial Officer, Carondelet St. Joseph's Hospital–Tucson, Tucson, AZ, p. A37
   Chief Financial Officer, Carondelet St. Mary's Hospital–Tucson, Tucson, AZ, p. A37

PERAUD, M.D., Joseph, President Medical Staff, Mercy Medical Center–New Hampton, New Hampton, IA, p. A238

PERCELLO, Thomas, Vice President Financial Services, Community Medical Center, Toms River, NJ, p. A437

PERCIVAL, Steve, Director Human Resources, Washington Regional Medical Center, Fayetteville, AR, p. A43

PERECKO, Gary L., President, Saint Joseph Regional Medical Center, South Bend, IN, p. A225

PEREL, Michael
   Regional Chief Financial Officer, Kauai Veterans Memorial Hospital, Waimea, HI, p. A176
   Regional Chief Financial Officer, Samuel Mahelona Memorial Hospital, Kapaa, HI, p. A175

PERET, Jason, Chief Financial Officer, Mt. San Rafael Hospital, Trinidad, CO, p. A110

PEREZ, David, Chief Information Officer, Eisenhower Memorial Hospital and Betty Ford Center at Eisenhower, Rancho Mirage, CA, p. A83

PEREZ, Francisco, Management Informatio Systems, Hospital de la Universidad de Puerto Rico/Dr. Federico Trilla, Carolina, PR, p. A744

PEREZ, Francisco J., FACHE, Network Chief Executive Officer, Kettering Medical Center–Network, Dayton, OH, p. B65

PEREZ, Gabriel, Chief Executive Officer and Medical Director, Aleda E. Lutz Veterans Affairs Medical Center, Saginaw, MI, p. A344

PEREZ, George
   President and Chief Executive Officer, Petaluma Valley Hospital, Petaluma, CA, p. A81
   President and Chief Executive Officer, Santa Rosa Memorial Hospital, Santa Rosa, CA, p. A93
   President and Chief Executive Officer, St. Mary Medical Center, Apple Valley, CA, p. A53

PEREZ, Homar
Chief Executive Officer and Vice President Administration, Hospital Dr. Cayetano Coll Y Toste, Arecibo, PR, p. A743
Administrator, Hospital Dr. Susoni, Arecibo, PR, p. A744

PEREZ, Jim, Interim Chief Information Officer, Memorial Medical Center, Johnstown, PA, p. A561

PEREZ, Joseph, Director Human Resources, South Shore Hospital, Chicago, IL, p. A190

PEREZ, Karla, Chief Executive Officer and Managing Director, Spring Valley Hospital Medical Center, Las Vegas, NV, p. A417

PERGERSON, Larry, Director Information Systems, Scotland Memorial Hospital, Laurinburg, NC, p. A486

PERI, M.D., Srihari, President, Medical Dental Staff, Beebe Medical Center, Lewes, DE, p. A119

PERILLI, Ernest N., Chief Operating Officer, St. Agnes Continuing Care Center, Philadelphia, PA, p. A569

PERILLI, John, M.D., Health Services Director, Ossining Correctional Facilities Hospital, Ossining, NY, p. A468

PERILLO, M.D., Louis, Senior Vice President Medical Affairs, West Florida Hospital, Pensacola, FL, p. A143

PERKET, William, Human Resources Director, SEARHC MT. Edgecumbe Hospital, Sitka, AK, p. A28

PERKINS, Gary A., President and Chief Executive Officer, Children's Hospital, Omaha, NE, p. A411

PERKINS, Richard, Chief Financial Officer, Hillcrest Baptist Medical Center, Waco, TX, p. A672

PERKINS, Steven J., President and Chief Executive Officer, Spanish Peaks Regional Health Center, Walsenburg, CO, p. A110

PERLIN, Jonathan, Acting Secretary, Department of Veterans Affairs, Washington, DC, p. B37

PERLIN, Mitch, Chief Information Officer, Medical Center of Louisiana at New Orleans, New Orleans, LA, p. A289

PERLMAN, Joel A., Senior Vice President Finance, Montefiore Medical Center, New York, NY, p. A462

PERMETTI, Thomas, Chief Executive Officer, Christus St. John Hospital, Houston, TX, p. A644

PEROT, Cathy, Administrator, Sterlington Rehabilitation Hospital, Sterlington, LA, p. A293

PERRA, Scott H., Executive Vice President and Chief Operating Officer, Faxton–St. Luke's Healthcare, Utica, NY, p. A474

PERRIGOT, Keri, Assistant Administrator Human Resources, Cassia Regional Medical Center, Burley, ID, p. A178

PERRITT, Daniel, Senior Vice President and Chief Financial Officer, Riverside Community Hospital, Riverside, CA, p. A84

PERROTT, M.D., David, Vice President and Medical Director, Salinas Valley Memorial Healthcare System, Salinas, CA, p. A86

PERROTTI, CPA, Paul R.
Chief Financial Officer, West Georgia Health System, La Grange, GA, p. A164
Chief Financial Officer, West Georgia Health System, La Grange, GA, p. A164

PERRY, Alan S., Director, Veterans Affairs Medical Center, Fresno, CA, p. A62

PERRY, Christopher, Director Human Resources, Memorial Hospital West, Pembroke Pines, FL, p. A142

PERRY, Denise, Chief Operating Officer, Tulare Local Health Care District, Tulare, CA, p. A96

PERRY, George H., Ph.D., Chief Executive Officer, Belmont Pines Hospital, Youngstown, OH, p. A525

PERRY, J. Steve, Chief Executive Officer, Star Valley Medical Center, Afton, WY, p. A739

PERRY, Karen, Chief Information Resource Management Services, James H. Quillen Veterans Affairs Medical Center, Mountain Home, TN, p. A614

PERRY, L. Gene, Chief Executive Officer, Bloomington Hospital of Orange County, Paoli, IN, p. A223

PERRY, Matthew J., President, Carilion New River Valley Medical Center, Christiansburg, VA, p. A686

PERRY, Megan R., Senior Vice President and Administrator, Sentara CarePlex Hospital, Hampton, VA, p. A689

PERRY, Pat, Manager Information Systems, Transylvania Community Hospital, Brevard, NC, p. A478

PERRY, Phil, Chief Information Officer, Valley Medical Center, Renton, WA, p. A706

PERRY, Rhonda, Chief Financial Officer, Medical Center of Central Georgia, Macon, GA, p. A165

PERRY, Rick, Vice President Information Services, St. Joseph's Hospital, Tampa, FL, p. A148

PERRY, Tim, Coordinator Human Resources, Baptist Regional Medical Center, Corbin, KY, p. A263

PERRY, V Mark, Chief Financial Officer, Adventist Medical Center, Portland, OR, p. A547

PERRYMAN, Daniel L., Chief Executive Officer, L. V. Stabler Memorial Hospital, Greenville, AL, p. A19

PERRYMAN, Margaret E., Chief Executive Officer, Gillette Children's Specialty Healthcare, Saint Paul, MN, p. A362

PERRYMAN, Mike
Administrator and Chief Executive Officer, Baptist Memorial Hospital–Union City, Union City, TN, p. A618
Administrator, Baptist Memorial Hospital–Union City, Union City, TN, p. A618

PERRYMAN, Scott, Vice President and Chief Financial Officer, South Coast Medical Center, Laguna Beach, CA, p. A66

PERSAUD, M.D., Pitamber, Chief Medical Staff, Rochelle Community Hospital, Rochelle, IL, p. A206

PERSON, Peter E., M.D., President and Chief Executive Officer, St. Mary's/Duluth Clinic Health System, Duluth, MN, p. B102

PERT, Robert M., Chief Financial Officer, Citizens Medical Center, Victoria, TX, p. A672

PERTTULA, Greg, Chief Financial Officer, Bell Hospital, Ishpeming, MI, p. A337

PERUSHEK, John R., Administrator, Quincy Valley Medical Center, Quincy, WA, p. A706

PERUZZI, M.D., William, Chief Medical Officer, Memorial Hermann Hospital, Houston, TX, p. A646

PERVINE, Ken, Management Information Systems Director, Bladen County Hospital, Elizabethtown, NC, p. A482

PESSAGNO, Paul, Chief Financial Officer, Richard L. Roudebush Veterans Affairs Medical Center, Indianapolis, IN, p. A218

PESTA, M.D., Carl, Medical Director, Henry Ford Bi–County Hospital, Warren, MI, p. A347

PETASNICK, William D., President and Chief Executive Officer, Froedtert Memorial Lutheran Hospital, Milwaukee, WI, p. A731

PETER, Chad, Administrator, Mercy Hospital of Defiance, Defiance, OH, p. A512

PETER, Edith S., Chief Financial Officer and Vice President Finance, Cooley Dickinson Hospital, Northampton, MA, p. A321

PETERS, Brian, Director Information Systems, St. Joseph Hospital, Kokomo, IN, p. A220

PETERS, Bruce, Vice President and Chief Operating Officer, Bakersfield Memorial Hospital, Bakersfield, CA, p. A53

PETERS, Chris, Vice President Finance, Fayette County Memorial Hospital, Washington Court House, OH, p. A524

PETERS, Connie, R.N., Regional Health Administrator, Alegent Health–Memorial Hospital, Schuyler, NE, p. A412

PETERS, Curtis A., Chief Executive Officer, J. D. McCarty Center for Children With Developmental Disabilities, Norman, OK, p. A534

PETERS, Dave, Chief Human Resources Officer, Veterans Affairs Medical Center, Omaha, NE, p. A411

PETERS, David, Chief, Veterans Affairs Nebraska–Western Iowa Health Care System, Lincoln, NE, p. A409

PETERS, M.D., Jamie, Vice President, Medical Services, Fairview Ridges Hospital, Burnsville, MN, p. A351

PETERS, Janna S.
Vice President and Chief Information Officer, Vista Health–Provena Saint Therese Medical Center, Waukegan, IL, p. A210
Vice President and Chief Information Officer, Vista Health–Victory Memorial Hospital, Waukegan, IL, p. A210

PETERS, John, Chief Financial Officer, Sunrise Hospital and Medical Center, Las Vegas, NV, p. A417

PETERS, Karen, Interim Chief Executive Officer, United Memorial Medical Center, Batavia, NY, p. A447

PETERS, Mark, M.D., President and Chief Executive Officer, East Jefferson General Hospital, Metairie, LA, p. A286

PETERS, Patrick, Chief Executive Officer, Keokuk County Health Center, Sigourney, IA, p. A241

PETERS, Sally Ann, Director Human Resources, Lourdes Medical Center, Pasco, WA, p. A705

PETERS, Stephen, Chief Nursing Officer and Chief Operating Officer, Logan Memorial Hospital, Russellville, KY, p. A274

PETERS, Sue, Vice President Human Resources, Munson Medical Center, Traverse City, MI, p. A346

PETERS, Tricia, Vice President Human Resources, Kaiser Sunnyside Medical Center, Clackamas, OR, p. A542

PETERS, Violeta, Chief Executive Officer, Specialty Hospital at Monmouth, Long Branch, NJ, p. A431

PETERS, M.D., William H., Vice President of Medical Affairs, Forrest General Hospital, Hattiesburg, MS, p. A369

PETERSCHICK, Anthony, Administrator, Central Montana Surgical Hospital, Great Falls, MT, p. A399

PETERSEN, Gary L., Chief Executive Officer, Gibson Area Hospital and Health Services, Gibson City, IL, p. A195

PETERSEN, Julie, Director Financial Services, Prosser Memorial Hospital, Prosser, WA, p. A706

PETERSEN, Keith J.
Chief Executive Officer, Phoebe Worth Medical Center, Sylvester, GA, p. A170
Chief Executive Officer, Phoebe Worth Medical Center, Sylvester, GA, p. A170

PETERSON, Anne, Director, Community Behavioral Health Center, Fresno, CA, p. A61

PETERSON, Brent A., Administrator, Cherry County Hospital, Valentine, NE, p. A413

PETERSON, Brian, Telecommunications Officer, Banner Baywood Medical Center, Mesa, AZ, p. A32

PETERSON, Chad, Chief Information Officer, Northwood Deaconess Health Center, Northwood, ND, p. A500

PETERSON, Cheryl
President and Chief Executive Officer, Memorial Healthcare, Owosso, MI, p. A342
Director Human Resources, Winslow Memorial Hospital, Winslow, AZ, p. A39

PETERSON, Clayton R., Chief Executive Officer, Mercy Hospital and Health Care Center, Moose Lake, MN, p. A358

PETERSON, Daniel, Chief Human Resource Management Service, Central Arkansas Veterans Healthcare System, Little Rock, AR, p. A46

PETERSON, Dave, Manager Human Resources, Gunnison Valley Hospital, Gunnison, UT, p. A676

PETERSON, David, Chief Information Officer, Baltimore Washington Medical Center, Glen Burnie, MD, p. A308

PETERSON, David A., President and Chief Executive Officer, Aroostook Medical Center, Presque Isle, ME, p. A300

PETERSON, David B., Executive Vice President and Chief Operating Officer, Mount Nittany Medical Center, State College, PA, p. A576

PETERSON, M.D., Debra G., Chief of Staff, Meeker County Memorial Hospital, Litchfield, MN, p. A355

PETERSON, Douglas R., President and Chief Executive Officer, Chippewa Valley Hospital and Oakview Care Center, Durand, WI, p. A724

PETERSON, M.D., Gary, Vice President Medical Affairs and Medical Director, St. Luke's Hospital, Duluth, MN, p. A352

PETERSON, Howard, Senior Vice President, St. John Medical Center, Tulsa, OK, p. A540

PETERSON, James, Chief Financial Officer, Habersham County Medical Center, Demorest, GA, p. A160

PETERSON, Jeffrey D., President and Chief Executive Officer, St. Vincent Mercy Medical Center, Toledo, OH, p. A523

PETERSON, John, Director Information Systems, Longmont United Hospital, Longmont, CO, p. A108

PETERSON, Larry
  Chief Executive Officer, Lake Chelan Community Hospital, Chelan, WA, p. A701
  Chief Financial Officer, Allen County Hospital, Iola, KS, p. A249
PETERSON, Leland W., President and Chief Executive Officer, Sun Health Corporation, Sun City, AZ, p. B103
PETERSON, Linda, Director Information Systems, Advocate Bethany Hospital, Chicago, IL, p. A186
PETERSON, Margaret R., Ph.D., President and Chief Executive Officer, Simi Valley Hospital and Health Care Services, Simi Valley, CA, p. A94
PETERSON, Noel R., MS, President and Chief Executive Officer, Olmsted Medical Center, Rochester, MN, p. A360
PETERSON, Patricia, President and Chief Executive Officer, St. Mary's Hospital, Passaic, NJ, p. A434
PETERSON, Philip, Senior Vice President Finance, Mercy Medical Center, Cedar Rapids, IA, p. A229
PETERSON, Randy, President and Chief Executive Officer, Salina Regional Health Center, Salina, KS, p. A256
PETERSON, Richard H., President and Chief Executive Officer, Swedish Health Services, Seattle, WA, p. A708
PETERSON, Robert, Chief Operating Officer, West Florida Hospital, Pensacola, FL, p. A143
PETERSON, Robert M., Chief Executive Officer, Riverton Memorial Hospital, Riverton, WY, p. A741
PETERSON, Ron, President, Regional Medical Center of Hopkins County, Madisonville, KY, p. A270
PETERSON, Ronald R.
  President, Johns Hopkins Health System, Baltimore, MD, p. B64
  President, Johns Hopkins Hospital, Baltimore, MD, p. A303
PETERSON, Sharon H., Chief Executive Officer, Physicians Hospital, El Paso, TX, p. A637
PETERSON, Thomas, Chief Executive Officer, Richard P. Stadter Psychiatric Center, Grand Forks, ND, p. A498
PETERSON, Todd L., Executive Vice President and Chief Operating Officer, University of North Carolina Hospitals, Chapel Hill, NC, p. A479
PETHIS, James D., Chief Executive Officer, Wichita Specialty Hospital, Wichita, KS, p. A260
PETIK, Jason, Chief Executive Officer, Custer Community Hospital, Custer, SD, p. A595
PETITT, Michael, Director Finance, St. Francis Hospital, Milwaukee, WI, p. A731
PETRALIA, Pat, Vice President and Chief Operating Officer, Potomac Ridge Behavioral Health System, Rockville, MD, p. A310
PETRAY, David, Chief Resource Management, Tripler Army Medical Center, Honolulu, HI, p. A174
PETREY, Brenda, Director of Human Resources, Jellico Community Hospital, Jellico, TN, p. A608
PETRICK, Teresa A.
  President, UPMC Passavant, Pittsburgh, PA, p. A572
  Chief Executive Officer, UPMC Passavant Cranberry, Cranberry, PA, p. A556
PETRINA, Robert, Chief Financial Officer, Alta Bates Summit Medical Center – Summit Campus, Oakland, CA, p. A78
PETRU, Sue, Vice President Finance and Chief Financial Officer, Rockford Memorial Hospital, Rockford, IL, p. A206
PETTEY, Robbie, Chief Financial Officer, National Park Medical Center, Hot Springs, AR, p. A44
PETTIGREW, Dennis, Chief Financial Officer, Washoe Medical Center, Reno, NV, p. A418
PETTIJOHN, Kelly J., Vice President Finance, Park Ridge Hospital, Fletcher, NC, p. A483
PETTINGILL, Richard R., President and Chief Executive Officer, Allina Hospitals & Clinics, Minneapolis, MN, p. B8
PETTIT, Dave, Chief Financial Officer, Cleveland Clinic Hospital, Weston, FL, p. A151
PETTRY, Harvey H., FACHE, President and Chief Executive Officer, Richland Memorial Hospital, Olney, IL, p. A203
PEYERL, John, Chief Financial Officer, Redwood Area Hospital, Redwood Falls, MN, p. A360

PEYOK, David M., Chief Executive Officer, Big Horn County Memorial Hospital, Hardin, MT, p. A399
PEZZIA, Marlene, Director, Tomball Regional Hospital, Tomball, TX, p. A670
PFAFF, Lawrence W., President and Chief Executive Officer, Fairview University Medical Center–Mesabi, Hibbing, MN, p. A355
PFAFF, Wanda, Vice President Human Resources, St. Alexius Medical Center, Bismarck, ND, p. A496
PFANNENSTIEL, Dan, Manager Finance, St. Michael Hospital, Milwaukee, WI, p. A732
PFEIFER, Brad, Area Technology Director, Kaiser Foundation Hospital and Rehabilitation Center, Vallejo, CA, p. A97
PFEIFER, M.D., Mark P., Chief of Staff, University of Louisville Hospital, Louisville, KY, p. A270
PFEIFFER, James A.
  President and Chief Executive Officer, Mease Countryside Hospital, Safety Harbor, FL, p. A144
  President and Chief Executive Officer, Mease Hospital Dunedin, Dunedin, FL, p. A127
PFISTER, Pam, Director Human Resources, Morrison Community Hospital, Morrison, IL, p. A201
PFISTER, Scott, Chief Financial Officer, River Region Health System, Vicksburg, MS, p. A376
PFITZER, Anthony D., Executive Vice President and Administrator, St. Mary's Hospital, Decatur, IL, p. A192
PFLIGER, Tom, Assistant Administrator, St. Joseph Regional Medical Center, Lewiston, ID, p. A180
PFRANK, Kim, Vice President Information Systems, Union Hospital, Terre Haute, IN, p. A226
PHARR, Jr, John K., Director Human Resources, Satilla Regional Medical Center, Waycross, GA, p. A172
PHAUP, Michael B., Director, Hunter Holmes McGuire Veterans Affairs Medical Center, Richmond, VA, p. A695
PHELPS, M.D., Craig, Chief of Staff, Great Plains Regional Medical Center, Elk City, OK, p. A530
PHELPS, Darla, Director Human Resources, Hanford Community Medical Center, Hanford, CA, p. A63
PHELPS, David E., President and Chief Executive Officer, Berkshire Health Systems, Inc., Pittsfield, MA, p. B17
PHELPS, Gary L., Senior Vice President and Chief Operating Officer, Athens Regional Medical Center, Athens, GA, p. A152
PHELPS, M.D., Greg, Medical Director, St. Mary's Medical Center, Knoxville, TN, p. A610
PHELPS, Kathleen, Director Human Resources, HEALTHSOUTH Treasure Valley Hospital, Boise, ID, p. A177
PHELPS, M. Randell, Chief Executive Officer, Memorial Hospital, Craig, CO, p. A103
PHELPS, M.D., Rick, Senior Vice President Medical Affairs, Elliot Hospital, Manchester, NH, p. A422
PHELPS SELLS, Angie, Human Resource Manager, Harrison County Hospital, Corydon, IN, p. A213
PHILBRICK, Teri, Chief Executive Officer, Oklahoma Center for Orthopedic and Multi–Specialty Surgery, Oklahoma City, OK, p. A535
PHILEBAR, Wayne, Chief Information Officer, River Parishes Hospital, La Place, LA, p. A283
PHILIPP, M.D., Joseph, Chief Medical Officer, Mercy Regional Health Center, New York, KS, p. A252
PHILLIP, Joyce, Vice President and Human Resources, Anne Arundel Medical Center, Annapolis, MD, p. A302
PHILLIPE, James R., President, Holzer Medical Center, Gallipolis, OH, p. A514
PHILLIPS, Andrew J., Ed.D., Chief Executive Officer, Western State Hospital, Tacoma, WA, p. A710
PHILLIPS, Annette, Vice President and Chief Financial Officer, Henry Ford Wyandotte Hospital, Wyandotte, MI, p. A348
PHILLIPS, Bob D., CHE, Administrator and Chief Executive Officer, Skaggs Community Health Center, Branson, MO, p. A379
PHILLIPS, Courtney, Chief Financial Officer, Delta Regional Medical Center, Greenville, MS, p. A368
PHILLIPS, Donna, President, Bryn Mawr Rehabilitation Hospital, Malvern, PA, p. A564
PHILLIPS, Glenn, Director Information Systems, Gadsden Regional Medical Center, Gadsden, AL, p. A19

PHILLIPS, J. Randall, CHE, Administrator, Mitchell County Hospital, Camilla, GA, p. A157
PHILLIPS, Jacki W., CHE, Chief Executive Officer, Medical Center Blount, Oneonta, AL, p. A23
PHILLIPS, M.D., James R., Chief of Staff, Gadsden Regional Medical Center, Gadsden, AL, p. A19
PHILLIPS, James Sandy, Vice President and Chief Information Officer, Jackson Memorial Hospital, Miami, FL, p. A137
PHILLIPS, Jim, Business Strategy and Finance Leader, Kaiser Foundation Hospital, San Francisco, CA, p. A89
PHILLIPS, Joan, Administrator, Greater Southeast Community Hospital, Washington, DC, p. A121
PHILLIPS, John, Vice President Information Services, St. Joseph Regional Health Center, Bryan, TX, p. A627
PHILLIPS, John E., Chief Executive Officer, Eastland Memorial Hospital, Eastland, TX, p. A636
PHILLIPS, John H., Administrator and Chief Financial Officer, Hardy Wilson Memorial Hospital, Hazlehurst, MS, p. A370
PHILLIPS, Joseph, Director Information Systems, Aurelia Osborn Fox Memorial Hospital, Oneonta, NY, p. A468
PHILLIPS, Kim, Director Finance, Children's Home of Pittsburgh, Pittsburgh, PA, p. A571
PHILLIPS, Larry, Chief Financial Officer, Moore County Hospital District, Dumas, TX, p. A636
PHILLIPS, Lionel J., Vice President Financial Services, Fauquier Hospital, Warrenton, VA, p. A698
PHILLIPS, M.D., Lloyd, Chief of Staff, Overton Brooks Veterans Affairs Medical Center, Shreveport, LA, p. A292
PHILLIPS, Mike, Chief Strategy Officer, San Juan Regional Medical Center, Farmington, NM, p. A442
PHILLIPS, Richard
  Chief Financial Officer, Shasta Regional Medical Center, Redding, CA, p. A83
  Chief Financial Officer, Sierra Vista Regional Medical Center, San Luis Obispo, CA, p. A91
PHILLIPS, Tammy, Director Information Services, Medical Center of Arlington, Arlington, TX, p. A622
PHILLIPS, Thad, Chief Information Officer, Veterans Affairs Medical Center, Birmingham, AL, p. A15
PHILLIPS, Thomas, Chief of Staff, Carolinas Hospital System, Florence, SC, p. A587
PHILLIPS, William
  Senior Vice President Finance and Chief Financial Officer, Jersey Shore University Medical Center, Neptune, NJ, p. A432
  Senior Vice President Finance and Chief Financial Officer, Ocean Medical Center, Brick Township, NJ, p. A426
PHIPPS, Bonnie, President and Chief Executive Officer, Saint Joseph's Hospital of Atlanta, Atlanta, GA, p. A154
PHIPPS, Jackie G., Executive Director Human Resources, Johnston Memorial Hospital, Abingdon, VA, p. A685
PHIPPS, M.D., Ronny, Chief of Staff, Northwest Medical Center of Benton County, Bentonville, AR, p. A40
PIAZZA, Tony, Vice President Human Resources, RHD Memorial Medical Center, Dallas, TX, p. A634
PICA, Erin, Chief Executive Officer, Kindred Hospital–Woming Valley, Wilkes–Barre, PA, p. A579
PICCONE, Robert, President, Clear Brook Manor, Wilkes–Barre, PA, p. A579
PICHE, Mary–Ellen, Director, Veterans Affairs Medical Center, Albany, NY, p. A446
PICHE, William K., Chief Executive Officer, Good Samaritan Hospital, San Jose, CA, p. A90
PICKENS, Paula, Chief Financial Officer, Decatur County Hospital, Leon, IA, p. A237
PICKENS, Troy, Chief Financial Officer, Edgefield County Hospital, Edgefield, SC, p. A587
PICKERING, Debbie, Executive Assistant Human Resources, Sparta Community Hospital, Sparta, IL, p. A208
PICKETT, Stephen A., Chief Financial Officer, University of Alabama Hospital, Birmingham, AL, p. A15
PICKOFF, M.D., Robert M., Vice President Medical Administration, Hunterdon Medical Center, Flemington, NJ, p. A428
PICKTON, Robert J., Senior Vice President, Baylor University Medical Center, Dallas, TX, p. A632

PIEKARCZYK, Wally, Chief Financial Officer, Iberia Medical Center, New Iberia, LA, p. A288

PIEKEN, Nathan, Chief Information Officer, Clarke County Hospital, Osceola, IA, p. A239

PIEPER, Blaine, Chief Executive Officer, Ohio County Hospital, Hartford, KY, p. A266

PIEPER, Jr, Samuel, Interim Chief of Staff, Veterans Affairs Tennessee Valley Healthcare System, Nashville, TN, p. A616

PIERANGELI, Ray
Regional Vice President Information Services, Mercy Franciscan Hospital Mount Airy, Cincinnati, OH, p. A507
Vice President and Chief Information Officer, Mercy Hospital Anderson, Cincinnati, OH, p. A507
Regional Vice President Information Services, Mercy Hospital Clermont, Batavia, OH, p. A503
Senior Vice President and Chief Information Officer, Mercy Hospital Fairfield, Fairfield, OH, p. A513

PIERCE, Carol, Commander, Ireland Army Community Hospital, Fort Knox, KY, p. A264

PIERCE, James M., Vice President Operations, Sarah Bush Lincoln Health Center, Mattoon, IL, p. A200

PIERCE, Jeff, Vice President Human Resources, Jackson County Memorial Hospital, Altus, OK, p. A527

PIERCE, Laura, Human Resources Director, Memorial Medical Center, Las Cruces, NM, p. A443

PIERCE, Michael L., Chief Operating Officer, Skaggs Community Health Center, Branson, MO, p. A379

PIERCE, Peggy, Administrator, Calhoun Memorial Hospital, Arlington, GA, p. A152

PIERSON, John, Chief Executive Officer, Kindred Hospital–Indianapolis, Indianapolis, IN, p. A218

PIERSON, Kari, Manager, Howard County Community Hospital, Saint Paul, NE, p. A412

PIERSON, Richard, Executive Director, UAMS Medical Center, Little Rock, AR, p. A47

PIETERS, Donald R., Asst Administrator Financial and Support Services, St. Nicholas Hospital, Sheboygan, WI, p. A735

PIETRAFESA, M.D., Charles, Executive Medical Director, Saint John's Health Center, Santa Monica, CA, p. A93

PIETRANGELO, Steve, Director Information Services, War Memorial Hospital, Sault Ste. Marie, MI, p. A345

PIETRO, M.D., Daniel, Medical Director, Sturdy Memorial Hospital, Attleboro, MA, p. A312

PIETSCH, CPA, Al
Vice President Finance, Baltimore Washington Medical Center, Glen Burnie, MD, p. A308
Director Finance, Mt. Washington Pediatric Hospital, Baltimore, MD, p. A304

PIGG, Jody
Interim Administrator, Shoals Hospital, Muscle Shoals, AL, p. A22
Chief Financial Officer, Eliza Coffee Memorial Hospital, Florence, AL, p. A18

PIGG, Russell, Chief Operating Officer, Conroe Regional Medical Center, Conroe, TX, p. A630

PIKE, M.D., Irving, Vice President Medical Affairs, Sentara Bayside Hospital, Virginia Beach, VA, p. A697

PILARCZYK, Penny, Vice President, Human Resources, Advocate Lutheran General Hospital, Park Ridge, IL, p. A204

PILE, Larry, Director Human Resources, Deaconess Hospital, Evansville, IN, p. A214

PILEGGI, Gale S., Chief Financial Officer, JPS Health Network, Fort Worth, TX, p. A640

PILKINGTON III, Albert, Chief Executive Officer, Fairmont General Hospital, Fairmont, WV, p. A715

PILLION, Scott, Chief Financial Officer, Helen Newberry Joy Hospital, Newberry, MI, p. A341

PILON, Crystal, Chief Information Officer, Westerly Hospital, Westerly, RI, p. A582

PINA, Maria, Chief of Staff, Carondelet Holy Cross Hospital, Nogales, AZ, p. A32

PINAC, Gil, Chief Executive Officer, Crowley Rehabilitation Hospital, Crowley, LA, p. A280

PINCETL, M.D., Pierre, Chief Information Officer and Associate Vice President for Health Sciences Information Technology Services, University of Utah Hospitals and Clinics, Salt Lake City, UT, p. A680

PINCKNEY, Frank D., President and Chief Executive Officer, Greenville Hospital System, Greenville, SC, p. B47

PINE, Richard M., President and Chief Executive Officer, Livengrin Foundation, Bensalem, PA, p. A552

PINEIRO, Carlos M., President, Hospital Interamericano De Medicina Avanzada, Caguas, PR, p. A744

PINEVICH, M.D., A J., Vice President Quality and Patient Safety, Mercy Hospital of Pittsburgh, Pittsburgh, PA, p. A572

PINION, Andrea, Vice President, Regional Medical Center–Bayonet Point, Hudson, FL, p. A131

PINKERMAN, Charles F., Chief Executive Officer, McCready Health Services Foundation, Crisfield, MD, p. A307

PINKHAM, Margaret G., President and Chief Executive Officer, St. Andrews Hospital and Healthcare Center, Boothbay Harbor, ME, p. A297

PINSON, C Wright, Chief Medical Officer, Vanderbilt University Medical Center, Nashville, TN, p. A616

PIPER, Ed, Chief Executive Officer, Onslow Memorial Hospital, Jacksonville, NC, p. A485

PIPICELLI, Thomas P., President and Chief Executive Officer, The William W. Backus Hospital, Norwich, CT, p. A116

PIPPIN, Saundra, Director of Human Resources, Hardin Medical Center, Savannah, TN, p. A617

PIRIZ, J. E., Administrator, Memorial Regional Hospital, Hollywood, FL, p. A131

PIRO, Michael, Vice President Facilities and Management Information Systems, Barnert Hospital, Paterson, NJ, p. A434

PIRO, Paul, Senior Vice President and Chief Financial Officer, Central DuPage Hospital, Winfield, IL, p. A210

PIROG, Steve, Vice President Finance, Saint Mary's Health Care, Grand Rapids, MI, p. A335

PIRTLE, Kathleen, Human Resources Manager, HEALTHSOUTH Rehabilitation Hospital–Wichita Falls, Wichita Falls, TX, p. A674

PIRTLE, Randy B., Chief Financial Officer, Metropolitan Nashville General Hospital, Nashville, TN, p. A615

PIRTLE, M.D., Stephen E., Chief of Staff, South Mississippi County Regional Medical Center, Osceola, AR, p. A49

PISCIOTTA, James M., Chief Executive Officer, Southwest Connecticut Mental Health System, Bridgeport, CT, p. A112

PISHIONERI, Thomas P., Associate Director, Veterans Affairs Medical Center, Cincinnati, OH, p. A508

PITCHER, Karen, Chief Executive Officer, Promise Specialty Hospital of San Antonio, San Antonio, TX, p. A665

PITLICK, Tom, Chief Financial Officer, Mid Dakota Medical Center, Chamberlain, SD, p. A594

PITMAN, David R., Chief Financial Officer, Grant Regional Health Center, Lancaster, WI, p. A728

PITTMAN, Deanna, Administrator, Wilson County Hospital, Neodesha, KS, p. A253

PITTMAN, Jennifer, Chief Financial Officer, North Shore Medical Center, Miami, FL, p. A138

PITTMAN, Jill, Regional Human Resources Director, HEALTHSOUTH Rehabilitation Hospital, Dothan, AL, p. A17

PITTMAN, Kenneth, Interim Chief Executive Officer, Medical Center at Terrell, Terrell, TX, p. A669

PITTMAN, Patricia O., Director, Veterans Affairs Medical Center, Memphis, TN, p. A614

PITTMAN, Scott M., President and Chief Executive Officer, East Pasco Medical Center, Zephyrhills, FL, p. A151

PITTS, Dee, Interim Chief Financial Officer, Mercer County Hospital, Aledo, IL, p. A183

PITTS, Pam, Director Personnel, Blowing Rock Hospital, Blowing Rock, NC, p. A478

PITTS, Sherry J., Administrator, Woman's Hospital at River Oaks, Jackson, MS, p. A371

PITTS, Stephen, Administrator, East Texas Medical Center–Mount Vernon, Mount Vernon, TX, p. A657

PIVIROTTO, Gregory A., President and Chief Executive Officer, University Medical Center, Tucson, AZ, p. A38

PIZZARD, M.D., Oscar, President Medical Staff, Christ Hospital, Jersey City, NJ, p. A430

PIZZUTELLI, El Reta, Director Human Resources, Central Carolina Hospital, Sanford, NC, p. A491

PLACEK, Lynn, Payroll and Personnel Coordinator, Box Butte General Hospital, Alliance, NE, p. A404

PLACENCIA, M.D., Cecilia, Chief of Staff, Rusk County Memorial Hospital and Nursing Home, Ladysmith, WI, p. A728

PLADSON, Terrance, M.D., President and Chief Executive Officer, CentraCare Health System, Saint Cloud, MN, p. B28

PLAISANCE, Stephen, Chief Financial Officer, Sauk Prairie Memorial Hospital, Prairie Du Sac, WI, p. A734

PLAMONDON, Richard, Vice President Finance, St. Joseph Hospital, Nashua, NH, p. A423

PLANT, Robert, Ph.D., Superintendent, Riverview Hospital for Children and Youth, Middletown, CT, p. A114

PLASZCZ, Bob, Executive Vice President Information Services and Chief Information Oficer, Unity Hospital, Fridley, MN, p. A354

PLASZCZ, Robert, Chief Information Officer, Mercy Hospital, Coon Rapids, MN, p. A351

PLATER, Queenie, Vice President Human Resources, Sibley Memorial Hospital, Washington, DC, p. A122

PLATOU, Kenneth E. S., Chief Executive Officer, Montrose Memorial Hospital, Montrose, CO, p. A108

PLATT, Anne, Chief Executive Officer, Sutter Amador Hospital, Jackson, CA, p. A65

PLATT, C. James, Chief Executive Officer, Fort Madison Community Hospital, Fort Madison, IA, p. A234

PLATT, Melvin J., Chief Executive Officer, Worthington Regional Hospital, Worthington, MN, p. A365

PLATYKE, Samantha, Chief Financial Officer, St. Anne Mercy Hospital, Toledo, OH, p. A523

PLATZKE, Samantha M., Senior Vice President Finance and Chief Financial Officer, St. Vincent Mercy Medical Center, Toledo, OH, p. A523

PLESHAR, Samuel G., Chief Executive Officer, Livingston Memorial Hospital, Livingston, MT, p. A400

PLESKOW, Eric D., President and Chief Executive Officer, Brylin Hospitals, Buffalo, NY, p. A448

PLETCHER, Daniel
Director Information System, Geneva General Hospital, Geneva, NY, p. A452
Director Information System, Soldiers and Sailors Memorial Hospital of Yates County, Penn Yan, NY, p. A469

PLETZ, Rick, Chief Executive Officer, Kindred Hospital–Cleveland, Cleveland, OH, p. A509

PLEVICH, Trish, Human Resource Director, HEALTHSOUTH MountainView Regional Rehabilitation Hospital, Morgantown, WV, p. A718

PLOTSKY, M.D., Carol, President Medical and Affiliate Staff, Shady Grove Adventist Hospital, Rockville, MD, p. A310

PLUARD, Dennis, Chief Financial Officer, Sarah Bush Lincoln Health Center, Mattoon, IL, p. A200

PLUCKER, Jay, Administrator, Landmann–Jungman Memorial Hospital, Scotland, SD, p. A598

PLUCKHORN, Fred, Senior Vice President, The Methodist Hospital, Houston, TX, p. A648

PLUMMER, Carey W., Chief Executive Officer, Focus Healthcare of Ohio, Maumee, OH, p. A518

PLUMMER, Deborah, Chief Executive Officer, Kindred Hospital–Boston, Boston, MA, p. A314

PLUMMER, James S., Chief Executive Officer, Aurora Behavioral HealthCare/San Diego, San Diego, CA, p. A86

PLUTA, Dave, Chief Information Officer, Vail Valley Medical Center, Vail, CO, p. A110

POBLETE, M.D., Ronald, President Medical and Dental Staff, St. Mary's Hospital, Passaic, NJ, p. A434

POCCIA, Thomas E., Vice President and Chief Financial Officer, Lenox Hill Hospital, New York, NY, p. A461

POCCIA, Tom, Chief Financial Officer, Manhattan Eye, Ear and Throat Hospital, New York, NY, p. A462

POCHYBOVA, Erika, Director Management Information Systems, Highland Medical Center, Lubbock, TX, p. A654

PODESTA, Charles
Chief Information Officer, Fairview Hospital, Great Barrington, MA, p. A318
Vice President and Chief Information Officer, Saint Mary's Hospital, Waterbury, CT, p. A117

PODGES, Christopher J.
Chief Information Officer, Leelanau Memorial Health Center, Northport, MI, p. A341
Chief Information Officer, Munson Medical Center, Traverse City, MI, p. A346

PODOLSKY, M.D., Howard, Vice President and Chief Medical Officer, SSM St. Mary's Health Center, Saint Louis, MO, p. A392

POE, Bernard, Administrator, New Horizons Health Systems, Inc., Owenton, KY, p. A273

POEHLING, James C., Director, Columbia Regional Hospital, Columbia, MO, p. A380

POEL, M.D., Mary L., Vice President Medical Affairs, Rehoboth McKinley Christian Hospital, Gallup, NM, p. A442

POGARCH, Dennis, Vice President Human Resources, Mercy Memorial Hospital System, Monroe, MI, p. A340

POGAS, George, Vice President and Chief Financial Officer, Witham Memorial Hospital, Lebanon, IN, p. A221

POGUE, Tom, Vice President, Thomasville Medical Center, Thomasville, NC, p. A493

POHJALA, Eric, Vice President and Chief Financial Officer, Lima Memorial Health System, Lima, OH, p. A516

POHLMAN, Dale, Chief Financial Officer, Faith Regional Health Services, Norfolk, NE, p. A410

POHREN, Allen E., Administrator, Montgomery County Memorial Hospital, Red Oak, IA, p. A240

POHSCILLI, Donna, Chief Operating Officer, Franciscan Hospital for Children and Rehabilitation Center, Boston, MA, p. A314

POINDEXTER, Judy, Executive Assistant and Human Resources Coordinator, R. J. Reynolds–Patrick County Memorial Hospital, Stuart, VA, p. A697

POIRIER, Alex M., Chief Executive Officer, Berwick Hospital Center, Berwick, PA, p. A552

POISSON, Keith R., President, St. John West Shore Hospital, Cleveland, OH, p. A509

POKORNEY, M.D., Bruce H., Senior Vice President Medical Affairs, Lancaster General Hospital, Lancaster, PA, p. A562

POKORNEY, Georgia, Chief Executive Officer, Pioneer Memorial Hospital and Health Services, Viborg, SD, p. A600

POLAHAR, Robert G., President, Wellmont Lonesome Pine Hospital, Big Stone Gap, VA, p. A685

POLAND, Dave, Chief Financial Officer, Meadville Medical Center, Meadville, PA, p. A564

POLANOWICZ, John, President and Chief Executive Officer, UMass Memorial–Marlborough Hospital, Marlborough, MA, p. A320

POLGE, David J., President and Chief Executive Officer, Delaware Valley Hospital, Walton, NY, p. A475

POLHAMUS, Bonnie, Director Human Resources, Columbia Basin Hospital, Ephrata, WA, p. A702

POLHEBER, Richard, Senior Vice President and Chief Executive Officer, Carondelet Holy Cross Hospital, Nogales, AZ, p. A32

POLICASTRO, M.D., Anthony M., Senior Vice President Medical Affairs, Nanticoke Memorial Hospital, Seaford, DE, p. A119

POLICH, M.D., Vance, Vice President Medical Affairs and Chief Medical Officer, Huntington Memorial Hospital, Pasadena, CA, p. A81

POLING, Sara, Senior Vice President and Chief Operating Officer, Allen Memorial Hospital, Waterloo, IA, p. A242

POLK, M.D., J Robert, Vice President Physician and Clinical Care Services, Saint Alphonsus Regional Medical Center, Boise, ID, p. A177

POLKOW, Craig, Chief Financial Officer, DeKalb Memorial Hospital, Auburn, IN, p. A211

POLLA, Dale E., Administrator, Okanogan Douglas District Hospital, Brewster, WA, p. A701

POLLARD, Timothy J., Chief Financial Officer, Greene Memorial Hospital, Xenia, OH, p. A525

POLLESCH, Bobbie, Chief Financial Officer, Ripon Medical Center, Ripon, WI, p. A735

POLLMAN, Jerri, Finance Director, Kremmling Memorial Hospital, Kremmling, CO, p. A107

POLLOCK, David, Director Information Systems, Twin Cities Community Hospital, Templeton, CA, p. A95

POLLOCK, Gale, Commander, Tripler Army Medical Center, Honolulu, HI, p. A174

POLLOCK, Jeffrey, Vice President Information Services and Chief Information Officer, Riverside Medical Center, Kankakee, IL, p. A198

POLLOCK, Tracy, Controller, Baptist Memorial Hospital–Forrest City, Forrest City, AR, p. A43

POLLY, M.D., Stuart, Medical Director, Regional Medical Center at Memphis, Memphis, TN, p. A613

POLOVICH, Joyce, Director Information Mangement, Ohio Valley General Hospital, McKees Rocks, PA, p. A564

POLSTER, Peggy, Personnel Manager and Administrative Assistant, Falls Community Hospital and Clinic, Marlin, TX, p. A655

POLUNAS, David M., Chief Executive Officer, Kindred Hospital–Greensboro, Greensboro, NC, p. A484

POLYS, Mary Kay, President and Chief Executive Officer, Mercy Medical, Daphne, AL, p. A17

POMA, Frank W., President, St. John River District Hospital, East China, MI, p. A332

POMEROY, Chuck, Vice President Finance, St. Luke's Regional Medical Center, Boise, ID, p. A178

POMMETT Jr, Francis A., Executive Director and Senior Vice President, Sacred Heart Hospital, Cumberland, MD, p. A307

POND, Mark, Administrator, Garfield County Health Center, Jordan, MT, p. A400

POOLAW, Bryce, Clinical Director, U. S. Public Health Service Indian Hospital, Lawton, OK, p. A532

POOLE, Ken, Information Systems Coordinator, Stone County Medical Center, Mountain View, AR, p. A48

POOLE, Rob, Director, Jane Phillips Medical Center, Bartlesville, OK, p. A528

POOLE ADAMS, Veronica, Vice President, Chief Operating Officer and Chief Nursing Executive, Cleveland Regional Medical Center, Shelby, NC, p. A491

POORE, Michael, Vice President and Administrator, WellStar Douglas Hospital, Douglasville, GA, p. A161

POORTEN, Kevin P., President and Chief Executive Officer, Kishwaukee Health System, De Kalb, IL, p. B67

POOTOOGOOLUK, Helen, Chief Operating Officer, Norton Sound Regional Hospital, Nome, AK, p. A28

POPE, Alice H., Vice President, Finance and Operations, Wellmont Holston Valley Medical Center, Kingsport, TN, p. A609

POPE, C Ron, Chief Operating Officer, Maury Regional Hospital, Columbia, TN, p. A604

POPE, J Larry, Vice President Finance, Palmetto Health Baptist Easley, Easley, SC, p. A587

POPE, James W., FACHE, President and Chief Executive Officer, Wadsworth–Rittman Hospital, Wadsworth, OH, p. A524

POPE, Jerry, Administrator and Chief Executive Officer, Baptist Memorial Hospital–Forrest City, Forrest City, AR, p. A43

POPE, Pat, Vice President Human Resources, Saline Memorial Hospital, Benton, AR, p. A40

POPIEL, Gary W., Chief Executive Officer, Henry Ford Bi–County Hospital, Warren, MI, p. A347

POPKIN, Steve, Chief Executive Officer, Memorial Hospital of Gardena, Gardena, CA, p. A62

POPP, Dennis A., Administrator and Chief Executive Officer, Enumclaw Community Hospital, Enumclaw, WA, p. A702

POQUETTE, Gary R., FACHE, Executive Director, Memorial Hospital, North Conway, NH, p. A423

PORCO, Al, Chief Information Officer, Kings County Hospital Center, New York, NY, p. A460

PORTCHY, Mindy, Manager Human Resources, Mark Reed Hospital, McCleary, WA, p. A704

PORTELA, Joyce, Chief Operating Officer, Tennessee Christian Medical Center, Madison, TN, p. A611

PORTEN, Hank J., President and Chief Executive Officer, Holyoke Medical Center, Holyoke, MA, p. A318

PORTER, Becky, Information Management Director, Howard Memorial Hospital, Nashville, AR, p. A48

PORTER, Cliff, Director Information Services, Noble Hospital, Westfield, MA, p. A325

PORTER, Glen, Vice President Human Resources, St. Mary's Medical Center, Duluth, MN, p. A352

PORTER, Greg, Chief Financial Officer, Rio Grande Hospital, Del Norte, CO, p. A103

PORTER, Jackie, Controller, Oakwood Heritage Hospital, Taylor, MI, p. A346

PORTER, James
Director Information Services, Comanche County Memorial Hospital, Lawton, OK, p. A532
Vice President and Chief Financial Officer, Riverview Hospital, Noblesville, IN, p. A223

PORTER, M.D., James, Vice President Medical Affairs, Deaconess Hospital, Evansville, IN, p. A214

PORTER, Jerry L., Chief Executive Officer, Westview Hospital, Indianapolis, IN, p. A219

PORTER Jr, John M., President and Chief Executive Officer, Ephrata Community Hospital, Ephrata, PA, p. A558

PORTER, John T., President and Chief Executive Officer, Avera Health, Yankton, SD, p. B13

PORTER, Nicolas, Associate Center Director for Administration, H. Lee Moffitt Cancer Center and Research Institute, Tampa, FL, p. A148

PORTER, Paul E., Chief Executive Officer, Fort Washington Medical Center, Fort Washington, MD, p. A308

PORTER, Sharon, Chief Financial Officer, Massachusetts Hospital School, Canton, MA, p. A316

PORTER, Thomas C., President, Morton Hospital and Medical Center, Taunton, MA, p. A324

PORTWOOD, David A., Chief Operating Officer, Coliseum Medical Centers, Macon, GA, p. A165

PORTWOOD, Lee, Vice President, Trinity Mother Frances Health System, Tyler, TX, p. A671

POSECAI, Scott J., Executive Vice President and Chief Financial Officer, Ochsner Clinic Foundation, New Orleans, LA, p. A289

POSEY, M. Kenneth, FACHE, Administrator, Jasper General Hospital, Bay Springs, MS, p. A366

POSMOGA, Paul, Chief Financial Officer, Twin Cities Community Hospital, Templeton, CA, p. A95

POST, M.D., Gregory, Senior Executive and Chief of Staff, MeritCare Medical Center, Fargo, ND, p. A497

POSTLER–SLATTERY, Ph.D., Diane, President and Chief Operating Officer, Aspirus Wausau Hospital, Wausau, WI, p. A737

POSTLETHWAIT, Betsy, Chief Operating Officer and Chief Financial Officer, Baptist Princeton, Birmingham, AL, p. A14

POTEETE, Kenneth W., President and Chief Executive Officer, Georgetown Healthcare System, Georgetown, TX, p. A641

POTHAST, Joyce, Vice President Human and Environmental Services, Van Wert County Hospital, Van Wert, OH, p. A523

POTTENGER, Jay, Administrator, Missouri River Medical Center, Fort Benton, MT, p. A398

POTTER, M.D., Joe, Chief of Staff, Integris Marshall County Medical Center, Madill, OK, p. A533

POTTER, Larry, Chief Executive Officer, Crook County Medical Services District, Sundance, WY, p. A742

POTTER, Michael S., FACHE, President and Chief Executive Officer, Wadley Regional Medical Center, Texarkana, TX, p. A670

POTTER, Stephen W., Chief Information Officer, Canton–Potsdam Hospital, Potsdam, NY, p. A470

POTTER, Terri L., President and Chief Executive Officer, Meriter Hospital, Madison, WI, p. A728

POTTS, Michael P., M.D., Interim Chief Executive Officer, Governor Juan F. Louis Hospital, Christiansted, VI, p. A749

POULIOT, Erika, Manager Human Resources, HEALTHSOUTH Rehabilitation Hospital, Concord, NH, p. A420

POULSON, Thomas
Vice President Finance, Mercy Hospital of Tiffin, Tiffin, OH, p. A522
Vice President Finance, Mercy Hospital of Willard, Willard, OH, p. A525

POUND, Steven, Vice President, Hamilton Medical Center, Dalton, GA, p. A160

POUNDS, Bet, Human Resources Director, Bogalusa Medical Center, Bogalusa, LA, p. A278

POWEL, M.D., Linda J., Medical Director, Odessa Memorial Healthcare Center, Odessa, WA, p. A705

POWELL, Charles
Chief Financial Officer, Golden Plains Community Hospital, Borger, TX, p. A626
Chief Financial Officer, Mena Medical Center, Mena, AR, p. A47

POWELL, D Jerome, Director Information Services, Strong Memorial Hospital of the University of Rochester, Rochester, NY, p. A471

POWELL, Daniel D., Chief Financial Officer, St. Luke's Medical Center, Phoenix, AZ, p. A35

POWELL, Darnell, Executive Director, Rolling Hills Hospital, Ada, OK, p. A527

POWELL, David G., Vice President Human Resources, Providence Hospital, Mobile, AL, p. A21

POWELL, Denny W., President, Mercy General Hospital, Sacramento, CA, p. A85

POWELL, Frank R.
Chief Financial Officer, Houston Medical Center, Warner Robins, GA, p. A172
Chief Financial Officer, Perry Hospital, Perry, GA, p. A167

POWELL, Jennifer, President Medical Staff, Dr. John Warner Hospital, Clinton, IL, p. A191

POWELL, Jerry, Chief Information Officer, Highland Hospital of Rochester, Rochester, NY, p. A470

POWELL, Joe, Director Human Resources, HEALTHSOUTH Rehabilitation of Mechanicsburg, Mechanicsburg, PA, p. A564

POWELL, Kay, Director Human Resources, Christus Jasper Memorial Hospital, Jasper, TX, p. A650

POWELL, Ricky, Chief Executive Officer, Red River Hospital, Wichita Falls, TX, p. A674

POWELL, Jr, Ronald P., Chief Financial Officer, Retreat Hospital, Richmond, VA, p. A695

POWELL, Roy A., President, Frankford Hospital of the City of Philadelphia, Philadelphia, PA, p. A568

POWELL, Steve, Administrator, Renaissance Women's Hospital of Edmond, Edmond, OK, p. A530

POWELL, M.D., Theo, Medical Director, Three Rivers Community Hospital and Health Center, Grants Pass, OR, p. A544

POWELL, Troy
Administrator, HEALTHSOUTH Rehabilitation Hospital of Charleston, Charleston, SC, p. A584
Administrator, HEALTHSOUTH Rehabilitation Hospital–Charleston, North Charleston, SC, p. A590

POWELSON, Jeffrey A., Chief Executive Officer, Broaddus Hospital, Philippi, WV, p. A719

POWERS, Daniell
Chief Executive Officer, Lynn County Hospital District, Tahoka, TX, p. A668
Chief Executive Officer, Lynn County Hospital District, Tahoka, TX, p. A668

POWERS, Donald, Chairman, President and Chief Executive Officer, Community Healthcare System, Hammond, IN, p. B32

POWERS, Greg, Administrative Officer, U. S. Public Health Service Indian Hospital, Mescalero, NM, p. A444

POWERS, Jack, Director Human Resources, Central Washington Hospital, Wenatchee, WA, p. A711

POWERS, Lisa, Chief Executive Officer, Trigg County Hospital, Cadiz, KY, p. A262

POWERS, Michael K., FACHE, Chief Executive Officer, Fairbanks Memorial Hospital, Fairbanks, AK, p. A27

POWERS, Paul A., Vice President, Lakeland Regional Medical Center, Lakeland, FL, p. A134

POWERS, Tina, Human Resource Directpr, Fayette County Memorial Hospital, Washington Court House, OH, p. A524

POWERS, Tom, Vice President Information Systems, Ball Memorial Hospital, Muncie, IN, p. A222

POYNTER, Carmen, Director Human Resources, Rockcastle Hospital and Respiratory Care Center, Mount Vernon, KY, p. A272

PRABHUDESAI, M.D., Sarita, Chief of Staff, Veterans Affairs Illiana Health Care System, Danville, IL, p. A191

PRACHT, Matthew, Vice President Finance, Scotland Memorial Hospital, Laurinburg, NC, p. A486

PRAGER, Jay E., Chief Operating Officer, Reynolds Memorial Hospital, Glen Dale, WV, p. A715

PRATER, Robin, Director of Human Resources, Howard A. Rusk Rehabilitation Center, Columbia, MO, p. A381

PRATHER, Bobbie L., Chief Financial Officer, Central Baptist Hospital, Lexington, KY, p. A267

PRATT, Audra, Vice President Human Resources, Mercy Medical Center, Nampa, ID, p. A180

PRATT, Lisa, Director Human Resources, McLean Hospital, Belmont, MA, p. A312

PRATT, Mary Ellen, Chief Executive Officer, University Hospital and Clinics – Holmes County, Lexington, MS, p. A372

PRATT, M.D., William, President Medical Staff, Marymount Medical Center, London, KY, p. A268

PRATT, William T., Administrator, Waukesha County Mental Health Center, Waukesha, WI, p. A737

PREATO, Robert, Chief Financial Officer, Palms West Hospital, Loxahatchee, FL, p. A135

PREECE, James, Chief Information Officer, Enloe Medical Center, Chico, CA, p. A56

PRESCOTT, Tina, Administrator, Camden General Hospital, Camden, TN, p. A602

PRESLAR Jr, Len B.
President and Chief Executive Officer, North Carolina Baptist Hospital, Winston–Salem, NC, p. B79
President and Chief Executive Officer, North Carolina Baptist Hospital (Wake Forest University Baptist Medical Center), Winston–Salem, NC, p. A494

PRESLEY, James, Chief Information Resources, Veterans Affairs Central Iowa Health Care System, Des Moines, IA, p. A233

PRESSLEY, Larry S., Administrator, Indian Valley Health Care District, Greenville, CA, p. A63

PRESTON, Jennifer, Human Resources Director, Fairview University Medical Center–Mesabi, Hibbing, MN, p. A355

PRESTON, Laura, Controller, Cozby–Germany Hospital, Grand Saline, TX, p. A642

PRESTON, R. Craig, Chief Executive Officer, Odessa Regional Hospital, Odessa, TX, p. A659

PRESTON, Sheila, Information Systems Director, Community Health Center of Branch County, Coldwater, MI, p. A330

PRESTRIDGE, Tim, Chief Financial Officer, Polk Medical Center, Cedartown, GA, p. A157

PRESZLER, Ron, Business Officer Manager, Jonathan M. Wainwright Memorial VA Medical Center, Walla Walla, WA, p. A711

PRETE, M.D., Mark, Vice President Medical Affairs, The Charlotte Hungerford Hospital, Torrington, CT, p. A117

PRETTYMAN, Edgar F., M.D.,
Chief Executive Officer, Compass Hospital of San Antonio, San Antonio, TX, p. A663
Chief Executive Officer, Texas Neuro Rehabilitation Center, Austin, TX, p. A624

PREUITT, Judy, Director Information Systems, St. Joseph's Mercy Health Center, Hot Springs National Park, AR, p. A45

PREWITT, Connie, Chief Financial Officer, Montrose Memorial Hospital, Montrose, CO, p. A108

PRICE, Andrea
Interim President and Chief Executive Officer, Hurley Medical Center, Flint, MI, p. A333
Executive Vice President and Operating Officer, Hurley Medical Center, Flint, MI, p. A333

PRICE, Brad H., Vice President Finance and Operations, Wellmont Bristol Regional Medical Center, Bristol, TN, p. A602

PRICE, Jack
Director, Dorchester General Hospital, Cambridge, MD, p. A306
Director, Memorial Hospital at Easton Maryland, Easton, MD, p. A307

PRICE, Jerry L., Executive Vice President and Chief Operating Officer, Sibley Memorial Hospital, Washington, DC, p. A122

PRICE, John D., Chief Financial Officer, FirstHealth Richmond Memorial Hospital, Rockingham, NC, p. A490

PRICE, Julie, Chief Financial Officer, Rooks County Health Center, Plainville, KS, p. A255

PRICE, Leeann, Director Human Resources, Tyrone Hospital, Tyrone, PA, p. A577

PRICE, Linda, Human Resources Director, Burnett Medical Center, Grantsburg, WI, p. A726

PRICE, Lori
President, Saint Joseph Regional Medical Center–Mishawaka Campus, Mishawaka, IN, p. A222
President, Saint Joseph Regional Medical Center–Plymouth Campus, Plymouth, IN, p. A224
President, Saint Joseph Regional Medical Center–Plymouth Campus, Plymouth, IN, p. A224

PRICE, Lorraine B., Associate Director, Veterans Affairs Medical Center, Hampton, VA, p. A689

PRICE, Mandy, Financial and Accounting Coordinator, Nemaha County Hospital, Auburn, NE, p. A404

PRICE, Manuel, Director Information Systems, Brookwood Medical Center, Birmingham, AL, p. A14

PRICE, Marsha, Supervisor Medical Records, Okeene Municipal Hospital, Okeene, OK, p. A534

PRICE, Norman M., FACHE, Administrator, Southwest Mississippi Regional Medical Center, McComb, MS, p. A372

PRICE, Sam, Vice President Finance, East Alabama Medical Center, Opelika, AL, p. A23

PRICE, Shelby
Chief Executive Officer, Louisiana State Hospitals, New Orleans, LA, p. B70
Chief Executive Officer, New Orleans Adolescent Hospital, New Orleans, LA, p. A289

PRICE, Wendy, Manager Human Resources, Nicholas County Hospital, Carlisle, KY, p. A262

PRIDGEN, Brenda, Director Personnel, Smith Northview Hospital, Valdosta, GA, p. A171

PRIEST, David, Information Systems Director, Charlevoix Area Hospital, Charlevoix, MI, p. A329

PRIEST, M.D., Geoff, Senior Vice President Medical Affairs, Meriter Hospital, Madison, WI, p. A728

PRINCE, Kellie, Director Human Resources, South Austin Hospital, Austin, TX, p. A624

PRINCE, Timothy, Vice President Planning and Ancillary Services, Mercy Hospital of Portland, Portland, ME, p. A300

PRINGLE, M.D., Robert W., Vice President Medical Affairs and Medical Director, Glens Falls Hospital, Glens Falls, NY, p. A453

PRINS, M.D., Bob, Chief of Staff, Island Hospital, Anacortes, WA, p. A700

PRINTY, Wayne
Vice President Finance, Miles Memorial Hospital, Damariscotta, ME, p. A298
Vice President Finance, Miles Memorial Hospital, Damariscotta, ME, p. A298
Vice President, St. Andrews Hospital and Healthcare Center, Boothbay Harbor, ME, p. A297

PRINTZ, David, Vice President and Chief Information Officer, Central DuPage Hospital, Winfield, IL, p. A210

PRIOR, M.D., Roderick
Medical Director and Chief Information Officer, Franklin Memorial Hospital, Farmington, ME, p. A298
Medical Director and Chief Information Officer, Franklin Memorial Hospital, Farmington, ME, p. A298

PRISCO, Michele, Director, North General Hospital, New York, NY, p. A464

PRISELAC, Thomas M., President and Chief Executive Officer, Cedars–Sinai Medical Center, Los Angeles, CA, p. A69

PRISTER, James R., President and Chief Executive Officer, R M L Specialty Hospital, Hinsdale, IL, p. A197

PRITCHARD, Eugene
President, Condell Medical Center, Libertyville, IL, p. A199
President, Condell Medical Center, Libertyville, IL, p. A199

PRITCHARD, Fred A., Executive Director, Incline Village Community Hospital, Incline Village, NV, p. A416

PRITCHETT, Greg, Controller, Cuero Community Hospital, Cuero, TX, p. A631

PROBSTFIELD, Dan, Senior Vice President Finance, Lake Regional Health System, Osage Beach, MO, p. A388

PROBUS, Jeff L., Administrator and Chief Exective Officer, Saint Mary's Standish Community Hospital, Standish, MI, p. A345

PROCHILO, John F., Chief Executive Officer and Administrator, Northeast Rehabilitation Hospital, Salem, NH, p. A423

PROCHNOW, Bryan, Chief Financial Officer, Matagorda General Hospital, Bay City, TX, p. A624

PROCTOR, Deborah A., President and Chief Executive Officer, St. Joseph Health System, Orange, CA, p. B102

PROCTOR, George
Chief Operating Officer and Chief Financial Officer, Kings County Hospital Center, New York, NY, p. A460
Chief Operating Officer and Chief Financial Officer, Kings County Hospital Center, New York, NY, p. A460

PROCTOR, Ken, Director Human Resources, Mayo Regional Hospital, Dover–Foxcroft, ME, p. A298

PROCTOR, Steven M., President, Matheny Medical and Educational Center, Peapack, NJ, p. A434

PROFFITT, David S., Superintendent, Riverview Psychiatric Center, Augusta, ME, p. A296

PROKOSCH, M.D., Brian, Vice President Medical Affairs, St. Francis Regional Medical Center, Shakopee, MN, p. A363

PROSSER, Alita, Director Finance, SSM St. Joseph Hospital of Kirkwood, Saint Louis, MO, p. A392

PROUJANSKY, M.D., Roy, Medical Director, Alfred I. duPont Hospital for Children, Wilmington, DE, p. A119

PROUL, Dennis, Chief Information Officer, Stony Brook University Hospital, Stony Brook, NY, p. A473

PROULX, Ronald, Director Public Relations and Marketing, South Bay Hospital, Sun City Center, FL, p. A147

PROUT, John S.
President and Chief Executive Officer, Bethesda North Hospital, Cincinnati, OH, p. A506
President and Chief Executive Officer, Good Samaritan Hospital, Cincinnati, OH, p. A507

PROVAZNIK, Joe, Manager Information Systems, SSM Cardinal Glennon Children's Hospital, Saint Louis, MO, p. A391

PROVENZANO, Jeff, Chief Financial Officer, Blue Hill Memorial Hospital, Blue Hill, ME, p. A297

PROVENZANO, William F., President and Chief Executive Officer, Ohio Valley General Hospital, McKees Rocks, PA, p. A564

PRPICH, Jen, Director Human Resources, War Memorial Hospital, Sault Ste. Marie, MI, p. A345

PRUIETT, Bobby, Chief Financial Officer, Texoma Medical Center, Denison, TX, p. A635

PRUIETT, Linda, Vice President Human Resources, North Suburban Medical Center, Thornton, CO, p. A110

PRUITT, D.O., Bart, President Medical Staff, Presbyterian Hospital of Winnsboro, Winnsboro, TX, p. A674

PRUITT, Bob, Director Human Resources, Parkview Noble Hospital, Kendallville, IN, p. A220

PRUITT, Elizabeth, Vice President Operations, Massillon Community Hospital, Massillon, OH, p. A518

PRUITT, John, Chief Executive Officer, Colorado River Medical Center, Needles, CA, p. A77

PRUITT, Michael W., Chief Executive Officer, Scenic Mountain Medical Center, Big Spring, TX, p. A626

PRUNCHUNAS, Edward, Senior Vice President and Chief Financial Officer, Cedars–Sinai Medical Center, Los Angeles, CA, p. A69

PRUNTE, Dominic, Director Human Resources, Fairfield Medical Center, Lancaster, OH, p. A515

PRUSAK, Thomas K., President, St. Joseph's Medical Center, Brainerd, MN, p. A350

PRUSHAN, Michael, Chief Learning Officer, Temple University Children's Medical Center, Philadelphia, PA, p. A570

PRYOR, Curtis R., Chief Executive Officer, Purcell Municipal Hospital, Purcell, OK, p. A537

PRYOR, Dennis P., Administrator, Salem Memorial District Hospital, Salem, MO, p. A393

PRYOR, M.D., Robert, Chief Medical Officer, St. Joseph's Hospital and Medical Center, Phoenix, AZ, p. A35

PRYOR, Vincent, Chief Financial Officer, Ingalls Memorial Hospital, Harvey, IL, p. A196

PTAK, Leonard, Executive Vice President Information Systems, Good Samaritan Hospital, Suffern, NY, p. A473

PUCKETT, Kristi, Director of Human Resources, Grande Ronde Hospital, La Grande, OR, p. A545

PUDLAK, Robert A., Executive Vice President and Chief Financial Officer, Bergen Regional Medical Center, Paramus, NJ, p. A433

PUFFENBERGER, James
Interim Chief Executive Officer, Flagstaff Medical Center, Flagstaff, AZ, p. A30
President and Chief Executive Officer, Northern Arizona Healthcare, Flagstaff, AZ, p. B80
Executive Vice President and Chief Financial Officer, Verde Valley Medical Center, Cottonwood, AZ, p. A30

PUGH, Bob, Interim Chief Executive Officer, Madison County Memorial Hospital, Madison, FL, p. A135

PUGH, Brian L., Interim Chief Executive Officer, Kindred Hospital–Louisville, Louisville, KY, p. A269

PUGH, Janelle, Vice President Finance, Gateway Regional Health System, Mount Sterling, KY, p. A272

PUGH, Larry W., Vice President Finance, Simi Valley Hospital and Health Care Services, Simi Valley, CA, p. A94

PUGH, Richard E., President and Chief Executive Officer, New Milford Hospital, New Milford, CT, p. A115

PUGH, Thomas E., Chief Executive Officer, John Heinz Institute of Rehabilitation Medicine, Wilkes–Barre, PA, p. A579

PUGH, William H., Senior Vice President and Chief Financial Officer, Frederick Memorial Hospital, Frederick, MD, p. A308

PUHY, Dorothy E., Executive Vice President and Chief Financial Officer, Dana–Farber Cancer Institute, Boston, MA, p. A313

PUJOLS–MCKEE, M.D., Ana, Chief Medical Officer and Associate Executive Director, Presbyterian Medical Center of the University of Pennsylvania Health System, Philadelphia, PA, p. A569

PULEO, Dominic J., Executive Vice President Finance and Chief Financial Officer, VCU Health System, Richmond, VA, p. A696

PULETTI, M.D., Ernesto, Chief Medical Staff, St. Luke's Hospital, San Francisco, CA, p. A89

PULIAFITO, M.D., Carmen, Chairman of the Department of Ophthalmology, Bascom Palmer Eye Institute–Anne Bates Leach Eye Hospital, Miami, FL, p. A136

PULLEN, Shelly, Chief Human Resources Management Service, Aleda E. Lutz Veterans Affairs Medical Center, Saginaw, MI, p. A344

PULLEYBLANK, Sylvia, Chief Executive Officer, Lawrence County Memorial Hospital, Lawrenceville, IL, p. A199

PULLMAN, Debbie
Business Manager, Hand County Memorial Hospital/Avera Health, Miller, SD, p. A597
Business Manager, Hand County Memorial Hospital/Avera Health, Miller, SD, p. A597

PULS, Dennis, Information Systems Director, Penobscot Bay Medical Center, Rockport, ME, p. A300

PULSIPHER, Gary W., President and Chief Executive Officer, Columbus Community Hospital, Columbus, NE, p. A406

PUMAREJO, M.D., Raymond, Head Information Resources Management, U. S. Naval Hospital, Roosevelt Roads, PR, p. A748

PUNDYS, Aras, Administrator, W. J. Barge Memorial Hospital, Greenville, SC, p. A588

PUNZIRUDU, Debbie, Controller, HEALTHSOUTH Rehabilitation Hospital of Spring Hill, Brooksville, FL, p. A125

PUORRO, Anthony, Chief Executive Officer, Aliquippa Community Hospital, Aliquippa, PA, p. A551

PURCELL, Sandra, Administrator Director Finance, Illini Community Hospital, Pittsfield, IL, p. A205

PURCELL, Terry, Vice President Human Resources, Gnaden Huetten Memorial Hospital, Lehighton, PA, p. A563

PURDY, Ann, Senior Vice President and Chief Financial Officer, St. Vincent's Hospital, Birmingham, AL, p. A15

PURDY, M.D., Bruce, Chief of Staff, Muleshoe Area Medical Center, Muleshoe, TX, p. A658

PURINGTON, Denise, Vice President and Chief Information Officer, Elliot Hospital, Manchester, NH, p. A422

PUROHIT, Shamb, Chief Financial Officer, Smith Northview Hospital, Valdosta, GA, p. A171

PURRINGTON, Janice, Medical Records Coordinator, Hand County Memorial Hospital/Avera Health, Miller, SD, p. A597

PURSLEY, Roger, Chief Executive Officer, Western Mental Health Institute, Bolivar, TN, p. A602

PURTELL, Nancy, Chief Executive Officer, Sierra Vista Hospital, Sacramento, CA, p. A85

PURTLE, M.D., Mark
Vice President Medical Affairs, Iowa Lutheran Hospital, Des Moines, IA, p. A232
Vice President Medical Affairs, Iowa Methodist Medical Center, Des Moines, IA, p. A232

PURVES, Stephen A., CHE, President and Chief Executive Officer, Sisters of Charity Providence Hospitals, Columbia, SC, p. A586

PURVIANCE, Bruce, Chief Executive Officer, Niobrara Valley Hospital, Lynch, NE, p. A409

PURVIS, Jay, Administrator, Wabash General Hospital District, Mount Carmel, IL, p. A201

PURVIS, Michael L.
President and Chief Executive Officer, Redwood Memorial Hospital, Fortuna, CA, p. A60
President and Chief Executive Officer, St. Joseph Hospital, Eureka, CA, p. A59

PUSEY, Cathy, Chf Executive Officer, Kindred Hospital – Delaware County, Darby, PA, p. A556

PUSTINA, Karl, Assistant Administrator for Finance, Upland Hills Health, Dodgeville, WI, p. A724

PUTHOFF, Tim, Chief Executive Officer, Regional Hospital of Jackson, Jackson, TN, p. A608

PUTNAM, Larry E., Administrator, Phillips County Medical Center, Malta, MT, p. A400

PUTNAM, Stewart, Executive Vice President, Cod Unity Health, Park Ridge Hospital, Rochester, NY, p. A471

PUTNAM, Timothy, Administrator and Chief Executive Officer, Mercer County Hospital, Aledo, IL, p. A183

PUTNICK, John, Director Information Systems, Catawba Valley Medical Center, Hickory, NC, p. A484

PUTT, CHE, David G., Administrator, University Hospitals and Clinics, University of Mississippi Medical Center, Jackson, MS, p. A371

PUTTER, Joshua S., Chief Executive Officer, Charlotte Regional Medical Center, Punta Gorda, FL, p. A144

PUVALOWSKI, Caren, Business Manager, Deckerville Community Hospital, Deckerville, MI, p. A330

PYE, Irma, Senior Vice President and Chief Human Resource Officer, Valley Baptist Health System, Harlingen, TX, p. A643

PYFER, Steve, Manager Information Systems, South Peninsula Hospital, Homer, AK, p. A27

PYLE, Anne D., Chief Information Officer, Lafayette General Medical Center, Lafayette, LA, p. A283

PYLE, David, Vice President Medical Affairs, St. Bernards Medical Center, Jonesboro, AR, p. A45

PYLE, Joseph
Executive Vice President and Chief Operating Officer, Friends Behavioral Health System, Philadelphia, PA, p. A568
Executive Vice President and Chief Operating Officer, Friends Behavioral Health System, Philadelphia, PA, p. A568

PYNE, Mel, Division President, Oakwood Hospital and Medical Center–Dearborn, Dearborn, MI, p. A330

PYNN, Chryl, Director Management Information Systems, Hudson Valley Hospital Center, Cortlandt Manor, NY, p. A451

PYNN, David, President and Chief Executive Officer, St. John Medical Center, Tulsa, OK, p. A540

PYRON, Jerry, Chief Executive Officer, Specialty Hospital of Midwest City, Midwest City, OK, p. A533

Q

QAYYUM, Jennifer, Administrator, Edgewood Hospital, Marion, LA, p. A286

QAZI, M.D., Nazimuddin, Chief Medicine, Trenton Psychiatric Hospital, Trenton, NJ, p. A438

QUADRI, Rob, Management Information Systems Director, Barton Memorial Hospital, South Lake Tahoe, CA, p. A94

QUAGLIATA, Joseph A., President and Chief Executive Officer, South Nassau Communities Hospital, Oceanside, NY, p. A467

QUAIN, Suzane, Director Human Resources, Elliot Hospital, Manchester, NH, p. A422

QUALES, Brenda, Chief Financial Officer, Norton Community Hospital, Norton, VA, p. A693

QUALLS, Judi, Director Human Resources, Elba General Hospital, Elba, AL, p. A18

QUANCE, MSC, USN, D E., Director Resources, Naval Hospital, Cherry Point, NC, p. A480

QUANSTROM, Julie, Information Systems Director and Reimbursement Specialist, Wilson County Hospital, Neodesha, KS, p. A253

QUARTIER, Michael J., Vice President, Administrative Services, Huntington Hospital, Huntington, NY, p. A454

QUATTROCCHI, Robert, President and Chief Executive Officer, Northside Hospital, Atlanta, GA, p. A154

QUICHOCHO, Vince, Management Information Systems, Guam Memorial Hospital Authority, Tamuning, GU, p. A743

QUIGLEY, Philip, Chief Financial Officer, Gooding County Memorial Hospital, Gooding, ID, p. A179

QUIGLEY, Scott, Director Management Information Systems, Good Samaritan Community Healthcare, Puyallup, WA, p. A706

QUIGLEY, Stephen J., Chief Executive Officer, Riveredge Hospital, Forest Park, IL, p. A194

QUILLMAN, Jerri, Senior Vice President and Chief Operating Officer, Floyd Memorial Hospital and Health Services, New Albany, IN, p. A222

QUINLAN, Patrick J., M.D., Chief Executive Officer, Ochsner Clinic Foundation, New Orleans, LA, p. A289

QUINLAN, M.D., Patrick J., Chief Executive Officer, Ochsner Clinic Foundation, New Orleans, LA, p. A289

QUINLIVAN, John, Vice President and Chief Operating Officer, North Florida Regional Medical Center, Gainesville, FL, p. A130

QUINLIVAN, Kathy, Management Information Systems Director, Avera Sacred Heart Hospital, Yankton, SD, p. A601

QUINN, J. Clifton, Administrator, Gulf States LTAC of Denham Springs, Denham Springs, LA, p. A280

QUINN, John A.
Chief Executive Officer, Spalding Regional Medical Center, Griffin, GA, p. A163
Chief Executive Officer, Sylvan Grove Hospital, Jackson, GA, p. A164

QUINN, Mary Anna, Vice President, St. Jude Children's Research Hospital, Memphis, TN, p. A614

QUINN, Thomas P., President and Chief Executive Officer, Community–General Hospital of Greater Syracuse, Syracuse, NY, p. A473

QUINONEZ, Yolanda, Director Finance, I. Gonzalez Martinez Oncologic Hospital, Hato Rey, PR, p. A747

QUINTANA, Humberto, Chief Information Officer, Antelope Valley Hospital, Lancaster, CA, p. A67

QUINTANA, Jay, Chief Executive Officer, SCCI Hospital – El Paso, El Paso, TX, p. A638

QUINTON, Byron, Administrator, Wayne Medical Center, Waynesboro, TN, p. A619

QUINTON, J. Ben, Administrator and Chief Executive Officer, Rooks County Health Center, Plainville, KS, p. A255

QUIRIN, Julie, Chief Executive Officer, Saint Luke's South Hospital, Overland Park, KS, p. A255

QUIRING, Robert, Vice President Human Resources, Integris Baptist Medical Center, Oklahoma City, OK, p. A535

QUON, Linda, Public Affairs Leader, Kaiser Foundation Hospital, Los Angeles, CA, p. A71

R

RAAB, Daniel J., President and Chief Executive Officer, St. Vincent Memorial Hospital, Taylorville, IL, p. A209

RAAB, Vincent R., Vice President Finance and Chief Financial Officer, New York Eye and Ear Infirmary, New York, NY, p. A463

RAB, Shafiq, Chief Information Officer, St. Mary's Hospital, Passaic, NJ, p. A434

RABER, Conrad, Chief, Information Resources Management Service, Durham Veterans Affairs Medical Center, Durham, NC, p. A481

RABIN, M.D., Barry, Medical Director, Linden Oaks Hospital at Edward, Naperville, IL, p. A202

RABNER, Barry S., President and Chief Executive Officer, University Medical Center at Princeton, Princeton, NJ, p. A435

RACHAL, I M., Chief Fiscal Service, South Texas Veterans Health Care System, San Antonio, TX, p. A665

RACHAL, M.D., Paul, Chief of Staff, Pointe Coupee General Hospital, New Roads, LA, p. A290

RACHUIG, Sue, Director Information Services, Tulane University Hospital and Clinic, New Orleans, LA, p. A290

RACKOW, Eric, M.D., President and Chief Executive Officer, New York University Medical Center, New York, NY, p. A463

RADCLIFFE, M.D., Eric, Medical Director, United Hospital Center, Clarksburg, WV, p. A715

RADER, Mark, Chief Operating Officer, Lewis–Gale Medical Center, Salem, VA, p. A696

RADFORD, Joanna, Chief Human Resources Officer, Shoshone Medical Center, Kellogg, ID, p. A179

RADFORD, Juanita, Team Resource Coordinator, South Florida Baptist Hospital, Plant City, FL, p. A143

RADICE, Barbara, Vice President and Chief Information Officer, San Diego Hospice & Palliative Care, San Diego, CA, p. A87

RADO, M.D., Thomas, Chief of Staff, Kadlec Medical Center, Richland, WA, p. A707

RADOTICH, Maureen, Director Human Resources, Providence Valdez Medical Center, Valdez, AK, p. A29

RADZIKOWSKI, M.D., Ronald A., Chief Medical Officer, Our Lady of the Lake Regional Medical Center, Baton Rouge, LA, p. A277

RAEL, Chris, Vice President Operations, Porter–Valparaiso Hospital Campus, Valparaiso, IN, p. A226

RAFALSKI, Mark, Vice President Finance and Chief Financial Officer, La Porte Regional Health System, La Porte, IN, p. A220

RAFELO, Wilfredo, Administrator, Mepsi Center, Bayamon, PR, p. A744

RAFFAELE, Virginia, Vice President Human Resources, Brookhaven Memorial Hospital Medical Center, Patchogue, NY, p. A469

RAFFERTY, Joyce, Vice President Finance, Champlain Valley Physicians Hospital Medical Center, Plattsburgh, NY, p. A469

RAFFERTY, Patrick W., Chief Executive Officer, Western Medical Center Anaheim, Anaheim, CA, p. A52

RAFFOUL, John, Vice President Finance, White Memorial Medical Center, Los Angeles, CA, p. A73

RAFOWICZ, Charles, Vice President, Community Hospital, Grand Junction, CO, p. A106

RAFTER, William A., Director, Julian F. Keith Alcohol and Drug Abuse Treatment Center, Black Mountain, NC, p. A478

RAFTERY, Anne, Vice President Human Resources, Valley Hospital, Ridgewood, NJ, p. A435

RAGGIO, James J., Administrator and Chief Executive Officer, Lompoc Healthcare District, Lompoc, CA, p. A68

RAGLAND, Kenneth E., Chief Executive Officer, Pungo District Hospital, Belhaven, NC, p. A478

RAGLE, Bertha, Director Personnel, CrossRidge Community Hospital, Wynne, AR, p. A51

RAHN, Douglas L., Chief Operating Officer, Leesburg Regional Medical Center, Leesburg, FL, p. A135

RAILEY, M.D., Bruce, Chief of Staff, Medical Center of Arlington, Arlington, TX, p. A622

RAINEY, Jackie, Accountant, Cornerstone Regional Hospital, Edinburg, TX, p. A636

RAINEY, John W., Administrator, Kearney County Health Services, Minden, NE, p. A409

RAINS, Jeffrey, Interim Chief Executive Officer, Williamson Memorial Hospital, Williamson, WV, p. A721

RAINS, Steve, Director Information Services, McKee Medical Center, Loveland, CO, p. A108

RAINSFORD, M.D., George, Chief of Medical Staff, Edgefield County Hospital, Edgefield, SC, p. A587

RAIZEN, Larry, Area Director Information Systems, St. Joseph Hospital, Eureka, CA, p. A59

RAJNIC, Sharon J., Administrator, Shriners Hospitals for Children, Philadelphia, Philadelphia, PA, p. A569

RALPH, Chandler M., President and Chief Executive Officer, Adirondack Medical Center, Saranac Lake, NY, p. A471

RALPH, Stephen A., President and Chief Executive Officer, Huntington Memorial Hospital, Pasadena, CA, p. A81

RALSTON, Kathleen, Vice President and Chief Financial Officer, Detroit Receiving Hospital and University Health Center, Detroit, MI, p. A331

RAMAN, Jayashree, Vice President and Chief Information Officer, Reading Hospital and Medical Center, West Reading, PA, p. A579

RAMAZANI, Regina, Chief Financial Officer, Garden Park Medical Center, Gulfport, MS, p. A369

RAMER, Gary, Information Management Manager, Jonathan M. Wainwright Memorial VA Medical Center, Walla Walla, WA, p. A711

RAMEY, M.D., E Ross, Medical Director, Monadnock Community Hospital, Peterborough, NH, p. A423

RAMEY, Rita, Director of Information Systems, Buchanan General Hospital, Grundy, VA, p. A689

RAMIREZ, Magdalena, Chief Executive Officer, Helen Hayes Hospital, West Haverstraw, NY, p. A476

RAMIREZ, Rafael E., M.D., Center Director, Veterans Affairs Medical Center, San Juan, PR, p. A748

RAMIREZ, Victor, Chief Human Resources, El Centro Regional Medical Center, El Centro, CA, p. A59

RAMOS, Ivette, Human Resources, Hospital Episcopal Cristo Redentor, Guayama, PR, p. A745

RAMPAGE, Bruce E., President and Chief Executive Officer, Saint Anthony Memorial Health Centers, Michigan City, IN, p. A222

RAMPAT, Ananda, Chief Financial Office, Columbia Hospital, West Palm Beach, FL, p. A150

RAMSEY, M.D., Alice, Chief of Staff, Palo Pinto General Hospital, Mineral Wells, TX, p. A657

RAMSEY, Barbara, Ph.D., Chief Executive Officer, Lincoln Regional Center, Lincoln, NE, p. A408

RAMSEY, David L.
President and Chief Executive Officer, Charleston Area Medical Center, Charleston, WV, p. A714
President and Chief Executive Officer, Charleston Area Medical Center Health System, Inc., Charleston, WV, p. B28

RAMSEY, Elizabeth, Chief Operating Officer, University of South Alabama Medical Center, Mobile, AL, p. A21

RAMSEY, Gina B., Vice President Financial Services and Chief Financial Officer, North Carolina Baptist Hospital (Wake Forest University Baptist Medical Center), Winston–Salem, NC, p. A494

RAMSEY, James, Vice President Finance and Chief Financial Officer, Lincoln Medical Center, Lincolnton, NC, p. A486

RAMSEY, Robert, Chief Financial Officer, Our Lady of the Lake Regional Medical Center, Baton Rouge, LA, p. A277

RAMSEY, Steve
Chief Executive Officer, SCCI Hospital – Aurora, Aurora, CO, p. A101
Chief Financial Officer, Powell Valley Healthcare, Powell, WY, p. A741

RAMSEY, Tom, Chief Financial Officer, Doctors Hospital of Stark County, Massillon, OH, p. A518

RAMSKI, Nancy, Director Human Resources, La Rabida Children's Hospital, Chicago, IL, p. A187

RAND, M.D., Kevin, Clinical Director, Chinle Comprehensive Health Care Facility, Chinle, AZ, p. A30

RAND, Sharon, Chief Financial Officer, Kindred Hospital–Milwaukee, Milwaukee, WI, p. A731

RANDALL, JoEllen, Vice President Human Resources, Ottumwa Regional Health Center, Ottumwa, IA, p. A240

RANDALL, Kenneth W., Chief Executive Officer, Western Arizona Regional Medical Center, Bullhead City, AZ, p. A30

RANDEL, Anna, Business Office Manager, Weisbrod Memorial County Hospital, Eads, CO, p. A105

RANDELL, M.D., David, Chief of Staff, Castle Medical Center, Kailua, HI, p. A174

RANDO, Andrew, Senior Controller, HEALTHSOUTH Braintree Rehabilitation Hospital, Braintree, MA, p. A315

RANDOLPH, M.D., James, Chief of Staff, Washakie Medical Center, Worland, WY, p. A742

RANDOLPH, Karsten, Chief Financial Officer, Adventist GlenOaks Hospital, Glendale Heights, IL, p. A195

RANDOLPH, Jr, M.D., Leonard M.
Chief Medical Officer, Mercy Franciscan Hospital Mount Airy, Cincinnati, OH, p. A507
Chief Medical Officer, Mercy Hospital Fairfield, Fairfield, OH, p. A513

RANDON, Christian, Chief Information Officer and Vice President Information Technology, Norwalk Hospital, Norwalk, CT, p. A115

RANERI, Samuel, Chief Operating Officer, Excela Frick Hospital, Mount Pleasant, PA, p. A565

RANGAVIZ, Rassoul, Vice President Finance, Copley Hospital, Morrisville, VT, p. A683

RANGE, Richard L., Chief Executive Officer, Baldwin Area Medical Center, Baldwin, WI, p. A722

RANGHELLI, Gloria, Deputy Chief Financial Officer, Coler–Goldwater Specialty Hospital and Nursing Facility, New York, NY, p. A459

RANKIN, David, Chief Human Resources Management Services, Veterans Affairs Medical Center, Togus, ME, p. A301

RANKIN III, Fred M., President and Chief Executive Officer, Mary Washington Hospital, Fredericksburg, VA, p. A688

RANSDELL, Lewis A., Administrator, Long Term Hospital of Montgomery, Montgomery, AL, p. A22

RANZENBERGER, Bev, Senior Vice President Operations, Salinas Valley Memorial Healthcare System, Salinas, CA, p. A86

RAO, M.D., Noel, Medical Director, Marianjoy Rehabilitation Hospital, Wheaton, IL, p. A210

RAPAPORT, Gary D., Chief Executive Officer, Sutter Tracy Community Hospital, Tracy, CA, p. A96

RAPENSKE, Jennifer, Manager Financial Services, Mercy Medical Center–New Hampton, New Hampton, IA, p. A238

RAPERT, Debra K., Director Human Resources, Marion General Hospital, Marion, OH, p. A517

RAPP, Larry, M.D., Chief Medical and Executive Officer, ELEAH Medical Center, Elbow Lake, MN, p. A353

RAPP, M.D., Larry
Chief Medical and Executive Officer, ELEAH Medical Center, Elbow Lake, MN, p. A353
Chief Medical and Executive Officer, ELEAH Medical Center, Elbow Lake, MN, p. A353

RAPP, Peter F., Vice President and Executive Director, OHSU Hospital, Portland, OR, p. A547

RAPPAPORT, Mark J., Chief Executive Officer, Lewis County General Hospital, Lowville, NY, p. A456

RARDIN, Jim, Chief Operating Officer, Trident Medical Center, Charleston, SC, p. A585

RAREY, Kanute, Administrator, Providence Valdez Medical Center, Valdez, AK, p. A29

RASKO, Sylvia, Director Human Resources, Norton Sound Regional Hospital, Nome, AK, p. A28

RASMUSSEN, Diane, Director of Human Resources, New Ulm Medical Center, New Ulm, MN, p. A358

RASMUSSEN, M.D., Steven, Medical Director, Butler Hospital, Providence, RI, p. A581

RASMUSSON, Duane, Human Resources Vice President, St. Cloud Hospital, Saint Cloud, MN, p. A361

RASMUSSON, Thomas P., President and Chief Executive Officer, Avera Queen of Peace, Mitchell, SD, p. A597

RASNER, George, Vice President, Human Resources, Winthrop–University Hospital, Mineola, NY, p. A457

RASOR, Linda, R.N., Chief Executive Officer, Plains Memorial Hospital, Dimmitt, TX, p. A635

RASPER, Deborah Y., FACHE, Administrator, St. Vincent Mercy Hospital, Elwood, IN, p. A214

RATCLIFF, M.D., David, Chief Medical Affairs, Washington Regional Medical Center, Fayetteville, AR, p. A43

RATCLIFF, Paul, Director Information Services, Trinity Medical Center, Carrollton, TX, p. A628

RATCLIFFE, M.D., Alma, Executive Vice President, Saint Clare's Hospital, Dover, NJ, p. A427

RATCLIFFE, Denise, Executive Vice President and Chief Operating Officer, Christian Health Care Center, Wyckoff, NJ, p. A439

RATHGEBER, Anita L., Administrator, Bucktail Medical Center, Renovo, PA, p. A574

RATLIFF, Ada, Chief Information Officer, Claiborne County Hospital, Port Gibson, MS, p. A375

RATLIFF, Ginger, Director Human Resources, Integris Baptist Regional Health Center, Miami, OK, p. A533

RATLIFF, Maggie, Director Information Services, Good Samaritan Hospital, San Jose, CA, p. A90

RATLIFF, Robert W., FACHE, Acting Director, Central Texas Veterans Healthcare System, Temple, TX, p. A668

RATLIFF, Ph.D., F, Robert W., Deputy Director, Central Texas Veterans Healthcare System, Temple, TX, p. A668

RATTRAY, Scott, Vice President and Chief Information Officer, St. Francis Hospital, Inc., Columbus, GA, p. A158

RAU, John, President, Stevens Community Medical Center, Morris, MN, p. A358

RAU, Robin, Administrator, Early Memorial Hospital, Blakely, GA, p. A156

RAUSCH, M.D., Daniel, Chief of Staff, Marias Medical Center, Shelby, MT, p. A402

RAUSCH, Gwenn A., Chief Operating Officer, Saint Anthony Hospital, Chicago, IL, p. A189

RAVELING, Lynn, Chief Financial Officer, Pocahontas Community Hospital, Pocahontas, IA, p. A240

RAVEN, Mark, Chief Financial Officer, Wayne County Hospital, Corydon, IA, p. A231

RAVENCRAFT, Jarrod, Director Human Resources, Mississippi State Hospital, Whitfield, MS, p. A377

RAVER, M.D., James M.
Senior Vice President Medical Affairs, Memorial Hospital and Medical Center of Cumberland, Cumberland, MD, p. A307
Senior Vice President Medical Affairs, Sacred Heart Hospital, Cumberland, MD, p. A307

RAWSON, Richard L.
President and Chief Executive Officer, Hanford Community Medical Center, Hanford, CA, p. A63
President and Chief Executive Officer, Selma Community Hospital, Selma, CA, p. A94
President, Selma Community Hospital, Selma, CA, p. A94

RAWSTHORNE, M.D., Larry, Vice President Medical Affairs, Sparrow Health System, Lansing, MI, p. A338

RAY, Brenda, Director Human Resources, Twelve Oaks Medical Center, Houston, TX, p. A648

RAY, Donald, Attorney, North General Hospital, New York, NY, p. A464

RAY, Dwayne, Chief Financial Officer, Medical Center of McKinney, McKinney, TX, p. A656

RAY, Fran, Manager Human Resources, Purcell Municipal Hospital, Purcell, OK, p. A537

RAY, John T., Chief Executive Officer, Doctor's Memorial Hospital, Perry, FL, p. A143

RAY, Kimberly, Director Risk Management and Health Information, Sullivan County Memorial Hospital, Milan, MO, p. A387

RAY, Kirk M., Chief Executive Officer, Select Specialty Hospital, Fort Wayne, IN, p. A215

RAY, Rachel, Chief Financial Officer, Unity Medical Center, Grafton, ND, p. A498

RAY, M.D., Roger, Chief Medical Officer, Morton Plant Hospital, Clearwater, FL, p. A125

RAY, M.D., Sanjay, Chief of Staff, Sutter Delta Medical Center, Antioch, CA, p. A52

RAY, Susan, Vice President Human Resources, St. Andrews Hospital and Healthcare Center, Boothbay Harbor, ME, p. A297

RAY, Todd, Director Human Resources, St. Vincent Memorial Hospital, Taylorville, IL, p. A209

RAY, Toni, Information Systems Supervisor, Community Hospital Association, Fairfax, MO, p. A381

RAYAS, Elizabeth, Director of Community Relations, NCED Mental Health Center, El Paso, TX, p. A637

RAYMOND, Edward, Vice President Human Resources, Maria Parham Medical Center, Henderson, NC, p. A484

RAYMOND, Jane, Vice President and Chief Operating Officer, Reston Hospital Center, Reston, VA, p. A694

RAYMOND, Michael J., Chief Executive Officer, Grand River Hospital District, Rifle, CO, p. A109

RAYMOND, M.D., Robert, President Medical Staff, Baptist DeKalb Medical Center, Fort Payne, AL, p. A18

RAYMOR, Charlotte, Chief Executive Officer, Meadowbrook Rehabilitation Hospital of West Gables, Miami, FL, p. A137

RAYNER, Evan J., Chief Executive Officer, Corcoran District Hospital, Corcoran, CA, p. A57

RAYNES, Scott, President and Chief Executive Officer, Northcrest Medical Center, Springfield, TN, p. A618

RAYNOR, James E., Chief Executive Officer, Fairview Park Hospital, Dublin, GA, p. A161

RAZAVI, Antonio, Chief Information Officer, Veterans Affairs Medical Center, Iowa City, IA, p. A236

REA, Jerry, Interim Superintendent, Parsons State Hospital and Training Center, Parsons, KS, p. A255

READ, J. Larry, President and Chief Executive Officer, University Health Care System, Augusta, GA, p. A155

READING, Ann, Human Resource Director, Bridges Medical Services, Ada, MN, p. A349

READING, Matt, Director Human Resources, Indiana Regional Medical Center, Indiana, PA, p. A561

REAGAN, M.D., Ph, David, Chief of Staff, James H. Quillen Veterans Affairs Medical Center, Mountain Home, TN, p. A614

REAGAN Jr, James H., Ph.D., Chief Executive Officer, Morris County Hospital, Council Grove, KS, p. A246

REAMER, Roger J., Chief Executive Officer, Memorial Health Care Systems, Seward, NE, p. A413

REAMEY, Herbert K., Chief Executive Officer, Ozark Health Medical Center, Clinton, AR, p. A41

REAMEY III, Herbert K., Chief Executive Officer and Administrator, Ozark Health Medical Center, Clinton, AR, p. A41

REARDON, M.D., David, President Medical Staff, Gulf Coast Hospital, Fort Myers, FL, p. A129

REARDON, Jerry, Director Information Systems, Rowan Regional Medical Center, Salisbury, NC, p. A491

REASY, Stephanie, Administrator, Marshall County Healthcare Center/Avera Health, Britton, SD, p. A594

REBENACK, M.D., Paul, President Medical Staff, St. Luke's Hospital, Jacksonville, FL, p. A132

REBER, James P., President and Chief Executive Officer, St. Rita's Medical Center, Lima, OH, p. A516

REBERG, Sherry, Chief Operating Officer and Director of Nursing, Sibley Medical Center, Arlington, MN, p. A349

RECTOR, Stephen A., Chief Executive Officer, South Bay Hospital, Sun City Center, FL, p. A147

RECUPERO, David, Vice President and Chief Financial Officer, Ottumwa Regional Health Center, Ottumwa, IA, p. A240

RECUPERO, Patricia R., M.D., President and Chief Executive Officer, Butler Hospital, Providence, RI, p. A581

REDAY, Stephen A., Vice President of Human Resources, Hospital for Special Surgery, New York, NY, p. A460

REDDISH, Robert R., Administrator and Chief Executive Officer, Chicot Memorial Hospital, Lake Village, AR, p. A46

REDDOCH Jr, James F., Director, Taylor Hardin Secure Medical Facility, Tuscaloosa, AL, p. A24

REDDY, M.D., C J., Medical Staff President, Coffee Regional Medical Center, Douglas, GA, p. A161

REDDY, Lex, President and Chief Executive Officer, Desert Valley Hospital, Wildomar, CA, p. A99

REDMAN, Paulette, Health Information Management Manager, St. Peter Community Hospital, Saint Peter, MN, p. A362

REDMOND, Charles, Head Information Resources Management, U. S. Naval Hospital, Roosevelt Roads, PR, p. A748

RENCHER, W. David, President and Chief Executive Officer, War Memorial Hospital, Sault Ste. Marie, MI, p. A345

RENDLE, Lynne, Regional Director Human Resources, HEALTHSOUTH Reading Rehabilitation Hospital, Reading, PA, p. A574

RENDON, Eloise, Human Resources Director, Twin Cities Community Hospital, Templeton, CA, p. A95

RENEMANS, Edmond R., Vice President and Chief Financial Officer, Wyoming Medical Center, Casper, WY, p. A739

RENFREE, Elizabeth
Chief Information Officer, Palomar Medical Center, Escondido, CA, p. A59
Director Information Systems, Pomerado Hospital, Poway, CA, p. A82

RENFREW, Roger, Medical Director, Redington–Fairview General Hospital, Skowhegan, ME, p. A301

RENFRO, F Traylor, Senior Vice President Human Resources, Carolinas Medical Center, Charlotte, NC, p. A479

RENIER, M.D., Hugh, Vice President Medical Affairs, St. Mary's Medical Center, Duluth, MN, p. A352

RENNEGARBE, Richelle, Ph.D., President, Salem Township Hospital, Salem, IL, p. A207

RENNER, John K., Finance Director, Christ Hospital, Cincinnati, OH, p. A506

RENO, Kathy, Executive Vice President and Chief Operating Officer, Clinical Services, Northwest Community Healthcare, Arlington Heights, IL, p. A183

RENSHAW, Dee, Chief Executive Officer, Henryetta Medical Center, Henryetta, OK, p. A531

RENTAS, Roberto A., Administrator, Hospital De Damas, Ponce, PR, p. A746

RENTFRO, Larry D., FACHE, President and Chief Executive Officer, Grant Regional Health Center, Lancaster, WI, p. A728

RENTSCH, Richard E., Senior Vice President and Chief Financial Officer, St. Paul University Hospital, Dallas, TX, p. A634

RENTZ, Norman G., President and Chief Executive Officer, Cannon Memorial Hospital, Pickens, SC, p. A591

RENTZ, M.D., T Wayne, Chief of Staff, Southeast Georgia Health System Brunswick Campus, Brunswick, GA, p. A157

REPAC, Kimberly S.
Senior Vice President and Chief Financial Officer, Memorial Hospital and Medical Center of Cumberland, Cumberland, MD, p. A307
Senior Vice President and Chief Financial Officer, Sacred Heart Hospital, Cumberland, MD, p. A307

REPETTI, Greg, Executive Vice President Operations, Silver Cross Hospital, Joliet, IL, p. A198

REPLOGLE, Raymond L.
President and Chief Executive Officer, Continuous Care Center of Tulsa, Tulsa, OK, p. A539
President and Chief Executive Officer, St. John Sapulpa, Sapulpa, OK, p. A538

REPPERT, Joseph A., Vice President and Chief Financial Officer, Good Shepherd Medical Center, Longview, TX, p. A653

RESCA, Michael, Commandant, Lawrence F. Quigley Memorial Hospital, Chelsea, MA, p. A316

RESEL, Paul, Chief Financial Officer, Veterans Affairs Medical Center, Minneapolis, MN, p. A358

RESENDEZ, Linda, R.N., Administrator and Chief Executive Officer, Cornerstone Regional Hospital, Edinburg, TX, p. A636

RESENDEZ, R.N., Linda, Administrator and Chief Executive Officer, Cornerstone Regional Hospital, Edinburg, TX, p. A636

RESENDEZ, Tom, Chief Executive Officer, West Valley Hospital, Goodyear, AZ, p. A31

RESETAR, Gayle L., Chief Operating Officer, Waccamaw Community Hospital, Murrells Inlet, SC, p. A590

RESNICK, Peter V., Executive Director, Dearborn County Hospital, Lawrenceburg, IN, p. A221

RESSLER, David R., Chief Executive Officer, Aspen Valley Hospital District, Aspen, CO, p. A101

RESSLER, Dennis, Chief Financial Officer, St. Joseph Hospital, Kokomo, IN, p. A220

RESTO, Leslie, Chief Financial Officer, Hospital de la Universidad de Puerto Rico/Dr. Federico Trilla, Carolina, PR, p. A744

REUSSNER, M.D., Lee, Chief of Staff, Lawrence Memorial Hospital, Lawrence, KS, p. A251

REUTER, M.D., Cathy, Medical Director, Memorial Health Center, Medford, WI, p. A729

REVERMAN, Larry, Director Information Systems, Clark Memorial Hospital, Jeffersonville, IN, p. A219

REVILL, Larry, Chief Financial Officer, University of Texas Medical Branch Hospitals, Galveston, TX, p. A641

REX–WALLER, John G., President and Chief Executive Officer, National Surgical Hospitals, Chicago, IL, p. B77

REYES, Arnold, Administrator, U. S. Penitentiary Infirmary, Lewisburg, PA, p. A563

REYES, Marco, Executive Director, Hospital Buen Samaritano, Aguadilla, PR, p. A743

REYMAN, Reed
Administrator, Prairie Community Health Center, Terry, MT, p. A402
Administrator, Prairie Community Health Center, Terry, MT, p. A402

REYNERTSON, Cathy, Management Information Systems Manager, Riverside Medical Center, Waupaca, WI, p. A737

REYNOLDS, Arlen, Interim Chief Executive Officer, Inova Mount Vernon Hospital, Alexandria, VA, p. A685

REYNOLDS, M.D., Curt, Senior Vice President Medical Affairs, Mercy Medical Center, Cedar Rapids, IA, p. A229

REYNOLDS, Doug, Chief Financial Officer, Kaiser Foundation Hospital, Redwood City, CA, p. A83

REYNOLDS, M.D., Jay, Vice President Medical Affairs, Aroostook Medical Center, Presque Isle, ME, p. A300

REYNOLDS, John R., President and Chief Executive Officer, Hospital for Special Surgery, New York, NY, p. A460

REYNOLDS, Karen, Chief Financial Officer, Integris Baptist Regional Health Center, Miami, OK, p. A533

REYNOLDS, Mark, Director Information Technology, Unity Hospital, Muscatine, IA, p. A238

REYNOLDS, Richard M., President, MidMichigan Medical Center–Midland, Midland, MI, p. A340

REYNOLDS, Stephen Curtis, President and Chief Executive Officer, Baptist Memorial Health Care Corporation, Memphis, TN, p. B16

REYNOLDS, Todd, Chief Information Officer, Memorial Medical Center, Ashland, WI, p. A722

REYNOLDS, Vance, Chief Executive Officer, Chesterfield General Hospital, Cheraw, SC, p. A585

REZAC, Pamela J., President and Chief Executive Officer, Avera Sacred Heart Hospital, Yankton, SD, p. A601

RHENEY, Joseph, Chief, Resources Management Division, Keller Army Community Hospital, West Point, NY, p. A476

RHINE, Andy, Information Technology Specialist, Jefferson Community Health Center, Fairbury, NE, p. A406

RHINE, Kathleen, Vice President Human Resources and Organizational Development, Saint Joseph Mercy Health System, Ypsilanti, MI, p. A348

RHINE, Scott, Administrator and Chief Executive Officer, Whidbey General Hospital, Coupeville, WA, p. A702

RHINEHART, Jennie R., Administrator and Chief Executive Officer, Community Hospital, Tallassee, AL, p. A24

RHOADES, M.D., Marques, Vice President Medical Service, Avera Sacred Heart Hospital, Yankton, SD, p. A601

RHOADES, Michael, Chief Human Resources Officer, Edmond Medical Center, Edmond, OK, p. A530

RHODES, J. Gary, Chief Executive Officer, Kane Community Hospital, Kane, PA, p. A562

RHODES, M.D., Kent, Chief Medicl Staff, Lane Memorial Hospital, Zachary, LA, p. A295

RHODES, Lee, Chief Executive Officer, Roundup Memorial Healthcare, Roundup, MT, p. A402

RHODES, Liz, Director Information Services, Specialty Hospital Jacksonville, Jacksonville, FL, p. A132

RHODES, Pam, Vice President, Human Resources, Christus St. Joseph Hospital, Houston, TX, p. A644

RHODES, Shannon, Chief Information Officer, Veterans Affairs Ann Arbor Healthcare System, Ann Arbor, MI, p. A327

RHODES ZOROVFY, M.D., Darius, President Medical Staff, North Country Hospital and Health Center, Newport, VT, p. A683

RHUDY, Kenneth D., Administrator, Grady General Hospital, Cairo, GA, p. A157

RIAD, M.D., Ash, Chief of Staff, Southwest Mississippi Regional Medical Center, McComb, MS, p. A372

RIALS, Loren
Chief Financial Officer, Henryetta Medical Center, Henryetta, OK, p. A531
Chief Financial Officer, Wagoner Community Hospital, Wagoner, OK, p. A541

RIBA, Chris, Human Resoure Manager, Holy Family Hospital, New Richmond, WI, p. A732

RICCITELLI, Anthony, Chief Operating Officer, Worcester State Hospital, Worcester, MA, p. A326

RICE, Ann Madden, Associate Director and Chief Operating Officer, University of Iowa Hospitals and Clinics, Iowa City, IA, p. A236

RICE, Charles, Chief Information Officer, South Jersey Healthcare, Bridgeton, NJ, p. A426

RICE, David O., President, Haywood Regional Medical Center, Clyde, NC, p. A480

RICE, James P., Commanding Officicer, Naval Hospital, Corpus Christi, TX, p. A631

RICE, Kathleen A., President and Chief Operating Officer, Cuyahoga Falls General Hospital, Cuyahoga Falls, OH, p. A511

RICE, Mark J.
Administrator, HEALTHSOUTH North Louisiana Rehabilitation Hospital, Ruston, LA, p. A291
Administrator, HEALTHSOUTH Specialty Hospital of Winnfield, Winnfield, LA, p. A294

RICE, Pam
Chief Financial Officer, Comanche Community Hospital, Comanche, TX, p. A629
Chief Financial Officer, De Leon Hospital, De Leon, TX, p. A634

RICE, R. Timothy, President and Chief Executive Officer, Moses Cone Health System, Greensboro, NC, p. A484

RICE, Thomas J., President and Chief Executive Officer, Fawcett Memorial Hospital, Port Charlotte, FL, p. A144

RICE, Thomas R., FACHE, President and Chief Operating Officer, Physicians Hospital, Oklahoma City, OK, p. A536

RICE, Tim, President, Lakewood Health System, Staples, MN, p. A363

RICE, Timothy, President and Chief Executive Officer, Moses Cone Health System, Greensboro, NC, p. B76

RICH, M.D., Barry, Chief Medical Staff, La Rabida Children's Hospital, Chicago, IL, p. A187

RICH, Chris, Administrator and Chief Executive Officer, Hubbard Regional Hospital, Webster, MA, p. A324

RICH, Dan, Director Finance, Presbyterian Hospital of Allen, Allen, TX, p. A620

RICH, Jeri, Assistant Administrator and Chief Financial Officer, Hunt Memorial Hospital District, Greenville, TX, p. A642

RICH, Judy F., Senior Vice President and Chief Operations Officer, Tucson Medical Center, Tucson, AZ, p. A38

RICH, Mark, Director Information Services, Ashley Valley Medical Center, Vernal, UT, p. A681

RICH–MCLERRAN, Andrea, Chief Executive Officer, Cumberland River Hospital, Celina, TN, p. A603

RICHARD, Brent, Director Information Systems, Southern Ohio Medical Center, Portsmouth, OH, p. A521

RICHARD, Charlene, Director Human Resources, Harrington Memorial Hospital, Southbridge, MA, p. A323

RICHARD, Marilyn, Director, Human Resources, Dukes Memorial Hospital, Peru, IN, p. A223

RICHARD, Robert J., Administrator, Buchanan County Health Center, Independence, IA, p. A235

RICHARD, Tracey S., Administrator, Dubuis Hospital of Corpus Christi, Corpus Christi, TX, p. A631

RICHARDS III, Davis A., Chief Executive Officer, Rankin Medical Center, Brandon, MS, p. A367

RICHARDS, Frank
Chief Information Officer, Geisinger Medical Center, Danville, PA, p. A556
Chief Information Officer, Geisinger Wyoming Valley Medical Center, Wilkes–Barre, PA, p. A579

RICHARDS, Jaena, Chief Financial Officer, Powell County Memorial Hospital, Deer Lodge, MT, p. A397

RICHARDS, Joan K.
Chief Executive Officer, Crozer–Chester Medical Center, Upland, PA, p. A577
Chief Executive Officer, Delaware County Memorial Hospital, Drexel Hill, PA, p. A557

RICHARDS, Kelley, Director Human Resources, J. Arthur Dosher Memorial Hospital, Southport, NC, p. A492

RICHARDS, Patrick, Vice President Finance and Chief Financial Officer, St. Joseph Medical Center, Reading, PA, p. A574

RICHARDS, Randy R., Chief Executive Officer, Permian Regional Medical Center, Andrews, TX, p. A621

RICHARDS, Robert J., Vice President Finance and Chief Financial Officer, The Good Samaritan Hospital, Lebanon, PA, p. A563

RICHARDSON, A. D., Administrator, Hood Memorial Hospital, Amite, LA, p. A276

RICHARDSON, M.D., Alan, Medical Staff President, Memorial Hospital of Sweetwater County, Rock Springs, WY, p. A741

RICHARDSON, Brandy, Human Resources Director, Laird Memorial Hospital, Kilgore, TX, p. A651

RICHARDSON, C Joan, Chief of Medical Staff, University of Texas Medical Branch Hospitals, Galveston, TX, p. A641

RICHARDSON, Darrel C.
Executive Vice President and Chief Operations Officer, Bristol Bay Area Health Corporation, Dillingham, AK, p. A27
Executive Vice President and Chief Operations Officer, Bristol Bay Area Health Corporation, Dillingham, AK, p. A27

RICHARDSON, Eileen, Director Human Resources, Natchez Regional Medical Center, Natchez, MS, p. A373

RICHARDSON, Greg, Director Human Resources, Newton Medical Center, Covington, GA, p. A159

RICHARDSON, Guy B.
Acting Director, Veterans Affairs Medical Center, Martinsburg, WV, p. A717
Associate Director Finance, Veterans Affairs Maryland Health Care System–Baltimore Division, Baltimore, MD, p. A305

RICHARDSON, James, FACHE, Chief Executive Officer, Saline Memorial Hospital, Benton, AR, p. A40

RICHARDSON, Janice, Chief Executive Officer, Rivendell Behavioral Health, Bowling Green, KY, p. A262

RICHARDSON, Karin, Chief Financial Officer, Nye Regional Medical Center, Tonopah, NV, p. A419

RICHARDSON, Kim
Information Systems Director, Logan Memorial Hospital, Russellville, KY, p. A274
Chief Financial Officer, St. Mary's Medical Center of Evansville, Evansville, IN, p. A215

RICHARDSON, Mark D., President and Chief Executive Officer, Great River Medical Center, West Burlington, IA, p. A243

RICHARDSON, Mindy, Associate Administrator, Banner Baywood Medical Center, Mesa, AZ, p. A32

RICHARDSON, Randy, Chief Financial Officer, Milan General Hospital, Milan, TN, p. A614

RICHARDSON, M.D., Steven, Chief Medical Staff, Madison County Hospital, London, OH, p. A516

RICHARDSON, M.D., Timothy J., Chief of Staff, Veterans Affairs Medical Center, Togus, ME, p. A301

RICHARDSON, Todd, Regional Vice President Information Services, Sartori Memorial Hospital, Cedar Falls, IA, p. A229

RICHARDSON, Tony, Controller, HEALTHSOUTH Rehabilitation Hospital, Memphis, TN, p. A613

RICHARDSON, William T., President and Chief Executive Officer, Tift Regional Medical Center, Tifton, GA, p. A171

RICHARDT, Claudia, Chairman, St. Mary's Medical Center of Evansville, Evansville, IN, p. A215

RICHARDVILLE, Craig, Chief Information Officer, Cleveland Regional Medical Center, Shelby, NC, p. A491

RICHEL, William, Director Information System, Citrus Memorial Hospital, Inverness, FL, p. A131

RICHENS, Ken, Chief Information Officer, Central Valley Medical Center, Nephi, UT, p. A677

RICHER, R. David, Administrator, HEALTHSOUTH Rehabilitation Hospital of Western Massachusetts, Ludlow, MA, p. A320

RICHETTI, Michael, Chief Financial Officer, Chilton Memorial Hospital, Pompton Plains, NJ, p. A435

RICHEY, M.D., Jason, Chief Medical Officer, Mercy Hospital–Turner Memorial, Ozark, AR, p. A49

RICHHART, David, Chief Financial Officer, Community Medical Center, Missoula, MT, p. A400

RICHINS, Suzanne, Chief Operating Officer, Kadlec Medical Center, Richland, WA, p. A707

RICHMAN, Martin I., President and Chief Executive Officer, Jamestown Hospital, Jamestown, ND, p. A499

RICHMOND, John W., President and Chief Executive Officer, Northwest Medical Center, Albany, MO, p. A378

RICHMOND, Joseph M., Chief Financial Officer, MountainView Hospital, Las Vegas, NV, p. A416

RICHTER, M.D., Daniel, Chief of Staff, Baum Harmon Mercy Hospital, Primghar, IA, p. A240

RICHTER, Kurt, Chief Human Resources Officer, Othello Community Hospital, Othello, WA, p. A705

RICHTER, Thomas, Chief Executive Officer, Madison Hospital, Madison, MN, p. A356

RICKARD, Ph.D., Angela, Human Resources Coordinator, William S. Middleton Memorial Veterans Hospital, Madison, WI, p. A728

RICKARD, Roland K., Administrator, North Runnels Hospital, Winters, TX, p. A674

RICKARD, Sheryl, Chief Executive Officer, Bonner General Hospital, Sandpoint, ID, p. A181

RICKERT, Maria, Chief Executive Officer, Public Health Service Indian Hospital, Albuquerque, NM, p. A441

RIDDLE, Brian L., President and Chief Executive Officer, Oconee Regional Medical Center, Milledgeville, GA, p. A166

RIDDLE, Greg, Information Systems Director, Washington County Memorial Hospital, Potosi, MO, p. A389

RIDDLE, James E., Vice President Finance, Northeast Alabama Regional Medical Center, Anniston, AL, p. A13

RIDER III, Harrison J., President, Union Memorial Hospital, Baltimore, MD, p. A304

RIDGE, Burt, Chief Information Officer, Laughlin Memorial Hospital, Greeneville, TN, p. A607

RIDLEY, Diane, Senior Systems Analyst, UMass Memorial–Marlborough Hospital, Marlborough, MA, p. A320

RIDLEY, Pam, Director Information Systems, Henry County Medical Center, Paris, TN, p. A616

RIDOUT, Les, Interim Human Resources Officer, Ohio State University Medical Center, Columbus, OH, p. A511

RIDYARD, M.D., Herbert, Chief of Staff, Windham Community Memorial Hospital, Willimantic, CT, p. A118

RIEBER, Jim, Director Information Systems, Perham Memorial Hospital and Home, Perham, MN, p. A359

RIEDMANN, Gary P., President and Chief Executive Officer, St. Anthony Regional Hospital, Carroll, IA, p. A229

RIEF, Kathleen A., Commanding Officer, U. S. Naval Hospital, Agana, GU, p. A743

RIEGE, Michael J., Chief Executive Officer, Virginia Gay Hospital, Vinton, IA, p. A242

RIEHLE, M.D., Robert, Chief Medical Officer, Spartanburg Regional Medical Center, Spartanburg, SC, p. A592

RIEMER, Jim, Medical Director, Pawnee Municipal Hospital, Pawnee, OK, p. A537

RIEMER–MATUZAK, Stephanie J., Chief Executive Officer, Mercy Hospital Grayling, Grayling, MI, p. A335

RIES, Douglas A., FACHE, President, SSM Cardinal Glennon Children's Hospital, Saint Louis, MO, p. A391

RIES, John, Director Information Systems, St. Marys Hospital Medical Center, Madison, WI, p. A728

RIES, William G., President, Lake Forest Hospital, Lake Forest, IL, p. A199

RIETSEMA, M.D., Wouter, Medical Director, Champlain Valley Physicians Hospital Medical Center, Plattsburgh, NY, p. A469

RIFKIN, Scott, Administrator, HEALTHSOUTH Tustin Rehabilitation Hospital, Tustin, CA, p. A97

RIGAS, Sonny
Senior Vice President, Floyd Medical Center, Rome, GA, p. A168
Senior Vice President, Floyd Medical Center, Rome, GA, p. A168

RIGGS, Debra, Chief Financial Officer, Caverna Memorial Hospital, Horse Cave, KY, p. A266

RIGGS, Nancy, Director Human Resources, Gibson General Hospital, Trenton, TN, p. A618

RIGGS, M.D., Paul, President, Mahaska Health Partnership, Oskaloosa, IA, p. A239

RIGLER, M.D., Wilson, Chief of Staff, Clarke County Hospital, Osceola, IA, p. A239

RIGNEY, Alice, Human Resource Director, Memorial Hospital, Craig, CO, p. A103

RIGSBY, Jimmy, Chief Executive Officer, Campbellton Graceville Hospital, Graceville, FL, p. A130

RIKER, M.D., Howard, Chief Medical Staff, U. S. Air Force Hospital, MacDill AFB, FL, p. A135

RIKKOLA, David, Vice President Finance and Chief Financial Officer, Newton Memorial Hospital, Newton, NJ, p. A433

RILEY, Amy, Administrator, Advance Care Hospital of Fort Smith, Fort Smith, AR, p. A43

RILEY, Betty, Chief Financial Officer, Ellsworth Municipal Hospital, Iowa Falls, IA, p. A236

RILEY, Carolyn E., Chief Executive Officer, Mt. San Rafael Hospital, Trinidad, CO, p. A110

RILEY, Daniel J., Chief Financial Officer, UAMS Medical Center, Little Rock, AR, p. A47

RILEY, Diane, Controller, HEALTHSOUTH Deaconess Rehabilitation Hospital, Evansville, IN, p. A214

RILEY, Doug, Director Information Services, Skagit Valley Hospital, Mount Vernon, WA, p. A704

RILEY, Edward E., Chief Financial Officer, Mitchell County Regional Health Center, Osage, IA, p. A239

RILEY, Joe B., Chief Executive Officer, Poplar Bluff Regional Medical Center, Poplar Bluff, MO, p. A389

RILEY, John, Chief Financial Officer, Kewanee Hospital, Kewanee, IL, p. A199

RILEY, Kurt, Administrative Officer, Public Health Service Indian Hospital, Albuquerque, NM, p. A441

RILEY, Robert, Chief Financial Officer, Prince William Hospital, Manassas, VA, p. A691

RILEY, Sharon L.
President, St. Paul University Hospital, Dallas, TX, p. A634
Chief Executive Officer, University of Texas Southwestern Medical Center, Dallas, TX, p. A634
Chief Executive Officer, UT Southwestern Medical Center at Dallas, Dallas, TX, p. B118

RIMA, Pat, Health Care Manager, State Penitentiary Hospital, Walla Walla, WA, p. A711

RIMAR, M.D., Stephen, Executive Vice President Medical Affairs, Cooper Health System, Camden, NJ, p. A426

RIMEL, Jeff, Chief Financial Officer, Cibola General Hospital, Grants, NM, p. A443

RIMMER, Jeffery
Chief Resource Management Division, Moncrief Army Community Hospital, Fort Jackson, SC, p. A588
Chief Resource Management Division, Moncrief Army Community Hospital, Fort Jackson, SC, p. A588

RINALDI, Daniel
Senior Vice President Finance and Chief Financial Officer, Benedictine Hospital, Kingston, NY, p. A455
Vice President and Chief Financial Officer, Saint Vincents Catholic Medical Centers of New York, New York, NY, p. A465

RINDFLEISCH, Jody, Human Resource Manager, Redwood Area Hospital, Redwood Falls, MN, p. A360

RINDLISBACHER, Diane
Information Systems Manager, American Fork Hospital, American Fork, UT, p. A676
Information Systems Manager, Orem Community Hospital, Orem, UT, p. A678
Acting Director Information Systems, Utah Valley Regional Medical Center, Provo, UT, p. A679

RINE, Thomas L., President and Chief Executive Officer, Southwestern Medical Center, Lawton, OK, p. A532

RINEHARDT, Mark, Chief Operating Officer, Lake City Medical Center–Mayo, Lake City, MN, p. A355

RING, M.D., Ernest, Chief Medical Officer, UCSF Medical Center, San Francisco, CA, p. A89

RINGSWALD, Madonna, Medical Staff President, Baptist Hospital Northeast, La Grange, KY, p. A267

RINKER, Franklin M., President and Chief Executive Officer, Gwinnett Hospital System, Lawrenceville, GA, p. A164

RINTOUL, M.D., James N., President Medical Staff, Fulton County Medical Center, McConnellsburg, PA, p. A564

RIORDAN, M.D., Charles, Vice President Medical Affairs, Hospital of Saint Raphael, New Haven, CT, p. A115

RIORDAN, Michael C., President and Chief Executive Officer, University of Chicago Hospitals, Chicago, IL, p. A191

RIOS, Margot, Vice President and Administrator, Christus Spohn Hospital Alice, Alice, TX, p. A620

RIOS, Ramon, Information Systems Manager, Hospital De Damas, Ponce, PR, p. A746

RIPSCH, Sue, Chief Operating Officer, Mercy Harvard Hospital, Harvard, IL, p. A196

RISER, Donna, Administrator, S. E. Lackey Memorial Hospital, Forest, MS, p. A368

RISLOW, Deb, Director Information Systems, Gundersen Lutheran Medical Center, La Crosse, WI, p. A727

RISPOLI, Anthony C., Chief Financial Officerf, Wilkes Regional Medical Center, North Wilkesboro, NC, p. A488

RISSE, Thomas
Chief Financial Officer, Providence Centralia Hospital, Centralia, WA, p. A701
Chief Financial Officer, Providence St. Peter Hospital, Olympia, WA, p. A705

RISSI, M.D., Daniel, Vice President Medical Affairs, Olean General Hospital, Olean, NY, p. A468

RITCHIE, Jim, Director Management Information Systems, South Shore Hospital, Chicago, IL, p. A190

RITCHIE, M.D., R Samantha, President Medical Staff, Mark Reed Hospital, McCleary, WA, p. A704

RITER, Pamela M., R.N., Chief Executive Officer, Kindred Hospital–St. Petersburg, Saint Petersburg, FL, p. A145

RITMAN, Claude, Executive Director, Coler–Goldwater Specialty Hospital and Nursing Facility, New York, NY, p. A459

RITTENHOUSE, Belinda, Director Human Resources, Dr. John Warner Hospital, Clinton, IL, p. A191

RITTER, Cheryl, Vice President and Chief Financial Officer, Skiff Medical Center, Newton, IA, p. A239

RITZ, Robert P., President and Chief Executive Officer, Saint Mary's Hospital, Waterbury, CT, p. A117

RIVAS, Ray, Chief Financial Officer, Promise Hospital of East Los Angeles, Suburban Medical Center Campus, Paramount, CA, p. A81

RIVERA, Cristina, Chief Operating Officer, Valley Regional Medical Center, Brownsville, TX, p. A627

RIVERA, Enrique, Chief Financial Officer, Bella Vista Hospital, Mayaguez, PR, p. A745

RIVERA, Luis Perez, Administrator, San Juan Capestrano Hospital, San Juan, PR, p. A748

RIVERA, M.D., Marcelo, Chairman, Palomar Medical Center, Escondido, CA, p. A59

RIVERA, Margaret, Commander, Martin Army Community Hospital, Fort Benning, GA, p. A162

RIVERA, Marta, Executive Director, First Hospital Panamericano, Cidra, PR, p. A744

RIVERA, Myrna, Director Medical Records, Hospital Del Maestro, San Juan, PR, p. A747

RIVERA, Pedro, Administrator, Doctors Center, Manati, PR, p. A745

RIVERA, Phillip, Chief Financial Officer, Memorial Medical Center, Las Cruces, NM, p. A443

RIVERA, Santiago, Executive Administrator, Hospital Oncologico Andres Grillasca, Ponce, PR, p. A746

RIVERS, Gene, Manager Employment Services, Massachusetts Hospital School, Canton, MA, p. A316

RIVES, Mark, Information Technology Officer, U. S. Public Health Service Comprehensive Indian Health Facility, Claremore, OK, p. A529

RIVEST, Jeffrey A., President and Chief Executive Officer, University of Maryland Medical Center, Baltimore, MD, p. A304

ROACH, David, Vice President Information System, Kadlec Medical Center, Richland, WA, p. A707

ROACH, M.D., Dee A., Chief of Staff, Mitchell County Hospital, Colorado City, TX, p. A629

ROACH, Joseph, Chief Executive Officer, Memorial Hospital, Martinsville, VA, p. A691

ROADER, Charles, Vice President Finance, Memorial Community Hospital, Edgerton, WI, p. A725

ROARK, Robert, Director of Human Resources, Laughlin Memorial Hospital, Greeneville, TN, p. A607

ROBBINS, M.D., Howard M., Chief Medical Officer, Martin Memorial Health Systems, Stuart, FL, p. A147

ROBBINS, John N., President and Chief Executive Officer, Conway Regional Medical Center, Conway, AR, p. A41

ROBBIO, Joan M., Senior Vice President Human Resources, Lahey Clinic Hospital, Burlington, MA, p. A316

ROBERSON, Madeleine, President and Chief Executive Officer, Presbyterian–St. Luke's Medical Center, Denver, CO, p. A104

ROBERSON, Ron, Chief Financial Officer, Mercy Medical Center–Sioux City, Sioux City, IA, p. A241

ROBERT, M.D., Marshall, Medical Staff President, Sarah D. Culbertson Memorial Hospital, Rushville, IL, p. A207

ROBERTS, CPA, Allyson, Chief Financial Officer, Nor–Lea General Hospital, Lovington, NM, p. A443

ROBERTS, Barbara, Chief Financial Officer, Veterans Affairs Medical Center–Louisville, Louisville, KY, p. A270

ROBERTS, Bill, Information Systems Director, Community Hospital, Watervliet, MI, p. A347

ROBERTS, Cathy, Human Resource Director, Mercy Medical Center, Durango, CO, p. A104

ROBERTS, Curt L., Chief Executive Officer, Flint River Community Hospital, Montezuma, GA, p. A166

ROBERTS, M.D., Floyd, Chief Medical Officer, Baton Rouge General Medical Center, Baton Rouge, LA, p. A277

ROBERTS, Gregory P., Chief Executive Officer, Trenton Psychiatric Hospital, Trenton, NJ, p. A438

ROBERTS, Jack
Chief Executive Officer, Madison Center and Hospital, South Bend, IN, p. A225
Chief Executive Officer, Riverside Hospital, South Bend, IN, p. A225

ROBERTS, Jean E., Administrator, Mark Reed Hospital, McCleary, WA, p. A704

ROBERTS, John W., President and Chief Executive Officer, Union Regional Medical Center, Monroe, NC, p. A487

ROBERTS, Kathy, Interim Administrator, Healthbridge Children's Hospital of Houston, Houston, TX, p. A645

ROBERTS, Kenneth D., President, John T. Mather Memorial Hospital, Port Jefferson, NY, p. A469

ROBERTS, Kevin, President and Chief Executive Officer, Castle Medical Center, Kailua, HI, p. A174

ROBERTS, Mickey, Information Systems Director, Huey P. Long Medical Center, Pineville, LA, p. A291

ROBERTS, Pamela W., Administrator, McNairy Regional Hospital, Selmer, TN, p. A617

ROBERTS, Paul, Chief of Staff, Reynolds Army Community Hospital, Fort Sill, OK, p. A531

ROBERTS, Shane H., Chief Executive Officer, St. Luke Community Hospital, Ronan, MT, p. A401

ROBERTS, Shelia, Director Human Resources, Hocking Valley Community Hospital, Logan, OH, p. A516

ROBERTS, William, Commanding Officer, Naval Hospital, Bremerton, WA, p. A701

ROBERTSON, Carla, Chief Financial Officer, Saline Memorial Hospital, Benton, AR, p. A40

ROBERTSON, David J., Chief Executive Officer, Monongalia General Hospital, Morgantown, WV, p. A718

ROBERTSON, Gary W.
Chief Executive Officer, Big Horn County Memorial Hospital, Hardin, MT, p. A399
Chief Executive Officer, Rosebud Health Care Center, Forsyth, MT, p. A398

ROBERTSON Jr, James E., Chief Executive Officer, Ocean Beach Hospital, Ilwaco, WA, p. A703

ROBERTSON, Jeffrey J., Chief Executive Officer, Lakeview Hospital, Stillwater, MN, p. A363

ROBERTSON, Jimmy
Chief Financial Officer, Baptist Memorial Hospital–Lauderdale, Ripley, TN, p. A617
Chief Financial Officer, Baptist Memorial Hospital–Tipton, Covington, TN, p. A605

ROBERTSON, John L., Chief Executive Officer, Randolph Medical Center, Roanoke, AL, p. A23

ROBERTSON, Ken, Director Information Systems, Jennie Stuart Medical Center, Hopkinsville, KY, p. A266

ROBERTSON, Patricia L., Executive Vice President and Administrator, Mary Immaculate Hospital, Newport News, VA, p. A692

ROBERTSON, Patrick, Chief Financial Officer, Ohio State University Hospitals East, Columbus, OH, p. A510

ROBERTSON, M.D., Rick, Chief of Staff, Fayette Memorial Hospital, Connersville, IN, p. A213

ROBERTSON, Tana, Chief Operating Officer, McCamey Hospital, McCamey, TX, p. A656

ROBERTSON, William G., President and Chief Executive Officer, Adventist HealthCare, Rockville, MD, p. B5

ROBERTSON–KECK, Karen, Assistant Vice President Human Resources, Franklin Square Hospital Center, Baltimore, MD, p. A302

ROBERTSTAD, John R., FACHE, President and Chief Executive Officer, Oconomowoc Memorial Hospital, Oconomowoc, WI, p. A733

ROBINS, Dan, Regional Director Information System, Providence Holy Cross Medical Center, San Fernando, CA, p. A88

ROBINSON, Alan, Chief Financial Officer, Logan Regional Hospital, Logan, UT, p. A677

ROBINSON, Brian C., Chief Executive Officer, Sunrise Hospital and Medical Center, Las Vegas, NV, p. A417

ROBINSON, Christopher, Chief Financial Officer, Southern Maine Medical Center, Biddeford, ME, p. A297

ROBINSON, M.D., Girard, Chief Medical Officer, Spring Harbor Hospital, Westbrook, ME, p. A301

ROBINSON, Glenn A., Chief Executive Officer, Mary Black Health System, Spartanburg, SC, p. A592

ROBINSON Sr, James M., Chief Executive Officer, Colorado–Fayette Medical Center, Weimar, TX, p. A673

ROBINSON, Jan King, Vice President Human Resources and Organizational Development, Albemarle Hospital, Elizabeth City, NC, p. A482

ROBINSON, M.D., Jeffrey D., President Medical Staff, Leesburg Regional Medical Center, Leesburg, FL, p. A135

ROBINSON, John, Clinical Director, U.S. Public Health Service Indian Hospital, Redlake, MN, p. A360

ROBINSON, Kenneth C., Senior Vice President and Chief Financial Officer, St. Mary–Rogers Memorial Hospital, Rogers, AR, p. A49

ROBINSON, Larry, Director Finance, St. Luke Community Hospital, Ronan, MT, p. A401

ROBINSON, Mark
Chief Operating Officer, Gulf Coast Medical Center, Panama City, FL, p. A142
Associate Administrator and Chief Financial Officer, Hazel Hawkins Memorial Hospital, Hollister, CA, p. A64

ROBINSON, Melvin D., Chief Financial Officer, Geary Community Hospital, Junction City, KS, p. A250

ROBINSON, Michael, Executive Vice President and Administrator, Memorial Regional Medical Center, Mechanicsville, VA, p. A691

ROBINSON, Pat, Accounting Manager, St. Vincent Rehabilitation Hospital, Sherwood, AR, p. A50

ROBINSON, Patrick C., M.D., Administrator, Walter Olin Moss Regional Medical Center, Lake Charles, LA, p. A285

ROBINSON, Philip C., Executive Vice President and Chief Operating Officer, United Regional Health Care System, Wichita Falls, TX, p. A674

ROBINSON, Phillip D., Chief Executive Officer, Bayshore Medical Center, Pasadena, TX, p. A660

ROBINSON, Richard H., Chief Executive Officer, Eastern New Mexico Medical Center, Roswell, NM, p. A444

ROBINSON, Roger, Interim President, The Outer Banks Hospital, Nags Head, NC, p. A488

ROBINSON, Terry F., Chief Executive Officer and Administrator, SCCI Hospital of Victoria, Victoria, TX, p. A672

ROBINSON, Thomas, Chief Financial Officer, Veterans Affairs Medical Center, Coatesville, PA, p. A556

ROBINSON, Tim, Chief Financial Officer and Treasurer, Children's Hospital, Columbus, OH, p. A510

ROBINSON, William, Director Human Resources, HEALTHSOUTH Rehabilitation Hospital of Erie, Erie, PA, p. A558

ROBINSON, William J.
Senior Vice President and Treasurer, Shands at the University of Florida, Gainesville, FL, p. A130
Senior Vice President and Chief Financial Officer, Shands Rehab Hospital, Gainesville, FL, p. A130

ROBIRDS, Mark, Director of Medical Staff, Self Regional Healthcare, Greenwood, SC, p. A589

ROBISCH, Christine, Chief Operating Officer, Kaiser Foundation Hospital, Walnut Creek, CA, p. A98

ROBISON, R.N., Debbie, Assistant Administrator Nursing, Atlanta Memorial Hospital, Atlanta, TX, p. A622

ROBISON, Keith, Chief Information Officer, Woman's Christian Association Hospital, Jamestown, NY, p. A454

ROBISON, M.D., Wendell, Chief of Staff, Veterans Affairs Medical Center, Sheridan, WY, p. A742

ROBLES, Bert, Chief Information Officer, SUNY Downstate Medical Center University Hospital, New York, NY, p. A466

ROBY, William J., Executive Vice President, Mountain Manor Treatment Center, Emmitsburg, MD, p. A308

ROCHE, Jerome J., Chief Medical Officer, Fairfield Medical Center, Lancaster, OH, p. A515

ROCHE, Joseph E., Administrator, St. Vincent Jennings Hospital, North Vernon, IN, p. A223

ROCHE, Richard J., Vice President for Human Resources, University Health Care System, Augusta, GA, p. A155

ROCHER, M.D., Leslie, Vice President Clinical Affairs and Chairman Internal Medicine, William Beaumont Hospital–Royal Oak, Royal Oak, MI, p. A343

ROCK, Lauren, Chief Administrative Officer, Euclid Hospital, Euclid, OH, p. A513

ROCK, M.D., Michael
Chair Hospital Practice Commitee, Rochester Methodist Hospital, Rochester, MN, p. A360
Chair practice Commitee, Saint Marys Hospital, Rochester, MN, p. A360

ROCKERS, Thomas H., President and Chief Executive Officer, St. Anthony's Medical Center, Saint Louis, MO, p. A392

ROCKEY, Debra, Site Director Information Services, Saint Mary's Health Care, Grand Rapids, MI, p. A335

ROCKOWITZ, Elizabeth, Director Business Information Management Systems, Bascom Palmer Eye Institute–Anne Bates Leach Eye Hospital, Miami, FL, p. A136

ROCKOWITZ, Liz, Director Information System, University of Miami Hospital and Clinics, Miami, FL, p. A138

ROCKWELL, Roger, Director of Human Resources, St. Joseph's Hospital, Elmira, NY, p. A452

ROCKWOOD Jr, John M., President and Chief Executive Officer, Munson Healthcare, Traverse City, MI, p. B77

RODEGHIERO, Helen, Manager Human Resources, Roundup Memorial Healthcare, Roundup, MT, p. A402

RODENBAUGH, Cathy, Human Resource Director, Holy Rosary Healthcare, Miles City, MT, p. A400

RODERICK, Jonathan, Chief Information Officer, Mercy Hospital of Portland, Portland, ME, p. A300

RODERICK, Willard P., Chief Executive Officer, Barberton Citizens Hospital, Barberton, OH, p. A503

RODGERS, M.D., H Lynn, President, Presbyterian Hospital of Allen, Allen, TX, p. A620

RODGERS, W Lance, Manager Managed Care Flight Commander, U. S. Air Force Hospital Shaw, Shaw AFB, SC, p. A591

RODIS, M.D., John, Senior Vice President Medical Services and Chief Clinical Officer, Stamford Health System, Stamford, CT, p. A116

RODRIGUES, David, Information Systems Manager, Oak Valley District Hospital, Oakdale, CA, p. A78

RODRIGUEZ, Alex
Vice President Information Systems Technology, St. Luke Hospital East, Fort Thomas, KY, p. A264
Vice President Information Systems Technology, St. Luke Hospital West, Florence, KY, p. A264
Senior Vice President and Chief Information Officer, University Hospital, Cincinnati, OH, p. A507

RODRIGUEZ, Edgardo, Management Information Systems Director, Auxilio Mutuo Hospital, San Juan, PR, p. A746

RODRIGUEZ, M.D., Gilbert, Chief Medical Officer, Southwest Washington Medical Center, Vancouver, WA, p. A711

RODRIGUEZ, M.D., Gilberto, Chief Medical Officer, St. Luke's Episcopal Hospital, Ponce, PR, p. A746

RODRIGUEZ, M.D., Jose O., Medical Director, Castaner General Hospital, Castaner, PR, p. A744

RODRIGUEZ, Julio Andino, Chief Executive Officer, Dr. Ramon E. Betances Hospital–Mayaguez Medical Center Branch, Mayaguez, PR, p. A745

RODRIGUEZ, Maria Elena, Patient Relations Director, Hospital San Pablo Del Este, Fajardo, PR, p. A745

RODRIGUEZ, Maritza
Chief Financial Officer, Hospital Dr. Cayetano Coll Y Toste, Arecibo, PR, p. A743
Chief Financial Officer, Hospital Metropolitan, San Juan, PR, p. A747

RODRIGUEZ, Patricia, Chief Operating Officer, Kaiser Permanente Medical Center, Honolulu, HI, p. A173

RODRIGUEZ, M.D., Reynaldo, Medical Director, State Psychiatric Hospital, San Juan, PR, p. A748

RODRIGUEZ, M.D., Richard P., Senior Vice President and Chief Medical Officer, Tucson Medical Center, Tucson, AZ, p. A38

RODRIGUEZ, Roy, Chief Executive Officer, University Community Hospital, San Diego, CA, p. A87

RODRIGUEZ, Vilma, Human Resources Director, Hospital San Pablo Del Este, Fajardo, PR, p. A745

RODRIGUEZ, M.D., Wilfredo, Chief of Staff, West Texas VA Health Care System, Big Spring, TX, p. A626

RODRIGUEZ SOLIS, M.D., Jaime, President Medical Staff, Wilma N. Vazquez Medical Center, Vega Baja, PR, p. A748

RODY, M.D., Brent, Vice President Medical Affairs, Via Christi Regional Medical Center, Wichita, KS, p. A259

ROE, Luis, Chief Executive Officer, Select Specialty Hospital–Charleston, Charleston, WV, p. A714

ROE, William, Chief Financial Officer, Moses Taylor Hospital, Scranton, PA, p. A575

ROEBACK, Jason N.
Administrator, HEALTHSOUTH Treasure Coast Rehabilitation Hospital, Vero Beach, FL, p. A150
Chief Executive Officer, HEALTHSOUTH Treasure Coast Rehabilitation Hospital, Vero Beach, FL, p. A150

ROEBER, Edward
Senior Vice President Finance and Chief Financial Officer, Mercy Franciscan Hospital Mount Airy, Cincinnati, OH, p. A507
Vice President Finance, Mercy Hospital Anderson, Cincinnati, OH, p. A507
Vice President Finance, Mercy Hospital Clermont, Batavia, OH, p. A503
Senior Vice President Finance and Chief Financial Officer, Mercy Hospital Fairfield, Fairfield, OH, p. A513

ROEDER, M.D., Werner, Vice President Medical Affairs, Lawrence Hospital Center, Bronxville, NY, p. A448

ROEDERER, Chris, Chief Corporate Services, City of Hope National Medical Center, Duarte, CA, p. A59

ROEDL, Madelene, President, Select Specialty Hospital–Oklahoma City East, Oklahoma City, OK, p. A536

ROEHRL, Andreas, Chief Financial Officer, Sentara Williamsburg Community Hospital, Williamsburg, VA, p. A698

ROEMER, Dennis, Executive Vice President and Chief Financial Officer, Cooper Health System, Camden, NJ, p. A426

ROEMHILDT, Julie, Administrator, Tilden Community Hospital, Tilden, NE, p. A413

ROESLER, Bruce E., Chief Executive Officer, Avera Marshall Regional Medical Center, Marshall, MN, p. A356

ROETHLE, Linda, President, Bellin Psychiatric Center, Green Bay, WI, p. A726

ROETMAN, James D., President and Chief Executive Officer, Pocahontas Community Hospital, Pocahontas, IA, p. A240

ROGALSKI, Dayton, Executive Officer, Mike O'Callaghan Federal Hospital, Nellis AFB, NV, p. A417

ROGERS, Cindy J., FACHE, Chief Executive Officer, St. Patrick's Psychiatric Hospital, Monroe, LA, p. A287

ROGERS, Gregory H., Senior Vice President and Treasurer, MidMichigan Medical Center–Midland, Midland, MI, p. A340

ROGERS, Joel, Chief Operating Officer, Minidoka Memorial Hospital and Extended Care Facility, Rupert, ID, p. A181

ROGERS, Keith, Administrator, Advance Care Hospital, Hot Springs National Park, AR, p. A44

ROGERS, LaDonna, Director Human Resources, T. J. Samson Community Hospital, Glasgow, KY, p. A265

ROGERS, Lucy, Chief Information Resource Management Systems, Veterans Affairs North Texas Health Care System, Dallas, TX, p. A634

ROGERS, Michael, Vice President Fiscal Services, Brattleboro Memorial Hospital, Brattleboro, VT, p. A682

ROGERS, Rhonda, Chief Financial Officer, Nacogdoches Medical Center, Nacogdoches, TX, p. A658

ROGERS, Rich
Vice President Information Technology and Chief Information Officer, Cape Canaveral Hospital/Health First, Cocoa Beach, FL, p. A126
Vice President Information Technology, Holmes Regional Medical Center, Melbourne, FL, p. A136

ROGERS, II, M.D., Robert T., Medical Director, Canton–Potsdam Hospital, Potsdam, NY, p. A470

ROGERS, Teri Jo, Human Resources Assistant, Conejos County Hospital, La Jara, CO, p. A107

ROGERS, Tracy A., Chief Executive Officer, Louis A. Weiss Memorial Hospital, Chicago, IL, p. A188

ROGERS, Virginia, Human Resources Director, Pawnee Municipal Hospital, Pawnee, OK, p. A537

ROGERSON, Russell E., Superintendent, Mental Health Institute, Mount Pleasant, IA, p. A238

ROGGERO, Ann, Director Human Resources, Venice Regional Medical Center, Venice, FL, p. A149

ROGNESS, Robin, Chief Financial Officer, Mercy Hospital of Folsom, Folsom, CA, p. A60

ROGOFF, Jeffrey, Deputy Executive Director, Harlem Hospital Center, New York, NY, p. A460

ROGOLS, Kevin L.
Chief Executive Officer, Knox Community Hospital, Mount Vernon, OH, p. A519
Chief Executive Officer, Knox Community Hospital, Mount Vernon, OH, p. A519

ROGOZ, Brian, Vice President Finance and Chief Financial Officer, Bradley Memorial Hospital and Health Center, Southington, CT, p. A116

ROHAN, Heather J., Chief Executive Officer, Palms West Hospital, Loxahatchee, FL, p. A135

ROHLEDER, Howard E., President and Chief Executive Officer, Salem Community Hospital, Salem, OH, p. A521

ROHLFING, Sandra, R.N., Chief Executive Officer, Horizon Specialty Hospital, Las Vegas, NV, p. A416

ROHRBACH, William K., Vice President Fiscal Affairs, Memorial Hospital, Towanda, PA, p. A577

ROHRER, Harry
Chief Financial Officer, Bascom Palmer Eye Institute–Anne Bates Leach Eye Hospital, Miami, FL, p. A136
Chief Financial Officer, University of Miami Hospital and Clinics, Miami, FL, p. A138

ROHRICH, George A., Chief Executive Officer, Washakie Medical Center, Worland, WY, p. A742

ROHWEDER, Gordon, Chief Information Officer, Owensboro Medical Health System, Owensboro, KY, p. A272

ROIG, Ruben Norat, Chief Financial Officer, Mennonite General Hospital, Aibonito, PR, p. A743

ROKOSZ, D.O., Gregory, Senior Vice President Medical and Academic Affairs, Saint Barnabas Medical Center, Livingston, NJ, p. A430

ROLFE, Randall H., President, Bakersfield Heart Hospital, Bakersfield, CA, p. A53

ROLL, Susan, Chief of Human Resources, National Jewish Medical and Research Center, Denver, CO, p. A103

ROLON, Waleska, Manager, Hospital Santa Rosa, Guayama, PR, p. A745

ROLPH, Michael F., Chief Financial Officer, Sarasota Memorial Hospital, Sarasota, FL, p. A146

ROLSTON, Richard, M.D., President and Chief Executive Officer, Lovelace Medical Center, Albuquerque, NM, p. A440

ROMAIN, Don, Chief Executive Officer, Sparrow Specialty Hospital, Lansing, MI, p. A339

ROMAINE, Alison, Director Management Information Systems, Palisades Medical Center, North Bergen, NJ, p. A433

ROMAN, Edward, Assistant Vice President and Chief Information Officer, Moses Taylor Hospital, Scranton, PA, p. A575

ROMAN, Elena, Administrator, HEALTHSOUTH Rehabilitation Hospital of Southern Arizona, Tucson, AZ, p. A38

ROMAN, M.D., Marina, Medical Director, Hospital de la Universidad de Puerto Rico/Dr. Federico Trilla, Carolina, PR, p. A744

ROMAN, Susan, Community Chief Executive Officer, Morgan County Appalachian Regional Hospital, West Liberty, KY, p. A275

ROMANO, M.D., C James, President Medical Staff, St. Francis Medical Center, Trenton, NJ, p. A437

ROMANO, John A., Chief Executive Officer, Mountain View Hospital, Gadsden, AL, p. A19

ROMANO, Kathy, Chief Operating Officer, Sequoia Hospital, Redwood City, CA, p. A83

ROMANO, M.D., Michael A., Vice President Medical Affairs, Jennie Edmundson Memorial Hospital, Council Bluffs, IA, p. A231

ROMANO Jr, Patrick A., Chief Executive Officer, Gateway Regional Health System, Mount Sterling, KY, p. A272

ROMANS, Juanita F., Chief Executive Officer, Memorial Hermann Hospital, Houston, TX, p. A646

ROMARY, Paul, Chief Executive Officer, Lemuel Shattuck Hospital, Jamaica Plain, MA, p. A319

ROMER, Deborah D., Senior Vice President and Area Manager, Kaiser Foundation Hospital and Rehabilitation Center, Vallejo, CA, p. A97

ROMERO, Ed, Chief Financial Officer, San Angelo Community Medical Center, San Angelo, TX, p. A663

ROMERO, Marcella A., Administrator, Espanola Hospital, Espanola, NM, p. A442

ROMERO, Matt, Vice President Finance and Chief Financial Officer, SouthCrest Hospital, Tulsa, OK, p. A540

ROMERO–ERLANSON, Carla, Director Human Resources, Teton Valley Hospital and Surgicenter, Driggs, ID, p. A179

ROMEZI, M.D., Masoud, Chief of Staff, East Texas Medical Center Trinity, Trinity, TX, p. A670

ROMIG, Glenn, Chief Financial Officer, Community Hospital, New Port Richey, FL, p. A139

ROMINE, Donnie L., Chief Executive Officer, Lake Granbury Medical Center, Granbury, TX, p. A642

ROMITO, Ed, Director Information Systems, Genesis HealthCare System, Zanesville, OH, p. A526

ROMOFF, Jeffrey A., President, University of Pittsburgh Medical Center, Pittsburgh, PA, p. B117

RONA, J. Michael, President, Virginia Mason Medical Center, Seattle, WA, p. A708

RONES, M.D., Kathie, Medical Director, Kings County Hospital Center, New York, NY, p. A460

RONEY, Michael J., Vice President Finance and Chief Financial Officer, Washington Hospital, Washington, PA, p. A578

RONK, Earlene, Administrator, Brown County Human Services Mental Health Center, Green Bay, WI, p. A726

RONKE, Lisa, Director of Finance and Business Office, St. Michael's Hospital, Tyndall, SD, p. A600

RONSTROM, Stephen F., Executive Vice President and Administrator, Sacred Heart Hospital, Eau Claire, WI, p. A725

ROODMAN, Richard D., Chief Executive Officer, Valley Medical Center, Renton, WA, p. A706

ROOKER, Mark, Director Information Systems, Susan B. Allen Memorial Hospital, El Dorado, KS, p. A246

ROONEY, Jeffrey, Vice President Finance, Rush North Shore Medical Center, Skokie, IL, p. A208

ROONEY, Ronald K., President, Arkansas Methodist Medical Center, Paragould, AR, p. A49

ROOT, Darwin E., Chief Executive Officer, Harrison Memorial Hospital, Cynthiana, KY, p. A263

ROOT, Jim, Director, Human Resources, Saint Elizabeth's Medical Center, Wabasha, MN, p. A364

RORAFF, Greg, President and Chief Executive Officer, Memorial Health Center, Medford, WI, p. A729

ROSA, Luis, Controller, Wilma N. Vazquez Medical Center, Vega Baja, PR, p. A748

ROSA, Thomas, Director Human Resources, Lawrence F. Quigley Memorial Hospital, Chelsea, MA, p. A316

ROSADO, M.D., Marcos, Chief of Staff, Good Hope Hospital, Erwin, NC, p. A482

ROSARIO, Bradalic, Administrator, Hospital San Gerardo, Rio Piedras, PR, p. A747

ROSARIO, Felisa, Accountant, Hale Ho'ola Hamakua, Honokaa, HI, p. A173

ROSARIO, Kim, Chief Information Officer, Holy Family Hospital, New Richmond, WI, p. A732

ROSAS, Victoria, Chief Human Resources, James A. Haley Veterans Hospital, Tampa, FL, p. A148

ROSBOROUGH, Heidi, Manager, Human Resources, Benedictine Hospital, Kingston, NY, p. A455

ROSBOROUGH, M.D., Rob, President Medical Staff, Silverton Hospital, Silverton, OR, p. A549

ROSCHER, Barbara, Director Information Systems, Providence Health Center, Waco, TX, p. A672

ROSCOE, Joan, Chief Information Officer, Winchester Medical Center, Winchester, VA, p. A698

ROSE, Hugh, Chief Financial Officer, University of Illinois Medical Center at Chicago, Chicago, IL, p. A191

ROSE, J. Anthony, President and Chief Executive Officer, Catawba Valley Medical Center, Hickory, NC, p. A484

ROSE, Joanne, Administrator, HEALTHSOUTH Rehabilitation Hospital of Texarkana, Texarkana, TX, p. A669

ROSE, Laurie, Director Human Resources, Sutter Medical Center, Sacramento, Sacramento, CA, p. A85

ROSE, Steven P., Chief Financial Officer, Conway Regional Medical Center, Conway, AR, p. A41

ROSE, M.D., Vera, Vice President Medical Affairs, St. Mary's Medical Center, Huntington, WV, p. A716

ROSE, Virginia, Vice President Human Resources, Medical City Dallas Hospital, Dallas, TX, p. A633

ROSEBOROUGH, James W., CHE, Director, Veterans Affairs Ann Arbor Healthcare System, Ann Arbor, MI, p. A327

ROSEN, M.D., Barry, Vice President Medical Management, Advocate Good Shepherd Hospital, Barrington, IL, p. A184

ROSEN, David P.
President and Chief Executive Officer, Brookdale Hospital Medical Center, New York, NY, p. A458
President and Chief Executive Officer, Flushing Hospital Medical Center, New York, NY, p. A459
President, Jamaica Hospital Medical Center, New York, NY, p. A460

ROSEN, Raymond, Vice President Operations, York Hospital, York, PA, p. A580

ROSENBERG, Jeff, Chief Operating Officer, St. Mary's Medical Center, West Palm Beach, FL, p. A150

ROSENBERG, Steven, Senior Vice President and Chief Financial Officer, Saint Francis Hospital and Medical Center, Hartford, CT, p. A113

ROSENCRANTZ, M.D., David, President Medical Staff, Samaritan North Lincoln Hospital, Lincoln City, OR, p. A545

ROSENDAHL, Lisa, Director, Human Resources, Veterans Affairs Medical Center, Saint Cloud, MN, p. A361

ROSENDORFF, M.D., Clive, Chief Medical Program, Veterans Affairs Medical Center, New York, NY, p. A466

ROSENFELD, Merryll, Vice President Human Resources, Southern New Hampshire Medical Center, Nashua, NH, p. A422

ROSENFELD, M.D., Paul S., Chief of Staff, Veterans Affairs Medical Center, New Orleans, LA, p. A290

ROSENFELD, Stephen, Chief Information Officer and Director Clinical Research Information Systems, Warren G. Magnuson Clinical Center, National Institutes of Health, Bethesda, MD, p. A306

ROSENFELD, M.D., William, Senior Vice President Clinical Integration, Bayhealth Medical Center, Dover, DE, p. A119

ROSENSTEIN, M.D., Beryl, Vice President Medical Affairs, Johns Hopkins Hospital, Baltimore, MD, p. A303

ROSENSTEIN, Gaynor, Vice President Operations, Bon Secours Community Hospital, Port Jervis, NY, p. A470

ROSENTHAL, David S., M.D., Director, Stillman Infirmary, Harvard University Health Services, Cambridge, MA, p. A316

ROSENTHAL, M.D., J Robert, Vice President, Medical Affairs, New York Eye and Ear Infirmary, New York, NY, p. A463

ROSENTHAL, M.D., J Thomas, Chief Medical Officer, University of California Los Angeles Medical Center, Los Angeles, CA, p. A73

ROSENTHAL, Philip, Executive Director, Manhattan Eye, Ear and Throat Hospital, New York, NY, p. A462

ROSENVALL, Greg, Administrator, Gunnison Valley Hospital, Gunnison, UT, p. A676

ROSKOSKI, Stephen, Director of Human Resources, Virginia Regional Medical Center, Virginia, MN, p. A364

ROSS, Aletha, Vice President Human Resources, Advocate South Suburban Hospital, Hazel Crest, IL, p. A196

ROSS, M.D., Charles
Vice President Medical Affairs, Chilton Memorial Hospital, Pompton Plains, NJ, p. A435
Vice President Information Technology System and Chief Information Officer, Summa Health System, Akron, OH, p. A502

ROSS, David, President, Barnes–Jewish St. Peters Hospital, Saint Peters, MO, p. A393

ROSS, M.D., David, Chief Medical Officer, Methodist Hospitals, Gary, IN, p. A216

ROSS, M.D., Eugene, Chief of Staff, Carl T. Hayden Veterans Affairs Medical Center, Phoenix, AZ, p. A33

ROSS, J Shane, Chief of Staff, Southwestern Medical Center, Lawton, OK, p. A532

ROSS, James E., FACHE, Chief Executive Officer, James Lawrence Kernan Hospital, Baltimore, MD, p. A303

ROSS, James H., Chief Executive Officer, University of Missouri Health Care, Columbia, MO, p. B117

ROSS, James W., Chief Information Officer, Veterans Affairs Black Hills Health Care System, Fort Meade, SD, p. A596

ROSS, Joseph, Chief Financial Officer, Livingston Regional Hospital, Livingston, TN, p. A611

ROSS, Joseph P.
President and Chief Executive Officer, Dorchester General Hospital, Cambridge, MD, p. A306
President and Chief Executive Officer, Memorial Hospital at Easton Maryland, Easton, MD, p. A307
President and Chief Executive Officer, Shore Health System, Easton, MD, p. B97

ROSS, Kenneth R., Chief Executive Officer, Kindred Hospital– Oklahoma City, Oklahoma City, OK, p. A535

ROSS, Mary, Administrator, Gravette Medical Center Hospital, Gravette, AR, p. A44

ROSS, Pattie, Director Finance, Presbyterian Hospital of Kaufman, Kaufman, TX, p. A650

ROSS, Phil, Chief Executive Officer, Surgical Hospital of Oklahoma, Oklahoma City, OK, p. A536

ROSS, Robert, Vice President Operations, St. Luke's Cornwall Hospital – Newburgh Campus, Newburgh, NY, p. A467

ROSS, M.D., Samuel
Senior Vice President and Medical Director, Parkland Health & Hospital System, Dallas, TX, p. A633
Senior Vice President and Medical Director, Parkland Health & Hospital System, Dallas, TX, p. A633

ROSS Jr, Semmes, Administrator, Lawrence County Hospital, Monticello, MS, p. A373

ROSS, Steve, Financial Director, Norton Southwest Hospital, Louisville, KY, p. A270

ROSS, Tammy, Interim Chief Executive Officer, Desert Springs Medical Center, Midland, TX, p. A656

ROSS, Zeff, Administrator, Memorial Hospital West, Pembroke Pines, FL, p. A142

ROSSETTI, Stephen J., Ph.D., President and Chief Executive Officer, Saint Luke Institute, Silver Spring, MD, p. A311

ROSSFELD, John, Chief Executive Officer, Gila Regional Medical Center, Silver City, NM, p. A445

ROSSI, Alfred N., M.D., Chief Executive Officer, Hopedale Medical Complex, Hopedale, IL, p. A197

ROSSI, Thom, Director Human Resources, Riddle Memorial Hospital, Media, PA, p. A565

ROSSINI, Becky P., Information Systems Manager, Chicot Memorial Hospital, Lake Village, AR, p. A46

ROSSIO, Gary J., Director, Veterans Affairs San Diego Healthcare System, San Diego, CA, p. A88

ROSSMAN, Mark, Vice President Finance and Chief Financial Officer, Mercy Memorial Hospital System, Monroe, MI, p. A340

ROSSMANN, Barbara, President and Chief Executive Officer, St. Joseph's Mercy of Macomb, Clinton Township, MI, p. A330

ROSSO, M.D., James, Chief of Staff, Mercy Hospital of Willard, Willard, OH, p. A525

ROSSWAY, Richard, Director Community Relations, Bell Hospital, Ishpeming, MI, p. A337

ROTELLA, William, Vice President for Human Resources, Frederick Memorial Hospital, Frederick, MD, p. A308

ROTH, Chris, Vice President Operations, Northwest Hospital, Seattle, WA, p. A707

ROTH III, Edward J., President, Aultman Hospital, Canton, OH, p. A505

ROTH, M.D., Elliot J., Senior Vice President and Medical Director, Rehabilitation Institute of Chicago, Chicago, IL, p. A189

ROTH, Eugene, Chief Information Officer, High Point Regional Health System, High Point, NC, p. A485

ROTHERY, Daniel J., Administrator, The Rehabilitation Institute of St. Louis, Saint Louis, MO, p. A393

ROTHSCHILD, M.D., Marylee, Chief of Staff, Veterans Affairs Medical Center–Louisville, Louisville, KY, p. A270

ROTHSTEIN, Fred C., M.D., President and Chief Executive Officer, University Hospitals of Cleveland, Cleveland, OH, p. A509

ROTHSTEIN, Ronald, President and Chief Operating Officer, Levindale Hebrew Geriatric Center and Hospital, Baltimore, MD, p. A303

ROTOLO, Robert S., Chief Executive Officer and Administrator, St. John's Specialty Hospital, New Orleans, LA, p. A289

ROUNDS, M.D., George, Chief of Staff, Big Fork Valley Hospital, Bigfork, MN, p. A350

ROUNDY, Ann, Director of Employee Services, Columbus Community Hospital, Columbus, WI, p. A724

ROUNSLEY, Karen, Accounting Manager, HEALTHSOUTH Chesapeake Rehabilitation Hospital, Salisbury, MD, p. A310

ROUNTREE, Renee K., Vice President and Administrator, Riverside Rehabilitation Institute, Newport News, VA, p. A692

ROURK, Mike, Chief Medical Services, Annie Penn Hospital, Reidsville, NC, p. A490

ROURKE, Thomas E., CHE, Chief Executive Officer, Millwood Hospital, Arlington, TX, p. A622

ROUSH, Cynthia, Vice President Finance and Chief Financial Officer, St. Joseph Mercy Oakland, Pontiac, MI, p. A343

ROUSH, Sharon L., Chief Executive Officer, Capital Regional Medical Center, Tallahassee, FL, p. A147

ROUSSEAU, Mickie, Director Human Resources, Thibodaux Regional Medical Center, Thibodaux, LA, p. A294

ROUVELL, Paul, Vice President Finance, Kimball Medical Center, Lakewood, NJ, p. A430

ROUZER, Cindy, Human Resources Director, Spooner Health System, Spooner, WI, p. A736

ROVELLI, John A., Chief Financial Officer, Auburn Memorial Hospital, Auburn, NY, p. A447

ROVITO, Kevin, Interim Chief Financial Officer, Jackson Hospital, Marianna, FL, p. A136

ROWBERG, Donald L., Chief of Staff, Jonathan M. Wainwright Memorial VA Medical Center, Walla Walla, WA, p. A711

ROWE, David B., Chief Executive Officer, OakBend Medical Center, Richmond, TX, p. A662

ROWE, Gary L., President and Chief Executive Officer, St. John's Regional Medical Center, Joplin, MO, p. A384

ROWE, James Scott, Administrator, HEALTHSOUTH Rehabilitation Hospital, Florence, SC, p. A587

ROWE, Janice, Director Information Resources, Children's Hospital, Omaha, NE, p. A411

ROWE, Marsha, Chief Operating Officer, Mercy Catholic Medical Center, Darby, PA, p. A557

ROWE, Paul W., Director Information Technology, St. Francis Hospital, Wilmington, DE, p. A120

ROWELL, James, Vice President Human Resources, Rutherford Hospital, Rutherfordton, NC, p. A491

ROWLAND, Kathy M., Administrator, Bernice Community Rehabilitation Hospital – Minden, Minden, LA, p. A286

ROWLEY, Dave, Vice President Information Technology and Chief Information Officer, Rex Healthcare, Raleigh, NC, p. A489

ROWLEY, Michael, Chief Executive Officer, Copper Hills Youth Center, West Jordan, UT, p. A681

ROWLEY, Scott, Executive Director for Operations, Adventist GlenOaks Hospital, Glendale Heights, IL, p. A195

ROWSON, James S., Vice President Operations and Chief Financial Officer, Harrison Memorial Hospital, Bremerton, WA, p. A700

ROWTON, William, Chief Executive Officer, Cozby–Germany Hospital, Grand Saline, TX, p. A642

ROY, Craig A., Chief Financial Officer, Avoyelles Hospital, Marksville, LA, p. A286

ROY, Juanita, Vice President Finance, Providence Medical Center, Kansas City, KS, p. A250

ROY, Rob, Hospital Director Information Services, Dominion Hospital, Falls Church, VA, p. A687

ROYAL, Jennifer A., Administrator, Burke Medical Center, Waynesboro, GA, p. A172

ROYAL, Ty, Director Human Resources, Gibson Area Hospital and Health Services, Gibson City, IL, p. A195

ROYER, Thomas C., M.D., President, Christus Health, Irving, TX, p. B28

ROYESKY, Raymond, Director Human Resources, Brownsville General Hospital, Brownsville, PA, p. A553

ROZEK, Thomas M., President and Chief Executive Officer, Miami Children's Hospital, Miami, FL, p. A137

ROZELL, Becky, Director Human Resources, Madison County Hospital, London, OH, p. A516

ROZENBOOM, Steve, Chief Financial Officer, United Hospital District, Blue Earth, MN, p. A350

ROZMUS, Mike, Director of Information Systems, Rockingham Memorial Hospital, Harrisonburg, VA, p. A689

ROZONKIEWIECZ, Mitchell P., Corporate Vice President Information Systems, Community–General Hospital of Greater Syracuse, Syracuse, NY, p. A473

RUBEL, Eric J., Deputy Commander Clinical Services, Darnall Army Community Hospital, Fort Hood, TX, p. A638

RUBEN, Maureen L., Executive Director, Mohawk Valley Psychiatric Center, Utica, NY, p. A474

RUBERTE, Henry, Chief Executive Officer and Managing Director, Caribbean Pediatric and Surgery Hospital, San Juan, PR, p. A747

RUBIN, Amir Dan, Chief Operating Officer, Stony Brook University Hospital, Stony Brook, NY, p. A473

RUBIN, Linda, Chief Operating Officer, Spectrum Health–Reed City Campus, Reed City, MI, p. A343

RUBIN, Ron, Director Information Services, Presbyterian–St. Luke's Medical Center, Denver, CO, p. A104

RUCHIM, M.D., Michael, Vice President Academic and Medical Affairs, Louis A. Weiss Memorial Hospital, Chicago, IL, p. A188

RUCHTI, Robert, Vice President and Chief of Operations, East Pasco Medical Center, Zephyrhills, FL, p. A151

RUCKEL, Michael R., Vice President Finance, Decatur County Memorial Hospital, Greensburg, IN, p. A217

RUCKER, Craig
Senior Vice President and Chief Financial Officer, Covenant Children's Hospital, Lubbock, TX, p. A654
Senior Vice President and Chief Financial Officer, Covenant Medical Center, Lubbock, TX, p. A654

RUCKER, Sheryl, Memorial Community Hospital, Edgerton, WI, p. A725

RUDAWSKY, Sandra, Corporate Senior Vice President and Chief Operating Officer, Berger Health System, Circleville, OH, p. A508

RUDD, John, Chief Financial Officer, Cayuga Medical Center at Ithaca, Ithaca, NY, p. A454

RUDOLPH, Tabitha, Vice President Financial Services, Charlevoix Area Hospital, Charlevoix, MI, p. A329

RUDZIK, Donna, Director of Human Resources, Hopkins County Memorial Hospital, Sulphur Springs, TX, p. A668

RUEDEL, Karen, Chief Resource Officer, Veterans Affairs Ann Arbor Healthcare System, Ann Arbor, MI, p. A327

RUELLO, Rocky, Vice President Human Resources, St. John's Mercy Medical Center, Saint Louis, MO, p. A392

RUESCH, M.D., McLaren, Chief of Staff, Cobre Valley Community Hospital, Globe, AZ, p. A31

RUFFNER, Lori
Chief Executive Officer, Community Medical Center–Clovis, Clovis, CA, p. A57
Chief Executive Officer, Community Medical Center–Fresno, Fresno, CA, p. A61

RUFFOLO, M.D., Aldo, President Medical Staff, Sarah Bush Lincoln Health Center, Mattoon, IL, p. A200

RUFFOLO, Joseph A., President and Chief Executive Officer, Niagara Falls Memorial Medical Center, Niagara Falls, NY, p. A467

RUFLIN, Patricia A., President and Chief Executive Officer, Parma Community General Hospital, Parma, OH, p. A520

RUGGERO, Robert, Senior Vice President Operations, Lourdes Medical Center of Burlington County, Willingboro, NJ, p. A438

RUH, JoAnne, Vice President Information Technology, Roswell Park Cancer Institute, Buffalo, NY, p. A449

RUH, M.D., Richard, Vice President Medical Affairs and Medical Director, Mercy Hospital, Buffalo, NY, p. A449

RUIZ, Mary, Chief Executive Officer, Manatee Glen Hospital, Bradenton, FL, p. A124

RUIZ, Roberto, Administrator, Doctors Hospital, San Juan, PR, p. A747

RUKSTAD, Julie, Chief Financial Officer, Hilo Medical Center, Hilo, HI, p. A173

RULLAN, Johnny V., M.D., Secretary of Health, Puerto Rico Department of Health, San Juan, PR, p. B88

RUMANS, M.D., Mark C., Chief of Staff, Deaconess Billings Clinic, Billings, MT, p. A396

RUMLEY, Darrell, Service Unit Director, U. S. Public Health Service Indian Hospital, Sells, AZ, p. A36

RUMMELL, Jennifer, Director Human Resources, East Texas Medical Center Fairfield, Fairfield, TX, p. A638

RUNDLE, Eduard, Vice President Human Resources, Mercy Hospital, Miami, FL, p. A137

RUNT, David
Chief Information Officer, Del E. Webb Memorial Hospital, Sun City West, AZ, p. A37
Vice President Information Services and Chief Information Officer, Walter O. Boswell Memorial Hospital, Sun City, AZ, p. A37

RUPERT, Mike, Chief Fiscal Services, Veterans Affairs Medical Center, Battle Creek, MI, p. A328

RUPP, William, M.D., President and Chief Executive Officer, Immanuel St. Joseph's–Mayo Health System, Mankato, MN, p. A356

RUPPEL, Rick, Chief Financial Officer, Memorial Hospital, Fremont, OH, p. A514

RUPPERT, James C., Regional Administrator, Alegent Health Mercy Hospital, Corning, IA, p. A231

RUSH, Cindy, Human Resources Director, Clay County Medical Center, Clay Center, KS, p. A245

RUSH, Donald J., Chief Executive Officer, Providence Kodiak Island Medical Center, Kodiak, AK, p. A27

RUSH, Ed, President and Chief Executive Officer, Iredell Memorial Hospital, Statesville, NC, p. A492

RUSH, Matthew, President and Chief Executive Officer, Hayes–Green–Beach Memorial Hospital, Charlotte, MI, p. A329

RUSHING, R. Lynn, Chief Executive Officer, Brook Lane Health Services, Hagerstown, MD, p. A308

RUSK, Ronald A., Chief Financial Officer, Pulaski Memorial Hospital, Winamac, IN, p. A227

RUSKAN, Jeff, Administrator, HEALTHSOUTH Rehabilitation Hospital of Virginia, Richmond, VA, p. A695

RUSNAK, Greg, Vice President, Greenville Memorial Hospital, Greenville, SC, p. A588

RUSSEL, Kimberly A., President and Chief Executive Officer, Mary Greeley Medical Center, Ames, IA, p. A228

RUSSELL, Alnita B., Director Quality and Access Services, UHHS Brown Memorial Hospital, Conneaut, OH, p. A511

RUSSELL, Curtis R., Chief Financial Officer, Harry S. Truman Memorial Veterans Hospital, Columbia, MO, p. A380

RUSSELL, M.D., Dee B., Chief Executive Officer, Floyd Medical Center, Rome, GA, p. A168

RUSSELL, Galen, Chief Financial Officer, Clear Lake Regional Medical Center, Webster, TX, p. A673

RUSSELL, Georgette, Director Human Resources, Carson City Hospital, Carson City, MI, p. A329

RUSSELL, Gerald L., Senior Vice President and Chief Operating Officer, St. Francis Medical Center, Lynwood, CA, p. A74

RUSSELL, Jack, Director Human Resources, Central Arkansas Hospital, Searcy, AR, p. A50

RUSSELL, James D. M., President and Chief Executive Officer, St. Mary's Healthcare Center, Pierre, SD, p. A597

RUSSELL, Kathie, Director Information Services, Plaza Medical Center of Fort Worth, Fort Worth, TX, p. A640

RUSSELL, Leisa, Senior Vice President Finance and Chief Financial Officer, Washington Hospital Center, Washington, DC, p. A122

RUSSELL, Linda B., Chief Executive Officer, The Woman's Hospital of Texas, Houston, TX, p. A648

RUSSELL, Michael, Director of Human Resources, Oswego Hospital, Oswego, NY, p. A468

RUSSELL, Michelle L., Vice and Administrator, Howard Regional Health System West Campus Specialty Hospital, Kokomo, IN, p. A220

RUSSELL, Paul, Director Information Services, Johnson Memorial Hospital, Stafford Springs, CT, p. A116

RUSSELL, Penelope, Director of Health Information Services, Regional Rehabilitation Hospital, Phenix City, AL, p. A23

RUSSELL, Tim, Administrator, Stillwater Community Hospital, Columbus, MT, p. A397

RUSSELL–SCOTT, Terrie, Director Information System, Woodland Heights Medical Center, Lufkin, TX, p. A655

RUTENBERG, Howard J., Administrator, Hot Springs Rehabilitation Center, Hot Springs National, AR, p. A44

RUTHERFORD, George, Vice President Planning, Ancillary and Support Services, Ionia County Memorial Hospital, Ionia, MI, p. A337

RUTHERFORD, Michael, Chief Financial Officer, Summa Health System, Akron, OH, p. A502

RUTKOWSKI, James C., Senior Vice President Financial Operations, Culpeper Regional Hospital, Culpeper, VA, p. A687

RUTLEDGE, Valinda, Chief Executive Officer, Bon Secours St. Francis Health System, Greenville, SC, p. A588

RUTLEDGE, Virginia, Assistant Administrator, Barton County Memorial Hospital, Lamar, MO, p. A386

RUWOLDT, Steve, Chief Administrative Officer, Lutheran Hospital, Cleveland, OH, p. A509

RUYLE, W. Kenneth, Director, Veterans Affairs Medical Center, Tuscaloosa, AL, p. A24

RUYTER, Mary, Chief Executive Officer, Jackson Medical Center, Jackson, MN, p. A355

RUZYCKI, Frank C., Executive Director, Roosevelt Warm Springs Institute for Rehabilitation, Warm Springs, GA, p. A171

RYALS, Billie, Director Human Resources, Sullivan County Memorial Hospital, Milan, MO, p. A387

RYAN, Bill
Chief Financial Officer, Shands Jacksonville Medical Center, Jacksonville, FL, p. A132
Chief Financial Officer, Shands Jacksonville Medical Center, Jacksonville, FL, p. A132

RYAN, Christina M., Chief Executive Officer, The Women's Hospital, Newburgh, IN, p. A223

RYAN, David, Vice President Human Resources, Quincy Medical Center, Quincy, MA, p. A322

RYAN, D.O., David, Cheif Medical Staff, Ellinwood District Hospital, Ellinwood, KS, p. A246

RYAN, Dennis, Senior Vice President and Chief Financial Officer, Children's Hospital of The King's Daughters, Norfolk, VA, p. A692

RYAN, Frank, Chief Financial Officer, Veterans Affairs Medical Center, Manchester, NH, p. A422

RYAN, M.D., J Thomas, Executive Vice President, Medical Affairs, Mary Washington Hospital, Fredericksburg, VA, p. A688

RYAN, M.D., Jacy, Chief Medical Service, Veterans Affairs Medical Center, Spokane, WA, p. A709

RYAN, Keith, Vice President Information Systems and Chief Information Officer, Stamford Health System, Stamford, CT, p. A116

RYAN, Margaret, Director Health Information, Deer Park Hospital, Deer Park, WA, p. A702

RYAN, Mary Jean, President and Chief Executive Officer, SSM Health Care, Saint Louis, MO, p. B101

RYAN, Michael
Administrator, Osseo Medical Center, Osseo, WI, p. A733
Senior Vice President Finance, Memorial Hospital of Rhode Island, Pawtucket, RI, p. A581

RYAN, Michael J., Chief Executive Officer, Hillsboro Community Medical Center, Hillsboro, KS, p. A248

RYAN, Patrick, Chief Executive Officer, Regency Hospital of Northwest Indiana, East Chicago, IN, p. A214

RYAN, Thomas E., President, Alamance Regional Medical Center, Burlington, NC, p. A478

RYAN, Timothy, Director, Human Resources, Lewis County General Hospital, Lowville, NY, p. A456

RYBA, Thomas L., Chief Executive Officer, Holly Hill Hospital, Raleigh, NC, p. A489

RYBA, Tomi S., Chief Operating Officer, UCSF Medical Center, San Francisco, CA, p. A89

RYBOLT, S Andrew, Vice President and Chief Financial Officer, Merle West Medical Center, Klamath Falls, OR, p. A545

RYDER, Doug, Vice President Operations, Advocate Good Shepherd Hospital, Barrington, IL, p. A184

RYDER, Jeff, Director Information Systems, Gateway Regional Health System, Mount Sterling, KY, p. A272

RYERSON, Nancy, Director Information Systems, Central Florida Regional Hospital, Sanford, FL, p. A146

RYLE, Deborah L., Administrator and Chief Executive Officer, Round Rock Medical Center, Round Rock, TX, p. A662

RYSCHON, Tim, Clinical Director, U. S. Public Health Service Indian Hospital, Rosebud, SD, p. A598

RZEMINSKI, Peter, Vice President Human Resources, New Hanover Regional Medical Center, Wilmington, NC, p. A494

S

SABA, Francis M., President and Chief Executive Officer, Milford Regional Medical Center, Milford, MA, p. A320

SABANEGH, Edmund, Chief Medical Staff, Wilford Hall Medical Center, Lackland AFB, TX, p. A652

SABARATNAM, Rudra, M.D.,
Chief Executive Officer, Bayview Hospital and Mental Health System, Chula Vista, CA, p. A56
President and Chief Executive Officer, City of Angels Medical Center, Los Angeles, CA, p. A69

SABO, Michael A., Director, Veterans Affairs Hudson Valley Health Care System–F.D. Roosevelt Hospital, Montrose, NY, p. A457

SABONYA, M.D., Linda M., Executive Medical Director, Riverside Behavioral Health Center, Hampton, VA, p. A689

SACCO, Frank V., FACHE, Chief Executive Officer, Memorial Healthcare System, Los Angeles, FL, p. B74

SACCO, Santo, Vice President Human Resources, Barnert Hospital, Paterson, NJ, p. A434

SACHAR, M.D., Rajinder, Vice President, Medical Affairs, St. Joseph Hospital, Cheektowaga, NY, p. A450

SACK, Michael V., President and Chief Executive Officer, Hallmark Health System, Melrose, MA, p. A320

SACKETT, John, Chief Executive Officer, Avista Adventist Hospital, Louisville, CO, p. A108

SACKETT, Walter, Chief Executive Officer, North Valley Rehabilitation Hospital, Thornton, CO, p. A110

SACKRISON, Jeffrey N., CHE,
President, Bertie Memorial Hospital, Windsor, NC, p. A494
President, Chowan Hospital, Edenton, NC, p. A482

SACKS, M.D., Robert, Chief of Staff, Olympia Medical Center, Los Angeles, CA, p. A72

SADLER, Blair L., President and Chief Executive Officer, Children's Hospital and Health Center, San Diego, CA, p. A86

SADLER, D.O., Michele, Chief Medical Staff, Guttenberg Municipal Hospital, Guttenberg, IA, p. A234

SADLER, Wanda H., Chief Executive Officer, Hallmark Youthcare – Richmond, Richmond, VA, p. A695

SADVARY, Thomas J., FACHE, Senior Vice President and Chief Executive Officer, Scottsdale Healthcare, Scottsdale, AZ, p. B96

SAFDAR, M.D., Feroz, Chief of Staff, Robert Wood Johnson University Hospital at Hamilton, Hamilton, NJ, p. A429

SAFF, Eric, Chief Information Officer, Mt. Diablo Medical Pavilion, Concord, CA, p. A57

SAFFIER, M.D., Sandon, Vice President, St. Joseph's Medical Center, Stockton, CA, p. A95

SAFIAN, Keith F., President and Chief Executive Officer, Phelps Memorial Hospital Center, Sleepy Hollow, NY, p. A472

SAFLEY, Thomas
Vice President Finance and Chief Financial Officer, St. Charles Medical Center – Bend, Bend, OR, p. A542
Vice President Finance, St. Charles Medical Center – Redmond, Redmond, OR, p. A548

SAFYER, M.D., Steven M., Senior Vice President and Chief Medical Officer, Montefiore Medical Center, New York, NY, p. A462

SAGER, Marc M.
Administrator, Wilford Hall Medical Center, Lackland AFB, TX, p. A652
Administrator, Wilford Hall Medical Center, Lackland AFB, TX, p. A652

SAGO, Glenn R., Administrator, Arkansas State Hospital, Little Rock, AR, p. A46

SAHAI, M.D., Anurag, Medical Director, Albert Lindley Lee Memorial Hospital, Fulton, NY, p. A452

SAILE, Anne, President and Chief Executive Officer, Bellevue Woman's Hospital, Schenectady, NY, p. A472

SAINTZ, Jeffrey, Vice President Human Resources, Titusville Area Hospital, Titusville, PA, p. A576

SAIYED, M.D., Ashfaq, Medical Director, Irwin County Hospital, Ocilla, GA, p. A167

SAKS, Stephen H., Chief Executive Officer, John F. Kennedy Memorial Hospital, Philadelphia, PA, p. A568

SAKUMOTO, Glenn, Regional Director Human Resources, Leahi Hospital, Honolulu, HI, p. A174

SALA, Jr, Anthony S., Chief Operating Officer, Rio Grande Regional Hospital, McAllen, TX, p. A656

SALANGER, Matthew J.
President and Chief Executive Officer, United Health Services, Binghamton, NY, p. B113
President and Chief Executive Officer, United Health Services Hospitals–Binghamton, Binghamton, NY, p. A448

SALAZAR, Macario, Vice President and Chief Financial Officer, Rush–Copley Medical Center, Aurora, IL, p. A184

SALAZAR, Margie, Human Resources Director, Valley Regional Medical Center, Brownsville, TX, p. A627

SALEAPAGA, Iotamo T., M.D., Director Health, Lyndon B. Johnson Tropical Medical Center, Pago Pago, AS, p. A743

SALEM, M.D., Robert J.
Chief Medical Officer, Covenant Children's Hospital, Lubbock, TX, p. A654
Chief Medical Officer, Covenant Medical Center, Lubbock, TX, p. A654

SALERNO, Richard E., Senior Vice President and Chief Operating Officer, Carraway Methodist Medical Center, Birmingham, AL, p. A14

SALERNO, Thomas A., Chief Executive Officer, Shasta Regional Medical Center, Redding, CA, p. A83

SALETA, Manuel, Service Chief, Veterans Affairs Medical Center, Miami, FL, p. A138

SALGADO, Joe, Chief of Staff, Artesia General Hospital, Artesia, NM, p. A441

SALHANY, Richard, Vice President Operations, Clara Maass Medical Center, Belleville, NJ, p. A425

SALIPANTE, M.D., Joseph, Vice President Medical Affairs, Park Ridge Hospital, Rochester, NY, p. A471

SALISBURY, Margaret A., Director Marketing, Runnells Specialized Hospital of Union County, Berkeley Heights, NJ, p. A425

SALISBURY, Renee, Executive Director Human Resources, Kewanee Hospital, Kewanee, IL, p. A199

SALISBURY, Tim, Vice President Finance, Bay Area Hospital, Coos Bay, OR, p. A543

SALKIL, Bennie, Director Human Resources, Integris Bass Baptist Health Center, Enid, OK, p. A530

SALLER, Bill, Chief Financial Officer, Doctors Hospital of Columbus, Columbus, GA, p. A158

SALLEY, Wanda, Administrative Director Human Resources, Gulf Coast Medical Center, Panama City, FL, p. A142

SALLUZO, Richard, M.D., President and Chief Executive Officer, Wellmont Health System, Kingsport, TN, p. B121

SALMON, Robert J.
Chief Executive Officer, Deuel County Memorial Hospital, Clear Lake, SD, p. A595
Chief Executive Officer, Sioux Valley Canby Campus, Canby, MN, p. A351

SALO, Saliba, Senior Vice President Finance and Chief Financial Officer, Northridge Hospital Medical Center–Roscoe Boulevard Campus, Los Angeles, CA, p. A72

SALOUM, M.D., Herbert A., Medical Director, St. Michael's Hospital, Tyndall, SD, p. A600

SALSBERRY, David, Vice President and Chief Financial Officer, West Virginia University Hospitals, Morgantown, WV, p. A718

SALSGIVER, Carolyn, Senior Vice President Planning and Marketing, Bridgeport Hospital, Bridgeport, CT, p. A112

SALTER, Michael, Chief Operating Officer, Park Plaza Hospital, Houston, TX, p. A647

SALTHOUSE, Alice, Administrator and Chief Executive Officer, Blowing Rock Hospital, Blowing Rock, NC, p. A478

SALTZMAN, M.D., Steven, Senior Vice President and Medical Director, Atlanta Medical Center, Atlanta, GA, p. A153

SALVIA, Richard, Vice President Finance and Chief Financial Officer, Palisades Medical Center, North Bergen, NJ, p. A433

SALVINO, Sonia, Director Finance, UHHS Bedford Medical Center, Bedford, OH, p. A503

SALVO, Stephen, Vice President Human Resources, Anna Jaques Hospital, Newburyport, MA, p. A321

SALYARDS, Lona, Director, Health Information Management, Haxtun Hospital District, Haxtun, CO, p. A106

SAMBRANO, Arlene, Chief Human Resources Management Services, Veterans Affairs Palo Alto Health Care System, Palo Alto, CA, p. A80

SAMET, Kenneth A., President and Chief Operating Officer, MedStar Health, Columbia, MD, p. B73

SAMMER, M.D., Edwin, Vice President and Chief Medical Officer, Lakeland Regional Medical Center, Lakeland, FL, p. A134

SAMMONS, Craig, Chief Financial Officer, Sky Ridge Medical Center, Lone Tree, CO, p. A108

SAMPLES, Beth
Human Resource Director, Georgetown Memorial Hospital, Georgetown, SC, p. A588
Human Resource Director, Waccamaw Community Hospital, Murrells Inlet, SC, p. A590

SAMPSON, Arthur J., President and Chief Executive Officer, Newport Hospital, Newport, RI, p. A581

SAMPSON, Bob, Vice President Human Resources, St. Joseph Hospital, Eureka, CA, p. A59

SAMS, Tom, Assistant Administrator Human Resources, Montrose Memorial Hospital, Montrose, CO, p. A108

SAN FILIPPO, M.D., Bruce, Vice President and Chief Medical Officer, Memorial Medical Center, Las Cruces, NM, p. A443

SANCHEZ, Carmen, Director Human Resources, Hospital Dr. Cayetano Coll Y Toste, Arecibo, PR, p. A743

SANCHEZ, Eduardo J., M.P.H., Commissioner of Health, Texas Department of State Health Services, Austin, TX, p. B107

SANCHEZ, George, Director Information Services, Gnaden Huetten Memorial Hospital, Lehighton, PA, p. A563

SANCHEZ, M.D., George, Chief Medical Officer, Jackson Hospital, Marianna, FL, p. A136

SANCHEZ, Jose R., Executive Director, Lincoln Medical and Mental Health Center, New York, NY, p. A461

SANCHEZ, Linda, Health Information Management Manager, HEALTHSOUTH Rehabilitation Hospital of New Jersey, Toms River, NJ, p. A437

SANDELL, Sue, Director Information Services, Catskill Regional Medical Center, Harris, NY, p. A453

SANDENE, Jeff, Chief of Finance, Sioux Valley Hospital University Medical Center, Sioux Falls, SD, p. A599

SANDERS, David S., Chief Executive Officer, Martin General Hospital, Williamston, NC, p. A493

SANDERS, Gale H., Director, Gadsden Regional Medical Center, Gadsden, AL, p. A19

SANDERS, Greggory, Information Systems Director, Parkway Regional Medical Center, North Miami Beach, FL, p. A139

SANDERS, Harv, Chief Financial Officer, Rhea Medical Center, Dayton, TN, p. A605

SANDERS, M.D., Jack, Chief Medical Officer, Campbellton Graceville Hospital, Graceville, FL, p. A130

SANDERS, CPA, Jerry L., Assistant Administrator, Southeast Missouri Hospital, Cape Girardeau, MO, p. A379

SANDERS, Kyle, Chief Operating Officer, Northwest Texas Healthcare System, Amarillo, TX, p. A621

SANDERS, Larry, FACHE, Chairman and Chief Executive Officer, Columbus Regional Healthcare System, Columbus, GA, p. B30

SANDERS, Michael B., President and Chief Executive Officer, The Monroe Clinic, Monroe, WI, p. A732

SANDERS, M.D., Robert, Executive Vice President of Medical Staff Affairs, Texoma Medical Center, Denison, TX, p. A635

SANDERS, Sandi, Chief Operating Officer, Chickasaw Nation Health System, Ada, OK, p. A527

SANDERS, Sherri, Manager Information Systems, Mountains Community Hospital, Lake Arrowhead, CA, p. A66

SANDERS, D.O., Steve
Vice President Medical Affairs, Saint Joseph Medical Center, Kansas City, MO, p. A385
Vice President Medical Affairs, St. Mary's Medical Center, Blue Springs, MO, p. A378

SANDERS, Thomas J., CHE, Director, Robert J. Dole Veterans Affairs Medical Center, Wichita, KS, p. A259

SANDLIN, Keith, Chief Executive Officer, Emory Cartersville Medical Center, Cartersville, GA, p. A157

SANDORA, George, Director Finance, Alle–Kiski Medical Center, Natrona Heights, PA, p. A566

SANDOVAL, Donald D., FACHE, Administrator, McLeod Medical Center–Dillon, Dillon, SC, p. A587

SANDSTROM, C Bruce, Senior Vice President Finance, Aroostook Medical Center, Presque Isle, ME, p. A300

SANFORD, Edward J., Chief Executive Officer, Cumberland County Hospital, Burkesville, KY, p. A262

SANG, Louis Fung, Chief Financial Officer, North Broward Medical Center, Pompano Beach, FL, p. A144

SANGER, M.D., David, Chief Medical Officer, St. Joseph Memorial Hospital, Larned, KS, p. A251

SANGIORGIO, M.D., Frank E., President Medical Staff, Bon Secours Hospital Campus, Altoona, PA, p. A552

SANNER, Melinda, Director of Information Systems, West Calcasieu Cameron Hospital, Sulphur, LA, p. A293

SANTAMARIA, Mark A., Vice President and Chief Operating Officer, The William W. Backus Hospital, Norwich, CT, p. A116

SANTANGELO, CPA, Charles J., Senior Vice President and Chief Financial Officer, Susquehanna Health System, Williamsport, PA, p. A580

SANTIAGO, M.D., Jose M.
Senior Vice President and Chief Medical Officer, Carondelet St. Joseph's Hospital–Tucson, Tucson, AZ, p. A37
Senior Vice President and Chief Medical Officer, Carondelet St. Mary's Hospital–Tucson, Tucson, AZ, p. A37

SANTIAGO, Orlando, HumanResources Officer, Hospital Del Maestro, San Juan, PR, p. A747

SANTIAGO–VEGA, Francisco, Consultor, Lafayette Hospital, Arroyo, PR, p. A744

SANTILLI, Arthur E., President, Masonic Healthcare Center, Wallingford, CT, p. A117

SANTILLI, Robert J., Vice President and Chief Operating Officer, Riddle Memorial Hospital, Media, PA, p. A565

SANTISTEVAN, Steven, Director Information Systems, Los Alamos Medical Center, Los Alamos, NM, p. A443

SANTORO, Barbara, Director Information Systems, Northern Westchester Hospital, Mount Kisco, NY, p. A457

SANTOS, Jack, Chief Information Officer, Catholic Medical Center, Manchester, NH, p. A422

SANVILLE, David, Chief Financial Officer, Gifford Medical Center, Randolph, VT, p. A683

SANZ, Lawrence, Vice President Finance and Chief Financial Officer, Midland Memorial Hospital, Midland, TX, p. A657

SARANTAKIS, John
Director Human Resources, SSM St. Joseph Health Center, Saint Charles, MO, p. A390
Director Human Resources, SSM St. Joseph Hospital West, Lake Saint Louis, MO, p. A386

SARDO, James, Chief of Staff, Berger Health System, Circleville, OH, p. A508

SARDONE, Frank J.
President and Chief Executive Officer, Bronson Healthcare Group, Inc., Kalamazoo, MI, p. B20
President and Chief Executive Officer, Bronson Methodist Hospital, Kalamazoo, MI, p. A338
President, Bronson Vicksburg Hospital, Vicksburg, MI, p. A347

SARGENT, M.D., Dale, Executive Vice President Medical Affairs, Wellmont Bristol Regional Medical Center, Bristol, TN, p. A602

SARGENT, M.D., David, Chief Medical Officer, Wilkes Regional Medical Center, North Wilkesboro, NC, p. A488

SARGENT, M.D., J Dale, Executive Vice President Medical Affairs, Wellmont Holston Valley Medical Center, Kingsport, TN, p. A609

SARGENT, Reed
Assistant Administrator Finance, Garfield Memorial Hospital and Clinics, Panguitch, UT, p. A678
Assistant Administrator Finance, Valley View Medical Center, Cedar City, UT, p. A676

SARLE, C. Richard, FACHE, President and Chief Executive Officer, Carrier Clinic, Belle Mead, NJ, p. A425

SARNESO, Mark, Chief Executive Officer, Cove Forge Behavioral Health System, Williamsburg, PA, p. A579

SARRICO, Christine, Chief Financial Officer, Enloe Medical Center, Chico, CA, p. A56

SARROS, Steve, Interim Director Information Systems, Mercy Medical Center, Springfield, OH, p. A522

SASS, Gregg, Chief Financial Officer, San Francisco General Hospital Medical Center, San Francisco, CA, p. A89

SASSER, Kelley, Director Information Systems, East Pasco Medical Center, Zephyrhills, FL, p. A151

SATCHER, Richard H., President and Chief Executive Officer, St. Petersburg General Hospital, Saint Petersburg, FL, p. A145

SATEY, Phil
Vice President Human Resources, Grace Hospital, Morganton, NC, p. A488
Vice President Human Resources, Valdese General Hospital, Valdese, NC, p. A493

SATKOSKI, R.N., Linda L., Vice President Physician Relations and Patient Care Services, La Porte Regional Health System, La Porte, IN, p. A220

SATO, Dennis, Chief Information Officer, Salem Hospital, Salem, OR, p. A549

SATTERFIELD, Jr, John B., Vice President Finance, Craven Regional Medical Center, New Bern, NC, p. A488

SATTLER, Alan, Senior Vice President, Finance, Flower Hospital, Sylvania, OH, p. A522

SATZGER, Bruce G., President, Commmunity Hospital of San Bernardino, San Bernardino, CA, p. A86

SAUCEDO, Jesse
Vice President and Chief Financial Officer, Central Kansas Medical Center, Great Bend, KS, p. A247
Vice President and Chief Financial Officer, St. Joseph Memorial Hospital, Larned, KS, p. A251

SAUER, Christie, Human Resources Officer, Cavalier County Memorial Hospital, Langdon, ND, p. A499

SAUK, Michael, Chief Information Officer, City of Hope National Medical Center, Duarte, CA, p. A59

SAUL, Neal, Vice President Finance, Piedmont Healthcare System, Rock Hill, SC, p. A591

SAULS, Randy, Chief Operating Officer, South Georgia Medical Center, Valdosta, GA, p. A171

SAULSBERY, Patricia A. H., Commander, Colonel Florence A. Blanchfield Army Community Hospital, Fort Campbell, KY, p. A264

SAULTERS, W. Dale, Administrator, Winston Medical Center, Louisville, MS, p. A372

SAUM, Anita, Manager Human Resoruces, Rehabilitation Hospital of Tinton Falls, Eatontown, NJ, p. A427

SAUNDERS, Jack, Chief of Staff, Mercy Medical Center Mount Shasta, Mount Shasta, CA, p. A77

SAUNDERS, Joseph, Chief Operating Officer, Crozer-Chester Medical Center, Upland, PA, p. A577

SAUNDERS, Kristi K., Director and Compliance Officer, Calais Regional Hospital, Calais, ME, p. A297

SAUNDERS, Sharon, Chief Clinical Officer, Delta County Memorial Hospital, Delta, CO, p. A103

SAUVIGNE, M.D., Arthur E., Medical Director, Veterans Affairs Medical Center, White River Junction, VT, p. A684

SAVAGE, M.D., Douglas, President Medical Staff, Southwest Florida Regional Medical Center, Fort Myers, FL, p. A129

SAVAGE, Elizabeth, Senior Vice President Human Resources, Good Samaritan Hospital, Suffern, NY, p. A473

SAVAGE, Jennifer, Chief Human Resources, Pella Regional Health Center, Pella, IA, p. A240

SAVAGE, Robert L., President and Chief Executive Officer, Saint Francis Hospital, Poughkeepsie, NY, p. A470

SAVELL, M.D., Randy
Chief of Staff, Harris Regional Hospital, Sylva, NC, p. A492
Chief of Staff, Swain County Hospital, Bryson City, NC, p. A478

SAVINO, Linda A., Administrator, Rehabilitation Hospital of Tinton Falls, Eatontown, NJ, p. A427

SAVOY, Cheryl, Administrative Manager and Fiscal Officer, Walter Olin Moss Regional Medical Center, Lake Charles, LA, p. A285

SAVOY III, F. Peter, Chief Executive Officer, Acadia–St. Landry Hospital, Church Point, LA, p. A279

SAWYER, Cecelia, Administrator, Methodist Healthcare–University Hospital, Memphis, TN, p. A613

SAWYER, M.D., Charles, Medical Director, Geisinger HEALTHSOUTH Rehabilitation Hospital, Danville, PA, p. A556

SAWYER, Dorothy, Chief Executive Officer, Havasu Regional Medical Center, Lake Havasu City, AZ, p. A32

SAWYER, John, Executive Director, Porterville Developmental Center, Porterville, CA, p. A82

SAWYER, M.D., John, Chief of Staff, Lompoc Healthcare District, Lompoc, CA, p. A68

SAWYERS Jr, Irving B., Chief Executive Officer, Specialty Hospital of New Orleans, New Orleans, LA, p. A289

SAYER, Michelle, Chief Operating Officer, San Gorgonio Memorial Hospital, Banning, CA, p. A54

SAYLOR, Roger, Finance Officer, Veterans Affairs Medical and Regional Office Center, Fargo, ND, p. A498

SBERNA, M.D., Joseph G., Chief of Staff, Wyandot Memorial Hospital, Upper Sandusky, OH, p. A523

SCADDAN, M.D., Paul, Chief of Staff, Scheurer Hospital, Pigeon, MI, p. A342

SCAFIDI, Frank, Vice President Information Systems and Chief Information Officer, Elmhurst Memorial Hospital, New York, IL, p. A193

SCAIFE, Debbie, MSN, Administrator and Director of Nursing, Jerold Phelps Community Hospital, Garberville, CA, p. A62

SCALES, Royce C., Chief Executive Officer, Sanger General Hospital, Sanger, CA, p. A92

SCALLEN, Jr, Joseph, Senior Vice President Finance and Chief Financial Officer, Mount Clemens General Hospital, Mount Clemens, MI, p. A340

SCAMARDO, II, M.D., L P., Chief of Staff, Grimes St. Joseph Health Center, Navasota, TX, p. A658

SCANLON, Dennis P., Vice President Finance, Doctors Community Hospital, Lanham, MD, p. A309

SCANLON, Donald, Chief Financial Officer, Mount Sinai Hosptial, New York, NY, p. A462

SCANLON, Shaun J., Senior Vice President Finance and Chief Financial Officer, Vail Valley Medical Center, Vail, CO, p. A110

SCANNELL, Stephen, Chief Financial Officer, Southern Indiana Rehabilitation Hospital, New Albany, IN, p. A223

SCANNELL, Steve, Assistant Vice President Financial Services, Frazier Rehab Institute, Louisville, KY, p. A269

SCARBROUGH, Greg, Senior Vice President Finance and Chief Financial Officer, Oconee Memorial Hospital, Seneca, SC, p. A591

SCARPATI, Randy, Chief Information Officer, Lawrence & Memorial Hospital, New London, CT, p. A115

SCARPINO, Dave, Vice President Finance and Chief Financial Officer, St. John's Riverside Hosptial, Yonkers, NY, p. A476

SCARROW, Lloyd, Chief Executive Officer, Arizona Spine and Joint Hospital, Mesa, AZ, p. A32

SCEENNA, Maria, Chief Human Resources Officer, St. Christopher's Hospital for Children, Philadelphia, PA, p. A570

SCHAACK, Gregory J., Vice President and Chief Financial Officer, St. Joseph's/Candler, Candler Hospital, Savannah, GA, p. A169

SCHABBING, Mark, Chief of Staff, Perry County Memorial Hospital, Perryville, MO, p. A389

SCHACKMAN, M.D., Paul, President Medical Staff, Robert Wood Johnson University Hospital at Rahway, Rahway, NJ, p. A435

SCHADE, Sue, Chief Information Officer, Brigham and Women's Hospital, Boston, MA, p. A313

SCHAEFBAUER, Paula, Administrator and Chief Executive Officer, White Community Hospital, Aurora, MN, p. A349

SCHAEFER, Carol, Director Human Resources, Hermann Area District Hospital, Hermann, MO, p. A383

SCHAEFER, Michael J., Executive Vice President and Chief Financial Officer, Methodist Charlton Medical Center, Dallas, TX, p. A633

SCHAEFER, Michele, Chief Executive Officer, Saint Joseph Medical Center, Kansas City, MO, p. A385

SCHAEFER, Michelle, Chief Financial Officer, Lillian M. Hudspeth Memorial Hospital, Sonora, TX, p. A667

SCHAEFFER, M.D., Andre, Chief of Staff, Union General Hospital, Blairsville, GA, p. A156

SCHAENGOLD, Phillip S., JD, Executive Director, Upstate Medical University, Syracuse, NY, p. A474

SCHAENGOLD, JD, Phillip S., Chief Operating Officer, Upstate Medical University, Syracuse, NY, p. A474

SCHAETZLE, Daniel J., Administrator, Community Hospital–Lakeview, Eufaula, OK, p. A530

SCHAFER, Michael, Chief Executive Officer and Administrator, Spooner Health System, Spooner, WI, p. A736

SCHAFFER, Arnold R., Chief Executive Officer, Providence Saint Joseph Medical Center, Burbank, CA, p. A55

SCHAFFER, Gregory F., President, Johns Hopkins Bayview Medical Center, Baltimore, MD, p. A303

SCHAFFNER, R.N., Julie W., Chief Operating Officer and Chief Nurse Executive, Advocate Lutheran General Hospital, Park Ridge, IL, p. A204

SCHAFFNER, Leroy, Chief Executive Officer, Coon Memorial Hospital and Home, Dalhart, TX, p. A631

SCHAFFNER, Richard, Executive Vice President, Beebe Medical Center, Lewes, DE, p. A119

SCHAFFNER, Rick, Associate Executive Director and Chief Operating Officer, Carlisle Regional Medical Center, Carlisle, PA, p. A554

SCHALK, Lawrence E.
Chief Financial Officer, Florida Hospital – Deland, De Land, FL, p. A127
Senior Vice President and Chief Financial Officer, Florida Hospital Fish Memorial, Orange City, FL, p. A140

SCHAMEL, Kaylyn, Director Human Resources, South Central Kansas Regional Medical Center, Arkansas City, KS, p. A244

SCHAMP, Cindy K., President, Alle–Kiski Medical Center, Natrona Heights, PA, p. A566

SCHANDLER, Jon B., President and Chief Executive Officer, White Plains Hospital Center, White Plains, NY, p. A476

SCHANWALD, Pamela R., Chief Executive Officer, Children's Home of Pittsburgh, Pittsburgh, PA, p. A571

SCHAPER, Robert F., President and Chief Executive Officer, Tomball Regional Hospital, Tomball, TX, p. A670

SCHAPPER, Robert A., Chief Executive Officer, Tahoe Forest Hospital District, Truckee, CA, p. A96

SCHARFF, Tom, Director Information Services, University Hospital and Medical Center, Tamarac, FL, p. A147

SCHARN, Lynn, Director Information Systems, Spencer Hospital, Spencer, IA, p. A242

SCHARWATH, Kim, Director Medical Records, St. James Parish Hospital, Lutcher, LA, p. A285

SCHATZLEIN, Michael H., M.D., Chief Executive Officer, Dupont Hospital, Fort Wayne, IN, p. A215

SCHAUER, Charles A., Ph.D., President and Chief Executive Officer, Brooks Rehabilitation Hospital, Jacksonville, FL, p. A132

SCHAUER, Raymond W., Vice President Finance, Sharon Regional Health System, Sharon, PA, p. A576

SCHAUER, Thomas, Assistant Executive Director and Chief Financial Officer, Pleasant Valley Hospital, Point Pleasant, WV, p. A719

SCHAUMBURG, John, Administrator, Kula Hospital, Kula, HI, p. A175

SCHAY, Maria, Chief Information Officer, Veterans Administration New York Harbor Healthcare System, New York, NY, p. A466

SCHECHTERLY, Charles, Director Information Systems, St. Agnes Continuing Care Center, Philadelphia, PA, p. A569

SCHECTER, M.D., Lawrence, Chief Medical Officer, Providence Everett Medical Center, Everett, WA, p. A703

SCHEEL, Paul D., Associate Director for Operations, Veterans Affairs Ann Arbor Healthcare System, Ann Arbor, MI, p. A327

SCHEETS, Frank, Vice President, Lutheran Medical Center, New York, NY, p. A461

SCHEFFLER, Tom, Chief Fiscal Officer, Veterans Affairs Maryland Health Care System–Baltimore Division, Baltimore, MD, p. A305

SCHEIG, William, Chief of Staff, Monticello Big Lake Hospital, Monticello, MN, p. A358

SCHELLING, LaRae, Vice President Operations and Chief Nursing Officer, Marshalltown Medical and Surgical Center, Marshalltown, IA, p. A237

SCHELLPFEFFER, M.D., Donald A., Medical Director, Sioux Falls Surgical Center, Sioux Falls, SD, p. A599

SCHEMPP, Jennifer, Manager Information Systems, St. Alexius Hospital, Saint Louis, MO, p. A392

SCHENEMAN, Karolyn, Vice President Patient Care Services and Chief Nursing Officer, South Coast Medical Center, Laguna Beach, CA, p. A66

SCHENK, M.D., Curtis, Chief of Staff, Watonga Municipal Hospital, Watonga, OK, p. A541

SCHERNECK, Michael D.
Vice President and Chief Financial Officer, Southeast Georgia Health System Brunswick Campus, Brunswick, GA, p. A157
Vice President Finance, Southeast Georgia Health System Camden Campus, Saint Marys, GA, p. A168

SCHERTZ, David A., Administrator, OSF Saint Anthony Medical Center, Rockford, IL, p. A206

SCHEUEN, Marlyn, Chief Financial Officer, St. John's Hospital – Aurora, Aurora, MO, p. A378

SCHEVITZ, Chuck, Manager Human Resources, University Specialty Hospital, Baltimore, MD, p. A305

SCHIEBEL, Annette, Controller, Elmbrook Memorial Hospital, Brookfield, WI, p. A723

SCHIFFNER, Wayne C., Executive Vice President, South Jersey Healthcare, Bridgeton, NJ, p. A426

SCHILLING, M.D., Debra, Medical Director, Regional Rehabilitation Hospital, Phenix City, AL, p. A23

SCHINDEL, Lester P., President and Chief Executive Officer, New England Sinai Hospital and Rehabilitation Center, Stoughton, MA, p. A324

SCHINDELAR, Carl J., President, Franklin Square Hospital Center, Baltimore, MD, p. A302

SCHIRRIPA, Robert, Administrative Director Finance, Community Hospital of Long Beach, Long Beach, CA, p. A68

SCHITTONE, Angelo, Chief Information Officer, Irvington General Hospital, Irvington, NJ, p. A430

SCHLADER, Rod G., Chief Financial Officer, Mercy Medical Center – North Iowa, Mason City, IA, p. A238

SCHLAGER, M.D., Robert, Chief of Staff, Calvert Memorial Hospital, Prince Frederick, MD, p. A309

SCHLAPPER, M.D., Brent, Chief of Staff, Florida Hospital – Deland, De Land, FL, p. A127

SCHLAUTMAN, Jacolyn M.
Executive Vice President and Administrator, St. Joseph's Hospital, Breese, IL, p. A185
Executive Vice President and Administrator, St. Joseph's Hospital, Breese, IL, p. A185

SCHLEGEL, Dale, Associate Hospital Director Operations, Temple East, Northeastern Hospital, Philadelphia, PA, p. A570

SCHLEGEL, Susie, Human Resources Director, Ness County Hospital, Ness City, KS, p. A253

SCHLEGELMILCH, M.D., John, Medical Director for Healthcare Improvement Services, Cheshire Medical Center, Keene, NH, p. A421

SCHLEGELMILCH, Kurt W., CHE, Director, Veterans Affairs Sierra Nevada Health Care System, Reno, NV, p. A418

SCHLENKER, Jim, Chief Financial Officer, Sunnyside Community Hospital, Sunnyside, WA, p. A710

SCHLENKER, John, Chief Information Officer, St. Mary's Medical Center, Knoxville, TN, p. A610

SCHLENKER, Patrick A., President, Northwest Florida Community Hospital, Chipley, FL, p. A125

SCHLESENBERG, Avery
Chief Financial Officer, Sutter Lakeside Hospital, Lakeport, CA, p. A67
Chief Financial Officer, Sutter Medical Center of Santa Rosa, Santa Rosa, CA, p. A93

SCHLEY, Kurt, Chief Operating Officer, Hutcheson Medical Center, Fort Oglethorpe, GA, p. A162

SCHLICHTING, Nancy M., President and Chief Executive Officer, Henry Ford Health System, Detroit, MI, p. B59

SCHLUTER, Robin M.
Chief Operating Officer, Truman Medical Center–Lakewood, Kansas City, MO, p. A385
Chief Operating Officer, Truman Medical Center–Lakewood, Kansas City, MO, p. A385

SCHMALL, Cindy, Vice President Human Resources, Hi–Desert Medical Center, Joshua Tree, CA, p. A65

SCHMALTZ, Vern J., Vice President Finance, Tipton County Memorial Hospital, Tipton, IN, p. A226

SCHMETZER, Alan D., M.D., Superintendent, Larue D. Carter Memorial Hospital, Indianapolis, IN, p. A218

SCHMIDLY, Scott, Chief Operating Officer, Medical Center of Arlington, Arlington, TX, p. A622

SCHMIDT, Barbara, Administrator, Lifecare Hospitals of Fort Worth, Fort Worth, TX, p. A640

SCHMIDT, Brent, Chief Financial Officer, St. Joseph's Area Health Services, Park Rapids, MN, p. A359

SCHMIDT, Craig W. C., President and Chief Executive Officer, Berlin Memorial Hospital, Berlin, WI, p. A723

SCHMIDT, Esther, Supervisor Human Resources, Kennewick General Hospital, Kennewick, WA, p. A703

SCHMIDT, Gene E., President, Hutchinson Hospital Corporation, Hutchinson, KS, p. A249

SCHMIDT, Joan E., Director, Human Resources, St. Francis Health Care Centre, Green Springs, OH, p. A514

SCHMIDT, Julie A., Chief Executive Officer, Woodwinds Health Campus, Woodbury, MN, p. A365

SCHMIDT, Kristi, Vice President Human Resources, Missouri Baptist Medical Center, Town and Country, MO, p. A394

SCHMIDT, Mark, President and Chief Executive Officer, Gettysburg Medical Center, Gettysburg, SD, p. A596

SCHMIDT, Michael A., President, Saint Joseph's Hospital, Marshfield, WI, p. A729

SCHMIDT Jr, Richard O.
President and Chief Executive Officer, United Health System–Kenosha Campus, Kenosha, WI, p. A727
President and Chief Executive Officer, United Hospital System, St. Catherine's Medical Center Campus, Pleasant Prairie, WI, p. A734

SCHMIDT, CPA, Stephen, Chief Financial Officer, Pekin Hospital, Pekin, IL, p. A204

SCHMIDT, Terri, Director, U. S. Public Health Service Indian Hospital, Clinton, OK, p. A529

SCHMIDT, Timothy E., Chief Executive Officer, Heartland Regional Medical Center, Marion, IL, p. A200

SCHMIDT, Wesley, Director Human Resources, Simi Valley Hospital and Health Care Services, Simi Valley, CA, p. A94

SCHMIDT, William, President and Chief Executive Officer, New London Family Medical Center, New London, WI, p. A732

SCHMIER, Joe, Director Human Resources, Capital Medical Center, Olympia, WA, p. A705

SCHMITT, M.D., Gary, Medical Staff President, St. Luke Hospital West, Florence, KY, p. A264

SCHMITT, Henry, Assistant Administrator and Director Finance, Inova Fair Oaks Hospital, Fairfax, VA, p. A687

SCHMITT, III, Joseph, Vice President Finance and Chief Financial Officer, Henry Ford Hospital, Detroit, MI, p. A331

SCHMITT, Jr, M.D., Milton G., Chief Medical Officer, Rockford Memorial Hospital, Rockford, IL, p. A206

SCHMITT, Rob, Chief Financial Officer, Gibson Area Hospital and Health Services, Gibson City, IL, p. A195

SCHMITT, Thomas, Chief Executive Officer, Haywood Park Community Hospital, Brownsville, TN, p. A602

SCHMITT, M.D., Tim, Medical Staff President, Tri–County Hospital, Wadena, MN, p. A364

SCHMITTER, Angela, Director Health Information Management, Scotland County Memorial Hospital, Memphis, MO, p. A387

SCHMITZ, Brenda, Financial Manager, Central Alabama Veterans Health Care System, Montgomery, AL, p. A22

SCHMITZ, Vince, Vice President and Chief Financial Officer, Tacoma General Hospital, Tacoma, WA, p. A710

SCHMUCKEN, M.D., M Lee, Chief of Staff, Arkansas Valley Regional Medical Center, La Junta, CO, p. A107

SCHNECK, David, Director Health Information Management and Technology, Good Samaritan Regional Medical Center, Pottsville, PA, p. A573

SCHNEDLER, Lisa, Administrator, Van Buren County Hospital, Keosauqua, IA, p. A236

SCHNEIDER, Alan, Vice President Operations, Hinsdale Hospital, Hinsdale, IL, p. A197

SCHNEIDER, Barbara, R.N., Chief Executive Officer, Community and Mission Hospitals of Huntington Park, Huntington Park, CA, p. A64

SCHNEIDER, C. W., President and Chief Executive Officer, Northwest Hospital, Seattle, WA, p. A707

SCHNEIDER, David R., Executive Director, Langlade Memorial Hospital, Antigo, WI, p. A722

SCHNEIDER, Doug, Director Information Systems, Raulerson Hospital, Okeechobee, FL, p. A140

SCHNEIDER, Karen, Chief Operating Officer, Children's Home of Pittsburgh, Pittsburgh, PA, p. A571

SCHNEIDER, Ken, Chair, Department of Human Resources, Saint Marys Hospital, Rochester, MN, p. A360

SCHNEIDER, Palmer, Chief Executive Officer, Hamilton Hospital, Webster City, IA, p. A243

SCHNEIDER, Thomas R., Administrator, Shriners Hospitals for Children, Honolulu, Honolulu, HI, p. A174

SCHNEIDERMAN, M.D., Henry, Vice President Medical Services and Physician in Chief, Hebrew Health Care, West Hartford, CT, p. A117

SCHNIEDERS, Michael H., Executive Vice President and Administrator, Good Samaritan Hospital, Suffern, NY, p. A473

SCHOCK, Carl, Superintendent, Austin State Hospital, Austin, TX, p. A622

SCHOEN, M.D., Greg, Regional Medical Director, Fairview Northland Regional Health Care, Princeton, MN, p. A360

SCHOENHOLTZ, Jack C., M.D., Medical Director, Administrator, President and Chief Executive Officer, Rye Hospital Center, Rye, NY, p. A471

SCHOENIG, Tom, Director Information Systems, Driscoll Children's Hospital, Corpus Christi, TX, p. A630

SCHOENMAKERS, Steve, Superintendent, Colorado Mental Health Institute at Pueblo, Pueblo, CO, p. A109

SCHOFIELD, Sherry, Director Human Resources, Memorial Hospital, Martinsville, VA, p. A691

SCHOLL, Edward C., Assistant Administrator Finance, Jackson Hospital and Clinic, Montgomery, AL, p. A22

SCHOLL, Sonja, Administrator, West Virginia Rehabilitation Center, Institute, WV, p. A716

SCHOLL, R.N., Susan K., Executive Vice President and Chief Operating Officer, SSM St. Mary's Health Center, Saint Louis, MO, p. A392

SCHOLTEN, Randall J., Chief Financial Officer, Southern Coos Hospital and Health Center, Bandon, OR, p. A542

SCHOLTZ, Simon, Vice President and Chief Financial Officer, Lawrence Memorial Hospital, Lawrence, KS, p. A251

SCHON, John, Administrator and Chief Executive Officer, Dickinson County Healthcare System, Iron Mountain, MI, p. A337

SCHOOLER, Rick, Vice President and Chief Information Officer, Orlando Regional Medical Center, Orlando, FL, p. A141

SCHOONMAKER, John T., Senior Vice President and Chief Financial Officer, Texas Scottish Rite Hospital for Children, Dallas, TX, p. A634

SCHORI, M.D., Melissa, Medical Director, Lincoln Medical and Mental Health Center, New York, NY, p. A461

SCHORN, M.D., Larry, Vice President Medical Affairs, Baylor Medical Center at Irving, Irving, TX, p. A649

SCHOTT, Carol, Chief Financial Officer and Assistant Administrator, Odessa Memorial Healthcare Center, Odessa, WA, p. A705

SCHOULTIES, M.D., Daniel L., Vice President Medical Affairs, Good Samaritan Hospital, Dayton, OH, p. A512

SCHRADER, Ann M.
Vice President and Chief Operating Officer, Bethesda Rehabilitation Hospital, Saint Paul, MN, p. A361
Vice President and Chief Operating Officer, St. Joseph's Hospital, Saint Paul, MN, p. A362

SCHRAMM, Howard K., Executive Vice President and Chief Financial Officer, St. Luke's Episcopal Hospital, Houston, TX, p. A647

SCHRAMM, Michael, Chief Executive Officer, Meeker County Memorial Hospital, Litchfield, MN, p. A355

SCHRAMM, Steven R., Chief Financial Officer, Mountain View Hospital, Payson, UT, p. A678

SCHRAMM, William, Vice President Operations, Henry Ford Hospital, Detroit, MI, p. A331

SCHRECK, Ted
Chief Executive Officer, University of Southern California–Norris Comprehensive Cancer Center and Hospital, Los Angeles, CA, p. A73
Chief Executive Officer, USC University Hospital, Los Angeles, CA, p. A73

SCHREEG, Timothy M., President and Chief Executive Officer, Jasper County Hospital, Rensselaer, IN, p. A224

SCHREIBMAN, M.D., Paul, Chief of Staff, Highland District Hospital, Hillsboro, OH, p. A515

SCHREIVOGEL, Herman
Chief Executive Officer, Lincoln Community Hospital and Nursing Home, Hugo, CO, p. A107
Administrator and Chief Executive Officer, Lincoln Community Hospital and Nursing Home, Hugo, CO, p. A107

SCHROCK, Richard, Chief Financial Officer, Ohio State University Medical Center, Columbus, OH, p. A511

SCHRODER, Kathy, Director, Administrative Services and Human Resources, Hebrew Health Care, West Hartford, CT, p. A117

SCHRODER, Loren D.
Chief Financial Officer, Phelps Memorial Health Center, Holdrege, NE, p. A408
Chief Financial Officer, Phelps Memorial Health Center, Holdrege, NE, p. A408

SCHROEDER, Connie L., Chief Executive Officer, Illini Community Hospital, Pittsfield, IL, p. A205

SCHROEDER, David, Ph.D., Chief Executive Officer, Highland Ridge Hospital, Midvale, UT, p. A677

SCHROEDER, Larry, Chief Operating Officer, Sauk Prairie Memorial Hospital, Prairie Du Sac, WI, p. A734

SCHROEDER, Richard J., Chief Financial Officer, Veterans Affairs Medical Center, Salem, VA, p. A696

SCHROEDL, M.D., Greg, Vice President Medical and Chief Quality Officer, Northwest Hospital, Seattle, WA, p. A707

SCHROER, Patricia A., President and Chief Executive Officer, Mercy Hospital Anderson, Cincinnati, OH, p. A507

SCHROFFEL, Bruce, Director and Chief Executive Officer, Stony Brook University Hospital, Stony Brook, NY, p. A473

SCHRUPP, Richard, President and Chief Executive Officer, Mercy Hospital of Franciscan Sisters, Oelwein, IA, p. A239

SCHUELER, Joe, Chief Financial Officer, Morrow County Hospital, Mount Gilead, OH, p. A519

SCHUETT, Susan M., Assistant Administrator Information Systems, Olmsted Medical Center, Rochester, MN, p. A360

SCHUETZ, M.D., Perry N., Chief Medical Staff, Central Kansas Medical Center, Great Bend, KS, p. A247

SCHUH, Deb, Director Human Resources, Genesis Medical Center, DeWitt, De Witt, IA, p. A232

SCHULER, William J., Chief Executive Officer, Portsmouth Regional Hospital, Portsmouth, NH, p. A423

SCHULLER, David E., M.D., Chief Executive Officer, Ohio State University James Cancer Hospital, Columbus, OH, p. A510

SCHULTE, James E., Administrator, Redwood Area Hospital, Redwood Falls, MN, p. A360

SCHULTE, Jody, Director Employee Relations, Fort Madison Community Hospital, Fort Madison, IA, p. A234

SCHULTE, Patricia A., Chief Operations and Chief Nursing Executive, Provena Covenant Medical Center, Urbana, IL, p. A209

SCHULTHEIS, Hal, Director Information Systems, Hendersonville Medical Center, Hendersonville, TN, p. A607

SCHULTZ, Bradley, Chief Financial Officer, Skyline Medical Center, Nashville, TN, p. A615

SCHULTZ, Greg, Chief Financial Officer, Colorado River Medical Center, Needles, CA, p. A77

SCHULTZ, Mary Kay, Director Human Resources, Sturgis Hospital, Sturgis, MI, p. A346

SCHULTZ, Michael H., Chief Executive Officer, Park Ridge Hospital, Fletcher, NC, p. A483

SCHULTZ, Rachelle H., President and Chief Executive Officer, Winona Health, Winona, MN, p. A365

SCHULTZ, Sheri, Director Health Information, Salem Township Hospital, Salem, IL, p. A207

SCHULTZ, Steven J., Chief Executive Officer, LifeCare Hospitals of Milwaukee, Milwaukee, WI, p. A731

SCHULZ, Charles K., Chief Executive Officer, York General Health Care Services, York, NE, p. A414

SCHULZ, Janet, Executive Vice President, Oconomowoc Memorial Hospital, Oconomowoc, WI, p. A733

SCHULZ, Richard, Administrator, HEALTHSOUTH Scottsdale Rehabilitation Hospital, Scottsdale, AZ, p. A36

SCHUMACHER, Larry P., R.N., President and Chief Executive Officer, Via Christi Regional Medical Center, Wichita, KS, p. A259

SCHUMACHER, Paul, Administrative Director, Tuomey Healthcare System, Sumter, SC, p. A592

SCHUMANN, Dan, Director Information Systems, Valley Hospital, Palmer, AK, p. A28

SCHUMM, M.D., Herbert, Vice Persident Medical Affairs, St. Rita's Medical Center, Lima, OH, p. A516

SCHURMEIER, L. Jon, President and Chief Executive Officer, Southwest General Health Center, Middleburg Heights, OH, p. A518

SCHURRA, Ronald J., Chief Executive Officer, Hilo Medical Center, Hilo, HI, p. A173

SCHUSTER, Christine C., President and Chief Executive Officer, Emerson Hospital, Concord, MA, p. A317

SCHUSTER, Jolene, Director Information Technology, Trego County–Lemke Memorial Hospital, Wakeeney, KS, p. A258

SCHUSTER, Robert, Director, Veterans Affairs Medical Center, Northport, NY, p. A467

SCHUTTER, Mark E., Ph.D., Superintendent, Larned State Hospital, Larned, KS, p. A251

SCHUUR, Bill, Director of Material Management, Borgess–Lee Memorial Hospital, Dowagiac, MI, p. A332

SCHWAB, Caryn A., Executive Director, The Mount Sinai Hospital of Queens, New York, NY, p. A466

SCHWADRON, Kate, Director Human Resources, Kenneth Hall Regional Hospital, East St. Louis, IL, p. A192

SCHWAIGER, M.D., Jim, Chief of Staff, Huron Regional Medical Center, Huron, SD, p. A596

SCHWANER, III, Charles, Chief Financial Officer, Englewood Community Hospital, Englewood, FL, p. A128

SCHWANKE, Dan, Executive Director, Defiance Regional Medical Center, Defiance, OH, p. A512

SCHWARM, Tony, President, Missouri Baptist Hospital–Sullivan, Sullivan, MO, p. A394

SCHWARTZ, Andrew, Medical Staff President, Shawnee Mission Medical Center, Shawnee Mission, KS, p. A257

SCHWARTZ, John N., President, Advocate Trinity Hospital, Chicago, IL, p. A186

SCHWARTZ, M.D., Kenneth V., Medical Director, Griffin Hospital, Derby, CT, p. A112

SCHWARTZ, Mark, Administrator, Aurora Medical Center of Washington County, Hartford, WI, p. A727

SCHWARTZ, M.D., Matthew, Medical Director, Chestnut Hill Rehabilitation Hospital, Glenside, PA, p. A559

SCHWARTZ, Michael J., President and Chief Executive Officer, Prince William Hospital, Manassas, VA, p. A691

SCHWARTZ, Peter, Chief Information Officer, Friends Behavioral Health System, Philadelphia, PA, p. A568

SCHWARTZ, M.D., Ronald, Medical Director, Masonic Healthcare Center, Wallingford, CT, p. A117

SCHWARTZ, Sharon, Medical Records and Information Systems Director, Trinity Community Medical Center of Brenham, Brenham, TX, p. A626

SCHWARZKOPF, Karl H., Regional Hospital Administrator, Northwest Georgia Regional Hospital, Rome, GA, p. A168

SCHWEIGERT, Byron F., Chief Executive Officer, Long Beach Memorial Medical Center, Long Beach, CA, p. A68

SCHWEITZER, Alex, Superintendent and Chief Executive Officer, North Dakota State Hospital, Jamestown, ND, p. A499

SCHWIENTEK, Barbara, Chief Executive Officer, Monticello Big Lake Hospital, Monticello, MN, p. A358

SCHWIETERMAN, James, Chief of Staff, Mercer County Joint Township Community Hospital, Coldwater, OH, p. A510

SCHWINGLER, Joyce, Finance Officer, Eureka Community Health Services/Avera Health, Eureka, SD, p. A595

SCIALDONE, Michael A., Chief Financial Officer, Penrose–St. Francis Health Services, Colorado Springs, CO, p. A102

SCIBELLI, Tony, Vice President Human Resources, Faxton–St. Luke's Healthcare, Utica, NY, p. A474

SCIESZINSKI, Robert C., Vice President Finance, Door County Memorial Hospital, Sturgeon Bay, WI, p. A736

SCIFRES, Kim, Director Financial and Support Services, Washington County Memorial Hospital, Salem, IN, p. A224

SCIOLA, Anthony, President, Shaughnessy–Kaplan Rehabilitation Hospital, Salem, MA, p. A323

SCIULLO, Louis A., Associate Director Operations, Excela Latrobe Area Hospital, Latrobe, PA, p. A563

SCIULLO, Susan G., Chief Financial Officer, DeKalb Medical Center, Decatur, GA, p. A160

SCIURBA, John, Vice President and Chief Financial Officer, White Plains Hospital Center, White Plains, NY, p. A476

SCLAIR, Max, Vice President, Jamaica Hospital Medical Center, New York, NY, p. A460

SCLAMA, M.D., Tony, Vice President Medical Affairs, Franklin Square Hospital Center, Baltimore, MD, p. A302

SCOCCIA, D.O., Vincent, Chief Medical Staff, Nye Regional Medical Center, Tonopah, NV, p. A419

SCONIERS, Alan, Director Human Resources, HEALTHSOUTH Medical Center, Birmingham, AL, p. A15

SCOPAC, Paul A., Chief Operating Officer, Oneida Healthcare Center, Oneida, NY, p. A468

SCOPPETTA, M.D., Daniel J., Chief of Staff, Bristol Hospital, Bristol, CT, p. A112

SCOTT, Camille, Administrator, Forks Community Hospital, Forks, WA, p. A703

SCOTT, Charles F., President and Chief Executive Officer, Glenwood Regional Medical Center, West Monroe, LA, p. A294

SCOTT, Colleen M., Vice President Finance, Waterbury Hospital, Waterbury, CT, p. A117

SCOTT, Daryl, Human Resources Director, Jefferson Regional Medical Center, Pine Bluff, AR, p. A49

SCOTT, Ginger, Director Human Resources, Columbus County Hospital, Whiteville, NC, p. A493

SCOTT, Harold, Chief Information Officer, Medical College of Georgia Hospital and Clinics, Augusta, GA, p. A155

SCOTT, Henry, Management Information Systems Director, Newnan Hospital East, Newnan, GA, p. A167

SCOTT, Jackie, Risk Manager and Director of Information Services and Safety, Putnam General Hospital, Hurricane, WV, p. A716

SCOTT, Joseph F., Chief Executive Officer, Broward General Medical Center, Fort Lauderdale, FL, p. A128

SCOTT, Kathy
Administrator, Bluegrass Community Hospital, Versailles, KY, p. A275
Associate Administrator and Chief Nursing Officer, Banner Thunderbird Medical Center, Glendale, AZ, p. A31

SCOTT, Monica, Chief Financial Officer, Sayre Memorial Hospital, Sayre, OK, p. A538

SCOTT, Robert F., Director, Human Resources, St. Francis Hospital, Milwaukee, WI, p. A731

SCOTT, Ronald, Vice President Human Resources, Queen of the Valley Hospital, Napa, CA, p. A77

SCOTT, Vanda
Chief Executive Officer, Select Specialty Hospital–Knoxville, Knoxville, TN, p. A610
Chief Executive Officer, Select Specialty Hospital–North Knoxville, Knoxville, TN, p. A610

SCOVILL, Terry, Chief Executive Officer, Intracare Medical Center Hospital, Houston, TX, p. A645

SCREMIN, Karen, Chief Financial Officer, Banner Baywood Medical Center, Mesa, AZ, p. A32

SCRIBER, Betty P., FACHE, Chief Executive Officer, North Monroe Medical Center, Monroe, LA, p. A287

SCRUGGS, Sherry, Administrator, Gibson General Hospital, Trenton, TN, p. A618

SCUDESE, Frank, Director Fiscal Services, Bacharach Institute for Rehabilitation, Pomona, NJ, p. A435

SCULCO, M.D., Thomas P., Chief Medical Officer, Hospital for Special Surgery, New York, NY, p. A460

SCULLY, Charles, Chief Information Officer, Washoe Medical Center, Reno, NV, p. A418

SCZYGELSKI, Sidney C., Senior Vice President Finance and Chief Financial Officer, Aspirus Wausau Hospital, Wausau, WI, p. A737

SEABOLT, Shellie, Director Human Resources, Perry Memorial Hospital, Perry, OK, p. A537

SEAFORD, Jeff, Director Human Resources, Hugh Chatham Memorial Hospital, Elkin, NC, p. A482

SEAGLE, M.D., Melissa, President Medical Staff, Davie County Hospital, Mocksville, NC, p. A487

SEAGRAVES, David H., President and Chief Executive Officer, Sumter Regional Hospital, Americus, GA, p. A152

SEAL, Ronald T., Chief Executive Officer, Wesley Medical Center, Hattiesburg, MS, p. A369

SEALE, Corey A., Administrator, Moreno Valley Community Hospital, Moreno Valley, CA, p. A77

SEALE, Paul E., Chief Executive Officer, New Island Hospital, Bethpage, NY, p. A448

SEALS, Frank, Chief Financial Officer, Reeves County Hospital, Pecos, TX, p. A660

SEALS, Molly
Senior Vice President Human Resources and Organizational Development, St. Elizabeth Health Center, Youngstown, OH, p. A526
Senior Vice President Human Resources and Organizational Development, St. Joseph Health Center, Warren, OH, p. A524

SEALS–BROWN, Sylvia, Vice President Human Resources, East Pasco Medical Center, Zephyrhills, FL, p. A151

SEARLE, Anne, Vice President and Chief Information Officer, Holy Redeemer Hospital and Medical Center, Jenkintown, PA, p. A561

SEARLS, Barbara, Chief Financial Officer, SEARHC MT. Edgecumbe Hospital, Sitka, AK, p. A28

SEARLS, Gary, Chief Financial Officer, Doctors Hospital of Sarasota, Sarasota, FL, p. A146

SEARS, Frank
Vice President Information Services, Franklin Hospital, Benton, IL, p. A184
Vice President Information Services, St. Joseph Memorial Hospital, Murphysboro, IL, p. A202

SEARS, M.D., James, Chief of Staff, St. Joseph Hospital, Bangor, ME, p. A296

SEARS, Marilyn, Chief Financial Officer, Shelby Memorial Hospital, Shelbyville, IL, p. A207

SEARS, M.D., Stephen, Chief Medical Officer, MaineGeneral Medical Center–Waterville Campus, Waterville, ME, p. A301

SEASE, R.N., Laura, Vice President and Chief Operating Officer, Ranken Jordan, Maryland Heights, MO, p. A387

SEAVER, Roger E., President and Chief Executive Officer, Henry Mayo Newhall Memorial Hospital, Valencia, CA, p. A97

SEBASTIANELLI, Joseph T., President and Chief Executive Officer, Jefferson Health System, Wayne, PA, p. B63

SEBBAS, M.D., Leslie, Medical Director, Anna Jaques Hospital, Newburyport, MA, p. A321

SECHRIST, Cindy, Director Human Resources, Baptist Medical Center–Beaches, Jacksonville Beach, FL, p. A133

SECK, Lawrence E., Senior Vice President, Morton Hospital and Medical Center, Taunton, MA, p. A324

SECK, William G., Chief Financial Officer, Adams Memorial Hospital, Decatur, IN, p. A214

SECKINGER, John, Vice President Corporate Services and Chief Financial Officer, St. Cloud Hospital, Saint Cloud, MN, p. A361

SECKINGER, Mark R., Administrator and Chief Executive Officer, Hardin Memorial Hospital, Kenton, OH, p. A515

SECREST, Stephanie, Human Resources Director, Hennepin County Medical Center, Minneapolis, MN, p. A357

SEDA, Michael, Chief Executive Officer, Sioux Center Community Hospital and Health Center/Avera Health, Sioux Center, IA, p. A241

SEDGWICK, Kevin, Chief Financial Officer, Maine Coast Memorial Hospital, Ellsworth, ME, p. A298

SEEHAFER, Kevin
Chief Financial Officer, Kenmare Community Hospital, Kenmare, ND, p. A499
Controller, Trinity Health, Minot, ND, p. A499

SEGAL, Janet Z., Chief Operating Officer, Four Winds Hospital, Katonah, NY, p. A455

SEGELEON, Kurt, Director Health Information Management, Kindred Hospital–Pittsburgh, Oakdale, PA, p. A566

SEGERS, Tina, Accounting Officer, Wiregrass Medical Center, Geneva, AL, p. A19

SEGLER, Randall K., Chief Executive Officer, Comanche County Memorial Hospital, Lawton, OK, p. A532

SEGURA, Ezra, Administrator, Heber Valley Medical Center, Heber City, UT, p. A676

SEIBER, Tom, Chief Executive Officer, Select Specialty Hospital–Zanesville, Zanesville, OH, p. A526

SEIDLER, Richard A., FACHE, Chief Executive Officer, Allen Memorial Hospital, Waterloo, IA, p. A242

SEIGLER, Leslie, Public Relations, Edgefield County Hospital, Edgefield, SC, p. A587

SEILER, Edward H., Director, Veterans Affairs Medical Center, West Palm Beach, FL, p. A150

SEILER, Gregory A., Chief Operating Officer, Riverside Community Hospital, Riverside, CA, p. A84

SEIM, Richard L., President and Chief Executive Officer, York Hospital, York, PA, p. A580

SEITZ, Stewart R., Chief Executive Officer, Gladys Spellman Specialty Hospital and Nursing Center, Cheverly, MD, p. A306

SEITZINGER, James M., President and Chief Executive Officer, Sacred Heart Hospital, Allentown, PA, p. A551

SELBERG, Jeffrey D., President and Chief Executive Officer, Exempla Healthcare, Inc., Denver, CO, p. B44

SELDEN, Thomas A., Chief Operating Officer, Cleveland Clinic Health System, Cleveland, OH, p. B29

SELENKE, M.D., Darcy, Chief of Staff, St. John's Maude Norton Memorial Hospital, Columbus, KS, p. A245

SELEY, Jim, Chief Information Officer, Clay County Medical Center, Clay Center, KS, p. A245

SELF, Doug, Executive Vice President and Chief Operating Officer, River Oaks Hospital, Jackson, MS, p. A371

SELIGMAN, Joel, President and Chief Executive Officer, Northern Westchester Hospital, Mount Kisco, NY, p. A457

SELIGMAN, M.D., Morris H.
Senior Vice President and Chief Operating Officer and Chief Medical Officer, Salina Regional Health Center, Salina, KS, p. A256
Senior Vice President and Chief Operating Officer and Chief Medical Officer, Salina Regional Health Center, Salina, KS, p. A256
Director Medical Affairs, Southeast Missouri Hospital, Cape Girardeau, MO, p. A379

SELL, Paula, Director Human Resources, Allen County Hospital, Iola, KS, p. A249

SELLA, John, Chief Financial Officer, Jefferson Memorial Hospital, Ranson, WV, p. A719

SELLARDS, Michael G., President and Chief Executive Officer, St. Mary's Medical Center, Huntington, WV, p. A716

SELLERS, Bill, Chief Financial Officer, Grady General Hospital, Cairo, GA, p. A157

SELLERS, David, Director Information Services, Shelby Baptist Medical Center, Alabaster, AL, p. A13

SELLERS, Jr, J William
Senior Vice President and Chief Financial Officer, John D. Archbold Memorial Hospital, Thomasville, GA, p. A170
Senior Vice President and Chief Financial Officer, Mitchell County Hospital, Camilla, GA, p. A157

SELLERS, M.D., Larry W., Chief Medical Officer, Mercy Medical Center–Sioux City, Sioux City, IA, p. A241

SELLERS, Robert R., Regional Health Administrator, Alegent Health Community Memorial Hospital, Missouri Valley, IA, p. A238

SELLERS, William H., Senior Vice President, Early Memorial Hospital, Blakely, GA, p. A156

SELLICK, Kathleen, Executive Director, University of Washington Medical Center, Seattle, WA, p. A708

SELLNER, William
Vice President and Chief Financial Officer, Del E. Webb Memorial Hospital, Sun City West, AZ, p. A37
Vice President and Chief Financial Officer, Walter O. Boswell Memorial Hospital, Sun City, AZ, p. A37

SELMAN, Dave, Corporate Vice President Information Systems, Fostoria Community Hospital, Fostoria, OH, p. A514

SELMAN, David B.
Chief Executive Officer, Hi–Desert Medical Center, Joshua Tree, CA, p. A65
Chief Executive Officer, Hi–Desert Medical Center, Joshua Tree, CA, p. A65

SELMAN, David G.
Vice President Information, Flower Hospital, Sylvania, OH, p. A522
Corporate Vice President Information Resources, The Toledo Hospital, Toledo, OH, p. A523

SELMAN, J. Peter
Chief Executive Officer, Baptist Cherokee, Centre, AL, p. A16
Chief Executive Officer, Baptist DeKalb Medical Center, Fort Payne, AL, p. A18

SELTZER, Charlotte, Executive Director, Creedmoor Psychiatric Center, New York, NY, p. A459

SELZ, Timothy P., President and Chief Executive Officer, Provena Mercy Center, Aurora, IL, p. A183

SELZER, Stephen R.
Chief Executive Officer, Bellaire Medical Center, Houston, TX, p. A644
Chief Executive Officer, St Luke's Community Medical Center–The Woodlands, The Woodlands, TX, p. A670

SEMENZA, Peter, Vice President Financial Operations, Mount Auburn Hospital, Cambridge, MA, p. A316

SEMRAD, Marianne, Associate Director for Administrative Services, Veterans Affairs Medical Center, North Chicago, IL, p. A203

SENCHAK, David, Vice President Ancillary and Support Services, McLaren Regional Medical Center, Flint, MI, p. A333

SENCHAK, Michael, President and Chief Executive Officer, Mahoning Valley Hospital, Youngstown, OH, p. A525

SENDACH, Jon, Associate Executive Director Finance, Glen Cove Hospital, Glen Cove, NY, p. A453

SENELICK, Richard, Medical Director, HEALTHSOUTH Rehabilitation Institute of San Antonio, San Antonio, TX, p. A664

SENESAC, Marc, Vice President Human Resources, Advocate Illinois Masonic Medical Center, Chicago, IL, p. A186

SENETTE, Robbie, R.N., Administrator, Louisiana Rehabilitation Hospital of Morgan City, Morgan City, LA, p. A287

SENGER, Richard, Chief Financial Officer, Portsmouth Regional Hospital, Portsmouth, NH, p. A423

SENGER, Tricia, Chief Financial Officer, Elmore Medical Center, Mountain Home, ID, p. A180

SENGEWALT, Mike, Senior Vice President and Chief Financial Officer, Fairmont General Hospital, Fairmont, WV, p. A715

SENKER, Thomas J., President and Chief Executive Officer, Forbes Regional Hospital, Monroeville, PA, p. A565

SENNEFF, Robert G., CHE, President and Chief Executive Officer, Perry Memorial Hospital, Princeton, IL, p. A205

SENSOR, Wayne A., President and Chief Executive Officer, Alegent Health, Omaha, NE, p. B7

SENTELL, John, Commanding Officer, Naval Hospital, Jacksonville, FL, p. A132

SEPICH, CHE, Charles E., Associate Director, South Texas Veterans Health Care System, San Antonio, TX, p. A665

SEPP Jr, Howard W., Administrator, Southeast Georgia Health System Camden Campus, Saint Marys, GA, p. A168

SEPPALA, M.D., Fay E., Chief Medical Officer, St. Joseph Health System, Tawas City, MI, p. A346

SEPULVEDA, Terry, Chief Operating Officer, Barlow Respiratory Hospital, Los Angeles, CA, p. A69

SEQUIN, Donny, Chief Operating Officer, Scott and White Memorial Hospital, Temple, TX, p. A669

SERAPHINE, Jeffrey G., Chief Executive Officer, Lake Cumberland Regional Hospital, Somerset, KY, p. A274

SERFLING, G. Aubrey, President and Chief Executive Officer, Eisenhower Memorial Hospital and Betty Ford Center at Eisenhower, Rancho Mirage, CA, p. A83

SERGEANT, Jim, Administrator, Salina Surgical Hospital, Salina, KS, p. A256

SERLE, John, President and Chief Executive Officer, Lourdes Medical Center, Pasco, WA, p. A705

SERNULKA, John M.
President and Chief Executive Officer, Carroll Hospital Center, Westminster, MD, p. A311
President and Chief Executive Officer, Carroll Hospital Center, Westminster, MD, p. A311

SERRILL, G B., Chief Operating Officer, Wesley Medical Center, Wichita, KS, p. A260

SESSIONS, David, Administrator, St. John North Shores Hospital, Harrison Township, MI, p. A336

SETTLE, Andrea, Director Human Resources, Taylor Regional Hospital, Campbellsville, KY, p. A262

SETTLE, Brian, Vice President Human Resources, Naples Community Hospital, Naples, FL, p. A139

SETTLES, Laura, Director Human Resources, Medical Center of McKinney, McKinney, TX, p. A656

SETZKORN–MEYER, Marsha, Public Relations and Marketing Director, Hillsboro Community Medical Center, Hillsboro, KS, p. A248

SEUBERT, Greg, Chief Financial Officer, Washington County Hospital, Washington, IA, p. A242

SEVCO, Mark, President, UPMC Braddock, Braddock, PA, p. A553

SEVERANCE, Matthew J., Chief Executive Officer, Roper Hospital, Charleston, SC, p. A585

SEVERNS, Mark D., Chief Executive Officer, Extended Care of Southwest Louiasiana, Lake Charles, LA, p. A285

SEVERUD, Michael, Director Management Information Systems, Brazosport Memorial Hospital, Lake Jackson, TX, p. A652

SEWARD Jr, James P., Chief Executive Officer, Town and Country Hospital, Tampa, FL, p. A148

SEWARD, M.D., Paul, Vice President Medical Affairs, Adirondack Medical Center, Saranac Lake, NY, p. A471

SEWELL, Hybart D., Administrator, Grove Hill Memorial Hospital, Grove Hill, AL, p. A19

SEWELL, Jon, Chief Executive Officer, Chalmette Medical Center, Chalmette, LA, p. A279

SEXTON, Bill, Chief Executive Officer, Wyoming Behavioral Institute, Casper, WY, p. A739

SEXTON, Charles F., Chief Executive Officer, Valley Regional Medical Center, Brownsville, TX, p. A627

SEXTON, Cindy, Chief Financial Officer, North Austin Medical Center, Austin, TX, p. A623

SEXTON, James J., President and Chief Executive Officer, Henry Ford Wyandotte Hospital, Wyandotte, MI, p. A348

SEXTON, Karen H., Ph.D., Vice President and Chief Executive Officer, University of Texas Medical Branch Hospitals, Galveston, TX, p. A641

SEXTON, Kevin J., President and Chief Executive Officer, Holy Cross Hospital, Silver Spring, MD, p. A311

SEXTON, Kim, Director of Human Resources, Hutcheson Medical Center, Fort Oglethorpe, GA, p. A162

SEXTON, William P., Chief Executive, Providence Seaside Hospital, Seaside, OR, p. A549

SEYAL, M.D., Saleem, President Medical Staff, Clark Memorial Hospital, Jeffersonville, IN, p. A219

SEYFERT, Beverly, Information Technology Leader, Kaiser Foundation Hospital, San Francisco, CA, p. A89

SEYLER, Dean, Chief Executive Officer, U. S. Public Health Service Indian Hospital–Whiteriver, Whiteriver, AZ, p. A39

SEYMOUR, Jose, Chief Information Resource Management, James A. Haley Veterans Hospital, Tampa, FL, p. A148

SHABINO, Charles L., M.D., President and Chief Executive Officer, Aspirus Wausau Hospital, Wausau, WI, p. A737

SHACHNER, M.D., Mark, Chief of Staff, Coral Springs Medical Center, Coral Springs, FL, p. A126

SHAFER, Duane, Chief Financial Officer, Mecosta County Medical Center, Big Rapids, MI, p. A328

SHAFER, James R., Administrator, Hamilton General Hospital, Hamilton, TX, p. A643

SHAFFER, David D., Chief Executive Officer, Stonewall Jackson Memorial Hospital, Weston, WV, p. A721

SHAFFER, George, Director Information Technology, Madison County Hospital, London, OH, p. A516

SHAFFER, Linda, Director Human Resources, Defiance Regional Medical Center, Defiance, OH, p. A512

SHAFFER, Scott, Vice President of Human Resources, Baptist Hospital of East Tennessee, Knoxville, TN, p. A609

SHAFFETT, Donald A., Chief Executive Officer, Clear Lake Regional Medical Center, Webster, TX, p. A673

SHAFFNER, Linda, Chief Information Officer, Keokuk Area Hospital, Keokuk, IA, p. A236

SHAH, M.D., Jayendra H., Chief Medical Officer, Southern Arizona Veterans Affairs Health Care System, Tucson, AZ, p. A38

SHAH, Paresh, Director Hospital Information Systems, Reston Hospital Center, Reston, VA, p. A694

SHAH, M.D., Rizwan, Medical Director, HEALTHSOUTH Rehabilitation Hospital of Arlington, Arlington, TX, p. A622

SHAH, Sanjay, Vice President and Chief Information Officer, Cabell Huntington Hospital, Huntington, WV, p. A716

SHAH, Shalin, Chief Financial Officer, Northside Hospital and Heart Institute, Saint Petersburg, FL, p. A145

SHALLASH, M.D., Anthony J., Chief Medical Officer, Brookhaven Memorial Hospital Medical Center, Patchogue, NY, p. A469

SHAMBLES, Terry W.
Chief Financial Officer, Craig General Hospital, Vinita, OK, p. A540
Chief Financial Officer, Craig General Hospital, Vinita, OK, p. A540

SHAMMAS, Karen, Chief Operating Officer, Huhukam Memorial Hospital, Sacaton, AZ, p. A35

SHANAHAN, M.D., M Kelly, Chief of Staff, Barton Memorial Hospital, South Lake Tahoe, CA, p. A94

SHANAHAN, Thomas, Chief Financial Officer and Senior Vice President, Raritan Bay Medical Center, Perth Amboy, NJ, p. A434

SHANKLE, Bob, Chief Information Management, Bassett Army Community Hospital, Fort Wainwright, AK, p. A27

SHANLEY, Kevin
Vice President Finance and Chief Financial Officer, Morristown Memorial Hospital, Morristown, NJ, p. A431
Vice President Finance and Chief Financial Officer, Mountainside Hospital, Montclair, NJ, p. A431
Vice President Finance and Chief Financial Officer, Overlook Hospital, Summit, NJ, p. A436

SHANNON, Greg, Director Human Resources, Ozarks Medical Center, West Plains, MO, p. A395

SHANNON, Ruth, Director Human Resources, Sharp Grossmont Hospital, La Mesa, CA, p. A66

SHAPIRO, Edward R., M.D., Medical Director and Chief Executive Officer, Austen Riggs Center, Stockbridge, MA, p. A324

SHAPIRO, M.D., Edward R.
Medical Director and Chief Executive Officer, Austen Riggs Center, Stockbridge, MA, p. A324
Medical Director and Chief Executive Officer, Austen Riggs Center, Stockbridge, MA, p. A324

SHAPIRO, Jack Nathan, Chief Executive Officer, Kindred Hospital–Chicago North, Chicago, IL, p. A187

SHAPIRO, Louis A., Chief Operating Officer, Clinical Enterprise, Geisinger Medical Center, Danville, PA, p. A556

SHAPIRO, M.D., Steven D., Interim Vice President for Medical Affairs, Roper Hospital, Charleston, SC, p. A585

SHARER, Beth, R.N., Interim Chief Executive Officer, Washington County Memorial Hospital, Salem, IN, p. A224

SHARFSTEIN, Steven S., M.D., President and Chief Executive Officer, Sheppard and Enoch Pratt Hospital, Baltimore, MD, p. A304

SHARIGIAN, Kenneth J., Chief Financial Officer, Stanford Hospital and Clinics, Palo Alto, CA, p. A80

SHARMA, M.D., Chandini, Chief of Staff, Comanche County Hospital, Coldwater, KS, p. A245

SHARMA, M.D., Ranjana, Chief of Staff, Washington Township Health Care District, Fremont, CA, p. A61

SHARMA, Timothy, M.D., President, Cambridge International, Inc,, Houston, TX, p. B20

SHARP, Charles S., Chief Executive Officer, Wilmington Treatment Center, Wilmington, NC, p. A494

SHARP, Gina, Controller, Linden Oaks Hospital at Edward, Naperville, IL, p. A202

SHARP, John, Chief Financial Officer, Brownwood Regional Medical Center, Brownwood, TX, p. A627

SHARP, Joseph, Chief Executive Officer, Capital Medical Center, Olympia, WA, p. A705

SHARP, Joseph W., Administrator, Runnells Specialized Hospital of Union County, Berkeley Heights, NJ, p. A425

SHARP, Julie, Director Business Operations, Falls Community Hospital and Clinic, Marlin, TX, p. A655

SHARP, Raymond, Vice President and Chief Information Officer, CGH Medical Center, Sterling, IL, p. A209

SHARPE, Dean, Vice President Medical Affairs, St. Charles Medical Center – Bend, Bend, OR, p. A542

SHARRER, Steve, Vice President Human Resources, St. Louise Regional Hospital, Gilroy, CA, p. A62

SHARROTT, Larry, President InfoShare, Atlanticare Regional Medical Center, Atlantic City, NJ, p. A425

SHARTLE, William, Vice President Human Resources, Holy Spirit Hospital, Camp Hill, PA, p. A554

SHAULL, Ty, Chief Operating Officer, Wyandot Memorial Hospital, Upper Sandusky, OH, p. A523

SHAVER, Jim, Director Information Systems, Good Hope Hospital, Erwin, NC, p. A482

SHAW, Benjamin T., Senior Vice President Human Resources, Christiana Care Health System, Wilmington, DE, p. A120

SHAW, David, Vice President and Chief Operating Officer, Susan B. Allen Memorial Hospital, El Dorado, KS, p. A246

SHAW, David B., Chief Executive Officer and Administrator, Nor–Lea General Hospital, Lovington, NM, p. A443

SHAW, Douglas A., Administrator, Mad River Community Hospital, Arcata, CA, p. A53

SHAW, Gene, Chief Information Officer, Yuma Regional Medical Center, Yuma, AZ, p. A39

SHAW, J. Michael, Administrator, Rusk County Memorial Hospital and Nursing Home, Ladysmith, WI, p. A728

SHAW, M.D., John C., Medical Director, Southern Indiana Rehabilitation Hospital, New Albany, IN, p. A223

SHAW, Phil, Interim President and Chief Executive Officer, Heart Hospital of New Mexico, Albuquerque, NM, p. A440

SHAW, Tammy
Chief Financial Officer, Haskell County Healthcare System, Stigler, OK, p. A538
Chief Financial Officer, Haskell County Healthcare System, Stigler, OK, p. A538

SHAW, Ted, Interim Chief Executive Officer, Maricopa Integrated Health System, Phoenix, AZ, p. A34

SHEA, Timothy P., FACHE, Director, Veterans Affairs Medical Center–Louisville, Louisville, KY, p. A270

SHEAGREN, Craig, Senior Vice President, McDonough District Hospital, Macomb, IL, p. A200

SHEALY, M.D., Gerald, Chief, Bon Secours–St. Francis Xavier Hospital, Charleston, SC, p. A584

SHEAR, Bruce A., President and Chief Executive Officer, Pioneer Behavioral Health, Peabody, MA, p. B84

SHECKLER, Robert L., Administrator, Webster County Community Hospital, Red Cloud, NE, p. A412

SHEEDY, Lucille K., Administrator and Chief Executive Officer, Wyoming County Community Hospital, Warsaw, NY, p. A475

SHEEHAN, Daniel F., Chief Executive Officer, Henry County Health Center, Mount Pleasant, IA, p. A238

SHEEHAN, John C., Executive Vice President and Chief Operating Officer, St. Luke's Hospital, Cedar Rapids, IA, p. A229

SHEEHAN, Karen, Information Systems Director, Swedish Covenant Hospital, Chicago, IL, p. A190

SHEEHAN, Kevin P., Chairman, President and Chief Executive Officer, Youth and Family Centered Services, Austin, TX, p. B123

SHEEHAN, M.D., Terrance J., Chief Medical Officer, Southern Maine Medical Center, Biddeford, ME, p. A297

SHEEHAN, M.D., Terrence P., Medical Director, Adventist Rehabilitation Hospital of Maryland, Rockville, MD, p. A310

SHEEHY, Earl N., President and Chief Executive Officer, Saunders County Health Service, Wahoo, NE, p. A413

SHEEHY, Joseph, Chief Executive Officer, The Pavilion, Champaign, IL, p. A186

SHEERIN, Rick, Vice President Fiscal Services, Floyd Medical Center, Rome, GA, p. A168

SHEETS, Cindy, Chief Information Officer, Mount Carmel, Columbus, OH, p. A510

SHEHATA, Nady, Vice President Medical Affairs, Sisters of Charity Hospital of Buffalo, Buffalo, NY, p. A449

SHEHORN, Patricia, Chief Executive Officer, Westlake Hospital, Melrose Park, IL, p. A201

SHEIKH, M.D., Javaid, Chief of Staff, Veterans Affairs Palo Alto Health Care System, Palo Alto, CA, p. A80

SHELBURNE, M.D., John D., Chief of Staff, Durham Veterans Affairs Medical Center, Durham, NC, p. A481

SHELBY, Dennis R., Chief Executive Officer, Yuma Rehabilitation Hospital, Yuma, AZ, p. A39

SHELBY, Joyce, Personnel Manager, Hardin County General Hospital, Rosiclare, IL, p. A207

SHELBY–DRABNER, Marla, FACHE, Administrator and Chief Executive Officer, Allen Memorial Hospital, Moab, UT, p. A677

SHELDON, M.D., Donald, Vice President Medical Affairs, EMH Regional Medical Center, Elyria, OH, p. A513

SHELDON, Kellie, Vice President Human Resources, Holy Family Hospital, Spokane, WA, p. A709

SHELDON, Lyle Ernest, FACHE,
President and Chief Executive Officer, Harford Memorial Hospital, Havre De Grace, MD, p. A308
President and Chief Executive Officer, Upper Chesapeake Health System, Bel Air, MD, p. B118
President and Chief Executive Officer, Upper Chesapeake Medical Center, Bel Air, MD, p. A305

SHELDON, Mo S., Chief Operating Officer, Glen Rose Medical Center, Glen Rose, TX, p. A642

SHELOR, Bonnie, Vice President Human Resources, Memorial Regional Medical Center, Mechanicsville, VA, p. A691

SHELT, Elizabeth, Civilian Personnel Officer, Dwight David Eisenhower Army Medical Center, Fort Gordon, GA, p. A162

SHELTON, Arneda, Director Human Resources, Community Relations and Education, Coffeyville Regional Medical Center, Coffeyville, KS, p. A245

SHELTON, M.D., Carl, Medical Director, HEALTHSOUTH Southern Hills Rehabilitation Hospital, Princeton, WV, p. A719

SHELTON, James D., Chairman and Chief Executive Officer, Triad Hospitals, Inc., Plano, TX, p. B108

SHELTON, John, Chief Operating Officer, DeKalb Medical Center, Decatur, GA, p. A160

SHELTON, Stan, Vice President, Woman's Hospital, Baton Rouge, LA, p. A278

SHELTON, Timothy S., Administrator, Medical Park Hospital, Winston–Salem, NC, p. A494

SHEMBERGER, Kaylor E., FACHE, Chief Executive Officer, Watsonville Community Hospital, Watsonville, CA, p. A98

SHENNAR, Arek, Director Information Services, St. Patrick Hospital, Missoula, MT, p. A401

SHEPARD, Bruce, Administrator, Dorminy Medical Center, Fitzgerald, GA, p. A162

SHEPARD, M.D., Charles, Medical Director, Winona Health, Winona, MN, p. A365

SHEPARD, Karen, Vice President Finance, Sacred Heart Medical Center, Eugene, OR, p. A543

SHEPARD, Tate, Vice President, Human Resources, Margaret Mary Community Hospital, Batesville, IN, p. A211

SHEPHERD, Douglas, FACHE, President and Chief Executive Officer, Laurel Regional Hospital, Laurel, MD, p. A309

SHEPHERD, Richard W., Chief Executive Officer, Weisman Children's Rehabilitation Hospital, Marlton, NJ, p. A431

SHERBELL, Stanley, Executive Vice President for Medical Affairs, New York Methodist Hospital, New York, NY, p. A463

SHERER, Susan, Chief Information Resource Management, Veterans Affairs Medical Center, Dayton, OH, p. A512

SHERMAN, M.D., Frederick C., Medical Director, Carrie Tingley Hospital, Albuquerque, NM, p. A440

SHERMAN, Jim, President and Chief Exeuctive Officer, Los Robles Hospital and Medical Center, Thousand Oaks, CA, p. A95

SHERMAN, Linda, Chief Financial Officer, Kansas Rehabilitation Hospital, Topeka, KS, p. A257

SHERMAN, Thomas, President Medical Staff, Fauquier Hospital, Warrenton, VA, p. A698

SHERO, John, Deputy Commander for Administration, Brooke Army Medical Center, Fort Sam Houston, TX, p. A638

SHERON, William E., Chief Executive Officer, Wooster Community Hospital, Wooster, OH, p. A525

SHERRILL, Angela
Director Information System, Rush Foundation Hospital, Meridian, MS, p. A373
Corporate Director Information System, Specialty Hospital of Meridian, Meridian, MS, p. A373

SHERRILL, Reece, Administrator, Choctaw Nation Health Care Center, Talihina, OK, p. A539

SHERROD, Rhonda, Administrator, Shands at Live Oak, Live Oak, FL, p. A135

SHERRY, Bernard
President and Chief Executive Officer, Baptist Hospital, Nashville, TN, p. A615
President and Chief Executive Officer, Baptist Hospital, Nashville, TN, p. A615

SHERSETH, Lee
Chief Financial Officer, Tanner Medical Center, Carrollton, GA, p. A157
Chief Financial Officer, Tanner Medical Center–Villa Rica, Villa Rica, GA, p. A171

SHERWOOD, Edward J., M.D.,
Chief Executive Officer, Cornerstone Hospital of Austin, Austin, TX, p. A623
Chief Executive Officer, Cornerstone Hospital of Central Texas, Austin, TX, p. A623

SHERWOOD, John M., FACHE, Chief Executive Officer, Jefferson Memorial Hospital, Ranson, WV, p. A719

SHERWOOD, Paul G., Senior Vice President and Chief Operating Officer, Halifax Regional Medical Center, Roanoke Rapids, NC, p. A490

SHERWOOD, Rose, Information Technology Specialist, Kingfisher Regional Hospital, Kingfisher, OK, p. A532

SHETLER, CPA, Charles L., Chief Financial Officer, Bedford Regional Medical Center, Bedford, IN, p. A211

SHEW, Angel, Area Technology Director, Kaiser Foundation Hospital, Redwood City, CA, p. A83

SHIELDS, Carol, Director Human Resources, Bert Fish Medical Center, New Smyrna Beach, FL, p. A139

SHIELDS, Diane, Chief Human Resources Officer, Alpena Regional Medical Center, Alpena, MI, p. A327

SHIELDS, Michael L., President and Chief Executive Officer, Maria Parham Medical Center, Henderson, NC, p. A484

SHIELDS, Paula, Director Human Resources, Orange Park Medical Center, Orange Park, FL, p. A140

SHIFFERMILLER, M.D., William, Vice President Medical Affairs, Nebraska Methodist Hospital, Omaha, NE, p. A411

SHILL, James, Chief Executive Officer and Managing Director, North Star Behavioral Health System, Anchorage, AK, p. A26

SHIMP, Shakila, Director, Human Resources, St. Joseph's Regional Medical Center, Milwaukee, WI, p. A731

SHIN, Peter, DPM, President and Chairman of the Board, MedLink Hospital and Nursing Center at Capitol Hill, Washington, DC, p. A121

SHINAMAN, Keith C McLean, Senior Vice President Finance, Baystate Medical Center, Springfield, MA, p. A323

SHINE, Tom, Vice President Human Resources, Bay Area Hospital, Coos Bay, OR, p. A543

SHINGLER, Raymond, Vice President Information System, Spartanburg Regional Medical Center, Spartanburg, SC, p. A592

SHINGLETON, Kathy, Chiefuman Resoruces Officer, University of Texas Medical Branch Hospitals, Galveston, TX, p. A641

SHININGER, Kim, Director of Human Resources, Wabash County Hospital, Wabash, IN, p. A227

SHIPMAN, Deborah A., Chief Financial Officer, Monadnock Community Hospital, Peterborough, NH, p. A423

SHIRCLIFF, Robert L., President and Chief Executive Officer, Jewish Hospital HealthCare Services, Louisville, KY, p. B64

SHIREY, Richard, Chief Information Officer, Baptist Montclair, Birmingham, AL, p. A14

SHIRK, Michael B., President and Senior Executive Officer, Boone Hospital Center, Columbia, MO, p. A380

SHIRLEY, Christian, Director Human Resources, Geisinger HEALTHSOUTH Rehabilitation Hospital, Danville, PA, p. A556

SHIRLEY, Tom, Chief Information Officer, Christus St. Joseph Hospital, Houston, TX, p. A644

SHIRTCLIFF, Christine, Executive Vice President, Mary Lane Hospital, Ware, MA, p. A324

SHIVERY, Toni
Vice President Human Resources, Harford Memorial Hospital, Havre De Grace, MD, p. A308
Vice President Human Resources, Upper Chesapeake Medical Center, Bel Air, MD, p. A305

SHOBE, Franklin, Administrator and Chief Executive Officer, Black Hills Surgery Center, Rapid City, SD, p. A598

SHOCK, Lynn, Controller, Stuttgart Regional Medical Center, Stuttgart, AR, p. A51

SHOCKEY, Carolyn, Director Human Resources, Norman Regional Hospital, Norman, OK, p. A534

SHOCKEY, Kathryn L., Director Human Resources, Northern Hills General Hospital, Deadwood, SD, p. A595

SHOCKLEY, Mary, Director Human Resources, Russell Medical Center, Alexander City, AL, p. A13

SHOCKNEY, Brian T., President and Chief Executive Officer, Memorial Hospital, Logansport, IN, p. A221

SHOEN, Jay, Chief Financial Officer, HEALTHSOUTH Rehabilitation Hospital of York, York, PA, p. A580

SHOEN, M.D., Timothy, Vice President Medical Staff Services, St. Mary's Hospital, Amsterdam, NY, p. A447

SHOENER, Carl
Chief Information Officer, Hazleton General Hospital, Hazleton, PA, p. A560
Chief Information Officer, Hazleton–St. Joseph Medical Center, Hazleton, PA, p. A560

SHOLL, Steven, President Medical Staff, Rush North Shore Medical Center, Skokie, IL, p. A208

SHOMAKER, CPA, James, Assistant Administrator and Chief Financial Officer, J. Arthur Dosher Memorial Hospital, Southport, NC, p. A492

SHOMAKER, Susan, Director Information Management Systems, J. Arthur Dosher Memorial Hospital, Southport, NC, p. A492

SHONTZ, Maggie
Vice President Human Resources, Edward Hospital, Naperville, IL, p. A202
Vice President Human Resources, Linden Oaks Hospital at Edward, Naperville, IL, p. A202

SHOOK, Rod, Controller, Parkview Hospital, El Reno, OK, p. A530

SHORB, Gary S., Chief Executive Officer, Methodist Healthcare, Memphis, TN, p. B75

SHORT, John, Associate Administrator and Chief Operating Officer, St. John's Hospital, Springfield, IL, p. A208

SHORT, Margaret W., Chief Information Officer, Webster County Memorial Hospital, Webster Springs, WV, p. A720

SHORT, M.D., Peter H., Senior Vice President Medical Affairs, Beverly Hospital, Beverly, MA, p. A312

SHORT, Steve, Executive Vice President Finance and Administration, Tampa General Hospital, Tampa, FL, p. A148

SHORT, Ted, Chief Financial Officer, Fairview Park Hospital, Dublin, GA, p. A161

SHORT, Val, Vice President Human Resources, Halifax Regional Medical Center, Roanoke Rapids, NC, p. A490

SHOUP, Chris, Chief Executive Officer, The Spine Hospital of South Texas, San Antonio, TX, p. A666

SHOVELIN, Wayne F., President and Chief Executive Officer, Gaston Memorial Hospital, Gastonia, NC, p. A483

SHOWALTER, Richard H., Senior Vice President Finance, Mary Hitchcock Memorial Hospital, Lebanon, NH, p. A422

SHOWALTER, William, Vice President Chief Information Officer, University of Minnesota Medical Center, Minneapolis, MN, p. A357

SHREEVE, Susan
Chief Financial Officer, Research Belton Hospital, Belton, MO, p. A378
Chief Financial Officer, Research Medical Center, Kansas City, MO, p. A384

SHREVE, Susan, Executive Director Information Technology, Boone Memorial Hospital, Madison, WV, p. A717

SHREWSBURY, Kim, Vice President Finance, Cullman Regional Medical Center, Cullman, AL, p. A16

SHRODER, Robert W.
President and Chief Executive Officer, St. Elizabeth Health Center, Youngstown, OH, p. A526
President and Chief Executive Officer, St. Joseph Health Center, Warren, OH, p. A524

SHROPSHIRE, Toni, Vice President, Mary Greeley Medical Center, Ames, IA, p. A228

SHUFFLEBARGER, Tom, Chief Operating Officer, The Children's Hospital of Alabama, Birmingham, AL, p. A15

SHUGARMAN, Mark D., President and Chief Executive Officer, Mercy Hospital Clermont, Batavia, OH, p. A503

SHUGART, Susan C., Chief Operating Officer, Clarendon Memorial Hospital, Manning, SC, p. A590

SHUGRUE, Dianne, Executive Vice President Operations and Chief Operating Officer, Ellis Hospital, Schenectady, NY, p. A472

SHULER, M.D., Conrad K., Chief Medical Officer, Oconee Memorial Hospital, Seneca, SC, p. A591

SHULKIN, David, M.D., President and Chief Executive Officer, Beth Israel Medical Center, New York, NY, p. A458

SHULMAN, M.D., Joel, Chief of Staff, Westside Regional Medical Center, Plantation, FL, p. A143

SHUMWAY, Barbara, Human Resources Officer, North Big Horn Hospital District, Lovell, WY, p. A741

SHUMWAY, Donald L., Chief Executive Officer, Crotched Mountain Rehabilitation Center, Greenfield, NH, p. A421

SHUNTICH, MaryJo, Chief Executive Officer, Select Specialty Hospital–Youngstown, Youngstown, OH, p. A525

SHUPP, Susie, Director Human Resources, Nemaha County Hospital, Auburn, NE, p. A404

SHUR, Kenneth L., Vice President and Chief Operating Officer, Waynesboro Hospital, Waynesboro, PA, p. A578

SHURSON, Richard, Information Systems Director, Kishwaukee Community Hospital, De Kalb, IL, p. A191

SHUTE, Leonard J.
Chief Financial Officer, Highland Hospital of Rochester, Rochester, NY, p. A470
Senior Director Finance, Strong Memorial Hospital of the University of Rochester, Rochester, NY, p. A471

SHUTER, Mark H., President and Chief Executive Officer, Adena Health System, Chillicothe, OH, p. A506

SHYAVITZ, Linda, President and Chief Executive Officer, Sturdy Memorial Hospital, Attleboro, MA, p. A312

SIBERY, Donald C., President and Chief Executive Officer, Roseland Community Hospital, Chicago, IL, p. A189

SICILIA, M.D., Bruce, Medical Director, HEALTHSOUTH Rehabilitation Hospital of York, York, PA, p. A580

SICURELLA, John, Chief Executive Officer, Reynolds Memorial Hospital, Glen Dale, WV, p. A715

SIDDIQI, M.D., Syed, Chief of Staff, Beckley Appalachian Regional Hospital, Beckley, WV, p. A713

SIDDIQUI, Hugh, System Specialist, Linden Oaks Hospital at Edward, Naperville, IL, p. A202

SIDELL, M.D., Jonathan, Chief Medical Officer, Mountain View Hospital District, Madras, OR, p. A545

SIDENER, Tom, Director Information Systems, Carlinville Area Hospital, Carlinville, IL, p. A185

SIDERAS, John, President, MetroHealth Medical Center, Cleveland, OH, p. A509

SIEBENALER, Christopher
Chief Operating Officer and Chief Financial Officer, San Jacinto Methodist Hospital, Baytown, TX, p. A625
Chief Operating Officer and Chief Financial Officer, San Jacinto Methodist Hospital, Baytown, TX, p. A625

SIEBER, Thomas L., President and Chief Executive Officer, Genesis HealthCare System, Zanesville, OH, p. A526

SIEFKIN, M.D., Allan, Chief Medical Officer, University of California, Davis Medical Center, Sacramento, CA, p. A85

SIEGELMAN, M.D., Gary M., Vice President Medical Affairs, Atlanticare Regional Medical Center, Atlantic City, NJ, p. A425

SIEMEN, Terry, Chief Information Officer, Skyline Medical Center, Nashville, TN, p. A615

SIERRAS, Jennifer, Chief Information Officer, Memorial Hospitals Association, Modesto, CA, p. A76

SIFSOF, Victor, Human Resources Director, Bristol Bay Area Health Corporation, Dillingham, AK, p. A27

SIGLAR, Harold L., Chief Executive Officer, Moberly Regional Medical Center, Moberly, MO, p. A388

SIGLER, Vanessa, Director of Health Information Management, Perry Memorial Hospital, Perry, OK, p. A537

SIGLER, Wes, Administrator, Lakeland Community Hospital, Haleyville, AL, p. A20

SIGSBURY, John R., President and Chief Executive Officer, Emanuel Medical Center, Turlock, CA, p. A96

SIKORYAK, John, Director Human Resources, Long Beach Medical Center, Long Beach, NY, p. A455

SILBERNAGEL, Gilbert, Administrator, HEALTHSOUTH Rehabilitation Hospital–Las Vegas, Las Vegas, NV, p. A416

SILIC, Scott, Vice President Operations and Chief Financial Officer, Rehabilitation Institute at Santa Barbara, Santa Barbara, CA, p. A92

SILLS, Doug, Chief Executive Officer, North Okaloosa Medical Center, Crestview, FL, p. A126

SILSBEE, Dave, Chief Information Officer, Cary Medical Center, Caribou, ME, p. A298

SILVA, Carmen, Chief Operating Officer and Chief Nursing Officer, Doctors Hospital of Manteca, Manteca, CA, p. A74

SILVA, William G., Executive Director, Metropolitan State Hospital, Norwalk, CA, p. A78

SILVER, M.D., Michael R., Vice President Medical Affairs, Rush Oak Park Hospital, Oak Park, IL, p. A203

SILVERBERG, Marcia
Vice President Human Resources, Seton Medical Center, Austin, TX, p. A623
Vice President Human Resources, Seton Shoal Creek Hospital, Austin, TX, p. A624

SILVERIA, Wayne
Chief Financial Officer, St. Joseph's Behavioral Health Center, Stockton, CA, p. A95
Chief Financial Officer, St. Joseph's Medical Center, Stockton, CA, p. A95

SILVERMAN, M.D., Michael, Medical Director, Miami Jewish Home and Hospital for Aged, Miami, FL, p. A137

SILVERNALE, Vern
Administrator and Chief Executive Officer, Glacial Ridge Health System, Glenwood, MN, p. A354
Administrator and Chief Executive Officer, Glacial Ridge Health System, Glenwood, MN, p. A354

SILVERSCHLAG, Kelly, Administrator, HEALTHSOUTH Rehabilitation Institute of Tucson, Tucson, AZ, p. A38

SILVIA, M.D., Charles B., President Medical Staff, Peninsula Regional Health System, Salisbury, MD, p. A310

SILVIA, Clarence J.
President and Chief Executive Officer, Bradley Memorial Hospital and Health Center, Southington, CT, p. A116
Senior Vice President and Chief Operating Officer, New Britain General Hospital, New Britain, CT, p. A114

SIM, Carol, President and Chief Executive Officer, Rehabilitation Hospital of the Cape and Islands, East Sandwich, MA, p. A317

SIMIA, Greg, Vice President Finance, St. Anthony Hospital, Oklahoma City, OK, p. A536

SIMKINS, Palma, Chief Human Resources Management Services, Veterans Affairs Medical Center, Battle Creek, MI, p. A328

SIMMONS, Allyn, Associate Vice President of Operations, Norton Hospital, Louisville, KY, p. A270

SIMMONS, R.N., Barbara, Chief Operating Officer, Plantation General Hospital, Plantation, FL, p. A143

SIMMONS, Daniel F., Chief Financial Officer, Monongahela Valley Hospital, Monongahela, PA, p. A565

SIMMONS, Preston M., Senior Operations Officer, University of Washington Medical Center, Seattle, WA, p. A708

SIMMONS, Randy, Chief Executive Officer, Crawford Memorial Hospital, Robinson, IL, p. A206

SIMMONS, Renae, Director Information Systems, Minden Medical Center, Minden, LA, p. A287

SIMMONS, M.D., Robert, Vice President Medical Affairs, Providence Hospital, Washington, DC, p. A122

SIMMONS, Roger
Chief Financial Officer, Coliseum Medical Centers, Macon, GA, p. A165
Chief Financial Officer, Coliseum Psychiatric Center, Macon, GA, p. A165

SIMMONS, Steve, Vice President, Human Resources, Crouse Hospital, Syracuse, NY, p. A473

SIMMONS, Terry, Chief Fiscal Services, Veterans Affairs Tennessee Valley Healthcare System, Nashville, TN, p. A616

SIMMS, Jennifer, Director of Human Resources, University Medical Center, Lafayette, LA, p. A284

SIMMS, John L.
President and Chief Executive Officer, Trinity Community Medical Center of Brenham, Brenham, TX, p. A626
President and Chief Executive Officer, Trinity Community Medical Center of Brenham, Brenham, TX, p. A626

SIMMS, Sr, Michael S., Vice President Human Resources, Northeast Alabama Regional Medical Center, Anniston, AL, p. A13

SIMODEJKA, John E., President and Chief Executive Officer, Pottsville Hospital and Warne Clinic, Pottsville, PA, p. A573

SIMON, Debbie, Senior Vice President Operations and Chief Nursing Officer, Methodist Medical Center of Illinois, Peoria, IL, p. A205

SIMON, M.D., John, Chief of Staff, Platte Valley Medical Center, Brighton, CO, p. A101

SIMON, Judith A., Chief Resources Management Services, Veterans Affairs Medical Center, Grand Junction, CO, p. A106

SIMON, Patricia, Manager Information Systems, Veterans Affairs Medical Center, Canandaigua, NY, p. A450

SIMON, M.D., Richard, Chief of Staff, University of Connecticut Health Center, John Dempsey Hospital, Farmington, CT, p. A113

SIMON, Sylvia, Chief of Staff, Drew Memorial Hospital, Monticello, AR, p. A48

SIMONIN, Steven J., Chief Executive Officer, Wright Medical Center, Clarion, IA, p. A230

SIMONIS, Iris, Chief Executive Officer, Pioneer Valley Hospital, West Valley City, UT, p. A681

SIMONS, Betty, Director, Human Resources, Eastern Idaho Regional Medical Center, Idaho Falls, ID, p. A179

SIMPATICO, Thomas, M.D., Facility Director and Network System Manager, Chicago–Read Mental Health Center, Chicago, IL, p. A186

SIMPSON, Bob, Chief Financial Officer, Richardson RegionalMedical Center, Richardson, TX, p. A662

SIMPSON, Chris, Chief Executive Officer, Cornerstone Hospital–West Monroe, West Monroe, LA, p. A294

SIMPSON, Ed, Vice President Finance, Johnston Memorial Hospital, Smithfield, NC, p. A491

SIMPSON, Elizabeth B., Senior Vice President Human Resources, Baystate Medical Center, Springfield, MA, p. A323

SIMPSON, Hank, M.D., Chief Executive Officer, Myrtle Werth Hospital–Mayo Health System, Menomonie, WI, p. A729

SIMPSON, Janis H., Chief Financial Officer, Deer Park Hospital, Deer Park, WA, p. A702

SIMPSON Jr, Lee A., Administrator, St. Bernard's Behavioral Health, Jonesboro, AR, p. A45

SIMPSON, Tim, Chief Executive Officer, Kindred Hospital North Florida, Green Cove Springs, FL, p. A130

SIMS, Charles, Director Human Resources, Children's Hospital and Regional Medical Center, Seattle, WA, p. A707

SIMS, Gregory F., Chief Executive Officer, Crossroads Community Hospital, Mount Vernon, IL, p. A202

SIMS Jr, John H., Director, Veterans Affairs Medical Center, Togus, ME, p. A301

SIMS, Sheila, Human Resources Director, Stuttgart Regional Medical Center, Stuttgart, AR, p. A51

SIMS, Tom, Chief Information Officer, Mt. Ascutney Hospital and Health Center, Windsor, VT, p. A684

SIMS, W Larry, Chief Financial Officer and Vice President Financial Services, Colquitt Regional Medical Center, Moultrie, GA, p. A166

SINACORE–JABERG, Janie, FACHE, Chief Executive Officer, Doctors Hospital of Stark County, Massillon, OH, p. A518

SINCLAIR, Mike, Administrator, Kane County Hospital, Kanab, UT, p. A677

SINCLAIR, M.D., Terry, Senior Vice President Medical Staff Affairs, Winchester Medical Center, Winchester, VA, p. A698

SINCOCK, Gregory M., Information Technology Leader, Kaiser Foundation Hospital–West Los Angeles, Los Angeles, CA, p. A71

SINDONI, John E., Senior Vice President Human Resources, Ocean Medical Center, Brick Township, NJ, p. A426

SINEK, James J., President and Senior Executive Officer, Verde Valley Medical Center, Cottonwood, AZ, p. A30

SINGER, Gary, Chief Financial Officer, Doctors Hospital of Dallas, Dallas, TX, p. A632

SINGER, Susan, Director, Human Resources, New York Eye and Ear Infirmary, New York, NY, p. A463

SINGH, Amar Jit, M.D., Chief Executive Officer, Brunswick General Hospital, Amityville, NY, p. A446

SINGH, M.D., Amrit, Medical Staff President, Medina Memorial Hospital, Medina, NY, p. A456

SINGH, M.D., Inderjeet, Chief of Staff, Kings Mountain Hospital, Kings Mountain, NC, p. A486

SINGH, M.D., Kuldeep, Chief of Staff, Clinch Memorial Hospital, Homerville, GA, p. A163

SINGLE, John L.
  Chief Executive Officer and Administrator, De Smet Memorial Hospital, De Smet, SD, p. A595
  Chief Executive Officer, Huron Regional Medical Center, Huron, SD, p. A596

SINGLETON, J Verne, Chief Administrative Officer, National Jewish Medical and Research Center, Denver, CO, p. A103

SINGLETON, J. Knox, President and Chief Executive Officer, Inova Health System, Falls Church, VA, p. B61

SINGMASTER, Margie
  Chief Information Officer and Vice President Support Services, Mercy Health System of Kansas, Fort Scott, KS, p. A247
  Chief Information Officer and Vice President Support Services, Mercy Health System of Kansas, Independence, KS, p. A249

SINHA, M.D., Anil, President Medical Staff, Brazosport Memorial Hospital, Lake Jackson, TX, p. A652

SINICROPE, Jr, Frank J., Vice President Financial Services, Princeton Community Hospital, Princeton, WV, p. A719

SINNER, James, Chief Executive Officer, Medina Memorial Hospital, Medina, NY, p. A456

SINNONI, John, Senior Vice President Human Resources, Jersey Shore University Medical Center, Neptune, NJ, p. A432

SINNOTT, Daniel J., Executive Director and Chief Executive Officer, Temple University Hospital, Philadelphia, PA, p. A570

SINNOTT, M.D., James, Chief of Medical Staff, Coquille Valley Hospital, Coquille, OR, p. A543

SIPES, Don, Chief Executive Officer, Saint Luke's Northland Hospital–Smithville Campus, Smithville, MO, p. A393

SIPKOSKI, Michael, Executive Vice President and Administrator, St. Francis Hospital, Litchfield, IL, p. A199

SIRK, David R., Chief Executive Officer, Medical Center of Southern Indiana, Charlestown, IN, p. A213

SIRK, Donald, Director Information Systems, St. Mary's Hospital, Leonardtown, MD, p. A309

SIROIS, Peter, Associate Administrator, Northern Maine Medical Center, Fort Kent, ME, p. A298

SIROTTA, Ted
  Chief Financial Officer and Chief Information Officer, Barlow Respiratory Hospital, Los Angeles, CA, p. A69
  Chief Financial Officer and Chief Information Officer, Barlow Respiratory Hospital, Los Angeles, CA, p. A69

SIRVENT, Mauricio, Chief Financial Officer, Kendall Regional Medical Center, Miami, FL, p. A137

SISK, Glenn C., President, Coosa Valley Medical Center, Sylacauga, AL, p. A24

SISK, Jack, Chief Financial Officer, Punxsutawney Area Hospital, Punxsutawney, PA, p. A574

SISSON, William G., President, Central Baptist Hospital, Lexington, KY, p. A267

SISTO, Dennis, President and Chief Executive Officer, Queen of the Valley Hospital, Napa, CA, p. A77

SISTO, Steve
  Chief Operating Officer, Irvine Regional Hospital and Medical Center, Irvine, CA, p. A65
  Chief Operating Officer, Lakewood Regional Medical Center, Lakewood, CA, p. A67

SISTY, John, Associate Director, Veterans Affairs Palo Alto Health Care System, Palo Alto, CA, p. A80

SITARIK, Sherrie, Executive Vice President, Orlando Regional Medical Center, Orlando, FL, p. A141

SIX, Deborah, Data Processing Coordinator, Wayne Memorial Hospital, Jesup, GA, p. A164

SKABELUND, Hoyt, Administrator, Socorro General Hospital, Socorro, NM, p. A445

SKADEN, John, Chief Financial Officer, Saint Joseph's Hospital, Marshfield, WI, p. A729

SKAGGS, M.D., Gregory, President Medical Staff, Twin Lakes Regional Medical Center, Leitchfield, KY, p. A267

SKAGGS, Jo Ann, Chief Executive Officer, Creek Nation Community Hospital, Okemah, OK, p. A534

SKALA, Pat, Chief Information Officer, Laguna Honda Hospital and Rehabilitation Center, San Francisco, CA, p. A89

SKARULIS, Patricia, Vice President Information Systems, Memorial Sloan–Kettering Cancer Center, New York, NY, p. A462

SKELDON, Timothy K., Senior Vice President and Chief Financial Officer, Parrish Medical Center, Titusville, FL, p. A149

SKELLEY, Dennis B., President and Chief Executive Officer, Walton Rehabilitation Hospital, Augusta, GA, p. A156

SKIDMORE, James, Financial Manager, James A. Haley Veterans Hospital, Tampa, FL, p. A148

SKIDMORE, Jocelyn, Finance Director, St. Francis Hospital and Health Services, Maryville, MO, p. A387

SKILLINGS, Charles E., President and Chief Executive Officer, Unity Health Center, Shawnee, OK, p. A538

SKINNER, Ann, Director Human Resources, University of California San Diego Medical Center, San Diego, CA, p. A88

SKINNER, Bob
  Vice President Information Services, Dr. Dan C. Trigg Memorial Hospital, Tucumcari, NM, p. A445
  Chief Information Officer, Presbyterian Hospital, Albuquerque, NM, p. A440
  Chief Information Officer, Presbyterian Kaseman Hospital, Albuquerque, NM, p. A441

SKINNER, Davis D., Chief Executive Officer, Drumright Regional Hospital, Drumright, OK, p. A529

SKINNER, Eileen F., President and Chief Executive Officer, Mercy Hospital of Portland, Portland, ME, p. A300

SKINNER, Gloria, Chief Executive Officer, Select Specialty Hospital of Bloomington, Bloomington, IN, p. A212

SKINNER, Jon, Executive Director, Baylor Medical Center at Southwest Fort Worth, Fort Worth, TX, p. A639

SKINNER, Marjorie, Director Finance, Pershing General Hospital, Lovelock, NV, p. A417

SKINNER, Michael D., President, Franklin Medical Center, Greenfield, MA, p. A318

SKINNER, Rick, Vice President Information Services and Chief Information Officer, Providence Newberg Hospital, Newberg, OR, p. A546

SKOGSBERGH, James H., President and Chief Executive Officer, Advocate Health Care, Oak Brook, IL, p. B6

SKOLD, Colleen, Administrator, Bloomer Memorial Medical Center, Bloomer, WI, p. A723

SKOMOROCH, Orianna A.
  Regional Chief Executive Officer, Kauai Veterans Memorial Hospital, Waimea, HI, p. A176
  Regional Chief Executive Officer, Samuel Mahelona Memorial Hospital, Kapaa, HI, p. A175

SKORICK, Cynthia, Chief Executive Officer, Fergus Falls Regional Treatment Center, Fergus Falls, MN, p. A353

SKOWLUND, Kathleen, MS, Administrator and Chief Nurse Executive, Aurora Lakeland Medical Center, Elkhorn, WI, p. A725

SKRINDE, Tracie, Director Human Resources, United General Hospital, Sedro–Woolley, WA, p. A708

SKRIPPS, Michele M., Administrator, AnMed HEALTHOUTH Rehabilitation Hospital, Anderson, SC, p. A583

SKRYPAK, Karl T., Executive Vice President and Chief Operating Officer, Brownsville General Hospital, Brownsville, PA, p. A553

SKUBA, Herbert S., President and Chief Executive Officer, Ellwood City Hospital, Ellwood City, PA, p. A558

SKUBITZ, Doug, Administrator, Kingsburg Medical Center, Kingsburg, CA, p. A65

SLABACH, Brock A., Administrator, Field Memorial Community Hospital, Centreville, MS, p. A367

SLACK, M.D., John, Chief Medical Officer, Memorial Hospital, Colorado Springs, CO, p. A102

SLACK, Randy
  Interim Chief Executive Officer, Mission Hospital, Mission, TX, p. A657
  Chief Financial Officer, Mission Hospital, Mission, TX, p. A657

SLADKY, Todd J., Chief Financial Officer, Great River Medical Center, West Burlington, IA, p. A243

SLATER, M.D., Craig M., Senior Vice President, Medical Affairs, Memorial Hospital at Gulfport, Gulfport, MS, p. A369

SLATER, M.D., Douglas, Vice President Medical Affairs, Mercy Hospital Grayling, Grayling, MI, p. A335

SLATON, Charles R., President and Chief Operating Officer, MedCath, Inc., Charlotte, NC, p. B73

SLATTERY, Sue, Director Human Resources, St. Luke's Hospital, Cedar Rapids, IA, p. A229

SLAUBAUGH, D. Ray, President, Graham Hospital, Canton, IL, p. A185

SLAVIN, Kevin, President and Chief Executive Officer, East Orange General Hospital, East Orange, NJ, p. A427

SLAVIN, Peter L., M.D., President, Massachusetts General Hospital, Boston, MA, p. A314

SLAYTON, Lisa, Vice President Human Resources, Bon Secours St. Francis Health System, Greenville, SC, p. A588

SLETTE, Katie, Communication Coordinator, Windom Area Hospital, Windom, MN, p. A365

SLICE, M.D., Roy, Chief Medical Officer, Hegg Memorial Health Center/Avera Health, Rock Valley, IA, p. A240

SLINGERLAND, Micki J., Chief Financial Officer, Centennial Medical Center and Parthenon Pavilion, Nashville, TN, p. A615

SLIWINSKI, Jeff, Chief Financial Officer, The Woman's Hospital of Texas, Houston, TX, p. A648

SLOAN, Gary, Chief Executive Officer, San Ramon Regional Medical Center, San Ramon, CA, p. A91

SLOAN, Joseph F., CHE, Chief Executive Officer, Seymour Hospital, Seymour, TX, p. A666

SLOAN, Robert L., President and Chief Executive Officer, Sibley Memorial Hospital, Washington, DC, p. A122

SLOAN, Ronald A., Administrator, Swain County Hospital, Bryson City, NC, p. A478

SLOAN, Steve, Chief Financial Officer, Northcrest Medical Center, Springfield, TN, p. A618

SLOCUM, Brandon H., Chief Financial Officer, Hancock Medical Center, Bay Saint Louis, MS, p. A366

SLOCUM, Gregg Y., Chief Financial Officer, Valley Forge Medical Center and Hospital, Norristown, PA, p. A566

SLONAKER, Jody, Chief, Fiscal Section, Veterans Affairs Medical Center, Martinsburg, WV, p. A717

SLONE, Judy, Division Director, Kosciusko Community Hospital, Warsaw, IN, p. A227

SLONIM, Sheryl A., President and Chief Executive Officer, Saint Peter's University Hospital, New Brunswick, NJ, p. A432

SLUNECKA, Fredrick, Regional President, Avera McKennan Hospital and University Health Center, Sioux Falls, SD, p. A599

SLUSKY, Richard, Administrator, Mt. Ascutney Hospital and Health Center, Windsor, VT, p. A684

SLYTER, Mark, Administrator, Baptist Medical Center–Beaches, Jacksonville Beach, FL, p. A133

SMALARA, M.D., Douglas, Medical Director, New Horizons Health Systems, Inc., Owenton, KY, p. A273

SMALE, Cindy, Director Human Resources, Bedford Regional Medical Center, Bedford, IN, p. A211

SMALL, Jonathan, Vice President Human Resources, University Hospital, Cincinnati, OH, p. A507

SMALL, Margaret, Director Human Resources, Greater El Monte Community Hospital, El Monte, CA, p. A59

SMALL, Sandi, Senior Vice President and Administrator, Kaiser Foundation Hospital, Walnut Creek, CA, p. A98

SMALL WARNER, Stephen, Deputy Executive Director, Network Human Resources, Kings County Hospital Center, New York, NY, p. A460

SMANIK, Robert E., FACHE, President and Chief Executive Officer, Ellis Hospital, Schenectady, NY, p. A472

SMART, Andrea, Controller, HEALTHSOUTH Rehabilitation Hospital of Baton Rouge, Baton Rouge, LA, p. A277

SMART, Dan, Chief Information Management, Permian Regional Medical Center, Andrews, TX, p. A621

SMART, George, Vice President of Finance and System Services, Zeeland Community Hospital, Zeeland, MI, p. A348

SMART, M.D., Martin, Chief of Medical Staff, Yuma District Hospital, Yuma, CO, p. A111

SMART, CPA, Paul, Chief Financial Officer, Franklin County Medical Center, Preston, ID, p. A181

SMILEY, Jon D., Chief Executive Officer, Sunnyside Community Hospital, Sunnyside, WA, p. A710

SMITH, Allen F.
Senior Vice President Financial Services, Baptist Health Medical Center – North Little Rock, North Little Rock, AR, p. A48
Senior Vice President Financial Services, Baptist Health Medical Center–Little Rock, Little Rock, AR, p. A46
Senior Vice President Financial Services, Baptist Health Rehabilitation Institute, Little Rock, AR, p. A46

SMITH, Andrew, Chief Financial Officer, Edward White Hospital, Saint Petersburg, FL, p. A145

SMITH, Becky, Director Human Resources, De Soto Regional Health System, Mansfield, LA, p. A286

SMITH, Bernadette M.
President and Chief Executive Officer, Seton Medical Center, Daly City, CA, p. A58
President and Chief Executive Officer, Seton Medical Center Coastside, Moss Beach, CA, p. A77

SMITH, Bernie, Chief Financial Officer, Troy Community Hospital, Troy, PA, p. A577

SMITH, M.D., Bill, Chief of Staff, Cullman Regional Medical Center, Cullman, AL, p. A16

SMITH, Brad, Chief Executive Officer, Rush Memorial Hospital, Rushville, IN, p. A224

SMITH, Brian, Executive Vice President and Chief Operating Officer, St. Rita's Medical Center, Lima, OH, p. A516

SMITH, C. W., President and Chief Executive Officer, Parkview Medical Center, Pueblo, CO, p. A109

SMITH, Carl, Director Information Systems, King's Daughters Medical Center, Brookhaven, MS, p. A367

SMITH, M.D., Charles W., Medical Director, UAMS Medical Center, Little Rock, AR, p. A47

SMITH Jr, Charles W., President and Chief Executive Officer, Lakeside Memorial Hospital, Brockport, NY, p. A448

SMITH, Chris, Vice President and Chief Information Officer, Saint Mary's Regional Medical Center, Reno, NV, p. A418

SMITH, M.D., Christopher R., President Medical Staff, Fort Washington Medical Center, Fort Washington, MD, p. A308

SMITH, Cindy, Chief Executive Officer, Kindred Hospital–Sycamore, Sycamore, IL, p. A209

SMITH, M.D., Coke R., Chief of Staff, Sunnyside Community Hospital, Sunnyside, WA, p. A710

SMITH, Connie, Chief Executive Officer, The Medical Center at Bowling Green, Bowling Green, KY, p. A262

SMITH, Dale, Director Human Resources, Harris Methodist–HEB, Bedford, TX, p. A625

SMITH, Dan
Vice President Finance, Samaritan Albany General Hospital, Albany, OR, p. A542
Vice President Finance, Samaritan Lebanon Community Hospital, Lebanon, OR, p. A545

SMITH, Daniel, Chief Financial Officer, Rebsamen Medical Center, Jacksonville, AR, p. A45

SMITH, Daniel B., Vice President Finance, Good Samaritan Regional Medical Center, Corvallis, OR, p. A543

SMITH, Daniel L., President and Chief Executive Officer, Bay Area Hospital, Coos Bay, OR, p. A543

SMITH, Danny, Chief Financial Officer, Redmond Regional Medical Center, Rome, GA, p. A168

SMITH, R.N., Darline, Chief Nursing Officer, Glenwood Regional Medical Center, West Monroe, LA, p. A294

SMITH, Darwin K., Vice President, Human Resources, Union Hospital, Dover, OH, p. A513

SMITH, David
Data Center Manager, Huguley Memorial Medical Center, Fort Worth, TX, p. A640
Chief Financial Officer, Memorial Regional Hospital, Hollywood, FL, p. A131
Director Support Services, St. Mary's Hospital, Streator, IL, p. A209

SMITH, David A., Vice President and Chief Operating Officer, Avista Adventist Hospital, Louisville, CO, p. A108

SMITH, M.D., David M., Associate Director Information Management, Veterans Affairs Medical Center, Portland, OR, p. A548

SMITH, M.D., David N., Vice President, Medical Affairs, Rowan Regional Medical Center, Salisbury, NC, p. A491

SMITH, Debbie, Medical Records and Information Systems Director, Crawford Memorial Hospital, Robinson, IL, p. A206

SMITH, Debra A., Acting Chief Executive Officer, Senator Garrett W. Hagedorn Psychiatric Hospital, Glen Gardner, NJ, p. A428

SMITH, Debra B., Senior Vice President and Chief Operating Officer, Stanly Memorial Hospital, Albemarle, NC, p. A477

SMITH, Denise
Chief Executive Officer, Good Hope Hospital, Erwin, NC, p. A482
Health Information Director, HEALTHSOUTH Chattanooga Rehabilitation Hospital, Chattanooga, TN, p. A603

SMITH, Dennis H., Director, Veterans Affairs Maryland Health Care System–Baltimore Division, Baltimore, MD, p. A305

SMITH, Donnie, Director Human Resources, Rush Foundation Hospital, Meridian, MS, p. A373

SMITH, Doug, Chief Financial Officer, McKay–Dee Hospital Center, Ogden, UT, p. A678

SMITH, M.D., Edward J., Chief of Staff, Prowers Medical Center, Lamar, CO, p. A107

SMITH, Ellen, President and Chief Executive Officer, Dubuis Health System, Houston, TX, p. B42

SMITH, Ericka, Chief Operating Officer, Monterey Park Hospital, Monterey Park, CA, p. A76

SMITH, Eugene, Chief Information Officer, Maniilaq Health Center, Kotzebue, AK, p. A28

SMITH, F. Curtis, President, Massachusetts Eye and Ear Infirmary, Boston, MA, p. A314

SMITH, Frank M., Vice President Human Resources and Organizational Development, Greater Baltimore Medical Center, Baltimore, MD, p. A302

SMITH, Gary, Information Technology Manager, Paynesville Area Health Care System, Paynesville, MN, p. A359

SMITH, Ph.D., Gary J., Chief Operating Officer, St. Luke's Rehabilitation Institute, Spokane, WA, p. A709

SMITH, Gloria, Vice President Human Resources, Tucson Medical Center, Tucson, AZ, p. A38

SMITH, Gordon, Administrator and Chief Executive Officer, Merrill Pioneer Community Hospital, Rock Rapids, IA, p. A240

SMITH, Gregory M.
Chief Executive Officer, Allentown State Hospital, Allentown, PA, p. A551
Chief Executive Officer, Harrisburg State Hospital, Harrisburg, PA, p. A559

SMITH, Hal E., Executive Director, Central New York Psychiatric Center, Marcy, NY, p. A456

SMITH, Harley, Chief Executive Officer, Miller County Hospital, Colquitt, GA, p. A158

SMITH Jr, Harry, President and Senior Administrative Officer, Sisters of Charity Hospital of Buffalo, Buffalo, NY, p. A449

SMITH, Heidi, Administrative Director, Guttenberg Municipal Hospital, Guttenberg, IA, p. A234

SMITH, Herman, Senior Assistant Executive Director, Lincoln Medical and Mental Health Center, New York, NY, p. A461

SMITH, J. Paul, Chief Executive Officer, Brentwood Behavioral Health Company, Shreveport, LA, p. A292

SMITH, James, Chief Financial Officer, Ira Davenport Memorial Hospital, Bath, NY, p. A447

SMITH, James E., Superintendent, North Texas State Hospital, Wichita Falls Campus, Wichita Falls, TX, p. A674

SMITH, James R., Chief Fiscal Service, Veterans Affairs Southern Nevada Healthcare System, North Las Vegas, NV, p. A418

SMITH, Jeanna, Administrative Assistant and Human Resources Officer, Polk Medical Center, Cedartown, GA, p. A157

SMITH, Jeff, M.D., Executive Director, Contra Costa Regional Medical Center, Martinez, CA, p. A75

SMITH, Jeff, Director Human Resources, Carilion New River Valley Medical Center, Christiansburg, VA, p. A686

SMITH, Jeffrey
Chief Executive Officer, Triumph Hospital Northwest, Houston, TX, p. A648
Senior Vice President and Chief Operating Officer, Mercy Medical Center, Canton, OH, p. A505

SMITH, Jeffrey H., Ph.D., Superintendent, Logansport State Hospital, Logansport, IN, p. A221

SMITH, M.D., Jennifer, Chief of Staff, Miles Memorial Hospital, Damariscotta, ME, p. A298

SMITH, Jill, Director Human Resources, Tyler Memorial Hospital, Tunkhannock, PA, p. A577

SMITH, Jody, Organizational Support Officer, Monticello Big Lake Hospital, Monticello, MN, p. A358

SMITH, Johnson L.
Interim President and Chief Executive Officer, Carrington Health Center, Carrington, ND, p. A497
President and Chief Executive Officer, Mercy Hospital, Valley City, ND, p. A500

SMITH, Joni, Director of Finance, Baptist Medical Center–Beaches, Jacksonville Beach, FL, p. A133

SMITH, Joseph B., Vice President Finance, Union Memorial Hospital, Baltimore, MD, p. A304

SMITH, Joseph S., Chief Executive Officer, Boone County Hospital, Boone, IA, p. A229

SMITH, Judy, Medical Director, Roswell Park Cancer Institute, Buffalo, NY, p. A449

SMITH, Julia, Regional Controller, HEALTHSOUTH Chattanooga Rehabilitation Hospital, Chattanooga, TN, p. A603

SMITH, Karen S., Director Information Services, Chilton Memorial Hospital, Pompton Plains, NJ, p. A435

SMITH, Katherine, Chief Operating Officer, Putnam County Memorial Hospital, Unionville, MO, p. A395

SMITH, Kathleen, Chief Executive Officer, Kindred Hospital–Brea, Brea, CA, p. A55

SMITH, Kevin
Director Information Systems, Palm Beach Gardens Medical Center, Palm Beach Gardens, FL, p. A141
Vice President Finance and Administrative Services, Winchester Hospital, Winchester, MA, p. A325

SMITH, Kevin J., Chief Operating Officer, Northwest Medical Center, Thief River Falls, MN, p. A363

SMITH, Kimberly A., President and Chief Executive Officer, Jewish Memorial Hospital and Rehabilitation Center, Boston, MA, p. A314

SMITH, Larry J., Chief Financial Officer, Phoenix Children's Hospital, Phoenix, AZ, p. A34

SMITH, M.D., Leighton B., Vice President Medical Affairs, Northwest Community Healthcare, Arlington Heights, IL, p. A183

SMITH, Lex, Administrator, Parkview Hospital, El Reno, OK, p. A530

SMITH, Linda, Administrator, Aurora BayCare Medical Center, Green Bay, WI, p. A726

SMITH, Lori, Chief Financial Officer, Meade District Hospital, Meade, KS, p. A252

SMITH, R.N., Marguerite, Vice President and Chief Nursing Officer, Chandler Regional Hospital, Chandler, AZ, p. A30

SMITH, Marshall E., Executive Vice President and Chief Operating Officer, St. Marys Health Center, Jefferson City, MO, p. A383

SMITH, Martin D., Chief Executive Officer, Pottstown Memorial Medical Center, Pottstown, PA, p. A573

SMITH, M.D., Michael, Medical Director, St. Joseph's Behavioral Health Center, Stockton, CA, p. A95

SMITH, M.D., Michael L., Chief Medical Staff, Hardin Medical Center, Savannah, TN, p. A617

SMITH, Mickey, Chief Executive Officer, Oak Hill Hospital, Brooksville, FL, p. A125

SMITH, Mike J., Chief Information Officer, Lee Memorial Health System, Fort Myers, FL, p. A129

SMITH, Nadine, Director Human Resources, Reeves County Hospital, Pecos, TX, p. A660

SMITH, Nanette, Vice President Human Resources, Caritas St. Elizabeth's Medical Center, Brighton, MA, p. A315

SMITH, Ollie, Vice President Human Resources, Paris Community Hospital, Paris, IL, p. A204

SMITH Jr, P. Paul, Executive Director, Lake Norman Regional Medical Center, Mooresville, NC, p. A487

SMITH Jr, P. W., Administrator and Chief Executive Officer, Pomerene Hospital, Millersburg, OH, p. A519

SMITH, M.D., Paul T., Chief of Staff, Florida Hospital Fish Memorial, Orange City, FL, p. A140

SMITH, Paul W., Vice President General Services, Providence Hospital, Washington, DC, p. A122

SMITH, Paula
Chief Information Officer, Delta Memorial Hospital, Dumas, AR, p. A42
Leader Information Services and Chief Information Officer, Oakwood Heritage Hospital, Taylor, MI, p. A346
Leader Information Services and Chief Information Officer, Oakwood Hospital and Medical Center–Dearborn, Dearborn, MI, p. A330
Vice President Information Services and Chief Information Officer, Oakwood Southshore Medical Center, Trenton, MI, p. A347
Chief Operating Officer, St. Luke's Wood River Medical Center, Ketchum, ID, p. A179

SMITH, Raymond N., Chief Executive Officer, Community Hospital of Gardena, Gardena, CA, p. A62

SMITH, Rebecca, Vice President, Caldwell Memorial Hospital, Lenoir, NC, p. A486

SMITH, Richard
Assistant Administrator, Providence Milwaukie Hospital, Milwaukie, OR, p. A546
Vice President Information Systems, Southcoast Hospitals Group, Fall River, MA, p. A317

SMITH, Richard G., Chief Executive Officer, Oneida Healthcare Center, Oneida, NY, p. A468

SMITH, Robbie, Administrator, Higgins General Hospital, Bremen, GA, p. A156

SMITH, III, M.D., Robert B., Medical Director, Emory University Hospital, Atlanta, GA, p. A153

SMITH, Robert J., Chief of Staff, Grant Regional Health Center, Lancaster, WI, p. A728

SMITH, Rodney, Director Human Resources and Development, Harrisburg Medical Center, Harrisburg, IL, p. A196

SMITH, Rodney R., Chief Executive Officer, Central Florida Regional Hospital, Sanford, FL, p. A146

SMITH, Ron, Chief Financial Officer, Wickenburg Regional Medical Center, Wickenburg, AZ, p. A39

SMITH, Roy, Chief Financial Officer, Onslow Memorial Hospital, Jacksonville, NC, p. A485

SMITH, M.D., Sam, Chief of Staff, Longmont United Hospital, Longmont, CO, p. A108

SMITH, Sandra K., Director and Chief Executive Officer, Deer's Head Hospital Center, Salisbury, MD, p. A310

SMITH, R.N., Sandy, Senior Vice President Operations, Margaret R. Pardee Memorial Hospital, Hendersonville, NC, p. A484

SMITH, Scott
Chief Executive Officer, River West Medical Center, Plaquemine, LA, p. A291
Director Information Systems, EMH Regional Medical Center, Elyria, OH, p. A513

SMITH, Shawn, Fiscal Director, Shaughnessy–Kaplan Rehabilitation Hospital, Salem, MA, p. A323

SMITH, Sherry, Director Human Resources, Dallas County Hospital, Perry, IA, p. A240

SMITH, Shirley M., Chief Financial Officer, Andalusia Regional Hospital, Andalusia, AL, p. A13

SMITH, Stacy, Chief Executive Officer, Valir Rehabilitation Hospital, Oklahoma City, OK, p. A536

SMITH, M.D., Stephen B., Chief Medical Officer, Nebraska Medical Center, Omaha, NE, p. A411

SMITH, Stephen R., Vice President Human Resources, Duke University Hospital, Durham, NC, p. A481

SMITH, Steve, Chief Executive Officer, Kindred Hospital – Phoenix, Phoenix, AZ, p. A34

SMITH, M.D., Steve, Chief Medical Staff, Providence Kodiak Island Medical Center, Kodiak, AK, p. A27

SMITH, Steven
Healthcare Director Information Services, CJW Medical Center, Richmond, VA, p. A695
Chief Financial Officer, Pampa Regional Medical Center, Pampa, TX, p. A659
Chief Information Officer, Saint's Mary & Elizabeth Medical Center, Division Street, Chicago, IL, p. A190

SMITH, Stuart
Vice President Clinical Operations and Executive Director, MUSC Medical Center of Medical University of South Carolina, Charleston, SC, p. B77
Vice President Clinical Operations and Executive Director, MUSC Medical Center of Medical University of South Carolina, Charleston, SC, p. A584

SMITH, Suellen, Chief Operating Officer, Twin Cities Community Hospital, Templeton, CA, p. A95

SMITH, Tammy, Director Human Resources, St. Anthony's Healthcare Center, Morrilton, AR, p. A48

SMITH, Terry J., Administrator, Bibb Medical Center, Centreville, AL, p. A16

SMITH, Thomas, Chief Information Officer, Evanston Northwestern Healthcare, Evanston, IL, p. A194

SMITH III, Thomas C., Chief Executive Officer, St. Luke Hospital and Living Center, Marion, KS, p. A252

SMITH, Thomas G., Chief Executive Officer, Audubon County Memorial Hospital, Audubon, IA, p. A228

SMITH, Tim, Chief Executive Officer, Fountain Valley Regional Hospital and Medical Center, Fountain Valley, CA, p. A60

SMITH, Todd A., Chief Executive Officer, Aurora Behavioral HealthCare–Charter Oak, Covina, CA, p. A58

SMITH, M.D., Tommy, President Medical Staff, Lincoln General Hospital, Ruston, LA, p. A292

SMITH, Tommy J., President and Chief Executive Officer, Baptist Healthcare System, Louisville, KY, p. B16

SMITH, Trevor, Chief Management Information Services, Gunnison Valley Hospital, Gunnison, CO, p. A106

SMITH, M.D., Tyson, Senior Vice President Medical Affairs and Strategic Planning, Cortland Memorial Hospital, Cortland, NY, p. A451

SMITH, W Stuart, Vice President of Clinical Operations and Executive Director, Charleston Memorial Hospital, Charleston, SC, p. A584

SMITH, W. David, Director, Veterans Affairs Medical Center, Canandaigua, NY, p. A450

SMITH, Wayne T., Chairman, President and Chief Executive Officer, Community Health Systems, Inc., Brentwood, TN, p. B30

SMITH, Wes, Chief Financial Officer, Jamestown Hospital, Jamestown, ND, p. A499

SMITH, Windell, Chief Operating Officer, Satilla Regional Medical Center, Waycross, GA, p. A172

SMITH–BURROWS, Susan, Senior Vice President Human Resources, St. Vincent Medical Center, Los Angeles, CA, p. A72

SMITHBURG, Donald R., Chief Executive Officer, LSU Health Sciences Center, Baton Rouge, LA, p. B71

SMITHMIER, Kenneth L., President and Chief Executive Officer, Decatur Memorial Hospital, Decatur, IL, p. A192

SMITHSON, Jr, M.D., John, Vice President, Jane Phillips Medical Center, Bartlesville, OK, p. A528

SMITHSON, Randell, Chief, Systems, U. S. Air Force Hospital Luke, Glendale, AZ, p. A31

SMOCK, Dennis, Chief Executive Officer, DeKalb Hospital, Smithville, TN, p. A617

SMOCYNSKI, Nancy, Payroll/Personnel and Human Resource Director, Kindred Hospital–Pittsburgh, Oakdale, PA, p. A566

SMOKER, Bret, Clinical Director, PHS Santa Fe Indian Hospital, Santa Fe, NM, p. A444

SMOOT, Steven, Administrator, Valley View Medical Center, Cedar City, UT, p. A676

SMOOT, Todd, Chief Information Officer, Jefferson Memorial Hospital, Ranson, WV, p. A719

SMOTHERS, Margaret Shawn, Administrator, Kenmare Community Hospital, Kenmare, ND, p. A499

SMYTHE, Robert C., Chief Operating Officer, Henry Ford Wyandotte Hospital, Wyandotte, MI, p. A348

SNAVELY, Gretchen, Director Human Resources, Holton Community Hospital, Holton, KS, p. A249

SNEAD, Benjamin E., President and Chief Executive Officer, St. Clair Memorial Hospital, Pittsburgh, PA, p. A572

SNEATH, Roger, Vice President and Chief Financial Officer, Columbus Community Hospital, Columbus, WI, p. A724

SNEDIGAR, Rudy C., Administrator and Chief Executive Officer, Barton County Memorial Hospital, Lamar, MO, p. A386

SNELL, Donald F., President and Chief Executive Officer, Medical College of Georgia Hospital and Clinics, Augusta, GA, p. A155

SNELL, Peggy, Chief Finance Officer, Cherry County Hospital, Valentine, NE, p. A413

SNIDER, Charles, Director Human Resources, Clinton Memorial Hospital, Wilmington, OH, p. A525

SNIDER, Dean, Chief Financial Officer, King's Daughters Medical Center, Brookhaven, MS, p. A367

SNIDERMAN, Howard, Vice President Professional and Support Services, Fairfield Medical Center, Lancaster, OH, p. A515

SNIFF, D. David, Administrator, Sarah D. Culbertson Memorial Hospital, Rushville, IL, p. A207

SNIFFEN, Michael J., Interim President and Chief Executive Officer, St. Mary Hospital, Hoboken, NJ, p. A429

SNOW, Brian, Information Systems Manager, Appling Healthcare System, Baxley, GA, p. A156

SNOW, Charlyn, Human Resources Director, Northwest Texas Healthcare System, Amarillo, TX, p. A621

SNOW, Diane, Director Human Resources, Methodist Willowbrook Hospital, Houston, TX, p. A646

SNOW, Leonard, Chief Quality Officer, San Luis Valley Regional Medical Center, Alamosa, CO, p. A101

SNOW, Mel L., Chief Executive Officer, West Holt Memorial Hospital, Atkinson, NE, p. A404

SNOWDEN, Raymond W., President and Chief Executive Officer, Memorial Hospital and Health Care Center, Jasper, IN, p. A219

SNYDER, Cathy, Director Human Resources, Richland Memorial Hospital, Olney, IL, p. A203

SNYDER, Darleen, Chief Business Analysis Division, Reynolds Army Community Hospital, Fort Sill, OK, p. A531

SNYDER, David M., Interim President and Chief Executive Officer, Hutcheson Medical Center, Fort Oglethorpe, GA, p. A162

SNYDER, George E., Warden, Federal Medical Center, Lexington, KY, p. A267

SNYDER, John, Vice President Human Resources, Olean General Hospital, Olean, NY, p. A468

SNYDER, John T., Executive Vice President, Carle Foundation Hospital, Urbana, IL, p. A209

SNYDER, LeeAnn, Vice President Human Resources, Montgomery General Hospital, Montgomery, WV, p. A717

SNYDER, Mary E., Associate Administrator, Montrose Memorial Hospital, Montrose, CO, p. A108

SNYDER, Paul, Chief Financial Officer, Oswego Hospital, Oswego, NY, p. A468

SNYDER, Renae, Business Office Manager, Sakakawea Medical Center, Hazen, ND, p. A498

SNYDER, M.D., Richard, Chief of Staff, Medical City Dallas Hospital, Dallas, TX, p. A633

SNYDER, Rick, Vice President and Chief Financial Officer, Via Christi Oklahoma Regional Medical Center, Ponca City, OK, p. A537

SNYDER, Ron, Chief Financial Officer, Hardin Memorial Hospital, Kenton, OH, p. A515

SOBOTA, Richard E., President and Chief Executive Officer, Pike Community Hospital, Waverly, OH, p. A524

SODERBLOM, Alan, President and Chief Executive Officer, Paradise Valley Hospital, National City, CA, p. A77

SODERHOLM, Jon, President, Avera Heart Hospital of South Dakota, Sioux Falls, SD, p. A598

SODOMKA, FACHE, Patricia, Executive Vice President/Chief Operating Officer, Medical College of Georgia Hospital and Clinics, Augusta, GA, p. A155

SOEKORO, Julie, Chief Financial Officer, Lea Regional Medical Center, Hobbs, NM, p. A443

SOGGE, Gary, Chief Financial Officer, Meeker County Memorial Hospital, Litchfield, MN, p. A355

SOJKA, M.D., Matthew, Chief of Staff, Unity Hospital, Muscatine, IA, p. A238

SOKOLOW, Norman J., Chairman and Chief Executive Officer, Cornerstone of Medical Arts Center Hospital, New York, NY, p. A459

SOLARE, Frank A., President and Chief Executive Officer, Thorek Hospital and Medical Center, Chicago, IL, p. A191

SOLBERG, Bradley, FACHE, Chief Executive Officer, Hammond–Henry Hospital, Geneseo, IL, p. A195

SOLHEIM, John H., President and Chief Executive Officer, St. Peter's Hospital, Helena, MT, p. A399

SOLIE, M.D., Carol M., Vice President Medical Affairs, Marion General Hospital, Marion, OH, p. A517

SOLIMAN, Russell
Regional Director Information Services, Adventist GlenOaks Hospital, Glendale Heights, IL, p. A195
Regional Director Information Services, Hinsdale Hospital, Hinsdale, IL, p. A197

SOLIMON, Russ, Chief Information Officer, Adventist La Grange Memorial Hospital, La Grange, IL, p. A199

SOLL, M.D., Mark, Chief of Staff, French Hospital Medical Center, San Luis Obispo, CA, p. A91

SOLLENBERGER, Donna K., President and Chief Executive Officer, University of Wisconsin Hospital and Clinics, Madison, WI, p. A728

SOLOMON, M.D., Barry, Senior Vice President Clinical Affairs, Genesys Regional Medical Center, Grand Blanc, MI, p. A334

SOLOMON, Bruce, Chief Operating Officer, Cambridge Health Alliance, Cambridge, MA, p. A316

SOLOMON, Steve, Director Human Resources, West Shore Medical Center, Manistee, MI, p. A339

SOMMER, Randall, Chief Business Office, Veterans Affairs Medical Center, West Palm Beach, FL, p. A150

SOMMER, Robert, Vice President Human Resources, New Milford Hospital, New Milford, CT, p. A115

SOMMERKAMP, James, Director Finance, St. Luke Hospital East, Fort Thomas, KY, p. A264

SOMMERKAMP, Jim, Director Financial Services, St. Luke Hospital West, Florence, KY, p. A264

SOMMERS, Belinda, Chief Information Officer, Lake Charles Memorial Hospital, Lake Charles, LA, p. A285

SOMMERS, Thomas W., President and Chief Executive Officer, Beatrice Community Hospital and Health Center, Beatrice, NE, p. A405

SONDECKER, James, President, St. Joseph's Behavioral Health Center, Stockton, CA, p. A95

SONDERMAN, M.D., Thomas, Vice President and Chief Medical Officer, Columbus Regional Hospital, Columbus, IN, p. A213

SONDUCK, Allan C., President and Chief Executive Officer, St. Joseph's Hospital and Health Center, Dickinson, ND, p. A497

SONENREICH, Steven D., President and Chief Executive Officer, Mount Sinai Medical Center, Miami Beach, FL, p. A138

SONESON, Jeanine, Chief Financial Officer, Howard County Community Hospital, Saint Paul, NE, p. A412

SONG, M.D., Mark, Chief of Staff, St. Jude Medical Center, Fullerton, CA, p. A62

SONNENBERG, M.D., William, Medical Staff President, Titusville Area Hospital, Titusville, PA, p. A576

SONNENSCHEIN, Silvia, Chief of Staff, Kohala Hospital, Kohala, HI, p. A175

SONNENSHEIN, Mona, Senior Vice President for Hospital Administration, New York University Medical Center, New York, NY, p. A463

SOOD, M.D., Harish, Medical Director, Long Beach Medical Center, Long Beach, NY, p. A455

SOOHO, M.D., Alan M., Chief of Staff, Veterans Affairs Medical Center, Battle Creek, MI, p. A328

SOOHOO, Richard, Administrative Director Finance, Sutter Auburn Faith Hospital, Auburn, CA, p. A53

SOPTELEAN, Walter, Chief Financial Officer, Blackford Community Hospital, Hartford City, IN, p. A217

SORAN, Andrei, Chief Executive Officer, Nashoba Valley Medical Center, Ayer, MA, p. A312

SORBER, Lin, Vice President Human Resources, Butler Health System, Butler, PA, p. A554

SORENSEN, CPA, Damone, Chief Financial Officer, Alpena Regional Medical Center, Alpena, MI, p. A327

SORENSEN, Jon, Director Business Services, Delta Memorial Hospital, Dumas, AR, p. A42

SORENSEN, Todd, M.D., Chief Executive Officer, Regional West Medical Center, Scottsbluff, NE, p. A413

SORRELL, Sr, Ralph W., Chief Financial Officer, Adena Health System, Chillicothe, OH, p. A506

SORRENTINI, Cesar Ortiz, Director, Hospital Universitario Dr. Ramon Ruiz Arnau, Bayamon, PR, p. A744

SOSA, Fernando, Chief Operating Officer, San Juan City Hospital, San Juan, PR, p. A748

SOUCY, Robert, Chief Operating Officer, Brattleboro Retreat, Brattleboro, VT, p. A682

SOURNI, Jan, Health Information Officer, Middlesboro Appalachian Regional Hospital, Middlesboro, KY, p. A271

SOUSA, Francine, Director Management Information Service, New England Sinai Hospital and Rehabilitation Center, Stoughton, MA, p. A324

SOUTHALL, M.D., Anthony, Chief of Staff, St. John North Shores Hospital, Harrison Township, MI, p. A336

SOUTHARD, Suzanne, Director Finance, Community Hospital Association, Fairfax, MO, p. A381

SOUTHERLAND, David, Senior Vice President and Administrator, Woods Memorial Hospital District, Etowah, TN, p. A606

SOUTHERS, Nancy J.
Vice President and Chief Information Officer, Hospital for Sick Children, Washington, DC, p. A121
Vice President and Chief Information Officer, Hospital for Sick Children, Washington, DC, p. A121

SOUZA, Catherine, Chief Financial Officer, Washington Township Health Care District, Fremont, CA, p. A61

SOVETSKHY, Ed, Director Information Services, Portsmouth Regional Hospital, Portsmouth, NH, p. A423

SOWA, Phillip E., Chief Executive Officer, Meadowcrest Hospital, Gretna, LA, p. A281

SOWDERS, Dale, President and Chief Executive Officer, Holland Hospital, Holland, MI, p. A336

SOWELL, Ron, Executive Vice President, The Medical Center at Bowling Green, Bowling Green, KY, p. A262

SOWERS, R.N., MS, Kevin W., Chief Operating Officer, Duke University Hospital, Durham, NC, p. A481

SPACK, Stan, Director Information Technology, Buena Vista Regional Medical Center, Storm Lake, IA, p. A242

SPAETH, Steve, Interim Chief Executive Officer, Bridges Medical Services, Ada, MN, p. A349

SPANGENBERG, Nancy, Vice President and Chief Operating Officer, Passavant Area Hospital, Jacksonville, IL, p. A198

SPANGLER, M.D., Elizabeth, Vice President Medical Affairs, Charleston Area Medical Center, Charleston, WV, p. A714

SPANN, Chuck, Chief Financial Officer, Northwest Medical Center, Winfield, AL, p. A25

SPARKS, David G., Senior Vice President Finance, Providence Hospital, Washington, DC, p. A122

SPARKS, Gary R., Administrator, CrossRidge Community Hospital, Wynne, AR, p. A51

SPARKS, Glenn, Assistant Administrator, Kona Community Hospital, Kealakekua, HI, p. A175

SPARKS, Richard G., President, Watauga Medical Center, Boone, NC, p. A478

SPARTZ, Dale
Vice President Human Resources, John C. Lincoln Hospital – North Mountain, Phoenix, AZ, p. A34
Vice President Human Resources, John C. Lincoln Hospital–Deer Valley, Phoenix, AZ, p. A34

SPARTZ, Jeff, Administrator, Hennepin County Medical Center, Minneapolis, MN, p. A357

SPARZO, M.D., John, Vice President Medical Affairs, Hendricks Regional Health, Danville, IN, p. A213

SPAUDE, Paul A., FACHE, President and Chief Executive Officer, Borgess Medical Center, Kalamazoo, MI, p. A338

SPEACH, Lisa, Chief Operating Officer, Crouse Hospital, Syracuse, NY, p. A473

SPEAR, Robert M., Superintendent, Evansville State Hospital, Evansville, IN, p. A214

SPEARE, Mark, Senior Asociate Director Human Resourcdes, University of California Los Angeles Medical Center, Los Angeles, CA, p. A73

SPEARS Jr, Julius D., President and Chief Executive Officer, Providence Hospital, Washington, DC, p. A122

SPEARS, LaLana, Supervisor Accounting, U. S. Public Health Service Comprehensive Indian Health Facility, Claremore, OK, p. A529

SPEER, Michael N., Senior Vice President, Human Resources, Theda Clark Medical Center, Neenah, WI, p. A732

SPEER, Sandra, Administrative Director Human Resources, Sutter Delta Medical Center, Antioch, CA, p. A52

SPEIDEL, M.D., Francis X., Senior Vice President Medical Affairs and Chief Quality Officer, Mount Nittany Medical Center, State College, PA, p. A576

SPEIGHT, Marianne, Vice President Information System and Chief Information Officer, Children's Hospital Medical Center, Cincinnati, OH, p. A506

SPELL, Dale
Chief Executive Officer, Appling Healthcare System, Baxley, GA, p. A156
Chief Operating Officer, Appling Healthcare System, Baxley, GA, p. A156

SPELLMAN, Warren K., Chief Executive Officer, Holy Cross Hospital, Taos, NM, p. A445

SPELTZ, David E., Chief Executive Officer, Saint Vincent Catholic Medical Centers, New York, NY, p. B95

SPENCE, Stephen L., President and Chief Executive Officer, Lakeland Regional Hospital, Springfield, MO, p. A394

SPENCER, Corte J., Chief Executive Officer, Oswego Hospital, Oswego, NY, p. A468

SPENCER, Dale, Chief Financial Officer, Anson Community Hospital, Wadesboro, NC, p. A493

SPENCER, John, Director Human Resources, Alleghany Memorial Hospital, Sparta, NC, p. A492

SPENCER, Lynie, Director Finance, Baptist Medical Center Nassau, Fernandina Beach, FL, p. A128

SPENCER, Mike, Chief Information Officer, Henry County Memorial Hospital, New Castle, IN, p. A223

SPENCER, Neil O., President, Ogden Regional Medical Center, Ogden, UT, p. A678

SPENCER, Roy, Chief Financial Officer, T. J. Samson Community Hospital, Glasgow, KY, p. A265

SPENCER, Susan, Chief Financial Officer, Samaritan Memorial Hospital, Macon, MO, p. A387

SPERBER, Edward E., Chief of Staff, Veterans Affairs Medical Center, Dayton, OH, p. A512

SPERL, Katy, Human Resources Director, Bridgton Hospital, Bridgton, ME, p. A297

SPERLING, Ronald K.
Chief Financial Officer, Swedish Health Services, Seattle, WA, p. A708
Chief Financial Officer, Swedish Medical Center–Providence Campus, Seattle, WA, p. A708

SPERTI, Patrick J., Chief Executive Officer, Oakland Regional Hospital, Southfield, MI, p. A343

SPEZIA, Anthony L., President and Chief Executive Officer, Covenant Health, Knoxville, TN, p. B34

SPHAR, Jessica, Director Human Resources, St. Francis Medical Center–West, Ewa Beach, HI, p. A173

SPICER, Charles, Chf Oper Officer, University of Texas Health Center at Tyler, Tyler, TX, p. A671

SPICER, John R.
President and Chief Executive Officer, Mount Vernon Hospital, Mount Vernon, NY, p. A457
President and Chief Executive Officer, Sound Shore Medical Center of Westchester, New Rochelle, NY, p. A458
Interim President and Chief Executive Officer, Westchester Medical Center, Valhalla, NY, p. A475

SPICER, Michael J., President and Chief Executive Officer, St. Joseph's Medical Center, Yonkers, NY, p. A476

SPIEGEL, Robert W., Chief Executive Officer, Westwood Lodge Hospital, Westwood, MA, p. A325

SPIEL, Bob, Chief Executive Officer, Idaho Falls Recovery Center, Idaho Falls, ID, p. A179

SPIER, M.D., Scott A., Senior Vice President Medical Affairs, Mercy Medical Center, Baltimore, MD, p. A304

SPIGNER, Jason, Vice President Human Resources, Advocate Bethany Hospital, Chicago, IL, p. A186

SPIKE, Colleen A., Administrator, St. Peter Community Hospital, Saint Peter, MN, p. A362

SPILLANE, Rosemarie, Chief of Medical Staff, Piedmont Mountainside Hospital, Jasper, GA, p. A164

SPILLER, M.D., James, Chief of Staff, Daviess Community Hospital, Washington, IN, p. A227

SPILLERS, Brian, Chief Financial Officer, St. Luke's Hospital, Chesterfield, MO, p. A380

SPILLERS, David S., Chief Operating Officer, Mission Hospitals, Asheville, NC, p. A477

SPINELL, Laura, Director Human Resources, Twin City Hospital, Dennison, OH, p. A513

SPINELLA, Judy L., R.N., President and Chief Executive Officer, Gunnison Valley Hospital, Gunnison, CO, p. A106

SPINHARNEY, Sarah, Senior Vice President, Baptist Medical Center, San Antonio, TX, p. A663

SPINNEY, M.D., Carmen, President Medical and Dental Staff, Jersey Shore Hospital, Jersey Shore, PA, p. A561

SPIRES, Madis, Vice President of Patient Services, Colquitt Regional Medical Center, Moultrie, GA, p. A166

SPIRES, M.D., Timothy, Chief Medical Staff, Morehouse General Hospital, Bastrop, LA, p. A277

SPIRITUS, M.D., Eugene, Chief Medical Officer, University of California, Irvine Medical Center, Orange, CA, p. A79

SPISSO, Johnese, Chief Operating Officer, Harborview Medical Center, Seattle, WA, p. A707

SPITLER, David, Chief Financial Officer, Riverside County Regional Medical Center, Moreno Valley, CA, p. A77

SPIVAK, Natalie, Director Information Services, Oaklawn Hospital, Marshall, MI, p. A340

SPIVEY, David A., President and Chief Executive Officer, St. Mary Mercy Hospital, Livonia, MI, p. A339

SPIVEY, Sue
Administrator, Charlton Memorial Hospital, Folkston, GA, p. A162
Administrator, Irwin County Hospital, Ocilla, GA, p. A167

SPIVEY–PAUL, Cathi, Acting Director, Veterans Affairs Illiana Health Care System, Danville, IL, p. A191

SPOELMAN, Roger, President and Chief Executive Officer, Mercy General Health Partners, Muskegon, MI, p. A341

SPOONER, Jim, Executive Director, St. Lawrence Psychiatric Center, Ogdensburg, NY, p. A468

SPOONER, Michael A., Chief of Staff, Northern Arizona VA Health Care System, Prescott, AZ, p. A35

SPOONER, William T.
Senior Vice President and Chief Information Officer, Sharp Grossmont Hospital, La Mesa, CA, p. A66
Senior Vice President and Chief Information Officer, Sharp Memorial Hospital, San Diego, CA, p. A87

SPRAGUE, M.D., Remington, Chief Medical Officer, Mercy General Health Partners, Muskegon, MI, p. A341

SPRAGUE, Todd, Marketing and Community Relations Director, St. Charles Medical Center – Bend, Bend, OR, p. A542

SPRATLING, M.D., Larry, Chief Medical Officer, Banner Baywood Medical Center, Mesa, AZ, p. A32

SPRAY, William Russell, Chief Executive Officer, Southern Tennessee Medical Center, Winchester, TN, p. A619

SPREITLER, Danny, President and Chief Executive Officer, Gilmore Memorial Hospital, Amory, MS, p. A366

SPRIGGS, Larry, Controller, HEALTHSOUTH Rehabilitation Institute of San Antonio, San Antonio, TX, p. A664

SPRIGGS, Phyllis, Vice President, Human Resources, Muskogee Regional Medical Center, Muskogee, OK, p. A534

SPRING, Jason A., Chief Executive Officer and Administrator, Healthpark Hospital, Hot Springs National Park, AR, p. A45

SPRINGER, Colleen, Director Human Resources, Marshalltown Medical and Surgical Center, Marshalltown, IA, p. A237

SPRINGER, M.D., David, Medical Staff President, Merrill Pioneer Community Hospital, Rock Rapids, IA, p. A240

SPRINGER, R.N., MS, Karen, Chief Operting Officer and Chief Nursing Officer, Dupont Hospital, Fort Wayne, IN, p. A215

SPRINGER, Madge, Director of Human Resources, Florida Hospital Waterman, Tavares, FL, p. A149

SPRINGFIELD, James G., FACHE, President and Chief Executive Officer, Valley Baptist Health System, Harlingen, TX, p. A643

SPRINGMANN, Tressa, Chief Information Officer, Greater Baltimore Medical Center, Baltimore, MD, p. A302

SPRINKEL, George, Financial Officer, Pender Memorial Hospital, Burgaw, NC, p. A478

SPUHLER, Richard
Chief Financial Officer and Chief Operating Officer, Brigham City Community Hospital, Brigham City, UT, p. A676
Chief Financial Officer, Brigham City Community Hospital, Brigham City, UT, p. A676

SPURGEON, Sharon, Interim Chief Executive Officer, Coalinga Regional Medical Center, Coalinga, CA, p. A57

SQUIRES, David, Chief Information Officer, United Medical Center, Cheyenne, WY, p. A739

SQUIRES, Jared, Chief Financial Officer, Covenant Hospital–Levelland, Levelland, TX, p. A652

SREBINSKI, Ron, Chief Financial Officer, McKenzie Memorial Hospital, Sandusky, MI, p. A345

SROCK, Timothy, Vice President Human Resources, McLaren Regional Medical Center, Flint, MI, p. A333

ST CLAIR, M.D., Stephen, President, North Adams Regional Hospital, North Adams, MA, p. A321

ST GEORGE, Scott, Chief Financial Officer, Seton Health System, Troy, NY, p. A474

ST JOHN, Keith, Controller, St. Luke's Hospital, Bluefield, WV, p. A713

ST PIERRE, Jay, Chief Financial Officer, Valley Regional Medical Center, Brownsville, TX, p. A627

ST. GEORGE, George H., Chief Executive Officer, Screven County Hospital, Sylvania, GA, p. A170

STAAS Jr, William E., M.D., President, Chief Executive Officer and Medical Director, Magee Rehabilitation Hospital, Philadelphia, PA, p. A568

STACEY, Bryan, Chief Executive Officer, Kiowa District Hospital and Manor, Kiowa, KS, p. A250

STACK, R. Timothy, FACHE, President and Chief Executive Officer, Piedmont Healthcare, Atlanta, GA, p. B84

STACY, Doug, Chief Information Officer, Coffeyville Regional Medical Center, Coffeyville, KS, p. A245

STAFFORD, Benny, Interim Finance Director, Sutter Solano Medical Center, Vallejo, CA, p. A98

STAFFORD, James, Director Information Systems, Aliquippa Community Hospital, Aliquippa, PA, p. A551

STAFFORD, John Scott, Chief Executive Officer, De Soto Regional Health System, Mansfield, LA, p. A286

STAFFORD, Shelly, Director Human Resources, River West Medical Center, Plaquemine, LA, p. A291

STAFFORD, Tom, Director Information Systems, Tri–City Medical Center, Oceanside, CA, p. A79

STAFFORD, Troy D., Assistant Administrator Finance, Olmsted Medical Center, Rochester, MN, p. A360

STAGEBERG, Kerrie
Director Finance and Information Systems, Stevens Community Medical Center, Morris, MN, p. A358
Director Finance and Information Systems, Stevens Community Medical Center, Morris, MN, p. A358

STAGG, Kevin, Vice President Finance and Chief Financial Officer, Christian Health Care Center, Wyckoff, NJ, p. A439

STAGNER, Barbara, Human Resources Director, Palo Pinto General Hospital, Mineral Wells, TX, p. A657

STAHELI, Michael, Chief Executive Officer, Cache Valley Specialty Hospital, North Logan, UT, p. A678

STAIMAN, M.D., JD, Richard, Vice President Medical Affairs, Dorchester General Hospital, Cambridge, MD, p. A306

STALCUP, Linda, Chief Executive Officer, Stevens County Hospital, Hugoton, KS, p. A249

STALDER, James C., Senior Vice President and Chief Information Officer, Mercy Medical Center, Baltimore, MD, p. A304

STALLINGS, Crystal, Chief Information Officer, Skaggs Community Health Center, Branson, MO, p. A379

STALLINGS, Elizabeth, Chief Operating Officer, Mt. Diablo Medical Pavilion, Concord, CA, p. A57

STAMM, Scott C., Chief Executive Officer, River Park Hospital, Huntington, WV, p. A716

STAMPOHAR, Jeffry, Chief Executive Officer, Deer River HealthCare Center, Deer River, MN, p. A352

STANBERRY, Pamela, Administrator, Wesley Rehabilitation Hospital, Wichita, KS, p. A260

STANCIL, Stan, Deputy Commander, U. S. Air Force Regional Hospital, Elmendorf AFB, AK, p. A27

STANCILL, Linda, Vice President and Chief Financial Officer, St. Joseph Health System, Tawas City, MI, p. A346

STANDER, M.D., Paul, Physician Director, Banner Good Samaritan Medical Center, Phoenix, AZ, p. A33

STANDLEY, Ron, Director Information Systems, Doctors Hospital, Jackson, MI, p. A337

STANDRIDGE, Debra
President, St. Francis Hospital, Milwaukee, WI, p. A731
President, St. Francis Hospital, Milwaukee, WI, p. A731

STANEK, Janet, Chief Information Officer, Stormont–Vail HealthCare, Topeka, KS, p. A258

STANEK, Robert V., President and Chief Executive Officer, Catholic Health East, Newtown Square, PA, p. B23

STANFILL, Timothy, Chief Financial Officer, Summit Medical Center, Hermitage, TN, p. A607

STANIC, Steve, Chief Information Officer, Memorial Health, Savannah, GA, p. A169

STANIFER, M.D., Ralph M., Vice President Medical Affairs and Chief Medical Officer, St. Luke's Regional Medical Center, Sioux City, IA, p. A242

STANLEY, Barbara, Human Resources Director, Mountain View Regional Medical Center, Norton, VA, p. A693

STANLEY, John T., Vice President Planning and Information Systems, Riverside Regional Medical Center, Newport News, VA, p. A692

STANSBERRY, David L., Administrator, University of Miami Hospital and Clinics, Miami, FL, p. A138

STANSBURY, Kevin M., Chief Operating Officer, Carson Tahoe Hospital, Carson City, NV, p. A415

STANTON, Jackie, Coordinator Human Resources, Wesley Rehabilitation Hospital, Wichita, KS, p. A260

STANTON, Lowell, Chief Financial Officer, Methodist Sugar Land Hospital, Sugar Land, TX, p. A668

STANTON, Melanie, Administrator, North Side Hospital, Johnson City, TN, p. A609

STAPEK, Roger, Vice President and Chief Financial Officer, Northfield Hospital, Northfield, MN, p. A359

STAPLES, Janet, Director Human Resources, South Central Regional Medical Center, Laurel, MS, p. A372

STARK, Charles A., CHE, President and Chief Executive Officer, Firelands Regional Health System, Sandusky, OH, p. A522

STARK, David A.
Chief Operating Officer and Chief Development Officer, Iowa Lutheran Hospital, Des Moines, IA, p. A232
Executive Vice President and Chief Operating Officer, Iowa Methodist Medical Center, Des Moines, IA, p. A232

STARKEBAUM, M.D., Gordon, Chief of Staff, Veterans Affairs Puget Sound Health Care System, Seattle, WA, p. A708

STARKEY, Tim
Chief Executive Officer, Memorial Hospital of Texas County, Guymon, OK, p. A531
Chief Executive Officer, Memorial Hospital of Texas County, Guymon, OK, p. A531

STARLING, Susan, President and Chief Executive Officer, Marcum and Wallace Memorial Hospital, Irvine, KY, p. A266

STARNS, M.D., Harry, Chief Medical Staff, Ozark Health Medical Center, Clinton, AR, p. A41

STARR Jr, Hickory
Chief Executive Officer, U. S. Public Health Service Indian Hospital, Lawton, OK, p. A532
Administrator, William W. Hastings Indian Hospital, Tahlequah, OK, p. A539

STASTNY, Mark, Vice President Information Technology, Saint Francis Hospital, Tulsa, OK, p. A540

STASZAK, M.D., Chris, Chief of Staff, Poudre Valley Hospital, Fort Collins, CO, p. A105

STATEN, Gary L., Chief Executive Officer, Trace Regional Hospital, Houston, MS, p. A370

STATEN, James, Senior Vice President Finance, Yale–New Haven Hospital, New Haven, CT, p. A115

STATES, Chuck, Director Information Systems, Punxsutawney Area Hospital, Punxsutawney, PA, p. A574

STATON, Paul, Chief Financial Officer, University of California Los Angeles Medical Center, Los Angeles, CA, p. A73

STATUTO, Richard, President and Chief Executive Officer, Bon Secours Health System, Inc., Marriottsville, MD, p. B18

STATZ, M.D., Lila, Chief of Staff, Haxtun Hospital District, Haxtun, CO, p. A106

STAUDER, Mark S., Executive Vice President and Chief Operating Officer, St. John's Mercy Medical Center, Saint Louis, MO, p. A392

STAUFFER, Keith, Regional Information Technology Director, St. Francis Hospital, Federal Way, WA, p. A703

STAVELEY, Melinda, President and Chief Executive Officer, Rehabilitation Institute at Santa Barbara, Santa Barbara, CA, p. A92

STEAD, M.D., William, Director Informatics Center, Vanderbilt University Medical Center, Nashville, TN, p. A616

STEARNS, Regina, Human Resource Director, Sullivan County Community Hospital, Sullivan, IN, p. A225

STEBBINS, Trish, Director of Management Information Systems, Florida Hospital Fish Memorial, Orange City, FL, p. A140

STEC, Juli, Chief Executive Officer, HEALTHSOUTH Rehabilitation Hospital of Fort Smith, Fort Smith, AR, p. A43

STECHER, Delores, Director Human Resources, Unity Hospital, Muscatine, IA, p. A238

STECK, Stacey, Chief Information Officer, Providence St. Peter Hospital, Olympia, WA, p. A705

STECK, Stacy, Chief Information Officer, Providence Centralia Hospital, Centralia, WA, p. A701

STECKLER, Michael J., President and Chief Executive Officer, Jennie M. Melham Memorial Medical Center, Broken Bow, NE, p. A405

STED, Charles A., Pesident and Chief Executive Officer, Hawaii Pacific Health, Honolulu, HI, p. B48

STEED, Edie, Chief Information Officer, Gila Regional Medical Center, Silver City, NM, p. A445

STEED, Larry N., Administrator, Tanner Medical Center–Villa Rica, Villa Rica, GA, p. A171

STEED, Robert A., Director Information Systems, Capital Regional Medical Center, Tallahassee, FL, p. A147

STEEDMAN, M.D., Robert, Chief of Staff, Western Medical Center–Santa Ana, Santa Ana, CA, p. A92

STEEGE, Armin L., Administrator and Vice President, Seton Shoal Creek Hospital, Austin, TX, p. A624

STEELE, Barbara, President, The Toledo Hospital, Toledo, OH, p. A523

STEELE, Franklin W., President of Valdese Hospital Medical Staff, Valdese General Hospital, Valdese, NC, p. A493

STEELE Jr, Glenn, Ph.D., President and Chief Executive Officer, Geisinger Health System, Danville, PA, p. B46

STEELE, Kenneth R., President, St. Mary's Medical Center, San Francisco, CA, p. A89

STEELE, M.D., Mark
Chief Medical Officer, Truman Medical Center–Hospital Hill, Kansas City, MO, p. A385
Chief Medical Officer, Truman Medical Center–Lakewood, Kansas City, MO, p. A385

STEELE, Terry L., Vice President Finance and Chief Financial Officer, Holland Hospital, Holland, MI, p. A336

STEELE, Tina, Chief Financial Officer, Pawnee Municipal Hospital, Pawnee, OK, p. A537

STEELEY, Hubert, Administrator, Gulf Pines Hospital, Port Saint Joe, FL, p. A144

STEELMAN, Jeffrey, Director Information Systems, Alleghany Regional Hospital, Low Moor, VA, p. A690

STEEVENS, Alan, Director Management Information, St. Clare Hospital and Health Services, Baraboo, WI, p. A723

STEFANIDES, Christine M., CHE, President and Chief Executive Officer, Civista Health, La Plata, MD, p. A309

STEFFEN, Keith E., Administrator and Chief Executive Officer, OSF Saint Francis Medical Center, Peoria, IL, p. A205

STEFKA, Darryl, Administrator, Cuero Community Hospital, Cuero, TX, p. A631

STEFL, William, Chief Information Officer, Mercy Memorial Hospital System, Monroe, MI, p. A340

STEFO, Andrew, Senior Vice President and Chief Financial Officer, Palos Community Hospital, Palos Heights, IL, p. A204

STEGNER, Kenneth, Interim Chief Executive Officer, Dodge County Hospital, Eastman, GA, p. A161

STEHLEY, Felicia, Chief Executive Officer, Meadows Psychiatric Center, Centre Hall, PA, p. A554

STEICHEN, Barry L., Senior Vice President and Chief Financial Officer, Saint Francis Hospital, Tulsa, OK, p. A540

STEIGER, Linda, Administrator, Select Specialty Hospital–Mount Clemens, Mount Clemens, MI, p. A341

STEIGER, Nancy, Chief Executive Officer, San Mateo Medical Center, San Mateo, CA, p. A91

STEIGMEYER, Robert, Chief Financial Officer, Northwest Hospital, Seattle, WA, p. A707

STEIN, Bob, Chief Executive Officer, Kindred Hospital–Houston, Houston, TX, p. A646

STEIN, Eric H., FACHE, Administrator and Chief Executive Officer, Bassett Hospital of Schoharie County, Cobleskill, NY, p. A450

STEIN, Gary M., CHE, Chief Executive Officer, Touro Rehabilitation Center, New Orleans, LA, p. A290

STEIN, M.D., Joel, Chief Medical Officer, Spaulding Rehabilitation Hospital, Boston, MA, p. A314

STEIN, M.D., Keith
Senior Vice President Medical Affairs, Baptist Medical Center, Jacksonville, FL, p. A132
Chief Medical Officer, Baptist Medical Center–Beaches, Jacksonville Beach, FL, p. A133

STEIN, M.D., Norman, Vice President Medical Affairs and Medical Director, Orange Regional Medical Center, Middletown, NY, p. A457

STEIN, Norman V., President, University Community Health, Tampa, FL, p. B116

STEIN, M.D., Robert, Vice President, Medical Management, Advocate Christ Medical Center, Oak Lawn, IL, p. A203

STEIN, Sheldon J.
President and Chief Executive Officer, Mt. Washington Pediatric Hospital, Baltimore, MD, p. A304
President and Chief Executive Officer, Mt. Washington Pediatric Hospital, Baltimore, MD, p. A304

STEINBACH, Gary
Administrator, Southeast Colorado Hospital and Long Term Care, Springfield, CO, p. A109
Chief Executive Officer, Southeast Colorado Hospital and Long Term Care, Springfield, CO, p. A109

STEINBERG, Marc, Vice President Community Relations and Physician Recruitment, Passavant Area Hospital, Jacksonville, IL, p. A198

STEINBERG, M.D., Marc, Chief of Staff, Mountainview Medical Center, White Sulphur Springs, MT, p. A402

STEINER, Garith W., Chief Executive Officer and Administrator, Vernon Memorial Healthcare, Viroqua, WI, p. A737

STEINER, Keith M., Chief Executive Officer, Madison Memorial Hospital, Rexburg, ID, p. A181

STEINER, Mary, Administrator, Herington Municipal Hospital, Herington, KS, p. A248

STEINES, Brian D., Chief Financial Officer, Midwest Regional Medical Center, Midwest City, OK, p. A533

STEINHAUER, Bruce W., M.D., President and Chief Executive Officer, Regional Medical Center at Memphis, Memphis, TN, p. A613

STEINKIRCHNER, Jim, Regional Controller, HEALTHSOUTH Harmarville Rehabilitation Hospital, Pittsburgh, PA, p. A571

STELLE, Walter, Ph.D., Director, Dorothea Dix Hospital, Raleigh, NC, p. A489

STELLER, Tim, Chief Executive Officer, North Central Health Care Facilities, Wausau, WI, p. A737

STENCE, Sue, Administrator, Continuous Care Centers of Bartlesville, Bartlesville, OK, p. A528

STENHOUSE, Andrew C., M.D., Acting Director and Chief Executive Officer, Amarillo Veterans Affairs Health Care System, Amarillo, TX, p. A620

STENHOUSE, M.D., Andrew C., Chief of Staff, Amarillo Veterans Affairs Health Care System, Amarillo, TX, p. A620

STENSAGER, Mark, President and Chief Executive Officer, Guthrie Healthcare System, Sayre, PA, p. B48

STENSON, Richard, President and Chief Executive Officer, Tuality Healthcare, Hillsboro, OR, p. A544

STENSRUD, Kirk, Chief Executive Officer, Hendricks Community Hospital, Hendricks, MN, p. A355

STEPANIK, Mark J., Chief Executive Officer, Kindred Hospital Kansas City, Kansas City, MO, p. A384

STEPANSKY, M.D., David, Chief Medical Officer, Phoenixville Hospital, Phoenixville, PA, p. A571

STEPHAN, M.D., William, Vice President Medical Affairs, St. Joseph Hospital, Nashua, NH, p. A423

STEPHEN, Ann, Director Public Relations, Southeastern Regional Medical Center, Lumberton, NC, p. A487

STEPHENS, Donita, Administrative Assistant to Financial Services, Choctaw Health Center, Philadelphia, MS, p. A374

STEPHENS Jr, Jack T., President and Chief Executive Officer, Lakeland Regional Medical Center, Lakeland, FL, p. A134

STEPHENS, Kenneth R., Executive Vice President, Cumberland Medical Center, Crossville, TN, p. A605

STEPHENS, Kimbro, President and Chief Executive Officer, Living Hope Texarkana, Texarkana, AR, p. A51

STEPHENS, Lee, Vice President Finance, Walker Baptist Medical Center, Jasper, AL, p. A20

STEPHENS, Maria, Director of Human Resources, Henderson Memorial Hospital, Henderson, TX, p. A643

STEPHENS, Michael D., President and Chief Executive Officer, Hoag Memorial Hospital Presbyterian, Newport Beach, CA, p. A78

STEPHENS, Michael R., President, Greene Memorial Hospital, Xenia, OH, p. A525

STEPHENS, Norman F., Chief Executive Officer, Valley Hospital, Palmer, AK, p. A28

STEPHENS, M.D., Ron, Chief of Staff, Parkview Regional Hospital, Mexia, TX, p. A656

STEPHENS, M.D., Todd, Chief of Staff, Minneola District Hospital, Minneola, KS, p. A253

STEPHENS, Tony, Chief Information Officer, Central Arkansas Veterans Healthcare System, Little Rock, AR, p. A46

STEPHENSON, Christy, Chief Executive Officer, Robert Wood Johnson University Hospital at Hamilton, Hamilton, NJ, p. A429

STEPHENSON, Melinda, Chief Operating Officer, Clear Lake Regional Medical Center, Webster, TX, p. A673

STERBACH, Maureen, Vice President Human Resources, St. Joseph's Hospital and Medical Center, Phoenix, AZ, p. A35

STERLING, Jane, Director Information Systems, Barnes–Jewish West County Hospital, Saint Louis, MO, p. A390

STERLING, Julie, Information System Manager, South Sunflower County Hospital, Indianola, MS, p. A370

STERLING, Mike, Director Human Resources, Brown County General Hospital, Georgetown, OH, p. A514

STERN, M.D., David, Chief of Staff, Columbia Hospital, West Palm Beach, FL, p. A150

STERNBERG, Charles D., Chief Information Resources Management Service, Veterans Affairs Medical Center, Memphis, TN, p. A614

STERNFELS, Bobbie, Medical Records Supervisor, Prevost Memorial Hospital, Donaldsonville, LA, p. A280

STETTHEIMER, Timothy, Vice President and Chief Information Officer, St. Vincent's Hospital, Birmingham, AL, p. A15

STEUSSY, William, Chief Financial Officer, Greene County Medical Center, Jefferson, IA, p. A236

STEVEN, M.D., James, Chief Medical Officer, Children's Hospital of Philadelphia, Philadelphia, PA, p. A567

STEVENS, Ann Marie, Director of Operations, Mid–Valley Hospital, Peckville, PA, p. A567

STEVENS, Beth, Vice President of Human Resources, St. Mary's Hospital, Amsterdam, NY, p. A447

STEVENS, Chris E., Chief Information Officer, Deaconess Billings Clinic, Billings, MT, p. A396

STEVENS, Diana R., Administrator, Garden County Hospital, Oshkosh, NE, p. A412

STEVENS, Essimae, Service Unit Director, U.S. Public Health Service Indian Hospital, Redlake, MN, p. A360

STEVENS, Harry H., President and Chief Executive Officer, Bradley County Medical Center, Warren, AR, p. A51

STEVENS, Helen L., Chief Executive Officer, Heartland Behavioral Healthcare, Massillon, OH, p. A518

STEVENS, Janis, Director Human Resources, Raulerson Hospital, Okeechobee, FL, p. A140

STEVENS, Jeff, Vice President Human Resources, North Adams Regional Hospital, North Adams, MA, p. A321

STEVENS, Robert, President and Chief Executive Officer, Ridgeview Medical Center, Waconia, MN, p. A364

STEVENS, Velinda
President, Health Center Northwest, Kalispell, MT, p. A400
President, Kalispell Regional Medical Center, Kalispell, MT, p. A400

STEVENS Jr, Vernon R., Administrator, Riverland Medical Center, Ferriday, LA, p. A280

STEVENS III, Ward W., CHE, Chief Executive Officer, Montgomery Regional Hospital, Blacksburg, VA, p. A686

STEVENSON, Jerry L., Chief Executive Officer, St. Edward Mercy Medical Center, Fort Smith, AR, p. A44

STEVENSON, M.D., John, Medical Director, HEALTHSOUTH Braintree Rehabilitation Hospital, Braintree, MA, p. A315

STEVENSON, Mike, Administrator, Murphy Medical Center, Murphy, NC, p. A488

STEVES, Sonja, Vice President Marketing, Legacy Good Samaritan Hospital and Medical Center, Portland, OR, p. A547

STEWARD, Todd, President and Chief Executive Officer, North Suburban Medical Center, Thornton, CO, p. A110

STEWART, Bruce E.
Acting Director, Jonathan M. Wainwright Memorial VA Medical Center, Walla Walla, WA, p. A711
Acting Director, Jonathan M. Wainwright Memorial VA Medical Center, Walla Walla, WA, p. A711

STEWART, Charles L., Administrator, Northport Medical Center, Northport, AL, p. A22

STEWART, Charles R., Vice President Business, Finance and Corporate Compliance, Southern Maryland Hospital Center, Clinton, MD, p. A306

STEWART, Christine R., Administrator, Russellville Hospital, Russellville, AL, p. A23

STEWART, Dalton, Chief Executive Officer, Kindred Hospital–Mansfield, Mansfield, TX, p. A655

STEWART, David K.
Vice President Finance, St. John West Shore Hospital, Cleveland, OH, p. A509
Vice President Financial Operations, St. Vincent Charity Hospital, Cleveland, OH, p. A509

STEWART, M.D., Deborah G., Chief Medical Officer and Medical Director, Brooks Rehabilitation Hospital, Jacksonville, FL, p. A132

STEWART, Diane, Chief Operating Officer, Kell West Regional Hospital, Wichita Falls, TX, p. A674

STEWART, Diane Gail
Chief Administrative Officer, Sutter Center for Psychiatry, Sacramento, CA, p. A85
Chief Administrative Officer, Sutter Center for Psychiatry, Sacramento, CA, p. A85

STEWART, Evelyn G., Chief Executive Officer, Mesa Hill Specialty Hospital, El Paso, TX, p. A637

STEWART, Gregory, Commander, Medical Support Squadron, Wilford Hall Medical Center, Lackland AFB, TX, p. A652

STEWART, Hedda, Director Human Resources, Neshoba County General Hospital, Philadelphia, MS, p. A374

STEWART, Jane, Director Information Services, J. F. K. Medical Center, Atlantis, FL, p. A123

STEWART, John
Interim Chief Executive Officer, The Heart Center of Indiana, Indianapolis, IN, p. A219
Director Information Systems, Anaheim Memorial Medical Center, Anaheim, CA, p. A52

STEWART, Joseph A., Chief Executive Officer, Butler Health System, Butler, PA, p. A554

STEWART, M.D., Kendall, Medical Director, Southern Ohio Medical Center, Portsmouth, OH, p. A521

STEWART, M.D., Marian, Chief of Staff, Jay Hospital, Jay, FL, p. A133

STEWART, Nova
Chief Information Officer, Western Medical Center Anaheim, Anaheim, CA, p. A52
Chief Information Officer, Western Medical Center–Santa Ana, Santa Ana, CA, p. A92

STEWART, Patrick, Vice President of Information Systems, Self Regional Healthcare, Greenwood, SC, p. A589

STEWART, Patty, Chief Financial Officer, Memorial Hospital, Gonzales, TX, p. A642

STEWART, Paul R., President and Chief Executive Officer, Merle West Medical Center, Klamath Falls, OR, p. A545

STEWART, M.D., Paula, Medical Director, HEALTHSOUTH Lakeshore Rehabilitation Hospital, Birmingham, AL, p. A15

STEWART, M.D., D., Russell L., Chief Medical Officer, Braxton County Memorial Hospital, Gassaway, WV, p. A715

STEWART, Scott, Director Management Information Systems, Rochelle Community Hospital, Rochelle, IL, p. A206

STEWART, Shirley A., CHE, Chief Executive Officer, Lakeside Hospital, Metairie, LA, p. A286

STEWART, Terry
Director Information Systems, Dauterive Hospital, New Iberia, LA, p. A288
Chief Management and Learning Resources, Veterans Affairs New Jersey Health Care System, East Orange, NJ, p. A427

STEWART, Thomas, Medical Information Services Flight Commander, U. S. Air Force Hospital, MacDill AFB, FL, p. A135

STEWART RATTRAY, Cindy, Human Resources Director, Jewish Hospital–Shelbyville, Shelbyville, KY, p. A274

STHAY, M.D., Michael, Chief Medical Officer, Ocean Beach Hospital, Ilwaco, WA, p. A703

STIEB, Pamela, Finance Coordinator, Sterling Regional MedCenter, Sterling, CO, p. A109

STIER, M.D., Jeffrey, Medical Director, Sound Shore Medical Center of Westchester, New Rochelle, NY, p. A458

STIFFARM, Duane, Chief Information Officer, U. S. Public Health Service Indian Hospital, Harlem, MT, p. A399

STIFFARM, Kevin, Chief Executive Officer, Crow/Northern Cheyenne Hospital, Crow Agency, MT, p. A397

STIGLEMAN, Randy, Chief Financial Officer, Stewart–Webster Hospital, Richland, GA, p. A167

STILLER, Brian, Chief Operating Officer, Veterans Affairs Medical Center, Minneapolis, MN, p. A358

STILLMAN, Diane, Chief Operating Officer, Mason General Hospital, Shelton, WA, p. A709

STILLMAN, Elizabeth M., Acting Director, Colorado Mental Health Institute at Fort Logan, Denver, CO, p. A103

STILLO, M.D., Joseph, Medical Director, HEALTHSOUTH Rehabilitation Hospital of New Jersey, Toms River, NJ, p. A437

STILLWELL, James M., Director, Impact Drug and Alcohol Treatment Center, Pasadena, CA, p. A81

STILLWELL, M.D., Paul, Physician in Chief, Phoenix Children's Hospital, Phoenix, AZ, p. A34

STILTNER, Wanda, Director Human Resources, Buchanan General Hospital, Grundy, VA, p. A689

STIMSON–RUSIN, Judi, Chief Financial Officer, Palm Beach Gardens Medical Center, Palm Beach Gardens, FL, p. A141

STINDT, John L., CHE, Chief Executive Officer, Daniels Memorial Hospital, Scobey, MT, p. A402

STINSON, John C., President and Chief Executive Officer, Quorum Health Resources, Plano, TX, p. B88

STINSON, Katy, Director Information Services, Medical Center of Southeastern Oklahoma, Durant, OK, p. A530

STINSON, Martha, Director, Columbia Hospital, West Palm Beach, FL, p. A150

STINSON, Mary, Chief Financial Officer, Choctaw Memorial Hospital, Hugo, OK, p. A532

STINSON, Sandi, Director Human Resources, Lompoc Healthcare District, Lompoc, CA, p. A68

STIPE, Christopher, Administrator and Chief Executive Officer, Clara Barton Hospital, Hoisington, KS, p. A248

STIRE, David R., Chief Executive Officer, Jane Phillips Medical Center, Bartlesville, OK, p. A528

STIRLING, Thomas, Chief Information Officer, Franklin Foundation Hospital, Franklin, LA, p. A281

STITT, Janice, Vice President and Chief Financial Officer, Clinton Memorial Hospital, Saint Johns, MI, p. A344

STIVER, M.D., Ken, Vice President Medical Affairs, St. Joseph Hospital, Eureka, CA, p. A59

STIVERS, Richard M., Senior Vice President Health System Services, Deaconess Hospital, Evansville, IN, p. A214

STOCK, Fred
Chief Operating Officer and Executive Director of Nursing Home, Miami Jewish Home and Hospital for Aged, Miami, FL, p. A137
Chief Operating Officer and Executive Director of Nursing Home, Miami Jewish Home and Hospital for Aged, Miami, FL, p. A137

STOCK, Greg K., Chief Executive Officer, Thibodaux Regional Medical Center, Thibodaux, LA, p. A294

STOCK, Neil, Executive Director Information Services, Mercy Medical Center, Durango, CO, p. A104

STOCKS, Jere D., President, Washington Adventist Hospital, Takoma Park, MD, p. A311

STODDARD, Mark R.
President, Central Valley Medical Center, Nephi, UT, p. A677
President, Rural Health Management Corporation, Nephi, UT, p. B94

STOFER, Gordon, Vice President Fiscal Services, Pratt Regional Medical Center, Pratt, KS, p. A255

STOFFERSON, Terry, Chief Financial Officer, Western Plains Medical Complex, Dodge City, KS, p. A246

STOGSDILL, Vicki, Chief Operating Officer, Owensboro Medical Health System, Owensboro, KY, p. A272

STOJAKOVICH, Edward R., Chief Financial Officer, Reston Hospital Center, Reston, VA, p. A694

STOKER, Teresa, Chief Executive Officer, Hillside Hospital, Atlanta, GA, p. A154

STOKES, Elia, Chief Financial Officer, Denton Regional Medical Center, Denton, TX, p. A635

STOKES, Gary L.
Chief Executive Officer, Nacogdoches Medical Center, Nacogdoches, TX, p. A658
Chief Executive Officer, Shelby Regional Medical Center, Center, TX, p. A628

STOKES, Nancy, Director, Bon Secours Baltimore Health System, Baltimore, MD, p. A302

STOKES, Randall G., Chief Executive Officer, LifeCare Hospitals of San Antonio, San Antonio, TX, p. A664

STOKES, CPA, Richard, Chief Financial Officer, Clarendon Memorial Hospital, Manning, SC, p. A590

STOLBA, Robert J., Chief Financial Officer, Mason District Hospital, Havana, IL, p. A196

STOLDT, Garrick J., Chief Financial Officer, Clara Maass Medical Center, Belleville, NJ, p. A425

STOLL, Sherry, Chief Operating Officer, Valley General Hospital, Monroe, WA, p. A704

STOLLIE, Claire, Acting Chief Information Management Services, Veterans Affairs Medical Center, Minneapolis, MN, p. A358

STOLT, James, Vice President Administration and Chief Financial Officer, La Rabida Children's Hospital, Chicago, IL, p. A187

STOLTZ, Kyla, Director Human Resources, Research Belton Hospital, Belton, MO, p. A378

STOLTZFUS, M.D., Richard, Chief of Staff, Harlan ARH Hospital, Harlan, KY, p. A265

STOLZE, Jeffery, Chief Operating Officer, Trinity at Terrace Park, Bettendorf, IA, p. A228

STOMP, Gregory, Chief Executive Officer, Cooperstown Medical Center, Cooperstown, ND, p. A497

STONE, M.D., Chester, Chief of Staff, Newman Regional Health, Emporia, KS, p. A246

STONE, Darlene
Vice President Human Resources, Leesburg Regional Medical Center, Leesburg, FL, p. A135
Vice President Human Resources, The Villages Regional Hospital, The Villages, FL, p. A149

STONE, M.D., Duncan, Chief Medical Staff, Mississippi State Hospital, Whitfield, MS, p. A377

STONE, Jeff, Director Human Resources, Marshall Medical Center North, Guntersville, AL, p. A19

STONE, John, Interim Director, Santa Monica–UCLA Medical Center, Santa Monica, CA, p. A93

STONE, Maxine, Superintendent, Eastern Oregon Psychiatric Center, Pendleton, OR, p. A547

STONE, M.D., Richard, Medical Director, Metropolitan Hospital Center, New York, NY, p. A462

STONE, Ronald, Regional Chief Human Resource Officer, North Shore University Hospital, Manhasset, NY, p. A456

STONE, Susan, Director of Human Resources, Claiborne County Hospital, Tazewell, TN, p. A618

STONE, Thomas J., Chief Executive Officer, Lincoln General Hospital, Ruston, LA, p. A292

STONE, Jr, Timothy D., Executive Vice President and Chief Operating Officer, Decatur Memorial Hospital, Decatur, IL, p. A192

STONE, Trish, Controller, Nicholas County Hospital, Carlisle, KY, p. A262

STONEBURG, John, Chief Information Officer, Tuality Healthcare, Hillsboro, OR, p. A544

STORDAHL, Dean R., Director, Jerry L. Pettis Memorial Veterans Medical Center, Loma Linda, CA, p. A67

STORDAHL, Todd, Chief Financial Officer, Melrose Area Hospital – Centra Care, Melrose, MN, p. A357

STORER, Gregory T., Chief Executive Officer, Select Specialty Hospital–Akron, Akron, OH, p. A502

STOREY, Kevin, Chief Financial Officer, Henderson Memorial Hospital, Henderson, TX, p. A643

STORM, Dave, Director Business Support, St. Anthony's Memorial Hospital, Effingham, IL, p. A193

STORY, Charles, Director Human Resources, Poplar Springs Hospital, Petersburg, VA, p. A693

STORY Jr, James L., M.D., President, John D. Archbold Memorial Hospital, Thomasville, GA, p. A170

STORY, R.N., Joyce A., Chief Nursing Officer, Henderson Memorial Hospital, Henderson, TX, p. A643

STOUGH, Teresa, Chief Information Officer, Mountain View Regional Medical Center, Norton, VA, p. A693

STOUPA, Raymond, Vice President, Nebraska Methodist Hospital, Omaha, NE, p. A411

STOUT, Deanna, Vice President Financial Services, Good Samaritan Hospital of Maryland, Baltimore, MD, p. A302

STOUT, Dick L., Chief Operating Officer, Cuero Community Hospital, Cuero, TX, p. A631

STOUT, Don, Administrator, Fond Du Lac County Mental Health Center, Fond Du Lac, WI, p. A725

STOUT, Janet S., Director, Veterans Affairs Medical Center, Fayetteville, NC, p. A483

STOVER, Kathleen, Business Manager, Grace Cottage Hospital, Townshend, VT, p. A684

STOVER, Ray, Vice President and Chief Financial Officer, MidMichigan Medical Center–Clare, Clare, MI, p. A330

STOVERINK, Mike, Chief Financial Officer, Clay County Hospital, Flora, IL, p. A194

STOYANOFF, Pam
Senior Vice President and Chief Financial Officer, St. Vincent Infirmary Medical Center, Little Rock, AR, p. A47
Senior Vice President and Chief Financial Officer, St. Vincent Medical Center–North, Sherwood, AR, p. A50

STRACHAHN, Ronald, Chief Information Officer, St. John's Hospital, Saint Paul, MN, p. A362

STRACHAN, Ron
Chief Information Officer, Bethesda Rehabilitation Hospital, Saint Paul, MN, p. A361
Chief Information Officer, St. Joseph's Hospital, Saint Paul, MN, p. A362

STRACK, J. Gary, President and Chief Executive Officer, Boca Raton Community Hospital, Boca Raton, FL, p. A124

STRADLEY, Sarah, Director Finance, Elizabethtown Community Hospital, Elizabethtown, NY, p. A452

STRAIN, Sandra, Controller, Elkview General Hospital, Hobart, OK, p. A531

STRAIT, Annette, Chief Financial Officer, Lakeside Hospital, Metairie, LA, p. A286

STRALKA, Susan, Administrator and Chief Executive Officer, Baptist Rehabilitation–Germantown, Germantown, TN, p. A606

STRAND, Ed, Assistant Administrator Finance and Chief Financial Officer, Lake Region Healthcare Corporation, Fergus Falls, MN, p. A353

STRAND, Joy, Chief Operating Officer, Schoolcraft Memorial Hospital, Manistique, MI, p. A340

STRANGE, John, President and Chief Executive Officer, St. Luke's Hospital, Duluth, MN, p. A352

STRANGE, Kim, Senior Vice President and Chief Operating Officer, Glendale Memorial Hospital and Health Center, Glendale, CA, p. A62

STRANGE, Roger, Chief Information Officer, Saint John's Health System, Anderson, IN, p. A211

STRASH, Shawn G., Chief Operating Officer, Redmond Regional Medical Center, Rome, GA, p. A168

STRASSER, Michael, Assistant Administrator Fiscal Services, Providence Medford Medical Center, Medford, OR, p. A546

STRATTA, Leslie, Director Human Resources, Grimes St. Joseph Health Center, Navasota, TX, p. A658

STRATTON, Jim, Vice President Finance, Graham Hospital, Canton, IL, p. A185

STRAUB, M.D., Kim, President, Medical Staff, Saint Elizabeth's Medical Center, Wabasha, MN, p. A364

STRAUCH, Tim, Director Information Services, Watertown Memorial Hospital, Watertown, WI, p. A737

STRAUSS, Thomas J., President and Chief Executive Officer, Summa Health System, Akron, OH, p. A502

STRECK, M.D., Richard J., Senior Vice President Medical Affairs, Akron General Medical Center, Akron, OH, p. A502

STRECK, William F., M.D., President and Chief Executive Officer, Mary Imogene Bassett Hospital, Cooperstown, NY, p. A450

STREET, LaVerne, Associate Vice President, Providence Hospital, Washington, DC, p. A122

STREET, Rex, Vice President Finance, Alamance Regional Medical Center, Burlington, NC, p. A478

STREET, Scott, President and Chief Executive Officer, Duncan Regional Hospital, Duncan, OK, p. A529

STREETER, Alan W., Chief Financial Officer, Scott County Hospital, Scott City, KS, p. A256

STREETMAN, Lynn, Administrator, HEALTHSOUTH Rehabilitation Hospital of Tallahassee, Tallahassee, FL, p. A147

STRENGTH, Perry, Director Information Services, San Antonio Community Hospital, Upland, CA, p. A97

STRICKER, Sean, Administrator, Liberty–Dayton Community Hospital, Liberty, TX, p. A653

STRICKER, Steve, Physician–in–Chief, Kaiser Foundation Hospital and Rehabilitation Center, Vallejo, CA, p. A97

STRICKLAND, Allen, Chief Financial Officer, McKenna Memorial Hospital, New Braunfels, TX, p. A658

STRICKLAND, Barrie, Chief Financial Officer, Memorial Hermann Hospital, Houston, TX, p. A646

STRICKLAND, Connie
Administrator, Centris, Oklahoma City, OK, p. A535
Administrator, Select Specialty Hospital–Oklahoma City West, Oklahoma City, OK, p. A536

STRICKLAND, Morris S., Chief Financial Officer, Helen Keller Hospital, Sheffield, AL, p. A24

STRICKLAND, Pat, Information Systems Manager, Marion County Medical Center, Mullins, SC, p. A590

STRICKLAND, Wallace
President and Chief Executive Officer, Rush Foundation Hospital, Meridian, MS, p. A373
President and Chief Executive Officer, Rush Health Systems, Meridian, MS, p. B94
President and Chief Executive Officer, Specialty Hospital of Meridian, Meridian, MS, p. A373

STRICKLING, Keith, Chief Accountant, Jay Hospital, Jay, FL, p. A133

STRIEBY, John F., Chief Executive Officer, Nix Health Care System, San Antonio, TX, p. A664

STRIGHT, Joni, Senior Vice President, McCall Memorial Hospital, McCall, ID, p. A180

STRINGER, Peggy, Assistant Administrator Human Resources, Morehouse General Hospital, Bastrop, LA, p. A277

STRITTMATTER, Julie
Director Human Resources, Baylor All Saints Medical Center at Fort Worth, Fort Worth, TX, p. A639
Director Human Resources, Baylor Medical Center at Southwest Fort Worth, Fort Worth, TX, p. A639

STRODE, Jayson B., Vice President Human Resources, Elmhurst Memorial Hospital, New York, IL, p. A193

STROMAN, W. Neil, Administrator, Newark–Wayne Community Hospital, Newark, NY, p. A467

STROMBERG, Audrey, Administrator, Roosevelt Memorial Medical Center, Culbertson, MT, p. A397

STROMBOM, Peter, Vice President Information System, Meriter Hospital, Madison, WI, p. A728

STROMSTAD, Darlene, Chief Executive Officer, Henrietta D. Goodall Hospital, Sanford, ME, p. A301

STRONG, David W., President, Rex Healthcare, Raleigh, NC, p. A489

STRONG, Doug, Chief Financial Officer, University of Michigan Hospitals and Health Centers, Ann Arbor, MI, p. A327

STRONG, Gary J., President, Fairview Southdale Hospital, Edina, MN, p. A353

STRONG, Jim, Chief Financial Officer, St. Luke's Hospital, San Francisco, CA, p. A89

STRONGWATER, Steven, M.D., Associate Dean Clinical Affairs and Hospital Director, University of Connecticut Health Center, John Dempsey Hospital, Farmington, CT, p. A113

STROP, Judith, Director Finance, Rusk County Memorial Hospital and Nursing Home, Ladysmith, WI, p. A728

STROPLE, Ken, Senior Vice President Operations, Community Memorial Hospital of San Buenaventura, Ventura, CA, p. A98

STRUBLE, Lynne M., MSN, Chief Executive Officer, Southwood Psychiatric Hospital, Pittsburgh, PA, p. A572

STRUXNESS, Ronald E., Chief Executive Officer, Saint Joseph Hospital, Chicago, IL, p. A190

STRUYK, Douglas A., President and Chief Executive Officer, Christian Health Care Center, Wyckoff, NJ, p. A439

STUART, Donald, Information Systems Director, Pulaski Community Hospital, Pulaski, VA, p. A694

STUART, Jerri J., R.N., President, Baylor Medical Center at Waxahachie, Waxahachie, TX, p. A672

STUART, Jimmy D., Chief Executive Officer, Parkview Regional Hospital, Mexia, TX, p. A656

STUART, Philip, Administrator and Chief Executive Officer, Tomah Memorial Hospital, Tomah, WI, p. A736

STUART, M.D., Robert J., Vice President for Medical Affairs, United Medical Center, Cheyenne, WY, p. A739

STUBBLEFIELD, Alfred G., President, Baptist Health Care Corporation, Pensacola, FL, p. B15

STUBBS, M.D., W Richard, Vice President Medical Affairs, Tacoma General Hospital, Tacoma, WA, p. A710

STUBER, Joseph A., Chief Executive Officer, Perry County Memorial Hospital, Tell City, IN, p. A226

STUCK, M.D., Deborah, Chief Medical Officer, Fairfield Memorial Hospital, Winnsboro, SC, p. A593

STUCZYNSKI, Joseph, Assistant Administrator Finance and Support, Memorial Hospital Pembroke, Pembroke Pines, FL, p. A142

STUDEBAKER, Shelly, Management Information Systems, Clinch Memorial Hospital, Homerville, GA, p. A163

STUDER, Vince, Chief Financial Officer, Shawano Medical Center, Shawano, WI, p. A735

STUENKEL, Kurt, FACHE, President and Chief Executive Officer, Floyd Medical Center, Rome, GA, p. A168

STULTZ, James R.
Senior Vice President, Human Resources, East Ohio Regional Hospital, Martins Ferry, OH, p. A517
Senior Vice President, Human Resources, Ohio Valley Medical Center, Wheeling, WV, p. A721

STULTZ, Robert G., Vice President Human Resources, Forrest General Hospital, Hattiesburg, MS, p. A369

STUMBO, Kathy, Chief Executive Officer, Our Lady of the Way Hospital, Martin, KY, p. A271

STURCH, M.D., Chris, Chief of Staff, Medical Center of Southeastern Oklahoma, Durant, OK, p. A530

STURGEON, Richard, M.D., Interim President, Abbott Northwestern Hospital, Minneapolis, MN, p. A357

STURGEON, M.D., Richard, Medical Affairs Vice President, Abbott Northwestern Hospital, Minneapolis, MN, p. A357

STURGEON, Wade, Chief Financial Officer, Klickitat Valley Health Services, Goldendale, WA, p. A703

STURM, M.D., Peter F., Chief of Staff, Shriners Hospitals for Children–Chicago, Chicago, IL, p. A190

STURSA, Robin, Director Information Systems, Community Health Partners Regional Medical Center, Lorain, OH, p. A516

STUTE, William, Chief Financial Officer, Temple University Children's Medical Center, Philadelphia, PA, p. A570

STYLES, Kelly R., Chief Information Officer, Children's National Medical Center, Washington, DC, p. A121

SUBER, Mandy, Controller, Calhoun Health Services, Calhoun City, MS, p. A367

SUCHARSKI, Allan, Controller, Washington County Memorial Hospital, Potosi, MO, p. A389

SUDA, M.D., Shirley, Associate Area Medical Director, Kaiser Foundation Hospital, Los Angeles, CA, p. A71

SUDDUTH, Debbie, Director Information Services, Bedford County Medical Center, Shelbyville, TN, p. A617

SUDDUTH, CPA, Tony G.
Chief Financial Officer, Samaritan Hospital, Lexington, KY, p. A268
Chief Financial Officer, Samaritan Hospital, Lexington, KY, p. A268

SUDOLCAN, Joseph, Medical Director, Reagan Memorial Hospital, Big Lake, TX, p. A626

SUEIRO, Edwin, Administrator, HEALTHSOUTH Rehabilitation Hospital, San Juan, PR, p. A747

SUGAR, Bev, Associate Administrator and Director Human Resources, Inova Mount Vernon Hospital, Alexandria, VA, p. A685

SUGARMAN, Stuart
Senior Vice President and Chief Information Officer, Hospital for Joint Diseases Orthopaedic Institute, New York, NY, p. A460
Senior Vice President and Chief Information Officer, New York University Medical Center, New York, NY, p. A463

SUGDEN, M.D., Elizabeth, Director Medical Staff Affairs, St. Benedicts Family Medical Center, Jerome, ID, p. A179

SUGG, William T., President and Chief Executive Officer, Sumner Regional Health Systems, Gallatin, TN, p. B103

SUGHRUE, Timothy H., Chief Executive Officer, Rapid City Regional Hospital System of Care, Rapid City, SD, p. A598

SUGIYAMA, Deborah
President, NorthBay Medical Center, Fairfield, CA, p. A60
President, Northbay VacaValley Hospital, Vacaville, CA, p. A97

SUITER, Clarissa, Chief Financial Officer, Fredonia Regional Hospital, Fredonia, KS, p. A247

SUITTER, Marie, Chief Financial Officer, Acadia Hospital, Bangor, ME, p. A296

SULLINS, Sandy, Chief Financial Officer, Lawrence Memorial Hospital, Walnut Ridge, AR, p. A51

SULLIVAN, Billy, Chief Fiscal Service, West Texas VA Health Care System, Big Spring, TX, p. A626

SULLIVAN, Charles, President and Chief Executive Officer, Reading Hospital and Medical Center, West Reading, PA, p. A579

SULLIVAN, George, Director Management Information Systems, Mary Lanning Memorial Hospital, Hastings, NE, p. A407

SULLIVAN, Ginny, Vice President Human Resources, Bethesda Rehabilitation Hospital, Saint Paul, MN, p. A361

SULLIVAN, M.D., J Andy, Chief Medical Officer, OU Medical Center, Oklahoma City, OK, p. A536

SULLIVAN, D.O., J D., Chief of Staff, Medical Center of Manchester, Manchester, TN, p. A612

SULLIVAN, Jane, Chief Information Resource Management Service, Veterans Affairs Sierra Nevada Health Care System, Reno, NV, p. A418

SULLIVAN, John
Vice President Human Resources, Antelope Valley Hospital, Lancaster, CA, p. A67
Vice President Human Resources, Health Central, Ocoee, FL, p. A140

SULLIVAN, Joseph, Senior Vice President Information Systems, Union Hospital, Union, NJ, p. A438

SULLIVAN, Keith, Acting Associate Director, Veterans Affairs Medical Center, Chillicothe, OH, p. A506

SULLIVAN, Mark J.
Vice President Human Resources, Memorial Hospital and Medical Center of Cumberland, Cumberland, MD, p. A307
Vice President Human Resources, Sacred Heart Hospital, Cumberland, MD, p. A307

SULLIVAN, Martha, Director Information Services, Harrison Memorial Hospital, Cynthiana, KY, p. A263

SULLIVAN, M.D., Maurice, Medical Director, Lafayette General Medical Center, Lafayette, LA, p. A283

SULLIVAN, Michael, Medical Director, Kenmore Mercy Hospital, Kenmore, NY, p. A455

SULLIVAN, Michael J., Director, Veterans Affairs Medical Center, Philadelphia, PA, p. A570

SULLIVAN, Patrick L., Director, Veterans Affairs Medical Center, North Chicago, IL, p. A203

SULLIVAN, Sandra, Director Human Resources and Payroll, Mitchell County Hospital, Colorado City, TX, p. A629

SULLIVAN, Theresa, Administrator of Organizational Support, Cuyuna Regional Medical Center, Crosby, MN, p. A352

SULLIVAN, William, Chief Financial Officer, MetroWest Medical Center, Framingham, MA, p. A318

SULLIVANT, Henry, President Medical Staff, Baptist Memorial Hospital for Women, Memphis, TN, p. A612

SUMMERER, M.D., Mike H., Chief Medical Officer, Hallmark Health System, Melrose, MA, p. A320

SUMMERHILL, Ron
Chief Human Resources, Mercy Hospital–Turner Memorial, Ozark, AR, p. A49
Vice President Human Resources, St. Edward Mercy Medical Center, Fort Smith, AR, p. A44

SUMMERS, David A., Chief Financial Officer, Terre Haute Regional Hospital, Terre Haute, IN, p. A226

SUMMERS, Linda, Chief Operating Officer, Charles Cole Memorial Hospital, Coudersport, PA, p. A556

SUMMERS, Stephen M., CHE, Chief Executive Officer, Wise Regional Health System, Decatur, TX, p. A635

SUMMERS, William L., Executive Director, Patton State Hospital, Patton, CA, p. A81

SUMNER, Carrel, Chief Executive Officer, Commonwealth Regional Specialty Hospital, Bowling Green, KY, p. A261

SUMNER, Clara M., Chief Executive Officer, The Medical Center at Franklin, Franklin, KY, p. A265

SUMNER, Jack R., Assistant Administrator Finance, Providence Newberg Hospital, Newberg, OR, p. A546

SUNDBERG, Jim, Director Information Systems, Marquette General Health System, Marquette, MI, p. A340

SUNDRUD, Diane, Human Resource Director, First Care Medical Services, Fosston, MN, p. A353

SUNGA, M.D., M N., Chief of Staff, Hardin County General Hospital, Rosiclare, IL, p. A207

SUNQUIST, Joanne, Chief Information Officer, Hennepin County Medical Center, Minneapolis, MN, p. A357

SURACI, M.D., Aldo, President Medical Staff, Bloomsburg Hospital, Bloomsburg, PA, p. A553

SURI, Satinder, Director Management Information Service, The Institute for Rehabilitation and Research, Houston, TX, p. A648

SUROWITZ, Dale
Chief Executive Officer, Encino–Tarzana Regional Medical Center Encino Campus, Los Angeles, CA, p. A70
Chief Executive Officer, Encino–Tarzana Regional Medical Center Tarzana Campus, Los Angeles, CA, p. A70

SUSI, Jeffrey L., President and Chief Executive Officer, Indian River Memorial Hospital, Vero Beach, FL, p. A150

SUSSMAN, Elliot J., M.D.,
President and Chief Executive Officer, Lehigh Valley Hospital, Allentown, PA, p. A551
President and Chief Executive Officer, Lehigh Valley Hospital–Muhlenberg, Bethlehem, PA, p. A552

SUTER, Mia, Senior Vice President Organizational Development, Owensboro Medical Health System, Owensboro, KY, p. A272

SUTHERLAND, III, John M., Vice President Finance, Women and Infants Hospital of Rhode Island, Providence, RI, p. A582

SUTHERLAND, Pam, Chief Financial Officer, Harlan ARH Hospital, Harlan, KY, p. A265

SUTHERLAND, M.D., William, Medical Director, Memorial Hospital, Belleville, IL, p. A184

SUTLIFF, Jack P.
Vice President and Chief Financial Officer, Eagle River Memorial Hospital, Eagle River, WI, p. A725
Vice President and Chief Financial Officer, Howard Young Medical Center, Woodruff, WI, p. A738
Vice President and Chief Financial Officer, Sacred Heart–St. Mary's Hospitals, Rhinelander, WI, p. A734

SUTTERMAN, Kristie, Director of Human Resources, Baptist Memorial Hospital for Women, Memphis, TN, p. A612

SUTTLES, Robert
Vice President Human Resources, Cape Canaveral Hospital/Health First, Cocoa Beach, FL, p. A126
Vice President Human Resources, Holmes Regional Medical Center, Melbourne, FL, p. A136

SUTTON, Brooks, R.N., Chief Operating Officer, St. Clare Hospital, Tacoma, WA, p. A710

SUTTON, R.N., Brooks, Chief Operating Officer, St. Clare Hospital, Tacoma, WA, p. A710

SUTTON, Frank, Vice President Hospital Services, SEARHC MT. Edgecumbe Hospital, Sitka, AK, p. A28

SUTTON, Nelson L., Chief Operating Officer, Willow Crest Hospital, Miami, OK, p. A533

SUTTON, Pat, Director Human Resources, Dearborn County Hospital, Lawrenceburg, IN, p. A221

SUTTON, Richard O., Chief Executive Officer, McKee Medical Center, Loveland, CO, p. A108

SUTTON, Thomas, Associate Director, Malcom Randall Veterans Affairs Medical Center, Gainesville, FL, p. A129

SUYENAGA, Lee, Acting Chief Executive Officer, Olympia Medical Center, Los Angeles, CA, p. A72

SVENDSEN, M.D., Craig, Medical Director, Woodwinds Health Campus, Woodbury, MN, p. A365

SVIHOVEC, Angelia K., Chief Executive Officer, Mobridge Regional Hospital, Mobridge, SD, p. A597

SWAFFORD, Donald, President, St. John's St. Francis Hospital, Mountain View, MO, p. A388

SWAGERTY, Jill, Director Human Resources, Union County General Hospital, Clayton, NM, p. A442

SWAIN, Art, Vice President Support Services, Joint Township District Memorial Hospital, Saint Marys, OH, p. A521

SWAIN, M.D., Cindy, Chief of Staff, Humboldt General Hospital, Humboldt, TN, p. A607

SWAINE, Richard P., Vice President, William Beaumont Hospital–Royal Oak, Royal Oak, MI, p. A343

SWALLER, R.N., Pat, Chief Operating Officer and Chief Nursing Officer, Placentia Linda Hospital, Placentia, CA, p. A81

SWAN, Dennis A., President and Chief Executive Officer, Sparrow Health System, Lansing, MI, p. A338

SWAN, Ruth, Director, Akron Children's Hospital, Akron, OH, p. A502

SWANGER, Cae, Director Information Services, MountainView Hospital, Las Vegas, NV, p. A416

SWANK, Mike, Executive Director Physician Network Development, Butler Health System, Butler, PA, p. A554

SWANN, Steven
Deputy Commander for Clinical Services, Bayne–Jones Army Community Hospital, Fort Polk, LA, p. A281
Deputy Commander for Clinical Services, Lyster U. S. Army Community Hospital, Fort Rucker, AL, p. A19

SWANSON, Darlene, Business Manager, Hillsboro Medical Center, Hillsboro, ND, p. A499

SWANSON, M.D., Heather, Chief of Staff, Albany Area Hospital and Medical Center, Albany, MN, p. A349

SWANSON, Karen, Director, Human Resources, Baptist Memorial Hospital–Collierville, Collierville, TN, p. A604

SWANSON, Peter, Assistant Administrator Fiscal Services, Island Hospital, Anacortes, WA, p. A700

SWANSON, Sandy, Director of Information System, Garrett County Memorial Hospital, Oakland, MD, p. A309

SWART, Steve, Administrator, Doctors Hospital Nelsonville, Nelsonville, OH, p. A519

SWARTOUT, Judi, Chief Financial Officer, Sutter Coast Hospital, Crescent City, CA, p. A58

SWARTWOUT, John A., Administrator, Shriners Hospitals for Children, Galveston Burns Hospital, Galveston, TX, p. A641

SWARTZ, Donn, Director Human Resources, Sonora Regional Medical Center, Sonora, CA, p. A94

SWARTZ, MaryLynn, Chief Executive Officer, Northwest Medical Center, Margate, FL, p. A136

SWARTZ, Michael J., Associate Medical Center Director, Veterans Affairs Medical Center, Syracuse, NY, p. A474

SWEDIEN, Scott, Information Services Director, Baldwin Area Medical Center, Baldwin, WI, p. A722

SWEDISH, Joseph R., President and Chief Executive Officer, Trinity Health, Novi, MI, p. B110

SWEENEY, Jen, Chief Operating Officer, Southern Hills Hospital and Medical Center, Las Vegas, NV, p. A417

SWEENEY, Kathleen, Chief Information Officer, North Hills Hospital, North Richland Hills, TX, p. A658

SWEENEY, Thomas, Senior Vice President and Chief Clinical Operations Officer, Union Hospital, Elkton, MD, p. A307

SWEENEY, Ty, Vice President and Chief Information Officer, Texoma Medical Center, Denison, TX, p. A635

SWEET, Berney, Chief Executive Officer, Ennis Regional Medical Center, Ennis, TX, p. A638

SWEET, Michael H., Human Resources Business Partner, Kaiser Foundation Hospital, San Francisco, CA, p. A89

SWEGER, Pam, Director Human Resources, Nevada Regional Medical Center, Nevada, MO, p. A388

SWEITER, Kim, Vice President, Willow Creek Women's Hospital, Johnson, AR, p. A45

SWENSON, Cathy, Chief Executive Officer, Nelson County Health System, McVille, ND, p. A499

SWENSON, Daniel J., Chief Executive Officer and Administrator, Appleton Municipal Hospital and Nursing Home, Appleton, MN, p. A349

SWENSON, M.D., Ronald, Chief Medical Information Officer, Sparrow Health System, Lansing, MI, p. A338

SWETNAM, M.D., Charles, Vice President Medical Affairs, Flagstaff Medical Center, Flagstaff, AZ, p. A30

SWETT, Austin, Chief Financial Officer, Guam Memorial Hospital Authority, Tamuning, GU, p. A743

SWICEGOOD, Debbie, Director Human Resources, Chowan Hospital, Edenton, NC, p. A482

SWICK, Michael D., President and Chief Executive Officer, Lima Memorial Health System, Lima, OH, p. A516

SWIDERSKI, Frederick A., Commander, Reynolds Army Community Hospital, Fort Sill, OK, p. A531

SWIETER, Kim
Vice President Human Resources, Northwest Medical Center of Benton County, Bentonville, AR, p. A40
Vice President Human Resources, Northwest Medical Center of Washington County, Springdale, AR, p. A50

SWIFT, Nick
Senior Vice President Finance, Carthage General Hospital, Carthage, TN, p. A603
Senior Vice President Finance, Sumner Regional Medical Center, Gallatin, TN, p. A606

SWILLEY, Bryanie W., Chief Executive Officer, Jordan Valley Hospital, West Jordan, UT, p. A681

SWINDELL, Terry
Controller, Bolivar General Hospital, Bolivar, TN, p. A602
Controller, Gibson General Hospital, Trenton, TN, p. A618
Controller, Humboldt General Hospital, Humboldt, TN, p. A607

SWINDLE, Dean, Chief Financial Officer, Forsyth Medical Center, Winston–Salem, NC, p. A494

SWINEY, Margie, Administrator and Chief Nursing Officer, Ridgeview Psychiatric Hospital and Center, Oak Ridge, TN, p. A616

SWINFARD, M.D., Ronald W.
Chief Medical Officer, Lehigh Valley Hospital, Allentown, PA, p. A551
Chief Medical Officer, Lehigh Valley Hospital–Muhlenberg, Bethlehem, PA, p. A552

SWINK, Gary W., Chief Financial Officer, Stonewall Jackson Hospital, Lexington, VA, p. A690

SWINNEY, Keith L., Chief Executive Officer, Baptist Medical Center, San Antonio, TX, p. A663

SWINT, Ken, Vice President Finance and Chief Financial Officer, Fostoria Community Hospital, Fostoria, OH, p. A514

SWITEK, Teresa, Manager Human Resources, Veterans Affairs Western New York Healthcare System–Buffalo Division, Buffalo, NY, p. A449

SWOFFORD, Lisa, Human Resource Director and Administrative Assistant, Ozark Health Medical Center, Clinton, AR, p. A41

SWOPE, Jon
President and Chief Executive Officer, Mercy Health System of Kansas, Fort Scott, KS, p. A247
President and Chief Executive Officer, Mercy Health System of Kansas, Independence, KS, p. A249

SWORD, Russ D., Administrator, Ashley County Medical Center, Crossett, AR, p. A41

SYKES, Carmia, Resource Management Flight Commander, Scott Medical Center, Scott AFB, IL, p. A207

SYLVIA, Bane, Vice President Human Resources, Southern Ohio Medical Center, Portsmouth, OH, p. A521

SYLVIA–HUTCHINSON, Doreen M., Vice Vice President Operations and Chief Nurse Executive, Fairview Hospital, Great Barrington, MA, p. A318

SYNDER, Kristy, Human Resources Director, Fulton County Health Center, Wauseon, OH, p. A524

SYNDULKO, Ph.D., Karl, Director Information Management, Veterans Affairs Greater Los Angeles Healthcare System, Los Angeles, CA, p. A73

SYNNESTVEDT, Eric, Director Information Services, Reid Hospital and Health Care Services, Richmond, IN, p. A224

SYPIEN, Troy, Director Information Services, Sunrise Hospital and Medical Center, Las Vegas, NV, p. A417

SYPNIEWSKI, Al, Administrator and Chief Executive Officer, Baptist Memorial Hospital–Booneville, Booneville, MS, p. A367

SYTSMA, Judy, Chief Nursing Officer, Community Memorial Hospital, Oconto Falls, WI, p. A733

SZABO, M.D., Ph, Sandor, Chief of Staff, Veterans Affairs Long Beach Healthcare System, Long Beach, CA, p. A69

SZALWINSKI, Mark A., Vice President and Administrator, Sentara Leigh Hospital, Norfolk, VA, p. A693

SZENCZY, Catherine, Chief Information Officer and Senior Vice President Information Systems, Saint Francis Hospital and Medical Center, Hartford, CT, p. A113

SZEWCZYK, Edwin, Chief Financial Officer, Charles Cole Memorial Hospital, Coudersport, PA, p. A556

SZUBSKI, Michael, Senior Vice President and Chief Financial Officer, University Hospitals of Cleveland, Cleveland, OH, p. A509

SZYMANSKI, Candra, Vice President for Patient Care and Hospital Operations and Chief Nursing Officer, UMass Memorial–Marlborough Hospital, Marlborough, MA, p. A320

SZYMULA, M.D., Norbert J., Medical Director, Inter–Community Memorial Hospital, Newfane, NY, p. A467

T

TABB, M.D., Doziier, Chief of Staff, Johnson County Healthcare Center, Buffalo, WY, p. A739

TABBAH, M.D., Isam, Chief of Staff, Harrison Community Hospital, Cadiz, OH, p. A504

TABIBI, M.D., Wasae S., President of Staff, Plaza Specialty Hospital, Houston, TX, p. A647

TACHOVSKY, Barbara J., President, Paoli Hospital, Paoli, PA, p. A567

TACKER, Tim, Director Information System, Riveredge Hospital, Forest Park, IL, p. A194

TAFFE, Patrick, Vice President Information Services, North Memorial Health Care, Robbinsdale, MN, p. A360

TAFT, Char, Service Line and Human Resources Management Manager, Veterans Affairs Medical Center, Bath, NY, p. A447

TAFT, Kenneth L.
    Executive Vice President and Chief Operating Officer, Bronson Methodist Hospital, Kalamazoo, MI, p. A338
    Executive Vice President and Chief Operating Officer, Bronson Vicksburg Hospital, Vicksburg, MI, p. A347

TAGAI, Lee, Director Human Resources, Lafayette Regional Health Center, Lexington, MO, p. A386

TAIT, Karen, Vice President, Howard Young Medical Center, Woodruff, WI, p. A738

TAKAS, M.D., Steven, Chief Medical Staff, Duplin General Hospital, Kenansville, NC, p. A485

TALALAI, James, Chief Information Officer, Kessler Institute for Rehabilitation, West Orange, NJ, p. A438

TALBERT, Kara, Director Human Resources, Keefe Memorial Hospital, Cheyenne Wells, CO, p. A102

TALBOT, Jack
    Director Human Resources, St. Luke Hospital East, Fort Thomas, KY, p. A264
    Director Human Resources, St. Luke Hospital West, Florence, KY, p. A264

TALBOT, Lisa, Human Resource Manager, Lakeside Hospital, Metairie, LA, p. A286

TALBOT, M.D., Paul, President Medical Staff, Wesley Medical Center, Hattiesburg, MS, p. A369

TALBOTT, Drew, Director Information Systems, Mt. Carmel Regional Medical Center, Pittsburg, KS, p. A255

TALLON, Joe, Director Finance, Arlington Memorial Hospital, Arlington, TX, p. A622

TALLON, Richard, Chief Financial Officer, Jefferson County Hospital, Waurika, OK, p. A541

TALLY, James E., Ph.D., President and Chief Executive Officer, Children's Healthcare of Atlanta, Atlanta, GA, p. A153

TAMAR, Earl J., Chief Operating Officer, Rockford Memorial Hospital, Rockford, IL, p. A206

TAMME, Susan Stout, President, Baptist Hospital East, Louisville, KY, p. A268

TAMMINEN, M.D., John, President, Medical Staff, Carilion Giles Memorial Hospital, Pearisburg, VA, p. A693

TAN, M.D., Ariel, Chief of Medical Staff, Kansas Rehabilitation Hospital, Topeka, KS, p. A257

TAN, M.D., Jamie, Chief of Staff, Harbor Beach Community Hospital, Harbor Beach, MI, p. A336

TANBERG, Darci, Director of Human Resources, Fairview Lakes Regional Health Care, Wyoming, MN, p. A365

TANDY, William, Driectror Human Resources, U. S. Public Health Service Owyhee Community Health Facility, Owyhee, NV, p. A418

TANET, Mark, Director Management Information Systems, Mainland Medical Center, Texas City, TX, p. A670

TANIS, Earl P., Senior Vice President Financial Operations, Bayhealth Medical Center, Dover, DE, p. A119

TANNENBAUM, M.D., Scott, Medical Director, HEALTHSOUTH Sunrise Rehabilitation Hospital, Fort Lauderdale, FL, p. A128

TANNER, Arlan, Chief Information Officer, Kit Carson County Memorial Hospital, Burlington, CO, p. A101

TANNER, Debora S., Vice President and Administrator, Riverside Behavioral Health Center, Hampton, VA, p. A689

TANNER, Douglas, Administrator, Washington County Hospital and Nursing Home, Chatom, AL, p. A16

TANNER, Laureen K., MSN, Chief Executive Officer, Ranken Jordan, Maryland Heights, MO, p. A387

TANNER, Laurence A., President and Chief Executive Officer, New Britain General Hospital, New Britain, CT, p. A114

TANNER, Sharon M., President and Chief Executive Officer, Albemarle Hospital, Elizabeth City, NC, p. A482

TANO, M.D., Albert, Chief of Staff, Palmetto General Hospital, Hialeah, FL, p. A131

TANPIENGCO, Nestorio, Senior Vice President and Chief Financial Officer, Tucson Medical Center, Tucson, AZ, p. A38

TANSINO, M.D., Gary F., Chief of Staff, MidState Medical Center, Meriden, CT, p. A114

TAPNIO, Rogelio, Director Health Information Services, Alvarado Hospital Medical Center, San Diego, CA, p. A86

TAPPAN, Hugh C., Chief Operating Officer, Presbyterian–St. Luke's Medical Center, Denver, CO, p. A104

TAQI, Mohammad, Chief of Staff, Borgess–Lee Memorial Hospital, Dowagiac, MI, p. A332

TARASOVITCH, James, Senior Vice President and Chief Financial Officer, Bradford Regional Medical Center, Bradford, PA, p. A553

TARBET, Michele T., R.N., Chief Executive Officer, Sharp Grossmont Hospital, La Mesa, CA, p. A66

TARNOWSKI, Tim, Chief Information Officer, Columbus Regional Hospital, Columbus, IN, p. A213

TARR, Judith, Chief Executive Officer, Miles Memorial Hospital, Damariscotta, ME, p. A298

TARRANT, Jeffrey S., CHE, Chief Executive Officer, Integris Blackwell Regional Hospital, Blackwell, OK, p. A528

TARRANT, Maureen, Chief Executive Officer, Sky Ridge Medical Center, Lone Tree, CO, p. A108

TART, Karen, Vice President Human Resources, Eagle River Memorial Hospital, Eagle River, WI, p. A725

TARTAGLIONE, Angelo J., Chief Financial Officer, Jewish Memorial Hospital and Rehabilitation Center, Boston, MA, p. A314

TARULLI, Pamela, Corporatae Vice President Human Resources, St. Vincent's Medical Center, Bridgeport, CT, p. A112

TARVER, Jennifer, Chief Financial Officer, Winn Parish Medical Center, Winnfield, LA, p. A294

TARWATER, Michael C., President and Chief Executive Officer, Carolinas HealthCare System, Charlotte, NC, p. B22

TASCONE, Deborah, MS,
    Executive Director, North Shore University Hospital at Plainview, Plainview, NY, p. A469
    Executive Director, North Shore University Hospital at Syosset, Syosset, NY, p. A473

TASSE, Joseph M.
    President, St. John Macomb Hospital, Warren, MI, p. A347
    President, St. John Macomb Hospital, Warren, MI, p. A347

TASSIN, Bruce, Chief Operating Officer, Christus St. Frances Cabrini Hospital, Alexandria, LA, p. A276

TATE, Charles, Information Technology Director, Lallie Kemp Medical Center, Independence, LA, p. A282

TATE, Gary, Chief Financial Officer, Athens–Limestone Hospital, Athens, AL, p. A13

TATE, Jean, Manager, Riverview Healthcare Association, Crookston, MN, p. A352

TATE, Joel W., FACHE, President, Walker Baptist Medical Center, Jasper, AL, p. A20

TATRO, David, Vice President Human Resources, Fauquier Hospital, Warrenton, VA, p. A698

TATTICH, Diane, Group Manager, Christian Hospital, Saint Louis, MO, p. A390

TATUM, Martha, Chief Financial Officer, Evans Memorial Hospital, Claxton, GA, p. A158

TATUM, Jr, Ronald E., Vice President Finance, Community Memorial Healthcenter, South Hill, VA, p. A697

TATUM, Stanley D., President, Baylor Medical Center at Garland, Garland, TX, p. A641

TAUBENHEIM, Troy, Chief Executive Officer, Woodward Regional Hospital, Woodward, OK, p. A541

TAUSSIG, Lynn M., M.D., President and Chief Executive Officer, National Jewish Medical and Research Center, Denver, CO, p. A103

TAVARY, James, Administrator, Prosser Memorial Hospital, Prosser, WA, p. A706

TAVERNARO, Mary Louise
    Director Human Resources, WellStar Cobb Hospital, Austell, GA, p. A156
    Director Human Resources, WellStar Windy Hill Hospital, Marietta, GA, p. A165

TAWNEY, M.D., Michael W., Senior Vice President Medical Affairs, Mount Clemens General Hospital, Mount Clemens, MI, p. A340

TAYLOR, Adam, manager Information Technology, Northern Inyo Hospital, Bishop, CA, p. A55

TAYLOR, Alfred P., Chief Executive Officer, Betsy Johnson Regional Hospital, Dunn, NC, p. A481

TAYLOR, M.D., Bonnie, Senior Vice President and Medical Director, Arkansas Children's Hospital, Little Rock, AR, p. A46

TAYLOR, Cherie, Chief Executive Officer, Northern Rockies Medical Center, Cut Bank, MT, p. A397

TAYLOR, Clay, Chief Executive Officer, Yoakum County Hospital, Denver City, TX, p. A635

TAYLOR, Dennis A., Chief Executive Officer, West Florida Hospital, Pensacola, FL, p. A143

TAYLOR, M.D., Donald A., Medical Director, Children's Hospital, Richmond, VA, p. A695

TAYLOR, Dwayne, Chief Executive Officer, Sycamore Shoals Hospital, Elizabethton, TN, p. A605

TAYLOR, Gary, Manager Information Services, Paris Community Hospital, Paris, IL, p. A204

TAYLOR Jr, George Peach, M.D., Surgeon General, Department of the Air Force, Washington, DC, p. B36

TAYLOR, Gil, Chief Human Resources Officer, Pomerado Hospital, Poway, CA, p. A82

TAYLOR, M.D., Gregory W., Senior Vice President and Chief Medical Director, High Point Regional Health System, High Point, NC, p. A485

TAYLOR, Irene, Chief Executive Officer, Wernersville State Hospital, Wernersville, PA, p. A578

TAYLOR, Iris, Ph.D., President, Detroit Receiving Hospital and University Health Center, Detroit, MI, p. A331

TAYLOR, James H., President and Chief Executive Officer, University of Louisville Hospital, Louisville, KY, p. A270

TAYLOR, Janetta, Director Information Systems, Mercy Medical Center–New Hampton, New Hampton, IA, p. A238

TAYLOR, Jim, Chief Business Office, Malcom Randall Veterans Affairs Medical Center, Gainesville, FL, p. A129

TAYLOR, Judd, Chief Financial Officer, West Valley Medical Center, Caldwell, ID, p. A178

TAYLOR, Lee, Vice President, Medical and Clinical Services, Muskogee Regional Medical Center, Muskogee, OK, p. A534

TAYLOR, Mark R., President, St. John Hospital and Medical Center, Detroit, MI, p. A332

TAYLOR, Marti, Human Resources Director, Harmon Memorial Hospital, Hollis, OK, p. A532

TAYLOR, Meredith, Chief Executive Officer, Kindred Hospital–Sacramento, Folsom, CA, p. A60

TAYLOR, Michael
    Chief Information Officer, Bon Secours–St. Francis Xavier Hospital, Charleston, SC, p. A584
    Chief Information Officer, Roper Hospital, Charleston, SC, p. A585

TAYLOR, Michael H., Vice President Human Resources, Memorial Health System of East Texas, Lufkin, TX, p. A655

TAYLOR, Michael L., President and Chief Executive Officer, Baylor Jack and Jane Hamilton Heart and Vascular Hospital, Dallas, TX, p. A632

TAYLOR, Michael V., Vice President Human Resources, Sentara Bayside Hospital, Virginia Beach, VA, p. A697

TAYLOR, Mimi
    Corporate Vice President, Baptist Hospital of Miami, Miami, FL, p. A136
    Corporate Vice President Information Technology, Homestead Hospital, Homestead, FL, p. A131
    Vice President Information Technology, Mariners Hospital, Tavernier, FL, p. A149

TAYLOR, Pam, Human Resource Director, Bonner General Hospital, Sandpoint, ID, p. A181

TAYLOR, Paul, Administrator, Doctors Hospital of Springfield, Springfield, MO, p. A393

TAYLOR, Robbie, Director Human Resources, North Sunflower Medical Center, Ruleville, MS, p. A375

TAYLOR, III, M.D, Robert, Vice President Medical Affairs, Our Lady of Lourdes Memorial Hospital, Binghamton, NY, p. A448

TAYLOR, Jr, Robert B., Vice President Finance and Chief Financial Officer, Bethesda Memorial Hospital, Boynton Beach, FL, p. A124

TAYLOR, Robert M., Chief Financial Officer, University Health Care System, Augusta, GA, p. A155

TAYLOR, Sarah, Chief Operating Officer, Monadnock Community Hospital, Peterborough, NH, p. A423

TAYLOR, Scott J., President and Chief Executive Officer, St. Catherine Hospital, Garden City, KS, p. A247

TAYLOR, Steve, Chief Financial Officer, Logan Medical Center, Guthrie, OK, p. A531

TAYLOR, M.D., Steve, Executive Vice President and Chief Medical Officer, Piedmont Hospital, Atlanta, GA, p. A154

TAYLOR, Steven, Vice President and Chief Financial Officer, St. Anthony Hospital, Pendleton, OR, p. A547

TAYLOR, Steven L., Chief Executive Officer, Harrison County Hospital, Corydon, IN, p. A213

TAYLOR, Summer, Director Information Systems, Hilo Medical Center, Hilo, HI, p. A193

TAYLOR, M.D., Thomas, President Medical Staff, Skyline Medical Center, Nashville, TN, p. A615

TEAGUE, Michael E., Chief Executive Officer, Southeast Louisiana Hospital, Mandeville, LA, p. A286

TEBRAKE, Larry, Site Director, St. Peter Regional Treatment Center, Saint Peter, MN, p. A362

TEDDER, Deborah, Chief Operating Officer, Memorial Regional Hospital, Hollywood, FL, p. A131

TEDESCHI, M.D., Anthony, Chief Operating Officer, Roseland Community Hospital, Chicago, IL, p. A189

TEDESCO, Art, Chief Financial Officer, Danbury Hospital, Danbury, CT, p. A112

TEDESCO, David, Vice President Human Resources, New England Sinai Hospital and Rehabilitation Center, Stoughton, MA, p. A324

TEEGARDEN, M.D., David, President and Chief Medical Officer, Trinity Mother Frances Health System, Tyler, TX, p. A671

TEEL, M.D., Dudley, Vice President Medical Management, Indian River Memorial Hospital, Vero Beach, FL, p. A150

TEEL, Kerry, Chief Executive Officer, Twelve Oaks Medical Center, Houston, TX, p. A648

TEEUWEN, Pat, Director Human Resources, St. Joseph's Hospital, Tampa, FL, p. A148

TEFFETELLER, Scott, Chief Operating Officer, Terre Haute Regional Hospital, Terre Haute, IN, p. A226

TEGETHOFF, Gretchen, Vice President Information Resources, George Washington University Hospital, Washington, DC, p. A121

TEIGEN, Bobbe, Administrator, Aurora Medical Center – Manitowoc, Two Rivers, WI, p. A737

TEITELBAUM, Karen, Senior Vice President Operations and Chief Business Development Officer, Swedish Covenant Hospital, Chicago, IL, p. A190

TEJIDOR, Roberto, Chief Executive Officer, Pan American Hospital, Miami, FL, p. A138

TELL, Marge, Director Information Services, Riverview Hospital Association, Wisconsin Rapids, WI, p. A738

TELLES, Ron, Chief Financial Officer, Ashland Community Hospital, Ashland, OR, p. A542

TELTHORSTER, Marcia, Vice President Human Resources, St. Mary Medical Center, Langhorne, PA, p. A562

TEMBREULL, John P., Administrator, Baraga County Memorial Hospital, L'Anse, MI, p. A338

TEMECK, M.D., Barbara, Chief of Staff, Veterans Affairs Edward Hines, Jr. Hospital, Hines, IL, p. A197

TEMIZER, M.D., Dogan, Chief of Staff, Mercy Hospital Clermont, Batavia, OH, p. A503

TEMME, M.D., Joel, President, Medical Staff, Inova Alexandria Hospital, Alexandria, VA, p. A685

TEMPLE, Debbie, Director Human Resources, King's Daughters' Hospital and Health Services, Madison, IN, p. A221

TEMPLE, John, Director Information Systems, York General Health Care Services, York, NE, p. A414

TEMPLE, Richard, Chief Information Officer, Saint Clare's Hospital, Dover, NJ, p. A427

TEMPLETON, Sheryl, Chief Financial Officer, Scotland County Memorial Hospital, Memphis, MO, p. A387

TENAGLIA, Nicholas, M.D., Chairman of the Board, Progressions Group, Inc., Lafayette Hill, PA, p. B85

TENHOUSE, Steve, Chief Executive Officer, John and Mary Kirby Hospital, Monticello, IL, p. A201

TENNANT, Gail, Director, H. Douglas Singer Mental Health and Developmental Center, Rockford, IL, p. A206

TEPLICK, M.D., Richard, Chief of Staff, USA Children's and Women's Hospital, Mobile, AL, p. A21

TEPPING, Mark, Chief Information Officer, Bridgeport Hospital, Bridgeport, CT, p. A112

TERNES, Howard, Chief Executive Officer, Whittier Hospital Medical Center, Whittier, CA, p. A99

TERPSTRA, D.O., Dale, Medical Director, Zeeland Community Hospital, Zeeland, MI, p. A348

TERRANOVA, Gail, Director Human Resources, Wing Memorial Hospital and Medical Centers, Palmer, MA, p. A322

TERREBONNE, Terry J., Chief Executive Officer, Jennings American Legion Hospital, Jennings, LA, p. A282

TERRELL, Greg, Vice President Operations, Norman Regional Hospital, Norman, OK, p. A534

TERRELL, Michael T., Chief Financial Officer, Brandon Regional Hospital, Brandon, FL, p. A124

TERRELL, Richard L., Chief Financial Officer, Veterans Affairs Medical Center, Salisbury, NC, p. A491

TERRELL, William, Vice President, Medical Center East, Birmingham, AL, p. A15

TERRENCE, M.D., Christopher F., Chief of Staff, Veterans Affairs New Jersey Health Care System, East Orange, NJ, p. A427

TERRESON, Gregg, Assistant Administrator Finance and Chief Financial Officer, Kindred Hospital Seattle, Seattle, WA, p. A707

TERRINONI, Gary G., Treasurer and Senior Vice President Finance, Suburban Hospital Healthcare System, Bethesda, MD, p. A305

TERRY, Micheal, Chief Executive Officer, Gulf Coast Medical Center, Biloxi, MS, p. A366

TERRY, Richard
Chief Information Officer, Carson City Hospital, Carson City, MI, p. A329
Financial Manager, U. S. Air Force Academy Hospital, USAF Academy, CO, p. A110

TERSHAKOVEC, M.D., George, President Medical Staff, South Miami Hospital, Miami, FL, p. A138

TERSIGNI, Anthony R., FACHE, President and Chief Executive Officer, Ascension Health, Saint Louis, MO, p. B10

TESAR, James D., Chief Executive Officer, North Oak Regional Medical Center, Senatobia, MS, p. A375

TESKE, Martie, Human Resources Director, Providence Seaside Hospital, Seaside, OR, p. A549

TESLER, M.D., Peter, Associate Medical Director, St. Luke's–Roosevelt Hospital Center, New York, NY, p. A465

TEST, Stefan, Chief, Information Resource Management Services, Veterans Affairs Medical Center, Alexandria, LA, p. A276

TETER, Heather, Chief Financial Officer, Los Alamos Medical Center, Los Alamos, NM, p. A443

TEUBNER, Sandra, Chief Financial Officer, Towner County Medical Center, Cando, ND, p. A496

TEUFEL, George, Vice President Finance, Advocate Good Shepherd Hospital, Barrington, IL, p. A184

TEUT, Gary, Assistant Administrator, Horn Memorial Hospital, Ida Grove, IA, p. A235

TEW, David, Chief Operating Officer, Sharp Memorial Hospital, San Diego, CA, p. A87

TEWAHAFTEWA, Thelma, Finance Officer, Hopi Health Care Center, Keams Canyon, AZ, p. A31

TEWKSBURY, Randy, Vice President Finance, Lewistown Hospital, Lewistown, PA, p. A563

THABES, Rudd, Chief Medical Staff, Clearwater Health Services, Bagley, MN, p. A350

THACKER, Danena, Controller, Marcum and Wallace Memorial Hospital, Irvine, KY, p. A266

THACKER, Roland, Senior Vice President and Chief Financial Officer, The Medical Center, Columbus, GA, p. A159

THAKUR, Lisa, Chief Financial Executive, Scripps Memorial Hospital–La Jolla, La Jolla, CA, p. A66

THALKEN, Mary Kay, R.N., Interim Vice President and Chief Operating Officer, Alegent Health Bergan Mercy Medical Center, Omaha, NE, p. A410

THAMES, Stephen, Chief Financial Officer, Woodward Regional Hospital, Woodward, OK, p. A541

THARP, Ed, Administrative Director Information Systems, Blessing Hospital, Quincy, IL, p. A206

THATCHER, Patricia, Executive Director Human Resources and Customer Services, University of California, Irvine Medical Center, Orange, CA, p. A79

THATE, Mark
Director Human Resources, Kishwaukee Community Hospital, De Kalb, IL, p. A191
Director Human Resources, Valley West Community Hospital, Sandwich, IL, p. A207

THAVASEELAN, M.D., Dorairaju, Vice President Medical Affairs, Caritas Holy Family Hospital and Medical Center, Methuen, MA, p. A320

THAW, James G., President and Chief Executive Officer, Lafayette General Medical Center, Lafayette, LA, p. A283

THAXTON, James D., President, Baylor Medical Center at Irving, Irving, TX, p. A649

THAYER, M.D., Devin, Medical Director, HEALTHSOUTH Rehabilitation Hospital, Columbia, SC, p. A585

THEBEAU, Debbie, Human Resources Director, Tehachapi Valley Healthcare District, Tehachapi, CA, p. A95

THEISS, Robert, Chief Information Officer, Bloomsburg Hospital, Bloomsburg, PA, p. A553

THEKEN, Richard, Vice President Human Resources, Central Vermont Medical Center, Barre, VT, p. A682

THERING, Jami, Manager Information Systems, Clinton Memorial Hospital, Saint Johns, MI, p. A344

THERIOT, Lyle, Director Human Resources, Lakeview Regional Medical Center, Covington, LA, p. A279

THEUER, Christopher, Chief Medical Officer, Jewish Hospital–Shelbyville, Shelbyville, KY, p. A274

THEUS, M.D., Thomas L., Chief of Medicine, Doctors Hospital of Columbus, Columbus, GA, p. A158

THIBAULT, Bonnie, Chief Information Officer, Spring Harbor Hospital, Westbrook, ME, p. A301

THIELE, Rosemary, Chief Executive Officer, Progressive Hospital, Las Vegas, NV, p. A416

THIELEMIER, Kevin, Director Human Resources, NEA Medical Center, Jonesboro, AR, p. A45

THIELKE, Jayne
Chief Financial Officer, Swift County–Benson Hospital, Benson, MN, p. A350
Chief Financial Officer, Swift County–Benson Hospital, Benson, MN, p. A350

THIGPEN, Kevin, Vice President Human Resources, Athens Regional Medical Center, Athens, GA, p. A152

THILGES, Michael
Chief Operating Officer and Chief Financial Officer, Clarke County Hospital, Osceola, IA, p. A239
Chief Operating Officer and Chief Financial Officer, Clarke County Hospital, Osceola, IA, p. A239

THIRINGER, John, Chief Medical Officer, Naval Medical Center, San Diego, CA, p. A87

THOMAS, M.D., Bill
Vice President Medical Affairs and Chief Information Officer, Saline Memorial Hospital, Benton, AR, p. A40
Vice President Medical Affairs and Chief Information Officer, Saline Memorial Hospital, Benton, AR, p. A40

THOMAS, Brian, Chief Operating Officer, John F. Kennedy Memorial Hospital, Indio, CA, p. A64

THOMAS, Brian E., Aministrator, Chester Mental Health Center, Chester, IL, p. A186

THOMAS, Chris, CHE, President and Chief Executive Officer, Central Kansas Medical Center, Great Bend, KS, p. A247

THOMAS, Cristina, Vice President and Chief Information Officer, Mercy Medical Center–Des Moines, Des Moines, IA, p. A233

THOMAS, M.D., Daniel, Chief of Staff, Enloe Medical Center, Chico, CA, p. A56

THOMAS, David, Chief Financial Officer, Carolinas Medical Center–Mercy, Charlotte, NC, p. A479

THOMAS, Debbie, Vice President and Chief Financial Officer, Florida Hospital–Flagler, Palm Coast, FL, p. A142

THOMAS, Debora, Chief Financial Officer, Florida Hospital–Ormond Memorial, Ormond Beach, FL, p. A141

THOMAS, Denise, Chief Financial Officer, Spring View Hospital, Lebanon, KY, p. A267

THOMAS, Dick, Executive Director Human Resources, Western Baptist Hospital, Paducah, KY, p. A273

THOMAS, Dwayne, M.D., Chief Executive Officer, Medical Center of Louisiana at New Orleans, New Orleans, LA, p. A289

THOMAS, M.D., F Ardell, Chief Medical Officer, Soldiers and Sailors Memorial Hospital, Wellsboro, PA, p. A578

THOMAS, Frank, Director Informatio Systems, Spectrum Health–Kent Community Campus, Grand Rapids, MI, p. A335

THOMAS, Gloria, Vice President Human Resources, Regional Medical Center at Memphis, Memphis, TN, p. A613

THOMAS, James, Chief Financial Officer, Montfort Jones Memorial Hospital, Kosciusko, MS, p. A371

THOMAS, James R., Chief Executive Officer, North Florida Regional Medical Center, Gainesville, FL, p. A130

THOMAS, Jerry, Administrator, Shreveport Rehabilitation Hospital, Shreveport, LA, p. A293

THOMAS, Joan, Chief Financial Officer, Brunswick Community Hospital, Supply, NC, p. A492

THOMAS, Joanna, Chief Executive Officer, Southern Kentucky Rehabilitation Hospital, Bowling Green, KY, p. A262

THOMAS, M.D., John H., Chief of Staff, Collingsworth General Hospital, Wellington, TX, p. A673

THOMAS, Kathy, Director Human Resources, Chatham Hospital, Siler City, NC, p. A491

THOMAS, Lacy L., CPA, Chief Executive Officer, University Medical Center, Las Vegas, NV, p. A417

THOMAS, Maggie, Chief Human Resources Officer, South County Hospital, Wakefield, RI, p. A582

THOMAS, Marcile, Administrator, Providence Medical Center, Wayne, NE, p. A414

THOMAS, CPA, Mark, Chief Financial Officer, Eastland Memorial Hospital, Eastland, TX, p. A636

THOMAS, Michael P., Administrator, Meade District Hospital, Meade, KS, p. A252

THOMAS, Mitch, Chief Financial Officer, Providence Holy Cross Medical Center, San Fernando, CA, p. A88

THOMAS, Mitchell T., Chief Financial Officer, Providence Saint Joseph Medical Center, Burbank, CA, p. A55

THOMAS, D.O., R Russell, Chief of Staff, Rice Medical Center, Eagle Lake, TX, p. A636

THOMAS, Richard Lee, Superintendent, Lakeshore Mental Health Institute, Knoxville, TN, p. A610

THOMAS, Robert, Administrator, Columbus Community Hospital, Columbus, TX, p. A629

THOMAS, Steve, Vice President Human Resources, Cape Fear Valley Health System, Fayetteville, NC, p. A482

THOMAS, Stuart J., Interim Executive Director, Memorial Hospital of Sweetwater County, Rock Springs, WY, p. A741

THOMAS, Sue, Human Resource Manager, Beckley Appalachian Regional Hospital, Beckley, WV, p. A713

THOMAS, Telford W., President and Chief Executive Officer, Washington Hospital, Washington, PA, p. A578

THOMAS, Timothy, Administrator, Newton Regional Hospital, Newton, MS, p. A374

THOMAS, M.D., Walter, Chief of Staff, Fayette Memorial Hospital, La Grange, TX, p. A651

THOMAS, Warner L., President and Chief Operating Officer, Ochsner Clinic Foundation, New Orleans, LA, p. A289

THOMAS, Wiley, Director Information Systems, Good Shepherd Medical Center, Longview, TX, p. A653

THOMASON, Joe, Chief Executive Officer, RHD Memorial Medical Center, Dallas, TX, p. A634

THOMASON, Rose, Administration Director Human Resources, Campbell Health System, Weatherford, TX, p. A673

THOMEIER, M.D., William, President Medical Staff, Canonsburg General Hospital, Canonsburg, PA, p. A554

THOMPSON, Belinda, Human Resources Coordinator, HEALTHSOUTH Chesapeake Rehabilitation Hospital, Salisbury, MD, p. A310

THOMPSON, Bobby G., President and Chief Executive Officer, Mercy Memorial Health Center, Ardmore, OK, p. A527

THOMPSON, M.D., Charles, Chief of Staff, Abilene Regional Medical Center, Abilene, TX, p. A620

THOMPSON, Charolette, Chief Executive Officer and Chief Financial Officer, Tri–Ward General Hospital, Bernice, LA, p. A278

THOMPSON, Chris
Chief Financial Officer, Delta Community Medical Center, Delta, UT, p. A676
Chief Financial Officer, Fillmore Community Medical Center, Fillmore, UT, p. A676
Chief Financial Officer, Sanpete Valley Hospital, Mount Pleasant, UT, p. A677
Chief Financial Officer, Sevier Valley Hospital, Richfield, UT, p. A679

THOMPSON, Dale, President and Chief Executive Officer, Benedictine Health System, Duluth, MN, p. B17

THOMPSON, David
Chief Information Officer, Borgess Medical Center, Kalamazoo, MI, p. A338
Chief Financial Officer, Primary Children's Medical Center, Salt Lake City, UT, p. A679

THOMPSON, Deborah, Vice President Human Resources, Lawrence Memorial Hospital, Lawrence, KS, p. A251

THOMPSON, Deborah A., Director, Northern Arizona VA Health Care System, Prescott, AZ, p. A35

THOMPSON, Donald, Commanding Officer, Naval Hospital, Cherry Point, NC, p. A480

THOMPSON, Dwight, Chief Financial Officer, Altru Health System, Grand Forks, ND, p. A498

THOMPSON, Floyd, Chief Executive Officer, Gallup Indian Medical Center, Gallup, NM, p. A442

THOMPSON, Frederick G., Ph.D., Administrator and Chief Executive Officer, Anson Community Hospital, Wadesboro, NC, p. A493

THOMPSON, H H., Chief Financial Officer, St. Joseph's Hospital, Parkersburg, WV, p. A718

THOMPSON, Helen
Chief Information Officer, Heartland Regional Medical Center, Saint Joseph, MO, p. A390
Administrative Officer, Indian Health Service Hospital, Rapid City, SD, p. A598

THOMPSON, James H., Ph.D., Owner and Chief Executive Officer, HealthMark Regional Medical Center, DeFuniak Springs, FL, p. A127

THOMPSON, Jane, Administrator and Chief Operating Officer, York General Health Care Services, York, NE, p. A414

THOMPSON, Jeffrey E., M.D., Chief Executive Officer, Gundersen Lutheran Medical Center, La Crosse, WI, p. A727

THOMPSON, John W., Ph.D., Chief Executive Officer, Sandypines, Tequesta, FL, p. A149

THOMPSON, Kelly, Director Finance, SSM Cardinal Glennon Children's Hospital, Saint Louis, MO, p. A391

THOMPSON, Kevin, Chief Financial Officer, Sharp Memorial Hospital, San Diego, CA, p. A87

THOMPSON, M.D., Lynn, Vice President and Chief Medical Officer, Lima Memorial Health System, Lima, OH, p. A516

THOMPSON, Mary, Manager, Human Resources, The Women's Hospital, Newburgh, IN, p. A223

THOMPSON, Michael S., Chief Executive Officer, Preston Memorial Hospital, Kingwood, WV, p. A717

THOMPSON, Michael W., Administrator, HEALTHSOUTH Rehabilitation of Gadsden, Gadsden, AL, p. A19

THOMPSON, Michele T.
Interim Chief Operating Officer, Provident Hospital of Cook County, Chicago, IL, p. A189
Interim Chief Operating Officer, Provident Hospital of Cook County, Chicago, IL, p. A189

THOMPSON, Pat, Chief Information Officer, Parkview Huntington Hospital, Huntington, IN, p. A218

THOMPSON, Patricia
Senior Vice President and Chief Information Officer, Parkview Hospital, Fort Wayne, IN, p. A215
Chief Information Officer, Parkview Noble Hospital, Kendallville, IN, p. A220

THOMPSON, Ray, Executive Vice President and Chief Operating Officer, Trinity Mother Frances Health System, Tyler, TX, p. A671

THOMPSON, Shari, Chief Information Officer, Boone County Health Center, Albion, NE, p. A404

THOMPSON, Stephanie, Vice President Nursing Services, The Good Samaritan Hospital, Lebanon, PA, p. A563

THOMPSON, Thomas R., Chief Executive Officer, St. Mary's Regional Health Center, Detroit Lakes, MN, p. A352

THOMPSON, Thomas W., Chief Operating Officer, Eastern Idaho Regional Medical Center, Idaho Falls, ID, p. A179

THOMPSON, Wayne
Manager Information Systems, Benefis Healthcare, Great Falls, MT, p. A399
Chief Financial Officer, Christus Schumpert Health System, Shreveport, LA, p. A292
Chief Financial Officer, Memorial Medical Center, New Orleans, LA, p. A289

THOMSEN, Greg, Chief Executive Officer, Columbus Specialty Hospital, Columbus, GA, p. A158

THOPPIL, M.D., Cecil, Chief of Staff, Northern Hospital of Surry County, Mount Airy, NC, p. A488

THORDARSON, M.D., David, Chief of Staff, USC University Hospital, Los Angeles, CA, p. A73

THORE, Joe, Chief Operating Officer, Ashe Memorial Hospital, Jefferson, NC, p. A485

THOREEN, Peter W., President and Chief Executive Officer, St. Luke's Regional Medical Center, Sioux City, IA, p. A242

THORESON, Scott D., Administrator, Springfield Medical Center–Mayo Health System, Springfield, MN, p. A363

THORLAND, Mark, Chief Financial Officer, McKenzie County Healthcare System, Watford City, ND, p. A500

THORN, III, Eugene A., Vice President, Finance and Chief Financial Officer, Union Hospital, Dover, OH, p. A513

THORNHILL, Larry, President and Chief Executive Officer, Berger Health System, Circleville, OH, p. A508

THORNTON, Bob, Chief Financial Officer, Bayfront Medical Center, Saint Petersburg, FL, p. A145

THORNTON, Dale E., CHE, President and Chief Executive Officer, Mercy Hospital of Tiffin, Tiffin, OH, p. A522

THORNTON, Fred, Director Information Systems, Grande Ronde Hospital, La Grande, OR, p. A545

THORNTON, Reggie, Chief Information Officer, Ashland Community Hospital, Ashland, OR, p. A542

THORNTON Jr, Robert M., Chief Executive Officer, Sunlink Healthcare, Atlanta, GA, p. B103

THORNTON, Robert S., Associate Director and Chief Financial Officer, Excela Latrobe Area Hospital, Latrobe, PA, p. A563

THORNTON, Timothy J., Chief Executive Officer, UAB Medical West, Bessemer, AL, p. A14

THORNTON, William M., President and Chief Executive Officer, Miami Valley Hospital, Dayton, OH, p. A512

THORPE, Linda, Finance Manager, East Morgan County Hospital, Brush, CO, p. A101

THORSEN, Erik, Chief Financial Officer, Columbia Memorial Hospital, Astoria, OR, p. A542

THORSLAND Jr, Ed, Director, Veterans Affairs Eastern Colorado Health Care System, Denver, CO, p. A104

THRASHER, Charlotte
Chief Operating Officer and Administrator, Seton Medical Center, Austin, TX, p. A623
Chief Operating Officer and Administrator, Seton Medical Center, Austin, TX, p. A623

THRONEBERRY, M.D., Bart, Chief of Staff, Conway Regional Medical Center, Conway, AR, p. A41

THURMAND, Karen, Administrator, Andrew McFarland Mental Health Center, Springfield, IL, p. A208

THURMER, DeAnn, Interim President and Chief Executive Officer, Waupun Memorial Hospital, Waupun, WI, p. A737

THURSTON, Leigh, System Director, Information Technology, Fairbanks Memorial Hospital, Fairbanks, AK, p. A27

THWEATT Jr, James W., Chief Executive Officer, Lewis–Gale Medical Center, Salem, VA, p. A696

TIBBITS, Richard M., Chief People Officer, Florida Hospital, Orlando, FL, p. A141

TIBBITTS, Mitch, Chief Financial Officer, St. Mark's Hospital, Salt Lake City, UT, p. A680

TIBBITTS, Tom, President, Trinity Regional Medical Center, Fort Dodge, IA, p. A234

TIBBOTT, Jane, Director, Magee–Womens Hospital of UPMC, Pittsburgh, PA, p. A571

TIBBS, E. W., President and Chief Executive Officer, Bedford Memorial Hospital, Bedford, VA, p. A685

TICE, Darlette, Vice President Operations and Chief Nursing Executive, Forbes Regional Hospital, Monroeville, PA, p. A565

TICE, Kirk C., President and Chief Executive Officer, Robert Wood Johnson University Hospital at Rahway, Rahway, NJ, p. A435

TICKLE, M Rita, Director, Human Resources, Albert Lindley Lee Memorial Hospital, Fulton, NY, p. A452

TIEDEMANN, Frank, President and Chief Executive Officer, Children's Hospital and Research Center at Oakland, Oakland, CA, p. A78

TIEMAN, Brian, Director Human Resources, Carlinville Area Hospital, Carlinville, IL, p. A185

TIERMAN, Kelley, Chief Financial Officer, Massena Memorial Hospital, Massena, NY, p. A456

TIERNEY, Thomas, Chief Information Officer, Veterans Affairs Medical Center, Wilmington, DE, p. A120

TIETJEN, M.D., George, Chief of Staff, Wayne Memorial Hospital, Honesdale, PA, p. A560

TILLER, Gary L., Chief Executive Officer, Ninnescah Valley Health System, Kingman, KS, p. A250

TILLERY, Iris, Vice President Patient Services, Baptist Cherokee, Centre, AL, p. A16

TILLIRSON, Mike, Executive Vice President, AnMED Health Medical Center, Anderson, SC, p. A583

TILLMAN, David, President and Chief Executive Officer, Motion Picture and Television Fund Hospital and Residential Services, Los Angeles, CA, p. A71

TILLMAN, Jason, Chief Financial Officer, Green Oaks Hospital, Dallas, TX, p. A632

TILLMAN, Jill
    Chief Executive Officer, St. Christopher's Hospital for Children, Philadelphia, PA, p. A570
    Chief Executive Officer, St. Christopher's Hospital for Children, Philadelphia, PA, p. A570

TILLMAN, Michael, Vice President Patient Servies and Chief Operating Officer, United Hospital Center, Clarksburg, WV, p. A715

TILSON, Natalie
    Accounting Manager, HEALTHSOUTH Rehabilitation Hospital, Kingsport, TN, p. A609
    Controller, HEALTHSOUTH Rehabilitation Hospital, Kingsport, TN, p. A609

TILTON, David P., President and Chief Executive Officer, Atlanticare Regional Medical Center, Atlantic City, NJ, p. A425

TIMCHO, Thomas P., President and Chief Executive Officer, Jefferson Regional Medical Center, Pittsburgh, PA, p. A571

TIMMONS, Bret, Chief Medical Staff, Harms Memorial Hospital District, American Falls, ID, p. A177

TIMMONS, William, Chief Executive Officer, Los Ninos Hospital, Phoenix, AZ, p. A34

TIMPE, Ronald, Associate Administrator, Buchanan County Health Center, Independence, IA, p. A235

TING, M.D., Robert, Chief Medical Staff, Gritman Medical Center, Moscow, ID, p. A180

TINGELSTAD, D.O., Kaare, Chief Medical Staff, Wallowa Memorial Hospital, Enterprise, OR, p. A543

TINKER, A. James, President and Chief Executive Officer, Mercy Medical Center, Cedar Rapids, IA, p. A229

TINKER, Peter, Chief, Human Resources, Veterans Affairs Medical Center, New York, NY, p. A466

TINNIN, Fran, Controller, Rolling Plains Memorial Hospital, Sweetwater, TX, p. A668

TINSA, Udom, Medical Director, Ashley Medical Center, Ashley, ND, p. A496

TINSLEY, Kay
    Vice President Fiscal Services, Good Samaritan Regional Health Center, Mount Vernon, IL, p. A202
    Vice President Finance, St. Mary's Hospital, Centralia, IL, p. A186

TINTLE, Keith D., Chief Executive Officer, Timpanogos Regional Hospital, Orem, UT, p. A678

TIPPETS, Wayne C., Director, Veterans Affairs Medical Center, Boise, ID, p. A178

TIPPIN, Russell, Administrator and Chief Executive Officer, Pecos County Memorial Hospital, Fort Stockton, TX, p. A639

TIPPINS, Doug, Director Information Services, Marian Community Hospital, Carbondale, PA, p. A554

TIPTON, Bob, Chief Financial Officer, Weston County Health Services, Newcastle, WY, p. A741

TIRADO, Norma, Vice President Employee Relations and Staff Organizational Development, Agnesian HealthCare, Fond Du Lac, WI, p. A725

TISCHER, Jesse, Administrator, Wheaton Community Hospital, Wheaton, MN, p. A365

TISCHLER, M.D., James F., Chief of Staff, Veterans Affairs Medical Center, Coatesville, PA, p. A556

TISDALE, Bruce, Vice President Human Resources, Saint Anthony's Health Center, Alton, IL, p. A183

TISDALL, Renae, Chief Financial Officer, Mobridge Regional Hospital, Mobridge, SD, p. A597

TISHER, Paul W., Vice President and Chief Medical Officer, Acadia Hospital, Bangor, ME, p. A296

TITUS III, Rexford W., President and Chief Executive Officer, ProHealth Care, Waukesha, WI, p. B85

TIURCHY, Payvand, Chief of Staff, Brooks County Hospital, Quitman, GA, p. A167

TKACH, M.D., Thomas, Chief of Staff, Bone and Joint Hospital, Oklahoma City, OK, p. A535

TOBIN, John H., President and Chief Executive Officer, Waterbury Hospital, Waterbury, CT, p. A117

TOBIN, Patricia, Administrative Director, Human Resources, Fawcett Memorial Hospital, Port Charlotte, FL, p. A144

TOBIN, Timothy C.
    President and Chief Executive Officer, Alleghany Regional Hospital, Low Moor, VA, p. A690
    President and Chief Executive Officer, Clinch Valley Medical Center, Richlands, VA, p. A694

TOCHE, Gary, President, Tucson Heart Hospital, Tucson, AZ, p. A38

TODD, Bob, Director Information Systems, Mount Auburn Hospital, Cambridge, MA, p. A316

TODD, Fred O., Vice President, Finance, Loris Community Hospital, Loris, SC, p. A590

TODD, John, M.D., President and Chief Executive Officer, Stevens Healthcare, Edmonds, WA, p. A702

TODHUNTER, Neil E., President, UPMC Northwest, Seneca, PA, p. A575

TODOROW, Thomas, Chief Financial Officer, Children's Hospital of Philadelphia, Philadelphia, PA, p. A567

TOEBBE, Nelson, Chief Executive Officer, Ivinson Memorial Hospital, Laramie, WY, p. A741

TOFANI, Gerald, Chief Financial Officer, Monmouth Medical Center, Long Branch, NJ, p. A430

TOKHEIM, Thomas J., Vice President and Chief Financial Officer, Eisenhower Memorial Hospital and Betty Ford Center at Eisenhower, Rancho Mirage, CA, p. A83

TOL, Daryl
    Administrator, Florida Hospital–Flagler, Palm Coast, FL, p. A142
    Chief Operating Officer, Florida Hospital–Ormond Memorial, Ormond Beach, FL, p. A141

TOLBERT, Sue, Chief Financial Officer, Earl K. Long Medical Center, Baton Rouge, LA, p. A277

TOLCHIN, M.D., Sanford, Chief Medical Officer, Borgess Medical Center, Kalamazoo, MI, p. A338

TOLER, M.D., Douglas, President Medical Staff, Huguley Memorial Medical Center, Fort Worth, TX, p. A640

TOLES, Rex, Director Information Management Service Line, Harry S. Truman Memorial Veterans Hospital, Columbia, MO, p. A380

TOLLIVER, Gerald, Associate Director Finance and Administration, St. Elizabeths Hospital, Washington, DC, p. A122

TOLMAN, Dennis, Chief Executive Officer, Mountain View Hospital, Idaho Falls, ID, p. A179

TOLMIE, John Kerr, President and Chief Executive Officer, St. Joseph Medical Center, Towson, MD, p. A311

TOLOSKY, Mark R.
    President and Chief Executive Officer, Baystate Health System, Inc., Springfield, MA, p. B17
    President and Chief Executive Officer, Baystate Medical Center, Springfield, MA, p. A323

TOLSON, Rick, Vice President Human Resources, Saint Joseph Hospital, Lexington, KY, p. A267

TOM, Adrian, Management Information Systems Supervisor, Hopi Health Care Center, Keams Canyon, AZ, p. A31

TOM, Beatrice
    Chief Executive Officer, St. Francis Medical Center, Honolulu, HI, p. A174
    Chief Executive Officer, St. Francis Medical Center–West, Ewa Beach, HI, p. A173

TOM, Malcolm J., Chief Operations Officer, St. Francis Medical Center–West, Ewa Beach, HI, p. A173

TOMAS, George, Director Information Services, Griffin Hospital, Derby, CT, p. A112

TOMASINO, Tom, Chief Information Officer, Whidbey General Hospital, Coupeville, WA, p. A702

TOMBERLIN, Don E., Chief Executive Officer, Effingham Hospital, Springfield, GA, p. A169

TOMLIN, Kerry W., Associate Administrator, Clay County Hospital, Ashland, AL, p. A13

TOMLINSON, D Ronald, Executive Vice President and Chief Financial Officer, Wilson Medical Center, Wilson, NC, p. A494

TOMLON, Kenneth, Chief Operating Officer, Via Christi Regional Medical Center, Wichita, KS, p. A259

TOMORY, M.D., Gerald
    Regional Medical Director, Kauai Veterans Memorial Hospital, Waimea, HI, p. A176
    Regional Medical Director, Samuel Mahelona Memorial Hospital, Kapaa, HI, p. A175

TOMPKINS, Kim, Director Information Services, DeTar Healthcare System, Victoria, TX, p. A672

TOMPKINS, III, William F., Vice President and Medical Director, Martha Jefferson Hospital, Charlottesville, VA, p. A686

TONEY, M.D., Steven, Chief Medical Officer, Davis Memorial Hospital, Elkins, WV, p. A715

TONG, M.D., Beverly, Chief of Staff, Mercy Medical Center, Williston, ND, p. A501

TONG, Hon–Chung, Chief Financial Officer, Eagleville Hospital, Eagleville, PA, p. A557

TONGATE, Scott, Administrator, Carthage General Hospital, Carthage, TN, p. A603

TONJES, Ken, Assistant Administrator Finance, Ketchikan General Hospital, Ketchikan, AK, p. A27

TONKINSON, Robert, Vice President Finance, Carle Foundation Hospital, Urbana, IL, p. A209

TONKOVIC, Kathie, Director Health Information Management, Shriners Hospitals for Children–Chicago, Chicago, IL, p. A190

TOOLE, LaDon
    Administrator, Brooks County Hospital, Quitman, GA, p. A167
    Administrator, Brooks County Hospital, Quitman, GA, p. A167
    Administrator, Brooks County Hospital, Quitman, GA, p. A167

TOOMEY, Joseph F., President and Chief Executive Officer, Resurrection Health Care Corporation, Chicago, IL, p. B93

TOOMEY, Richard Kirk, President and Chief Executive Officer, Nash Health Care Systems, Rocky Mount, NC, p. A490

TOOT, Gregory P., Administrator and Chief Executive Officer, HEALTHSOUTH Rehabilitation of Mechanicsburg, Mechanicsburg, PA, p. A564

TOPMILLER, Darrell, Director Finance, Fulton County Health Center, Wauseon, OH, p. A524

TOPPER, David
    Chief Executive Officer, Alta Healthcare System, Bellflower, CA, p. B8
    Chief Executive Officer, Los Angeles Community Hospital, Los Angeles, CA, p. A71

TOPPER, John E., Senior Vice President and Chief Financial Officer, Mercy Medical Center, Baltimore, MD, p. A304

TORBETT, Russell, Manager, Creek Nation Community Hospital, Okemah, OK, p. A534

TORCHIA, Jude, Chief Executive Officer, Cleveland Regional Medical Center, Cleveland, TX, p. A629

TORIANO, Sharon, Chief Human Resources, Kona Community Hospital, Kealakekua, HI, p. A175

TORNES, Cindy, Coordinator Human Resources, Selby General Hospital, Marietta, OH, p. A517

TOROK, Peter G., Commander, Keller Army Community Hospital, West Point, NY, p. A476

TORRES, Carlos V.
Christus Santa Rosa Children's Hospital, San Antonio, TX, p. A663
Regional Vice President, Human Resources, Christus Santa Rosa Health Care, San Antonio, TX, p. A663

TORRES, Diane D., R.N., Administrator, McKenzie Memorial Hospital, Sandusky, MI, p. A345

TORRES, M.D., Francisco de, Medical Director, Ashford Presbyterian Community Hospital, San Juan, PR, p. A746

TORRES, Matthew, Chief Information Officer, Memorial Medical Center, Port Lavaca, TX, p. A661

TORRES, M.D., Shivaun, Chief Medical Staff, Dundy County Hospital, Benkelman, NE, p. A405

TORRES AYALA, Eugenio, Director Information Systems, Cardiovascular Center of Puerto Rico and the Caribbean, San Juan, PR, p. A746

TORRES CASTRO, M.D., Jadmmal, Medical Director, Hospital Metropolitan, San Juan, PR, p. A747

TOSI, M.D., Stephen, Chief Medical Officer, UMass Memorial Medical Center, Worcester, MA, p. A326

TOTH, Jackie, Administrator, Acute Care Specialty Hospital of Aultman, Canton, OH, p. A505

TOTTEN, M.D., Mark, President Medical Staff, King's Daughters' Hospital and Health Services, Madison, IN, p. A221

TOUPS, Sharon A., Senior Vice President and Chief Operating Officer, St. Tammany Parish Hospital, Covington, LA, p. A279

TOURVILLE, James C., Administrator, Douglas County Health Center, Omaha, NE, p. A411

TOUSSAINT, John S., M.D., President and Chief Executive Officer, ThedaCare, Inc., Appleton, WI, p. B108

TOWER, David W., Chief Operating Officer, Huggins Hospital, Wolfeboro, NH, p. A424

TOWERY, M.D., O B., Chief of Staff, Mt. Diablo Medical Pavilion, Concord, CA, p. A57

TOWLE, Sonya, Human Resources Director, Mille Lacs Health System, Onamia, MN, p. A359

TOWLER, Robert D., Chief Executive Officer, Southern Virginia Regional Medical Center, Emporia, VA, p. A687

TOWN, Alex, Chief Financial Officer, Tri-State Memorial Hospital, Clarkston, WA, p. A701

TOWNES, Tim, Director, Information Systems, Carraway Methodist Medical Center, Birmingham, AL, p. A14

TOWNSEND, Charlotte, Financial Manager, North Sunflower Medical Center, Ruleville, MS, p. A375

TOWNSEND, Gary, Chief Information Officer, Hurley Medical Center, Flint, MI, p. A333

TOWNSEND, Jamie, Chief Financial Officer, Henry County Medical Center, Paris, TN, p. A616

TOWNSEND, Pam, Vice President Finance, Coosa Valley Medical Center, Sylacauga, AL, p. A24

TOWNSEND, Theodore E., President and Chief Executive Officer, St. Luke's Hospital, Cedar Rapids, IA, p. A229

TOWNSON, Charles, Chief Operating Officer, Spartanburg Regional Medical Center, Spartanburg, SC, p. A592

TOY, Gale S., Manager Information Systems, Mid Coast Hospital, Brunswick, ME, p. A297

TOY, Joseph A., President and Chief Executive Officer, Eastern State Hospital, Lexington, KY, p. A267

TRACEY, Allen, Manager Information Systems, James Lawrence Kernan Hospital, Baltimore, MD, p. A303

TRACEY, Robert M.
Administrator, Regional Hospitals, Franciscan Skemp Healthcare–Arcadia Campus, Arcadia, WI, p. A722
Administrator, Franciscan Skemp Healthcare–Sparta Campus, Sparta, WI, p. A735

TRACHTA, Michael D., Chief Executive Officer, Waverly Health Center, Waverly, IA, p. A243

TRACY, Tim, Executive Vice President and Chief Executive Officer, John C. Lincoln Hospital–Deer Valley, Phoenix, AZ, p. A34

TRACY, Timothy J., Chief Executive Officer, Sioux Valley Vermillion Medical Center, Vermillion, SD, p. A600

TRACZ, Robert, Chief Financial Officer, Lake Hospital System, Painesville, OH, p. A520

TRADER, Harold R., Vice President and Chief Financial Officer, Lexington Memorial Hospital, Lexington, NC, p. A486

TRAHAN, Alcus, Administrator and Chief Executive Officer, St. Helena Parish Hospital, Greensburg, LA, p. A281

TRAHAN, Daniel M., Administrator, Leonard J. Chabert Medical Center, Houma, LA, p. A282

TRAHAN, Lyman, Chief Executive Officer, Abrom Kaplan Memorial Hospital, Kaplan, LA, p. A282

TRAHERN, Sheri, Chief Financial Officer, St. Thomas More Hospital, Canon City, CO, p. A102

TRAINOR, Sara, Chief Financial Officer, Community Memorial Hospital, Sumner, IA, p. A242

TRAMP, Francis, President, Burgess Health Center, Onawa, IA, p. A239

TRAN, Vinh, Chief Financial Officer, Veterans Affairs Medical Center, Philadelphia, PA, p. A570

TRANTHAM, Susan, Director of Human Resources, HEALTHSOUTH Rehabilitation Hospital, Florence, SC, p. A587

TRASK, Jonathan, Director Management Information Services, The Charlotte Hungerford Hospital, Torrington, CT, p. A117

TRAUB, Bruce, Vice President Finance, University Medical Center at Princeton, Princeton, NJ, p. A435

TRAUTMAN, Robert J., Chief Executive Officer, Lancaster Community Hospital, Lancaster, CA, p. A67

TRAVERS, M.D., Richard D.,Prince William Hospital, Manassas, VA, p. A691

TRAVERSE, Bruce L., President, Carson City Hospital, Carson City, MI, p. A329

TRAVIS, Bob, Director Information Systems, Wheeling Hospital, Wheeling, WV, p. A721

TRAVIS, David A.
Chief Financial Officer, East Texas Medical Center Athens, Athens, TX, p. A622
Chief Financial Officer, East Texas Medical Center Fairfield, Fairfield, TX, p. A638

TRAVIS, Dee Dee, Director Community Relations, Calais Regional Hospital, Calais, ME, p. A297

TRAVIS, Keith, Vice President Human Resources, Murray–Calloway County Hospital, Murray, KY, p. A272

TRAYNOR, Karen, Chief Financial Officer, Baldwin Area Medical Center, Baldwin, WI, p. A722

TREACY, Nancy, Chief Financial Officer, Falls Memorial Hospital, International Falls, MN, p. A355

TREADWAY, Michael G., Controller, HEALTHSOUTH Rehabilitation Hospital–Tyler, Tyler, TX, p. A671

TREASURE, Martin, Director Human Resources, Pottsville Hospital and Warne Clinic, Pottsville, PA, p. A573

TREFRY, Robert J., President and Chief Executive Officer, Bridgeport Hospital, Bridgeport, CT, p. A112

TREGLOWN, Brad, Director Information Systems, Redmond Regional Medical Center, Rome, GA, p. A168

TREGLOWN, Jim, Vice President Human Resources, Southeast Alabama Medical Center, Dothan, AL, p. A17

TREMBULAK, Frank J., Executive Vice President and Chief Operating Officer, Geisinger Medical Center, Danville, PA, p. A556

TRENTHAM, MC, Nathan, Chief of Staff, Woods Memorial Hospital District, Etowah, TN, p. A606

TREPAGNIER, Kat, Human Resource Director, River Parishes Hospital, La Place, LA, p. A283

TRETT, Jenny, Chief Financial Officer, Chickasaw Nation Health System, Ada, OK, p. A527

TREVATHAN, Phyllis, Human Resources Director, Northcrest Medical Center, Springfield, TN, p. A618

TREXLER, David V., President, Decatur County Memorial Hospital, Greensburg, IN, p. A217

TRIANA, Milton, Administrator, St. Mary Medical Center, Hobart, IN, p. A217

TRIEBES, David G., Chief Executive Officer, Samaritan Albany General Hospital, Albany, OR, p. A542

TRIGG, Pat, Direcor of Human Resources and Public Relations, Memorial Medical Center, Port Lavaca, TX, p. A661

TRIGGS, Jonna, Chief Executive Officer, Southern Nevada Adult Mental Health Services, Las Vegas, NV, p. A417

TRIMBLE, Deborah L., Chief Executive Officer, Paul B. Hall Regional Medical Center, Paintsville, KY, p. A273

TRIMBLE, R.N., Kevin, Senior Vice President and Chief Nursing Officer, Saint Luke's Northland Hospital–Smithville Campus, Smithville, MO, p. A393

TRIMBLE, Melody, Chief Executive Officer, Venice Regional Medical Center, Venice, FL, p. A149

TRIMM, Robert M., President and Chief Executive Officer, Satilla Regional Medical Center, Waycross, GA, p. A172

TRIMMER, Matt, Director Information Services, Mercy Medical Center–Dubuque, Dubuque, IA, p. A233

TRIPPEL, Cheryl, Finance Director, Glencoe Regional Health Services, Glencoe, MN, p. A354

TRIPPEL, Donald E., Chief Financial Officer, Hugh Chatham Memorial Hospital, Elkin, NC, p. A482

TROSCLAIR, Andrea, Vice President Human Resources, Arkansas Children's Hospital, Little Rock, AR, p. A46

TROST, Carnie, Director Human Resources, Memorial Health Center, Sidney, NE, p. A413

TROTTER, M.D., R C., Chief Medical Staff, Western Plains Medical Complex, Dodge City, KS, p. A246

TROTTIER, Timothy, Chief Executive Officer, Yakima Regional Medical and Heart Center, Yakima, WA, p. A712

TROUP, Matthew, President, Presbyterian Hospital of Winnsboro, Winnsboro, TX, p. A674

TROUT, Gene, Chief Financial Officer, Canonsburg General Hospital, Canonsburg, PA, p. A554

TROUTMAN, CPA, Gary, Vice President Finance, Women and Children's Hospital, Lake Charles, LA, p. A285

TROVINI, Kevin, Manager, Information Systems, Advocate Illinois Masonic Medical Center, Chicago, IL, p. A186

TROWER, G. Wil, President and Chief Executive Officer, North Broward Hospital District, Fort Lauderdale, FL, p. B79

TROYER, David, Manager Information Resources Management, Veterans Affairs Northern Indiana Health Care System, Fort Wayne, IN, p. A216

TRSTENSKY, Jomary, President, Hospital Sisters Health System, Springfield, IL, p. B60

TRUELL, George, Director Human Resources, Ripon Medical Center, Ripon, WI, p. A735

TRUELOVE, Lynn, Administrator, Singing River Hospital System, Pascagoula, MS, p. A374

TRUESDALE, M.D., Bruce H., Chief of Staff, Lexington Medical Center, West Columbia, SC, p. A593

TRUESDALE Jr, Fred A., Chief Executive Officer, H. C. Watkins Memorial Hospital, Quitman, MS, p. A375

TRUFANT, Richard, Chief Financial Officer, Community Health Center of Branch County, Coldwater, MI, p. A330

TRUITT, Louise, Director of Human Resources, Doctors Hospital of Columbus, Columbus, GA, p. A158

TRULL, David J., President, Faulkner Hospital, Boston, MA, p. A313

TRUMBLE, Rebecca, Director Human Resources, Forbes Regional Hospital, Monroeville, PA, p. A565

TRUNFIO, Joseph A., Ph.D.,
President and Chief Executive Officer, Atlantic Health System, Florham Park, NJ, p. B12
President and Chief Executive Officer, Morristown Memorial Hospital, Morristown, NJ, p. A431
President and Chief Executive Officer, Mountainside Hospital, Montclair, NJ, p. A431
President and Chief Executive Officer, Overlook Hospital, Summit, NJ, p. A436

TRUNNELL, David, Chief Financial Officer, Inland Hospital, Waterville, ME, p. A301

TRUNZ, III, Charles M., Chief Information Officer and Chief Administrative Officer, North Shore University Hospital at Syosset, Syosset, NY, p. A473

TRUSLEY III, James F., Director, Veterans Affairs Medical Center, Augusta, GA, p. A155

TRUSSEL, Paul, Director Human Resources, University Hospitals and Clinics, University of Mississippi Medical Center, Jackson, MS, p. A371

TRUSTY, Kevin, Information Technology Director and Materials Manager, Pulaski Memorial Hospital, Winamac, IN, p. A227

TRYON, Ellen, Chief Operating Officer, San Joaquin Community Hospital, Bakersfield, CA, p. A54

TSALATE, Cynthia, Human Resource Specialist, U. S. Public Health Service Indian Hospital, Zuni, NM, p. A445

TSCHIDER, Richard A., FACHE, President and Chief Executive Officer, St. Alexius Medical Center, Bismarck, ND, p. A496

TSCHIRHART, M.D., Donald, Chief of Staff, St. Vincent Medical Center, Los Angeles, CA, p. A72

TSENG, Allen, Administrative Director, Harris Methodist Southwest, Fort Worth, TX, p. A639

TSENG, M.D., Angela, Chief of Staff, East Texas Medical Center Clarksville, Clarksville, TX, p. A628

TSO, Ronald, Chief Executive Officer, Chinle Comprehensive Health Care Facility, Chinle, AZ, p. A30

TSOSIE, Fawn, Finance Manager, U. S. Public Health Service Indian Hospital, Crownpoint, NM, p. A442

TUCHSCHMIDT, James, M.D., Director, Veterans Affairs Medical Center, Portland, OR, p. A548

TUCKER, Jr, Allen D., Senior Executive Vice President and Chief Operating Officer, Genesys Regional Medical Center, Grand Blanc, MI, p. A334

TUCKER, Denis, Director Information Services, Riddle Memorial Hospital, Media, PA, p. A565

TUCKER, Edgar L., Director, Michael E. Debakey Veterans Affairs Medical Center, Houston, TX, p. A646

TUCKER, Jr, G Edward
Chief Financial Officer, Forrest General Hospital, Hattiesburg, MS, p. A369
Chief Financial Officer, Forrest General Hospital, Hattiesburg, MS, p. A369

TUCKER, Gene
Interim Chief Executive Officerf, Marion County Medical Center, Mullins, SC, p. A590
Chief Financial Officer, Marion County Medical Center, Mullins, SC, p. A590

TUCKER, Joseph B., Chief Financial Officer, Fort Washington Medical Center, Fort Washington, MD, p. A308

TUCKER, Lisa, Chief Information Officer, McDuffie Regional Medical Center, Thomson, GA, p. A170

TUCKER, Paul, Administrator, Highline Medical Center, Seattle, WA, p. A707

TUCKER, Ron, Chief Financial Officer, Kiowa County Memorial Hospital, Greensburg, KS, p. A248

TUCKER, Sidney, Administrator, Reagan Memorial Hospital, Big Lake, TX, p. A626

TUCKER, Steven, Chief Executive Officer, Select Specialty Hospital–San Antonio, San Antonio, TX, p. A665

TUCKER, Steven E., President, Memorial Medical Center, Johnstown, PA, p. A561

TUDOR, Chuck, Information Services Director, Marion General Hospital, Marion, OH, p. A517

TUDOR, Lorie, Chief Financial Officer, De Queen Regional Medical Center, De Queen, AR, p. A42

TUELL, William J., MSN, Facility Director, Commonwealth Center for Children and Adolescents, Staunton, VA, p. A697

TUESLEY, Sid
Chief Information Officer, Dupont Hospital, Fort Wayne, IN, p. A215
Chief Information Officer, Lutheran Hospital of Indiana, Fort Wayne, IN, p. A215
Chief Information Officer, St. Joseph Hospital, Fort Wayne, IN, p. A216

TUGWELL, M.D., Terry, Chf of Staff, P & S Surgical Hospital, Monroe, LA, p. A287

TULIN, Matthew, Chief Financial Officer, Southern Tennessee Medical Center, Winchester, TN, p. A619

TULLISON, David L., Comptroller, U. S. Naval Hospital, Roosevelt Roads, PR, p. A748

TULLMAN, Steven M., Chief Executive Officer, Phoenixville Hospital, Phoenixville, PA, p. A571

TUMA, Scott
Chief Operating Officer and Director Human Resources, Bell Hospital, Ishpeming, MI, p. A337
Chief Operating Officer and Director Human Resources, Bell Hospital, Ishpeming, MI, p. A337

TUMLIN, Richard, Chief Operating Officer, Emory Eastside Medical Center, Snellville, GA, p. A169

TUMMUTU, M.D., Ramireddy K., Chief Medical Officer, Porter–Valparaiso Hospital Campus, Valparaiso, IN, p. A226

TUNGATE, Rex A.
Administrator, Casey County Hospital, Liberty, KY, p. A268
Administrator, Westlake Regional Hospital, Columbia, KY, p. A263

TUNNEY, Niona, Director Human Resources, Cochran Memorial Hospital, Morton, TX, p. A657

TUPPER, Dave, Chief Operating Officer, HEALTHSOUTH Rehabilitation Institute of Tucson, Tucson, AZ, p. A38

TUPPER, David L., Administrator and Chief Executive Officer, Lifecare Hospitals of South Texas, Edinburg, TX, p. A636

TUPPER, Kevin, Director Information Technology, Windham Community Memorial Hospital, Willimantic, CT, p. A118

TUREK, Beth, Manager Information Systems, Advocate South Suburban Hospital, Hazel Crest, IL, p. A196

TURK, Edward, Chief Financial Officer, Scripps Mercy Hospital, San Diego, CA, p. A87

TURK, Herbert A., FACHE, Administrator, Sweeny Community Hospital, Sweeny, TX, p. A668

TURK, Jan, Chief Executive Officer, Kindred Hospital – New Orleans, New Orleans, LA, p. A288

TURK, M.D., Jay, Chief of Staff, Bowie Memorial Hospital, Bowie, TX, p. A626

TURKEL, Brooks, Chief Executive Officer, MacNeal Hospital, Berwyn, IL, p. A184

TURLEY, Susan S., Chief Financial Officer, Rio Grande Regional Hospital, McAllen, TX, p. A656

TURNBULL, James, Vice President and Chief Information Officer, Children's Hospital, Denver, CO, p. A103

TURNER, A. Ronald, President and Chief Executive Officer, Associated Healthcare Systems, Inc., Brentwood, TN, p. B12

TURNER, Cindy R.
Interim Chief Executive Officer, Bacon County Hospital and Health System, Alma, GA, p. A152
Chief Financial Officer and Chief Operating Officer, Bacon County Hospital and Health System, Alma, GA, p. A152
Chief Financial Officer, Bacon County Hospital and Health System, Alma, GA, p. A152

TURNER, Deborah, Vice President Human Resources, St. Luke's Cornwall Hospital – Newburgh Campus, Newburgh, NY, p. A467

TURNER, Doug, Chief Information Officer, Maury Regional Hospital, Columbia, TN, p. A604

TURNER, Farrell, Interim Administrator, Wedowee Hospital, Wedowee, AL, p. A25

TURNER, Glenn, Director, Information Systems, Memorial Medical Center, New Orleans, LA, p. A289

TURNER, FACHE, Jeff, Chief Operating Officer, Brownwood Regional Medical Center, Brownwood, TX, p. A627

TURNER, John, Chief Executive Officer, Quillen Rehabilitation Hospital, Johnson City, TN, p. A609

TURNER Jr, Joseph F., Chief Executive Officer, Wetzel County Hospital, New Martinsville, WV, p. A718

TURNER, Kathy, Human Resources Director, East Texas Medical Center Trinity, Trinity, TX, p. A670

TURNER, Kelly, Senior Vice President Finance, Glendale Adventist Medical Center, Glendale, CA, p. A62

TURNER, Mark J., Chief Operating Officer, Memorial Hospital, Belleville, IL, p. A184

TURNER, Michael, Director Human Resources, Yampa Valley Medical Center, Steamboat Springs, CO, p. A109

TURNER, Robert, M.D., Chief Executive Officer, Laurel Oaks Behavioral Center, Dothan, AL, p. A17

TURNER, Robert J.
Chief Operating Officer, St. Elizabeth Hospital, Appleton, WI, p. A722
Chief Operating Officer, St. Elizabeth Hospital, Appleton, WI, p. A722

TURNER, M.D., Roy, Chief of Staff, Harris Methodist–HEB, Bedford, TX, p. A625

TURNER Sr, Samuel H., Chief Executive Officer, Shawnee Mission Medical Center, Shawnee Mission, KS, p. A257

TURNER, Spencer, Chief Operating Officer, Trinity Medical Center, Carrollton, TX, p. A628

TURNEY, Brian, Chief Executive Officer, Kingman Regional Medical Center, Kingman, AZ, p. A31

TURNEY, Larry, Interim Administrator, Cochran Memorial Hospital, Morton, TX, p. A657

TURNQUIST, Carrie, Director Human Resources, Buena Vista Regional Medical Center, Storm Lake, IA, p. A242

TUSLER, Robert G., Chief Financial Officer, Wallace Thomson Hospital, Union, SC, p. A592

TWARDY, Cindi, Human Resources Department Manager, Meeker County Memorial Hospital, Litchfield, MN, p. A355

TWIEST, M.D., Mel, Senior Vice President Medical Affairs and Chief Medical Officer, Erlanger Medical Center, Chattanooga, TN, p. A603

TYGRETT, Holley, Director Human Resources, Abraham Lincoln Memorial Hospital, Lincoln, IL, p. A199

TYK, Robert C., Vice President Finance, Rehoboth McKinley Christian Hospital, Gallup, NM, p. A442

TYLER, Alan, Associate Director, Veterans Affairs Medical Center, Leeds, MA, p. A319

TYLER, Angie, Network Technician, University Specialty Hospital, Baltimore, MD, p. A305

TYLER, James E., Administrator and Chief Executive Officer, Carilion Giles Memorial Hospital, Pearisburg, VA, p. A693

TYLER, Rob, Chief Financial Officer, HEALTHSOUTH Rehabilitation Hospital of North Houston, Conroe, TX, p. A630

TYLER, Rosamond M., Administrator, Tyler Holmes Memorial Hospital, Winona, MS, p. A377

TYNER, W. Russell, President and Chief Executive Officer, Baptist Health, Montgomery, AL, p. B14

TYRA, J. Allen, Executive Director, Natchez Community Hospital, Natchez, MS, p. A373

TYRER, Ron, Interim Chief Executive Officer, Starke Memorial Hospital, Knox, IN, p. A220

TYSON, Kenneth L., Senior Vice President Operations, Newark Beth Israel Medical Center, Newark, NJ, p. A432

TYSON, Shelly, Director Human Resources, Medical Center of Lewisville, Lewisville, TX, p. A653

U

UBBING, Mina H., President and Chief Executive Officer, Fairfield Medical Center, Lancaster, OH, p. A515

UBOLDI, Michael J., R.N., President, Mercy San Juan Medical Center, Carmichael, CA, p. A56

UCHMAN, Stanley F., Deputy Commander, U. S. Air Force Medical Center Keesler, Keesler AFB, MS, p. A371

UDEH, M.D., C John, Chief of Staff, St. Bernardine Medical Center, San Bernardino, CA, p. A86

UDOVICH, Bill, Information Systems Director, Havasu Regional Medical Center, Lake Havasu City, AZ, p. A32

UGWUEKE, Michael O., Vice President Operations, Provena Saint Joseph Medical Center, Joliet, IL, p. A198

UHLHORN, Raymond W., Executive Director and Chief Executive Officer, Temple University Children's Medical Center, Philadelphia, PA, p. A570

ULAND, Jonas S.
Executive Director, Greene County General Hospital, Linton, IN, p. A221
Executive Director, Greene County General Hospital, Linton, IN, p. A221

ULBRICHT, William G.
Chief Operating Officer, South Florida Baptist Hospital, Plant City, FL, p. A143
Chief Operating Officer, South Florida Baptist Hospital, Plant City, FL, p. A143

ULICNY, Gary R., Ph.D., President and Chief Executive Officer, Shepherd Center, Atlanta, GA, p. A154

ULLIAN, Elaine S., President and Chief Executive Officer, Boston Medical Center, Boston, MA, p. A313

ULM, Michael, Chief Executive Officer, Mangum City Hospital, Mangum, OK, p. A533

ULMER, Carlton, Chief Operating Officer, Parkridge Medical Center, Chattanooga, TN, p. A604

ULMER, Carol, Chief Executive Officer, Select Specialty Hospital–Sioux Falls, Sioux Falls, SD, p. A599

ULMER, Evonne G., JD, Chief Executive Officer, Ionia County Memorial Hospital, Ionia, MI, p. A337

ULRICH, Alan, Chief Financial Officer, Wahiawa General Hospital, Wahiawa, HI, p. A176

ULRICH, D.O., Russell, Chief of Staff, Jacksonville Medical Center, Jacksonville, AL, p. A20

ULRICH, Tanya, Director Human Resources, Western Pennsylvania Hospital, Pittsburgh, PA, p. A573

ULSETH, Randy, Chief Executive Officer, Kanabec Hospital, Mora, MN, p. A358

ULSHAFER, Susan, Vice President Human Resources, Bronson Vicksburg Hospital, Vicksburg, MI, p. A347

ULSHATE, Susan M., Senior Vice President Human Resources, Bronson Methodist Hospital, Kalamazoo, MI, p. A338

UMBDENSTOCK, Richard J., President and Chief Executive Officer, Providence Services, Spokane, WA, p. B86

UMPHREY, Thomas, Senior Vice President, Aroostook Medical Center, Presque Isle, ME, p. A300

UNDERDAHL, Rosalind, Director, Rainbow Mental Health Facility, Kansas City, KS, p. A250

UNDERKOFLER, Joseph, Director, Veterans Affairs Montana Healthcare System, Fort Harrison, MT, p. A398

UNDERRINER, David T., Administrator, Providence Portland Medical Center, Portland, OR, p. A547

UNDERWOOD, Claudia, Vice President Human Resources, Hillcrest Medical Center, Tulsa, OK, p. A539

UNDERWOOD, Greg G., Chief Financial Officer, Alliance HealthCare System, Holly Springs, MS, p. A370

UNDERWOOD, Jill, Vice President Human Resources, Methodist Hospital of Southern California, Arcadia, CA, p. A53

UNDERWOOD, Ken, Chief Executive Officer, Hazel Hawkins Memorial Hospital, Hollister, CA, p. A64

UNDERWOOD, Martha, Chief Human Resources Officer, Baptist Hospital, Nashville, TN, p. A615

UNDERWOOD, Patricia A., Chief Financial Officer, Magee Rehabilitation Hospital, Philadelphia, PA, p. A568

UNGER, Dayle, Administrator, HEALTHSOUTH Cane Creek Rehabilitation Hospital, Martin, TN, p. A612

UNGER, Kevin, Vice President Operations, Poudre Valley Hospital, Fort Collins, CO, p. A105

UNGER, Michael, Vice President Medical Affairs, Community Memorial Hospital, Menomonee Falls, WI, p. A729

UNGER, Roger R., Administrator, Linton Hospital, Linton, ND, p. A499

UNROE, Larry J., President, Marietta Memorial Hospital, Marietta, OH, p. A517

UNRUH, Greg, Chief Executive Officer, Scott County Hospital, Scott City, KS, p. A256

UNZEN, John, Chief Financial Officer, Mercy Hospital and Health Care Center, Moose Lake, MN, p. A358

UPCHURCH, Valerie, Chief Physician Relations, Smith County Memorial Hospital, Carthage, TN, p. A603

UPTON, Daniel, Chief Financial Officer, University of Connecticut Health Center, John Dempsey Hospital, Farmington, CT, p. A113

URBACH, Marlene, Director Human Resources, Doctors Hospital of Dallas, Dallas, TX, p. A632

URBAN, Pamela, Senior Vice President Operations, St. James Mercy Hospital, Hornell, NY, p. A454

URBANSKI, Joanne, Chief Operating Officer, South Haven Community Hospital, South Haven, MI, p. A345

URBISTONDO, Lisa, Chief Financial Officer, Peach Regional Medical Center, Fort Valley, GA, p. A162

URCIUOLI, Robert A., President and Chief Executive Officer, Roger Williams Medical Center, Providence, RI, p. A582

URLAUB, C J, Chief Administrative Officer, Mercy Hospital of Scranton, Scranton, PA, p. A575

URLAUB, C. J., Chief Administrative Officer, Mercy Hospital of Scranton, Scranton, PA, p. A575

URSO, Susan, Administrator, Mendota Community Hospital, Mendota, IL, p. A201

URVAND, Leslie O., Administrator, St. Luke's Hospital, Crosby, ND, p. A497

USHAK, Don, Director of Information Systems, New York Eye and Ear Infirmary, New York, NY, p. A463

USHER, David, Vice President of Operations, Lake Charles Memorial Hospital, Lake Charles, LA, p. A285

USHER, Paul, Vice President Finance and Chief Financial Officer, Marion General Hospital, Marion, IN, p. A221

USHIJIMA, Arthur A., President and Chief Executive Officer, Queen's Medical Center, Honolulu, HI, p. A174

USMANI, M.D., Shahid, Chief of Staff, Health Central, Ocoee, FL, p. A140

UTTENDORFSKY, Rob, Director Information Management, Lewis County General Hospital, Lowville, NY, p. A456

V

VAAGENES, Carl P., President and Chief Executive Officer, St. Gabriel's Hospital, Little Falls, MN, p. A356

VAALER, M.D., Mark
Chief Medical Officer, South Florida Baptist Hospital, Plant City, FL, p. A143
Chief Medical Officer, St. Joseph's Hospital, Tampa, FL, p. A148

VACHON, Susan, Administrative Director Human Resources, Sutter Medical Center of Santa Rosa, Santa Rosa, CA, p. A93

VACLAVIK, Linda, Administrator, Victoria Warm Springs Rehabilitation Hospital, Victoria, TX, p. A672

VADELLA, Anthony J., President and Chief Executive Officer, Poplar Springs Hospital, Petersburg, VA, p. A693

VAIDYA, Shrikart, President Medical Staff, Pleasant Valley Hospital, Point Pleasant, WV, p. A719

VAIL, M.D., Connie, Chief of Staff, Central Valley Medical Center, Nephi, UT, p. A677

VAIL, Lucy, Director Human Resources, William Beaumont Hospital–Troy, Troy, MI, p. A347

VALADJA, Nicholas J., Vice President Information Systems, Allegheny General Hospital, Pittsburgh, PA, p. A571

VALDERA, Trummell, Senior Vice President and Chief Human Resources Officer, Jackson Memorial Hospital, Miami, FL, p. A137

VALDESPINO, Gustavo A., Chief Executive Officer, St. Vincent Medical Center, Los Angeles, CA, p. A72

VALDEZ, J. Alex, JD, Chief Executive Officer, St. Vincent Hospital, Santa Fe, NM, p. A444

VALDEZ, Wendy, Chief Information Officer, Mercy Hospital, Bakersfield, CA, p. A54

VALENCIA, Walena, Chief Financial Officer, Oak Forest Hospital of Cook County, Oak Forest, IL, p. A203

VALENTE, M.D., Anthony
Vice President Medical Affairs, Hazleton General Hospital, Hazleton, PA, p. A560
Vice President Medical Affairs, Hazleton–St. Joseph Medical Center, Hazleton, PA, p. A560

VALENTI, James N., FACHE, President and Chief Executive Officer, R. E. Thomason General Hospital, El Paso, TX, p. A637

VALENTIN, MSN, USN, Eleanor, Executive Officer, Naval Hospital, Corpus Christi, TX, p. A631

VALENTINE, Greg, Superintendent, Osawatomie State Hospital, Osawatomie, KS, p. A254

VALENTINE, Lisa R., Chief Operating Officer, Henrico Doctors' Hospital, Richmond, VA, p. A695

VALENZUELA, Lisa, Director Human Resources, Olympia Medical Center, Los Angeles, CA, p. A72

VALERIAN, D.O., Christopher, Vice President Medical Affairs, St. Mary Hospital, Hoboken, NJ, p. A429

VALEYKO, James F.
Interim Chief Executive Officer, St. Luke's Hospital, Bluefield, WV, p. A713
Vice President Operations, Princeton Community Hospital, Princeton, WV, p. A719

VALK, Keith, Vice President, Human Resources, Aurelia Osborn Fox Memorial Hospital, Oneonta, NY, p. A468

VALLIANT, Robert F., Chief Executive Officer, Bartlett Regional Hospital, Juneau, AK, p. A27

VALLIERE, M.D., Mark
Vice President Medical Affairs and Chief Medical Officer, Trinity at Terrace Park, Bettendorf, IA, p. A228
Vice President Medical Affairs and Chief Medical Officer, Trinity Medical Center–West, Rock Island, IL, p. A206

VAN ACKER, Patricia, R.N., Administrator, Eagle River Memorial Hospital, Eagle River, WI, p. A725

VAN BEEK, Jannette, Chief Executive Officer, Five Counties Hospital, Lemmon, SD, p. A596

VAN BOENING, Jon, President, Bakersfield Memorial Hospital, Bakersfield, CA, p. A53

VAN BREE, Dr.PH, Margaret M., Chief Operations Officer, University of Virginia Medical Center, Charlottesville, VA, p. A686

VAN BRUNT, Norene, Manager Human Resources, Mid–Valley Hospital, Omak, WA, p. A705

VAN BUREN, M.D., David, Chief of Staff, Navapache Regional Medical Center, Show Low, AZ, p. A36

VAN BUREN, Shelly, Director, Human Resources, Frances Mahon Deaconess Hospital, Glasgow, MT, p. A398

VAN BUSKIRK, M.D., George F., Chief of Staff, Veterans Affairs Medical Center, Bay Pines, FL, p. A123

VAN CAMP, Kathy, Senior Vice President and Chief Operating Officer, Somerset Medical Center, Somerville, NJ, p. A436

VAN CAMP, Keith, Vice President Information Services, St. Dominic–Jackson Memorial Hospital, Jackson, MS, p. A371

VAN DIVIER, Arthur, Executive Director, La Hacienda Treatment Center, Hunt, TX, p. A649

VAN DORNICK, James, Administrator, Community Memorial Hospital, Oconto Falls, WI, p. A733

VAN DRIEL, Allen, CHE, Administrator, Harlan County Health System, Alma, NE, p. A404

VAN DUSER, Maureen, Vice President Human Resources, Akron General Medical Center, Akron, OH, p. A502

VAN DYK, Kathryn, Director, Western Medical Center Anaheim, Anaheim, CA, p. A52

VAN DYKE, Karin, Director Human Resources, Portage Health System, Hancock, MI, p. A336

VAN DYKE, Walter S., Chief Executive Officer, Tyrone Hospital, Tyrone, PA, p. A577

VAN EPPS, John, Director Human Resources, Community–General Hospital of Greater Syracuse, Syracuse, NY, p. A473

VAN ERT, M.D., Gary, Chief Medical Staff, Mid Dakota Medical Center, Chamberlain, SD, p. A594

VAN GHELUWE, Betty, Chief Operating Officer, Elmore Medical Center, Mountain Home, ID, p. A180

VAN GORDER, Chris D., President and Chief Executive Officer, Scripps Health, San Diego, CA, p. B96

VAN GORP, M.D., David, Physician, Ellsworth Municipal Hospital, Iowa Falls, IA, p. A236

VAN HORN, Jeff, Chief Financial Officer, Palestine Regional Rehabilitation Center, Palestine, TX, p. A659

VAN LANINGHAM, Nathan
Vice President and Chief Financial Officer, Barberton Citizens Hospital, Barberton, OH, p. A503
Vice President and Chief Financial Officer, Doctors Hospital, Columbus, OH, p. A510

VAN LITH, Richard, Chief Executive Officer, Cottage Hospital, Grosse Pointe Farms, MI, p. A336

VAN LOOY, M.D., James, Chief Medical Executive, Altru Health System, Grand Forks, ND, p. A498

VAN METEREN, Robert, Chief Executive Officer, Sleepy Eye Medical Center, Sleepy Eye, MN, p. A363

VAN METER, Rex, Chief Financial Officer, Integris Blackwell Regional Hospital, Blackwell, OK, p. A528

VAN NATTA, Gretchen, Vice President Human Resources, Marianjoy Rehabilitation Hospital, Wheaton, IL, p. A210

VAN NATTA, D.O., Michael, President Medical Staff, Knoxville Area Community Hospital and Clinic, Knoxville, IA, p. A236

VAN NES, M.D., W Gordon, Medical Director, The William W. Backus Hospital, Norwich, CT, p. A116

VAN NORMAN, M.D., Steven, Medical Director, Dixie Regional Medical Center, Saint George, UT, p. A679

VAN RYBROEK, Greg, Chief Executive Officer, Mendota Mental Health Institute, Madison, WI, p. A728

VAN SCOY, Mitch, Manager, Delta County Memorial Hospital, Delta, CO, p. A103

VAN SLUYTER, Charles K., Interim Administrator, Shands at AGH, Gainesville, FL, p. A130

VAN STRATEN, Elizabeth, President and Chief Executive Officer, St. Bernard Hospital and Health Care Center, Chicago, IL, p. A190

VAN VRANKEN, Matthew, President, Spectrum Health, Grand Rapids, MI, p. A335

VAN VRANKEN, Ross, Chief Executive Officer, University of Utah Neuropsychiatric Institute, Salt Lake City, UT, p. A680

VAN WORMER, M.D., Valerie H., Chief of Staff, Central Texas Veterans Healthcare System, Temple, TX, p. A668

VANARKEL, Terence, Chief Financial Officer, J. F. K. Medical Center, Atlantis, FL, p. A123

VANASKIE, William F., CHE, President and Chief Executive Officer, Robert Packer Hospital, Sayre, PA, p. A574

VANCE, Derek, Vice President Business Development and Operations, Labette County Medical Center, Parsons, KS, p. A255

VANCE, M.D., Mark, Chief Medical Officer, Quincy Valley Medical Center, Quincy, WA, p. A706

VANCE, Ruth, Director Information Systems, Quincy Valley Medical Center, Quincy, WA, p. A706

VANCOURT, Bernie, Chief Operating Officer, Bay Area Medical Center, Marinette, WI, p. A729

VANCUREN, M.D., James, Vice President Medical Affairs, Goshen General Hospital, Goshen, IN, p. A216

VANDEHAAR, R.N., Donna J., Chief Clinical Director, Dallas County Hospital, Perry, IA, p. A240

VANDEN BERG, Peter, Information Services Specialist, Silverton Hospital, Silverton, OR, p. A549

VANDENBOSCH, Darryl, Senior Vice President and Chief Financial Officer, St. Bernardine Medical Center, San Bernardino, CA, p. A86

VANDER DOES, Victor, Administrator, Pioneer Memorial Hospital, Heppner, OR, p. A544

VANDERHOEF, Virginia D., Chief Information Officer, Breckinridge Memorial Hospital, Hardinsburg, KY, p. A265

VANDERPOL, Antoinette, Chief of Staff, Avera St. Benedict Health Center, Parkston, SD, p. A597

VANDERPOOL, Lee, Vice President, Dominican Hospital, Santa Cruz, CA, p. A92

VANDERSTEEG, James, Administrator and Chief Executive Officer, Baptist Memorial Hospital – Memphis, Memphis, TN, p. A612

VANDERSTEK, Eliott R., Chief, Fiscal Service, Veterans Affairs Eastern Colorado Health Care System, Denver, CO, p. A104

VANDERVEER, Robert W., President and Chief Executive Officer, Knapp Medical Center, Weslaco, TX, p. A673

VANDERVORT, Darryl L., President and Chief Executive Officer, Katherine Shaw Bethea Hospital, Dixon, IL, p. A192

VANDETTE, Joan, Vice President, Human Resources, Brooks Memorial Hospital, Dunkirk, NY, p. A451

VANDEVEER, Alden, Chief Operating Officer, Northeast Medical Center Hospital, Humble, TX, p. A649

VANDEWATER, David T., President and Chief Executive Officer, Ardent Health Services, Nashville, TN, p. B9

VANEK, James, Chief Executive Officer, Lavaca Medical Center, Hallettsville, TX, p. A643

VANES, Wendell, Chief Financial Officer, Saint Mary's Regional Medical Center, Russellville, AR, p. A50

VANGENDEREN, Nathan, Assistant Vice President Finance, Jefferson Regional Medical Center, Pine Bluff, AR, p. A49

VANHEININGEN, Robert, Administrative Leader, Rutland Regional Medical Center, Rutland, VT, p. A683

VANHORN, Jeffrey, Chief Financial Officer, Willamette Valley Medical Center, McMinnville, OR, p. A546

VANHYNING, Jill, Director Human Resources and Marketing, Clay County Hospital, Flora, IL, p. A194

VANNOY, Patricia, Controller, Oakwood Southshore Medical Center, Trenton, MI, p. A347

VANORSDALE, Beth, Manager, Human Resources, Mary Black Health System, Spartanburg, SC, p. A592

VANOVER, Patricia, Chief of Medical Staff, Dickenson Community Hospital, Clintwood, VA, p. A687

VANVEEN, M.D., Thomas, Chief Medical Officer, Santiam Memorial Hospital, Stayton, OR, p. A549

VARA, Ray
Chief Executive Officer, Kapiolani Medical Center at Pali Momi, Aiea, HI, p. A173
Chief Executive Officer, Kapiolani Medical Center for Women & Children, Honolulu, HI, p. A173
Chief Executive Officer, Straub Clinic & Hospital, Honolulu, HI, p. A174

VARGA, M.D., Daniel W.
Chief Medical Officer, Norton Audubon Hospital, Louisville, KY, p. A269
Senior Vice President and Chief Medical Officer, Norton Hospital, Louisville, KY, p. A270
Senior Vice President and Chief Medical Officer, Norton Southwest Hospital, Louisville, KY, p. A270
Senior Vice President and Chief Medical Officer, Norton Suburban Hospital, Louisville, KY, p. A270

VARGAS, Frank, Director Information Management Systems, San Gabriel Valley Medical Center, San Gabriel, CA, p. A90

VARGAS, Laura, Chief Executive Officer and Managing Director, San Juan Capestrano Hospital, San Juan, PR, p. A748

VARGAS, Margie, Director Human Resources, Memorial Hospital Pembroke, Pembroke Pines, FL, p. A142

VARGAS, Marisol, Finance Director, Hospital Del Maestro, San Juan, PR, p. A747

VARGAS, Milagros, Executive Director, I. Gonzalez Martinez Oncologic Hospital, Hato Rey, PR, p. A747

VARGHESE, Shibu, Director Human Resources, Clear Lake Regional Medical Center, Webster, TX, p. A673

VARGO, M.D., James, Medical Director, Ridgeview Institute, Smyrna, GA, p. A169

VARIAN, M.D., Grant, Medical Director, Mary Rutan Hospital, Bellefontaine, OH, p. A504

VARK, Lawrence, Chief Medical Officer, Creek Nation Community Hospital, Okemah, OK, p. A534

VARLEY, Kevin, Chief Financial Officer, Kindred Hospital–Pittsburgh, Oakdale, PA, p. A566

VARMUS, Harold, M.D., President and Chief Executive Officer, Memorial Sloan–Kettering Cancer Center, New York, NY, p. A462

VARNADOE, Milo, Director of Systems, Warm Springs Medical Center, Warm Springs, GA, p. A171

VARNELL, Karen, Director Finance, Walls Regional Hospital, Cleburne, TX, p. A629

VARNER, Clara, Business Office Manager, Weston County Health Services, Newcastle, WY, p. A741

VARNER, Terry, Administrator, Yalobusha General Hospital, Water Valley, MS, p. A376

VARNUM, James W., President, Mary Hitchcock Memorial Hospital, Lebanon, NH, p. A422

VARONA, Angela, Administrator Fiscal Services, Auxilio Mutuo Hospital, San Juan, PR, p. A746

VARRELL, M.D., James, Medical Director, Friends Behavioral Health System, Philadelphia, PA, p. A568

VARY, M.D., Mark, Chief Medical Officer, Riverside Methodist Hospital, Columbus, OH, p. A511

VASA, Brad, Chief of Staff, St. Mary's Hospital, Nebraska City, NE, p. A409

VASKELIS, Glenna L., President and Administrator, Sequoia Hospital, Redwood City, CA, p. A83

VASQUEZ, Alberto, Administrator, Garfield Memorial Hospital and Clinics, Panguitch, UT, p. A678

VASQUEZ, Chris M., Vice President and Chief Executive Officer, Memorial Hermann Southwest Hospital, Houston, TX, p. A646

VASQUEZ, Joe, Chief Human Resource Officer, Knapp Medical Center, Weslaco, TX, p. A673

VAUGHAN, M.D., Peggy
Senior Vice President Medical Affairs, Harford Memorial Hospital, Havre De Grace, MD, p. A308
Senior Vice President Medical Affairs, Upper Chesapeake Medical Center, Bel Air, MD, p. A305

VAUGHN, Anita, Administrator and Chief Executive Officer, Baptist Memorial Hospital for Women, Memphis, TN, p. A612

VAUGHN, David L., Administrator, St. Luke's Rehabilitation Hospital, Lafayette, LA, p. A284

VAUGHN, Kerry, Director Information Services, St. Mary's Health Care System, Athens, GA, p. A153

VAUGHN, Sandy
Director of Information Services, Baylor All Saints Medical Center at Fort Worth, Fort Worth, TX, p. A639
Director Information Technology, Baylor Medical Center at Southwest Fort Worth, Fort Worth, TX, p. A639

VAUGHT, Chris, Community Chief Executive Officer, Summers County Appalachian Regional Hospital, Hinton, WV, p. A716

VAUGHT, Richard H., Administrator, William Newton Hospital, Winfield, KS, p. A260

VAUTRAIN, M.D., Robert, Medical Director, Memorial Medical Center, Springfield, IL, p. A208

VAZIRI, H. Kevin, President, Woodland Healthcare, Woodland, CA, p. A99

VAZQUEZ, Francisco
General Manager and Executive Director, Lafayette Hospital, Arroyo, PR, p. A744
General Manager and Executive Director, Lafayette Hospital, Arroyo, PR, p. A744

VAZQUEZ, Manuel J., Administrator, Hospital Matilde Brenes, Bayamon, PR, p. A744

VEACH, Shae, Administrator, Stanton County Health Care Facility, Johnson, KS, p. A249

VECCHIONE, George A., President, Lifespan Corporation, Providence, RI, p. B70

VEENSTRA, Henry A.
President, Zeeland Community Hospital, Zeeland, MI, p. A348
President, Zeeland Community Hospital, Zeeland, MI, p. A348

VEERKAMP, Marshall, Chief Information Officer, Jefferson Regional Medical Center, Pine Bluff, AR, p. A49

VEGA, Maria, Human Resources Director, Auxilio Mutuo Hospital, San Juan, PR, p. A746

VEILLETTE, David, Chief Executive Officer, Indiana Heart Hospital, Indianapolis, IN, p. A218

VEILLETTE, Stephen, Director Management Information Systems, New Milford Hospital, New Milford, CT, p. A115

VEILLON, CPA, Paul
Chief Financial Officer, Advance Care Hospital, Hot Springs National Park, AR, p. A44
Chief Financial Officer, Dubuis Hospital of Houston, Houston, TX, p. A645

VEIT, Kathy, Director Health Information Services, Loring Hospital, Sac City, IA, p. A241

VEIT, M.D., Kirk, Medical Director, Agnesian HealthCare, Fond Du Lac, WI, p. A725

VEITZ, Larry W., Chief Executive Officer, Lookout Memorial Hospital, Spearfish, SD, p. A599

VELASQUEZ, Carolina, Chief Information Officer, Uvalde County Hospital Authority, Uvalde, TX, p. A671

VELAZCO, M.D., Juan Carlos, Director Staff Medicine, Hospital Metropolitano Dr. Tito Mattei, Yauco, PR, p. A749

VELEZ, Abel, Chief Information Officer, Hospital Metropolitan, San Juan, PR, p. A747

VELINE, Jim, Interim Director Information Technology, Nebraska Medical Center, Omaha, NE, p. A411

VELLINGA, David H., President and Chief Executive Officer, Mercy Medical Center–Des Moines, Des Moines, IA, p. A233

VELLMAN, M.D., Pete, Chief Medical Officer, St. Anthony Central Hospital, Denver, CO, p. A104

VELLOZO, M.D., Paul, Chief Medical Officer and Chief of Staff, Lawrence Memorial Hospital, Walnut Ridge, AR, p. A51

VELTE, Carl J., Chief Executive Officer, Munising Memorial Hospital, Munising, MI, p. A341

VENABLE, Chip, Chief Information Officer, St. Joseph's Hospital and Medical Center, Phoenix, AZ, p. A35

VENEREO, M.D., Miguel, Director Medical Staff, Memorial Hospital West, Pembroke Pines, FL, p. A142

VENTRESS, William L., Superintendent, Moccasin Bend Mental Health Institute, Chattanooga, TN, p. A604

VENTURA, Lawrence, Chief Executive Officer, Memphis Mental Health Institute, Memphis, TN, p. A613

VENUTO, Frank
    Vice President Human Resources, Laurel Regional Hospital, Laurel, MD, p. A309
    Vice President, Human Resources, Prince George's Hospital Center, Cheverly, MD, p. A306

VENUTO, Kenneth, Chief Financial Officer, Saint Thomas Hospital, Nashville, TN, p. A615

VERCHOTA, Robert, Vice President of Ancillary Service and Human Resources, North Country Regional Hospital, Bemidji, MN, p. A350

VERCILLA, Regina, Chief Executive Officer, Select Specialty Hospital–Pittsburgh, Pittsburgh, PA, p. A572

VERGNE, Roger T., Chief, Fiscal Service, Hunter Holmes McGuire Veterans Affairs Medical Center, Richmond, VA, p. A695

VERMEER, Kevin, Chief Financial Officer, Trinity Medical Center–West, Rock Island, IL, p. A206

VERMILLION, Kathy, Medical Records Supervisor, Watonga Municipal Hospital, Watonga, OK, p. A541

VERNEGAARD, Niels P., Chief Executive Officer, Research Medical Center, Kansas City, MO, p. A384

VERNON, Janice, Supervisory Information Technology Specialist, John J. Pershing Veterans Affairs Medical Center, Poplar Bluff, MO, p. A389

VERNON-YOUNG, Karen, Vice President Human Resources and Communications, Thoms Rehabilitation Hospital, Asheville, NC, p. A477

VERONIE, Arris S., Chief Financial Officer, Friends Behavioral Health System, Philadelphia, PA, p. A568

VERRET, Deborah, Administrator, Winnie Community Hospital, Winnie, TX, p. A674

VESTA, Mike, Chief Information Resource Management Service, Overton Brooks Veterans Affairs Medical Center, Shreveport, LA, p. A292

VESTAL, Charlotte, Chief Financial Officer, Crisp Regional Hospital, Cordele, GA, p. A159

VESTER, Nancy
    Vice President Information Technology, Leesburg Regional Medical Center, Leesburg, FL, p. A135
    Vice President Information Technology, The Villages Regional Hospital, The Villages, FL, p. A149

VIA, Bob, Chief Executive Officer, Emanuel Medical Hospital, Swainsboro, GA, p. A170

VIATOR, Dionne, Senior Vice President and Chief Financial Officer, Baton Rouge General Medical Center, Baton Rouge, LA, p. A277

VIATOR, Kyle J., Chief Executive Officer, Dauterive Hospital, New Iberia, LA, p. A288

VIAU ZEEB, Sandy, Employee and Community Relations, Landmann–Jungman Memorial Hospital, Scotland, SD, p. A598

VICE, Jon E., President and Chief Executive Officer, Children's Hospital of Wisconsin, Milwaukee, WI, p. A730

VICENS, Jr, Enrique A., Corporate Vice President and Legal Counsel, Hospital De Damas, Ponce, PR, p. A746

VICENTE, Oscar, Chief Financial Officer, Palmetto General Hospital, Hialeah, FL, p. A131

VICENTI, M.D., Darren, Clinical Director, Hopi Health Care Center, Kearns Canyon, AZ, p. A31

VICK, Terrell, Chief Executive Officer, St. Clair Regional Hospital, Pell City, AL, p. A23

VICKERS, Dave, Chief Financial Officer, Los Alamitos Medical Center, Los Alamitos, CA, p. A69

VICKNAIR, Joseph, Chief Information Officer, P & S Surgical Hospital, Monroe, LA, p. A287

VICKROY, Joseph, Medical Director, HEALTHSOUTH Rehabilitation Hospital of Utah, Sandy, UT, p. A680

VICTORY, Ronald D., Chief Executive Officer, Penobscot Valley Hospital, Lincoln, ME, p. A299

VIDAURRI, Ph.D., Mary, Senior Vice President and Chief Operating Officer, Ingalls Memorial Hospital, Harvey, IL, p. A196

VIDRINE, CPA, Charmaine, Chief Financial Officer, American Legion Hospital, Crowley, LA, p. A279

VIELKIND, James, Chief Financial Officer, Little Falls Hospital, Little Falls, NY, p. A455

VIENNEAU, Marie E., R.N., Chief Executive Officer, Millinocket Regional Hospital, Millinocket, ME, p. A299

VIESSMAN, Bruce, Director Finance, Worthington Regional Hospital, Worthington, MN, p. A365

VIGUS, Ronald J., Chief Executive Officer, Granville Medical Center, Oxford, NC, p. A489

VILAR, Ramon J., Administrator, Wilma N. Vazquez Medical Center, Vega Baja, PR, p. A748

VILBIG, Joe, Director Information Systems, Eastern Idaho Regional Medical Center, Idaho Falls, ID, p. A179

VILHAUER, Beverly, Director Finance, Wishek Community Hospital and Clinics, Wishek, ND, p. A501

VILLALOBOS, Max, Chief Operating Officer, Kaiser Foundation Hospital, Sacramento, CA, p. A84

VILLANI, Cheryl, Vice President Human Resources, Cooley Dickinson Hospital, Northampton, MA, p. A321

VILLANUEVA, Alice, Vice President Human Resources, Mt. Diablo Medical Pavilion, Concord, CA, p. A57

VILLANUEVA, Yvette, Senior Associate Executive Director, Woodhull Medical and Mental Health Center, New York, NY, p. A466

VILLAREAL, Xavier, Chief Operating Officer, Abilene Regional Medical Center, Abilene, TX, p. A620

VILLARREAL, Troy, Chief Executive Officer, Plaza Medical Center of Fort Worth, Fort Worth, TX, p. A640

VILLASUSO, M.D., Raul, Medical Staff President, Gottlieb Memorial Hospital, Melrose Park, IL, p. A201

VILUMS, Karl, Chief Financial Officer, St. Mary's Hospital, Nebraska City, NE, p. A409

VINARDI, Gregory B., President and Chief Executive Officer, Western Missouri Medical Center, Warrensburg, MO, p. A395

VINAS, Elmo, Director of Human Resources, Denton Regional Medical Center, Denton, TX, p. A635

VINCENT, Benjamin, Administrator, Braxton County Memorial Hospital, Gassaway, WV, p. A715

VINCENT, Donna, Vice President Corporate Services, Bay Medical Center, Panama City, FL, p. A142

VINCENT, Mark A., Vice President and Chief Financial Officer, Mary Lanning Memorial Hospital, Hastings, NE, p. A407

VINCENT, Paula, Vice President Community Acute Services, Presbyterian Hospital–Matthews, Matthews, NC, p. A487

VINCENZ, Felix T., Ph.D., Chief Executive Officer, Fulton State Hospital, Fulton, MO, p. A382

VINES, Amy, Chief Executive Officer, De Queen Regional Medical Center, De Queen, AR, p. A42

VINSON, Ronald, Director Finance, Sentara Virginia Beach General Hospital, Virginia Beach, VA, p. A698

VINSON, Roy C., President, Heart Hospital of Austin, Austin, TX, p. A623

VINTYARD, Theresa, Chief Financial Officer, St. Mary's Health Care System, Athens, GA, p. A153

VINYARD II, Roy G., President and Chief Executive Officer, Asante Health System, Medford, OR, p. B9

VIPOND, Kathleen, Assistant Administrator and Director, Abraham Lincoln Memorial Hospital, Lincoln, IL, p. A199

VIPPERMAN, Mark, Executive Vice President and Chief Operating Officer, Mount Clemens General Hospital, Mount Clemens, MI, p. A340

VISAGGIO, Stella, Chief Financial Officer, Hackettstown Community Hospital, Hackettstown, NJ, p. A429

VITALE, Nickolas A., Chief Financial Officer, William Beaumont Hospital–Troy, Troy, MI, p. A347

VITRANO, M.D., Craig, Assistant Vice President Patient Care Services, St. Elizabeth Hospital, Gonzales, LA, p. A281

VIVALDI, Domingo Cruz, Administrator, San Jorge Children's Hospital, San Juan, PR, p. A747

VIVIT, Romeo, Chief Surgeon, U. S. Public Health Service Indian Hospital, Rosebud, SD, p. A598

VLAARDINGERBROEK, Loretta, Executive Director, Sonoma Developmental Center, Eldridge, CA, p. A59

VLACH, Karen, Administrator, Oakland Memorial Hospital, Oakland, NE, p. A410

VOELKEL, Jonathan, Director Human Resources, Mena Medical Center, Mena, AR, p. A47

VOELPEL, Stuart
    Senior Vice President Operations Hospital and Chief Operating Officer, FirstHealth Moore Regional Hospital, Pinehurst, NC, p. A489
    Senior Vice President Operations Hospital and Chief Operating Officer, FirstHealth Moore Regional Hospital, Pinehurst, NC, p. A489

VOGAN, Gary, Chief Financial Officer, Holy Cross Hospital, Silver Spring, MD, p. A311

VOGEL, M.D., Daryl, Chief Medical Officer, United General Hospital, Sedro–Woolley, WA, p. A708

VOGEL, Lynn H., Vice President and Chief Information Officer, University of Texas M. D. Anderson Cancer Center, Houston, TX, p. A648

VOGELSANG, M.D., Glenn, Chief Medical Staff, Lucas County Health Center, Chariton, IA, p. A230

VOGELSANG, Mark, Director Information Services, Holy Family Hospital, Spokane, WA, p. A709

VOGT, Allen J., Administrator, Cook Hospital and Convalescent Nursing Care Unit, Cook, MN, p. A351

VOGT, Dennis, Director Information Services, Adena Health System, Chillicothe, OH, p. A506

VOHRA, M.D., Rahal, Medical Director, Methodist Rehabilitation Center, Jackson, MS, p. A370

VOLCKERS, Alfredo E.
    Executive Vice President, Hospital Pavia–Hato Rey, San Juan, PR, p. A747
    Executive Director, Hospital Pavia–Santurce, San Juan, PR, p. A747

VOLK, Ronald J., President and Chief Executive Officer, St. Aloisius Medical Center, Harvey, ND, p. A498

VOLKMAR, Larry E.
    President, Mount Sinai Hospital Medical Center of Chicago, Chicago, IL, p. A188
    President, Schwab Rehabilitation Hospital, Chicago, IL, p. A190

VOLPE, Buddy, Director, Human Resources, Sid Peterson Memorial Hospital, Kerrville, TX, p. A651

VOLPE, Michele M., Executive Director and Chief Executive Officer, Presbyterian Medical Center of the University of Pennsylvania Health System, Philadelphia, PA, p. A569

VOLTAIRE, Adler, Chief Administrative Officer, Medical Center of Louisiana at New Orleans, New Orleans, LA, p. A289

VON BEHREN, Rachel, Director Financial Services, Jones Regional Medical Center, Anamosa, IA, p. A228

VON ZYCHLIN, Claus, Executive Vice President and Chief Operating Officer, Good Samaritan Hospital, Cincinnati, OH, p. A507

VONDERFECHT, Dennis, President and Chief Executive Officer, Mountain States Health Alliance, Johnson City, TN, p. B76

VONDRAK, Darrell E., Chief Executive Officer, Decatur County Hospital, Leon, IA, p. A237

VOORDE, Christine T., Chief Executive Officer, Our Lady of Peace Hospital, South Bend, IN, p. A225

VORNBROCK, John G., Senior Vice President and Chief Financial Officer, Yakima Valley Memorial Hospital, Yakima, WA, p. A712

VOSS, Daryle, Chief Executive Officer, Matagorda General Hospital, Bay City, TX, p. A624

VOSS, Jeanie, Manager Information Systems, St. Anthony's Healthcare Center, Morrilton, AR, p. A48

VOSS, Sarah, Chief Executive Officer, Pembina County Memorial Hospital and Wedgewood Manor, Cavalier, ND, p. A497

VOSS, Wayne M., Chief Executive Officer, Memorial Hermann Memorial City Hospital, Houston, TX, p. A646

VOSSLER, Jeffrey W., Vice President Financial Services, Joint Township District Memorial Hospital, Saint Marys, OH, p. A521

VOZOS, Frank J., FACS, Executive Director, Monmouth Medical Center, Long Branch, NJ, p. A430

VUCHAK, Jerry, Vice President Information Systems, The Methodist Hospital, Houston, TX, p. A648

VUGRINEC, Barbara P., Vice President Information Systems, Beebe Medical Center, Lewes, DE, p. A119

VUJAN, M.D., Alexander, Acting Clinical Director, U. S. Public Health Service Indian Hospital, Crownpoint, NM, p. A442

VUKICH, M.D., David, Senior Vice President and Chief Medical Officer, Shands Jacksonville Medical Center, Jacksonville, FL, p. A132

VUKOVICH, Pamela S.
Senior Vice President and Chief Financial Officer, Legacy Emanuel Hospital and Health Center, Portland, OR, p. A547
Vice President Financial Services, Legacy Good Samaritan Hospital and Medical Center, Portland, OR, p. A547
Senior Vice President and Chief Financial Officer, Legacy Meridian Park Hospital, Tualatin, OR, p. A550

VUMBACCO, Joseph V., President and Chief Executive Officer, Health Management Associates, Naples, FL, p. B54

W

WACHACHA, Arnold, Administrator, Cherokee Indian Hospital Authority, Cherokee, NC, p. A480

WACHTEL, R Andrew
Vice President Operations, Deaconess Hospital, Oklahoma City, OK, p. A535
Vice President Operations, Deaconess Hospital, Oklahoma City, OK, p. A535

WACHTER, Hal, Director Information Systems, Long Island College Hospital, New York, NY, p. A461

WADDELTON, D.O., Beverly, Chief Medical Staff, East Texas Medical Center–Quitman, Quitman, TX, p. A662

WADE, Charles, Interim Administrator, Sequoyah Memorial Hospital, Sallisaw, OK, p. A538

WADE, Donald, Chief Financial Officer, Angel Medical Center, Franklin, NC, p. A483

WADE, John
Chief Information Officer, Saint Luke's Hospital of Kansas City, Kansas City, MO, p. A385
Chief Information Officer, Saint Luke's Northland Hospital–Smithville Campus, Smithville, MO, p. A393
Chief Information Officer, Saint Luke's South Hospital, Overland Park, KS, p. A255

WADE, Jonathan, Vice President, St. John's Hospital – Lebanon, Lebanon, MO, p. A386

WADE, Linda, Administrator, HEALTHSOUTH Rehabilitation Hospital of Montgomery, Montgomery, AL, p. A22

WADE, M.D., Robert B., President Medical Staff, Reynolds Memorial Hospital, Glen Dale, WV, p. A715

WADHWANI, M.D., Bhagwan, Chief of Staff, Brownsville General Hospital, Brownsville, PA, p. A553

WADMAN, Timothy, Executive Vice President and Chief Operating Officer, Sherman Hospital, Elgin, IL, p. A193

WAETZMAN, Ronald, Senior Vice President and Chief Human Resources, Henry Ford Hospital, Detroit, MI, p. A331

WAGERS, Rick, Chief Financial Officer, Vanderbilt University Medical Center, Nashville, TN, p. A616

WAGES, Gerald D., Executive Vice President Finance, North Mississippi Medical Center – Tupelo, Tupelo, MS, p. A376

WAGES, N. Gary, President and Chief Executive Officer, Saint Luke's Northland Hospital, Kansas City, MO, p. A385

WAGGENER, Robert S., Chief Executive Officer, Lakeside Behavioral Health System, Memphis, TN, p. A613

WAGGONER, Michelle
Chief Operating Officer, Community Memorial Hospital, Hicksville, OH, p. A515
Chief Operating Officer, Community Memorial Hospital, Hicksville, OH, p. A515

WAGNER, Alan, Director Human Resources, St. Luke's Rehabilitation Institute, Spokane, WA, p. A709

WAGNER, Arnold, Controller, McCamey Hospital, McCamey, TX, p. A656

WAGNER, Arthur
Chief Operating Officer, Jacobi Medical Center, New York, NY, p. A460
Chief Operating Officer, North Central Bronx Hospital, New York, NY, p. A464

WAGNER, Craig M., Chief Financial Officer, Havasu Regional Medical Center, Lake Havasu City, AZ, p. A32

WAGNER, David D., Chief Information Management Service, Veterans Affairs Gulf Coast Veterans Health Care System, Biloxi, MS, p. A367

WAGNER, David S., Vice President and Administrator, Christus Spohn Hospital Beeville, Beeville, TX, p. A625

WAGNER, M.D., Elaine, Executive Officer, Naval Hospital, Jacksonville, FL, p. A132

WAGNER, Janet, R.N., Chief Administrative Officer, Sutter Davis Hospital, Davis, CA, p. A58

WAGNER, Joe
Vice President and Chief Information Officer, Broward General Medical Center, Fort Lauderdale, FL, p. A128
Vice President Chief Information Officer, North Broward Medical Center, Pompano Beach, FL, p. A144

WAGNER, Russell R., Senior Vice President Finance, Holy Redeemer Hospital and Medical Center, Jenkintown, PA, p. A561

WAGNER, Suzie, Human Resource Director, HEALTHSOUTH Rehabilitation Hospital of Alexandria, Alexandria, LA, p. A276

WAGNER, Terry, Chief Information Officer, Upstate Medical University, Syracuse, NY, p. A474

WAGNON, LaNell, Medical Records Director, Comanche County Hospital, Coldwater, KS, p. A245

WAGNON, William, Chief Operating Officer, Swedish Medical Center, Englewood, CO, p. A105

WAGONER, Dean, Director, Good Samaritan Hospital, Vincennes, IN, p. A226

WAGONER, Lynn, Chief Operating Officer, Valley Hospital, Palmer, AK, p. A28

WAGONER, Michael, Director Human Resources, St. Joseph's Hospital, Highland, IL, p. A196

WAHAB, M.D., Amir John, Medical Staff President, Abraham Lincoln Memorial Hospital, Lincoln, IL, p. A199

WAHL, Tony, Chief Executive Officer, Texas Spine & Joint Hospital, Tyler, TX, p. A671

WAHLMEIER, James, Chief Financial Officer, Smith County Memorial Hospital, Smith Center, KS, p. A257

WAID, Julie, Director Human Resources, Smithville Regional Hospital, Smithville, TX, p. A667

WAINER, Gary, Medical Director, MacNeal Hospital, Berwyn, IL, p. A184

WAINZ, M.D., Ronald, Vice President Medical Affairs, The Toledo Hospital, Toledo, OH, p. A523

WAITE, Douglas D.
Chief Financial Officer, Brackenridge Hospital, Austin, TX, p. A623
Chief Financial Officer, Seton Edgar B. Davis Hospital, Luling, TX, p. A655
Senior Vice President and Chief Financial Officer, Seton Highland Lakes, Burnet, TX, p. A627
Chief Financial Officer, Seton Medical Center, Austin, TX, p. A623
Chief Financial Officer, Seton Shoal Creek Hospital, Austin, TX, p. A624

WAJDA, David, Chief Financial Officer, Nazareth Hospital, Philadelphia, PA, p. A569

WAKEFIELD, Brett, Vice President Human Resources, Gottlieb Memorial Hospital, Melrose Park, IL, p. A201

WAKEMAN, Daniel L., President and Chief Executive Officer, Mercy Memorial Hospital System, Monroe, MI, p. A340

WAKIM, Tina, Vice President, Operations, Northside Hospital, Atlanta, GA, p. A154

WALB, William R., CHE, President and Chief Executive Officer, Hanover Hospital, Hanover, PA, p. A559

WALCEK, Peter, Vice President Finance, Wentworth–Douglass Hospital, Dover, NH, p. A420

WALDBILLIG, Kurt, Chief Executive Officer, Jacobson Memorial Hospital Care Center, Elgin, ND, p. A497

WALDOW, Dee, Chief Financial Officer, Palo Pinto General Hospital, Mineral Wells, TX, p. A657

WALDROUP, Gerald E., Senior Vice President, Good Samaritan Hospital, Vincennes, IN, p. A226

WALK, Rex D., President and Chief Executive Officer, Memorial Hospital, McPherson, KS, p. A252

WALKER, Billy, Chief Financial Officer, Memorial Hospital and Manor, Bainbridge, GA, p. A156

WALKER, Bruce, Chief Executive Officer, New Orleans East Rehabilitation Hospital, New Orleans, LA, p. A289

WALKER, Chris, Vice President Human Resources, Adirondack Medical Center, Saranac Lake, NY, p. A471

WALKER, Christie, Director Health Information Management, Muhlenberg Community Hospital, Greenville, KY, p. A265

WALKER, M.D., Dean, Chief of Staff, Sutter Maternity and Surgery Center of Santa Cruz, Santa Cruz, CA, p. A93

WALKER, M.D., Ed, Medical Director, University of Washington Medical Center, Seattle, WA, p. A708

WALKER, Gale, President and Chief Executive Officer, Avera St. Benedict Health Center, Parkston, SD, p. A597

WALKER, Gaye, Controller, Humphreys County Memorial Hospital, Belzoni, MS, p. A366

WALKER, Gregory J., Chief Executive Officer, Wentworth–Douglass Hospital, Dover, NH, p. A420

WALKER, James R., FACHE, President and Chief Executive Officer, Baltimore Washington Medical Center, Glen Burnie, MD, p. A308

WALKER, James R., Vice President of Human Resources, Spartanburg Regional Medical Center, Spartanburg, SC, p. A592

WALKER, Jan, Vice President Human Resources, Glenwood Regional Medical Center, West Monroe, LA, p. A294

WALKER, R.N., Janice L., Chief Operating Officer, Freeman Neosho Hospital, Neosho, MO, p. A388

WALKER, John E., FACHE, Chief Executive Officer, Parkway Regional Medical Center, North Miami Beach, FL, p. A139

WALKER, Ken
Director Human Resources, Orem Community Hospital, Orem, UT, p. A678
Director Human Resources, Utah Valley Regional Medical Center, Provo, UT, p. A679

WALKER, Larry, Chief Information Officer, Helen Keller Hospital, Sheffield, AL, p. A24

WALKER, Larry D., President and Chief Executive Officer, Louisiana Heart Hospital, Lacombe, LA, p. A283

WALKER, LeRoy
Vice President Human Resources, St. Vincent Infirmary Medical Center, Little Rock, AR, p. A47
Vice President Human Resources, St. Vincent Medical Center–North, Sherwood, AR, p. A50

WALKER, Melissa, Vice President and Chief Financial Officer, Duncan Regional Hospital, Duncan, OK, p. A529

WALKER, Paul A., Chief Executive Officer, St. Mary's Medical Center, West Palm Beach, FL, p. A150

WALKER, Paula H., R.N., Chief Executive Officer, Franklin Medical Center, Winnsboro, LA, p. A294

WALKER, Randy, Vice President, Methodist Dallas Medical Center, Dallas, TX, p. A633

WALKER, Robert, Manager Information Services, Carteret General Hospital, Morehead City, NC, p. A488

WALKER, Ron, Chief Executive Officer, Smith County Memorial Hospital, Carthage, TN, p. A603

WALKER, Shirley, Director Human Resources, Mercy Hospital Clermont, Batavia, OH, p. A503

WALKER, Tim, Manager Information Services, Ketchikan General Hospital, Ketchikan, AK, p. A27

WALKER, Troy, Director Finance, St. Clare Hospital and Health Services, Baraboo, WI, p. A723

WALKLEY, M.D., Peter
Chief of Staff, Franklin Regional Hospital, Franklin, NH, p. A421
Chief of Staff, Lakes Region General Hospital, Laconia, NH, p. A421

WALKLEY Jr, Philip H., Chief Executive Officer, Northeast Regional Medical Center, Kirksville, MO, p. A386

WALL, Daniel J., President and Chief Executive Officer, Emma Pendleton Bradley Hospital, East Providence, RI, p. A581

WALL, M.D., H James, Chief of Staff, Colorado–Fayette Medical Center, Weimar, TX, p. A673

WALL, Jonathan, Chief Financial Officer, Lake Cumberland Regional Hospital, Somerset, KY, p. A274

WALL, Kathryn, Executive Vice President Human Resources and Organizational Development, Mary Washington Hospital, Fredericksburg, VA, p. A688

WALL, Michael L., President, Northridge Hospital Medical Center–Roscoe Boulevard Campus, Los Angeles, CA, p. A72

WALLACE, Archie T.
Chief Executive Officer, Clifton T. Perkins Hospital Center, Jessup, MD, p. A308
Chief Executive Officer, Thomas B. Finan Center, Cumberland, MD, p. A307

WALLACE, M.D., Brent, Chief of Staff, Walls Regional Hospital, Cleburne, TX, p. A629

WALLACE, Daniela, Chief Operating Officer, Plaza Medical Center of Fort Worth, Fort Worth, TX, p. A640

WALLACE, Donna Geiken
Chief Operating Officer, Hopkins County Memorial Hospital, Sulphur Springs, TX, p. A668
Chief Operating Officer and Chief Financial Officer, Hopkins County Memorial Hospital, Sulphur Springs, TX, p. A668

WALLACE, Glenn, Chief Operating Officer, North Hills Hospital, North Richland Hills, TX, p. A658

WALLACE, D.O., James, Chief of Staff, Community Memorial Hospital, Oconto Falls, WI, p. A733

WALLACE, James D., Executive Director, Choctaw Health Center, Philadelphia, MS, p. A374

WALLACE, Kelly, Vice President and Chief Financial Officer, Children's Hospital and Regional Medical Center, Seattle, WA, p. A707

WALLACE, Linda, Director of Human Resources, Lea Regional Medical Center, Hobbs, NM, p. A443

WALLACE, Lloyd E., President and Chief Executive Officer, Valdese General Hospital, Valdese, NC, p. A493

WALLACE, Mark, Director Human Resources, Lodi Memorial Hospital, Lodi, CA, p. A67

WALLACE, Mark A., President and Chief Executive Officer, Texas Children's Hospital, Houston, TX, p. A647

WALLACE, Patrick L., Administrator, East Texas Medical Center Athens, Athens, TX, p. A622

WALLACE, Penny, Chief Financial Officer, Guadalupe Valley Hospital, Seguin, TX, p. A666

WALLACE, M.D., Peter D., Vice President Medical Staff Affairs, Mercy Hospital, Iowa City, IA, p. A235

WALLACE, Rick, FACHE, Chief Executive Officer, St. Mary's Regional Medical Center, Enid, OK, p. A530

WALLACE, Samuel T., President, Iowa Health System, Des Moines, IA, p. B63

WALLACE, Sheri, Chief Operating Officer, North Austin Medical Center, Austin, TX, p. A623

WALLACE–MOORE, Patrice, Executive Director, Arms Acres, Carmel, NY, p. A450

WALLDO, Allen, Chief Operating Officer, Citizens Memorial Hospital, Bolivar, MO, p. A378

WALLEN, Carla, Manager Human Resources, Cass Medical Center, Harrisonville, MO, p. A382

WALLENHAUPT, M.D., Stephen
Executive Vice President Medical Affairs, Presbyterian Hospital, Charlotte, NC, p. A480
Executive Vice President Medical Affairs, Presbyterian Hospital–Matthews, Matthews, NC, p. A487

WALLIS, Carla, Director Human Resources, North Ottawa Community Hospital, Grand Haven, MI, p. A334

WALLMAN, Gerald H., Administrator, Doctors Hospital of West Covina, West Covina, CA, p. A99

WALMSLEY III, George J., CPA, President and Chief Executive Officer, North Philadelphia Health System, Philadelphia, PA, p. A569

WALSH, Daniel P., President and Chief Executive Officer, Winthrop–University Hospital, Mineola, NY, p. A457

WALSH, Debbie, Chief Operating Officer, USC University Hospital, Los Angeles, CA, p. A73

WALSH, Edward J., Vice President Financial Services, Pocono Medical Center, East Stroudsburg, PA, p. A557

WALSH, Gerard M.
Senior Vice President and Chief Operating Officer, Dorchester General Hospital, Cambridge, MD, p. A306
Senior Vice President and Chief Operating Officer, Memorial Hospital at Easton Maryland, Easton, MD, p. A307

WALSH, John, Chief Fiscal Services, Veterans Affairs Hudson Valley Health Care System–F.D. Roosevelt Hospital, Montrose, NY, p. A457

WALSH, Len, Chief Executive Officer, St. Vincent's Midtown Hospital, New York, NY, p. A465

WALSH, Leon, Director Finance, Othello Community Hospital, Othello, WA, p. A705

WALSH, M.P.H., Marcia S., Chief Operating Officer, Community Hospital Onaga, Onaga, KS, p. A254

WALSH, Mary Beth, M.D., Chief Executive Officer, Burke Rehabilitation Hospital, White Plains, NY, p. A476

WALSH, Michael, Vice President Finance, Abington Memorial Hospital, Abington, PA, p. A551

WALSH, Michael T., Chief Financial Officer, University Medical Center, Las Vegas, NV, p. A417

WALSH, Peter T., Commander, U. S. Air Force Academy Hospital, USAF Academy, CO, p. A110

WALSH, Raoul M., Chief Executive Officer, Greene County Memorial Hospital, Waynesburg, PA, p. A578

WALSH, Richard
President, SwedishAmerican Hospital, Rockford, IL, p. A207
President, SwedishAmerican Hospital, Rockford, IL, p. A207

WALSH, Ph.D., Richard J., Chief Human Resources Officer, Durham Regional Hospital, Durham, NC, p. A481

WALSH, Timothy J., Chief Executive Officer, Martha's Vineyard Hospital, Oak Bluffs, MA, p. A322

WALSH, M.D., Tom, Chief of Staff, Community Hospital Onaga, Onaga, KS, p. A254

WALSH, William P.
Executive Director, Jacobi Medical Center, New York, NY, p. A460
Executive Director, North Central Bronx Hospital, New York, NY, p. A464

WALSTATLER, M.D., Bennett, President, Spectrum Health–United Memorial, Greenville, MI, p. A335

WALSTROM, Kevin, Chief Financial Officer, Holy Family Hospital, Spokane, WA, p. A709

WALTER, Beth, Human Resources Director, Cheboygan Memorial Hospital, Cheboygan, MI, p. A329

WALTER, Stephen
Chief Financial Officer, Marin General Hospital, Greenbrae, CA, p. A63
Chief Financial Officer, Novato Community Hospital, Novato, CA, p. A78

WALTERS, Joan, Interim Chief Executive Officer, Prague Municipal Hospital, Prague, OK, p. A537

WALTERS, Kevin, Chief Financial Officer, Bakersfield Memorial Hospital, Bakersfield, CA, p. A53

WALTERS, M.D., Ron, Chief of Staff, Columbus County Hospital, Whiteville, NC, p. A493

WALTHER, Robert H., Chief Financial Officer, Sid Peterson Memorial Hospital, Kerrville, TX, p. A651

WALTMAN, Karl, Vice President Finance, Holy Spirit Hospital, Camp Hill, PA, p. A554

WALTON, Beverly, Manager Human Resources, Washakie Medical Center, Worland, WY, p. A742

WALTON, Carlyle L. E., President, Takoma Adventist Hospital, Greeneville, TN, p. A607

WALTON, Frank, Chief Operating Officer, Horizon Medical Center, Dickson, TN, p. A605

WALTON, Greg, Senior Vice President and Chief Information Officer, Carilion Medical Center, Roanoke, VA, p. A696

WALTON, III, FAC, Ira F., Chief Executive Officer, Kona Community Hospital, Kealakekua, HI, p. A175

WALTON III, Ira F., FACHE,
Chief Executive Officer, Kohala Hospital, Kohala, HI, p. A175
Chief Executive Officer, Kona Community Hospital, Kealakekua, HI, p. A175

WALTON, M.D., Michael, Chief of Staff, St. Joseph's Hospital, Chippewa Falls, WI, p. A724

WALTZ, Brenda M., FACHE, Chief Executive Officer, Redmond Regional Medical Center, Rome, GA, p. A168

WALZ, George, CHE, President and Chief Executive Officer, Breckinridge Memorial Hospital, Hardinsburg, KY, p. A265

WALZ, Pat, Chief Financial Officer, Yuma Regional Medical Center, Yuma, AZ, p. A39

WANG, M.D., Peter, Chief of Staff, Garden Grove Hospital and Medical Center, Garden Grove, CA, p. A62

WANGLER, Patricia, Chief Executive Officer, First Care Medical Services, Fosston, MN, p. A353

WANGSMO, Gary L., President, Board of Commissioner, Stevens Healthcare, Edmonds, WA, p. A702

WANNER, David, Director Information Systems, St. Joseph Health System, Tawas City, MI, p. A346

WANTUCK, M.D., Donald, Chief of Staff, St. John's Hospital, Springfield, MO, p. A394

WANTZ, M.D., Mark, Chief of Staff, Summersville Memorial Hospital, Summersville, WV, p. A720

WANTZ, Steve, Senior Vice President, Human Resources, Clarian Health Partners, Indianapolis, IN, p. A218

WARD, Beth, Vice President and Chief Financial Officer, Moses Cone Health System, Greensboro, NC, p. A484

WARD, Cheryl Y., Executive Vice President and Chief Operating Officer, Providence Hospital, Mobile, AL, p. A21

WARD, David, Business Manager, Cleveland Area Hospital, Cleveland, OK, p. A529

WARD, David M., Senior Vice President and Chief Financial Officer, Cabell Huntington Hospital, Huntington, WV, p. A716

WARD, Greg, Vice President and Chief Financial Officer, Rehabilitation Institute of Chicago, Chicago, IL, p. A189

WARD, Henry J., Vice President Finance and Chief Financial Officer, Westfield Memorial Hospital, Westfield, NY, p. A476

WARD, Jeanne L., President, Oconee Memorial Hospital, Seneca, SC, p. A591

WARD, Lisa, Director Management Information Systems, Columbus County Hospital, Whiteville, NC, p. A493

WARD, Michael, Information Services Director, Anderson Hospital, Maryville, IL, p. A200

WARD, Rory, Chief Financial Officer, Valley View Regional Hospital, Ada, OK, p. A527

WARD, Jr, Roy J., Chief Financial Officer, Henrico Doctors' Hospital, Richmond, VA, p. A695

WARD, Sandy
Administrator, Johnson County Healthcare Center, Buffalo, WY, p. A739
Administrator, Johnson County Healthcare Center, Buffalo, WY, p. A739

WARD, Susan, Public Affairs Officer, Veterans Affairs Medical Center, Miami, FL, p. A138

WARD–RIGGS, Mary, Director Human Resources, Ocean Beach Hospital, Ilwaco, WA, p. A703

WARDELL, Kevin S., Chief Administrative Officer, Norton Hospital, Louisville, KY, p. A270

WARDEN, Michael S.
Director, Human Resources, Banner Baywood Medical Center, Mesa, AZ, p. A32
Senior Vice President Information Technology, Banner Good Samaritan Medical Center, Phoenix, AZ, p. A33

WARDEN, Richard, Chief Executive Officer, Windsor Hospital, Chagrin Falls, OH, p. A505

WARDWELL, Robert D., Vice President and Chief Financial Officer, Tri–City Medical Center, Oceanside, CA, p. A79

WARE, Judy, Director Human Resources, Johnson Memorial Hospital, Franklin, IN, p. A216

WARFIELD, William, Acting Chief Human Resources Management, Veterans Affairs Boston Healthcare System, Boston, MA, p. A315

WARLITNER, Todd, Vice President of Business Operations, The Outer Banks Hospital, Nags Head, NC, p. A488

WARM, Ira, Senior Vice President Human Resources, New York University Medical Center, New York, NY, p. A463

WARMAN Jr, Harold C., President and Chief Executive Officer, Highlands Regional Medical Center, Prestonsburg, KY, p. A273

WARNER, James L.
Vice President Operations, University Specialty Hospital, Baltimore, MD, p. A305
Vice President Operations, University Specialty Hospital, Baltimore, MD, p. A305

WARNER, Lori, Public Relations Manager, Madonna Rehabilitation Hospital, Lincoln, NE, p. A409

WARNER, Todd, Interim Chief Financial Officer, St. Charles Mercy Hospital, Oregon, OH, p. A520

WARNKEN, James A., Executive Vice President and Chief Financial Officer, Naples Community Hospital, Naples, FL, p. A139

WARREN, Danny, Chief Financial Officer, Smith County Memorial Hospital, Carthage, TN, p. A603

WARREN, M.D., Ellen, Chief of Staff, Holy Cross Hospital, Taos, NM, p. A445

WARREN, Gorman, Director Finance, Presbyterian Hospital of Winnsboro, Winnsboro, TX, p. A674

WARREN, Jennifer, Chief Financial Officer, Purcell Municipal Hospital, Purcell, OK, p. A537

WARREN, Larry, Director and Chief Executive Officer, University of Michigan Hospitals and Health Centers, Ann Arbor, MI, p. A327

WARREN, Richard
Vice President Health Information Systems, Foote Health System, Jackson, MI, p. A337
Director Information Systems, Hillcrest Baptist Medical Center, Waco, TX, p. A672

WARREN, Roger D., M.D., Administrator, Washington County Hospital District 1, Hanover, KS, p. A248

WARREN, Seth, President, St. Anthony Medical Center, Crown Point, IN, p. A213

WARREN, Steve, Vice President Finance, Baptist Hospital East, Louisville, KY, p. A268

WARREN, Tony, Vice President Development, Henry County Health Center, Mount Pleasant, IA, p. A238

WAS, CPA, Gregory J., Vice President Finance, Garrett County Memorial Hospital, Oakland, MD, p. A309

WASHAM, Jim, Human Resources Manager, Silverton Hospital, Silverton, OR, p. A549

WASHBURN, Geoffrey, Vice President Human Resources, Memorial Healthcare, Owosso, MI, p. A342

WASHINGTON, Glen, Senior Vice President Operations, Bradford Regional Medical Center, Bradford, PA, p. A553

WASHINGTON, Maurice, Director Controls and Accountability, Roseland Community Hospital, Chicago, IL, p. A189

WASHKO, Albert B., Director, Veterans Affairs Medical Center, Omaha, NE, p. A411

WASSERMAN, Joseph A., President and Chief Executive Officer, Lakeland Hospital–St. Joseph, Saint Joseph, MI, p. A344

WASSILAK, Leighton, Director Information Systems, SSM St. Joseph Hospital of Kirkwood, Saint Louis, MO, p. A392

WASSON, Phil, Chief Information Officer, FHN Memorial Hospital, Freeport, IL, p. A194

WATERMAN, Matt, Chief Executive Officer, Cooper County Memorial Hospital, Boonville, MO, p. A379

WATERS, Charles, Director Human Resources, Shore Memorial Hospital, Nassawadox, VA, p. A692

WATERS, Gina, Director Human Resources, Evans Memorial Hospital, Claxton, GA, p. A158

WATERS, Glenn D., Chief Operating Officer, Moses Cone Health System, Greensboro, NC, p. A484

WATERS, Kristy, Chief Financial Officer, Rio Vista Physical Rehabilitation Hospital, El Paso, TX, p. A637

WATERS, Mickey, Director Information Technology, Conway Medical Center, Conway, SC, p. A587

WATERS, Nancy, Director Human Resources, Wallowa Memorial Hospital, Enterprise, OR, p. A543

WATERS, Robert E., Chief Executive Officer, Barnwell County Hospital, Barnwell, SC, p. A583

WATERS, W. Charles, President and Chief Executive Officer, Via Christi Oklahoma Regional Medical Center, Ponca City, OK, p. A537

WATERSTON, Judith C., President, Spaulding Rehabilitation Hospital, Boston, MA, p. A314

WATHEN, James A., Chief Executive Officer, Southern Coos Hospital and Health Center, Bandon, OR, p. A542

WATKINS, Aundria, Administrator, Select Specialty Hospital – Kansas City, Overland Park, KS, p. A255

WATKINS, Barbara C., Director, Veterans Affairs Medical Center, Alexandria, LA, p. A276

WATKINS, M.D., David R.
Chief of Staff, Frazier Rehab Institute, Louisville, KY, p. A269
Chief of Staff, Jewish Hospital, Louisville, KY, p. A269

WATKINS, Johnny, Chief Financial Officer, St. Alexius Hospital, Saint Louis, MO, p. A392

WATKINS, W. Mackey, M.D., President and Chief Executive Officer, Texoma Medical Center, Denison, TX, p. A635

WATKO, Peter, Vice President Medical Affairs and Quality, St. Mary's Regional Medical Center, Lewiston, ME, p. A299

WATSON, Alan, Chief Executive Officer, Bradley Memorial Hospital, Cleveland, TN, p. A604

WATSON, Betty A., Administrator, Syringa General Hospital, Grangeville, ID, p. A179

WATSON, M.D., Christopher, Chief Medical Officer, Bellin Memorial Hospital, Green Bay, WI, p. A726

WATSON, Craig B., Chief Executive Officer, Delta Medical Center, Memphis, TN, p. A613

WATSON, Heath, Controller, HEALTHSOUTH Rehabilitation Hospital of Montgomery, Montgomery, AL, p. A22

WATSON, Ian W., Chief Executive Officer, Great River Medical Center, Blytheville, AR, p. A41

WATSON, James B., Chief Executive Officer, Ira Davenport Memorial Hospital, Bath, NY, p. A447

WATSON, Jill, Chief of Staff, Purcell Municipal Hospital, Purcell, OK, p. A537

WATSON, Jim, Chief Financial Officer, OU Medical Center, Oklahoma City, OK, p. A536

WATSON, M.D., Michael, Chief of Staff, Memorial Hospital, Seminole, TX, p. A666

WATSON, Michelle, Chief Nursing Officer and Chief Operating Officer, Livingston Regional Hospital, Livingston, TN, p. A611

WATSON, Ronald L., Chief Financial Officer, Houston Northwest Medical Center, Houston, TX, p. A645

WATSON, M.D., Thelma Ruth, Medical Director, Roy Lester Schneider Hospital, Saint Thomas, VI, p. A749

WATSON, Virgil, Administrator, Sumner County Hospital District One, Caldwell, KS, p. A245

WATTS, M.D., Charles M., Senior Vice President Medical Affairs, Northwestern Memorial Hospital, Chicago, IL, p. A188

WATTS Jr, Claude D.
Chief Executive Officer, Alameda County Medical Center–Fairmont Campus, San Leandro, CA, p. A90
Chief Executive Officer, Alameda Medical Center, San Leandro, CA, p. B6

WATTS, Donna, Director Staff and Community Relations, Marengo Memorial Hospital, Marengo, IA, p. A237

WAUTERS, Ron, Chief Financial Officer, Pella Regional Health Center, Pella, IA, p. A240

WAY, M.D., Arnold, Chief of Staff, Southern Hills Hospital and Medical Center, Las Vegas, NV, p. A417

WAY, Harold
Chief Financial Officer, Garfield Medical Center, Monterey Park, CA, p. A76
Chief Financial Officer, Greater El Monte Community Hospital, El Monte, CA, p. A59

WAY, M.D., John, Vice President Corporate Medical Affairs, Bay Regional Medical Center, Bay City, MI, p. A328

WAYNE, Jim, Chief Financial Officer, OSF St. Francis Hospital, Escanaba, MI, p. A332

WAYNE, Richard, M.D., Vice President and Administrator, Christus Santa Rosa Children's Hospital, San Antonio, TX, p. A663

WEADICK, James F., Administrator and Chief Executive Officer, Newton Medical Center, Covington, GA, p. A159

WEAR, Sondra, Administrator, Dardanelle Hospital, Dardanelle, AR, p. A42

WEARMOUTH, Christopher L., President and Chief Executive Officer, Tazewell Community Hospital, Tazewell, VA, p. A697

WEAST, Brad, Chief Business Operations, U. S. Air Force Hospital Luke, Glendale, AZ, p. A31

WEATHERFORD, Dennis, Chief Executive Officer, Putnam County Hospital, Greencastle, IN, p. A217

WEATHERWAX, Marlene, Vice President and Chief Financial Officer, Columbus Regional Hospital, Columbus, IN, p. A213

WEAVER, Beth, Human Resources Director, Bourbon Community Hospital, Paris, KY, p. A273

WEAVER, Clifford, Management Information Systems Director, Memorial Hospital, York, PA, p. A580

WEAVER, M.D., Darrel, Vice President Medical Staff Affairs, Shelby Baptist Medical Center, Alabaster, AL, p. A13

WEAVER, Daryl W., Chief Executive Officer, Madison County Medical Center, Canton, MS, p. A367

WEAVER, Douglas K., Chief Operating Officer, Comanche County Memorial Hospital, Lawton, OK, p. A532

WEAVER, Jeff, Chief Financial Officer, Morton County Health System, Elkhart, KS, p. A246

WEBB, Barnetta, Director, Wagoner Community Hospital, Wagoner, OK, p. A541

WEBB Jr, Charles L., Administrator, Lincoln Trail Behavioral Health System, Radcliff, KY, p. A274

WEBB, Dee, Vice President Human Resources, St. Bernardine Medical Center, San Bernardino, CA, p. A86

WEBB, Denise, Administrator, Virginia Beach Psychiatric Center, Virginia Beach, VA, p. A698

WEBB, Dennis, Director Information Technology, Banner Desert Medical Center, Mesa, AZ, p. A32

WEBB, Donald, Chief Financial Officer, Williamson Medical Center, Franklin, TN, p. A606

WEBB, CPA, Jeffrey D., Controller, Jasper County Hospital, Rensselaer, IN, p. A224

WEBB, M.D., Karen
Chief Medical Officer, Des Peres Hospital, Saint Louis, MO, p. A390
Chief Medical Officer, Saint Louis University Hospital, Saint Louis, MO, p. A391

WEBB, Kevin C., FACHE, President, Flower Hospital, Sylvania, OH, p. A522

WEBB, Kimberly, Acting Vice President, Heywood Hospital, Gardner, MA, p. A318

WEBB, Lynn, Chief Financial Officer, HEALTHSOUTH Rehabilitation Hospital of Beaumont, Beaumont, TX, p. A625

WEBB, Mike, Information Systems Director, Southern Tennessee Medical Center, Winchester, TN, p. A619

WEBB, Patricia, Vice President Human Resources, Boston Medical Center, Boston, MA, p. A313

WEBB, Ronald W., President and Chief Executive Officer, Valley View Regional Hospital, Ada, OK, p. A527

WEBB, W Larry, Senior Vice President and Chief Financial Officer, Athens Regional Medical Center, Athens, GA, p. A152

WEBBER, Cathy, Chief Information Officer, Franklin County Memorial Hospital, Franklin, NE, p. A406

WEBBER, Joyce, Chief Financial Officer, Spalding Rehabilitation Hospital, Aurora, CO, p. A101

WEBBER, Lora A., Director Financial Services, St. Vincent Mercy Hospital, Elwood, IN, p. A214

WEBDALE, Ralph, Vice President Finance, Brooks Memorial Hospital, Dunkirk, NY, p. A451

WEBER, Ben, Chief Financial Officer, Kenneth Hall Regional Hospital, East St. Louis, IL, p. A192

WEBER, David, Chief Executive Officer, Wenatchee Valley Hospital, Wenatchee, WA, p. A712

WEBER Jr, Everett P., President and Chief Executive Officer, Grady Memorial Hospital, Delaware, OH, p. A512

WEBER, Frank, Administrator, HEALTHSOUTH Huntington Rehabilitation Hospital, Huntington, WV, p. A716

WEBER, Mark F., FACHE,
President and Chief Executive Officer, Gulf Coast Hospital, Fort Myers, FL, p. A129
President and Chief Executive Officer, Southwest Florida Regional Medical Center, Fort Myers, FL, p. A129

WEBER, Michael T., President and Chief Executive Officer, Putnam Hospital Center, Carmel, NY, p. A450

WEBER, Peter M., President and Chief Executive Officer, Huguley Memorial Medical Center, Fort Worth, TX, p. A640

WEBER, Rebecca
Vice President Information Technology, Jersey Shore University Medical Center, Neptune, NJ, p. A432
Vice President Information System and Chief Information Officer, Ocean Medical Center, Brick Township, NJ, p. A426

WEBER, Wilson J., Chief Operating Officer, Memorial Hermann Baptist Beaumont Hospital, Beaumont, TX, p. A625

WEBSTER, Carolyn, R.N., Interim Chief Executive Officer, Fresno Heart Hospital, Fresno, CA, p. A61

WEBSTER, Jackie, Director Human Resources, New Horizons Health Systems, Inc., Owenton, KY, p. A273

WEBSTER, Jeffrey, Administrator, Christus St. Joseph Hospital, Houston, TX, p. A644

WEBSTER, Joanne, Director Human Resources, Community Hospital of the Monterey Peninsula, Monterey, CA, p. A76

WEBSTER, Lana J., Vice President Finance, Great Plains Regional Medical Center, North Platte, NE, p. A410

WEBSTER, Mark
President, Claxton–Hepburn Medical Center, Ogdensburg, NY, p. A468
Vice President Finance, Hudson Valley Hospital Center, Cortlandt Manor, NY, p. A451

WEBSTER, Victoria, President and Chief Executive Officer, Doctors Hospital, Jackson, MI, p. A337

WEBSTER, William W., Chief Executive Officer, Medical Center Hospital, Odessa, TX, p. A659

WEDDELL, Bruce B., Chief Financial Officer, Golden Valley Memorial Hospital, Clinton, MO, p. A380

WEDDLE, Peggy, Information Systems Manager, North Valley Hospital, Tonasket, WA, p. A711

WEDEL, Cindy, Chief Operations Officer, Saint Thomas Hospital, Nashville, TN, p. A615

WEE, Donald J., Executive Director, Pioneer Memorial Hospital, Prineville, OR, p. A548

WEED, Warren, Director Human Resources, River Oaks Hospital, Jackson, MS, p. A371

WEEKS, Dennis, Director Information Services, Jennie Edmundson Memorial Hospital, Council Bluffs, IA, p. A231

WEEKS, Donnie J., President and Chief Executive Officer, Kershaw County Medical Center, Camden, SC, p. A584

WEEKS, James, Chief Information Officer, Greenwich Hospital, Greenwich, CT, p. A113

WEEKS, Margaret, Manager Personnel, Tippah County Hospital, Ripley, MS, p. A375

WEEKS, Mike
Chief Financial Officer, Stone County Medical Center, Mountain View, AR, p. A48
Chief Financial Officer, White River Medical Center, Batesville, AR, p. A40

WEEKS, Steven Douglas, Senior Vice President and Administrator, Baptist Health Medical Center–Little Rock, Little Rock, AR, p. A46

WEERTS, Michael, Director, Grand River Hospital District, Rifle, CO, p. A109

WEGENER, Brian, Chief Financial Officer, Trinity Regional Medical Center, Fort Dodge, IA, p. A234

WEGG, M.D., Daniel, Medical Director, St. Vincent Randolph Hospital, Winchester, IN, p. A227

WEHNER, Jill, Vice President Financial Services, Harbor Beach Community Hospital, Harbor Beach, MI, p. A336

WEIDER, Will, Chief Information Officer, St. Elizabeth Hospital, Appleton, WI, p. A722

WEIDMAN, Samuel G., Vice President and Chief Financial Officer, Children's Hospital, Richmond, VA, p. A695

WEIDNER, Peter, Director Management Information Systems, St. John's Riverside Hosptial, Yonkers, NY, p. A476

WEIGEL, Patricia, Controller, HEALTHSOUTH Plano Rehabilitation Hospital, Plano, TX, p. A661

WEINBERG, Arnold N., M.D., Director, M. I. T. Medical Department, Cambridge, MA, p. A316

WEINBERG, M.D., Mitch, Chief of Staff, Evergreen Healthcare, Kirkland, WA, p. A703

WEINBURGER, Terry, Vice President Human Resources, St. Mary's Hospital and Medical Center, Grand Junction, CO, p. A106

WEINER, Gary, Chief Information Officer, St. Vincent's Medical Center, Bridgeport, CT, p. A112

WEINER, Jack, President and Chief Executive Officer, St. Joseph Mercy Oakland, Pontiac, MI, p. A343

WEINER, M.D., Martin E., Chief of Staff, Seton Edgar B. Davis Hospital, Luling, TX, p. A655

WEINHOLD, Keith J., Chief Executive Officer, Select Specialty Hospital, Pittsburgh, PA, p. A572

WEINMEISTER, Karl, Interim Administrator, Integris Bass Baptist Health Center, Enid, OK, p. A530

WEINMEISTER, Kurt, Chief Operating Officer and Executive Vice President, Pomona Valley Hospital Medical Center, Pomona, CA, p. A82

WEINSTEIN, Barry S., Chief Financial Officer, Four Winds Hospital, Katonah, NY, p. A455

WEINSTEIN, M.D., Benjamin, Senior Vice President and Medical Director, CentraState Healthcare System, Freehold, NJ, p. A428

WEINSTEIN, Gary B., Executive Vice President, Washington Hospital, Washington, PA, p. A578

WEINSTOCK, Dean R., R.N., Acting Executive Director, Pilgrim Psychiatric Center, Brentwood, NY, p. A448

WEIS, Charles
Chief Financial Officer, Mount Sinai Hospital Medical Center of Chicago, Chicago, IL, p. A188
Chief Financial Officer, Schwab Rehabilitation Hospital, Chicago, IL, p. A190

WEIS, Timothy, Chief Financial Officer, Saint Vincent's Hospital – Manhattan, New York, NY, p. A464

WEISE, M.D., Charles, Medical Director, Highland Hospital, Charleston, WV, p. A714

WEISFIELD, Phyllis, Interim Chief Executive Officer, Horsham Clinic, Ambler, PA, p. A552

WEISHOLTZ, M.D., Steven, President Medical Staff, Englewood Hospital and Medical Center, Englewood, NJ, p. A428

WEISNER, Brad, Executive Vice President and Chief Operating Officer, Nash Health Care Systems, Rocky Mount, NC, p. A490

WEISPFENNING, Diane
Chief Operating Officer, Lisbon Area Health Services, Lisbon, ND, p. A499
Vice President of Operations, Oakes Community Hospital, Oakes, ND, p. A500

WEISS, M.D., Alan R., Chief of Staff, California Hospital Medical Center, Los Angeles, CA, p. A69

WEISS, Allen, President, Naples Community Hospital, Naples, FL, p. A139

WEISS, Barry J., Chairman of the Board, College Health Enterprises, Santa Fe Springs, CA, p. B30

WEISS, David, Vice President Information System, Alton Memorial Hospital, Alton, IL, p. A183

WEISS, Linda, Acting Director, Veterans Affairs Medical Center, Bath, NY, p. A447

WEISS, Phyllis, Director Human Resources, San Leandro Hospital, San Leandro, CA, p. A91

WEISS, Steven J., Chief Financial Officer, Forest Park Hospital, Saint Louis, MO, p. A391

WEISSER, Lisa, Finance Supervisor, Wagner Community Memorial Hospital, Wagner, SD, p. A600

WEISSMAN, M.D., Joel, Chief Medical Officer, Jeanes Hospital, Philadelphia, PA, p. A568

WEISUL, M.D., Jonathan, Vice President Medical Affairs & Chief Medical Officer, Christus St. Frances Cabrini Hospital, Alexandria, LA, p. A276

WEITEKAMP, M.D., Michael, Chief Medical Officer, Penn State Milton S. Hershey Medical Center, Hershey, PA, p. A560

WELCH, Cheryl, Acting Director, Louis A. Johnson Veterans Affairs Medical Center, Clarksburg, WV, p. A714

WELCH, Donald E., Chief Financial Officer, East Pasco Medical Center, Zephyrhills, FL, p. A151

WELCH, Donna, Resources Service Line Manager, Veterans Affairs Medical Center, Tomah, WI, p. A736

WELCH, Douglas, Chief Executive Officer, Las Colinas Medical Center, Irving, TX, p. A649

WELCH, Melissa, Health Information Management Director, Oakdale Community Hospital, Oakdale, LA, p. A290

WELCH, Rob, Chief Operating Officer, Ridgeview Medical Center, Waconia, MN, p. A364

WELCH, Tammy
Controller, HEALTHSOUTH Rehabilitation Hospital of Texarkana, Texarkana, TX, p. A669
Chief Financial Officer, Laird Memorial Hospital, Kilgore, TX, p. A651

WELCH, Tony, Vice President Human Resources, Hardin Memorial Hospital, Elizabethtown, KY, p. A263

WELCH, William L., CHE, Chief Executive Officer, Jefferson Community Health Center, Fairbury, NE, p. A406

WELDAY, Douglas D., Executive Vice President and Chief Financial Officer, Oakwood Hospital and Medical Center–Dearborn, Dearborn, MI, p. A330

WELDON, M.D., Donald, Chief of Staff, Beatrice Community Hospital and Health Center, Beatrice, NE, p. A405

WELDON, FACHE, Marie, Associate Director, Harry S. Truman Memorial Veterans Hospital, Columbia, MO, p. A380

WELDON, William W., Ph.D., Chief Executive Officer, Highland Medical Center, Lubbock, TX, p. A654

WELKER, Suzanne, Corporate Vice President Human Resources, Berger Health System, Circleville, OH, p. A508

WELLER, Karen A., Chief Executive Officer, North Country Hospital and Health Center, Newport, VT, p. A683

WELLS, Alphe, Chief Human Resources Officer, Delta Regional Medical Center, Greenville, MS, p. A368

WELLS, Barbara, Human Resources Director, Sutter Amador Hospital, Jackson, CA, p. A65

WELLS, M.D., Bruce, Chief of Staff, William Newton Hospital, Winfield, KS, p. A260

WELLS, Dawn L., Administrator, St. James Health Services, Saint James, MN, p. A361

WELLS, Hank, Interim Chief Executive Officer, LAC–King–Drew Medical Center, Los Angeles, CA, p. A71

WELLS, M.D., Kristy G., President Medical Staff, Muhlenberg Community Hospital, Greenville, KY, p. A265

WELLS, Mary, Administrator, Community Memorial Hospital, Sumner, IA, p. A242

WELLS, Robert, Chief Information Officer, Castle Medical Center, Kailua, HI, p. A174

WELLS, Stephanie, Chief Executive Officer, Advance Care Hospital, Marrero, LA, p. A286

WELSH Jr, J. L., President and Chief Executive Officer, Southeastern Regional Medical Center, Lumberton, NC, p. A487

WELSH, John H., Chief Executive Officer, Rumford Hospital, Rumford, ME, p. A300

WELSH, M.D., Randall, Chief of Staff, Wilson Memorial Hospital, Sidney, OH, p. A522

WELTON, George, Vice President Information Services, Exempla Lutheran Medical Center, Wheat Ridge, CO, p. A110

WELTON, R. C., Chief Commander, Naval Hospital, Camp Lejeune, NC, p. A479

WENDELL, M.D., Gary D., President Medical and Dental Staff, Crozer–Chester Medical Center, Upland, PA, p. A577

WENGARD, Gary, Interim President and Chief Executive Officer, Community Health Partners Regional Medical Center, Lorain, OH, p. A516

WENGER, Jill, Vice President Human Resources, Memorial Hospital, McPherson, KS, p. A252

WENGER, Mike, Chief Financial Officer, Via Christi Regional Medical Center, Wichita, KS, p. A259

WENGERD, Gary, Vice President Finance and Chief Financial Officer, Community Health Partners Regional Medical Center, Lorain, OH, p. A516

WENTE, James W., CHE, President and Chief Executive Officer, Southeast Missouri Hospital, Cape Girardeau, MO, p. A379

WENTWORTH, Philip M., FACHE, President, Presbyterian Hospital of Plano, Plano, TX, p. A661

WENTZ, Jim, Associate Vice President and Chief Financial Officer, University of Texas Southwestern Medical Center, Dallas, TX, p. A634

WENTZ, Robert J., President and Chief Executive Officer, Oroville Hospital, Oroville, CA, p. A80

WENTZ, Terri, Chief Operating Officer, Jupiter Medical Center, Jupiter, FL, p. A133

WEOT, M.D., Christine, Medical Director, HEALTHSOUTH Rehabilitation Hospital of Spring Hill, Brooksville, FL, p. A125

WEPPLER, M.D., Angie, Chief of Staff, Cass County Memorial Hospital, Atlantic, IA, p. A228

WERBYLO, Linda
Vice President Human Resources, Carondelet St. Joseph's Hospital–Tucson, Tucson, AZ, p. A37
Vice President Human Resources, Carondelet St. Mary's Hospital–Tucson, Tucson, AZ, p. A37

WERFT, Ronald C.
President and Chief Executive Officer, Cottage Health System, Santa Barbara, CA, p. B33
President and Chief Executive Officer, Santa Barbara Cottage Hospital, Santa Barbara, CA, p. A92

WERKOWSKI, Richard F., Chief Financial Officer, Johnson Memorial Hospital, Stafford Springs, CT, p. A116

WERMERT, James A., Chief Financial Officer, Mercer County Joint Township Community Hospital, Coldwater, OH, p. A510

WERNER, Daniel J., President and Chief Executive Officer, Nanticoke Memorial Hospital, Seaford, DE, p. A119

WERNER, Dennis, Chief Financial Officer, National Rehabilitation Hospital, Washington, DC, p. A122

WERNER, Thomas L., President, Adventist Health System Sunbelt Health Care Corporation, Winter Park, FL, p. B4

WERNER, Todd S., Chief Executive Officer, Hinsdale Hospital, Hinsdale, IL, p. A197

WERNER, William, Vice President Medical Management, Advocate Illinois Masonic Medical Center, Chicago, IL, p. A186

WERNICK, Joel
President and Chief Executive Officer, Phoebe Putney Health Systems, Albany, GA, p. B83
President and Chief Executive Officer, Phoebe Putney Memorial Hospital, Albany, GA, p. A152

WERNTZ, Beverly, Chief Operating Officer, Kaiser Foundation Hospital, Sacramento, CA, p. A84

WERTHMAN, Ronald J., Vice President Finance, Chief Financial Officer and Treasurer, Johns Hopkins Hospital, Baltimore, MD, p. A303

WERTZ, Randy S., Chief Executive Officer, Golden Valley Memorial Hospital, Clinton, MO, p. A380

WESLEY, James A., Chief Information Officer, New Britain General Hospital, New Britain, CT, p. A114

WESLEY, John, Deputy Chief for Clinical Services, Dwight David Eisenhower Army Medical Center, Fort Gordon, GA, p. A162

WESLEY, M.D., Sue, Senior Vice President Medical Staff Affairs, St. James Mercy Hospital, Hornell, NY, p. A454

WESOLOWSKI, Jaime A., President and Chief Executive Officer, Riverside Community Hospital, Riverside, CA, p. A84

WESSNER, David K.
President and Chief Executive Officer, Methodist Hospital, Saint Louis Park, MN, p. A361
President and Chief Executive Officer, Park Nicollet Health Services, Saint Louis Park, MN, p. B83

WESSON, Jim, Chief Executive Officer, Valley Baptist Medical Center–Brownsville, Brownsville, TX, p. A627

WEST, Andrea, Manager Human Resources, Thomasville Medical Center, Thomasville, NC, p. A493

WEST, Chris, President and Chief Executive Officer, Alliant Management Services, Louisville, KY, p. B7

WEST, Dan, Chief Executive Officer, Select Specialty Hospital–Columbus, Columbus, OH, p. A511

WEST, David, Supervisor Information Technology, Deckerville Community Hospital, Deckerville, MI, p. A330

WEST, M.D., George, President Medical Staff, Lenoir Memorial Hospital, Kinston, NC, p. A486

WEST, James R., CHE, President and Chief Executive Officer, Presbyterian Intercommunity Hospital, Whittier, CA, p. A99

WEST, Julie, Chief Administrative Officer, Memorial Hospital of Texas County, Guymon, OK, p. A531

WEST, Michele, Director Human Resources, Doctors Medical Center, Modesto, CA, p. A76

WEST, Rachel, Vice President Human Resources, Southeast Georgia Health System Brunswick Campus, Brunswick, GA, p. A157

WEST, Stephanie, R.N., Administrator, Ellett Memorial Hospital, Appleton City, MO, p. A378

WEST, Steven J., Chief Executive Officer, Blackford Community Hospital, Hartford City, IN, p. A217

WEST, Warren K., President, Copley Hospital, Morrisville, VT, p. A683

WESTENBERG, Diane, Executive Assistant, Sioux Valley Luverne Medical Center, Luverne, MN, p. A356

WESTENHOFER, Steve, Chief Executive Officer, Volunteer Community Hospital, Martin, TN, p. A612

WESTER, K. Scott, FACHE, President and Chief Executive Officer, St. Francis Medical Center, Monroe, LA, p. A287

WESTERCAMP, Lois, Manager Human Resources, Davis County Hospital, Bloomfield, IA, p. A229

WESTFALL, M.D., David, Vice President Medical Affairs, Northeast Georgia Medical Center, Gainesville, GA, p. A163

WESTGARD, M.D., David E., Chief Medical Officer, Olmsted Medical Center, Rochester, MN, p. A360

WESTMAN, Ken, Chief Executive Officer, Big Fork Valley Hospital, Bigfork, MN, p. A350

WESTON, Katy, Chief Human Resources, San Gorgonio Memorial Hospital, Banning, CA, p. A54

WESTON, M.D., Terry, Vice President Medical Affairs, MedCentral Health System, Mansfield, OH, p. A517

WESTON–HALL, Patricia, Executive Director, Glenbeigh Hospital and Outpatient Centers, Rock Creek, OH, p. A521

WETHERELL, Russell, Vice Preesident Finance and Operations, Grandview Hospital and Medical Center, Dayton, OH, p. A512

WETHINGTON, Bud
Chief Executive Officer, Palmyra Medical Centers, Albany, GA, p. A152
Chief Operating Officer, Southwest Florida Regional Medical Center, Fort Myers, FL, p. A129

WETTON, Darlene, Chief Operating Officer, Alvarado Hospital Medical Center, San Diego, CA, p. A86

WETZEL, Myra, Administrator, HEALTHSOUTH Hospital of Terre Haute, Terre Haute, IN, p. A226

WEXLER, Erik G., President and Chief Operating Officer, Northwest Hospital Center, Randallstown, MD, p. A310

WEXNER, M.D., Steven D., Chief of Staff, Cleveland Clinic Hospital, Weston, FL, p. A151

WEYHMULLER, Gary, Vice President Human Resources, Fox Chase Cancer Center–American Oncologic Hospital, Philadelphia, PA, p. A567

WEYMOUTH, Deborah
Senior Vice President Operations and Chief Financial Officer, Thompson Health, Canandaigua, NY, p. A449
Senior Vice President Operations and Chief Financial Officer, Thompson Health, Canandaigua, NY, p. A449

WHALEN, David, Chief Executive Officer, Twin Cities Hospital, Niceville, FL, p. A139

WHALEN, Keith
Administrative Director and Chief Information Officer, Mercy Medical Center Merced–Community Campus, Merced, CA, p. A75
Administrative Director and Chief Information Officer, Mercy Medical Center Merced–Dominican Campus, Merced, CA, p. A75

WHALEN, M Colleen, Chief Operating Officer, Exempla Lutheran Medical Center, Wheat Ridge, CO, p. A110

WHALEY, Lisa, Vice President, Human Resources, Memorial Health Care System, Chattanooga, TN, p. A603

WHARTON, M.D., George W., Medical Director, HEALTHSOUTH Medical Center, Dallas, TX, p. A632

WHARTON, Glenda, Vice President Nursing, Mercy Hospital Fairfield, Fairfield, OH, p. A513

WHATLEY, Gary Lex, Senior Vice President and Chief Operating Officer, Willis–Knighton Medical Center, Shreveport, LA, p. A293

WHEATLEY, Jane, Chief Executive Officer, Taylor Regional Hospital, Campbellsville, KY, p. A262

WHEATLEY, Richard
Vice President Information Services, Community Medical Center, Toms River, NJ, p. A437
Vice President Information Services, Monmouth Medical Center, Long Branch, NJ, p. A430

WHEELEHAN, Phil, Information Systems Manager, Norton Sound Regional Hospital, Nome, AK, p. A28

WHEELER, David, Administrator, Eureka Springs Hospital, Eureka Springs, AR, p. A42

WHEELER, James F.
Vice President Finance, Lenawee Health Alliance – Bixby Campus, Adrian, MI, p. A327
Vice President Finance, Lenawee Health Alliance–Herrick Campus, Tecumseh, MI, p. A346

WHEELER, MSN, R.N. Joan, Associate Administrator, Runnells Specialized Hospital of Union County, Berkeley Heights, NJ, p. A425

WHEELER, Juanita, Interim Chief Executive Officer, Rankin Hospital District, Rankin, TX, p. A662

WHEELER, Katrina, Chief Financial Officer, Satilla Regional Medical Center, Waycross, GA, p. A172

WHEELER, Larry, Vice President Communications and External Affairs, Kaiser Sunnyside Medical Center, Clackamas, OR, p. A542

WHEELER, Michael K., Director, John D. Dingell Veterans Affairs Medical Center, Detroit, MI, p. A331

WHEELER, Robert
Controller, HEALTHSOUTH Rehabilitation Hospital, Florence, SC, p. A587
Vice President Human Resources, South Shore Hospital, South Weymouth, MA, p. A323

WHEELER, Tammy, Controller, Putnam County Memorial Hospital, Unionville, MO, p. A395

WHEELER, Terry J., Chief Executive Officer, Cypress Fairbanks Medical Center, Houston, TX, p. A644

WHEELER, William G., M.D., President and Chief Executive Officer, Lourdes Hospital, Paducah, KY, p. A273

WHEELER, Zach, Vice President Human Resources, John D. Archbold Memorial Hospital, Thomasville, GA, p. A170

WHELAN, Laurie A., Vice President Finance and Chief Financial Officer, Hospital for Special Care, New Britain, CT, p. A114

WHELAN, Thomas, President, Lodi Community Hospital, Lodi, OH, p. A516

WHICHARD, Forrest, Chief Financial Officer, Teche Regional Medical Center, Morgan City, LA, p. A287

WHIDDON, Mike, Director Information Systems, Orange Park Medical Center, Orange Park, FL, p. A140

WHILES, David, Director Health Information Systems, Midland Memorial Hospital, Midland, TX, p. A657

WHINERY, Robert N., Vice President Finance, Grande Ronde Hospital, La Grande, OR, p. A545

WHIPKEY, Neil, Administrator, Shands at Lake Shore, Lake City, FL, p. A134

WHIPPLE, Ingrid L., Chief Executive Officer, Montevista Hospital, Las Vegas, NV, p. A416

WHIPPLE, James, Administrator, Marshall Hospital, Placerville, CA, p. A81

WHISMAN, R.N., Lynn, Chief Nursing Executive and Vice President, Operations, Memorial Health Care System, Chattanooga, TN, p. A603

WHITAKER, David D., FACHE, President and Chief Executive Officer, Norman Regional Hospital, Norman, OK, p. A534

WHITAKER, David L., Chief Executive Officer, Crane Memorial Hospital, Crane, TX, p. A631

WHITAKER, Doris, Human Resources Director, Booneville Community Hospital, Booneville, AR, p. A41

WHITAKER, E. Berton, President and Chief Executive Officer, Wellmont Holston Valley Medical Center, Kingsport, TN, p. A609

WHITAKER, James B., President, Circles of Care, Melbourne, FL, p. A136

WHITAKER, Jimmy, Director Information Systems, Central Carolina Hospital, Sanford, NC, p. A491

WHITAKER, M.D., Neil
Chief Medical Director, Orem Community Hospital, Orem, UT, p. A678
Medical Director, Utah Valley Regional Medical Center, Provo, UT, p. A679

WHITBY, Lea, President and Chief Executive Officer, Calumet Medical Center, Chilton, WI, p. A724

WHITCHURCH, Walter D., Controller, HEALTHSOUTH Sunrise Rehabilitation Hospital, Fort Lauderdale, FL, p. A128

WHITE, Al, Senior Vice President Business Services, Broadlawns Medical Center, Des Moines, IA, p. A232

WHITE, Carol, Associate Executive Director, Elmhurst Hospital Center, New York, NY, p. A459

WHITE, Cindy, Chief Financial Officer, INTEGRIS Canadian Valley Regional Hospital, Yukon, OK, p. A541

WHITE, Dale A., Chief Executive Officer, Northeast Kansas Center for Health and Wellness, Horton, KS, p. A249

WHITE, David R., Chairman and Chief Executive Officer, IASIS Healthcare, Franklin, TN, p. B61

WHITE, Doug, Chief Executive Officer, Grand Strand Regional Medical Center, Myrtle Beach, SC, p. A590

WHITE, Douglas, Director of Medical Affairs, Day Kimball Hospital, Putnam, CT, p. A116

WHITE, Dudley R., Administrator and Chief Executive Officer, Concho County Hospital, Eden, TX, p. A636

WHITE, Harvey, Medical Director, Heart Hospital of New Mexico, Albuquerque, NM, p. A440

WHITE, J B., Chief Information Officer, River Region Health System, Vicksburg, MS, p. A376

WHITE, James, Vice President Human Resources, North Memorial Health Care, Robbinsdale, MN, p. A360

WHITE, M.D., James P., Chief Medical Officer, Integris Baptist Medical Center, Oklahoma City, OK, p. A535

WHITE, Jean, Vice President of Finance, Avera Heart Hospital of South Dakota, Sioux Falls, SD, p. A598

WHITE, Jim, Chief Information Officer, Lompoc Healthcare District, Lompoc, CA, p. A68

WHITE, Joanne, Chief Information Officer, Wood County Hospital, Bowling Green, OH, p. A504

WHITE, Jody, Executive Vice President and Chief Operating Officer, Lowell General Hospital, Lowell, MA, p. A319

WHITE, John R., Chief Executive Officer and Superintendent, Samaritan Healthcare, Moses Lake, WA, p. A704

WHITE, Kevin A., Administrator, Medicine Lodge Memorial Hospital, Medicine Lodge, KS, p. A252

WHITE Jr, Lawrence L., Interim President and Chief Executive Officer, Clark Fork Valley Hospital, Plains, MT, p. A401

WHITE, Linda E.
President and Chief Executive Officer, Deaconess Health System, Evansville, IN, p. B35
President and Chief Executive Officer, Deaconess Hospital, Evansville, IN, p. A214

WHITE, Lindy, Chief Financial Officer, Smyth County Community Hospital, Marion, VA, p. A691

WHITE, Mariann, Chief Operating Officer, Kaiser Foundation Hospital and Rehabilitation Center, Vallejo, CA, p. A97

WHITE, Mary M., President and Chief Executive Officer, Swedish Medical Center, Englewood, CO, p. A105

WHITE, M.D., Michael, President, Medical Staff, Allegheny General Hospital, Pittsburgh, PA, p. A571

WHITE, Nathan, Admin Director Information Systems, Frye Regional Medical Center, Hickory, NC, p. A485

WHITE, Olinda, Chief Financial Officer, Wrangell Medical Center, Wrangell, AK, p. A29

WHITE, R.N., MS, Patricia, Chief Operating Officer, St. Joseph's Hospital and Medical Center, Phoenix, AZ, p. A35

WHITE, Robert, Chief of Staff, East Texas Medical Center–Mount Vernon, Mount Vernon, TX, p. A657

WHITE, M.D., Robert, Assistant Administrator Medical Affairs, OSF Saint Anthony Medical Center, Rockford, IL, p. A206

WHITE, Robin, Director Human Resources, Parkview Adventist Medical Center, Brunswick, ME, p. A297

WHITE, Roger, Chief Financial Officer, Memorial Hospital, Craig, CO, p. A103

WHITE, Ronald, Director Human Resources, Western Plains Medical Complex, Dodge City, KS, p. A246

WHITE, Rory, Information Systems Operations Manager, Veterans Affairs Medical Center, Bath, NY, p. A447

WHITE, Roy E., Chief Executive Officer, Cloud County Health Center, Concordia, KS, p. A245

WHITE, Sheli, Director Health Information, Sabetha Community Hospital, Sabetha, KS, p. A256

WHITE, Shelia, Director Human Resources, Bon Secours–Richmond Community Hospital, Richmond, VA, p. A694

WHITE, Shirley, Director Human Resources, Ashley County Medical Center, Crossett, AR, p. A41

WHITE, Stephani, Vice President and Site Administrator, Legacy Emanuel Hospital and Health Center, Portland, OR, p. A547

WHITE, M.D., Steve, Chief of Staff, Guadalupe Valley Hospital, Seguin, TX, p. A666

WHITE, Thomas, President and Chief Executive Officer, Jameson Hospital, New Castle, PA, p. A566

WHITE, Wesley, Chief Financial Officer, Plains Regional Medical Center, Clovis, NM, p. A442

WHITE, William J., Interim Chief Executive Officer, Tewksbury Hospital, Tewksbury, MA, p. A324

WHITE, Woody, Chief Financial Officer, DeTar Healthcare System, Victoria, TX, p. A672

WHITEAKER, Les, Vice President for Finance and Information, Memorial Medical Center, Ashland, WI, p. A722

WHITEHEAD, M.D., Alva W., Vice President Medical Services, McLeod Health, Florence, SC, p. A588

WHITEHEAD, M.D., Deborah A., President, Medical Staff, Middlesex Hospital, Middletown, CT, p. A114

WHITEHORN, Jeffrey T., Chief Executive Officer, Summit Medical Center, Hermitage, TN, p. A607

WHITEHOUSE, Edward J.
Interim Chief Executive Office, West Hills Hospital, Reno, NV, p. A418
Chief Operating Officer, Sylvan Grove Hospital, Jackson, GA, p. A164

WHITEHURST, Angela, Finance Manager, HEALTHSOUTH Emerald Coast Rehabilitation Hospital, Panama City, FL, p. A142

WHITELOCK, M.D., Paul, Medical Director, Seton Shoal Creek Hospital, Austin, TX, p. A624

WHITENACK, Barbara, Manager, Human Resources, St. Vincent Mercy Hospital, Elwood, IN, p. A214

WHITESEL, John
Senior Vice President and Chief Financial Officer, Bon Secours Community Hospital, Port Jervis, NY, p. A470
Senior Vice President and Chief Financial Officer, Good Samaritan Hospital, Suffern, NY, p. A473
Senior Vice President and Chief Financial Officer, St. Anthony Community Hospital, Warwick, NY, p. A475

WHITFIELD, Bruce, Chief Financial Officer, St. James Healthcare, Butte, MT, p. A397

WHITFIELD Jr, Charles H., President and Chief Executive Officer, Laughlin Memorial Hospital, Greeneville, TN, p. A607

WHITFIELD, Jay, Chief Financial Officer, Baylor Medical Center at Irving, Irving, TX, p. A649

WHITLEY, R.N., Pam, Chief Operating Officer and Chief Nursing Officer, Green Oaks Hospital, Dallas, TX, p. A632

WHITLOCK, M.D., Dan, Chief Medical Officer, St. Cloud Hospital, Saint Cloud, MN, p. A361

WHITLOCK, Kenneth W., Medical Information Services Flight Commander, U. S. Air Force Hospital Shaw, Shaw AFB, SC, p. A591

WHITMORE, Ray B., Chief Financial Officer, McCurtain Memorial Hospital, Idabel, OK, p. A532

WHITNEY, Nancy, Chief Financial Officer, St. Francis Medical Center, Breckenridge, MN, p. A350

WHITSON, CPA, Charles P., Vice President Finance, Lake Charles Memorial Hospital, Lake Charles, LA, p. A285

WHITTEKER, Lynn, Vice President, Bluefield Regional Medical Center, Bluefield, WV, p. A713

WHITTEMORE, Anthony, Chief Medical Officer, Brigham and Women's Hospital, Boston, MA, p. A313

WHITTENBURG, Pat, Director, Human Resources and Corporate Compliance Officer, Cumberland Medical Center, Crossville, TN, p. A605

WHITTINGTON, Bruce, Vice President Human Resources, Hays Medical Center, Hays, KS, p. A248

WHITTINGTON, M.D., Kenneth W., Vice President Medical Affairs, Deaconess Hospital, Oklahoma City, OK, p. A535

WHITTINGTON, Laurie A., Chief Operating Officer, Memorial Hospital of Union County, Marysville, OH, p. A517

WHITTINGTON, Shane, Chief Financial Officer, Caldwell County Hospital, Princeton, KY, p. A274

WHITTINGTON, Terry G., Chief Executive Officer, Randolph County Medical Center, Pocahontas, AR, p. A49

WHORLEY, Douglas, Director Information Systems, R. J. Reynolds–Patrick County Memorial Hospital, Stuart, VA, p. A697

WHORTON, Jeff, Director Human Resources, Noble Hospital, Westfield, MA, p. A325

WHYTE, M.D., Thomas, Chief of Staff, Randolph Hospital, Asheboro, NC, p. A477

WICK, Betty, Assistant Administrator, Colorado–Fayette Medical Center, Weimar, TX, p. A673

WICK, Timothy J., Chief Executive Officer, Burnett Medical Center, Grantsburg, WI, p. A726

WICKE, III, Julius, Controller, Baylor Specialty Hospital, Dallas, TX, p. A632

WICKER, Mary, Chief Operating Officer, Southwestern Vermont Medical Center, Bennington, VT, p. A682

WIDHALM, M.D., Timothy, Chief of Staff, Memorial Hospital, Aurora, NE, p. A404

WIDMER, M.D., James, Chief of Staff, Henry County Health Center, Mount Pleasant, IA, p. A238

WIEGAND, Deborah, R.N., Chief Executive Officer, Christus Jasper Memorial Hospital, Jasper, TX, p. A650

WIEGEL, Gregory, Vice President Finance and Chief Financial Officer, Civista Health, La Plata, MD, p. A309

WIEMAN, Jeffrey, M.D., Chief Executive Officer, The Cancer Institute, Kansas City, MO, p. A385

WIEMAN, M.D., Michael, Senior Vice President and Chief Medical Officer, St. Vincent Hospitals and Health Services, Indianapolis, IN, p. A219

WIENER, Mark S.
Regional President and Chief Executive Officer, Provena Covenant Medical Center, Urbana, IL, p. A209
President and Chief Executive Officer, Provena United Samaritans Medical Center, Danville, IL, p. A191

WIENS, Ron, Chief Financial Officer, St. John's Lutheran Hospital, Libby, MT, p. A400

WIERCINSKI, John P., President and Chief Executive Officer, Shamokin Area Community Hospital, Coal Township, PA, p. A555

WIESEL, M.D., Sam, Senior Vice President and Chief Medical Officer, MedStar–Georgetown Medical Center, Washington, DC, p. A121

WIESNER, Gerald, Administrator, Miami County Medical Center, Paola, KS, p. A255

WIEST, John K., Chief Financial and Insitutional Service Officer, Lee Memorial Health System, Fort Myers, FL, p. A129

WIETRZYKOWSKI, Kevin, Information Mangement Systems Director, Defiance Regional Medical Center, Defiance, OH, p. A512

WIETSTOCK, Les, Chief Executive Officer, Towner County Medical Center, Cando, ND, p. A496

WIGGERS, Terri, Chief Financial Officer, Woodland Heights Medical Center, Lufkin, TX, p. A655

WIGGINS, Celeste M., Chief Executive Officer, Surgical Specialty Centre, Baton Rouge, LA, p. A278

WIGGINS, Gary K., Chief Financial Officer, Alameda Hospital, Alameda, CA, p. A52

WIGGINS, John, Vice President Finance and Chief Financial Officer, Albemarle Hospital, Elizabeth City, NC, p. A482

WIGGINS, Leslie, Associate Director, John D. Dingell Veterans Affairs Medical Center, Detroit, MI, p. A331

WIGGINS, Stephen P., Director, Western State Hospital, Hopkinsville, KY, p. A266

WIGHTMAN, Lori L., Administrator, New Ulm Medical Center, New Ulm, MN, p. A358

WIGNALL, Terry A., Director of Human Resources, St. Elizabeth Ann Seton Hospital of Carmel, Carmel, IN, p. A212

WIJEWARDANE, Chamath, Director Information Technology, Oktibbeha County Hospital, Starkville, MS, p. A376

WILBANKS, John F., Chief Operating Officer, Baptist Medical Center, Jacksonville, FL, p. A132

WILBERDING, Deborah, Controller, Rush Oak Park Hospital, Oak Park, IL, p. A203

WILBUR, Thomas W., Chief Executive Officer and Superintendent, Newport Community Hospital, Newport, WA, p. A704

WILBURN, Tyree, Chaiman, President and Chief Executive Officer, Merit Health Systems, Louisville, KY, p. B75

WILCOX, Alex, R.N., Chief Executive Officer, Kindred Hospital – Tucson, Tucson, AZ, p. A38

WILCOX, Dale R., Executive Vice President and Chief Operating Officer, Parkview Hospital, Fort Wayne, IN, p. A215

WILCOX, Jack, Chief Financial Officer, Medical Park Hospital, Hope, AR, p. A44

WILCOX, James, Chief Executive Officer, Las Encinas Hospital, Pasadena, CA, p. A81

WILCOX, William, President and Chief Executive Officer, United Surgical Partners International, Addison, TX, p. B114

WILD, Philip, Controller, St. John River District Hospital, East China, MI, p. A332

WILD, Ronald, Controller, Yuma Rehabilitation Hospital, Yuma, AZ, p. A39

WILDE, Brent, Vice President, Fairview Southdale Hospital, Edina, MN, p. A353

WILDE, Gary, Chief Executive Officer, Community Memorial Hospital of San Buenaventura, Ventura, CA, p. A98

WILDE, Kathy
Vice President Operations and Patient Care, Mercy Hospital, Coon Rapids, MN, p. A351
Vice President Operations and Patient Care, Unity Hospital, Fridley, MN, p. A354

WILDER, M.D., Carol, Medical Director, Kau Hospital, Pahala, HI, p. A176

WILDER, Norman, Director Information Services, Cibola General Hospital, Grants, NM, p. A443

WILDER, M.D., Norman, Vice President Medical Affairs, Alaska Regional Hospital, Anchorage, AK, p. A26

WILDMAN, Darrell, Chief Financial Officer, Rush Foundation Hospital, Meridian, MS, p. A373

WILES, Ellie, Manager Human Resources, FirstHealth Montgomery Memorial Hospital, Troy, NC, p. A493

WILES, Paul M., President and Chief Executive Officer, Novant Health, Winston–Salem, NC, p. B80

WILEY, Chuck, Information Systems Manager, Harrison County Hospital, Corydon, IN, p. A213

WILEY, Donald J., President, St. Joseph's Medical Center, Stockton, CA, p. A95

WILEY, George, Chief Financial Officer, Georgetown Community Hospital, Georgetown, KY, p. A265

WILEY, R.N., Rebecca, Chief Operating Officer and Associate Director, G.V. Montgomery Veterans Affairs Medical Center, Jackson, MS, p. A370

WILFORD, Linda, Chief Financial Officer, Holy Cross Hospital, Fort Lauderdale, FL, p. A128

WILHELM, Andrew, Director Information Technology Services, Mercy Medical, Daphne, AL, p. A17

WILHELM, Charles M., Vice President Financial Services and Chief Financial Officer, Provena St. Mary's Hospital, Kankakee, IL, p. A198

WILHELM, Jr, John O., Executive Vice President and Chief Financial Officer, Beverly Hospital, Beverly, MA, p. A312

WILHELM, Kenneth F., President and Chief Executive Officer, Huron Medical Center, Bad Axe, MI, p. A328

WILHELM, Paul, Chief of Staff, Kiowa District Hospital and Manor, Kiowa, KS, p. A250

WILHELMSEN Jr, Thomas E., President and Chief Executive Officer, Southern New Hampshire Medical Center, Nashua, NH, p. A422

WILHITE, Milton, Chief Operating Officer, Sierra Vista Hospital, Truth or Consequences, NM, p. A445

WILHOIT, Ellen, President and Chief Administrative Officer, Fort Sanders–Sevier Medical Center, Sevierville, TN, p. A617

WILHOITE, David, Chief Financial Officer, Mercy Medical Center, Springfield, OH, p. A522

WILK, Ann Marie, Chief Financial Officer, Veterans Affairs Greater Los Angeles Healthcare System, Los Angeles, CA, p. A73

WILK, Leonard E., Administrator, Aurora Sinai Medical Center, Milwaukee, WI, p. A730

WILK, Terry, Vice President Information Technology and Chief Information Officer, Southern Regional Medical Center, Riverdale, GA, p. A167

WILKER, John, Vice President and Chief Financial Officer, Portneuf Medical Center, Pocatello, ID, p. A181

WILKERSON, Donald H., Chief Executive Officer, North Austin Medical Center, Austin, TX, p. A623

WILKERSON, Natalie, Director Information Technology Services, Henry Medical Center, Stockbridge, GA, p. A170

WILKINS, Janice F.
Administrator, R. J. Reynolds–Patrick County Memorial Hospital, Stuart, VA, p. A697
Administrator, R. J. Reynolds–Patrick County Memorial Hospital, Stuart, VA, p. A697

WILKINS, Jeff, Interim Chief Information Officer, Ohio State University Medical Center, Columbus, OH, p. A511

WILKINS, Jr, M.D., William E., Chief Medical Officer, Mercy Health System of Kansas, Independence, KS, p. A249

WILKINSON, Gary L., Director, Veterans Affairs Medical Center, Iowa City, IA, p. A236

WILKINSON, Linda, Coordinator Human Resources, East Texas Medical Center Carthage, Carthage, TX, p. A628

WILKINSON, Robyn, Vice President Human Resources, Mercy Medical Center–Des Moines, Des Moines, IA, p. A233

WILKINSON, Steven D., President and Chief Executive Officer, Menorah Medical Center, Overland Park, KS, p. A254

WILL, Nicki, Ph.D., President and Chief Executive Officer, Lower Keys Medical Center, Key West, FL, p. A133

WILLARD, Mary Beth, Director Nursing, Coon Memorial Hospital and Home, Dalhart, TX, p. A631

WILLARS, Susan, Human Resource Director, Mission Hospital, Mission, TX, p. A657

WILLCOXON, Phil, Chief Executive Officer, Freeman Neosho Hospital, Neosho, MO, p. A388

WILLEKE, Louis R., Administrator, Refugio County Memorial Hospital, Refugio, TX, p. A662

WILLEMSEN, Jane, Executive Vice President and Chief Operating Officer, Queen of the Valley Hospital, Napa, CA, p. A77

WILLERT, Todd, Administrator, Story County Medical Center, Nevada, IA, p. A238

WILLETT, Richard, Chief Executive Officer, Redington–Fairview General Hospital, Skowhegan, ME, p. A301

WILLETT, Simon, Director Administrative Operations, South Texas Veterans Health Care System, San Antonio, TX, p. A665

WILLHELM, Judene, Administrator, Winkler County Memorial Hospital, Kermit, TX, p. A650

WILLIAMS, Allyson, Chief Operating Officer, Delta Regional Medical Center, Greenville, MS, p. A368

WILLIAMS, Althea, Vice President Human Resources, JPS Health Network, Fort Worth, TX, p. A640

WILLIAMS, Carlene, Chief Financial Officer, Glades General Hospital, Belle Glade, FL, p. A123

WILLIAMS, M.D., Catherine, Medical Director, Lewis County General Hospital, Lowville, NY, p. A456

WILLIAMS, Cheryl, Human Resource Director, Seton Edgar B. Davis Hospital, Luling, TX, p. A655

WILLIAMS, Dan B., Senior Vice President and Chief Human Resources Officer, Montgomery Hospital Medical Center, Norristown, PA, p. A566

WILLIAMS, Dana, Assistant Administrator and Chief Financial Officer, Baptist Memorial Hospital–North Mississippi, Oxford, MS, p. A374

WILLIAMS, M.D., Daniel G., Chief of Staff, St. Luke's Hospital, Maumee, OH, p. A518

WILLIAMS, Daniel J., Chief Financial Officer, Truman Medical Center–Lakewood, Kansas City, MO, p. A385

WILLIAMS, Darlene, R.N., Administrator, Memorial Medical Center – San Augustine, San Augustine, TX, p. A666

WILLIAMS, David R., Chief Executive Officer, Regional Medical Center–Bayonet Point, Hudson, FL, p. A131

WILLIAMS, R.N., Deborah J., Chief Nursing Officer, Meadowview Regional Medical Center, Maysville, KY, p. A271

WILLIAMS, Don
Director Human Resources, Feather River Hospital, Paradise, CA, p. A80
Director Information Systems, Hutcheson Medical Center, Fort Oglethorpe, GA, p. A162

WILLIAMS, Douglas, Administrator, Cascade Medical Center, Leavenworth, WA, p. A704

WILLIAMS, Ed, Chief Financial Officer, Harris County Psychiatric Center, Houston, TX, p. A645

WILLIAMS Jr, Elton L., FACHE, President, Lake Charles Memorial Hospital, Lake Charles, LA, p. A285

WILLIAMS, Gary
Chief Financial Officer, Gulf Coast Medical Center, Wharton, TX, p. A673
Chief Operating Officer and Chief Nursing Officer, St. Vincent Hospital, Santa Fe, NM, p. A444

WILLIAMS, M.D., Gary, Chief Medical Staff, Sunnyview Rehabilitation Hospital, Schenectady, NY, p. A472

WILLIAMS, George, Director Human Resources, Bolivar Medical Center, Cleveland, MS, p. A368

WILLIAMS, Gerald L., Director, James E. Van Zandt Veterans Affairs Medical Center, Altoona, PA, p. A552

WILLIAMS, Harriett, Director Management Information, Stonewall Jackson Memorial Hospital, Weston, WV, p. A721

WILLIAMS, M.D., Herman, Chief Medical Officer, Baptist Medical Center, San Antonio, TX, p. A663

WILLIAMS, Homer, Chief Civilian Personnel Branch, Reynolds Army Community Hospital, Fort Sill, OK, p. A531

WILLIAMS, Jeff, Director of Human Resources and Business Development, Major Hospital, Shelbyville, IN, p. A225

WILLIAMS, Jim R., Chief Financial Officer, Bolivar Medical Center, Cleveland, MS, p. A368

WILLIAMS, Joan, Administrative Assistant, Lamb Healthcare Center, Littlefield, TX, p. A653

WILLIAMS, Joan H., Vice President Human Resources, Cooper Health System, Camden, NJ, p. A426

WILLIAMS, John
Chief Financial Officer, Upson Regional Medical Center, Thomaston, GA, p. A170
Chief Information Resources Management Service, Veterans Affairs Medical Center, Bay Pines, FL, p. A123

WILLIAMS, John G., President and Chief Executive Officer, St. Luke's Hospital, San Francisco, CA, p. A89

WILLIAMS, Joseph, Director, Veterans Affairs Medical Center, Hampton, VA, p. A689

WILLIAMS, Julie, Chief Financial Officer, Graham County Hospital, Hill City, KS, p. A248

WILLIAMS, M.D., Karen, Chief of Staff, Bayfront Medical Center, Saint Petersburg, FL, p. A145

WILLIAMS, Kim, Vice President Medical Affairs, St. Claire Regional Medical Center, Morehead, KY, p. A272

WILLIAMS, Kurt, Controller and Vice President Financial Services, Jersey Shore Hospital, Jersey Shore, PA, p. A561

WILLIAMS, M.D., Michael, Medical Director, Kosciusko Community Hospital, Warsaw, IN, p. A227

WILLIAMS, Michael L., Interim President, Howard Regional Health System, Kokomo, IN, p. A220

WILLIAMS, Pam
Director Information Management Systems, Taylor Regional Hospital, Campbellsville, KY, p. A262
Human Resources Director, White County Medical Center, Searcy, AR, p. A50

WILLIAMS, Patricia, Chief Financial Officer, Conroe Regional Medical Center, Conroe, TX, p. A630

WILLIAMS, Sr, Perry E., Administrator, Alliance HealthCare System, Holly Springs, MS, p. A370

WILLIAMS Sr, Perry E., Administrator and Chief Executive Officer, Alliance HealthCare System, Holly Springs, MS, p. A370

WILLIAMS, R Martin, Chief Financial Officer, Hospital District Number 1 of Crawford County, Girard, KS, p. A247

WILLIAMS, R. D., Administrator and Chief Executive Officer, Ashe Memorial Hospital, Jefferson, NC, p. A485

WILLIAMS, Ralph D., Chief Financial Officer, BJC Medical Center, Commerce, GA, p. A159

WILLIAMS, Randy, Director Management Information Systems, Maria Parham Medical Center, Henderson, NC, p. A484

WILLIAMS III, Raymond, Interim Chief Executive Officer, Phillips County Hospital, Phillipsburg, KS, p. A255

WILLIAMS, Richard, Chief, Medical Staff, U. S. Air Force Hospital Luke, Glendale, AZ, p. A31

WILLIAMS, Robert B.
Chief Executive Officer, Bert Fish Medical Center, New Smyrna Beach, FL, p. A139
Health Central, Ocoee, FL, p. A140

WILLIAMS, Robert D., Vice President and Administrator, Mercy Special Care Hospital, Nanticoke, PA, p. A566

WILLIAMS, Roby D., Administrator, Hardin County General Hospital, Rosiclare, IL, p. A207

WILLIAMS, M.D., JD, Rodney W., Executive Vice President and Chief Medical Officer, Greater Baltimore Medical Center, Baltimore, MD, p. A302

WILLIAMS, Scott, Administrator, Rivendell Behavioral Health Services, Benton, AR, p. A40

WILLIAMS, Sean, Chief Executive Officer, Jones Regional Medical Center, Anamosa, IA, p. A228

WILLIAMS, Shannon
Chief Information Officer, Northwest Medical Center of Benton County, Bentonville, AR, p. A40
Chief Information Officer, Northwest Medical Center of Washington County, Springdale, AR, p. A50

WILLIAMS, Sharon
Vice President Information and Financial Services, Avera Marshall Regional Medical Center, Marshall, MN, p. A356
Assistant Administrator Information and Financial Services, Avera Marshall Regional Medical Center, Marshall, MN, p. A356
Human Resources Director, Southwest Memorial Hospital, Cortez, CO, p. A102

WILLIAMS, Sheila, Chief Financial Officer, H.S.C. Medical Center, Malvern, AR, p. A47

WILLIAMS, Stephen A., President, Norton Healthcare, Louisville, KY, p. B80

WILLIAMS, Stuart W., President and Chief Executive Officer, Westfield Memorial Hospital, Westfield, NY, p. A476

WILLIAMS, Thomas
Clinical Administrator, Banner Behavioral Health Hospital, Scottsdale, AZ, p. A36
Chief Human Resources Management Service, Veterans Affairs Medical Center, Spokane, WA, p. A709

WILLIAMS, Timothy B., Director, Veterans Affairs Puget Sound Health Care System, Seattle, WA, p. A708

WILLIAMS, Tobi, Manager Human Resources, HEALTHSOUTH Tustin Rehabilitation Hospital, Tustin, CA, p. A97

WILLIAMS, Tom, Director Human Resources, Lake Regional Health System, Osage Beach, MO, p. A388

WILLIAMS, M.D., Tom, Chief of Staff, Sullivan County Memorial Hospital, Milan, MO, p. A387

WILLIAMS, Vernell, Vice President Operations, Sinai-Grace Hospital, Detroit, MI, p. A332

WILLIAMS, Wade, Information Systems Director, Laurens County Healthcare System, Clinton, SC, p. A585

WILLIAMS, CPA, Warren, Fiscal Services Director, Mississippi State Hospital, Whitfield, MS, p. A377

WILLIAMS, Jr, M.D., Wendell H., Medical Director, Specialty Hospital Jacksonville, Jacksonville, FL, p. A132

WILLIAMS CARLSON, Laishy
Chief Information Officer, Mary Immaculate Hospital, Newport News, VA, p. A692
Chief Information Officer, Maryview Medical Center, Portsmouth, VA, p. A694

WILLIAMS-SCRUTON, Kathleen, Director of Information Systems, Wing Memorial Hospital and Medical Centers, Palmer, MA, p. A322

WILLIAMSON, M.D., Alan, Chief Medical Officer, Eisenhower Memorial Hospital and Betty Ford Center at Eisenhower, Rancho Mirage, CA, p. A83

WILLIAMSON, David, Director Human Resources, Franklin Foundation Hospital, Franklin, LA, p. A281

WILLIAMSON, Don, Chief Financial Officer, Valley County Hospital, Ord, NE, p. A411

WILLIAMSON, Doug, Director of Support Services, Avera Gregory Healthcare Center, Gregory, SD, p. A596

WILLIAMSON, Robert, Chief Medical Staff, Malcolm Grow Medical Center, Andrews AFB, MD, p. A302

WILLIAMSON, Stacey, Director of Human Resources, St. Luke's Wood River Medical Center, Ketchum, ID, p. A179

WILLIAMSON, Tina, Director Human Resources, Beartooth Hospital and Health Center, Red Lodge, MT, p. A401

WILLIE, Dave, Chief Financial Officer and Vice President Fiscal Services, Gaston Memorial Hospital, Gastonia, NC, p. A483

WILLIE, Debra, Director Medical Records, Lakeview Regional Medical Center, Covington, LA, p. A279

WILLINGHAM, John, Chief Executive Officer, Carolina Center for Behavioral Health, Greer, SC, p. A589

WILLIS, Cathy, Director Human Resources, Memorial Hospital and Manor, Bainbridge, GA, p. A156

WILLIS, Gary, Director Human Resources, Shodair Children's Hospital, Helena, MT, p. A399

WILLIS, M.D., Walt, Medical Director, Neshoba County General Hospital, Philadelphia, MS, p. A374

WILLIS, William L., Chief Executive Officer, Women and Children's Hospital, Lake Charles, LA, p. A285

WILLMON, Gary R., Administrator, Grafton City Hospital, Grafton, WV, p. A715

WILLOUGHBY, Sandra, Chief Human Resources, Veterans Affairs Medical Center, Cheyenne, WY, p. A739

WILLS, Larry, Senior Assistant Administrator and Chief Operating Officer, OSF St. Joseph Medical Center, Bloomington, IL, p. A185

WILLS, Laura S., Chief Executive Officer, Kindred Hospital – Albuquerque, Albuquerque, NM, p. A440

WILLS, Lynda, Interim Administrator, Hemet Valley Medical Center, Hemet, CA, p. A64

WILMOT, M.D., Clare, President Medical Staff, Littleton Regional Hospital, Littleton, NH, p. A422

WILSHIRE, Brian, Supervisor Information Systems, Veterans Affairs Medical Center, Erie, PA, p. A558

WILSON, Allen, Director Human Resources, St. Joseph's Hospital of Buckhannon, Buckhannon, WV, p. A714

WILSON, Charlene, Vice President Human Resources, Casa Grande Regional Medical Center, Casa Grande, AZ, p. A30

WILSON, Cheryl, Chief Operating Officer, Rapides Regional Medical Center, Alexandria, LA, p. A276

WILSON, Corrine, Chief Financial Officer, Huhukam Memorial Hospital, Sacaton, AZ, p. A35

WILSON, Craig, Assistant Administrator Patient Care Services, Kittitas Valley Community Hospital, Ellensburg, WA, p. A702

WILSON, M.D., D Mark, Chief of Staff, Conway Medical Center, Conway, SC, p. A587

WILSON, David C., Chief Executive Officer, Saint Francis Hospital-Bartlett, Bartlett, TN, p. A602

WILSON, Deborah, Senior Vice President Human Resources and Organizational Development, Glendale Memorial Hospital and Health Center, Glendale, CA, p. A62

WILSON, Dennis, Customer Service Representative, Bay Regional Medical Center, Bay City, MI, p. A328

WILSON, Diane, Chief Financial Officer, Baptist Memorial Hospital-Booneville, Booneville, MS, p. A367

WILSON, Douglas, Chief Executive Officer, Pekin Hospital, Pekin, IL, p. A204

WILSON, Jr, Floyd, Chief Human Resources Officer, Spectrum Health-Kent Community Campus, Grand Rapids, MI, p. A335

WILSON, Fred
Chief Financial Officer, Bourbon Community Hospital, Paris, KY, p. A273
Director Management Information Services, Northeast Alabama Regional Medical Center, Anniston, AL, p. A13

WILSON, Hamlin J.
Senior Vice President Human Resources, Wellmont Bristol Regional Medical Center, Bristol, TN, p. A602
Senior Vice President Human Resources, Wellmont Holston Valley Medical Center, Kingsport, TN, p. A609

WILSON, Harold E., Chief Executive Officer, Eastern State Hospital, Medical Lake, WA, p. A704

WILSON, Helen, Chief Operating Officer, Memorial Hospital, Manchester, KY, p. A271

WILSON, Hugh D., Chief Executive Officer, Doctors Hospital of Columbus, Columbus, GA, p. A158

WILSON, Jeff
Data Processing Manager, Illinois Valley Community Hospital, Peru, IL, p. A205
Chief of Staff, T. J. Samson Community Hospital, Glasgow, KY, p. A265

WILSON, Jim, President and Chief Executive Officer, Susan B. Allen Memorial Hospital, El Dorado, KS, p. A246

WILSON, John P., Chief Financial Officer, Heartland Regional Medical Center, Saint Joseph, MO, p. A390

WILSON, Judi, Director Human Resources, Medical Center of South Arkansas, El Dorado, AR, p. A42

WILSON, Kim, Director Human Resources, University of Kentucky Hospital, Lexington, KY, p. A268

WILSON, Kirk G., President and Chief Operating Officer, Our Lady of the Lake Regional Medical Center, Baton Rouge, LA, p. A277

WILSON, L. Steven, Administrator, Dixie Regional Medical Center, Saint George, UT, p. A679

WILSON, Lois, Controller, Roger Mills Memorial Hospital, Cheyenne, OK, p. A528

WILSON, Lynn, Chief Financial Officer, Ridgeview Institute, Smyrna, GA, p. A169

WILSON, Mark D., President and Chief Executive Officer, Regina Medical Center, Hastings, MN, p. A354

WILSON, Pat, Diector Human Resources, Kalispell Regional Medical Center, Kalispell, MT, p. A400

WILSON, Paul J., Chief Executive Officer, Innovis Health, Fargo, ND, p. A497

WILSON, Preshie, Vice President Finance, Baylor Medical Center at Waxahachie, Waxahachie, TX, p. A672

WILSON, D.O., Robert, Director Medical Services, Eagleville Hospital, Eagleville, PA, p. A557

WILSON, Robert E.
Vice President and Chief Information Officer, Crozer-Chester Medical Center, Upland, PA, p. A577
Vice President and Chief Information Officer, Delaware County Memorial Hospital, Drexel Hill, PA, p. A557

WILSON, M.D., Roger D., Medical Director, St. John Sapulpa, Sapulpa, OK, p. A538

WILSON, CPA, Stephan, Chief Financial Officer, Sumner Regional Medical Center, Wellington, KS, p. A259

WILSON, Steve, Chief Financial Officer, Takoma Adventist Hospital, Greeneville, TN, p. A607

WILSON, Susan, Controller, HEALTHSOUTH Tustin Rehabilitation Hospital, Tustin, CA, p. A97

WILSON, Terrance E., President and Chief Executive Officer, Greater Lafayette Health Services, Lafayette, IN, p. A220

WILSON, Timothy, Vice President for Finance and Chief Financial Officer, Cardinal Hill Rehabilitation Hospital, Lexington, KY, p. A267

WILSON, Vicki, Chief Human Resources Officer, Dixie Regional Medical Center, Saint George, UT, p. A679

WILSON, William G., President and Chief Executive Officer, Jackson County Memorial Hospital, Altus, OK, p. A527

WILT, Carroll, Vice President and Chief Information Officer, Tacoma General Hospital, Tacoma, WA, p. A710

WILTERS, M.D., John, Chief Medical Officer, Tennessee Christian Medical Center, Madison, TN, p. A611

WILTGEN, Sarah, Chief Executive Officer, Brynn Marr Behavioral Healthcare System, Jacksonville, NC, p. A485

WIND, D.O., Brian E., Chief of Staff, Doctors Hospital of Stark County, Massillon, OH, p. A518

WINDER, Todd, Administrator and Chief Executive Officer, Oneida County Hospital, Malad City, ID, p. A180

WINDHAM, Hailey, Chief Information Management, Brooke Army Medical Center, Fort Sam Houston, TX, p. A638

WINDHAM, Joel, Vice President Human Resources, St. Vincent's Hospital, Birmingham, AL, p. A15

WINEGARNER, Rodney, Chief Financial Officer, Mercy Hospital, Bakersfield, CA, p. A54

WINFIELD, Wynona C., Director, South Mississippi State Hospital, Purvis, MS, p. A375

WINFREE, M.D., Kersey, Chief Medical Officer, St. Anthony Hospital, Oklahoma City, OK, p. A536

WING, Susan M., Chief Operating Officer, Falmouth Hospital, Falmouth, MA, p. A317

WING, Yakesun, Business Strategy and Finance Leader, Kaiser Foundation Hospital, Walnut Creek, CA, p. A98

WINGATE–JONES, Phyllis, Senior Vice President Operations, Carolinas Medical Center, Charlotte, NC, p. A479

WINGER, Mark, Director People Resoruces and Organizational Planning, Platte County Memorial Hospital, Wheatland, WY, p. A742

WINGER, Ronald C., Chief Executive Officer, Porter–Valparaiso Hospital Campus, Valparaiso, IN, p. A226

WINGET, Mary, Human Resource Director, Minden Medical Center, Minden, LA, p. A287

WINGFIELD, Gena, Chief Financial Officer, Arkansas Children's Hospital, Little Rock, AR, p. A46

WINGO, Margaret, Chief Financial Officer, Faith Community Hospital, Jacksboro, TX, p. A650

WINGO, Paul W., Troop Commander, Tripler Army Medical Center, Honolulu, HI, p. A174

WINIARSKI, Michael H., Vice President Finance, East Liverpool City Hospital, East Liverpool, OH, p. A513

WINKELS, Patty, Human Resources and Payroll Supervisor, Sioux Valley Luverne Medical Center, Luverne, MN, p. A356

WINKLER, Gordon W., Administrator, Ringgold County Hospital, Mount Ayr, IA, p. A238

WINKLER, Robert E., Chief Executive Officer, Doctors Memorial Hospital, Bonifay, FL, p. A124

WINKLER, Walter, Chief Financial Officer, Keokuk Area Hospital, Keokuk, IA, p. A236

WINN, Brian, Controller, Howard A. Rusk Rehabilitation Center, Columbia, MO, p. A381

WINN, George, President and Chief Executive Officer, St. Elizabeth Health Services, Baker City, OR, p. A542

WINN, Grant M.
Interim Chief Executive Officer, North Big Horn Hospital District, Lovell, WY, p. A741
Interim Chief Executive Officer, North Big Horn Hospital District, Lovell, WY, p. A741

WINN, Karla, Chief Information Officer, Greater Community Hospital, Creston, IA, p. A231

WINN, Michael R., Director, Veterans Affairs Medical Center, Fayetteville, AR, p. A43

WINN, Roger P.
President, UPMC Bedford Memorial, Everett, PA, p. A559
President, UPMC Lee Regional, Johnstown, PA, p. A562

WINNENBERG, William
Vice President Information Services, Grant Medical Center, Columbus, OH, p. A510
Vice President Information Services, Riverside Methodist Hospital, Columbus, OH, p. A511

WINSCHEL, Don, Director Information Services, Baptist St. Anthony Health System, Amarillo, TX, p. A621

WINSELL, Susan, Director Human Resources, French Hospital Medical Center, San Luis Obispo, CA, p. A91

WINSHIP, Daniel, Chief, Cook County Bureau of Health Services, Chicago, IL, p. B33

WINSLETT, Charlene, Director of Human Resources, Warm Springs Medical Center, Warm Springs, GA, p. A171

WINSTEAD, Dwain, Director Financial Management, Veterans Affairs Medical Center, Tuscaloosa, AL, p. A24

WINSTON, Nat T., Medical Director, Pathways of Tennessee, Jackson, TN, p. A608

WINTER, Bill, Director Information Technology, Sacred Heart Hospital of Pensacola, Pensacola, FL, p. A143

WINTER, William E., Administrative Director, Silverton Hospital, Silverton, OR, p. A549

WINTERBOTTOM, Rocky, Chief Information Officer, John and Mary Kirby Hospital, Monticello, IL, p. A201

WINTERS, Gene, Chief Financial Officer, Regency Hospital of Akron, Barberton, OH, p. A503

WINTHROP, Michael K., President, Bellevue Hospital, Bellevue, OH, p. A504

WIRTH, Pamela R., Vice President and Chief Information Officer, Susquehanna Health System, Williamsport, PA, p. A580

WIRTZ, Carman, Vice President Human Resources, Memorial Hospital of Union County, Marysville, OH, p. A517

WISBY, Diane, Administrator, Goleta Valley Cottage Hospital, Santa Barbara, CA, p. A92

WISCOMBE, Shawn D., Administrator, Grover C. Dils Medical Center, Caliente, NV, p. A415

WISDOM, Karen J., Chief Operating Officer and Senior Vice President, Hamilton Medical Center, Dalton, GA, p. A160

WISE, Dorinda, Information Technology Manager, Clarendon Memorial Hospital, Manning, SC, p. A590

WISE, Franklin E., Administrator, Fulton County Hospital, Salem, AR, p. A50

WISE, M.D., Gregory
Vice President Medical Affiars, Charles F. Kettering Memorial Hospital, Kettering, OH, p. A515
Vice President Medical Affiars, Sycamore Hospital, Miamisburg, OH, p. A518

WISE, Jerry R., Administrator and Vice President, Hart County Hospital, Hartwell, GA, p. A163

WISE, Robert P., President and Chief Executive Officer, Hunterdon Medical Center, Flemington, NJ, p. A428

WISEMAN, Patrick, Director Information Systems, Olympia Medical Center, Los Angeles, CA, p. A72

WISEMAN, Roger D., Senior Vice President and Chief Financial Officer, North Shore Medical Center, Salem, MA, p. A323

WISNER, Donna, Chief Financial Officer, Dr. John Warner Hospital, Clinton, IL, p. A191

WISNIEWSKI, John, Chief Financial Officer, Metropolitan Methodist Hospital, San Antonio, TX, p. A664

WISNIEWSKI, Richard, Senior Vice President Finance and Chief Financial Officer, Mount Nittany Medical Center, State College, PA, p. A576

WISSLER, James, President and Chief Executive Officer, Nicholas H. Noyes Memorial Hospital, Dansville, NY, p. A451

WITHAM, Gary, Vice President Finance, Hutchinson Hospital Corporation, Hutchinson, KS, p. A249

WITHERSPOON, Lynn, Vice President and Chief Information Officer, Ochsner Clinic Foundation, New Orleans, LA, p. A289

WITHIAM, Cathy, Vice President Human Resources, Mercy Health Center, Oklahoma City, OK, p. A535

WITKOWICZ, Victor J., Senior Vice President and Chief Financial Officer, Madonna Rehabilitation Hospital, Lincoln, NE, p. A409

WITKOWSKI, Richard J., Director Management Information Systems, Mount St. Mary's Hospital and Health Center, Lewiston, NY, p. A455

WITT, II, M.D., David R., Chief of Staff, Longview Regional Medical Center, Longview, TX, p. A654

WITT, Laura, Administrator Human Resources, Banner Thunderbird Medical Center, Glendale, AZ, p. A31

WITT, Stephen, Chief Executive Officer, College Hospital, Cerritos, CA, p. A56

WITT, Thomas J., M.D., President and Chief Executive Officer, Lake City Medical Center–Mayo, Lake City, MN, p. A355

WITTES, M.D., Robert E., Physician in Chief, Memorial Sloan–Kettering Cancer Center, New York, NY, p. A462

WITTGAN, Larry F., Executive Director, Cornerstone Hospital of Houston, Houston, TX, p. A644

WITTHAUS, Patty, Director Information Services, Valley Regional Hospital, Claremont, NH, p. A420

WITTMAN, Thomas, Director Information Systems, CARITAS Medical Center, Louisville, KY, p. A269

WITTON, David, Manager, St. John's Medical Center and Living Center, Jackson, WY, p. A740

WITZ, Steve, President, St. Patrick Hospital, Missoula, MT, p. A401

WITZLSTEINER, Gail, Marketing Director, Sonora Regional Medical Center, Sonora, CA, p. A94

WIVODA, Joe, Chief Information Officer, Fairview University Medical Center–Mesabi, Hibbing, MN, p. A355

WOERMAN, Barry M., Administrator, Tuolumne General Hospital, Sonora, CA, p. A94

WOERNER, Steve
Chief Executive Officer, Corpus Christi Medical Center, Corpus Christi, TX, p. A630
Chief Executive Officer, Corpus Christi Medical Center Bay Area, Corpus Christi, TX, p. A630

WOERZ, Paul, Vice President Human Resources, Riverside Community Hospital, Riverside, CA, p. A84

WOHLFORD, Steve, Chief Operating Officer, Fayette Memorial Hospital, Connersville, IN, p. A213

WOJCIK, M.D., Robert, Chief of Staff and Medical Staff President, Illinois Valley Community Hospital, Peru, IL, p. A205

WOJTALEWICZ, Jeanette, Vice President Finance, Saint Elizabeth Regional Medical Center, Lincoln, NE, p. A409

WOJTOWICZ, Linda, Vice President Patient Care Services and Chief Operating Officer, Sierra Vista Regional Health Center, Sierra Vista, AZ, p. A37

WOLAK, Robert, Chief Information Resource Management Service, G.V. Montgomery Veterans Affairs Medical Center, Jackson, MS, p. A370

WOLENSKI, Marianne, Director Information Systems, Bayonne Medical Center, Bayonne, NJ, p. A425

WOLF, M.D., Alan, Chief of Staff, Ketchikan General Hospital, Ketchikan, AK, p. A27

WOLF, Edward H., President and Chief Executive Officer, Lakeview Medical Center, Rice Lake, WI, p. A734

WOLF, Jack, Vice President Management Information Systems, Montefiore Medical Center, New York, NY, p. A462

WOLF, James N., Chief Executive Officer, District One Hospital, Faribault, MN, p. A353

WOLF, Laura J., President, Franciscan Sisters of Christian Charity HealthCare Ministry, Inc, Manitowoc, WI, p. B46

WOLF, Peter, Executive Director, Coney Island Hospital, New York, NY, p. A459

WOLF, R. Chris, Chief Executive Officer, Payson Regional Medical Center, Payson, AZ, p. A33

WOLF, Randall, Vice President Finance, Perry County Memorial Hospital, Perryville, MO, p. A389

WOLF–ROSENBLUM, M.D., Stephanie, Vice President Medical Affairs, Southern New Hampshire Medical Center, Nashua, NH, p. A422

WOLFE, Barry, Director Human Resources, Baptist Memorial Hospital–North Mississippi, Oxford, MS, p. A374

WOLFE, M.D., Brad, President, Baptist Memorial Hospital–Desoto, Southaven, MS, p. A375

WOLFE, John, Chief Financial Officer, Saint Elizabeth's Medical Center, Wabasha, MN, p. A364

WOLFE, M.D., Joseph, President Medical Staff, Baptist Memorial Hospital–Booneville, Booneville, MS, p. A367

WOLFE, Linda, Finance Manager, Morton Plant North Bay Hospital, New Port Richey, FL, p. A139

WOLFE, M.D., Paul D., Chief of Staff, Marion General Hospital, Marion, IN, p. A221

WOLFE, Philip R., President and Chief Executive Officer, Enloe Medical Center, Chico, CA, p. A56

WOLFE, CPA, Scott R., Senior Vice President and Chief Operating Officer, Reading Hospital and Medical Center, West Reading, PA, p. A579

WOLFE, Stephen A., President and Chief Executive Officer, Indiana Regional Medical Center, Indiana, PA, p. A561

WOLFE, M.D., Timothy, President Medical Staff, New London Hospital, New London, NH, p. A423

WOLFERSTEIG, Jean L., Acting Executive Director, Hudson River Psychiatric Center, Poughkeepsie, NY, p. A470

WOLFF, Cathy, Vice President of Financial Services and Chief Financial Officer, Yuma District Hospital, Yuma, CO, p. A111

WOLFF, David, Director Information Technology, Miami Jewish Home and Hospital for Aged, Miami, FL, p. A137

WOLFF, Ronald V., Interim Chief Executive Officer, Memorial Community Hospital, Edgerton, WI, p. A725

WOLFF, Susan, Chief Information Officer, Naples Community Hospital, Naples, FL, p. A139

WOLFMAN, Barry A., Senior Vice President and Area Manager, Kaiser Foundation Hospital, Los Angeles, CA, p. A70

WOLFORD, Dennis A., FACHE, Chief Executive Officer, Macon County General Hospital, Lafayette, TN, p. A610

WOLFRAM, Karen, Director of Human Resources, St. Marys Hospital Medical Center, Madison, WI, p. A728

WOLFRAM, Patricia L., R.N., Chief Executive Officer, La Palma Intercommunity Hospital, La Palma, CA, p. A66

WOLFSON, M.D., Donn, Vice President Medical Affairs, Parma Community General Hospital, Parma, OH, p. A520

WOLIN, Harry, Administrator and Chief Executive Officer, Mason District Hospital, Havana, IL, p. A196

WOLKOV, M.D., Jay, Chief of Staff, Gunnison Valley Hospital, Gunnison, CO, p. A106

WOLLEBEN, Robert G., Chief Operating Officer, Orange Regional Medical Center, Middletown, NY, p. A457

WOLLEN, Nancy L., CHE, Executive Director and Chief Administrative Officer, Community Medical Center, Toms River, NJ, p. A437

WOLOSZYN, Daniel B., Administrator, Van Matre HEALTHSOUTH Rehabilitation Hospital, Rockford, IL, p. A207

WOLOWICKI, Donna Marie
Executive Vice President and Chief Executive Officer, Holy Family Medical Center, Des Plaines, IL, p. A192
Executive Vice President and Chief Executive Officer, Resurrection Medical Center, Chicago, IL, p. A189

WOLTER, Nicholas J., M.D., President and Chief Executive Officer, Deaconess Billings Clinic, Billings, MT, p. A396

WOLTERMAN, Daniel J., President and Chief Executive Officer, Memorial Hermann Healthcare System, Houston, TX, p. B74

WOLTHWZEN, Dianne, Human Resources Director, Northwest Iowa Health Center, Sheldon, IA, p. A241

WOMBLE, Matthew, Chief Executive Officer, Select Specialty Hospital of Durham, Durham, NC, p. A481

WONG, Caroline, Chief Financial Officer, Toppenish Community Hospital, Toppenish, WA, p. A711

WONG, M.D., K S., Chief Medical Staff, Culberson Hospital District, Van Horn, TX, p. A671

WONG, Leslie H., Chief Executive Officer, Antelope Valley Hospital, Lancaster, CA, p. A67

WONG, Lily, Director Psychiatry, Trinity Springs Pavilion, Fort Worth, TX, p. A640

WOO, M.D., Joseph, Chief of Staff, Chinese Hospital, San Francisco, CA, p. A88

WOOD, Aaron, Chief Executive Officer, Haxtun Hospital District, Haxtun, CO, p. A106

WOOD, Alice L., Director, Veterans Affairs Medical Center, Battle Creek, MI, p. A328

WOOD, David, Director, Veterans Affairs Medical Center, Butler, PA, p. A554

WOOD, Gary
Vice President of Facilities and Chief Information Officer, Lourdes Hospital, Paducah, KY, p. A273
Vice President of Facilities and Chief Information Officer, Lourdes Hospital, Paducah, KY, p. A273

WOOD, Gregory C., Chief Executive Officer, Scotland Memorial Hospital, Laurinburg, NC, p. A486

WOOD, Jack L., Director, Catawba Hospital, Catawba, VA, p. A686

WOOD, James B., President and Chief Executive Officer, Ocala Regional Medical Center, Ocala, FL, p. A140

WOOD, Jeanne, Manager Human Resources, Veterans Affairs Medical Center, Sheridan, WY, p. A742

WOOD, Joe, Vice President and Chief Information Officer, The Medical Center, Columbus, GA, p. A159

WOOD, Kenneth W., President and Chief Executive Officer, Grace Hospital, Morganton, NC, p. A488

WOOD, Latanya, Chief Executive Officer, Ancora Psychiatric Hospital, Ancora, NJ, p. A425

WOOD, M L., Vice President Human Resources, Deaconess Hospital, Oklahoma City, OK, p. A535

WOOD, M.D., Michael K., Chief of Staff, Mills–Peninsula Health Services, Burlingame, CA, p. A55

WOOD, Robin, Director Information Systems, Platte County Memorial Hospital, Wheatland, WY, p. A742

WOODALL, Jay, Chief Executive Officer, Texas Orthopedic Hospital, Houston, TX, p. A648

WOODALL, Lois, Director Human Resources, Touro Infirmary, New Orleans, LA, p. A290

WOODARD, Betty, Health Information Management Manager, D. M. Cogdell Memorial Hospital, Snyder, TX, p. A667

WOODBECK, Terry L., Administrator, Tulsa Spine Hospital, Tulsa, OK, p. A540

WOODCOCK, David, Director Information Systems, Yavapai Regional Medical Center, Prescott, AZ, p. A35

WOODFORD, Steve, Chief Financial Officer, East Cooper Regional Medical Center, Mount Pleasant, SC, p. A590

WOODIN, Joseph L., President and Chief Executive Officer, Gifford Medical Center, Randolph, VT, p. A683

WOODLAND, Dave, President, Brim Healthcare, Inc., Brentwood, TN, p. B18

WOODLAND, M.D., John, Medical Director, Vail Valley Medical Center, Vail, CO, p. A110

WOODLIFF, Brian K., Chief Executive Officer, Tahlequah City Hospital, Tahlequah, OK, p. A539

WOODRELL, Frederick, CHE, Chief Executive Officer, University Hospitals and Clinics, University of Mississippi Medical Center, Jackson, MS, p. A371

WOODRICH, John, Chief Executive Officer, Wright Memorial Hospital, Trenton, MO, p. A394

WOODS, Bob, Chief Information Officer, ValleyCare Medical Center, Pleasanton, CA, p. A82

WOODS, Daniel J., Executive Vice President and Administrator, St. Anthony's Memorial Hospital, Effingham, IL, p. A193

WOODS, Eugene A.
President and Chief Executive Officer, Saint Joseph Hospital, Lexington, KY, p. A267
President and Chief Executive Officer, Saint Joseph Hospital East, Lexington, KY, p. A268

WOODS, Josh, Director Information Systems, Camden–Clark Memorial Hospital, Parkersburg, WV, p. A718

WOODS, Kim, R.N., President and Chief Executive Officer, Kimball Health Services, Kimball, NE, p. A408

WOODS, Linda, Vice President Information Services, Bayshore Community Hospital, Holmdel, NJ, p. A429

WOODS, MSN, R.N, Theresa, Chief Operating Officer, West Calcasieu Cameron Hospital, Sulphur, LA, p. A293

WOODWARD, James L., President and Chief Administrative Officer, Winchester Medical Center, Winchester, VA, p. A698

WOODY, Fred, Chief Executive Officer, Carlsbad Medical Center, Carlsbad, NM, p. A441

WOOL, Julius
Chief Financial Officer, Elmhurst Hospital Center, New York, NY, p. A459
Chief Financial Officer, Queens Hospital Center, New York, NY, p. A464

WOOLF, Louis J., Senior Vice President and Chief Executive Officer, North Shore Medical Center, Salem, MA, p. A323

WOOLLEY, Jacqueline, Vice President Human Resources, St. Joseph Hospital, Nashua, NH, p. A423

WORDELMAN, Scott, President and Chief Executive Officer, Fairview Red Wing Medical Center, Red Wing, MN, p. A360

WORDEN, Jerry L., Vice President and Chief Financial Officer, St. Luke's Hospital, Cedar Rapids, IA, p. A229

WORKMAN, Jennifer, Director Human Resources, Jane Phillips Medical Center, Bartlesville, OK, p. A528

WORKMAN, John R., Chief Executive Officer, Athens Regional Medical Center, Athens, TN, p. A602

WORLEY, Steve, President and Chief Executive Officer, Children's Hospital, New Orleans, LA, p. A288

WORRELL, Lou, Director Information Systems, Raleigh General Hospital, Beckley, WV, p. A713

WORRICK, Gerald M., President and Chief Executive Officer, Door County Memorial Hospital, Sturgeon Bay, WI, p. A736

WORSHAM, Sharon, Chief Executive Officer, Shadow Mountain Behavioral Health System, Tulsa, OK, p. A540

WORSOWICZ, M.D., Gregory, Medical Director, Howard A. Rusk Rehabilitation Center, Columbia, MO, p. A381

WORSTELL, Carl, Chief Information Officer, Veterans Affairs Salt Lake City Health Care System, Salt Lake City, UT, p. A680

WORTHAM, Turner, Chief Financial Officer, Grand Strand Regional Medical Center, Myrtle Beach, SC, p. A590

WORTHINGTON, M.D., Dennis, Chief of Staff, Lincoln County Medical Center, Ruidoso, NM, p. A444

WORTMAN, Rand J., President and Chief Executive Officer, Kadlec Medical Center, Richland, WA, p. A707

WOZNIAK, Andrea L., R.N., Chief Executive Officer, East Cooper Regional Medical Center, Mount Pleasant, SC, p. A590

WOZNIAK, Gregory T., President and Chief Executive Officer, St. Mary Medical Center, Langhorne, PA, p. A562

WOZNIAK, R.N., Susan C., Chief Operating Officer, OSF Saint Francis Medical Center, Peoria, IL, p. A205

WRAALSTAD, Kimber, President and Chief Executive Officer, Presentation Medical Center, Rolla, ND, p. A500

WRAY, Christine R., President and Chief Executive Officer, St. Mary's Hospital, Leonardtown, MD, p. A309

WRAY, Dean, Vice President Finance, Southern Ohio Medical Center, Portsmouth, OH, p. A521

WREN, Timothy, Chief Financial Officer, Winneshiek Medical Center, Decorah, IA, p. A232

WRIGHT, Adam, Interim Administrator, Long Term Hospital of Anniston, Anniston, AL, p. A13

WRIGHT, Albert
Chief Executive Officer, Select Specialty Hospital–Columbus, Columbus, OH, p. A511
Chief Executive Officer, Select Specialty Hospital–Columbus, Columbus, OH, p. A511

WRIGHT, Betsy T., President and Chief Executive Officer, Woman's Christian Association Hospital, Jamestown, NY, p. A454

WRIGHT, Charles T., Chief Executive, Southern Oregon Service Area, Providence Medford Medical Center, Medford, OR, p. A546

WRIGHT, Charlie
Assistant Administrator Human Resources, Stone County Medical Center, Mountain View, AR, p. A48
Assistant Administrator Human Resources, White River Medical Center, Batesville, AR, p. A40

WRIGHT, Connie, Director Human Resources, Richardson RegionalMedical Center, Richardson, TX, p. A662

WRIGHT, M.D., Creighton, Chief of Staff, Veterans Affairs Medical Center, Cincinnati, OH, p. A508

WRIGHT, Dan, Vice President Human Resources, Children's Mercy Hospital, Kansas City, MO, p. A384

WRIGHT, Dennis
Vice President Human Resources, Lenawee Health Alliance – Bixby Campus, Adrian, MI, p. A327
Vice President Human Resources, Lenawee Health Alliance–Herrick Campus, Tecumseh, MI, p. A346

WRIGHT, Fred W., Chief Financial Officer, Johnston Memorial Hospital, Abingdon, VA, p. A685

WRIGHT, Gary R., Chief Financial Officer, Jupiter Medical Center, Jupiter, FL, p. A133

WRIGHT, Gene B., Interim Chief Executive Officer, Upson Regional Medical Center, Thomaston, GA, p. A170

WRIGHT, James, Chief Financial Officer, Cypress Fairbanks Medical Center, Houston, TX, p. A644

WRIGHT, M.D., James, Vice President Medical Affairs, Loris Community Hospital, Loris, SC, p. A590

WRIGHT, Jeffrey, Chief Financial Officer, Kaiser Permanente Medical Center, Honolulu, HI, p. A173

WRIGHT, Jeffrey T., Chief Financial Officer, Geisinger Wyoming Valley Medical Center, Wilkes–Barre, PA, p. A579

WRIGHT, Jerry, Chief Financial Officer, Gordon Memorial Hospital, Gordon, NE, p. A407

WRIGHT, Joseph, Chief Executive Officer, Southwestern General Hospital, El Paso, TX, p. A638

WRIGHT, Kemp, Administrator, HEALTHSOUTH Rehabilitation Hospital of Alexandria, Alexandria, LA, p. A276

WRIGHT, Kim, Executive Director Human Resources, Anaheim Memorial Medical Center, Anaheim, CA, p. A52

WRIGHT, Krista, Director of Human Resources, St. Vincent Frankfort Hospital, Frankfort, IN, p. A216

WRIGHT, Linda, Director Information, Ottawa County Health Center, Minneapolis, KS, p. A253

WRIGHT, Marcel, Director, Potomac Ridge Behavioral Health System, Rockville, MD, p. A310

WRIGHT, Margaret, President, Palos Community Hospital, Palos Heights, IL, p. A204

WRIGHT, Mark J., Vice President and Chief Financial Officer, Aultman Hospital, Canton, OH, p. A505

WRIGHT, Patricia, Administrator, Meadow Wood Behavioral Health System, New Castle, DE, p. A119

WRIGHT, Randall P., Chief Operating Officer, Texas Children's Hospital, Houston, TX, p. A647

WRIGHT, Robert N., President and Chief Executive Officer, Bay Regional Medical Center, Bay City, MI, p. A328

WRIGHT, M.D., Robert R., Chief of Staff, Sutter Medical Center of Santa Rosa, Santa Rosa, CA, p. A93

WRIGHT, Roy, FACHE, President and Chief Executive Officer, Cape Canaveral Hospital/Health First, Cocoa Beach, FL, p. A126

WRIGHT, Skip, Vice President and Administrator, Dekalb Medical Center at Decatur, Decatur, GA, p. A160

WRIGHT, Stephanie, Director Human Resources Management, Veterans Affairs San Diego Healthcare System, San Diego, CA, p. A88

WRIGHT, M.D., Stephen C., Chief Medical Officer, Faulkner Hospital, Boston, MA, p. A313

WRIGHT, Stephen F., President and Chief Executive Officer, Christus St. Frances Cabrini Hospital, Alexandria, LA, p. A276

WRIGHT, Susan, Chief Operating Officer, Hamilton Hospital, Webster City, IA, p. A243

WRIGHT, M.D., Terry, President Medical Staff, Our Lady of the Way Hospital, Martin, KY, p. A271

WRIGHT, Tony, Chief Financial Officer, McCune–Brooks Hospital, Carthage, MO, p. A380

WRINKLE, Sharyn, Director Human Resources, University of Texas Health Center at Tyler, Tyler, TX, p. A671

WU, Jonathan, M.D., President and Chairman, AHMC, Inc, Alhambra, CA, p. B6

WUELLNER, James F., Vice President and Chief Financial Officer, Lake Forest Hospital, Lake Forest, IL, p. A199

WUERSTLE, Gregory, Vice President Finance, Grand View Hospital, Sellersville, PA, p. A575

WUESTE, David, Director Information Services, University of Southern California–Norris Comprehensive Cancer Center and Hospital, Los Angeles, CA, p. A73

WURGLER, Brad D., Chief Financial Officer, Perham Memorial Hospital and Home, Perham, MN, p. A359

WURTH, Marie, Vice President Human Resources and Public Relations Officer, Sierra Vista Regional Health Center, Sierra Vista, AZ, p. A37

WYANT, Sandy, Director Human Resources, St. Mary's Medical Center, West Palm Beach, FL, p. A150

WYATT, Basil, Chief Financial Officer, Continuous Care Center of Tulsa, Tulsa, OK, p. A539

WYATT, Jana, Chief Financial Officer, Mizell Memorial Hospital, Opp, AL, p. A23

WYATT, M.D., John, Medical Director, HEALTHSOUTH Rehabilitation Hospital of Erie, Erie, PA, p. A558

WYATT, Leslie G.
President and Chief Executive Officer, Children's Hospital, Richmond, VA, p. A695
President and Chief Executive Officer, Children's Hospital, Richmond, VA, p. A695

WYATT, Vincent N., Chief Financial Officer, Fort Walton Beach Medical Center, Fort Walton Beach, FL, p. A129

WYERS, Michael, Chief Financial Officer, Northern Virginia Community Hospital, Arlington, VA, p. A685

WYLES, Rick, Chief Financial Officer, McLaren Regional Medical Center, Flint, MI, p. A333

WYLIE, Eugene, Chief Human Resources Officer, Jerry L. Pettis Memorial Veterans Medical Center, Loma Linda, CA, p. A67

WYLIE, Patrick
Director Information Systems, Petaluma Valley Hospital, Petaluma, CA, p. A81
Director Information Systems, Santa Rosa Memorial Hospital, Santa Rosa, CA, p. A93

WYLIE, Steve, Interim Chief Executive Officer, Crossroads Regional Medical Center, Wentzville, MO, p. A395

WYMAN, Alan, Vice President Information Technology, Aspirus Wausau Hospital, Wausau, WI, p. A737

WYNN, Chester A., President and Chief Executive Officer, Passavant Area Hospital, Jacksonville, IL, p. A198

WYSE, LaMar L., President and Chief Executive Officer, Galion Community Hospital, Galion, OH, p. A514

WYSZKOWSKI, Bob, Director of Information Systems, Northwest Medical Center, Margate, FL, p. A136

X

XINIS, James J., President and Chief Executive Officer, Calvert Memorial Hospital, Prince Frederick, MD, p. A309

Y

YAHR, M.D., William, Director Medical Affairs, Capital Regional Medical Center, Tallahassee, FL, p. A147

YAJKO, Gene, Director Human Resources, Soldiers and Sailors Memorial Hospital, Wellsboro, PA, p. A578

YAKLIN, Shellye, Chief Executive Officer, Kindred Hospital–Detroit, Lincoln Park, MI, p. A339

YANAI, Christopher, Warden and Chief Executive Officer, Oakwood Correctional Facility, Lima, OH, p. A516

YANCER, Deborah A., R.N., President, Shady Grove Adventist Hospital, Rockville, MD, p. A310

YANES, John C., Chief Executive Officer, Lock Haven Hospital, Lock Haven, PA, p. A564

YARBOROUGH, Dianne, Director Information Systems, Doctors Hospital of Dallas, Dallas, TX, p. A632

YARBOROUGH, James, Chief Executive Officer, BJC Medical Center, Commerce, GA, p. A159

YARBROUGH, J. Douglas, Chief Executive Officer, Duplin General Hospital, Kenansville, NC, p. A485

YARMEL, Jeffrey N., Executive Vice President and Chief Operating Officer, Cooper Health System, Camden, NJ, p. A426

YATES, R.N., Ann C., Director Patient Care and Clinical Services, St. Vincent Mercy Hospital, Elwood, IN, p. A214

YATES, M.D., Gary R., Vice President and Executive Medical Director, Clinical Effectiveness, Sentara CarePlex Hospital, Hampton, VA, p. A689

YATES, Viki, Interim Administrator, Ward Memorial Hospital, Monahans, TX, p. A657

YATES, Vinson, Vice President Finance, Riverside Methodist Hospital, Columbus, OH, p. A511

YAZIGI, M.D., Ghassan, Medical Staff President, Livingston Hospital and Healthcare Services, Salem, KY, p. A274

YAZZIE, Bennie C., Administratrative Officer, Gallup Indian Medical Center, Gallup, NM, p. A442

YAZZIE, Earleen, Financial Manager, Gallup Indian Medical Center, Gallup, NM, p. A442

YEAGER, David, Chief Financial Officer, California Hospital Medical Center, Los Angeles, CA, p. A69

YEAGER–LOWRY, Kathy, Chief, Business Administration, Veterans Affairs Medical Center, Fresno, CA, p. A62

YEAGLE, M.D., Charles, Chief Medical Officer, Mt. San Rafael Hospital, Trinidad, CO, p. A110

YEATES, Alan H.
Vice President Fiscal Services, Doctors Hospital, Jackson, MI, p. A337
Vice President Fiscal Services, Wyandot Memorial Hospital, Upper Sandusky, OH, p. A523

YEATES, Diane, Senior Vice President Financial Services, Terrebonne General Medical Center, Houma, LA, p. A282

YECNY, Rick, Vice President and Chief Financial Officer, Peace Harbor Hospital, Florence, OR, p. A543

YEE, Brenda, MSN, Chief Executive Officer, Chinese Hospital, San Francisco, CA, p. A88

YEE, Stevan, Director Information Systems, Wilcox Memorial Hospital, Lihue, HI, p. A175

YELLAN, Robert J., President, Huron Valley–Sinai Hospital, Commerce Township, MI, p. A330

YELLAND, M.D., Grace, Physician, Mid–Valley Hospital, Omak, WA, p. A705

YELLOW, Tim, Director, U. S. Public Health Service Indian Hospital, Fort Yates, ND, p. A498

YELVINGTON, Fleury, President and Chief Executive Officer, Saint Mary's Medical Center, Saginaw, MI, p. A344

YENAWINE, Kelly R., Executive Director, Pathways of Tennessee, Jackson, TN, p. A608

YILMAZ, M.D., Mehmet, Medical Director, Southwest Regional Rehabilitation Center, Battle Creek, MI, p. A328

YIM, Nathan, Chief Financial Officer, Leahi Hospital, Honolulu, HI, p. A174

YOCHUM, Richard E., President and Chief Executive Officer, Pomona Valley Hospital Medical Center, Pomona, CA, p. A82

YODER, Cathy
Chief Financial Officer, South Florida Baptist Hospital, Plant City, FL, p. A143
Chief Financial Officer, St. Joseph's Hospital, Tampa, FL, p. A148

YODER, David, Chief Executive Officer, Irving Coppell Surgical Hospital, Irving, TX, p. A649

YODER, John H., Chief Operating Officer, West Virginia University Hospitals, Morgantown, WV, p. A718

YODER, M.D., Steven M., Chief of Staff, St. Luke Community Hospital, Ronan, MT, p. A401

YODER, Vince, Information Technology Manager, Prowers Medical Center, Lamar, CO, p. A107

YOKOBOSKY, Jr, Walter J.
Chief Financial Officer, Our Lady of Bellefonte Hospital, Ashland, KY, p. A261
Assistant Administrator Finance, St. Elizabeth's Hospital, Belleville, IL, p. A184

YONKER, Rich, Director Information Systems, Pike County Memorial Hospital, Louisiana, MO, p. A387

YOON, M.D., Chris, Medical Director, HEALTHSOUTH Bakersfield Rehabilitation Hospital, Bakersfield, CA, p. A54

YORK, Don, Vice President Human Resources, Merle West Medical Center, Klamath Falls, OR, p. A545

YORK, Linda, Manager Human Resources, Memorial Hospital of Converse County, Douglas, WY, p. A740

YORK, Nancy, Director Information Services, Dukes Memorial Hospital, Peru, IN, p. A223

YORK, Russell W., Vice President and Chief Financial Officer, Mississippi Baptist Health Systems, Jackson, MS, p. A370

YORK, Teisha, Chief Executive Officer, Intracare North Hospital, Houston, TX, p. A645

YORKE, Harvey M., President and Chief Executive Officer, Southwestern Vermont Medical Center, Bennington, VT, p. A682

YOSHII, Brian, Chief Information Officer, Kaiser Permanente Medical Center, Honolulu, HI, p. A173

YOSHIOKA, James T.
President and Chief Executive Officer, Citrus Valley Health Partners, Covina, CA, p. B29
President and Chief Executive Officer, Citrus Valley Medical Center–Inter–Community Campus, Covina, CA, p. A58
President and Chief Executive Officer, Citrus Valley Medical Center–Queen of the Valley Campus, West Covina, CA, p. A99

YOSKO, Kathleen C., President and Chief Executive Officer, Marianjoy Rehabilitation Hospital, Wheaton, IL, p. A210

YOUNG, Angela, Human Resources Officer, Veterans Affairs Medical Center, Chillicothe, OH, p. A506

YOUNG, Ann, Vice President, Mercy Medical Center–Centerville, Centerville, IA, p. A230

YOUNG, Anthony R., Chief Executive Officer, SouthCrest Hospital, Tulsa, OK, p. A540

YOUNG, Barbara, Director Community Relations, Providence Hood River Memorial Hospital, Hood River, OR, p. A544

YOUNG, Bev, Director Human Resources, Frankfort Regional Medical Center, Frankfort, KY, p. A264

YOUNG, Billy, Chief Executive Officer, KeyStone Center, Chester, PA, p. A555

YOUNG, Brad, Human Resources Director, Memorial Community Hospital, Edgerton, WI, p. A725

YOUNG, Bryce, Chief Operating Officer, Hays Medical Center, Hays, KS, p. A248

YOUNG, Charles R., Administrator, Shriners Hospitals for Children–Spokane, Spokane, WA, p. A709

YOUNG, Chris
  Chief Information Officer, Baptist Hospital, Nashville, TN, p. A615
  Chief Information Officer, Saint Thomas Hospital, Nashville, TN, p. A615

YOUNG, David
  Chief Information Officer, Carthage General Hospital, Carthage, TN, p. A603
  Senior Vice President of Planning and Technology, Sumner Regional Medical Center, Gallatin, TN, p. A606

YOUNG, Eric
  Chief Financial Officer, Madison County Hospital, London, OH, p. A516
  Chief of Staff, Veterans Affairs Ann Arbor Healthcare System, Ann Arbor, MI, p. A327

YOUNG, Horace, Manager Human Resources, Barnes–Jewish West County Hospital, Saint Louis, MO, p. A390

YOUNG, James W., President and Chief Executive Officer, Pacific Health Corporation, Tustin, CA, p. B82

YOUNG, John E.
  President and Chief Executive Officer, Cleveland Regional Medical Center, Shelby, NC, p. A491
  President and Chief Executive Officer, Kings Mountain Hospital, Kings Mountain, NC, p. A486

YOUNG, Kimberly, Chief Financial Officer, Baptist Memorial Hospital for Women, Memphis, TN, p. A612

YOUNG, Mary Ann, R.N., Administrator, Utah Valley Regional Medical Center, Provo, UT, p. A679

YOUNG, Michael A., FACHE, Chief Executive Officer, Erie County Medical Center, Buffalo, NY, p. A449

YOUNG, Nancy, Director Human Resources, Lake Chelan Community Hospital, Chelan, WA, p. A701

YOUNG, Phil, President, Heart Hospital of Lafayette, Lafayette, LA, p. A283

YOUNG, Randall A., Administrator, Lamb Healthcare Center, Littlefield, TX, p. A653

YOUNG, Rick, Chief Operating Officer, Henry Ford Kingswood Hospital, Ferndale, MI, p. A333

YOUNG, Steven W., Associate Director, James A. Haley Veterans Hospital, Tampa, FL, p. A148

YOUNG, Sylvia, President and Chief Executive Officer, Medical Center of Aurora, Aurora, CO, p. A101

YOUNG, Tammy, Controller, HEALTHSOUTH Lakeshore Rehabilitation Hospital, Birmingham, AL, p. A15

YOUNG, William, Chief Information Officer, Ellis Hospital, Schenectady, NY, p. A472

YOUNG, Jr, William A., Chief Operating Officer, St. Joseph Health Center, Warren, OH, p. A524

YOUNGBLOOD, Lee, Administrator, Physicians' Hospital in Anadarko, Anadarko, OK, p. A527

YOUNGER, Christina, Vice President Human Resources, Washington Hospital Center, Washington, DC, p. A122

YOUNGER, Lonnie D., Senior Vice President and Chief Financial Officer, Mission Hospitals, Asheville, NC, p. A477

YOUNGS, Patsy, Assistant Administrator and Chief Operating Officer, Hunt Memorial Hospital District, Greenville, TX, p. A642

YOUNKER, Ben, Information Systems Manager, Ira Davenport Memorial Hospital, Bath, NY, p. A447

YOUREE, James H., FACHE, Chief Executive Officer, Iberia Medical Center, New Iberia, LA, p. A288

YOUSO, Michael, President, Fairview Northland Regional Health Care, Princeton, MN, p. A360

YOX, John, Chief Financial Officer, St. Catherine Hospital, Garden City, KS, p. A247

YSEBAERT, John, Director Human Resources, Ivinson Memorial Hospital, Laramie, WY, p. A741

YU, Derrick, Chief Executive Officer, Mimbres Memorial Hospital, Deming, NM, p. A442

YUHAS, Joel, Chief Operating Officer, St. Mary Medical Center, Long Beach, CA, p. A68

YUHAS, D.O., John, Medical Director, St. Francis Health Care Centre, Green Springs, OH, p. A514

YULE, Warren, Administrator and Chief Executive Officer, Weisbrod Memorial County Hospital, Eads, CO, p. A105

YUTANI, M.D., Dennis, Chief of Staff, Memorial Hospital of Converse County, Douglas, WY, p. A740

YUTZY, LaVern J., Chief Executive Officer, Philhaven, Behavioral Healthcare Services, Mount Gretna, PA, p. A565

Z

ZACCAGNINO, Joseph A.
  President and Chief Executive Officer, Yale New Haven Health System, New Haven, CT, p. B123
  President and Chief Executive Officer, Yale–New Haven Hospital, New Haven, CT, p. A115

ZACHARIE, Scott, Director Finance, Soldiers' Home in Holyoke, Holyoke, MA, p. A319

ZACHARY, Beth D., President and Chief Executive Officer, White Memorial Medical Center, Los Angeles, CA, p. A73

ZACHRY, Lori, Director Human Resources, Iberia Medical Center, New Iberia, LA, p. A288

ZACKOSKI, Colleen, Executive Director, Richard H. Hutchings Psychiatric Center, Syracuse, NY, p. A473

ZADE, Ken, Information Technology Manager, Shawano Medical Center, Shawano, WI, p. A735

ZAGER, Joseph P., President and Chief Executive Officer, Shore Memorial Hospital, Nassawadox, VA, p. A692

ZAIDBERG, Edward A., Senior Vice President Finance, New York Methodist Hospital, New York, NY, p. A463

ZAKS, M.D., Jeffrey, Vice President Medical Affairs, Providence Hospital and Medical Center, Southfield, MI, p. A345

ZALAR, Karl, Administrator and Chief Executive Officer, Mercy Memorial Hospital, Urbana, OH, p. A523

ZAMBERLETTI, Romeo, Chief Fiscal Service, Veterans Affairs Illiana Health Care System, Danville, IL, p. A191

ZAMBITO, Paolo
  Interim Chief Executive Officer, Kenner Regional Medical Center, Kenner, LA, p. A283
  Chief Operating Officer, Kenner Regional Medical Center, Kenner, LA, p. A283

ZAMMAM, M.D., Hassan, President Medical Staff, St. Vincent Jennings Hospital, North Vernon, IN, p. A223

ZAMORA, Diana, Administrator, HEALTHSOUTH Surgical Hospital of Austin, Austin, TX, p. A623

ZANE, Ellen, Chief Executive Officer, Tufts–New England Medical Center, Boston, MA, p. A314

ZANI, Carl, Director Information Systems, Memorial Hospital of Union County, Marysville, OH, p. A517

ZANI, Paul, Chief Executive Officer, Pembroke Hospital, Pembroke, MA, p. A322

ZAPPALA, Phyllis, Vice President Human Resources, Danbury Hospital, Danbury, CT, p. A112

ZAPPAS, Barbara, Senior Vice President Clinical Operations, Legacy Meridian Park Hospital, Tualatin, OR, p. A550

ZARA, George A., Chief Executive Officer, St. Anthony Central Hospital, Denver, CO, p. A104

ZASTOCKI, Deborah K., FACHE, President and Chief Executive Officer, Chilton Memorial Hospital, Pompton Plains, NJ, p. A435

ZASTROW, Allan, FACHE, Chief Executive Officer, Keokuk Area Hospital, Keokuk, IA, p. A236

ZAUNBRECHER, Nick, CPA, Chief Operating Officer, Meadowbrook Rehabilitation Hospital of Lafayette, Lafayette, LA, p. A284

ZAVALA, M.D., Jeff, Chief of Staff, Beartooth Hospital and Health Center, Red Lodge, MT, p. A401

ZBOROWSKI, Richard, Executive Director Human Resources, McDowell ARH Hospital, McDowell, KY, p. A271

ZECHMAN Jr, Edwin K., President and Chief Executive Officer, Children's National Medical Center, Washington, DC, p. A121

ZECK, M.D., Robert
  Regional Vice President and Chief Medical Officer, Adventist La Grange Memorial Hospital, La Grange, IL, p. A199
  Regional Vice President and Chief Medical Officer, Hinsdale Hospital, Hinsdale, IL, p. A197

ZEGAR, Eugene
  Vice President Human Resources, Crozer–Chester Medical Center, Upland, PA, p. A577
  Vice President Human Resources, Delaware County Memorial Hospital, Drexel Hill, PA, p. A557

ZEH, Jeffrey C., Executive Director, St. Clare Medical Center, Crawfordsville, IN, p. A213

ZEHM, Laura, Vice President and Chief Financial Officer, Community Hospital of the Monterey Peninsula, Monterey, CA, p. A76

ZEHNER, Douglas, Chief Financial Officer, North Suburban Medical Center, Thornton, CO, p. A110

ZEHNTNER, R.N., Maureen, Chief Operating Officer, University of California, Irvine Medical Center, Orange, CA, p. A79

ZEICHNER, Veronica, Chief Financial Officer, Newark Beth Israel Medical Center, Newark, NJ, p. A432

ZEIGLER, Michael, Vice President and Chief Information Officer, Chambersburg Hospital, Chambersburg, PA, p. A555

ZEIHER, Tim, Director Information Services, Mount Desert Island Hospital, Bar Harbor, ME, p. A296

ZEILER, John, Chief Financial Officer, Ozark Health Medical Center, Clinton, AR, p. A41

ZEITLER, D.O., Irvin, Vice President Medical Affairs, Shannon Medical Center, San Angelo, TX, p. A663

ZEITLIN, Alan P., M.D., Chief Executive Officer, Parkway Hospital, New York, NY, p. A464

ZELL, John, Chief Financial Officer, OSF St. Joseph Medical Center, Bloomington, IL, p. A185

ZELLERS, M.D., Thomas, Interim Chief Medical Officer, Children's Medical Center of Dallas, Dallas, TX, p. A632

ZELLERS, Thomas J., President and Chief Executive Officer, Vail Valley Medical Center, Vail, CO, p. A110

ZELNIK, Ken, Director Information, Cedars Medical Center, Miami, FL, p. A137

ZELONIS, Jaloo, Acting Director, U. S. Public Health Service Blackfeet Community Hospital, Browning, MT, p. A396

ZENDER, Dale, Regional Vice President Finance and Chief Financial Officer, St. Joseph Hospital, Bellingham, WA, p. A700

ZENKER, M.D., Steven, Medical Director, Saint Anthony's Health Center, Alton, IL, p. A183

ZENN, Michael B., Executive Vice President and Chief Operating Officer, Corporate Services, Northwest Community Healthcare, Arlington Heights, IL, p. A183

ZENONE, Michael, Controller, HEALTHSOUTH Rehabilitation Hospital of Altoona, Altoona, PA, p. A552

ZENTY III, Thomas F., President and Chief Executive Officer, University Hospitals Health System, Cleveland, OH, p. B116

ZEPHIER, Richard L., Ph.D., Chief Executive Officer, PHS Santa Fe Indian Hospital, Santa Fe, NM, p. A444

ZETTERMAN, M.D., Rowen K., Chief of Staff, Veterans Affairs Nebraska–Western Iowa Health Care System, Lincoln, NE, p. A409

ZEVENBERGEN, Glenn, Chief Executive Officer, Hegg Memorial Health Center/Avera Health, Rock Valley, IA, p. A240

ZIAYA, Paul, Commander, U. S. Air Force Hospital, Hampton, VA, p. A689

ZICHAL, Frances, Chief Executive Officer, Central Community Hospital, Elkader, IA, p. A233

ZIDANSEK, John A., Executive Vice President, Sharon Regional Health System, Sharon, PA, p. A576

ZIEGELE, Paul, Chief Financial Officer, Adventist La Grange Memorial Hospital, La Grange, IL, p. A199

ZIEGLER, John, Director Human Resources, Claxton–Hepburn Medical Center, Ogdensburg, NY, p. A468

ZIELAZINSKI, Mark, Chief Information Officer, El Camino Hospital, Mountain View, CA, p. A77

ZIELINSKI, Dennis G., Chief Executive Officer, Coquille Valley Hospital, Coquille, OR, p. A543

ZIELINSKI, Sharon, Chief Information Resource Officer, Veterans Affairs Maryland Health Care System–Baltimore Division, Baltimore, MD, p. A305

ZIENIEWICZ, Stephen, Chief Operating Officer, Saint Louis University Hospital, Saint Louis, MO, p. A391

ZIENTS, Deborah T.
Chief Operating Officer, Hospital for Sick Children, Washington, DC, p. A121
Chief Operating Officer, Hospital for Sick Children, Washington, DC, p. A121

ZIEROLD, Bob, Vice President Human Resources, Christian Health Care Center, Wyckoff, NJ, p. A439

ZIETZ, M.D., Barry, Chief of Staff, West Houston Medical Center, Houston, TX, p. A649

ZIGLINSKI, Thomas J., Director Information Systems, Veterans Affairs Medical Center, Marion, IL, p. A200

ZILKOW, Jon, Chief Financial Officer, North Fulton Regional Hospital, Roswell, GA, p. A168

ZILLI, David, Chief Financial Officer, Cottage Hospital, Grosse Pointe Farms, MI, p. A336

ZILLNER, Dan, Information Systems Director, Idaho Elks Rehabilitation Hospital, Boise, ID, p. A177

ZIMMER, Kaylene, Chief Information Officer, Veterans Affairs Medical Center, Sheridan, WY, p. A742

ZIMMERMAN, Mark, Vice President Human Resources, Rockingham Memorial Hospital, Harrisonburg, VA, p. A689

ZIMMERMAN, Michael, Chief Financial Officer, Lane Memorial Hospital, Zachary, LA, p. A295

ZIMMERMAN, Nancy, R.N., Administrator, Comanche County Hospital, Coldwater, KS, p. A245

ZIMMERMANN, William
Chief Information Officer, Grady General Hospital, Cairo, GA, p. A157
Vice President Information Services, John D. Archbold Memorial Hospital, Thomasville, GA, p. A170
Chief Information Officer, Mitchell County Hospital, Camilla, GA, p. A157

ZIMPFER, Mary, Vice President Quality Management, Grace Hospital, Cleveland, OH, p. A508

ZINKULA, Lisa, Chief Financial Officer, Grundy County Memorial Hospital, Grundy Center, IA, p. A234

ZINNEN Jr, Robert O., President and Chief Executive Officer, Northwest Suburban Community Hospital, Belvidere, IL, p. A184

ZIOLKOWSKI, David, Chief Information Officer, Sampson Regional Medical Center, Clinton, NC, p. A480

ZIRKLE, William, Information Systems Manager, Halifax Regional Health System, South Boston, VA, p. A696

ZISKIN, Robert, Chief Information Officer, Veterans Affairs Medical Center, Northport, NY, p. A467

ZISKIND, Andrew A., M.D., President and Chief Executive Officer, Barnes–Jewish Hospital, Saint Louis, MO, p. A390

ZNAMIROWSKI, Maria, Vice President Human Resources, Midland Memorial Hospital, Midland, TX, p. A657

ZOGELMAN, Sharon, Human Resources Director, St. Luke Hospital and Living Center, Marion, KS, p. A252

ZOLKIWSKY, M.D., Walter R., Vice President Medical Affairs, Reston Hospital Center, Reston, VA, p. A694

ZOMOK, Robert, Director, Human Resources, Indian River Memorial Hospital, Vero Beach, FL, p. A150

ZOPH, Tim, Vice President Information Services, Northwestern Memorial Hospital, Chicago, IL, p. A188

ZOPOLSKY, M.D., Paul, Chief of Staff, Lake Pointe Medical Center, Rowlett, TX, p. A662

ZORGER, Charles, Senior Vice President Finance, Altoona Hospital Campus, Altoona, PA, p. A551

ZOROMSKI, Dave, Director Information Systems, Memorial Health Center, Medford, WI, p. A729

ZUBER, Eugene, Administrator, Newport Hospital and Clinic, Newport, AR, p. A48

ZUBER, Michael P., Ph.D., Executive Director, Rochester Psychiatric Center, Rochester, NY, p. A471

ZUBKE, Martha, Vice President Human Resources, Jennie Edmundson Memorial Hospital, Council Bluffs, IA, p. A231

ZUBKO, Elizabeth, Finance Administrator, Franklin Hospital Medical Center, Valley Stream, NY, p. A475

ZUBKOFF, William, Ph.D., Chief Executive Officer, South Shore Hospital and Medical Center, Miami Beach, FL, p. A138

ZUCKER, Michael C., FACHE, President, USMD Hospital at Arlington, Arlington, TX, p. A622

ZUCKERMAN, M.D., Nathan, Vice President Medical Affairs, Lourdes Medical Center of Burlington County, Willingboro, NJ, p. A438

ZUIDEMA, Paul, Chief Financial Officer, Ivinson Memorial Hospital, Laramie, WY, p. A741

ZULIANI, Michael E., Chief Executive Officer, Angel Medical Center, Franklin, NC, p. A483

ZUMPANO, Anthony, Chief Financial Officer, Warminster Hospital, Warminster, PA, p. A577

ZUPA, Robert, Vice President Finance, St. Vincent's Hospital, New York, NY, p. A465

ZWANZIGER, Marcia, Vice President Finance, Huron Regional Medical Center, Huron, SD, p. A596

ZWARTVERWER, M.D., Rick, Vice President Medical Affairs, Merle West Medical Center, Klamath Falls, OR, p. A545

ZWEIGHAFT, M.D., Ronald, Chief of Staff, Memorial Hermann Memorial City Hospital, Houston, TX, p. A646

ZWICKEY, Timothy, Administrator and Chief Executive Officer, Pine Medical Center, Sandstone, MN, p. A362

ZWINGER, Glenn, Manager Information Systems Services, Veterans Affairs Puget Sound Health Care System, Seattle, WA, p. A708

AHA Membership Categories

The American Hospital Association is primarily an organization of hospitals and related institutions. Its object, according to its bylaws, is "to promote high–quality health care and health services for all the people through leadership in the development of public policy, leadership in the representation and advocacy of hospital and health care organization interests, and leadership in the provision of services to assist hospitals and health care organizations in meeting the health care needs of their communities."

The major source of income for the AHA is its membership dues, which are established by the membership through the House of Delegates. The types of membership are described in the following paragraphs.

Institutional Members

Type I–Hospitals or health services organizations or systems which provide a continuum of integrated, community health resources and which include at least one licensed hospital that is owned, leased, managed or religiously sponsored.

Type I members include hospitals, health care systems, integrated delivery systems, and physician hospital organizations (PHOs) and health maintenance organizations (HMOs) wholly or partially owned by or owning a member hospital or system. A Type I member hospital, health care system or integrated delivery system may, at its discretion and upon approval of a membership application by the Association chief executive officer, extend membership to the health care provider organizations, other than a hospital that it owns, leases, or fully controls.

Type II–Freestanding Health Care Provider Organizations

These are health provider organizations, other than registered hospitals, that provide patient care services, including, but not limited to, ambulatory, preventive, rehabilitative, specialty, post–acute and continuing care, as well as physician groups, health insurance services, and staff and group model health maintenance organizations without a hospital component. Type II members are not owned or controlled by a Type I hospital, health care system or integrated delivery system member. They may, however, be part of an organization eligible for, but not holding, Type I membership.

Type III–Other Organizations

Type III membership includes organizations interested in the objectives of the Association, but not eligible for Type I or Type II membership. Organizations eligible for Type III membership shall include, but not be limited to, associations, societies, foundations, corporations, educational and academic institutions, companies, government agencies, international health providers, and organizations having an interest in and a desire to support the objectives of the Association.

Provisional Members

Hospitals that are in the planning or construction stage and that, on completion, will be eligible for institutional membership type I or type II. Provisional membership may also be granted to applicant institutions that cannot, at present, meet the requirements of type I or type II membership.

Government Institution Group Members

Groups of government hospitals operated by the same unit of government may obtain institutional membership under a group plan. Membership dues are based on a special schedule set forth in the bylaws of the AHA.

Contracting Hospitals

The AHA also provides membership services to certain hospitals that are prevented from holding membership because of legal or other restrictions.

Other Institutional Members

U.S. hospitals and hospitals in areas associated with the U.S. that are type IA members of the American Hospital Association are included in the list of hospitals in section A. Canadian types I members of the American Hospital Association are listed below.

Canada

ALBERTA

Lamont: LAMONT HEALTH CARE CENTRE, P.O. Bag 10, Zip T0B 2R0; tel. 780/895–2211; Harold James, Executive Director

MANITOBA

Winnipeg: RIVERVIEW HEALTH CENTRE, 1 Morley Avenue East, Zip R3L 2P4; tel. 204/452–3411; Norman R. Kasian, President and Chief Executive Officer

ONTARIO

Alliston: STEVENSON MEMORIAL HOSPITAL, 200 Fletcher Crescent, Zip L9R 1W7; tel. 705/435–6281; E. Takacs, Executive Director

London: ST. JOSEPH'S HEALTH CENTRE, P.O. Box 5777, Zip N6A 4V2; tel. 519/646–6000; Clifford A. Nordal, President and Chief Executive Officer

North York: BAYCREST CENTRE–GERIATRIC CARE, 3560 Bathurst Street, Zip M6A 2E1; tel. 416/789–5131; Stephen W. Herbert, President and Chief Executive Officer

Ottawa: ROYAL OTTAWA HOSPITAL, 1145 Carling Avenue, Zip K1Z 7K4; tel. 613/722–6521; George F. Langill, Executive Director

Parry Sound: WEST PARRY SOUND HEALTH CENTRE, 10 James Street, Zip P2A 1T3; tel. 705/746–9321; Norman Maciver, Chief Executive Officer

Renfrew: RENFREW VICTORIA HOSPITAL, 499 Raglan Street North, Zip K7V 1P6; tel. 613/432–4851; Randy V. Penney, Executive Director

Thornhill: SHOULDICE HOSPITAL, P.O. Box 370, Zip L3T 4A3; tel. 905/889–1125; Alan O'Dell, Administrator

Toronto: MOUNT SINAI HOSPITAL, 600 University Avenue, Zip M5G 1X5; tel. 416/596–4200; Joseph Mapa, FACHE, Executive Vice President and Chief Operating Officer

ST. JOSEPH'S HEALTH CENTRE, 30 the Queensway, Zip M6R 1B5; tel. 416/530–6008; Vas Georgiou, Interim President and Chief Executive Officer

TORONTO REHABILITATION INSTITUTE, 550 University Avenue, Zip M5G 2A2; tel. 416/597–5111; Mark Rochon, President and Chief Executive Officer

QUEBEC

Montreal: MOUNT SINAI HOSPITAL CENTER, 5690 Cavendish Cote St–Luc', Zip H4W 1S7; tel. 514/369–2222; Joseph Rothbart, Executive Director

Associated University Programs in Health Administration

CALIFORNIA

San Diego: CALIFORNIA COLLEGE SAN DIEGO, 2820 Camino Del Rio South, Suite 300, Zip 92108–3821; tel. 619/295–5784; Jeff Welsh, President

IOWA

Iowa City: DEPARTMENT OF HEALTH MANAGEMENT AND POLICY, UNIVERSITY OF IOWA, 200 Hawkins Drive, E211 GH, Zip 52242; tel. 319/384–5120; Douglas Wakefield, Ph.D., Head

MARYLAND

Bethesda: NAVAL SCHOOL OF HEALTH SCIENCES, Naval Medical Command, National Region, Zip 20889–5611; tel. 301/295–1251

MISSOURI

Saint Louis: WASHINGTON UNIVERSITY, SCHOOL OF MEDICINE, 4547 Clayton Avenue, Zip 63110; tel. 314/362–2477; Stuart Boxerman, Interim Director

NEW YORK

Valhalla: NEW YORK MEDICAL COLLEGE, Administration Building, Zip 10595; tel. 914/347–5044; Father Harry C. Barrett, M.P.H., President and Chief Executive Officer

OHIO

Cleveland: HEALTH CARE ADMINISTRATION PROGRAMS AT CLEVELAND STATE UNIVERSITY, 1860 East 18th Street, BU 435, Zip 44114–3610; tel. 216/687–4711; Brenda Stevenson Marshall, Ph.D., Program Director, Health Care Administration

PENNSYLVANIA

Philadelphia: TEMPLE UNIVERSITY, DEPARTMENT OF HEALTH ADMINISTRATION, SCHOOL OF BUSINESS ADMINISTRATION, Zip 19122–6083; tel. 215/787–8082; William Aaronson, Professor and Chairman

University Park: PENNSYLVANIA STATE UNIVERSITY, 116 Henderson Building, Zip 16802; tel. 814/863–2859; Diane Brannon, Ph.D., Interim Department Head, Health Policy and Administration

TEXAS

Brooks AFB: U. S. AIR FORCE SCHOOL OF AEROSPACE MEDICINE, USAFSAM–CCE, Zip 78235–5301; tel. 512/536–3342

San Antonio: ARMY–BAYLOR UNIVERSITY PROGRAM IN HEALTH CARE ADMINISTRATION, Academy of Health Sciences–USA, Zip 78234–6135; tel. 210/221–6443; Colonel Daniel Dominguez, Program Director

TRINITY UNIVERSITY, 715 Stadium Drive, Suite 58, Zip 78212–7200; tel. 210/736–8107; Mary E. Stefl, Ph.D., Chairman

Sheppard AFB: U. S. AIR FORCE SCHOOL OF HEALTH CARE SCIENCES, Building 1900, MSTL/114, Academic Library, Zip 76311; tel. 817/851–2511

PUERTO RICO

San Juan: SCHOOL OF PUBLIC HEALTH, P.O. Box 5067, Zip 00936; tel. 809/767–9626; Orlando Nieves, Dean

Hospital Schools of Nursing

ILLINOIS

Canton: GRAHAM HOSPITAL School of Nursing

NEW JERSEY

Plainfield: MUHLENBERG REGIONAL MEDICAL CENTER School of Nursing

NEW YORK

Elmira: ARNOT–OGDEN MEMORIAL HOSPITAL School of Nursing

OHIO

Canton: AULTMAN HOSPITAL School of Nursing
Cincinnati: CHRIST HOSPITAL School of Nursing

PENNSYLVANIA

Johnstown: CONEMAUGH VALLEY MEDICAL CENTER School of Nursing
New Castle: JAMESON HOSPITAL School of Nursing
Pittsburgh: WESTERN PENNSYLVANIA HOSPITAL School of Nursing

TENNESSEE

Memphis: BAPTIST COLLEGE OF HEALTH SCIENCES

Nonhospital Preacute and Postacute Care Facilities

ALABAMA

Fort McClellan: NOBLE ARMY HEALTH CLINIC, Zip 36205–5083; tel. 256/820–9135
Montgomery: MAXWELL CLINIC, 330 Kirkpatrick Avenue East, Zip 36112–6219; tel. 334/953–7801; Colonel Bart O. Iddins, Commander
Redstone Arsenal: FOX ARMY HEALTH CENTER, Building 4100, Zip 35809–7000; tel. 256/876–4147; Colonel Robert Nobak, Commander

ALASKA

Anchorage: DEPARTMENT OF VETERANS AFFAIRS ALASKA MEDICAL AND REGIONAL OFFICE CENTER, 2925 Debarr Road, Zip 99508–2989; tel. 907/257–6930; Alonzo M. Poteet, III, Director
SOUTHCENTRAL FOUNDATION, 4501 Diplomacy Drive, Suite 200, Zip 99508; tel. 907/265–4955; Katherine Gottlieb, President and Chief Executive Officer

ARIZONA

Davis–Monthan AFB: U. S. AIR FORCE CLINIC, 4175 South Alamo Avenue, Zip 85707–4405; tel. 520/228–2930; Colonel Thomas E. Scott, Commander
Fort Huachuca: RAYMOND W. BLISS ARMY HEALTH CENTER, 45001 Winrow Avenue, Zip 85613–7040; tel. 520/533–2350

ARKANSAS

Jacksonville: U. S. AIR FORCE CLINIC LITTLE ROCK, Little Rock AFB, Zip 72099–5057; tel. 501/987–7411; Colonel Rebecca A. Russell, USAF, Commander
Little Rock: CENTRAL ARKANSAS RADIATION THERAPY INSTITUTE, P.O. Box 55050, Zip 72215; tel. 501/664–8573; Janice E. Burford, President and Chief Executive Officer

CALIFORNIA

Beale AFB: U. S. AIR FORCE HOSPITAL, 15301 Warren Shingle Road, Zip 95903–1907; tel. 530/634–4838; Lieutenant Colonel Robert G. Quinn, MSC, USAF, FACHE, Administrator
Edwards AFB: U. S. AIR FORCE CLINIC, 30 Hospital Road, Building 5500, Zip 93524–1730; tel. 661/277–2010; Colonel Sally Petty, Commander
Los Angeles: DEPARTMENT OF VETERANS AFFAIRS, OUTPATIENT CLINIC, 351 East Temple Street, Room A–102, Zip 90012; tel. 213/253–5000; Jules Morevac, Ph.D., Director
Martinez: VETERANS AFFAIRS NORTHERN CALIFORNIA HEALTH SYSTEM, 150 Muir Road, Zip 94553; tel. 925/372–2000; Lawrence S. Sandler, Director
Port Hueneme: NAVAL AMBULATORY CARE CENTER, Zip 93043; tel. 805/982–6301; Captain Fred White, Officer–in–Charge
San Francisco: VETERANS AFFAIRS OUTPATIENT CLINIC, 4150 Clement Street, Zip 94121; tel. 415/221–4810; Lawrence C. Stewart, Director
Sepulveda: VETERANS AFFAIRS MEDICAL CENTER, 16111 Plummer Street, Zip 91343; tel. 818/891–7711; Charles M. Doorman, Acting Director
Vandenberg AFB: U. S. AIR FORCE HOSPITAL, 338 South Dakota Street, Zip 93437–6307; tel. 805/606–1110; Colonel Alan D. Newton, Commander

CONNECTICUT

Groton: NAVAL HOSPITAL, 1 Wahoo Drive, Box 600, Zip 06349–5600; tel. 860/694–3261

Newington: VETERANS AFFAIRS MEDICAL CENTER–NEWINGTON CAMPUS, 555 Willard Avenue, Zip 06111–2600; tel. 860/666–6951; Roger L. Johnson, Director

DELAWARE

New Castle: CHRISTIANA CARE VISITING NURSE ASSOCIATION, One Reads Way, Zip 19720; tel. 302/327–8200; Gary W. Ferguson, Chief Operating Officer
SCHWEIZER'S THERAPY AND REHABILITATION, 1 Reads Way, Suite 300, Zip 19720; tel. 302/326–8755; Steven Rombach, Chief Executive Officer
Newark: CHRISTIANA CARE IMAGING CENTER, 4751 Ogletown–Stanton Road, Zip 19713; tel. 302/731–9800; Gary W. Ferguson, Chief Executive Officer
CHRISTIANA INFUSION SERVICES, 200 Hygeia Drive, Zip 19713; Mary Fitzpatrick, Director
CHRISTIANA SURGICENTER, 4755 Ogletown–Stanton Road, Zip 19718; tel. 302/733–6900; Vicky Leccia, Coordinator
HEALTH CARE CENTER AT CHRISTIANA, 200 Hygeia Drive, Zip 19714
Wilmington: EUGENE DUPONT PREVENTIVE MEDICINE AND REHABILITATION INSTITUTE, 3506 Kennett Pike, Zip 19807; tel. 302/655–4041

FLORIDA

Jacksonville: BAPTIST HOME HEALTH CARE, 3563 Philips Highway, Suite 202, Zip 32207; tel. 904/202–4300; Diane Jones, Director
BAPTIST OCCUPATIONAL HEALTH, 1325 San Marco Boulevard, Suite 301, Zip 32207; tel. 904/202–2395; Donna Snider, Director
BAPTIST PRIMARY CARE, 3563 Philips Highway, Suite 101, Zip 32207; tel. 904/376–3744; Mother Superior Berl O'Malley, Administrator
PAVILION INFUSION THERAPY, 3563 Philips Highway, Suite 202, Zip 32207; tel. 904/202–5730; Diane Jones, Director
PSYCHIATRIC AND PSYCHOLOGICAL CARE, 4160 University Boulevard South, Zip 32216; tel. 904/376–3800; Mark A. Masters, Ph.D., Director
Key West: NAVAL REGIONAL MEDICAL CLINIC, 1500 Douglas Circle, Zip 33040; tel. 305/293–4613; Commander Stephen Lanier, Officer–in–Charge
Riverview: TAMPA BAY ACADEMY, 12012 Boyette Road, Zip 33569; tel. 813/677–6700; Edward C. Hoefle, Administrator
Tyndall AFB: U. S. AIR FORCE CLINIC, 340 Magnolia Avenue, Zip 32403–5612; tel. 850/283–7515; Colonel Michael J. Murphy, Commander

GEORGIA

Calhoun: ALLIANT HEALTH PLANS, INC., 401 South Wall Street, Suite 201, Zip 30701; tel. 706/629–8848; Louis G. Smith, Jr, Chief Executive Officer
GEORGIA HEALTH PLUS, 401 South Wall Street, Suite 201, Zip 30701; tel. 706/629–1833; Louis G. Smith, Jr, Chief Executive Officer
Moody AFB: U. S. AIR FORCE HOSPITAL MOODY, 3278 Mitchell Boulevard, Zip 31699–1500; tel. 229/257–3772; Colonel Dominic DeFrancis, Commander
Robins AFB: U. S. AIR FORCE CLINIC, 655 Seventh Street, Zip 31098–2227; tel. 912/327–7996; Colonel John A. Lee, USAF, MSC, Commander
Rome: CENTREX, 420 East Second Avenue, Zip 30161; tel. 706/235–1006; Dee B. Russell, M.D., Chief Executive Officer
COMMUNITY HOSPICECARE, P.O. Box 233, Zip 30162–0233; tel. 706/232–0807; Kurt Stuenkel, FACHE, President and Chief Executive Officer
FLOYD HOME HEALTH AGENCY, P.O. Box 6248, Zip 30162–6248; tel. 706/802–4600; Kurt Stuenkel, FACHE, President and Chief Executive Officer

FLOYD MEDICAL OUTPATIENT SURGERY, P.O. Box 233, Zip 30162–0233; tel. 706/802–2070; Kurt Stuenkel, FACHE, President and Chief Executive Officer
FLOYD REHABILITATION CENTER, P.O. Box 233, Zip 30162–0233; tel. 706/802–2091; Kurt Stuenkel, FACHE, President and Chief Executive Officer

HAWAII

Honolulu: VETERANS AFFAIRS MEDICAL REGIONAL OFFICE, 459 Patterson Road, Zip 96819; tel. 808/541–1582
Pearl Harbor: NAVAL REGIONAL MEDICAL CLINIC, Box 121, Building 1750, Zip 96860–5080; tel. 808/471–3025; Captain Joseph Moore, Commanding Officer

IDAHO

Mountain Home AFB: U. S. AIR FORCE CLINIC, 90 Hope Drive, Building 600, Zip 83648–5300; tel. 208/828–7610; Lieutenant Colonel Gregory W. Carson, Administrator

KANSAS

Fort Leavenworth: MUNSON ARMY HEALTH CENTER, 550 Pope Avenue, Zip 66027–2332; tel. 913/684–6420; Colonel William Davis, Commander
Wichita: U. S. AIR FORCE HOSPITAL, 59570 Leavenworth Street, Suite 6E4, Zip 67221–5300; tel. 316/759–5421

LOUISIANA

Barksdale AFB: U. S. AIR FORCE CLINIC, 243 Curtiss Road, Suite 100, Zip 71110–5300; tel. 318/456–6004; Colonel James M. Benge, Commander
New Orleans: NAVAL MEDICAL CLINIC, 1 Sanctuary Drive, Zip 70142–5300; tel. 504/678–2400; Captain David Shiveley, Officer in Charge

MAINE

Damariscotta: MILES MEDICAL GROUP, INC., 35 Miles Street, Zip 04543; tel. 207/563–1234; Stacey Miller–Friant, Director
Kennebunk: SOUTHERN MAINE HEALTH AND HOME SERVICES, P.O. Box 739, Zip 04043; tel. 207/985–4767; Elaine Brady, R.N., Executive Director

MARYLAND

Annapolis: NAVAL MEDICAL CLINIC, Zip 21402; tel. 410/293–1330
Baltimore: ST. AGNES HEALTH SERVICES, 900 Caton Avenue, Zip 21229; tel. 410/368–2945; Peter Clay, Senior Vice President Managed Care
ST. AGNES HOME CARE AND HOSPICE, 3421 Benson Avenue, Suite G100, Zip 21227; tel. 410/368–2825; Robin Dowell, Director
Fort George G Meade: KIMBROUGH ARMY COMMUNITY HOSPITAL, 2480 Llewellyn Avenue, Zip 20755; tel. 301/677–4171; Colonel Billie J. Mielcarek, Commanding Officer
Fort Howard: VETERANS AFFAIRS MARYLAND HEALTH CARE SYSTEM–FORT HOWARD DIVISION, 9600 North Point Road, Zip 21052–9989; tel. 410/477–1800
Patuxent River: NAVAL MEDICAL CLINIC, 47149 Buse Road, Zip 20670–5370; tel. 301/342–1418; Captain Ralph A. Puckett, MC, USN, Commanding Officer

MASSACHUSETTS

Springfield: VISITING NURSE ASSOCIATION AND HOSPICE OF WESTERN NEW ENGLAND, INC., 50 Maple Street, Zip 01105; tel. 413/781–5070; Maureen Skipper, President

MICHIGAN

Big Rapids: MECOSTA HEALTH SERVICES, 650 Linden Street, Zip 49307; tel. 231/796–3200; Gail Bullard, Director

Detroit: ST. JOHN NORTHEAST COMMUNITY HOSPITAL, 4777 East Outer Drive, Zip 48234–0401; tel. 313/369–9100; Michael F. Breen, President

Port Huron: TRI-HOSPITAL E.M.S., 309 Grand River Street, Zip 48060; tel. 313/985–7115; Ken Cummings, Chief Executive Officer

WILLOW ENTERPRISES, INC., 1221 Pine Grove Avenue, Zip 48060; tel. 313/989–3737; James B. Bridge, Chief Executive Officer

Sault Sainte Marie: SAULT SAINTE MARIE TRIBAL HEALTH AND HUMAN SERVICES CENTER, 2864 Ashmun Street, Zip 49783; tel. 906/495–5651; Russell Vizina, Division Director Health

MINNESOTA

Bemidji: BEMIDJI SAME DAY SURGERY, 1233 34th Street N.W., Zip 56601; tel. 218/333–5000; Randy D. Beck

MERITCARE DIALYSIS CTR BEMIDJI, 1300 Anne Street N.W., Zip 56601; tel. 218/333–5000; Maria Regnier

MERITCARE PHYSICAL THERAPY BEMIDJI, 3604 Bemidji Avenue North, Zip 56601; tel. 218/333–5000; Don Martin

MERITCARE RADIATION ONCOLOGY PHYSICS, 1233 34th Street N.W., Zip 56601; tel. 218/333–4600; Randy D. Beck, Executive Partner

Detroit Lakes: MERITCARE DIALYSIS CENTER DETROIT LAKES, 1027 Washington Avenue, Zip 56501; tel. 218/847–0825; Roger L. Gilbertson, M.D., President and Chief Executive Officer

MERITCARE PHYSICAL THERAPY DETROIT LAKES, 1245 Washington Avenue, Zip 56501; tel. 218/846–2000; Brenda Muckenhirn

Morris: MERITCARE DIALYSIS CENTER MORRIS, P.O. Box 660, Zip 56267–0660; tel. 320/586–2832; Maria Regnier

Pelican Rapids: MERITCARE HOME HEALTH CARE PELICAN RAPIDS, P.O. Box 737, Zip 56572–0737; tel. 218/863–2273; Marsha Sjulstad

Saint Paul: HEALTHEAST CARE, INC., 1690 University Avenue W, Suite 370, Zip 55104–3729; tel. 651/232–5070

HEALTHEAST HOME CARE, INC., 1700 University Avenue, Zip 55104; tel. 651/232–2800; Scott Batulis, Vice President and Administrator

HEALTHEAST MEDICAL RESEARCH INSTITUTE, 559 Capitol Boulevard, Zip 55103; tel. 651/232–2300; Timothy H. Hanson, President and Chief Executive Officer

MISSISSIPPI

Columbus: U. S. AIR FORCE CLINIC, 201 Independence, Suite 235, Zip 39701–5300; tel. 662/434–2297; Colonel Dave Armstrong, Commander

MISSOURI

Independence: SURGI-CARE CENTER OF INDEPENDENCE, 2311 Redwood Avenue, Zip 64057; tel. 816/373–7995

Whiteman AFB: U. S. AIR FORCE CLINIC WHITEMAN, 331 Sijan Avenue, Zip 65305–5001; tel. 660/687–1194; Lieutenant Colonel David Wilmot, USAF, MSC, Administrator

MONTANA

Malmstrom AFB: U. S. AIR FORCE CLINIC, Zip 59402–5300; tel. 406/731–3863; Colonel David L. Doty, Administrator

Miles City: VETERANS AFFAIRS MEDICAL CENTER, 210 South Winchester Avenue, Zip 59301–4742; tel. 406/232–3060

NEBRASKA

Grand Island: GRAND ISLAND DIVISION, 2211 North Broadwell Avenue, Zip 68803–2196; tel. 308/382–3660; Gary N. Nugent, Chief Executive Officer

North Platte: GREAT PLAINS PHO, INC., P.O. Box 1167, Zip 69103; tel. 308/535–7496; Todd Hlavaty, M.D., Chairman

---

Offutt AFB: EHRLING BERGQUIST HOSPITAL, 2501 Capehart Road, Zip 68113–2160; tel. 402/294–7312; Colonel Howard Googins, Deputy Commander

NEW HAMPSHIRE

Portsmouth: NAVAL MEDICAL CLINIC, Building H–1, Zip 03801; tel. 207/439–1000; Captain F. M. Richardson, Commanding Officer

NEW JERSEY

Atlantic City: ATLANTICARE SURGERY CENTER, 1925 Pacific Avenue, Zip 08401; tel. 609/407–2200; William Aarons, M.D., President

Egg Harbor City: ATLANTICARE BEHAVIORAL HEALTH, 2511 Fire Road, Suite B10, Zip 08234; tel. 609/272–6392; Theodore Stryker, President and Chief Executive

ATLANTICARE HEALTH SERVICES, 2500 English Creek Avenue, Building C., Zip 08234; tel. 609/272–6392; Donald Parker, President and Chief Executive Officer

Fort Monmouth: PATTERSON ARMY HEALTH CLINIC, Stephenson Avenue, Building 1075, Zip 07703–5504; tel. 908/532–1266

Millburn: ATLANTIC HOME CARE AND HOSPICE, 33 Bleeker Street, Zip 07041; tel. 973/379–8400; Susan Quinn, Administrator

Morristown: ALLIANCE IMAGING CENTER, 65 Maple Street, Zip 07960; tel. 973/267–5700; Barbara Picorale, Administrator

Succasunna: DIALYSIS CENTER OF NORTHWEST NEW JERSEY, 170 Righter Road, Zip 07876; tel. 973/584–1117; Carol Cahill, Administrator

NEW MEXICO

Cannon AFB: U. S. AIR FORCE CLINIC, 208 West Casablanca Avenue, Zip 88103–5300; tel. 505/784–6318; Lieutenant Colonel James M. Davis, Jr, Administrator

Holloman AFB: U. S. AIR FORCE CLINIC, 280 First Street, Zip 88330–8273; tel. 505/572–5587

Kirtland AFB: U. S. AIR FORCE CLINIC–KIRTLAND, 2050 A Second Street S.E., Zip 87117–5559; tel. 505/846–3547; Colonel Regina Aune, Commander

NEW YORK

Bronx: MORRISANIA DIAGNOSTIC AND TREATMENT CENTER, 1225 Gerard Avenue, Zip 10452; tel. 718/960–2777; Victor Hernandez, Administrator

SEGUNDO RUIZ BELVIS DIAGNOSTIC AND TREATMENT CENTER, 545 East 142nd Street, Zip 10454; tel. 718/579–4000; Victor Hernandez, Administrator

Brooklyn: CUMBERLAND DIAGNOSTIC AND TREATMENT CENTER, 100 North Portland Avenue, Zip 11205; tel. 718/260–7500; K. Candis Best, Administrator

DR. SUSAN SMITH NURSING REHABILITATION CENTER, 594 Albany Avenue, Zip 11203; tel. 718/245–7000; Ruth Ogieste, Administrator

EAST NEW YORK DIAGNOSTIC AND TREATMENT CENTER, 2094 Pitkin Avenue, Zip 11207; tel. 718/240–0400; Yvette Isaac, Administrator

Cheektowaga: MCAULEY SETON HOME CARE, 2875 Union Road, Suite 14, Zip 14227; tel. 716/685–4870; Mark A. Sullivan, President and Senior Administrative Officer

MERCY HOME CARE, 2875 Union Road, Suite 14, Zip 14227; tel. 716/685–4870; Mark A. Sullivan, President and Senior Administrative Officer

Fort Drum: 11050 MOUNT BELVEDERE BOULEVARD, 11050 Mount Belvedere Boulevard, Zip 13602–5004; tel. 315/772–4024

New York: RENAISSANCE DIAGNOSTIC AND TREATMENT CENTER, 215 West 125 Street, Zip 10027; tel. 212/932–6500; Rose Garcia, Administrator

Tuckahoe: HOME NURSING ASSOCIATION OF WESTCHESTER, 69 Main Street, Zip 10707; tel. 919/961–2818; Mary Wehrberger, Director

NORTH CAROLINA

Jamestown: MERITCARE PHYSICAL THERAPY, 904 Fifth Avenue N.E., Zip 58401; tel. 702/253–4000; Jim Schaefer, Regional Clinic Manager

---

Seymour Johnson AFB: U. S. AIR FORCE HOSPITAL SEYMOUR JOHNSON, 1050 Curtis Avenue, Zip 27531–5300; tel. 919/722–1812; Colonel Donna M. Lake, Commanding Officer

NORTH DAKOTA

Grand Forks AFB: U. S. AIR FORCE HOSPITAL, 220 G Street, Zip 58205–6332; tel. 701/747–5391

Minot: U. S. AIR FORCE REGIONAL HOSPITAL, 10 Missile Avenue, Zip 58705–5024; tel. 701/723–5103; Colonel Lawrence Riddles, Commander

OHIO

Cleveland: KAISER PERMANENTE, 1001 Lakeside, Zip 44114; tel. 216/362–2000; Patricia Kennedy–Scott, President

Columbus: OHIOHEALTH GROUP, 445 Hutchinson Avenue, Suite 300, Zip 43235–5677; tel. 614/566–0123; John Burns, Chief Executive Officer

VETERANS AFFAIRS OUTPATIENT CLINIC, 543 Taylor Avenue, Zip 43203–1278; tel. 614/257–5200; Lillian Thone, Chief Executive Officer

Worthington: HOMEREACH, 404 East Wilson Bridge Road, Suite H., Zip 43085; tel. 614/566–0888; Fran Baby, Vice President Home and Hospice Services

OKLAHOMA

Altus: U. S. AIR FORCE CLINIC ALTUS, 301 North First Street, Zip 73523–5005; tel. 580/481–5204; Colonel Charles W. Cotta, USAF, Commander

Enid: U. S. AIR FORCE CLINIC, Vance AFB, Building 810, Zip 73705–5000; tel. 405/249–7494; Lieutenant Colonel Andrew F. Love, MSC, USAF, Commander Medical Group

Eufaula: EUFALA INDIAN HEALTH CENTER, 800 Forest Avenue, Zip 74432; tel. 918/689–2547; Shelly Crow, Health System Administrator

Okmulgee: OKMULGEE INDIAN HEALTH SYSTEM, 1313 East 20th, Zip 74447; tel. 918/758–1926; Steve Landsberry, Administrator

Sapulpa: SAPULPA INDIAN HEALTH CENTER, 1125 East Clevelend, Zip 74066; tel. 918/224–9310; Judy Aaron, Health System Administrator

Tinker AFB: U. S. AIR FORCE HOSPITAL TINKER, 5700 Arnold Street, Zip 73145; tel. 405/736–2084; Colonel Lloyd A. Reinke, Commander

PENNSYLVANIA

Chester: COMMUNITY HOSPITAL, DIVISION OF THE CROZER–CHESTER MEDICAL CENTER, Ninth and Wilson Streets, Zip 19013–2098; tel. 610/494–0700; Kevin Caupeto, Vice President Operations

Dallastown: WELLSPAN MEDICAL GROUP, Zip 17313; tel. 717/851–6515

York: SOUTH CENTRAL PREFERRED, 45 Monument Road, Suite 200, Zip 17403; tel. 717/741–9511; Charles H. Chodroff, M.D., Executive Director

WELLSPAN HEALTH CARE SERVICES, 1001 South George Street, Zip 17405; tel. 717/851–2121; Bruce M. Bartels, President

RHODE ISLAND

Newport: NAVAL HOSPITAL, 1 Riggs Road, Zip 02841–1002; tel. 401/841–3771; Captain Andre Greedan, Deputy Commander

SOUTH DAKOTA

Ellsworth AFB: U. S. AIR FORCE CLINIC, 2900 Doolittle Drive, Zip 57706–4821; tel. 605/385–3201; Colonel Chris Gray, Commanding Officer

TEXAS

Abilene: U. S. AIR FORCE CLINIC, 7th Medical Group, Dyess AFB, Zip 79607–1367; tel. 915/696–5429; Major John G. Wiseman, Administrator

Corpus Christi: NORTHWEST REGIONAL HOSPITAL, 13725 Northwest Boulevard, Zip 78410–5199; tel. 361/241–4243; Steve Woerner, Chief Executive Officer

---

Dallas: SURGICARE OF TRAVIS CENTER, INC., 13355 Noel Road, Suite 650, Zip 75240–6694; tel. 713/520–1782

El Paso: VETERANS AFFAIRS HEALTHCARE CENTER, 5001 North Piedras Street, Zip 79930–4211; tel. 915/564–6100; Edward Valenzuela, Director

Houston: GRAMERCY OUTPATIENT SURGERY CENTER. LTD., 2727 Gramercy, Zip 77025; Carol Simons, Administrator

WEST HOUSTON SURGICARE, 970 Campbell Road, Zip 77024; tel. 713/461–3547; Edward Downs, Administrator

Laughlin AFB: U. S. AIR FORCE HOSPITAL, 590 Mitchell Boulevard, Zip 78843–5200; tel. 210/298–6311

San Antonio: U. S. AIR FORCE CLINIC BROOKS, Building 615, Zip 78235–5300; tel. 210/536–2087; Lieutenant Colonel Donald Sampson, Commanding Officer

Universal City: U. S. AIR FORCE CLINIC RANDOLPH, 221 3rd Street West, Zip 78150–4801; tel. 210/652–5701; Lieutenant Colonel Dennis E. Franks, Administrator

Webster: BAY AREA SURGICARE CENTER, 502 Medical Center Boulevard, Zip 77598; tel. 281/332–2433; Carol Simons, Administrator

VIRGINIA

Fort Lee: KENNER ARMY HEALTH CLINIC, 700 24th Street, Zip 23801–1716; tel. 804/734–9256; Colonel Betty Wiley, Commander

Quantico: NAVAL REGIONAL MEDICAL CLINIC, Zip 22134; tel. 703/784–1699; Captain Janee Przybyl, Commanding Officer

WASHINGTON

Fairchild AFB: U. S. AIR FORCE CLINIC, 701 Hospital Loop, Suite 102, Zip 99011–8701; tel. 509/247–5217; Colonel Richard G. Griffith, Commanding Officer

WISCONSIN

Green Bay: UNITY HOSPICE, P.O. Box 28345, Zip 54324–8345; tel. 920/494–0225; Donald Seibel, Executive Director

WYOMING

Cheyenne: U. S. AIR FORCE HOSPITAL, 6900 Alden Drive, Zip 82005–3913; tel. 307/773–2045; Major Brenda Bullard, Administrator

Provisional Hospitals

This listing includes organizations that, as of June 1, 2005, were in the planning or construction stage and that, on completion, will be eligible for Type I institutional membership. Some hospitals are granted provisional membership for reasons related to other Association requirements. Hospitals classified as provisional members for reasons other than being under construction are indicated by a bullet (●).

ARIZONA

Phoenix: SELECT SPECIALTY HOSPITAL – PHOENIX, 350 West Thomas Road, Zip 85013; tel. 602/406–6800; Meridell Sloterbeek, R.N., Chief Executive Officer

MICHIGAN

Detroit: BARBARA ANN KARMANOS CANCER INSTITUTE, 4100 John R, Zip 48201; tel. 313/993–7773

Associate Members

Ambulatory Centers and Home Care Agencies

United States

FLORIDA

NEMOURS CHILDREN'S CLINIC, 807 Children's Way, Jacksonville, Zip 32207; tel. 904/390–3600; Traci Pezall, Associate Administrator

NEW HAMPSHIRE

DARTMOUTH COLLEGE HEALTH SERVICE, 7 Rope Ferry Road, Hanover, Zip 03755–1421; tel. 603/650–1400; John H. Turco, M.D., Director

NEW YORK

WESTFALL SURGERY CENTER, 1065 Senator Keating Boulevard, Rochester, Zip 14618; tel. 716/256–1330; Gary J. Scott, Administrative Director

PENNSYLVANIA

CRAIG ACADEMY, 751 North Negley Avenue, Pittsburgh, Zip 15206; tel. 412/361–2801; Roberta Mack, Program Director

WASHINGTON

PACIFIC MEDICAL CENTERS, 1200 12th Avenue South, Seattle, Zip 98144; tel. 206/621–4489; Harvey W. Smith, President and Chief Executive Officer

Philippines

DEPARTMENT OF VETERANS AFFAIRS, OUTPATIENT CLINIC, Manila, Zip 96440; tel. 632/521–7116

Blue Cross Plans

United States

ARIZONA

BLUE CROSS AND BLUE SHIELD OF ARIZONA, Box 13466, Phoenix, Zip 85002–3466; tel. 602/864–4100; Richard Boals, President and Chief Financial Officer

NEW YORK

EXCELLUS HEALTH PLAN, INC., 165 Court Street, Rochester, Zip 14647; tel. 716/454–1700; David Mack, Senior Vice President Corporate Relations

PENNSYLVANIA

CAPITAL BLUE CROSS, 2500 Elmerton Avenue, Harrisburg, Zip 17110; tel. 717/541–7000; Anita Smith, President and Chief Executive Officer

HIGHMARK BLUE CROSS BLUE SHIELD, 120 Fifth Avenue Place, Suite 3014, Pittsburgh, Zip 15222; tel. 412/544–7646; Sandra R. Tomlinson, Senior Vice President Provider Services

INDEPENDENCE BLUE CROSS, 1901 Market Street, Philadelphia, Zip 19103; tel. 215/241–3300; Denise Dodd, Manager

Other Members

UNITED STATES

Alliance:

PREMIER, INC., 3 Westbrook Corporate Center, 9th Floor, San Diego, California Zip 92130; tel. 858/481–2727; Richard A. Norling, Chief Executive Officer; www.premierinc.com

THE NEW JERSEY COUNCIL OF TEACHING HOSPITALS, 154 West State Street, Trenton, New Jersey Zip 08608; tel. 609/656–9600; J. Richard Goldstein, President; www.njcth.org

UNIVERSITY HEALTHSYSTEM CONSORTIUM, INC., 2001 Spring Road, Suite 700, Oak Brook, Illinois Zip 60523; tel. 630/954–1700; Robert J. Baker, President and Chief Executive Officer; www.uhc.edu

VHA, INC., P.O. Box 140909, Irving, Texas Zip 75014–0909; tel. 972/830–0000; Curtis W. Nonomaque, President and Chief Executive Officer

Architecture:

BURT HILL KOSAR RITTELMANN ASSOCIATES, 400 Morgan Center, Butler, Pennsylvania Zip 16001–5977; tel. 412/285–4761; John E. Brock, Vice President; www.burthill.com

EARL SWENSSON ASSOCIATES, INC., 2100 West End Avenue, Suite 1200, Nashville, Tennessee Zip 37203; tel. 615/329–9445; Richard L. Miller, President; www.esarch.com

HDR ARCHITECTURE, 8404 Indian Hills Drive, Omaha, Nebraska Zip 68114; tel. 402/399–1000; Jim Pine, Executive Vice President; www.hdrinc.com

LEGAT MEDICAL ARCHITECTS, 24 North Chapel, Waukegan, Illinois Zip 60085; tel. 847/605–0234; Casimir Frankiewicz, President

MARSHALL CRAFT ASSOCIATES, INC., 6112 York Road, Baltimore, Maryland Zip 21212; tel. 410/532–3131; Tonia Burnette, Principal

MATTHEI AND COLIN ASSOCIATES, 332 South Michigan Avenue, Suite 614, Chicago, Illinois Zip 60604; tel. 312/939–4002; Ronald G. Kobold, Managing Partner

SMITHGROUP, INC., 225 Bush Street, 11th Floor, San Francisco, California Zip 94104; tel. 415/227–0100; James T. Hannon, Senior Vice President; www.sf.smithgroup.com

Behavioral Health Center:

DEVEREUX–VICTORIA, P.O. Box 2666, Victoria, Texas Zip 77902–2666; tel. 361/575–8271; Fred Williams, Executive Director

Construction Firm:

BE & K BUILDING GROUP, INC., 3001 Armory Drive, Suite 250, Nashville, Tennessee Zip 37204; tel. 615/742–6610; Burk Waugh, Principal In Charge and Executive Vice President

HBE CORPORATION, P.O. Box 419039, Saint Louis, Missouri Zip 63141; tel. 314/567–9000; Stephen G. Dailey, Senior Vice President

Consulting Firm:

ARAMARK HEALTHCARE MANAGEMENT SERVICES, 1101 Market Street, Philadelphia, Pennsylvania Zip 19107–2988; tel. 215/238–4054; Jonathan J. Cutler, Senior Vice President Marketing; www.aramark.com

BOLDT CONSULTING SERVICES, 1110 North Old World 3rd Street, Suite 610, Milwaukee, Wisconsin Zip 53203; tel. 414/276–4666; Kenneth R. Greve, Principal; www.boldtconsulting.com

CAMPBELL WILSON, 9400 Central Expressway, Suite 613, Dallas, Texas Zip 75231; tel. 214/373–7077; Manie Campbell, Partner

ERNST & YOUNG, 5 Times Square, 14th Floor, New York, Zip 10036–6530; tel. 212/773–3000; Frank Bresz, Senior Manager; www.ey.com/global/content.nsf/us/home

EXECUTIVE HEALTH RESOURCES, INC., 15 Campus Boulevard, Suite 200, Newtown Square, Zip 19073; tel. 610/446–6100; Robert Corrato, President and Chief Executive Officer; www.ehrdocs.com

HEIDRICK AND STRUGGLES, 233 South Wacker, Suite 7000, Chicago, Illinois Zip 60606; tel. 312/372–8811; Richard P. Gustafson, Partner

KAUFMAN HALL, One Northfield Plaza, Suite 240, Northfield, Zip 60093; tel. 847/441–8780; Jason Sussman, Partner; www.kaufmanhall.com

KURT SALMON ASSOCIATES, 1355 Peachtree Street N.E., Suite 900, Atlanta, Georgia Zip 30309–0900; tel. 404/892–0321; C. B. Souther, Communication Director; www.kurtsalmon.com

MARSHALL ERDMAN & ASSOCIATES, INC., 5117 University Avenue, Madison, Wisconsin Zip 53705; tel. 608/238–0211; Ronald S. Luskin, Vice President and Director Marketing; www.erdman.com

MCKESSON HBO, 5995 Windward Parkway, Alpharetta, Georgia Zip 30005; tel. 404/338–3519; Louise Smith, Manager, Regulatory Assessment and Operations

PHOENIX HEALTH SYSTEMS, INC., 9200 Wightman Road, Suite 400, Montgomery Village, Maryland Zip 20886; tel. 301/869–7300; Richard A. Lind, Chief Executive Officer; www.phoenixhealth.com

PRESS, GANEY ASSOCIATES, INC., 404 Columbia Place, South Bend, Zip 46601; tel. 800/232–8032; Martin Ma, Vice President Marketing; www.pressganey.com

PRICEWATERHOUSECOOPERS, 2001 Ross Avenue, Suite 1800, Dallas, Texas Zip 75201; tel. 214/999–1400; Kelly Barnes, Partner

TIBER GROUP, LLC, 200 South Wacker Drive, Suite 2620, Chicago, Illinois Zip 60601; tel. 312/609–9900; Matt Terry

WIPFLI LLP, P.O. Box 690, Eau Claire, Wisconsin Zip 54702–0690; tel. 715/858–3407; Sylvia Weise; www.wipfli.com

Facilities Management:

JOHNSON CONTROLS, INC., 3354 Perimeter Hill Drive, Suite 105, Antioch, Tennessee Zip 37013; tel. 615/501–7327; Iona Canada, Manager Business Development; www.johnsoncontrols.com

Information Systems:

3M HEALTH INFORMATION SYSTEMS, 575 West Murray Boulevard, Murray, Utah Zip 84157; tel. 801/265–4400; Scott Slivka, Marketing Manager

CERNER CORPORATION, 2800 Rockcreek Parkway, Kansas City, Missouri Zip 64117; tel. 816/221–1024; Jack Newman, Jr, Executive Vice President

KPMG LLP, 303 East Wacker Drive, 19th Floor, Chicago, Illinois Zip 60601; tel. 312/665–2073; Edward J. Giniat, Partner

MICROMEDEX, INC., 6200 South Syracuse Way, Suite 300, Englewood, Colorado Zip 80111–4740; tel. 303/486–6437; Dana Guilfoyle

Insurance Broker:

AMERICAN FIDELITY ASSURANCE COMPANY, 2000 North Classen Boulevard, Oklahoma City, Zip 73106; tel. 877/967–5748; Barry Koonce, National Sales Director; www.af–group.com

BOSTON MUTUAL LIFE INSURANCE COMPANY, 120 Royall Street, Canton, Zip 02021; tel. 781/828–7000; Peter Tillson, Vice President; www.bostonmutual.com

DYE & ESKIN, 1324 Vincent Place, Mc Lean, Zip 22101; tel. 703/556–0744; Major Rick Eskin, President

G. E. FINANCIAL, GE Appliance Park Building, 100, Louisville, Zip 40225; tel. 502/452–5396; Greg Miller, Business Development Director; www.ge.com

LOCKTON COMPANIES, 444 West 47th Street, Suite 900, Kansas City, Missouri Zip 64112–1906; tel. 816/960–9000; Becky Sullivan, Senior Vice President and Unit Manager; www.lockton.com

NEBCO, 1264 Knollwood Drive West, West Chester, Zip 19380; tel. 877/739–3330; James M. Mattison, Vice President; www.nebenefit.com

PRINCIPAL FINANCIAL GROUP, 711 High Street, Des Moines, Iowa Zip 50392–5440; tel. 515/248–4455; Pat Burch, Senior Technical Consultant; www.goldfarb@shands.ufl.edu

THE ALLEN J. FLOOD COMPANIES, INC., 2 Madison Avenue, Larchmont, Zip 10538; tel. 914/834–9326; Allen J. Flood, President; www.ajfusa.com

UNITED CONCORDIA COMPANY, INC., 4401 Deer Path Road, Harrisburg, Zip 17110; tel. 717/260–6800; Denise Adams, Manager Sales Support; www.ucci.com

WEST LAKE FINANCIAL GROUP, 1477 Barday Boulevard, Buffalo Grove, Zip 60089; tel. 847/353–6150; Paul Burt, President; www.westlakefg.com

Investment Broker:

STEPHENS, INC., 111 Center Street, Little Rock, Arkansas Zip 72201; tel. 501/377–2544; Nancy Weaver, Research Analyst

Manufacturer/Supplier:

ABBOTT LABORATORIES, 100 Abbott Park Road, Abbott Park, Zip 60064; tel. 847/937–4537; William D. Motley, Jr, Divisional Vice President; www.abbot.com

AMGEN, INC., 1840 Dehavilland Drive, Department 631, Thousand Oaks, California Zip 91320; tel. 805/447–2106; Kevin Sharer, President and Chief Executive Officer; www.amgen.com

BAXTER HEALTHCARE CORPORATION, Route 120 and Wilson Road, Round Lake, Illinois Zip 60073; tel. 847/270–5440; Joseph Darling, Vice President Marketing and Medication Delivery

CARDINAL HEALTH, 7000 Cardinal Place, Dublin, Zip 43017; tel. 614/757–5000; Nat Findlay, General Manager; www.cardinal.com

COLGATE–PALMOLIVE COMPANY, 191 East Hanover Avenue, Morristown, New Jersey Zip 07960; tel. 973/630–1247; Steve Kaulfuss, Health Care Sales Manager; www.colgate.com

ELI LILLY AND COMPANY, Lilly Corporate Center, Suite 18, Indianapolis, Indiana Zip 46285–4113; tel. 317/277–8173; John H. Poulin, Professional Relations Manager; www.lilly.com

GE HEALTHCARE, 3000 North Grandview Boulevard, Waukesha, Wisconsin Zip 53188; tel. 262/312–7915; Jim Orheim, Marketing Manager

HILL–ROM, 1069 State Route 46 East, Batesville, Indiana Zip 47006–9167; tel. 812/934–7958; Thomas J. Jeffers, Director Government Relations; www.hill–rom.com

JOHNSON & JOHNSON, 425 Hoes Lane, Piscataway, New Jersey Zip 08855; tel. 732/562–3058; Cathi Brozena, Manager Professional Affairs

MANAGEMENT SCIENCE ASSOCIATES, INC., 700 West 47th Street, Suite 400, Kansas City, Missouri Zip 64112–1805; tel. 816/795–1947; Robert Erra

MERCK & COMPANY INC, MARKETING INFORMATION CENTER, 351 North Sumneytown Road, UG2BC–10, North Wales, Pennsylvania Zip 19454–2505; tel. 215/652–3244; Leonardo Mendez

PFIZER U.S. PHARMACEUTICALS GROUP, 235 East 42nd Street, New York, New York Zip 10017; tel. 212/573–3192; Thomas McPhillips, Vice President Trade Relations

RIVERAIN MEDICAL, 3020 South Tech Boulevard, Miamisburg, Ohio Zip 45342; tel. 937/425–6811; Martha Quarles, Director Customer Care; www.riverainmedical.com

SPECIALTY MEDICAL ELECTRONICS, INC., 254 Garden Road, River Ridge, Louisiana Zip 70123; tel. 504/464–1134; Ralph A. Marshall, III, President

SUBURBAN SURGICAL COMPANY, INC., 275 Twelfth Street, Wheeling, Illinois Zip 60090; tel. 847/537–9320; Todd Pinkerman, Vice President; www.suburban–surgical.com

*The members listed in **bold** are Associate Advantage members.* © 2005 AHA Guide

Metro Health Care Assn:

HOSPITAL ASSOCIATION OF SOUTHERN CALIFORNIA, 201 North Figueroa Street, 4th Floor, Los Angeles, California Zip 90071–3322; tel. 213/538–0700; James D. Barber, President

Other:

901 EAST ST LOUIS STREET, SUITE 1800, 901 East St. Louis Street, Suite 1800, Springfield, Missouri Zip 65806; tel. 417/831–7283; Ann King, Partner; www.bkd.com

ALLIANCE IMAGING, INC., 1900 South State College Boulevard, Suite 600, Anaheim, California Zip 92806; tel. 714/688–3301; Paul S. Viviano, Chairman and Chief Executive Officer; www.allianceimaging.com

AMERICA'S BLOOD CENTERS, 725 15th Street N.W., Suite 700, Washington, District of Columbia Zip 20005; tel. 202/393–5725; Jim MacPherson, Executive Director

AMERICAN ASSOCIATION OF NURSE ANESTHETISTS, 222 South Prospect Avenue, Park Ridge, Illinois Zip 60068–4001; tel. 847/692–7050; Jeff Beutler, Executive Director; www.aana.com

AMERICAN BOARD OF MEDICAL SPECIALTIES, 1007 Church Street, Suite 404, Evanston, Illinois Zip 60201–5913; tel. 847/491–9091; Stephen H. Miller, President; www.abms.org

AMERICAN COLLEGE OF HEALTHCARE EXECUTIVES, One North Franklin, Suite 1700, Chicago, Illinois Zip 60606–3491; tel. 312/424–2800; Thomas C. Dolan, President and Chief Executive Officer; www.ache.org

AMERICAN HEALTH INFORMATION MANAGEMENT ASSOCIATION, 233 North Michigan Avenue, Suite 2150, Chicago, Illinois Zip 60601–5519; tel. 312/233–1100; David A. Sweet, Director Library Services

AMERICAN RED CROSS BIOMEDICAL SERVICES, 2025 East Street, N.W., Washington, District of Columbia Zip 20006; tel. 703/206–6000; Marsha Johnson Evans, President and Chief Executive Officer

AMERICAN SOCIETY OF HOSPITAL PHARMACISTS, 7272 Wisconsin Avenue, Bethesda, Maryland Zip 20814; tel. 301/657–3000; Henri R. Manasse, Executive Vice President and Chief Executive Officer

AMERICAN VALET, 8902 North Central Avenue, Phoenix, Arizona Zip 85020; tel. 602/861–9182; Michael Pendergraft, President and Chief Executive Officer; www.americanvalet.com

AMERICANA PROGRAM UNDERWRITERS, 355 North 21st Street, Suite 300, Camp Hill, Zip 17011; tel. 717/214–7601; Ben Francavilla, Senior Managing Directoe; www.amwins.com

AMERINET, INC., 2060 Craigshire Road, Saint Louis, Missouri Zip 63146; tel. 800/388–2638; Robert P. Bowen, Chief Executive Officer; www.amerinet-gpo.com

AMN HEALTHCARE, INC., 12400 High Bluff Drive, Suite 100, San Diego, California Zip 92130–3581; tel. 866/871–8519; Steve Wehn, Senior Vice President of Corporate Development

APTIUM ONCOLOGY, INC., 8201 Beverly Boulevard, Los Angeles, California Zip 90048; tel. 323/966–3400; Rod Cooley, Vice President Revenue Cycle; www.aptiumoncology.com

ARJO, 13166 Lakeshore Drive, Fenton, Zip 48430; tel. 800/323–1245; Andrew Hepburn, Vice President; www.arjousa.com

ARMED FORCES INSTITUTE OF PATHOLOGY, 6825 16th Street N.W., Building 54, Washington, District of Columbia Zip 20306–6000; tel. 202/782–2100; Renata Greenspan, Director

ASSOCIATION OF UNIVERSITY PROGRAMS IN HEALTH ADMINISTRATION, 1911 North Fort Myer Drive, Suite 503, Arlington, Virginia Zip 22201–2543; tel. 703/894–0940; Lydia Reed, President and Chief Executive Officer; www.aupha.org

AVP, INC, 4400 West 107th Street, Overland Park, Kansas Zip 66207; tel. 913/385–1220; Greg Dennis, President of Operations; www.avpco.com

BILLIAN'S HEALTHDATA GROUP, 2100 Powers Ferry Road, Suite 300, Atlanta, Georgia Zip 30339; tel. 800/533–8484; Joyce A. Metzer, Editor in Chief; www.billianshealthdata.com

BLUE CROSS AND BLUE SHIELD ASSOCIATION, 225 North Michigan Avenue, Chicago, Illinois Zip 60601–7680; tel. 312/297–6000; Scott Serota, President

BRIGGS CORPORATION, 7300 Westown Parkway, West Des Moines, Iowa Zip 50266; tel. 515/327–6400; Carrie Bozis Sears

BROADLANE INC, 13727 Noel Road, Suite 1400, Dallas, Texas Zip 75240; tel. 972/813–7500; Kerry Gordon, Marketing Manager; www.info@broadlane.com

C. R. BARD, 730 Central Avenue, Murray Hill, New Jersey Zip 07974; tel. 908/277–8018; James L. Natale, Senior Vice President; www.crbard.com

CAMBIO HEALTH SOLUTIONS, LLC, 100 Westwood Place, Suite 350, Brentwood, Tennessee Zip 37027; tel. 615/324–8500; Thomas W. Singleton, President; www.cambiohealth.com

CCM ADVISORS, LLC, 190 South LaSalle Street, Suite 2800, Chicago, Zip 60603; tel. 312/444–6200; Michael Randall, Director Sales and Marketing; www.ahafunds.org

CHUBB HEALTH CARE, P.O. Box 2002, Simsbury, Connecticut Zip 06070; tel. 860/408–2000; Susan Huntington, Senior Vice President; www.chubb.com

CIT EQUIPMENT FINANCE, 1540 West Fountainhead Parkway, Tempe, Arizona Zip 85282; tel. 480/784–2392; John Medina, Senior Vice President

CLAREDI CORPORATION, 7201 North Classen, Suite 202, Oklahoma City, Zip 73116; tel. 801/444–0339; Skip McKinstry, Vice President Sales and Marketing; www.claredi.com

COGENT HEALTHCARE, INC., 2600 Michelson Drive, Suite 1400, Irvine, California Zip 92612–6529; tel. 949/399–6008; Eugene Fleming, President and Chief Executive Officer; www.cogenthealthcare.com

COMMERCE INSURANCE SERVICES, INC., P.O. Box 2060, Cherry Hill, New Jersey Zip 08003; tel. 856/470–6174; Barbara H. Smith, Senior Vice President and Health Care Unit Manager; www.commerceonline.com

COMPREHENSIVE PHARMACY SERVICES, 6409 North Quail Hollow Road, Memphis, Tennessee Zip 38120–1414; tel. 901/748–0470; Donald Nickleson, President

COMPUTER ASSOCIATES, 4601 Touchton Road E, Suite 3210, Jacksonville, Zip 32246; tel. 904/371–6200; Michael McDermand, Vice President Healthcare; www.ca.com

CONCUITY, 22320 Foothill Boulevard, Suite 250, Hayward, Zip 94541; tel. 510/581–5646; James Farrar, Vice President Sales; www.concuity.com

CRANEWARE, INC., 5770 Hoffner Avenue, Suite 102, Orlando, Florida Zip 32822; tel. 407/384–1711; Derek Morkel, Chief Executive Officer US Operations; www.craneware.com

CSI FINANCIAL SERVICES, 4320 La Jolla Village Drive, Suite 250, San Diego, California Zip 92122; tel. 858/200–9200; Mitch Patridge, Chairman and Chief Executive Officer

CURBELL, INC., ELECTRONICS DIVISION, 7 Cobham Drive, Orchard Park, New York Zip 14127–4180; tel. 716/667–3377; Michael P. Donovan, Marketing Manager

CXTEC, 5404 South Bay Road, Syracuse, New York Zip 13221; tel. 315/476–3000; Brian Vislosky, Strategic Information Manager; www.cxtec.com

DASCO COMPANIES, 11360 Jog Road, Suite 200, Palm Beach Gardens, Florida Zip 33418–1751; tel. 561/691–9900; Jim Galgano, President; www.dascomed.com

DAVITA, INC., 1423 Pacific Avenue, Tacoma, Washington Zip 98402; tel. 800/477–1916; Daniel Evans, Director of Acute Support Services and Marketing; www.davita.com

DEPARTMENT OF AIR FORCE MEDICAL SERVICE, HQ USAF/SG, Bolling AFB, District of Columbia Zip 20332–6188; tel. 202/545–6700

DEPARTMENT OF THE ARMY, OFFICE OF THE SURGEON GENERAL, 5109 Leesburg Pike, Falls Church, Virginia Zip 22041; tel. 202/690–6467

DEPARTMENT OF THE NAVY, BUREAU OF MEDICINE AND SURGERY, 2300 East Street N.W., Washington, District of Columbia Zip 20372–5300; tel. 202/762–3701; Rear Admiral Donald C. Arthur, Commander

DEPARTMENT OF VETERANS AFFAIRS, 201 Walnut Avenue, Suite 201, Vallejo, California Zip 94592–1107; Linda Pierce, Director, Sierra Pacific Network

DEPARTMENT OF VETERANS AFFAIRS, 810 Vermont Avenue N.W., Washington, District of Columbia Zip 20420; tel. 202/273–5400; Jonathan Perlin, Acting Secretary

DHHS, PUBLIC HEALTH SERVICE, DIVISION OF INDIAN HEALTH, HEALTH CARE ADMINISTRATION BRANCH, 5600 Fisher Lane, Room 6A–25, Rockville, Maryland Zip 20857; tel. 301/443–1085; Charles Grim, Interim Director

DIVERSIFIED INVESTMENT ADVISORS, 4 Manhattanville Road, Purchase, Zip 10577; tel. 914/697–8952; Eric Henon, Vice President; www.divinvest.com

DIVERSIFIED MAINTENANCE, 5110 Eisenhower Boulevard, Suite 250, Tampa, Florida Zip 33634; tel. 800/351–1557; Rebecca Addington, Director Marketing; www.diveinc.com

EMERGENCY CONSULTANTS, INC., 4075 Copper Ridge Drive, Traverse City, Michigan Zip 49684–4796; tel. 800/253–1795; James Johnson, President; www.eci–med.com

EMERGENCY PHYSICAN MEDICAL GROUP, PC, 2000 Green Road, Suite 300, Ann Arbor, Michigan Zip 48105; David Badour, Vice President of Business Development; www.epmgpc.com

ERNST & YOUNG, 1225 Connecticut Avenue N.W., Washington, District of Columbia Zip 20036; tel. 202/327–8854; Sherry Hayes, Director

FASTAFF NURSING, 6501 South Fiddlers Green Circle, Suite 200, Englewood, Colorado Zip 80111; tel. 800/736–8773; Sheryl Hinton, Director Marketing; www.fastaff.com

FEDERAL MEDICAL, INC., 6903 Rockledge Drive, 8th Floor, Rockville, Maryland Zip 20850–5979; tel. 301/214–8900; Brian Moffitt

GLAXOSMITHKLINE, Five Moore Drive, Research Traingle Park, North Carolina Zip 27709–3398; tel. 919/483–2031; Peter G. Kaylid, Head, GPO Segments and Institutional Sales; www.gsk.com

GULDMANN INC., 5505 Johns Road, Suite 700, Tampa, Florida Zip 33634–4307; tel. 813/880–0619; Anders Drechsler, President; www.guldmann.com

HAWAII MEDICAL SERVICE ASSOCIATION, P.O. Box 860, Honolulu, Hawaii Zip 96808–0860; tel. 808/948–5482; Gina Marting, Manager Facility Reimbursement

HEALTHCARE MANAGEMENT SYSTEMS, INC., 3102 West End Avenue, Suite 400, Nashville, Tennessee Zip 37203; tel. 615/383–7300; Christy Wright, Marketing Manager; www.hmstn.com

HEALTHMEANS, INC., 1333 Corporate Drive, Suite 360, Irving, Texas Zip 75038; tel. 972/488–6633; Vicki Judd, Director Marketing; www.healthmeans.com

HOVERTECH INTERNATIONAL, 513 South Clewell Street, Bethlehem, Pennsylvania Zip 18015; tel. 610/694–9600; David T. Davis, President; www.hovermatt.com

HQ ACC/SGMS, 162 Dodd, Suite 100, Langley AFB, Virginia Zip 23665–1995

HQ AETC/SGAL, 63 Main Circle, Suite 3, Randolph AFB, Texas Zip 78150–4549

HQ AFMC/SGAR, 4225 Logistics Avenue, N–209, Dayton, Ohio Zip 45433–5761; tel. 937/656–3655; Alice Rohrbach

HQ AFSPC/SGAL, 150 Vandenberg Street, Suite 1105, Petterson AFB, Colorado Zip 80914–4550

HQ AMC/SGSL, 203 West Losey Street, Room 1180, Scott A F B, Illinois Zip 62225–5219

HQ PACAF/SGAL, 25 East Street, Suite D1, Hickam AFB, Hawaii Zip 96853–5418

HQ USAFA/SGAL, Pinion Drive, Building 4102, Suite 3, U South A F Academy, Colorado Zip 80840–2325

HURON CONSULTING GROUP, 550 West Van Buren, Chicago, Illinois Zip 60607; tel. 312/880–3335; Mukesh Gangwal, Managing Director; www.huronconsultinggroup.com

HYLAND SOFTWARE, INC., 28500 Clemens Road, Westlake, Zip 44145; tel. 440/788–5814; Michael Kortan, Director Health Care Solutions; www.onbase.com

INSITE PROPERTIES, INC., 3400 East Bayaud Avenue, Suite 250, Denver, Colorado Zip 80206–4814; tel. 303/320–0505; James C. Turpen, President; www.insiteproperties.com

INTERNATIONAL ASSOCIATION FOR HEALTHCARE SECURITY AND SAFETY, P.O. Box 5038, Glendale Heights, Illinois Zip 60139; tel. 630/871–9936; Nancy Felesena, Executive Assistant; www.iahss.org

J. STEPHENS MAYHUGH AND ASSOCIATES, INC., P.O. Box 77458, Baton Rouge, Louisiana Zip 70879; tel. 225/295–7000; Melanie Johnson, Chief Executive Officer

JOHNSON & LEE CONSULTING, LLC, 6203 Abercorn, Suite 100, Savannah, Georgia Zip 31405; tel. 912/596–5565; Franky L. Johnson, President

KEPPLER ASSOCIATES, INC., 4350 North Fairfax Drive, Suite 700, Arlington, Virginia Zip 22203; tel. 703/516–4000; Kevin O'Hare

LIFE ALLIANCE ORGAN RECOVERY AGENCY–UNIVERSITY OF MIAMI, 1801 N.W. 9th Avenue, Suite 150–A, Miami, Florida Zip 33136; tel. 800/232–2892; Karen Garcia, Assistant Director; www.laora.med.miami.edu

---

*The members listed in **bold** are Associate Advantage members.*

MAG MUTUAL, 3025 Breckenridge Boulevard, 120, Duluth, Zip 30096; tel. 678/226–0035; David A. Miller; www.magmutual.com

MEDEX, INC., 2231 Rutherford Road, Carlsbad, California Zip 92008; tel. 760/602–4427; Eileen Lane, Vice President Marketing

MEMORIAL BLOOD CENTERS, 2304 Park Avenue, Minneapolis, Minnesota Zip 55404; tel. 612/871–3300; Donald C. Berglund, Chief Executive Officer; www.memorialbloodcenters.org

MITRETEK SYSTEMS, 3150 Fairview Park South, Falls Church, Zip 22042; tel. 703/610–2255; Richard Fiddleman, Deputy Health Program Manager; www.mitretek.org

MODERN HEALTHCARE, 360 North Michigan Avenue, Chicago, Illinois Zip 60601–3806; tel. 312/649–5491; Fawn Lopez, Publisher; www.modernhealthcare.com

MRI INTERNATIONAL, INC./CLAIMS SERVICING OF AMERICA, 5330 South Durango Drive, Las Vegas, Nevada Zip 89113–1835; tel. 702/396–8822; Linda Martinez

NAVAL REGIONAL MEDICAL CENTER, PSC 1005, Box 36, FPO, APO/FPO Europe Zip 09593–0136

NDCHEALTH, NDC Plaza, Atlanta, Georgia Zip 30329; tel. 404/728–2000; Vijay Tummala, Director Product Marketing; www.ndchealth.com

NORTH CENTRAL HEALTH SERVICES, INC., P.O. Box 528, Lafayette, Indiana Zip 47902; tel. 765/423–1604; John R. Walling, President and Chief Executive Officer

OLYMPUS AMERICA, INC., P.O. Box 9058, Melville, New York Zip 11747–9058; tel. 631/844–5000; Steven K. Wendt, Senior Manager National Accounts

PEDIATRIX SCREENING, INC., P.O. Box 219, Bridgeville, Pennsylvania Zip 15017; tel. 412/220–2300; Joseph M. Quashnock, Laboratory Director; www.pediatrixscreening.com

PER–SE TECHNOLOGIES, 1145 Sanctuary Parkway, Suite 200, Alpharetta, Zip 30004–4785; tel. 770/237–7714; Ann Marie Brown, Vice President Marketing

PEROT SYSTEMS HEALTHCARE, 101 Cumberland Avenue, Madison, Tennessee Zip 37115; tel. 800/659–8883; Glenn Heath, Vice President Sales; www.perotsystems.com/revenuecycle

PIPER MARBURY RUDNICK & WOLFE LLP, 6225 Smith Avenue, Baltimore, Maryland Zip 21209–3600; tel. 410/580–4179; Sandra Jarva Weiss, Attorney

POSTX CORPORATION, 3 Results Way, Cupertino, Zip 95014; tel. 773/354–6512; Scott Olechowski, Vice President Product Strategy

PPO CHECK, P.O. Box 2873, Houston, Texas Zip 77252; tel. 713/651–1533; Ryne Manahan, Chief Operating Officer

PROCARE USA, LLC, 2 Bridgewater Road, Farmington, Connecticut Zip 06032; tel. 860/677–6525; Richard Anderson, Vice President Business Development

PROCTER AND GAMBLE COMPANY, 8700 Mason–Montgomery Road, Mason, Zip 45040–9462; tel. 513/622–4672; John E. Roney, Associate Director

PROFITLINE, 9920 Pacific Hts Boulevard, 200, San Diego, California Zip 92121; tel. 858/202–1203; Kathleen Glass, Assistant Vice President; www.profitline.com

QUADRAMED CORPORATION, 12110 Sunset Hills Road, Suite 600, Reston, Virginia Zip 20190; tel. 800/393–0278; Kevin Cleary, Marketing Manager; www.quadramed.com

R & J HEALTH, 35 Waterview Boulevard, Parsippany, New Jersey Zip 07054; tel. 973/331–1070; Steven Parkins, Director Business Development; www.randjhealth.com

RED CAPITAL GROUP, 7720 A. Shedhorn Drive, PMB 97, Bozeman, Montana Zip 59718; tel. 406/763–5670; Charles C. Ervin, Jr, Managing Director; www.redcapitalgroup.com

REHABCARE GROUP, INC., 7733 Forsyth Boulevard, Suite 1700, Saint Louis, Missouri Zip 63105–1817; tel. 314/202–8400; John Short, President; www.rehabcare.com

RISK MANAGEMENT LOGISTICS PROACTIVE, 2255 Glades Road, Suite 324, Boca Raton, Florida Zip 33431; tel. 561/482–8900; Lawrence E. Lafferty, Vice President

ROSARIO INCORPORATED, P.O. Box 5265, Clover, North Carolina Zip 29710; tel. 803/631–4391; Sandra R. Robinson, President and Chief Executive Officer; www.rosarioinc.com

RURAL HEALTH RESOURCE CENTER, 600 East Superior Street, Suite 404, Duluth, Minnesota Zip 55802; tel. 218/727–9390; Terry J. Hill, Executive Director; www.ruralcenter.org

SENTINEL FIDUCIARY SERVICES, INC., 605 Delaney Avenue, Orlando, Florida Zip 32801; tel. 407/246–7221; Stephen J. Lansing, President; www.sfs.cc

SPRINT, 1400 East Rochelle Boulevard, Irving, Texas Zip 75039; tel. 972/405–7652; Charles P. Tipay, Manager Healthcare Marketing

TEKNION, 12000 Horizon Way, Mount Laurel, New Jersey Zip 08054; tel. 877/835–8466; Steve Knippen, Manager Education and Healthcare Markets; www.teknion.com

TENNANT, 701 North Lilac Drive, Minneapolis, Minnesota Zip 55422; tel. 763/513–2272; David Stanley, Market Research Specialist

TEXAS MEDICAL CENTER, 406 Jesse Jones Library Building, Houston, Texas Zip 77030; tel. 713/797–0100; Richard E. Wainerdi, President and Chief Executive Officer

TEXAS ORGANIZATION OF RURAL & COMMUNITY HOSPITALS, P.O. Box 14547, Austin, Texas Zip 78761; tel. 512/873–0045; John F. Boff, President and Chief Executive Officer; www.torchnet.org

THE ADVISORY BOARD COMPANY, 2445 M Street N.W., Washington, District of Columbia Zip 20037–2403; tel. 202/266–5600; Scott Fassbach, Chief Research Officer; www.advisory.com

THE GOVERNANCE INSTITUTE, 6333 Greenwich Drive, Suite 200, San Diego, California Zip 92122; tel. 858/909–0811; Gordon R. Clark, President and Chief Executive Officer; www.governanceinstitute.com

THE JEWISH GUILD FOR THE BLIND, 15 West 65th Street, New York, New York Zip 10023; tel. 212/769–6200; Alan R. Morse, President and Chief Executive Officer; www.jgb.org

THE WALKER COMPANY, 4848 Hastings Drive, Lake Oswego, Zip 97035; tel. 503/534–9461; Larry W. Walker, Principal; www.walkercompany.com

THE WHITING TURNER CONTRACTING COMPANY, 300 East Joppa Road, Baltimore, Maryland Zip 21286; tel. 410/337–7422; Kim Bates, Market Coordinator; www.whiting–turner.com

THEREX, INC., 341 Cool Springs Boulevard, Franklin, Tennessee Zip 37067; tel. 615/236–2550; Robert A. Metry, Executive Vice President

THERMO USCS, 120 Bishop's Way, Brookfield, Zip 53008; tel. 262/784–5600; Christine Miller, Executive Vice President Healthcare Group; www.us-cs.com

TRANSUNION, 2500 Regency Parkway, Cary, Zip 27511; Geoffrey Hakel, Vice President Vertical Markets; www.transunion.com

U. S. ARMY MEDICAL COMMAND, 2050 Worth Road, Suite 3, Fort Sam Houston, Texas Zip 78234; tel. 210/221–2212

U.S. POWER CORPORATION, 115 Castle Heights Avenue North –Suite 206, Lebanon, Connecticut Zip 37087; tel. 860/868–6696; William Ross, President

UNITED HOSPITAL FUND OF NEW YORK, 350 Fifth Avenue, 23rd Floor, New York, New York Zip 10118; tel. 212/494–0700; James R. Tallon, Jr, President

VERTICAL CLAIMS MANAGEMENT, L.L.C., Three Gateway Center, 15 North, Pittsburgh, Zip 15222; tel. 800/501–6248; Clare Bello, President; www.vcm–llc.com

VETERANS AFFAIRS EASTERN REGION OFFICE, 9600 North Point Road, Fort Howard, Maryland Zip 21052

VISN 1 OFFICE, 200 Spring Road, Building 61, Bedford, Massachusetts Zip 01730

VISN 10 OFFICE, 11500 Northlake Drive, Suite 200, Cincinnati, Ohio Zip 45259–1655

VISN 11 OFFICE, P.O. Box 134002, Ann Arbor, Michigan Zip 48113–4002; Linda Belton, Network Director

VISN 12 OFFICE, P.O. Box 5000, Building 18, Hines, Illinois Zip 60141–5000; tel. 708/202–8400; Renee Oshinski, Acting Network Director

VISN 15 OFFICE, 4801 Linwood Boulevard, Kansas City, Missouri Zip 64128

VISN 16 OFFICE, 1600 East Woodrow Wilson Drive, Suite A, 3rd Floor, Jackson, Mississippi Zip 39216; tel. 601/364–7901; Rica Lewis Payton, Deputy Network Director

VISN 17 OFFICE, 2301 East Lamar Boulevard, Suite 650, Arlington, Texas Zip 76006–7435

VISN 18 OFFICE, 6950 East Williams Field Road, Mesa, Arizona Zip 85212–6033; tel. 602/222–2681; Patricia A. McKlem, Director; www.va.gov/VISN18

VISN 19 OFFICE, 4100 East Mississippi Avenue, Suite 510, Glendale, Colorado Zip 80222

VISN 2 OFFICE, P.O. Box 8980, Albany, New York Zip 12208–0980; tel. 518/472–1055

VISN 20 OFFICE, P.O. Box 1035, Portland, Oregon Zip 97207

VISN 21 OFFICE, 201 Walnut Avenue, Mare Island, California Zip 94592

VISN 22 OFFICE, 5901 East Seventh Street, Long Beach, California Zip 90822; tel. 562/494–5963; Kenneth J. Clark, Director

VISN 23 OFFICE, 5445 Minnehaha Avenue South, 2nd Floor, Minneapolis, Minnesota Zip 55417; tel. 612/727–5967; Robert A. Petzel, Network Director; www.visn23.med.va.gov

VISN 3 OFFICE, 130 West Kingsbridge Road, Building 16, Bronx, New York Zip 10468; James J. Farsetta, Director

VISN 4 OFFICE, Delafield Road, Pittsburgh, Pennsylvania Zip 15240

VISN 5 OFFICE, 849 International Drive, Suite 275, Linthicum Heights, Maryland Zip 21090

VISN 6 OFFICE, 300 West Morgan Street, Suite 1402, Durham, North Carolina Zip 27701

VISN 7 OFFICE, 3700 Crestwood Parkway N.E., Suite 260, Duluth, Georgia Zip 30096–5585

VISN 8 OFFICE, P.O. Box 406, Bay Pines, Florida Zip 33744

VISN 9 OFFICE, 1310 24th Avenue South, Nashville, Tennessee Zip 37212–2637

VOCERA COMMUNICATIONS, 20600 Lazaneo Drive, Cupertino, California Zip 95014; tel. 408/790–4100; Angie Airhart, Sales Administrator; www.vocera.com

WACHOVIA, 80 South 8th Street, Suite 3400, Minneapolis, Minnesota Zip 55402; tel. 612/342–0789; Bill Bonello, Senior Research Analyst; www.wachovia.com

WALGREENS HEALTH INITIATIVES, 1417 Lake Cook Road, MS 468, Deerfield, Zip 60015; tel. 847/374–2640; Gregg Cygan, Director Clinical Pharmacy

WIELAND FURNITURE, P.O. Box 1000, Grabill, Indiana Zip 46741; tel. 260/627–3686; Dennis Balgavy, Director Marketing; www.wielandfurniture.com

University Program:

HOUSTON BAPTIST UNIVERSITY, 7502 Fondren Road, Houston, Texas Zip 77074; tel. 281/649–3325; Ray G. Newman, Dean, College of Business and Economics; www.hbu.edu

CANADA

Other:

DARCOR CASTERS, 7 Staffordshire Place, Toronto, Ontario Zip M8W 1T1; tel. 416/255–8563; Cyril J. Muhic, Regional Sales Manager

SIGMA ASSISTEL, INC., 1100 Boul Rene–Levesque Quest, Suite 1500, Montreal, Quebec Zip H3B 4N4; tel. 800/465–6390; Louise Des Ormeaux, General Manager

ST. JOSEPH'S HEALTH CARE SYSTEM, P.O. Box 155, LCD 1, Hamilton, Ontario Zip L8L 7V7; tel. 905/528–0138; Brian Guest, Executive Director

FOREIGN

BAHAMAS

Other:

PRINCESS MARGARET HOSPITAL, P.O. Box N–8700, Nassau, tel. 242/322–2861; Coralee Adderly, Chief Hospital Administrator; www.phabahamas.org

BAHRAIN

Other:

INTERNATIONAL HOSPITAL OF BAHRAIN, P.O. Box 1084, Manama, F. S. Zeerah, President

*The members listed in **bold** are Associate Advantage members.*

BERMUDA

Other:

KING EDWARD VII MEMORIAL HOSPITAL, P.O. Box HM1023, Hamilton, L. Keitha Bassett, Health Sciences Librarian

BRAZIL

Other:

HOSPITAL ISRAELITA ALBERT EINSTEIN, Avenue Albert Einstein, 627, Sao Paulo 05651–901, Jairo Tabacow Hidal, Vice President; www.einstein.br

HOSPITAL SAMARITANO, Rua Conselheiro Brotero, 1486, Sao Paulo, Zip 01232–010; Jose Antonio de Lima, General Superintendent; www.samaritano.com.br

SANTA MARINA HOSPITAL AND MATERNIDADE, Av Santa Catarina, 2785, Jabaquara, Sao Paulo, SP, Zip 04378–500; Daniela Maria de Almeida, Gestao Integrada

CHINA

Other:

ELECTRICAL AND MECHANICAL SERVICES DEPARTMENT, HONGKONG SPECIAL ADMINISTRATIVE REGION GOVERNMENT, 3 Lok Man Road, Chai Wan, Hongkong, Alfred Sit Wing–hang, Health Sector Manager

COLUMBIA

Other:

ASOCIACION COLOMBIANA DE HOSPITALES Y CLINICAS, Carrera 4, No 73–15, Bogota, Juan Carlos Giraldo Valencia, Director General; www.achc.org.co

FUNDACION SANTA FE DE BOGOTA, Calle 119 No 9–02, Bogota, Ana Catalina Vesquez Quintero, Manager

CYPRUS

Other:

NEAPOLIS HEALTH CENTER, 111 Agiou Pavlou Avenue, Paphos, Zip CY–8129; Constantin Mavros, Chief Executive Officer and Managing Director

ECUADOR

Other:

HOSPITAL VOZANDES – QUITO, Villengua 022–37, Casilla17–17–691, Quito, Dan Shedd, Administrator; www.hcjb.org

JUNTA DE BENEFICENCIA DE GUAYAQUIL, P.O. Box 09–01–789, Guayaquil, Lautaro Aspiazu Wright, Director; www.jbg.org.ec

GERMANY

Other:

HQ USAFE/SGPXL, Unit 3050, Box 130, Ramstein AB, Zip 09094–5001

INTERNATIONAL SPINE CLINIC BERLIN, Tauentzienstr 17, Berlin 10789, Munther Sabarini, Medical Director; www.spine–clinic.de

GREECE

Other:

DIAGNOSTIC AND THERAPEUTIC CENTRE OF ATHENS HYGEIA, S A, 4 Erythrou Stavrou & Kifissiap, Athens, C. Kitsionas, Executive Director

IASO S.A. DIAGNOSTIC THERAPEUTIC AND RESEARCH CENTER, OBSTETRICS AND GYNECOLOGY HOSPITAL, 37–39 Kifissias Avenue, Maroussi Athens, Zip 15123

ISRAEL

Other:

HADASSAH MEDICAL ORGANIZATION, Box 12000, Jerusalem, Zip 91120; Shlomo Mor–Yosef, Director General; www.hadassah.org.il

S.A.R.E.L. SUPPLIES AND SERVICES FOR MEDICINE LTD., P.O. Box 8466, Netanya 42504, Moshe Modai, Chief Executive Officer; www.sarel.co.il

JAPAN

Other:

NAVAL REGIONAL MEDICAL CENTER, U.S. Naval Base, FPO, Zip 96362

ST. LUKE'S INTERNATIONAL HOSPITAL, 10–1 Akashi–Cho, Chuo–Ku, Tokyo 104, Shigeaki Hinohara, Honorary President

LEBANON

Other:

AMERICAN UNIVERSITY OF BEIRUT MEDICAL CENTER, 3 Dag Hammarskjold Plaza, 8th Floor, New York, Zip 10017–2303; John Rhoder, Medical Center Director

MAKASSED GENERAL HOSPITAL, P.O. Box 6301, Beirut, Moh'd Firikh, Director

SAINT GEORGE HOSPITAL, P.O. Box 166378, Beirut, Zip 1100–2807; Ziad Kamel, Administrative Director; www.stgeorgehospital.org

MEXICO

Consulting Firm:

ASOCIACION NACIONAL DE HOSPITALES PRIVADOS, Viaducto Rio Becerra 97 Colonel Napoles, Mexico City, Ernesto Perusquia, President

Other:

SHRINERS HOSPITAL FOR CHILDREN, Suchil 152, Colonel El Rosario, Mexico City, Zip 04380; Araceli Nagore, Administrator

UNIVERSIDAD AUTONOMA DE GUADALAJARA, 4715 Fredericksburg Road, 300, San Antonio, Zip 78229; tel. 210/366–1611; Susana Leano, Dean

Other Inpatient Care:

OASIS HOSPITAL, 2247 San Diego Avenue, Suite 235, San Ysidro, Zip 92143; tel. 800/700–1850; Francisco Contreras, Director

NETHERLANDS ANTILLES

Other:

SINT MAARTEN MEDICAL CENTER FOUNDATION, Welgelegen Road 30 Ut 1 Cay Hill, Sint Maarten, tel. 599/543–1111; George Scot, General Director

PANAMA

Other:

CLINICA SAN FERNANDO, S. A., Dept PTY 1663, P.O. Box 25207, Miami, Zip 33102–5207; tel. 507/229–1699; Edgardo Fernandez, Medical Director; www.hospitalsanfernando.com

FAMILY HOSPITAL GROUP OF COMPANIES, PO Box 87–3715 – Zona 7, Panama, tel. 507/227–8354; Randall D. Arlett, Vice President Finance

PERU

Other:

BRITISH AMERICAN HOSPITAL, Avenue Alfredo Salazar 3 Era, Lima 27, tel. 511/712–3000; Gonzalo Garrido–Lecca, Director; www.clinangloamericana.com.pe

PHILIPPINES

Other:

SPCASTRO AND ASSOCIATES, INC., Gabriel III Condominium, San Miguel Avenue, Suite 601, Pasig City 1603, Salvador P. Castro, Jr, Chairman and Managing Director; www.spcastro.com

ST. LUKE'S MEDICAL CENTER, 279 East Rodriguez Sr Boulevard, Quezon City, Jose F. G. Ledesma, Chief Executive Officer

SAUDI ARABIA

Other:

ABDUL RAHMAN AL MISHARI GENERAL HOSPITAL, Olaya, Riyadh 11564, Abdul Rahman Al Mishari, President

DR. ERFAN AND BAGEDO GENERAL HOSPITAL, P.O. Box 6519, Jeddah 21452, Zip 21452; Mohamed Erfan, Owner and General Director; www.erfanbagedohospital.med.sa

ELAJ MEDICAL SERVICES COMPANY, LTD., P.O. Box 51141, Jeddah 21463, Mohamed Amin, Medical Director

MUHAMMAD S BASHARAHIL HOSPITAL, P.O. Box 10505, Madinah Road, Omora Gadida, Makkah, Sameer M. Basharahil, Vice President

SAAD SPECIALIST HOSPITAL, P.O. Box 30353, Al–Khobar 31952S, Gordon Pincock, Chief Operating Officer

TAIWAN

Other:

CHANG GUNG MEMORIAL HOSPITAL, 199 Tun Hwa North Road, Taipei, Yi–Chou Chuang, Director Administration Center

TURKEY

Other:

ISTANBUL MEMORIAL HOSPITAL, Piyale Pasa Bulvari, Okmeydani, Istanbul, Zip 80270; Hakan Ertufan, Quality and Human Resources Coordinator

UNITED ARAB EMIRATES

Other:

AMERICAN HOSPITAL–DUBAI, P.O. Box 59, Dubai, Saeed M. Almulla, Chairman

VENEZUELA

Other:

POLICLINICA METROPOLITANA, C.A., Calle A–1, URB, Caurimare, Caracas 1060, Pedro Del Medico, Medical Director

Notes

Notes

B Health Care Systems, Networks and Alliances

Section B

Introduction

This section includes listings for networks, health care systems and alliances.

Health Care Systems

To reflect the diversity that exists among health care organizations, this publication uses the term health care system to identify both multihospital and diversified single hospital systems.

Multihospital Systems

A multihospital health care system is two or more hospitals owned, leased, sponsored, or contract managed by a central organization.

Single Hospital Systems

Single, freestanding member hospitals may be categorized as health care systems by bringing into membership three or more, and at least 25 percent, of their owned or leased non–hospital preacute and postacute health care organizations. (For purposes of definition, health care delivery is the availability of professional healthcare staff during all hours of the organization's operations). Organizations provide, or provide and finance, diagnostic, therapeutic, and/or consultative patient or client services that normally precede or follow acute, inpatient, hospitalization; or that serve to prevent or substitute for such hospitalization. These services are provided in either a freestanding facility not eligible for licensure as a hospital under state statue or through one that is a subsidiary of a hospital.

The first part of this section is an alphabetical list of multihospital health care systems. Each system listed contains two or more hospitals, which are listed under the system by state. Data for this section were compiled from the 2004 *Annual Survey* and the membership information base as published in section A of the *AHA Guide*.

One of the following codes appears after the name of each system listed to indicate the type of organizational control reported by that system:

CC	Catholic (Roman) church–related system, not–for–profit
CO	Other church–related system, not–for–profit
NP	Other not–for–profit system, including nonfederal, governmental systems
IO	Investor–owned, for profit system
FG	Federal Government

One of the following codes appears after the name of each hospital to indicate how that hospital is related to the system:

O	Owned
L	Leased
S	Sponsored
CM	Contract–managed

Health System Classification System

An identification system for Health Systems was developed jointly by the American Hospital Association's Health Research and Education Trust and Health Forum, and the University of California-Berkeley.[1] A health system is assigned to one of five categories based on how much they differentiate and centralize their hospital services, physician arrangements, and provider-based insurance products. Differentiation refers to the number of different products or services that the organization offers. Centralization refers to whether decision-making and service delivery emanate from the system level more so than individual hospitals.

The Categories Are:

Centralized Health System: A delivery system in which the system centrally organizes individual hospital service delivery, physician arrangements, and insurance product development. The number of different products/services that are offered across the system is moderate.

Centralized Physician/Insurance Health System: A delivery system with highly centralized physician arrangements and insurance product development. Within this group, hospital services are relatively decentralized with individual hospitals having discretion over the array of services they offer. The number of different products/services that are offered across the system is moderate.

Moderately Centralized Health System: A delivery system that is distinguished by the presence of both centralized and decentralized activity for hospital services, physician arrangements, and insurance product development. For example, a system within this group may have centralized care of expensive, high technology services, such as open heart surgery, but allows individual hospitals to provide an array of other health services based on local needs. The number of different products/services that are offered across the system is moderate.

Decentralized Health System: A delivery system with a high degree of decentralized of hospital services, physician arrangements, and insurance product development. Within this group, systems may lack an overarching structure for coordination. Service and product differentiation is high, which may explain why centralization is hard to achieve. In this group, the system may simply service a role in sharing information and providing administrative support to highly developed local delivery systems centered around hospitals.

Independent Hospital System: A delivery system with limited differentiation in hospital services, physician arrangements, and insurance product development. These systems are largely horizontal affiliations of autonomous hospitals.

No Assignment: For some systems sufficient data from the Annual Survey were not available to determine a cluster assignment.

The second part of this section lists health care systems indexed geographically by state and city. Every effort has been made to be as inclusive and accurate as possible. However, as in all efforts of this type, there may be omissions. For further information, write to the section for Health Care Systems, American Hospital Association, One North Franklin, Chicago, IL 60606–3401.

Networks

The *AHA Guide* shows listings of networks. A network is defined as a group of hospitals, physicians, other providers, insurers and/or community agencies that work together to coordinate and deliver a broad spectrum of services to their community. Organizations listed represent the lead or hub of the network activity. Networks are listed by state, then alphabetically by name including participating partners.

The network identification process has purposely been designed to capture networks of varying organization type. Sources include but are not limited to the following: *AHA Annual Survey,* national, state and metropolitan associations, national news and periodical searches, and the networks and their health care providers themselves. Therefore, networks are included regardless of whether a hospital or healthcare system is the network lead. When an individual hospital does appear in the listing, it is indicative of the role the hospital plays as the network lead. In addition, the network listing is **not** mutually exclusive of the hospital, health care system or alliance listings within this publication.

Networks are very fluid in their composition as goals evolve and partners change. Therefore, some of the networks included in this listing may have dissolved, reformed, or simply been renamed as this section was being produced for publication.

The network identification process is an ongoing and responsive initiative. As more information is collected and validated, it will be made available in other venues, in addition to the *AHA Guide.* For more information concerning the network identification process, please contact The American Hospital Association Resource Center at 312/422–2050.

Alliances

An alliance is a formal organization, usually owned by shareholders/members, that works on behalf of its individual members in the provision of services and products and in the promotion of activities and ventures. The organization functions under a set of bylaws or other written rules to which each member agrees to abide.

Alliances are listed alphabetically by name. Its members are listed alphabetically by state, city, and then by member name.

---

[1] Bazzoli, CJ; Shortell, SM; Dubbs, N; Chan, C; and Kralovec, P; "A Taxonomy of Health networks and Systems: Bringing Order Out of Chaos" *Health Services Research*, February; 1999

Statistics for Multihospital Health Care Systems and their Hospitals

The following tables describing multihospital health care systems refer to information in section B of the 2006 *AHA Guide*.

Table 1 shows the number of multihospital health care systems by type of control. Table 2 provides a breakdown of the number of systems that own, lease, sponsor or contract manage hospitals within each control category. Table 3 gives the number of hospitals and beds in each control category as well as total hospitals and beds. Finally, Table 4 shows the percentage of hospitals and beds in each control category.

For more information on multihospital health care systems, please write to the Section for Health Care Systems, One North Franklin, Chicago, Illinois 60606–3401 or call 312/422–3000.

Table 1. Multihospital Health Care Systems, by Type of Organizaton Control

Type of Control	Code	Number of Systems
Catholic (Roman) church–related	CC	43
Other church–related	CO	13
Subtotal, church–related		56
Other not–for–profit	NP	235
Subtotal, not–for–profit		291
Investor Owned	IO	61
Federal Government	FG	5
Total		357

Table 2. Multihospital Health Care Systems, by Type of Ownership and Control

Type of Ownership	Catholic Church–Related (CC)	Other Church–Related (CO)	Total Church–Related (CC + CO)	Other Not–for–Profit (NP)	Total Not–for–Profit (CC, CO, + NP)	Investor–Owned (IO)	Federal Government	All Systems
Systems that only own, lease or sponsor	37	12	49	203	252	52	5	309
Systems that only contract–manage	0	0	0	1	1	3	0	4
Systems that manage, own, lease, or sponsor	6	1	7	31	38	6	0	44
Total	43	13	56	235	291	61	5	357

Table 3. Hospitals and Beds in Multihospital Health Care Systems, by Type of Ownership and Control

Type of Ownership	Catholic Church–Related (CC) H	B	Other Church–Related (CO) H	B	Total Church–Related (CC + CO) H	B	Other Not–for–Profit (NP) H	B	Total Not–for–Profit (CC, CO, + NP) H	B	Investor–Owned (IO) H	B	Federal Government H	B	All Systems H	B
Owned, leased or sponsored	518	108,178	111	21,737	629	129,915	1,093	254,293	1,722	384,208	997	129,208	245	47,801	2,964	561,217
Contract–managed	42	2,071	1	268	43	2,339	91	7,640	134	9,979	199	15,398	0	0	333	25,377
Total	560	110,249	112	22,005	672	132,254	1,184	261,933	1,856	394,187	1,196	144,606	245	47,801	3,297	586,594

H = hospitals; **B** = beds.

Table 4. Hospitals and Beds in Multihospital Health Care Systems, by Type of Ownership and Control as a Percentage of All Systems

Type of Ownership	Catholic Church–Related (CC) H	B	Other Church–Related (CO) H	B	Total Church–Related (CC + CO) H	B	Other Not–for–Profit (NP) H	B	Total Not–for–Profit (CC, CO, + NP) H	B	Investor–Owned (IO) H	B	Federal Government H	B	All Systems H	B
Owned, leased or sponsored	17.5	19.3	3.7	3.9	21.2	23.1	36.9	45.3	58.1	68.5	33.6	23.0	8.3	8.5	100.0	100.0
Contract–managed	12.6	8.2	0.3	1.1	12.9	9.2	27.3	30.1	40.2	39.3	59.8	60.7	0.0	0.0	100.0	100.0
Total	17.0	18.8	3.4	3.8	20.4	22.5	35.9	44.7	56.3	67.2	36.3	24.7	7.4	8.1	100.0	100.0

H = hospitals; **B** = beds.
*Please note that figures may not always equal the provided subtotal or total percentages due to rounding.

Section B

0071: ACCORD HEALTH CARE CORPORATION (IO)
14010 Roosevelt Road, Clearwater, FL Zip 33762;
tel. 727/573–1755; Stephen H. Noble, President
(Independent Hospital System)

GEORGIA: STEWART–WEBSTER HOSPITAL (O, 25 beds) 300 Alston Street, Richland, GA Zip 31825–1406, Mailing Address: P.O. Box 190, Zip 31825–0190; tel. 229/887–3366; Stephen H. Noble, President

WHEELER COUNTY HOSPITAL (O, 73 beds) 111 Third Street, Glenwood, GA Zip 30428–2301, Mailing Address: P.O. Box 398, Zip 30428–0398; tel. 912/523–5113; Brenda Josey, Administrator

Owned, leased, sponsored:	2 hospitals	98 beds
Contract–managed:	0 hospitals	0 beds
Totals:	2 hospitals	98 beds

★0235: ADVENTIST HEALTH (CO)
2100 Douglas Boulevard, Roseville, CA Zip 95661–3898, Mailing Address: P.O. Box 619002, Zip 95661–9002; tel. 916/781–2000; Donald R. Ammon, President and Chief Executive Officer
(Decentralized Health System)

CALIFORNIA: CENTRAL VALLEY GENERAL HOSPITAL (O, 26 beds) 1025 North Douty Street, Hanford, CA Zip 93230–3722, Mailing Address: P.O. Box 480, Zip 93232–0480; tel. 559/583–2100; Douglas L. Lafferty, Administrator
Web address: www.hanfordhealth.com

FEATHER RIVER HOSPITAL (O, 80 beds) 5974 Pentz Road, Paradise, CA Zip 95969–5509; tel. 530/877–9361; A. Wayne Ferch, President and Chief Executive Officer
Web address: www.frhosp.org

FRANK R. HOWARD MEMORIAL HOSPITAL (L, 25 beds) One Madrone Street, Willits, CA Zip 95490–4225; tel. 707/459–6801; Kevin R. Erich, President and Chief Executive Officer
Web address: www.howardhospital.com

GLENDALE ADVENTIST MEDICAL CENTER (O, 394 beds) 1509 Wilson Terrace, Glendale, CA Zip 91206–4098; tel. 818/409–8000; Scott Reiner, President and Chief Executive Officer
Web address: www.glendaleadventist.com

HANFORD COMMUNITY MEDICAL CENTER (O, 50 beds) 450 Greenfield Avenue, Hanford, CA Zip 93230–3513, Mailing Address: P.O. Box 240, Zip 93232–0240; tel. 559/582–9000; Richard L. Rawson, President and Chief Executive Officer
Web address: www.hanfordhealth.com

PARADISE VALLEY HOSPITAL (O, 207 beds) 2400 East Fourth Street, National City, CA Zip 91950–2099; tel. 619/470–4321; Alan Soderblom, President and Chief Executive Officer
Web address: www.adventisthealth.org

REDBUD COMMUNITY HOSPITAL (O, 32 beds) 15630 18th Avenue, Clearlake, CA Zip 95422–9339, Mailing Address: P.O. Box 6720, Zip 95422–6720; tel. 707/994–6486; Kendall R. Fults, President and Chief Executive Officer
Web address: www.adventisthealth.org

SAN JOAQUIN COMMUNITY HOSPITAL (O, 166 beds) 2615 Eye Street, Bakersfield, CA Zip 93301–2006, Mailing Address: P.O. Box 2615, Zip 93303–2615; tel. 661/395–3000; Robert J. Beehler, President and Chief Executive Officer
Web address: www.sanjoaquinhospital.org

SELMA COMMUNITY HOSPITAL (O, 24 beds) 1141 Rose Avenue, Selma, CA Zip 93662–3241; tel. 559/891–1000; Richard L. Rawson, President and Chief Executive Officer
Web address: www.adventisthealth.org

SIMI VALLEY HOSPITAL AND HEALTH CARE SERVICES (O, 191 beds) 2975 North Sycamore Drive, Simi Valley, CA Zip 93065–1201; tel. 805/955–6000; Margaret R. Peterson, Ph.D., President and Chief Executive Officer
Web address: www.simivalleyhospital.com

SONORA REGIONAL MEDICAL CENTER (O, 147 beds) 1000 Greenley Road, Sonora, CA Zip 95370–4819; tel. 209/532–5000; Lary Davis, President and Chief Executive Officer
Web address: www.sonorahospital.org

SOUTH COAST MEDICAL CENTER (O, 208 beds) 31872 Coast Highway, Laguna Beach, CA Zip 92651–6775; tel. 949/499–1311; Gary G. Irish, President and Chief Executive Officer
Web address: www.southcoastmedcenter.com

ST HELENA HOSPITAL–CENTER FOR BEHAVIORAL HEALTH (O, 61 beds) 525 Oregon Street, Vallejo, CA Zip 94590–3201; tel. 707/648–2200; JoAline Olson, R.N., President and Chief Executive Officer
Web address:
www.sthelenahospital.org/Hospital/HS_California/Cal_child.html

ST. HELENA HOSPITAL (O, 242 beds) 10 Woodland Road, Saint Helena, CA Zip 94574; tel. 707/963–3611; JoAline Olson, R.N., President and Chief Executive Officer
Web address: www.sthelenahospital.org

UKIAH VALLEY MEDICAL CENTER (O, 56 beds) 275 Hospital Drive, Ukiah, CA Zip 95482–4531; tel. 707/462–3111; Mark LaRose, President and Chief Executive Officer
Web address: www.adventisthealth.org

WHITE MEMORIAL MEDICAL CENTER (O, 369 beds) 1720 Cesar E Chavez Avenue, Los Angeles, CA Zip 90033–2481; tel. 323/268–5000; Beth D. Zachary, President and Chief Executive Officer
Web address: www.whitememorial.com

HAWAII: CASTLE MEDICAL CENTER (O, 157 beds) 640 Ulukahiki Street, Kailua, HI Zip 96734–4498; tel. 808/263–5500; Kevin Roberts, President and Chief Executive Officer
Web address: www.castlemed.com

NORTH HAWAII COMMUNITY HOSPITAL (O, 35 beds) 67–1125 Mamalahoa Highway, Kamuela, HI Zip 96743; tel. 808/885–4444; Stan B. Berry, FACHE, Chief Executive Officer
Web address: www.northhawaiicommunityhospital.org

OREGON: ADVENTIST MEDICAL CENTER (O, 252 beds) 10123 S.E. Market Street, Portland, OR Zip 97216–2599; tel. 503/257–2500; Deryl L. Jones, President and Chief Executive Officer
Web address: www.adventisthealthnw.com

TILLAMOOK COUNTY GENERAL HOSPITAL (L, 25 beds) 1000 Third Street, Tillamook, OR Zip 97141–3430; tel. 503/842–4444; Wendell Hesseltine, President and Chief Executive Officer
Web address: www.tcgh.com

WASHINGTON: WALLA WALLA GENERAL HOSPITAL (O, 72 beds) 1025 South Second Avenue, Walla Walla, WA Zip 99362–1398, Mailing Address: P.O. Box 1398, Zip 99362–1398; tel. 509/525–0480; Morre Dean, President and Chief Executive Officer
Web address: www.wwgh.com

Owned, leased, sponsored:	21 hospitals	2819 beds
Contract–managed:	0 hospitals	0 beds
Totals:	21 hospitals	2819 beds

★4165: ADVENTIST HEALTH SYSTEM SUNBELT HEALTH CARE CORPORATION (CO)
111 North Orlando Avenue, Winter Park, FL Zip 32789–3675; tel. 407/975–1417; Thomas L. Werner, President
(Decentralized Health System)

COLORADO: AVISTA ADVENTIST HOSPITAL (O, 85 beds) 100 Health Park Drive, Louisville, CO Zip 80027–9583; tel. 303/673–1000; John Sackett, Chief Executive Officer
Web address: www.avistahosp.org

LITTLETON ADVENTIST HOSPITAL (O, 134 beds) 7700 South Broadway Street, Littleton, CO Zip 80122–2628; tel. 303/730–8900; David Crane, Chief Executive Officer
Web address: www.centura.org

For explanation of codes following names, see page B2.
★ Indicates Type III membership in the American Hospital Association.

PARKER ADVENTIST HOSPITAL (O, 10 beds) 9395 Crown Crest Boulevard, Parker, CO Zip 80138; tel. 303/269–6000; Ken Bacon, President

PORTER ADVENTIST HOSPITAL (O, 239 beds) 2525 South Downing Street, Denver, CO Zip 80210–5876; tel. 303/778–1955; James W. Boyle, Chief Executive Officer
Web address: www.centura.org

FLORIDA: EAST PASCO MEDICAL CENTER (O, 154 beds) 7050 Gall Boulevard, Zephyrhills, FL Zip 33541–1399; tel. 813/788–0411; Scott M. Pittman, President and Chief Executive Officer
Web address: www.epmc.org

FLORIDA HOSPITAL (O, 1758 beds) 601 East Rollins Street, Orlando, FL Zip 32803–1489; tel. 407/303–6611; Donald L. Jernigan, Ph.D., President
Web address: www.flhosp.org

FLORIDA HOSPITAL – DELAND (O, 156 beds) 701 West Plymouth Avenue, De Land, FL Zip 32720; tel. 386/734–3320; Rob Fulbright, Administrator
Web address: www.fhdeland.org

FLORIDA HOSPITAL FISH MEMORIAL (O, 139 beds) 1055 Saxon Boulevard, Orange City, FL Zip 32763–8468; tel. 386/917–5000; Joe Johnson, President and Chief Executive Officer
Web address: www.fhfishmemorial.org

FLORIDA HOSPITAL HEARTLAND MEDICAL CENTER (O, 186 beds) 4200 Sun'n Lake Boulevard, Sebring, FL Zip 33872–1986, Mailing Address: P.O. Box 9400, Zip 33871–9400; tel. 863/314–4466; John R. Harding, President and Chief Executive Officer
Web address: www.flhosp–heartland.org

FLORIDA HOSPITAL WATERMAN (O, 204 beds) 1000 Waterman Way, Tavares, FL Zip 32778–5266; tel. 352/253–3333; Kenneth R. Mattison, President and Chief Executive Officer
Web address: www.fhwat.org

FLORIDA HOSPITAL WAUCHULA (O, 25 beds) 533 West Carlton Street, Wauchula, FL Zip 33873; tel. 863/773–3101; David Ottati, Administrator
Web address: www.flhosp–heartland.org/Facilities/Wauchula.htm

FLORIDA HOSPITAL–FLAGLER (O, 81 beds) 60 Memorial Medical Parkway, Palm Coast, FL Zip 32164; tel. 386/586–2000; Daryl Tol, Administrator
Web address: www.fhmd.com

FLORIDA HOSPITAL–ORMOND MEMORIAL (O, 324 beds) 875 Sterthaus Avenue, Ormond Beach, FL Zip 32174–5197; tel. 386/676–6000; Michael V. Gentry, President
Web address: www.memorial–health.com

GEORGIA: EMORY–ADVENTIST HOSPITAL (O, 69 beds) 3949 South Cobb Drive S.E., Smyrna, GA Zip 30080–6300; tel. 770/434–0710; Dennis Kiley, President
Web address: www.ahss.org

GORDON HOSPITAL (O, 65 beds) 1035 Red Bud Road, Calhoun, GA Zip 30701–2082, Mailing Address: P.O. Box 12938, Zip 30703–7013; tel. 706/629–2895; Carlene Jamerson, President and Chief Executive Officer
Web address: www.gordonhospital.com

ILLINOIS: ADVENTIST GLENOAKS HOSPITAL (O, 149 beds) 701 Winthrop Avenue, Glendale Heights, IL Zip 60139–1403; tel. 630/545–8000; Brinsley B. Lewis, Chief Executive Officer
Web address: www.keepingyouwell.com

ADVENTIST LA GRANGE MEMORIAL HOSPITAL (O, 178 beds) 5101 South Willow Spring Road, La Grange, IL Zip 60525–2680; tel. 708/352–1200; Timothy W. Cook, Chief Executive Officer
Web address: www.keepingyouwell.com/facilities/LaGrange.asp

HINSDALE HOSPITAL (O, 333 beds) 120 North Oak Street, Hinsdale, IL Zip 60521–3890; tel. 630/856–9000; Todd S. Werner, Chief Executive Officer
Web address: www.keepingyouwell.com

KANSAS: SHAWNEE MISSION MEDICAL CENTER (O, 304 beds) 9100 West 74th Street, Shawnee Mission, KS Zip 66204–4004, Mailing Address: Box 2923, Zip 66201–1323; tel. 913/676–2000; Samuel H. Turner Sr, Chief Executive Officer
Web address: www.shawneemission.org

KENTUCKY: MEMORIAL HOSPITAL (O, 63 beds) 210 Marie Langdon Drive, Manchester, KY Zip 40962–9156; tel. 606/598–5104; Dennis Meyers, President and Chief Executive Officer
Web address: www.manchestermemorial.com

NORTH CAROLINA: PARK RIDGE HOSPITAL (O, 98 beds) Naples Road, Fletcher, NC Zip 28732, Mailing Address: P.O. Box 1569, Zip 28732–1569; tel. 828/684–8501; Michael H. Schultz, Chief Executive Officer
Web address: www.parkridgehospital.org

PUERTO RICO: HOSPITAL METROPOLITANO DR. TITO MATTEI (O, 106 beds) Carretera 128 KM 1, Yauco, PR Zip 00698, Mailing Address: P.O. Box 68, Zip 00698; tel. 787/856–1000; Pedro Barez, Chief Executive Officer
Web address: www.hmyauco.com

TENNESSEE: JELLICO COMMUNITY HOSPITAL (L, 46 beds) 188 Hospital Lane, Jellico, TN Zip 37762–4432; tel. 423/784–7252; David A. Butler, Chief Executive Officer and President
Web address: www.ahss.org

TAKOMA ADVENTIST HOSPITAL (O, 100 beds) 401 Takoma Avenue, Greeneville, TN Zip 37743–4647; tel. 423/639–3151; Carlyle L. E. Walton, President
Web address: www.takoma.org

TENNESSEE CHRISTIAN MEDICAL CENTER (O, 284 beds) 500 Hospital Drive, Madison, TN Zip 37115–5032; tel. 615/865–2373; Jimm Bunch, President and Chief Executive Officer
Web address: www.tennesseechristian.com

TEXAS: CENTRAL TEXAS MEDICAL CENTER (O, 113 beds) 1301 Wonder World Drive, San Marcos, TX Zip 78666–7544; tel. 512/753–3500; Gary L. Jepson, President and Chief Executive Officer
Web address: www.ctmc.org

HUGULEY MEMORIAL MEDICAL CENTER (O, 199 beds) 11801 South Freeway, Fort Worth, TX Zip 76134, Mailing Address: P.O. Box 6337, Zip 76115–6337; tel. 817/293–9110; Peter M. Weber, President and Chief Executive Officer
Web address: www.huguley.org

METROPLEX ADVENTIST HOSPITAL (O, 177 beds) 2201 South Clear Creek Road, Killeen, TX Zip 76549–4110; tel. 254/526–7523; Kenneth A. Finch, Chief Executive Officer
Web address: www.mplex.org

ROLLINS–BROOK COMMUNITY HOSPITAL (O, 25 beds) 608 North Key Avenue, Lampasas, TX Zip 76550, Mailing Address: Box 589, Zip 76550; tel. 512/556–3682; Kenneth A. Finch, Chief Executive Officer
Web address: www.mplex.org

WISCONSIN: CHIPPEWA VALLEY HOSPITAL AND OAKVIEW CARE CENTER (O, 83 beds) 1220 Third Avenue West, Durand, WI Zip 54736–1600, Mailing Address: P.O. Box 224, Zip 54736–0224; tel. 715/672–4211; Douglas R. Peterson, President and Chief Executive Officer

Owned, leased, sponsored:	30 hospitals	5887 beds
Contract–managed:	0 hospitals	0 beds
Totals:	30 hospitals	5887 beds

★**0214: ADVENTIST HEALTHCARE** (NP)
1801 Research Boulevard, Suite 400, Rockville, MD Zip 20850; tel. 301/315–3030; William G. Robertson, President and Chief Executive Officer
(Moderately Centralized Health System)

MARYLAND: ADVENTIST REHABILITATION HOSPITAL OF MARYLAND (O, 77 beds) 9909 Medical Center Drive, Rockville, MD Zip 20850; tel. 240/864–6000; Doris B. Reinhart, Vice President and Administrator
Web address: www.adventisthealthcare.com

POTOMAC RIDGE BEHAVIORAL HEALTH SYSTEM (O, 85 beds) 14901 Broschart Road, Rockville, MD Zip 20850–3395; tel. 301/251–4500; Craig S. Juengling, President
Web address: www.potomacridge.com

SHADY GROVE ADVENTIST HOSPITAL (O, 265 beds) 9901 Medical Center Drive, Rockville, MD Zip 20850–3395; tel. 301/279–6000; Deborah A. Yancer, R.N., President
Web address: www.adventisthealthcare.com

WASHINGTON ADVENTIST HOSPITAL (O, 291 beds) 7600 Carroll Avenue, Takoma Park, MD Zip 20912–6392; tel. 301/891–7600; Jere D. Stocks, President
Web address: www.adventisthealthcare.com

For explanation of codes following names, see page B2.
★ Indicates Type III membership in the American Hospital Association.

Section B

NEW JERSEY: HACKETTSTOWN COMMUNITY HOSPITAL (O, 92 beds) 651 Willow Grove Street, Hackettstown, NJ Zip 07840–1792; tel. 908/852–5100; Gene C. Milton, President and Chief Executive Officer
Web address: www.hch.org

Owned, leased, sponsored:	5 hospitals	810 beds
Contract–managed:	0 hospitals	0 beds
Totals:	5 hospitals	810 beds

★0064: ADVOCATE HEALTH CARE (NP)
2025 Windsor Drive, Oak Brook, IL Zip 60523; tel. 630/990–5010; James H. Skogsbergh, President and Chief Executive Officer
(Moderately Centralized Health System)

ILLINOIS: ADVOCATE BETHANY HOSPITAL (O, 136 beds) 3435 West Van Buren Street, Chicago, IL Zip 60624–3399; tel. 773/265–7700; Lena Dobbs–Johnson, President
Web address: www.advocatehealth.com

ADVOCATE CHRIST MEDICAL CENTER (O, 649 beds) 4440 West 95th Street, Oak Lawn, IL Zip 60453–2699; tel. 708/684–8000; Jonathan R. Bruss, Interim President
Web address: www.advocatehealth.com/christ

ADVOCATE GOOD SAMARITAN HOSPITAL (O, 278 beds) 3815 Highland Avenue, Downers Grove, IL Zip 60515–1590; tel. 630/275–5900; David S. Fox, President
Web address: www.advocatehealth.com

ADVOCATE GOOD SHEPHERD HOSPITAL (O, 142 beds) 450 West Highway 22, Barrington, IL Zip 60010–1901; tel. 847/381–9600; Karen A. Lambert, President
Web address: www.advocatehealth.com

ADVOCATE ILLINOIS MASONIC MEDICAL CENTER (O, 346 beds) 836 West Wellington Avenue, Chicago, IL Zip 60657–5193; tel. 773/975–1600; Susan Nordstrom Lopez, President
Web address: www.advocatehealth.com

ADVOCATE LUTHERAN GENERAL HOSPITAL (O, 569 beds) 1775 Dempster Street, Park Ridge, IL Zip 60068–1174; tel. 847/723–2210; Bruce C. Campbell, President
Web address: www.advocatehealth.com

ADVOCATE SOUTH SUBURBAN HOSPITAL (O, 245 beds) 17800 South Kedzie Avenue, Hazel Crest, IL Zip 60429–0989; tel. 708/213–3000; Patricia A. Martin, President
Web address: www.advocatehealth.com/ssub/

ADVOCATE TRINITY HOSPITAL (O, 158 beds) 2320 East 93rd Street, Chicago, IL Zip 60617–9984; tel. 773/967–2000; John N. Schwartz, President
Web address: www.advocatehealth.com/trinity

Owned, leased, sponsored:	8 hospitals	2523 beds
Contract–managed:	0 hospitals	0 beds
Totals:	8 hospitals	2523 beds

0312: AHMC, INC (IO)
100 South Raymond Avenue, Alhambra, CA Zip 91801–3199; tel. 626/458–4789; Jonathan Wu, M.D., President and Chairman

CALIFORNIA: ALHAMBRA HOSPITAL MEDICAL CENTER (O, 144 beds) 100 South Raymond Avenue, Alhambra, CA Zip 91801–3199, Mailing Address: P.O. Box 510, Zip 91802–0510; tel. 626/570–1606; Iris Lai, Acting Chief Executive Officer
Web address: www.alhambrahospital.com

DOCTORS HOSPITAL MEDICAL CENTER OF MONTCLAIR (O, 102 beds) 5000 San Bernardino Street, Montclair, CA Zip 91763–2326; tel. 909/625–5411; David Chu, Chief Executive Officer
Web address: www.dhmcm.com

GARFIELD MEDICAL CENTER (O, 208 beds) 525 North Garfield Avenue, Monterey Park, CA Zip 91754–1205; tel. 626/573–2222; Philip A. Cohen, Chief Executive Officer
Web address: www.garfieldmedicalcenter.com

GREATER EL MONTE COMMUNITY HOSPITAL (O, 117 beds) 1701 Santa Anita Avenue, El Monte, CA Zip 91733–3411; tel. 626/579–7777; Philip A. Cohen, Chief Executive Officer
Web address: www.greaterelmonte.com

MONTEREY PARK HOSPITAL (O, 101 beds) 900 South Atlantic Boulevard, Monterey Park, CA Zip 91754–4780; tel. 626/570–9000; Philip A. Cohen, Chief Executive Officer
Web address: www.montereyparkhosp.com

WHITTIER HOSPITAL MEDICAL CENTER (O, 171 beds) 9080 Colima Road, Whittier, CA Zip 90605–1600; tel. 562/945–3561; Howard Ternes, Chief Executive Officer
Web address: www.whittierhospital.com

Owned, leased, sponsored:	6 hospitals	843 beds
Contract–managed:	0 hospitals	0 beds
Totals:	6 hospitals	843 beds

0247: AKRON GENERAL HEALTH SYSTEM (NP)
400 Wabash Avenue, Akron, OH Zip 44307–2433; tel. 330/344–6000; Alan J. Bleyer, President and Chief Executive Officer
(Moderately Centralized Health System)

OHIO: AKRON GENERAL MEDICAL CENTER (O, 462 beds) 400 Wabash Avenue, Akron, OH Zip 44307–2433; tel. 330/344–6000; Alan J. Bleyer, President
Web address: www.akrongeneral.org

LODI COMMUNITY HOSPITAL (O, 23 beds) 225 Elyria Street, Lodi, OH Zip 44254–1096; tel. 330/948–1222; Thomas Whelan, President
Web address: www.lodihospital.com

MASSILLON COMMUNITY HOSPITAL (O, 139 beds) 875 Eighth Street N.E., Massillon, OH Zip 44646–8503, Mailing Address: P.O. Box 805, Zip 44648–8503; tel. 330/832–8761; Michael L. Reichfield, President
Web address: www.mchosp.org

Owned, leased, sponsored:	3 hospitals	624 beds
Contract–managed:	0 hospitals	0 beds
Totals:	3 hospitals	624 beds

0225: ALAMEDA MEDICAL CENTER (NP)
15400 Foothill Boulevard, San Leandro, CA Zip 94578; tel. 510/677–7920; Claude D. Watts Jr, Chief Executive Officer
(Independent Hospital System)

CALIFORNIA: ALAMEDA COUNTY MEDICAL CENTER–FAIRMONT CAMPUS (O, 399 beds) 15400 Foothill Boulevard, San Leandro, CA Zip 94578–1009; tel. 510/437–4800; Claude D. Watts Jr, Chief Executive Officer
Web address: www.acmedctr.org

ALAMEDA COUNTY MEDICAL CENTER–HIGHLAND CAMPUS (O, 420 beds) 1411 East 31st Street, Oakland, CA Zip 94602–1018; tel. 510/437–4800; Kenneth B. Cohen, Chief Executive Officer
Web address: www.acmedctr.org

Owned, leased, sponsored:	2 hospitals	819 beds
Contract–managed:	0 hospitals	0 beds
Totals:	2 hospitals	819 beds

1685: ALBERT EINSTEIN HEALTHCARE NETWORK (NP)
5501 Old York Road, Philadelphia, PA Zip 19141–3098; tel. 215/456–7890; Barry R. Freedman, President and Chief Executive Officer

PENNSYLVANIA: ALBERT EINSTEIN MEDICAL CENTER (O, 701 beds) 5501 Old York Road, Philadelphia, PA Zip 19141–3098; tel. 215/456–7890; Barry R. Freedman, President and Chief Executive Officer
Web address: www.einstein.edu

BELMONT CENTER FOR COMPREHENSIVE TREATMENT (O, 146 beds) 4200 Monument Road, Philadelphia, PA Zip 19131–1625; tel. 215/877–2000; Sharon A. Bergen, Chief Operating Officer
Web address: www.einstein.edu

MOSS REHAB, EINSTEIN AT ELKINS PARK (O, 158 beds) 60 East Township Line Road, Elkins Park, PA Zip 19027–2220; tel. 215/663–6000; Ruth Lefton, Chief Operating Officer

---

For explanation of codes following names, see page B2.
★ Indicates Type III membership in the American Hospital Association.

Section B

Owned, leased, sponsored:	3 hospitals	1005 beds
Contract–managed:	0 hospitals	0 beds
Totals:	3 hospitals	1005 beds

Owned, leased, sponsored:	3 hospitals	653 beds
Contract–managed:	0 hospitals	0 beds
Totals:	3 hospitals	653 beds

0278: ALEGENT HEALTH (CO)
1010 North 96th Street, Suite 200, Omaha, NE Zip 68114–2595; tel. 402/343–4300; Wayne A. Sensor, President and Chief Executive Officer
(Moderately Centralized Health System)

IOWA: ALEGENT HEALTH COMMUNITY MEMORIAL HOSPITAL (O, 25 beds) 631 North Eighth Street, Missouri Valley, IA Zip 51555–1199; tel. 712/642–2784; Robert R. Sellers, Regional Health Administrator
Web address: www.alegent.org

ALEGENT HEALTH MERCY HOSPITAL (S, 22 beds) 603 Rosary Drive, Corning, IA Zip 50841–1685, Mailing Address: P.O. Box 368, Zip 50841–0368; tel. 641/322–3121; James C. Ruppert, Regional Administrator
Web address: www.alegent.com

ALEGENT HEALTH MERCY HOSPITAL (S, 181 beds) 800 Mercy Drive, Council Bluffs, IA Zip 51503–3128, Mailing Address: P.O. Box 1C, Zip 51502–3001; tel. 712/328–5000; Marie E. Knedler, R.N., Vice President and Chief Operating Officer
Web address: www.alegent.com/mercy

NEBRASKA: ALEGENT HEALTH BERGAN MERCY MEDICAL CENTER (S, 327 beds) 7500 Mercy Road, Omaha, NE Zip 68124–2319; tel. 402/398–6060; Mary Kay Thalken, R.N., Interim Vice President and Chief Operating Officer
Web address: www.alegent.com/bergan

ALEGENT HEALTH IMMANUEL MEDICAL CENTER (O, 489 beds) 6901 North 72nd Street, Omaha, NE Zip 68122–1799; tel. 402/572–2121; Barbara K. Goodrich, R.N., Vice President and Chief Operating Officer
Web address: www.alegent.com/immanuel

ALEGENT HEALTH LAKESIDE HOSPITAL (O, 45 beds) 16901 Lakeside Hills Court, Omaha, NE Zip 68130–2318; tel. 402/717–8000; Cindy Alloway, R.N., Vice President and Chief Operating Officer
Web address: www.alegent.org

ALEGENT HEALTH–MEMORIAL HOSPITAL (O, 15 beds) 104 West 17th Street, Schuyler, NE Zip 68661–1396; tel. 402/352–2441; Connie Peters, R.N., Regional Health Administrator
Web address: www.alegent.org

ALEGENT–HEALTH MIDLANDS COMMUNITY HOSPITAL (O, 100 beds) 11111 South 84th Street, Papillion, NE Zip 68046–4157; tel. 402/593–3000; Kevin Nokels, Vice President and Chief Operating Officer
Web address: www.alegent.org/midlands

MEMORIAL COMMUNITY HOSPITAL AND HEALTH SYSTEM (O, 25 beds) 810 North 22nd Street, Blair, NE Zip 68008–1199, Mailing Address: P.O. Box 250, Zip 68008–0250; tel. 402/426–2182; Sally Harvey, R.N., Regional Administrator
Web address: www.mchhs.org

Owned, leased, sponsored:	9 hospitals	1229 beds
Contract–managed:	0 hospitals	0 beds
Totals:	9 hospitals	1229 beds

0065: ALEXIAN BROTHERS HEALTH SYSTEM (CC)
3040 Salt Creek Lane, Arlington Heights, IL Zip 60005; tel. 847/463–8910; Brother Thomas Keusenkothen, President and Chief Executive Officer
(Moderately Centralized Health System)

ILLINOIS: ALEXIAN BROTHERS BEHAVIORAL HEALTH HOSPITAL (O, 94 beds) 1650 Moon Lake Boulevard, Hoffman Estates, IL Zip 60194–5000; tel. 847/882–1600; Mark A. Frey, President and Chief Executive Officer
Web address: www.abbhh.net

ALEXIAN BROTHERS MEDICAL CENTER (O, 348 beds) 800 Biesterfield Road, Elk Grove Village, IL Zip 60007–3397; tel. 847/437–5500; Roger Johnson, President and Chief Executive Officer
Web address: www.alexian.org

ST. ALEXIUS MEDICAL CENTER (O, 211 beds) 1555 Barrington Road, Hoffman Estates, IL Zip 60194–1018; tel. 847/843–2000; Edward M. Goldberg, President and Chief Executive Officer
Web address: www.stalexius.org

0317: ALLIANT MANAGEMENT SERVICES (IO)
2501 Nelson Miller Parkway, Suite 104, Louisville, KY Zip 40223; tel. 502/992–3525; Chris West, President and Chief Executive Officer

FAIRFIELD MEMORIAL HOSPITAL (C, 163 beds) 303 N.W. 11th Street, Fairfield, IL Zip 62837–1203; tel. 618/842–2611; Katherine Bunting, Chief Nurse Executive
Web address: www.fairfieldmemorial.org

FAYETTE COUNTY HOSPITAL (O, 145 beds) 650 West Taylor Street, Vandalia, IL Zip 62471–1296; tel. 618/283–1231; Dennis L. Hutchison, Chief Executive Officer
Web address: www.bjc.org

FERRELL HOSPITAL (C, 25 beds) 1201 Pine Street, Eldorado, IL Zip 62930–1634; tel. 618/273–3361; William Hartley, FACHE, President and Chief Executive Officer
Web address: www.sih.net

FRANKLIN HOSPITAL (C, 25 beds) 201 Bailey Lane, Benton, IL Zip 62812–1999; tel. 618/439–3161; Hervey E. Davis, Chief Executive Officer
Web address: www.sih.net

PARIS COMMUNITY HOSPITAL (C, 25 beds) 721 East Court Street, Paris, IL Zip 61944–2420; tel. 217/465–4141; John D. Fajt, FACHE, President and Chief Executive Officer
Web address: www.pariscommunityhospital.com

WABASH GENERAL HOSPITAL DISTRICT (C, 25 beds) 1418 College Drive, Mount Carmel, IL Zip 62863–2638; tel. 618/262–8621; Jay Purvis, Administrator
Web address: www.wabashgeneral.com

INDIANA: GIBSON GENERAL HOSPITAL (C, 70 beds) 1808 Sherman Drive, Princeton, IN Zip 47670–1043; tel. 812/385–3401; Michael J. Budnick, FACHE, Chief Executive Officer
Web address: www.gibsongeneral.com

PERRY COUNTY MEMORIAL HOSPITAL (C, 25 beds) 1 Hospital Road, Tell City, IN Zip 47586–0362; tel. 812/547–7011; Joseph A. Stuber, Chief Executive Officer
Web address: www.pchospital.org

WABASH COUNTY HOSPITAL (C, 50 beds) 710 North East Street, Wabash, IN Zip 46992–1924, Mailing Address: P.O. Box 548, Zip 46992–0548; tel. 260/563–3131; Jeffrey L. Buckley, President and Chief Executive Officer
Web address: www.wchospital.com

KENTUCKY: BRECKINRIDGE MEMORIAL HOSPITAL (C, 43 beds) 1011 Old Highway 60, Hardinsburg, KY Zip 40143–2597; tel. 270/756–7000; George Walz, CHE, President and Chief Executive Officer
Web address: www.breckhealth.org

CAVERNA MEMORIAL HOSPITAL (C, 25 beds) 1501 South Dixie Street, Horse Cave, KY Zip 42749–1477; tel. 270/786–2191; Alan B. Alexander, Chief Executive Officer

MUHLENBERG COMMUNITY HOSPITAL (C, 135 beds) 440 Hopkinsville Street, Greenville, KY Zip 42345–1172, Mailing Address: P.O. Box 387, Zip 42345–0387; tel. 270/338–8000; Lloyd Ford, Chief Executive Officer
Web address: www.mchky.org

THE JAMES B. HAGGIN MEMORIAL HOSPITAL (C, 59 beds) 464 Linden Avenue, Harrodsburg, KY Zip 40330–1862; tel. 859/734–5441; Earl James Motzer, Ph.D., FACHE, Chief Executive Officer

TWIN LAKES REGIONAL MEDICAL CENTER (C, 75 beds) 910 Wallace Avenue, Leitchfield, KY Zip 42754–1499; tel. 270/259–9400; Stephen L. Meredith, Chief Executive Officer
Web address: www.tlrmc.com

Owned, leased, sponsored:	1 hospital	145 beds
Contract–managed:	13 hospitals	745 beds
Totals:	14 hospitals	890 beds

For explanation of codes following names, see page B2.
★ Indicates Type III membership in the American Hospital Association.

★0041: ALLINA HOSPITALS & CLINICS (NP)
710 East 24th Street, Minneapolis, MN Zip 55404–3840, Mailing
Address: P.O. Box 1469, Zip 55440–1469; tel. 612/775–5000;
Richard R. Pettingill, President and Chief Executive Officer
(Moderately Centralized Health System)

MINNESOTA: ABBOTT NORTHWESTERN HOSPITAL (O, 627 beds) 800 East
28th Street, Minneapolis, MN Zip 55407–3799; tel. 612/863–4000;
Richard Sturgeon, M.D., Interim President
Web address: www.allina.com

BUFFALO HOSPITAL (O, 38 beds) 303 Catlin Street, Buffalo, MN
Zip 55313–1947; tel. 763/682–1212; Lenore Day, Interim President
Web address: www.buffalohospital.org

CAMBRIDGE MEDICAL CENTER (O, 81 beds) 701 South Dellwood Street,
Cambridge, MN Zip 55008–1920; tel. 763/689–7700; Dennis J. Doran,
President
Web address: www.allina.com/ahs/cambridge.nsf

HUTCHINSON AREA HEALTH CARE (C, 190 beds) 1095 Highway 15 South,
Hutchinson, MN Zip 55350–3182; tel. 320/234–5000; Philip G. Graves,
President
Web address: www.hahc–hmc.com

MERCY HOSPITAL (O, 266 beds) 4050 Coon Rapids Boulevard, Coon Rapids,
MN Zip 55433–2586; tel. 763/236–6000; Venetia Kudrle, President
Web address: www.allina.com

NEW ULM MEDICAL CENTER (O, 47 beds) 1324 Fifth Street North, New Ulm,
MN Zip 56073–1553, Mailing Address: P.O. Box 577, Zip 56073–0577;
tel. 507/233–1000; Lori L. Wightman, Administrator
Web address: www.newulmmedicalcenter.com

OWATONNA HOSPITAL (O, 48 beds) 903 South Oak Street, Owatonna, MN
Zip 55060–3234; tel. 507/451–3850; Dorothy Erdmann, President
Web address: www.allina.com

PHILLIPS EYE INSTITUTE (O, 10 beds) 2215 Park Avenue, Minneapolis, MN
Zip 55404–3756; tel. 612/336–6000; Shari E. Levy, President
Web address: www.allina.com

ST. FRANCIS REGIONAL MEDICAL CENTER (O, 61 beds) 1455 St. Francis
Avenue, Shakopee, MN Zip 55379–3380; tel. 952/403–3000; Thomas
O'Connor, President
Web address: www.stfrancis–shakopee.com

UNITED HOSPITAL (O, 418 beds) 333 North Smith Avenue, Saint Paul, MN
Zip 55102–2389; tel. 651/220–8000; Mark G. Mishek, President
Web address: www.allina.com

UNITY HOSPITAL (O, 228 beds) 550 Osborne Road N.E., Fridley, MN
Zip 55432–2799; tel. 763/236–5000; Venetia Kudrle, President
Web address: www.allina.com

WISCONSIN: RIVER FALLS AREA HOSPITAL (O, 27 beds) 1629 East Division
Street, River Falls, WI Zip 54022–1571; tel. 715/425–6155; Randy
Farrow, President
Web address: www.allina.com

Owned, leased, sponsored:	11 hospitals	1851 beds
Contract–managed:	1 hospital	190 beds
Totals:	12 hospitals	2041 beds

0187: ALTA HEALTHCARE SYSTEM (IO)
10230 East Artesia Boulevard, Suite 206, Bellflower, CA Zip 90706;
tel. 562/925–0201; David Topper, Chief Executive Officer

CALIFORNIA: HOLLYWOOD COMMUNITY HOSPITAL (O, 45 beds) 6245 De
Longpre Avenue, Los Angeles, CA Zip 90028–9001; tel. 323/462–2271;
Casey Fatch, Chief Executive Officer

LOS ANGELES COMMUNITY HOSPITAL (O, 180 beds) 4081 East Olympic
Boulevard, Los Angeles, CA Zip 90023–3330; tel. 323/267–0477; David
Topper, Chief Executive Officer

Owned, leased, sponsored:	2 hospitals	225 beds
Contract–managed:	0 hospitals	0 beds
Totals:	2 hospitals	225 beds

**2295: AMERICAN PROVINCE OF LITTLE COMPANY OF MARY
SISTERS** (CC)
9350 South California Avenue, Evergreen Park, IL Zip 60805–2595;
tel. 708/229–5491; Sister Carol Pacini, Provincialate Superior
(Moderately Centralized Health System)

ILLINOIS: LITTLE COMPANY OF MARY HOSPITAL AND HEALTH CARE
CENTERS (O, 294 beds) 2800 West 95th Street, Evergreen Park, IL
Zip 60805–2795; tel. 708/422–6200; Dennis A. Reilly, President and
Chief Executive Officer
Web address: www.lcmh.org

INDIANA: MEMORIAL HOSPITAL AND HEALTH CARE CENTER (O, 124 beds)
800 West Ninth Street, Jasper, IN Zip 47546–2516; tel. 812/482–2345;
Raymond W. Snowden, President and Chief Executive Officer
Web address: www.mhhcc.org

Owned, leased, sponsored:	2 hospitals	418 beds
Contract–managed:	0 hospitals	0 beds
Totals:	2 hospitals	418 beds

0316: AMERIS HEALTH SYSTEMS (IO)
1114 17th Avenue South, Suite 205, Nashville, TN Zip 37212–2215;
tel. 615/327–4440; Sam Lewis, Chairman and Chief Executive
Officer

ARKANSAS: GREAT RIVER MEDICAL CENTER (O, 111 beds) 1520 North
Division Street, Blytheville, AR Zip 72315–1448, Mailing Address: P.O.
Box 108, Zip 72316–0108; tel. 870/838–7300; Ian W. Watson, Chief
Executive Officer
Web address: www.greatrivermc.com

SOUTH MISSISSIPPI COUNTY REGIONAL MEDICAL CENTER (O, 25 beds) 611
West Lee Avenue, Osceola, AR Zip 72370–3001, Mailing Address: P.O. Box
607, Zip 72370–0607; tel. 870/563–7000; Andrea Conley, Chief Executive
Officer

GEORGIA: SMITH NORTHVIEW HOSPITAL (C, 29 beds) 4280 North Valdosta
Road, Valdosta, GA Zip 31602, Mailing Address: P.O. Box 10010,
Zip 31604; tel. 229/671–2000; Robert Bauer, Chief Executive Officer
Web address: www.smithhospital.com

MISSISSIPPI: JEFFERSON DAVIS COMMUNITY HOSPITAL (C, 101 beds) 1102
Rose Street, Prentiss, MS Zip 39474, Mailing Address: P.O. Box 1288,
Zip 39474; tel. 601/792–4276; Mary Curtis, Administrator

Owned, leased, sponsored:	2 hospitals	136 beds
Contract–managed:	2 hospitals	130 beds
Totals:	4 hospitals	266 beds

0244: AMT GROUP, INC. (IO)
3700 Crestwood Parkway, Suite 150, Duluth, GA Zip 30096;
tel. 770/923–6500; Thomas E. McNaull, President and Chief
Executive Officer
(Independent Hospital System)

TEXAS: BELLAIRE MEDICAL CENTER (O, 194 beds) 5314 Dashwood Street,
Houston, TX Zip 77081–4689; tel. 713/512–1200; Stephen R. Selzer,
Chief Executive Officer
Web address: www.bellairemedicalcenter.com

MEDICAL CENTER AT LANCASTER (O, 90 beds) 2600 West Pleasant Run
Road, Lancaster, TX Zip 75146–1199; tel. 972/223–9600; Barry L. Mousa,
Chief Executive Officer
Web address: www.medicalcenteratlancaster.com

NORTH BAY HOSPITAL (O, 64 beds) 1711 West Wheeler Avenue, Aransas
Pass, TX Zip 78336–4536; tel. 361/758–8585; Christopher W. Dux, Chief
Executive Officer
Web address: www.nbhtx.com

Owned, leased, sponsored:	3 hospitals	348 beds
Contract–managed:	0 hospitals	0 beds
Totals:	3 hospitals	348 beds

For explanation of codes following names, see page B2.
★ Indicates Type III membership in the American Hospital Association.

★0145: APPALACHIAN REGIONAL HEALTHCARE (NP)
2285 Executive Drive, Suite 400, Lexington, KY Zip 40505, Mailing Address: P.O. Box 8086, Zip 40533–8086; tel. 859/226–2440; Jerry Haynes, Interim President and Chief Executive Officer
(Centralized Physician/Insurance Health System)

KENTUCKY: HARLAN ARH HOSPITAL (O, 150 beds) 81 Ball Park Road, Harlan, KY Zip 40831–1792; tel. 606/573–8201; Michael G. Layfield, Community Chief Executive Officer
Web address: www.arh.org

HAZARD ARH REGIONAL MEDICAL CENTER (O, 308 beds) 100 Medical Center Drive, Hazard, KY Zip 41701–1000; tel. 606/439–6600; Wayne B. Griffith, FACHE, Regional Chief Executive Officer
Web address: www.arh.org

MCDOWELL ARH HOSPITAL (O, 46 beds) Route 122, McDowell, KY Zip 41647, Mailing Address: P.O. Box 247, Zip 41647–0247; tel. 606/377–3400; Russel Barker, Chief Executive Officer
Web address: www.arh.org

MIDDLESBORO APPALACHIAN REGIONAL HOSPITAL (O, 96 beds) 3600 West Cumberland Avenue, Middlesboro, KY Zip 40965–2614, Mailing Address: P.O. Box 340, Zip 40965–0340; tel. 606/242–1300; J. Gene Faile, Community Chief Executive Officer
Web address: www.arh.org/middlesboro

MORGAN COUNTY APPALACHIAN REGIONAL HOSPITAL (L, 40 beds) 476 Liberty Road, West Liberty, KY Zip 41472–2049, Mailing Address: P.O. Box 579, Zip 41472–0579; tel. 606/743–3186; Susan Roman, Community Chief Executive Officer
Web address: www.arh.org/morgan

WHITESBURG APPALACHIAN REGIONAL HOSPITAL (O, 82 beds) 240 Hospital Road, Whitesburg, KY Zip 41858–1254; tel. 606/633–3600; Donald Fields, Community Chief Executive Officer
Web address: www.arh.org/whitesburg

WILLIAMSON ARH HOSPITAL (O, 163 beds) 260 Hospital Drive, South Williamson, KY Zip 41503–4072; tel. 606/237–1710; Wesley Dangerfield, Community Chief Executive Officer
Web address: www.arh.org

WEST VIRGINIA: BECKLEY APPALACHIAN REGIONAL HOSPITAL (O, 173 beds) 306 Stanaford Road, Beckley, WV Zip 25801–3142; tel. 304/255–3000; Rocco K. Massey, Community Chief Executive Officer
Web address: www.arh.org

SUMMERS COUNTY APPALACHIAN REGIONAL HOSPITAL (L, 61 beds) Terrace Street, Hinton, WV Zip 25951–2407, Mailing Address: Drawer 940, Zip 25951–0940; tel. 304/466–1000; Chris Vaught, Community Chief Executive Officer
Web address: www.arh.org

Owned, leased, sponsored:	9 hospitals	1119 beds
Contract–managed:	0 hospitals	0 beds
Totals:	9 hospitals	1119 beds

★0104: ARCHBOLD MEDICAL CENTER (NP)
910 South Broad Street, Thomasville, GA Zip 31792–6113; tel. 229/228–2739; Ken B. Beverly, President and Chief Executive Officer
(Moderately Centralized Health System)

GEORGIA: BROOKS COUNTY HOSPITAL (L, 35 beds) 903 North Court Street, Quitman, GA Zip 31643–1315, Mailing Address: P.O. Box 5000, Zip 31643–5000; tel. 229/263–4171; LaDon Toole, Administrator
Web address: www.archbold.org/BrooksCountyHospital

EARLY MEMORIAL HOSPITAL (L, 152 beds) 11740 Columbia Street, Blakely, GA Zip 39823–9604; tel. 229/723–4241; Robin Rau, Administrator
Web address: www.archbold.org

GRADY GENERAL HOSPITAL (L, 48 beds) 1155 Fifth Street S.E., Cairo, GA Zip 39828–0360, Mailing Address: P.O. Box 360, Zip 39828–0360; tel. 229/377–1150; Kenneth D. Rhudy, Administrator
Web address: www.archbold.org

JOHN D. ARCHBOLD MEMORIAL HOSPITAL (O, 328 beds) Gordon Avenue at Mimosa Drive, Thomasville, GA Zip 31792–6113, Mailing Address: P.O. Box 1018, Zip 31799–1018; tel. 229/228–2000; James L. Story Jr, M.D., President
Web address: www.archbold.org

MITCHELL COUNTY HOSPITAL (L, 181 beds) 90 Stephens Street, Camilla, GA Zip 31730, Mailing Address: P.O. Box 639, Zip 31730–0639; tel. 229/336–5284; J. Randall Phillips, CHE, Administrator
Web address: www.archbold.org/mitchellcountyhospital

Owned, leased, sponsored:	5 hospitals	744 beds
Contract–managed:	0 hospitals	0 beds
Totals:	5 hospitals	744 beds

0069: ARDENT HEALTH SERVICES (IO)
1 Burton Hills Boulevard, Suite 250, Nashville, TN Zip 37215; tel. 615/296–3000; David T. Vandewater, President and Chief Executive Officer
(Moderately Centralized Health System)

LOUISIANA: SUMMIT HOSPITAL (O, 94 beds) 17000 Medical Center Drive, Baton Rouge, LA Zip 70816–3224; tel. 225/752–2470; Robert F. Jernigan Jr, Chief Executive Officer
Web address: www.ahssummithospital.com

NEW MEXICO: ALBUQUERQUE REGIONAL MEDICAL CENTER (O, 128 beds) 601 Martin Luther King Jr. Avenue N.E., Albuquerque, NM Zip 87102–3670, Mailing Address: P.O. Box 25555, Zip 87125–0555; tel. 505/727–8000; Michael F. O'Keefe, FACHE, Chief Executive Officer
Web address: www.albuquerquehospital.com

LOVELACE MEDICAL CENTER (O, 212 beds) 5400 Gibson Boulevard S.E., Albuquerque, NM Zip 87108–4763; tel. 505/262–7000; Richard Rolston, M.D., President and Chief Executive Officer
Web address: www.lovelace.com

REHABILITATION HOSPITAL OF NEW MEXICO (O, 62 beds) 505 Elm Street N.E., Albuquerque, NM Zip 87102–2500, Mailing Address: P.O. Box 25555, Zip 87125–5555; tel. 505/727–4700; Dale Olson, Chief Executive Officer
Web address: www.sjhs.org

WEST MESA MEDICAL CENTER (O, 48 beds) 10501 Golf Course Road N.W., Albuquerque, NM Zip 87114–5000, Mailing Address: P.O. Box 25555, Zip 87125–0555; tel. 505/727–2000; Angela M. Marchi, Chief Executive Officer
Web address: www.lovelacesandiahealthsystem.com

WOMEN'S HOSPITAL (O, 84 beds) 4701 Montgomery Boulevard N.E., Albuquerque, NM Zip 87109–1251, Mailing Address: P.O. Box 25555, Zip 87125–0555; tel. 505/727–7800; Sheri Milone, Chief Executive Officer and Administrator
Web address: www.lovelacesandia.com

OKLAHOMA: HILLCREST SPECIALTY HOSPITAL (O, 100 beds) 744 West 9th Street, Tulsa, OK Zip 74127–9028; tel. 918/599–4000; Kenneth Noteboom, Chief Executive Officer
Web address: www.hillcrestspecialty.com

PENNSYLVANIA: BROOKE GLEN BEHAVIORAL HOSPITAL (O, 146 beds) 7170 Lafayette Avenue, Fort Washington, PA Zip 19034–0209; tel. 215/641–5300; Robert Fleming, Administrator

Owned, leased, sponsored:	8 hospitals	874 beds
Contract–managed:	0 hospitals	0 beds
Totals:	8 hospitals	874 beds

★0094: ASANTE HEALTH SYSTEM (NP)
2650 Siskiyou Boulevard, Suite 200, Medford, OR Zip 97504–8177; tel. 541/789–4100; Roy G. Vinyard II, President and Chief Executive Officer
(Moderately Centralized Health System)

OREGON: ROGUE VALLEY MEDICAL CENTER (O, 260 beds) 2825 East Barnett Road, Medford, OR Zip 97504–8332; tel. 541/789–7000; Roseanne McLaren, Administrator
Web address: www.asante.org

THREE RIVERS COMMUNITY HOSPITAL AND HEALTH CENTER (O, 98 beds) 500 S.W. Ramsey Avenue, Grants Pass, OR Zip 97527; tel. 541/472–7000; Paul Janke, Senior Vice President
Web address: www.asante.org

Owned, leased, sponsored:	2 hospitals	358 beds
Contract–managed:	0 hospitals	0 beds
Totals:	2 hospitals	358 beds

For explanation of codes following names, see page B2.
★ Indicates Type III membership in the American Hospital Association.

★0198: ASCENSION HEALTH (CC)
4600 Edmundson Road, Saint Louis, MO Zip 63134–3806;
tel. 314/733–8000; Anthony R. Tersigni, Ed.D., FACHE, President
and Chief Executive Officer
(Decentralized Health System)

ALABAMA: PROVIDENCE HOSPITAL (S, 349 beds) 6801 Airport Boulevard,
Mobile, AL Zip 36608–3785, Mailing Address: P.O. Box 850429,
Zip 36685–0429; tel. 251/633–1000; Clark P. Christianson, President
and Chief Executive Officer
Web address: www.providencehospital.org

ST. VINCENT'S HOSPITAL (S, 274 beds) 810 St. Vincent's Drive, Birmingham,
AL Zip 35205–1695, Mailing Address: P.O. Box 12407, Zip 35202–2407;
tel. 205/939–7000; Curtis James, President and Chief Executive Officer
Web address: www.stv.org

ARIZONA: CARONDELET HOLY CROSS HOSPITAL (S, 79 beds) 1171 West
Target Range Road, Nogales, AZ Zip 85621–2496; tel. 520/285–3000;
Richard Polheber, Senior Vice President and Chief Executive Officer
Web address: www.carondelet.org

CARONDELET ST. JOSEPH'S HOSPITAL–TUCSON (S, 287 beds) 350 North
Wilmot Road, Tucson, AZ Zip 85711–2678; tel. 520/296–3211; Wesley E.
Colvin, Chief Executive Officer
Web address: www.carondelet.org

CARONDELET ST. MARY'S HOSPITAL–TUCSON (S, 402 beds) 1601 West St.
Mary's Road, Tucson, AZ Zip 85745–2682; tel. 520/872–3000; Gregory R.
Angle, Chief Executive Officer
Web address: www.carondelet.org

CONNECTICUT: ST. VINCENT'S MEDICAL CENTER (S, 320 beds) 2800 Main
Street, Bridgeport, CT Zip 06606–4292; tel. 203/576–6000; Susan L.
Davis, R.N., Ed.D., President and Chief Executive Officer
Web address: www.stvincents.org

DISTRICT OF COLUMBIA: PROVIDENCE HOSPITAL (S, 522 beds) 1150
Varnum Street N.E., Washington, DC Zip 20017–2180;
tel. 202/269–7000; Julius D. Spears Jr, President and Chief Executive
Officer
Web address: www.provhosp.org

FLORIDA: SACRED HEART HOSPITAL OF PENSACOLA (S, 449 beds) 5151
North Ninth Avenue, Pensacola, FL Zip 32504–8795, Mailing Address:
P.O. Box 2700, Zip 32513–2700; tel. 850/416–7000; William R.
McLaughlin, President
Web address: www.sacred–heart.org

SACRED HEART HOSPITAL ON THE EMERALD COAST (S, 50 beds) 7800
Highway 98 West, Destin, FL Zip 32550; tel. 850/278–3000; Roger L. Hall,
Chief Executive Officer
Web address: www.sacredheartemerald.org

ST. VINCENT'S MEDICAL CENTER (S, 528 beds) 1800 Barrs Street,
Jacksonville, FL Zip 32204–2982, Mailing Address: P.O. Box 2982,
Zip 32203–2982; tel. 904/308–7300; Margaret Mortensen, Interim
Executive Vice President and Chief Operating Officer
Web address: www.jaxhealth.com

GEORGIA: ST. JOSEPH HOSPITAL (S, 142 beds) 2260 Wrightsboro Road,
Augusta, GA Zip 30904–4726; tel. 706/481–7000; Andrew A. Lasser,
Dr.PH, President and Chief Executive Officer
Web address: www.stjosephhospital.org

IDAHO: ST. JOSEPH REGIONAL MEDICAL CENTER (S, 156 beds) 415 Sixth
Street, Lewiston, ID Zip 83501–0816; tel. 208/743–2511; Howard A.
Hayes, President and Chief Executive Officer
Web address: www.sjrmc.org

ILLINOIS: SAINT ANTHONY HOSPITAL (S, 151 beds) 2875 West 19th Street,
Chicago, IL Zip 60623–3596; tel. 773/484–1000; Kathleen K. DeVine,
Chief Executive Officer
Web address: www.cath–health.org

INDIANA: SAINT JOHN'S HEALTH SYSTEM (S, 206 beds) 2015 Jackson
Street, Anderson, IN Zip 46016–4339; tel. 765/649–2511; Kyle De Fur,
FACHE, President
Web address: www.stjohnshealthsystem.org

ST. ELIZABETH ANN SETON HOSPITAL OF CARMEL (S, 36 beds) 13500
North Meridian Street, Carmel, IN Zip 46032, Mailing Address: P.O. Box
1906, Zip 46082–1906; tel. 317/582–8500; Peter H. Alexander,
Administrator
Web address: www.stvincent.org

ST. ELIZABETH ANN SETON SPECIALTY CARE HOSPITAL (S, 31 beds) 3700
Washington Avenue, Evansville, IN Zip 47750; tel. 812/485–7540; Carol
Godsey, Chief Executive Officer
Web address: www.stmarys.org

ST. JOSEPH HOSPITAL (S, 136 beds) 1907 West Sycamore Street, Kokomo,
IN Zip 46901–4197, Mailing Address: P.O. Box 9010, Zip 46904–9010;
tel. 765/452–5611; Darcy K. Burthay, R.N., Interim President and Chief
Nursing Officer
Web address: www.stjosephhospital.net

ST. MARY'S WARRICK HOSPITAL (S, 40 beds) 1116 Millis Avenue, Boonville,
IN Zip 47601–0629, Mailing Address: Box 629, Zip 47601–0629;
tel. 812/897–4800; Mark Dooley, Executive Vice President and Administrator
Web address: www.stmarys.org

ST. MARY'S MEDICAL CENTER OF EVANSVILLE (S, 459 beds) 3700
Washington Avenue, Evansville, IN Zip 47750–0002; tel. 812/485–4000;
Timothy A. Flesch, President and Chief Executive Officer
Web address: www.stmarys.org

ST. VINCENT CLAY HOSPITAL (S, 25 beds) 1206 East National Avenue,
Brazil, IN Zip 47834–2797; tel. 812/442–2500; Jerry Laue, Administrator
Web address: www.stvincent.org

ST. VINCENT FRANKFORT HOSPITAL (S, 25 beds) 1300 South Jackson
Street, Frankfort, IN Zip 46041–3394, Mailing Address: P.O. Box 669,
Zip 46041–0669; tel. 765/656–3000; Thomas Crawford, Chief Executive
Officer
Web address: www.stvincent.org

ST. VINCENT HOSPITALS AND HEALTH SERVICES (S, 889 beds) 2001 West
86th Street, Indianapolis, IN Zip 46260–1991, Mailing Address: P.O. Box
40970, Zip 46240–0970; tel. 317/338–2345; Patricia A. Maryland, Dr.PH,
President
Web address: www.stvincent.org

ST. VINCENT JENNINGS HOSPITAL (S, 25 beds) 301 Henry Street, North
Vernon, IN Zip 47265–1097; tel. 812/352–4200; Joseph E. Roche,
Administrator
Web address: www.stvincent.org

ST. VINCENT MERCY HOSPITAL (S, 25 beds) 1331 South A Street, Elwood,
IN Zip 46036–1942; tel. 765/552–4600; Deborah Y. Rasper, FACHE,
Administrator
Web address: www.stvincent.org

ST. VINCENT RANDOLPH HOSPITAL (S, 25 beds) 473 Greenville Avenue,
Winchester, IN Zip 47394–2235, Mailing Address: P.O. Box 407,
Zip 47394–0407; tel. 765/584–0004; Wayne G. Deschambeau, Chief
Executive Officer
Web address: www.stvincent.org

ST. VINCENT WILLIAMSPORT HOSPITAL (S, 16 beds) 412 North Monroe
Street, Williamsport, IN Zip 47993–0215; tel. 765/762–4000; Jane Craigin,
Chief Executive Officer
Web address: www.stvincent.org

ST. VINCENT WOMEN'S HOSPITAL (O, 102 beds) 8111 Township Line Road,
Indianapolis, IN Zip 46260–8043; tel. 317/415–8111; Mary Lane Jackson,
Administrator
Web address: www.stvincent.org

MARYLAND: MEMORIAL HOSPITAL AND MEDICAL CENTER OF CUMBERLAND
(O, 160 beds) 600 Memorial Avenue, Cumberland, MD Zip 21502–3797;
tel. 301/723–4000; Thomas C. Dowdell, Executive Director and Senior
Vice President
Web address: www.wmhs.com

SACRED HEART HOSPITAL (S, 243 beds) 900 Seton Drive, Cumberland, MD
Zip 21502–1874; tel. 301/723–4200; Francis A. Pommett Jr, Executive
Director and Senior Vice President
Web address: www.wmhs.com

ST. AGNES HEALTHCARE (S, 327 beds) 900 Caton Avenue, Baltimore, MD
Zip 21229–5299; tel. 410/368–6000; Kenneth H. Bancroft, President and
Chief Executive Officer
Web address: www.stagnes.org

MICHIGAN: BORGESS MEDICAL CENTER (S, 381 beds) 1521 Gull Road,
Kalamazoo, MI Zip 49048–1666; tel. 269/226–4800; Paul A. Spaude,
FACHE, President and Chief Executive Officer
Web address: www.borgess.com

BORGESS–LEE MEMORIAL HOSPITAL (S, 15 beds) 420 West High Street,
Dowagiac, MI Zip 49047–1907; tel. 269/782–8681; William Daam, Chief
Operating Officer
Web address: www.borgess.com

For explanation of codes following names, see page B2.
★ Indicates Type III membership in the American Hospital Association.

B10 Health Care Systems, Networks and Alliances

© 2005 AHA Guide

BRIGHTON HOSPITAL (S, 92 beds) 12851 East Grand River Avenue, Brighton, MI Zip 48116–8596; tel. 810/227–1211; Denise Bertin–Epp, Chief Executive Officer
Web address: www.brightonhospital.org

DOCTORS HOSPITAL (S, 65 beds) 110 North Elm Avenue, Jackson, MI Zip 49202–3595; tel. 517/787–1440; Victoria Webster, President and Chief Executive Officer

GENESYS REGIONAL MEDICAL CENTER (S, 389 beds) One Genesys Parkway, Grand Blanc, MI Zip 48439–8066; tel. 810/606–5000; Norma R. Hagenow, R.N., President and Chief Executive Officer
Web address: www.genesys.org

PROVIDENCE HOSPITAL AND MEDICAL CENTER (S, 384 beds) 16001 West Nine Mile Road, Southfield, MI Zip 48075–4854, Mailing Address: Box 2043, Zip 48037–2043; tel. 248/424–3000; Robert F. Casalou, President
Web address: www.providence–stjohnhealth.org

SAINT MARY'S MEDICAL CENTER (S, 268 beds) 800 South Washington Avenue, Saginaw, MI Zip 48601–2594; tel. 989/776–8000; Fleury Yelvington, President and Chief Executive Officer
Web address: www.saintmarys–saginaw.org

SAINT MARY'S STANDISH COMMUNITY HOSPITAL (S, 68 beds) 805 West Cedar Street, Standish, MI Zip 48658–9526; tel. 989/846–4521; Jeff L. Probus, Administrator and Chief Exective Officer
Web address: www.saintmarys–standish.org

ST. JOHN DETROIT RIVERVIEW HOSPITAL – NORTHEAST CAMPUS (S, 262 beds) 7733 East Jefferson Avenue, Detroit, MI Zip 48214–2598; tel. 313/499–4000; Anthony E. Munroe, President and Chief Executive Officer
Web address: www.stjohn.org/detroitriverview

ST. JOHN HOSPITAL AND MEDICAL CENTER (S, 607 beds) 22101 Moross Road, Detroit, MI Zip 48236–2172; tel. 313/343–4000; Mark R. Taylor, President
Web address: www.stjohn.org

ST. JOHN MACOMB HOSPITAL (S, 349 beds) 11800 East Twelve Mile Road, Warren, MI Zip 48093–3494; tel. 586/573–5000; Joseph M. Tasse, President
Web address: www.stjohn.org

ST. JOHN NORTH SHORES HOSPITAL (S, 55 beds) 26755 Ballard Road, Harrison Township, MI Zip 48045–2458; tel. 586/465–5501; David Sessions, Administrator
Web address: www.stjohn.org

ST. JOHN OAKLAND HOSPITAL (S, 164 beds) 27351 Dequindre, Madison Heights, MI Zip 48071–3499; tel. 248/967–7000; Robert Deputat, President
Web address: www.stjohn.org

ST. JOHN RIVER DISTRICT HOSPITAL (S, 68 beds) 4100 River Road, East China, MI Zip 48054–2909; tel. 810/329–7111; Frank W. Poma, President
Web address: www.stjohn.org

ST. JOSEPH HEALTH SYSTEM (S, 49 beds) 200 Hemlock Street, Tawas City, MI Zip 48763–9360, Mailing Address: P.O. Box 659, Zip 48764–0659; tel. 989/362–3411; Patrick Murtha, President and Chief Executive Officer
Web address: www.sjhsys.org

MISSOURI: SAINT JOSEPH MEDICAL CENTER (S, 272 beds) 1000 Carondelet Drive, Kansas City, MO Zip 64114–4673; tel. 816/942–4400; Michele Schaefer, Chief Executive Officer
Web address: www.carondelethealth.org

ST. MARY'S MEDICAL CENTER (S, 134 beds) 201 West R. D. Mize Road, Blue Springs, MO Zip 64014–2533; tel. 816/228–5900; Gordon Docking, Chief Executive Officer
Web address: www.carondelethealth.org

NEW YORK: MOUNT ST. MARY'S HOSPITAL AND HEALTH CENTER (S, 175 beds) 5300 Military Road, Lewiston, NY Zip 14092–1997; tel. 716/297–4800; Angelo G. Calbone, President and Chief Executive Officer
Web address: www.msmh.org

OUR LADY OF LOURDES MEMORIAL HOSPITAL (S, 159 beds) 169 Riverside Drive, Binghamton, NY Zip 13905–4198; tel. 607/798–5111; John D. O'Neil, President and Chief Executive Officer
Web address: www.lourdes.com

SETON HEALTH SYSTEM (S, 179 beds) 1300 Massachusetts Avenue, Troy, NY Zip 12180–1695; tel. 518/268–5000; Gino J. Pazzaglini, FACHE, President and Chief Executive Officer
Web address: www.setonhealth.org

ST. MARY'S HOSPITAL (S, 143 beds) 427 Guy Park Avenue, Amsterdam, NY Zip 12010–1095; tel. 518/842–1900; Victor Giulianelli, President and Chief Executive Officer
Web address: www.smha.org

PENNSYLVANIA: GOOD SAMARITAN REGIONAL MEDICAL CENTER (S, 147 beds) 700 East Norwegian Street, Pottsville, PA Zip 17901–2798; tel. 570/621–4000; Peter Bergmann, President and Chief Executive Officer
Web address: www.gsrmc.com

TENNESSEE: BAPTIST HOSPITAL (S, 454 beds) 2000 Church Street, Nashville, TN Zip 37236–0002; tel. 615/284–5555; Bernard Sherry, President and Chief Executive Officer
Web address: www.baptisthospital.com

DEKALB HOSPITAL (S, 51 beds) 520 West Main Street, Smithville, TN Zip 37166–0640, Mailing Address: P.O. Box 640, Zip 37166–0640; tel. 615/597–7171; Dennis Smock, Chief Executive Officer
Web address: www.baptistdekalbhospital.com

HICKMAN COMMUNITY HOSPITAL (S, 65 beds) 135 East Swan Street, Centerville, TN Zip 37033–1446; tel. 931/729–4271; Jack M. Keller, Administrator
Web address: www.hickmanhospital.com

MIDDLE TENNESSEE MEDICAL CENTER (S, 199 beds) 400 North Highland Avenue, Murfreesboro, TN Zip 37130–3854, Mailing Address: P.O. Box 1178, Zip 37133–1178; tel. 615/396–4100; Donald R. Gintzig, CHE, Chief Executive Officer
Web address: www.mtmc.org

SAINT THOMAS HOSPITAL (S, 485 beds) 4220 Harding Road, Nashville, TN Zip 37205–2095, Mailing Address: P.O. Box 380, Zip 37202–0380; tel. 615/222–2111; Dale Batchelor, M.D., Interim President and Chief Executive Officer
Web address: www.stthomas.org

TEXAS: BRACKENRIDGE HOSPITAL (L, 382 beds) 601 East 15th Street, Austin, TX Zip 78701–1996; tel. 512/324–7000; Jesus Garza, President and Chief Executive Officer
Web address: www.seton.net

PROVIDENCE HEALTH CENTER (S, 549 beds) 6901 Medical Parkway, Waco, TX Zip 76712–7998, Mailing Address: P.O. Box 2589, Zip 76702–2589; tel. 254/751–4000; Kent A. Keahey, President and Chief Executive Officer
Web address: www.providence.net

SETON EDGAR B. DAVIS HOSPITAL (S, 27 beds) 130 Hays Street, Luling, TX Zip 78648–3207; tel. 830/875–7000; Neal Kelley, Administrator
Web address: www.seton.net

SETON HIGHLAND LAKES (S, 28 beds) Highway 281 South, Burnet, TX Zip 78611–7219, Mailing Address: P.O. Box 1219, Zip 78611–7219; tel. 512/715–3000; Janna Maturo, R.N., Vice President and Chief Operating Officer
Web address: www.seton.net

SETON MEDICAL CENTER (S, 446 beds) 1201 West 38th Street, Austin, TX Zip 78705–1056; tel. 512/324–1000; John C. Brindley, President and Chief Executive Officer
Web address: www.seton.net

SETON SHOAL CREEK HOSPITAL (S, 89 beds) 3501 Mills Avenue, Austin, TX Zip 78731–6391; tel. 512/324–2040; Armin L. Steege, Administrator and Vice President
Web address: www.seton.net

WASHINGTON: LOURDES COUNSELING CENTER (S, 32 beds) 1175 Carondelet Drive, Richland, WA Zip 99352–3396; tel. 509/943–9104; Barbara Mead, Executive Director
Web address: www.lourdesonline.org

LOURDES MEDICAL CENTER (S, 52 beds) 520 North Fourth Avenue, Pasco, WA Zip 99301–2568, Mailing Address: P.O. Box 2568, Zip 99302–2568; tel. 509/547–7704; John Serle, President and Chief Executive Officer
Web address: www.lourdesonline.org

WISCONSIN: COLUMBIA ST. MARY'S OZAUKEE CAMPUS (S, 106 beds) 13111 North Port Washington Road, Mequon, WI Zip 53097–2416; tel. 262/243–7300; Leo P. Brideau, President and Chief Executive Officer
Web address: www.columbia–stmarys.com

COLUMBIA ST. MARY'S–COLUMBIA CAMPUS (S, 287 beds) 2025 East Newport Avenue, Milwaukee, WI Zip 53211–2990; tel. 414/961–3300; Leo P. Brideau, President and Chief Executive Officer
Web address: www.columbia–stmarys.com

For explanation of codes following names, see page B2.
★ Indicates Type III membership in the American Hospital Association.

COLUMBIA ST. MARY'S–MILWAUKEE CAMPUS (S, 237 beds) 2323 North Lake Drive, Milwaukee, WI Zip 53211–9682, Mailing Address: P.O. Box 503, Zip 53201–0503; tel. 414/291–1000; Leo P. Brideau, President and Chief Executive Officer
Web address: www.columbia–stmarys.com

SACRED HEART REHABILITATION INSTITUTE (S, 49 beds) 2025 East Newport Avenue, Milwaukee, WI Zip 53211–2906; tel. 414/298–6700; Jack Burke, Administrator
Web address: www.columbia–stmarys.com

Owned, leased, sponsored:	69 hospitals	14442 beds
Contract–managed:	0 hospitals	0 beds
Totals:	69 hospitals	14442 beds

0229: ASSOCIATED HEALTHCARE SYSTEMS, INC. (IO)
214 Overlook Court, Suite 260, Brentwood, TN Zip 37027; tel. 615/309–0940; A. Ronald Turner, President and Chief Executive Officer
(Independent Hospital System)

ARKANSAS: RANDOLPH COUNTY MEDICAL CENTER (O, 45 beds) 2801 Medical Center Drive, Pocahontas, AR Zip 72455–9497; tel. 870/892–6000; Terry G. Whittington, Chief Executive Officer

GEORGIA: BERRIEN COUNTY HOSPITAL (O, 171 beds) 1221 East McPherson Street, Nashville, GA Zip 31639–2326, Mailing Address: P.O. Box 665, Zip 31639–0665; tel. 229/543–7100; Rick Langosch, Interim Chief Executive Officer
Web address: www.berriencountyhospital.com

KENTUCKY: CARROLL COUNTY HOSPITAL (L, 25 beds) 309 11th Street, Carrollton, KY Zip 41008–1400; tel. 502/732–4321; Kim Dees, Chief Executive Officer
Web address: www.nortonhealthcare.com

SAMARITAN HOSPITAL (L, 271 beds) 310 South Limestone Street, Lexington, KY Zip 40508–3008; tel. 859/226–7000; Frank Beirne, Chief Executive Officer
Web address: www.samaritanhospital.com

LOUISIANA: SABINE MEDICAL CENTER (O, 44 beds) 240 Highland Drive, Many, LA Zip 71449–3718; tel. 318/256–5691; Patrick W. Gandy, Chief Executive Officer

TENNESSEE: CUMBERLAND RIVER HOSPITAL (O, 34 beds) 100 Old Jefferson Street, Celina, TN Zip 38551–4040, Mailing Address: P. O. Box 427, Zip 38551–0427; tel. 931/243–3581; Andrea Rich–McLerran, Chief Executive Officer

THREE RIVERS HOSPITAL (O, 25 beds) 451 Highway 13 South, Waverly, TN Zip 37185–2149, Mailing Address: P.O. Box 437, Zip 37185–2149; tel. 931/296–4203; Kent Koster, Chief Executive Officer

TRINITY HOSPITAL (O, 31 beds) 353 Main Street, Erin, TN Zip 37061–0489, Mailing Address: P.O. Box 489, Zip 37061–0489; tel. 931/289–4211; Yvette Gillespie, Chief Executive Officer
Web address: www.trinityhospitaltn.com

Owned, leased, sponsored:	8 hospitals	646 beds
Contract–managed:	0 hospitals	0 beds
Totals:	8 hospitals	646 beds

★0865: ATLANTIC HEALTH SYSTEM (NP)
325 Columbia Turnpike, Florham Park, NJ Zip 07932; tel. 973/660–3270; Joseph A. Trunfio, Ph.D., President and Chief Executive Officer
(Moderately Centralized Health System)

NEW JERSEY: MORRISTOWN MEMORIAL HOSPITAL (O, 601 beds) 100 Madison Avenue, Morristown, NJ Zip 07962–1956; tel. 973/971–5000; Joseph A. Trunfio, Ph.D., President and Chief Executive Officer
Web address: www.atlantichealth.org/cons/hospitals/at_MMH

MOUNTAINSIDE HOSPITAL (O, 261 beds) 1 Bay Avenue, Montclair, NJ Zip 07042–4898; tel. 973/429–6000; Joseph A. Trunfio, Ph.D., President and Chief Executive Officer
Web address: www.atlantichealth.org/cons/hospitals/at_MSH

OVERLOOK HOSPITAL (O, 363 beds) 99 Beauvoir Avenue, Summit, NJ Zip 07902–0220; tel. 908/522–2000; Joseph A. Trunfio, Ph.D., President and Chief Executive Officer
Web address: www.atlantichealth.org/cons/hospitals/at_OH

Owned, leased, sponsored:	3 hospitals	1225 beds
Contract–managed:	0 hospitals	0 beds
Totals:	3 hospitals	1225 beds

● ★0293: ATLANTICARE (NP)
2500 English Creek Avenue, Building C., Egg Harbor City, NJ Zip 08234; tel. 609/407–2300; George F. Lynn, President
(Centralized Physician/Insurance Health System)

ATLANTICARE REGIONAL MEDICAL CENTER (O, 442 beds) 1925 Pacific Avenue, Atlantic City, NJ Zip 08401–6713; tel. 609/345–4000; David P. Tilton, President and Chief Executive Officer
Web address: www.atlanticare.org

Owned, leased, sponsored:	1 hospital	442 beds
Contract–managed:	0 hospitals	0 beds
Totals:	1 hospital	442 beds

★2215: AURORA HEALTH CARE (NP)
3000 West Montana, Milwaukee, WI Zip 53215–3268, Mailing Address: P.O. Box 343910, Zip 53234–3910; tel. 414/647–3000; G. Edwin Howe, President
(Centralized Health System)

WISCONSIN: AURORA BAYCARE MEDICAL CENTER (O, 126 beds) 2845 Greenbrier Road, Green Bay, WI Zip 54311, Mailing Address: P.O. Box 8900, Zip 54308; tel. 920/288–8000; Linda Smith, Administrator
Web address: www.aurorabaycare.com

AURORA LAKELAND MEDICAL CENTER (O, 75 beds) W3985 County Road NN, Elkhorn, WI Zip 53121–4389; tel. 262/741–2000; Kathleen Skowlund, R.N., MS, Administrator and Chief Nurse Executive
Web address: www.aurorahealthcare.org

AURORA MEDICAL CENTER (O, 72 beds) 10400 South 75th Street, Kenosha, WI Zip 53142; tel. 262/948–5600; Christine Olson, Administrator
Web address: www.aurorahealthcare.org

AURORA MEDICAL CENTER – MANITOWOC (O, 69 beds) 5000 Memorial Drive, Two Rivers, WI Zip 54241–2399; tel. 920/794–5000; Bobbe Teigen, Administrator
Web address: www.aurorahealthcare.org

AURORA MEDICAL CENTER OF OSHKOSH (O, 84 beds) 855 North Westhaven Drive, Oshkosh, WI Zip 54904; tel. 920/456–6000; Frances R. Finley, Administrator
Web address: www.aurorahealthcare.com

AURORA MEDICAL CENTER OF WASHINGTON COUNTY (O, 55 beds) 1032 East Sumner Street, Hartford, WI Zip 53027–1698; tel. 262/673–2300; Mark Schwartz, Administrator
Web address: www.aurorahealthcare.org

AURORA PSYCHIATRIC HOSPITAL (O, 105 beds) 1220 Dewey Avenue, Wauwatosa, WI Zip 53213–2598; tel. 414/454–6600; Peter Carlson, Executive Director
Web address: www.aurorahealthcare.org

AURORA SHEBOYGAN MEMORIAL MEDICAL CENTER (O, 233 beds) 2629 North Seventh Street, Sheboygan, WI Zip 53083–4998; tel. 920/451–5000; Daniel Meyer, Administrator
Web address: www.aurorahealthcare.org

AURORA SINAI MEDICAL CENTER (O, 236 beds) 945 North 12th Street, Milwaukee, WI Zip 53233–1337, Mailing Address: P.O. Box 342, Zip 53201–0342; tel. 414/219–2000; Leonard E. Wilk, Administrator
Web address: www.aurorahealthcare.org

MEMORIAL HOSPITAL CORPORATION OF BURLINGTON (O, 65 beds) 252 McHenry Street, Burlington, WI Zip 53105–1828; tel. 262/767–6000; Ann R. Navera, R.N., Administrator and Chief Nurse Executive
Web address: www.aurorahealthcare.org

ST. LUKE'S MEDICAL CENTER (O, 752 beds) 2900 West Oklahoma Avenue, Milwaukee, WI Zip 53215–4330, Mailing Address: P.O. Box 2901, Zip 53201–2901; tel. 414/649–6000; Mark R. Ambrosius, Administrator
Web address: www.aurorahealthcare.org

For explanation of codes following names, see page B2.
★ Indicates Type III membership in the American Hospital Association.
● Single hospital health care system

WEST ALLIS MEMORIAL HOSPITAL (O, 227 beds) 8901 West Lincoln Avenue, West Allis, WI Zip 53227–0901, Mailing Address: P.O. Box 27901, Zip 53227–0901; tel. 414/328–6000; Richard A. Kellar, Administrator
Web address: www.aurora.org

Owned, leased, sponsored:	12 hospitals	2099 beds
Contract–managed:	0 hospitals	0 beds
Totals:	12 hospitals	2099 beds

★**5255: AVERA HEALTH** (CC)
610 West 23rd Street, Yankton, SD Zip 57078, Mailing Address: P.O. Box 38, Zip 57078–0038; tel. 605/322–7050; John T. Porter, President and Chief Executive Officer
(Decentralized Health System)

IOWA: AVERA HOLY FAMILY HOSPITAL (O, 25 beds) 826 North Eighth Street, Estherville, IA Zip 51334–1598; tel. 712/362–2631; William Bumgarner, Chief Executive Officer
Web address: www.avera–holyfamily.org

FLOYD VALLEY HOSPITAL/AVERA HEALTH (C, 44 beds) 714 Lincoln Street N.E., Le Mars, IA Zip 51031–0010, Mailing Address: P.O. Box 10, Zip 51031–0010; tel. 712/546–7871; Michael T. Donlin, Administrator
Web address: www.floydvalleyhospital.org

HEGG MEMORIAL HEALTH CENTER/AVERA HEALTH (C, 120 beds) 1202 21st Avenue, Rock Valley, IA Zip 51247–1497; tel. 712/476–8000; Glenn Zevenbergen, Chief Executive Officer
Web address: www.heggmemorialhealthcenter.org

OSCEOLA COMMUNITY HOSPITAL (C, 25 beds) Ninth Avenue North, Sibley, IA Zip 51249–0258, Mailing Address: P.O. Box 258, Zip 51249–0258; tel. 712/754–2574; Janet Dykstra, Administrator
Web address: www.osceolacommunityhospital.org

SIOUX CENTER COMMUNITY HOSPITAL AND HEALTH CENTER/AVERA HEALTH (C, 90 beds) 605 South Main Avenue, Sioux Center, IA Zip 51250–1398; tel. 712/722–1271; Michael Seda, Chief Executive Officer
Web address: www.schospital.org

MINNESOTA: AVERA MARSHALL REGIONAL MEDICAL CENTER (C, 108 beds) 300 South Bruce Street, Marshall, MN Zip 56258–3900; tel. 507/532–9661; Bruce E. Roesler, Chief Executive Officer
Web address: www.wmmc.org

DIVINE PROVIDENCE HEALTH CENTER/AVERA HEALTH (C, 56 beds) 312 East George Street, Ivanhoe, MN Zip 56142–0136, Mailing Address: P.O. Box 136, Zip 56142–0136; tel. 507/694–1414; Mary Maertens, Interim Administrator
Web address: www.dphc.org

PIPESTONE COUNTY MEDICAL CENTER/AVERA HEALTH (C, 76 beds) 916 4th Avenue S.W., Pipestone, MN Zip 56164–0370; tel. 507/825–6125; Jody Jenner, Chief Executive Officer and Administrator
Web address: www.pcmchealth.org

TYLER HEALTHCARE CENTER/AVERA HEALTH (C, 63 beds) 240 Willow Street, Tyler, MN Zip 56178–0280, Mailing Address: P.O. Box 280, Zip 56178–0280; tel. 507/247–5521; Dale Kruger, Chief Executive Officer & Chief Financial Officer

NEBRASKA: AVERA ST. ANTHONY'S HOSPITAL (O, 27 beds) Second and Adams Streets, O'Neill, NE Zip 68763–1569; tel. 402/336–2611; Ronald J. Cork, President and Chief Executive Officer
Web address: www.avera–sta.org

SOUTH DAKOTA: AVERA GREGORY HEALTHCARE CENTER (O, 94 beds) 400 Park Avenue, Gregory, SD Zip 57533–0400, Mailing Address: P.O. Box 408, Zip 57533–0408; tel. 605/835–8394; Mark Klosterman, Chief Executive Officer
Web address: www.gregoryhealthcare.org

AVERA MCKENNAN HOSPITAL AND UNIVERSITY HEALTH CENTER (O, 651 beds) 800 East 21st Street, Sioux Falls, SD Zip 57105–1096, Mailing Address: P.O. Box 5045, Zip 57117–5045; tel. 605/322–8000; Fredrick Slunecka, Regional President
Web address: www.averamckennan.org

AVERA QUEEN OF PEACE (O, 213 beds) 525 North Foster, Mitchell, SD Zip 57301–2999; tel. 605/995–2000; Thomas P. Rasmusson, President and Chief Executive Officer
Web address: www.averaqueenofpeace.org

AVERA SACRED HEART HOSPITAL (O, 297 beds) 501 Summit Avenue, Yankton, SD Zip 57078–3899; tel. 605/668–8000; Pamela J. Rezac, President and Chief Executive Officer
Web address: www.averasacredheart.com

AVERA ST. BENEDICT HEALTH CENTER (O, 100 beds) 401 Glynn Drive, Parkston, SD Zip 57366–2031; tel. 605/928–3311; Gale Walker, President and Chief Executive Officer
Web address: www.averastbenedict.org

AVERA ST. LUKE'S (O, 269 beds) 305 South State Street, Aberdeen, SD Zip 57402–4450; tel. 605/622–5000; Ronald L. Jacobson, President and Chief Executive Officer
Web address: www.averastlukes.org

AVERA WESKOTA MEMORIAL MEDICAL CENTER (L, 25 beds) 604 First Street N.E., Wessington Springs, SD Zip 57382, Mailing Address: P.O. Box 429, Zip 57382; tel. 605/539–1201; Kayleen R. Lee, Chief Executive Officer
Web address: www.averaweskota.org

DELLS AREA HEALTH CENTER (L, 20 beds) 909 North Iowa Avenue, Dell Rapids, SD Zip 57022–1231; tel. 605/428–5431; James A. Faulwell, Chief Executive Officer and Administrator

EUREKA COMMUNITY HEALTH SERVICES/AVERA HEALTH (C, 6 beds) 410 Ninth Street, Eureka, SD Zip 57437–0517, Mailing Address: P.O. Box 517, Zip 57437–0517; tel. 605/284–2661; Robert A. Dockter, Administrator
Web address: www.avera.org/facilities/eureka.htm

FLANDREAU MEDICAL CENTER/AVERA HEALTH (L, 18 beds) 214 North Prairie Avenue, Flandreau, SD Zip 57028–1243; tel. 605/997–2433; Randy Anderson, Administrator and Chief Executive Officer
Web address: www.flandreaumedical.org

HAND COUNTY MEMORIAL HOSPITAL/AVERA HEALTH (C, 44 beds) 300 West Fifth Street, Miller, SD Zip 57362–1238; tel. 605/853–2421; Bryan Breitling, Administrator
Web address: www.avera.org

LANDMANN–JUNGMAN MEMORIAL HOSPITAL (C, 19 beds) 600 Billars Street, Scotland, SD Zip 57059–2026; tel. 605/583–2226; Jay Plucker, Administrator
Web address: www.ljmh.org

MARSHALL COUNTY HEALTHCARE CENTER/AVERA HEALTH (C, 20 beds) 413 Ninth Street, Britton, SD Zip 57430; tel. 605/448–2253; Stephanie Reasy, Administrator
Web address: www.avera.org

MILBANK AREA HOSPITAL/AVERA HEALTH (L, 25 beds) 901 East Virgil Avenue, Milbank, SD Zip 57252; tel. 605/432–4538; Jeffrey M. Lang, Administrator

PLATTE HEALTH CENTER/AVERA HEALTH (C, 63 beds) 601 East Seventh, Platte, SD Zip 57369–2123, Mailing Address: P.O. Box 200, Zip 57369–0200; tel. 605/337–3364; Mark Burket, Chief Executive Officer
Web address: www.phcavera.org

ST. MICHAEL'S HOSPITAL (C, 34 beds) 410 West 16th Avenue, Tyndall, SD Zip 57066, Mailing Address: P.O. Box 27, Zip 57066–0027; tel. 605/589–3341; Carol Deurmier, Chief Executive Officer

WAGNER COMMUNITY MEMORIAL HOSPITAL (C, 20 beds) Third and Walnut, Wagner, SD Zip 57380, Mailing Address: P.O. Box 280, Zip 57380–0280; tel. 605/384–3611; Jeremy Armstrong, Administrator

Owned, leased, sponsored:	12 hospitals	1764 beds
Contract–managed:	15 hospitals	788 beds
Totals:	27 hospitals	2552 beds

★**0194: BANNER HEALTH** (NP)
1441 North 12th Street, Phoenix, AZ Zip 85006, Mailing Address: P.O. Box 25489, Zip 85002–5489; tel. 602/495–4000; Peter S. Fine, FACHE, President and Chief Executive Officer
(Decentralized Health System)

ALASKA: FAIRBANKS MEMORIAL HOSPITAL (L, 162 beds) 1650 Cowles Street, Fairbanks, AK Zip 99701–5998; tel. 907/452–8181; Michael K. Powers, FACHE, Chief Executive Officer
Web address: www.bannerhealth.com

ARIZONA: BANNER BAYWOOD HEART HOSPITAL (O, 111 beds) 6750 East Baywood Avenue, Mesa, AZ Zip 85206; tel. 480/854–5000; Kathy Bollinger, Chief Executive Officer
Web address: www.bannerhealth.com

For explanation of codes following names, see page B2.
★ Indicates Type III membership in the American Hospital Association.

BANNER BAYWOOD MEDICAL CENTER (O, 242 beds) 6644 Baywood Avenue, Mesa, AZ Zip 85206–1797; tel. 480/981–2000; Don A. Evans, FACHE, Chief Executive Officer
Web address: www.bannerhealth.com

BANNER BEHAVIORAL HEALTH HOSPITAL (O, 100 beds) 7575 East Earll Drive, Scottsdale, AZ Zip 85251–6915; tel. 480/941–7500; Patricia A. Little–Upah, Chief Executive Officer
Web address: www.bannerhealth.com

BANNER DESERT MEDICAL CENTER (O, 611 beds) 1400 South Dobson Road, Mesa, AZ Zip 85202–9879; tel. 480/512–3000; Bruce E. Pearson, Chief Executive Officer
Web address: www.bannerhealth.com

BANNER ESTRELLA MEDICAL (O, 172 beds) 9201 West Thomas Road, Phoenix, AZ Zip 85037–3332, Mailing Address: P.O. Box 120, Zip 85001–0120; tel. 623/327–4000; Constance Harmsen, R.N., Chief Executive Officer
Web address: www.bannerhealth.org

BANNER GOOD SAMARITAN MEDICAL CENTER (O, 577 beds) 1111 East McDowell Road, Phoenix, AZ Zip 85006–2666, Mailing Address: P.O. Box 2989, Zip 85062–2989; tel. 602/239–2000; Paul Mullings, FACHE, Chief Executive Officer
Web address: www.bannerhealth.com

BANNER MESA MEDICAL CENTER (O, 201 beds) 1010 North Country Club Drive, Mesa, AZ Zip 85201–3299; tel. 480/834–1211; Rebecca C. Kuhn, Chief Executive Officer
Web address: www.bannerhealth.com

BANNER THUNDERBIRD MEDICAL CENTER (O, 369 beds) 5555 West Thunderbird Road, Glendale, AZ Zip 85306–4696; tel. 602/865–5555; Colleen Hallberg, Chief Executive Officer
Web address: www.bannerhealth.com

PAGE HOSPITAL (C, 25 beds) 501 North Navajo Drive, Page, AZ Zip 86040, Mailing Address: P.O. Box 1447, Zip 86040–1447; tel. 928/645–2424; Sandy Haryasz, R.N., Chief Executive Officer
Web address: www.bannerhealth.com

CALIFORNIA: BANNER LASSEN MEDICAL CENTER (O, 38 beds) 1800 Spring Ridge Drive, Susanville, CA Zip 96130–4809; tel. 530/252–2000; David S. Anderson, FACHE, Chief Executive Officer
Web address: www.bannerhealth.com

COLORADO: EAST MORGAN COUNTY HOSPITAL (L, 15 beds) 2400 West Edison Street, Brush, CO Zip 80723–1640; tel. 970/842–6200; Larry E. Leaming, Chief Executive Officer
Web address: www.emchbrush.com

MCKEE MEDICAL CENTER (O, 109 beds) 2000 Boise Avenue, Loveland, CO Zip 80538–4281, Mailing Address: P.O. Box 830, Zip 80539–0830; tel. 970/669–4640; Richard O. Sutton, Chief Executive Officer
Web address: www.mckeeloveland.com

NORTH COLORADO MEDICAL CENTER (L, 276 beds) 1801 16th Street, Greeley, CO Zip 80631–5199; tel. 970/352–4121; Gene L. O'Hara, Chief Executive Officer
Web address: www.ncmcgreeley.com

STERLING REGIONAL MEDCENTER (O, 36 beds) 615 Fairhurst Street, Sterling, CO Zip 80751–0500; tel. 970/522–0122; Michael J. Gillen, Chief Executive Officer
Web address: www.bannerhealth.com

NEBRASKA: OGALLALA COMMUNITY HOSPITAL (L, 18 beds) 2601 North Spruce Street, Ogallala, NE Zip 69153–2465; tel. 308/284–4011; Margie Molitor, R.N., Chief Executive Officer

NEVADA: BANNER CHURCHILL COMMUNITY HOSPITAL (O, 40 beds) 801 East Williams Avenue, Fallon, NV Zip 89406–3052; tel. 775/423–3151; Charles Myers, Chief Executive Officer
Web address: www.churchillhospital.com

WYOMING: COMMUNITY HOSPITAL (O, 25 beds) 2000 Campbell Drive, Torrington, WY Zip 82240–1597; tel. 307/532–4181; Gordon Lewis, Chief Executive Officer
Web address: www.torringtonhealth.com

PLATTE COUNTY MEMORIAL HOSPITAL (L, 68 beds) 201 14th Street, Wheatland, WY Zip 82201–3201, Mailing Address: P.O. Box 848, Zip 82201–0848; tel. 307/322–3636; Kenneth W. Leisher, Chief Executive Officer
Web address: www.plattecountyhospital.com

WASHAKIE MEDICAL CENTER (L, 25 beds) 400 South 15th Street, Worland, WY Zip 82401–3531, Mailing Address: P.O. Box 700, Zip 82401–0700; tel. 307/347–3221; George A. Rohrich, Chief Executive Officer
Web address: www.washakiemedicalcenter.com

Owned, leased, sponsored:	19 hospitals	3195 beds
Contract–managed:	1 hospital	25 beds
Totals:	20 hospitals	3220 beds

★0005: BAPTIST HEALTH (CO)
800 Prudential Drive, Jacksonville, FL Zip 32207; tel. 904/202–4011; Hugh Greene, Chief Executive Officer
(Moderately Centralized Health System)

FLORIDA: BAPTIST MEDICAL CENTER (O, 547 beds) 800 Prudential Drive, Jacksonville, FL Zip 32207–8203; tel. 904/202–2000; Joseph Mitrick, Administrator
Web address: www.e–baptisthealth.com

BAPTIST MEDICAL CENTER NASSAU (O, 32 beds) 1250 South 18th Street, Fernandina Beach, FL Zip 32034–3098; tel. 904/321–3500; Jim L. Mayo, Administrator
Web address: www.e–baptisthealth.com

BAPTIST MEDICAL CENTER–BEACHES (O, 98 beds) 1350 13th Avenue South, Jacksonville Beach, FL Zip 32250–3205; tel. 904/247–2900; Mark Slyter, Administrator
Web address: www.e–baptisthealth.com

Owned, leased, sponsored:	3 hospitals	677 beds
Contract–managed:	0 hospitals	0 beds
Totals:	3 hospitals	677 beds

★0150: BAPTIST HEALTH (NP)
301 Brown Springs Road, Montgomery, AL Zip 36117; tel. 334/273–4400; W. Russell Tyner, President and Chief Executive Officer
(Independent Hospital System)

ALABAMA: BAPTIST MEDICAL CENTER EAST (O, 138 beds) 400 Taylor Road, Montgomery, AL Zip 36117–3512, Mailing Address: P.O. Box 241267, Zip 36124–1267; tel. 334/277–8330; Mindy Burdick, Administrator
Web address: www.baptistfirst.org

BAPTIST MEDICAL CENTER SOUTH (O, 342 beds) 2105 East South Boulevard, Montgomery, AL Zip 36116–2498, Mailing Address: Box 11010, Zip 36111–0010; tel. 334/288–2100; Lynne Parker, Administrator
Web address: www.baptistfirst.org

PRATTVILLE BAPTIST HOSPITAL (O, 47 beds) 124 South Memorial Drive, Prattville, AL Zip 36067–3619, Mailing Address: P.O. Box 681630, Zip 36067–1638; tel. 334/365–0651; Ginger Irsik, Administrator
Web address: www.baptistfirst.org

Owned, leased, sponsored:	3 hospitals	527 beds
Contract–managed:	0 hospitals	0 beds
Totals:	3 hospitals	527 beds

★0355: BAPTIST HEALTH (NP)
9601 Interstate 630, Exit 7, Little Rock, AR Zip 72205–7299; tel. 501/202–2000; Russell D. Harrington Jr, President and Chief Executive Officer
(Centralized Health System)

ARKANSAS: BAPTIST HEALTH MEDICAL CENTER – NORTH LITTLE ROCK (O, 210 beds) 3333 Springhill Drive, North Little Rock, AR Zip 72117–2922; tel. 501/202–3000; Harrison M. Dean, Senior Vice President and Administrator
Web address: www.baptist–health.org

BAPTIST HEALTH MEDICAL CENTER–ARKADELPHIA (L, 25 beds) 3050 Twin Rivers Drive, Arkadelphia, AR Zip 71923–4299; tel. 870/245–2622; Dan Gathright, Senior Vice President and Administrator
Web address: www.baptist–health.org

BAPTIST HEALTH MEDICAL CENTER–HEBER SPRINGS (L, 18 beds) 2319 Highway 110 West, Heber Springs, AR Zip 72543–3442; tel. 501/206–3000; Edward L. Lacy, Vice President and Administrator
Web address: www.baptist–health.com

For explanation of codes following names, see page B2.
★ Indicates Type III membership in the American Hospital Association.

BAPTIST HEALTH MEDICAL CENTER–LITTLE ROCK (O, 692 beds) 9601 Interstate 630, Exit 7, Little Rock, AR Zip 72205–7299; tel. 501/202–2000; Steven Douglas Weeks, Senior Vice President and Administrator
Web address: www.baptist–health.org

BAPTIST HEALTH REHABILITATION INSTITUTE (O, 100 beds) 9601 Interstate 630, Exit 7, Little Rock, AR Zip 72205–7249; tel. 501/202–7000; Greg Crain, Vice President
Web address: www.baptist–health.com

Owned, leased, sponsored:	5 hospitals	1045 beds
Contract–managed:	0 hospitals	0 beds
Totals:	5 hospitals	1045 beds

0185: BAPTIST HEALTH CARE CORPORATION (NP)
1717 North E Street, Suite 320, Pensacola, FL Zip 32501–6335; tel. 850/469–7643; Alfred G. Stubblefield, President
(Moderately Centralized Health System)

ALABAMA: ATMORE COMMUNITY HOSPITAL (L, 51 beds) 401 Medical Park Drive, Atmore, AL Zip 36502–3091; tel. 251/368–2500; Robert E. Gowing, Administrator

FLORIDA: BAPTIST HOSPITAL (O, 492 beds) 1000 West Moreno, Pensacola, FL Zip 32501–2393, Mailing Address: P.O. Box 17500, Zip 32522–7500; tel. 850/469–2313; Robert Murphy, R.N., JD, Administrator
Web address: www.ebaptisthealthcare.org

GULF BREEZE HOSPITAL (O, 60 beds) 1110 Gulf Breeze Parkway, Gulf Breeze, FL Zip 32561, Mailing Address: P.O. Box 159, Zip 32562–0159; tel. 850/934–2000; Robert Harriman, Administrator
Web address: www.e–baptisthealthcare.org

JAY HOSPITAL (L, 55 beds) 14114 South Alabama Street, Jay, FL Zip 32565–1070; tel. 850/675–8000; Michael T. Hutchins, Administrator
Web address: www.e–baptisthealthcare.org

THE FRIARY OF BAPTIST HEALTH CENTER (O, 30 beds) 4400 Hickory Shores Boulevard, Gulf Breeze, FL Zip 32561–9113; tel. 850/932–9375; Leo J. Donnelly, Executive Director

Owned, leased, sponsored:	5 hospitals	688 beds
Contract–managed:	0 hospitals	0 beds
Totals:	5 hospitals	688 beds

★0122: BAPTIST HEALTH SOUTH FLORIDA (NP)
6855 Red Road, Suite 600, Coral Gables, FL Zip 33143–3632; tel. 786/662–7111; Brian E. Keeley, President and Chief Executive Officer
(Moderately Centralized Health System)

BAPTIST HOSPITAL OF MIAMI (O, 541 beds) 8900 North Kendall Drive, Miami, FL Zip 33176–2197; tel. 786/596–1960; Lee S. Huntley, Chief Executive Officer
Web address: www.baptisthealth.net

DOCTORS HOSPITAL (O, 281 beds) 5000 University Drive, Coral Gables, FL Zip 33146–2094; tel. 305/666–2111; Lincoln S. Mendez, Chief Executive Officer
Web address: www.baptisthealth.net

HOMESTEAD HOSPITAL (O, 116 beds) 160 N.W. 13th Street, Homestead, FL Zip 33030–4299; tel. 786/243–8000; Bo Boulenger, Chief Executive Officer
Web address: www.baptisthealth.net

MARINERS HOSPITAL (O, 42 beds) 91500 Overseas Highway, Tavernier, FL Zip 33070–2547; tel. 305/434–1582; Robert H. Luse, Chief Executive Officer
Web address: www.baptisthealth.net

SOUTH MIAMI HOSPITAL (O, 336 beds) 6200 S.W. 73rd Street, Miami, FL Zip 33143–9990; tel. 786/662–4000; D. Wayne Brackin, Chief Executive Officer
Web address: www.baptisthealth.net

Owned, leased, sponsored:	5 hospitals	1316 beds
Contract–managed:	0 hospitals	0 beds
Totals:	5 hospitals	1316 beds

★0345: BAPTIST HEALTH SYSTEM (CO)
3201 4th Avenue South, Birmingham, AL Zip 35222, Mailing Address: P.O. Box 830605, Zip 35283–0605; tel. 205/715–5319; Mary Elizabeth O'Brien, President and Chief Executive Officer
(Centralized Physician/Insurance Health System)

ALABAMA: BAPTIST CHEROKEE (O, 45 beds) 400 Northwood Drive, Centre, AL Zip 35960–1023; tel. 256/927–5531; J. Peter Selman, Chief Executive Officer
Web address: www.bhsala.com/cherokee/index.asp

BAPTIST DEKALB MEDICAL CENTER (O, 103 beds) 200 Medical Center Drive, Fort Payne, AL Zip 35968–3415, Mailing Address: P.O. Box 680778, Zip 35968–1608; tel. 256/845–3150; J. Peter Selman, Chief Executive Officer
Web address: www.bhsala.com

BAPTIST MONTCLAIR (O, 350 beds) 800 Montclair Road, Birmingham, AL Zip 35213–1984; tel. 205/592–1000; Michael Cowling, President
Web address: www.bhsala.com

BAPTIST PRINCETON (O, 299 beds) 701 Princeton Avenue S.W., Birmingham, AL Zip 35211–1305; tel. 205/783–3000; Charlie Faulkner, President
Web address: www.bhsala.com

CITIZENS BAPTIST MEDICAL CENTER (O, 106 beds) 604 Stone Avenue, Talladega, AL Zip 35160–2217, Mailing Address: P.O. Box 978, Zip 35161–0978; tel. 256/362–8111; Steven Gautney, President
Web address: www.bhsala.com

SHELBY BAPTIST MEDICAL CENTER (O, 187 beds) 1000 First Street North, Alabaster, AL Zip 35007–0488; tel. 205/620–8100; Charles C. Colvert, President
Web address: www.baptistmedical.org

WALKER BAPTIST MEDICAL CENTER (O, 195 beds) 3400 Highway 78 East, Jasper, AL Zip 35501–8956, Mailing Address: P.O. Box 3547, Zip 35502–3547; tel. 205/387–4000; Joel W. Tate, FACHE, President
Web address: www.bhsala.com

Owned, leased, sponsored:	7 hospitals	1285 beds
Contract–managed:	0 hospitals	0 beds
Totals:	7 hospitals	1285 beds

2155: BAPTIST HEALTH SYSTEM OF EAST TENNESSEE (NP)
137 Blount Avenue S.E., Knoxville, TN Zip 37920–1643, Mailing Address: P.O. Box 1788, Zip 37901–1788; tel. 865/632–5011; Dale Collins, President and Chief Executive Officer
(Moderately Centralized Health System)

TENNESSEE: BAPTIST HOSPITAL FOR WOMEN (O, 16 beds) 10820 Parkside Drive, Knoxville, TN Zip 37922–1956; tel. 865/218–7090; Martha O'Regan Chill, Senior Vice President and Administrator

BAPTIST HOSPITAL OF COCKE COUNTY (O, 103 beds) 435 Second Street, Newport, TN Zip 37821–3799; tel. 423/625–2200; James Lee Decker, Senior Vice President and Administrator
Web address: www.baptistoneword.org/

BAPTIST HOSPITAL OF EAST TENNESSEE (O, 274 beds) 137 Blount Avenue S.E., Knoxville, TN Zip 37920–1643, Mailing Address: P.O. Box 1788, Zip 37901–1788; tel. 865/632–5011; Brue Chandler, Senior Vice President and Administrator
Web address: www.bhset.org

BAPTIST HOSPITAL WEST (O, 75 beds) 10820 Parkside Drive, Knoxville, TN Zip 37922–1956; tel. 865/218–7011; Martha O'Regan Chill, Senior Vice President and Administrator

CLAIBORNE COUNTY HOSPITAL (C, 45 beds) 1850 Old Knoxville Road, Tazewell, TN Zip 37879–3625, Mailing Address: P.O. Box 219, Zip 37879–0219; tel. 423/626–4211; Tim S. Brown, Senior Vice President and Administrator
Web address: www.claibornehospital.org

WOODS MEMORIAL HOSPITAL DISTRICT (C, 46 beds) 886 Highway 411 North, Etowah, TN Zip 37331–1912; tel. 423/263–3600; David Southerland, Senior Vice President and Administrator
Web address: www.woodshospital.org

Owned, leased, sponsored:	4 hospitals	468 beds
Contract–managed:	2 hospitals	91 beds
Totals:	6 hospitals	559 beds

Section B

For explanation of codes following names, see page B2.
★ Indicates Type III membership in the American Hospital Association.

★0315: BAPTIST HEALTHCARE SYSTEM (CO)
4007 Kresge Way, Louisville, KY Zip 40207–4677;
tel. 502/896–5000; Tommy J. Smith, President and Chief Executive
Officer
(Moderately Centralized Health System)

KENTUCKY: BAPTIST HOSPITAL EAST (O, 407 beds) 4000 Kresge Way,
Louisville, KY Zip 40207–4676; tel. 502/897–8100; Susan Stout Tamme,
President
Web address: www.baptisteast.com

BAPTIST HOSPITAL NORTHEAST (O, 82 beds) 1025 New Moody Lane, La
Grange, KY Zip 40031–0559; tel. 502/222–5388; Dennis B. Johnson,
Administrator
Web address: www.baptistnortheast.com

BAPTIST REGIONAL MEDICAL CENTER (O, 240 beds) 1 Trillium Way, Corbin,
KY Zip 40701–8420; tel. 606/528–1212; John S. Henson, President
Web address: www.baptistregional.com

CENTRAL BAPTIST HOSPITAL (O, 348 beds) 1740 Nicholasville Road,
Lexington, KY Zip 40503–1499; tel. 859/260–6100; William G. Sisson,
President
Web address: www.centralbap.com

HARDIN MEMORIAL HOSPITAL (C, 268 beds) 913 North Dixie Avenue,
Elizabethtown, KY Zip 42701; tel. 270/737–1212; David L. Gray, President
Web address: www.hmh.net

WESTERN BAPTIST HOSPITAL (O, 288 beds) 2501 Kentucky Avenue,
Paducah, KY Zip 42003–3200; tel. 270/575–2100; Larry O. Barton,
President
Web address: www.westernbaptist.com

Owned, leased, sponsored:	5 hospitals	1365 beds
Contract–managed:	1 hospital	268 beds
Totals:	**6 hospitals**	**1633 beds**

★1625: BAPTIST MEMORIAL HEALTH CARE CORPORATION
(NP)
350 North Humphreys Boulevard, Memphis, TN Zip 38120–2177;
tel. 901/227–5117; Stephen Curtis Reynolds, President and Chief
Executive Officer
(Moderately Centralized Health System)

ARKANSAS: BAPTIST MEMORIAL HOSPITAL–FORREST CITY (O, 70 beds)
1601 Newcastle Road, Forrest City, AR Zip 72335, Mailing Address: P.O.
Box 667, Zip 72336–0667; tel. 870/261–0000; Jerry Pope,
Administrator and Chief Executive Officer
Web address: www.bmhcc.org

MISSISSIPPI: BAPTIST MEMORIAL HOSPITAL–BOONEVILLE (L, 66 beds) 100
Hospital Street, Booneville, MS Zip 38829–3359; tel. 662/720–5000; Al
Sypniewski, Administrator and Chief Executive Officer
Web address: www.bmhcc.org

BAPTIST MEMORIAL HOSPITAL–DESOTO (O, 199 beds) 7601 Southcrest
Parkway, Southaven, MS Zip 38671–4742; tel. 662/349–4000; Randy King,
Administrator and Chief Executive Officer
Web address: www.bmhcc.org

BAPTIST MEMORIAL HOSPITAL–GOLDEN TRIANGLE (L, 328 beds) 2520 Fifth
Street North, Columbus, MS Zip 39705–2095, Mailing Address: P.O. Box
1307, Zip 39703–1307; tel. 662/244–1000; Jason Little, Administrator and
Chief Executive Officer
Web address: www.bmhcc.org

BAPTIST MEMORIAL HOSPITAL–NORTH MISSISSIPPI (L, 217 beds) 2301
South Lamar Boulevard, Oxford, MS Zip 38655–5373, Mailing Address: P.O.
Box 946, Zip 38655–0946; tel. 662/232–8100; Zachary Chandler,
Administrator and Chief Executive Officer
Web address: www.bmhcc.org

BAPTIST MEMORIAL HOSPITAL–UNION COUNTY (L, 153 beds) 200 Highway
30 West, New Albany, MS Zip 38652–3197; tel. 662/538–7631; Mitchell
Johnson, Administrator and Chief Executive Officer
Web address: www.bmhcc.org

TENNESSEE: BAPTIST MEMORIAL HOSPITAL – MEMPHIS (O, 625 beds) 6019
Walnut Grove Road, Memphis, TN Zip 38120–2173; tel. 901/226–5000;
James VanderSteeg, Administrator and Chief Executive Officer
Web address: www.baptistonline.org

BAPTIST MEMORIAL HOSPITAL FOR WOMEN (O, 140 beds) 6225 Humphreys
Boulevard, Memphis, TN Zip 38120–2373; tel. 901/227–9000; Anita
Vaughn, Administrator and Chief Executive Officer
Web address: www.bmhcc.org

BAPTIST MEMORIAL HOSPITAL–COLLIERVILLE (O, 61 beds) 1500 West Poplar
Avenue, Collierville, TN Zip 38017; tel. 901/861–9400; Glenn Baker,
Administrator and Chief Executive Officer
Web address: www.bmhcc.org

BAPTIST MEMORIAL HOSPITAL–HUNTINGDON (O, 45 beds) 631 R. B. Wilson
Drive, Huntingdon, TN Zip 38344–1675; tel. 731/986–4461; Susan M.
Breeden, Administrator and Chief Executive Officer
Web address: www.bmhcc.org

BAPTIST MEMORIAL HOSPITAL–LAUDERDALE (O, 14 beds) 326 Asbury
Avenue, Ripley, TN Zip 38063–9701; tel. 731/221–2200; Keon Falkner,
Administrator and Chief Executive Officer
Web address: www.lauderdale.baptistonline.org

BAPTIST MEMORIAL HOSPITAL–TIPTON (O, 54 beds) 1995 Highway 51
South, Covington, TN Zip 38019–3635; tel. 901/476–2621; Paul Betz,
Administrator and Chief Executive Officer
Web address: www.bmhcc.org

BAPTIST MEMORIAL HOSPITAL–UNION CITY (O, 136 beds) 1201 Bishop
Street, Union City, TN Zip 38261–5403, Mailing Address: P.O. Box 310,
Zip 38281–0310; tel. 731/884–8601; Mike Perryman, Administrator and
Chief Executive Officer
Web address: www.bmhcc.org

BAPTIST REHABILITATION–GERMANTOWN (O, 51 beds) 2100 Exeter Road,
Germantown, TN Zip 38138–3978; tel. 901/757–1350; Susan Stralka,
Administrator and Chief Executive Officer
Web address: www.bmhcc.org

Owned, leased, sponsored:	14 hospitals	2159 beds
Contract–managed:	0 hospitals	0 beds
Totals:	**14 hospitals**	**2159 beds**

★0095: BAYLOR HEALTH CARE SYSTEM (CO)
3500 Gaston Avenue, Dallas, TX Zip 75246; tel. 214/820–0111;
Joel T. Allison, President and Chief Executive Officer
(Centralized Health System)

TEXAS: BAYLOR ALL SAINTS MEDICAL CENTER AT FORT WORTH (O, 275
beds) 1400 Eighth Avenue, Fort Worth, TX Zip 76104–4192, Mailing
Address: P.O. Box 31, Zip 76101–0031; tel. 817/926–2544; Steven R.
Newton, President and Chief Executive Officer
Web address: www.baylorhealth.com

BAYLOR INSTITUTE FOR REHABILITATION (O, 92 beds) 3505 Gaston Avenue,
Dallas, TX Zip 75246–2018; tel. 214/820–9300; Luci Neumann, President
Web address: www.bhcs.com

BAYLOR MEDICAL CENTER AT GARLAND (O, 205 beds) 2300 Marie Curie
Boulevard, Garland, TX Zip 75042–5706; tel. 972/487–5000; Stanley D.
Tatum, President
Web address: www.baylorhealth.com

BAYLOR MEDICAL CENTER AT IRVING (L, 222 beds) 1901 North MacArthur
Boulevard, Irving, TX Zip 75061–2291; tel. 972/579–8100; James D.
Thaxton, President
Web address: www.bhcs.com/irving

BAYLOR MEDICAL CENTER AT SOUTHWEST FORT WORTH (O, 59 beds) 7100
Oakmont Boulevard, Fort Worth, TX Zip 76132–3999; tel. 817/926–2544;
Jon Skinner, Executive Director
Web address: www.baylorhealth.com

BAYLOR MEDICAL CENTER AT WAXAHACHIE (O, 53 beds) 1405 West
Jefferson Street, Waxahachie, TX Zip 75165–2275; tel. 972/923–7000; Jerri
J. Stuart, R.N., President
Web address: www.bhcs.com

BAYLOR REGIONAL MEDICAL CENTER AT GRAPEVINE (O, 102 beds) 1650
West College Street, Grapevine, TX Zip 76051–1650; tel. 817/481–1588;
Laura J. Lycan, President
Web address: www.bhcs.com

BAYLOR REGIONAL MEDICAL CENTER AT PLANO (O, 96 beds) 4700 Alliance
Boulevard, Plano, TX Zip 75093; tel. 469/814–2000; Arthur E. Aenchbacher
Jr, President

BAYLOR SPECIALTY HOSPITAL (O, 96 beds) 3504 Swiss Avenue, Dallas, TX
Zip 75204–6224; tel. 214/820–9700; Geraldine Brueckner, R.N., President
Web address: www.bhcs.com

For explanation of codes following names, see page B2.
★ Indicates Type III membership in the American Hospital Association.

BAYLOR UNIVERSITY MEDICAL CENTER (O, 939 beds) 3500 Gaston Avenue, Dallas, TX Zip 75246–2088; tel. 214/820–0111; John B. McWhorter III, Interim President
Web address: www.baylorhealth.com
OUR CHILDREN'S HOUSE AT BAYLOR (O, 37 beds) 3504 Swiss Avenue, Dallas, TX Zip 75204–6219; tel. 214/820–9838; Geraldine Brueckner, R.N., President
Web address: www.bhcs.com

Owned, leased, sponsored:	11 hospitals	2176 beds
Contract–managed:	0 hospitals	0 beds
Totals:	11 hospitals	2176 beds

★**1095: BAYSTATE HEALTH SYSTEM, INC.** (NP)
759 Chestnut Street, Springfield, MA Zip 01199–0001; tel. 413/794–0000; Mark R. Tolosky, President and Chief Executive Officer
(Centralized Physician/Insurance Health System)

MASSACHUSETTS: BAYSTATE MEDICAL CENTER (O, 594 beds) 759 Chestnut Street, Springfield, MA Zip 01199–0001; tel. 413/794–0000; Mark R. Tolosky, President and Chief Executive Officer
Web address: www.baystatehealth.com
FRANKLIN MEDICAL CENTER (O, 95 beds) 164 High Street, Greenfield, MA Zip 01301–2613; tel. 413/773–0211; Michael D. Skinner, President
Web address: www.baystatehealth.com
MARY LANE HOSPITAL (O, 31 beds) 85 South Street, Ware, MA Zip 01082–1697; tel. 413/967–6211; Christine Shirtcliff, Executive Vice President
Web address: www.baystatehealth.com

Owned, leased, sponsored:	3 hospitals	720 beds
Contract–managed:	0 hospitals	0 beds
Totals:	3 hospitals	720 beds

0515: BENEDICTINE HEALTH SYSTEM (CC)
503 East Third Street, Duluth, MN Zip 55805–1964; tel. 218/786–2370; Dale Thompson, President and Chief Executive Officer
(Moderately Centralized Health System)

IDAHO: CLEARWATER VALLEY HOSPITAL AND CLINICS (L, 23 beds) 301 Cedar, Orofino, ID Zip 83544–9029; tel. 208/476–4555; Casey Meza, Chief Executive Officer
Web address: www.clearwatervalleyhospital.com
ST. MARY'S HOSPITAL (O, 28 beds) Lewiston and North Streets, Cottonwood, ID Zip 83522–9750, Mailing Address: P.O. Box 137, Zip 83522–0137; tel. 208/962–3251; Casey Meza, Chief Executive Officer
Web address: www.stmaryshospital.net

MINNESOTA: BRIDGES MEDICAL SERVICES (L, 14 beds) 201 9th Street West, Ada, MN Zip 56510–1243; tel. 218/784–5000; Steve Spaeth, Interim Chief Executive Officer
ST. JOSEPH'S MEDICAL CENTER (O, 162 beds) 523 North Third Street, Brainerd, MN Zip 56401–3098; tel. 218/829–2861; Thomas K. Prusak, President
Web address: www.sjmcmn.org
ST. MARY'S REGIONAL HEALTH CENTER (O, 154 beds) 1027 Washington Avenue, Detroit Lakes, MN Zip 56501–3598; tel. 218/847–5611; Thomas R. Thompson, Chief Executive Officer
Web address: www.smrhc.com

Owned, leased, sponsored:	5 hospitals	381 beds
Contract–managed:	0 hospitals	0 beds
Totals:	5 hospitals	381 beds

0545: BENEDICTINE SISTERS OF THE ANNUNCIATION (CC)
7520 University Drive, Bismarck, ND Zip 58504–9653; tel. 701/255–1520; Sister Susan Berger, Prioress
(Moderately Centralized Health System)

NORTH DAKOTA: GARRISON MEMORIAL HOSPITAL (S, 46 beds) 407 Third Avenue S.E., Garrison, ND Zip 58540–0039; tel. 701/463–2275; Dennis Goebel, President and Chief Executive Officer

ST. ALEXIUS MEDICAL CENTER (S, 282 beds) 900 East Broadway, Bismarck, ND Zip 58501–4586, Mailing Address: P.O. Box 5510, Zip 58506–5510; tel. 701/530–7000; Richard A. Tschider, FACHE, President and Chief Executive Officer
Web address: www.st.alexius.org

Owned, leased, sponsored:	2 hospitals	328 beds
Contract–managed:	0 hospitals	0 beds
Totals:	2 hospitals	328 beds

★**2435: BERKSHIRE HEALTH SYSTEMS, INC.** (NP)
725 North Street, Pittsfield, MA Zip 01201–4124; tel. 413/447–2743; David E. Phelps, President and Chief Executive Officer
(Centralized Health System)

MASSACHUSETTS: BERKSHIRE MEDICAL CENTER (O, 280 beds) 725 North Street, Pittsfield, MA Zip 01201–4124; tel. 413/447–2000; Helen Downey, Chief Operating Officer
Web address: www.berkshirehealthsystems.com
FAIRVIEW HOSPITAL (O, 25 beds) 29 Lewis Avenue, Great Barrington, MA Zip 01230–1713; tel. 413/528–0790; Eugene A. Dellea, President
Web address: www.berkshirehealthsystems.com

Owned, leased, sponsored:	2 hospitals	305 beds
Contract–managed:	0 hospitals	0 beds
Totals:	2 hospitals	305 beds

★**0051: BJC HEALTHCARE** (NP)
4444 Forest Park Avenue, Suite 500, Saint Louis, MO Zip 63108–2259; tel. 314/286–2000; Steven H. Lipstein, President and Chief Executive Officer
(Moderately Centralized Health System)

ILLINOIS: ALTON MEMORIAL HOSPITAL (O, 217 beds) One Memorial Drive, Alton, IL Zip 62002–6722; tel. 618/463–7311; Ronald B. McMullen, President
Web address: www.altonmemorialhospital.org
CLAY COUNTY HOSPITAL (C, 24 beds) 911 Stacy Burk Drive, Flora, IL Zip 62839–1823, Mailing Address: P.O. Box 280, Zip 62839–0280; tel. 618/662–2131; Susan G. Batchelor, President
Web address: www.bjc.org

MISSOURI: BARNES–JEWISH HOSPITAL (O, 962 beds) One Barnes–Jewish Hospital Plaza, Saint Louis, MO Zip 63110–1094; tel. 314/747–3000; Andrew A. Ziskind, M.D., President and Chief Executive Officer
Web address: www.barnesjewish.org
BARNES–JEWISH ST. PETERS HOSPITAL (O, 90 beds) 10 Hospital Drive, Saint Peters, MO Zip 63376–1691; tel. 636/916–9000; David Ross, President
Web address: www.bjc.org/bjsph.html
BARNES–JEWISH WEST COUNTY HOSPITAL (O, 74 beds) 12634 Olive Boulevard, Saint Louis, MO Zip 63141–6337; tel. 314/996–8000; Mary Patricia Mohrman, R.N., MSN, President
Web address: www.bjc.org/bjwch.html
BOONE HOSPITAL CENTER (L, 353 beds) 1600 East Broadway, Columbia, MO Zip 65201–5897; tel. 573/815–8000; Michael B. Shirk, President and Senior Executive Officer
Web address: www.boone.org
CHRISTIAN HOSPITAL (O, 463 beds) 11133 Dunn Road, Saint Louis, MO Zip 63136–6192; tel. 314/653–5000; Paul E. Macek, President
Web address: www.bjc.org
MISSOURI BAPTIST HOSPITAL–SULLIVAN (O, 46 beds) 751 Sappington Bridge Road, Sullivan, MO Zip 63080–2354; tel. 573/468–4186; Tony Schwarm, President
Web address: www.bjc.org/mbhs.html
MISSOURI BAPTIST MEDICAL CENTER (O, 379 beds) 3015 North Ballas Road, Town and Country, MO Zip 63131–2374; tel. 314/996–5000; Carmelo J. Moceri, President
Web address: www.bjc.org/mbmc
PARKLAND HEALTH CENTER (O, 94 beds) 1101 West Liberty Street, Farmington, MO Zip 63640–1921; tel. 573/756–6451; Richard L. Conklin, President
Web address: www.parklandhealthcenter.org

Section B

PARKLAND HEALTH CENTER–BONNE TERRE 7245 Raider Road, Bonne Terre, MO Zip 63628; tel. 573/358–1400; Richard L. Conklin, President
Web address: www.parklandhealthcenter.org

ST. LOUIS CHILDREN'S HOSPITAL (O, 235 beds) One Children's Place, Saint Louis, MO Zip 63110–1081; tel. 314/454–6000; Lee F. Fetter, President and Senior Executive Officer
Web address: www.stlouischildrens.org

Owned, leased, sponsored:	10 hospitals	2913 beds
Contract–managed:	1 hospital	24 beds
Totals:	11 hospitals	2937 beds

0300: BLUE MOUNTAIN HEALTH SYSTEM (NP)
211 North 12th Street, Lehighton, PA Zip 18235–1138; tel. 610/377–1300; Robert J. Clark, FACHE, President and Chief Executive Officer
(Independent Hospital System)

PENNSYLVANIA: GNADEN HUETTEN MEMORIAL HOSPITAL (O, 202 beds) 211 North 12th Street, Lehighton, PA Zip 18235–1138; tel. 610/377–1300; Robert J. Clark, FACHE, President and Chief Executive Officer
Web address: www.bluemountainhealthsystem.org

PALMERTON HOSPITAL (O, 70 beds) 135 Lafayette Avenue, Palmerton, PA Zip 18071–1596; tel. 610/826–3141; Robert J. Clark, FACHE, President and Chief Executive Officer
Web address: www.palmertonhospital.com

Owned, leased, sponsored:	2 hospitals	272 beds
Contract–managed:	0 hospitals	0 beds
Totals:	2 hospitals	272 beds

●★**0053: BLUE WATER HEALTH SERVICES CORPORATION** (NP)
1221 Pine Grove Avenue, Port Huron, MI Zip 48061–5011; tel. 810/989–3717; Brian M. Connolly, President and Chief Executive Officer
(Moderately Centralized Health System)

MICHIGAN: PORT HURON HOSPITAL (O, 186 beds) 1221 Pine Grove Avenue, Port Huron, MI Zip 48061–5011; tel. 810/987–5000; Brian M. Connolly, President and Chief Executive Officer
Web address: www.porthuronhosp.org

Owned, leased, sponsored:	1 hospital	186 beds
Contract–managed:	0 hospitals	0 beds
Totals:	1 hospital	186 beds

★**5085: BON SECOURS HEALTH SYSTEM, INC.** (CC)
1505 Marriottsville Road, Marriottsville, MD Zip 21104–1399; tel. 410/442–5511; Richard Statuto, President and Chief Executive Officer
(Decentralized Health System)

KENTUCKY: OUR LADY OF BELLEFONTE HOSPITAL (O, 214 beds) St. Christopher Drive, Ashland, KY Zip 41101–7071, Mailing Address: P.O. Box 789, Zip 41105–0789; tel. 606/833–3333; Mark M. Gordon, Chief Executive Officer
Web address: www.olbh.com

MARYLAND: BON SECOURS BALTIMORE HEALTH SYSTEM (O, 148 beds) 2000 West Baltimore Street, Baltimore, MD Zip 21223–1597; tel. 410/362–3000; Percy Allen II, FACHE, Chief Executive Officer
Web address: www.bonsecours.org

MICHIGAN: BON SECOURS HOSPITAL (O, 221 beds) 468 Cadieux Road, Grosse Pointe, MI Zip 48230–1592; tel. 313/343–1000; Jeffrey A. Collins, Interim Chief Executive Officer
Web address: www.bschealth.com

COTTAGE HOSPITAL (O, 54 beds) 159 Kercheval Avenue, Grosse Pointe Farms, MI Zip 48236–3692; tel. 313/640–1000; Richard Van Lith, Chief Executive Officer
Web address: www.bonsecourscottage.org

NEW JERSEY: ST. MARY HOSPITAL (O, 401 beds) 308 Willow Avenue, Hoboken, NJ Zip 07030–3889; tel. 201/418–1000; Michael J. Sniffen, Interim President and Chief Executive Officer
Web address: www.bonsecoursnj.org

NEW YORK: BON SECOURS COMMUNITY HOSPITAL (O, 187 beds) 160 East Main Street, Port Jervis, NY Zip 12771–2245, Mailing Address: P.O. Box 1014, Zip 12771–1014; tel. 845/858–7000; Thomas R. Brunelle, Executive Vice President and Administrator
Web address: www.bonsecourscommunityhosp.org

GOOD SAMARITAN HOSPITAL (O, 308 beds) 255 Lafayette Avenue, Suffern, NY Zip 10901–4869; tel. 845/368–5000; Michael H. Schnieders, Executive Vice President and Administrator
Web address: www.goodsamhosp.org

ST. ANTHONY COMMUNITY HOSPITAL (O, 61 beds) 15 Maple Avenue, Warwick, NY Zip 10990–5180; tel. 845/987–5173; Leah Cerkvenik, Executive Vice President, Administrator and Chief Executive Officer
Web address: www.stanthonycommunityhosp.org

SOUTH CAROLINA: BON SECOURS ST. FRANCIS HEALTH SYSTEM (O, 237 beds) One St. Francis Drive, Greenville, SC Zip 29601–3207; tel. 864/255–1000; Valinda Rutledge, Chief Executive Officer
Web address: www.stfrancishealth.org

VIRGINIA: BON SECOURS ST. MARY'S HOSPITAL (O, 320 beds) 5801 Bremo Road, Richmond, VA Zip 23226–1907; tel. 804/285–2011; Michael K. Kerner, Executive Vice President and Administrator
Web address: www.bonsecours.com

BON SECOURS–DEPAUL MEDICAL CENTER (O, 238 beds) 150 Kingsley Lane, Norfolk, VA Zip 23505–4650; tel. 757/889–5000; Susan A. Erickson, Executive Vice President and Administrator
Web address: www.bonsecourshamptonroads.com

BON SECOURS–RICHMOND COMMUNITY HOSPITAL (O, 88 beds) 1500 North 28th Street, Richmond, VA Zip 23223–5396, Mailing Address: Box 27184, Zip 23261–7184; tel. 804/225–1700; Paula R. Autry, Executive Vice President and Administrator
Web address: www.bonsecours.com

MARY IMMACULATE HOSPITAL (O, 225 beds) 2 Bernardine Drive, Newport News, VA Zip 23602–4499; tel. 757/886–6000; Patricia L. Robertson, Executive Vice President and Administrator
Web address: www.bonsecourshamptonroads.com

MARYVIEW MEDICAL CENTER (O, 466 beds) 3636 High Street, Portsmouth, VA Zip 23707–3270; tel. 757/398–2200; Jack McNamara, Interim Executive Vice President and Administrator
Web address: www.bonsecourshamptonroads.com

MEMORIAL REGIONAL MEDICAL CENTER (O, 225 beds) 8260 Atlee Road, Mechanicsville, VA Zip 23116–1844; tel. 804/764–6000; Michael Robinson, Executive Vice President and Administrator
Web address: www.bonsecours.com

Owned, leased, sponsored:	15 hospitals	3393 beds
Contract–managed:	0 hospitals	0 beds
Totals:	15 hospitals	3393 beds

●**2455: BRADFORD HEALTH SERVICES** (IO)
2101 Magnolia Avenue South, Suite 518, Birmingham, AL Zip 35205; tel. 205/251–7753; Jerry W. Crowder, President and Chief Executive Officer

ALABAMA: BRADFORD HEALTH SERVICES AT HUNTSVILLE (O, 84 beds) 1600 Browns Ferry Road, Madison, AL Zip 35758–9769, Mailing Address: P.O. Box 176, Zip 35758–0176; tel. 256/461–7272; Bob Hinds, Executive Director
Web address: www.bradfordhealth.com

Owned, leased, sponsored:	1 hospital	84 beds
Contract–managed:	0 hospitals	0 beds
Totals:	1 hospital	84 beds

★**0585: BRIM HEALTHCARE, INC.** (IO)
105 Westwood Place, Suite 300, Brentwood, TN Zip 37027; tel. 615/309–6053; Dave Woodland, President
(Decentralized Health System)

ARIZONA: COBRE VALLEY COMMUNITY HOSPITAL (C, 43 beds) 5880 South Hospital Drive, Globe, AZ Zip 85501–9454; tel. 928/425–3261; James H. Gingerich, Chief Executive Officer
Web address: www.cvchospital.com

NAVAPACHE REGIONAL MEDICAL CENTER (C, 66 beds) 2200 Show Low Lake Road, Show Low, AZ Zip 85901–7800; tel. 928/537–4375; Leigh Cox, Chief Executive Officer
Web address: www.nrmc.org

CALIFORNIA: HAZEL HAWKINS MEMORIAL HOSPITAL (C, 113 beds) 911 Sunset Drive, Hollister, CA Zip 95023–5695; tel. 831/637–5711; Ken Underwood, Chief Executive Officer
Web address: www.hazelhawkins.com

HI–DESERT MEDICAL CENTER (C, 140 beds) 6601 White Feather Road, Joshua Tree, CA Zip 92252–6601; tel. 760/366–3711; David B. Selman, Chief Executive Officer
Web address: www.hdmc.org

PIONEERS MEMORIAL HEALTHCARE DISTRICT (C, 105 beds) 207 West Legion Road, Brawley, CA Zip 92227–7780; tel. 760/351–3333; Richard L. Mendoza, Chief Executive Officer
Web address: www.pmhd.org

SAN GORGONIO MEMORIAL HOSPITAL (C, 70 beds) 600 North Highland Springs Avenue, Banning, CA Zip 92220–3046; tel. 909/845–1121; Donald N. Larkin, Chief Executive Officer
Web address: www.sgmh.org

FLORIDA: JUPITER MEDICAL CENTER (C, 276 beds) 1210 South Old Dixie Highway, Jupiter, FL Zip 33458–7299; tel. 561/747–2234; R. Michael Barry, Chief Executive Officer
Web address: www.jupitermed.com

GEORGIA: UPSON REGIONAL MEDICAL CENTER (C, 115 beds) 801 West Gordon Street, Thomaston, GA Zip 30286–2831, Mailing Address: P.O. Box 1059, Zip 30286–1059; tel. 706/647–8111; Gene B. Wright, Interim Chief Executive Officer
Web address: www.urmc.org

ILLINOIS: CARLINVILLE AREA HOSPITAL (C, 33 beds) 1001 East Morgan Street, Carlinville, IL Zip 62626–1499; tel. 217/854–3141; Steven Hannah, Interim President and Chief Executive Officer
Web address: www.cahcare.com

HAMMOND–HENRY HOSPITAL (C, 74 beds) 600 North College Avenue, Geneseo, IL Zip 61254–1099; tel. 309/944–4625; Bradley Solberg, FACHE, Chief Executive Officer
Web address: www.hammondhenry.com

HILLSBORO AREA HOSPITAL (C, 66 beds) 1200 East Tremont Street, Hillsboro, IL Zip 62049–1900; tel. 217/532–6111; Rex H. Brown, Chief Executive Officer
Web address: www.hillsboroareahospital.org

INDIANA: ST. JOSEPH'S HOSPITAL (C, 25 beds) 1900 Medical Arts Drive, Huntingburg, IN Zip 47542–9521; tel. 812/683–2121; Jonathan Brenn, Chief Executive Officer
Web address: www.stjh.info

LOUISIANA: DE SOTO REGIONAL HEALTH SYSTEM (C, 57 beds) 207 Jefferson Street, Mansfield, LA Zip 71052–2603, Mailing Address: P.O. Box 1636, Zip 71052–2603; tel. 318/871–3100; John Scott Stafford, Chief Executive Officer
Web address: www.desotoregional.com

IBERIA MEDICAL CENTER (C, 63 beds) 2315 East Main Street, New Iberia, LA Zip 70560–4031, Mailing Address: P.O. Box 13338, Zip 70562–3338; tel. 337/364–0441; James H. Youree, FACHE, Chief Executive Officer
Web address: www.iberiamedicalcenter.com

LADY OF THE SEA GENERAL HOSPITAL (C, 49 beds) 200 West 134th Place, Cut Off, LA Zip 70345–4145; tel. 985/632–6401; Raymond L. Ford, FACHE, Chief Executive Officer
Web address: www.losgh.com

MONTANA: BARRETT HOSPITAL & HEALTHCARE (C, 20 beds) 90 Highway 91 South, Dillon, MT Zip 59725–3597; tel. 406/683–3000; John M. Mootry, Chief Executive Officer
Web address: www.barretthospital.org

MINERAL COMMUNITY HOSPITAL (C, 41 beds) 1208 6th Avenue East, Superior, MT Zip 59872–9603, Mailing Address: P.O. Box 66, Zip 59872–0066; tel. 406/822–4841; James P. Henshaw, Chief Executive Officer

ROUNDUP MEMORIAL HEALTHCARE (C, 48 beds) 1202 Third Street West, Roundup, MT Zip 59072–1816, Mailing Address: P.O. Box 40, Zip 59072–0040; tel. 406/323–2302; Lee Rhodes, Chief Executive Officer

NEBRASKA: TRI–VALLEY HEALTH SYSTEM (C, 51 beds) West Highway 6 and 34, Cambridge, NE Zip 69022–0488, Mailing Address: P.O. Box 488, Zip 69022–0488; tel. 308/697–3329; Lynn Milnes, Chief Executive Officer
Web address: www.trivalleyhealth.com

NEW MEXICO: UNION COUNTY GENERAL HOSPITAL (C, 21 beds) 301 Harding Street, Clayton, NM Zip 88415–3321, Mailing Address: P.O. Box 489, Zip 88415–0489; tel. 505/374–2585; Stephen J. Campbell, Administrator
Web address: www.unioncountygeneral.com

NEW YORK: ADIRONDACK MEDICAL CENTER (C, 77 beds) 2233 State Route 86, Saranac Lake, NY Zip 12983, Mailing Address: P.O. Box 471, Zip 12983–0471; tel. 518/891–4141; Chandler M. Ralph, President and Chief Executive Officer
Web address: www.amccares.org

OKLAHOMA: HOLDENVILLE GENERAL HOSPITAL (C, 25 beds) 100 McDougal Drive, Holdenville, OK Zip 74848–9700; tel. 405/379–4200; Deryl E. Gulliford, Ph.D., Chief Executive Officer

OREGON: BLUE MOUNTAIN HOSPITAL (C, 68 beds) 170 Ford Road, John Day, OR Zip 97845–2009; tel. 541/575–1311; Robert Houser, Chief Executive Officer
Web address: www.bluemountainhospital.org

WASHINGTON: KLICKITAT VALLEY HEALTH SERVICES (C, 18 beds) 310 South Roosevelt, Goldendale, WA Zip 98620–9201, Mailing Address: P.O. Box 5, Zip 98620–0005; tel. 509/773–4022; Sharon Cox, Chief Executive Officer
Web address: www.kvhs.net

SUNNYSIDE COMMUNITY HOSPITAL (C, 25 beds) 1016 Tacoma Avenue, Sunnyside, WA Zip 98944–0719, Mailing Address: P.O. Box 719, Zip 98944–0719; tel. 509/837–1500; Jon D. Smiley, Chief Executive Officer
Web address: www.sunnysidehospital.com

WISCONSIN: BURNETT MEDICAL CENTER (C, 70 beds) 257 West St. George Avenue, Grantsburg, WI Zip 54840–7827; tel. 715/463–5353; Timothy J. Wick, Chief Executive Officer
Web address: www.burnettmedicalcenter.com

COMMUNITY MEMORIAL HOSPITAL (C, 25 beds) 855 South Main Street, Oconto Falls, WI Zip 54154–1296; tel. 920/846–3444; James Van Dornick, Administrator
Web address: www.cmhospital.org

GRANT REGIONAL HEALTH CENTER (C, 29 beds) 507 South Monroe Street, Lancaster, WI Zip 53813–2099; tel. 608/723–2143; Larry D. Rentfro, FACHE, President and Chief Executive Officer
Web address: www.grantregional.com

MEMORIAL COMMUNITY HOSPITAL (C, 86 beds) 313 Stoughton Road, Edgerton, WI Zip 53534–1198; tel. 608/884–3441; Ronald V. Wolff, Interim Chief Executive Officer
Web address: www.edgertonhospital.com

RIPON MEDICAL CENTER (C, 19 beds) 933 Newbury Street, Ripon, WI Zip 54971–1798, Mailing Address: P.O. Box 390, Zip 54971–0390; tel. 920/748–3101; Tommy Hobbs, Chief Executive Officer
Web address: www.riponmedicalcenter.com

SHAWANO MEDICAL CENTER (C, 39 beds) 309 North Bartlette Street, Shawano, WI Zip 54166–0477; tel. 715/526–2111; James E. Baer, FACHE, Chief Executive Officer
Web address: www.shawanomed.org

SOUTHWEST HEALTH CENTER (C, 132 beds) 1400 Eastside Road, Platteville, WI Zip 53818–9800; tel. 608/348–2331; Anne K. Klawiter, President and Chief Executive Officer
Web address: www.southwesthealth.org

SPOONER HEALTH SYSTEM (C, 115 beds) 819 Ash Street, Spooner, WI Zip 54801–1299; tel. 715/635–2111; Michael Schafer, Chief Executive Officer and Administrator
Web address: www.spoonerhealthsystem.com

TOMAH MEMORIAL HOSPITAL (C, 25 beds) 321 Butts Avenue, Tomah, WI Zip 54660–1412; tel. 608/372–2181; Philip Stuart, Administrator and Chief Executive Officer
Web address: www.tomahhospital.org

For explanation of codes following names, see page B2.
★ Indicates Type III membership in the American Hospital Association.

WYOMING: HOT SPRINGS COUNTY MEMORIAL HOSPITAL (C, 25 beds) 150 East Arapahoe Street, Thermopolis, WY Zip 82443–2498; tel. 307/864–3121; Trudy Chittick, Chief Executive Officer
Web address: www.hscmh.com

POWELL VALLEY HEALTHCARE (C, 125 beds) 777 Avenue H, Powell, WY Zip 82435–2296; tel. 307/754–2267; Rod Barton, Chief Executive Officer
Web address: www.pvhc.org

Owned, leased, sponsored:	0 hospitals	0 beds
Contract–managed:	36 hospitals	2379 beds
Totals:	36 hospitals	2379 beds

★**0595: BRONSON HEALTHCARE GROUP, INC.** (NP)
One Healthcare Plaza, Kalamazoo, MI Zip 49007–5345; tel. 269/341–6000; Frank J. Sardone, President and Chief Executive Officer
(Centralized Physician/Insurance Health System)

MICHIGAN: BRONSON METHODIST HOSPITAL (O, 307 beds) 601 John Street, Kalamazoo, MI Zip 49007–5345; tel. 269/341–6000; Frank J. Sardone, President and Chief Executive Officer
Web address: www.bronsonhealth.com

BRONSON VICKSBURG HOSPITAL (O, 21 beds) 13326 North Boulevard, Vicksburg, MI Zip 49097–1099; tel. 269/649–2321; Frank J. Sardone, President
Web address: www.bronsonhealth.com

Owned, leased, sponsored:	2 hospitals	328 beds
Contract–managed:	0 hospitals	0 beds
Totals:	2 hospitals	328 beds

9655: BUREAU OF MEDICINE AND SURGERY, DEPARTMENT OF THE NAVY (FG)
2300 East Street N.W., Washington, DC Zip 20372–5300; tel. 202/762–3701; Rear Admiral Kathleen L. Martin, Deputy Surgeon General
(Moderately Centralized Health System)

CALIFORNIA: NAVAL HOSPITAL (O, 16 beds) 937 Franklin Avenue, Lemoore, CA Zip 93246–5004; tel. 559/998–4201; Captain Sandra DeGroot, Commanding Officer
Web address: www.lemoore.med.navy.mil

NAVAL HOSPITAL (O, 83 beds) Camp Pendleton, CA Mailing Address: Box 555191, Zip 92055–5191; tel. 760/725–1304; Captain Richard Jeffries, Commanding Officer
Web address: www.enhcp.com

NAVAL HOSPITAL (O, 29 beds) Twentynine Palms, CA Mailing Address: Box 788250, MCAGCC, Zip 92278–8250; tel. 760/830–2190; Captain Robert Engelhart, Commanding Officer
Web address: www.nhtp.med.navy.mil/nhtp

NAVAL MEDICAL CENTER (O, 272 beds) 34800 Bob Wilson Drive, San Diego, CA Zip 92134–5000; tel. 619/532–6400; Rear Admiral John M. Mateczun, MC, USN, Commander
Web address: www.nmcsd.med.navy.mil

FLORIDA: NAVAL HOSPITAL (O, 60 beds) 2080 Child Street, Jacksonville, FL Zip 32214–5000; tel. 904/542–7300; Captain John Sentell, Commanding Officer
Web address: www.199.208.118.223/

NAVAL HOSPITAL (O, 63 beds) 6000 West Highway 98, Pensacola, FL Zip 32512–0003; tel. 850/505–6413; Captain Matthew L. Nathan, Commanding Officer
Web address: www.psa10.med.navy.mil

GUAM: U. S. NAVAL HOSPITAL (O, 55 beds) Agana, GU Mailing Address: PSC 490, Box 7607, FPO, APZip 96538–1600; tel. 671/344–9340; Captain Kathleen A. Rief, Commanding Officer
Web address: www.usnhgvam.med.navy.mil

ILLINOIS: NAVAL HOSPITAL (O, 47 beds) 3001A Sixth Street, Great Lakes, IL Zip 60088–5230; tel. 847/688–4560; Captain Michael Anderson, Commanding Officer
Web address: www.greatlakes.med.navy.mil

MARYLAND: NATIONAL NAVAL MEDICAL CENTER (O, 240 beds) 8901 Wisconsin Avenue, Bethesda, MD Zip 20889–5600; tel. 301/295–5800; Rear Admiral Donald C. Arthur, MC, USN, Commander
Web address: www.nnmc.med.navy.mil

NORTH CAROLINA: NAVAL HOSPITAL (O, 76 beds) Camp Lejeune, NC Mailing Address: P.O. Box 10100, Zip 28547–0100; tel. 910/450–4300; Captain R. C. Welton, Chief Commander
Web address: www.nhcl.med.navy.mil

NAVAL HOSPITAL (O, 23 beds) Cherry Point, NC Mailing Address: PSC Box 8023, Zip 28533–0023; tel. 252/466–0266; Captain Donald Thompson, Commanding Officer
Web address: www.cpoint–www.med.navy.mil

PUERTO RICO: U. S. NAVAL HOSPITAL (O, 36 beds) Roosevelt Roads, PR Mailing Address: P.O. Box 3007, FPO, AAZip 34051–8100; tel. 787/865–5762; Captain Patricia H. Netzer, Commanding Officer
Web address: www.rooseyroads.med.navy.mil

SOUTH CAROLINA: NAVAL HOSPITAL (O, 20 beds) 1 Pinckney Boulevard, Beaufort, SC Zip 29902–6148; tel. 843/228–5301; Captain James Hoffower, Commanding Officer

NAVAL HOSPITAL (O, 15 beds) 3600 Rivers Avenue, North Charleston, SC Zip 29405; tel. 843/743–7000; Captain Margaret Allard, Commanding Officer
Web address: www.nhchasn.med.navy.mil

TEXAS: NAVAL HOSPITAL (O, 25 beds) 10651 E Street, Corpus Christi, TX Zip 78419–5131; tel. 361/961–2688; Captain James P. Rice, Commanding Officicer
Web address: www.nhcc.med.navy.mil

VIRGINIA: NAVAL MEDICAL CENTER (O, 274 beds) 620 John Paul Jones Circle, Portsmouth, VA Zip 23708–2197; tel. 757/953–7424; Admiral Thomas Burkhard, Commander

WASHINGTON: NAVAL HOSPITAL (O, 51 beds) One Boone Road, Bremerton, WA Zip 98312–1898; tel. 360/475–4000; Captain William Roberts, Commanding Officer
Web address: www.nh_bremerton.med.navy.mil

NAVAL HOSPITAL (O, 25 beds) 3475 North Saratoga Street, Oak Harbor, WA Zip 98278–8800; tel. 360/257–9500; Captain Susan Herrold, Commanding Officer
Web address: www.nhoh.med.navy.mil/

Owned, leased, sponsored:	18 hospitals	1410 beds
Contract–managed:	0 hospitals	0 beds
Totals:	18 hospitals	1410 beds

0077: CAMBRIDGE INTERNATIONAL, INC, (IO)
7505 Fannin, Suite 680, Houston, TX Zip 77225; tel. 713/790–1153; Timothy Sharma, M.D., President
(Independent Hospital System)

TEXAS: INTRACARE MEDICAL CENTER HOSPITAL (O, 120 beds) 7601 Fannin Street, Houston, TX Zip 77054–1905; tel. 713/790–0949; Terry Scovill, Chief Executive Officer
Web address: www.intracarehospital.com

INTRACARE NORTH HOSPITAL (O, 68 beds) 1120 Cypress Station Drive, Houston, TX Zip 77090–3031; tel. 281/893–7200; Teisha York, Chief Executive Officer
Web address: www.intracarehospital.com

Owned, leased, sponsored:	2 hospitals	188 beds
Contract–managed:	0 hospitals	0 beds
Totals:	2 hospitals	188 beds

0113: CANCER TREATMENT CENTERS OF AMERICA (IO)
3150 Salt Creek Lane, Arlington Heights, IL Zip 60005–1080; tel. 847/342–7400; Stephen B. Bonner, President and Chief Executive Officer
(Independent Hospital System)

ILLINOIS: MIDWESTERN REGIONAL MEDICAL CENTER (O, 73 beds) 2520 Elisha Avenue, Zion, IL Zip 60099–2587; tel. 847/872–4561; Roger C. Cary, President and Chief Executive Officer
Web address: www.cancercenter.com

For explanation of codes following names, see page B2.
★ Indicates Type III membership in the American Hospital Association.

Section B

OKLAHOMA: SOUTHWESTERN REGIONAL MEDICAL CENTER (O, 40 beds) 2408 East 81st Street, Tulsa, OK Zip 74137–4210; tel. 918/496–5000; James H. Bruer, President and Chief Executive Officer
Web address: www.cancercenter.com

Owned, leased, sponsored:	2 hospitals	113 beds
Contract–managed:	0 hospitals	0 beds
Totals:	2 hospitals	113 beds

0124: CAPE COD HEALTHCARE, INC. (NP)
88 Lewis Bay Road, Hyannis, MA Zip 02601–5210; tel. 508/862–5010; Stephen L. Abbott, President and Chief Executive Officer
(Centralized Health System)

MASSACHUSETTS: CAPE COD HOSPITAL (O, 223 beds) 27 Park Street, Hyannis, MA Zip 02601–5203; tel. 508/771–1800; Margaret Hanson, Chief Administrative Officer
Web address: www.capecodhealth.org

FALMOUTH HOSPITAL (O, 95 beds) 100 Ter Heun Drive, Falmouth, MA Zip 02540–2599; tel. 508/548–5300; Susan M. Wing, Chief Operating Officer
Web address: www.capecodhealth.org

Owned, leased, sponsored:	2 hospitals	318 beds
Contract–managed:	0 hospitals	0 beds
Totals:	2 hospitals	318 beds

0297: CAPITAL HEALTH SYSTEM (NP)
750 Brunswick Avenue, Trenton, NJ Zip 08638–4174; tel. 609/394–6000; Al Maghazehe, President and Chief Executive Officer
(Moderately Centralized Health System)

NEW JERSEY: CAPITAL HEALTH SYSTEM AT FULD (O, 186 beds) 750 Brunswick Avenue, Trenton, NJ Zip 08638–4174; tel. 609/394–6000; Al Maghazehe, Chief Executive Officer
Web address: www.capitalhealth.org

CAPITAL HEALTH SYSTEM AT MERCER (O, 260 beds) 446 Bellevue Avenue, Trenton, NJ Zip 08618–4597, Mailing Address: P.O. Box 1658, Zip 08607–1658; tel. 609/394–4000; Al Maghazehe, Chief Executive Officer
Web address: www.capitalhealth.org

Owned, leased, sponsored:	2 hospitals	446 beds
Contract–managed:	0 hospitals	0 beds
Totals:	2 hospitals	446 beds

0262: CARDINAL HEALTH SYSTEM (NP)
2401 University Avenue, Muncie, IN Zip 47303; tel. 765/747–3139; Robert S. Curtis, President and Chief Executive Officer
(Moderately Centralized Health System)

INDIANA: BALL MEMORIAL HOSPITAL (O, 393 beds) 2401 University Avenue, Muncie, IN Zip 47303–3499; tel. 765/747–3111; Brent L. Batman, President
Web address: www.cardinalhealthsystem.org

BLACKFORD COMMUNITY HOSPITAL (O, 25 beds) 410 Pilgrim Boulevard, Hartford City, IN Zip 47348–1897; tel. 765/348–0300; Steven J. West, Chief Executive Officer

JAY COUNTY HOSPITAL (C, 25 beds) 500 West Votaw Street, Portland, IN Zip 47371–1322; tel. 260/726–7131; Joe Johnston, Chief Executive Officer
Web address: www.jaycountyhospital.com

Owned, leased, sponsored:	2 hospitals	418 beds
Contract–managed:	1 hospital	25 beds
Totals:	3 hospitals	443 beds

0301: CARDINAL HILL HEALTHCARE SYSTEM (NP)
2050 Versailes Road, Lexington, KY Zip 40504; tel. 859/254–5701; Kerry G. Gillihan, FACHE, President and Chief Executive Officer
(Independent Hospital System)

KENTUCKY: CARDINAL HILL REHABILITATION HOSPITAL (O, 108 beds) 2050 Versailles Road, Lexington, KY Zip 40504–1499; tel. 859/254–5701; Kerry G. Gillihan, FACHE, President and Chief Executive Officer
Web address: www.cardinalhill.org

CARDINAL HILL SPECIALTY HOSPITAL (O, 20 beds) 85 North Grand Avenue, Fort Thomas, KY Zip 41075; tel. 859/572–3880; Janice Bauer, Administrator
Web address: www.cardinalhill.org/ltach.html

Owned, leased, sponsored:	2 hospitals	128 beds
Contract–managed:	0 hospitals	0 beds
Totals:	2 hospitals	128 beds

★0099: CARE NEW ENGLAND HEALTH SYSTEM (NP)
45 Willard Avenue, Providence, RI Zip 02905–3218; tel. 401/453–7900; John J. Hynes, President and Chief Executive Officer
(Centralized Health System)

RHODE ISLAND: BUTLER HOSPITAL (O, 113 beds) 345 Blackstone Boulevard, Providence, RI Zip 02906–4829; tel. 401/455–6200; Patricia R. Recupero, JD, M.D., President and Chief Executive Officer
Web address: www.butler.org

KENT COUNTY MEMORIAL HOSPITAL (O, 320 beds) 455 Tollgate Road, Warwick, RI Zip 02886–2770; tel. 401/737–7000; Robert E. Baute, M.D., President and Chief Executive Officer
Web address: www.kentri.org

WOMEN AND INFANTS HOSPITAL OF RHODE ISLAND (O, 197 beds) 101 Dudley Street, Providence, RI Zip 02905–2499; tel. 401/274–1100; Constance A. Howes, President and Chief Executive Officer
Web address: www.womenandinfants.org

Owned, leased, sponsored:	3 hospitals	630 beds
Contract–managed:	0 hospitals	0 beds
Totals:	3 hospitals	630 beds

★0070: CARILION HEALTH SYSTEM (NP)
Belleview at Jefferson Street, Roanoke, VA Zip 24014, Mailing Address: P.O. Box 13367, Zip 24033; tel. 540/981–7893; Edward G. Murphy, M.D., President and Chief Executvie Officer
(Moderately Centralized Health System)

VIRGINIA: BEDFORD MEMORIAL HOSPITAL (O, 161 beds) 1613 Oakwood Street, Bedford, VA Zip 24523–0688, Mailing Address: P.O. Box 688, Zip 24523–0688; tel. 540/586–2441; E. W. Tibbs, President and Chief Executive Officer
Web address: www.bmhva.com

CARILION FRANKLIN MEMORIAL HOSPITAL (O, 37 beds) 180 Floyd Avenue, Rocky Mount, VA Zip 24151–1389; tel. 540/483–5277; Chad E. Boore, Vice President and Administrator
Web address: www.carilion.com

CARILION GILES MEMORIAL HOSPITAL (O, 32 beds) 1 Taylor Avenue, Pearisburg, VA Zip 24134–1932; tel. 540/921–6000; James E. Tyler, Administrator and Chief Executive Officer
Web address: www.carilion.com

CARILION MEDICAL CENTER (O, 723 beds) Belleview at Jefferson Street, Roanoke, VA Zip 24014, Mailing Address: P.O. Box 13367, Zip 24033–3367; tel. 540/981–7000; Edward G. Murphy, M.D., Chief Executive Officer
Web address: www.carilion.com

CARILION NEW RIVER VALLEY MEDICAL CENTER (O, 97 beds) 2900 Lamb Circle, Christiansburg, VA Zip 24073–5041, Mailing Address: P.O. Box 5, Radford, Zip 24143–0005; tel. 540/731–2000; Matthew J. Perry, President
Web address: www.carilion.com

SMYTH COUNTY COMMUNITY HOSPITAL (O, 285 beds) 565 Radio Hill Road, Marion, VA Zip 24354–3526, Mailing Address: P.O. Box 880, Zip 24354–0880; tel. 276/782–1234; William Mahone V, President and Chief Executive Officer
Web address: www.scchosp.org

TAZEWELL COMMUNITY HOSPITAL (C, 34 beds) 141 Ben Bolt Avenue, Tazewell, VA Zip 24651–9700; tel. 276/988–8700; Christopher L. Wearmouth, President and Chief Executive Officer
Web address: www.tazecommhospital.org

For explanation of codes following names, see page B2.
★ Indicates Type III membership in the American Hospital Association.

Owned, leased, sponsored:	6 hospitals	1335 beds
Contract–managed:	1 hospital	34 beds
Totals:	7 hospitals	1369 beds

★**0141: CARITAS CHRISTI HEALTH CARE** (NP)
736 Cambridge Street, Boston, MA Zip 02135–2997;
tel. 617/789–2500; Robert M. Haddad, M.D., President
(Moderately Centralized Health System)

MASSACHUSETTS: CARITAS CARNEY HOSPITAL (S, 186 beds) 2100
Dorchester Avenue, Dorchester, MA Zip 02124–5666;
tel. 617/296–4000; Joyce A. Murphy, President
Web address: www.carneyhospital.org

CARITAS GOOD SAMARITAN MEDICAL CENTER (S, 231 beds) 235 North Pearl
Street, Brockton, MA Zip 02401–1794; tel. 508/427–3000; John J. Holiver,
President
Web address: www.caritasgoodsam.org

CARITAS HOLY FAMILY HOSPITAL AND MEDICAL CENTER (S, 256 beds) 70
East Street, Methuen, MA Zip 01844–4597; tel. 978/687–0151; Peter J.
Holden, President and Chief Executive Officer
Web address: www.holyfamilyhosp.org

CARITAS NORWOOD HOSPITAL (S, 200 beds) 800 Washington Street,
Norwood, MA Zip 02062–3487; tel. 781/769–4000; Richard Cunningham,
President
Web address: www.caritasnorwood.org

CARITAS ST. ELIZABETH'S MEDICAL CENTER (S, 247 beds) 736 Cambridge
Street, Brighton, MA Zip 02135–2997; tel. 617/789–3000; Robert M.
Haddad, M.D., President
Web address: www.semc.org

SAINT ANNE'S HOSPITAL (S, 106 beds) 795 Middle Street, Fall River, MA
Zip 02721–1798; tel. 508/674–5741; Michael W. Metzler, President
Web address: www.saintanneshospital.org

Owned, leased, sponsored:	6 hospitals	1226 beds
Contract–managed:	0 hospitals	0 beds
Totals:	6 hospitals	1226 beds

★**0705: CAROLINAS HEALTHCARE SYSTEM** (NP)
1000 Blythe Boulevard, Charlotte, NC Zip 28203–5871, Mailing
Address: P.O. Box 32861, Zip 28232–2861; tel. 704/355–2000;
Michael C. Tarwater, President and Chief Executive Officer
(Moderately Centralized Health System)

NORTH CAROLINA: ANSON COMMUNITY HOSPITAL (O, 125 beds) 500
Morven Road, Wadesboro, NC Zip 28170–2745; tel. 704/694–5131;
Frederick G. Thompson, Ph.D., Administrator and Chief Executive Officer
Web address: www.carolinashealthcare.org

CAROLINAS MEDICAL CENTER (O, 861 beds) 1000 Blythe Boulevard,
Charlotte, NC Zip 28203–5871, Mailing Address: P.O. Box 32861,
Zip 28232–2861; tel. 704/355–2000; Suzanne H. Freeman, R.N., President
Web address: www.carolinashealthcare.org

CAROLINAS MEDICAL CENTER–MERCY (O, 224 beds) 2001 Vail Avenue,
Charlotte, NC Zip 28207–1289; tel. 704/379–5000; C. Curtis Copenhaver,
President
Web address: www.carolinashealthcare.org

CAROLINAS MEDICAL CENTER–PINEVILLE (O, 108 beds) 10628 Park Road,
Charlotte, NC Zip 28210; tel. 704/543–2025; William K. Brown, Vice
President and Administrator
Web address: www.carolinashealthcare.org

CAROLINAS MEDICAL CENTER–UNIVERSITY (O, 122 beds) 8800 North Tryon
Street, Charlotte, NC Zip 28262–8415, Mailing Address: P.O. Box 560727,
Zip 28256–0727; tel. 704/548–6000; W. Spencer Lilly, Administrator
Web address: www.carolinashealthcare.org

CHARLOTTE INSTITUTE OF REHABILITATION (O, 120 beds) 1100 Blythe
Boulevard, Charlotte, NC Zip 28203–5864; tel. 704/355–4300; Thomas M.
Nojunas, Vice President and Administrator
Web address: www.carolinashealthcare.org

CLEVELAND REGIONAL MEDICAL CENTER (L, 306 beds) 201 East Grover
Street, Shelby, NC Zip 28150; tel. 704/487–3000; John E. Young, President
and Chief Executive Officer
Web address: www.carolinas.org

CRAWLEY MEMORIAL HOSPITAL (C, 60 beds) 315 West College Avenue,
Boiling Springs, NC Zip 28017, Mailing Address: P.O. Box 996,
Zip 28017–0996; tel. 704/434–9466; Gail McKillop, President
Web address: www.carolinas.org

GRACE HOSPITAL (C, 269 beds) 2201 South Sterling Street, Morganton, NC
Zip 28655–4058; tel. 828/580–5000; Kenneth W. Wood, President and
Chief Executive Officer
Web address: www.gracehcs.org

KINGS MOUNTAIN HOSPITAL (L, 72 beds) 706 West King Street, Kings
Mountain, NC Zip 28086–2708; tel. 704/739–3601; John E. Young,
President and Chief Executive Officer
Web address: www.carolinas.org

LINCOLN MEDICAL CENTER (C, 87 beds) 200 Gamble Drive, Lincolnton, NC
Zip 28092–4421, Mailing Address: Box 677, Zip 28093–0677;
tel. 704/735–3071; Peter W. Acker, President and Chief Executive Officer
Web address: www.lincolnmedical.org

UNION REGIONAL MEDICAL CENTER (L, 215 beds) 600 Hospital Drive,
Monroe, NC Zip 28112–6000, Mailing Address: P.O. Box 5003,
Zip 28111–5003; tel. 704/283–3100; John W. Roberts, President and Chief
Executive Officer
Web address: www.unionregional.org

VALDESE GENERAL HOSPITAL (O, 199 beds) 720 Malcolm Boulevard,
Valdese, NC Zip 28690, Mailing Address: P.O. Box 700, Zip 28690–0700;
tel. 828/874–2251; Lloyd E. Wallace, President and Chief Executive Officer
Web address: www.blueridgehealth.org

SOUTH CAROLINA: BON SECOURS–ST. FRANCIS XAVIER HOSPITAL (C, 145
beds) 2095 Henry Tecklenburg Drive, Charleston, SC Zip 29414–0001,
Mailing Address: P.O. Box 160001, Zip 29414–0001;
tel. 843/402–1000; Allen P. Carroll, Chief Executive Officer
Web address: www.ropersaintfrancis.com

ROPER HOSPITAL (C, 345 beds) 316 Calhoun Street, Charleston, SC
Zip 29401–1125; tel. 843/724–2000; Matthew J. Severance, Chief
Executive Officer
Web address: www.carealliance.com

Owned, leased, sponsored:	10 hospitals	2352 beds
Contract–managed:	5 hospitals	906 beds
Totals:	15 hospitals	3258 beds

★**0250: CASCADE HEALTHCARE COMMUNITY** (NP)
2500 N.E. Neff Road, Bend, OR Zip 97701–6015;
tel. 541/382–4321; Jim R. Hobbs, President and Chief Executive
Officer
(Moderately Centralized Health System)

OREGON: ST. CHARLES MEDICAL CENTER – BEND (O, 172 beds) 2500 N.E.
Neff Road, Bend, OR Zip 97701–6015; tel. 541/382–4321; Jim R.
Hobbs, President and Chief Executive Officer
Web address: www.scmc.org

ST. CHARLES MEDICAL CENTER – REDMOND (O, 48 beds) 1253 North Canal
Boulevard, Redmond, OR Zip 97756–1395; tel. 541/548–8131; Jim R.
Hobbs, President and Chief Executive Officer
Web address: www.codh.org

Owned, leased, sponsored:	2 hospitals	220 beds
Contract–managed:	0 hospitals	0 beds
Totals:	2 hospitals	220 beds

6545: CATHEDRAL HEALTHCARE SYSTEM, INC. (CC)
219 Chestnut Street, Newark, NJ Zip 07105–1558;
tel. 973/690–3600; Henry Amoroso, President and Chief Executive
Officer

NEW JERSEY: COLUMBUS HOSPITAL (O, 169 beds) 495 North 13th Street,
Newark, NJ Zip 07107–1397; tel. 973/268–1400; Richard Giorgino,
Administrator

SAINT JAMES HOSPITAL OF NEWARK (O, 189 beds) 155 Jefferson Street,
Newark, NJ Zip 07105–1791; tel. 973/589–1300; Ceu Cirne–Neves,
Administrator
Web address: www.cathedralhealth.org

For explanation of codes following names, see page B2.
★ Indicates Type III membership in the American Hospital Association.

SAINT MICHAEL'S MEDICAL CENTER (O, 223 beds) 268 Dr. Martin Luther King Jr. Boulevard, Newark, NJ Zip 07102–2094; tel. 973/877–5000; Felicia Karsos, Acting Administrator
Web address: www.cathedralhealthcare.org

Owned, leased, sponsored:	3 hospitals	581 beds
Contract–managed:	0 hospitals	0 beds
Totals:	3 hospitals	581 beds

★**0136: CATHOLIC HEALTH EAST** (CC)
14 Campus Boulevard, Suite 300, Newtown Square, PA Zip 19073–3277; tel. 610/355–2000; Robert V. Stanek, President and Chief Executive Officer
(Moderately Centralized Health System)

ALABAMA: MERCY MEDICAL (O, 162 beds) 101 Villa Drive, Daphne, AL Zip 36526–4653, Mailing Address: P.O. Box 1090, Zip 36526–1090; tel. 251/621–4200; Mary Kay Polys, President and Chief Executive Officer
Web address: www.mercymedical.com

DELAWARE: ST. FRANCIS HOSPITAL (O, 129 beds) Seventh and Clayton Streets, Wilmington, DE Zip 19805–0500, Mailing Address: P.O. Box 2500, Zip 19805–0500; tel. 302/421–4100; Richard A. Long, President and Chief Executive Officer
Web address: www.stfrancishealthcare.org

FLORIDA: HOLY CROSS HOSPITAL (O, 450 beds) 4725 North Federal Highway, Fort Lauderdale, FL Zip 33308–4668, Mailing Address: P.O. Box 23460, Zip 33307–3460; tel. 954/771–8000; John C. Johnson, Chief Executive Officer
Web address: www.holy–cross.com

MERCY HOSPITAL (O, 339 beds) 3663 South Miami Avenue, Miami, FL Zip 33133–4237; tel. 305/854–4400; John E. Matuska, President and Chief Executive Officer
Web address: www.mercymiami.com

SOUTH FLORIDA BAPTIST HOSPITAL (S, 147 beds) 301 North Alexander Street, Plant City, FL Zip 33563–9058, Mailing Address: Drawer H, Zip 33564–9058; tel. 813/757–1200; William G. Ulbricht, Chief Operating Officer
Web address: www.sjbhealth.org

ST. ANTHONY'S HOSPITAL (S, 370 beds) 1200 Seventh Avenue North, Saint Petersburg, FL Zip 33705–1388, Mailing Address: P.O. Box 12588, Zip 33733–2588; tel. 727/825–1100; Ford Kyes, President
Web address: www.stanthonys.org

ST. JOSEPH'S HOSPITAL (S, 883 beds) 3001 West Martin Luther King Jr. Boulevard, Tampa, FL Zip 33607–6387, Mailing Address: P.O. Box 4227, Zip 33677–4227; tel. 813/870–4000; Isaac Mallah, President and Chief Executive Officer
Web address: www.sjbhealth.org

GEORGIA: SAINT JOSEPH'S HOSPITAL OF ATLANTA (O, 346 beds) 5665 Peachtree Dunwoody Road N.E., Atlanta, GA Zip 30342–1764; tel. 404/851–7001; Bonnie Phipps, President and Chief Executive Officer
Web address: www.stjosephsatlanta.org

ST. MARY'S HEALTH CARE SYSTEM (O, 302 beds) 1230 Baxter Street, Athens, GA Zip 30606–3791; tel. 706/389–3000; Thomas E. Fitz Jr, FACHE, President and Chief Executive Officer
Web address: www.stmarysathens.com

MAINE: MERCY HOSPITAL OF PORTLAND (O, 168 beds) 144 State Street, Portland, ME Zip 04101–3795; tel. 207/879–3000; Eileen F. Skinner, President and Chief Executive Officer
Web address: www.mercyhospital.com

MASSACHUSETTS: MERCY MEDICAL CENTER (O, 327 beds) 271 Carew Street, Springfield, MA Zip 01104–2398, Mailing Address: P.O. Box 9012, Zip 01102–9012; tel. 413/748–9000; Vincent J. McCorkle, President and Chief Executive Officer
Web address: www.mercycares.com

NEW JERSEY: LOURDES MEDICAL CENTER OF BURLINGTON COUNTY (O, 165 beds) 218–A Sunset Road, Willingboro, NJ Zip 08046–1162; tel. 609/835–2900; John L. Nespoli, Chief Administrative Officer
Web address: www.lourdesnet.org

OUR LADY OF LOURDES MEDICAL CENTER (O, 289 beds) 1600 Haddon Avenue, Camden, NJ Zip 08103–3117; tel. 856/757–3500; Mark T. Bateman, Chief Administrative Officer
Web address: www.lourdesnet.org

ST. FRANCIS MEDICAL CENTER (O, 165 beds) 601 Hamilton Avenue, Trenton, NJ Zip 08629–1986; tel. 609/599–5000; Gerald J. Jablonowski, President and Chief Executive Officer
Web address: www.stfrancismedical.com

NEW YORK: ST. JAMES MERCY HOSPITAL (O, 225 beds) 411 Canisteo Street, Hornell, NY Zip 14843–2197; tel. 607/324–8000; Clarence R. La Liberty Jr, President and Chief Executive Officer
Web address: www.stjamesmercy.org

ST. PETER'S HOSPITAL (O, 442 beds) 315 South Manning Boulevard, Albany, NY Zip 12208–1789; tel. 518/525–1550; Steven P. Boyle, President and Chief Executive Officer
Web address: www.stpetershealthcare.org

PENNSYLVANIA: MARIAN COMMUNITY HOSPITAL (O, 104 beds) 100 Lincoln Avenue, Carbondale, PA Zip 18407–2198; tel. 570/281–1000; Sister Jean Coughlin, President and Chief Executive Officer
Web address: www.marianhospital.org

MERCY CATHOLIC MEDICAL CENTER (O, 470 beds) 1500 South Lansdowe Avenue, Darby, PA Zip 19023; tel. 610/237–4000; R. Alan Larson, Chief Executive Officer
Web address: www.mercyhealth.org

MERCY HOSPITAL OF PITTSBURGH (O, 495 beds) 1400 Locust Street, Pittsburgh, PA Zip 15219–5166; tel. 412/232–8111; Kenneth A. Eshak, President and Chief Executive Officer
Web address: www.mercylink.org

MERCY HOSPITAL–NORTH SHORE CAMPUS (O, 132 beds) 1004 Arch Street, Pittsburgh, PA Zip 15212–5235; tel. 412/323–5600; Mary Anne Foley, Aministrator
Web address: www.mercylink.org

MERCY JEANNETTE HOSPITAL (O, 138 beds) 600 Jefferson Avenue, Jeannette, PA Zip 15644–2599; tel. 724/527–3551; Julie A. Hester, Administrator
Web address: www.jdmh.org/

MERCY SUBURBAN HOSPITAL (O, 141 beds) 2701 DeKalb Pike, Norristown, PA Zip 19401–1820; tel. 610/278–2000; Mark C. Barabas, President and Chief Executive Officer
Web address: www.mercyhealth.org

NAZARETH HOSPITAL (O, 233 beds) 2601 Holme Avenue, Philadelphia, PA Zip 19152–2096; tel. 215/335–6000; Patricia B. DeAngelis, President and Chief Executive Officer
Web address: www.nazarethhospital.org

ST. AGNES CONTINUING CARE CENTER (O, 172 beds) 1900 South Broad Street, Philadelphia, PA Zip 19145–2304; tel. 215/339–4100; James J. Flowers, D.O., President and Chief Executive Officer
Web address: www.stagnesphila.org

ST. MARY MEDICAL CENTER (O, 262 beds) Langhorne–Newtown Road, Langhorne, PA Zip 19047–1295; tel. 215/710–2000; Gregory T. Wozniak, President and Chief Executive Officer
Web address: www.stmaryhealthcare.org

Owned, leased, sponsored:	25 hospitals	7056 beds
Contract–managed:	0 hospitals	0 beds
Totals:	25 hospitals	7056 beds

★**0092: CATHOLIC HEALTH INITIATIVES** (CC)
1999 Broadway, Suite 2600, Denver, CO Zip 80202–4004; tel. 303/298–9100; Kevin E. Lofton, President and Chief Executive Officer
(Decentralized Health System)

ARKANSAS: ST. VINCENT INFIRMARY MEDICAL CENTER (S, 542 beds) Two St. Vincent Circle, Little Rock, AR Zip 72205–5499; tel. 501/552–3000; Stephen L. Mansfield, President and Chief Executive Officer
Web address: www.stvincenthealth.com

ST. VINCENT MEDICAL CENTER–NORTH (S, 35 beds) 2215 Wildwood Avenue, Sherwood, AR Zip 72120; tel. 501/552–7100; Randall R. Cason, Administrator and Chief Executive Officer
Web address: www.stvincenthealth.com

ST. VINCENT REHABILITATION HOSPITAL (S, 60 beds) 2201 Wildwood Avenue, Sherwood, AR Zip 72120–5074, Mailing Address: P.O. Box 6930, Zip 72124–6930; tel. 501/834–1800; Robert Shane Everett, Administrator
Web address: www.healthsouth.com

For explanation of codes following names, see page B2.
★ Indicates Type III membership in the American Hospital Association.

Section B

COLORADO: MERCY MEDICAL CENTER (S, 75 beds) 375 East Park Avenue, Durango, CO Zip 81301–5089; tel. 970/247–4311; Kirk Dignum, Ph.D., President and Chief Executive Officer
Web address: www.mercydurango.org

PENROSE–ST. FRANCIS HEALTH SERVICES (S, 392 beds) 2215 North Cascade Avenue, Colorado Springs, CO Zip 80907–6799, Mailing Address: P.O. Box 7021, Zip 80933–7021; tel. 719/776–5000; Rick O'Connell, President and Chief Executive Officer
Web address: www.penrosestfrancis.org

ST. ANTHONY CENTRAL HOSPITAL (S, 319 beds) 4231 West 16th Avenue, Denver, CO Zip 80204–4098; tel. 303/629–3511; George A. Zara, Chief Executive Officer
Web address: www.stanthonyhosp.org

ST. ANTHONY NORTH HOSPITAL (S, 132 beds) 2551 West 84th Avenue, Westminster, CO Zip 80031; tel. 303/426–2151; James F. Dover, FACHE, Administrator
Web address: www.centura.org

ST. MARY–CORWIN MEDICAL CENTER (S, 254 beds) 1008 Minnequa Avenue, Pueblo, CO Zip 81004–3798; tel. 719/560–4000; Thomas E. Anderson, Administrator
Web address: www.centura.org

ST. THOMAS MORE HOSPITAL (S, 55 beds) 1338 Phay Avenue, Canon City, CO Zip 81212–2221; tel. 719/269–2000; C. Ray Honaker, President and Chief Executive Officer
Web address: www.centura.org

IDAHO: MERCY MEDICAL CENTER (S, 104 beds) 1512 12th Avenue Road, Nampa, ID Zip 83686–6008; tel. 208/467–1171; Joseph Messmer, President and Chief Executive Officer
Web address: www.mercynampa.org

IOWA: MERCY MEDICAL CENTER–CENTERVILLE (S, 51 beds) 1 St. Joseph's Drive, Centerville, IA Zip 52544–8055; tel. 641/437–4111; Clinton J. Christianson, Chief Executive Officer
Web address: www.mercycenterville.org

MERCY MEDICAL CENTER–DES MOINES (S, 561 beds) 1111 6th Avenue, Des Moines, IA Zip 50314–2611; tel. 515/247–3121; David H. Vellinga, President and Chief Executive Officer
Web address: www.mercydesmoines.org

KANSAS: CENTRAL KANSAS MEDICAL CENTER (S, 61 beds) 3515 Broadway Street, Great Bend, KS Zip 67530–3633; tel. 620/792–2511; Chris Thomas, CHE, President and Chief Executive Officer
Web address: www.ckmc.org

ST. CATHERINE HOSPITAL (S, 101 beds) 401 East Spuce Street, Garden City, KS Zip 67846–5679; tel. 620/272–2561; Scott J. Taylor, President and Chief Executive Officer
Web address: www.stcath–hosp.org

ST. JOHN'S MAUDE NORTON MEMORIAL HOSPITAL (S, 18 beds) 220 North Pennsylvania Street, Columbus, KS Zip 66725–1110; tel. 620/429–2545; Cindy Neely, Administrator

ST. JOSEPH MEMORIAL HOSPITAL (S, 55 beds) 923 Carroll Avenue, Larned, KS Zip 67550; tel. 620/285–3161; Danielle Johnson, Administrator
Web address: www.ckmc.org

KENTUCKY: BEREA HOSPITAL (S, 150 beds) 305 Estill Street, Berea, KY Zip 40403–1909; tel. 859/986–3151; Angela Carman, President and Chief Executive Officer
Web address: www.bereahospital.com

CARITAS MEDICAL CENTER (S, 473 beds) 1850 Bluegrass Avenue, Louisville, KY Zip 40215–1199; tel. 502/361–6000; Robert M. Lovell, Interim President and Chief Executive Officer
Web address: www.caritas.org

CARITAS PEACE CENTER (S, 206 beds) 2020 Newburg Road, Louisville, KY Zip 40205–1879; tel. 502/451–3330; Robert M. Lovell, Interim President and Chief Executive Officer
Web address: www.caritas.org

FLAGET MEMORIAL HOSPITAL (S, 52 beds) 4305 New Shepherdsville Road, Bardstown, KY Zip 40004; tel. 502/350–5000; Bruce A. Klockars, President and Chief Executive Officer
Web address: www.flaget.com

MARYMOUNT MEDICAL CENTER (S, 87 beds) 310 East Ninth Street, London, KY Zip 40741–1299; tel. 606/878–6520; Virginia B. Dempsey, Chief Executive Officer
Web address: www.marymount.com

OUR LADY OF THE WAY HOSPITAL (S, 25 beds) 11203 Main Street, Martin, KY Zip 41649–0910; tel. 606/285–5181; Kathy Stumbo, Chief Executive Officer
Web address: www.olwh.org

SAINT JOSEPH HOSPITAL (S, 344 beds) One St. Joseph Drive, Lexington, KY Zip 40504–3754; tel. 859/278–3436; Eugene A. Woods, President and Chief Executive Officer
Web address: www.sjhlex.org

SAINT JOSEPH HOSPITAL EAST (S, 116 beds) 150 North Eagle Creek Drive, Lexington, KY Zip 40509–1807; tel. 859/268–4800; Eugene A. Woods, President and Chief Executive Officer
Web address: www.sjhlex.org

MARYLAND: ST. JOSEPH MEDICAL CENTER (S, 359 beds) 7601 Osler Drive, Towson, MD Zip 21204–7582; tel. 410/337–1000; John Kerr Tolmie, President and Chief Executive Officer
Web address: www.sjmcmd.org

MINNESOTA: ALBANY AREA HOSPITAL AND MEDICAL CENTER (S, 15 beds) 300 Third Avenue, Albany, MN Zip 56307–9363; tel. 320/845–2121; Benjamin Koppelman, Administrator
Web address: www.albanyareahospital.com

LAKEWOOD HEALTH CENTER (S, 65 beds) 600 Main Avenue South, Baudette, MN Zip 56623–2855; tel. 218/634–2120; SharRay Palm, President and Chief Executive Officer
Web address: www.lakewood–baudette.org

ST. FRANCIS MEDICAL CENTER (S, 145 beds) 415 Oak Street, Breckenridge, MN Zip 56520–1298; tel. 218/643–3000; David A. Nelson, President and Chief Executive Officer
Web address: www.sfcare.org

ST. GABRIEL'S HOSPITAL (S, 199 beds) 815 Second Street S.E., Little Falls, MN Zip 56345–3596; tel. 320/632–5441; Carl P. Vaagenes, President and Chief Executive Officer
Web address: www.stgabriels.com

ST. JOSEPH'S AREA HEALTH SERVICES (S, 43 beds) 600 Pleasant Avenue, Park Rapids, MN Zip 56470–1432; tel. 218/732–3311; Peter Jacobson, President and Chief Executive Officer
Web address: www.sjahs.org

MISSOURI: ST. JOHN'S REGIONAL MEDICAL CENTER (S, 367 beds) 2727 McClelland Boulevard, Joplin, MO Zip 64804–1694; tel. 417/781–2727; Gary L. Rowe, President and Chief Executive Officer
Web address: www.stj.org

NEBRASKA: GOOD SAMARITAN HEALTH SYSTEMS (S, 185 beds) 10 East 31st Street, Kearney, NE Zip 68847–2926, Mailing Address: P.O. Box 1990, Zip 68848–1990; tel. 308/865–7100; John Allen, President and Chief Executive Officer
Web address: www.gshs.org

RICHARD H. YOUNG PSYCHIATRIC HOSPITAL (S, 43 beds) 1755 Prairie View Place, Kearney, NE Zip 68848; tel. 308/865–2000;
Web address: www.gshs.org

SAINT ELIZABETH REGIONAL MEDICAL CENTER (S, 242 beds) 555 South 70th Street, Lincoln, NE Zip 68510–2494; tel. 402/219–8000; Robert J. Lanik, President and Chief Executive Officer
Web address: www.saintelizabethonline.com

SAINT FRANCIS MEDICAL CENTER (S, 200 beds) 2620 West Faidley Avenue, Grand Island, NE Zip 68803–4297, Mailing Address: P.O. Box 9804, Zip 68802–9804; tel. 308/384–4600; Michael R. Gloor, FACHE, President and Chief Executive Officer
Web address: www.saintfrancisgi.org

ST. MARY'S HOSPITAL (S, 18 beds) 1314 Third Avenue, Nebraska City, NE Zip 68410–1999; tel. 402/873–3321; Daniel J. Kelly, President and Chief Executive Officer
Web address: www.stmaryshospitalnecity.org

NORTH DAKOTA: CARRINGTON HEALTH CENTER (S, 49 beds) 800 North Fourth Street, Carrington, ND Zip 58421–1217; tel. 701/652–3141; Johnson L. Smith, Interim President and Chief Executive Officer
Web address: www.carringtonhealthcenter.com

LISBON AREA HEALTH SERVICES (S, 65 beds) 905 Main Street, Lisbon, ND Zip 58054–0353, Mailing Address: P.O. Box 353, Zip 58054–0353; tel. 701/683–5241; Bradley D. Burris, President and Chief Executive Officer
Web address: www.lhsnet.org

MERCY HOSPITAL (S, 35 beds) 1031 Seventh Street N.E., Devils Lake, ND Zip 58301–2798; tel. 701/662–2131; Marlene J. Krein, President and Chief Executive Officer
Web address: www.mercyhospitaldl.com

For explanation of codes following names, see page B2.
★ Indicates Type III membership in the American Hospital Association.

MERCY HOSPITAL (S, 25 beds) 570 Chautauqua Boulevard, Valley City, ND Zip 58072–3199; tel. 701/845–6400; Johnson L. Smith, President and Chief Executive Officer
Web address: www.mercyhospital.biz

MERCY MEDICAL CENTER (S, 45 beds) 1301 15th Avenue West, Williston, ND Zip 58801–3896; tel. 701/774–7400; Kimberly J. Miller, CHE, President and Chief Executive Officer
Web address: www.mercy–williston.org

OAKES COMMUNITY HOSPITAL (S, 25 beds) 314 South Eighth Street, Oakes, ND Zip 58474–2099; tel. 701/742–3291; Bradley D. Burris, President and Chief Executive Officer

ST. JOSEPH'S HOSPITAL AND HEALTH CENTER (S, 83 beds) 30 Seventh Street West, Dickinson, ND Zip 58601–4399; tel. 701/456–4000; Allan C. Sonduck, President and Chief Executive Officer
Web address: www.stjoeshospital.org

OHIO: GOOD SAMARITAN HOSPITAL (S, 468 beds) 375 Dixmyth Avenue, Cincinnati, OH Zip 45220–2489; tel. 513/872–1400; John S. Prout, President and Chief Executive Officer
Web address: www.trihealth.com

GOOD SAMARITAN HOSPITAL (S, 348 beds) 2222 Philadelphia Drive, Dayton, OH Zip 45406–1813; tel. 937/278–2612; James R. Pancoast, President and Chief Executive Officer
Web address: www.goodsamdayton.com

OREGON: HOLY ROSARY MEDICAL CENTER (S, 49 beds) 351 S.W. Ninth Street, Ontario, OR Zip 97914–2693; tel. 541/881–7000; Mark F. Dalley, President and Chief Executive Officer
Web address: www.holyrosary–ontario.org

MERCY MEDICAL CENTER (S, 153 beds) 2700 Stewart Parkway, Roseburg, OR Zip 97470–1297; tel. 541/673–0611; Victor J. Fresolone, FACHE, President and Chief Executive Officer
Web address: www.mercyrose.org

ST. ANTHONY HOSPITAL (S, 25 beds) 1601 S.E. Court Avenue, Pendleton, OR Zip 97801–3297; tel. 541/276–5121; Jeffrey S. Drop, President and Chief Executive Officer
Web address: www.sahpendleton.org

ST. ELIZABETH HEALTH SERVICES (S, 75 beds) 3325 Pocahontas Road, Baker City, OR Zip 97814–1464; tel. 541/523–6461; George Winn, President and Chief Executive Officer
Web address: www.stelizabethhealth.com

PENNSYLVANIA: ST. JOSEPH MEDICAL CENTER (S, 267 beds) 215 North 12th Street, Reading, PA 19604, Mailing Address: P.O. Box 316, Zip 19603–0316; tel. 610/378–2000; John R. Morahan, President and Chief Executive Officer
Web address: www.sjmcberks.org

SOUTH DAKOTA: GETTYSBURG MEDICAL CENTER (S, 58 beds) 606 East Garfield Avenue, Gettysburg, SD Zip 57442–1398; tel. 605/765–2480; Mark Schmidt, President and Chief Executive Officer
Web address: www.catholichealthinit.org

ST. MARY'S HEALTHCARE CENTER (S, 165 beds) 800 East Dakota Avenue, Pierre, SD Zip 57501–3313; tel. 605/224–3100; James D. M. Russell, President and Chief Executive Officer
Web address: www.st–marys.com

TENNESSEE: MEMORIAL HEALTH CARE SYSTEM (S, 394 beds) 2525 De Sales Avenue, Chattanooga, TN Zip 37404–3322; tel. 423/495–8656; Ruth W. Brinkley, President and Chief Executive Officer
Web address: www.memorial.org

WASHINGTON: ST. CLARE HOSPITAL (S, 106 beds) 11315 Bridgeport Way S.W., Tacoma, WA Zip 98499–3004, Mailing Address: P.O. Box 99998, Lakewood, Zip 98499–0998; tel. 253/588–1711; Brooks Sutton, R.N., Chief Operating Officer
Web address: www.fhshealth.org

ST. FRANCIS HOSPITAL (S, 108 beds) 34515 Ninth Avenue South, Federal Way, WA Zip 98003–6799; tel. 253/927–9700; Syd Bersante, Chief Operating Officer
Web address: www.fhshealth.org

ST. JOSEPH MEDICAL CENTER (S, 290 beds) 1717 South J Street, Tacoma, WA Zip 98405–3004, Mailing Address: P.O. Box 2197, Zip 98401–2197; tel. 253/426–4101; June C. Bowman, R.N., Chief Operating Officer and Nurse Executive
Web address: www.fhshealth.org

Owned, leased, sponsored:	56 hospitals	8982 beds
Contract–managed:	0 hospitals	0 beds
Totals:	56 hospitals	8982 beds

★0233: CATHOLIC HEALTH SERVICES OF LONG ISLAND (CC)
1 Huntington Quadrangle, Suite 4C04, Rockville Centre, NY Zip 11570; tel. 516/705–3700; James Harden, President and Chief Executive Officer
(Centralized Health System)

NEW YORK: GOOD SAMARITAN HOSPITAL MEDICAL CENTER (O, 531 beds) 1000 Montauk Highway, West Islip, NY Zip 11795–4958; tel. 631/376–3000; Richard J. Murphy, President and Chief Executive Officer
Web address: www.good–samaritan–hospital.org

MERCY MEDICAL CENTER (O, 387 beds) 1000 North Village Avenue, Rockville Centre, NY Zip 11570–1098; tel. 516/705–2525; Martin A. Bieber, President and Chief Executive Officer
Web address: www.mercymedicalcenter.org

ST. CATHERINE OF SIENA MEDICAL CENTER (O, 490 beds) 50 Route 25–A, Smithtown, NY Zip 11787–1398; tel. 631/862–3000; Vincent DiRubbio, President and Chief Executive Officer
Web address: www.stcatherinemedicalcenter.org

ST. CHARLES HOSPITAL (O, 289 beds) 200 Belle Terre Road, Port Jefferson, NY Zip 11777–1928; tel. 631/474–6000; James O'Connor, President and Chief Executive Officer
Web address: www.stcharleshospital.chsli.org

ST. FRANCIS HOSPITAL (O, 321 beds) 100 Port Washington Boulevard, Roslyn, NY Zip 11576–1348; tel. 516/562–6000; Alan D. Guerci, M.D., Chief Executive Officer
Web address: www.stfrancisheartcenter.chsli.org

Owned, leased, sponsored:	5 hospitals	2018 beds
Contract–managed:	0 hospitals	0 beds
Totals:	5 hospitals	2018 beds

★0234: CATHOLIC HEALTH SYSTEM (CC)
515 Abbott Road, Suite 508, Buffalo, NY Zip 14220; tel. 716/828–2750; Joseph D. McDonald, President and Chief Executive Officer
(Centralized Health System)

KENMORE MERCY HOSPITAL (O, 308 beds) 2950 Elmwood Avenue, Kenmore, NY Zip 14217–1390; tel. 716/447–6100; Mary Hoffman, President and Senior Administrative Officer
Web address: www.chsbuffalo.org

MERCY HOSPITAL (O, 389 beds) 565 Abbott Road, Buffalo, NY Zip 14220–2095; tel. 716/826–7000; John P. Davanzo, President and Chief Executive Officer
Web address: www.chsbuffalo.org

SISTERS OF CHARITY HOSPITAL OF BUFFALO (O, 307 beds) 2157 Main Street, Buffalo, NY Zip 14214–2692; tel. 716/862–1000; Harry Smith Jr, President and Senior Administrative Officer
Web address: www.chsbuffalo.org

ST. JOSEPH HOSPITAL (O, 132 beds) 2605 Harlem Road, Cheektowaga, NY Zip 14225–4097; tel. 716/891–2400; James M. Millard, President and Senior Administrative Officer
Web address: www.chsbuffalo.org

Owned, leased, sponsored:	4 hospitals	1136 beds
Contract–managed:	0 hospitals	0 beds
Totals:	4 hospitals	1136 beds

★5155: CATHOLIC HEALTHCARE PARTNERS (CC)
615 Elsinore Place, Cincinnati, OH Zip 45202; tel. 513/639–2800; Michael D. Connelly, President and Chief Executive Officer
(Decentralized Health System)

For explanation of codes following names, see page B2.
★ Indicates Type III membership in the American Hospital Association.

Section B

KENTUCKY: LOURDES HOSPITAL (O, 289 beds) 1530 Lone Oak Road, Paducah, KY Zip 42003–7900, Mailing Address: P.O. Box 7100, Zip 42002–7100; tel. 270/444–2444; William G. Wheeler, M.D., President and Chief Executive Officer
Web address: www.lourdes-pad.org

MARCUM AND WALLACE MEMORIAL HOSPITAL (O, 25 beds) 60 Mercy Court, Irvine, KY Zip 40336–1331; tel. 606/723–2115; Susan Starling, President and Chief Executive Officer

OHIO: ALLEN MEDICAL CENTER (O, 25 beds) 200 West Lorain Street, Oberlin, OH Zip 44074–1077; tel. 440/775–1211; Edwin M. Oley, President and Chief Executive Officer
Web address: www.ehealthconnection.com/lorain

COMMUNITY HEALTH PARTNERS REGIONAL MEDICAL CENTER (O, 318 beds) 3700 Kolbe Road, Lorain, OH Zip 44053–1697; tel. 440/960–4000; Gary Wengard, Interim President and Chief Executive Officer
Web address: www.community–health–partners.com

COMMUNITY HOSPITAL (O, 204 beds) 2615 East High Street, Springfield, OH Zip 45505–1422, Mailing Address: Box 1228, Zip 45501–1228; tel. 937/325–0531; Andrew R. McCulloch, President and Chief Executive Officer
Web address: www.communityhospital.com

INSTITUTE FOR ORTHOPAEDIC SURGERY (O, 3 beds) 801 Medical Drive, Suite B., Lima, OH Zip 45804; tel. 419/224–7586; Cindy Hauck, Administrator

MERCY FRANCISCAN HOSPITAL MOUNT AIRY (O, 246 beds) 2446 Kipling Avenue, Cincinnati, OH Zip 45239–6650; tel. 513/853–5000; James Gravell, President and Chief Executive Officer
Web address: www.mercy.health–partners.org

MERCY FRANCISCAN HOSPITAL–WESTERN HILLS (O, 163 beds) 3131 Queen City Avenue, Cincinnati, OH Zip 45238–2396; tel. 513/389–5000; James Chadwick Patrick, President and Chief Executive Officer
Web address: www.mercy.health–partners.org

MERCY HOSPITAL ANDERSON (O, 160 beds) 7500 State Road, Cincinnati, OH Zip 45255–2492; tel. 513/624–4500; Patricia A. Schroer, President and Chief Executive Officer
Web address: www.mercy.health–partners.org

MERCY HOSPITAL CLERMONT (O, 124 beds) 3000 Hospital Drive, Batavia, OH Zip 45103–1998; tel. 513/732–8200; Mark D. Shugarman, President and Chief Executive Officer
Web address: www.e–mercy.com

MERCY HOSPITAL FAIRFIELD (O, 168 beds) 3000 Mack Road, Fairfield, OH Zip 45014; tel. 513/870–7000; Jeffrey A. Ashin, Interim President and Chief Executive Officer
Web address: www.e–mercy.com

MERCY HOSPITAL OF DEFIANCE (O, 23 beds) 1404 East Second Street, Defiance, OH Zip 43512; tel. 419/782–8444; Chad Peter, Administrator
Web address: www.ehealthconnection.com/regions/toledo/

MERCY HOSPITAL OF TIFFIN (O, 65 beds) 485 West Market Street, Tiffin, OH Zip 44883–0727; tel. 419/447–3130; Dale E. Thornton, M.P.H., CHE, President and Chief Executive Officer
Web address: www.mhsnr.org

MERCY HOSPITAL OF WILLARD (O, 25 beds) 110 East Howard Street, Willard, OH Zip 44890–1611; tel. 419/964–5000; Robert E. Gospodarek, President and Chief Executive Officer
Web address: www.mhsnr.org

MERCY MEDICAL CENTER (O, 158 beds) 1343 North Fountain Boulevard, Springfield, OH Zip 45501–1380; tel. 937/390–5000; Andrew R. McCulloch, President and Chief Executive Officer
Web address: www.mercy–health.org

MERCY MEMORIAL HOSPITAL (O, 12 beds) 904 Scioto Street, Urbana, OH Zip 43078–2200; tel. 937/653–5231; Karl Zalar, Administrator and Chief Executive Officer
Web address: www.mercy–health.org

ST. ANNE MERCY HOSPITAL (O, 142 beds) 3404 West Sylvania Avenue, Toledo, OH Zip 43623; tel. 419/407–2663; Karen H. Connors, President and Chief Executive Officer
Web address: www.mercyweb.org

ST. CHARLES MERCY HOSPITAL (O, 390 beds) 2600 Navarre Avenue, Oregon, OH Zip 43616–3297; tel. 419/696–7200; David J. Ameen, President and Chief Executive Officer
Web address: www.mercyweb.org

ST. ELIZABETH HEALTH CENTER (O, 482 beds) 1044 Belmont Avenue, Youngstown, OH Zip 44504–1096, Mailing Address: P.O. Box 1790, Zip 44501–1790; tel. 330/746–7211; Robert W. Shroder, President and Chief Executive Officer
Web address: www.hmpartners.org

ST. JOSEPH HEALTH CENTER (O, 158 beds) 667 Eastland Avenue S.E., Warren, OH Zip 44484–4531; tel. 330/841–4000; Robert W. Shroder, President and Chief Executive Officer
Web address: www.hmpartners.org

ST. RITA'S MEDICAL CENTER (O, 383 beds) 730 West Market Street, Lima, OH Zip 45801–4670; tel. 419/227–3361; James P. Reber, President and Chief Executive Officer
Web address: www.stritas.org

ST. VINCENT MERCY MEDICAL CENTER (O, 556 beds) 2213 Cherry Street, Toledo, OH Zip 43608–2691; tel. 419/251–3232; Jeffrey D. Peterson, President and Chief Executive Officer
Web address: www.mercyweb.org

PENNSYLVANIA: MERCY HOSPITAL OF SCRANTON (O, 251 beds) 746 Jefferson Avenue, Scranton, PA Zip 18501–1697; tel. 570/348–7100; C. J. Urlaub, Chief Administrative Officer
Web address: www.mhs–nepa.com

MERCY HOSPITAL OF WILKES–BARRE (O, 188 beds) 25 Church Street, Wilkes–Barre, PA Zip 18765–0999, Mailing Address: P.O. Box 658, Zip 18765–0658; tel. 570/826–3100; Eugene Bassett, Chief Administrative Officer
Web address: www.mhs–nepa.com

MERCY SPECIAL CARE HOSPITAL (L, 56 beds) 128 West Washington Street, Nanticoke, PA Zip 18634–3113; tel. 570/735–5000; Robert D. Williams, Vice President and Administrator
Web address: www.mhs–nepa.com

TENNESSEE: ST. MARY'S JEFFERSON MEMORIAL HOSPITAL (O, 58 beds) 110 Hospital Drive, Jefferson City, TN Zip 37760–5281; tel. 865/471–2500; Michael C. Hicks, Administrator
Web address: www.jeffersonhealthinc.com

ST. MARY'S MEDICAL CENTER (O, 385 beds) 900 East Oak Hill Avenue, Knoxville, TN Zip 37917–4556; tel. 865/545–8000; Debra K. London, President and Chief Executive Officer
Web address: www.stmaryshealth.com

ST. MARY'S MEDICAL CENTER OF CAMPBELL COUNTY (L, 164 beds) 923 East Central Avenue, La Follette, TN Zip 37766–3106, Mailing Address: P.O. Box 1301, Zip 37766–1301; tel. 423/907–1200; Nicholas P. Lewis, Administrator
Web address: www.stmaryshealth.com

Owned, leased, sponsored:	28 hospitals	5221 beds
Contract–managed:	0 hospitals	0 beds
Totals:	28 hospitals	5221 beds

★5205: CATHOLIC HEALTHCARE WEST (CC)
185 Berry Street, Suite 300, San Francisco, CA Zip 94107–1773; tel. 415/438–5500; Lloyd H. Dean, President and Chief Executive Officer
(Moderately Centralized Health System)

ARIZONA: CHANDLER REGIONAL HOSPITAL (O, 147 beds) 475 South Dobson Road, Chandler, AZ Zip 85224–4230; tel. 480/963–4561; David G. Covert, President and Chief Administrative Officer
Web address: www.chandlerregional.com

ST. JOSEPH'S HOSPITAL AND MEDICAL CENTER (S, 536 beds) 350 West Thomas Road, Phoenix, AZ Zip 85013–4496, Mailing Address: P.O. Box 2071, Zip 85001–2071; tel. 602/406–3000; Linda A. Hunt, President
Web address: www.ichosestjoes.com

CALIFORNIA: ARROYO GRANDE COMMUNITY HOSPITAL (O, 65 beds) 345 South Halcyon Road, Arroyo Grande, CA Zip 93420–3899; tel. 805/489–4261; Rick Castro, President and Chief Executive Officer
Web address: www.agfh.org

BAKERSFIELD MEMORIAL HOSPITAL (O, 339 beds) 420 34th Street, Bakersfield, CA Zip 93301–2237, Mailing Address: P.O. Box 1888, Zip 93303–1888; tel. 661/327–1792; Jon Van Boening, President
Web address: www.chw.edu

For explanation of codes following names, see page B2.
★ Indicates Type III membership in the American Hospital Association.

CALIFORNIA HOSPITAL MEDICAL CENTER (O, 316 beds) 1401 South Grand Avenue, Los Angeles, CA Zip 90015–3010; tel. 213/748–2411; Mark A. Meyers, President
Web address: www.chmcla.org

COMMMUNICH HOSPITAL OF SAN BERNARDINO (O, 374 beds) 1805 Medical Center Drive, San Bernardino, CA Zip 92411–1214; tel. 909/887–6333; Bruce G. Satzger, President
Web address: www.communityhospitalsb.org

DOMINICAN HOSPITAL (S, 282 beds) 1555 Soquel Drive, Santa Cruz, CA Zip 95065–1794; tel. 831/462–7700; Sister Julie Hyer, President
Web address: www.dominicanhospital.org

FRENCH HOSPITAL MEDICAL CENTER (O, 112 beds) 1911 Johnson Avenue, San Luis Obispo, CA Zip 93401–4131; tel. 805/543–5353; Alan Iftiniuk, President
Web address: www.agfh.org

GLENDALE MEMORIAL HOSPITAL AND HEALTH CENTER (O, 334 beds) 1420 South Central Avenue, Glendale, CA Zip 91204–2594; tel. 818/502–1900; Catherine M. Pelley, President
Web address: www.glendalememorial.com

MARIAN MEDICAL CENTER (S, 242 beds) 1400 East Church Street, Santa Maria, CA Zip 93454–5906, Mailing Address: P.O. Box 1238, Zip 93456–1238; tel. 805/739–3000; Charles J. Cova, President
Web address: www.marianmedicalcenter.org

MARK TWAIN ST. JOSEPH'S HOSPITAL (O, 30 beds) 768 Mountain Ranch Road, San Andreas, CA Zip 95249–9707; tel. 209/754–3521; Michael P. Lawson, President
Web address: www.marktwainhospital.com

MERCY GENERAL HOSPITAL (S, 329 beds) 4001 J Street, Sacramento, CA Zip 95819–3600; tel. 916/453–4545; Denny W. Powell, President
Web address: www.mercygeneral.org

MERCY HOSPITAL (S, 261 beds) 2215 Truxtun Avenue, Bakersfield, CA Zip 93301–3698, Mailing Address: P.O. Box 119, Zip 93302–0119; tel. 661/632–5000; Russell V. Judd, President
Web address: www.chw.edu

MERCY HOSPITAL OF FOLSOM (S, 85 beds) 1650 Creekside Drive, Folsom, CA Zip 95630–3405; tel. 916/983–7400; Donald C. Hudson, President
Web address: www.mercyfolsom.org

MERCY MEDICAL CENTER MERCED–COMMUNITY CAMPUS (O, 174 beds) 301 East 13th Street, Merced, CA Zip 95340–6211; tel. 209/385–7000; David S. Dunham, President
Web address: www.sutterhealth.org

MERCY MEDICAL CENTER MERCED–DOMINICAN CAMPUS (S, 115 beds) 2740 M Street, Merced, CA Zip 95340–2880; tel. 209/384–6444; David S. Dunham, President
Web address: www.mercymercedcares.org

MERCY MEDICAL CENTER MOUNT SHASTA (S, 80 beds) 914 Pine Street, Mount Shasta, CA Zip 96067–2143; tel. 530/926–6111; Chuck Gersdorf, President
Web address: www.mercy.org

MERCY MEDICAL CENTER REDDING (S, 250 beds) 2175 Rosaline Avenue, Redding, CA Zip 96001–2509, Mailing Address: P.O. Box 496009, Zip 96049–6009; tel. 530/225–6000; Richard J. Barnett, President
Web address: www.mercy.org

MERCY SAN JUAN MEDICAL CENTER (S, 260 beds) 6501 Coyle Avenue, Carmichael, CA Zip 95608–0306, Mailing Address: P.O. Box 479, Zip 95608–0479; tel. 916/537–5000; Michael J. Uboldi, R.N., President
Web address: www.mercysanjuan.org

METHODIST HOSPITAL OF SACRAMENTO (O, 333 beds) 7500 Hospital Drive, Sacramento, CA Zip 95823–5477; tel. 916/423–3000; Timothy M. Moran, President
Web address: www.mercyhospitals.org

NORTHRIDGE HOSPITAL MEDICAL CENTER–ROSCOE BOULEVARD CAMPUS (O, 370 beds) 18300 Roscoe Boulevard, Northridge, CA Zip 91328–4167; tel. 818/885–8500; Michael L. Wall, President
Web address: www.nmhc–roscoe.org

OAK VALLEY DISTRICT HOSPITAL (O, 150 beds) 350 South Oak Street, Oakdale, CA Zip 95361–3519; tel. 209/847–3011; John P. Friel, Chief Executive Officer
Web address: www.oakvalleycares.org

SAINT FRANCIS MEMORIAL HOSPITAL (O, 210 beds) 900 Hyde Street, San Francisco, CA Zip 94109–4899, Mailing Address: Box 7726, Zip 94120–7726; tel. 415/353–6000; Cheryl A. Fama, President and Chief Executive Officer
Web address: www.chw.edu

SAN GABRIEL VALLEY MEDICAL CENTER (O, 190 beds) 438 West Las Tunas Drive, San Gabriel, CA Zip 91776–1216, Mailing Address: P.O. Box 1507, Zip 91778–1507; tel. 626/289–5454; Makoto Nakayama, President
Web address: www.sgvmc.org

SEQUOIA HOSPITAL (O, 205 beds) 170 Alameda De Las Pulgas, Redwood City, CA Zip 94062–2799; tel. 650/369–5811; Glenna L. Vaskelis, President and Administrator
Web address: www.sequoiahospital.org

SIERRA NEVADA MEMORIAL HOSPITAL (O, 75 beds) 155 Glasson Way, Grass Valley, CA Zip 95945–5723, Mailing Address: P.O. Box 1029, Zip 95945–1029; tel. 530/274–6000; C. Thomas Collier, President and Chief Executive Officer
Web address: www.snmh.org

ST. BERNARDINE MEDICAL CENTER (S, 280 beds) 2101 North Waterman Avenue, San Bernardino, CA Zip 92404–4836; tel. 909/883–8711; Steven R. Barron, President
Web address: www.stbernardinemedicalcenter.com

ST. ELIZABETH COMMUNITY HOSPITAL (S, 64 beds) 2550 Sister Mary Columba Drive, Red Bluff, CA Zip 96080–4397; tel. 530/529–8000; Jon W. Halfhide, President
Web address: www.mercy.org

ST. JOHN'S PLEASANT VALLEY HOSPITAL (S, 163 beds) 2309 Antonio Avenue, Camarillo, CA Zip 93010–1414; tel. 805/389–5800; T. Michael Murray, President
Web address: www.catholichealthcarewest.org

ST. JOHN'S REGIONAL MEDICAL CENTER (S, 218 beds) 1600 North Rose Avenue, Oxnard, CA Zip 93030–3723; tel. 805/988–2500; T. Michael Murray, President
Web address: www.chw.edu

ST. JOSEPH'S BEHAVIORAL HEALTH CENTER (S, 35 beds) 2510 North California Street, Stockton, CA Zip 95204–5502; tel. 209/461–2000; James Sondecker, President
Web address: www.stjosephscanhelp.org

ST. JOSEPH'S MEDICAL CENTER (S, 294 beds) 1800 North California Street, Stockton, CA Zip 95204–6019, Mailing Address: P.O. Box 213008, Zip 95213–3008; tel. 209/943–2000; Donald J. Wiley, President
Web address: www.stjosephsCARES.org

ST. MARY MEDICAL CENTER (S, 236 beds) 1050 Linden Avenue, Long Beach, CA Zip 90801–3393, Mailing Address: P.O. Box 887, Zip 90813–0887; tel. 562/491–9000; Christopher DiCicco, Chief Executive Officer
Web address: www.sc.chw.edu

ST. MARY'S MEDICAL CENTER (S, 232 beds) 450 Stanyan Street, San Francisco, CA Zip 94117–1079; tel. 415/668–1000; Kenneth R. Steele, President
Web address: www.stmarysmedicalcenter.com

WOODLAND HEALTHCARE (O, 111 beds) 1325 Cottonwood Street, Woodland, CA Zip 95695–5199; tel. 530/662–3961; H. Kevin Vaziri, President
Web address: www.chw.edu

NEVADA: ST. ROSE DOMINICAN HOSPITALS – ROSE DE LIMA CAMPUS (S, 138 beds) 102 East Lake Mead Parkway, Henderson, NV Zip 89015–5524; tel. 702/616–5000; Renato V. Baciarelli, President
Web address: www.strosecares.com

ST. ROSE DOMINICAN HOSPITALS – SIENA CAMPUS (S, 214 beds) 3001 St. Rose Parkway, Henderson, NV Zip 89015; tel. 702/616–5000; Rod A. Davis, President and Chief Executive Officer
Web address: www.strosecares.com

Owned, leased, sponsored:	37 hospitals	7849 beds
Contract–managed:	0 hospitals	0 beds
Totals:	37 hospitals	7849 beds

0298:   CENTEGRA HEALTH SYSTEM (NP)
527 West South Street, Woodstock, IL Zip 60098; tel. 815/338–2500; Michael S. Eesley, President and Chief Executive Officer
(Independent Hospital System)

For explanation of codes following names, see page B2.
★ Indicates Type III membership in the American Hospital Association.

ILLINOIS: CENTEGRA MEMORIAL MEDICAL CENTER (O, 140 beds) 3701 Doty Road, Woodstock, IL Zip 60098–3797, Mailing Address: P.O. Box 1990, Zip 60098–1990; tel. 815/338–2500; Michael S. Eesley, President and Chief Executive Officer
Web address: www.centegra.org

CENTEGRA NORTHERN ILLINOIS MEDICAL CENTER (O, 168 beds) 4201 Medical Center Drive, McHenry, IL Zip 60050–9506; tel. 815/344–5000; Michael S. Eesley, President and Chief Executive Officer
Web address: www.centegra.org

Owned, leased, sponsored:	2 hospitals	308 beds
Contract–managed:	0 hospitals	0 beds
Totals:	2 hospitals	308 beds

0321: CENTINELA FREEMAN HEALTHSYSTEM (IO)
555 East Hardy Street, Inglewood, CA Zip 90301; tel. 310/673–4660; Michael A. Rembis, FACHE, Chief Executive Officer

CALIFORNIA: CENTINELA FREEMAN REGIONAL MEDICAL CENTER, CENTINELA CAMPUS (O, 333 beds) 555 East Hardy Street, Inglewood, CA Zip 90301–4011, Mailing Address: P.O. Box 720, Zip 90307–0720; tel. 310/673–4660; Michael A. Rembis, FACHE, Chief Executive Officer
Web address: www.centinelafreeman.com

CENTINELA FREEMAN REGIONAL MEDICAL CENTER, MARINA CAMPUS (O, 90 beds) 4650 Lincoln Boulevard, Marina Del Rey, CA Zip 90292–6360; tel. 310/823–8911; Michael A. Rembis, FACHE, Chief Executive Officer
Web address: www.centinelafreeman.com

CENTINELA FREEMAN REGIONAL MEDICAL CENTER, MEMORIAL CAMPUS (O, 221 beds) 333 North Prairie Avenue, Inglewood, CA Zip 90301–4514; tel. 310/674–7050; Harris Koenig, Chief Executive Officer

Owned, leased, sponsored:	3 hospitals	644 beds
Contract–managed:	0 hospitals	0 beds
Totals:	3 hospitals	644 beds

★0184: CENTRACARE HEALTH SYSTEM (NP)
1406 Sixth Avenue North, Saint Cloud, MN Zip 56303; tel. 320/251–2700; Terrance Pladson, M.D., President and Chief Executive Officer
(Moderately Centralized Health System)

MINNESOTA: LONG PRAIRIE MEMORIAL HOSPITAL AND HOME (O, 120 beds) 20 Ninth Street S.E., Long Prairie, MN Zip 56347–1404; tel. 320/732–2141; Roger Oberg, Administrator
Web address: www.centracare.com

MELROSE AREA HOSPITAL – CENTRA CARE (L, 93 beds) 11 North Fifth Avenue West, Melrose, MN Zip 56352–1098; tel. 320/256–4231; Joan Jackson, Administrator
Web address: www.centracare.com

ST. CLOUD HOSPITAL (O, 425 beds) 1406 Sixth Avenue North, Saint Cloud, MN Zip 56303–1901; tel. 320/251–2700; Craig J. Broman, President and Chief Executive Officer
Web address: www.centracare.com

Owned, leased, sponsored:	3 hospitals	638 beds
Contract–managed:	0 hospitals	0 beds
Totals:	3 hospitals	638 beds

★0955: CHARLESTON AREA MEDICAL CENTER HEALTH SYSTEM, INC. (NP)
501 Morris Street, Charleston, WV Zip 25301–1300, Mailing Address: P.O. Box 1547, Zip 25326–1547; tel. 304/388–5432; David L. Ramsey, President and Chief Executive Officer
(Moderately Centralized Health System)

WEST VIRGINIA: BRAXTON COUNTY MEMORIAL HOSPITAL (O, 25 beds) 100 Hoylman Drive, Gassaway, WV Zip 26624–9320; tel. 304/364–5156; Benjamin Vincent, Administrator
Web address: www.braxmh.org

CHARLESTON AREA MEDICAL CENTER (O, 793 beds) 501 Morris Street, Charleston, WV Zip 25301–1300, Mailing Address: P.O. Box 1547, Zip 25326–1547; tel. 304/388–5432; David L. Ramsey, President and Chief Executive Officer
Web address: www.camc.org

Owned, leased, sponsored:	2 hospitals	818 beds
Contract–managed:	0 hospitals	0 beds
Totals:	2 hospitals	818 beds

0331: CHILDREN'S HOSPITALS AND CLINICS OF MINNESOTA (NP)
2525 Chicago Avenue South, Minneapolis, MN Zip 55404; tel. 612/813–6100; Alan L. Goldbloom, M.D., President and Chief Executive Officer

MINNESOTA: CHILDREN'S HOSPITAL AND CLINICS (O, 126 beds) 345 North Smith Avenue, Saint Paul, MN Zip 55102–2392; tel. 651/220–6000; Alan L. Goldbloom, M.D., President and Chief Executive Officer
Web address: www.childrenshc.org

CHILDREN'S HOSPITALS AND CLINICS (O, 173 beds) 2525 Chicago Avenue South, Minneapolis, MN Zip 55404–9976; tel. 612/813–6100; Alan L. Goldbloom, M.D., President and Chief Executive Officer
Web address: www.childrenshc.org

Owned, leased, sponsored:	2 hospitals	299 beds
Contract–managed:	0 hospitals	0 beds
Totals:	2 hospitals	299 beds

● ★0131: CHRISTIANA CARE HEALTH SYSTEM (NP)
501 West 14th Street, Wilmington, DE Zip 19899, Mailing Address: P.O. Box 1668, Zip 19899; tel. 302/733–1000; Robert J. Laskowski, M.D., President and Chief Executive Officer
(Centralized Physician/Insurance Health System)

DELAWARE: CHRISTIANA CARE HEALTH SYSTEM (O, 865 beds) 501 West 14th Street, Wilmington, DE Zip 19801; tel. 302/428–2570; Robert J. Laskowski, M.D., President and Chief Executive Officer
Web address: www.christianacare.org

Owned, leased, sponsored:	1 hospital	865 beds
Contract–managed:	0 hospitals	0 beds
Totals:	1 hospital	865 beds

★0192: CHRISTUS HEALTH (CC)
6363 North Highway 161, Suite 450, Irving, TX Zip 75038; tel. 877/980–0100; Thomas C. Royer, M.D., President
(Moderately Centralized Health System)

ARKANSAS: MAGNOLIA HOSPITAL (C, 62 beds) 101 Hospital Drive, Magnolia, AR Zip 71753–2416, Mailing Address: P.O. Box 629, Zip 71753–0629; tel. 870/235–3000; Terry L. Amstutz, CHE, Chief Executive Officer
Web address: www.magnoliahospital.org

LOUISIANA: CHRISTUS COUSHATTA HEALTH CARE CENTER (O, 25 beds) 1635 Marvel Street, Coushatta, LA Zip 71019–9022, Mailing Address: P.O. Box 589, Zip 71019–0589; tel. 318/932–2000; Karen Mixon, Interim Administrator
Web address: www.christushealth.org

CHRISTUS SCHUMPERT HEALTH SYSTEM (O, 745 beds) One St. Mary Place, Shreveport, LA Zip 71101–4399; tel. 318/681–4500; Charles J. Paine, M.D., President and Chief Executive Officer
Web address: www.christussantarosa.org

CHRISTUS ST. FRANCES CABRINI HOSPITAL (O, 258 beds) 3330 Masonic Drive, Alexandria, LA Zip 71301–3899; tel. 318/487–1122; Stephen F. Wright, President and Chief Executive Officer
Web address: www.christushealth.org/sfcabrini

CHRISTUS ST. PATRICK HOSPITAL OF LAKE CHARLES (O, 290 beds) 524 South Ryan Street, Lake Charles, LA Zip 70601–5799, Mailing Address: P.O. Box 3401, Zip 70602–3401; tel. 337/436–2511; Ellen M. Jones, President and Chief Executive Officer
Web address: www.sphchristushealth.org

For explanation of codes following names, see page B2.
★ Indicates Type III membership in the American Hospital Association.
● Single hospital health care system

B28 Health Care Systems, Networks and Alliances

© 2005 AHA Guide

NATCHITOCHES PARISH HOSPITAL (C, 190 beds) 501 Keyser Avenue, Natchitoches, LA Zip 71457–6036, Mailing Address: P.O. Box 2009, Zip 71457–2009; tel. 318/214–4200; Mark E. Marley, CHE, Administrator
Web address: www.natchitochesparishhospital.org

TEXAS: CHRISTUS JASPER MEMORIAL HOSPITAL (L, 50 beds) 1275 Marvin Hancock Drive, Jasper, TX Zip 75951–4995; tel. 409/384–5461; Deborah Wiegand, R.N., Chief Executive Officer
Web address: www.christusjasper.org

CHRISTUS SANTA ROSA CHILDREN'S HOSPITAL (O, 187 beds) 333 North Santa Rosa Street, San Antonio, TX Zip 78207; tel. 210/704–2011; Richard Wayne, M.D., Vice President and Administrator
Web address: www.christussantarosa.org/childrenshospital.html

CHRISTUS SANTA ROSA HEALTH CARE (O, 378 beds) 333 North Santa Rosa, San Antonio, TX Zip 78207–3108; tel. 210/704–2011; Don A. Beeler, President and Chief Executive Officer
Web address: www.christussantarosa.org

CHRISTUS SPOHN HOSPITAL ALICE (O, 73 beds) 2500 East Main Street, Alice, TX Zip 78332–4794; tel. 361/661–8000; Margot Rios, Vice President and Administrator
Web address: www.christusspohn.org/locations_alice.htm

CHRISTUS SPOHN HOSPITAL BEEVILLE (L, 63 beds) 1500 East Houston Street, Beeville, TX Zip 78102–5312; tel. 361/354–2000; David S. Wagner, Vice President and Administrator
Web address: www.christushealth.org

CHRISTUS SPOHN HOSPITAL CORPUS CHRISTI MEMORIAL (O, 784 beds) 2606 Hospital Boulevard, Corpus Christi, TX Zip 78405–1818, Mailing Address: P.O. Box 5280, Zip 78465–5280; tel. 361/902–4000; Peter Banko, Vice President and Administrator
Web address: www.christusspohn.org

CHRISTUS SPOHN HOSPITAL KLEBERG (O, 100 beds) 1311 General Cavazos Boulevard, Kingsville, TX Zip 78363–1197, Mailing Address: P.O. Box 1197, Zip 78363–1197; tel. 361/595–9701; Ernesto M. Flores Jr, Vice President and Administrator
Web address: www.christusspohn.org

CHRISTUS ST. CATHERINE HOSPITAL (O, 58 beds) 701 Fry Road, Katy, TX Zip 77450; tel. 281/599–5700; Sheila Fata, Administrator
Web address: www.christusstcatherine.org

CHRISTUS ST. ELIZABETH HOSPITAL (O, 432 beds) 2830 Calder Avenue, Beaumont, TX Zip 77702–1809, Mailing Address: P.O. Box 5405, Zip 77726–5405; tel. 409/892–7171; Joel Fagerstrom, Chief Executive Officer
Web address: www.christusste.org

CHRISTUS ST. JOHN HOSPITAL (O, 128 beds) 18300 St. John Drive, Houston, TX Zip 77058–6302; tel. 281/333–5503; Thomas Permetti, Chief Executive Officer
Web address: www.christushealth.org

CHRISTUS ST. JOSEPH HOSPITAL (O, 433 beds) 1401 St. Joseph Parkway, Houston, TX Zip 77002–8321; tel. 713/757–1000; Jeffrey Webster, Administrator
Web address: www.christusstjoseph.org

CHRISTUS ST. MARY HOSPITAL (O, 196 beds) 3600 Gates Boulevard, Port Arthur, TX Zip 77642–3601, Mailing Address: P.O. Box 3696, Zip 77643–3696; tel. 409/985–7431; Wayne Moore, Administrator
Web address: www.christusstmary.org

CHRISTUS ST. MICHAEL HEALTH SYSTEM (O, 278 beds) 2600 St. Michael Drive, Texarkana, TX Zip 75503–2372; tel. 903/614–1000; Chris Karam, President and Chief Executive Officer
Web address: www.christusstmichael.org

CHRISTUS ST. MICHAEL REHABILITATION HOSPITAL (O, 80 beds) 2400 St. Michael Drive, Texarkana, TX Zip 75503; tel. 903/614–4000; Cookie Gender, Administrator
Web address: www.christusstmichael.org

RICE MEDICAL CENTER (C, 25 beds) 600 South Austin Road, Eagle Lake, TX Zip 77434–3298, Mailing Address: P.O. Box 277, Zip 77434–0277; tel. 979/234–5571; Steven L. Henderson, Administrator
Web address: www.ricemedicalcenter.org

Owned, leased, sponsored:	18 hospitals	4558 beds
Contract–managed:	3 hospitals	277 beds
Totals:	21 hospitals	4835 beds

0101: CITRUS VALLEY HEALTH PARTNERS (NP)
210 West San Bernardino Road, Covina, CA Zip 91723; tel. 626/331–7331; James T. Yoshioka, President and Chief Executive Officer

CALIFORNIA: CITRUS VALLEY MEDICAL CENTER–INTER–COMMUNITY CAMPUS (O, 252 beds) 210 West San Bernardino Road, Covina, CA Zip 91723–1901, Mailing Address: P.O. Box 6108, Zip 91722–5108; tel. 626/331–7331; James T. Yoshioka, President and Chief Executive Officer
Web address: www.cvhp.org

CITRUS VALLEY MEDICAL CENTER–QUEEN OF THE VALLEY CAMPUS (O, 263 beds) 1115 South Sunset Avenue, West Covina, CA Zip 91790–3940, Mailing Address: P.O. Box 1980, Zip 91793–1980; tel. 626/962–4011; James T. Yoshioka, President and Chief Executive Officer
Web address: www.cvhp.org

FOOTHILL PRESBYTERIAN HOSPITAL–MORRIS L. JOHNSTON MEMORIAL (O, 106 beds) 250 South Grand Avenue, Glendora, CA Zip 91741–4218; tel. 626/963–8411; Larry S. Fetters, Administrator
Web address: www.cvhp.org

Owned, leased, sponsored:	3 hospitals	621 beds
Contract–managed:	0 hospitals	0 beds
Totals:	3 hospitals	621 beds

★0231: CLARIAN HEALTH PARTNERS (NP)
I–65 at 21st Street, Indianapolis, IN Zip 46202–5250, Mailing Address: P.O. Box 1367, Zip 46206–1367; tel. 317/962–5900; Daniel F. Evans Jr, President and Chief Executive Officer
(Moderately Centralized Health System)

INDIANA: BEDFORD REGIONAL MEDICAL CENTER (O, 49 beds) 2900 West 16th Street, Bedford, IN Zip 47421–3583; tel. 812/275–1200; Bradford W. Dykes, President and Chief Executive Officer
Web address: www.brmchealthcare.com

CLARIAN HEALTH PARTNERS (O, 1357 beds) I–65 at 21st Street, Indianapolis, IN Zip 46202–5250, Mailing Address: P.O. Box 1367, Zip 46206–1367; tel. 317/962–2000; Daniel F. Evans Jr, President and Chief Executive Officer
Web address: www.clarian.org

CLARIAN WEST MEDICAL CENTER (O, 76 beds) 1111 North Ronald Reagan Parkway, Avon, IN Zip 46123; tel. 317/217–3000; Alfonso W. Gatmaitan, Chief Executive Officer

GOSHEN GENERAL HOSPITAL (O, 116 beds) 200 High Park Avenue, Goshen, IN Zip 46526–4899, Mailing Address: P.O. Box 139, Zip 46527–0139; tel. 574/533–2141; James O. Dague, President and Chief Executive Officer
Web address: www.goshenhealth.com

LA PORTE REGIONAL HEALTH SYSTEM (O, 227 beds) 1007 Lincolnway, La Porte, IN Zip 46350–3201, Mailing Address: P.O. Box 250, Zip 46352–0250; tel. 219/326–1234; Michael E. Haley, President and Chief Executive Officer
Web address: www.laportehealth.org

TIPTON COUNTY MEMORIAL HOSPITAL (C, 75 beds) 1000 South Main Street, Tipton, IN Zip 46072–9799; tel. 765/675–8500; Michael Harlowe, President and Chief Executive Officer
Web address: www.tiptonhospital.org

Owned, leased, sponsored:	5 hospitals	1825 beds
Contract–managed:	1 hospital	75 beds
Totals:	6 hospitals	1900 beds

0212: CLEVELAND CLINIC HEALTH SYSTEM (NP)
9500 Euclid, Cleveland, OH Zip 44195–5108; tel. 216/444–2200; Michael O'Boyle, Chief Operating Officer
(Centralized Health System)

FLORIDA: CLEVELAND CLINIC HOSPITAL–NAPLES (O, 70 beds) 6101 Pine Ridge Road, Naples, FL Zip 34119; tel. 239/348–4468; Geoffrey D. Moebius, Administrator
Web address: www.clevelandclinic.org/florida/naples/hospital/

Section B

For explanation of codes following names, see page B2.
★ Indicates Type III membership in the American Hospital Association.

OHIO: CLEVELAND CLINIC CHILDREN'S HOSPITAL FOR REHABILITATION (O, 47 beds) Cleveland, OH Mailing Address: 2801 Martin Luther King Jr. Drive, Zip 44104–3865; tel. 216/721–5400; David Kenogy, M.D., Medical Director
Web address: www.clevelandclinic.org/childrensrehab

CLEVELAND CLINIC FOUNDATION (O, 1032 beds) 9500 Euclid Avenue, Cleveland, OH Zip 44195–5108; tel. 216/444–2200; Delos Cosgrove, M.D., President and Chief Executive Officer
Web address: www.clevelandclinic.org

EUCLID HOSPITAL (O, 219 beds) 18901 Lake Shore Boulevard, Euclid, OH Zip 44119–1090; tel. 216/531–9000; Lauren Rock, Chief Administrative Officer
Web address: www.meridia.org

FAIRVIEW HOSPITAL (O, 414 beds) 18101 Lorain Avenue, Cleveland, OH Zip 44111–5656; tel. 216/476–7000; Fred M. DeGrandis, Chief Executive Officer
Web address: www.fairviewhospital.org

HILLCREST HOSPITAL (O, 431 beds) 6780 Mayfield Road, Cleveland, OH Zip 44124–2202; tel. 440/449–4500; Glenn Levy, Chief Administrative Officer
Web address: www.meridia.org

HURON HOSPITAL (O, 183 beds) 13951 Terrace Road, Cleveland, OH Zip 44112–4399; tel. 216/761–3300; A. Gus Kious, M.D., Chief Administrative Officer
Web address: www.meridia.org

LAKEWOOD HOSPITAL (O, 334 beds) 14519 Detroit Avenue, Lakewood, OH Zip 44107–4383; tel. 216/521–4200; Jack D. Gustin, Chief Administrative Officer
Web address: www.lakewoodhospital.org

LUTHERAN HOSPITAL (O, 185 beds) 1730 West 25th Street, Cleveland, OH Zip 44113–3170; tel. 216/696–4300; Steve Ruwoldt, Chief Administrative Officer
Web address: www.lutheranhospital.org

MARYMOUNT HOSPITAL (O, 237 beds) 12300 McCracken Road, Garfield Heights, OH Zip 44125–2975; tel. 216/581–0500; David J. Kilarski, President and Chief Executive Officer
Web address: www.marymount.org

SOUTH POINTE HOSPITAL (O, 234 beds) 4110 Warrensville Center Road, Warrensville Heights, OH Zip 44122–7099; tel. 216/491–6000; Beverly Lozar, Chief Administrative Officer
Web address: www.southpointehospital.org

Owned, leased, sponsored:	11 hospitals	3386 beds
Contract–managed:	0 hospitals	0 beds
Totals:	11 hospitals	3386 beds

★0152: COFFEE HEALTH GROUP (NP)
205 Marengo Street, Florence, AL Zip 35630–6033; tel. 256/768–9191; Carl W. Bailey, President and Chief Executive Officer
(Independent Hospital System)

ALABAMA: ELIZA COFFEE MEMORIAL HOSPITAL (O, 322 beds) 205 Marengo Street, Florence, AL Zip 35630–6033, Mailing Address: P.O. Box 818, Zip 35631–0818; tel. 256/768–9191; Carl W. Bailey, Administrator
Web address: www.chgroup.org

SHOALS HOSPITAL (O, 100 beds) 201 Avalon Avenue, Muscle Shoals, AL Zip 35661–2805, Mailing Address: P.O. Box 3359, Zip 35662–3359; tel. 256/386–1600; Jody Pigg, Interim Administrator
Web address: www.chgroup.org

Owned, leased, sponsored:	2 hospitals	422 beds
Contract–managed:	0 hospitals	0 beds
Totals:	2 hospitals	422 beds

0076: COLLEGE HEALTH ENTERPRISES (IO)
11627 Telegraph Road, Suite 200, Santa Fe Springs, CA Zip 90670; tel. 562/923–9449; Barry J. Weiss, Chairman of the Board
(Independent Hospital System)

CALIFORNIA: COLLEGE HOSPITAL (O, 125 beds) 10802 College Place, Cerritos, CA Zip 90703–1579; tel. 562/924–9581; Stephen Witt, Chief Executive Officer
Web address: www.collegehospitals.com

COLLEGE HOSPITAL COSTA MESA (O, 84 beds) 301 Victoria Street, Costa Mesa, CA Zip 92627–7131; tel. 949/642–2734; Wayne M. Lingenfelter, Ed.D., Chief Executive Officer
Web address: www.collegehospitals.com

Owned, leased, sponsored:	2 hospitals	209 beds
Contract–managed:	0 hospitals	0 beds
Totals:	2 hospitals	209 beds

●★0161: COLUMBUS REGIONAL HEALTHCARE SYSTEM (NP)
707 Center Street, Suite 400, Columbus, GA Zip 31901; tel. 706/660–6100; Larry Sanders, FACHE, Chairman and Chief Executive Officer
(Centralized Physician/Insurance Health System)

GEORGIA: THE MEDICAL CENTER (O, 537 beds) 710 Center Street, Columbus, GA Zip 31901–1527, Mailing Address: P.O. Box 951, Zip 31902–0951; tel. 706/571–1000; Lance B. Duke, FACHE, President and Chief Executive Officer
Web address: www.columbusregional.com

Owned, leased, sponsored:	1 hospital	537 beds
Contract–managed:	0 hospitals	0 beds
Totals:	1 hospital	537 beds

0080: COMMUNITY HEALTH SYSTEMS, INC. (IO)
155 Franklin Road, Suite 400, Brentwood, TN Zip 37027–4600, Mailing Address: P.O. Box 217, Zip 37024–0217; tel. 615/373–9600; Wayne T. Smith, Chairman, President and Chief Executive Officer
(Decentralized Health System)

ALABAMA: HARTSELLE MEDICAL CENTER (O, 119 beds) 201 Pine Street N.W., Hartselle, AL Zip 35640–2309, Mailing Address: P.O. Box 969, Zip 35640–0969; tel. 256/773–6511; David R. Jones, Chief Executive Officer
Web address: www.hartsellemedicalcenter.com

L. V. STABLER MEMORIAL HOSPITAL (O, 72 beds) 29 L. V. Stabler Drive, Greenville, AL Zip 36037–3800; tel. 334/382–2671; Daniel L. Perryman, Chief Executive Officer
Web address: www.lvstabler.com

PARKWAY MEDICAL CENTER (O, 120 beds) 1874 Beltline Road S.W., Decatur, AL Zip 35601–5509, Mailing Address: P.O. Box 2211, Zip 35609–2211; tel. 256/350–2211; Tom R. McDougal Jr, Chief Executive Officer

SOUTH BALDWIN REGIONAL MEDICAL CENTER (L, 82 beds) 1613 North McKenzie Street, Foley, AL Zip 36535–2299; tel. 251/949–3400; Stephen Pennington, Chief Executive Officer
Web address: www.southbaldwinrmc.com

WOODLAND MEDICAL CENTER (O, 70 beds) 1910 Cherokee Avenue S.W., Cullman, AL Zip 35055–5502; tel. 256/739–3500; David W. Fuller, Chief Executive Officer
Web address: www.woodlandmedicalcenter.com

ARIZONA: PAYSON REGIONAL MEDICAL CENTER (L, 34 beds) 807 South Ponderosa Street, Payson, AZ Zip 85541–5599; tel. 928/474–3222; R. Chris Wolf, Chief Executive Officer
Web address: www.paysonhospital.com

WESTERN ARIZONA REGIONAL MEDICAL CENTER (O, 115 beds) 2735 Silver Creek Road, Bullhead City, AZ Zip 86442–8303; tel. 928/763–2273; Kenneth W. Randall, Chief Executive Officer
Web address: www.warmc.com

ARKANSAS: HARRIS HOSPITAL (O, 83 beds) 1205 McLain Street, Newport, AR Zip 72112–3533; tel. 870/523–8911; George F. Naylor III, FACHE, Chief Executive Officer
Web address: www.harrishospital.com

HELENA REGIONAL MEDICAL CENTER (L, 100 beds) 1801 Martin Luther King Drive, Helena, AR Zip 72342, Mailing Address: P.O. Box 788, Zip 72342–0788; tel. 870/338–5800; Tom Kinnebrew, Chief Executive Officer
Web address: www.helenaregionalmedicalcenter.com

For explanation of codes following names, see page B2.
★ Indicates Type III membership in the American Hospital Association.
● Single hospital health care system

CALIFORNIA: BARSTOW COMMUNITY HOSPITAL (L, 24 beds) 555 South Seventh Street, Barstow, CA Zip 92311–3086; tel. 760/256–1761; Randall Hempling, Chief Executive Officer
Web address: www.barstowhospital.com

FALLBROOK HOSPITAL (L, 179 beds) 624 East Elder Street, Fallbrook, CA Zip 92028–3099; tel. 760/728–1191; Larry W. Payton, Chief Executive Officer

WATSONVILLE COMMUNITY HOSPITAL (O, 64 beds) 75 Nielson Street, Watsonville, CA Zip 95076–2468; tel. 831/724–4741; Kaylor E. Shemberger, FACHE, Chief Executive Officer
Web address: www.watsonvillehospital.com

FLORIDA: LAKE WALES MEDICAL CENTERS (O, 154 beds) 410 South 11th Street, Lake Wales, FL Zip 33853–4256; tel. 863/676–1433; Carol Negoshian, Administrator
Web address: www.winterhavenhospital.org/fac/lwmc/

NORTH OKALOOSA MEDICAL CENTER (O, 110 beds) 151 Redstone Avenue S.E., Crestview, FL Zip 32539–6026; tel. 850/689–8100; Doug Sills, Chief Executive Officer
Web address: www.nomc.net

GEORGIA: FANNIN REGIONAL HOSPITAL (O, 34 beds) 2855 Old Highway 5, Blue Ridge, GA Zip 30513–6248; tel. 706/632–3711; Michael H. Huff, Interim Chief Executive Officer
Web address: www.fanninregionalhospital.com

ILLINOIS: CROSSROADS COMMUNITY HOSPITAL (O, 41 beds) 8 Doctors Park Road, Mount Vernon, IL Zip 62864–6224; tel. 618/244–5500; Gregory F. Sims, Chief Executive Officer
Web address: www.crossroadscommunityhospital.com

GALESBURG COTTAGE HOSPITAL (O, 150 beds) 695 North Kellogg Street, Galesburg, IL Zip 61401–2885; tel. 309/343–8131; Steven D. Patonai, Chief Executive Officer
Web address: www.cottagehospital.com

HEARTLAND REGIONAL MEDICAL CENTER (O, 84 beds) 3333 West DeYoung, Marion, IL Zip 62959; tel. 618/998–7000; Timothy E. Schmidt, Chief Executive Officer
Web address: www.heartlandregional.com

RED BUD REGIONAL HOSPITAL (O, 190 beds) 325 Spring Street, Red Bud, IL Zip 62278–1194; tel. 618/282–3831; Robert J. Moore, FACHE, Chief Executive Officer
Web address: www.redbudhospital.com

KENTUCKY: KENTUCKY RIVER MEDICAL CENTER (L, 54 beds) 540 Jett Drive, Jackson, KY Zip 41339–9620; tel. 606/666–6000; O. David Bevins, Chief Executive Officer
Web address: www.kentuckyrivermc.com

PARKWAY REGIONAL HOSPITAL (O, 70 beds) 2000 Holiday Lane, Fulton, KY Zip 42041–8468; tel. 270/472–2522; Michael Patterson, Chief Executive Officer

THREE RIVERS MEDICAL CENTER (O, 90 beds) Highway 644, Louisa, KY Zip 41230–9632, Mailing Address: P.O. Box 769, Zip 41230–0769; tel. 606/638–9451; Greg Kiser, Chief Executive Officer
Web address: www.threeriversmedicalcenter.com

LOUISIANA: BYRD REGIONAL HOSPITAL (O, 60 beds) 1020 Fertitta Boulevard, Leesville, LA Zip 71446–4697; tel. 337/239–9041; Roger C. LeDoux, Chief Executive Officer
Web address: www.byrdregional.com

RIVER WEST MEDICAL CENTER (L, 75 beds) 59355 River West Drive, Plaquemine, LA Zip 70764–0737, Mailing Address: P.O. Box 737, Zip 70764–0737; tel. 225/687–9222; Scott Smith, Chief Executive Officer
Web address: www.riverwestmc.com

MISSOURI: MOBERLY REGIONAL MEDICAL CENTER (O, 96 beds) 1515 Union Avenue, Moberly, MO Zip 65270–9449; tel. 660/263–8400; Harold L. Siglar, Chief Executive Officer
Web address: www.moberlyhospital.com

NORTHEAST REGIONAL MEDICAL CENTER (L, 109 beds) 315 South Osteopathy, Kirksville, MO Zip 63501–8599, Mailing Address: P.O. Box C8502, Zip 63501–8599; tel. 660/785–1000; Philip H. Walkley Jr, Chief Executive Officer
Web address: www.nermc.com

NEW JERSEY: MEMORIAL HOSPITAL OF SALEM COUNTY (O, 110 beds) 310 Woodstown Road, Salem, NJ Zip 08079–2080; tel. 856/935–1000; Robert W. Allen, Chief Executive Officer
Web address: www.salemhospitalnj.org

NEW MEXICO: ALTA VISTA REGIONAL HOSPITAL (O, 54 beds) 104 Legion Drive, Las Vegas, NM Zip 87701, Mailing Address: P.O. Box 248, Zip 87701; tel. 505/426–3500; Benjamin J. Everett, Chief Executive Officer
Web address: www.altavistaregionalhospital.com

EASTERN NEW MEXICO MEDICAL CENTER (L, 149 beds) 405 West Country Club Road, Roswell, NM Zip 88201–9981; tel. 505/622–8170; Richard H. Robinson, Chief Executive Officer
Web address: www.enmmc.com

MIMBRES MEMORIAL HOSPITAL (O, 119 beds) 900 West Ash Street, Deming, NM Zip 88030–4098, Mailing Address: P.O. Box 710, Zip 88031–0710; tel. 505/546–2761; Derrick Yu, Chief Executive Officer
Web address: www.mimbresmemorial.com

NORTH CAROLINA: MARTIN GENERAL HOSPITAL (L, 49 beds) 310 South McCaskey Road, Williamston, NC Zip 27892–2150, Mailing Address: P.O. Box 1128, Zip 27892–1128; tel. 252/809–6179; David S. Sanders, Chief Executive Officer
Web address: www.martingeneral.com

PENNSYLVANIA: BERWICK HOSPITAL CENTER (O, 341 beds) 701 East 16th Street, Berwick, PA Zip 18603–2397; tel. 570/759–5000; Alex M. Poirier, Chief Executive Officer
Web address: www.berwick–hospital.com

BRANDYWINE HOSPITAL (O, 164 beds) 201 Reeceville Road, Coatesville, PA Zip 19320–1536; tel. 610/383–8000; Warren E. Callaway, FACHE, Chief Executive Officer
Web address: www.brandywinehospital.com

CHESTNUT HILL HEALTH SYSTEM (O, 212 beds) 8835 Germantown Avenue, Philadelphia, PA Zip 19118–2765; tel. 215/248–8200; Rodney D. Reider, Chief Executive Officer
Web address: www.chh.org

EASTON HOSPITAL (O, 231 beds) 250 South 21st Street, Easton, PA Zip 18042–3892; tel. 610/250–4000; Cornelio R. Catena, President and Chief Executive Officer
Web address: www.easton–hospital.com

JENNERSVILLE REGIONAL HOSPITAL (O, 59 beds) 1015 West Baltimore Pike, West Grove, PA Zip 19390–9499; tel. 610/869–1000; Bryan J. Hargis, President and Chief Executive Officer
Web address: www.jennersville.com

LOCK HAVEN HOSPITAL (O, 195 beds) 24 Cree Drive, Lock Haven, PA Zip 17745–2699; tel. 570/893–5000; John C. Yanes, Chief Executive Officer
Web address: www.lhhospital.com

PHOENIXVILLE HOSPITAL (O, 136 beds) 140 Nutt Road, Phoenixville, PA Zip 19460–3900; tel. 610/983–1000; Steven M. Tullman, Chief Executive Officer
Web address: www.pennhealth.com/phoenix

POTTSTOWN MEMORIAL MEDICAL CENTER (O, 222 beds) 1600 East High Street, Pottstown, PA Zip 19464–5093; tel. 610/327–7000; Martin D. Smith, Chief Executive Officer
Web address: www.pmmctr.org

SOUTH CAROLINA: CHESTERFIELD GENERAL HOSPITAL (L, 59 beds) 711 Chesterfield Highway, Cheraw, SC Zip 29520, Mailing Address: P.O. Box 151, Zip 29520–0151; tel. 843/537–7881; Vance Reynolds, Chief Executive Officer
Web address: www.chesterfieldgeneral.com

MARLBORO PARK HOSPITAL (L, 98 beds) 1138 Cheraw Highway, Bennettsville, SC Zip 29512–0738, Mailing Address: P.O. Box 738, Zip 29512–0738; tel. 843/479–2881; Bobby Ginn, Chief Executive Officer
Web address: www.marlboroparkhospital.com

SPRINGS MEMORIAL HOSPITAL (O, 194 beds) 800 West Meeting Street, Lancaster, SC Zip 29720–2298; tel. 803/286–1214; Daniel E. McKay, Chief Executive Officer
Web address: www.springsmemorial.com

TENNESSEE: CLEVELAND COMMUNITY HOSPITAL (O, 73 beds) 2800 Westside Drive N.W., Cleveland, TN Zip 37312–3599; tel. 423/339–4100; Jim Coleman Jr, Chief Executive Officer
Web address: www.clevelandcommunity.com

DYERSBURG REGIONAL MEDICAL CENTER (O, 105 beds) 400 Tickle Street, Dyersburg, TN Zip 38024–3182; tel. 731/285–2410; R. Coleman Foss, Chief Executive Officer
Web address: www.dyersburgregionalmc.com

For explanation of codes following names, see page B2.
★ Indicates Type III membership in the American Hospital Association.

Section B

HAYWOOD PARK COMMUNITY HOSPITAL (O, 44 beds) 2545 North Washington Avenue, Brownsville, TN Zip 38012–1697; tel. 731/772–4110; Thomas Schmitt, Chief Executive Officer
Web address: www.haywoodparkcommunity.com

HENDERSON COUNTY COMMUNITY HOSPITAL (O, 36 beds) 200 West Church Street, Lexington, TN Zip 38351–2014; tel. 731/968–3646; Holly Fowler, M.D., Administrator

LAKEWAY REGIONAL HOSPITAL (O, 135 beds) 726 McFarland Street, Morristown, TN Zip 37814–3990; tel. 423/586–2302; Priscilla Millis, Chief Executive Officer
Web address: www.lakewayregionalhospital.com

MCKENZIE REGIONAL HOSPITAL (O, 29 beds) 161 Hospital Drive, McKenzie, TN Zip 38201–1636; tel. 731/352–5344; Robert D. Miller, Chief Executive Officer
Web address: www.mckenzieregionalhospital.com

MCNAIRY REGIONAL HOSPITAL (O, 38 beds) 705 East Poplar Avenue, Selmer, TN Zip 38375–1828; tel. 731/645–3221; Pamela W. Roberts, Administrator
Web address: www.mcnairyregionalhospital.com

REGIONAL HOSPITAL OF JACKSON (O, 127 beds) 367 Hospital Boulevard, Jackson, TN Zip 38305–4518; tel. 731/661–2000; Tim Puthoff, Chief Executive Officer
Web address: www.regionalhospital.com

VOLUNTEER COMMUNITY HOSPITAL (O, 65 beds) 161 Mount Pelia Road, Martin, TN Zip 38237–0967; tel. 731/587–4261; Steve Westenhofer, Chief Executive Officer
Web address: www.chs.net

WHITE COUNTY COMMUNITY HOSPITAL (O, 44 beds) 401 Sewell Road, Sparta, TN Zip 38583–1223; tel. 931/738–9211; Mark Cain, Chief Executive Officer
Web address: www.chs.net

TEXAS: BIG BEND REGIONAL MEDICAL CENTER (O, 35 beds) 2600 Highway 118 North, Alpine, TX Zip 79830–2002; tel. 432/837–3447; John Krogness, CHE, Administrator
Web address: www.bigbendhealthcare.com

CLEVELAND REGIONAL MEDICAL CENTER (L, 107 beds) 300 East Crockett Street, Cleveland, TX Zip 77327–4062, Mailing Address: P.O. Box 1688, Zip 77328–1688; tel. 281/593–1811; Jude Torchia, Chief Executive Officer
Web address: www.clevelandregionalmedicalcenter.com

HIGHLAND MEDICAL CENTER (O, 95 beds) 2412 50th Street, Lubbock, TX Zip 79412–2494; tel. 806/788–4100; William W. Weldon, Ph.D., Chief Executive Officer
Web address: www.highlandmedcenter.com

HILL REGIONAL HOSPITAL (O, 84 beds) 101 Circle Drive, Hillsboro, TX Zip 76645–2670; tel. 254/580–8950; Jan McClure, Chief Executive Officer
Web address: www.chs.net

LAKE GRANBURY MEDICAL CENTER (L, 38 beds) 1310 Paluxy Road, Granbury, TX Zip 76048–5699; tel. 817/573–2683; Donnie L. Romine, Chief Executive Officer
Web address: www.lakegranburymedicalcenter.com

LAREDO MEDICAL CENTER (O, 312 beds) 1700 East Saunders Avenue, Laredo, TX Zip 78041–5401, Mailing Address: Drawer 2068, Zip 78044–2068; tel. 956/796–5000; Abraham Martinez, Chief Executive Officer
Web address: www.laredomedical.com

SCENIC MOUNTAIN MEDICAL CENTER (O, 122 beds) 1601 West 11th Place, Big Spring, TX Zip 79720–4198; tel. 432/263–1211; Michael W. Pruitt, Chief Executive Officer
Web address: www.smmccares.com

SOUTH TEXAS REGIONAL MEDICAL CENTER (O, 47 beds) 1905 Highway 97 East, Jourdanton, TX Zip 78026–1504; tel. 830/769–3515; Dennis Barts, Chief Executive Officer
Web address: www.strmc.com

UTAH: MOUNTAIN WEST MEDICAL CENTER (O, 35 beds) 2055 North Main, Tooele, UT Zip 84074–2794; tel. 435/843–3600; Charles A. Davis, Chief Executive Officer
Web address: www.mountainwestmc.com

VIRGINIA: RUSSELL COUNTY MEDICAL CENTER (O, 78 beds) Carroll and Tate Streets, Lebanon, VA Zip 24266–4510, Mailing Address: P.O. Box 3600, Zip 24266–3600; tel. 276/889–1224; David L. Brash, Chief Executive Officer
Web address: www.rcmc.net

SOUTHAMPTON MEMORIAL HOSPITAL (O, 203 beds) 100 Fairview Drive, Franklin, VA Zip 23851–1206, Mailing Address: P.O. Box 817, Zip 23851–0817; tel. 757/569–6100; Sean T. Dardeau, Chief Executive Officer
Web address: www.smhfranklin.com

SOUTHERN VIRGINIA REGIONAL MEDICAL CENTER (O, 154 beds) 727 North Main Street, Emporia, VA Zip 23847–1482; tel. 434/348–4400; Robert D. Towler, Chief Executive Officer
Web address: www.svrmc.com

SOUTHSIDE REGIONAL MEDICAL CENTER (L, 283 beds) 801 South Adams Street, Petersburg, VA Zip 23803–5133; tel. 804/862–5000; David J. Fikse, Chief Executive Officer
Web address: www.srmconline.com

WEST VIRGINIA: PLATEAU MEDICAL CENTER, INC. (O, 25 beds) 430 Main Street, Oak Hill, WV Zip 25901–3455; tel. 304/469–8600; David V. Bunch, Chief Executive Officer
Web address: www.camc.org

WYOMING: EVANSTON REGIONAL HOSPITAL (O, 42 beds) 190 Arrowhead Drive, Evanston, WY Zip 82930–9266; tel. 307/789–3636; R. Clifford Park, Chief Executive Officer
Web address: www.evanstonregionalhospital.com

Owned, leased, sponsored:	67 hospitals	7127 beds
Contract–managed:	0 hospitals	0 beds
Totals:	67 hospitals	7127 beds

0249: COMMUNITY HEALTHCARE SYSTEM (NP)
901 MacArthur Boulevard, Hammond, IN Zip 46321–2959; tel. 219/836–1600; Donald Powers, Chairman, President and Chief Executive Officer
(Moderately Centralized Health System)

INDIANA: COMMUNITY HOSPITAL (O, 362 beds) 901 MacArthur Boulevard, Munster, IN Zip 46321–2959; tel. 219/836–1600; John Gorski, Interim Administrator
Web address: www.comhs.org

ST. CATHERINE HOSPITAL (O, 200 beds) 4321 Fir Street, East Chicago, IN Zip 46312–3097; tel. 219/392–7000; JoAnn Birdzell, President and Chief Executive Officer
Web address: www.stcatherinehospital.org

ST. MARY MEDICAL CENTER (O, 176 beds) 1500 South Lake Park Avenue, Hobart, IN Zip 46342–6699; tel. 219/942–0551; Milton Triana, Administrator
Web address: www.stmary–hobart.com

Owned, leased, sponsored:	3 hospitals	738 beds
Contract–managed:	0 hospitals	0 beds
Totals:	3 hospitals	738 beds

1085: COMMUNITY MEDICAL CENTERS (NP)
Fresno and Maddy Drive, Fresno, CA Zip 93721, Mailing Address: P.O. Box 1232, Zip 93715–1232; tel. 559/459–6000; Tim A. Joslin, President and Chief Executive Officer
(Moderately Centralized Health System)

CALIFORNIA: COMMUNITY BEHAVIORAL HEALTH CENTER (O, 670 beds) 7171 North Cedar Avenue, Fresno, CA Zip 93720–3311; tel. 559/449–8000; Anne Peterson, Director

COMMUNITY MEDICAL CENTER–CLOVIS (O, 110 beds) 2755 Herndon Avenue, Clovis, CA Zip 93611–6800; tel. 559/324–4000; Lori Ruffner, Chief Executive Officer
Web address: www.communitymedical.org

COMMUNITY MEDICAL CENTER–FRESNO (O, 1004 beds) 2823 Fresno Street, Fresno, CA Zip 93721–1324, Mailing Address: P.O. Box 1232, Zip 93715–1232; tel. 559/459–6000; Lori Ruffner, Chief Executive Officer
Web address: www.communitymedical.org

UNIVERSITY MEDICAL CENTER (O, 334 beds) 445 South Cedar Avenue, Fresno, CA Zip 93702–2998; tel. 559/459–4000; Bruce Kinder, R.N., Chief Operating Officer
Web address: www.communitymedical.org

For explanation of codes following names, see page B2.
★ Indicates Type III membership in the American Hospital Association.

Owned, leased, sponsored:	4 hospitals	2118 beds
Contract–managed:	0 hospitals	0 beds
Totals:	4 hospitals	2118 beds

0014: CONNECTICUT DEPARTMENT OF MENTAL HEALTH AND ADDICTION SERVICES (NP)

410 Capitol Avenue, Hartford, CT Zip 06134, Mailing Address: P.O. Box 341431, Zip 06134–1431; tel. 860/418–7000; Thomas A. Kirk Jr, Ph.D., Commissioner
(Independent Hospital System)

CONNECTICUT: CEDARCREST HOSPITAL (O, 135 beds) 525 Russell Road, Newington, CT Zip 06111–1595; tel. 860/666–4613; Susan Graham, R.N., MSN, Chief Executive Officer

CONNECTICUT MENTAL HEALTH CENTER (O, 29 beds) 34 Park Street, New Haven, CT Zip 06519–1187, Mailing Address: P.O. Box 1842, Zip 06508–1842; tel. 203/974–7144; Selby Jacobs, M.D., Chief Executive Officer
Web address: www.dmhas.state.ct.us/lmha.htm

CONNECTICUT VALLEY HOSPITAL (O, 548 beds) Eastern Drive, Middletown, CT Zip 06457–3947, Mailing Address: P.O. Box 351, Zip 06457–0351; tel. 860/262–5000; Garrell S. Mullaney, Chief Executive Officer

SOUTHWEST CONNECTICUT MENTAL HEALTH SYSTEM (O, 62 beds) 97 Middle Street, Bridgeport, CT Zip 06604; tel. 203/551–7400; James M. Pisciotta, Chief Executive Officer

Owned, leased, sponsored:	4 hospitals	774 beds
Contract–managed:	0 hospitals	0 beds
Totals:	4 hospitals	774 beds

★0127: CONTINUUM HEALTH PARTNERS (NP)

555 West 57th Street, New York, NY Zip 10019; tel. 212/523–8130; Stanley Brezenoff, President and Chief Executive Officer
(Centralized Health System)

NEW YORK: BETH ISRAEL MEDICAL CENTER (O, 821 beds) First Avenue and 16th Street, New York, NY Zip 10003–3803; tel. 212/420–2000; David Shulkin, M.D., President and Chief Executive Officer
Web address: www.bethisraelny.org

LONG ISLAND COLLEGE HOSPITAL (O, 432 beds) 339 Hicks Street, Brooklyn, NY Zip 11201–5509; tel. 718/780–1000; Rita Battles, President and Chief Executive Officer
Web address: www.wehealny.org

NEW YORK EYE AND EAR INFIRMARY (O, 32 beds) 310 East 14th Street, New York, NY Zip 10003–4201; tel. 212/979–4000; Joseph P. Corcoran, President and Chief Executive Officer
Web address: www.nyee.edu

ST. LUKE'S–ROOSEVELT HOSPITAL CENTER (O, 718 beds) 1000 Tenth Avenue, New York, NY Zip 10019; tel. 212/523–4000; Richard F. Daines, M.D., President and Chief Executive Officer
Web address: www.slrhc.org

Owned, leased, sponsored:	4 hospitals	2003 beds
Contract–managed:	0 hospitals	0 beds
Totals:	4 hospitals	2003 beds

0016: COOK COUNTY BUREAU OF HEALTH SERVICES (NP)

1900 West Polk Street, Suite 200, Chicago, IL Zip 60612; tel. 312/633–6820; Daniel Winship, Chief
(Moderately Centralized Health System)

ILLINOIS: JOHN H. STROGER JR. HOSPITAL OF COOK COUNTY (O, 460 beds) 1835 West Harrison Street, Chicago, IL Zip 60612–3785; tel. 312/864–6000; Johnny C. Brown, Chief Operating Officer
Web address: www.ccbhs.org

OAK FOREST HOSPITAL OF COOK COUNTY (O, 450 beds) 15900 South Cicero Avenue, Oak Forest, IL Zip 60452–4006; tel. 708/687–7200; Sylvia Edwards, Acting Chief Operating Officer
Web address: www.cookcountygov.com

PROVIDENT HOSPITAL OF COOK COUNTY (O, 119 beds) 500 East 51st Street, Chicago, IL Zip 60615–2494; tel. 312/572–2000; Michele T. Thompson, Interim Chief Operating Officer
Web address: www.ccbhs.org/pages/ProvidentHospitalofCookCounty.htm

Owned, leased, sponsored:	3 hospitals	1029 beds
Contract–managed:	0 hospitals	0 beds
Totals:	3 hospitals	1029 beds

0905: CORNERSTONE HEALTHCARE GROUP (IO)

7600 Chevy Chase Drive, Building 2, Suite 500, Austin, TX Zip 78752, Mailing Address: 7600 Chevy Chase, Building 2, Suite 500, Zip 78752; tel. 512/533–2400; Michael D. Cress, President
(Independent Hospital System)

ARIZONA: CORNERSTONE HOSPITAL OF SOUTHEAST ARIZONA (O, 34 beds) 7220 East Rosewood Drive, Tucson, AZ Zip 85710; tel. 520/546–4595; Louise Cassidy, Chief Executive Officer
Web address: www.cornerstonehealthcaregroup.com

LOUISIANA: CORNERSTONE HOSPITAL OF BOSSIER CITY (O, 54 beds) 4900 Medical Drive, Bossier City, LA Zip 71112–4596; tel. 318/747–9500; Jack Cook, Chief Executive Officer and Administrator

CORNERSTONE HOSPITAL OF SOUTHWEST LOUISIANA (O, 30 beds) 703 Cypress Street, Sulphur, LA Zip 70663; tel. 337/527–1102; Wade K. Lester, Chief Executive Officer

CORNERSTONE HOSPITAL–WEST MONROE (O, 40 beds) 6198 Cypress Street, West Monroe, LA Zip 71291–9010; tel. 318/396–5600; Chris Simpson, Chief Executive Officer

NEW YORK: CORNERSTONE OF MEDICAL ARTS CENTER HOSPITAL (O, 162 beds) 57 West 57th Street, New York, NY Zip 10019–2802; tel. 212/755–0200; Norman J. Sokolow, Chairman and Chief Executive Officer
Web address: www.cornerstoneny.com

OHIO: SPECIALTY HOSPITAL OF LORAIN (C, 30 beds) 205 West 20th Street, Suite 200, Lorain, OH Zip 44052; tel. 440/204–3500; Julia M. Meeks, President and Chief Executive Officer
Web address: www.specialtyhospitaloflorain.com

TEXAS: CORNERSTONE HOSPITAL OF AUSTIN (O, 122 beds) 4207 Burnet Road, Austin, TX Zip 78756–3396; tel. 512/706–1900; Edward J. Sherwood, M.D., Chief Executive Officer
Web address: www.marinerhealthcare.com

CORNERSTONE HOSPITAL OF CENTRAL TEXAS (O, 39 beds) 8402 Cross Park Drive, Austin, TX Zip 78754; tel. 512/837–6233; Edward J. Sherwood, M.D., Chief Executive Officer
Web address: www.cornerstonehealthcaregroup.com

CORNERSTONE HOSPITAL OF HOUSTON (O, 174 beds) 5556 Gasmer Drive, Houston, TX Zip 77035–4598; tel. 713/551–5300; Larry F. Wittgan, Executive Director
Web address: www.marinerhealthcare.com

CORNERSTONE REGIONAL HOSPITAL (O, 14 beds) 2302 Cornerstone Boulevard, Edinburg, TX Zip 78539–8471; tel. 956/618–4444; Linda Resendez, R.N., Administrator and Chief Executive Officer

Owned, leased, sponsored:	9 hospitals	669 beds
Contract–managed:	1 hospital	30 beds
Totals:	10 hospitals	699 beds

★0103: COTTAGE HEALTH SYSTEM (NP)

Pueblo at Bath Streets, Santa Barbara, CA Zip 93105, Mailing Address: P.O. Box 689, Zip 93102–0689; tel. 805/569–7290; Ronald C. Werft, President and Chief Executive Officer
(Independent Hospital System)

CALIFORNIA: GOLETA VALLEY COTTAGE HOSPITAL (O, 109 beds) 351 South Patterson Avenue, Santa Barbara, CA Zip 93111–2496, Mailing Address: Box 6306, Zip 93160–6306; tel. 805/967–3411; Diane Wisby, Administrator
Web address: www.sbch.org

SANTA BARBARA COTTAGE HOSPITAL (O, 307 beds) Pueblo at Bath Streets, Santa Barbara, CA Zip 93105–4390, Mailing Address: P.O. Box 689, Zip 93102–0689; tel. 805/682–7111; Ronald C. Werft, President and Chief Executive Officer
Web address: www.cottagehealthsystem.org

For explanation of codes following names, see page B2.
★ Indicates Type III membership in the American Hospital Association.

SANTA YNEZ VALLEY COTTAGE HOSPITAL (O, 6 beds) 700 Alamo Pintado Road, Solvang, CA Zip 93463–2295; tel. 805/688–6431; Wende Cappetta, Administrator
Web address: www.cottagehealthsystem.org

Owned, leased, sponsored:	3 hospitals	422 beds
Contract–managed:	0 hospitals	0 beds
Totals:	3 hospitals	422 beds

★**0123: COVENANT HEALTH** (NP)
100 Fort Sanders West Boulevard, Knoxville, TN Zip 37922; tel. 865/531–5555; Anthony L. Spezia, President and Chief Executive Officer
(Centralized Physician/Insurance Health System)

TENNESSEE: FORT LOUDOUN MEDICAL CENTER (L, 30 beds) 550 Fort Loudoun Medical Center Drive, Lenoir City, TN Zip 37772; tel. 865/458–8222; Jeffrey Feike, President and Chief Administrative Officer
Web address: www.covenanthealth.com
FORT SANDERS REGIONAL MEDICAL CENTER (O, 431 beds) 1901 Clinch Avenue S.W., Knoxville, TN Zip 37916–2394; tel. 865/541–1111; Keith Altshuler, Administrator
Web address: www.covenanthealth.com
FORT SANDERS–SEVIER MEDICAL CENTER (L, 108 beds) 709 Middle Creek Road, Sevierville, TN Zip 37862–5016, Mailing Address: P.O. Box 8005, Zip 37864–8005; tel. 865/429–6100; Ellen Wilhoit, President and Chief Administrative Officer
Web address: www.covenanthealth.com
METHODIST MEDICAL CENTER OF OAK RIDGE (O, 219 beds) 990 Oak Ridge Turnpike, Oak Ridge, TN Zip 37830–6976, Mailing Address: P.O. Box 2529, Zip 37831–2529; tel. 865/481–1000; Jan McNally, President and Chief Administrative Officer
Web address: www.mccoakridge.com
PARKWEST MEDICAL CENTER (O, 277 beds) 9352 Park West Boulevard, Knoxville, TN Zip 37923–4387, Mailing Address: P.O. Box 22993, Zip 37933–0993; tel. 865/373–1001; Wayne S. Heatherly, President and Chief Administrative Officer
Web address: www.yesparkwest.com

Owned, leased, sponsored:	5 hospitals	1065 beds
Contract–managed:	0 hospitals	0 beds
Totals:	5 hospitals	1065 beds

★**0036: COVENANT HEALTH SYSTEM** (NP)
3615 19th Street, Lubbock, TX Zip 79410–1201; tel. 806/725–1011; Steven L. Hunter, President and Chief Executive Officer
(Decentralized Health System)

NEW MEXICO: NOR–LEA GENERAL HOSPITAL (C, 12 beds) 1600 North Main Avenue, Lovington, NM Zip 88260–2871; tel. 505/396–6611; David B. Shaw, Chief Executive Officer and Administrator
Web address: www.nlgh.org
ROOSEVELT GENERAL HOSPITAL (C, 22 beds) 14121 U.S. Highway 70, Portales, NM Zip 88130, Mailing Address: P.O. Box 868, Zip 88130–0868; tel. 505/359–1800; James P. D'Agostino, Chief Executive Officer

TEXAS: COVENANT CHILDREN'S HOSPITAL (O, 73 beds) 3610 21st Street, Lubbock, TX Zip 79410–1218; tel. 806/725–1011; Steven L. Hunter, President and Chief Executive Officer
Web address: www.covenanthealth.org
COVENANT HOSPITAL PLAINVIEW (L, 31 beds) 2601 Dimmitt Road, Plainview, TX Zip 79072–1833; tel. 806/296–5531; Joe S. Langford, Chief Executive Officer
Web address: www.covenantplainview.org
COVENANT HOSPITAL–LEVELLAND (L, 22 beds) 1900 South College Avenue, Levelland, TX Zip 79336–6508; tel. 806/894–4963; Jerry Osburn, Administrator
Web address: www.covenanthealth.org
COVENANT MEDICAL CENTER (O, 868 beds) 3615 19th Street, Lubbock, TX Zip 79410–1201, Mailing Address: P.O. Box 1201, Zip 79408–1201; tel. 806/725–1011; Steven L. Hunter, President and Chief Executive Officer
Web address: www.covenanthealth.org

CROSBYTON CLINIC HOSPITAL (C, 25 beds) 710 West Main Street, Crosbyton, TX Zip 79322–2143; tel. 806/675–2382; John D. Brock, Chief Executive Officer
LAMB HEALTHCARE CENTER (C, 41 beds) 1500 South Sunset, Littlefield, TX Zip 79339–4899; tel. 806/385–6411; Randall A. Young, Administrator
MEDICAL ARTS HOSPITAL (C, 38 beds) 1600 North Bryan Avenue, Lamesa, TX Zip 79331–3145; tel. 806/872–2183; Charles N. Butts, Chief Executive Officer
Web address: www.medicalartshospital.org
MEMORIAL HOSPITAL (C, 37 beds) 209 N.W. Eighth Street, Seminole, TX Zip 79360–3447; tel. 432/758–5811; Steve Beck, Chief Executive Officer and Administrator
Web address: www.semmem.com
MULESHOE AREA MEDICAL CENTER (C, 25 beds) 708 South First Street, Muleshoe, TX Zip 79347; tel. 806/272–4524; Jim G. Bone, Administrator
Web address: www.mahdservices.org
YOAKUM COUNTY HOSPITAL (C, 24 beds) 412 Mustang Avenue, Denver City, TX Zip 79323–2750, Mailing Address: P.O. Drawer 1130, Zip 79323–1130; tel. 806/592–2121; Clay Taylor, Chief Executive Officer

Owned, leased, sponsored:	4 hospitals	994 beds
Contract–managed:	8 hospitals	224 beds
Totals:	12 hospitals	1218 beds

★**5885: COVENANT HEALTH SYSTEMS, INC.** (CC)
420 Bedford Street, Lexington, MA Zip 02420–1502; tel. 781/862–1634; David R. Lincoln, President and Chief Executive Officer
(Moderately Centralized Health System)

MAINE: ST. MARY'S REGIONAL MEDICAL CENTER (O, 171 beds) 330 Sabattus Street, Lewiston, ME Zip 04240, Mailing Address: P.O. Box 291, Zip 04243–0291; tel. 207/777–8100; James E. Cassidy, President and Chief Executive Officer
Web address: www.stmarysmaine.com

MASSACHUSETTS: YOUVILLE HOSPITAL AND REHABILITATION CENTER (O, 130 beds) 1575 Cambridge Street, Cambridge, MA Zip 02138–4398; tel. 617/876–4344; Daniel P. Leahey, President and Chief Executive Officer
Web address: www.youville.org

NEW HAMPSHIRE: ST. JOSEPH HOSPITAL (O, 144 beds) 172 Kinsley Street, Nashua, NH Zip 03060–3688; tel. 603/882–3000; Peter B. Davis, President and Chief Executive Officer
Web address: www.stjosephhealthcare.com

Owned, leased, sponsored:	3 hospitals	445 beds
Contract–managed:	0 hospitals	0 beds
Totals:	3 hospitals	445 beds

0179: COXHEALTH (NP)
1423 North Jefferson Avenue, Springfield, MO Zip 65802–1988; tel. 417/269–3108; Robert H. Bezanson, President and Chief Executive Officer
(Centralized Physician/Insurance Health System)

MISSOURI: COX MONETT HOSPITAL (O, 47 beds) 801 Lincoln Avenue, Monett, MO Zip 65708–1698; tel. 417/235–3144; Gregory D. Johnson, Administrator and Chief Executive Officer
Web address: www.coxhealth.com
LESTER E. COX MEDICAL CENTERS (O, 719 beds) 1423 North Jefferson Street, Springfield, MO Zip 65802–1988; tel. 417/269–3000; Robert H. Bezanson, President and Chief Executive Officer
Web address: www.coxhealth.com

Owned, leased, sponsored:	2 hospitals	766 beds
Contract–managed:	0 hospitals	0 beds
Totals:	2 hospitals	766 beds

For explanation of codes following names, see page B2.
★ Indicates Type III membership in the American Hospital Association.

★0008: **CROZER–KEYSTONE HEALTH SYSTEM** (NP)
100 West Sproul Road, Springfield, PA Zip 19064;
tel. 610/338–8211; Gerald Miller, President and Chief Executive
Officer
(Centralized Health System)

PENNSYLVANIA: CROZER–CHESTER MEDICAL CENTER (O, 600 beds) One
Medical Center Boulevard, Upland, PA Zip 19013–3995;
tel. 610/447–2000; Joan K. Richards, Chief Executive Officer
Web address: www.crozer.org

DELAWARE COUNTY MEMORIAL HOSPITAL (O, 215 beds) 501 North
Lansdowne Avenue, Drexel Hill, PA Zip 19026–1114; tel. 610/284–8100;
Joan K. Richards, Chief Executive Officer
Web address: www.crozer.org

Owned, leased, sponsored:	2 hospitals	815 beds
Contract–managed:	0 hospitals	0 beds
Totals:	2 hospitals	815 beds

0835: **CUMBERLAND COUNTY HOSPITAL SYSTEM** (NP)
1638 Owen Drive, Fayetteville, NC Zip 28304, Mailing Address: P.O.
Box 2000, Zip 28302–2000; tel. 910/609–4000; Richard H. Parks,
FACHE, Chief Executive Officer
(Moderately Centralized Health System)

NORTH CAROLINA: BEHAVIORAL HEALTH CARE OF CAPE FEAR VALLEY
HEALTH SYSTEM (O, 32 beds) 3425 Melrose Road, Fayetteville, NC
Zip 28304–1695; tel. 910/609–3000; Stanley D. Dodson, Director for
Psychiatric Services
Web address: www.capefearvalley.com

CAPE FEAR VALLEY HEALTH SYSTEM (O, 581 beds) 1638 Owen Drive,
Fayetteville, NC Zip 28304–3431, Mailing Address: P.O. Box 2000,
Zip 28302–2000; tel. 910/609–4000; Richard H. Parks, FACHE, Chief
Executive Officer
Web address: www.capefearvalley.com

Owned, leased, sponsored:	2 hospitals	613 beds
Contract–managed:	0 hospitals	0 beds
Totals:	2 hospitals	613 beds

0239: **DASSEE COMMUNITY HEALTH SYSTEM** (IO)
23186 Blue Star Highway, Quincy, FL Zip 32351, Mailing Address:
P.O. Box 1589, Zip 32353; tel. 850/875–1100; Michael C. Lake,
Chief Executive Officer
(Independent Hospital System)

FLORIDA: CALHOUN–LIBERTY HOSPITAL (O, 25 beds) 20370 N.E. Burns
Avenue, Blountstown, FL Zip 32424–1097, Mailing Address: P.O. Box
419, Zip 32424–0419; tel. 850/674–5411; Ben Burnham, Administrator

GADSDEN COMMUNITY HOSPITAL (O, 25 beds) 23186 Blue Star Highway,
Quincy, FL Zip 32351–2857, Mailing Address: P.O. Box 1979,
Zip 32353–1979; tel. 850/875–1100; Alma Jones, Administrator

GEORGE E. WEEMS MEMORIAL HOSPITAL (O, 25 beds) 135 Avenue G.,
Apalachicola, FL Zip 32320–1613, Mailing Address: P.O. Box 580,
Zip 32329–0580; tel. 850/653–8853; Michael C. Lake, Chief Executive
Officer

Owned, leased, sponsored:	3 hospitals	75 beds
Contract–managed:	0 hospitals	0 beds
Totals:	3 hospitals	75 beds

★1075: **DAUGHTERS OF CHARITY HEALTH SYSTEM** (CC)
26000 Altamont Road, Los Altos Hills, CA Zip 94022;
tel. 650/917–4500; Bain J. Farris, President and Chief Executive
Officer
(Moderately Centralized Health System)

CALIFORNIA: O'CONNOR HOSPITAL (O, 225 beds) 2105 Forest Avenue, San
Jose, CA Zip 95128–1471; tel. 408/947–2500; Robert H. Curry,
President and Chief Executive Officer
Web address: www.oconnorhospital.org

SETON MEDICAL CENTER (O, 263 beds) 1900 Sullivan Avenue, Daly City, CA
Zip 94015–2229; tel. 650/992–4000; Bernadette M. Smith, President and
Chief Executive Officer
Web address: www.setonmedicalcenter.org

SETON MEDICAL CENTER COASTSIDE (O, 121 beds) 600 Marine Boulevard,
Moss Beach, CA Zip 94038–9641; tel. 650/563–7100; Bernadette M. Smith,
President and Chief Executive Officer
Web address: www.setonmedicalcenter.com/coastside

ST. FRANCIS MEDICAL CENTER (O, 353 beds) 3630 East Imperial Highway,
Lynwood, CA Zip 90262–2636; tel. 310/900–8900; Gerald T. Kozai,
President
Web address: www.dochs.org

ST. LOUISE REGIONAL HOSPITAL (O, 93 beds) 9400 No Name Uno, Gilroy,
CA Zip 95020–3528; tel. 408/848–2000; Theodore P. Fox, President and
Chief Operating Officer
Web address: www.dochs.org

ST. VINCENT MEDICAL CENTER (O, 314 beds) 2131 West Third Street, Los
Angeles, CA Zip 90057–7992, Mailing Address: P.O. Box 57992,
Zip 90057–7992; tel. 213/484–7111; Gustavo A. Valdespino, Chief
Executive Officer
Web address: www.stvincentmedicalcenter.com

Owned, leased, sponsored:	6 hospitals	1369 beds
Contract–managed:	0 hospitals	0 beds
Totals:	6 hospitals	1369 beds

1825: **DCH HEALTH SYSTEM** (NP)
809 University Boulevard East, Tuscaloosa, AL Zip 35401;
tel. 205/759–7111; Bryan N. Kindred, President and Chief Executive
Officer
(Moderately Centralized Health System)

ALABAMA: DCH REGIONAL MEDICAL CENTER (O, 414 beds) 809 University
Boulevard East, Tuscaloosa, AL Zip 35401–9961; tel. 205/759–7111;
William H. Cassels, Administrator
Web address: www.dchsystem.com

FAYETTE MEDICAL CENTER (L, 183 beds) 1653 Temple Avenue North,
Fayette, AL Zip 35555–1314, Mailing Address: P.O. Drawer 710,
Zip 35555–0710; tel. 205/932–5966; Harold Reed, Administrator
Web address: www.dchsystem.com

NORTHPORT MEDICAL CENTER (O, 196 beds) 2700 Hospital Drive,
Northport, AL Zip 35476–1079, Mailing Address: P.O. Box 1079,
Zip 35476–1079; tel. 205/333–4500; Charles L. Stewart, Administrator
Web address: www.dchsystem.com

Owned, leased, sponsored:	3 hospitals	793 beds
Contract–managed:	0 hospitals	0 beds
Totals:	3 hospitals	793 beds

0313: **DEACONESS HEALTH SYSTEM** (NP)
600 Mary Street, Evansville, IN Zip 47747; tel. 812/450–5000;
Linda E. White, President and Chief Executive Officer

INDIANA: DEACONESS CROSS POINTE CENTER (O, 60 beds) 7200 East
Indiana Street, Evansville, IN Zip 47715; tel. 812/476–7200; David W.
Morris, Chief Executive Officer
Web address: www.deaconess.com

DEACONESS HOSPITAL (O, 348 beds) 600 Mary Street, Evansville, IN
Zip 47747–0001; tel. 812/450–5000; Linda E. White, President and Chief
Executive Officer
Web address: www.deaconess.com

THE WOMEN'S HOSPITAL (O, 78 beds) 4199 Gateway Boulevard, Newburgh,
IN Zip 47630; tel. 812/842–4200; Christina M. Ryan, Chief Executive Officer
Web address: www.deaconess.com

Owned, leased, sponsored:	3 hospitals	486 beds
Contract–managed:	0 hospitals	0 beds
Totals:	3 hospitals	486 beds

0330: **DEKALB MEDICAL CENTER** (NP)
2701 North Decatur Road, Decatur, GA Zip 30033;
tel. 404/501–1000; Eric P. Norwood, President and Chief Executive
Officer

For explanation of codes following names, see page B2.
★ Indicates Type III membership in the American Hospital Association.

GEORGIA: DEKALB MEDICAL CENTER (O, 389 beds) 2701 North Decatur Road, Decatur, GA Zip 30033–5995; tel. 404/501–1000; Eric P. Norwood, President and Chief Executive Officer
Web address: www.dekalbmedicalcenter.org

DEKALB MEDICAL CENTER AT DECATUR (O, 84 beds) 450 North Candler Street, Decatur, GA Zip 30030–2671; tel. 404/501–6700; Skip Wright, Vice President and Administrator
Web address: www.dekalbmedicalcenter.org

Owned, leased, sponsored:	2 hospitals	473 beds
Contract–managed:	0 hospitals	0 beds
Totals:	2 hospitals	473 beds

9495: DEPARTMENT OF THE AIR FORCE (FG)
1420 Pentagon, Room 4E1084, Washington, DC Zip 20330–1420; tel. 202/767–4765; Lieutenant General George Peach Taylor Jr, M.D., Surgeon General
(Moderately Centralized Health System)

ALASKA: U. S. AIR FORCE REGIONAL HOSPITAL (O, 64 beds) 5955 Zeamer Avenue, Elmendorf AFB, AK Zip 99506–3700; tel. 907/560–6260; Colonel Deborah Kretzchmer, Commander
Web address: www.elmendorf.af.mil/units/3mdg

ARIZONA: U. S. AIR FORCE HOSPITAL LUKE (O, 23 beds) Luke AFB, 7219 North Litchfield Road, Glendale, AZ Zip 85309–1525; tel. 623/856–7502; Colonel Schuyler K. Geller, Commander
Web address: www.luke.af.mil/56mg/

CALIFORNIA: DAVID GRANT MEDICAL CENTER (O, 172 beds) 101 Bodin Circle, Travis AFB, CA Zip 94535–1800; tel. 707/423–7300; Colonel George Johnson, Administrator

COLORADO: U. S. AIR FORCE ACADEMY HOSPITAL (O, 24 beds) 4102 Pinion Drive, USAF Academy, CO Zip 80840–4000; tel. 719/333–5102; Colonel Peter T. Walsh, Commander
Web address: www.usafa.af.mil

DELAWARE: U. S. AIR FORCE HOSPITAL DOVER (O, 16 beds) 300 Tuskegee Boulevard, Dover, DE Zip 19902–7307; tel. 302/677–2525; Colonel Genanne Hansen–Bayless, Administrator

FLORIDA: U. S. AIR FORCE HOSPITAL (O, 12 beds) 8415 Bayshore Boulevard, MacDill AFB, FL Zip 33621–1607; tel. 813/827–9521; Colonel Charles W. Mackett, Commander

U. S. AIR FORCE REGIONAL HOSPITAL (O, 51 beds) 307 Boatner Road, Suite 114, Eglin AFB, FL Zip 32542–1282; tel. 850/883–8221; Lieutenant Colonel Gary S. Forthman, MSC, USAF, Commander

ILLINOIS: SCOTT MEDICAL CENTER (O, 25 beds) 310 West Losey Street, Scott AFB, IL Zip 62225–5252; tel. 618/256–7000; Colonel Steven H. Regner, Administrator
Web address: www.satx.disa.mil/mtf375/

MARYLAND: MALCOLM GROW MEDICAL CENTER (O, 68 beds) 1050 West Perimeter, Andrews AFB, MD Zip 20762–6600, Mailing Address: 1050 West Perimeter, Suite A1–19, Zip 20762–6600; tel. 240/857–3001; Brigadier General William Germann, Commanding Officer
Web address: www.mgmc.af.mil

MISSISSIPPI: U. S. AIR FORCE MEDICAL CENTER KEESLER (O, 185 beds) 301 Fisher Street, Suite 1A132, Keesler AFB, MS Zip 39534–2519; tel. 228/377–6510; Colonel Randy Borg, MSC, USAF, Administrator
Web address: www.81mdg06.keesler.af.mil/index.cgi

NEVADA: MIKE O'CALLAGHAN FEDERAL HOSPITAL (O, 94 beds) 4700 Las Vegas Boulevard North, Suite 2419, Nellis AFB, NV Zip 89191–6601; tel. 702/653–2000; Colonel John Korlaske, MSC, Administrator

OHIO: WRIGHT PATTERSON MEDICAL CENTER (O, 70 beds) 4881 Sugar Maple Drive, Wright–Patterson AFB, OH Zip 45433–5529; tel. 937/257–0837; Colonel Loretta Bailey, Administrator
Web address: www.wpmc1.wpafb.af.mil

SOUTH CAROLINA: U. S. AIR FORCE HOSPITAL SHAW (O, 11 beds) 431 Meadowlark Street, Shaw AFB, SC Zip 29152–5019; tel. 803/895–6324; Colonel Troy Molnar, Commander
Web address: www.shaw.af.mil

TEXAS: U. S. AIR FORCE REGIONAL HOSPITAL–SHEPPARD (O, 65 beds) 149 Hart Street, Suite 1, Sheppard AFB, TX Zip 76311–3478; tel. 940/676–5874; Lieutenant Colonel Joseph Kennedy, Administrator
Web address: www.sheppard.af.mil

WILFORD HALL MEDICAL CENTER (O, 284 beds) 2200 Bergquist Drive, Suite 1, Lackland AFB, TX Zip 78236–5300; tel. 210/292–7412; Colonel Marc M. Sager, Administrator
Web address: www.whmc.af.mil

VIRGINIA: U. S. AIR FORCE HOSPITAL (O, 59 beds) 45 Pine Street, Hampton, VA Zip 23665–2080; tel. 757/764–6969; Colonel David C. Houglum, MC, Administrator

Owned, leased, sponsored:	16 hospitals	1223 beds
Contract–managed:	0 hospitals	0 beds
Totals:	16 hospitals	1223 beds

9395: DEPARTMENT OF THE ARMY, OFFICE OF THE SURGEON GENERAL (FG)
5109 Leesburg Pike, Falls Church, VA Zip 22041; tel. 703/681–3000; Lieutenant General Kevin C. Kiley, M.D., Surgeon General
(Moderately Centralized Health System)

ALABAMA: LYSTER U. S. ARMY COMMUNITY HOSPITAL (O, 37 beds) U.S. Army Aeromedical Center, Fort Rucker, AL Zip 36362–5333; tel. 334/255–7361; Colonel Suzan Denny, Commanding Officer
Web address: www.rucker.amedd.army.mil

ALASKA: BASSETT ARMY COMMUNITY HOSPITAL (O, 32 beds) 1060 Gaffney Road, Box 7400, Fort Wainwright, AK Zip 99703–7400; tel. 907/353–5172; Colonel Koji Nishimura, Commander
Web address: www.alaska.amedd.army.mil

CALIFORNIA: WEED ARMY COMMUNITY HOSPITAL (O, 19 beds) Fort Irwin, CA Mailing Address: P.O. Box 105109, Zip 92310–5109; tel. 760/380–3108; Colonel Ronald Eskew, Commander
Web address: www.irwin.amedd.army.mil

COLORADO: EVANS U. S. ARMY COMMUNITY HOSPITAL (O, 78 beds) 7500 Cochrane Circle, Fort Carson, CO Zip 80913–5101; tel. 719/526–7200; Colonel Brian C. Lein, Commander
Web address: www.evans.amedd.army.mil

DISTRICT OF COLUMBIA: WALTER REED ARMY MEDICAL CENTER (O, 261 beds) 6900 Georgia Avenue N.W., Washington, DC Zip 20307–5001; tel. 202/782–6395; Colonel James K. Gilman, Commander
Web address: www.wramc.amedd.army.mil

GEORGIA: DWIGHT DAVID EISENHOWER ARMY MEDICAL CENTER (O, 111 beds) Hospital Drive, Building 300, Fort Gordon, GA Zip 30905–5650; tel. 706/787–5811; Colonel Donald M. Bradshaw, Commander
Web address: www.ddeamc.amedd.army.mil

MARTIN ARMY COMMUNITY HOSPITAL (O, 62 beds) 7950 Martin Loop, Fort Benning, GA Zip 31905–6100, Mailing Address: P.O. Box 56100, Building 9200, Zip 31905–6100; tel. 706/544–2516; Colonel Margaret Rivera, Commander
Web address: www.martin.amedd.army.mil

WINN ARMY COMMUNITY HOSPITAL (O, 79 beds) 1061 Harmon Avenue, Hinesville, GA Zip 31314–5611; tel. 912/435–6965; Colonel Scott Goodrich, Commander

HAWAII: TRIPLER ARMY MEDICAL CENTER (O, 209 beds) 1 Jarret White Road, Honolulu, HI Zip 96859–5000; tel. 808/433–6661; Major General Gale Pollock, Commander
Web address: www.tamc.amedd.army.mil

KANSAS: IRWIN ARMY COMMUNITY HOSPITAL (O, 27 beds) 600 Caisson Hill Road, Junction City, KS Zip 66442–5037; tel. 785/239–7555; Colonel Marilyn Brooks, Commander
Web address: www.iach.amedd.army.mil

KENTUCKY: COLONEL FLORENCE A. BLANCHFIELD ARMY COMMUNITY HOSPITAL (O, 107 beds) 650 Joel Drive, Fort Campbell, KY Zip 42223–5349; tel. 270/798–8040; Colonel Patricia A. H. Saulsbery, Commander
Web address: www.198.250.216.210/

IRELAND ARMY COMMUNITY HOSPITAL (O, 76 beds) 851 Ireland Avenue, Fort Knox, KY Zip 40121–5520; tel. 502/624–0467; Colonel Carol Pierce, Commander

For explanation of codes following names, see page B2.
★ Indicates Type III membership in the American Hospital Association.

LOUISIANA: BAYNE–JONES ARMY COMMUNITY HOSPITAL (O, 33 beds) 1585 Third Street, Fort Polk, LA Zip 71459–5110; tel. 337/531–3928; Colonel Steven Swann, Deputy Commander for Clinical Services
Web address: www.polk.amedd.army.mil

MARSHALL ISLANDS: KWAJALEIN HOSPITAL (O, 100 beds) U.S. Army Kwajalein Atoll, Kwajalein Island, MH Zip 96960, Mailing Address: Box 1702, APO, APZip 96555–5000; tel. 805/355–2225; Elaine McMahon, Administrator

MISSOURI: GENERAL LEONARD WOOD ARMY COMMUNITY HOSPITAL (O, 62 beds) 126 Missouri Avenue, Fort Leonard Wood, MO Zip 65473–8952; tel. 573/596–0414; Colonel Sharon DeRuvo, Commander
Web address: www.glwach.leonardwood.amedd.army.mil

NEW YORK: KELLER ARMY COMMUNITY HOSPITAL (O, 35 beds) U.S. Military Academy, West Point, NY Zip 10996–1197; tel. 845/938–5169; Colonel Peter G. Torok, Commander
Web address: www.wramc.amedd.army.mil/wp

NORTH CAROLINA: WOMACK ARMY MEDICAL CENTER (O, 129 beds) Normandy Drive, Fort Bragg, NC Zip 28307–5000; tel. 910/907–6000; Colonel Ronald Maul, Commander
Web address: www.wamc.amedd.army.mil/

OKLAHOMA: REYNOLDS ARMY COMMUNITY HOSPITAL (O, 32 beds) 4301 Mow–way Street, Fort Sill, OK Zip 73503–6300; tel. 580/458–3000; Colonel Frederick A. Swiderski, Commander
Web address: www.rach.sill.amedd.army.mil

SOUTH CAROLINA: MONCRIEF ARMY COMMUNITY HOSPITAL (O, 60 beds) 4500 Stuart Street, Fort Jackson, SC Zip 29207–5720; tel. 803/751–2284; Colonel James M. Baunchalk, Commander
Web address: www.moncrief.amedd.army.mil

TEXAS: BROOKE ARMY MEDICAL CENTER (O, 226 beds) 3851 Roger Brookes Drive, Fort Sam Houston, TX Zip 78234–6200; tel. 210/916–4141; Brigadier General C. William Fox Jr, Deputy Commander for Administration
Web address: www.gprmc.amedd.army.mil

DARNALL ARMY COMMUNITY HOSPITAL (O, 109 beds) 36000 Darnall Loop, Fort Hood, TX Zip 76544–4752; tel. 254/288–8000; Colonel Bernard DeKoning, Commander
Web address: www.hood–meddac.army.mil

WILLIAM BEAUMONT ARMY MEDICAL CENTER (O, 209 beds) 5005 North Piedras Street, El Paso, TX Zip 79920–5001; tel. 915/569–2121; Colonel James J. Leach, MC, Commander
Web address: www.wbamc.amedd.army.mil

VIRGINIA: DEWITT ARMY COMMUNITY HOSPITAL (O, 43 beds) 9501 Farrell Road, Fort Belvoir, VA Zip 22060–5901, Mailing Address: 9501 Farrell Road, Suite GC11, Zip 22060–5901; tel. 703/805–0510; Colonel Patricia Horoho, Commander
Web address: www.dewitt.wramc.amedd.army.mil

MCDONALD ARMY COMMUNITY HOSPITAL (O, 30 beds) Jefferson Avenue, Fort Eustis, VA Zip 23604–5548; tel. 757/314–7501; Colonel Steven Hunte, Commander
Web address: www.narmc.amedd.army.mil/mcdonald/

WASHINGTON: MADIGAN ARMY MEDICAL CENTER (O, 169 beds) Fitzsimmons Drive, Building 9040, Tacoma, WA Zip 98431–1100; tel. 253/968–1110; Brigadier General Michael A. Dunn, M.D., Commanding General
Web address: www.mamc.amedd.army.mil

Owned, leased, sponsored:	25 hospitals	2335 beds
Contract–managed:	0 hospitals	0 beds
Totals:	25 hospitals	2335 beds

9295: DEPARTMENT OF VETERANS AFFAIRS (FG)
810 Vermont Avenue N.W., Washington, DC Zip 20420; tel. 202/273–5781; Jonathan Perlin, Acting Secretary
(Decentralized Health System)

ALABAMA: CENTRAL ALABAMA VETERANS HEALTH CARE SYSTEM (O, 270 beds) 215 Perry Hill Road, Montgomery, AL Zip 36109–3798; tel. 334/272–4670; N. Rao Chava, M.D., Director
Web address: www.va.gov/sta/guide/home.asp

VETERANS AFFAIRS MEDICAL CENTER (O, 134 beds) 700 South 19th Street, Birmingham, AL Zip 35233–1927; tel. 205/933–8101; Y. C. Parris, Director
Web address: www.va.gov/sta/guide/home.asp

VETERANS AFFAIRS MEDICAL CENTER (O, 324 beds) 3701 Loop Road, Tuscaloosa, AL Zip 35404–5015; tel. 205/554–2000; W. Kenneth Ruyle, Director
Web address: www.va.gov/sta/guide/home.asp

ARIZONA: CARL T. HAYDEN VETERANS AFFAIRS MEDICAL CENTER (O, 188 beds) 650 East Indian School Road, Phoenix, AZ Zip 85012–1892; tel. 602/277–5551; John R. Fears, Director
Web address: www.phoenix.med.va.gov

NORTHERN ARIZONA VA HEALTH CARE SYSTEM (O, 236 beds) 500 Highway 89 North, Prescott, AZ Zip 86313–5000; tel. 928/445–4860; Deborah A. Thompson, Director
Web address: www.va.gov/sta/guide/home.asp

SOUTHERN ARIZONA VETERANS AFFAIRS HEALTH CARE SYSTEM (O, 279 beds) 3601 South 6th Avenue, Tucson, AZ Zip 85723–0002; tel. 520/792–1450; Jonathan H. Gardner, Chief Executive Officer
Web address: www.va.gov/sta/guide/home.asp

ARKANSAS: CENTRAL ARKANSAS VETERANS HEALTHCARE SYSTEM (O, 551 beds) 4300 West Seventh Street, Little Rock, AR Zip 72205–5484; tel. 501/257–1000; Nicholas P. Lang, M.D., Interim Director
Web address: www.va.gov/sta/guide/home.asp

VETERANS AFFAIRS MEDICAL CENTER (O, 53 beds) 1100 North College Avenue, Fayetteville, AR Zip 72703–6995; tel. 479/443–4301; Michael R. Winn, Director
Web address: www.va.gov/sta/guide/home.asp

CALIFORNIA: JERRY L. PETTIS MEMORIAL VETERANS MEDICAL CENTER (O, 205 beds) 11201 Benton Street, Loma Linda, CA Zip 92357; tel. 909/825–7084; Dean R. Stordahl, Director
Web address: www.va.gov/sta/guide/home.asp

VETERANS AFFAIRS GREATER LOS ANGELES HEALTHCARE SYSTEM (O, 589 beds) 11301 Wilshire Boulevard, Los Angeles, CA Zip 90073–1003; tel. 310/478–3711; Charles M. Dorman, Acting Director
Web address: www.va.gov/sta/guide/home.asp

VETERANS AFFAIRS LONG BEACH HEALTHCARE SYSTEM (O, 327 beds) 5901 East Seventh Street, Long Beach, CA Zip 90822–5201; tel. 562/826–8000; Ronald Norby, Director
Web address: www.long–beach.va.gov

VETERANS AFFAIRS MEDICAL CENTER (O, 125 beds) 2615 East Clinton Avenue, Fresno, CA Zip 93703–2223; tel. 559/225–6100; Alan S. Perry, Director
Web address: www.fresno.med.va.gov

VETERANS AFFAIRS MEDICAL CENTER (O, 244 beds) 4150 Clement Street, San Francisco, CA Zip 94121–1598; tel. 415/221–4810; Sheila M. Cullen, Director
Web address: www.va.gov/sta/guide/home.asp

VETERANS AFFAIRS PALO ALTO HEALTH CARE SYSTEM (O, 913 beds) 3801 Miranda Avenue, Palo Alto, CA Zip 94304–1207; tel. 650/493–5000; Elizabeth Joyce Freeman, Director
Web address: www.va.gov/sta/guide/home.asp

VETERANS AFFAIRS SAN DIEGO HEALTHCARE SYSTEM (O, 238 beds) 3350 LaJolla Village Drive, San Diego, CA Zip 92161–0002; tel. 858/552–8585; Gary J. Rossio, Director
Web address: www.va.gov/sta/guide/home.asp

COLORADO: VETERANS AFFAIRS EASTERN COLORADO HEALTH CARE SYSTEM (O, 228 beds) 1055 Clermont Street, Denver, CO Zip 80220–3877; tel. 303/399–8020; Ed Thorsland Jr, Director
Web address: www.va.gov/sta/guide/home.asp

VETERANS AFFAIRS MEDICAL CENTER (O, 53 beds) 2121 North Avenue, Grand Junction, CO Zip 81501–6499; tel. 970/242–0731; William R. Berryman, M.D., Acting Director
Web address: www.va.gov/sta/guide/home.asp

CONNECTICUT: VETERANS AFFAIRS CONNECTICUT HEALTHCARE SYSTEM–NEW HAVEN DIVISION (O, 200 beds) 950 Campbell Avenue, West Haven, CT Zip 06516–2770; tel. 203/932–5711; Roger L. Johnson, Director
Web address: www.va.gov/sta/guide/home.asp

DELAWARE: VETERANS AFFAIRS MEDICAL CENTER (O, 118 beds) 1601 Kirkwood Highway, Wilmington, DE Zip 19805–4989; tel. 302/994–2511; Richard S. Citron, Director
Web address: www.va.gov/sta/guide/home.asp

For explanation of codes following names, see page B2.
★ Indicates Type III membership in the American Hospital Association.

Section B

DISTRICT OF COLUMBIA: VETERANS AFFAIRS MEDICAL CENTER (O, 291 beds) 50 Irving Street N.W., Washington, DC Zip 20422–0002; tel. 202/745–8100; Sanford M. Garfunkel, Director
Web address: www.va.gov/sta/guide/home.asp

FLORIDA: JAMES A. HALEY VETERANS HOSPITAL (O, 321 beds) 13000 Bruce B. Downs Boulevard, Tampa, FL Zip 33612–4798; tel. 813/972–2000; Forest Farley, Director
Web address: www.va.gov/visn8/tampa

MALCOM RANDALL VETERANS AFFAIRS MEDICAL CENTER (O, 589 beds) 1601 S.W. Archer Road, Gainesville, FL Zip 32608–1197; tel. 352/376–1611; Frederick L. Malphurs, Director
Web address: www.va.gov/visn8/nfsg

VETERANS AFFAIRS MEDICAL CENTER (O, 469 beds) 10000 Bay Pines Boulevard, Bay Pines, FL Zip 33744, Mailing Address: P.O. Box 5005, Zip 33744–5005; tel. 727/398–6661; Wallace M. Hopkins, FACHE, Director
Web address: www.va.gov/sta/guide/home.asp

VETERANS AFFAIRS MEDICAL CENTER (O, 186 beds) 7305 North Military Trail, West Palm Beach, FL Zip 33410–6400; tel. 561/422–8262; Edward H. Seiler, Director
Web address: www.va.gov/sta/guide/home.asp

VETERANS AFFAIRS MEDICAL CENTER (O, 347 beds) 1201 N.W. 16th Street, Miami, FL Zip 33125–1624; tel. 305/575–7000; Stephen M. Lucas, FACHE, Director
Web address: www.va.gov/miami

VETERANS AFFAIRS MEDICAL CENTER (O, 360 beds) 619 South Marion Avenue, Lake City, FL Zip 32025–5898; tel. 386/755–3016; Frederick L. Malphurs, Director
Web address: www.va.gov/sta/guide/home.asp

GEORGIA: CARL VINSON VETERANS AFFAIRS MEDICAL CENTER (O, 339 beds) 1826 Veterans Boulevard, Dublin, GA Zip 31021–3620; tel. 478/272–1210; Richard W. Fry, Director
Web address: www.va.gov/sta/guide/home.asp

VETERANS AFFAIRS MEDICAL CENTER (O, 173 beds) 1670 Clairmont Road, Decatur, GA Zip 30033–4004; tel. 404/321–6111; Thomas A. Cappello, Director
Web address: www.va.gov/sta/guide/home.asp

VETERANS AFFAIRS MEDICAL CENTER (O, 305 beds) 1 Freedom Way, Augusta, GA Zip 30904–6285; tel. 706/733–0188; James F. Trusley III, Director
Web address: www.va.gov/sta/guide/home.asp

IDAHO: VETERANS AFFAIRS MEDICAL CENTER (O, 176 beds) 500 West Fort Street, Boise, ID Zip 83702–4598; tel. 208/422–1000; Wayne C. Tippets, Director
Web address: www.va.gov/sta/guide/home.asp

ILLINOIS: JESSE BROWN VETERANS AFFAIRS CHICAGO HEALTH CARE SYSTEM (O, 205 beds) 820 South Damen, Chicago, IL Zip 60612–3776; tel. 312/569–8387; Stan Johnson, Acting Director
Web address: www.va.gov/sta/guide/home.asp

VETERANS AFFAIRS EDWARD HINES, JR. HOSPITAL (O, 484 beds) Fifth Avenue and Roosevelt Road, Hines, IL Zip 60141–5000, Mailing Address: P.O. Box 5000, Zip 60141–5000; tel. 708/202–8387; Jack G. Hetrick, Director
Web address: www.va.gov/sta/guide/home.asp

VETERANS AFFAIRS ILLIANA HEALTH CARE SYSTEM (O, 370 beds) 1900 East Main Street, Danville, IL Zip 61832–5198; tel. 217/554–3000; Cathi Spivey–Paul, Acting Director
Web address: www.va.gov/sta/guide/home.asp

VETERANS AFFAIRS MEDICAL CENTER (O, 520 beds) 3001 Green Bay Road, North Chicago, IL Zip 60064–3049; tel. 847/688–1900; Patrick L. Sullivan, Director
Web address: www.va.gov/sta/guide/home.asp

VETERANS AFFAIRS MEDICAL CENTER (O, 115 beds) 2401 West Main Street, Marion, IL Zip 62959–1194; tel. 618/997–5311; Robert D. Morrel, Director
Web address: www.va.gov/sta/guide/home.asp

INDIANA: RICHARD L. ROUDEBUSH VETERANS AFFAIRS MEDICAL CENTER (O, 150 beds) 1481 West Tenth Street, Indianapolis, IN Zip 46202–2884; tel. 317/554–0000; Susan P. Bowers, Director
Web address: www.va.gov/sta/guide/home.asp

VETERANS AFFAIRS NORTHERN INDIANA HEALTH CARE SYSTEM (O, 423 beds) 2121 Lake Avenue, Fort Wayne, IN Zip 46805–5347; tel. 260/460–1310; Robert H. Beller, Acting Director

IOWA: VETERANS AFFAIRS CENTRAL IOWA HEALTH CARE SYSTEM (O, 327 beds) 3600 30th Street, Des Moines, IA Zip 50310–5774; tel. 515/699–5999; Donald C. Cooper, Director
Web address: www.va.gov/sta/guide/home.asp

VETERANS AFFAIRS MEDICAL CENTER (O, 93 beds) 601 Highway 6 West, Iowa City, IA Zip 52246–2208; tel. 319/338–0581; Gary L. Wilkinson, Director
Web address: www.va.gov/sta/guide/home.asp

KANSAS: ROBERT J. DOLE VETERANS AFFAIRS MEDICAL CENTER (O, 71 beds) 5500 East Kellogg, Wichita, KS Zip 67218; tel. 316/685–2221; Thomas J. Sanders, CHE, Director
Web address: www.va.gov/sta/guide/home.asp

VETERANS AFFAIRS EASTERN KANSAS HEALTH CARE SYSTEM (O, 597 beds) 2200 Gage Boulevard, Topeka, KS Zip 66622–0002; tel. 785/350–3111; Robert M. Malone Jr, Director
Web address: www.va.gov/sta/guide/home.asp

KENTUCKY: VETERANS AFFAIRS MEDICAL CENTER–LEXINGTON (O, 168 beds) 2250 Leestown Pike, Lexington, KY Zip 40511–1093; tel. 859/233–4511; Forest Farley, Director
Web address: www.va.gov/sta/guide/home.asp

VETERANS AFFAIRS MEDICAL CENTER–LOUISVILLE (O, 110 beds) 800 Zorn Avenue, Louisville, KY Zip 40206–1499; tel. 502/895–3401; Timothy P. Shea, FACHE, Director
Web address: www.va.gov/603louisville

LOUISIANA: OVERTON BROOKS VETERANS AFFAIRS MEDICAL CENTER (O, 112 beds) 510 East Stoner Avenue, Shreveport, LA Zip 71101–4295; tel. 318/221–8411; George M. Moore Jr, Director
Web address: www.va.gov/sta/guide/home.asp

VETERANS AFFAIRS MEDICAL CENTER (O, 292 beds) 2495 Shreveport Highway, 71 North, Alexandria, LA Zip 71306–6002, Mailing Address: P.O. Box 69004, Zip 71306–9004; tel. 318/473–0010; Barbara C. Watkins, Director
Web address: www.va.gov/sta/guide/home.asp

VETERANS AFFAIRS MEDICAL CENTER (O, 206 beds) 1601 Perdido Street, New Orleans, LA Zip 70112–1262; tel. 504/568–0811; John D. Church Jr, FACHE, Director
Web address: www.va.gov/new–orleans

MAINE: VETERANS AFFAIRS MEDICAL CENTER (O, 167 beds) 1 VA Center, Togus, ME Zip 04330; tel. 207/623–8411; John H. Sims Jr, Director
Web address: www.visn1.med.va.gov/togus/

MARYLAND: VETERANS AFFAIRS MARYLAND HEALTH CARE SYSTEM–BALTIMORE DIVISION (O, 754 beds) 10 North Greene Street, Baltimore, MD Zip 21201–1524; tel. 410/605–7001; Dennis H. Smith, Director
Web address: www.va.gov/sta/guide/home.asp

MASSACHUSETTS: BROCKTON VETERANS AFFAIRS MEDICAL CENTER (O, 531 beds) 940 Belmont Street, Brockton, MA Zip 02401–5596; tel. 508/583–4500; Michael E. Lawson, Director
Web address: www.va.gov/sta/guide/home.asp

EDITH NOURSE ROGERS MEMORIAL VETERANS HOSPITAL (O, 453 beds) 200 Springs Road, Bedford, MA Zip 01730–1198; tel. 781/687–2000; William A. Conte, Director
Web address: www.va.gov/sta/guide/home.asp

VETERANS AFFAIRS BOSTON HEALTHCARE SYSTEM (O, 531 beds) 1400 VFW Parkway, Boston, MA Zip 02132; tel. 617/232–9500; Michael M. Lawson, Director
Web address: www.va.gov/sta/guide/home.asp

VETERANS AFFAIRS MEDICAL CENTER (O, 181 beds) 421 North Main Street, Leeds, MA Zip 01053–9764; tel. 413/584–4040; Bruce A. Gordon, Director
Web address: www.va.gov/sta/guide/home.asp

MICHIGAN: ALEDA E. LUTZ VETERANS AFFAIRS MEDICAL CENTER (O, 114 beds) 1500 Weiss Street, Saginaw, MI Zip 48602–5298; tel. 989/497–2500; Gabriel Perez, Chief Executive Officer and Medical Director
Web address: www.va.gov/sta/guide/home.asp

JOHN D. DINGELL VETERANS AFFAIRS MEDICAL CENTER (O, 217 beds) 4646 John R Street, Detroit, MI Zip 48201–1932; tel. 313/576–1000; Michael K. Wheeler, Director
Web address: www.va.gov/sta/guide/home.asp

For explanation of codes following names, see page B2.
★ Indicates Type III membership in the American Hospital Association.

VETERANS AFFAIRS ANN ARBOR HEALTHCARE SYSTEM (O, 140 beds) 2215 Fuller Road, Ann Arbor, MI Zip 48105-2399; tel. 734/769-7100; James W. Roseborough, CHE, Director
Web address: www.va.gov/sta/guide/home.asp

VETERANS AFFAIRS MEDICAL CENTER (O, 368 beds) 5500 Armstrong Road, Battle Creek, MI Zip 49015; tel. 269/966-5600; Alice L. Wood, Director
Web address: www.va.gov/sta/guide/home.asp

VETERANS AFFAIRS MEDICAL CENTER (O, 57 beds) 325 East H Street, Iron Mountain, MI Zip 49801-4792; tel. 906/774-3300; Janice M. Boss, CHE, Director
Web address: www.va.gov/sta/guide/home.asp

MINNESOTA: VETERANS AFFAIRS MEDICAL CENTER (O, 340 beds) One Veterans Drive, Minneapolis, MN Zip 55417-2399; tel. 612/725-2000; Steven Kleinglass, Director
Web address: www.va.gov/sta/guide/home.asp

VETERANS AFFAIRS MEDICAL CENTER (O, 391 beds) 4801 Veterans Drive, Saint Cloud, MN Zip 56303-2099; tel. 320/252-1670; Barry I. Bahl, Director
Web address: www.visn13.med.va.gov

MISSISSIPPI: G.V. MONTGOMERY VETERANS AFFAIRS MEDICAL CENTER (O, 443 beds) 1500 East Woodrow Wilson Drive, Jackson, MS Zip 39216-5199; tel. 601/364-1201; Richard J. Baltz, Director
Web address: www.va.gov

VETERANS AFFAIRS GULF COAST VETERANS HEALTH CARE SYSTEM (O, 552 beds) 400 Veterans Avenue, Biloxi, MS Zip 39531-2410; tel. 228/523-5000; Julie A. Catellier, Director
Web address: www.va.gov/sta/guide/home.asp

MISSOURI: HARRY S. TRUMAN MEMORIAL VETERANS HOSPITAL (O, 118 beds) 800 Hospital Drive, Columbia, MO Zip 65201-5297; tel. 573/814-6000; Gary L. Campbell, CHE, Director
Web address: www.va.gov/sta/guide/home.asp

JOHN J. PERSHING VETERANS AFFAIRS MEDICAL CENTER (O, 58 beds) 1500 North Westwood Boulevard, Poplar Bluff, MO Zip 63901-3318; tel. 573/686-4151; Nancy Arnold, R.N., Director
Web address: www.va.gov/sta/guide/home.asp

VETERANS AFFAIRS MEDICAL CENTER (O, 339 beds) 915 North Grand, Saint Louis, MO Zip 63106; tel. 314/652-4100; Peter M. McBrady, Interim Director
Web address: www.va.gov/sta/guide/home.asp

VETERANS AFFAIRS MEDICAL CENTER (O, 155 beds) 4801 Linwood Boulevard, Kansas City, MO Zip 64128-2295; tel. 816/861-4700; Kent D. Hill, Director
Web address: www.va.gov/sta/guide/home.asp

MONTANA: VETERANS AFFAIRS MONTANA HEALTHCARE SYSTEM (O, 80 beds) 1892 Williams Street, Fort Harrison, MT Zip 59636; tel. 406/442-6410; Joseph Underkofler, Director
Web address: www.va.gov/sta/guide/home.asp

NEBRASKA: VETERANS AFFAIRS MEDICAL CENTER (O, 202 beds) 4101 Woolworth Avenue, Omaha, NE Zip 68105-1873; tel. 402/346-8800; Albert B. Washko, Director
Web address: www.va.gov/sta/guide/home.asp

VETERANS AFFAIRS NEBRASKA-WESTERN IOWA HEALTH CARE SYSTEM (O, 186 beds) 600 South 70th Street, Lincoln, NE Zip 68510-2493; tel. 402/489-3802; Denise Harrison, Site Manager

NEVADA: VETERANS AFFAIRS SIERRA NEVADA HEALTH CARE SYSTEM (O, 113 beds) 1000 Locust Street, Reno, NV Zip 89502-2597; tel. 775/786-7200; Kurt W. Schlegelmilch, M.D., CHE, Director
Web address: www.va.gov/sta/guide/home.asp

VETERANS AFFAIRS SOUTHERN NEVADA HEALTHCARE SYSTEM (O, 52 beds) North Las Vegas, NV Mailing Address: P.O. Box 360001, Zip 89036; tel. 702/636-3000; John Hempel, Director
Web address: www.va.gov/sta/guide/home.asp

NEW HAMPSHIRE: VETERANS AFFAIRS MEDICAL CENTER (O, 90 beds) 718 Smyth Road, Manchester, NH Zip 03104-4098; tel. 603/624-4366; Marc Levenson, Administrator
Web address: www.va.gov/sta/guide/home.asp

NEW JERSEY: VETERANS AFFAIRS NEW JERSEY HEALTH CARE SYSTEM (O, 845 beds) 385 Tremont Avenue, East Orange, NJ Zip 07018-1095; tel. 973/676-1000; Kenneth H. Mizrach, Director
Web address: www.va.gov/visns/visn03/default.asp

NEW MEXICO: VETERANS AFFAIRS MEDICAL CENTER (O, 181 beds) 1501 San Pedro S.E., Albuquerque, NM Zip 87108-5138; tel. 505/265-1711; Mary A. Dowling, Director
Web address: www.va.gov/sta/guide/home.asp

NEW YORK: VETERANS ADMINISTRATION NEW YORK HARBOR HEALTHCARE SYSTEM (O, 549 beds) 800 Poly Place, Brooklyn, NY Zip 11209-7104; tel. 718/630-3500; John J. Donnellan Jr, Director
Web address: www.vaww.va.gov

VETERANS AFFAIRS HUDSON VALLEY HEALTH CARE SYSTEM-F.D. ROOSEVELT HOSPITAL (O, 413 beds) Montrose, NY Mailing Address: P.O. Box 100, Zip 10548-0110; tel. 914/737-4400; Michael A. Sabo, Director
Web address: www.va.gov/sta/guide/home.asp

VETERANS AFFAIRS MEDICAL CENTER (O, 133 beds) 113 Holland Avenue, Albany, NY Zip 12208-3473; tel. 518/626-5000; Mary-Ellen Piche, Director
Web address: www.va.gov/sta/guide/home.asp

VETERANS AFFAIRS MEDICAL CENTER (O, 360 beds) 76 Veterans Avenue, Bath, NY Zip 14810-0842; tel. 607/664-4000; Linda Weiss, Acting Director
Web address: www.va.gov/sta/guide/home.asp

VETERANS AFFAIRS MEDICAL CENTER (O, 238 beds) 400 Fort Hill Avenue, Canandaigua, NY Zip 14424-1197; tel. 585/394-2000; W. David Smith, Director
Web address: www.va.gov/visns/visn02/can_nf.html

VETERANS AFFAIRS MEDICAL CENTER (O, 326 beds) 130 West Kingsbridge Road, Bronx, NY Zip 10468-3992; tel. 718/584-9000; Maryann Musumeci, Director
Web address: www.va.gov/sta/guide/home.asp

VETERANS AFFAIRS MEDICAL CENTER (O, 332 beds) 79 Middleville Road, Northport, NY Zip 11768-2293; tel. 631/261-4400; Robert Schuster, Director
Web address: www.va.gov/sta/guide/home.asp

VETERANS AFFAIRS MEDICAL CENTER (O, 154 beds) 800 Irving Avenue, Syracuse, NY Zip 13210-2796; tel. 315/425-4400; James Cody, Director
Web address: www.va.gov/sta/guide/home.asp

VETERANS AFFAIRS WESTERN NEW YORK HEALTHCARE SYSTEM-BATAVIA DIVISION (O, 158 beds) 222 Richmond Avenue, Batavia, NY Zip 14020-1288; tel. 585/343-7500; Michael S. Finegan, Director
Web address: www.va.gov/sta/guide/home.asp

VETERANS AFFAIRS WESTERN NEW YORK HEALTHCARE SYSTEM-BUFFALO DIVISION (O, 233 beds) 3495 Bailey Avenue, Buffalo, NY Zip 14215-1129; tel. 716/834-9200; Michael S. Finegan, Director
Web address: www.va.gov/visn/visn02

NORTH CAROLINA: DURHAM VETERANS AFFAIRS MEDICAL CENTER (O, 232 beds) 508 Fulton Street, Durham, NC Zip 27705-3897; tel. 919/286-0411; Alan K. Begbie, Acting Director
Web address: www.va.gov/sta/guide/facility.asp?id=43

VETERANS AFFAIRS MEDICAL CENTER (O, 159 beds) 2300 Ramsey Street, Fayetteville, NC Zip 28301-3899; tel. 910/822-7059; Janet S. Stout, Director
Web address: www.va.gov/sta/guide/home.asp

VETERANS AFFAIRS MEDICAL CENTER (O, 297 beds) 1100 Tunnel Road, Asheville, NC Zip 28805-2087; tel. 828/298-7911; James A. Christian, Director
Web address: www.va.gov/sta/guide/home.asp

VETERANS AFFAIRS MEDICAL CENTER (O, 429 beds) 1601 Brenner Avenue, Salisbury, NC Zip 28144-2559; tel. 704/638-9000;
Web address: www.va.gov/sta/guide/home.asp

NORTH DAKOTA: VETERANS AFFAIRS MEDICAL AND REGIONAL OFFICE CENTER (O, 71 beds) 2101 Elm Street, Fargo, ND Zip 58102-2498; tel. 701/232-3241; Douglas M. Kenyon, Director
Web address: www.va.gov/sta/guide/home.asp

OHIO: VETERANS AFFAIRS MEDICAL CENTER (O, 459 beds) 10701 East Boulevard, Cleveland, OH Zip 44106-1702; tel. 216/791-3800; William D. Montague, Director
Web address: www.va.gov/sta/guide/home.asp

VETERANS AFFAIRS MEDICAL CENTER (O, 297 beds) 17273 State Route 104, Chillicothe, OH Zip 45601-0999; tel. 740/773-1141; Douglas A. Moorman, Medical Center Director

VETERANS AFFAIRS MEDICAL CENTER (O, 113 beds) 3200 Vine Street, Cincinnati, OH Zip 45220-2288; tel. 513/861-3100; Carlos B. Lott Jr, Director
Web address: www.va.gov/sta/guide/home.asp

Section B

For explanation of codes following names, see page B2.
★ Indicates Type III membership in the American Hospital Association.

Section B

VETERANS AFFAIRS MEDICAL CENTER (O, 500 beds) 4100 West Third Street, Dayton, OH Zip 45428–1002; tel. 937/268–6511; Steven M. Cohen, M.D., Director
Web address: www.va.gov/sta/guide/home.asp

OKLAHOMA: VETERANS AFFAIRS MEDICAL CENTER (O, 50 beds) 1011 Honor Heights Drive, Muskogee, OK Zip 74401–1399; tel. 918/683–3261; Benjamin Campeau, Interim Director
Web address: www.va.gov/sta/guide/home.asp

VETERANS AFFAIRS MEDICAL CENTER (O, 169 beds) 921 N.E. 13th Street, Oklahoma City, OK Zip 73104–5028; tel. 405/270–0501; Steven J. Gentling, FACHE, Director
Web address: www.va.gov/sta/guide/home.asp

OREGON: VETERANS AFFAIRS MEDICAL CENTER (O, 221 beds) 3710 S.W. U.S. Veterans Hospital Road, Portland, OR Zip 97201; tel. 503/220–8262; James Tuchschmidt, M.D., Director
Web address: www.va.gov/sta/guide/home.asp

VETERANS AFFAIRS ROSEBURG HEALTHCARE SYSTEM (O, 143 beds) 913 N.W. Garden Valley Boulevard, Roseburg, OR Zip 97470–6513; tel. 541/440–1000; George Marnell, Director
Web address: www.va.gov/sta/guide/home.asp

PENNSYLVANIA: JAMES E. VAN ZANDT VETERANS AFFAIRS MEDICAL CENTER (O, 68 beds) 2907 Pleasant Valley Boulevard, Altoona, PA Zip 16602–4377; tel. 814/943–8164; Gerald L. Williams, Director
Web address: www.va.gov/sta/guide/home.asp

VETERANS AFFAIRS MEDICAL CENTER (O, 149 beds) 325 New Castle Road, Butler, PA Zip 16001–2480; tel. 724/287–4781; David Wood, Director
Web address: www.va.gov/station/529–butler

VETERANS AFFAIRS MEDICAL CENTER (O, 526 beds) 1400 Black Horse Hill Road, Coatesville, PA Zip 19320–2040; tel. 610/384–7711; Gary W. Devansky, Director
Web address: www.va.gov/sta/guide/home.asp

VETERANS AFFAIRS MEDICAL CENTER (O, 78 beds) 135 East 38th Street, Erie, PA Zip 16504–1596; tel. 814/860–2576; Michael Adelman, M.D., Acting Director
Web address: www.va.gov/sta/guide/home.asp

VETERANS AFFAIRS MEDICAL CENTER (O, 257 beds) 1700 South Lincoln Avenue, Lebanon, PA Zip 17042–7529; tel. 717/272–6621; Terry M. Gerigk, Director
Web address: www.va.gov/sta/guide/home.asp

VETERANS AFFAIRS MEDICAL CENTER (O, 389 beds) University and Woodland Avenues, Philadelphia, PA Zip 19104–4594; tel. 215/823–5800; Michael J. Sullivan, Director
Web address: www.va.gov/sta/guide/home.asp

VETERANS AFFAIRS MEDICAL CENTER (O, 184 beds) 1111 East End Boulevard, Wilkes–Barre, PA Zip 18711–0026; tel. 570/824–3521; Roland E. Moore, Director
Web address: www.va.gov/sta/guide/home.asp

VETERANS AFFAIRS PITTSBURGH HEALTHCARE SYSTEM (O, 692 beds) Delafield Road, Pittsburgh, PA Zip 15240–1001; tel. 412/688–6000; Michael E. Moreland, Director
Web address: www.va.gov/pittsburgh

PUERTO RICO: VETERANS AFFAIRS MEDICAL CENTER (O, 468 beds) 10 Casia Street, San Juan, PR Zip 00921–3201; tel. 787/641–7582; Rafael E. Ramirez, M.D., Center Director
Web address: www.va.gov/visn8/sanjuan

RHODE ISLAND: VETERANS AFFAIRS MEDICAL CENTER (O, 75 beds) 830 Chalkstone Avenue, Providence, RI Zip 02908–4799; tel. 401/457–3042; Vincent Ng, Director
Web address: www.va.gov/sta/guide/home.asp

SOUTH CAROLINA: RALPH H. JOHNSON VETERANS AFFAIRS MEDICAL CENTER (O, 85 beds) 109 Bee Street, Charleston, SC Zip 29401–5703; tel. 843/577–5011; William A. Mountcastle, CHE, Director
Web address: www.va.gov/sta/guide/home.asp

WM. JENNINGS BRYAN DORN VETERANS AFFAIRS MEDICAL CENTER (O, 180 beds) 6439 Garners Ferry Road, Columbia, SC Zip 29209–1639; tel. 803/776–4000; Brian Heckert, Chief Executive Officer
Web address: www.va.gov/sta/guide/home.asp

SOUTH DAKOTA: ROYAL C. JOHNSON VETERANS MEMORIAL HOSPITAL (O, 103 beds) 2501 West 22nd Street, Sioux Falls, SD Zip 57105–9920, Mailing Address: P.O. Box 5046, Zip 57117–5046; tel. 605/336–3230; Joseph M. Dalpiaz, Director
Web address: www.visn23.med.va.gov

VETERANS AFFAIRS BLACK HILLS HEALTH CARE SYSTEM (O, 351 beds) 113 Comanche Road, Fort Meade, SD Zip 57741–1099; tel. 605/347–2511; Peter P. Henry, CHE, Director
Web address: www.va.gov/sta/guide/home.asp

TENNESSEE: JAMES H. QUILLEN VETERANS AFFAIRS MEDICAL CENTER (O, 603 beds) Mountain Home, TN Mailing Address: P.O. Box 4000, Zip 37684–4000; tel. 423/926–1171; Carl J. Gerber, M.D., Ph.D., Director
Web address: www.va.gov/621quillen

VETERANS AFFAIRS MEDICAL CENTER (O, 263 beds) 1030 Jefferson Avenue, Memphis, TN Zip 38104–2193; tel. 901/523–8990; Patricia O. Pittman, Director
Web address: www.va.gov/sta/guide/home.asp

VETERANS AFFAIRS TENNESSEE VALLEY HEALTHCARE SYSTEM (O, 510 beds) 1310 24th Avenue South, Nashville, TN Zip 37212–2637; tel. 615/327–4751; David N. Pennington, FACHE, Chief Executive Officer
Web address: www.va.gov/sta/guide/home.asp

TEXAS: AMARILLO VETERANS AFFAIRS HEALTH CARE SYSTEM (O, 189 beds) 6010 Amarillo Boulevard West, Amarillo, TX Zip 79106–1992; tel. 806/355–9703; Andrew C. Stenhouse, M.D., Acting Director and Chief Executive Officer
Web address: www.va.gov/sta/guide/home.asp

CENTRAL TEXAS VETERANS HEALTHCARE SYSTEM (O, 1852 beds) 1901 South First Street, Temple, TX Zip 76504–7493; tel. 254/778–4811; Robert W. Ratliff, Ph.D., FACHE, Acting Director
Web address: www.texvet.com

MICHAEL E. DEBAKEY VETERANS AFFAIRS MEDICAL CENTER (O, 859 beds) 2002 Holcombe Boulevard, Houston, TX Zip 77030–4298; tel. 713/791–1414; Edgar L. Tucker, Director
Web address: www.va.gov/sta/guide/home.asp

SOUTH TEXAS VETERANS HEALTH CARE SYSTEM (O, 1112 beds) 7400 Merton Minter Boulevard, San Antonio, TX Zip 78284–5799; tel. 210/617–5140; Jose R. Coronado, FACHE, Director
Web address: www.vasthcs.med.va.gov

VETERANS AFFAIRS NORTH TEXAS HEALTH CARE SYSTEM (O, 875 beds) 4500 South Lancaster Road, Dallas, TX Zip 75216–7167; tel. 214/742–8387; Alan G. Harper, Director
Web address: www.va.gov/sta/guide/home.asp

WEST TEXAS VA HEALTH CARE SYSTEM (O, 189 beds) 300 Veterans Boulevard, Big Spring, TX Zip 79720–5500; tel. 432/263–7361; Lou Ann Atkins, Director
Web address: www.va.gov/sta/guide/home.asp

UTAH: VETERANS AFFAIRS SALT LAKE CITY HEALTH CARE SYSTEM (O, 121 beds) 500 Foothill Drive, Salt Lake City, UT Zip 84148–0002; tel. 801/582–1565; James R. Floyd, Director
Web address: www.va.gov/sta/guide/home.asp

VERMONT: VETERANS AFFAIRS MEDICAL CENTER (O, 60 beds) 215 North Main Street, White River Junction, VT Zip 05009–0001; tel. 802/295–9363; Gary M. De Gasta, Director
Web address: www.va.gov/sta/guide/home.asp

VIRGINIA: HUNTER HOLMES MCGUIRE VETERANS AFFAIRS MEDICAL CENTER (O, 427 beds) 1201 Broad Rock Boulevard, Richmond, VA Zip 23249–0002; tel. 804/675–5000; Michael B. Phaup, Director
Web address: www.va.gov/sta/guide/home.asp

VETERANS AFFAIRS MEDICAL CENTER (O, 485 beds) 100 Emancipation Drive, Hampton, VA Zip 23667–0001; tel. 757/722–9961; Joseph Williams, Director
Web address: www.va.gov/sta/guide/home.asp

VETERANS AFFAIRS MEDICAL CENTER (O, 298 beds) 1970 Roanoke Boulevard, Salem, VA Zip 24153–6478; tel. 540/982–2463; Stephen L. Lemons, Ed.D., Director
Web address: www.va.gov/sta/guide/home.asp

WASHINGTON: JONATHAN M. WAINWRIGHT MEMORIAL VA MEDICAL CENTER (O, 66 beds) 77 Wainwright Drive, Walla Walla, WA Zip 99362–3994; tel. 509/525–5200; Bruce E. Stewart, Acting Director
Web address: www.va.gov/sta/guide/home.asp

For explanation of codes following names, see page B2.
★ Indicates Type III membership in the American Hospital Association.

VETERANS AFFAIRS MEDICAL CENTER (O, 92 beds) North 4815 Assembly Street, Spokane, WA Zip 99205–6197; tel. 509/434–7000; Joseph M. Manley, Director
Web address: www.spokane.med.va.gov

VETERANS AFFAIRS PUGET SOUND HEALTH CARE SYSTEM (O, 512 beds) 1660 South Columbian Way, Seattle, WA Zip 98108–1597; tel. 206/762–1010; Timothy B. Williams, Director
Web address: www.va.gov/sta/guide/home.asp

WEST VIRGINIA: LOUIS A. JOHNSON VETERANS AFFAIRS MEDICAL CENTER (O, 98 beds) 1 Medical Center Drive, Clarksburg, WV Zip 26301–4199; tel. 304/623–3461; Cheryl Welch, Acting Director
Web address: www.va.gov/sta/guide/home.asp

VETERANS AFFAIRS MEDICAL CENTER (O, 90 beds) 200 Veterans Avenue, Beckley, WV Zip 25801–6499; tel. 304/255–2121; Gerard P. Husson, Director
Web address: www.va.gov/sta/guide/home.asp

VETERANS AFFAIRS MEDICAL CENTER (O, 80 beds) 1540 Spring Valley Drive, Huntington, WV Zip 25704–9300; tel. 304/429–6741; Betty Bolin Brown, Ed.D., Chief Executive Officer
Web address: www.va.gov/sta/guide/home.asp

VETERANS AFFAIRS MEDICAL CENTER (O, 559 beds) 510 Butler Avenue, Martinsburg, WV Zip 25401–0205; tel. 304/263–0811; Guy B. Richardson, Acting Director
Web address: www.va.gov/sta/guide/home.asp

WISCONSIN: CLEMENT J. ZABLOCKI VETERANS AFFAIRS MEDICAL CENTER (O, 566 beds) 5000 West National Avenue, Milwaukee, WI Zip 53295; tel. 414/384–2000; Glen W. Grippen, Director
Web address: www.va.gov/sta/guide/home.asp

VETERANS AFFAIRS MEDICAL CENTER (O, 331 beds) 500 East Veterans Street, Tomah, WI Zip 54660; tel. 608/372–3971; Stan Johnson, Medical Center Director
Web address: www.va.gov/tomahvamc

WILLIAM S. MIDDLETON MEMORIAL VETERANS HOSPITAL (O, 87 beds) 2500 Overlook Terrace, Madison, WI Zip 53705–2286; tel. 608/256–1901; Nathan L. Geraths, Director
Web address: www.madison.med.va.gov

WYOMING: VETERANS AFFAIRS MEDICAL CENTER (O, 71 beds) 2360 East Pershing Boulevard, Cheyenne, WY Zip 82001–5392; tel. 307/778–7550; David M. Kilpatrick, M.D., Director
Web address: www.va.gov/sta/guide/home.asp

VETERANS AFFAIRS MEDICAL CENTER (O, 149 beds) 1898 Fort Road, Sheridan, WY Zip 82801–8320; tel. 307/672–3473; Maureen Humphrys, Director
Web address: www.va.gov/sta/guide/home.asp

Owned, leased, sponsored:	136 hospitals	40917 beds
Contract–managed:	0 hospitals	0 beds
Totals:	136 hospitals	40917 beds

★2145: DETROIT MEDICAL CENTER (NP)
3990 John R., Detroit, MI Zip 48201; tel. 313/745–1250; Michael Duggan, President and Chief Executive Officer
(Centralized Health System)

MICHIGAN: CHILDREN'S HOSPITAL OF MICHIGAN (O, 228 beds) 3901 Beaubien Street, Detroit, MI Zip 48201–9985; tel. 313/966–5110; Larry Fleischmann, M.D., President
Web address: www.chmkids.org

DETROIT RECEIVING HOSPITAL AND UNIVERSITY HEALTH CENTER (O, 217 beds) 4201 St. Antoine Boulevard, Detroit, MI Zip 48201–2194; tel. 313/745–3603; Iris Taylor, Ph.D., President
Web address: www.dmc.org

HARPER UNIVERSITY HOSPITAL (O, 601 beds) 3990 John R., Detroit, MI Zip 48201–9027; tel. 313/745–8040; Brooks Bock, M.D., President
Web address: www.harperhospital.org

HURON VALLEY–SINAI HOSPITAL (O, 153 beds) 1 William Carls Drive, Commerce Township, MI Zip 48382–2201; tel. 248/937–3300; Robert J. Yellan, President
Web address: www.hvsh.org

MICHIGAN ORTHOPAEDIC SPECIATY HOSPITAL (O, 64 beds) 30671 Stephenson Highway, Madison Heights, MI Zip 48071–1678; tel. 248/733–2200; Frank P. Iacobell, President
Web address: www.michiganorthopaedic.org

REHABILITATION INSTITUTE OF MICHIGAN (O, 94 beds) 261 Mack Boulevard, Detroit, MI Zip 48201–2495; tel. 313/745–1203; Terry Reiley, President
Web address: www.rimrehab.org

SINAI–GRACE HOSPITAL (O, 404 beds) 6071 West Outer Drive, Detroit, MI Zip 48235–2679; tel. 313/966–3300; Conrad L. Mallett Jr, President
Web address: www.sinaigrace.org

Owned, leased, sponsored:	7 hospitals	1761 beds
Contract–managed:	0 hospitals	0 beds
Totals:	7 hospitals	1761 beds

0845: DEVEREUX (NP)
444 Devereux Drive, Villanova, PA Zip 19085, Mailing Address: P.O. Box 638, Zip 19085–0638; tel. 610/520–3000; Robert Q. Kreider, President and Chief Executive
(Independent Hospital System)

FLORIDA: DEVEREUX HOSPITAL AND CHILDREN'S CENTER OF FLORIDA (O, 100 beds) 8000 Devereux Drive, Melbourne, FL Zip 32940–7907; tel. 321/242–9100; Patty Hurst, Administrator
Web address: www.devereux.org

GEORGIA: DEVEREUX GEORGIA TREATMENT NETWORK (O, 187 beds) 1291 Stanley Road N.W., Kennesaw, GA Zip 30152–4359, Mailing Address: P.O. Box 1688, Zip 30156–8688; tel. 770/422–2135; Mario Bolivar, Executive Director
Web address: www.devereuxga.org

PENNSYLVANIA: DEVEREUX CHILDREN'S BEHAVIORAL HEALTH CENTER (O, 13 beds) 655 Sugartown Road, Malvern, PA Zip 19355–0275, Mailing Address: P.O. Box 275, Zip 19355–0275; tel. 484/595–6777; Walter J. Grono, Executive Director
Web address: www.devereux.org

TEXAS: DEVEREUX TEXAS TREATMENT NETWORK (O, 74 beds) 1150 Devereux Drive, League City, TX Zip 77573–2043; tel. 281/335–1000; L. Gail Atkinson, Executive Director
Web address: www.devereux.org

Owned, leased, sponsored:	4 hospitals	374 beds
Contract–managed:	0 hospitals	0 beds
Totals:	4 hospitals	374 beds

★0029: DIMENSIONS HEALTHCARE SYSTEM (NP)
3001 Hospital Drive, 3rd Floor, Cheverly, MD Zip 20785; tel. 301/583–4000; G. T. Dunlop Ecker, President and Chief Executive Officer
(Moderately Centralized Health System)

MARYLAND: LAUREL REGIONAL HOSPITAL (O, 115 beds) 7300 Van Dusen Road, Laurel, MD Zip 20707–9266; tel. 301/725–4300; Douglas Shepherd, FACHE, President and Chief Executive Officer
Web address: www.laurelregionalhospital.org

PRINCE GEORGE'S HOSPITAL CENTER (O, 403 beds) 3001 Hospital Drive, Cheverly, MD Zip 20785–1189; tel. 301/618–2000; G. T. Dunlop Ecker, President and Chief Executive Officer
Web address: www.princegeorgeshospital.org

Owned, leased, sponsored:	2 hospitals	518 beds
Contract–managed:	0 hospitals	0 beds
Totals:	2 hospitals	518 beds

0010: DIVISION OF MENTAL HEALTH SERVICES, DEPARTMENT OF HUMAN SERVICES, STATE OF NEW JERSEY (NP)
Capital Center, P.O. Box 727, Trenton, NJ Zip 08625–0727; tel. 609/777–0702; Alan G. Kaufman, Director
(Independent Hospital System)

NEW JERSEY: ANCORA PSYCHIATRIC HOSPITAL (O, 709 beds) 202 Spring Garden Road, Ancora, NJ Zip 08037–9699; tel. 609/561–1700; Latanya Wood, Chief Executive Officer

For explanation of codes following names, see page B2.
★ Indicates Type III membership in the American Hospital Association.

GREYSTONE PARK PSYCHIATRIC HOSPITAL (O, 578 beds) Central Avenue, Morris Plains, NJ Zip 07950–1005, Mailing Address: P.O. Box A, Zip 07950–1005; tel. 973/538–1800; Janet Monroe, Chief Executive Officer
Web address: www.state.nj.us/humanservices/pfnurse/greystone.htm

SENATOR GARRETT W. HAGEDORN PSYCHIATRIC HOSPITAL (O, 181 beds) 200 Sanitorium Road, Glen Gardner, NJ Zip 08826–3291; tel. 908/537–2141; Debra A. Smith, Acting Chief Executive Officer

TRENTON PSYCHIATRIC HOSPITAL (O, 511 beds) Route 29 and Sullivan Way, Trenton, NJ Zip 08628–3425, Mailing Address: P.O. Box 7500, West Trenton, Zip 08628–7500; tel. 609/633–1500; Gregory P. Roberts, Chief Executive Officer

Owned, leased, sponsored:	4 hospitals	1979 beds
Contract–managed:	0 hospitals	0 beds
Totals:	4 hospitals	1979 beds

★0226: **DUBUIS HEALTH SYSTEM** (CC)
10333 Richmond Avenue, Suite 300, Houston, TX Zip 77042; tel. 713/339–7000; Ellen Smith, President and Chief Executive Officer
(Independent Hospital System)

ARKANSAS: ADVANCE CARE HOSPITAL (O, 27 beds) 300 Werner Street, 3rd Floor East, Hot Springs National Park, AR Zip 71913; tel. 501/609–4300; Keith Rogers, Administrator
Web address: www.dubuis.org

ADVANCE CARE HOSPITAL OF FORT SMITH (C, 25 beds) 7301 Rogers Avenue, 4th Floor, Fort Smith, AR Zip 72917; tel. 479/314–4900; Amy Riley, Administrator
Web address: www.dubuis.org

GEORGIA: SOUTHERN CRESCENT HOSPITAL FOR SPECIALTY CARE (C, 30 beds) 11 Upper Riverdale Road S.W., 6th Floor, Riverdale, GA Zip 30274; tel. 770/897–7603; Janice Harrison, Administrator

LOUISIANA: DUBUIS HOSPITAL OF ALEXANDRIA (O, 33 beds) 3330 Masonic Drive, 4th Floor, Alexandria, LA Zip 71301; tel. 318/448–6505; Ray Owens, Administrator and Chief Executive Officer

DUBUIS HOSPITAL OF LAKE CHARLES (O, 20 beds) 524 South Ryan, 5th Floor, Lake Charles, LA Zip 70601–5725; tel. 337/491–7752; Michael M. Fuselier, FACHE, Administrator

DUBUIS HOSPITAL OF SHREVEPORT (O, 36 beds) One St. Mary Place, 6th Floor, Shreveport, LA Zip 71101; tel. 318/221–3802; Kay B. Allen, R.N., Administrator
Web address: www.dubuis.org

MISSOURI: ALL SAINTS SPECIAL CARE HOSPITAL (C, 20 beds) 12303 De Paul Drive, 2nd Floor, Bridgeton, MO Zip 63044–2588; tel. 314/344–7830; David L. Adcock, Administrator
Web address: www.dubuis.org

OKLAHOMA: ADVANCE CARE HOSPITAL OF OKLAHOMA CITY (O, 34 beds) 4300 West Memorial Road, 5th Floor, Oklahoma City, OK Zip 73120; tel. 405/486–8800; George H. Dashner, FACHE, Administrator
Web address: www.dubuis.org

TEXAS: DUBUIS HOSPITAL OF BEAUMONT (O, 51 beds) 2830 Calder Avenue, 4th Floor, Beaumont, TX Zip 77702; tel. 409/899–8154; Stephen Mills, Regional Administrator
Web address: www.dubuis.org

DUBUIS HOSPITAL OF CORPUS CHRISTI (O, 12 beds) 600 Elizabeth Street, 3rd Floor, Corpus Christi, TX Zip 78404; tel. 361/881–3640; Tracey S. Richard, Administrator
Web address: www.dubuis.org

DUBUIS HOSPITAL OF HOUSTON (O, 30 beds) 1919 Labranch 7GWS Street, Houston, TX Zip 77002; tel. 713/756–8660; Stephen Mills, Regional Administrator
Web address: www.dubuis.org

DUBUIS HOSPITAL OF PARIS (O, 25 beds) 865 Deshong Drive, 5th Floor, Paris, TX Zip 75462; tel. 903/782–2960; Berry Gilbert, Administrator
Web address: www.dubuis.org

DUBUIS HOSPITAL OF PORT ARTHUR (O, 15 beds) 3600 Gates Boulevard, Port Arthur, TX Zip 77642; tel. 409/989–5300; Stephen Mills, Administrator

DUBUIS HOSPITAL OF TEXARKANA (O, 34 beds) 2600 St. Michael Drive, 6th Floor, Texarkana, TX Zip 75503–2372; tel. 903/899–7168; Tim Freeman, Administrator
Web address: www.dubuis.org

Owned, leased, sponsored:	11 hospitals	317 beds
Contract–managed:	3 hospitals	75 beds
Totals:	14 hospitals	392 beds

★0190: **DUKE UNIVERSITY HEALTH SYSTEM** (NP)
Erwin Road, Durham, NC Zip 27710, Mailing Address: P.O. Box 3701, Zip 27710–3701; tel. 919/684–2255; Victor J. Dzau, M.D., President and Chief Executive Officer
(Centralized Health System)

NORTH CAROLINA: DUKE HEALTH RALEIGH HOSPITAL (O, 150 beds) 3400 Wake Forest Road, Raleigh, NC Zip 27609–7373, Mailing Address: P.O. Box 28280, Zip 27611–8280; tel. 919/954–3000; James P. Knight, Chief Executive Officer
Web address: www.dukehealthraleigh.org

DUKE UNIVERSITY HOSPITAL (O, 753 beds) Erwin Road, Durham, NC Zip 27710–0001, Mailing Address: P.O. Box 3708, Zip 27710–3708; tel. 919/684–8111; William J. Fulkerson, M.D., Chief Executive Officer
Web address: www.mc.duke.edu

DURHAM REGIONAL HOSPITAL (L, 269 beds) 3643 North Roxboro Road, Durham, NC Zip 27704–2763; tel. 919/470–4000; David P. McQuaid, Chief Executive Officer
Web address: www.durhamregional.org

PERSON MEMORIAL HOSPITAL (C, 110 beds) 615 Ridge Road, Roxboro, NC Zip 27573–4630; tel. 336/599–2121; Craig B. James, Chief Executive Officer
Web address: www.personhospital.com

Owned, leased, sponsored:	3 hospitals	1172 beds
Contract–managed:	1 hospital	110 beds
Totals:	4 hospitals	1282 beds

0286: **DYNACQ HEALTHCARE, INC.** (IO)
10304 Interstate 10 East, Suite 369, Houston, TX Zip 77029; tel. 713/673–6432; Chiu Moon Chan, Chairman, President and Chief Executive Officer
(Independent Hospital System)

LOUISIANA: VISTA SURGICAL HOSPITAL OF BATON ROUGE (O, 39 beds) 9032 Perkins Road, Baton Rouge, LA Zip 70810; tel. 225/819–4100; Gary Guidry, Chief Executive Officer

TEXAS: VISTA HOSPITAL OF DALLAS (O, 14 beds) 2696 West Walnut Street, Garland, TX Zip 75042–6499; tel. 972/487–2401; James Bryant, Chief Executive Officer and Chief Nursing Officer
Web address: www.lelandmedical.com

VISTA MEDICAL CENTER HOSPITAL (O, 37 beds) 4301B Vista, Pasadena, TX Zip 77504; tel. 713/378–3000; Rick Dicapo, Chief Executive Officer
Web address: www.dynacq.com

Owned, leased, sponsored:	3 hospitals	90 beds
Contract–managed:	0 hospitals	0 beds
Totals:	3 hospitals	90 beds

★1895: **EAST TEXAS MEDICAL CENTER REGIONAL HEALTHCARE SYSTEM** (NP)
1000 South Beckham Street, Tyler, TX Zip 75701–1996, Mailing Address: P.O. Box 6400, Zip 75711–6400; tel. 903/535–6211; Elmer G. Ellis, FACHE, President and Chief Executive Officer
(Centralized Physician/Insurance Health System)

EAST TEXAS MEDICAL CENTER ATHENS (L, 117 beds) 2000 South Palestine Street, Athens, TX Zip 75751–5610; tel. 903/676–1000; Patrick L. Wallace, Administrator
Web address: www.etmc.org

EAST TEXAS MEDICAL CENTER CARTHAGE (L, 37 beds) 409 Cottage Road, Carthage, TX Zip 75633–1466, Mailing Address: P.O. Box 549, Zip 75633–0549; tel. 903/693–3841; Gary Mikeal Hudson, Administrator
Web address: www.etmc.org

For explanation of codes following names, see page B2.
★ Indicates Type III membership in the American Hospital Association.

EAST TEXAS MEDICAL CENTER CLARKSVILLE (L, 36 beds) 3000 West Main Street, Clarksville, TX Zip 75426, Mailing Address: P.O. Box 1270, Zip 75426–1270; tel. 903/427–3851; Jack R. Endres, Interim Administrator
Web address: www.etmc.org

EAST TEXAS MEDICAL CENTER CROCKETT (L, 54 beds) 1100 Loop 304 East, Crockett, TX Zip 75835–1810; tel. 936/546–3862; Terry Cutler, Administrator and Chief Operating Officer
Web address: www.etmc.org

EAST TEXAS MEDICAL CENTER FAIRFIELD (L, 44 beds) 125 Newman Street, Fairfield, TX Zip 75840–1499; tel. 903/389–2121; Ruth Cook, Administrator
Web address: www.etmc.org

EAST TEXAS MEDICAL CENTER JACKSONVILLE (O, 58 beds) 501 South Ragsdale Street, Jacksonville, TX Zip 75766–2413; tel. 903/541–5000; Steve Bowen, President
Web address: www.etmc.org

EAST TEXAS MEDICAL CENTER PITTSBURG (L, 42 beds) 414 Quitman Street, Pittsburg, TX Zip 75686–1032; tel. 903/856–6663; W. Perry Henderson, Administrator
Web address: www.etmc.org

EAST TEXAS MEDICAL CENTER REHABILITATION CENTER (O, 49 beds) 701 Olympic Plaza Circle, Tyler, TX Zip 75701–1996; tel. 903/596–3000; Eddie L. Howard, Vice President and Chief Operating Officer
Web address: www.etmc.org

EAST TEXAS MEDICAL CENTER SPECIALTY HOSPITAL (O, 36 beds) 1000 South Beckham, 5th Floor, Tyler, TX Zip 75701; tel. 903/596–3600; Eddie L. Howard, Vice President, Chief Operating Officer and Administrator
Web address: www.etmc.org

EAST TEXAS MEDICAL CENTER TRINITY (L, 22 beds) 317 Prospect Drive, Trinity, TX Zip 75862, Mailing Address: P.O. Box 3169, Zip 75862; tel. 936/594–3541; Terry Cutler, Administrator and Chief Operating Officer
Web address: www.etmc.org

EAST TEXAS MEDICAL CENTER TYLER (O, 422 beds) 1000 South Beckham Street, Tyler, TX Zip 75701–1996, Mailing Address: Box 6400, Zip 75711–6400; tel. 903/597–0351; Robert B. Evans, Administrator and Chief Executive Officer
Web address: www.etmc.org

EAST TEXAS MEDICAL CENTER–GILMER (O, 37 beds) 712 North Wood Street, Gilmer, TX Zip 75644; tel. 903/841–7100; Kenneth May, Chief Executive Officer
Web address: www.etmc.org

EAST TEXAS MEDICAL CENTER–MOUNT VERNON (L, 30 beds) 500 Highway 37 South, Mount Vernon, TX Zip 75457–3602, Mailing Address: P.O. Box 477, Zip 75457–0477; tel. 903/537–8000; Stephen Pitts, Administrator
Web address: www.etmc.org

EAST TEXAS MEDICAL CENTER–QUITMAN (L, 28 beds) 117 Winnsboro Street, Quitman, TX Zip 75783–2144, Mailing Address: P.O. Box 1000, Zip 75783–1000; tel. 903/763–6300; Ernest R. Parisi, CHE, Administrator and Chief Executive Officer
Web address: www.etmc.org

Owned, leased, sponsored:	14 hospitals	1012 beds
Contract–managed:	0 hospitals	0 beds
Totals:	14 hospitals	1012 beds

0270: EASTERN CONNECTICUT HEALTH NETWORK (NP)
71 Haynes Street, Manchester, CT Zip 06040; tel. 860/533–3429; Peter J. Karl, President and Chief Executive Officer
(Centralized Health System)

CONNECTICUT: MANCHESTER MEMORIAL HOSPITAL (O, 145 beds) 71 Haynes Street, Manchester, CT Zip 06040–4188; tel. 860/646–1222; Peter J. Karl, President and Chief Executive Officer
Web address: www.echn.org

ROCKVILLE GENERAL HOSPITAL (O, 57 beds) 31 Union Street, Vernon Rockville, CT Zip 06066–3160; tel. 860/872–0501; Peter J. Karl, President and Chief Executive Officer
Web address: www.echn.org

Owned, leased, sponsored:	2 hospitals	202 beds
Contract–managed:	0 hospitals	0 beds
Totals:	2 hospitals	202 beds

★0100: EASTERN HEALTH SYSTEM, INC. (NP)
50 Medical Park East Drive, Birmingham, AL Zip 35235; tel. 205/838–3999; Robert C. Chapman, FACHE, President and Chief Executive Officer
(Moderately Centralized Health System)

ALABAMA: MEDICAL CENTER BLOUNT (L, 40 beds) 150 Gilbreath, Oneonta, AL Zip 35121–2534, Mailing Address: P.O. Box 1000, Zip 35121–1000; tel. 205/274–3000; Jacki W. Phillips, CHE, Chief Executive Officer
Web address: www.medicalcenterblount.com

MEDICAL CENTER EAST (O, 269 beds) 50 Medical Park East Drive, Birmingham, AL Zip 35235–9987; tel. 205/838–3000; George McGowan, FACHE, Chief Executive Officer
Web address: www.ehs.org

ST. CLAIR REGIONAL HOSPITAL (L, 40 beds) 2805 Drive John Haynes Drive, Pell City, AL Zip 35125–1499; tel. 205/338–3301; Terrell Vick, Chief Executive Officer
Web address: www.stclairregional.com

Owned, leased, sponsored:	3 hospitals	349 beds
Contract–managed:	0 hospitals	0 beds
Totals:	3 hospitals	349 beds

★0555: EASTERN MAINE HEALTHCARE (NP)
489 State Street, Bangor, ME Zip 04401–6674, Mailing Address: P.O. Box 404, Zip 04402–0404; tel. 207/973–7045; Norman A. Ledwin, President and Chief Executive Officer
(Moderately Centralized Health System)

MAINE: ACADIA HOSPITAL (O, 91 beds) 268 Stillwater Avenue, Bangor, ME Zip 04401–3945, Mailing Address: P.O. Box 422, Zip 04402–0422; tel. 207/973–6100; Dorothy E. Hill, Chief Executive Officer and Chief Nursing Officer
Web address: www.acadiahospital.org

AROOSTOOK MEDICAL CENTER (O, 147 beds) 140 Academy Street, Presque Isle, ME Zip 04769–3171, Mailing Address: P.O. Box 151, Zip 04769–0151; tel. 207/768–4000; David A. Peterson, President and Chief Executive Officer
Web address: www.tamc.org

CHARLES A. DEAN MEMORIAL HOSPITAL AND NURSING HOME (O, 36 beds) Pritham Avenue, Greenville, ME Zip 04441–1395, Mailing Address: P.O. Box 1129, Zip 04441–1129; tel. 207/695–5200; Geno Murray, President and Chief Executive Officer
Web address: www.cadean.org

EASTERN MAINE MEDICAL CENTER (O, 329 beds) 489 State Street, Bangor, ME Zip 04401–6674, Mailing Address: P.O. Box 404, Zip 04402–0404; tel. 207/973–7000; Deborah Carey Johnson, R.N., President and Chief Executive Officer
Web address: www.emh.org

INLAND HOSPITAL (O, 48 beds) 200 Kennedy Memorial Drive, Waterville, ME Zip 04901–4595; tel. 207/861–3000; Sally Conary, President and Chief Executive Officer
Web address: www.inlandhospital.org

SEBASTICOOK VALLEY HOSPITAL (O, 25 beds) 99 Grove Street, Pittsfield, ME Zip 04967–1199; tel. 207/487–5141; John C. May, Chief Executive Officer
Web address: www.sebasticookhospital.org

Owned, leased, sponsored:	6 hospitals	676 beds
Contract–managed:	0 hospitals	0 beds
Totals:	6 hospitals	676 beds

★0256: EMORY HEALTHCARE (NP)
1440 Clifton Road, N.E., Suite 420, Atlanta, GA Zip 30322–1102, Mailing Address: 1440 Clifton Road N.E., Suite 420, Zip 30322–1102; tel. 404/778–5000; John T. Fox, Chief Executive Officer
(Centralized Health System)

GEORGIA: EMORY CRAWFORD LONG HOSPITAL (O, 419 beds) 550 Peachtree Street N.E., Atlanta, GA Zip 30308; tel. 404/686–4411; John T. Fox, Chief Executive Officer
Web address: www.emoryhealthcare.org

For explanation of codes following names, see page B2.
★ Indicates Type III membership in the American Hospital Association.

EMORY UNIVERSITY HOSPITAL (O, 508 beds) 1364 Clifton Road N.E., Atlanta, GA Zip 30322–1102; tel. 404/712–2000; John T. Fox, Chief Executive Officer
Web address: www.emory.org

WESLEY WOODS CENTER OF EMORY UNIVERSITY (O, 304 beds) 1821 Clifton Road N.E., Atlanta, GA Zip 30329–5102; tel. 404/728–6200; John T. Fox, Chief Executive Officer
Web address: www.emory.org

Owned, leased, sponsored:	3 hospitals	1231 beds
Contract–managed:	0 hospitals	0 beds
Totals:	3 hospitals	1231 beds

★0945: EMPIRE HEALTH SERVICES (NP)
West 800 Fifth Avenue, Spokane, WA Zip 99204, Mailing Address: P.O. Box 248, Zip 99210–0248; tel. 509/473–7960; Jeffrey Nelson, Interim President and Chief Executive Officer
(Moderately Centralized Health System)

WASHINGTON: DEACONESS MEDICAL CENTER–SPOKANE (O, 287 beds) 800 West Fifth Avenue, Spokane, WA Zip 99204–2803, Mailing Address: P.O. Box 248, Zip 99210–0248; tel. 509/458–5800; Michael T. Liepman, Chief Operating Officer
Web address: www.deaconess–spokane.org

VALLEY HOSPITAL AND MEDICAL CENTER (O, 93 beds) 12606 East Mission Avenue, Spokane, WA Zip 99216–1090; tel. 509/924–6650; Keith J. Baldwin, Chief Operating Officer
Web address: www.valleyhospital.org

Owned, leased, sponsored:	2 hospitals	380 beds
Contract–managed:	0 hospitals	0 beds
Totals:	2 hospitals	380 beds

0525: ERLANGER HEALTH SYSTEM (NP)
975 East Third Street, Chattanooga, TN Zip 37403; tel. 423/778–7000; James L. Brexler, President
(Moderately Centralized Health System)

TENNESSEE: ERLANGER BLEDSOE HOSPITAL (C, 28 beds) 71 Wheeler Avenue, Pikeville, TN Zip 37367, Mailing Address: P.O. Box 699, Zip 37367–0699; tel. 423/447–2112; Stephanie Boynton, Administrator
Web address: www.erlanger.org

ERLANGER MEDICAL CENTER (O, 519 beds) 975 East Third Street, Chattanooga, TN Zip 37403–2112; tel. 423/778–7000; James L. Brexler, President and Chief Executive Officer
Web address: www.erlanger.org

Owned, leased, sponsored:	1 hospital	519 beds
Contract–managed:	1 hospital	28 beds
Totals:	2 hospitals	547 beds

0241: ESSENT HEALTHCARE (IO)
3100 West End Avenue, Suite 900, Nashville, TN Zip 37203; tel. 615/312–5100; W. Hudson Connery Jr, President and Chief Executive Officer
(Moderately Centralized Health System)

CONNECTICUT: SHARON HOSPITAL (O, 78 beds) 50 Hospital Hill Road, Sharon, CT Zip 06069–0789, Mailing Address: P.O. Box 789, Zip 06069–0789; tel. 860/364–4141; Daniel R. Kelly, Chief Executive Officer
Web address: www.sharonhospital.com

MASSACHUSETTS: MERRIMACK VALLEY HOSPITAL (O, 109 beds) 140 Lincoln Avenue, Haverhill, MA Zip 01830–6798; tel. 978/374–2000;
Web address: www.merrimackvalleyhospital.com

NASHOBA VALLEY MEDICAL CENTER (O, 41 beds) 200 Groton Road, Ayer, MA Zip 01432–3300; tel. 978/784–9000; Andrei Soran, Chief Executive Officer
Web address: www.nashoba.caregroup.org

MISSOURI: CROSSROADS REGIONAL MEDICAL CENTER (O, 73 beds) 500 Medical Drive, Wentzville, MO Zip 63385–3421; tel. 636/327–1000; Steve Wylie, Interim Chief Executive Officer
Web address: www.crossroadsregional.com

TEXAS: PARIS REGIONAL MEDICAL CENTER (O, 445 beds) 820 Clarksville Street, Paris, TX Zip 75460–9070; tel. 903/785–4521; Andrew Knizley, Chief Executive Officer
Web address: www.parisrmc.com

Owned, leased, sponsored:	5 hospitals	746 beds
Contract–managed:	0 hospitals	0 beds
Totals:	5 hospitals	746 beds

2395: EXCELA HEALTH (IO)
532 West Pittsburgh Street, Greensburg, PA Zip 15601; tel. 724/832–5050; David S. Gallatin, Chief Executive Officer
(Moderately Centralized Health System)

PENNSYLVANIA: EXCELA FRICK HOSPITAL (O, 100 beds) 508 South Church Street, Mount Pleasant, PA Zip 15666–1790; tel. 724/547–1500; David S. Gallatin, Chief Executive Officer
Web address: www.frickhospital.org

EXCELA LATROBE AREA HOSPITAL (O, 188 beds) 121 West Second Avenue, Latrobe, PA Zip 15650–1096; tel. 724/537–1000; Douglas A. Clark, FACHE, President
Web address: www.lah.com

EXCELA WESTMORELAND REGIONAL HOSPITAL (O, 290 beds) 532 West Pittsburgh Street, Greensburg, PA Zip 15601–2282; tel. 724/832–4000; David S. Gallatin, Chief Executive Officer
Web address: www.excelahealth.org

Owned, leased, sponsored:	3 hospitals	578 beds
Contract–managed:	0 hospitals	0 beds
Totals:	3 hospitals	578 beds

★0134: EXEMPLA HEALTHCARE, INC. (NP)
600 Grant Street, Suite 700, Denver, CO Zip 80203; tel. 303/813–5000; Jeffrey D. Selberg, President and Chief Executive Officer
(Moderately Centralized Health System)

COLORADO: EXEMPLA GOOD SAMARITAN MEDICAL CENTER (O, 143 beds) 2600 Campus Drive, Suite C., Lafayette, CO Zip 80026; tel. 303/689–4000; David Hamm, President and Chief Executive Officer
Web address: www.exempla.org

EXEMPLA LUTHERAN MEDICAL CENTER (O, 494 beds) 8300 West 38th Avenue, Wheat Ridge, CO Zip 80033–6005; tel. 303/425–4500; Robert H. Malte, President and Chief Executive Officer
Web address: www.exempla.org

EXEMPLA SAINT JOSEPH HOSPITAL (C, 436 beds) 1835 Franklin Street, Denver, CO Zip 80218–1191; tel. 303/837–7111;
Web address: www.exempla.org

Owned, leased, sponsored:	2 hospitals	637 beds
Contract–managed:	1 hospital	436 beds
Totals:	3 hospitals	1073 beds

★1325: FAIRVIEW HEALTH SERVICES (NP)
2450 Riverside Avenue, Minneapolis, MN Zip 55454–1400; tel. 612/672–6300; David R. Page, President and Chief Executive Officer
(Moderately Centralized Health System)

MINNESOTA: FAIRVIEW LAKES REGIONAL HEALTH CARE (O, 50 beds) 5200 Fairview Boulevard, Wyoming, MN Zip 55092–8013; tel. 651/982–7000; Daniel K. Anderson, President
Web address: www.fairview.org/lakes/flrmc.htm

FAIRVIEW NORTHLAND REGIONAL HEALTH CARE (O, 41 beds) 911 Northland Drive, Princeton, MN Zip 55371–2173; tel. 763/389–1313; Michael Youso, President
Web address: www.fairview.org/northland/

FAIRVIEW RED WING MEDICAL CENTER (O, 135 beds) 701 Fairview Boulevard, Red Wing, MN Zip 55066–2848, Mailing Address: P.O. Box 95, Zip 55066–0095; tel. 651/267–5000; Scott Wordelman, President and Chief Executive Officer
Web address: www.fairview.org

For explanation of codes following names, see page B2.
★ Indicates Type III membership in the American Hospital Association.

FAIRVIEW RIDGES HOSPITAL (O, 147 beds) 201 East Nicollet Boulevard, Burnsville, MN Zip 55337–5799; tel. 952/892–2000; Sara Criger, President and Chief Executive Officer
Web address: www.fairview.org

FAIRVIEW SOUTHDALE HOSPITAL (O, 329 beds) 6401 France Avenue South, Edina, MN Zip 55435–2199; tel. 952/924–5000; Gary J. Strong, President
Web address: www.fairview.org

FAIRVIEW UNIVERSITY MEDICAL CENTER–MESABI (O, 111 beds) 750 East 34th Street, Hibbing, MN Zip 55746–4600; tel. 218/262–4881; Lawrence W. Pfaff, President and Chief Executive Officer
Web address: www.range.fairview.org

UNIVERSITY OF MINNESOTA MEDICAL CENTER (O, 829 beds) 2450 Riverside Avenue, Minneapolis, MN Zip 55454–1400; tel. 612/672–6000; Gordon L. Alexander, President
Web address: www.fairview.org

Owned, leased, sponsored:	7 hospitals	1642 beds
Contract–managed:	0 hospitals	0 beds
Totals:	7 hospitals	1642 beds

0328: FIRST HEALTH, INC. (IO)
6450 U.S. Highway 1, Rockledge, FL Zip 32955; tel. 321/434–7000; Michael D. Means, President and Chief Executive Officer

FLORIDA: CAPE CANAVERAL HOSPITAL/HEALTH FIRST (O, 150 beds) 701 West Cocoa Beach Causeway, Cocoa Beach, FL Zip 32931–5595, Mailing Address: P.O. Box 320069, Zip 32932–0069; tel. 321/799–7111; Roy Wright, FACHE, President and Chief Executive Officer
Web address: www.health–first.org

HOLMES REGIONAL MEDICAL CENTER (O, 504 beds) 1350 South Hickory Street, Melbourne, FL Zip 32901–3276; tel. 321/434–7000; Christopher S. Kennedy, President and Chief Executive Officer
Web address: www.health–first.org

Owned, leased, sponsored:	2 hospitals	654 beds
Contract–managed:	0 hospitals	0 beds
Totals:	2 hospitals	654 beds

★0243: FIRSTHEALTH OF THE CAROLINAS (NP)
155 Memorial Drive, Pinehurst, NC Zip 28374–8710, Mailing Address: P.O. Box 3000, Zip 28374–3000; tel. 910/715–1000; Charles T. Frock, President and Chief Executive Officer
(Centralized Physician/Insurance Health System)

NORTH CAROLINA: FIRSTHEALTH MONTGOMERY MEMORIAL HOSPITAL (O, 55 beds) 520 Allen Street, Troy, NC Zip 27371–2802, Mailing Address: P.O. Box 486, Zip 27371–0486; tel. 910/572–1301; Kerry A. Hensley, R.N., Vice President Operations
Web address: www.firsthealth.org

FIRSTHEALTH MOORE REGIONAL HOSPITAL (O, 356 beds) 155 Memorial Drive, Pinehurst, NC Zip 28374–8710, Mailing Address: P.O. Box 3000, Zip 28374–3000; tel. 910/215–1000; Stuart Voelpel, Senior Vice President Operations Hospital and Chief Operating Officer
Web address: www.firsthealth.org

FIRSTHEALTH RICHMOND MEMORIAL HOSPITAL (O, 141 beds) 925 Long Drive, Rockingham, NC Zip 28379–4815; tel. 910/417–3000; John J. Jackson, Vice President Operations
Web address: www.firsthealth.org

Owned, leased, sponsored:	3 hospitals	552 beds
Contract–managed:	0 hospitals	0 beds
Totals:	3 hospitals	552 beds

0174: FORUM HEALTH (NP)
3530 Belmont Avenue, Suite 7, Youngstown, OH Zip 44505; tel. 330/759–4090; N. Kristopher Hoce, President and Chief Executive Officer

OHIO: FORUM HEALTH TRUMBULL MEMORIAL HOSPITAL (O, 292 beds) 1350 East Market Street, Warren, OH Zip 44482–6628; tel. 330/841–9011; N. Kristopher Hoce, President and Chief Executive Officer
Web address: www.forumhealth.org

FORUM HILLSIDE REHABILITATION HOSPITAL (O, 47 beds) 8747 Squires Lane N.E., Warren, OH Zip 44484–1649; tel. 330/841–3700; Rodney Jones, Chief Operating Officer
Web address: www.forumhealth.org

WESTERN RESERVE CARE SYSTEM (O, 373 beds) 500 Gypsy Lane, Youngstown, OH Zip 44501–0240, Mailing Address: P.O. Box 990, Zip 44501–0990; tel. 330/747–1444; N. Kristopher Hoce, President and Chief Executive Officer
Web address: www.forumhealth.org

Owned, leased, sponsored:	3 hospitals	712 beds
Contract–managed:	0 hospitals	0 beds
Totals:	3 hospitals	712 beds

★1475: FRANCISCAN MISSIONARIES OF OUR LADY HEALTH SYSTEM, INC. (CC)
4200 Essen Lane, Baton Rouge, LA Zip 70809; tel. 225/923–2701; John J. Finan Jr, President and Chief Executive Officer
(Moderately Centralized Health System)

LOUISIANA: ASSUMPTION COMMUNITY HOSPITAL (O, 6 beds) 135 Highway 402, Napoleonville, LA Zip 70390; tel. 985/369–3600; Wayne M. Arboneaux, Administrator
Web address: www.ololrmc.com

OUR LADY OF LOURDES REGIONAL MEDICAL CENTER (O, 264 beds) 611 St. Landry Street, Lafayette, LA Zip 70506–4627, Mailing Address: P.O. Box 4027, Zip 70502–4027; tel. 337/289–2000; Robert Peebles, President and Chief Executive Officer
Web address: www.lourdes.net

OUR LADY OF THE LAKE REGIONAL MEDICAL CENTER (O, 626 beds) 5000 Hennessy Boulevard, Baton Rouge, LA Zip 70808–4350; tel. 225/765–6565; Robert C. Davidge, Chief Executive Officer
Web address: www.olormc.com

ST. ELIZABETH HOSPITAL (O, 83 beds) 1125 West Highway 30, Gonzales, LA Zip 70737; tel. 225/647–5000; Dee LeJeune, Chief Executive Officer
Web address: www.steh.com

ST. FRANCIS MEDICAL CENTER (O, 316 beds) 309 Jackson Street, Monroe, LA Zip 71201–7407, Mailing Address: P.O. Box 1901, Zip 71210–1901; tel. 318/327–4000; K. Scott Wester, FACHE, President and Chief Executive Officer
Web address: www.stfran.com

ST. PATRICK'S PSYCHIATRIC HOSPITAL (O, 28 beds) 309 Jackson Street, Monroe, LA Zip 71201, Mailing Address: P.O. Box 1901, Zip 71201–1901; tel. 318/327–4686; Cindy J. Rogers, FACHE, Chief Executive Officer
Web address: www.stpatrickshospital.net

Owned, leased, sponsored:	6 hospitals	1323 beds
Contract–managed:	0 hospitals	0 beds
Totals:	6 hospitals	1323 beds

5375: FRANCISCAN SERVICES CORPORATION (CC)
6832 Convent Boulevard, Sylvania, OH Zip 43560–2897; tel. 419/882–8373; John W. O'Connell, President
(Moderately Centralized Health System)

OHIO: TRINITY HEALTH SYSTEM (S, 350 beds) 380 Summit Avenue, Steubenville, OH Zip 43952–2699; tel. 740/283–7000; Fred B. Brower, President and Chief Executive Officer
Web address: www.trinityhealth.com

TEXAS: BURLESON ST. JOSEPH HEALTH CENTER (S, 25 beds) 1101 Woodson Drive, Caldwell, TX Zip 77836–1052, Mailing Address: P.O. Drawer 360, Zip 77836–0360; tel. 979/567–3245; Reed Edmundson, Administrator
Web address: www.st–joseph.org/

GRIMES ST. JOSEPH HEALTH CENTER (S, 25 beds) 210 South Judson Street, Navasota, TX Zip 77868–3704, Mailing Address: P.O. Box 1390, Zip 77868–1390; tel. 936/825–6585; Molly Hurst, Administrator
Web address: www.st–joseph.org

MADISON ST. JOSEPH HEALTH CENTER (S, 25 beds) 100 West Cross Street, Madisonville, TX Zip 77864–0698, Mailing Address: Box 698, Zip 77864–0698; tel. 936/348–2631; Reed Edmundson, Administrator

For explanation of codes following names, see page B2.
★ Indicates Type III membership in the American Hospital Association.

Section B

ST. JOSEPH REGIONAL HEALTH CENTER (S, 285 beds) 2801 Franciscan Drive, Bryan, TX Zip 77802–2599; tel. 979/776–3777; John J. Buckley Jr, President and Chief Executive Officer
Web address: www.st–joseph.org

TRINITY COMMUNITY MEDICAL CENTER OF BRENHAM (S, 60 beds) 700 Medical Parkway, Brenham, TX Zip 77833–5498; tel. 979/836–6173; John L. Simms, President and Chief Executive Officer
Web address: www.trinitymed.org

Owned, leased, sponsored:	6 hospitals	770 beds
Contract–managed:	0 hospitals	0 beds
Totals:	6 hospitals	770 beds

★1455: FRANCISCAN SISTERS OF CHRISTIAN CHARITY HEALTHCARE MINISTRY, INC (CC)
1415 South Rapids Road, Manitowoc, WI Zip 54220–9302; tel. 920/684–7071; Sister Laura J. Wolf, President
(Moderately Centralized Health System)

NEBRASKA: ST. FRANCIS MEMORIAL HOSPITAL (O, 95 beds) 430 North Monitor Street, West Point, NE Zip 68788–1595; tel. 402/372–2404; Ronald O. Briggs, FACHE, President and Chief Executive Officer
Web address: www.fcswp.org

OHIO: GENESIS HEALTHCARE SYSTEM (O, 405 beds) 2951 Maple Avenue, Zanesville, OH Zip 43701–2881; tel. 740/454–5000; Thomas L. Sieber, President and Chief Executive Officer
Web address: www.genesishcs.org

WISCONSIN: HOLY FAMILY MEMORIAL MEDICAL CENTER (O, 148 beds) 2300 Western Avenue, Manitowoc, WI Zip 54220, Mailing Address: P.O. Box 1450, Zip 54221–1450; tel. 920/684–2011; Mark P. Herzog, President and Chief Executive Officer
Web address: www.hfmhealth.org

Owned, leased, sponsored:	3 hospitals	648 beds
Contract–managed:	0 hospitals	0 beds
Totals:	3 hospitals	648 beds

★0271: FREEMAN HEALTH SYSTEM (NP)
1102 West 32nd Street, Joplin, MO Zip 64804; tel. 417/347–1111; Gary D. Duncan, President and Chief Executive Officer
(Centralized Health System)

MISSOURI: FREEMAN HEALTH SYSTEM (O, 320 beds) 1102 West 32nd Street, Joplin, MO Zip 64804–3599; tel. 417/347–1111; Gary D. Duncan, President and Chief Executive Officer
Web address: www.freemanhealth.com

FREEMAN NEOSHO HOSPITAL (O, 63 beds) 113 West Hickory Street, Neosho, MO Zip 64850–1705; tel. 417/455–4352; Phil Willcoxon, Chief Executive Officer
Web address: www.freemanhospitals.org

Owned, leased, sponsored:	2 hospitals	383 beds
Contract–managed:	0 hospitals	0 beds
Totals:	2 hospitals	383 beds

2115: FREMONT–RIDEOUT HEALTH GROUP (NP)
989 Plumas Street, Yuba City, CA Zip 95991; tel. 530/751–4010; Thomas P. Hayes, Chief Executive Officer
(Centralized Health System)

CALIFORNIA: FREMONT MEDICAL CENTER (O, 90 beds) 970 Plumas Street, Yuba City, CA Zip 95991–4087; tel. 530/751–4000; Thomas P. Hayes, Chief Executive Officer
Web address: www.frhg.org

RIDEOUT MEMORIAL HOSPITAL (O, 281 beds) 726 Fourth Street, Marysville, CA Zip 95901–5600, Mailing Address: P.O. Box 2128, Zip 95901–2128; tel. 530/749–4300; Thomas P. Hayes, Chief Executive Officer
Web address: www.frhg.org

Owned, leased, sponsored:	2 hospitals	371 beds
Contract–managed:	0 hospitals	0 beds
Totals:	2 hospitals	371 beds

★5570: GEISINGER HEALTH SYSTEM (NP)
100 North Academy Avenue, Danville, PA Zip 17822; tel. 570/271–6211; Glenn Steele Jr, M.D., Ph.D., President and Chief Executive Officer
(Centralized Physician/Insurance Health System)

PENNSYLVANIA: GEISINGER MEDICAL CENTER (O, 368 beds) 100 North Academy Avenue, Danville, PA Zip 17822–2201; tel. 570/271–6211; Louis A. Shapiro, Chief Operating Officer, Clinical Enterprise
Web address: www.geisinger.org

GEISINGER WYOMING VALLEY MEDICAL CENTER (O, 138 beds) 1000 East Mountain Drive, Wilkes–Barre, PA Zip 18711–0027; tel. 570/826–7300; Lissa Bryan–Smith, Chief Administrative Officer
Web address: www.geisinger.org

Owned, leased, sponsored:	2 hospitals	506 beds
Contract–managed:	0 hospitals	0 beds
Totals:	2 hospitals	506 beds

0311: GENESIS HEALTH SYSTEM (IO)
1227 East Rusholme Street, Davenport, IA Zip 52803–2498; tel. 563/421–1000; Leo A. Bressanelli, FACHE, President and Chief Executive Officer

ILLINOIS: GENESIS MEDICAL CENTER, ILLINI CAMPUS (O, 110 beds) 801 Illini Drive, Silvis, IL Zip 61282–1893; tel. 309/792–9363; Charles E. Bruhn, Chief Executive Officer
Web address: www.genesishealth.com

IOWA: GENESIS MEDICAL CENTER, DAVENPORT (O, 427 beds) 1227 East Rusholme Street, Davenport, IA Zip 52803–2498; tel. 563/421–1000; Leo A. Bressanelli, FACHE, Chief Executive Officer
Web address: www.genesishealth.com

GENESIS MEDICAL CENTER, DEWITT (O, 90 beds) 1118 11th Street, De Witt, IA Zip 52742–1296; tel. 563/659–4200; Jeffrey M. Cooper, President and Chief Executive Officer
Web address: www.genesishealth.com

Owned, leased, sponsored:	3 hospitals	627 beds
Contract–managed:	0 hospitals	0 beds
Totals:	3 hospitals	627 beds

0283: GILLIARD HEALTH SERVICES (IO)
3091 Carter Hill Road, Montgomery, AL Zip 36111; tel. 334/265–5009; William G. McKenzie, President and Chief Executive Officer
(Independent Hospital System)

ALABAMA: EVERGREEN MEDICAL CENTER (O, 42 beds) 101 Crestview Avenue, Evergreen, AL Zip 36401–0706, Mailing Address: P.O. Box 706, Zip 36401–0706; tel. 251/578–2480; L. E. Peace III, Administrator
Web address: www.evergreenmedical.org

JACKSON MEDICAL CENTER (O, 26 beds) 220 Hospital Drive, Jackson, AL Zip 36545–2459, Mailing Address: P.O. Box 428, Zip 36545–0428; tel. 251/246–9021; Teresa F. Grimes, Administrator
Web address: www.jacksonmedicalcenter.com

RANDOLPH MEDICAL CENTER (O, 40 beds) 59928 Highway 22, Roanoke, AL Zip 36274–2410, Mailing Address: P.O. Box 670, Zip 36274–0670; tel. 334/863–4111; John L. Robertson, Chief Executive Officer
Web address: www.randolphmedicalcenter.com

Owned, leased, sponsored:	3 hospitals	108 beds
Contract–managed:	0 hospitals	0 beds
Totals:	3 hospitals	108 beds

★1535: GREAT PLAINS HEALTH ALLIANCE, INC. (NP)
625 Third Street, Phillipsburg, KS Zip 67661–2138, Mailing Address: P.O. Box 366, Zip 67661–0366; tel. 785/543–2111; Roger S. John, President and Chief Executive Officer
(Decentralized Health System)

For explanation of codes following names, see page B2.
★ Indicates Type III membership in the American Hospital Association.

Section B

KANSAS: ASHLAND HEALTH CENTER (C, 47 beds) 709 Oak Street, Ashland, KS Zip 67831–0188, Mailing Address: P.O. Box 188, Zip 67831–0188; tel. 620/635–2241; Daryl Marshall, Administrator
Web address: www.phn.org

CHEYENNE COUNTY HOSPITAL (L, 16 beds) 210 West First Street, Saint Francis, KS Zip 67756–0547, Mailing Address: P.O. Box 547, Zip 67756–0547; tel. 785/332–2104; Leslie Lacy, Administrator
Web address: www.cheyennecountyhospital.com

COMANCHE COUNTY HOSPITAL (C, 14 beds) 202 South Frisco Street, Coldwater, KS Zip 67029, Mailing Address: HC 65, Box 8A, Zip 67029; tel. 620/582–2144; Nancy Zimmerman, R.N., Administrator
Web address: www.gpha.com

EDWARDS COUNTY HOSPITAL AND HEALTHCARE CENTER (C, 12 beds) 620 West Eighth Street, Kinsley, KS Zip 67547–2329, Mailing Address: P.O. Box 99, Zip 67547–0099; tel. 620/659–3621; Shaun Keef, Administrator

ELLINWOOD DISTRICT HOSPITAL (L, 25 beds) 605 North Main Street, Ellinwood, KS Zip 67526–1440; tel. 620/564–2548; David Haneke, Administrator
Web address: www.gpha.com

FREDONIA REGIONAL HOSPITAL (C, 51 beds) 1527 Madison Street, Fredonia, KS Zip 66736–1751, Mailing Address: P.O. Box 579, Zip 66736–0579; tel. 620/378–2121; Terry Deschaine, Chief Executive Officer
Web address: www.gpha.com

GREELEY COUNTY HEALTH SERVICES (L, 50 beds) 506 Third Street, Tribune, KS Zip 67879–0338, Mailing Address: P.O. Box 338, Zip 67879–0338; tel. 620/376–4221; Todd Burch, Administrator and Chief Executive Officer
Web address: www.phn.org

GRISELL MEMORIAL HOSPITAL DISTRICT ONE (C, 46 beds) 210 South Vermont Avenue, Ransom, KS Zip 67572; tel. 785/731–2231; Kristine Ochs, R.N., Administrator
Web address: www.gpha.com

KIOWA COUNTY MEMORIAL HOSPITAL (L, 25 beds) 501 South Walnut Street, Greensburg, KS Zip 67054–1951, Mailing Address: P.O. Box 616, Zip 67054–0616; tel. 620/723–3341; Mary Colclazier, Administrator
Web address: www.gpha.com

LANE COUNTY HOSPITAL (C, 31 beds) 235 West Vine, Dighton, KS Zip 67839–0969, Mailing Address: P.O. Box 969, Zip 67839–0969; tel. 620/397–5321; Donna McGowan, Administrator

MEDICINE LODGE MEMORIAL HOSPITAL (C, 25 beds) 710 North Walnut Street, Medicine Lodge, KS Zip 67104–1019, Mailing Address: P.O. Drawer C, Zip 67104; tel. 620/886–3771; Kevin A. White, Administrator

MINNEOLA DISTRICT HOSPITAL (C, 54 beds) 212 Main Street, Minneola, KS Zip 67865–0127, Mailing Address: P.O. Box 127, Zip 67865–0127; tel. 620/885–4264; Donald J. Kessen, Administrator and Chief Executive Officer
Web address: www.gpha.com

OSBORNE COUNTY MEMORIAL HOSPITAL (C, 25 beds) 424 West New Hampshire Street, Osborne, KS Zip 67473–0070, Mailing Address: P.O. Box 70, Zip 67473–0070; tel. 785/346–2121; Kiley Floyd, Administrator
Web address: www.ocmh.org

OTTAWA COUNTY HEALTH CENTER (L, 52 beds) 215 East Eighth, Minneapolis, KS Zip 67467–1999, Mailing Address: P.O. Box 290, Zip 67467–0290; tel. 785/392–2122; Joy Johnson, R.N., Administrator
Web address: www.gpha.com

PHILLIPS COUNTY HOSPITAL (L, 58 beds) 1150 State Street, Phillipsburg, KS Zip 67661–1799, Mailing Address: P.O. Box 607, Zip 67661–0607; tel. 785/543–5226; Raymond Williams III, Interim Chief Executive Officer
Web address: www.phillipshospital.org

RAWLINS COUNTY HEALTH CENTER (C, 24 beds) 707 Grant Street, Atwood, KS Zip 67730–4700, Mailing Address: P.O. Box 47, Zip 67730–4700; tel. 785/626–3211; Robert Garrison, Administrator and Chief Executive Officer
Web address: www.gpha.com

REPUBLIC COUNTY HOSPITAL (L, 63 beds) 2420 G Street, Belleville, KS Zip 66935–2400; tel. 785/527–2254; Blaine K. Miller, Administrator
Web address: www.republiccountyhospital.org

SABETHA COMMUNITY HOSPITAL (L, 25 beds) 14th and Oregon Streets, Sabetha, KS Zip 66534–0229, Mailing Address: P.O. Box 229, Zip 66534–0229; tel. 785/284–2121; Rita K. Buurman, Chief Executive Officer
Web address: www.sabethahospital.com

SATANTA DISTRICT HOSPITAL (C, 57 beds) 401 South Cheyenne Street, Satanta, KS Zip 67870–0159, Mailing Address: P.O. Box 159, Zip 67870–0159; tel. 620/649–2761; Curt Colson, Administrator
Web address: www.satanta.org

SMITH COUNTY MEMORIAL HOSPITAL (L, 54 beds) 614 South Main Street, Smith Center, KS Zip 66967–0349, Mailing Address: P.O. Box 349, Zip 66967–0349; tel. 785/282–6845; Carolyn K. Hess, R.N., Administrator
Web address: www.gpha.com

TREGO COUNTY–LEMKE MEMORIAL HOSPITAL (C, 62 beds) 320 North 13th Street, Wakeeney, KS Zip 67672–2099; tel. 785/743–2182; Daniel R. Bartz, Administrator
Web address: www.gpha.com

NEBRASKA: HARLAN COUNTY HEALTH SYSTEM (C, 25 beds) 717 North Brown Street, Alma, NE Zip 68920–0836, Mailing Address: P.O. Box 836, Zip 68920–0836; tel. 308/928–2151; Allen Van Driel, CHE, Administrator
Web address: www.gpha.com

Owned, leased, sponsored:	9 hospitals	368 beds
Contract–managed:	13 hospitals	473 beds
Totals:	22 hospitals	841 beds

0279: GREATER HAZLETON HEALTH ALLIANCE (NP)
687 North Church Street, Hazleton, PA Zip 18201–3198; tel. 570/501–6000; James D. Edwards, President
(Independent Hospital System)

PENNSYLVANIA: HAZLETON GENERAL HOSPITAL (C, 127 beds) 700 East Broad Street, Hazleton, PA Zip 18201–6897; tel. 570/501–4000; James Edwards, President
Web address: www.ghha.org

HAZLETON–ST. JOSEPH MEDICAL CENTER (C, 11 beds) 687 North Church Street, Hazleton, PA Zip 18201–3198; tel. 570/501–6000; James Edwards, President
Web address: www.ghha.org

Owned, leased, sponsored:	0 hospitals	0 beds
Contract–managed:	2 hospitals	138 beds
Totals:	2 hospitals	138 beds

★1555: GREENVILLE HOSPITAL SYSTEM (NP)
701 Grove Road, Greenville, SC Zip 29605–4211; tel. 864/455–7000; Frank D. Pinckney, President and Chief Executive Officer
(Centralized Health System)

SOUTH CAROLINA: ALLEN BENNETT HOSPITAL (O, 68 beds) 313 Memorial Drive, Greer, SC Zip 29650–1521; tel. 864/848–8200; Phil Feisal, Administrator
Web address: www.ghs.org

GREENVILLE MEMORIAL HOSPITAL (O, 806 beds) 701 Grove Road, Greenville, SC Zip 29605–4295; tel. 864/455–7000; Greg Rusnak, Vice President
Web address: www.ghs.org

HILLCREST HOSPITAL (O, 43 beds) 729 S.E. Main Street, Simpsonville, SC Zip 29681–3280; tel. 864/967–6100; Dennis R. Burns, FACHE, Administrator
Web address: www.ghs.org

Owned, leased, sponsored:	3 hospitals	917 beds
Contract–managed:	0 hospitals	0 beds
Totals:	3 hospitals	917 beds

2025: GULF HEALTH HOSPITALS (NP)
5 Mobile Infirmary Circle, Mobile, AL Zip 36607–3520; tel. 251/435–5500; E. Chandler Bramlett Jr, President and Chief Executive Officer
(Independent Hospital System)

ALABAMA: MOBILE INFIRMARY MEDICAL CENTER (O, 704 beds) 5 Mobile Infirmary Drive North, Mobile, AL Zip 36607–3513, Mailing Address: P.O. Box 2144, Zip 36652–2144; tel. 251/435–2400; E. Chandler Bramlett Jr, President and Chief Executive Officer
Web address: www.mobileinfirmary.org

For explanation of codes following names, see page B2.
★ Indicates Type III membership in the American Hospital Association.

NORTH BALDWIN INFIRMARY (L, 130 beds) 1815 Hand Avenue, Bay Minette, AL Zip 36507–4110, Mailing Address: P.O. Box 1409, Zip 36507–1409; tel. 251/937–5521; John S. Eads, Administrator
Web address: www.mobileinfirmary.org

Owned, leased, sponsored:	2 hospitals	834 beds
Contract–managed:	0 hospitals	0 beds
Totals:	2 hospitals	834 beds

★**0675: GUTHRIE HEALTHCARE SYSTEM** (NP)
Guthrie Square, Sayre, PA Zip 18840; tel. 570/888–6666; Mark Stensager, President and Chief Executive Officer
(Moderately Centralized Health System)

NEW YORK: CORNING HOSPITAL (O, 99 beds) 176 Denison Parkway East, Corning, NY Zip 14830–2899; tel. 607/937–7200; Marilyn J. Custer–Mitchell, Chief Operating Officer
Web address: www.corninghospital.com

PENNSYLVANIA: ROBERT PACKER HOSPITAL (O, 222 beds) 1 Guthrie Square, Sayre, PA Zip 18840–1698; tel. 570/888–6666; William F. Vanaskie, CHE, President and Chief Executive Officer
Web address: www.guthrie.org

TROY COMMUNITY HOSPITAL (O, 30 beds) 100 John Street, Troy, PA Zip 16947–0036; tel. 570/297–2121; Staci Covey, Administrator
Web address: www.guthrie.org

Owned, leased, sponsored:	3 hospitals	351 beds
Contract–managed:	0 hospitals	0 beds
Totals:	3 hospitals	351 beds

0303: HACKLEY HEALTH SYSTEM (NP)
2700 Clinton Street, Muskegon, MI Zip 49442; tel. 231/726–3511; Gordon A. Mudler, President and Chief Executive Officer
(Centralized Health System)

MICHIGAN: HACKLEY HEALTH (O, 181 beds) 1700 Clinton Street, Muskegon, MI Zip 49443–3302, Mailing Address: P.O. Box 3302, Zip 49443–3302; tel. 231/726–3511; Gordon A. Mudler, President and Chief Executive Officer
Web address: www.hackley.org

HACKLEY LAKESHORE HOSPITAL (O, 24 beds) 72 South State Street, Shelby, MI Zip 49455–1299; tel. 231/861–2156; Jay Bryan, Chief Executive Officer

Owned, leased, sponsored:	2 hospitals	205 beds
Contract–managed:	0 hospitals	0 beds
Totals:	2 hospitals	205 beds

★**3555: HAWAII HEALTH SYSTEMS CORPORATION** (NP)
3675 Kilauea Avenue, Honolulu, HI Zip 96816; tel. 808/733–4151; Thomas M. Driskill Jr, President and Chief Executive Officer
(Independent Hospital System)

HAWAII: HALE HO'OLA HAMAKUA (O, 50 beds) 45–547 Plumeria Street, Honokaa, HI Zip 96727–6902; tel. 808/775–7211; Romel Dela Cruz, Administrator
Web address: www.hhsc.org

HILO MEDICAL CENTER (O, 275 beds) 1190 Waianuenue Avenue, Hilo, HI Zip 96720–2095; tel. 808/974–4700; Ronald J. Schurra, Chief Executive Officer
Web address: www.hmc.hhsc.org

KAU HOSPITAL (O, 21 beds) 1 Kamani Street, Pahala, HI Zip 96777, Mailing Address: P.O. Box 40, Zip 96777–0040; tel. 808/928–8331; Merilyn Harris, Administrator
Web address: www.hhsc.org

KAUAI VETERANS MEMORIAL HOSPITAL (O, 45 beds) Waimea Canyon Road, Waimea, HI Zip 96796, Mailing Address: P.O. Box 337, Zip 96796–0337; tel. 808/338–9431; Orianna A. Skomoroch, Regional Chief Executive Officer
Web address: www.kvmh.hhsc.org

KOHALA HOSPITAL (O, 26 beds) 54–383 Hospital Road, Kohala, HI Zip 96755, Mailing Address: P.O. Box 10, Kapaau, Zip 96755–0010; tel. 808/889–6211; Ira F. Walton III, FACHE, Chief Executive Officer
Web address: www.koh.hhsc.org

KONA COMMUNITY HOSPITAL (O, 88 beds) 79–1019 Haukapila Street, Kealakekua, HI Zip 96750–7920; tel. 808/322–4430; Ira F. Walton III, FACHE, Chief Executive Officer
Web address: www.kch.hhsc.org

KULA HOSPITAL (O, 115 beds) 204 Kula Highway, Kula, HI Zip 96790–9499; tel. 808/878–1221; John Schaumburg, Administrator
Web address: www.hhsc.org

LANAI COMMUNITY HOSPITAL (O, 14 beds) 628 Seventh Street, Lanai City, HI Zip 96763–0650, Mailing Address: P.O. Box 630650, Zip 96763–0650; tel. 808/565–6411; Mary Catiel, Acting Administrator
Web address: www.lch.hhsc.org

LEAHI HOSPITAL (O, 192 beds) 3675 Kilauea Avenue, Honolulu, HI Zip 96816–2398; tel. 808/733–8000; Vincent H. S. Lee, FACHE, Administrator
Web address: www.hhsc.org

MAUI MEMORIAL MEDICAL CENTER (O, 193 beds) 221 Mahalani Street, Wailuku, HI Zip 96793–2581; tel. 808/244–9056; Wesley Lo, Chief Executive Officer
Web address: www.mmmc.hhsc.org

SAMUEL MAHELONA MEMORIAL HOSPITAL (O, 81 beds) 4800 Kawaihau Road, Kapaa, HI Zip 96746–1998; tel. 808/822–4961; Orianna A. Skomoroch, Regional Chief Executive Officer
Web address: www.mahelona.org

Owned, leased, sponsored:	11 hospitals	1100 beds
Contract–managed:	0 hospitals	0 beds
Totals:	11 hospitals	1100 beds

0266: HAWAII PACIFIC HEALTH (NP)
55 Merchant Street, Honolulu, HI Zip 96813; tel. 808/535–7414; Charles A. Sted, Pesident and Chief Executive Officer
(Moderately Centralized Health System)

KAPIOLANI MEDICAL CENTER AT PALI MOMI (O, 100 beds) 98–1079 Moanalua Road, Aiea, HI Zip 96701–4713; tel. 808/486–6000; Ray Vara, Chief Executive Officer
Web address: www.kapiolani.org

KAPIOLANI MEDICAL CENTER FOR WOMEN & CHILDREN (O, 225 beds) 1319 Punahou Street, Honolulu, HI Zip 96826–1032; tel. 808/983–6000; Ray Vara, Chief Executive Officer
Web address: www.kapiolani.org

STRAUB CLINIC & HOSPITAL (O, 143 beds) 888 South King Street, Honolulu, HI Zip 96813–3083; tel. 808/522–4000; Ray Vara, Chief Executive Officer
Web address: www.straubhealth.com

WILCOX MEMORIAL HOSPITAL (O, 181 beds) 3420 Kuhio Highway, Lihue, HI Zip 96766–1099; tel. 808/245–1100; Lee Evslin, M.D., President and Chief Executive Officer
Web address: www.wilcoxhealth.org

Owned, leased, sponsored:	4 hospitals	649 beds
Contract–managed:	0 hospitals	0 beds
Totals:	4 hospitals	649 beds

★**0048: HCA** (IO)
One Park Plaza, Nashville, TN Zip 37203–1548; tel. 615/344–9551; Jack O. Bovender Jr, Chairman and Chief Executive Officer
(Decentralized Health System)

ALASKA: ALASKA REGIONAL HOSPITAL (O, 178 beds) 2801 Debarr Road, Anchorage, AK Zip 99508–2997, Mailing Address: P.O. Box 143889, Zip 99514–3889; tel. 907/264–1754; Edward H. Lamb, FACHE, President and Chief Executive Officer
Web address: www.alaskaregional.com

CALIFORNIA: GOOD SAMARITAN HOSPITAL (O, 269 beds) 2425 Samaritan Drive, San Jose, CA Zip 95124–3997, Mailing Address: P.O. Box 240002, Zip 95154–2402; tel. 408/559–2011; William K. Piche, Chief Executive Officer
Web address: www.goodsamsanjose.com

LOS ROBLES HOSPITAL AND MEDICAL CENTER (O, 265 beds) 215 West Janss Road, Thousand Oaks, CA Zip 91360–1847; tel. 805/497–2727; Jim Sherman, President and Chief Exeuctive Officer
Web address: www.losrobleshospital.com

For explanation of codes following names, see page B2.
★ Indicates Type III membership in the American Hospital Association.

REGIONAL MEDICAL CENTER OF SAN JOSE (O, 204 beds) 225 North Jackson Avenue, San Jose, CA Zip 95116–1691; tel. 408/729–2801; William L. Gilbert, Chief Executive Officer
Web address: www.regionalmedicalsanjose.com

RIVERSIDE COMMUNITY HOSPITAL (O, 338 beds) 4445 Magnolia Avenue, Riverside, CA Zip 92501–4199, Mailing Address: P.O. Box 1669, Zip 92502–1669; tel. 951/788–3000; Jaime A. Wesolowski, President and Chief Executive Officer
Web address: www.riversidecommunityhospital.com

WEST HILLS HOSPITAL AND MEDICAL CENTER (O, 120 beds) 7300 Medical Center Drive, Canoga Park, CA Zip 91307–1902; tel. 818/676–4000; Beverly Gilmore, President and Chief Executive Officer
Web address: www.westhillshospital.com

COLORADO: MEDICAL CENTER OF AURORA (O, 314 beds) 1501 South Potomac Street, Aurora, CO Zip 80012–5499; tel. 303/695–2600; Sylvia Young, President and Chief Executive Officer
Web address: www.auroramed.com

NORTH SUBURBAN MEDICAL CENTER (O, 140 beds) 9191 Grant Street, Thornton, CO Zip 80229–4341; tel. 303/451–7800; Todd Steward, President and Chief Executive Officer
Web address: www.northsuburban.com

PRESBYTERIAN–ST. LUKE'S MEDICAL CENTER (O, 400 beds) 1719 East 19th Avenue, Denver, CO Zip 80218–1281; tel. 303/839–6000; Madeleine Roberson, President and Chief Executive Officer
Web address: www.pslmc.com

ROSE MEDICAL CENTER (O, 246 beds) 4567 East Ninth Avenue, Denver, CO Zip 80220–3941; tel. 303/320–2121; Kenneth H. Feiler, President and Chief Executive Officer
Web address: www.rosebabies.com

SKY RIDGE MEDICAL CENTER (O, 106 beds) 10101 Ridge Gate Parkway, Lone Tree, CO Zip 80124; tel. 720/225–1000; Maureen Tarrant, Chief Executive Officer
Web address: www.skyridgemedcenter.com

SPALDING REHABILITATION HOSPITAL (O, 122 beds) 900 Potomac Street, Aurora, CO Zip 80011–6716; tel. 303/367–1166; Cynthia Kruetz, President and Chief Executive Officer
Web address: www.spaldingrehab.com

SWEDISH MEDICAL CENTER (O, 333 beds) 501 East Hampden Avenue, Englewood, CO Zip 80110–0101; tel. 303/788–5000; Mary M. White, President and Chief Executive Officer
Web address: www.swedishhospital.com

FLORIDA: AVENTURA HOSPITAL AND MEDICAL CENTER (O, 407 beds) 20900 Biscayne Boulevard, Aventura, FL Zip 33180–1407; tel. 305/682–7000; Davide M. Carbone, Chief Executive Officer
Web address: www.aventurahospital.com

BLAKE MEDICAL CENTER (O, 298 beds) 2020 59th Street West, Bradenton, FL Zip 34209–4669; tel. 941/792–6611; Daniel J. Friedrich III, Chief Executive Officer
Web address: www.blakemedicalcenter.com

BRANDON REGIONAL HOSPITAL (O, 327 beds) 119 Oakfield Drive, Brandon, FL Zip 33511–5799; tel. 813/681–5551; Michael M. Fencel, Chief Executive Officer
Web address: www.brandonhospital.com

CAPITAL REGIONAL MEDICAL CENTER (O, 198 beds) 2626 Capital Medical Boulevard, Tallahassee, FL Zip 32308–4499; tel. 850/325–5000; Sharon L. Roush, Chief Executive Officer
Web address: www.capitalregionalmedicalcenter.com

CEDARS MEDICAL CENTER (O, 515 beds) 1400 N.W. 12th Avenue, Miami, FL Zip 33136–1003; tel. 305/325–5511; Michael G. Joseph, Administrator
Web address: www.cedarsmedicalcenter.com

CENTRAL FLORIDA REGIONAL HOSPITAL (O, 226 beds) 1401 West Seminole Boulevard, Sanford, FL Zip 32771–6764; tel. 407/321–4500; Rodney R. Smith, Chief Executive Officer
Web address: www.centralfloridaregional.com

COLUMBIA HOSPITAL (O, 250 beds) 2201 45th Street, West Palm Beach, FL Zip 33407–2069; tel. 561/842–6141; Valerie A. Jackson, Chief Executive Officer
Web address: www.columbiahospital.com

COMMUNITY HOSPITAL (O, 414 beds) 5637 Marine Parkway, New Port Richey, FL Zip 34652–4331, Mailing Address: P.O. Box 996, Zip 34656–0996; tel. 727/848–1733; Kathryn Gillette, Chief Executive Officer
Web address: www.communityhospitalnpr.com

DOCTORS HOSPITAL OF SARASOTA (O, 168 beds) 5731 Bee Ridge Road, Sarasota, FL Zip 34233–5056; tel. 941/342–1100; Robert C. Meade, Chief Executive Officer
Web address: www.doctorsofsarasota.com

EDWARD WHITE HOSPITAL (O, 113 beds) 2323 Ninth Avenue North, Saint Petersburg, FL Zip 33713–6898, Mailing Address: P.O. Box 12018, Zip 33733–2018; tel. 727/323–1111; Roland Metivier, Chief Executive Officer
Web address: www.edwardwhitehospital.com

ENGLEWOOD COMMUNITY HOSPITAL (O, 100 beds) 700 Medical Boulevard, Englewood, FL Zip 34223–3978; tel. 941/475–6571; Robert C. Meade, Chief Executive Officer
Web address: www.englewoodcommunityhospital.com

FAWCETT MEMORIAL HOSPITAL (O, 200 beds) 21298 Olean Boulevard, Port Charlotte, FL Zip 33952–6765, Mailing Address: P.O. Box 494960, Punta Gorda, Zip 33949–4960; tel. 941/629–1181; Thomas J. Rice, President and Chief Executive Officer
Web address: www.fawcetthospital.com

FORT WALTON BEACH MEDICAL CENTER (O, 247 beds) 1000 Mar–Walt Drive, Fort Walton Beach, FL Zip 32547–6795; tel. 850/862–1111; Wayne Campbell, Chief Executive Officer
Web address: www.fwbmedicalcenter.com

GULF COAST HOSPITAL (O, 107 beds) 13681 Doctors Way, Fort Myers, FL Zip 33912–4309; tel. 239/768–5000; Mark F. Weber, FACHE, President and Chief Executive Officer
Web address: www.gulfcoasthospital.com

GULF COAST MEDICAL CENTER (O, 176 beds) 449 West 23rd Street, Panama City, FL Zip 32405–4593, Mailing Address: P.O. Box 15309, Zip 32406–5309; tel. 850/769–8341; Todd Gallati, Chief Executive Officer
Web address: www.egulfcoastmedical.com

J. F. K. MEDICAL CENTER (O, 387 beds) 5301 South Congress Avenue, Atlantis, FL Zip 33462–1197; tel. 561/965–7300; Gina Melby, Chief Executive Officer
Web address: www.jfkmc.com

KENDALL REGIONAL MEDICAL CENTER (O, 322 beds) 11750 Bird Road, Miami, FL Zip 33175–3530; tel. 305/223–3000; Victor Maya, Chief Executive Officer
Web address: www.kendallmed.com

LAKE CITY MEDICAL CENTER (O, 67 beds) 340 N.W. Commerce Drive, Lake City, FL Zip 32055–3718; tel. 386/719–9000; Garry L. Karsner, Chief Executive Officer
Web address: www.lakecitymedical.com

LARGO MEDICAL CENTER (O, 243 beds) 201 14th Street S.W., Largo, FL Zip 33770–3133, Mailing Address: P.O. Box 2905, Zip 33779–2905; tel. 727/588–5200; Thomas L. Herron, FACHE, President and Chief Executive Officer
Web address: www.largomedical.com

LAWNWOOD REGIONAL MEDICAL CENTER (O, 345 beds) 1700 South 23rd Street, Fort Pierce, FL Zip 34950–0188; tel. 772/461–4000; Thomas R. Pentz, President and Chief Executive Officer
Web address: www.lawnwoodmed.com

MEMORIAL HOSPITAL OF JACKSONVILLE (O, 353 beds) 3625 University Boulevard South, Jacksonville, FL Zip 32216–4240, Mailing Address: P.O. Box 16325, Zip 32216–6325; tel. 904/399–6111; H. Rex Etheredge, President and Chief Executive Officer
Web address: www.memorialhospitaljax.com

NORTH FLORIDA REGIONAL MEDICAL CENTER (O, 267 beds) 6500 Newberry Road, Gainesville, FL Zip 32605–4392, Mailing Address: P.O. Box 147006, Zip 32614–7006; tel. 352/333–4000; James R. Thomas, Chief Executive Officer
Web address: www.nfrmc.com

NORTHSIDE HOSPITAL AND HEART INSTITUTE (O, 288 beds) 6000 49th Street North, Saint Petersburg, FL Zip 33709–2145; tel. 727/521–4411; Ward Boston III, Chief Executive Officer
Web address: www.northsidehospital.com

NORTHWEST MEDICAL CENTER (O, 175 beds) 2801 North State Road 7, Margate, FL Zip 33063; tel. 954/978–4000; MaryLynn Swartz, Chief Executive Officer
Web address: www.northwestmed.com

OAK HILL HOSPITAL (O, 204 beds) 11375 Cortez Boulevard, Brooksville, FL Zip 34613, Mailing Address: P.O. Box 5300, Spring Hill, Zip 34611–5300; tel. 352/596–6632; Mickey Smith, Chief Executive Officer
Web address: www.oakhillhospital.com

For explanation of codes following names, see page B2.
★ Indicates Type III membership in the American Hospital Association.

Section B

OCALA REGIONAL MEDICAL CENTER (O, 270 beds) 1431 S.W. First Avenue, Ocala, FL Zip 34474–4058, Mailing Address: P.O. Box 2200, Zip 34478–2200; tel. 352/401–1000; James B. Wood, President and Chief Executive Officer
Web address: www.ocalaregional.com

ORANGE PARK MEDICAL CENTER (O, 230 beds) 2001 Kingsley Avenue, Orange Park, FL Zip 32073–5156; tel. 904/276–8500; Robert M. Krieger, Chief Executive Officer
Web address: www.opmedical.com

OSCEOLA REGIONAL MEDICAL CENTER (O, 231 beds) 700 West Oak Street, Kissimmee, FL Zip 34741–4996; tel. 407/846–2266; E. Tim Cook, Chief Executive Officer
Web address: www.osceolaregional.com

PALMS WEST HOSPITAL (O, 140 beds) 13001 Southern Boulevard, Loxahatchee, FL Zip 33470–1150; tel. 561/798–3300; Heather J. Rohan, Chief Executive Officer
Web address: www.palmswesthospital.com

PLANTATION GENERAL HOSPITAL (O, 264 beds) 401 N.W. 42nd Avenue, Plantation, FL Zip 33317–2882; tel. 954/587–5010; Anthony M. Degina Jr, Chief Executive Officer
Web address: www.plantationgeneral.com

RAULERSON HOSPITAL (O, 101 beds) 1796 Highway 441 North, Okeechobee, FL Zip 34972–1918, Mailing Address: P.O. Box 1307, Zip 34973–1307; tel. 863/763–2151; Robert H. Lee, President
Web address: www.raulersonhospital.com

REGIONAL MEDICAL CENTER–BAYONET POINT (O, 243 beds) 14000 Fivay Road, Hudson, FL Zip 34667–7199; tel. 727/863–2411; David R. Williams, Chief Executive Officer
Web address: www.rmchealth.com

SOUTH BAY HOSPITAL (O, 122 beds) 4016 State Road 674, Sun City Center, FL Zip 33573–5298; tel. 813/634–3301; Stephen A. Rector, Chief Executive Officer
Web address: www.southbayhospital.com

SOUTHWEST FLORIDA REGIONAL MEDICAL CENTER (O, 279 beds) 2727 Winkler Avenue, Fort Myers, FL Zip 33901–9396; tel. 239/939–1147; Mark F. Weber, FACHE, President and Chief Executive Officer
Web address: www.swfrmc.com

ST. LUCIE MEDICAL CENTER (O, 194 beds) 1800 S.E. Tiffany Avenue, Port St. Lucie, FL Zip 34952–7580; tel. 772/335–4000; Gary Cantrell, President and Chief Executive Officer
Web address: www.stluciemed.com

ST. PETERSBURG GENERAL HOSPITAL (O, 219 beds) 6500 38th Avenue North, Saint Petersburg, FL Zip 33710–1629; tel. 727/384–1414; Richard H. Satcher, President and Chief Executive Officer
Web address: www.stpetegeneral.com

TWIN CITIES HOSPITAL (O, 65 beds) 2190 Highway 85 North, Niceville, FL Zip 32578–1045; tel. 850/678–4131; David Whalen, Chief Executive Officer
Web address: www.tchealthcare.com

UNIVERSITY HOSPITAL AND MEDICAL CENTER (O, 271 beds) 7201 North University Drive, Tamarac, FL Zip 33321–2996; tel. 954/721–2200; James A. Cruickshank, Chief Executive Officer
Web address: www.uhmchealth.com

WEST FLORIDA HOSPITAL (O, 339 beds) 8383 North Davis Highway, Pensacola, FL Zip 32514–6088; tel. 850/494–4000; Dennis A. Taylor, Chief Executive Officer
Web address: www.westfloridahospital.com

WESTSIDE REGIONAL MEDICAL CENTER (O, 224 beds) 8201 West Broward Boulevard, Plantation, FL Zip 33324–9937; tel. 954/473–6600; Earl H. Denning, Chief Executive Officer
Web address: www.westsideregional.com

GEORGIA: COLISEUM MEDICAL CENTERS (O, 214 beds) 350 Hospital Drive, Macon, GA Zip 31217–3871; tel. 478/765–7000; Allen Golson, Chief Executive Officer
Web address: www.coliseumhealthsystem.com

COLISEUM PSYCHIATRIC CENTER (O, 32 beds) 340 Hospital Drive, Macon, GA Zip 31217–8002; tel. 478/741–1355; Mark Nichols, FACHE, Chief Executive Officer, Coliseum Psychiatric Center
Web address: www.hcahealthcare.com

DOCTORS HOSPITAL (O, 255 beds) 3651 Wheeler Road, Augusta, GA Zip 30909–6426; tel. 706/651–3232; C. Shayne George, President and Chief Executive Officer
Web address: www.doctors–hospital.net

DOCTORS HOSPITAL OF COLUMBUS (O, 171 beds) 616 19th Street, Columbus, GA Zip 31901–1528, Mailing Address: P.O. Box 2188, Zip 31902–2188; tel. 706/494–4262; Hugh D. Wilson, Chief Executive Officer
Web address: www.doctorshospital.net

EMORY CARTERSVILLE MEDICAL CENTER (O, 80 beds) 960 Joe Frank Harris Parkway, Cartersville, GA Zip 30120–2129, Mailing Address: P.O. Box 200008, Zip 30120–9001; tel. 770/382–1530; Keith Sandlin, Chief Executive Officer
Web address: www.cartersvillemedical.com

EMORY DUNWOODY MEDICAL CENTER (O, 118 beds) 4575 North Shallowford Road, Atlanta, GA Zip 30338–6499; tel. 770/454–2000; Thomas D. Gilbert, President and Chief Executive Officer
Web address: www.emorydunwoody.com

EMORY EASTSIDE MEDICAL CENTER (O, 171 beds) 1700 Medical Way, Snellville, GA Zip 30078–2195, Mailing Address: P.O. Box 587, Zip 30078–0587; tel. 770/979–0200; Les Beard, Chief Executive Officer
Web address: www.emoryeastside.com

FAIRVIEW PARK HOSPITAL (O, 190 beds) 200 Industrial Boulevard, Dublin, GA Zip 31021–2997, Mailing Address: P.O. Box 1408, Zip 31040–1408; tel. 478/275–2000; James E. Raynor, Chief Executive Officer
Web address: www.fairviewparkhospital.com

HUGHSTON ORTHOPEDIC HOSPITAL (O, 100 beds) 100 Frist Court, Columbus, GA Zip 31908–7188, Mailing Address: P.O. Box 7188, Zip 31908–7188; tel. 706/576–2101; Donald R. Avery, FACHE, President and Chief Executive Officer
Web address: www.hughstonsports.com

MACON NORTHSIDE HOSPITAL (O, 103 beds) 400 Charter Boulevard, Macon, GA Zip 31210–4853, Mailing Address: P.O. Box 4627, Zip 31208–4627; tel. 478/757–8200; Bud Costello, Administrator and Chief Executive Officer
Web address: www.coliseumhealthsystem.com

NORTHLAKE MEDICAL CENTER (O, 116 beds) 1455 Montreal Road, Tucker, GA Zip 30084–8100; tel. 770/270–3000; Daniel W. Jackson, Chief Executive Officer
Web address: www.northlakemedical.com

PALMYRA MEDICAL CENTERS (O, 174 beds) 2000 Palmyra Road, Albany, GA Zip 31702–1908, Mailing Address: P.O. Box 1908, Zip 31702–1908; tel. 229/434–2000; Bud Wethington, Chief Executive Officer
Web address: www.palmyramedicalcenters.com

POLK MEDICAL CENTER (O, 22 beds) 424 North Main Street, Cedartown, GA Zip 30125–2698; tel. 770/748–2500; Steve C. Hoelscher, Chief Executive Officer
Web address: www.polkmedicalcenter.com

REDMOND REGIONAL MEDICAL CENTER (O, 191 beds) 501 Redmond Road, Rome, GA Zip 30165–7001, Mailing Address: Box 107001, Zip 30164–7001; tel. 706/291–0291; Brenda M. Waltz, FACHE, Chief Executive Officer
Web address: www.redmondregional.com

IDAHO: EASTERN IDAHO REGIONAL MEDICAL CENTER (O, 291 beds) 3100 Channing Way, Idaho Falls, ID Zip 83404–7533, Mailing Address: P.O. Box 2077, Zip 83403–2077; tel. 208/529–6111; Douglas Crabtree, Chief Executive Officer
Web address: www.eirmc.com

WEST VALLEY MEDICAL CENTER (O, 122 beds) 1717 Arlington, Caldwell, ID Zip 83605–4864; tel. 208/459–4641; Mark B. Adams, Chief Executive Officer
Web address: www.westvalleymedctr.com

INDIANA: TERRE HAUTE REGIONAL HOSPITAL (O, 207 beds) 3901 South Seventh Street, Terre Haute, IN Zip 47802–4299; tel. 812/232–0021; E. Kenneth Hutchenrider, Chief Executive Officer
Web address: www.regionalhospital.com

KANSAS: ALLEN COUNTY HOSPITAL (O, 25 beds) 101 South First Street, Iola, KS Zip 66749–3505, Mailing Address: P.O. Box 540, Zip 66749–0540; tel. 620/365–1000; Michael C. Carter, Interim Chief Executive Officer
Web address: www.allencountyhospital.com

MENORAH MEDICAL CENTER (O, 158 beds) 5721 West 119th Street, Overland Park, KS Zip 66209–3722; tel. 913/498–6000; Steven D. Wilkinson, President and Chief Executive Officer
Web address: www.menorahmedicalcenter.com

For explanation of codes following names, see page B2.
★ Indicates Type III membership in the American Hospital Association.

OVERLAND PARK REGIONAL MEDICAL CENTER (O, 256 beds) 10500 Quivira Road, Overland Park, KS Zip 66215–2306, Mailing Address: P.O. Box 15959, Zip 66215–5959; tel. 913/541–5000; Kevin J. Hicks, Chief Executive Officer
Web address: www.oprmc.com

WESLEY MEDICAL CENTER (O, 503 beds) 550 North Hillside, Wichita, KS Zip 67214–4976; tel. 316/962–2000; David S. Nevill, President and Chief Executive Officer
Web address: www.wesleymc.com

KENTUCKY: FRANKFORT REGIONAL MEDICAL CENTER (O, 146 beds) 299 King's Daughters Drive, Frankfort, KY Zip 40601–4186; tel. 502/875–5240; Michael A. Mayo, FACHE, Chief Executive Officer
Web address: www.frankfortregional.com

GREENVIEW REGIONAL HOSPITAL (O, 211 beds) 1801 Ashley Circle, Bowling Green, KY Zip 42104–3384, Mailing Address: P.O. Box 90024, Zip 42102–9024; tel. 270/793–1000; Mark A. Marsh, Chief Executive Officer
Web address: www.greenviewhospital.com

LOUISIANA: AVOYELLES HOSPITAL (O, 47 beds) 4231 Highway 1192, Marksville, LA Zip 71351, Mailing Address: P.O. Box 249, Zip 71351–0249; tel. 318/253–8611; David M. Mitchel, Chief Executive Officer
Web address: www.avoyelleshospital.com

DAUTERIVE HOSPITAL (O, 103 beds) 600 North Lewis Street, New Iberia, LA Zip 70560–2043; tel. 337/365–7311; Kyle J. Viator, Chief Executive Officer
Web address: www.dauterivehospital.com

LAKESIDE HOSPITAL (O, 75 beds) 4700 I–10 Service Road, Metairie, LA Zip 70001–1269; tel. 504/780–8282; Shirley A. Stewart, CHE, Chief Executive Officer
Web address: www.lakesidehospital.com

LAKEVIEW REGIONAL MEDICAL CENTER (O, 178 beds) 95 East Fairway Drive, Covington, LA Zip 70433–7507; tel. 985/867–3800; Max Lauderdale, Chief Executive Officer
Web address: www.lakeviewregional.com

NORTH MONROE MEDICAL CENTER (O, 239 beds) 3421 Medical Park Drive, Monroe, LA Zip 71203–2399; tel. 318/388–1946; Betty P. Scriber, FACHE, Chief Executive Officer
Web address: www.northmonroe.net

OAKDALE COMMUNITY HOSPITAL (O, 59 beds) 130 North Hospital Drive, Oakdale, LA Zip 71463, Mailing Address: P.O. Box 629, Zip 71463–0629; tel. 318/335–3700; H. J. Gaspard, Chief Executive Officer
Web address: www.oakdalecommunityhospital.com

RAPIDES REGIONAL MEDICAL CENTER (O, 323 beds) 211 Fourth Street, Alexandria, LA Zip 71301–8421, Mailing Address: Box 30101, 211 Fourth Street, Zip 71306–0146; tel. 318/473–3000; A. C. Buchanan, President and Chief Executive Officer
Web address: www.rapidesregional.com

SAVOY MEDICAL CENTER (O, 180 beds) 801 Poinciana Avenue, Mamou, LA Zip 70554–2298; tel. 337/468–5261; Gerald A. Fornoff, Chief Executive Officer
Web address: www.savoymedicalcenter.com

SOUTHWEST MEDICAL CENTER (O, 135 beds) 2810 Ambassador Caffery Parkway, Lafayette, LA Zip 70506–5900; tel. 337/981–2949; Stephen K. Jones Jr, FACHE, Chief Executive Officer
Web address: www.southwestmc.com

TULANE UNIVERSITY HOSPITAL AND CLINIC (O, 353 beds) 1415 Tulane Avenue, New Orleans, LA Zip 70112–2605; tel. 504/988–5263; James T. Montgomery, CHE, President and Chief Executive Officer
Web address: www.tuhc.com

WINN PARISH MEDICAL CENTER (O, 60 beds) 301 West Boundary Street, Winnfield, LA Zip 71483–3427, Mailing Address: P.O. Box 152, Zip 71483–0152; tel. 318/648–3000; Bobby Jordan, Chief Executive Officer
Web address: www.winnparishmedical.com

WOMEN'S AND CHILDREN'S HOSPITAL (O, 157 beds) 4600 Ambassador Caffery Parkway, Lafayette, LA Zip 70508–6923, Mailing Address: P.O. Box 88030, Zip 70598–8030; tel. 337/521–9100; Kathy J. Bobbs, Chief Executive Officer
Web address: www.womens–childrens.com

MISSISSIPPI: GARDEN PARK MEDICAL CENTER (O, 130 beds) 15200 Community Road, Gulfport, MS Zip 39503–3085, Mailing Address: P.O. Box 1240, Zip 39502–1240; tel. 228/575–7000; William E. Peaks, Chief Executive Officer
Web address: www.gardenparkmedical.com

MISSOURI: BAPTIST–LUTHERAN MEDICAL CENTER (O, 265 beds) 6601 Rockhill Road, Kansas City, MO Zip 64131–1197; tel. 816/276–7000; Darrell W. Moore, President and Chief Executive Officer
Web address: www.b–lmc.com

INDEPENDENCE REGIONAL HEALTH CENTER (O, 213 beds) 1509 West Truman Road, Independence, MO Zip 64050–3498; tel. 816/836–8100; Dan L. Jones Jr, Chief Executive Officer
Web address: www.independenceregionalhealthcenter.com

LAFAYETTE REGIONAL HEALTH CENTER (O, 25 beds) 1500 State Street, Lexington, MO Zip 64067–1199; tel. 660/259–2203; Bret Kolman, CPA, Chief Executive Officer
Web address: www.lafayetteregionalhealthcenter.com

LEE'S SUMMIT HOSPITAL (O, 83 beds) 530 North Murray Road, Lees Summit, MO Zip 64081–1497; tel. 816/969–6000; Carolyn W. Caldwell, Chief Executive Officer
Web address: www.leessummithospital.com

MEDICAL CENTER OF INDEPENDENCE (O, 123 beds) 17203 East 23rd Street South, Independence, MO Zip 64057–1899; tel. 816/478–5000; Dan L. Jones Jr, Chief Executive Officer
Web address: www.medicalcenterofindependence.com

RESEARCH BELTON HOSPITAL (O, 38 beds) 17065 South 71 Highway, Belton, MO Zip 64012–2165; tel. 816/348–1200; Todd Krass, President and Chief Executive Officer
Web address: www.researchbeltonhospital.com

RESEARCH MEDICAL CENTER (O, 446 beds) 2316 East Meyer Boulevard, Kansas City, MO Zip 64132–1199; tel. 816/276–4000; Niels P. Vernegaard, Chief Executive Officer
Web address: www.researchmedicalcenter.com

RESEARCH PSYCHIATRIC CENTER (O, 100 beds) 2323 East 63rd Street, Kansas City, MO Zip 64130–3495; tel. 816/444–8161; Todd Krass, President and Chief Executive Officer
Web address: www.researchpsychiatriccenter.com

NEVADA: MOUNTAINVIEW HOSPITAL (O, 199 beds) 3100 North Tenaya Way, Las Vegas, NV Zip 89128–0436; tel. 702/255–5000; Mark J. Howard, President and Chief Executive Officer
Web address: www.mountainview–hospital.com

SOUTHERN HILLS HOSPITAL AND MEDICAL CENTER (O, 130 beds) 9300 West Sunset Road, Las Vegas, NV Zip 89148; tel. 702/880–2100; Stephen E. Dixon, Chief Executive Officer
Web address: www.southernhillshospital.com

SUNRISE HOSPITAL AND MEDICAL CENTER (O, 655 beds) 3186 Maryland Parkway, Las Vegas, NV Zip 89109–2306, Mailing Address: P.O. Box 98530, Zip 89193–8530; tel. 702/731–8000; Brian C. Robinson, Chief Executive Officer
Web address: www.sunrisehospital.com

NEW HAMPSHIRE: PARKLAND MEDICAL CENTER (O, 82 beds) One Parkland Drive, Derry, NH Zip 03038–2750; tel. 603/432–1500; Anne Jamieson, Chief Executive Officer
Web address: www.parklandmedicalcenter.com

PORTSMOUTH REGIONAL HOSPITAL (O, 165 beds) 333 Borthwick Avenue, Portsmouth, NH Zip 03801–7004; tel. 603/436–5110; William J. Schuler, Chief Executive Officer
Web address: www.portsmouthhospital.com

NORTH CAROLINA: BRUNSWICK COMMUNITY HOSPITAL (O, 60 beds) 1 Medical Center Drive, Supply, NC Zip 28462–3350, Mailing Address: P.O. Box 139, Zip 28462–0139; tel. 910/755–8121; Hugh Brown, Chief Executive Officer
Web address: www.brunswickcommunityhospital.com

OKLAHOMA: EDMOND MEDICAL CENTER (O, 87 beds) 1 South Bryant Street, Edmond, OK Zip 73034–4798; tel. 405/341–6100; Ed Gray, Chief Executive Officer
Web address: www.edmondhospital.com

OU MEDICAL CENTER (O, 578 beds) 1200 Everett Drive, Oklahoma City, OK Zip 73104–5047, Mailing Address: P.O. Box 26307, Zip 73126; tel. 405/271–4700; Gerald J. Maier, FACHE, Chief Executive Officer
Web address: www.oumedcenter.com

SOUTHWESTERN MEDICAL CENTER (O, 162 beds) 5602 S.W. Lee Boulevard, Lawton, OK Zip 73505–9635, Mailing Address: P.O. Box 7290, Zip 73506–7290; tel. 580/531–4700; Thomas L. Rine, President and Chief Executive Officer
Web address: www.swmconline.com

Section B

For explanation of codes following names, see page B2.
★ Indicates Type III membership in the American Hospital Association.

SOUTH CAROLINA: COLLETON MEDICAL CENTER (O, 131 beds) 501 Robertson Boulevard, Walterboro, SC Zip 29488–5714; tel. 843/549–2000; Rebecca T. Brewer, FACHE, Chief Executive Officer
Web address: www.colletonmedical.com

GRAND STRAND REGIONAL MEDICAL CENTER (O, 219 beds) 809 82nd Parkway, Myrtle Beach, SC Zip 29572–1413; tel. 843/692–1000; Doug White, Chief Executive Officer
Web address: www.grandstrandmed.com

TRIDENT MEDICAL CENTER (O, 275 beds) 9330 Medical Plaza Drive, Charleston, SC Zip 29406–9195; tel. 843/797–7000; Terry J. Gunn, President and Chief Executive Officer
Web address: www.tridenthealthsystem.com

TENNESSEE: CENTENNIAL MEDICAL CENTER AND PARTHENON PAVILION (O, 556 beds) 2300 Patterson Street, Nashville, TN Zip 37203–1528; tel. 615/342–1000; Lawrence Kloess, President and Chief Executive Officer
Web address: www.centennialmedctr.com

CENTENNIAL MEDICAL CENTER AT ASHLAND CITY (O, 8 beds) 313 North Main Street, Ashland City, TN Zip 37015–1358; tel. 615/792–3030; Lawrence Kloess, President
Web address: www.centennialmedicalcenter.com

GRANDVIEW MEDICAL CENTER (O, 68 beds) 1000 Highway 28, Jasper, TN Zip 37347–3638; tel. 423/837–9500; George Asbell, Interim President
Web address: www.grandviewhospital.com

HENDERSONVILLE MEDICAL CENTER (O, 70 beds) 355 New Shackle Island Road, Hendersonville, TN Zip 37075–2393; tel. 615/338–1000; Mike Esposito, Chief Executive Officer
Web address: www.hendersonvillemedicalcenter.com

HORIZON MEDICAL CENTER (O, 116 beds) 111 Highway 70 East, Dickson, TN Zip 37055–2033; tel. 615/446–0446; John A. Marshall, Chief Executive Officer
Web address: www.horizonmedicalcenter.com

PARKRIDGE MEDICAL CENTER (O, 517 beds) 2333 McCallie Avenue, Chattanooga, TN Zip 37404–3285; tel. 423/698–6061; Jeff Fee, President and Chief Executive Officer
Web address: www.parkridgemedicalcenter.com

RIVER PARK HOSPITAL (O, 127 beds) 1559 Sparta Road, McMinnville, TN Zip 37110–1399; tel. 931/815–4000; George Asbell, Interim President
Web address: www.riverparkhospital.com

SKYLINE MEDICAL CENTER (O, 202 beds) 3441 Dickerson Pike, Nashville, TN Zip 37207–2539; tel. 615/769–2000; Robert Klein, Chief Executive Officer
Web address: www.skylinemedicalcenter.com

SOUTHERN HILLS MEDICAL CENTER (O, 120 beds) 391 Wallace Road, Nashville, TN Zip 37211–4859; tel. 615/781–4000; Victor Giovanetti, Chief Executive Officer
Web address: www.southernhills.com

STONECREST MEDICAL CENTER (O, 75 beds) 200 StoneCrest Boulevard, Smyrna, TN Zip 37167; tel. 615/768–2000; Neil A. Heatherly, CHE, Chief Executive Officer
Web address: www.stonecrestmedical.com

SUMMIT MEDICAL CENTER (O, 188 beds) 5655 Frist Boulevard, Hermitage, TN Zip 37076–2053; tel. 615/316–3000; Jeffrey T. Whitehorn, Chief Executive Officer
Web address: www.summitmedctr.com

TEXAS: BAYSHORE MEDICAL CENTER (O, 360 beds) 4000 Spencer Highway, Pasadena, TX Zip 77504–1294; tel. 713/359–2000; Phillip D. Robinson, Chief Executive Officer
Web address: www.bayshoremedical.com

CLEAR LAKE REGIONAL MEDICAL CENTER (O, 391 beds) 500 Medical Center Boulevard, Webster, TX Zip 77598–4286; tel. 281/332–2511; Donald A. Shaffett, Chief Executive Officer
Web address: www.clearlakermc.com

CONROE REGIONAL MEDICAL CENTER (O, 266 beds) 504 Medical Boulevard, Conroe, TX Zip 77304, Mailing Address: P.O. Box 1538, Zip 77305–1538; tel. 936/539–1111; Jerry A. Nash, Chief Executive Officer
Web address: www.conroeregional.com

CORPUS CHRISTI MEDICAL CENTER (O, 237 beds) 3315 South Alameda Street, Corpus Christi, TX Zip 78411–1883, Mailing Address: P.O. Box 8991, Zip 78468–8991; tel. 361/761–1400; Steve Woerner, Chief Executive Officer
Web address: www.ccmedicalcenter.com

CORPUS CHRISTI MEDICAL CENTER BAY AREA (O, 325 beds) 7101 South Padre Island Drive, Corpus Christi, TX Zip 78412–4999; tel. 361/985–1200; Steve Woerner, Chief Executive Officer
Web address: www.ccmedicalcenter.com

DEL SOL MEDICAL CENTER (O, 293 beds) 10301 Gateway West, El Paso, TX Zip 79925–7798; tel. 915/595–9000; Douglas A. Matney, Chief Executive Officer
Web address: www.delsolmedicalcenter.com

DEL SOL REHABILITATION HOSPITAL (O, 40 beds) 300 Waymore Drive, El Paso, TX Zip 79902–1628; tel. 915/577–2600; Douglas A. Matney, Chief Executive Officer

DENTON REGIONAL MEDICAL CENTER (O, 184 beds) 3535 South 1–35 East, Denton, TX Zip 76205; tel. 940/384–3535; Bob Haley, Chief Executive Officer
Web address: www.dentonregional.com

EAST HOUSTON REGIONAL MEDICAL CENTER (O, 131 beds) 13111 East Freeway, Houston, TX Zip 77015–5820; tel. 713/393–2000; Todd Caliva, Chief Executive Officer
Web address: www.easthoustonrmc.com

GREEN OAKS HOSPITAL (O, 97 beds) 7808 Clodus Fields Drive, Dallas, TX Zip 75251–2206; tel. 972/991–9504; Thomas M. Collins, Chief Executive Officer
Web address: www.greenoakspsych.com

KINGWOOD MEDICAL CENTER (O, 149 beds) 22999 U.S. Highway 59, Kingwood, TX Zip 77339; tel. 281/348–8000; Gay Nord, Chief Executive Officer
Web address: www.kingwoodmedical.com

LAS COLINAS MEDICAL CENTER (O, 70 beds) 6800 North MacArthur Boulevard, Irving, TX Zip 75039–2422; tel. 972/969–2000; Douglas Welch, Chief Executive Officer
Web address: www.lascolinasmedical.com

LAS PALMAS MEDICAL CENTER (O, 266 beds) 1801 North Oregon Street, El Paso, TX Zip 79902–3591; tel. 915/521–1200; Hank Hernandez, Chief Executive Officer
Web address: www.laspalmashealth.com

MAINLAND MEDICAL CENTER (O, 206 beds) 6801 E F Lowry Expressway, Texas City, TX Zip 77591; tel. 409/938–5000; Dean Alexander, Chief Executive Officer
Web address: www.mainlandmedical.com

MEDICAL CENTER OF ARLINGTON (O, 271 beds) 3301 Matlock Road, Arlington, TX Zip 76015–2998; tel. 817/465–3241; Patrick D. Brilliant, Chief Executive Officer
Web address: www.medicalcenterarlington.com

MEDICAL CENTER OF LEWISVILLE (O, 202 beds) 500 West Main, Lewisville, TX Zip 75057–3699; tel. 972/420–1000; Raymond M. Dunning Jr, Chief Executive Officer
Web address: www.lewisvillemedical.com

MEDICAL CENTER OF MCKINNEY (O, 179 beds) 4500 Medical Center Drive, McKinney, TX Zip 75069–3499; tel. 972/547–8000; Ernest C. Lynch III, Chief Executive Officer
Web address: www.ncentralmedical.com

MEDICAL CENTER OF PLANO (O, 348 beds) 3901 West 15th Street, Plano, TX Zip 75075–7799; tel. 972/596–6800; Harvey L. Fishero, President and Chief Executive Officer
Web address: www.medicalcenterplano.com

MEDICAL CITY DALLAS HOSPITAL (O, 537 beds) 7777 Forest Lane, Dallas, TX Zip 75230–2598; tel. 972/566–7000; Britt Berrett, President and Chief Executive Officer
Web address: www.medicalcityhospital.com

METHODIST AMBULATORY SURGERY HOSPITAL (O, 27 beds) 9150 Huebner Road, Suite 100, San Antonio, TX Zip 78240–1545; tel. 210/691–8000; Elaine F. Morris, Administrator
Web address: www.mas.sahealth.com

METHODIST CHILDREN'S HOSPITAL OF SOUTH TEXAS (O, 150 beds) 7700 Floyd Curl Drive, San Antonio, TX Zip 78229–3383; tel. 210/575–7138; Annie Holt, FACHE, Chief Executive Officer
Web address: www.mch.sahealth.com/

METHODIST HOSPITAL (O, 1338 beds) 7700 Floyd Curl Drive, San Antonio, TX Zip 78229–3993; tel. 210/575–4000; John E. Hornbeak, FACHE, Chief Executive Officer
Web address: www.sahealth.com

For explanation of codes following names, see page B2.
★ Indicates Type III membership in the American Hospital Association.

B52 Health Care Systems, Networks and Alliances

© 2005 AHA Guide

METROPOLITAN METHODIST HOSPITAL (O, 244 beds) 1310 McCullough Avenue, San Antonio, TX Zip 78212–2617; tel. 210/208–2200; Mark L. Bernard, Chief Executive Officer
Web address: www.metro.sahealth.com

NORTH AUSTIN MEDICAL CENTER (O, 210 beds) 12221 MoPac Expressway North, Austin, TX Zip 78758–2496; tel. 512/901–1000; Donald H. Wilkerson, Chief Executive Officer
Web address: www.northaustin.com

NORTH HILLS HOSPITAL (O, 140 beds) 4401 Booth Calloway Road, North Richland Hills, TX Zip 76180–7399; tel. 817/255–1000; Randolph Moresi, Chief Executive Officer
Web address: www.northhillshospital.com

PLAZA MEDICAL CENTER OF FORT WORTH (O, 264 beds) 900 Eighth Avenue, Fort Worth, TX Zip 76104–3986; tel. 817/336–2100; Troy Villarreal, Chief Executive Officer
Web address: www.plazamedicalcenter.com

RIO GRANDE REGIONAL HOSPITAL (O, 319 beds) 101 East Ridge Road, McAllen, TX Zip 78503–1299; tel. 956/632–6000; William A. Burns, Chief Executive Officer
Web address: www.riohealth.com

ROUND ROCK MEDICAL CENTER (O, 114 beds) 2400 Round Rock Avenue, Round Rock, TX Zip 78681–4097; tel. 512/341–1000; Deborah L. Ryle, Administrator and Chief Executive Officer
Web address: www.roundrockmc.com

SOUTH AUSTIN HOSPITAL (O, 193 beds) 901 West Ben White Boulevard, Austin, TX Zip 78704–6903; tel. 512/447–2211; Erol R. Akdamar, Chief Executive Officer
Web address: www.southaustinhospital.com

SPRING BRANCH MEDICAL CENTER (O, 305 beds) 8850 Long Point Road, Houston, TX Zip 77055–3082; tel. 713/467–6555; Scott Koenig, Chief Executive Officer
Web address: www.springbranchmedical.com

ST. DAVID'S MEDICAL CENTER (O, 290 beds) 919 East 32nd Street, Austin, TX Zip 78705–2709, Mailing Address: P.O. Box 4039, Zip 78765–4039; tel. 512/476–7111; Cole C. Eslyn, Chief Executive Officer
Web address: www.stdavids.com

ST. DAVID'S PAVILION (O, 20 beds) 1025 East 32nd Street, Austin, TX Zip 78765–2705; tel. 512/867–5800; Cole C. Eslyn, Chief Executive Officer
Web address: www.stdavids.com

ST. DAVID'S REHABILITATION CENTER (O, 62 beds) 1005 East 32nd Street, Austin, TX Zip 78705–2705, Mailing Address: P.O. Box 4270, Zip 78765–4270; tel. 512/867–5100; Cole C. Eslyn, Chief Executive Officer
Web address: www.stdavids.com

TEXAS ORTHOPEDIC HOSPITAL (O, 49 beds) 7401 South Main Street, Houston, TX Zip 77030–4509; tel. 713/799–8600; Jay Woodall, Chief Executive Officer
Web address: www.texasorthopedic.com

THE WOMAN'S HOSPITAL OF TEXAS (O, 248 beds) 7600 Fannin Street, Houston, TX Zip 77054–1900; tel. 713/790–1234; Linda B. Russell, Chief Executive Officer
Web address: www.womanshospital.com

VALLEY REGIONAL MEDICAL CENTER (O, 214 beds) 100A Alton Gloor Boulevard, Brownsville, TX Zip 78526–3346, Mailing Address: P.O. Box 3710, Zip 78521–3710; tel. 956/350–7101; Charles F. Sexton, Chief Executive Officer
Web address: www.valleyregionalmedicalcenter.com

WEST HOUSTON MEDICAL CENTER (O, 175 beds) 12141 Richmond Avenue, Houston, TX Zip 77082–2499; tel. 281/558–3444; Jeffrey S. Holland, Chief Executive Officer
Web address: www.westhoustonmedical.com

UTAH: BRIGHAM CITY COMMUNITY HOSPITAL (O, 49 beds) 950 South Medical Drive, Brigham City, UT Zip 84302; tel. 435/734–9471; Steven B. Bateman, Chief Executive Officer
Web address: www.brighamcityhospital.com

LAKEVIEW HOSPITAL (O, 128 beds) 630 East Medical Drive, Bountiful, UT Zip 84010–4996; tel. 801/292–6231; Steven M. Anderson, CHE, Chief Executive Officer
Web address: www.lakeviewhospital.com

MOUNTAIN VIEW HOSPITAL (O, 114 beds) 1000 East 100 North, Payson, UT Zip 84651–1690; tel. 801/465–7000; Kevin Johnson, Chief Executive Officer
Web address: www.mvhpayson.com

OGDEN REGIONAL MEDICAL CENTER (O, 167 beds) 5475 South 500 East, Ogden, UT Zip 84405–6978; tel. 801/479–2111; Steven B. Bateman, Chief Executive Officer
Web address: www.ogdenregional.com

ST. MARK'S HOSPITAL (O, 293 beds) 1200 East 3900 South, Salt Lake City, UT Zip 84124–1390; tel. 801/268–7111; John Hanshaw, Chief Executive Officer
Web address: www.stmarkshospital.com

TIMPANOGOS REGIONAL HOSPITAL (O, 51 beds) 750 West 800 North, Orem, UT Zip 84059–3660; tel. 801/714–6000; Keith D. Tintle, Chief Executive Officer
Web address: www.timpanogosregionalhospital.com

VIRGINIA: ALLEGHANY REGIONAL HOSPITAL (O, 89 beds) One ARH Lane, Low Moor, VA Zip 24457, Mailing Address: P.O. Box 7, Zip 24457–0007; tel. 540/862–6011; Timothy C. Tobin, President and Chief Executive Officer
Web address: www.alleghanyregional.com

CJW MEDICAL CENTER (O, 758 beds) 7101 Jahnke Road, Richmond, VA Zip 23225–4044; tel. 804/320–3911; Peter A. Marmerstein, Chief Executive Officer
Web address: www.cjwmedical.com

CLINCH VALLEY MEDICAL CENTER (O, 140 beds) 2949 West Front Street, Richlands, VA Zip 24641–2099; tel. 276/596–6000; Timothy C. Tobin, President and Chief Executive Officer
Web address: www.clinchvalleymedicalcenter.com

DOMINION HOSPITAL (O, 100 beds) 2960 Sleepy Hollow Road, Falls Church, VA Zip 22044–2001; tel. 703/536–2000; Bryan K. Dearing, Chief Executive Officer
Web address: www.dominionhospital.com

HENRICO DOCTORS' HOSPITAL (O, 496 beds) 1602 Skipwith Road, Richmond, VA Zip 23229–5205; tel. 804/289–4500; Patrick W. Farrell, Chief Executive Officer
Web address: www.henricodoctorshospital.com

JOHN RANDOLPH MEDICAL CENTER (O, 264 beds) 411 West Randolph Road, Hopewell, VA Zip 23860–2938; tel. 804/541–1600; Elwood Bernard Boone III, Chief Executive Officer
Web address: www.johnrandolphmed.com

LEWIS–GALE MEDICAL CENTER (O, 521 beds) 1900 Electric Road, Salem, VA Zip 24153–7494; tel. 540/776–4000; James W. Thweatt Jr, Chief Executive Officer
Web address: www.lewis–gale.com

MONTGOMERY REGIONAL HOSPITAL (O, 89 beds) 3700 South Main Street, Blacksburg, VA Zip 24060–7081, Mailing Address: P.O. Box 90004, Zip 24062–9004; tel. 540/951–1111; Ward W. Stevens III, CHE, Chief Executive Officer
Web address: www.mrhospital.com

NORTHERN VIRGINIA COMMUNITY HOSPITAL (O, 100 beds) 601 South Carlin Springs Road, Arlington, VA Zip 22204–1096; tel. 703/671–1200; Bryan K. Dearing, Chief Executive Officer
Web address: www.nvchospital.com

PULASKI COMMUNITY HOSPITAL (O, 72 beds) 2400 Lee Highway, Pulaski, VA Zip 24301–0759, Mailing Address: P.O. Box 759, Zip 24301–0759; tel. 540/994–8100; Jackson Nunley, Chief Executive Officer
Web address: www.pch–va.com

RESTON HOSPITAL CENTER (O, 160 beds) 1850 Town Center Parkway, Reston, VA Zip 20190–3210; tel. 703/689–9000; William A. Adams, President and Chief Executive Officer
Web address: www.restonhospital.com

RETREAT HOSPITAL (O, 116 beds) 2621 Grove Avenue, Richmond, VA Zip 23220–4308; tel. 804/254–5100; Paul L. Baldwin, Chief Executive Officer
Web address: www.retreathospital.com

WASHINGTON: CAPITAL MEDICAL CENTER (O, 105 beds) 3900 Capital Mall Drive S.W., Olympia, WA Zip 98502–5026, Mailing Address: P.O. Box 19002, Zip 98507–9002; tel. 360/754–5858; Joseph Sharp, Chief Executive Officer
Web address: www.capitalmedical.com

WEST VIRGINIA: PUTNAM GENERAL HOSPITAL (O, 68 beds) 1400 Hospital Drive, Hurricane, WV Zip 25526–9210; tel. 304/757–1700; Dan Lauffer, FACHE, Chief Executive Officer
Web address: www.putnamgeneralhospital.com

For explanation of codes following names, see page B2.
★ Indicates Type III membership in the American Hospital Association.

RALEIGH GENERAL HOSPITAL (O, 225 beds) 1710 Harper Road, Beckley, WV Zip 25801–3397; tel. 304/256–4100; Karen L. Bowling, Chief Executive Officer
Web address: www.raleighgeneral.com

SAINT FRANCIS HOSPITAL (O, 114 beds) 333 Laidley Street, Charleston, WV Zip 25301–1628, Mailing Address: P.O. Box 471, Zip 25322–0471; tel. 304/347–6500; Dan Lauffer, FACHE, Chief Executive Officer
Web address: www.stfrancishospital.com

ST. JOSEPH'S HOSPITAL (O, 194 beds) 1824 Murdoch Avenue, Parkersburg, WV Zip 26101–3246, Mailing Address: P.O. Box 327, Zip 26102–0327; tel. 304/424–4111; Patsy A. Hardy, Chief Executive Officer
Web address: www.stjosephs–hospital.com

Owned, leased, sponsored:	180 hospitals	37929 beds
Contract–managed:	0 hospitals	0 beds
Totals:	180 hospitals	37929 beds

★**0082: HEALTH ALLIANCE OF GREATER CINCINNATI** (NP) 3200 Burnet Avenue, Cincinnati, OH Zip 45229; tel. 513/585–6000; Kenneth Hanover, President and Chief Executive Officer
(Centralized Health System)

KENTUCKY: ST. LUKE HOSPITAL EAST (O, 222 beds) 85 North Grand Avenue, Fort Thomas, KY Zip 41075–1796; tel. 859/572–3100; Nancy Kremer, Senior Vice President
Web address: www.health–alliance.com

ST. LUKE HOSPITAL WEST (O, 177 beds) 7380 Turfway Road, Florence, KY Zip 41042–1337; tel. 859/962–5200; Nancy Kremer, Senior Vice President
Web address: www.health–alliance.com

OHIO: CHRIST HOSPITAL (O, 440 beds) 2139 Auburn Avenue, Cincinnati, OH Zip 45219–2989; tel. 513/585–2000; Susan Croushore, Executive Director and Senior Vice President
Web address: www.health–alliance.com/hospitals/christ_control.html

FORT HAMILTON HOSPITAL (O, 181 beds) 630 Eaton Avenue, Hamilton, OH Zip 45013–2770; tel. 513/867–2000; Lynn M. Oswald, R.N., Senior Vice President
Web address: www.health–alliance.com/forthamilton.html

JEWISH HOSPITAL (O, 200 beds) 4777 East Galbraith Road, Cincinnati, OH Zip 45236–2725; tel. 513/686–3000; M. Aurora Lambert, Senior Vice President
Web address: www.health–alliance.com/jewish.html

UNIVERSITY HOSPITAL (O, 448 beds) 234 Goodman Street, Cincinnati, OH Zip 45219–2316; tel. 513/584–1000; James A. Kingsbury, Executive Director and Senior Vice President
Web address: www.health–alliance.com/Univ_control.html

Owned, leased, sponsored:	6 hospitals	1668 beds
Contract–managed:	0 hospitals	0 beds
Totals:	6 hospitals	1668 beds

1775: HEALTH MANAGEMENT ASSOCIATES (IO) 5811 Pelican Bay Boulevard, Suite 500, Naples, FL Zip 34108; tel. 239/598–3131; Joseph V. Vumbacco, President and Chief Executive Officer
(Decentralized Health System)

ALABAMA: RIVERVIEW REGIONAL MEDICAL CENTER (O, 281 beds) 600 South Third Street, Gadsden, AL Zip 35901–5399, Mailing Address: P.O. Box 268, Zip 35999–0268; tel. 256/543–5200; J. Matthew Hayes, Executive Director
Web address: www.riverviewregional.com

STRINGFELLOW MEMORIAL HOSPITAL (L, 125 beds) 301 East 18th Street, Anniston, AL Zip 36207–0038, Mailing Address: P.O. Box 38, Zip 36207–0038; tel. 256/235–8900; David Orcutt, Chief Executive Officer
Web address: www.stringfellowhealth.com

ARKANSAS: CRAWFORD MEMORIAL HOSPITAL (L, 103 beds) East Main and South 20th Streets, Van Buren, AR Zip 72956–5715, Mailing Address: P.O. Box 409, Zip 72957–0409; tel. 479/474–3401; Kevin Clement, Chief Executive Officer
Web address: www.crawfordmemorial.com

SOUTHWEST REGIONAL MEDICAL CENTER (O, 125 beds) 11401 Interstate 30, Little Rock, AR Zip 72209–7056; tel. 501/455–7100; Nancy C. Fodi, R.N., Chief Executive Officer
Web address: www.hma–corp.com

FLORIDA: BARTOW REGIONAL MEDICAL CENTER (O, 56 beds) 2200 Osprey Boulevard, Bartow, FL Zip 33830–3308, Mailing Address: P.O. Box 1050, Zip 33830–1050; tel. 863/533–8111; Justin Davis, Chief Executive Officer
Web address: www.lifepointhospitals.com

BROOKSVILLE REGIONAL HOSPITAL (L, 91 beds) 55 Ponce De Leon Boulevard, Brooksville, FL Zip 34601, Mailing Address: P.O. Box 37, Zip 34605–0037; tel. 352/796–5111; Thomas D. Barb, Executive Director
Web address: www.hernandohealthcare.com

CHARLOTTE REGIONAL MEDICAL CENTER (O, 208 beds) 809 East Marion Avenue, Punta Gorda, FL Zip 33950–3898, Mailing Address: P.O. Box 51–1328, Zip 33951–1328; tel. 941/639–3131; Joshua S. Putter, Chief Executive Officer
Web address: www.charlotteregional.com

FISHERMEN'S HOSPITAL (L, 58 beds) 3301 Overseas Highway, Marathon, FL Zip 33050–0068; tel. 305/743–5533; Michael Kissner, Chief Executive Officer
Web address: www.fishermenshospital.com

HEART OF FLORIDA REGIONAL MEDICAL CENTER (O, 142 beds) 40100 Highway 27, Davenport, FL Zip 33837–5902, Mailing Address: P.O. Box 67, Haines City, Zip 33844–0067; tel. 863/419–2259; Ann Barnhart, Chief Executive Officer
Web address: www.heartofflorida.com

HIGHLANDS REGIONAL MEDICAL CENTER (L, 64 beds) 3600 South Highlands Avenue, Sebring, FL Zip 33870–5495, Mailing Address: Drawer 2066, Zip 33871–2066; tel. 863/471–5800; Linda Harrison, Chief Executive Officer
Web address: www.highlandsregional.com

LEHIGH REGIONAL MEDICAL CENTER (O, 88 beds) 1500 Lee Boulevard, Lehigh Acres, FL Zip 33936–4897; tel. 239/369–2101; Dan Buckner, Chief Executive Officer
Web address: www.lehighregional.com

LOWER KEYS MEDICAL CENTER (L, 115 beds) 5900 College Road, Key West, FL Zip 33040–4396, Mailing Address: P.O. Box 9107, Zip 33041–9107; tel. 305/294–5531; Nicki Will, Ph.D., President and Chief Executive Officer
Web address: www.lkmc.com

PASCO REGIONAL MEDICAL CENTER (O, 120 beds) 13100 Fort King Road, Dade City, FL Zip 33525–5294; tel. 352/521–1100; Michael J. Arno, Chief Executive Officer
Web address: www.pascoregionalmc.com

PEACE RIVER REGIONAL MEDICAL CENTER (O, 314 beds) 2500 Harbor Boulevard, Port Charlotte, FL Zip 33952–5396; tel. 941/766–4122; David McCormack, Chief Executive Officer
Web address: www.bssjconnections.com

SANDYPINES (O, 78 beds) 11301 S.E. Tequesta Terrace, Tequesta, FL Zip 33469–8146; tel. 561/744–0211; John W. Thompson, Ph.D., Chief Executive Officer

SANTA ROSA MEDICAL CENTER (O, 77 beds) 1450 Berryhill Road, Milton, FL Zip 32570–4028, Mailing Address: P.O. Box 648, Zip 32572–0648; tel. 850/626–7762; M. P. Gandy Jr, Chief Executive Officer

SEBASTIAN RIVER MEDICAL CENTER (O, 129 beds) 13695 North U.S. Highway 1, Sebastian, FL Zip 32958–3230, Mailing Address: Box 780838, Zip 32978–0838; tel. 772/589–3186; Kathy A. Burke, Chief Executive Officer
Web address: www.srmcenter.com

SEVEN RIVERS REGIONAL MEDICAL CENTER (O, 128 beds) 6201 North Suncoast Boulevard, Crystal River, FL Zip 34428–6712; tel. 352/795–6560; Joyce Brancato, Chief Executive Officer
Web address: www.srrmc.com

SPRING HILL REGIONAL HOSPITAL (L, 85 beds) 10461 Quality Drive, Brooksville, FL Zip 34609–9634; tel. 352/688–8200; James R. Beatty, Executive Director
Web address: www.hernandohealthcare.com

VENICE REGIONAL MEDICAL CENTER (O, 128 beds) 540 The Rialto, Venice, FL Zip 34285–2900; tel. 941/485–7711; Melody Trimble, Chief Executive Officer

For explanation of codes following names, see page B2.
★ Indicates Type III membership in the American Hospital Association.

GEORGIA: EAST GEORGIA REGIONAL MEDICAL CENTER (O, 114 beds) 1499 Fair Road, Statesboro, GA Zip 30458–5105, Mailing Address: P.O. Box 1048, Zip 30459–1048; tel. 912/486–1000; Robert F. Bigley, Executive Director
Web address: www.egrmc.com

WALTON REGIONAL MEDICAL CENTER (O, 115 beds) 330 Alcovy Street, Monroe, GA Zip 30655–2140, Mailing Address: P.O. Box 1346, Zip 30655–1346; tel. 770/267–8461; Alan E. George, Chief Executive Officer
Web address: www.waltonregional.org

KENTUCKY: PAUL B. HALL REGIONAL MEDICAL CENTER (O, 72 beds) 625 James S Trimble Boulevard, Paintsville, KY Zip 41240–0000; tel. 606/789–3511; Deborah L. Trimble, Chief Executive Officer
Web address: www.pbhrmc.com

MISSISSIPPI: BILOXI REGIONAL MEDICAL CENTER (L, 153 beds) 150 Reynoir Street, Biloxi, MS Zip 39530–4199, Mailing Address: P.O. Box 128, Zip 39533–0128; tel. 228/432–1571; Timothy W. Mitchell, Chief Executive Officer
Web address: www.hmamississippi.com

CENTRAL MISSISSIPPI MEDICAL CENTER (L, 429 beds) 1850 Chadwick Drive, Jackson, MS Zip 39204–3479, Mailing Address: P.O. Box 59001, Zip 39204–9001; tel. 601/376–1000; John R. Finnegan, Chief Executive Officer
Web address: www.centralmississippimedicalcenter.com

MADISON COUNTY MEDICAL CENTER (O, 34 beds) Highway 16 East, Canton, MS Zip 39046–8823, Mailing Address: P.O. Box 1607, Zip 39046–1607; tel. 601/859–1331; Daryl W. Weaver, Chief Executive Officer

NATCHEZ COMMUNITY HOSPITAL (O, 101 beds) 129 Jefferson Davis Boulevard, Natchez, MS Zip 39120–5100, Mailing Address: P.O. Box 1203, Zip 39121–1203; tel. 601/445–6200; J. Allen Tyra, Executive Director
Web address: www.hmamississippi.com

NORTHWEST MISSISSIPPI REGIONAL MEDICAL CENTER (L, 175 beds) 1970 Hospital Drive, Clarksdale, MS Zip 38614–7204, Mailing Address: P.O. Box 1218, Zip 38614–1218; tel. 662/627–3211; Douglas Arnold, Chief Executive Officer
Web address: www.hmamississippi.com

RANKIN MEDICAL CENTER (L, 134 beds) 350 Crossgates Boulevard, Brandon, MS Zip 39042–2698; tel. 601/825–2811; Davis A. Richards III, Chief Executive Officer
Web address: www.rankinmedcenter.com

RILEY HOSPITAL (O, 120 beds) 1102 21st Avenue, Meridian, MS Zip 39301–4096, Mailing Address: P.O. Box 1810, Zip 39301–1810; tel. 601/693–2511; Stephen Nichols, Chief Executive Officer
Web address: www.hmamississippi.com

RIVER OAKS HOSPITAL (O, 109 beds) 1030 River Oaks Drive, Jackson, MS Zip 39232, Mailing Address: P.O. Box 5100, Zip 39296–5100; tel. 601/932–1030; John J. Cleary, President and Chief Executive Officer
Web address: www.riveroakshospital.org

WOMAN'S HOSPITAL AT RIVER OAKS (O, 61 beds) 1026 North Flowood Drive, Jackson, MS Zip 39232, Mailing Address: P.O. Box 4546, Zip 39296–4546; tel. 601/932–1000; Sherry J. Pitts, Administrator
Web address: www.womanshospitalms.com

MISSOURI: POPLAR BLUFF REGIONAL MEDICAL CENTER (O, 257 beds) 2620 North Westwood Boulevard, Poplar Bluff, MO Zip 63901–2341, Mailing Address: P.O. Box 88, Zip 63901–2341; tel. 573/785–7721; Joe B. Riley, Chief Executive Officer
Web address: www.three–rivershealthcare.com

TWIN RIVERS REGIONAL MEDICAL CENTER (O, 116 beds) 1301 First Street, Kennett, MO Zip 63857–2508, Mailing Address: P.O. Box 728, Zip 63857–0728; tel. 573/888–4522; John W. McClellan, Chief Executive Officer
Web address: www.twinriversmedctr.com

NORTH CAROLINA: DAVIS REGIONAL MEDICAL CENTER (O, 123 beds) 218 Old Mocksville Road, Statesville, NC Zip 28625–1930, Mailing Address: P.O. Box 1823, Zip 28687–1823; tel. 704/873–0281; Vincent T. Cherry Jr, Chief Executive Director
Web address: www.davisregional.com

FRANKLIN REGIONAL MEDICAL CENTER (O, 56 beds) 100 Hospital Drive, Louisburg, NC Zip 27549–2256, Mailing Address: P.O. Box 609, Zip 27549–0609; tel. 919/497–8401; Thomas Dunning, Executive Director
Web address: www.franklinregionalmedicalctr.com

LAKE NORMAN REGIONAL MEDICAL CENTER (O, 129 beds) 171 Fairview Road, Mooresville, NC Zip 28117–9500, Mailing Address: P.O. Box 3250, Zip 28117–3250; tel. 704/660–4000; P. Paul Smith Jr, Executive Director
Web address: www.lnrmc.com

SANDHILLS REGIONAL MEDICAL CENTER (O, 64 beds) 1000 West Hamlet Avenue, Hamlet, NC Zip 28345–4522, Mailing Address: P.O. Box 1109, Zip 28345–1109; tel. 910/205–8000; William H. Leonard, Chief Executive Officer
Web address: www.hma–corp.com

OKLAHOMA: MEDICAL CENTER OF SOUTHEASTERN OKLAHOMA (O, 120 beds) 1800 University Boulevard, Durant, OK Zip 74701–3006, Mailing Address: P.O. Box 1207, Zip 74702–1207; tel. 580/924–3080; Jacquelyn Harms, R.N., Executive Director
Web address: www.mcsohealth.com

MIDWEST REGIONAL MEDICAL CENTER (L, 255 beds) 2825 Parklawn Drive, Midwest City, OK Zip 73110–4258; tel. 405/610–4411; Brian L. Clemens, Chief Executive Officer
Web address: www.midwestregional.com

PENNSYLVANIA: CARLISLE REGIONAL MEDICAL CENTER (O, 133 beds) 246 Parker Street, Carlisle, PA Zip 17013–3661; tel. 717/249–1212;
Web address: www.carlislermc.com

HEART OF LANCASTER REGIONAL MEDICAL CENTER (O, 139 beds) 1500 Highlands Avenue, Lititz, PA Zip 17543; tel. 717/625–5000; Lee Christenson, Chief Executive Officer
Web address: www.chol.org

LANCASTER REGIONAL MEDICAL CENTER (O, 226 beds) 250 College Avenue, Lancaster, PA Zip 17603, Mailing Address: P.O. Box 3434, Zip 17604–3434; tel. 717/291–8211; Brad K. Nurkin, Chief Executive Officer

SOUTH CAROLINA: CAROLINA PINES REGIONAL MEDICAL CENTER (O, 120 beds) 1304 West BoBo Newsom Highway, Hartsville, SC Zip 29550–4710; tel. 843/339–2100; David L. Castleberry, Chief Executive Officer
Web address: www.cprmc.com

CHESTER COUNTY HOSPITAL AND NURSING CENTER (O, 154 beds) 1 Medical Park Drive, Chester, SC Zip 29706–9799; tel. 803/581–3151; William H. Bundy, Chief Executive Officer
Web address: www.chospital.org

UPSTATE CAROLINA MEDICAL CENTER (O, 125 beds) 1530 North Limestone Street, Gaffney, SC Zip 29340–4738; tel. 864/487–4271; Joe D. Howell, Executive Director
Web address: www.upstatecarolina.org

TENNESSEE: HARTON REGIONAL MEDICAL CENTER (O, 110 beds) 1801 North Jackson Street, Tullahoma, TN Zip 37388–2201; tel. 931/393–3000; Dwayne Blaylock, Chief Executive Officer
Web address: www.hartonmedicalcenter.com

JAMESTOWN REGIONAL MEDICAL CENTER (O, 71 beds) 436 Central Avenue West, Jamestown, TN Zip 38556–1500, Mailing Address: P.O. Box 1500, Zip 38556–1500; tel. 931/879–8171; James P. Frazier III, Chief Executive Officer
Web address: www.jamestownregional.org

UNIVERSITY MEDICAL CENTER/MCFARLAND HOSPITAL (O, 245 beds) 1411 Baddour Parkway, Lebanon, TN Zip 37087–2595; tel. 615/444–8262; Mark W. Crawford, Chief Executive Officer
Web address: www.universitymedicalcenter.com

TEXAS: MEDICAL CENTER OF MESQUITE (O, 156 beds) 1011 North Galloway Avenue, Mesquite, TX Zip 75149–2433; tel. 214/320–7000; Raymond P. De Blasi, Chief Executive Officer
Web address: www.hma–corp.com

MESQUITE COMMUNITY HOSPITAL (O, 137 beds) 3500 Interstate 30, Mesquite, TX Zip 75150–2696; tel. 972/698–3300; Raymond P. De Blasi, Chief Executive Officer
Web address: www.mchtx.com

VIRGINIA: LEE REGIONAL MEDICAL CENTER (O, 52 beds) West Morgan Avenue, Pennington Gap, VA Zip 24277–0070, Mailing Address: P.O. Box 70, Zip 24277–0070; tel. 276/546–1440; S. Scott McIntyre, Chief Executive Officer
Web address: www.leeregional.com

MOUNTAIN VIEW REGIONAL MEDICAL CENTER (O, 133 beds) Third Street N.E., Norton, VA Zip 24273–1131, Mailing Address: P.O. Box 620, Zip 24273–0620; tel. 276/679–9100; Jamie Guin, Chief Executive Officer
Web address: www.smhnorton.org

For explanation of codes following names, see page B2.
★ Indicates Type III membership in the American Hospital Association.

Section B

WASHINGTON: TOPPENISH COMMUNITY HOSPITAL (O, 50 beds) 502 West Fourth Avenue, Toppenish, WA Zip 98948–0672, Mailing Address: P.O. Box 672, Zip 98948–0672; tel. 509/865–3105; Monte Bostwick, Administrator and Chief Operating Officer
Web address: www.hma–corp.com

YAKIMA REGIONAL MEDICAL AND HEART CENTER (O, 169 beds) 110 South Ninth Avenue, Yakima, WA Zip 98902–3397; tel. 509/575–5000; Timothy Trottier, Chief Executive Officer

WEST VIRGINIA: WILLIAMSON MEMORIAL HOSPITAL (O, 76 beds) 859 Alderson Street, Williamson, WV Zip 25661–3215, Mailing Address: P.O. Box 1980, Zip 25661–1980; tel. 304/235–2500; Jeffrey Rains, Interim Chief Executive Officer
Web address: www.hmawmh.com

Owned, leased, sponsored:	56 hospitals	7348 beds
Contract–managed:	0 hospitals	0 beds
Totals:	56 hospitals	7348 beds

0307: HEALTH QUEST (IO)
45 Reade Place, Poughkeepsie, NY Zip 12601; tel. 845/431–5601; Adil M. Ameer, Chief Executive Officer
(Moderately Centralized Health System)

NEW YORK: NORTHERN DUTCHESS HOSPITAL (O, 68 beds) 6511 Springbrook Avenue, Rhinebeck, NY Zip 12572–5002, Mailing Address: P.O. Box 5002, Zip 12572–5002; tel. 845/876–3001; Michael Mimoso, President and Chief Executive Officer
Web address: www.ndhosp.com

PUTNAM HOSPITAL CENTER (O, 144 beds) 670 Stoneleigh Avenue, Carmel, NY Zip 10512–9948; tel. 845/279–5711; Michael T. Weber, President and Chief Executive Officer
Web address: www.putnamhospital.org

VASSAR BROTHERS MEDICAL CENTER (O, 315 beds) 45 Reade Place, Poughkeepsie, NY Zip 12601–3990; tel. 845/454–8500; Daniel Z. Aronzon, M.D., Acting President and Chief Executive Officer
Web address: www.vassarbrothers.org

Owned, leased, sponsored:	3 hospitals	527 beds
Contract–managed:	0 hospitals	0 beds
Totals:	3 hospitals	527 beds

★2185: HEALTHEAST CARE SYSTEM (NP)
559 Capitol Boulevard, 6–South, Saint Paul, MN Zip 55103–0000; tel. 651/232–2300; Timothy H. Hanson, President and Chief Executive Officer
(Centralized Health System)

MINNESOTA: BETHESDA REHABILITATION HOSPITAL (O, 172 beds) 559 Capitol Boulevard, Saint Paul, MN Zip 55103–2101; tel. 651/232–2000; Frank Indihar, M.D., Chief Executive Officer
Web address: www.healtheast.org

ST. JOHN'S HOSPITAL (O, 189 beds) 1575 Beam Avenue, Saint Paul, MN Zip 55109–1126; tel. 651/232–7000; Scott North, Chief Executive Officer
Web address: www.stjohnshospital-mn.org

ST. JOSEPH'S HOSPITAL (O, 258 beds) 69 West Exchange Street, Saint Paul, MN Zip 55102–1053; tel. 651/232–3000; Scott Batulis, Chief Executive Officer
Web address: www.healtheast.org

WOODWINDS HEALTH CAMPUS (O, 53 beds) 1925 Woodwinds Drive, Woodbury, MN Zip 55125; tel. 651/232–0100; Julie A. Schmidt, Chief Executive Officer
Web address: www.woodwinds.org

Owned, leased, sponsored:	4 hospitals	672 beds
Contract–managed:	0 hospitals	0 beds
Totals:	4 hospitals	672 beds

0296: HEALTHPLUS (IO)
509 West Tidwell Road, Houston, TX Zip 77091; tel. 713/490–0700; Mac Burt, President and Chief Executive Officer
(Independent Hospital System)

CALIFORNIA: EAST LOS ANGELES DOCTORS HOSPITAL (O, 127 beds) 4060 East Whittier Boulevard, Los Angeles, CA Zip 90023–2526; tel. 323/268–5514; Araceli Lonergan, Administrator and Chief Executive Officer

MEMORIAL HOSPITAL OF GARDENA (O, 107 beds) 1145 West Redondo Beach Boulevard, Gardena, CA Zip 90247–3528; tel. 310/532–4200; Steve Popkin, Chief Executive Officer

TEXAS: DOCTORS HOSPITAL PARKWAY (O, 134 beds) 233 West Parker Road, Houston, TX Zip 77076–2999; tel. 281/765–2600; Alan A. Beauchamp, Chief Executive Officer

DOCTORS HOSPITAL–TIDWELL (O, 200 beds) 510 West Tidwell Road, Houston, TX Zip 77091–4399; tel. 713/691–1111; Alan A. Beauchamp, Chief Executive Officer
Web address: www.health–plus.net

Owned, leased, sponsored:	4 hospitals	568 beds
Contract–managed:	0 hospitals	0 beds
Totals:	4 hospitals	568 beds

★0023: HEALTHSOUTH CORPORATION (IO)
One Healthsouth Parkway, Birmingham, AL Zip 35243; tel. 205/967–7116; Jay Grinney, President
(Decentralized Health System)

ALABAMA: HEALTHSOUTH LAKESHORE REHABILITATION HOSPITAL (O, 100 beds) 3800 Ridgeway Drive, Birmingham, AL Zip 35209–5599; tel. 205/868–2000; Terry Brown, Administrator and Chief Executive Officer
Web address: www.healthsouth.com

HEALTHSOUTH MEDICAL CENTER (O, 153 beds) 1201 11th Avenue South, Birmingham, AL Zip 35205–5299; tel. 205/930–7000; Don Lilly, Interim Administrator
Web address: www.healthsouth.com

HEALTHSOUTH REHABILITATION HOSPITAL (O, 34 beds) 1736 East Main Street, Dothan, AL Zip 36301, Mailing Address: P.O. Box 6708, Zip 36302–6708; tel. 334/712–6333; Margaret Futch, Chief Operating Officer and Administrator
Web address: www.healthsouth.com

HEALTHSOUTH REHABILITATION HOSPITAL OF MONTGOMERY (O, 80 beds) 4465 Narrow Lane Road, Montgomery, AL Zip 36116–2900; tel. 334/284–7700; Linda Wade, Administrator
Web address: www.healthsouth.com

HEALTHSOUTH REHABILITATION HOSPITAL OF NORTH ALABAMA (O, 50 beds) 107 Governors Drive S.W., Huntsville, AL Zip 35801–4329; tel. 256/535–2300; Douglas H. Beverly, CHE, Administrator
Web address: www.healthsouth.com

HEALTHSOUTH REHABILITATION OF GADSDEN (O, 40 beds) 801 Goodyear Avenue, Gadsden, AL Zip 35903; tel. 256/439–5000; Michael W. Thompson, Administrator

REGIONAL REHABILITATION HOSPITAL (O, 38 beds) 3715 Highway 280, Phenix City, AL Zip 36869; tel. 334/732–2200; Jill Jordan, Administrator
Web address: www.healthsouth.com

ARIZONA: HEALTHSOUTH REHABILITATION HOSPITAL OF SOUTHERN ARIZONA (O, 60 beds) 1921 West Hospital Drive, Tucson, AZ Zip 85704–7806; tel. 520/742–2800; Elena Roman, Administrator
Web address: www.healthsouth.com

HEALTHSOUTH REHABILITATION INSTITUTE OF TUCSON (O, 80 beds) 2650 North Wyatt Drive, Tucson, AZ Zip 85712–6108; tel. 520/325–1300; Kelly Silverschlag, Administrator
Web address: www.healthsouth.com

HEALTHSOUTH SCOTTSDALE REHABILITATION HOSPITAL (O, 46 beds) 9630 East Shea Boulevard, Scottsdale, AZ Zip 85260; tel. 480/551–5400; Richard Schulz, Administrator
Web address: www.healthsouth.com

HEALTHSOUTH VALLEY OF THE SUN REHABILITATION HOSPITAL (O, 60 beds) 13460 North 67th Avenue, Glendale, AZ Zip 85304–1042; tel. 623/878–8800; Beth Bacher, Administrator
Web address: www.healthsouth.com

YUMA REHABILITATION HOSPITAL (O, 41 beds) 901 West 24th Street, Yuma, AZ Zip 85364; tel. 928/726–5000; Dennis R. Shelby, Chief Executive Officer

---

For explanation of codes following names, see page B2.
★ Indicates Type III membership in the American Hospital Association.

ARKANSAS: HEALTHSOUTH REHABILITATION HOSPITAL (O, 60 beds) 153 East Monte Painter Drive, Fayetteville, AR Zip 72703–4002; tel. 479/444–2200; Jeffrey Huff, Administrator
Web address: www.healthsouth.com

HEALTHSOUTH REHABILITATION HOSPITAL OF FORT SMITH (O, 80 beds) 1401 South J Street, Fort Smith, AR Zip 72901–5155; tel. 479/785–3300; Juli Stec, Chief Executive Officer
Web address: www.healthsouth.com

HEALTHSOUTH REHABILITATION HOSPITAL OF JONESBORO (O, 67 beds) 1201 Fleming Avenue, Jonesboro, AR Zip 72401–4311, Mailing Address: P.O. Box 1680, Zip 72403–1680; tel. 870/932–0440; Donna Bloodworth, Administrator
Web address: www.healthsouth.com

CALIFORNIA: HEALTHSOUTH BAKERSFIELD REHABILITATION HOSPITAL (O, 60 beds) 5001 Commerce Drive, Bakersfield, CA Zip 93309–0689; tel. 661/323–5500; Ann Feaver, Administrator
Web address: www.healthsouth.com

HEALTHSOUTH TUSTIN REHABILITATION HOSPITAL (O, 48 beds) 14851 Yorba Street, Tustin, CA Zip 92780–2925; tel. 714/832–9200; Scott Rifkin, Administrator
Web address: www.healthsouth.com

COLORADO: HEALTHSOUTH REHABILITATION HOSPITAL OF COLORADO SPRINGS (O, 56 beds) 325 Parkside Drive, Colorado Springs, CO Zip 80910; tel. 719/630–8000; Ellen DeAustin, Administrator

FLORIDA: HEALTHSOUTH EMERALD COAST REHABILITATION HOSPITAL (O, 65 beds) 1847 Florida Avenue, Panama City, FL Zip 32405–4640; tel. 850/914–8600; Tony N. Bennett, Administrator
Web address: www.healthsouth.com

HEALTHSOUTH REHABILITATION HOSPITAL (O, 60 beds) 901 North Clearwater–Largo Road, Largo, FL Zip 33770–4126; tel. 727/586–2999; Elaine D. Ebaugh, Administrator
Web address: www.healthsouth.com

HEALTHSOUTH REHABILITATION HOSPITAL (O, 60 beds) 20601 Old Cutler Road, Miami, FL Zip 33189–2400; tel. 305/251–3800; Jacqueline Arocho, Administrator
Web address: www.healthsouth.com

HEALTHSOUTH REHABILITATION HOSPITAL OF SARASOTA (O, 76 beds) 3251 Proctor Road, Sarasota, FL Zip 34231–8538; tel. 941/921–8600; Margaret Holloway, Administrator
Web address: www.healthsouth.com

HEALTHSOUTH REHABILITATION HOSPITAL OF SPRING HILL (O, 60 beds) 12440 Cortez Boulevard, Brooksville, FL Zip 34613–2628; tel. 352/592–4250; Mario A. Mudano, Administrator
Web address: www.healthsouth.com

HEALTHSOUTH REHABILITATION HOSPITAL OF TALLAHASSEE (O, 70 beds) 1675 Riggins Road, Tallahassee, FL Zip 32308–5315; tel. 850/656–4800; Lynn Streetman, Administrator
Web address: www.healthsouth.com

HEALTHSOUTH SEA PINES REHABILITATION HOSPITAL (O, 90 beds) 101 East Florida Avenue, Melbourne, FL Zip 32901–9966; tel. 321/984–4600; Denise B. McGrath, Administrator
Web address: www.healthsouth.com

HEALTHSOUTH SUNRISE REHABILITATION HOSPITAL (O, 116 beds) 4399 Nob Hill Road, Fort Lauderdale, FL Zip 33351–5899; tel. 954/749–0300; Kevin R. Conn, Administrator
Web address: www.healthsouth.com

HEALTHSOUTH TREASURE COAST REHABILITATION HOSPITAL (O, 90 beds) 1600 37th Street, Vero Beach, FL Zip 32960–6549; tel. 772/778–2100; Jason N. Roeback, Administrator
Web address: www.healthsouth.com

GEORGIA: HEALTHSOUTH CENTRAL GEORGIA REHABILITATION HOSPITAL (O, 58 beds) 3351 Northside Drive, Macon, GA Zip 31210–2591; tel. 478/471–3500; Elbert T. McQueen, Administrator
Web address: www.healthsouth.com

IDAHO: HEALTHSOUTH TREASURE VALLEY HOSPITAL (O, 9 beds) 8800 West Emerald Street, Boise, ID Zip 83704; tel. 208/373–5000; Michael L. Long, Administrator

ILLINOIS: VAN MATRE HEALTHSOUTH REHABILITATION HOSPITAL (O, 40 beds) 950 South Mulford Road, Rockford, IL Zip 61108; tel. 815/381–8500; Daniel B. Woloszyn, Administrator
Web address: www.healthsouth.com

INDIANA: HEALTHSOUTH DEACONESS REHABILITATION HOSPITAL (O, 80 beds) 4100 Covert Avenue, Evansville, IN Zip 47714–5567, Mailing Address: P.O. Box 5349, Zip 47716–5349; tel. 812/476–9983; Barbara Butler, Administrator
Web address: www.healthsouth.com

HEALTHSOUTH HOSPITAL OF TERRE HAUTE (O, 58 beds) 501 East St. Anthony Drive, Terre Haute, IN Zip 47802–9135; tel. 812/235–5656; Myra Wetzel, Administrator
Web address: www.healthsouth.com

KANSAS: KANSAS REHABILITATION HOSPITAL (O, 69 beds) 1504 S.W. Eighth Avenue, Topeka, KS Zip 66606–1632; tel. 785/235–6600; Paul Livingston, Administrator
Web address: www.kansasrehab.com

MID–AMERICA REHABILITATION HOSPITAL (O, 80 beds) 5701 West 110th Street, Shawnee Mission, KS Zip 66211–2503; tel. 913/491–2400; Kristen De Hart, Administrator
Web address: www.selectmedicalcorp.com

WESLEY REHABILITATION HOSPITAL (O, 65 beds) 8338 West 13th Street North, Wichita, KS Zip 67212–2984; tel. 316/729–9999; Pamela Stanberry, Administrator
Web address: www.healthsouth.com

KENTUCKY: HEALTHSOUTH NORTHERN KENTUCKY REHABILITATION HOSPITAL (O, 40 beds) 201 Medical Village Drive, Edgewood, KY Zip 41017–3407; tel. 859/341–2044; Brenda Gosney, Administrator
Web address: www.healthsouth.com

HEALTHSOUTH REHABILITATION HOSPITAL OF CENTRAL KENTUCKY (O, 40 beds) 134 Heartland Drive, Elizabethtown, KY Zip 42701–2778; tel. 270/769–3100; Eileen Nelson, Administrator
Web address: www.healthsouth.com

LOUISIANA: HEALTHSOUTH NORTH LOUISIANA REHABILITATION HOSPITAL (O, 90 beds) 1401 Ezell Street, Ruston, LA Zip 71270–7221; tel. 318/251–5354; Mark J. Rice, Administrator
Web address: www.healthsouth.com

HEALTHSOUTH REHABILITATION HOSPITAL OF ALEXANDRIA (O, 47 beds) 104 North Third Street, Alexandria, LA Zip 71301–8581; tel. 318/449–1370; Kemp Wright, Administrator
Web address: www.healthsouth.com

HEALTHSOUTH REHABILITATION HOSPITAL OF BATON ROUGE (O, 80 beds) 8595 United Plaza Boulevard, Baton Rouge, LA Zip 70809–2251; tel. 225/927–0567; Kenneth E. Alexander, Administrator
Web address: www.healthsouth.com

HEALTHSOUTH RIVERSIDE HOSPITAL OF ALEXANDRIA (O, 28 beds) 211 Fourth Street, 5th Floor, Alexandria, LA Zip 71301; tel. 318/449–8381; Bryan Day, Administrator

HEALTHSOUTH SPECIALTY HOSPITAL OF NEW ORLEANS (O, 28 beds) 5620 Read Boulevard, 6th Floor N., New Orleans, LA Zip 70127; tel. 504/240–4260; Susan R. Davis, Administrator

HEALTHSOUTH SPECIALTY HOSPITAL OF WINNFIELD (O, 20 beds) 915 First Street, Winnfield, LA Zip 71483; tel. 318/648–0212; Mark J. Rice, Administrator

MAINE: NEW ENGLAND REHABILITATION HOSPITAL OF PORTLAND (O, 76 beds) 335 Brighton Avenue, Portland, ME Zip 04102–9735; tel. 207/775–4000; Amy Morse, Administrator
Web address: www.healthsouth.com

MARYLAND: HEALTHSOUTH CHESAPEAKE REHABILITATION HOSPITAL (O, 42 beds) 220 Tilghman Road, Salisbury, MD Zip 21804–1921; tel. 410/546–4600; Gary Crowley, Administrator
Web address: www.healthsouth.com

MASSACHUSETTS: FAIRLAWN REHABILITATION HOSPITAL (O, 110 beds) 189 May Street, Worcester, MA Zip 01602–4399; tel. 508/791–6351; Peter M. Mantegazza, Chief Executive Officer
Web address: www.healthsouth.com

HEALTHSOUTH BRAINTREE REHABILITATION HOSPITAL (O, 117 beds) 250 Pond Street, Braintree, MA Zip 02185–9020; tel. 781/348–2078; Randy Doherty, Administrator
Web address: www.healthsouth.com

HEALTHSOUTH NEW ENGLAND REHABILITATION HOSPITAL (O, 210 beds) Two Rehabilitation Way, Woburn, MA Zip 01801–6098; tel. 781/935–5050; Eileen Gibbons, Administrator
Web address: www.healthsouth.com

For explanation of codes following names, see page B2.
★ Indicates Type III membership in the American Hospital Association.

HEALTHSOUTH REHABILITATION HOSPITAL OF WESTERN MASSACHUSETTS (O, 40 beds) 14 Chestnut Place, Ludlow, MA Zip 01056–3460; tel. 413/589–7581; R. David Richer, Administrator
Web address: www.healthsouth.com

MISSOURI: HOWARD A. RUSK REHABILITATION CENTER (O, 60 beds) 315 Business Loop 70 West, Columbia, MO Zip 65203–3248; tel. 573/817–2703; Patrick N. Lee, CHE, Administrator
Web address: www.healthsouth.com

THE REHABILITATION INSTITUTE OF ST. LOUIS (O, 72 beds) 4455 Duncan Avenue, Saint Louis, MO Zip 63110–1111; tel. 314/658–3800; Daniel J. Rothery, Administrator
Web address: www.healthsouth.com

NEVADA: HEALTHSOUTH HOSPITAL OF TENAYA (O, 70 beds) 2500 North Tenaya, Las Vegas, NV Zip 89128; tel. 702/562–2021; Jerry Amato, Administrator

HEALTHSOUTH REHABILITATION HOSPITAL – HENDERSON (O, 60 beds) 10301 Jeffreys Street, Henderson, NV Zip 89052; tel. 702/939–9400; Thomas Maher, Administrator

HEALTHSOUTH REHABILITATION HOSPITAL–LAS VEGAS (O, 79 beds) 1250 South Valley View Boulevard, Las Vegas, NV Zip 89102–1861; tel. 702/877–8898; Gilbert Silbernagel, Administrator
Web address: www.healthsouth.com

NEW HAMPSHIRE: HEALTHSOUTH REHABILITATION HOSPITAL (O, 50 beds) 254 Pleasant Street, Concord, NH Zip 03301–2508; tel. 603/226–9800; Lori Manor Underwood, Administrator
Web address: www.healthsouth.com

NEW JERSEY: HEALTHSOUTH REHABILITATION HOSPITAL OF NEW JERSEY (O, 125 beds) 14 Hospital Drive, Toms River, NJ Zip 08755–6470; tel. 732/244–3100; Patricia Ostaszewski, Administrator
Web address: www.healthsouth.com

REHABILITATION HOSPITAL OF TINTON FALLS (O, 60 beds) 2 Centre Plaza, Eatontown, NJ Zip 07724; tel. 732/460–5320; Linda A. Savino, Administrator
Web address: www.healthsouth.com

NEW MEXICO: HEALTHSOUTH REHABILITATION CENTER (O, 60 beds) 7000 Jefferson N.E., Albuquerque, NM Zip 87109–4357; tel. 505/344–9478; Sylvia K. Kelly, Administrator
Web address: www.healthsouth.com

PENNSYLVANIA: GEISINGER HEALTHSOUTH REHABILITATION HOSPITAL (O, 40 beds) 2 Rehab Lane, Danville, PA Zip 17821; tel. 570/271–6733; Lorie Dillon, Administrator
Web address: www.healthsouth.com

HEALTHSOUTH HARMARVILLE REHABILITATION HOSPITAL (O, 202 beds) Guys Run Road, Pittsburgh, PA Zip 15238–0460, Mailing Address: P.O. Box 11460, Zip 15238–0460; tel. 412/828–1300; Sharon Noro, Administrator
Web address: www.healthsouth.com

HEALTHSOUTH HOSPITAL OF PITTSBURGH (O, 89 beds) 2380 McGinley Road, Monroeville, PA Zip 15146–4400; tel. 412/856–2400; Timothy Bugin, Chief Operating Officer
Web address: www.healthsouth.com

HEALTHSOUTH NITTANY VALLEY REHABILITATION HOSPITAL (O, 85 beds) 550 West College Avenue, Pleasant Gap, PA Zip 16823–7416; tel. 814/359–3421; Susan Hartman, Administrator
Web address: www.healthsouth.com

HEALTHSOUTH READING REHABILITATION HOSPITAL (O, 95 beds) 1623 Morgantown Road, Reading, PA Zip 19607–9455; tel. 610/796–6000; Tammy L. Ober, Administrator
Web address: www.healthsouth.com

HEALTHSOUTH REGIONAL SPECIALTY HOSPITAL (O, 46 beds) 4950 Wilson Lane, Mechanicsburg, PA Zip 17055; tel. 717/697–7706; Brent Burger, Administrator

HEALTHSOUTH REHABILITATION HOSPITAL (O, 44 beds) 303 Camp Meeting Road, Sewickley, PA Zip 15143–8322; tel. 412/741–9500; Sharon Noro, Administrator
Web address: www.healthsouth.com

HEALTHSOUTH REHABILITATION HOSPITAL OF ALTOONA (O, 70 beds) 2005 Valley View Boulevard, Altoona, PA Zip 16602–4598; tel. 814/944–3535; Scott Filler, Administrator
Web address: www.healthsouth.com

HEALTHSOUTH REHABILITATION HOSPITAL OF ERIE (O, 108 beds) 143 East Second Street, Erie, PA Zip 16507–1501; tel. 814/878–1200; Louis M. Condrasky, Administrator
Web address: www.healthsouth.com

HEALTHSOUTH REHABILITATION HOSPITAL OF YORK (O, 90 beds) 1850 Normandie Drive, York, PA Zip 17404–1534; tel. 717/767–6941; Cheryl Fleming, Administrator
Web address: www.healthsouth.com

HEALTHSOUTH REHABILITATION OF MECHANICSBURG (O, 103 beds) 175 Lancaster Boulevard, Mechanicsburg, PA Zip 17055–0736, Mailing Address: P.O. Box 2016, Zip 17055–2016; tel. 717/691–3700; Gregory P. Toot, Administrator and Chief Executive Officer
Web address: www.healthsouth.com

PUERTO RICO: HEALTHSOUTH REHABILITATION HOSPITAL (O, 32 beds) University Hospital, 3rd Floor, San Juan, PR Zip 00923, Mailing Address: P.O. Box 70344, Zip 00923; tel. 787/274–5100; Edwin Sueiro, Administrator

SOUTH CAROLINA: ANMED HEALTHOUTH REHABILITATION HOSPITAL (O, 40 beds) 1 Spring Back Way, Anderson, SC Zip 29621; tel. 864/716–2600; Michele M. Skripps, Administrator

HEALTHSOUTH REHABILITATION HOSPITAL (O, 96 beds) 2935 Colonial Drive, Columbia, SC Zip 29203–6811; tel. 803/254–7777; Candace Knox, Administrator
Web address: www.healthsouth.com

HEALTHSOUTH REHABILITATION HOSPITAL (O, 88 beds) 900 East Cheves Street, Florence, SC Zip 29506–2704; tel. 843/679–9000; James Scott Rowe, Administrator
Web address: www.healthsouth.com

HEALTHSOUTH REHABILITATION HOSPITAL (O, 34 beds) 1795 Frank Gaston Boulevard, Rock Hill, SC Zip 29732; tel. 803/362–3500; Anthony W. Jackson, Administrator
Web address: www.healthsouth.org

HEALTHSOUTH REHABILITATION HOSPITAL OF CHARLESTON (O, 46 beds) 9181 Medcom Street, Charleston, SC Zip 29406–9168; tel. 843/820–7777; Troy Powell, Administrator
Web address: www.healthsouth.com

TENNESSEE: HEALTHSOUTH CANE CREEK REHABILITATION HOSPITAL (O, 40 beds) 180 Mt Pelia Road, Martin, TN Zip 38237; tel. 731/587–4231; Dayle Unger, Administrator

HEALTHSOUTH CHATTANOOGA REHABILITATION HOSPITAL (O, 54 beds) 2412 McCallie Avenue, Chattanooga, TN Zip 37404–3398; tel. 423/698–0221; Donna Bourdon, Administrator
Web address: www.healthsouth.com

HEALTHSOUTH REHABILITATION HOSPITAL (O, 42 beds) 113 Cassel Drive, Kingsport, TN Zip 37660–3775; tel. 423/246–7240; Terri Alsbrook, Administrator
Web address: www.healthsouth.com

HEALTHSOUTH REHABILITATION HOSPITAL (O, 80 beds) 1282 Union Avenue, Memphis, TN Zip 38104–3414; tel. 901/722–2000; Mark A. Kelly, Administrator
Web address: www.healthsouth.com

HEALTHSOUTH REHABILITATION HOSPITAL (O, 40 beds) 4100 Austin Peay Highway, Memphis, TN Zip 38128; tel. 901/213–5400; Brenda M. Antwine, Administrator

VANDERBILT STALLWORTH REHABILITATION HOSPITAL (O, 80 beds) 2201 Childrens Way, Nashville, TN Zip 37212–3165; tel. 615/320–7600; Susan Heath, Administrator
Web address: www.healthsouth.com

TEXAS: HEALTHSOUTH HOUSTON REHABILITATION INSTITUTE (O, 79 beds) 17506 Red Oak Drive, Houston, TX Zip 77090–7721, Mailing Address: P.O. Box 73684, Zip 77273–3684; tel. 281/580–1212; Edward Downs, Administrator
Web address: www.healthsouth.com

HEALTHSOUTH INTEGRATED MEDICAL PLAZA (O, 6 beds) 4243 East Southcross Boulevard, San Antonio, TX Zip 78222; tel. 210/368–7400

HEALTHSOUTH MEDICAL CENTER (O, 106 beds) 2124 Research Row, Dallas, TX Zip 75235–2504; tel. 214/904–6100; Russell Bailey, Administrator
Web address: www.healthsouth.com

HEALTHSOUTH PLANO REHABILITATION HOSPITAL (O, 65 beds) 2800 West 15th Street, Plano, TX Zip 75075–7526; tel. 972/612–9000; Chester Crouch, Administrator
Web address: www.healthsouth.com

For explanation of codes following names, see page B2.
★ Indicates Type III membership in the American Hospital Association.

HEALTHSOUTH REHABILITATION HOSPITAL (O, 60 beds) 1212 West Lancaster Avenue, Fort Worth, TX Zip 76102–4510; tel. 817/870–2336; Sandra Collins, Administrator
Web address: www.healthsouth.com

HEALTHSOUTH REHABILITATION HOSPITAL (O, 28 beds) 515 North Adams, 3rd Floor, Odessa, TX Zip 79760; tel. 432/550–1800; William Grey, Administrator
Web address: www.healthsouth.com

HEALTHSOUTH REHABILITATION HOSPITAL (O, 60 beds) 19002 McKay Drive, Humble, TX Zip 77338–5701; tel. 281/446–6148; Robyne Pack, Administrator
Web address: www.healthsouth.com

HEALTHSOUTH REHABILITATION HOSPITAL MIDLAND–ODESSA (O, 30 beds) 1800 Heritage Boulevard, Midland, TX Zip 79707–9750; tel. 432/520–1600; William Grey, Administrator
Web address: www.healthsouth.com

HEALTHSOUTH REHABILITATION HOSPITAL OF ARLINGTON (O, 65 beds) 3200 Matlock Road, Arlington, TX Zip 76015–2911; tel. 817/468–4000; Bruce Lambdin, Interim Chief Executive Officer
Web address: www.healthsouth.com

HEALTHSOUTH REHABILITATION HOSPITAL OF AUSTIN (O, 83 beds) 1215 Red River Street, Austin, TX Zip 78701–1921; tel. 512/474–5700; Denise Lynch, Administrator
Web address: www.healthsouth.com

HEALTHSOUTH REHABILITATION HOSPITAL OF BEAUMONT (O, 61 beds) 3340 Plaza 10 Boulevard, Beaumont, TX Zip 77707–2551; tel. 409/835–0835; Bill Klamforth, Administrator
Web address: www.healthsouth.com

HEALTHSOUTH REHABILITATION HOSPITAL OF NORTH HOUSTON (O, 73 beds) 18550 I 45 South, Conroe, TX Zip 77384; tel. 281/364–2000; Robyne Pack, Administrator
Web address: www.healthsouth.com

HEALTHSOUTH REHABILITATION HOSPITAL OF TEXARKANA (O, 60 beds) 515 West 12th Street, Texarkana, TX Zip 75501–4416; tel. 903/793–0088; Joanne Rose, Administrator
Web address: www.healthsouth.com

HEALTHSOUTH REHABILITATION HOSPITAL–CITYVIEW (O, 62 beds) 6701 Oakmont Boulevard, Fort Worth, TX Zip 76132–2957; tel. 817/370–4700; Jason Jennings, Administrator
Web address: www.healthsouth.com

HEALTHSOUTH REHABILITATION HOSPITAL–TYLER (O, 62 beds) 3131 Troup Highway, Tyler, TX Zip 75701–8352; tel. 903/510–7000; Sharla Anderson, Administrator
Web address: www.healthsouth.com

HEALTHSOUTH REHABILITATION HOSPITAL–WICHITA FALLS (O, 63 beds) 3901 Armory Road, Wichita Falls, TX Zip 76302–2204; tel. 940/720–5700; Michael L. Bullitt, Administrator
Web address: www.healthsouth.com

HEALTHSOUTH REHABILITATION INSTITUTE OF SAN ANTONIO (O, 96 beds) 9119 Cinnamon Hill, San Antonio, TX Zip 78240–5401; tel. 210/691–0737; Diane B. Lampe, Administrator
Web address: www.healthsouth.com

HEALTHSOUTH SURGICAL HOSPITAL OF AUSTIN (O, 8 beds) 6818 Austin Center Boulevard, Austin, TX Zip 78731–3165; tel. 512/346–1994; Diana Zamora, Administrator
Web address: www.healthsouth.com

UTAH: HEALTHSOUTH REHABILITATION HOSPITAL OF UTAH (O, 84 beds) 8074 South 1300 East, Sandy, UT Zip 84094–0743; tel. 801/561–3400; Tom Almerico, Administrator
Web address: www.healthsouth.com

VIRGINIA: HEALTHSOUTH REHABILITATION HOSPITAL OF VIRGINIA (O, 40 beds) 5700 Fitzhugh Avenue, Richmond, VA Zip 23226–1877; tel. 804/288–5700; Jeff Ruskan, Administrator
Web address: www.healthsouth.com

UVA–HEALTHSOUTH REHABILITATION HOSPITAL (O, 50 beds) 515 Ray C. Hunt Drive, Charlottesville, VA Zip 22903; tel. 434/244–2000; Thomas J. Cook, Administrator

WEST VIRGINIA: HEALTHSOUTH HUNTINGTON REHABILITATION HOSPITAL (O, 52 beds) 6900 West Country Club Drive, Huntington, WV Zip 25705–2000; tel. 304/733–1060; Frank Weber, Administrator
Web address: www.healthsouth.com

HEALTHSOUTH MOUNTAINVIEW REGIONAL REHABILITATION HOSPITAL (O, 96 beds) 1160 Van Voorhis Road, Morgantown, WV Zip 26505–3435; tel. 304/598–1100; John C. Forester, Administrator
Web address: www.healthsouth.com

HEALTHSOUTH SOUTHERN HILLS REHABILITATION HOSPITAL (O, 60 beds) 120 Twelfth Street, Princeton, WV Zip 24740–2312; tel. 304/487–8000; Marion Houser, Administrator
Web address: www.healthsouth.com

HEALTHSOUTH WESTERN HILLS REHABILITATION CENTER (O, 40 beds) 3 Western Hills Drive, Parkersburg, WV Zip 26101–8122; tel. 304/420–1300; Dean Hatcher, Administrator
Web address: www.healthsouth.com

Owned, leased, sponsored:	106 hospitals	7036 beds
Contract–managed:	0 hospitals	0 beds
Totals:	106 hospitals	7036 beds

★9505:   HENRY FORD HEALTH SYSTEM (NP)
One Ford Place, Detroit, MI Zip 48202–3450; tel. 313/876–8705; Nancy M. Schlichting, President and Chief Executive Officer
(Centralized Physician/Insurance Health System)

MICHIGAN: HENRY FORD BI–COUNTY HOSPITAL (O, 170 beds) 13355 East Ten Mile Road, Warren, MI Zip 48089–2065; tel. 586/759–7300; Gary W. Popiel, Chief Executive Officer
Web address: www.bicountyhospital.org

HENRY FORD HOSPITAL (O, 673 beds) 2799 West Grand Boulevard, Detroit, MI Zip 48202–2689; tel. 313/916–2600; Anthony A. Armada, President and Chief Executive Officer
Web address: www.henryfordhealth.org

HENRY FORD KINGSWOOD HOSPITAL (O, 64 beds) 10300 West Eight Mile Road, Ferndale, MI Zip 48220–2198; tel. 248/398–3200; Marilyn Grazio, Clinical Administrator

HENRY FORD WYANDOTTE HOSPITAL (O, 336 beds) 2333 Biddle Avenue, Wyandotte, MI Zip 48192–4693; tel. 734/246–6000; James J. Sexton, President and Chief Executive Officer
Web address: www.henryfordhealth.org

Owned, leased, sponsored:	4 hospitals	1243 beds
Contract–managed:	0 hospitals	0 beds
Totals:	4 hospitals	1243 beds

0309:   HERITAGE VALLEY HEALTH SYSTEM (IO)
1000 Dutch Ridge Road, Beaver, PA Zip 15009–9727; tel. 724/728–7000; Norman F. Mitry, President and Chief Executive Officer

PENNSYLVANIA: SEWICKLEY VALLEY HOSPITAL, (A DIVISION OF VALLEY MEDICAL FACILITIES) (O, 182 beds) 720 Blackburn Road, Sewickley, PA Zip 15143–1459; tel. 412/741–6600; Norman F. Mitry, President and Chief Executive Officer
Web address: www.heritagevalley.org

THE MEDICAL CENTER, BEAVER (O, 359 beds) 1000 Dutch Ridge Road, Beaver, PA Zip 15009–9727; tel. 724/728–7000; Norman F. Mitry, President and Chief Executive Officer
Web address: www.heritagevalley.org

Owned, leased, sponsored:	2 hospitals	541 beds
Contract–managed:	0 hospitals	0 beds
Totals:	2 hospitals	541 beds

★0130:   HILLCREST HEALTHCARE SYSTEM (NP)
110 West 7th Street, Suite 2540, Tulsa, OK Zip 74119; tel. 918/579–1070; Kevin J. Gross, President and Chief Executive Officer
(Moderately Centralized Health System)

OKLAHOMA: BRISTOW MEMORIAL HOSPITAL (O, 17 beds) 700 West 7th Street, Suite 6, Bristow, OK Zip 74010; tel. 918/367–2215; Ryan Gehrig, Chief Executive Officer
Web address: www.bristowmedicalcenter.com

For explanation of codes following names, see page B2.
★ Indicates Type III membership in the American Hospital Association.

Section B

CLEVELAND AREA HOSPITAL (O, 17 beds) 1401 West Pawnee Street, Cleveland, OK Zip 74020–3019; tel. 918/358–2501; Samuel T. Guild, Chief Executive Officer
Web address: www.hillcrest.com

CUSHING REGIONAL HOSPITAL (O, 75 beds) 1027 East Cherry Street, Cushing, OK Zip 74023–4101, Mailing Address: P.O. Box 1409, Zip 74023–1409; tel. 918/225–2915; Ron Cackler, President and Chief Executive Officer
Web address: www.hillcrest.com

HENRYETTA MEDICAL CENTER (O, 42 beds) Dewey Bartlett and Main Streets, Henryetta, OK Zip 74437–6820, Mailing Address: P.O. Box 1269, Zip 74437–1269; tel. 918/652–4463; Dee Renshaw, Chief Executive Officer
Web address: www.henryetta.org/medical

HILLCREST MEDICAL CENTER (O, 432 beds) 1120 South Utica, Tulsa, OK Zip 74104–4090; tel. 918/579–1000; Steve Dobbs, Chief Executive Officer
Web address: www.hillcrest.com

PAWNEE MUNICIPAL HOSPITAL (O, 20 beds) 1212 Fourth Street, Pawnee, OK Zip 74058–4046, Mailing Address: P.O. Box 467, Zip 74058–0467; tel. 918/762–2577; Samuel T. Guild, Chief Executive Officer
Web address: www.hillcrest.com

TULSA REGIONAL MEDICAL CENTER (O, 212 beds) 744 West Ninth Street, Tulsa, OK Zip 74127–9990; tel. 918/587–2561; Dan Fieker, Chief Executive Officer
Web address: www.hillcrest.com

WAGONER COMMUNITY HOSPITAL (O, 100 beds) 1200 West Cherokee, Wagoner, OK Zip 74467–4681, Mailing Address: Box 407, Zip 74477–0407; tel. 918/485–5514; John W. Crawford, Chief Executive Officer

Owned, leased, sponsored:	8 hospitals	915 beds
Contract–managed:	0 hospitals	0 beds
Totals:	8 hospitals	915 beds

0306: HORIZON HEALTH CORPORATION (IO)
1500 Waters Ridge Drive, Lewisville, TX Zip 75057; tel. 972/420–8222; Ken Newman, President and Chief Executive Officer
(Independent Hospital System)

INDIANA: MICHIANA BEHAVIORAL HEALTH CENTER (O, 76 beds) 1800 North Oak Road, Plymouth, IN Zip 46563–3492; tel. 574/936–3784; Bryan W. Lett, Chief Executive Officer
Web address: www.michianabhc.com

PENNSYLVANIA: FRIENDS BEHAVIORAL HEALTH SYSTEM (O, 192 beds) 4641 Roosevelt Boulevard, Philadelphia, PA Zip 19124–2399; tel. 215/831–4600; Joseph Pyle, Executive Vice President and Chief Operating Officer
Web address: www.friendshospitalonline.org

VIRGINIA: POPLAR SPRINGS HOSPITAL (O, 161 beds) 350 Poplar Drive, Petersburg, VA Zip 23805–4657, Mailing Address: P.O. Box 3060, Zip 23805–3060; tel. 804/733–6874; Anthony J. Vadella, President and Chief Executive Officer
Web address: www.poplarsprings.com

Owned, leased, sponsored:	3 hospitals	429 beds
Contract–managed:	0 hospitals	0 beds
Totals:	3 hospitals	429 beds

0289: HOSPITAL PARTNERS OF AMERICA (IO)
2320 Cascade Pointe Boulevard, Suite 310, Charlotte, NC Zip 28208; tel. 704/424–6800; Todd Johnson, President and Chief Executive Officer
(Moderately Centralized Health System)

CALIFORNIA: SHASTA REGIONAL MEDICAL CENTER (O, 238 beds) 1100 Butte Street, Redding, CA Zip 96001–0853, Mailing Address: Box 496072, Zip 96049–6072; tel. 530/244–5454; Thomas A. Salerno, Chief Executive Officer
Web address: www.reddingmedicalcenter.com

TEXAS: AUSTIN SURGICAL HOSPITAL (O, 23 beds) 3003 Bee Caves Road, Austin, TX Zip 78746; tel. 512/314–3800; Jess N. Judy, President and Chief Executive Officer
Web address: www.austinsurgicalhospital.com

TWELVE OAKS MEDICAL CENTER (O, 356 beds) 4200 Twelve Oaks Drive, Houston, TX Zip 77027–6899; tel. 713/623–2500; Kerry Teel, Chief Executive Officer
Web address: www.twelveoaksmedicalcenter.com

Owned, leased, sponsored:	3 hospitals	617 beds
Contract–managed:	0 hospitals	0 beds
Totals:	3 hospitals	617 beds

★**5355: HOSPITAL SISTERS HEALTH SYSTEM** (CC)
Springfield, IL Mailing Address: P.O. Box 19456, Zip 62794–9456; tel. 217/523–4747; Sister Jomary Trstensky, President
(Moderately Centralized Health System)

ILLINOIS: ST. ANTHONY'S MEMORIAL HOSPITAL (O, 146 beds) 503 North Maple Street, Effingham, IL Zip 62401–2099; tel. 217/342–2121; Daniel J. Woods, Executive Vice President and Administrator
Web address: www.stanthonyshospital.org

ST. ELIZABETH'S HOSPITAL (O, 278 beds) 211 South Third Street, Belleville, IL Zip 62220–1998; tel. 618/234–2120; Timothy F. Brady, FACHE, Administrator
Web address: www.steliz.org

ST. FRANCIS HOSPITAL (O, 85 beds) 1215 Franciscan Drive, Litchfield, IL Zip 62056–1799, Mailing Address: P.O. Box 1215, Zip 62056–1215; tel. 217/324–2191; Michael Sipkoski, Executive Vice President and Administrator
Web address: www.stfrancis–litchfield.org

ST. JOHN'S HOSPITAL (O, 539 beds) 800 East Carpenter Street, Springfield, IL Zip 62769–0002; tel. 217/544–6464; Richard J. Carlson, Executive Vice President and Administrator
Web address: www.st-johns.org

ST. JOSEPH'S HOSPITAL (O, 60 beds) 9515 Holy Cross Lane, Breese, IL Zip 62230–0099; tel. 618/526–4511; Jacolyn M. Schlautman, Executive Vice President and Administrator
Web address: www.stjoebreese.com

ST. JOSEPH'S HOSPITAL (O, 55 beds) 1515 Main Street, Highland, IL Zip 62249–1656; tel. 618/654–7421; Claudio Fort, Executive Vice President and Administrator
Web address: www.stjosephs–highland.org

ST. MARY'S HOSPITAL (O, 224 beds) 1800 East Lake Shore Drive, Decatur, IL Zip 62521–3883; tel. 217/464–2966; Anthony D. Pfitzer, Executive Vice President and Administrator
Web address: www.stmarys–hospital.com

ST. MARY'S HOSPITAL (O, 109 beds) 111 Spring Street, Streator, IL Zip 61364–3399; tel. 815/673–2311; Mark S. O'Halla, Executive Vice President and Administrator
Web address: www.stmaryshospital.org

WISCONSIN: SACRED HEART HOSPITAL (O, 194 beds) 900 West Clairemont Avenue, Eau Claire, WI Zip 54701–6122; tel. 715/839–4121; Stephen F. Ronstrom, Executive Vice President and Administrator
Web address: www.sacredhearthospital-ec.org

ST. JOSEPH'S HOSPITAL (O, 127 beds) 2661 County Highway I, Chippewa Falls, WI Zip 54729–1498; tel. 715/723–1811; David B. Fish, Executive Vice President and Administrator
Web address: www.stjoeschipfalls.com

ST. MARY'S HOSPITAL MEDICAL CENTER (O, 94 beds) 1726 Shawano Avenue, Green Bay, WI Zip 54303–3282; tel. 920/498–4200; James G. Coller, Executive Vice President and Administrator
Web address: www.stmgb.org

ST. NICHOLAS HOSPITAL (O, 78 beds) 3100 Superior Avenue, Sheboygan, WI Zip 53081; tel. 920/459–8300; Mary T. Brasseaux, Executive Vice President and Administrator
Web address: www.stnicholashospital.org

ST. VINCENT HOSPITAL (O, 275 beds) 835 South Van Buren Street, Green Bay, WI Zip 54307–3508, Mailing Address: P.O. Box 13508, Zip 54307–3508; tel. 920/433–0111; Joseph J. Neidenbach, Executive Vice President and Administrator
Web address: www.stvgb.org

Owned, leased, sponsored:	13 hospitals	2264 beds
Contract–managed:	0 hospitals	0 beds
Totals:	13 hospitals	2264 beds

For explanation of codes following names, see page B2.
★ Indicates Type III membership in the American Hospital Association.

0201: IASIS HEALTHCARE (IO)

117 Seaborad Lane, Building E., Franklin, TN Zip 37067, Mailing Address: 117 Seaboard Lane, Building E., Zip 37067; tel. 615/844–2747; David R. White, Chairman and Chief Executive Officer

(Moderately Centralized Health System)

ARIZONA: MESA GENERAL HOSPITAL MEDICAL CENTER (O, 143 beds) 515 North Mesa Drive, Mesa, AZ Zip 85201–5989; tel. 480/969–9111; C. Mark Gregson, Chief Executive Officer
Web address: www.mesageneralhospital.com

ST. LUKE'S BEHAVIORAL HEALTH CENTER (O, 85 beds) 1800 East Van Buren, Phoenix, AZ Zip 85006–3742; tel. 602/251–8546; Paul M. Jenson, Chief Executive Officer
Web address: www.iasishealthcare.com

ST. LUKE'S MEDICAL CENTER (O, 225 beds) 1800 East Van Buren Street, Phoenix, AZ Zip 85006–3742; tel. 602/251–8100; Paul M. Jenson, Chief Executive Officer
Web address: www.iasishealthcare.com

TEMPE ST. LUKE'S HOSPITAL (O, 110 beds) 1500 South Mill Avenue, Tempe, AZ Zip 85281–6699; tel. 480/784–5510; Jeff R. Egbert, Chief Executive Officer
Web address: www.tempestlukehospital.com

FLORIDA: MEMORIAL HOSPITAL OF TAMPA (O, 149 beds) 2901 Swann Avenue, Tampa, FL Zip 33609–4057; tel. 813/873–6400; John J. Mainieri, Chief Executive Officer
Web address: www.memorialhospitaltampa.com

PALMS OF PASADENA HOSPITAL (O, 307 beds) 1501 Pasadena Avenue South, Saint Petersburg, FL Zip 33707–3798; tel. 727/381–1000; Steven J. Greene, Chief Executive Officer
Web address: www.palmspasadena.com

TOWN AND COUNTRY HOSPITAL (O, 127 beds) 6001 Webb Road, Tampa, FL Zip 33615–3291; tel. 813/888–7060; James P. Seward Jr, Chief Executive Officer
Web address: www.townandcountryhospital.com

NEVADA: NORTH VISTA HOSPITAL (O, 198 beds) 1409 East Lake Mead Boulevard, North Las Vegas, NV Zip 89030–7197; tel. 702/649–7711; Anthony Marinello, Chief Executive Officer
Web address: www.lakemeadhospital.com

TEXAS: ODESSA REGIONAL HOSPITAL (O, 146 beds) 520 East Sixth Street, Odessa, TX Zip 79761–4565, Mailing Address: P.O. Box 4859, Zip 79760–4859; tel. 432/334–8200; R. Craig Preston, Chief Executive Officer
Web address: www.odessaregionalhospital.com

SOUTHWEST GENERAL HOSPITAL (O, 266 beds) 7400 Barlite Boulevard, San Antonio, TX Zip 78224–1399; tel. 210/921–2000; Richard D. Gonzalez, Chief Executive Officer
Web address: www.swgeneralhospital.com

THE MEDICAL CENTER OF SOUTHEAST TEXAS (O, 216 beds) 2555 Jimmy Johnson Boulevard, Port Arthur, TX Zip 77640; tel. 409/724–7389; P. Craig Desmond, Chief Executive Officer
Web address: www.medicalcentersetexas.com

UTAH: DAVIS HOSPITAL AND MEDICAL CENTER (O, 136 beds) 1600 West Antelope Drive, Layton, UT Zip 84041–1142; tel. 801/825–9561; Michael E. Jensen, President and Chief Executive Officer
Web address: www.davishospital.com

JORDAN VALLEY HOSPITAL (O, 50 beds) 3580 West 9000 South, West Jordan, UT Zip 84088–8811; tel. 801/561–8888; Bryanie W. Swilley, Chief Executive Officer
Web address: www.jordanvalleyhospital.com

PIONEER VALLEY HOSPITAL (O, 100 beds) 3460 South Pioneer Parkway, West Valley City, UT Zip 84120–2648; tel. 801/964–3100; Iris Simonis, Chief Executive Officer
Web address: www.pioneervalleyhospital.com

SALT LAKE REGIONAL MEDICAL CENTER (O, 132 beds) 1050 East South Temple, Salt Lake City, UT Zip 84102–1599; tel. 801/350–4111; Brian E. Dunn, Chief Executive Officer
Web address: www.saltlakeregional.com

Owned, leased, sponsored:	15 hospitals	2390 beds
Contract–managed:	0 hospitals	0 beds
Totals:	15 hospitals	2390 beds

★1305: INOVA HEALTH SYSTEM (NP)

8110 Gatehouse Road, Falls Church, VA Zip 22042; tel. 703/289–2069; J. Knox Singleton, President and Chief Executive Officer

(Centralized Health System)

VIRGINIA: INOVA ALEXANDRIA HOSPITAL (O, 330 beds) 4320 Seminary Road, Alexandria, VA Zip 22304–1594; tel. 703/504–3000; Kenneth H. Kozloff, FACHE, Administrator
Web address: www.inova.org

INOVA FAIR OAKS HOSPITAL (O, 174 beds) 3600 Joseph Siewick Drive, Fairfax, VA Zip 22033–1798; tel. 703/391–3600; John L. Fitzgerald, Vice President and Administrator
Web address: www.inova.org

INOVA FAIRFAX HOSPITAL (O, 924 beds) 3300 Gallows Road, Falls Church, VA Zip 22042–3300; tel. 703/776–4001; Douglas P. Cropper, Administrator
Web address: www.inova.com

INOVA LOUDOUN HOSPITAL (O, 92 beds) 44045 Riverside Parkway, Leesburg, VA Zip 20176–2799, Mailing Address: P.O. Box 6000, Zip 20176–6000; tel. 703/858–6000; Rodney N. Huebbers, President and Chief Executive Officer
Web address: www.loudounhospital.org

INOVA MOUNT VERNON HOSPITAL (O, 236 beds) 2501 Parker's Lane, Alexandria, VA Zip 22306; tel. 703/664–7000; Arlen Reynolds, Interim Chief Executive Officer
Web address: www.inova.org

Owned, leased, sponsored:	5 hospitals	1756 beds
Contract–managed:	0 hospitals	0 beds
Totals:	5 hospitals	1756 beds

0182: INTEGRATED HEALTH SERVICES (IO)

910 Ridgebrook Road, Sparks Glencoe, MD Zip 21152; tel. 410/773–1000; Joseph A. Bondi, Chairman and Chief Executive Officer

(Independent Hospital System)

KANSAS: SPECIALTY HOSPITAL OF MID–AMERICA (O, 37 beds) 6509 West 103rd Street, Overland Park, KS Zip 66212–1728; tel. 913/649–3701; Jerry Lindenbaum, Administrator
Web address: www.thicare.com/SpecHospOfMidAmerica/

WICHITA SPECIALTY HOSPITAL (O, 26 beds) 8080 East Pawnee Street, Wichita, KS Zip 67207–5475; tel. 316/682–0004; James D. Pethis, Chief Executive Officer
Web address: www.thicare.com/WichitaSpecialty/default.aspx

OKLAHOMA: EDMOND SPECIALTY HOSPITAL (O, 42 beds) 1100 East Ninth Street, Edmond, OK Zip 73034–5755; tel. 405/341–8150; Gayla Campbell, Executive Director
Web address: www.thicare.com/EdmondSpecialty/

SPECIALTY HOSPITAL OF MIDWEST CITY (O, 42 beds) 8210 National Avenue, Midwest City, OK Zip 73110; tel. 405/739–0800; Jerry Pyron, Chief Executive Officer

TEXAS: CORPUS CHRISTI SPECIALTY HOSPITAL (O, 31 beds) 1310 Third Street, Corpus Christi, TX Zip 78404–2208; tel. 361/888–4323; Sammy E. Davis, Administrator

GULF POINTE SPECIALTY HOSPITAL (O, 59 beds) 6160 South Loop East, Houston, TX Zip 77087–1010; tel. 713/640–2400; Shelley R. Cochran, Executive Director
Web address: www.ihsweb.his–inc.com

MESA HILL SPECIALTY HOSPITAL (O, 32 beds) 2311 North Oregon Street, El Paso, TX Zip 79902–3216; tel. 915/545–1823; Evelyn G. Stewart, Chief Executive Officer
Web address: www.ihs–inc.com

PLANO SPECIALTY HOSPITAL (O, 30 beds) 1621 Coit Road, Plano, TX Zip 75075; tel. 972/758–5200; Terry Kepler, Administrator and Chief Executive Officer

PLUM CREEK SPECIALTY HOSPITAL (O, 32 beds) 5601 Plum Creek Drive, Amarillo, TX Zip 79124–1801; tel. 806/351–1000; LeeAnn Griffin, Chief Executive Officer

SOUTHWEST REGIONAL MEDICAL COMPLEX (O, 30 beds) 1409 9th Street, Lubbock, TX Zip 79401–2601; tel. 806/767–9133; Deanna Graves, Chief Executive Officer
Web address: www.ihsoflubbock.com

For explanation of codes following names, see page B2.
★ Indicates Type III membership in the American Hospital Association.

Section B

TEXAS SPECIALTY HOSPITAL AT DALLAS (O, 66 beds) 7955 Harry Hines Boulevard, Dallas, TX Zip 75235–3395; tel. 214/637–0000; Cathy Campbell, Chief Executive Officer
Web address: www.thicare.com

TEXAS SPECIALTY HOSPITAL AT SAN ANTONIO (O, 24 beds) 7310 Oak Manor Drive, San Antonio, TX Zip 78229–4509; tel. 210/308–0261; Peggy Cliffe, Administrator
Web address: www.thicare.com

TEXAS SPECIALTY HOSPITAL AT WICHITA FALLS (O, 31 beds) 1103 Grace Street, Wichita Falls, TX Zip 76301–4414; tel. 940/720–6633; Billy Blasingame, Administrator
Web address: www.thicare.com

Owned, leased, sponsored:	13 hospitals	482 beds
Contract–managed:	0 hospitals	0 beds
Totals:	13 hospitals	482 beds

★**0305: INTEGRIS HEALTH** (NP)
3366 N.W. Expressway, Suite 800, Oklahoma City, OK Zip 73112–9756; tel. 405/949–6068; Stanley F. Hupfeld, President and Chief Executive Officer
(Decentralized Health System)

OKLAHOMA: INTEGRIS BAPTIST MEDICAL CENTER (O, 483 beds) 3300 N.W. Expressway, Oklahoma City, OK Zip 73112–4481; tel. 405/949–3011; C. Bruce Lawrence, President and Chief Operating Officer
Web address: www.integris–health.com

INTEGRIS BAPTIST REGIONAL HEALTH CENTER (O, 100 beds) 200 Second Street S.W., Miami, OK Zip 74354–6830, Mailing Address: P.O. Box 1207, Zip 74355–1207; tel. 918/542–6611; Joel A. Hart, FACHE, Chief Executive Officer
Web address: www.integris–health.com

INTEGRIS BASS BAPTIST HEALTH CENTER (O, 151 beds) 600 South Monroe Street, Enid, OK Zip 73701–7211, Mailing Address: P.O. Box 3168, Zip 73702–3168; tel. 580/233–2300; Karl Weinmeister, Interim Administrator
Web address: www.integris–health.com

INTEGRIS BLACKWELL REGIONAL HOSPITAL (L, 34 beds) 710 South 13th Street, Blackwell, OK Zip 74631–3700; tel. 580/363–2311; Jeffrey S. Tarrant, CHE, Chief Executive Officer
Web address: www.integris–health.com

INTEGRIS CANADIAN VALLEY REGIONAL HOSPITAL (O, 40 beds) 1201 Health Center Parkway, Yukon, OK Zip 73099; tel. 405/717–6800; James D. Moore, FACHE, Chief Executive Officer and Administrator
Web address: www.integris–health.com

INTEGRIS CLINTON REGIONAL HOSPITAL (L, 49 beds) 100 North 30th Street, Clinton, OK Zip 73601–3117, Mailing Address: P.O. Box 1569, Zip 73601–1569; tel. 580/323–2363; Jerry Jones, Administrator

INTEGRIS GROVE GENERAL HOSPITAL (O, 50 beds) 1310 South Main Street, Grove, OK Zip 74344–1310; tel. 918/786–2243; Greg Martin, Administrator and Chief Executive Officer
Web address: www.integris–health.com

INTEGRIS MARSHALL COUNTY MEDICAL CENTER (L, 20 beds) 1 Hospital Drive, Madill, OK Zip 73446, Mailing Address: P.O. Box 827, Zip 73446–0827; tel. 580/795–3384; C. David Hill, Chief Executive Officer
Web address: www.integris–health.com

INTEGRIS MAYES COUNTY MEDICAL CENTER (L, 52 beds) 111 North Bailey Street, Pryor, OK Zip 74361–4211, Mailing Address: P.O. Box 278, Zip 74362–0278; tel. 918/825–1600; W. Charles Jordan, Administrator

INTEGRIS SOUTHWEST MEDICAL CENTER (O, 361 beds) 4401 South Western, Oklahoma City, OK Zip 73109–3441; tel. 405/636–7000; C. Bruce Lawrence, President and Chief Operating Officer
Web address: www.integris–health.com

Owned, leased, sponsored:	10 hospitals	1340 beds
Contract–managed:	0 hospitals	0 beds
Totals:	10 hospitals	1340 beds

★**1815: INTERMOUNTAIN HEALTH CARE, INC.** (NP)
36 South State Street, 22nd Floor, Salt Lake City, UT Zip 84111–1453; tel. 801/442–2000; William H. Nelson, President and Chief Executive Officer
(Decentralized Health System)

IDAHO: CASSIA REGIONAL MEDICAL CENTER (O, 25 beds) 1501 Hiland Avenue, Burley, ID Zip 83318–2648; tel. 208/678–4444; Ken Harman, Administrator
Web address: www.ihc.com

UTAH: ALTA VIEW HOSPITAL (O, 73 beds) 9660 South 1300 East, Sandy, UT Zip 84094–3793; tel. 801/501–2600; Tim Bricker, Administrator and Chief Executive Officer
Web address: www.ihc.com

AMERICAN FORK HOSPITAL (O, 81 beds) 170 North 1100 East, American Fork, UT Zip 84003–2096; tel. 801/855–3300; Michael R. Olson, Administrator
Web address: www.ihc.com

BEAR RIVER VALLEY HOSPITAL (O, 58 beds) 440 West 600 North, Tremonton, UT Zip 84337–2497; tel. 435/257–7441; Eric Packer, Administrator
Web address: www.ihc.com

COTTONWOOD HOSPITAL MEDICAL CENTER (O, 172 beds) 5770 South 300 East, Murray, UT Zip 84107–6186, Mailing Address: P.O. Box 57800, Salt Lake City, Zip 84107–0800; tel. 801/314–5300; David Grauer, Administrator and Chief Executive Officer
Web address: www.ihc.com

DELTA COMMUNITY MEDICAL CENTER (O, 20 beds) 126 South White Sage Avenue, Delta, UT Zip 84624–8928; tel. 435/864–5591; James E. Beckstrand, Administrator
Web address: www.ihc.com

DIXIE REGIONAL MEDICAL CENTER (O, 212 beds) 544 South 400 East, Saint George, UT Zip 84770–3799; tel. 435/634–4000; L. Steven Wilson, Administrator
Web address: www.ihc.com

FILLMORE COMMUNITY MEDICAL CENTER (O, 20 beds) 674 South Highway 99, Fillmore, UT Zip 84631–9701; tel. 435/743–5591; James E. Beckstrand, Administrator
Web address: www.ihc.com

GARFIELD MEMORIAL HOSPITAL AND CLINICS (C, 44 beds) 200 North 400 East, Panguitch, UT Zip 84759, Mailing Address: P.O. Box 389, Zip 84759–0389; tel. 435/676–8811; Alberto Vasquez, Administrator
Web address: www.ihc.com/xp/ihc/garfield

HEBER VALLEY MEDICAL CENTER (O, 19 beds) 1485 South Highway 40, Heber City, UT Zip 84032–3522; tel. 435/654–2500; Ezra Segura, Administrator
Web address: www.ihc.com

LDS HOSPITAL (O, 468 beds) Eighth Avenue and C Street, Salt Lake City, UT Zip 84143–0001; tel. 801/408–1100; Mikelle D. Moore, CHE, Chief Executive Officer
Web address: www.ihc.com/xp/ihc/lds

LOGAN REGIONAL HOSPITAL (O, 127 beds) 1400 North 500 East, Logan, UT Zip 84341–2499; tel. 435/716–1000; Robert C. Cash, CHE, Administrator
Web address: www.ihc.com

MCKAY–DEE HOSPITAL CENTER (O, 299 beds) 4401 Harrison Boulevard, Ogden, UT Zip 84403, Mailing Address: Box 9370, Zip 84409–0370; tel. 801/387–2800; Timothy T. Pehrson, Chief Executive Officer
Web address: www.ihc.com/xp/ihc/mckaydee

OREM COMMUNITY HOSPITAL (O, 20 beds) 331 North 400 West, Orem, UT Zip 84057–1999; tel. 801/224–4080; Gail McGuill, Administrator and Chief Executive Officer
Web address: www.ihc.com

PRIMARY CHILDREN'S MEDICAL CENTER (O, 225 beds) 100 North Medical Drive, Salt Lake City, UT Zip 84113–1100; tel. 801/588–2000; Joseph R. Horton, Chief Executive Officer and Administrator

SANPETE VALLEY HOSPITAL (O, 20 beds) 1100 South Medical Drive, Mount Pleasant, UT Zip 84647–2222; tel. 435/462–2441; Ned Hill, Administrator
Web address: www.ihc.com

SEVIER VALLEY HOSPITAL (O, 27 beds) 1000 North Main Street, Richfield, UT Zip 84701–1843; tel. 435/896–8271; Gary E. Beck, Administrator
Web address: www.ihc.com

For explanation of codes following names, see page B2.
★ Indicates Type III membership in the American Hospital Association.

UTAH VALLEY REGIONAL MEDICAL CENTER (O, 355 beds) 1034 North 500 West, Provo, UT Zip 84604–3337; tel. 801/373–7850; Mary Ann Young, R.N., Administrator
Web address: www.ihc.com

VALLEY VIEW MEDICAL CENTER (O, 42 beds) 1303 North Main Street, Cedar City, UT Zip 84720–3462; tel. 435/868–5000; Steven Smoot, Administrator
Web address: www.ihc.com

Owned, leased, sponsored:	18 hospitals	2263 beds
Contract–managed:	1 hospital	44 beds
Totals:	19 hospitals	2307 beds

★0061: IOWA HEALTH SYSTEM (NP)
1200 Pleasant Street, Des Moines, IA Zip 50309–1453; tel. 515/241–6161; Samuel T. Wallace, President
(Decentralized Health System)

ILLINOIS: TRINITY MEDICAL CENTER–WEST (O, 327 beds) 2701 17th Street, Rock Island, IL Zip 61201–5393; tel. 309/779–5000; William B. Leaver, President and Chief Executive Officer
Web address: www.trinityqc.com

IOWA: ALLEN MEMORIAL HOSPITAL (O, 222 beds) 1825 Logan Avenue, Waterloo, IA Zip 50703–1916; tel. 319/235–3941; Richard A. Seidler, FACHE, Chief Executive Officer
Web address: www.allenhospital.org

BUENA VISTA REGIONAL MEDICAL CENTER (C, 42 beds) 1525 West Fifth Street, Storm Lake, IA Zip 50588–0309, Mailing Address: P.O. Box 309, Zip 50588–0309; tel. 712/732–4030; Todd Hudspeth, Chief Executive Officer
Web address: www.bvrmc.org

CLARKE COUNTY HOSPITAL (C, 55 beds) 800 South Fillmore Street, Osceola, IA Zip 50213–1619; tel. 641/342–2184; Brian Evans, Interim Chief Executive Officer
Web address: www.clarkehosp.org

COMMUNITY MEMORIAL HOSPITAL (C, 25 beds) 909 West First Street, Sumner, IA Zip 50674–1203, Mailing Address: P.O. Box 148, Zip 50674–0148; tel. 563/578–3275; Mary Wells, Administrator

DALLAS COUNTY HOSPITAL (C, 25 beds) 610 10th Street, Perry, IA Zip 50220–2221; tel. 515/465–3547; Laurie A. Conner, Chief Executive Officer
Web address: www.dallascohospital.org

FINLEY HOSPITAL (O, 124 beds) 350 North Grandview Avenue, Dubuque, IA Zip 52001–6392; tel. 563/582–1881; John E. Knox, President and Chief Executive Officer
Web address: www.finleyhospital.com

GREATER COMMUNITY HOSPITAL (C, 34 beds) 1700 West Townline, Creston, IA Zip 50801–1099; tel. 641/782–7091; Monte Neitzel, Administrator and Chief Executive Officer
Web address: www.greaterch.com

GREENE COUNTY MEDICAL CENTER (C, 101 beds) 1000 West Lincolnway, Jefferson, IA Zip 50129–1697; tel. 515/386–2114; Karen L. Bossard, Administrator and Chief Executive Officer
Web address: www.gcmchealth.com

GRUNDY COUNTY MEMORIAL HOSPITAL (C, 80 beds) 201 East J Avenue, Grundy Center, IA Zip 50638–2096; tel. 319/824–5421; Pamela K. Delagardelle, Chief Executive Officer
Web address: www.grundyhospital.com

GUTHRIE COUNTY HOSPITAL (C, 25 beds) 710 North 12th Street, Guthrie Center, IA Zip 50115–1544; tel. 641/332–2201; Gerald D. Neal, Chief Executive Officer
Web address: www.gcho.org

GUTTENBERG MUNICIPAL HOSPITAL (C, 25 beds) Second and Main Street, Guttenberg, IA Zip 52052–0550, Mailing Address: P.O. Box 550, Zip 52052–0550; tel. 563/252–1121; Kimberley Gau, Chief Executive Officer
Web address: www.guttenberghospital.org

HUMBOLDT COUNTY MEMORIAL HOSPITAL (C, 49 beds) 1000 North 15th Street, Humboldt, IA Zip 50548–1008; tel. 515/332–4200; Charles Kelch, Administrator
Web address: www.humboldthealth.org

IOWA LUTHERAN HOSPITAL (O, 217 beds) 700 East University Avenue, Des Moines, IA Zip 50316–2392; tel. 515/263–5612; Eric T. Crowell, President and Chief Executive Officer
Web address: www.ihsdesmoines.org

IOWA METHODIST MEDICAL CENTER (O, 461 beds) 1200 Pleasant Street, Des Moines, IA Zip 50309–9976; tel. 515/241–6212; Eric T. Crowell, President and Chief Executive Officer
Web address: www.ihsdesmoines.org

JACKSON COUNTY PUBLIC HOSPITAL (C, 43 beds) 700 West Grove Street, Maquoketa, IA Zip 52060–0910; tel. 563/652–2474; Curt Coleman, CHE, Chief Executive Officer

JONES REGIONAL MEDICAL CENTER (L, 25 beds) 104 Broadway Place, Anamosa, IA Zip 52205–1100; tel. 319/462–6131; Sean Williams, Chief Executive Officer
Web address: www.jonesregional.org

LORING HOSPITAL (C, 44 beds) 211 Highland Avenue, Sac City, IA Zip 50583–0217; tel. 712/662–7105; Michael S. Ketcham, President and Chief Executive Officer
Web address: www.loringhospital.org

POCAHONTAS COMMUNITY HOSPITAL (C, 20 beds) 606 N.W. Seventh, Pocahontas, IA Zip 50574–1099; tel. 712/335–3501; James D. Roetman, President and Chief Executive Officer
Web address: www.pchiowa.com

ST. LUKE'S HOSPITAL (O, 375 beds) 1026 A Avenue N.E., Cedar Rapids, IA Zip 52402–3026, Mailing Address: P.O. Box 3026, Zip 52406–3026; tel. 319/369–7211; Theodore E. Townsend, President and Chief Executive Officer
Web address: www.crstlukes.com

ST. LUKE'S REGIONAL MEDICAL CENTER (O, 158 beds) 2720 Stone Park Boulevard, Sioux City, IA Zip 51104–2000; tel. 712/279–3500; Peter W. Thoreen, President and Chief Executive Officer
Web address: www.stlukes.org

TRINITY AT TERRACE PARK (O, 93 beds) 4500 Utica Ridge Road, Bettendorf, IA Zip 52722–1626; tel. 563/742–5000; William B. Leaver, President and Chief Executive Officer
Web address: www.trinityqc.com

TRINITY REGIONAL MEDICAL CENTER (O, 154 beds) 802 Kenyon Road, Fort Dodge, IA Zip 50501–5795; tel. 515/573–3101; Tom Tibbitts, President
Web address: www.trmc.org

Owned, leased, sponsored:	10 hospitals	2156 beds
Contract–managed:	13 hospitals	568 beds
Totals:	23 hospitals	2724 beds

★0277: JACKSON HEALTH SYSTEM (NP)
1611 N.W. 12th Avenue, Miami, FL Zip 33136–1094; tel. 305/585–1111; Marvin O'Quinn, President and Chief Executive Officer
(Moderately Centralized Health System)

FLORIDA: JACKSON MEMORIAL HOSPITAL (O, 1764 beds) 1611 N.W. 12th Avenue, Miami, FL Zip 33136–1094; tel. 305/585–6754; Marvin O'Quinn, President and Chief Executive Officer
Web address: www.um–jmh.org/JHS/Jackson.html

JACKSON SOUTH COMMUNITY HOSPITAL (O, 233 beds) 9333 S.W. 152nd Street, Miami, FL Zip 33157–1780; tel. 305/251–2500; Leigh Massengill, Chief Administrative Officer
Web address: www.um–jmh.org/JHS/JSCH/Jaxsouth.html

Owned, leased, sponsored:	2 hospitals	1997 beds
Contract–managed:	0 hospitals	0 beds
Totals:	2 hospitals	1997 beds

7775: JEFFERSON HEALTH SYSTEM (NP)
259 Radnor–Chester Road, Suite 290, Wayne, PA Zip 19087–5288; tel. 610/225–6200; Joseph T. Sebastianelli, President and Chief Executive Officer
(Moderately Centralized Health System)

PENNSYLVANIA: BRYN MAWR HOSPITAL (O, 320 beds) 130 South Bryn Mawr Avenue, Bryn Mawr, PA Zip 19010–3160; tel. 610/526–3000; Andrea F. Gilbert, CHE, President
Web address: www.brynmawrhospital.org

BRYN MAWR REHABILITATION HOSPITAL (O, 143 beds) 414 Paoli Pike, Malvern, PA Zip 19355–3300, Mailing Address: P.O. Box 3007, Zip 19355–3300; tel. 610/251–5400; Donna Phillips, President
Web address: www.mainlinehealth.org

For explanation of codes following names, see page B2.
★ Indicates Type III membership in the American Hospital Association.

Section B

FRANKFORD HOSPITAL OF THE CITY OF PHILADELPHIA (O, 436 beds) Knights and Red Lion Roads, Philadelphia, PA Zip 19114–4208; tel. 215/612–4000; Roy A. Powell, President
Web address: www.frankfordhospitals.org

LANKENAU HOSPITAL (O, 330 beds) 100 Lancaster Avenue West, Wynnewood, PA Zip 19096–3411; tel. 610/645–2000; Gail A. Egan, President
Web address: www.jeffersonhealth.org

MAGEE REHABILITATION HOSPITAL (O, 96 beds) 1513 Race Street, Philadelphia, PA Zip 19102–1177; tel. 215/587–3000; William E. Staas Jr, M.D., President, Chief Executive Officer and Medical Director
Web address: www.mageerehab.org

PAOLI HOSPITAL (O, 147 beds) 255 West Lancaster Avenue, Paoli, PA Zip 19301–1792; tel. 610/648–1000; Barbara J. Tachovsky, President
Web address: www.mainlinehealth.org

THOMAS JEFFERSON UNIVERSITY HOSPITAL (O, 905 beds) 111 South 11th Street, Philadelphia, PA Zip 19107–5096; tel. 215/955–6000; Thomas J. Lewis, CHE, President and Chief Executive Officer
Web address: www.jeffersonhospital.org

Owned, leased, sponsored:	7 hospitals	2377 beds
Contract–managed:	0 hospitals	0 beds
Totals:	7 hospitals	2377 beds

★**0052:   JEWISH HOSPITAL HEALTHCARE SERVICES** (NP)
200 Abraham Flexner Way, Louisville, KY Zip 40202–1886; tel. 502/587–4011; Robert L. Shircliff, President and Chief Executive Officer
(Moderately Centralized Health System)

INDIANA: CLARK MEMORIAL HOSPITAL (C, 241 beds) 1220 Missouri Avenue, Jeffersonville, IN Zip 47130–3743, Mailing Address: P.O. Box 69, Zip 47131–0069; tel. 812/282–6631; Martin Padgett, President and Chief Executive Officer
Web address: www.clarkmemorial.org

SCOTT MEMORIAL HOSPITAL (C, 56 beds) 1415 North Gardner Street, Scottsburg, IN Zip 47170–0430, Mailing Address: Box 430, Zip 47170–0430; tel. 812/752–8500; Clifford D. Nay, Executive Director
Web address: www.scottmemorial.com

SOUTHERN INDIANA REHABILITATION HOSPITAL (O, 60 beds) 3104 Blackiston Boulevard, New Albany, IN Zip 47150–9579; tel. 812/941–8300; Randy L. Napier, President and Chief Executive Officer
Web address: www.sirh.org

WASHINGTON COUNTY MEMORIAL HOSPITAL (C, 15 beds) 911 North Shelby Street, Salem, IN Zip 47167–1694; tel. 812/883–5881; Beth Sharer, R.N., Interim Chief Executive Officer

KENTUCKY: FRAZIER REHAB INSTITUTE (O, 135 beds) 220 Abraham Flexner Way, Louisville, KY Zip 40202–1887; tel. 502/582–7400; Joanne Berryman, Senior Vice President
Web address: www.frazierrehab.org

JEWISH HOSPITAL (O, 442 beds) 217 East Chestnut Street, Louisville, KY Zip 40202–1886, Mailing Address: One Audubon Plaza Drive #100, Zip 40217; tel. 502/587–4011; Timothy L. Jarm, President
Web address: www.jewishhospital.org

JEWISH HOSPITAL–SHELBYVILLE (O, 70 beds) 727 Hospital Drive, Shelbyville, KY Zip 40065–1699; tel. 502/647–4000; Michael L. Collins, President and Chief Executive Officer
Web address: www.jhhs.org

TAYLOR REGIONAL HOSPITAL (C, 90 beds) 1700 Old Lebanon Road, Campbellsville, KY Zip 42718–9600; tel. 270/465–3561; Jane Wheatley, Chief Executive Officer
Web address: www.tchosp.org

Owned, leased, sponsored:	4 hospitals	707 beds
Contract–managed:	4 hospitals	402 beds
Totals:	8 hospitals	1109 beds

★**0218:   JOHN C. LINCOLN HEALTH NETWORK** (NP)
250 East Dunlap Avenue, Phoenix, AZ Zip 85020–2446; tel. 602/943–2381; Dan C. Coleman, President and Chief Executive Officer
(Centralized Health System)

ARIZONA: JOHN C. LINCOLN HOSPITAL – NORTH MOUNTAIN (O, 262 beds) 250 East Dunlap Avenue, Phoenix, AZ Zip 85020–2446; tel. 602/943–2381; Rhonda Forsyth, Executive Vice President and Chief Executive Officer
Web address: www.jcl.com

JOHN C. LINCOLN HOSPITAL–DEER VALLEY (O, 143 beds) 19829 North 27th Avenue, Phoenix, AZ Zip 85027–4002; tel. 623/879–6100; Tim Tracy, Executive Vice President and Chief Executive Officer
Web address: www.jcl.com

Owned, leased, sponsored:	2 hospitals	405 beds
Contract–managed:	0 hospitals	0 beds
Totals:	2 hospitals	405 beds

★**0324:   JOHN MUIR/MOUNT DIABLO HEALTH SYSTEM** (NP)
1400 Treat Boulevard, Walnut Creek, CA Zip 94596–2142; tel. 925/947–2100

CALIFORNIA: JOHN MUIR MEDICAL CENTER (O, 380 beds) 1601 Ygnacio Valley Road, Walnut Creek, CA Zip 94598–3194; tel. 925/939–3000; Kenneth L. Meehan, President and Chief Administrative Officer
Web address: www.jmmdhs.com/index.php/jmmdhs_jmmc.html

MOUNT DIABLO MEDICAL CENTER (O, 188 beds) 2540 East Street, Concord, CA Zip 94520; tel. 925/682–8200; Thomas M. Harlan, President and Chief Administrative Officer
Web address: www.jmmdhs.com/index.php/jmmdhs_mdmc.html

Owned, leased, sponsored:	2 hospitals	568 beds
Contract–managed:	0 hospitals	0 beds
Totals:	2 hospitals	568 beds

★**1015:   JOHNS HOPKINS HEALTH SYSTEM** (NP)
733 North Broadway, BRB 104, Baltimore, MD Zip 21205; tel. 410/955–5000; Ronald R. Peterson, President
(Centralized Physician/Insurance Health System)

MARYLAND: HOWARD COUNTY GENERAL HOSPITAL (O, 204 beds) 5755 Cedar Lane, Columbia, MD Zip 21044–2999; tel. 410/740–7890; Victor A. Broccolino, President and Chief Executive Officer
Web address: www.hcgh.org

JOHNS HOPKINS BAYVIEW MEDICAL CENTER (O, 586 beds) 4940 Eastern Avenue, Baltimore, MD Zip 21224–2780; tel. 410/550–0100; Gregory F. Schaffer, President
Web address: www.jhbmc.jhu.edu

JOHNS HOPKINS HOSPITAL (O, 909 beds) 600 North Wolfe Street, Baltimore, MD Zip 21287–2182; tel. 410/955–5000; Ronald R. Peterson, President
Web address: www.hopkinsmedicine.org

Owned, leased, sponsored:	3 hospitals	1699 beds
Contract–managed:	0 hospitals	0 beds
Totals:	3 hospitals	1699 beds

★**2105:   KAISER FOUNDATION HOSPITALS** (NP)
One Kaiser Plaza, Oakland, CA Zip 94612–3600; tel. 510/271–5910; George C. Halvorson, M.D., Chairman and Chief Executive Officer
(Decentralized Health System)

CALIFORNIA: KAISER FOUNDATION HOSPITAL (O, 247 beds) 2200 O'Farrell Street, San Francisco, CA Zip 94115–3358; tel. 415/833–2000; R. Michael Alexander, Senior Vice President and Area Manager
Web address: www.kaiserpermanente.org

KAISER FOUNDATION HOSPITAL (O, 117 beds) 401 Bicentennial Way, Santa Rosa, CA Zip 95403–2192; tel. 707/571–4000; Susan Janvrin, R.N., Senior Vice President and Administrator
Web address: www.ca.kaiserpermanente.org

KAISER FOUNDATION HOSPITAL (O, 475 beds) 4867 Sunset Boulevard, Los Angeles, CA Zip 90027–5969; tel. 323/783–4011; Barry A. Wolfman, Senior Vice President and Area Manager
Web address: www.kaiserpermanente.org

KAISER FOUNDATION HOSPITAL (O, 121 beds) 7300 North Fresno Street, Fresno, CA Zip 93720–2941; tel. 559/448–4040; Corwin Harper, Vice President and Administrator
Web address: www.kaiserpermanente.org

For explanation of codes following names, see page B2.
★ Indicates Type III membership in the American Hospital Association.

KAISER FOUNDATION HOSPITAL (O, 341 beds) 280 West MacArthur Boulevard, Oakland, CA Zip 94611–5693; tel. 510/752–1000; Bettie L. Coles, R.N., Senior Vice President and Administrator
Web address: www.kaiserpermanente.org

KAISER FOUNDATION HOSPITAL (O, 288 beds) 1425 South Main Street, Walnut Creek, CA Zip 94596–5300; tel. 925/295–4000; Sandi Small, Senior Vice President and Administrator
Web address: www.kaiserpermanente.org

KAISER FOUNDATION HOSPITAL (O, 393 beds) 9961 Sierra Avenue, Fontana, CA Zip 92335–6720; tel. 909/427–5000; Terry A. Belmont, Senior Vice President and Administrator
Web address: www.kaiserpermanente.org

KAISER FOUNDATION HOSPITAL (O, 193 beds) 25825 South Vermont Avenue, Harbor City, CA Zip 90710–3599; tel. 310/325–5111; Gerald A. McCall, Senior Vice President and Administrator
Web address: www.kaiserpermanente.org

KAISER FOUNDATION HOSPITAL (O, 208 beds) 27400 Hesperian Boulevard, Hayward, CA Zip 94545–4235; tel. 510/784–4000; Kim Pardini–Keily, Chief Operating Officer
Web address: www.kaiserpermanente.org

KAISER FOUNDATION HOSPITAL (O, 392 beds) 4647 Zion Avenue, San Diego, CA Zip 92120–2507; tel. 619/528–5000; Arthur Flippin, M.D., Administrator
Web address: www.kaiserpermanente.org

KAISER FOUNDATION HOSPITAL (O, 168 beds) 1150 Veterans Boulevard, Redwood City, CA Zip 94063–2037; tel. 650/299–2000; Linda Jensen, Senior Vice President and Area Manager
Web address: www.kaiserpermanente.org

KAISER FOUNDATION HOSPITAL (O, 463 beds) 2025 Morse Avenue, Sacramento, CA Zip 95825–2115; tel. 916/973–5000; Beverly Werntz, Chief Operating Officer
Web address: www.kp.org

KAISER FOUNDATION HOSPITAL (O, 162 beds) 6600 Bruceville Road, Sacramento, CA Zip 95823–4671; tel. 916/688–2430; Max Villalobos, Chief Operating Officer
Web address: www.kp.org

KAISER FOUNDATION HOSPITAL (O, 110 beds) 99 Montecillo Road, San Rafael, CA Zip 94903–3308; tel. 415/444–2000; Jill Magri, Senior Vice President and Administrator
Web address: www.kaiserpermanente.org

KAISER FOUNDATION HOSPITAL (O, 265 beds) 900 Kiely Boulevard, Santa Clara, CA Zip 95051–5329; tel. 408/236–6400; Charles S. Koch, Chief Operating Officer
Web address: www.kaiserpermanente.org

KAISER FOUNDATION HOSPITAL (O, 105 beds) 1200 El Camino Real, South San Francisco, CA Zip 94080–3299; tel. 650/742–2000; Linda Jensen, Senior Vice President and Administrator
Web address: www.kaiserpermanente.org

KAISER FOUNDATION HOSPITAL (O, 205 beds) 13652 Cantara Street, Panorama City, CA Zip 91402–5497; tel. 818/375–2000; Jane Finley, Interim Service Area Manager
Web address: www.kaiserpermanente.org

KAISER FOUNDATION HOSPITAL (O, 218 beds) 5601 DeSoto Avenue, Woodland Hills, CA Zip 91365–6701; tel. 818/719–3800; Jane Finley, Interim Service Area Manager
Web address: www.kaiserpermanente.org

KAISER FOUNDATION HOSPITAL – ORANGE COUNTY (O, 167 beds) 441 North Lakeview Avenue, Anaheim, CA Zip 92807–3089; tel. 714/279–4100; Julie K. Miller–Phipps, Senior Vice President and Service Area Manager
Web address: www.kaiserpermanente.org

KAISER FOUNDATION HOSPITAL – SANTA TERESA (O, 228 beds) 250 Hospital Parkway, San Jose, CA Zip 95119–1199; tel. 408/972–7000; Terry L. Austen, Senior Vice President and Area Manager
Web address: www.kaiserpermanente.org

KAISER FOUNDATION HOSPITAL AND REHABILITATION CENTER (O, 270 beds) 975 Sereno Drive, Vallejo, CA Zip 94589–2441; tel. 707/651–1000; Deborah D. Romer, Senior Vice President and Area Manager
Web address: www.kaiserpermanente.org

KAISER FOUNDATION HOSPITAL–BALDWIN PARK (O, 207 beds) 1011 Baldwin Park Boulevard, Baldwin Park, CA Zip 91706–5806; tel. 626/851–1011; Gerald A. McCall, Senior Vice President and Administrator
Web address: www.kp.org

KAISER FOUNDATION HOSPITAL–BELLFLOWER (O, 307 beds) 9400 East Rosecrans Avenue, Bellflower, CA Zip 90706–2246; tel. 562/461–3000; Gerald A. McCall, Senior Vice President and Administrator
Web address: www.kaiserpermanente.org

KAISER FOUNDATION HOSPITAL–RIVERSIDE (O, 215 beds) 10800 Magnolia Avenue, Riverside, CA Zip 92505–3000; tel. 909/353–4600; Terry A. Belmont, Senior Vice President and Administrator
Web address: www.kaiserpermanente.org

KAISER FOUNDATION HOSPITAL–WEST LOS ANGELES (O, 166 beds) 6041 Cadillac Avenue, Los Angeles, CA Zip 90034–1702; tel. 323/857–2201; Gloria Blackburn, Director Operations and Chief Nursing Executive
Web address: www.kaiserpermanente.org

ST. DOMINIC'S HOSPITAL (O, 65 beds) 1777 West Yosemite Avenue, Manteca, CA Zip 95337–5187; tel. 209/825–3500; Margaret Hepburn, President
Web address: www.stdominicscares.org

HAWAII: KAISER PERMANENTE MEDICAL CENTER (O, 270 beds) 3288 Moanalua Road, Honolulu, HI Zip 96819–1469; tel. 808/432–0000; Susan R. Murray, Administrator
Web address: www.kaiserhawaii.com

OREGON: KAISER SUNNYSIDE MEDICAL CENTER (O, 185 beds) 10180 S.E. Sunnyside Road, Clackamas, OR Zip 97015–9303; tel. 503/652–2880; Jesse M. Gamez, Administrator
Web address: www.kaiserpermanente.org

Owned, leased, sponsored:	28 hospitals	6551 beds
Contract–managed:	0 hospitals	0 beds
Totals:	28 hospitals	6551 beds

0102: KALEIDA HEALTH (NP)
901 Washington Street, Buffalo, NY Zip 14203; tel. 716/859–2155; William D. McGuire, President and Chief Executive Officer
(Moderately Centralized Health System)

NEW YORK: BUFFALO GENERAL HOSPITAL (O, 1691 beds) 100 High Street, Buffalo, NY Zip 14203–1154; tel. 716/859–5600; William D. McGuire, Chief Executive Officer
Web address: www.kaleidahealth.org

WOMEN AND CHILDREN'S HOSPITAL (O, 200 beds) 219 Bryant Street, Buffalo, NY Zip 14222–2099; tel. 716/878–7000; Cheryl Klass, President

Owned, leased, sponsored:	2 hospitals	1891 beds
Contract–managed:	0 hospitals	0 beds
Totals:	2 hospitals	1891 beds

★0258: KETTERING MEDICAL CENTER–NETWORK (NP)
3965 Southern Boulevard, Dayton, OH Zip 45429–1221; tel. 937/395–8150; Francisco J. Perez, FACHE, Network Chief Executive Officer
(Centralized Health System)

OHIO: CHARLES F. KETTERING MEMORIAL HOSPITAL (O, 521 beds) 3535 Southern Boulevard, Kettering, OH Zip 45429; tel. 937/298–4331; Fred M. Manchur, President
Web address: www.kmcnetwork.org

GRANDVIEW HOSPITAL AND MEDICAL CENTER (O, 330 beds) 405 Grand Avenue, Dayton, OH Zip 45405–4796; tel. 937/226–3200; Roy G. Chew, Ph.D., President
Web address: www.kmcnetwork.org

SYCAMORE HOSPITAL (O, 142 beds) 2150 Leiter Road, Miamisburg, OH Zip 45342; tel. 937/866–0551; Richard Haas, Senior Executive Officer
Web address: www.kmcnetwork.org

Owned, leased, sponsored:	3 hospitals	993 beds
Contract–managed:	0 hospitals	0 beds
Totals:	3 hospitals	993 beds

For explanation of codes following names, see page B2.
★ Indicates Type III membership in the American Hospital Association.

0026: KINDRED HEALTHCARE (IO)
680 South Fourth Street, Louisville, KY Zip 40202–2412; tel. 502/596–7300; Paul J. Diaz, President and Chief Operating Officer
(Independent Hospital System)

ARIZONA: KINDRED HOSPITAL – PHOENIX (O, 58 beds) 40 East Indianola Avenue, Phoenix, AZ Zip 85012–2059; tel. 602/280–7000; Steve Smith, Chief Executive Officer
Web address: www.kindredhealthcare.com

KINDRED HOSPITAL – TUCSON (O, 51 beds) 355 North Wilmot Road, Tucson, AZ Zip 85711–2635; tel. 520/584–4500; Alex Wilcox, R.N., Chief Executive Officer
Web address: www.kindredhealthcare.com

CALIFORNIA: KINDRED HOSPITAL–BREA (O, 48 beds) 875 North Brea Boulevard, Brea, CA Zip 92821–2606; tel. 714/529–6842; Kathleen Smith, Chief Executive Officer
Web address: www.kindredhealthcare.com

KINDRED HOSPITAL–LOS ANGELES (O, 81 beds) 5525 West Slauson Avenue, Los Angeles, CA Zip 90056–1067; tel. 310/642–0325; Adam Darvish, M.P.H., Chief Executive Officer
Web address: www.kindredhealthcare.com

KINDRED HOSPITAL–ONTARIO (O, 91 beds) 550 North Monterey Avenue, Ontario, CA Zip 91764–3399; tel. 909/391–0333; Scott Floden, Chief Executive Officer
Web address: www.kindredhealthcare.com

KINDRED HOSPITAL–SACRAMENTO (O, 34 beds) 223 Fargo Way, Folsom, CA Zip 95630–2961; tel. 916/351–9151; Meredith Taylor, Chief Executive Officer
Web address: www.kindredhealthcare.com

KINDRED HOSPITAL–SAN DIEGO (O, 70 beds) 1940 El Cajon Boulevard, San Diego, CA Zip 92104–1096; tel. 619/543–4500; Susan Bailey, Chief Executive Officer
Web address: www.kindredsandiego.com

KINDRED HOSPITAL–SAN FRANCISCO BAY AREA (O, 80 beds) 2800 Benedict Drive, San Leandro, CA Zip 94577–6840; tel. 510/357–8300; Jim Linhares, Chief Executive Officer
Web address: www.kindredhospitalsfba.com

KINDRED HOSPITAL–WESTMINSTER (O, 99 beds) 200 Hospital Circle, Westminster, CA Zip 92683–3910; tel. 714/893–4541; Virgis Narbutas, Chief Executive Officer
Web address: www.kindredhealthcare.com

MENLO PARK SURGICAL HOSPITAL (O, 16 beds) 570 Willow Road, Menlo Park, CA Zip 94025–2617; tel. 650/324–8500; Sean P. McCarthy, Chief Executive Officer
Web address: www.kindredhealthcare.com

COLORADO: KINDRED HOSPITAL–DENVER (O, 55 beds) 1920 High Street, Denver, CO Zip 80218–1213; tel. 303/320–5871; April Myers, Chief Executive Officer
Web address: www.kindredhealthcare.com

FLORIDA: KINDRED HOSPITAL – CENTRAL TAMPA (O, 73 beds) 4801 North Howard Avenue, Tampa, FL Zip 33603–1484; tel. 813/874–7575; Danny R. Edwards, Chief Executive Officer
Web address: www.kindredhealthcare.com

KINDRED HOSPITAL BAY AREA –TAMPA (O, 73 beds) 4555 South Manhattan Avenue, Tampa, FL Zip 33611–2397; tel. 813/839–6341; Sally Hoffmann, Chief Executive Officer
Web address: www.kindredhealthcare.com

KINDRED HOSPITAL NORTH FLORIDA (O, 60 beds) 801 Oak Street, Green Cove Springs, FL Zip 32043–4317; tel. 904/284–9230; Tim Simpson, Chief Executive Officer
Web address: www.khnorthflorida.com

KINDRED HOSPITAL–FORT LAUDERDALE (O, 64 beds) 1516 East Las Olas Boulevard, Fort Lauderdale, FL Zip 33301–2399; tel. 954/764–8900; Clifford J. Bauer, Chief Executive Officer
Web address: www.kindredhealthcare.com

KINDRED HOSPITAL–SOUTH FLORIDA/CORAL GABLES (O, 53 beds) 5190 S.W. Eighth Street, Coral Gables, FL Zip 33134–2495; tel. 305/445–1364; Charles Doten, Chief Executive Officer
Web address: www.kindredhealthcare.com

KINDRED HOSPITAL–ST. PETERSBURG (O, 112 beds) 3030 Sixth Street South, Saint Petersburg, FL Zip 33705–3720; tel. 727/894–8719; Pamela M. Riter, R.N., Chief Executive Officer
Web address: www.kindredstpete.com

GEORGIA: KINDRED HOSPITAL–ATLANTA (O, 70 beds) 705 Juniper Street N.E., Atlanta, GA Zip 30365–2500; tel. 404/873–2871; Craig Hoover, Chief Executive Officer
Web address: www.kindredhealthcare.com

ILLINOIS: KINDRED CHICAGO CENTRAL HOSPITAL (O, 76 beds) 4058 West Melrose Street, Chicago, IL Zip 60641–4797; tel. 773/736–7000; Larry Foster, Chief Executive Officer
Web address: www.kindredhealthcare.com

KINDRED HOSPITAL–CHICAGO NORTH (O, 164 beds) 2544 West Montrose Avenue, Chicago, IL Zip 60618–1589; tel. 773/267–2622; Jack Nathan Shapiro, Chief Executive Officer
Web address: www.kindredhealthcare.com

KINDRED HOSPITAL–CHICAGO NORTHLAKE (O, 86 beds) 365 East North Avenue, Northlake, IL Zip 60164–2628; tel. 708/345–8100; Michele Dionne, Chief Executive Officer
Web address: www.kindredhealthcare.com

KINDRED HOSPITAL–SYCAMORE (O, 69 beds) 225 Edward Street, Sycamore, IL Zip 60178–2197; tel. 815/895–2144; Cindy Smith, Chief Executive Officer
Web address: www.kindredhealthcare.com

INDIANA: KINDRED HOSPITAL INDIANAPOLIS SOUTH (O, 36 beds) 898 East Main Street, Greenwood, IN Zip 46143–1400; tel. 317/888–8155; Mona Euler, Chief Executive Officer
Web address: www.kindredhealthcare.com

KINDRED HOSPITAL–INDIANAPOLIS (O, 59 beds) 1700 West 10th Street, Indianapolis, IN Zip 46222–3802; tel. 317/636–4400; John Pierson, Chief Executive Officer
Web address: www.kindredhealthcare.com

KENTUCKY: KINDRED HOSPITAL–LOUISVILLE (O, 170 beds) 1313 St. Anthony Place, Louisville, KY Zip 40204–1765; tel. 502/587–7001; Brian L. Pugh, Interim Chief Executive Officer
Web address: www.kindredhealthcare.com

LOUISIANA: KINDRED HOSPITAL – NEW ORLEANS (O, 94 beds) 3601 Coliseum Street, New Orleans, LA Zip 70115–3606; tel. 504/899–1555; Jan Turk, Chief Executive Officer
Web address: www.kindredhealthcare.com

MASSACHUSETTS: KINDRED HOSPITAL BOSTON NORTH SHORE (O, 50 beds) 15 King Street, Peabody, MA Zip 01960–4268; tel. 978/531–2900; Andrew Escamilla, Chief Executive Officer
Web address: www.kindredbns.com

KINDRED HOSPITAL–BOSTON (O, 36 beds) 1515 Commonwealth Avenue, Boston, MA Zip 02135–3696; tel. 617/254–1100; Deborah Plummer, Chief Executive Officer
Web address: www.kindredhealthcare.com

MISSOURI: KINDRED HOSPITAL KANSAS CITY (O, 94 beds) 8701 Troost Avenue, Kansas City, MO Zip 64131–2767; tel. 816/995–2000; Mark J. Stepanik, Chief Executive Officer
Web address: www.kindredhospitalkc.com

KINDRED HOSPITAL–ST. LOUIS (O, 60 beds) 4930 Lindell Boulevard, Saint Louis, MO Zip 63108–1510; tel. 314/361–8700; Michael Moody, Interim Chief Executive Officer
Web address: www.kindredhealthcare.com

NEVADA: KINDRED HOSPITAL–LAS VEGAS (O, 92 beds) 5110 West Sahara Avenue, Las Vegas, NV Zip 89146–3406; tel. 702/871–1418; Linn P. Billingsley, Chief Executive Officer
Web address: www.kindredhealthcare.com

NEW MEXICO: KINDRED HOSPITAL – ALBUQUERQUE (O, 61 beds) 700 High Street N.E., Albuquerque, NM Zip 87102–2565; tel. 505/242–4444; Laura S. Wills, Chief Executive Officer
Web address: www.kindredhealthcare.com

NORTH CAROLINA: KINDRED HOSPITAL–GREENSBORO (O, 124 beds) 2401 Southside Boulevard, Greensboro, NC Zip 27406–3311; tel. 336/271–2800; David M. Polunas, Chief Executive Officer
Web address: www.kindredhealthcare.com/hospitals/greensboro

OKLAHOMA: KINDRED HOSPITAL– OKLAHOMA CITY (O, 59 beds) 1407 North Robinson Avenue, Oklahoma City, OK Zip 73103; tel. 405/232–8000; Kenneth R. Ross, Chief Executive Officer
Web address: www.kindredhealthcare.com

PENNSYLVANIA: KINDRED HOSPITAL–PHILADELPHIA (O, 52 beds) 6129 Palmetto Street, Philadelphia, PA Zip 19111–5729; tel. 215/722–8555; Margaret M. Murphy, Chief Executive Officer
Web address: www.kindredhealthcare.com

For explanation of codes following names, see page B2.
★ Indicates Type III membership in the American Hospital Association.

KINDRED HOSPITAL–PITTSBURGH (O, 63 beds) 7777 Steubenville Pike, Oakdale, PA Zip 15071–3409; tel. 412/494–5500; Gregory J. Kuntz, Chief Executive Officer
Web address: www.kindredhealthcare.com

TENNESSEE: KINDRED HOSPITAL–CHATTANOOGA (O, 44 beds) 709 Walnut Street, Chattanooga, TN Zip 37402; tel. 423/266–7721; William J. Bryant, Chief Executive Officer
Web address: www.kindredhealthcare.com

TEXAS: KINDRED HOSPITAL – DALLAS (O, 130 beds) 9525 Greenville Avenue, Dallas, TX Zip 75243–4116; tel. 214/355–2600; Dorothy J. Elford, Chief Executive Officer
Web address: www.kindredhealthcare.com

KINDRED HOSPITAL OF TARRANT COUNTY (O, 79 beds) 1000 North Cooper Street, Arlington, TX Zip 76011–5540; tel. 817/548–3400; Robert C. Gladney, Chief Executive Officer
Web address: www.kindredhealthcare.com

KINDRED HOSPITAL–BAY AREA (O, 78 beds) 1004 Seymour Street, Pasadena, TX Zip 77506–2699; tel. 713/473–9700; Randy E. Johnson, Chief Executive Officer
Web address: www.kindredhealthcare.com

KINDRED HOSPITAL–FORT WORTH SOUTHWEST (O, 68 beds) 7800 Oakmont Boulevard, Fort Worth, TX Zip 76132–4299; tel. 817/346–0094; Robert L. McNew, Chief Executive Officer
Web address: www.kindredhealthcare.com

KINDRED HOSPITAL–HOUSTON (O, 92 beds) 6441 Main Street, Houston, TX Zip 77030–1596; tel. 713/790–0500; Bob Stein, Chief Executive Officer
Web address: www.kindredhealthcare.com

KINDRED HOSPITAL–HOUSTON NORTHWEST (O, 84 beds) 11297 Fallbrook Drive, Houston, TX Zip 77065–4292; tel. 281/897–8114; Mary Anne Craig, Chief Executive Officer
Web address: www.kindredhealthcare.com

KINDRED HOSPITAL–MANSFIELD (O, 39 beds) 1802 Highway 157 North, Mansfield, TX Zip 76063–9555; tel. 817/473–6101; Dalton Stewart, Chief Executive Officer
Web address: www.kindredmansfield.com

KINDRED HOSPITAL–SAN ANTONIO (O, 59 beds) 3636 Medical Drive, San Antonio, TX Zip 78229–3184; tel. 210/616–0616; John M. Griffes, Chief Executive Officer
Web address: www.kindredhealthcare.com

WASHINGTON: KINDRED HOSPITAL SEATTLE (O, 42 beds) 10560 Fifth Avenue N.E., Seattle, WA Zip 98125–0977; tel. 206/364–2050; Cheryl Payseno, Chief Executive Officer
Web address: www.kindredhealthcare.com

WISCONSIN: KINDRED HOSPITAL–MILWAUKEE (O, 56 beds) 5017 South 110th Street, Milwaukee, WI Zip 53228–3131; tel. 414/427–8282; Linda Newberry–Ferguson, Chief Executive Officer
Web address: www.kindredhealthcare.com

Owned, leased, sponsored:	47 hospitals	3404 beds
Contract–managed:	0 hospitals	0 beds
Totals:	47 hospitals	3404 beds

★0149: KISHWAUKEE HEALTH SYSTEM (NP)
626 Bethany Road, De Kalb, IL Zip 60115–4939, Mailing Address: P.O. Box 707, Zip 60115–4939; tel. 815/756–1521; Kevin P. Poorten, President and Chief Executive Officer
(Independent Hospital System)

ILLINOIS: KISHWAUKEE COMMUNITY HOSPITAL (O, 102 beds) 626 Bethany Road, De Kalb, IL Zip 60115–4939, Mailing Address: P.O. Box 707, Zip 60115–0707; tel. 815/756–1521; Brad Copple, Administrator
Web address: www.kishhospital.org

VALLEY WEST COMMUNITY HOSPITAL (O, 25 beds) 11 East Pleasant Avenue, Sandwich, IL Zip 60548–0901; tel. 815/786–8484; Brad Copple, Administrator
Web address: www.vwch.org

Owned, leased, sponsored:	2 hospitals	127 beds
Contract–managed:	0 hospitals	0 beds
Totals:	2 hospitals	127 beds

★2755: LEGACY HEALTH SYSTEM (NP)
1919 N.W. Lovejoy Street, Portland, OR Zip 97209–1503; tel. 503/415–5600; Robert Pallari, President and Chief Executive Officer
(Centralized Health System)

OREGON: LEGACY EMANUEL HOSPITAL AND HEALTH CENTER (O, 403 beds) 2801 North Gantenbein Avenue, Portland, OR Zip 97227–1674; tel. 503/413–2200; Stephani White, Vice President and Site Administrator
Web address: www.legacyhealth.org

LEGACY GOOD SAMARITAN HOSPITAL AND MEDICAL CENTER (O, 274 beds) 1015 N.W. 22nd Avenue, Portland, OR Zip 97210–3099; tel. 503/413–7711; Robert Pallari, President and Chief Executive Officer
Web address: www.legacyhealth.org

LEGACY MERIDIAN PARK HOSPITAL (O, 133 beds) 19300 S.W. 65th Avenue, Tualatin, OR Zip 97062–9741; tel. 503/692–1212; Allyson Anderson, Vice President and Administrator
Web address: www.legacyhealth.org

LEGACY MOUNT HOOD MEDICAL CENTER (O, 55 beds) 24800 S.E. Stark, Gresham, OR Zip 97030–0154; tel. 503/667–1122; Thomas S. Parker, Site Administrator
Web address: www.legacyhealth.org

Owned, leased, sponsored:	4 hospitals	865 beds
Contract–managed:	0 hospitals	0 beds
Totals:	4 hospitals	865 beds

0206: LIBERTY MANAGEMENT GROUP, INC. (IO)
19 Spear Road, Suite 305, Ramsey, NJ Zip 07446; tel. 201/236–8880; William J. Hartigan, President and Chief Executive Officer
(Independent Hospital System)

FLORIDA: SAVANNAS HOSPITAL (O, 75 beds) 2550 S.E. Walton Road, Port St. Lucie, FL Zip 34952–7197; tel. 772/335–0400; Maria Nixon, Executive Director

NEW YORK: HOLLISWOOD HOSPITAL (C, 110 beds) 87–37 Palermo Street, Jamaica, NY Zip 11423–1209; tel. 718/776–8181; Jeffrey Borenstein, M.D., Chief Executive Officer and Medical Director
Web address: www.holliswoodhospital.com

OKLAHOMA: ROLLING HILLS HOSPITAL (O, 40 beds) 1000 Rolling Hills Lane, Ada, OK Zip 74820–9415; tel. 580/436–3600; Darnell Powell, Executive Director
Web address: www.rollinghillshospital.com

Owned, leased, sponsored:	2 hospitals	115 beds
Contract–managed:	1 hospital	110 beds
Totals:	3 hospitals	225 beds

0173: LIBERTYHEALTH (NP)
355 Grand Street, Jersey City, NJ Zip 07302; tel. 201/915–2000; Jonathan M. Metsch, Dr.PH, President and Chief Executive Officer
(Independent Hospital System)

NEW JERSEY: LIBERTYHEALTH–GREENVILLE HOSPITAL (O, 100 beds) 1825 John F. Kennedy Boulevard, Jersey City, NJ Zip 07305–2198; tel. 201/547–6100; Jean A. Murray, Administrator and Senior Vice President of Operations
Web address: www.libertyhcs.org

LIBERTYHEALTH–JERSEY CITY MEDICAL CENTER (O, 366 beds) 355 Grand Street, Jersey City, NJ Zip 07302; tel. 201/915–2000; Jonathan M. Metsch, Dr.PH, President and Chief Executive Officer
Web address: www.libertyhcs.org

LIBERTYHEALTH–MEADOWLANDS HOSPITAL MEDICAL CENTER (O, 147 beds) 55 Meadowland Parkway, Secaucus, NJ Zip 07096–1580; tel. 201/392–3100; Martin W. Baicker, CHE, Senior Vice President and Administrator
Web address: www.libertyhcs.com

Owned, leased, sponsored:	3 hospitals	613 beds
Contract–managed:	0 hospitals	0 beds
Totals:	3 hospitals	613 beds

Section B

For explanation of codes following names, see page B2.
★ Indicates Type III membership in the American Hospital Association.

★0158: LIFEBRIDGE HEALTH (NP)
2401 West Belvedere Avenue, Baltimore, MD Zip 21215;
tel. 410/601–9789; Warren A. Green, President and Chief Executive Officer
(Moderately Centralized Health System)

MARYLAND: LEVINDALE HEBREW GERIATRIC CENTER AND HOSPITAL (O, 443 beds) 2434 West Belvedere Avenue, Baltimore, MD Zip 21215–5299; tel. 410/466–8700; Ronald Rothstein, President and Chief Operating Officer
Web address: www.sinai–balt.com

NORTHWEST HOSPITAL CENTER (O, 198 beds) 5401 Old Court Road, Randallstown, MD Zip 21133–5185; tel. 410/521–2200; Erik G. Wexler, President and Chief Operating Officer
Web address: www.lifebridgehealth.org

SINAI HOSPITAL OF BALTIMORE (O, 423 beds) 2401 West Belvedere Avenue, Baltimore, MD Zip 21215–5271; tel. 410/601–9000; Neil M. Meltzer, President and Chief Operating Officer
Web address: www.lifebridgehealth.org

Owned, leased, sponsored:	3 hospitals	1064 beds
Contract–managed:	0 hospitals	0 beds
Totals:	3 hospitals	1064 beds

0191: LIFECARE MANAGEMENT SERVICES (IO)
5560 Tennyson Parkway, Plano, TX Zip 75024; tel. 469/241–2100; Thomas W. Erickson, Board Chairman and Chief Executive Officer
(Independent Hospital System)

COLORADO: COLORADO ACUTE SPECIALTY CARE HOSPITAL (O, 24 beds) 1601 North Lowell Boulevard, Denver, CO Zip 80204–1545; tel. 303/899–5166; William Fox, Interim Chief Executive Officer
Web address: www.lifecare–hospitals.com

LOUISIANA: LIFECARE HOSPITALS OF NEW ORLEANS–BAPTIST CAMPUS (O, 130 beds) 2700 Napoleon Avenue, New Orleans, LA Zip 70115; tel. 504/896–5524; Tim Burke, Chief Executive Officer

LIFECARE HOSPITALS OF SHREVEPORT (O, 130 beds) 9320 Linwood Avenue, Shreveport, LA Zip 71106–7003; tel. 318/688–8504; Douglas Parker, Chief Executive Officer
Web address: www.lifecare–hospitals.com

LIFECARE HOSPITALS–KENNER CAMPUS (O, 28 beds) 180 West Esplanade Avenue, Kenner, LA Zip 70065; tel. 504/461–0710; Tim Burke, Chief Executive Officer

MICHIGAN: LIFECARE HOSPITALS OF WEST MICHIGAN (O, 20 beds) 1700 Oak Avenue, 3rd Floor, Muskegon, MI Zip 49442; tel. 231/777–6202; Jevne Conover, Administrator
Web address: www.lifecare–hospital.com

NEVADA: TAHOE PACIFIC HOSPITALS (O, 29 beds) 10405 Double R Boulevard, Reno, NV Zip 89512; tel. 775/355–5970; Paul C. Miller, Chief Executive Officer
Web address: www.lifecare–hospitals.com

NORTH CAROLINA: LIFECARE HOSPITALS OF NORTH CAROLINA (O, 43 beds) 1051 Noell Lane, Rocky Mount, NC Zip 27804–1761; tel. 252/451–2300; Kevin S. Cooper, R.N., Chief Executive Officer and Administrator
Web address: www.lifecare–hospitals.com

OHIO: LIFECARE HOSPITAL OF DAYTON (O, 42 beds) 2150 Leiter Road, Miamisburg, OH Zip 45342; tel. 937/384–8300; Ken D'Amico, Chief Executive Officer

PENNSYLVANIA: LIFECARE HOSPITALS OF PITTSBURGH (O, 132 beds) 225 Penn Avenue, Pittsburgh, PA Zip 15221–2173; tel. 412/247–2424; Clifton Neal Orme, FACHE, Administrator and Chief Executive Officer
Web address: www.lifecare–hospitals.com

TEXAS: LIFECARE HOSPITALS OF FORT WORTH (O, 68 beds) 6201 Overton Ridge Boulevard, Fort Worth, TX Zip 76132; tel. 817/370–6078; Barbara Schmidt, Administrator
Web address: www.lifecare–hospitals.com

LIFECARE HOSPITALS OF NORTH TEXAS–DALLAS (O, 64 beds) 6161 Harry Hines Boulevard, Suite 100, Dallas, TX Zip 75235–5306; tel. 214/525–6300; Louis Bradley, Chief Executive Officer
Web address: www.lifecare–hospitals.com

LIFECARE HOSPITALS OF PLANO (O, 66 beds) 6800 Preston Road, Plano, TX Zip 75024; tel. 214/473–8822; Kent Ashley, Chief Executive Officer
Web address: www.lifecare–hospitals.com

LIFECARE HOSPITALS OF SAN ANTONIO (O, 38 beds) 8026 Floyd Curl Drive, San Antonio, TX Zip 78229; tel. 210/575–8005; Randall G. Stokes, Chief Executive Officer
Web address: www.lifecare–hospitals.com

LIFECARE HOSPITALS OF SOUTH TEXAS (O, 39 beds) 333 West Freddy Gonzalez Drive, Edinburg, TX Zip 78539–6132; tel. 956/388–1800; David L. Tupper, Administrator and Chief Executive Officer
Web address: www.lifecare–hospitals.com

WISCONSIN: LIFECARE HOSPITALS OF MILWAUKEE (O, 35 beds) 5000 West Chambers Street, 8th FL, Milwaukee, WI Zip 53210; tel. 414/447–3600; Steven J. Schultz, Chief Executive Officer
Web address: www.lifecare–hospitals.com

Owned, leased, sponsored:	15 hospitals	888 beds
Contract–managed:	0 hospitals	0 beds
Totals:	15 hospitals	888 beds

★0180: LIFEPOINT HOSPITALS, INC. (IO)
103 Powell Court, Suite 200, Brentwood, TN Zip 37027; tel. 615/372–8500; Kenneth C. Donahey, Chairman and Chief Executive Officer
(Decentralized Health System)

ALABAMA: ANDALUSIA REGIONAL HOSPITAL (O, 99 beds) 849 South Three Notch Street, Andalusia, AL Zip 36420–5325, Mailing Address: P.O. Box 760, Zip 36420–0760; tel. 334/222–8466; Michael A. Callahan, Chief Executive Officer
Web address: www.andalusiaregionalhospital.com

LAKELAND COMMUNITY HOSPITAL (O, 42 beds) Highway 195 East, Haleyville, AL Zip 35565–9536, Mailing Address: P.O. Box 780, Zip 35565–0780; tel. 205/486–5213; Wes Sigler, Administrator
Web address: www.lifepointhospitals.com

NORTHWEST MEDICAL CENTER (O, 66 beds) 1530 U.S. Highway 43, Winfield, AL Zip 35594–5056; tel. 205/487–7000; Barry L. Keel, Chief Executive Officer
Web address: www.northwestmedcenter.com

RUSSELLVILLE HOSPITAL (O, 100 beds) 15155 Highway 43, Russellville, AL Zip 35653–1975, Mailing Address: P.O. Box 1089, Zip 35653–1089; tel. 256/332–1611; Christine R. Stewart, Administrator
Web address: www.chgroup.com

VAUGHAN REGIONAL MEDICAL CENTER (O, 149 beds) 1015 Medical Center Parkway, Selma, AL Zip 36701–6352; tel. 334/418–4100; Stephen Mahan, Chief Executive Officer
Web address: www.uabsfm.org/vaughan.html

ARIZONA: HAVASU REGIONAL MEDICAL CENTER (O, 138 beds) 101 Civic Center Lane, Lake Havasu City, AZ Zip 86403–5683; tel. 928/855–8185; Dorothy Sawyer, Chief Executive Officer
Web address: www.havasuregional.com

CALIFORNIA: COLORADO RIVER MEDICAL CENTER (O, 49 beds) 1401 Bailey Avenue, Needles, CA Zip 92363–3103; tel. 760/326–4531; John Pruitt, Chief Executive Officer

PALO VERDE HOSPITAL (O, 35 beds) 250 North First Street, Blythe, CA Zip 92225–1702; tel. 760/922–4115; Dale R. Mulder, Chief Executive Officer

COLORADO: COLORADO PLAINS MEDICAL CENTER (O, 50 beds) 1000 Lincoln Street, Fort Morgan, CO Zip 80701–3298; tel. 970/867–3391; Michael A. Anaya Sr, FACHE, Chief Executive Officer

FLORIDA: PUTNAM COMMUNITY MEDICAL CENTER (O, 141 beds) Highway 20 West, Palatka, FL Zip 32177–8118, Mailing Address: P.O. Box 778, Zip 32178–0778; tel. 386/328–5711; Bruce A. Baldwin, Chief Executive Officer
Web address: www.pcmcfl.com

INDIANA: MEDICAL CENTER OF SOUTHERN INDIANA (O, 77 beds) 2200 Market Street, Charlestown, IN Zip 47111–0069, Mailing Address: P.O. Box 69, Zip 47111–0069; tel. 812/256–3301; David R. Sirk, Chief Executive Officer
Web address: www.mcsi–charlestown.com

For explanation of codes following names, see page B2.
★ Indicates Type III membership in the American Hospital Association.

STARKE MEMORIAL HOSPITAL (O, 35 beds) 102 East Culver Road, Knox, IN Zip 46534–2299, Mailing Address: P.O. Box 339, Zip 46534–2299; tel. 574/772–6231; Ron Tyrer, Interim Chief Executive Officer

KANSAS: WESTERN PLAINS MEDICAL COMPLEX (O, 99 beds) 3001 Avenue A, Dodge City, KS Zip 67801–6508, Mailing Address: P.O. Box 1478, Zip 67801–1478; tel. 620/225–8400; Steven G. Daniel, President and Chief Executive Officer
Web address: www.westernplainsmc.com

KENTUCKY: BLUEGRASS COMMUNITY HOSPITAL (L, 25 beds) 360 Amsden Avenue, Versailles, KY Zip 40383–1286; tel. 859/873–3111; Kathy Scott, Administrator

BOURBON COMMUNITY HOSPITAL (O, 58 beds) 9 Linville Drive, Paris, KY Zip 40361–2196; tel. 859/987–3600; Clay Holderman, Chief Executive Officer
Web address: www.bourbonhospital.com

GEORGETOWN COMMUNITY HOSPITAL (O, 60 beds) 1140 Lexington Road, Georgetown, KY Zip 40324–9362; tel. 502/868–1100; Michael Clark, Chief Executive Officer
Web address: www.georgetowncommunityhospital.com

JACKSON PURCHASE MEDICAL CENTER (O, 107 beds) 1099 Medical Center Circle, Mayfield, KY Zip 42066–1179; tel. 270/251–4100; Mary Jo Lewis, Chief Executive Officer
Web address: www.jacksonpurchase.com

LAKE CUMBERLAND REGIONAL HOSPITAL (O, 227 beds) 305 Langdon Street, Somerset, KY Zip 42501–2750, Mailing Address: P.O. Box 620, Zip 42502–2750; tel. 606/679–7441; Jeffrey G. Seraphine, Chief Executive Officer
Web address: www.lcrh.ky

LOGAN MEMORIAL HOSPITAL (O, 92 beds) 1625 South Nashville Road, Russellville, KY Zip 42276–8834, Mailing Address: P.O. Box 10, Zip 42276–0010; tel. 270/726–4011; Greg Moore, Chief Executive Officer
Web address: www.loganmemorial.com

MEADOWVIEW REGIONAL MEDICAL CENTER (O, 101 beds) 989 Medical Park Drive, Maysville, KY Zip 41056–8750; tel. 606/759–5311; David E. Loving, Chief Executive Officer
Web address: www.meadowviewregional.com

SPRING VIEW HOSPITAL (O, 60 beds) 320 Loretto Road, Lebanon, KY Zip 40033–0320; tel. 270/692–3161; Barry A. Papania, Chief Executive Officer
Web address: www.springviewhospital.com

LOUISIANA: DOCTOR'S HOSPITAL OF OPELOUSAS (O, 145 beds) 3983 I–49 South Service Road, Opelousas, LA Zip 70570–8975; tel. 337/948–2100; Mark W. Caton, Chief Executive Officer
Web address: www.doctorshospital.com

EUNICE COMMUNITY MEDICAL CENTER (O, 52 beds) 400 Moosa Boulevard, Eunice, LA Zip 70535–3628; tel. 337/457–5244; Charlotte Dupre, Chief Executive Officer
Web address: www.eunicemedical.com

MINDEN MEDICAL CENTER (O, 159 beds) 1 Medical Plaza, Minden, LA Zip 71055–3330, Mailing Address: P.O. Box 5003, Zip 71058–5003; tel. 318/377–2321; George E. French III, CHE, Chief Executive Officer
Web address: www.mindenmedicalcenter.com

RIVER PARISHES HOSPITAL (O, 60 beds) 500 Rue de Sante, La Place, LA Zip 70068–5420; tel. 985/652–7000; Scott Boudreaux, Chief Executive Officer
Web address: www.riverparisheshospital.com

TECHE REGIONAL MEDICAL CENTER (L, 50 beds) 1125 Marguerite Street, Morgan City, LA Zip 70380–1855, Mailing Address: P.O. Box 2308, Zip 70381–2308; tel. 985/384–2200; Michael J. Landry, Chief Executive Officer
Web address: www.techeregional.com

VILLE PLATTE MEDICAL CENTER (O, 81 beds) 800 East Main Street, Ville Platte, LA Zip 70586–4618, Mailing Address: P.O. Box 349, Zip 70586–0349; tel. 337/363–5684; Steven Downs, Chief Executive Officer and Administrator
Web address: www.vpmc.com

MISSISSIPPI: BOLIVAR MEDICAL CENTER (L, 143 beds) 901 Sunflower Road, Cleveland, MS Zip 38732–9722, Mailing Address: P.O. Box 1380, Zip 38732–1380; tel. 662/846–0061; Ruth A. McDaniel, Chief Executive Officer
Web address: www.bolivarmedical.com

NEVADA: NORTHEASTERN NEVADA REGIONAL HOSPITAL (O, 50 beds) 2001 Errecart Boulevard, Elko, NV Zip 89801–3499; tel. 775/738–5151; David L. Henson, Chief Executive Officer
Web address: www.nnrhospital.com

NEW MEXICO: LOS ALAMOS MEDICAL CENTER (O, 36 beds) 3917 West Road, Los Alamos, NM Zip 87544–2293; tel. 505/662–4201; Gary A. Nicholds, FACHE, Chief Executive Officer
Web address: www.losalamosmedicalcenter.com

MEMORIAL MEDICAL CENTER (L, 240 beds) 2450 South Telshor Boulevard, Las Cruces, NM Zip 88011–5076; tel. 505/522–8641; Paul F. Herzog, Chief Executive Officer
Web address: www.mmclc.org

PENNSYLVANIA: ASHLAND REGIONAL MEDICAL CENTER (O, 123 beds) 101 Broad Street, Ashland, PA Zip 17921–0000; tel. 570/875–2000; Cindy Gorr, Chief Executive Officer
Web address: www.ashlandregional.com

SOUTH CAROLINA: COASTAL CAROLINA MEDICAL CENTER (O, 41 beds) 1000 Medical Center Drive, Hardeeville, SC Zip 29926, Mailing Address: P.O. Box 1758, Zip 29927–1758; tel. 843/784–8000; Eric Deaton, Chief Executive Officer
Web address: www.coastalcarolinamedicalcenter.com

TENNESSEE: ATHENS REGIONAL MEDICAL CENTER (O, 97 beds) 1114 West Madison Avenue, Athens, TN Zip 37303–4150, Mailing Address: P.O. Box 250, Zip 37371–0250; tel. 423/745–1411; John R. Workman, Chief Executive Officer
Web address: www.athensrmc.com

CROCKETT HOSPITAL (O, 98 beds) U.S. Highway 43 South, Lawrenceburg, TN Zip 38464–0847, Mailing Address: P.O. Box 847, Zip 38464–0847; tel. 931/762–6571; Jack S. Buck, Chief Executive Officer
Web address: www.crocketthospital.com

HILLSIDE HOSPITAL (O, 87 beds) 1265 East College Street, Pulaski, TN Zip 38478–4500; tel. 931/363–7531; James H. Edmondson, Chief Executive Officer
Web address: www.hillsidehospital.com

LIVINGSTON REGIONAL HOSPITAL (O, 67 beds) 315 Oak Street, Livingston, TN Zip 38570, Mailing Address: P.O. Box 550, Zip 38570–0550; tel. 931/823–5611; Timothy W. McGill, Chief Executive Officer
Web address: www.livingston–hospital.com

SMITH COUNTY MEMORIAL HOSPITAL (O, 63 beds) 158 Hospital Drive, Carthage, TN Zip 37030–1096; tel. 615/735–1560; Ron Walker, Chief Executive Officer

SOUTHERN TENNESSEE MEDICAL CENTER (O, 198 beds) 185 Hospital Road, Winchester, TN Zip 37398–9504; tel. 931/967–8200; William Russell Spray, Chief Executive Officer
Web address: www.southerntennessee.com

TEXAS: ENNIS REGIONAL MEDICAL CENTER (O, 42 beds) 803 West Lampasas Street, Ennis, TX Zip 75119; tel. 972/875–0900; Berney Sweet, Chief Executive Officer
Web address: www.ennisregional.com

PALESTINE REGIONAL MEDICAL CENTER–EAST (O, 124 beds) 2900 South Loop 256, Palestine, TX Zip 75801–6958; tel. 903/731–1000; Randall L. Hoover, Chief Executive Officer
Web address: www.palestineregional.com

PALESTINE REGIONAL REHABILITATION CENTER (O, 22 beds) 4000 South Loop 256, Palestine, TX Zip 75801–8467, Mailing Address: P.O. Box 4070, Zip 75802–4070; tel. 903/731–1000; Randall L. Hoover, Chief Executive Officer
Web address: www.palestineregional.com

PARKVIEW REGIONAL HOSPITAL (O, 59 beds) 600 South Bonham, Mexia, TX Zip 76667–3608; tel. 254/562–0408; Jimmy D. Stuart, Chief Executive Officer
Web address: www.parkviewregional.com

UTAH: ASHLEY VALLEY MEDICAL CENTER (O, 31 beds) 151 West 200 North, Vernal, UT Zip 84078–1907; tel. 435/789–3342; Si Hutt, Chief Executive Officer
Web address: www.avmc–hospital.com

CASTLEVIEW HOSPITAL (O, 57 beds) 300 North Hospital Drive, Price, UT Zip 84501–4200; tel. 435/637–4800; Jeffrey J. Manley, Chief Executive Officer
Web address: www.castleviewhospital.net

For explanation of codes following names, see page B2.
★ Indicates Type III membership in the American Hospital Association.

VIRGINIA: DANVILLE REGIONAL MEDICAL CENTER (O, 201 beds) 142 South Main Street, Danville, VA Zip 24541–2922; tel. 434/799–2100; Tod N. Lambert, Interim President and Chief Executive Officer
Web address: www.danvilleregional.org

MEMORIAL HOSPITAL (O, 152 beds) 320 Hospital Drive, Martinsville, VA Zip 24112–1981, Mailing Address: P.O. Box 4788, Zip 24115–4788; tel. 276/666–7200; Joseph Roach, Chief Executive Officer
Web address: www.martinsvillehospital.com

WYTHE COUNTY COMMUNITY HOSPITAL (L, 90 beds) 600 West Ridge Road, Wytheville, VA Zip 24382–1099; tel. 276/228–0200; John R. McLain, Administrator
Web address: www.wcch.org

WEST VIRGINIA: GUYAN VALLEY HOSPITAL (O, 15 beds) 396 Dingess Street, Logan, WV Zip 25601–3695; tel. 304/831–1700; Kevin N. Fowler, Chief Executive Officer
Web address: www.loganregionalmedicalcenter.com/gvh.shtml

LOGAN REGIONAL MEDICAL CENTER (O, 129 beds) 20 Hospital Drive, Logan, WV Zip 25601–3473; tel. 304/831–1101; Kevin N. Fowler, Chief Executive Officer
Web address: www.loganregionalmedicalcenter.com

WYOMING: LANDER VALLEY MEDICAL CENTER (O, 89 beds) 1320 Bishop Randall Drive, Lander, WY Zip 82520–3996; tel. 307/332–4420; Phil Eaton, Chief Executive Officer
Web address: www.landerhospital.com

RIVERTON MEMORIAL HOSPITAL (O, 70 beds) 2100 West Sunset Drive, Riverton, WY Zip 82501–2274; tel. 307/856–4161; Robert M. Peterson, Chief Executive Officer
Web address: www.riverton–hospital.com

Owned, leased, sponsored:	52 hospitals	4681 beds
Contract–managed:	0 hospitals	0 beds
Totals:	52 hospitals	4681 beds

0060: LIFESPAN CORPORATION (NP)
167 Point Street, Providence, RI Zip 02903–4771; tel. 401/444–3500; George A. Vecchione, President
(Centralized Health System)

RHODE ISLAND: EMMA PENDLETON BRADLEY HOSPITAL (O, 51 beds) 1011 Veterans Memorial Parkway, East Providence, RI Zip 02915–5099; tel. 401/432–1000; Daniel J. Wall, President and Chief Executive Officer
Web address: www.lifespan.org

MIRIAM HOSPITAL (O, 208 beds) 164 Summit Avenue, Providence, RI Zip 02906–2895; tel. 401/793–2500; Kathleen C. Hittner, M.D., President and Chief Executive Officer
Web address: www.lifespan.org

NEWPORT HOSPITAL (O, 130 beds) 11 Friendship Street, Newport, RI Zip 02840–2299; tel. 401/846–6400; Arthur J. Sampson, President and Chief Executive Officer
Web address: www.newporthospital.org

RHODE ISLAND HOSPITAL (O, 579 beds) 593 Eddy Street, Providence, RI Zip 02903–4900; tel. 401/444–4000; Joseph F. Amaral, M.D., President and Chief Executive Officer
Web address: www.lifespan.org

Owned, leased, sponsored:	4 hospitals	968 beds
Contract–managed:	0 hospitals	0 beds
Totals:	4 hospitals	968 beds

2175: LOMA LINDA UNIVERSITY ADVENTIST HEALTH SCIENCES CENTER (NP)
11175 Campus Street, Loma Linda, CA Zip 92354; tel. 909/558–7572; B. Lyn Behrens, President and Chief Executive Officer
(Moderately Centralized Health System)

CALIFORNIA: LOMA LINDA UNIVERSITY BEHAVIORAL MEDICINE CENTER (O, 89 beds) 1710 Barton Road, Redlands, CA Zip 92373–5304; tel. 909/558–9200; Ruthita J. Fike, President
Web address: www.llu.edu

LOMA LINDA UNIVERSITY MEDICAL CENTER (O, 701 beds) 11234 Anderson Street, Loma Linda, CA Zip 92354–2870, Mailing Address: P.O. Box 2000, Zip 92354–0200; tel. 909/558–4000; Ruthita J. Fike, Chief Executive Officer
Web address: www.llumc.edu

Owned, leased, sponsored:	2 hospitals	790 beds
Contract–managed:	0 hospitals	0 beds
Totals:	2 hospitals	790 beds

5755: LOS ANGELES COUNTY–DEPARTMENT OF HEALTH SERVICES (NP)
313 North Figueroa Street, Room 912, Los Angeles, CA Zip 90012–2691; tel. 213/240–8101; Thomas L. Garthwaite, M.D., Director and Chief Medical Officer
(Moderately Centralized Health System)

LAC–HARBOR–UNIVERSITY OF CALIFORNIA AT LOS ANGELES MEDICAL CENTER (O, 325 beds) 1000 West Carson Street, Torrance, CA Zip 90502–2004; tel. 310/222–2345; Tecla A. Mickoseff, Chief Executive Officer
Web address: www.humc.edu

LAC–KING–DREW MEDICAL CENTER (O, 206 beds) 12021 South Wilmington Avenue, Los Angeles, CA Zip 90059–3019; tel. 310/668–4321; Hank Wells, Interim Chief Executive Officer
Web address: www.ladhs.org/mlk

LAC–OLIVE VIEW–UCLA MEDICAL CENTER (O, 226 beds) 14445 Olive View Drive, Sylmar, CA Zip 91342–1495; tel. 818/364–1555; Melinda Anderson, Chief Executive Officer
Web address: www.ladhs.org

LAC/UNIVERSITY OF SOUTHERN CALIFORNIA MEDICAL CENTER (O, 737 beds) 1200 North State Street, Los Angeles, CA Zip 90033–1029; tel. 323/226–2622; Pete Delgado, Chief Executive Officer
Web address: www.lacusc.org

RANCHO LOS AMIGOS NATIONAL REHABILITATION CENTER (O, 167 beds) 7601 East Imperial Highway, Downey, CA Zip 90242–3496; tel. 562/401–7022; Valerie Orange, Chief Executive Officer
Web address: www.rancho.org

Owned, leased, sponsored:	5 hospitals	1661 beds
Contract–managed:	0 hospitals	0 beds
Totals:	5 hospitals	1661 beds

0047: LOUISIANA STATE HOSPITALS (NP)
210 State Street, New Orleans, LA Zip 70118–5797; tel. 504/897–4616; Shelby Price, Chief Executive Officer
(Independent Hospital System)

LOUISIANA: CENTRAL LOUISIANA STATE HOSPITAL (O, 180 beds) 242 West Shamrock Avenue, Pineville, LA Zip 71361–5031, Mailing Address: P.O. Box 5031, Zip 71360–5031; tel. 318/484–6200; Thomas L. Davis, Chief Executive Officer
Web address: www.dhh.state.us.la/omh/inpatient–serv/clsh.htm

EASTERN LOUISIANA MENTAL HEALTH SYSTEM (O, 605 beds) 4502 Highway 951, Jackson, LA Zip 70748–5842, Mailing Address: P.O. Box 498, Zip 70748–0498; tel. 225/634–0100; Herbert Erwin, Chief Executive Officer

NEW ORLEANS ADOLESCENT HOSPITAL (O, 30 beds) 210 State Street, New Orleans, LA Zip 70118–5797; tel. 504/897–3400; Shelby Price, Chief Executive Officer

SOUTHEAST LOUISIANA HOSPITAL (O, 162 beds) 23515 Highway 190, Mandeville, LA Zip 70448–5612, Mailing Address: P.O. Box 3850, Zip 70470–3850; tel. 985/626–6300; Michael E. Teague, Chief Executive Officer
Web address: www.dhh.state.la.us/OMH/inpatient–serv/seast–la–hosp.htm

Owned, leased, sponsored:	4 hospitals	977 beds
Contract–managed:	0 hospitals	0 beds
Totals:	4 hospitals	977 beds

0320: LRG HEALTHCARE (NP)
80 Highland Street, Laconia, NH Zip 03246–3298; tel. 603/524–3211; Thomas Clairmont, President

---

For explanation of codes following names, see page B2.
★ Indicates Type III membership in the American Hospital Association.

NEW HAMPSHIRE: FRANKLIN REGIONAL HOSPITAL (O, 31 beds) 15 Aiken Avenue, Franklin, NH Zip 03235–1299; tel. 603/934–2060; Thomas Clairmont, President
Web address: www.lrgh.org

LAKES REGION GENERAL HOSPITAL (O, 106 beds) 80 Highland Street, Laconia, NH Zip 03246–3298; tel. 603/524–3211; Thomas Clairmont, President
Web address: www.lrgh.org

Owned, leased, sponsored:	2 hospitals	137 beds
Contract–managed:	0 hospitals	0 beds
Totals:	2 hospitals	137 beds

★**0715: LSU HEALTH SCIENCES CENTER** (NP)
8550 United Plaza Boulevard, 4th Floor, Baton Rouge, LA Zip 70809; tel. 225/922–0490; Donald R. Smithburg, Chief Executive Officer
(Moderately Centralized Health System)

LOUISIANA: BOGALUSA MEDICAL CENTER (O, 66 beds) 433 Plaza Street, Bogalusa, LA Zip 70427–3793; tel. 985/732–1722; LeVern S. Meades, Administrator

EARL K. LONG MEDICAL CENTER (O, 144 beds) 5825 Airline Highway, Baton Rouge, LA Zip 70805–2498; tel. 225/358–1000; Clay Dunaway, Administrator
Web address: www.lsuhsc.edu

HUEY P. LONG MEDICAL CENTER (O, 60 beds) 352 Hospital Boulevard, Pineville, LA Zip 71360, Mailing Address: P.O. Box 5352, Zip 71361–5352; tel. 318/448–0811; James E. Morgan, Administrator
Web address: www.lsuhsc.edu/hcsd/hpl

LALLIE KEMP MEDICAL CENTER (O, 28 beds) 52579 Highway 51 South, Independence, LA Zip 70443–2231; tel. 985/878–9421; LeVern S. Meades, Administrator
Web address: www.lak.lsuhsc.edu

LEONARD J. CHABERT MEDICAL CENTER (O, 83 beds) 1978 Industrial Boulevard, Houma, LA Zip 70363–7094; tel. 985/873–2200; Daniel M. Trahan, Administrator

MEDICAL CENTER OF LOUISIANA AT NEW ORLEANS (O, 449 beds) 2021 Perdido Street, New Orleans, LA Zip 70112–1396; tel. 504/903–3000; Dwayne Thomas, M.D., Chief Executive Officer
Web address: www.mclno.org

UNIVERSITY MEDICAL CENTER (O, 124 beds) 2390 West Congress Street, Lafayette, LA Zip 70506–4298, Mailing Address: P.O. Box 69300, Zip 70596–9300; tel. 337/261–6001; Lawrence T. Dorsey, Administrator and Chief Executive Officer

WALTER OLIN MOSS REGIONAL MEDICAL CENTER (O, 32 beds) 1000 Walters Street, Lake Charles, LA Zip 70605–4647; tel. 337/475–8100; Patrick C. Robinson, M.D., Administrator

Owned, leased, sponsored:	8 hospitals	986 beds
Contract–managed:	0 hospitals	0 beds
Totals:	8 hospitals	986 beds

★**5305: MARIAN HEALTH SYSTEM** (CC)
Tulsa, OK Mailing Address: P.O. Box 4753, Zip 74159–0753; tel. 918/742–9988; Sister M. Therese Gottschalk, President
(Decentralized Health System)

MINNESOTA: SAINT ELIZABETH'S MEDICAL CENTER (O, 179 beds) 1200 Grant Boulevard West, Wabasha, MN Zip 55981–1098; tel. 651/565–4531; Thomas Crowley, President
Web address: www.stelizabethswabasha.org

NEW JERSEY: SAINT CLARE'S HOSPITAL (O, 650 beds) 400 West Blackwell Street, Dover, NJ Zip 07801; tel. 973/625–6000; David Lundquist, President and Chief Executive Officer
Web address: www.saintclares.org

OKLAHOMA: JANE PHILLIPS MEDICAL CENTER (O, 132 beds) 3500 East Frank Phillips Boulevard, Bartlesville, OK Zip 74006–2409; tel. 918/333–7200; David R. Stire, Chief Executive Officer
Web address: www.jpmc.org

ST. JOHN MEDICAL CENTER (O, 557 beds) 1923 South Utica Avenue, Tulsa, OK Zip 74104–5445; tel. 918/744–2345; David Pynn, President and Chief Executive Officer
Web address: www.sjmc.org

ST. JOHN SAPULPA (O, 25 beds) 519 South Division Street, Sapulpa, OK Zip 74066–4501, Mailing Address: P.O. Box 1368, Zip 74067–1368; tel. 918/224–4280; Raymond L. Replogle, President and Chief Executive Officer
Web address: www.sjmc.org

WISCONSIN: DOOR COUNTY MEMORIAL HOSPITAL (O, 73 beds) 323 South 18th Avenue, Sturgeon Bay, WI Zip 54235–1495; tel. 920/743–5566; Gerald M. Worrick, President and Chief Executive Officer
Web address: www.dcmh.org

EAGLE RIVER MEMORIAL HOSPITAL (O, 8 beds) 201 Hospital Road, Eagle River, WI Zip 54521–8835; tel. 715/479–7411; Patricia Van Acker, R.N., Administrator
Web address: www.ministryhealth.org

FLAMBEAU HOSPITAL (O, 25 beds) 98 Sherry Avenue, Park Falls, WI Zip 54552–1467, Mailing Address: P.O. Box 310, Zip 54552–0310; tel. 715/762–2484; David A. Grundstrom, Administrator
Web address: www.flambeauhospital.org

GOOD SAMARITAN HEALTH CENTER OF MERRILL (O, 14 beds) 601 Center Avenue South, Merrill, WI Zip 54452–3404; tel. 715/536–5511; Michael Hammer, President and Chief Operating Officer
Web address: www.gshc.org

HOWARD YOUNG MEDICAL CENTER (O, 65 beds) 240 Maple Street, Woodruff, WI Zip 54568, Mailing Address: P.O. Box 470, Zip 54568–0470; tel. 715/356–8000; Brian Kief, President and Chief Executive Officer
Web address: www.hyhc.com

OUR LADY OF VICTORY HOSPITAL (O, 24 beds) 1120 Pine Street, Stanley, WI Zip 54768–0220, Mailing Address: P.O. Box 220, Zip 54768–0220; tel. 715/644–5571; Cynthia Eichman, Chief Executive Officer and Administrator
Web address: www.ministryhealth.org

SACRED HEART–ST. MARY'S HOSPITALS (O, 44 beds) 2251 North Shore Drive, Rhinelander, WI Zip 54501–3998; tel. 715/361–2000; Kevin J. O'Donnell, President and Chief Executive Officer
Web address: www.ministryhealth.org

SAINT JOSEPH'S HOSPITAL (O, 319 beds) 611 St. Joseph Avenue, Marshfield, WI Zip 54449–1898; tel. 715/387–1713; Michael A. Schmidt, President
Web address: www.stjosephs–marshfield.org

SAINT MICHAEL'S HOSPITAL (O, 122 beds) 900 Illinois Avenue, Stevens Point, WI Zip 54481–3196; tel. 715/346–5000; Bradley Neet, President and Chief Operating Officer
Web address: www.saintmichaelshospital.org

Owned, leased, sponsored:	14 hospitals	2237 beds
Contract–managed:	0 hospitals	0 beds
Totals:	14 hospitals	2237 beds

1975: MARSHALL COUNTY HEALTH CARE AUTHORITY (NP)
227 Britany Road, Guntersville, AL Zip 35976; tel. 256/894–6615; Gary R. Gore, Chief Executive Officer
(Independent Hospital System)

ALABAMA: MARSHALL MEDICAL CENTER NORTH (O, 90 beds) 8000 Alabama Highway 69, Guntersville, AL Zip 35976; tel. 256/753–8000; Cheryl M. Hays, FACHE, Administrator
Web address: www.mmcenters.com

MARSHALL MEDICAL CENTER SOUTH (O, 102 beds) U.S. Highway 431 North, Boaz, AL Zip 35957–0999, Mailing Address: P.O. Box 758, Zip 35957–0758; tel. 256/593–8310; John D. Anderson, Administrator
Web address: www.mmcs.org

Owned, leased, sponsored:	2 hospitals	192 beds
Contract–managed:	0 hospitals	0 beds
Totals:	2 hospitals	192 beds

0013: MASSACHUSETTS DEPARTMENT OF MENTAL HEALTH (NP)
25 Staniford Street, Boston, MA Zip 02114–2575; tel. 617/626–8123; Ken Duckworth, Interim Commissioner

MASSACHUSETTS: DR. J. CORRIGAN MENTAL HEALTH CENTER (O, 16 beds) 49 Hillside Street, Fall River, MA Zip 02720–5266; tel. 508/235–7200; Daniel K. Amigone, Director

Section B

For explanation of codes following names, see page B2.
★ Indicates Type III membership in the American Hospital Association.

TAUNTON STATE HOSPITAL (O, 187 beds) 60 Hodges Avenue Extension, Taunton, MA Zip 02780–3034, Mailing Address: P.O. Box 4007, Zip 02780–4007; tel. 508/977–3000; Roberta H. Guez, Administrator and Chief Operating Officer

WESTBOROUGH STATE HOSPITAL (O, 220 beds) Lyman Street, Westborough, MA Zip 01581–0288, Mailing Address: P.O. Box 288, Zip 01581–0288; tel. 508/616–2100; Theodore E. Kirousis, Area Director

WORCESTER STATE HOSPITAL (O, 176 beds) 305 Belmont Street, Worcester, MA Zip 01604–1695; tel. 508/368–3300; Anthony Riccitelli, Chief Operating Officer

Owned, leased, sponsored:	4 hospitals	599 beds
Contract–managed:	0 hospitals	0 beds
Totals:	4 hospitals	599 beds

0280:   MASSSCHUSETTS DEPARTMENT OF PUBLIC HEALTH (NP)
250 Washington Street, Boston, MA Zip 02108–4619; tel. 617/624–6000; Christine C. Ferguson, Commissioner
(Independent Hospital System)

LEMUEL SHATTUCK HOSPITAL (O, 255 beds) 170 Morton Street, Jamaica Plain, Jamaica Plain, MA Zip 02130–3787; tel. 617/522–8110; Paul Romary, Chief Executive Officer
Web address: www.shattuckhospital.org

MASSACHUSETTS HOSPITAL SCHOOL (O, 88 beds) 3 Randolph Street, Canton, MA Zip 02021–2397; tel. 781/828–2440; Mederic D. McLaughlin, Chief Executive Officer
Web address: www.state.ma.us/dph/hosp/mhs.htm

TEWKSBURY HOSPITAL (O, 540 beds) 365 East Street, Tewksbury, MA Zip 01876–1998; tel. 978/851–7321; William J. White, Interim Chief Executive Officer
Web address: www.state.ma.us/dph/hosp/th.htm

WESTERN MASSACHUSETTS HOSPITAL (O, 80 beds) 91 East Mountain Road, Westfield, MA Zip 01085; tel. 413/562–4131; Blake M. Molleur, Executive Director
Web address: www.mass.gov/dph/hosp/wmh.htm

Owned, leased, sponsored:	4 hospitals	963 beds
Contract–managed:	0 hospitals	0 beds
Totals:	4 hospitals	963 beds

★1875:   MAYO FOUNDATION (NP)
200 S.W. First Street, Rochester, MN Zip 55905–0002; tel. 507/284–2511; Denis A. Cortese, M.D., President and Chief Executive Officer
(Moderately Centralized Health System)

ARIZONA: MAYO CLINIC HOSPITAL (O, 202 beds) 5777 East Mayo Boulevard, Phoenix, AZ Zip 85054–4502; tel. 480/515–6296; Thomas C. Bour, Administrator
Web address: www.mayoclinic.org

FLORIDA: ST. LUKE'S HOSPITAL (L, 289 beds) 4201 Belfort Road, Jacksonville, FL Zip 32216–5898; tel. 904/296–3700; Hilary G. Mathews, Administrator
Web address: www.mayoclinic.org

IOWA: FLOYD COUNTY MEMORIAL HOSPITAL (C, 25 beds) 800 Eleventh Street, Charles City, IA Zip 50616–3499; tel. 641/228–6830; Bill D. Faust, Administrator

MINNESOTA: ALBERT LEA MEDICAL CENTER (O, 129 beds) 404 West Fountain Street, Albert Lea, MN Zip 56007–2473; tel. 507/373–2384; Mark Ciota, M.D., Chief Executive Officer
Web address: www.almedcenter.org

AUSTIN MEDICAL CENTER (O, 73 beds) 1000 First Drive N.W., Austin, MN Zip 55912–2904; tel. 507/437–4551; Timothy Johnson, M.D., President
Web address: www.austinmedicalcenter.org

FAIRMONT MEDICAL CENTER–MAYO HEALTH SYSTEM (O, 97 beds) 800 Medical Center Drive, Fairmont, MN Zip 56031–0800, Mailing Address: P.O. Box 835, Zip 56031–0835; tel. 507/238–8100; Larry Gleason, Chief Administrative Officer
Web address: www.fch.org

IMMANUEL ST. JOSEPH'S–MAYO HEALTH SYSTEM (O, 174 beds) 1025 Marsh Street, Mankato, MN Zip 56002–8673, Mailing Address: P.O. Box 8673, Zip 56002–8673; tel. 507/625–4031; William Rupp, M.D., President and Chief Executive Officer
Web address: www.isj–mhs.org

LAKE CITY MEDICAL CENTER–MAYO (O, 116 beds) 500 West Grant Street, Lake City, MN Zip 55041–1143; tel. 651/345–3321; Thomas J. Witt, M.D., President and Chief Executive Officer
Web address: www.lakecitymedicalcenter.org

ROCHESTER METHODIST HOSPITAL (O, 335 beds) 201 West Center Street, Rochester, MN Zip 55902–3084; tel. 507/266–7890; Lynn Frederick, Administrator
Web address: www.mayoclinic.org

SAINT MARYS HOSPITAL (O, 797 beds) 1216 Second Street S.W., Rochester, MN Zip 55902–1970; tel. 507/255–5123; Lynn Frederick, Administrator
Web address: www.mayoclinic.org

SPRINGFIELD MEDICAL CENTER–MAYO HEALTH SYSTEM (O, 24 beds) 625 North Jackson Avenue, Springfield, MN Zip 56087–1714, Mailing Address: P.O. Box 146, Zip 56087–0146; tel. 507/723–6201; Scott D. Thoreson, Administrator
Web address: www.smc–mhs.org

ST. JAMES HEALTH SERVICES (C, 12 beds) 1207 Sixth Avenue South, Saint James, MN Zip 56081–2415, Mailing Address: P.O. Box 460, Zip 56081–0460; tel. 507/375–3261; Dawn L. Wells, Administrator
Web address: www.stjmc.org

WASECA MEDICAL CENTER (O, 25 beds) 501 North State Street, Waseca, MN Zip 56093–2811; tel. 507/835–1210; Michael Milbrath, Executive Vice President
Web address: www.wmc–mhs.org

WISCONSIN: BARRON MEDICAL CENTER–MAYO HEALTH SYSTEM (O, 75 beds) 1222 Woodland Avenue, Barron, WI Zip 54812–1798; tel. 715/537–3186; Bradley D. Groseth, Administrator
Web address: www.barronmedicalcenter.org

BLOOMER MEMORIAL MEDICAL CENTER (O, 70 beds) 1501 Thompson Street, Bloomer, WI Zip 54724–1299; tel. 715/568–2000; Colleen Skold, Administrator
Web address: www.bloomermedicalcenter.org

FRANCISCAN SKEMP HEALTHCARE–ARCADIA CAMPUS (O, 100 beds) 464 South St. Joseph Avenue, Arcadia, WI Zip 54612–1401; tel. 608/323–3341; Robert M. Tracey, Administrator, Regional Hospitals
Web address: www.mayo.edu/fsh/

FRANCISCAN SKEMP HEALTHCARE–LA CROSSE CAMPUS (O, 226 beds) 700 West Avenue South, La Crosse, WI Zip 54601–4783; tel. 608/785–0940; Robert Nesse, M.D., President and Chief Executive Officer
Web address: www.franciscanskemp.org

FRANCISCAN SKEMP HEALTHCARE–SPARTA CAMPUS (O, 55 beds) 310 West Main Street, Sparta, WI Zip 54656–2171; tel. 608/269–2132; Robert M. Tracey, Administrator
Web address: www.mayo.edu/fsh

LUTHER HOSPITAL (O, 172 beds) 1221 Whipple Street, Eau Claire, WI Zip 54702–4105, Mailing Address: P.O. Box 5, Zip 54702–0005; tel. 715/838–3311; Randall Linton, M.D., President and Chief Executive Officer
Web address: www.mhs.mayo.edu

MYRTLE WERTH HOSPITAL–MAYO HEALTH SYSTEM (O, 43 beds) 2321 Stout Road, Menomonie, WI Zip 54751–2397; tel. 715/235–5531; Hank Simpson, M.D., Chief Executive Officer
Web address: www.rcmc–mhs.org

OSSEO MEDICAL CENTER (C, 72 beds) 13025 Eighth Street, Osseo, WI Zip 54758–7673, Mailing Address: P.O. Box 70, Zip 54758–0070; tel. 715/597–3121; Michael Ryan, Administrator
Web address: www.osseomedicalcenter.org

Owned, leased, sponsored:	18 hospitals	3002 beds
Contract–managed:	3 hospitals	109 beds
Totals:	21 hospitals	3111 beds

0252:   MCLAREN HEALTH CARE CORPORATION (NP)
G3235 Beecher Road, Suite B., Flint, MI Zip 48532; tel. 810/342–1100; Philip A. Incarnati, President and Chief Executive Officer
(Centralized Physician/Insurance Health System)

For explanation of codes following names, see page B2.
★ Indicates Type III membership in the American Hospital Association.

B72   Health Care Systems, Networks and Alliances   © 2005 AHA Guide

MICHIGAN: BAY REGIONAL MEDICAL CENTER (O, 313 beds) 1900 Columbus Avenue, Bay City, MI Zip 48708–6880; tel. 989/894–3000; Robert N. Wright, President and Chief Executive Officer
Web address: www.baymed.org

INGHAM REGIONAL MEDICAL CENTER (O, 356 beds) 401 West Greenlawn Avenue, Lansing, MI Zip 48910–2819; tel. 517/334–2121; Dennis M. Litos, President and Chief Executive Officer
Web address: www.irmc.org

LAPEER REGIONAL MEDICAL CENTER (O, 145 beds) 1375 North Main Street, Lapeer, MI Zip 48446–1376; tel. 810/667–5500; Barton Buxton, Chief Executive Officer
Web address: www.lapeerhospital.org

MCLAREN REGIONAL MEDICAL CENTER (O, 378 beds) 401 South Ballenger Highway, Flint, MI Zip 48532–3685; tel. 810/342–2000; Donald C. Kooy, President and Chief Executive Officer
Web address: www.mclaren.org

Owned, leased, sponsored:	4 hospitals	1192 beds
Contract–managed:	0 hospitals	0 beds
Totals:	4 hospitals	1192 beds

0200: MEDCATH, INC. (IO)
10720 Sikes Place, Suite 300, Charlotte, NC Zip 28277–8143; tel. 704/708–6610; Charles R. Slaton, President and Chief Operating Officer
(Independent Hospital System)

ARIZONA: ARIZONA HEART HOSPITAL (O, 59 beds) 1930 East Thomas Road, Phoenix, AZ Zip 85016; tel. 602/532–1000; Kenneth Howell, President and Chief Executive Officer
Web address: www.azheart.com

TUCSON HEART HOSPITAL (O, 60 beds) 4888 North Stone Avenue, Tucson, AZ Zip 85704; tel. 520/696–2328; Gary Toche, President
Web address: www.tucsonhearthospital.com

ARKANSAS: ARKANSAS HEART HOSPITAL (O, 84 beds) 1701 South Shackleford Road, Little Rock, AR Zip 72211–4335; tel. 501/219–7000; Charles Mitchener Jr, President
Web address: www.arheart.com

CALIFORNIA: BAKERSFIELD HEART HOSPITAL (O, 47 beds) 3001 Sillect Avenue, Bakersfield, CA Zip 93308–6337; tel. 661/316–6000; Randall H. Rolfe, President
Web address: www.bakersfieldhearthospital.com

LOUISIANA: HEART HOSPITAL OF LAFAYETTE (O, 24 beds) 1105 Kaliste Saloom, Lafayette, LA Zip 70508; tel. 337/521–1000; Phil Young, President
Web address: www.hearthospitaloflafayette.com

LOUISIANA HEART HOSPITAL (O, 58 beds) 64030 Highway 434, Lacombe, LA Zip 70445; tel. 985/690–7500; Larry D. Walker, President and Chief Executive Officer
Web address: www.louisianahearthospital.com

NEW MEXICO: HEART HOSPITAL OF NEW MEXICO (O, 55 beds) 504 Elm Street, Albuquerque, NM Zip 87102; tel. 505/724–2000; Phil Shaw, Interim President and Chief Executive Officer
Web address: www.hearthospitalnm.com

OHIO: DAYTON HEART HOSPITAL (O, 47 beds) 707 South Edwin C. Moses Boulevard, Dayton, OH Zip 45408; tel. 937/221–8000; Chad Carpenter, President and Chief Executive Officer
Web address: www.daytonhearthospital.com

SOUTH DAKOTA: AVERA HEART HOSPITAL OF SOUTH DAKOTA (O, 55 beds) 4500 West 69th Street, Sioux Falls, SD Zip 57108–8148; tel. 605/977–7000; Jon Soderholm, President
Web address: www.southdakotaheart.com

TEXAS: HARLINGEN MEDICAL CENTER (O, 80 beds) 5501 South Expressway 77, Harlingen, TX Zip 78550; tel. 956/365–1000; Richard L. Gamber, President and Chief Executive Officer
Web address: www.harlingenmedicalcenter.com

HEART HOSPITAL OF AUSTIN (O, 58 beds) 3801 North Lamar Boulevard, Austin, TX Zip 78756; tel. 512/407–7000; Roy C. Vinson, President
Web address: www.hearthospitalofaustin.com

TEXSAN HEART HOSPITAL (O, 60 beds) 6700 IH–10 West, San Antonio, TX Zip 78201; tel. 210/736–6700; Robert S. Freymuller, Chief Executive Officer
Web address: www.texsanhearthospital.com

Owned, leased, sponsored:	12 hospitals	687 beds
Contract–managed:	0 hospitals	0 beds
Totals:	12 hospitals	687 beds

★0154: MEDSTAR HEALTH (NP)
5565 Sterrett Place, 5th Floor, Columbia, MD Zip 21044; tel. 410/772–6500; Kenneth A. Samet, President and Chief Operating Officer
(Centralized Health System)

DISTRICT OF COLUMBIA: MEDSTAR–GEORGETOWN MEDICAL CENTER (O, 367 beds) 3800 Reservoir Road N.W., Washington, DC Zip 20007–2197; tel. 202/444–3000; Joy Drass, M.D., President
Web address: www.georgetownuniversityhospital.org

NATIONAL REHABILITATION HOSPITAL (O, 137 beds) 102 Irving Street N.W., Washington, DC Zip 20010–2949; tel. 202/877–1000; Edward A. Eckenhoff, President and Chief Executive Officer
Web address: www.nrhrehab.org

WASHINGTON HOSPITAL CENTER (O, 786 beds) 110 Irving Street N.W., Washington, DC Zip 20010–2975; tel. 202/877–7000; James F. Caldas, President
Web address: www.whcenter.org

MARYLAND: FRANKLIN SQUARE HOSPITAL CENTER (O, 358 beds) 9000 Franklin Square Drive, Baltimore, MD Zip 21237–2998; tel. 443/777–7000; Carl J. Schindelar, President
Web address: www.franklinsquare.org

GOOD SAMARITAN HOSPITAL OF MARYLAND (O, 244 beds) 5601 Loch Raven Boulevard, Baltimore, MD Zip 21239–2995; tel. 410/532–8000; Lawrence M. Beck, President
Web address: www.goodsam-md.org

HARBOR HOSPITAL CENTER (O, 145 beds) 3001 South Hanover Street, Baltimore, MD Zip 21225–1290; tel. 410/350–3200; Joseph M. Oddis, President and Chief Executive Officer
Web address: www.harborhospital.org

UNION MEMORIAL HOSPITAL (O, 327 beds) 201 East University Parkway, Baltimore, MD Zip 21218–2895; tel. 410/554–2000; Harrison J. Rider III, President
Web address: www.unionmemorial.org

Owned, leased, sponsored:	7 hospitals	2364 beds
Contract–managed:	0 hospitals	0 beds
Totals:	7 hospitals	2364 beds

0084: MEMORIAL HEALTH SERVICES (NP)
2801 Atlantic Avenue, Long Beach, CA Zip 90806, Mailing Address: P.O. Box 1428, Zip 90801–1428; tel. 562/933–2000; Barry S. Arbuckle, Ph.D., President and Chief Executive Officer
(Centralized Health System)

CALIFORNIA: ANAHEIM MEMORIAL MEDICAL CENTER (O, 217 beds) 1111 West La Palma Avenue, Anaheim, CA Zip 92801–2881; tel. 714/774–1450; Melinda D. Beswick, Chief Executive Officer
Web address: www.memorialcare.org

LONG BEACH MEMORIAL MEDICAL CENTER (O, 462 beds) 2801 Atlantic Avenue, Long Beach, CA Zip 90806–1737, Mailing Address: P.O. Box 1428, Zip 90801–1428; tel. 562/933–2000; Byron F. Schweigert, Chief Executive Officer
Web address: www.memorialcare.org

MILLER CHILDREN'S HOSPITAL (O, 281 beds) 2801 Atlantic Avenue, Long Beach, CA Zip 90806; tel. 562/933–2000; Melvin Marks, M.D., Administrator
Web address: www.memorialcare.org

ORANGE COAST MEMORIAL MEDICAL CENTER (O, 172 beds) 9920 Talbert Avenue, Fountain Valley, CA Zip 92708–5153; tel. 714/378–7000; Marcia Manker, Chief Executive Officer
Web address: www.memorialcare.org

SADDLEBACK MEMORIAL MEDICAL CENTER (O, 252 beds) 24451 Health Center Drive, Laguna Hills, CA Zip 92653–3689; tel. 949/837–4500; Steve Geidt, Chief Executive Officer
Web address: www.memorialcare.org

SADDLEBACK MEMORIAL MEDICAL CENTER – SAN CLEMENTE CAMPUS (O, 73 beds) 654 Camino De Los Mares, San Clemente, CA Zip 92673–2827; tel. 949/496–1122; Diana Hendel, PharmD, Administrator
Web address: www.sanclementehospital.com

For explanation of codes following names, see page B2.
★ Indicates Type III membership in the American Hospital Association.

Section B

Owned, leased, sponsored:	6 hospitals	1457 beds
Contract–managed:	0 hospitals	0 beds
Totals:	6 hospitals	1457 beds

2335: MEMORIAL HEALTH SERVICES (IO)
706 North Parrish Avenue, Adel, GA Zip 31620–2064, Mailing Address: P.O. Box 677, Zip 31620–0677; tel. 229/896–8077; Greg Griffith, Chief Executive Officer
(Independent Hospital System)
GEORGIA: BLECKLEY MEMORIAL HOSPITAL (C, 25 beds) 408 Peacock Street, Cochran, GA Zip 31014–1559, Mailing Address: P.O. Box 536, Zip 31014–0536; tel. 478/934–6211; Cary Martin, Administrator
TAYLOR–TELFAIR REGIONAL HOSPITAL (C, 25 beds) U.S. 341 South, McRae, GA Zip 31055, Mailing Address: P.O. Box 150, Zip 31055–0150; tel. 229/868–5621; Joan Hartley, Chief Executive Officer

Owned, leased, sponsored:	0 hospitals	0 beds
Contract–managed:	2 hospitals	50 beds
Totals:	2 hospitals	50 beds

★0086: MEMORIAL HEALTH SYSTEM (NP)
701 North First Street, Springfield, IL Zip 62781–0001; tel. 217/788–3000; Robert T. Clarke, President and Chief Executive Officer
(Centralized Physician/Insurance Health System)
ILLINOIS: ABRAHAM LINCOLN MEMORIAL HOSPITAL (O, 25 beds) 315 8th Street, Lincoln, IL Zip 62656–2698; tel. 217/732–2161; Forrest G. Hester, President and Chief Executive Officer
Web address: www.almh.org
MEMORIAL MEDICAL CENTER (O, 443 beds) 701 North First Street, Springfield, IL Zip 62781–0001; tel. 217/788–3000; Robert T. Clarke, President and Chief Executive Officer
Web address: www.memorialmedical.com
ST. VINCENT MEMORIAL HOSPITAL (S, 75 beds) 201 East Pleasant Street, Taylorville, IL Zip 62568–1597; tel. 217/824–3331; Daniel J. Raab, President and Chief Executive Officer
Web address: www.svmh.org

Owned, leased, sponsored:	3 hospitals	543 beds
Contract–managed:	0 hospitals	0 beds
Totals:	3 hospitals	543 beds

0176: MEMORIAL HEALTH SYSTEM OF EAST TEXAS (NP)
1201 West Frank Avenue, Lufkin, TX Zip 75904–3357; tel. 936/634–8111; Bryant H. Krenek Jr, President and Chief Executive Officer
(Centralized Physician/Insurance Health System)
TEXAS: MEMORIAL HEALTH SYSTEM OF EAST TEXAS (O, 180 beds) 1201 West Frank Avenue, Lufkin, TX Zip 75904–3357, Mailing Address: P.O. Box 1447, Zip 75902–1447; tel. 936/634–8111; Bryant H. Krenek Jr, President and Chief Executive Officer
Web address: www.memorialhealth.org
MEMORIAL MEDICAL CENTER – LIVINGSTON (O, 35 beds) 1717 Highway 59 Bypass, Livingston, TX Zip 77351–1257, Mailing Address: P.O. Box 1257, Zip 77351–1257; tel. 936/327–4381; James C. Dickson, Administrator
Web address: www.memorialhealth.org
MEMORIAL MEDICAL CENTER – SAN AUGUSTINE (O, 18 beds) 511 East Hospital Street, San Augustine, TX Zip 75972–2121, Mailing Address: P.O. Box 658, Zip 75972–0658; tel. 936/275–3446; Darlene Williams, R.N., Administrator
Web address: www.memorialhealth.org
MEMORIAL SPECIALTY HOSPITAL (O, 17 beds) 1201 West Frank Avenue, Lufkin, TX Zip 75904; tel. 936/639–7975; Les Leach, Administrator
Web address: www.memorialhealth.org

Owned, leased, sponsored:	4 hospitals	250 beds
Contract–managed:	0 hospitals	0 beds
Totals:	4 hospitals	250 beds

★0083: MEMORIAL HEALTHCARE SYSTEM (NP)
3501 Johnson Street, Hollywood, FL Zip 33021–5421; tel. 954/985–5805; Frank V. Sacco, FACHE, Chief Executive Officer
(Centralized Health System)
FLORIDA: MEMORIAL HOSPITAL MIRAMAR (O, 100 beds) 1901 S.W. 172nd Avenue, Miramar, FL Zip 33029; tel. 954/538–5000; C. Kennon Hetlage, Administrator
MEMORIAL HOSPITAL PEMBROKE (L, 149 beds) 7800 Sheridan Street, Pembroke Pines, FL Zip 33024–2536; tel. 954/962–9650; Martha Garcia, Administrator
Web address: www.mhs–net.com
MEMORIAL HOSPITAL WEST (O, 237 beds) 703 North Flamingo Road, Pembroke Pines, FL Zip 33028–1014; tel. 954/436–5000; Zeff Ross, Administrator
Web address: www.mhs.net
MEMORIAL REGIONAL HOSPITAL (O, 684 beds) 3501 Johnson Street, Hollywood, FL Zip 33021–5421; tel. 954/987–2000; J. E. Piriz, Administrator
Web address: www.mhs.net

Owned, leased, sponsored:	4 hospitals	1170 beds
Contract–managed:	0 hospitals	0 beds
Totals:	4 hospitals	1170 beds

★2645: MEMORIAL HERMANN HEALTHCARE SYSTEM (NP)
7737 S.W. Freeway, Suite 200, Houston, TX Zip 77074–1800; tel. 713/456–5550; Daniel J. Wolterman, President and Chief Executive Officer
(Centralized Health System)
TEXAS: MEMORIAL HERMANN BAPTIST BEAUMONT HOSPITAL (C, 365 beds) 3080 College Street, Beaumont, TX Zip 77701–4689, Mailing Address: P.O. Box 1591, Zip 77704–1591; tel. 409/212–5000; David N. Parmer, President and Chief Executive Officer
Web address: www.mhbh.org
MEMORIAL HERMANN BAPTIST IN ORANGE (C, 154 beds) 608 Strickland Drive, Orange, TX Zip 77630–4717; tel. 409/883–9361; Rosanne Akin, Chief Administrative Officer
Web address: www.mhhs.org
MEMORIAL HERMANN CONTINUING CARE HOSPITAL (L, 162 beds) 3043 Gessner Drive, Houston, TX Zip 77080–2597; tel. 713/462–2515; Joe G. Baldwin, Chief Executive Officer
Web address: www.mhhs.org
MEMORIAL HERMANN FORT BEND HOSPITAL (O, 65 beds) 3803 FM 1092 at Highway 6, Missouri City, TX Zip 77459; tel. 281/499–4800; Rod Brace, Chief Executive Officer
Web address: www.mhhs.org
MEMORIAL HERMANN HOSPITAL (O, 711 beds) 6411 Fannin, Houston, TX Zip 77030–1501; tel. 713/704–4000; Juanita F. Romans, Chief Executive Officer
Web address: www.mhhs.org
MEMORIAL HERMANN KATY HOSPITAL (O, 90 beds) 5602 Medical Center Drive, Katy, TX Zip 77494–6399; tel. 281/392–1111; Brian S. Barbe, Chief Executive Officer
Web address: www.mhhs.org
MEMORIAL HERMANN MEMORIAL CITY HOSPITAL (L, 400 beds) 920 Frostwood Drive, Houston, TX Zip 77024–9173; tel. 713/932–3000; Wayne M. Voss, Chief Executive Officer
Web address: www.mhhs.org
MEMORIAL HERMANN SOUTHWEST HOSPITAL (O, 525 beds) 7600 Beechnut, Houston, TX Zip 77074–1850; tel. 713/776–5000; Chris M. Vasquez, Vice President and Chief Executive Officer
Web address: www.mhhs.org

Owned, leased, sponsored:	6 hospitals	1953 beds
Contract–managed:	2 hospitals	519 beds
Totals:	8 hospitals	2472 beds

For explanation of codes following names, see page B2.
★ Indicates Type III membership in the American Hospital Association.

Section B

★0257: MERIDIAN HEALTH (NP)
1350 Campus Parkway, Neptune, NJ Zip 07753;
tel. 732/751–7510; John K. Lloyd, President and Chief Executive Officer
(Centralized Health System)

NEW JERSEY: JERSEY SHORE UNIVERSITY MEDICAL CENTER (O, 446 beds) 1945 Route 33, Neptune, NJ Zip 07754–0397; tel. 732/775–5500; Steven G. Littleson, President
Web address: www.meridianhealth.com

OCEAN MEDICAL CENTER (O, 210 beds) 425 Jack Martin Boulevard, Brick Township, NJ Zip 08724; tel. 732/840–2200; W. Peter Daniels, President
Web address: www.meridianhealth.com

RIVERVIEW MEDICAL CENTER (O, 282 beds) 1 Riverview Plaza, Red Bank, NJ Zip 07701–9982; tel. 732/741–2700; Timothy J. Hogan, President
Web address: www.meridianhealth.com

Owned, leased, sponsored:	3 hospitals	938 beds
Contract–managed:	0 hospitals	0 beds
Totals:	3 hospitals	938 beds

0291: MERIT HEALTH SYSTEMS (NP)
333 East Main Street, Suite 300, Louisville, KY Zip 40202; tel. 502/753–0890; Tyree Wilburn, Chaiman, President and Chief Executive Officer
(Independent Hospital System)

ILLINOIS: LINCOLN PARK HOSPITAL (O, 155 beds) 550 Webster Avenue, Chicago, IL Zip 60614–9980; tel. 773/883–2000; Gregory A. Cierlik, President and Chief Executive Officer
Web address: www.lincolnparkhospital.com

TEXAS: NIX HEALTH CARE SYSTEM (O, 181 beds) 414 Navarro Street, San Antonio, TX Zip 78205–2522; tel. 210/271–1800; John F. Strieby, Chief Executive Officer
Web address: www.nixhealth.com

Owned, leased, sponsored:	2 hospitals	336 beds
Contract–managed:	0 hospitals	0 beds
Totals:	2 hospitals	336 beds

★0287: MERITCARE HEALTH SYSTEM (NP)
720 Fourth Street North, Fargo, ND Zip 58122; tel. 701/234–6000; Roger L. Gilbertson, M.D., President and Chief Executive Officer
(Moderately Centralized Health System)

MINNESOTA: MAHNOMEN HEALTH CENTER (C, 63 beds) 414 Jefferson Avenue, Mahnomen, MN Zip 56557–4912, Mailing Address: P.O. Box 396, Zip 56557–0396; tel. 218/935–2511; Sue Klabo, Administrator

PERHAM MEMORIAL HOSPITAL AND HOME (C, 123 beds) 665 Third Street S.W., Perham, MN Zip 56573–1199; tel. 218/346–4500; Chuck Hofius, Administrator
Web address: www.pmhh.com

NORTH DAKOTA: MERITCARE MEDICAL CENTER (O, 522 beds) 720 Fourth Street North, Fargo, ND Zip 58122; tel. 701/234–6000; Roger L. Gilbertson, M.D., President
Web address: www.meritcare.com

Owned, leased, sponsored:	1 hospital	522 beds
Contract–managed:	2 hospitals	186 beds
Totals:	3 hospitals	708 beds

★2735: METHODIST HEALTH SYSTEM (NP)
1441 North Beckley Avenue, Dallas, TX Zip 75203–1201, Mailing Address: P.O. Box 655999, Zip 75265–5999; tel. 214/947–8181; Howard M. Chase, FACHE, President and Chief Executive Officer
(Independent Hospital System)

TEXAS: METHODIST CHARLTON MEDICAL CENTER (O, 204 beds) 3500 West Wheatland Road, Dallas, TX Zip 75237–3460, Mailing Address: Box 225357, Zip 75222–5357; tel. 214/947–7777; Kim N. Hollon, FACHE, Executive Vice President, Operations
Web address: www.mhs.com

METHODIST DALLAS MEDICAL CENTER (O, 394 beds) 1441 North Beckley Avenue, Dallas, TX Zip 75203–1201, Mailing Address: Box 655999, Zip 75265–5999; tel. 214/947–8181; Kim N. Hollon, FACHE, Executive Vice President Operations
Web address: www.mhd.com

Owned, leased, sponsored:	2 hospitals	598 beds
Contract–managed:	0 hospitals	0 beds
Totals:	2 hospitals	598 beds

9345: METHODIST HEALTHCARE (CO)
1211 Union Avenue, Suite 700, Memphis, TN Zip 38104–6600; tel. 901/516–0543; Gary S. Shorb, Chief Executive Officer
(Moderately Centralized Health System)

TENNESSEE: METHODIST HEALTHCARE – EXTENDED CARE HOSPITAL (O, 36 beds) 225 South Claybrook Street, Memphis, TN Zip 38104–3537; tel. 901/726–2113; Sandra Bailey, Administrator
Web address: www.methodisthealth.org

METHODIST HEALTHCARE–FAYETTE HOSPITAL (O, 10 beds) 214 Lakeview Drive, Somerville, TN Zip 38068–9737; tel. 901/465–3594; Michael Blome', Administrator
Web address: www.methodisthealth.org

METHODIST HEALTHCARE–UNIVERSITY HOSPITAL (O, 1281 beds) 1211 Union Avenue, Memphis, TN Zip 38104–3499; tel. 901/726–7000; Cecelia Sawyer, Administrator
Web address: www.methodisthealth.org

Owned, leased, sponsored:	3 hospitals	1327 beds
Contract–managed:	0 hospitals	0 beds
Totals:	3 hospitals	1327 beds

0208: MID ATLANTIC HEALTH MANAGEMENT, INC. (IO)
1220 Butterworth Court, Stevensville, MD Zip 21666–2504; tel. 410/643–3393; Harold A. McBee Jr, President
(Independent Hospital System)

WEST VIRGINIA: HAMPSHIRE MEMORIAL HOSPITAL (O, 44 beds) 549 Center Avenue, Romney, WV Zip 26757–1199; tel. 304/822–4561; Roberta D. McCauley, Chief Executive Officer

POTOMAC VALLEY HOSPITAL (O, 30 beds) 167 South Mineral Street, Keyser, WV Zip 26726–2699; tel. 304/788–3141; Michael Makosky, Administrator

WISCONSIN: INDIANHEAD MEDICAL CENTER (O, 49 beds) 113 Fourth Avenue, Shell Lake, WI Zip 54871, Mailing Address: P.O. Box 300, Zip 54871–0300; tel. 715/468–7833; Paul Naglosky, Administrator

Owned, leased, sponsored:	3 hospitals	123 beds
Contract–managed:	0 hospitals	0 beds
Totals:	3 hospitals	123 beds

★0001: MIDMICHIGAN HEALTH (NP)
4005 Orchard Drive, Midland, MI Zip 48670–0001; tel. 989/839–3000; Terence F. Moore, President
(Moderately Centralized Health System)

MICHIGAN: MIDMICHIGAN MEDICAL CENTER–CLARE (O, 64 beds) 703 North McEwan Street, Clare, MI Zip 48617–1409; tel. 989/802–5000; Lawrence F. Barco, President
Web address: www.midmichigan.org

MIDMICHIGAN MEDICAL CENTER–GLADWIN (O, 42 beds) 515 South Quarter Street, Gladwin, MI Zip 48624–1918; tel. 989/426–9286; Mark E. Bush, Executive Vice President
Web address: www.midmichigan.org

MIDMICHIGAN MEDICAL CENTER–MIDLAND (O, 250 beds) 4005 Orchard Drive, Midland, MI Zip 48670–0001; tel. 989/839–3000; Richard M. Reynolds, President
Web address: www.midmichigan.org

Owned, leased, sponsored:	3 hospitals	356 beds
Contract–managed:	0 hospitals	0 beds
Totals:	3 hospitals	356 beds

Section B

For explanation of codes following names, see page B2.
★ Indicates Type III membership in the American Hospital Association.

2855: MISSIONARY BENEDICTINE SISTERS AMERICAN PROVINCE (CC)
300 North 18th Street, Norfolk, NE Zip 68701–3687;
tel. 402/371–3438; Sister Kevin Hermsen, Prioress
(Moderately Centralized Health System)

MINNESOTA: GRACEVILLE HEALTH CENTER (O, 112 beds) 115 West Second Street, Graceville, MN Zip 56240–0157, Mailing Address: P.O. Box 157, Zip 56240–0157; tel. 320/748–7223; Helen Jorve, Chief Executive Officer

NEBRASKA: FAITH REGIONAL HEALTH SERVICES (O, 222 beds) 2700 Norfolk Avenue, Norfolk, NE Zip 68701, Mailing Address: P.O. BOX 869, Zip 68702–0869; tel. 402/644–7201; Robert L. Driewer, CHE, Chief Executive Officer
Web address: www.frhs.org

PROVIDENCE MEDICAL CENTER (O, 25 beds) 1200 Providence Road, Wayne, NE Zip 68787–1299; tel. 402/375–3800; Marcile Thomas, Administrator
Web address: www.providencemedical.com

Owned, leased, sponsored:	3 hospitals	359 beds
Contract–managed:	0 hospitals	0 beds
Totals:	3 hospitals	359 beds

0017: MISSISSIPPI STATE DEPARTMENT OF MENTAL HEALTH (NP)
1101 Robert E Lee Building, Jackson, MS Zip 39201–1101;
tel. 601/359–1288; Roger McMurtry, Chief Mental Health Bureau
(Independent Hospital System)

MISSISSIPPI: EAST MISSISSIPPI STATE HOSPITAL (O, 543 beds) 4555 Highland Park Drive, Meridian, MS Zip 39307–5498, Mailing Address: Box 4128, West Station, Zip 39304–4128; tel. 601/482–6186; Charles Carlisle, Director
Web address: www.emsh.state.ms.us

MISSISSIPPI STATE HOSPITAL (O, 1303 beds) 3550 Highway 468 West, Whitfield, MS Zip 39193, Mailing Address: P.O. Box 157–A, Zip 39193–0157; tel. 601/351–8000; James G. Chastain, CHE, Director
Web address: www.msh.state.ms.us

NORTH MISSISSIPPI STATE HOSPITAL (O, 74 beds) 1937 Briar Ridge Road, Tupelo, MS Zip 38804; tel. 662/690–4200; Paul A. Callens, Ph.D., Director
Web address: www.nmsh.state.ms.us

SOUTH MISSISSIPPI STATE HOSPITAL (O, 50 beds) 823 Highway 589, Purvis, MS Zip 39475–4194; tel. 601/794–0100; Wynona C. Winfield, Director
Web address: www.smsh.state.ms.us

Owned, leased, sponsored:	4 hospitals	1970 beds
Contract–managed:	0 hospitals	0 beds
Totals:	4 hospitals	1970 beds

1335: MORTON PLANT MEASE HEALTH CARE (NP)
601 Main Street, Dunedin, FL Zip 34698, Mailing Address: P.O. Box 760, Zip 34697–0760; tel. 727/733–1111; Philip K. Beauchamp, FACHE, President and Chief Executive Officer

FLORIDA: MEASE COUNTRYSIDE HOSPITAL (O, 100 beds) 3231 McMullen–Booth Road, Safety Harbor, FL Zip 34695–1098, Mailing Address: P.O. 1098, Zip 34695–1098; tel. 727/725–6111; James A. Pfeiffer, President and Chief Executive Officer
Web address: www.measehospitals.com

MEASE HOSPITAL DUNEDIN (O, 258 beds) 601 Main Street, Dunedin, FL Zip 34698–5891, Mailing Address: P.O. Box 760, Zip 34697–0760; tel. 727/733–1111; James A. Pfeiffer, President and Chief Executive Officer
Web address: www.measehospitals.com

MORTON PLANT HOSPITAL (S, 524 beds) 300 Pinellas Street, Clearwater, FL Zip 33756–3825, Mailing Address: P.O. Box 210, Zip 34657–0210; tel. 727/462–7000; Philip K. Beauchamp, FACHE, President and Chief Executive Officer
Web address: www.mortonplant.com

MORTON PLANT NORTH BAY HOSPITAL (S, 122 beds) 6600 Madison Street, New Port Richey, FL Zip 34652–1900; tel. 727/842–8468; William M. Jennings, Administrator and Chief Operating Officer

Owned, leased, sponsored:	4 hospitals	1004 beds
Contract–managed:	0 hospitals	0 beds
Totals:	4 hospitals	1004 beds

★2225: MOSES CONE HEALTH SYSTEM (NP)
1200 North Elm Street, Greensboro, NC Zip 27401–1020;
tel. 336/832–7000; Timothy Rice, President and Chief Executive Officer
(Centralized Health System)

NORTH CAROLINA: ANNIE PENN HOSPITAL (O, 179 beds) 618 South Main Street, Reidsville, NC Zip 27320–5094; tel. 336/951–4000; Susan H. Fitzgibbon, President and Executive Vice President
Web address: www.mosescone.com

BEHAVIORAL HEALTH CENTER (O, 80 beds) 700 Walter Reed Drive, Greensboro, NC Zip 27403–1129; tel. 336/852–4821; Paul A. Jeffrey, Vice President
Web address: www.mosescone.com

MOSES CONE HEALTH SYSTEM (O, 1324 beds) 1200 North Elm Street, Greensboro, NC Zip 27401–1020; tel. 336/832–7000; R. Timothy Rice, President and Chief Executive Officer
Web address: www.mosescone.com

Owned, leased, sponsored:	3 hospitals	1583 beds
Contract–managed:	0 hospitals	0 beds
Totals:	3 hospitals	1583 beds

0167: MOUNTAIN STATES HEALTH ALLIANCE (NP)
701 North State of Franklin, Suite 1, Johnson City, TN Zip 37604;
tel. 423/431–6040; Dennis Vonderfecht, President and Chief Executive Officer
(Centralized Health System)

TENNESSEE: INDIAN PATH MEDICAL CENTER (O, 222 beds) 2000 Brookside Drive, Kingsport, TN Zip 37660–4682; tel. 423/857–7000; Monty E. McLaurin, President and Chief Executive Officer
Web address: www.msha.com

JOHNSON CITY MEDICAL CENTER (O, 481 beds) 400 North State of Franklin Road, Johnson City, TN Zip 37604–6094; tel. 423/431–6111; John W. Melton, Senior Vice President Operations and Chief Executive Officer
Web address: www.jcmc.com

JOHNSON CITY SPECIALTY HOSPITAL (O, 49 beds) 203 East Watauga Avenue, Johnson City, TN Zip 37601–4651; tel. 423/434–1400; Rhonda Mann, Director Nursing and Operations
Web address: www.msha.com/facilities/jchs.htm

JOHNSON COUNTY HEALTH CENTER (O, 2 beds) 1901 South Shady Street, Mountain City, TN Zip 37683; tel. 423/727–1100; Lisa Heaton, Administrator and Chief Nursing Officer
Web address: www.msha.com

NORTH SIDE HOSPITAL (O, 80 beds) 401 Princeton Road, Johnson City, TN Zip 37601–2097; tel. 423/854–5600; Melanie Stanton, Administrator
Web address: www.msha.com

QUILLEN REHABILITATION HOSPITAL (O, 60 beds) 2511 Wesley Street, Johnson City, TN Zip 37601–1723; tel. 423/283–0700; John Turner, Chief Executive Officer
Web address: www.msha.com

SYCAMORE SHOALS HOSPITAL (O, 121 beds) 1501 West Elk Avenue, Elizabethton, TN Zip 37643–2874; tel. 423/542–1300; Dwayne Taylor, Chief Executive Officer
Web address: www.msha.com

WOODRIDGE HOSPITAL (O, 64 beds) 403 State of Franklin Road, Johnson City, TN Zip 37604–6009; tel. 423/928–7111; Ensign Randall E. Jessee, M.D., Administrator
Web address: www.frontierhealth.org

Owned, leased, sponsored:	8 hospitals	1079 beds
Contract–managed:	0 hospitals	0 beds
Totals:	8 hospitals	1079 beds

For explanation of codes following names, see page B2.
★ Indicates Type III membership in the American Hospital Association.

Section B

6555: MULTICARE HEALTH SYSTEM (NP)
315 Martin Luther King Jr. Way, Tacoma, WA Zip 98415, Mailing Address: P.O. Box 5299, Zip 98415–0299; tel. 253/403–1000; Diane Cecchettini, President and Chief Executive Officer
(Centralized Physician/Insurance Health System)

WASHINGTON: MARY BRIDGE CHILDREN'S HOSPITAL AND HEALTH CENTER (O, 68 beds) 317 Martin Luther King Jr. Way, Tacoma, WA Zip 98405–0299, Mailing Address: Box 5299, Zip 98405–0299; tel. 253/403–1400; Diane Cecchettini, President and Chief Executive Officer
Web address: www.multicare.org

TACOMA GENERAL HOSPITAL (O, 308 beds) 315 Martin Luther King Jr. Way, Tacoma, WA Zip 98405–0299, Mailing Address: P.O. Box 5299, Zip 98415–0299; tel. 253/403–1000; Diane Cecchettini, President and Chief Executive Officer
Web address: www.multicare.org

Owned, leased, sponsored:	2 hospitals	376 beds
Contract–managed:	0 hospitals	0 beds
Totals:	2 hospitals	376 beds

★1465: MUNSON HEALTHCARE (NP)
1105 Sixth Street, Traverse City, MI Zip 49684–2386; tel. 231/935–6502; John M. Rockwood Jr, President and Chief Executive Officer
(Moderately Centralized Health System)

MICHIGAN: KALKASKA MEMORIAL HEALTH CENTER (C, 96 beds) 419 South Coral Street, Kalkaska, MI Zip 49646–9438; tel. 231/258–7500; James D. Austin, FACHE, Administrator
Web address: www.munsonhealthcare.org

LEELANAU MEMORIAL HEALTH CENTER (O, 95 beds) 215 South High Street, Northport, MI Zip 49670–9755, Mailing Address: P.O. Box 217, Zip 49670–0217; tel. 231/386–0000; Kathrine Garthe, Administrator
Web address: www.munsonhealthcare.org

MUNSON MEDICAL CENTER (O, 368 beds) 1105 Sixth Street, Traverse City, MI Zip 49684–2386; tel. 231/935–5000; Edwin Ness, President and Chief Executive Officer
Web address: www.munsonhealthcare.org

PAUL OLIVER MEMORIAL HOSPITAL (O, 48 beds) 224 Park Avenue, Frankfort, MI Zip 49635–9658; tel. 231/352–2200; James D. Austin, FACHE, Administrator
Web address: www.munsonhealthcare.org

Owned, leased, sponsored:	3 hospitals	511 beds
Contract–managed:	1 hospital	96 beds
Totals:	4 hospitals	607 beds

0248: MUSC MEDICAL CENTER OF MEDICAL UNIVERSITY OF SOUTH CAROLINA (NP)
169 Ashley Avenue, Charleston, SC Zip 29425–5836; tel. 843/792–2300; Stuart Smith, Vice President Clinical Operations and Executive Director
(Moderately Centralized Health System)

SOUTH CAROLINA: CHARLESTON MEMORIAL HOSPITAL (O, 20 beds) 326 Calhoun Street, Charleston, SC Zip 29401–1189; tel. 843/792–2300; Thomas F. Moore, Administrator
Web address: www.musc.edu

MUSC MEDICAL CENTER OF MEDICAL UNIVERSITY OF SOUTH CAROLINA (O, 590 beds) 169 Ashley Avenue, Charleston, SC Zip 29425; tel. 843/792–2300; Stuart Smith, Vice President Clinical Operations and Executive Director
Web address: www.musc.edu

Owned, leased, sponsored:	2 hospitals	610 beds
Contract–managed:	0 hospitals	0 beds
Totals:	2 hospitals	610 beds

0261: NATIONAL SURGICAL HOSPITALS (IO)
30 South Wacker Drive, Suite 2302, Chicago, IL Zip 60606; tel. 312/627–8400; John G. Rex–Waller, President and Chief Executive Officer
(Independent Hospital System)

ARIZONA: ARIZONA SPINE AND JOINT HOSPITAL (O, 22 beds) 4620 East Baseline Road, Mesa, AZ Zip 85206; tel. 480/832–4770; Lloyd Scarrow, Chief Executive Officer

IDAHO: NORTHWEST SPECIALTY HOSPITAL (O, 12 beds) 1593 East Polston, Post Falls, ID Zip 83854; tel. 208/262–2300; Nick Genna, Chief Executive Officer

MICHIGAN: SOUTHEAST MICHIGAN SURGICAL HOSPITAL (O, 13 beds) 21230 Dequindre, Warren, MI Zip 48091–2287; tel. 586/427–1000; Brian J. Peltz, Chief Executive Office
Web address: www.nshinc.com

NORTH CAROLINA: NORTH CAROLINA SPECIALTY HOSPITAL (O, 14 beds) 1110 West Main Street, Durham, NC Zip 27701–2000; tel. 919/956–9300

TEXAS: EL PASO SPECIALTY HOSPITAL (O, 31 beds) 1755 Curie Drive, El Paso, TX Zip 79902; tel. 915/533–7465; Mitchell McBeth, Chief Executive Officer
Web address: www.elpasospecialtyhospital.com

THE SPINE HOSPITAL OF SOUTH TEXAS (O, 30 beds) 18600 Hardy Oak Boulevard, San Antonio, TX Zip 78258; tel. 210/404–0800; Chris Shoup, Chief Executive Officer
Web address: www.shst.net

UTAH: CACHE VALLEY SPECIALTY HOSPITAL (O, 33 beds) 2380 North 400 East, North Logan, UT Zip 84341; tel. 435/713–9700; Michael Staheli, Chief Executive Officer
Web address: www.cvsh.com

Owned, leased, sponsored:	7 hospitals	155 beds
Contract–managed:	0 hospitals	0 beds
Totals:	7 hospitals	155 beds

★9265: NEBRASKA METHODIST HEALTH SYSTEM, INC. (CO)
8511 West Dodge Road, Omaha, NE Zip 68114; tel. 402/354–4844; Stephen D. Long, President and Executive Officer
(Moderately Centralized Health System)

IOWA: JENNIE EDMUNDSON MEMORIAL HOSPITAL (O, 118 beds) 933 East Pierce Street, Council Bluffs, IA Zip 51503–4652, Mailing Address: P.O. Box 2C, Zip 51502–3002; tel. 712/396–6000; David M. Holcomb, President and Chief Executive Officer
Web address: www.bestcare.org

NEBRASKA: NEBRASKA METHODIST HOSPITAL (O, 345 beds) 8303 Dodge Street, Omaha, NE Zip 68114–4199; tel. 402/354–4000; John M. Fraser, President and Chief Executive Officer
Web address: www.bestcare.org

Owned, leased, sponsored:	2 hospitals	463 beds
Contract–managed:	0 hospitals	0 beds
Totals:	2 hospitals	463 beds

★0213: NEW HANOVER HEALTH NETWORK (NP)
2131 South 17th Street, Wilmington, NC Zip 28401–9000; tel. 910/343–7040; John K. Barto Jr, Chief Executive Officer
(Moderately Centralized Health System)

NORTH CAROLINA: NEW HANOVER REGIONAL MEDICAL CENTER (O, 655 beds) 2131 South 17th Street, Wilmington, NC Zip 28401–7483, Mailing Address: P.O. Box 9000, Zip 28402–9000; tel. 910/343–7000; John K. Barto Jr, Chief Executive Officer
Web address: www.nhhn.org

PENDER MEMORIAL HOSPITAL (C, 68 beds) 507 Freemont Street, Burgaw, NC Zip 28425–5131; tel. 910/259–5451; Matthew Mendez, Administrator
Web address: www.nhhn.org

For explanation of codes following names, see page B2.
★ Indicates Type III membership in the American Hospital Association.

Section B

Owned, leased, sponsored:	1 hospital	655 beds
Contract–managed:	1 hospital	68 beds
Totals:	2 hospitals	723 beds

★**3075: NEW YORK CITY HEALTH AND HOSPITALS CORPORATION** (NP)
125 Worth Street, Room 514, New York, NY Zip 10013–4006; tel. 212/788–3321; Alan D. Aviles, Acting President
(Decentralized Health System)

NEW YORK: BELLEVUE HOSPITAL CENTER (O, 771 beds) 462 First Avenue, New York, NY Zip 10016–9198; tel. 212/562–4141; Linda Curtis, Acting Executive Director
Web address: www.nyc.gov/bellevue

COLER–GOLDWATER SPECIALTY HOSPITAL AND NURSING FACILITY (O, 2016 beds) One Main Street, New York, NY Zip 10044; tel. 212/318–8000; Claude Ritman, Executive Director
Web address: www.coler-goldwater.org

CONEY ISLAND HOSPITAL (O, 376 beds) 2601 Ocean Parkway, Brooklyn, NY Zip 11235–7795; tel. 718/616–3000; Peter Wolf, Executive Director
Web address: www.ci.nyc.ny.us/html/hhc/html/coneyisland.html

ELMHURST HOSPITAL CENTER (O, 525 beds) 79–01 Broadway, Flushing, NY Zip 11373–1368; tel. 718/334–4000; Chris D. Constantino, Executive Director
Web address: www.elmhursthospitalcenter.org

HARLEM HOSPITAL CENTER (O, 275 beds) 506 Lenox Avenue, New York, NY Zip 10037–1894; tel. 212/939–1000; John M. Palmer, Ph.D., Executive Director
Web address: www.nyclink.org/hhc

JACOBI MEDICAL CENTER (O, 556 beds) Pelham Parkway South and Eastchester Road, Bronx, NY Zip 10461–1197; tel. 718/918–5000; William P. Walsh, Executive Director
Web address: www.ci.nyc.ny.us/html/hhc/html/jacobi.html

KINGS COUNTY HOSPITAL CENTER (O, 627 beds) 451 Clarkson Avenue, Brooklyn, NY Zip 11203–2097; tel. 718/245–3131; Jean G. Leon, R.N., Senior Vice President
Web address: www.ci.nyc.ny.us/html/hhc/html/kings.html

LINCOLN MEDICAL AND MENTAL HEALTH CENTER (O, 322 beds) 234 East 149th Street, Bronx, NY Zip 10451–9998; tel. 718/579–5700; Jose R. Sanchez, Executive Director

METROPOLITAN HOSPITAL CENTER (O, 325 beds) 1901 First Avenue, New York, NY Zip 10029–7496; tel. 212/423–6262; Louis Martir, Executive Director

NORTH CENTRAL BRONX HOSPITAL (O, 210 beds) 3424 Kossuth Avenue, Bronx, NY Zip 10467–2489; tel. 718/519–3500; William P. Walsh, Executive Director
Web address: www.ci.nyc.ny.us/html/hhc/html/northcentralbronx.html

QUEENS HOSPITAL CENTER (O, 248 beds) 82–68 164th Street, Jamaica, NY Zip 11432–1104; tel. 718/883–3000; Antonio D. Martin, Executive Director
Web address: www.ci.nyc.ny.us/html/hhc/html/facilities/queens/shtml

WOODHULL MEDICAL AND MENTAL HEALTH CENTER (O, 406 beds) 760 Broadway Street, Brooklyn, NY Zip 11206–5383; tel. 718/963–8000; Lynda D. Curtis, Executive Director
Web address: www.nyc.gov/html/hhc/home/html

Owned, leased, sponsored:	12 hospitals	6657 beds
Contract–managed:	0 hospitals	0 beds
Totals:	12 hospitals	6657 beds

0142: NEW YORK PRESBYTERIAN HEALTHCARE SYSTEM (NP)
525 East 68th Street, New York, NY Zip 10021–4885; tel. 212/746–3745; Herbert Pardes, M.D., Chief Executive Officer
(Moderately Centralized Health System)

NEW JERSEY: PALISADES MEDICAL CENTER (S, 202 beds) 7600 River Road, North Bergen, NJ Zip 07047–6217; tel. 201/854–5000; Bruce J. Markowitz, President and Chief Executive Officer
Web address: www.palisadesmedical.org

NEW YORK: BROOKLYN HOSPITAL CENTER (S, 653 beds) 121 DeKalb Avenue, Brooklyn, NY Zip 11201–5493; tel. 718/250–8000; Samuel Lehrfeld, President and Chief Executive Officer
Web address: www.tbh.org

GRACIE SQUARE HOSPITAL (S, 157 beds) 420 East 76th Street, New York, NY Zip 10021–3104; tel. 212/988–4400; Frank Bruno, Chief Executive Officer
Web address: www.nygsh.org

HOSPITAL FOR SPECIAL SURGERY (S, 142 beds) 535 East 70th Street, New York, NY Zip 10021–4898; tel. 212/606–1000; John R. Reynolds, President and Chief Executive Officer
Web address: www.hss.edu

NEW YORK COMMUNITY HOSPITAL (S, 125 beds) 2525 Kings Highway, Brooklyn, NY Zip 11229–1798, Mailing Address: 2513 Avenue O, Zip 11210; tel. 718/692–5300; Lin H. Mo, President and Chief Executive Officer
Web address: www.nycommunityhospital.com

NEW YORK HOSPITAL MEDICAL CENTER OF QUEENS (S, 439 beds) 56–45 Main Street, Flushing, NY Zip 11355–5000; tel. 718/670–1231; Stephen S. Mills, President and Chief Executive Officer
Web address: www.nyhq.org

NEW YORK METHODIST HOSPITAL (S, 570 beds) 506 Sixth Street, Brooklyn, NY Zip 11215–3645; tel. 718/780–3000; Mark J. Mundy, President and Chief Executive Officer
Web address: www.nym.org

NEW YORK UNITED HOSPITAL MEDICAL CENTER (S, 203 beds) 406 Boston Post Road, Port Chester, NY Zip 10573–7300; tel. 914/934–3000; Philip G. Dionne, President and Chief Executive Officer
Web address: www.uhmc.com

NEW YORK WESTCHESTER SQUARE MEDICAL CENTER (S, 165 beds) 2475 St. Raymond Avenue, Bronx, NY Zip 10461–3198; tel. 718/430–7300; Alan Kopman, President and Chief Executive Officer
Web address: www.nywsmc.org

NEW YORK–PRESBYTERIAN HOSPITAL (O, 2095 beds) 525 East 68th Street, New York, NY Zip 10021–4885; tel. 212/746–5454; Herbert Pardes, M.D., President and Chief Executive Officer
Web address: www.nyp.org

WYCKOFF HEIGHTS MEDICAL CENTER (S, 305 beds) 374 Stockholm Street, Brooklyn, NY Zip 11237–4099; tel. 718/963–7272; Dominick J. Gio, President and Chief Executive Officer
Web address: www.wyckoffhospital.org

Owned, leased, sponsored:	11 hospitals	5056 beds
Contract–managed:	0 hospitals	0 beds
Totals:	11 hospitals	5056 beds

0009: NEW YORK STATE OFFICE OF MENTAL HEALTH (NP)
44 Holland Avenue, Albany, NY Zip 12229–3411; tel. 518/474–4403; Sharon E. Carpinello, R.N., Ph.D., Commissioner
(Independent Hospital System)

BRONX CHILDREN'S PSYCHIATRIC CENTER (O, 75 beds) 1000 Waters Place, Bronx, NY Zip 10461–2799; tel. 718/239–3600; Mark D. Bienstock, Executive Director

BRONX PSYCHIATRIC CENTER (O, 450 beds) 1500 Waters Place, Bronx, NY Zip 10461–2796; tel. 718/931–0600; LeRoy Carmichael, Executive Director
Web address: www.omh.state.ny.us

BUFFALO PSYCHIATRIC CENTER (O, 240 beds) 400 Forest Avenue, Buffalo, NY Zip 14213–1298; tel. 716/885–2261; Thomas Dodson, Executive Director
Web address: www.omh.state.ny.us

CAPITAL DISTRICT PSYCHIATRIC CENTER (O, 200 beds) 75 New Scotland Avenue, Albany, NY Zip 12208–3474; tel. 518/447–9611; Lou Campbell, Acting Executive Director

CENTRAL NEW YORK PSYCHIATRIC CENTER (O, 206 beds) Marcy, NY Mailing Address: P.O. Box 300, Zip 13403–0300; tel. 315/736–8271; Hal E. Smith, Executive Director

CREEDMOOR PSYCHIATRIC CENTER (O, 456 beds) Jamaica, NY Mailing Address: 80–45 Winchester Boulevard, Queens Village, Zip 11427–2199; tel. 718/264–3600; Charlotte Seltzer, Executive Director
Web address: www.omh.state.ny.us

ELMIRA PSYCHIATRIC CENTER (O, 93 beds) 100 Washington Street, Elmira, NY Zip 14901–2898; tel. 607/737–4739; William Benedict, Executive Director
Web address: www.omh.state.ny.us/omhweb/facilities/elpc/facility.htm

For explanation of codes following names, see page B2.
★ Indicates Type III membership in the American Hospital Association.

GREATER BINGHAMTON HEALTH CENTER (O, 154 beds) 425 Robinson Street, Binghamton, NY Zip 13901–4198; tel. 607/724–1391; Margaret R. Dugan, Executive Director

HUDSON RIVER PSYCHIATRIC CENTER (O, 460 beds) 10 Ross Circle, Poughkeepsie, NY Zip 12601–1078; tel. 845/452–8000; Jean L. Wolfersteig, Acting Executive Director
Web address: www.omh.state.ny.us

KINGSBORO PSYCHIATRIC CENTER (O, 290 beds) 681 Clarkson Avenue, Brooklyn, NY Zip 11203–2199; tel. 718/221–7395; Martin Darcy, Acting Executive Director
Web address: www.omh.state.ny.us/omhweb/facilities/kbpc/facility/htm

MANHATTAN PSYCHIATRIC CENTER–WARD'S ISLAND (O, 745 beds) 600 East 125th Street, New York, NY Zip 10035–9998; tel. 212/369–0500; Eileen Consilvio, R.N., MS, Executive Director

MID–HUDSON FORENSIC PSYCHIATRIC CENTER (O, 268 beds) Route 17M, New Hampton, NY Zip 10958, Mailing Address: P.O. Box 158, Zip 10958–0158; tel. 845/374–3171; Howard Holanchock, Executive Director
Web address: www.omh.state.ny.us

MIDDLETOWN PSYCHIATRIC CENTER (O, 112 beds) 122 Dorothea Dix Drive, Middletown, NY Zip 10940–6198; tel. 845/342–5511; James H. Bopp, Executive Director
Web address: www.omh.state.ny.us/omhweb/facilities/mipc/facility.htm

MOHAWK VALLEY PSYCHIATRIC CENTER (O, 614 beds) 1400 Noyes Street, Utica, NY Zip 13502–3803; tel. 315/797–6800; Maureen L. Ruben, Executive Director

NEW YORK STATE PSYCHIATRIC INSTITUTE (O, 58 beds) 1051 Riverside Drive, New York, NY Zip 10032–2695; tel. 212/543–5000; Jeffrey A. Lieberman, M.D., Executive Director
Web address: www.nyspi.org

PILGRIM PSYCHIATRIC CENTER (O, 744 beds) 998 Crooked Hill Road, Brentwood, NY Zip 11717–1087; tel. 631/761–3500; Dean R. Weinstock, R.N., Acting Executive Director

QUEENS CHILDREN'S PSYCHIATRIC CENTER (O, 84 beds) 74–03 Commonwealth Boulevard, Jamaica, NY Zip 11426–1890; tel. 718/264–4506; Keith Little, Acting Executive Director
Web address: www.omh.state.ny.us

RICHARD H. HUTCHINGS PSYCHIATRIC CENTER (O, 131 beds) 620 Madison Street, Syracuse, NY Zip 13210–2319; tel. 315/473–4980; Colleen Zackoski, Executive Director
Web address: www.omh.state.ny.us

ROCHESTER PSYCHIATRIC CENTER (O, 180 beds) 1111 Elmwood Avenue, Rochester, NY Zip 14620–3005; tel. 585/473–3230; Michael P. Zuber, Ph.D., Executive Director
Web address: www.omh.state.ny.us/omhweb/facilities/ropc/facility.htm

ROCKLAND CHILDREN'S PSYCHIATRIC CENTER (O, 54 beds) 599 Convent Road, Orangeburg, NY Zip 10962; tel. 845/359–7400; Barry Kutok, Interim Executive Director

ROCKLAND PSYCHIATRIC CENTER (O, 525 beds) 140 Old Orangeburg Road, Orangeburg, NY Zip 10962–0071; tel. 845/359–1000; James H. Bopp, Executive Director

SAGAMORE CHILDREN'S PSYCHIATRIC CENTER (O, 69 beds) 197 Half Hollow Road, Huntington Station, NY Zip 11746–5861; tel. 631/673–7700; Dennis Dubey, Ph.D., Executive Director
Web address: www.omh.state.ny.us/ombweb/facilities/scpc/facility.htm

SOUTH BEACH PSYCHIATRIC CENTER (O, 325 beds) 777 Seaview Avenue, Staten Island, NY Zip 10305–3499; tel. 718/667–2300; William Henri, Executive Director
Web address: www.omh.state.ny.us

ST. LAWRENCE PSYCHIATRIC CENTER (O, 114 beds) 1 Chimney Point Drive, Ogdensburg, NY Zip 13669–2291; tel. 315/541–2001; Jim Spooner, Executive Director

WESTERN NEW YORK CHILDREN'S PSYCHIATRIC CENTER (O, 46 beds) 1010 East and West Road, Buffalo, NY Zip 14224–3698; tel. 716/674–9730; David Heffler, Ph.D., Executive Director
Web address: www.omh.state.ny.us

Owned, leased, sponsored:	25 hospitals	6693 beds
Contract–managed:	0 hospitals	0 beds
Totals:	25 hospitals	6693 beds

★**3115: NORTH BROWARD HOSPITAL DISTRICT** (NP)
303 S.E. 17th Street, Fort Lauderdale, FL Zip 33316–2510; tel. 954/355–5100; G. Wil Trower, President and Chief Executive Officer
(Centralized Health System)

FLORIDA: BROWARD GENERAL MEDICAL CENTER (O, 567 beds) 1600 South Andrews Avenue, Fort Lauderdale, FL Zip 33316–2510; tel. 954/355–4400; Joseph F. Scott, Chief Executive Officer
Web address: www.nbhd.org

CORAL SPRINGS MEDICAL CENTER (O, 200 beds) 3000 Coral Hills Drive, Coral Springs, FL Zip 33065; tel. 954/344–3000; Deborah Mulvihill, Chief Executive Officer
Web address: www.nbhd.org

IMPERIAL POINT MEDICAL CENTER (O, 180 beds) 6401 North Federal Highway, Fort Lauderdale, FL Zip 33308–1495; tel. 954/776–8500; Dorothy J. Mancini, R.N., Chief Executive Officer
Web address: www.nbhd.org

NORTH BROWARD MEDICAL CENTER (O, 337 beds) 201 Sample Road, Pompano Beach, FL Zip 33064–3502; tel. 954/941–8300; Pauline Grant, Chief Executive Officer
Web address: www.nbhd.org

Owned, leased, sponsored:	4 hospitals	1284 beds
Contract–managed:	0 hospitals	0 beds
Totals:	4 hospitals	1284 beds

★**0221: NORTH CAROLINA BAPTIST HOSPITAL** (NP)
Medical Center Boulevard, Winston–Salem, NC Zip 27157; tel. 336/716–2011; Len B. Preslar Jr, President and Chief Executive Officer
(Moderately Centralized Health System)

NORTH CAROLINA: HOOTS MEMORIAL HOSPITAL (L, 22 beds) 624 West Main Street, Yadkinville, NC Zip 27055–7804, Mailing Address: P.O. Box 68, Zip 27055–0068; tel. 336/679–2041; Lance C. Labine, President
Web address: www.bgsm.edu/hoots/

NORTH CAROLINA BAPTIST HOSPITAL (WAKE FOREST UNIVERSITY BAPTIST MEDICAL CENTER) (O, 937 beds) Medical Center Boulevard, Winston–Salem, NC Zip 27157–0001; tel. 336/716–2011; Len B. Preslar Jr, President and Chief Executive Officer
Web address: www.wfubmc.edu

STOKES–REYNOLDS MEMORIAL HOSPITAL (L, 65 beds) 1570 Highway 8 and 89 North, Danbury, NC Zip 27016, Mailing Address: P.O. Box 10, Zip 27016–0010; tel. 336/593–2831; Lance C. Labine, President
Web address: www.wfubmc.edu/stokes

Owned, leased, sponsored:	3 hospitals	1024 beds
Contract–managed:	0 hospitals	0 beds
Totals:	3 hospitals	1024 beds

★**0032: NORTH MISSISSIPPI HEALTH SERVICES, INC.** (NP)
830 South Gloster Street, Tupelo, MS Zip 38801–4996; tel. 662/377–3136; John R. Heer, President and Chief Executive Officer
(Centralized Physician/Insurance Health System)

ALABAMA: NORTH MISSISSIPPI MEDICAL CENTER–HAMILTON (O, 111 beds) 1256 Military Street South, Hamilton, AL Zip 35570–5001; tel. 205/921–6200; Donald J. Jones, Administrator
Web address: www.nmhs.net

MISSISSIPPI: NORTH MISSISSIPPI MEDICAL CENTER – TUPELO (O, 757 beds) 830 South Gloster Street, Tupelo, MS Zip 38801–4934; tel. 662/377–3000; John R. Heer, President and Chief Executive Officer
Web address: www.nmhs.net

NORTH MISSISSIPPI MEDICAL CENTER–EUPORA (O, 74 beds) 500 Highway 9 South, Eupora, MS Zip 39744–2215; tel. 662/258–6221; K. Michael Bailey, Ph.D., Administrator

NORTH MISSISSIPPI MEDICAL CENTER–IUKA (O, 48 beds) 1777 Curtis Drive, Iuka, MS Zip 38852–1001, Mailing Address: P.O. Box 860, Zip 38852–0860; tel. 662/423–6051; James R. Carter Jr, Administrator
Web address: www.nmhs.net

For explanation of codes following names, see page B2.
★ Indicates Type III membership in the American Hospital Association.

NORTH MISSISSIPPI MEDICAL CENTER–PONTOTOC HOSPITAL AND NURSING HOME (L, 73 beds) 176 South Main Street, Pontotoc, MS Zip 38863–3311, Mailing Address: P.O. Box 790, Zip 38863–0790; tel. 662/488–7640; Fred B. Hood, Administrator
Web address: www.nmhs.net

NORTH MISSISSIPPI MEDICAL CENTER–WEST POINT (O, 60 beds) 835 Medical Center Drive, West Point, MS Zip 39773–9320; tel. 662/495–2300; Timothy H. Moore, Administrator

Owned, leased, sponsored:	6 hospitals	1123 beds
Contract–managed:	0 hospitals	0 beds
Totals:	6 hospitals	1123 beds

★**0062: NORTH SHORE–LIJ HEALTH SYSTEM** (NP)
150 Community Drive, Great Neck, NY Zip 11021; tel. 516/465–8100; Michael J. Dowling, President and Chief Executive Officer
(Centralized Health System)

NEW YORK: FRANKLIN HOSPITAL MEDICAL CENTER (O, 370 beds) 900 Franklin Avenue, Valley Stream, NY Zip 11580–2190; tel. 516/256–6000; Joseph Lamantia, Executive Director
Web address: www.fhmc.org

GLEN COVE HOSPITAL (O, 210 beds) 101 St. Andrews Lane, Glen Cove, NY Zip 11542–2254; tel. 516/674–7300; Dennis Connors, Executive Director
Web address: www.northshorelij.com

HUNTINGTON HOSPITAL (S, 259 beds) 270 Park Avenue, Huntington, NY Zip 11743–2799; tel. 631/351–2200; J. Ronald Gaudreault, President and Chief Executive Officer
Web address: www.hunthosp.org

LONG ISLAND JEWISH MEDICAL CENTER (O, 795 beds) 270–05 76th Avenue, New Hyde Park, NY Zip 11040–1496; tel. 718/470–7000; Dennis Dowling, Executive Director
Web address: www.lij.edu

NORTH SHORE UNIVERSITY HOSPITAL (O, 788 beds) 300 Community Drive, Manhasset, NY Zip 11030–3876; tel. 516/562–0100; Dennis Dowling, Executive Director
Web address: www.northshorelij.com

NORTH SHORE UNIVERSITY HOSPITAL AT PLAINVIEW (O, 211 beds) 888 Old Country Road, Plainview, NY Zip 11803–4978; tel. 516/719–3000; Deborah Tascone, R.N., MS, Executive Director
Web address: www.northshorelij.com

NORTH SHORE UNIVERSITY HOSPITAL AT SYOSSET (O, 64 beds) 221 Jericho Turnpike, Syosset, NY Zip 11791–4567; tel. 516/496–6400; Deborah Tascone, R.N., MS, Executive Director
Web address: www.northshorelij.com

NORTH SHORE UNIVERSITY HOSPITAL–FOREST HILLS (O, 223 beds) Flushing, NY Mailing Address: 102–01 66th Road, Zip 11375–2029; tel. 718/830–4000; Robert T. Hettenbach, Executive Director
Web address: www.northshorelij.com

SOUTHSIDE HOSPITAL (S, 371 beds) 301 East Main Street, Bay Shore, NY Zip 11706–8458; tel. 631/968–3000; Michael L. Nolan, Prseident and Chief Executive Officer
Web address: www.southsidehospital.org

STATEN ISLAND UNIVERSITY HOSPITAL (S, 686 beds) 475 Seaview Avenue, Staten Island, NY Zip 10305–9998; tel. 718/226–9000; Anthony C. Ferreri, President and Chief Executive Officer
Web address: www.siuh.edu

Owned, leased, sponsored:	10 hospitals	3977 beds
Contract–managed:	0 hospitals	0 beds
Totals:	10 hospitals	3977 beds

★**2075: NORTHBAY HEALTHCARE SYSTEM** (NP)
1200 B. Gale Wilson Boulevard, Fairfield, CA Zip 94533–3587; tel. 707/429–7809; Gary J. Passama, President and Chief Executive Officer
(Centralized Health System)

CALIFORNIA: NORTHBAY MEDICAL CENTER (O, 113 beds) 1200 B. Gale Wilson Boulevard, Fairfield, CA Zip 94533–3587; tel. 707/429–3600; Deborah Sugiyama, President
Web address: www.northbay.org

NORTHBAY VACAVALLEY HOSPITAL (O, 49 beds) 1000 Nut Tree Road, Vacaville, CA Zip 95687–4100; tel. 707/446–4000; Deborah Sugiyama, President
Web address: www.northbay.org

Owned, leased, sponsored:	2 hospitals	162 beds
Contract–managed:	0 hospitals	0 beds
Totals:	2 hospitals	162 beds

★**0281: NORTHERN ARIZONA HEALTHCARE** (NP)
1200 North Beaver Street, Flagstaff, AZ Zip 86001; tel. 928/773–2001; James Puffenberger, President and Chief Executive Officer
(Moderately Centralized Health System)

ARIZONA: FLAGSTAFF MEDICAL CENTER (O, 267 beds) 1200 North Beaver Street, Flagstaff, AZ Zip 86001–3198; tel. 928/779–3366; James Puffenberger, Interim Chief Executive Officer
Web address: www.flagstaffmedicalcenter.com

VERDE VALLEY MEDICAL CENTER (O, 99 beds) 269 South Candy Lane, Cottonwood, AZ Zip 86326–4170; tel. 928/634–2251; James J. Sinek, President and Senior Executive Officer
Web address: www.nahealth.com

Owned, leased, sponsored:	2 hospitals	366 beds
Contract–managed:	0 hospitals	0 beds
Totals:	2 hospitals	366 beds

★**2285: NORTON HEALTHCARE** (NP)
234 East Gray Street, Suite 225, Louisville, KY Zip 40202, Mailing Address: P.O. Box 35070, Zip 40232–5070; tel. 502/629–8000; Stephen A. Williams, President
(Centralized Health System)

KENTUCKY: NORTON AUDUBON HOSPITAL (O, 276 beds) One Audubon Plaza Drive, Louisville, KY Zip 40217–1397, Mailing Address: P.O. Box 17550, Zip 40217–0550; tel. 502/636–7111; Thomas D. Kmetz, President
Web address: www.nortonhealthcare.org

NORTON HOSPITAL (O, 677 beds) 200 East Chestnut Street, Louisville, KY Zip 40202–1800, Mailing Address: P.O. Box 35070, Zip 40232–5070; tel. 502/629–8000; Kevin S. Wardell, Chief Administrative Officer
Web address: www.nortonhealthcare.org

NORTON SOUTHWEST HOSPITAL (O, 126 beds) 9820 Third Street Road, Louisville, KY Zip 40272–9984; tel. 502/933–8100; Teresa Parker, Administrator
Web address: www.nortonhealthcare.org

NORTON SUBURBAN HOSPITAL (O, 311 beds) 4001 Dutchmans Lane, Louisville, KY Zip 40207–4799; tel. 502/893–1000; John D. Harryman, President and Administrator
Web address: www.nortonhealthcare.com

Owned, leased, sponsored:	4 hospitals	1390 beds
Contract–managed:	0 hospitals	0 beds
Totals:	4 hospitals	1390 beds

★**0139: NOVANT HEALTH** (NP)
2085 Frontis Plaza Boulevard, Winston–Salem, NC Zip 27103–3090; tel. 336/718–2023; Paul M. Wiles, President and Chief Executive Officer
(Centralized Health System)

NORTH CAROLINA: FORSYTH MEDICAL CENTER (O, 776 beds) 3333 Silas Creek Parkway, Winston–Salem, NC Zip 27103–3090; tel. 336/718–5000; Gregory J. Beier, President
Web address: www.novanthealth.org

MEDICAL PARK HOSPITAL (O, 40 beds) 1950 South Hawthorne Road, Winston–Salem, NC Zip 27103–3993, Mailing Address: P.O. Box 24728, Zip 27114–4728; tel. 336/718–0600; Timothy S. Shelton, Administrator
Web address: www.novanthealth.org

PRESBYTERIAN HOSPITAL (O, 547 beds) 200 Hawthorne Lane, Charlotte, NC Zip 28204–2528, Mailing Address: P.O. Box 33549, Zip 28233–3549; tel. 704/384–4000; Carl Armato, President
Web address: www.presbyterian.org

For explanation of codes following names, see page B2.
★ Indicates Type III membership in the American Hospital Association.

PRESBYTERIAN HOSPITAL HUNTERSVILLE (O, 50 beds) 10030 Gilead Road, Huntersville, NC Zip 28078, Mailing Address: P.O. Box 3508, Zip 28070–3508; tel. 704/316–4000; Denise B. Mihal, R.N., Chief Executive Officer

PRESBYTERIAN HOSPITAL–MATTHEWS (O, 94 beds) 1500 Matthews Township Parkway, Matthews, NC Zip 28105–4656, Mailing Address: P.O. Box 3310, Zip 28106–3310; tel. 704/384–6500; Paula Vincent, Vice President Community Acute Services
Web address: www.presbyterian.org

PRESBYTERIAN–ORTHOPAEDIC HOSPITAL (O, 76 beds) 1901 Randolph Road, Charlotte, NC Zip 28207–1195; tel. 704/375–6792; Tanya Blackmon, Executive Director Orthopaedic Services
Web address: www.novanthealth.org

THOMASVILLE MEDICAL CENTER (O, 81 beds) 207 Old Lexington Road, Thomasville, NC Zip 27360–3428, Mailing Address: P.O. Box 789, Zip 27361–0789; tel. 336/472–2000; Gabrielle K. Causby, President
Web address: www.thomasvillemedicalcenter.org

Owned, leased, sponsored:	7 hospitals	1664 beds
Contract–managed:	0 hospitals	0 beds
Totals:	7 hospitals	1664 beds

★1165: OAKWOOD HEALTHCARE, INC. (NP)
One Parklane Boulevard, Suite 1000E, Dearborn, MI Zip 48126; tel. 313/253–6050; Gerald D. Fitzgerald, President and Chief Executive Officer
(Centralized Health System)

MICHIGAN: OAKWOOD ANNAPOLIS HOSPITAL (O, 196 beds) 33155 Annapolis Road, Wayne, MI Zip 48184–2493; tel. 734/467–4000; Thomas Kochis, Division President
Web address: www.oakwood.org

OAKWOOD HERITAGE HOSPITAL (O, 233 beds) 10000 Telegraph Road, Taylor, MI Zip 48180–3349; tel. 313/295–5000; Richard Hillbom, Division President
Web address: www.oakwood.org

OAKWOOD HOSPITAL AND MEDICAL CENTER–DEARBORN (O, 619 beds) 18101 Oakwood Boulevard, Dearborn, MI Zip 48124–4093, Mailing Address: P.O. Box 2500, Zip 48123–2500; tel. 313/593–7000; Mel Pyne, Division President
Web address: www.oakwood.org

OAKWOOD SOUTHSHORE MEDICAL CENTER (O, 148 beds) 5450 Fort Street, Trenton, MI Zip 48183–4625; tel. 734/671–3800; Edith M. Hughes, Division President
Web address: www.oakwood.org

Owned, leased, sponsored:	4 hospitals	1196 beds
Contract–managed:	0 hospitals	0 beds
Totals:	4 hospitals	1196 beds

0251: OHIO STATE UNIVERSITY HEALTH SYSTEM (NP)
370 West 10th Avenue, Columbus, OH Zip 43210–1240; tel. 614/293–8000; Peter E. Geier, Chief Executive Officer
(Moderately Centralized Health System)

OHIO: OHIO STATE UNIVERSITY HOSPITALS EAST (O, 175 beds) 1492 East Broad Street, Columbus, OH Zip 43205–1546; tel. 614/257–3000; Karen Mlawsky, Executive Director
Web address: www.medicalcenter.osu.edu

OHIO STATE UNIVERSITY JAMES CANCER HOSPITAL (O, 156 beds) 300 West Tenth Avenue, Columbus, OH Zip 43210–1240; tel. 614/293–5485; David E. Schuller, M.D., Chief Executive Officer
Web address: www.jamesline.com

OHIO STATE UNIVERSITY MEDICAL CENTER (O, 654 beds) 410 West 10th Avenue, Columbus, OH Zip 43210–1240; tel. 614/293–8000; Peter E. Geier, Chief Executive Officer
Web address: www.osumedcenter.edu

Owned, leased, sponsored:	3 hospitals	985 beds
Contract–managed:	0 hospitals	0 beds
Totals:	3 hospitals	985 beds

★3315: OHIO VALLEY HEALTH SERVICES AND EDUCATION CORPORATION (NP)
2000 Eoff Street, Wheeling, WV Zip 26003; tel. 304/234–8383; Brian K. Felici, President and Chief Executive Officer
(Moderately Centralized Health System)

EAST OHIO REGIONAL HOSPITAL (O, 172 beds) 90 North Fourth Street, Martins Ferry, OH Zip 43935–1648; tel. 740/633–1100; Brian K. Felici, President and Chief Executive Officer
Web address: www.eastohioregionalhospital.com

WEST VIRGINIA: OHIO VALLEY MEDICAL CENTER (O, 171 beds) 2000 Eoff Street, Wheeling, WV Zip 26003–3870; tel. 304/234–0123; Brian K. Felici, President and Chief Executive Officer
Web address: www.ohiovalleymedicalcenter.com

Owned, leased, sponsored:	2 hospitals	343 beds
Contract–managed:	0 hospitals	0 beds
Totals:	2 hospitals	343 beds

★0162: OHIOHEALTH (NP)
1087 Dennison Avenue, Columbus, OH Zip 43201; tel. 614/544–5430; David P. Blom, President and Chief Executive Officer
(Moderately Centralized Health System)

OHIO: DOCTORS HOSPITAL (O, 209 beds) 5100 West Broad Street, Columbus, OH Zip 43228; tel. 614/544–1000; Kreg Gruber, President
Web address: www.ohiohealth.com

DOCTORS HOSPITAL NELSONVILLE (O, 70 beds) 1950 Mount Saint Mary Drive, Nelsonville, OH Zip 45764–1193; tel. 740/753–1931; Steve Swart, Administrator
Web address: www.ohiohealth.com

GRADY MEMORIAL HOSPITAL (O, 75 beds) 561 West Central Avenue, Delaware, OH Zip 43015–1485; tel. 740/369–8711; Everett P. Weber Jr, President and Chief Executive Officer
Web address: www.gradyhospital.com

GRANT MEDICAL CENTER (O, 385 beds) 111 South Grant Avenue, Columbus, OH Zip 43215–1898; tel. 614/566–9000; Robert Falcone, M.D., President
Web address: www.ohiohealth.com

HARDIN MEMORIAL HOSPITAL (O, 25 beds) 921 East Franklin Street, Kenton, OH Zip 43326–2099, Mailing Address: P.O. Box 710, Zip 43326–0710; tel. 419/673–0761; Mark R. Seckinger, Administrator and Chief Executive Officer
Web address: www.hardinmemorial.org

MARION GENERAL HOSPITAL (O, 131 beds) 1000 McKinley Park Drive, Marion, OH Zip 43302–6397; tel. 740/383–8400; Ronald J. Bachman, President and Chief Executive Officer
Web address: www.mariongeneral.com

MORROW COUNTY HOSPITAL (C, 53 beds) 651 West Marion Road, Mount Gilead, OH Zip 43338–1096; tel. 419/946–5015; Diana D. Fisher, President and Chief Executive Officer
Web address: www.morrowcountyhospital.com

RIVERSIDE METHODIST HOSPITAL (O, 813 beds) 3535 Olentangy River Road, Columbus, OH Zip 43214–3998; tel. 614/566–5000; Bruce P. Hagen, President
Web address: www.ohiohealth.com

SOUTHERN OHIO MEDICAL CENTER (O, 222 beds) 1805 27th Street, Portsmouth, OH Zip 45662–2400; tel. 740/354–5000; Randal M. Arnett, President and Chief Executive Officer
Web address: www.somc.org

Owned, leased, sponsored:	8 hospitals	1930 beds
Contract–managed:	1 hospital	53 beds
Totals:	9 hospitals	1983 beds

0018: OKLAHOMA STATE DEPARTMENT OF MENTAL HEALTH AND SUBSTANCE ABUSE SERVICES (NP)
1200 N.E. 13th Street, Oklahoma City, OK Zip 73117, Mailing Address: P.O. Box 53277, Zip 73152–3277; tel. 405/522–3878; Terry Cline, Ph.D., Commissioner
(Independent Hospital System)

For explanation of codes following names, see page B2.
★ Indicates Type III membership in the American Hospital Association.

Section B

OKLAHOMA: GRIFFIN MEMORIAL HOSPITAL (O, 150 beds) 900 East Main Street, Norman, OK Zip 73071–5305, Mailing Address: P.O. Box 151, Zip 73070–0151; tel. 405/321–4880; Don Bowen, Executive Director
Web address: www.odmhsas.org

NORTHWESTERN CENTER FOR BEHAVIORAL HEALTH (O, 84 beds) 1222 10th Street, Suite 211, Woodward, OK Zip 73801; tel. 580/571–3233; Steve Norwood, Executive Director

OKLAHOMA FORENSIC CENTER (O, 221 beds) Vinita, OK Mailing Address: P.O. Box 69, Zip 74301–0069; tel. 918/256–7841; William T. Burkett, Chief Executive Officer

Owned, leased, sponsored:	3 hospitals	455 beds
Contract–managed:	0 hospitals	0 beds
Totals:	3 hospitals	455 beds

3355: ORLANDO REGIONAL HEALTHCARE (NP)
1414 Kuhl Avenue, Orlando, FL Zip 32806–2093; tel. 407/841–5111; John Hillenmeyer, President and Chief Executive Officer
(Moderately Centralized Health System)

FLORIDA: ORLANDO REGIONAL MEDICAL CENTER (O, 1354 beds) 1414 Kuhl Avenue, Orlando, FL Zip 32806–2093; tel. 407/841–5111; Sherrie Sitarik, Executive Vice President
Web address: www.orhs.org

ORLANDO REGIONAL SOUTH SEMINOLE HOSPITAL (O, 206 beds) 555 West State Road 434, Longwood, FL Zip 32750–4999; tel. 407/767–1200; Stephen M. Glazier, Executive Director

SOUTH LAKE HOSPITAL (O, 80 beds) 1099 Citrus Tower Boulevard, Clermont, FL Zip 34711–2787; tel. 352/394–4071; Leslie Longacre, Executive Director and Chief Executive Officer
Web address: www.southlakehospital.com

ST. CLOUD HOSPITAL (O, 68 beds) 2906 17th Street, Saint Cloud, FL Zip 34769–6099; tel. 407/892–2135; Mark Aanonson, Executive Director

Owned, leased, sponsored:	4 hospitals	1708 beds
Contract–managed:	0 hospitals	0 beds
Totals:	4 hospitals	1708 beds

★5335: OSF HEALTHCARE SYSTEM (CC)
800 N.E. Glen Oak Avenue, Peoria, IL Zip 61603–3200; tel. 309/655–2850; James M. Moore, Chief Executive Officer
(Decentralized Health System)

ILLINOIS: OSF SAINT ANTHONY MEDICAL CENTER (O, 238 beds) 5666 East State Street, Rockford, IL Zip 61108–2472; tel. 815/226–2000; David A. Schertz, Administrator
Web address: www.osfhealthcare.org

OSF SAINT FRANCIS MEDICAL CENTER (O, 523 beds) 530 N.E. Glen Oak Avenue, Peoria, IL Zip 61637–0001; tel. 309/655–2000; Keith E. Steffen, Administrator and Chief Executive Officer
Web address: www.osfsaintfrancis.org

OSF SAINT JAMES – JOHN W. ALBRECHT MEDICAL CENTER (O, 42 beds) 2500 West Reynolds, Pontiac, IL Zip 61764–2194; tel. 815/842–2828; David T. Ochs, Administrator
Web address: www.osfsaintjames.org

OSF ST. JOSEPH MEDICAL CENTER (O, 157 beds) 2200 East Washington Street, Bloomington, IL Zip 61701–4323; tel. 309/662–3311; Kenneth J. Natzke, Administrator
Web address: www.osfhealthcare.org

OSF ST. MARY MEDICAL CENTER (O, 99 beds) 3333 North Seminary Street, Galesburg, IL Zip 61401–1299; tel. 309/344–3161; Richard S. Kowalski, Administrator and Chief Executive Officer
Web address: www.osfhealthcare.org

MICHIGAN: OSF ST. FRANCIS HOSPITAL (O, 64 beds) 3401 Ludington Street, Escanaba, MI Zip 49829–1377; tel. 906/786–3311; Peter G. Jennings, Chief Executive Officer
Web address: www.osfstfrancis.org

Owned, leased, sponsored:	6 hospitals	1123 beds
Contract–managed:	0 hospitals	0 beds
Totals:	6 hospitals	1123 beds

0435: PACIFIC HEALTH CORPORATION (IO)
14642 Newport Avenue, Suite 388, Tustin, CA Zip 92780; tel. 714/669–2085; James W. Young, President and Chief Executive Officer

CALIFORNIA: ANAHEIM GENERAL HOSPITAL (O, 143 beds) 3350 West Ball Road, Anaheim, CA Zip 92804–3799; tel. 714/827–6700; Josh Luke, Chief Executive Officer
Web address: www.anaheimgeneral.com

BELLFLOWER MEDICAL CENTER (O, 113 beds) 9542 East Artesia Boulevard, Bellflower, CA Zip 90706–6511; tel. 562/925–8355; James Linhares, Chief Executive Officer

LOS ANGELES METROPOLITAN MEDICAL CENTER (O, 213 beds) 2231 South Western Avenue, Los Angeles, CA Zip 90018–1302; tel. 323/730–7342; John V. Fenton, Chief Executive Officer

TUSTIN HOSPITAL AND MEDICAL CENTER (O, 64 beds) 14662 Newport Avenue, Tustin, CA Zip 92680–6064; tel. 714/838–9600; R. Michael Hartman, Chief Executive Officer
Web address: www.tustinhospital.com

Owned, leased, sponsored:	4 hospitals	533 beds
Contract–managed:	0 hospitals	0 beds
Totals:	4 hospitals	533 beds

★4155: PALMETTO HEALTH ALLIANCE (CO)
1301 Taylor Street, Suite 9–A, Columbia, SC Zip 29201, Mailing Address: P.O. Box 2266, Zip 29202–2266; tel. 803/296–2100; Charles D. Beaman Jr, President
(Moderately Centralized Health System)

SOUTH CAROLINA: PALMETTO HEALTH BAPTIST EASLEY (O, 79 beds) 200 Fleetwood Drive, Easley, SC Zip 29640–2076, Mailing Address: P.O. Box 2129, Zip 29641–2129; tel. 864/442–7200; Roddey E. Gettys III, Executive Vice President and Chief Operating Officer
Web address: www.palmettohealth.org

PALMETTO HEALTH BAPTIST/COLUMBIA (O, 409 beds) Taylor at Marion Street, Columbia, SC Zip 29220–0001; tel. 803/296–5010; James M. Bridges, Executive Vice President and Chief Operating Officer
Web address: www.palmettohealth.org

PALMETTO HEALTH RICHLAND (O, 633 beds) Five Richland Medical Park Drive, Columbia, SC Zip 29203–6897, Mailing Address: P.O. Box 2266, Zip 29203–2266; tel. 803/434–7000; James E. Lathren, Executive Vice President and Chief Operating Officer
Web address: www.palmettohealth.org

Owned, leased, sponsored:	3 hospitals	1121 beds
Contract–managed:	0 hospitals	0 beds
Totals:	3 hospitals	1121 beds

★7555: PALOMAR POMERADO HEALTH (NP)
15255 Innovation Drive, Suite 204, San Diego, CA Zip 92128–3410; tel. 858/675–5100; Michael H. Covert, FACHE, Chief Executive Officer
(Moderately Centralized Health System)

CALIFORNIA: PALOMAR MEDICAL CENTER (O, 315 beds) 555 East Valley Parkway, Escondido, CA Zip 92025–3084; tel. 760/739–3000; Gerald E. Bracht, Chief Administrative Officer
Web address: www.pph.org

POMERADO HOSPITAL (O, 188 beds) 15615 Pomerado Road, Poway, CA Zip 92064–2460; tel. 858/485–6511; James T. Flinn, Chief Administrative Officer
Web address: www.pphs.org

Owned, leased, sponsored:	2 hospitals	503 beds
Contract–managed:	0 hospitals	0 beds
Totals:	2 hospitals	503 beds

For explanation of codes following names, see page B2.
★ Indicates Type III membership in the American Hospital Association.

Section B

★1985: PARK NICOLLET HEALTH SERVICES (NP)
6500 Excelsior Boulevard, Saint Louis Park, MN Zip 55426–4702; tel. 952/993–5000; David K. Wessner, President and Chief Executive Officer
(Moderately Centralized Health System)

MINNESOTA: GLENCOE REGIONAL HEALTH SERVICES (C, 135 beds) 1805 Hennepin Avenue North, Glencoe, MN Zip 55336–1416; tel. 320/864–3121; Jon D. Braband, President and Chief Executive Officer
Web address: www.grhsonline.com

METHODIST HOSPITAL (O, 382 beds) 6500 Excelsior Boulevard, Saint Louis Park, MN Zip 55426–4702; tel. 952/993–5000; David K. Wessner, President and Chief Executive Officer
Web address: www.parknicollet.com

Owned, leased, sponsored:	1 hospital	382 beds
Contract–managed:	1 hospital	135 beds
Totals:	2 hospitals	517 beds

0159: PARKVIEW HEALTH (NP)
10501 Corporate Drive, Fort Wayne, IN Zip 46895–5600, Mailing Address: P.O. Box 5600, Zip 46895–5600; tel. 260/373–7001; Charles H. Mason Jr, President and Chief Executive Officer
(Centralized Physician/Insurance Health System)

INDIANA: PARKVIEW HOSPITAL (O, 654 beds) 2200 Randallia Drive, Fort Wayne, IN Zip 46805–4699; tel. 260/373–4000; Duane L. Erwin, President
Web address: www.parkview.com

PARKVIEW HUNTINGTON HOSPITAL (O, 36 beds) 2001 Stults Road, Huntington, IN Zip 46750–3696; tel. 260/356–3000; Darlene Garrett, Chief Operating Officer
Web address: www.parkview.com

PARKVIEW LAGRANGE HOSPITAL (O, 50 beds) 207 North Townline Road, LaGrange, IN Zip 46761–1325; tel. 260/463–2143; Debra Close, Interim Chief Executive Officer
Web address: www.lagrangech.com

PARKVIEW NOBLE HOSPITAL (O, 30 beds) 401 Sawyer Road, Kendallville, IN Zip 46755–2293, Mailing Address: P.O. Box 728, Zip 46755–0728; tel. 260/347–8700; David C. Hunter, Chief Operating Officer
Web address: www.parkview.com

PARKVIEW WHITLEY HOSPITAL (O, 118 beds) 353 North Oak Street, Columbia City, IN Zip 46725–1623; tel. 260/248–9000; Bridget Johnson, Interim Chief Operating Officer
Web address: www.parkview.com

Owned, leased, sponsored:	5 hospitals	888 beds
Contract–managed:	0 hospitals	0 beds
Totals:	5 hospitals	888 beds

★1785: PARTNERS HEALTHCARE SYSTEM, INC. (NP)
800 Boylston Street, Suite 1150, Boston, MA Zip 02199–8001; tel. 617/278–1004; James J. Mongan, M.D., President and Chief Executive Officer
(Centralized Health System)

MASSACHUSETTS: BRIGHAM AND WOMEN'S HOSPITAL (O, 735 beds) 75 Francis Street, Boston, MA Zip 02115–6195; tel. 617/732–5500; Gary L. Gottlieb, M.D., Chief Executive Officer
Web address: www.brighamandwomens.org

FAULKNER HOSPITAL (O, 124 beds) Boston, MA Mailing Address: 1153 Centre Sreet, Zip 02130–3400; tel. 617/983–7000; David J. Trull, President
Web address: www.faulknerhospital.org

MASSACHUSETTS GENERAL HOSPITAL (O, 898 beds) 55 Fruit Street, Boston, MA Zip 02114–2696; tel. 617/726–2000; Peter L. Slavin, M.D., President
Web address: www.partners.org

MCLEAN HOSPITAL (O, 169 beds) 115 Mill Street, Belmont, MA Zip 02478–9106; tel. 617/855–2000; Bruce M. Cohen, M.D., Ph.D., President and Psychiatrist–in–Chief
Web address: www.mclean.harvard.edu

NEWTON–WELLESLEY HOSPITAL (O, 226 beds) 2014 Washington Street, Newton Lower Falls, MA Zip 02462–1699; tel. 617/243–6000; Michael Jellinek, M.D., President
Web address: www.nwh.org

NORTH SHORE MEDICAL CENTER (O, 417 beds) 81 Highland Avenue, Salem, MA Zip 01970–2768; tel. 978/741–1200; Robert G. Norton, President and Chief Executive Officer
Web address: www.nsmc.partners.org

SHAUGHNESSY–KAPLAN REHABILITATION HOSPITAL (O, 160 beds) Dove Avenue, Salem, MA Zip 01970–2999; tel. 978/745–9000; Anthony Sciola, President
Web address: www.shaughnessy–kaplan.org

SPAULDING REHABILITATION HOSPITAL (O, 296 beds) 125 Nashua Street, Boston, MA Zip 02114–1198; tel. 617/573–7000; Judith C. Waterston, President
Web address: www.spauldingrehab.org

Owned, leased, sponsored:	8 hospitals	3025 beds
Contract–managed:	0 hospitals	0 beds
Totals:	8 hospitals	3025 beds

★5415: PEACEHEALTH (CC)
14432 S.E. Eastgate Way, Suite 300, Bellevue, WA Zip 98007–6412; tel. 425/747–1711; John Hayward, President and Chief Executive Officer
(Moderately Centralized Health System)

ALASKA: KETCHIKAN GENERAL HOSPITAL (L, 64 beds) 3100 Tongass Avenue, Ketchikan, AK Zip 99901–5746; tel. 907/225–5171; Patrick J. Branco, Chief Executive Officer
Web address: www.peacehealth.org

OREGON: COTTAGE GROVE COMMUNITY HOSPITAL (O, 14 beds) 1515 Village Drive, Cottage Grove, OR Zip 97424; tel. 541/942–0511; Tim Herrmann, Administrator

PEACE HARBOR HOSPITAL (O, 21 beds) 400 Ninth Street, Florence, OR Zip 97439–7398; tel. 541/997–8412; James R. Barnhart, Chief Executive Officer
Web address: www.peacehealth.org

SACRED HEART MEDICAL CENTER (O, 463 beds) 1255 Hilyard Street, Eugene, OR Zip 97401–3700, Mailing Address: P.O. Box 10905, Zip 97440–0905; tel. 541/686–7300; Jill Hoggard Green, R.N., Ph.D., Administrator
Web address: www.peacehealth.org

WASHINGTON: ST. JOHN MEDICAL CENTER (O, 202 beds) 1615 Delaware Street, Longview, WA Zip 98632–2310, Mailing Address: P.O. Box 3002, Zip 98632–3002; tel. 360/414–2000; Medrice Coluccio, Chief Executive Officer
Web address: www.peacehealth.org

ST. JOSEPH HOSPITAL (O, 235 beds) 2901 Squalicum Parkway, Bellingham, WA Zip 98225–1898; tel. 360/734–5400; Nancy J. Bitting, Regional Chief Executive Officer
Web address: www.peacehealth.org

Owned, leased, sponsored:	6 hospitals	999 beds
Contract–managed:	0 hospitals	0 beds
Totals:	6 hospitals	999 beds

0314: PHOEBE PUTNEY HEALTH SYSTEMS (NP)
417 Third Avenue, Albany, GA Zip 31702; tel. 229/312–1000; Joel Wernick, President and Chief Executive Officer

GEORGIA: PHOEBE PUTNEY MEMORIAL HOSPITAL (O, 439 beds) 417 Third Avenue, Albany, GA Zip 31701–1828, Mailing Address: P.O. Box 1828, Zip 31703–1828; tel. 229/883–1800; Joel Wernick, President and Chief Executive Officer
Web address: www.phoebeputney.com

PHOEBE WORTH MEDICAL CENTER (O, 25 beds) 807 South Isabella Street, Sylvester, GA Zip 31791–0545, Mailing Address: P.O. Box 545, Zip 31791–0545; tel. 229/776–6961; Keith J. Petersen, Chief Executive Officer
Web address: www.ppmh.org

Section B

For explanation of codes following names, see page B2.
★ Indicates Type III membership in the American Hospital Association.

Owned, leased, sponsored:	2 hospitals	464 beds
Contract–managed:	0 hospitals	0 beds
Totals:	2 hospitals	464 beds

0310: PIEDMONT HEALTHCARE (NP)

2001 Peachtree Road N.E., Suite 400, Atlanta, GA Zip 30309; tel. 404/605–3215; R. Timothy Stack, FACHE, President and Chief Executive Officer

PIEDMONT FAYETTE HOSPITAL (O, 100 beds) 1255 Highway 54 West, Fayetteville, GA Zip 30214; tel. 770/719–7000; W. Darrell Cutts, President and Chief Executive Officer

PIEDMONT HOSPITAL (O, 441 beds) 1968 Peachtree Road N.W., Atlanta, GA Zip 30309–1231; tel. 404/605–5000; Robert W. Maynard, President and Chief Executive Officer
Web address: www.piedmonthospital.org

PIEDMONT MOUNTAINSIDE HOSPITAL (O, 40 beds) 1266 Highway 515 South, Jasper, GA Zip 30143; tel. 706/692–2441; Ed Lovern, President and Chief Executive Officer
Web address: www.piedmontmountainsidehospital.org

Owned, leased, sponsored:	3 hospitals	581 beds
Contract–managed:	0 hospitals	0 beds
Totals:	3 hospitals	581 beds

0091: PIONEER BEHAVIORAL HEALTH (IO)

200 Lake Street, Suite 102, Peabody, MA Zip 01960–4780; tel. 978/536–2777; Bruce A. Shear, President and Chief Executive Officer
(Independent Hospital System)

MICHIGAN: HARBOR OAKS HOSPITAL (O, 64 beds) 35031 23 Mile Road, New Baltimore, MI Zip 48047–2097; tel. 586/725–5777; Patrick Moalleman, Chief Executive Officer
Web address: www.harboroaks.com

UTAH: HIGHLAND RIDGE HOSPITAL (O, 32 beds) 7309 South 180 West, Midvale, UT Zip 84047–3769; tel. 801/569–2153; David Schroeder, Ph.D., Chief Executive Officer
Web address: www.highlandridgehospital.com

VIRGINIA: MOUNT REGIS CENTER (O, 25 beds) 405 Kimball Avenue, Salem, VA Zip 24153–6299; tel. 540/389–4761; Gail S. Basham, Chief Executive Officer
Web address: www.mtregis.com

Owned, leased, sponsored:	3 hospitals	121 beds
Contract–managed:	0 hospitals	0 beds
Totals:	3 hospitals	121 beds

0326: PIONEER HEALTH SERVICES (IO)

301 Eighth Avenue S.W., Magee, MS Zip 39111, Mailing Address: P.O. Box 1100, Zip 39111; tel. 601/849–6440; Joseph S. McNulty, President and Chief Executive Officer

MISSISSIPPI: PIONEER COMMUNITY HOSPITAL OF ABERDEEN (O, 25 beds) 400 South Chestnut Street, Aberdeen, MS Zip 39730–3335, Mailing Address: P.O. Box 548, Zip 39730–0747; tel. 662/369–2455; Steven M. Fontaine, Administrator
Web address: www.pchaberdeen.com

S. E. LACKEY MEMORIAL HOSPITAL (O, 55 beds) 330 Broad Street, Forest, MS Zip 39074–0428, Mailing Address: P.O. Box 428, Zip 39074–0428; tel. 601/469–4151; Donna Riser, Administrator
Web address: www.selackey.com

Owned, leased, sponsored:	2 hospitals	80 beds
Contract–managed:	0 hospitals	0 beds
Totals:	2 hospitals	80 beds

0240: PREFERRED MANAGEMENT CORPORATION (IO)

120 West MacArthur, Suite 121, Shawnee, OK Zip 74804–2028; tel. 405/878–0202; Donald Freeman, President and Chief Executive Officer
(Independent Hospital System)

MISSOURI: COMMUNITY HOSPITAL ASSOCIATION (C, 25 beds) 405 East Main, Fairfax, MO Zip 64446–0107, Mailing Address: P.O. Box 107, Zip 64446–0107; tel. 660/686–2211; Myra Evans, Administrator

OKLAHOMA: ARBUCKLE MEMORIAL HOSPITAL (C, 25 beds) 2011 West Broadway Street, Sulphur, OK Zip 73086–4221; tel. 580/622–2161; Darin Farrell, Chief Executive Officer

TEXAS: COLLINGSWORTH GENERAL HOSPITAL (L, 16 beds) 1014 15th Street, Wellington, TX Zip 79095–3704, Mailing Address: P.O. Box 1112, Zip 79095–1112; tel. 806/447–2521; Mike Easley, Administrator
CULBERSON HOSPITAL DISTRICT (L, 14 beds) Eisenhower–Farm Market Road 2185, Van Horn, TX Zip 79855, Mailing Address: P.O. Box 609, Zip 79855–0609; tel. 432/283–2760; Mike Easley, Administrator
Web address: www.culbersonhospital.com
PARMER COUNTY COMMUNITY HOSPITAL (C, 25 beds) 1307 Cleveland Street, Friona, TX Zip 79035–1121; tel. 806/250–2754; Brandon L. Gatlin, Administrator
SCHLEICHER COUNTY MEDICAL CENTER (C, 14 beds) 400 West Murchison, Eldorado, TX Zip 76936, Mailing Address: Box V, Zip 76936; tel. 325/853–2507; Sharon Dietz, Administrator

Owned, leased, sponsored:	2 hospitals	30 beds
Contract–managed:	4 hospitals	89 beds
Totals:	6 hospitals	119 beds

★3505: PRESBYTERIAN HEALTHCARE SERVICES (CO)

2501 Buena Vista, S.E., Albuquerque, NM Zip 87106, Mailing Address: P.O. Box 26666, Zip 87125–6666; tel. 505/841–1234; James H. Hinton, President and Chief Executive Officer
(Centralized Physician/Insurance Health System)

NEW MEXICO: DR. DAN C. TRIGG MEMORIAL HOSPITAL (L, 25 beds) 301 East Miel De Luna Avenue, Tucumcari, NM Zip 88401–3810, Mailing Address: P.O. Box 608, Zip 88401–0608; tel. 505/461–0141; Bo Beames, Administrator
Web address: www.phs.org
ESPANOLA HOSPITAL (O, 80 beds) 1010 Spruce Street, Espanola, NM Zip 87532–2746; tel. 505/753–7111; Marcella A. Romero, Administrator
Web address: www.phs.org
LINCOLN COUNTY MEDICAL CENTER (L, 25 beds) 211 Sudderth Drive, Ruidoso, NM Zip 88345–6043, Mailing Address: P.O. Box 8000, Zip 88345–8000; tel. 505/257–7381; James P. Gibson, Administrator
Web address: www.phs.org
PLAINS REGIONAL MEDICAL CENTER (O, 106 beds) 2100 Martin Luther King, Jr. Boulevard, Clovis, NM Zip 88101–9412, Mailing Address: P.O. Box 1688, Zip 88101–1688; tel. 505/769–2141; Brian S. Bentley, Administrator
Web address: www.phs.org
PRESBYTERIAN HOSPITAL (O, 349 beds) 1100 Central Avenue S.E., Albuquerque, NM Zip 87106–4934, Mailing Address: P.O. Box 26666, Zip 87125–6666; tel. 505/841–1234; Mark W. Reifsteck, Senior Vice President and Chief Operating Officer
Web address: www.phs.org
PRESBYTERIAN KASEMAN HOSPITAL (O, 115 beds) 8300 Constitution Avenue N.E., Albuquerque, NM Zip 87110–7624, Mailing Address: P.O. Box 26666, Zip 87125–6666; tel. 505/291–2000; Robert A. Garcia, Administrative Director
Web address: www.phs.org
SOCORRO GENERAL HOSPITAL (O, 15 beds) 1202 Highway 60 West, Socorro, NM Zip 87801, Mailing Address: P.O. Box 1009, Zip 87801–1009; tel. 505/835–1140; Hoyt Skabelund, Administrator
Web address: www.phs.org/facilities/facsocorro.htm

Owned, leased, sponsored:	7 hospitals	715 beds
Contract–managed:	0 hospitals	0 beds
Totals:	7 hospitals	715 beds

For explanation of codes following names, see page B2.
★ Indicates Type III membership in the American Hospital Association.

© 2005 AHA Guide

Section B

0209: PROGRESSIONS GROUP, INC. (IO)
660 Thomas Road, Lafayette Hill, PA Zip 19444;
tel. 215/836–7700; Nicholas Tenaglia, M.D., Chairman of the Board

PENNSYLVANIA: EUGENIA HOSPITAL (O, 126 beds) 660 Thomas Road, Lafayette Hill, PA Zip 19444–1199; tel. 215/836–7700

MALVERN INSTITUTE (O, 40 beds) 940 King Road, Malvern, PA Zip 19355–3167; tel. 610/647–0330; Richard Mangano, Administrator and Chief Executive Officer

Owned, leased, sponsored:	2 hospitals	166 beds
Contract–managed:	0 hospitals	0 beds
Totals:	2 hospitals	166 beds

★0153: PROHEALTH CARE (NP)
N17 W24199 Riverwood Drive, Suite 130, Waukesha, WI Zip 53188, Mailing Address: N17 W24100 Riverwood Drive, Suite 130, Zip 53188; tel. 262/928–2244; Rexford W. Titus III, President and Chief Executive Officer
(Moderately Centralized Health System)

WISCONSIN: OCONOMOWOC MEMORIAL HOSPITAL (O, 74 beds) 791 Summit Avenue, Oconomowoc, WI Zip 53066–3896; tel. 262/569–9400; John R. Robertstad, FACHE, President and Chief Executive Officer
Web address: www.oconomowocmemorial.org

WAUKESHA MEMORIAL HOSPITAL (O, 319 beds) 725 American Avenue, Waukesha, WI Zip 53188–5099; tel. 262/928–1000; Edward A. Olson, President and Chief Executive Officer
Web address: www.waukeshamemorial.org

Owned, leased, sponsored:	2 hospitals	393 beds
Contract–managed:	0 hospitals	0 beds
Totals:	2 hospitals	393 beds

★0197: PROMEDICA HEALTH SYSTEM (NP)
2121 Hughes Drive, 4th Floor, Toledo, OH Zip 43606; tel. 419/291–7176; Alan W. Brass, FACHE, Chief Executive Officer and President
(Decentralized Health System)

MICHIGAN: LENAWEE HEALTH ALLIANCE – BIXBY CAMPUS (O, 66 beds) 818 Riverside Avenue, Adrian, MI Zip 49221–1496; tel. 517/265–0900; Randall D. Oostra, FACHE, President
Web address: www.promedica.org

LENAWEE HEALTH ALLIANCE–HERRICK CAMPUS (O, 95 beds) 500 East Pottawatamie Street, Tecumseh, MI Zip 49286–2097; tel. 517/424–3000; Randall D. Oostra, FACHE, President
Web address: www.promedica.org

OHIO: BAY PARK COMMUNITY HOSPITAL (O, 70 beds) 2801 Bay Park Drive, Oregon, OH Zip 43616; tel. 419/690–7900; Terri L. McLain, R.N., MSN, CHE, President
Web address: www.promedica.org

DEFIANCE REGIONAL MEDICAL CENTER (O, 61 beds) 1200 Ralston Avenue, Defiance, OH Zip 43512–1396; tel. 419/783–6955; John E. Horns, President
Web address: www.promedica.org

FLOWER HOSPITAL (O, 252 beds) 5200 Harroun Road, Sylvania, OH Zip 43560–2196; tel. 419/824–1444; Kevin C. Webb, FACHE, President
Web address: www.promedica.org

FOSTORIA COMMUNITY HOSPITAL (O, 25 beds) 501 Van Buren Street, Fostoria, OH Zip 44830–0907, Mailing Address: P.O. Box 907, Zip 44830–0907; tel. 419/435–7734; Timothy Jakacki, President
Web address: www.fchosp.org

THE TOLEDO HOSPITAL (O, 610 beds) 2142 North Cove Boulevard, Toledo, OH Zip 43606–3896; tel. 419/291–4000; Barbara Steele, President
Web address: www.promedica.org

Owned, leased, sponsored:	7 hospitals	1179 beds
Contract–managed:	0 hospitals	0 beds
Totals:	7 hospitals	1179 beds

0230: PROMISE HEALTHCARE (IO)
400 East Kaliste Saloom Road, 7100, Lafayette, LA Zip 70508; tel. 337/325–8555; Howard B. Koslow, President and Chief Executive Officer
(Independent Hospital System)

ARIZONA: PROMISE SPECIALTY HOSPITAL OF PHOENIX (O, 36 beds) 1800 East Van Buren Street, 2nd Floor, Phoenix, AZ Zip 85006; tel. 602/251–8525; Brian Holt, Chief Executive Officer
Web address: www.promise–phoenix.com

ARKANSAS: DE QUEEN REGIONAL MEDICAL CENTER (O, 44 beds) 1306 Collin Raye Drive, De Queen, AR Zip 71832–2198; tel. 870/584–4111; Amy Vines, Chief Executive Officer
Web address: www.dequeenmedicalcenter.com

CALIFORNIA: PROMISE HOSPITAL OF EAST LOS ANGELES, SUBURBAN MEDICAL CENTER CAMPUS (O, 182 beds) 16453 South Colorado Avenue, Paramount, CA Zip 90723–5000; tel. 562/531–3110; Richard McCarthy, Chief Executive Officer
Web address: www.promiseeastla.com

LOUISIANA: DEQUINCY MEMORIAL HOSPITAL (O, 19 beds) 110 West Fourth Street, DeQuincy, LA Zip 70633–3508, Mailing Address: P.O. Box 1166, Zip 70633–1166; tel. 337/786–1200; Barbara Hollingsworth, Administrator and Chief Executive Officer
Web address: www.dequincyhospital.com

PROMISE SPECIALTY HOSPITAL OF FERRIDAY (O, 40 beds) 6818–A Highway 84, Ferriday, LA Zip 71334–5101; tel. 318/757–7575; Lee Huckaby, Chief Executive Officer
Web address: www.camelothealthcare.net

PROMISE SPECIALTY HOSPITAL OF SHREVEPORT (O, 137 beds) 1800 Irving Place, Shreveport, LA Zip 71101–4608; tel. 318/425–4096; Michael O. Choo, Chief Executive Officer
Web address: www.promise–shreveport.com

SOUTH CAMERON MEMORIAL HOSPITAL (O, 33 beds) 5360 West Creole Highway, Cameron, LA Zip 70631–5127; tel. 337/542–4111; David Byrns, Chief Executive Officer

SPECIALTY HOSPITAL OF NEW ORLEANS (O, 27 beds) 1401 Foucher Street, New Orleans, LA Zip 70115; tel. 504/897–8942; Irving B. Sawyers Jr, Chief Executive Officer

MISSISSIPPI: PROMISE SPECIALTY HOSPITAL OF VICKSBURG (O, 33 beds) 1111 North Frontage Road, 2nd Floor, Vicksburg, MS Zip 39180; tel. 601/619–3526; Lee Huckaby, Chief Executive Officer
Web address: www.promise–vicksburg.com

TEXAS: PROMISE SPECIALTY HOSPITAL OF SAN ANTONIO (O, 26 beds) 7400 Barlite Boulevard, 2nd Floor, San Antonio, TX Zip 78224; tel. 210/921–3550; Karen Pitcher, Chief Executive Officer
Web address: www.promise–sanantonio.com

Owned, leased, sponsored:	10 hospitals	577 beds
Contract–managed:	0 hospitals	0 beds
Totals:	10 hospitals	577 beds

★0132: PROVENA HEALTH (CO)
19065 Hickory Creek Drive, Suite 300, Mokena, IL Zip 60448; tel. 708/478–6300; William T. Foley, Chief Executive Officer
(Moderately Centralized Health System)

ILLINOIS: PROVENA COVENANT MEDICAL CENTER (O, 120 beds) 1400 West Park Street, Urbana, IL Zip 61801–2396; tel. 217/337–2000; Mark S. Wiener, Regional President and Chief Executive Officer
Web address: www.provenacovenant.org

PROVENA MERCY CENTER (O, 254 beds) 1325 North Highland Avenue, Aurora, IL Zip 60506–1449; tel. 630/859–2222; Timothy P. Selz, President and Chief Executive Officer
Web address: www.provenamercy.com

PROVENA SAINT JOSEPH HOSPITAL (O, 174 beds) 77 North Airlite Street, Elgin, IL Zip 60123–4912; tel. 847/695–3200; William A. Brown, CHE, President and Chief Executive Officer
Web address: www.provenahealth.com

PROVENA SAINT JOSEPH MEDICAL CENTER (O, 454 beds) 333 North Madison Street, Joliet, IL Zip 60435–6595; tel. 815/725–7133; Jeffrey Brickman, President and Chief Executive Officer
Web address: www.provenasaintjoe.org

Section B

For explanation of codes following names, see page B2.
★ Indicates Type III membership in the American Hospital Association.

PROVENA ST. MARY'S HOSPITAL (O, 160 beds) 500 West Court Street, Kankakee, IL Zip 60901–3661; tel. 815/937–2490; George N. Miller Jr, President and Chief Executive Officer
Web address: www.provena–stmarys.com

PROVENA UNITED SAMARITANS MEDICAL CENTER (O, 170 beds) 812 North Logan, Danville, IL Zip 61832–3788; tel. 217/443–5000; Mark S. Wiener, President and Chief Executive Officer
Web address: www.provenausmc.org

Owned, leased, sponsored:	6 hospitals	1332 beds
Contract–managed:	0 hospitals	0 beds
Totals:	6 hospitals	1332 beds

★**5275: PROVIDENCE HEALTH SYSTEM** (CC)
506 Second Avenue, Suite 1200, Seattle, WA Zip 98104–2329; tel. 206/464–3355; John Koster, M.D., President and Chief Executive Officer
(Decentralized Health System)

ALASKA: PROVIDENCE ALASKA MEDICAL CENTER (O, 345 beds) 3200 Providence Drive, Anchorage, AK Zip 99508–4615, Mailing Address: P.O. Box 196604, Zip 99519–6604; tel. 907/562–2211; E. Al Parrish, Vice President and Chief Executive Officer
Web address: www.providence.org/alaska/pamc/default.htm

PROVIDENCE KODIAK ISLAND MEDICAL CENTER (L, 25 beds) 1915 East Rezanof Drive, Kodiak, AK Zip 99615–6602; tel. 907/486–3281; Donald J. Rush, Chief Executive Officer
Web address: www.providence.org

PROVIDENCE SEWARD MEDICAL CENTER (L, 6 beds) 417 First Avenue, Seward, AK Zip 99664, Mailing Address: P.O. Box 365, Zip 99664–0365; tel. 907/224–5205; Kathy Kloster, Administrator
Web address: www.providence.org

CALIFORNIA: PROVIDENCE HOLY CROSS MEDICAL CENTER (O, 254 beds) 15031 Rinaldi Street, San Fernando, CA Zip 91346–9600; tel. 818/365–8051; Kerry Carmody, Administrator
Web address: www.providence.org/losangeles/facilities/providence_holy_cross/

PROVIDENCE SAINT JOSEPH MEDICAL CENTER (O, 427 beds) 501 South Buena Vista Street, Burbank, CA Zip 91505–4866; tel. 818/843–5111; Arnold R. Schaffer, Chief Executive Officer
Web address: www.providence.org

PROVIDENCE–LITTLE COMPANY OF MARY SERVICE AREA (O, 360 beds) 4101 Torrance Boulevard, Torrance, CA Zip 90503–4698; tel. 310/540–7676; Blair Contratto, Chief Executive Officer
Web address: www.lcmweb.org

SAN PEDRO PENINSULA HOSPITAL (O, 521 beds) 1300 West Seventh Street, San Pedro, CA Zip 90732–3505; tel. 310/514–5233; Nancy Carlson, Administrator
Web address: www.lcmhs.org

OREGON: PROVIDENCE HOOD RIVER MEMORIAL HOSPITAL (O, 25 beds) 811 13th Street, Hood River, OR Zip 97031–1204, Mailing Address: P.O. Box 149, Zip 97031–0149; tel. 541/386–3911; James Arp, Chief Executive Officer
Web address: www.providence.org/hoodriver

PROVIDENCE MEDFORD MEDICAL CENTER (O, 127 beds) 1111 Crater Lake Avenue, Medford, OR Zip 97504–6241; tel. 541/732–5000; Charles T. Wright, Chief Executive, Southern Oregon Service Area
Web address: www.providence.org

PROVIDENCE MILWAUKIE HOSPITAL (O, 56 beds) 10150 S.E. 32nd Avenue, Milwaukie, OR Zip 97222–6593; tel. 503/513–8300; Jacquelyn Gaines, Administrator
Web address: www.providence.org

PROVIDENCE NEWBERG HOSPITAL (O, 36 beds) 501 Villa Road, Newberg, OR Zip 97132–1832; tel. 503/537–1555; Larry Bowe, Chief Executive, Yamhill Service Area
Web address: www.phsor.org

PROVIDENCE PORTLAND MEDICAL CENTER (O, 402 beds) 4805 N.E. Glisan Street, Portland, OR Zip 97213–2967; tel. 503/215–1111; David T. Underriner, Administrator
Web address: www.providence.org

PROVIDENCE SEASIDE HOSPITAL (L, 47 beds) 725 South Wahanna Road, Seaside, OR Zip 97138–7735; tel. 503/717–7000; William P. Sexton, Chief Executive
Web address: www.providence.org

PROVIDENCE ST. VINCENT MEDICAL CENTER (O, 483 beds) 9205 S.W. Barnes Road, Portland, OR Zip 97225–6661; tel. 503/216–1234; Donald Elsom, Administrator
Web address: www.providence.org/portland/hospitals

WASHINGTON: PROVIDENCE CENTRALIA HOSPITAL (O, 114 beds) 914 South Scheuber Road, Centralia, WA Zip 98531–9027; tel. 360/736–2803; Steven A. Burdick, Administrator
Web address: www.providence.org

PROVIDENCE EVERETT MEDICAL CENTER (O, 325 beds) 1321 Colby Street, Everett, WA Zip 98206–1147, Mailing Address: P.O. Box 1147, Zip 98206–1147; tel. 425/261–2000; Gail C. Larson, Chief Executive Officer
Web address: www.providence.org

PROVIDENCE ST. PETER HOSPITAL (O, 317 beds) 413 Lilly Road N.E., Olympia, WA Zip 98506–5166; tel. 360/491–9480; C. Scott Bond, Administrator and Chief Executive Officer
Web address: www.providence.org/swsa/facilities/st_peter_hospital

Owned, leased, sponsored:	17 hospitals	3870 beds
Contract–managed:	0 hospitals	0 beds
Totals:	17 hospitals	3870 beds

★**5265: PROVIDENCE SERVICES** (CC)
9 East Ninth Avenue, Spokane, WA Zip 99202; tel. 509/474–7337; Richard J. Umbdenstock, President and Chief Executive Officer
(Moderately Centralized Health System)

MONTANA: BENEFIS HEALTHCARE (S, 470 beds) 1101 26th Street South, Great Falls, MT Zip 59405–5104; tel. 406/455–5000; John H. Goodnow, President and Chief Executive Officer
Web address: www.benefis.org

COMMUNITY HOSPITAL OF ANACONDA (C, 87 beds) 401 West Pennsylvania Street, Anaconda, MT Zip 59711–1999; tel. 406/563–8500; Steve McNeece, Chief Executive Officer

MISSOURI RIVER MEDICAL CENTER (C, 52 beds) 1501 St. Charles Street, Fort Benton, MT Zip 59442–0249, Mailing Address: P.O. Box 249, Zip 59442–0249; tel. 406/622–3331; Jay Pottenger, Administrator
Web address: www.fortbenton.com/hospital.index.htm

MOUNTAINVIEW MEDICAL CENTER (C, 37 beds) 16 West Main Street, White Sulphur Springs, MT Zip 59645, Mailing Address: P.O. Box Q, Zip 59645; tel. 406/547–3321; Katharine Ann Campbell, Chief Executive Officer and Administrator
Web address: www.mvmc.org

ST. JOSEPH HOSPITAL (S, 22 beds) 6 Thirteenth Avenue East, Polson, MT Zip 59860–5316, Mailing Address: P.O. Box 1010, Zip 59860–1010; tel. 406/883–5377; John W. Glueckert, President
Web address: www.saintjoes.org

ST. PATRICK HOSPITAL (S, 200 beds) 500 West Broadway, Missoula, MT Zip 59802–4096, Mailing Address: P.O. Box 4587, Zip 59806–4587; tel. 406/543–7271; Steve Witz, President
Web address: www.saintpatrick.org

WASHINGTON: DEER PARK HOSPITAL (S, 25 beds) 1015 East D Street, Deer Park, WA Zip 99006–0742, Mailing Address: P.O. Box 742, Zip 99006–0742; tel. 509/276–3500; M. Colleen Febach, Administrator

HOLY FAMILY HOSPITAL (S, 198 beds) North 5633 Lidgerwood Avenue, Spokane, WA Zip 99208–2533; tel. 509/482–0111; Thomas Corley, President
Web address: www.holy–family.org

MOUNT CARMEL HOSPITAL (S, 25 beds) 982 East Columbia Street, Colville, WA Zip 99114–3352; tel. 509/684–2561; Gordon C. McLean, President
Web address: www.mtcarmelhospital.org

SACRED HEART MEDICAL CENTER (S, 610 beds) 101 West Eighth Avenue, Spokane, WA Zip 99204–2364, Mailing Address: P.O. Box 2555, Zip 99220–2555; tel. 509/474–3040; Ryland P. Davis, Chief Executive Officer
Web address: www.shmc.org

ST. JOSEPH'S HOSPITAL (S, 65 beds) 500 East Webster Street, Chewelah, WA Zip 99109–0197, Mailing Address: P.O. Box 197, Zip 99109–0197; tel. 509/935–8211; Gary V. Peck, Administrator
Web address: www.sjhospital.org

For explanation of codes following names, see page B2.
★ Indicates Type III membership in the American Hospital Association.

ST. MARY MEDICAL CENTER (S, 103 beds) 401 West Poplar Street, Walla Walla, WA Zip 99362–1477, Mailing Address: Box 1477, Zip 99362–1477; tel. 509/525–3320; John A. Isely, President
Web address: www.smmc.org

WHITMAN HOSPITAL AND MEDICAL CENTER (C, 33 beds) 1200 West Fairview, Colfax, WA Zip 99111–9579; tel. 509/397–3435; Jon R. Davis, FACHE, Chief Executive Officer
Web address: www.whitmanhospital.com

Owned, leased, sponsored:	9 hospitals	1718 beds
Contract–managed:	4 hospitals	209 beds
Totals:	13 hospitals	1927 beds

0263: PSYCHIATRIC SOLUTIONS (IO)
840 Crescent Centre Drive, Suite 460, Franklin, TN Zip 37067; tel. 615/312–5700; Joey Jacobs, President and Chief Executive Officer
(Independent Hospital System)

ALABAMA: HILL CREST BEHAVIORAL HEALTH SERVICES (O, 76 beds) 6869 Fifth Avenue South, Birmingham, AL Zip 35212–1866; tel. 205/833–9000; Steve McCabe, Chief Executive Officer
Web address: www.psysolutions.com

LAUREL OAKS BEHAVIORAL CENTER (O, 24 beds) 700 East Cottonwood Road, Dothan, AL Zip 36301; tel. 334/794–7373; Robert Turner, M.D., Chief Executive Officer
Web address: www.psysolutions.com

ARKANSAS: PINNACLE POINTE HOSPITAL (O, 102 beds) 11501 Financial Center Parkway, Little Rock, AR Zip 72211–3715; tel. 501/223–3322; Lucinda DeBruce, Chief Executive Officer
Web address: www.bhcpinnaclepoint.com

CALIFORNIA: ALHAMBRA HOSPITAL (O, 85 beds) 4619 North Rosemead Boulevard, Rosemead, CA Zip 91770–1478, Mailing Address: P.O. Box 369, Zip 91770–0369; tel. 626/286–1191; Peggy Minnick, R.N., Chief Executive Officer
Web address: www.ardenthealth.com

FREMONT HOSPITAL (O, 78 beds) 39001 Sundale Drive, Fremont, CA Zip 94538–2005; tel. 510/796–1100; Terry Bridges, Chief Executive Officer
Web address: www.fremonthospital.com

HERITAGE OAKS HOSPITAL (O, 76 beds) 4250 Auburn Boulevard, Sacramento, CA Zip 95841–4164; tel. 916/489–3336; Nancy Faulkner, Chief Executive Officer
Web address: www.bhcheritageoaks.com

SIERRA VISTA HOSPITAL (O, 72 beds) 8001 Bruceville Road, Sacramento, CA Zip 95823–2329; tel. 916/423–2000; Nancy Purtell, Chief Executive Officer
Web address: www.bhcsierravista.com

COLORADO: CEDAR SPRINGS HOSPITAL (O, 110 beds) 2135 Southgate Road, Colorado Springs, CO Zip 80906–2693; tel. 719/633–4114; Robert E. Marshall, Chief Executive Officer
Web address: www.psysolutions.com

FLORIDA: FORT LAUDERDALE HOSPITAL (O, 100 beds) 1601 East Las Olas Boulevard, Fort Lauderdale, FL Zip 33301–2393; tel. 954/463–4321; Tim Kenna, Administrator

IDAHO: INTERMOUNTAIN HOSPITAL (O, 125 beds) 303 North Allumbaugh Street, Boise, ID Zip 83704–9266; tel. 208/377–8400; Richard Failla, Chief Executive Officer
Web address: www.bhcintermountain.com

ILLINOIS: RIVEREDGE HOSPITAL (O, 210 beds) 8311 West Roosevelt Road, Forest Park, IL Zip 60130–2500; tel. 708/771–7000; Stephen J. Quigley, Chief Executive Officer
Web address: www.psysolutions.com

STREAMWOOD BEHAVIORAL HEALTH CENTER (O, 238 beds) 1400 East Irving Park Road, Streamwood, IL Zip 60107–3203; tel. 630/837–9000; Jeff Bergren, Regional Chief Executive Officer
Web address: www.streamwoodhospital.com

INDIANA: MEADOWS HOSPITAL (O, 78 beds) 3600 North Prow Road, Bloomington, IN Zip 47404; tel. 812/331–8000; Leann Moren Hutchinson, Chief Executive Officer

VALLE VISTA HEALTH SYSTEM (O, 88 beds) 898 East Main Street, Greenwood, IN Zip 46143–1400; tel. 317/887–1348; David Bell, Chief Executive Officer
Web address: www.vallevistahospital.com

LOUISIANA: BRENTWOOD BEHAVIORAL HEALTH COMPANY (O, 150 beds) 1006 Highland Avenue, Shreveport, LA Zip 71101–4103; tel. 318/618–7500; J. Paul Smith, Chief Executive Officer

MICHIGAN: HAVENWYCK HOSPITAL (O, 152 beds) 1525 University Drive, Auburn Hills, MI Zip 48326–2675; tel. 248/373–9200; Robert A. Kercorian, Chief Executive Officer
Web address: www.havenwyckhospital.com

MISSISSIPPI: ALLIANCE HEALTH CENTER (O, 149 beds) 5000 Highway 39 North, Meridian, MS Zip 39301; tel. 601/483–6211; William M. Patterson, Chief Executive Officer
Web address: www.alliancehealthcenter.com

BRENTWOOD BEHAVIORAL HEALTHCARE OF MISSISSIPPI (O, 107 beds) 3531 East Lakeland Drive, Jackson, MS Zip 39296–9794; tel. 601/936–2024; Michael J. Carney, Chief Executive Officer

MISSOURI: HEARTLAND BEHAVIORAL HEALTH SERVICES (O, 159 beds) 1500 West Ashland Street, Nevada, MO Zip 64772–1710; tel. 417/667–2666; Mike Ham, Chief Executive Officer
Web address: www.heartlandbhs.com

NEVADA: MONTEVISTA HOSPITAL (O, 80 beds) 5900 West Rochelle Avenue, Las Vegas, NV Zip 89103–3327; tel. 702/364–1111; Ingrid L. Whipple, Chief Executive Officer
Web address: www.bhcmontevista.com

WEST HILLS HOSPITAL (O, 95 beds) 1240 East Ninth Street, Reno, NV Zip 89512–2997, Mailing Address: P.O. Box 30012, Zip 89520–0012; tel. 775/323–0478; Edward J. Whitehouse, Interim Chief Executive Office
Web address: www.bhcwesthills.com

WILLOW SPRINGS RESIDENTIAL TREATMENT CENTER (O, 74 beds) 690 Edison Way, Reno, NV Zip 89502–4135; tel. 775/858–3303; Nancy N. Dandliker, Executive Director
Web address: www.bhcwillowsprings.com

NEW JERSEY: SUMMIT HOSPITAL (O, 90 beds) 19 Prospect Street, Summit, NJ Zip 07902–0100; tel. 908/522–7000; James E. Ledbetter, Ph.D., Chief Executive Officer

NEW MEXICO: MESILLA VALLEY HOSPITAL (O, 125 beds) 3751 Del Rey Boulevard, Las Cruces, NM Zip 88012–8526; tel. 505/382–3500; Robert Mansfield, Chief Executive Officer
Web address: www.mesillavalleyhospital.com

PEAK BEHAVIORAL HEALTH SERVICES (O, 36 beds) 5065 McNut Road, Santa Teresa, NM Zip 88008; tel. 505/589–3000; James Baca, Chief Executive Officer

NORTH CAROLINA: BRYNN MARR BEHAVIORAL HEALTHCARE SYSTEM (O, 88 beds) 192 Village Drive, Jacksonville, NC Zip 28546–7299; tel. 910/577–1400; Sarah Wiltgen, Chief Executive Officer
Web address: www.brynnmarr.org

HOLLY HILL HOSPITAL (O, 105 beds) 3019 Falstaff Road, Raleigh, NC Zip 27610–1812; tel. 919/250–7000; Thomas L. Ryba, Chief Executive Officer
Web address: www.hollyhillhospital.com

OHIO: BELMONT PINES HOSPITAL (O, 46 beds) 615 Churchill–Hubbard Road, Youngstown, OH Zip 44505–1379; tel. 330/759–2700; George H. Perry, Ph.D., Chief Executive Officer
Web address: www.belmontpines.com

FOX RUN HOSPITAL (O, 74 beds) 67670 Traco Drive, Saint Clairsville, OH Zip 43950–9375; tel. 740/695–2131; Karen Maxwell, Chief Executive Officer
Web address: www.bhcfoxrun.com

WINDSOR HOSPITAL (O, 47 beds) 115 East Summit Street, Chagrin Falls, OH Zip 44022–2750; tel. 440/247–5300; Richard Warden, Chief Executive Officer
Web address: www.bhcwindsor.com

OKLAHOMA: SHADOW MOUNTAIN BEHAVIORAL HEALTH SYSTEM (O, 100 beds) 6262 South Sheridan Road, Tulsa, OK Zip 74133–4099; tel. 918/492–8200; Sharon Worsham, Chief Executive Officer

SOUTH CAROLINA: PALMETTO LOWCOUNTRY BEHAVIORAL HEALTH SYSTEM (O, 70 beds) 2777 Speissegger Drive, Charleston, SC Zip 29405–8299; tel. 843/747–5830; Anne Battin, Administrator
Web address: www.plbhs.com

TEXAS: COMPASS HOSPITAL OF SAN ANTONIO (O, 35 beds) 14743 Jones Maltsberger Avenue, San Antonio, TX Zip 78247–3713; tel. 210/402–0029; Edgar F. Prettyman, M.D., Chief Executive Officer

For explanation of codes following names, see page B2.
★ Indicates Type III membership in the American Hospital Association.

CYPRESS CREEK HOSPITAL (O, 96 beds) 17750 Cali Drive, Houston, TX Zip 77090–2700; tel. 281/586–7600; Ronald Mays, Chief Executive Officer
Web address: www.psysolutions.com

LAUREL RIDGE HOSPITAL (O, 94 beds) 17720 Corporate Woods Drive, San Antonio, TX Zip 78259–3500, Mailing Address: P.O. Box 700590, Zip 78259–3500; tel. 210/491–9400; Ramona T. Key, Chief Executive Officer
Web address: www.brownschools.com

MILLWOOD HOSPITAL (O, 98 beds) 1011 North Cooper Street, Arlington, TX Zip 76011–5517; tel. 817/261–3121; Thomas E. Rourke, CHE, Chief Executive Officer
Web address: www.millwoodhospital.com

MISSION VISTA GERIATRIC PSYCHIATRIC HOSPITAL (O, 34 beds) 14747 Jones Maltsberger, San Antonio, TX Zip 78247–3713; tel. 210/490–0000; Ramona T. Key, Chief Executive Officer
Web address: www.missionvistabhc.com

TEXAS NEURO REHABILITATION CENTER (O, 31 beds) 1106 West Dittmar, Austin, TX Zip 78745–6388, Mailing Address: P.O. Box 150459, Zip 78715–0459; tel. 512/444–4835; Edgar F. Prettyman, M.D., Chief Executive Officer
Web address: www.psysolutions.com

TEXAS WEST OAKS HOSPITAL (O, 144 beds) 6500 Hornwood Drive, Houston, TX Zip 77074–5095; tel. 713/995–0909; Charlene Arnett, MS, FACHE, Chief Executive Officer
Web address: www.psysolutions.com

UTAH: BENCHMARK BEHAVIORAL HEALTH SYSTEMS (O, 104 beds) 592 West 1350 South, Woods Cross, UT Zip 84087–1665; tel. 801/299–5300; John A. Holter, Chief Executive Officer
Web address: www.bbhsnet.com

VIRGINIA: CUMBERLAND HOSPITAL FOR CHILDREN AND ADOLESCENTS (O, 132 beds) 9407 Cumberland Road, New Kent, VA Zip 23124–0150; tel. 804/966–2242; Patrice Gay Brooks, Chief Operating Officer
Web address: www.cumberlandhospital.com

WHISPER RIDGE AT LEESBURG (O, 77 beds) 42009 Victory Lane, Leesburg, VA Zip 20176–6269; tel. 703/777–0800; Bill Bailey, Chief Executive Officer

WASHINGTON: FAIRFAX HOSPITAL (O, 65 beds) 10200 N.E. 132nd Street, Kirkland, WA Zip 98034–2899; tel. 425/821–2000; Ron Escarda, Chief Executive Officer
Web address: www.fairfaxhospital.com

Owned, leased, sponsored:	43 hospitals	4119 beds
Contract–managed:	0 hospitals	0 beds
Totals:	43 hospitals	4119 beds

★0011: PUERTO RICO DEPARTMENT OF HEALTH (NP)
Building A – Medical Center, San Juan, PR Zip 00936, Mailing Address: Call Box 70184, Zip 00936; tel. 787/274–7676; Johnny V. Rullan, M.D., Secretary of Health

PUERTO RICO: CARDIOVASCULAR CENTER OF PUERTO RICO AND THE CARIBBEAN (O, 122 beds) Americo Miranda Centro Medico, San Juan, PR Zip 00936, Mailing Address: P.O. Box 366528, Zip 00936–6528; tel. 787/754–8500; Carlos G. Melendez, Executive Director
Web address: www.cardiovascularpr.com

HOSPITAL UNIVERSITARIO DR. RAMON RUIZ ARNAU (O, 148 beds) Avenue Laurel, Santa Juanita, Bayamon, PR Zip 00956; tel. 787/787–5151; Rafael Garcia, Chief Executive Officer

SAN JUAN BAUTISTA MEDICAL CENTER (C, 195 beds) Carretera Caguas A Cidra, Caguas, PR Zip 00725, Mailing Address: Call Box 4964, Zip 00726–4964; tel. 787/744–2500; Rosita Esteras, Executive Director

STATE PSYCHIATRIC HOSPITAL (O, 153 beds) Monacillos Avenue, San Juan, PR Zip 00936, Mailing Address: Call Box 2100, Caparra Heights Station, Zip 00922–2100; tel. 787/766–4646; Rafael Garcia Alvarez, Executive Director

UNIVERSITY HOSPITAL (O, 260 beds) San Juan, PR Mailing Address: P.O. Box 2116, Zip 00922; tel. 787/754–0101; Roberto Burgos, Executive Director

UNIVERSITY PEDIATRIC HOSPITAL (O, 145 beds) San Juan, PR Mailing Address: Call Box 191079, Zip 00910–1079; tel. 787/777–3535; Sylvette Llovet, Executive Director

Owned, leased, sponsored:	5 hospitals	828 beds
Contract–managed:	1 hospital	195 beds
Totals:	6 hospitals	1023 beds

★0040: QUEEN'S HEALTH SYSTEMS (NP)
1099 Alakea Street, Suite 1100, Honolulu, HI Zip 96813; tel. 808/532–6100; Gary Okamoto, President and Chief Executive Officer
(Moderately Centralized Health System)

HAWAII: MOLOKAI GENERAL HOSPITAL (O, 30 beds) Kaunakakai, HI Mailing Address: P.O. Box 408, Zip 96748–0408; tel. 808/553–5331; Janice Kalanihuia, Administrator
Web address: www.queens.org

QUEEN'S MEDICAL CENTER (O, 456 beds) 1301 Punchbowl Street, Honolulu, HI Zip 96813–2499; tel. 808/538–9011; Arthur A. Ushijima, President and Chief Executive Officer
Web address: www.queens.org

Owned, leased, sponsored:	2 hospitals	486 beds
Contract–managed:	0 hospitals	0 beds
Totals:	2 hospitals	486 beds

★0002: QUORUM HEALTH RESOURCES (IO)
5800 Tennyson Parkway, Plano, TX Zip 75024; tel. 214/473–3700; John C. Stinson, President and Chief Executive Officer
(Decentralized Health System)

ALABAMA: MONROE COUNTY HOSPITAL (C, 62 beds) 1901 South Alabama Avenue, Monroeville, AL Zip 36460, Mailing Address: P.O. Box 886, Zip 36461–0886; tel. 251/575–3111; Chris Johns, Chief Executive Officer
Web address: www.mchcare.com

ALASKA: BARTLETT REGIONAL HOSPITAL (C, 72 beds) 3260 Hospital Drive, Juneau, AK Zip 99801–7808; tel. 907/586–2611; Robert F. Valliant, Chief Executive Officer
Web address: www.bartletthospital.org

ARKANSAS: CHICOT MEMORIAL HOSPITAL (C, 35 beds) 2729 Highway 65 and 82 South, Lake Village, AR Zip 71653; tel. 870/265–5351; Robert R. Reddish, Administrator and Chief Executive Officer

DELTA MEMORIAL HOSPITAL (C, 50 beds) 300 East Pickens Street, Dumas, AR Zip 71639–2710, Mailing Address: P.O. Box 887, Zip 71639–0887; tel. 870/382–4303; Mark Deal, Chief Executive Officer
Web address: www.deltafasthealth.com

HOWARD MEMORIAL HOSPITAL (C, 25 beds) 800 West Leslie Street, Nashville, AR Zip 71852–0381, Mailing Address: P.O. Box 381, Zip 71852–0381; tel. 870/845–4400; Brian E. Bickel, President and Chief Executive Officer

MENA MEDICAL CENTER (C, 58 beds) 311 North Morrow Street, Mena, AR Zip 71953–2516; tel. 479/394–6100; Vince DiFranco, Chief Executive Officer
Web address: www.menamedical.com

REBSAMEN MEDICAL CENTER (C, 87 beds) 1400 West Braden Street, Jacksonville, AR Zip 72076–3788; tel. 501/985–7000; Kurt Meyer, Chief Executive Officer
Web address: www.rebsamenmedicalcenter.com

SALINE MEMORIAL HOSPITAL (C, 106 beds) 1 Medical Park Drive, Benton, AR Zip 72015–3354; tel. 501/776–6000; James Richardson, FACHE, Chief Executive Officer
Web address: www.scmc.com

COLORADO: ARKANSAS VALLEY REGIONAL MEDICAL CENTER (C, 176 beds) 1100 Carson Avenue, La Junta, CO Zip 81050–2799; tel. 719/383–6000; Lynn Crowell, Chief Executive Officer
Web address: www.avrmc.org

MEMORIAL HOSPITAL (C, 25 beds) 785 Russell Street, Craig, CO Zip 81625–9906; tel. 970/824–9411; M. Randell Phelps, Chief Executive Officer
Web address: www.thememorialhospital.com

MONTROSE MEMORIAL HOSPITAL (C, 51 beds) 800 South Third Street, Montrose, CO Zip 81401–4291; tel. 970/249–2211; Kenneth E. S. Platou, Chief Executive Officer
Web address: www.montrosehospital.com

For explanation of codes following names, see page B2.
★ Indicates Type III membership in the American Hospital Association.

© 2005 AHA Guide

PARKVIEW MEDICAL CENTER (C, 287 beds) 400 West 16th Street, Pueblo, CO Zip 81003–2781; tel. 719/584–4000; C. W. Smith, President and Chief Executive Officer
Web address: www.parkviewmc.org

PIONEERS HOSPITAL OF RIO BLANCO COUNTY (C, 48 beds) 345 Cleveland Street, Meeker, CO Zip 81641–3238; tel. 970/878–5047; Robert W. Omer, FACHE, Chief Executive Officer
Web address: www.pioneershospital.com

PROWERS MEDICAL CENTER (C, 25 beds) 401 Kendall Drive, Lamar, CO Zip 81052–3993; tel. 719/336–4343; Greg D. Gerard, Administrator and Chief Executive Officer
Web address: www.lpmc.org

SOUTHWEST MEMORIAL HOSPITAL (C, 61 beds) 1311 North Mildred Road, Cortez, CO Zip 81321–2299; tel. 970/565–6666; Charles E. Bill, CHE, Chief Executive Officer
Web address: www.swhealth.org

VALLEY VIEW HOSPITAL (C, 71 beds) 1906 Blake Avenue, Glenwood Springs, CO Zip 81601–4259, Mailing Address: P.O. Box 1970, Zip 81602–1970; tel. 970/945–6535; Gary L. Brewer, Chief Executive Officer
Web address: www.vvh.org

FLORIDA: HENDRY REGIONAL MEDICAL CENTER (C, 25 beds) 500 West Sugarland Highway, Clewiston, FL Zip 33440–3094; tel. 863/983–9121; Craig R. Cudworth, Chief Executive Officer
Web address: www.hendryregional.org

JACKSON HOSPITAL (C, 86 beds) 4250 Hospital Drive, Marianna, FL Zip 32446–1939, Mailing Address: P.O. Box 1608, Zip 32447–1608; tel. 850/526–2200; David L. Hample, Chief Executive Officer
Web address: www.jacksonhosp.com

GEORGIA: ELBERT MEMORIAL HOSPITAL (C, 52 beds) 4 Medical Drive, Elberton, GA Zip 30635–1897; tel. 706/283–3151; Mark LeNeave, Chief Executive Officer
Web address: www.elbertmemorialhospital.net

HABERSHAM COUNTY MEDICAL CENTER (C, 159 beds) 541 Historic Highway 441, Demorest, GA Zip 30535–3118, Mailing Address: P.O. Box 37, Zip 30535–0037; tel. 706/754–2161; C. Richard Dwozan, Chief Executive Officer
Web address: www.hcmcmed.org

MCDUFFIE REGIONAL MEDICAL CENTER (C, 35 beds) 521 Hill Street S.W., Thomson, GA Zip 30824–2199; tel. 706/595–1411; Douglas C. Keir, Chief Executive Officer
Web address: www.mrmc.org

WARM SPRINGS MEDICAL CENTER (C, 25 beds) 5995 Spring Street, Warm Springs, GA Zip 31830–2149, Mailing Address: P.O. Box 8, Zip 31830–0008; tel. 706/655–3331; Jon L. Dixon, Chief Executive Officer

WAYNE MEMORIAL HOSPITAL (C, 84 beds) 865 South First Street, Jesup, GA Zip 31598–0210, Mailing Address: P.O. Box 410, Zip 31598–0410; tel. 912/427–6811; Charles R. Morgan, Chief Executive Officer
Web address: www.wmhweb.com

IDAHO: BENEWAH COMMUNITY HOSPITAL (C, 20 beds) 229 South Seventh Street, Saint Maries, ID Zip 83861–1894; tel. 208/245–5551; Erik Fox, Chief Executive Officer

GRITMAN MEDICAL CENTER (C, 25 beds) 700 South Main Street, Moscow, ID Zip 83843–3047; tel. 208/882–4511; Jeffrey W. Martin, Chief Executive Officer
Web address: www.gritman.org

SHOSHONE MEDICAL CENTER (C, 25 beds) 25 Jacobs Gulch, Kellogg, ID Zip 83837–2096; tel. 208/784–1221; Gary Moore, Chief Executive Officer
Web address: www.shomed.org

STEELE MEMORIAL HOSPITAL (C, 18 beds) 707 Van Dreff, Salmon, ID Zip 83467–4109, Mailing Address: P.O. Box 700, Zip 83467–0700; tel. 208/756–4291; Victoria A. Alexander, Chief Executive Officer
Web address: www.steelemh.org

ILLINOIS: COMMUNITY MEMORIAL HOSPITAL (C, 25 beds) 400 Caldwell Street, Staunton, IL Zip 62088–1499; tel. 618/635–2200; Patrick B. Heise, Chief Executive Officer
Web address: www.stauntonhospital.org

CRAWFORD MEMORIAL HOSPITAL (C, 64 beds) 1000 North Allen Street, Robinson, IL Zip 62454–1167; tel. 618/546–1234; Randy Simmons, Chief Executive Officer
Web address: www.crawfordmh.com

GIBSON AREA HOSPITAL AND HEALTH SERVICES (C, 80 beds) 1120 North Melvin Street, Gibson City, IL Zip 60936, Mailing Address: P.O. Box 429, Zip 60936–0429; tel. 217/784–4251; Gary L. Petersen, Chief Executive Officer
Web address: www.gibsonhospital.org

MEMORIAL HOSPITAL (C, 15 beds) 402 South Adams Street, Carthage, IL Zip 62321–1600, Mailing Address: P.O. Box 160, Zip 62321–0160; tel. 217/357–3131; Ada Bair, Chief Executive Officer
Web address: www.mhtlc.com

PEKIN HOSPITAL (C, 107 beds) 600 South 13th Street, Pekin, IL Zip 61554–5098; tel. 309/347–1151; Douglas Wilson, Chief Executive Officer
Web address: www.pekinhospital.org

INDIANA: DAVIESS COMMUNITY HOSPITAL (C, 70 beds) 1314 East Walnut Street, Washington, IN Zip 47501–2198, Mailing Address: P.O. Box 760, Zip 47501–0760; tel. 812/254–2760; Robert J. Heckert Jr, Chief Executive Officer
Web address: www.dchosp.org

SULLIVAN COUNTY COMMUNITY HOSPITAL (C, 37 beds) 2200 North Section Street, Sullivan, IN Zip 47882, Mailing Address: P.O. Box 10, Zip 47882–0010; tel. 812/268–4311; Patricia Holden, Chief Executive Officer
Web address: www.schosp.com

IOWA: BOONE COUNTY HOSPITAL (C, 48 beds) 1015 Union Street, Boone, IA Zip 50036–4821; tel. 515/432–3140; Joseph S. Smith, Chief Executive Officer
Web address: www.boonehospital.com

FORT MADISON COMMUNITY HOSPITAL (C, 50 beds) 5445 Avenue O, Fort Madison, IA Zip 52627–0174, Mailing Address: P.O. Box 174, Zip 52627–0174; tel. 319/372–6530; C. James Platt, Chief Executive Officer
Web address: www.fmchosp.com

KNOXVILLE AREA COMMUNITY HOSPITAL AND CLINIC (C, 25 beds) 1002 South Lincoln Street, Knoxville, IA Zip 50138–3155; tel. 641/842–2151; Ann M. Helwig, Chief Executive Officer
Web address: www.kach.org

KANSAS: COFFEYVILLE REGIONAL MEDICAL CENTER (C, 105 beds) 1400 West Fourth, Coffeyville, KS Zip 67337–0856; tel. 620/251–1200; Gerald J. Marquette Jr, Chief Executive Officer
Web address: www.crmcinc.com

NEOSHO MEMORIAL REGIONAL MEDICAL CENTER (C, 59 beds) 629 South Plummer, Chanute, KS Zip 66720–0426, Mailing Address: P.O. Box 426, Zip 66720–0426; tel. 620/431–4000; Murray L. Brown, Chief Executive Officer
Web address: www.nmrmc.com

NEWMAN REGIONAL HEALTH (C, 122 beds) 1201 West 12th Avenue, Emporia, KS Zip 66801–2597; tel. 620/343–6800; Terry R. Lambert, CHE, Chief Executive Officer
Web address: www.newmanrh.org

ST. LUKE HOSPITAL AND LIVING CENTER (C, 54 beds) 535 South Freeborn, Marion, KS Zip 66861–1299; tel. 620/382–2179; Thomas C. Smith III, Chief Executive Officer

KENTUCKY: CALDWELL COUNTY HOSPITAL (C, 48 beds) 101 Hospital Drive, Princeton, KY Zip 42445–0410; tel. 270/365–0300; Charles D. Lovell Jr, President and Chief Executive Officer
Web address: www.caldwellhosp.org

CRITTENDEN COUNTY HOSPITAL (C, 228 beds) Highway 60 South, Marion, KY Zip 42064–6201, Mailing Address: P.O. Box 386, Zip 42064–0386; tel. 270/965–5281; Claudia Ann Eisenmann, Chief Executive Officer
Web address: www.crittenden–health.org

CUMBERLAND COUNTY HOSPITAL (C, 25 beds) Highway 90 West, Burkesville, KY Zip 42717–0280, Mailing Address: P.O. Box 280, Zip 42717–0280; tel. 270/864–2511; Edward J. Sanford, Chief Executive Officer
Web address: www.cchospital.org

FLEMING COUNTY HOSPITAL (C, 32 beds) 920 Elizaville Avenue, Flemingsburg, KY Zip 41041, Mailing Address: P.O. Box 388, Zip 41041–0388; tel. 606/849–5000; Harrell L. Connelly, Interim Chief Executive Officer
Web address: www.flemingcountyhospital.org

Section B

For explanation of codes following names, see page B2.
★ Indicates Type III membership in the American Hospital Association.

JENNIE STUART MEDICAL CENTER (C, 139 beds) 320 West 18th Street, Hopkinsville, KY Zip 42241–2400, Mailing Address: P.O. Box 2400, Zip 42241–2400; tel. 270/887–0100; Lewis T. Peeples, Chief Executive Officer
Web address: www.jsmc.org

MARSHALL COUNTY HOSPITAL (C, 80 beds) 503 George McClain Drive, Benton, KY Zip 42025–1399, Mailing Address: P.O. Box 630, Zip 42025–0630; tel. 270/527–4800; Kathy Long, Chief Executive Officer
Web address: www.marshallcountyhospital.org

MONROE COUNTY MEDICAL CENTER (C, 49 beds) 529 Capp Harlan Road, Tompkinsville, KY Zip 42167–1840; tel. 270/487–9231; Vicky McFall, Chief Executive Officer
Web address: www.mcmccares.com

OHIO COUNTY HOSPITAL (C, 25 beds) 1211 Main Street, Hartford, KY Zip 42347–1619; tel. 270/298–7411; Blaine Pieper, Chief Executive Officer
Web address: www.ohiocountyhospital.com

LOUISIANA: FRANKLIN FOUNDATION HOSPITAL (C, 25 beds) 1501 Hospital Avenue, Franklin, LA Zip 70538–3724, Mailing Address: P.O. Box 577, Zip 70538–0577; tel. 337/828–0760; J. Calvin Green, Chief Executive Officer
Web address: www.franklinfoundation.org

OPELOUSAS GENERAL HEALTH SYSTEM (C, 154 beds) 539 East Prudhomme Street, Opelousas, LA Zip 70570, Mailing Address: P.O. Box 1389, Zip 70571–1389; tel. 337/948–3011; William F. Barrow II, Chief Executive Officer
Web address: www.opelousasgeneral.com

THIBODAUX REGIONAL MEDICAL CENTER (C, 140 beds) 602 North Acadia Road, Thibodaux, LA Zip 70301–4847, Mailing Address: P.O. Box 1118, Zip 70302–1118; tel. 985/447–5500; Greg K. Stock, Chief Executive Officer
Web address: www.thibodaux.com

MAINE: CALAIS REGIONAL HOSPITAL (C, 25 beds) 22 Hospital Lane, Calais, ME Zip 04619–1398; tel. 207/454–7521; Ray H. Davis Jr, Chief Executive Officer
Web address: www.calaishospital.com

CARY MEDICAL CENTER (C, 49 beds) 163 Van Buren Road, Suite 1, Caribou, ME Zip 04736–2599; tel. 207/498–3111; Kris Doody–Chabre, Chief Executive Officer
Web address: www.carymedicalcenter.org

DOWN EAST COMMUNITY HOSPITAL (C, 34 beds) Upper Court Street, Machias, ME Zip 04654, Mailing Address: Rural Route 1, Box 11, Zip 04654–9702; tel. 207/255–3356; Wayne Dodwell, Chief Executive Officer
Web address: www.dech.org

MILLINOCKET REGIONAL HOSPITAL (C, 25 beds) 200 Somerset Street, Millinocket, ME Zip 04462–1298; tel. 207/723–5161; Marie E. Vienneau, R.N., Chief Executive Officer
Web address: www.mrhme.org

PENOBSCOT VALLEY HOSPITAL (C, 25 beds) 7 Transalpine Road, Lincoln, ME Zip 04457–0368, Mailing Address: P.O. Box 368, Zip 04457–0368; tel. 207/794–3321; Ronald D. Victory, Chief Executive Officer
Web address: www.pvhhealthcare.org

MICHIGAN: ALLEGAN GENERAL HOSPITAL (C, 63 beds) 555 Linn Street, Allegan, MI Zip 49010–1594; tel. 269/673–8424; Gerald J. Barbini, President and Chief Executive Officer
Web address: www.aghosp.org

COMMUNITY HOSPITAL (C, 56 beds) 400 Medical Park Drive, Watervliet, MI Zip 49098–9225; tel. 269/463–3111; Fritz Fahrenbacher, Interim President and Chief Executive Officer
Web address: www.communityhospitalwatervliet.com

HAYES–GREEN–BEACH MEMORIAL HOSPITAL (C, 32 beds) 321 East Harris Street, Charlotte, MI Zip 48813–1697; tel. 517/543–1050; Matthew Rush, President and Chief Executive Officer
Web address: www.hgbhealth.com

LAKEVIEW COMMUNITY HOSPITAL (C, 174 beds) 408 Hazen Street, Paw Paw, MI Zip 49079–0209, Mailing Address: P.O. Box 209, Zip 49079–0209; tel. 269/657–3141; Rick Ament, President and Chief Executive Officer
Web address: www.lakeviewcares.com

MARLETTE COMMUNITY HOSPITAL (C, 91 beds) 2770 Main Street, Marlette, MI Zip 48453–0307, Mailing Address: P.O. Box 307, Zip 48453–0307; tel. 989/635–4000; David S. McEwen, Chief Executive Officer
Web address: www.marlettecommunityhospital.com

MECOSTA COUNTY MEDICAL CENTER (C, 64 beds) 605 Oak Street, Big Rapids, MI Zip 49307–2099; tel. 231/796–8691; Thomas E. Daugherty, Administrator
Web address: www.mcmcbr.com

STURGIS HOSPITAL (C, 49 beds) 916 Myrtle, Sturgis, MI Zip 49091–2001; tel. 269/651–7824; Robert J. LaBarge, Chief Executive Officer
Web address: www.sturgishospital.com

THREE RIVERS HEALTH (C, 60 beds) 701 South Health Parkway, Three Rivers, MI Zip 49093–9362; tel. 269/278–1145; Matthew Chambers, Chief Executive Officer
Web address: www.trah.org

MINNESOTA: FALLS MEMORIAL HOSPITAL (C, 25 beds) 1400 Highway 71, International Falls, MN Zip 56649–2189; tel. 218/283–4481; Ty W. Erickson, Chief Executive Officer
Web address: www.fmh–mn.com

MISSISSIPPI: HANCOCK MEDICAL CENTER (C, 104 beds) 149 Drinkwater Boulevard, Bay Saint Louis, MS Zip 39521–2790, Mailing Address: P.O. Box 2790, Zip 39521–2790; tel. 228/467–8600; Hal W. Leftwich, FACHE, Administrator
Web address: www.hmc.org

KING'S DAUGHTERS MEDICAL CENTER (C, 109 beds) 427 Highway 51 North, Brookhaven, MS Zip 39601–2600, Mailing Address: P.O. Box 948, Zip 39602–0948; tel. 601/833–6011; Phillip L. Grady, Chief Executive Officer
Web address: www.kdmc.org

NATCHEZ REGIONAL MEDICAL CENTER (C, 109 beds) Seargent S Prentiss Drive, Natchez, MS Zip 39120–4726, Mailing Address: P.O. Box 1488, Zip 39121–1488; tel. 601/443–2100; Jack F. Houghton, Chief Executive Officer
Web address: www.natchezregional.com

NESHOBA COUNTY GENERAL HOSPITAL (C, 204 beds) 1001 Holland Avenue, Philadelphia, MS Zip 39350–2161, Mailing Address: P.O. Box 648, Zip 39350–0648; tel. 601/663–1200; Lawrence Graeber, Chief Executive Officer

UNIVERSITY HOSPITAL AND CLINICS – HOLMES COUNTY (C, 42 beds) 239 Bowling Green Road, Lexington, MS Zip 39095–9332; tel. 662/834–1321; Mary Ellen Pratt, Chief Executive Officer

UNIVERSITY HOSPITALS AND CLINICS, UNIVERSITY OF MISSISSIPPI MEDICAL CENTER (C, 774 beds) 2500 North State Street, Jackson, MS Zip 39216–4505; tel. 601/984–1000; Frederick Woodrell, CHE, Chief Executive Officer
Web address: www.umc.edu

MISSOURI: NEVADA REGIONAL MEDICAL CENTER (C, 53 beds) 800 South Ash Street, Nevada, MO Zip 64772–3223; tel. 417/667–3355; Judith K. Feuquay, Chief Executive Officer
Web address: www.nrmchealth.com

MONTANA: CENTRAL MONTANA MEDICAL CENTER (C, 124 beds) 408 Wendell Avenue, Lewistown, MT Zip 59457–2261; tel. 406/538–7711; David M. Faulkner, Chief Executive Officer
Web address: www.cmmccares.com

NORTH VALLEY HOSPITAL (C, 25 beds) 6575 Highway 93 South, Whitefish, MT Zip 59937–2990; tel. 406/863–3500; Craig E. Aasved, Chief Executive Officer
Web address: www.nvhosp.org

NEBRASKA: GREAT PLAINS REGIONAL MEDICAL CENTER (C, 98 beds) 601 West Leota Street, North Platte, NE Zip 69101–6598, Mailing Address: P.O. Box 1167, Zip 69103–1167; tel. 308/534–9310; Lucinda A. Bradley, Chief Executive Officer
Web address: www.gprmc.com

PHELPS MEMORIAL HEALTH CENTER (C, 30 beds) 1215 Tibbals Street, Holdrege, NE Zip 68949–1280; tel. 308/995–2211; Joyce Grove Hein, Administrator and Chief Executive Officer
Web address: www.phelpsmemorial.com

NEW HAMPSHIRE: LITTLETON REGIONAL HOSPITAL (C, 25 beds) 600 Saint Johnsbury Road, Littleton, NH Zip 03561–3436; tel. 603/444–9000; William E. Holmes, Chief Executive Officer
Web address: www.littletonhospital.org

NEW MEXICO: CIBOLA GENERAL HOSPITAL (C, 25 beds) 1016 Roosevelt Avenue, Grants, NM Zip 87020–2104; tel. 505/287–4446; Vincent Ashley, Chief Executive Officer
Web address: www.cibolahospital.com

For explanation of codes following names, see page B2.
★ Indicates Type III membership in the American Hospital Association.

Section B

GERALD CHAMPION REGIONAL MEDICAL CENTER (C, 99 beds) 2669 North Scenic Drive, Alamogordo, NM Zip 88310–8799; tel. 505/439–6100; Carl W. Mantey, Chief Executive Officer
Web address: www.gcrmc.org

GILA REGIONAL MEDICAL CENTER (C, 68 beds) 1313 East 32nd Street, Silver City, NM Zip 88061; tel. 505/538–4000; John Rossfeld, Chief Executive Officer
Web address: www.grmc.org

HOLY CROSS HOSPITAL (C, 49 beds) 1397 Weimer Road, Taos, NM Zip 87571–6284, Mailing Address: P.O. Box DD, Zip 87571–6284; tel. 505/758–8883; Warren K. Spellman, Chief Executive Officer
Web address: www.taoshospital.org

NORTH CAROLINA: ALLEGHANY MEMORIAL HOSPITAL (C, 46 beds) 233 Doctors Street, Sparta, NC Zip 28675–0009, Mailing Address: P.O. Box 9, Zip 28675–0009; tel. 336/372–5511; Kevin Harlan, Chief Executive Officer
Web address: www.amhsparta.org

ANGEL MEDICAL CENTER (C, 59 beds) Riverview and White Oak Streets, Franklin, NC Zip 28734, Mailing Address: P.O. Box 1209, Zip 28744; tel. 828/524–8411; Michael E. Zuliani, Chief Executive Officer
Web address: www.angelmed.org

ASHE MEMORIAL HOSPITAL (C, 115 beds) 200 Hospital Avenue, Jefferson, NC Zip 28640–9244; tel. 336/846–7101; R. D. Williams, Administrator and Chief Executive Officer
Web address: www.ashememorial.org

CHATHAM HOSPITAL (C, 25 beds) West Third Street and Ivy Avenue, Siler City, NC Zip 27344–2343, Mailing Address: P.O. Box 649, Zip 27344; tel. 919/663–2113; Woodrow W. Hathaway Jr, Chief Executive Officer
Web address: www.chathamhospital.org

COLUMBUS COUNTY HOSPITAL (C, 113 beds) 500 Jefferson Street, Whiteville, NC Zip 28472–9987; tel. 910/642–8011; William S. Clark, Chief Executive Officer
Web address: www.cchospital.com

GOOD HOPE HOSPITAL (C, 47 beds) 410 Denim Drive, Erwin, NC Zip 28339–0668; tel. 910/897–6151; Donald E. Annis, Chief Executive Officer
Web address: www.goodhopehospital.org

GRANVILLE MEDICAL CENTER (C, 142 beds) 1010 College Street, Oxford, NC Zip 27565–2507, Mailing Address: P.O. Box 947, Zip 27565–0947; tel. 919/690–3000; Ronald J. Vigus, Chief Executive Officer
Web address: www.granvillemedical.com

HUGH CHATHAM MEMORIAL HOSPITAL (C, 220 beds) 180 Parkwood Drive, Elkin, NC Zip 28621–0560, Mailing Address: P.O. Box 560, Zip 28621–0560; tel. 336/527–7000; Richard D. Osmus, Chief Executive Officer
Web address: www.hughchatham.org

JOHNSTON MEMORIAL HOSPITAL (C, 160 beds) 509 North Bright Leaf Boulevard, Smithfield, NC Zip 27577–1376, Mailing Address: P.O. Box 1376, Zip 27577–1376; tel. 919/934–8171; Leland E. Farnell, President
Web address: www.johnstonmemorial.org

MOREHEAD MEMORIAL HOSPITAL (C, 242 beds) 117 East King's Highway, Eden, NC Zip 27288–5299; tel. 336/623–9711; Robert Enders, President
Web address: www.morehead.org

NORTHERN HOSPITAL OF SURRY COUNTY (C, 113 beds) 830 Rockford Street, Mount Airy, NC Zip 27030–5365, Mailing Address: P.O. Box 1101, Zip 27030–1101; tel. 336/719–7000; William B. James, Chief Executive Officer
Web address: www.northernhospital.com

RUTHERFORD HOSPITAL (C, 143 beds) 288 South Ridgecrest Avenue, Rutherfordton, NC Zip 28139–3097; tel. 828/286–5000; Robert D. Jones, President
Web address: www.rutherfordhosp.org

OHIO: BROWN COUNTY GENERAL HOSPITAL (C, 59 beds) 425 Home Street, Georgetown, OH Zip 45121–1407; tel. 937/378–7500; Bruce A. Bennett, Chief Executive Officer
Web address: www.browncountygeneralhospital.org

KNOX COMMUNITY HOSPITAL (C, 82 beds) 1330 Coshocton Road, Mount Vernon, OH Zip 43050–1495; tel. 740/393–9000; Kevin L. Rogols, Chief Executive Officer
Web address: www.knoxcommhosp.org

MEMORIAL HOSPITAL (C, 120 beds) 715 South Taft Avenue, Fremont, OH Zip 43420–3200; tel. 419/332–7321; John A. Gorman, Chief Executive Officer
Web address: www.fremontmemorial.org

SELBY GENERAL HOSPITAL (C, 25 beds) 1106 Colegate Drive, Marietta, OH Zip 45750–1323; tel. 740/568–2000; Kevin P. Calhoun, Chief Executive Officer
Web address: www.selbygeneralhospital.com

WOOSTER COMMUNITY HOSPITAL (C, 114 beds) 1761 Beall Avenue, Wooster, OH Zip 44691–2342; tel. 330/263–8100; William E. Sheron, Chief Executive Officer
Web address: www.woosterhospital.org

OKLAHOMA: CHOCTAW MEMORIAL HOSPITAL (C, 34 beds) 1405 East Kirk Road, Hugo, OK Zip 74743–3603; tel. 580/326–6414; Steven K. Jacobson, Chief Executive Officer and Administrator

HASKELL COUNTY HEALTHCARE SYSTEM (C, 29 beds) 401 N.W. H Street, Stigler, OK Zip 74462–1625; tel. 918/967–4682; Mark Harrel, Chief Executive Officer

KINGFISHER REGIONAL HOSPITAL (C, 25 beds) 500 South Ninth Street, Kingfisher, OK Zip 73750–3528, Mailing Address: P.O. Box 59, Zip 73750–0059; tel. 405/375–3141; Damon Benson, Chief Executive Officer
Web address: www.kingfisherhospital.com

LOGAN MEDICAL CENTER (C, 25 beds) Highway 33 West at Academy Road, Guthrie, OK Zip 73044–3700, Mailing Address: P.O. Box 1017, Zip 73044–1017; tel. 405/282–6700; Shawn Morrow, Chief Executive Officer
Web address: www.loganhosp.com

PERRY MEMORIAL HOSPITAL (C, 26 beds) 501 14th Street, Perry, OK Zip 73077–5099; tel. 580/336–3541; Joe Duerr, Chief Executive Officer
Web address: www.pmh–ok.org

PURCELL MUNICIPAL HOSPITAL (C, 30 beds) 1500 North Green Avenue, Purcell, OK Zip 73080–1699, Mailing Address: P.O. Box 511, Zip 73080–0511; tel. 405/527–6524; Curtis R. Pryor, Chief Executive Officer
Web address: www.purcellhospital.com

SAYRE MEMORIAL HOSPITAL (C, 35 beds) 501 East Washington Street, Sayre, OK Zip 73662–1337; tel. 580/928–5541; Rex Jones, Chief Executive Officer

SHARE MEDICAL CENTER (C, 117 beds) 800 Share Drive, Alva, OK Zip 73717–3699, Mailing Address: P.O. Box 727, Zip 73717–0727; tel. 580/327–2800; Barbara Oestmann, Chief Executive Officer
Web address: www.smcok.com

PENNSYLVANIA: CLARION HOSPITAL (C, 83 beds) One Hospital Drive, Clarion, PA Zip 16214–8599; tel. 814/226–9500; Edward J. Hannon, President and Chief Executive Officer
Web address: www.clarionhospital.org

J. C. BLAIR MEMORIAL HOSPITAL (C, 71 beds) 1225 Warm Springs Avenue, Huntingdon, PA Zip 16652–2398; tel. 814/643–2290; Roger D. Feldt, FACHE, Interim President and Chief Executive Officer
Web address: www.jcblair.org

JERSEY SHORE HOSPITAL (C, 25 beds) 1020 Thompson Street, Jersey Shore, PA Zip 17740–1794; tel. 570/398–0100; Louis A. Ditzel Jr, President and Chief Executive Officer
Web address: www.jsh.org

MEMORIAL HOSPITAL (C, 162 beds) One Hospital Drive, Towanda, PA Zip 18848–9702; tel. 570/265–2191; Gary A. Baker, President
Web address: www.memorialhospital.org

OHIO VALLEY GENERAL HOSPITAL (C, 89 beds) 25 Heckel Road, McKees Rocks, PA Zip 15136–1694; tel. 412/777–6161; William F. Provenzano, President and Chief Executive Officer
Web address: www.ohiovalleyhospital.org

TYRONE HOSPITAL (C, 59 beds) One Hospital Drive, Tyrone, PA Zip 16686–1810; tel. 814/684–1255; Walter S. Van Dyke, Chief Executive Officer
Web address: www.tyronehospital.org

SOUTH CAROLINA: ABBEVILLE COUNTY MEMORIAL HOSPITAL (C, 40 beds) 901 West Greenwood Street, Abbeville, SC Zip 29620–0887, Mailing Address: P.O. Box 887, Zip 29620–0887; tel. 864/366–5011; Alvin Hoover, CHE, Chief Executive Officer

For explanation of codes following names, see page B2.
★ Indicates Type III membership in the American Hospital Association.

GEORGETOWN MEMORIAL HOSPITAL (C, 135 beds) 606 Black River Road, Georgetown, SC Zip 29440–3368, Mailing Address: Drawer 1718, Zip 29442–1718; tel. 843/527–7000; Bruce P. Bailey, Chief Executive Officer
Web address: www.gmhsc.com

LAKE CITY COMMUNITY HOSPITAL (C, 40 beds) 258 North Ron McNair Boulevard, Lake City, SC Zip 29560–1029, Mailing Address: P.O. Box 1479, Zip 29560–1479; tel. 843/374–2036; Clarence W. Bowman, Chief Executive Officer

LAURENS COUNTY HEALTHCARE SYSTEM (C, 90 beds) Highway 76 East, Clinton, SC Zip 29325–2331, Mailing Address: P.O. Box 976, Zip 29325–0976; tel. 864/833–9100; Richard E. D'Alberto, FACHE, Chief Executive Officer
Web address: www.lchcs.org

NEWBERRY COUNTY MEMORIAL HOSPITAL (C, 77 beds) 2669 Kinard Street, Newberry, SC Zip 29108–0497, Mailing Address: P.O. Box 497, Zip 29108–0497; tel. 803/276–7570; Lynn W. Beasley, President and Chief Executive Officer
Web address: www.newberryhospital.org

REGIONAL MEDICAL CENTER OF ORANGEBURG AND CALHOUN COUNTIES (C, 286 beds) 3000 St. Matthews Road, Orangeburg, SC Zip 29118–1470; tel. 803/395–2200; Thomas C. Dandridge, President
Web address: www.regmed.com

WACCAMAW COMMUNITY HOSPITAL (C, 83 beds) 4070 Highway 17 Bypass, Murrells Inlet, SC Zip 29576, Mailing Address: P.O. Drawer 3350, Zip 29576; tel. 843/652–1000; Gayle L. Resetar, Chief Operating Officer
Web address: www.gmhsc.com

WALLACE THOMSON HOSPITAL (C, 220 beds) 322 West South Street, Union, SC Zip 29379–2857, Mailing Address: P.O. Box 789, Zip 29379–0789; tel. 864/429–2600; Karen A. Fiducia, Interim Chief Executive Officer
Web address: www.wallacethomson.com

SOUTH DAKOTA: HURON REGIONAL MEDICAL CENTER (C, 61 beds) 172 Fourth Street S.E., Huron, SD Zip 57350–2590; tel. 605/353–6200; John L. Single, Chief Executive Officer
Web address: www.huronregional.org

TENNESSEE: BEDFORD COUNTY MEDICAL CENTER (C, 176 beds) 845 Union Street, Shelbyville, TN Zip 37160–2609; tel. 931/685–5433; William P. Macri, Chief Executive Officer
Web address: www.bcmctn.com

LINCOLN COUNTY HEALTH SYSTEM (C, 327 beds) 106 Medical Center Boulevard, Fayetteville, TN Zip 37334–2684; tel. 931/438–1100; Gary G. Kendrick, Chief Executive Officer
Web address: www.lchealthsystem.com

MACON COUNTY GENERAL HOSPITAL (C, 25 beds) 204 Medical Drive, Lafayette, TN Zip 37083–1799, Mailing Address: P.O. Box 378, Zip 37083–0378; tel. 615/666–2147; Dennis A. Wolford, FACHE, Chief Executive Officer
Web address: www.mcgh.net

RHEA MEDICAL CENTER (C, 114 beds) 7900 Rhea County Highway, Dayton, TN Zip 37321–5912; tel. 423/775–1121; Kennedy L. Croom Jr, Administrator and Chief Executive Officer
Web address: www.rheamedical.org

TEXAS: BRAZOSPORT MEMORIAL HOSPITAL (C, 156 beds) 100 Medical Drive, Lake Jackson, TX Zip 77566–9983; tel. 979/297–4411; Daniel L. Buche, Chief Executive Officer
Web address: www.brazosportmemorial.com

CAMPBELL HEALTH SYSTEM (C, 78 beds) 713 East Anderson Street, Weatherford, TX Zip 76086–9971; tel. 817/596–8751; Scott M. Landrum, Chief Executive Officer
Web address: www.campbellhealth.com

HENDERSON MEMORIAL HOSPITAL (C, 76 beds) 300 Wilson Street, Henderson, TX Zip 75652–5956; tel. 903/657–7541; David Klein, Interim Chief Executive Officer
Web address: www.hmhnet.org

MATAGORDA GENERAL HOSPITAL (C, 67 beds) 1115 Avenue G, Bay City, TX Zip 77414–3544; tel. 979/245–6383; Daryle Voss, Chief Executive Officer
Web address: www.matagordageneral.org

MEMORIAL HOSPITAL (C, 34 beds) Highway 90A By-Pass, Gonzales, TX Zip 78629–2021, Mailing Address: P.O. Box 587, Zip 78629–0587; tel. 830/672–7581; Charles Norris, Chief Executive Officer
Web address: www.gonzaleshealthcare.com

VERMONT: NORTHWESTERN MEDICAL CENTER (C, 52 beds) 133 Fairfield Street, Saint Albans, VT Zip 05478–1734, Mailing Address: P.O. Box 1370, Zip 05478–1370; tel. 802/524–5911; Peter A. Hofstetter, Chief Executive Officer
Web address: www.nmcinc.org

VIRGINIA: DICKENSON COMMUNITY HOSPITAL (C, 15 beds) Hospital Drive, Clintwood, VA Zip 24228, Mailing Address: P.O. Box 1440, Zip 24228–1440; tel. 276/926–0300; Kenneth Boyd, Chief Executive Officer
Web address: www.dchosp.com

NORTON COMMUNITY HOSPITAL (C, 129 beds) 100 15th Street N.W., Norton, VA Zip 24273–1699; tel. 276/679–9600; David G. Fuqua, Chief Executive Officer
Web address: www.nchosp.org

WASHINGTON: KADLEC MEDICAL CENTER (C, 166 beds) 888 Swift Boulevard, Richland, WA Zip 99352–3542; tel. 509/946–4611; Rand J. Wortman, President and Chief Executive Officer
Web address: www.kadlecmed.org

WISCONSIN: AMERY REGIONAL MEDICAL CENTER (C, 13 beds) 225 Scholl Court, Amery, WI Zip 54001–1292; tel. 715/268–8000; Michael Karuschak Jr, Chief Executive Officer
Web address: www.amerymedicalcenter.org

RIVERSIDE MEDICAL CENTER (C, 25 beds) 800 Riverside Drive, Waupaca, WI Zip 54981–1999; tel. 715/258–1000; Craig A. Kantos, Chief Executive Officer
Web address: www.riversidemedical.org

WYOMING: IVINSON MEMORIAL HOSPITAL (C, 99 beds) 255 North 30th Street, Laramie, WY Zip 82072–5195; tel. 307/742–2141; Nelson Toebbe, Chief Executive Officer
Web address: www.ivinsonhospital.org

WEST PARK HOSPITAL (C, 153 beds) 707 Sheridan Avenue, Cody, WY Zip 82414–3409; tel. 307/527–7501; Douglas A. McMillan, Administrator and Chief Executive Officer
Web address: www.westparkhospital.org

Owned, leased, sponsored:	0 hospitals	0 beds
Contract-managed:	139 hospitals	11681 beds
Totals:	139 hospitals	11681 beds

★0260: REGENCY HOSPITAL COMPANY (IO)
30000 Mill Creek Avenue, Suite 250, Alpharetta, GA Zip 30022; tel. 770/772–4345; Rod Laughlin, President and Chief Executive Officer

ARKANSAS: REGENCY HOSPITAL OF NORTHWEST ARKANSAS (O, 25 beds) 1125 North College, Fayetteville, AR Zip 72703; tel. 479/713–7000; Michael A. McLean, Chief Executive Officer
Web address: www.regencyhospital.com

REGENCY HOSPITAL OF SPRINGDALE (O, 15 beds) 609 West Maple Avenue, 6th Floor, Springdale, AR Zip 72764; tel. 479/757–2600;
Web address: www.regencyhospital.com

GEORGIA: REGENCY HOSPITAL OF CENTRAL GEORGIA (O, 34 beds) 700 Spring Street, Macon, GA Zip 31201; tel. 478/633–8260; Richard W. Graham, Chief Executive Officer

REGENCY HOSPITAL OF SOUTH ATLANTA (O, 25 beds) 1170 Cleveland Avenue, 4th Floor, East Point, GA Zip 30344; tel. 404/466–6250; Carolyn S. Gray, Chief Executive Officer

INDIANA: REGENCY HOSPITAL OF NORTHWEST INDIANA (O, 25 beds) 4321 Fir Street, 4th Floor, East Chicago, IN Zip 46312; tel. 219/392–7790; Patrick Ryan, Chief Executive Officer

LOUISIANA: REGENCY HOSPITAL OF COVINGTON (O, 24 beds) 195 Highland Park Entrance, Covington, LA Zip 70433; tel. 985/867–3977; Laurence J. Frayne, Chief Executive Officer

MINNESOTA: REGENCY HOSPITAL OF MINNEAPOLIS (O, 15 beds) 1300 Hidden Lakes Parkway, Golden Valley, MN Zip 55422–4299; tel. 612/588–2771; Douglas Beardsley, Administrator

MISSISSIPPI: REGENCY HOSPITAL OF HATTIESBURG (O, 37 beds) 125 South 25th Avenue, Hattiesburg, MS Zip 39401; tel. 601/288–8510; James S. Kaigler, FACHE, Chief Executive Officer
Web address: www.regencyhospital.com/hattiesburg.htm

For explanation of codes following names, see page B2.
★ Indicates Type III membership in the American Hospital Association.

REGENCY HOSPITAL OF MERIDIAN (O, 37 beds) 1102 Constitution Avenue, 2nd Floor, Meridian, MS Zip 39301, Mailing Address: 1102 Constitution Avenue, 2nd Floor, Zip 39301; tel. 601/484–7900; Benny Costello, Chief Executive Officer
Web address: www.ltac.com

OHIO: REGENCY HOSPITAL OF AKRON (O, 36 beds) 155 Fifth Street N.E., Barberton, OH Zip 44203; tel. 330/861–2065; Richard L. Adams, Chief Executive Officer
Web address: www.regencyhospital.com

REGENCY HOSPITAL OF RAVENNA (O, 19 beds) 6847 North Chestnut Street, Ravenna, OH Zip 44266; tel. 330/296–2350; Robert A. Leonhard Jr, Chief Executive Officer

SOUTH CAROLINA: REGENCY HOSPITAL OF FLORENCE (O, 28 beds) 121 East Cedar Street, Florence, SC Zip 29506; tel. 843/661–3499; Daniel C. Dunmyer, Chief Executive Officer
Web address: www.regencyhospital.com

TEXAS: REGENCY HOSPITAL OF ODESSA (O, 36 beds) 500 West 4th Street, Suite 701, Odessa, TX Zip 79761; tel. 432/552–4000; Patrick A. Auman, Ph.D., Chief Executive Officer

Owned, leased, sponsored:	13 hospitals	356 beds
Contract–managed:	0 hospitals	0 beds
Totals:	13 hospitals	356 beds

8495: REGIONAL HEALTH (NP)
353 Fairmont Boulevard, Rapid City, SD Zip 57701, Mailing Address: P.O. Box 6000, Zip 57709–6000; tel. 605/719–1000; Charles Hart, M.D., President and Chief Executive Officer
(Moderately Centralized Health System)

NEBRASKA: GORDON MEMORIAL HOSPITAL (C, 65 beds) 300 East Eighth Street, Gordon, NE Zip 69343–9990; tel. 308/282–0401; Mehdi Merred, Chief Executive Officer
Web address: www.gordonhospital.org

SOUTH DAKOTA: CUSTER COMMUNITY HOSPITAL (L, 87 beds) 1039 Montgomery Street, Custer, SD Zip 57730–1397; tel. 605/673–2229; Jason Petik, Chief Executive Officer
Web address: www.custerhospital.org

FIVE COUNTIES HOSPITAL (C, 47 beds) 405 Sixth Avenue West, Lemmon, SD Zip 57638–1318, Mailing Address: P.O. Box 479, Zip 57638–0479; tel. 605/374–3871; Jannette Van Beek, Chief Executive Officer
Web address: www.rcrh.org/facilities/hospitals/fivecounties.asp

HANS P. PETERSON MEMORIAL HOSPITAL (C, 48 beds) 503 West Pine Street, Philip, SD Zip 57567, Mailing Address: P.O. Box 790, Zip 57567–0790; tel. 605/859–2511; David Dick, Chief Executive Officer
Web address: www.rcrh.org/Facilities/Hospitals/HPPMemorial.asp

LOOKOUT MEMORIAL HOSPITAL (O, 40 beds) 1440 North Main Street, Spearfish, SD Zip 57783–1504; tel. 605/644–4000; Larry W. Veitz, Chief Executive Officer
Web address: www.rcrh.org

NORTHERN HILLS GENERAL HOSPITAL (O, 18 beds) 61 Charles Street, Deadwood, SD Zip 57732–1303; tel. 605/722–6101; Don A. Nelson, Chief Executive Officer
Web address: www.rcrh.org

RAPID CITY REGIONAL HOSPITAL SYSTEM OF CARE (O, 371 beds) 353 Fairmont Boulevard, Rapid City, SD Zip 57701–7393, Mailing Address: P.O. Box 6000, Zip 57709–6000; tel. 605/719–1000; Timothy H. Sughrue, Chief Executive Officer
Web address: www.rcrh.org

STURGIS COMMUNITY HEALTH CARE CENTER (O, 109 beds) 949 Harmon Street, Sturgis, SD Zip 57785–2452; tel. 605/347–2536; Van Hyde, Chief Executive Officer
Web address: www.rcrh.org/Facilities/Hospitals/SCHCC/Default.asp

WYOMING: WESTON COUNTY HEALTH SERVICES (C, 69 beds) 1124 Washington Boulevard, Newcastle, WY Zip 82701–2996; tel. 307/746–4491; George Minder, Chief Executive Officer
Web address: www.wchs-wy.org

Owned, leased, sponsored:	5 hospitals	625 beds
Contract–managed:	4 hospitals	229 beds
Totals:	9 hospitals	854 beds

0290: RESURGENCE HEALTH GROUP (IO)
1400 Buford Highway, Building R–3, Sugar Hill, GA Zip 30518; tel. 770/904–6731; Philip H. Eastman III, President
(Independent Hospital System)

ALABAMA: SOUTHWEST ALABAMA MEDICAL CENTER (O, 27 beds) 33700 Highway 43, Thomasville, AL Zip 36784–3351; tel. 334/636–4431; Kevin Bierschenk, Chief Executive Officer
Web address: www.resurgencehealthgroup.com

GEORGIA: FLINT RIVER COMMUNITY HOSPITAL (O, 49 beds) 509 Sumter Street, Montezuma, GA Zip 31063–0770, Mailing Address: P.O. Box 770, Zip 31063–0770; tel. 478/472–3100; Curt L. Roberts, Chief Executive Officer
Web address: www.resurgencehealthgroup.com

TATTNALL COMMUNITY HOSPITAL (O, 25 beds) 247 South Main Street, Reidsville, GA Zip 30453; tel. 912/557–1000; Karen O'Neal, Chief Executive Officer
Web address: www.resurgencehealthgroup.com

TEXAS: MEDICAL CENTER AT TERRELL (O, 130 beds) 1551 Highway 34 South, Terrell, TX Zip 75160–4833; tel. 972/563–7611; Kenneth Pittman, Interim Chief Executive Officer
Web address: www.medcenter–terrell.com

Owned, leased, sponsored:	4 hospitals	231 beds
Contract–managed:	0 hospitals	0 beds
Totals:	4 hospitals	231 beds

0171: RESURRECTION HEALTH CARE CORPORATION (CC)
7435 West Talcott Avenue, Chicago, IL Zip 60631; tel. 773/792–5150; Joseph F. Toomey, President and Chief Executive Officer
(Moderately Centralized Health System)

ILLINOIS: HOLY FAMILY MEDICAL CENTER (O, 165 beds) 100 North River Road, Des Plaines, IL Zip 60016–1255; tel. 847/297–1800; Sister Donna Marie Wolowicki, Executive Vice President and Chief Executive Officer
Web address: www.reshealth.org

OUR LADY OF THE RESURRECTION MEDICAL CENTER (O, 265 beds) 5645 West Addison Street, Chicago, IL Zip 60634–4455; tel. 773/282–7000; Ivette Estrada, Executive Vice President and Chief Executive Officer
Web address: www.reshealthcare.org

RESURRECTION MEDICAL CENTER (O, 398 beds) 7435 West Talcott Avenue, Chicago, IL Zip 60631–3746; tel. 773/774–8000; Sister Donna Marie Wolowicki, Executive Vice President and Chief Executive Officer
Web address: www.reshealthcare.org

SAINT FRANCIS HOSPITAL (O, 236 beds) 355 Ridge Avenue, Evanston, IL Zip 60202–3399; tel. 847/316–4000; Sherlyn Hailstone, Chief Executive Officer
Web address: www.reshealth.org

SAINT JOSEPH HOSPITAL (O, 345 beds) 2900 North Lake Shore Drive, Chicago, IL Zip 60657–6274; tel. 773/665–3000; Ronald E. Struxness, Chief Executive Officer
Web address: www.reshealth.org

SAINT'S MARY & ELIZABETH MEDICAL CENTER, CLAREMONT AVENUE (O, 252 beds) 1431 North Claremont Avenue, Chicago, IL Zip 60622–1791; tel. 773/278–2000; Margaret McDermott, Chief Executive Officer
Web address: www.reshealthcare.org

SAINT'S MARY & ELIZABETH MEDICAL CENTER, DIVISION STREET (O, 305 beds) 2233 West Division Street, Chicago, IL Zip 60622–3086; tel. 312/770–2000; Margaret McDermott, Chief Executive Officer
Web address: www.stmaryofnazareth.org

WEST SUBURBAN MEDICAL CENTER (O, 246 beds) 3 Erie Court, Oak Park, IL Zip 60302–2599; tel. 708/383–6200; Jay E. Kreuzer, FACHE, President and Chief Executive Officer
Web address: www.westsub.com

WESTLAKE HOSPITAL (O, 180 beds) 1225 Lake Street, Melrose Park, IL Zip 60160–4000; tel. 708/681–3000; Patricia Shehorn, Chief Executive Officer
Web address: www.reshealth.org

Owned, leased, sponsored:	9 hospitals	2392 beds
Contract–managed:	0 hospitals	0 beds
Totals:	9 hospitals	2392 beds

For explanation of codes following names, see page B2.
★ Indicates Type III membership in the American Hospital Association.

4810: RIVERSIDE HEALTH SYSTEM (NP)
701 Town Center Drive, Suite 1000, Newport News, VA Zip 23606; tel. 757/534–7000; Richard J. Pearce, President and Chief Executive Officer
(Centralized Health System)

VIRGINIA: RIVERSIDE BEHAVIORAL HEALTH CENTER (O, 125 beds) 2244 Executive Drive, Hampton, VA Zip 23666–2430; tel. 757/827–1001; Debora S. Tanner, Vice President and Administrator
Web address: www.riversideonline.com

RIVERSIDE REGIONAL MEDICAL CENTER (O, 237 beds) 500 J. Clyde Morris Boulevard, Newport News, VA Zip 23601–1976; tel. 757/594–2000; William B. Downey, Executive Vice President and Administrator
Web address: www.riverside-online.com

RIVERSIDE REHABILITATION INSTITUTE (O, 41 beds) 245 Chesapeake Avenue, Newport News, VA Zip 23607–6038; tel. 757/928–8000; Renee K. Rountree, Vice President and Administrator
Web address: www.riverside-online.com

RIVERSIDE TAPPAHANNOCK HOSPITAL (O, 28 beds) 618 Hospital Road, Tappahannock, VA Zip 22560–5000; tel. 804/443–3311; Elizabeth J. Martin, Vice President and Administrator
Web address: www.riverside-online.com

RIVERSIDE WALTER REED HOSPITAL (O, 27 beds) 7519 Hospital Drive, Gloucester, VA Zip 23061–4178, Mailing Address: P.O. Box 1130, Zip 23061–1130; tel. 804/693–8800; Robert E. Bryant, Vice President and Administrator
Web address: www.riversideonline.com/rwrh/index.html

Owned, leased, sponsored:	5 hospitals	458 beds
Contract–managed:	0 hospitals	0 beds
Totals:	5 hospitals	458 beds

0268: ROBERT WOOD JOHNSON HEALTH SYSTEM & NETWORK (NP)
1 Robert Wood Johnson Place, New Brunswick, NJ Zip 08903–2601; tel. 732/828–3000; Andrew Greene, Chief Executive Officer
(Moderately Centralized Health System)

NEW JERSEY: CHILDREN'S SPECIALIZED HOSPITAL (O, 109 beds) 150 New Providence Road, Mountainside, NJ Zip 07092–2590; tel. 908/233–3720; Amy B. Mansue, President and Chief Executive Officer
Web address: www.childrens-specialized.org

ROBERT WOOD JOHNSON UNIVERSITY HOSPITAL (O, 482 beds) 1 Robert Wood Johnson Place, New Brunswick, NJ Zip 08903–2601; tel. 732/828–3000; Clifton R. Lacy, M.D., President and Chief Executive Officer
Web address: www.rwjuh.edu

ROBERT WOOD JOHNSON UNIVERSITY HOSPITAL AT HAMILTON (O, 204 beds) One Hamilton Health Place, Hamilton, NJ Zip 08690–3599; tel. 609/586–7900; Christy Stephenson, Chief Executive Officer
Web address: www.rwjhamilton.org

ROBERT WOOD JOHNSON UNIVERSITY HOSPITAL AT RAHWAY (O, 157 beds) 865 Stone Street, Rahway, NJ Zip 07065–2797; tel. 732/381–4200; Kirk C. Tice, President and Chief Executive Officer
Web address: www.rahwayhospital.com

Owned, leased, sponsored:	4 hospitals	952 beds
Contract–managed:	0 hospitals	0 beds
Totals:	4 hospitals	952 beds

★0109: RURAL HEALTH MANAGEMENT CORPORATION (NP)
48 West 1500 North, Nephi, UT Zip 84648–1226; tel. 435/623–4924; Mark R. Stoddard, President
(Independent Hospital System)

UTAH: ALLEN MEMORIAL HOSPITAL (L, 25 beds) 719 West 400 North Street, Moab, UT Zip 84532–2297, Mailing Address: P.O. Box 998, Zip 84532–0998; tel. 435/259–7191; Marla Shelby–Drabner, FACHE, Administrator and Chief Executive Officer
Web address: www.amh-moab.org

CENTRAL VALLEY MEDICAL CENTER (L, 19 beds) 48 West 1500 North, Nephi, UT Zip 84648; tel. 435/623–3000; Mark R. Stoddard, President
Web address: www.centralvalleymed.com

Owned, leased, sponsored:	2 hospitals	44 beds
Contract–managed:	0 hospitals	0 beds
Totals:	2 hospitals	44 beds

0220: RUSH HEALTH SYSTEMS (NP)
1314 19th Avenue, Meridian, MS Zip 39301; tel. 601/483–0011; Wallace Strickland, President and Chief Executive Officer
(Moderately Centralized Health System)

MISSISSIPPI: RUSH FOUNDATION HOSPITAL (O, 182 beds) 1314 19th Avenue, Meridian, MS Zip 39301–4195; tel. 601/483–0011; Wallace Strickland, President and Chief Executive Officer
Web address: www.rushhealthsystems.org

SPECIALTY HOSPITAL OF MERIDIAN (O, 49 beds) 1314 19th Avenue, Meridian, MS Zip 39301–4116; tel. 601/703–4211; Wallace Strickland, President and Chief Executive Officer
Web address: www.rushhealthsystems.org

Owned, leased, sponsored:	2 hospitals	231 beds
Contract–managed:	0 hospitals	0 beds
Totals:	2 hospitals	231 beds

★3855: RUSH UNIVERSITY MEDICAL CENTER (NP)
1653 West Congress Parkway, Chicago, IL Zip 60612–3864; tel. 312/942–5000; Larry J. Goodman, M.D., President
(Moderately Centralized Health System)

ILLINOIS: RUSH NORTH SHORE MEDICAL CENTER (O, 239 beds) 9600 Gross Point Road, Skokie, IL Zip 60076–1257; tel. 847/677–9600; James T. Frankenbach, President and Chief Executive Officer
Web address: www.rnsmc.org

RUSH UNIVERSITY MEDICAL CENTER (O, 679 beds) 1653 West Congress Parkway, Chicago, IL Zip 60612–3833; tel. 312/942–5000; Larry J. Goodman, M.D., President and Chief Executive Officer
Web address: www.rush.edu

RUSH–COPLEY MEDICAL CENTER (O, 148 beds) 2000 Ogden Avenue, Aurora, IL Zip 60504–4206; tel. 630/978–6200; Barry C. Finn, President and Chief Executive Officer
Web address: www.rushcopley.com

Owned, leased, sponsored:	3 hospitals	1066 beds
Contract–managed:	0 hospitals	0 beds
Totals:	3 hospitals	1066 beds

★0118: SAINT BARNABAS HEALTH CARE SYSTEM (NP)
95 Old Short Hills Road, West Orange, NJ Zip 07052; tel. 973/322–4001; Ronald J. Del Mauro, President and Chief Executive Officer
(Moderately Centralized Health System)

NEW JERSEY: CLARA MAASS MEDICAL CENTER (O, 301 beds) One Clara Maass Drive, Belleville, NJ Zip 07109–3557; tel. 973/450–2000; Thomas A. Biga, Executive Director
Web address: www.sbhcs.com

COMMUNITY MEDICAL CENTER (O, 494 beds) 99 Route 37 West, Toms River, NJ Zip 08755–6423; tel. 732/557–8000; Nancy L. Wollen, R.N., CHE, Executive Director and Chief Administrative Officer
Web address: www.sbhcs.com

IRVINGTON GENERAL HOSPITAL (O, 111 beds) 832 Chancellor Avenue, Irvington, NJ Zip 07111–0709; tel. 973/399–6000; Patricia Carroll, Executive Director
Web address: www.sbhcs.com

KIMBALL MEDICAL CENTER (O, 302 beds) 600 River Avenue, Lakewood, NJ Zip 08701–4281; tel. 732/363–1900; Joe Hicks, Executive Director
Web address: www.sbhcs.com

MONMOUTH MEDICAL CENTER (O, 232 beds) 300 Second Avenue, Long Branch, NJ Zip 07740–6303; tel. 732/222–5200; Frank J. Vozos, M.D., FACS, Executive Director
Web address: www.sbhcs.com

NEWARK BETH ISRAEL MEDICAL CENTER (O, 567 beds) 201 Lyons Avenue, Newark, NJ Zip 07112–2027; tel. 973/926–7000; Paul A. Mertz, Executive Director
Web address: www.sbhcs.com

For explanation of codes following names, see page B2.
★ Indicates Type III membership in the American Hospital Association.

SAINT BARNABAS MEDICAL CENTER (O, 592 beds) 94 Old Short Hills Road, Livingston, NJ Zip 07039–5668; tel. 973/322–5000; John F. Bonamo, M.D., Executive Director
Web address: www.sbhcs.com

UNION HOSPITAL (O, 142 beds) 1000 Galloping Hill Road, Union, NJ Zip 07083–1652; tel. 908/687–1900; Kathryn W. Coyne, Executive Director
Web address: www.sbhcs.com

Owned, leased, sponsored:	8 hospitals	2741 beds
Contract–managed:	0 hospitals	0 beds
Totals:	8 hospitals	2741 beds

0318: SAINT FRANCIS CARE, INC. (NP)
114 Woodland Street, Hartford, CT Zip 06105; tel. 860/714–5541; Christopher M. Dadlez, President and Chief Executive Officer

CONNECTICUT: SAINT FRANCIS HOSPITAL AND MEDICAL CENTER (O, 515 beds) 114 Woodland Street, Hartford, CT Zip 06105–1299; tel. 860/714–7440; Christopher M. Dadlez, President and Chief Executive Officer
Web address: www.saintfranciscare.com

THE REHABILITATION HOSPITAL OF CONNECTICUT (O, 38 beds) 490 Blue Hills Avenue, Hartford, CT Zip 06112; tel. 860/714–3500; Christopher M. Dadlez, President and Chief Executive Officer

Owned, leased, sponsored:	2 hospitals	553 beds
Contract–managed:	0 hospitals	0 beds
Totals:	2 hospitals	553 beds

★0254: SAINT FRANCIS HEALTH SYSTEM (NP)
6161 South Yale Avenue, Tulsa, OK Zip 74136–1902; tel. 918/494–8454; Jake Henry Jr, President and Chief Executive Officer
(Centralized Health System)

OKLAHOMA: LAUREATE PSYCHIATRIC CLINIC AND HOSPITAL (O, 75 beds) 6655 South Yale Avenue, Tulsa, OK Zip 74136–3329; tel. 918/481–4000; Reese Jackson, Senior Vice President and Administrator
Web address: www.laureate.com

SAINT FRANCIS HEART HOSPITAL (O, 52 beds) 10501 East 91st Street South, Tulsa, OK Zip 74133; tel. 918/307–6000; Robert S. Dolan, Chief Executive Officer
Web address: www.saintfrancisheart.com

SAINT FRANCIS HOSPITAL (O, 666 beds) 6161 South Yale Avenue, Tulsa, OK Zip 74136–1902; tel. 918/494–2200; Reese Jackson, Senior Vice President and Administrator
Web address: www.saintfrancis.com

SAINT FRANCIS HOSPITAL AT BROKEN ARROW (O, 74 beds) 3000 South Elm Place, Broken Arrow, OK Zip 74012–7952; tel. 918/455–3535; Joseph H. Neely, Senior Vice President and Administrator
Web address: www.stfrancis.com

Owned, leased, sponsored:	4 hospitals	867 beds
Contract–managed:	0 hospitals	0 beds
Totals:	4 hospitals	867 beds

0120: SAINT LUKE'S HEALTH SYSTEM (NP)
10920 Elm Avenue, Kansas City, MO Zip 64134–4108; tel. 816/932–2000; G. Richard Hastings, President and Chief Executive Officer
(Centralized Health System)

KANSAS: ANDERSON COUNTY HOSPITAL (O, 47 beds) 421 South Maple, Garnett, KS Zip 66032–1334, Mailing Address: P.O. Box 309, Zip 66032–0309; tel. 785/448–3131; Dennis A. Hachenberg, CHE, Chief Executive Officer
Web address: www.saint–lukes.org

CUSHING MEMORIAL HOSPITAL (L, 74 beds) 711 Marshall Street, Leavenworth, KS Zip 66048–3235; tel. 913/684–1100; Bob S. Edwards Jr, Chief Executive Officer
Web address: www.cushinghospital.org

SAINT LUKE'S SOUTH HOSPITAL (O, 93 beds) 12300 Metcalf Avenue, Overland Park, KS Zip 66213; tel. 913/317–7000; Julie Quirin, Chief Executive Officer
Web address: www.saint–lukes.org

MISSOURI: CRITTENTON CHILDREN'S CENTER (O, 54 beds) 10918 Elm Avenue, Kansas City, MO Zip 64134–4199; tel. 816/765–6600; Stephen W. Churchill, M.D., Chief Executive Officer and Medical Director
Web address: www.saintlukeshealthsystem.org/app/hpcrittenton.asp

HEDRICK MEDICAL CENTER (O, 30 beds) 100 Central Avenue, Chillicothe, MO Zip 64601–1599; tel. 660/646–1480; James K. Johnson, Chief Executive Officer
Web address: www.saintlukeshealthsystem.org

SAINT LUKE'S HOSPITAL OF KANSAS CITY (O, 482 beds) 4401 Wornall Road, Kansas City, MO Zip 64111–3238; tel. 816/932–2000; G. Richard Hastings, Chief Executive Officer
Web address: www.saintlukeshealthsystem.org/app/hpslh.asp

SAINT LUKE'S NORTHLAND HOSPITAL (O, 79 beds) 5830 N.W. Barry Road, Kansas City, MO Zip 64154–2778; tel. 816/891–6000; N. Gary Wages, President and Chief Executive Officer
Web address: www.saint–lukes.org

SAINT LUKE'S NORTHLAND HOSPITAL–SMITHVILLE CAMPUS (O, 40 beds) 601 South 169 Highway, Smithville, MO Zip 64089–9317; tel. 816/532–3700; Don Sipes, Chief Executive Officer
Web address: www.saintlukeshealthsystem.org

WRIGHT MEMORIAL HOSPITAL (O, 25 beds) 701 East First Street, Trenton, MO Zip 64683–2402, Mailing Address: P.O. Box 628, Zip 64683–0628; tel. 660/359–5621; John Woodrich, Chief Executive Officer
Web address: www.saintlukeshealthsystem.org

Owned, leased, sponsored:	9 hospitals	924 beds
Contract–managed:	0 hospitals	0 beds
Totals:	9 hospitals	924 beds

★0274: SAINT VINCENT CATHOLIC MEDICAL CENTERS (CC)
130 West 12th Street, Suite 1G, New York, NY Zip 10011; tel. 212/604–2300; David E. Speltz, Chief Executive Officer

NEW YORK: SAINT VINCENT'S HOSPITAL – MANHATTAN (O, 978 beds) 170 West 12th Street, New York, NY Zip 10011–8397; tel. 212/604–7000; Kathleen Galvin, Executive Director
Web address: www.svcmcny.org

SAINT VINCENTS CATHOLIC MEDICAL CENTERS OF NEW YORK (O, 1584 beds) 88–25 153rd Street, Jamaica, NY Zip 11432–3731; tel. 718/558–6900; Rose Britt, Executive Director
Web address: www.svcmc.org

ST. VINCENT'S HOSPITAL (O, 449 beds) 355 Bard Avenue, Staten Island, NY Zip 10310–1699; tel. 718/818–1234; Dawn M. Gideon, Executive Director
Web address: www.svcmc.org/statenisland/

Owned, leased, sponsored:	3 hospitals	3011 beds
Contract–managed:	0 hospitals	0 beds
Totals:	3 hospitals	3011 beds

★0186: SAMARITAN HEALTH SERVICES (NP)
3600 N.W. Samaritan Drive, Corvallis, OR Zip 97330, Mailing Address: P.O. Box 1068, Zip 97339; tel. 541/768–5001; Larry A. Mullins, FACHE, President and Chief Executive Officer
(Centralized Physician/Insurance Health System)

OREGON: GOOD SAMARITAN REGIONAL MEDICAL CENTER (O, 134 beds) 3600 N.W. Samaritan Drive, Corvallis, OR Zip 97330–3737, Mailing Address: P.O. Box 1068, Zip 97339–1068; tel. 541/768–5111; Steven W. Jasperson, Chief Executive Officer
Web address: www.samhealth.org

SAMARITAN ALBANY GENERAL HOSPITAL (O, 63 beds) 1046 West Sixth Avenue, Albany, OR Zip 97321–1999; tel. 541/812–4000; David G. Triebes, Chief Executive Officer
Web address: www.samhealth.org

SAMARITAN LEBANON COMMUNITY HOSPITAL (O, 49 beds) 525 North Santiam Highway, Lebanon, OR Zip 97355–4363, Mailing Address: P.O. Box 739, Zip 97355–0739; tel. 541/258–2101; Becky A. Pape, R.N., Chief Executive Officer
Web address: www.samhealth.org

For explanation of codes following names, see page B2.
★ Indicates Type III membership in the American Hospital Association.

SAMARITAN NORTH LINCOLN HOSPITAL (C, 25 beds) 3043 N.E. 28th Street, Lincoln City, OR Zip 97367–4523, Mailing Address: P.O. Box 767, Zip 97367–0767; tel. 541/994–3661; Jack T. Flaig, Chief Executive Officer
Web address: www.samhealth.org

SAMARITAN PACIFIC COMMUNITIES HOSPITAL (C, 42 beds) 930 S.W. Abbey Street, Newport, OR Zip 97365–4820, Mailing Address: P.O. Box 945, Zip 97365–4820; tel. 541/265–2244; David C. Bigelow, Chief Executive Officer
Web address: www.samhealth.org/pch

Owned, leased, sponsored:	3 hospitals	246 beds
Contract–managed:	2 hospitals	67 beds
Totals:	5 hospitals	313 beds

★**0037: SCOTTSDALE HEALTHCARE** (NP)
3621 Wells Fargo Avenue, Scottsdale, AZ Zip 85251–5607; tel. 480/882–4000; Thomas J. Sadvary, FACHE, Senior Vice President and Chief Executive Officer
(Moderately Centralized Health System)

ARIZONA: SCOTTSDALE HEALTHCARE–OSBORN (O, 300 beds) 7400 East Osborn Road, Scottsdale, AZ Zip 85251–6403; tel. 480/882–4000; Gary E. Baker, Vice President
Web address: www.shc.org

SCOTTSDALE HEALTHCARE–SHEA (O, 343 beds) 9003 East Shea Boulevard, Scottsdale, AZ Zip 85260–6771; tel. 480/323–3000; Peggy Reiley, Senior Vice President and Chief Clinical Officer
Web address: www.shc.org

Owned, leased, sponsored:	2 hospitals	643 beds
Contract–managed:	0 hospitals	0 beds
Totals:	2 hospitals	643 beds

★**1505: SCRIPPS HEALTH** (NP)
4275 Campus Point Court, San Diego, CA Zip 92121; tel. 858/678–7200; Chris D. Van Gorder, President and Chief Executive Officer
(Moderately Centralized Health System)

CALIFORNIA: SCRIPPS GREEN HOSPITAL (O, 153 beds) 10666 North Torrey Pines Road, La Jolla, CA Zip 92037–1093; tel. 858/455–9100; Robin Brown, Chief Executive Officer
Web address: www.scrippshealth.org

SCRIPPS MEMORIAL HOSPITAL–ENCINITAS (O, 109 beds) 354 Santa Fe Drive, Encinitas, CA Zip 92024–5182, Mailing Address: P.O. Box 230817, Zip 92023–0817; tel. 760/753–6501; Carl J. Etter, Chief Executive
Web address: www.scrippshealth.org/scripps_locations_1458.asp

SCRIPPS MEMORIAL HOSPITAL–LA JOLLA (O, 278 beds) 9888 Genesee Avenue, La Jolla, CA Zip 92037–1200, Mailing Address: P.O. Box 28, Zip 92038–0028; tel. 858/626–4123; Gary G. Fybel, Chief Executive Officer
Web address: www.scrippshealth.org

SCRIPPS MERCY HOSPITAL (O, 517 beds) 4077 Fifth Avenue, San Diego, CA Zip 92103–2105; tel. 619/294–8111; Thomas A. Gammiere, Chief Executive
Web address: www.scrippshealth.org

Owned, leased, sponsored:	4 hospitals	1057 beds
Contract–managed:	0 hospitals	0 beds
Totals:	4 hospitals	1057 beds

0181: SELECT MEDICAL CORPORATION (IO)
4718 Old Gettysburg Road, Mechanicsburg, PA Zip 17055; tel. 717/972–1100; Robert Ortenzio, Chief Executive Officer
(Independent Hospital System)

ARKANSAS: SELECT SPECIALTY HOSPITAL–LITTLE ROCK (O, 43 beds) 2 St. Vincent Circle, 6th Floor, Little Rock, AR Zip 72204; tel. 501/661–4198; Maureen Henneken, Chief Executive Officer
Web address: www.selectmedicalcorp.com

KANSAS: SELECT SPECIALTY HOSPITAL – KANSAS CITY (O, 34 beds) 10550 Quivira Road, Overland Park, KS Zip 66215; tel. 913/541–5886; Aundria Watkins, Administrator
Web address: www.selectmedicalcorp.com

SELECT SPECIALTY HOSPITAL – TOPEKA (O, 34 beds) 1700 S.W. Seventh Street, Suite 840, Topeka, KS Zip 66606–1660; tel. 785/295–5551; Mark Davis, Chief Executive Officer
Web address: www.selectmedicalcorp.com

LOUISIANA: SELECT SPECIALTY HOSPITAL–JEFFERSON PARISH (O, 32 beds) 4200 Houma Boulevard, Metairie, LA Zip 70006; tel. 504/780–3020; Meg McNally, Chief Executive Officer
Web address: www.selectmedicalcorp.com

MISSOURI: SELECT SPECIALTY HOSPITAL – WESTERN MISSOURI (O, 15 beds) 2316 East Meyer Boulevard, 3–West, Kansas City, MO Zip 64132; tel. 816/276–9444; Jerry Janssen, Chief Executive Officer
Web address: www.selectmedicalcorp.com

NEBRASKA: SELECT SPECIALTY HOSPITAL–OMAHA (O, 30 beds) 11111 South 84th Street, Papillion, NE Zip 68046; tel. 402/898–2700; Linda Mertz, Administrator
Web address: www.selectmedicalcorp.com

NEW JERSEY: KESSLER INSTITUTE FOR REHABILITATION (O, 322 beds) 1199 Pleasant Valley Way, West Orange, NJ Zip 07052–1419; tel. 973/731–3600; Robert Brehm, President
Web address: www.kessler–rehab.com

OKLAHOMA: SELECT SPECIALTY HOSPITAL – TULSA (O, 32 beds) 744 West Ninth Street, Tulsa, OK Zip 74127–9096; tel. 918/502–1400; David Bennett, Chief Executive Officer

PENNSYLVANIA: SELECT SPECIALTY HOSPITAL–DANVILLE (O, 30 beds) 100 North Academy Avenue, 3rd Floor, Danville, PA Zip 17822–3050; tel. 570/214–9657; Lori Metzer, Chief Executive Officer

TENNESSEE: SELECT SPECIALTY HOSPITAL OF NASHVILLE (O, 35 beds) 2021 Church Street, Nashville, TN Zip 37236; tel. 615/284–4599; William Bryan Lee, Chief Executive Officer

TEXAS: SELECT SPECIALTY HOSPITAL – DALLAS (O, 55 beds) 10 Medical Parkway, Suite 205, Dallas, TX Zip 75234–7845; tel. 972/488–9167; Joy Dier, R.N., MS, Administrtor and Chief Executive Officer
Web address: www.selectmedicalcorp.com

SELECT SPECIALTY HOSPITAL–HOUSTON HEIGHTS (O, 221 beds) 1917 Ashland Street, Houston, TX Zip 77008–3994; tel. 713/861–6161; Teresa L. Davis, Administrator
Web address: www.selectmedicalcorp.com

SELECT SPECIALTY HOSPITAL–HOUSTON MEDICAL CENTER (O, 34 beds) 6447 Main Street, Houston, TX Zip 77030–1502, Mailing Address: 6500 Fannin Street, Suite 907, Zip 77030–1502; tel. 713/363–9393; Brock Hardaway, Administrator
Web address: www.selectmedicalcorp.com

Owned, leased, sponsored:	13 hospitals	917 beds
Contract–managed:	0 hospitals	0 beds
Totals:	13 hospitals	917 beds

★**2565: SENTARA HEALTHCARE** (NP)
6015 Poplar Hall Drive, Norfolk, VA Zip 23502–3819; tel. 757/455–7000; David L. Bernd, Chief Executive Officer
(Centralized Health System)

VIRGINIA: SENTARA BAYSIDE HOSPITAL (O, 99 beds) 800 Independence Boulevard, Virginia Beach, VA Zip 23455–6076; tel. 757/363–6100; Larry T. DePriest, Vice President and Administrator
Web address: www.sentara.com

SENTARA CAREPLEX HOSPITAL (O, 194 beds) 3000 Coliseum Drive, Hampton, VA Zip 23666–5963; tel. 757/736–2656; Megan R. Perry, Senior Vice President and Administrator
Web address: www.sentara.com

SENTARA LEIGH HOSPITAL (O, 223 beds) 830 Kempsville Road, Norfolk, VA Zip 23502–3920; tel. 757/466–6000; Mark A. Szalwinski, Vice President and Administrator
Web address: www.sentara.com

SENTARA NORFOLK GENERAL HOSPITAL (O, 461 beds) 600 Gresham Drive, Norfolk, VA Zip 23507; tel. 757/668–3000; Bruce E. Holstien, Senior Vice President and Administrator
Web address: www.sentara.com

SENTARA VIRGINIA BEACH GENERAL HOSPITAL (O, 240 beds) 1060 First Colonial Road, Virginia Beach, VA Zip 23454–3002; tel. 757/395–8000; Les A. Donahue, Vice President and Administrator
Web address: www.sentara.com

For explanation of codes following names, see page B2.
★ Indicates Type III membership in the American Hospital Association.

SENTARA WILLIAMSBURG COMMUNITY HOSPITAL (O, 110 beds) 301 Monticello Avenue, Williamsburg, VA Zip 23185, Mailing Address: P.O. Box 8700, Zip 23187–8700; tel. 757/259–6000; Robert L. Graves, Vice President and Administrator
Web address: www.sentara.com

Owned, leased, sponsored:	6 hospitals	1327 beds
Contract–managed:	0 hospitals	0 beds
Totals:	6 hospitals	1327 beds

★**0111: SHANDS HEALTHCARE** (NP)
1600 S.W. Archer Road, Gainesville, FL Zip 32610–0326; tel. 352/265–8929; Timothy M. Goldfarb, Chief Executive Officer
(Moderately Centralized Health System)

FLORIDA: SHANDS AT AGH (O, 269 beds) 801 S.W. Second Avenue, Gainesville, FL Zip 32601–6289; tel. 352/372–4321; Charles K. Van Sluyter, Interim Administrator
Web address: www.shands.org/hospitals/agh

SHANDS AT LAKE SHORE (L, 87 beds) 368 N.E. Franklin Street, Lake City, FL Zip 32055–3047; tel. 386/754–8000; Neil Whipkey, Administrator
Web address: www.shands.org

SHANDS AT LIVE OAK (O, 15 beds) 1100 S.W. 11th Street, Live Oak, FL Zip 32060–3608; tel. 386/362–1413; Rhonda Sherrod, Administrator
Web address: www.shands.org

SHANDS AT STARKE (O, 25 beds) 922 East Call Street, Starke, FL Zip 32091–3699; tel. 904/368–2300; Jeannie Baker, Administrator
Web address: www.shands.org

SHANDS AT THE UNIVERSITY OF FLORIDA (O, 602 beds) 1600 S.W. Archer Road, Gainesville, FL Zip 32610–0326, Mailing Address: P.O. Box 100326, Zip 32610–0326; tel. 352/265–0111; Timothy J. Goldfarb, Chief Executive Officer
Web address: www.shands.org

SHANDS JACKSONVILLE MEDICAL CENTER (O, 508 beds) 655 West Eighth Street, Jacksonville, FL Zip 32209–6595; tel. 904/244–0411; James R. Burkhart, FACHE, President and Administrator
Web address: www.shandsjacksonville.org

SHANDS REHAB HOSPITAL (O, 35 beds) 4101 N.W. 89th Boulevard, Gainesville, FL Zip 32606–3813; tel. 352/265–5491; Marina T. Cecchini, Administrator
Web address: www.shands.org

Owned, leased, sponsored:	7 hospitals	1541 beds
Contract–managed:	0 hospitals	0 beds
Totals:	7 hospitals	1541 beds

★**2065: SHARP HEALTHCARE** (NP)
8695 Spectrum Center Boulevard, San Diego, CA Zip 92123–1489; tel. 858/499–4000; Michael Murphy, President and Chief Executive Officer
(Moderately Centralized Health System)

CALIFORNIA: SHARP CHULA VISTA MEDICAL CENTER (O, 326 beds) 751 Medical Center Court, Chula Vista, CA Zip 91911–6617, Mailing Address: P.O. Box 1297, Zip 91912–1297; tel. 619/482–5800; Christopher L. Boyd, Chief Executive Officer
Web address: www.sharp.com

SHARP CORONADO HOSPITAL AND HEALTH CENTER (C, 204 beds) 250 Prospect Place, Coronado, CA Zip 92118–1943; tel. 619/522–3600; Marcia K. Hall, Chief Executive Officer
Web address: www.sharp.com

SHARP GROSSMONT HOSPITAL (C, 457 beds) 5555 Grossmont Center Drive, La Mesa, CA Zip 91942–3019, Mailing Address: P.O. Box 158, Zip 91944–0158; tel. 619/740–6000; Michele T. Tarbet, R.N., Chief Executive Officer
Web address: www.sharp.com

SHARP MEMORIAL HOSPITAL (O, 731 beds) 7901 Frost Street, San Diego, CA Zip 92123–2701; tel. 858/939–3400; Daniel Gross, Chief Executive Officer
Web address: www.sharp.com

Owned, leased, sponsored:	2 hospitals	1057 beds
Contract–managed:	2 hospitals	661 beds
Totals:	4 hospitals	1718 beds

0304: SHORE HEALTH SYSTEM (NP)
219 South Washington Street, Easton, MD Zip 21601; tel. 410/822–1000; Joseph P. Ross, President and Chief Executive Officer
(Independent Hospital System)

MARYLAND: DORCHESTER GENERAL HOSPITAL (O, 64 beds) 300 Byrn Street, Cambridge, MD Zip 21613–1908; tel. 410/228–5511; Joseph P. Ross, President and Chief Executive Officer
Web address: www.shorehealth.org

MEMORIAL HOSPITAL AT EASTON MARYLAND (O, 111 beds) 219 South Washington Street, Easton, MD Zip 21601–2996; tel. 410/822–1000; Joseph P. Ross, President and Chief Executive Officer
Web address: www.shorehealth.org

Owned, leased, sponsored:	2 hospitals	175 beds
Contract–managed:	0 hospitals	0 beds
Totals:	2 hospitals	175 beds

4125: SHRINERS HOSPITALS FOR CHILDREN (NP)
2900 Rocky Point Drive, Tampa, FL Zip 33607–1435, Mailing Address: Box 31356, Zip 33631–3356; tel. 813/281–0300; Joseph E. Melchiorre Jr, CHE, Executive Administrator
(Independent Hospital System)

CALIFORNIA: SHRINERS HOSPITALS FOR CHILDREN, LOS ANGELES (O, 60 beds) 3160 Geneva Street, Los Angeles, CA Zip 90020–1199; tel. 213/388–3151; Frank LaBonte, FACHE, Administrator
Web address: www.shrinehg.com

SHRINERS HOSPITALS FOR CHILDREN, NORTHERN CALIFORNIA (O, 70 beds) 2425 Stockton Boulevard, Sacramento, CA Zip 95817–2215; tel. 916/453–2000; Margaret Bryan, Administrator
Web address: www.shrinershq.org

FLORIDA: SHRINERS HOSPITALS FOR CHILDREN, TAMPA (O, 60 beds) 12502 North Pine Drive, Tampa, FL Zip 33612–9499; tel. 813/972–2250; Alice Reed Lanford, R.N., Administrator
Web address: www.shrinershq.org

HAWAII: SHRINERS HOSPITALS FOR CHILDREN, HONOLULU (O, 40 beds) 1310 Punahou Street, Honolulu, HI Zip 96826–1099; tel. 808/941–4466; Thomas R. Schneider, Administrator
Web address: www.shrinershq.org

ILLINOIS: SHRINERS HOSPITALS FOR CHILDREN–CHICAGO (O, 60 beds) 2211 North Oak Park Avenue, Chicago, IL Zip 60707–3361; tel. 773/622–5400; Shana Jones, Ph.D., Administrator
Web address: www.shrinershq.org

KENTUCKY: SHRINERS HOSPITALS FOR CHILDREN–LEXINGTON (O, 50 beds) 1900 Richmond Road, Lexington, KY Zip 40502–1298; tel. 859/266–2101; Tony Lewgood, Administrator
Web address: www.shrinershq.com

LOUISIANA: SHRINERS HOSPITALS FOR CHILDREN, SHREVEPORT (O, 45 beds) 3100 Samford Avenue, Shreveport, LA Zip 71103–4289; tel. 318/222–5704; Garry K. Green, Administrator
Web address: www.shriners.com

MASSACHUSETTS: SHRINERS HOSPITALS FOR CHILDREN, SHRINERS BURNS HOSPITAL–BOSTON (O, 30 beds) 51 Blossom Street, Boston, MA Zip 02114–2699; tel. 617/722–3000; Janet L. Mulligan, R.N., MS, Administrator
Web address: www.shrinershq.org

SHRINERS HOSPITALS FOR CHILDREN, SPRINGFIELD (O, 40 beds) 516 Carew Street, Springfield, MA Zip 01104–2396; tel. 413/787–2000; Mark L. Niederpruem, Administrator
Web address: www.shrinerhq.org

MINNESOTA: SHRINERS HOSPITALS FOR CHILDREN, TWIN CITIES (O, 40 beds) 2025 East River Parkway, Minneapolis, MN Zip 55414–3696; tel. 612/596–6100; Laurence E. Johnson, Administrator
Web address: www.shrinershq.org

Section B

For explanation of codes following names, see page B2.
★ Indicates Type III membership in the American Hospital Association.

MISSOURI: SHRINERS HOSPITALS FOR CHILDREN, ST. LOUIS (O, 42 beds) 2001 South Lindbergh Boulevard, Saint Louis, MO Zip 63131–3597; tel. 314/432–3600; Josephine B. Holtz, R.N., Interim Administrator
Web address: www.shrinershq.org

OHIO: SHRINERS HOSPITALS FOR CHILDREN, SHRINERS BURNS HOSPITAL, CINCINNATI (O, 30 beds) 3229 Burnet Avenue, Cincinnati, OH Zip 45229–3095; tel. 513/872–6000; Ronald R. Hitzler, Administrator
Web address: www.shrinershq.org

OREGON: SHRINERS HOSPITALS FOR CHILDREN, PORTLAND (O, 40 beds) 3101 S.W. Sam Jackson Park Road, Portland, OR Zip 97239; tel. 503/241–5090; C. Thomas D'Esmond, Administrator
Web address: www.shcc.org

PENNSYLVANIA: SHRINERS HOSPITALS FOR CHILDREN, ERIE (O, 30 beds) 1645 West 8th Street, Erie, PA Zip 16505–5007; tel. 814/875–8700; Richard W. Brzuz, FACHE, Administrator
Web address: www.shrinershq.org

SHRINERS HOSPITALS FOR CHILDREN, PHILADELPHIA (O, 80 beds) 3551 North Broad Street, Philadelphia, PA Zip 19140–4131; tel. 215/430–4000; Sharon J. Rajnic, Administrator
Web address: www.shrinershq.org

SOUTH CAROLINA: SHRINERS HOSPITALS FOR CHILDREN, GREENVILLE (O, 50 beds) 950 West Faris Road, Greenville, SC Zip 29605–4277; tel. 864/271–3444; Gary F. Fraley, Administrator
Web address: www.shrinershq.org

TEXAS: SHRINERS HOSPITALS FOR CHILDREN, GALVESTON BURNS HOSPITAL (O, 30 beds) 815 Market Street, Galveston, TX Zip 77550–2725; tel. 409/770–6600; John A. Swartwout, Administrator
Web address: www.shrinershq.org

SHRINERS HOSPITALS FOR CHILDREN, HOUSTON (O, 40 beds) 6977 Main Street, Houston, TX Zip 77030–3701; tel. 713/797–1616; Steven B. Reiter, Administrator
Web address: www.shrineshq.org

UTAH: SHRINERS HOSPITALS FOR CHILDREN–INTERMOUNTAIN (O, 40 beds) Fairfax Road and Virginia Street, Salt Lake City, UT Zip 84103–4399; tel. 801/536–3500; J. Craig Patchin, Administrator
Web address: www.shriners.com

WASHINGTON: SHRINERS HOSPITALS FOR CHILDREN–SPOKANE (O, 30 beds) 911 West Fifth Avenue, Spokane, WA Zip 99204–2901, Mailing Address: P.O. Box 2472, Zip 99210–2472; tel. 509/455–7844; Charles R. Young, Administrator
Web address: www.shrinershq.org

Owned, leased, sponsored:	20 hospitals	907 beds
Contract–managed:	0 hospitals	0 beds
Totals:	20 hospitals	907 beds

0284: SINAI HEALTH SYSTEM (NP)
California Avenue at 15th Street, Chicago, IL Zip 60608; tel. 773/542–2000; Alan H. Channing, President and Chief Executive Officer
(Centralized Health System)

ILLINOIS: MOUNT SINAI HOSPITAL MEDICAL CENTER OF CHICAGO (O, 312 beds) California Avenue and 15th Street, Chicago, IL Zip 60608–1610; tel. 773/542–2000; Larry E. Volkmar, President
Web address: www.sinai.org

SCHWAB REHABILITATION HOSPITAL (O, 104 beds) 1401 South California Boulevard, Chicago, IL Zip 60608–1612; tel. 773/522–2010; Larry E. Volkmar, President
Web address: www.schwabrehab.org

Owned, leased, sponsored:	2 hospitals	416 beds
Contract–managed:	0 hospitals	0 beds
Totals:	2 hospitals	416 beds

★0078: SIOUX VALLEY HOSPITALS AND HEALTH SYSTEM (NP)
1305 West 18th Street, Sioux Falls, SD Zip 57105–0496, Mailing Address: P.O. Box 5039, Zip 57117–5039; tel. 605/333–1000; Kelby K. Krabbenhoft, President and Chief Executive Officer
(Decentralized Health System)

IOWA: MERRILL PIONEER COMMUNITY HOSPITAL (L, 16 beds) 801 South Greene Street, Rock Rapids, IA Zip 51246–1998; tel. 712/472–2591; Gordon Smith, Administrator and Chief Executive Officer
Web address: www.merrillpioneer.org

NORTHWEST IOWA HEALTH CENTER (L, 95 beds) 118 North Seventh Avenue, Sheldon, IA Zip 51201–1235, Mailing Address: P.O. Box 250, Zip 51201–0250; tel. 712/324–5041; Charles R. Miller, Chief Executive Officer
Web address: www.nwiowahealthcenter.org

ORANGE CITY HEALTH SYSTEM (C, 108 beds) 400 Central Avenue N.W., Orange City, IA Zip 51041–1398; tel. 712/737–4984; Martin W. Guthmiller, Administrator and Chief Executive Officer
Web address: www.ochealthsystem.org

MINNESOTA: JACKSON MEDICAL CENTER (L, 20 beds) 1430 North Highway, Jackson, MN Zip 56143–1098; tel. 507/847–2420; Mary Ruyter, Chief Executive Officer
Web address: www.jacksonmedical.org

MURRAY COUNTY MEMORIAL HOSPITAL (C, 25 beds) 2042 Juniper Avenue, Slayton, MN Zip 56172–1016; tel. 507/836–6111; Rick Nordahl, Administrator and Chief Executive Officer
Web address: www.murraycountymemorial.org

ORTONVILLE AREA HEALTH SERVICES (C, 89 beds) 450 Eastvold Avenue, Ortonville, MN Zip 56278–1133; tel. 320/839–2502; Kenneth W. Archer, Chief Executive Officer
Web address: www.ortonvilleareahealth.org

SIOUX VALLEY CANBY CAMPUS (L, 100 beds) 112 St. Olaf Avenue South, Canby, MN Zip 56220–1433; tel. 507/223–7277; Robert J. Salmon, Chief Executive Officer
Web address: www.svcanbycampus.org

SIOUX VALLEY LUVERNE MEDICAL CENTER (O, 28 beds) 1600 North Kniss, Luverne, MN Zip 56156–2519, Mailing Address: P.O. Box 1019, Zip 56156–2519; tel. 507/283–2321; Gerald E. Carl, Chief Executive Officer
Web address: www.luvernecommunityhospital.org

TRACY AREA MEDICAL SERVICES (L, 23 beds) 251 Fifth Street East, Tracy, MN Zip 56175–1536; tel. 507/629–3200; Rick Nordahl, Administrator and Chief Executive Officer
Web address: www.tracyareamedical.org

WESTBROOK HEALTH CENTER (L, 13 beds) 920 Bell Avenue, Westbrook, MN Zip 56183–0188, Mailing Address: P.O. Box 188, Zip 56183–0188; tel. 507/274–6121; Rick Nordahl, Administrator and Chief Executive Officer
Web address: www.westbrookhealthcenter.org

WINDOM AREA HOSPITAL (C, 25 beds) 2150 Hospital Drive, Windom, MN Zip 56101–1287, Mailing Address: P.O. Box 339, Zip 56101–0339; tel. 507/831–2400; Geraldine Burmeister, Chief Executive Officer and Administrator
Web address: www.windomareahospital.com

WORTHINGTON REGIONAL HOSPITAL (C, 66 beds) 1018 Sixth Avenue, Worthington, MN Zip 56187–2202, Mailing Address: P.O. Box 997, Zip 56187–0997; tel. 507/372–2941; Melvin J. Platt, Chief Executive Officer
Web address: www.worthingtonhospital.com

NEBRASKA: NIOBRARA VALLEY HOSPITAL (C, 20 beds) Lynch, NE Mailing Address: P.O. Box 118, Zip 68746–0118; tel. 402/569–2451; Bruce Purviance, Chief Executive Officer

WEST HOLT MEMORIAL HOSPITAL (C, 18 beds) 406 West Neely Street, Atkinson, NE Zip 68713–0200; tel. 402/925–2811; Mel L. Snow, Chief Executive Officer
Web address: www.westholtmed.org

SOUTH DAKOTA: CANTON–INWOOD MEMORIAL HOSPITAL (L, 18 beds) 440 North Hiawatha Drive, Canton, SD Zip 57013–9404; tel. 605/987–2621; Eric Hilmoe, Chief Executive Officer
Web address: www.cantoninwoodhospital.org

COMMUNITY MEMORIAL HOSPITAL (C, 16 beds) Eighth and Jackson, Burke, SD Zip 57523, Mailing Address: P.O. Box 319, Zip 57523–0319; tel. 605/775–2621; Michelle Murphy, Chief Executive Officer

---

For explanation of codes following names, see page B2.
★ Indicates Type III membership in the American Hospital Association.

DEUEL COUNTY MEMORIAL HOSPITAL (L, 20 beds) 701 Third Avenue South, Clear Lake, SD Zip 57226–2016; tel. 605/874–2141; Robert J. Salmon, Chief Executive Officer
Web address: www.siouxvalley.org

LAKE AREA HOSPITAL (L, 25 beds) North First Street, Webster, SD Zip 57274–1816, Mailing Address: P.O. Box 489, Zip 57274–0489; tel. 605/345–3336; Donald J. Finn, Chief Executive Officer
Web address: www.lakeareahospital.org

MID DAKOTA MEDICAL CENTER (O, 70 beds) 300 South Byron Boulevard, Chamberlain, SD Zip 57325–9741; tel. 605/234–5511; Maureen Cadwell, Chief Executive Officer
Web address: www.middakotamedicalcenter.org

PIONEER MEMORIAL HOSPITAL AND HEALTH SERVICES (C, 64 beds) 315 North Washington Street, Viborg, SD Zip 57070–2002, Mailing Address: P.O. Box 368, Zip 57070–0368; tel. 605/326–5161; Georgia Pokorney, Chief Executive Officer
Web address: www.pioneermemorial.org

PRAIRIE LAKES HEALTHCARE SYSTEM (C, 119 beds) 401 9th Avenue N.W., Watertown, SD Zip 57201–6210, Mailing Address: P.O. Box 1210, Zip 57201–1210; tel. 605/882–7000; Paul A. Hanson, Chief Executive Officer
Web address: www.prairielakes.com

SIOUX VALLEY HOSPITAL UNIVERSITY MEDICAL CENTER (O, 492 beds) 1305 West 18th Street, Sioux Falls, SD Zip 57105–0496, Mailing Address: P.O. Box 5039, Zip 57117–5039; tel. 605/333–1000; Becky Nelson, President
Web address: www.siouxvalley.org

SIOUX VALLEY VERMILLION MEDICAL CENTER (L, 116 beds) 20 South Plum Street, Vermillion, SD Zip 57069–3346; tel. 605/624–2611; Timothy J. Tracy, Chief Executive Officer
Web address: www.siouxvalleyvermillion.org

WINNER REGIONAL HEALTHCARE CENTER (C, 106 beds) 745 East Eighth Street, Winner, SD Zip 57580–2677; tel. 605/842–7100; Michael Hall, Chief Executive Officer
Web address: www.winnerregional.org

Owned, leased, sponsored:	13 hospitals	1036 beds
Contract–managed:	11 hospitals	656 beds
Totals:	24 hospitals	1692 beds

★5095: SISTERS OF CHARITY OF LEAVENWORTH HEALTH SYSTEM (CC)
9801 Renner Boulevard, Suite 100, Lenexa, KS Zip 66219; tel. 913/895–2800; William M. Murray, President
(Moderately Centralized Health System)

CALIFORNIA: SAINT JOHN'S HEALTH CENTER (O, 195 beds) 1328 Twenty Second Street, Santa Monica, CA Zip 90404–2091; tel. 310/829–5511; Lou Lazatin, Interim President
Web address: www.stjohns.org

COLORADO: ST. MARY'S HOSPITAL AND MEDICAL CENTER (O, 300 beds) 2635 North 7th Street, Grand Junction, CO Zip 81501–8204, Mailing Address: P.O. Box 1628, Zip 81502–1628; tel. 970/244–2273; Robert W. Ladenburger, President and Chief Executive Officer
Web address: www.stmarygj.com

KANSAS: PROVIDENCE MEDICAL CENTER (O, 257 beds) 8929 Parallel Parkway, Kansas City, KS Zip 66112–1636; tel. 913/596–4000; James T. Paquette, President and Chief Executive Officer
Web address: www.providence–health.org

SAINT JOHN HOSPITAL (O, 56 beds) 3500 South Fourth Street, Leavenworth, KS Zip 66048–5043; tel. 913/680–6000; Greg Madsen, Vice President and Administrator
Web address: www.providence–health.org/sjh

ST. FRANCIS HEALTH CENTER (O, 274 beds) 1700 West Seventh Street, Topeka, KS Zip 66606–1690; tel. 785/295–8000; Sister Loretto Marie Colwell, President and Chief Executive Officer
Web address: www.stfrancistopeka.org

MONTANA: HOLY ROSARY HEALTHCARE (O, 136 beds) 2600 Wilson Street, Miles City, MT Zip 59301–5094; tel. 406/233–2600; Greg Nielsen, Chief Administrative Officer
Web address: www.hrh–mt.org

ST. JAMES HEALTHCARE (O, 69 beds) 400 South Clark Street, Butte, MT Zip 59701–2328, Mailing Address: P.O. Box 3300, Zip 59702–3300; tel. 406/723–2500; James Kiser II, Chief Administrative Officer
Web address: www.stjameshealthcare.org

ST. VINCENT HEALTHCARE (O, 268 beds) 1233 North 30th Street, Billings, MT Zip 59101–0165, Mailing Address: P.O. Box 35200, Zip 59107–5200; tel. 406/237–7000; M. Michelle Hood, President and Chief Executive Officer
Web address: www.stvincenthealthcare.org

Owned, leased, sponsored:	8 hospitals	1555 beds
Contract–managed:	0 hospitals	0 beds
Totals:	8 hospitals	1555 beds

5125: SISTERS OF CHARITY OF ST. AUGUSTINE HEALTH SYSTEM (CC)
2351 East 22nd Street, Cleveland, OH Zip 44115–3197; tel. 216/696–5560; Sister Judith Ann Karam, President and Chief Executive Officer
(Moderately Centralized Health System)

OHIO: MERCY MEDICAL CENTER (O, 352 beds) 1320 Mercy Drive N.W., Canton, OH Zip 44708–2641; tel. 330/489–1000; Thomas E. Cecconi, President and Chief Executive
Web address: www.thequalityhospital.com

ST. JOHN WEST SHORE HOSPITAL (O, 160 beds) 29000 Center Ridge Road, Cleveland, OH Zip 44145–5219; tel. 440/835–8000; Keith R. Poisson, President
Web address: www.sjws.net

ST. VINCENT CHARITY HOSPITAL (O, 222 beds) 2351 East 22nd Street, Cleveland, OH Zip 44115–3111; tel. 216/861–6200; Jeffrey S. Jeney, President and Chief Executive Officer
Web address: www.svch.net

SOUTH CAROLINA: SISTERS OF CHARITY PROVIDENCE HOSPITALS (O, 251 beds) 2435 Forest Drive, Columbia, SC Zip 29204–2098; tel. 803/865–4500; Stephen A. Purves, CHE, President and Chief Executive Officer
Web address: www.provhosp.com

Owned, leased, sponsored:	4 hospitals	985 beds
Contract–managed:	0 hospitals	0 beds
Totals:	4 hospitals	985 beds

5805: SISTERS OF MARY OF THE PRESENTATION HEALTH SYSTEM (CC)
1102 Page Drive S.W., Fargo, ND Zip 58106–0007, Mailing Address: P.O. Box 10007, Zip 58106–0007; tel. 701/237–9290; Aaron Alton, President and Chief Executive Officer
(Independent Hospital System)

ILLINOIS: ST. MARGARET'S HOSPITAL (O, 93 beds) 600 East First Street, Spring Valley, IL Zip 61362–2034; tel. 815/664–5311; Tim Muntz, President and Chief Executive Officer
Web address: www.st-margarets.com

NORTH DAKOTA: PRESENTATION MEDICAL CENTER (O, 25 beds) 213 Second Avenue N.E., Rolla, ND Zip 58367–7153, Mailing Address: P.O. Box 759, Zip 58367–0759; tel. 701/477–3161; Kimber Wraalstad, President and Chief Executive Officer
Web address: www.pmc–rolla.com

ST. ALOISIUS MEDICAL CENTER (O, 131 beds) 325 East Brewster Street, Harvey, ND Zip 58341–1605; tel. 701/324–4651; Ronald J. Volk, President and Chief Executive Officer
Web address: www.staloisius.com

ST. ANDREW'S HEALTH CENTER (O, 25 beds) 316 Ohmer Street, Bottineau, ND Zip 58318–1018; tel. 701/228–9300; Jodi Atkinson, President and Chief Executive Officer
Web address: www.standrewshealth.com

Owned, leased, sponsored:	4 hospitals	274 beds
Contract–managed:	0 hospitals	0 beds
Totals:	4 hospitals	274 beds

For explanation of codes following names, see page B2.
★ Indicates Type III membership in the American Hospital Association.

Section B

★5185: SISTERS OF MERCY HEALTH SYSTEM (CC)

14528 South Outer 40, Suite 100, Chesterfield, MO
Zip 63017–5743; tel. 314/579–6100; Ronald B. Ashworth, Chief
Executive Officer
(Decentralized Health System)

ARKANSAS: MERCY HOSPITAL OF SCOTT COUNTY (O, 24 beds) 895 West
6th Street, Waldron, AR Zip 72958–7001; tel. 479/637–4135; Jim L.
Maddox, Administrator
Web address: www.stedwardmercy.com

MERCY HOSPITAL–TURNER MEMORIAL (L, 25 beds) 801 West River Street,
Ozark, AR Zip 72949–3000; tel. 479/667–4138; Jim L. Maddox,
Administrator
Web address: www.gravettehospital.org

NORTH LOGAN MERCY HOSPITAL (L, 16 beds) 500 East Academy, Paris, AR
Zip 72855–4099; tel. 479/963–6101; Jim L. Maddox, Administrator
Web address: www.stedwardmercy.com

ST. EDWARD MERCY MEDICAL CENTER (O, 370 beds) 7301 Rogers Avenue,
Fort Smith, AR Zip 72903–4189, Mailing Address: P.O. Box 17000,
Zip 72917–7000; tel. 479/314–6000; Jerry L. Stevenson, Chief Executive
Officer
Web address: www.stedwardmercy.com

ST. JOHN'S HOSPITAL–BERRYVILLE (L, 45 beds) 214 Carter Street,
Berryville, AR Zip 72616–4303; tel. 870/423–3355; David Dennis, President
Web address: www.stjohnsberryville.com

ST. JOSEPH'S MERCY HEALTH CENTER (O, 261 beds) 300 Werner Street,
Hot Springs National Park, AR Zip 71913–9937, Mailing Address: P.O. Box
29001, Zip 71913–9001; tel. 501/622–1000; Randall J. Fale, FACHE,
President and Chief Executive Officer
Web address: www.saintjosephs.com

ST. MARY–ROGERS MEMORIAL HOSPITAL (O, 133 beds) 1200 West Walnut
Street, Rogers, AR Zip 72756–3599; tel. 479/636–0200; Susan Barrett,
President and Chief Executive Officer
Web address: www.mercyhealthnwa.smhs.com

KANSAS: MERCY HEALTH SYSTEM OF KANSAS (O, 94 beds) 401 Woodland
Hills Boulevard, Fort Scott, KS Zip 66701–8797; tel. 620/223–2200; Jon
Swope, President and Chief Executive Officer
Web address: www.mhsk.smhs.com

MISSOURI: ST. JOHN'S HOSPITAL (O, 601 beds) 1235 East Cherokee Street,
Springfield, MO Zip 65804–2263; tel. 417/820–2000; Robert T.
Brodhead, President
Web address: www.stjohns.com

ST. JOHN'S HOSPITAL – AURORA (L, 25 beds) 500 Porter Street, Aurora, MO
Zip 65605–2399; tel. 417/678–2122; Gary W. Jordan, President
Web address: www.stjohns.com/aboutus/aurora.aspx

ST. JOHN'S HOSPITAL – CASSVILLE (L, 18 beds) 94 Main Street, Cassville,
MO Zip 65625–1610; tel. 417/847–6000; Gary W. Jordan, President
Web address: www.southbarrycountyhospital.com

ST. JOHN'S HOSPITAL – LEBANON (O, 48 beds) 100 Hospital Drive, Lebanon,
MO Zip 65536–9210; tel. 417/533–6100; Timothy J. Johnsen, President
Web address: www.stjohnslebanon.com

ST. JOHN'S MERCY HOSPITAL (O, 122 beds) 901 East Fifth Street,
Washington, MO Zip 63090; tel. 636/239–8000;
Web address: www.stjohnsmercy.org/sjmh/default.asp

ST. JOHN'S MERCY MEDICAL CENTER (O, 852 beds) 615 South New Ballas
Road, Saint Louis, MO Zip 63141–8277; tel. 314/569–6000; Margaret
Denielle DeNarvaez, President and Chief Executive Officer
Web address: www.stjohnsmercy.org

ST. JOHN'S ST. FRANCIS HOSPITAL (O, 20 beds) Highway 60, Mountain View,
MO Zip 65548–7125, Mailing Address: P.O. Box 82, Zip 65548–0082;
tel. 417/934–7000; Donald Swafford, President
Web address: www.stjohns.com/aboutus/stfrancis.aspx

OKLAHOMA: MERCY HEALTH CENTER (O, 351 beds) 4300 West Memorial
Road, Oklahoma City, OK Zip 73120–8362; tel. 405/755–1515; Michael
J. Packnett, President and Chief Executive Officer
Web address: www.mhso.okla.smhs.com

MERCY MEMORIAL HEALTH CENTER (O, 199 beds) 1011 14th Street N.W.,
Ardmore, OK Zip 73401–1889; tel. 580/223–5400; Bobby G. Thompson,
President and Chief Executive Officer
Web address: www.mercyok.org

Owned, leased, sponsored:	17 hospitals	3204 beds
Contract–managed:	0 hospitals	0 beds
Totals:	17 hospitals	3204 beds

5955: SISTERS OF SAINT FRANCIS (CC)

2500 Grant Boulevard, Syracuse, NY Zip 13208–1713;
tel. 315/634–7000; Sister Grace Anne Dillenschneider, Assistant
General Minister
(Moderately Centralized Health System)

HAWAII: ST. FRANCIS MEDICAL CENTER (S, 240 beds) 2230 Liliha Street,
Honolulu, HI Zip 96817–9979, Mailing Address: P.O. Box 30100,
Zip 96820–0100; tel. 808/547–6011; Sister Beatrice Tom, Chief
Executive Officer
Web address: www.stfrancishawaii.org

ST. FRANCIS MEDICAL CENTER–WEST (S, 102 beds) 91–2141 Fort Weaver
Road, Ewa Beach, HI Zip 96706–1993; tel. 808/678–7000; Sister Beatrice
Tom, Chief Executive Officer
Web address: www.sfhs–hi.org

NEW YORK: ST. ELIZABETH MEDICAL CENTER (S, 190 beds) 2209 Genesee
Street, Utica, NY Zip 13501–5999; tel. 315/798–8100; Sister M.
Johanna DeLelys, President and Chief Executive Officer
Web address: www.stemc.org

ST. JOSEPH'S HOSPITAL HEALTH CENTER (S, 431 beds) 301 Prospect
Avenue, Syracuse, NY Zip 13203–1895; tel. 315/448–5111; Theodore M.
Pasinski, President
Web address: www.SJHSYR.ORG

Owned, leased, sponsored:	4 hospitals	963 beds
Contract–managed:	0 hospitals	0 beds
Totals:	4 hospitals	963 beds

5345: SISTERS OF ST. FRANCIS HEALTH SERVICES, INC. (CC)

1515 Dragoon Trail, Mishawaka, IN Zip 46546–1290, Mailing
Address: P.O. Box 1290, Zip 46546–1290; tel. 574/256–3935;
Kevin D. Leahy, President and Chief Executive Officer
(Moderately Centralized Health System)

ILLINOIS: ST. JAMES HOSPITALS AND HEALTH CENTERS (O, 494 beds)
20201 South Crawford Avenue, Olympia Fields, IL Zip 60461–1080;
tel. 708/747–4000; Peter J. Murphy, President and Chief Executive
Officer
Web address: www.stjameshhc.org

INDIANA: GREATER LAFAYETTE HEALTH SERVICES (O, 440 beds) 2400
South Street, Lafayette, IN Zip 47904–3027; tel. 765/447–6811;
Terrance E. Wilson, President and Chief Executive Officer
Web address: www.glhsi.org

SAINT ANTHONY MEMORIAL HEALTH CENTERS (O, 224 beds) 301 West
Homer Street, Michigan City, IN Zip 46360–4358; tel. 219/879–8511; Bruce
E. Rampage, President and Chief Executive Officer
Web address: www.sahhc.org

SAINT MARGARET MERCY HEALTHCARE CENTERS (O, 624 beds) 5454
Hohman Avenue, Hammond, IN Zip 46320–1999; tel. 219/933–2074;
Thomas J. Gryzbek, President
Web address: www.smmhc.com

ST. ANTHONY MEDICAL CENTER (O, 267 beds) 1201 South Main Street,
Crown Point, IN Zip 46307–8483; tel. 219/738–2100; Seth Warren,
President
Web address: www.stanthonymedicalcenter.com

ST. CLARE MEDICAL CENTER (O, 86 beds) 1710 Lafayette Road,
Crawfordsville, IN Zip 47933–1099; tel. 765/362–2800; Jeffrey C. Zeh,
Executive Director
Web address: www.stclaremedical.org

ST. FRANCIS HOSPITAL AND HEALTH CENTERS – NORTH CAMPUS (O, 463
beds) 1600 Albany Street, Beech Grove, IN Zip 46107–1593;
tel. 317/787–3311; Robert J. Brody, President and Chief Executive Officer
Web address: www.stfrancishospitals.org

ST. FRANCIS HOSPITAL–MOORESVILLE (O, 54 beds) 1201 Hadley Road N.W.,
Mooresville, IN Zip 46158–1789; tel. 317/831–1160; D. Keith Jewell,
President and Executive Officer

For explanation of codes following names, see page B2.
★ Indicates Type III membership in the American Hospital Association.

Owned, leased, sponsored:	8 hospitals	2652 beds
Contract–managed:	0 hospitals	0 beds
Totals:	8 hospitals	2652 beds

★8855:   SOLARIS HEALTH SYSTEM (NP)
80 James Street, 2nd Floor, Edison, NJ Zip 08820–3998;
tel. 732/632–1501; John P. McGee, President and Chief Executive
Officer
(Moderately Centralized Health System)

NEW JERSEY: JFK JOHNSON REHABILITATION INSTITUTE (O, 92 beds) 65
James Street, Edison, NJ Zip 08818–3059; tel. 732/321–7050; Anthony
Cuzzola, Vice President Rehabilitation Services
Web address: www.solarishs.org

JFK MEDICAL CENTER (O, 325 beds) 65 James Street, Edison, NJ
Zip 08818–3059; tel. 732/321–7000; Scott Gebhard, Executive Vice
President and Chief Executive Officer
Web address: www.solarishs.org

MUHLENBERG REGIONAL MEDICAL CENTER (O, 301 beds) Park Avenue and
Randolph Road, North Plainfield, NJ Zip 07060; tel. 908/668–2000; Nancy A.
Fiamingo, Senior Vice President and Chief Operating Officer
Web address: www.solarishs.org

Owned, leased, sponsored:	3 hospitals	718 beds
Contract–managed:	0 hospitals	0 beds
Totals:	3 hospitals	718 beds

0253:   SOUTHEAST GEORGIA HEALTH SYSTEM (NP)
2415 Parkwood Drive, Brunswick, GA Zip 31520–4252, Mailing
Address: P.O. Box 1518, Zip 31521–1518; tel. 912/466–7000;
Gary R. Colberg, CHE, President and Chief Executive Officer
(Independent Hospital System)

GEORGIA: SOUTHEAST GEORGIA HEALTH SYSTEM BRUNSWICK CAMPUS (O,
247 beds) 2415 Parkwood Drive, Brunswick, GA Zip 31520–4252,
Mailing Address: P.O. Box 1518, Zip 31521–1518; tel. 912/466–7000;
Gary R. Colberg, CHE, President and Chief Executive Officer
Web address: www.sghs.org

SOUTHEAST GEORGIA HEALTH SYSTEM CAMDEN CAMPUS (O, 40 beds)
2000 Dan Proctor Drive, Saint Marys, GA Zip 31558–3810;
tel. 912/576–6200; Howard W. Sepp Jr, Administrator
Web address: www.sghs.org

Owned, leased, sponsored:	2 hospitals	287 beds
Contract–managed:	0 hospitals	0 beds
Totals:	2 hospitals	287 beds

4175:   SOUTHERN ILLINOIS HOSPITAL SERVICES (NP)
1239 East Main Street, Carbondale, IL Zip 62901, Mailing Address:
P.O. Box 3988, Zip 62902–3988; tel. 618/457–5200; Thomas J.
Firestone, M.D., President and Chief Executive Officer
(Moderately Centralized Health System)

ILLINOIS: HERRIN HOSPITAL (O, 89 beds) 201 South 14th Street, Herrin, IL
Zip 62948–3631; tel. 618/942–2171; Becky Ashton, Administrator
Web address: www.sih.net

MEMORIAL HOSPITAL OF CARBONDALE (O, 142 beds) 405 West Jackson
Street, Carbondale, IL Zip 62901–1467, Mailing Address: P.O. Box 10000,
Zip 62902–9000; tel. 618/549–0721; George Maroney, Senior Vice
President and Administrator
Web address: www.sih.net

ST. JOSEPH MEMORIAL HOSPITAL (O, 25 beds) 2 South Hospital Drive,
Murphysboro, IL Zip 62966–3333; tel. 618/684–3156; Stephen Pautler,
FACHE, Administrator
Web address: www.sih.net

Owned, leased, sponsored:	3 hospitals	256 beds
Contract–managed:	0 hospitals	0 beds
Totals:	3 hospitals	256 beds

★4195:   SPARTANBURG REGIONAL HEALTHCARE SYSTEM
(NP)
101 East Wood Street, Spartanburg, SC Zip 29303–3016;
tel. 864/560–6000; Ingo Angermeier, FACHE, President and Chief
Executive Officer
(Moderately Centralized Health System)

SOUTH CAROLINA: SPARTANBURG HOSPITAL FOR RESTORATIVE CARE (O,
82 beds) 389 Serpentine Drive, Spartanburg, SC Zip 29303–3026;
tel. 864/560–3280; Anita M. Butler, Chief Executive Officer
Web address: www.srhs.com

SPARTANBURG REGIONAL MEDICAL CENTER (O, 465 beds) 101 East Wood
Street, Spartanburg, SC Zip 29303–3016; tel. 864/560–6000; Ingo
Angermeier, FACHE, President and Chief Executive Officer
Web address: www.spartanburgregional.com

Owned, leased, sponsored:	2 hospitals	547 beds
Contract–managed:	0 hospitals	0 beds
Totals:	2 hospitals	547 beds

0177:   SPECTRUM HEALTH (NP)
100 Michigan Street N.E., Grand Rapids, MI Zip 49503–2551;
tel. 616/391–1774; Richard C. Breon, President and Chief Executive
Officer
(Centralized Physician/Insurance Health System)

MICHIGAN: SPECTRUM HEALTH (O, 912 beds) 1840 Wealthy Street S.E.,
Grand Rapids, MI Zip 49506–2921; tel. 616/774–7444; Matthew Van
Vranken, President
Web address: www.spectrum–health.org

SPECTRUM HEALTH–KENT COMMUNITY CAMPUS (O, 373 beds) 750 Fuller
Avenue N.E., Grand Rapids, MI Zip 49503–1995; tel. 616/486–3000;
Stephanie Hearn, Administrator
Web address: www.kentcommunity.spectrum–health.org

SPECTRUM HEALTH–REED CITY CAMPUS (O, 82 beds) 300 North Patterson
Road, Reed City, MI Zip 49677–0075, Mailing Address: P.O. Box 75,
Zip 49677–0075; tel. 231/832–3271; Thomas D. Kaufman, President and
Chief Executive Officer
Web address: www.spectrum–health.org

SPECTRUM HEALTH–UNITED MEMORIAL (O, 65 beds) 615 South Bower
Street, Greenville, MI Zip 48838–2628; tel. 616/754–4691; Paul Bonis, Chief
Executive Officer
Web address: www.umha.org

Owned, leased, sponsored:	4 hospitals	1432 beds
Contract–managed:	0 hospitals	0 beds
Totals:	4 hospitals	1432 beds

★5455:   SSM HEALTH CARE (CC)
477 North Lindbergh Boulevard, Saint Louis, MO Zip 63141–7813;
tel. 314/994–7800; Sister Mary Jean Ryan, President and Chief
Executive Officer
(Moderately Centralized Health System)

ILLINOIS: GOOD SAMARITAN REGIONAL HEALTH CENTER (O, 149 beds) 605
North 12th Street, Mount Vernon, IL Zip 62864–2899;
tel. 618/242–4600; Leo F. Childers Jr, FACHE, President
Web address: www.smgsi.com

ST. FRANCIS HOSPITAL & HEALTH CENTER (O, 260 beds) 12935 South
Gregory Street, Blue Island, IL Zip 60406–2470; tel. 708/597–2000; Colleen
Kannaday, President
Web address: www.stfrancisblueisland.com

ST. MARY'S HOSPITAL (C, 125 beds) 400 North Pleasant Avenue, Centralia,
IL Zip 62801–3091; tel. 618/436–8000; Bruce Merrell, President
Web address: www.smgsi.com

MISSOURI: SSM CARDINAL GLENNON CHILDREN'S HOSPITAL (O, 164 beds)
1465 South Grand Boulevard, Saint Louis, MO Zip 63104–1095;
tel. 314/577–5600; Douglas A. Ries, FACHE, President
Web address: www.cardinalglennon.com

SSM DEPAUL HEALTH CENTER (O, 412 beds) 12303 DePaul Drive, Saint
Louis, MO Zip 63044–2588; tel. 314/344–6000; Melinda Clark, FACHE,
President and Chief Executive Officer
Web address: www.ssmdepaul.com

For explanation of codes following names, see page B2.
★ Indicates Type III membership in the American Hospital Association.

Section B

SSM REHAB (O, 100 beds) 6420 Clayton Road, Suite 600, Saint Louis, MO Zip 63117–1811; tel. 314/768–5300; Steven P. Johnson, Ph.D., President
Web address: www.ssmrehab.com

SSM ST. JOSEPH HEALTH CENTER (O, 276 beds) 300 First Capitol Drive, Saint Charles, MO Zip 63301–2844; tel. 636/947–5000; Paul Convery, M.D., Interim President and Chief Executive Officer
Web address: www.ssmstjoseph.com

SSM ST. JOSEPH HOSPITAL OF KIRKWOOD (O, 202 beds) 525 Couch Avenue, Saint Louis, MO Zip 63122–5536; tel. 314/966–1500; Sherry Hausmann, President
Web address: www.st josephkirkwood.com

SSM ST. JOSEPH HOSPITAL WEST (O, 83 beds) 100 Medical Plaza, Lake Saint Louis, MO Zip 63367–1395; tel. 636/625–5200; Paul Convery, M.D., Interim President and Chief Executive Officer
Web address: www.ssmstjoseph.com

SSM ST. MARY'S HEALTH CENTER (O, 365 beds) 6420 Clayton Road, Saint Louis, MO Zip 63117–1872; tel. 314/768–8000; Kenneth W. Lukhard, President
Web address: www.stlapps.ssmhc.com/intranet/home/smhcstl.nsf

ST. FRANCIS HOSPITAL AND HEALTH SERVICES (O, 55 beds) 2016 South Main Street, Maryville, MO Zip 64468–2693; tel. 660/562–2600; Michael Baumgartner, President
Web address: www.stfrancismaryville.com

ST. MARYS HEALTH CENTER (O, 167 beds) 100 St. Marys Medical Plaza, Jefferson City, MO Zip 65101–1601; tel. 573/761–7000; Elizabeth Aderholdt, President
Web address: www.stmarys–jeffcity.com

OKLAHOMA: BONE AND JOINT HOSPITAL (O, 80 beds) 1111 North Dewey Avenue, Oklahoma City, OK Zip 73103–2615; tel. 405/552–9100; James A. Hyde, Administrator
Web address: www.boneandjoint.com

ST. ANTHONY HOSPITAL (O, 543 beds) 1000 North Lee Street, Oklahoma City, OK Zip 73102–1080, Mailing Address: P.O. Box 205, Zip 73101–0205; tel. 405/272–7000; Joe Hodges, President
Web address: www.saintsok.com

WISCONSIN: ST. CLARE HOSPITAL AND HEALTH SERVICES (O, 84 beds) 707 14th Street, Baraboo, WI Zip 53913–1597; tel. 608/356–1400; Sandra L. Anderson, President
Web address: www.stclare.com

ST. MARYS HOSPITAL MEDICAL CENTER (O, 307 beds) 707 South Mills Street, Madison, WI Zip 53715–0450; tel. 608/251–6100; Frank D. Byrne, M.D., President
Web address: www.stmarysmadison.com

Owned, leased, sponsored:	15 hospitals	3247 beds
Contract–managed:	1 hospital	125 beds
Totals:	16 hospitals	3372 beds

★5425:   ST. JOSEPH HEALTH SYSTEM (CC)
500 South Main Street, Suite 1000, Orange, CA Zip 92868, Mailing Address: P.O. Box 14132, Zip 92863–1532; tel. 714/347–7500; Deborah A. Proctor, President and Chief Executive Officer
(Moderately Centralized Health System)

CALIFORNIA: MISSION HOSPITAL (O, 272 beds) 27700 Medical Center Road, Mission Viejo, CA Zip 92691–6426; tel. 949/364–1400; Peter F. Bastone, President and Chief Executive Officer
Web address: www.mission4health.com

PETALUMA VALLEY HOSPITAL (L, 69 beds) 400 North McDowell Boulevard, Petaluma, CA Zip 94954–2369; tel. 707/778–1111; George Perez, President and Chief Executive Officer
Web address: www.stjosephhealth.org/petalumavalley

QUEEN OF THE VALLEY HOSPITAL (O, 179 beds) 1000 Trancas Street, Napa, CA Zip 94558–2906, Mailing Address: P.O. Box 2340, Zip 94558–2340; tel. 707/252–4411; Dennis Sisto, President and Chief Executive Officer
Web address: www.thequeen.org

REDWOOD MEMORIAL HOSPITAL (O, 46 beds) 3300 Renner Drive, Fortuna, CA Zip 95540–3198; tel. 707/725–3361; Michael L. Purvis, President and Chief Executive Officer

SANTA ROSA MEMORIAL HOSPITAL (O, 325 beds) 1165 Montgomery Drive, Santa Rosa, CA Zip 95405–4897, Mailing Address: P.O. Box 522, Zip 95402–0522; tel. 707/546–3210; George Perez, President and Chief Executive Officer
Web address: www.stjosephhealth.org

ST. JOSEPH HOSPITAL (O, 159 beds) 2700 Dolbeer Street, Eureka, CA Zip 95501–4799; tel. 707/445–8121; Michael L. Purvis, President and Chief Executive Officer
Web address: www.stjosepheureka.org

ST. JOSEPH HOSPITAL (O, 366 beds) 1100 West Stewart Drive, Orange, CA Zip 92668–3891, Mailing Address: P.O. Box 5600, Zip 92613–5600; tel. 714/633–9111; Larry K. Ainsworth, President and Chief Executive Officer
Web address: www.sjo.stjoe.org

ST. JUDE MEDICAL CENTER (O, 293 beds) 101 East Valencia Mesa Drive, Fullerton, CA Zip 92835–3809; tel. 714/992–3000; Robert J. Fraschetti, President and Chief Executive Officer
Web address: www.stjudemedicalcenter.org

ST. MARY MEDICAL CENTER (O, 186 beds) 18300 Highway 18, Apple Valley, CA Zip 92307–2255, Mailing Address: P.O. Box 7025, Zip 92307–0725; tel. 760/242–2311; George Perez, President and Chief Executive Officer

Owned, leased, sponsored:	9 hospitals	1895 beds
Contract–managed:	0 hospitals	0 beds
Totals:	9 hospitals	1895 beds

0269:   ST. JOSEPH'S HEALTHCARE SYSTEM (CC)
703 Main Street, Paterson, NJ Zip 07503–2691; tel. 973/754–2000; William A. McDonald, Interim Chief Executive Officer
(Independent Hospital System)

NEW JERSEY: ST. JOSEPH'S REGIONAL MEDICAL CENTER (O, 651 beds) 703 Main Street, Paterson, NJ Zip 07503–2691; tel. 973/754–2000; William A. McDonald, Interim Chief Executive Officer
Web address: www.sjhmc.org

ST. JOSEPH'S WAYNE HOSPITAL (O, 122 beds) 224 Hamburg Turnpike, Wayne, NJ Zip 07470–2100; tel. 973/942–6900; William A. McDonald, Interim Chief Executive Officer
Web address: www.sjwh.net

Owned, leased, sponsored:	2 hospitals	773 beds
Contract–managed:	0 hospitals	0 beds
Totals:	2 hospitals	773 beds

0302:   ST. LUKE'S EPISCOPAL HEALTH SYSTEM (NP)
6624 Fannin Street, Suite 1100, Houston, TX Zip 77030; tel. 832/355–7661; David J. Fine, Chief Executive Officer
(Moderately Centralized Health System)

TEXAS: ST LUKE'S COMMUNITY MEDICAL CENTER–THE WOODLANDS (O, 76 beds) 17200 St. Luke's Way, The Woodlands, TX Zip 77384; tel. 936/266–2000; Stephen R. Selzer, Chief Executive Officer
Web address: www.stlukeswoodlands.com

ST. LUKE'S EPISCOPAL HOSPITAL (O, 685 beds) 6720 Bertner Avenue, Houston, TX Zip 77030–2697, Mailing Address: Box 20269, Zip 77225–0269; tel. 832/355–1000; David J. Fine, Chief Executive Officer
Web address: www.sleh.com

Owned, leased, sponsored:	2 hospitals	761 beds
Contract–managed:	0 hospitals	0 beds
Totals:	2 hospitals	761 beds

0242:   ST. MARY'S/DULUTH CLINIC HEALTH SYSTEM (NP)
407 East Third Street, Duluth, MN Zip 55805–1984; tel. 218/786–4000; Peter E. Person, M.D., President and Chief Executive Officer
(Moderately Centralized Health System)

MINNESOTA: MILLER–DWAN MEDICAL CENTER (O, 152 beds) 502 East Second Street, Duluth, MN Zip 55805–1982; tel. 218/727–8762; Rocklon B. Chapin, Chief Operating Officer and Administrator
Web address: www.miller–dwan.com

For explanation of codes following names, see page B2.
★ Indicates Type III membership in the American Hospital Association.

Section B

PINE MEDICAL CENTER (O, 94 beds) 109 Court Avenue South, Sandstone, MN Zip 55072–5120; tel. 320/245–2212; Timothy Zwickey, Administrator and Chief Executive Officer
Web address: www.pinemedical.org

ST. MARY'S MEDICAL CENTER (O, 315 beds) 407 East Third Street, Duluth, MN Zip 55805–1984; tel. 218/786–4000; Susan E. McClernon, Chief Operating Officer
Web address: www.smdc.org

WISCONSIN: ST. MARY'S HOSPITAL OF SUPERIOR (O, 24 beds) 3500 Tower Avenue, Superior, WI Zip 54880–5395; tel. 715/392–8281; Maribeth Olson, Interim Administrator
Web address: www.smdc.org

Owned, leased, sponsored:	4 hospitals	585 beds
Contract–managed:	0 hospitals	0 beds
Totals:	4 hospitals	585 beds

0264: ST. VINCENT HEALTH SYSTEM (CC)
232 West 25th Street, Erie, PA Zip 16544–0002; tel. 814/452–5000; C. Angela Bontempo, President and Chief Executive Officer
(Moderately Centralized Health System)

NEW YORK: WESTFIELD MEMORIAL HOSPITAL (O, 19 beds) 189 East Main Street, Westfield, NY Zip 14787–1195; tel. 716/326–4921; Stuart W. Williams, President and Chief Executive Officer
Web address: www.wmhinc.org

PENNSYLVANIA: SAINT VINCENT HEALTH CENTER (O, 456 beds) 232 West 25th Street, Erie, PA Zip 16544–0002; tel. 814/452–5000; C. Angela Bontempo, President and Chief Executive Officer
Web address: www.svhs.org

Owned, leased, sponsored:	2 hospitals	475 beds
Contract–managed:	0 hospitals	0 beds
Totals:	2 hospitals	475 beds

0156: STANFORD HEALTH CARE (NP)
300 Pasteur Drive, Palo Alto, CA Zip 94304–2299; tel. 650/723–4000; Martha H. Marsh, President and Chief Executive Officer
(Moderately Centralized Health System)

CALIFORNIA: LUCILE SALTER PACKARD CHILDREN'S HOSPITAL AT STANFORD (O, 248 beds) 725 Welch Road, Palo Alto, CA Zip 94304–1601; tel. 650/497–8000; Christopher G. Dawes, President and Chief Executive Officer
Web address: www.lpch.org

STANFORD HOSPITAL AND CLINICS (O, 439 beds) 300 Pasteur Drive, Palo Alto, CA Zip 94304–2299; tel. 650/723–4000; Martha H. Marsh, President and Chief Executive Officer
Web address: www.stanfordhospital.com/

Owned, leased, sponsored:	2 hospitals	687 beds
Contract–managed:	0 hospitals	0 beds
Totals:	2 hospitals	687 beds

0223: STRONG MEMORIAL HOSPITAL (NP)
601 Elmwood Avenue, Rochester, NY Zip 14642–0002; tel. 585/275–2100; Steven I. Goldstein, General Director and Chief Executive Officer
(Centralized Health System)

NEW YORK: HIGHLAND HOSPITAL OF ROCHESTER (O, 241 beds) 1000 South Avenue, Rochester, NY Zip 14620–2782; tel. 585/473–2200; Steven I. Goldstein, President and Chief Executive Officer
Web address: www.stronghealth.com

STRONG MEMORIAL HOSPITAL OF THE UNIVERSITY OF ROCHESTER (O, 695 beds) 601 Elmwood Avenue, Rochester, NY Zip 14642–0002; tel. 585/275–2100; Steven I. Goldstein, General Director and Chief Executive Officer
Web address: www.urmc.rochester.edu

Owned, leased, sponsored:	2 hospitals	936 beds
Contract–managed:	0 hospitals	0 beds
Totals:	2 hospitals	936 beds

★0189: SUMMIT HEALTH (NP)
112 North Seventh Street, Chambersburg, PA Zip 17201; tel. 717/267–7138; Norman B. Epstein, CHE, President
(Moderately Centralized Health System)

PENNSYLVANIA: CHAMBERSBURG HOSPITAL (O, 231 beds) 112 North Seventh Street, Chambersburg, PA Zip 17201–0187, Mailing Address: P.O. Box 6005, Zip 17201–6005; tel. 717/267–3000; Norman B. Epstein, CHE, President
Web address: www.summithealth.org

WAYNESBORO HOSPITAL (O, 62 beds) 501 East Main Street, Waynesboro, PA Zip 17268–2394; tel. 717/765–4000; Kenneth L. Shur, Vice President and Chief Operating Officer
Web address: www.summithealth.org

Owned, leased, sponsored:	2 hospitals	293 beds
Contract–managed:	0 hospitals	0 beds
Totals:	2 hospitals	293 beds

0292: SUMNER REGIONAL HEALTH SYSTEMS (NP)
555 Hartsville Pike, Gallatin, TN Zip 37066; tel. 615/452–4210; William T. Sugg, President and Chief Executive Officer
(Independent Hospital System)

TENNESSEE: CARTHAGE GENERAL HOSPITAL (O, 25 beds) 130 Lebanon Highway, Carthage, TN Zip 37030–2955, Mailing Address: P.O. Box 319, Zip 37030–0319; tel. 615/735–9815; Scott Tongate, Administrator
Web address: www.sumner.org

SUMNER REGIONAL MEDICAL CENTER (O, 115 beds) 555 Hartsville Pike, Gallatin, TN Zip 37066–2449, Mailing Address: P.O. Box 1558, Zip 37066–1558; tel. 615/452–4210; Bruce James, Administrator
Web address: www.sumner.org

TROUSDALE MEDICAL CENTER (O, 25 beds) 500 Church Street, Hartsville, TN Zip 37074, Mailing Address: P.O. Box 319, Carthage, Zip 37030; tel. 615/374–2221; William D. Mize, Administrator
Web address: www.sumner.org

Owned, leased, sponsored:	3 hospitals	165 beds
Contract–managed:	0 hospitals	0 beds
Totals:	3 hospitals	165 beds

★0030: SUN HEALTH CORPORATION (NP)
13180 North 103rd Drive, Sun City, AZ Zip 85351–3038, Mailing Address: P.O. Box 1278, Zip 85372–1278; tel. 623/876–5301; Leland W. Peterson, President and Chief Executive Officer
(Centralized Health System)

ARIZONA: DEL E. WEBB MEMORIAL HOSPITAL (O, 334 beds) 14502 West Meeker Boulevard, Sun City West, AZ Zip 85375–5299, Mailing Address: P.O. Box 5169, Sun City, Zip 85375–5169; tel. 623/214–4000; Jo Adkins, Chief Executive Officer
Web address: www.sunhealth.org

WALTER O. BOSWELL MEMORIAL HOSPITAL (O, 324 beds) 10401 West Thunderbird Boulevard, Sun City, AZ Zip 85351–3092, Mailing Address: P.O. Box 1690, Zip 85372–1690; tel. 623/977–7211; Thomas C. Dickson, Chief Executive Officer
Web address: www.sunhealth.org

Owned, leased, sponsored:	2 hospitals	658 beds
Contract–managed:	0 hospitals	0 beds
Totals:	2 hospitals	658 beds

0237: SUNLINK HEALTHCARE (IO)
900 Circle 75 Parkway, Suite 1300, Atlanta, GA Zip 30339; tel. 770/933–7000; Robert M. Thornton Jr, Chief Executive Officer
(Independent Hospital System)

For explanation of codes following names, see page B2.
★ Indicates Type III membership in the American Hospital Association.

ALABAMA: CHILTON MEDICAL CENTER (O, 60 beds) 1010 Lay Dam Road, Clanton, AL Zip 35045–2306; tel. 205/755–2500; Terry Frech, Chief Executive Officer
Web address: www.sunlinkhealth.com/chilton.html

GEORGIA: CHESTATEE REGIONAL HOSPITAL (O, 49 beds) 227 Mountain Drive, Dahlonega, GA Zip 30533–1606; tel. 706/864–6136; Rob Followell, Chief Executive Officer
Web address: www.chestateeregionalhospital.com

MEMORIAL HOSPITAL OF ADEL (O, 155 beds) 706 North Parrish Avenue, Adel, GA Zip 31620–0677, Mailing Address: 705 North Parrish Avenue, Zip 31620–0677; tel. 229/896–8000; William Hawley, Chief Executive Officer
Web address: www.sunlinkhealth.com/memorial.html

NORTH GEORGIA MEDICAL CENTER (O, 150 beds) 1362 South Main Street, Ellijay, GA Zip 30540–0346, Mailing Address: P.O. Box 2239, Zip 30540–0346; tel. 706/276–4741; Jeffrey Dunn, Chief Executive Officer

MISSISSIPPI: TRACE REGIONAL HOSPITAL (O, 84 beds) Highway 8 East, Houston, MS Zip 38851–9396, Mailing Address: P.O. Box 626, Zip 38851–0626; tel. 662/456–3700; Gary L. Staten, Chief Executive Officer
Web address: www.traceregional.com

MISSOURI: CALLAWAY COMMUNITY HOSPITAL (O, 31 beds) 10 South Hospital Drive, Fulton, MO Zip 65251–2513; tel. 573/642–3376; John T. Graves, Chief Executive Officer
Web address: www.sunlinkhealth.com/callaway.html

MISSOURI SOUTHERN HEALTHCARE (L, 41 beds) 1200 North One Mile Road, Dexter, MO Zip 63841–1000; tel. 573/624–5566; Jim Crawford, Chief Executive Officer
Web address: www.msh–hospital.com

Owned, leased, sponsored:	7 hospitals	570 beds
Contract–managed:	0 hospitals	0 beds
Totals:	7 hospitals	570 beds

★**8795: SUTTER HEALTH** (NP)
2200 River Plaza Drive, Sacramento, CA Zip 95833; tel. 916/733–8800; Patrick E. Fry, Chief Executive Officer
(Decentralized Health System)

CALIFORNIA: ALTA BATES SUMMIT MEDICAL CENTER (O, 509 beds) 2450 Ashby Avenue, Berkeley, CA Zip 94705–2067; tel. 510/204–4444; Warren J. Kirk, Chief Executive Officer
Web address: www.altabates.com

ALTA BATES SUMMIT MEDICAL CENTER – SUMMIT CAMPUS (O, 877 beds) 350 Hawthorne Avenue, Oakland, CA Zip 94609–3100; tel. 510/655–4000; Warren J. Kirk, President and Chief Executive Officer
Web address: www.altabatessummit.com

CALIFORNIA PACIFIC MEDICAL CENTER (C, 783 beds) 2333 Buchanan Street, San Francisco, CA Zip 94115–1925, Mailing Address: P.O. Box 7999, Zip 94120–7999; tel. 415/563–4321; Martin Brotman, M.D., President and Chief Executive Officer
Web address: www.cpmc.org

MARIN GENERAL HOSPITAL (O, 235 beds) 250 Bon Air Road, Greenbrae, CA Zip 94904–1784, Mailing Address: P.O. Box 8010, San Rafael, Zip 94912–8010; tel. 415/925–7000; David Bradley, Chief Executive Officer
Web address: www.maringeneral.sutterhealth.org

MEMORIAL HOSPITALS ASSOCIATION (O, 313 beds) Modesto, CA Mailing Address: P.O. Box 942, Zip 95353–0942; tel. 209/526–4500; David P. Benn, Chief Executive Officer
Web address: www.memorialmedicalcenter.org

MILLS–PENINSULA HEALTH SERVICES (O, 398 beds) 1783 El Camino Real, Burlingame, CA Zip 94010–3282; tel. 650/696–5400; Robert W. Merwin, Chief Executive Officer
Web address: www.mills–pensinsula.org

NOVATO COMMUNITY HOSPITAL (O, 47 beds) 180 Rowland Way, Novato, CA Zip 94945–5009, Mailing Address: P.O. Box 1108, Zip 94948–1108; tel. 415/209–1300; Anne L. Hosfeld, Chief Administrative Officer
Web address: www.novatocommunity.sutterhealth.org

ST. LUKE'S HOSPITAL (O, 220 beds) 3555 Cesar Chavez Street, San Francisco, CA Zip 94110–4490; tel. 415/647–8600; John G. Williams, President and Chief Executive Officer
Web address: www.stlukes–sf.org

SUTTER AMADOR HOSPITAL (O, 66 beds) 200 Mission Boulevard, Jackson, CA Zip 95642–2132; tel. 209/223–7500; Anne Platt, Chief Executive Officer
Web address: www.sutteramador.com

SUTTER AUBURN FAITH HOSPITAL (O, 82 beds) 11815 Education Street, Auburn, CA Zip 95602–2410; tel. 530/888–4500; Mitchell J. Hanna, Chief Administrative Officer
Web address: www.sutterhealth.org

SUTTER CENTER FOR PSYCHIATRY (O, 69 beds) 7700 Folsom Boulevard, Sacramento, CA Zip 95826–2608; tel. 916/386–3000; Diane Gail Stewart, Chief Administrative Officer
Web address: www.sutterhealth.org

SUTTER COAST HOSPITAL (O, 59 beds) 800 East Washington Boulevard, Crescent City, CA Zip 95531–8359; tel. 707/464–8511; John E. Menaugh, Chief Executive Officer
Web address: www.sutterhealth.org

SUTTER DAVIS HOSPITAL (O, 48 beds) 2000 Sutter Place, Davis, CA Zip 95616–6201, Mailing Address: P.O. Box 1617, Zip 95617–1617; tel. 530/756–6440; Janet Wagner, R.N., Chief Administrative Officer
Web address: www.sutterhealth.org

SUTTER DELTA MEDICAL CENTER (O, 111 beds) 3901 Lone Tree Way, Antioch, CA Zip 94509–6200; tel. 925/779–7200; Linda Horn, Chief Executive Officer
Web address: www.sutterdelta.org

SUTTER LAKESIDE HOSPITAL (O, 53 beds) 5176 Hill Road East, Lakeport, CA Zip 95453–6300; tel. 707/262–5001; Kelly Mather, Chief Executive Officer
Web address: www.sutterlake.org

SUTTER MATERNITY AND SURGERY CENTER OF SANTA CRUZ (O, 28 beds) 2900 Chanticleer Avenue, Santa Cruz, CA Zip 95065–1816; tel. 831/477–2200; Richard Nichols, Administrator
Web address: www.suttermatsurg.org

SUTTER MEDICAL CENTER OF SANTA ROSA (O, 181 beds) 3325 Chanate Road, Santa Rosa, CA Zip 95404–1707; tel. 707/576–4000; Michael J. Cohill, Chief Executive Officer
Web address: www.sutterhealth.org

SUTTER MEDICAL CENTER, SACRAMENTO (O, 742 beds) 5151 F Street, Sacramento, CA Zip 95819–3295; tel. 916/454–3333; Thomas C. Gagen, Chief Executive Officer
Web address: www.sutterhealth.org

SUTTER ROSEVILLE MEDICAL CENTER (O, 172 beds) One Medical Plaza, Roseville, CA Zip 95661–3037; tel. 916/781–1000; Patrick R. Brady, Chief Executive Officer
Web address: www.sutterroseville.org

SUTTER SOLANO MEDICAL CENTER (O, 111 beds) 300 Hospital Drive, Vallejo, CA Zip 94589–2517, Mailing Address: P.O. Box 3189, Zip 94589–3189; tel. 707/554–4444; Theresa Glubka, Chief Executive Officer
Web address: www.suttersolano.org

SUTTER TRACY COMMUNITY HOSPITAL (O, 79 beds) 1420 North Tracy Boulevard, Tracy, CA Zip 95376–3497; tel. 209/835–1500; Gary D. Rapaport, Chief Executive Officer
Web address: www.suttertracy.org

HAWAII: KAHI MOHALA BEHAVIORAL HEALTH (O, 88 beds) 91–2301 Old Fort Weaver Road, Ewa Beach, HI Zip 96706–3602; tel. 808/671–8511; Mark R. Mitchell, Ph.D., Chief Executive Officer
Web address: www.kahi.org

Owned, leased, sponsored:	21 hospitals	4488 beds
Contract–managed:	1 hospital	783 beds
Totals:	22 hospitals	5271 beds

0039: TARRANT COUNTY HOSPITAL DISTRICT (NP)
1500 South Main Street, Fort Worth, TX Zip 76104–4941; tel. 817/927–1230; David M. Cecero, President and Chief Executive Officer
(Centralized Physician/Insurance Health System)

TEXAS: JPS HEALTH NETWORK (O, 378 beds) 1500 South Main Street, Fort Worth, TX Zip 76104–4941; tel. 817/921–3431; David M. Cecero, President and Chief Executive Officer
Web address: www.jpshealthnet.org

TRINITY SPRINGS PAVILION (O, 34 beds) 1500 South Main Street, Fort Worth, TX Zip 76104–4917; tel. 817/927–3636; Lily Wong, Director Psychiatry

For explanation of codes following names, see page B2.
★ Indicates Type III membership in the American Hospital Association.

Owned, leased, sponsored:	2 hospitals	412 beds
Contract–managed:	0 hospitals	0 beds
Totals:	2 hospitals	412 beds

★**0169:** **TEMPLE UNIVERSITY HEALTH SYSTEM** (NP)
3509 North Broad Street, 9th Floor, Philadelphia, PA Zip 19140;
tel. 215/707–0900; Joseph W. Marshall III, Chairman and Chief
Executive Officer
(Centralized Health System)

PENNSYLVANIA: JEANES HOSPITAL (O, 207 beds) 7600 Central Avenue,
Philadelphia, PA Zip 19111–2499; tel. 215/728–2000; Linda J. Grass,
Executive Director and Chief Executive Officer
Web address: www.jeanes.com

TEMPLE EAST, NORTHEASTERN HOSPITAL (O, 185 beds) 2301 East
Allegheny Avenue, Philadelphia, PA Zip 19134–4497; tel. 215/291–3000;
John J. Buckley, Executive Director and Chief Executive Officer
Web address: www.health.temple.edu/northeastern.html

TEMPLE UNIVERSITY CHILDREN'S MEDICAL CENTER (O, 68 beds) 3509 North
Broad Street, Philadelphia, PA Zip 19140; tel. 215/707–6038; Raymond W.
Uhlhorn, Executive Director and Chief Executive Officer
Web address: www.health.temple.edu/tucmc/index.htm

TEMPLE UNIVERSITY HOSPITAL (O, 640 beds) Broad and Ontario Streets,
Philadelphia, PA Zip 19140–5192; tel. 215/707–2000; Daniel J. Sinnott,
Executive Director and Chief Executive Officer
Web address: www.health.temple.edu/tuh/

Owned, leased, sponsored:	4 hospitals	1100 beds
Contract–managed:	0 hospitals	0 beds
Totals:	4 hospitals	1100 beds

★**0063:** **TENET HEALTHCARE CORPORATION** (IO)
13737 Noel Road, Suite 100, Dallas, TX Zip 75240–2200;
tel. 469/893–2200; Trevor Fetter, President and Chief Executive
Officer
(Decentralized Health System)

ALABAMA: BROOKWOOD MEDICAL CENTER (O, 568 beds) 2010 Brookwood
Medical Center Drive, Birmingham, AL Zip 35209–6875;
tel. 205/877–1000; Garry L. Gause, Chief Executive Officer
Web address: www.brookwood–medical.com

CALIFORNIA: ALVARADO HOSPITAL MEDICAL CENTER (O, 151 beds) 6655
Alvarado Road, San Diego, CA Zip 92120–5208; tel. 619/287–3270;
Mark R. Palmer, Chief Executive Officer
Web address: www.alvaradohospital.com

BROTMAN MEDICAL CENTER (O, 250 beds) 3828 Delmas Terrace, Culver
City, CA Zip 90232–6806, Mailing Address: P.O. Box 2459,
Zip 90231–2459; tel. 310/836–7000; Maurine Cate, Chief Executive Officer
Web address: www.brotmanmedicalcenter.com

COMMUNITY AND MISSION HOSPITALS OF HUNTINGTON PARK (L, 157 beds)
2623 East Slauson Avenue, Huntington Park, CA Zip 90255–2900;
tel. 323/583–1931; Barbara Schneider, R.N., Chief Executive Officer
Web address: www.communityhosp.com

COMMUNITY HOSPITAL OF LOS GATOS (L, 77 beds) 815 Pollard Road, Los
Gatos, CA Zip 95032–1438; tel. 408/378–6131; Gary Honts, Chief
Executive Officer
Web address: www.communityhospitallg.com

DESERT REGIONAL MEDICAL CENTER (L, 325 beds) 1150 North Indian
Canyon Drive, Palm Springs, CA Zip 92262–4872, Mailing Address: P.O. Box
2739, Zip 92263–2739; tel. 760/323–6511; Barry Dykes, President and
Chief Executive Officer
Web address: www.desertmedctr.com

DOCTORS HOSPITAL OF MANTECA (O, 73 beds) 1205 East North Street,
Manteca, CA Zip 95336–4900; tel. 209/823–3111; Katherine Medeiros,
Chief Executive Officer
Web address: www.doctorsmanteca.com

DOCTORS MEDICAL CENTER (O, 398 beds) 1441 Florida Avenue, Modesto,
CA Zip 95350–4418, Mailing Address: P.O. Box 4138, Zip 95352–4138;
tel. 209/578–1211; Katherine Medeiros, Interim Chief Executive Officer
Web address: www.dmc–modesto.com

ENCINO–TARZANA REGIONAL MEDICAL CENTER ENCINO CAMPUS (L, 232
beds) 16237 Ventura Boulevard, Encino, CA Zip 91436–2201;
tel. 818/995–5000; Dale Surowitz, Chief Executive Officer
Web address: www.encino–tarzana.com

ENCINO–TARZANA REGIONAL MEDICAL CENTER TARZANA CAMPUS (L, 286
beds) 18321 Clark Street, Tarzana, CA Zip 91356–3521;
tel. 818/881–0800; Dale Surowitz, Chief Executive Officer
Web address: www.encino–tarzana.com

FOUNTAIN VALLEY REGIONAL HOSPITAL AND MEDICAL CENTER (O, 360
beds) 17100 Euclid Street, Fountain Valley, CA Zip 92708–4043;
tel. 714/966–7200; Tim Smith, Chief Executive Officer
Web address: www.fountainvalleyhospital.com

GARDEN GROVE HOSPITAL AND MEDICAL CENTER (O, 79 beds) 12601
Garden Grove Boulevard, Garden Grove, CA Zip 92843–1908;
tel. 714/537–5160; Maxine T. Cooper, Chief Executive Officer
Web address: www.gardengrovehospital.com

IRVINE REGIONAL HOSPITAL AND MEDICAL CENTER (L, 176 beds) 16200
Sand Canyon Avenue, Irvine, CA Zip 92618–3714; tel. 949/753–2000; Dan
F. Ausman, Chief Executive Officer
Web address: www.irvineregionalhospital.com

JOHN F. KENNEDY MEMORIAL HOSPITAL (O, 145 beds) 47–111 Monroe
Street, Indio, CA Zip 92201; tel. 760/347–6191; John J. Ferrelli, Chief
Executive Officer
Web address: www.jfkmemorialhosp.com

LAKEWOOD REGIONAL MEDICAL CENTER (O, 161 beds) 3700 East South
Street, Lakewood, CA Zip 90712–1498, Mailing Address: P.O. Box 6070,
Zip 90714–6070; tel. 562/531–2550; Michael Hunn, Chief Executive Officer
Web address: www.lakewoodregional.com

LOS ALAMITOS MEDICAL CENTER (O, 167 beds) 3751 Katella Avenue, Los
Alamitos, CA Zip 90720–3164; tel. 562/598–1311; Michele Finney, Chief
Executive Officer
Web address: www.losalamitosmedctr.com

PLACENTIA LINDA HOSPITAL (O, 114 beds) 1301 Rose Drive, Placentia, CA
Zip 92870–3899; tel. 714/993–2000; Kent G. Clayton, President and Chief
Executive Officer
Web address: www.placentialinda.com

SAN DIMAS COMMUNITY HOSPITAL (O, 93 beds) 1350 West Covina
Boulevard, San Dimas, CA Zip 91773–3219; tel. 909/599–6811; Dan
Bowers, Chief Executive Officer
Web address: www.sandimashospital.com

SAN RAMON REGIONAL MEDICAL CENTER (O, 123 beds) 6001 Norris Canyon
Road, San Ramon, CA Zip 94583–5400; tel. 925/275–9200; Gary Sloan,
Chief Executive Officer
Web address: www.sanramonmedctr.com

SIERRA VISTA REGIONAL MEDICAL CENTER (O, 160 beds) 1010 Murray
Street, San Luis Obispo, CA Zip 93405–8800, Mailing Address: P.O. Box
1367, Zip 93406–1367; tel. 805/546–7600; Candace L. Markwith, Chief
Executive Officer
Web address: www.sierravistaregional.com

TWIN CITIES COMMUNITY HOSPITAL (O, 60 beds) 1100 Las Tablas Road,
Templeton, CA Zip 93465–9704; tel. 805/434–3500; Richard D. Lyons,
Chief Executive Officer
Web address: www.twincitieshospital.com

UNIVERSITY OF SOUTHERN CALIFORNIA–NORRIS COMPREHENSIVE CANCER
CENTER AND HOSPITAL (L, 60 beds) 1441 Eastlake Avenue, Los Angeles, CA
Zip 90033–3804; tel. 323/865–3000; Ted Schreck, Chief Executive Officer
Web address: www.uscnorris.com

USC UNIVERSITY HOSPITAL (L, 269 beds) 1500 San Pablo Street, Los
Angeles, CA Zip 90033–4587; tel. 323/442–8500; Ted Schreck, Chief
Executive Officer
Web address: www.uscuh.com

FLORIDA: CLEVELAND CLINIC HOSPITAL (O, 150 beds) 3100 Weston Road,
Weston, FL Zip 33331–3602; tel. 954/689–5000;
Web address: www.clevelandclinic.org/florida

CORAL GABLES HOSPITAL (O, 188 beds) 3100 Douglas Road, Coral Gables,
FL Zip 33134–6990; tel. 305/445–8461; Jay S. Miranda, Chief Executive
Officer
Web address: www.coralgableshospital.com

DELRAY MEDICAL CENTER (O, 372 beds) 5352 Linton Boulevard, Delray
Beach, FL Zip 33484–6580; tel. 561/498–4440; Mitchell S. Feldman, Chief
Executive Officer
Web address: www.delraymedicalctr.com

Section B

For explanation of codes following names, see page B2.
★ Indicates Type III membership in the American Hospital Association.

FLORIDA MEDICAL CENTER (O, 459 beds) 5000 West Oakland Park Boulevard, Fort Lauderdale, FL Zip 33313–1585; tel. 954/735–6000; Aurelio Fernandez, Chief Executive Officer
Web address: www.floridamedicalctr.com

GOOD SAMARITAN MEDICAL CENTER (O, 341 beds) Flagler Drive at Palm Beach Lakes Boulevard, West Palm Beach, FL Zip 33401–3499; tel. 561/655–5511; Paul D. Echelard, Chief Executive Officer

HIALEAH HOSPITAL (O, 220 beds) 651 East 25th Street, Hialeah, FL Zip 33013–3878; tel. 305/693–6100; Ana J. Mederos, Chief Executive Officer
Web address: www.hialeahhosp.com

HOLLYWOOD MEDICAL CENTER (O, 324 beds) 3600 Washington Street, Hollywood, FL Zip 33021–8216; tel. 954/966–4500; Larry Melby, Chief Executive Officer
Web address: www.hollywoodmedicalctr.com

NORTH RIDGE MEDICAL CENTER (O, 391 beds) 5757 North Dixie Highway, Fort Lauderdale, FL Zip 33334–4182, Mailing Address: P.O. Box 23160, Zip 33307; tel. 954/776–6000; Jeffrey A. Feeney, Interim Chief Executive Officer
Web address: www.northridgemedical.com

NORTH SHORE MEDICAL CENTER (O, 185 beds) 1100 N.W. 95th Street, Miami, FL Zip 33150–2098; tel. 305/835–6000; Edward D. Banos, Chief Executive Officer
Web address: www.northshoremedical.com

PALM BEACH GARDENS MEDICAL CENTER (L, 204 beds) 3360 Burns Road, Palm Beach Gardens, FL Zip 33410–4304; tel. 561/622–1411; Mary Jo Gregory, Chief Executive Officer
Web address: www.pbgmc.com

PALMETTO GENERAL HOSPITAL (O, 360 beds) 2001 West 68th Street, Hialeah, FL Zip 33016–1898; tel. 305/823–5000; Ralph A. Aleman, Chief Executive Officer
Web address: www.palmettogeneral.com

PARKWAY REGIONAL MEDICAL CENTER (O, 347 beds) 160 N.W. 170th Street, North Miami Beach, FL Zip 33169–5576; tel. 305/651–1100; John E. Walker, FACHE, Chief Executive Officer
Web address: www.parkwayregionalmedctr.com

PINECREST REHABILITATION HOSPITAL (O, 90 beds) 5360 Linton Boulevard, Delray Beach, FL Zip 33484–6538; tel. 561/495–0400; Mitchell S. Feldman, Chief Executive Officer
Web address: www.pinecrestrehab.com

ST. MARY'S MEDICAL CENTER (O, 460 beds) 901 45th Street, West Palm Beach, FL Zip 33407–2495, Mailing Address: P.O. Box 24620, Zip 33416–4620; tel. 561/844–6300; Paul A. Walker, Chief Executive Officer
Web address: www.stmarysmc.com

WEST BOCA MEDICAL CENTER (O, 185 beds) 21644 State Road 7, Boca Raton, FL Zip 33428–1899; tel. 561/488–8000; Walt Mickens, Chief Executive Officer
Web address: www.westbocamedctr.com

GEORGIA: ATLANTA MEDICAL CENTER (O, 408 beds) 303 Parkway Drive N.E., Atlanta, GA Zip 30312–1212; tel. 404/265–4000; William T. Moore, Chief Executive Officer
Web address: www.atlantamedcenter.com

NORTH FULTON REGIONAL HOSPITAL (L, 167 beds) 3000 Hospital Boulevard, Roswell, GA Zip 30076–3899; tel. 770/751–2500; John F. Holland, Chief Executive Officer
Web address: www.northfultonregional.com

SOUTH FULTON MEDICAL CENTER (O, 260 beds) 1170 Cleveland Avenue, Atlanta, GA Zip 30344–3665; tel. 404/305–3500; Christopher Hummer, Chief Executive Officer
Web address: www.southfultonmedicalcenter.com

SPALDING REGIONAL MEDICAL CENTER (O, 160 beds) 601 South Eighth Street, Griffin, GA Zip 30224–4294, Mailing Address: P.O. Drawer V, Zip 30224–1168; tel. 770/228–2721; John A. Quinn, Chief Executive Officer
Web address: www.spaldingregional.com

SYLVAN GROVE HOSPITAL (L, 21 beds) 1050 McDonough Road, Jackson, GA Zip 30233–1599; tel. 770/775–7861; John A. Quinn, Chief Executive Officer
Web address: www.sylvangrovehospital.com

LOUISIANA: KENNER REGIONAL MEDICAL CENTER (O, 104 beds) 180 West Esplanade Avenue, Kenner, LA Zip 70065–6001; tel. 504/468–8600; Paolo Zambito, Interim Chief Executive Officer
Web address: www.kennerregional.com

MEADOWCREST HOSPITAL (O, 221 beds) 2500 Belle Chase Highway, Gretna, LA Zip 70056–7196; tel. 504/392–3131; Phillip E. Sowa, Chief Executive Officer
Web address: www.meadowcresthosp.com

MEMORIAL MEDICAL CENTER (O, 603 beds) New Orleans, LA L. Rene' Goux, Chief Executive Officer
Web address: www.memmedctr.com

NORTHSHORE REGIONAL MEDICAL CENTER (L, 165 beds) 100 Medical Center Drive, Slidell, LA Zip 70461–8572; tel. 985/646–5025; Michael O'Bryan, M.D., Chief Executive Officer
Web address: www.northshoremedctr.com

MISSISSIPPI: GULF COAST MEDICAL CENTER (O, 189 beds) 180–A Debuys Road, Biloxi, MS Zip 39531–4405; tel. 228/388–6711; Micheal Terry, Chief Executive Officer
Web address: www.gulfcoastmedicalcenter.com

MISSOURI: DES PERES HOSPITAL (O, 127 beds) 2345 Dougherty Ferry Road, Saint Louis, MO Zip 63122–3313; tel. 314/821–5850; Michele C. Meyer, Chief Executive Officer
Web address: www.despereshospital.com

SAINT LOUIS UNIVERSITY HOSPITAL (O, 337 beds) 3635 Vista at Grand Boulevard, Saint Louis, MO Zip 63110–0250, Mailing Address: P.O. Box 15250, Zip 63110–0250; tel. 314/577–8000; Crystal L. Haynes, Chief Executive Officer
Web address: www.sluhospital.com

NEBRASKA: CREIGHTON UNIVERSITY MEDICAL CENTER (O, 278 beds) 601 North 30th Street, Omaha, NE Zip 68131–2197; tel. 402/449–5021; Philip P. Gustafson, Chief Executive Officer
Web address: www.saintjosephhospital.com

NORTH CAROLINA: CENTRAL CAROLINA HOSPITAL (O, 137 beds) 1135 Carthage Street, Sanford, NC Zip 27330–4111; tel. 919/774–2100; Dale Armstrong, Chief Executive Officer
Web address: www.centralcarolinahosp.com

FRYE REGIONAL MEDICAL CENTER (L, 355 beds) 420 North Center Street, Hickory, NC Zip 28601–5049; tel. 828/322–6070; Dennis Ray Bruns, Chief Executive Officer
Web address: www.fryemedctr.com

PENNSYLVANIA: GRADUATE HOSPITAL (O, 181 beds) One Graduate Plaza, Philadelphia, PA Zip 19146–1407; tel. 215/893–2000; Brian Finestein, President
Web address: www.graduatehospital.com

HAHNEMANN UNIVERSITY HOSPITAL (O, 447 beds) Broad and Vine Streets, Philadelphia, PA Zip 19102–1192; tel. 215/762–7000; Michael P. Halter, Chief Executive Officer
Web address: www.hahnemannhospital.com

ROXBOROUGH MEMORIAL HOSPITAL (O, 125 beds) 5800 Ridge Avenue, Philadelphia, PA Zip 19128–1737; tel. 215/483–9900; John J. Donnelly Jr, Chief Executive Officer
Web address: www.roxboroughmemorial.com

ST. CHRISTOPHER'S HOSPITAL FOR CHILDREN (O, 178 beds) Erie Avenue at Front Street, Philadelphia, PA Zip 19134–1095; tel. 215/427–5000; Jill Tillman, Chief Executive Officer
Web address: www.stchristophershospital.com

WARMINSTER HOSPITAL (O, 151 beds) 225 Newtown Road, Warminster, PA Zip 18974–5221; tel. 215/441–6600; Andrew E. Harris, Chief Executive Officer
Web address: www.warminsterhospital.com

SOUTH CAROLINA: EAST COOPER REGIONAL MEDICAL CENTER (O, 106 beds) 1200 Johnnie Dodds Boulevard, Mount Pleasant, SC Zip 29464–3294; tel. 843/881–0100; Andrea L. Wozniak, R.N., Chief Executive Officer
Web address: www.eastcoopermedctr.com

HILTON HEAD REGIONAL MEDICAL CENTER (O, 93 beds) 25 Hospital Center Boulevard, Hilton Head Island, SC Zip 29926–2738, Mailing Address: P.O. Box 21117, Zip 29925–1117; tel. 843/681–6122; Elizabeth Lamkin, President and Chief Executive Officer
Web address: www.hiltonheadmedctr.com

PIEDMONT HEALTHCARE SYSTEM (O, 266 beds) 222 Herlong Avenue, Rock Hill, SC Zip 29732–1952; tel. 803/329–1234; Charles F. Miller, President and Chief Executive Officer
Web address: www.piedmonthealth.com

For explanation of codes following names, see page B2.
★ Indicates Type III membership in the American Hospital Association.

TENNESSEE: SAINT FRANCIS HOSPITAL (O, 562 beds) 5959 Park Avenue, Memphis, TN Zip 38119–5198, Mailing Address: P.O. Box 171808, Zip 38187–1808; tel. 901/765–1000; David L. Archer, Chief Executive Officer
Web address: www.saintfrancishosp.com

SAINT FRANCIS HOSPITAL–BARTLETT (O, 44 beds) 2986 Kate Bond Road, Bartlett, TN Zip 38133–4003; tel. 901/820–7000; David C. Wilson, Chief Executive Officer
Web address: www.saintfrancisbartlett.com

TEXAS: CENTENNIAL MEDICAL CENTER (O, 72 beds) 12505 Lebanon Road, Frisco, TX Zip 75035–8298; tel. 972/963–3333; Lynn M. Mergen, Chief Executive Officer
Web address: www.centennialmedcenter.com

CYPRESS FAIRBANKS MEDICAL CENTER (O, 146 beds) 10655 Steepletop Drive, Houston, TX Zip 77065–4297; tel. 281/890–4285; Terry J. Wheeler, Chief Executive Officer
Web address: www.cyfairhospital.com

DOCTORS HOSPITAL OF DALLAS (O, 156 beds) 9440 Poppy Drive, Dallas, TX Zip 75218–3694; tel. 214/324–6100; Mitch Edgeworth, Chief Executive Officer
Web address: www.doctorshospitaldallas.com

HOUSTON NORTHWEST MEDICAL CENTER (O, 378 beds) 710 FM 1960 West, Houston, TX Zip 77090–3496; tel. 281/440–1000; Louis O. Garcia, Chief Executive Officer
Web address: www.hnmc.com

LAKE POINTE MEDICAL CENTER (O, 99 beds) 6800 Scenic Drive, Rowlett, TX Zip 75088–4552, Mailing Address: P.O. Box 1550, Zip 75030–1550; tel. 972/412–2273; John Harris, Chief Executive Officer
Web address: www.lakepointemedical.com

NACOGDOCHES MEDICAL CENTER (O, 150 beds) 4920 N.E. Stallings, Nacogdoches, TX Zip 75965–1200, Mailing Address: P.O. Box 631604, Zip 75963–1604; tel. 936/569–9481; Gary L. Stokes, Chief Executive Officer
Web address: www.nacmedicalcenter.com

PARK PLAZA HOSPITAL (O, 373 beds) 1313 Hermann Drive, Houston, TX Zip 77004–7092; tel. 713/527–5000; Lex A. Guinn, Chief Executive Officer
Web address: www.parkplazahospital.com

PLAZA SPECIALTY HOSPITAL (O, 61 beds) 1300 Binz, Houston, TX Zip 77004; tel. 713/285–1000; J. Michael Leger, Interim Chief Executive Officer
Web address: www.plazaspecialtyhospital.com

PROVIDENCE MEMORIAL HOSPITAL (O, 359 beds) 2001 North Oregon Street, El Paso, TX Zip 79902–3368; tel. 915/577–6011; Thomas E. Casaday, Chief Executive Officer
Web address: www.sphn.com/sphn/aboutus/providencememorialhospital.asp

RHD MEMORIAL MEDICAL CENTER (L, 114 beds) Seven Medical Parkway, Dallas, TX Zip 75381–7829, Mailing Address: P.O. Box 819094, Zip 75381–9094; tel. 972/247–1000; Joe Thomason, Chief Executive Officer
Web address: www.rhdmemorial.com

RIO VISTA PHYSICAL REHABILITATION HOSPITAL (O, 48 beds) 1740 Curie Drive, El Paso, TX Zip 79902–2900; tel. 915/544–3399; Thomas E. Casaday, Chief Executive Officer
Web address: www.sphn.com/sphn/aboutus/riovistaphysicalrehabilitationhospital.asp

SHELBY REGIONAL MEDICAL CENTER (O, 46 beds) 602 Hurst Street, Center, TX Zip 75935–3414, Mailing Address: P.O. Box 1749, Zip 75935–1749; tel. 936/598–2781; Gary L. Stokes, Chief Executive Officer
Web address: www.shelbyregional.com

SIERRA MEDICAL CENTER (O, 334 beds) 1625 Medical Center Drive, El Paso, TX Zip 79902–5044; tel. 915/747–4000; Thomas E. Casaday, President and Chief Executive Officer
Web address: www.sphn.com

TRINITY MEDICAL CENTER (L, 207 beds) 4343 North Josey Lane, Carrollton, TX Zip 75010–4691; tel. 972/492–1010; Ernie Bovio, Chief Executive Officer
Web address: www.trinitymedicalcenter.com

Owned, leased, sponsored:	77 hospitals	16988 beds
Contract–managed:	0 hospitals	0 beds
Totals:	77 hospitals	16988 beds

0020: TEXAS DEPARTMENT OF STATE HEALTH SERVICES (NP)
1100 West 49th Street, Austin, TX Zip 78756–3199; tel. 512/458–7111; Eduardo J. Sanchez, M.D., M.P.H., Commissioner of Health
(Independent Hospital System)

AUSTIN STATE HOSPITAL (O, 297 beds) 4110 Guadalupe Street, Austin, TX Zip 78751–4296; tel. 512/452–0381; Carl Schock, Superintendent
Web address: www.mhmr.state.tx.us

BIG SPRING STATE HOSPITAL (O, 151 beds) 1901 North Highway 87, Big Spring, TX Zip 79720; tel. 915/267–8216; Edward Moughon, Superintendent
Web address: www.mhmr.state.tx.us/hospitals/bigspringSH/bigspringsh.html

EL PASO PSYCHIATRIC CENTER (O, 64 beds) 4615 Alameda Avenue, El Paso, TX Zip 79905–2702; Zulema Carrillo, Chief Executive Officer

KERRVILLE STATE HOSPITAL (O, 177 beds) 721 Thompson Drive, Kerrville, TX Zip 78028–5154; tel. 830/896–2211; Gloria P. Olsen, Ph.D., Superintendent
Web address: www.dshs.state.tx.us/lmhhospitals/kerrvillesh

RIO GRANDE STATE CENTER (O, 130 beds) 1401 South Rangerville Road, Harlingen, TX Zip 78552–7638; tel. 956/425–8900; Sonia Hernandez–Keeble, Superintendent
Web address: www.dshs.state.tx.us/mentalhealth

RUSK STATE HOSPITAL (O, 271 beds) Jacksonville Highway North, Rusk, TX Zip 75785, Mailing Address: P.O. Box 318, Zip 75785–0318; tel. 903/683–3421; Ted Debbs, Administrator
Web address: www.mhmr.state.tx.us/hospitals/rusksh/rusksh.html

SAN ANTONIO STATE HOSPITAL (O, 292 beds) 6711 South New Braunfels, San Antonio, TX Zip 78223–3006, Mailing Address: Box 23991, Highland Hills Station, Zip 78223–3006; tel. 210/531–7711; Robert C. Arizpe, Superintendent
Web address: www.mhmr.state.tx.us

SOUTH TEXAS HEALTH CARE SYSTEM (O, 35 beds) 1301 Rangerville Road, Harlingen, TX Zip 78552–7609, Mailing Address: P.O. Box 592, Zip 78551–0592; tel. 956/423–3420; Sonia Hernandez–Keeble, Superintendent
Web address: www.tdh.texas.gov

TERRELL STATE HOSPITAL (O, 273 beds) 1200 East Brin Street, Terrell, TX Zip 75160–2938; tel. 972/524–6452; Fred Hale, Superintendent
Web address: www.dshs.state.tx.us

TEXAS CENTER FOR INFECTIOUS DISEASE (O, 72 beds) 2303 S.E. Military Drive, San Antonio, TX Zip 78223–3597; tel. 210/534–8857; James N. Elkins, FACHE, Director
Web address: www.dshs.state.tx.us/tcid/default/shtm

Owned, leased, sponsored:	10 hospitals	1762 beds
Contract–managed:	0 hospitals	0 beds
Totals:	10 hospitals	1762 beds

★0129: TEXAS HEALTH RESOURCES (NP)
611 Ryan Plaza Drive, Suite 900, Arlington, TX Zip 76011; tel. 817/462–7900; Douglas D. Hawthorne, FACHE, President and Chief Executive Officer
(Moderately Centralized Health System)

ARLINGTON MEMORIAL HOSPITAL (O, 369 beds) 800 West Randol Mill Road, Arlington, TX Zip 76012–2503; tel. 817/548–6100; Oscar Amparan, President
Web address: www.arlingtonmemorial.org

HARRIS CONTINUED CARE HOSPITAL (O, 10 beds) 1301 Pennsylvania Avenue, 4th Floor, Fort Worth, TX Zip 76104–2190; tel. 817/878–5500; Louise Baldwin, R.N., President
Web address: www.texashealth.org

HARRIS METHODIST FORT WORTH (O, 553 beds) 1301 Pennsylvania Avenue, Fort Worth, TX Zip 76104–2895; tel. 817/882–2000; Barclay E. Berdan, CHE, President
Web address: www.texashealth.org

HARRIS METHODIST NORTHWEST (O, 30 beds) 108 Denver Trail, Azle, TX Zip 76020–3697; tel. 817/444–8600; Brett McClung, President
Web address: www.hmhs.com

For explanation of codes following names, see page B2.
★ Indicates Type III membership in the American Hospital Association.

Section B

HARRIS METHODIST SOUTHWEST (O, 85 beds) 6100 Harris Parkway, Fort Worth, TX Zip 76132–4199; tel. 817/433–6550; Stansel Harvey, FACHE, President
Web address: www.texashealth.org

HARRIS METHODIST–ERATH COUNTY (O, 55 beds) 411 North Belknap Street, Stephenville, TX Zip 76401–3415, Mailing Address: P.O. Box 1399, Zip 76401–1399; tel. 254/965–1500; Deborah Paganelli, CHE, President
Web address: www.texashealth.org

HARRIS METHODIST–HEB (O, 216 beds) 1600 Hospital Parkway, Bedford, TX Zip 76022–6913, Mailing Address: P.O. Box 669, Zip 76095–0669; tel. 817/685–4000; Jack McCabe, FACHE, President
Web address: www.texashealth.org

PRESBYTERIAN HOSPITAL OF ALLEN (O, 29 beds) 1105 Central Expressway North, Allen, TX Zip 75013, Mailing Address: 1105 Central Expressway North, Suite 100, Zip 75013; tel. 972/747–1000; Sheila A. McKinney, President
Web address: www.texashealth.org

PRESBYTERIAN HOSPITAL OF DALLAS (O, 734 beds) 8200 Walnut Hill Lane, Dallas, TX Zip 75231–4402; tel. 214/345–6789; Mark H. Merrill, President
Web address: www.texashealth.org

PRESBYTERIAN HOSPITAL OF KAUFMAN (O, 68 beds) 850 Highway 243 West, Kaufman, TX Zip 75142–9998, Mailing Address: P.O. Box 310, Zip 75142–0310; tel. 972/932–7200; Kirk King, CHE, President
Web address: www.texashealth.org

PRESBYTERIAN HOSPITAL OF PLANO (O, 203 beds) 6200 West Parker Road, Plano, TX Zip 75093–7914; tel. 972/981–8000; Philip M. Wentworth, FACHE, President
Web address: www.texashealth.org

PRESBYTERIAN HOSPITAL OF WINNSBORO (O, 46 beds) 719 West Coke Road, Winnsboro, TX Zip 75494–3098, Mailing Address: P.O. Box 628, Zip 75494–0628; tel. 903/342–5227; Matthew Troup, President
Web address: www.texashealth.org

WALLS REGIONAL HOSPITAL (O, 125 beds) 201 Walls Drive, Cleburne, TX Zip 76033–4008; tel. 817/641–2551; Brent D. Magers, FACHE, President
Web address: www.texashealth.org

Owned, leased, sponsored:	13 hospitals	2523 beds
Contract–managed:	0 hospitals	0 beds
Totals:	13 hospitals	2523 beds

★**7235: THE METHODIST HOSPITAL SYSTEM** (CO)
6565 Fannin Street, D–200, Houston, TX Zip 77030–2707; tel. 713/790–2221; Ronald G. Girotto, President and Chief Executive Officer
(Moderately Centralized Health System)

METHODIST SUGAR LAND HOSPITAL (O, 54 beds) 16655 S.W. Freeway, Sugar Land, TX Zip 77479–2343; tel. 281/274–8000; James F. Heitzenrater, Administrator
Web address: www.methodisthealth.com

METHODIST WILLOWBROOK HOSPITAL (O, 110 beds) 18220 Tomball Parkway, Houston, TX Zip 77070; tel. 281/477–1000; Andrew Cochrane, Chief Executive Officer
Web address: www.methodisthealth.com/willowbrook

SAN JACINTO METHODIST HOSPITAL (O, 266 beds) 4401 Garth Road, Baytown, TX Zip 77521–3160; tel. 281/420–8600; S. Jeffrey Ackerman, M.D., President and Chief Executive Officer
Web address: www.methodisthealth.com

THE METHODIST HOSPITAL (O, 911 beds) 6565 Fannin Street, Houston, TX Zip 77030–2707; tel. 713/790–3311; Ronald G. Girotto, President and Chief Executive Officer
Web address: www.methodisthealth.com

Owned, leased, sponsored:	4 hospitals	1341 beds
Contract–managed:	0 hospitals	0 beds
Totals:	4 hospitals	1341 beds

★**2445: THEDACARE, INC.** (NP)
122 East College Avenue, Appleton, WI Zip 54911, Mailing Address: P.O. Box 8025, Zip 54912; tel. 920/830–5880; John S. Toussaint, M.D., President and Chief Executive Officer
(Centralized Physician/Insurance Health System)

WISCONSIN: APPLETON MEDICAL CENTER (O, 156 beds) 1818 North Meade Street, Appleton, WI Zip 54911–3496; tel. 920/731–4101; Kathryn Correia, Senior Vice President
Web address: www.thedacare.org

NEW LONDON FAMILY MEDICAL CENTER (O, 15 beds) 1405 Mill Street, New London, WI Zip 54961–2155, Mailing Address: P.O. Box 307, Zip 54961–0307; tel. 920/982–5330; William Schmidt, President and Chief Executive Officer
Web address: www.newlondon.thedacare.org

THEDA CLARK MEDICAL CENTER (O, 166 beds) 130 Second Street, Neenah, WI Zip 54956–2883, Mailing Address: P.O. Box 2021, Zip 54957–2021; tel. 920/729–3100; Kathryn Correia, Senior Vice President
Web address: www.thedacare.org

Owned, leased, sponsored:	3 hospitals	337 beds
Contract–managed:	0 hospitals	0 beds
Totals:	3 hospitals	337 beds

★**0294: TMC HEALTHCARE** (NP)
5301 East Grant Road, Tucson, AZ Zip 85712; tel. 520/327–5461; Frank D. Alvarez, President and Chief Executive Officer
(Independent Hospital System)

ARIZONA: EL DORADO HOSPITAL (O, 90 beds) 1400 North Wilmot Road, Tucson, AZ Zip 85712–4498, Mailing Address: P.O. Box 13070, Zip 85732–3070; tel. 520/886–6361; Rhonda Dean, Chief Executive Officer
Web address: www.eldoradohospital.com

TUCSON MEDICAL CENTER (O, 533 beds) 5301 East Grant Road, Tucson, AZ Zip 85712–2874; tel. 520/327–5461; Frank D. Alvarez, President and Chief Executive Officer
Web address: www.tmcaz.com

Owned, leased, sponsored:	2 hospitals	623 beds
Contract–managed:	0 hospitals	0 beds
Totals:	2 hospitals	623 beds

★**0178: TRIAD HOSPITALS, INC.** (IO)
5800 Tennyson Parkway, Plano, TX Zip 75024; tel. 214/473–7000; James D. Shelton, Chairman and Chief Executive Officer
(Decentralized Health System)

ALABAMA: CRESTWOOD MEDICAL CENTER (O, 120 beds) One Hospital Drive, Huntsville, AL Zip 35801–3403; tel. 256/882–3100; Bradley E. Jones, Chief Executive Officer
Web address: www.crestwoodmedcenter.com

FLOWERS HOSPITAL (O, 235 beds) 4370 West Main Street, Dothan, AL Zip 36305–4000, Mailing Address: P.O. Box 6907, Zip 36302–6907; tel. 334/793–5000; Keith Granger, President and Chief Executive Officer
Web address: www.flowershospital.com

GADSDEN REGIONAL MEDICAL CENTER (O, 259 beds) 1007 Goodyear Avenue, Gadsden, AL Zip 35903–1195; tel. 256/494–4000; Douglas P. DeGraaf, Chief Executive Officer
Web address: www.gadsdenregional.com

JACKSONVILLE MEDICAL CENTER (O, 56 beds) 1701 Pelham Road South, Jacksonville, AL Zip 36265–3399, Mailing Address: P.O. Box 999, Zip 36265–0999; tel. 256/435–4970; Roger Collins, Chief Executive Officer
Web address: www.jmcfirst.com

MEDICAL CENTER ENTERPRISE (O, 117 beds) 400 North Edwards Street, Enterprise, AL Zip 36330; tel. 334/347–0584; Jeffrey M. Brannon, Chief Executive Officer
Web address: www.mcehospital.com

ALASKA: VALLEY HOSPITAL (O, 36 beds) 515 East Dahlia Street, Palmer, AK Zip 99645–6489, Mailing Address: P.O. Box 1687, Zip 99645–1687; tel. 907/746–8600; Norman F. Stephens, Chief Executive Officer
Web address: www.valley–hosp.com

ARIZONA: NORTHWEST MEDICAL CENTER (O, 250 beds) 6200 North La Cholla Boulevard, Tucson, AZ Zip 85741–3599; tel. 520/742–9000; W. Jefferson Comer Sr, FACHE, Chief Executive Officer
Web address: www.northwestmedicalcenter.com

For explanation of codes following names, see page B2.
★ Indicates Type III membership in the American Hospital Association.

NORTHWEST MEDICAL CENTER, ORO VALLEY (O, 96 beds) 1551 East Tangerine Road, Oro Valley, AZ Zip 85737; tel. 520/901–3500; Paul Kappelman, Chief Executive Officer
Web address: www.nmcorovalley.com

ARKANSAS: CENTRAL ARKANSAS HOSPITAL (O, 145 beds) 1200 South Main Street, Searcy, AR Zip 72143–7397; tel. 501/278–3100; Ben Frank, Chief Executive Officer
Web address: www.centralarkhospital.com

MEDICAL CENTER OF SOUTH ARKANSAS (O, 140 beds) 700 West Grove Street, El Dorado, AR Zip 71730–4416, Mailing Address: P.O. Box 1998, Zip 71731–1998; tel. 870/864–3200; Luther J. Lewis, FACHE, Chief Executive Officer
Web address: www.themedcenter.net

MEDICAL PARK HOSPITAL (O, 79 beds) 2001 South Main Street, Hope, AR Zip 71801–8194; tel. 870/777–2323; Jimmy Leopard, Chief Executive Officer
Web address: www.mphhope.com

NATIONAL PARK MEDICAL CENTER (O, 181 beds) 1910 Malvern Avenue, Hot Springs, AR Zip 71901–7799; tel. 501/321–1000; Jerry D. Mabry, Chief Executive Officer
Web address: www.nationalparkmedical.com

NEA MEDICAL CENTER (O, 104 beds) 3024 Stadium Boulevard, Jonesboro, AR Zip 72401–7493; tel. 870/972–7000; William C. Lievense, Chief Executive Officer
Web address: www.neamedicalcenter.com

NORTHWEST MEDICAL CENTER OF BENTON COUNTY (O, 73 beds) 3000 Medical Center Parkway, Bentonville, AR Zip 72712; tel. 479/553–1000; Gary N. Looper, Chief Executive Officer
Web address: www.northwesthealth.com

NORTHWEST MEDICAL CENTER OF WASHINGTON COUNTY (O, 180 beds) 609 West Maple Avenue, Springdale, AR Zip 72764; tel. 479/751–5711; Gary N. Looper, Chief Executive Officer
Web address: www.northwesthealth.com

SAINT MARY'S REGIONAL MEDICAL CENTER (O, 154 beds) 1808 West Main Street, Russellville, AR Zip 72801–2724; tel. 479/968–2841; Mike McCoy, Chief Executive Officer
Web address: www.saintmarysregional.com

WILLOW CREEK WOMEN'S HOSPITAL (O, 30 beds) 4301 Greathouse Springs Road, Johnson, AR Zip 72741–0544, Mailing Address: P.O. Box 544, Zip 72741–0544; tel. 479/684–3000; Gary N. Looper, Chief Executive Officer
Web address: www.northwesthealth.com

INDIANA: BLUFFTON REGIONAL MEDICAL CENTER (O, 79 beds) 303 South Main Street, Bluffton, IN Zip 46714–2529; tel. 260/824–3210; Thomas A. Clark, Chief Executive Officer
Web address: www.blufftonregional.com

DUKES MEMORIAL HOSPITAL (O, 27 beds) 275 West 12th Street, Peru, IN Zip 46970–1698; tel. 765/472–8000; Michael J. Funk, President and Chief Executive Officer
Web address: www.dukeshospital.org

DUPONT HOSPITAL (O, 86 beds) 2520 East Dupont Road, Fort Wayne, IN Zip 46825; tel. 260/416–3000; Michael H. Schatzlein, M.D., Chief Executive Officer
Web address: www.theduponthospital.com

KOSCIUSKO COMMUNITY HOSPITAL (O, 72 beds) 2101 East Dubois Drive, Warsaw, IN Zip 46580–3288; tel. 574/267–3200; Michael L. Mullins, Chief Executive Officer
Web address: www.kch.com

LUTHERAN HOSPITAL OF INDIANA (O, 366 beds) 7950 West Jefferson Boulevard, Fort Wayne, IN Zip 46804–1677; tel. 260/435–7001; Thomas D. Miller, Chief Executive Officer
Web address: www.lutheran–hosp.com

REHABILITATION HOSPITAL OF FORT WAYNE (O, 36 beds) 7970 West Jefferson Boulevard, Fort Wayne, IN Zip 46804–4140; tel. 260/435–6100; Darlene Degener, Chief Operating Officer
Web address: www.rehabhospital.com

ST. JOSEPH HOSPITAL (O, 211 beds) 700 Broadway, Fort Wayne, IN Zip 46802–1493; tel. 260/425–3000; Jerry Beasley, Chief Executive Officer
Web address: www.stjoehospital.com

LOUISIANA: WOMEN AND CHILDREN'S HOSPITAL (O, 114 beds) 4200 Nelson Road, Lake Charles, LA Zip 70605–4118; tel. 337/474–6370; William L. Willis, Chief Executive Officer
Web address: www.women–childrens.com

MISSISSIPPI: RIVER REGION HEALTH SYSTEM (O, 381 beds) 2100 Highway 61 North, Vicksburg, MS Zip 39183, Mailing Address: P.O. Box 590, Zip 39181–0590; tel. 601/883–5000; Phillip A. Clendenin, Chief Executive Officer
Web address: www.riverregion.com

WESLEY MEDICAL CENTER (O, 211 beds) 5001 Hardy Street, Hattiesburg, MS Zip 39402–1366, Mailing Address: P.O. Box 16509, Zip 39404–6509; tel. 601/268–8000; Ronald T. Seal, Chief Executive Officer
Web address: www.wesley.com

NEVADA: MESA VIEW REGIONAL HOSPITAL (O, 21 beds) 1299 Bertha Howe Avenue, Mesquite, NV Zip 89027; tel. 702/346–8040; Sue Conley, Chief Executive Officer
Web address: www.mesaviewhospital.com

NEW MEXICO: CARLSBAD MEDICAL CENTER (O, 127 beds) 2430 West Pierce Street, Carlsbad, NM Zip 88220–3597; tel. 505/887–4100; Fred Woody, Chief Executive Officer
Web address: www.triadhospitals.com

LEA REGIONAL MEDICAL CENTER (O, 214 beds) 5419 North Lovington Highway, Hobbs, NM Zip 88240–9125, Mailing Address: P.O. Box 3000, Zip 88240–3000; tel. 505/492–5000; Larry C. Bozeman, Chief Executive Officer
Web address: www.learegionalmedicalcenter.com

MOUNTAINVIEW REGIONAL MEDICAL CENTER (O, 163 beds) 4311 East Lohman Avenue, Las Cruces, NM Zip 88011; tel. 505/556–7600; John L. Hummer, Chief Executive Officer
Web address: www.mountainviewregional.com

OHIO: BARBERTON CITIZENS HOSPITAL (O, 226 beds) 155 Fifth Street N.E., Barberton, OH Zip 44203–3398; tel. 330/745–1611; Willard P. Roderick, Chief Executive Officer
Web address: www.barbertonhospital.com

DOCTORS HOSPITAL OF STARK COUNTY (O, 133 beds) 400 Austin Avenue N.W., Massillon, OH Zip 44646–3554; tel. 330/837–7200; Janie Sinacore–Jaberg, R.N., MS, FACHE, Chief Executive Officer
Web address: www.drshospital.com

OKLAHOMA: CLAREMORE REGIONAL HOSPITAL (O, 46 beds) 1202 North Muskogee Place, Claremore, OK Zip 74017–3036; tel. 918/341–2556; David Chaussard, Chief Executive Officer
Web address: www.claremorereghospital.com

DEACONESS HOSPITAL (O, 267 beds) 5501 North Portland Avenue, Oklahoma City, OK Zip 73112–2099; tel. 405/604–6000; Paul Dougherty, President and Chief Executive Officer
Web address: www.deaconessokc.org

SOUTHCREST HOSPITAL (O, 180 beds) 8801 South 101st East Avenue, Tulsa, OK Zip 74133; tel. 918/294–4000; Anthony R. Young, Chief Executive Officer
Web address: www.southcresthospital.com

WOODWARD REGIONAL HOSPITAL (L, 68 beds) 900 17th Street, Woodward, OK Zip 73801–2423; tel. 580/256–5511; Troy Taubenheim, Chief Executive Officer
Web address: www.woodwardhospital.com

OREGON: MCKENZIE–WILLAMETTE MEDICAL CENTER (O, 105 beds) 1460 G Street, Springfield, OR Zip 97477–4197; tel. 541/726–4400; Roy J. Orr, Chief Executive Officer
Web address: www.mckweb.com

WILLAMETTE VALLEY MEDICAL CENTER (O, 67 beds) 2700 S.E. Stratus Avenue, McMinnville, OR Zip 97128–6498; tel. 503/472–6131; Rosemari Davis, Chief Executive Officer
Web address: www.wvmcweb.com

SOUTH CAROLINA: CAROLINAS HOSPITAL SYSTEM (O, 66 beds) 805 Pamplico Highway, Florence, SC Zip 29505–6050, Mailing Address: P.O. Box 100550, Zip 29501–0550; tel. 843/674–5000; James O'Laughlin, Chief Executive Officer
Web address: www.carolinashospital.com

MARY BLACK HEALTH SYSTEM (O, 168 beds) 1700 Skylyn Drive, Spartanburg, SC Zip 29307–1061, Mailing Address: P.O. Box 3217, Zip 29304–3217; tel. 864/573–3000; Glenn A. Robinson, Chief Executive Officer
Web address: www.maryblack.org

Section B

For explanation of codes following names, see page B2.
★ Indicates Type III membership in the American Hospital Association.

TEXAS: ABILENE REGIONAL MEDICAL CENTER (O, 178 beds) 6250 Highway 83–84 at Antilley Road, Abilene, TX Zip 79606–5299; tel. 325/695–9900; Michael D. Murphy, Chief Executive Officer
Web address: www.abileneregional.com

BROWNWOOD REGIONAL MEDICAL CENTER (O, 174 beds) 1501 Burnet Drive, Brownwood, TX Zip 76801–5933, Mailing Address: P.O. Box 760, Zip 76804–0760; tel. 325/646–8541; Matt T. Maxfield, CHE, Chief Executive Officer
Web address: www.brmc-cares.com

COLLEGE STATION MEDICAL CENTER (O, 115 beds) 1604 Rock Prairie Road, College Station, TX Zip 77845–8345, Mailing Address: P.O. Box 10000, Zip 77842–3500; tel. 979/764–5100; Thomas W. Jackson, Chief Executive Officer
Web address: www.csmedcenter.com

DETAR HEALTHCARE SYSTEM (O, 329 beds) 506 East San Antonio Street, Victoria, TX Zip 77901–6060, Mailing Address: P.O. Box 2089, Zip 77902–2089; tel. 361/575–7441; William R. Blanchard, Chief Executive Officer
Web address: www.detar.com

GULF COAST MEDICAL CENTER (O, 128 beds) 1400 Highway 59, Wharton, TX Zip 77488–3004, Mailing Address: P.O. Box 3004, Zip 77488–3004; tel. 979/532–2500; Donald J. Frederic, Chief Executive Officer
Web address: www.gulfcoastmedical.com

LONGVIEW REGIONAL MEDICAL CENTER (O, 166 beds) 2901 North Fourth Street, Longview, TX Zip 75605–5191, Mailing Address: P.O. Box 14000, Zip 75607–4000; tel. 903/758–1818; Vicki L. Briggs, Chief Executive Officer
Web address: www.longviewregional.com

NAVARRO REGIONAL HOSPITAL (O, 144 beds) 3201 West State Highway 22, Corsicana, TX Zip 75110–2469; tel. 903/654–6800; Nancy A. Byrnes, Chief Executive Officer
Web address: www.navarrohospital.com

PAMPA REGIONAL MEDICAL CENTER (O, 91 beds) One Medical Plaza, Pampa, TX Zip 79065; tel. 806/665–3721; Alan N. King, Chief Executive Officer
Web address: www.triadhospitals.com

PRESBYTERIAN HOSPITAL OF DENTON (O, 112 beds) 3000 I. 35 North, Denton, TX Zip 76201–3798; tel. 940/898–7000; Stan C. Morton, Chief Executive Officer
Web address: www.dentonhospital.com

SAN ANGELO COMMUNITY MEDICAL CENTER (O, 127 beds) 3501 Knickerbocker Road, San Angelo, TX Zip 76904–7698; tel. 325/949–9511; Samuel G. Feazell, Chief Executive Officer
Web address: www.sacmc.com

WOODLAND HEIGHTS MEDICAL CENTER (O, 146 beds) 505 South John Redditt Drive, Lufkin, TX Zip 75904–3157, Mailing Address: P.O. Box 150610, Zip 75915–0610; tel. 936/634–8311; Lance Jones, Chief Executive Officer
Web address: www.woodlandheights.net

WEST VIRGINIA: GREENBRIER VALLEY MEDICAL CENTER (O, 101 beds) 202 Maplewood Avenue, Ronceverte, WV Zip 24970–0497, Mailing Address: P.O. Box 497, Zip 24970–0497; tel. 304/647–4411; Mark Nosacka, Chief Executive Officer
Web address: www.gvmc.com

Owned, leased, sponsored:	53 hospitals	7500 beds
Contract–managed:	0 hospitals	0 beds
Totals:	53 hospitals	7500 beds

★0219: TRINITY HEALTH (CC)
27870 Cabot Drive, Novi, MI Zip 48377; tel. 248/489–5004; Joseph R. Swedish, President and Chief Executive Officer
(Decentralized Health System)

CALIFORNIA: SAINT AGNES MEDICAL CENTER (O, 330 beds) 1303 East Herndon Avenue, Fresno, CA Zip 93720–3309; tel. 559/450–3000; Mathew Abraham, President and Chief Executive Officer
Web address: www.samc.com

IDAHO: CASCADE MEDICAL CENTER (C, 10 beds) 402 Old State Highway, Cascade, ID Zip 83611, Mailing Address: P.O. Box 1330, Zip 83611–1330; tel. 208/382–4242; Kay Garcia, Administrator

SAINT ALPHONSUS REGIONAL MEDICAL CENTER (O, 392 beds) 1055 North Curtis Road, Boise, ID Zip 83706–1370; tel. 208/367–2121; Sandra B. Bruce, President and Chief Executive Officer
Web address: www.saintalphonsus.org

ST. BENEDICTS FAMILY MEDICAL CENTER (O, 65 beds) 709 North Lincoln Street, Jerome, ID Zip 83338–1851, Mailing Address: P.O. Box 586, Zip 83338–0586; tel. 208/324–4301; Ken Belke, Interim Administrator

WEISER MEMORIAL HOSPITAL (C, 18 beds) 645 East Fifth Street, Weiser, ID Zip 83672–2202; tel. 208/549–0370; Anne Oglevie, Administrator
Web address: www.weisermemorialhospital.org

ILLINOIS: MORRISON COMMUNITY HOSPITAL (C, 63 beds) 303 North Jackson Street, Morrison, IL Zip 61270–3042; tel. 815/772–4003; Terry L. Amstutz, CHE, Administrator

INDIANA: SAINT JOSEPH REGIONAL MEDICAL CENTER (O, 286 beds) 801 East LaSalle, South Bend, IN Zip 46617–2800; tel. 574/237–7111; Gary L. Perecko, President
Web address: www.sjmed.com

SAINT JOSEPH REGIONAL MEDICAL CENTER–MISHAWAKA CAMPUS (O, 95 beds) 215 West Fourth Street, Mishawaka, IN Zip 46544–1999; tel. 574/259–2431; Lori Price, President
Web address: www.sjmed.com

SAINT JOSEPH REGIONAL MEDICAL CENTER–PLYMOUTH CAMPUS (O, 45 beds) 1915 Lake Avenue, Plymouth, IN Zip 46563–9905, Mailing Address: P.O. Box 670, Zip 46563–9905; tel. 574/936–3181; Lori Price, President
Web address: www.sjmed.com

IOWA: BAUM HARMON MERCY HOSPITAL (O, 13 beds) 255 North Welch Avenue, Primghar, IA Zip 51245–1034, Mailing Address: P.O. Box 528, Zip 51245–0528; tel. 712/957–2300; Robert Monical, Chief Executive Officer and Administrator
Web address: www.baumharmon.org

BELMOND MEDICAL CENTER (C, 22 beds) 403 First Street S.E., Belmond, IA Zip 50421–1201; tel. 641/444–3223; Suzan Brunes, Administrator and Director of Nursing
Web address: www.belmondmedicalcenter.com

CENTRAL COMMUNITY HOSPITAL (C, 15 beds) 901 Davidson Street N.W., Elkader, IA Zip 52043–9015; tel. 563/245–7000; Frances Zichal, Chief Executive Officer

ELLSWORTH MUNICIPAL HOSPITAL (C, 40 beds) 110 Rocksylvania Avenue, Iowa Falls, IA Zip 50126–2400; tel. 641/648–4631; John O'Brien, Administrator
Web address: www.emhia.com

FRANKLIN GENERAL HOSPITAL (C, 77 beds) 1720 Central Avenue East, Hampton, IA Zip 50441–1859; tel. 641/456–5000; Ronald D. Baker, Chief Executive Officer
Web address: www.franklingeneral.com

HANCOCK COUNTY MEMORIAL HOSPITAL (C, 25 beds) 532 First Street N.W., Britt, IA Zip 50423; tel. 641/843–5000; Toni Ebeling, Administrator
Web address: www.hancockmemhospital.com

HAWARDEN COMMUNITY HOSPITAL (C, 18 beds) 1111 11th Street, Hawarden, IA Zip 51023–1999; tel. 712/551–3100; Brian Monsma, Chief Executive Officer

KOSSUTH REGIONAL HEALTH CENTER (C, 22 beds) 1515 South Phillips Street, Algona, IA Zip 50511–3649; tel. 515/295–2451; Scott Curtis, Administrator
Web address: www.krhc.com

MERCY MEDICAL CENTER – NORTH IOWA (O, 238 beds) 1000 Fourth Street S.W., Mason City, IA Zip 50401–2800; tel. 641/422–7000; James G. FitzPatrick, President and Chief Executive Officer
Web address: www.mercynorthiowa.com

MERCY MEDICAL CENTER–CLINTON (O, 349 beds) 1410 North Fourth Street, Clinton, IA Zip 52732–2999; tel. 563/244–5555; Donna M. Oliver, Chief Executive Officer
Web address: www.mercyclinton.com

MERCY MEDICAL CENTER–DUBUQUE (O, 320 beds) 250 Mercy Drive, Dubuque, IA Zip 52001–7360; tel. 563/589–8000; Russell M. Knight, President and Chief Executive Officer
Web address: www.mercydubuque.com

MERCY MEDICAL CENTER–NEW HAMPTON (O, 53 beds) 308 North Maple Avenue, New Hampton, IA Zip 50659–1142; tel. 641/394–4121; Carolyn Martin–Shaw, Chief Executive Officer
Web address: www.mercynewhampton.com

MERCY MEDICAL CENTER–SIOUX CITY (O, 272 beds) 801 Fifth Street, Sioux City, IA Zip 51101–1326, Mailing Address: P.O. Box 3168, Zip 51102–3168; tel. 712/279–2010; Peter E. Makowski, President and Chief Executive Officer
Web address: www.mercysiouxcity.com

For explanation of codes following names, see page B2.
★ Indicates Type III membership in the American Hospital Association.

Section B

MITCHELL COUNTY REGIONAL HEALTH CENTER (C, 25 beds) 616 North Eighth Street, Osage, IA Zip 50461–1498; tel. 641/732–6000; Sylvia Getman, Chief Executive Officer
Web address: www.osagehospital.com

PALO ALTO COUNTY HEALTH SYSTEM (C, 47 beds) 3201 First Street, Emmetsburg, IA Zip 50536; tel. 712/852–5500; Thomas J. Lee, Chief Executive Officer
Web address: www.pachs.com

REGIONAL HEALTH SERVICES OF HOWARD COUNTY (C, 25 beds) 235 Eighth Avenue West, Cresco, IA Zip 52136–1098; tel. 563/547–2101; Elizabeth A. Doty, Chief Executive Officer
Web address: www.rhshc.com

MARYLAND: HOLY CROSS HOSPITAL (O, 406 beds) 1500 Forest Glen Road, Silver Spring, MD Zip 20910–1487; tel. 301/754–7000; Kevin J. Sexton, President and Chief Executive Officer
Web address: www.holycrosshealth.org

MICHIGAN: BATTLE CREEK HEALTH SYSTEM (O, 393 beds) Battle Creek, MI tel. 269/966–8000; Patrick R. Garrett, President and Chief Executive Officer
Web address: www.bchealth.com

MERCY GENERAL HEALTH PARTNERS (O, 201 beds) 1500 East Sherman Boulevard, Muskegon, MI Zip 49443–1849; tel. 231/739–9341; Roger Spoelman, President and Chief Executive Officer
Web address: www.mghp.com

MERCY HOSPITAL (O, 119 beds) 2601 Electric Avenue, Port Huron, MI Zip 48060–6518; tel. 810/985–1500; Peter Karadjoff, President and Chief Executive Officer
Web address: www.mercyporthuron.com

MERCY HOSPITAL CADILLAC (O, 79 beds) 400 Hobart Street, Cadillac, MI Zip 49601–9596; tel. 231/876–7200; John L. MacLeod, Chief Executive Officer
Web address: www.munsonhealthcare.org

MERCY HOSPITAL GRAYLING (O, 89 beds) 1100 East Michigan Avenue, Grayling, MI Zip 49738–1398; tel. 989/348–5461; Stephanie J. Riemer–Matuzak, Chief Executive Officer
Web address: www.mercygrayling.munsonhealthcare.org

SAINT JOSEPH MERCY HEALTH SYSTEM (O, 631 beds) 5301 East Huron River Drive, Ypsilanti, MI Zip 48197, Mailing Address: P.O. Box 995, Ann Arbor, Zip 48106–0995; tel. 734/712–3456; Garry C. Faja, President and Chief Executive Officer
Web address: www.sjmh.com

SAINT JOSEPH MERCY LIVINGSTON HOSPITAL (O, 50 beds) 620 Byron Road, Howell, MI Zip 48843–1093; tel. 517/545–6000; Patricia Claffey, Executive Director
Web address: www.sjmh.com/who/mcphersn.shtml

SAINT JOSEPH MERCY SALINE HOSPITAL (O, 28 beds) 400 West Russell Street, Saline, MI Zip 48176–1101; tel. 734/429–1500; Stacey Breedveld, Executive Director
Web address: www.sjmh.com

SAINT MARY'S HEALTH CARE (O, 324 beds) 200 Jefferson Avenue S.E., Grand Rapids, MI Zip 49503–4598; tel. 616/752–6090; Philip H. McCorkle Jr, President and Chief Executive Officer
Web address: www.smhealthcare.org

ST. JOSEPH MERCY OAKLAND (O, 478 beds) 44405 Woodward Avenue, Pontiac, MI Zip 48341–2985; tel. 248/858–3000; Jack Weiner, President and Chief Executive Officer
Web address: www.stjoesoakland.com

ST. JOSEPH'S MERCY OF MACOMB (O, 389 beds) Clinton Township, MI Barbara Rossmann, President and Chief Executive Officer
Web address: www.stjoe–macomb.com

ST. MARY MERCY HOSPITAL (O, 247 beds) 36475 West Five Mile Road, Livonia, MI Zip 48154–1988; tel. 734/655–4800; David A. Spivey, President and Chief Executive Officer
Web address: www.stmarymercy.org

NEBRASKA: OAKLAND MEMORIAL HOSPITAL (C, 23 beds) 601 East Second Street, Oakland, NE Zip 68045–1499; tel. 402/685–5601; Karen Vlach, Administrator
Web address: www.oaklandhospital.org

PENDER COMMUNITY HOSPITAL (C, 133 beds) 603 Earl Street, Pender, NE Zip 68047–0100, Mailing Address: P.O. Box 100, Zip 68047–0100; tel. 402/385–3083;
Web address: www.pendercommunityhospital.com

OHIO: FAYETTE COUNTY MEMORIAL HOSPITAL (C, 34 beds) 1430 Columbus Avenue, Washington Court House, OH Zip 43160–1791; tel. 740/335–1210; Francis G. Albarano, Chief Executive Officer
Web address: www.fcmh.org

MOUNT CARMEL (O, 843 beds) Columbus, OH Mailing Address: 793 West State Street, Zip 43222–1551; tel. 614/234–5000; Joseph T. Calvaruso, President and Chief Executive Officer
Web address: www.mountcarmelhealth.com

MOUNT CARMEL ST. ANN'S (O, 272 beds) 500 South Cleveland Avenue, Westerville, OH Zip 43081–8998; tel. 614/898–4000; Joseph T. Calvaruso, Chief Executive Officer
Web address: www.mountcarmelhealth.com

Owned, leased, sponsored:	27 hospitals	7007 beds
Contract–managed:	16 hospitals	597 beds
Totals:	43 hospitals	7604 beds

0319: TRIUMPH HEALTHCARE (IO)
7333 North Freeway, Suite 500, Houston, TX Zip 77076; tel. 832/200–6000; Charlie Allen, President and Chief Executive

TEXAS: TRIUMPH HOSPITAL EAST HOUSTON (O, 93 beds) 15101 East Freeway, Channelview, TX Zip 77530; tel. 832/200–5500; Mike Files, Chief Executive Officer

TRIUMPH HOSPITAL NORTH HOUSTON (O, 130 beds) 7333 North Freeway, Houston, TX Zip 77076; tel. 832/200–6000; Michael R. Bullard, Chief Executive Officer

TRIUMPH HOSPITAL NORTHWEST (O, 115 beds) 205 Hollow Tree Lane, Houston, TX Zip 77090; tel. 832/249–2700; Jeffrey Smith, Chief Executive Officer

TRIUMPH HOSPITAL SOUTHWEST (O, 85 beds) 1550 First Colony Boulevard, Sugar Land, TX Zip 77479; tel. 281/275–6000; Joan Damon, Chief Executive Officer

Owned, leased, sponsored:	4 hospitals	423 beds
Contract–managed:	0 hospitals	0 beds
Totals:	4 hospitals	423 beds

★9255: TRUMAN MEDICAL CENTERS (NP)
2301 Holmes Street, Kansas City, MO Zip 64108–2677; tel. 816/404–1000; John W. Bluford, President and Chief Executive Officer
(Centralized Health System)

MISSOURI: TRUMAN MEDICAL CENTER–HOSPITAL HILL (O, 206 beds) 2301 Holmes Street, Kansas City, MO Zip 64108–2677; tel. 816/404–1000; John W. Bluford, Chief Executive Officer
Web address: www.trumanmed.org

TRUMAN MEDICAL CENTER–LAKEWOOD (O, 295 beds) 7900 Lee's Summit Road, Kansas City, MO Zip 64139–1246; tel. 816/404–7000; Robin M. Schluter, Chief Operating Officer
Web address: www.trumanmed.org

Owned, leased, sponsored:	2 hospitals	501 beds
Contract–managed:	0 hospitals	0 beds
Totals:	2 hospitals	501 beds

0238: TY COBB HEALTHCARE SYSTEM, INC. (NP)
461 Cook Street, Suite A., Royston, GA Zip 30662, Mailing Address: P.O. Box 589, Zip 30662; tel. 706/245–1825; Charles T. Adams, Chief Executive Officer
(Independent Hospital System)

GEORGIA: BARROW COMMUNITY HOSPITAL (O, 56 beds) 316 North Broad Street, Winder, GA Zip 30680–2150, Mailing Address: P.O. Box 768, Zip 30680–0768; tel. 770/867–3400; Jim Litchford, Administrator
Web address: www.barrowcommunityhospital.com

COBB MEMORIAL HOSPITAL (O, 331 beds) 521 Franklin Springs Street, Royston, GA Zip 30662–3909, Mailing Address: P.O. Box 589, Zip 30662–0589; tel. 706/245–5071; John M. Herron, Administrator
Web address: www.tycobbhealthcare.org

For explanation of codes following names, see page B2.
★ Indicates Type III membership in the American Hospital Association.

Section B

HART COUNTY HOSPITAL (L, 174 beds) Gibson and Cade Streets, Hartwell, GA Zip 30643–0280, Mailing Address: P.O. Box 280, Zip 30643–0280; tel. 706/856–6100; Jerry R. Wise, Administrator and Vice President
Web address: www.tycobbhealthcare.org

Owned, leased, sponsored:	3 hospitals	561 beds
Contract–managed:	0 hospitals	0 beds
Totals:	3 hospitals	561 beds

9195: U. S. INDIAN HEALTH SERVICE (FG)
801 Thompson Avenue, Rockville, MD Zip 20852; tel. 301/443–1083; Charles Grim, D.D.S., Acting Director
(Moderately Centralized Health System)

ALASKA: ALASKA NATIVE MEDICAL CENTER (O, 150 beds) 4315 Diplomacy Drive, Anchorage, AK Zip 99508; tel. 907/563–2662; Dee Hutchison, R.N., Administrator
Web address: www.anmc.org

BRISTOL BAY AREA HEALTH CORPORATION (O, 14 beds) 6000 Kanakanak Road, Dillingham, AK Zip 99576, Mailing Address: P.O. Box 130, Zip 99576; tel. 907/842–5201; Darrel C. Richardson, Executive Vice President and Chief Operations Officer
Web address: www.bbahc.org

MANIILAQ HEALTH CENTER (O, 17 beds) Kotzebue, AK Zip 99752–0043; tel. 907/442–3321; Hugh R. Hallgren, Administrator
Web address: www.maniilaq.org

NORTON SOUND REGIONAL HOSPITAL (O, 34 beds) Bering Straits, Nome, AK Zip 99762, Mailing Address: P.O. Box 966, Zip 99762–0966; tel. 907/443–3311; Angela Gorn, Vice President
Web address: www.nortonsoundhealth.org

SAMUEL SIMMONDS MEMORIAL HOSPITAL (O, 14 beds) 1296 Agvik Street, Barrow, AK Zip 99723, Mailing Address: P.O. Box 29, Zip 99723; tel. 907/852–4611; Michael S. Herring, Administrator

SEARHC MT. EDGECUMBE HOSPITAL (O, 49 beds) 222 Tongass Drive, Sitka, AK Zip 99835–9416; tel. 907/966–2411; Frank Sutton, Vice President Hospital Services
Web address: www.searhc.org

YUKON–KUSKOKWIM DELTA REGIONAL HOSPITAL (O, 54 beds) Bethel, AK Mailing Address: P.O. Box 528, Zip 99559–3000; tel. 907/543–6300; Jack Crow, Vice President Health Services
Web address: www.ykhc.org

ARIZONA: CHINLE COMPREHENSIVE HEALTH CARE FACILITY (O, 52 beds) Highway 191, Chinle, AZ Zip 86503, Mailing Address: P.O. Drawer PH, Zip 86503; tel. 928/674–7011; Ronald Tso, Chief Executive Officer

FORT DEFIANCE INDIAN HEALTH SERVICE HOSPITAL (O, 39 beds) Fort Defiance, AZ Mailing Address: P.O. Box 649, Zip 86504–0649; tel. 928/729–5741; Franklin R. Freeland, Ed.D., Chief Executive Officer

HOPI HEALTH CARE CENTER (O, 6 beds) Keams Canyon, AZ Mailing Address: P.O. Box 4000, Polacca, Zip 86042; tel. 928/737–6000; Daryl Melvin, Chief Executive Officer

HUHUKAM MEMORIAL HOSPITAL (O, 10 beds) Seed Farm and Skill Center Road, Sacaton, AZ Zip 85247–0038, Mailing Address: P.O. Box 38, Zip 85247–0038; tel. 602/528–1200; Loren Ellery, M.P.H., Chief Executive Officer
Web address: www.grhc.org

TUBA CITY INDIAN MEDICAL CENTER (O, 69 beds) 167 Main Street, Tuba City, AZ Zip 86045–0611, Mailing Address: P.O. Box 600, Zip 86045–0600; tel. 928/283–2501; Scott Deasy, M.D., Acting Chief Executive Officer
Web address: www.tcrhcc.org

U. S. PUBLIC HEALTH SERVICE INDIAN HOSPITAL (O, 20 beds) Parker, AZ Mailing Address: Route 1, Box 12, Zip 85344; tel. 928/669–2137; Robert O'Rielly, Deputy Chief Executive Officer

U. S. PUBLIC HEALTH SERVICE INDIAN HOSPITAL (O, 34 beds) Sells, AZ Mailing Address: P.O. Box 548, Zip 85634–0548; tel. 520/383–7251; Darrell Rumley, Service Unit Director

U. S. PUBLIC HEALTH SERVICE INDIAN HOSPITAL (O, 8 beds) San Carlos, AZ Mailing Address: P.O. Box 208, Zip 85550–0208; tel. 928/475–2371; Nella J. Ben, Chief Executive Officer

U. S. PUBLIC HEALTH SERVICE INDIAN HOSPITAL–WHITERIVER (O, 15 beds) State Route 73, Box 860, Whiteriver, AZ Zip 85941–0860; tel. 928/338–4911; Dean Seyler, Chief Executive Officer
Web address: www.ihs.gov

U. S. PUBLIC HEALTH SERVICE PHOENIX INDIAN MEDICAL CENTER (O, 84 beds) 4212 North 16th Street, Phoenix, AZ Zip 85016–5389; tel. 602/263–1200; John Meeth, M.D., Acting Chief Executive Officer
Web address: www.ihs.gov

CALIFORNIA: U. S. PUBLIC HEALTH SERVICE INDIAN HOSPITAL (O, 15 beds) 1 Indian Hill Road, Winterhaven, CA Zip 92283–1368, Mailing Address: P.O. Box 1368, Yuma, AZ Zip 85366–1368; tel. 760/572–0217; Hortense Miguel, R.N., Service Unit Director

MARYLAND: WARREN G. MAGNUSON CLINICAL CENTER, NATIONAL INSTITUTES OF HEALTH (O, 265 beds) 9000 Rockville Pike, Bethesda, MD Zip 20892–1504; tel. 301/496–4114; John I. Gallin, M.D., Director
Web address: www.cc.nih.gov

MINNESOTA: U. S. PUBLIC HEALTH SERVICE INDIAN HOSPITAL (O, 13 beds) 7th Street and Grant Utley Avenue N.W., Cass Lake, MN Zip 56633, Mailing Address: Rural Route 3, Box 211, Zip 56633; tel. 218/335–3200; Jennifer Jenkins, Service Unit Director

U.S. PUBLIC HEALTH SERVICE INDIAN HOSPITAL (O, 23 beds) Highway 1, Redlake, MN Zip 56671, Mailing Address: P.O. Box 497, Zip 56671–0497; tel. 218/679–3912; Essimae Stevens, Service Unit Director

MISSISSIPPI: CHOCTAW HEALTH CENTER (O, 35 beds) 210 Hospital Circle, Philadelphia, MS Zip 39350–6781; tel. 601/656–2211; James D. Wallace, Executive Director

MONTANA: CROW/NORTHERN CHEYENNE HOSPITAL (O, 24 beds) Crow Agency, MT Mailing Address: P.O. Box 9, Zip 59022–0009; tel. 406/638–2626; Kevin Stiffarm, Chief Executive Officer

U. S. PUBLIC HEALTH SERVICE BLACKFEET COMMUNITY HOSPITAL (O, 25 beds) Browning, MT Mailing Address: P.O. Box 760, Zip 59417–0760; tel. 406/338–6100; Jaloo Zelonis, Acting Director
Web address: www.phs.ihs.gov

U. S. PUBLIC HEALTH SERVICE INDIAN HOSPITAL (O, 6 beds) Rural Route 1, Box 67, Harlem, MT Zip 59526; tel. 406/353–3100; Daryl A. Brockie, Director

NEBRASKA: U. S. PUBLIC HEALTH SERVICE INDIAN HOSPITAL (O, 30 beds) Highway 7577, Winnebago, NE Zip 68071; tel. 402/878–2231; Donald Lee, Service Unit Director

NEVADA: U. S. PUBLIC HEALTH SERVICE OWYHEE COMMUNITY HEALTH FACILITY (O, 15 beds) Owyhee, NV Mailing Address: P.O. Box 130, Zip 89832–0130; tel. 775/757–2415; Alan J. Burgess, CHE, FAAMA, Administrator

NEW MEXICO: ACOMA–CANONCITO–LAGUNA HOSPITAL (O, 14 beds) San Fidel, NM Mailing Address: P.O. Box 130, Zip 87049–0130; tel. 505/552–5300; R. C. Begay, Chief Executive Officer

GALLUP INDIAN MEDICAL CENTER (O, 99 beds) 516 East Nizhoni Boulevard, Gallup, NM Zip 87301–5748, Mailing Address: P.O. Box 1337, Zip 87305–1337; tel. 505/722–1000; Floyd Thompson, Chief Executive Officer
Web address: www.ihs.gov

NORTHERN NAVAJO MEDICAL CENTER (O, 64 beds) Shiprock, NM Mailing Address: P.O. Box 160, Zip 87420–0160; tel. 505/368–6001; Carla Baha–Alchesay, Chief Executive Officer
Web address: www.home.nnmc.ihs.gov

PHS SANTA FE INDIAN HOSPITAL (O, 39 beds) 1700 Cerrillos Road, Santa Fe, NM Zip 87505–3554; tel. 505/988–9821; Richard L. Zephier, Ph.D., Chief Executive Officer

PUBLIC HEALTH SERVICE INDIAN HOSPITAL (O, 28 beds) 801 Vassar Drive N.E., Albuquerque, NM Zip 87106–2799; tel. 505/248–4000; Maria Rickert, Chief Executive Officer

U. S. PUBLIC HEALTH SERVICE INDIAN HOSPITAL (O, 25 beds) Crownpoint, NM Mailing Address: P.O. Box 358, Zip 87313–0358; tel. 505/786–5291; Anita Muneta, Chief Executive Officer
Web address: www.ihs.gov

U. S. PUBLIC HEALTH SERVICE INDIAN HOSPITAL (O, 11 beds) Mescalero, NM Mailing Address: Box 210, Zip 88340–0210; tel. 505/671–4441; Matthew Anderson, Administrator

U. S. PUBLIC HEALTH SERVICE INDIAN HOSPITAL (O, 29 beds) Route 301 North B. Street, Zuni, NM Zip 87327, Mailing Address: P.O. Box 467, Zip 87327–0467; tel. 505/782–4431; Jean Othole, Service Unit Director

NORTH CAROLINA: CHEROKEE INDIAN HOSPITAL AUTHORITY (O, 28 beds) Hospital Road, Cherokee, NC Zip 28719, Mailing Address: Caller Box C–26, Zip 28719; tel. 828/497–9163; Arnold Wachacha, Administrator

For explanation of codes following names, see page B2.
★ Indicates Type III membership in the American Hospital Association.

Section B

NORTH DAKOTA: U. S. PUBLIC HEALTH SERVICE INDIAN HOSPITAL (O, 27 beds) Belcourt, ND Mailing Address: P.O. Box 160, Zip 58316–0160; tel. 701/477–6111; Linus Everling, JD, M.P.H., Chief Executive Officer

U. S. PUBLIC HEALTH SERVICE INDIAN HOSPITAL (O, 14 beds) N 10 North River Road, Fort Yates, ND Zip 58538, Mailing Address: P.O. Box J, Zip 58538; tel. 701/854–3831; Tim Yellow, Director

OKLAHOMA: CHICKASAW NATION HEALTH SYSTEM (O, 52 beds) 1001 North Country Club Road, Ada, OK Zip 74820–2847; tel. 580/436–3980; Bill Lance, Administrator
Web address: www.ihs.gov

CHOCTAW NATION HEALTH CARE CENTER (O, 37 beds) One Choctaw Way, Talihina, OK Zip 74571–9517; tel. 918/567–7000; Reece Sherrill, Administrator
Web address: www.choctawnationhealth.com

CREEK NATION COMMUNITY HOSPITAL (O, 34 beds) 309 North 14th Street, Okemah, OK Zip 74859–2099; tel. 918/623–1424; Jo Ann Skaggs, Chief Executive Officer

U. S. PUBLIC HEALTH SERVICE COMPREHENSIVE INDIAN HEALTH FACILITY (O, 46 beds) 101 South Moore Avenue, Claremore, OK Zip 74017–5091; tel. 918/342–6434; James F. Cussen, Director

U. S. PUBLIC HEALTH SERVICE INDIAN HOSPITAL (O, 11 beds) Clinton, OK Mailing Address: Route 1, Box 3060, Zip 73601–9303; tel. 580/323–2884; Terri Schmidt, Director
Web address: www.ihs.gov

U. S. PUBLIC HEALTH SERVICE INDIAN HOSPITAL (O, 44 beds) 1515 Lawrie Tatum Road, Lawton, OK Zip 73507–3099; tel. 580/353–0350; Hickory Starr Jr, Chief Executive Officer

WILLIAM W. HASTINGS INDIAN HOSPITAL (O, 60 beds) 100 South Bliss Avenue, Tahlequah, OK Zip 74464–3399; tel. 918/458–3100; Hickory Starr Jr, Administrator

SOUTH DAKOTA: INDIAN HEALTH SERVICE HOSPITAL (O, 32 beds) 3200 Canyon Lake Drive, Rapid City, SD Zip 57702–8197; tel. 605/355–2280; Ray Grandbois, M.P.H., Director
Web address: www.ihs.gov

U. S. PUBLIC HEALTH SERVICE INDIAN HOSPITAL (O, 11 beds) Eagle Butte, SD Mailing Address: P.O. Box 1012, Zip 57625–1012; tel. 605/964–7724; Donald D. Annis, Service Unit Director

U. S. PUBLIC HEALTH SERVICE INDIAN HOSPITAL (O, 45 beds) Pine Ridge, SD Mailing Address: P.O. Box 1201, Zip 57770–1201; tel. 605/867–5131; Vern F. Donnell, Service Unit Director

U. S. PUBLIC HEALTH SERVICE INDIAN HOSPITAL (O, 35 beds) Highway 18, Soldier Creek Road, Rosebud, SD Zip 57570; tel. 605/747–2231; Dixie Gaikowski, Acting Chief Executive Officer

U. S. PUBLIC HEALTH SERVICE INDIAN HOSPITAL (O, 11 beds) Chestnut Street, Sisseton, SD Zip 57262, Mailing Address: P.O. Box 189, Zip 57262–0189; tel. 605/698–7606; Richard Huff, Administrator
Web address: www.home.aberdeen.his.gov

Owned, leased, sponsored:	50 hospitals	1916 beds
Contract–managed:	0 hospitals	0 beds
Totals:	50 hospitals	1916 beds

9105: UAB HEALTH SYSTEM (NP)
500 22nd Street South, Suite 408, Birmingham, AL Zip 35233; tel. 205/975–5362; David E. Hoidal, Chief Executive Officer
(Moderately Centralized Health System)

ALABAMA: CALLAHAN EYE FOUNDATION HOSPITAL (O, 20 beds) 1720 University Boulevard, Birmingham, AL Zip 35233–1816; tel. 205/325–8100; Raymond Butler, President
Web address: www.health.uab.edu/eyes

UAB MEDICAL WEST (O, 226 beds) 995 Ninth Avenue S.W., Bessemer, AL Zip 35022–4527, Mailing Address: P.O. Box 847, Zip 35021–0847; tel. 205/481–7000; Timothy J. Thornton, Chief Executive Officer
Web address: www.health.uab.edu

UNIVERSITY OF ALABAMA HOSPITAL (O, 867 beds) 619 South 19th Street, Birmingham, AL Zip 35233–6505; tel. 205/934–4011; David E. Hoidal, Chief Executive Officer
Web address: www.health.uab.edu

Owned, leased, sponsored:	3 hospitals	1113 beds
Contract–managed:	0 hospitals	0 beds
Totals:	3 hospitals	1113 beds

★0224: UMASS MEMORIAL HEALTH CARE, INC. (NP)
1 Biotech Park, Worcester, MA Zip 01605–2982; tel. 508/334–0100; John G. O'Brien, President and Chief Executive Officer
(Moderately Centralized Health System)

MASSACHUSETTS: CLINTON HOSPITAL (O, 41 beds) 201 Highland Street, Clinton, MA Zip 01510–1096; tel. 978/368–3000; Sheila Daly, Chief Executive Officer
Web address: www.umassmemorial.org/ummhc/hospitals/clinton

HEALTH ALLIANCE HOSPITALS (O, 103 beds) 60 Hospital Road, Leominster, MA Zip 01453–8004; tel. 978/466–2000; Patrick L. Muldoon, President and Chief Executive Officer
Web address: www.healthalliance.com

UMASS MEMORIAL MEDICAL CENTER (O, 726 beds) 119 Belmont Street, Worcester, MA Zip 01605–2982; tel. 508/334–1000; Walter Ettinger, M.D., President
Web address: www.umassmemorial.org

UMASS MEMORIAL–MARLBOROUGH HOSPITAL (O, 67 beds) 157 Union Street, Marlborough, MA Zip 01752–1297; tel. 508/481–5000; John Polanowicz, President and Chief Executive Officer
Web address: www.marlboroughhospital.org

WING MEMORIAL HOSPITAL AND MEDICAL CENTERS (O, 39 beds) 40 Wright Street, Palmer, MA Zip 01069–1138; tel. 413/283–7651; Charles E. Cavagnaro, M.D., President and Chief Executive Officer
Web address: www.winghealth.org

Owned, leased, sponsored:	5 hospitals	976 beds
Contract–managed:	0 hospitals	0 beds
Totals:	5 hospitals	976 beds

0288: UNITED HEALTH SERVICES (NP)
10–42 Mitchell Avenue, Binghamton, NY Zip 13903; tel. 607/762–2200; Matthew J. Salanger, President and Chief Executive Officer
(Moderately Centralized Health System)

NEW YORK: CHENANGO MEMORIAL HOSPITAL (O, 138 beds) 179 North Broad Street, Norwich, NY Zip 13815–1097; tel. 607/337–4111; Frank W. Mirabito, President
Web address: www.uhs.net/aboutus/hospitals/chenango/index.asp

DELAWARE VALLEY HOSPITAL (O, 33 beds) 1 Titus Place, Walton, NY Zip 13856–1498; tel. 607/865–2100; David J. Polge, President and Chief Executive Officer
Web address: www.uhs.net

UNITED HEALTH SERVICES HOSPITALS–BINGHAMTON (O, 425 beds) 10–42 Mitchell Avenue, Binghamton, NY Zip 13903–1678; tel. 607/763–6000; Matthew J. Salanger, President and Chief Executive Officer
Web address: www.uhs.net

Owned, leased, sponsored:	3 hospitals	596 beds
Contract–managed:	0 hospitals	0 beds
Totals:	3 hospitals	596 beds

9605: UNITED MEDICAL CORPORATION (IO)
603 Main Street, Windermere, FL Zip 34786–3548, Mailing Address: P.O. Box 1100, Zip 34786–1100; tel. 407/876–2200; Donald R. Dizney, Chairman and Chief Executive Officer
(Independent Hospital System)

FLORIDA: TEN BROECK HOSPITAL JACKSONVILLE (O, 99 beds) 6300 Beach Boulevard, Jacksonville, FL Zip 32216–2782; tel. 904/724–9202; Paul Andrews, Chief Executive Officer
Web address: www.tenbroeck.com

KENTUCKY: TEN BROECK HOSPITAL (O, 94 beds) 8521 Old LaGrange Road, Louisville, KY Zip 40242–3800; tel. 502/426–6380; John Hollinsworth, Executive Director
Web address: www.tenbroeck.com

For explanation of codes following names, see page B2.
★ Indicates Type III membership in the American Hospital Association.

LOUISIANA: BYWATER HOSPITAL (O, 136 beds) 3419 St. Claude Avenue, New Orleans, LA Zip 70117–6198; tel. 504/948–8200; John McGee, Chief Executive Officer

PUERTO RICO: HOSPITAL PAVIA–HATO REY (O, 180 beds) San Juan, PR Mailing Address: 435 Ponce De Leon, Hato Rey, Zip 00917–3428; tel. 787/754–0909; Alfredo E. Volckers, Executive Vice President
Web address: www.paviahealth.com

HOSPITAL PAVIA–SANTURCE (O, 309 beds) 1462 Asia Street, San Juan, PR Zip 00909–2143, Mailing Address: Box 11137, Santurce Station, Zip 00910–1137; tel. 787/727–6060; Alfredo E. Volckers, Executive Director
Web address: www.paviahealth.com

HOSPITAL PEREA (O, 103 beds) 15 Basora Street, Mayaguez, PR Zip 00681, Mailing Address: P.O. Box 170, Zip 00681; tel. 787/834–0101; Rafael Alvarado, Chief Executive Officer
Web address: www.paviahealth.com/perea_hospital.htm

SAN JORGE CHILDREN'S HOSPITAL (O, 125 beds) 258 San Jorge Avenue, San Juan, PR Zip 00912–3310; tel. 787/727–1000; Domingo Cruz Vivaldi, Administrator
Web address: www.sanjorgechildrenhospital.com

Owned, leased, sponsored:	7 hospitals	1046 beds
Contract–managed:	0 hospitals	0 beds
Totals:	7 hospitals	1046 beds

0322: UNITED SURGICAL PARTNERS INTERNATIONAL (IO) 15305 Dallas Parkway, Suite 1600, Addison, TX Zip 75001–6491; tel. 972/713–3500; William Wilcox, President and Chief Executive Officer

ARIZONA: ARIZONA ORTHOPEDIC SURGICAL HOSPITAL (O, 16 beds) 2905 West Warner Road, Chandler, AZ Zip 85224; tel. 480/603–9000; Robert Conoway, Chief Executive Officer

OKLAHOMA: OKLAHOMA CENTER FOR ORTHOPEDIC AND MULTI–SPECIALTY SURGERY (O, 10 beds) 8100 South Walker, Suite C., Oklahoma City, OK Zip 73139; tel. 405/602–6500; Teri Philbrick, Chief Executive Officer

TEXAS: FRISCO MEDICAL CENTER (O, 25 beds) 5601 Warren Parkway, Frisco, TX Zip 75034; tel. 214/618–2000; William A. Keaton, Chief Executive Officer
Web address: www.friscomedicalcenter.com

IRVING COPPELL SURGICAL HOSPITAL (O, 20 beds) 440 West Interstate 635, Irving, TX Zip 75063; tel. 972/868–4000; David Yoder, Chief Executive Officer

MARY SHIELS HOSPITAL (O, 14 beds) 3515 Howell Street, Dallas, TX Zip 75204–2895; tel. 214/443–3000; Suzanne Greever, Chief Executive Officer
Web address: www.maryshiels.com

SUGAR LAND SURGICAL HOSPITAL (O, 6 beds) 1211 Highway 6, Suite 70, Sugar Land, TX Zip 77478; tel. 281/243–1000; Carol Champagne, Chief Executive Officer

TOPS SURGICAL SPECIALTY HOSPITAL (O, 18 beds) 17080 Red Oak Drive, Houston, TX Zip 77090; tel. 281/539–2900; J. L. Flotte', Administrator
Web address: www.unitedsurgical.com

Owned, leased, sponsored:	7 hospitals	109 beds
Contract–managed:	0 hospitals	0 beds
Totals:	7 hospitals	109 beds

9555: UNIVERSAL HEALTH SERVICES, INC. (IO) 367 South Gulph Road, King of Prussia, PA Zip 19406–0958, Mailing Address: P.O. Box 61558, Zip 19406–0958; tel. 610/768–3300; Alan B. Miller, President and Chief Executive Officer
(Decentralized Health System)

ALASKA: NORTH STAR BEHAVIORAL HEALTH SYSTEM (O, 117 beds) 2530 DeBarr Road, Anchorage, AK Zip 99508–2948; tel. 907/258–7575; James Shill, Chief Executive Officer and Managing Director
Web address: www.northstarbehavioral.com

ARKANSAS: BRIDGEWAY (L, 98 beds) 21 Bridgeway Road, North Little Rock, AR Zip 72113–9516; tel. 501/771–1500; Joel Klein, Chief Executive Officer and Managing Director
Web address: www.thebridgeway.com

RIVENDELL BEHAVIORAL HEALTH SERVICES (O, 77 beds) 100 Rivendell Drive, Benton, AR Zip 72015–9100; tel. 501/316–1255; Scott Williams, Administrator
Web address: www.ccskids.com

CALIFORNIA: CORONA REGIONAL MEDICAL CENTER (O, 228 beds) 800 South Main Street, Corona, CA Zip 92882–3420; tel. 951/737–4343; John A. Calderone, Ph.D., Chief Executive Officer
Web address: www.coronaregional.com

DEL AMO HOSPITAL (O, 70 beds) 23700 Camino Del Sol, Torrance, CA Zip 90505–5000; tel. 310/530–1151; Lisa K. Montes, Chief Executive Officer
Web address: www.delamohospital.com

INLAND VALLEY MEDICAL CENTER (L, 80 beds) 36485 Inland Valley Drive, Wildomar, CA Zip 92595–9700; tel. 951/677–1111; Linda Bradley, Chief Executive Officer
Web address: www.ivrmc–rsmc.com

LANCASTER COMMUNITY HOSPITAL (O, 117 beds) 43830 North Tenth Street West, Lancaster, CA Zip 93534–4895; tel. 661/948–4781; Robert J. Trautman, Chief Executive Officer
Web address: www.lancastercommunityhospital.net

RANCHO SPRINGS MEDICAL CENTER (O, 51 beds) 25500 Medical Center Drive, Murrieta, CA Zip 92562–5965; tel. 951/696–6000; Linda Bradley, Chief Executive Officer
Web address: www.ivrmc–rsmc.com

DELAWARE: ROCKFORD CENTER (O, 74 beds) 100 Rockford Drive, Newark, DE Zip 19713–2121; tel. 302/996–5480; John F. McKenna, Chief Executive Officer
Web address: www.rockfordcenter.com

DISTRICT OF COLUMBIA: GEORGE WASHINGTON UNIVERSITY HOSPITAL (O, 326 beds) 900 23rd Street N.W., Washington, DC Zip 20037–2377; tel. 202/715–4000; Richard B. Becker, M.D., Chief Executive Officer
Web address: www.gwhospital.com

FLORIDA: LAKEWOOD RANCH MEDICAL CENTER (O, 120 beds) 8330 Lakewood Ranch Boulevard, Bradenton, FL Zip 34202; tel. 941/782–2100; Lynn M. Mergen, Interim Chief Executive Officer and Managing Director

MANATEE MEMORIAL HOSPITAL (O, 512 beds) 206 Second Street East, Bradenton, FL Zip 34208–1000; tel. 941/746–5111; Brian T. Flynn, Chief Executive Officer
Web address: www.manateememorial.com

WELLINGTON REGIONAL MEDICAL CENTER (L, 108 beds) 10101 Forest Hill Boulevard, West Palm Beach, FL Zip 33414–6199; tel. 561/798–8500; Kevin DiLallo, Chief Executive Officer
Web address: www.wellingtonregional.com

GEORGIA: ANCHOR HOSPITAL (O, 92 beds) 5454 Yorktowne Drive, Atlanta, GA Zip 30349–5305; tel. 770/991–6044; Trey Carter, Chief Executive Officer
Web address: www.anchorhospital.com

COASTAL HARBOR TREATMENT CENTER (O, 112 beds) 1150 Cornell Avenue, Savannah, GA Zip 31406–2797; tel. 912/354–3911; Ray Heckerman, Chief Executive Officer
Web address: www.coastalharbor.com

PEACHFORD BEHAVIORAL HEALTH SYSTEM (O, 224 beds) 2151 Peachford Road, Atlanta, GA Zip 30338–6599; tel. 770/455–3200; Matthew Crouch, Chief Executive Officer
Web address: www.peachfordhospital.com

TURNING POINT HOSPITAL (O, 59 beds) 3015 East By–Pass, Moultrie, GA Zip 31768–6705, Mailing Address: P.O. Box 1177, Zip 31776–1177; tel. 229/985–4815; Ben Marion, Chief Executive Officer
Web address: www.turningpointcare.com

ILLINOIS: HARTGROVE HOSPITAL (O, 128 beds) 520 North Ridgeway Avenue, Chicago, IL Zip 60624–1299; tel. 773/722–3113; Steven Airhart, Chief Executive Officer
Web address: www.uhsinc.com

THE PAVILION (O, 46 beds) 809 West Church Street, Champaign, IL Zip 61820–3399; tel. 217/373–1700; Joseph Sheehy, Chief Executive Officer
Web address: www.info@pavilionhospital.com

For explanation of codes following names, see page B2.
★ Indicates Type III membership in the American Hospital Association.

KENTUCKY: RIDGE BEHAVIORAL HEALTH SYSTEM (O, 110 beds) 3050 Rio Dosa Drive, Lexington, KY Zip 40509–9990; tel. 859/269–2325; Nina W. Eisner, Chief Executive Officer and Managing Director
Web address: www.ridgebhs.com

RIVENDELL BEHAVIORAL HEALTH (O, 72 beds) 1035 Porter Pike, Bowling Green, KY Zip 42103; tel. 270/843–1199; Janice Richardson, Chief Executive Officer
Web address: www.rivendellbehavioral.com

LOUISIANA: CHALMETTE MEDICAL CENTER (O, 194 beds) 9001 Patricia Street, Chalmette, LA Zip 70043–1769; tel. 504/620–6000; Jon Sewell, Chief Executive Officer
Web address: www.chalmettemedical.com

METHODIST HOSPITAL (O, 295 beds) 5620 Read Boulevard, New Orleans, LA Zip 70127–3154; tel. 504/244–5100;
Web address: www.methodisthospitalnola.org

RIVER OAKS HOSPITAL (O, 126 beds) 1525 River Oaks Road West, New Orleans, LA Zip 70123–2199; tel. 504/734–1740; Jennifer Nolan, Chief Executive Officer
Web address: www.riveroakshospital.com

MASSACHUSETTS: ARBOUR H. R. I. HOSPITAL (O, 68 beds) 227 Babcock Street, Brookline, MA Zip 02146–6799; tel. 617/731–3200; Marcia Hoch, Interim Chief Executive Officer
Web address: www.arbourhealth.com

ARBOUR HOSPITAL (O, 118 beds) 49 Robinwood Avenue, Boston, MA Zip 02130–2156, Mailing Address: P.O. Box 9, Zip 02130; tel. 617/522–4400; Roy A. Ettlinger, Chief Executive Officer, Managing Director and Regional Vice President
Web address: www.arbourhealth.com

ARBOUR–FULLER HOSPITAL (O, 46 beds) 200 May Street, Attleboro, MA Zip 02703–5515; tel. 508/761–8500; Gary M. Gilberti, Regional Vice President
Web address: www.arbourhealth.com

PEMBROKE HOSPITAL (O, 80 beds) 199 Oak Street, Pembroke, MA Zip 02359–1953; tel. 781/826–8161; Paul Zani, Chief Executive Officer

WESTWOOD LODGE HOSPITAL (O, 65 beds) 45 Clapboardtree Street, Westwood, MA Zip 02090–2930; tel. 781/762–7764; Robert W. Spiegel, Chief Executive Officer
Web address: www.westwoodpembroke.com

MICHIGAN: FOREST VIEW PSYCHIATRIC HOSPITAL (O, 62 beds) 1055 Medical Park Drive S.E., Grand Rapids, MI Zip 49546–3671; tel. 616/942–9610; Wayne T. Miller, Chief Executive Officer
Web address: www.forestview.com

MISSISSIPPI: PARKWOOD BEHAVIORAL HEALTH SYSTEM (O, 72 beds) 8135 Goodman Road, Olive Branch, MS Zip 38654–2199; tel. 662/895–4900; M. Andrew Mayo, Ph.D., Chief Executive Officer
Web address: www.parkwoodbhs.com

MISSOURI: TWO RIVERS PSYCHIATRIC HOSPITAL (O, 76 beds) 5121 Raytown Road, Kansas City, MO Zip 64133–2141; tel. 816/356–5688; Linda Berridge, Chief Executive Officer
Web address: www.tworivershospital.com

NEVADA: DESERT SPRINGS HOSPITAL (O, 346 beds) 2075 East Flamingo Road, Las Vegas, NV Zip 89119–5121, Mailing Address: P.O. Box 19204, Zip 89132–9204; tel. 702/733–8800; Samuel Kaufman, Chief Executive Officer and Managing Director
Web address: www.desertspringshosp.com

NORTHERN NEVADA MEDICAL CENTER (O, 100 beds) 2375 East Prater Way, Sparks, NV Zip 89434–9900; tel. 775/331–7000; Margaret S. Cleary, Chief Executive Officer
Web address: www.nnmc.com

SPRING VALLEY HOSPITAL MEDICAL CENTER (O, 90 beds) 5400 South Rainbow Boulevard, Las Vegas, NV Zip 89118; tel. 702/853–3333; Karla Perez, Chief Executive Officer and Managing Director

SUMMERLIN HOSPITAL MEDICAL CENTER (O, 148 beds) 657 Town Center Drive, Las Vegas, NV Zip 89134; tel. 702/233–7000; Tim Hingtgen, Chief Executive Officer and Managing Director
Web address: www.summerlinhospital.org

VALLEY HOSPITAL MEDICAL CENTER (O, 365 beds) 620 Shadow Lane, Las Vegas, NV Zip 89106–4119; tel. 702/388–4000; Gregory E. Boyer, Chief Executive Officer
Web address: www.valleyhospital.net

NEW JERSEY: HAMPTON HOSPITAL (O, 83 beds) 650 Rancocas Road, Mount Holly, NJ Zip 08060–5613, Mailing Address: P.O. Box 7000, Rancocas, Zip 08073–7000; tel. 609/267–7000; James P. Gallagher, Chief Executive Officer
Web address: www.hamptonhospital.com

OKLAHOMA: ST. MARY'S REGIONAL MEDICAL CENTER (O, 160 beds) 305 South Fifth Street, Enid, OK Zip 73701–5899, Mailing Address: Box 232, Zip 73702–0232; tel. 580/233–6100; Rick Wallace, FACHE, Chief Executive Officer
Web address: www.stmarysregional.com

PENNSYLVANIA: CENTRAL MONTGOMERY MEDICAL CENTER (O, 119 beds) 100 Medical Campus Drive, Lansdale, PA Zip 19446–1200; tel. 215/368–2100; George E. Miller, Chief Executive Officer
Web address: www.cmmc–uhs.com

CLARION PSYCHIATRIC CENTER (O, 52 beds) 2 Hospital Drive, Clarion, PA Zip 16214–9424; tel. 814/226–9545; Jeffrey Barnett, Chief Executive Officer
Web address: www.clarioncenter.com

FAIRMOUNT BEHAVIORAL HEALTH SYSTEM (O, 180 beds) 561 Fairthorne Avenue, Philadelphia, PA Zip 19128–2499; tel. 215/487–4000; Geoff Botak, Chief Executive Officer
Web address: www.fairmountbhs.com

HORSHAM CLINIC (O, 138 beds) 722 East Butler Pike, Ambler, PA Zip 19002–2310; tel. 215/643–7800; Phyllis Weisfield, Interim Chief Executive Officer
Web address: www.horshamclinic.com

KEYSTONE CENTER (O, 84 beds) 2001 Providence Avenue, Chester, PA Zip 19013–5504; tel. 610/876–9000; Billy Young, Chief Executive Officer
Web address: www.keystonecenter.net

MEADOWS PSYCHIATRIC CENTER (O, 101 beds) 132 The Meadows Drive, Centre Hall, PA Zip 16828–9798; tel. 814/364–2161; Felicia Stehley, Chief Executive Officer
Web address: www.themeadow.net

PUERTO RICO: SAN JUAN CAPESTRANO HOSPITAL (O, 108 beds) San Juan, PR Mailing Address: Rural Route 2, Box 11, Zip 00926; tel. 787/760–0222; Laura Vargas, Chief Executive Officer and Managing Director
Web address: www.sjcapestrano.com

SOUTH CAROLINA: AIKEN REGIONAL MEDICAL CENTERS (O, 269 beds) 302 University Parkway, Aiken, SC Zip 29801–2757, Mailing Address: P.O. Box 1117, Zip 29802–1117; tel. 803/641–5000; Kathryn D. Justyn, Chief Executive Officer
Web address: www.aikenregional.com

CAROLINA CENTER FOR BEHAVIORAL HEALTH (O, 66 beds) 2700 East Phillips Road, Greer, SC Zip 29650–4816; tel. 864/968–6300; John Willingham, Chief Executive Officer
Web address: www.thecarolinacenter.com

TENNESSEE: LAKESIDE BEHAVIORAL HEALTH SYSTEM (O, 219 beds) 2911 Brunswick Road, Memphis, TN Zip 38133–4199; tel. 901/377–4700; Robert S. Waggener, Chief Executive Officer
Web address: www.lakesidebhs.com

TEXAS: DOCTORS HOSPITAL OF LAREDO (O, 180 beds) 10700 McPherson Road, Laredo, TX Zip 78045; tel. 956/523–2000; Al Chapa, Chief Executive Officer and Managing Director
Web address: www.doctorshoslaredo.com

EDINBURG REGIONAL MEDICAL CENTER (O, 151 beds) 1102 West Trenton Road, Edinburg, TX Zip 78539–6199; tel. 956/388–6000; Daniel P. McLean, Chief Executive Officer
Web address: www.edinburgregional.com

FORT DUNCAN MEDICAL CENTER (O, 73 beds) 350 South Adams Street, Eagle Pass, TX Zip 78852–5110; tel. 830/773–5321; Alfredo Ontiveros Jr, Chief Executive Officer
Web address: www.fortduncanmedicalcenter.com

GLEN OAKS HOSPITAL (O, 54 beds) 301 East Division, Greenville, TX Zip 75402–4199; tel. 903/454–6000; John Baker, Chief Executive Officer and Managing Director
Web address: www.glenoakshospital.com

MCALLEN MEDICAL CENTER (L, 552 beds) 301 West Expressway 83, McAllen, TX Zip 78503–3045; tel. 956/632–4000; Daniel P. McLean, Chief Executive Officer and Managing Director
Web address: www.mcallenmedicalcenter.com

For explanation of codes following names, see page B2.
★ Indicates Type III membership in the American Hospital Association.

Section B

MERIDELL ACHIEVEMENT CENTER (O, 78 beds) 12550 West Highway 29, Liberty Hill, TX Zip 78642, Mailing Address: P.O. Box 87, Zip 78642–0087; tel. 800/366–8656; Gail M. Oberta, FACHE, Chief Executive Officer and Managing Director
Web address: www.meridell.com

NORTHWEST TEXAS HEALTHCARE SYSTEM (O, 433 beds) 1501 South Coulter Avenue, Amarillo, TX Zip 79106–1790, Mailing Address: P.O. Box 1110, Zip 79175–1110; tel. 806/354–1000; Frank Lopez, FACHE, Chief Executive Officer and Managing Director
Web address: www.nwtexashealthcare.com

RIVER CREST HOSPITAL (O, 80 beds) 1636 Hunters Glen Road, San Angelo, TX Zip 76901–5016; tel. 325/949–5722; Larry Grimes, Chief Executive Officer and Managing Director
Web address: www.rivercresthospital.com

TIMBERLAWN MENTAL HEALTH SYSTEM (O, 124 beds) 4600 Samuell Boulevard, Dallas, TX Zip 75228–6800; tel. 214/381–7181; Craig Nuckles, Chief Executive Officer, Managing Director and Group Director
Web address: www.timberlawn.com

WASHINGTON: AUBURN REGIONAL MEDICAL CENTER (O, 120 beds) 202 North Division, Plaza One, Auburn, WA Zip 98001–4908; tel. 253/833–7711; Leonard Freehof, Chief Executive Officer and Managing Director
Web address: www.auburnregional.com

Owned, leased, sponsored:	59 hospitals	8496 beds
Contract–managed:	0 hospitals	0 beds
Totals:	59 hospitals	8496 beds

0246: UNIVERSITY COMMUNITY HEALTH (NP)
3100 East Fletcher Avenue, Tampa, FL Zip 33613; tel. 813/971–6000; Norman V. Stein, President
(Moderately Centralized Health System)

FLORIDA: HELEN ELLIS MEMORIAL HOSPITAL (O, 168 beds) 1395 South Pinellas Avenue, Tarpon Springs, FL Zip 34689–3721, Mailing Address: P.O. Box 1487, Zip 34688–1487; tel. 727/942–5000; Steven MacLauchlan, Chief Executive Officer
Web address: www.helenellis.com

SUN COAST HOSPITAL (O, 300 beds) 2025 Indian Rocks Road, Largo, FL Zip 33774–1096, Mailing Address: P.O. Box 2025, Zip 33779–2025; tel. 727/581–9474; Larry J. Archbell, Chief Executive Officer
Web address: www.suncoasthealthcare.com

UNIVERSITY COMMUNITY HOSPITAL (O, 360 beds) 3100 East Fletcher Avenue, Tampa, FL Zip 33613–4688; tel. 813/971–6000; Calvin Glidewell, Chief Executive Officer
Web address: www.uch.org

UNIVERSITY COMMUNITY HOSPITAL–CARROLLWOOD (O, 90 beds) 7171 North Dale Mabry Highway, Tampa, FL Zip 33614–2699; tel. 813/932–2222; Donald D. Evans, Chief Executive Officer
Web address: www.uch.org

Owned, leased, sponsored:	4 hospitals	918 beds
Contract–managed:	0 hospitals	0 beds
Totals:	4 hospitals	918 beds

★0217: UNIVERSITY HEALTH SYSTEMS OF EASTERN CAROLINA (NP)
2100 Stantonsburg Road, Greenville, NC Zip 27834, Mailing Address: P.O. Box 6028, Zip 27835–6028; tel. 252/847–4100; Dave C. McRae, Chief Executive Officer
(Moderately Centralized Health System)

NORTH CAROLINA: BERTIE MEMORIAL HOSPITAL (L, 6 beds) 1403 South King Street, Windsor, NC Zip 27983–1726, Mailing Address: P.O. Box 40, Zip 27983–1726; tel. 252/794–6600; Jeffrey N. Sackrison, CHE, President
Web address: www.bertie.uhseast.com

CHOWAN HOSPITAL (L, 76 beds) 211 Virginia Road, Edenton, NC Zip 27932–0629, Mailing Address: P.O. Box 629, Zip 27932–0629; tel. 252/482–8451; Jeffrey N. Sackrison, CHE, President
Web address: www.uhseast.com

HERITAGE HOSPITAL (O, 127 beds) 111 Hospital Drive, Tarboro, NC Zip 27886–2011; tel. 252/641–7700; Wendell H. Baker Jr, President
Web address: www.heritage.uhseast.com

PITT COUNTY MEMORIAL HOSPITAL (O, 745 beds) 2100 Stantonsburg Road, Greenville, NC Zip 27834, Mailing Address: P.O. Box 6028, Zip 27835–6028; tel. 252/847–4100; Deborah W. Davis, President
Web address: www.uhseast.com

ROANOKE–CHOWAN HOSPITAL (L, 105 beds) 500 South Academy Street, Ahoskie, NC Zip 27910–3261, Mailing Address: P.O. Box 1385, Zip 27910–1385; tel. 252/209–3000; Susan S. Lassiter, President
Web address: www.uhseast.com

THE OUTER BANKS HOSPITAL (O, 19 beds) 4800 South Croatan Highway, Nags Head, NC Zip 27959–9704; tel. 252/449–4500; Roger Robinson, Interim President
Web address: www.theouterbankshospital.com

Owned, leased, sponsored:	6 hospitals	1078 beds
Contract–managed:	0 hospitals	0 beds
Totals:	6 hospitals	1078 beds

0112: UNIVERSITY HOSPITALS HEALTH SYSTEM (NP)
11100 Euclid Avenue, Cleveland, OH Zip 44106–5000; tel. 216/844–1000; Thomas F. Zenty III, President and Chief Executive Officer
(Centralized Physician/Insurance Health System)

OHIO: HEATHER HILL HOSPITAL AND HEALTH PARTNERSHIP (O, 320 beds) 12340 Bass Lake Road, Chardon, OH Zip 44024–8327; tel. 440/285–4040; Richard J. Frenchie, President and Chief Executive Officer
Web address: www.healtherhill.org

SOUTHWEST GENERAL HEALTH CENTER 18697 Bagley Road, Middleburg Heights, OH Zip 44130–3497; tel. 440/816–8000; L. Jon Schurmeier, President and Chief Executive Officer
Web address: www.swgeneral.com

UHHS BEDFORD MEDICAL CENTER (O, 103 beds) 44 Blaine Avenue, Bedford, OH Zip 44146–2799; tel. 440/735–3900; Sean McKibben, President
Web address: www.uhhsbmc.com

UHHS BROWN MEMORIAL HOSPITAL (O, 25 beds) 158 West Main Road, Conneaut, OH Zip 44030–2039; tel. 440/593–1131; William P. Lawrence, President
Web address: www.uhhs.com

UHHS GEAUGA REGIONAL HOSPITAL (O, 125 beds) 13207 Ravenna Road, Chardon, OH Zip 44024–9012; tel. 440/269–6000; Richard J. Frenchie, President and Chief Executive Officer
Web address: www.uhhsgrh.com

UHHS RICHMOND HEIGHTS HOSPITAL (O, 100 beds) 27100 Chardon Road, Richmond Heights, OH Zip 44143–1198; tel. 440/585–6500; William P. Lawrence, President
Web address: www.uhhsrh.org

UHHS–MEMORIAL HOSPITAL OF GENEVA (O, 25 beds) 870 West Main Street, Geneva, OH Zip 44041–1295; tel. 440/466–1141; Laurie Delgado, President and Chief Executive Officer
Web address: www.uhhs.com/geneva

UNIVERSITY HOSPITALS OF CLEVELAND (O, 580 beds) 11100 Euclid Avenue, Cleveland, OH Zip 44106–2602; tel. 216/844–1000; Fred C. Rothstein, M.D., President and Chief Executive Officer
Web address: www.uhhs.com

Owned, leased, sponsored:	7 hospitals	1278 beds
Contract–managed:	0 hospitals	0 beds
Totals:	7 hospitals	1278 beds

★6405: UNIVERSITY OF CALIFORNIA–SYSTEMWIDE ADMINISTRATION (NP)
1111 Franklin Street, 11th Floor, Oakland, CA Zip 94607–5200; tel. 510/987–9071; William Gurtner, Vice President Clinical Services
(Moderately Centralized Health System)

CALIFORNIA: SANTA MONICA–UCLA MEDICAL CENTER (O, 221 beds) 1250 16th Street, Santa Monica, CA Zip 90404; tel. 310/319–4000; John Stone, Interim Director
Web address: www.healthcare.ucla.edu

For explanation of codes following names, see page B2.
★ Indicates Type III membership in the American Hospital Association.

Section B

UCSF MEDICAL CENTER (O, 574 beds) 500 Parnassus Avenue, San Francisco, CA Zip 94143–0296, Mailing Address: 505 Parnassus Avenue, Box 0296, Zip 94143–0296; tel. 415/476–1000; Mark R. Laret, Chief Executive Officer
Web address: www.ucsfhealth.org

UNIVERSITY OF CALIFORNIA LOS ANGELES MEDICAL CENTER (L, 592 beds) 10833 Le Conte Avenue, Los Angeles, CA Zip 90095–3075; tel. 310/825–9111; David L. Callender, M.D., Director
Web address: www.healthcare.ucla.edu

UNIVERSITY OF CALIFORNIA LOS ANGELES NEUROPSYCHIATRIC HOSPITAL (O, 70 beds) 760 Westwood Plaza, Los Angeles, CA Zip 90095–8353; tel. 310/825–0511; Fawzy I. Fawzy, M.D., Chief Executive Officer
Web address: www.npi.ucla.edu

UNIVERSITY OF CALIFORNIA SAN DIEGO MEDICAL CENTER (O, 485 beds) 200 West Arbor Drive, San Diego, CA Zip 92103–8970; tel. 619/543–6222; Richard Liekweg, Director
Web address: www.health.ucsd.edu

UNIVERSITY OF CALIFORNIA, DAVIS MEDICAL CENTER (O, 526 beds) 2315 Stockton Boulevard, Sacramento, CA Zip 95817–2282; tel. 916/734–2011; Robert E. Chason, Chief Executive Officer
Web address: www.ucdmc.ucdavis.edu

UNIVERSITY OF CALIFORNIA, IRVINE MEDICAL CENTER (O, 383 beds) 101 The City Drive, Orange, CA Zip 92868–3298; tel. 714/456–6011; Ralph Cygan, M.D., Chief Executive Officer
Web address: www.ucihealth.com

Owned, leased, sponsored:	7 hospitals	2851 beds
Contract–managed:	0 hospitals	0 beds
Totals:	7 hospitals	2851 beds

★0216: UNIVERSITY OF MARYLAND MEDICAL SYSTEM (NP) 250 West Pratt Street, Suite 880, Baltimore, MD Zip 21201–1595; tel. 410/328–8667; Edmond F. Notebaert, President and Chief Executive Officer
(Centralized Health System)

MARYLAND: BALTIMORE WASHINGTON MEDICAL CENTER (O, 253 beds) 301 Hospital Drive, Glen Burnie, MD Zip 21061–5899; tel. 410/787–4000; James R. Walker, FACHE, President and Chief Executive Officer
Web address: www.northarundel.org

JAMES LAWRENCE KERNAN HOSPITAL (O, 131 beds) 2200 Kernan Drive, Baltimore, MD Zip 21207–6697; tel. 410/448–2500; James E. Ross, FACHE, Chief Executive Officer
Web address: www.umm.edu

MARYLAND GENERAL HOSPITAL (O, 242 beds) 827 Linden Avenue, Baltimore, MD Zip 21201–4681; tel. 410/225–8000; Colene Daniel, President and Chief Executive Officer
Web address: www.marylandgeneral.org

MT. WASHINGTON PEDIATRIC HOSPITAL (O, 70 beds) 1708 West Rogers Avenue, Baltimore, MD Zip 21209–4537; tel. 410/578–8600; Sheldon J. Stein, President and Chief Executive Officer
Web address: www.mwph.org

UNIVERSITY OF MARYLAND MEDICAL CENTER (O, 607 beds) 22 South Greene Street, Baltimore, MD Zip 21201–1595; tel. 410/328–8667; Jeffrey A. Rivest, President and Chief Executive Officer
Web address: www.umm.edu

UNIVERSITY SPECIALTY HOSPITAL (O, 135 beds) 601 South Charles Street, Baltimore, MD Zip 21230–3898; tel. 410/547–8500; James L. Warner, Vice President Operations
Web address: www.umm.edu/ush/

Owned, leased, sponsored:	6 hospitals	1438 beds
Contract–managed:	0 hospitals	0 beds
Totals:	6 hospitals	1438 beds

0227: UNIVERSITY OF MISSOURI HEALTH CARE (NP) MA204 Medical Science Building, Columbia, MO Zip 65212–0001; tel. 573/884–8738; James H. Ross, Chief Executive Officer
(Moderately Centralized Health System)

MISSOURI: CAPITAL REGION MEDICAL CENTER (O, 134 beds) 1125 Madison Street, Jefferson City, MO Zip 65101–5227, Mailing Address: P.O. Box 1128, Zip 65102–1128; tel. 573/632–5000; Edward F. Farnsworth, FACHE, President
Web address: www.crmc.org

COLUMBIA REGIONAL HOSPITAL (O, 237 beds) 404 Keene Street, Columbia, MO Zip 65201–6698; tel. 573/875–9000; James C. Poehling, Director
Web address: www.columbiaregional.org

COOPER COUNTY MEMORIAL HOSPITAL (C, 49 beds) 17651 B Highway, Boonville, MO Zip 65233–2839, Mailing Address: P.O. Box 88, Zip 65233–0088; tel. 660/882–7461; Matt Waterman, Chief Executive Officer

MISSOURI REHABILITATION CENTER (O, 139 beds) 600 North Main, Mount Vernon, MO Zip 65712–1099; tel. 417/466–3711; Dennis Nicely, Director
Web address: www.muhealth.org/~rehab/

UNIVERSITY OF MISSOURI HOSPITALS AND CLINICS (O, 260 beds) One Hospital Drive, Columbia, MO Zip 65212–0001; tel. 573/882–4141; Cynthia M. Grueber, Director
Web address: www.hsc.missouri.edu/~2000

Owned, leased, sponsored:	4 hospitals	770 beds
Contract–managed:	1 hospital	49 beds
Totals:	5 hospitals	819 beds

0021: UNIVERSITY OF NEW MEXICO (NP) 915 Camino De Salud, Albuquerque, NM Zip 87131–0001; tel. 505/272–5849; R. Philip Eaton, M.D., Vice President Health Sciences
(Moderately Centralized Health System)

NEW MEXICO: CARRIE TINGLEY HOSPITAL (O, 30 beds) 1127 University Boulevard N.E., Albuquerque, NM Zip 87102–1715; tel. 505/272–5200; Barbara Ohm, Executive Director
Web address: www.hospitals.unm.edu/cth/index.shtml

UNIVERSITY HOSPITAL (O, 292 beds) 2211 Lomas Boulevard N.E., Albuquerque, NM Zip 87106–2745; tel. 505/272–2111; Stephen W. McKernan, Chief Executive Officer
Web address: www.unm.edu

Owned, leased, sponsored:	2 hospitals	322 beds
Contract–managed:	0 hospitals	0 beds
Totals:	2 hospitals	322 beds

0168: UNIVERSITY OF PENNSYLVANIA HEALTH SYSTEM (NP) 399 South 34th Street, 21st Floor, Philadelphia, PA Zip 19104–4385; tel. 215/662–2203; Ralph W. Muller, President and Chief Executive Officer
(Centralized Health System)

PENNSYLVANIA: HOSPITAL OF THE UNIVERSITY OF PENNSYLVANIA (O, 624 beds) 3400 Spruce Street, Philadelphia, PA Zip 19104–4283; tel. 215/662–4000; Ralph W. Muller, President and Chief Executive Officer
Web address: www.med.upenn.edu

PENNSYLVANIA HOSPITAL (O, 409 beds) 800 Spruce Street, Philadelphia, PA Zip 19107–6192; tel. 215/829–3000; Timothy O. Morgan, Executive Director
Web address: www.pahosp.com

PRESBYTERIAN MEDICAL CENTER OF THE UNIVERSITY OF PENNSYLVANIA HEALTH SYSTEM (O, 277 beds) 39th and Market Street, Philadelphia, PA Zip 19104–2699; tel. 215/662–8000; Michele M. Volpe, Executive Director and Chief Executive Officer
Web address: www.health.upenn.edu/pmc

Owned, leased, sponsored:	3 hospitals	1310 beds
Contract–managed:	0 hospitals	0 beds
Totals:	3 hospitals	1310 beds

0137: UNIVERSITY OF PITTSBURGH MEDICAL CENTER (NP) 200 Lothrop Street, Pittsburgh, PA Zip 15213; tel. 412/647–2345; Jeffrey A. Romoff, President
(Moderately Centralized Health System)

Section B

For explanation of codes following names, see page B2.
★ Indicates Type III membership in the American Hospital Association.

CHILDREN'S HOSPITAL OF PITTSBURGH OF UPMC (O, 260 beds) 3705 Fifth Avenue at De Soto Street, Pittsburgh, PA Zip 15213–2583; tel. 412/692–5325; Roger A. Oxendale, President and Chief Executive Officer
Web address: www.chp.edu

MAGEE–WOMENS HOSPITAL OF UPMC (O, 205 beds) 300 Halket Street, Pittsburgh, PA Zip 15213–3180; tel. 412/641–1000; Leslie C. Davis, President
Web address: www.magee.edu

UPMC BEDFORD MEMORIAL (O, 27 beds) 10455 Lincoln Highway, Everett, PA Zip 15537–7046; tel. 814/623–6161; Roger P. Winn, President
Web address: www.bedford.org

UPMC BRADDOCK (O, 133 beds) 400 Holland Avenue, Braddock, PA Zip 15104–1598; tel. 412/636–5000; Mark Sevco, President
Web address: www.upmc.edu

UPMC HORIZON (O, 212 beds) Greenville, PA Dean Eckenrode, Chief Executive Officer
Web address: www.horizon.upmc.com

UPMC LEE REGIONAL (O, 209 beds) 320 Main Street, Johnstown, PA Zip 15901–1694; tel. 814/533–0123; Roger P. Winn, President
Web address: www.upmc.edu/lee

UPMC MCKEESPORT (O, 181 beds) 1500 Fifth Avenue, McKeesport, PA Zip 15132–2482; tel. 412/664–2000; Ronald H. Ott, President
Web address: www.mckeesport.upmc.com

UPMC NORTHWEST (O, 209 beds) 100 Fairfield Drive, Seneca, PA Zip 16346; tel. 814/676–7600; Neil E. Todhunter, President
Web address: www.upmc.com

UPMC PASSAVANT (O, 258 beds) 9100 Babcock Boulevard, Pittsburgh, PA Zip 15237–5815; tel. 412/367–6700; Teresa A. Petrick, President
Web address: www.upmc.edu/passavant

UPMC PASSAVANT CRANBERRY (O, 185 beds) One St. Francis Way, Cranberry, PA Zip 16066; tel. 724/772–5300; Teresa A. Petrick, Chief Executive Officer

UPMC PRESBYTERIAN (O, 1412 beds) 200 Lothrop Street, Pittsburgh, PA Zip 15213–2585; tel. 412/647–2345; Elizabeth B. Concordia, President
Web address: www.upmc.edu

UPMC SOUTH SIDE (O, 126 beds) 2000 Mary Street, Pittsburgh, PA Zip 15203–2095; tel. 412/488–5550; Nancy Magee, President
Web address: www.upmc.edu/southside/

UPMC ST. MARGARET (O, 208 beds) 815 Freeport Road, Pittsburgh, PA Zip 15215–3399; tel. 412/784–4000; David T. Martin, President
Web address: www.upmc.edu/stmargaret

Owned, leased, sponsored:	13 hospitals	3625 beds
Contract–managed:	0 hospitals	0 beds
Totals:	13 hospitals	3625 beds

★**0057:** **UNIVERSITY OF SOUTH ALABAMA HOSPITALS** (NP) 5600 Girby Road, Mobile, AL Zip 36693–3398; tel. 251/471–7000; Stanley K. Hammack, Associate Vice President Hospital Affairs/Chief Executive Officer
(Independent Hospital System)

ALABAMA: UNIVERSITY OF SOUTH ALABAMA KNOLLWOOD PARK HOSPITAL (O, 88 beds) 5600 Girby Road, Mobile, AL Zip 36693–3398; tel. 251/660–5120; Thomas J. Gibson, Administrator
Web address: www.southalabama.edu/usakph/index.html

UNIVERSITY OF SOUTH ALABAMA MEDICAL CENTER (O, 112 beds) 2451 Fillingim Street, Mobile, AL Zip 36617–2293; tel. 251/471–7000; Beth Anderson, Administrator
Web address: www.usahospitals.org

USA CHILDREN'S AND WOMEN'S HOSPITAL (O, 185 beds) 1700 Center Street, Mobile, AL Zip 36604–3301; tel. 251/415–1000; Becky DeVillier, Administrator
Web address: www.southalabama.edu/usacwh

Owned, leased, sponsored:	3 hospitals	385 beds
Contract–managed:	0 hospitals	0 beds
Totals:	3 hospitals	385 beds

0033: **UNIVERSITY OF TEXAS SYSTEM** (NP) 601 Colorado Street, Austin, TX Zip 78701–2982; tel. 512/499–4224; James C. Guckian, M.D., Executive Vice Chancellor
(Moderately Centralized Health System)

TEXAS: HARRIS COUNTY PSYCHIATRIC CENTER (O, 203 beds) 2800 South MacGregor Way, Houston, TX Zip 77021–1000, Mailing Address: P.O. Box 20249, Zip 77225–0249; tel. 713/741–5000; Robert W. Guynn, M.D., Executive Director
Web address: www.uth.tmc.edu

UNIVERSITY OF TEXAS HEALTH CENTER AT TYLER (O, 109 beds) 11937 Highway 271, Tyler, TX Zip 75708–3154; tel. 903/877–3451; Kirk A. Calhoun, M.D., President
Web address: www.uthct.edu

UNIVERSITY OF TEXAS M. D. ANDERSON CANCER CENTER (O, 482 beds) 1515 Holcombe Boulevard, Box 91, Houston, TX Zip 77030–4095; tel. 713/792–2121; John Mendelsohn, M.D., President
Web address: www.mdanderson.org

UNIVERSITY OF TEXAS MEDICAL BRANCH HOSPITALS (O, 764 beds) 301 University Boulevard, Galveston, TX Zip 77555–0518; tel. 409/772–1011; Karen H. Sexton, R.N., Ph.D., Vice President and Chief Executive Officer
Web address: www.utmb.edu

Owned, leased, sponsored:	4 hospitals	1558 beds
Contract–managed:	0 hospitals	0 beds
Totals:	4 hospitals	1558 beds

★**0038:** **UPPER CHESAPEAKE HEALTH SYSTEM** (NP) 520 Upper Chesapeake Drive, Suite 405, Bel Air, MD Zip 21014–4324; tel. 443/643–3303; Lyle Ernest Sheldon, FACHE, President and Chief Executive Officer
(Independent Hospital System)

MARYLAND: HARFORD MEMORIAL HOSPITAL (O, 102 beds) 501 South Union Avenue, Havre De Grace, MD Zip 21078–3493; tel. 443/843–5000; Lyle Ernest Sheldon, FACHE, President and Chief Executive Officer
Web address: www.uchs.org

UPPER CHESAPEAKE MEDICAL CENTER (O, 152 beds) 500 Upper Chesapeake Drive, Bel Air, MD Zip 21014–4324; tel. 443/643–1000; Lyle Ernest Sheldon, FACHE, President and Chief Executive Officer
Web address: www.uchs.org

Owned, leased, sponsored:	2 hospitals	254 beds
Contract–managed:	0 hospitals	0 beds
Totals:	2 hospitals	254 beds

★**0232:** **UT SOUTHWESTERN MEDICAL CENTER AT DALLAS** (NP) 5151 Harry Hines Boulevard, Dallas, TX Zip 75235–7786; tel. 214/590–3000; Sharon L. Riley, Chief Executive Officer
(Centralized Health System)

TEXAS: ST. PAUL UNIVERSITY HOSPITAL (O, 324 beds) 5909 Harry Hines Boulevard, Dallas, TX Zip 75235–6285; tel. 214/879–1000; Sharon L. Riley, President
Web address: www.stpauldallas.com

UNIVERSITY OF TEXAS SOUTHWESTERN MEDICAL CENTER (O, 152 beds) 5151 Harry Hines Boulevard, Dallas, TX Zip 75390–9265; tel. 214/590–3000; Sharon L. Riley, Chief Executive Officer
Web address: www.utsouthwestern.edu

Owned, leased, sponsored:	2 hospitals	476 beds
Contract–managed:	0 hospitals	0 beds
Totals:	2 hospitals	476 beds

★**0043:** **VALLEY HEALTH SYSTEM** (NP) 1117 East Devonshire Avenue, Hemet, CA Zip 92543; tel. 909/652–2811; Susan Ballard, Chief Executive Officer
(Independent Hospital System)

For explanation of codes following names, see page B2.
★ Indicates Type III membership in the American Hospital Association.

Section B

CALIFORNIA: HEMET VALLEY MEDICAL CENTER (O, 356 beds) 1117 East Devonshire Avenue, Hemet, CA Zip 92543–3083; tel. 909/652–2811; Lynda Wills, Interim Administrator
Web address: www.valleyhealthsystem.com

MENIFEE VALLEY MEDICAL CENTER (O, 84 beds) 28400 McCall Boulevard, Sun City, CA Zip 92585–9537; tel. 951/679–8888; Kim Eastman, R.N., Administrator

MORENO VALLEY COMMUNITY HOSPITAL (O, 101 beds) 27300 Iris Avenue, Moreno Valley, CA Zip 92555–4800; tel. 951/243–0811; Corey A. Seale, Administrator
Web address: www.valleyhealthsystem.com

Owned, leased, sponsored:	3 hospitals	541 beds
Contract–managed:	0 hospitals	0 beds
Totals:	3 hospitals	541 beds

★0128: VALLEY HEALTH SYSTEM (NP)
190 Campus Boulevard, Suite 220, Winchester, VA Zip 22601, Mailing Address: P.O. Box 3340, Zip 22604–1334; tel. 540/536–8024; Michael J. Halseth, President and Chief Executive Officer
(Moderately Centralized Health System)

VIRGINIA: SHENANDOAH MEMORIAL HOSPITAL (O, 23 beds) 759 South Main Street, Woodstock, VA Zip 22664–1127; tel. 540/459–1100; Floyd Heater, Chief Executive Officer
Web address: www.shenmemhosp.com

WARREN MEMORIAL HOSPITAL (O, 166 beds) 1000 Shenandoah Avenue, Front Royal, VA Zip 22630–3598; tel. 540/636–0300; Patrick B. Nolan, President and Chief Executive Officer
Web address: www.valleyhealthlink.com

WINCHESTER MEDICAL CENTER (O, 411 beds) 1840 Amherst Street, Winchester, VA Zip 22601–2540, Mailing Address: P.O. Box 3340, Zip 22604–3340; tel. 540/536–8000; James L. Woodward, President and Chief Administrative Officer
Web address: www.valleyhealthlink.com

WEST VIRGINIA: MORGAN COUNTY WAR MEMORIAL HOSPITAL (C, 41 beds) 109 War Memorial Drive, Berkeley Springs, WV Zip 25411–1718; tel. 304/258–1234; John H. Borg, Administrator
Web address: www.warmemorialhospital.com

Owned, leased, sponsored:	3 hospitals	600 beds
Contract–managed:	1 hospital	41 beds
Totals:	4 hospitals	641 beds

0193: VANGUARD HEALTH SYSTEM (IO)
20 Burton Hills Boulevard, Suite 10, Nashville, TN Zip 37215; tel. 615/665–6000; Charles N. Martin Jr, Chairman and Chief Executive Officer
(Moderately Centralized Health System)

ARIZONA: ARROWHEAD COMMUNITY HOSPITAL AND MEDICAL CENTER (O, 115 beds) 18701 North 67th Avenue, Glendale, AZ Zip 85308–5722; tel. 623/561–1000; Jonathan W. Bartlett, Chief Executive Officer
Web address: www.baptisthealth.com

MARYVALE HOSPITAL MEDICAL CENTER (O, 175 beds) 5102 West Campbell Avenue, Phoenix, AZ Zip 85031–1799; tel. 623/848–5000; Gregory Padilla, Chief Executive Officer
Web address: www.maryvalehospital.com

PARADISE VALLEY HOSPITAL (O, 126 beds) 3929 East Bell Road, Phoenix, AZ Zip 85032–2196; tel. 602/923–5000; John L. Harrington Jr, FACHE, President and Chief Executive Officer
Web address: www.paradisevalleyhospital.com

PHOENIX BAPTIST HOSPITAL (O, 201 beds) 2000 West Bethany Home Road, Phoenix, AZ Zip 85015–2110; tel. 602/249–0212; Dennis M. Knox, Chief Executive Officer
Web address: www.baptisthealth.com

PHOENIX MEMORIAL HOSPITAL (O, 159 beds) 1201 South Seventh Avenue, Phoenix, AZ Zip 85007–3995; tel. 602/258–5111; Sonja Hagel, Vice President Operations and Chief Executive Officer
Web address: www.phxmemorialhospital.com

CALIFORNIA: HUNTINGTON BEACH HOSPITAL (O, 102 beds) 17772 Beach Boulevard, Huntington Beach, CA Zip 92647–6819; tel. 714/842–1473; Mary Botticella, Chief Executive Officer
Web address: www.hbhospital.com

LA PALMA INTERCOMMUNITY HOSPITAL (O, 141 beds) 7901 Walker Street, La Palma, CA Zip 90623–1722, Mailing Address: P.O. Box 5850, Buena Park, Zip 90622–5850; tel. 714/670–7400; Patricia L. Wolfram, R.N., Chief Executive Officer
Web address: www.lapalmaintercommunityhospital.com

WEST ANAHEIM MEDICAL CENTER (O, 219 beds) 3033 West Orange Avenue, Anaheim, CA Zip 92804–3184; tel. 714/827–3000; David K. Culberson, Chief Executive Officer
Web address: www.westanaheimmedctr.com

ILLINOIS: LOUIS A. WEISS MEMORIAL HOSPITAL (O, 192 beds) 4646 North Marine Drive, Chicago, IL Zip 60640–1501; tel. 773/878–8700; Tracy A. Rogers, Chief Executive Officer
Web address: www.weisshospital.com

MACNEAL HOSPITAL (O, 320 beds) 3249 South Oak Park Avenue, Berwyn, IL Zip 60402–0715; tel. 708/783–9100; Brooks Turkel, Chief Executive Officer
Web address: www.macneal.com

MASSACHUSETTS: METROWEST MEDICAL CENTER (O, 372 beds) 115 Lincoln Street, Framingham, MA Zip 01702–6342; tel. 508/383–1000; Patrick F. Mutch, Chief Executive Officer
Web address: www.mwmc.com

TEXAS: BAPTIST MEDICAL CENTER (O, 375 beds) 111 Dallas Street, San Antonio, TX Zip 78205–1230; tel. 210/297–7000; Keith L. Swinney, Chief Executive Officer
Web address: www.baptisthealth.com/bmc.asp

NORTH CENTRAL BAPTIST HOSPITAL (O, 126 beds) 520 Madison Oak Drive, San Antonio, TX Zip 78258–3912; tel. 210/297–4000; Mark W. Clayton, Chief Executive Officer
Web address: www.baptisthealthsystem.com

NORTHEAST BAPTIST HOSPITAL (O, 221 beds) 8811 Village Drive, San Antonio, TX Zip 78217–5440; tel. 210/297–2000; Bruce F. Buchanan, FACHE, Chief Executive Officer
Web address: www.baptisthealth.org

SOUTHEAST BAPTIST HOSPITAL (O, 146 beds) 4214 East Southcross Boulevard, San Antonio, TX Zip 78222–3740; tel. 210/297–3000; Richard Marsh, Chief Executive officer
Web address: www.baptisthealth.org/SBH.asp

ST. LUKE'S BAPTIST HOSPITAL (O, 248 beds) 7930 Floyd Curl Drive, San Antonio, TX Zip 78229–0100; tel. 210/297–5000; Dominic J. Dominguez, Chief Executive Officer
Web address: www.baptisthealthsystem.org

Owned, leased, sponsored:	16 hospitals	3238 beds
Contract–managed:	0 hospitals	0 beds
Totals:	16 hospitals	3238 beds

5435: VIA CHRISTI HEALTH SYSTEM (CC)
3720 East Bayley, Wichita, KS Zip 67218–3002; tel. 316/858–4900; Kevin P. Conlin, President and Chief Executive Officer
(Centralized Health System)

KANSAS: KANSAS SURGERY AND RECOVERY CENTER 2770 North Webb Road, Wichita, KS Zip 67226–8112; tel. 316/634–0090; Ely Bartal, M.D., Administrator and Chief Executive Officer
Web address: www.ksrc.org

MERCY REGIONAL HEALTH CENTER (O, 121 beds) 1823 College Avenue, Manhattan, KS Zip 66502, Mailing Address: P.O. Box 1289, Zip 66505–1289; tel. 785/776–3322; Richard L. Allen, President and Chief Executive Officer
Web address: www.mercyregional.org

MT. CARMEL REGIONAL MEDICAL CENTER (O, 141 beds) 1102 East Centennial Drive, Pittsburg, KS Zip 66762–6643; tel. 620/231–6100; John Daniel Lingor, President and Chief Executive Officer
Web address: www.mtcarmel.org

VIA CHRISTI REGIONAL MEDICAL CENTER (O, 811 beds) 929 North St. Francis Street, Wichita, KS Zip 67214–3882; tel. 316/268–5000; Larry P. Schumacher, R.N., President and Chief Executive Officer
Web address: www.via–christi.org

Section B

For explanation of codes following names, see page B2.
★ Indicates Type III membership in the American Hospital Association.

VIA CHRISTI REHABILITATION CENTER (O, 60 beds) 1151 North Rock Road, Wichita, KS Zip 67206–1262; tel. 316/634–3400; Laurie Labarca, Chief Operating Officer
Web address: www.via–christi.org

VIA CHRISTI RIVERSIDE MEDICAL CENTER (S, 88 beds) 2622 West Central Avenue, Wichita, KS Zip 67203–4902; tel. 316/946–5000; John Coslett, Administrator
Web address: www.via–christiriverside.org

OKLAHOMA: VIA CHRISTI OKLAHOMA REGIONAL MEDICAL CENTER (O, 97 beds) 1900 North 14th Street, Ponca City, OK Zip 74601–2035, Mailing Address: P.O. Box 1270, Zip 74602–1270; tel. 580/765–3321; W. Charles Waters, President and Chief Executive Officer
Web address: www.viachristiok.org

Owned, leased, sponsored:	6 hospitals	1318 beds
Contract–managed:	0 hospitals	0 beds
Totals:	6 hospitals	1318 beds

0046: VIAHEALTH (NP)

1425 Portland Avenue, 5th Floor, Rochester, NY Zip 14621; tel. 585/922–4437; Samuel R. Huston, President and Chief Executive Officer
(Centralized Health System)

NEW YORK: NEWARK–WAYNE COMMUNITY HOSPITAL (O, 275 beds) Driving Park Avenue, Newark, NY Zip 14513, Mailing Address: P.O. Box 111, Zip 14513–0111; tel. 315/332–2022; W. Neil Stroman, Administrator
Web address: www.viahealth.org

ROCHESTER GENERAL HOSPITAL (O, 492 beds) 1425 Portland Avenue, Rochester, NY Zip 14621–3099; tel. 585/922–4000; Samuel R. Huston, President and Chief Executive Officer
Web address: www.viahealth.org/

Owned, leased, sponsored:	2 hospitals	767 beds
Contract–managed:	0 hospitals	0 beds
Totals:	2 hospitals	767 beds

0299: VIBRA HEALTHCARE (IO)

4550 Lena Drive, Suite 225, Mechanicsburg, PA Zip 17055; tel. 717/591–5700; Brad Hollinger, Chairman and Chief Executive Officer
(Independent Hospital System)

CALIFORNIA: KENTFIELD REHABILITATION HOSPITAL (O, 57 beds) 1125 Sir Francis Drake Boulevard, San Rafael, CA Zip 94904–1455; tel. 415/456–9680; Ann Gors, Chief Executive Officer
Web address: www.nbhd.org

SAN JOAQUIN VALLEY REHABILITATION HOSPITAL (O, 38 beds) 7173 North Sharon Avenue, Fresno, CA Zip 93720–3329; tel. 559/436–3600; Edward C. Palacios, R.N., Chief Executive Officer
Web address: www.sjvrehab.com

COLORADO: NORTH VALLEY REHABILITATION HOSPITAL (O, 117 beds) 8451 Pearl Street, Thornton, CO Zip 80229–4804; tel. 303/288–3000; Walter Sackett, Chief Executive Officer
Web address: www.mediplexhospital.com

KENTUCKY: SOUTHERN KENTUCKY REHABILITATION HOSPITAL (O, 60 beds) 1300 Campbell Lane, Bowling Green, KY Zip 42104–4162; tel. 270/782–6900; Joanna Thomas, Chief Executive Officer
Web address: www.mediplex–bowlinggreen.com

MASSACHUSETTS: NEW BEDFORD REHABILITATION HOSPITAL (O, 90 beds) 4499 Acushnet Avenue, New Bedford, MA Zip 02745; tel. 508/995–6900; Edward B. Leary, Chief Executive Officer

NEW JERSEY: MARLTON REHABILITATION HOSPITAL (O, 46 beds) 92 Brick Road, Marlton, NJ Zip 08053–2020; tel. 856/988–8778; Christopher Gillies, Chief Executive Officer

OHIO: ST. FRANCIS HEALTH CARE CENTRE (C, 184 beds) 401 North Broadway, Green Springs, OH Zip 44836–9653; tel. 419/639–2626; Kim D. Eicher, Chief Executive Officer
Web address: www.sfhcc.org

Owned, leased, sponsored:	6 hospitals	408 beds
Contract–managed:	1 hospital	184 beds
Totals:	7 hospitals	592 beds

0012: VIRGINIA DEPARTMENT OF MENTAL HEALTH (NP)

1220 Bank Street, Richmond, VA Zip 23219, Mailing Address: P.O. Box 1797, Zip 23218–1797; tel. 804/786–3921; James S. Reinhard, M.D., Commissioner
(Independent Hospital System)

VIRGINIA: CATAWBA HOSPITAL (O, 110 beds) 5525 Catawba Hospital Drive, Catawba, VA Zip 24070–2115, Mailing Address: P.O. Box 200, Zip 24070–0200; tel. 540/375–4200; Jack L. Wood, Director
Web address: www.catawba.state.va.us

CENTRAL STATE HOSPITAL (O, 277 beds) 26317 West Washington Street, Petersburg, VA Zip 23803, Mailing Address: P.O. Box 4030, Zip 23803–4030; tel. 804/524–7000; Charles S. Davis, M.D., Ph.D., Director
Web address: www.csh.state.va.us

CENTRAL VIRGINIA TRAINING CENTER (O, 1112 beds) 210 East Colony Road, Madison Heights, VA Zip 24572–2005, Mailing Address: P.O. Box 1098, Lynchburg, Zip 24505–1098; tel. 434/947–6326; Denise D. Micheletti, Acting Director
Web address: www.cvtc.state.va.us

COMMONWEALTH CENTER FOR CHILDREN AND ADOLESCENTS (O, 60 beds) 1355 Richmond Road, Staunton, VA Zip 24401–1091, Mailing Address: Box 4000, Zip 24402–4000; tel. 540/332–2100; William J. Tuell, MSN, Facility Director
Web address: www.ccca.state.va.us

EASTERN STATE HOSPITAL (O, 488 beds) 4601 Ironbound Road, Williamsburg, VA Zip 23187–8791, Mailing Address: P.O. Box 8791, Zip 23187–8791; tel. 757/253–5161; John M. Favret, Director
Web address: www.esh.state.va.us

NORTHERN VIRGINIA MENTAL HEALTH INSTITUTE (O, 137 beds) 3302 Gallows Road, Falls Church, VA Zip 22042–3398; tel. 703/207–7110; Lynn Delacy, R.N., MS, Facility Director
Web address: www.nvmhi.state.va.us

PIEDMONT GERIATRIC HOSPITAL (O, 150 beds) 5001 East Patrick Henry Highway, Burkeville, VA Zip 23922–0427, Mailing Address: P.O. Box 427, Zip 23922–0427; tel. 434/767–4401; Stephen M. Herrick, Ph.D., Acting Director
Web address: www.pgh.state.va.us

SOUTHERN VIRGINIA MENTAL HEALTH INSTITUTE (O, 80 beds) 382 Taylor Drive, Danville, VA Zip 24541–4023; tel. 434/799–6220; David M. Lyon, Director
Web address: www.svmhi.dmhmrsas.virginia.gov

SOUTHWESTERN VIRGINIA MENTAL HEALTH INSTITUTE (O, 266 beds) 340 Bagley Circle, Marion, VA Zip 24354–3390; tel. 276/783–1200; Cynthia McClure, Ph.D., Director

WESTERN STATE HOSPITAL (O, 488 beds) 1301 Richmond Avenue, Staunton, VA Zip 24401–9146, Mailing Address: P.O. Box 2500, Zip 24402–2500; tel. 540/332–8000; Jack W. Barber, M.D., Director
Web address: www.wsh.state.va.us

Owned, leased, sponsored:	10 hospitals	3168 beds
Contract–managed:	0 hospitals	0 beds
Totals:	10 hospitals	3168 beds

6725: VIRTUA HEALTH (NP)

94 Brick Road, Suite 200, Marlton, NJ Zip 08053; tel. 856/355–0010; Richard P. Miller, President and Chief Executive Officer
(Moderately Centralized Health System)

NEW JERSEY: VIRTUA MEMORIAL HOSPITAL BURLINGTON COUNTY (O, 296 beds) 175 Madison Avenue, Mount Holly, NJ Zip 08060–2099; tel. 609/267–0700; Stephen Kolesk, M.D., Vice President and Chief Operating Officer
Web address: www.virtua.org

For explanation of codes following names, see page B2.
★ Indicates Type III membership in the American Hospital Association.

VIRTUA WEST JERSEY HOSPITAL–BERLIN (O, 95 beds) 100 Townsend Avenue, Berlin, NJ Zip 08009–9035; tel. 856/322–3000; Gary L. Long, Vice President and Chief Operating Officer
Web address: www.virtua.org

VIRTUA WEST JERSEY HOSPITAL–MARLTON (O, 165 beds) 90 Brick Road, Marlton, NJ Zip 08053–9697; tel. 856/355–6000; Ellen Guarnieri, Vice President and Chief Operating Officer
Web address: www.virtua.org

VIRTUA WEST JERSEY HOSPITAL–VOORHEES (O, 260 beds) 101 Carnie Boulevard, Voorhees, NJ Zip 08043–1597; tel. 856/325–3000; Michael S. Kotzen, Vice President and Chief Operating Officer
Web address: www.virtua.org

Owned, leased, sponsored:	4 hospitals	816 beds
Contract–managed:	0 hospitals	0 beds
Totals:	4 hospitals	816 beds

★**6705: WAKEMED** (NP)
3000 New Bern Avenue, Raleigh, NC Zip 27610; tel. 919/350–8000; William K. Atkinson II, Ph.D., President and Chief Executive Officer
(Moderately Centralized Health System)

NORTH CAROLINA: WAKEMED CARY HOSPITAL (O, 150 beds) 1900 Kildaire Farm Road, Cary, NC Zip 27511; tel. 919/233–2300;
Web address: www.wakemed.org

WAKEMED RALEIGH CAMPUS (O, 602 beds) 3000 New Bern Avenue, Raleigh, NC Zip 27610–1295; tel. 919/350–8000; William K. Atkinson II, Ph.D., President and Chief Executive Officer
Web address: www.wakemed.org

Owned, leased, sponsored:	2 hospitals	752 beds
Contract–managed:	0 hospitals	0 beds
Totals:	2 hospitals	752 beds

0327: WARM SPRINGS REHABILITATION SYSTEM (NP)
909 N.E. Loop 410, San Antonio, TX Zip 78209; tel. 210/616–0100

TEXAS: VICTORIA WARM SPRINGS REHABILITATION HOSPITAL (O, 22 beds) 102 Medical Drive, Victoria, TX Zip 77904; tel. 210/829–0009; Linda Vaclavik, Administrator
Web address: www.warmsprings.org

WARM SPRINGS REHABILITATION HOSPITAL (O, 22 beds) 2606 Hospital Boulevard, Corpus Christi, TX Zip 78405–1818; tel. 361/888–4458; Patrick Flannery, Administrator
Web address: www.warmsprings.org

WARM SPRINGS REHABILITATION HOSPITAL (O, 64 beds) 5101 Medical Drive, San Antonio, TX Zip 78229–6098; tel. 210/616–0100; Rick Marek, President and Chief Executive Officer
Web address: www.warmsprings.org

WARM SPRINGS SPECIALTY HOSPITAL (O, 36 beds) 200 Memorial Drive, Luling, TX Zip 78648; tel. 830/875–8400; Brenda Miles, Administrator
Web address: www.warmsprings.org

Owned, leased, sponsored:	4 hospitals	144 beds
Contract–managed:	0 hospitals	0 beds
Totals:	4 hospitals	144 beds

2625: WASHOE HEALTH SYSTEM (NP)
77 Pringle Way, Reno, NV Zip 89502–1474; tel. 775/982–4100; Jim Miller, President and Chief Executive Officer
(Centralized Physician/Insurance Health System)

NEVADA: WASHOE MEDICAL CENTER (O, 529 beds) 77 Pringle Way, Reno, NV Zip 89502–1474; tel. 775/982–4100; James I. Miller, President and Chief Executive Officer
Web address: www.washoehealth.com

WASHOE MEDICAL CENTER REHABILITATION HOSPITAL (O, 62 beds) 555 Gould Street, Reno, NV Zip 89502–1449; tel. 775/348–5500; Michael R. Klepin, Administrator
Web address: www.washoehealth.com

WASHOE MEDICAL CENTER SOUTH MEADOWS (O, 36 beds) 10101 Double R Boulevard, Reno, NV Zip 89511; tel. 775/982–7000; Alan C. Olive, Chief Executive Officer

Owned, leased, sponsored:	3 hospitals	627 beds
Contract–managed:	0 hospitals	0 beds
Totals:	3 hospitals	627 beds

0188: WELLMONT HEALTH SYSTEM (NP)
1905 American Way, Kingsport, TN Zip 37662–0224; tel. 423/230–8200; Richard Salluzo, M.D., President and Chief Executive Officer
(Centralized Physician/Insurance Health System)

TENNESSEE: WELLMONT BRISTOL REGIONAL MEDICAL CENTER (O, 348 beds) 1 Medical Park Boulevard, Bristol, TN Zip 37620–7434; tel. 423/844–1121; Barton A. Hove, President
Web address: www.wellmont.org

WELLMONT HAWKINS COUNTY MEMORIAL HOSPITAL (L, 50 beds) 851 Locust Street, Rogersville, TN Zip 37857–2407, Mailing Address: P.O. Box 130, Zip 37857–0130; tel. 423/921–7000; Fred L. Pelle, President
Web address: www.wellmont.org

WELLMONT HOLSTON VALLEY MEDICAL CENTER (O, 347 beds) 130 West Ravine Street, Kingsport, TN Zip 37660, Mailing Address: P.O. Box 238, Zip 37662–0238; tel. 423/224–4000; E. Berton Whitaker, President and Chief Executive Officer
Web address: www.wellmont.org

VIRGINIA: WELLMONT LONESOME PINE HOSPITAL (O, 60 beds) 1990 Holton Avenue East, Big Stone Gap, VA Zip 24219–0230; tel. 276/523–3111; Robert G. Polahar, President
Web address: www.wellmont.org

Owned, leased, sponsored:	4 hospitals	805 beds
Contract–managed:	0 hospitals	0 beds
Totals:	4 hospitals	805 beds

★**0068: WELLSPAN HEALTH** (NP)
45 Monument Road, Suite 200, York, PA Zip 17403; tel. 717/851–2121; Bruce M. Bartels, President
(Centralized Physician/Insurance Health System)

PENNSYLVANIA: GETTYSBURG HOSPITAL (O, 95 beds) 147 Gettys Street, Gettysburg, PA Zip 17325–2534; tel. 717/334–2121; Kevin H. Mosser, M.D., Chief Executive Officer
Web address: www.wellspan.org

YORK HOSPITAL (O, 460 beds) 1001 South George Street, York, PA Zip 17405–3645; tel. 717/851–2345; Richard L. Seim, President and Chief Executive Officer
Web address: www.wellspan.org

Owned, leased, sponsored:	2 hospitals	555 beds
Contract–managed:	0 hospitals	0 beds
Totals:	2 hospitals	555 beds

★**0995: WELLSTAR HEALTH SYSTEM** (NP)
805 Sandy Plains Road, Marietta, GA Zip 30066; tel. 770/792–5012; Robert A. Lipson, M.D., President and Chief Executive Officer
(Centralized Health System)

GEORGIA: WELLSTAR COBB HOSPITAL (O, 342 beds) 3950 Austell Road, Austell, GA Zip 30106–1121; tel. 770/732–4000; Randy Cook, Vice President and Administrator
Web address: www.wellstar.org

WELLSTAR DOUGLAS HOSPITAL (O, 71 beds) 8954 Hospital Drive, Douglasville, GA Zip 30134–2282; tel. 770/949–1500; Michael Poore, Vice President and Administrator
Web address: www.wellstar.org

WELLSTAR KENNESTONE HOSPITAL (O, 487 beds) 677 Church Street, Marietta, GA Zip 30060–1148; tel. 770/793–5000; Linda A. Clark, Senior Vice President and Administrator
Web address: www.wellstar.org

Section B

For explanation of codes following names, see page B2.
★ Indicates Type III membership in the American Hospital Association.

WELLSTAR PAULDING HOSPITAL (O, 216 beds) 600 West Memorial Drive, Dallas, GA Zip 30132–1335; tel. 770/445–4411; John Law, Site Administrator
Web address: www.wellstar.org

WELLSTAR WINDY HILL HOSPITAL (O, 29 beds) 2540 Windy Hill Road, Marietta, GA Zip 30067–8632; tel. 770/644–1000; Lou Little, Vice President and Administrator
Web address: www.wellstar.org

Owned, leased, sponsored:	5 hospitals	1145 beds
Contract–managed:	0 hospitals	0 beds
Totals:	5 hospitals	1145 beds

★0199:   WEST PENN ALLEGHENY HEALTH SYSTEM (NP)
4800 Friendship Avenue, Pittsburgh, PA Zip 15224; tel. 412/578–4703; Jerry J. Fedele, President and Chief Executive Officer
(Moderately Centralized Health System)

PENNSYLVANIA: ALLE–KISKI MEDICAL CENTER (O, 250 beds) 1301 Carlisle Street, Natrona Heights, PA Zip 15065–1192; tel. 724/224–5100; Cindy K. Schamp, President
Web address: www.wpahs.org

ALLEGHENY GENERAL HOSPITAL (O, 426 beds) 320 East North Avenue, Pittsburgh, PA Zip 15212–4756; tel. 412/359–3131; Connie M. Cibrone, President and Chief Executive Officer
Web address: www.wpahs.org

CANONSBURG GENERAL HOSPITAL (O, 104 beds) 100 Medical Boulevard, Canonsburg, PA Zip 15317–9762; tel. 724/745–6100; Kim Malinky, President and Chief Executive Officer
Web address: www.wpahs.org

FORBES REGIONAL HOSPITAL (O, 231 beds) 2570 Haymaker Road, Monroeville, PA Zip 15146–3592; tel. 412/858–2000; Thomas J. Senker, President and Chief Executive Officer
Web address: www.wpahs.org

WESTERN PENNSYLVANIA HOSPITAL (O, 479 beds) 4800 Friendship Avenue, Pittsburgh, PA Zip 15224–1722; tel. 412/578–5000; James M. Collins, President and Chief Executive Officer
Web address: www.wpahs.org

Owned, leased, sponsored:	5 hospitals	1490 beds
Contract–managed:	0 hospitals	0 beds
Totals:	5 hospitals	1490 beds

★0004:   WEST TENNESSEE HEALTHCARE (NP)
708 West Forest Avenue, Jackson, TN Zip 38301–3901; tel. 731/425–5000; James T. Moss, President
(Centralized Physician/Insurance Health System)

TENNESSEE: BOLIVAR GENERAL HOSPITAL (O, 37 beds) 650 Nuckolls Road, Bolivar, TN Zip 38008–1532, Mailing Address: P.O. Box 509, Zip 38008–0509; tel. 731/658–3100; Ruby Kirby, Administrator
Web address: www.wth.net

CAMDEN GENERAL HOSPITAL (O, 30 beds) 175 Hospital Drive, Camden, TN Zip 38320–1617; tel. 731/584–6135; Tina Prescott, Administrator
Web address: www.wth.net

GIBSON GENERAL HOSPITAL (O, 34 beds) 200 Hospital Drive, Trenton, TN Zip 38382–3313; tel. 731/855–7900; Sherry Scruggs, Administrator
Web address: www.wth.net

HUMBOLDT GENERAL HOSPITAL (O, 42 beds) 3525 Chere Carol Road, Humboldt, TN Zip 38343–3699; tel. 731/784–0301; Bill Kail, Administrator
Web address: www.wth.net

JACKSON–MADISON COUNTY GENERAL HOSPITAL (O, 635 beds) 708 West Forest Avenue, Jackson, TN Zip 38301–3956; tel. 731/425–5000; Jim Dockins, Chief Executive Officer
Web address: www.wth.org

MILAN GENERAL HOSPITAL (O, 41 beds) 4039 South Highland, Milan, TN Zip 38358–3167; tel. 731/686–1591; John M. Carruth, Administrator
Web address: www.wth.net

PATHWAYS OF TENNESSEE (O, 23 beds) 238 Summar Drive, Jackson, TN Zip 38301–3982; tel. 731/935–8200; Kelly R. Yenawine, Executive Director
Web address: www.wth.net

Owned, leased, sponsored:	7 hospitals	842 beds
Contract–managed:	0 hospitals	0 beds
Totals:	7 hospitals	842 beds

★0119:   WEST VIRGINIA UNITED HEALTH SYSTEM (NP)
1000 Technology Drive, Sutie 2320, Fairmont, WV Zip 26554, Mailing Address: 1000 Technology Drive, Suite 2320, Zip 26554; tel. 304/368–2700; J. Thomas Jones, President and Chief Executive Officer
(Centralized Physician/Insurance Health System)

WEST VIRGINIA: CITY HOSPITAL (O, 143 beds) Dry Run Road, Martinsburg, WV Zip 25401, Mailing Address: P.O. Box 1418, Zip 25402–1418; tel. 304/264–1000; Jon D. Applebaum, Chief Executive Officer
Web address: www.cityhospital.org

JEFFERSON MEMORIAL HOSPITAL (O, 60 beds) 300 South Preston Street, Ranson, WV Zip 25438–1699; tel. 304/728–1600; John M. Sherwood, FACHE, Chief Executive Officer
Web address: www.jeffmem.com

UNITED HOSPITAL CENTER (O, 369 beds) Route 19 South, Clarksburg, WV Zip 26301, Mailing Address: P.O. Box 1680, Zip 26302–1680; tel. 304/624–2121; Bruce C. Carter, President
Web address: www.uhcwv.org

WEST VIRGINIA UNIVERSITY HOSPITALS (O, 440 beds) Medical Center Drive, Morgantown, WV Zip 26506–4749; tel. 304/598–4000; Bruce McClymonds, President
Web address: www.health.wvu.edu

Owned, leased, sponsored:	4 hospitals	1012 beds
Contract–managed:	0 hospitals	0 beds
Totals:	4 hospitals	1012 beds

0323:   WESTCARE HEALTH SYSTEM (NP)
68 Hospital Road, Sylva, NC Zip 28779; tel. 828/586–7000; Mark T. Leonard, Chief Executive Officer

NORTH CAROLINA: HARRIS REGIONAL HOSPITAL (O, 201 beds) 68 Hospital Road, Sylva, NC Zip 28779–2795; tel. 828/586–7000; Mark T. Leonard, Chief Executive Officer
Web address: www.westcare.org

SWAIN COUNTY HOSPITAL (O, 25 beds) 45 Plateau Street, Bryson City, NC Zip 28713–6784; tel. 828/488–4013; Ronald A. Sloan, Administrator
Web address: www.westcare.org

Owned, leased, sponsored:	2 hospitals	226 beds
Contract–managed:	0 hospitals	0 beds
Totals:	2 hospitals	226 beds

★6745:   WHEATON FRANCISCAN SERVICES, INC. (CC)
26W171 Roosevelt Road, Wheaton, IL Zip 60189–0667, Mailing Address: P.O. Box 667, Zip 60189–0667; tel. 630/462–9271; John D. Oliverio, President and Chief Executive Officer
(Moderately Centralized Health System)

ILLINOIS: MARIANJOY REHABILITATION HOSPITAL (O, 116 beds) 26 West 171 Roosevelt Road, Wheaton, IL Zip 60187–0795, Mailing Address: P.O. Box 795, Zip 60189–0795; tel. 630/462–4000; Kathleen C. Yosko, President and Chief Executive Officer
Web address: www.marianjoy.org

RUSH OAK PARK HOSPITAL (O, 176 beds) 520 South Maple Avenue, Oak Park, IL Zip 60304–1097; tel. 708/383–9300; Bruce M. Elegant, President and Chief Executive Officer
Web address: www.oakparkhospital.org

IOWA: COVENANT MEDICAL CENTER (O, 281 beds) 3421 West Ninth Street, Waterloo, IA Zip 50702–5499; tel. 319/272–8000; Jack Dusenbery, President and Chief Executive Officer
Web address: www.covhealth.com

MERCY HOSPITAL OF FRANCISCAN SISTERS (O, 64 beds) 201 Eighth Avenue S.E., Oelwein, IA Zip 50662–2447; tel. 319/283–6000; Richard Schrupp, President and Chief Executive Officer
Web address: www.covhealth.com

For explanation of codes following names, see page B2.
★ Indicates Type III membership in the American Hospital Association.

SARTORI MEMORIAL HOSPITAL (O, 67 beds) 515 College Street, Cedar Falls, IA Zip 50613–2500; tel. 319/268–3000; Sherri Greenwood, Administrator
Web address: www.covhealth.com

WISCONSIN: ALL SAINTS HEALTHCARE (O, 200 beds) 3801 Spring Street, Racine, WI Zip 53405–1690; tel. 262/687–4011; Kenneth R. Buser, President and Chief Executive Officer
Web address: www.allsaintshealthcare.org

ELMBROOK MEMORIAL HOSPITAL (O, 92 beds) 19333 West North Avenue, Brookfield, WI Zip 53045–4198; tel. 262/785–2000; Kimry A. Johnsrud, President
Web address: www.covhealth.org

ST. ELIZABETH HOSPITAL (O, 191 beds) 1506 South Oneida Street, Appleton, WI Zip 54915–1397; tel. 920/738–2000; Robert J. Turner, Chief Operating Officer
Web address: www.affinityhealth.org

ST. FRANCIS HOSPITAL (S, 212 beds) 3237 South 16th Street, Milwaukee, WI Zip 53215–4592; tel. 414/647–5000; Debra Standridge, President
Web address: www.stfrancishospital.net

ST. JOSEPH'S REGIONAL MEDICAL CENTER (O, 396 beds) 5000 West Chambers Street, Milwaukee, WI Zip 53210–9988; tel. 414/447–2000; Ron Groepper, President
Web address: www.covhealth.org

ST. LUKE'S HOSPITAL (O, 175 beds) 1320 Wisconsin Avenue, Racine, WI Zip 53403–1987; tel. 262/687–2011; Kenneth R. Buser, President and Chief Executive Officer
Web address: www.allsaintshealth.com

ST. MICHAEL HOSPITAL (O, 121 beds) 2400 West Villard Avenue, Milwaukee, WI Zip 53209–4999; tel. 414/527–8000; Alicia Modjeska, President
Web address: www.stmichaelhospital.net

THE WISCONSIN HEART HOSPITAL 10000 West Bluemound Road, Wauwatosa, WI Zip 53226; tel. 414/778–7800; Norma J. McCutcheon, President
Web address: www.twhh.org

UNITED HOSPITAL SYSTEM, ST. CATHERINE'S MEDICAL CENTER CAMPUS (O, 114 beds) 9555 76th Street, Pleasant Prairie, WI Zip 53158; tel. 262/656–2011; Richard O. Schmidt Jr, President and Chief Executive Officer

Owned, leased, sponsored:	13 hospitals	2205 beds
Contract–managed:	0 hospitals	0 beds
Totals:	13 hospitals	2205 beds

★9575: WILLIAM BEAUMONT HOSPITALS (NP)
3601 West Thirteen Mile Road, Royal Oak, MI Zip 48073–6769; tel. 248/551–5000; Kenneth J. Matzick, President and Chief Executive Officer
(Moderately Centralized Health System)

MICHIGAN: WILLIAM BEAUMONT HOSPITAL–ROYAL OAK (O, 1061 beds) 3601 West Thirteen Mile Road, Royal Oak, MI Zip 48073–6769; tel. 248/551–5000; John D. Labriola, Senior Vice President and Hospital Director
Web address: www.beaumonthospitals.com

WILLIAM BEAUMONT HOSPITAL–TROY (O, 254 beds) 44201 Dequindre Road, Troy, MI Zip 48085; tel. 248/964–5000; Eugene F. Michalski, Senior Vice President and Director
Web address: www.beaumonthospitals.com

Owned, leased, sponsored:	2 hospitals	1315 beds
Contract–managed:	0 hospitals	0 beds
Totals:	2 hospitals	1315 beds

1945: WILLIS–KNIGHTON HEALTH SYSTEM (NP)
2600 Greenwood Road, Shreveport, LA Zip 71130–2600; tel. 318/212–4000; James K. Elrod, President and Chief Executive Officer
(Centralized Physician/Insurance Health System)

LOUISIANA: WILLIS–KNIGHTON BOSSIER HEALTH CENTER (O, 115 beds) 2400 Hospital Drive, Bossier City, LA Zip 71111; tel. 318/212–7000; Donald R. Hebert, FACHE, Administrator

WILLIS–KNIGHTON MEDICAL CENTER (O, 719 beds) 2600 Greenwood Road, Shreveport, LA Zip 71103–2600, Mailing Address: P.O. Box 32600, Zip 71130–2600; tel. 318/212–4600; Ira L. Moss, Vice President and Administrator
Web address: www.wkhs.com

Owned, leased, sponsored:	2 hospitals	834 beds
Contract–managed:	0 hospitals	0 beds
Totals:	2 hospitals	834 beds

0282: WUESTHOFF HEALTH SYSTEM (NP)
110 Longwood Avenue, Rockledge, FL Zip 32955; tel. 321/636–2211; Emil P. Miller, President and Chief Executive Officer

FLORIDA: WUESTHOFF MEDICAL CENTER – MELBOURNE (O, 115 beds) 250 North Wickham Road, Melbourne, FL Zip 32935; tel. 321/752–1200; Donald McKenna, Administrator
Web address: www.wuesthoff.org

WUESTHOFF MEDICAL CENTER – ROCKLEDGE (O, 359 beds) 110 Longwood Avenue, Rockledge, FL Zip 32955–2887, Mailing Address: P.O. Box 565002, Mail Stop 1, Zip 32956–5002; tel. 321/636–2211; Emil P. Miller, President and Chief Executive Officer
Web address: www.wuesthoff.org

Owned, leased, sponsored:	2 hospitals	474 beds
Contract–managed:	0 hospitals	0 beds
Totals:	2 hospitals	474 beds

★0157: YALE NEW HAVEN HEALTH SYSTEM (NP)
789 Howard Avenue, New Haven, CT Zip 06519; tel. 203/688–4608; Joseph A. Zaccagnino, President and Chief Executive Officer
(Moderately Centralized Health System)

CONNECTICUT: BRIDGEPORT HOSPITAL (O, 383 beds) 267 Grant Street, Bridgeport, CT Zip 06610–0120, Mailing Address: P.O. Box 5000, Zip 06610–5000; tel. 203/384–3000; Robert J. Trefry, President and Chief Executive Officer
Web address: www.bridgeporthospital.org

GREENWICH HOSPITAL (O, 175 beds) 5 Perryridge Road, Greenwich, CT Zip 06830–4697; tel. 203/863–3000; Frank A. Corvino, President and Chief Executive Officer
Web address: www.greenhosp.org

YALE–NEW HAVEN HOSPITAL (O, 830 beds) 20 York Street, New Haven, CT Zip 06510–3202; tel. 203/688–4242; Joseph A. Zaccagnino, President and Chief Executive Officer
Web address: www.ynhh.org

Owned, leased, sponsored:	3 hospitals	1388 beds
Contract–managed:	0 hospitals	0 beds
Totals:	3 hospitals	1388 beds

0211: YOUTH AND FAMILY CENTERED SERVICES (IO)
1705 Capital of Texas Highway South, Austin, TX Zip 78746; tel. 512/327–1119; Kevin P. Sheehan, Chairman, President and Chief Executive Officer
(Independent Hospital System)

MISSOURI: LAKELAND REGIONAL HOSPITAL (O, 60 beds) 440 South Market Street, Springfield, MO Zip 65806–2090; tel. 417/865–5581; Stephen L. Spence, President and Chief Executive Officer
Web address: www.yfcs.com

NEW MEXICO: MEMORIAL PSYCHIATRIC HOSPITAL (O, 58 beds) 806 Central Avenue S.E., Albuquerque, NM Zip 87102–3671, Mailing Address: P.O. Box 26568, Zip 87125–6568; tel. 505/247–0220; Kay DeLage, Chief Executive Officer
Web address: www.yfcs.com

For explanation of codes following names, see page B2.
★ Indicates Type III membership in the American Hospital Association.

PENNSYLVANIA: SOUTHWOOD PSYCHIATRIC HOSPITAL (O, 119 beds) 2575
Boyce Plaza Road, Pittsburgh, PA Zip 15241–3925; tel. 412/257–2290;
Lynne M. Struble, MSN, Chief Executive Officer
Web address: www.southwoodhospital.com

Owned, leased, sponsored:	3 hospitals	237 beds
Contract–managed:	0 hospitals	0 beds
Totals:	3 hospitals	237 beds

For explanation of codes following names, see page B2.
★ Indicates Type III membership in the American Hospital Association.

B124 / Health Care Systems, Networks and Alliances

© 2005 AHA Guide

Geographically

United States

ALABAMA

Birmingham: ★ BAPTIST HEALTH SYSTEM 3201 4th Avenue South, Zip 35222, Mailing Address: P.O. Box 830605, Zip 35283–0605; tel. 205/715–5319; Mary Elizabeth O'Brien, President and Chief Executive Officer, p. B15

BRADFORD HEALTH SERVICES 2101 Magnolia Avenue South, Suite 518, Zip 35205; tel. 205/251–7753; Jerry W. Crowder, President and Chief Executive Officer, p. B18

★ EASTERN HEALTH SYSTEM, INC. 50 Medical Park East Drive, Zip 35235; tel. 205/838–3999; Robert C. Chapman, FACHE, President and Chief Executive Officer, p. B43

★ HEALTHSOUTH CORPORATION One Healthsouth Parkway, Zip 35243; tel. 205/967–7116; Jay Grinney, President, p. B56

UAB HEALTH SYSTEM 500 22nd Street South, Suite 408, Zip 35233; tel. 205/975–5362; David E. Hoidal, Chief Executive Officer, p. B113

Florence: ★ COFFEE HEALTH GROUP 205 Marengo Street, Zip 35630–6033; tel. 256/768–9191; Carl W. Bailey, President and Chief Executive Officer, p. B30

Guntersville: MARSHALL COUNTY HEALTH CARE AUTHORITY 227 Britany Road, Zip 35976; tel. 256/894–6615; Gary R. Gore, Chief Executive Officer, p. B71

Mobile: GULF HEALTH HOSPITALS 5 Mobile Infirmary Circle, Zip 36607–3520; tel. 251/435–5500; E. Chandler Bramlett Jr, President and Chief Executive Officer, p. B47

★ UNIVERSITY OF SOUTH ALABAMA HOSPITALS 5600 Girby Road, Zip 36693–3398; tel. 251/471–7000; Stanley K. Hammack, Associate Vice President Hospital Affairs/Chief Executive Officer, p. B118

Montgomery: ★ BAPTIST HEALTH 301 Brown Springs Road, Zip 36117; tel. 334/273–4400; W. Russell Tyner, President and Chief Executive Officer, p. B14

GILLIARD HEALTH SERVICES 3091 Carter Hill Road, Zip 36111; tel. 334/265–5009; William G. McKenzie, President and Chief Executive Officer, p. B46

Tuscaloosa: DCH HEALTH SYSTEM 809 University Boulevard East, Zip 35401; tel. 205/759–7111; Bryan N. Kindred, President and Chief Executive Officer, p. B35

ARIZONA

Flagstaff: ★ NORTHERN ARIZONA HEALTHCARE 1200 North Beaver Street, Zip 86001; tel. 928/773–2001; James Puffenberger, President and Chief Executive Officer, p. B80

Phoenix: ★ BANNER HEALTH 1441 North 12th Street, Zip 85006, Mailing Address: P.O. Box 25489, Zip 85002–5489; tel. 602/495–4000; Peter S. Fine, FACHE, President and Chief Executive Officer, p. B13

★ JOHN C. LINCOLN HEALTH NETWORK 250 East Dunlap Avenue, Zip 85020–2446; tel. 602/943–2381; Dan C. Coleman, President and Chief Executive Officer, p. B64

Scottsdale: ★ SCOTTSDALE HEALTHCARE 3621 Wells Fargo Avenue, Zip 85251–5607; tel. 480/882–4000; Thomas J. Sadvary, FACHE, Senior Vice President and Chief Executive Officer, p. B96

Sun City: ★ SUN HEALTH CORPORATION 13180 North 103rd Drive, Zip 85351–3038, Mailing Address: P.O. Box 1278, Zip 85372–1278; tel. 623/876–5301; Leland W. Peterson, President and Chief Executive Officer, p. B103

Tucson: ★ TMC HEALTHCARE 5301 East Grant Road, Zip 85712; tel. 520/327–5461; Frank D. Alvarez, President and Chief Executive Officer, p. B108

ARKANSAS

Little Rock: ★ BAPTIST HEALTH 9601 Interstate 630, Exit 7, Zip 72205–7299; tel. 501/202–2000; Russell D. Harrington Jr, President and Chief Executive Officer, p. B14

CALIFORNIA

Alhambra: AHMC, INC 100 South Raymond Avenue, Zip 91801–3199; tel. 626/458–4789; Jonathan Wu, M.D., President and Chairman, p. B6

Bellflower: ALTA HEALTHCARE SYSTEM 10230 East Artesia Boulevard, Suite 206, Zip 90706; tel. 562/925–0201; David Topper, Chief Executive Officer, p. B8

Covina: CITRUS VALLEY HEALTH PARTNERS 210 West San Bernardino Road, Zip 91723; tel. 626/331–7331; James T. Yoshioka, President and Chief Executive Officer, p. B29

Fairfield: ★ NORTHBAY HEALTHCARE SYSTEM 1200 B. Gale Wilson Boulevard, Zip 94533–3587; tel. 707/429–7809; Gary J. Passama, President and Chief Executive Officer, p. B80

Fresno: COMMUNITY MEDICAL CENTERS Fresno and Maddy Drive, Zip 93721, Mailing Address: P.O. Box 1232, Zip 93715–1232; tel. 559/459–6000; Tim A. Joslin, President and Chief Executive Officer, p. B32

Hemet: ★ VALLEY HEALTH SYSTEM 1117 East Devonshire Avenue, Zip 92543; tel. 909/652–2811; Susan Ballard, Chief Executive Officer, p. B118

Inglewood: CENTINELA FREEMAN HEALTHSYSTEM 555 East Hardy Street, Zip 90301; tel. 310/673–4660; Michael A. Rembis, FACHE, Chief Executive Officer, p. B28

Loma Linda: LOMA LINDA UNIVERSITY ADVENTIST HEALTH SCIENCES CENTER 11175 Campus Street, Zip 92354; tel. 909/558–7572; B. Lyn Behrens, President and Chief Executive Officer, p. B70

Long Beach: MEMORIAL HEALTH SERVICES 2801 Atlantic Avenue, Zip 90806, Mailing Address: P.O. Box 1428, Zip 90801–1428; tel. 562/933–2000; Barry S. Arbuckle, Ph.D., President and Chief Executive Officer, p. B73

Los Altos Hills: ★ DAUGHTERS OF CHARITY HEALTH SYSTEM 26000 Altamont Road, Zip 94022; tel. 650/917–4500; Bain J. Farris, President and Chief Executive Officer, p. B35

Los Angeles: LOS ANGELES COUNTY–DEPARTMENT OF HEALTH SERVICES 313 North Figueroa Street, Room 912, Zip 90012–2691; tel. 213/240–8101; Thomas L. Garthwaite, M.D., Director and Chief Medical Officer, p. B70

Oakland: ★ KAISER FOUNDATION HOSPITALS One Kaiser Plaza, Zip 94612–3600; tel. 510/271–5910; George C. Halvorson, M.D., Chairman and Chief Executive Officer, p. B64

★ UNIVERSITY OF CALIFORNIA–SYSTEMWIDE ADMINISTRATION 1111 Franklin Street, 11th Floor, Zip 94607–5200; tel. 510/987–9071; William Gurtner, Vice President Clinical Services, p. B116

Orange: ★ ST. JOSEPH HEALTH SYSTEM 500 South Main Street, Suite 1000, Zip 92868, Mailing Address: P.O. Box 14132, Zip 92863–1532; tel. 714/347–7500; Deborah A. Proctor, President and Chief Executive Officer, p. B102

Palo Alto: STANFORD HEALTH CARE 300 Pasteur Drive, Zip 94304–2299; tel. 650/723–4000; Martha H. Marsh, President and Chief Executive Officer, p. B103

Roseville: ★ ADVENTIST HEALTH 2100 Douglas Boulevard, Zip 95661–3898, Mailing Address: P.O. Box 619002, Zip 95661–9002; tel. 916/781–2000; Donald R. Ammon, President and Chief Executive Officer, p. B4

Sacramento: ★ SUTTER HEALTH 2200 River Plaza Drive, Zip 95833; tel. 916/733–8800; Patrick E. Fry, Chief Executive Officer, p. B104

San Diego: ★ PALOMAR POMERADO HEALTH 15255 Innovation Drive, Suite 204, Zip 92128–3410; tel. 858/675–5100; Michael H. Covert, FACHE, Chief Executive Officer, p. B82

★ SCRIPPS HEALTH 4275 Campus Point Court, Zip 92121; tel. 858/678–7200; Chris D. Van Gorder, President and Chief Executive Officer, p. B96

★ SHARP HEALTHCARE 8695 Spectrum Center Boulevard, Zip 92123–1489; tel. 858/499–4000; Michael Murphy, President and Chief Executive Officer, p. B97

San Francisco: ★ CATHOLIC HEALTHCARE WEST 185 Berry Street, Suite 300, Zip 94107–1773; tel. 415/438–5500; Lloyd H. Dean, President and Chief Executive Officer, p. B26

San Leandro: ALAMEDA MEDICAL CENTER 15400 Foothill Boulevard, Zip 94578; tel. 510/677–7920; Claude D. Watts Jr, Chief Executive Officer, p. B6

Santa Barbara: ★ COTTAGE HEALTH SYSTEM Pueblo at Bath Streets, Zip 93105, Mailing Address: P.O. Box 689, Zip 93102–0689; tel. 805/569–7290; Ronald C. Werft, President and Chief Executive Officer, p. B33

Santa Fe Springs: COLLEGE HEALTH ENTERPRISES 11627 Telegraph Road, Suite 200, Zip 90670; tel. 562/923–9449; Barry J. Weiss, Chairman of the Board, p. B30

Tustin: PACIFIC HEALTH CORPORATION 14642 Newport Avenue, Suite 388, Zip 92780; tel. 714/669–2085; James W. Young, President and Chief Executive Officer, p. B82

Walnut Creek: ★ JOHN MUIR/MOUNT DIABLO HEALTH SYSTEM 1400 Treat Boulevard, Zip 94596–2142; tel. 925/947–2100, p. B64

Yuba City: FREMONT–RIDEOUT HEALTH GROUP 989 Plumas Street, Zip 95991; tel. 530/751–4010; Thomas P. Hayes, Chief Executive Officer, p. B46

COLORADO

Denver: ★ CATHOLIC HEALTH INITIATIVES 1999 Broadway, Suite 2600, Zip 80202–4004; tel. 303/298–9100; Kevin E. Lofton, President and Chief Executive Officer, p. B23

★ EXEMPLA HEALTHCARE, INC. 600 Grant Street, Suite 700, Zip 80203; tel. 303/813–5000; Jeffrey D. Selberg, President and Chief Executive Officer, p. B44

CONNECTICUT

Hartford: CONNECTICUT DEPARTMENT OF MENTAL HEALTH AND ADDICTION SERVICES 410 Capitol Avenue, Zip 06134, Mailing Address: P.O. Box 341431, Zip 06134–1431; tel. 860/418–7000; Thomas A. Kirk Jr, Ph.D., Commissioner, p. B33

SAINT FRANCIS CARE, INC. 114 Woodland Street, Zip 06105; tel. 860/714–5541; Christopher M. Dadlez, President and Chief Executive Officer, p. B95

Manchester: EASTERN CONNECTICUT HEALTH NETWORK 71 Haynes Street, Zip 06040; tel. 860/533–3429; Peter J. Karl, President and Chief Executive Officer, p. B43

New Haven: ★ YALE NEW HAVEN HEALTH SYSTEM 789 Howard Avenue, Zip 06519; tel. 203/688–4608; Joseph A. Zaccagnino, President and Chief Executive Officer, p. B123

DELAWARE

Wilmington: ★ CHRISTIANA CARE HEALTH SYSTEM 501 West 14th Street, Zip 19899, Mailing Address: P.O. Box 1668, Zip 19899; tel. 302/733–1000; Robert J. Laskowski, M.D., President and Chief Executive Officer, p. B28

DISTRICT OF COLUMBIA

Washington: BUREAU OF MEDICINE AND SURGERY, DEPARTMENT OF THE NAVY 2300 East Street N.W., Zip 20372–5300; tel. 202/762–3701; Rear Admiral Kathleen L. Martin, Deputy Surgeon General, p. B20

DEPARTMENT OF THE AIR FORCE 1420 Pentagon, Room 4E1084, Zip 20330–1420; tel. 202/767–4765; Lieutenant General George Peach Taylor Jr, M.D., Surgeon General, p. B36

DEPARTMENT OF VETERANS AFFAIRS 810 Vermont Avenue N.W., Zip 20420; tel. 202/273–5781; Jonathan Perlin, Acting Secretary, p. B37

FLORIDA

Clearwater: ACCORD HEALTH CARE CORPORATION 14010 Roosevelt Road, Zip 33762; tel. 727/573–1755; Stephen H. Noble, President, p. B4

Coral Gables: ★ BAPTIST HEALTH SOUTH FLORIDA 6855 Red Road, Suite 600, Zip 33143–3632; tel. 786/662–7111; Brian E. Keeley, President and Chief Executive Officer, p. B15

Dunedin: MORTON PLANT MEASE HEALTH CARE 601 Main Street, Zip 34698, Mailing Address: P.O. Box 760, Zip 34697–0760; tel. 727/733–1111; Philip K. Beauchamp, FACHE, President and Chief Executive Officer, p. B76

Fort Lauderdale: ★ NORTH BROWARD HOSPITAL DISTRICT 303 S.E. 17th Street, Zip 33316–2510; tel. 954/355–5100; G. Wil Trower, President and Chief Executive Officer, p. B79

Gainesville: ★ SHANDS HEALTHCARE 1600 S.W. Archer Road, Zip 32610–0326; tel. 352/265–8929; Timothy M. Goldfarb, Chief Executive Officer, p. B97

Hollywood: ★ MEMORIAL HEALTHCARE SYSTEM 3501 Johnson Street, Zip 33021–5421; tel. 954/985–5805; Frank V. Sacco, FACHE, Chief Executive Officer, p. B74

Jacksonville: ★ BAPTIST HEALTH 800 Prudential Drive, Zip 32207; tel. 904/202–4011; Hugh Greene, Chief Executive Officer, p. B14

Miami: ★ JACKSON HEALTH SYSTEM 1611 N.W. 12th Avenue, Zip 33136–1094; tel. 305/585–1111; Marvin O'Quinn, President and Chief Executive Officer, p. B63

Naples: HEALTH MANAGEMENT ASSOCIATES 5811 Pelican Bay Boulevard, Suite 500, Zip 34108; tel. 239/598–3131; Joseph V. Vumbacco, President and Chief Executive Officer, p. B54

Orlando: ORLANDO REGIONAL HEALTHCARE 1414 Kuhl Avenue, Zip 32806–2093; tel. 407/841–5111; John Hillenmeyer, President and Chief Executive Officer, p. B82

Pensacola: BAPTIST HEALTH CARE CORPORATION 1717 North E Street, Suite 320, Zip 32501–6335; tel. 850/469–7643; Alfred G. Stubblefield, President, p. B15

Quincy: DASSEE COMMUNITY HEALTH SYSTEM 23186 Blue Star Highway, Zip 32351, Mailing Address: P.O. Box 1589, Zip 32353; tel. 850/875–1100; Michael C. Lake, Chief Executive Officer, p. B35

Rockledge: FIRST HEALTH, INC. 6450 U.S. Highway 1, Zip 32955; tel. 321/434–7000; Michael D. Means, President and Chief Executive Officer, p. B45

WUESTHOFF HEALTH SYSTEM 110 Longwood Avenue, Zip 32955; tel. 321/636–2211; Emil P. Miller, President and Chief Executive Officer, p. B123

Tampa: SHRINERS HOSPITALS FOR CHILDREN 2900 Rocky Point Drive, Zip 33607–1435, Mailing Address: Box 31356, Zip 33631–3356; tel. 813/281–0300; Joseph E. Melchiorre Jr, CHE, Executive Administrator, p. B97

UNIVERSITY COMMUNITY HEALTH 3100 East Fletcher Avenue, Zip 33613; tel. 813/971–6000; Norman V. Stein, President, p. B116

Windermere: UNITED MEDICAL CORPORATION 603 Main Street, Zip 34786–3548, Mailing Address: P.O. Box 1100, Zip 34786–1100; tel. 407/876–2200; Donald R. Dizney, Chairman and Chief Executive Officer, p. B113

Winter Park: ★ ADVENTIST HEALTH SYSTEM SUNBELT HEALTH CARE CORPORATION 111 North Orlando Avenue, Zip 32789–3675; tel. 407/975–1417; Thomas L. Werner, President, p. B4

GEORGIA

Adel: MEMORIAL HEALTH SERVICES 706 North Parrish Avenue, Zip 31620–2064, Mailing Address: P.O. Box 677, Zip 31620–0677; tel. 229/896–8077; Greg Griffith, Chief Executive Officer, p. B74

Albany: PHOEBE PUTNEY HEALTH SYSTEMS 417 Third Avenue, Zip 31702; tel. 229/312–1000; Joel Wernick, President and Chief Executive Officer, p. B83

Alpharetta: ★ REGENCY HOSPITAL COMPANY 30000 Mill Creek Avenue, Suite 250, Zip 30022; tel. 770/772–4345; Rod Laughlin, President and Chief Executive Officer, p. B92

Atlanta: ★ EMORY HEALTHCARE 1440 Clifton Road, N.E., Suite 420, Zip 30322–1102, Mailing Address: 1440 Clifton Road N.E., Suite 420, Zip 30322–1102; tel. 404/778–5000; John T. Fox, Chief Executive Officer, p. B43

PIEDMONT HEALTHCARE 2001 Peachtree Road N.E., Suite 400, Zip 30309; tel. 404/605–3215; R. Timothy Stack, FACHE, President and Chief Executive Officer, p. B84

SUNLINK HEALTHCARE 900 Circle 75 Parkway, Suite 1300, Zip 30339; tel. 770/933–7000; Robert M. Thornton Jr, Chief Executive Officer, p. B103

Brunswick: SOUTHEAST GEORGIA HEALTH SYSTEM 2415 Parkwood Drive, Zip 31520–4252, Mailing Address: P.O. Box 1518, Zip 31521–1518; tel. 912/466–7000; Gary R. Colberg, CHE, President and Chief Executive Officer, p. B101

Columbus: ★ COLUMBUS REGIONAL HEALTHCARE SYSTEM 707 Center Street, Suite 400, Zip 31901; tel. 706/660–6100; Larry Sanders, FACHE, Chairman and Chief Executive Officer, p. B30

Decatur: DEKALB MEDICAL CENTER 2701 North Decatur Road, Zip 30033; tel. 404/501–1000; Eric P. Norwood, President and Chief Executive Officer, p. B35

Duluth: AMT GROUP, INC. 3700 Crestwood Parkway, Suite 150, Zip 30096; tel. 770/923–6500; Thomas E. McNaull, President and Chief Executive Officer, p. B8

Marietta: ★ WELLSTAR HEALTH SYSTEM 805 Sandy Plains Road, Zip 30066; tel. 770/792–5012; Robert A. Lipson, M.D., President and Chief Executive Officer, p. B121

Royston: TY COBB HEALTHCARE SYSTEM, INC. 461 Cook Street, Suite A., Zip 30662, Mailing Address: P.O. Box 589, Zip 30662; tel. 706/245–1825; Charles T. Adams, Chief Executive Officer, p. B111

Sugar Hill: RESURGENCE HEALTH GROUP 1400 Buford Highway, Building R–3, Zip 30518; tel. 770/904–6731; Philip H. Eastman III, President, p. B93

Thomasville: ★ ARCHBOLD MEDICAL CENTER 910 South Broad Street, Zip 31792–6113; tel. 229/228–2739; Ken B. Beverly, President and Chief Executive Officer, p. B9

HAWAII

Honolulu: ★ HAWAII HEALTH SYSTEMS CORPORATION 3675 Kilauea Avenue, Zip 96816; tel. 808/733–4151; Thomas M. Driskill Jr, President and Chief Executive Officer, p. B48

HAWAII PACIFIC HEALTH 55 Merchant Street, Zip 96813; tel. 808/535–7414; Charles A. Sted, Pesident and Chief Executive Officer, p. B48

★ QUEEN'S HEALTH SYSTEMS 1099 Alakea Street, Suite 1100, Zip 96813; tel. 808/532–6100; Gary Okamoto, President and Chief Executive Officer, p. B88

ILLINOIS

Arlington Heights: ALEXIAN BROTHERS HEALTH SYSTEM 3040 Salt Creek Lane, Zip 60005; tel. 847/463–8910; Brother Thomas Keusenkothen, President and Chief Executive Officer, p. B7

CANCER TREATMENT CENTERS OF AMERICA 3150 Salt Creek Lane, Zip 60005–1080; tel. 847/342–7400; Stephen B. Bonner, President and Chief Executive Officer, p. B20

Carbondale: SOUTHERN ILLINOIS HOSPITAL SERVICES 1239 East Main Street, Zip 62901, Mailing Address: P.O. Box 3988, Zip 62902–3988; tel. 618/457–5200; Thomas J. Firestone, M.D., President and Chief Executive Officer, p. B101

Chicago: COOK COUNTY BUREAU OF HEALTH SERVICES 1900 West Polk Street, Suite 200, Zip 60612; tel. 312/633–6820; Daniel Winship, Chief, p. B33

NATIONAL SURGICAL HOSPITALS 30 South Wacker Drive, Suite 2302, Zip 60606; tel. 312/627–8400; John G. Rex–Waller, President and Chief Executive Officer, p. B77

RESURRECTION HEALTH CARE CORPORATION 7435 West Talcott Avenue, Zip 60631; tel. 773/792–5150; Joseph F. Toomey, President and Chief Executive Officer, p. B93

★ RUSH UNIVERSITY MEDICAL CENTER 1653 West Congress Parkway, Zip 60612–3864; tel. 312/942–5000; Larry J. Goodman, M.D., President, p. B94

SINAI HEALTH SYSTEM California Avenue at 15th Street, Zip 60608; tel. 773/542–2000; Alan H. Channing, President and Chief Executive Officer, p. B98

De Kalb: ★ KISHWAUKEE HEALTH SYSTEM 626 Bethany Road, Zip 60115–4939, Mailing Address: P.O. Box 707, Zip 60115–4939; tel. 815/756–1521; Kevin P. Poorten, President and Chief Executive Officer, p. B67

Evergreen Park: AMERICAN PROVINCE OF LITTLE COMPANY OF MARY SISTERS 9350 South California Avenue, Zip 60805–2595; tel. 708/229–5491; Sister Carol Pacini, Provincialate Superior, p. B8

Mokena: ★ PROVENA HEALTH 19065 Hickory Creek Drive, Suite 300, Zip 60448; tel. 708/478–6300; William T. Foley, Chief Executive Officer, p. B85

Oak Brook: ★ ADVOCATE HEALTH CARE 2025 Windsor Drive, Zip 60523; tel. 630/990–5010; James H. Skogsbergh, President and Chief Executive Officer, p. B6

Peoria: ★ OSF HEALTHCARE SYSTEM 800 N.E. Glen Oak Avenue, Zip 61603–3200; tel. 309/655–2850; James M. Moore, Chief Executive Officer, p. B82

Springfield: ★ HOSPITAL SISTERS HEALTH SYSTEM Mailing Address: P.O. Box 19456, Zip 62794–9456; tel. 217/523–4747; Sister Jomary Trstensky, President, p. B60

★ MEMORIAL HEALTH SYSTEM 701 North First Street, Zip 62781–0001; tel. 217/788–3000; Robert T. Clarke, President and Chief Executive Officer, p. B74

Wheaton: ★ WHEATON FRANCISCAN SERVICES, INC. 26W171 Roosevelt Road, Zip 60189–0667, Mailing Address: P.O. Box 667, Zip 60189–0667; tel. 630/462–9271; John D. Oliverio, President and Chief Executive Officer, p. B122

Woodstock: CENTEGRA HEALTH SYSTEM 527 West South Street, Zip 60098; tel. 815/338–2500; Michael S. Eesley, President and Chief Executive Officer, p. B27

INDIANA

Evansville: DEACONESS HEALTH SYSTEM 600 Mary Street, Zip 47747; tel. 812/450–5000; Linda E. White, President and Chief Executive Officer, p. B35

Fort Wayne: PARKVIEW HEALTH 10501 Corporate Drive, Zip 46895–5600, Mailing Address: P.O. Box 5600, Zip 46895–5600; tel. 260/373–7001; Charles H. Mason Jr, President and Chief Executive Officer, p. B83

Hammond: COMMUNITY HEALTHCARE SYSTEM 901 MacArthur Boulevard, Zip 46321–2959; tel. 219/836–1600; Donald Powers, Chairman, President and Chief Executive Officer, p. B32

Indianapolis: ★ CLARIAN HEALTH PARTNERS I–65 at 21st Street, Zip 46202–5250, Mailing Address: P.O. Box 1367, Zip 46206–1367; tel. 317/962–5900; Daniel F. Evans Jr, President and Chief Executive Officer, p. B29

Mishawaka: SISTERS OF ST. FRANCIS HEALTH SERVICES, INC. 1515 Dragoon Trail, Zip 46546–1290, Mailing Address: P.O. Box 1290, Zip 46546–1290; tel. 574/256–3935; Kevin D. Leahy, President and Chief Executive Officer, p. B100

Muncie: CARDINAL HEALTH SYSTEM 2401 University Avenue, Zip 47303; tel. 765/747–3139; Robert S. Curtis, President and Chief Executive Officer, p. B21

IOWA

Davenport: GENESIS HEALTH SYSTEM 1227 East Rusholme Street, Zip 52803–2498; tel. 563/421–1000; Leo A. Bressanelli, FACHE, President and Chief Executive Officer, p. B46

Des Moines: ★ IOWA HEALTH SYSTEM 1200 Pleasant Street, Zip 50309–1453; tel. 515/241–6161; Samuel T. Wallace, President, p. B63

KANSAS

Lenexa: ★ SISTERS OF CHARITY OF LEAVENWORTH HEALTH SYSTEM 9801 Renner Boulevard, Suite 100, Zip 66219; tel. 913/895–2800; William M. Murray, President, p. B99

Phillipsburg: ★ GREAT PLAINS HEALTH ALLIANCE, INC. 625 Third Street, Zip 67661–2138, Mailing Address: P.O. Box 366, Zip 67661–0366; tel. 785/543–2111; Roger S. John, President and Chief Executive Officer, p. B46

Wichita: VIA CHRISTI HEALTH SYSTEM 3720 East Bayley, Zip 67218–3002; tel. 316/858–4900; Kevin P. Conlin, President and Chief Executive Officer, p. B119

KENTUCKY

Lexington: ★ APPALACHIAN REGIONAL HEALTHCARE 2285 Executive Drive, Suite 400, Zip 40505, Mailing Address: P.O. Box 8086, Zip 40533–8086; tel. 859/226–2440; Jerry Haynes, Interim President and Chief Executive Officer, p. B9

CARDINAL HILL HEALTHCARE SYSTEM 2050 Versailes Road, Zip 40504; tel. 859/254–5701; Kerry G. Gillihan, FACHE, President and Chief Executive Officer, p. B21

Louisville: ALLIANT MANAGEMENT SERVICES 2501 Nelson Miller Parkway, Suite 104, Zip 40223; tel. 502/992–3525; Chris West, President and Chief Executive Officer, p. B7

★ BAPTIST HEALTHCARE SYSTEM 4007 Kresge Way, Zip 40207–4677; tel. 502/896–5000; Tommy J. Smith, President and Chief Executive Officer, p. B16

★ JEWISH HOSPITAL HEALTHCARE SERVICES 200 Abraham Flexner Way, Zip 40202–1886; tel. 502/587–4011; Robert L. Shircliff, President and Chief Executive Officer, p. B64

KINDRED HEALTHCARE 680 South Fourth Street, Zip 40202–2412; tel. 502/596–7300; Paul J. Diaz, President and Chief Operating Officer, p. B66

MERIT HEALTH SYSTEMS 333 East Main Street, Suite 300, Zip 40202; tel. 502/753–0890; Tyree Wilburn, Chaiman, President and Chief Executive Officer, p. B75

★ NORTON HEALTHCARE 234 East Gray Street, Suite 225, Zip 40202, Mailing Address: P.O. Box 35070, Zip 40232–5070; tel. 502/629–8000; Stephen A. Williams, President, p. B80

LOUISIANA

Baton Rouge: ★ FRANCISCAN MISSIONARIES OF OUR LADY HEALTH SYSTEM, INC. 4200 Essen Lane, Zip 70809; tel. 225/923–2701; John J. Finan Jr, President and Chief Executive Officer, p. B45

★ LSU HEALTH SCIENCES CENTER 8550 United Plaza Boulevard, 4th Floor, Zip 70809; tel. 225/922–0490; Donald R. Smithburg, Chief Executive Officer, p. B71

Lafayette: PROMISE HEALTHCARE 400 East Kaliste Saloom Road, 7100, Zip 70508; tel. 337/325–8555; Howard B. Koslow, President and Chief Executive Officer, p. B85

New Orleans: LOUISIANA STATE HOSPITALS 210 State Street, Zip 70118–5797; tel. 504/897–4616; Shelby Price, Chief Executive Officer, p. B70

Shreveport: WILLIS–KNIGHTON HEALTH SYSTEM 2600 Greenwood Road, Zip 71130–2600; tel. 318/212–4000; James K. Elrod, President and Chief Executive Officer, p. B123

MAINE

Bangor: ★ EASTERN MAINE HEALTHCARE 489 State Street, Zip 04401–6674, Mailing Address: P.O. Box 404, Zip 04402–0404; tel. 207/973–7045; Norman A. Ledwin, President and Chief Executive Officer, p. B43

MARYLAND

Baltimore: ★ JOHNS HOPKINS HEALTH SYSTEM 733 North Broadway, BRB 104, Zip 21205; tel. 410/955–5000; Ronald R. Peterson, President, p. B64

★ LIFEBRIDGE HEALTH 2401 West Belvedere Avenue, Zip 21215; tel. 410/601–9789; Warren A. Green, President and Chief Executive Officer, p. B68

★ UNIVERSITY OF MARYLAND MEDICAL SYSTEM 250 West Pratt Street, Suite 880, Zip 21201–1595; tel. 410/328–8667; Edmond F. Notebaert, President and Chief Executive Officer, p. B117

Bel Air: ★ UPPER CHESAPEAKE HEALTH SYSTEM 520 Upper Chesapeake Drive, Suite 405, Zip 21014–4324; tel. 443/643–3303; Lyle Ernest Sheldon, FACHE, President and Chief Executive Officer, p. B118

Cheverly: ★ DIMENSIONS HEALTHCARE SYSTEM 3001 Hospital Drive, 3rd Floor, Zip 20785; tel. 301/583–4000; G. T. Dunlop Ecker, President and Chief Executive Officer, p. B41

Columbia: ★ MEDSTAR HEALTH 5565 Sterrett Place, 5th Floor, Zip 21044; tel. 410/772–6500; Kenneth A. Samet, President and Chief Operating Officer, p. B73

Easton: SHORE HEALTH SYSTEM 219 South Washington Street, Zip 21601; tel. 410/822–1000; Joseph P. Ross, President and Chief Executive Officer, p. B97

Marriottsville: ★ BON SECOURS HEALTH SYSTEM, INC. 1505 Marriottsville Road, Zip 21104–1399; tel. 410/442–5511; Richard Statuto, President and Chief Executive Officer, p. B18

Rockville: ★ ADVENTIST HEALTHCARE 1801 Research Boulevard, Suite 400, Zip 20850; tel. 301/315–3030; William G. Robertson, President and Chief Executive Officer, p. B5

U. S. INDIAN HEALTH SERVICE 801 Thompson Avenue, Zip 20852; tel. 301/443–1083; Charles Grim, D.D.S., Acting Director, p. B112

Sparks Glencoe: INTEGRATED HEALTH SERVICES 910 Rudgebrook Road, Zip 21152; tel. 410/773–1000; Joseph A. Bondi, Chairman and Chief Executive Officer, p. B61

Stevensville: MID ATLANTIC HEALTH MANAGEMENT, INC. 1220 Butterworth Court, Zip 21666–2504; tel. 410/643–3393; Harold A. McBee Jr, President, p. B75

MASSACHUSETTS

Boston: ★ CARITAS CHRISTI HEALTH CARE 736 Cambridge Street, Zip 02135–2997; tel. 617/789–2500; Robert M. Haddad, M.D., President, p. B22

MASSACHUSETTS DEPARTMENT OF MENTAL HEALTH 25 Staniford Street, Zip 02114–2575; tel. 617/626–8123; Ken Duckworth, Interim Commissioner, p. B71

MASSSCHUSETTS DEPARTMENT OF PUBLIC HEALTH 250 Washington Street, Zip 02108–4619; tel. 617/624–6000; Christine C. Ferguson, Commissioner, p. B72

★ PARTNERS HEALTHCARE SYSTEM, INC. 800 Boylston Street, Suite 1150, Zip 02199–8001; tel. 617/278–1004; James J. Mongan, M.D., President and Chief Executive Officer, p. B83

Hyannis: CAPE COD HEALTHCARE, INC. 88 Lewis Bay Road, Zip 02601–5210; tel. 508/862–5010; Stephen L. Abbott, President and Chief Executive Officer, p. B21

Lexington: ★ COVENANT HEALTH SYSTEMS, INC. 420 Bedford Street, Zip 02420–1502; tel. 781/862–1634; David R. Lincoln, President and Chief Executive Officer, p. B34

Peabody: PIONEER BEHAVIORAL HEALTH 200 Lake Street, Suite 102, Zip 01960–4780; tel. 978/536–2777; Bruce A. Shear, President and Chief Executive Officer, p. B84

Pittsfield: ★ BERKSHIRE HEALTH SYSTEMS, INC. 725 North Street, Zip 01201–4124; tel. 413/447–2743; David E. Phelps, President and Chief Executive Officer, p. B17

Springfield: ★ BAYSTATE HEALTH SYSTEM, INC. 759 Chestnut Street, Zip 01199–0001; tel. 413/794–0000; Mark R. Tolosky, President and Chief Executive Officer, p. B17

Worcester: ★ UMASS MEMORIAL HEALTH CARE, INC. 1 Biotech Park, Zip 01605–2982; tel. 508/334–0100; John G. O'Brien, President and Chief Executive Officer, p. B113

MICHIGAN

Dearborn: ★ OAKWOOD HEALTHCARE, INC. One Parklane Boulevard, Suite 1000E, Zip 48126; tel. 313/253–6050; Gerald D. Fitzgerald, President and Chief Executive Officer, p. B81

Detroit: ★ DETROIT MEDICAL CENTER 3990 John R., Zip 48201; tel. 313/745–1250; Michael Duggan, President and Chief Executive Officer, p. B41

★ HENRY FORD HEALTH SYSTEM One Ford Place, Zip 48202–3450; tel. 313/876–8705; Nancy M. Schlichting, President and Chief Executive Officer, p. B59

Flint: MCLAREN HEALTH CARE CORPORATION G3235 Beecher Road, Suite B., Zip 48532; tel. 810/342–1100; Philip A. Incarnati, President and Chief Executive Officer, p. B72

Grand Rapids: SPECTRUM HEALTH 100 Michigan Street N.E., Zip 49503–2551; tel. 616/391–1774; Richard C. Breon, President and Chief Executive Officer, p. B101

Kalamazoo: ★ BRONSON HEALTHCARE GROUP, INC. One Healthcare Plaza, Zip 49007–5345; tel. 269/341–6000; Frank J. Sardone, President and Chief Executive Officer, p. B20

Midland: ★ MIDMICHIGAN HEALTH 4005 Orchard Drive, Zip 48670–0001; tel. 989/839–3000; Terence F. Moore, President, p. B75

Muskegon: HACKLEY HEALTH SYSTEM 2700 Clinton Street, Zip 49442; tel. 231/726–3511; Gordon A. Mudler, President and Chief Executive Officer, p. B48

Novi: ★ TRINITY HEALTH 27870 Cabot Drive, Zip 48377; tel. 248/489–5004; Joseph R. Swedish, President and Chief Executive Officer, p. B110

Port Huron: ★ BLUE WATER HEALTH SERVICES CORPORATION 1221 Pine Grove Avenue, Zip 48061–5011; tel. 810/989–3717; Brian M. Connolly, President and Chief Executive Officer, p. B18

Royal Oak: ★ WILLIAM BEAUMONT HOSPITALS 3601 West Thirteen Mile Road, Zip 48073–6769; tel. 248/551–5000; Kenneth J. Matzick, President and Chief Executive Officer, p. B123

Traverse City: ★ MUNSON HEALTHCARE 1105 Sixth Street, Zip 49684–2386; tel. 231/935–6502; John M. Rockwood Jr, President and Chief Executive Officer, p. B77

MINNESOTA

Duluth: BENEDICTINE HEALTH SYSTEM 503 East Third Street, Zip 55805–1964; tel. 218/786–2370; Dale Thompson, President and Chief Executive Officer, p. B17

ST. MARY'S/DULUTH CLINIC HEALTH SYSTEM 407 East Third Street, Zip 55805–1984; tel. 218/786–4000; Peter E. Person, M.D., President and Chief Executive Officer, p. B102

Minneapolis: ★ ALLINA HOSPITALS & CLINICS 710 East 24th Street, Zip 55404–3840, Mailing Address: P.O. Box 1469, Zip 55440–1469; tel. 612/775–5000; Richard R. Pettingill, President and Chief Executive Officer, p. B8

CHILDREN'S HOSPITALS AND CLINICS OF MINNESOTA 2525 Chicago Avenue South, Zip 55404; tel. 612/813–6100; Alan L. Goldbloom, M.D., President and Chief Executive Officer, p. B28

★ FAIRVIEW HEALTH SERVICES 2450 Riverside Avenue, Zip 55454–1400; tel. 612/672–6300; David R. Page, President and Chief Executive Officer, p. B44

Rochester: ★ MAYO FOUNDATION 200 S.W. First Street, Zip 55905–0002; tel. 507/284–2511; Denis A. Cortese, M.D., President and Chief Executive Officer, p. B72

Saint Cloud: ★ CENTRACARE HEALTH SYSTEM 1406 Sixth Avenue North, Zip 56303; tel. 320/251–2700; Terrance Pladson, M.D., President and Chief Executive Officer, p. B28

Saint Louis Park: ★ PARK NICOLLET HEALTH SERVICES 6500 Excelsior Boulevard, Zip 55426–4702; tel. 952/993–5000; David K. Wessner, President and Chief Executive Officer, p. B83

Saint Paul: ★ HEALTHEAST CARE SYSTEM 559 Capitol Boulevard, 6–South, Zip 55103–0000; tel. 651/232–2300; Timothy H. Hanson, President and Chief Executive Officer, p. B56

MISSISSIPPI

Jackson: MISSISSIPPI STATE DEPARTMENT OF MENTAL HEALTH 1101 Robert E Lee Building, Zip 39201–1101; tel. 601/359–1288; Roger McMurtry, Chief Mental Health Bureau, p. B76

Magee: PIONEER HEALTH SERVICES 301 Eighth Avenue S.W., Zip 39111, Mailing Address: P.O. Box 1100, Zip 39111; tel. 601/849–6440; Joseph S. McNulty, President and Chief Executive Officer, p. B84

Meridian: RUSH HEALTH SYSTEMS 1314 19th Avenue, Zip 39301; tel. 601/483–0011; Wallace Strickland, President and Chief Executive Officer, p. B94

Health Care Systems Index

Tupelo: ★ NORTH MISSISSIPPI HEALTH SERVICES, INC. 830 South Gloster Street, Zip 38801–4996; tel. 662/377–3136; John R. Heer, President and Chief Executive Officer, p. B79

MISSOURI

Chesterfield: ★ SISTERS OF MERCY HEALTH SYSTEM 14528 South Outer 40, Suite 100, Zip 63017–5743; tel. 314/579–6100; Ronald B. Ashworth, Chief Executive Officer, p. B100

Columbia: UNIVERSITY OF MISSOURI HEALTH CARE MA204 Medical Science Building, Zip 65212–0001; tel. 573/884–8738; James H. Ross, Chief Executive Officer, p. B117

Joplin: ★ FREEMAN HEALTH SYSTEM 1102 West 32nd Street, Zip 64804; tel. 417/347–1111; Gary D. Duncan, President and Chief Executive Officer, p. B46

Kansas City: SAINT LUKE'S HEALTH SYSTEM 10920 Elm Avenue, Zip 64134–4108; tel. 816/932–2000; G. Richard Hastings, President and Chief Executive Officer, p. B95

★ TRUMAN MEDICAL CENTERS 2301 Holmes Street, Zip 64108–2677; tel. 816/404–1000; John W. Bluford, President and Chief Executive Officer, p. B111

Saint Louis: ★ ASCENSION HEALTH 4600 Edmundson Road, Zip 63134–3806; tel. 314/733–8000; Anthony R. Tersigni, Ed.D., FACHE, President and Chief Executive Officer, p. B10

★ BJC HEALTHCARE 4444 Forest Park Avenue, Suite 500, Zip 63108–2259; tel. 314/286–2000; Steven H. Lipstein, President and Chief Executive Officer, p. B17

★ SSM HEALTH CARE 477 North Lindbergh Boulevard, Zip 63141–7813; tel. 314/994–7800; Sister Mary Jean Ryan, President and Chief Executive Officer, p. B101

Springfield: COXHEALTH 1423 North Jefferson Avenue, Zip 65802–1988; tel. 417/269–3108; Robert H. Bezanson, President and Chief Executive Officer, p. B34

NEBRASKA

Norfolk: MISSIONARY BENEDICTINE SISTERS AMERICAN PROVINCE 300 North 18th Street, Zip 68701–3687; tel. 402/371–3438; Sister Kevin Hermsen, Prioress, p. B76

Omaha: ALEGENT HEALTH 1010 North 96th Street, Suite 200, Zip 68114–2595; tel. 402/343–4300; Wayne A. Sensor, President and Chief Executive Officer, p. B7

★ NEBRASKA METHODIST HEALTH SYSTEM, INC. 8511 West Dodge Road, Zip 68114; tel. 402/354–4844; Stephen D. Long, President and Executive Officer, p. B77

NEVADA

Reno: WASHOE HEALTH SYSTEM 77 Pringle Way, Zip 89502–1474; tel. 775/982–4100; Jim Miller, President and Chief Executive Officer, p. B121

NEW HAMPSHIRE

Laconia: LRG HEALTHCARE 80 Highland Street, Zip 03246–3298; tel. 603/524–3211; Thomas Clairmont, President, p. B70

NEW JERSEY

Edison: ★ SOLARIS HEALTH SYSTEM 80 James Street, 2nd Floor, Zip 08820–3998; tel. 732/632–1501; John P. McGee, President and Chief Executive Officer, p. B101

Egg Harbor City: ★ ATLANTICARE 2500 English Creek Avenue, Building C., Zip 08234; tel. 609/407–2300; George F. Lynn, President, p. B12

Florham Park: ★ ATLANTIC HEALTH SYSTEM 325 Columbia Turnpike, Zip 07932; tel. 973/660–3270; Joseph A. Trunfio, Ph.D., President and Chief Executive Officer, p. B12

Jersey City: LIBERTYHEALTH 355 Grand Street, Zip 07302; tel. 201/915–2000; Jonathan M. Metsch, Dr.PH, President and Chief Executive Officer, p. B67

Marlton: VIRTUA HEALTH 94 Brick Road, Suite 200, Zip 08053; tel. 856/355–0010; Richard P. Miller, President and Chief Executive Officer, p. B120

Neptune: ★ MERIDIAN HEALTH 1350 Campus Parkway, Zip 07753; tel. 732/751–7510; John K. Lloyd, President and Chief Executive Officer, p. B75

New Brunswick: ROBERT WOOD JOHNSON HEALTH SYSTEM & NETWORK 1 Robert Wood Johnson Place, Zip 08903–2601; tel. 732/828–3000; Clifton R. Lacy, M.D., President and Chief Executive Officer, p. B94

Newark: CATHEDRAL HEALTHCARE SYSTEM, INC. 219 Chestnut Street, Zip 07105–1558; tel. 973/690–3600; Henry Amoroso, President and Chief Executive Officer, p. B22

Paterson: ST. JOSEPH'S HEALTHCARE SYSTEM 703 Main Street, Zip 07503–2691; tel. 973/754–2000; William A. McDonald, Interim Chief Executive Officer, p. B102

Ramsey: LIBERTY MANAGEMENT GROUP, INC. 19 Spear Road, Suite 305, Zip 07446; tel. 201/236–8880; William J. Hartigan, President and Chief Executive Officer, p. B67

Trenton: CAPITAL HEALTH SYSTEM 750 Brunswick Avenue, Zip 08638–4174; tel. 609/394–6000; Al Maghazehe, President and Chief Executive Officer, p. B21

DIVISION OF MENTAL HEALTH SERVICES, DEPARTMENT OF HUMAN SERVICES, STATE OF NEW JERSEY Capital Center, P.O. Box 727, Zip 08625–0727; tel. 609/777–0702; Alan G. Kaufman, Director, p. B41

West Orange: ★ SAINT BARNABAS HEALTH CARE SYSTEM 95 Old Short Hills Road, Zip 07052; tel. 973/322–4001; Ronald J. Del Mauro, President and Chief Executive Officer, p. B94

NEW MEXICO

Albuquerque: ★ PRESBYTERIAN HEALTHCARE SERVICES 2501 Buena Vista, S.E., Zip 87106, Mailing Address: P.O. Box 26666, Zip 87125–6666; tel. 505/841–1234; James H. Hinton, President and Chief Executive Officer, p. B84

UNIVERSITY OF NEW MEXICO 915 Camino De Salud, Zip 87131–0001; tel. 505/272–5849; R. Philip Eaton, M.D., Vice President Health Sciences, p. B117

NEW YORK

Albany: NEW YORK STATE OFFICE OF MENTAL HEALTH 44 Holland Avenue, Zip 12229–3411; tel. 518/474–4403; Sharon E. Carpinello, R.N., Ph.D., Commissioner, p. B78

Binghamton: UNITED HEALTH SERVICES 10–42 Mitchell Avenue, Zip 13903; tel. 607/762–2200; Matthew J. Salanger, President and Chief Executive Officer, p. B113

Buffalo: ★ CATHOLIC HEALTH SYSTEM 515 Abbott Road, Suite 508, Zip 14220; tel. 716/828–2750; Joseph D. McDonald, President and Chief Executive Officer, p. B25

KALEIDA HEALTH 901 Washington Street, Zip 14203; tel. 716/859–2155; William D. McGuire, President and Chief Executive Officer, p. B65

Great Neck: ★ NORTH SHORE–LIJ HEALTH SYSTEM 150 Community Drive, Zip 11021; tel. 516/465–8100; Michael J. Dowling, President and Chief Executive Officer, p. B80

New York: ★ CONTINUUM HEALTH PARTNERS 555 West 57th Street, Zip 10019; tel. 212/523–8130; Stanley Brezenoff, President and Chief Executive Officer, p. B33

★ NEW YORK CITY HEALTH AND HOSPITALS CORPORATION 125 Worth Street, Room 514, Zip 10013–4006; tel. 212/788–3321; Alan D. Aviles, Acting President, p. B78

NEW YORK PRESBYTERIAN HEALTHCARE SYSTEM 525 East 68th Street, Zip 10021–4885; tel. 212/746–3745; Herbert Pardes, M.D., Chief Executive Officer, p. B78

★ SAINT VINCENT CATHOLIC MEDICAL CENTERS 130 West 12th Street, Suite 1G, Zip 10011; tel. 212/604–2300; David E. Speltz, Chief Executive Officer, p. B95

Poughkeepsie: HEALTH QUEST 45 Reade Place, Zip 12601; tel. 845/431–5601; Adil M. Ameer, Chief Executive Officer, p. B56

Rochester: STRONG MEMORIAL HOSPITAL 601 Elmwood Avenue, Zip 14642–0002; tel. 585/275–2100; Steven I. Goldstein, General Director and Chief Executive Officer, p. B103

VIAHEALTH 1425 Portland Avenue, 5th Floor, Zip 14621; tel. 585/922–4437; Samuel R. Huston, President and Chief Executive Officer, p. B120

Rockville Centre: ★ CATHOLIC HEALTH SERVICES OF LONG ISLAND 1 Huntington Quadrangle, Suite 4C04, Zip 11570; tel. 516/705–3700; James Harden, President and Chief Executive Officer, p. B25

Syracuse: SISTERS OF SAINT FRANCIS 2500 Grant Boulevard, Zip 13208–1713; tel. 315/634–7000; Sister Grace Anne Dillenschneider, Assistant General Minister, p. B100

NORTH CAROLINA

Charlotte: ★ CAROLINAS HEALTHCARE SYSTEM 1000 Blythe Boulevard, Zip 28203–5871, Mailing Address: P.O. Box 32861, Zip 28232–2861; tel. 704/355–2000; Michael C. Tarwater, President and Chief Executive Officer, p. B22

HOSPITAL PARTNERS OF AMERICA 2320 Cascade Pointe Boulevard, Suite 310, Zip 28208; tel. 704/424–6800; Todd Johnson, President and Chief Executive Officer, p. B60

MEDCATH, INC. 10720 Sikes Place, Suite 300, Zip 28277–8143; tel. 704/708–6610; Charles R. Slaton, President and Chief Operating Officer, p. B73

Durham: ★ DUKE UNIVERSITY HEALTH SYSTEM Erwin Road, Zip 27710, Mailing Address: P.O. Box 3701, Zip 27710–3701; tel. 919/684–2255; Victor J. Dzau, M.D., President and Chief Executive Officer, p. B42

Fayetteville: CUMBERLAND COUNTY HOSPITAL SYSTEM 1638 Owen Drive, Zip 28304, Mailing Address: P.O. Box 2000, Zip 28302–2000; tel. 910/609–4000; Richard H. Parks, FACHE, Chief Executive Officer, p. B35

Greensboro: ★ MOSES CONE HEALTH SYSTEM 1200 North Elm Street, Zip 27401–1020; tel. 336/832–7000; Timothy Rice, President and Chief Executive Officer, p. B76

Greenville: ★ UNIVERSITY HEALTH SYSTEMS OF EASTERN CAROLINA 2100 Stantonsburg Road, Zip 27834, Mailing Address: P.O. Box 6028, Zip 27835–6028; tel. 252/847–4100; Dave C. McRae, Chief Executive Officer, p. B116

Pinehurst: ★ FIRSTHEALTH OF THE CAROLINAS 155 Memorial Drive, Zip 28374–8710, Mailing Address: P.O. Box 3000, Zip 28374–3000; tel. 910/715–1000; Charles T. Frock, President and Chief Executive Officer, p. B45

Raleigh: ★ WAKEMED 3000 New Bern Avenue, Zip 27610; tel. 919/350–8000; William K. Atkinson II, Ph.D., President and Chief Executive Officer, p. B121

Sylva: WESTCARE HEALTH SYSTEM 68 Hospital Road, Zip 28779; tel. 828/586–7000; Mark T. Leonard, Chief Executive Officer, p. B122

Wilmington: ★ NEW HANOVER HEALTH NETWORK 2131 South 17th Street, Zip 28401–9000; tel. 910/343–7040; John K. Barto Jr, Chief Executive Officer, p. B77

Winston–Salem: ★ NORTH CAROLINA BAPTIST HOSPITAL Medical Center Boulevard, Zip 27157; tel. 336/716–2011; Len B. Preslar Jr, President and Chief Executive Officer, p. B79

★ NOVANT HEALTH 2085 Frontis Plaza Boulevard, Zip 27103–3090; tel. 336/718–2023; Paul M. Wiles, President and Chief Executive Officer, p. B80

NORTH DAKOTA

Bismarck: BENEDICTINE SISTERS OF THE ANNUNCIATION 7520 University Drive, Zip 58504–9653; tel. 701/255–1520; Sister Susan Berger, Prioress, p. B17

Fargo: ★ MERITCARE HEALTH SYSTEM 720 Fourth Street North, Zip 58122; tel. 701/234–6000; Roger L. Gilbertson, M.D., President and Chief Executive Officer, p. B75

SISTERS OF MARY OF THE PRESENTATION HEALTH SYSTEM 1102 Page Drive S.W., Zip 58106–0007, Mailing Address: P.O. Box 10007, Zip 58106–0007; tel. 701/237–9290; Aaron Alton, President and Chief Executive Officer, p. B99

OHIO

Akron: AKRON GENERAL HEALTH SYSTEM 400 Wabash Avenue, Zip 44307–2433; tel. 330/344–6000; Alan J. Bleyer, President and Chief Executive Officer, p. B6

Cincinnati: ★ CATHOLIC HEALTHCARE PARTNERS 615 Elsinore Place, Zip 45202; tel. 513/639–2800; Michael D. Connelly, President and Chief Executive Officer, p. B25

★ HEALTH ALLIANCE OF GREATER CINCINNATI 3200 Burnet Avenue, Zip 45229; tel. 513/585–6000; Kenneth Hanover, President and Chief Executive Officer, p. B54

Cleveland: CLEVELAND CLINIC HEALTH SYSTEM 9500 Euclid, Zip 44195–5108; tel. 216/444–2200; Thomas A. Selden, Chief Operating Officer, p. B29

SISTERS OF CHARITY OF ST. AUGUSTINE HEALTH SYSTEM 2351 East 22nd Street, Zip 44115–3197; tel. 216/696–5560; Sister Judith Ann Karam, President and Chief Executive Officer, p. B99

UNIVERSITY HOSPITALS HEALTH SYSTEM 11100 Euclid Avenue, Zip 44106–5000; tel. 216/844–1000; Thomas F. Zenty III, President and Chief Executive Officer, p. B116

Columbus: OHIO STATE UNIVERSITY HEALTH SYSTEM 370 West 10th Avenue, Zip 43210–1240; tel. 614/293–8000; Peter E. Geier, Chief Executive Officer, p. B81

★ OHIOHEALTH 1087 Dennison Avenue, Zip 43201; tel. 614/544–5430; David P. Blom, President and Chief Executive Officer, p. B81

Dayton: ★ KETTERING MEDICAL CENTER–NETWORK 3965 Southern Boulevard, Zip 45429–1221; tel. 937/395–8150; Francisco J. Perez, FACHE, Network Chief Executive Officer, p. B65

Sylvania: FRANCISCAN SERVICES CORPORATION 6832 Convent Boulevard, Zip 43560–2897; tel. 419/882–8373; John W. O'Connell, President, p. B45

Toledo: ★ PROMEDICA HEALTH SYSTEM 2121 Hughes Drive, 4th Floor, Zip 43606; tel. 419/291–7176; Alan W. Brass, FACHE, Chief Executive Officer and President, p. B85

Youngstown: FORUM HEALTH 3530 Belmont Avenue, Suite 7, Zip 44505; tel. 330/759–4090; N. Kristopher Hoce, President and Chief Executive Officer, p. B45

OKLAHOMA

Oklahoma City: ★ INTEGRIS HEALTH 3366 N.W. Expressway, Suite 800, Zip 73112–9756; tel. 405/949–6068; Stanley F. Hupfeld, President and Chief Executive Officer, p. B62

OKLAHOMA STATE DEPARTMENT OF MENTAL HEALTH AND SUBSTANCE ABUSE SERVICES 1200 N.E. 13th Street, Zip 73117, Mailing Address: P.O. Box 53277, Zip 73152–3277; tel. 405/522–3878; Terry Cline, Ph.D., Commissioner, p. B81

Shawnee: PREFERRED MANAGEMENT CORPORATION 120 West MacArthur, Suite 121, Zip 74804–2028; tel. 405/878–0202; Donald Freeman, President and Chief Executive Officer, p. B84

Tulsa: ★ HILLCREST HEALTHCARE SYSTEM 110 West 7th Street, Suite 2540, Zip 74119; tel. 918/579–1070; Kevin J. Gross, President and Chief Executive Officer, p. B59

★ MARIAN HEALTH SYSTEM Mailing Address: P.O. Box 4753, Zip 74159–0753; tel. 918/742–9988; Sister M. Therese Gottschalk, President, p. B71

★ SAINT FRANCIS HEALTH SYSTEM 6161 South Yale Avenue, Zip 74136–1902; tel. 918/494–8454; Jake Henry Jr, President and Chief Executive Officer, p. B95

OREGON

Bend: ★ CASCADE HEALTHCARE COMMUNITY 2500 N.E. Neff Road, Zip 97701–6015; tel. 541/382–4321; Jim R. Hobbs, President and Chief Executive Officer, p. B22

Corvallis: ★ SAMARITAN HEALTH SERVICES 3600 N.W. Samaritan Drive, Zip 97330, Mailing Address: P.O. Box 1068, Zip 97339; tel. 541/768–5001; Larry A. Mullins, FACHE, President and Chief Executive Officer, p. B95

Medford: ★ ASANTE HEALTH SYSTEM 2650 Siskiyou Boulevard, Suite 200, Zip 97504–8177; tel. 541/789–4100; Roy G. Vinyard II, President and Chief Executive Officer, p. B9

Portland: ★ LEGACY HEALTH SYSTEM 1919 N.W. Lovejoy Street, Zip 97209–1503; tel. 503/415–5600; Robert Pallari, President and Chief Executive Officer, p. B67

PENNSYLVANIA

Beaver: HERITAGE VALLEY HEALTH SYSTEM 1000 Dutch Ridge Road, Zip 15009–9727; tel. 724/728–7000; Norman F. Mitry, President and Chief Executive Officer, p. B59

Chambersburg: ★ SUMMIT HEALTH 112 North Seventh Street, Zip 17201; tel. 717/267–7138; Norman B. Epstein, CHE, President, p. B103

Danville: ★ GEISINGER HEALTH SYSTEM 100 North Academy Avenue, Zip 17822; tel. 570/271–6211; Glenn Steele Jr, M.D., Ph.D., President and Chief Executive Officer, p. B46

Erie: ST. VINCENT HEALTH SYSTEM 232 West 25th Street, Zip 16544–0002; tel. 814/452–5000; C. Angela Bontempo, President and Chief Executive Officer, p. B103

Greensburg: EXCELA HEALTH 532 West Pittsburgh Street, Zip 15601; tel. 724/832–5050; David S. Gallatin, Chief Executive Officer, p. B44

Hazleton: GREATER HAZLETON HEALTH ALLIANCE 687 North Church Street, Zip 18201–3198; tel. 570/501–6000; James D. Edwards, President, p. B47

King of Prussia: UNIVERSAL HEALTH SERVICES, INC. 367 South Gulph Road, Zip 19406–0958, Mailing Address: P.O. Box 61558, Zip 19406–0958; tel. 610/768–3300; Alan B. Miller, President and Chief Executive Officer, p. B114

Lafayette Hill: PROGRESSIONS GROUP, INC. 660 Thomas Road, Zip 19444; tel. 215/836–7700; Nicholas Tenaglia, M.D., Chairman of the Board, p. B85

Lehighton: BLUE MOUNTAIN HEALTH SYSTEM 211 North 12th Street, Zip 18235–1138; tel. 610/377–1300; Robert J. Clark, FACHE, President and Chief Executive Officer, p. B18

Mechanicsburg: SELECT MEDICAL CORPORATION 4718 Old Gettysburg Road, Zip 17055; tel. 717/972–1100; Robert Ortenzio, Chief Executive Officer, p. B96

VIBRA HEALTHCARE 4550 Lena Drive, Suite 225, Zip 17055; tel. 717/591–5700; Brad Hollinger, Chairman and Chief Executive Officer, p. B120

Newtown Square: ★ CATHOLIC HEALTH EAST 14 Campus Boulevard, Suite 300, Zip 19073–3277; tel. 610/355–2000; Robert V. Stanek, President and Chief Executive Officer, p. B23

Philadelphia: ALBERT EINSTEIN HEALTHCARE NETWORK 5501 Old York Road, Zip 19141–3098; tel. 215/456–7890; Barry R. Freedman, President and Chief Executive Officer, p. B6

★ TEMPLE UNIVERSITY HEALTH SYSTEM 3509 North Broad Street, 9th Floor, Zip 19140; tel. 215/707–0900; Joseph W. Marshall III, Chairman and Chief Executive Officer, p. B105

UNIVERSITY OF PENNSYLVANIA HEALTH SYSTEM 399 South 34th Street, 21st Floor, Zip 19104–4385; tel. 215/662–2203; Ralph W. Muller, President and Chief Executive Officer, p. B117

Pittsburgh: UNIVERSITY OF PITTSBURGH MEDICAL CENTER 200 Lothrop Street, Zip 15213; tel. 412/647–2345; Jeffrey A. Romoff, President, p. B117

★ WEST PENN ALLEGHENY HEALTH SYSTEM 4800 Friendship Avenue, Zip 15224; tel. 412/578–4703; Jerry J. Fedele, President and Chief Executive Officer, p. B122

Sayre: ★ GUTHRIE HEALTHCARE SYSTEM Guthrie Square, Zip 18840; tel. 570/888–6666; Mark Stensager, President and Chief Executive Officer, p. B48

Springfield: ★ CROZER–KEYSTONE HEALTH SYSTEM 100 West Sproul Road, Zip 19064; tel. 610/338–8211; Gerald Miller, President and Chief Executive Officer, p. B35

Villanova: DEVEREUX 444 Devereux Drive, Zip 19085, Mailing Address: P.O. Box 638, Zip 19085–0638; tel. 610/520–3000; Robert Q. Kreider, President and Chief Executive, p. B41

Wayne: JEFFERSON HEALTH SYSTEM 259 Radnor–Chester Road, Suite 290, Zip 19087–5288; tel. 610/225–6200; Joseph T. Sebastianelli, President and Chief Executive Officer, p. B63

York: ★ WELLSPAN HEALTH 45 Monument Road, Suite 200, Zip 17403; tel. 717/851–2121; Bruce M. Bartels, President, p. B121

PUERTO RICO

San Juan: ★ PUERTO RICO DEPARTMENT OF HEALTH Building A – Medical Center, Zip 00936, Mailing Address: Call Box 70184, Zip 00936; tel. 787/274–7676; Johnny V. Rullan, M.D., Secretary of Health, p. B88

RHODE ISLAND

Providence: ★ CARE NEW ENGLAND HEALTH SYSTEM 45 Willard Avenue, Zip 02905–3218; tel. 401/453–7900; John J. Hynes, President and Chief Executive Officer, p. B21

LIFESPAN CORPORATION 167 Point Street, Zip 02903–4771; tel. 401/444–3500; George A. Vecchione, President, p. B70

SOUTH CAROLINA

Charleston: MUSC MEDICAL CENTER OF MEDICAL UNIVERSITY OF SOUTH CAROLINA 169 Ashley Avenue, Zip 29425–5836; tel. 843/792–2300; Stuart Smith, Vice President Clinical Operations and Executive Director, p. B77

Columbia: ★ PALMETTO HEALTH ALLIANCE 1301 Taylor Street, Suite 9–A, Zip 29201, Mailing Address: P.O. Box 2266, Zip 29202–2266; tel. 803/296–2100; Charles D. Beaman Jr, President, p. B82

Greenville: ★ GREENVILLE HOSPITAL SYSTEM 701 Grove Road, Zip 29605–4211; tel. 864/455–7000; Frank D. Pinckney, President and Chief Executive Officer, p. B47

Spartanburg: ★ SPARTANBURG REGIONAL HEALTHCARE SYSTEM 101 East Wood Street, Zip 29303–3016; tel. 864/560–6000; Ingo Angermeier, FACHE, President and Chief Executive Officer, p. B101

SOUTH DAKOTA

Rapid City: REGIONAL HEALTH 353 Fairmont Boulevard, Zip 57701, Mailing Address: P.O. Box 6000, Zip 57709–6000; tel. 605/719–1000; Charles Hart, M.D., President and Chief Executive Officer, p. B93

Sioux Falls: ★ SIOUX VALLEY HOSPITALS AND HEALTH SYSTEM 1305 West 18th Street, Zip 57105–0496, Mailing Address: P.O. Box 5039, Zip 57117–5039; tel. 605/333–1000; Kelby K. Krabbenhoft, President and Chief Executive Officer, p. B98

Yankton: ★ AVERA HEALTH 610 West 23rd Street, Zip 57078, Mailing Address: P.O. Box 38, Zip 57078–0038; tel. 605/322–7050; John T. Porter, President and Chief Executive Officer, p. B13

TENNESSEE

Brentwood: ASSOCIATED HEALTHCARE SYSTEMS, INC. 214 Overlook Court, Suite 260, Zip 37027; tel. 615/309–0940; A. Ronald Turner, President and Chief Executive Officer, p. B12

★ BRIM HEALTHCARE, INC. 105 Westwood Place, Suite 300, Zip 37027; tel. 615/309–6053; Dave Woodland, President, p. B18

COMMUNITY HEALTH SYSTEMS, INC. 155 Franklin Road, Suite 400, Zip 37027–4600, Mailing Address: P.O. Box 217, Zip 37024–0217; tel. 615/373–9600; Wayne T. Smith, Chairman, President and Chief Executive Officer, p. B30

★ LIFEPOINT HOSPITALS, INC. 103 Powell Court, Suite 200, Zip 37027; tel. 615/372–8500; Kenneth C. Donahey, Chairman and Chief Executive Officer, p. B68

Chattanooga: ERLANGER HEALTH SYSTEM 975 East Third Street, Zip 37403; tel. 423/778–7000; James L. Brexler, President, p. B44

Franklin: IASIS HEALTHCARE 117 Seaborad Lane, Building E., Zip 37067, Mailing Address: 117 Seaboard Lane, Building E., Zip 37067; tel. 615/844–2747; David R. White, Chairman and Chief Executive Officer, p. B61

PSYCHIATRIC SOLUTIONS 840 Crescent Centre Drive, Suite 460, Zip 37067; tel. 615/312–5700; Joey Jacobs, President and Chief Executive Officer, p. B87

Gallatin: SUMNER REGIONAL HEALTH SYSTEMS 555 Hartsville Pike, Zip 37066; tel. 615/452–4210; William T. Sugg, President and Chief Executive Officer, p. B103

Jackson: ★ WEST TENNESSEE HEALTHCARE 708 West Forest Avenue, Zip 38301–3901; tel. 731/425–5000; James T. Moss, President, p. B122

Johnson City: MOUNTAIN STATES HEALTH ALLIANCE 701 North State of Franklin, Suite 1, Zip 37604; tel. 423/431–6040; Dennis Vonderfecht, President and Chief Executive Officer, p. B76

Kingsport: WELLMONT HEALTH SYSTEM 1905 American Way, Zip 37662–0224; tel. 423/230–8200; Richard Salluzo, M.D., President and Chief Executive Officer, p. B121

Knoxville: BAPTIST HEALTH SYSTEM OF EAST TENNESSEE 137 Blount Avenue S.E., Zip 37920–1643, Mailing Address: P.O. Box 1788, Zip 37901–1788; tel. 865/632–5011; Dale Collins, President and Chief Executive Officer, p. B15

★ COVENANT HEALTH 100 Fort Sanders West Boulevard, Zip 37922; tel. 865/531–5555; Anthony L. Spezia, President and Chief Executive Officer, p. B34

Memphis: ★ BAPTIST MEMORIAL HEALTH CARE CORPORATION 350 North Humphreys Boulevard, Zip 38120–2177; tel. 901/227–5117; Stephen Curtis Reynolds, President and Chief Executive Officer, p. B16

METHODIST HEALTHCARE 1211 Union Avenue, Suite 700, Zip 38104–6600; tel. 901/516–0543; Gary S. Shorb, Chief Executive Officer, p. B75

Nashville: AMERIS HEALTH SYSTEMS 1114 17th Avenue South, Suite 205, Zip 37212–2215; tel. 615/327–4440; Sam Lewis, Chairman and Chief Executive Officer, p. B8

ARDENT HEALTH SERVICES 1 Burton Hills Boulevard, Suite 250, Zip 37215; tel. 615/296–3000; David T. Vandewater, President and Chief Executive Officer, p. B9

ESSENT HEALTHCARE 3100 West End Avenue, Suite 900, Zip 37203; tel. 615/312–5100; W. Hudson Connery Jr, President and Chief Executive Officer, p. B44

★ HCA One Park Plaza, Zip 37203–1548; tel. 615/344–9551; Jack O. Bovender Jr, Chairman and Chief Executive Officer, p. B48

VANGUARD HEALTH SYSTEM 20 Burton Hills Boulevard, Suite 10, Zip 37215; tel. 615/665–6000; Charles N. Martin Jr, Chairman and Chief Executive Officer, p. B119

TEXAS

Addison: UNITED SURGICAL PARTNERS INTERNATIONAL 15305 Dallas Parkway, Suite 1600, Zip 75001–6491; tel. 972/713–3500; William Wilcox, President and Chief Executive Officer, p. B114

Arlington: ★ TEXAS HEALTH RESOURCES 611 Ryan Plaza Drive, Suite 900, Zip 76011; tel. 817/462–7900; Douglas D. Hawthorne, FACHE, President and Chief Executive Officer, p. B107

Austin: CORNERSTONE HEALTHCARE GROUP 7600 Chevy Chase Drive, Building 2, Suite 500, Zip 78752, Mailing Address: 7600 Chevy Chase, Building 2, Suite 500, Zip 78752; tel. 512/533–2400; Michael D. Cress, President, p. B33

TEXAS DEPARTMENT OF STATE HEALTH SERVICES 1100 West 49th Street, Zip 78756–3199; tel. 512/458–7111; Eduardo J. Sanchez, M.D., M.P.H., Commissioner of Health, p. B107

UNIVERSITY OF TEXAS SYSTEM 601 Colorado Street, Zip 78701–2982; tel. 512/499–4224; James C. Guckian, M.D., Executive Vice Chancellor, p. B118

YOUTH AND FAMILY CENTERED SERVICES 1705 Capital of Texas Highway South, Zip 78746; tel. 512/327–1119; Kevin P. Sheehan, Chairman, President and Chief Executive Officer, p. B123

Dallas: ★ BAYLOR HEALTH CARE SYSTEM 3500 Gaston Avenue, Zip 75246; tel. 214/820–0111; Joel T. Allison, President and Chief Executive Officer, p. B16

★ METHODIST HEALTH SYSTEM 1441 North Beckley Avenue, Zip 75203–1201, Mailing Address: P.O. Box 655999, Zip 75265–5999; tel. 214/947–8181; Howard M. Chase, FACHE, President and Chief Executive Officer, p. B75

★ TENET HEALTHCARE CORPORATION 13737 Noel Road, Suite 100, Zip 75240–2200; tel. 469/893–2200; Trevor Fetter, President and Chief Executive Officer, p. B105

★ UT SOUTHWESTERN MEDICAL CENTER AT DALLAS 5151 Harry Hines Boulevard, Zip 75235–7786; tel. 214/590–3000; Sharon L. Riley, Chief Executive Officer, p. B118

Fort Worth: TARRANT COUNTY HOSPITAL DISTRICT 1500 South Main Street, Zip 76104–4941; tel. 817/927–1230; David M. Cecero, President and Chief Executive Officer, p. B104

Houston: CAMBRIDGE INTERNATIONAL, INC, 7505 Fannin, Suite 680, Zip 77225; tel. 713/790–1153; Timothy Sharma, M.D., President, p. B20

★ DUBUIS HEALTH SYSTEM 10333 Richmond Avenue, Suite 300, Zip 77042; tel. 713/339–7000; Ellen Smith, President and Chief Executive Officer, p. B42

DYNACQ HEALTHCARE, INC. 10304 Interstate 10 East, Suite 369, Zip 77029; tel. 713/673–6432; Chiu Moon Chan, Chairman, President and Chief Executive Officer, p. B42

HEALTHPLUS 509 West Tidwell Road, Zip 77091; tel. 713/490–0700; Mac Burt, President and Chief Executive Officer, p. B56

★ MEMORIAL HERMANN HEALTHCARE SYSTEM 7737 S.W. Freeway, Suite 200, Zip 77074–1800; tel. 713/456–5550; Daniel J. Wolterman, President and Chief Executive Officer, p. B74

ST. LUKE'S EPISCOPAL HEALTH SYSTEM 6624 Fannin Street, Suite 1100, Zip 77030; tel. 832/355–7661; David J. Fine, Chief Executive Officer, p. B102

★ THE METHODIST HOSPITAL SYSTEM 6565 Fannin Street, D–200, Zip 77030–2707; tel. 713/790–2221; Ronald G. Girotto, President and Chief Executive Officer, p. B108

TRIUMPH HEALTHCARE 7333 North Freeway, Suite 500, Zip 77076; tel. 832/200–6000; Charlie Allen, President and Chief Executive, p. B111

Irving: ★ CHRISTUS HEALTH 6363 North Highway 161, Suite 450, Zip 75038; tel. 877/980–0100; Thomas C. Royer, M.D., President, p. B28

Lewisville: HORIZON HEALTH CORPORATION 1500 Waters Ridge Drive, Zip 75057; tel. 972/420–8222; Ken Newman, President and Chief Executive Officer, p. B60

Lubbock: ★ COVENANT HEALTH SYSTEM 3615 19th Street, Zip 79410–1201; tel. 806/725–1011; Steven L. Hunter, President and Chief Executive Officer, p. B34

Lufkin: MEMORIAL HEALTH SYSTEM OF EAST TEXAS 1201 West Frank Avenue, Zip 75904–3357; tel. 936/634–8111; Bryant H. Krenek Jr, President and Chief Executive Officer, p. B74

Plano: LIFECARE MANAGEMENT SERVICES 5560 Tennyson Parkway, Zip 75024; tel. 469/241–2100; Thomas W. Erickson, Board Chairman and Chief Executive Officer, p. B68

★ QUORUM HEALTH RESOURCES 5800 Tennyson Parkway, Zip 75024; tel. 214/473–3700; John C. Stinson, President and Chief Executive Officer, p. B88

★ TRIAD HOSPITALS, INC. 5800 Tennyson Parkway, Zip 75024; tel. 214/473–7000; James D. Shelton, Chairman and Chief Executive Officer, p. B108

San Antonio: WARM SPRINGS REHABILITATION SYSTEM 909 N.E. Loop 410, Zip 78209; tel. 210/616–0100, p. B121

Tyler: ★ EAST TEXAS MEDICAL CENTER REGIONAL HEALTHCARE SYSTEM 1000 South Beckham Street, Zip 75701–1996, Mailing Address: P.O. Box 6400, Zip 75711–6400; tel. 903/535–6211; Elmer G. Ellis, FACHE, President and Chief Executive Officer, p. B42

UTAH

Nephi: ★ RURAL HEALTH MANAGEMENT CORPORATION 48 West 1500 North, Zip 84648–1226; tel. 435/623–4924; Mark R. Stoddard, President, p. B94

Salt Lake City: ★ INTERMOUNTAIN HEALTH CARE, INC. 36 South State Street, 22nd Floor, Zip 84111–1453; tel. 801/442–2000; William H. Nelson, President and Chief Executive Officer, p. B62

VIRGINIA

Falls Church: DEPARTMENT OF THE ARMY, OFFICE OF THE SURGEON GENERAL 5109 Leesburg Pike, Zip 22041; tel. 703/681–3000; Lieutenant General Kevin C. Kiley, M.D., Surgeon General, p. B36

★ INOVA HEALTH SYSTEM 8110 Gatehouse Road, Zip 22042; tel. 703/289–2069; J. Knox Singleton, President and Chief Executive Officer, p. B61

Newport News: RIVERSIDE HEALTH SYSTEM 701 Town Center Drive, Suite 1000, Zip 23606; tel. 757/534–7000; Richard J. Pearce, President and Chief Executive Officer, p. B94

Norfolk: ★ SENTARA HEALTHCARE 6015 Poplar Hall Drive, Zip 23502–3819; tel. 757/455–7000; David L. Bernd, Chief Executive Officer, p. B96

Richmond: VIRGINIA DEPARTMENT OF MENTAL HEALTH 1220 Bank Street, Zip 23219, Mailing Address: P.O. Box 1797, Zip 23218–1797; tel. 804/786–3921; James S. Reinhard, M.D., Commissioner, p. B120

Roanoke: ★ CARILION HEALTH SYSTEM Belleview at Jefferson Street, Zip 24014, Mailing Address: P.O. Box 13367, Zip 24033; tel. 540/981–7893; Edward G. Murphy, M.D., President and Chief Executvie Officer, p. B21

Winchester: ★ VALLEY HEALTH SYSTEM 190 Campus Boulevard, Suite 220, Zip 22601, Mailing Address: P.O. Box 3340, Zip 22604–1334; tel. 540/536–8024; Michael J. Halseth, President and Chief Executive Officer, p. B119

WASHINGTON

Bellevue: ★ PEACEHEALTH 14432 S.E. Eastgate Way, Suite 300, Zip 98007–6412; tel. 425/747–1711; John Hayward, President and Chief Executive Officer, p. B83

Seattle: ★ PROVIDENCE HEALTH SYSTEM 506 Second Avenue, Suite 1200, Zip 98104–2329; tel. 206/464–3355; John Koster, M.D., President and Chief Executive Officer, p. B86

Spokane: ★ EMPIRE HEALTH SERVICES West 800 Fifth Avenue, Zip 99204, Mailing Address: P.O. Box 248, Zip 99210–0248; tel. 509/473–7960; Jeffrey Nelson, Interim President and Chief Executive Officer, p. B44

★ PROVIDENCE SERVICES 9 East Ninth Avenue, Zip 99202; tel. 509/474–7337; Richard J. Umbdenstock, President and Chief Executive Officer, p. B86

Tacoma: MULTICARE HEALTH SYSTEM 315 Martin Luther King Jr. Way, Zip 98415, Mailing Address: P.O. Box 5299, Zip 98415–0299; tel. 253/403–1000; Diane Cecchettini, President and Chief Executive Officer, p. B77

WEST VIRGINIA

Charleston: ★ CHARLESTON AREA MEDICAL CENTER HEALTH SYSTEM, INC. 501 Morris Street, Zip 25301–1300, Mailing Address: P.O. Box 1547, Zip 25326–1547; tel. 304/388–5432; David L. Ramsey, President and Chief Executive Officer, p. B28

Fairmont: ★ WEST VIRGINIA UNITED HEALTH SYSTEM 1000 Technology Drive, Sutie 2320, Zip 26554, Mailing Address: 1000 Technology Drive, Suite 2320, Zip 26554; tel. 304/368–2700; J. Thomas Jones, President and Chief Executive Officer, p. B122

Wheeling: ★ OHIO VALLEY HEALTH SERVICES AND EDUCATION CORPORATION 2000 Eoff Street, Zip 26003; tel. 304/234–8383; Brian K. Felici, President and Chief Executive Officer, p. B81

WISCONSIN

Appleton: ★ THEDACARE, INC. 122 East College Avenue, Zip 54911, Mailing Address: P.O. Box 8025, Zip 54912; tel. 920/830–5880; John S. Toussaint, M.D., President and Chief Executive Officer, p. B108

Manitowoc: ★ FRANCISCAN SISTERS OF CHRISTIAN CHARITY HEALTHCARE MINISTRY, INC 1415 South Rapids Road, Zip 54220–9302; tel. 920/684–7071; Sister Laura J. Wolf, President, p. B46

Milwaukee: ★ AURORA HEALTH CARE 3000 West Montana, Zip 53215–3268, Mailing Address: P.O. Box 343910, Zip 53234–3910; tel. 414/647–3000; G. Edwin Howe, President, p. B12

Waukesha: ★ PROHEALTH CARE N17 W24199 Riverwood Drive, Suite 130, Zip 53188, Mailing Address: N17 W24100 Riverwood Drive, Suite 130, Zip 53188; tel. 262/928–2244; Rexford W. Titus III, President and Chief Executive Officer, p. B85

ALASKA

KETCHIKAN GENERAL HOSPITAL
3100 Tongass Avenue, Ketchikan, AK 99901; tel. 907/225-5171; Ed Mahn, President

KETCHIKAN GENERAL HOSPITAL, 3100 Tongass Avenue, Ketchikan, AK, Zip 99901-5746; tel. 907/225-5171; Patrick J. Branco, Chief Executive Officer

NORTON SOUND REGIONAL HOSPITAL
P.O. Box 966, Nome, AK 99762; tel. 907/443-3311; H. Mack, Network Contact

NORTON SOUND REGIONAL HOSPITAL, Bering Straits, Nome, AK, Zip 99762, Mailing Address: P.O. Box 966, Zip 99762-0966; tel. 907/443-3311; Angela Gorn, Vice President

ARIZONA

NORTHERN ARIZONA HEALTHCARE
1200 North Beaver Street, Flagstaff, AZ 86001; tel. 520/773-2180; Joseph M. Kortum, President

FLAGSTAFF MEDICAL CENTER, 1200 North Beaver Street, Flagstaff, AZ, Zip 86001-3198; tel. 928/779-3366; James Puffenberger, Interim Chief Executive Officer

VERDE VALLEY MEDICAL CENTER, 269 South Candy Lane, Cottonwood, AZ, Zip 86326-4170; tel. 928/634-2251; James J. Sinek, President and Senior Executive Officer

CALIFORNIA

ADVENTIST HEALTH SOUTHERN CALIFORNIA
1505 Wilson Terrace, Suite 220, Glendale, CA 91206; tel. 818/409-8300; Theresa M. Day, Vice President Finance

GLENDALE ADVENTIST MEDICAL CENTER, 1509 Wilson Terrace, Glendale, CA, Zip 91206-4098; tel. 818/409-8000; Scott Reiner, President and Chief Executive Officer

SIMI VALLEY HOSPITAL AND HEALTH CARE SERVICES, 2975 North Sycamore Drive, Simi Valley, CA, Zip 93065-1201; tel. 805/955-6000; Margaret R. Peterson, Ph.D., President and Chief Executive Officer

SOUTH COAST MEDICAL CENTER, 31872 Coast Highway, Laguna Beach, CA, Zip 92651-6775; tel. 949/499-1311; Gary G. Irish, President and Chief Executive Officer

WHITE MEMORIAL MEDICAL CENTER, 1720 Cesar E Chavez Avenue, Los Angeles, CA, Zip 90033-2481; tel. 323/268-5000; Beth D. Zachary, President and Chief Executive Officer

EAST BAY MEDICAL NETWORK
2000 Powell Street 9th Floor, Emeryville, CA 94608; tel. 510/450-9850; Belina Rule, Provider Relations

ALAMEDA HOSPITAL, 2070 Clinton Avenue, Alameda, CA, Zip 94501-4397; tel. 510/522-3700; Stuart A. Jed, Chief Executive Officer

ALTA BATES SUMMIT MEDICAL CENTER, 2450 Ashby Avenue, Berkeley, CA, Zip 94705-2067; tel. 510/204-4444; Warren J. Kirk, Chief Executive Officer

PATTON STATE HOSPITAL, 3102 East Highland Avenue, Patton, CA, Zip 92369; tel. 909/425-7000; William L. Summers, Executive Director

SAN LEANDRO HOSPITAL, 13855 East 14th Street, San Leandro, CA, Zip 94578-2600; tel. 510/357-6500; Ronnie Bayduza, Administrator

SUTTER DELTA MEDICAL CENTER, 3901 Lone Tree Way, Antioch, CA, Zip 94509-6200; tel. 925/779-7200; Linda Horn, Chief Executive Officer

WASHINGTON TOWNSHIP HEALTH CARE DISTRICT, 2000 Mowry Avenue, Fremont, CA, Zip 94538-1746; tel. 510/797-1111; Nancy D. Farber, Chief Executive Officer

ESSENTIAL HEALTHCARE NETWORK
525 North Garfield Park, Monterey Park, CA 91754; tel. 818/573-2222; A. Schaffer, Acting Executive Director

COMMUNITY AND MISSION HOSPITALS OF HUNTINGTON PARK, 2623 East Slauson Avenue, Huntington Park, CA, Zip 90255-2900; tel. 323/583-1931; Barbara Schneider, R.N., Chief Executive Officer

GARFIELD MEDICAL CENTER, 525 North Garfield Avenue, Monterey Park, CA, Zip 91754-1205; tel. 626/573-2222; Philip A. Cohen, Chief Executive Officer

GREATER EL MONTE COMMUNITY HOSPITAL, 1701 Santa Anita Avenue, El Monte, CA, Zip 91733-3411; tel. 626/579-7777; Philip A. Cohen, Chief Executive Officer

HOLLYWOOD PRESBYTERIAN MEDICAL CENTER, 1300 North Vermont Avenue, Los Angeles, CA, Zip 90027-0069; tel. 323/913-4800; Albert L. Greene, Chief Executive Officer

PACIFIC ALLIANCE MEDICAL CENTER, 531 West College Street, Los Angeles, CA, Zip 90012-2315; tel. 213/624-8411; John R. Edwards, Administrator and Chief Executive Officer

PROMISE HOSPITAL OF EAST LOS ANGELES, SUBURBAN MEDICAL CENTER CAMPUS, 16453 South Colorado Avenue, Paramount, CA, Zip 90723-5000; tel. 562/531-3110; Richard McCarthy, Chief Executive Officer

ST. FRANCIS MEDICAL CENTER, 3630 East Imperial Highway, Lynwood, CA, Zip 90262-2636; tel. 310/900-8900; Gerald T. Kozai, President

FRIENDLY HILLS HEALTHCARE NETWORK
501 South Idaho Street, LaHabra, CA 90631; tel. 562/905-5204; Dr. Marvin Rice, Chairman and CEO

PLACENTIA LINDA HOSPITAL, 1301 Rose Drive, Placentia, CA, Zip 92870-3899; tel. 714/993-2000; Kent G. Clayton, President and Chief Executive Officer

WHITTIER HOSPITAL MEDICAL CENTER, 9080 Colima Road, Whittier, CA, Zip 90605-1600; tel. 562/945-3561; Howard Ternes, Chief Executive Officer

INTERMOUNTAIN HEALTHCARE NETWORK
228 McDowell Street, Alturas, CA 96101; Theresa Jacques, Network Contact

INDIAN VALLEY HEALTH CARE DISTRICT, 184 Hot Springs Road, Greenville, CA, Zip 95947-9747; tel. 530/284-7191; Larry S. Pressley, Administrator

MAYERS MEMORIAL HOSPITAL DISTRICT, 43563 Highway 299 East, Fall River Mills, CA, Zip 96028-0459, Mailing Address: P.O. Box 459, Zip 96028-0459; tel. 530/336-5511; Jerald Fikes, Administrator and Chief Executive Officer

MODOC MEDICAL CENTER, 228 McDowell Street, Alturas, CA, Zip 96101-3915; tel. 530/233-5131; Teresa Jacques, Chief Executive Officer

SURPRISE VALLEY HEALTHCARE DISTRICT, Main and Washington Streets, Cedarville, CA, Zip 96104, Mailing Address: P.O. Box 246, Zip 96104-0246; tel. 530/279-6111; Dannette E. DePaul, Administrator

LITTLE COMPANY OF MARY HEALTH SERVICES
4101 Torrance Boulevard, Torrance, CA 90503; tel. 310/793-8152; Blair Contratto, Chief Executive Officer

PROVIDENCE–LITTLE COMPANY OF MARY SERVICE AREA, 4101 Torrance Boulevard, Torrance, CA, Zip 90503-4698; tel. 310/540-7676; Blair Contratto, Chief Executive Officer

SAN PEDRO PENINSULA HOSPITAL, 1300 West Seventh Street, San Pedro, CA, Zip 90732-3505; tel. 310/514-5233; Nancy Carlson, Administrator

COLORADO

COMMUNITY HEALTH PROVIDERS ORGANIZATION
2021 North 12th Street, Grand Junction, CO 81501; tel. 303/256-6200; Randall Phillips, Chief Executive Officer

COMMUNITY HOSPITAL, 2021 North 12th Street, Grand Junction, CO, Zip 81501-2999; tel. 970/242-0920; Mark J. Francis, President and Chief Executive Officer

HEALTHONE
4900 South Monaco Street, Suite 380, Denver, CO 80237; tel. 303/788-2500; Jeffrey A. Dorsey, President and CEO

MEDICAL CENTER OF AURORA, 1501 South Potomac Street, Aurora, CO, Zip 80012-5499; tel. 303/695-2600; Sylvia Young, President and Chief Executive Officer

NORTH SUBURBAN MEDICAL CENTER, 9191 Grant Street, Thornton, CO, Zip 80229-4341; tel. 303/451-7800; Todd Steward, President and Chief Executive Officer

ROSE MEDICAL CENTER, 4567 East Ninth Avenue, Denver, CO, Zip 80220-3941; tel. 303/320-2121; Kenneth H. Feiler, President and Chief Executive Officer

SKY RIDGE MEDICAL CENTER, 10101 Ridge Gate Parkway, Lone Tree, CO, Zip 80124; tel. 720/225-1000; Maureen Tarrant, Chief Executive Officer

SWEDISH MEDICAL CENTER, 501 East Hampden Avenue, Englewood, CO, Zip 80110-0101; tel. 303/788-5000; Mary M. White, President and Chief Executive Officer

THE COLORADO NETWORK, INC.
4450 Arapahoe Avenue #200, Boulder, CO 80303; tel. 303/440-5511; John Leavitt, Executive Director

ARKANSAS VALLEY REGIONAL MEDICAL CENTER, 1100 Carson Avenue, La Junta, CO, Zip 81050-2799; tel. 719/383-6000; Lynn Crowell, Chief Executive Officer

HEART OF THE ROCKIES REGIONAL MEDICAL CENTER, 448 East First Street, Salida, CO, Zip 81201-0429, Mailing Address: P.O. Box 429, Zip 81201-0429; tel. 719/539-6661; Nathan C. Olson, Chief Executive Officer

MEMORIAL HOSPITAL, 785 Russell Street, Craig, CO, Zip 81625-9906; tel. 970/824-9411; M. Randell Phelps, Chief Executive Officer

MONTROSE MEMORIAL HOSPITAL, 800 South Third Street, Montrose, CO, Zip 81401–4291; tel. 970/249–2211; Kenneth E. S. Platou, Chief Executive Officer

MT. SAN RAFAEL HOSPITAL, 410 Benedicta Avenue, Trinidad, CO, Zip 81082–2093; tel. 719/846–9213; Carolyn E. Riley, Chief Executive Officer

PARKVIEW MEDICAL CENTER, 400 West 16th Street, Pueblo, CO, Zip 81003–2781; tel. 719/584–4000; C. W. Smith, President and Chief Executive Officer

PROWERS MEDICAL CENTER, 401 Kendall Drive, Lamar, CO, Zip 81052–3993; tel. 719/336–4343; Greg D. Gerard, Administrator and Chief Executive Officer

VALLEY VIEW HOSPITAL, 1906 Blake Avenue, Glenwood Springs, CO, Zip 81601–4259, Mailing Address: P.O. Box 1970, Zip 81602–1970; tel. 970/945–6535; Gary L. Brewer, Chief Executive Officer

CONNECTICUT

DANBURY HEALTH SYSTEMS, INC.
24 Hospital Avenue, Danbury, CT 06810; tel. 203/797–7066; Frank J. Kelly, President and Chief Executive Officer

DANBURY HOSPITAL, 24 Hospital Avenue, Danbury, CT, Zip 06810–6099; tel. 203/797–7000; Frank J. Kelly, President and Chief Executive Officer

EASTERN CONNECTICUT HEALTH NETWORK, INC.
71 Haynes Street, Manchester, CT 06040; tel. 860/533–3458; Peter J. Karl, President and Chief Executive Officer

MANCHESTER MEMORIAL HOSPITAL, 71 Haynes Street, Manchester, CT, Zip 06040–4188; tel. 860/646–1222; Peter J. Karl, President and Chief Executive Officer

ROCKVILLE GENERAL HOSPITAL, 31 Union Street, Vernon Rockville, CT, Zip 06066–3160; tel. 860/872–0501; Peter J. Karl, President and Chief Executive Officer

HARTFORD HEALTH CARE CORPORATION
80 Seymour Street, P.O. Box 5037, Hartford, CT 06102; tel. 860/545–1490; John J. Meehan, VP Network Development

BRADLEY MEMORIAL HOSPITAL AND HEALTH CENTER, 81 Meriden Avenue, Southington, CT, Zip 06489–3297; tel. 860/276–5000; Clarence J. Silvia, President and Chief Executive Officer

HARTFORD HOSPITAL, 80 Seymour Street, Hartford, CT, Zip 06102–5037, Mailing Address: P.O. Box 5037, Zip 06102–5037; tel. 860/545–5000; John J. Meehan, President and Chief Executive Officer

HOSPITAL FOR SPECIAL CARE, 2150 Corbin Avenue, New Britain, CT, Zip 06053–2263; tel. 860/827–4758; David Crandall, FACHE, President and Chief Executive Officer

HOSPITAL OF SAINT RAPHAEL, 1450 Chapel Street, New Haven, CT, Zip 06511–1450; tel. 203/789–3000; David W. Benfer, FACHE, President and Chief Executive Officer

JOHNSON MEMORIAL HOSPITAL, 201 Chestnut Hill Road, Stafford Springs, CT, Zip 06076–0860, Mailing Address: P.O. Box 860, Zip 06076–0860; tel. 860/684–4251; Alfred A. Lerz, President and Chief Executive Officer

MIDSTATE MEDICAL CENTER, 435 Lewis Avenue, Meriden, CT, Zip 06451–2101; tel. 203/694–8200; Lucille A. Janatka, President and Chief Executive Officer

NEW BRITAIN GENERAL HOSPITAL, 100 Grand Street, New Britain, CT, Zip 06052–2017, Mailing Address: P.O. Box 100, Zip 06050–0100; tel. 860/224–5011; Laurence A. Tanner, President and Chief Executive Officer

ST. VINCENT'S MEDICAL CENTER, 2800 Main Street, Bridgeport, CT, Zip 06606–4292; tel. 203/576–6000; Susan L. Davis, R.N., Ed.D., President and Chief Executive Officer

STAMFORD HEALTH SYSTEM, 30 Shelburne Road, Stamford, CT, Zip 06902, Mailing Address: P.O. Box 9317, Zip 06904–9317; tel. 203/325–7000; Brian G. Grissler, President and Chief Executive Officer

THE CHARLOTTE HUNGERFORD HOSPITAL, 540 Litchfield Street, Torrington, CT, Zip 06790–0988, Mailing Address: P.O. Box 988, Zip 06790–0988; tel. 860/496–6666; Daniel J. McIntyre, President and Chief Executive Officer

ST. MARY'S HOSPITAL INTEGRATED DELIVERY NETWORK
56 Franklin Street, Waterbury, CT 06702; tel. 203/574–6000; Sr. Marguerite Waite, President

SAINT FRANCIS HOSPITAL AND MEDICAL CENTER, 114 Woodland Street, Hartford, CT, Zip 06105–1299; tel. 860/714–7440; Christopher M. Dadlez, President and Chief Executive Officer

SAINT MARY'S HOSPITAL, 56 Franklin Street, Waterbury, CT, Zip 06706–1281; tel. 203/709–6000; Robert P. Ritz, President and Chief Executive Officer

FLORIDA

LAKE OKEECHOBEE RURAL HEALTH NETWORK, INC.
185 U.S. Highway 27 South, South Bay, FL 33493; tel. 561/993–4221; Andrew Behman, Chief Executive Officer

GLADES GENERAL HOSPITAL, 1201 South Main Street, Belle Glade, FL, Zip 33430–4911; tel. 561/996–6571; Dan Aranda, Chief Executive Officer

HENDRY REGIONAL MEDICAL CENTER, 500 West Sugarland Highway, Clewiston, FL, Zip 33440–3094; tel. 863/983–9121; Craig R. Cudworth, Chief Executive Officer

MID–FLORIDA MEDICAL SERVICES
200 Avenue F Northeast, Winter Haven, FL 33881; tel. 863/297–1899; Lance Anastasio, President

WINTER HAVEN HOSPITAL, 200 Avenue F. N.E., Winter Haven, FL, Zip 33881–4193; tel. 863/293–1121; Lance W. Anastasio, President

GEORGIA

EMORY HEALTHCARE
1365 Clifton Road Northeast, Atlanta, GA 30322; tel. 404/778–5434; Michael Johns, M.D., Chief Executive Officer

EMORY CRAWFORD LONG HOSPITAL, 550 Peachtree Street N.E., Atlanta, GA, Zip 30308; tel. 404/686–4411; John T. Fox, Chief Executive Officer

EMORY UNIVERSITY HOSPITAL, 1364 Clifton Road N.E., Atlanta, GA, Zip 30322–1102; tel. 404/712–2000; John T. Fox, Chief Executive Officer

WESLEY WOODS CENTER OF EMORY UNIVERSITY, 1821 Clifton Road N.E., Atlanta, GA, Zip 30329–5102; tel. 404/728–6200; John T. Fox, Chief Executive Officer

GEORGIA FIRST NETWORK
150 East Ponce de Leon #320, Decatur, GA 30030; tel. 404/778–4939; Russ Toal, President

APPLING HEALTHCARE SYSTEM, 163 East Tollison Street, Baxley, GA, Zip 31513–2898; tel. 912/367–9841; Dale Spell, Chief Executive Officer

ATHENS REGIONAL MEDICAL CENTER, 1199 Prince Avenue, Athens, GA, Zip 30606–2793; tel. 706/475–7000; John A. Drew, President and Chief Executive Officer

BROOKS COUNTY HOSPITAL, 903 North Court Street, Quitman, GA, Zip 31643–1315, Mailing Address: P.O. Box 5000, Zip 31643–5000; tel. 229/263–4171; LaDon Toole, Administrator

CANDLER COUNTY HOSPITAL, 400 Cedar Road, Metter, GA, Zip 30439–1448, Mailing Address: P.O. Box 597, Zip 30439–0597; tel. 912/685–5741; Michael Alexander, President and Chief Executive Officer

CRISP REGIONAL HOSPITAL, 902 North Seventh Street, Cordele, GA, Zip 31015–5007; tel. 229/276–3100; D. Wayne Martin, President and Chief Executive Officer

EARLY MEMORIAL HOSPITAL, 11740 Columbia Street, Blakely, GA, Zip 39823–9604; tel. 229/723–4241; Robin Rau, Administrator

EFFINGHAM HOSPITAL, 459 Highway 119 South, Springfield, GA, Zip 31329–3021, Mailing Address: P.O. Box 386, Zip 31329–0386; tel. 912/754–6451; Don E. Tomberlin, Chief Executive Officer

ELBERT MEMORIAL HOSPITAL, 4 Medical Drive, Elberton, GA, Zip 30635–1897; tel. 706/283–3151; Mark LeNeave, Chief Executive Officer

EMORY CRAWFORD LONG HOSPITAL, 550 Peachtree Street N.E., Atlanta, GA, Zip 30308; tel. 404/686–4411; John T. Fox, Chief Executive Officer

EMORY EASTSIDE MEDICAL CENTER, 1700 Medical Way, Snellville, GA, Zip 30078–2195, Mailing Address: P.O. Box 587, Zip 30078–0587; tel. 770/979–0200; Les Beard, Chief Executive Officer

EMORY UNIVERSITY HOSPITAL, 1364 Clifton Road N.E., Atlanta, GA, Zip 30322–1102; tel. 404/712–2000; John T. Fox, Chief Executive Officer

EMORY–ADVENTIST HOSPITAL, 3949 South Cobb Drive S.E., Smyrna, GA, Zip 30080–6300; tel. 770/434–0710; Dennis Kiley, President

FAIRVIEW PARK HOSPITAL, 200 Industrial Boulevard, Dublin, GA, Zip 31021–2997, Mailing Address: P.O. Box 1408, Zip 31040–1408; tel. 478/275–2000; James E. Raynor, Chief Executive Officer

FLOYD MEDICAL CENTER, 304 Turner McCall Boulevard, Rome, GA, Zip 30165–2734, Mailing Address: P.O. Box 233, Zip 30162–0233; tel. 706/802–2000; Kurt Stuenkel, FACHE, President and Chief Executive Officer

GRADY GENERAL HOSPITAL, 1155 Fifth Street S.E., Cairo, GA, Zip 39828–0360, Mailing Address: P.O. Box 360, Zip 39828–0360; tel. 229/377–1150; Kenneth D. Rhudy, Administrator

HABERSHAM COUNTY MEDICAL CENTER, 541 Historic Highway 441, Demorest, GA, Zip 30535–3118, Mailing Address: P.O. Box 37, Zip 30535–0037; tel. 706/754–2161; C. Richard Dwozan, Chief Executive Officer

HIGGINS GENERAL HOSPITAL, 200 Allen Memorial Drive, Bremen, GA, Zip 30110–2012, Mailing Address: P.O. Box 655, Zip 30110–0655; tel. 770/537–5851; Robbie Smith, Administrator

HOUSTON MEDICAL CENTER, 1601 Watson Boulevard, Warner Robins, GA, Zip 31093–3431, Mailing Address: P.O. Box 2886, Zip 31099–2886; tel. 478/922–4281; Arthur P. Christie, Administrator

JOHN D. ARCHBOLD MEMORIAL HOSPITAL, Gordon Avenue at Mimosa Drive, Thomasville, GA, Zip 31792–6113, Mailing Address: P.O. Box 1018, Zip 31799–1018; tel. 229/228–2000; James L. Story, Jr, M.D., President

LIBERTY REGIONAL MEDICAL CENTER, 462 East G. Parkway, Hinesville, GA, Zip 31313, Mailing Address: P.O. Box 919, Zip 31313; tel. 912/369–9438; H. Scott Kroell, Jr, Chief Executive Officer

LOUIS SMITH MEMORIAL HOSPITAL, 852 West Thigpen Avenue, Lakeland, GA, Zip 31635–1099; tel. 229/482–3110; Neil W. Ginty, Administrator

MEDICAL CENTER OF CENTRAL GEORGIA, 777 Hemlock Street, Macon, GA, Zip 31201–2155, Mailing Address: P.O. Box 6000, Zip 31208–6000; tel. 478/633–1000; A. Donald Faulk, FACHE, President

MEDICAL COLLEGE OF GEORGIA HOSPITAL AND CLINICS, 1120 15th Street, Augusta, GA, Zip 30912–5000; tel. 706/721–0211; Donald F. Snell, President and Chief Executive Officer

MITCHELL COUNTY HOSPITAL, 90 Stephens Street, Camilla, GA, Zip 31730, Mailing Address: P.O. Box 639, Zip 31730–0639; tel. 229/336–5284; J. Randall Phillips, CHE, Administrator

NEWTON MEDICAL CENTER, 5126 Hospital Drive, Covington, GA, Zip 30014–2567; tel. 770/786–7053; James F. Weadick, Administrator and Chief Executive Officer

NORTHSIDE HOSPITAL, 1000 Johnson Ferry Road N.E., Atlanta, GA, Zip 30342–1611; tel. 404/851–8000; Robert Quattrocchi, President and Chief Executive Officer

OCONEE REGIONAL MEDICAL CENTER, 821 North Cobb Street, Milledgeville, GA, Zip 31061–2351, Mailing Address: P.O. Box 690, Zip 31061–0690; tel. 478/454–3500; Brian L. Riddle, President and Chief Executive Officer

PALMYRA MEDICAL CENTERS, 2000 Palmyra Road, Albany, GA, Zip 31702–1908, Mailing Address: P.O. Box 1908, Zip 31702–1908; tel. 229/434–2000; Bud Wethington, Chief Executive Officer

SOUTH GEORGIA MEDICAL CENTER, 2501 North Patterson Street, Valdosta, GA, Zip 31602–1735, Mailing Address: P.O. Box 1727, Zip 31603–1727; tel. 229/333–1000; James McGahee, Administrator and Chief Executive Officer

SOUTHEAST GEORGIA HEALTH SYSTEM BRUNSWICK CAMPUS, 2415 Parkwood Drive, Brunswick, GA, Zip 31520–4252, Mailing Address: P.O. Box 1518, Zip 31521–1518; tel. 912/466–7000; Gary R. Colberg, CHE, President and Chief Executive Officer

SOUTHEAST GEORGIA HEALTH SYSTEM CAMDEN CAMPUS, 2000 Dan Proctor Drive, Saint Marys, GA, Zip 31558–3810; tel. 912/576–6200; Howard W. Sepp, Jr, Administrator

SOUTHERN REGIONAL MEDICAL CENTER, 11 Upper Riverdale Road S.W., Riverdale, GA, Zip 30274–2600; tel. 770/991–8000; Edward J. Bonn, President and Chief Executive Officer

SPALDING REGIONAL MEDICAL CENTER, 601 South Eighth Street, Griffin, GA, Zip 30224–4294, Mailing Address: P.O. Drawer V, Zip 30224–1168; tel. 770/228–2721; John A. Quinn, Chief Executive Officer

ST. JOSEPH'S/CANDLER, CANDLER HOSPITAL, 5353 Reynolds Street, Savannah, GA, Zip 31405–6013; tel. 912/819–6000; Paul P. Hinchey, President and Chief Executive Officer

SUMTER REGIONAL HOSPITAL, 100 Wheatley Drive, Americus, GA, Zip 31709–3799; tel. 229/924–6011; David H. Seagraves, President and Chief Executive Officer

TANNER MEDICAL CENTER, 705 Dixie Street, Carrollton, GA, Zip 30117–3818; tel. 770/836–9666; Loy M. Howard, Chief Executive Officer

TANNER MEDICAL CENTER–VILLA RICA, 601 Dallas Road, Villa Rica, GA, Zip 30180–1202, Mailing Address: P.O. Box 638, Zip 30180–0638; tel. 770/456–3100; Larry N. Steed, Administrator

TATTNALL COMMUNITY HOSPITAL, 247 South Main Street, Reidsville, GA, Zip 30453; tel. 912/557–1000; Karen O'Neal, Chief Executive Officer

THE MEDICAL CENTER, 710 Center Street, Columbus, GA, Zip 31901–1527, Mailing Address: P.O. Box 951, Zip 31902–0951; tel. 706/571–1000; Lance B. Duke, FACHE, President and Chief Executive Officer

TIFT REGIONAL MEDICAL CENTER, 901 East 18th Street, Tifton, GA, Zip 31794–3648, Mailing Address: Drawer 747, Zip 31793–0747; tel. 229/382–7120; William T. Richardson, President and Chief Executive Officer

UPSON REGIONAL MEDICAL CENTER, 801 West Gordon Street, Thomaston, GA, Zip 30286–2831, Mailing Address: P.O. Box 1059, Zip 30286–1059; tel. 706/647–8111; Gene B. Wright, Interim Chief Executive Officer

WALTON REGIONAL MEDICAL CENTER, 330 Alcovy Street, Monroe, GA, Zip 30655–2140, Mailing Address: P.O. Box 1346, Zip 30655–1346; tel. 770/267–8461; Alan E. George, Chief Executive Officer

WEST GEORGIA HEALTH SYSTEM, 1514 Vernon Road, La Grange, GA, Zip 30240–4199; tel. 706/882–1411; Gerald N. Fulks, President and Chief Executive Officer

NATIONAL CARDIOVASCULAR NETWORK
6 Concourse Parkway, Atlanta, GA 30328; Michael Lanzilotta, President

BAPTIST HOSPITAL OF EAST TENNESSEE, 137 Blount Avenue S.E., Knoxville, TN, Zip 37920–1643, Mailing Address: P.O. Box 1788, Zip 37901–1788; tel. 865/632–5011; Brue Chandler, Senior Vice President and Administrator

PHOEBE PUTNEY MEMORIAL HOSPITAL, 417 Third Avenue, Albany, GA, Zip 31701–1828, Mailing Address: P.O. Box 1828, Zip 31703–1828; tel. 229/883–1800; Joel Wernick, President and Chief Executive Officer

ST. JOSEPH'S/CANDLER HEALTH SYSTEM, INC.
5353 Reynolds Street, Savannah, GA 31412; tel. 912/692–6606; Paul Hinchey, President

APPLING HEALTHCARE SYSTEM, 163 East Tollison Street, Baxley, GA, Zip 31513–2898; tel. 912/367–9841; Dale Spell, Chief Executive Officer

CANDLER COUNTY HOSPITAL, 400 Cedar Road, Metter, GA, Zip 30439–1448, Mailing Address: P.O. Box 597, Zip 30439–0597; tel. 912/685–5741; Michael Alexander, President and Chief Executive Officer

EFFINGHAM HOSPITAL, 459 Highway 119 South, Springfield, GA, Zip 31329–3021, Mailing Address: P.O. Box 386, Zip 31329–0386; tel. 912/754–6451; Don E. Tomberlin, Chief Executive Officer

EMORY UNIVERSITY HOSPITAL, 1364 Clifton Road N.E., Atlanta, GA, Zip 30322–1102; tel. 404/712–2000; John T. Fox, Chief Executive Officer

LIBERTY REGIONAL MEDICAL CENTER, 462 East G. Parkway, Hinesville, GA, Zip 31313, Mailing Address: P.O. Box 919, Zip 31313; tel. 912/369–9438; H. Scott Kroell, Jr, Chief Executive Officer

MEADOWS REGIONAL MEDICAL CENTER, 1703 Meadows Lane, Vidalia, GA, Zip 30474–8915, Mailing Address: P.O. Box 1048, Zip 30475–1048; tel. 912/537–8921; Alan Kent, Chief Executive Officer

ST. JOSEPH'S/CANDLER, CANDLER HOSPITAL, 5353 Reynolds Street, Savannah, GA, Zip 31405–6013; tel. 912/819–6000; Paul P. Hinchey, President and Chief Executive Officer

WILLINGWAY HOSPITAL, 311 Jones Mill Road, Statesboro, GA, Zip 30458–4765; tel. 912/764–6236; Jimmy Mooney, Chief Executive Officer

UNIVERSITY HEALTH, INC.
1350 Walton Way, Augusta, GA 30901; tel. 706/722–9011; Jim Showman, M.S.N., R.N., Director, Outreach Services

BARNWELL COUNTY HOSPITAL, 811 Reynolds Road, Barnwell, SC, Zip 29812–1555; tel. 803/259–1000; Robert E. Waters, Chief Executive Officer

BURKE MEDICAL CENTER, 351 Liberty Street, Waynesboro, GA, Zip 30830–9686; tel. 706/554–4435; Jennifer A. Royal, Administrator

EDGEFIELD COUNTY HOSPITAL, 300 Ridge Medical Plaza, Edgefield, SC, Zip 29824; tel. 803/637–3174; Samuel S. Gregory, Chief Executive Officer

EMANUEL MEDICAL HOSPITAL, 117 Kite Road, Swainsboro, GA, Zip 30401–3231, Mailing Address: P.O. Box 879, Zip 30401–0879; tel. 478/237–9911; Bob Via, Chief Executive Officer

JEFFERSON HOSPITAL, 1067 Peachtree Street, Louisville, GA, Zip 30434–1599; tel. 478/625–7000; Rita Culvern, Administrator

JENKINS COUNTY HOSPITAL, 931 East Winthrope Avenue, Millen, GA, Zip 30442–1839; tel. 478/982–4221; Pete Mills, Chief Executive Officer

MCDUFFIE REGIONAL MEDICAL CENTER, 521 Hill Street S.W., Thomson, GA, Zip 30824–2199; tel. 706/595–1411; Douglas C. Keir, Chief Executive Officer

MINNIE G. BOSWELL MEMORIAL HOSPITAL, 1201 Siloam Highway, Greensboro, GA, Zip 30642–2811; tel. 706/453–7331; Floyd D. Bounds, Chief Executive Officer

UNIVERSITY HEALTH CARE SYSTEM, 1350 Walton Way, Augusta, GA, Zip 30901–2629; tel. 706/722–9011; J. Larry Read, President and Chief Executive Officer

WALTON REHABILITATION HOSPITAL, 1355 Independence Drive, Augusta, GA, Zip 30901–1037; tel. 706/724–7746; Dennis B. Skelley, President and Chief Executive Officer

WILLS MEMORIAL HOSPITAL, 120 Gordon Street, Washington, GA, Zip 30673–1602, Mailing Address: P.O. Box 370, Zip 30673–0370; tel. 706/678–2151; T. Marvin Goldman, Chief Executive Officer

IDAHO

NORTH IDAHO HEALTH NETWORK
700 Ironwood Drive, Suite 220, Coeur D'Alene, ID 83814; tel. 208/666–3212; Richard McMaster, Executive Director

BENEWAH COMMUNITY HOSPITAL, 229 South Seventh Street, Saint Maries, ID, Zip 83861–1894; tel. 208/245–5551; Erik Fox, Chief Executive Officer

BONNER GENERAL HOSPITAL, 520 North Third Avenue, Sandpoint, ID, Zip 83864–0877, Mailing Address: Box 1448, Zip 83864–0877; tel. 208/263–1441; Sheryl Rickard, Chief Executive Officer

BOUNDARY COMMUNITY HOSPITAL, 6640 Kaniksu Street, Bonners Ferry, ID, Zip 83805–7532; tel. 208/267–3141; Craig A. Johnson, Chief Executive Officer and Chief Financial Officer

KOOTENAI MEDICAL CENTER, 2003 Lincoln Way, Coeur D'Alene, ID, Zip 83814–2677; tel. 208/666–2000; Joseph E. Morris, Chief Executive Officer

SHOSHONE MEDICAL CENTER, 25 Jacobs Gulch, Kellogg, ID, Zip 83837–2096; tel. 208/784–1221; Gary Moore, Chief Executive Officer

ILLINOIS

FAMILY HEALTH NETWORK, INC.
910 West Van Buren–6th, Chicago, IL 60607; tel. 312/491–1956; Phillip C. Bradley, President

MERCY HOSPITAL AND MEDICAL CENTER, 2525 South Michigan Avenue, Chicago, IL, Zip 60616–2477; tel. 312/567–2000; Sister Sheila Lyne, President and Chief Executive Officer

MOUNT SINAI HOSPITAL MEDICAL CENTER OF CHICAGO, California Avenue and 15th Street, Chicago, IL, Zip 60608–1610; tel. 773/542–2000; Larry E. Volkmar, President

NORWEGIAN–AMERICAN HOSPITAL, Chicago, IL, Mailing Address: 1044 North Francisco Avenue, Zip 60622–2794; tel. 773/292–8200; Michael J. O'Grady, Jr, President and Chief Executive Officer

SAINT'S MARY & ELIZABETH MEDICAL CENTER, DIVISION STREET, 2233 West Division Street, Chicago, IL, Zip 60622–3086; tel. 312/770–2000; Margaret McDermott, Chief Executive Officer

ST. BERNARD HOSPITAL AND HEALTH CARE CENTER, 326 West 64th Street, Chicago, IL, Zip 60621–3146; tel. 773/962–3900; Sister Elizabeth Van Straten, President and Chief Executive Officer

SWEDISH AMERICAN HEALTH SYSTEM
1313 East State Street, Rockford, IL 61104; tel. 815/968–4400; Dr Bill Gorski, President and Chief Executive Officer

SWEDISHAMERICAN HOSPITAL, 1401 East State Street, Rockford, IL, Zip 61104–2315; tel. 815/968–4400; Richard Walsh, President

INDIANA

MEMORIAL HEALTH SYSTEM, INC
707 North Michigan Street, Suite 100, South Bend, IN 46601; tel. 574/647–1822; Phillip Newshold, Vice President

MEMORIAL HOSPITAL OF SOUTH BEND, 615 North Michigan Street, South Bend, IN, Zip 46601–9986; tel. 574/647–9041; Philip A. Newbold, President and Chief Executive Officer

ST. VINCENT HEALTH
8425 Harcourt Road, Indianapolis, IN 46260; tel. 317/338–7080; Vincent Caponi, Chief Executive Officer

SAINT JOHN'S HEALTH SYSTEM, 2015 Jackson Street, Anderson, IN, Zip 46016–4339; tel. 765/649–2511; Kyle De Fur, FACHE, President

ST. ELIZABETH ANN SETON SPECIALTY CARE HOSPITAL, 3700 Washington Avenue, Evansville, IN, Zip 47750; tel. 812/485–7540; Carol Godsey, Chief Executive Officer

ST. JOSEPH HOSPITAL, 1907 West Sycamore Street, Kokomo, IN, Zip 46901–4197, Mailing Address: P.O. Box 9010, Zip 46904–9010; tel. 765/452–5611; Darcy K. Burthay, R.N., Interim President and Chief Nursing Officer

ST. VINCENT CLAY HOSPITAL, 1206 East National Avenue, Brazil, IN, Zip 47834–2797; tel. 812/442–2500; Jerry Laue, Administrator

ST. VINCENT FRANKFORT HOSPITAL, 1300 South Jackson Street, Frankfort, IN, Zip 46041–3394, Mailing Address: P.O. Box 669, Zip 46041–0669; tel. 765/656–3000; Thomas Crawford, Chief Executive Officer

ST. VINCENT HOSPITALS AND HEALTH SERVICES, 2001 West 86th Street, Indianapolis, IN, Zip 46260–1991, Mailing Address: P.O. Box 40970, Zip 46240–0970; tel. 317/338–2345; Patricia A. Maryland, Dr.PH, President

ST. VINCENT JENNINGS HOSPITAL, 301 Henry Street, North Vernon, IN, Zip 47265–1097; tel. 812/352–4200; Joseph E. Roche, Administrator

ST. VINCENT MERCY HOSPITAL, 1331 South A Street, Elwood, IN, Zip 46036–1942; tel. 765/552–4600; Deborah Y. Rasper, FACHE, Administrator

ST. VINCENT RANDOLPH HOSPITAL, 473 Greenville Avenue, Winchester, IN, Zip 47394–2235, Mailing Address: P.O. Box 407, Zip 47394–0407; tel. 765/584–0004; Wayne G. Deschambeau, Chief Executive Officer

ST. VINCENT WILLIAMSPORT HOSPITAL, 412 North Monroe Street, Williamsport, IN, Zip 47993–0215; tel. 765/762–4000; Jane Craigin, Chief Executive Officer

SUBURBAN HEALTH ORGANIZATION
2780 Waterfront Parkway, East Drive, Suite 300, Indianapolis, IN 46214; tel. 317/692–5222; Julie M. Carmichael, President

HANCOCK MEMORIAL HOSPITAL AND HEALTH SERVICES, 801 North State Street, Greenfield, IN, Zip 46140–1270, Mailing Address: P.O. Box 827, Zip 46140–0827; tel. 317/462–5544; Robert C. Keen, Ph.D., FACHE, President and Chief Executive Officer

HENDRICKS REGIONAL HEALTH, 1000 East Main Street, Danville, IN, Zip 46122–0409, Mailing Address: P.O. Box 409, Zip 46122–0409; tel. 317/745–4451; Dennis W. Dawes, FACHE, President

HENRY COUNTY MEMORIAL HOSPITAL, 1000 North 16th Street, New Castle, IN, Zip 47362–4319, Mailing Address: P.O. Box 490, Zip 47362–0490; tel. 765/521–0890; Blake A. Dye, President and Chief Executive Officer

MORGAN HOSPITAL AND MEDICAL CENTER, 2209 John R. Wooden Drive, Martinsville, IN, Zip 46151–1840, Mailing Address: P.O. Box 1717, Zip 46151–1717; tel. 765/342–8441; Thomas W. Laux, President and Chief Executive Officer

RIVERVIEW HOSPITAL, 395 Westfield Road, Noblesville, IN, Zip 46060–1425, Mailing Address: P.O. Box 220, Zip 46061–0220; tel. 317/773–0760; Patricia K. Fox, President and Chief Executive Officer

WESTVIEW HOSPITAL, 3630 Guion Road, Indianapolis, IN, Zip 46222–1699; tel. 317/924–6661; Jerry L. Porter, Chief Executive Officer

WITHAM MEMORIAL HOSPITAL, 2605 North Lebanon Street, Lebanon, IN, Zip 46052, Mailing Address: P.O. Box 1200, Zip 46052–3005; tel. 765/485–8000; Raymond V. Ingham, Ph.D., President and Chief Executive Officer

IOWA

GENESIS HEALTH SYSTEM
1227 East Rusholme Street, Davenport, IA 52803; tel. 319/421–1000; Leo Bressanelli, Chief Executive Officer

GENESIS MEDICAL CENTER, DAVENPORT, 1227 East Rusholme Street, Davenport, IA, Zip 52803–2498; tel. 563/421–1000; Leo A. Bressanelli, FACHE, Chief Executive Officer

GENESIS MEDICAL CENTER, DEWITT, 1118 11th Street, De Witt, IA, Zip 52742–1296; tel. 563/659–4200; Jeffrey M. Cooper, President and Chief Executive Officer

GENESIS MEDICAL CENTER, ILLINI CAMPUS, 801 Illini Drive, Silvis, IL, Zip 61282–1893; tel. 309/792–9363; Charles E. Bruhn, Chief Executive Officer

MERCY HEALTH NETWORK – NORTH IOWA
1000 4th Street, Southwest, Mason City, IA 50401; tel. 515/422–7008; James Fitzpatrick, President/Chief Executive Officer

BELMOND MEDICAL CENTER, 403 First Street S.E., Belmond, IA, Zip 50421–1201; tel. 641/444–3223; Suzan Brunes, Administrator and Director of Nursing

ELLSWORTH MUNICIPAL HOSPITAL, 110 Rocksylvania Avenue, Iowa Falls, IA, Zip 50126–2400; tel. 641/648–4631; John O'Brien, Administrator

FRANKLIN GENERAL HOSPITAL, 1720 Central Avenue East, Hampton, IA, Zip 50441–1859; tel. 641/456–5000; Ronald D. Baker, Chief Executive Officer

HANCOCK COUNTY MEMORIAL HOSPITAL, 532 First Street N.W., Britt, IA, Zip 50423; tel. 641/843–5000; Toni Ebeling, Administrator

KOSSUTH REGIONAL HEALTH CENTER, 1515 South Phillips Street, Algona, IA, Zip 50511–3649; tel. 515/295–2451; Scott Curtis, Administrator

MERCY MEDICAL CENTER – NORTH IOWA, 1000 Fourth Street S.W., Mason City, IA, Zip 50401–2800; tel. 641/422–7000; James G. FitzPatrick, President and Chief Executive Officer

MERCY MEDICAL CENTER–NEW HAMPTON, 308 North Maple Avenue, New Hampton, IA, Zip 50659–1142; tel. 641/394–4121; Carolyn Martin–Shaw, Chief Executive Officer

MITCHELL COUNTY REGIONAL HEALTH CENTER, 616 North Eighth Street, Osage, IA, Zip 50461–1498; tel. 641/732–6000; Sylvia Getman, Chief Executive Officer

PALO ALTO COUNTY HEALTH SYSTEM, 3201 First Street, Emmetsburg, IA, Zip 50536; tel. 712/852–5500; Thomas J. Lee, Chief Executive Officer

REGIONAL HEALTH SERVICES OF HOWARD COUNTY, 235 Eighth Avenue West, Cresco, IA, Zip 52136–1098; tel. 563/547–2101; Elizabeth A. Doty, Chief Executive Officer

MERCY NETWORK
400 University, Des Moines, IA 50309; tel. 515/247–4277; Sara Drobnick, Vice President

ADAIR COUNTY MEMORIAL HOSPITAL, 609 S.E. Kent Street, Greenfield, IA, Zip 50849–9454; tel. 641/743–2123; Myrna Erb–Gundel, Administrator

AUDUBON COUNTY MEMORIAL HOSPITAL, 515 Pacific Street, Audubon, IA, Zip 50025–1052; tel. 712/563–2611; Thomas G. Smith, Chief Executive Officer

DAVIS COUNTY HOSPITAL, 507 North Madison Street, Bloomfield, IA, Zip 52537–1271; tel. 641/664–2145; John E. Monnahan, Chief Executive Officer

HAMILTON HOSPITAL, 800 Ohio Street, Webster City, IA, Zip 50595–2824, Mailing Address: P.O. Box 430, Zip 50595–0430; tel. 515/832–9400; Palmer Schneider, Chief Executive Officer

MADISON COUNTY HEALTH CARE SYSTEM, 300 Hutchings Street, Winterset, IA, Zip 50273–2199; tel. 515/462–2373; Marcia Harris, Chief Executive Officer

MANNING REGIONAL HEALTHCARE CENTER, 410 Main Street, Manning, IA, Zip 51455–1093; tel. 712/655–2072; Jeanne Goche, Chief Executive Officer and Administrator

MERCY MEDICAL CENTER–CENTERVILLE, 1 St. Joseph's Drive, Centerville, IA, Zip 52544–8055; tel. 641/437–4111; Clinton J. Christianson, Chief Executive Officer

MERCY MEDICAL CENTER–DES MOINES, 1111 6th Avenue, Des Moines, IA, Zip 50314–2611; tel. 515/247–3121; David H. Vellinga, President and Chief Executive Officer

MONROE COUNTY HOSPITAL, 1901 South Alabama Avenue, Monroeville, AL, Zip 36460, Mailing Address: P.O. Box 886, Zip 36461–0886; tel. 251/575–3111; Chris Johns, Chief Executive Officer

RINGGOLD COUNTY HOSPITAL, 211 Shellway Drive, Mount Ayr, IA, Zip 50854–1299; tel. 641/464–3226; Gordon W. Winkler, Administrator

ST. ANTHONY REGIONAL HOSPITAL, 311 South Clark Street, Carroll, IA, Zip 51401–3038, Mailing Address: P.O. Box 628, Zip 51401–0628; tel. 712/792–3581; Gary P. Riedmann, President and Chief Executive Officer

STORY COUNTY MEDICAL CENTER, 630 Sixth Street, Nevada, IA, Zip 50201–2266; tel. 515/382–2111; Todd Willert, Administrator

WAYNE COUNTY HOSPITAL, 417 South East Street, Corydon, IA, Zip 50060–1860, Mailing Address: P.O. Box 305, Zip 50060–0305; tel. 641/872–2260; Brian Burnside, Administrator

KANSAS

COMMUNITY HEALTH ALLIANCE
240 West 18th Street, Horton, KS 66439; tel. 816/276–7580; Dale White, Chairman

COMMUNITY HOSPITAL ONAGA, 120 West Eighth Street, Onaga, KS, Zip 66521-0120; tel. 785/889-4272; Joseph T. Engelken, Chief Executive Officer

COMMUNITY MEMORIAL HEALTHCARE, 708 North 18th Street, Marysville, KS, Zip 66508-1338; tel. 785/562-2311; David Bailey, Chief Executive Officer

GEARY COMMUNITY HOSPITAL, 1102 St. Mary's Road, Junction City, KS, Zip 66441-4196, Mailing Address: P.O. Box 490, Zip 66441-0490; tel. 785/238-4131; David K. Bradley, CHE, Chief Executive Officer

HOLTON COMMUNITY HOSPITAL, 1110 Columbine Drive, Holton, KS, Zip 66436-1545; tel. 785/364-2116; James W. Fairchild, Chief Executive Officer

MERCY REGIONAL HEALTH CENTER, 1823 College Avenue, Manhattan, KS, Zip 66502, Mailing Address: P.O. Box 1289, Zip 66505-1289; tel. 785/776-3322; Richard L. Allen, President and Chief Executive Officer

MORRIS COUNTY HOSPITAL, 600 North Washington Street, Council Grove, KS, Zip 66846-0275, Mailing Address: P.O. Box 275, Zip 66846-0275; tel. 620/767-6811; James H. Reagan, Jr, Ph.D., Chief Executive Officer

NEMAHA VALLEY COMMUNITY HOSPITAL, 1600 Community Drive, Seneca, KS, Zip 66538-9739; tel. 785/336-6181; Stan Regehr, Chief Executive Officer

NORTHEAST KANSAS CENTER FOR HEALTH AND WELLNESS, 240 West 18th Street, Horton, KS, Zip 66439-1245; tel. 785/486-2642; Dale A. White, Chief Executive Officer

ST. FRANCIS HEALTH CENTER, 1700 West Seventh Street, Topeka, KS, Zip 66606-1690; tel. 785/295-8000; Sister Loretto Marie Colwell, President and Chief Executive Officer

WAMEGO CITY HOSPITAL, 711 Genn Drive, Wamego, KS, Zip 66547-1179; tel. 785/456-2295; Mark Aldridge, Chief Executive Officer

GREAT PLAINS HEALTH ALLIANCE
P.O. Box 366, Phillipsberg, KS 67661; tel. 800/432-2779; Roger John, President

SATANTA DISTRICT HOSPITAL, 401 South Cheyenne Street, Satanta, KS, Zip 67870-0159, Mailing Address: P.O. Box 159, Zip 67870-0159; tel. 620/649-2761; Curt Colson, Administrator

MED-OP, INC.
202 Center Avenue, Oakley, KS 67748; tel. 785/672-3540; David Britain, Executive Director

CITIZENS MEDICAL CENTER, 100 East College Drive, Colby, KS, Zip 67701-3799; tel. 785/462-7511; Janice McCart, Chief Executive Officer

CLARA BARTON HOSPITAL, 250 West Ninth Street, Hoisington, KS, Zip 67544-1706; tel. 620/653-2114; Christopher Stipe, Administrator and Chief Executive Officer

DECATUR COUNTY HOSPITAL AND CEDAR LIVING CENTER, 810 West Columbia Street, Oberlin, KS, Zip 67749-2450, Mailing Address: P.O. Box 268, Zip 67749-0268; tel. 785/475-2208; Lynn Doeden, Chief Executive Officer

GOODLAND REGIONAL MEDICAL CENTER, 220 West Second Street, Goodland, KS, Zip 67735-1602; tel. 785/890-3625; Jay P. Jolly, Chief Executive Officer

GOVE COUNTY MEDICAL CENTER, 520 West Fifth Street, Quinter, KS, Zip 67752-0129, Mailing Address: P.O. Box 129, Zip 67752-0129; tel. 785/754-3341; Paul Davis, Administrator

GRAHAM COUNTY HOSPITAL, 304 West Prout Street, Hill City, KS, Zip 67642-1435, Mailing Address: P.O. Box 339, Zip 67642-0339; tel. 785/421-2121; Fred J. Meis, Administrator and Chief Executive Officer

LOGAN COUNTY HOSPITAL, 211 Cherry Street, Oakley, KS, Zip 67748-1201; tel. 785/672-3211; Kyle Hahn, Administrator

MEMORIAL HOSPITAL, 511 N.E. Tenth Street, Abilene, KS, Zip 67410; tel. 785/263-2100; Mark A. Miller, Chief Executive Officer

NESS COUNTY HOSPITAL, 312 Custer Street, Ness City, KS, Zip 67560-1654; tel. 785/798-2291; Richard Q. Bergling, Administrator and Chief Executive Officer

NORTON COUNTY HOSPITAL, 102 East Holme, Norton, KS, Zip 67654-0250, Mailing Address: P.O. Box 250, Zip 67654-0250; tel. 785/877-3351; Richard Miller, Administrator and Chief Executive Officer

RICE COUNTY HOSPITAL DISTRICT NUMBER ONE, 619 South Clark Street, Lyons, KS, Zip 67554-0828, Mailing Address: P.O. Box 828, Zip 67554-0828; tel. 620/257-5173; Robert L. Mullen, Chief Executive Officer

RUSH COUNTY MEMORIAL HOSPITAL, 801 Locust Street, La Crosse, KS, Zip 67548-9673, Mailing Address: P.O. Box 520, Zip 67548-0520; tel. 785/222-2545; Teresa L. Deuel, Administrator and Chief Executive Officer

RUSSELL REGIONAL HOSPITAL, 200 South Main Street, Russell, KS, Zip 67665-2997; tel. 785/483-3131; Roger Knak, R.N., Administrator and Chief Executive Officer

SCOTT COUNTY HOSPITAL, 310 East Third Street, Scott City, KS, Zip 67871-1203; tel. 620/872-5811; Greg Unruh, Chief Executive Officer

SHERIDAN COUNTY HEALTH COMPLEX, 826 18th Street, Hoxie, KS, Zip 67740-0167, Mailing Address: P.O. Box 167, Zip 67740-0167; tel. 785/675-3281; Paul Hammeke, Chief Executive Officer

STAFFORD DISTRICT HOSPITAL, 502 South Buckeye Street, Stafford, KS, Zip 67578-2035, Mailing Address: P.O. Box 190, Zip 67578-0190; tel. 620/234-5221; Vernon Minnis, Administrator and Chief Executive Officer

NORTHWEST KANSAS HEALTH ALLIANCE (CAH NETWORK)
2220 Canterbury Drive, Hays, KS 67601; tel. 785/623-2301; Jodi A. Schmidt, VP/Chief Development Officer

CHEYENNE COUNTY HOSPITAL, 210 West First Street, Saint Francis, KS, Zip 67756-0547, Mailing Address: P.O. Box 547, Zip 67756-0547; tel. 785/332-2104; Leslie Lacy, Administrator

CITIZENS MEDICAL CENTER, 100 East College Drive, Colby, KS, Zip 67701-3799; tel. 785/462-7511; Janice McCart, Chief Executive Officer

CLARA BARTON HOSPITAL, 250 West Ninth Street, Hoisington, KS, Zip 67544-1706; tel. 620/653-2114; Christopher Stipe, Administrator and Chief Executive Officer

EDWARDS COUNTY HOSPITAL AND HEALTHCARE CENTER, 620 West Eighth Street, Kinsley, KS, Zip 67547-2329, Mailing Address: P.O. Box 99, Zip 67547-0099; tel. 620/659-3621; Shaun Keef, Administrator

GOVE COUNTY MEDICAL CENTER, 520 West Fifth Street, Quinter, KS, Zip 67752-0129, Mailing Address: P.O. Box 129, Zip 67752-0129; tel. 785/754-3341; Paul Davis, Administrator

GRAHAM COUNTY HOSPITAL, 304 West Prout Street, Hill City, KS, Zip 67642-1435, Mailing Address: P.O. Box 339, Zip 67642-0339; tel. 785/421-2121; Fred J. Meis, Administrator and Chief Executive Officer

GRISELL MEMORIAL HOSPITAL DISTRICT ONE, 210 South Vermont Avenue, Ransom, KS, Zip 67572; tel. 785/731-2231; Kristine Ochs, R.N., Administrator

HARLAN COUNTY HEALTH SYSTEM, 717 North Brown Street, Alma, NE, Zip 68920-0836, Mailing Address: P.O. Box 836, Zip 68920-0836; tel. 308/928-2151; Allen Van Driel, CHE, Administrator

KIOWA COUNTY MEMORIAL HOSPITAL, 501 South Walnut Street, Greensburg, KS, Zip 67054-1951, Mailing Address: P.O. Box 616, Zip 67054-0616; tel. 620/723-3341; Mary Colclazier, Administrator

LANE COUNTY HOSPITAL, 235 West Vine, Dighton, KS, Zip 67839-0969, Mailing Address: P.O. Box 969, Zip 67839-0969; tel. 620/397-5321; Donna McGowan, Administrator

LOGAN COUNTY HOSPITAL, 211 Cherry Street, Oakley, KS, Zip 67748-1201; tel. 785/672-3211; Kyle Hahn, Administrator

MINNEOLA DISTRICT HOSPITAL, 212 Main Street, Minneola, KS, Zip 67865-0127, Mailing Address: P.O. Box 127, Zip 67865-0127; tel. 620/885-4264; Donald J. Kessen, Administrator and Chief Executive Officer

NORTON COUNTY HOSPITAL, 102 East Holme, Norton, KS, Zip 67654-0250, Mailing Address: P.O. Box 250, Zip 67654-0250; tel. 785/877-3351; Richard Miller, Administrator and Chief Executive Officer

PHILLIPS COUNTY HOSPITAL, 1150 State Street, Phillipsburg, KS, Zip 67661-1799, Mailing Address: P.O. Box 607, Zip 67661-0607; tel. 785/543-5226; Raymond Williams, III, Interim Chief Executive Officer

RAWLINS COUNTY HEALTH CENTER, 707 Grant Street, Atwood, KS, Zip 67730-4700, Mailing Address: P.O. Box 47, Zip 67730-4700; tel. 785/626-3211; Robert Garrison, Administrator and Chief Executive Officer

ROOKS COUNTY HEALTH CENTER, 304 South Colorado Avenue, Plainville, KS, Zip 67663-0389; tel. 785/434-4553; J. Ben Quinton, Administrator and Chief Executive Officer

RUSH COUNTY MEMORIAL HOSPITAL, 801 Locust Street, La Crosse, KS, Zip 67548-9673, Mailing Address: P.O. Box 520, Zip 67548-0520; tel. 785/222-2545; Teresa L. Deuel, Administrator and Chief Executive Officer

RUSSELL REGIONAL HOSPITAL, 200 South Main Street, Russell, KS, Zip 67665-2997; tel. 785/483-3131; Roger Knak, R.N., Administrator and Chief Executive Officer

SCOTT COUNTY HOSPITAL, 310 East Third Street, Scott City, KS, Zip 67871-1203; tel. 620/872-5811; Greg Unruh, Chief Executive Officer

SHERIDAN COUNTY HEALTH COMPLEX, 826 18th Street, Hoxie, KS, Zip 67740-0167, Mailing Address: P.O. Box 167, Zip 67740-0167; tel. 785/675-3281; Paul Hammeke, Chief Executive Officer

WAMEGO CITY HOSPITAL, 711 Genn Drive, Wamego, KS, Zip 66547-1179; tel. 785/456-2295; Mark Aldridge, Chief Executive Officer

SUNFLOWER HEALTH NETWORK
139 North Penn, Salina, KS 67401; tel. 785/452-6102; Rob Colerick, Executive Director

CLAY COUNTY MEDICAL CENTER, 617 Liberty Street, Clay Center, KS, Zip 67432-0512, Mailing Address: P.O. Box 512, Zip 67432-0512; tel. 785/632-2144; Ronald Bender, Chief Executive Officer

CLOUD COUNTY HEALTH CENTER, 1100 Highland Drive, Concordia, KS, Zip 66901-3923; tel. 785/243-1234; Roy E. White, Chief Executive Officer

ELLSWORTH COUNTY MEDICAL CENTER, 1604 Aylward Street, Ellsworth, KS, Zip 67439-0087, Mailing Address: P.O. Box 87, Zip 67439-0087; tel. 785/472-3111; Roger W. Pearson, Administrator

HERINGTON MUNICIPAL HOSPITAL, 100 East Helen Street, Herington, KS, Zip 67449-1606; tel. 785/258-2207; Mary Steiner, Administrator

JEWELL COUNTY HOSPITAL, 100 Crestvue Avenue, Mankato, KS, Zip 66956-2407, Mailing Address: P.O. Box 327, Zip 66956-0327; tel. 785/378-3137; Deanna Freeman, Administrator

Section B

LINCOLN COUNTY HOSPITAL, 624 North Second Street, Lincoln, KS, Zip 67455-1738, Mailing Address: P.O. Box 406, Zip 67455-0406; tel. 785/524-4403; Greg R. McNeil, Chief Executive Officer

LINDSBORG COMMUNITY HOSPITAL, 605 West Lincoln Street, Lindsborg, KS, Zip 67456-2328; tel. 785/227-3308; Greg Lundstrom, Administrator and Chief Executive Officer

MEMORIAL HOSPITAL, 511 N.E. Tenth Street, Abilene, KS, Zip 67410; tel. 785/263-2100; Mark A. Miller, Chief Executive Officer

MEMORIAL HOSPITAL, 1000 Hospital Drive, McPherson, KS, Zip 67460-2321; tel. 620/241-2250; Rex D. Walk, President and Chief Executive Officer

MITCHELL COUNTY HOSPITAL, 400 West Eighth, Beloit, KS, Zip 67420-1605, Mailing Address: P.O. Box 399, Zip 67420-0399; tel. 785/738-2266; John M. Osse, Administrator

OSBORNE COUNTY MEMORIAL HOSPITAL, 424 West New Hampshire Street, Osborne, KS, Zip 67473-0070, Mailing Address: P.O. Box 70, Zip 67473-0070; tel. 785/346-2121; Kiley Floyd, Administrator

OTTAWA COUNTY HEALTH CENTER, 215 East Eighth, Minneapolis, KS, Zip 67467-1999, Mailing Address: P.O. Box 290, Zip 67467-0290; tel. 785/392-2122; Joy Johnson, R.N., Administrator

REPUBLIC COUNTY HOSPITAL, 2420 G Street, Belleville, KS, Zip 66935-2400; tel. 785/527-2254; Blaine K. Miller, Administrator

SALINA REGIONAL HEALTH CENTER, 400 South Santa Fe Avenue, Salina, KS, Zip 67401-4198, Mailing Address: P.O. Box 5080, Zip 67401-5080; tel. 785/452-7000; Randy Peterson, President and Chief Executive Officer

SMITH COUNTY MEMORIAL HOSPITAL, 614 South Main Street, Smith Center, KS, Zip 66967-0349, Mailing Address: P.O. Box 349, Zip 66967-0349; tel. 785/282-6845; Carolyn K. Hess, R.N., Administrator

KENTUCKY

CARITAS HEALTH SERVICES
1850 Bluegrass Avenue, Louisville, KY 40215; tel. 502/361-6000;
Robert M. Lovell, Interim President and CEO

CARITAS MEDICAL CENTER, 1850 Bluegrass Avenue, Louisville, KY, Zip 40215-1199; tel. 502/361-6000; Robert M. Lovell, Interim President and Chief Executive Officer

CARITAS PEACE CENTER, 2020 Newburg Road, Louisville, KY, Zip 40205-1879; tel. 502/451-3330; Robert M. Lovell, Interim President and Chief Executive Officer

CHA HMO, INC.
300 West Vine Street, Lexington, KY 40507; tel. 859/232-8686;
Theresa Kline, Chief Executive Officer

ADAMS COUNTY HOSPITAL, 210 North Wilson Drive, West Union, OH, Zip 45693-1574; tel. 937/544-5571; Linda Niles, Chief Executive Officer

BAPTIST HOSPITAL EAST, 4000 Kresge Way, Louisville, KY, Zip 40207-4676; tel. 502/897-8100; Susan Stout Tamme, President

BAPTIST HOSPITAL FOR WOMEN, 10820 Parkside Drive, Knoxville, TN, Zip 37922-1956; tel. 865/218-7090; Martha O'Regan Chill, Senior Vice President and Administrator

BAPTIST HOSPITAL NORTHEAST, 1025 New Moody Lane, La Grange, KY, Zip 40031-0559; tel. 502/222-5388; Dennis B. Johnson, Administrator

BAPTIST HOSPITAL OF EAST TENNESSEE, 137 Blount Avenue S.E., Knoxville, TN, Zip 37920-1643, Mailing Address: P.O. Box 1788, Zip 37901-1788; tel. 865/632-5011; Brue Chandler, Senior Vice President and Administrator

BAPTIST HOSPITAL WEST, 10820 Parkside Drive, Knoxville, TN, Zip 37922-1956; tel. 865/218-7011; Martha O'Regan Chill, Senior Vice President and Administrator

BAPTIST REGIONAL MEDICAL CENTER, 1 Trillium Way, Corbin, KY, Zip 40701-8420; tel. 606/528-1212; John S. Henson, President

BECKLEY APPALACHIAN REGIONAL HOSPITAL, 306 Stanaford Road, Beckley, WV, Zip 25801-3142; tel. 304/255-3000; Rocco K. Massey, Community Chief Executive Officer

BEREA HOSPITAL, 305 Estill Street, Berea, KY, Zip 40403-1909; tel. 859/986-3151; Angela Carman, President and Chief Executive Officer

BLUEGRASS COMMUNITY HOSPITAL, 360 Amsden Avenue, Versailles, KY, Zip 40383-1286; tel. 859/873-3111; Kathy Scott, Administrator

BOONE MEMORIAL HOSPITAL, 701 Madison Avenue, Madison, WV, Zip 25130-1699; tel. 304/369-1230; Tommy H. Mullins, Administrator

BOURBON COMMUNITY HOSPITAL, 9 Linville Drive, Paris, KY, Zip 40361-2196; tel. 859/987-3600; Clay Holderman, Chief Executive Officer

BRECKINRIDGE MEMORIAL HOSPITAL, 1011 Old Highway 60, Hardinsburg, KY, Zip 40143-2597; tel. 270/756-7000; George Walz, CHE, President and Chief Executive Officer

CALDWELL COUNTY HOSPITAL, 101 Hospital Drive, Princeton, KY, Zip 42445-0410; tel. 270/365-0300; Charles D. Lovell, Jr, President and Chief Executive Officer

CARDINAL HILL REHABILITATION HOSPITAL, 2050 Versailles Road, Lexington, KY, Zip 40504-1499; tel. 859/254-5701; Kerry G. Gillihan, FACHE, President and Chief Executive Officer

CARDINAL HILL SPECIALTY HOSPITAL, 85 North Grand Avenue, Fort Thomas, KY, Zip 41075; tel. 859/572-3880; Janice Bauer, Administrator

CARITAS MEDICAL CENTER, 1850 Bluegrass Avenue, Louisville, KY, Zip 40215-1199; tel. 502/361-6000; Robert M. Lovell, Interim President and Chief Executive Officer

CARITAS PEACE CENTER, 2020 Newburg Road, Louisville, KY, Zip 40205-1879; tel. 502/451-3330; Robert M. Lovell, Interim President and Chief Executive Officer

CARROLL COUNTY HOSPITAL, 309 11th Street, Carrollton, KY, Zip 41008-1400; tel. 502/732-4321; Kim Dees, Chief Executive Officer

CASEY COUNTY HOSPITAL, 187 Wolford Avenue, Liberty, KY, Zip 42539; tel. 606/787-6275; Rex A. Tungate, Administrator

CAVERNA MEMORIAL HOSPITAL, 1501 South Dixie Street, Horse Cave, KY, Zip 42749-1477; tel. 270/786-2191; Alan B. Alexander, Chief Executive Officer

CENTRAL BAPTIST HOSPITAL, 1740 Nicholasville Road, Lexington, KY, Zip 40503-1499; tel. 859/260-6100; William G. Sisson, President

CHILDREN'S HOSPITAL MEDICAL CENTER, 3333 Burnet Avenue, Cincinnati, OH, Zip 45229-3039; tel. 513/636-4200; James M. Anderson, President and Chief Executive Officer

CHRIST HOSPITAL, 2139 Auburn Avenue, Cincinnati, OH, Zip 45219-2989; tel. 513/585-2000; Susan Croushore, Executive Director and Senior Vice President

CLAIBORNE COUNTY HOSPITAL, 1850 Old Knoxville Road, Tazewell, TN, Zip 37879-3625, Mailing Address: P.O. Box 219, Zip 37879-0219; tel. 423/626-4211; Tim S. Brown, Senior Vice President and Administrator

CLARK MEMORIAL HOSPITAL, 1220 Missouri Avenue, Jeffersonville, IN, Zip 47130-3743, Mailing Address: P.O. Box 69, Zip 47131-0069; tel. 812/282-6631; Martin Padgett, President and Chief Executive Officer

CLARK REGIONAL MEDICAL CENTER, 1107 West Lexington Avenue, Winchester, KY, Zip 40391-1138, Mailing Address: P.O. Box 630, Zip 40392-0630; tel. 859/745-3500; Robert D. Fraraccio, Chief Executive Officer

CLINTON COUNTY HOSPITAL, 723 Burkesville Road, Albany, KY, Zip 42602-1654; tel. 606/387-6421; Randel Flowers, Ph.D., Administrator

CONTINUING CARE HOSPITAL, 150 North Eagle Creek Drive, 5th Floor, Lexington, KY, Zip 40515; tel. 859/268-4800; Eric Gilliam, Administrator

CRITTENDEN COUNTY HOSPITAL, Highway 60 South, Marion, KY, Zip 42064-6201, Mailing Address: P.O. Box 386, Zip 42064-0386; tel. 270/965-5281; Claudia Ann Eisenmann, Chief Executive Officer

CUMBERLAND COUNTY HOSPITAL, Highway 90 West, Burkesville, KY, Zip 42717-0280, Mailing Address: P.O. Box 280, Zip 42717-0280; tel. 270/864-2511; Edward J. Sanford, Chief Executive Officer

CUMBERLAND HALL HOSPITAL, 210 West 17th Street, Hopkinsville, KY, Zip 42240-1999; tel. 270/886-1919; Alan G. Chapman, Chief Executive Officer

DEACONESS CROSS POINTE CENTER, 7200 East Indiana Street, Evansville, IN, Zip 47715; tel. 812/476-7200; David W. Morris, Chief Executive Officer

DEACONESS HOSPITAL, 600 Mary Street, Evansville, IN, Zip 47747-0001; tel. 812/450-5000; Linda E. White, President and Chief Executive Officer

DICKENSON COMMUNITY HOSPITAL, Hospital Drive, Clintwood, VA, Zip 24228, Mailing Address: P.O. Box 1440, Zip 24228-1440; tel. 276/926-0300; Kenneth Boyd, Chief Executive Officer

DRAKE CENTER, 151 West Galbraith Road, Cincinnati, OH, Zip 45216-1096; tel. 513/948-2500; Roberta J. Bradford, President and Chief Executive Officer

EPHRAIM MCDOWELL REGIONAL MEDICAL CENTER, 217 South Third Street, Danville, KY, Zip 40422-9983; tel. 859/239-1000; Barry Michael, President

FLAGET MEMORIAL HOSPITAL, 4305 New Shepherdsville Road, Bardstown, KY, Zip 40004; tel. 502/350-5000; Bruce A. Klockars, President and Chief Executive Officer

FLEMING COUNTY HOSPITAL, 920 Elizaville Avenue, Flemingsburg, KY, Zip 41041, Mailing Address: P.O. Box 388, Zip 41041-0388; tel. 606/849-5000; Harrell L. Connelly, Interim Chief Executive Officer

FLOYD MEMORIAL HOSPITAL AND HEALTH SERVICES, 1850 State Street, New Albany, IN, Zip 47150-4997; tel. 812/949-5500; Bryant R. Hanson, President and Chief Executive Officer

FORT HAMILTON HOSPITAL, 630 Eaton Avenue, Hamilton, OH, Zip 45013-2770; tel. 513/867-2000; Lynn M. Oswald, R.N., Senior Vice President

FORT LOGAN HOSPITAL, 124 Portman Avenue, Stanford, KY, Zip 40484-1200; tel. 606/365-2187; Mike Jackson, President and Chief Executive Officer

FORT LOUDOUN MEDICAL CENTER, 550 Fort Loudoun Medical Center Drive, Lenoir City, TN, Zip 37772; tel. 865/458-8222; Jeffrey Feike, President and Chief Administrative Officer

FORT SANDERS REGIONAL MEDICAL CENTER, 1901 Clinch Avenue S.W., Knoxville, TN, Zip 37916-2394; tel. 865/541-1111; Keith Altshuler, Administrator

FORT SANDERS-SEVIER MEDICAL CENTER, 709 Middle Creek Road, Sevierville, TN, Zip 37862-5016, Mailing Address: P.O. Box 8005, Zip 37864-8005; tel. 865/429-6100; Ellen Wilhoit, President and Chief Administrative Officer

FRANKFORT REGIONAL MEDICAL CENTER, 299 King's Daughters Drive, Frankfort, KY, Zip 40601-4186; tel. 502/875-5240; Michael A. Mayo, FACHE, Chief Executive Officer

FRAZIER REHAB INSTITUTE, 220 Abraham Flexner Way, Louisville, KY, Zip 40202-1887; tel. 502/582-7400; Joanne Berryman, Senior Vice President

GATEWAY REGIONAL HEALTH SYSTEM, 50 Sterling Avenue, Mount Sterling, KY, Zip 40353–1158, Mailing Address: P.O. Box 7, Zip 40353–0007; tel. 859/497–6000; Patrick A. Romano, Jr, Chief Executive Officer

GATEWAY REHABILITATION HOSPITAL, 5940 Merchant Street, Florence, KY, Zip 41042; tel. 859/426–2400; Jim Burcham, Chief Executive Officer

GATEWAY REHABILITATION HOSPITAL, 315 East Broadway, Louisville, KY, Zip 40202; tel. 502/315–8300; James Parobek, Chief Executive Officer

GEORGETOWN COMMUNITY HOSPITAL, 1140 Lexington Road, Georgetown, KY, Zip 40324–9362; tel. 502/868–1100; Michael Clark, Chief Executive Officer

GREENVIEW REGIONAL HOSPITAL, 1801 Ashley Circle, Bowling Green, KY, Zip 42104–3384, Mailing Address: P.O. Box 90024, Zip 42102–9024; tel. 270/793–1000; Mark A. Marsh, Chief Executive Officer

HARDIN MEMORIAL HOSPITAL, 913 North Dixie Avenue, Elizabethtown, KY, Zip 42701; tel. 270/737–1212; David L. Gray, President

HARLAN ARH HOSPITAL, 81 Ball Park Road, Harlan, KY, Zip 40831–1792; tel. 606/573–8201; Michael G. Layfield, Community Chief Executive Officer

HARRISON COUNTY HOSPITAL, 245 Atwood Street, Corydon, IN, Zip 47112–1774; tel. 812/738–4251; Steven L. Taylor, Chief Executive Officer

HARRISON MEMORIAL HOSPITAL, 1210 KY Highway 36E, Cynthiana, KY, Zip 41031–7498; tel. 859/234–2300; Darwin E. Root, Chief Executive Officer

HAZARD ARH REGIONAL MEDICAL CENTER, 100 Medical Center Drive, Hazard, KY, Zip 41701–1000; tel. 606/439–6600; Wayne B. Griffith, FACHE, Regional Chief Executive Officer

HEALTHSOUTH DEACONESS REHABILITATION HOSPITAL, 4100 Covert Avenue, Evansville, IN, Zip 47714–5567, Mailing Address: P.O. Box 5349, Zip 47716–5349; tel. 812/476–9983; Barbara Butler, Administrator

HEALTHSOUTH NORTHERN KENTUCKY REHABILITATION HOSPITAL, 201 Medical Village Drive, Edgewood, KY, Zip 41017–3407; tel. 859/341–2044; Brenda Gosney, Administrator

HIGHLANDS REGIONAL MEDICAL CENTER, 5000 Kentucky Route 321, Prestonsburg, KY, Zip 41653–1273, Mailing Address: P.O. Box 668, Zip 41653–0668; tel. 606/886–8511; Harold C. Warman, Jr, President and Chief Executive Officer

HORIZON MEDICAL CENTER, 111 Highway 70 East, Dickson, TN, Zip 37055–2033; tel. 615/446–0446; John A. Marshall, Chief Executive Officer

JACKSON PURCHASE MEDICAL CENTER, 1099 Medical Center Circle, Mayfield, KY, Zip 42066–1179; tel. 270/251–4100; Mary Jo Lewis, Chief Executive Officer

JANE TODD CRAWFORD HOSPITAL, 202–206 Milby Street, Greensburg, KY, Zip 42743–1100, Mailing Address: P.O. Box 220, Zip 42743–0220; tel. 270/932–4211; Jack Grimsley, Interim Chief Executive Officer

JELLICO COMMUNITY HOSPITAL, 188 Hospital Lane, Jellico, TN, Zip 37762–4432; tel. 423/784–7252; David A. Butler, Chief Executive Officer and President

JENKINS COMMUNITY HOSPITAL, Main Street, Jenkins, KY, Zip 41537–9614, Mailing Address: P.O. Box 472, Zip 41537–0472; tel. 606/832–2171; Sherrie Newcomb, Administrator

JENNIE STUART MEDICAL CENTER, 320 West 18th Street, Hopkinsville, KY, Zip 42241–2400, Mailing Address: P.O. Box 2400, Zip 42241–2400; tel. 270/887–0100; Lewis T. Peeples, Chief Executive Officer

JEWISH HOSPITAL, 4777 East Galbraith Road, Cincinnati, OH, Zip 45236–2725; tel. 513/686–3000; M. Aurora Lambert, Senior Vice President

JEWISH HOSPITAL, 217 East Chestnut Street, Louisville, KY, Zip 40202–1886, Mailing Address: One Audubon Plaza Drive #100, Zip 40217; tel. 502/587–4011; Timothy L. Jarm, President

JEWISH HOSPITAL–SHELBYVILLE, 727 Hospital Drive, Shelbyville, KY, Zip 40065–1699; tel. 502/647–4000; Michael L. Collins, President and Chief Executive Officer

KENTUCKY RIVER MEDICAL CENTER, 540 Jett Drive, Jackson, KY, Zip 41339–9620; tel. 606/666–6000; O. David Bevins, Chief Executive Officer

KING'S DAUGHTERS MEDICAL CENTER, 2201 Lexington Avenue, Ashland, KY, Zip 41101–2874, Mailing Address: P.O. Box 151, Zip 41105–0151; tel. 606/327–4000; Fred L. Jackson, Chief Executive Officer

KNOX COUNTY HOSPITAL, One Hospital Drive, Barbourville, KY, Zip 40906–1317, Mailing Address: P.O. Box 160, Zip 40906–0160; tel. 606/546–4175; Connie Hensley, Acting Chief Operating Officer

LAKE CUMBERLAND REGIONAL HOSPITAL, 305 Langdon Street, Somerset, KY, Zip 42501–2750, Mailing Address: P.O. Box 620, Zip 42502–2750; tel. 606/679–7441; Jeffrey G. Seraphine, Chief Executive Officer

LIVINGSTON HOSPITAL AND HEALTHCARE SERVICES, 131 Hospital Drive, Salem, KY, Zip 42078–8043; tel. 270/988–2299; Yvonne Maddux, Chief Executive Officer

LIVINGSTON REGIONAL HOSPITAL, 315 Oak Street, Livingston, TN, Zip 38570, Mailing Address: P.O. Box 550, Zip 38570–0550; tel. 931/823–5611; Timothy W. McGill, Chief Executive Officer

LOGAN MEMORIAL HOSPITAL, 1625 South Nashville Road, Russellville, KY, Zip 42276–8834, Mailing Address: P.O. Box 10, Zip 42276–0010; tel. 270/726–4011; Greg Moore, Chief Executive Officer

LOURDES HOSPITAL, 1530 Lone Oak Road, Paducah, KY, Zip 42003–7900, Mailing Address: P.O. Box 7100, Zip 42002–7100; tel. 270/444–2444; William G. Wheeler, M.D., President and Chief Executive Officer

MARCUM AND WALLACE MEMORIAL HOSPITAL, 60 Mercy Court, Irvine, KY, Zip 40336–1331; tel. 606/723–2115; Susan Starling, President and Chief Executive Officer

MARSHALL COUNTY HOSPITAL, 503 George McClain Drive, Benton, KY, Zip 42025–1399, Mailing Address: P.O. Box 630, Zip 42025–0630; tel. 270/527–4800; Kathy Long, Chief Executive Officer

MARY BRECKINRIDGE HOSPITAL, 130 Kate Ireland Drive, Hyden, KY, Zip 41749–0000; tel. 606/672–2901; Mallie S. Noble, Administrator

MARYMOUNT MEDICAL CENTER, 310 East Ninth Street, London, KY, Zip 40741–1299; tel. 606/878–6520; Virginia B. Dempsey, Chief Executive Officer

MASSAC MEMORIAL HOSPITAL, 28 Chick Street, Metropolis, IL, Zip 62960, Mailing Address: P.O. Box 850, Zip 62960–0850; tel. 618/524–2176; Jeffrey L. Durham, Chief Executive Officer

MCDOWELL ARH HOSPITAL, Route 122, McDowell, KY, Zip 41647, Mailing Address: P.O. Box 247, Zip 41647–0247; tel. 606/377–3400; Russel Barker, Chief Executive Officer

MEADOWVIEW REGIONAL MEDICAL CENTER, 989 Medical Park Drive, Maysville, KY, Zip 41056–8750; tel. 606/759–5311; David E. Loving, Chief Executive Officer

MEDICAL CENTER OF SOUTHERN INDIANA, 2200 Market Street, Charlestown, IN, Zip 47111–0069, Mailing Address: P.O. Box 69, Zip 47111–0069; tel. 812/256–3301; David R. Sirk, Chief Executive Officer

MEMORIAL HOSPITAL, 210 Marie Langdon Drive, Manchester, KY, Zip 40962–9156; tel. 606/598–5104; Dennis Meyers, President and Chief Executive Officer

MERCY FRANCISCAN HOSPITAL MOUNT AIRY, 2446 Kipling Avenue, Cincinnati, OH, Zip 45239–6650; tel. 513/853–5000; James Gravell, President and Chief Executive Officer

MERCY FRANCISCAN HOSPITAL–WESTERN HILLS, 3131 Queen City Avenue, Cincinnati, OH, Zip 45238–2396; tel. 513/389–5000; James Chadwick Patrick, President and Chief Executive Officer

MERCY HOSPITAL ANDERSON, 7500 State Road, Cincinnati, OH, Zip 45255–2492; tel. 513/624–4500; Patricia A. Schroer, President and Chief Executive Officer

MERCY HOSPITAL CLERMONT, 3000 Hospital Drive, Batavia, OH, Zip 45103–1998; tel. 513/732–8200; Mark D. Shugarman, President and Chief Executive Officer

MERCY HOSPITAL FAIRFIELD, 3000 Mack Road, Fairfield, OH, Zip 45014; tel. 513/870–7000; Jeffrey A. Ashin, Interim President and Chief Executive Officer

METHODIST HOSPITAL, 1305 North Elm Street, Henderson, KY, Zip 42420–2775, Mailing Address: P.O. Box 48, Zip 42420–0048; tel. 270/827–7700; Bruce D. Begley, Executive Director

METHODIST HOSPITAL UNION COUNTY, 4604 Highway 60 West, Morganfield, KY, Zip 42437–9570; tel. 270/389–5000; Patrick Donahue, Administrator

METHODIST MEDICAL CENTER OF OAK RIDGE, 990 Oak Ridge Turnpike, Oak Ridge, TN, Zip 37830–6976, Mailing Address: P.O. Box 2529, Zip 37831–2529; tel. 865/481–1000; Jan McNally, President and Chief Administrative Officer

MIDDLESBORO APPALACHIAN REGIONAL HOSPITAL, 3600 West Cumberland Avenue, Middlesboro, KY, Zip 40965–2614, Mailing Address: P.O. Box 340, Zip 40965–0340; tel. 606/242–1300; J. Gene Faile, Community Chief Executive Officer

MONROE COUNTY MEDICAL CENTER, 529 Capp Harlan Road, Tompkinsville, KY, Zip 42167–1840; tel. 270/487–9231; Vicky McFall, Chief Executive Officer

MORGAN COUNTY APPALACHIAN REGIONAL HOSPITAL, 476 Liberty Road, West Liberty, KY, Zip 41472–2049, Mailing Address: P.O. Box 579, Zip 41472–0579; tel. 606/743–3186; Susan Roman, Community Chief Executive Officer

MUHLENBERG COMMUNITY HOSPITAL, 440 Hopkinsville Street, Greenville, KY, Zip 42345–1172, Mailing Address: P.O. Box 387, Zip 42345–0387; tel. 270/338–8000; Lloyd Ford, Chief Executive Officer

MURRAY–CALLOWAY COUNTY HOSPITAL, 803 Poplar Street, Murray, KY, Zip 42071–2432; tel. 270/762–1100; Jon C. O'Shaughnessy, Chief Executive Officer

NEW HORIZONS HEALTH SYSTEMS, INC., 330 Roland Avenue, Owenton, KY, Zip 40359–1502; tel. 502/484–3663; Bernard Poe, Administrator

NICHOLAS COUNTY HOSPITAL, 2323 Concrete Road, Carlisle, KY, Zip 40311–9721, Mailing Address: P.O. Box 232, Zip 40311–0232; tel. 859/289–7181; Doris Ecton, Administrator and Chief Executive Officer

NORTON AUDUBON HOSPITAL, One Audubon Plaza Drive, Louisville, KY, Zip 40217–1397, Mailing Address: P.O. Box 17550, Zip 40217–0550; tel. 502/636–7111; Thomas D. Kmetz, President

NORTON COMMUNITY HOSPITAL, 100 15th Street N.W., Norton, VA, Zip 24273–1699; tel. 276/679–9600; David G. Fuqua, Chief Executive Officer

NORTON HOSPITAL, 200 East Chestnut Street, Louisville, KY, Zip 40202–1800, Mailing Address: P.O. Box 35070, Zip 40232–5070; tel. 502/629–8000; Kevin S. Wardell, Chief Administrative Officer

NORTON SOUTHWEST HOSPITAL, 9820 Third Street Road, Louisville, KY, Zip 40272–9984; tel. 502/933–8100; Teresa Parker, Administrator

NORTON SUBURBAN HOSPITAL, 4001 Dutchmans Lane, Louisville, KY, Zip 40207–4799; tel. 502/893–1000; John D. Harryman, President and Administrator

OHIO COUNTY HOSPITAL, 1211 Main Street, Hartford, KY, Zip 42347–1619; tel. 270/298–7411; Blaine Pieper, Chief Executive Officer

OUR LADY OF BELLEFONTE HOSPITAL, St. Christopher Drive, Ashland, KY, Zip 41101–7071, Mailing Address: P.O. Box 789, Zip 41105–0789; tel. 606/833–3333; Mark M. Gordon, Chief Executive Officer

OUR LADY OF THE WAY HOSPITAL, 11203 Main Street, Martin, KY, Zip 41649–0910; tel. 606/285–5181; Kathy Stumbo, Chief Executive Officer

OWENSBORO MEDICAL HEALTH SYSTEM, 811 East Parrish Avenue, Owensboro, KY, Zip 42303, Mailing Address: P.O. Box 20007, Zip 42304–0007; tel. 270/688–2000; Jeffrey B. Barber, Dr.PH, President and Chief Executive Officer

PARKWAY REGIONAL HOSPITAL, 2000 Holiday Lane, Fulton, KY, Zip 42041–8468; tel. 270/472–2522; Michael Patterson, Chief Executive Officer

PATTIE A. CLAY REGIONAL MEDICAL CENTER, 801 Eastern Bypass, Richmond, KY, Zip 40475–2405, Mailing Address: P.O. Box 1600, Zip 40476–2603; tel. 859/623–3131; Robert J. Hudson, Chief Executive Officer and President

PAUL B. HALL REGIONAL MEDICAL CENTER, 625 James S Trimble Boulevard, Paintsville, KY, Zip 41240–0000; tel. 606/789–3511; Deborah L. Trimble, Chief Executive Officer

PENINSULA HOSPITAL, 2347 Jones Bend Road, Louisville, TN, Zip 37777–5213, Mailing Address: P.O. Box 2000, Zip 37777–2000; tel. 865/970–9800; Barbara S. Blevins, President and Chief Administrative Officer

PIKEVILLE MEDICAL CENTER, 911 Bypass Road, Pikeville, KY, Zip 41501–1595; tel. 606/218–3500; Joann Anderson, Chief Executive Officer

PINEVILLE COMMUNITY HOSPITAL ASSOCIATION, 850 Riverview Avenue, Pineville, KY, Zip 40977–0850; tel. 606/337–3051; J. Milton Brooks, III, Administrator

RIDGE BEHAVIORAL HEALTH SYSTEM, 3050 Rio Dosa Drive, Lexington, KY, Zip 40509–9990; tel. 859/269–2325; Nina W. Eisner, Chief Executive Officer and Managing Director

RIVENDELL BEHAVIORAL HEALTH, 1035 Porter Pike, Bowling Green, KY, Zip 42103; tel. 270/843–1199; Janice Richardson, Chief Executive Officer

RIVER PARK HOSPITAL, 1230 Sixth Avenue, Huntington, WV, Zip 25701–2312, Mailing Address: P.O. Box 1875, Zip 25719–1875; tel. 304/526–9111; Scott C. Stamm, Chief Executive Officer

ROCKCASTLE HOSPITAL AND RESPIRATORY CARE CENTER, 145 Newcomb Avenue, Mount Vernon, KY, Zip 40456–2733, Mailing Address: P.O. Box 1310, Zip 40456–1310; tel. 606/256–2195; Stephen A. Estes, Chief Executive Officer

RUSSELL COUNTY HOSPITAL, 153 Dowell Road, Russell Springs, KY, Zip 42642–4236, Mailing Address: P.O. Box 1610, Zip 42642–1610; tel. 270/866–4141; Patricia Ekdahl, R.N., President and Chief Executive Officer

SAINT JOSEPH HOSPITAL, One St. Joseph Drive, Lexington, KY, Zip 40504–3754; tel. 859/278–3436; Eugene A. Woods, President and Chief Executive Officer

SAINT JOSEPH HOSPITAL EAST, 150 North Eagle Creek Drive, Lexington, KY, Zip 40509–1807; tel. 859/268–4800; Eugene A. Woods, President and Chief Executive Officer

SAINT THOMAS HOSPITAL, 4220 Harding Road, Nashville, TN, Zip 37205–2095, Mailing Address: P.O. Box 380, Zip 37202–0380; tel. 615/222–2111; Dale Batchelor, M.D., Interim President and Chief Executive Officer

SAMARITAN HOSPITAL, 310 South Limestone Street, Lexington, KY, Zip 40508–3008; tel. 859/226–7000; Frank Beirne, Chief Executive Officer

SCOTT COUNTY HOSPITAL, 18797 Alberta Avenue, Oneida, TN, Zip 37841–4939, Mailing Address: P.O. Box 4939, Zip 37841–4939; tel. 423/569–8521; Larry R. Jeter, Chief Executive Officer

SCOTT MEMORIAL HOSPITAL, 1415 North Gardner Street, Scottsburg, IN, Zip 47170–0430, Mailing Address: Box 430, Zip 47170–0430; tel. 812/752–8500; Clifford D. Nay, Executive Director

SELECT SPECIALTY HOSPITAL OF EVANSVILLE, 600 Mary Street, Suite 3325, Evansville, IN, Zip 47747; tel. 812/450–5270; Tracy Conroy, Chief Executive Officer

SOUTHERN INDIANA REHABILITATION HOSPITAL, 3104 Blackiston Boulevard, New Albany, IN, Zip 47150–9579; tel. 812/941–8300; Randy L. Napier, President and Chief Executive Officer

SOUTHERN OHIO MEDICAL CENTER, 1805 27th Street, Portsmouth, OH, Zip 45662–2400; tel. 740/354–5000; Randal M. Arnett, President and Chief Executive Officer

SPRING VIEW HOSPITAL, 320 Loretto Road, Lebanon, KY, Zip 40033–0320; tel. 270/692–3161; Barry A. Papania, Chief Executive Officer

ST. CLAIRE REGIONAL MEDICAL CENTER, 222 Medical Circle, Morehead, KY, Zip 40351–1180; tel. 606/783–6500; Mark J. Neff, President and Chief Executive Officer

ST. ELIZABETH MEDICAL CENTER–GRANT COUNTY, 238 Barnes Road, Williamstown, KY, Zip 41097–9460; tel. 859/824–8240; Chris Carle, Administrator

ST. ELIZABETH MEDICAL CENTER–SOUTH, 1 Medical Village Drive, Covington, KY, Zip 41017–3403; tel. 859/344–2000; Joseph W. Gross, President and Chief Executive Officer

ST. LUKE HOSPITAL EAST, 85 North Grand Avenue, Fort Thomas, KY, Zip 41075–1796; tel. 859/572–3100; Nancy Kremer, Senior Vice President

ST. LUKE HOSPITAL WEST, 7380 Turfway Road, Florence, KY, Zip 41042–1337; tel. 859/962–5200; Nancy Kremer, Senior Vice President

ST. MARY'S MEDICAL CENTER, 2900 First Avenue, Huntington, WV, Zip 25702–1272; tel. 304/526–1234; Michael G. Sellards, President and Chief Executive Officer

ST. MARY'S MEDICAL CENTER, 900 East Oak Hill Avenue, Knoxville, TN, Zip 37917–4556; tel. 865/545–8000; Debra K. London, President and Chief Executive Officer

ST. MARY'S MEDICAL CENTER OF CAMPBELL COUNTY, 923 East Central Avenue, La Follette, TN, Zip 37766–3106, Mailing Address: P.O. Box 1301, Zip 37766–1301; tel. 423/907–1200; Nicholas P. Lewis, Administrator

SUMMERS COUNTY APPALACHIAN REGIONAL HOSPITAL, Terrace Street, Hinton, WV, Zip 25951–2407, Mailing Address: Drawer 940, Zip 25951–0940; tel. 304/466–1000; Chris Vaught, Community Chief Executive Officer

T. J. SAMSON COMMUNITY HOSPITAL, 1301 North Race Street, Glasgow, KY, Zip 42141–3483; tel. 270/651–4444; Dwayne Moss, Chief Executive Officer

TEN BROECK HOSPITAL, 8521 Old LaGrange Road, Louisville, KY, Zip 40242–3800; tel. 502/426–6380; John Hollinsworth, Executive Director

THE JAMES B. HAGGIN MEMORIAL HOSPITAL, 464 Linden Avenue, Harrodsburg, KY, Zip 40330–1862; tel. 859/734–5441; Earl James Motzer, Ph.D., FACHE, Chief Executive Officer

THE MEDICAL CENTER AT BOWLING GREEN, 250 Park Street, Bowling Green, KY, Zip 42101–1795, Mailing Address: P.O. Box 90010, Zip 42102–9010; tel. 270/745–1000; Connie Smith, Chief Executive Officer

THE MEDICAL CENTER AT FRANKLIN, 1100 Brookhaven Road, Franklin, KY, Zip 42134–2746; tel. 270/598–4800; Clara M. Sumner, Chief Executive Officer

THE WOMEN'S HOSPITAL, 4199 Gateway Boulevard, Newburgh, IN, Zip 47630; tel. 812/842–4200; Christina M. Ryan, Chief Executive Officer

THREE RIVERS MEDICAL CENTER, Highway 644, Louisa, KY, Zip 41230–9632, Mailing Address: P.O. Box 769, Zip 41230–0769; tel. 606/638–9451; Greg Kiser, Chief Executive Officer

TRIGG COUNTY HOSPITAL, 254 Main Street, Cadiz, KY, Zip 42211–9153, Mailing Address: P.O. Box 312, Zip 42211–0312; tel. 270/522–3215; Lisa Powers, Chief Executive Officer

UNIVERSITY HOSPITAL, 234 Goodman Street, Cincinnati, OH, Zip 45219–2316; tel. 513/584–1000; James A. Kingsbury, Executive Director and Senior Vice President

UNIVERSITY OF KENTUCKY HOSPITAL, 800 Rose Street, N100, Lexington, KY, Zip 40536–0293; tel. 859/323–5000; Murray B. Clark, Jr, Associate Vice President Operations

UNIVERSITY OF LOUISVILLE HOSPITAL, 530 South Jackson Street, Louisville, KY, Zip 40202–3611; tel. 502/562–3000; James H. Taylor, President and Chief Executive Officer

VANDERBILT UNIVERSITY MEDICAL CENTER, 1211 22nd Avenue South, Nashville, TN, Zip 37232–2102; tel. 615/322–5000; Larry Goldberg, Executive Director and Chief Executive Officer

WASHINGTON COUNTY MEMORIAL HOSPITAL, 911 North Shelby Street, Salem, IN, Zip 47167–1694; tel. 812/883–5881; Beth Sharer, R.N., Interim Chief Executive Officer

WAYNE COUNTY HOSPITAL, 166 Hospital Street, Monticello, KY, Zip 42633–2416; tel. 606/348–9343; Patricia Brinson, Administrator

WELLMONT HOLSTON VALLEY MEDICAL CENTER, 130 West Ravine Street, Kingsport, TN, Zip 37660, Mailing Address: P.O. Box 238, Zip 37662–0238; tel. 423/224–4000; E. Berton Whitaker, President and Chief Executive Officer

WELLMONT LONESOME PINE HOSPITAL, 1990 Holton Avenue East, Big Stone Gap, VA, Zip 24219–0230; tel. 276/523–3111; Robert G. Polahar, President

WESTERN BAPTIST HOSPITAL, 2501 Kentucky Avenue, Paducah, KY, Zip 42003–3200; tel. 270/575–2100; Larry O. Barton, President

WESTLAKE REGIONAL HOSPITAL, 901 Westlake Drive, Columbia, KY, Zip 42728–1149, Mailing Address: P.O. Box 1269, Zip 42728–1269; tel. 270/384–4753; Rex A. Tungate, Administrator

WHITESBURG APPALACHIAN REGIONAL HOSPITAL, 240 Hospital Road, Whitesburg, KY, Zip 41858–1254; tel. 606/633–3600; Donald Fields, Community Chief Executive Officer

WILLIAMSON ARH HOSPITAL, 260 Hospital Drive, South Williamson, KY, Zip 41503–4072; tel. 606/237–1710; Wesley Dangerfield, Community Chief Executive Officer

COMMONWEALTH HEALTH CORPORATION
800 Park Street, Bowling Green, KY 42103; tel. 270/745–1500; John Desmarais, Chief Executive Officer

THE MEDICAL CENTER AT BOWLING GREEN, 250 Park Street, Bowling Green, KY, Zip 42101–1795, Mailing Address: P.O. Box 90010, Zip 42102–9010; tel. 270/745–1000; Connie Smith, Chief Executive Officer

THE MEDICAL CENTER AT FRANKLIN, 1100 Brookhaven Road, Franklin, KY, Zip 42134–2746; tel. 270/598–4800; Clara M. Sumner, Chief Executive Officer

COMMUNITY CARE NETWORK
110 A. Second Street, Henderson, KY 42420; tel. 502/827–7380; Elizabeth Johnson, Director of Marketing

CALDWELL COUNTY HOSPITAL, 101 Hospital Drive, Princeton, KY, Zip 42445–0410; tel. 270/365–0300; Charles D. Lovell, Jr, President and Chief Executive Officer

CARITAS MEDICAL CENTER, 1850 Bluegrass Avenue, Louisville, KY, Zip 40215–1199; tel. 502/361–6000; Robert M. Lovell, Interim President and Chief Executive Officer

CRITTENDEN COUNTY HOSPITAL, Highway 60 South, Marion, KY, Zip 42064–6201, Mailing Address: P.O. Box 386, Zip 42064–0386; tel. 270/965–5281; Claudia Ann Eisenmann, Chief Executive Officer

JENNIE STUART MEDICAL CENTER, 320 West 18th Street, Hopkinsville, KY, Zip 42241–2400, Mailing Address: P.O. Box 2400, Zip 42241–2400; tel. 270/887–0100; Lewis T. Peeples, Chief Executive Officer

LIVINGSTON HOSPITAL AND HEALTHCARE SERVICES, 131 Hospital Drive, Salem, KY, Zip 42078–8043; tel. 270/988–2299; Yvonne Maddux, Chief Executive Officer

METHODIST HOSPITAL, 1305 North Elm Street, Henderson, KY, Zip 42420–2775, Mailing Address: P.O. Box 48, Zip 42420–0048; tel. 270/827–7700; Bruce D. Begley, Executive Director

METHODIST HOSPITAL UNION COUNTY, 4604 Highway 60 West, Morganfield, KY, Zip 42437–9570; tel. 270/389–5000; Patrick Donahue, Administrator

MURRAY–CALLOWAY COUNTY HOSPITAL, 803 Poplar Street, Murray, KY, Zip 42071–2432; tel. 270/762–1100; Jon C. O'Shaughnessy, Chief Executive Officer

REGIONAL MEDICAL CENTER OF HOPKINS COUNTY, 900 Hospital Drive, Madisonville, KY, Zip 42431–1694; tel. 270/825–5100; Ron Peterson, President

THE MEDICAL CENTER AT FRANKLIN, 1100 Brookhaven Road, Franklin, KY, Zip 42134–2746; tel. 270/598–4800; Clara M. Sumner, Chief Executive Officer

COMMUNITY HEALTH DELIVERY SYSTEM, INC.
2020 Newbrug Road, Louisville, KY 40205; tel. 502/451–3330; Fran Dotson, Network Contact

BAPTIST HOSPITAL EAST, 4000 Kresge Way, Louisville, KY, Zip 40207–4676; tel. 502/897–8100; Susan Stout Tamme, President

BAPTIST HOSPITAL NORTHEAST, 1025 New Moody Lane, La Grange, KY, Zip 40031–0559; tel. 502/222–5388; Dennis B. Johnson, Administrator

BAPTIST REGIONAL MEDICAL CENTER, 1 Trillium Way, Corbin, KY, Zip 40701–8420; tel. 606/528–1212; John S. Henson, President

BRECKINRIDGE MEMORIAL HOSPITAL, 1011 Old Highway 60, Hardinsburg, KY, Zip 40143–2597; tel. 270/756–7000; George Walz, CHE, President and Chief Executive Officer

CALDWELL COUNTY HOSPITAL, 101 Hospital Drive, Princeton, KY, Zip 42445–0410; tel. 270/365–0300; Charles D. Lovell, Jr, President and Chief Executive Officer

CARITAS MEDICAL CENTER, 1850 Bluegrass Avenue, Louisville, KY, Zip 40215–1199; tel. 502/361–6000; Robert M. Lovell, Interim President and Chief Executive Officer

CARITAS PEACE CENTER, 2020 Newburg Road, Louisville, KY, Zip 40205–1879; tel. 502/451–3330; Robert M. Lovell, Interim President and Chief Executive Officer

CARROLL COUNTY HOSPITAL, 309 11th Street, Carrollton, KY, Zip 41008–1400; tel. 502/732–4321; Kim Dees, Chief Executive Officer

CAVERNA MEMORIAL HOSPITAL, 1501 South Dixie Street, Horse Cave, KY, Zip 42749–1477; tel. 270/786–2191; Alan B. Alexander, Chief Executive Officer

CENTRAL BAPTIST HOSPITAL, 1740 Nicholasville Road, Lexington, KY, Zip 40503–1499; tel. 859/260–6100; William G. Sisson, President

FLAGET MEMORIAL HOSPITAL, 4305 New Shepherdsville Road, Bardstown, KY, Zip 40004; tel. 502/350–5000; Bruce A. Klockars, President and Chief Executive Officer

JANE TODD CRAWFORD HOSPITAL, 202–206 Milby Street, Greensburg, KY, Zip 42743–1100, Mailing Address: P.O. Box 220, Zip 42743–0220; tel. 270/932–4211; Jack Grimsley, Interim Chief Executive Officer

MARYMOUNT MEDICAL CENTER, 310 East Ninth Street, London, KY, Zip 40741–1299; tel. 606/878–6520; Virginia B. Dempsey, Chief Executive Officer

NORTON HOSPITAL, 200 East Chestnut Street, Louisville, KY, Zip 40202–1800, Mailing Address: P.O. Box 35070, Zip 40232–5070; tel. 502/629–8000; Kevin S. Wardell, Chief Administrative Officer

SAINT JOSEPH HOSPITAL, One St. Joseph Drive, Lexington, KY, Zip 40504–3754; tel. 859/278–3436; Eugene A. Woods, President and Chief Executive Officer

ST. ELIZABETH MEDICAL CENTER–GRANT COUNTY, 238 Barnes Road, Williamstown, KY, Zip 41097–9460; tel. 859/824–8240; Chris Carle, Administrator

ST. ELIZABETH MEDICAL CENTER–SOUTH, 1 Medical Village Drive, Covington, KY, Zip 41017–3403; tel. 859/344–2000; Joseph W. Gross, President and Chief Executive Officer

TRIGG COUNTY HOSPITAL, 254 Main Street, Cadiz, KY, Zip 42211–9153, Mailing Address: P.O. Box 312, Zip 42211–0312; tel. 270/522–3215; Lisa Powers, Chief Executive Officer

TWIN LAKES REGIONAL MEDICAL CENTER, 910 Wallace Avenue, Leitchfield, KY, Zip 42754–1499; tel. 270/259–9400; Stephen L. Meredith, Chief Executive Officer

WESTERN BAPTIST HOSPITAL, 2501 Kentucky Avenue, Paducah, KY, Zip 42003–3200; tel. 270/575–2100; Larry O. Barton, President

ST. ELIZABETH MEDICAL CENTER
1 Medical Village Drive, Edgewood, KY 41017; tel. 606/344–2000; Joseph W. Gross, President

ST. ELIZABETH MEDICAL CENTER–GRANT COUNTY, 238 Barnes Road, Williamstown, KY, Zip 41097–9460; tel. 859/824–8240; Chris Carle, Administrator

ST. ELIZABETH MEDICAL CENTER–SOUTH, 1 Medical Village Drive, Covington, KY, Zip 41017–3403; tel. 859/344–2000; Joseph W. Gross, President and Chief Executive Officer

LOUISIANA

OCHSNER HEALTH PLAN
One Galleria Boulevard, Suite 850, Metairie, LA 70001; tel. 504/836–6600; Leslie Borel, Manager, Marketing Research an

ABBEVILLE GENERAL HOSPITAL, 118 North Hospital Drive, Abbeville, LA, Zip 70510–4077, Mailing Address: P.O. Box 580, Zip 70511–0580; tel. 337/893–5466; Ray A. Landry, Chief Executive Officer

ACADIA–ST. LANDRY HOSPITAL, 810 South Broadway Street, Church Point, LA, Zip 70525–4497; tel. 337/684–5435; F. Peter Savoy, III, Chief Executive Officer

ALLEN PARISH HOSPITAL, 108 North Sixth Avenue, Kinder, LA, Zip 70648–3519, Mailing Address: P.O. Box 1670, Zip 70648–1670; tel. 337/738–2527; Scott Barrilleaux, Chief Executive Officer and Administrator

ASCENSION HOSPITAL, 615 East Worthey Road, Gonzales, LA, Zip 70737–4240; tel. 225/621–1248; Michael J. Nolan, Chief Executive Officer

BATON ROUGE GENERAL MEDICAL CENTER, 3600 Florida Street, Baton Rouge, LA, Zip 70806–3889, Mailing Address: P.O. Box 2511, Zip 70821–2511; tel. 225/387–7000; William R. Holman, CHE, President and Chief Executive Officer

BEAUREGARD MEMORIAL HOSPITAL, 600 South Pine Street, De Ridder, LA, Zip 70634–4998, Mailing Address: P.O. Box 730, Zip 70634–0730; tel. 337/462–7100; Theodore J. Badger, Jr, CHE, Chief Executive Officer

BUNKIE GENERAL HOSPITAL, 427 Evergreen Highway, Bunkie, LA, Zip 71322–3901, Mailing Address: P.O. Box 380, Zip 71322–0380; tel. 318/346–6681; Donald L. Kannady, Chief Executive Officer

BYRD REGIONAL HOSPITAL, 1020 Fertitta Boulevard, Leesville, LA, Zip 71446–4697; tel. 337/239–9041; Roger C. LeDoux, Chief Executive Officer

CHRISTUS COUSHATTA HEALTH CARE CENTER, 1635 Marvel Street, Coushatta, LA, Zip 71019–9022, Mailing Address: P.O. Box 589, Zip 71019–0589; tel. 318/932–2000; Karen Mixon, Interim Administrator

CHRISTUS SCHUMPERT HEALTH SYSTEM, One St. Mary Place, Shreveport, LA, Zip 71101–4399; tel. 318/681–4500; Charles J. Paine, M.D., President and Chief Executive Officer

CHRISTUS ST. FRANCES CABRINI HOSPITAL, 3330 Masonic Drive, Alexandria, LA, Zip 71301–3899; tel. 318/487–1122; Stephen F. Wright, President and Chief Executive Officer

DE SOTO REGIONAL HEALTH SYSTEM, 207 Jefferson Street, Mansfield, LA, Zip 71052–2603, Mailing Address: P.O. Box 1636, Zip 71052–2603; tel. 318/871–3100; John Scott Stafford, Chief Executive Officer

DEQUINCY MEMORIAL HOSPITAL, 110 West Fourth Street, DeQuincy, LA, Zip 70633–3508, Mailing Address: P.O. Box 1166, Zip 70633–1166; tel. 337/786–1200; Barbara Hollingsworth, Administrator and Chief Executive Officer

HARDTNER MEDICAL CENTER, 1102 North Pine Road, Olla, LA, Zip 71465; tel. 318/495–3131; Paul G. Mathews, Administrator

HOMER MEMORIAL HOSPITAL, 620 East College Street, Homer, LA, Zip 71040–3202; tel. 318/927–2024; Douglas P. Efferson, Administrator

HOOD MEMORIAL HOSPITAL, 301 West Walnut Street, Amite, LA, Zip 70422–2098; tel. 504/748–9485; A. D. Richardson, Administrator

JENNINGS AMERICAN LEGION HOSPITAL, 1634 Elton Road, Jennings, LA, Zip 70546–3614; tel. 337/616–7000; Terry J. Terrebonne, Chief Executive Officer

LADY OF THE SEA GENERAL HOSPITAL, 200 West 134th Place, Cut Off, LA, Zip 70345–4145; tel. 985/632–6401; Raymond L. Ford, FACHE, Chief Executive Officer

LAKE CHARLES MEMORIAL HOSPITAL, 1701 Oak Park Boulevard, Lake Charles, LA, Zip 70601–8911, Mailing Address: P.O. Drawer M, Zip 70602; tel. 337/494–3000; Elton L. Williams, Jr, CPA, FACHE, President

LALLIE KEMP MEDICAL CENTER, 52579 Highway 51 South, Independence, LA, Zip 70443–2231; tel. 985/878–9421; LeVern S. Meades, Administrator

LANE MEMORIAL HOSPITAL, 6300 Main Street, Zachary, LA, Zip 70791–9990; tel. 225/658–4000; Randall M. Olson, Chief Executive Officer

LEONARD J. CHABERT MEDICAL CENTER, 1978 Industrial Boulevard, Houma, LA, Zip 70363–7094; tel. 985/873–2200; Daniel M. Trahan, Administrator

MINDEN MEDICAL CENTER, 1 Medical Plaza, Minden, LA, Zip 71055–3330, Mailing Address: P.O. Box 5003, Zip 71058–5003; tel. 318/377–2321; George E. French, III, CHE, Chief Executive Officer

NATCHITOCHES PARISH HOSPITAL, 501 Keyser Avenue, Natchitoches, LA, Zip 71457–6036, Mailing Address: P.O. Box 2009, Zip 71457–2009; tel. 318/214–4200; Mark E. Marley, CHE, Administrator

OCHSNER CLINIC FOUNDATION, 1514 Jefferson Highway, New Orleans, LA, Zip 70121–2484; tel. 504/842–3000; Patrick J. Quinlan, M.D., Chief Executive Officer

OPELOUSAS GENERAL HEALTH SYSTEM, 539 East Prudhomme Street, Opelousas, LA, Zip 70570, Mailing Address: P.O. Box 1389, Zip 70571–1389; tel. 337/948–3011; William F. Barrow, II, Chief Executive Officer

OUR LADY OF LOURDES REGIONAL MEDICAL CENTER, 611 St. Landry Street, Lafayette, LA, Zip 70506–4627, Mailing Address: P.O. Box 4027, Zip 70502–4027; tel. 337/289–2000; Robert Peebles, President and Chief Executive Officer

OUR LADY OF THE LAKE REGIONAL MEDICAL CENTER, 5000 Hennessy Boulevard, Baton Rouge, LA, Zip 70808–4350; tel. 225/765–6565; Robert C. Davidge, Chief Executive Officer

POINTE COUPEE GENERAL HOSPITAL, 2202 False River Drive, New Roads, LA, Zip 70760–2698; tel. 225/638–6331; Larry J. Ayres, Administrator and Chief Executive Officer

PREVOST MEMORIAL HOSPITAL, 301 Memorial Drive, Donaldsonville, LA, Zip 70346–4376; tel. 225/473–7931; Vincent A. Cataldo, Administrator

RIVER WEST MEDICAL CENTER, 59355 River West Drive, Plaquemine, LA, Zip 70764–0737, Mailing Address: P.O. Box 737, Zip 70764–0737; tel. 225/687–9222; Scott Smith, Chief Executive Officer

RIVERLAND MEDICAL CENTER, 1700 North E 'E' Wallace Boulevard, Ferriday, LA, Zip 71334–0111, Mailing Address: P.O. Box 111, Zip 71334–0111; tel. 318/757–6551; Vernon R. Stevens, Jr, Administrator

SABINE MEDICAL CENTER, 240 Highland Drive, Many, LA, Zip 71449–3718; tel. 318/256–5691; Patrick W. Gandy, Chief Executive Officer

SLIDELL MEMORIAL HOSPITAL AND MEDICAL CENTER, 1001 Gause Boulevard, Slidell, LA, Zip 70458–2987; tel. 985/643–2200; Robert L. Hawley, Jr, Chief Executive Officer

ST. ANNE GENERAL HOSPITAL, 4608 Highway 1, Raceland, LA, Zip 70394–2623; tel. 985/537–6841; Milton D. Bourgeois, Jr, Chief Executive Officer

ST. CHARLES PARISH HOSPITAL, 1057 Paul Maillard Road, Luling, LA, Zip 70070–0087, Mailing Address: P.O. Box 87, Zip 70070–0087; tel. 985/785–6242; Fred Martinez, Jr, Chief Executive Officer

ST. HELENA PARISH HOSPITAL, Highway 43 North, Greensburg, LA, Zip 70441, Mailing Address: P.O. Box 337, Zip 70441–0337; tel. 225/222–6111; Alcus Trahan, Administrator and Chief Executive Officer

ST. JAMES PARISH HOSPITAL, 2471 Louisiana Avenue, Lutcher, LA, Zip 70071; tel. 225/869–5512; Joan Z. Murray, R.N., Administrator and Chief Executive Officer

ST. TAMMANY PARISH HOSPITAL, 1202 South Tyler Street, Covington, LA, Zip 70433–2394; tel. 985/898–4000; Patti M. Ellish, R.N., President and Chief Executive Officer

TOURO INFIRMARY, 1401 Foucher Street, New Orleans, LA, Zip 70115–3593; tel. 504/897–7011; Leslie D. Hirsch, President and Chief Executive Officer

VILLE PLATTE MEDICAL CENTER, 800 East Main Street, Ville Platte, LA, Zip 70586–4618, Mailing Address: P.O. Box 349, Zip 70586–0349; tel. 337/363–5684; Steven Downs, Chief Executive Officer and Administrator

WEST FELICIANA PARISH HOSPITAL, 5266 Commerce Street, Saint Francisville, LA, Zip 70775–0368, Mailing Address: P.O. Box 368, Zip 70775–0368; tel. 225/635–3811; Mark Chustz, Administrator

WEST JEFFERSON MEDICAL CENTER, 1101 Medical Center Boulevard, Marrero, LA, Zip 70072–3191; tel. 504/347–5511; A. Gary Muller, FACHE, President and Chief Executive Officer

WOMAN'S HOSPITAL, 9050 Airline Highway, Baton Rouge, LA, Zip 70815–4192, Mailing Address: P.O. Box 95009, Zip 70895–5009; tel. 225/927–1300; Teri G. Fontenot, CHE, President and Chief Executive Officer

MAINE

BLUE HILL MEMORIAL HOSPITAL
P.O. Box 823, Blue Hill, ME 04614; tel. 207/374–2836; Timothy Gamity, FACHE, CEO

BLUE HILL MEMORIAL HOSPITAL, 57 Water Street, Blue Hill, ME, Zip 04614–0823, Mailing Address: P.O. Box 823, Zip 04614–0823; tel. 207/374–3400; Timothy Garrity, Chief Executive Officer

MAINE NETWORK FOR HEALTH
Key Plaza, 23 Water Street, Bangor, ME 04401; tel. 207/942–2844; Stephen P. Ryan, President/Chief Executive Officer

ACADIA HOSPITAL, 268 Stillwater Avenue, Bangor, ME, Zip 04401–3945, Mailing Address: P.O. Box 422, Zip 04402–0422; tel. 207/973–6100; Dorothy E. Hill, Chief Executive Officer and Chief Nursing Officer

AROOSTOOK MEDICAL CENTER, 140 Academy Street, Presque Isle, ME, Zip 04769–3171, Mailing Address: P.O. Box 151, Zip 04769–0151; tel. 207/768–4000; David A. Peterson, President and Chief Executive Officer

BLUE HILL MEMORIAL HOSPITAL, 57 Water Street, Blue Hill, ME, Zip 04614–0823, Mailing Address: P.O. Box 823, Zip 04614–0823; tel. 207/374–3400; Timothy Garrity, Chief Executive Officer

CHARLES A. DEAN MEMORIAL HOSPITAL AND NURSING HOME, Pritham Avenue, Greenville, ME, Zip 04441–1395, Mailing Address: P.O. Box 1129, Zip 04441–1129; tel. 207/695–5200; Geno Murray, President and Chief Executive Officer

EASTERN MAINE MEDICAL CENTER, 489 State Street, Bangor, ME, Zip 04401–6674, Mailing Address: P.O. Box 404, Zip 04402–0404; tel. 207/973–7000; Deborah Carey Johnson, R.N., President and Chief Executive Officer

INLAND HOSPITAL, 200 Kennedy Memorial Drive, Waterville, ME, Zip 04901–4595; tel. 207/861–3000; Sally Conary, President and Chief Executive Officer

MILLINOCKET REGIONAL HOSPITAL, 200 Somerset Street, Millinocket, ME, Zip 04462–1298; tel. 207/723–5161; Marie E. Vienneau, R.N., Chief Executive Officer

MOUNT DESERT ISLAND HOSPITAL, 10 Wayman Lane, Bar Harbor, ME, Zip 04609–0008, Mailing Address: P.O. Box 8, Zip 04609–0008; tel. 207/288–5081; Arthur J. Blank, President and Chief Executive Officer

NORTHERN MAINE MEDICAL CENTER, 194 East Main Street, Fort Kent, ME, Zip 04743–1497; tel. 207/834–3155; Martin B. Bernstein, Chief Executive Officer

SEBASTICOOK VALLEY HOSPITAL, 99 Grove Street, Pittsfield, ME, Zip 04967–1199; tel. 207/487–5141; John C. May, Chief Executive Officer

SYNERNET, INC.
222 St. John Street, Suite 329, Portland, ME 04102; tel. 207/771–3456; Gerald Vicenzi, President/Chief Executive Officer

FRANKLIN MEMORIAL HOSPITAL, 111 Franklin Health Commons, Farmington, ME, Zip 04938–9990; tel. 207/778–6031; Richard A. Batt, President and Chief Executive Officer

HENRIETTA D. GOODALL HOSPITAL, 25 June Street, Sanford, ME, Zip 04073–2645; tel. 207/324–4310; Darlene Stromstad, Chief Executive Officer

HOULTON REGIONAL HOSPITAL, 20 Hartford Street, Houlton, ME, Zip 04730–9998; tel. 207/532–9471; Thomas J. Moakler, Chief Executive Officer

MOUNT DESERT ISLAND HOSPITAL, 10 Wayman Lane, Bar Harbor, ME, Zip 04609–0008, Mailing Address: P.O. Box 8, Zip 04609–0008; tel. 207/288–5081; Arthur J. Blank, President and Chief Executive Officer

NORTHERN MAINE MEDICAL CENTER, 194 East Main Street, Fort Kent, ME, Zip 04743–1497; tel. 207/834–3155; Martin B. Bernstein, Chief Executive Officer

PENOBSCOT BAY MEDICAL CENTER, 6 Glen Cove Drive, Rockport, ME, Zip 04856–4241; tel. 207/596–8000; Roy A. Hitchings, Jr, FACHE, President and Chief Executive Officer

REDINGTON–FAIRVIEW GENERAL HOSPITAL, Fairview Avenue, Skowhegan, ME, Zip 04976, Mailing Address: P.O. Box 468, Zip 04976–0468; tel. 207/474–5121; Richard Willett, Chief Executive Officer

ST. JOSEPH HOSPITAL, 360 Broadway, Bangor, ME, Zip 04401–3897, Mailing Address: P.O. Box 403, Zip 04402–0403; tel. 207/262–1000; Sister Mary Norberta Malinowski, President

MARYLAND

MARYLAND HEALTH NETWORK
1508 Woodlawn Drive, Suite 13, Baltimore, MD 21044; tel. 410/594–2401; Peter Clay, President

GREATER BALTIMORE MEDICAL CENTER, 6701 North Charles Street, Baltimore, MD, Zip 21204–6892; tel. 443/849–2000; Laurence M. Merlis, President and Chief Executive Officer

HOLY CROSS HOSPITAL, 1500 Forest Glen Road, Silver Spring, MD, Zip 20910–1487; tel. 301/754–7000; Kevin J. Sexton, President and Chief Executive Officer

MONTGOMERY GENERAL HOSPITAL, 18101 Prince Philip Drive, Olney, MD, Zip 20832–1512; tel. 301/774–8882; Peter W. Monge, President and Chief Executive Officer

NORTHWEST HOSPITAL CENTER, 5401 Old Court Road, Randallstown, MD, Zip 21133–5185; tel. 410/521–2200; Erik G. Wexler, President and Chief Operating Officer

ST. AGNES HEALTHCARE, 900 Caton Avenue, Baltimore, MD, Zip 21229–5299; tel. 410/368–6000; Kenneth H. Bancroft, President and Chief Executive Officer

MASSACHUSETTS

LAHEY CLINIC MEDICAL CENTER
41 Mall Road, Burlington, MA 01805; tel. 781/744–8733; David M. Barrett, M.D., Manager, Media Relations

LAHEY CLINIC HOSPITAL, 41 Mall Road, Burlington, MA, Zip 01805–0001; tel. 781/744–5100; David M. Barrett, M.D., Chief Executive Officer

NORTHEAST HEALTH SYSTEM
85 Herrick Street, Beverly, MA 01915; tel. 978/922–3000; Steven R. Laverty, President

BEVERLY HOSPITAL, 85 Herrick Street, Beverly, MA, Zip 01915–1777; tel. 978/922–3000; Stephen R. Laverty, President and Chief Executive Officer

PATHWAY HEALTH NETWORK
1 Deaconess Road, Boston, MA 02215; tel. 617/667–7000; Susan K. Glazer, Vice President – Planning

BETH ISRAEL DEACONESS MEDICAL CENTER, 330 Brookline Avenue, Boston, MA, Zip 02215–5491; tel. 617/667–7000; Paul F. Levy, Chief Executive Officer

MOUNT AUBURN HOSPITAL, 330 Mount Auburn Street, Cambridge, MA, Zip 02138–5597; tel. 617/492–3500; Jeanette G. Clough, President and Chief Executive Officer

NASHOBA VALLEY MEDICAL CENTER, 200 Groton Road, Ayer, MA, Zip 01432–3300; tel. 978/784–9000; Andrei Soran, Chief Executive Officer

NEW ENGLAND BAPTIST HOSPITAL, 125 Parker Hill Avenue, Boston, MA, Zip 02120–3297; tel. 617/754–5800; Joseph D. Dionisio, President and Chief Executive Officer

SISTERS OF PROVIDENCE HEALTH SYSTEM
271 Carew /Street, Springfield, MA 01104; tel. 413/736–5494; Vincent McCorkle, President and Chief Executive

MERCY MEDICAL CENTER, 271 Carew Street, Springfield, MA, Zip 01104–2398, Mailing Address: P.O. Box 9012, Zip 01102–9012; tel. 413/748–9000; Vincent J. McCorkle, President and Chief Executive Officer

MICHIGAN

GENESYS HEALTH SYSTEM
302 Kensington Avenue, Flint, MI 48503; tel. 810/606–5000; Norma Hagenow, Chief Executive Officer/COO

GENESYS REGIONAL MEDICAL CENTER, One Genesys Parkway, Grand Blanc, MI, Zip 48439–8066; tel. 810/606–5000; Norma R. Hagenow, R.N., President and Chief Executive Officer

HOSPITAL NETWORK, INC.
252 East Lovell Street, Box 42, Kalamazoo, MI 49007; tel. 616/341–8888; George D. Angelidis, President

ALLEGAN GENERAL HOSPITAL, 555 Linn Street, Allegan, MI, Zip 49010–1594; tel. 269/673–8424; Gerald J. Barbini, President and Chief Executive Officer

BRONSON METHODIST HOSPITAL, 601 John Street, Kalamazoo, MI, Zip 49007–5345; tel. 269/341–6000; Frank J. Sardone, President and Chief Executive Officer

BRONSON VICKSBURG HOSPITAL, 13326 North Boulevard, Vicksburg, MI, Zip 49097–1099; tel. 269/649–2321; Frank J. Sardone, President

OAKLAWN HOSPITAL, 200 North Madison Street, Marshall, MI, Zip 49068–1199; tel. 269/781–4271; Rob Covert, President and Chief Executive Officer

PENNOCK HOSPITAL, 1009 West Green Street, Hastings, MI, Zip 49058–1790; tel. 269/945–3451; Harry Doele, Chief Executive Officer

STURGIS HOSPITAL, 916 Myrtle, Sturgis, MI, Zip 49091–2001; tel. 269/651–7824; Robert J. LaBarge, Chief Executive Officer

LAKELAND REGIONAL HEALTH SYSTEM
1234 Napier Avenue, St. Joseph, MI 49085; tel. 616/983–8300; Joseph Wasserman, President and Chief Executive Officer

LAKELAND HOSPITAL–ST. JOSEPH, 1234 Napier Avenue, Saint Joseph, MI, Zip 49085–2112; tel. 269/983–8300; Joseph A. Wasserman, President and Chief Executive Officer

ST. JOHN HEALTH SYSTEM
22101 Moross Road, Detroit, MI 48236; tel. 810/753–0394; Anthony R. Tersigni, President

POH MEDICAL CENTER, 50 North Perry Street, Pontiac, MI, Zip 48342–2253; tel. 248/338–5000; Patrick Lamberti, Chief Executive Officer

PORT HURON HOSPITAL, 1221 Pine Grove Avenue, Port Huron, MI, Zip 48061–5011; tel. 810/987–5000; Brian M. Connolly, President and Chief Executive Officer

PROVIDENCE HOSPITAL AND MEDICAL CENTER, 16001 West Nine Mile Road, Southfield, MI, Zip 48075–4854, Mailing Address: Box 2043, Zip 48037–2043; tel. 248/424–3000; Robert F. Casalou, President

ST. JOHN DETROIT RIVERVIEW HOSPITAL – NORTHEAST CAMPUS, 7733 East Jefferson Avenue, Detroit, MI, Zip 48214–2598; tel. 313/499–4000; Anthony E. Munroe, President and Chief Executive Officer

ST. JOHN MACOMB HOSPITAL, 11800 East Twelve Mile Road, Warren, MI, Zip 48093–3494; tel. 586/573–5000; Joseph M. Tasse, President

ST. JOHN NORTH SHORES HOSPITAL, 26755 Ballard Road, Harrison Township, MI, Zip 48045–2458; tel. 586/465–5501; David Sessions, Administrator

ST. JOHN OAKLAND HOSPITAL, 27351 Dequindre, Madison Heights, MI, Zip 48071–3499; tel. 248/967–7000; Robert Deputat, President

ST. JOHN RIVER DISTRICT HOSPITAL, 4100 River Road, East China, MI, Zip 48054–2909; tel. 810/329–7111; Frank W. Poma, President

MINNESOTA

AFFILIATED COMMUNITY HEALTH NETWORK, INC.
101 Wilmar Avenue S.W., Willmar, MN 56201; tel. 612/231–6719; Ronald L. Holmgren, President

AVERA MARSHALL REGIONAL MEDICAL CENTER, 300 South Bruce Street, Marshall, MN, Zip 56258–3900; tel. 507/532–9661; Bruce E. Roesler, Chief Executive Officer

AVERA MCKENNAN HOSPITAL AND UNIVERSITY HEALTH CENTER, 800 East 21st Street, Sioux Falls, SD, Zip 57105–1096, Mailing Address: P.O. Box 5045, Zip 57117–5045; tel. 605/322–8000; Fredrick Slunecka, Regional President

RICE MEDICAL CENTER, 600 South Austin Road, Eagle Lake, TX, Zip 77434–3298, Mailing Address: P.O. Box 277, Zip 77434–0277; tel. 979/234–5571; Steven L. Henderson, Administrator

U.S. PUBLIC HEALTH SERVICE INDIAN HOSPITAL, Highway 1, Redlake, MN, Zip 56671, Mailing Address: P.O. Box 497, Zip 56671–0497; tel. 218/679–3912; Essimae Stevens, Service Unit Director

WILLMAR REGIONAL TREATMENT CENTER, 1550 Highway 71 N.E., Willmar, MN, Zip 56201; tel. 320/231–5100; Sandra J. Butturff, Site Director

I-35 CORRIDOR HEALTH NETWORK
760 West Fourth Street, Rush City, MN 55069; tel. 612/358–4708; Lynn Clayton, Administrator

KANABEC HOSPITAL, 301 South Highway 65, Mora, MN, Zip 55051; tel. 320/679–1212; Randy Ulseth, Chief Executive Officer

MERCY HOSPITAL AND HEALTH CARE CENTER, 710 South Kenwood Avenue, Moose Lake, MN, Zip 55767–9405; tel. 218/485–4481; Clayton R. Peterson, Chief Executive Officer

PINE MEDICAL CENTER, 109 Court Avenue South, Sandstone, MN, Zip 55072–5120; tel. 320/245–2212; Timothy Zwickey, Administrator and Chief Executive Officer

UNIVERSITY OF MINNESOTA MEDICAL CENTER, 2450 Riverside Avenue, Minneapolis, MN, Zip 55454–1400; tel. 612/672–6000; Gordon L. Alexander, President

ITASCA PARTNERSHIP FOR QUALITY HEALTHCARE
126 S.E. First Avenue, Grand Rapids, MN 55744; tel. 218/326–7791; Betsy Johnson, Volunteer Co-Chair

BIG FORK VALLEY HOSPITAL, 258 Pine Tree Drive, Bigfork, MN, Zip 56628, Mailing Address: P.O. Box 258, Zip 56628–0258; tel. 218/743–3177; Daniel Odegaard, Chief Executive Officer

DEER RIVER HEALTHCARE CENTER, 1002 Comstock Drive, Deer River, MN, Zip 56636–9700; tel. 218/246–2900; Jeffry Stampohar, Chief Executive Officer

GRAND ITASCA CLINIC AND HOSPITAL, 126 First Avenue S.E., Grand Rapids, MN, Zip 55744–3698; tel. 218/326–3401; Dan McCormick, President and Chief Executive Officer

MINNESOTA RURAL HEALTH COOPERATIVE
P.O. Box 104, Willmar, MN 56201; tel. 612/231–3849; Lyle Munneke, M.D., President and Chairperson

APPLETON MUNICIPAL HOSPITAL AND NURSING HOME, 30 South Behl Street, Appleton, MN, Zip 56208–1699; tel. 320/289–2422; Daniel J. Swenson, Chief Executive Officer and Administrator

AVERA MARSHALL REGIONAL MEDICAL CENTER, 300 South Bruce Street, Marshall, MN, Zip 56258–3900; tel. 507/532–9661; Bruce E. Roesler, Chief Executive Officer

CHIPPEWA COUNTY–MONTEVIDEO HOSPITAL, 824 North 11th Street, Montevideo, MN, Zip 56265–1683; tel. 320/269–8877; Mark E. Paulson, Administrator

DIVINE PROVIDENCE HEALTH CENTER/AVERA HEALTH, 312 East George Street, Ivanhoe, MN, Zip 56142–0136, Mailing Address: P.O. Box 136, Zip 56142–0136; tel. 507/694–1414; Mary Maertens, Interim Administrator

GRACEVILLE HEALTH CENTER, 115 West Second Street, Graceville, MN, Zip 56240–0157, Mailing Address: P.O. Box 157, Zip 56240–0157; tel. 320/748–7223; Helen Jorve, Chief Executive Officer

GRANITE FALLS MUNICIPAL HOSPITAL AND MANOR, 345 Tenth Avenue, Granite Falls, MN, Zip 56241–1499; tel. 320/564–3111; George Gerlach, Administrator

HENDRICKS COMMUNITY HOSPITAL, 503 East Lincoln Street, Hendricks, MN, Zip 56136–0106, Mailing Address: P.O. Box 1016, Zip 56136–0106; tel. 507/275–3134; Kirk Stensrud, Chief Executive Officer

JOHNSON MEMORIAL HEALTH SERVICES, 1282 Walnut Street, Dawson, MN, Zip 56232–2333; tel. 320/769–4323; Glenn Haugo, Administrator

MADISON HOSPITAL, 820 Third Avenue, Madison, MN, Zip 56256–1014, Mailing Address: 900 Second Avenue, Zip 56256–1006; tel. 320/598–7556; Thomas Richter, Chief Executive Officer

ORTONVILLE AREA HEALTH SERVICES, 450 Eastvold Avenue, Ortonville, MN, Zip 56278–1133; tel. 320/839–2502; Kenneth W. Archer, Chief Executive Officer

RENVILLE COUNTY HOSPITAL, 611 East Fairview Avenue, Olivia, MN, Zip 56277–0800; tel. 320/523–1261; Tim Middendorf, Administrator

RICE MEDICAL CENTER, 600 South Austin Road, Eagle Lake, TX, Zip 77434–3298, Mailing Address: P.O. Box 277, Zip 77434–0277; tel. 979/234–5571; Steven L. Henderson, Administrator

SIOUX VALLEY CANBY CAMPUS, 112 St. Olaf Avenue South, Canby, MN, Zip 56220–1433; tel. 507/223–7277; Robert J. Salmon, Chief Executive Officer

SWIFT COUNTY–BENSON HOSPITAL, 1815 Wisconsin Avenue, Benson, MN, Zip 56215–1653; tel. 320/843–4232; Frank Lawatsch, Chief Executive Officer

Section B

TYLER HEALTHCARE CENTER/AVERA HEALTH, 240 Willow Street, Tyler, MN, Zip 56178–0280, Mailing Address: P.O. Box 280, Zip 56178–0280; tel. 507/247–5521; Dale Kruger, Chief Executive Officer & Chief Financial Officer

U.S. PUBLIC HEALTH SERVICE INDIAN HOSPITAL, Highway 1, Redlake, MN, Zip 56671, Mailing Address: P.O. Box 497, Zip 56671–0497; tel. 218/679–3912; Essimae Stevens, Service Unit Director

WHEATON COMMUNITY HOSPITAL, 401 12th Street North, Wheaton, MN, Zip 56296–1099; tel. 320/563–8226; Jesse Tischer, Administrator

NORTHERN LAKES HEALTH CONSORTIUM
600 East Superior Street, Suite 404, Duluth, MN 55802;
tel. 218/727–9393; Terry J. Hill, Executive Director

BIG FORK VALLEY HOSPITAL, 258 Pine Tree Drive, Bigfork, MN, Zip 56628, Mailing Address: P.O. Box 258, Zip 56628–0258; tel. 218/743–3177; Daniel Odegaard, Chief Executive Officer

CLOQUET COMMUNITY MEMORIAL HOSPITAL, 512 Skyline Boulevard, Cloquet, MN, Zip 55720–1199; tel. 218/879–4641; Rick Breuer, Chief Executive Officer and Administrator

COOK COUNTY NORTH SHORE HOSPITAL, 515 West 5th Street, Grand Marais, MN, Zip 55604–9716, Mailing Address: P.O. Box 10, Zip 55604–0010; tel. 218/387–3040; Diane L. Pearson, Administrator

COOK HOSPITAL AND CONVALESCENT NURSING CARE UNIT, 10 Fifth Street S.E., Cook, MN, Zip 55723–9745; tel. 218/666–5945; Allen J. Vogt, Administrator

CUYUNA REGIONAL MEDICAL CENTER, 320 East Main Street, Crosby, MN, Zip 56441–1690; tel. 218/546–7000; Thomas F. Reek, Chief Executive Officer

DEER RIVER HEALTHCARE CENTER, 1002 Comstock Drive, Deer River, MN, Zip 56636–9700; tel. 218/246–2900; Jeffry Stampohar, Chief Executive Officer

ELY–BLOOMENSON COMMUNITY HOSPITAL, 328 West Conan Street, Ely, MN, Zip 55731–1198; tel. 218/365–3271; John Fossum, Chief Executive Officer and Administrator

FAIRVIEW UNIVERSITY MEDICAL CENTER–MESABI, 750 East 34th Street, Hibbing, MN, Zip 55746–4600; tel. 218/262–4881; Lawrence W. Pfaff, President and Chief Executive Officer

FALLS MEMORIAL HOSPITAL, 1400 Highway 71, International Falls, MN, Zip 56649–2189; tel. 218/283–4481; Ty W. Erickson, Chief Executive Officer

GRAND ITASCA CLINIC AND HOSPITAL, 126 First Avenue S.E., Grand Rapids, MN, Zip 55744–3698; tel. 218/326–3401; Dan McCormick, President and Chief Executive Officer

LAKE VIEW MEMORIAL HOSPITAL AND HOME, 325 11th Avenue, Two Harbors, MN, Zip 55616–1360; tel. 218/834–7300; Brian J. Carlson, FACHE, President and Chief Executive Officer

LAKEVIEW MEDICAL CENTER, 1100 North Main Street, Rice Lake, WI, Zip 54868–1238; tel. 715/234–1515; Edward H. Wolf, President and Chief Executive Officer

MERCY HOSPITAL AND HEALTH CARE CENTER, 710 South Kenwood Avenue, Moose Lake, MN, Zip 55767–9405; tel. 218/485–4481; Clayton R. Peterson, Chief Executive Officer

MILLE LACS HEALTH SYSTEM, 200 North Elm Street, Onamia, MN, Zip 56359–7978; tel. 320/532–3154; Daniel Reiner, Administrator and Chief Executive Officer

ONTONAGON MEMORIAL HOSPITAL, 601 Seventh Street, Ontonagon, MI, Zip 49953–1496; tel. 906/884–4134; Fred Nelson, Administrator

PINE MEDICAL CENTER, 109 Court Avenue South, Sandstone, MN, Zip 55072–5120; tel. 320/245–2212; Timothy Zwickey, Administrator and Chief Executive Officer

RIVERWOOD HEALTHCARE CENTER, 200 Bunker Hill Drive, Aitkin, MN, Zip 56431–1844; tel. 218/927–2121; Michael Hagen, Chief Executive Officer

SPOONER HEALTH SYSTEM, 819 Ash Street, Spooner, WI, Zip 54801–1299; tel. 715/635–2111; Michael Schafer, Chief Executive Officer and Administrator

ST. LUKE'S HOSPITAL, 915 East First Street, Duluth, MN, Zip 55805–2193; tel. 218/249–5555; John Strange, President and Chief Executive Officer

VIRGINIA REGIONAL MEDICAL CENTER, 901 Ninth Street North, Virginia, MN, Zip 55792–2398; tel. 218/741–3340; Keith D. Harvey, Chief Executive Officer

WHITE COMMUNITY HOSPITAL, 5211 Highway 110, Aurora, MN, Zip 55705–1599; tel. 218/229–2211; Paula Schaefbauer, Administrator and Chief Executive Officer

MISSOURI

FREEMAN HEALTH SYSTEM
1102 West 32nd, Joplin, MO 64804; tel. 417/347–6601; Gary Duncan, President/Chief Executive Officer

FREEMAN HEALTH SYSTEM, 1102 West 32nd Street, Joplin, MO, Zip 64804–3599; tel. 417/347–1111; Gary D. Duncan, President and Chief Executive Officer

FREEMAN NEOSHO HOSPITAL, 113 West Hickory Street, Neosho, MO, Zip 64850–1705; tel. 417/455–4352; Phil Willcoxon, Chief Executive Officer

HEARTLAND HEALTH
5325 Faraon Street, St. Joseph, MO 64506; tel. 816/271–6000; Lowell Kruse, President/Chief Executive Officer

HEARTLAND REGIONAL MEDICAL CENTER, 5325 Faraon Street, Saint Joseph, MO, Zip 64506–3398; tel. 816/271–6000; Lowell C. Kruse, President and Chief Executive Officer

ST. JOHN'S MERCY HEALTH CARE
615 S. New Ballas Road, St. Louis, MO 63141; tel. 314/569–6000; Michael Morgan, President/Chief Executive Officer

ST. JOHN'S MERCY MEDICAL CENTER, 615 South New Ballas Road, Saint Louis, MO, Zip 63141–8277; tel. 314/569–6000; Margaret Denielle DeNarvaez, President and Chief Executive Officer

MONTANA

MONTANA HEALTH NETWORK INC.
11 South 7th Street, Suite 160, Miles City, MT 59301;
tel. 406/232–1420; Janet Bastian, Chief Executive Officer

BEARTOOTH HOSPITAL AND HEALTH CENTER, 600 West 20th Street, Red Lodge, MT, Zip 59068, Mailing Address: P.O. Box 590, Zip 59068–0590; tel. 406/446–2345; Kelley Evans, Administrator

CENTRAL MONTANA MEDICAL CENTER, 408 Wendell Avenue, Lewistown, MT, Zip 59457–2261; tel. 406/538–7711; David M. Faulkner, Chief Executive Officer

DANIELS MEMORIAL HOSPITAL, 105 Fifth Avenue East, Scobey, MT, Zip 59263, Mailing Address: P.O. Box 400, Zip 59263–0400; tel. 406/487–2296; John L. Stindt, CHE, Chief Executive Officer

DEACONESS BILLINGS CLINIC, 2800 10th Avenue North, Billings, MT, Zip 59101–0799, Mailing Address: P.O. Box 37000, Zip 59107–7000; tel. 406/657–4000; Nicholas J. Wolter, M.D., President and Chief Executive Officer

FALLON MEDICAL COMPLEX, 202 South 4th Street West, Baker, MT, Zip 59313–0820, Mailing Address: P.O. Box 820, Zip 59313–0820; tel. 406/778–3331; David Espeland, Chief Executive Officer

FRANCES MAHON DEACONESS HOSPITAL, 621 Third Street South, Glasgow, MT, Zip 59230–2699; tel. 406/228–3500; Randall G. Holom, Chief Executive Officer

GLENDIVE MEDICAL CENTER, 202 Prospect Drive, Glendive, MT, Zip 59330–1999; tel. 406/345–3306; Scott Duke, Chief Executive Officer

HOLY ROSARY HEALTHCARE, 2600 Wilson Street, Miles City, MT, Zip 59301–5094; tel. 406/233–2600; Greg Nielsen, Chief Administrative Officer

MCCONE COUNTY HEALTH CENTER, Circle, MT, Mailing Address: P.O. Box 48, Zip 59215–0048; tel. 406/485–3381; Nancy Hansen, Administrator

PHILLIPS COUNTY MEDICAL CENTER, 417 South Fourth East, Malta, MT, Zip 59538, Mailing Address: P.O. Box 640, Zip 59538–0640; tel. 406/654–1100; Larry E. Putnam, Administrator

ROOSEVELT MEMORIAL MEDICAL CENTER, 818 Second Avenue East, Culbertson, MT, Zip 59218, Mailing Address: P.O. Box 419, Zip 59218–0419; tel. 406/787–6281; Audrey Stromberg, Administrator

ROUNDUP MEMORIAL HEALTHCARE, 1202 Third Street West, Roundup, MT, Zip 59072–1816, Mailing Address: P.O. Box 40, Zip 59072–0040; tel. 406/323–2302; Lee Rhodes, Chief Executive Officer

SHERIDAN MEMORIAL HOSPITAL, 440 West Laurel Avenue, Plentywood, MT, Zip 59254–1596; tel. 406/765–1420; Wayne Nelson, Chief Executive Officer

SIDNEY HEALTH CENTER, 216 14th Avenue S.W., Sidney, MT, Zip 59270–3586; tel. 406/488–2100; Richard Haraldson, Chief Executive Officer

STILLWATER COMMUNITY HOSPITAL, 44 West Fourth Avenue North, Columbus, MT, Zip 59019–7126, Mailing Address: P.O. Box 959, Zip 59019–0959; tel. 406/322–5316; Tim Russell, Administrator

NEBRASKA

ALEGENT HEALTH
1010 North 96th Street Suite 200, Omaha, NE 68114;
tel. 402/343–4410; Wayne A. Sensor, Chief Executive Officer

ALEGENT HEALTH BERGAN MERCY MEDICAL CENTER, 7500 Mercy Road, Omaha, NE, Zip 68124–2319; tel. 402/398–6060; Mary Kay Thalken, R.N., Interim Vice President and Chief Operating Officer

ALEGENT HEALTH COMMUNITY MEMORIAL HOSPITAL, 631 North Eighth Street, Missouri Valley, IA, Zip 51555–1199; tel. 712/642–2784; Robert R. Sellers, Regional Health Administrator

ALEGENT HEALTH IMMANUEL MEDICAL CENTER, 6901 North 72nd Street, Omaha, NE, Zip 68122–1799; tel. 402/572–2121; Barbara K. Goodrich, R.N., Vice President and Chief Operating Officer

ALEGENT HEALTH MERCY HOSPITAL, 603 Rosary Drive, Corning, IA, Zip 50841–1685, Mailing Address: P.O. Box 368, Zip 50841–0368; tel. 641/322–3121; James C. Ruppert, Regional Administrator

ALEGENT HEALTH MERCY HOSPITAL, 800 Mercy Drive, Council Bluffs, IA, Zip 51503–3128, Mailing Address: P.O. Box 1C, Zip 51502–3001; tel. 712/328–5000; Marie E. Knedler, R.N., Vice President and Chief Operating Officer

ALEGENT HEALTH–MEMORIAL HOSPITAL, 104 West 17th Street, Schuyler, NE, Zip 68661–1396; tel. 402/352–2441; Connie Peters, R.N., Regional Health Administrator

ALEGENT–HEALTH MIDLANDS COMMUNITY HOSPITAL, 11111 South 84th Street, Papillion, NE, Zip 68046–4157; tel. 402/593–3000; Kevin Nokels, Vice President and Chief Operating Officer

BLUE RIVER VALLEY HEALTH NETWORK
2222 Lincoln Avenue, York, NE 68467; tel. 402/362–0445; Charles Schulz, President

ANNIE JEFFREY MEMORIAL COUNTY HEALTH CENTER, 531 Beebe Street, Osceola, NE, Zip 68651, Mailing Address: P.O. Box 428, Zip 68651–0428; tel. 402/747–2031; Terry L. Hoffart, Administrator

BUTLER COUNTY HEALTH CARE CENTER, 372 South Ninth Street, David City, NE, Zip 68632–2199; tel. 402/367–3115; Donald T. Naiberk, Administrator

CRETE AREA MEDICAL CENTER, 1540 Grove Street, Crete, NE, Zip 68333–0220, Mailing Address: P.O. Box 220, Zip 68333–0220; tel. 402/826–6800; Joseph W. Lohrman, Administrator

FILLMORE COUNTY HOSPITAL, 1325 H Street, Geneva, NE, Zip 68361–1325, Mailing Address: P.O. Box 193, Zip 68361–0193; tel. 402/759–3167; Larry Eichelberger, Administrator

LITZENBERG MEMORIAL COUNTY HOSPITAL, 1715 26th Street, Central City, NE, Zip 68826–9620, Mailing Address: Route 2, Box 1, Zip 68826–0001; tel. 308/946–3015; Michael R. Bowman, Administrator

MEMORIAL HEALTH CARE SYSTEMS, 300 North Columbia Avenue, Seward, NE, Zip 68434–9907; tel. 402/643–2971; Roger J. Reamer, Chief Executive Officer

MEMORIAL HOSPITAL, 1423 Seventh Street, Aurora, NE, Zip 68818–1197; tel. 402/694–3171; Diane R. Keller, Administrator

THAYER COUNTY HEALTH SERVICES, 120 Park Avenue, Hebron, NE, Zip 68370–2019, Mailing Address: P.O. Box 49, Zip 68370–0049; tel. 402/768–6041; Joyce Beck, Administrator

WARREN MEMORIAL HOSPITAL, 905 Second Street, Friend, NE, Zip 68359–1198; tel. 402/947–2541; Amy Fish, Administrator

YORK GENERAL HEALTH CARE SERVICES, 2222 North Lincoln Avenue, York, NE, Zip 68467–1095; tel. 402/362–6671; Charles K. Schulz, Chief Executive Officer

CENTRAL NEBRASKA PRIMARY
1518 J. Street, Ord, NE 68862; tel. 308/728–3011; Victoria Bauer, Executive Director

BOX BUTTE GENERAL HOSPITAL, 2101 Box Butte Avenue, Alliance, NE, Zip 69301–0810, Mailing Address: P.O. Box 810, Zip 69301–0810; tel. 308/762–6660; Dan Griess, Chief Executive Officer

VALLEY COUNTY HOSPITAL, 217 Westridge Drive, Ord, NE, Zip 68862–1675; tel. 308/728–3211; Neelam Bhardwaj, Chief Executive Officer and Administrator

NORTHEAST HEALTH SERVICES
P.O. Box 186, Creighton, NE 68729; tel. 402/358–5700; Paul Hurd, President

CREIGHTON AREA HEALTH SERVICES, 1503 Main Street, Creighton, NE, Zip 68729–0186, Mailing Address: P.O. Box 186, Zip 68729–0186; tel. 402/358–5700; Paul Hurd, CHE, Chief Executive Officer

OSMOND GENERAL HOSPITAL, 5th and Maple Street, Osmond, NE, Zip 68765–0429, Mailing Address: P.O. Box 429, Zip 68765–0429; tel. 402/748–3393; Celine M. Mlady, Chief Executive Officer

PLAINVIEW AREA HEALTH SYSTEM, 705 North Third Street, Plainview, NE, Zip 68769, Mailing Address: P.O. Box 489, Zip 68769–0489; tel. 402/582–4245; Becky Lambrecht, Administrator

RURAL HEALTHCARE NETWORK
821 Morehead Street, Chadron, NE 69337; tel. 308/432–5586; Harold L. Krueger, Chief Executive Officer

CHADRON COMMUNITY HOSPITAL AND HEALTH SERVICES, 821 Morehead Street, Chadron, NE, Zip 69337–2599; tel. 308/432–5586; Harold L. Krueger, Jr, Chief Executive Officer

GARDEN COUNTY HOSPITAL, 1100 West Second Street, Oshkosh, NE, Zip 69154, Mailing Address: P.O. Box 320, Zip 69154–0320; tel. 308/772–3283; Diana R. Stevens, Administrator

GORDON MEMORIAL HOSPITAL, 300 East Eighth Street, Gordon, NE, Zip 69343–9990; tel. 308/282–0401; Mehdi Merred, Chief Executive Officer

KIMBALL HEALTH SERVICES, 505 South Burg Street, Kimball, NE, Zip 69145–1398; tel. 308/235–1952; Kim Woods, R.N., President and Chief Executive Officer

MEMORIAL HEALTH CENTER, 645 Osage Street, Sidney, NE, Zip 69162–1799; tel. 308/254–5825; Kent Aland, Chief Executive Officer

MORRILL COUNTY COMMUNITY HOSPITAL, 1313 S Street, Bridgeport, NE, Zip 69336–0579, Mailing Address: P.O. Box 579, Zip 69336–0579; tel. 308/262–1616; Julia Morrow, Administrator

PERKINS COUNTY HEALTH SERVICES, 900 Lincoln Avenue, Grant, NE, Zip 69140–9799, Mailing Address: Rural Route 1, Box 26, Zip 69140–9799; tel. 308/352–7200; Carol A. Kraus, Administrator and Chief Executive Officer

REGIONAL WEST MEDICAL CENTER, 4021 Avenue B, Scottsbluff, NE, Zip 69361–4695; tel. 308/635–3711; Todd Sorensen, M.D., Chief Executive Officer

WESTERN PLAINS COMMUNITY HEALTH SERVICES
302 West 27th Street, Scottsbluff, NE 69361; tel. 308/635–2260; Steve Hetzel, Executive Vice President

BOX BUTTE GENERAL HOSPITAL, 2101 Box Butte Avenue, Alliance, NE, Zip 69301–0810, Mailing Address: P.O. Box 810, Zip 69301–0810; tel. 308/762–6660; Dan Griess, Chief Executive Officer

CHADRON COMMUNITY HOSPITAL AND HEALTH SERVICES, 821 Morehead Street, Chadron, NE, Zip 69337–2599; tel. 308/432–5586; Harold L. Krueger, Jr, Chief Executive Officer

GARDEN COUNTY HOSPITAL, 1100 West Second Street, Oshkosh, NE, Zip 69154, Mailing Address: P.O. Box 320, Zip 69154–0320; tel. 308/772–3283; Diana R. Stevens, Administrator

GORDON MEMORIAL HOSPITAL, 300 East Eighth Street, Gordon, NE, Zip 69343–9990; tel. 308/282–0401; Mehdi Merred, Chief Executive Officer

KIMBALL HEALTH SERVICES, 505 South Burg Street, Kimball, NE, Zip 69145–1398; tel. 308/235–1952; Kim Woods, R.N., President and Chief Executive Officer

MORRILL COUNTY COMMUNITY HOSPITAL, 1313 S Street, Bridgeport, NE, Zip 69336–0579, Mailing Address: P.O. Box 579, Zip 69336–0579; tel. 308/262–1616; Julia Morrow, Administrator

REGIONAL WEST MEDICAL CENTER, 4021 Avenue B, Scottsbluff, NE, Zip 69361–4695; tel. 308/635–3711; Todd Sorensen, M.D., Chief Executive Officer

NEVADA

SAINT MARY'S HEALTH NETWORK
235 West Sixth Street, Reno, NV 89520; tel. 775/770–3000; Jeffrey Bills, President

SAINT MARY'S REGIONAL MEDICAL CENTER, 235 West Sixth Street, Reno, NV, Zip 89503; tel. 775/770–3000; Lawrence F. O'Brien, Chief Executive Officer

NEW HAMPSHIRE

CARING COMMUNITY NETWORK OF THE TWIN RIVERS
c/o Health First 841 Central Avenue, Franklin, NH 03235; tel. 603/934–0177; Rick Silverberg, Managing Director

FRANKLIN REGIONAL HOSPITAL, 15 Aiken Avenue, Franklin, NH, Zip 03235–1299; tel. 603/934–2060; Thomas Clairmont, President

HEALTHLINK
80 Highland Street, Laconia, NH 03246; tel. 603/527–2801; Thomas Clairmont, President

CATHOLIC MEDICAL CENTER, 100 McGregor Street, Manchester, NH, Zip 03102–3770; tel. 603/668–3545; Alyson Pitman Giles, President and Chief Executive Officer

CONCORD HOSPITAL, 250 Pleasant Street, Concord, NH, Zip 03301–2598; tel. 603/225–2711; Michael B. Green, President and Chief Executive Officer

ELLIOT HOSPITAL, One Elliot Way, Manchester, NH, Zip 03103–3599; tel. 603/669–5300; Douglas F. Dean, Jr, President and Chief Executive Officer

LAKES REGION GENERAL HOSPITAL, 80 Highland Street, Laconia, NH, Zip 03246–3298; tel. 603/524–3211; Thomas Clairmont, President

MARY HITCHCOCK MEMORIAL HOSPITAL, One Medical Center Drive, Lebanon, NH, Zip 03756–0001; tel. 603/650–5000; James W. Varnum, President

NEW JERSEY

ATLANTICARE
6725 Delilah Road, Egg Harbor Township, NJ 08234; tel. 609/272–6316; George F. Lynn, VP of Finance

ATLANTICARE REGIONAL MEDICAL CENTER, 1925 Pacific Avenue, Atlantic City, NJ, Zip 08401–6713; tel. 609/345–4000; David P. Tilton, President and Chief Executive Officer

BURDETTE TOMLIN HEALTH SYSTEM
Two Stone Habor Boulevard, Cape May, NJ 08210; tel. 609/463–2266; Joanne Carrocino, President and Chief Executive Officer

BURDETTE TOMLIN MEMORIAL HOSPITAL, 2 Stone Harbor Boulevard, Cape May Court House, NJ, Zip 08210–9990; tel. 609/463–2000; Joanne Carrocino, FACHE, President and Chief Executive Officer

FIRST OPTION HEALTH PLAN
2 Bridge Street, Red Bank, NJ 07701; tel. 908/842–5000; Marc Stein, Vice President Finance

BARNERT HOSPITAL, 680 Dr. Martin Luther King Jr. Way, Paterson, NJ, Zip 07514–1472; tel. 973/977–6600; Joseph S. Orlando, Interim Chief Executive Officer

BAYSHORE COMMUNITY HOSPITAL, 727 North Beers Street, Holmdel, NJ, Zip 07733–1598; tel. 732/739–5900; Raimonda Clark, President and Chief Executive Officer

Section B

BURDETTE TOMLIN MEMORIAL HOSPITAL, 2 Stone Harbor Boulevard, Cape May Court House, NJ, Zip 08210–9990; tel. 609/463–2000; Joanne Carrocino, FACHE, President and Chief Executive Officer

CENTRASTATE HEALTHCARE SYSTEM, 901 West Main Street, Freehold, NJ, Zip 07728–2549; tel. 732/431–2000; John T. Gribbin, President and Chief Executive Officer

CHILTON MEMORIAL HOSPITAL, 97 West Parkway, Pompton Plains, NJ, Zip 07444–1696; tel. 973/831–5000; Deborah K. Zastocki, FACHE, President and Chief Executive Officer

CHRIST HOSPITAL, 176 Palisade Avenue, Jersey City, NJ, Zip 07306–1196, Mailing Address: P.O. Box J–1, Zip 07306–1196; tel. 201/795–8200; Peter A. Kelly, President and Chief Executive Officer

CLARA MAASS MEDICAL CENTER, One Clara Maass Drive, Belleville, NJ, Zip 07109–3557; tel. 973/450–2000; Thomas A. Biga, Executive Director

COMMUNITY MEDICAL CENTER, 99 Route 37 West, Toms River, NJ, Zip 08755–6423; tel. 732/557–8000; Nancy L. Wollen, R.N., CHE, Executive Director and Chief Administrative Officer

EAST ORANGE GENERAL HOSPITAL, 300 Central Avenue, East Orange, NJ, Zip 07019–2897; tel. 973/672–8400; Kevin Slavin, President and Chief Executive Officer

ENGLEWOOD HOSPITAL AND MEDICAL CENTER, 350 Engle Street, Englewood, NJ, Zip 07631–1898; tel. 201/894–3000; Douglas A. Duchak, President and Chief Executive Officer

HACKETTSTOWN COMMUNITY HOSPITAL, 651 Willow Grove Street, Hackettstown, NJ, Zip 07840–1792; tel. 908/852–5100; Gene C. Milton, President and Chief Executive Officer

HOLY NAME HOSPITAL, 718 Teaneck Road, Teaneck, NJ, Zip 07666–4281; tel. 201/833–3000; Michael Maron, President and Chief Executive Officer

HUNTERDON MEDICAL CENTER, 2100 Wescott Drive, Flemington, NJ, Zip 08822–4604; tel. 908/788–6100; Robert P. Wise, President and Chief Executive Officer

IRVINGTON GENERAL HOSPITAL, 832 Chancellor Avenue, Irvington, NJ, Zip 07111–0709; tel. 973/399–6000; Patricia Carroll, Executive Director

JFK MEDICAL CENTER, 65 James Street, Edison, NJ, Zip 08818–3059; tel. 732/321–7000; Scott Gebhard, Executive Vice President and Chief Executive Officer

KIMBALL MEDICAL CENTER, 600 River Avenue, Lakewood, NJ, Zip 08701–4281; tel. 732/363–1900; Joe Hicks, Executive Director

MONMOUTH MEDICAL CENTER, 300 Second Avenue, Long Branch, NJ, Zip 07740–6303; tel. 732/222–5200; Frank J. Vozos, M.D., FACS, Executive Director

MUHLENBERG REGIONAL MEDICAL CENTER, Park Avenue and Randolph Road, North Plainfield, NJ, Zip 07060; tel. 908/668–2000; Nancy A. Fiamingo, Senior Vice President and Chief Operating Officer

NEWARK BETH ISRAEL MEDICAL CENTER, 201 Lyons Avenue, Newark, NJ, Zip 07112–2027; tel. 973/926–7000; Paul A. Mertz, Executive Director

NEWTON MEMORIAL HOSPITAL, 175 High Street, Newton, NJ, Zip 07860–1004; tel. 973/383–2121; Dennis H. Collette, President and Chief Executive Officer

OUR LADY OF LOURDES MEDICAL CENTER, 1600 Haddon Avenue, Camden, NJ, Zip 08103–3117; tel. 856/757–3500; Mark T. Bateman, Chief Administrative Officer

PALISADES MEDICAL CENTER, 7600 River Road, North Bergen, NJ, Zip 07047–6217; tel. 201/854–5000; Bruce J. Markowitz, President and Chief Executive Officer

PASCACK VALLEY HOSPITAL, 250 Old Hook Road, Westwood, NJ, Zip 07675–3181; tel. 201/358–3000; Sidney E. Mitchell, President and Chief Executive Officer

PBI REGIONAL MEDICAL CENTER, 70 Parker Avenue, Passaic, NJ, Zip 07055–7000; tel. 973/365–5000; Jeffrey S. Moll, President and Chief Executive Officer

ROBERT WOOD JOHNSON UNIVERSITY HOSPITAL, 1 Robert Wood Johnson Place, New Brunswick, NJ, Zip 08903–2601; tel. 732/828–3000; Harvey A. Holzberg, President and Chief Executive Officer

SAINT BARNABAS MEDICAL CENTER, 94 Old Short Hills Road, Livingston, NJ, Zip 07039–5668; tel. 973/322–5000; John F. Bonamo, M.D., Executive Director

SAINT PETER'S UNIVERSITY HOSPITAL, 254 Easton Avenue, New Brunswick, NJ, Zip 08901–1780, Mailing Address: P.O. Box 591, Zip 08903–0591; tel. 732/745–8600; Sheryl A. Slonim, President and Chief Executive Officer

SHORE MEMORIAL HOSPITAL, 1 East New York Avenue, Somers Point, NJ, Zip 08244–2387; tel. 609/653–3500; Albert Gutierrez, President and Chief Executive Officer

SOMERSET MEDICAL CENTER, 110 Rehill Avenue, Somerville, NJ, Zip 08876–2598; tel. 908/685–2200; Kenneth Bateman, President and Chief Executive Officer

SOUTH JERSEY HEALTHCARE, 333 Irving Avenue, Bridgeton, NJ, Zip 08302–2100; tel. 856/575–4500; Chester B. Kaletkowski, President and Chief Executive Officer

SOUTHERN OCEAN COUNTY HOSPITAL, 1140 Route 72 West, Manahawkin, NJ, Zip 08050–2499; tel. 609/978–8900; Joseph P. Coyle, President and Chief Executive Officer

ST. FRANCIS MEDICAL CENTER, 601 Hamilton Avenue, Trenton, NJ, Zip 08629–1986; tel. 609/599–5000; Gerald J. Jablonowski, President and Chief Executive Officer

ST. JOSEPH'S REGIONAL MEDICAL CENTER, 703 Main Street, Paterson, NJ, Zip 07503–2691; tel. 973/754–2000; William A. McDonald, Interim Chief Executive Officer

TRINITAS HOSPITAL–WILLIAMSON STREET CAMPUS, 225 Williamson Street, Elizabeth, NJ, Zip 07202–3600; tel. 908/994–5000; Gary S. Horan, FACHE, President and Chief Executive Officer

UNDERWOOD–MEMORIAL HOSPITAL, 509 North Broad Street, Woodbury, NJ, Zip 08096–1697, Mailing Address: P.O. Box 359, Zip 08096–7359; tel. 856/845–0100; Steven W. Jackmuff, President and Chief Executive Officer

UNION HOSPITAL, 1000 Galloping Hill Road, Union, NJ, Zip 07083–1652; tel. 908/687–1900; Kathryn W. Coyne, Executive Director

UNIVERSITY MEDICAL CENTER AT PRINCETON, 253 Witherspoon Street, Princeton, NJ, Zip 08540–3213; tel. 609/497–4000; Barry S. Rabner, President and Chief Executive Officer

VALLEY HOSPITAL, 223 North Van Dien Avenue, Ridgewood, NJ, Zip 07450–9982; tel. 201/447–8000; Audrey Meyers, President and Chief Executive Officer

VIRTUA MEMORIAL HOSPITAL BURLINGTON COUNTY, 175 Madison Avenue, Mount Holly, NJ, Zip 08060–2099; tel. 609/267–0700; Stephen Kolesk, M.D., Vice President and Chief Operating Officer

VIRTUA WEST JERSEY HOSPITAL–BERLIN, 100 Townsend Avenue, Berlin, NJ, Zip 08009–9035; tel. 856/322–3000; Gary L. Long, Vice President and Chief Operating Officer

VIRTUA WEST JERSEY HOSPITAL–MARLTON, 90 Brick Road, Marlton, NJ, Zip 08053–9697; tel. 856/355–6000; Ellen Guarnieri, Vice President and Chief Operating Officer

VIRTUA WEST JERSEY HOSPITAL–VOORHEES, 101 Carnie Boulevard, Voorhees, NJ, Zip 08043–1597; tel. 856/325–3000; Michael S. Kotzen, Vice President and Chief Operating Officer

WILLIAM B. KESSLER MEMORIAL HOSPITAL, 600 South White Horse Pike, Hammonton, NJ, Zip 08037–2099; tel. 609/561–6700; Michael J. Gonnella, President and Chief Executive Officer

QUALCARE, INC.
242 Old Brunswick Road, Piscataway, NJ 08854; tel. 908/562–2800; Jerry Eisenberg, Network Contact

BARNERT HOSPITAL, 680 Dr. Martin Luther King Jr. Way, Paterson, NJ, Zip 07514–1472; tel. 973/977–6600; Joseph S. Orlando, Interim Chief Executive Officer

CAPITAL HEALTH SYSTEM AT MERCER, 446 Bellevue Avenue, Trenton, NJ, Zip 08618–4597, Mailing Address: P.O. Box 1658, Zip 08607–1658; tel. 609/394–4000; Al Maghazehe, Chief Executive Officer

CHILTON MEMORIAL HOSPITAL, 97 West Parkway, Pompton Plains, NJ, Zip 07444–1696; tel. 973/831–5000; Deborah K. Zastocki, FACHE, President and Chief Executive Officer

CHRIST HOSPITAL, 176 Palisade Avenue, Jersey City, NJ, Zip 07306–1196, Mailing Address: P.O. Box J–1, Zip 07306–1196; tel. 201/795–8200; Peter A. Kelly, President and Chief Executive Officer

CLARA MAASS MEDICAL CENTER, One Clara Maass Drive, Belleville, NJ, Zip 07109–3557; tel. 973/450–2000; Thomas A. Biga, Executive Director

DEBORAH HEART AND LUNG CENTER, 200 Trenton Road, Browns Mills, NJ, Zip 08015–1799; tel. 609/893–6611; John R. Ernst, Executive Director

ENGLEWOOD HOSPITAL AND MEDICAL CENTER, 350 Engle Street, Englewood, NJ, Zip 07631–1898; tel. 201/894–3000; Douglas A. Duchak, President and Chief Executive Officer

HACKETTSTOWN COMMUNITY HOSPITAL, 651 Willow Grove Street, Hackettstown, NJ, Zip 07840–1792; tel. 908/852–5100; Gene C. Milton, President and Chief Executive Officer

JFK MEDICAL CENTER, 65 James Street, Edison, NJ, Zip 08818–3059; tel. 732/321–7000; Scott Gebhard, Executive Vice President and Chief Executive Officer

MEMORIAL HOSPITAL OF SALEM COUNTY, 310 Woodstown Road, Salem, NJ, Zip 08079–2080; tel. 856/935–1000; Robert W. Allen, Chief Executive Officer

MUHLENBERG REGIONAL MEDICAL CENTER, Park Avenue and Randolph Road, North Plainfield, NJ, Zip 07060; tel. 908/668–2000; Nancy A. Fiamingo, Senior Vice President and Chief Operating Officer

OCEAN MEDICAL CENTER, 425 Jack Martin Boulevard, Brick Township, NJ, Zip 08724; tel. 732/840–2200; W. Peter Daniels, President

PIEDMONT MOUNTAINSIDE HOSPITAL, 1266 Highway 515 South, Jasper, GA, Zip 30143; tel. 706/692–2441; Ed Lovern, President and Chief Executive Officer

RARITAN BAY MEDICAL CENTER, 530 New Brunswick Avenue, Perth Amboy, NJ, Zip 08861; tel. 732/442–3700; Michael R. D'Agnes, President and Chief Executive Officer

RIVERVIEW MEDICAL CENTER, 1 Riverview Plaza, Red Bank, NJ, Zip 07701–9982; tel. 732/741–2700; Timothy J. Hogan, President

ROBERT WOOD JOHNSON UNIVERSITY HOSPITAL, 1 Robert Wood Johnson Place, New Brunswick, NJ, Zip 08903–2601; tel. 732/828–3000; Harvey A. Holzberg, President and Chief Executive Officer

SAINT JAMES HOSPITAL OF NEWARK, 155 Jefferson Street, Newark, NJ, Zip 07105–1791; tel. 973/589–1300; Ceu Cirne-Neves, Administrator

SAINT MICHAEL'S MEDICAL CENTER, 268 Dr. Martin Luther King Jr. Boulevard, Newark, NJ, Zip 07102–2094; tel. 973/877–5000; Felicia Karsos, Acting Administrator

SOUTH JERSEY HEALTHCARE, 333 Irving Avenue, Bridgeton, NJ, Zip 08302–2100; tel. 856/575–4500; Chester B. Kaletkowski, President and Chief Executive Officer

ST. MARY'S HOSPITAL, 211 Pennington Avenue, Passaic, NJ, Zip 07055–4698; tel. 973/470–3000; Patricia Peterson, President and Chief Executive Officer

UNIVERSITY MEDICAL CENTER AT PRINCETON, 253 Witherspoon Street, Princeton, NJ, Zip 08540–3213; tel. 609/497–4000; Barry S. Rabner, President and Chief Executive Officer

UNIVERSITY OF MEDICINE AND DENTISTRY OF NEW JERSEY–UNIVERSITY HOSPITAL, 150 Bergen Street, Newark, NJ, Zip 07103–2496; tel. 973/972–4300; Darlene L. Cox, President and Chief Executive Officer

VIRTUA WEST JERSEY HOSPITAL–BERLIN, 100 Townsend Avenue, Berlin, NJ, Zip 08009–9035; tel. 856/322–3000; Gary L. Long, Vice President and Chief Operating Officer

VIRTUA WEST JERSEY HOSPITAL–MARLTON, 90 Brick Road, Marlton, NJ, Zip 08053–9697; tel. 856/355–6000; Ellen Guarnieri, Vice President and Chief Operating Officer

NEW YORK

ALLEGANY WESTERN STEUBEN RURAL HEALTH NETWORK
15 Loder Street, Wellsville, NY 14895; tel. 585/596–4006; Carrie Whitwood, Director

JONES MEMORIAL HOSPITAL, 191 North Main Street, Wellsville, NY, Zip 14895–1197, Mailing Address: P.O. Box 72, Zip 14895–0072; tel. 585/593–1100; Ann C. Gilpin, President and Chief Executive Officer

ST. JAMES MERCY HOSPITAL, 411 Canisteo Street, Hornell, NY, Zip 14843–2197; tel. 607/324–8000; Clarence R. La Liberty, Jr, President and Chief Executive Officer

ARNOT HEALTH
600 Roe Avenue, Elmira, NY 14905; tel. 607/737–4100; Anthony J. Cooper, FACHE, President

ARNOT OGDEN MEDICAL CENTER, 600 Roe Avenue, Elmira, NY, Zip 14905–1629; tel. 607/737–4100; Anthony J. Cooper, FACHE, President and Chief Executive Officer

BASSETT HEALTHCARE
1 Atwell Road, Cooperstown, NY 13326; tel. 607/547–3100; William F. Streck, M.D., President and Chief Executive Officer

BASSETT HOSPITAL OF SCHOHARIE COUNTY, 178 Grandview Drive, Cobleskill, NY, Zip 12043–1331; tel. 518/254–3456; Eric H. Stein, FACHE, Administrator and Chief Executive Officer

MARY IMOGENE BASSETT HOSPITAL, One Atwell Road, Cooperstown, NY, Zip 13326–1394; tel. 607/547–3100; William F. Streck, M.D., President and Chief Executive Officer

O'CONNOR HOSPITAL, 460 Andes Road, Route 28, Delhi, NY, Zip 13753; tel. 607/746–0300

HAMILTON–BASSETT–CROUSE RURAL HEALTH NETWORK
150 South Broad Street, Hamilton, NY 13346; tel. 315/598–4735; David Felton, President and Chief Executive Officer

BASSETT HOSPITAL OF SCHOHARIE COUNTY, 178 Grandview Drive, Cobleskill, NY, Zip 12043–1331; tel. 518/254–3456; Eric H. Stein, FACHE, Administrator and Chief Executive Officer

COMMUNITY MEMORIAL HOSPITAL, 150 Broad Street, Hamilton, NY, Zip 13346–9518; tel. 315/824–1100; David Felton, President and Chief Executive Officer

CROUSE HOSPITAL, 736 Irving Avenue, Syracuse, NY, Zip 13210–1690; tel. 315/470–7111; Paul J. Kronenberg, M.D., President and Chief Executive Officer

HEALTH STAR NETWORK
1 North Greenwich Road, Armonk, NY 10504; tel. 914/273–2850; Kevin P. Murphy, Vice President and CEO

LAWRENCE HOSPITAL CENTER, 55 Palmer Avenue, Bronxville, NY, Zip 10708–3491; tel. 914/787–1000; Edward M. Dinan, President and Chief Executive Officer

NORTHERN WESTCHESTER HOSPITAL, 400 East Main Street, Mount Kisco, NY, Zip 10549–3477; tel. 914/666–1200; Joel Seligman, President and Chief Executive Officer

PHELPS MEMORIAL HOSPITAL CENTER, 701 North Broadway, Sleepy Hollow, NY, Zip 10591–1096; tel. 914/366–3000; Keith F. Safian, President and Chief Executive Officer

WHITE PLAINS HOSPITAL CENTER, Davis Avenue and Post Road, White Plains, NY, Zip 10601–4699; tel. 914/681–0600; Jon B. Schandler, President and Chief Executive Officer

MOHAWK VALLEY NETWORK, INC.
P.O. Box 4308, Utica, NY 13504; tel. 315/624–5116; Keith A. Fenstemacher, President and Chief Executive Officer

FAXTON–ST. LUKE'S HEALTHCARE, 1676 Sunset Avenue, Utica, NY, Zip 13502–5475, Mailing Address: P.O. Box 479, Zip 13503–0479; tel. 315/624–6000; Keith A. Fenstemacher, President and Chief Executive Officer

MOUNT SINAI NYU HEALTH NETWORK
P.O. Box 1068, New York, NY 10029; tel. 212/241–3427; Barry Freedman, Acting President

CABRINI MEDICAL CENTER, 227 East 19th Street, New York, NY, Zip 10003–2600; tel. 212/995–6000; Robert S. Chaloner, President and Chief Executive Officer

ELMHURST HOSPITAL CENTER, 79–01 Broadway, Flushing, NY, Zip 11373–1368; tel. 718/334–4000; Chris D. Constantino, Executive Director

ENGLEWOOD HOSPITAL AND MEDICAL CENTER, 350 Engle Street, Englewood, NJ, Zip 07631–1898; tel. 201/894–3000; Douglas A. Duchak, President and Chief Executive Officer

HOSPITAL FOR JOINT DISEASES ORTHOPAEDIC INSTITUTE, 301 East 17th Street, New York, NY, Zip 10003–3890; tel. 212/598–6000; David A. Dibner, FACHE, Chief Executive Officer

LIBERTYHEALTH–GREENVILLE HOSPITAL, 1825 John F. Kennedy Boulevard, Jersey City, NJ, Zip 07305–2198; tel. 201/547–6100; Jean A. Murray, Administrator and Senior Vice President of Operations

LIBERTYHEALTH–JERSEY CITY MEDICAL CENTER, 355 Grand Street, Jersey City, NJ, Zip 07302; tel. 201/915–2000; Jonathan M. Metsch, Dr.PH, President and Chief Executive Officer

LIBERTYHEALTH–MEADOWLANDS HOSPITAL MEDICAL CENTER, 55 Meadowland Parkway, Secaucus, NJ, Zip 07096–1580; tel. 201/392–3100; Martin W. Baicker, CHE, Senior Vice President and Administrator

LONG BEACH MEDICAL CENTER, 455 East Bay Drive, Long Beach, NY, Zip 11561–2300, Mailing Address: P.O. Box 300, Zip 11561–2300; tel. 516/897–1000; Douglas L. Melzer, Chief Executive Officer

LUTHERAN MEDICAL CENTER, 150 55th Street, Brooklyn, NY, Zip 11220–2570; tel. 718/630–7000; Wendy Z. Goldstein, President and Chief Executive Officer

MAIMONIDES MEDICAL CENTER, 4802 Tenth Avenue, Brooklyn, NY, Zip 11219–2916; tel. 718/283–6000; Pamela S. Brier, President and Chief Executive Officer

NEW YORK UNIVERSITY MEDICAL CENTER, 550 First Avenue, New York, NY, Zip 10016–4576; tel. 212/263–7300; Eric Rackow, M.D., President and Chief Executive Officer

NYU DOWNTOWN HOSPITAL, 170 William Street, New York, NY, Zip 10038–2649; tel. 212/312–5000; Bruce D. Logan, M.D., President and Chief Executive Officer

PHELPS MEMORIAL HOSPITAL CENTER, 701 North Broadway, Sleepy Hollow, NY, Zip 10591–1096; tel. 914/366–3000; Keith F. Safian, President and Chief Executive Officer

QUEENS HOSPITAL CENTER, 82–68 164th Street, Jamaica, NY, Zip 11432–1104; tel. 718/883–3000; Antonio D. Martin, Executive Director

SAINT FRANCIS HOSPITAL, 241 North Road, Poughkeepsie, NY, Zip 12601–1399; tel. 845/483–5000; Robert L. Savage, President and Chief Executive Officer

ST. JOSEPH'S REGIONAL MEDICAL CENTER, 703 Main Street, Paterson, NJ, Zip 07503–2691; tel. 973/754–2000; William A. McDonald, Interim Chief Executive Officer

THE MOUNT SINAI HOSPITAL OF QUEENS, 25–10 30th Avenue, Long Island City, NY, Zip 11102–2495; tel. 718/932–1000; Caryn A. Schwab, Executive Director

VASSAR BROTHERS MEDICAL CENTER, 45 Reade Place, Poughkeepsie, NY, Zip 12601–3990; tel. 845/454–8500; Daniel Z. Aronzon, M.D., Acting President and Chief Executive Officer

VETERANS AFFAIRS MEDICAL CENTER, 130 West Kingsbridge Road, Bronx, NY, Zip 10468–3992; tel. 718/584–9000; Maryann Musumeci, Director

NORTHERN NY RURAL HEALTH CARE ALLIANCE
200 Washington Street, Suite 300, Watertown, NY 13601; tel. 315/786–0565; James C. Bellinger, Chairman

CARTHAGE AREA HOSPITAL, 1001 West Street, Carthage, NY, Zip 13619–9703; tel. 315/493–1000; Walter S. Becker, Chief Executive Officer

RIVER HOSPITAL, 4 Fuller Street, Alexandria Bay, NY, Zip 13607; tel. 315/482–2511; Michael J. McLean, Chief Executive Officer

SAMARITAN MEDICAL CENTER, 830 Washington Street, Watertown, NY, Zip 13601–4066; tel. 315/785–4121; Thomas H. Carman, President and Chief Executive Officer

SISTERS OF CHARITY HEALTHCARE
75 Vanderbilt Avenue, Staten Island, NY 10304; tel. 354/718–5080; John J. DePierro, FACHE, President and Chief Executive Officer

ST. VINCENT'S HOSPITAL, 355 Bard Avenue, Staten Island, NY, Zip 10310–1699; tel. 718/818–1234; Dawn M. Gideon, Executive Director

THE RURAL HEALTH NETWORK OF OSWEGO COUNTY
157 West First Street, Oswego, NY 13126; tel. 315/343–2344; Collene Dare, Director

ALBERT LINDLEY LEE MEMORIAL HOSPITAL, 510 South Fourth Street, Fulton, NY, Zip 13069–2994; tel. 315/591–9400; Dennis A. Casey, Executive Director

OSWEGO HOSPITAL, 110 West Sixth Street, Oswego, NY, Zip 13126–9985; tel. 315/349–5511; Corte J. Spencer, Chief Executive Officer

NORTH CAROLINA

BLADEN COUNTY HOSPITAL
P.O. Box 398, Elizabethtown, NC 28337; tel. 910/862–5179; David Masterson, Chief Executive Officer

BLADEN COUNTY HOSPITAL, 501 South Poplar Street, Elizabethtown, NC, Zip 28337–0398, Mailing Address: P.O. Box 398, Zip 28337–0398; tel. 910/862–5100; David J. Masterson, Chief Executive Officer

HOSPITAL ALLIANCE FOR COMMUNITY HEALTH
P.O. Box 46833, Raleigh, NC 27620; tel. 919/250–3813; Gary Park, Chairman

DUKE HEALTH RALEIGH HOSPITAL, 3400 Wake Forest Road, Raleigh, NC, Zip 27609–7373, Mailing Address: P.O. Box 28280, Zip 27611–8280; tel. 919/954–3000; James P. Knight, Chief Executive Officer

WAKEMED RALEIGH CAMPUS, 3000 New Bern Avenue, Raleigh, NC, Zip 27610–1295; tel. 919/350–8000; William K. Atkinson, II, Ph.D., President and Chief Executive Officer

MISSION ST. JOSEPH'S HEALTH SYSTEM
509 Biltmore Avenue, Asheville, NC 28801; tel. 828/213–1144; John Graeter, Director

MISSION HOSPITALS, 509 Biltmore Avenue, Asheville, NC, Zip 28801–4690; tel. 828/213–1111; Joseph F. Damore, President and Chief Executive Officer

SPRUCE PINE COMMUNITY HOSPITAL, 125 Hospital Drive, Spruce Pine, NC, Zip 28777, Mailing Address: P.O. Drawer 9, Zip 28777; tel. 828/765–4201; Keith S. Holtsclaw, Chief Executive Officer

WNC HEALTH NETWORK, INC.
501 Bittmore Avenue, Asheville, NC 28801; tel. 828/257–2983; Gary Bowers, Executive Director

ANGEL MEDICAL CENTER, Riverview and White Oak Streets, Franklin, NC, Zip 28734, Mailing Address: P.O. Box 1209, Zip 28744; tel. 828/524–8411; Michael E. Zuliani, Chief Executive Officer

CHEROKEE INDIAN HOSPITAL AUTHORITY, Hospital Road, Cherokee, NC, Zip 28719, Mailing Address: Caller Box C–26, Zip 28719; tel. 828/497–9163; Arnold Wachacha, Administrator

HARRIS REGIONAL HOSPITAL, 68 Hospital Road, Sylva, NC, Zip 28779–2795; tel. 828/586–7000; Mark T. Leonard, Chief Executive Officer

HAYWOOD REGIONAL MEDICAL CENTER, 262 Leroy George Drive, Clyde, NC, Zip 28721–9434; tel. 828/456–7311; David O. Rice, President

HIGHLANDS–CASHIERS HOSPITAL, 190 Hospital Drive, Highlands, NC, Zip 28741–7600, Mailing Address: P.O. Drawer 190, Zip 28741–0190; tel. 828/526–1200; H. James Graham, Administrator

MARGARET R. PARDEE MEMORIAL HOSPITAL, 800 North Justice Street, Hendersonville, NC, Zip 28791–2563; tel. 828/696–1000; Robert P. Goodwin, President and Chief Executive Officer

MCDOWELL HOSPITAL, 430 Rankin Drive, Marion, NC, Zip 28752–4989, Mailing Address: P.O. Box 730, Zip 28752–0730; tel. 828/659–5000; Sonya Greck, Chief Executive Officer

MISSION HOSPITALS, 509 Biltmore Avenue, Asheville, NC, Zip 28801–4690; tel. 828/213–1111; Joseph F. Damore, President and Chief Executive Officer

MURPHY MEDICAL CENTER, 4130 U.S. Highway 64 East, Murphy, NC, Zip 28906–7917; tel. 828/837–8161; Mike Stevenson, Administrator

PARK RIDGE HOSPITAL, Naples Road, Fletcher, NC, Zip 28732, Mailing Address: P.O. Box 1569, Zip 28732–1569; tel. 828/684–8501; Michael H. Schultz, Chief Executive Officer

RUTHERFORD HOSPITAL, 288 South Ridgecrest Avenue, Rutherfordton, NC, Zip 28139–3097; tel. 828/286–5000; Robert D. Jones, President

SPRUCE PINE COMMUNITY HOSPITAL, 125 Hospital Drive, Spruce Pine, NC, Zip 28777, Mailing Address: P.O. Drawer 9, Zip 28777; tel. 828/765–4201; Keith S. Holtsclaw, Chief Executive Officer

ST. LUKE'S HOSPITAL, 101 Hospital Drive, Columbus, NC, Zip 28722–9473; tel. 828/894–3311; C. Cameron Highsmith, President and Chief Executive Officer

SWAIN COUNTY HOSPITAL, 45 Plateau Street, Bryson City, NC, Zip 28713–6784; tel. 828/488–4013; Ronald A. Sloan, Administrator

THOMS REHABILITATION HOSPITAL, 68 Sweeten Creek Road, Asheville, NC, Zip 28803–1599, Mailing Address: P.O. Box 5779, Zip 28813–5779; tel. 828/274–2400; Charles D. Norvell, President and Chief Executive Officer

TRANSYLVANIA COMMUNITY HOSPITAL, Hospital Drive, Brevard, NC, Zip 28712–1116, Mailing Address: Box 1116, Zip 28712–1116; tel. 828/884–9111; Robert J. Bednarek, President and Chief Executive Officer

NORTH DAKOTA

MEDCENTER ONE HEALTH SERVICES
300 North 7th Street, Bismarck, ND 58506; tel. 701/323–6000; James Cooper, President/Chief Executive Officer

JACOBSON MEMORIAL HOSPITAL CARE CENTER, 601 East Street North, Elgin, ND, Zip 58533–0376; tel. 701/584–2792; Kurt Waldbillig, Chief Executive Officer

MCKENZIE COUNTY HEALTHCARE SYSTEM, 516 North Main Street, Watford City, ND, Zip 58854–0548, Mailing Address: P.O. Box 548, Zip 58854–0548; tel. 701/842–3000; Kris Pacheco, Chief Executive Officer

MEDCENTER ONE, 300 North Seventh Street, Bismarck, ND, Zip 58501–4439, Mailing Address: P.O. Box 5525, Zip 58506–5525; tel. 701/323–6000; James C. Cooper, President and Chief Executive Officer

RICHARDTON HEALTH CENTER, 212 Third Avenue West, Richardton, ND, Zip 58652–7103, Mailing Address: P.O. Box H, Zip 58652; tel. 701/974–3304; Bruce Howe, Jr, Chief Executive Officer

SOUTHWEST HEALTHCARE SERVICES, 202 Sixth Avenue S.W., Bowman, ND, Zip 58623–0009, Mailing Address: P.O. Drawer C, Zip 58623; tel. 701/523–5265; Darrold Bertsch, Administrator

ST. JOSEPH'S HOSPITAL AND HEALTH CENTER, 30 Seventh Street West, Dickinson, ND, Zip 58601–4399; tel. 701/456–4000; Allan C. Sonduck, President and Chief Executive Officer

MERIT CARE HEALTH SYSTEM
720 Fourth Street North, Fargo, ND 58122; tel. 701/234–2600; Dr. Roger Gilbetson, MD, Chief Executive Officer

MERITCARE MEDICAL CENTER, 720 Fourth Street North, Fargo, ND, Zip 58122; tel. 701/234–6000; Roger L. Gilbertson, M.D., President

OHIO

BLANCHARD VALLEY HEALTH ASSOCIATION
145 West Wallace, Findlay, OH 45840; tel. 419/423–5201; Scott Malaney, President and Chief Executive Officer

BLANCHARD VALLEY HEALTH ASSOCIATION, 145 West Wallace Street, Findlay, OH, Zip 45840–1299; tel. 419/423–4500; Scott C. Malaney, President and Chief Executive Officer

BLUFFTON REGIONAL MEDICAL CENTER, 303 South Main Street, Bluffton, IN, Zip 46714–2529; tel. 260/824–3210; Thomas A. Clark, Chief Executive Officer

CLEVELAND HEALTH NETWORK
6000 W. Creek Road, Independence, OH 44131; tel. 216/328–7550; Dennis Pijor, Executive Vice President and COO

AKRON CHILDREN'S HOSPITAL, One Perkins Square, Akron, OH, Zip 44308–1062; tel. 330/543–1000; William H. Considine, President

ASHTABULA COUNTY MEDICAL CENTER, 2420 Lake Avenue, Ashtabula, OH, Zip 44004–4993; tel. 440/997–2262; Kevin J. Miller, FACHE, President and Chief Executive Officer

BARBERTON CITIZENS HOSPITAL, 155 Fifth Street N.E., Barberton, OH, Zip 44203–3398; tel. 330/745–1611; Willard P. Roderick, Chief Executive Officer

CLEVELAND CLINIC FOUNDATION, 9500 Euclid Avenue, Cleveland, OH, Zip 44195–5108; tel. 216/444–2200; Delos Cosgrove, M.D., President and Chief Executive Officer

CUYAHOGA FALLS GENERAL HOSPITAL, 1900 23rd Street, Cuyahoga Falls, OH, Zip 44223–1499; tel. 330/971–7000; Kathleen A. Rice, President and Chief Operating Officer

DOCTORS HOSPITAL OF STARK COUNTY, 400 Austin Avenue N.W., Massillon, OH, Zip 44646–3554; tel. 330/837–7200; Janie Sinacore–Jaberg, R.N., MS, FACHE, Chief Executive Officer

EMH REGIONAL MEDICAL CENTER, 630 East River Street, Elyria, OH, Zip 44035–5902; tel. 440/329–7500; Kevin C. Martin, President and Chief Executive Officer

EUCLID HOSPITAL, 18901 Lake Shore Boulevard, Euclid, OH, Zip 44119–1090; tel. 216/531–9000; Lauren Rock, Chief Administrative Officer

FAIRVIEW HOSPITAL, 18101 Lorain Avenue, Cleveland, OH, Zip 44111–5656; tel. 216/476–7000; Fred M. DeGrandis, Chief Executive Officer

FIRELANDS REGIONAL HEALTH SYSTEM, 1101 Decatur Street, Sandusky, OH, Zip 44870–3335; tel. 419/626–7400; Charles A. Stark, CHE, President and Chief Executive Officer

FISHER–TITUS MEDICAL CENTER, 272 Benedict Avenue, Norwalk, OH, Zip 44857–2374; tel. 419/668–8101; Patrick J. Martin, President and Chief Executive Officer

HAMOT MEDICAL CENTER, 201 State Street, Erie, PA, Zip 16550–0002; tel. 814/877–6000; John T. Malone, President and Chief Executive Officer

HILLCREST HOSPITAL, 6780 Mayfield Road, Cleveland, OH, Zip 44124–2202; tel. 440/449–4500; Glenn Levy, Chief Administrative Officer

HURON HOSPITAL, 13951 Terrace Road, Cleveland, OH, Zip 44112–4399; tel. 216/761–3300; A. Gus Kious, M.D., Chief Administrative Officer

LAKEWOOD HOSPITAL, 14519 Detroit Avenue, Lakewood, OH, Zip 44107–4383; tel. 216/521–4200; Jack D. Gustin, Chief Administrative Officer

LUTHERAN HOSPITAL, 1730 West 25th Street, Cleveland, OH, Zip 44113–3170; tel. 216/696–4300; Steve Ruwoldt, Chief Administrative Officer

MARYMOUNT HOSPITAL, 12300 McCracken Road, Garfield Heights, OH, Zip 44125–2975; tel. 216/581–0500; David J. Kilarski, President and Chief Executive Officer

METROHEALTH MEDICAL CENTER, 2500 MetroHealth Drive, Cleveland, OH, Zip 44109–1998; tel. 216/778–7800; John Sideras, President

PARMA COMMUNITY GENERAL HOSPITAL, 7007 Powers Boulevard, Parma, OH, Zip 44129–5495; tel. 440/743–3000; Patricia A. Ruflin, President and Chief Executive Officer

ST. ELIZABETH HEALTH CENTER, 1044 Belmont Avenue, Youngstown, OH, Zip 44504–1096, Mailing Address: P.O. Box 1790, Zip 44501–1790; tel. 330/746–7211; Robert W. Shroder, President and Chief Executive Officer

ST. JOSEPH HEALTH CENTER, 667 Eastland Avenue S.E., Warren, OH, Zip 44484–4531; tel. 330/841–4000; Robert W. Shroder, President and Chief Executive Officer

SUMMA HEALTH SYSTEM, Akron, OH, Thomas J. Strauss, President and Chief Executive Officer

THE HOSPITAL FOR ORTHOPAEDIC AND SPECIALTY SERVICES, 254 Cleveland Avenue, Amherst, OH, Zip 44001–1699; tel. 440/988–6000; Kevin C. Martin, President and Chief Executive Officer

WADSWORTH–RITTMAN HOSPITAL, 195 Wadsworth Road, Wadsworth, OH, Zip 44281–9505; tel. 330/334–1504; James W. Pope, FACHE, President and Chief Executive Officer

COMPREHENSIVE HEALTHCARE OF OHIO, INC.
630 East River Street, Elyria, OH 44035; tel. 440/329–7700; Kevin Martin, President and Chief Executive Officer

EMH REGIONAL MEDICAL CENTER, 630 East River Street, Elyria, OH, Zip 44035–5902; tel. 440/329–7500; Kevin C. Martin, President and Chief Executive Officer

THE HOSPITAL FOR ORTHOPAEDIC AND SPECIALTY SERVICES, 254 Cleveland Avenue, Amherst, OH, Zip 44001–1699; tel. 440/988–6000; Kevin C. Martin, President and Chief Executive Officer

LAKE HOSPITAL SYSTEM
10 East Washington, Painesville, OH 44077; tel. 440/354–2400; Cynthia Moore–Hardy, President and Chief Executive Officer

LAKE HOSPITAL SYSTEM, 10 East Washington, Painesville, OH, Zip 44077–3472; tel. 440/354–2400; Cynthia Ann Moore–Hardy, President and Chief Executive Officer

MERCY HEALTH PARTNERS – SOUTHWEST OHIO
4600 McAuley Place, Cincinnati, OH 45242; tel. 513/981–6000; Thomas Urban, President and Chief Executive Officer

MERCY FRANCISCAN HOSPITAL MOUNT AIRY, 2446 Kipling Avenue, Cincinnati, OH, Zip 45239–6650; tel. 513/853–5000; James Gravell, President and Chief Executive Officer

MERCY FRANCISCAN HOSPITAL–WESTERN HILLS, 3131 Queen City Avenue, Cincinnati, OH, Zip 45238–2396; tel. 513/389–5000; James Chadwick Patrick, President and Chief Executive Officer

MERCY HOSPITAL ANDERSON, 7500 State Road, Cincinnati, OH, Zip 45255–2492; tel. 513/624–4500; Patricia A. Schroer, President and Chief Executive Officer

MERCY HOSPITAL CLERMONT, 3000 Hospital Drive, Batavia, OH, Zip 45103–1998; tel. 513/732–8200; Mark D. Shugarman, President and Chief Executive Officer

MERCY HOSPITAL FAIRFIELD, 3000 Mack Road, Fairfield, OH, Zip 45014; tel. 513/870–7000; Jeffrey A. Ashin, Interim President and Chief Executive Officer

OHIO STATE HEALTH NETWORK
1375 Perry, Suite 518, Columbus, OH 43201; tel. 614/293–3756; Joann Ort, Executive Director

BARNESVILLE HOSPITAL ASSOCIATION, 639 West Main Street, Barnesville, OH, Zip 43713–0309, Mailing Address: P.O. Box 309, Zip 43713–0309; tel. 740/425–3941; Richard L. Doan, CHE, Chief Executive Officer

BUCYRUS COMMUNITY HOSPITAL, 629 North Sandusky Avenue, Bucyrus, OH, Zip 44820–0627; tel. 419/562–4677; Gerard D. Klein, President and Chief Executive Officer

MADISON COUNTY HOSPITAL, 210 North Main Street, London, OH, Zip 43140–1115; tel. 740/852–1372; Fred L. Kolb, Chief Executive Officer

MARY RUTAN HOSPITAL, 205 Palmer Avenue, Bellefontaine, OH, Zip 43311–2298; tel. 937/592–4015; Mandy C. Goble, President & Chief Executive Officer

OHIO STATE UNIVERSITY MEDICAL CENTER, 410 West 10th Avenue, Columbus, OH, Zip 43210–1240; tel. 614/293–8000; Peter E. Geier, Chief Executive Officer

WYANDOT MEMORIAL HOSPITAL, 885 North Sandusky Avenue, Upper Sandusky, OH, Zip 43351–1098; tel. 419/294–4991; Joseph A. D'Ettorre, Chief Executive Officer

TRIHEALTH INC.
619 Oak Street Corporate Administration, Cincinnati, OH 45206; tel. 513/569–6507; John Prout, Project Manager

BETHESDA NORTH HOSPITAL, 10500 Montgomery Road, Cincinnati, OH, Zip 45242–4415; tel. 513/745–1111; John S. Prout, President and Chief Executive Officer

GOOD SAMARITAN HOSPITAL, 375 Dixmyth Avenue, Cincinnati, OH, Zip 45220–2489; tel. 513/872–1400; John S. Prout, President and Chief Executive Officer

UNITED HEALTH PARTNERSHIP
2200 Jefferson Avenue, Toledo, OH 43624–1181; tel. 419/251–2137; Cathleen Nelson, President and Chief Executive Officer

BELLEVUE HOSPITAL, 1400 West Main Street, Bellevue, OH, Zip 44811, Mailing Address: P.O. Box 8004, Zip 44811–8004; tel. 419/483–4040; Michael K. Winthrop, President

FIRELANDS REGIONAL HEALTH SYSTEM, 1101 Decatur Street, Sandusky, OH, Zip 44870–3335; tel. 419/626–7400; Charles A. Stark, CHE, President and Chief Executive Officer

FISHER–TITUS MEDICAL CENTER, 272 Benedict Avenue, Norwalk, OH, Zip 44857–2374; tel. 419/668–8101; Patrick J. Martin, President and Chief Executive Officer

FULTON COUNTY HEALTH CENTER, 725 South Shoop Avenue, Wauseon, OH, Zip 43567–2015; tel. 419/335–2015; E. Dean Beck, Administrator

H. B. MAGRUDER MEMORIAL HOSPITAL, 615 Fulton Street, Port Clinton, OH, Zip 43452–2034; tel. 419/734–3131; David R. Norwine, FACHE, President and Chief Executive Officer

HENRY COUNTY HOSPITAL, 11600 State Route 424, Napoleon, OH, Zip 43545–9399; tel. 419/592–4015; Kimberly Bordenkircher, Chief Executive Officer

MEDICAL COLLEGE OF OHIO HOSPITALS, 3000 Arlington Avenue, Toledo, OH, Zip 43614–5805; tel. 419/383–4000; Lloyd A. Jacobs, M.D., President

MEMORIAL HOSPITAL, 715 South Taft Avenue, Fremont, OH, Zip 43420–3200; tel. 419/332–7321; John A. Gorman, Chief Executive Officer

MERCY HOSPITAL OF TIFFIN, 485 West Market Street, Tiffin, OH, Zip 44883–0727; tel. 419/447–3130; Dale E. Thornton, M.P.H., CHE, President and Chief Executive Officer

MERCY HOSPITAL OF WILLARD, 110 East Howard Street, Willard, OH, Zip 44890–1611; tel. 419/964–5000; Robert E. Gospodarek, President and Chief Executive Officer

ST. ANNE MERCY HOSPITAL, 3404 West Sylvania Avenue, Toledo, OH, Zip 43623; tel. 419/407–2663; Karen H. Connors, President and Chief Executive Officer

ST. CHARLES MERCY HOSPITAL, 2600 Navarre Avenue, Oregon, OH, Zip 43616–3297; tel. 419/696–7200; David J. Ameen, President and Chief Executive Officer

ST. VINCENT MERCY MEDICAL CENTER, 2213 Cherry Street, Toledo, OH, Zip 43608–2691; tel. 419/251–3232; Jeffrey D. Peterson, President and Chief Executive Officer

WOOD COUNTY HOSPITAL, 950 West Wooster Street, Bowling Green, OH, Zip 43402–2699; tel. 419/354–8900; Stanley R. Korducki, President

WEST CENTRAL OHIO REGIONAL HEALTHCARE ALLIANCE, LLC
730 West Market Street, Lima, OH 45801; tel. 419/226–9085; Sheryl Darnell, Executive Director

JOINT TOWNSHIP DISTRICT MEMORIAL HOSPITAL, 200 St. Clair Street, Saint Marys, OH, Zip 45885–2400; tel. 419/394–3387; James R. Chick, President

MARY RUTAN HOSPITAL, 205 Palmer Avenue, Bellefontaine, OH, Zip 43311–2298; tel. 937/592–4015; Mandy C. Goble, President & Chief Executive Officer

MERCER COUNTY JOINT TOWNSHIP COMMUNITY HOSPITAL, 800 West Main Street, Coldwater, OH, Zip 45828–1698; tel. 419/678–2341; Terrance J. Padden, Chief Executive Officer

ST. RITA'S MEDICAL CENTER, 730 West Market Street, Lima, OH, Zip 45801–4670; tel. 419/227–3361; James P. Reber, President and Chief Executive Officer

VAN WERT COUNTY HOSPITAL, 1250 South Washington Street, Van Wert, OH, Zip 45891–2599; tel. 419/238–2390; Mark J. Minick, President and Chief Executive Officer

OKLAHOMA

EASTERN OKLAHOMA HEALTH NETWORK
110 West 7th Street, Suite 2520, Tulsa, OK 74114; tel. 918/579–7856; Dale Harris, Regional Development

HILLCREST MEDICAL CENTER, 1120 South Utica, Tulsa, OK, Zip 74104–4090; tel. 918/579–1000; Steve Dobbs, Chief Executive Officer

WAGONER COMMUNITY HOSPITAL, 1200 West Cherokee, Wagoner, OK, Zip 74467–4681, Mailing Address: Box 407, Zip 74477–0407; tel. 918/485–5514; John W. Crawford, Chief Executive Officer

MERCY HEALTH SYSTEM OF OKLAHOMA
4300 West Memorial Road, Oklahoma City, OK 73120; tel. 405/752–3756; Michael Packnett, President and CEO

MERCY HEALTH CENTER, 4300 West Memorial Road, Oklahoma City, OK, Zip 73120–8362; tel. 405/755–1515; Michael J. Packnett, President and Chief Executive Officer

MERCY MEMORIAL HEALTH CENTER, 1011 14th Street N.W., Ardmore, OK, Zip 73401–1889; tel. 580/223–5400; Bobby G. Thompson, President and Chief Executive Officer

OU MEDICAL CENTER
6501 North Broadway, Oklahoma City, OK 73116; tel. 405/271–5911; Gerald Maier, Chief Executive Officer

EDMOND MEDICAL CENTER, 1 South Bryant Street, Edmond, OK, Zip 73034–4798; tel. 405/341–6100; Ed Gray, Chief Executive Officer

SOUTHWESTERN MEDICAL CENTER, 5602 S.W. Lee Boulevard, Lawton, OK, Zip 73505–9635, Mailing Address: P.O. Box 7290, Zip 73506–7290; tel. 580/531–4700; Thomas L. Rine, President and Chief Executive Officer

OREGON

HEALTH FUTURE, LLC
825 East Main Street, Suite D., Medford, OR 97504; tel. 541/772–3062; Hans G. Wiik, President and CEO

COQUILLE VALLEY HOSPITAL, 940 East Fifth Street, Coquille, OR, Zip 97423–1699; tel. 541/396–3101; Dennis G. Zielinski, Chief Executive Officer

IDAHO FALLS RECOVERY CENTER, 1957 East 17th Street, Idaho Falls, ID, Zip 83404–6429; tel. 208/529–5285; Bob Spiel, Chief Executive Officer

LAKE DISTRICT HOSPITAL, 700 South J Street, Lakeview, OR, Zip 97630–1679; tel. 541/947–2114; Gordon Ensley, Chief Executive Officer

LODI MEMORIAL HOSPITAL, 975 South Fairmont Avenue, Lodi, CA, Zip 95240–5179, Mailing Address: P.O. Box 3004, Zip 95241–1908; tel. 209/334–3411; Joseph P. Harrington, Chief Executive Officer

SAMARITAN ALBANY GENERAL HOSPITAL, 1046 West Sixth Avenue, Albany, OR, Zip 97321–1999; tel. 541/812–4000; David G. Triebes, Chief Executive Officer

SAMARITAN LEBANON COMMUNITY HOSPITAL, 525 North Santiam Highway, Lebanon, OR, Zip 97355–4363, Mailing Address: P.O. Box 739, Zip 97355–0739; tel. 541/258–2101; Becky A. Pape, R.N., Chief Executive Officer

SAMARITAN NORTH LINCOLN HOSPITAL, 3043 N.E. 28th Street, Lincoln City, OR, Zip 97367–4523, Mailing Address: P.O. Box 767, Zip 97367–0767; tel. 541/994–3661; Jack T. Flaig, Chief Executive Officer

SAMARITAN PACIFIC COMMUNITIES HOSPITAL, 930 S.W. Abbey Street, Newport, OR, Zip 97365–4820, Mailing Address: P.O. Box 945, Zip 97365–4820; tel. 541/265–2244; David C. Bigelow, Chief Executive Officer

SOUTHERN COOS HOSPITAL AND HEALTH CENTER, 900 11th Street S.E., Bandon, OR, Zip 97411–9114; tel. 541/347–2426; James A. Wathen, Chief Executive Officer

ST. CHARLES MEDICAL CENTER – REDMOND, 1253 North Canal Boulevard, Redmond, OR, Zip 97756–1395; tel. 541/548–8131; Jim R. Hobbs, President and Chief Executive Officer

INTERCOMMUNITY HEALTH NETWORK
3600 North Samaritan Drive, Corvallis, OR 97330; tel. 541/768–5377; Larry Mullins, Board Chairman

GOOD SAMARITAN REGIONAL MEDICAL CENTER, 3600 N.W. Samaritan Drive, Corvallis, OR, Zip 97330–3737, Mailing Address: P.O. Box 1068, Zip 97339–1068; tel. 541/768–5111; Steven W. Jasperson, Chief Executive Officer

SAMARITAN ALBANY GENERAL HOSPITAL, 1046 West Sixth Avenue, Albany, OR, Zip 97321–1999; tel. 541/812–4000; David G. Triebes, Chief Executive Officer

SAMARITAN LEBANON COMMUNITY HOSPITAL, 525 North Santiam Highway, Lebanon, OR, Zip 97355–4363, Mailing Address: P.O. Box 739, Zip 97355–0739; tel. 541/258–2101; Becky A. Pape, R.N., Chief Executive Officer

PENNSYLVANIA

DUBOIS REGIONAL MEDICAL
P.O. Box 447, DuBois, PA 15801; tel. 814/371–2200; Raymond A. Garcia, President

DU BOIS REGIONAL MEDICAL CENTER, 100 Hospital Avenue, Du Bois, PA, Zip 15801–1440, Mailing Address: P.O. Box 447, Zip 15801–0447; tel. 814/371–2200; Raymond A. Graeca, President and Chief Executive Officer

GREAT LAKES HEALTH NETWORK
201 State Street, Erie, PA 16550; tel. 814/877–7053; Andrew J. Glass, President

ELK REGIONAL HEALTH CENTER, 763 Johnsonburg Road, Saint Marys, PA, Zip 15857–3498; tel. 814/788–8000; Scott A. Berlucchi, President and Chief Executive Officer

HAMOT MEDICAL CENTER, 201 State Street, Erie, PA, Zip 16550–0002; tel. 814/877–6000; John T. Malone, President and Chief Executive Officer

KANE COMMUNITY HOSPITAL, 4372 Route 5, Kane, PA, Zip 16735, Mailing Address: 4372 Route 6, Zip 16735; tel. 814/837–8585; J. Gary Rhodes, Chief Executive Officer

MARYLAND GENERAL HOSPITAL, 827 Linden Avenue, Baltimore, MD, Zip 21201–4681; tel. 410/225–8000; Colene Daniel, President and Chief Executive Officer

WOMAN'S CHRISTIAN ASSOCIATION HOSPITAL, 207 Foote Avenue, Jamestown, NY, Zip 14702–9975, Mailing Address: P.O. Box 840, Zip 14702–0840; tel. 716/487–0141; Betsy T. Wright, President and Chief Executive Officer

LAUREL HEALTH SYSTEM
22 Walnut Street, Wellsboro, PA 16901; tel. 570/723–0500; Ronald Butler, President and Chief Executive Officer

SOLDIERS AND SAILORS MEMORIAL HOSPITAL, 32–36 Central Avenue, Wellsboro, PA, Zip 16901–1899; tel. 570/724–1631; Jan E. Fisher, President and Chief Executive Officer

SAINT VINCENT HEALTH SYSTEM
232 West 25th Street, Erie, PA 16544; tel. 814/452–5000; Sr. Catherine Manning, Chief Executive Officer

SAINT VINCENT HEALTH CENTER, 232 West 25th Street, Erie, PA, Zip 16544–0002; tel. 814/452–5000; C. Angela Bontempo, President and Chief Executive Officer

WESTFIELD MEMORIAL HOSPITAL, 189 East Main Street, Westfield, NY, Zip 14787–1195; tel. 716/326–4921; Stuart W. Williams, President and Chief Executive Officer

VANTAGE HEALTHCARE NETWORK, INC.
11031 Perry Highway, Meadville, PA 16335; tel. 814/337–0000; Gerald P. Alonge, CEO/Administrator

MEADVILLE MEDICAL CENTER, 751 Liberty Street, Meadville, PA, Zip 16335–2555; tel. 814/333–5000; Anthony J. DeFail, FACHE, President and Chief Executive Officer

MILLCREEK COMMUNITY HOSPITAL, 5515 Peach Street, Erie, PA, Zip 16509–2695; tel. 814/864–4031; Mary L. Eckert, President and Chief Executive Officer

SAINT VINCENT HEALTH CENTER, 232 West 25th Street, Erie, PA, Zip 16544–0002; tel. 814/452–5000; C. Angela Bontempo, President and Chief Executive Officer

TITUSVILLE AREA HOSPITAL, 406 West Oak Street, Titusville, PA, Zip 16354–1404; tel. 814/827–1851; Anthony J. Nasralla, FACHE, President and Chief Executive Officer

UPMC HORIZON, Greenville, PA, Dean Eckenrode, Chief Executive Officer

UPMC NORTHWEST, 100 Fairfield Drive, Seneca, PA, Zip 16346; tel. 814/676–7600; Neil E. Todhunter, President

WARREN GENERAL HOSPITAL, Two Crescent Park West, Warren, PA, Zip 16365–0068, Mailing Address: P.O. Box 68, Zip 16365–0068; tel. 814/723–4973; John P. Papalia, CHE, Chief Executive Officer

SOUTH CAROLINA

CAROLINA HEALTHCHOICE NETWORK
1718 Saint Julian Place, Columbia, SC 29204; tel. 803/254–0984; Suzanne H. Catalano, Executive Director

CLARENDON MEMORIAL HOSPITAL, 10 Hospital Street, Manning, SC, Zip 29102–3153, Mailing Address: P.O. Box 550, Zip 29102–0550; tel. 803/435–8463; Edward R. Frye, Jr, Chief Executive Officer

FAIRFIELD MEMORIAL HOSPITAL, 102 U.S. Highway 321 By–Pass North, Winnsboro, SC, Zip 29180–9251, Mailing Address: P.O. Box 620, Zip 29180–0620; tel. 803/635–5548; J. Larry Dozier, Jr, FACHE, Chief Executive Officer

KERSHAW COUNTY MEDICAL CENTER, 1315 Roberts Street, Camden, SC, Zip 29020–7003, Mailing Address: P.O. Box 7003, Zip 29020–7003; tel. 803/432–4311; Donnie J. Weeks, President and Chief Executive Officer

NEWBERRY COUNTY MEMORIAL HOSPITAL, 2669 Kinard Street, Newberry, SC, Zip 29108–0497, Mailing Address: P.O. Box 497, Zip 29108–0497; tel. 803/276–7570; Lynn W. Beasley, President and Chief Executive Officer

REGIONAL MEDICAL CENTER OF ORANGEBURG AND CALHOUN COUNTIES, 3000 St. Matthews Road, Orangeburg, SC, Zip 29118–1470; tel. 803/395–2200; Thomas C. Dandridge, President

TUOMEY HEALTHCARE SYSTEM, 129 North Washington Street, Sumter, SC, Zip 29150–4983; tel. 803/778–9000; Jay Cox, President and Chief Executive Officer

SOUTH DAKOTA

BANNER HEALTH – BLACK HILLS
930 10th Street, Spearfish, SD 57783; tel. 605/642–4641; Rachelle Schultz, Chief Executive Officer/ADM

LOOKOUT MEMORIAL HOSPITAL, 1440 North Main Street, Spearfish, SD, Zip 57783–1504; tel. 605/644–4000; Larry W. Veitz, Chief Executive Officer

STURGIS COMMUNITY HEALTH CARE CENTER, 949 Harmon Street, Sturgis, SD, Zip 57785–2452; tel. 605/347–2536; Van Hyde, Chief Executive Officer

REGIONAL HEALTH, INC.
P.O. Box 6000, Rapid City, SD 57709; tel. 605/719–1000; Charles E. Hart, M.D., President

CUSTER COMMUNITY HOSPITAL, 1039 Montgomery Street, Custer, SD, Zip 57730–1397; tel. 605/673–2229; Jason Petik, Chief Executive Officer

FIVE COUNTIES HOSPITAL, 405 Sixth Avenue West, Lemmon, SD, Zip 57638–1318, Mailing Address: P.O. Box 479, Zip 57638–0479; tel. 605/374–3871; Jannette Van Beek, Chief Executive Officer

GORDON MEMORIAL HOSPITAL, 300 East Eighth Street, Gordon, NE, Zip 69343–9990; tel. 308/282–0401; Mehdi Merred, Chief Executive Officer

HANS P. PETERSON MEMORIAL HOSPITAL, 503 West Pine Street, Philip, SD, Zip 57567, Mailing Address: P.O. Box 790, Zip 57567-0790; tel. 605/859-2511; David Dick, Chief Executive Officer

LOOKOUT MEMORIAL HOSPITAL, 1440 North Main Street, Spearfish, SD, Zip 57783-1504; tel. 605/644-4000; Larry W. Veitz, Chief Executive Officer

NORTHERN HILLS GENERAL HOSPITAL, 61 Charles Street, Deadwood, SD, Zip 57732-1303; tel. 605/722-6101; Don A. Nelson, Chief Executive Officer

STURGIS COMMUNITY HEALTH CARE CENTER, 949 Harmon Street, Sturgis, SD, Zip 57785-2452; tel. 605/347-2536; Van Hyde, Chief Executive Officer

WESTON COUNTY HEALTH SERVICES, 1124 Washington Boulevard, Newcastle, WY, Zip 82701-2996; tel. 307/746-4491; George Minder, Chief Executive Officer

TEXAS

CENTRAL TEXAS RURAL HEALTH NETWORK
503 East 4th Street, Harrietsville, TX 77964; tel. 512/798-2302; Marcella V. Henke, Executive Director

CENTRAL TEXAS HOSPITAL, 806 North Crockett Avenue, Cameron, TX, Zip 76520-2599; tel. 254/697-6591; Tariq Mahmood, Chief Executive Officer

FALLS COMMUNITY HOSPITAL AND CLINIC, 322 Coleman Street, Marlin, TX, Zip 76661-2358, Mailing Address: Box 60, Zip 76661-0060; tel. 254/803-3561; Willis L. Reese, Administrator

GOODALL-WITCHER HEALTHCARE, 101 South Avenue T, Clifton, TX, Zip 76634-1897, Mailing Address: P.O. Box 549, Zip 76634-0549; tel. 254/675-8322; Clarence Fields, Jr, President and Chief Executive Officer

HAMILTON GENERAL HOSPITAL, 400 North Brown Street, Hamilton, TX, Zip 76531-1598; tel. 254/386-3151; James R. Shafer, Administrator

HILL REGIONAL HOSPITAL, 101 Circle Drive, Hillsboro, TX, Zip 76645-2670; tel. 254/580-8950; Jan McClure, Chief Executive Officer

LAKE WHITNEY MEDICAL CENTER, 200 North San Jacinto Street, Whitney, TX, Zip 76692-2388, Mailing Address: P.O. Box 458, Zip 76692-0458; tel. 254/694-3165; Ted Howard, Administrator

LIMESTONE MEDICAL CENTER, 701 McClintic Street, Groesbeck, TX, Zip 76642-2105; tel. 254/729-3281; Penny Gray, Administrator and Chief Executive Officer

CHRISTUS PRIMARY CARENET OF TEXAS
62443 IH 10 W, Suite 1001, San Antonio, TX 78201; tel. 210/704-4800; Jeffrey M. Puckett, President

CHRISTUS SANTA ROSA HEALTH CARE, 333 North Santa Rosa, San Antonio, TX, Zip 78207-3108; tel. 210/704-2011; Don A. Beeler, President and Chief Executive Officer

HEALTHCARE PARTNERS OF EAST TEXAS, INC
P.O. Box 6340, Tyler, TX 75711; tel. 903/238-8845; Joy McGee-Cory

CHRISTUS ST. MICHAEL HEALTH SYSTEM, 2600 St. Michael Drive, Texarkana, TX, Zip 75503-2372; tel. 903/614-1000; Chris Karam, President and Chief Executive Officer

COZBY-GERMANY HOSPITAL, 707 North Waldrip Street, Grand Saline, TX, Zip 75140-1555; tel. 903/962-4242; William Rowton, Chief Executive Officer

EAST TEXAS MEDICAL CENTER ATHENS, 2000 South Palestine Street, Athens, TX, Zip 75751-5610; tel. 903/676-1000; Patrick L. Wallace, Administrator

EAST TEXAS MEDICAL CENTER CARTHAGE, 409 Cottage Road, Carthage, TX, Zip 75633-1466, Mailing Address: P.O. Box 549, Zip 75633-0549; tel. 903/693-3841; Gary Mikeal Hudson, Administrator

EAST TEXAS MEDICAL CENTER CLARKSVILLE, 3000 West Main Street, Clarksville, TX, Zip 75426, Mailing Address: P.O. Box 1270, Zip 75426-1270; tel. 903/427-3851; Jack R. Endres, Interim Administrator

EAST TEXAS MEDICAL CENTER CROCKETT, 1100 Loop 304 East, Crockett, TX, Zip 75835-1810; tel. 936/546-3862; Terry Cutler, Administrator and Chief Operating Officer

EAST TEXAS MEDICAL CENTER FAIRFIELD, 125 Newman Street, Fairfield, TX, Zip 75840-1499; tel. 903/389-2121; Ruth Cook, Administrator

EAST TEXAS MEDICAL CENTER JACKSONVILLE, 501 South Ragsdale Street, Jacksonville, TX, Zip 75766-2413; tel. 903/541-5000; Steve Bowen, President

EAST TEXAS MEDICAL CENTER PITTSBURG, 414 Quitman Street, Pittsburg, TX, Zip 75686-1032; tel. 903/856-6663; W. Perry Henderson, Administrator

EAST TEXAS MEDICAL CENTER REHABILITATION CENTER, 701 Olympic Plaza Circle, Tyler, TX, Zip 75701-1996; tel. 903/596-3000; Eddie L. Howard, Vice President and Chief Operating Officer

EAST TEXAS MEDICAL CENTER TRINITY, 317 Prospect Drive, Trinity, TX, Zip 75862, Mailing Address: P.O. Box 3169, Zip 75862; tel. 936/594-3541; Terry Cutler, Administrator and Chief Operating Officer

EAST TEXAS MEDICAL CENTER TYLER, 1000 South Beckham Street, Tyler, TX, Zip 75701-1996, Mailing Address: Box 6400, Zip 75711-6400; tel. 903/597-0351; Robert B. Evans, Administrator and Chief Executive Officer

EAST TEXAS MEDICAL CENTER-MOUNT VERNON, 500 Highway 37 South, Mount Vernon, TX, Zip 75457-3602, Mailing Address: P.O. Box 477, Zip 75457-0477; tel. 903/537-8000; Stephen Pitts, Administrator

EAST TEXAS MEDICAL CENTER-QUITMAN, 117 Winnsboro Street, Quitman, TX, Zip 75783-2144, Mailing Address: P.O. Box 1000, Zip 75783-1000; tel. 903/763-6300; Ernest R. Parisi, CHE, Administrator and Chief Executive Officer

GOOD SHEPHERD MEDICAL CENTER, 700 East Marshall Avenue, Longview, TX, Zip 75601-5571; tel. 903/315-2000; Jerry D. Adair, President and Chief Executive Officer

HENDERSON MEMORIAL HOSPITAL, 300 Wilson Street, Henderson, TX, Zip 75652-5956; tel. 903/657-7541; David Klein, Interim Chief Executive Officer

LAIRD MEMORIAL HOSPITAL, 1612 South Henderson Boulevard, Kilgore, TX, Zip 75662-3594; tel. 903/984-3505; Bob Ellzey, Administrator

LINDEN MUNICIPAL HOSPITAL, 404 North Kaufman Street, Linden, TX, Zip 75563-5235; tel. 903/756-5561; Sam DeNunzio, Administrator

MEMORIAL HEALTH SYSTEM OF EAST TEXAS, 1201 West Frank Avenue, Lufkin, TX, Zip 75904-3357, Mailing Address: P.O. Box 1447, Zip 75902-1447; tel. 936/634-8111; Bryant H. Krenek, Jr, President and Chief Executive Officer

MEMORIAL MEDICAL CENTER - LIVINGSTON, 1717 Highway 59 Bypass, Livingston, TX, Zip 77351-1257, Mailing Address: P.O. Box 1257, Zip 77351-1257; tel. 936/327-4381; James C. Dickson, Administrator

NACOGDOCHES MEDICAL CENTER, 4920 N.E. Stallings, Nacogdoches, TX, Zip 75965-1200, Mailing Address: P.O. Box 631604, Zip 75963-1604; tel. 936/569-9481; Gary L. Stokes, Chief Executive Officer

NACOGDOCHES MEMORIAL HOSPITAL, 1204 North Mound Street, Nacogdoches, TX, Zip 75961-4061; tel. 936/564-4611; Tim Hayward, Administrator

PALESTINE REGIONAL MEDICAL CENTER-EAST, 2900 South Loop 256, Palestine, TX, Zip 75801-6958; tel. 903/731-1000; Randall L. Hoover, Chief Executive Officer

PRESBYTERIAN HOSPITAL OF WINNSBORO, 719 West Coke Road, Winnsboro, TX, Zip 75494-3098, Mailing Address: P.O. Box 628, Zip 75494-0628; tel. 903/342-5227; Matthew Troup, President

SABINE COUNTY HOSPITAL, Highway 83 West, Hemphill, TX, Zip 75948, Mailing Address: P.O. Box 750, Zip 75948-0750; tel. 409/787-3300; Edith McCauley, Administrator

SHELBY REGIONAL MEDICAL CENTER, 602 Hurst Street, Center, TX, Zip 75935-3414, Mailing Address: P.O. Box 1749, Zip 75935-1749; tel. 936/598-2781; Gary L. Stokes, Chief Executive Officer

TITUS REGIONAL MEDICAL CENTER, 2001 North Jefferson Avenue, Mount Pleasant, TX, Zip 75455-2398; tel. 903/577-6000; Ronald D. Davis, Chief Executive Officer

TYLER COUNTY HOSPITAL, 1100 West Bluff Street, Woodville, TX, Zip 75979-4799, Mailing Address: P.O. Box 549, Zip 75979-0549; tel. 409/283-8141; Sandra S. Jackson, Ed.D., R.N., Administrator

UNIVERSITY HEALTH SYSTEM, 4502 Medical Drive, San Antonio, TX, Zip 78229-4493; tel. 210/358-4000; George B. Hernandez, Jr, President and Chief Executive Officer

WEST HOUSTON MEDICAL CENTER, 12141 Richmond Avenue, Houston, TX, Zip 77082-2499; tel. 281/558-3444; Jeffrey S. Holland, Chief Executive Officer

NORTH TEXAS HEALTHCARE NETWORK
5601 MacArthur Suite 300, Irving, TX 75038; tel. 972/751-2326; Robert J. Brown, President and CEO

ARLINGTON MEMORIAL HOSPITAL, 800 West Randol Mill Road, Arlington, TX, Zip 76012-2503; tel. 817/548-6100; Oscar Amparan, President

BAYLOR MEDICAL CENTER AT WAXAHACHIE, 1405 West Jefferson Street, Waxahachie, TX, Zip 75165-2275; tel. 972/923-7000; Jerri J. Stuart, R.N., President

BAYLOR SPECIALTY HOSPITAL, 3504 Swiss Avenue, Dallas, TX, Zip 75204-6224; tel. 214/820-9700; Geraldine Brueckner, R.N., President

BAYLOR UNIVERSITY MEDICAL CENTER, 3500 Gaston Avenue, Dallas, TX, Zip 75246-2088; tel. 214/820-0111; John B. McWhorter, III, Interim President

CAMPBELL HEALTH SYSTEM, 713 East Anderson Street, Weatherford, TX, Zip 76086-9971; tel. 817/596-8751; Scott M. Landrum, Chief Executive Officer

COOK CHILDREN'S MEDICAL CENTER, 801 Seventh Avenue, Fort Worth, TX, Zip 76104-2796; tel. 682/885-4000; Nancy C. Cychol, President

DENTON REGIONAL MEDICAL CENTER, 3535 South I-35 East, Denton, TX, Zip 76205; tel. 940/384-3535; Bob Haley, Chief Executive Officer

GLEN ROSE MEDICAL CENTER, 1021 Holden Street, Glen Rose, TX, Zip 76043-4937, Mailing Address: P.O. Box 2099, Zip 76043-2099; tel. 254/897-2215; Gary A. Marks, Executive Director

GREEN OAKS HOSPITAL, 7808 Clodus Fields Drive, Dallas, TX, Zip 75251-2206; tel. 972/991-9504; Thomas M. Collins, Chief Executive Officer

HARRIS CONTINUED CARE HOSPITAL, 1301 Pennsylvania Avenue, 4th Floor, Fort Worth, TX, Zip 76104-2190; tel. 817/878-5500; Louise Baldwin, R.N., President

HARRIS METHODIST FORT WORTH, 1301 Pennsylvania Avenue, Fort Worth, TX, Zip 76104-2895; tel. 817/882-2000; Barclay E. Berdan, CHE, President

Section B

HARRIS METHODIST NORTHWEST, 108 Denver Trail, Azle, TX, Zip 76020–3697; tel. 817/444–8600; Brett McClung, President

HARRIS METHODIST SOUTHWEST, 6100 Harris Parkway, Fort Worth, TX, Zip 76132–4199; tel. 817/433–6550; Stansel Harvey, FACHE, President

HARRIS METHODIST–ERATH COUNTY, 411 North Belknap Street, Stephenville, TX, Zip 76401–3415, Mailing Address: P.O. Box 1399, Zip 76401–1399; tel. 254/965–1500; Deborah Paganelli, CHE, President

HARRIS METHODIST–HEB, 1600 Hospital Parkway, Bedford, TX, Zip 76022–6913, Mailing Address: P.O. Box 669, Zip 76095–0669; tel. 817/685–4000; Jack McCabe, FACHE, President

HUGULEY MEMORIAL MEDICAL CENTER, 11801 South Freeway, Fort Worth, TX, Zip 76134, Mailing Address: P.O. Box 6337, Zip 76115–6337; tel. 817/293–9110; Peter M. Weber, President and Chief Executive Officer

JPS HEALTH NETWORK, 1500 South Main Street, Fort Worth, TX, Zip 76104–4941; tel. 817/921–3431; David M. Cecero, President and Chief Executive Officer

LAKE GRANBURY MEDICAL CENTER, 1310 Paluxy Road, Granbury, TX, Zip 76048–5699; tel. 817/573–2683; Donnie L. Romine, Chief Executive Officer

LAKE POINTE MEDICAL CENTER, 6800 Scenic Drive, Rowlett, TX, Zip 75088–4552, Mailing Address: P.O. Box 1550, Zip 75030–1550; tel. 972/412–2273; John Harris, Chief Executive Officer

LIFECARE HOSPITALS OF FORT WORTH, 6201 Overton Ridge Boulevard, Fort Worth, TX, Zip 76132; tel. 817/370–6078; Barbara Schmidt, Administrator

LIFECARE HOSPITALS OF NORTH TEXAS–DALLAS, 6161 Harry Hines Boulevard, Suite 100, Dallas, TX, Zip 75235–5306; tel. 214/525–6300; Louis Bradley, Chief Executive Officer

MEDICAL CENTER OF LEWISVILLE, 500 West Main, Lewisville, TX, Zip 75057–3699; tel. 972/420–1000; Raymond M. Dunning, Jr, Chief Executive Officer

MEDICAL CENTER OF MCKINNEY, 4500 Medical Center Drive, McKinney, TX, Zip 75069–3499; tel. 972/547–8000; Ernest C. Lynch, III, Chief Executive Officer

METHODIST DALLAS MEDICAL CENTER, 1441 North Beckley Avenue, Dallas, TX, Zip 75203–1201, Mailing Address: Box 655999, Zip 75265–5999; tel. 214/947–8181; Kim N. Hollon, FACHE, Executive Vice President Operations

NORTH HILLS HOSPITAL, 4401 Booth Calloway Road, North Richland Hills, TX, Zip 76180–7399; tel. 817/255–1000; Randolph Moresi, Chief Executive Officer

PARIS REGIONAL MEDICAL CENTER, 820 Clarksville Street, Paris, TX, Zip 75460–9070; tel. 903/785–4521; Andrew Knizley, Chief Executive Officer

PARKLAND HEALTH & HOSPITAL SYSTEM, 5201 Harry Hines Boulevard, Dallas, TX, Zip 75235–7731; tel. 214/590–8000; Ron J. Anderson, M.D., President and Chief Executive Officer

PRESBYTERIAN HOSPITAL OF DALLAS, 8200 Walnut Hill Lane, Dallas, TX, Zip 75231–4402; tel. 214/345–6789; Mark H. Merrill, President

RHD MEMORIAL MEDICAL CENTER, Seven Medical Parkway, Dallas, TX, Zip 75381–7829, Mailing Address: P.O. Box 819094, Zip 75381–9094; tel. 972/247–1000; Joe Thomason, Chief Executive Officer

ST. PAUL UNIVERSITY HOSPITAL, 5909 Harry Hines Boulevard, Dallas, TX, Zip 75235–6285; tel. 214/879–1000; Sharon L. Riley, President

TEXOMA MEDICAL CENTER, 1000 Memorial Drive, Denison, TX, Zip 75020–2035, Mailing Address: P.O. Box 890, Zip 75021–9988; tel. 903/416–4000; W. Mackey Watkins, M.D., President and Chief Executive Officer

TRINITY MEDICAL CENTER, 4343 North Josey Lane, Carrollton, TX, Zip 75010–4691; tel. 972/492–1010; Ernie Bovio, Chief Executive Officer

WALLS REGIONAL HOSPITAL, 201 Walls Drive, Cleburne, TX, Zip 76033–4008; tel. 817/641–2551; Brent D. Magers, FACHE, President

WISE REGIONAL HEALTH SYSTEM, 2000 South FM 51, Decatur, TX, Zip 76234–9295; tel. 940/627–5921; Stephen M. Summers, CPA, CHE, Chief Executive Officer

PERMIAN BASIN RURAL HEALTH NETWORK
P.O. Box 1648, Fort Stockton, TX 79735; tel. 915/336–2241; George Miller, Jr., President

BIG BEND REGIONAL MEDICAL CENTER, 2600 Highway 118 North, Alpine, TX, Zip 79830–2002; tel. 432/837–3447; John Krogness, CHE, Administrator

BIG SPRING STATE HOSPITAL, 1901 North Highway 87, Big Spring, TX, Zip 79720; tel. 915/267–8216; Edward Moughon, Superintendent

CRANE MEMORIAL HOSPITAL, 1310 South Alford Street, Crane, TX, Zip 79731–3899; tel. 432/558–3555; David L. Whitaker, Chief Executive Officer

IRAAN GENERAL HOSPITAL, 305 West Fifth Street, Iraan, TX, Zip 79744, Mailing Address: P.O. Box 665, Zip 79744–2057; tel. 432/639–2871; Teresa Callahan, R.N., MSN, Chief Executive Officer

MARTIN COUNTY HOSPITAL DISTRICT, 610 North St. Peter Street, Stanton, TX, Zip 79782, Mailing Address: P.O. Box 640, Zip 79782–0640; tel. 432/756–3345; William G. Jones, Administrator

MCCAMEY HOSPITAL, Highway 305 South, McCamey, TX, Zip 79752, Mailing Address: P.O. Box 1200, Zip 79752–1200; tel. 432/652–8626; Bill Boswell, Chief Executive Officer

MEDICAL ARTS HOSPITAL, 1600 North Bryan Avenue, Lamesa, TX, Zip 79331–3145; tel. 806/872–2183; Charles N. Butts, Chief Executive Officer

MEDICAL CENTER HOSPITAL, 500 West Fourth Street, Odessa, TX, Zip 79761–5059, Mailing Address: P.O. Drawer 7239, Zip 79760–7239; tel. 432/640–4000; William W. Webster, Chief Executive Officer

MEMORIAL HOSPITAL, 209 N.W. Eighth Street, Seminole, TX, Zip 79360–3447; tel. 432/758–5811; Steve Beck, Chief Executive Officer and Administrator

MIDLAND MEMORIAL HOSPITAL, 2200 West Illinois Avenue, Midland, TX, Zip 79701–6499; tel. 432/685–1111; Russell Meyers, President and Chief Executive Officer

PECOS COUNTY MEMORIAL HOSPITAL, 387 West I. H–10, Fort Stockton, TX, Zip 79735–8912, Mailing Address: P.O. Box 1648, Zip 79735–1648; tel. 432/336–2241; Russell Tippin, Administrator and Chief Executive Officer

PERMIAN REGIONAL MEDICAL CENTER, Northeast By–Pass, Andrews, TX, Zip 79714, Mailing Address: P.O. Box 2108, Zip 79714–2108; tel. 432/523–2200; Randy R. Richards, Chief Executive Officer

RANKIN HOSPITAL DISTRICT, 1105 Elizabeth Street, Rankin, TX, Zip 79778, Mailing Address: P.O. Box 327, Zip 79778–0327; tel. 432/693–2443; Juanita Wheeler, Interim Chief Executive Officer

REAGAN MEMORIAL HOSPITAL, 805 North Main Street, Big Lake, TX, Zip 76932–3999; tel. 325/884–2561; Sidney Tucker, Administrator

REEVES COUNTY HOSPITAL, 2323 Texas Street, Pecos, TX, Zip 79772–7338; tel. 432/447–3551; Bill Conder, Administrator and Chief Executive Officer

SCENIC MOUNTAIN MEDICAL CENTER, 1601 West 11th Place, Big Spring, TX, Zip 79720–4198; tel. 432/263–1211; Michael W. Pruitt, Chief Executive Officer

WARD MEMORIAL HOSPITAL, 406 South Gary Street, Monahans, TX, Zip 79756–4798, Mailing Address: P.O. Box 40, Zip 79756–0040; tel. 432/943–2511; Viki Yates, Interim Administrator

WEST TEXAS VA HEALTH CARE SYSTEM, 300 Veterans Boulevard, Big Spring, TX, Zip 79720–5500; tel. 432/263–7361; Lou Ann Atkins, Director

WINKLER COUNTY MEMORIAL HOSPITAL, 821 Jeffee Drive, Kermit, TX, Zip 79745–4696, Mailing Address: Drawer H, Zip 79745–6008; tel. 915/586–5864; Judene Willhelm, Administrator

REGIONAL HEALTHCARE ALLIANCE
800 East Dawson, Tyler, TX 75701; tel. 903/531–4449; John Webb, President

ATLANTA MEMORIAL HOSPITAL, Highway 77 at South William, Atlanta, TX, Zip 75551, Mailing Address: P.O. Box 1049, Zip 75551–1049; tel. 903/799–3000; Tom Crow, Administrator

BAYLOR UNIVERSITY MEDICAL CENTER, 3500 Gaston Avenue, Dallas, TX, Zip 75246–2088; tel. 214/820–0111; John B. McWhorter, III, Interim President

CHILDREN'S MEDICAL CENTER OF DALLAS, 1935 Motor Street, Dallas, TX, Zip 75235–7794; tel. 214/456–7000; Christopher J. Durovich, President and Chief Executive Officer

CHRISTUS SCHUMPERT HEALTH SYSTEM, One St. Mary Place, Shreveport, LA, Zip 71101–4399; tel. 318/681–4500; Charles J. Paine, M.D., President and Chief Executive Officer

COZBY–GERMANY HOSPITAL, 707 North Waldrip Street, Grand Saline, TX, Zip 75140–1555; tel. 903/962–4242; William Rowton, Chief Executive Officer

EAST TEXAS MEDICAL CENTER CARTHAGE, 409 Cottage Road, Carthage, TX, Zip 75633–1466, Mailing Address: P.O. Box 549, Zip 75633–0549; tel. 903/693–3841; Gary Mikeal Hudson, Administrator

EAST TEXAS MEDICAL CENTER FAIRFIELD, 125 Newman Street, Fairfield, TX, Zip 75840–1499; tel. 903/389–2121; Ruth Cook, Administrator

EAST TEXAS MEDICAL CENTER–QUITMAN, 117 Winnsboro Street, Quitman, TX, Zip 75783–2144, Mailing Address: P.O. Box 1000, Zip 75783–1000; tel. 903/763–6300; Ernest R. Parisi, CHE, Administrator and Chief Executive Officer

GOOD SHEPHERD MEDICAL CENTER, 700 East Marshall Avenue, Longview, TX, Zip 75601–5571; tel. 903/315–2000; Jerry D. Adair, President and Chief Executive Officer

HEALTHSOUTH REHABILITATION HOSPITAL–TYLER, 3131 Troup Highway, Tyler, TX, Zip 75701–8352; tel. 903/510–7000; Sharla Anderson, Administrator

HENDERSON MEMORIAL HOSPITAL, 300 Wilson Street, Henderson, TX, Zip 75652–5956; tel. 903/657–7541; David Klein, Interim Chief Executive Officer

HOPKINS COUNTY MEMORIAL HOSPITAL, 115 Airport Road, Sulphur Springs, TX, Zip 75482–0115; tel. 903/885–7671; Michael McAndrew, Chief Executive Officer

LAIRD MEMORIAL HOSPITAL, 1612 South Henderson Boulevard, Kilgore, TX, Zip 75662–3594; tel. 903/984–3505; Bob Ellzey, Administrator

LINDEN MUNICIPAL HOSPITAL, 404 North Kaufman Street, Linden, TX, Zip 75563–5235; tel. 903/756–5561; Sam DeNunzio, Administrator

MARSHALL REGIONAL MEDICAL CENTER, 811 South Washington Avenue, Marshall, TX, Zip 75670–5336, Mailing Address: P.O. Box 1599, Zip 75671–1599; tel. 903/927–6000; Russell J. Collier, Chief Executive Officer and Chief Financial Officer

NACOGDOCHES MEDICAL CENTER, 4920 N.E. Stallings, Nacogdoches, TX, Zip 75965–1200, Mailing Address: P.O. Box 631604, Zip 75963–1604; tel. 936/569–9481; Gary L. Stokes, Chief Executive Officer

PRESBYTERIAN HOSPITAL OF DALLAS, 8200 Walnut Hill Lane, Dallas, TX, Zip 75231–4402; tel. 214/345–6789; Mark H. Merrill, President

PRESBYTERIAN HOSPITAL OF KAUFMAN, 850 Highway 243 West, Kaufman, TX, Zip 75142–9998, Mailing Address: P.O. Box 310, Zip 75142–0310; tel. 972/932–7200; Kirk King, CHE, President

PRESBYTERIAN HOSPITAL OF WINNSBORO, 719 West Coke Road, Winnsboro, TX, Zip 75494–3098, Mailing Address: P.O. Box 628, Zip 75494–0628; tel. 903/342–5227; Matthew Troup, President

TITUS REGIONAL MEDICAL CENTER, 2001 North Jefferson Avenue, Mount Pleasant, TX, Zip 75455–2398; tel. 903/577–6000; Ronald D. Davis, Chief Executive Officer

TRINITY MOTHER FRANCES HEALTH SYSTEM, 910 East Houston, Tyler, TX, Zip 75702–8369; tel. 903/593–8441; J. Lindsey Bradley, Jr, FACHE, President and Chief Administrative Officer

UNIVERSITY OF TEXAS HEALTH CENTER AT TYLER, 11937 Highway 271, Tyler, TX, Zip 75708–3154; tel. 903/877–3451; Kirk A. Calhoun, M.D., President

WILLIS–KNIGHTON MEDICAL CENTER, 2600 Greenwood Road, Shreveport, LA, Zip 71103–2600, Mailing Address: P.O. Box 32600, Zip 71130–2600; tel. 318/212–4600; Ira L. Moss, Vice President and Administrator

SE TEXAS HOSPITAL SYSTEM
233 West 10th Street, Dallas, TX 75208; tel. 214/943–3582; Bob McElearney, Interim President

CITIZENS MEDICAL CENTER, 2701 Hospital Drive, Victoria, TX, Zip 77901–5749; tel. 361/573–9181; David P. Brown, Administrator

CUERO COMMUNITY HOSPITAL, 2550 North Esplanade Street, Cuero, TX, Zip 77954–4716; tel. 361/275–6191; Darryl Stefka, Administrator

DETAR HEALTHCARE SYSTEM, 506 East San Antonio Street, Victoria, TX, Zip 77901–6060, Mailing Address: P.O. Box 2089, Zip 77902–2089; tel. 361/575–7441; William R. Blanchard, Chief Executive Officer

DRISCOLL CHILDREN'S HOSPITAL, 3533 South Alameda Street, Corpus Christi, TX, Zip 78411–1785, Mailing Address: P.O. Box 6530, Zip 78466–6530; tel. 361/694–5000; Rick W. Merrill, President and Chief Executive Officer

EL CAMPO MEMORIAL HOSPITAL, 303 Sandy Corner Road, El Campo, TX, Zip 77437–9535; tel. 979/543–6251; Steve Gularte, Administrator

JACKSON COUNTY HOSPITAL DISTRICT, 1013 South Wells Street, Edna, TX, Zip 77957–4098; tel. 361/782–5241; Marcella V. Henke, Administrator and Chief Executive Officer

LAVACA MEDICAL CENTER, 1400 North Texana Street, Hallettsville, TX, Zip 77964–2099; tel. 361/798–3671; James Vanek, Chief Executive Officer

MEMORIAL MEDICAL CENTER, 815 North Virginia Street, Port Lavaca, TX, Zip 77979–3025, Mailing Address: P.O. Box 25, Zip 77979–0025; tel. 361/552–6713; Elwood E. Currier, Jr, CHE, Administrator

REFUGIO COUNTY MEMORIAL HOSPITAL, 107 Swift Street, Refugio, TX, Zip 78377–2425; tel. 361/526–2321; Louis R. Willeke, Administrator

YOAKUM COUNTY HOSPITAL, 412 Mustang Avenue, Denver City, TX, Zip 79323–2750, Mailing Address: P.O. Drawer 1130, Zip 79323–1130; tel. 806/592–2121; Clay Taylor, Chief Executive Officer

SOUTHWEST TEXAS RURAL HEALTH ALLIANCE
143 East Garza, New Braunfels, TX 78130; tel. 210/606–9111; Johnny Johnson, President

CENTRAL TEXAS MEDICAL CENTER, 1301 Wonder World Drive, San Marcos, TX, Zip 78666–7544; tel. 512/753–3500; Gary L. Jepson, President and Chief Executive Officer

CONNALLY MEDICAL CENTER, 499 10th Street, Floresville, TX, Zip 78114–2798; tel. 830/393–1300; Frances L. Chilek, R.N., Administrator

DIMMIT COUNTY MEMORIAL HOSPITAL, 704 Hospital Drive, Carrizo Springs, TX, Zip 78834–3836; tel. 830/876–2424; Ernest Flores, Jr, Administrator

FRIO REGIONAL HOSPITAL, 200 South I. H. 35, Pearsall, TX, Zip 78061–3998; tel. 830/334–3617; Alan D. Holmes, Chief Executive Officer

GUADALUPE VALLEY HOSPITAL, 1215 East Court Street, Seguin, TX, Zip 78155–5189; tel. 830/379–2411; Robert Haynes, Administrator

HILL COUNTRY MEMORIAL HOSPITAL, 1020 Highway 16 South, Fredericksburg, TX, Zip 78624, Mailing Address: P.O. Box 835, Zip 78624–0835; tel. 830/997–4353; Jeff A. Bourgeois, Chief Executive Officer

KIMBLE HOSPITAL, 2101 Main Street, Junction, TX, Zip 76849–2101; tel. 325/446–3321; Marlene Jones, Chief Executive Officer

MCKENNA MEMORIAL HOSPITAL, 600 North Union Avenue, New Braunfels, TX, Zip 78130–4191; tel. 830/606–9111; Tim Brierty, Chief Executive Officer

MEDINA COMMUNITY HOSPITAL, 3100 Avenue E., Hondo, TX, Zip 78861–3599; tel. 830/426–7838; Beverly Gruber, Administrator

MEMORIAL HOSPITAL, Highway 90A By–Pass, Gonzales, TX, Zip 78629–2021, Mailing Address: P.O. Box 587, Zip 78629–0587; tel. 830/672–7581; Charles Norris, Chief Executive Officer

OTTO KAISER MEMORIAL HOSPITAL, 3349 South Highway 181, Kenedy, TX, Zip 78119–5240; tel. 830/583–3401; Nancy Kinkler, Administrator

SETON EDGAR B. DAVIS HOSPITAL, 130 Hays Street, Luling, TX, Zip 78648–3207; tel. 830/875–7000; Neal Kelley, Administrator

SID PETERSON MEMORIAL HOSPITAL, 710 Water Street, Kerrville, TX, Zip 78028–5398; tel. 830/896–4200; James Patrick Murray, Chief Executive Officer

SOUTH TEXAS REGIONAL MEDICAL CENTER, 1905 Highway 97 East, Jourdanton, TX, Zip 78026–1504; tel. 830/769–3515; Dennis Barts, Chief Executive Officer

UVALDE COUNTY HOSPITAL AUTHORITY, 1025 Garner Field Road, Uvalde, TX, Zip 78801–1025; tel. 830/278–6251; James E. Buckner, Jr, CHE, Administrator

VAL VERDE REGIONAL MEDICAL CENTER, 801 Bedell Avenue, Del Rio, TX, Zip 78840–4185, Mailing Address: P.O. Box 1527, Zip 78840–1527; tel. 830/775–8566; Patrick J. Jacobus, Chief Executive Officer

WARM SPRINGS SPECIALTY HOSPITAL, 200 Memorial Drive, Luling, TX, Zip 78648; tel. 830/875–8400; Brenda Miles, Administrator

ST. DAVID'S HEALTH NETWORK
P.O. Box 49192, Austin, TX 78765; Sharon J. Alvis, Executive Director

ROUND ROCK MEDICAL CENTER, 2400 Round Rock Avenue, Round Rock, TX, Zip 78681–4097; tel. 512/341–1000; Deborah L. Ryle, Administrator and Chief Executive Officer

SOUTH AUSTIN HOSPITAL, 901 West Ben White Boulevard, Austin, TX, Zip 78704–6903; tel. 512/447–2211; Erol R. Akdamar, Chief Executive Officer

ST. DAVID'S MEDICAL CENTER, 919 East 32nd Street, Austin, TX, Zip 78705–2709, Mailing Address: P.O. Box 4039, Zip 78765–4039; tel. 512/476–7111; Cole C. Eslyn, Chief Executive Officer

ST. DAVID'S PAVILION, 1025 East 32nd Street, Austin, TX, Zip 78765–2705; tel. 512/867–5800; Cole C. Eslyn, Chief Executive Officer

ST. DAVID'S REHABILITATION CENTER, 1005 East 32nd Street, Austin, TX, Zip 78705–2705, Mailing Address: P.O. Box 4270, Zip 78765–4270; tel. 512/867–5100; Cole C. Eslyn, Chief Executive Officer

VIRGINIA

CENTRAL VIRGINIA HEALTH NETWORK
2201 West Broad Street Suite 202, Richmond, VA 23220–2022; tel. 804/359–4500; Michael Matthews, Chief Executive Officer

BON SECOURS ST. MARY'S HOSPITAL, 5801 Bremo Road, Richmond, VA, Zip 23226–1907; tel. 804/285–2011; Michael K. Kerner, Executive Vice President and Administrator

BON SECOURS–RICHMOND COMMUNITY HOSPITAL, 1500 North 28th Street, Richmond, VA, Zip 23223–5396, Mailing Address: Box 27184, Zip 23261–7184; tel. 804/225–1700; Paula R. Autry, Executive Vice President and Administrator

COMMUNITY MEMORIAL HEALTHCENTER, 125 Buena Vista Circle, South Hill, VA, Zip 23970–0090, Mailing Address: P.O. Box 90, Zip 23970–0090; tel. 434/447–3151; W. Scott Burnette, President and Chief Executive Officer

MARY IMMACULATE HOSPITAL, 2 Bernardine Drive, Newport News, VA, Zip 23602–4499; tel. 757/886–6000; Patricia L. Robertson, Executive Vice President and Administrator

MEMORIAL REGIONAL MEDICAL CENTER, 8260 Atlee Road, Mechanicsville, VA, Zip 23116–1844; tel. 804/764–6000; Michael Robinson, Executive Vice President and Administrator

RAPPAHANNOCK GENERAL HOSPITAL, 101 Harris Drive, Kilmarnock, VA, Zip 22482, Mailing Address: P.O. Box 1449, Zip 22482–1449; tel. 804/435–8000; James M. Holmes, Jr, President and Chief Executive Officer

SHELTERING ARMS REHABILITATION HOSPITAL, 8254 Atlee Road, Mechanicsville, VA, Zip 23116–1844; tel. 804/764–6000; Jack A. Carroll, Ph.D., President and Chief Executive Officer

SOUTHSIDE COMMUNITY HOSPITAL, 800 Oak Street, Farmville, VA, Zip 23901–1199; tel. 434/392–8811; Gwen S. Eddleman, R.N., President and Chief Executive Officer

UNIVERSITY OF VIRGINIA MEDICAL CENTER, Jefferson Park Avenue, Charlottesville, VA, Zip 22908–0001, Mailing Address: P.O. Box 800809, Zip 22908–0809; tel. 434/924–0211; R. Edward Howell, Vice President and Chief Executive Officer

PREFERRED CARE OF RICHMOND
P.O. Box 13739, Richmond, VA 23225; tel. 804/560–4160; Richard Morrow, Network Coordinator

JOHN RANDOLPH MEDICAL CENTER, 411 West Randolph Road, Hopewell, VA, Zip 23860–2938; tel. 804/541–1600; Elwood Bernard Boone, III, Chief Executive Officer

RETREAT HOSPITAL, 2621 Grove Avenue, Richmond, VA, Zip 23220–4308; tel. 804/254–5100; Paul L. Baldwin, Chief Executive Officer

VIRGINIA HEALTH NETWORK
7400 Beaufont Springs Drive, Suite 505, Richmond, VA 23225; James Brittain, President

ALLEGHANY REGIONAL HOSPITAL, One ARH Lane, Low Moor, VA, Zip 24457, Mailing Address: P.O. Box 7, Zip 24457–0007; tel. 540/862–6011; Timothy C. Tobin, President and Chief Executive Officer

AUGUSTA HEALTH CARE, 78 Medical Center Drive, Fishersville, VA, Zip 22939–2332, Mailing Address: P.O. Box 1000, Zip 22939–1000; tel. 540/932–4000; Richard H. Graham, President and Chief Executive Officer

BEDFORD MEMORIAL HOSPITAL, 1613 Oakwood Street, Bedford, VA, Zip 24523–0688, Mailing Address: P.O. Box 688, Zip 24523–0688; tel. 540/586–2441; E. W. Tibbs, President and Chief Executive Officer

Section B

BON SECOURS ST. MARY'S HOSPITAL, 5801 Bremo Road, Richmond, VA, Zip 23226–1907; tel. 804/285–2011; Michael K. Kerner, Executive Vice President and Administrator

BON SECOURS–DEPAUL MEDICAL CENTER, 150 Kingsley Lane, Norfolk, VA, Zip 23505–4650; tel. 757/889–5000; Susan A. Erickson, Executive Vice President and Administrator

BON SECOURS–RICHMOND COMMUNITY HOSPITAL, 1500 North 28th Street, Richmond, VA, Zip 23223–5396, Mailing Address: Box 27184, Zip 23261–7184; tel. 804/225–1700; Paula R. Autry, Executive Vice President and Administrator

BUCHANAN GENERAL HOSPITAL, Grundy, VA, Mailing Address: Route 5, Box 20, Zip 24614–9611; tel. 276/935–1000; Joan Jamison, Interim Chief Executive Officer

CARILION GILES MEMORIAL HOSPITAL, 1 Taylor Avenue, Pearisburg, VA, Zip 24134–1932; tel. 540/921–6000; James E. Tyler, Administrator and Chief Executive Officer

CARILION MEDICAL CENTER, Belleview at Jefferson Street, Roanoke, VA, Zip 24014, Mailing Address: P.O. Box 13367, Zip 24033–3367; tel. 540/981–7000; Edward G. Murphy, M.D., Chief Executive Officer

CARILION NEW RIVER VALLEY MEDICAL CENTER, 2900 Lamb Circle, Christiansburg, VA, Zip 24073–5041, Mailing Address: P.O. Box 5, Radford, Zip 24143–0005; tel. 540/731–2000; Matthew J. Perry, President

CHESAPEAKE GENERAL HOSPITAL, 736 Battlefield Boulevard North, Chesapeake, VA, Zip 23320–4941, Mailing Address: P.O. Box 2028, Zip 23327–2028; tel. 757/312–8121; Christopehr R. Mosley, President and Chief Executive Officer

CHILDREN'S HOSPITAL, 2924 Brook Road, Richmond, VA, Zip 23220–1298; tel. 804/321–7474; Leslie G. Wyatt, President and Chief Executive Officer

CHILDREN'S HOSPITAL OF THE KING'S DAUGHTERS, 601 Children's Lane, Norfolk, VA, Zip 23507–1969; tel. 757/668–7000; James D. Dahling, President and Chief Executive Officer

CJW MEDICAL CENTER, 7101 Jahnke Road, Richmond, VA, Zip 23225–4044; tel. 804/320–3911; Peter A. Marmerstein, Chief Executive Officer

COMMUNITY MEMORIAL HEALTHCENTER, 125 Buena Vista Circle, South Hill, VA, Zip 23970–0090, Mailing Address: P.O. Box 90, Zip 23970–0090; tel. 434/447–3151; W. Scott Burnette, President and Chief Executive Officer

CULPEPER REGIONAL HOSPITAL, 501 Sunset Lane, Culpeper, VA, Zip 22701–3917, Mailing Address: Box 592, Zip 22701–0592; tel. 540/829–4100; H. Lee Kirk, Jr, President and Chief Executive Officer

DOMINION HOSPITAL, 2960 Sleepy Hollow Road, Falls Church, VA, Zip 22044–2001; tel. 703/536–2000; Bryan K. Dearing, Chief Executive Officer

FAUQUIER HOSPITAL, 500 Hospital Drive, Warrenton, VA, Zip 20186–3099; tel. 540/349–0531; Rodger H. Baker, President and Chief Executive Officer

FRANKLIN MEMORIAL HOSPITAL, 111 Franklin Health Commons, Farmington, ME, Zip 04938–9990; tel. 207/778–6031; Richard A. Batt, President and Chief Executive Officer

HEALTHSOUTH REHABILITATION HOSPITAL OF VIRGINIA, 5700 Fitzhugh Avenue, Richmond, VA, Zip 23226–1877; tel. 804/288–5700; Jeff Ruskan, Administrator

HENRICO DOCTORS' HOSPITAL, 1602 Skipwith Road, Richmond, VA, Zip 23229–5205; tel. 804/289–4500; Patrick W. Farrell, Chief Executive Officer

INOVA ALEXANDRIA HOSPITAL, 4320 Seminary Road, Alexandria, VA, Zip 22304–1594; tel. 703/504–3000; Kenneth H. Kozloff, FACHE, Administrator

INOVA FAIR OAKS HOSPITAL, 3600 Joseph Siewick Drive, Fairfax, VA, Zip 22033–1798; tel. 703/391–3600; John L. Fitzgerald, Vice President and Administrator

INOVA FAIRFAX HOSPITAL, 3300 Gallows Road, Falls Church, VA, Zip 22042–3300; tel. 703/776–4001; Douglas P. Cropper, Administrator

INOVA LOUDOUN HOSPITAL, 44045 Riverside Parkway, Leesburg, VA, Zip 20176–2799, Mailing Address: P.O. Box 6000, Zip 20176–6000; tel. 703/858–6000; Rodney N. Huebbers, President and Chief Executive Officer

INOVA MOUNT VERNON HOSPITAL, 2501 Parker's Lane, Alexandria, VA, Zip 22306; tel. 703/664–7000; Arlen Reynolds, Interim Chief Executive Officer

JOHN RANDOLPH MEDICAL CENTER, 411 West Randolph Road, Hopewell, VA, Zip 23860–2938; tel. 804/541–1600; Elwood Bernard Boone, III, Chief Executive Officer

JOHNSTON MEMORIAL HOSPITAL, 351 Court Street N.E., Abingdon, VA, Zip 24210–2955; tel. 276/676–7000; Sean S. McMurray, CHE, Chief Executive Officer

LOUISE OBICI MEMORIAL HOSPITAL, 2800 Godwin Boulevard, Suffolk, VA, Zip 23434–4323, Mailing Address: P.O. Box 1100, Zip 23439–1100; tel. 757/934–4000; Rosemary C. Check, President and Chief Executive Officer

MARTHA JEFFERSON HOSPITAL, 459 Locust Avenue, Charlottesville, VA, Zip 22902–9940; tel. 434/982–7000; James E. Haden, President and Chief Executive Officer

MARY IMMACULATE HOSPITAL, 2 Bernardine Drive, Newport News, VA, Zip 23602–4499; tel. 757/886–6000; Patricia L. Robertson, Executive Vice President and Administrator

MARY WASHINGTON HOSPITAL, 1001 Sam Perry Boulevard, Fredericksburg, VA, Zip 22401–3354; tel. 540/741–1100; Fred M. Rankin, III, President and Chief Executive Officer

MARYVIEW MEDICAL CENTER, 3636 High Street, Portsmouth, VA, Zip 23707–3270; tel. 757/398–2200; Jack McNamara, Interim Executive Vice President and Administrator

MEMORIAL HOSPITAL, 320 Hospital Drive, Martinsville, VA, Zip 24112–1981, Mailing Address: P.O. Box 4788, Zip 24115–4788; tel. 276/666–7200; Joseph Roach, Chief Executive Officer

MEMORIAL REGIONAL MEDICAL CENTER, 8260 Atlee Road, Mechanicsville, VA, Zip 23116–1844; tel. 804/764–6000; Michael Robinson, Executive Vice President and Administrator

MOUNT REGIS CENTER, 405 Kimball Avenue, Salem, VA, Zip 24153–6299; tel. 540/389–4761; Gail S. Basham, Chief Executive Officer

MOUNTAIN VIEW REGIONAL MEDICAL CENTER, Third Street N.E., Norton, VA, Zip 24273–1131, Mailing Address: P.O. Box 620, Zip 24273–0620; tel. 276/679–9100; Jamie Guin, Chief Executive Officer

NORTHERN HOSPITAL OF SURRY COUNTY, 830 Rockford Street, Mount Airy, NC, Zip 27030–5365, Mailing Address: P.O. Box 1101, Zip 27030–1101; tel. 336/719–7000; William B. James, Chief Executive Officer

NORTHERN VIRGINIA COMMUNITY HOSPITAL, 601 South Carlin Springs Road, Arlington, VA, Zip 22204–1096; tel. 703/671–1200; Bryan K. Dearing, Chief Executive Officer

POTOMAC HOSPITAL, 2300 Opitz Boulevard, Woodbridge, VA, Zip 22191–3399; tel. 703/670–1313; William Mason Moss, President

PRINCE WILLIAM HOSPITAL, 8700 Sudley Road, Manassas, VA, Zip 20110–4418, Mailing Address: P.O. Box 2610, Zip 20108–0867; tel. 703/369–8000; Michael J. Schwartz, President and Chief Executive Officer

R. J. REYNOLDS–PATRICK COUNTY MEMORIAL HOSPITAL, 18688 Jeb Stuart Highway, Stuart, VA, Zip 24171–1559; tel. 276/694–3151; Janice F. Wilkins, Administrator

RAPPAHANNOCK GENERAL HOSPITAL, 101 Harris Drive, Kilmarnock, VA, Zip 22482, Mailing Address: P.O. Box 1449, Zip 22482–1449; tel. 804/435–8000; James M. Holmes, Jr, President and Chief Executive Officer

RESTON HOSPITAL CENTER, 1850 Town Center Parkway, Reston, VA, Zip 20190–3210; tel. 703/689–9000; William A. Adams, President and Chief Executive Officer

RETREAT HOSPITAL, 2621 Grove Avenue, Richmond, VA, Zip 23220–4308; tel. 804/254–5100; Paul L. Baldwin, Chief Executive Officer

RIVERSIDE BEHAVIORAL HEALTH CENTER, 2244 Executive Drive, Hampton, VA, Zip 23666–2430; tel. 757/827–1001; Debora S. Tanner, Vice President and Administrator

RIVERSIDE REGIONAL MEDICAL CENTER, 500 J. Clyde Morris Boulevard, Newport News, VA, Zip 23601–1976; tel. 757/594–2000; William B. Downey, Executive Vice President and Administrator

RIVERSIDE REHABILITATION INSTITUTE, 245 Chesapeake Avenue, Newport News, VA, Zip 23607–6038; tel. 757/928–8000; Renee K. Rountree, Vice President and Administrator

RIVERSIDE TAPPAHANNOCK HOSPITAL, 618 Hospital Road, Tappahannock, VA, Zip 22560–5000; tel. 804/443–3311; Elizabeth J. Martin, Vice President and Administrator

RIVERSIDE WALTER REED HOSPITAL, 7519 Hospital Drive, Gloucester, VA, Zip 23061–4178, Mailing Address: P.O. Box 1130, Zip 23061–1130; tel. 804/693–8800; Robert E. Bryant, Vice President and Administrator

RUSSELL COUNTY MEDICAL CENTER, Carroll and Tate Streets, Lebanon, VA, Zip 24266–4510, Mailing Address: P.O. Box 3600, Zip 24266–3600; tel. 276/889–1224; David L. Brash, Chief Executive Officer

SENTARA CAREPLEX HOSPITAL, 3000 Coliseum Drive, Hampton, VA, Zip 23666–5963; tel. 757/736–2656; Megan R. Perry, Senior Vice President and Administrator

SENTARA LEIGH HOSPITAL, 830 Kempsville Road, Norfolk, VA, Zip 23502–3920; tel. 757/466–6000; Mark A. Szalwinski, Vice President and Administrator

SENTARA NORFOLK GENERAL HOSPITAL, 600 Gresham Drive, Norfolk, VA, Zip 23507; tel. 757/668–3000; Bruce E. Holstien, Senior Vice President and Administrator

SENTARA VIRGINIA BEACH GENERAL HOSPITAL, 1060 First Colonial Road, Virginia Beach, VA, Zip 23454–3002; tel. 757/395–8000; Les A. Donahue, Vice President and Administrator

SENTARA WILLIAMSBURG COMMUNITY HOSPITAL, 301 Monticello Avenue, Williamsburg, VA, Zip 23185, Mailing Address: P.O. Box 8700, Zip 23187–8700; tel. 757/259–6000; Robert L. Graves, Vice President and Administrator

SHELTERING ARMS REHABILITATION HOSPITAL, 8254 Atlee Road, Mechanicsville, VA, Zip 23116–1844; tel. 804/764–6000; Jack A. Carroll, Ph.D., President and Chief Executive Officer

SHORE MEMORIAL HOSPITAL, 9507 Hospital Avenue, Nassawadox, VA, Zip 23413–1821, Mailing Address: P.O. Box 17, Zip 23413–0017; tel. 757/414–8000; Joseph P. Zager, President and Chief Executive Officer

SMYTH COUNTY COMMUNITY HOSPITAL, 565 Radio Hill Road, Marion, VA, Zip 24354–3526, Mailing Address: P.O. Box 880, Zip 24354–0880; tel. 276/782–1234; William Mahone, V, President and Chief Executive Officer

SOUTHAMPTON MEMORIAL HOSPITAL, 100 Fairview Drive, Franklin, VA, Zip 23851–1206, Mailing Address: P.O. Box 817, Zip 23851–0817; tel. 757/569–6100; Sean T. Dardeau, Chief Executive Officer

SOUTHERN VIRGINIA REGIONAL MEDICAL CENTER, 727 North Main Street, Emporia, VA, Zip 23847–1482; tel. 434/348–4400; Robert D. Towler, Chief Executive Officer

SOUTHSIDE COMMUNITY HOSPITAL, 800 Oak Street, Farmville, VA, Zip 23901–1199; tel. 434/392–8811; Gwen S. Eddleman, R.N., President and Chief Executive Officer

SOUTHSIDE REGIONAL MEDICAL CENTER, 801 South Adams Street, Petersburg, VA, Zip 23803–5133; tel. 804/862–5000; David J. Fikse, Chief Executive Officer

STONEWALL JACKSON HOSPITAL, 1 Health Circle, Lexington, VA, Zip 24450–2492; tel. 540/458–3300; Chad E. Boore, Interim President and Chief Executive Officer

TAZEWELL COMMUNITY HOSPITAL, 141 Ben Bolt Avenue, Tazewell, VA, Zip 24651–9700; tel. 276/988–8700; Christopher L. Wearmouth, President and Chief Executive Officer

TWIN COUNTY REGIONAL HOSPITAL, 200 Hospital Drive, Galax, VA, Zip 24333–2283; tel. 276/236–8181; Marcus G. Kuhn, President and Chief Executive Officer

UNIVERSITY OF VIRGINIA MEDICAL CENTER, Jefferson Park Avenue, Charlottesville, VA, Zip 22908–0001, Mailing Address: P.O. Box 800809, Zip 22908–0809; tel. 434/924–0211; R. Edward Howell, Vice President and Chief Executive Officer

UVA–HEALTHSOUTH REHABILITATION HOSPITAL, 515 Ray C. Hunt Drive, Charlottesville, VA, Zip 22903; tel. 434/244–2000; Thomas J. Cook, Administrator

VCU HEALTH SYSTEM, 1250 East Marshall Street, Richmond, VA, Zip 23219, Mailing Address: P.O. Box 980510, Zip 23298–0510; tel. 804/828–9000; John Duval, Chief Executive Officer

VIRGINIA HOSPITAL CENTER – ARLINGTON, 1701 North George Mason Drive, Arlington, VA, Zip 22205–3698; tel. 703/558–5000; James B. Cole, Chief Executive Officer

WYTHE COUNTY COMMUNITY HOSPITAL, 600 West Ridge Road, Wytheville, VA, Zip 24382–1099; tel. 276/228–0200; John R. McLain, Administrator

WASHINGTON

GROUP HEALTH COOPERATIVE
521 Wall Street, Seattle, WA 98121; tel. 206/326–3000; Scott Armstrong, Chief Executive Officer

GROUP HEALTH COOPERATIVE, 2700 152nd Avenue N.E., Redmond, WA, Zip 98052–5560; tel. 425/883–5151; Susan Kropelnicki, Administrator

LINCOLN COUNTY PUBLIC HEALTH
90 Nicholls, Davenport, WA 99122; tel. 509/725–1001; Thomas J. Martin, Administrator

LINCOLN HOSPITAL, 10 Nicholls Street, Davenport, WA, Zip 99122–9729; tel. 509/725–7101; Thomas J. Martin, Administrator

ODESSA MEMORIAL HEALTHCARE CENTER, 502 East Amende Drive, Odessa, WA, Zip 99159–0368, Mailing Address: P.O. Box 368, Zip 99159–0368; tel. 509/982–2611; Mark Barglof, Administrator

WEST VIRGINIA

EASTERN PANHANDLE INTEGRATED DELIVERY SYSTEM
P.O. Box 758, Martinsburg, WV 25402; tel. 304/262–0201; Jeffrey Debord, Chairman

CITY HOSPITAL, Dry Run Road, Martinsburg, WV, Zip 25401, Mailing Address: P.O. Box 1418, Zip 25402–1418; tel. 304/264–1000; Jon D. Applebaum, Chief Executive Officer

GRANT MEMORIAL HOSPITAL, Route 55 West, Petersburg, WV, Zip 26847, Mailing Address: P.O. Box 1019, Zip 26847–1019; tel. 304/257–1026; Robert L. Harman, Chief Executive Officer

JEFFERSON MEMORIAL HOSPITAL, 300 South Preston Street, Ranson, WV, Zip 25438–1699; tel. 304/728–1600; John M. Sherwood, FACHE, Chief Executive Officer

MORGAN COUNTY WAR MEMORIAL HOSPITAL, 109 War Memorial Drive, Berkeley Springs, WV, Zip 25411–1718; tel. 304/258–1234; John H. Borg, Administrator

HEALTH PARTNERS NETWORK, INC.
1000 Technology Drive, Suite 2320, Fairmont, WV 26554; tel. 304/368–2740; William G. Maclean, Chief Operating Officer

BROADDUS HOSPITAL, Mansfield Hill, Philippi, WV, Zip 26416–1051; tel. 304/457–1760; Jeffrey A. Powelson, Chief Executive Officer

CAMDEN–CLARK MEMORIAL HOSPITAL, 800 Garfield Avenue, Parkersburg, WV, Zip 26101–5378, Mailing Address: P.O. Box 718, Zip 26102–0718; tel. 304/424–2111; Thomas J. Corder, President and Chief Executive Officer

CITY HOSPITAL, Dry Run Road, Martinsburg, WV, Zip 25401, Mailing Address: P.O. Box 1418, Zip 25402–1418; tel. 304/264–1000; Jon D. Applebaum, Chief Executive Officer

DAVIS MEMORIAL HOSPITAL, Gorman Avenue and Reed Street, Elkins, WV, Zip 26241, Mailing Address: P.O. Box 1484, Zip 26241–1484; tel. 304/636–3300; Mark Doak, President and Chief Executive Officer

FAIRMONT GENERAL HOSPITAL, 1325 Locust Avenue, Fairmont, WV, Zip 26554–1435; tel. 304/367–7100; Albert Pilkington, III, Chief Executive Officer

GRAFTON CITY HOSPITAL, 500 Market Street, Grafton, WV, Zip 26354–1187; tel. 304/265–0400; Gary R. Willmon, Administrator

HEALTHSOUTH HUNTINGTON REHABILITATION HOSPITAL, 6900 West Country Club Drive, Huntington, WV, Zip 25705–2000; tel. 304/733–1060; Frank Weber, Administrator

HEALTHSOUTH MOUNTAINVIEW REGIONAL REHABILITATION HOSPITAL, 1160 Van Voorhis Road, Morgantown, WV, Zip 26505–3435; tel. 304/598–1100; John C. Forester, Administrator

HEALTHSOUTH WESTERN HILLS REHABILITATION CENTER, 3 Western Hills Drive, Parkersburg, WV, Zip 26101–8122; tel. 304/420–1300; Dean Hatcher, Administrator

JEFFERSON MEMORIAL HOSPITAL, 300 South Preston Street, Ranson, WV, Zip 25438–1699; tel. 304/728–1600; John M. Sherwood, FACHE, Chief Executive Officer

MINNIE HAMILTON HEALTHCARE CENTER, Hospital Hill, Grantsville, WV, Zip 26147, Mailing Address: 186 Hospital Drive, Zip 26147; tel. 304/354–9244; Barbara Lay, Administrator

ST. JOSEPH'S HOSPITAL OF BUCKHANNON, 1 Amalia Drive, Buckhannon, WV, Zip 26201–2222; tel. 304/473–2000; Tony E. Atkins, Chief Executive Officer

STONEWALL JACKSON MEMORIAL HOSPITAL, 230 Hospital Plaza, Weston, WV, Zip 26452–8558; tel. 304/269–8000; David D. Shaffer, Chief Executive Officer

UNITED HOSPITAL CENTER, Route 19 South, Clarksburg, WV, Zip 26301, Mailing Address: P.O. Box 1680, Zip 26302–1680; tel. 304/624–2121; Bruce C. Carter, President

WEBSTER COUNTY MEMORIAL HOSPITAL, 324 Miller Mountain Drive, Webster Springs, WV, Zip 26288–1087, Mailing Address: P.O. Box 312, Zip 26288–0312; tel. 304/847–5682; Stephen M. Gavalchik, Administrator

WEST VIRGINIA UNIVERSITY HOSPITALS, Medical Center Drive, Morgantown, WV, Zip 26506–4749; tel. 304/598–4000; Bruce McClymonds, President

INTEGRATED PROVIDER NETWORK
7000 Hampton Center, Suite F., Morgantown, WV 26505; tel. 304/598–3911; Brad Minton, Network Contact

UNITED HOSPITAL CENTER, Route 19 South, Clarksburg, WV, Zip 26301, Mailing Address: P.O. Box 1680, Zip 26302–1680; tel. 304/624–2121; Bruce C. Carter, President

WEST VIRGINIA UNIVERSITY HOSPITALS, Medical Center Drive, Morgantown, WV, Zip 26506–4749; tel. 304/598–4000; Bruce McClymonds, President

PARTNERS IN HEALTH NETWORK, INC.
501 Morris Streets, Charleston, WV 25301; tel. 304/388–7385; Albert H. Michael, Executive Director

BOONE MEMORIAL HOSPITAL, 701 Madison Avenue, Madison, WV, Zip 25130–1699; tel. 304/369–1230; Tommy H. Mullins, Administrator

BRAXTON COUNTY MEMORIAL HOSPITAL, 100 Hoylman Drive, Gassaway, WV, Zip 26624–9320; tel. 304/364–5156; Benjamin Vincent, Administrator

CHARLESTON AREA MEDICAL CENTER, 501 Morris Street, Charleston, WV, Zip 25301–1300, Mailing Address: P.O. Box 1547, Zip 25326–1547; tel. 304/388–5432; David L. Ramsey, President and Chief Executive Officer

EYE AND EAR CLINIC OF CHARLESTON, 1306 Kanawha Boulevard East, Charleston, WV, Zip 25301–3001, Mailing Address: P.O. Box 2271, Zip 25328–2271; tel. 304/343–4371; Christina Arvon, Acting Administrator and Chief Executive Officer

JACKSON GENERAL HOSPITAL, Pinnell Street, Ripley, WV, Zip 25271–1009, Mailing Address: P.O. Box 720, Zip 25271–0720; tel. 304/372–2731; Sandra Elza, Chief Executive Officer

MONTGOMERY GENERAL HOSPITAL, 401 Sixth Avenue, Montgomery, WV, Zip 25136–0270, Mailing Address: P.O. Box 270, Zip 25136–0270; tel. 304/442–5151; Vickie Gay, Chief Executive Officer

RICHWOOD AREA COMMUNITY HOSPITAL, 75 Avenue B., Richwood, WV, Zip 26261; tel. 304/846–2573; Elaine Butler, Chief Executive Officer

ROANE GENERAL HOSPITAL, 200 Hospital Drive, Spencer, WV, Zip 25276–1060; tel. 304/927–4444; Doug Bentz, Chief Executive Officer

STONEWALL JACKSON MEMORIAL HOSPITAL, 230 Hospital Plaza, Weston, WV, Zip 26452–8558; tel. 304/269–8000; David D. Shaffer, Chief Executive Officer

SUMMERSVILLE MEMORIAL HOSPITAL, 400 Fairview Heights Road, Summersville, WV, Zip 26651–0400; tel. 304/872–2891; Deborah A. Hill, R.N., Chief Executive Officer

WEBSTER COUNTY MEMORIAL HOSPITAL, 324 Miller Mountain Drive, Webster Springs, WV, Zip 26288–1087, Mailing Address: P.O. Box 312, Zip 26288–0312; tel. 304/847–5682; Stephen M. Gavalchik, Administrator

SOUTHERN VIRGINIA RURAL
500 A. Cherry Street, Suite 7, Bluefield, WV 24701; tel. 304/324–7123; Jean Henshaw, Network Coordinator

BLUEFIELD REGIONAL MEDICAL CENTER, 500 Cherry Street, Bluefield, WV, Zip 24701–3390; tel. 304/327–1100; Steven A. Caywood, Interim Chief Executive Officer

PRINCETON COMMUNITY HOSPITAL, 122 12th Street, Princeton, WV, Zip 24740–1369, Mailing Address: P.O. Box 1369, Zip 24740–1369; tel. 304/487–7000; Clinton Matthews, Chief Executive Officer

VALLEY PRIMARY CARE
601 Colliers Way, Weirton, WV 26062; tel. 304/797–6323; Cynthia R. Nixon, Chief Financial Officer

WEIRTON MEDICAL CENTER, 601 Colliers Way, Weirton, WV, Zip 26062–5091; tel. 304/797–6000; Joseph Endrich, M.D., President and Chief Executive Officer

WISCONSIN

AFFINITY HEALTH SYSTEM
1570 Midway Place, Menasha, WI 54954; tel. 920/720–1713; Kevin E. Nolan, Chief Executive Officer

CALUMET MEDICAL CENTER, 614 Memorial Drive, Chilton, WI, Zip 53014–1597; tel. 920/849–2386; Lea Whitby, President and Chief Executive Officer

MERCY MEDICAL CENTER, 500 South Oakwood, Oshkosh, WI, Zip 54903–3370, Mailing Address: P.O. Box 3370, Zip 54903–3370; tel. 920/223–2000; Clifford R. Lehman, Chief Operating Officer

ST. ELIZABETH HOSPITAL, 1506 South Oneida Street, Appleton, WI, Zip 54915–1397; tel. 920/738–2000; Robert J. Turner, Chief Operating Officer

ALL SAINTS HEALTHCARE SYSTEM
3801 Spring Street, Racine, WI 53405; tel. 414/636–4860; Ken Buser, President and CEO

ALL SAINTS HEALTHCARE, 3801 Spring Street, Racine, WI, Zip 53405–1690; tel. 262/687–4011; Kenneth R. Buser, President and Chief Executive Officer

ST. LUKE'S HOSPITAL, 1320 Wisconsin Avenue, Racine, WI, Zip 53403–1987; tel. 262/687–2011; Kenneth R. Buser, President and Chief Executive Officer

ASPIRUS, INC.
425 Pine Ridge Boulevard, Wausau, WI 54401; tel. 715/847–2121; Charles L. Shabino, M.D, President & Chief Executive Officer

ASPIRUS WAUSAU HOSPITAL, 333 Pine Ridge Boulevard, Wausau, WI, Zip 54401–4187, Mailing Address: P.O. Box 1847, Zip 54402–1847; tel. 715/847–2121; Charles L. Shabino, M.D., President and Chief Executive Officer

COLUMBIA ST. MARY'S
2323 N. Lake Drive, Milwaukee, WI 53211; tel. 414/291–1042; Leo Brideau, President

COLUMBIA ST. MARY'S OZAUKEE CAMPUS, 13111 North Port Washington Road, Mequon, WI, Zip 53097–2416; tel. 262/243–7300; Leo P. Brideau, President and Chief Executive Officer

COLUMBIA ST. MARY'S–COLUMBIA CAMPUS, 2025 East Newport Avenue, Milwaukee, WI, Zip 53211–2990; tel. 414/961–3300; Leo P. Brideau, President and Chief Executive Officer

COLUMBIA ST. MARY'S–MILWAUKEE CAMPUS, 2323 North Lake Drive, Milwaukee, WI, Zip 53211–9682, Mailing Address: P.O. Box 503, Zip 53201–0503; tel. 414/291–1000; Leo P. Brideau, President and Chief Executive Officer

SACRED HEART REHABILITATION INSTITUTE, 2025 East Newport Avenue, Milwaukee, WI, Zip 53211–2906; tel. 414/298–6700; Jack Burke, Administrator

COMMUNITY HEALTH NETWORK, INC.
225 Memorial Drive, Berlin, WI 54923; tel. 920/361–5580; Craig W. C. Schmidt, President & Chief Executive Officer

BERLIN MEMORIAL HOSPITAL, 225 Memorial Drive, Berlin, WI, Zip 54923–1295; tel. 920/361–1313; Craig W. C. Schmidt, President and Chief Executive Officer

WILD ROSE COMMUNITY MEMORIAL HOSPITAL, 601 Grove Avenue, Wild Rose, WI, Zip 54984, Mailing Address: P.O. Box 243, Zip 54984–0243; tel. 920/622–3257; Donald Caves, Chief Executive Officer

COVENANT HEALTHCARE SYSTEM, INC.
400 W. River Woods Parkway, Milwaukee, WI 53212; tel. 414/456–2300; Paul Dell Uomo, President & Chief Executive Officer

ELMBROOK MEMORIAL HOSPITAL, 19333 West North Avenue, Brookfield, WI, Zip 53045–4198; tel. 262/785–2000; Kimry A. Johnsrud, President

ST. FRANCIS HOSPITAL, 3237 South 16th Street, Milwaukee, WI, Zip 53215–4592; tel. 414/647–5000; Debra Standridge, President

ST. JOSEPH'S REGIONAL MEDICAL CENTER, 5000 West Chambers Street, Milwaukee, WI, Zip 53210–9988; tel. 414/447–2000; Ron Groepper, President

ST. MICHAEL HOSPITAL, 2400 West Villard Avenue, Milwaukee, WI, Zip 53209–4999; tel. 414/527–8000; Alicia Modjeska, President

FELICIAN HEALTH CARE, INC.
3237 South 16th, Milwaukee, WI 53215; tel. 414/647–5622; Sister Mary Clarette, President

ST. FRANCIS HOSPITAL, 3237 South 16th Street, Milwaukee, WI, Zip 53215–4592; tel. 414/647–5000; Debra Standridge, President

ST. MARY'S HOSPITAL, 400 North Pleasant Avenue, Centralia, IL, Zip 62801–3091; tel. 618/436–8000; Bruce Merrell, President

LUTHERAN HEALTH SYSTEM
1910 South Avenue, LaCrosse, WI 54601; tel. 608/775–2219; Jeffrey Thompson, MD, Chief Executive Officer

GUNDERSEN LUTHERAN MEDICAL CENTER, 1910 South Avenue, La Crosse, WI, Zip 54601–9980; tel. 608/785–0530; Jeffrey E. Thompson, M.D., Chief Executive Officer

TRI-COUNTY MEMORIAL HOSPITAL, 18601 Lincoln Street, Whitehall, WI, Zip 54773–0065; tel. 715/538–4361; Curtis A. Johnson, President and Chief Executive Officer

MERCY ALLIANCE, INC.
1000 Mineral Point Avenue, Janesville, WI 53547; tel. 608/756–6080; Javon R. Bea, President & Chief Executive Officer

MERCY HARVARD HOSPITAL, 901 Grant Street, Harvard, IL, Zip 60033–1898, Mailing Address: P.O. Box 850, Zip 60033–0850; tel. 815/943–5431; Sue Ripsch, Chief Operating Officer

MERCY HEALTH SYSTEM, 1000 Mineral Point Avenue, Janesville, WI, Zip 53547–2982, Mailing Address: P.O. Box 5003, Zip 53547–5003; tel. 608/756–6000; Javon R. Bea, President and Chief Executive Officer

MINISTRY HEALTH CARE
11925 West Lake Park Drive, Suite 100, Milwaukee, WI 53224; tel. 414/359–1060; Nicholas Desien, President

CALUMET MEDICAL CENTER, 614 Memorial Drive, Chilton, WI, Zip 53014–1597; tel. 920/849–2386; Lea Whitby, President and Chief Executive Officer

DOOR COUNTY MEMORIAL HOSPITAL, 323 South 18th Avenue, Sturgeon Bay, WI, Zip 54235–1495; tel. 920/743–5566; Gerald M. Worrick, President and Chief Executive Officer

FLAMBEAU HOSPITAL, 98 Sherry Avenue, Park Falls, WI, Zip 54552–1467, Mailing Address: P.O. Box 310, Zip 54552–0310; tel. 715/762–2484; David A. Grundstrom, Administrator

MERCY MEDICAL CENTER, 500 South Oakwood, Oshkosh, WI, Zip 54903–3370, Mailing Address: P.O. Box 3370, Zip 54903–3370; tel. 920/223–2000; Clifford R. Lehman, Chief Operating Officer

OUR LADY OF VICTORY HOSPITAL, 1120 Pine Street, Stanley, WI, Zip 54768–0220, Mailing Address: P.O. Box 220, Zip 54768–0220; tel. 715/644–5571; Cynthia Eichman, Chief Executive Officer and Administrator

SACRED HEART–ST. MARY'S HOSPITALS, 2251 North Shore Drive, Rhinelander, WI, Zip 54501–3998; tel. 715/361–2000; Kevin J. O'Donnell, President and Chief Executive Officer

SAINT ELIZABETH'S MEDICAL CENTER, 1200 Grant Boulevard West, Wabasha, MN, Zip 55981–1098; tel. 651/565–4531; Thomas Crowley, President

SAINT JOSEPH'S HOSPITAL, 611 St. Joseph Avenue, Marshfield, WI, Zip 54449–1898; tel. 715/387–1713; Michael A. Schmidt, President

SAINT MICHAEL'S HOSPITAL, 900 Illinois Avenue, Stevens Point, WI, Zip 54481–3196; tel. 715/346–5000; Bradley Neet, President and Chief Operating Officer

WYOMING

WYOMING INTEGRATED NETWORK
1233 East 2nd Street, Casper, WY 82601; tel. 307/577–2153; Dan Hampton, Network Contact

IVINSON MEMORIAL HOSPITAL, 255 North 30th Street, Laramie, WY, Zip 82072–5195; tel. 307/742–2141; Nelson Toebbe, Chief Executive Officer

WYOMING MEDICAL CENTER, 1233 East Second Street, Casper, WY, Zip 82601–2988; tel. 307/577–7201; Pam Fulks, President and Chief Executive Officer

ALLIANCE OF INDEPENDENT ACADEMIC MEDICAL CENTERS

233 East Erie Street, Ste 306, Chicago, IL Zip 60611; tel. 312/988–7572; Ms Nancie Noie Thompson, Executive Director

ARIZONA
Phoenix
Member
Maricopa Integrated Health System
St. Joseph's Hospital and Medical Center

CALIFORNIA
Los Angeles
Member
Cedars–Sinai Medical Center

CONNECTICUT
Hartford
Member
Saint Francis Hospital and Medical Center

DELAWARE
Wilmington
Member
Christiana Care Health System

DISTRICT OF COLUMBIA
Washington
Member
National Rehabilitation Hospital
Washington Hospital Center

FLORIDA
Miami
Member
Miami Children's Hospital

Miami Beach
Member
Mount Sinai Medical Center

ILLINOIS
Oak Brook
Member
Advocate Health Care

Peoria
Member
OSF Saint Francis Medical Center

LOUISIANA
New Orleans
Member
Ochsner Clinic Foundation

MARYLAND
Baltimore
Sinai Hospital of Baltimore
Member
Franklin Square Hospital Center
Good Samaritan Hospital of Maryland
Harbor Hospital Center
Union Memorial Hospital

Columbia
Member
MedStar Health

MASSACHUSETTS
Springfield
Member
Baystate Medical Center

MICHIGAN
Dearborn
Member
Oakwood Healthcare, Inc.

Grand Rapids
Member
Spectrum Health

Royal Oak
Member
William Beaumont Hospital–Royal Oak

MISSOURI
Kansas City
Member
Saint Luke's Hospital of Kansas City

Saint Louis
Member
St. John's Mercy Medical Center

NEW JERSEY
Florham Park
Member
Atlantic Health System

Neptune
Member
Jersey Shore University Medical Center
Meridian Health

NEW YORK
Brooklyn
Member
Maimonides Medical Center

Mineola
Member
Winthrop–University Hospital

Rochester
Member
Rochester General Hospital

NORTH CAROLINA
Charlotte
Member
Carolinas Medical Center

OHIO
Akron
Member
Akron General Medical Center

Columbus
Member
Riverside Methodist Hospital

PENNSYLVANIA
Bethlehem
Member
St. Luke's Hospital – Bethlehem Campus

Pittsburgh
Member
Western Pennsylvania Hospital

York
Member
York Hospital

TEXAS
Dallas
Member
Baylor Health Care System

VIRGINIA
Falls Church
Member
Inova Fairfax Hospital

CATHOLIC CEO HEALTHCARE CONNECTION

3333 Warrenville Rd, Ste 200, Lisle, IL Zip 60532; tel. 630/799–8315; Mr Roger N Butler, Executive Director

CALIFORNIA
Orange
Member
St. Joseph Health System

San Francisco
Member
Catholic Healthcare West

COLORADO
Denver
Member
Catholic Health Initiatives

ILLINOIS
Mokena
Member
Provena Health

Wheaton
Member
Wheaton Franciscan Services, Inc.

INDIANA
Mishawaka
Member
Sisters of St. Francis Health Services, Inc.

KANSAS
Lenexa
Shareholder
Sisters of Charity of Leavenworth Health System

Wichita
Member
Via Christi Health System

LOUISIANA
Baton Rouge
Member
Franciscan Missionaries of Our Lady Health System, Inc.

MARYLAND
Marriottsville
Member
Bon Secours Health System, Inc.

MASSACHUSETTS
Lexington
Member
Covenant Health Systems, Inc.

MICHIGAN
Novi
Member
Trinity Health

MISSOURI
Chesterfield
Member
Sisters of Mercy Health System

Saint Louis
Member
Ascension Health

OHIO
Cincinnati
Member
Catholic Healthcare Partners

Sylvania
Member
Franciscan Services Corporation

PENNSYLVANIA
Newtown Square
Member
Catholic Health East

SOUTH DAKOTA
Yankton
Member
Avera Health

TEXAS
Irving
Member
Christus Health

WASHINGTON
Bellevue
Member
PeaceHealth

Seattle
Member
Providence Health System

Spokane
Member
Providence Services

WISCONSIN

Manitowoc
Member
   Franciscan Sisters of Christian Charity HealthCare
   Ministry, Inc

CHILD HEALTH CORPORATION OF AMERICA

6803 West 64th Street, Ste 208,
Shawnee Mission, KS Zip 66202;
tel. 913/262–1436; Mr Don C Black,
President and Chief Executive Officer

ALABAMA

Birmingham
Member
   The Children's Hospital of Alabama

ARIZONA

Phoenix
Member
   Phoenix Children's Hospital

ARKANSAS

Little Rock
Member
   Arkansas Children's Hospital

CALIFORNIA

Los Angeles
Member
   Childrens Hospital Los Angeles

Madera
Member
   Children's Hospital Central California

Oakland
Member
   Children's Hospital and Research Center at Oakland

Orange
Member
   Children's Hospital of Orange County

Palo Alto
Member
   Lucile Salter Packard Children's Hospital at Stanford

San Diego
Member
   Children's Hospital and Health Center

COLORADO

Denver
Member
   Children's Hospital

CONNECTICUT

Hartford
Member
   Connecticut Children's Medical Center

DISTRICT OF COLUMBIA

Washington
Member
   Children's National Medical Center

FLORIDA

Miami
Member
   Miami Children's Hospital

Saint Petersburg
Member
   All Children's Hospital

GEORGIA

Atlanta
Member
   Children's Healthcare of Atlanta

ILLINOIS

Chicago
Member
   Children's Memorial Hospital

LOUISIANA

New Orleans
Member
   Children's Hospital

MASSACHUSETTS

Boston
Member
   Children's Hospital Boston

MICHIGAN

Detroit
Member
   Children's Hospital of Michigan

MINNESOTA

Minneapolis
Member
   Children's Hospitals and Clinics

MISSOURI

Kansas City
Member
   Children's Mercy Hospital

Saint Louis
Member
   St. Louis Children's Hospital

NEBRASKA

Omaha
Member
   Children's Hospital

NEW YORK

Buffalo
Member
   Women and Children's Hospital

OHIO

Akron
Member
   Akron Children's Hospital

Cincinnati
Member
   Children's Hospital Medical Center

Columbus
Member
   Children's Hospital

Dayton
Member
   Children's Medical Center

PENNSYLVANIA

Philadelphia
Member
   Children's Hospital of Philadelphia

Pittsburgh
Member
   Children's Hospital of Pittsburgh of UPMC

TENNESSEE

Memphis
Member
   Le Bonheur Children's Medical Center
   St. Jude Children's Research Hospital

TEXAS

Corpus Christi
Member
   Driscoll Children's Hospital

Dallas
Member
   Children's Medical Center of Dallas

Fort Worth
Member
   Cook Children's Medical Center

Houston
Member
   Texas Children's Hospital

VIRGINIA

Norfolk
Member
   Children's Hospital of The King's Daughters

WASHINGTON

Seattle
Member
   Children's Hospital and Regional Medical Center

WISCONSIN

Milwaukee
Member
   Children's Hospital of Wisconsin

HOSPITAL NETWORK, INC.

4510 Commercial Avenue, Portage, MI
Zip 49002; tel. 269/341–8888; Mr
George Angelidis, President and Chief
Executive Officer

MICHIGAN

Allegan
Member
   Allegan General Hospital

Hastings
Member
   Pennock Hospital

Kalamazoo
Member
   Bronson Healthcare Group, Inc.
   Bronson Methodist Hospital

Marshall
Member
   Oaklawn Hospital

Sturgis
Member
   Sturgis Hospital

Vicksburg
Member
   Bronson Vicksburg Hospital

MEDI-SOTA, INC.

669 Sixth Street, Suite 3, Dawson, MN
Zip 56232; tel. 320/769–2269

MINNESOTA

Arlington
Member
   Sibley Medical Center

Benson
Member
   Swift County–Benson Hospital

Canby
Member
   Sioux Valley Canby Campus

Dawson
Member
   Johnson Memorial Health Services

Glencoe
Member
   Glencoe Regional Health Services

Graceville
Member
   Graceville Health Center

Granite Falls
Member
   Granite Falls Municipal Hospital and Manor

Hendricks
Member
   Hendricks Community Hospital

Ivanhoe
Member
   Divine Providence Health Center/Avera Health

Litchfield
Member
   Meeker County Memorial Hospital

Madelia
Member
   Madelia Community Hospital

Madison
Member
   Madison Lutheran Home

Marshall
Member
   Avera Marshall Regional Medical Center

Montevideo
Member
   Chippewa County–Montevideo Hospital

Olivia
Member
   Renville County Hospital

Ortonville
Member
   Ortonville Area Health Services

Paynesville
Member
    Paynesville Area Health Care System

Perham
Member
    Perham Memorial Hospital and Home

Pipestone
Member
    Pipestone County Medical Center/Avera Health

Redwood Falls
Member
    Redwood Area Hospital

Slayton
Member
    Murray County Memorial Hospital

Sleepy Eye
Member
    Sleepy Eye Medical Center

Tracy
Member
    Tracy Area Medical Services

Tyler
Member
    Tyler Healthcare Center/Avera Health

Willmar
Member
    Rice Memorial Hospital

Windom
Member
    Windom Area Hospital

SOUTH DAKOTA
Watertown
Member
    Prairie Lakes Healthcare System

PREMIER, INC.
    3 Westbrook Corporate Center, 9th Floor,
    San Diego, CA Zip 92130;
    tel. 858/481–2727; Mr Richard A
    Norling, Chief Executive Officer

ALABAMA
Birmingham
Member
    Callahan Eye Foundation Hospital
    The Children's Hospital of Alabama

Dadeville
Member
    Lake Martin Community Hospital

Daphne
Member
    Mercy Medical

Dothan
Member
    Flowers Hospital
Owner
    Southeast Alabama Medical Center

Enterprise
Member
    Medical Center Enterprise

Gadsden
Member
    Gadsden Regional Medical Center

Geneva
Member
    Wiregrass Medical Center

Jacksonville
Member
    Jacksonville Medical Center

Monroeville
Member
    Monroe County Hospital

Opelika
Owner
    East Alabama Medical Center

Valley
Member
    Lanier Health Services

ALASKA
Anchorage
Member
    Providence Alaska Medical Center

Cordova
Affiliate
    Cordova Community Medical Center

Fairbanks
Member
    Fairbanks Memorial Hospital

Homer
Member
    South Peninsula Hospital

Juneau
Member
    Bartlett Regional Hospital

Ketchikan
Member
    Ketchikan General Hospital

Kodiak
Member
    Providence Kodiak Island Medical Center

Palmer
Member
    Valley Hospital

Seward
Affiliate
    Providence Seward Medical Center

Soldotna
Member
    Central Peninsula General Hospital

Valdez
Member
    Providence Valdez Medical Center

ARIZONA
Bullhead City
Member
    Western Arizona Regional Medical Center

Casa Grande
Member
    Casa Grande Regional Medical Center

Ganado
Member
    Sage Memorial Hospital

Glendale
Member
    Arrowhead Community Hospital and Medical Center

Mesa
Member
    Banner Baywood Medical Center
    Banner Mesa Medical Center

Phoenix
Member
    Maricopa Integrated Health System
    Phoenix Baptist Hospital
Owner
    Banner Health

Prescott
Member
    Yavapai Regional Medical Center

ARKANSAS
Ashdown
Member
    Little River Memorial Hospital

Batesville
Owner
    White River Medical Center

Benton
Member
    Saline Memorial Hospital

Camden
Member
    Ouachita Medical Center

Crossett
Shareholder
    Ashley County Medical Center

Danville
Shareholder
    Chambers Memorial Hospital

Dardanelle
Shareholder
    Dardanelle Hospital

De Witt
Shareholder
    DeWitt Hospital

Dumas
Member
    Delta Memorial Hospital

Gravette
Shareholder
    Gravette Medical Center Hospital

Harrison
Shareholder
    North Arkansas Regional Medical Center

Hot Springs National Park
Shareholder
    Levi Hospital

Jacksonville
Member
    Rebsamen Medical Center

Lake Village
Member
    Chicot Memorial Hospital

Little Rock
Owner
    Arkansas Children's Hospital

Magnolia
Shareholder
    Magnolia Hospital

McGehee
Shareholder
    McGehee–Desha County Hospital

Mena
Member
    Mena Medical Center

Monticello
Shareholder
    Drew Memorial Hospital

Nashville
Member
    Howard Memorial Hospital

Paragould
Shareholder
    Arkansas Methodist Medical Center

Pine Bluff
Owner
    Jefferson Regional Medical Center

Siloam Springs
Member
    Siloam Springs Memorial Hospital

Warren
Shareholder
    Bradley County Medical Center

West Memphis
Shareholder
    Crittenden Memorial Hospital

CALIFORNIA
Alhambra
Member
    Alhambra Hospital Medical Center

Apple Valley
Member
    St. Mary Medical Center

Arroyo Grande
Member
    Arroyo Grande Community Hospital

Bakersfield
Member
    Kern Medical Center
    San Joaquin Community Hospital

Burbank
Member
    Providence Saint Joseph Medical Center

Chula Vista
Member
    Sharp Chula Vista Medical Center

Section B

Clearlake
Member
    Redbud Community Hospital

Corona
Member
    Corona Regional Medical Center

Coronado
Member
    Sharp Coronado Hospital and Health Center

Delano
Member
    Delano Regional Medical Center

Escondido
Member
    Palomar Medical Center

Fortuna
Member
    Redwood Memorial Hospital

Fullerton
Member
    St. Jude Medical Center

Glendale
Member
    Glendale Adventist Medical Center
    Glendale Memorial Hospital and Health Center

Hanford
Member
    Hanford Community Medical Center

La Mesa
Member
    Sharp Grossmont Hospital

La Palma
Member
    La Palma Intercommunity Hospital

Laguna Beach
Member
    South Coast Medical Center

Lompoc
Member
    Lompoc Healthcare District

Los Angeles
Member
    California Hospital Medical Center
    Childrens Hospital Los Angeles
    White Memorial Medical Center

Madera
Member
    Children's Hospital Central California

Mission Viejo
Member
    Mission Hospital

Murrieta
Member
    Rancho Springs Medical Center

Napa
Member
    Queen of the Valley Hospital

National City
Member
    Paradise Valley Hospital

Northridge
Member
    Northridge Hospital Medical Center–Roscoe Boulevard
        Campus

Oakland
Member
    Children's Hospital and Research Center at Oakland
Owner
    Alta Bates Summit Medical Center – Summit Campus

Orange
Affiliate
    Children's Hospital of Orange County
Member
    St. Joseph Hospital
Owner
    St. Joseph Health System

Palo Alto
Member
    Lucile Salter Packard Children's Hospital at Stanford

Paradise
Member
    Feather River Hospital

Petaluma
Member
    Petaluma Valley Hospital

Poway
Member
    Pomerado Hospital

Rancho Mirage
Owner
    Eisenhower Memorial Hospital and Betty Ford Center
        at Eisenhower

Roseville
Owner
    Adventist Health

Saint Helena
Member
    St. Helena Hospital

San Diego
Member
    Children's Hospital and Health Center
    Sharp Memorial Hospital
Owner
    Palomar Pomerado Health
    Sharp Healthcare

San Fernando
Member
    Providence Holy Cross Medical Center

San Francisco
Owner
    Catholic Healthcare West

San Gabriel
Member
    San Gabriel Valley Medical Center

San Luis Obispo
Member
    French Hospital Medical Center

San Pedro
Member
    San Pedro Peninsula Hospital

Selma
Member
    Selma Community Hospital

Simi Valley
Member
    Simi Valley Hospital and Health Care Services

Sonora
Member
    Sonora Regional Medical Center

Susanville
Member
    Banner Lassen Medical Center

Torrance
Owner
    Providence–Little Company of Mary Service Area

Ukiah
Member
    Ukiah Valley Medical Center

Vallejo
Member
    St Helena Hospital–Center for Behavioral Health

Wildomar
Member
    Victor Valley Community Hospital

Willits
Member
    Frank R. Howard Memorial Hospital

COLORADO

Brush
Member
    East Morgan County Hospital

Cortez
Member
    Southwest Memorial Hospital

Craig
Member
    Memorial Hospital

Delta
Member
    Delta County Memorial Hospital

Denver
Member
    Children's Hospital

Glenwood Springs
Member
    Valley View Hospital

Greeley
Member
    North Colorado Medical Center

Holyoke
Member
    Melissa Memorial Hospital

Lamar
Member
    Prowers Medical Center

Loveland
Member
    McKee Medical Center

Meeker
Member
    Pioneers Hospital of Rio Blanco County

Montrose
Member
    Montrose Memorial Hospital

Pueblo
Member
    Parkview Medical Center

Rifle
Member
    Grand River Hospital District

Salida
Member
    Heart of the Rockies Regional Medical Center

Sterling
Member
    Sterling Regional MedCenter

Trinidad
Member
    Mt. San Rafael Hospital

Yuma
Affiliate
    Yuma District Hospital

CONNECTICUT

Bristol
Member
    Bristol Hospital

Hartford
Owner
    Saint Francis Hospital and Medical Center

New Haven
Member
    Hospital of Saint Raphael

Stafford Springs
Member
    Johnson Memorial Hospital

DELAWARE

Dover
Owner
    Bayhealth Medical Center

Lewes
Owner
    Beebe Medical Center

Seaford
Member
    Nanticoke Memorial Hospital

Wilmington
Affiliate
    Christiana Care Health System
Member
    Alfred I. duPont Hospital for Children
    Eugene Dupont Preventive Medicine and Rehabilitation
        Institute
Owner
    Christiana Care Health System

DISTRICT OF COLUMBIA
Washington
Member
  Children's National Medical Center
  George Washington University Hospital
  Greater Southeast Community Hospital
Owner
  Sibley Memorial Hospital

FLORIDA
Altamonte Springs
Member
  Florida Hospital–Altamonte

Apopka
Member
  Florida Hospital–Apopka

Arcadia
Member
  DeSoto Memorial Hospital

Belle Glade
Member
  Glades General Hospital

Brooksville
Member
  Brooksville Regional Hospital
  Spring Hill Regional Hospital

Clearwater
Member
  Accord Health Care Corporation

Clewiston
Member
  Hendry Regional Medical Center

Coral Gables
Owner
  Baptist Health South Florida

Coral Springs
Member
  Coral Springs Medical Center

De Land
Member
  Florida Hospital – Deland

Dunedin
Member
  Mease Hospital Dunedin

Fernandina Beach
Member
  Baptist Medical Center Nassau

Fort Lauderdale
Member
  Broward General Medical Center
  Holy Cross Hospital
  Imperial Point Medical Center
Owner
  North Broward Hospital District

Gainesville
Member
  AvMed–Santa Fe

Hollywood
Member
  Memorial Regional Hospital
Owner
  Memorial Healthcare System

Homestead
Member
  Homestead Hospital

Jacksonville
Member
  St. Vincent's Medical Center

Jacksonville Beach
Member
  Baptist Medical Center–Beaches

Jupiter
Member
  Jupiter Medical Center

Kissimmee
Member
  Florida Hospital Kissimmee

Largo
Member
  Sun Coast Hospital

Marianna
Member
  Jackson Hospital

Miami
Member
  Baptist Hospital of Miami
  Bascom Palmer Eye Institute–Anne Bates Leach Eye
    Hospital
  Miami Children's Hospital
  Pan American Hospital
  South Miami Hospital

Miami Beach
Owner
  Mount Sinai Medical Center

Naples
Owner
  Naples Community Hospital

New Port Richey
Member
  Morton Plant North Bay Hospital

New Smyrna Beach
Member
  Bert Fish Medical Center

Orange City
Member
  Florida Hospital Fish Memorial

Orlando
Member
  Florida Hospital

Ormond Beach
Member
  Florida Hospital–Ormond Memorial

Palm Coast
Member
  Florida Hospital–Flagler

Pembroke Pines
Member
  Memorial Hospital Pembroke
  Memorial Hospital West

Plant City
Member
  South Florida Baptist Hospital

Pompano Beach
Member
  North Broward Medical Center

Port Charlotte
Member
  Peace River Regional Medical Center

Rockledge
Owner
  Wuesthoff Medical Center – Rockledge

Safety Harbor
Member
  Mease Countryside Hospital

Saint Petersburg
Member
  All Children's Hospital
  Bayfront Medical Center
  St. Anthony's Hospital

Sebring
Member
  Florida Hospital Heartland Medical Center

Tampa
Member
  H. Lee Moffitt Cancer Center and Research Institute
  St. Joseph's Hospital
  St. Joseph's Hospital, St. Joseph's Women's Hospital
    – Tampa

Tarpon Springs
Owner
  Helen Ellis Memorial Hospital

Tavares
Member
  Florida Hospital Waterman

Tavernier
Member
  Mariners Hospital

Titusville
Member
  Parrish Medical Center

Venice
Member
  Venice Regional Medical Center

Vero Beach
Owner
  Indian River Memorial Hospital

Weston
Member
  Cleveland Clinic Hospital

Winter Haven
Owner
  Winter Haven Hospital

Winter Park
Owner
  Adventist Health System Sunbelt Health Care
    Corporation

Zephyrhills
Member
  East Pasco Medical Center

GEORGIA
Athens
Owner
  St. Mary's Health Care System

Atlanta
Member
  Northside Hospital
  Saint Joseph's Hospital of Atlanta

Augusta
Member
  University Health Care System
  Walton Rehabilitation Hospital
Owner
  Medical College of Georgia Hospital and Clinics

Blairsville
Member
  Union General Hospital

Bremen
Member
  Higgins General Hospital

Brunswick
Member
  Southeast Georgia Health System Brunswick Campus

Calhoun
Member
  Gordon Hospital

Carrollton
Member
  Tanner Medical Center

Columbus
Owner
  St. Francis Hospital, Inc.

Cumming
Member
  Northside Hospital Forsyth

Demorest
Member
  Habersham County Medical Center

Elberton
Member
  Elbert Memorial Hospital

Fort Oglethorpe
Owner
  Hutcheson Medical Center

Glenwood
Member
  Wheeler County Hospital

Greensboro
Member
  Minnie G. Boswell Memorial Hospital

Jesup
Member
  Wayne Memorial Hospital

La Grange
Owner
  West Georgia Health System

Macon
Member
  Macon Northside Hospital

Milledgeville
Member
    Oconee Regional Medical Center

Monroe
Member
    Walton Regional Medical Center

Richland
Member
    Stewart–Webster Hospital

Saint Marys
Member
    Southeast Georgia Health System Camden Campus

Savannah
Owner
    Memorial Health
    St. Joseph's/Candler, Candler Hospital
    St. Joseph's/Candler, St. Joseph's Hospital

Smyrna
Member
    Emory–Adventist Hospital

Sylvania
Member
    Screven County Hospital

Sylvester
Member
    Phoebe Worth Medical Center

Thomaston
Member
    Upson Regional Medical Center

Thomson
Member
    McDuffie Regional Medical Center

Tifton
Owner
    Tift Regional Medical Center

Villa Rica
Member
    Tanner Medical Center–Villa Rica

Warm Springs
Member
    Warm Springs Medical Center

Washington
Member
    Wills Memorial Hospital

HAWAII

Honolulu
Owner
    Kuakini Medical Center

IDAHO

Blackfoot
Member
    Bingham Memorial Hospital

Moscow
Member
    Gritman Medical Center

ILLINOIS

Aurora
Member
    Provena Mercy Center

Barrington
Member
    Advocate Good Shepherd Hospital

Blue Island
Member
    St. Francis Hospital & Health Center

Canton
Member
    Graham Hospital

Carmi
Member
    White County Medical Center

Carrollton
Member
    Thomas H. Boyd Memorial Hospital

Carthage
Member
    Memorial Hospital

Centralia
Member
    St. Mary's Hospital

Chicago
Member
    Advocate Trinity Hospital
    Children's Memorial Hospital
    Our Lady of the Resurrection Medical Center
    Resurrection Medical Center
    Thorek Hospital and Medical Center
Owner
    Mercy Hospital and Medical Center
    Mount Sinai Hospital Medical Center of Chicago

Downers Grove
Member
    Advocate Good Samaritan Hospital

Elk Grove Village
Member
    Alexian Brothers Medical Center

Galesburg
Member
    Galesburg Cottage Hospital

Geneva
Member
    Delnor–Community Hospital

Gibson City
Member
    Gibson Area Hospital and Health Services

Hazel Crest
Member
    Advocate South Suburban Hospital

Hinsdale
Member
    Hinsdale Hospital

Hoopeston
Member
    Hoopeston Community Memorial Hospital

Melrose Park
Member
    Gottlieb Memorial Hospital

Metropolis
Member
    Massac Memorial Hospital

Morrison
Member
    Morrison Community Hospital

Mount Carmel
Member
    Wabash General Hospital District

Mount Vernon
Member
    Good Samaritan Regional Health Center

Nashville
Member
    Washington County Hospital

Oak Brook
Owner
    Advocate Health Care

Oak Lawn
Member
    Advocate Christ Medical Center

Ottawa
Member
    Community Hospital of Ottawa

Paris
Member
    Paris Community Hospital

Park Ridge
Member
    Advocate Lutheran General Hospital

Peoria
Member
    Methodist Medical Center of Illinois
Owner
    Methodist Health Services Corporation

Pinckneyville
Member
    Pinckneyville Community Hospital

Pittsfield
Member
    Illini Community Hospital

Robinson
Member
    Crawford Memorial Hospital

Staunton
Member
    Community Memorial Hospital

Urbana
Owner
    Carle Foundation Hospital

Winfield
Owner
    Central DuPage Hospital

INDIANA

Brazil
Member
    St. Vincent Clay Hospital

Charlestown
Member
    Medical Center of Southern Indiana

Frankfort
Member
    St. Vincent Frankfort Hospital

Gary
Owner
    Methodist Hospitals

Greensburg
Member
    Decatur County Memorial Hospital

Hartford City
Member
    Blackford Community Hospital

Jeffersonville
Member
    Clark Memorial Hospital

Princeton
Member
    Gibson General Hospital

Rushville
Member
    Rush Memorial Hospital

Salem
Member
    Washington County Memorial Hospital

Scottsburg
Member
    Scott Memorial Hospital

Sullivan
Member
    Sullivan County Community Hospital

Tell City
Member
    Perry County Memorial Hospital

Wabash
Member
    Wabash County Hospital

Washington
Member
    Daviess Community Hospital

Winchester
Member
    St. Vincent Randolph Hospital

IOWA

Algona
Member
    Kossuth Regional Health Center

Ames
Member
    Mary Greeley Medical Center

Anamosa
Member
    Jones Regional Medical Center

Belmond
Member
    Belmond Medical Center

Boone
Member
    Boone County Hospital

Britt
Member
　Hancock County Memorial Hospital

Cedar Rapids
Member
　Mercy Medical Center
　St. Luke's Hospital

Chariton
Member
　Lucas County Health Center

Charles City
Member
　Floyd County Memorial Hospital

Clarion
Member
　Wright Medical Center

Clinton
Member
　Mercy Medical Center–Clinton

Corning
Member
　Alegent Health Mercy Hospital

Council Bluffs
Member
　Alegent Health Mercy Hospital

Cresco
Member
　Regional Health Services of Howard County

Davenport
Member
　Genesis Medical Center, Davenport

De Witt
Member
　Genesis Medical Center, DeWitt

Des Moines
Member
　Harrison Treat and Rehabilitation Center
　Iowa Lutheran Hospital
　Iowa Methodist Medical Center
Owner
　Iowa Health System

Dubuque
Member
　Finley Hospital
　Mercy Medical Center–Dubuque

Dyersville
Member
　Mercy Medical Center–Dyersville

Elkader
Member
　Central Community Hospital

Emmetsburg
Member
　Palo Alto County Health System

Estherville
Member
　Avera Holy Family Hospital

Fairfield
Member
　Jefferson County Hospital

Fort Dodge
Member
　Trinity Regional Medical Center

Fort Madison
Member
　Fort Madison Community Hospital

Grinnell
Member
　Grinnell Regional Medical Center

Hampton
Member
　Franklin General Hospital

Hawarden
Member
　Hawarden Community Hospital

Humboldt
Member
　Humboldt County Memorial Hospital

Iowa City
Member
　Mercy Hospital

Iowa Falls
Member
　Ellsworth Municipal Hospital

Knoxville
Member
　Knoxville Area Community Hospital and Clinic

Manchester
Member
　Regional Medical Center

Maquoketa
Member
　Jackson County Public Hospital

Marengo
Member
　Marengo Memorial Hospital

Marshalltown
Member
　Marshalltown Medical and Surgical Center

Mason City
Member
　Mercy Medical Center – North Iowa

Missouri Valley
Owner
　Alegent Health Community Memorial Hospital

New Hampton
Member
　Mercy Medical Center–New Hampton

Newton
Member
　Skiff Medical Center

Osage
Member
　Mitchell County Regional Health Center

Osceola
Member
　Clarke County Hospital

Oskaloosa
Member
　Mahaska Health Partnership

Ottumwa
Member
　Ottumwa Regional Health Center

Pella
Member
　Pella Regional Health Center

Pocahontas
Member
　Pocahontas Community Hospital

Primghar
Member
　Baum Harmon Mercy Hospital

Rock Valley
Member
　Hegg Memorial Health Center/Avera Health

Sac City
Member
　Loring Hospital

Shenandoah
Member
　Shenandoah Medical Center

Sibley
Member
　Osceola Community Hospital

Sioux City
Member
　Mercy Medical Center–Sioux City
　St. Luke's Regional Medical Center

Spencer
Member
　Spencer Hospital

Storm Lake
Member
　Buena Vista Regional Medical Center

Washington
Member
　Washington County Hospital

Waterloo
Member
　Allen Memorial Hospital

West Burlington
Member
　Great River Medical Center

Winterset
Member
　Madison County Health Care System

KANSAS

Chanute
Member
　Neosho Memorial Regional Medical Center

Coffeyville
Member
　Coffeyville Regional Medical Center

Emporia
Member
　Newman Regional Health

Eureka
Member
　Greenwood County Hospital

Iola
Member
　Allen County Hospital

Lawrence
Member
　Lawrence Memorial Hospital

Marion
Member
　St. Luke Hospital and Living Center

Neodesha
Member
　Wilson County Hospital

Oberlin
Member
　Decatur County Hospital and Cedar Living Center

Overland Park
Member
　Menorah Medical Center

Ulysses
Member
　Bob Wilson Memorial Grant County Hospital

KENTUCKY

Benton
Member
　Marshall County Hospital

Berea
Member
　Berea Hospital

Bowling Green
Member
　The Medical Center at Bowling Green

Burkesville
Owner
　Cumberland County Hospital

Cadiz
Member
　Trigg County Hospital

Campbellsville
Member
　Taylor Regional Hospital

Carrollton
Member
　Carroll County Hospital

Corbin
Member
　Baptist Regional Medical Center

Elizabethtown
Member
　Hardin Memorial Hospital

Flemingsburg
Member
　Fleming County Hospital

Franklin
Member
　The Medical Center at Franklin

Glasgow
Owner
  T. J. Samson Community Hospital

Greensburg
Member
  Jane Todd Crawford Hospital

Greenville
Member
  Muhlenberg Community Hospital

Hardinsburg
Member
  Breckinridge Memorial Hospital

Harrodsburg
Member
  The James B. Haggin Memorial Hospital

Hartford
Member
  Ohio County Hospital

Henderson
Owner
  Methodist Hospital

Hopkinsville
Member
  Jennie Stuart Medical Center

Horse Cave
Member
  Caverna Memorial Hospital

Irvine
Member
  Marcum and Wallace Memorial Hospital

La Grange
Member
  Baptist Hospital Northeast

Leitchfield
Member
  Twin Lakes Regional Medical Center

Lexington
Member
  Central Baptist Hospital
  Saint Joseph Hospital East

Louisville
Member
  Baptist Hospital East
  Frazier Rehab Institute
  Jewish Hospital
  Jewish Hospital HealthCare Services
  Kosair Children's Hospital
  Norton Hospital
  University of Louisville Hospital
Owner
  Baptist Healthcare System
  Norton Healthcare

Manchester
Member
  Memorial Hospital

Marion
Member
  Crittenden County Hospital

Morganfield
Member
  Methodist Hospital Union County

Mount Sterling
Member
  Gateway Regional Health System

Mount Vernon
Member
  Rockcastle Hospital and Respiratory Care Center

Murray
Owner
  Murray–Calloway County Hospital

Paducah
Member
  Lourdes Hospital
  Western Baptist Hospital

Pikeville
Owner
  Pikeville Medical Center

Pineville
Member
  Pineville Community Hospital Association

Princeton
Member
  Caldwell County Hospital

Richmond
Member
  Pattie A. Clay Regional Medical Center

Russell Springs
Member
  Russell County Hospital

Salem
Member
  Livingston Hospital and Healthcare Services

Shelbyville
Member
  Jewish Hospital–Shelbyville

Tompkinsville
Member
  Monroe County Medical Center

Winchester
Member
  Clark Regional Medical Center

LOUISIANA

Alexandria
Member
  Christus St. Frances Cabrini Hospital

Baton Rouge
  Baton Rouge General Medical Center
Member
  Woman's Hospital

Breaux Bridge
Affiliate
  St. Martin Hospital

Farmerville
Member
  Union General Hospital

Franklin
Member
  Franklin Foundation Hospital

Hammond
Member
  North Oaks Medical Center

Homer
Member
  Homer Memorial Hospital

Houma
Owner
  Terrebonne General Medical Center

Jena
Member
  LaSalle General Hospital

Kaplan
Member
  Abrom Kaplan Memorial Hospital

Lafayette
Owner
  Lafayette General Medical Center

Lake Charles
Member
  Christus St. Patrick Hospital of Lake Charles
  Dubuis Hospital of Lake Charles

Lutcher
Member
  St. James Parish Hospital

Marrero
Owner
  West Jefferson Medical Center

Morgan City
Member
  Teche Regional Medical Center

Natchitoches
Member
  Natchitoches Parish Hospital

New Orleans
Member
  Children's Hospital
Owner
  Touro Infirmary

Opelousas
Member
  Opelousas General Health System

Raceland
Member
  St. Anne General Hospital

Tallulah
Member
  Madison Parish Hospital

Thibodaux
Member
  Thibodaux Regional Medical Center

Ville Platte
Member
  Ville Platte Medical Center

West Monroe
Owner
  Glenwood Regional Medical Center

Zachary
  Lane Memorial Hospital

MAINE

Blue Hill
Member
  Blue Hill Memorial Hospital

Brunswick
Member
  Parkview Adventist Medical Center

Calais
Member
  Calais Regional Hospital

Caribou
Member
  Cary Medical Center

Dover–Foxcroft
Member
  Mayo Regional Hospital

Ellsworth
Member
  Maine Coast Memorial Hospital

Houlton
Member
  Houlton Regional Hospital

Lewiston
Member
  St. Mary's Regional Medical Center

Lincoln
Member
  Penobscot Valley Hospital

Machias
Member
  Down East Community Hospital

Millinocket
Member
  Millinocket Regional Hospital

Portland
Member
  Mercy Hospital of Portland

MARYLAND

Annapolis
Owner
  Anne Arundel Medical Center

Baltimore
Member
  Bon Secours Baltimore Health System
  Franklin Square Hospital Center
  Good Samaritan Hospital of Maryland
  Harbor Hospital Center
  Mercy Medical Center
  Mt. Washington Pediatric Hospital
  Sinai Hospital of Baltimore
  Union Memorial Hospital
Owner
  LifeBridge Health

Berlin
Member
  Atlantic General Hospital

Bethesda
Owner
  Suburban Hospital Healthcare System

Cheverly
Member
  Prince George's Hospital Center

Columbia
Owner
  Howard County General Hospital
  MedStar Health

Cumberland
Owner
  Memorial Hospital and Medical Center of Cumberland
  Sacred Heart Hospital

Elkton
Owner
  Union Hospital

Fort Washington
Member
  Fort Washington Medical Center

Frederick
Owner
  Frederick Memorial Hospital

Glen Burnie
Member
  Baltimore Washington Medical Center

Hagerstown
Owner
  Washington County Health System

Lanham
Owner
  Doctors Community Hospital

Laurel
Member
  Laurel Regional Hospital

Marriottsville
Owner
  Bon Secours Health System, Inc.

Olney
Owner
  Montgomery General Hospital

Randallstown
Member
  Northwest Hospital Center

Rockville
Member
  Shady Grove Adventist Hospital
Owner
  Adventist HealthCare

Salisbury
Owner
  Peninsula Regional Health System

Takoma Park
Member
  Washington Adventist Hospital

Westminster
Owner
  Carroll Hospital Center

MASSACHUSETTS
Andover
Owner
  Yankee Alliance

Attleboro
Member
  Sturdy Memorial Hospital

Ayer
Member
  Nashoba Valley Medical Center

Boston
Member
  Beth Israel Deaconess Medical Center
  Boston Medical Center
  Children's Hospital Boston
  New England Baptist Hospital

Braintree
Member
  Northeast Specialty Hospital

Brockton
Member
  Brockton Hospital
  Caritas Good Samaritan Medical Center

Cambridge
Member
  Youville Hospital and Rehabilitation Center

Fall River
Owner
  Southcoast Hospitals Group

Great Barrington
Member
  Fairview Hospital

Greenfield
Member
  Franklin Medical Center

Haverhill
Member
  Merrimack Valley Hospital

Lexington
Member
  Covenant Health Systems, Inc.

Lowell
Member
  Saints Memorial Medical Center

Palmer
Member
  Wing Memorial Hospital and Medical Centers

Pittsfield
Member
  Berkshire Medical Center

Plymouth
Member
  Jordan Hospital

Quincy
Member
  Quincy Medical Center

Springfield
Member
  Baystate Medical Center
Owner
  Baystate Health System, Inc.

Ware
Member
  Mary Lane Hospital

Webster
Member
  Hubbard Regional Hospital

Winchester
Member
  Winchester Hospital

Worcester
Owner
  UMass Memorial Medical Center

MICHIGAN
Allegan
Member
  Allegan General Hospital

Alma
Member
  Gratiot Medical Center

Battle Creek
Member
  Battle Creek Health System

Big Rapids
Member
  Mecosta County Medical Center

Cadillac
Member
  Mercy Hospital Cadillac

Carson City
Member
  Carson City Hospital

Chelsea
Member
  Chelsea Community Hospital

Clinton Township
Member
  St. Joseph's Mercy of Macomb

Commerce Township
Member
  Huron Valley–Sinai Hospital

Detroit
Member
  Detroit Receiving Hospital and University Health
    Center
  Henry Ford Hospital
  Sinai–Grace Hospital
  St. John Detroit Riverview Hospital – Northeast
    Campus
Owner
  Detroit Medical Center
  Henry Ford Health System

Dowagiac
Member
  Borgess–Lee Memorial Hospital

Farmington Hills
Member
  Botsford General Hospital

Flint
Owner
  McLaren Regional Medical Center

Frankfort
Member
  Paul Oliver Memorial Hospital

Garden City
Member
  Garden City Hospital

Grand Rapids
Member
  Metropolitan Hospital
  Saint Mary's Health Care

Grayling
Member
  Mercy Hospital Grayling

Grosse Pointe
Member
  Bon Secours Hospital

Grosse Pointe Farms
Member
  Cottage Hospital

Hillsdale
Member
  Hillsdale Community Health Center

Jackson
Member
  Doctors Hospital
  Foote Health System

Kalamazoo
Member
  Borgess Medical Center
Owner
  Borgess Health Alliance

Kalkaska
Member
  Kalkaska Memorial Health Center

Lansing
Member
  Ingham Regional Medical Center
Owner
  Sparrow Health System

Lapeer
Member
  Lapeer Regional Medical Center

Madison Heights
Member
  Michigan Orthopaedic Specialty Hospital
  St. John Oakland Hospital

Marlette
Member
  Marlette Community Hospital

Mount Clemens
Member
  Mount Clemens General Hospital

Mount Pleasant
Member
  Central Michigan Community Hospital

Muskegon
Member
  Mercy General Health Partners

Northport
Member
  Leelanau Memorial Health Center

Section B

Novi
Owner
  Trinity Health

Paw Paw
Member
  LakeView Community Hospital

Pontiac
Member
  POH Medical Center
  St. Joseph Mercy Oakland

Port Huron
Member
  Mercy Hospital

Rochester
Member
  Crittenton Hospital Medical Center

Romeo
Member
  St. Joseph's Mercy–North

Saginaw
Member
  HealthSource Saginaw

Saint Johns
Member
  Clinton Memorial Hospital

Saline
Member
  Saint Joseph Mercy Saline Hospital

Southfield
Member
  Straith Hospital for Special Surgery

Sturgis
Member
  Sturgis Hospital

Tecumseh
Member
  Lenawee Health Alliance–Herrick Campus

Three Rivers
Member
  Three Rivers Health

Traverse City
Member
  Munson Medical Center

Warren
Member
  Henry Ford Bi–County Hospital
  St. John Macomb Hospital

Watervliet
Member
  Community Hospital

Wyandotte
Member
  Henry Ford Wyandotte Hospital

Ypsilanti
Member
  Saint Joseph Mercy Health System

MINNESOTA

Aitkin
Member
  Riverwood HealthCare Center

Alexandria
Member
  Douglas County Hospital

Austin
Member
  Austin Medical Center

Burnsville
Member
  Fairview Ridges Hospital

Cloquet
Member
  Cloquet Community Memorial Hospital

Cook
Member
  Cook Hospital and Convalescent Nursing Care Unit

Crosby
Member
  Cuyuna Regional Medical Center

Duluth
Member
  Miller–Dwan Medical Center

Edina
Member
  Fairview Southdale Hospital

Ely
Member
  Ely–Bloomenson Community Hospital

Fairmont
Member
  Fairmont Medical Center–Mayo Health System

Glencoe
Member
  Glencoe Regional Health Services

Hibbing
Member
  Fairview University Medical Center–Mesabi

International Falls
Member
  Falls Memorial Hospital

Litchfield
Member
  Meeker County Memorial Hospital

Minneapolis
Member
  University of Minnesota Medical Center
Owner
  Fairview Health Services

Monticello
Member
  Monticello Big Lake Hospital

Moose Lake
Member
  Mercy Hospital and Health Care Center

Mora
Member
  Kanabec Hospital

New Prague
Member
  Queen of Peace Hospital

Northfield
Member
  Northfield Hospital

Ortonville
Member
  Ortonville Area Health Services

Pipestone
Member
  Pipestone County Medical Center/Avera Health

Princeton
Member
  Fairview Northland Regional Health Care

Red Wing
Member
  Fairview Red Wing Medical Center

Robbinsdale
Member
  North Memorial Health Care

Rochester
Member
  Olmsted Medical Center

Saint Louis Park
Member
  Park Nicollet Health Services

Sandstone
Member
  Pine Medical Center

Staples
Member
  Lakewood Health System

Stillwater
Member
  Lakeview Hospital

Tyler
Member
  Tyler Healthcare Center/Avera Health

Virginia
Member
  Virginia Regional Medical Center

Wadena
Member
  Tri–County Hospital

Winona
Member
  Winona Health

Wyoming
Member
  Fairview Lakes Regional Health Care

MISSISSIPPI

Amory
Member
  Gilmore Memorial Hospital

Bay Saint Louis
Member
  Hancock Medical Center

Bay Springs
Member
  Jasper General Hospital

Brookhaven
Member
  King's Daughters Medical Center

Centreville
Member
  Field Memorial Community Hospital

Cleveland
Member
  Bolivar Medical Center

Columbia
Member
  Marion General Hospital

Corinth
Member
  Magnolia Regional Health Center

Greenville
Member
  Delta Regional Medical Center
  The King's Daughters Hospital

Grenada
Owner
  Grenada Lake Medical Center

Hattiesburg
Member
  Wesley Medical Center

Jackson
Member
  Central Mississippi Medical Center
Owner
  Mississippi Baptist Health Systems
  University Hospitals and Clinics, University of
    Mississippi Medical Center

Laurel
Owner
  South Central Regional Medical Center

Lexington
Member
  University Hospital and Clinics – Holmes County

Louisville
Member
  Winston Medical Center

Magee
Member
  Magee General Hospital

Meridian
Member
  Rush Foundation Hospital
Owner
  Rush Health Systems

Natchez
Member
  Natchez Regional Medical Center

Philadelphia
Member
  Neshoba County General Hospital

Picayune
Member
  Crosby Memorial Hospital

Prentiss
Member
　Jefferson Davis Community Hospital

Quitman
Member
　H. C. Watkins Memorial Hospital

Union
Member
　Laird Hospital

Yazoo City
Member
　King's Daughters Hospital

MISSOURI
Albany
Member
　Northwest Medical Center

Belton
Member
　Research Belton Hospital

Bethany
Member
　Harrison County Community Hospital

Carrollton
Member
　Carroll County Memorial Hospital

Fairfax
Member
　Community Hospital Association

Farmington
Member
　Mineral Area Regional Medical Center

Harrisonville
Member
　Cass Medical Center

Independence
Member
　Medical Center of Independence

Jefferson City
Member
　St. Marys Health Center

Kansas City
Member
　Baptist–Lutheran Medical Center
　Children's Mercy Hospital
　Research Medical Center

Lake Saint Louis
Member
　SSM St. Joseph Hospital West

Lees Summit
Member
　Lee's Summit Hospital

Lexington
Member
　Lafayette Regional Health Center

Louisiana
Member
　Pike County Memorial Hospital

Maryville
Member
　St. Francis Hospital and Health Services

Mexico
Member
　Audrain Medical Center

Nevada
Member
　Nevada Regional Medical Center

Rolla
Member
　Phelps County Regional Medical Center

Saint Charles
Member
　SSM St. Joseph Health Center

Saint Joseph
Owner
　Heartland Regional Medical Center

Saint Louis
Member
　SSM Cardinal Glennon Children's Hospital
　SSM St. Joseph Hospital of Kirkwood
　SSM St. Mary's Health Center
Owner
　SSM Health Care

West Plains
Member
　Ozarks Medical Center

MONTANA
Anaconda
Member
　Community Hospital of Anaconda

Cut Bank
Member
　Northern Rockies Medical Center

Great Falls
Member
　Benefis Health Care–West Campus

Harlowton
Member
　Wheatland Memorial Hospital

Lewistown
Member
　Central Montana Medical Center

Missoula
Member
　St. Patrick Hospital

Plains
Member
　Clark Fork Valley Hospital

Polson
Member
　St. Joseph Hospital

Whitefish
Member
　North Valley Hospital

NEBRASKA
Ainsworth
Member
　Brown County Hospital

Albion
Member
　Boone County Health Center

Atkinson
Member
　West Holt Memorial Hospital

Auburn
Member
　Nemaha County Hospital

Aurora
Member
　Memorial Hospital

Bassett
Member
　Rock County Hospital

Central City
Member
　Litzenberg Memorial County Hospital

Chadron
Member
　Chadron Community Hospital and Health Services

Cozad
Member
　Cozad Community Hospital

Creighton
Member
　Creighton Area Health Services

Fairbury
Member
　Jefferson Community Health Center

Fremont
Member
　Fremont Area Medical Center

Geneva
Member
　Fillmore County Hospital

Genoa
Member
　Genoa Community Hospital

Gordon
Member
　Gordon Memorial Hospital

Gothenburg
Member
　Gothenburg Memorial Hospital

Hebron
Member
　Thayer County Health Services

Henderson
Member
　Henderson Health Care Services

Holdrege
Member
　Phelps Memorial Health Center

Imperial
Member
　Chase County Community Hospital

Lynch
Member
　Niobrara Valley Hospital

North Platte
Member
　Great Plains Regional Medical Center

O'Neill
Member
　Avera St. Anthony's Hospital

Oakland
Member
　Oakland Memorial Hospital

Ogallala
Member
　Ogallala Community Hospital

Omaha
Member
　Boys Town National Research Hospital
Owner
　Alegent Health Bergan Mercy Medical Center
　Alegent Health Immanuel Medical Center

Ord
Member
　Valley County Hospital

Osceola
Member
　Annie Jeffrey Memorial County Health Center

Papillion
Owner
　Alegent–Health Midlands Community Hospital

Pawnee City
Member
　Pawnee County Memorial Hospital

Pender
Member
　Pender Community Hospital

Red Cloud
Member
　Webster County Community Hospital

Saint Paul
Member
　Howard County Community Hospital

Schuyler
Owner
　Alegent Health–Memorial Hospital

Seward
Member
　Memorial Health Care Systems

Superior
Member
　Brodstone Memorial Hospital

Syracuse
Member
　Community Memorial Hospital

Tecumseh
Member
　Johnson County Hospital

Valentine
Member
Cherry County Hospital

Wahoo
Member
Saunders County Health Service

Wayne
Member
Providence Medical Center

West Point
Member
St. Francis Memorial Hospital

NEVADA
Fallon
Member
Banner Churchill Community Hospital

Las Vegas
Member
Desert Springs Hospital

Lovelock
Member
Pershing General Hospital

NEW HAMPSHIRE
Exeter
Member
Exeter Hospital

Littleton
Member
Littleton Regional Hospital

Manchester
Member
Catholic Medical Center
Elliot Hospital

Nashua
Member
St. Joseph Hospital

NEW JERSEY
Belleville
Member
Clara Maass Medical Center

Edison
Member
JFK Medical Center
Solaris Health System

Englewood
Owner
Englewood Hospital and Medical Center

Freehold
Member
CentraState Healthcare System

Hackensack
Member
Hackensack University Medical Center

Hackettstown
Member
Hackettstown Community Hospital

Holmdel
Member
Bayshore Community Hospital

Irvington
Member
Irvington General Hospital

Jersey City
Member
LibertyHealth–Greenville Hospital
LibertyHealth–Jersey City Medical Center

Lakewood
Member
Kimball Medical Center

Livingston
Member
Saint Barnabas Medical Center

Long Branch
Member
Monmouth Medical Center

Manahawkin
Member
Southern Ocean County Hospital

Newark
Member
Newark Beth Israel Medical Center

Passaic
Member
PBI Regional Medical Center

Paterson
Member
Barnert Hospital
St. Joseph's Regional Medical Center

Salem
Member
Memorial Hospital of Salem County

Secaucus
Member
LibertyHealth–Meadowlands Hospital Medical Center

Toms River
Member
Community Medical Center

Union
Member
Union Hospital

Wayne
Member
St. Joseph's Wayne Hospital

West Orange
Member
Saint Barnabas Health Care System

NEW MEXICO
Alamogordo
Member
Gerald Champion Regional Medical Center

Albuquerque
Member
Presbyterian Hospital
Presbyterian Kaseman Hospital
Owner
Presbyterian Healthcare Services

Artesia
Member
Artesia General Hospital

Clovis
Member
Plains Regional Medical Center

Espanola
Member
Espanola Hospital

Grants
Member
Cibola General Hospital

Los Alamos
Member
Los Alamos Medical Center

Ruidoso
Member
Lincoln County Medical Center

Silver City
Member
Gila Regional Medical Center

Socorro
Member
Socorro General Hospital

Taos
Member
Holy Cross Hospital

Truth or Consequences
Member
Sierra Vista Hospital

Tucumcari
Member
Dr. Dan C. Trigg Memorial Hospital

NEW YORK
Albany
Member
Albany Medical Center
St. Peter's Hospital

Amityville
Affiliate
South Oaks Hospital

Amsterdam
Member
Amsterdam Memorial Hospital

Batavia
Member
United Memorial Medical Center

Bath
Member
Ira Davenport Memorial Hospital

Bayside
Member
St. Mary's Hospital for Children

Beacon
Member
Saint Francis Hospital

Bethpage
Member
New Island Hospital
Owner
Episcopal Health Services Inc.

Brockport
Member
Lakeside Memorial Hospital

Bronx
St. Barnabas Hospital
Member
Bronx–Lebanon Hospital Center
Calvary Hospital
Fulton Division
Jewish Home and Hospital for Aged
Our Lady of Mercy Medical Center
Owner
Montefiore Medical Center

Brooklyn
Member
Brookdale Hospital Medical Center
Interfaith Medical Center
Kingsbrook Jewish Medical Center
Long Island College Hospital
Lutheran Medical Center
New York Methodist Hospital
St. Mary's Hospital of Brooklyn
SUNY Downstate Medical Center University Hospital
Victory Memorial Hospital
Owner
Maimonides Medical Center

Buffalo
Member
Brylin Hospitals
Mercy Hospital
Sheehan Memorial Hospital
Women and Children's Hospital

Canandaigua
Member
Thompson Health

Cheektowaga
Member
St. Joseph Hospital

Clifton Springs
Member
Clifton Springs Hospital and Clinic

Corning
Member
Corning Hospital

Cortlandt Manor
Member
Hudson Valley Hospital Center

Dansville
Member
Nicholas H. Noyes Memorial Hospital

Dobbs Ferry
Member
Community Hospital at Dobbs Ferry

Elizabethtown
Member
Elizabethtown Community Hospital

Elmira
Member
Arnot Ogden Medical Center
St. Joseph's Hospital

Far Rockaway
Member
 Peninsula Hospital Center
 St. John's Episcopal Hospital–South Shore

Flushing
Member
 Parkway Hospital
 St. John's Queens Hospital
 St. Joseph's Hospital

Glen Oaks
Member
 Zucker Hillside Hospital

Glens Falls
Member
 Glens Falls Hospital

Great Neck
Owner
 North Shore–LIJ Health System

Hornell
Member
 St. James Mercy Hospital

Irving
Member
 Lake Shore Health Care Center

Jamaica
Member
 Jamaica Hospital Medical Center
Owner
 Saint Vincents Catholic Medical Centers of New York

Kenmore
Member
 Kenmore Mercy Hospital

Lackawanna
Member
 Our Lady of Victory Hospital

Long Beach
Member
 Long Beach Medical Center

Long Island City
Member
 The Mount Sinai Hospital of Queens

Medina
Member
 Medina Memorial Hospital

Mineola
Member
 Winthrop–University Hospital

Montour Falls
Member
 Schuyler Hospital

Mount Vernon
Member
 Mount Vernon Hospital

New Hyde Park
Member
 Long Island Jewish Medical Center
 Schneider Children's Hospital

New York
Member
 Cabrini Medical Center
 Hospital for Special Surgery
 Lenox Hill Hospital
 Manhattan Eye, Ear and Throat Hospital
 New York Eye and Ear Infirmary
 North General Hospital
 Saint Vincent's Hospital – Manhattan
 St. Luke's–Roosevelt Hospital Center
 St. Vincent's Midtown Hospital

Newfane
Member
 Inter–Community Memorial Hospital

Oceanside
Member
 South Nassau Communities Hospital

Oneonta
Member
 Aurelia Osborn Fox Memorial Hospital

Patchogue
Member
 Brookhaven Memorial Hospital Medical Center

Penn Yan
Member
 Soldiers and Sailors Memorial Hospital of Yates
  County

Plattsburgh
Member
 Champlain Valley Physicians Hospital Medical Center

Port Jefferson
Member
 John T. Mather Memorial Hospital
Owner
 St. Charles Hospital

Poughkeepsie
Member
 Saint Francis Hospital
Owner
 Vassar Brothers Medical Center

Rochester
Member
 Monroe Community Hospital
 Rochester General Hospital
Owner
 ViaHealth

Rockville Centre
Member
 Mercy Medical Center

Roslyn
Member
 St. Francis Hospital

Schenectady
Member
 Ellis Hospital

Smithtown
Member
 St. Catherine of Siena Medical Center

Staten Island
Member
 Sisters of Charity Healthcare
 St. Vincent's Hospital
 Staten Island University Hospital–Concord
Owner
 Staten Island University Hospital

Syracuse
Member
 Upstate Medical University

Troy
Member
 Samaritan Hospital

Valhalla
Member
 Blythedale Children's Hospital

Warsaw
Member
 Wyoming County Community Hospital

West Islip
Member
 Good Samaritan Hospital Medical Center

Westfield
Member
 Westfield Memorial Hospital

Yonkers
Member
 St. John's Riverside Hosptial

NORTH CAROLINA

Albemarle
Owner
 Stanly Memorial Hospital

Asheboro
Owner
 Randolph Hospital

Asheville
Member
 Thoms Rehabilitation Hospital
Owner
 Mission Hospitals

Blowing Rock
Member
 Blowing Rock Hospital

Boiling Springs
Member
 Crawley Memorial Hospital

Boone
Owner
 Watauga Medical Center

Brevard
Member
 Transylvania Community Hospital

Bryson City
Member
 Swain County Hospital

Burgaw
Member
 Pender Memorial Hospital

Burlington
Owner
 Alamance Regional Medical Center

Clinton
Member
 Sampson Regional Medical Center

Clyde
Owner
 Haywood Regional Medical Center

Columbus
Member
 St. Luke's Hospital

Danbury
Member
 Stokes–Reynolds Memorial Hospital

Durham
Owner
 Durham Regional Hospital

Eden
Member
 Morehead Memorial Hospital

Edenton
Member
 Chowan Hospital

Elizabethtown
Member
 Bladen County Hospital

Elkin
Member
 Hugh Chatham Memorial Hospital

Erwin
Member
 Good Hope Hospital

Fayetteville
 Cape Fear Valley Health System
Member
 Behavioral Health Care of Cape Fear Valley Health
  System

Fletcher
Member
 Park Ridge Hospital

Franklin
Member
 Angel Medical Center

Gastonia
Owner
 Gaston Memorial Hospital

Goldsboro
Owner
 Wayne Memorial Hospital

Henderson
Member
 Maria Parham Medical Center

Hendersonville
Owner
 Margaret R. Pardee Memorial Hospital

Hickory
Owner
 Catawba Valley Medical Center

Jefferson
Member
 Ashe Memorial Hospital

Kenansville
Member
 Duplin General Hospital

Section B

Kinston
Owner
Lenoir Memorial Hospital

Laurinburg
Member
Scotland Memorial Hospital

Lenoir
Owner
Caldwell Memorial Hospital

Lexington
Member
Lexington Memorial Hospital

Lumberton
Owner
Southeastern Regional Medical Center

Marion
Member
McDowell Hospital

Matthews
Member
Presbyterian Hospital–Matthews

Morganton
Owner
Grace Hospital

Mount Airy
Member
Northern Hospital of Surry County

Murphy
Member
Murphy Medical Center

North Wilkesboro
Member
Wilkes Regional Medical Center

Oxford
Member
Granville Medical Center

Pinehurst
Owner
FirstHealth Moore Regional Hospital

Plymouth
Member
Washington County Hospital

Raleigh
Owner
Rex Healthcare

Roanoke Rapids
Owner
Halifax Regional Medical Center

Roxboro
Member
Person Memorial Hospital

Rutherfordton
Member
Rutherford Hospital

Shelby
Owner
Cleveland Regional Medical Center

Siler City
Member
Chatham Hospital

Smithfield
Member
Johnston Memorial Hospital

Sparta
Member
Alleghany Memorial Hospital

Spruce Pine
Member
Spruce Pine Community Hospital

Statesville
Owner
Iredell Memorial Hospital

Sylva
Owner
Harris Regional Hospital

Troy
Owner
FirstHealth Montgomery Memorial Hospital

Whiteville
Member
Columbus County Hospital

Williamston
Member
Martin General Hospital

Wilmington
Owner
New Hanover Regional Medical Center

Wilson
Owner
Wilson Medical Center

Winston–Salem
Owner
North Carolina Baptist Hospital (Wake Forest
University Baptist Medical Center)

Yadkinville
Member
Hoots Memorial Hospital

NORTH DAKOTA

Cavalier
Member
Pembina County Memorial Hospital and Wedgewood
Manor

Kenmare
Member
Kenmare Community Hospital

Lisbon
Member
Lisbon Area Health Services

OHIO

Akron
Member
Akron Children's Hospital
Akron City Hospital
Edwin Shaw Hospital for Rehabilitation
Saint Thomas Hospital
Owner
Summa Health System

Alliance
Member
Alliance Community Hospital

Amherst
Member
The Hospital for Orthopaedic and Specialty Services

Ashtabula
Member
Ashtabula County Medical Center

Barberton
Member
Barberton Citizens Hospital

Batavia
Member
Mercy Hospital Clermont

Cincinnati
Member
Children's Hospital Medical Center
Mercy Hospital Anderson
Owner
Bethesda North Hospital
Catholic Healthcare Partners
Good Samaritan Hospital

Cleveland
Member
Cleveland Clinic Children's Hospital for Rehabilitation
Fairview Hospital
Grace Hospital
Lutheran Hospital
MetroHealth Medical Center
Owner
Cleveland Clinic Foundation
Hillcrest Hospital
Huron Hospital

Columbus
Member
Children's Hospital
Ohio State University Hospitals East

Dayton
Member
Children's Medical Center
Good Samaritan Hospital

Defiance
Member
Defiance Regional Medical Center

Dennison
Member
Twin City Hospital

East Liverpool
Member
East Liverpool City Hospital

Elyria
Member
EMH Regional Medical Center

Euclid
Member
Euclid Hospital

Fremont
Member
Memorial Hospital

Garfield Heights
Member
Marymount Hospital

Georgetown
Member
Brown County General Hospital

Green Springs
Member
St. Francis Health Care Centre

Greenfield
Member
Greenfield Area Medical Center

Lakewood
Member
Lakewood Hospital

Lima
Member
St. Rita's Medical Center

Lodi
Member
Lodi Community Hospital

Lorain
Member
Community Health Partners Regional Medical Center

Marietta
Member
Selby General Hospital

Marysville
Member
Memorial Hospital of Union County

Massillon
Member
Doctors Hospital of Stark County
Massillon Community Hospital

Middleburg Heights
Member
Southwest General Health Center

Mount Vernon
Member
Knox Community Hospital

Oberlin
Member
Allen Medical Center

Oregon
Member
St. Charles Mercy Hospital

Parma
Member
Parma Community General Hospital

Paulding
Member
Paulding County Hospital

Springfield
Member
Mercy Medical Center

Tiffin
Member
Mercy Hospital of Tiffin

Toledo
Member
St. Vincent Mercy Medical Center

Urbana
Member
Mercy Memorial Hospital

Van Wert
Member
Van Wert County Hospital

Wadsworth
Member
Wadsworth–Rittman Hospital

Warren
Member
Forum Hillside Rehabilitation Hospital
St. Joseph Health Center

Warrensville Heights
Owner
South Pointe Hospital

Washington Court House
Member
Fayette County Memorial Hospital

Willard
Member
Mercy Hospital of Willard

Wooster
Member
Wooster Community Hospital

Youngstown
Member
St. Elizabeth Health Center

OKLAHOMA
Alva
Member
Share Medical Center

Atoka
Member
Atoka Memorial Hospital

Cordell
Member
Cordell Memorial Hospital

Cushing
Member
Cushing Regional Hospital

Frederick
Member
Memorial Hospital and Physician Group

Guthrie
Member
Logan Medical Center

Henryetta
Member
Henryetta Medical Center

Holdenville
Member
Holdenville General Hospital

Idabel
Member
McCurtain Memorial Hospital

Kingfisher
Member
Kingfisher Regional Hospital

Lawton
Member
Comanche County Memorial Hospital

Mangum
Member
Mangum City Hospital

Oklahoma City
Member
Bone and Joint Hospital
St. Anthony Hospital

Okmulgee
Affiliate
Okmulgee Memorial Hospital
Member
Okmulgee Memorial Hospital Authority

Perry
Member
Perry Memorial Hospital

Purcell
Member
Purcell Municipal Hospital

Sayre
Member
Sayre Memorial Hospital

Seiling
Member
Seiling Hospital

Seminole
Member
Seminole Medical Center

Tahlequah
Member
Tahlequah City Hospital

Tulsa
Member
Laureate Psychiatric Clinic and Hospital
Owner
Saint Francis Hospital

Watonga
Member
Watonga Municipal Hospital

Woodward
Member
Woodward Regional Hospital

OREGON
Dallas
Member
West Valley Hospital

Eugene
Member
Sacred Heart Medical Center

Florence
Member
Peace Harbor Hospital

Gold Beach
Member
Curry General Hospital

Gresham
Member
Legacy Mount Hood Medical Center

Heppner
Member
Pioneer Memorial Hospital

Lakeview
Member
Lake District Hospital

Lebanon
Member
Samaritan Lebanon Community Hospital

Lincoln City
Member
Samaritan North Lincoln Hospital

Medford
Providence Medford Medical Center

Milwaukie
Member
Providence Milwaukie Hospital

Newberg
Member
Providence Newberg Hospital

Newport
Member
Samaritan Pacific Communities Hospital

Portland
Member
Adventist Medical Center
Colonial Manor Sanitarium
Legacy Good Samaritan Hospital and Medical Center
Providence St. Vincent Medical Center
Owner
Legacy Health System

Prineville
Member
Pioneer Memorial Hospital

Salem
Member
Salem Hospital

Seaside
Member
Providence Seaside Hospital

Springfield
Member
McKenzie–Willamette Medical Center

Stayton
Member
Santiam Memorial Hospital

Tillamook
Member
Tillamook County General Hospital

Tualatin
Member
Legacy Meridian Park Hospital

PENNSYLVANIA
Altoona
Member
Bon Secours Hospital Campus

Berwick
Member
Berwick Hospital Center

Bethlehem
Owner
St. Luke's Hospital – Bethlehem Campus

Brownsville
Member
Brownsville General Hospital

Bryn Mawr
Member
Bryn Mawr Hospital
Bryn Mawr Hospital

Carlisle
Member
Carlisle Regional Medical Center

Clarion
Member
Clarion Hospital

Coaldale
Owner
St. Luke's Miner's Memorial Hospital

Corry
Member
Corry Memorial Hospital

Danville
Member
Geisinger Health System
Geisinger Medical Center

Darby
Member
Mercy Fitzgerald Hospital

East Stroudsburg
Member
Pocono Medical Center

Easton
Member
Easton Hospital

Erie
Member
Millcreek Community Hospital
Saint Vincent Health Center

Hastings
Member
Miners Medical Center

Havertown
Member
Mercy Community Hospital

Hazleton
Member
Hazleton–St. Joseph Medical Center

Hershey
Owner
Penn State Milton S. Hershey Medical Center

Huntingdon
Member
J. C. Blair Memorial Hospital

Jersey Shore
Member
Jersey Shore Hospital

Kane
Member
Kane Community Hospital

Lock Haven
Member
  Lock Haven Hospital

Malvern
Member
  Bryn Mawr Rehabilitation Hospital

McKees Rocks
Member
  Ohio Valley General Hospital

Meadville
Member
  Meadville Medical Center

Media
Member
  Riddle Memorial Hospital

Monroeville
Member
  Forbes Regional Hospital

Nanticoke
Member
  Mercy Special Care Hospital

Newtown Square
Owner
  Catholic Health East

Palmerton
Owner
  Palmerton Hospital

Paoli
Member
  Paoli Hospital

Philadelphia
Member
  Albert Einstein Medical Center
  Belmont Center for Comprehensive Treatment
  Children's Hospital of Philadelphia
  Mercy Hospital of Philadelphia
  Methodist Hospital
  Thomas Jefferson University Hospital
  Wills Eye Hospital
Owner
  Albert Einstein Healthcare Network

Pittsburgh
Member
  Children's Hospital of Pittsburgh of UPMC
  LifeCare Hospitals of Pittsburgh
  Mercy Hospital of Pittsburgh
  Mercy Hospital–North Shore Campus
Owner
  Western Pennsylvania Hospital

Pottsville
Member
  Pottsville Hospital and Warne Clinic

Ridley Park
Member
  Taylor Hospital

Scranton
Member
  Mercy Hospital of Scranton

Titusville
Member
  Titusville Area Hospital

Towanda
Member
  Memorial Hospital

Tyrone
Member
  Tyrone Hospital

Union City
Member
  Saint Vincent Outpatient Center – Union City

Warren
Owner
  Warren General Hospital

Wayne
Owner
  Jefferson Health System

Waynesburg
Member
  Greene County Memorial Hospital

West Grove
Member
  Jennersville Regional Hospital

Wilkes–Barre
Member
  Geisinger Wyoming Valley Medical Center
  Mercy Hospital of Wilkes–Barre

Wynnewood
Member
  Lankenau Hospital

York
Member
  Memorial Hospital

PUERTO RICO

Mayaguez
Member
  Bella Vista Hospital

Ponce
Member
  Hospital De Damas

RHODE ISLAND

Providence
Member
  Roger Williams Medical Center

SOUTH CAROLINA

Abbeville
Member
  Abbeville County Memorial Hospital

Anderson
Owner
  AnMED Health Medical Center

Beaufort
Member
  Beaufort Memorial Hospital

Camden
Member
  Kershaw County Medical Center

Charleston
Member
  Bon Secours–St. Francis Xavier Hospital
Owner
  Roper Hospital

Clinton
Member
  Laurens County Healthcare System

Columbia
Member
  Palmetto Health Richland
Owner
  Palmetto Health Alliance

Conway
Owner
  Conway Medical Center

Dillon
Member
  McLeod Medical Center–Dillon

Edgefield
Member
  Edgefield County Hospital

Florence
Member
  Carolinas Hospital System
Owner
  McLeod Health

Greenville
Member
  Greenville Memorial Hospital
  Shriners Hospitals for Children, Greenville
Owner
  Greenville Hospital System

Greenwood
Owner
  Self Regional Healthcare

Greer
Member
  Allen Bennett Hospital

Kingstree
Member
  Williamsburg Regional Hospital

Lake City
Member
  Lake City Community Hospital

Lexington
Member
  Keisler Nursing Home

Loris
Member
  Loris Community Hospital

Newberry
Member
  Newberry County Memorial Hospital

Orangeburg
Member
  Regional Medical Center of Orangeburg and Calhoun
    Counties

Pickens
Member
  Cannon Memorial Hospital

Simpsonville
Member
  Hillcrest Hospital

Spartanburg
Member
  Mary Black Health System
Owner
  Spartanburg Regional Medical Center

Sumter
Member
  Tuomey Healthcare System

Union
Member
  Wallace Thomson Hospital

West Columbia
Owner
  Lexington Medical Center

Winnsboro
Member
  Fairfield Memorial Hospital

SOUTH DAKOTA

Aberdeen
Member
  Avera St. Luke's

Armour
Member
  Douglas County Memorial Hospital

Britton
Member
  Marshall County Healthcare Center/Avera Health

Burke
Member
  Community Memorial Hospital

Custer
Member
  Custer Community Hospital

Deadwood
Member
  Northern Hills General Hospital

Dell Rapids
Member
  Dells Area Health Center

Eureka
Member
  Eureka Community Health Services/Avera Health

Faulkton
Member
  Faulk County Memorial Hospital

Flandreau
Member
  Flandreau Medical Center/Avera Health

Gregory
Member
  Avera Gregory Healthcare Center

Hoven
Member
  Holy Infant Hospital

Huron
Member
  Huron Regional Medical Center

Martin
Member
Bennett County Healthcare Center

Milbank
Member
Milbank Area Hospital/Avera Health

Miller
Member
Hand County Memorial Hospital/Avera Health

Mitchell
Member
Avera Queen of Peace

Parkston
Member
Avera St. Benedict Health Center

Platte
Member
Platte Health Center/Avera Health

Rapid City
Owner
Rapid City Regional Hospital System of Care

Redfield
Member
Community Memorial Hospital

Scotland
Member
Landmann–Jungman Memorial Hospital

Sioux Falls
Member
Avera McKennan Hospital and University Health Center

Spearfish
Member
Lookout Memorial Hospital

Sturgis
Member
Sturgis Community Health Care Center

Tyndall
Member
St. Michael's Hospital

Wagner
Member
Wagner Community Memorial Hospital

Watertown
Member
Prairie Lakes Healthcare System

Wessington Springs
Member
Avera Weskota Memorial Medical Center

Yankton
Member
Avera Sacred Heart Hospital
Owner
Avera Health

TENNESSEE

Bristol
Member
Wellmont Bristol Regional Medical Center

Brownsville
Member
Haywood County Memorial Hospital

Chattanooga
Member
Siskin Hospital for Physical Rehabilitation

Cleveland
Member
Bradley Memorial Hospital

Copperhill
Member
Copper Basin Medical Center

Crossville
Member
Cumberland Medical Center

Dayton
Member
Rhea Medical Center

Dyersburg
Member
Dyersburg Regional Medical Center

Erwin
Member
Unicoi County Memorial Hospital

Etowah
Member
Woods Memorial Hospital District

Fayetteville
Member
Lincoln County Health System

Gallatin
Owner
Sumner Regional Medical Center

Greeneville
Member
Takoma Adventist Hospital

Jackson
Member
Jackson–Madison County General Hospital

Jefferson City
Member
St. Mary's Jefferson Memorial Hospital

Jellico
Member
Jellico Community Hospital

Johnson City
Member
Johnson City Medical Center
Owner
Mountain States Health Alliance

Kingsport
Member
Wellmont Holston Valley Medical Center
Owner
Wellmont Health System

Knoxville
Member
Baptist Hospital of East Tennessee
St. Mary's Medical Center
Owner
Baptist Health System of East Tennessee

La Follette
Member
St. Mary's Medical Center of Campbell County

Lafayette
Member
Macon County General Hospital

Lexington
Member
Henderson County Community Hospital

Madison
Member
Tennessee Christian Medical Center

Maryville
Owner
Blount Memorial Hospital

McKenzie
Member
McKenzie Regional Hospital

Memphis
Member
Extendicare of Memphis
Methodist Healthcare
Methodist Healthcare–University Hospital
Regional Medical Center at Memphis
St. Jude Children's Research Hospital

Morristown
Member
Morristown–Hamblen Hospital

Nashville
Owner
Vanderbilt University Medical Center

Newport
Member
Baptist Hospital of Cocke County

Rockwood
Member
Baptist Urgent Care

Rogersville
Member
Wellmont Hawkins County Memorial Hospital

Somerville
Owner
Methodist Healthcare–Fayette Hospital

Sweetwater
Member
Sweetwater Hospital

Tazewell
Member
Claiborne County Hospital

TEXAS

Abilene
Member
Abilene Regional Medical Center
Owner
Hendrick Health System

Anahuac
Member
Bayside Community Hospital

Anson
Member
Anson General Hospital

Arlington
Owner
Texas Health Resources

Aspermont
Member
Stonewall Memorial Hospital

Azle
Member
Harris Methodist Northwest

Ballinger
Member
Ballinger Memorial Hospital

Bay City
Member
Matagorda General Hospital

Beaumont
Member
Christus St. Elizabeth Hospital

Bedford
Member
Harris Methodist–HEB

Big Lake
Member
Reagan Memorial Hospital

Bowie
Member
Bowie Memorial Hospital

Brady
Member
Heart of Texas Memorial Hospital

Breckenridge
Member
Stephens Memorial Hospital

Brenham
Member
Trinity Community Medical Center of Brenham

Bryan
Owner
St. Joseph Regional Health Center

Burnet
Member
Seton Highland Lakes

Caldwell
Member
Burleson St. Joseph Health Center

Canadian
Member
Hemphill County Hospital

Carrizo Springs
Member
Dimmit County Memorial Hospital

Childress
Member
Childress Regional Medical Center

Chillicothe
Member
Chillicothe Hospital District

Section B

Cleburne
Member
  Walls Regional Hospital

Clifton
Member
  Goodall–Witcher Healthcare

Coleman
Member
  Coleman County Medical Center

Columbus
Member
  Columbus Community Hospital

Comanche
Member
  Comanche Community Hospital

Commerce
Member
  Presbyterian Hospital of Commerce

Corpus Christi
Member
  Driscoll Children's Hospital

Crane
Member
  Crane Memorial Hospital

Crosbyton
Member
  Crosbyton Clinic Hospital

Dallas
Member
  Children's Medical Center of Dallas
  Methodist Charlton Medical Center
  Methodist Dallas Medical Center
  Presbyterian Hospital of Dallas
  St. Paul University Hospital
Owner
  Methodist Health System

Decatur
Member
  Wise Regional Health System

Denison
Member
  Texoma Medical Center Restorative Care Hospital
Owner
  Texoma Medical Center

Denver City
Member
  Yoakum County Hospital

Dimmitt
Member
  Plains Memorial Hospital

Eagle Lake
Member
  Rice Medical Center

Eagle Pass
Member
  Fort Duncan Medical Center

Eastland
Member
  Eastland Memorial Hospital

Eden
Member
  Concho County Hospital

Edna
Member
  Jackson County Hospital District

El Campo
Member
  El Campo Memorial Hospital

El Paso
Owner
  R. E. Thomason General Hospital

Eldorado
Member
  Schleicher County Medical Center

Fort Stockton
Member
  Pecos County Memorial Hospital

Fort Worth
Member
  Cook Children's Medical Center
  Harris Methodist Fort Worth
  Harris Methodist Health System
  Harris Methodist Southwest
  Huguley Memorial Medical Center

Fredericksburg
Member
  Hill Country Memorial Hospital

Friona
Member
  Parmer County Community Hospital

Galveston
Member
  University of Texas Medical Branch Hospitals

Graham
Member
  Graham Regional Medical Center

Greenville
Member
  Presbyterian Hospital of Greenville

Groves
Member
  Doctors Hospital

Hallettsville
Member
  Lavaca Medical Center

Hamilton
Member
  Hamilton General Hospital

Hamlin
Member
  Hamlin Memorial Hospital

Haskell
Member
  Haskell Memorial Hospital

Henderson
Member
  Henderson Memorial Hospital

Hondo
Member
  Medina Community Hospital

Houston
Member
  Christus St. John Hospital
  Christus St. Joseph Hospital
  Texas Children's Hospital
  The Methodist Hospital
Owner
  St. Luke's Episcopal Hospital
  The Methodist Hospital System
  University of Texas M. D. Anderson Cancer Center

Irving
Owner
  Christus Health

Jasper
Member
  Christus Jasper Memorial Hospital

Junction
Member
  Kimble Hospital

Kaufman
Member
  Presbyterian Hospital of Kaufman

Kenedy
Member
  Otto Kaiser Memorial Hospital

Kermit
Member
  Winkler County Memorial Hospital

Killeen
Member
  Metroplex Adventist Hospital

Knox City
Member
  Knox County Hospital

Lake Jackson
Member
  Brazosport Memorial Hospital

Lamesa
Member
  Medical Arts Hospital

Livingston
Member
  Memorial Medical Center – Livingston

Lockney
Member
  W. J. Mangold Memorial Hospital

Lubbock
Owner
  University Medical Center

Lufkin
Owner
  Memorial Health System of East Texas

Luling
Member
  Seton Edgar B. Davis Hospital

Madisonville
Member
  Madison St. Joseph Health Center

McAllen
Member
  McAllen Medical Center

Midland
Member
  Midland Memorial Hospital

Mineral Wells
Member
  Palo Pinto General Hospital

Mission
Member
  Mission Hospital

Monahans
Member
  Ward Memorial Hospital

Morton
Member
  Cochran Memorial Hospital

Mount Pleasant
Member
  Titus Regional Medical Center

Muleshoe
Member
  Muleshoe Area Medical Center

Nacogdoches
Owner
  Nacogdoches Memorial Hospital

Navasota
Member
  Grimes St. Joseph Health Center

Nocona
Member
  Nocona General Hospital

Olney
Member
  Hamilton Hospital

Pecos
Member
  Reeves County Hospital

Plano
Member
  Presbyterian Hospital of Plano

Port Arthur
Member
  Christus St. Mary Hospital

Quanah
Member
  Hardeman County Memorial Hospital

Rockdale
Member
  Richards Memorial Hospital

Rotan
Member
  Fisher County Hospital District

San Augustine
Member
  Memorial Medical Center – San Augustine

San Marcos
Member
  Central Texas Medical Center

Seminole
Member
  Memorial Hospital

Seymour
Member
  Seymour Hospital

Shamrock
Member
  Shamrock General Hospital

Snyder
Member
  D. M. Cogdell Memorial Hospital

Sonora
Member
  Lillian M. Hudspeth Memorial Hospital

Spearman
Member
  Hansford Hospital

Stamford
Member
  Stamford Memorial Hospital

Stanton
Member
  Martin County Hospital District

Stephenville
Member
  Harris Methodist–Erath County

Sweetwater
Member
  Rolling Plains Memorial Hospital

Tahoka
Member
  Lynn County Hospital District

Texarkana
Member
  Christus St. Michael Health System

Throckmorton
Member
  Throckmorton County Memorial Hospital

Tulia
Member
  Swisher Memorial Hospital District

Van Horn
Member
  Culberson Hospital District

Weatherford
Member
  Campbell Health System

Wellington
Member
  Collingsworth General Hospital

Weslaco
Owner
  Knapp Medical Center

Whitney
Member
  Lake Whitney Medical Center

Winnsboro
Member
  Presbyterian Hospital of Winnsboro

Winters
Member
  North Runnels Hospital

UTAH
Monticello
Member
  San Juan Hospital

VERMONT
Saint Albans
Member
  Northwestern Medical Center

Saint Johnsbury
Member
  Northeastern Vermont Regional Hospital

VIRGINIA
Abingdon
Owner
  Johnston Memorial Hospital

Alexandria
Member
  Inova Alexandria Hospital
  Inova Mount Vernon Hospital

Bedford
Member
  Bedford Memorial Hospital

Big Stone Gap
Member
  Wellmont Lonesome Pine Hospital

Chesapeake
Owner
  Chesapeake General Hospital

Christiansburg
Member
  Carilion New River Valley Medical Center

Culpeper
Member
  Culpeper Regional Hospital

Danville
Owner
  Danville Regional Medical Center

Emporia
Member
  Southern Virginia Regional Medical Center

Fairfax
Member
  Inova Fair Oaks Hospital

Falls Church
Member
  Inova Fairfax Hospital
Owner
  Inova Health System

Farmville
Member
  Southside Community Hospital

Front Royal
Member
  Warren Memorial Hospital

Galax
Owner
  Twin County Regional Hospital

Gloucester
Member
  Riverside Walter Reed Hospital

Grundy
Member
  Buchanan General Hospital

Kilmarnock
Member
  Rappahannock General Hospital

Leesburg
Member
  Inova Loudoun Hospital

Lexington
Member
  Stonewall Jackson Hospital

Luray
Member
  Page Memorial Hospital

Manassas
Member
  Prince William Hospital

Marion
Owner
  Smyth County Community Hospital

Martinsville
Member
  Memorial Hospital

Mechanicsville
Member
  Memorial Regional Medical Center

Nassawadox
Member
  Shore Memorial Hospital

Newport News
Member
  Mary Immaculate Hospital
  Riverside Regional Medical Center
  Riverside Rehabilitation Institute
Owner
  Riverside Health System

Norfolk
Member
  Bon Secours–DePaul Medical Center
  Children's Hospital of The King's Daughters

Norton
Member
  Norton Community Hospital

Pearisburg
Member
  Carilion Giles Memorial Hospital

Pennington Gap
Member
  Lee Regional Medical Center

Petersburg
Member
  Southside Regional Medical Center

Portsmouth
Member
  Maryview Medical Center

Richmond
Member
  Bon Secours St. Mary's Hospital
  Bon Secours–Richmond Community Hospital
  Children's Hospital
  Stony Point Surgery Center

Roanoke
Member
  Carilion Medical Center
Owner
  Carilion Health System

Rocky Mount
Member
  Carilion Franklin Memorial Hospital

South Boston
Member
  Halifax Regional Health System

South Hill
Owner
  Community Memorial Healthcenter

Stuart
Member
  R. J. Reynolds–Patrick County Memorial Hospital

Suffolk
Owner
  Louise Obici Memorial Hospital

Tappahannock
Member
  Riverside Tappahannock Hospital

Tazewell
Member
  Tazewell Community Hospital

Virginia Beach
Member
  Sentara Virginia Beach General Hospital
  Tidewater Health Care, Inc.

Warrenton
Member
  Fauquier Hospital

Winchester
Member
  Winchester Medical Center
Owner
  Valley Health System

Woodbridge
Member
  Potomac Hospital

Woodstock
Member
  Shenandoah Memorial Hospital

Wytheville
Member
  Wythe County Community Hospital

WASHINGTON

Aberdeen
Member
　Grays Harbor Community Hospital

Bellevue
Member
　Overlake Hospital Medical Center
Owner
　PeaceHealth

Bellingham
Member
　St. Joseph Hospital

Brewster
Member
　Okanogan Douglas District Hospital

Centralia
Member
　Providence Centralia Hospital

Chelan
Member
　Lake Chelan Community Hospital

Chewelah
Member
　St. Joseph's Hospital

Clarkston
Member
　Tri–State Memorial Hospital

Colfax
Member
　Whitman Hospital and Medical Center

Colville
Member
　Mount Carmel Hospital

Coupeville
Member
　Whidbey General Hospital

Davenport
Member
　Lincoln Hospital

Deer Park
Member
　Deer Park Hospital

Edmonds
Member
　Stevens Healthcare

Ephrata
Member
　Columbia Basin Hospital

Everett
Member
　Providence Everett Medical Center

Grand Coulee
Member
　Coulee Community Hospital

Kirkland
Member
　Evergreen Healthcare

Longview
Member
　St. John Medical Center

Morton
Member
　Morton General Hospital

Moses Lake
Member
　Samaritan Healthcare

Newport
Member
　Newport Community Hospital

Odessa
Member
　Odessa Memorial Healthcare Center

Olympia
Member
　Providence St. Peter Hospital

Omak
Member
　Mid–Valley Hospital

Othello
Member
　Othello Community Hospital

Prosser
Member
　Prosser Memorial Hospital

Pullman
Member
　Pullman Regional Hospital

Puyallup
Member
　Good Samaritan Community Healthcare

Quincy
Member
　Quincy Valley Medical Center

Redmond
Member
　Group Health Cooperative

Renton
Member
　Valley Medical Center

Republic
Member
　Ferry County Memorial Hospital

Richland
Member
　Kadlec Medical Center

Ritzville
Member
　East Adams Rural Hospital

Seattle
Member
　Children's Hospital and Regional Medical Center
　Highline Medical Center
　Providence Health System
　Regional Hospital for Respiratory and Complex Care
　Swedish Medical Center–Providence Campus
Owner
　Northwest Hospital

Shelton
Member
　Mason General Hospital

Spokane
Member
　Deaconess Medical Center–Spokane
　Empire Health Services
　Holy Family Hospital
　Sacred Heart Medical Center
　Shriners Hospitals for Children–Spokane
　St. Luke's Rehabilitation Institute
　Valley Hospital and Medical Center
Owner
　Providence Services

Tonasket
Member
　North Valley Hospital

Toppenish
Member
　Toppenish Community Hospital

Vancouver
Member
　Southwest Washington Medical Center
　Woodside Hospital

Walla Walla
Member
　St. Mary Medical Center
　Walla Walla General Hospital

Wenatchee
Member
　Central Washington Hospital

Yakima
Member
　Yakima Regional Medical and Heart Center

WEST VIRGINIA

Berkeley Springs
Member
　Morgan County War Memorial Hospital

Bluefield
Owner
　Bluefield Regional Medical Center

Buckhannon
Member
　St. Joseph's Hospital of Buckhannon

Clarksburg
Member
　United Hospital Center

Elkins
Owner
　Davis Memorial Hospital

Fairmont
Member
　Fairmont General Hospital
Owner
　West Virginia United Health System

Huntington
Owner
　St. Mary's Medical Center

Keyser
Member
　Potomac Valley Hospital

Kingwood
Member
　Preston Memorial Hospital

Martinsburg
Member
　City Hospital

Morgantown
Owner
　Monongalia General Hospital

Parkersburg
Owner
　Camden–Clark Memorial Hospital

Petersburg
Member
　Grant Memorial Hospital

Philippi
Member
　Broaddus Hospital

Point Pleasant
Owner
　Pleasant Valley Hospital

Ranson
Member
　Jefferson Memorial Hospital

Romney
Member
　Hampshire Memorial Hospital

Sistersville
Member
　Sistersville General Hospital

South Charleston
Owner
　Thomas Memorial Hospital

Summersville
Member
　Summersville Memorial Hospital

Weirton
Owner
　Weirton Medical Center

Weston
Member
　Stonewall Jackson Memorial Hospital

WISCONSIN

Amery
Member
　Amery Regional Medical Center

Baldwin
Member
　Baldwin Area Medical Center

Baraboo
Member
　St. Clare Hospital and Health Services

Barron
Member
　Barron Medical Center–Mayo Health System

Berlin
Member
　Berlin Memorial Hospital

Burlington
Member
  Memorial Hospital Corporation of Burlington

Cumberland
Member
  Cumberland Memorial Hospital

Durand
Member
  Chippewa Valley Hospital and Oakview Care Center

Elkhorn
Member
  Aurora Lakeland Medical Center

Green Bay
Member
  Bellin Memorial Hospital

Hartford
Member
  Aurora Medical Center of Washington County

Janesville
Member
  Mercy Health System

Madison
Member
  St. Marys Hospital Medical Center

Marinette
Member
  Bay Area Medical Center

Milwaukee
Member
  Aurora Sinai Medical Center
  Children's Hospital of Wisconsin
  St. Luke's Medical Center
Owner
  Aurora Health Care

Monroe
Member
  The Monroe Clinic

Osceola
Member
  Osceola Medical Center

Sheboygan
Member
  Aurora Sheboygan Memorial Medical Center

Two Rivers
Member
  Aurora Medical Center – Manitowoc

Viroqua
Member
  Vernon County Hospital

Waupaca
Member
  Riverside Medical Center

West Allis
Member
  West Allis Memorial Hospital

WYOMING
Buffalo
Member
  Johnson County Healthcare Center

Cody
Member
  West Park Hospital

Gillette
Member
  Campbell County Memorial Hospital

Jackson
Member
  St. John's Medical Center and Living Center

Newcastle
Member
  Weston County Health Services

Sundance
Member
  Crook County Medical Services District

Torrington
Member
  Community Hospital

Wheatland
Member
  Platte County Memorial Hospital Nursing Home

Worland
Member
  Washakie Medical Center

SYNERNET, INC.
222 St John Street, Portland, ME Zip 04102; tel. 207/775–6081; Mr Paul I Davis, III, President

MAINE
Bangor
Affiliate
  St. Joseph Hospital

Bar Harbor
Affiliate
  Mount Desert Island Hospital

Biddeford
Affiliate
  Southern Maine Medical Center

Boothbay Harbor
Owner
  St. Andrews Hospital and Healthcare Center

Brunswick
Affiliate
  Mid Coast Hospital

Damariscotta
Owner
  Miles Memorial Hospital

Farmington
Owner
  Franklin Memorial Hospital

Fort Kent
Affiliate
  Northern Maine Medical Center

Norway
Owner
  Stephens Memorial Hospital

Portland
Owner
  Maine Medical Center
  New England Rehabilitation Hospital of Portland

Rockport
Affiliate
  Penobscot Bay Medical Center

Sanford
Owner
  Henrietta D. Goodall Hospital

Skowhegan
Affiliate
  Redington–Fairview General Hospital

Waterville
Affiliate
  MaineGeneral Medical Center–Waterville Campus

Westbrook
Owner
  Spring Harbor Hospital

THE NEW JERSEY COUNCIL OF TEACHING HOSPITALS
154 West State Street, Trenton, NJ Zip 08608; tel. 609/656–9600; Dr J Richard Goldstein , M.D., President

NEW JERSEY
Camden
Member
  Cooper Health System

Florham Park
Member
  Atlantic Health System

Hamilton
Member
  Robert Wood Johnson University Hospital at Hamilton

Neptune
Member
  Meridian Health

New Brunswick
Member
  Robert Wood Johnson University Hospital

Newark
Member
  University of Medicine and Dentistry of New Jersey–University Hospital

Paterson
Member
  St. Joseph's Regional Medical Center

Phillipsburg
Member
  Warren Hospital

Somerville
Member
  Somerset Medical Center

UNIVERSITY HEALTHSYSTEM CONSORTIUM, INC.
2001 Spring Road, Suite 700, Oak Brook, IL Zip 60523; tel. 630/954–1700

ALABAMA
Birmingham
Member
  University of Alabama Hospital

Mobile
Affiliate
  University of South Alabama Knollwood Park Hospital
Member
  University of South Alabama Medical Center

ARIZONA
Tucson
Member
  University Medical Center

ARKANSAS
Little Rock
Member
  UAMS Medical Center

CALIFORNIA
Downey
Affiliate
  Rancho Los Amigos National Rehabilitation Center

Los Angeles
Member
  LAC–King–Drew Medical Center
  LAC/University of Southern California Medical Center
  University of California Los Angeles Medical Center

Martinez
Affiliate
  Contra Costa Regional Medical Center

Orange
Member
  University of California, Irvine Medical Center

Palo Alto
  Lucile Salter Packard Children's Hospital at Stanford
Member
  Stanford Hospital and Clinics

Sacramento
Member
  University of California, Davis Medical Center

San Diego
Member
  University of California San Diego Medical Center

San Francisco
Affiliate
  University of California–San Francisco Mount Zion Medical Center
Member
  San Francisco General Hospital Medical Center

San Jose
Affiliate
  Santa Clara Valley Medical Center

San Leandro
Affiliate
  Alameda County Medical Center–Fairmont Campus

Santa Monica
Affiliate
  Santa Monica–UCLA Medical Center

Sylmar
Affiliate
  LAC–Olive View–UCLA Medical Center

Section B

Torrance
Member
LAC–Harbor–University of California at Los Angeles Medical Center

Valencia
Affiliate
Henry Mayo Newhall Memorial Hospital

COLORADO
Denver
Affiliate
National Jewish Medical and Research Center
Member
Denver Health Medical Center
University of Colorado Hospital

CONNECTICUT
Farmington
Member
University of Connecticut Health Center, John Dempsey Hospital

New Haven
Member
Yale–New Haven Hospital

DISTRICT OF COLUMBIA
Washington
Member
Howard University Hospital
MedStar–Georgetown Medical Center

FLORIDA
Gainesville
Affiliate
Shands at AGH
Member
Shands at the University of Florida

Lake City
Affiliate
Shands at Lake Shore

Live Oak
Affiliate
Shands at Live Oak

Starke
Affiliate
Shands at Starke

Tampa
Member
Tampa General Hospital

GEORGIA
Atlanta
Wesley Woods Center of Emory University
Member
Emory Crawford Long Hospital
Emory University Hospital

Augusta
Member
Medical College of Georgia Hospital and Clinics

ILLINOIS
Chicago
Affiliate
Louis A. Weiss Memorial Hospital
Member
University of Chicago Hospitals
University of Illinois Medical Center at Chicago

Maywood
Member
Loyola University Medical Center

INDIANA
Indianapolis
Member
Clarian Health Partners
Wishard Health Services

IOWA
Iowa City
Member
University of Iowa Hospitals and Clinics

KANSAS
Kansas City
Member
University of Kansas Hospital

KENTUCKY
Lexington
Member
University of Kentucky Hospital

LOUISIANA
Shreveport
Member
LSU Medical Center–University Hospital

MARYLAND
Baltimore
Maryland General Hospital
Mt. Washington Pediatric Hospital
Affiliate
James Lawrence Kernan Hospital
Member
University of Maryland Medical Center

Glen Burnie
Baltimore Washington Medical Center

MASSACHUSETTS
Boston
Faulkner Hospital
Member
Brigham and Women's Hospital
Massachusetts General Hospital

Clinton
Affiliate
Clinton Hospital

Marlborough
Affiliate
UMass Memorial–Marlborough Hospital

Newton Lower Falls
Newton–Wellesley Hospital

Salem
North Shore Medical Center

MICHIGAN
Ann Arbor
Member
University of Michigan Hospitals and Health Centers

MINNESOTA
Burnsville
Fairview Ridges Hospital

Edina
Fairview Southdale Hospital

Hibbing
Fairview University Medical Center–Mesabi

Minneapolis
Affiliate
Hennepin County Medical Center

MISSOURI
Boonville
Cooper County Memorial Hospital

Columbia
Columbia Regional Hospital
Member
University of Missouri Hospitals and Clinics

Jefferson City
Capital Region Medical Center

Kansas City
Truman Medical Center–Hospital Hill
Truman Medical Center–Lakewood

NEBRASKA
Omaha
Member
Nebraska Medical Center

NEVADA
Las Vegas
Affiliate
University Medical Center

NEW JERSEY
New Brunswick
Member
Robert Wood Johnson University Hospital

Newark
Member
University of Medicine and Dentistry of New Jersey–University Hospital

NEW MEXICO
Albuquerque
Carrie Tingley Hospital
University Hospital

NEW YORK
Albany
Member
Albany Medical Center

Brooklyn
Kings County Hospital Center
Member
SUNY Downstate Medical Center University Hospital

Flushing
Elmhurst Hospital Center

New York
Bellevue Hospital Center
New York–Presbyterian Hospital

Stony Brook
Member
Stony Brook University Hospital

Syracuse
Member
Upstate Medical University

NORTH CAROLINA
Ahoskie
Affiliate
Roanoke–Chowan Hospital

Chapel Hill
Member
University of North Carolina Hospitals

Edenton
Chowan Hospital

Greenville
Member
Pitt County Memorial Hospital

Tarboro
Heritage Hospital

Windsor
Affiliate
Bertie Memorial Hospital

Winston–Salem
Old Vineyard Youth Services
Member
North Carolina Baptist Hospital (Wake Forest University Baptist Medical Center)

OHIO
Bedford
Affiliate
UHHS Bedford Medical Center

Canton
Mercy Medical Center

Chardon
Affiliate
UHHS Geauga Regional Hospital

Cincinnati
Member
University Hospital

Cleveland
St. John West Shore Hospital
St. Vincent Charity Hospital
Member
University Hospitals of Cleveland

Columbus
Member
Ohio State University Medical Center

Conneaut
Affiliate
UHHS Brown Memorial Hospital

Geneva
Affiliate
UHHS–Memorial Hospital of Geneva

Middleburg Heights
Southwest General Health Center

Richmond Heights
UHHS Richmond Heights Hospital

Toledo
Member
Medical College of Ohio Hospitals

Waverly
Affiliate
Pike Community Hospital

Willoughby
Affiliate
Laurelwood Hospital

OREGON

Portland
Member
OHSU Hospital

PENNSYLVANIA

Philadelphia
Affiliate
Friends Behavioral Health System
Presbyterian Medical Center of the University of
Pennsylvania Health System
Thomas Jefferson University Hospital
Member
Hospital of the University of Pennsylvania

Phoenixville
Affiliate
Phoenixville Hospital

Pittsburgh
Member
UPMC Presbyterian

SOUTH CAROLINA

Charleston
Affiliate
Charleston Memorial Hospital
Member
MUSC Medical Center of Medical University of South
Carolina

TENNESSEE

Knoxville
Member
University of Tennessee Medical Center

TEXAS

Baytown
San Jacinto Methodist Hospital

Dallas
St. Paul University Hospital
Member
University of Texas Southwestern Medical Center

Galveston
Member
University of Texas Medical Branch Hospitals

Houston
Methodist Willowbrook Hospital
The Methodist Hospital

Sugar Land
Methodist Sugar Land Hospital

Tyler
Affiliate
University of Texas Health Center at Tyler

UTAH

Salt Lake City
Member
University of Utah Hospitals and Clinics

VIRGINIA

Charlottesville
Member
University of Virginia Medical Center

Richmond
Member
VCU Health System

WASHINGTON

Seattle
Member
Harborview Medical Center
University of Washington Medical Center

WISCONSIN

Antigo
Affiliate
Langlade Memorial Hospital

Madison
Member
University of Wisconsin Hospital and Clinics

Medford
Affiliate
Memorial Health Center

Merrill
Affiliate
Good Samaritan Health Center of Merrill

Milwaukee
Member
Froedtert Memorial Lutheran Hospital

Wausau
Affiliate
Aspirus Wausau Hospital

VANTAGE HEALTH GROUP
265 Conneaut Lake Road, Meadville, PA
Zip 16335; tel. 814/337–0000; Mr David
C Petno, Vice President Business
Development

PENNSYLVANIA

Corry
Member
Corry Memorial Hospital

Du Bois
Member
Du Bois Regional Medical Center

Ellwood City
Member
Ellwood City Hospital

Erie
Member
Millcreek Community Hospital
Saint Vincent Health Center

Greenville
Member
UPMC Horizon

Kane
Member
Kane Community Hospital

Kittanning
Member
Armstrong County Memorial Hospital

Meadville
Member
Meadville Medical Center

Seneca
Member
UPMC Northwest

Titusville
Member
Titusville Area Hospital

Warren
Member
Warren General Hospital

VHA, INC.
220 East Las Colinas Boulevard, Irving,
TX Zip 75039–5500; tel. 972/830–0000;
Mr Curtis W Nonomaque, President and
Chief Executive Officer

ALABAMA

Alabaster
Shelby Baptist Medical Center

Anniston
Partner
Northeast Alabama Regional Medical Center

Athens
Partner
Athens–Limestone Hospital

Atmore
Atmore Community Hospital

Bay Minette
North Baldwin Infirmary

Birmingham
Baptist Montclair
Baptist Princeton
Shareholder
Baptist Health System

Boaz
Marshall Medical Center South

Brewton
D. W. McMillan Memorial Hospital

Carrollton
Pickens County Medical Center

Centre
Baptist Cherokee

Chatom
Washington County Hospital and Nursing Home

Cullman
Partner
Cullman Regional Medical Center

Decatur
Decatur General Hospital

Fairhope
Thomas Hospital

Fayette
Fayette Medical Center

Florence
Coffee Health Group

Fort Payne
Baptist DeKalb Medical Center

Grove Hill
Grove Hill Memorial Hospital

Guntersville
Marshall Medical Center North
Partner
Marshall County Health Care Authority

Hamilton
North Mississippi Medical Center–Hamilton

Huntsville
Huntsville Hospital

Jasper
Walker Baptist Medical Center

Luverne
Crenshaw Community Hospital

Mobile
Mobile Infirmary Medical Center

Montgomery
Baptist Medical Center East
Shareholder
Baptist Medical Center South

Moulton
Lawrence Medical Center

Muscle Shoals
Shoals Hospital

Northport
Northport Medical Center

Opp
Mizell Memorial Hospital

Ozark
Dale Medical Center

Prattville
Prattville Baptist Hospital

Scottsboro
Partner
Jackson County Hospital

Sylacauga
Coosa Valley Medical Center

Talladega
Citizens Baptist Medical Center

Tuscaloosa
DCH Regional Medical Center
Partner
DCH Health System

Union Springs
Bullock County Hospital

ALASKA

Anchorage
Providence Alaska Medical Center

Cordova
Cordova Community Medical Center

Kodiak
Providence Kodiak Island Medical Center

Seward
Providence Seward Medical Center

Valdez
Providence Valdez Medical Center

Wrangell
Wrangell Medical Center

ARIZONA

Bisbee
Copper Queen Community Hospital

Phoenix
Mayo Clinic Hospital

Safford
Mt. Graham Regional Medical Center

Tucson
El Dorado Hospital
TMC HealthCare
Tucson Medical Center

ARKANSAS

Arkadelphia
Baptist Health Medical Center–Arkadelphia

Booneville
Booneville Community Hospital

Clinton
Ozark Health Medical Center

Conway
Partner
Conway Regional Medical Center

Eureka Springs
Eureka Springs Hospital

Fayetteville
Partner
Washington Regional Medical Center

Forrest City
Baptist Memorial Hospital–Forrest City

Fort Smith
Shareholder
Sparks Regional Medical Center

Heber Springs
Baptist Health Medical Center–Heber Springs

Jonesboro
Partner
St. Bernards Medical Center

Little Rock
Baptist Health Medical Center–Little Rock
Shareholder
Baptist Health

North Little Rock
Baptist Health Medical Center – North Little Rock

Paragould
Partner
Arkansas Methodist Medical Center

Piggott
Piggott Community Hospital

Searcy
Partner
White County Medical Center

Walnut Ridge
Lawrence Memorial Hospital

Wynne
CrossRidge Community Hospital

CALIFORNIA

Alameda
Alameda Hospital

Anaheim
Partner
Anaheim Memorial Medical Center

Antioch
Sutter Delta Medical Center

Arcadia
Methodist Hospital of Southern California

Auburn
Sutter Auburn Faith Hospital

Berkeley
Alta Bates Medical Center–Herrick Campus
Alta Bates Summit Medical Center

Burbank
Providence Saint Joseph Medical Center

Burlingame
Mills–Peninsula Health Services

Clovis
Community Medical Center–Clovis

Concord
Mount Diablo Medical Center

Covina
Citrus Valley Health Partners
Citrus Valley Medical Center–Inter–Community
Campus

Crescent City
Sutter Coast Hospital

Davis
Sutter Davis Hospital

El Centro
El Centro Regional Medical Center

Encinitas
Scripps Memorial Hospital–Encinitas

Fountain Valley
Orange Coast Memorial Medical Center

Fresno
Community Medical Center–Fresno
University Medical Center
Shareholder
Community Medical Centers

Glendora
Foothill Presbyterian Hospital–Morris L. Johnston
Memorial

Greenbrae
Marin General Hospital

Jackson
Sutter Amador Hospital

La Jolla
Scripps Green Hospital
Shareholder
Scripps Memorial Hospital–La Jolla

Laguna Hills
Saddleback Memorial Medical Center

Lakeport
Sutter Lakeside Hospital

Lancaster
Partner
Antelope Valley Hospital

Long Beach
Long Beach Memorial Medical Center
Shareholder
Memorial Health Services

Los Angeles
Shareholder
Cedars–Sinai Medical Center

Modesto
Partner
Memorial Hospitals Association

Monterey
Community Hospital of the Monterey Peninsula

Napa
Queen of the Valley Hospital

Newport Beach
Shareholder
Hoag Memorial Hospital Presbyterian

Novato
Novato Community Hospital

Oakland
Alta Bates Summit Medical Center – Summit Campus

Ojai
Ojai Valley Community Hospital

Pasadena
Huntington Memorial Hospital

Pleasanton
ValleyCare Medical Center

Pomona
Partner
Pomona Valley Hospital Medical Center

Roseville
Sutter Roseville Medical Center

Sacramento
Sutter Medical Center, Sacramento
Shareholder
Sutter Health

San Diego
Scripps Health
Scripps Mercy Hospital

San Fernando
Providence Holy Cross Medical Center

San Francisco
California Pacific Medical Center–Davies Campus
Chinese Hospital
St. Luke's Hospital
Shareholder
California Pacific Medical Center

San Pedro
San Pedro Peninsula Hospital

Santa Barbara
Cottage Health System
Goleta Valley Cottage Hospital
Partner
Santa Barbara Cottage Hospital

Santa Cruz
Sutter Maternity and Surgery Center of Santa Cruz

Santa Rosa
Sutter Medical Center of Santa Rosa

Sonoma
Sonoma Valley Hospital

Torrance
Providence–Little Company of Mary Service Area
Partner
Torrance Memorial Medical Center

Tracy
Sutter Tracy Community Hospital

Turlock
Partner
Emanuel Medical Center

Vallejo
Sutter Solano Medical Center

Van Nuys
Partner
Valley Presbyterian Hospital

Ventura
Community Memorial Hospital of San Buenaventura

Walnut Creek
John Muir Medical Center
John Muir/Mount Diablo Health System

Whittier
Partner
Presbyterian Intercommunity Hospital

COLORADO

Alamosa
Partner
San Luis Valley Regional Medical Center

Aspen
Partner
Aspen Valley Hospital District

Boulder
Partner
Boulder Community Hospital

Colorado Springs
Partner
Memorial Hospital

Denver
Exempla Healthcare, Inc.
Exempla Saint Joseph Hospital

Englewood
Craig Hospital

Estes Park
Estes Park Medical Center

Fort Collins
Poudre Valley Hospital

Grand Junction
Partner
Community Hospital

Gunnison
Partner
Gunnison Valley Hospital

Haxtun
Haxtun Hospital District

La Jara
Conejos County Hospital

Lafayette
Exempla Good Samaritan Medical Center

Longmont
Partner
Longmont United Hospital

Rangely
Rangely District Hospital

Steamboat Springs
Partner
Yampa Valley Medical Center

Vail
Shareholder
Vail Valley Medical Center

Wheat Ridge
Shareholder
Exempla Lutheran Medical Center

Yuma
Yuma District Hospital

CONNECTICUT

Bridgeport
Bridgeport Hospital

Danbury
Partner
Danbury Hospital

Greenwich
Partner
   Greenwich Hospital

Hartford
   Connecticut Children's Medical Center
Shareholder
   Hartford Hospital

Manchester
   Eastern Connecticut Health Network
   Manchester Memorial Hospital

Meriden
Partner
   MidState Medical Center

Middletown
Partner
   Middlesex Hospital

New Britain
   Hospital for Special Care
   New Britain General Hospital

New Haven
   Yale New Haven Health System
   Yale–New Haven Hospital

New Milford
   New Milford Hospital

Putnam
   Day Kimball Hospital

Southington
   Bradley Memorial Hospital and Health Center

Stamford
Partner
   Stamford Health System

Torrington
Partner
   The Charlotte Hungerford Hospital

Vernon Rockville
   Rockville General Hospital

Waterbury
Partner
   Waterbury Hospital

DISTRICT OF COLUMBIA

Washington
   MedStar–Georgetown Medical Center
   Washington Hospital Center

FLORIDA

Boca Raton
Partner
   Boca Raton Community Hospital

Boynton Beach
Partner
   Bethesda Memorial Hospital

Cape Coral
   Cape Coral Hospital

Clermont
   South Lake Hospital

Cocoa Beach
   Cape Canaveral Hospital/Health First

Daytona Beach
   Atlantic Medical Center
   Halifax–Fish Community Health
Shareholder
   Halifax Fish Community Health

Fort Myers
Partner
   Lee Memorial Health System

Gainesville
   Shands at AGH
   Shands at the University of Florida
   Shands HealthCare
   Shands Rehab Hospital

Gulf Breeze
   Gulf Breeze Hospital

Inverness
Partner
   Citrus Memorial Hospital

Jacksonville
   Shands Jacksonville Medical Center
   St. Luke's Hospital

Jay
   Jay Hospital

Lake City
   Shands at Lake Shore

Lakeland
Shareholder
   Lakeland Regional Medical Center

Largo
   Sun Coast Hospital

Leesburg
   Leesburg Regional Medical Center

Live Oak
   Shands at Live Oak

Longwood
   Orlando Regional South Seminole Hospital

Melbourne
   Palm Bay Community Hospital
Shareholder
   Holmes Regional Medical Center

New Smyrna Beach
   Bert Fish Medical Center

Ocala
Partner
   Munroe Regional Medical Center

Ocoee
   Health Central

Orlando
   Orlando Regional Medical Center
Shareholder
   Orlando Regional Healthcare

Panama City
   Bay Medical Center

Pensacola
   Baptist Hospital
Shareholder
   Baptist Health Care Corporation

Rockledge
   First Health, Inc.

Saint Cloud
   St. Cloud Hospital

Sarasota
Partner
   Sarasota Memorial Hospital

Starke
   Shands at Starke

Tallahassee
Shareholder
   Tallahassee Memorial HealthCare

Tampa
Partner
   University Community Hospital

Tarpon Springs
   Helen Ellis Memorial Hospital

The Villages
   The Villages Regional Hospital

Titusville
Partner
   Parrish Medical Center

GEORGIA

Albany
   Phoebe Putney Health Systems
Partner
   Phoebe Putney Memorial Hospital

Americus
   Sumter Regional Hospital

Athens
Partner
   Athens Regional Medical Center

Atlanta
Partner
   Northside Hospital
Shareholder
   Piedmont Hospital

Augusta
   University Health Care System

Austell
   WellStar Cobb Hospital

Blakely
   Early Memorial Hospital

Cairo
   Grady General Hospital

Camilla
   Mitchell County Hospital

Chatsworth
   Murray Medical Center

Cochran
   Bleckley Memorial Hospital

Columbus
   Columbus Regional Healthcare System
   Columbus Specialty Hospital
Partner
   The Medical Center

Cordele
   Crisp Regional Hospital

Cuthbert
   Southwest Georgia Regional Medical Center

Dallas
   WellStar Paulding Hospital

Dalton
Partner
   Hamilton Medical Center

Decatur
Partner
   DeKalb Medical Center

Douglas
   Coffee Regional Medical Center

Douglasville
   WellStar Douglas Hospital

Fitzgerald
   Dorminy Medical Center

Gainesville
   Northeast Georgia Medical Center

Hawkinsville
   Taylor Regional Hospital

Homerville
   Clinch Memorial Hospital

Jasper
   Piedmont Mountainside Hospital

Lakeland
   Louis Smith Memorial Hospital

Lawrenceville
Partner
   Gwinnett Hospital System

Macon
Partner
   Medical Center of Central Georgia

Marietta
   WellStar Health System
   WellStar Windy Hill Hospital
Partner
   WellStar Kennestone Hospital

Moultrie
   Colquitt Regional Medical Center

Newnan
   Newnan Hospital East

Perry
   Perry Hospital

Quitman
   Brooks County Hospital

Riverdale
Partner
   Southern Regional Medical Center

Rome
   Specialty Hospital
Partner
   Floyd Medical Center

Sylvester
   Phoebe Worth Medical Center

Thomasville
Partner
   Archbold Medical Center
   John D. Archbold Memorial Hospital

Tifton
   Tift Regional Medical Center

Valdosta
Partner
   South Georgia Medical Center

Warner Robins
   Houston Medical Center

HAWAII

Honolulu
   Queen's Medical Center

Kaunakakai
   Molokai General Hospital

IDAHO

American Falls
Harms Memorial Hospital District

Arco
Lost Rivers District Hospital

Blackfoot
Bingham Memorial Hospital

Boise
Idaho Elks Rehabilitation Hospital
Shareholder
St. Luke's Regional Medical Center

Bonners Ferry
Boundary Community Hospital

Coeur D'Alene
Partner
Kootenai Medical Center

Emmett
Walter Knox Memorial Hospital

Gooding
Gooding County Memorial Hospital

Grangeville
Syringa General Hospital

Ketchum
St. Luke's Wood River Medical Center

Malad City
Oneida County Hospital

Montpelier
Bear Lake Memorial Hospital

Mountain Home
Elmore Medical Center

Pocatello
Portneuf Medical Center

Preston
Franklin County Medical Center

Rupert
Minidoka Memorial Hospital and Extended Care
Facility

Sandpoint
Partner
Bonner General Hospital

Twin Falls
Partner
Magic Valley Regional Medical Center

Weiser
Weiser Memorial Hospital

ILLINOIS

Arlington Heights
Partner
Northwest Community Healthcare

Belleville
Partner
Memorial Hospital

Canton
Graham Hospital Extended Care Facility

Carbondale
Memorial Hospital of Carbondale
Partner
Southern Illinois Hospital Services

Chester
Memorial Hospital

Chicago
Partner
Swedish Covenant Hospital
Shareholder
Northwestern Memorial Hospital

De Kalb
Kishwaukee Health System
Partner
Kishwaukee Community Hospital

Decatur
Decatur Memorial Hospital

Dixon
Partner
Katherine Shaw Bethea Hospital

Elgin
Partner
Sherman Hospital

Elmhurst
Partner
Elmhurst Memorial Hospital

Eureka
Eureka Community Hospital

Evanston
Evanston Northwestern Healthcare

Evergreen Park
Partner
Little Company of Mary Hospital and Health Care
Centers

Flora
Clay County Hospital

Freeport
Partner
FHN Memorial Hospital

Geneseo
Hammond–Henry Hospital

Geneva
Delnor–Community Hospital

Greenville
Greenville Regional Hospital

Harvey
Shareholder
Ingalls Memorial Hospital

Herrin
Herrin Hospital

Jacksonville
Partner
Passavant Area Hospital

Jerseyville
Jersey Community Hospital

Joliet
Partner
Silver Cross Hospital

Kankakee
Partner
Riverside Medical Center

Lake Forest
Partner
Lake Forest Hospital

Lincoln
Abraham Lincoln Memorial Hospital

Macomb
Partner
McDonough District Hospital

Maryville
Partner
Anderson Hospital

Mendota
Mendota Community Hospital

Monticello
John and Mary Kirby Hospital

Murphysboro
St. Joseph Memorial Hospital

Naperville
Edward Hospital

Normal
Partner
BroMenn Healthcare System

Peoria
Partner
Proctor Hospital

Pittsfield
Illini Community Hospital

Quincy
Partner
Blessing Hospital

Salem
Salem Township Hospital

Sandwich
Valley West Community Hospital

Shelbyville
Shelby Memorial Hospital

Springfield
Shareholder
Memorial Medical Center

Taylorville
St. Vincent Memorial Hospital

Vandalia
Fayette County Hospital

INDIANA

Anderson
Community Hospital of Anderson and Madison County

Batesville
Margaret Mary Community Hospital

Bedford
Bedford Regional Medical Center

Bloomington
Partner
Bloomington Hospital

Clinton
West Central Community Hospital

Columbia City
Parkview Whitley Hospital

Columbus
Partner
Columbus Regional Hospital

Danville
Partner
Hendricks Regional Health

Elkhart
Partner
Elkhart General Hospital

Evansville
Shareholder
Deaconess Hospital

Fort Wayne
Parkview Health
Partner
Parkview Hospital

Goshen
Goshen General Hospital

Greenfield
Hancock Memorial Hospital and Health Services

Greensburg
Decatur County Memorial Hospital

Hartford City
Blackford Community Hospital

Huntington
Parkview Huntington Hospital

Indianapolis
Community Hospital East
Community Hospital North
Indiana Heart Hospital
Methodist Hospital of Indiana
Westview Hospital
Shareholder
Clarian Health Partners
Community Health Network

Kendallville
Parkview Noble Hospital

Kokomo
Partner
Howard Regional Health System

La Porte
Partner
La Porte Regional Health System

Lafayette
Greater Lafayette Health Services
Partner
Lafayette Home Hospital

LaGrange
Parkview LaGrange Hospital

Madison
Partner
King's Daughters' Hospital and Health Services

Marion
Partner
Marion General Hospital

Martinsville
Morgan Hospital and Medical Center

Muncie
Cardinal Health System
Shareholder
Ball Memorial Hospital

New Albany
Partner
Floyd Memorial Hospital and Health Services

New Castle
Henry County Memorial Hospital

Newburgh
The Women's Hospital
Noblesville
Partner
Riverview Hospital
Paoli
Bloomington Hospital of Orange County
Portland
Jay County Hospital
Richmond
Partner
Reid Hospital and Health Care Services
Shelbyville
Major Hospital
South Bend
Madison Center and Hospital
Memorial Hospital of South Bend
Terre Haute
Partner
Union Hospital
Tipton
Tipton County Memorial Hospital
Valparaiso
Partner
Porter–Valparaiso Hospital Campus
Vincennes
Partner
Good Samaritan Hospital

IOWA
Atlantic
Shareholder
Cass County Memorial Hospital
Council Bluffs
Shareholder
Jennie Edmundson Memorial Hospital
Decorah
Winneshiek Medical Center
Hamburg
Grape Community Hospital
Harlan
Partner
Shelby County Myrtue Memorial Hospital
Keokuk
Shareholder
Keokuk Area Hospital
Le Mars
Partner
Floyd Valley Hospital/Avera Health
Muscatine
Unity Hospital
Onawa
Partner
Burgess Health Center
Orange City
Orange City Health System
Red Oak
Shareholder
Montgomery County Memorial Hospital
Rock Rapids
Merrill Pioneer Community Hospital
Sheldon
Northwest Iowa Health Center
Sioux City
Shareholder
St. Luke's Regional Medical Center
West Union
Palmer Lutheran Health Center

KANSAS
Abilene
Memorial Hospital
Atchison
Shareholder
Atchison Hospital
Atwood
Rawlins County Health Center
Belleville
Republic County Hospital
Beloit
Mitchell County Hospital

Clay Center
Clay County Medical Center
Colby
Shareholder
Citizens Medical Center
Coldwater
Comanche County Hospital
Concordia
Cloud County Health Center
Dighton
Lane County Hospital
Ellinwood
Ellinwood District Hospital
Ellsworth
Ellsworth County Medical Center
Fredonia
Fredonia Regional Hospital
Garnett
Anderson County Hospital
Goodland
Goodland Regional Medical Center
Greensburg
Kiowa County Memorial Hospital
Hays
Shareholder
Hays Medical Center
Herington
Herington Municipal Hospital
Hiawatha
Partner
Hiawatha Community Hospital
Hill City
Graham County Hospital
Hillsboro
Hillsboro Community Medical Center
Hoisington
Clara Barton Hospital
Hoxie
Sheridan County Health Complex
Hutchinson
Shareholder
Hutchinson Hospital Corporation
Junction City
Geary Community Hospital
Kinsley
Edwards County Hospital and Healthcare Center
La Crosse
Rush County Memorial Hospital
Lawrence
Lawrence Memorial Hospital
Leavenworth
Cushing Memorial Hospital
Leoti
Wichita County Health Center
Liberal
Shareholder
Southwest Medical Center
Lincoln
Lincoln County Hospital
Lindsborg
Lindsborg Community Hospital
Lyons
Rice County Hospital District Number One
Mankato
Jewell County Hospital
McPherson
Memorial Hospital
Medicine Lodge
Medicine Lodge Memorial Hospital
Minneapolis
Ottawa County Health Center
Minneola
Minneola District Hospital
Ness City
Ness County Hospital
Norton
Norton County Hospital
Oakley
Logan County Hospital
Osborne
Osborne County Memorial Hospital

Overland Park
Saint Luke's South Hospital
Parsons
Partner
Labette County Medical Center
Phillipsburg
Phillips County Hospital
Shareholder
Great Plains Health Alliance, Inc.
Pittsburg
Mt. Carmel Regional Medical Center
Plainville
Rooks County Health Center
Pratt
Shareholder
Pratt Regional Medical Center
Quinter
Gove County Medical Center
Ransom
Grisell Memorial Hospital District One
Russell
Russell Regional Hospital
Sabetha
Sabetha Community Hospital
Saint Francis
Cheyenne County Hospital
Salina
Partner
Salina Regional Health Center
Smith Center
Smith County Memorial Hospital
Stafford
Stafford District Hospital
Topeka
Shareholder
Stormont–Vail HealthCare
Tribune
Greeley County Health Services
Wakeeney
Trego County–Lemke Memorial Hospital
Wichita
Partner
Via Christi Health System

KENTUCKY
Florence
St. Luke Hospital West
Fort Thomas
Partner
St. Luke Hospital East
Harlan
Harlan ARH Hospital
Hazard
Hazard ARH Regional Medical Center
Lexington
Appalachian Regional Healthcare
McDowell
McDowell ARH Hospital
Middlesboro
Middlesboro Appalachian Regional Hospital
Pikeville
Pikeville Medical Center
South Williamson
Williamson ARH Hospital
West Liberty
Morgan County Appalachian Regional Hospital
Whitesburg
Whitesburg Appalachian Regional Hospital

LOUISIANA
Amite
Hood Memorial Hospital
Baton Rouge
Franciscan Missionaries of Our Lady Health System, Inc.
Member
Our Lady of the Lake Regional Medical Center
Partner
Woman's Hospital
Bossier City
Willis–Knighton Bossier Health Center
Bunkie
Bunkie General Hospital

Cameron
South Cameron Memorial Hospital

Church Point
Acadia–St. Landry Hospital

Columbia
Citizens Medical Center

Covington
Partner
St. Tammany Parish Hospital

Crowley
Partner
American Legion Hospital

De Ridder
Partner
Beauregard Memorial Hospital

Ferriday
Riverland Medical Center

Franklinton
Riverside Medical Center

Gonzales
St. Elizabeth Hospital

Greensburg
St. Helena Parish Hospital

Jennings
Jennings American Legion Hospital

Jonesboro
Jackson Parish Hospital

Lafayette
Partner
Our Lady of Lourdes Regional Medical Center

Lake Charles
Partner
Lake Charles Memorial Hospital

Mansfield
De Soto Regional Health System

Monroe
Partner
St. Francis Medical Center

Napoleonville
Assumption Community Hospital

Natchitoches
Natchitoches Parish Hospital

New Iberia
Iberia Medical Center

New Orleans
Shareholder
Ochsner Clinic Foundation

New Roads
Pointe Coupee General Hospital

Oak Grove
West Carroll Memorial Hospital

Olla
Hardtner Medical Center

Ruston
Partner
Lincoln General Hospital

Shreveport
Willis–Knighton Health System
Willis–Knighton Pierremont Health Center
Willis–Knighton South – The Center for Women's
Health
Shareholder
Willis–Knighton Medical Center

Slidell
Partner
Slidell Memorial Hospital and Medical Center

Sulphur
Partner
West Calcasieu Cameron Hospital

Vivian
North Caddo Medical Center

MAINE

Augusta
MaineGeneral Medical Center–Augusta Campus

Bangor
Acadia Hospital
Eastern Maine Medical Center
Partner
Eastern Maine Healthcare

Bar Harbor
Mount Desert Island Hospital

Biddeford
Shareholder
Southern Maine Medical Center

Blue Hill
Blue Hill Memorial Hospital

Bridgton
Bridgton Hospital

Brunswick
Mid Coast Hospital

Damariscotta
Miles Memorial Hospital

Dover–Foxcroft
Mayo Regional Hospital

Ellsworth
Maine Coast Memorial Hospital

Greenville
Charles A. Dean Memorial Hospital and Nursing Home

Houlton
Houlton Regional Hospital

Lewiston
Shareholder
Central Maine Medical Center

Norway
Stephens Memorial Hospital

Pittsfield
Sebasticook Valley Hospital

Portland
Shareholder
Maine Medical Center

Presque Isle
Aroostook Medical Center

Rockport
Penobscot Bay Medical Center

Rumford
Rumford Hospital

Waterville
Inland Hospital
Shareholder
MaineGeneral Medical Center–Waterville Campus

Westbrook
Spring Harbor Hospital

York
York Hospital

MARYLAND

Baltimore
Franklin Square Hospital Center
Good Samaritan Hospital of Maryland
Harbor Hospital Center
Union Memorial Hospital

Bel Air
Upper Chesapeake Medical Center
Partner
Upper Chesapeake Health System

Cambridge
Dorchester General Hospital

Columbia
MedStar Health

Easton
Shore Health System
Partner
Memorial Hospital at Easton Maryland

Havre De Grace
Harford Memorial Hospital

Prince Frederick
Calvert Memorial Hospital

MASSACHUSETTS

Belmont
McLean Hospital

Beverly
Partner
Beverly Hospital

Boston
Brigham and Women's Hospital
Faulkner Hospital
Massachusetts General Hospital
Spaulding Rehabilitation Hospital
Partner
Massachusetts Eye and Ear Infirmary
Shareholder
Partners HealthCare System, Inc.
Tufts–New England Medical Center

Burlington
Partner
Lahey Clinic Hospital

Cambridge
Partner
Mount Auburn Hospital

Clinton
Clinton Hospital

Concord
Partner
Emerson Hospital

East Sandwich
Rehabilitation Hospital of the Cape and Islands

Falmouth
Falmouth Hospital

Gardner
Partner
Heywood Hospital

Hyannis
Cape Cod Healthcare, Inc.
Partner
Cape Cod Hospital

Lawrence
Owner
Lawrence General Hospital

Leominster
Partner
Health Alliance Hospitals

Lowell
Partner
Lowell General Hospital

Marlborough
UMass Memorial–Marlborough Hospital

Melrose
Hallmark Health System
Partner
Melrose–Wakefield Hospital

Nantucket
Nantucket Cottage Hospital

Newton Lower Falls
Newton–Wellesley Hospital

Northampton
Cooley Dickinson Hospital

Palmer
Wing Memorial Hospital and Medical Centers

Plymouth
Jordan Hospital

Salem
North Shore Medical Center
Shaughnessy–Kaplan Rehabilitation Hospital

South Weymouth
Partner
South Shore Hospital

Southbridge
Partner
Harrington Memorial Hospital

Worcester
UMass Memorial Health Care, Inc.

MICHIGAN

Adrian
Lenawee Health Alliance – Bixby Campus

Allegan
Allegan General Hospital

Bad Axe
Huron Medical Center

Caro
Caro Community Hospital

Cass City
Hills and Dales General Hospital

Cheboygan
Cheboygan Memorial Hospital

Dearborn
Member
Oakwood Healthcare, Inc.
Partner
Oakwood Hospital and Medical Center–Dearborn

Detroit
St. John Detroit Riverview Hospital – Northeast
Campus
Partner
St. John Hospital and Medical Center

East China
St. John River District Hospital
Fremont
Gerber Memorial Health Services
Gaylord
Otsego Memorial Hospital
Grand Haven
North Ottawa Community Hospital
Grand Rapids
Mary Free Bed Rehabilitation Hospital
Metropolitan Hospital
Spectrum Health
Greenville
Spectrum Health–United Memorial
Harrison Township
St. John North Shores Hospital
Hastings
Pennock Hospital
Holland
Partner
Holland Hospital
Ionia
Ionia County Memorial Hospital
Jackson
Foote Health System
Kalamazoo
Partner
Bronson Healthcare Group, Inc.
Bronson Methodist Hospital
Ludington
Memorial Medical Center of West Michigan
Madison Heights
St. John Oakland Hospital
Marshall
Oaklawn Hospital
Monroe
Partner
Mercy Memorial Hospital System
Muskegon
Partner
Hackley Health
Niles
Lakeland Hospital–Niles
Owosso
Partner
Memorial Healthcare
Petoskey
Northern Michigan Regional Health System
Port Huron
Port Huron Hospital
Partner
Blue Water Health Services Corporation
Reed City
Spectrum Health–Reed City Campus
Royal Oak
Shareholder
William Beaumont Hospital–Royal Oak
Saginaw
Covenant Medical Center
Saint Joseph
Lakeland Hospital–St. Joseph
Sandusky
McKenzie Memorial Hospital
Shelby
Hackley Lakeshore Hospital
South Haven
South Haven Community Hospital
Southfield
Providence Hospital and Medical Center
Taylor
Oakwood Heritage Hospital
Tecumseh
Lenawee Health Alliance–Herrick Campus
Trenton
Oakwood Southshore Medical Center
Troy
William Beaumont Hospital–Troy
Vicksburg
Bronson Vicksburg Hospital
Warren
St. John Macomb Hospital

Wayne
Oakwood Annapolis Hospital
West Branch
Partner
West Branch Regional Medical Center
Zeeland
Zeeland Community Hospital

MINNESOTA

Albert Lea
Albert Lea Medical Center
Arlington
Sibley Medical Center
Austin
Austin Medical Center
Bemidji
Partner
North Country Regional Hospital
Benson
Swift County–Benson Hospital
Blue Earth
United Hospital District
Buffalo
Buffalo Hospital
Cambridge
Cambridge Medical Center
Canby
Sioux Valley Canby Campus
Coon Rapids
Mercy Hospital
Duluth
Partner
St. Luke's Hospital
Fairmont
Fairmont Medical Center–Mayo Health System
Fergus Falls
Partner
Lake Region Healthcare Corporation
Fosston
First Care Medical Services
Fridley
Unity Hospital
Hallock
Kittson Memorial Healthcare Center
Hutchinson
Hutchinson Area Health Care
Jackson
Jackson Medical Center
Lake City
Lake City Medical Center–Mayo
Long Prairie
Long Prairie Memorial Hospital and Home
Luverne
Sioux Valley Luverne Medical Center
Madelia
Madelia Community Hospital
Mahnomen
Mahnomen Health Center
Mankato
Partner
Immanuel St. Joseph's–Mayo Health System
Melrose
Melrose Area Hospital – Centra Care
Minneapolis
Abbott Northwestern Hospital
Shareholder
Allina Hospitals & Clinics
Morris
Stevens Community Medical Center
New Ulm
New Ulm Medical Center
Ortonville
Ortonville Area Health Services
Owatonna
Owatonna Hospital
Paynesville
Paynesville Area Health Care System
Perham
Perham Memorial Hospital and Home
Redwood Falls
Redwood Area Hospital

Robbinsdale
North Memorial Health Care
Rochester
Mayo Foundation
Rochester Methodist Hospital
Saint Marys Hospital
Roseau
Roseau Area Hospital and Homes
Saint Cloud
CentraCare Health System
Partner
St. Cloud Hospital
Saint James
St. James Health Services
Saint Paul
Bethesda Rehabilitation Hospital
St. Joseph's Hospital
United Hospital
Shareholder
HealthEast Care System
Saint Peter
St. Peter Community Hospital
Shakopee
St. Francis Regional Medical Center
Slayton
Murray County Memorial Hospital
Springfield
Springfield Medical Center–Mayo Health System
Tracy
Tracy Area Medical Services
Waconia
Partner
Ridgeview Medical Center
Warren
North Valley Health Center
Waseca
Waseca Medical Center
Westbrook
Westbrook Health Center
Willmar
Partner
Rice Memorial Hospital
Windom
Windom Area Hospital
Worthington
Worthington Regional Hospital

MISSISSIPPI

Batesville
Tri–Lakes Medical Center
Booneville
Baptist Memorial Hospital–Booneville
Calhoun City
Calhoun Health Services
Columbus
Baptist Memorial Hospital–Golden Triangle
Corinth
Magnolia Regional Health Center
Eupora
North Mississippi Medical Center–Eupora
Greenville
Delta Regional Medical Center
The King's Daughters Hospital
Greenwood
Partner
Greenwood Leflore Hospital
Gulfport
Partner
Memorial Hospital at Gulfport
Hattiesburg
Partner
Forrest General Hospital
Jackson
Partner
St. Dominic–Jackson Memorial Hospital
McComb
Partner
Southwest Mississippi Regional Medical Center
Meridian
Partner
Jeff Anderson Regional Medical Center

Monticello
Lawrence County Hospital

New Albany
Baptist Memorial Hospital–Union County

Oxford
Baptist Memorial Hospital–North Mississippi

Pascagoula
Singing River Hospital System

Pontotoc
North Mississippi Medical Center–Pontotoc Hospital
and Nursing Home

Ripley
Tippah County Hospital

Southaven
Baptist Memorial Hospital–Desoto

Starkville
Oktibbeha County Hospital

Tylertown
Walthall County General Hospital

West Point
North Mississippi Medical Center–West Point

MISSOURI

Bolivar
Partner
Citizens Memorial Hospital

Branson
Partner
Skaggs Community Health Center

Brookfield
General John J. Pershing Memorial Hospital

Cameron
Partner
Cameron Regional Medical Center

Cape Girardeau
Partner
Saint Francis Medical Center

Carthage
Partner
McCune–Brooks Hospital

Chillicothe
Hedrick Medical Center

Columbia
Boone Hospital Center

Crystal City
Jefferson Memorial Hospital

Florissant
Northwest HealthCare

Joplin
Freeman Health System
Freeman Hospital East
Partner
Freeman Hospital West

Kansas City
Crittenton Children's Center
Saint Luke's Northland Hospital
Shareholder
Saint Luke's Health System
Saint Luke's Hospital of Kansas City

Lamar
Barton County Memorial Hospital

Liberty
Partner
Liberty Hospital

Marshall
Fitzgibbon Hospital

Monett
Cox Monett Hospital

Neosho
Freeman Neosho Hospital

Potosi
Washington County Memorial Hospital

Saint Louis
Barnes–Jewish Hospital
Barnes–Jewish West County Hospital
Christian Hospital
St. Louis Children's Hospital
Shareholder
BJC HealthCare

Saint Peters
Barnes–Jewish St. Peters Hospital

Salem
Salem Memorial District Hospital

Sikeston
Missouri Delta Medical Center

Smithville
Saint Luke's Northland Hospital–Smithville Campus

Springfield
CoxHealth
Lester E. Cox Medical Center North
Shareholder
Lester E. Cox Medical Centers

Ste Genevieve
Ste. Genevieve County Memorial Hospital

Sullivan
Missouri Baptist Hospital–Sullivan

Town and Country
Missouri Baptist Medical Center

Trenton
Wright Memorial Hospital

MONTANA

Big Timber
Pioneer Medical Center

Billings
Partner
Deaconess Billings Clinic

Bozeman
Partner
Bozeman Deaconess Hospital

Forsyth
Rosebud Health Care Center

Glasgow
Frances Mahon Deaconess Hospital

Glendive
Partner
Glendive Medical Center

Great Falls
Benefis Healthcare

Hamilton
Partner
Marcus Daly Memorial Hospital

Helena
Partner
St. Peter's Hospital

Livingston
Livingston Memorial Hospital

Missoula
Partner
Community Medical Center

Plentywood
Sheridan Memorial Hospital

Red Lodge
Beartooth Hospital and Health Center

Ronan
Partner
St. Luke Community Hospital

Scobey
Daniels Memorial Hospital

Sidney
Partner
Sidney Health Center

NEBRASKA

Alliance
Box Butte General Hospital

Alma
Harlan County Health System

Atkinson
West Holt Memorial Hospital

Beatrice
Partner
Beatrice Community Hospital and Health Center

Bridgeport
Morrill County Community Hospital

Broken Bow
Jennie M. Melham Memorial Medical Center

Columbus
Partner
Columbus Community Hospital

Crete
Crete Area Medical Center

David City
Butler County Health Care Center

Falls City
Community Medical Center

Franklin
Franklin County Memorial Hospital

Hastings
Partner
Mary Lanning Memorial Hospital

Lexington
Partner
Tri–County Area Hospital

Lincoln
BryanLGH Medical Center
Partner
Madonna Rehabilitation Hospital

Lynch
Niobrara Valley Hospital

McCook
Partner
Community Hospital

Minden
Kearney County Health Services

Neligh
Antelope Memorial Hospital

Norfolk
Partner
Faith Regional Health Services

Omaha
Shareholder
Nebraska Methodist Hospital

Oshkosh
Garden County Hospital

Osmond
Osmond General Hospital

Plainview
Plainview Area Health System

Scottsbluff
Partner
Regional West Medical Center

Sidney
Partner
Memorial Health Center

Tilden
Tilden Community Hospital

York
Partner
York General Health Care Services

NEW HAMPSHIRE

Claremont
Valley Regional Hospital

Colebrook
Upper Connecticut Valley Hospital

Concord
Concord Hospital

Dover
Partner
Wentworth–Douglass Hospital

Keene
Partner
Cheshire Medical Center

Lancaster
Weeks Medical Center

Lebanon
Alice Peck Day Memorial Hospital
Mary Hitchcock Memorial Hospital

Nashua
Partner
Southern New Hampshire Medical Center

New London
New London Hospital

Peterborough
Monadnock Community Hospital

Rochester
Partner
Frisbie Memorial Hospital

NEW JERSEY

Bayonne
Bayonne Medical Center

Brick Township
  Ocean Medical Center
Bridgeton
  South Jersey Health System
  South Jersey Healthcare
Camden
Partner
  Our Lady of Lourdes Medical Center
East Orange
  East Orange Division
Edison
  Solaris Health System
Flemington
Partner
  Hunterdon Medical Center
Hackettstown
Partner
  Hackettstown Community Hospital
Neptune
  Jersey Shore University Medical Center
  Meridian Health
Newton
Partner
  Newton Memorial Hospital
North Plainfield
Partner
  Muhlenberg Regional Medical Center
Phillipsburg
Partner
  Warren Hospital
Pompton Plains
Partner
  Chilton Memorial Hospital
Red Bank
  Riverview Medical Center
Ridgewood
  Valley Hospital
Somers Point
Partner
  Shore Memorial Hospital
Trenton
  Capital Health System
  Capital Health System at Fuld
  Capital Health System at Mercer
Vineland
  Regional Medical Center
Willingboro
  Lourdes Medical Center of Burlington County
Woodbury
Partner
  Underwood–Memorial Hospital

NEW MEXICO
Artesia
  Artesia General Hospital
Farmington
Partner
  San Juan Regional Medical Center
Gallup
Partner
  Rehoboth McKinley Christian Hospital
Santa Fe
  St. Vincent Hospital
NEW YORK
Binghamton
Shareholder
  United Health Services Hospitals–Binghamton
Bronxville
  Lawrence Hospital Center
Brooklyn
  New York Community Hospital
  Wyckoff Heights Medical Center
Partner
  Brooklyn Hospital Center
Buffalo
  Roswell Park Cancer Institute
Cobleskill
Partner
  Bassett Hospital of Schoharie County
Cooperstown
Partner
  Mary Imogene Bassett Hospital

Corning
  Corning Hospital
Elmira
  St. Joseph's Hospital
Flushing
  New York Hospital Medical Center of Queens
Geneva
Partner
  Geneva General Hospital
Hamilton
  Community Memorial Hospital
Ithaca
Partner
  Cayuga Medical Center at Ithaca
Jamestown
  Woman's Christian Association Hospital
Little Falls
  Little Falls Hospital
Malone
  Alice Hyde Medical Center
Middletown
  Orange Regional Medical Center
Mount Kisco
Partner
  Northern Westchester Hospital
New York
  New York–Presbyterian Hospital
  NYU Downtown Hospital
  Rockefeller University Hospital
Shareholder
  New York–Presbyterian/Columbia University Medical
    Center
Norwich
  Chenango Memorial Hospital
Ogdensburg
  Claxton–Hepburn Medical Center
Penn Yan
  Soldiers and Sailors Memorial Hospital of Yates
    County
Potsdam
  Canton–Potsdam Hospital
Rochester
  Park Ridge Hospital
  Strong Memorial Hospital
  Strong Memorial Hospital of the University of
    Rochester
Partner
  Highland Hospital of Rochester
Sleepy Hollow
  Phelps Memorial Hospital Center
Syracuse
  Community–General Hospital of Greater Syracuse
Partner
  Crouse Hospital
Utica
  Faxton–St. Luke's Healthcare
Walton
  Delaware Valley Hospital
Watertown
Partner
  Samaritan Medical Center
White Plains
Partner
  White Plains Hospital Center

NORTH CAROLINA
Ahoskie
  Roanoke–Chowan Hospital
Cary
  WakeMed Cary Hospital
Charlotte
  Carolinas Medical Center
  Carolinas Medical Center–Mercy
  Carolinas Medical Center–Pineville
  Carolinas Medical Center–University
  Presbyterian Hospital
  Presbyterian–Orthopaedic Hospital
Shareholder
  Carolinas HealthCare System
Concord
Shareholder
  NorthEast Medical Center

Edenton
  Chowan Hospital
Greensboro
  Moses Cone Health System
Greenville
Shareholder
  Pitt County Memorial Hospital
High Point
Shareholder
  High Point Regional Health System
Huntersville
  Presbyterian Hospital Huntersville
Kings Mountain
  Kings Mountain Hospital
Lincolnton
  Lincoln Medical Center
Matthews
  Presbyterian Hospital–Matthews
Monroe
  Union Regional Medical Center
Morganton
  Blue Ridge HealthCare
  Grace Hospital
Nags Head
  The Outer Banks Hospital
New Bern
Shareholder
  Craven Regional Medical Center
North Wilkesboro
  Wilkes Regional Medical Center
Raleigh
  WakeMed
Partner
  WakeMed Raleigh Campus
Reidsville
  Annie Penn Hospital
Rocky Mount
Partner
  Nash Health Care Systems
Salisbury
Partner
  Rowan Regional Medical Center
Shelby
  Cleveland Regional Medical Center
Tarboro
  Heritage Hospital
Thomasville
Partner
  Thomasville Medical Center
Valdese
  Valdese General Hospital
Wadesboro
  Anson Community Hospital
Windsor
  Bertie Memorial Hospital
Winston–Salem
  Forsyth Medical Center
  Medical Park Hospital
  Novant Health
NORTH DAKOTA
Bismarck
Partner
  MedCenter One
Fargo
  MeritCare Health System
  MeritCare Medical Center
Grafton
  Unity Medical Center
Grand Forks
Partner
  Altru Health System
Hillsboro
  Hillsboro Medical Center
Jamestown
Partner
  Jamestown Hospital
Minot
  Trinity Health

OHIO

Akron
Akron General Health System
Shareholder
Akron General Medical Center

Athens
O'Bleness Memorial Hospital

Bellaire
Belmont Community Hospital

Bowling Green
Bowling Green University Medical Center

Cambridge
Partner
Southeastern Ohio Regional Medical Center

Cincinnati
Health Alliance of Greater Cincinnati
Jewish Hospital
Shareholder
Christ Hospital

Cleveland
University Hospitals of Cleveland

Columbus
Doctors Hospital
Grant Medical Center
Riverside Methodist Hospital
Member
OhioHealth

Dayton
Miami Valley Hospital
Partner
Good Samaritan Hospital

Defiance
Defiance Regional Medical Center

Delaware
Grady Memorial Hospital

Dover
Partner
Union Hospital

Findlay
Blanchard Valley Health Association

Fostoria
Fostoria Community Hospital

Fremont
Partner
Memorial Hospital

Galion
Galion Community Hospital

Hamilton
Partner
Fort Hamilton Hospital

Kenton
Hardin Memorial Hospital

Lima
Partner
Lima Memorial Health System

Lodi
Lodi Community Hospital

Mansfield
MedCentral Health System

Marion
Marion General Hospital

Massillon
Massillon Community Hospital

Maumee
Partner
St. Luke's Hospital

Middletown
Partner
Middletown Regional Hospital

Mount Gilead
Morrow County Hospital

Nelsonville
Doctors Hospital Nelsonville

Newark
Partner
Licking Memorial Hospital

Norwalk
Fisher–Titus Medical Center

Oregon
Bay Park Community Hospital

Painesville
Partner
Lake Hospital System

Portsmouth
Southern Ohio Medical Center

Ravenna
Robinson Memorial Hospital

Steubenville
Partner
Trinity Health System

Sylvania
Flower Hospital

Toledo
ProMedica Health System
Shareholder
The Toledo Hospital

Troy
Partner
Upper Valley Medical Center

Warren
Forum Hillside Rehabilitation Hospital

Wauseon
Fulton County Health Center

Xenia
Partner
Greene Memorial Hospital

Youngstown
Forum Health
Western Reserve Care System

Zanesville
Partner
Genesis HealthCare System

OKLAHOMA

Ada
Partner
Valley View Regional Hospital

Altus
Partner
Jackson County Memorial Hospital

Blackwell
Integris Blackwell Regional Hospital

Carnegie
Carnegie Tri–County Municipal Hospital

Chickasha
Partner
Grady Memorial Hospital

Clinton
Integris Clinton Regional Hospital

Duncan
Partner
Duncan Regional Hospital

El Reno
Parkview Hospital

Elk City
Great Plains Regional Medical Center

Enid
Integris Bass Baptist Health Center
Integris Bass Pavilion

Frederick
Memorial Hospital and Physician Group

Guymon
Partner
Memorial Hospital of Texas County

Hobart
Elkview General Hospital

Lawton
Partner
Comanche County Memorial Hospital

Madill
Integris Marshall County Medical Center

McAlester
Partner
McAlester Regional Health Center

Miami
Integris Baptist Regional Health Center

Muskogee
Partner
Muskogee Regional Medical Center

Norman
Partner
Norman Regional Hospital

Oklahoma City
Integris Baptist Medical Center
INTEGRIS Health
Integris Southwest Medical Center
Oklahoma Spine Hospital

Ponca City
Via Christi Oklahoma Regional Medical Center

Pryor
Integris Mayes County Medical Center

Shawnee
Unity Health Center

Stillwater
Partner
Stillwater Medical Center

Yukon
INTEGRIS Canadian Valley Regional Hospital

OREGON

Hillsboro
Partner
Tuality Healthcare

Hood River
Providence Hood River Memorial Hospital

Medford
Providence Medford Medical Center

Milwaukie
Providence Milwaukie Hospital

Newberg
Providence Newberg Hospital

Portland
Providence Portland Medical Center
Providence St. Vincent Medical Center

Seaside
Providence Seaside Hospital

Silverton
Silverton Hospital

PENNSYLVANIA

Abington
Partner
Abington Memorial Hospital

Allentown
Shareholder
Lehigh Valley Hospital

Altoona
Bon Secours Hospital Campus
Partner
Altoona Hospital Campus

Beaver
Heritage Valley Health System
The Medical Center, Beaver

Bethlehem
Lehigh Valley Hospital–Muhlenberg

Bradford
Bradford Regional Medical Center

Butler
Partner
Butler Health System

Chambersburg
Chambersburg Hospital
Summit Health

Drexel Hill
Delaware County Memorial Hospital

Du Bois
Du Bois Regional Medical Center

East Stroudsburg
Pocono Medical Center

Ephrata
Partner
Ephrata Community Hospital

Erie
Shareholder
Hamot Medical Center

Gettysburg
Gettysburg Hospital

Hanover
Hanover Hospital

Harrisburg
PinnacleHealth at Community General Osteopathic
Hospital
PinnacleHealth System

Indiana
Indiana Regional Medical Center

Jenkintown
Holy Redeemer Hospital and Medical Center
Johnstown
Memorial Medical Center
Lancaster
Partner
Lancaster General Hospital
Lebanon
The Good Samaritan Hospital
Lehighton
Gnaden Huetten Memorial Hospital
Lewisburg
Evangelical Community Hospital
Media
Riddle Memorial Hospital
Meyersdale
Meyersdale Medical Center
New Castle
Jameson Hospital
Norristown
Partner
Montgomery Hospital Medical Center
Philadelphia
Albert Einstein Medical Center
Florence Crittenton Home and Hospital
Friends Behavioral Health System
Hospital of the University of Pennsylvania
Jeanes Hospital
Presbyterian Medical Center of the University of
Pennsylvania Health System
Temple East, Northeastern Hospital
Temple University Health System
Temple University Hospital
University of Pennsylvania Health System
Shareholder
Pennsylvania Hospital
Pittsburgh
Jefferson Regional Medical Center
Partner
St. Clair Memorial Hospital
Renovo
Bucktail Medical Center
Ridgway
Ridgway Health Center
Saint Marys
Elk Regional Health Center
Sayre
Robert Packer Hospital
Shareholder
Guthrie Healthcare System
Scranton
Partner
Community Medical Center
Sellersville
Partner
Grand View Hospital
Sewickley
Sewickley Valley Hospital, (A Division of Valley Medical
Facilities)
Sharon
Partner
Sharon Regional Health System
State College
Mount Nittany Medical Center
Troy
Troy Community Hospital
Uniontown
Partner
Uniontown Hospital
Upland
Crozer–Chester Medical Center
Waynesboro
Waynesboro Hospital
West Chester
Partner
Chester County Hospital
West Reading
Reading Hospital and Medical Center
Williamsport
Divine Providence Hospital
Partner
Susquehanna Health System

Windber
Windber Medical Center
York
Partner
WellSpan Health
Shareholder
York Hospital

RHODE ISLAND
East Providence
Emma Pendleton Bradley Hospital
Newport
Newport Hospital
Pawtucket
Memorial Hospital of Rhode Island
Providence
Butler Hospital
Miriam Hospital
Women and Infants Hospital of Rhode Island
Shareholder
Lifespan Corporation
Rhode Island Hospital
Warwick
Kent County Memorial Hospital

SOUTH CAROLINA
Charleston
Bon Secours–St. Francis Xavier Hospital
Roper Hospital
Varnville
Hampton Regional Medical Center

SOUTH DAKOTA
Burke
Community Memorial Hospital
Canton
Canton–Inwood Memorial Hospital
Chamberlain
Mid Dakota Medical Center
Clear Lake
Deuel County Memorial Hospital
Sioux Falls
Sioux Valley Hospitals and Health System
Shareholder
Sioux Valley Hospital University Medical Center
Vermillion
Sioux Valley Vermillion Medical Center
Viborg
Pioneer Memorial Hospital and Health Services
Watertown
Prairie Lakes Healthcare System
Webster
Lake Area Hospital
Winner
Winner Regional Healthcare Center

TENNESSEE
Bolivar
Bolivar General Hospital
Camden
Camden General Hospital
Chattanooga
Erlanger Health System
Erlanger North Hospital
Clarksville
Partner
Gateway Health System
Collierville
Baptist Memorial Hospital–Collierville
Columbia
Partner
Maury Regional Hospital
Covington
Baptist Memorial Hospital–Tipton
Franklin
Williamson Medical Center
Harriman
Roane Medical Center
Humboldt
Humboldt General Hospital
Huntingdon
Baptist Memorial Hospital–Huntingdon
Jackson
Shareholder
Jackson–Madison County General Hospital

Knoxville
Covenant Health
East Tennessee Children's Hospital
Fort Sanders Regional Medical Center
Parkwest Medical Center
Lenoir City
Fort Loudoun Medical Center
Lewisburg
Marshall Medical Center
Louisville
Peninsula Hospital
Memphis
Baptist Memorial Health Care Corporation
Baptist Memorial Hospital – Memphis
Baptist Memorial Hospital for Women
Milan
Milan General Hospital
Oak Ridge
Partner
Methodist Medical Center of Oak Ridge
Oneida
Scott County Hospital
Paris
Henry County Medical Center
Parsons
Decatur County General Hospital
Pikeville
Erlanger Bledsoe Hospital
Ripley
Baptist Memorial Hospital–Lauderdale
Savannah
Hardin Medical Center
Sevierville
Fort Sanders–Sevier Medical Center
Trenton
Gibson General Hospital
Union City
Baptist Memorial Hospital–Union City
Waynesboro
Wayne Medical Center

TEXAS
Amarillo
Partner
Baptist St. Anthony Health System
Andrews
Permian Regional Medical Center
Angleton
Angleton Danbury Medical Center
Atlanta
Atlanta Memorial Hospital
Beaumont
Memorial Hermann Baptist Beaumont Hospital
Bellville
Bellville General Hospital
Dallas
Baylor Jack and Jane Hamilton Heart and Vascular
Hospital
Baylor Specialty Hospital
Baylor University Medical Center
Children's Medical Center of Dallas
Shareholder
Baylor Health Care System
Del Rio
Val Verde Regional Medical Center
Electra
Electra Memorial Hospital
Floresville
Connally Medical Center
Fort Worth
Baylor Medical Center at Southwest Fort Worth
Shareholder
Baylor All Saints Medical Center at Fort Worth
Gainesville
North Texas Medical Center
Garland
Baylor Medical Center at Garland
Gatesville
Coryell Memorial Hospital
Grapevine
Partner
Baylor Regional Medical Center at Grapevine

Section B

Harlingen
Partner
 Valley Baptist Health System

Henrietta
 Clay County Memorial Hospital

Houston
 Memorial Hermann Healthcare System
 Memorial Hermann Hospital
Shareholder
 Memorial Hermann Southwest Hospital

Humble
 Northeast Medical Center Hospital

Huntsville
 Huntsville Memorial Hospital

Irving
Partner
 Baylor Medical Center at Irving

Jacksonville
 Mother Frances Hospital – Jacksonville

Katy
 Memorial Hermann Katy Hospital

Kilgore
 Laird Memorial Hospital

La Grange
 Fayette Memorial Hospital

Levelland
 Covenant Hospital–Levelland

Longview
Partner
 Good Shepherd Medical Center

Lubbock
 Covenant Children's Hospital
 Covenant Medical Center
 Covenant Medical Center–Lakeside
Shareholder
 Covenant Health System

Marshall
Partner
 Marshall Regional Medical Center

Midland
 Midland Memorial Hospital
Partner
 Midland Memorial Hospital

Missouri City
 Memorial Hermann Fort Bend Hospital

Odessa
 Medical Center Hospital

Orange
 Continuecare Hospital of Southeast Texas
 Memorial Hermann Baptist in Orange

Pearsall
 Frio Regional Hospital

Plainview
 Covenant Hospital Plainview

Plano
 Baylor Regional Medical Center at Plano

Richardson
Partner
 Richardson RegionalMedical Center

Richmond
 OakBend Medical Center

Rockdale
 Richards Memorial Hospital

San Antonio
 Baptist Health System

Sherman
Partner
 Wilson N. Jones Medical Center

Sulphur Springs
 Hopkins County Memorial Hospital

Sweeny
 Sweeny Community Hospital

Temple
Partner
 King's Daughters Hospital

Texarkana
Partner
 Wadley Regional Medical Center

Tyler
 Tyler Continuecare Hospital at Mother Frances
Partner
 Trinity Mother Frances Health System

Vernon
 Wilbarger General Hospital

Waco
Partner
 Hillcrest Baptist Medical Center

Waxahachie
 Baylor Medical Center at Waxahachie

Wichita Falls
Partner
 United Regional Health Care System
 United Regional Health Care System–Eighth Street
 Campus

Yoakum
 Yoakum Community Hospital

VERMONT
Barre
Partner
 Central Vermont Medical Center

Bennington
 Southwestern Vermont Medical Center

Burlington
Shareholder
 Fletcher Allen Health Care

Morrisville
 Copley Hospital

Newport
 North Country Hospital and Health Center

Randolph
 Gifford Medical Center

Rutland
Partner
 Rutland Regional Medical Center

Saint Johnsbury
 Northeastern Vermont Regional Hospital

Windsor
 Mt. Ascutney Hospital and Health Center

VIRGINIA
Charlottesville
Partner
 Martha Jefferson Hospital

Fredericksburg
 Mary Washington Hospital

Hampton
 Sentara CarePlex Hospital

Harrisonburg
Partner
 Rockingham Memorial Hospital

Lynchburg
 Centra Health

Norfolk
 Sentara Leigh Hospital
 Sentara Norfolk General Hospital
Shareholder
 Sentara Healthcare

Virginia Beach
 Sentara Bayside Hospital
 Sentara Virginia Beach General Hospital

Williamsburg
 Sentara Williamsburg Community Hospital

WASHINGTON
Aberdeen
 Grays Harbor Community Hospital

Centralia
 Providence Centralia Hospital

Everett
 Providence Everett Medical Center

Morton
 Morton General Hospital

Olympia
 Providence St. Peter Hospital

Seattle
 Providence Health System

Tacoma
 Tacoma General Hospital
Shareholder
 MultiCare Health System

Wenatchee
 Central Washington Hospital

Yakima
Partner
 Yakima Valley Memorial Hospital

WEST VIRGINIA
Beckley
 Beckley Appalachian Regional Hospital

Bluefield
 St. Luke's Hospital

Charleston
 Charleston Area Medical Center
 Women and Children's Hospital
Shareholder
 Charleston Area Medical Center Health System, Inc.

Gassaway
 Braxton County Memorial Hospital

Glen Dale
Partner
 Reynolds Memorial Hospital

Hinton
 Summers County Appalachian Regional Hospital

Madison
 Boone Memorial Hospital

Montgomery
 Montgomery General Hospital

Princeton
Partner
 Princeton Community Hospital

Ripley
 Jackson General Hospital

Spencer
 Roane General Hospital

Wheeling
Partner
 Wheeling Hospital

WISCONSIN
Appleton
 Appleton Medical Center
Shareholder
 ThedaCare, Inc.

Arcadia
 Franciscan Skemp Healthcare–Arcadia Campus

Barron
 Barron Medical Center–Mayo Health System

Beaver Dam
Partner
 Beaver Dam Community Hospitals

Beloit
Partner
 Beloit Memorial Hospital

Bloomer
 Bloomer Memorial Medical Center

Eau Claire
Partner
 Luther Hospital

Green Bay
Partner
 Bellin Memorial Hospital

La Crosse
 Franciscan Skemp Healthcare
 Franciscan Skemp Healthcare–La Crosse Campus
Shareholder
 Gundersen Lutheran Medical Center

Madison
 St. Marys Hospital Medical Center
Shareholder
 Meriter Hospital

Menomonee Falls
Partner
 Community Memorial Hospital

Menomonie
 Myrtle Werth Hospital–Mayo Health System

Milwaukee
Partner
 Froedtert Memorial Lutheran Hospital

New London
 New London Family Medical Center

Oconomowoc
 Oconomowoc Memorial Hospital

Osseo
 Osseo Medical Center

Rice Lake
Partner
 Lakeview Medical Center

River Falls
River Falls Area Hospital
Saint Croix Falls
St. Croix Regional Medical Center
Sparta
Franciscan Skemp Healthcare–Sparta Campus
Watertown
Partner
Watertown Memorial Hospital
Waukesha
ProHealth Care
Waukesha Memorial Hospital
West Bend
Owner
St. Joseph's Community Hospital of West Bend
Whitehall
Tri–County Memorial Hospital

WYOMING
Afton
Star Valley Medical Center
Buffalo
Johnson County Healthcare Center
Casper
Partner
Wyoming Medical Center
Cheyenne
Partner
United Medical Center
Douglas
Memorial Hospital of Converse County
Gillette
Campbell County Memorial Hospital
Jackson
St. John's Medical Center and Living Center
Kemmerer
South Lincoln Medical Center
Laramie
Partner
Ivinson Memorial Hospital
Lovell
North Big Horn Hospital District

Rawlins
Memorial Hospital of Carbon County

YANKEE ALLIANCE
300 Brickstone Square, 5th Floor,
Andover, MA Zip 01810–1429;
tel. 978/475–2000; Mr R Paul O'Neill,
President

CONNECTICUT
New Haven
Member
Hospital of Saint Raphael

MAINE
Bangor
Member
St. Joseph Hospital

MASSACHUSETTS
Attleboro
Affiliate
Sturdy Memorial Hospital
Boston
Member
Boston Medical Center
Brockton
Member
Brockton Hospital
Cambridge
Member
Youville Hospital and Rehabilitation Center
Fall River
Member
Charlton Memorial Hospital
Southcoast Hospitals Group
Great Barrington
Member
Fairview Hospital
Lowell
Member
Saints Memorial Medical Center

New Bedford
Member
St. Luke's Hospital of New Bedford
North Adams
Affiliate
North Adams Regional Hospital
Pittsfield
Member
Berkshire Medical Center
Wareham
Member
Tobey Hospital
Winchester
Member
Winchester Hospital

NEW HAMPSHIRE
Manchester
Affiliate
Catholic Medical Center
Elliot Hospital
Nashua
Member
St. Joseph Hospital

NEW YORK
Albany
Member
Albany Medical Center
Elizabethtown
Affiliate
Elizabethtown Community Hospital
Glens Falls
Member
Glens Falls Hospital
Plattsburgh
Affiliate
Champlain Valley Physicians Hospital Medical Center
Troy
Member
Samaritan Hospital

Section B

C

Health Organizations, Agencies, and Providers

†List supplied by the Joint Commission on
Accreditation of Healthcare Organizations

Description of Lists

This section of AHA Guide was compiled to provide a directory of information useful to the health care field.

National and International Organizations

The national and international lists include many types of voluntary organizations concerned with matters of interest to the health care field. The organizational information includes address, telephone number, FAX number, and the contact person. The information was obtained directly from the organizations.

Organizations are searchable by state, then city within state, and "kind of organization."

Recent editions of AHA Guide included a listing for healthfinder®. While the information is not included in the 2006 edition, it can be accessed via the Internet at www.healthfinder.gov.

We present this organization listings simply as a convenient directory. Inclusion or omission of any organization's name indicates neither approval nor disapproval by Health Forum LLC, an American Hospital Association company.

United States Government Agencies

National agencies concerned with health–related matters are listed by the major department of government under which the different functions fall.

State and Local Organizations and Agencies

The lists of organizations in states, associated areas, and provinces include Blue Cross and Blue Shield plans, group purchasing organizations, health systems agencies, hospital associations and councils, hospital licensure agencies, medical and nursing licensure agencies, quality improvement organizations, state health planning and development agencies, and statewide health coordinating councils.

There are many active local organizations that do not fall within these categories. Contact the hospital association of the state or province for information about such additional groups. The hospital association and councils listed have offices with full-time executives.

The selected state and provincial government agencies include those within state departments of health and welfare, and other agencies, such as comprehensive health planning, crippled children's services, maternal and child health, mental health, and vocational rehabilitation.

Other Providers

Lists of State Government Agencies for Health Maintenance Organizations (HMO's), Freestanding Hospices, and Freestanding Ambulatory Surgery Centers (FASC's) are provided as a resource for obtaining the most current list of agencies in various states. A list of Freestanding Ambulatory Surgery Centers is provided.

Lists of JCAHO Accredited Long–Term Care Organizations, JCAHO Accredited Chemical Dependency Organizations, and JCAHO Accredited Mental Health Organizations are provided for your information.

These lists are provided simply as a convenient reference. Inclusion or omission of any organization's name

indicates neither approval or disapproval by Health Forum L.L.C.

Section C

A

AAMP (American Association on Mental Retardation), 444 North Capitol Street, N.W., Suite 846, Washington, DC 20001-1512; tel. 202/387-1968; FAX. 202/387-2193; M. Doreen Croser, Executive Director

Academy of Dentistry for Persons with Disabilities, 211 East Chicago Avenue, Suite 740, Chicago, IL 60611; tel. 312/440-2660; FAX. 312/440-2824; Vacant, Executive Director

Academy of Medical Management, 560 West Crossville Road, Suite 103, Roswell, GA 30075; tel. 770/649-7150; FAX. 770/649-7552; Jan McElroy, Director of Member Services

Academy of Oral Dynamics, P.O.Box 29, Fort Washington, PA 19034; tel. 215/957-0700; FAX. 215/957-0703; Dr. William J. Crielly, Treasurer

Accreditation Association for Ambulatory Health Care, 3201 Old Glenview Road, Suite 300, Wilmette, IL 60091; tel. 847/853-6060; FAX. 847/853-9028; John E. Burke, Ph. D., Executive Director

Accreditation Council for Pharmacy Education, 20 North Clark Street, Suite 2500, Chicago, IL 60602-5109; tel. 312/664-3575; FAX. 312/664-4652; Peter H. Vlasses, Pharm. D., MD, BCPS, FCCP, Executive Director

Acute Long Term Hospital Association, 1055 North Fairfax Street, Suite 201, Alexandria, VA 22314; tel. 703/299-5571; FAX. 703/299-5574; Brad Traverse, Executive Director, ALTHA

Advanced Medical Technology Association, 1200 G Street, N.W., Suite 400, Washington, DC 20005; tel. 202/783-8700; FAX. 202/783-8750; Pamela G. Bailey, President

Aerospace Medical Association, 320 South Henry Street, Alexandria, VA 22314-3579; tel. 703/739-2240; FAX. 703/739-9652; Russell B. Rayman, M.D., Executive Director

Alexander Graham Bell Association for the Deaf & Hard Of Hearing, 3417 Volta Place, NW, Washington, DC 20007; tel. 202/337-5220; FAX. 202/337-8314; Lisa Ruffin Schauf, Development Administrator

Allergy Associates, 2004 Grand Avenue, Baldwin, NY 11510; tel. 516/223-7656; FAX. 516/223-0583; Joe D' Amore, MD, President

Alliance for Children & Families, 11700 West Lake Park Drive, Milwaukee, WI 53224; tel. 414/359-1040; FAX. 414/359-1074; Peter B. Goldberg, President and CEO

Alzheimer's Association, (Alzheimer's Disease and Related Disorders Association, Inc.), 225 North Michigan Avenue, Suite 1700, Chicago, IL 60601; tel. 312/335-8700; FAX. 312/335-1110; Gary Berting,VP of Asministration

Ambulatory Pediatric Association, 6728 Old McLean Village Drive, McLean, VA 22101; tel. 703/556-9222; FAX. 703/556-8729; Marge Degnon, Executive Director

America's Blood Centers, 725 15th Street, N.W., Suite 700, Washington, DC 20005-2109; tel. 202/393-5725; FAX. 202/393-1282; Jim MacPherson, CEO

America's Health Insuranace Plans, 601 Pennsylvania Ave.NW, South Bldg, Suite 500, Washington, DC 20004; tel. 202/778-3200; FAX. 202/778-8486; Charles W. Stellar, Executive Vice President

American Academy for Cerebral Palsy and Developmental Medicine, 6300 North River Road, Suite 727, Rosemont, IL 60018-4226; tel. 847/698-1635; FAX. 847/823-0536; Sheril King, Executive Director

American Academy of Allergy, Asthma and Immunology, 555 East Wells Street, Suite 1100, Milwaukee, WI 53202; tel. 414/272-6071; FAX. 414/272-6070; Kay Whalen, Executive Vice President

American Academy of Child and Adolescent Psychiatry, 3615 Wisconsin Avenue, N.W., Washington, DC 20016; tel. 202/966-7300; FAX. 202/966-2891; Virginia Q. Anthony, Executive Director

American Academy of Dental Practice Administration, 1063 Whippoorwill Lane, Palatine, IL 60067; tel. 847/934-4404; Kathleen Uebel, Executive Director

American Academy of Dermatology, 930 East Woodfield Road, Schaumburg, IL 60173; tel. 847/330-0230; FAX. 847/330-0050; Robert S. Bolan, Ph D, Interim Executive Director

American Academy of Family Physicians, 11400 Tomahawk Creek Parkway, Leawood, KS 66211; tel. 913/906-6000; FAX. 913/906-6083

American Academy of Medical Administrators, 701 Lee Street, Suite 600, Des Plaines, IL 60016; tel. 847/759-8601; FAX. 847/759-8602; Renee Schleicher, CAE, President and CEO

American Academy of Neurology, 1080 Montreal Avenue, St. Paul, MN 55116-2325; tel. 651/695-1940; FAX. 612/695-2791; Catherine Rydell, Executive Director

American Academy of Ophthalmology, 655 Beach Street, P.O. Box 7424, San Francisco, CA 94120; tel. 415/561-8500; FAX. 415/561-8533; H. Dunbar Hoskins, Jr., M.D., Executive Vice President

American Academy of Optometry, 6110 Executive Boulevard, Suite 506, Rockville, MD 20852; tel. 301/984-1441; FAX. 301/984-4737; Lois Schoenbrun, CAE, FAAO Executive Director

American Academy of Oral Medicine, 2517 Eastlake Ave E Ste 200, Seattle, WA 98102-3278; tel. 206/267-4790; David Setumph, CAE, Executive Coordinator

American Academy of Orthopedic Surgeons, 6300 North River Road, Rosemont, IL 60018-4262; tel. 847/823-7186; FAX. 847/823-8125; Karen L. Hackett, FACHE, CAE, Chief Executive Officer

American Academy of Otolaryngic Allergy, 1990 M. Street,NW, Suite 680, Washington, DC 20036; tel. 202/955-5010; FAX. 202/955-5016; Jami Lucas, Executive Director

American Academy of Otolaryngology-Head and Neck Surgery, Inc., One Prince Street, Alexandria, VA 22314; tel. 703/836-4444; FAX. 703/519-1553; David R. Nielsen, MD, FACS

American Academy of Pain Management, 13947 Mono Way, Suite A, Sonora, CA 95370-2807; tel. 209/533-9744; FAX. 209/533-9750; Kathryn A. Padgett, Ph.D., Executive Director

American Academy of Pediatrics, 141 Northwest Point Boulevard, Elk Grove Village, IL 60007-1098; tel. 847/434-4000; FAX. 847/228-5027; Errol R. Alden MD.

American Academy of Physical Medicine and Rehabilitation, One IBM Plaza, Suite 2500, Chicago, IL 60611-3604; tel. 312/464-9700; FAX. 312/464-0227; Thomas E. Stautzenbach,Cae, Executive Director

American Academy of Physician Assistants, 950 North Washington Street, Alexandria, VA 22314-1552; tel. 703/836-2272; FAX. 703/684-1924; Stephen C. Crane, Ph.D., MPH, Executive Vice President/CEO

American Academy of Psychoanalysis And Dynamic Psychiatry, One Regency Drive, P.O. Box 30, Bloomfield, CT 06002; tel. 888/691-8281; FAX. 860/286-0787; Jacquelyn T. Coleman, CAE, Executive Director

American Academy of Restorative Dentistry, 1700 W. Koch, Suite 1, Bozeman, MT 59715; tel. 406/586-4559; FAX. 406/586-0397; Thad Langford, DDS, Secretary-Treasurer

American Aging Association, The Sally Balin Medical Center, 110 Chesley Drive, Media, PA 19063; tel. 610/627-2626; FAX. 610/565-9747; Arthur K. Balin, M.D., Ph D., FACP

American Alliance for Health, Physical Education, Recreation & Dance, 1900 Association Drive, Reston, VA 20191; tel. 703/476-3400; FAX. 703/476-9527; Michael G. Davis, CEO

American Ambulance Association, 8201 Greensboro Drive, Suite 300, McLean, VA 22102; tel. 703/610-9000; FAX. 703/610-9005; Maria Bianchi, Executive Vice President

American Art Therapy Association, 1202 Allanson Road, Mundelein, IL 60060; tel. 847/949-6064; FAX. 847/566-4580; Edward J. Stygar, Jr., Executive Director

American Arthritis Foundation, 1330 West Peachtree Street, Atlanta, GA 30309; tel. 404/872-7100; FAX. 404/872-9559; Tino Mantella, President

American Association for Clinical Chemistry, Inc., 2101 L Street, N.W., Suite 202, Washington, DC 20037; tel. 202/857-0717; FAX. 202/887-5093; Richard Flaherty, Executive Vice President

American Association for Dental Research, 1619 Duke Street, Alexandria, VA 22314-3406; tel. 703/548-0066; FAX. 703/548-1883; Christopher Fox, Executive Director

American Association For Homecare, 625 Slaters Lane, Suite 200, Alexandria, VA 22314-1171; tel. 703/836-6263; FAX. 703/836-6730; Kay Cox, President and CEO

American Association for Laboratory Animal Science, AALAS, 9190 Crestwyn Hills Drive, Memphis, TN 38125; tel. 901/754-8620; FAX. 901/753-0046; Ann T. Turner, PHD, CAE, Executive Director

American Association for Respiratory Care, 9425 N. MacArthur, Suite 100, Irving, TX 75063; tel. 972/243-2272; FAX. 972484-2720; Sam P. Giordano, Executive Director

American Association for the Advancement of Science, 1200 New York Avenue, N.W., Washington, DC 20005; tel. 202/326-6400; FAX. 202/321-5526; Alan Leshner, Chief Executive Officer

American Association for the Surgery of Trauma, Department of Surgery, F-1281, Pittsburgh, PA 15213; tel. 412/647-0635; FAX. 404/616-7333; Andrew B. Peitzman MD, Secretary-Treasurer

American Association of Ambulatory Surgery Centers, P.O. Box 5271, Johnson City, TN 37602-5271; tel. 423/915-1001; FAX. 423/282-9712; David Shapiro, M.D., President

American Association of Anatomists, Department of Anatomy, University of Mississippi Medical Center, Jackson, MS 39216-4505; tel. 601/984-1640; FAX. 601/984-1655; Duaine E. Haines, Secretary-Treasury

American Association of Bioanalysts, 906 Olive, Suite 1200, St. Louis, MO 63101-1434; tel. 314/241-1445; FAX. 314/241-1449; Mark S. Birenbaum, Ph.D., Administrator

American Association of Certified Orthoptists, UIHC-Ophthalmology, 200 Hawkins Drive, Iowa City, IA 52242; tel. 319/356-3863; FAX. 319/384-9831; Pamela J. Kutschke, C.O., President

American Association of Colleges of Nursing, One Dupont Circle, N.W., Suite 530, Washington, DC 20036; tel. 202/463-6930; FAX. 202/785-8320; Geraldine Bednash, Ph.D., RN, FAAN, Executive Director

American Association of Colleges of Pharmacy, 1426 Prince Street, Alexandria, VA 22314-2841; tel. 703/739-2330; FAX. 703/836-8982; Lucinda Maine, Ph.D., Executive Vice President

American Association of Colleges of Podiatric Medicine, 15850 Crabbs Branch Way, Suite 320, Rockville, MD 20855-2622; tel. 301/948-9760; FAX. 301/948-1928

American Association of Critical-Care Nurses, 101 Columbia, Aliso Viejo, CA 92656-1491; tel. 949/362-2000; FAX. 949/362-2020; Wanda L. Johansson, RN, MN, CEO

American Association of Dental Consultants, Inc., 10032 Wind Hill Drive, Greenville, IN 47124; tel. 812/923-2600; FAX. 812/923-2900; Judy Salisbury, Executive Director

American Association of Endodontists, 211 East Chicago Avenue, Suite 1100, Chicago, IL 60611; tel. 312/266-7255; FAX. 312/266-9867; James Drinan, Executive Director

American Association of Healthcare Administrative Management, 11240 Waples Mill Road, Suite 200, Fairfax, VA 22030; tel. 703/281–4043; FAX. 703/359–7562; Sharon Galler, Executive Director

American Association of Healthcare Consultants, 5 Revere Drive, #200, Northbrook, IL 60062; tel. 847/205–2718; FAX. 847/657–6819; Linda Campbell, CAE, Acting Executive Director

American Association of Homes and Services for the Aging, 2519 Connecticut Avenue, NW, Washington, DC 20008-1520; tel. 202/783–2242; FAX. 202/220–0020; William L. (Larry) Minnix Jr., D. Min, President and CEO

American Association of Kidney Patients, 3505 E. Frontage Road, Suite 315, Tampa, FL 33607; tel. 800/749–2257; FAX. 813/636–8122; Kris Robinson, Executive Director

American Association of Medical Assistants, 20 North Wacker Drive, Suite 1575, Chicago, IL 60606; tel. 312/899–1500; FAX. 312/899–1259; Donald A. Balasa, JD, MBA, Executive Director, Legal Counsel

American Association of Nurse Anesthetists, 222 South Prospect Avenue, Park Ridge, IL 60068-4001; tel. 847/692–7050; FAX. 847/692–6968; Jeffery M. Beutler, CRNA, MS, Executive Director

American Association of Occupational Health Nurses, 2920 Brandywine Road, Suite 100, Atlanta, GA 30341; tel. 770/455–7757; FAX. 770/455–7271; Ann R. Cox, CAE, Executive Director

American Association of Oral and Maxillofacial Surgeons, 9700 West Bryn Mawr Avenue, Rosemont, IL 60018-5701; tel. 847/678–6200; FAX. 847/678–6286; Robert C. Rinaldi, Ph.D., Executive Director

American Association of Orthodontists, 401 North Lindbergh Boulevard, St. Louis, MO 63141-7816; tel. 314/993–1700; FAX. 314/997–1745; Chris P. Vranas, Executive Director

American Association of Pastoral Counselors, 9504A Lee Highway, Fairfax, VA 22031-2303; tel. 703/385–6967; FAX. 703/352–7725; C. Roy Woodruff, Ph.D., Executive Director

American Association of Physicists in Medicine, One Physics Ellipse, College Park, MD 20740-3846; tel. 301/209–3350; FAX. 301/209–0862; Angela R. Keyser, Executive Director

American Association of Plastic Surgeons, 900 Cummings Center, Suite 221-u, Beverly, MA 01915; tel. 703/820–7400; FAX. 703/931–4520; David M. Cloud, Executive Secretary

American Association of Poison Control Centers, 3201 New Mexico Avenue, N.W., Suite 330, Washington, DC 20016; tel. 202/362–7217; Anne Flanangan, Ms, RN, Executive Director

American Association of Psychiatric Technicians, Inc., A.A.P.T., 2000 O Street, Suite 250, Sacramento, CA 95814-5286; tel. 800/391–7589; FAX. 916/329–9145; Keith Hearn, Executive Director

American Association of Public Health Dentistry, A.A.P.H.D. National Office, 3760 SW Lyle Court, Portland, OR 97221; tel. 503/242–0712; FAX. 503/242–0721; James Toothaker, D.D.S., MPH, Executive Director

American Baptist Homes and Hospitals Association, P.O. Box 851 (National Ministries), Valley Forge, PA 19482-0851; tel. 610/768–2411; FAX. 610/768–2453; Rosalie Norman-McNaney, Director

American Board of Allergy and Immunology, A Conjoint Board of the American Board of Internal Medicine and the American Board of Pediatrics, 510 Walnut Street, Suite 1701, Philadelphia, PA 19106-3699; tel. 215/592–9466; FAX. 215/592–9411; John W. Yunginger, M.D., Executive Secretary

American Board of Anesthesiology, 4101 Lake Boone Trail, Suite 510, Raleigh, NC 27607-7506; tel. 919/881–2570; FAX. 919/881–2575; Francis P. Hughes, Ph.D., Executive Vice President

American Board of Cardiovascular Perfusion, 207 North 25th Avenue, Hattiesburg, MS 39401; tel. 601/582–2227; FAX. 601/582–2271; Beth A. Richmond, Ph.D., Mark G. Richmond, Ed.D.

American Board of Colon and Rectal Surgery, 20600 Eureka Road, Suite 600, Taylor, MI 48180; tel. 734/282–9400; FAX. 734/282–9402; Herand Abcarian, M.D., Executive Director

American Board of Dermatology, Inc., Henry Ford Health System, One Ford Place, Detroit, MI 48202-3450; tel. 313/874–1088; FAX. 313/872–3221; Antoinette F. Hood, M.D., Executive Director

American Board of Emergency Medicine, 3000 Coolidge Road, East Lansing, MI 48823; tel. 517/332–4800; FAX. 517/332–2234; Mary Ann Reinhart, Ph.D., Executive Director

American Board of Family Practice, Inc., 2228 Young Drive, Lexington, KY 40505; tel. 859/269–5626; FAX. 859/335–7501; James Puffer, M.D., Executive Director

American Board of Internal Medicine, 510 Walnut Street, Suite 1700, Philadelphia, PA 19106-3699; tel. 215/446–3500; FAX. 215/446–3473; Christine K. Cassel, M.D., President

American Board of Medical Management, 4890 West Kennedy Boulevard, Suite 200, Tampa, FL 33609-2575; tel. 813/287–2815; FAX. 813/287–8993; Roger S. Schenke, Executive Vice President

American Board of Medical Specialties, 1007 Church Street, Suite 404, Evanston, IL 60201-5913; tel. 847/491–9091; FAX. 847/328–3596; Stephen H. Miller, M.D., MPH, President

American Board of Neurological Surgery, 6550 Fannin Street, Suite 2139, Houston, TX 77030; tel. 713/441–6015; FAX. 713/794–0207; Mary Louise Sanderson, Administrator

American Board of Nuclear Medicine, 900 Veteran Avenue, Los Angeles, CA 90024; tel. 310/825–6787; FAX. 310/794–4821; Henry D. Royal, M.D., Executive Director

American Board of Ophthalmology, 111 Presidential Boulevard, Suite 241, Bala Cynwyd, PA 19004; tel. 610/664–1175; FAX. 610/664–6503; Denis M. O'Day, M.D., Executive Director

American Board of Oral and Maxillofacial Surgery, 625 North Michigan Avenue, Suite 1820, Chicago, IL 60611; tel. 312/642–0070; FAX. 312/642–8584; Cheryl E. Mounts, Executive Secretary

American Board of Orthopedic Surgery, Inc., 400 Silver Cedar Court, Chapel Hill, NC 27514; tel. 919/929–7103; FAX. 919/942–8988; G. Paul De Rosa, M.D., Executive Director

American Board of Pathology, One Urban Centre, 4830 West Kennedy Boulevard, Suite 690, Tampa, FL 33622-5915; tel. 813/286–2444; FAX. 813/289–5279; Betsy D. Bennett M.D Ph D., Executive Vice President

American Board of Pediatrics, Inc., 111 Silver Cedar Court, Chapel Hill, NC 27514; tel. 919/929–0461; FAX. 919/929–9255; James A. Stockman III, M.D., President

American Board of Physical Medicine and Rehabilitation, 3015 Allegro Park, Lake SW, Rochester, MN 55902; tel. 507/282–1776; FAX. 507/282–9242; Anthony M. Tarvestad, JD, Executive Director

American Board of Podiatric Surgery, 445 Fillmore Street, San Francisco, CA 94117-3404; tel. 415/553–7800; FAX. 415/553–7801; James A. Lamb, Executive Director

American Board of Preventive Medicine, Inc., 330 S. Wells Street, Suite 1018, Chicago, IL 60606; tel. 312/939–2276; FAX. 312/939–2218; James M. Vanderploeg, M.D., M.P.H.

American Board of Prosthodontics, P.O. Box 271894, West Hartford, CT 06127-1894; tel. 860/679–2649; FAX. 860/679–1370; Thomas D. Taylor, D.D.S., M.S.D., Executive Director

American Board of Psychiatry and Neurology, Inc., 500 Lake Cook Road, Suite 335, Deerfield, IL 60015; tel. 847/945–7900; FAX. 847/945–1146; Stephen C. Scheiber, M.D., Executive Vice President

American Board of Quality Assurance and Utilization Review, 2120 Range Road, Clearwater, FL 33765; tel. 727/298–8777; FAX. 727/449–0555; H.E. Hartsell, Chief Operating Officer

American Board of Radiology, 5441 E. Williams Blvd, Suite 200, Tucson, AZ 85711; tel. 520/790–2900; FAX. 520/790–3200; Robert R. Hattery, MD, Executive Director

American Board of Surgery, Inc., 1617 John F. Kennedy Boulevard, Suite 860, Philadelphia, PA 19103; tel. 215/568–4000; FAX. 215/563–5718; Frank R. Lewis, M.D., Executive Director

American Board of Thoracic Surgery, 633 N. St. Clair Street, Suite 2320, Chicago, IL 60611; tel. 312/202–5900; FAX. 312/202–5960; William A. Gay, Jr., M.D., Executive Director

American Broncho-Esophagological Association, Office of the Secretary, University of Utah Medical Center, 50 North Medical Drive, Salt Lake City,, UT 84132; tel. 801/581–7514; FAX. 801/585–5744; R. Kim Davis, MD., Secretary

American Burn Association, 625 North Michigan Avenue, Suite 1530, Chicago, IL 60611; tel. 312/642–9260; FAX. 312/642–9130; John Krichbaum, JD, Executive Director

American Cancer Society, 1599 Clifton Road, N.E., Atlanta, GA 30329; tel. 404/320–3333; Gerald P. Murphy, M.D., Senior Vice President

American Center for the Alexander Technique, Inc., 39 W. 14th Street, #507, New York, NY 10011; tel. 212/633–2229; FAX. 212/633–2239; Jane Tomkiewiez, Executive Director

American Chiropractic Association, 1701 Clarendon Boulevard, Arlington, VA 22209; tel. 703/276–8800; FAX. 703/243–2593; Garrett F. Cuneo, Executive Vice President

American Cleft Palate-Craniofacial Association, 1504 E. Franklin St., Suite 102, Chapel Hill, NC 27514; tel. 919/933–9044; FAX. 919/933–9604; Nancy C. Smythe, Executive Director

American College Health Association, P.O. Box 28937, Baltimore, MD 21240-8937; tel. 410/859–1500; FAX. 410/859–1510; Doyle E. Randol, MS, Executive Director

American College of Allergy, Asthma and Immunology, 85 West Algonquin Road, Suite 550, Arlington Heights, IL 60005; tel. 847/427–1200; FAX. 847/427–1294; James R. Slawny, Executive Director

American College of Apothecaries, P.O. Box 341266, Bartlett, TN 38184; tel. 901/383–8119; FAX. 901/383–8882; D. C. Huffman, Jr., Ph.D., Executive Vice President

American College of Cardiology, 9111 Old Georgetown Road, Bethesda, MD 20814; tel. 800/253–4636; FAX. 301/897–9745; Christine McEntee, Chief Executive Officer

American College of Cardiovascular Nursing, 11219 Rice Creek Road, Riverview, FL 33569; tel. 813/677–1116; FAX. 813/671–8912; Jonni Cooper, BSN, MBA, PhD, FACCN-III, Chief Executive Officer

American College of Chest Physicians, 3300 Dundee Road, Northbrook, IL 60062-2348; tel. 847/498–1400; FAX. 847/498–5460; Alvin Lever, Executive Vice President and CEO

American College of Dentists, 8393 Quince Orchard Boulevard, Gaithersburg, MD 20878-1614; tel. 301/977–3223; FAX. 301/977–3330; Stephen A. Ralls, D.D.S.

American College of Emergency Physicians, P.O. Box 619911, Dallas, TX 75261-9911; tel. 972/550–0911; FAX. 972/580–2816; Michael E. Gallery, Ph.D, CAE, Interim Executive Director

American College of Foot and Ankle Surgeons, 8725 W. Higgins Rd, Suite 555, Chicago, IL 60631; tel. 773/693–9300; FAX. 773/693–9304; J.C. Mahaffey, CAE, Executive Director

American College of Gastroenterology, 4900B South 31st Street, Arlington, VA 22206; tel. 703/820–7400; FAX. 703/931–4520; Thomas F. Fise, Executive Director

American College of Healthcare Executives, One North Franklin, Suite 1700, Chicago, IL 60606-3491; tel. 312/424–2800; FAX. 312/424–0023; Thomas C. Dolan, Ph.D., FACHE, CAE, President and CEO

American College of Mohs Micrographic Surgery and Cutaneous Oncology, 555 E. Wells, Suite 1100, Milwaukee, WI 53202-3823; tel. 414/347–1103; FAX. 414/272–6070; Georganne Dixon, Executive Director

American College of Nurse-Midwives, Silver Spring Metro Plaza, 8403 Colesville Rd, Ste.1550, Silver Spring, MD 20910-6374; tel. 240/485–1800; FAX. 240/485–1818; Deanne Williams, Executive Director

American College of Obstetricians and Gynecologists, 409 12th Street, S.W., Washington, DC 20024-2188; tel. 202/638–5577; FAX. 202/484–5107; Ralph W. Hale, M.D., Executive Vice President

American College of Occupational and Environmental Medicine, (Includes Occupational & Environmental Health Fnd. & The Occupational Physicians Scholarship Fund, 1114 N. Arlington Heights Road, Arlington Heights, IL 60004; tel. 847/818–1800; FAX. 847/818–9289; Barry S. Eisenberg, CAE., Executive Director

American College of Physician Executives, 4890 West Kennedy Boulevard, Suite 200, Tampa, FL 33619-2575; tel. 813/287–2000; FAX. 813/287–8993; Roger S. Schenke, Executive Vice President

American College of Physicians, 190 North Independence Mall West, Philadelphia, PA 19106-1572; tel. 215/351–2800; FAX. 215/351–2829; John Tooker, M.D., MBA, F.A.C.P., Executive VP, CEO

American College of Preventive Medicine, 1660 L Street, N.W., Washington, DC 20036; tel. 202/466–2044; FAX. 202/466–2662; Jordan H. Richland, MPH, Executive Director

American College of Radiology, 1891 Preston White Drive, Reston, VA 20191-4397; tel. 703/648–8900; FAX. 703/648–9176; Harvey L. Neiman, M.D., Executive Director

American College of Rheumatology, 1800 Century Place, Suite 250, Atlanta, GA 30345; tel. 404/633–3777; FAX. 404/633–1870; Lynn Bonfiglio, Director of Membership

American College of Sports Medicine, P.O. Box 1440, Indianapolis, IN 46206-1440; tel. 317/637–9200; FAX. 317/634–7817; James R. Whitehead, Executive Vice President

American College of Surgeons, 633 N. Saint Clair Street, Chicago, IL 60611; tel. 312/202–5000; FAX. 312/202–5001; Thomas R. Russell, M.D., Executive Director

American Congress of Rehabilitation Medicine, 6801 Lake Plaza Drive, Suite B205, Indianapolis, IN 46220; tel. 317/915–2250; FAX. 317/915–2245; Richard D. Morgan, MBA

American Dental Assistants Association, 35 E. Wacker Driver, Suite 1730, Chicago, IL 60601; tel. 312/541–1550; FAX. 312/541–1496; Lawrence H. Sepin, Executive Director

American Dental Association, 211 East Chicago Avenue, Chicago, IL 60611; tel. 312/440–2500; FAX. 312/440–7494; James B. Bramson, DDS, Executive Director

American Dental Education Association, 1400 K. Street NW, Suite 1100, Washington, DC 20005; tel. 202/289–7201; FAX. 202/289–7204; Richard W. Valachovic, MPH, D.M.D.,Executive Director

American Dental Society of Anesthesiology, Inc., 211 East Chicago Avenue, Suite 780, Chicago, IL 60611; tel. 312/664–8270; FAX. 312/642–9713; R. Knight Charlton, Executive Director

American Diabetes Association, Inc., 1701 N. Beauregard Street, Alexandria, VA 22311; tel. 703/549–1500; FAX. 703/836–7439; John H. Graham IV, Interim Chief Executive Officer

American Dietetic Association, 120 South Riverside Plaza, Suite 2000, Chicago, IL 60606-6995; tel. 312/899–0040; FAX. 312/899–4765; Ronald S. Moen, Chief Executive Officer

American Foundation for Aging Research, North Carolina State University, Biochemistry Department, Raleigh, NC 27695-7622; tel. 919/515–5679; FAX. 919/515–2047; Paul F. Agris, President

American Foundation for AIDS Research (amfAR), 120 Wall Street, 13th Floor, New York, NY 10005-3902; tel. 212/806–1600; FAX. 212/806–1601; Deborah C. Hernan, Vice President, Public Information

American Foundation for the Blind, Inc., 11 Penn Plaza, Suite 300, New York, NY 10001; tel. 212/502–7600; FAX. 212/502–7770; Liz Greco - Rocks, Vice President, Communications

American Group Psychotherapy Association, Inc., 25 East 21st Street, Sixth Floor, New York, NY 10010; tel. 212/477–2677; FAX. 212/979–6627; Marsha S. Block, CAE, Chief Executive Officer

American Head and Neck Society, 11300 W. Olympic Blvd #600, Los Angles, CA 90064; tel. 310/437–0559; FAX. 310/437–0585; Erin Schwarz, Executive Director

American Headache Society, 19 Mantua Road, Mt. Royal, NJ 08061; tel. 856/423–0043; FAX. 856/423–0082; Linda McGillicuddy, Executive Director

American Health Care Association, 1201 L Street, N.W., Washington, DC 20005; tel. 202/842–4444; FAX. 202/842–3860; Charles H. Roadman II, M.D., President and CEO

American Health Information Management Association (AHIMA), 233 North Michigan Avenue, Suite 2150, Chicago, IL 60601-5800; tel. 312/233–1100; FAX. 312/233–1090; Linda Kloss, R.H.I.A., C.A.E.

American Health Lawyers Association, 1025 Connecticut Avenue, N.W., Suite 600, Washington, DC 20036; tel. 202/833–1100; FAX. 202/833–1105; Peter M. Leibold, Esq, Executive Vice President and CEO

American Health Planning Association, 7245 Arlington Boulevard, Suite 300, Falls Church, VA 22042; tel. 703/573–3103; FAX. 703/573–1276; Dean Montgomery

American Healthcare Radiology Administrators, 490 - B Boston, Post Road, Suite 101, Sudbury, MA 01776; tel. 978/443–7591; FAX. 978/443–8046; Mary S. Reitter, Executive Director

American Heart Association, Inc., 7272 Greenville Avenue, Dallas, TX 75231; tel. 214/706–1446; FAX. 214/373–9818; Rose Marie Robertson, MD, FAHA, Chief Executive Officer

American Hospital Association, One North Franklin, Chicago, Chicago, IL 60606-3491; tel. 312/422–3000; Richard J. Davidson, President

American Hospital Association, 325 Seventh Street, N.W., Washington, DC 20004; tel. 202/626–2363; FAX. 202/626–2303; Richard J. Davidson, President

American Hospital Association, Washington Office, 325 Seventh Street, N.W., Suite 700, Washington, DC 20004; tel. 202/638–1100; FAX. 202/626–2355; Rick Pollack, Executive Vice President

American Laryngological Association, Department of Otolaryngology/MonteFiore Medical Center, 3400 Bainbridge Ave, 3rd fl, Bronx, NY 10467-2404; tel. 718/920–8453; FAX. 615/343–7604; Marvin D. Fried MD.

American Library Association, 50 East Huron Street, Chicago, IL 60611; tel. 312/280–5044; FAX. 312/944–8520; Debra Davis, Director

American Lung Association, 61 Broadway, New York, NY 10006; tel. 212/315–8700; FAX. 212/315–8800; John L. Kirkwood, Pres. & CEO

American Lung Association of Ohio Southwest Region, Dayton Office, 7560 McEwen Road, Dayton, OH 45459; tel. 937/291–0451; FAX. 937/291–0453; Roberta M. Taylor, Regional Coordinator

American Medical Association, 515 North State Street, Chicago, IL 60610; tel. 312/464–5000; FAX. 312/464–4184

American Medical Association Alliance, 515 North State Street, 9th Floor, Chicago, IL 60610; tel. 312/464–4470; FAX. 312/464–5020; Hazel J. Lewis, Executive Director

American Medical Group Association, Inc., 1422 Duke Street, Alexandria, VA 22314-3430; tel. 703/838–0033; FAX. 703/548–1890; Donald W. Fisher, Ph.D., President and CEO

American Medical Student Association/Foundation, 1902 Association Drive, Reston, VA 20191; tel. 703/620–6600; FAX. 703/620–5873; Paul R. Wright, Executive Director

American Medical Technologists, 710 Higgins Road, Park Ridge, IL 60068; tel. 847/823–5169; FAX. 847/823–0458; Christopher Damon, Executive Director

American Medical Women's Association, Inc., 801 North Fairfax Street, Suite 400, Alexandria, VA 22314; tel. 703/838–0500; FAX. 703/549–3864; Linda D. Hallman, Executive Director

American Medical Writers Association, 40 West Gude Drive #101, Rockville, MD 20850-1192; tel. 301/294–5303; FAX. 301/294–9006

American Music Therapy Association, 8455 Colesville Road, Suite 1000, Silver Spring, MD 20910; tel. 301/589–3300; FAX. 301/589–5175; Andrea Farbman, Ed.D., Executive Director

American National Standards Institute, 25 West 43rd Street, Fourth Floor, New York, NY 10036; tel. 212/642–4900; FAX. 212/398–0023; Mark W. Hurwitz, CAE, President and CEO

American Nephrology Nurses' Association, East Holly Avenue, P.O. Box 56, Pitman, NJ 08071; tel. 856/256–2320; FAX. 856/589–7463

American Neurological Association, 5841 Cedar Lake Road, Suite 204, Minneapolis, MN 55416; tel. 952/545–6284; FAX. 952/545–6073; Linda Wilkerson, Executive Director

American Nurses Association, 600 Maryland Avenue, S.W., Suite 100 W, Washington, DC 20024-2571; tel. 202/651–7000; FAX. 202/651–7001; David Hennage, Ph.D., M.B.A.

American Occupational Therapy Association, Inc., 4720 Montgomery Lane, P.O. Box 31220, Bethesda, MD 20824-1220; tel. 301/652–2682; FAX. 301/652–7711; Frederick P. Somers, Executive Director

American Ophthalmological Society, P.O. Box 193940, San Francisco, CA 94119-3940; tel. 415/561–8578; FAX. 415/561–8531; Charles P. Wilkinson, M.D., Secretary-Treasurer

American Optometric Association, 243 North Lindbergh Boulevard, St. Louis, MO 63141; tel. 314/991–4100; FAX. 314/991–4101; Michael D. Jones, O.D., Executive Director

American Organization of Nurse Executives (AONE), 325 7th Street, NW, Washington, DC 20004; tel. 202/626–2240; FAX. 202/638–5499; Pamela Thompson, MS, RN, FAAN,Chief Executive Officer

American Orthopsychiatric Association, 2001 N. Beavereegard St., 12th Floor, Alexandria, VA 22311; tel. 703/797–2584; FAX. 212/564–6180; Renee Hyson, Sr. Admin Asst.

American Orthoptic Council, 3914 Nakoma Road, Madison, WI 53711; tel. 608/233–5383; FAX. 608/263–4247; Leslie France, Administrator

American Osteopathic Association, 142 East Ontario Street, Chicago, IL 60611; tel. 312/202–8000; FAX. 312/202–8210; John B. Crosby, J.D., Executive Director

American Otological Society, Inc., Administrative Office, 2720 Tartan Way, Springfield, IL 62711; tel. 217/483–6966; FAX. 217/483–6966; Shirley Gossard, Administrator

American Parkinson Disease Association, Inc., 1250 Hylan Boulevard, Suite 4B, Staten Island, NY 10305; tel. 800/223–2732; FAX. 718/981–4399; G. Maestrone, D.V.M., Scientific and Medical Affairs Director

American Pediatric Society, Inc., 3400 Research Forest Drive, Suite B7, The Woodlands, TX 77381; tel. 281/419–0052; FAX. 281/419–0082; Kathy Cannon, Associate Executive Director

American Pharmacists Association, 2215 Constitution Avenue, N.W., Washington, DC 20037; tel. 202/628–4410; FAX. 202/429–6300; John A. Gans, Pharm.D., Executive Vice President

American Physical Therapy Association, 1111 North Fairfax Street, Alexandria, VA 22314; tel. 703/684–2782; FAX. 703/684–7343; Francis J. Mallon, Esq., Chief Executive Officer

American Physiological Society, 9650 Rockville Pike, Bethesda, MD 20814-3991; tel. 301/634–7118; FAX. 301/634–7241; Martin Frank, Ph.D., Executive Director

American Podiatric Medical Association, 9312 Old Georgetown Road, Bethesda, MD 20814-1698; tel. 301/571–9200; FAX. 301/530–2752; Glenn B. Gastwirth, DPM, Executive Director

American Psychiatric Association, 1000 Wilson Boulevard, Suite 1825, Arlington, VA 22209; tel. 703/907–7300; FAX. 703/907–1085; James H. Scully Jr., M.D., Medical Director

American Psychoanalytic Association, 309 East 49th Street, New York, NY 10017; tel. 212/752–0450; FAX. 212/593–0571; Dean K. Stein, Executive Director

American Psychological Association, 750 First Street, N.E., Washington, DC 20002-4242; tel. 202/336–5800; FAX. 202/336–5797; Russ Newman, Ph.D., JD, Executive Director For Professional Practice

American Psychosomatic Society, 6728 Old McLean Village Drive, McLean, VA 22101-3906; tel. 703/556–9222; FAX. 703/556–8729; George K. Degnon, Executive Director

American Public Health Association, 800 I. Street, NW, Washington, DC 20001-3710; tel. 202/777–2742; FAX. 202/777–2534; George S. Benjamin, MD, FACP, Executive Director

American Public Human Services Association, 810 First Street, N.E., Suite 500, Washington, DC 20002; tel. 202/682–0100; FAX. 202/289–6555; Jerry W. Friedman, Executive Director

American Red Cross, National Headquarters, 2025 E. Street, NW, Washington, DC 20006; tel. 202/303–4498; FAX. 703/206–7765

American Registry of Medical Assistants, 69 Southwick Road, Westfield, MA 01085-4729; tel. 800/527–2762; FAX. 413/562–9021; Annette H. Heyman, R.M.A., Director

American Registry of Radiologic Technologists, 1255 Northland Drive, St. Paul, MN 55120; tel. 651/687–0048; Jerry B. Reid, Ph.D., Executive Director

American Rhinologic Society, Department of Otolaryngology, Montefiore Medical Center, Bronx, NY 10467; tel. 718/920–2991; FAX. 718/652–5194; Marvin P. Fried, M.D. Secretary

American Roentgen Ray Society, 44211 Slate Stone Court, Leesburg, VA 20176; tel. 703/729–3353; FAX. 703/729–4839; Susan Brown Cappitelli, Executive Director

American School Health Association, 7263 S.R. 43, P.O. Box 708, Kent, OH 44240-0708; tel. 330/678–1601; FAX. 330/678–4526; Susan Wooley, Ph.D., CHES, Executive Director

American Society for Adolescent Psychiatry, P.O. Box 570218, Dallas, TX 75357-0218; tel. 214/686–6166; FAX. 972/613–5532; Frances M. Roton, Executive Director

American Society for Biochemistry and Molecular Biology, Inc., 9650 Rockville Pike, Bethesda, MD 20814-3996; tel. 301634–7145; FAX. 301/634–7126; Charles C. Hancock, Executive Officer

American Society for Clinical Laboratory Science, 6701 Democracy Boulevard, Suite 300, Bethesda, MD 20817; tel. 301/657–2768; FAX. 301/657–2909; Elissa Passiment, Vice President

American Society for Clinical Pharmacology and Therapeutics, 528 North Washington Street, Alexandria, VA 22314; tel. 703/836–6981; FAX. 703/836–5223; Sharon J. Swan, CAE, Executive Director

American Society for Cytotechnology, 1500 Sunday Drive, Suite 102, Raleigh, NC 27607; tel. 800/948–3947; FAX. 919/787–4916; Joy Traynor, Executive Director

American Society for Healthcare Central Service Professionals (ASHCSP), One North Franklin, 31st Floor, Chicago, IL 60606; tel. 312/422–3700; FAX. 312/422–4577; Virginia Sylvestri, Executive Director

American Society for Healthcare Engineering (ASHE), One North Franklin St., 31st Floor, Chicago, IL 60606; tel. 312/422–3800; FAX. 312/422–4571; Albert J. Sunseri, PhD, Executive Director

American Society for Healthcare Environmental Services (ASHES), 1 N. Franklin Street, Suite 2800, Chicago, IL 60606; tel. 312/422–3860; FAX. 312/422–4578; Patti Costello, Executive Director

American Society for Healthcare Food Service Administrators (ASHFSA), 304 W. Liberty Street, Suite 201, Louisville, KY 40202; tel. 800/620–6422; FAX. 502/589–3602; Keith Howard, Executive VP

American Society for Healthcare Human Resources Administration (ASHHRA), One North Franklin, 31st Floor, Chicago, IL 60606; tel. 312/422–3720; FAX. 312/422–4577; Nadene Chambers, Executive Director

American Society for Healthcare Risk Management (ASHRM), One North Franklin, 31st Floor, Chicago, IL 60606; tel. 312/422–3980; FAX. 312/422–4580; Elizabeth Summy, Executive Director

American Society for Investigative Pathology, 9650 Rockville Pike, Bethesda, MD 20814-3993; tel. 301/530–7130; FAX. 301/571–1879; Frances A. Pitlick, Ph.D., Executive Officer

American Society for Laser Medicine and Surgery, Inc., 2404 Stewart Avenue, Wausau, WI 54401; tel. 715/845–9282; FAX. 715/848–2493; Richard O. Gregory, M.D., Secretary

American Society for Microbiology, 1752 North Street, NW, Washington, DC 20036; tel. 202/924–9265; FAX. 202/942–9333; Michael I. Goldberg, Ph.D., Executive Director

American Society for Pharmacology and Experimental Therapeutic, 9650 Rockville Pike, Bethesda, MD 20814-3995; tel. 301/634–7060; FAX. 301/634–7061; Christine K. Carrico, Ph. D., Executive Officer

American Society for Public Administration, 1120 G Street, N.W., Suite 700, Washington, DC 20005; tel. 202/393–7878; FAX. 202/638–4952; Glenn Cope, President

American Society for Reproductive Medicine, 1209 Montgomery Highway, Birmingham, AL 35216-2809; tel. 205/978–5000; FAX. 205/978–5005; Robert W. Rebart, M.D., Executive Director

American Society for the Advancement of Anesthesia and Sedation in Dentistry, Six East Union Avenue, P.O. Box 551, Bound Brook, NJ 08805; tel. 732/469–9050; FAX. 732/271–1985; David Crystal, D.D.S., Executive Secretary

American Society for Therapeutic Radiology and Oncology, 12500 Fair Lakes Circle, Suite 375, Fairfax, VA 22033-3882; tel. 703/502–1550; FAX. 703/502–7852; Laura Thevenot, Chief Executive Officer

American Society of Anesthesiologists, 520 North Northwest Highway, Park Ridge, IL 60068; tel. 847/825–5586; FAX. 847/825–1692; Ronald A. Bruns, Executive Director

American Society of Clinical Pathologists., (Includes Board of Registry), 2100 West Harrison Street, Chicago, IL 60612-3798; tel. 312/738–1336; FAX. 312/738–9798; Anna Graham, M.D., Acting Executive Vice President

American Society of Colon and Rectal Surgeons, 85 West Algonquin Road, Suite 550, Arlington Heights, IL 60005; tel. 847/290–9184; FAX. 847/290–9203; James Slawny, Executive Director

American Society of Consultant Pharmacists, 1321 Duke Street, Alexandria, VA 22314-3563; tel. 703/739–1300; FAX. 703/739–1321; John Feather, Executive Director

American Society of Contemporary Medicine and Surgery, 820 N. Orleans, Suite 208, Chicago, IL 60610; tel. 312/440–0699; FAX. 312/440–0580; Randall T. Bellows, M.D., Director

American Society of Cytopathology, 400 West Ninth Street, Suite 201, Wilmington, DE 19801; tel. 302/429–8802; FAX. 302/429–8807; Elizabeth A. Jenkins, Executive Director

American Society of Directors of Volunteer Services (ASDVS), One North Franklin, 31st Floor, Chicago, IL 60606; tel. 312/422–3939; FAX. 312/422–4575; Audrey L. Harris, Executive Director

American Society of Electroneurodiagnostic Technologists, Inc., 426 W. 42nd Street, Kansas City, MO 64111; tel. 816/931–1120; FAX. 816/931–1145; Sheila R. Navis, CAE, Executive Director

American Society of Health-System Pharmacists, 7272 Wisconsin Avenue, Bethesda, MD 20814; tel. 301/657–3000; FAX. 301/664–8877; Henri R. Manasse, Jr., Executive VP and CEO

American Society of Internal Medicine, 2011 Pennsylvania Avenue, N.W., Suite 800, Washington, DC 20006-1808; tel. 202/835–2746; FAX. 202/835–0443

American Society of Law, Medicine & Ethics, 765 Commonwealth Avenue, Suite 1634, Boston, MA 02215; tel. 617/262–4990; FAX. 617/437–7596; Benjamin W. Moulton, JD, MPH, Executive Director

American Society of Neuroimaging, 5841 Cedar Lake Road, Suite 204, Minneapolis, MN 55416; tel. 952/545–6291; FAX. 952/545–6073; Tisha Kehn, Associate Executive Director

American Society of Plastic Surgeons, 444 East Algonquin Road, Arlington Heights, IL 60005; tel. 847/228–9900; FAX. 847/228–9131; Executive Director

American Society of Radiologic Technologists, 15000 Central Avenue, S.E., Albuquerque, NM 87123-3917; tel. 505/298–4500; FAX. 505/298–5063; Joan L. Parsons, Executive Vice President

American Speech-Language-Hearing Association, 10801 Rockville Pike, Rockville, MD 20852; tel. 301/897–5700; FAX. 301/571–0457

American Surgical Association, 900 Cummings Center, Suite 221-U, Beverly, MA 01915; tel. 978/927–8330; FAX. 978/524–0461; Michael W. Mulholland, MD

American Thoracic Society, 61 Broadway, New York, NY 10006-2755; tel. 212/315–6444; FAX. 212/315–6498; Carl C. Booberg, Executive Director

American Trauma Society, 8903 Presidential Parkway, Suite 512, Upper Marlboro, MD 20772-2656; tel. 800/556–7890; FAX. 301/420–0617; Harry Teter, Executive Director - Sonny Oztas PR Dept.

American Urological Association, Inc., 1000 Corporate Boulevard, Linthicum, MD 21090; tel. 410/689–3700; G. James Gallagher, Executive Director

AORN, Association of Peri Operative Registered Nurses, 2170 South Parker Road, Suite 300, Denver, CO 80231-5711; tel. 303/755–6300; FAX. 303/750–2927; Tom Cooper, Executive Director

Arthritis Foundation, 1330 West Peachtree Street, Atlanta, GA 30309; tel. 404/872–7100; FAX. 404/965–7712; Tino J. Mantella, President and CEO

Association for Applied Psychophysiology and Biofeedback, 10200 West 44th Avenue, Suite 304, Wheat Ridge, CO 80033; tel. 303/422–8436; FAX. 303/422–8894; Francine Butler, Ph.D., Executive Director

Association for Clinical Pastoral Education, Inc., 1549 Clairmont Road, Suite 103, Decatur, GA 30033; tel. 404/320–1472; FAX. 404/320–0849; Teresa E. Snorton, Executive Director

Association for Community Health Improvement (ACHI), 180 Montgomery Street, Suite 1520, San Francisco, CA 94104; tel. 415/248–8411; FAX. 415/296–0519; Michael Bilton, Director

Association for Healthcare Philanthropy, 313 Park Avenue, Suite 400, Falls Church, VA 22046; tel. 703/532–6243; FAX. 703/532–7170; William C. McGinly,Ph.D., CAE, President & Chief Executive Officer

Association for Healthcare Resource & Materials Management (AHRMM), One North Franklin St., Suite 2800, Chicago, IL 60606-3491; tel. 312/422–3840; FAX. 312/422–4573; Deborah L. Sprindzunas, Executive Director

Association for Hospital Medical Education, 205 Sixth Street, Irwin, PA 15642; tel. 724/864–7321; FAX. 724/864–6151; Margie Kleppick, Executive Director

Association for Professionals in Infection Control and Epidemiology, 1275 K Street. NW, Suite 1000, Washington, DC 20036; tel. 202/789–1890; FAX. 202/789–1899; Kathy L. Warye, Executive Director

Association for the Advancement of Automotive Medicine (AAAM), P.O. Box 4176, Barrington, IL 60146; tel. 847/844–3880; FAX. 847/844–3884; Irene Herzau, Executive Director

Association of American Medical Colleges, 2450 N Street, N.W., Washington, DC 20037-1127; tel. 202/828–0400; FAX. 202/828–1125; Jordan J. Cohen, M.D., President

Association of American Physicians and Surgeons, Inc., 1601 North Tucson Boulevard, Suite Nine, Tucson, AZ 85716; tel. 520/327–4885; FAX. 520/325–4230; Jane M. Orient, M.D., Executive Director

Association of Community Cancer Centers, 11600 Nebel Street, Suite 201, Rockville, MD 20852-2557; tel. 301/984-9496; FAX. 301/770-1949; Lee E. Mortenson, DPA, Executive Director

Association of Professional Chaplains, 1701 East Woodfield Road, Suite 760, Schaumburg, IL 60173-5109; tel. 847/240-1014; FAX. 847/240-1015; Josephine N. Schrader,CAE, Executive Director

Association of Schools of Allied Health Professions, 1730 M Street, N.W., Suite 500, Washington, DC 20036; tel. 202/293-4848; FAX. 202/293-4852; Thomas W. Elwood, Dr. P.H., Executive Director

Association of Schools of Public Health, Inc., 1101 15th Street, N.W., Suite 910, Washington, DC 20005; tel. 202/296-1099; FAX. 202/296-1252; Harrison C. Spencer, MD, MPH, President and CEO

Association of Specialized and Cooperative Library Agencies, 50 East Huron Street, Chicago, IL 60611; tel. 312/280-4399; FAX. 312/944-8085; Cathleen Bourdon, ASCLA, Executive Director

Association of State and Territorial Health Officials, 1275 K Street, NW, Suite 800, Washington, DC 20005-4006; tel. 202/371-9090; FAX. 202/371-9797; George E. Hardy, Jr, M.D., MPH, Executive Director

Association of Surgical Technologists, Inc., 7108-C South Alton Way, Englewood, CO 80112-2106; tel. 303/694-9130; FAX. 303/694-9169; William J. Teutsch, Executive Director

Association of University Programs in Health Administration, 730 11th Street, NW, 4th Floor, Washington, DC 20001; tel. 202/638-1448; FAX. 202/638-3429; Lydia Reed, Vice President and COO

Asthma and Allergy Foundation of America, 1233 20th Street,NW, Suite 402, Washington, DC 20036; tel. 800-7-ASTHMA; FAX. 202/466-8940; William McLin, Executive Director

Asthma Foundation of Southern Arizona, P.O. Box 30069, Tucson, AZ 85751-0069; tel. 602/323-6046; FAX. 602/324-1137; Lynn Krust, Executive Director

B

BCS Financial Corporation, 676 North Saint Clair, Suite 1600, Chicago, IL 60611-2997; tel. 312/951-7700; FAX. 312/951-7777

Bereavement Services, Gundersen Lutheran Medical Foundation, 1900 South Avenue-Alex, La Crosse, WI 54601; tel. 608/775-4747; FAX. 608/775-5137; Rana Limbo, Director

Biological Stain Commission, Inc., University of Rochester, Department Pathology, Rochester, NY 14642-0001; tel. 585/275-6335; FAX. 585/442-8993; David P. Penney, Ph.D., Treasurer

Birth Defect Research for Children, 930 Woodcock Road, Suite 225, Orlando, FL 32803; tel. 407/895-0802; FAX. 407/895-0824; Betty Mekdeci, Executive Director

Blinded Veterans Association, 477 H Street, N.W., Washington, DC 20001; tel. 202/371-8880; FAX. 202/371-8258; Thomas H. Miller, Executive Director

Blue Cross and Blue Shield Association, 225 N. Michigan Avenue, Chicago, IL 60601; tel. 312/297-6267; FAX. 312/297-6120; Scott Serota, President and CEO

C

Catholic Health Association of the United States, 4455 Woodson Road, St. Louis, MO 63134-3797; tel. 314/427-2500; FAX. 314/427-0029; Michael F. Rodgers, Interim, President and CEO

Catholic Medical Association, 2020 Pennsylvania Avenue, NW, Suite 864, Washington, DC 20006; tel. 703/988-0588; FAX. 702/830-1308; Executive Director

Center for Health Administration Studies, University of Chicago, 969 East 60th Street, Chicago, IL 60637; tel. 773/702-7104; FAX. 773/702-7222; Kristiana Raube, Ph.D., Director

Center for Healthcare Governance, 1 N. Franklin Street, 29th Floor, Chicago, IL 60606; tel. 888/540-6111; FAX. 312/422-4650; John R. Combes, M.D., President and Chief Operating Officer

Central Surgical Association, University of Chicago, 5841 S. Maryland m/c 5094, Chicago, IL 60637; tel. 773/702-6237; FAX. 773/702-6120; Fabrizio Michelassi, Secretary-CSA

Christian Record Services, Inc., 4444 South 52nd Street, Lincoln, NE 68516; tel. 402/488-0981; FAX. 402/488-7582; Dwayne Bullock, Treasurer

College of American Pathologists, 325 Waukegan Road, Northfield, IL 60093-2750; tel. 847/832-7000; FAX. 847/832-8151; Lee VanBremen, Ph.D., Executive Vice President

Commission on Accreditation of Rehabilitation Facilities, 4891 East Grant Road, Tucson, AZ 85712; tel. 520/325-1044; FAX. 520/318-1129; Emmett Ervin,Managing Director

Cooley's Anemia Foundation, Inc., 129-09 26th Avenue, Suite 203, Flushing, NY 11354; tel. 800/522-7222; FAX. 718/321-3340; Jayne Restivo, National Executive Director

Corporate Angel Network, Inc., CAN (Arranges Free Air Transportation for Cancer Patients, Westchester County Airport, One Loop Road, White Plains, NY 10604; tel. 914/328-1313; FAX. 914/328-4226; Vicki Blucher, Director of Volunteers

Council of Medical Specialty Societies, 51 Sherwood Terrace, Suite M, Lake Bluff, IL 60044; tel. 847/295-3456; FAX. 847/295-3759; Sandra K. Trusky, Executive Administrator

Council on Education for Public Health, 800 Eye Street , NW, Washington, DC 20001-3710; tel. 202/789-1050; FAX. 202/789-1895; Patricia P. Evans, Executive Director

Crohn's & Colitis Foundation of America, Inc., 386 Park Avenue, S., 17th Floor, New York, NY 10016-8804; tel. 800/932-2423; FAX. 212/779-4098; Rodger DeRose President and CEO

Cystic Fibrosis Foundation, 6931 Arlington Road, Bethesda, MD 20814; tel. 301/951-4422; FAX. 301/951-6378; Robert J. Beall, Ph.D., President and CEO

D

Damien Dutton Society for Leprosy Aid, Inc., 616 Bedford Avenue, Bellmore, NY 11710; tel. 516/221-5829; FAX. 516/221-5909; Howard Crouch, President

Depression and Bipolar Support Alliance, 730 North Franklin Street, Suite 501, Chicago, IL 60610; tel. 312/642-0049; FAX. 312/642-7243; Lydia Lewis, President

Dietary Managers Association, 406 Surrey Woods Drive, St. Charles, IL 60174; tel. 630/587-6336; FAX. 630/587-6308; William St. John, President

Dysautonomia Foundation, Inc., 315 W. 39th Street, Suite 701, New York, NY 10018; tel. 212/279-1066; FAX. 212/279-2066; Lenore F. Roseman, Executive Director

E

Easter Seals, Inc., 230 West Monroe Street, Suite 1800, Chicago, IL 60606-4802; tel. 312/726-6200; FAX. 312/726-1494; James E. Williams, Jr., President and CEO

ECRI, 5200 Butler Pike, Plymouth Meeting, PA 19462; tel. 610/825-6000; FAX. 610/834-1275; Jeffery C. Lerner, Ph.D., CEO & President

Educational Commission for Foreign Medical Graduates, 3624 Market Street, Philadelphia, PA 19104-2685; tel. 215/386-5900; FAX. 215/387-9963; James A. Hallock, M.D., President and CEO

Ehlers-Danlos National Foundation, P.O. Box 13157, Richmond, VA 23225; tel. 804/276-9940; FAX. 804/276-9940; Susan L. Stephenson, Vice President, Patient Advocate

Emergency Nurses Association, 915 Lee Street, Des Plaines, IL 60016; tel. 847/460-4000; FAX. 847/460-4002; David Westman, Executive Director

Epilepsy Foundation, 4351 Garden City Drive, Landover, MD 20785-2267; tel. 301/459-3700; FAX. 301/577-2684; Eric Hargis, Chief Executive Officer

Epilepsy Foundation of Connecticut, 386 Main Street, Middletown, CT 06457; tel. 860/346-1924; FAX. 860/346-1928; Linda Wallace

F

Federated Ambulatory Surgery Association, 700 N. Fairfax Street, #306, Alexandria, VA 22314; tel. 703/836-8808; FAX. 703/549-0976; Kathy Bryant, Executive Director

Federation of American Hospitals, 801 Pennsylvania Ave N.W., Suite 245, Washington, DC 20004; tel. 202/624-1500; FAX. 202/737-6832; Chip Kahn, President

Federation of State Medical Boards of the United States, Inc., P.O. Box 619850, Dallas, TX 75261-9850; tel. 817/868-4000; FAX. 817/868-4097; James N. Thompson, MD, President and CEO

Financial Accounting Standards Board, 401 Merritt 7, P.O. Box 5116, Norwalk, CT 06856-5116; tel. 203/847-0700; FAX. 203/849-9714

Foundation for Chiropractic Education and Research, 1330 Beacon Street, Suite 315, Brookline, MA 02446-3202; tel. 617/734-3397; FAX. 617/734-0989; Anthony L. Rosner, Ph.D., L.L. D,. Hon. Director of Research and Education

G

Gerontological Society of America, 1030 15 Street, NW, Suite 250, Washington, DC 20005-1503; tel. 202/842-1275; FAX. 202/842-1150; Carol A. Schutz, Executive Director

Great Plains Health Alliance, Inc., 625 Third Street, Box 366, Phillipsburg, KS 67661; tel. 785/543-2111; FAX. 785/543-5098; Roger S. John, President and CEO

Guide Dog Users, Inc., 14311 Astrodome Dr., Silver Spring, MD 20906-2245; tel. 301/598-5771; FAX. 301/871-7591; Jane Sheehan, Office Manager

H

Health Care Executive Assistants, 1 N. Franklin Street, 31st Floor, Chicago, IL 60606; tel. 312/922-3907; FAX. 312/422-4575; Glen Brown, Executive Director

Health Industry Distributors Association, 310 Montgomery Street, Alexandria, VA 22314-1516; tel. 703/549-4432; FAX. 703/549-6495; Matthew J. Rowan, President & Chief Executive Officer

Health Research and Educational Trust, One North Franklin, Chicago, IL 60606; tel. 312/422–2622; FAX. 312/422–4568; Mary Pittman, Dr. P.H., President

Healthcare Council of MidMichigan, 3927 Beecher Road, Flint, MI 48532; tel. 810/766–8898; FAX. 810/762–4108; Bruce Trevithick, President

Healthcare Financial Management Association, Two Westbrook Corporate Center, Suite 700, Westchester, IL 60154; tel. 708/531–9600; FAX. 708/531–0032; Richard L. Clarke, President and CEO

Healthcare Information and Management Systems Society (HIMSS), 230 East Ohio Street, Suite 500, Chicago, IL 60611-3201; tel. 312/664–4467; FAX. 312/664–6143; H. Stephen Lieber, President, CEO

HealthCare Partnership, Inc., Quality Healthcare Partnership Inc., 1340 14th Street, Columbus, GA 31902; tel. 706/323–1777; FAX. 404/571–2650; James N. Railey,President

HEAR Center, 301 East Del Mar Boulevard, Pasadena, CA 91101; tel. 626/796–2016; FAX. 626/796–2320; Josephine Wilson, Executive Director

Histochemical Society, Inc., P.O. Box 85630, University Station, Seattle, WA 98195-1630; tel. 206/616–5894; FAX. 206/616–5842; W.L. Stahl, Ph.D., Executive Director

Huntington's Disease Society of America, Inc., 158 West 29th Street, 7th Floor, New York, NY 10001-5300; tel. 800/345–HDSA; FAX. 212/239–3430; Barbara T. Boyle, National Executive Director/CEO

I

Infusion Nurses Society, 220 Norwood Park South, Norwood, MA 02062; tel. 781/440–9408; FAX. 781/440–9409; Mary Alexander, Chief Executive Officer

Institute For Cancer Prevention, 390 Fifth Avenue, 3rd Floor, New York, NY 10595; tel. 212/551–2500; FAX. 212/687–2339; Daniel W. Nixon, M.D., President

Institutes for the Achievement of Human Potential, 8801 Stenton Avenue, Wyndmoor, PA 19038; tel. 215/233–2050; FAX. 215/233–3940; Coralee Thompson, M.D.

International Childbirth Education Association, Inc., P.O. Box 20048, Minneapolis, MN 55420-0048; tel. 612/854–8660; FAX. 612/854–8772

International College of Surgeons/United States Section, 1516 North Lake Shore Drive, Chicago, IL 60610-1694; tel. 312/787–6274; FAX. 312/787–9289; Maggie Kearney, Meeting and Publications Manager

International Council for Health, Physical Education, Recreation, Sport and Dance, 1900 Association Drive, Reston, VA 20191; tel. 703/476–3486; FAX. 703/476–9527; Dr. Dong Ja Yang, President

J

John Milton Society for the Blind, 475 Riverside Drive, Room 455, New York, NY 10115; tel. 212/870–3335; FAX. 212/870–3229; Darcy Quigley, Executive Director

Joint Commission on Accreditation of Healthcare Organizations, One Renaissance Boulevard, Oakbrook Terrace, IL 60181; tel. 630/792–5000; FAX. 630/792–5005; Dennis S. O'Leary, M.D., President

K

Krannert Institute of Cardiology, Indiana University School of Medicine, 1801 N. Senate Blvd., Suite 4000, Indianapolis, IN 46202-4800; tel. 317/962–0500; FAX. 317/962–0501

L

Lupus Foundation of America, Inc., 1300 Piccard Drive, Suite 200, Rockville, MD 20850-4303; tel. 301/670–9292; FAX. 301/670–9486; Karen Johnson, Health Educator

M

March of Dimes Birth Defects Foundation, 1275 Mamaroneck Avenue, White Plains, NY 10605; tel. 914/428–7100; FAX. 914/428–8203; Jennifer L. Howse, Ph.D., President

Medic Alert Foundation International, 2323 Colorado Avenue, Turlock, CA 95382; tel. 888/633–4298; FAX. 209/669–2495; Ramesh Srinvasar, Marketing Department

Medical Fitness Association, P.O. Box 73103, Richmond, VA 23235; tel. 804/327–0330; FAX. 804/327–1630; Cary Wing, Ed.D., Executive Director

Medical Group Management Association, 104 Inverness Terrace, E., Englewood, CO 80112-5306; tel. 877/275–6462; FAX. 303/643–4427; William F. Jessee, MD, FACMPE, President and CEO

Medical Library Association, 65 East Wacker Drive, Suite 1900, Chicago, IL 60601-7298; tel. 312/419–9094; FAX. 312/419–8950; Carla J. Funk, Executive Director

Mended Hearts, Inc., 7272 Greenville Avenue, Dallas, TX 75231; tel. 214/706–1224; FAX. 214/706–5245; Bonna Kol, Executive Director

Muscular Dystrophy Association, 3300 East Sunrise Drive, Tucson, AZ 85718; tel. 520/529–2000; FAX. 520/529–5300; Robert Ross, President & CEO

N

National Academy of Sciences, Division on Earth and Life Studies, 500 Fifth St., NW-Keck 611, Washington, DC 20001; tel. 202/334–2500; FAX. 202/334–3362; Warren R. Muir, PH.D, Executive Director

National Accreditation Council for Agencies Serving the Blind , 21475 Lorain Road, Suite300, Fairview, OH 44126; tel. 440/409–0340; Steven K. Hegedeos Executive Director

National Accrediting Agency for Clinical Laboratory Sciences, 8410 West Bryn Mawr, Suite 670, Chicago, IL 60631-3415; tel. 773/714–8880; FAX. 773/714–8886; Olive M. Kimball, CEO

National Alliance for the Mentally Ill, 2107 Wilson Blvd, Suite 300, Arlington, VA 22201-3042; tel. 703/524–7600; FAX. 703/524–9094; Richard C. Birkel, Ph.D., Executive Director

National Assembly on School Based Health Care, 666 11th Street, NW, Suite 735, Washington, DC 20001; tel. 202/638–5872; FAX. 202/638–5879; John Schlitt, Executive Director

National Association for Home Care & Hospice, 228 Seventh Street, S.E., Washington, DC 20003; tel. 202/547–7424; FAX. 202/547–3540; Val J. Halamandaris, President

National Association for Practical Nurse Education and Service, 3800 Powell LN STE CU-4, Falls Church, VA 22041; tel. 703/933–1003; FAX. 703/933–1004; Helen M. Larsen, JD, Executive Director

National Association Medical Staff Services, 631 East Butterfield, Suite 311, Lombard, IL 60148; tel. 630/271–9814; FAX. 630/271–0295; Robert A. Dengler, CAE, CMP, Executive Director

National Association of Boards of Pharmacy, 700 Busse Highway, Park Ridge, IL 60068; tel. 847/698–6227; FAX. 847/698–0124; Carmen A. Catizone, R.Ph., M.S., Executive Director/ Secretary

National Association of Children's Hospitals and Related Institutes, 401 Wythe Street, Alexandria, VA 22314; tel. 703/684–1355; FAX. 703/684–1589; Lawrence A. McAndrews, President and CEO

National Association of Dental Assistants, 900 South Washington Street, Suite G13, Falls Church, VA 22046; tel. 703/237–8616; FAX. 703/533–1153; S. Young, Director

National Association of Dental Laboratories, (Includes National Board for Certification in Dental Laboratory Technology), 1530 Metropolitan Boulevard, Tallahassee, FL 32308; tel. 800/950–1150; FAX. 850/222–0053; Bennett Napier, CAE, Executive Director

National Association of Health Services Executives, 8630 Fenton Street, Suite 126, Silver Spring, MD 20910; tel. 202/628–3953; FAX. 301/588–0011; Ozzie Jenkins, CMP, Association Manager

National Association of Psychiatric Health Systems, 325 Seventh Street, NW, Suite 625, Washington, DC 20004-2802; tel. 202/393–6700; FAX. 202/783–6041; Mark J. Covall, Executive Director

National Association of Social Workers, 750 First Street, N.E., Suite 700, Washington, DC 20002; tel. 202/408–8600; FAX. 202/336–8327; Elizabeth Clark, Ph.D., Executive Director

National Association of State Mental Health Program Directors, 66 Canal Center Plaza, Suite 302, Alexandria, VA 22314; tel. 703/739–9333; FAX. 703/548–9517; Robert W. Glover, Ph.D., Executive Director

National Board for Respiratory Care, 8310 Nieman Road, Lenexa, KS 66214; tel. 913/599–4200; FAX. 913/541–0156; Gary A. Smith, Executive Director

National Board of Anesthesiology, Inc, 11817 Summit, Kansas, MO 64114; tel. 785/842–7067; FAX. 816/836–8953; R. Scott Richart, JD, Executive Director

National Board of Medical Examiners, 3750 Market Street, Philadelphia, PA 19104; tel. 215/590–9500; FAX. 215/590–9755; Donald E. Melnick, M.D., President

National Children's Eye Care Foundation, P.O. Box 795069, Dallas, TX 75379-5069; tel. 972/407–0404; FAX. 972/407–0616

National Council of State Boards of Nursing, 111 E. Wacker Dr., Suite 2900, Chicago, IL 60601; tel. 312/525–3600; FAX. 312/279–1032

National Council on Alcoholism and Drug Dependence, Inc., 22 Cortland Street, 8th floor, New York, NY 1000; tel. 212/269–7797; FAX. 212/269–7510; Ames K. Sweet, Director of Communications

National Council on Radiation Protection and Measurements, 7910 Woodmont Avenue, Suite 400, Bethesda, MD 20814; tel. 301/657–2652; FAX. 301/907–8768; David A. Schauer, Executive Director

National Council on the Aging, Inc., 300 D Street, SW, Suite 801, Washington, DC 20024; tel. 202/479–1200; FAX. 202/479–0735; James Firman, President & CEO

National Dental Association, 3517 16th Street, NW, Washington, DC 20010; tel. 202/588–1697; FAX. 202/588–1244; Robert S. Johns, Executive Director

National Environmental Health Association, 720 South Colorado Boulevard, South Tower, Suite, Suite 970, Denver, CO 80246; tel. 303/756–9090; FAX. 303/691–9490; Nelson Fabian, Executive Director

National Federation of Licensed Practical Nurses, 605 Poole Dr., Garner, NC 27529; tel. 919/779–0046; FAX. 919/779–5642; Charlene Barbour, Executive Director

National Fire Protection Association, P.O. Box 9101, One Batterymarck Park, Quincy, MA 02269-9101; tel. 617/770–3000; FAX. 617/770–7110; Richard P. Bielen, P.E. Chief Systems and Applications Engineer

National Gaucher Foundation, 5410 Edson Lane, Suite 260, Rockville, MD 20852; tel. 301/816–1515; FAX. 301/816–1516; Rhonda Buyers, Executive Director

National Headache Foundation, 820 N. Orleans, Suite 217, Chicago, IL 60610-3132; tel. 888/NHF–5552; FAX. 312/640–9049; Suzanne Simons, Executive Director

National Health Council, Inc., 1730 M Street, N.W., Suite 500, Washington, DC 20036; tel. 202/785–3910; FAX. 202/785–5923; Myrl Weinberg, CAE, President

National Hemophilia Foundation, 116 West 32nd Street, 11th Floor, New York, NY 10001; tel. 212/328–3700; FAX. 212/328–3795; Alan J. Kinniburgh, PH.D, CEO

National Institute for Jewish Hospice, Central Telephone Network, P.O. Box 48025, Los Angeles, CA 90048; tel. 800/446–4448

National Kidney Foundation, 30 East 33rd Street, New York, NY 10016; tel. 800/622–9010; FAX. 212/779–0068; John Davis, Chief Executive Officer

National Mental Health Association, 1021 Prince Street, Alexandria, VA 22314-2971; tel. 800/969–6642; FAX. 703/684–5968; Michael M. Faenza, President and CEO

National Multiple Sclerosis Society, 733 Third Avenue, New York, NY 10017; tel. 212/986–3240; FAX. 212/986–7981; Dwayne Howell, Executive Vice President

National Parkinson Foundation, Inc., 1501 Northwest Ninth Avenue, Miami, FL 33136-1494; tel. 305/547–6666; FAX. 305/243–5540; Pamela Olmo, Controller

National Perinatal Association, 2090 Linglestown Rd, suite 107, Harrisburg, PA 17110; tel. 888/971–3295; FAX. 717/920–1390; Albert Pizzica, MD President

National Recreation and Park Association, 22377 Belmont Ridge Road, Ashburn, VA 20148; tel. 703/858–0784; FAX. 703/858–0794; John Thorner, Executive Director

National Registry of Emergency Medical Technicians, 6610 Busch Boulevard, P.O. Box 29233, Columbus, OH 43229; tel. 614/888–4484; FAX. 614/888–8920; William E. Brown, Jr., Executive Director

National Rehabilitation Association, (Includes Eight National Divisions and 58 Affiliate Chapters), 633 South Washington Street, Alexandria, VA 22314; tel. 703/836–0850; FAX. 703/836–0848; Linda R. Winslow, Executive Director

National Resident Matching Program, 2450 N Street, N.W., Washington, DC 1127; tel. 202/828–0676; FAX. 202/828–4797; Robert L. Beran, Ph. D., Executive Director

National Rural Health Association, 1307 Duke Street, Alexandria, VA 22314-3509; tel. 703/519–7910; FAX. 703/519–3865; Alan Morgan, Vice President for Government Affairs

National Safety Council, P.O. Box 558, Itasca, IL 60143-0558; tel. 800/621–7619; FAX. 630/285–0797; Customer Service Department

National Student Nurses' Association, Inc., 45 Main Street, Suite 606, Brooklyn, NY 11201; tel. 718/210–0705; FAX. 718/210–0710; Diane J. Mancino, Ed.D., RN, CAE, Executive Director

National Tay-Sachs and Allied Diseases Association, 2001 Beacon Street, Suite 204, Brighton, MA 02135; tel. 800/90–NTSAD; FAX. 617/277–0134; Jayne C. Gershkowitz, Executive Director

New England Gerontological Association, One Cutts Road, Durham, NH 03824-3102; tel. 603/868–5757; Eugene E. Tillock, Ed.D., Executive Director

New York State Nurses Association, NYSNA, 11 Cornel Road, Latham, NY 12110-1499; tel. 518/782–9400; FAX. 518/782–9530; Gene Tranbarger Ed. D., RN

NSF International, 789 Dixboro Road, P.O. Box 130140, Ann Arbor, MI 48113-0140; tel. 313/769–8010; FAX. 313/769–0109; Dennis R. Mangino, Ph. D., President and CEO

O

Osteogenesis Imperfecta Foundation, Inc., 804 West Diamond Avenue, Suite 210, Gaithersburg, MD 20878; tel. 301/947–0083; FAX. 301/947–0456; Heller An Shapiro, Executive Director

P

Pan American Health Organization/Regional Office of the World Health Organization, 525 23rd Street, N.W., Washington, DC 20037; tel. 202/974–3221; FAX. 202/974–3613; Director Of Program Manager (DPH)

Parkinson's Disease Foundation, Inc, (Formerly United Parkinson Foundation), 833 West Washington Boulevard, Chicago, IL 60607; tel. 312/733–1893; FAX. 312/733–1896; Jeanne Lee - Rosner, Manager

Physician Executive Management Center, 3403 West Fletcher Avenue, Tampa, FL 33618-2813; tel. 813/963–1800; FAX. 813/264–2207; David R. Kirschman, President

Pilot Dogs, Inc., 625 West Town Street, Columbus, OH 43215; tel. 614/221–6367; FAX. 614/221–1577; J. Jay Gray, Executive Director

Prevent Blindness America, 211 W. Wacker Drive, Suite 1700, Chicago, IL 60606; tel. 800/331–2020; FAX. 312/363–6052; Hugh Parry, President & Chief Executive Officer

Public Relations Society of America, 33 Maiden Lane 11th Floor, New York, NY 10038-5150; tel. 212/460–1400; FAX. 212/995–0757; Catherine A. Bolton, Executive Director and COO

R

Radiological Society of North America, Inc., 820 Jorie Boulevard, Oak Brook, IL 60523-2251; tel. 630/571–2670; FAX. 630/571–7837; Joe Taylor, Marketing Communications

Recording for the Blind and Dyslexic, 20 Roszel Road, Princeton, NJ 08540; tel. 609/452–0606; FAX. 609/520–7990; Richard O. Scribner, President

Renal Physicians Association, 2011 Pennsylvania Avenue, N.W., Suite 800, Washington, DC 20006-1808; tel. 202/835–0436; FAX. 202/835–0443; Dale Singer, MHA, Executive Director

Robert Wood Johnson Foundation, P.O. Box 2316, Route One and College Road East, Princeton, NJ 08543-2316; tel. 609/452–8701; FAX. 888/727–1966; Richard J. Toth, Director, Office of Proposal Management

S

Shriners Hospitals for Children, P.O. Box 31356, Tampa, FL 33631-3356; tel. 813/281–0300; FAX. 813/281–8113; Lewis K. Molnar, Executive Vice President

Sickle Cell Institute, 521 5th Avenue, New York, NY 10175; tel. 212/292–4332; FAX. 212/682–5844

Society for Academic Emergency Medicine, 901 North Washington Avenue, Lansing, MI 48906; tel. 517/485–5484; FAX. 517/485–0801; Mary Ann Schropp, Executive Director

Society for Adolescent Medicine, Inc., 1916 NW Copper Oaks Circle, Blue Springs, MO 64015; tel. 816/224–8010; FAX. 816/224–8009; Edie Moore, Executive Director

Society for Healthcare Consumer Advocacy (SHCA), One North Franklin, 31st Floor, Chicago, IL 60606; tel. 312/422–3907; FAX. 312/422–4575; Glen Brown, Executive Director

Society for Healthcare Strategy and Market Development, of the American Hospital Association, One North Franklin, 28th Floor, Chicago, IL 60606; tel. 312/422–3888; FAX. 312/422–4579; Lauren A. Barnett, Executive Director

Society for Occupational and Environmental Health, 6728 Old McLean Village Drive, McLean, VA 22101; tel. 703/556–9222; FAX. 703/556–8729; Connie MacKay, Account Manager

Society for Pediatric Pathology, 3643 Walton Way, Augusta, GA 30909; tel. 706/364–3375; FAX. 706/733–8033; James Crimmins, Administrator

Society for Social Work Leadership in Health Care (SSWLHC), 1211 Locust Street, Philadelphia, PA 19107; tel. 866/237–9542; FAX. 215/545–8107; Joe Braden, President

Society of Critical Care Medicine, 701 Lee Street, Suite 200, Des Plaines, IL 60016; tel. 847/827–6869; FAX. 847/827–6886; David J. Martin, CAE, Chief Executive Officer/EVP

Society of Neurological Surgeons, New England Medical Center, Department of Neurosurgery, Boston, MA 02111; tel. 617/636–5858; William Shucart, M.D., Secretary

Society of Nuclear Medicine, 1850 Samuel Morse Drive, Reston, VA 20190-5316; tel. 703/708–9000; FAX. 703/708–9777; Mac Cannon, Administrator

Society of University Otolaryngologists-Head and Neck Surgeons, USC School of Medicine, Department of Otolaryngology, Los Angeles, CA 90033; tel. 323/226–7315; FAX. 323/226–2780; Donna Hoffman, M.A., Executive Director

Southeastern Healthcare Association, 4150 Carmichael Court, P.O. Box 11126, Montgomery, AL 36111-0126; tel. 334/260–8600; FAX. 205/260–0023; Tommy R. McDougal, FACHE, President

Special Care Dentistry, 401 N. Michigan Ave, Chicago, IL 60611; tel. 312/527–6764; FAX. 312/440–2824; Kristen Smith

T

Technologist Section, Society of Nuclear Medicine, 1850 Samuel Morse Drive, Reston, VA 20190; tel. 703/708–9000; FAX. 703/708–9013; Virginia M. Pappas, Executive Director

The American Association of Immunologists, 9650 Rockville Pike, Bethesda, MD 20814; tel. 301/530–7178; FAX. 301/571–1816; M. Michele Hogan, Ph.D., Executive Director

The American Board of Obstetrics and Gynecology, Inc., 2915 Vine Street, Dallas, TX 75204; tel. 214/871–1619; FAX. 214/871–1943; Dr. Norman F. Gant, Executive Director

The American Board of Pediatric Dentistry, 325 E. Washington Street, Suite 101, Iowa City, IA 52240-3959; tel. 319/341–8488; FAX. 319/341–9499; Arthur J. Nowak, Executive Director

Section C

The American Board of Plastic Surgery, Inc., Seven Penn Center, Suite 400, 1635 Market Street, Philadelphia, PA 19103-2204; tel. 215/587–9322; FAX. 215/587–9622; Terry M. Cullison, RN, MSN, Administrator

The American Board of Professional Disability Consultants, 1350 Beverly Road, Suite 115-327, McLean, VA 22101; tel. 703/790–8644; Taras J. Cerkevitch, Ph.D., Director, Operations

The American Board of Urology, Inc., 2216 Ivy Road, Suite 210, Charlottesville, VA 22903; tel. 434/979–0059; FAX. 434/979–0266; Stuart S. Howards, M.D., Executive Secretary

The American Orthopaedic Association, 6300 North River Road, Suite 505, Rosemont, IL 60018-4263; tel. 847/318–7330; FAX. 847/318–7339; Christine C. Eme Director Of Academic and Members Services

The Arc of the United States, 1010 Wayne Ave, Suite 650, Silver Spring, MD 60910; tel. 301/565–3842; FAX. 301/565–3843; Steven M. Eidelman, Executive Director

The Association for Research in Vision and Ophthalmology, 12300 Twinbrook Parkway, Suite 250, Rockville, MD 20852-1606; tel. 240/221–2900; FAX. 240/221–0370; Joanne G. Angle, Executive Director

The Association of Medical Illustrators, 245 1st Street, Suite 1800, Cambridge, MA 02142; tel. 617/395–8186; FAX. 617/812–0208; Janet McAndless, Executive Director

The Association of Women's Health, Obstetric and Neonatal Nurses, 2000 L. Street, NW, Suite 740, Washington, DC 20036; tel. 202/261–2400; FAX. 202/728–0575; Gail G. Kincaide, Executive Director

The Duke Endowment, 100 North Tryon Street, Suite 3500, Charlotte, NC 28202; tel. 704/376–0291; FAX. 704/376–9336; Elizabeth H. Locke, President

The Endocrine Society, 4350 East West Highway, Suite 500, Bethesda, MD 20814-4410; tel. 301/941–0200; FAX. 301/941–0259; Susan Koppi, Director, Public Affairs

The Foundation Fighting Blindness, 11435 Crohill Drive, Owings Mill,, MD 21117-2220; tel. 410/568–0150; FAX. 410/363–2393; Mitsy Palmer, Constat. Serv. Coord.

The Foundation for Ichthyosis and Related Skin Types, Inc., (F.I.R.S.T.), 1601 Valley Forge Road, Lansdale, PA 19446; tel. 215/631–1411; FAX. 215/631–1413; Jean Pickford, Executive Director

The Institute for Rehabilitation and Research Systems, 5100 Travis, Houston, TX 77002; tel. 713/528–0123; FAX. 713/528–4554; John Kajander, President & CEO

The International Dyslexia Association, (Formerly The Orton Dyslexia Society), Chester Building, Suite 382, 8600 LaSalle Road, Baltimore, MD 21286-2044; tel. 410/296–0232; FAX. 410/321–5069; Judith Dudek, Director, Marketing and Membership

The Leukemia & Lymphoma Society, 1311 Mamaroneck Avenue, White Plains, NY 10650; tel. 914/949–5213; FAX. 914/949–6691; Dwayne Howell, President and CEO

The Salvation Army National Corporation, 615 Slaters Lane, P.O. Box 269, Alexandria, VA 22313; tel. 703/684–5500; FAX. 703/684–3478; Lt. Colonel Paul E. Bollwahn, National Social Services Secretary

The Seeing Eye, Inc., P.O. Box 375, Morristown, NJ 07963-0375; tel. 973/539–4425; FAX. 973/539–0922; Kenneth Rosenthal, President

The Southwestern Surgical Congress, 401 North Michigan Avenue, Chicago, IL 60611-4267; tel. 312/527–6667; FAX. 312/527–6658; Mary Beth Hepp, Executive Director

U

UCLA Medical Center, Neurosurgery, Box 957039, Room 74-134 CHS, Los Angeles, CA 90095-7039; tel. 310/794–1222; FAX. 310/825–7245; Donald P. Becker, M.D.

United Cerebral Palsy Associations, Inc., 1660 L Street, N.W., Suite 700, Washington, DC 20036; tel. 800/872–5827; Stephen Bennett, President and CEO

United Methodist Association of Health and Welfare Ministries, 407 Corporate Center Dr., Suite B, Vandalia, OH 45377; tel. 937/227–9494; FAX. 937/222–7364; Mearle L. Griffith, President and CEO

United Ostomy Association, Inc., 19772 MacArthur Boulevard, Suite 200, Irvine, CA 92613; tel. 800/826–0826; FAX. 949/660–9262; Nancy Italia, Executive Director

United Way of America, 701 North Fairfax Street, Alexandria, VA 22314-2045; tel. 703/836–7100; FAX. 703/683–7846; Brian A. Gallagher, President and CEO

USP, 12601 Twinbrook Parkway, Rockville, MD 20852; tel. 301/881–0666; FAX. 301/816–8299; Angela G. Long, Program Director, Professional Affairs

W

Western Orthopedic Association, 1834 First Street, Suite 3, Napa, CA 94559-2353; tel. 707/259–9481; FAX. 707/259–9486; Stephen Oliver, Executive Director

Western Surgical Association, Mayo Clinic, 200 First Street, S.W., Rochester, MN 55905; Jon A. VanHeerden, M.D., Secretary

ARGENTINA

Argentinean Association of Dermatology (AAD), Asociacion Argentina De Dermatologia, Mexico 1720, 1100 Buenos Aires; tel. 1143812737; FAX. 1143831153; Dra. Lidia Ester Valle, Chairman

Camara Argentina De Empresas De Salud, (Argentina Hospital Association), Tucuman 1668, 2 Piso, C.P. 1050 Buenos Aires; tel. 541143725915; FAX. 541143723229; Norberto Larroca-President

AUSTRALIA

Australian Healthcare Association, P.O. Box 54, Deakin West, 2600; tel. +612 6285148; FAX. +612 6282235; Executive Director

BELGIUM

International Federation of Oto-Rhino-Laryngological Societies, IFOS-MISA-NKO Oosterveldlaan 24, 2610 WILRIJK; tel. *32/34433614; FAX. *32/34433611; Ms. Wydoodts, Administrator, Publication Manager

Verbond der Verzorgingsinstellingen V.Z.W., 1, Guimardstraat, Brussels 1040; tel. 003225070150; FAX. 2 5135269; Mrs. C. Boonen, M.D., General Manager

BRAZIL

Fraternidade Crista De Doentes E Deficientes, Cap. Correa Pacheco 134, Americana, SP; tel. 0 194 619754; Celso Zoppi

CANADA

Association des Medecins de langue francaise du Canada, 8355 St. Laurent Boulevard, Montreal, PQ H2P 2Z6; tel. 514/388–2228; FAX. 514/388–5335; Andre' de Seve, General Director

Canadian Anesthesiologists' Society, One Eglinton Avenue East, Suite 208, Toronto, ON M4P 3A1; tel. 416/480–0602; FAX. 416/480–0320; Angela Snider, Executive Director

Canadian Association of Pathologists, Office of the Secretariat, 774 Echo Drive, Ottawa, ON K1S 5N8; tel. 613–730–6230; FAX. 613/730–1116; Dr. Laurette Geldenhuys, Secretary-Treasurer

Canadian Association of Social Workers, 383 Parkdale Avenue, Suite 402, Ottawa, ON K1Y 4R4; tel. 613/729–6668; FAX. 613/729–9608; Eugenia Repetur Moreno, Executive Director

Canadian Blood Services, Head Office, 1800 Alta Vista Drive, Ottawa, ON K1G 4J5; tel. 613/739–2300; FAX. 613/731–1411; Graham Sher, CEO

Canadian Cancer Society, 10 Alcorn Avenue, Suite 200, Toronto, ON M4V 3B1; tel. 416/961–7223; FAX. 416/961–4189; Barbara Whylie,Chief Executive Officer

Canadian Cardiovascular Society, 222 Queen Street, Suite 1403, Ottawa, On K1P 5V9; tel. 613/569–3407; FAX. 613/569–6574; Anne Fegruson, Executive Director

Canadian College of Health Record Administrators, Canadian Health Record Association, 1090 Don Mills Road, Suite 501, Don Mills, ON M3C 3R6; tel. 416/447–4900; FAX. 416/447–4598; Gail Crook, Executive Director

Canadian Council of the Blind, 396 Cooper Street, Suite 401, Ottawa, ON K2P 2H7; tel. 613/567–0311; FAX. 613/567–2728; Jim Prolose, Executive Director- National

Canadian Council on Social Development, 309 Cooper Street, 5th floor, Ottawa, ON K2P 0G5; tel. 613/236–8977; FAX. 613/236–2750; Nancy Perkins, Communications Coordinator

Canadian Dental Association, 1815 Alta Vista Drive, Ottawa, ON K1G 3Y6; tel. 613/523–1770; FAX. 613/523–5675; Mr. George Weber, Executive Director

Canadian Healthcare Association, 17 York Street, Suite 100, Ottawa, ON K1N 9J6; tel. 613/241–8005; FAX. 613/241–5055; Sharon Sholzberg-Gray, President & CEO

Canadian Medical Engineering Consultants, 594 Bush Street, Belfountain, ON LON 1B0; tel. 519/927–3286; FAX. 519/927–9440; A. M. Dolan, President

Canadian Mental Health Association, 8 King Street, East, Suite 810, Toronto, ON MSC 1B5; tel. 416/484–7750; FAX. 416/484–4617; Penelope Marrat, General Director

Canadian National Institute for the Blind, 320 McLeod Street, Ottawa, ON K2P1A3; tel. 416/480–7445; FAX. 416/480–7677; Angelo Nikias, National Director

Canadian Nurses Association, 50 Driveway, Ottawa, ON K2P 1E2; tel. 613/237–2133; FAX. 613/237–3520; Lucille Auffrey, RN, MN, Executive Director

Canadian Orthopaedic Association, 1440 Ste. Catherine Street, W., Suite 718, Montreal, PQ H3G 1R8; tel. 514/874–9003; FAX. 514/874–0464; Doug Thomson, CEO

Canadian Pharmacists Association, 1785 Alta Vista Drive, Ottawa, ON K1G 3Y6; tel. 613/523–7877; FAX. 613/523–0445; Jeff Poston, Executive Director

Canadian Physiotherapy Association, National Office, 2345 Yonge Street, Suite 410, Toronto, ON M4P 2E5; tel. 416/932–1888; FAX. 416/932–9708; Pamela C. Fralick, CEO

Canadian Psychiatric Association, 701-141 Laurier Ave W., Ottawa, ON KIP5J3; tel. 613/234–2815; FAX. 613/234–9857; Alex Saunders, Chief Executive Officer

Canadian Public Health Association, 1565 Carling Avenue, Suite 400, Ottawa, ON K1Z 8R1; tel. 613/725–3769; FAX. 613/725–9826; Elinor Wilson, RN, PhD, Chief Executive Officer

Canadian Society for Medical Laboratory Science, Box 2830, LCD 1, Hamilton, ON L8N 3N8; tel. 905/528–8642; FAX. 905/528–4968; Kurt H. Davis, Executive Director

Canadian Society of Hospital Pharmacists, 30 Concourse Gate, Unit 3, Ottawa, ON K2E7V7; tel. 613/736–9733; FAX. 613/736–5660; Janet Lett, Executive Assistant

Catholic Health Association of Canada, 1247 Kilborn Place, Ottawa, ON K1H 6K9; tel. 613/731–7148; FAX. 613/731–7797; Dr. Richard Haughian, President

College des medecins du Quebec, 2170, boul. Rene-Levesque Quest, Montreal, PQ H3H 2T8; tel. 514/933–4441; FAX. 514/993–3112; Andre Garon, M.D., Secretary General

Dietitians of Canada/Les dietetistes du Canada, 480 University Avenue, Suite 604, Toronto, ON M5G 1V2; tel. 416/596–0857; FAX. 416/596–0603; Marsha Sharp, Chief Executive Officer

National Cancer Institute of Canada, 10 Alcorn Avenue, Suite 200, Toronto, ON M4V 3B1; tel. 416/961–7223; FAX. 416/961–4189; Barbara Whylie, CEO

The Canadian Hearing Society, 271 Spadina Road, Toronto, ON M5R 2V3; tel. 416/928–2500; FAX. 416/928–2506; Kelly Duffin, President & CEO

The Canadian Medical Association, 1867 Alta Vista Drive, Ottawa, ON K1G 3Y60G8; tel. 613/731–9331; FAX. 613/731–7314; Dana Hanson, M.D., President

The College of Family Physicians of Canada, 2630 Skymark Avenue, Mississauga, ON L4W 5A4; tel. 905/629–0900; FAX. 905/629–0893

The College of Physicians and Surgeons of New Brunswick, One Hampton Road, Suite 300, Rothesay, NB E2E 5K8; tel. 506/849–5050; FAX. 506/849–5069; Ed Schollenberg, M.D., Registrar

The Royal College of Physicians and Surgeons of Canada, 774 Echo Drive, Ottawa, ON K1S 5N8; tel. 613/730–6201; FAX. 613/730–8250; Ms. Pierrette Leonard, APR, Public Affairs Officer

World Federation of Hemophilia, 1425 Rene Levesque Blvd. West, Suite 1010, Montreal, PQ H3G 1T7; tel. 514/8757944; FAX. 514/8758916; Mr. Miklos Fulop, Executive Director

COSTA RICA

Associacion Coctarricense De Hospitales, (Costa Rica Hospital Association), Aparatado 267, 1005 San Jose; tel. 506/255–0363; FAX. 506/221–4919; Carlos Enrique Fuentes Bolanos

DENMARK

Amtsradsforeningen, Dampfaergevej 22, Postboks 2593, Copenhagen; tel. +453529 8196; FAX. +453529 8337; Peder Ring, Assistant Director

Danish Dental Association, Amaliegade 17, Postboks 143, Copenhagen; tel. 45 70257711; FAX. 45 251537; Eric Schmaker, Chairman

Danish Regions, DAMPFAEORGEVEJ 22, P.O. Box 2593; tel. +453529800100; FAX. +4535298300; Peter Ring, Assistant Director

National Committee for Danish Hospitals, Dampfaergevej 22, Postboks 2593; tel. 45 35298196; FAX. 45 35298337; Peder Ring, Assistant Director

ENGLAND

British Medical Association, B.M.A. House Tavistock Square, London, WCIH 9JP; tel. 02073874499; FAX. 02073836400; Mr. J. Strachan, M.A. LLM Barrister Secretary

European Association of Poisons/Centres and Clinical Toxicology, Hopitaux Universitaires de Strasbourg, Hospital de Hautepierre, Cedex; tel. 33/388127906; FAX. 33/388127908; Dr. Bateman, President

Institute of Healthcare Management, 7-10 Chandos Street, London,WIM,9DE; tel. 02078819235; FAX. 02078819236; Sandra White, Chair

International Hospital Federation, International Hospital Federation, 46 Grosvenor Gardens, London, SW1WOEB; tel. 44/207881922; FAX. 44/207881922; Professor Per-Gunnar Svensson, Director General

King's Fund, 11-13 Cavendish Square, London, W1G 0AN; tel. 020 73072400; FAX. 020 73072801; Rabbi Julia Neuberger, Chief Executive

Nuffield Trust, 59 New Cavendish Street, London WIG 7LP; tel. 02076318450; FAX. 02076318451; John Wyn Owen, Secretary

FINLAND

National Research and Development Centre for Welfare and Health Stakes, Lintulahdenkuja4, P.O. Box 220, 00531 Helsinki; Ilmo Keskimaki, Research Director

FRANCE

Federation hospitaliere De France, (France Hospital Association), Avenue d'Italie 33, Paris 75013; tel. 003314406486; FAX. 003314406844; Pascal Garel- Deputy Director

World Medical Association, P.O. Box 63 - 01212 Ferney-Voltaire Cedex; tel. 33450407575; FAX. 33450405937; Dr. Otmar Kloiber, Secretary General

GERMANY

Deutsche Krankenhausgesellschaft e.v., (German Hospital Federation), Wegelstrabe 3, D - 10623 Berlin; tel. +4930398040; FAX. 493039087307; Jorg Robbers, Managing Director

International Academy of Cytology, Burgunderstr. 1, 79104 Freiburg; tel. 497612923801; FAX. 497612923802; Volker Schneider, M.D., FIAC, Office of Secretary General

HUNGARY

Magyar Korhazszovetseg, (Hungarian Hospital Association), Fogaskereku U.4-6., 1125 Budapest; tel. 36–12145118; FAX. 36–12149715; Dr. Zoltan Ajkay, President

INDIA

Indian Hospital Association, B-401 Sarita Vihar, New Delhi, 110044; tel. 69699; FAX. 91–11–694126; Dr. P.Ghez, Secretary General

INDONESIA

Indonesian Hospital Association (PERSI), Jl. Danau Sunter Utara, Blok J 12/68, Sunter Podomoro, Jakarta,, Utara, 14350; tel. 6221 6510962; FAX. 6221 6514531; Adib A. Yahya, MD President

ITALY

Federazione Italiana delle Aziende Sanitarie e Ospedaliere (FIASO), (Italy Hospital Association), Azienda Ospedaliera S Orsola Malpoghi Via Albertoni 15, 40138 Bologna

KOREA

Korean Hospital Association, (Mapo Hyun Dai Building), 35-1 Mapo-dong; tel. 2 7187521; FAX. 2 7187522; (Internation Cooperation Officer)

MANGOLIA

Mongolian Hospital Association, P.O. Box 48/146, MHSW Olympic Street

MEXICO

Asociacion Mexicana De Hospitales AC, (Mexico Hospital Association), Queretaro 210, Col Roma Mexico DF, 06700; tel. 55740135; FAX. 55841882; LIC. Francisco Spindola Salazar, Manager

Federacion Latinoamericana de Hospitales, Apartado Postal 107-076, C.P. 06741; tel. 5 482650; Dr. Guillermo Fajardo, Representative

NORWAY

Norsk Sykehus Helsetjenesten, (Norway Hospital Association), Nedre Slottsgt 7, 0157 Oslo, Norske Kommuners sentralforbund, Vika Oslo 1

Section C

PANAMA

Asociacion Panamena De Hospitales Privados, (Panama Hospital Association), Apartado 0816 - 03075, Panama, Rep. De Panama; tel. 507/265–8881; FAX. 507/265–8862; Rodrigo A. Moreno T/., President

PERU

Peruvian Hospital Association, Av. Dos De Mayo 8502 Of. 203, San Isidro, L; tel. 14 419546; Arturo Vasi Paez, President

PHILIPPINES

Philippine Hospital Association, 14 Kamias Road, Quezon City-1; tel. 2 9227674/75; Thelma Navarrete-Clemente, M.D., M.H.A., President

SOUTH AFRICA

Provincial Administration, Health Services Branch, P.O. Box 517; tel. 051/4055818; FAX. 051/304958; Dr. J. H. Kotze

South African Hospital Federation, Department of Health, Facilities Planning and Hospital, Private Bag X828, Pretoria 0001

SWEDEN

Federation of Swedish County Councils, S-118 82 Stockholm; tel. +4684527200; FAX. +4684527210; Kicki Nilsson, Assistant

SWITZERLAND

H+ Die Spitaler der Schweiz, (Swiss Hospital Association), Lorrainestrasse 4A; tel. 044^3^335^^^; FAX. 004^3^335^^7; Geschaftsstelle

TAIWAN

Hospital Association of Taiwan, 25 F, No 29-5, Section 2, Jhongheng East Road; tel. 886228083300; FAX. 886228083304; Grace Y. L. Hsu, Head of Department

UNITED STATES

Association for Assessment and Accreditation of Laboratory Animal Care International, 11300 Rockville Pike, Suite 1211, Rockville, MD 20852-3035; tel. 301/231–5353; FAX. 301/231–8282; Dr. John G. Miller, Executive Director

Association for Volunteer Administration, P.O. Box 32092, Richmond, VA 23294; tel. 804/672–3353; FAX. 804/346–3318; John Throop, Executive Director

ASTM International, 100 Barr Harbor Drive, West Conshoho, PA 19428-2959; tel. 610/832–9672; FAX. 610/832–9666; Kenneth C. Pearson, Vice President

International Aid, 17011 West Hickory, Spring Lake, MI 49456-9712; tel. 616/846–7490; FAX. 616/846–3842; Sonny Enriquez, VP of International Programs

International Association for Dental Research, 1619 Duke Street, Alexandria, VA 22314-3406; tel. 703/548–0066; FAX. 703/548–1883; Christopher Fox, Executive Director

International Association of Ocular Surgeons, 820 North Orleans, Suite 208, Chicago, IL 60610; tel. 800/621–4002; FAX. 312/440–0580; Randall T. Bellows, M.D., Director

International Association of Society for Quality of Life Research, 6728 Old McLean Village Drive, McLean, VA 22101; tel. 703/556–9222; FAX. 703/556–8729; Bette Anne German, Association Mgr.

International Essential Tremor Foundation, P. O. Box 14005, Lenexa, KS 66285-4005; tel. 888/387–3667; FAX. 913/341–1296; Catherine S. Rice, Executive Director

International Executive Housekeepers Association, Inc., 1001 Eastwind Drive, Suite 301, Westerville, OH 43081-3361; tel. 800/200–6342; FAX. 614/895–1248; Beth Risinger, CEO/ Executive Director

Rehabilitation International, 25 East 21st Street, New York, NY 10010; tel. 212/420–1500; FAX. 212/505–0871; Thomas Lagerwall, Secretary General

Sigma Theta Tau International Honor Society of Nursing, 550 West North Street, Indianapolis, IN 46202; tel. 317/634–8171; FAX. 317/634–8188; Nancy A. Dickenson-Hazard, Chief Executive Officer

U.S. Council on International Social Welfare, 750 First Street, N.E., Washington, DC 20002; tel. 202/336–8274; FAX. 202/336–8311; Helen Whetzel, Secretary; M. Carpenter, Volunteer Coordinator

World Federation of Public Health Associations, c/o APHA, 800 I Street NW, Washington, DC 20001-3710; tel. 202/777–2487; FAX. 202/777–2533; Allen K. Jones, Ph.D., Secretary - General

VENEZUELA

Latin American Association for the Study of the Liver (LAASL), P.O. Box 51890, Sabana Grande, Venezuela; tel. 58–2–9799380; FAX. 58–2–9799380; Dr. Miguel A. Garassini, President

U. S. GOVERNMENT AGENCIES

The following information is based on data available as of June, 2005.
For more information about U.S. government agencies, consult the U.S. Government Manual, available from the
Office of the Federal Register, National Archives and Records Service, Washington, DC 20408. A telephone
directory of the U.S. Department of Health and Human Services is available from the Superintendent of Documents,
Government Printing Office, Washington, DC 20402. Additional assistance may be obtained by contacting the
American Hospital Association's Washington office, 325 Seventh Street, N.W., Washington, DC 20004.

Centers for Disease Control and Prevention
1600 Clifton Avenue Road NE
Atlanta, GA 30333
404/639-3311
Dr. Julie L. Gerberding, Director
http://www.cdc.gov

Centers for Medicare & Medicaid Services
200 Independence
Washington, DC 20201
202/690-6726
Mark B. McClellan, Administrator
http://www.cms.gov

Council of Economic Advisors
Old Executive Office Building
Washington, DC 20502
202/395-5084
Ben S. Bernanke, Chairman
http://www.whitehouse.gov/wh/eop/cea/html

Council on Environmental Quality
Old Executive Office Building
Room 360
Washington, DC 20503
202/395-5750
James Connaughton, Chairman
http://www.whitehouse.gov/ceq

Department of Agriculture
Fourteenth Street and Independence Avenue SW
Washington, DC 20250
202/720-2791
Mike Johanns, Secretary of Agriculture
http://www.usda.gov

Department of Commerce
Fourteenth Street between Constitution and
Pennsylvania Avenues NW
Washington, DC 20230
202/482-2000
Carlos Gutierrez, Secretary of Commerce
http://www.doc.gov

Department of Defense
Office of the Secretary
The Pentagon
Washington, DC 20301-1155
703/545-6700
Donald Rumsfeld, Secretary of Defense
http://www.defenselink.mil

Department of Education
600 Independence Avenue SW
Washington, DC 20202
800/USA-LEAR
Margaret Spellings, Secretary of Education
http://www.ed.gov

Department of Energy
1000 Independence Avenue SW
Washington, DC 20585
202/586-5000

Samuel Bodman, Secretary of Energy
http://www.doe.gov

Department of Health and Human Services
200 Independence Avenue SW
Washington, DC 20201
202/619-0257
Mike Leavitt, Secretary of Health and Human Services
http://www.dhhs.gov

Department of Justice
Tenth Street and Constitution Avenue, NW
Washington, DC 20530
202/514-2000
Alberto R. Gonzales, The Attorney General
http://www.usdoj.gov

Department of Labor
200 Constitution Avenue NW
Washington, DC 20210
202/219-5000
Elaine L. Chao, Secretary of Labor
http://www.dol.gov

Department of State
2201 C. Street NW
Washington, DC 20520
202/647-4000
Condoleezza Rice, Secretary of State
http://www.state.gov

Department of the Air Force
1670 Air Force Pentagon
Washington, DC 20330-1670
202/720-3631
James G. Roche, Secretary of the Air Force

Department of the ARMY
The Pentagon
Washington, DC 20310
703/545-6700
Thomas E. White, Secretary of the ARMY
http://www.army.mil

Department of the NAVY
The Pentagon
Washington, DC 20350
703/545-6700
Gordon R. England, Secretary of the NAVY
http://www.navy.mil

Department of the Treasury
1500 Pennsylvania NW,
Washington, DC 20220
202/622-2000
John W. Snow, Secretary of the Treasury
http://www.treas.gov

Drug Enforcement Administration
600-700 Army Navy Drive
Arlington, VA 22202
202/307-1000
William B. Simpkins, Administrator

Environmental Protection Agency
401 M. Street SW
Washington, DC 20460
202/260-2090
Stephen L. Johnson, Administrator
http://www.epa.gov

Equal Employment Opportunity Commission
1801 L. Street NW
Washington, DC 20507
202/663-4900
Cari M. Dominguez, Chairwoman
http://www.eeoc.gov

Executive Office of the President, The White House
1600 Pennsylvania Avenue NW
Washington, DC 20500
202/456-1414
George W. Bush, President of the United States
http://www.whitehouse.gov

Food and Drug Administration
5600 Fishers Lane
Rockville, MD 20857
301/443-1544
Lester M. Crawford, Commissioner
http://www.fda.gov

Health Resources and Services Administration
5600 Fishers Lane
Rockville, MD 20857
301/443-2086
Elizabeth James Duke, Administrator
http://www.dhhs.gov/hsra

Office of Management and Budget
Executive Office Building
Washington, DC 20503
202/395-3080
Joshua Bolden, Director

Office of National Drug Policy
Executive Office of the President
Washington, DC 20503
202/395-6700
John P. Walters, Director
http://www.whitehousedrugpolicy.gov

Office of the Vice President of the United States
Old Executive Office Building
Washington, DC 20501
202/452-2326
Richard B. Cheney, Vice President of the United States

Substance Abuse and Mental Health Services Administration
5600 Fishers Lane
Rockville, MD 20857
301/443-4797
Charles Curi, Administrator
http://www.samhsa.gov

Blue Cross–Blue Shield Plans

The following listing is based on information provided by the agencies themselves and the Blue Cross and Blue Shield Association. Inclusion or omission of any organization's name indicates neither approval nor disapproval by Health Forum LLC, an American Hospital Association Company.

United States

ALABAMA: Blue Cross and Blue Shield of Alabama, Blue Cross and Blue Shield of Alabama, 450 Riverchase Parkway, East, Birmingham, AL 35244; tel. 205/220-2100; FAX. 205/220-2949; Phillip G. Pope, President and CEO

ARIZONA: Blue Cross and Blue Shield of Arizona, Blue Cross and Blue Shield of Arizona, 2444 W. Las Palmaritas Drive, Phoenix, AZ 85021; tel. 602/864-4100; FAX. 602/864-4376; Richard L. Boals, President and Chief Executive Officer

ARKANSAS: Arkansas Blue Cross and Blue Shield, Arkansas Blue Cross and Blue Shield, 601 Gaines Street, Little Rock, AR 72201; tel. 501/378-2000; FAX. 501/378-2037; Robert Shoptaw, President and Chief Executive Officer

CALIFORNIA: California Physician's Service, Blue Shield of California, 50 Beale Street, San Francisco, CA 94105; tel. 415/229-5000; FAX. 415/229-5056; Bruce Bodaken, Chairman, President and Chief Executive Officer

DELAWARE: Blue Cross Blue Shield of Delaware, Inc., 201 West 14th Street, Wilmington, DE 19801; tel. 302/421-3000; FAX. 302/421-2089; Timothy J. Constantine, President

DISTRICT OF COLUMBIA: CareFirst BlueCross BlueShield, Group Hospitalization and Medical Services, Inc, 840 First Street, N.E., Washington, DC 20065; tel. 202/479-8000; FAX. 202/479-3520; William L. Jews, President and Chief Executive Officer

FLORIDA: Blue Cross and Blue Shield of Florida, Blue Cross and Blue Shield of Florida, Inc., 4800 Deerwood Campus Parkway, Jacksonville, FL 32246-8273; tel. 904/791-6111; FAX. 904/905-0806; Robert I. Lufrano, MD, President and Chief Executive Officer

GEORGIA: Blue Cross and Blue Shield of Georgia, Blue Cross and Blue Shield of Georgia, Inc., 3350 Peachtree Road NE, Capital City Plaza, Atlanta, GA 30326; tel. 404/842-8000; FAX. 404/842-8010; John Watts, Jr, President

HAWAII: Hawaii Medical Service Association, Blue Cross and Blue Shield of Hawaii, 818 Keeaumoku Street, Honolulu, HI 96822; tel. 808/948-5110; FAX. 808/948-6555; Robert P. Hiam, President and Chief Executive Officer

IDAHO: Blue Cross of Idaho Health Service, Inc., Blue Cross of Idaho Health Service Inc., 3000 East Pine Avenue, Meridian, ID 83642-5995; tel. 208/345-4550; FAX. 208/331-7311; Ray Flachbart, President and Chief Executive Officer
Regence BlueShield of Idaho, 1602 21st Ave., Lewiston, ID 83501; tel. 208/746-2671; FAX. 208/798-2099; John M. Stellmon, President and CEO

ILLINOIS: Blue Cross and Blue Shield of Illinois, 300 E. Randolph Street, Chicago, IL 60601-5099; tel. 312/653-6000; FAX. 312/819-1220; Raymond F. McCaskey, President and Chief Executive Officer

INDIANA: Anthem Insurance Companies, Inc. (IN), Anthem Blue Cross and Blue Shield, 120 Monument Circle, Indianapolis, IN 46204; tel. 317/488-6000; FAX. 317/488-6371; Larry C Glasscock, Chairman and Chief Executive Officer

IOWA: Wellmark Blue Cross and Blue Shield, Wellmark Blue Cross Blue Shield of Iowa, 636 Grand Avenue, Des Moines, IA 50309; tel. 515/245-4500; FAX. 515/245-4651; John D. Forsyth, Chairman and Chief Executive Officer

LOUISIANA: Louisiana Health Service and Indemnity Company, Blue Cross and Blue Shield of Louisiana, 5525 Reitz Ave., Baton Rouge, LA 70809-3802; tel. 225/295-3307; FAX. 225/295-2054; Gery J. Barry, President and CEO

MARYLAND: CareFirst of Maryland, Inc., CareFirst BlueCross BlueShield, 10455 Mill Run Circle, Owings Mills, MD 21117-5559; tel. 410/581-3000; FAX. 410/998-5576; William L. Jews, President and Chief Executive Officer

MASSACHUSETTS: Blue Cross and Blue Shield of Massachusetts, The Landmark Center, 401 Park Drive, Boston, MA 02215-3326; tel. 617/246-5000; FAX. 617/246-3309; William C. Van Faasen, President and Chief Executive Officer

MICHIGAN: Blue Cross and Blue Shield of Michigan, Blue Cross Blue Shield of Michigan, 600 E. Lafayette, Detroit, MI 48226-2998; tel. 313/225-9000; FAX. 313/225-6239; Richard E. Whitmer, President and Chief Executive Officer

MINNESOTA: Blue Cross and Blue Shield of Minnesota, 3535 Blue Cross Road, St. Paul, MN 55122-1154; tel. 651/662-8000; FAX. 651/662-7767; Mark W. Banks, MD, Chief Executive Officer

MISSISSIPPI: Blue Cross & Blue Shield of Mississippi, 3545 Lakeland Dr., Flowood, MS 39232-9799; tel. 601/932-3704; FAX. 601/939-7035; Richard J. Hale, President and Chief Executive Officer

MISSOURI: Blue Cross and Blue Shield of Kansas City, 2301 Main Street, Kansas City, MO 64108; tel. 816/395-2222; FAX. 816/802-4451; Tom Bowser, President and Chief Executive Officer

NEBRASKA: Blue Cross and Blue Shield of Nebraska, 7261 Mercy Road, Omaha, NE 68180-0001; tel. 402/390-1800; FAX. 402/391-2141; Steven S. Martin, President and Chief Executive Officer

NEW JERSEY: Horizon Healthcare Services, Inc., Horizon Blue Cross and Blue Shield of New Jersey Inc., 3 Penn Plaza East, Newark, NJ 07105; tel. 973/466-4000; FAX. 973 466-6606; William J. Marino, President and Chief Executive Officer

NEW MEXICO: Health Care Service Corporation, Blue Cross and Blue Shield of New Mexico, 12800 Indian School Road., N.E., Albuquerque, NM 87112; tel. 505/291-3500; FAX. 505/816-5324; Elizabeth Liz Watrin, President

NEW YORK: Empre HealthChoice Assurance, Inc., Empire Blue Cross and Blue Shield, 11 West 42nd Street, New York, NY 10036; tel. 212/476-1000; FAX. 212/476-1281; Michael A. Stocker, MD, President
Excellus Health Plan, Inc (Rochester), Excellus BlueCross BlueShield, 165 Court Street, Rochester, NY 14647; tel. 585/454-1700; FAX. 585/238-4400; Kevin N. Hill, President & COO
Excellus Health Plan, Inc. (Syracuse), Excellus BlueCross BlueShield, 344 South Warren Street, Syracuse, NY 13202; tel. 315/671-6400; FAX. 315/448-4922; James R. Smith, President

HealthNow New York, Inc., Blue Cross & Blue Shield of Western New York, 1901 Main Street, Buffalo, NY 14208; tel. 716/887-6900; FAX. 716/887-8981; Alphonso O'Neil-White, Esq.

NORTH CAROLINA: Blue Cross and Blue Shield of North Carolina, 5901 Chapel Hill Road, Durham, NC 27707; tel. 800/446-8053; FAX. 919/765-2433; Robert Greczyn Jr, President and Chief Executive Officer

NORTH DAKOTA: Noridian Mutual Insurance Company, BlueCross BlueShield of North Dakota, 4510 13th Avenue, South, Fargo, ND 58121-0001; tel. 701/282-1100; FAX. 701/282-1469; Michael B. Unhjem, President and CEO

OKLAHOMA: Group Health Service of Oklahoma, Inc., Blue Cross and Blue Shield of Oklahoma, 1215 South Boulder Avenue, Tulsa, OK 74119-2800; tel. 918/560-3500; FAX. 918/560-2095; Ronald F. King, Chairman, President and Chief Executive Officer

OREGON: Regence BlueCross BlueShield of Oregon, 100 S.W. Market Street, Portland, OR 97201; tel. 503/225-5221; FAX. 503/225-5232; J.B. McMullan, Jr., M.D., President

PENNSYLVANIA: Capital Blue Cross, 2500 Elmerton Avenue, Harrisburg, PA 17110; tel. 717/541-7000; FAX. 717/541-6072; Anita M. Smith, President & Chief Executive Officer
Highmark Blue Cross and Blue Shield, 120 Fifth Avenue, Pittsburgh, PA 15222-3099; tel. 412/544-7000; FAX. 412/544-7583; Kenneth R. Melani M.D., President and Chief Executive Officer
Hospital Service Association of Northeastern Pennsylvania, Blue Cross of Northeastern Pennsylvania, 19 North Main Street, Wilkes-Barre, PA 18711; tel. 570/200-4300; FAX. 570/200-6730; Denise S. Cesare, President and Chief Executive Officer
Independence Blue Cross, 1901 Market Street, Philadelphia, PA 19103; tel. 215/241-2400; FAX. 215/241-3824; Joseph A. Frick, Prsident and CEO

RHODE ISLAND: Blue Cross & Blue Shield of Rhode Island, 444 Westminster Street, Providence, RI 02903-3279; tel. 401/459-1000; FAX. 401/351-2050; James E. Purcell, Esq., President and CEO

SOUTH CAROLINA: Blue Cross and Blue Shield of South Carolina, I-20 East at Alpine Road, Columbia, SC 29219; tel. 803/788-3860; FAX. 803/736-3420; M. Edward Sellers, President and Chief Executive Officer

SOUTH DAKOTA: Wellmark, Inc., Wellmark Blue Cross and Blue Shield of South Dakota, 1601 West Madison Street, Sioux Falls, SD 57104; tel. 605/373-7401; FAX. 605/373-7497; Philip M. Davis, President and Chief Operating Officer

TENNESSEE: Blue Cross and Blue Shield of Tennessee, 801 Pine Street, Chattanooga, TN 37402; tel. 423/755-5600; FAX. 423/755-3178; Vicky Gregg, President and Chief Executive Officer

TEXAS: Blue Cross and Blue Shield of Texas, 901 South Central Expressway N. Bldg.-C, Richardson, TX 75080; tel. 972/766-6900; FAX. 972/766-0359; Patricia Hemingway-Hall, President

UTAH: Regence BlueCross BlueShield of Utah, 2890 E. Cottonwood Parkway, Salt Lake City, UT 84121; tel. 801/333-2000; FAX. 801/333-6516; D. Scott Ideson, President

VERMONT: Blue Cross and Blue Shield of Vermont, 455 Industrial Lane, Berlin, VT 05602; tel. 802/223–6131; FAX. 802/229–0511; William R. Milnes, Jr, President and Chief Executive Officer

VIRGINIA: Anthem Health Plans of Virginia, Anthem Blue Cross and Blue Shield, 2015 Staples Mill Road, Richmond, VA 23230-3119; tel. 804/354–3510; FAX. 804/354–3115; Thomas G. Snead Jr, President of Anthem BCBS Southeast

WASHINGTON: Premera Blue Cross, 7001 220th Street SW, Mountlake Terrace, WA 98043-2124; tel. 425/918–4000; FAX. 425/918–4900; Mr. H.R. Brereton(Gubby) Barlow, President and Chief Executive Officer

The Regence Group (WA), Regence BlueShield, 1800 Ninth Avenue, Seattle, WA 98101-1322; tel. 206/464–3756; FAX. 206/287–5413; Mary McWilliams, President

WEST VIRGINIA: Mountain State Blue Cross & Blue Shield, Highmark West Virginia, Inc., 700 Market Square, Parkersburg, WV 26101; tel. 304/424–7700; FAX. 304/424–7730; Gregory K. Smith, President and Chief Executive Officer

WISCONSIN: BlueCross BlueShield of Wisconsin, 401 West Michigan Street, Milwaukee, WI 53203-2804; tel. 414/226–5000; FAX. 414/226–5488; Kathy A. Ledvina, President and Chief Executive Officer

WYOMING: Blue Cross and Blue Shield of Wyoming, 4000 House Avenue, Cheyenne, WY 82001-2266; tel. 307/634–1393; FAX. 307/778–8582; Tim J. Crilly, President and Chief Executive Officer

U.S. Associated Areas

PUERTO RICO: La Cruz Azul de Puerto Rico, P.O. Box 366068, San Juan, PR 00926-6068; tel. 787/282–9898; FAX. 787/272–7867; Marcos Vidal, President

Triple-S, Inc., P.O. Box 363628, San Juan, PR 00936-3628; tel. 787/749–4190; FAX. 787/749–4190; Ramon M. Ruiz-Comas, President and CEO

Section C

Group Purchasing Organizations

The following list of Group Purchasing Organizations is derived from the AHA Annual Survey of Hospitals. It reflects Group Purchasing Organizations serving hospitals. Inclusion or omission of any organization's name indicates neither approval nor disapproval by Health Forum LLC, an American Hospital Association company.

A

Advantage Healthcare Net, 2100 South Columbia Road, Suite 104, Grand Forks, ND 58201; tel. 800/548-2744; F. Wade Johnson, Vice President & Chief Operating Officer ; www.advantage-healthcare. net

Affiliated Material Services, 925 Union Street, Bangor, ME 04401; tel. 207/973-6730; Miles Unobsky Theeman, Executive Vice President & COO; www.bigbluea.com/ams.htm

AHC
see Aurora Health Care

Alaska Federal Health Care Partnership, 1919 South Bragaw, Anchorage, AK 99508; tel. 907/729-4480; www.usarak.army.mil/afhcp

All Health, 4750 Lindle Road, P.O. Box 8800, Harrisburg, PA 17105-8800; tel. 800/377-8200; D. Patrick Mazzola, President & CEO; www.all-health.com

Allegiance Health Care Corporation
see CardinalHealth

Allen Health System, 1825 Logan Avenue, Waterloo, IA 50703-1916; tel. 319/235-3606; Rick Seidler, President & CEO; www.allenhospital.org

Alliance of Healthcare Organizations, 3 Riverchase Office Plaza, Suite 112, Birmingham, AL 35244; tel. 205/739-0407; James B. Baker, Sr., Executive Director; www.alliancehealthcare.org

Alliance Purchasing Group, 1610 Oak Park Boulevard, Suite 207, Pleasant Hill, CA 94523; tel. 925/932-6268; Steve Oakes; www.alliance-purchasing.com

Alliant Purchasing Organization, 2501 Nelson Miller Parkway, Suite 104, Louisville, KY 40223; tel. 800/528-3321; Joe Broyles, Vice President; www. alliantpurchasing.com

Amerinet, Inc., 2060 Craigshire Road, St. Louis, MO 63146; tel. 800/882-6385; Robert P. Bowen, President; www.amerinet-gpo.com

AmerisourceBergen, 1300 Morris Drive, Suite 100, Chesterbrook, PA 19087; tel. 800/829-3132; R. David Yost, CEO; www.amerisourcebergen.com

APG
see Alliance Purchasing Group

Associated Purchasing Services, 10401 Holmes Road, Suite 280, Kansas City, MO 64131-3406; tel. 816/941-3440; Tom Bell, President & CEO; www.apskc.org

Aurora Health Care, 3031 West Montana Street, P.O. Box 343910, Milwaukee, WI 53234-3910; tel. 414/647-3313; Ron Buettner, C.P.M., Purchasing Agent; www.aurorahealthcare.org

Avera PACE, 3900 West Avera Drive, Suite 100, Sioux Falls, SD 57108-5721; tel. 800/657-8095; Mary Kuper, Executive Director; www.averapace. com

B

Bergen Brunswig Drug Company
see AmerisourceBergen

Boone Hospital Center, 1600 East Broadway, Columbia, MO 65201; tel. 573/815-3210; Michael B. Shirk, President; www.boone.org/bhc

Brim Healthcare Inc., 105 Westwood Place, Suite 300, Brentwood, TN 37027; tel. 800/228-0647; Dave Woodland, President; www.brimhealthcare. com

Broadlane, 40 Gold Street, San Francisco, CA 94133; tel. 800/276-2356; Charles E. Saunders, M.D., CEO; www.broadlane.com

BuyPower
see Broadlane

C

Capital Region Health Care, 250 Pleasant Street, Concord, NH 03301-2598; tel. 603/225-2711; Kevin McCarthy, Vice President, Materials Management; www.crhc.org

CardinalHealth, 7000 Cardinal Place, Dublin, OH 43017; tel. 800/234-8701; Robert D. Walter, Chairman & CEO; www.cardinal.com

Catholic Materials Management Alliance
see Consorta, Inc.

Central Kansas Medical Center, 3515 Broadway, Great Bend, KS 67530; tel. 620/792-2511; Chris Thomas, President & CEO; www.ckmc.org

CHAMPS Management Services, 1226 Huron Road East, Cleveland, OH 44115; tel. 216/696-6900; Laura Gronowski, Senior Vice President; www. chanet.org

CHCA
see Child Health Corporation of America

Child Health Corporation of America, 6803 West 64th Street, Suite 208, Shawnee Mission , KS 66202; tel. 913/262-1436; Don C. Black, President & CEO; www.chca.com

Coastal Cooperative of New Jersey, L.L.C., Monmouth Shores Corporate Park, 1350 Campus Parkway, Wall, NJ 07753; tel. 732/751-3404; Patricia Klancer, Director of Network Services

COHR
see MasterPlan

Community Health Systems, Inc., 155 Franklin Road, Suite 400, Brentwood, TN 37027-4600; tel. 615/373-9600; Wayne Smith, Chairman, President & CEO; www.chs.net

Connecticut Hospital Association Shared Services Program, 110 Barnes Road, P.O. Box 90, Wallingford, CT 06492-0090; tel. 203/294-7380; Diane Mase, Assistant Vice President; www.chassp. com

Consorta, Inc., 1475 East Woodfield Road, Suite 400, Schaumburg, IL 60173; tel. 800/342-5333; John Strong, President & CEO; www.consorta.com

Cooperative Health Services of Florida
see LeeSar & Cooperative Services of Florida

D

Dartmouth-Hitchcock Alliance, One Medical Center Drive, Lebanon, NH 03756-1000; tel. 603/650-5000; James Varnum, President; www. dartmouth-hitchcock.org

Department of Defense
see United States Department of Defense

Department of Veterans Affairs
see United States Department of Veterans Affairs

Direct Sourcing Solutions, Inc., 26261 Evergreen Road, Suite 250, Southfield, MI 48076; tel. 248/208-8308; B.P. Thacker, CEO; www. directsourcing.com

DSSI
see Direct Sourcing Solutions, Inc.

E

East Texas Medical Center Regional Healthcare System, 1000 South Beckham Avenue, Tyler, TX 75701; tel. 903/535-6211; Elmer G. Ellis, President & CEO; www.etmc.org

F

Fairview Health Services, 2450 Riverside Avenue, Minneapolis, MN 55454-1450; tel. 612/672-6141; David R. Page, President & CEO; www.fairview.org

FirstChoice Cooperative, 4815 Troup Highway, Tyler, TX 75703; tel. 800/250-3457; Freddie Sanchez, Chairman; www.fccoop.org

Frontier Health, Center of Tri-Cities Business Park, P.O. Box 9054, Gray, TN 37615-6205; tel. 888/291-1935; E. Douglas Varney, President & CEO; www.frontierhealth.org

G

General Services Commission
see Texas Building & Procurement Commission

Georgia Shared Services
see Shared Services Healthcare, Inc.

Greater New York Hospital Association, 555 West 57th Street, 15th floor, New York, NY 10019; tel. 212/246-7100; Alfred J. LoBiondo, Senior Vice President, Supply Chain Management; www.gnyha. org

GSA & Consolidated
see United States General Services Administration

H

HCSC
see Hospital Central Services Cooperative

Health Enterprises, 4250 Glass Road, N.E., Cedar Rapids, IA 52402; tel. 319/368-3612; Glenn E. Potter, President & CEO; www.healthenterprises.org

Health Purchasing Group
see HealthTrust Purchasing Group

Health Services Corporation of America
see MedAssets HSCA

Healthcare Enterprises, P.O. Box 4449, Cary, NC 27519-4449; tel. 919/620–9506; Ken Davenport, Director of Resources; www.ncha.org/public/nche.html

Healthcare Purchasing Partners International, 125 East John Carpenter Freeway, Irving, TX 75062-2324; tel. 888/538–4662; Eldon Petersen, President; www.hppigpo.com.

Healthcare Services of New England, Inc., 859 Willard Street, Suite 510, Quincy, MA 02169-7428; tel. 888/848–4763; Martha A. Dula, President & CEO; www.hsne.com

HealthTrust Purchasing Group, 104 Continental Place, Suite 300, Brentwood, TN 37027; tel. 615/344–3000; Jim Fitzgerald, President & CEO; www.healthtrustpg.com

Hospital Central Services Cooperative, 2171 28th Street, S.W., Allentown, PA 18103; tel. 800/444–4272; J. Michael Lee, President & CEO; www.hcsc.org/index.shtml

Hospital Council of Western Pennsylvania, 500 Commonwealth Drive, Warrendale, PA 15086; tel. 800/704–8434; Ian G. Rawson, President; www.hcwp.org

Hospital Purchasing Service, 3275 North M-37 Highway, P.O. Box 247, Middleville, MI 49333-0040; tel. 800/632–4572; Jerry Welsh, President & CEO; www.hpsnet.com

Hospital Shared Services, 1395 South Platte River Drive, Denver, CO 80223; tel. 303/722–5566; George Schiel, President; www.hospitalshared.com

Hospital Shared Services Association, 300 Elliott Avenue West, Suite 300, Seattle, WA 98119; tel. 206/285–3937; Bud Musselman, President; www.hssagroup.org

HPG
see HealthTrust Purchasing Group

HPPI
see Healthcare Purchasing Partners International

HSCA
see MedAssets HSCA

HSNE
see Healthcare Services of New England, Inc.

HSS
see Hospital Shared Services

HSSA
see Hospital Shared Services Association

I

Idaho Department of Health and Welfare, 450 West State Street, Boise, ID 83720-0036; tel. 208/334–5500; Karl B. Kurtz, Director; www2.state.id.us/dhw/index.htm

InSource
see MedAssets HSCA

Iroquois Healthcare Alliance
see United Iroquois Shared Services

J

Jane Phillips Medical Center, 3500 S.E. Frank Phillips Boulevard, Bartlesville, OK 74006; tel. 918/333–7200; David Stire, President & CEO; www.jpmc.org

Jewish Hospital Healthcare Services, Regional Service Center, 5000 Commerce Crossing Drive, Louisville, KY 40299; tel. 502/962–6349; Alan Broude, President; www.jhhs.org

L

Lake Erie Health Alliance, 2142 North Cove Boulevard, Toledo, OH 43606; tel. 419/291–3450; Chuck Swisher, President; www.promedica.org/promedica

Lake Erie Regional Cooperative
see Lake Erie Health Alliance

LeeSar & Cooperative Services of Florida, 401 Leonard Boulevard North, Lehigh Acres, FL 33971; tel. 239/303–0606; Robert Simpson, President

Louisiana Office of State Purchasing & Travel, 1201 North 3rd Street, Suite 2-160, P.O. Box 94095, Baton Rouge, LA 70804-9095; tel. 225/342–8010; Denise M. Lea, State Purchasing Director; www.state.la.us/osp/osp.htm

M

Maine, Division of Purchases, Burton Cross Building, 4th Floor, 9 State House Station, Augusta, ME 04333; tel. 207/624–7340; Betty M. Lamoreau, Director; www.state.me.us/purchase

Managed Health Care Associates, Inc., 25-A Vreeland Road, Suite 203, P.O. Box 789, Florham Park, NJ 07932-0789; tel. 800/642–3020; Douglas Present, CEO; www.mhainc.com

Massachusetts Alliance for State Pharmaceutical Buying, 1 Ashburton Place, Room 1017, Boston, MA 02108-1552; tel. 617/720–3328; Brian Putnam, Procurement Manager; www.maspb.com

MasterPlan, 21540 Plummer Street, Chatsworth, CA 91311-4103; tel. 818/773–2647; Bruce Cree, Chairman & CEO; www.masterplan-inc.com

MCHC
see Metropolitan Chicago Healthcare Council, Group

McKesson Corporation, One Post Street, San Francisco, CA 94104; tel. 415/983–8300; John H. Hammergren, Chairman, President & CEO; www.mckesson.com

Med Assets HSCA, 100 North Point Center East, Suite 200, Alpharetta, GA 30022; tel. 678/323–2500; John Bardis, Chairman, President & CEO; www.medassets.com

MedEcon
see Managed Health Care Associates, Inc.

Medical Logistics Command
see United States Naval Medical Logistics Command

Mercy Health System of Oklahoma, 1011 Fourteenth Avenue, N.W., Ardmore, OK 73401; tel. 580/223–5400; Bobby G. Thompson, President & CEO; www.mercyok.com/mmhc

Mercy Resource Management, Inc., 280 Shuman Boulevard, Suite 110, Naperville, IL 60563-8401; tel. 630/778–2150; Michael D. Gray, President & CEO; www.mrmi.org

Metropolitan Chicago Healthcare Council, Group Purchasing Services, 222 South Riverside Plaza, Suite 1900, Chicago, IL 60606; tel. 312/906–6128; Jay Chibe, Director; www.mchc.org

MHA
see Managed Health Care Associates, Inc.

MHA Ventures, Inc., P.O. Box 5119, Helena, MT 59604; tel. 406/442–1911; Dick Brown, Executive Director; www.mtha.org/ventures1.htm

Midsouth Healthcare Network
see United States Department of Veterans Affairs

Minnesota Multi-State Contracting Alliance for Pharmacy, 50 Sherburne Avenue, Room 112, St. Paul, MN 55155; tel. 651/296–2600; Paul Stembler, Manager; www.mmd.admin.state.mn.us/mmcap

Missouri Procurement Office, 301 West High, Room 630, P.O. Box 809, Jefferson City, MO 65102-0809; tel. 573/751–2387; James Miluski, Director; www.oa.mo.gov/purch/purch.htm

MMCAP
see Minnesota Multi-State Contracting for Pharmacy

N

National Acquisition Center
see United States Department of Veterans Affairs N

Navajo Area Indian Health Service, P.O. Box 9020, Window Rock, AZ 86515; tel. 928/871–5811; John Hubbard, Jr., Director; www.ihs.gov/FacilitiesServices/AreaOffices/Navajo

New Jersey Hospital Association, 760 Alexander Road, P.O. Box 1, Princeton, NJ 08543; tel. 888/221–2182; Marilyn Zacks, Director of Materials Services; www.njha.com/corporate.services/bs.materials.aspx

New Mexico General Services Department, State Purchasing Division , P.O. Box 26110, Santa Fe, NM 87502-0110; tel. 505/827–0472; Michael C. Vinyard, State Purchasing Agent; www.state.nm.us/clients/spd/spd.html

New York City Health & Hospitals Corporation, 125 Worth Street, New York, NY 10013; tel. 212/788–3339; Benjamin Chu, M.D., President; www.nyc.gov/html/hhc/home.html

New York University Purchasing Services & Contract Administration, 269 Mercer Street, 5th floor, New York, NY 10003-6687; tel. 212/998–1212; Stephen Heller, Vice President, Administration; www.nyu.edu/purchasing.services

North Carolina Department of Correction, Division of Departmental Purchasing & Services, 2020 Yonkers Road, 4227 Mail Service Center, Raleigh, NC 27699-4227; tel. 919/716–3250; Barbara Baker, Chief Procurement Officer & Budget Officer; www.doc.state.nc.us/purchasing/index.htm

North Dakota Healthcare Association, P.O. Box 7340, 3205 East Thayer Avenue, Bismark, ND 58507; tel. 701/224–9732; Arnold Thomas, President; www.ndha.org

Northern Michigan Supply Alliance, LLC, 2651 Aero Park Drive, Traverse City, MI 49686-9101; tel. 231/935–8233; Mark Deponio, President

NOVATION, 123 East John Carpenter Freeway, Irving, TX 75062-2324; tel. 888/766–8283; Mark McKenna, President & CEO; www.novationco.com

O

Oklahoma Department of Central Services, 2401 Lincoln Boulevard, Suite 206, Oklahoma City, OK 73105; tel. 405/521–2121; John S. Richard, Director; www.dcs.state.ok.us/OKDCS.nsf

Owens & Minor, 4800 Cox Road, Glen Allen, VA 23060-6292; tel. 804/747–9794; G. Gilmer Minor, III, Chairman & CEO; www.owens-minor.com

P

PACE
see Avera PACE

Peconic Health Corporation, 116 Main Road, Aquebogue, NY 11931; tel. 631/369–7110; Thomas B. Doolan, President

Phoenix Area Indian Health Services, Two Renaissance Square, 40 North Central Ave, Phoenix, AZ 85004-4424; tel. 602/364–5039; Don J. Davis, Area Director; www.ihs.gov/FacilitiesServices/AreaOffices/Phoenix/index.cfm

PPG
see Professionals' Purchasing Group, Inc.

Premier, 700 Commerce Drive, Suite 100, Oak Brook, IL 60523; tel. 630/891–4100; Robert L. Hamon, Senior Vice President ; www.premierinc.com/groupbuy

Professionals' Purchasing Group, Inc., 2904 Eastpoint Parkway, Louisville, KY 40223; tel. 800/333–1774; John Deweese, President; www.ppginc.net/index.htm

Purchase Connection
see MedAssets HSCA

S

Seagate Alliance, 3445 Winton Place, Rochester, NY 14623; tel. 585/214–2413; Robert Swinnerton, President & CEO; www.seagatealliance.com

Shared Health Services Corporation, 2635 Hemstock Street, LaCrosse, WI 54603; tel. 608/781–4410; Wade Turner, Executive Director; www.shsc-gpo.com

Shared Services Healthcare, Inc., 2300 Windy Ridge Parkway, Suite 5605, Atlanta, GA 30339; tel. 800/827–0340; Sandra Green, CEO; www.sharedservices.org

Sun Healthcare Group, 18831 Von Karman, Suite 400, Irvine, CA 92612; tel. 800/729–6600; Richard K. Matos, Chairman & CEO; www.sunh.com/Production/shg/index.asp

T

Texas Building & Procurement Commission, 1711 San Jacinto, Austin, TX 78701; tel. 512/463–6363; Tom Beard, Chairman; www.tbpc.state.tx.us

The CHI Group of Superior Consultant Company, 130 South First Street, Ann Arbor, MI 48104; tel. 734/761–3912; www.superiorconsultant.com/solutions/Chi/TheChiGroup.asp

U

UHC
see University Healthsystem Consortium

United Iroquois Shared Service, 17 Halfmoon Executive Park Drive, Clifton Park, NY 12065; tel. 518/383–5060; J. Edward 'Jed' Potocar, Executive Vice President, UISS; www.iroquois.org/uiss.htm

United Shared Services , 1876 Niagara Falls Boulevard, Tonawanda, NY 14150; tel. 716/695–6370; William D. Pike, President; wnyha.com/uss/default.htm

United States Department of Defense, Defense Supply Center Philadelphia, 700 Robbins Avenue, Philadelphia, PA 19111-5092; tel. 888/352–2255; Col. Raymond V. Mason, U.S.A., Commander; www.dscp.dla.mil

United States Department of Veterans Affairs National Acquisition Center, P. O. Box 76, Building 37, Hines, IL 60141; tel. 708/786–5157; George Patterson, Executive Director & COO; www1.va.gov/oamm/nac/index.htm

United States Department of Veterans Affairs Veterans Integrated Services Network (VISN),

United States General Services Administration (Consolidated), 400 15th S.W., Auburn, WA 98001-6599; tel. 800/241–7246; Warren Jayashi, Business Management Specialist; www.gsa.gov

United States Naval Medical Logistics Command, Fort Detrick, MD 21702-5015; tel. 301/619–2157; 131.158.58.12/default.htm

Universal Hospital Services, Inc., 3800 American Boulevard West, Suite 1250, Bloomington, MN 55431-4442; tel. 800/847–7368; Gary D. Blackford, President & CEO; www.uhs.com

University Healthsystem Consortium, 2001 Spring Road, Suite 700, Oak Brook, IL 60523; tel. 630/954–1700; Robert J. Baker, President & CEO; www.uhc.edu

Upper Peninsula Health Care Network, 710 Chippewa Square, Suite 206, Marquette, MI 49855; tel. 906/225–3146; Gerald A. Messana, Executive Director; www.uphcn.org

V

VA Great Lakes Acquisition Center, 5000 West National Avenue, Building No. 5, Milwaukee, WI 53295-0005; tel. 414/902–5400

VA System
see United States Department of Veterans Affairs

Vector Amerinet
see Amerinet, Inc.

VHA, Inc., 220 East Las Colinas Boulevard, Irving, TX 75039-5500; tel. 972/830–0000; Curt Nonomaque, President & CEO; www.vha.com.

Virginia Department of Mental Health, Mental Retardation, and Substance Abuse Services, Office of Administrative Services, P.O. Box 1797, Richmond, VA 23218-1797; tel. 804/786–4512; Joy Lazarus, Director, OAS; www.dmhmrsas.state.va.us

VISN 1: VA New England Healthcare System, 200 Springs Road, Building No. 61, Bedford, MA 01730; tel. 781/687–3400; Jeanette Chirico-Post, M.D., Network Director; www.visn1.med.va.gov/default.htm

VISN 2: VA Healthcare Network Upstate New York, P.O. Box 8980, Albany, NY 12202-8980; tel. 518/626–7300; William F. Feeley, Network Director; www1.va.gov/visns/visn02

VISN 4: VA Stars & Stripes Healthcare Network, VAMC, Delafield Road, Pittsburgh, PA 15240; tel. 412/784–3939; Charleen R. Szabo, Acting Network Director; www.starsandstripes.med.va.gov/visn4

VISN 9: VA Mid South Healthcare Network, 1310-24th Avenue South, Nashville, TN 37212-2637; tel. 615/340–2389; John Dandridge, Jr., Director; vaww.va.gov/visn9

VISN 12: Great Lakes Health Care System, P.O. Box 5000, Building No. 18, Hines, IL 60141-5000; tel. 708/202–8400; Dr. Joan E. Cummings, Director; www.vagreatlakes.org

VISN 15: VA Heartland Network, 1201 Walnut Street, Suite 800, Kansas City, MO 64106; tel. 816/701–3000; Peter L. Almenoff, M.D., Director; www1.va.gov/directory/guide/region.asp?ID=1015

VISN 22: Desert Pacific Healthcare Network, 5901 East 7th Street, Long Beach, CA 90822; tel. 562/826–5963; Kenneth J. Clark, Network Director; www.visn22.med.va.gov/home.htm

Voluntary Hospital Association
see VHA

W

West Virginia Health Services , 100 Association Drive, Charleston, WV 25311; tel. 304/295–7450; Richard L. Miller, Vice President, Shared Services; www.wvhsi.com

Wisconsin Valley Health Network, LLC, 3000 Westhill Drive, Suite 300, Wausau, WI 54401; tel. 715/847–2999; www.wvhn.org

Health Systems Agencies

United States

The following list is based on information provided by the agencies themselves. For information about other local agencies and organizations that fulfill similar functions, contact the state or metropolitan hospital associations; see also the list of State Health Planning and Development Agencies in Section C.

FLORIDA: Broward Regional Health Planning Council (District 10), 915 Middle River Drive, Suite 120, Fort Lauderdale, FL 33304; tel. 954/561-9681; FAX. 954/561-9685; John H. Werner, Chief Executive Officer

Health Council of South Florida, Inc., 8095 Northwest 12th Street, Suite 300, Miami, FL 33126; tel. 305/592-1452; FAX. 305/592-0589; Sonya Albury, Executive Director

Health Planning Council of Northeast Florida, Inc., 900 University Blvd. N, Suite110, Jacksonville, FL 32211; tel. 904/745-3050; FAX. 904/745-3054; Lori A. Bilello, Executive Director

North Central Florida Health Planning Council, DBA. Well Florida Council, 18 N.W. 33rd Court, Gainesville, FL 32607; tel. 352/955-2264; FAX. 352/955-3109; Steven Oliva, Executive Director

Suncoast Health Council, Inc. (District Five), 9455 Koger Boulevard, Suite 104, St. Petersburg, FL 33702-2451; tel. 727/217-7070; FAX. 727/570-3033; Elizabeth Rugg, Executive Director

The Health Council of East Central Florida Inc., 1155 South Semoran Boulevard, Suite 1111, Winter Park, FL 32792-5505; tel. 407/671-2005; Karen Van Caulil, Executive Director

Treasure Coast Health Council, Inc. (District Nine), 4152 W. Blue Heron Blvd, Suite 229, Riviera Beach, FL 33404; tel. 561/844-4220; FAX. 561/844-3310; Barbara H. Jacobowitz, Executive Director

MARYLAND: Chesapeake Health Planning System, Inc., P.O. Box 773, Cambridge, MD 21613; tel. 410/221-0907; FAX. 410/221-2605; John Bennett, President

MINNESOTA: Region 1 (Northwest MN) and Region II (Northeast MN), Regional Coordinating Boards, Minnesota Department of Health, P.O. Box 64975, St. Paul, MN 55164-0975; tel. 612/282-5644; Michele Holten

NEW YORK: Central New York Health Systems Agency, Inc., (CNYHSA), 5700 Commons Park Drive, East Syracuse, NY 13057; tel. 315/472-8099; FAX. 315/472-8033; Timothy J. Bobo, Executive Director

Finger Lakes Health Systems Agency, 1150 University Avenue, Rochester, NY 14607; tel. 585/461-3520; FAX. 585/461-0997; Bonnie C. DeVinney, Executive Director

New York State Public Health Association, Pine West Plaza, One United Way, Albany, NY 12205-5558; tel. 518/427-5835; Robert Guerrin, Ph.D., President

OHIO: Health Planning and Resource Development Association of Central, Ohio River Valley, Cincinnati, OH 45219; tel. 513/221-4949; FAX. 513/221-4954; James F. Sandmann, President

Miami Valley Health Improvement Council, 2618 Needmore Road, Suite A, Dayton, OH 45414; tel. 937/754-9520; FAX. 937/275-0150; Rudolph P. Arnold, M.D., President and CEO

VIRGINIA: Central Virginia Health Planning Agency, Inc., P.O. Box 24287, Richmond, VA 23224; tel. 804/233-6206; FAX. 804/233-8834; Karen L. Cameron, CHE, Chief Executive Officer

Health Systems Agency of Northern Virginia, 7245 Arlington Boulevard, Suite 300, Falls Church, VA 22042; tel. 703/573-3100; FAX. 703/573-1276; Dean Montgomery, Executive Director

Northwestern Virginia Health Systems Agency, 1924 Arlington Boulevard, Suite 211, Charlottesville, VA 22903; tel. 434/977-6010; FAX. 434/977-0748; Margaret P. King, Executive Director

Hospital Associations

The following list of state and metropolitan hospital associations is derived from the American Hospital Association. For additional information visit the American Hospital Association website: www.aha.org.

United States

ALABAMA: Alabama Hospital Association, 500 North East Boulevard, Montgomery, AL 36117; tel. 334/272-8781; FAX. 334/270-9527; J. Michael Horsley, President and CEO

ALASKA: Alaska State Hospital and Nursing Home Association, 426 Main Street, Juneau, AK 99801; tel. 907/586-1790; FAX. 907/463-3573; Rod Betut, President and CEO

ARIZONA: Arizona Hospital and Healthcare Association, 2901 North Central Avenue,Suite 900, Phoenix, AZ 85012-2729; tel. 602/445-4300; FAX. 602/445-4299; John R. Rivers, President and CEO

ARKANSAS: Arkansas Hospital Association, 419 Natural Resources Drive, Little Rock, AR 72205-1539; tel. 501/224-7878; FAX. 501/224-0519; Phil E. Matthews, President and CEO

CALIFORNIA: California Hospital Association, 1215 K. Street, Suite 800, Sacramento, CA 95814; tel. 916/552-7547; FAX. 916/552-7618; C. Duane Dauner, President

Hospital Association of San Diego and Imperial Counties, 707 Broadway, Suite 905, San Diego, CA 92101-5391; tel. 619/544-0777; FAX. 619/544-0888; Steven A. Escoboza, President and CEO

Hospital Association of Southern California, 515 South Figueroa Street, Suite 1300, Los Angeles, CA 90071-3322; tel. 213/538-0700; FAX. 213/629-4272; James D. Barber, President and CEO

Hospital Council of Northern and Central California, 1215 K Street, Suite 730, Sacramento, CA 95814; tel. 916/552-7608; FAX. 916/552-2618; Arthur A. Sponseller, President and CEO

COLORADO: Colorado Health and Hospital Association, 7335 East Orchard Road, Suite 100, Greenwood Village, CO 80111; tel. 720/489-1630; FAX. 720/489-9400; Larry Wall, President

CONNECTICUT: Connecticut Hospital Association, 110 Barnes Road, P.O. Box 90, Wallingford, CT 06492-0090; tel. 203/294-7200; FAX. 203/269-7713; Jennifer Jackson, President and CEO

DELAWARE: Delaware Healthcare Association, 1280 South Governors Avenue, Dover, DE 19904-4802; tel. 302/674-2853; FAX. 302/734-2731; Joseph M. Letnaunchyn, President and CEO

DISTRICT OF COLUMBIA: District of Columbia Hospital Association, 1250 Eye Street, N.W., Suite 700, Washington, DC 20005-3930; tel. 202/682-1581; FAX. 202/371-8151; Robert A. Malson, President

FLORIDA: Florida Hospital Association, 306 East College Avenue, Tallahassee, FL 32301; tel. 850/222-9800; FAX. 850/561-6230; Wayne NeSmith, President

South Florida Hospital and Healthcare Association, Inc, 6363 Taft Street, Suite 200, Hollywood, FL 33024; tel. 954/964-1660; FAX. 954/962-1260; Linda S. Quick, President

GEORGIA: Georgia Hospital Association (GHA), 1675 Terrell Mill Road, Marietta, GA 30067; tel. 770/249-4500; FAX. 770/955-5801; Joseph A. Parker, President

HAWAII: Healthcare Association of Hawaii, 932 Ward Avenue, Suite 430, Honolulu, HI 96814-2126; tel. 808/521-8961; FAX. 808/599-2879; Richard E. Meiers, President and CEO

IDAHO: Idaho Hospital Association, 615 N. Seventh Street, Boise, ID 83701-1278; tel. 208/338-5100; FAX. 208/338-7800; Steven A. Millard, President

ILLINOIS: Illinois Hospital Association, 1151 East Warrenville Road, P.O. Box 3015, Naperville, IL 60566-7015; tel. 630/505-7777; FAX. 630/505-4237; Kenneth C. Robbins, President

Metropolitan Chicago Healthcare Council, 222 South Riverside Plaza, 19th Floor, Chicago, IL 60606; tel. 312/906-6000; FAX. 312/993-0779; Earl C. Bird, President/CEO

INDIANA: Indiana Hospital & Health Association, 1 American Square, Suite 1900, Indianapolis, IN 46282; tel. 317/633-4870; FAX. 317/633-4875; Kenneth G. Stella, President

IOWA: Iowa Hospital Association, 100 East Grand Avenue, Suite 100, Des Moines, IA 50309-1835; tel. 515/288-1955; FAX. 515/283-9366; Kirk Norris, President

KANSAS: Kansas Hospital Association, 215 SE 8th Street, Topeka, KS 66603; tel. 785/233-7436; FAX. 785/233-6955; Thomas L. Bell, President

KENTUCKY: Kentucky Hospital Association, 2501 Nelson Miller Parkway, P.O. Box 436629, Louisville, KY 402536629; tel. 502/426-6220; FAX. 502/426-6226; Michael T. Rust, President

LOUISIANA: Louisiana Hospital Association, 9521 Brookline Avenue, Baton Rouge, LA 70809-1431; tel. 225/928-0026; FAX. 225/923-1004; John Matessino, President & CEO

Metropolitan Hospital Council of New Orleans, 2450 Severn Avenue, Suite 210, Metairie, LA 70001; tel. 504/837-1171; FAX. 504/837-1174; John J. Finn, Ph.D., President

MAINE: Maine Hospital Association, 33 Fuller Road, Augusta, ME 04330; tel. 207/622-4794; FAX. 207/622-3073; Steven R. Michaud, President

MARYLAND: The Maryland Hospital Association, 6820 Deerpath Road, Elkridge, MD 21075-6234; tel. 410/379-6200; FAX. 410/379-8239; Calvin M. Pierson, President

Healthcare Council of the National Capital Area, 8201 Corporate Drive, Suite 410, Landover, MD 20785-2229; tel. 301/731-4700; FAX. 301/731-8286; Joseph P. Burns, President and CEO

MASSACHUSETTS: Massachusetts Hospital Association, Five New England Executive Park, Burlington, MA 01803; tel. 781/272-8000; FAX. 781/272-1524; Ronald M. Hollander, President

MICHIGAN: Michigan Health & Hospital Association, 6215 West St. Joseph Highway, Lansing, MI 48917; tel. 517/323-3443; FAX. 517/323-0946; Spencer C. Johnson, President

Healthcare Council of MidMichigan, 3927 Beecher Road, Flint, MI 48532-3803; tel. 810/766-8898; FAX. 810/762-4108; Bruce Trevithick,President

Hospital Council of East Central Michigan, 315 Mulholland Street, Bay City, MI 48703; tel. 989/891-8810; FAX. 989/891-8161; Elizabeth S. Schnettler, President

North Central Council of MHA, 616 Petoskey St., Suite 208, Petoskey, MI 49770; tel. 231/439-9812; FAX. 231/439-9813; Elizabeth Gertz, Executive Director

Southwestern Michigan Hospital Council, 6215 West St. Joseph Highway, Lansing, MI 48917; tel. 517/323-3443; FAX. 517/323-0946; Clark R. Ballard, President

MINNESOTA: Minnesota Hospital Association, 2550 University Avenue, W., Suite 350S, St. Paul, MN 55114-1900; tel. 651/641-1121; FAX. 651/659-1477; Bruce J. Rueben, President

MISSISSIPPI: Mississippi Hospital Association, 116 Woodgreen Crossing, P.O. Box 1909, Madison, MS 39130; tel. 800/289-8884; FAX. 601/368-3200; Sam W. Cameron, President and CEO

MISSOURI: Missouri Hospital Association, P.O. Box 60, Jefferson City, MO 65102-0060; tel. 573/893-3700; FAX. 573/893-2809; Marc D. Smith, President

The Health Alliance of MidAmerica, 10401 Holmes Road, Suite 280, Kansas City, MO 64131-3368; tel. 816/941-3800; FAX. 816/941-0818; Michael R. Dunaway, Senior Vice President

MONTANA: MHA...An Association of Montana Health Care Providers, 1720 Ninth Avenue, P.O. Box 5119, Helena, MT 59604; tel. 406/442-1911; FAX. 406/443-3894; James F. Ahrens, President

NEBRASKA: Nebraska Hospital Association, 1640 L Street, Suite D, Lincoln, NE 68508; tel. 402/458-4900; FAX. 402/475-4091; Laura J. Redoutey, FACHE, President

NEVADA: Nevada Hospital Association, 5250 Neil Road, Suite 302, Reno, NV 89502; tel. 775/827-0184; FAX. 775/827-0190; Bill M. Welch, President and CEO

NEW HAMPSHIRE: New Hampshire Hospital Association, Foundation for Healthy Communities, 125 Airport Road, Concord, NH 03301-7300; tel. 603/225-0900; FAX. 603/225-4346; Michael J. Hill, President

NEW JERSEY: New Jersey Hospital Association, P.O. Box One, 760 Alexander Road, Princeton, NJ 08543-0001; tel. 609/275-4000; FAX. 609/452-8097; Gary S. Carter, FACHE, President and CEO

NEW MEXICO: New Mexico Hospitals and Health Systems Association, 2121 Osuna Road, N.E., Albuquerque, NM 87113; tel. 505/343-0010; FAX. 505/343-0012; Jeff Pye, President and CEO

NEW YORK: Healthcare Association of New York State, One Empire Drive, Rensselaer, NY 12144; tel. 518/431-7600; FAX. 518/431-7915; Daniel Sisto, President

Greater New York Hospital Association, Subsidiaries, and Affiliates, 555 West 57 Street, 15th Floor, New York, NY 10019; tel. 212/246-7100; FAX. 212/262-6350; Kenneth E. Raske, President

Iroquois Healthcare Alliance, 17 Halfmoon Executive Park Drive, Clifton Park, NY 12065; tel. 518/383-5060; FAX. 518/383-2616; Gary J. Fitzgerald, President

Nassau-Suffolk Hospital Council, Inc, 1383 Veterans Memorial Highway, Suite 26, Hauppauge, NY 11788; tel. 631/435-3000; FAX. 631/435-2343; Paul J. Rowlad, VP/COO

Northern Metropolitan Hospital Association, 400 Stony Brook Court, Newburgh, NY 12550; tel. 845/562-7520; FAX. 845/562-0187; Neil Abitabilo, President

Rochester Regional Healthcare Association, 3445 Winton Place, Rochester, NY 14623; tel. 585/273-8180; FAX. 585/475-0266; Robert M. Swinnerton, President and CEO

Western New York Healthcare Association, 1876 Niagara Falls Boulevard, Tonawanda, NY 14150-6439; tel. 716/695-0843; FAX. 716/695-0073; Mary E. LaRowe, President

NORTH CAROLINA: North Carolina Hospital Association, P.O. Box 4449, Cary, NC 27519-4449; tel. 919/677-2400; FAX. 919/677-4200; William A. Pully, President

NORTH DAKOTA: North Dakota Healthcare Association, P.O. Box 7340, Bismarck, ND 585077340; tel. 701/224-9732; FAX. 701/224-9529; Arnold R. Thomas, President

OHIO: Ohio Hospital Association, 155 East Broad Street, Floor 15, Columbus, OH 43215; tel. 614/221-7614; FAX. 614/221-4771; James R. Castle, President and CEO

Greater Cincinnati Health Council, 2100 Sherman Avenue, Suite 100, Cincinnati, OH 45212-2775; tel. 513/531-0200; FAX. 513/531-0278; Lynn R. Olman, President

Greater Dayton Area Hospital Association, 32 North Main Street, Suite 1441, Dayton, OH 45402; tel. 937/228-1000; FAX. 937/228-1035; Gregory Sample, President

Hospital Council of Northwest Ohio, 3231 Central Park West Drive, Suite 200, Toledo, OH 43617; tel. 419/842-0800; FAX. 419/843-8889; W. Scott Fry, President and CEO

The Center for Health Affairs, 1226 Huron Road East, Cleveland, OH 44115; tel. 216/696-6900; FAX. 216/696-1875; William T. (Bill) Ryan, President and CEO

OKLAHOMA: Oklahoma Hospital Association, 4000 Lincoln Boulevard, Oklahoma City, OK 73105; tel. 405/427-9537; FAX. 405/424-4507; Craig W. Jones, President

Greater Oklahoma City Hospital Council, 4000 Lincoln Boulevard, Oklahoma City, OK 73105; tel. 405/949–3177; FAX. 405/949–3573; Bruce Lawrence, Chairman

OREGON: Oregon Association of Hospitals and Health Systems, 4000 Kruse Way Place, Building 2, Suite 100, Lake Oswego, OR 97035-2543; tel. 503/636–2204; FAX. 503/636–8310; Gwen Dayton, Interim President

PENNSYLVANIA: The Hospital & Healthsystem Association of Pennsylvania, 4750 Lindle Road, P.O. Box 8600, Harrisburg, PA 17105-8600; tel. 717/564–9200; FAX. 717/561–5334; Caroyln F. Scanlan, President and CEO
  Hospital Council of Western Pennsylvania, 500 Commonwealth Drive, Warrendale, PA 15086; tel. 724/772–7206; FAX. 724/772–8339; Alvin J. Harper, President
  The Delaware Valley Healthcare Council, 121 South Broad Street, 20th Floor, Philadelphia, PA 19107; tel. 215/735–9695; FAX. 215/790–1267; Andrew B. Wigglesworth, President

RHODE ISLAND: Hospital Association of Rhode Island, 880 Butler Drive, Suite One, Providence, RI 02906; tel. 401/946–7887; FAX. 401/946–8188; Edward Quinlan, President

SOUTH CAROLINA: South Carolina Hospital Association, 1000 Center Point Road, Columbia, SC 29210-5802; tel. 803/796–3080; FAX. 803/796–2938; Thorton Kirby, President

SOUTH DAKOTA: South Dakota Association of Healthcare Organizations, 3708 West Brooks Place, Sioux Falls, SD 57106; tel. 605/361–2281; FAX. 605/361–5175; David R. Hewett, President and CEO

TENNESSEE: Tennessee Hospital Association, 500 Interstate Boulevard, South, Nashville, TN 37210; tel. 615/256–8240; FAX. 615/242–4803; Craig A. Becker, President

TEXAS: Texas Hospital Association, 6225 U.S. Highway 290, E, P.O. Box 15587, Austin, TX 78761-5587; tel. 512/465–1000; FAX. 512/465–1090; Richard J. Bettis, CAE, President and CEO

Dallas-Fort Worth Hospital Council, 250 Decker Drive, Irving, TX 75062; tel. 972/719–4900; FAX. 972/719–4009; John C. Gavras, President
Greater San Antonio Hospital Council, 8610 North New Braunfels, Suite 105, San Antonio, TX 78217; tel. 210/820–3500; FAX. 210/820–3888; William Dean Rasco, FACHE, President and CEO

UTAH: UHA, Utah Hospitals and Health Systems Association, 2180 South 1300 East, Suite 440, Salt Lake City, UT 84106-2843; tel. 801/486–9915; FAX. 801/486–0882; Joseph M. Krella, CAE-President/CEO

VERMONT: Vermont Association of Hospitals and Health Systems, 148 Main Street, Montpelier, VT 05602; tel. 802/223–3461; FAX. 802/223–0364; Beatrice Grause, President and CEO

VIRGINIA: Virginia Hospital & Healthcare Association, 4200 Inslake Drive, P.O. Box 31394, Richmond, VA 23294; tel. 804/747–8600; FAX. 804/965–0475; Laurens Sartoris, President

WASHINGTON: Washington State Hospital Association, 300 Elliott Avenue, West, Suite 300, Seattle, WA 98119-4118; tel. 206/281–7211; FAX. 206/283–6122; Leo F. Greenawalt, President and CEO

WEST VIRGINIA: West Virginia Hospital Association, 100 Association Drive, Charleston, WV 25311-1571; tel. 304/344–9744; FAX. 304/344–9745; Steven J. Summer, President

WISCONSIN: Wisconsin Hospital Association, 5510 Research Park Dr., P.O.Box 259038, Madison, WI 53725-9038; tel. 608/274–1820; FAX. 608/274–8554; Stephen Brenton, President

WYOMING: Wyoming Hospital Association, P.O. Box 249, Cheyenne, WY 82003; tel. 307/632–9344; FAX. 307/632–9347; Robert C. Kidd, II, President

U.S. Associated Areas

PUERTO RICO: Puerto Rico Hospital Association, Officina 101-103, Villa Nevarez Professional Center, Centro Commercial Villa Nevarez, San Juan, PR 00927; tel. 787/764–0290; FAX. 787/753–9748; Juan Rivera, Executive Vice President

Canada

ALBERTA: Provincial Health Authorities of Alberta, 44 Capital Boulevard, 200-10044-108 Street, NW, Edmonton, AB AB T5J 3S7; tel. 780/426–8503; FAX. 780/424–4309; E. Michael Higgins, Executive Director

NEW BRUNSWICK: New Brunswick Healthcare Association, 861 Woodstock Road, Fredericton, NB E3B 7R7; tel. 506/451–0750; FAX. 506/451–0760; Robert Simpson, Executive Director

NOVA SCOTIA: Nova Scotia Association of Health Organizations, Bedford Professional Centre, 2 Dartmouth Road, Bedford, NS B4A-2K7; tel. 902–832–8500; FAX. 902/832–8505; Robert A. Cook, President and CEO

ONTARIO: Ontario Hospital Association, 200 Front Street, W, Suite 2800, Toronto, ON M5V-3L1; tel. 416–205–1305; FAX. 416/205–1310; David MacKinnon, President & CEO
  Catholic Health Association of Canada, 1247 Kilborn Place, Ottawa, ON K1H-6K9; tel. 613–731–7148; FAX. 613/731–7797; Richard Haughian, D.Th., President

PRINCE EDWARD ISLAND: Health Association of PEI, Inc., 10 Pownal Street, Charlottetown, PE C1A-3V6; tel. 902–368–3901; FAX. 902/368–3231; Ken Ezeard, Executive Director

QUEBEC: Quebec Hospital Association, 505 boulevard de Maisonneuve, W, Suite 400, Montreal, PQ H3A3C2; tel. 514–282–4200; FAX. 514/282–4271; Daniel Adam, Executive Vice President

SASKATCHEWAN: Saskatchewan Association of Health Organizations, 1445 Park Street, Regina, SK S4N-4C5; tel. 306–347–5500; FAX. 306/347–5500; R.M. Louise Simard, President and CEO

Hospital Licensure Agencies

Information for the following list of state hospital licensure agencies was obtained directly from the agencies.

United States

ALABAMA: Alabama Department of Public Health, Division of Health Care Facilities, The RSA Tower, Sixth Floor, P.O. Box 303017, Montgomery, AL 36130-3017; tel. 334/206-5075; FAX. 334/206-5088; Rick Harris, Director of Healthcare Standards

Alabama Department of Public Health, Division of Provider Services, The RSA Tower, 201 Monroe Street, Montgomery, AL 36130-3017; tel. 334/206-5086; FAX. 334/206-5219; Rick Harris, Director of Healthcare Standards

ALASKA: Health Facilities Licensing and Certification, 4730 Business Park Boulevard, Building H, Anchorage, AK 99503-7137; tel. 907/334-2481; FAX. 907/561-3011; Shelbert Larsen, Administrator

ARIZONA: Arizona Department of Health Services, Division of Licensing Services/Office of Medical Facilities, 150 N. 18th Avenue, Suite 460, Phoenix, AZ 85007; tel. 602/364-3030; FAX. 602/395-8913; Kathy McCanna, Program Manager

ARKANSAS: Division of Health Facility Services, Arkansas Department of Health, 5800 West 10th Street, Suite 400, Little Rock, AR 72204-9916; tel. 501/661-2201; FAX. 501/661-2165; Renee Mallory, Director

CALIFORNIA: State of California/DHS/L&C, 1615 Capitol Ave Suite 1, P.O. Box 997413/MS 3000, Sacramento, CA 94234-7320; tel. 916440-7360; FAX. 916/552-8758; Brenda Klutz, Deputy Director

COLORADO: Health Facilities Division, Colorado Department of Public Health and Environment, 4300 Cherry Creek Drive, S., Denver, CO 80246-1530; tel. 303/692-2800; FAX. 303/782-4883; Ellen Mangione, Director

CONNECTICUT: Department of Public Health, Division of Health Systems Regulation, 410 Capitol Avenue, MS 12HSR, P.O. Box 340308, Hartford, CT 06134-0308; tel. 860/509-7407; FAX. 860/509-7539; Wendy Furniss, RNC, MS, Branch Chief

DELAWARE: Department of Health and Social Services, Office of Health Facilities Licensing and Certification, 2055 Limestone Road, Suite 200, Wilmington, DE 19808; tel. 302/995-8521; FAX. 302/995-8529; Mary E. Peterson, Director

FLORIDA: Agency for Health Care Administration, Division of Health Facility Regulations, Hospital and Outpatient Services Unit, Mail Stop 31, 2727 Mahan Drive, Tallahassee, FL 32308; tel. 850/487-2717; FAX. 850/922-4351; Laura MacLafflerty, Unit Manager

GEORGIA: Health Care Section, Office of Regulatory Services, Georgia Department of Human Resources, Two Peachtree Street, N.W., Room 33-250, Atlanta, GA 30303-3142; tel. 404/657-5550; FAX. 404/657-8934; Carol Zafiratos, Director, Health Care Section

HAWAII: Hawaii Department of Health, Office of Health Care Assurance, P.O. Box 3378, Honolulu, HI 96801-3378; tel. 808/586-4080; FAX. 808/586-4791; Dianne Okumura, B.S.N., MPH, Chief, OHCA

IDAHO: Bureau of Facility Standards, Department of Health and Welfare, P.O. Box 83720, Boise, ID 83720-0036; tel. 208/334-6626; FAX. 208/364-1888; Sylvia Creswell, Supervisor, Non-Long Term Care

ILLINOIS: Division of Health Care Facilities and Programs, Illinois Department of Public Health, 525 West Jefferson Street, Springfield, IL 62761; tel. 217/782-7412; FAX. 217/782-0382; Enrique J. Unanue, AIA, ACHA, Deputy Director

INDIANA: Division of Acute Care, Indiana State Department of Health, Two North Meridian Street, Indianapolis, IN 46204; tel. 317/233-7472; FAX. 317/233-7157; Mary Azbill, Director

IOWA: Health Facilities Division, Iowa Department of Inspections and Appeals, Lucas State Office Building, 321 East 12th Street, Des Moines, IA 50319-0083; tel. 515/281-4115; FAX. 515/242-5022; David Werning, Public Information Officer

KANSAS: Kansas Department of Health and Environment, Bureau of Child Care &Health Facilities, 1000 Southwest Jackson, Suite 200, Topeka, KS 66612-1365; tel. 785/296-0131; FAX. 785/291-3419; Charles Moore, Director of Medical Facilities and Support

KENTUCKY: Division of Healthcare Facilities and Services, Cabinet for Health and Family Services, 275 East Main Street, 5E-A, Frankfort, KY 40621; tel. 502/564-2800; FAX. 502/564-6546; Jennifer Mitchell, Director

LOUISIANA: Health Standards Section, Louisiana Department of Health and Hospitals, P.O. Box 3767, Baton Rouge, LA 70821; tel. 225/342-0415; FAX. 225/342-5292; Lisa Deaton, RN, Manager

MAINE: Division of Licensing and Certification, Department of Human Services, State House, Station 11, Augusta, ME 04333; tel. 207/287-9300; FAX. 207/287-9304; Louis Dorogi, Assistant Director

MARYLAND: Department of Health and Mental Hygiene, Office of Health Care Quality, 55 Wade Avenue - SGHC, Catonsville, MD 21228; tel. 410/402-8007; FAX. 410/402-8167; Joseph I. Berman, Medical Director

MASSACHUSETTS: Massachusetts Department of Public Health, Division of Health Care Quality, 10 West Street, Fifth Floor, Boston, MA 02111; tel. 617/753-8000; FAX. 617/753-8125; Paul I. Dreyer, Ph.D., Director

MICHIGAN: Bureau of Health Systems, Michigan Department of Community Health, 525 West Ottawa, P.O. Box 30664, Lansing, MI 48909; tel. 517/241-4160; FAX. 517/241-3354; Darryl Horton, Director

MINNESOTA: Compliance Monitoring Division, Minnesota Department of Health, 85 East Seventh Place, P.O. Box 64900, St. Paul, MN 55164-0900; tel. 651/215-5611; FAX. 651/215-8710; David Giese, Director

MISSISSIPPI: Division of Health Facilities Licensure and Certification, Mississippi State Department of Health, P.O. Box 1700, Jackson, MS 39215; tel. 601/576-7300; FAX. 601/576-7350; Karen Selestak, Director

MISSOURI: Bureau of Health Facility Regulation, Missouri Department of Health, P.O. Box 570, Jefferson City, MO 65102; tel. 573/751-6303; FAX. 573/526-3621; Andrew Petti, Administrator

MONTANA: Division of Quality Assurance, Department of Public Health and Human Services, 2401 Colonial Drive, P.O. Box 202953, Helena, MT 59620-2953; tel. 406/444-2037; FAX. 406/444-1742; Roy Kemp, Licensure Bureau Chief

NEBRASKA: Nebraska Department of Health & Human Services Regulation and Licensure, Credentialing Division, 301 Centennial Mall, S., P.O. Box 94986, Lincoln, NE 68509-4986; tel. 402/471-4362; FAX. 402/471-0555; Nancy Brown, Program Manager

NEVADA: Bureau of Licensure and Certification, Nevada Health Division, 1550 East College Parkway, Suite 158, Carson City, NV 89706-7921; tel. 775/687-4475; FAX. 775/687-6588; Pam Graham, Chief

NEW HAMPSHIRE: Bureau of Health Facilities Administration, Office of Program Support, Licensure and Regulation, 129 Pleasant Street, Brown Building, Concord, NH 03301; tel. 603/271-4967; FAX. 603/271-8617; Robert Ehlers, Bureau Chief

NEW JERSEY: Certificate of Need and Acute Care Licensing, N.J. Department of Health and Senior Services, P.O. Box 360, Room 403, Trenton, NJ 08625-0360; tel. 609/292-8773; FAX. 609/292-3780; John Calabria, Director

NORTH CAROLINA: Division of Facility Services, Department of Health and Human Services, 2711 Mail Service Center, Raleigh, NC 27699-2711; tel. 919/733-7461; FAX. 919/733-8274; Jeff Horton, Section Chief

NORTH DAKOTA: Health Resources Section, North Dakota Department of Health, 600 East Boulevard Avenue, Dept 301, Bismarck, ND 58505-0200; tel. 701/328-2352; FAX. 701/328-1890; Darleen Bartz, Chief Health Resources Section

OHIO: Ohio Department of Health, Division of Quality Assurance, Bureau of Information & Operational Support-Hospital Registration, 246 N. High St. - P.O. Box 118, Columbus, OH 43215-2412; tel. 614/644-7238; FAX. 614/466-8692; Iris King, Administrative Assistant

OKLAHOMA: State Department of Health, 1000 Northeast 10th, Suite 305, Oklahoma City, OK 73117; tel. 405/271-4200; FAX. 405/271-3431; James Crutcher,Commissioner of Health

OREGON: Health Care Licensure and Certification, Department of Human Services, P.O. Box 14450, Portland, OR 97293-0450; tel. 503/731-4013; FAX. 503/731-4080; Kathleen Smail, Manager

PENNSYLVANIA: Division of Acute and Ambulatory Care Facilities, Pennsylvania Department of Health, Division of Acute and Ambulatory Care, Health & Welfare Bldg Room 532, Harrisburg, PA 17100; tel. 717/783-8980; FAX. 717/705-6663; Sandra Knoble, Director

RHODE ISLAND: Rhode Island Department of Health, Office of Facilities Regulation, Three Capitol Hill Room 306, Providence, RI 02908-5097; tel. 401/222-2566; FAX. 401/222-3999; Raymond Rusin, Chief

SOUTH CAROLINA: Department of Health and Environmental Control, Division of Health Licensing, 2600 Bull Street, Columbia, SC 29201; tel. 803/545-4370; FAX. 803/545-4212; Dennis Gibbs, Director,Division of Health Licensing

SOUTH DAKOTA: Office of Health Care Facilities Licensure and Certification, State Department of Health, Licensure and Certification, 615 E. 4th Street, Pierre, SD 57501-1700; tel. 605/773-3356; FAX. 605/773-6667; Robert Stahl, Administrator

TENNESSEE: Tennessee Department of Health, Division of Health Care Facilities, 425 5th Avenue North, Cordell Hull, 1st Floor, Nashville, TN 37247-0508; tel. 615/741–7294; FAX. 615/741–7051; Katy Gammon, Director

TEXAS: Texas Department of Health, Health Facility Licensing and Compliance Division, 1100 West 49th Street, Austin, TX 78756-3199; tel. 512/834–6650; FAX. 512/834–6653; Cindy Bednar, Director

UTAH: Utah State Department of Health, Bureau of Licensing, Box 142003, Salt Lake City, UT 84114-2003; tel. 801/538–6152; FAX. 801/538–6325; Debra Wynkoop, Director

VERMONT: Health Improvement, Vermont Department of Health, 108 Cherry Street, P.O. Box 70, Burlington, VT 05402; tel. 802/863–7606; FAX. 802/651–1634; Ellen B. Thompson, Planning Chief

VIRGINIA: Center for Quality Health Care Services and Consumer Protection, Virginia Department of Health, 3600 Centre, Suite 216, Richmond, VA 23230; tel. 804/367–2102; FAX. 804/367–2149; Nancy R. Hofheimer, Director

WASHINGTON: Office of Health Care Survey, Washington Department of Health, Point Plaza East, 310 Israel Road SE, Olympia, WA 98504-7852; tel. 360/236–2917; FAX. 360/236–2901; Byron Plan, Executive Manager

WEST VIRGINIA: Office of Health Facility Licensure and Certification, West Virginia Department of Health and Human Resources, 1 Davis Square, Suite 101, Charleston, WV 25301-1799; tel. 304/558–0050; FAX. 304/558–5607; John Wilkinson, Director

WISCONSIN: Bureau of Quality Assurance, Division of Disability and Elder Services, Department of Health and Family Services, One West Wilson Street, P.O. Box 2969, Madison, WI 53701-2969; tel. 608/267–7185; FAX. 608/267–0352; Cris Ros-Dukler,Director

WYOMING: Office of Health Quality, Health Facilities Licensing, 2020 Carey Avenue, Eighth Floor, Cheyenne, WY 82002; tel. 307/777–7123; FAX. 307/777–7127; Gene McClean, Nurse Administrator

Medical and Nursing Licensure Agencies

The following information is based on information provided by state government entities and the agencies themselves.

United States

ALABAMA
Alabama Board of Nursing, RSA Plaza, 770 Washington Ave., Suite 250, Montgomery, AL 36104; tel. 334/242–4060; FAX. 334/242–4360; N. Genell lee, RN, M.S.N. JD, Executive Officer

Alabama State Board of Medical Examiners, 848 Washington Avenue, P.O. Box 946, Montgomery, AL 36101-0946; tel. 334/242–4116; FAX. 334/242–4155; Larry D. Dixon, Executive Director

ALASKA
Alaska Board of Nursing, Division of Occupational Licensing, 550 W. 7th Ave. Suite. 1500, Anchorage, AK 99501; tel. 907/269–8161; FAX. 907/269–8196; Dorothy Fulton, Executive Administrator

Alaska State Board of Medical Examiners, 550 West Seventh Ave., Suite 1500, Anchorage, AK 99501; tel. 907/269–8163; FAX. 907/269–8196; Leslie A. Gallant, Executive Administrator

ARIZONA
Arizona Board of Osteopathic Examiners in Medicine and Surgery, 9535 E. Doubletree Ranch Road, Scottsdale, AZ 85258; tel. 480/657–7703; FAX. 480/657–7715; Jack Confer, Executive Director

Arizona State Board of Medical Examiners, 9545 E. Doubletree Ranch Road, Scottsdale, AZ 85258; tel. 877/255–2212; FAX. 480/551–2704; Claudia Foutz, Executive Director

Arizona State Board of Nursing, 1651 East Morten, Suite 210, Phoenix, AZ 85020; tel. 602/889–5150; FAX. 602/889–5155; Joey Ridenour, RN, MN., Executive Director

ARKANSAS
Arkansas State Board of Nursing, University Tower Building, Suite 800, 1123 South University Avenue, Little Rock, AR 72204; tel. 501/686–2700; FAX. 501/686–2714; Faith A. Fields, M.S.N., RN, Executive Director

Arkansas State Medical Board, 2100 Riverfront Drive, Little Rock, AR 72202; tel. 501/296–1802; FAX. 501/296–1805; Peggy Pryor Cryer, Executive Secretary

CALIFORNIA
California Board of Registered Nursing, 400 R Street, Suite 4030, Sacramento, CA 94244-2100; tel. 916/322–3350; FAX. 916/327–4402; Ruth Ann Terry, MPH, RN, Executive Officer

Medical Board of California, 1426 Howe Avenue, Suite 54, Sacramento, CA 95825; tel. 916/263–2382; FAX. 916/263–2487; Joyce HADnot, Chief Licensing Program

COLORADO
Colorado State Board of Medical Examiners, 1560 Broadway, Suite 1350, Denver, CO 80202-5140; tel. 303/894–7693; FAX. 303/894–7692; Susan Miller, Program Director

Colorado State Board of Nursing, 1560 Broadway, Suite 880, Denver, CO 80202; tel. 303/894–2430; FAX. 303/894–2821; Patricia Uris, RN, Ph.D., Program Administrator

CONNECTICUT
Connecticut Board of Examiners for Nursing, Department of Public Health, 410 Capitol Avenue, MS #13PHO, P.O. Box 340308, Hartford, CT 06134-0308; tel. 860/509–7624; FAX. 860/509–7553; Jan Wojick, Board Liaison

Connecticut Department of Public Health, 410 Capitol Avenue, MS #12 APP, P.O. Box 340308, Hartford, CT 06134-0308; tel. 860/509–7603; FAX. 860/509–8457; Stephen Carragher, Health Program Supervisor

DELAWARE
Delaware Board of Medical Practice, Cannon Building, 861 Silver Lake Boulevard, Suite 203, Dover, DE 19904; tel. 302/744–4522; FAX. 302/739–2711; Gayle Franzolino, Executive

Delaware Board of Nursing, Cannon Building, Suite 203, 861 Silver Lake Boulevard, Suite 203, Dover, DE 19904; tel. 302/739–4516; FAX. 302/739–2711; Iva J. Boardman, RN, M.S.N., Executive Director

DISTRICT OF COLUMBIA
District of Columbia Board of Medicine, 717 14th St. NW, Suite 600, Washington, DC 20005; tel. 202/442–9200; FAX. 202/724–8677; James R. Granger, Jr., Executive Director

FLORIDA
Florida Board of Medicine, 4052 Bald Cypress Way, Bin #C03, Tallahassee, FL 32399-3253; tel. 850/245–4131; FAX. 850/488–9325; Larry G. McPherson, Jr., J.D., Board Director

Florida Board of Nursing, Capital Circle Officer Center, 4052 Bald Cypress Way, Bin C02, Tallahassee, FL 32399-3252; tel. 850/245–4125; FAX. 850/487–9874; Dan Coble, RN, Ph.D., Executive Director

Florida Board of Osteopathic Medicine, 4052 Bald Cypress Way, Bin #C-06, Tallahassee, FL 32399-3256; tel. 850/488–0595; FAX. 850/487–9874; Christy Robinson, POA

GEORGIA
Georgia Board of Nursing, 237 Coliseum Drive, Macon, GA 31217; tel. 912/207–1640; FAX. 912/207–1660; Sylvia L. Bond, R.N. MSN, MBA, Executive Director

Georgia Composite State Board of Medical Examiners, 2 Peachtree Street, 36th Floor, Atlanta, GA 30303; tel. 404/656–3913; FAX. 404/656–9723; Physician Licensing

HAWAII
Hawaii Board of Medical Examiners, Department of Commerce and Consumer Affairs, 335 Merchants Street, Room 301, Honolulu, HI 96801; tel. 808/586–3000; Constance Cabral-Makanani, Executive Officer

Hawaii Board of Nursing, Professional and Vocational Licensing Division, P.O. Box 3469, Honolulu, HI 96801; tel. 808/586–3000; FAX. 808/586–2689; Kathy Yokouchi, MBA, BBA, Executive Officer

IDAHO
Idaho State Board of Medicine, P.O. Box 83720, Boise, ID 83720-0058; tel. 208/327–7000; FAX. 208/327–7005; Nancy Kerr, Executive Director

Idaho State Board of Nursing, 280 North 8th Street, Suite 210, P.O. Box 83720, Boise, ID 83720-0061; tel. 208/334–3110; FAX. 208/334–3262; Sandra Evans, MA.Ed., RN Executive Director

ILLINOIS
Illinois Department of Professional Regulation, 320 West Washington Street, 3rd Floor, Springfield, IL 62786; tel. 217/782–8556; FAX. 217/782–7645; Chris Ganschow, Director of Communications

Illinois Department of Professional Regulation, James R. Thompson Center, 100 West Randolph Street, Chicago, IL 60601; tel. 312/814–2715; FAX. 312/814–3145; Maryann Alexander,PhD,RN,Nursing Act Coordinator

INDIANA
Indiana Health Professions Bureau, Medical Licensing Board of Indiana, Indiana State Board of Nursing, 402 West Washington, Suite W066, Indianapolis, IN 46204; tel. 317/232–2960; FAX. 317/233–4236; Frances L. Kelly, Executive Director

Indiana State Board of Nursing, Health Professions Bureau, 402 West Washington, Suite 066, Indianapolis, IN 46204; tel. 317/234–2043; FAX. 317/233–4236; Tonja Thompson, Board Director

IOWA
Iowa Board of Medical Examiners, 400 S.W. 8th Street, Suite C, Des Moines, IA 50309-4686; tel. 515/281–5171; FAX. 515/242–5908; Ann E. Mowery, Ph.D., Executive Director

Iowa Board of Nursing, Riverpoint Business Park, 400 S.W. 8th Street, Des Moines, IA 50309-4685; tel. 515/281–3255; FAX. 515/281–4825; Lorinda K. Inman, RN, M.S.N., Executive Director

KANSAS
Kansas Board of Healing Arts, 235 SW Topeka Blvd., Topeka, KS 66603-3068; tel. 913/296–7413; FAX. 913/296–0852; Lawrence T. Buening, Jr., Executive Director

Kansas State Board of Nursing, Landon State Office Building, 900 SW Jackson, Topeka, KS 66612-1230; tel. 785/296–4929; FAX. 785/296–3929; Mary Blubaugh MSN, RN, Executive Administrator

KENTUCKY
Kentucky Board of Medical Licensure, The Hurstbourne Office Park, 310 Whittington Parkway, Suite 1B, Louisville, KY 40222; tel. 502/429–7150; FAX. 502/429–7158; C. William Schmidt, Executive Director

Kentucky Board of Nursing, 312 Whittington Parkway, Suite 300, Louisville, KY 40222; tel. 502/429–3000; FAX. 502/429–3311; Sharon M. Weisenbeck, M.S., RN, Executive Director

LOUISIANA
Louisiana State Board of Medical Examiners, 630 Camp Street, New Orleans, LA 70130; tel. 504/524–6763; FAX. 504/568–8893; Kim Edward LeBlank, M.D., Ph.D., President

Louisiana State Board of Nursing, 3510 N. Causeway Boulevard, Suite 601, Metarie, LA 70002; tel. 504/838–5332; FAX. 504/838–5349; Barbara L. Morvant, MN, RN, Executive Director

Louisiana State Board of Practical Nurse Examiners, 3421 N. Causeway Boulevard, Suite 505, Metairie, LA 70002; tel. 504/838–5791; FAX. 504/838–5279; Claire Glaviano, BSN, MN, RN, Executive Director

MAINE
Maine Board of Licensure in Medicine, Two Bangor Street, 137 State House Station, Augusta, ME 04333-0137; tel. 207/287–3601; FAX. 207/287–6590

Maine Board of Osteopathic Licensure, 142 State House Station, Two Bangor Street, Augusta, ME 04333-0142; tel. 207/287–2480; FAX. 207/287–3015; Susan E. Strout, Executive Secretary

Maine State Board of Nursing, 158 State House Station, Augusta, ME 04333; tel. 207/287–1133; FAX. 207/287–1149; Myra A. Broadway, JD, MS, RN, Executive Director

MARYLAND
Maryland Board of Nursing, 4140 Patterson Avenue, Baltimore, MD 21215; tel. 410/585–1900; FAX. 410/358–3530; Donna M. Dorsey, RN, M.S., Executive Director

Maryland Board of Physicians, 4201 Patterson Avenue, Third Floor, P.O. Box 2571, Baltimore, MD 21215-0095; tel. 800/492–6836; FAX. 410/358–2252; C.Irving Pinder, Jr., Executive Director

MASSACHUSETTS
Massachusetts Board of Registration in Medicine, 560 Harrison Avenue, Suite G4, Boston, MA 02118; tel. 617/654–9800; FAX. 617/426–9373; Nancy AchinAndesse, Executive Director

MICHIGAN
Michigan Board of Medicine, 611 West Ottawa Street, First Floor, P.O. Box 30670, Lansing, MI 48909; tel. 517/335–0918; FAX. 517/373–2179

Michigan Board of Nursing, Department of Consumer and Industry Service, 611 West Ottawa Street, P.O. Box 30670, Lansing, MI 48909; tel. 517/335–0918; FAX. 517/373–2179

Michigan Board of Osteopathic Medicine and Surgery, 611 West Ottawa Street, First Floor, P.O. Box 30670, Lansing, MI 48909; tel. 517/335–0918; FAX. 517/373–2179

MINNESOTA
Minnesota Board of Medical Practice, 2829 University Avenue, S.E., Suite 400, Minneapolis, MN 55414-3246; tel. 612/617–2130; FAX. 612/617–2166; Robert A. Leach, Executive Director

Minnesota Board of Nursing, 2829 University Avenue, S.E., Suite 200, Minneapolis, MN 55414-3253; tel. 612/617–2270; FAX. 612/617–2190; Shirley A. Brekken, Executive Director

MISSISSIPPI

Mississippi Board of Nursing, 1935 Lakeland Drive, Suite B, Jackson, MS 39216-5014; tel. 601/987-4188; FAX. 601/364-2352; Delia Owens, J.D, RN, Executive Director

Mississippi State Board of Medical Licensure, 1867 Crane Ridge Drive, Suite 200-B, Jackson, MS 39216; tel. 601/987-3079; FAX. 601/987-4159; W. Joseph Burnett, M.D., Executive Director

MISSOURI

Missouri State Board of Nursing, 3605 Missouri Boulevard, P.O. Box 656, Jefferson City, MO 65102; tel. 573/751-0681; FAX. 573/751-0075; Lori Scheidt, Executive Director

Missouri State Board of Registration for the Healing Arts, 3605 Missouri Boulevard, Zip 65109, P.O. Box 4, Jefferson City, MO 65102; tel. 573/751-0098; FAX. 573/751-3166; Tina Steinman, Exeuctive Director

MONTANA

Montana Board of Medical Examiners, 301 S. Park Avenue 4th Floor, P.O. Box 200513, Helena, MT 59620-0513; tel. 406/841-2364; FAX. 406/841-2305; Jeannie Worsech, Executive Secretary

Montana State Board of Nursing, 301 South Park, P.O. Box 200513, Helena, MT 59620-0513; tel. 406/841-2361; FAX. 406/841-2343; Anita Verbanac, Program Manager

NEBRASKA

Nebraska Board of Medicine and Surgery, 301 Centennial Mall, S., P.O. Box 94986, Lincoln, NE 68509-4986; tel. 402/471-2118; FAX. 402/471-3577; Becky Wisell, Executive Director

NEVADA

Nevada State Board of Medical Examiners, 1105 Terminal Way, Suite 301, Zip 89502, P.O. Box 7238, Reno, NV 89510; tel. 775/688-2559; FAX. 775/688-2321; Bonnie S. Brand,General Counsel

Nevada State Board of Nursing, 5011 Meadowood Mace Wy #201, Reno, NV 89502; tel. 775/688-2620; FAX. 775/688-2628; Debra Scott, Executive Director

Nevada State Board of Osteopathic Medicine, 2860 East Flamingo Road, Suite D, Las Vegas, NV 89121-5270; tel. 702/732-2147; FAX. 702/732-2079; Trey Dulap, Executive Director

NEW HAMPSHIRE

New Hampshire Board of Medicine, Two Industrial Park Drive, Suite Eight, Concord, NH 03301; tel. 603/271-1203; FAX. 603/271-6702; Penny Taylor, Administrator

NH Board of Nursing, 21 S. Fruit S, Suite 16, Concord, NH 03301-2431; tel. 603/271-2323; FAX. 603/271-6605; Margaret Walker, RN, Executive Director

NEW JERSEY

New Jersey Board of Nursing, P.O. Box 45010, Newark, NJ 07101; tel. 973/504-6430; FAX. 973/648-3481; George Hebert, Executive Director

New Jersey State Board of Medical Examiners, P.O. Box 183, Trenton, NJ 08625-0183; tel. 609/826-7100; FAX. 609/984-3930; William V. Roeder, Executive Director

NEW MEXICO

New Mexico Board of Osteopathic Medical Examiners, 2550 Cerrillos Rd., P.O. Box 25101, Santa Fe, NM 87504; tel. 505/476-4695; FAX. 505/476-7095; Annette Rodriguez Brumley, Board Administrator

New Mexico Medical Board, 2055 S. Pacheco #400, Santa Fe, NM 87505; tel. 505/476-2220; FAX. 505/476-7237; Charlotte Kinney, Executive Director

State of New Mexico Board of Nursing, 6301 Indian School NE Suite,710, Albuquerque, NM 87109; tel. 505/841-8340; FAX. 505/841-8347; Allison Kozeliski, Executive Director

NEW YORK

New York State Board for Nursing, State Education Department, Education Bldg. 2nd Floor, West/Wing, Albany, NY 12234-1000; tel. 518/474-3817; FAX. 518/474-3706; Barbara Zittel, Ph.D., RN, Executive Secretary

New York State Division of Professional Licensing Services, 89 Washington Avenue, 2nd Floor North, Albany, NY 12234; tel. 518/474-3817; FAX. 518/402-5265; Robert G. Bentley, Director of Professional Licensing

New York State Education Department, Office of the Professions Division of Professional Licensing Services, 89 Washington Avenue 2nd Floor, Albany, NY 12234; tel. 518/474-3817; FAX. 518/474-1449; Patricia E. Whitman

NORTH CAROLINA

North Carolina Board of Nursing, P.O. Box 2129, Raleigh, NC 27602-2129; tel. 919/782-3211; FAX. 919/781-9461; Mary P. Johnson, RN, MSN, Executive Director

North Carolina Medical Board, 1203 Front Street, Raleigh, NC 27609; tel. 919/326-1100; FAX. 919/326-1130; David Henderson, Executive Director

NORTH DAKOTA

North Dakota Board of Nursing, 919 South Seventh Street, Suite 504, Bismarck, ND 58504-5881; tel. 701/328-9777; FAX. 701/328-9785; Constance Kalanek, Ph D., RN, Executive Director

North Dakota State Board of Medical Examiners, 418 East Broadway Avenue, Bismarck, ND 58501; tel. 701/328-6500; FAX. 701/328-6505; Rolf P. Sletten, Executive Secretary-Treasurer

OHIO

Ohio Board of Nursing, 17 South High Street, Suite 400, Columbus, OH 43215-3413; tel. 614/466-3947; FAX. 614/466-0388; John M. Brion, RN, MS, Executive Director

State Medical Board of Ohio, 77 South High Street, 17th Floor, Columbus, OH 43215-6127; tel. 614/466-3934; FAX. 614/728-5946; Tom Dilling, Executive Director

OKLAHOMA

Oklahoma Board of Nursing, 2915 North Classen Boulevard, Suite 524, Oklahoma City, OK 73106; tel. 405/962-1800; FAX. 405/962-1821; Kimberly Glazier, M.Ed., RN, Executive Director

Oklahoma Board of Osteopathic Examiners, 4848 North Lincoln Boulevard, Suite 100, Oklahoma City, OK 73105-3321; tel. 405/528-8625; Gary R. Clark, Executive Director

Oklahoma State Board of Medical Licensure and Supervision, 5104 North Francis, Suite C, Oklahoma City, OK 73118, Oklahoma City, OK 73154-0256; tel. 405/848-6841; FAX. 405/848-8240; Lyle Kelsey, Executive Director

OREGON

Oregon Board of Medical Examiners, 620 Crown Plaza, Portland, OR 97201-5826; tel. 503/229-5770; FAX. 503/229-6543; Kathleen Haley, JD, Executive Director

Oregon State Board of Nursing, 800 Northeast Oregon Street, Suite 465, Portland, OR 97232-2162; tel. 503/731-4745; FAX. 503/731-4755; Joan C. Bouchard, Executive Director

PENNSYLVANIA

Pennsylvania State Board of Medicine, P.O. Box 2649, Harrisburg, PA 17105-2649; tel. 717/783-1400; FAX. 717/787-7769; Joanne T. Troutman, Administrative Officer

Pennsylvania State Board of Nursing, P.O. Box 2649, Harrisburg, PA 17105-2649; tel. 717/783-7142; FAX. 717/783-0822; Executive Secretary

Pennsylvania State Board of Osteopathic Medicine, P.O. Box 2649, Harrisburg, PA 17105-2649; tel. 717/783-4858; FAX. 717/787-7769; Gina Bittner, Administrative Assistant

Quality Insights of Pennsylvania, Commerce Court, 2601 Market Place, Harrisburg, PA 17110; tel. 304/346-9864; John C. Wiesendanger, CEO

RHODE ISLAND

Rhode Island Board of Medical Licensure & Discipline, Three Capitol Hill, Room 205, Providence, RI 02908-5097; tel. 401/222-3855; David R. Gifford, M.D., MPH, Director

Rhode Island Board of Nursing Education and Nurse Registration, Three Capitol Hill, Room 105, Providence, RI 02908-5097; tel. 401/222-5700; FAX. 401/222-3352; Jean Marie Rocha, Director

SOUTH CAROLINA

Department of Labor, Licensing and Regulation, State Board of Nursing for South Carolina, 110 Centerview Drive, Suite 202, Columbia, SC 29210; tel. 803/896-4550; FAX. 803/896-4525; Martha Summer Bursinger, RN, MSN, Med Administrator

South Carolina Department of Labor, Licensing and Regulation, Board of Medical Examiners, 110 Centerview Drive, Suite 202, Columbia, S.C. 29210, Columbia, SC 29211-1289; tel. 803/896-4500; FAX. 803/896-4515; John D. Volmer, Board Administrator

SOUTH DAKOTA

South Dakota Board of Nursing, 4305 South Louise Avenue, Suite 201, Sioux Falls, SD 57106; tel. 605/362-2760; FAX. 605/362-2768; Gloria Damgoard, Executive Secretary

South Dakota State Board of Medical and Osteopathic Examiners, 1323 South Minnesota Avenue, Sioux Falls, SD 57105; tel. 605/334-8343; FAX. 605/336-0270; L. Paul Jensen, Executive Secretary

TENNESSEE

Tennessee Board of Medical Examiners, Cordell Hull Building, 1st Floor, 425 Fifth Avenue, N, Nashville, TN 37247-1010; tel. 615/253-4123; FAX. 615/253-4484; Sandra Powell, Administrator

Tennessee Board of Nursing, Cordell Hull Building, 1st Floor, 425 Fifth Avenue, N, Nashville, TN 37247-1010; tel. 800/778-4123; FAX. 615/741-7899; Elizabeth J. Lund, MSN, RN, Executive Director

Tennessee State Board of Osteopathic Examination, Cordell Hull Building, 1st Floor, 425 Fifth Avenue, N., Nashville, TN 37247-1010; tel. 800/778-4123; FAX. 615/253-4484; Shelia Bush, Administrator

TEXAS

Board of Vocational Nurse Examiners, William P. Hobby Building, 333 Guadalupe Street, Austin, TX 78701; tel. 512/305-8100; FAX. 512/305-8101; Terrie L. Hairston, Executive Director

Texas Board of Nurse Examiners, 333 Guadalupe, Suite 3-460, Austin, TX 78701; tel. 512/305-7400; FAX. 512/305-7401; Katherine A. Thomas, M.S.N., RN., Executive Director

Texas Board of Vocational Nurse Examiners, William P. Hobby Building, 333 Guadalupe Street, Austin, TX 78701; tel. 512/305-8100; FAX. 512/305-8101; Terrie Hairston, RN, CHE, Executive Director

Texas State Board of Medical Examiners, 333 Guadalupe, Tower Three, Suite 610, P.O. Box 2018, Austin, TX 78768-2018; tel. 512/305-7010; FAX. 512/305-7008; Donald W. Patrick, MD, JD, Executive Director

UTAH

Utah Physicians Licensing Board, Division of Occupational and Professional Licensure, Heber M. Wells Building, First Floor, 160 East 300 South, Salt Lake City, UT 84114-6741; tel. 801/530-6628; FAX. 801/530-6511; Diana Baker, Bureau Manager

Utah State Board of Nursing, 160 East 300 South, Box 146741, Salt Lake City, UT 84114-6741; tel. 801/530-6628; FAX. 801/530-6511; Laura Poe, Executive Administrator

VERMONT

Vermont Board of Nursing, 81 River Street, Heritage Building, Montpelier, VT 05609-1106; tel. 802/828-2396; FAX. 802/828-2484; Anita Ristau, RN, M.S., Executive Director

Vermont Board of Osteopathic Physicians and Surgeons, 26 Terrace Street, Montpelier, VT 05609; tel. 802/828-1134; FAX. 802/828-2465; Kara Sanborn, Staff Secretary

VIRGINIA

Virginia Board of Medicine, 6603 West Broad Street, Fifth Floor, Richmond, VA 23230-1712; tel. 804/662-9908; FAX. 804/662-9517; William L. Harp, M.D., Executive Director

Virginia Board of Nursing, 6603 West Broad Street, Fifth Floor, Richmond, VA 23230; tel. 804/662-9909; FAX. 804/662-9512; Jay P. Douglas, RN, Executive Director

WASHINGTON

Washington State Board of Osteopathic Medicine and Surgery, Department of Health, 310 Israel Rd, SE, P.O.Box 47866, Tumwater, WA 98501; tel. 360/236-4943; FAX. 360/236-2406; Jennifer Wolfe, Program Representative

Washington State Medical Quality Assurance Commission, 310 Israel Road, P.O. Box 47866, Tumwater, WA 98501; tel. 360/236-4700; FAX. 360/586-4573; Beverly Thomas, Program Manager

Washington State Nursing Care Quality Assurance Commission, Department of Health, Point Plaza East, 310 Israel Rd. SE, Tumwater, WA 98501; tel. 360/236-4700; FAX. 360/236-4738; Paula Meyer, RN, M.S.N., Executive Director

Section C

WEST VIRGINIA

West Virginia Board of Examiners for Registered Professional Nurses, 101 Dee Drive, Charleston, WV 25311-1620; tel. 304/558–3596; FAX. 304/558–3666; Laura S. Rhodes, RN, M.S.N., Executive Director

West Virginia Board of Osteopathy, 334 Penco Road, Weirton, WV 26062; tel. 304/723–4638; FAX. 304/723–6723; Cheryl D. Schreiber, Executive Secretary

West Virginia State Board of Examiners for Licensed Practical Nurses, 101 Dee Drive, Suite 100, Charleston, WV 25311; tel. 304/558–3572; FAX. 304/558–4367; Lanette Anderson, RN, BSN, JD, Executive Director

WISCONSIN

Wisconsin Department of Regulation and Licensing, 1400 East Washington Avenue, Room 178, P.O. Box 8935, Madison, WI 53708-8935; tel. 608/266–2112; FAX. 608/267–3816; Kimberly Nania, Director, Ph.D

Wisconsin Medical Examining Board, 1400 East Washington Avenue, Zip 53702, P.O. Box 8935, Madison, WI 53704; tel. 608/266–2112; FAX. 608/261–7083; Tom Ryan

WYOMING

Wyoming Board of Medicine, The Colony Building, 211 West 19th Street, Cheyenne, WY 82002; tel. 307/778–7053; FAX. 307/778–2069; Carole Shotwell, Executive Secretary

Wyoming State Board of Nursing, 2020 Carey Avenue, Suite 110, Cheyenne, WY 82002; tel. 307/777–7601; FAX. 307/777–3519; Cheryl Koski, MN, RN, Executive Director

U.S. Associated Areas

GUAM

Guam Board of Medical Examiners, 651 Legacy Square Commercial Complex, S. Route 10, Suite 9, Mangilao, GU 96913; tel. 671/735–7406; FAX. 671/735–7413; Teresita L.G. Villagomez, Acting Administrator, HPLO

Guam Board of Nurse Examiners, Department of Public Health and Social Serv, 1304 East Sunset Boulevard, P.O. Box 2816, Barrigada, GU 96913; tel. 671/475–0251; FAX. 671/477–4733; Teofila P. Cruz, RN, M.S., Administrator

PUERTO RICO

Puerto Rico Board of Medical Examiners, Kennedy Avenue, ILA Building, Hogar del Obrero Portuario, Piso 8, Puert Nuevo, San Juan, PR 00908; tel. 787/782–8989; FAX. 787/782–8733; Ivonne M. Fernandez, Executive Director

Canada

ALBERTA

College of Physicians and Surgeons of Alberta, 900 Manulife Place, 10180-101 Street NW, Edmonton, AB T5J 4P8; tel. 780/423–4764; FAX. 780/420–0651; Robert A. Burns, Registrar

MANITOBA

College of Physicians and Surgeons of Manitoba, 1000-1661 Portage Avenue, Winnipeg, MB R3J 3T7; tel. 204/774–4344; FAX. 204/774–0750; William D.B. Pope, M.D., Registrar

NEW BRUNSWICK

College of Physicians and Surgeons of New Brunswick, One Hampton Road, Rothesay, NB E2E 5K8; tel. 506/849–5050; FAX. 506/849–5069; Dr. Ed Schollenberg, Registrar

NOVA SCOTIA

College of Physicians and Surgeons of Nova Scotia, Office of the Registrar, 1559 Brunswick Street, Suite 200, Halifax, NS B3J 2G1; tel. 902/422–5823; FAX. 902/422–5035; Dr. Cameron Little, Registrar

PRINCE EDWARD ISLAND

College of Physicians and Surgeons of Prince Edward Island, 199 Grafton Street, Charlottetown, PE C1A 1L2; tel. 902/566–3861; FAX. 902/566–3861; C.A. Moyse, M.D., Registrar

QUEBEC

College des medecins du Quebec, 2170, boul. Rene-Levesque Ouest, Montreal, PQ H3H 2T8; tel. 514/933–4441; FAX. 514/933–3112; Andre Garon, M.D., Director General & Secretary

SASKATCHEWAN

College of Physicians and Surgeons of Saskatchewan, 211 Fourth Avenue S., Saskatoon, SK S7K 1N1; tel. 306/244–7355; FAX. 306/244–0090; D. A. Kendel, M.D., Registrar

Quality Improvement Organizations

The following list of QIOs was obtained from the agencies themselves and the Centers for Medicare and Medicaid Services, Quality Improvement Organization programs.

United States

ALABAMA: Alabama Quality Assurance Foundation, Two Perimeter Park, S., Suite 200 West, Birmingham, AL 35243-2337; tel. 205/970–1600; FAX. 205/970–1616; Susan B. Holmes, C F O

ARIZONA: Health Services Advisory Group, Inc., 1600 E. Northern Avenue, Suite 100, Phoenix, AZ 85020; tel. 602/264–6382; FAX. 602/241–0757; Herbert S. Rigberg, CEO

ARKANSAS: Arkansas Foundation for Medical Care, Inc., 2201 Brooken Hill Drive, P.O. Box 180001, Fort Smith, AR 72918-0001; tel. 479/649–8501; FAX. 479/649–8180; Russell G. Brasher, Ph.D., Chief Executive Officer

CALIFORNIA: Lumetra (formerly CMRI), One Sansome Street, Suite 600, San Francisco, CA 94104; tel. 415/677–2000; FAX. 415/677–2195; Jo Ellen H. Ross, President and CEO

COLORADO: Colorado Foundation for Medical Care, 2851 South Parker Road, Suite 300, Aurora, CO 80014-2713; tel. 303/695–3300; FAX. 303/695–3343; Arja P. Adair, Jr., President and CEO

CONNECTICUT: Connecticut Peer Review Organization, Inc., d/b/a Qualidigm, 100 Roscommon Drive, Suite 200, Middletown, CT 06457; tel. 860/632–2008; FAX. 860/632–5865; Marcia K. Petrillo, Chief Executive Officer

DELAWARE: Quality Insights of Delaware, Plaza III, 1847 Marsh Road, Wilmington, DE 19810; tel. 302/475–8100; FAX. 302/475–7317; John C. Wiesendanger, CEO

DISTRICT OF COLUMBIA: Delmarva Foundation for Medical Care, Inc., 1620 L Street, NW, Suite 1275, Washington, DC 20036; tel. 202/293–9650; FAX. 202/293–7317; Maulik Joshi, CEO

FLORIDA: Florida Medical Quality Assurance, Inc., 4350 West Cypress Street, Suite 900, Tampa, FL 33607; tel. 813/354–9111; FAX. 813/354–0737; Logan Malone, Ed.D, Chief Executive Officer

GEORGIA: Georgia Medical Care Foundation, 1455 Lincoln Parkway, Suite 800, Atlanta, GA 30346; tel. 404/982–0411; FAX. 404/982–7584; Tom W. Williams, Chief Executive Officer

HAWAII: Mountain-Pacific Quality Health Foundation, 1360 South Beretania Street, Suite 501, Honolulu, HI 96814; tel. 808/545–2550; FAX. 808/440–6030; Dee Dee Nelson, Director of Hawaii Office

IDAHO: Qualis Health of Idaho Office, 720 Park Boulevard, Suite 120, Boise, ID 83712-7756; tel. 208/343–4617; FAX. 208/343–4705; Jonathan R. Sugarman MD, MPH, Chief Executive Officer

ILLINOIS: Illinois Foundation for Quality Healthcare, 2625 Butterfield Road, Suite 102E, Oak Brook, IL 60521; tel. 630/571–5540; FAX. 630/571–5611; Don Lavasz, CEO

INDIANA: Health Care Excel, Incorporated, 2629 Waterfront Parkway East Drive, Suite 150, Indianapolis, IN 46214; tel. 317/347–4500; FAX. 317/347–4567; Sharon Smith, Chief Executive Officer

IOWA: Iowa Foundation for Medical Care, 6000 Westtown Parkway, Suite 350E, West Des Moines, IA 50266-7771; tel. 515/223–2900; FAX. 515/222–2407; Don Lovasz, CEO

KANSAS: The Kansas Foundation for Medical Care, Inc., 2947 Southwest Wanamaker Drive, Topeka, KS 66614; tel. 785/273–2552; FAX. 785/273–0737; Larry Pitman, President and CEO

KENTUCKY: Health Care Excel of Kentucky Incorporated, 9300 Shelbyville Road, The Hurstborne Place, Suite 600, Louisville, KY 40222; tel. 502/339–7442; FAX. 502/339–8641; Sharon Smith, Chief Executive Officer

LOUISIANA: Louisiana Health Care Review, Inc., 8591 United Plaza Boulevard, Suite 270, Baton Rouge, LA 70809; tel. 504/926–6353; FAX. 504/923–0957; Leo Stanley, Chief Executive Officer

MARYLAND: Delmarva Foundation for Medical Care, Inc., 9240 Centreville Road, Easton, MD 21601; tel. 410/822–0697; FAX. 410/822–9572; Maulik S. Joshi, President and CEO

MASSACHUSETTS: Mass Pro. Inc., 235 Wyman Street, Waltham, MA 02154-1231; tel. 781/890–0011; FAX. 781/487–0083; Jeffery M. East, President and CEO

MICHIGAN: MPRO, 22670 Haggerty Rd, Suite 100, Farmington Hills, MI 48335-2611; tel. 248/465–7400; FAX. 248/465–7430; Debra L. Moss, MD, MBA, President/CEO

MINNESOTA: Stratis Health, 2901 Metro Drive, Suite 400, Bloomington, MN 55425; tel. 952/854–3306; FAX. 952/853–8503; Patricia Riley, Chief Executive Officer

MISSISSIPPI: I.Q.H., Information & Quality Healthcare, 385 Highland Colony Parkway, Suite 120, Ridgeland, MS 39157; tel. 601/957–1575; FAX. 601/956–1713; James McIlwain, M.D., President

MISSOURI: Primaris, 200 N. Keene Street, Columbia, MO 65201; tel. 573/817–8300; FAX. 573/817–8330; Richard A. Royer, Chief Executive Officer

MONTANA: Mountain-Pacific Quality Health Foundation, 3404 Cooney Drive, Helena, MT 59602; tel. 406/443–4020; FAX. 406/443–4585; Janice Connors, Executive Director

NEVADA: HealthInsight, 500 South Rancho Drive, Suite C-17, Las Vegas, NV 89106; tel. 702/385–9933; FAX. 702/385–4586; Marc Bennett, President & CEO

NEW HAMPSHIRE: Northeast Health Care Quality Foundation, 15 Old Rollinsford Road, Suite 302, Dover, NH 03820; tel. 603/749–1641; FAX. 603/7491195; Robert A. Aurilio, CEO
Northeast Health Care Quality Foundation, 15 Old Rollinsford Road, Suite 302, Dover, NH 03820-2830; tel. 603/749–1641; FAX. 603/749–1195; Robert A. Aurilio, CEO

NEW JERSEY: The Peer Review Organization of New Jersey, Inc., 557 Cranbury Road, Suite 21, East Brunswick, NJ 08816; tel. 732/238–5570; FAX. 732/238–7766; Martin P. Margolies, Chief Executive Officer

NEW MEXICO: NMMRA, (New Mexico Medical Review Association), 2340 Menaul Blvd., NE, Suite 300, P.O. Box 3200, Albuquerque, NM 87190-3200; tel. 505/998–9898; FAX. 505/998–9899; Dan Jaco, Chief Executive Officer

NEW YORK: IPRO, 1979 Marcus Avenue, First Floor, Lake Success, NY 11042-1002; tel. 516/326–7767; FAX. 516/326–7791; Theodore O. Will, Chief Executive Officer

NORTH CAROLINA: Medical Review of North Carolina, Inc., 100 Regency Forest Drive, Suite 200, Cary, NC 8598; tel. 919/380–9860; FAX. 919/380–7637; Charles Riddick, Executive Director

NORTH DAKOTA: North Dakota Health Care Review Inc., 800 31st Avenue S.W., Minot, ND 58701; tel. 701/852–4231; FAX. 701/838–6009; David Remillard, Chief Executive Officer

OHIO: Ohio KePRO, Inc, Rock Run Center, 5700 Lombardo Center Drive, Suite 100, Seven Hills, OH 44131; tel. 216/447–9604; FAX. 216/447–7925; Marcia Rynearson, Executive Director
Ohio KePRO, Inc., Rock Run Center, 5700 Lombardo Center Drive, Seven Hills, OH 44131; tel. 216/447–9604; FAX. 216/447–7925; Gayle Smith, CEO

OKLAHOMA: Oklahoma Foundation for Medical Quality, Inc., 14000 Quail Springs Parkway, Suite 400, Oklahoma City, OK 73134; tel. 405/840–2891; FAX. 405/840–1343; Jim L. Williams, President and CEO

OREGON: Oregon Medical Professional Review Organization, 2020 S.W. 4th Avenue, Suite 520, Portland, OR 97201-4960; tel. 503/279–0100; FAX. 503/279–0190; John Mitchell, FACHE, President and CEO

PENNSYLVANIA: KEPRO, Inc., 777 East Park Drive, P.O. Box 8310, Harrisburg, PA 17105-8310; tel. 717/564–8288; FAX. 717/564–3862; John DiNardi III, Executive Director

RHODE ISLAND: Rhode Island Quality Partners, Inc., 9 Hayes Street, Providence, RI 02908; tel. 401/528–3200; FAX. 401/528–3210; Marcia K. Petrillo, Executive Director

SOUTH CAROLINA: Carolina Medical Review, 250 Berryhill Road, Suite 101, Columbia, SC 29210; tel. 803/731–8225; FAX. 803/731–8229; Melinda Postal, Communications Manager

SOUTH DAKOTA: South Dakota Foundation for Medical Care, 1323 South Minnesota Avenue, Sioux Falls, SD 57105; tel. 605/336–3505; FAX. 605/336–0270; Mark Hoven, Chief Executive Officer

TENNESSEE: Q Source, Center For Healthcare Quality, Q Source, Center For Healthcare and Quality, 3175 Lenox Park Boulevard, Suite 309, Memphis, TN 38115; tel. 901/682–0381; FAX. 901/761–3786; Albert J. Grobmyer III, M.D., Chief Executive Officer

TEXAS: Texas Medical Foundation, Barton Oaks Plaza Two, Suite 200, 901 Mopac Expressway, S., Austin, TX 78746-5799; tel. 512/329–6610; FAX. 512/327–7159; William G. Gamel, MD

UTAH: Health Insight, 348 East 4500 South, Suite 300, Salt Lake City, UT 84107; tel. 801/892–0155; FAX. 801/892–0160; Marc Bennett, President and CEO

VIRGINIA: Virginia Health Quality Center, 1604 Santa Rosa Road, Suite 200, Richmond, VA 23288-0070; tel. 804/289–5320; FAX. 804/289–5324; Joy Hogan Rozman, Chief Executive Officer

WASHINGTON: Qualis Health, 10700 Meridian Avenue, N., Suite 100, Seattle, WA 98133-9075; tel. 206/364–9700; FAX. 206/368–2419; Jonathan Sugarman, MD, MPH, President and Chief Executive Officer

WEST VIRGINIA: West Virginia Medical Institute, Inc., 3001 Chesterfield Place, Charleston, WV 25304; tel. 304/346–9864; FAX. 304/346–9863; John Wiesendanger, Chief Executive Officer

WISCONSIN: MetaStar, Inc., 2909 Landmark Place, Madison, WI 53713; tel. 608/274–1940; FAX. 608/274–5008; Greg E. Simmons, President and CEO

U.S. Associated Areas

PUERTO RICO: Quality Improvement Professional Research Organization, Mercantile Plaza Building, 2 Ponce de Leon Ave., San Juan, PR 00918-1696; tel. 787/641–1240; FAX. 787/641–1248; Jose Robles, Chief Executive Officer

VIRGIN ISLANDS: Virgin Islands Medical Institute, Inc., 1AD Estate Diamond Ruby, P.O. Box 5989, Christiansted, VI 00823-5989; tel. 340/712–2400; FAX. 340/712–2449; Jill S. Doran, Chief Executive Officer

Section C

State Health Planning and Development Agencies

The following is a list of state health planning and development agencies. The information was obtained from the agencies themselves. For information about other state agencies and organizations that fulfill many of the same functions, contact the state or metropolitan hospital associations.

United States

ALABAMA: State Health Planning and Development Agency, 100 North Union Street, Suite 870, Montgomery, AL 36104; tel. 334/242–4103; FAX. 334/242–4113; Alva Lambert, Executive Director

ALASKA: Facilities and Planning Section, Department of Health and Social Services, P.O. Box 110650, Juneau, AK 99811-0650; tel. 907/465–3015; FAX. 907/465-2499; Larry J. Streuber, Section Chief

ARIZONA: Office of Health Planning, Evaluation and Statistics, 1647 East Morton, Phoenix, AZ 85007; tel. 602/542–1216; FAX. 602/542–1244; Barry Milcarek, Chief

CALIFORNIA: Healthcare Workforce, 1600 Ninth Street, Suite 440, Sacramento, CA 95814; tel. 916/654–2087; FAX. 916/654–3138; Pavlo Rosales, Deputy Director

COLORADO: Colorado Department of Public Health and Environment, Primary Care Office, 4300 Cherry Creek Drive, S., Denver, CO 80246-1530; tel. 303/692–2470; FAX. 303/758–3448; Kitty Stevens, Program Director

CONNECTICUT: Connecticut Department of Public Health, Office of Health Care Quality & Best Practice, 410 Capitol Avenue, MS# 13PPE, Hartford, CT 06134-0308; tel. 860/509–7123; FAX. 860/509-7160; Michael Hoffmann, Ph.D., Director

DELAWARE: Bureau of Health Planning and Resources Management, Department of Health and Social Services, P.O. Box 637, Dover, DE 19903; tel. 302/739–4776; FAX. 302/739–4784; Robert I. Welch, Director

DISTRICT OF COLUMBIA: District Of Columbia Department Of Health, 825 North Capital Street, N.E., Second Floor, Washington, DC 20002; tel. 202/442–9035; FAX. 202/442–4840; Michael Richardson, M.D., Senior Deputy, Medical Affairs

GEORGIA: Georgia Department of Community Health, 2 Peachtree Street, NW, 34th Floor, Suite 102, Atlanta, GA 30303-3159; tel. 404/656–0655; FAX. 404/656–0655; Richard L. Greene, Director, Division Of Health Planning

HAWAII: Hawaii State Health Planning and Development Agency, 1177 Alakea Street, Suite 402, Honolulu, HI 96813; tel. 808/587–0788; FAX. 808/587-0783; David Sakamoto, M.D. Administrator

IDAHO: Bureau of Health Policy Vital Statistics, Division of Health, Idaho Department of Health and Welfare, 450 West State Street, First Floor, P.O. Box 83720, Boise, ID 83720-0036; tel. 208/334–5976; FAX. 208/332–7260; Jane Smith, Chief

ILLINOIS: Illinois Department of Public Health, Division of Health Policy, 525 West Jefferson, Second Floor, Springfield, IL 62761; tel. 217/782–6235; FAX. 217/785–4308; Patti Kimmel, Chief Division of Health Policy

INDIANA: Indiana State Department of Health, Local Liaison Office, Two North Meridian Street, Suite Eight-B, Indianapolis, IN 46204-3003; tel. 317/233–7679; FAX. 317/233–7761; Nellie Simpson, Primary Care Officer

IOWA: Department of Public Health, Division of Administration, Lucas State Office Building, Des Moines, IA 50319-0075; tel. 515/281–4348; FAX. 515/281–4958; Louise Lex, Ph.D., Health 010 Iowans Coordinator

KANSAS: Health Care Commission, Rm 920-N, Landon State Office Bldg., 900 SW Jackson, Topeka, KS 66612-1251; tel. 785/296–6280; FAX. 785/368–7180; Linda DeCoursey, Benefits Administrator

MAINE: Office of Health Data and Program Management, Bureau of Health, Department of Human Services, 161 Capitol Street, SHS #11, Augusta, ME 04333-0011; tel. 207/287–5524; FAX. 207/287-5431; Sophie Glidden, Office of Rural Health & Primary Care

MARYLAND: Maryland Health Care Commission, 4160 Patterson Avenue, Baltimore, MD 21215-2299; tel. 410/764–3460; FAX. 410/358–1311; Barbara G. McLean, Executive Director

MISSISSIPPI: Mississippi State Department of Health, Health Planning and Resource Development Division, 570 East Woodrow Wilson, P.O. Box 1700, Jackson, MS 39215-1700; tel. 601/576–7874; FAX. 601/576–7530; Harold B. Armstrong, Office Director

MISSOURI: Missouri Department of Health and Senior Services, 912 Wildwood, P.O. Box 570, Jefferson City, MO 65102; tel. 573/751–6001; FAX. 573/751-6041; Richard C. Dunn, Director

MONTANA: Health Policy and Services Division, Department of Public Health and Human Services, Cogswell Building, P.O. Box 202951, Helena, MT 59620-2951; tel. 406/444–4540; FAX. 406/444-1861; Maggie Bullock, Administrator

NEBRASKA: Nebraska Health and Human Services, Finance and Support, Research and Performance Measurement, Nebraska State Office Building-5th Floor, 301 Centennial Mall South, Lincoln, NE 68509; tel. 402/471–8941; FAX. 402/471-7783; Paula Hartig, Administrator

NEVADA: State Health Division, Bureau of Health Planning and Statistics, 505 East King Street, Suite 102, Carson City, NV 89701-4749; tel. 775/684–4218; FAX. 775/684–4156; Emil DeJan, Chief

NEW HAMPSHIRE: Office of Health Services Planning and Review, Six Hazen Drive, Concord, NH 03301-6527; tel. 603/271–4606; FAX. 603/271–4141; Margaret Heatley, Administrator

NEW JERSEY: Certificate of Need and Acute Care Licensure Program, New Jersey Department of Health and Senior Services, CN 360, John Fitch Plaza, Trenton, NJ 08625-0360; tel. 609/292–8773; FAX. 609/292–3780; John A. Calabria, Director

NEW MEXICO: New Mexico Health Policy Commission, 2055 S. Pacheco Street, Suite 200, Santa Fe, NM 87505; tel. 505/424–3200; FAX. 505/424–3222; Patricia Larragoite, DDS, Director

NEW YORK: New York State Department of Health, Division of Planning, Policy and Resource Development, Corning Tower, Suite 1495, Empire State Plaza, Albany, NY 12237; tel. 518/474–0180; FAX. 518/474–5450; Judith Arnold, Deputy Commissioner

NORTH CAROLINA: Medical Facilities Planning Section, 2701 Mail Service Center, Raleigh, NC 27699-2701; tel. 919/855–3865; FAX. 919/733–4413; Mark Benton, Chief of Budget & Planning, Division of Facility Services

NORTH DAKOTA: North Dakota Department of Health, Office of Community Assistance, 600 East Boulevard Avenue, Dept 301, Bismarck, ND 58505-0200; tel. 701/328–2894; FAX. 701/328–1890; Gary Garland, Director of Community Assistance

OKLAHOMA: Oklahoma State Department of Health, Healthcare Information, 1000 Northeast 10th Street, Oklahoma City, OK 73117-1299; tel. 405/271–6225; FAX. 405/271–9061; Kristen Eberly, Asst Director of Health Care Information

PENNSYLVANIA: Bureau of Health Planning, Pennsylvania Department of Health, Health and Welfare Building, Room 1033, P.O. Box 90, Harrisburg, PA 17120; tel. 717/772–5298; FAX. 717/705-6525; Joseph B. May, Director

RHODE ISLAND: Rhode Island Department of Health, Cannon Building, Three Capitol Hill, Room 401, Providence, RI 02908; tel. 401/222–2231; FAX. 401/222-6548; William J. Waters, Jr., Ph.D., Deputy Director

SOUTH CAROLINA: DHEC, Division of Planning and Certificate of Need, 2600 Bull Street, Columbia, SC 29201; tel. 803/545–4200; FAX. 803/545-4579; Albert Whiteside, Director

SOUTH DAKOTA: South Dakota Department of Health, Division of Administration, 600 East Capitol Avenue, Pierre, SD 57501-2536; tel. 605/773–3361; FAX. 605/773–5683; Jerry Hofer, Director, Division of Administration

TENNESSEE: Assessment and Planning, Tennessee Department of Health, Cordell Hull Building, Sixth Floor, Nashville, TN 37247-5261; tel. 615/741–0244; FAX. 615/253–1688; Steven Taylor, Health Planner

TEXAS: Texas Department of Health, 1100 West 49th Street, Austin, TX 78756; tel. 512/458–7261; FAX. 512/458–7344; Rick A. Danko, Dr PH, Diretor Strategic Health Planning

VERMONT: Division of Health Care Administration, Department of Banking Insurance, Securities, and Health Care Administration, 89 Main Street, Drawer 20, Montpelier, VT 05620-3601; tel. 802/828–2900; FAX. 802/828–2949; Jennifer Garson, Certificate of Need Specialist

VIRGINIA: Virginia Department of Health, Division of Certificate of Public Need, 3600 West Broad Street, Suite 216, Richmond, VA 23220; tel. 804/367–2126; FAX. 804/367–2206; Erik O. Bodin, III

WASHINGTON: Washington State Board of Health, 1102 SE Quince Street, P.O. Box 47990, Olympia, WA 98504-7990; tel. 360/236–4100; FAX. 360/236-4088; Craig McLaughlin, MJ, Acting Executive Director

WEST VIRGINIA: West Virginia Health Care Authority, 100 Dee Drive, Charleston, WV 25311; tel. 304/558–7000; FAX. 304/558–7001; Sonia D. Chamber, Chair

WYOMING: Department of Health, Office of Rural Health, 2300 Capitol Avenue, Cheyenne, WY 82002; tel. 307/777–8651; FAX. 307/777–8776; Douglas Thiede, Assistant Manager

State and Provincial Government Agencies

The following list includes state departments of health and welfare, and their subagencies as well as such independent agencies as those for children's services, maternal and child health, mental health, and vocational rehabilitation. The information was obtained directly from the agencies. Additional licensing agencies are listed in Section C under Medical and Nursing Licensure Agencies and Hospital Licensure Agencies.

United States

ALABAMA
The Honorable Robert Riley, Governor, 334/242-7100

Health

Alabama Department of Public Health, Bureau Of Family Health Services, The RSA Tower, P.O. Box 303017, Montgomery, AL 36130-3017; tel. 334/206-2940; FAX. 334/206-2950; Thomas M. Miller, M.D., MPH, Director

Department of Public Health, The RSA Tower, Suite 1552, P.O. Box 303017, Montgomery, AL 36130-3017; tel. 334/206-5200; FAX. 334/206-2008; Donald E. Williamson, M.D., State Health Officer

Insurance

Department of Insurance, 201 Monroe Street, Suite 1700, Montgomery, AL 36130; tel. 334/241-4101; FAX. 334/241-4192; David Parsons, Commissioner

Social Services

Alabama Medicaid Agency, 501 Dexter Avenue, P.O. Box 5624, Montgomery, AL 36103-5624; tel. 334/242-5010; FAX. 334/242-5097; Carol A. Herrmann, Commissioner

Department of Human Resources, Gordon Persons Building, 50 Ripley Street, Montgomery, AL 36104; tel. 334/242-1160; FAX. 334/242-0198; Bill Fuller, Commissioner

Department of Rehabilitation Services, 2129 East South Boulevard, Montgomery, AL 36116; tel. 800/441-7607; FAX. 334/281-1973; Steve Shivers, Commissioner

Other

State Department of Education, Gordon Persons Building, P.O. Box 302101, Montgomery, AL 36130-2101; tel. 334/242-9700; FAX. 334/242-9708; Ed Richardson, Superintendent

ALASKA
The Honorable Frank Murkowski, Governor, 907/465-3500

Health

Division of Behavioral Health, P.O. Box 110620, Juneau, AK 99811-0620; tel. 907/465-3370; FAX. 907/465-2668; William H. Hogan, Director

Health Facilities Licensing and Certification, 4730 Business Park Boulevard, Suite 18, Anchorage, AK 99503-7137; tel. 907/334-2483; FAX. 907/561-3011; Shelbert Larsen, Administrator

Social Services

Department Health and Social Services, Division Alcoholism and Drug Abuse, 240 Main Street, Suite 701, P.O. Box 110607, Juneau, AK 99811-0607; tel. 907/465-2071; FAX. 907/465-2185; Russ Webb, Interim Director

Department of Health and Social Services, 350 Main Street, Room 229, P.O. Box 110601, Juneau, AK 99811-0601; tel. 907/465-3030; FAX. 907/465-3068; Joel Gilbertson, Commissioner

Division of Administrative Services, Department of Health and Social Services, P.O. Box 110650, Juneau, AK 99811-0650; tel. 907/465-1630; FAX. 907/465-2499; Janet E. Clarke, Director

Division of Health Care Services, P.O. Box 110660, Juneau, AK 99811-0660; tel. 907/465-3355; FAX. 907/465-2204; Dwayne Peoples, Director

Office of Children's Services, P.O. Box 110630, Juneau, AK 99811; tel. 907/465-3191; FAX. 907/465-3397; Tammy Sandoval, Acting Deputy Commissioner

State of Alaska, Department of Health and Social Services, P.O. Box 110601, Juneau, AK 99811-0601; tel. 907/465-3030; FAX. 907/465-3068; Bob Labbe, Deputy Commissioner

State of Alaska Division of Vocational Rehabilitation, 801 West 10th Street, Suite A, Juneau, AK 99801-1894; tel. 907/465-2814; FAX. 907/465-2856; Gale Sinnott, Director

State of Alaska, Department of Health and Social Services, 350 Main Street, Room 229, P.O. Box 110601, Juneau, AK 99811-0601; tel. 907/465-3030; FAX. 907/465-3068; Elmer Lindstrom, Deputy Commissioner

Other

Department of Education & Early Development, 801 West 10th Street, Suite 200, Juneau, AK 99801-1894; tel. 907/465-2887; FAX. 907/465-2713; Conchita McKnight, Program Assistant

ARIZONA
The Honorable Janet Napolitano, Governor, 602/542-4331

Health

Arizona Department of Health Services, 150 N. 18th Ave, Suite 500, Phoenix, AZ 85007; tel. 602/542-1025; FAX. 602/542-1062; Catherine R. Eden, Ph.D.

Arizona Department of Health Services, Division of Licensing Services, 150 N. 18th Ave., Suite 510, Phoenix, AZ 85007; tel. 602/364-3064; FAX. 602/364-4808; Mary Wiley, Assistant Director

Arizona Department of Health Services, Division of Public Health, Bureau of Epidemiology and Disease Control Services, 3815 North Black Canyon Highway, Phoenix, AZ 85015; tel. 602/230-5808; FAX. 602/230-5959; Lee A. Bland, Bureau Chief

Social Services

Bureau of Community and Family Health Services, 2927 N. 35th Avenue, Suite 100, Phoenix, AZ 85017; tel. 602/542-1223; FAX. 602/542-1265; Raul V. Munoz, MPH, Bureau Chief

Division of Behavioral Health Services, Arizona Department of Health Services, 150 N. 18th Ave, Ste 200, Phoenix, AZ 85007; tel. 602/364-4558; FAX. 602/364-4570; Dr. Jerry Dennis, Acting Deputy Director

Office for Children with Special Health Care Needs, OCSACN, 2927 N. 35th Avenue, Phoenix, AZ 85017; tel. 602/542-1860; FAX. 602/542-2589; Kathryn Echeverria, Ed. D, Chief

Rehabilitation Services Administration (930A), 1789 West Jefferson, Second Floor Northwest, Phoenix, AZ 85007; tel. 602/542-3332; FAX. 602/542-3778; Skip Bingham, Administrator

Other

Arizona Department of Environmental Quality, 1110 W. Washington Street, Phoenix, AZ 85007; tel. 602/771-2300; FAX. 602/771-2218; Stephen A. Owens, Director

Department of Economic Security, Site Code 010A, P.O. Box 6123, Phoenix, AZ 85005; tel. 602/542-5678; FAX. 602/542-5339; David A. Berns, Director

ARKANSAS
The Honorable Mike Huckabee, Governor, 501/682-2345

Health

Arkansas Department of Health, Agency Leadership Team, 4815 West Markham, Slot 55, Little Rock, AR 72205; tel. 501/661-2238; FAX. 501/661-2308; Fay Boozman, M.D.,Director

Children's Medical Service, Donaghey Plaza South, Seventh and Main Streets, Little Rock, AR 72203; tel. 501/682-8202; FAX. 501/682-8247; G. A. Buchanan, M.D., Medical Director

Division of Health Facility Services, Department of Health, 5800 West 10th Street, Suite 400, Little Rock, AR 72204; tel. 501/661-2201; FAX. 501/661-2165; Renee Mallory, Director, Health Facility Services

Division of Medical Services, 700 Main Street, Little Rock, AR 72203-1437; tel. 501/682-8292; FAX. 501/682-1197; Roy Jeffus, Director

Social Services

Arkansas Department of Human Services, P.O. Box 1437, Little Rock, AR 72203-1437; tel. 501/682-8650; FAX. 501/682-6836; Kurk Knickrehm, Director

Arkansas Division of Behavioral Health Services, Arkansas State Hospital, 4313 West Markham, Little Rock, AR 72205-4096; tel. 501/686-9000; FAX. 501/686-9182; Pat Dahlgren, Director

Arkansas Rehabilitation Services, 1616 Brookwood, P.O. Box 3781, Little Rock, AR 72203; tel. 501/296-1616; FAX. 501/296-1675; John C. Wyill

Bureau of Alcohol & Drug Abuse Prevention, Freeway Medical Center, Suite 907, 5800 West 10th Street, Little Rock, AR 72204; tel. 501/280-4501; FAX. 501/280-4532; Gary Horton, Team Leader

Division of Aging and Adult Services, P.O. Box 1437, Slot S530, Little Rock, AR 72203-1437; tel. 501/682-2441; FAX. 501/682-8155; Herb Sanderson, Director

Office of Long-Term Care, New Donaghey Plaza South, 7th & Main Street, Little Rock, AR 72203-8059; tel. 501/682-8487; FAX. 501/682-8551; Carol Shockley, Director

Statewide Services, Arkansas Department of Health, 4815 West Markham Street, Slot 41, Little Rock, AR 72205-3867; tel. 501/661-2292; FAX. 501/661-2055; Renee Patrick, Deputy Director

CALIFORNIA
The Honorable Arnold Schwarzenegger, Governor, 916/445-2841

Health

Department of Developmental Services, 1600 Ninth Street, Suite 240, MS 2-13, Sacramento, CA 95814; tel. 916/654-1897; FAX. 916/654-2167; Cliff Allenby, Director

Department of Health Services, P.O.Box 997413, MS00000, Sacramento, CA 95899-7413; tel. 916/440-7400; FAX. 916/440-7404; Sandra Slewry, Director

Licensing

Board of Vocational Nursing and Psychiatric Technicians, 2535 Capitol Oaks Drive, Suite 205, Sacramento, CA 95833; tel. 916/263-7800; FAX. 916/263-7859; Teresa Bello-Jones, JD, M.S.N., RN, Executive Officer

Social Services

CA Health And Human Services Agency, Office of the Secretary, 1600 Ninth Street, Suite 460, Sacramento, CA 95814; tel. 916/654-3454; FAX. 916/654-3343; Lynn Froelic, BSO

California Health and Human Services Agency, Office of the Secretary, 1600 Ninth Street, Suite 460, Sacramento, CA 95814; tel. 916/654-3454; FAX. 916/654-3342; Lynn Froelick, Business Services Officer

Community Resources Development Section, California Department of Rehabilitation, 2000 Evergreen Street, Sacramento, CA 95815; tel. 916/263-7374; FAX. 916/263-7456; Kent Thompson, Chief

Department of Alcohol and Drug Programs, 1700 K Street, Sacramento, CA 95814; tel. 916/445-1943; FAX. 916/323-5873; Kathryn Jett, Director

Department of Social Services, 744 P Street, Sacramento, CA 95814; tel. 916445-6951; FAX. 916/445-7333; Director

COLORADO
The Honorable Bill Owens, Governor, 303/866-2471

Health

Colorado Department of Public Health and Environment, 4300 Cherry Creek Drive, S., Denver, CO 80246-1530; tel. 303/692-2000; FAX. 303/691-7702; Jane E. Norton, Executive Director

State Department of Health Care Policy and Financing, 1570 Grant Street, 10th Floor, Denver, CO 80203-1714; tel. 303/866-2868; FAX. 303/866-4411; Karen Rcinertson, Executive Director

Insurance

Division of Insurance, 1560 Broadway, Suite 850, Denver, CO 80202; tel. 303/894-7499; FAX. 303/894-7455; Commissioner

Licensing

Department of Regulatory Agencies, 1560 Broadway, Suite 1550, Denver, CO 80202; tel. 303/894-7855; FAX. 303/894-7885; Tambor Williams, Executive Director

Social Services

Alcohol and Drug Abuse Division, Colorado Department of Human Services, 4055 S. Lowell Blvd., Denver, CO 80236; tel. 323/866-7480; FAX. 303/866-7481; Janet Wood, Director

Department of Human Services, 1575 Sherman Street, Eighth Floor, Denver, CO 80203; tel. 303/866-5096; FAX. 303/866-4740; Marva Livingston Hammons, Executive Director

Mental Health Services, 3824 West Princeton Circle, Denver, CO 80236; tel. 303/366-7400; FAX. 303/866-7428; Debra Kusfer, Acting Director

CONNECTICUT
The Honorable M. Jodi Rell, Governor, 800/406-1527

Health

Department of Public Health, 410 Capitol Avenue, Mail Stop 12APP, Hartford, CT 06134-0308; tel. 860/509-7590; FAX. 860/509-8457; Jennifer Filippone, Public Health Services Manager

Department of Public Health, Division of Health Systems Regulation, 410 Capitol Avenue, Mail Stop 12HSR, Hartford, CT 06134-0308; tel. 860/509-7407; FAX. 860/509-7539; Valerie Bryan, R.N., S.N.C.

Insurance

Department of Insurance, P.O. Box 816, Hartford, CT 06142-0816; tel. 860/297-3862; FAX. 860/297-3941; Mary Ellen Breault, Director, Life and Health Division

Licensing

Connecticut Board of Examiners for Nursing, Department of Public Health – MS#12APP, 410 Capitol Avenue, P.O. Box 340308, Hartford, CT 06134-0308; tel. 860/509-7603; FAX. 860/509-8457; Janice Wojick, Liaison

Social Services

Aging Services Division, Department of Social Services, 25 Sigourney Street, Hartford, CT 06106-5033; tel. 860/424-5277; FAX. 860/424-5301; Pamela A Giannini, Director

Department of Social Services, 25 Sigourney Street, Hartford, CT 06106; tel. 860/424-5008; FAX. 860/424-5129; Patricia A. Wilson-Coker, JD, MSW, Commissioner

State Department of Mental Health and Addiction Services, 410 Capitol Avenue, P.O. Box 341431, Hartford, CT 6134; tel. 860/418-7000; FAX. 860/418-6691; Thomas A. Kirk, Jr., Ph.D., Commissioner

Other

Department of Education, 165 Capitol Avenue, Hartford, CT 06106; tel. 203/566-5061; FAX. 203/566-8964

DELAWARE
The Honorable Ruth Ann Minner, Governor, 302/739-4101

Health

Delaware Office of Emergency Medical Services, Blue Hen Corporate Center, 655 South Bay Road, Dover, DE 19901; tel. 302/739-4710; FAX. 302/739-2352; Bill Stevenson, EMS Director

Delaware Public Health Laboratory, P.O. Box 1047, Smyrna, DE 19977-1047; tel. 302/653-2870; FAX. 302/653-2877; Deputy Director

Division of Public Health, Jesse Cooper Building,P.O. Box 637, Dover, DE 19903; tel. 302/744-4700; FAX. 302/739-6659; Barbara Jarrell, Senior Deputy, Chief Operating Officer

Division of Public Health, Community Health Care Access Section, Jesse S. Cooper Building, 417 Federal Street, Dover, DE 19903; tel. 302/744-4700; FAX. 302/739-6653; Jacqueline J. Christman, M.D., Section Administrator

Licensing

Department of Health and Social Services, Office of Health Facilities Licensing and Certification, 2055 Limestone Road, Suite 200, Wilmington, DE 19808; tel. 302/995-8521; FAX. 302/995-8529; Mary E. Peterson, Director

Social Services

Delaware Psychiatric Center, Division of Alcoholism, Drug Abuse and Mental Health, 1901 North DuPont Highway, New Castle, DE 19720; tel. 302/255-2700; FAX. 302/255-4417; Martha Boston, PhD

Department of Health and Social Services, 1901 North DuPont Highway, Main Administration Building, New Castle, DE 19720; tel. 302/255-9040; FAX. 302/255-4429; Vincent Meconi, Cabinet Secretary

Department of Labor, Division of Vocational Rehabilitation, 4425 North Market Street, P.O.Box 9969, Wilmington, DE 19809-0969; tel. 302/761-8275; FAX. 302/761-6611; Andrea Guest, Director

Division of Services for Aging and Adults with Physical Disabilities, 1901 North DuPont Highway, 2nd Floor Annex, New Castle, DE 19720; tel. 302/255-9390; FAX. 302/255-4445; Allan Zaback, Director

Division of Social Services, The Lewis Building, P.O. Box 906, New Castle, DE 19720; tel. 302/255-9668; FAX. 302/255-4433; Elaine Archangelo, Director

Family Health Services, Division of Public Health, P.O. Box 637, Dover, DE 19903; tel. 302/744-4553; FAX. 302/739-6653; Joan Powell, MPA, Director

DISTRICT OF COLUMBIA
Governor Swithboard, 202/727-1000

Social Services

Rehabilitation Services Administration, 810 First Street, N.E., 10th Floor, Washington, DC 20002; tel. 202/442-8663; FAX. 202/442-8742; Elizabeth B. Parker, Administrator

FLORIDA
The Honorable Jeb Bush, Governor, 850/488-2272

Health

Children's Medical Services, 4052 Bald Cypress Way, Bin A-06, Tallahassee, FL 32399-1700; tel. 850/245-4200; FAX. 904/488-3813; Phyllis Sloyer, RN, PhD, Division Director, CMS

Department of Health, Secretary's Office, 4052 Bald Cypress Way, Bin #A00, Tallahassee, FL 32399-1701; tel. 850/245-4321; FAX. 850/922-9453; John O. Agwunobi, MD, MBA, Secretary

Licensing

Agency for Health Care Administration, Division of Health Quality Assurance, 2727 Mahan Drive, Tallahassee, FL 32308; tel. 850/414-9796; FAX. 850/487-6240; Elizabeth Dudek, Deputy Secretary

Social Services

Adult Services, 1317 Winewood Boulevard, Building 6, Room 366, Tallahassee, FL 32399-0700; tel. 850/488-2881; FAX. 850/922-4193; Mr. Chris Shoemaker, Deputy Director, Adult Services

Department of Children and Families, Mental Health Program Office, 1317 Winewood Boulevard, Tallahassee, FL 32399-0700; tel. 904/488-8304; FAX. 904/487-2239

Department of Labor and Employment Security, 2012 Capital Circle, S.E., 303 Hartman Building, Tallahassee, FL 32399-2152; tel. 904/922-7021; FAX. 904/488-8930; Mary B. Hooks, Secretary

Division of Vocational Rehabilitation, 2002 Old St. Augustine Road, Building A, Tallahassee, FL 32301-4862; tel. 850/245-3400; FAX. 850/245-3316; Linda Parnell, Interim Director

Health Facility Regulation, Agency for Health Care Administration, 2727 Mahan Drive, Tallahassee, FL 32308; tel. 850/922-0791; FAX. 850/413-7955; Jeff Gregg, Chief

GEORGIA
The Honorable Sonny Perdue, Governor, 404/656-1776

Health

Division of Public Health, Two Peachtree Street, NW, Suite 15-470, Atlanta, GA 30303-3682; tel. 404/657-2700; FAX. 404/657-6709; Kathleen E. Toomay, M.D., MPH, Director

Insurance

Office of Commissioner of Insurance, Two Martin Luther King, Jr. Drive, Seventh Floor, West Tower, Floyd Build, Atlanta, GA 30334; tel. 404/656-2056; FAX. 404/656-4030; John W. Oxendine, Commissioner of Insurance

Licensing

Bright From The Start Georgia Department of Early Care and Learning, 10 Park Place South, Suite 600, Atlanta, GA 30303; tel. 404/657-5590; FAX. 404/657-8936; Kathy Wilxcox, Director, Family Care and Initial Licensing

Diagnostic Services Unit, Health Care Section, Office of Regulatory Services, Two Peachtree Street, N.W., 33rd Floor, Room 250, Atlanta, GA 30303-3142; tel. 404/657-5447; FAX. 404/657-5442; Betty J. Logan, Program Director, Diagnostic Services

Social Services

Department of Human Resources, Two Peachtree N.W., Suite 29.250, Atlanta, GA 30303-3142; tel. 404/656-5680; FAX. 404/651-8669; B.J. Walker, Commissioner

Department of Human Resources, Division of Mental Health, Develomental Disabilities & Addictive Diseases, Two Peachtree Street, NW., 22-224, Atlanta, GA 30303-3171; tel. 404/657-2252; FAX. 404/657-1137; Gregory C. Hoyt, Acting Director

Department of Human Resources, Office of Regulatory Services, Health Care Section, Two Peachtree Street, N.W., Suite 33.250, Atlanta, GA 30303-3142; tel. 404/657-5550; FAX. 404/657-8934; Carol Zafiratos, Director of the HCS

Office of Regulatory Services, Georgia Department of Human Resources, Two Peachtree Street, N.W., Room 32-415, Atlanta, GA 30303-3142; tel. 404/657-5700; FAX. 404/657-5708; Martin J. Rotter, Director

Personal Care Home Program, Office of Regulatory Services, Two Peachtree Street, 31st Floor, Atlanta, GA 30303-3167; tel. 404/657-4076; FAX. 404/657-3655; Victoria L. Flynn, Director

Rehabilitation Services of the Georgia, Department of Labor, 148 Andrew Young International Blvd., NE, Suite 510 Sussex Place, Atlanta, GA 30303-1751; tel. 404/232-3910; FAX. 404/657-3079; Bobby L. Pack, Assistant Commissioner

HAWAII
The Honorable Linda Lingle, Governor, 808/586-0034

Health

Adult Mental Health Division, P.O. Box 3378, Honolulu, HI 96801-3378; tel. 808/586-4688; FAX. 808/586-4745; Thomas W. Hester, M.D., Chief

Communicable Disease Division, P.O. Box 3378, Honolulu, HI 96801; tel. 808/586-4580; FAX. 808/586-7409; Paul V. Effler, M.D., M.P.H., State Epidemiologist

Dental Health Division, 1700 Lanakila Avenue, Suite 203, Honolulu, HI 96817-2199; tel. 808/832-5700; FAX. 808/832-5722; Mark H.K. Greer, D.M.D., MPH, Chief

Hawaii Department of Health, P.O. Box 3378, Honolulu, HI 96801; tel. 808/586-4410; FAX. 808/586-4368; Chiyome L. Fukino, M.D., Director

Licensing

Department of Health/Office of Health Care Assurance, Licensing and Certification, P.O. Box 3378, Honolulu, HI 96801-3378; tel. 808/586-4080; FAX. 808/586-4791; Dianne M. Okumura, B.S.N., MPH, Chief, OHCA

Social Services

Alcohol and Drug Abuse Division, Department of Health, State of Hawaii, 601 Kamokila Blvd., Room 360, Kapolei, HI 96707; tel. 808/692-7506; FAX. 808/692-7521; Jared Yurow, Psy.D., Acting Chief

Department of Human Services, Med-QUEST Division, P.O. Box 700190, Kapolei, HI 96709-0190; tel. 808/692-8050; FAX. 808/692-8173; Angie Payne, Acting Med-Quest Administrator

Department of Labor and Industrial Relations, Disability Compensation Division, P.O. Box 3769, Honolulu, HI 96812; tel. 808/586-9151; FAX. 808/586-9219; Gary S. Hamada, Administrator

Family Health Services Division, Hawaii State Department of Health, 1250 Punchbowl Street, Room 216, Honolulu, HI 96813; tel. 808/586-4122; FAX. 808/586-9303; Loretta J. Fuddy, A.C.S.W., M.P.H

Vocational Rehabilitation, 601 Kamokila Blvd, Room 515, Kapolei, HI 96707; tel. 808/692-7715; FAX. 808/692-7727; Neil Shim, Administrator

IDAHO

The Honorable Dirk Kempthorne, Governor, 208/334–2100

Health

Bureau of Emergency Medical Services, 590 West Washington Street, Boise, ID 83702–0036; tel. 208/334–4000; FAX. 208/334–4015; Dia Gainor, Bureau Chief

Bureau of Health Policy and Vital Statistics, Division of Health, Idaho Dept. of Health and Welfare, 450 West State, First Floor, P.O. Box 83720, Boise, ID 83720–0036; tel. 208/334–5976; FAX. 208/332–7260; Jane S. Smith, State Registrar, Chief

Insurance

Department of Insurance, 700 West State Street, Third Floor, P.O. Box 83720, Boise, ID 83720–0043; tel. 208/334–4250; FAX. 208/334–4398; Gary L. Smith, Director

Licensing

Bureau of Facility Standards, Department of Health and Welfare, P.O. Box 83720, Boise, ID 83720–0036; tel. 208/334–6626; FAX. 208/364–1888; Sylvia Creswell, Supervisor–Non LTC

Social Services

Bureau of Clinical and Preventive Services, 450 West State Street, P. O. Box 83720, Boise, ID 83720–0036; tel. 208/334–5930; FAX. 208/332–7362; Russell Duke, Chief

Department of Health and Welfare, Division of Health, 450 West State, Fourth Floor, P.O. Box 83720, Boise, ID 83720–0036; tel. 208/334–6996; FAX. 208/334–6581; Richard H. Schultz, Administrator

Department of Health and Welfare Division of Family and Community Services, Substance Abuse Program, 450 West State, 5th Floor, P.O. Box 83720, Boise, ID 83720–0036; tel. 208/334–5935; FAX. 208/334–6664; Pharis Stanger, Substance Abuse Program Manager

Vocational Rehabilitation, Len B. Jordan Building, 650 West State, Room 150, P. O. Box 83720, Boise, ID 83720–0096; tel. 208/334–3390; FAX. 208/334–5305; Barry J. Thompson, Administrator

Other

Idaho State Bureau of Laboratories, 2220 Old Penitentiary Road, Boise, ID 83712; tel. 208/334–2235; FAX. 208/334–2382; Richard F. Hudson, Ph.D., Chief

ILLINOIS

The Honorable Rod Blagojevich, Governor, 217/782–0244

Health

Illinois Department of Public Health, 535 West Jefferson Street, Springfield, IL 62761; tel. 217/782–4977; FAX. 217/557–3497; Eric E. Whitaker, M.D., MPH, Director

Illinois Department of Public Health, Office of Health Care Regulation, 525 West Jefferson Street, 5th floor, Springfield, IL 62761; tel. 217/782–2913; FAX. 217/524–6292; Enrique J. Unanue, AIA, NCARB, ACHA, Deputy Director

Illinois Department of Public Health, Office of Health Protection, 525 West Jefferson Street, Springfield, IL 62761; tel. 217/782–3984; FAX. 217/524–0802; Tom Hughes, Deputy Director

Illinois Department of Public Health, Office of Statistics Policy & Planning, 525 West Jefferson Street, Springfield, IL 62761; tel. 217/785–2040; FAX. 217/785–4308; David Carvalho, Deputy Director

Illinois Department of Public Health Laboratories, 825 North Rutledge Street, P.O. Box 19435, Springfield, IL 62794–9435; tel. 217/782–6562; FAX. 217/524–7924; Mr. Maserang, MD, State Laboratory Director

Illinois Department of Public Health, Office of Health Care Regulation, Bureau of Hospitals and Ambulatory Services, 525 West Jefferson Street, Fourth Floor, Springfield, IL 62761; tel. 217/782–7412; FAX. 217/782–0382; Catherine M. Stokes, Assistant Deputy Director

Insurance

Department of Financial & Professional Regulation, Division of Insurance, 320 West Washington Street, Fourth Floor, Springfield, IL 62767; tel. 217/782–4515; FAX. 217/782–5020; Michael T. McRaith, Director

Social Services

Department of Public Aid, 201 South Grand Avenue, E., Springfield, IL 62763; tel. 217/782–1200; FAX. 217/524–7979; Barry S. Maram, Director

Division of Specialized Care for Children, University of Illinois, (Illinois' Title V Program for Children with Special Health Care Needs), 2815 West Washington, Suite 300, Springfield, IL 62794–9481; tel. 217/793–2340; FAX. 217/793–0773; Charles N. Onufer, M.D., Director

Office of Finance and Administration, 535 West Jefferson Street, Springfield, IL 62761; tel. 217/785–2033; FAX. 217/782–3987; Gary Robinson, Deputy Director

INDIANA

The Honorable Mitch Daniels, Governor, 317/232–4567

Health

Children's Special Health Care Services, Indiana State Department of Health, Two North Meridian Street, Section 7B, Indianapolis, IN 46204; tel. 317/233–9247; FAX. 317/233–1342; Eric J. Vermeulen, J.D., Director

Indiana State Department of Health, Division of Acute Care, Two North Meridian Street, Indianapolis, IN 46204; tel. 317/233–7474; FAX. 317/233–7157; Mary Azbill, Director

Insurance

Department of Insurance, 311 West Washington Street, Suite 300, Indianapolis, IN 46204; tel. 317/232–2406; FAX. 317/232–5251; Adrienne Quill, Chief Deputy Commissioner

Social Services

Division of Long Term Care, Two North Meridian Street, Section 4–B, Indianapolis, IN 46204; tel. 317/233–7442; FAX. 317/233–7322; Suzanne Hornstein, Director

Indiana Family and Social Services Administration, 402 West Washington Street, P.O. Box 7083, Indianapolis, IN 46207–7083; tel. 317/233–4454; FAX. 317/233–4693; Cheryl G. Sullivan, Secretary

Indiana Family and Social Services Administration, Division of Mental Health and Addiction, Indiana Government Center–South, W353, 402 West Washington Street, Indianapolis, IN 46204; tel. 317/232–7800; FAX. 317/233–3472; Cathy Boggs, Interim Director

Indiana Family and Social Services Administration, Office of Medicaid Policy and Planning, Indiana Government Center–South, 402 West Washington, Room W 382, Indianapolis, IN 46204–2739; tel. 317/233–4455; FAX. 317/232–7382; Melanie Bella, Assistant Secretary

Maternal and Children's Special Health Care Services, Indiana State Department of Health, Two North Meridian Street, Section 8c, Indianapolis, IN 46204; tel. 317/233–1262; FAX. 317/233–1299; Judith A. Ganser, M.D., MPH, Medical Director

IOWA

The Honorable Thomas Vilsack, Governor, 515/281–5211

Health

Department of Public Health, Lucas State Office Building, 321 E. 12th Street, Des Moines, IA 50319–0075; tel. 515/281–7689; FAX. 515/281–4958; Mary Mincer Hansen, R.N., Ph.D.

Division Health Promotion and Chronic Disease Prevention, Iowa Department of Public Health, Lucas State Office Building, Fifth Floor, Des Moines, IA 50319; tel. 515/281–3104; FAX. 515/242–6384; Julie McMahon

Iowa Department of Public Health, Lucas State Office Building, 6th Floor, Des Moines, IA 50319; tel. 515/281–3126; FAX. 515/242–6384; Jeff Lobas,ND

Insurance

Division of Insurance, 330 E. Maple, Des Moines, IA 50319–0065; tel. 515/281–5705; FAX. 515/281–3059; Susan E. Voss, Commissioner

Licensing

Department of Inspection and Appeals, Division of Health Facilities, Lucas State Office Building, Des Moines, IA 50319; tel. 515/281–4115; FAX. 515/242–5022; Marvin Tooman, Administrator

Social Services

Child Health Specialty Clinics, 247 Center For Disabilities & Development, Iowa City, IA 52242–1011; tel. 319/356–1469; FAX. 319/356–3715; Jeffrey G. Lobas, M.D., Director

Department of Human Services, Hoover State Office Building, 1305 E. Walnut, Des Moines, IA 50319; tel. 515/281–5452; FAX. 515/281–4980; Director

Division of Behavioral, Developmental & Protective Services For Family, Adults & Children, 1305 E. Walnut Street 5th floor, Des Moines, IA 50319–0114; tel. 515/281–8746; FAX. 515/242–6036; Division Administrator

Division of Health Promotion, Prevention, and Addictive Behaviors, Lucas State Office Building – 4th Floor, 321 East 12th Street, Des Moines, IA 50319–0075; tel. 515/281–7689; FAX. 515/281–4535; Janet Zwick, Director

Governor's Office of Drug Control Policy, 321 E. 12th Street, 2nd Floor, Des Moines, IA 50319; 515/242–6391; FAX. 515/242–6390; Dale Woolery, Associate Director

Iowa Department of Elder Affairs, Clemens Building 200 – 10th, 3rd Floor, Des Moines, IA 50309–3609; tel. 515/242–3333; FAX. 515/242–3300; Mark Haverland, Executive Director

Other

Department of Education, Iowa Vocational Rehabilitation Services, 510 East 12th Street, Des Moines, IA 50319; tel. 515/281–6731; FAX. 515/281–4703; Stephen A. Wooderson, Administrator

KANSAS

The Honorable Kathleen Sebelius, Governor, 913/296–6240

Health

Kansas Department of Health and Environment, Curtis Building, 1000 S.W. Jackson, Topeka, KS 66612–1368; tel. 913/296–0461; FAX. 913/368–6368; Roderick Bremby, Secretary, Kansas Health and Environment

Insurance

Kansas Insurance Department, 420 Southwest Ninth, Topeka, KS 66612; tel. 785/296–3071; FAX. 785/296–2283; Sandy Praeger, Commissioner of Insurance

Kansas Insurance Department, Accident and Health Division, 420 Southwest Ninth, Topeka, KS 66612; tel. 785/296–7850; FAX. 785/291–3034; Jay J. Rogers, Director of Accident and Health

Social Services

Division of Health Care Policy, Docking State Office Building, Fifth Floor–N, Topeka, KS 66612; tel. 913/296–3773; FAX. 913/296–6142; J. Lyn Entrikin Goering, Assistant Secretary

Health Care Policy/Medicaid, Docking State Office Building, 915 Southwest Harrison, Topeka, KS 66612; tel. 913/296–3981; FAX. 913/296–4813; Scott Brunner, Director

Kansas Department of Health and Environment, Bureau of Child Care and Health Facilities, 1000 Southwest Jackson, Suite 200, Topeka, KS 66612–1365; tel. 913/296–1240; FAX. 913/291–3419; Charles Moore, Director of Medical Facilities and Survey Support

Kansas Rehabilitation Services, 3640 SW Topeka Blvd., Suite 150, Topeka, KS 66611–2373; tel. 785/267–5301; FAX. 785/267–0263; Dale Barnum, Director

State Department of Social and Rehabilitation Services, Economic & Employment Support, Docking State Office Building, 915 sw Harrison, Topeka, KS 66612–1505; tel. 785/296–3349; FAX. 913/296–6960; Bobbi Mariani, Director

KENTUCKY

The Honorable Ernie Fletcher, Governor, 502/564–2611

Health

Commission for Children with Special Health Care Needs, 982 Eastern Parkway, Louisville, KY 40217; tel. 502/595–4459; FAX. 502/595–4673; Eric Friedlander, Executive Director

Department For Mental Health/Mental Retardation Services, 100 Fair Oaks Lane, Frankfort, KY 40621–0001; tel. 502/564–4527; FAX. 502/564–5478; Margaret A. Pennington, MSSW, Commissioner

Department for Public Health, Cabinet for Health & Family Services, 275 East Main Street, Mail Stop HSIGWA, Frankfort, KY 40621; tel. 502/564–3970; FAX. 502/564–9377; William D. Hacker, MD. FAAP, CPE, Commissioner

Office of Certificate of Need, 275 East Main Street, HS1E–D, Frankfort, KY 40621; tel. 502/564–9589; FAX. 502/564–0302; John H. Gray, Director

Surveillance and Health Data Branch, 275 East Main Street, HSIE–C, Frankfort, KY 40621; tel. 502/564–2757; FAX. 502/564–4015; George Robertson, Manager

Insurance

Department of Insurance, Division of Health Policy and Managed Care, 215 West Main Street, P.O. Box 517, Frankfort, KY 40602; tel. 502/564–6088; FAX. 502/564–2728; Carrie Banahan, Director

Licensing

Division of Long Term Care, Office of Inspector General, CHS Building, Fifth Floor, E, 275 East Main Street – 5EA, Frankfort, KY 40621; tel. 502/564–2800; FAX. 502/564–4268; Edward A. Wilson, Director

Social Services

Department for Community Based Services, 3W–A, 275 East Main Street, Frankfort, KY 40621; tel. 502/564–3703; FAX. 502/564–6907; Mike Robinson, Commissioner

Department for Medicaid Services, 275 East Main Street, 6WA, Frankfort, KY 40621; tel. 502/564–4321; FAX. 502/564–0509; Shannon R. Turner, Commissioner

Department of Vocational Rehabilitation, 209 St. Clair Street, Frankfort, KY 40601; tel. 502/564–4440; FAX. 502/564–6745; Bruce Crump, Commissioner

LOUISIANA
The Honorable Kathleen Blanco, Governor, 225/342–7015

Health

Louisiana State University Health Sciences Center, Health Care Services Division–Medical Center of LA at New Orleans, 2021 Perdido Street, New Orleans, LA 70112–1352; tel. 504/903–3332; FAX. 504/903–3580; Dwayne A. Thomas, M.D. —— Chief Executive Officer

Louisiana State University Medical Center, Health Care Services Division, 8550 United Plaza Boulevard, Fourth Floor, Baton Rouge, LA 70809; tel. 504/922–0490; FAX. 504/922–2259; Cary M. Dougherty, Jr., Chief Operating Officer

Insurance

Department of Insurance, P.O. Box 94214, Baton Rouge, LA 70804; tel. 225/342–5900; FAX. 225/342–3078; J. Robert Wooley, Commissioner

Social Services

Office for Addictive Disorders, P.O. Box 2790, Baton Rouge, LA 70821–2790; tel. 225/342–6717; FAX. 225/342–3875; Michael Duffy, Assistant Secretary

Office of Community Services, P.O. Box 3318, Baton Rouge, LA 70821; tel. 504/342–4073; FAX. 504/342–2268; Carmen Weisner, Assistant Secretary

Office of Family Support, P.O. Box 94065, Baton Rouge, LA 70804–9065; tel. 225/342–3950; FAX. 225/219–9399; Mr. Adren O. Wilson, Assistant Secretary

Other

LA Dept. Of Health and Hospitals Office of the Secretary, P.O. Box 629, Baton Rouge, LA 70821–0629; tel. 225/342–9500; FAX. 225/342–5568; Frederick P. Cerise, M.D., M.P.H.

MAINE
The Honorable John E. Baldacci, Governor, 207/287–3531

Health

Bureau of Health, Department of Health and Human Services, 11 State House Station, 286 Water Street, Augusta, ME 04333–0011; tel. 207/287–8016; FAX. 207/287–9058; Dora Anne Mills, M.D., MPH, Director

Insurance

Bureau of Insurance, Department of Professional and Financial Regulation, 34 State House Station, Augusta, ME 04333; tel. 207/624–8475; FAX. 207/624–8599; David Trubee, Supervisor, Life and Disability

Licensing

Department of Professional and Financial Regulation, 35 State House Station, Augusta, ME 04333; tel. 207/624–8511; FAX. 207/624–8595

Division of Licensing and Certification, Department of Human Services, 442 Civic Center Drive, Station 11, Augusta, ME 04333; tel. 207/287–9300; FAX. 207/287–9304; Louis Dorogi, Assistant Director

Social Services

Bureau of Elder and Adult Services, 442 Civic Center Dr., 11 State House Station, Augusta, ME 04333; tel. 207/287–9200; FAX. 207/287–9229; Catherine Cobb, Acting Director

Bureau of Rehabilitation Services, 150 State House Station, Augusta, ME 04333–0150; tel. 207/624–5954; FAX. 207/624–5980; Jill Duson

Bureau of Rehabilitation Services, Division of Deafness, 150 State House Station, Augusta, ME 04333–0150; tel. 207/624–5964; FAX. 207/624–5980; Jan DeVinney, Director

Department of Health and Human Services, 11 State House Station, Augusta, ME 04333–0011; tel. 207/287–3707; FAX. 207/287–3005; John R. Nicholas, Commissioner

Department of Human Services, Bureau of Medical Services, State House, Station 11, Augusta, ME 04333; tel. 207/287–2674; FAX. 207/287–2675; Christine Zukas–Lessard, Acting Director

Division for the Blind and Visually Impaired, 150 State House Station, Augusta, ME 04333–0150; tel. 207/624–5959; FAX. 207/624–5980; Harold Lewis, Director

Maine Department of Human Services, Bureau of Medical Services, Division of Licensing, State House, Station 11 442 Civic Center Drive, Augusta, ME 04333; tel. 207/287–9300; FAX. 207/287–9304; Lou Dorogi, Assistant Director

MARYLAND
The Honorable Robert Ehrlich, Governor, 410/974–3901

Health

Community and Public Health Administration, 201 West Preston Street, Baltimore, MD 21201; tel. 410/767–5300; FAX. 410/333–7106; Russell Moy, M.D.,Director

Department of Health and Mental Hygiene, 201 West Preston Street, Suite 500, Baltimore, MD 21201; tel. 410/767–6500; FAX. 410/767–6489; S. Anthony McCann, Secretary

Insurance

Maryland Insurance Administration, 525 St. Paul Place, Baltimore, MD 21202; tel. 800/492–6116; FAX. 410/468–2020; Alfred W. Redmer Jr., Insurance Commissioner

Licensing

Office of Health Care Quality, Bland Bryant Building, Spring Grove Center, 55 Wade Avenue, Catonsville, MD 21228; tel. 410/402–8015; FAX. 410/402–8211; Carol Benner, Director

Social Services

Alcohol and Drug Abuse Administration, pluongo@dhmh.state.md.us, 55 Wade Avenue, Catonsville, MD 21228; tel. 410/402–8610; FAX. 410/402–8601; Peter F. Luongo, Ph.D., Director

Community Health Administration, Maryland Dept of Health and Mental Hygiene, 201 West Preston Street, Baltimore, MD 21201; tel. 410/767–6742; FAX. 410/333–5995; Diane L. Matuszak, MD, MPH, Director

Developmental Disabilities Administration, 201 West Preston Street, 4th Floor, Baltimore, MD 21201; tel. 410/767–5600; FAX. 410/767–5850; Diane K. Coughlin, Director

Division Of Mental Health, Dix Building Spring Grove Hospital, 55 Wade Avenue, Catonsville, MD 21228; tel. 410/402–8452; FAX. 410/402–8441; Brian Hepburn, M.D., Director

Division of Rehabilitation Services, 2301 Argonne Drive, Baltimore, MD 21218–1696; tel. 410/554–9385; FAX. 410/554–9412; Robert A. Burns, Assistant State Superintendent

Social Services Administration, 311 West Saratoga Street, Fifth Floor, Baltimore, MD 21201; tel. 410/767–7216; FAX. 410/333–0127; Linda E. Mouzon, Executive Director

Other

Laboratories Administration, 201 West Preston Street, Baltimore, MD 21201; tel. 410/767–6100; FAX. 410/333–5403; John M. DeBoy, Dr. P.H.

Maryland Department of the Environment, Office of Environmental Health Coordination, 2500 Broening Highway, Baltimore, MD 21224; tel. 410/631–3851; FAX. 410/631–4112; Tom Allen, Director

Maryland State Department of Education, 200 West Baltimore Street, Baltimore, MD 21201–1595; tel. 410/767–0100; FAX. 410/333–6033; Nancy S. Grasmick, State Superintendent of Schools

Office of Planning and Capital Financing, Maryland State Dept. Of Health and Mental Hygiene Office of Planning and Capital Financing, 201 West Preston Street, room 505, Baltimore, MD 21201; tel. 410/767–6816; FAX. 410/333–7525; Elizabeth G. Barnard, Director

MASSACHUSETTS
The Honorable Mitt Romney, Governor, 617/727–3600

Health

Bureau of Environmental Health Assessment, Massachusetts Department of Public Health, 250 Washington Street, Seventh Floor, Boston, MA 02108; tel. 617/624–5757; FAX. 617/624–5777; Suzanne K. Condon, Assistant Commissioner

Bureau of Health Quality Management, Massachusetts Department of Public Health, 250 Washington Street, Boston, MA 02108–4619; tel. 617/624–5280; FAX. 617/624–5046; Nancy Ridley, Assistant Commissioner

Center for Health Information, research and Evaluation, Massachusetts Department of Public Health, 250 Washington Street, Sixth Floor, Boston, MA 02108–4619; tel. 617/624–5613; FAX. 617/624–5698; Bruce Cohen, Ph.D.,Acting Director

Department of Transitional Assistance, 600 Washington Street, Boston, MA 02111; tel. 617/348–8402; FAX. 617/348–8575; Claire McIntire, Commissioner

Insurance

Division of Insurance, One South Station, Boston, MA 02110–2208; tel. 617/521–7794; FAX. 617/521–7773; Julianne M. Bowler, Commissioner

Licensing

Division of Health Care Quality, 10 West Street, Fifth Floor, Boston, MA 02111; tel. 617/753–8100; FAX. 617/753–8125; Paul I. Dreyer, Ph.D., Director

Social Services

Massachusetts Commission For The Blind, 48 Boylston Street, Boston, MA 02116–4718; tel. 617/727–5550; FAX. 617/626–7685; David Govostes, Commissioner

Massachusetts Department of Mental Health, Central Office, 25 Stanford Street, Boston, MA 02114; tel. 617/626–8123; FAX. 617/626–8131; Elizabeth Childs, MD, Commissioner

Massachusetts Department of Public Health, Bureau of Substance Abuse, 250 Washington Street, 3rd Floor, Boston, MA 02108–4619; tel. 617/624–5222; FAX. 617/624–5261; Deborah Klein Walker Ed.D. Assoc. Commissioner for Programs and Prevention

Massachusetts Rehabilitation Commission, Fort Point Place, 27 Wormwood Street, Boston, MA 02210–1606; tel. 617/204–3600; FAX. 617/727–1354; Elmer C. Bartels, Commissioner

MICHIGAN
The Honorable Jennifer Granholm, Governor, 517/335–3400

Health

Department of Community Health, Bureau of Health Systems, Division of Licensing and Certification, P.O. Box 30664, Lansing, MI 48909; tel. 517/241–4160; FAX. 517/241–3354; Darryl Horton, Director

Division of Chronic Disease and Injury Control, Michigan Department of Community Health, 3423 North Martin Luther King, Jr. Boulevard, P.O. Box 30195, Lansing, MI 48909; tel. 517/335–8368; FAX. 517/335–8593; Jean Chabut, Director

Medical Services Administration, 400 South Pine, P.O. Box 30037, Lansing, MI 48909; tel. 517/241–7882; FAX. 517/335–5007; Paul Reinhart, Deputy Director

Licensing

Department of Consumer and Industry Services, Michigan Insurance Bureau, 611 West Ottawa, Second Floor, P.O. Box 30220, Lansing, MI 48909–7720; tel. 877/999–6442; FAX. 517/335–4978; Linda A. Watters, Commissioner

Division of Licensing and Certification, 3500 North Logan Street, Lansing, MI 48909; tel. 517/335–8505; Nancy Graham, Supervisor

Managed Care Plan Division, Michigan Department of Community Health, P.O. Box 30479, Lansing, MI 48909; tel. 517/241–7933; FAX. 517/241–5713; Cheryl Bupp Director

Section C

Social Services

Division of Substance Abuse Quality & Planning, Michigan Department of Community Health, 3423 N. MLK Blvd., Lewis Cass Building, Lansing, MI 48909; tel. 517/335-0278; FAX. 517/241-2611; Deborah J. Hollis, Director

Michigan Department of Community Health, Health Policy Regulation & Professions Administration, 320 S. Walnut Street, Lewis Cass Building, 6th Floor, Lansing, MI 48933; tel. 517/373-2559; FAX. 517/241-1200; Jan Christensen, Deputy Director

Michigan Rehabilitation Services, Box 30010, Lansing, MI 48909; tel. 517/373-3390; Jaye N. Balthazar, State Director

Office of Drug Control Policy, Michigan Department of Community Health, 320 S. Walnut Street, 5th Floor, Lansing, MI 48913; tel. 517/373-4700; FAX. 517/335-3090; Yvonne Blackmond, Director

Office of Health and Human Services, State Budget Office, Michigan Department of Management and Budget, George W. Romney Building, Box 30026, Lansing, MI 48909; tel. 517/373-1076; FAX. 517/335-1521; Charles Overbey, Director

Office of Services to the Aging, P.O. Box 30676, Lansing, MI 48909; tel. 517/373-8230; FAX. 517/373-4092

Other

Department of Education, Office of School Support Services, Coordinated School, School Health & Safety Programs, P.O. Box 30008, Lansing, MI 48909; tel. 517/241-4292; FAX. 517/373-1233; Kim Kovalchick, Consultant, CSHSP

Michigan Department of Community Health, Bureau of Health Professions, Box 30670, Lansing, MI 48909; tel. 517/373-8068; FAX. 517/241-3082; Melanie Brim

Michigan Department of Consumer and Industry Services, Laboratories, Laboratory Improvement Section, P.O. Box 30664, Lansing, MI 48909; tel. 517/241-2640; FAX. 517/241-2629; Richard J. Benson, Chief

Michigan Family Independence Agency, 235 South Grand Avenue, P.O. Box 30037, Lansing, MI 48909; tel. 517/373-2035; FAX. 517/335-6101; Marianne Udow, Director

MINNESOTA
The Honorable Tim Pawlenty, Governor, 651/296-3391

Health

Division of Environmental Health, 121 East Seventh Place, P.O. Box 64975, St. Paul, MN 55164-0975; tel. 651/215-0731; FAX. 651/215-0979; Patricia A. Bloomgren, Director

Minnesota Department of Health, Finance and Administrative Management Bureau, 85 East 7th Place, P.O. Box 64882, St. Paul, MN 55164-0882; tel. 651/282-2999; FAX. 651/215-5801; David Johnson, Assistant Commissioner

Public Health Laboratory Division, Minnesota Department of Health, 717 Delaware Street, S.E., P.O. Box 9441, Minneapolis, MN 55440; tel. 612/676-5331; FAX. 612/676-5514; Norman A. Crouch, PhD, Director

Social Services

Minnesota Department of Health, Division of Community Health, Golden Rule Building, Suite 500, 85 East Seventh Place, Zip 55101, St. Paul, MN 55164-0882; tel. 651/296-9720; FAX. 651/296-9362; Mary Sheehan, Director

Minnesota Department of Health, Division of Disease Prevention and Control, 717 Southeast Delaware Street S.E., P.O. Box 9441, Minneapolis, MN 55440-9441; tel. 612/676-5414; FAX. 612/676-5666; Harry Hull, Director & State Epidemiologist

Minnesota Department of Human Services, 444 Lafayette Road, N., St. Paul, MN 55155; tel. 651/296-2701; FAX. 651/296-5868; Kevin Goodno, Commissioner

Rehabilitation Services Branch, Minnesota Department of Economic Security, 390 North Robert Street, Fifth Floor, St. Paul, MN 55101; tel. 651/296-7510; FAX. 651/296-0994; Howard E. Glad, Assistant Commissioner

MISSISSIPPI
The Honorable Haley Barbour, Governor, 601/737-9540

Health

Bureau of Health Services, Felix J. Underwood State Board of Health Building An, P.O. Box 1700, Jackson, MS 32915; tel. 601/960-7472; FAX. 601/960-7480; Michael J. Gandy, Ed.D., Bureau Director, Deputy

Department of Health, P.O. Box 1700, Jackson, MS 32915-1700; tel. 601/576-7634; FAX. 601/576-7931; Brian W. Amy, MD, MHA, MP

Health Informatics, Mississippi State Department of Health, Health Informatics, Box 1700, Jackson, MS 39215-1700; tel. 601/576-7960; FAX. 601/576-7505; Judy T. Moulder, Director

Health Planning and Resources Development Division, Mississippi State Department of Health, Osborne Building, 570 East Woodrow Wilson, Jackson, MS 39215-1700; tel. 601/576-7874; FAX. 601/576-7530; Harold B. Armstrong, Chief

Mississippi State Department of Health, P.O. Box 1700, Jackson, MS 32915-1700; tel. 601/576-7951; FAX. 601/576-7823; Kaye Bender, RN, PH.D, Deputy State Health Officer

Office of Environmental Health, Mississippi State Department of Health, 120 Osborne Building, P.O. Box 1700, Jackson, MS 32915-1700; tel. 601/576-7680; FAX. 601/576-7270; Rick Herrington, Director

Licensing

Division of Health Facilities Licensure and Certification, Mississippi State Department of Health, P.O. Box 1700, Jackson, MS 39215; tel. 601/576-7300; FAX. 601/576-7350; Karen Selestak, Director

Social Services

Children's Medical Program, MS State Department of Health, P.O. Box 1700, Jackson, MS 39215-1700; tel. 601/987-3965; FAX. 601/987-5560; Lawrence (Larry) Clark, Director

Department of Mental Health, 1101 Robert E. Lee Building, Jackson, MS 39201; tel. 601/359-1288; FAX. 601/359-6295; Randy Hendrix, Ph.D., Director

Mississippi Department of Human Services, P.O. Box 352, Jackson, MS 39205-0352; tel. 601/359-4480; FAX. 601/359-4910; Donald R. Taylor, Executive Director

State Department of Rehabilitation Services, P.O. Box 1698, Jackson, MS 39215-1698; tel. 601/853-5100; FAX. 601/853-5205; H.S. McMillian, Executive Director

Other

State Epidemiologist, 570 E. Woodrow Wilson, P.O Box 1700, Jackson, MS 32915-1700; tel. 601/576-7725; FAX. 601/576-7497; Mary Currier, M.D., MPH

MISSOURI
The Honorable Matt Blunt, Governor, 573/751-3222

Health

Center for Health Information Management and Evaluation (CHIME), Box 570, Jefferson City, MO 65102; tel. 573/751-6272; FAX. 573/526-4102; Garland H. Land, Director

Department of Health and Senior Services, 912 Wildwood, P.O. Box 570, Jefferson City, MO 65102; tel. 573/751-6001; FAX. 573/751-6041; Julia M. Eckstein, Director

Missouri Department of Health – Bureau of Special Health Care Needs, 930 Wildwood Drive, P.O. Box 570, Jefferson City, MO 65109; tel. 573/751-6246; FAX. 314/751-6237; Gary Harbison, Chief

Insurance

Department of Insurance, P.O. Box 690, Jefferson City, MO 65102; tel. 314/751-4126; FAX. 314/751-1165; Scott Lakin, Director

Licensing

Unit of Health Facility Regulation, Missouri Department of Health and Senior Services, P.O.Box 570, Jefferson City, MO 65102; tel. 573/751-6303; FAX. 573/526-3621; Terry Wenkel, Health Care Regulatory Supervisor

Social Services

Department of Mental Health, 1706 East Elm Street, P.O. Box 687, Jefferson City, MO 65102; tel. 573/751-4122; FAX. 573/526-7926; Mr. Dorn Schuffman, Director

Life and Health Section, Missouri Department of Insurance, P.O. Box 690, Jefferson City, MO 65102; tel. 573/751-4363; FAX. 573/526-6075; John S. Korte, Manager

Missouri Division of Vocational Rehabilitation, 3024 Dupont Circle, Jefferson City, MO 65109-0525; tel. 573/751-3251; FAX. 314/751-1441; C. Jeanne Loyd, Assistant Commissioner

Other

Department of Elementary and Secondary Education, 205 Jefferson, P.O. Box 480, Jefferson City, MO 65102; tel. 573/751-4446; FAX. 573/751-1179; Dr. D. Kent King, Commissioner of Education

Division of Community Health, P.O. Box 570, Jefferson City, MO 65102-0570; tel. 573/751-6252; FAX. 573/526-5348; Paula F. Nickelson, Director

MONTANA
The Honorable Brian Schweitzer, Governor, 406/444-3111

Health

Health Policy and Services Division, Montana Department of Public Health and Human Services, 1400 Broadway, P.O. Box 202951, Helena, MT 59620-2951; tel. 406/444-4540; FAX. 406/444-1861; Nancy Ellery, Administrator

Licensing

Quality Assurance Division, Department of Public Health and Human Services, Certification Bureau, 2401 Colonial Drive, 2nd Floor, P.O. Box 202953, Helena, MT 59620-2951; tel. 406/444-2099; FAX. 406/444-3456; Marjorie VanderAarde, Chief

Social Services

Aging Services, Senior and Long Term Care Division, Department of Public Health and Human Services, 111 Sanders, P.O. Box 4210, Helena, MT 59604; tel. 406/444-4676; FAX. 406/444-7743; Robin Homan, State Long Term Care Ombudsman

Child and Family Services Division, P.O. Box 8005, Helena, MT 59604-8005; tel. 406/444-5902; FAX. 406/444-5956; Hank Hudson, Administrator

Disability Services Division, P.O. Box 4210, Helena, MT 59604; tel. 406/444-2590; FAX. 406/444-3632; Joe A. Mathews, Administrator

Family and Community Health Bureau, Department of Public Health & Human Services, W. F. Cogswell Building, Helena, MT 59620; tel. 406/444-4740; FAX. 406/444-2606; JoAnn Walsh Dotson, RN MSN, Bureau Chief

Montana Department of Public Health and Human Services, 111 North Sanders, P.O. Box 4210, Helena, MT 59604; tel. 406/444-5622; FAX. 406/444-1970; Robert E. Wynia, M.D. Director

NEBRASKA
The Honorable Dave Heineman, Governor, 402/471-2244

Licensing

Nebraska Department of Health and Human Services Regulation and Licensure, Credentialing Division, 301 Centennial Mall, South 3rd Floor, P.O. Box 94986, Lincoln, NE 68509-4986; tel. 402/471-2115; FAX. 402/471-3557; Helen L. Meeks, Administrator

Office of Public Health, 301 Centennial Mall, S., P.O. Box 95007, Lincoln, NE 68509; tel. 402/471-0146; FAX. 402/471-8259; David Palm, Ph.D., Director

Social Services

Department of Health and Human Services – Regulation and Licensure, Credentialing Division, Certificate of Need Program, P.O. Box 94986, Lincoln, NE 68509; tel. 402/471-4963; FAX. 402/471-3577; Claire Titus, Program Manager

Nebraska Department of Health & Human Services, Regulation & Licensure, 301 Centennial Mall South, P.O. Box 95007, Lincoln, NE 68509-5007; tel. 402/471-3121; FAX. 402/471-9449; Richard A. Raymond, Director

Nebraska Department of Health and Human Services, Services, 301 Centennial Mall, S., P.O. Box 95044, Lincoln, NE 68509; tel. 402/471-0191; FAX. 402/471-8259; Sue Medinger, Administrator

Nebraska Department of Health and Human Services, Special Services for Children and Adults, 301 Centennial Mall, S., P.O. Box 95044, Lincoln, NE 68509-5044; tel. 402/471-9345; FAX. 402/471-6352; Mary Jo Iwan, Administrator

Section C

Nebraska Health and Human Services, Finance and Support Medicaid Division Medical Services Division, 301 Centennial Mall, S., P.O. Box 95026, Lincoln, NE 68509; tel. 402/471-9147; FAX. 402/471-9092; Cec Brady, Administrator

Nebraska Health and Human Services System, 301 Centennial Mall, South., P.O. Box 95026, Lincoln, NE 68509-5026; tel. 402/471-9433; FAX. 401/471-9449; Chris Peterson, Policy Secretary

Office of Family Health, Nebraska Department of Health and Human Services, 301 Centennial Mall South, P.O. Box 95044, Lincoln, NE 68509-5044; tel. 402/471-3980; FAX. 402/471-7049; Paula Eurek, R.D., Office Administrator

Other

Department of Education, Vocational Rehabilitation, 301 Centennial Mall, S., P.O. Box 94987, Lincoln, NE 68509; tel. 402/471-3644; FAX. 402/471-0788; Frank Lloyd, Assistant Commissioner

Nebraska Department of Health, Division of Radiological Health, 301 Centennial Mall, S., P.O. Box 95007, Lincoln, NE 68509; tel. 402/471-2168; FAX. 402/471-0169; Harold Borchert, Director

NEVADA
The Honorable Kenny C. Guinn, Governor, 702/684-5670

Health

Bureau of Health Planning and Statistics, Nevada State Health Division, 505 East King Street, Room 102, Carson City, NV 89701-4749; tel. 775/684-4155; FAX. 775/684-4156; Emil DeJan, Chief

Children With Special Health Care Needs Program, Nevada State Health Division, Kinkead Building, 3527 Goni Rd., Suite 108, Carson City, NV 89706; tel. 775/684-4285; FAX. 775/684-5840; Gloria Deyhle, MCH Nurse Consultant

Division of Mental Health and Developmental Services, Kinkead Building, Suite 602, 505 East King Street, Carson City, NV 89701-3790; tel. 775/684-5943; FAX. 775/684-5966; Carlos Brandenburg, Ph.D., Administrator

Nevada Division of Health, Kinkead Building, 505 East King Street, Room 201, Carson City, NV 89701-4761; tel. 775/684-4200; FAX. 775/684-4211; Yvonne Sylva, Administrator

Nevada State Health Division, Bureau of Community Health Services, 3656 Research Way, Suite 32, Carson City, NV 89706; tel. 775/687-6944; FAX. 775/687-7693; Mary D. Sassi, Bureau Chief

Nevada State Health Laboratory, 1660 North Virginia Street, Reno, NV 89503; tel. 702/688-1335; FAX. 702/688-1460; Arthur F. DiSalvo, M.D., Director

Insurance

Division of Insurance, 788 Fairview Drive, Suite 300, Carson City, NV 89701; tel. 775/687-4270; FAX. 775/687-3937; Alice A. Molasky-Arman, Commissioner

Licensing

Bureau of Licensure and Certification, Nevada Health Division, 1550 East College Parkway, Capitol Complex, Suite 158, Carson City, NV 89706-7921; tel. 775/687-4475; FAX. 775/687-6588; Pamela S. Graham BS, RN, LNC Chief

Social Services

Department of Human Resources, Kinkead Building, 505 East King, Room 600, Carson City, NV 89710; tel. 775/684-4000; FAX. 775/684-4010; Michael J. Willden, Director

Division of Health Care Financing & Policy, 1100 East William Street, Suite 101, Carson City, NV 89701; tel. 775/684-3677; FAX. 775/687-3893; Charles Duarte, Administrator

Division of Health Care Financing and Policy-Medicaid, 1100 E. William Street, Suite 102, Carson City, NV 89701; tel. 775/684-3600; FAX. 775/687-3893; Mary Wherry, MS, CS, RN, Deputy Administrator

Rehabilitation Division, Kinkead Building, 505 East King, Room 502, Carson City, NV 89701-3705; tel. 775/684-4040; FAX. 775/684-4184; Maynard R. Yasmer, Administrator

NEW HAMPSHIRE
The Honorable John Lynch, Governor, 603/271-2121

Health

Department of Health and Human Services, Six Hazen Drive, Concord, NH 03301-6527; tel. 603/271-8560; FAX. 603/271-8705; William J. Kassler, M.D., MPH, State Medical Director

Department of Health and Human Services, 129 Pleasant St., Concord, NH 03301-6527; tel. 603/271-8560; FAX. 603/271-7912; William J. Kassler, M.D., MPH, State Medical Director

NH Department of Health and Human Services, Office of The Commissioner, 129 Pleasant Street, Brown Building, Concord, NH 03301-3857; tel. 603/271-4602; FAX. 603/271-4912; Kathleen G. Sgambati, Deputy Commissioner

Office of Community and Public Health, Dept. of Health and Human Services, Six Hazen Drive, Concord, NH 03301; tel. 603/271-4501; FAX. 603/271-4779; Maryann Cooney, Director

Insurance

New Hampshire Insurance Department, 21 South Fruit Street, Suite 14, Concord, NH 03301; tel. 603/271-2261; FAX. 603/271-1406; Roger A. Sevigny, Insurance Commissioner

State of New Hampshire, Insurance Department, Examination Division, 56 Old Suncook Road, Concord, NH 03301-5151; tel. 603/271-2241; FAX. 603/271-1406; Thomas S. Burke, Director

Licensing

Office of Program Support, Licensing and Regulation, Health Facilities Administration, 129 Pleasant Street, Concord, NH 03301; tel. 603/271-4966; FAX. 603/271-5590; Theresa Jarvis, Bureau Chief

Social Services

Bureau of Behavioral Health, State Office Park, S., 105 Pleasant Street, Concord, NH 03301; tel. 603/271-5000; FAX. 603/271-5058; Geoffrey C. Souther, Bureau Chief

New Hampshire Department of Health and Human Services, Division of Public Health Success, 29 Hazen Drive, Concord, NH 03301; tel. 603/271-4496; FAX. 603/271-0545; Donna Sevesance, Administrator

Vocational Rehabilitation Division, 78 Regional Drive, Concord, NH 03301; tel. 603/271-3471; Paul K. Leather, Director

Other

Department of Environmental Services, Six Hazen Drive, Concord, NH 03301-3503; tel. 603/271-3503; FAX. 603/271-2867; Robert W. Varney, Commissioner

State Department of Education, 101 Pleasant Street, State Office Park, South, Concord, NH 03301; tel. 603/271-3494; FAX. 603/271-1953; Dr. Lyonel B. Trady

NEW JERSEY
The Honorable Richard Codey, Governor, 609/292-6000

Health

Division of Health Care Systems Analysis, CN-360, Trenton, NJ 08625; tel. 609/292-8772; FAX. 609/984-3165; Maria Morgan, Assistant Commissioner

New Jersey Department of Health and Senior Services, Certificate of Need and Acute Care Licensing, P.O. Box 360, Trenton, NJ 08625-0360; tel. 609/292-8773; FAX. 609/292-3780; John A. Calabria, Director

Office of Managed Care, New Jersey State Department of Health, P.O. Box 360, Trenton, NJ 08625; tel. 609/633-0660; FAX. 609/633-0807; Holly Gaenzle, Program Manager

Licensing

Division of Consumer Affairs, 124 Halsey Street, P.O. Box 45027, Newark, NJ 07101; tel. 201/504-6534; FAX. 201/648-3538

Social Services

Department of Law and Public Safety, P.O. Box 080, 25 Market Street, Trenton, NJ 08625; tel. 609/292-8740; FAX. 609/292-3508; Peter Harvey, Attorney General

Division of Family Development, 6 Quakerbridge Plaza, Trenton, NJ 08625-0716; tel. 609/588-2401; FAX. 609/588-3369; Pearl Elias, Acting Director

Division of Family Health Services, 50 East State Street, P.O. Box 364, Trenton, NJ 08625; tel. 609/292-4043; FAX. 609/292-9599; Celeste Andriot-Wood

Maternal, Child and Community Health, New Jersey Department of Health and Senior Services, 50 East State Street,, P.O. Box 364, Trenton, NJ 08625-0364; tel. 609/984-1384; FAX. 609/292-3580; Dr. Linda Jones-Hicks, Diretor of MCCH

N.J. Department of Health and Senior Services, Division Of Long Term Care Systems, P.O. Box 367, Trenton, NJ 08625; tel. 609/633-8997; FAX. 609/292-0053; William Conroy, Assistant Commissioner

New Jersey Department of Health and Senior Services, Office of the Commissioner, P.O. Box 360, Trenton, NJ 08625-0360; tel. 609/292-7837; FAX. 609/292-0053; Fred M. Jacobs, M.D, M.D., State Commissioner of Health and Senior Services

NEW MEXICO
The Honorable Bill Richardson, Governor, 505/827-3000

Health

Department of Health, P.O. Box 26110, Santa Fe, NM 87502-6110; tel. 505/827-2613; FAX. 505/827-2530; Patricia T. Montoya, Secretary

Public Health Division, New Mexico Department of Health, P.O. Box 26110, Santa Fe, NM 87502-6110; tel. 505/827-2389; FAX. 505/827-2329; Joyce Naseyowma – Chalam, Director

Insurance

New Mexico Department of Insurance, P.O. Drawer 1269, Santa Fe, NM 87504-1269; tel. 505/827-4601; FAX. 505/827-4734; Helen Hordes, Manager, Life and Health Forms Division

Public Regulation Commission, P.O. Drawer 1269, Santa Fe, NM 87504; tel. 505/827-4599; FAX. 505/476-0326; Eric P. Serna, Superintendent of Insurance

Social Services

Division of Vocational Rehabilitation, 435 St. Michaels Drive, Building D, Santa Fe, NM 87505; tel. 505/954-8511; FAX. 505/954-8562; Catherine Cross Maple, PhD.

Human Services Department, P.O. Box 2348, Santa Fe, NM 87504-2348; tel. 505/827-7750; FAX. 505/827-6286; Pamela S. Hyde, Secretary

Income Support Division, P.O. Box 2348, Santa Fe, NM 87504-2348; tel. 505/827-7252; FAX. 505/827-7203; Linda Chavez, Administrator

Protective Services Division, P.O. Box 5160, Santa Fe, NM 87502-5160; tel. 505/827-8400; FAX. 505/827-8480; Merry Ortiz Y Pino, Director

Other

Public Education Dept., Education Building Jerry Apodaca Education Bldg., 300 Don Gaspar, Santa Fe, NM 87501-2786; tel. 505/827-5800; FAX. 505/827-6520; Dr. Veronica C. Garcia, Sec. Of Education

NEW YORK
The Honorable George E. Pataki, Governor, 518/474-8390

Health

New York State Department of Health, Empire State Plaza, Corning Tower, Room 1495, Albany, NY 12237; tel. 518/474-2011; FAX. 518/474-5450; Antonia C. Novello, M.D., M.P.H., Dr.P.H., Commissioner of Health

New York State Department of Health, Office of Medicaid Management, Empire State Plaza, Corning Tower, Room 1466, Albany, NY 12237; tel. 518/474-3018; FAX. 518/486-6852; Kathryn Kuhmerker, Deputy Commissioner – Office of Medicaid Management

New York State Department of Health, Office of Managed Care, Bureau of Managed Care Certification and Surveillance, Room 1911 Corning Tower Building, Empire State Plaza, Albany, NY 12237; tel. 518/473-4842; FAX. 518/473-3583; Vallencia Lloyd, Director

Office of Clinical Affairs, New York State Department of Health OHSM, Corning Tower Room 1815, Albany, NY 12237; tel. 518/402-5914; FAX. 518/402-5902; Dr. Nancy Barhydt, Director

Licensing

New York State Board for Medicine, 89 Washington Avenue, West Wing 2nd Floor, Albany, NY 12234; tel. 518/474-3841; FAX. 518/486-4846; Thomas J. Monahan, Executive Secretary

Social Services

New York State Education Department, Vocational and Educational Services for Individuals with Disabilities, One Commerce Plaza, Suite 1606, Albany, NY 12234; tel. 518/474-2714; Rebecca H. Cort, Deputy Commissioner

New York State Office of Alcoholism and Substance Abuse Services, 1450 Western Avenue, Albany, NY 12203; tel. 518/457-2061; FAX. 518/457-5474; Shari Noonan, Acting Commisioner

New York State Office of Mental Health, 44 Holland Avenue, Albany, NY 12229; tel. 518/474-4403; FAX. 518/474-2149; Sharon E. Carpinello, RN, Ph.D,Commissioner

Office of Mental Retardation and Developmental Disabilities, 44 Holland Avenue, Albany, NY 12229; tel. 518/473-1997; FAX. 518/473-1271; Thomas A. Maul, Commissioner

Other

Bureau of Project Management, New York State Department of Health, 433 River Street, Suite 303, Troy, NY 12180-2299; tel. 518/402-0911; FAX. 518/402-0931; Diane M. Smith, Acting Director

Office of Health Systems Management, Tower Building, Empire State Plaza, Room 1415, Albany, NY 12237-0701; tel. 518/474-7028; FAX. 518/486-2564

Wadsworth Center for Laboratories and Research, Clinical Lab Evaluatioan, P.O. Box 509, Empire State Plaza, Albany, NY 12201-0509; tel. 518/474-7592; FAX. 518/474-3439; Lawrence S. Sturman, M.D., Ph.D., Director

NORTH CAROLINA
The Honorable Michael Easley, Governor, 919/733-4240

Health

Department of Health and Human Services, 2001 Mail Service Center, Raleigh, NC 27699-2001; tel. 919/733-4534; FAX. 919/715-4645; Carmen Hooker Odom, Secretary

Department of Health and Human Services, Division of Facility Services, 2701 Mail Service Center, Raleigh, NC 27699-2701; tel. 919/855-3750; FAX. 919/733-2757; Robert J. Fitzgerald, Director

Insurance

Department of Insurance, 1201 Mail Service Center, Raleigh, NC 27699-1201; tel. 919/733-2032; FAX. 919/733-0085; James E. Long, Commissioner

Social Services

Division of Medical Assistance, 2501Mail Service Center, Raleigh, NC 27699-2501; tel. 919/857-4011; FAX. 919/733-6608; Gary Fuquay, Director

Division of Mental Health, Developmental Disabilities and Substance Abuse Services, 3001 Mail Service Center, Raleigh, NC 27699-3001; tel. 919/733-7011; FAX. 919/733-1221; Michael Moseley

Division of Vocational Rehabilitation Services, 280 Mail Service Center, Raleigh, NC 27699-2801; tel. 919/733-3364; FAX. 919/733-7968; Bob H. Philbeck, Director

NORTH DAKOTA
The Honorable John Hoeven, Governor, 701/328-2200

Health

Children's Special Health Services, Department of Human Services, State Capitol, 600 East Boulevard Avenue, Dept 325, Bismarck, ND 58505-0269; tel. 701/328-2436; FAX. 701/328-1645; Tamara Gallup-Millner, Unit Director

Division of Health Facilities, North Dakota Department of Health, 600 East Boulevard Avenue, Dept 301, Bismarck, ND 58505-0200; tel. 701/328-2352; FAX. 701/328-1890; Darleen Bartz, Chief

Health Resources Section, North Dakota Department of Health, 600 East Boulevard Avenue, Dept 301, Bismarck, ND 58505-0200; tel. 701/328-2352; FAX. 701/328-1890; Daeleen Bartz, Chief, Health Resources Section

Medical Services Division, North Dakota Department of Human Services, 600 East Boulevard Avenue, Dept 325, Bismarck, ND 58505-0261; tel. 701/328-2321; FAX. 701/328-1544; David J. Zentner, Director

State Department of Health, 600 East Boulevard Avenue, Bismarck, ND 58505-0200; tel. 701/328-2372; FAX. 701/328-4727; Londa Rodahl, Administrative Assistant

Insurance

North Dakota Department of Insurance, State Capitol, 600 East Boulevard, 5th Floor, Bismarck, ND 58505-0320; tel. 701/328-2440; FAX. 701/328-4880; Jim Poolman, Commissioner

Social Services

Developmental Disabilities Unit, Disability Services Division, Department of Human Services, 600 South Second Street, Suite 1A, Bismarck, ND 58504-5729; tel. 701/328-8930; FAX. 701/328-8969; Gene Hysjulien, Director

Division of Family Health, North Dakota Department of Health, State Capitol, 600 East Boulevard Avenue, Bismarck, ND 58505-0200; tel. 701/328-2493; FAX. 701/328-1412; Kim Senn, Director

Division of Mental Health and Substance Abuse Services, 1237 W. Divide Avenue, Suite 1c, Bismarck, ND 58501-1208; tel. 701/328-8920; FAX. 701/328-8969; JoAnne Hoesel, Director

Economic Assistance Policy Division, North Dakota Department of Human Services, 600 East Boulevard Avenue Dept 325, Bismarck, ND 58505-0250; tel. 701/328-2332; FAX. 701/328-1060; Carol K. Olson, Executive Director

Other

Facility Management Division, Office of Management and Budget, 600 East Boulevard, Ave, Dept 130, State Capitol, Bismarck, ND 58505-0130; tel. 701/328-2471; FAX. 701/328-3230; Curt Zimmerman, Director, Facility Management

Program and Policy, State Capitol, 600 East Boulevard Avenue Dept 325, Bismarck, ND 58505-0265; tel. 701/328-2310; FAX. 701/328-2359; Carol K. Olson, Executive Director

OHIO
The Honorable Bob Taft, Governor, 614/466-3555

Health

Managed Care Division, 2100 Stella Court, Columbus, OH 43215-1067; tel. 614/644-3315; FAX. 614/728-5238; Teresa Reedus, Senior Contract Analyst

Ohio Department of Health, 246 North High Street, P.O. Box 118, Columbus, OH 43216-0118; tel. 614/466-3543; FAX. 614/644-0085; J.Nick Baird, M.D., Director

Ohio Department of Health, Bureau of Community Health Care Facilities & Services, 246 North High Street, P.O. Box 118, Columbus, OH 43216-0118; tel. 614/995-7466; FAX. 614/387-2763; Roy Croy, Bureau Chief, Health Planning Administrator

Ohio Department of Health –Division of Prevention, Bureau of Environmental Health, 246 North High Street, Columbus, OH 43216-0118; tel. 614/466-1390; FAX. 614/564-2410; Steve Wagner, Chief

Insurance

Department of Insurance, 2100 Stella Court, Columbus, OH 43215-1067; tel. 614/719-1589; FAX. 614/719-1661; Ann Womer Benjamin, Director

Licensing

Division of Quality Assurance, Ohio Department of Health, 246 North High Street, P. O. Box 118, Columbus, OH 43216-0118; tel. 614/466-7857; FAX. 614/644-0208; Rebecca S. Maust, Chief

Social Services

Bureau of Disability Determination, P.O. Box 359001, Columbus, OH 43235-9001; tel. 614/438-1545; FAX. 614/438-1504; Kathleen Johnson, Director

Department of Mental Health, 30 East Broad Street, Eighth Floor, Columbus, OH 43266-0414; tel. 614/466-2596; FAX. 614/752-9453; Michael F. Hogan, Ph.D., Director

Department of Mental Retardation and Developmental Disability, 1810 Sullivan Avenue, Columbus, OH 43223-0415; tel. 614/466-0129; FAX. 614/644-5013; Kenneth Ritchey, Director

Division of Family and Community Health Services, 246 North High Street, P.O. Box 118, Columbus, OH 43216-0118; tel. 614/466-3263; FAX. 614/728-9163; David P. Schor, MD, MPH, Chief

Ohio Department Jobs Family Services, Office of Ohio Health Plans, 30 East Broad Street, 31st Floor, Columbus, OH 43215-3414; tel. 614/466-4443; FAX. 614/752-3986; Barbara Coulter Edwards, Deputy Director

Ohio Department of Alcohol and Drug Addiction Services, 280 Plaza, 280 North High Street, 12th Floor, Columbus, OH 43215-2550; tel. 614/466-3445; FAX. 614/752-8645; Gary Q. Tester, Director

Ohio Department of Human Services, 30 East Broad Street, 32nd Floor, Columbus, OH 43215-3414; tel. 614/466-6282; FAX. 614/466-2815; Barbara Riley, Director

Ohio Rehabilitation Services Commission, Bureau of Services for the Visually Impaired, 400 East Campus View Boulevard, Columbus, OH 43235-4604; tel. 614/438-1438; FAX. 614/438-1257; William A. Casto II, Director

Ohio Rehabilitation Services Commission, Bureau of Vocational Rehabilitation, 400 East Campus View Boulevard (SW3), Columbus, OH 43235-4604; tel. 614/438-1438; FAX. 614/438-1257; Katherine A. Brown, Ph.D.

Other

Bureau of Plan Operations, 30 East Broad Street, 31st Floor, Columbus, OH 43266-0423; tel. 614/466-2365; FAX. 614/752-7701; Sheila J. Fuji, Bureau Chief

OKLAHOMA
The Honorable Brad Henry, Governor, 405/521-2342

Health

Oklahoma Health Care Authority, 4545 North Lincoln Boulevard, Suite 124, Oklahoma City, OK 73105; tel. 405/522-7300; FAX. 405/522-7187; Mike Fogarty, Chief Executive Officer

Protective Health Services, Oklahoma State Department of Health, 1000 Northeast 10th Street, Oklahoma City, OK 73117-1299; tel. 405/271-6576; FAX. 405/271-1308; Gary Glover, Chief, Medical Facilities

Public Health Laboratory Services, 1000 Northeast 10th, Oklahoma City, OK 73117-1299; tel. 405/271-5070; FAX. 405/271-4850; John J. Mathewson, Ph.D., Chief

State Department of Health, 1000 Northeast 10th, #305, Oklahoma City, OK 73117-1299; tel. 405/271-4200; FAX. 405/271-3431; James M. Crutcher,MD, MPH, Commissioner Of Health

State Department of Health, Dental Services, 1000 Northeast 10th Street, Oklahoma City, OK 73117-1299; tel. 405/271-5502; FAX. 405/271-6199; Michael L. Morgan, D.D.S., Chief

State Department of Health, Nursing Service, 1000 Northeast 10th Street, Oklahoma City, OK 73117-1299; tel. 405/271-5183; FAX. 405/271-1897; Diana Pistole, MPH, RN

State Department of Health, Special Health Services, 1000 Northeast 10th, Oklahoma City, OK 73117-1299; tel. 405/271-4200; FAX. 405/271-2632; Brent E. VanMeter, Deputy Commissioner

Social Services

Aging Services Division, Oklahoma Department of Human Services, Sheperd Mall 2401 NW. 23rd, Ste. 40 A, Oklahoma City, OK 73107-2422; tel. 405/521-2327; FAX. 405/521-2086; Roy R. Keen, Director

Department of Mental Health and Substance Abuse Services, 1200 N.E., 13th Street,, Oklahoma City, OK 73152-3277; tel. 405/522-3878; FAX. 405/522-0637; Terry Cline, Ph.D., Commissioner

Oklahoma State Department of Health, Family Health Services, 1000 Northeast 10th Street, Oklahoma City, OK 73117-1299; tel. 405/271-4200; FAX. 405/271-3632; Edd D. Rhoades, M.D., MPH, Deputy Commissioner

Rehabilitation Services, 3535 Northwest 58th Street, Suite 500, Oklahoma City, OK 73112-4815; tel. 405/951-3400; FAX. 405/951-3529; Linda Parker, Director

OREGON
The Honorable Ted Kulongoski, Governor, 503/378-3111

Health

Office of Health Planning & Community Relations, 800 Oregon Street, Suite 930, Portland, OR 97232; tel. 503/731-4000; FAX. 503/731-4078; Claudia Bingham, Administrator

---

Licensing

Department of Consumer and Business Services/Oregon, Insurance Division, PO Box 14480, Salem, OR 97301–0405; tel. 503/947–7216; FAX. 503/378–4351; Shelley Bain, Senior Policy Analyst

Oregon Health Services, Health Care Licensure and Certification, P.O. Box 14450, Portland, OR 97214–0450; tel. 503/731–4013; FAX. 503/731–4080; Kathleen Smail, Manager

Social Services

Child Development and Rehabilitation Center, Oregon Health Sciences University, Box 574, Portland, OR 97207; tel. 503/494–8362; FAX. 503/494–6868; Clifford J. Sells, M.D., Director

Children, Adults & Families, 500 Summer Street, N.E ., E–62, Salem, OR 97301–1067; tel. 503/945–5600; Ramona Foley, Assistant Director

Department of Human Services, Community Human Services, Office of Vocational Rehabilitation Services, 500 Summer Street N.E. E–87, Salem, OR 97301–1120; tel. 503/945–6621; FAX. 503/947–5010; Tina Treasurer, Acting Administrator

Office of Mental Health and Addiction Services, 500 Summer St. NE E86, Salem, OR 97301–1118; tel. 503/945–9704; FAX. 503/373–7327; Robert E. Nikkel, MSW, Adminstrator

Other

Oregon State Public Health Laboratory, P.O. Box 275, Portland, OR 97207–0275; tel. 503/229–5882; FAX. 503/229–5682; Michael R. Skeels, Ph.D., MPH

PENNSYLVANIA
The Honorable Edward Rendell, Governor, 717/787-2500

Health

Bureau of Health Planning, Pennsylvania Department of Health, Health and Welfare Building, Room 1033, P.O. Box 90, Harrisburg, PA 17120; tel. 717/772–5298; FAX. 717/705–6525; Joseph B. May, Director

Department of Health, Bureau of Laboratories, P.O. Box 500, Exton, PA 19341–0500; tel. 610/280–3464; FAX. 610/436–3346; Dr. Nancy Warren, Director

Division of Acute and Ambulatory Care, Pennsylvania Department of Health, Health and Welfare Building, Room 532, Harrisburg, PA 17120; tel. 717/783–8980; FAX. 717/705–6663

Pennsylvania Department of Health, Health and Welfare Building, Suite 802, Harrisburg, PA 17120; tel. 717/787–6436; FAX. 717/787–0191; Calvin B. Johnson, M.D., M.P.H., Secretary

Pennsylvania Department of Health, Division Home Health, 132 Kline Plaza, Suite A, Harrisburg, PA 17104; tel. 717/783–1379; FAX. 717/772–0232; Jan Staloski, Director

Pennsylvania Department of Health, Public Health Programs, 809 Health and Welfare Building, Harrisburg, PA 17120; tel. 717/787–9857; Stephen H. Suroviec, Deputy Secr. for Health Promotion & Disease Prevention

Insurance

Pennsylvania Insurance Department, 1326 Strawberry Square, Harrisburg, PA 17120; tel. 717/783–0442; FAX. 717/772–1969; M. Diane Koken, Insurance Commissioner

Pennsylvania Insurance Department, Office of Rate and Policy Regulation, 1311 Strawberry Square, Harrisburg, PA 17120; tel. 717/783–5079; FAX. 717/787–8555; Gregory Martino, Deputy Insurance Commissioner

Licensing

Bureau of Facility Licensure and Certification, Health and Welfare Building, Room 930, Harrisburg, PA 17120; tel. 717/787–8015; FAX. 717/787–1491; Gerald F. Radke, Bureau Director

Pennsylvania Department of Health, Quality Assurance, Health and Welfare Building, Room 805, P.O. Box 90, Harrisburg, PA 17108; tel. 717/783–1078; FAX. 717/772–6959; Richard H. Lee, Deputy Secretary

Social Services

Office of Children, Youth, and Families, Department of Public Welfare, P.O. Box 2675, Harrisburg, PA 17105–2675; tel. 717/787–4756; FAX. 717/787–0414; Vacant

Office of Income Maintenance, Health and Welfare Building, Room 432, Harrisburg, P, P.O. Box 2675, Harrisburg, PA 17105; tel. 717/783–3063; FAX. 717/787–6765; Kathy Yorkievitz, Deputy Secretary

Office of Mental Health and Substance Abuse Services, Health and Welfare Building, Room 502, P.O. Box 2675, Harrisburg, PA 17120; tel. 717/787–6443; FAX. 717/787–5394; Joan L. Erney, J.D., Deputy Secretary, Mental Health

Office of Vocational Rehabilitation, 1521 North Sixth Street, Harrisburg, PA 17102–2913; tel. 717/787–7312; FAX. 717/772–1629; William A. Gannon, Executive Director

Pennsylvania Department of Health, Bureau of Drug and Alcohol Programs, 02 Kline Plaza, Harrisburg, PA 17104; tel. 717/783–8200; FAX. 717/787–6285; Gene R. Boyle, Director

Pennsylvania Department of Public Welfare, Office of Medical Assistance Programs, Health and Welfare Building, Room 515, Harrisburg, PA 17120; tel. 717/787–1870; FAX. 717/787–4639; David S. Feinberg, Deputy Secretary

Other

Division of Laboratory Improvement, Bureau of Laboratories, 110 Pickering Way, Lionville, PA 19353; tel. 610/280–3464; FAX. 610/594–9763; Joseph W. Gasiewski, Director

RHODE ISLAND
The Honorable Don Carcieri, Governor, 401/222-2080

Health

Department of Health, Three Capitol Hill, Providence, RI 02908–5097; tel. 401/277–2231; FAX. 401/277–6548; Barbara A. DeBuono, M.D., MPH, Director, Health

Rhode Island Department of Health, Three Capitol Hill, Room 401, Providence, RI 02908–5097; tel. 401/222–2231; FAX. 401/222–6548; William J. Waters, Jr., Ph.D., Deputy Director

Rhode Island Department of Health, Division of Family Health, Three Capitol Hill, Room 302, Providence, RI 02908–5097; tel. 401/222–2312; FAX. 401/222–1442; William H. Hollinshead, M.D., MPH, Medical Director

Rhode Island Department of Health, Office of Health Systems Development, Three Capitol Hill, Providence, RI 02908–5097; tel. 401/222–2788; FAX. 401/273–4350; Michael K. Dexter, Chief

Rhode Island Department of Human Services, Division of Health Care Quality, Financing, and Purchasing, 600 New London Avenue, Cranston, RI 02920; tel. 401/464–5274; John Young, Associate Director

Insurance

Division of Insurance, 233 Richmond Street, Suite 233, Providence, RI 02903–4233; tel. 401/277–2223; FAX. 401/751–4887; Charles P. Kwolek, Jr., CPA, Associate Director, Supervisor

Licensing

Division of Professional Regulation, Rhode Island Department of Health, Three Capitol Hill, Suite 104, Providence, RI 02908–5097; tel. 401/222–2827; FAX. 401/222–1272; Russell J. Spaight, Administrator

Social Services

Office of Rehabilitation Services, 40 Fountain Street, Providence, RI 02903; tel. 401/421–7005; FAX. 401/222–3574; Raymond A. Carroll, Administrator

Rhode Island Department of Health, Office of Facilities Regulation, Three Capitol Hill, Providence, RI 02908–5097; tel. 401/222–2566; FAX. 401/222–3999; Raymond Rusin, Chief

Rhode Island Department of Human Division of Health Care Q, 600 New London Avenue, Cranston, RI 02920; tel. 401/464–3575; FAX. 401/464–2174; John Young, Associate Director, Division of Medical Services

Rhode Island Department of Mental Health, Retardation and Hospitals, Barry Hall, 14 Harrington Road, Cranston, RI 02920; tel. 401/462–3201; FAX. 401/462–3204; A. Kathryn Power, Director

Other

Department of Business Regulation, 233 Richmond Street, Suite 237, Providence, RI 02903–4237; tel. 401/222–2246; FAX. 401/222–6098; Barry G. Hittner, Director

SOUTH CAROLINA
The Honorable Mark Sanford, Governor, 803/734-9400

Health

Bureau of Maternal and Child Health, South Carolina Department of Health and Environmental Control, Robert Mills Complex, 1757 Calhoun Street, Columbia, SC 29201; tel. 803/898–0344; FAX. 803/898–2065; Candace Jones, MPH, RD, Acting Director

Department of Health and Environmental Control, 2600 Bull Street, Columbia, SC 29201; tel. 803/898–3300; FAX. 803/898–3323; C. Earl Hunter, Commissioner

Department of Health and Human Services, 1801 Main Street, P.O. Box 8206, Columbia, SC 29202–8206; tel. 803/898–2500; FAX. 803/898–4515; Robert M. Kerr, Director

Division of Preventive and Personal Health, South Carolina Department of Health and Environmental Control, 2600 Bull Street, Columbia, SC 29201; tel. 803/737–4040; FAX. 803/737–4036; Mick Henry, Division Chief

SC. DHEC Health Services Deputy Area, 2600 Bull Street, Columbia, SC 29201; tel. 803/898–0307; FAX. 803/898–0588; Richard L. Hatfield, Assistant Deputy Commissioner Public Health Services

Licensing

Department of Health and Environmental Control, Division of Health Licensing, 2600 Bull Street, Columbia, SC 29201; tel. 803/545–4370; FAX. 803/545–4212; Dennis Gibbs, Director

Social Services

Bureau of Drug Control, South Carolina Department of Health and Environmental Control, 2600 Bull Street, Columbia, SC 29201; tel. 803/896–063; FAX. 803/896–0625; Wilbur L. Harling, Director

LLRSC Board of Nursing, 110 Centerview Drive, Suite 202, Columbia, SC 29210; tel. 803/896–4550; FAX. 803/896–4525; Martha Summer Bursinger, RN, MSN,Med Administrator

South Carolina Commission for the Blind, P.O. Box 79, Columbia, SC 29202–0079; tel. 803/898–8822; FAX. 803/898–8852

South Carolina Department of Alcohol and Other Drug Abuse Services, 101 Business Park Boulevard, Columbia, SC 29203; tel. 803/896–5555; FAX. 803/896–5557; W. Lee Catoe, Director

South Carolina Department of Disabilities and Special Needs, 3440 Harden Street Extension, P.O. Box 4706, Columbia, SC 29240; tel. 803/898–9769; FAX. 803/898–9656; Stan Butkus, PhD, State Director

South Carolina Department of Health and Environmental Control, Bureau Community Health & Chronic Disease Prevention, 1777 St. Julian Place, Columbia, SC 29204; tel. 803/545–4481; FAX. 803/545–4921; Michael D. Byrd, Ph.D.,M.P.H.

South Carolina Department of Health and Human Services, Office of Senior and Long Term Care Services, 1801 Main Street, P.O. Box 8206, Columbia, SC 29202–8206; tel. 803/898–2500; FAX. 803/898–4515; Elizabeth M. Fuller, Deputy Director – Officer

South Carolina Department of Social Services, P.O. Box 1520, Columbia, SC 29202; tel. 803/898–7360; FAX. 803/898–7277; Kim S. Aydlette, State Director

State Department of Mental Health, 2414 Bull Street, P.O. Box 485, Columbia, SC 29202; tel. 803/898–8319; FAX. 803/898–8586; George P. Gintoli, State Director

Vocational Rehabilitation Department, 1410 Boston Avenue, P.O. Box 15, West Columbia, SC 29171–0015; tel. 803/896–6504; FAX. 803/896–6510; Larry C. Bryant, Commissioner

Other

Bureau of Laboratories, P.O. Box 2202, Columbia, SC 29202; tel. 803/935–7045; FAX. 803/935–7357; Sarah J. Robinson, Acting Chief

SOUTH DAKOTA
The Honorable Mike Rounds, Governor, 605/773-3212

Health

Division of Developmental Disabilities, Hillsview Plaza, E. Highway 34, c/o 500 East Capitol, Pierre, SD 57501–5070; tel. 605/773–3438; FAX. 605/773–7562; Wanda Seiler, Director

© 2005 AHA Guide

Division of Health Systems Development and Regulation, South Dakota Department of Health, Health Building, 600 East Capitol, Pierre, SD 57501; tel. 605/773-3364; FAX. 605/773-5904; Kevin Forsch, Division Director

South Dakota Department of Health, 600 East Capitol, Pierre, SD 57501-2536; tel. 605/773-3361; FAX. 605/773-5683; Doneen B. Hollingsworth, Secretary of Health

South Dakota Department of Health, Division of Health and Medical Services, 615 East Fourth Street, Pierre, SD 57501; tel. 605/773-3737; FAX. 605/773-5942; Laurie Gill, Director

Licensing

Office of Health Care Facilities Licensure and Certification, State Department of Health, 615 E. Fourth Street, Pierre, SD 57501; tel. 605/773-3356; FAX. 605/773-6667; Dan Thayer, Administrator

Social Services

Department of Human Services, East Highway 34, Hillsview Plaza, c/o 500 East Capitol, Pierre, SD 57501; tel. 605/773-5990; FAX. 605/773-5483; John N. Jones, Secretary

Department of Social Services, 700 Governors Drive, Pierre, SD 57501-2291; tel. 605/773-3165; FAX. 605/773-4855; Deborah K. Bowman, Secretary

Division of Alcohol and Drug Abuse, 3800 East Highway 34, Hillsview Plaza, Pierre, SD 57501; tel. 605/773-3123; FAX. 605/773-7076; Gilbert Sudbeck, Director

Office of Medical Services, 700 Governor's Drive, Pierre, SD 57501-2291; tel. 605/773-3495; FAX. 605/773-5246; Damian Prunty, Administrator

TENNESSEE
The Honorable Phil Bredesen, Governor, 615/741-2001

Health

Department of Health, Cordell Hull Building, 425 Fifth Avenue, N., Nashville, TN 37247-0101; tel. 615/741-3111; FAX. 615/741-2491; Kenneth S. Robinson, M.D., Commissioner

Licensing

Board for Licensing Health Care Facilities, Cordell Hull Building, 425 Fifth Avenue, N., Nashville, TN 37247-0530; tel. 615/741-7221; FAX. 615/741-7051; Katy Gammon, Director

Department of Health, Bureau of Health Licensure and Regulation, Cordell Hull Building, 425 Fifth Avenue, N., Nashville, TN 37247-0501; tel. 615/741-8402; FAX. 615/741-5542; Judy Eads, Assistant Commissioner

Tennessee Medical Laboratory Board, Cordell Hull Building, 425 Fifth Avenue, N., Nashville, TN 37247-1010; tel. 615/532-5128; FAX. 615/532-5369

Social Services

Bureau of Alcohol and Drug Abuse Services – TN Dept. of Health, Cordell Hull Building, 425 Fifth Avenue North, Nashville, TN 37247-4401; tel. 615/741-1921; FAX. 615/532-2419; Stephanie W. Perry, M.D., Assistant Commissioner

Department of Children's Services, Program Operations, 3712 Middlebrook Pk., Knoxville, TN 37921; tel. 865/594-7101; FAX. 865/637-8824; Cathy R. Smith, Assistant Commissioner, Department

Division of Health Care Facilities, Cordell Hull Building, 426 Fifth Avenue N., 1st Floor, Nashville, TN 37247-0508; tel. 615/741-7221; FAX. 615/741-7051; Kennard Murray, Director

Division of Rehabilitation Services, Citizens Plaza State Office Building, 15th Floor, Nashville, TN 37248-0060; tel. 615/313-4714; FAX. 615/741-4165; Carl Brown, Assistant Commissioner

Family Assistance, 400 Deaderick Street, Nashville, TN 37248-0070; tel. 615/313-5652; FAX. 615/313-6639; Susan Cowden, Director

Medicaid/TennCare, 729 Church Street, Nashville, TN 37247-6501; tel. 615/741-0213; FAX. 615/741-0882; Manny Martins, Deputy Commissioner

Tennessee Commission on Aging and Disability, 500 Deaderick Street, Ninth Floor, Nashville, TN 37243-0860; tel. 615/741-2056; FAX. 615/253-2302; Nancy Peace, Executive Director

Tennessee Department of Human Services, 400 Deaderick Street, Nashville, TN 37248; tel. 615/741-3241; FAX. 615/741-4165; Robert A. Grunow, Commissioner

Tennessee Department of Mental Health and Developmental Disabilities, Cordell Hull Building, 3rd floor, 425 Fifth Avenue, N, Nashville, TN 37243-0675; tel. 615/532-6500; FAX. 615/532-6514; Virginia Trotter Betts, Commissioner

Tennessee Rehabilitation Center, 460 Ninth Avenue, Smyrna, TN 37167; tel. 615/459-6811; FAX. 615/355-1373; David Holmes, Superintendent

Other

Bureau of Administrative Services, Tennessee Department of Health, Andrew Johnson Tower, Tenth Floor, Nashville, TN 37247-0301; tel. 615/741-3151; FAX. 615/253-1998; Trent Ridley, Assistant Commissioner

Tennessee Department of Environment and Conservation, L&C Annex, 1st Floor, 401 Church Street, Nashville, TN 37243-1530; tel. 615/532-0114; FAX. 615/532-0120; Karen Stachowski, Deputy Commissioner

TEXAS
The Honorable Rick Perry, Governor, 512/463-2000

Health

Bureau of Children's Health, (Texas Department of Health), 1100 West 49th Street, Austin, TX 78756; tel. 512/458-7700; FAX. 512/458-7203; L. Jann Melton-Kissel

Department of State Health Services, State Hospital Section, 909 West 45th Street, Austin, TX 78751; tel. 512/206-4855; FAX. 512/206-4774; Tex Killion, Deputy Medical Director for Administration

Health & Human Services Commission, 4900 N. Lamar, 4th Floor, Austin, TX 78751; tel. 512/424-6517; FAX. 512/424-6585; Randy P. Washington, Deputy Commissioner, Health Care

Texas Department of Health, 1100 West 49th Street, Austin, TX 78756; tel. 512/458-7375; FAX. 512/458-7477; Charles E. Bell, M.D., Executive Deputy Commissioner

Texas Department of Health, Center For Health Statistics, 1100 West 49th Street, Austin, TX 78756; tel. 512/458-7261; FAX. 512/458-7344; Director

Texas Department of Health, Health Facility Licensing and Compliance Division, 1100 West 49th Street, Austin, TX 78756; tel. 512/834-6650; FAX. 512/834-6653; Nance Stearman, RN, M.S.N., Director

Insurance

Texas Department of Insurance, P.O. Box 149104, Mail Code 106-1A, Austin, TX 78714-9104; tel. 512/322-3401; FAX. 512/322-3552; Ana M. Smith-Daley, Deputy Commissioner, Life/Health Division

UTAH
The Honorable Olene Walker, Governor, 801/538-1000

Health

Utah Department of Health, P.O. Box 14100, Salt Lake City, UT 84114-1000; tel. 801/538-6111; FAX. 801/538-6306; Rod L. Betit, Executive Director

Utah Department of Health, Bureau of Licensing, Box 142003, Salt Lake City, UT 84114-2003; tel. 801/538-6152; FAX. 801/538-6325; Debra Wynkoop, Director

Utah Department of Health, Community and Family Health Services Division, P.O. Box 142001, Salt Lake City, UT 84114-2001; tel. 801/538-6901; FAX. 801/538-6510; George Delavan, M.D., Director

Utah Department of Health, Division of Epidemiology and Laboratories, 46 North Medical Drive, Salt Lake City, UT 84113; tel. 801/584-8400; FAX. 801/584-8486; Charles D. Brokopp, Dr.P.H., Director

Utah Department of Health, Office of Primary Care and Rural Health, P.O. Box 142005, Salt Lake City, UT 84114-2005; tel. 801/538-6113; FAX. 801/538-6387; Don Beckwith, Manager

Insurance

Insurance Department, State Office Building, Suite 3110, Salt Lake City, UT 84114; tel. 801/538-3800; FAX. 801/538-3829; Merwin U. Stewart, Insurance Commissioner

Licensing

Division of Occupational and Professional Licensing, Heber M. Wells Building, 160 East 300 South, Salt Lake City, UT 84114-6741; tel. 801/530-6628; FAX. 801/530-6511; J. Craig Jackson, Division Director

Social Services

Department of Human Services, 120 North 200 West #319, Salt Lake City, UT 84103; tel. 801/538-4001; FAX. 801/538-4016; Lisa-Michele Church

Division of Aging and Adult Services, 120 North 200 West, Room 325, Salt Lake City, UT 84103; tel. 801/538-3910; FAX. 801/538-4395; Alan K. Ormsby

Division of Child and Family Services, 120 North. 200 W., Suite 225, Salt Lake City, UT 84103; tel. 801/538-4100; FAX. 801/538-3993; Richard Anderson, Director

Division of Health Care Financing (Utah Medicaid), P.O. Box 143101, Salt Lake City, UT 84114-3101; tel. 801/538-6406; FAX. 801/538-6099; Michael J. Deily, Director

Division of Services for People With Disabilities, 120 North 200 West, Suite 411, Salt Lake City, UT 84103; tel. 801/538-4200; FAX. 801/538-4279; George Kelner Ph.D

Mental Health, P.O. Box 45500, Salt Lake City, UT 84145-0500; tel. 801/538-4270; Paul Thorpe, Director

Utah Division of Substance Abuse, 120 North 200 West, Room 209, Salt Lake City, UT 84103; tel. 801/538-3939; FAX. 801/538-9892; Randall W. Bachman, M. Ed.

Utah State Office of Rehabilitation, 250 East 500 South, P.O.Box 1444200, Salt Lake City, UT 84114-4200; tel. 801/538-7530; FAX. 801/538-7522; Blaine Petersen, Ed.D., Executive Director

Youth Corrections, P.O. Box 45500, Salt Lake City, UT 84145-0500; tel. 801/538-4330; FAX. 801/538-4334; Gary K. Dalton, Director

Other

Department of Environmental Quality, 168 No 1950 West, Salt Lake City, UT 84116; tel. 801/536-4400; FAX. 801/536-0061; Dianne R. Nielson, Ph.D., Executive Director

VERMONT
The Honorable James H. Douglas, Governor, 802/828-3333

Health

Department of Developmental and Mental Health Services, Weeks Building, 103 South Main Street, Waterbury, VT 05671-1601; tel. 802/241-2610; FAX. 802/241-1129; Susan W. Besio, PhD, Commissioner

Environmental Health Division, 108 Cherry Street, P.O. Box 70, Burlington, VT 05402; tel. 802/863-7220; FAX. 802/863-7425; William C. Bress, Ph. D., Director

Vermont Department of Health, 108 Cherry Street, P.O. Box 70, Burlington, VT 05402; tel. 802/863-7280; FAX. 802/863-7425; Paul E. Jarris, MD, MBA, Commissioner

Vermont Department of Health, Division of Community Public Health, 108 Cherry Street, P.O. Box 70, Burlington, VT 05402-0070; tel. 802/863-7347; FAX. 802/863-7229; Patricia Berry, Director

Vermont Department of Health, Division of Health Surveillance, 108 Cherry Street, P.O. Box 70, Burlington, VT 05402; tel. 802/863-7246; FAX. 802/652-4157; William K. Apao, Ph.D., Director of Health Surveillance

Vermont Department of Health, Division of Health Surveillance, Public Health Statistics, 108 Cherry Street, P.O. Box 70, Burlington, VT 05402-0070; tel. 802/863-7300; FAX. 802/865-7701; Jeanette Voas, Health Surveillance Biostatistician

Vermont Department of Health Laboratory, 195 Colchester Avenue, P.O. Box 1125, Burlington, VT 05402-1125; tel. 802/863-7335; FAX. 802/863-7632; Mary Colotti, MS, Director

Insurance

Department of Banking, Insurance, Securities & Health Care Adm., 89 Main Street, Drawer 20, Montpelier, VT 05620-3101; tel. 802/828-3301; FAX. 802/828-3306; John P. Crowley, Commissioner

Section C

Licensing

Licensing and Protection, Ladd Hall, 103 South Main Street, Waterbury, VT 05671–2306; tel. 802/241–2345; FAX. 802/241–2358; Laine Lucenti, Director

Vermont Department of Aging and Independent Living, Division of Licensing and Protection, Ladd Hall, 103 South Main Street, Waterbury, VT 05671–2306; tel. 802/241–2345; FAX. 802/241–2358; Laine Lucenti, RN, Director

Social Services

Agency of Human Services, 103 South Main Street, Waterbury, VT 05676; tel. 802/241–2220; FAX. 802/241–2979; Cornelius Hogan, Secretary

Department for Children and Families, 103 South Main Street, Osgood Building 3rd floor, Waterbury, VT 05671–2401; tel. 802/241–2100; FAX. 802/241–2980; James L. Morse, Commissioner

Department of Social Welfare, 103 South Main Street, Waterbury, VT 05671–1201; tel. 802/241–2853; FAX. 802/241–2830; M. Jane Kitchel, Commissioner

Division of Alcohol and Drug Abuse Programs, 108 Cherry Street, Burlington, VT 05401; tel. 802/651–1550; FAX. 802/651–1573; Barbara Cimaglio, Director

Office of Vermont Health Access/Medicaid, 103 South Main Street, Waterbury, VT 05671–1201; tel. 802/241–2880; FAX. 802/241–2897; Paul Wallace–Brodeur, Director

Vocational Rehabilitation Division, 103 South Main Street, Waterbury, VT 05671–2303; tel. 802/241–2186; FAX. 802/241–3359; Diane P. Dalmasse, Director

VIRGINIA

The Honorable Mark Warner, Governor, 804/786–2211

Health

State Department of Health, Main Street Station, P.O. Box 2448, Richmond, VA 23218; tel. 804/786–3561; FAX. 804/786–4616; Robert B. Syroube, M.D., MPH, State Health Commissioner

Insurance

Bureau of Insurance, Virginia State Corporation Commission, P.O. Box 1157, Richmond, VA 23218; tel. 804/371–9691; FAX. 804/371–9944; Life and Health Consumer Services Section

State Corporation Commission Bureau of Insurance, Company Licensing and Regulatory Compliance Section, P.O. Box 1157, Richmond, VA 23209; tel. 904/371–9636; FAX. 904/371–9396; Andy Delbridge, Supervisor

State Corporation Commission–Bureau of Insurance, P.O. Box 1157, Richmond, VA 23218; tel. 804/371–9869; FAX. 804/371–9511; Douglas C. Stolte, Deputy Insurance Commissioner

Licensing

Center for Quality Health Care Services and Consumer Protection, Virginia Department of Health, 3600 Centre, Suite 216, 3600 West Broad Street, Richmond, VA 23230; tel. 804/367–2102; FAX. 804/367–2149; Nancy R. Hofheimer, Director

Social Services

Children with Special Health Care Needs Program, 109 Governor Street, Eighth Floor, Richmond, VA 23218; tel. 804/864–7706; FAX. 804/846–7723; Nancy R. Bullock, RN, MPH, Director

Department for the Aging, 1600 Forest Avenue, Suite 102, Richmond, VA 23229; tel. 804/662–9333; FAX. 804/662–9354; Jay W. DeBoer,Commissioner

Department of Medical Assistance Services, 600 East Broad Street, Suite 1300, Richmond, VA 23219; tel. 804/786–8099; FAX. 804/371–4981; Patrick W. Finnerty, Director

Department of Mental Health, Mental Retardation and Substance Abuse Services, 1220 Bank Street, P.O. Box 1797, Richmond, VA 23218–1797; tel. 804/786–3921; FAX. 804/371–6638; James S. Reinhard, M.D., Commissioner

Department of Rehabilitative Services, 8004 Franklin Farms Drive, Richmond, VA 23229; tel. 804/662–7000; FAX. 804/662–9532; James A. Rothrock, Commissioner

Division of Women's and Infants' Health, 109 Governor Street, P.O. Box 2448, Richmond, VA 23218–2448; tel. 804/864–7750; FAX. 804/864–7771; Joan Corder-Mabe, RNC, M.S., OGNP, Director

Virginia Department of Social Services, 730 East Broad Street, Richmond, VA 23219–1949; tel. 804/692–1900; FAX. 804/692–1964; Maurice A. Jones, Commissioner

WASHINGTON

The Honorable Christine Gregoire, Governor, 360/902–4111

Health

Department of Health, Facilities and Services Licensing, P.O. Box 47852, Olympia, WA 98504–7852; tel. 206/705–6652; FAX. 206/705–6654; Kathy Stout, Director

Department of Health, Office of Emergency Medical Services and Trauma System, P.O. Box 47853, Olympia, WA 98504–7853; tel. 360/236–2828; FAX. 360/236–2830; Janet Griffith,Kastl, Director

Washington State Department of Health, P.O. Box 47812, Mail Stop 7812, Olympia, WA 98504–7812; tel. 206/705–6060; FAX. 206/705–6043; Dan Rubin, Director, Special Projects Office

Insurance

Office of the Insurance Commissioner, Insurance Building, P.O. Box 40258, Olympia, WA 98504–0258; tel. 360/753–7300; FAX. 360/586–3109; Mike Kreidler, Insurance Commissioner

Licensing

Health Systems Quality Assurance, Department of Health, 310 Israel Rd. SE, Mail Stop 47850, Tumwater, WA 98504–7850; tel. 360/236–4600; FAX. 360/236–4626; Laurie Jinkins, Assistant Secretary

Social Services

Division of Alcohol and Substance Abuse, P.O. Box 45330, Mail Stop 45330, Olympia, WA 98504–5330; tel. 360/438–8200; FAX. 360/438–8078; Ken Stark, Director

Division of Vocational Rehabilitation, P.O. Box 45340, Olympia, WA 98504–5340; tel. 360/438–8000; FAX. 360/438–8007; Michael O'Brien, Director

Medical Assistance Administration, P.O. Box 45080, Olympia, WA 98504–5080; tel. 360/725–1867; FAX. 360/902–7855; Doug Porter, Assistant Secretary

State Department of Social and Health Services, P.O. Box 45500, Olympia, WA 98504–5500; tel. 360/725–1863; FAX. 360/586–7498; Douglas Porter, Assistant Secretary, Medical Assistance Administration

Other

Washington State Nursing Care Quality Assurance Commission, 310 Isreal Road, P.O. Box 47864, Tumwater, WA 98504–7864; tel. 360/236–4713; FAX. 360/236–4738; Paula R. Meyer, MSN, Executive Director

WEST VIRGINIA

The Honorable Joe Manchin III, Governor, 304/558–2000

Health

Bureau for Public Health, 350 Capital Street, Room 702, Charleston, WV 25301; tel. 304/558–2971; FAX. 304/558–1035; Chris Curtis, M.P.H., Acting Commissioner

Children's Specialty Care, 350 Capitol Street, Room 427, Charleston, WV 25301; tel. 304/558–5388; FAX. 304/558–2866; Janet E. Lucas, Director

Department of Health and Human Resources, Capitol Complex, Building Three, Room 206, Charleston, WV 25305; tel. 304/558–0685; FAX. 304/558–1130; Martha Yeager Walker, Secretary

Office of Community and Rural Health Services, Bureau for Public Health, 350 Capitol Street, Room 515, Charleston, WV 25301–3716; tel. 304/558–3210; FAX. 504/558–1437

Office of Environmental Health Services, Capitol and Washington Streets, 1 Davis Square, Charleston, WV 25301–1798; tel. 304/558–2981; FAX. 304/558–1291; Barbara S. Taylor

West Virginia Department of Health and Human Resources, Division of Primary Care, 350 Capitol Street, Room 515, Charleston, WV 25301–3716; tel. 304/558–4007; FAX. 304/558–1437; Nancy Bazzle, Director

Insurance

Office of the West Virginia Insurance Commissioner, 1124 Smith Street, Charleston, WV 25301; tel. 304/558–2100; FAX. 304/558–1365; J. Leah Cooper, Director, Chief Examiner

West Virginia Insurance Commission, P.O. Box 50540, Charleston, WV 25305–0540; tel. 304/558–3029; FAX. 304/558–0412; Jane L. Cline, Commissioner

Licensing

Office of Chief Medical Examiner, State of West Virginia, 701 Jefferson Road, South Charles, WV 25309; tel. 304/558–3920; FAX. 304/558–7886; James A. Kaplan, M.D., Chief Medical Examiner

Office of Health Facility Licensure and Certification, West Virginia Department of Health and Human Resources, 1 Davis Square, Suite 101, Charleston, WV 25301–1799; tel. 304/558–0050; FAX. 304/558–5607; John Wilkinson, Director

Social Services

Division of Rehabilitation Services, P.O. Box 50890, State Capitol Complex, Charleston, WV 25305–0890; tel. 304/766–4985; FAX. 304/766–4956; Sonja School, Administrator

Division on Alcoholism and Drug Abuse, 350 Capitol Street, Room 350, Charleston, WV 25305; tel. 304/558–2276; FAX. 304/558–1008; Stephen S. Mason, Director

WISCONSIN

The Honorable Jim Doyle, Governor, 608/266–1212

Health

Bureau of Health Services, P.O. Box 7925, Madison, WI 53707–7925; tel. 608/240–5120; FAX. 608/240–3311

Center for Health Statistics, P.O. Box 309, Madison, WI 53701–0309; tel. 608/266–1334; FAX. 608/261–6380; James John Vaura, Director

Division of Public Health, P.O. Box 2659, Madison, WI 53701–2659; tel. 608/266–1251; FAX. 608/267–2832; Herb H. Bostrom, Interim Administrator

Insurance

Office of the Commissioner of Insurance, 125 S. Webster St., P.O. Box 7873, Madison, WI 53707–7873; tel. 608/266–3585; FAX. 608/266–9935; Eileen Mallow, Assistant Deputy Commissioner

Licensing

State of Wisconsin, Department of Regulation and Licensing, 1400 East Washington Avenue, P.O. Box 8935, Madison, WI 53708–8935; tel. 608/266–2112; FAX. 608/267–0644

Social Services

Department of Health and Family Services, P.O. Box 7850, Madison, WI 53707–7850; tel. 608/266–9622; FAX. 608/266–7882; Helene Nelson, Secretary

Division for Learning Support: Equity and Advocacy, Wisconsin Department of Public Instruction, 125 South Webster Street, P.O. Box 7841, Madison, WI 53707–7841; tel. 608/266–1649; FAX. 608/267–3746; Carolyn S. Taylor, Assistant State Superintendent

Division of Health Care Financing (Wisconsin Medicaid), One West Wilson Street, Room 350, P.O. Box 309, Madison, WI 53701–0309; tel. 608/266–8922; FAX. 608/266–1096; Mark B. Moody, Administrator

Division of Vocational Rehabilitation, P.O. Box 7852, Madison, WI 53707–7852; tel. 608/261–0050; FAX. 608/266–1133; Charlene Dwyer, Administrator

Other

State Department of Public Instruction, 125 South Webster Street, P.O. Box 7841, Madison, WI 53707–7841; tel. 608/266–1771; FAX. 608/267–1052; Elizabeth Burmaster, State Superintendent

WYOMING

The Honorable Dave Freudenthal, Governor, 307/777–7434

Health

Children's Special Health, Department of Health, 4020 House Avenue, Cheyenne, WY 82002; tel. 307/777–7941; FAX. 307/777–7215; Dorothy Ailes, Program Manager

Department of Health, 117 Hathaway Building, Cheyenne, WY 82002; tel. 307/777–7656; FAX. 307/777–7439

Mental Health Division, 6101 Yellowstone Road, Suite 220, Cheyenne, WY 82002–0480; tel. 307/777–7094; FAX. 307/777–5580; Chuck Hayes, MSW, ALSW, Administrator

Wyoming Department of Health, Community & Family Health Division, 4020 House Avenue, Cheyenne, WY 82002; tel. 307/777–6004; FAX. 307/777–3617

Licensing

Health Facilities Licensing, Department of Health, Metropolitan Bank Building, Eighth Floor, Cheyenne, WY 82002; tel. 307/777–7123; FAX. 307/777–5970; Charlie Simineo, Program Manager

Social Services

Department of Family Services, Hathaway Building, Third Floor, 2300 Capitol Avenue, Cheyenne, WY 82002–0490; tel. 307/777–7561; FAX. 307/777–7747; Rodger McDaniel, Director

Division of Vocational Rehabilitation, Herschler Building, Room 1100, Cheyenne, WY 82002; tel. 307/777–7386; FAX. 307/777–5939; Jim McIntosh, Administrator

Wyoming Department of Health, Division on Aging, 6101 Yellowstone Road 259B, Cheyenne, WY 82002; tel. 800/442–2766; FAX. 307/777–5340; Beverly Morrow, Administrator

Wyoming Department of Health–Health Care Financing, Office of Medicaid, 6101 Yellowstone Rd., Suite 210, Cheyenne, WY 82002; tel. 307/777–7531; FAX. 307/777–6964; Iris Oleske, State Medicaid Agent

U.S. Associated Areas

GUAM

Social Services

Department of Public Health and Social Services, P.O. Box 2816, Hagatna, GU 96932; tel. 671/735–7102; FAX. 671/734–5910; Peter John D. Camacho, MPH, Acting Director

Division of Public Welfare, Box 2816, Hagatna, GU 96932; tel. 671/735–7274; FAX. 671/734–7015; Diana B. Calvo, Chief Human Services Administrator

PUERTO RICO

Health

Dental Health, Building A–Medical Center, P.O. Box 70184, San Juan, PR 00936; tel. 787/274–7842; FAX. 787/274–6859; Wanda Urbiztondo, D.M.D., MPH, Oral Health Coordinator

Department of Health, Secretary ship for Preventive Medicine and Family Health, Pan–American Health Org., Call Box 70184, San Juan, PR 00936; tel. 787/274–7698; FAX. 787/250–1119; Dr. Raul G. Castellanos Bran, Director, Division of FAA

Environmental Health, Department of Health, Building A, Psiq Hospital, Box 70184, San Juan, PR 00936–0184; tel. 787/274–7798; FAX. 787/758–6285; Alfredo Casta Velez, Assistant Secretary, Environmental Health

Government of Puerto Rico, Department of Health, P.O. Box 70184, San Juan, PR 00936–8184; tel. 787/274–7601; FAX. 787/250–6547; Carmen A. Feliciano–De–Melecio, Secretary of Health

Mental Health and Anti Addiction Services, P.O. Box 21414, San Juan, PR 00928–1414; tel. 787/764–3795; FAX. 787/765–5888; Johnny Rullan, MD, FACPM

Social Services

Department of Family, Call Box 11398, San Juan, PR 00910; tel. 809/721–4624; FAX. 809/723–1223; Yalonda Zayas, Secretary

Vocational Rehabilitation Administration, Department of Labor and Human Resources, PO Box 191118, San Juan, PR 00919–1118; tel. 787/728–3566; FAX. 787/728–7117; Ms. Maria S. Vega, Assistant Administrator for Operations

Other

, Building A–Medical Center, Call Box 70184, San Juan, PR 00936; tel. 787/274–7676; FAX. 787/274–7638; Nitza Pinzon, Assistant Secretary for Administration

Department of Health for the Commonwealth of Puerto Rico, Building A–Medical Center, Call Box 70184, San Juan, PR 00936; tel. 809/274–7604; FAX. 809/250–6547; Jr. Johnny V. Rullan, MD, FACPH, Secretary of Health

VIRGIN ISLANDS

Health

Department of Health, Division of Financial Services, Knud Hansen Complex, St. Thomas, VI 00802; tel. 809/774–3171; FAX. 809/777–5120; Alphonse J. Stalliard, Deputy Commissioner

Division of Environmental Health, John Moorehead Complex, Charlotte Amalie, St. Thomas, VI 00802; tel. 809/774–6880; FAX. 809/776–7899; Ethlyn T. Joseph, Director

Division of Hospitals and Medical Services, Roy Lester Schneider Hospital, 9048 Sugar Estate, St. Thomas, VI 00802; tel. 340/776–8311; FAX. 340/714–6340; Maureen G. Venzen, MPA, Vice President Administration

Prevention, Health, Promotion and Protection, Department of Health, Charles Harwood Hospital, 3500 Richmond Christiansted, St. Croix, VI 00820–4300; tel. 809/773–1311; FAX. 809/772–5895; Olaf G. Hendricks, M.D., Assistant Commissioner

Virgin Islands Department of Health, St. Thomas Hospital, St. Thomas, VI 00802; tel. 809/774–0117; FAX. 809/777–4001; Ralph A. de Chabert, M.D., Acting Commissioner

Social Services

Disabilities and Vocational Rehabilitation Services, Department of Human Services, Knud Hansen Complex–Building A, 1303 Hospital Ground, St. Thomas, VI 00802; tel. 809/774–0930; FAX. 809/774–3466; Beverly C. Plaskett, Administrator

Division of Maternal and Child Health Services, Virgin Islands Department of Health, #31012 Vitaraco Park, Estate Golden Park, St. Croix, VI 00820; tel. 340/773–9924; FAX. 340/713–9928; Mavis Matthew, MD, MPH Director

Division of Mental Health, Alcoholism and Drug Dependency, Department of Health, Barbel Plaza South, 2nd Floor, St. Thomas, VI 00802; tel. 340/774–4888; FAX. 340/774–4701; Jaslene Williams

Virgin Islands Department of Human Services, Knud Hansen Complex, Building A, St. Thomas, VI 00802; tel. 340/774–1166; FAX. 340/774–3466; Sedonie Halbert, Commissioner

Canada

ALBERTA

Social Services

Department of Family and Social Services, 109 Street and 97 Avenue, Edmonton, AB T5K 2B6; tel. 403/427–2606; FAX. 403/427–0954; Dr. Lyle Oberg, Minister

MANITOBA

Health

Department of Health, 302 Legislative Building, Winnipeg, MB R3C 0V8; tel. 204/945–3731; FAX. 204/945–0441; Hon. Jane Purves, Honourable Erie Stefanson, Minister

Social Services

Department of Manitoba Family Services and Housing, 450 Broadway, Room 357 Legislative Building, Winnipeg, MB R3C 0V8; tel. 204/945–4173; FAX. 204/945–5149; Honourable Drew Caldwell

NEWFOUNDLAND

Health

Department of Health and Community Services, Confederation Building (West Block), P.O. Box 8700, St. John's, NF A1B 4J6; tel. 709/729–3124; FAX. 709/729–0121; Elizabeth Marshall, Minister, Health and Community Services

NOVA SCOTIA

Health

Department of Health, P.O. Box 488, Halifax, NS B3J 2R8; tel. 902/424–3377; FAX. 902/424–0559; Hon. Angus MasIsaac

PRINCE EDWARD ISLAND

Social Services

Department of Health and Social Services, Sullivan Building, Second Floor, P.O. Box 2000, Charlottetown, PE C1A 7N8; tel. 902/368–4930; FAX. 902/368–4969; The Honorable Walter A. McEwen, Q.C./Minister

QUEBEC

Social Services

Ministry of Health and Social Services, Ministere de la Sante et des Services Sociaux, Quebec, PQ G1S 2M1; tel. 418/643–3160; FAX. 418/644–4534; Jean Rochon, Minister

SASKATCHEWAN

Health

Department of Health, 3475 Albert Street, Third Floor, Regina, SK S4S 6X6; tel. 306/787–3696; FAX. 306/787–8310; Minister, The Hon. John T. Nilson, Q.C.

Section C

State Government Agencies for HMO's

United States

ALABAMA: Department of Insurance, 201 Monroe Street, Suite 1700, Montgomery, AL 36104; tel. 334/269–3550; FAX. 334/241–4192; Walter Bell, Commissioner

ALASKA: Alaska Division of Insurance, P.O. Box 110805, Juneau, AK 99811-0805; tel. 907/465–2596; FAX. 907/465–3422; Linda Hall, Director

ARIZONA: Department of Insurance, 2910 North 44th Street, Suite 210, Phoenix, AZ 85018; tel. 602/912–8460; FAX. 602/912–8453; Alexandra Shafer, Assistant Director, Life and Health

ARKANSAS: Arkansas Insurance Department, 1200 West Third Street, Little Rock, AR 72201-1904; tel. 501/371–2800; FAX. 501/371–2618; Julie Benafield Bowman, Insurance Commissioner

CALIFORNIA: Department of Corporations, Health Care Service Plan Division, 3200 West 4th Street, Suite 750, Los Angeles, CA 90010; tel. 213/897–8921; FAX. 213/576–7660; Gary G. Hagen, Assistant Commissioner

COLORADO: Department of Regulatory Agencies, Colorado Division of Insurance, 1560 Broadway, Suite 850, Denver, CO 80202; tel. 303/894–7499; FAX. 303/894–7455; Doug Dean, Commissioner

CONNECTICUT: Department of Insurance, P.O. Box 816, Hartford, CT 06142-0816; tel. 860/297–3800; FAX. 860/566–7410; Susan P. Cogswell, Commissioner

DELAWARE: Department of Health and Social Services, Office of Health Facilities Licensing and Certification, 2055 Limestone Road, Suite 200, Wilmington, DE 19808; tel. 302/995–8521; FAX. 302/995–8529; Mary Peterson, Director

DISTRICT OF COLUMBIA: District of Columbia Department of Insurance and Securities and Banking, 810 1st Street NE, Room 701, Washington, DC 20002; tel. 202/727–8000; FAX. 202/535–1197; Florence Thomas,Insurance Operating Specialist,MGR.,Comsumer Services Branc

FLORIDA: Florida Department of Insurance, Bureau of Life and Health Insurer Solvency and Market Con, 200 East Gaines, Tallahassee, FL 32399-0327; tel. 850/413–3153; FAX. 850/413–9019; Beth Vecchioli, Director

GEORGIA: Department of Insurance, Two Martin Luther King Jr. Drive, Suite 604 West Tower, Atlanta, GA 30334; tel. 404/656–2074; FAX. 404/657–7743; John Oxendine, Commissioner

HAWAII: State of Hawaii Department of Labor and Industrial Relations, Disability Compensation Division, P.O. Box 3769, Honolulu, HI 96812; tel. 808/586–9151; FAX. 808/586–9219; Gary S. Hamada, Administrator

IDAHO: Department of Insurance, 700 West State Street, Third Floor, Boise, ID 83720-0043; tel. 208/334–4250; FAX. 208/334–4398; Joan Krosch, Ins. Policy/Progeram Spec. Health

ILLINOIS: Department of Insurance, 320 West Washington Street, Fourth Floor, Springfield, IL 62767-0001; tel. 217/782–6369; FAX. 217/524–2122; David E. Grant, Health Care Coordinator

INDIANA: Department of Insurance, 311 West Washington Street, Suite 300, Indianapolis, IN 46204; tel. 317/232–5695; FAX. 317/232–5251; Joy Long, Health Deputy

IOWA: Iowa Department of Commerce, Division of Insurance, 330 Maple, Des Moines, IA 50319-0065; tel. 515/281–5705; FAX. 515/281–3059; Susan E. Voss, Commissioner

KANSAS: Kansas Insurance Department, 420 Southwest Ninth Street, Topeka, KS 66612; tel. 785/296–3071; FAX. 785/296–2283; Sandy Praeger, Commissioner

KENTUCKY: Department of Insurance, Life and Health Division, 215 West Main Street, P.O. Box 517, Frankfort, KY 40602; tel. 502/564–6088; FAX. 502/564–2728; Carrie Banahan, Director

LOUISIANA: Department of Insurance, Attn: Company Licensing Division, P.O. Box 94214, Baton Rouge, LA 70804; tel. 225/219–4318; FAX. 225/219–9322; Mike Boutwell, Company Licensing Coordinator

MAINE: Department of Professional and Financial Regulation, Bureau of Insurance, 34 State House Station, Augusta, ME 04333; tel. 207/624–8416; FAX. 207/624–8599; Michael F. McGonigle, Senior Insurance Analyst

MASSACHUSETTS: Division of Insurance, 1 South State, Boston, MA 02110-2223; tel. 617/521–7794; FAX. 617/521–7575; Julienne Bowler

MICHIGAN: Department of Community Health, Bureau of Medicaid Program Operations and Quality Assurance, P.O. Box 30479, 400 S. Pine, Lansing, MI 48909-7979; tel. 517/241–8055; FAX. 517/335–5007; Susan Moran, Director

MINNESOTA: Minnesota Health Technology Advisory Committee (HTAC), 121 East Seventh Place, Suite 400, P.O. Box 64975, St. Paul, MN 55101-0975; tel. 651/282–5600; FAX. 651/282–5628; Brenda Holden, HTAC

MISSISSIPPI: Mississippi Department of Insurance, P.O. Box 79, Jackson, MS 39205; tel. 601/359–3577; FAX. 601/359–2474; J. Mark Haire, Special Assistant Attorney General

MISSOURI: Department of Insurance, Division of Market Regulation, Managed Care Section, P.O. Box 690, Jefferson City, MO 65102; tel. 573/751–4126; FAX. 573/526–6075; Molly White, Research Analyst 3

MONTANA: Montana State Auditor, Insurance Department, 840 Helena Avenue, Helena, MT 59604-4009; tel. 406/444–4372; FAX. 406/444–3497; Steve Mattahews, Chief Examiner

NEBRASKA: Department of Insurance, 941 O Street, Suite 400, Lincoln, NE 68508; tel. 402/471–2201; FAX. 402/471–4610; L Tim Wagner, Director

NEVADA: Nevada Division of Insurance, 788 Fairview Drive, Suite 300, Carson City, NV 89701; tel. 775/687–4270; FAX. 775/687–3937; Alice A. Molasky-Arman, Esq., Commissioner

NEW HAMPSHIRE: Department of Health and Human Services, Office of Community and Public Health, Medicaid Administration Bureau, 6 Hazen Drive, Concord, NH 03301-6521; tel. 603/271–4365; FAX. 603/271–4376; Diane Kemp, Administrator

NEW JERSEY: Department of Health, Office of Managed Care, P.O. Box 360, Room 603, Trenton, NJ 08625-0360; tel. 609/588–2510; FAX. 609/633–0807; Sylvia Allen-Ware, Director

NEW MEXICO: Public Regulation Commission, Insurance Division, P.O. Box 1269, Santa Fe, NM 87504; tel. 505/827–4601; FAX. 505/827–4734; Eric P. Serna, Superintendent

NEW YORK: The Bureau of Managed Care Certification and Surveillance, Empire State Plaza, Corning Tower, Room 1911, Albany, NY 12237; tel. 518/474–5515; FAX. 518/473–3583; Vallencia Lloyd, Director

NORTH CAROLINA: Department of Insurance, Financial Evaluation Division, P.O. Box 26387, Raleigh, NC 27611; tel. 919/733–7230; FAX. 919/715–6811; Jackie Obusek, Financial Analyst

NORTH DAKOTA: North Dakota Department of Insurance, State Capitol, 600 East Boulevard, 5th Floor, Bismarck, ND 58505-0320; tel. 701/328–2440; FAX. 701/328–4880; Jim Poolman, Commissioner

OHIO: Department of Insurance, Office of Life and Health Services, 2100 Stella Court, Columbus, OH 43215-1067; tel. 614/644–3311; FAX. 614/644–2658; Kay Thompson, Chief, Health Division

OKLAHOMA: Oklahoma State Department of Health, 1000 Northeast 10th Street, Oklahoma City, OK 73117-1299; tel. 405/271–5600; FAX. 405/271–7360; Randy Wray, Director of Managed Care

OREGON: Department of Consumer and Business Services, Insurance Division, 350 Winter St. NE #440, Salem, OR 97301-3883; tel. 503/947–7980; FAX. 503/378–4351; Cory Stresinger, Commissioner

PENNSYLVANIA: Pennsylvania Insurance Department, Company Licensing Division, 1345 Strawberry Square, Harrisburg, PA 17120; tel. 717/787–2735; FAX. 717/787–8557; Robert E. Brackbill, Chief of Company Licensing Division

RHODE ISLAND: Department of Business Regulation, Division of Insurance, 233 Richmond Street, Suite 233, Providence, RI 02903-4233; tel. 401/222–2223; FAX. 401/222–5475; Alfonso E. Mastrostefano, Associate Director

SOUTH CAROLINA: Office of Insurer Licensing and Solvency Services, 300 Arbor Lake Drive, Suite 1200, Columbia, SC 29223; tel. 803/737–6221; FAX. 803/737–6232; Timothy W. Campbell, Chief Financial Analyst

SOUTH DAKOTA: Division of Administration, South Dakota Department of Health, 600 East Capitol Avenue, Pierre, SD 57501-2536; tel. 605/773–3361; FAX. 605/773–5683; Jerry Hofer, Division Director

TENNESSEE: Department of Commerce and Insurance, 500 James Robertson Parkway, Nashville, TN 37243-1135; tel. 615/741–2280; FAX. 615/532–2788; Don Spann, Chief Financial Executive

TEXAS: Texas Department of Insurance, Mail Code 103-6A, P.O. Box 149104, Austin, TX 78714-9104; tel. 512/322–4266; FAX. 512/322–4260; Margaret Lazaretti, Deputy Commissioner

UTAH: Utah Insurance Department, State Office Building, Room 3110, Salt Lake City, UT 84114; tel. 801/538–3800; FAX. 801/538–3829; Jilane Whitby, Information Specialist

Section C

VERMONT: Department of Banking, Insurance and Securities, Division of Healthcare Administration, 89 Main Street, Drawer 20, Montpelier, VT 05620-2706; tel. 802/828–2900; FAX. 802/828–2949; Paulette Thabault, Deputy Commissioner

VIRGINIA: State Corporation Commission, Bureau of Insurance, P.O. Box 1157, Richmond, VA 23218; tel. 804/371–9901; FAX. 804/371–9511; Laura Lee Viergever, Senior Financial Analyst

WASHINGTON: Office of the Insurance Commissioner, Insurance Building, P.O. Box 40255, Olympia, WA 98504-0255; tel. 360/664–8002; FAX. 360/586–3535; Sharlene Bowman, Manager, Health Care

WEST VIRGINIA: Insurance Commissioner's Office, Financial Conditions Division, 1124 Smith Street, Charleston, WV 25301; tel. 304/558–2100; FAX. 304/558–1365; Jeffrey W. Van Gilder, Director, Chief Examiner

WISCONSIN: Office of the Commissioner of Insurance, Market Regulation, P.O. Box 7873, Madison, WI 53707-7873; tel. 608/266–3585; FAX. 608/266–9935; Eileen Mallow, Assistant Deputy Commissioner

WYOMING: Department of Insurance, Herschler Building, Third Floor East, Cheyenne, WY 82002; tel. 307/777–7401; FAX. 307/777–5895; Ken Vines, Commissioner

U.S. Associated Areas

GUAM: Department of Public Health and Social Services, Government of Guam, P.O. Box 2816, Agana, GU 96932; tel. 671/735–7102; FAX. 671/734–5910; Peter John D. Camacho,MPH

PUERTO RICO: Aurea Lopez, Chief Examiner, Office of the Commissioner of Insurance, P.O. Box 8330, Fernandez Juncos Station, Santurce, PR 00910-8330; tel. 787/722–8686; FAX. 809/722–4400; Aurea Lopez, Chief Examiner

Section C

State Government Agencies for FASC's

Information for the following list was obtained directly from the agencies. Hospital based ambulatory surgery centers are listed in Section A of AHA Guide and are identified by Facility Code F63. Please refer to that section for information on over 3,500 hospital based ambulatory surgery centers.

United States

ALABAMA
Alabama Department of Public Health, Division of Licensure and Certification, 434 Monroe Street, Montgomery, AL 36130-1701; tel. 334/240–3503; FAX. 334/240–3147; L. O'Neal Green, Director

ARIZONA
Arizona Department of Health Services, Health and Child Care Review Services, 1647 East Morten, Suite 220, Phoenix, AZ 85020; tel. 602/542–1100; FAX. 602/861–0645; Mary Wiley, Assistant Director

ARKANSAS
Department of Health, Division of Health Facility Services, 5800 West 10th Street, Suite 400, Little Rock, AR 72204-9916; tel. 501/661–2201; FAX. 501/661–2165; Renee Mallory, Director

CALIFORNIA
Department of Health Services, Licensing and Certification Program, 1800 Third Street, Suite 210, P.O. Box 942732, Sacramento, CA 94234-7320; tel. 916/445–2070; FAX. 916/327–4355; Brenda Klutz, Director

COLORADO
Department of Health, Division of Health Facilities, 4300 Cherry Creek Drive South, Denver, CO 80246; tel. 303/962–2800; FAX. 303/782–4883; Ellen Manigone, MD, Director

CONNECTICUT
Department of Public Health, Bureau of Healthcare Systems, 410 Capital Avenue, MS#12HCS, Hartford, CT 06134-0308; tel. 860/509–7406; FAX. 860/509–7539; Wendy Furniss,R.N.C.,M.S., Bureau Chief,Bureau of Healthcare Systems

DELAWARE
Department of Health and Social Services, Office of Health Facilities, Licensing and Certification, 2055 Limestone Road, Suite 200, Wilmington, DE 19808; tel. 302/995–8521; FAX. 302/995–8529; Mary Peterson, Director

DISTRICT OF COLUMBIA
Department of Health, Health Regulation Administration, 825 North Capital, NE, Room 2264, Washington, DC 20002; tel. 202/442–5888; FAX. 202/442–9430; Dennis Pope, Administrator

FLORIDA
Division of Health Quality Assurance, Agency for Health Care Administration, Fort Knox Executive Office Center, 2727 Mahan Drive, Suite 214, Tallahassee, FL 32308-5407; tel. 850/487–2527; Peter J. Buigas, Director

GEORGIA
Health Care Section - Georgia Dept. of Human Resources, Office of Regulatory Services, Two Peachtree Street, N.W., Room 33-250, Atlanta, GA 30303-3142; tel. 404/657–5550; FAX. 404/657–8934

HAWAII
Hawaii Department of Health, Office of Health Care Assurance, P.O. Box 3378, Honolulu, HI 96801; tel. 808/586–4080; FAX. 808/586–4791; Dianne Okumura, RSN,MPH, Chief,OHCA

IDAHO
Bureau of Facility Standards, Department of Health and Welfare, P.O. Box 83720, Boise, ID 83720-0036; tel. 208/334–6626; FAX. 208/364–1888; Sylvia Creswell, Supervisor-Non Long Term Care

ILLINOIS
Department of Public Health, Division of Health Care Facilities and Programs, 525 West Jefferson Street, 4th Floor, Springfield, IL 62761; tel. 217/782–7412; FAX. 217/782–0382; Gloria McDowell, Acting Division Chief

INDIANA
Indiana State Department of Health, Division of Acute Care, Two North Meridian Street, 4/A, Indianapolis, IN 46204; tel. 317/233–7474; FAX. 317/233–7157; Mary Azbill, Director

IOWA
Department of Inspection and Appeals, Division of Health Facilities, Lucas State Office Building, Des Moines, IA 50319; tel. 515/281–4115; FAX. 515/242–5022

KANSAS
Kansas Department of Health and Environment, Bureau of Child Care and Health Facilities, 1000 SW Jackson Suite 200, Topeka, KS 66612-1365; tel. 785/296–0131; FAX. 785/291–3419; Charles Moore, Director of Medical Facilities

KENTUCKY
Cabinet for Health and Family Services, Division of Health Care Facilities and Services, 275 East Main, 5th Floor East, Frankfort, KY 40621; tel. 502/564–2800; FAX. 502/564–6546; Jennifer Mitchell, Director

LOUISIANA
Department of Health and Hospitals, Bureau of Health Services Financing-Health Standards Section, P.O. Box 3767, Baton Rouge, LA 70821; tel. 225/342–0415; FAX. 225/342–5292; Lisa Deaton, RN, Manager

MAINE
Division of Licensing and Certification, Department of Human Services, 442 Civic Center Drive, Station 11, Augusta, ME 04333-0011; tel. 207/287–9300; FAX. 207/287–9304; Louis Dorogi,Assistant Director

MARYLAND
Department of Health and Mental Hygiene, Licensing and Certification, 55 Wade Avenue, Cantonville, MD 21228; tel. 410/402–8025; FAX. 410/402–8211; Carol Benner, Director

MASSACHUSETTS
Department of Public Health, Division of Health Care Quality, 10 West Street, Boston, MA 02101-2111; tel. 617/753–8000; Paul Dreyer, Director

MICHIGAN
Department of Community Health, Division of Licensing and Certification, P.O. Box 30664, Lansing, MI 48909; tel. 517/241–2626; FAX. 517/241–2635; Darryl Horton, Director

MINNESOTA
Department of Health, Division of Compliance Monitoring, Licensing and Certification Program, 85 East Seventh Place, Suite 300, St. Paul, MN 55164-0900; tel. 651/215–8719; FAX. 651/215–8709; Carol Hirschfeld, Program Assurance Unit

MISSISSIPPI
Department of Health, Division of Health Facilities Licensure and Certification, P.O. Box 1700, Jackson, MS 39215; tel. 601/576–7300; FAX. 601/576–7230; Karen Selescak, Director

MISSOURI
Missouri Department of Health, Unit of Health Facility Regulation, 1617 Southridge Drive, P.O. Box 570, Jefferson City, MO 65102; tel. 573/751–6303; FAX. 573/526–3621; Terry Wenkel, Health Care Regulatory Supervisor

MONTANA
Quality Assurance Division, Department of Public Health and Human Services, 2401 Colonial Drive, 2nd Floor, P.O. Box 202953, Helena, MT 59620-2953; tel. 406/444–2099; FAX. 406/444–3456; Mary Dalton, Division Administrator

NEBRASKA
Nebraska Department of Health and Human Services Regulation & Licensure, Credentialing Division, 301 Centennial Mall, S. 3rd Floor, P.O. Box 94986, Lincoln, NE 68509-4986; tel. 402/471–2116; FAX. 402/471–3577; Helen L. Meeks, Administrator

NEVADA
Bureau of Licensure & Certification, Nevada Health Division, 1550 E. College Parkway, Suite 158, Carson City, NV 89706-7921; tel. 775/687–4475; FAX. 775/687–6588; Pam Graham, Bureau Chief

NEW HAMPSHIRE
Health and Human Services, 129 Pleasant Street, Concord, NH 03301; tel. 603/271–4592; FAX. 603/271–4968; Bob Ehlers, Bureau Chief

NEW JERSEY
Division of Health Systems Analysis, Certificate of Need and Acute Care Licensing, P.O. Box 360, Trenton, NJ 08625-0360; tel. 609/292–5960; FAX. 609/292–3780; John A. Calabria, Director

NEW MEXICO
Department of Health and Environment, Health Facility Licensing and Certification Bureau, 525 Camino de los Marquez, Suite Two, Santa Fe, NM 87501; tel. 505/827–4200; FAX. 505/827–4203; Wilma Hammer, Bureau Chief

NEW YORK
Department of Health, P.O. Box 7126, Albany, NY 12224; tel. 518/473–8600; FAX. 518/439–7200

NORTH CAROLINA
Department of Human Resources, Division of Facility Services, 805 Biggs Drive, P.O. Box 29530, Raleigh, NC 27626-0530; tel. 919/733–7461; FAX. 919/733–8274; Jeff Horton, Bureau Chief

NORTH DAKOTA
North Dakota Department of Health, Health Resources Section, 600 East Boulevard Avenue, Bismarck, ND 58505-0200; tel. 701/328–2352; FAX. 701/328–1890; Darleen Bartz, Chief

OHIO
Division of Quality Assurance, Ohio Department of Health, 246 North High Street, P.O. Box 0118, Columbus, OH 43266-0118; tel. 614/466–7857; FAX. 614/644–0208; Rebecca Maust, Division Chief of Quality

OKLAHOMA
Department of Health, Special Health Services, 1000 Northeast 10th Street, Oklahoma City, OK 73117; tel. 405/271–6576; FAX. 405/271–1308; Gary Glover, Chief, Medical Facilities

OREGON
Health Care Licensure and Certification, Oregon Department of Human Services, 800 Northeast Oregon Street, Suite 640, P.O. Box 14450, Portland, OR 97232; tel. 503/731–4013; FAX. 503/731–4080; Kathleen Smail, Manager

PENNSYLVANIA
Bureau of Quality Assurance, Division of Acute and Ambulatory Care Facilities, Health and Welfare Building, Room 532, Harrisburg, PA 17120; tel. 717/783–8980; FAX. 717/705–6663; Sandra Knoble, Director

RHODE ISLAND
Rhode Island Department of Health, Office Room 306, Three Capitol Hill, Providence, RI 02908-5097; tel. 401/222–2566; FAX. 401/222–3999; Raymond Rusin, Chief

SOUTH CAROLINA
Department of Health and Environmental Control, Division of Health Licensing, 2600 Bull Street, Columbia, SC 29201; tel. 803/545–4370; FAX. 803/737–7212; Jerry Paul, Director

SOUTH DAKOTA
Department of Health, Office of Licensure and Certification, 615 East 4th Street, Pierre, SD 57501; tel. 605/773–3356; FAX. 605/773–6667; Kevin Forsch, Division Director

TENNESSEE
Department of Health, Division of Health Care Facilities, Cordell Hull Building, First Floor, 425 Fifth Avenue, N., Nashville, TN 37247-0508; tel. 615/741–7221; FAX. 615/741–7051; Katy Gammon, Director

TEXAS

Texas Department of Health, Health Facility Compliance Division, 1100 West 49th Street, Austin, TX 78756; tel. 512/834–6650; FAX. 512/834–6653; Nance Stearman, RN, M.S.N., Director

UTAH

Utah Department of Health, Bureau of Licensing, P.O. Box 142003, Salt Lake City, UT 84114-2003; tel. 801/538–6152; FAX. 801/538–6325; Debra Wynkoop, Director

VERMONT

Department of Aging and Disabilities, 103 South Main Street, Osgood, VT 05671; tel. 802/241–2400; FAX. 802/241–2325; Patrick Flood, Commissioner

VIRGINIA

Virginia Department of Health, Center for Quality Health Care Services and Consumer Protection, 3600 Centre, Suite 216, 3600 West Broad Street, Richmond, VA 23230; tel. 804/367–2102; FAX. 804/367–2149; Nancy R. Hofheimer, Director

WASHINGTON

Washington Department of Health, Facilities and Services Licensing, 310 Israel Road, SE, Point Plaza East Building, Tumwater, WA 98504; tel. 360/236–2900; FAX. 360/236–2901; Byron R. Plan,Executive Manager

WEST VIRGINIA

Office of Health Facility Licensure and Certification, West Virginia Division of Health, 1 Davis Square, Suite 101, Charleston, WV 25301-3718; tel. 304/558–0050; FAX. 304/588–2515; Anita Barnhouse, Program Manager

WISCONSIN

Bureau of Quality Assurance, Division of Disability & Elder Services, Department of Health and Family Services, P.O. Box 2969, Madison, WI 53701-2969; tel. 608/267–7185; FAX. 608/267–0352; Susan Schroder, Director, Bureau of Quality Assurance

WYOMING

Wyoming Department of Health, Office of Health Facilities Licensing and Surveys, 2020 Carey Avenue, Eighth Floor, Cheyenne, WY 82001; tel. 307/777–7123; FAX. 307/777–7127; Jean McLean, RD, Acting Manger

U.S. Associated Areas

PUERTO RICO

Department of Health, P. O. Box 70184, San Juan, PR 00936; tel. 809/766–1616; FAX. 809/766–2240; Carmen Feliciano de Melecio, M.D., Secretary of Health

Section C

Freestanding Ambulatory Surgery Centers

The following list of freestanding ambulatory surgery centers was developed with the assistance of state government agencies and the individual facilities listed.

The AHA Guide contains two types of ambulatory surgery center listings; those that are hospital based and those that are freestanding. Hospital based ambulatory surgery centers are listed in section A of the AHA Guide and are identified by Facility Code F63. Please refer to that section for information on the over 3,500 hospital based ambulatory surgery centers.

We present this list simply as a convenient directory. Inclusion or omission of any organization's name indicates neither approval nor disapproval by Health Forum LLC, an American Hospital Association company.

United States

ALABAMA

American Surgery Centers of Alabama, d/b/a American Surgery Center, 2802 Ross Clark Circle, S.W., Dothan, AL 36301; tel. 334/793-3411; FAX. 334/712-0227; Carlotta McCallister, Administrator

Baptist Surgery Center, 2035 East South Boulevard, Montgomery, AL 36111-0000; tel. 334/286-3180; FAX. 334/286-3381; Kay Catliffe, Nurse Manager

Birmingham Endoscopy Center, Inc., 2621 19th Street, South, Homewood, AL 35209; tel. 205/271-8200; Martha Otts,RN Director of Nursing

Birmingham Outpatient Surgery Center, Ltd., d/b/a HealthSouth Outpatient Surgery Center, 2720 University Boulevard, Birmingham, AL 35233; 205/933-0050; FAX. 205/933-8212; Jackie Harrison, RN, Administrator

Columbia Surgicare of Mobile, 2890 Dauphin Street, Mobile, AL 36606; tel. 334/473-2020; FAX. 334/478-6737; Sandy Bunch, Administrator

Dauphin West Surgery Center, 3701 Dauphin Street, Mobile, AL 36608; tel. 334/341-3405; FAX. 334/341-3404; James L. Spires, Executive Director

Decatur Ambulatory Surgery Center, 2828 Highway 31, S., Decatur, AL 35603; tel. 256/340-1212; FAX. 256/340-0252; Andrew Hetrick, Administrator

Dothan Surgery Center, 1450 Ross Clark Circle, S.E.Suite 4, Dothan, AL 36301; tel. 334/793-3442; FAX. 334/793-3318; Denise Harrington, Clinic Administrator

HealthSouth Florence Surgery Center, 103 Helton Court, Florence, AL 35630; tel. 256/760-0672; FAX. 256/766-4547; Pam Watson, Administrator

HealthSouth Gadsden Surgery Center, 418 South Fifth Street, Gadsden, AL 35901; tel. 205/543-1253; FAX. 205/543-1260; Mike Piver, Administrator

HealthSouth Surgical Center of Tuscaloosa, 1400 McFarland Boulevard, N., Tuscaloosa, AL 35406; tel. 205/345-5500; Jeff Hayes, Administrator

Huntsville Endoscopy Center, Inc., 119 Longwood Drive, Huntsville, AL 35801; tel. 205/533-6488; FAX. 205/533-6495; Michael W. Brown, M.D.

Medplex Outpatient Medical Centers, Inc., 4511 Southlake Parkway, Birmingham, AL 35422; tel. 205/985-4398; FAX. 205/985-4486; Dawn Ousley, RN, Administrator

Mobile Surgery Center, 1721 Springhill Avenue, Mobile, AL 36608; tel. 334/438-3614; Julie Saucier, RN, B.S.N., Facility Administrator

Montgomery Eye Surgery Center, 2752 Zelda Road, Montgomery, AL 36106; tel. 334/270-9677; FAX. 334/213-0622; Chris Green, Center Director

Montgomery Surgical Center, 855 East South Boulevard, Montgomery, AL 36116; tel. 334/284-9600; FAX. 334/284-4233; Susan N. Lamar, Administrator

Outpatient Services East, Inc., 52 Medical Park Drive, E., Suite 305, Birmingham, AL 35235; tel. 205/838-3874; FAX. 205/838-6181; James E. Stidham, President and CEO

The Kirklin Clinic, 2000 Sixth Avenue, S., Birmingham, AL 35233; tel. 205/801-8000; Nancy E. Dunlap, Chief Of Staff

The Surgery Center of Huntsville, 721 Madison Street, Huntsville, AL 35801; tel. 205/533-4888; FAX. 205/532-9510; William Sammons, Chief Executive Officer

Tuscaloosa Endoscopy Center, 100 Rice Mine Road, N.E, Suite E, Tuscaloosa, AL 35406; tel. 205/345-0010; FAX. 205/752-1175; A. B. Reddy, M.D., Medical Director

ALASKA

Alaska Women's Health Services, Inc., 4115 Lake Otis Parkway, Anchorage, AK 99508; tel. 907/563-7228; FAX. 907/563-6278; Ellen Cowgill, Administrative Director

Geneva Woods Surgical Center, 3730 Rhone Circle, Suite 100, Anchorage, AK 99508; tel. 907/562-4764; FAX. 907/561-8519; Barbara Cope, Administrator

Pacific Cataract & Laser Institute, 1600 'A' Street, Suite 200, Anchorage, AK 99501; tel. 907/272-2423; FAX. 907/272-2428

ARIZONA

32nd Street Outpatient Surgery Center, 2501 North 32nd Street, Phoenix, AZ 85008; tel. 602/957-6799; FAX. 602/957-0172; Gary W. Hall, M.D., President

A.I.M.S. Outpatient Surgery, 3636 Stockton Hill Road, Kingman, AZ 86401; tel. 602/757-3636; FAX. 602/757-7224; Bill Margita

Adobe Plastic Surgery, 2585 North Wyatt Drive, Tucson, AZ 85712; tel. 602/322-5295; FAX. 602/325-7763; Lucricia Banks, Administrator

Aesthetic Reconstructive Associates, P.C., 7101 E. Jackrabbit Road, Suite C, Paradise Valley, AZ 85253; tel. 480/994-3996; FAX. 480/994-3997; Martin L. Johnson, M.D.

Arizona Diagnostic and Surgical Center, 545 North Mesa Drive, Mesa, AZ 85201; tel. 602/461-4407; FAX. 602/461-4401; David Milton, Administrator

Arizona Medical Clinic, Ltd., 13640 North Plaza Del Rio Boulevard, Peoria, AZ 85381; tel. 602/876-3800; Jan Kaplan, Director, Operations

Arizona Surgical Arts, Inc., 1245 North Wilmot Road, Tucson, AZ 85712; tel. 520/296-7550; FAX. 520/298-5415; Dr. Robert M. Dryden

Banner BaywoodSurgicenter, 6424 East Broadway Road, Suite 102, Mesa, AZ 85206; tel. 480/641-9292; Christine Casto, RN, Administrator

Barnet Dulaney Eye Center, 825 20th Avenue, Safford, AZ 85546; tel. 602/428-6930; FAX. 602/428-7272; Beth Curtis, RN

Barnet Dulaney Perkin Eye Center, 1375 West 16th Street, Yuma, AZ 85364; tel. 602/955-1000; FAX. 602/508-4700; Imelda Kelly, Director of Nursing

Barnet Dulaney Perkins Eye Center, 4800 N. 22nd Street, Phoenix, AZ 85016; tel. 602/955-1000; FAX. 602/508-4700; Ronald W. Barnet, M.D.

Barnet Eye Center-Mesa, 6335 East Main Street, Mesa, AZ 85205; tel. 602/981-1000; FAX. 602/981-0467; Carolyn Miller, Administrator

Carriker Eye Center, 6425 North 16th Street, Phoenix, AZ 85016; tel. 602/274-1703; FAX. 602/274-3216; Richard G. Carriker, M.D.

Cataract Surgery Clinic, 215 South Power Road, Suite 112, Mesa, AZ 85206; tel. 480/981-1345; FAX. 480/981-3721; Robert P. Gervais, M.D., President

CIGNA Healthplan of Arizona, Outpatient Surgery, 755 East McDowell Road, Phoenix, AZ 85006; tel. 602/271-5207; Karen A. Miller, Administrator

Cochise Eye and Laser, PC, 2445 East Wilcox Drive, Sierra Vista, AZ 85635; tel. 520/458-8131; FAX. 520/458-0422; Sheree H. Christian, Administrator

Cottonwood Day Surgery Center, Inc., 55 South Sixth Street, Cottonwood, AZ 86326; tel. 602/634-8330; FAX. 520/634-8522; Linda Davis, Administrator

Desert Mountain Surgicenter, 7776 Pointe Parkway West, Suite 135, Phoenix, AZ 85044; tel. 602/431-8500; FAX. 602/431-1677; David M. Creech, M.D.

Desert Samaritan Surgicenter, 1500 South Dobson Road, Suite 101, Mesa, AZ 85202; tel. 602/835-3590; FAX. 480/835-8774; Brenda Mastopietro, Administrator

Dooley Outpatient Surgery Center, 151 Riviera Drive, Lake Havasu C, AZ 86403; tel. 602/855-9477; FAX. 602/855-2983; William J. Dooley, Jr., M.D., Medical Director

Eye Institute at Boswell, 10541 West Thunderbird Boulevard, Sun City, AZ 85351; tel. 602/933-3402; FAX. 602/972-5014; Jan Zellmann, Administrator

Fifty-Ninth Avenue Surgical Facility, Ltd., 8608 North 59th Avenue, Glendale, AZ 85302; tel. 623/934-3211; FAX. 623/930-1891; Mark Gorman, Administrator

Fishkind and Bakewell Eye Care and Surgery Center, 5599 North Oracle Road, Tucson, AZ 85704; tel. 520/293-6740; FAX. 520/293-6771; Kathleen A. Brown, Surgery Center Supervisor

Footcare Surgi Center, 10249 West Thunderbird, Suite 100, Sun City, AZ 85351; tel. 623/979-4466; FAX. 623/933-8354; Gary N. Friedlander, D.P.M.

Footcare Surgi Center of Northern Arizona, 10 West Columbus Avenue, Flagstaff, AZ 86001; tel. 928/774-4191; Dr. Edward L. Wiebe

Good Samaritan Surgicenter, 1111 B East McDowell Road, Phoenix, AZ 85006; tel. 602/239-2776; FAX. 602/239-5352; Brenda Mastopietro, Administrator

Greenbaum Outpatient Surgery and Recovery Care Center, 3624 Wells Fargo Avenue, Scottsdale, AZ 85251; tel. 602/481-4958; Craig Stout, Administrator

Grimm Eye Clinic and Cataract Institute, P.C., 1502 North Tucson Boulevard, Tucson, AZ 85716; tel. 520/326-4321; FAX. 520/326-4736; Stephen F. Grimm, M.D., President

Havasu Arthritis and Sports Medicine Institute, 1840 Mesquite Avenue, Suite G, Lake Havasu, AZ 86403; tel. 602/453-2663; Marc H. Zimmerman, M.D., Administrator

Havasu Foot and Ankle Surgi-Center, 90 Riviera Drive, Lake Havasu, AZ 86403; tel. 928/855-7800; FAX. 928/855-5392; Robert Novack, D.P.M., Director

HealthSouth Surgery Center of Tucson, 310 North Wilmot Road, Suite 309, Tucson, AZ 85711; tel. 520/296-7080; FAX. 520/886-6518; Deborah Danich, Administrator

Kokopelli Eye Care, P.C., 2820 North Glassford Hill Road, Suite 106, Prescott Vall, AZ 86314; tel. 928/775-5606; FAX. 928/772-4999; John Sabala

Mayo Clinic Scottsdale Ambulatory Surgery Center, 13400 East Shea Boulevard, Scottsdale, AZ 85259; tel. 602/342-2419; FAX. 602/342-2414; Karen A. Biel, Administrator

Metro Surgery Center, L.P., 3131 West Peoria Avenue, Phoenix, AZ 85029; tel. 602/375-1083; FAX. 602/789-6833; Camie Overton, Administrator

Mohave Surgery Center, Inc., 1919 Florence Avenue, Kingman, AZ 86401; tel. 928/753-5454; FAX. 928/753-7790; Lorrie Waits, Administrator

Nogales Medical Clinic Outpatient Surgery, 480 North Morley Avenue, Nogales, AZ 85621; tel. 520/287-2726; Imogene A. Bell, Administrator

Osborn Ambulatory Surgical Center, 3330 North Second Street, Suite 300, Phoenix, AZ 85012; tel. 602/265-0113; FAX. 602/277-8580; Donna Parker, RN, Administrator

Outpatient Surgical Care, Ltd., 1530 West Glendale, Suite 105, Phoenix, AZ 85021; tel. 602/995-3395; FAX. 602/995-1853; Steven Perlmutter, M.D., Medical Director

Outpatient Surgical Center, 456 North Mesa Drive, Mesa, AZ 85201; tel. 602/464-8000; FAX. 602/969-7107; Maddie Dauernheim, Administrator

Phoenix Eye Surgical Center, L.L.C., 5133 North Central Avenue, Suite 100, Phoenix, AZ 85012; tel. 602/279 2434; FAX. 602/279-6475; Beth Hurley, RN Nursing/Business Administrator

Physicians Surgery Center of Tempe, 1940 East Southern Avenue, Tempe, AZ 85282; tel. 602/820–7101; FAX. 602/820–9291; Susan Vitort, Administrator

Prescott Outpatient Surgery Center, Inc., 815 Ainsworth Drive, Prescott, AZ 86301; tel. 602/778–9770; Gail Reidhead, Administrative Director

Prescott Urocenter, Ltd., 811 Ainsworth, Suite 101, Prescott, AZ 86301; tel. 520/771–5282; FAX. 520/771–5283; Jeffrey Sanwick

Scottsdale Eye Surgery Center, P.C., 3320 North Miller Road, Scottsdale, AZ 85251; tel. 480/949–1208; FAX. 480/994–3316; Beth Hurley, RN Nursing/Business Administrator

Southwestern Eye Center, 1055 S. Stapley, Mesa, AZ 85204; tel. 480/833–9100; FAX. 480/833–6000; Penny Gold, RN

Southwestern Eye Center-Casa Grande, 1919 North Trekell Road, Casa Grande, AZ 85222; tel. 520/426–9224; FAX. 520/426–1554; Lothaire Bluth, Administrator

Southwestern Eye Center-Yuma, 2179 West 24th Street, Yuma, AZ 85364; tel. 520/726–4120; FAX. 520/341–0315; Lance K. Wozniak, M.D.

Southwestern Eye Surgicenter-Nogales, 1815 North Mastick Way, Nogales, AZ 85621; tel. 520/761–3533; Pat Bray, Administrator

Summit Surgery & Recovery Care Center, 1485 N. Turquoise Drive, #100, Flagstaff, AZ 86001; tel. 928/214–3211; FAX. 928/214–3219; Jantina Wilson, Administrator

Sun City Endoscopy Center, Inc., 13203 North 103rd Avenue, Suite C 3, Sun City, AZ 85351; tel. 623/972–2116; Jagdish Patel, M.D.

Surgery Center of Peoria, 13260 North 94th Drive, Suite 301, Peoria, AZ 85381; tel. 623/933–2900; FAX. 623/933–0017; Jeff Andrews, Administrator

Surgi-Care, 5115 North Central Avenue, Suite B, Phoenix, AZ 85012; tel. 602/264–1818; FAX. 602/264–2172; Ellison F. Herro, M.D., Administrator

SurgiCenter, 1040 East McDowell Road, Phoenix, AZ 85006; tel. 602/258–1521; FAX. 602/340–0889; Sharon Shafer, RN, Administrator

Surginet, 7725 North 43rd Avenue, Suite 510, Phoenix, AZ 85051; tel. 602/931–9400; FAX. 623/930–9884; Todd Corless, Administrator

Swagel Wootton Eye Center, 220 South 63rd Street, Mesa, AZ 85206; tel. 602/641–3937; FAX. 602/924–5096; S. Joyce Graham

T.A.S.I. Surgery Center, 5585 North Oracle Road, Suite B, Tucson, AZ 85704; tel. 520/293–4730; FAX. 520/293–7561; John A. Pierce, M.D., Medical Director

Tempe Surgical Center, Inc., 2000 East Southern Avenue, Suite 106, Tempe, AZ 85282; tel. 602/838–9313; Richard F. Pavese, M.D.

Thunderbird Samaritan Surgicenter, 5555 B West Thunderbird Road, Glendale, AZ 85306-4622; tel. 602/588–5475; FAX. 602/588–5472; Diane Elmore, RN, Administrator

Valley Outpatient Surgery Center, 160 West University Drive #1, Mesa, AZ 85201; tel. 602/835–7373; FAX. 602/969–7981; Craig R. Cassidy, D.O., President

Vital Sight ASC, dba Eye Institute of Southern Arizona, 5632 East Fifth Street, Tucson, AZ 85711; tel. 520/790–8888; FAX. 520/790–1427; Lianne McDowell, Aministrator

Warner Park Surgery Center, 604 West Warner Road, Building A, Chandler, AZ 85225; tel. 480/899–2571; FAX. 480/899–4263; Marlene Bell

White Mountain Ambulatory Surgery Center, 2650 East Show Low Lake Road, Suite Two, Show Low, AZ 85901; tel. 602/537–4240; William J. Waldo

Yuma Outpatient Surgery Center, L.P., dba HealthSouth Yuma Surgery Center, 2475 Avenue A, Suite B, Yuma, AZ 85364; tel. 928/726–6910; FAX. 928/726–7423; Stephen Renfro, Facility Administrator

ARKANSAS

Arkansas Endoscopy Center, P.A., 9501 Lile Drive, Suite 100, Little Rock, AR 72205; tel. 501/224–9100; FAX. 501/224–0420; Ronald D. Hardin, M.D.

Arkansas Surgery and Endoscopy Center, 4800 Hazel Street, Pine Bluff, AR 71603; tel. 870/536–4800; FAX. 870/534–5535; Syed Samad, M.D., FACP, FACG President

Arkansas Surgery Center, 10 Hospital Circle, Batesville, AR 72501; tel. 870/793–4040; FAX. 870/793–5649; Ronald L. Lowery, M.D., Administrator

BEC Surgery Center, One Mercy Lane, Suite 201, P.O. Box 6409, Hot Springs, AR 71902; tel. 501/623–0755; Terry D. Brown

Boozman-Hof Eye Surgery and Laser Center, LLC, 3737 West Walnut Street, P.O. Box 1353, Rogers, AR 72757-1353; tel. 501/246–1751; FAX. 501/631–2702; Donna R. Acord, Director

Cooper Clinic Ambulatory Surgery Center, 6801 Rogers Avenue, P.O. Box 3528, Fort Smith, AR 72903; tel. 501/452–2077; FAX. 501/452–4425; Jerry Stewart, M.D, Administrator

Dempsey-McKee, Inc., d/b/a McKee Outpatient Surgery Center, 601 East Matthews, Jonesboro, AR 72401; tel. 870/935–6396; FAX. 870/935–4063; Chris Blanchard, Administrator

Doctors Surgery Center PA, 303 West Polk Ave, Suite B, West Memphis, AR 72301; tel. 501/732–2100; Doris Davis, Administrator

Endoscopy Center of Hot Springs, 151 McGowan Court, Hot Springs, AR 71913; tel. 501/623–4101; FAX. 501/623–0103; Barbara Hulsey, Administrator

H. Lewis Pearson Eye Institute, 3211 Surger Hill Road, Texarkana, AR 71854-9265; tel. 501/772–4440; FAX. 501/772–7190; James Loomis, Comptroller

Hot Springs Outpatient Surgery, 100 Ridgeway Boulevard, Suite Seven, Hot Springs, AR 71901; tel. 501/624–4464; FAX. 501/623–7748; James Griffin, Administrator

James Trice, M.D., P.A., d/b/a Digestive Disease Center, 7005 South Hazel Street, Pine Bluff, AR 71603; tel. 870/536–3070; FAX. 870/536–3171; Louis Trice, Administrator

Little Rock Diagnostic Clinic ASC, 10001 Lile Drive, Little Rock, AR 72205; tel. 501/227–8000; Roger J. St. Onge, Administrator

Little Rock Surgery Center, 8820 Knoedl Court, Little Rock, AR 72205; tel. 501/224–6767; FAX. 501/224–8203; Patricia Reedy, Administrator

Lowery Medical/Surgical Eye Center, P.A., 105 Central Avenue, Searcy, AR 72143; tel. 501/268–7154; FAX. 501/268–9071; Benjamin R. Lowery, M.D., Administrator

North Hills Gastroenterology Endoscopy Center, Inc., 3344 North Futrall Drive, Fayetteville, AR 72703; tel. 501/582–7280; FAX. 510/582–7279; William C. Martin, M.D.

Northeast Arkansas Surgery Center, Inc., 505 East Matthews, Suite 103, Jonesboro, AR 72401; tel. 501/972–1723; FAX. 501/972–5941; Teresa D. Brown, Administrator

Ozark Eye Center, 360 Highway Five North, Mountain Home, AR 72653; tel. 870/425–2277; Renea LeMar, Administrator

Physicians Day Surgery Center, 3805 West 28th, Pine Bluff, AR 71603; tel. 501/536–4100; FAX. 501/536–3100; Joan Fletcher, Administrator

Physicians' Surgery Center of Fayetteville, 3873 North Parkview Drive, Suite One, Fayetteville, AR 72703; tel. 479/527–0050; FAX. 479/582–1338; Russ Greene R.N. Administrator

Russellville Surgery Center, L.L.C., 2205 West Main Street, P.O. Box 2654, Russellville, AR 72801; tel. 501/890–2654; FAX. 501/890–5101; James Kennedy, Administrator

South Arkansas Surgery Center, 4310 South Mulberry, Pine Bluff, AR 71603; tel. 501/535–7519; Tammy L. Studdard, Administrator

The Gastro-Intestinal Center, 405 North University, Little Rock, AR 72205; tel. 501/663–1074; James G. Dunlap, Administrator

CALIFORNIA

Los Gatos Surgical Center, 15195 National Avenue, Suite 100, Los Gatos, CA 95032; tel. 408/356–0454; FAX. 408/358–3924; Kate O'Connor, MBA

Advanced Surgery Center, 5771 North Fresno Street, Suite 101, Fresno, CA 93710; tel. 559/448–9900; FAX. 559/448–9546; B. David Singh M.D., Administrator

Aestheticare Outpatient Surgery Center, 30260 Rancho Viejo Road, San Juan Capital, CA 92675; tel. 949/661–1700; FAX. 949/661–4321; Ronald E. Moser, M.D.

Alliance Surgery Center, P.O. Box 22680, LongBeach, CA 90801-5680; tel. 562/446–2229; FAX. 562/446–2239; Judy Hopkins - Chief Operation Officer

Ambulatory Surgical Center of Southern California, Gastroentrology Diagnostic Center, 880 South Atlantic Boulevard G-10, Monterey Park, CA 91754; tel. 213/483–9080; FAX. 213/483–9086; Zelman Weingaren, M.D.

Ambulatory Surgical Center of Zeiter Eye, 117 North San Joaquin Street, Stockton, CA 95202; tel. 209/466–5566; FAX. 209/466–0535; Erin McCarthy/Office Manager

Ambulatory Surgical Center, Inc., 14400 Bear Valley Road, Suite 201, Victorville, CA 92392; tel. 760/951–5162; FAX. 818/985–0055; Garey L. Weber, D.P.M., Administrator

Antelope Valley Surgery Center, 44301 North Lorimer Avenue, Lancaster, CA 93534; tel. 805/940–1112; FAX. 805/940–6856; Yolanda Gomez

Apple Valley Surgery Center, 18122 Outer Highway 18, Apple Valley, CA 92307; tel. 760/946–1170; FAX. 760/946–2646; Jason Barker, Administrator

Arlington Podiatry Surgery Center, 7310 Magnolia Avenue, Riverside, CA 92504; tel. 951/354–8787; FAX. 951/354–0350; James A. De Silva, Administrator

Aspen Outpatient Center, 2750 North Sycamore Drive, Simi Valley, CA 93065; tel. 805/955–6200; FAX. 805/526–0837; Margaret Peterson, PhD

Associates Outpatient Surgery Center, 2128 Eureka Way, Redding, CA 96001; tel. 916/246–9737; FAX. 916/246–4052; Jesse M. Kramer, M.D., Administrator

Bakersfield Endoscopy Center, 1408 Commercial Way, Bakersfield, CA 93309; tel. 661/327–4455; FAX. 661/633–5484; Ramesh Gupta, M.D., Medical Director

Bakersfield Surgery Center, 2120 19th Street, Bakersfield, CA 93301; tel. 661/323–2020; FAX. 661/323–6552; Shirley Skelton, Administrator

Bedford Outpatient Surgery Center, 436 North Bedford, Suite 101, Beverly Hills, CA 90210; tel. 310/777–8820; FAX. 310/777–8890; Patricia Adams, RN,PHD, Director of Nursing

Beverly Hills Ambulatory Surgery Center, Inc., 9201 Sunset Boulevard, Suite 405, Los Angeles, CA 90069; tel. 310/887–1730; FAX. 310/887–1734; Amgad Awad, Administrator

Beverly Hills Outpatient Surgery Center, 250 North Robertson Boulevard, Suite 104, Los Angeles, CA 90211; tel. 310/273–9255; FAX. 310/273–6167; Peter Golden, M.D., Medical Director

Blackhawk Surgery Center, Inc., 4165 Blackhawk Plaza Circle, Suite 195, Danville, CA 94506; tel. 510/736–7881; Molly Healy, Administrator

Bolsa Out-Patient Surgery Center, 10362 Bolsa Avenue, Suite 100, Westminster, CA 92683; tel. 714/775–5690; FAX. 714/775–7405; CO D. L. PHAM, FACOG, M.D., Medical Director

Bonaventure Surgery Center, 221 North Jackson Avenue, San Jose, CA 95116; tel. 408/729–2848; FAX. 408/729–2880; Virginia Field, RN, MBA, Director

Brawley Endoscopy and Surgery Center, 205 West Legion Road, Brawley, CA 92227; tel. 619/351–3655; FAX. 619/351–3675; Mahomed Suliman, M.D., Administrator

Brockton Surgical Center, 5905 Brockton Avenue, Suite B, Riverside, CA 92506; tel. 909/686–5373; FAX. 909/778–9064; Michael N. Durrant, D.P.M., MPH/Donald G. Vogt, D.P.M.

California Eye Clinic, 3747 Sunset Lane, Suite A, Antioch, CA 94509; tel. 510/754–2300; Jean Kemp, Administrator

Camden Surgery Center of Beverly Hills, 414 North Camden Drive, Suite 800, Beverly Hills, CA 90210; tel. 310/859–3991; FAX. 310/859–7126; Yvette L. Lee Administrator

Capistrano Surgicenter, Inc., 30280 Rancho Viejo Road, San Juan Capital, CA 92675; tel. 714/248–5757; FAX. 714/248–9339; Jeffrey A. Klein, Administrator

Cardiac Surgery Mercy Medical Center, 2626 Edith Avenue # D, Redding, CA 96001; tel. 530/243–2626; Edward W. Pottmeyer, M.D.

Center for Ambulatory Medicine and Surgery, 111 East Noble Avenue, Visalia, CA 93277; tel. 559/739–8383; FAX. 209/739–7929; Renda Liden, Administrator

Center for Surgery of Encinitas, 477 North El Camino Real, Suite C-100, Encinitas, CA 92024; tel. 760/942–8800; FAX. 760/942–0106; Chris Clinton,RN, CAPA Administrator

Central Valley Surgery Center, 3796 North Fresno Street, Suite 101, Fresno, CA 93726; tel. 559/228–1491; Mark H. Scoffield, Administrator

Channel Islands Surgicenter, 2300 Wankel Way, Oxnard, CA 93030; tel. 805/485–1908; FAX. 805/485–5767; Mary K. Fish, Administrator

Charles S. Nicholson III D.D.S, 820 34th Street, Suite 201, Bakersfield, CA 93301; tel. 805/327–7878; Charles Nicholson III, Administrator

Children's Surgery Center, 744 Fifty-Second Street, Oakland, CA 94609; tel. 510/428–3133; FAX. 510/450–5606; Terry Hawes, Administrator

Columbia Surgicenter of South Bay, 23500 Madison Street, Torrance, CA 90505; tel. 310/539–5120; Debra Saxton

Columbia West Hills Surgical Center, 7240 Medical Center Drive, West Hills, CA 91307; tel. 818/226–9151; FAX. 818/226–6171; Christine Sherman, Administrator

Community Surgery Centre, 17190 Bernado Center Drive, Suite 100, San Diego, CA 92128; tel. 619/675–3270; FAX. 619/675–3260; Regina S. Boore, B.S.N., M.S.

Crown Valley Surgicenter, 26921 Crown Valley Parkway, Suite 110, Mission Viejo, CA 92691; tel. 949/348–7252; FAX. 949/348–7246; Maurice Chammas, M.D., Administrator

Cypress Outpatient Surgical Center, Inc., 1665 Dominican Way, Suite 120, Santa Cruz, CA 95065; tel. 831/476–6943; FAX. 831/476–1473; Sandra Warren, Administrator

Cypress Surgery Center, 842 South Akers St., Visalia, CA 93277; tel. 559/740–4094; FAX. 559/740–4100; Belen Kerstein, RN, BSN Administrator

Del Rey Surgery Center, 4640 Admiralty Way, Suite 1020, Marina Del Re, CA 90292; tel. 310/305–7570; Lee Estes, Administrator

Desert Surgery Center, 1180 North Palm Canyon, Palm Springs, CA 92262; tel. 760/320–7600; FAX. 760/320–1694; Rosemary Combs, Executive Director

Digestive Disease Center, 24411 Health Center Drive, Suite 450, Laguna Hills, CA 92653; tel. 949/586–9386; FAX. 949/586–0864; Robert Dyer, Medical Director

Downey Surgery Center, 8555 East Florence Avenue, Downey, CA 90240; tel. 310/923–9784; Marisol Magana, Administrator

E. N. T. Facial Surgery Center, 1351 East Spruce, Fresno, CA 93720; tel. 209/432–3724; FAX. 209/432–8579; JoAnn LoForti, RN, Division of Nursing

East Bay Medical Surgical Center, 20998 Redwood Road, Castro Valley, CA 94546; tel. 510/538–2828; FAX. 510/538–2508; Yoshitsugu Teramoto, M.D., Administrator

El Camino Surgery Center, 2480 Grant Road, Mountain View, CA 94040–4300; tel. 650/961–1200; FAX. 650/960–7041; Julie Butner, Executive Director

El Mirador Surgical Center, 1180 North Indian Canyon Drive, Suite 110, Palm Springs, CA 92262; tel. 760/416–4600; FAX. 760/416–4668; Carol Ann Campbell, RN, CNDR

Elite Surgical Centers, Point Loma, 3434 Midway Drive, Suite 1008, San Diego, CA 92110; tel. 619/223–0910; FAX. 619/221–4456; David M. Kupfer, M.D., Medical Director

Endoscopy Center of Chula Vista, 681 Third Avenue, Suite B, Chula Vista, CA 91910; tel. 619/425–2150; Robert Penner, M.D., Administrator

Endoscopy Center of Southern California, 2336 Santa Monica Boulevard, Suite 204, Santa Monica, CA 90404; tel. 310/453–4477; FAX. 310/453–4811; Richard F. Corlin M.D.

Endoscopy Center of the Central Coast, 77 Casa Street, Suite 106, San Luis Obis, CA 93405; tel. 805/541–1021; FAX. 805/541–3142; Sue McMillan, Nurse Manager

Escondido Surgery Center, 343 East Second Avenue, Escondido, CA 92025; tel. 760/480–6606; FAX. 760/480–6671; L. Richard Greenstein, M.D., Medical Director

Eye Center of Northern California Surgicenter, 6500 Fairmount Avenue, Suite Two, El Cerrito, CA 94530; tel. 510/525–2600; FAX. 510/524–1887; William Ellis

Eye Life Institute, 6283 Clark Road, Suite Seven, Paradise, CA 95969; tel. 916/877–2020; FAX. 916/877–4641; Almary Hivale, RN, Administrator

Eye Surgery Center of Southern California, Inc./ Med. Group, DBA: Tri-City Surgery Center, 2023 West Vista Way, Suite E, Vista, CA 92083; tel. 760/941–8152; FAX. 760/941–8967; Daniel Lee, DDS, Medical Director

Eye Surgery Center of the Desert, 39700 Bob Hope Drive, Suite 111, Rancho Mirage, CA 92270; tel. 760/340–3937; FAX. 760/340–1940; Timothy D. Milauskas, Administrator

Feather River Surgery Center, 370 Del Norte Avenue, Yuba City, CA 95991; tel. 916/751–4800; FAX. 916/751–4884; Elizabeth LaBouyer, RN, CNOR, Perioperative Coordinator

Foothill Ambulatory Surgery Center, 1030 East Foothill Boulevard, Suite 101B, Upland, CA 91786; tel. 909/981–5859; FAX. 909/981–8293; Montra M. Kanok, M.D.

Fort Sutter Surgery Center, 2801 K Street, Suite 525, Sacramento, CA 95816; tel. 916/733–5017; FAX. 916/733–8738; Bill Davis, Administrator

Fremont Surgery Center, 2675 Stevenson Boulevard-South, Fremont, CA 94538; tel. 510/793–4987; FAX. 510/793–5084; Debi Ford, RN, Director of Nursing

GastroDiagnostics, A Medical Group, 1140 West La Veta, Suite 550, Orange, CA 92868; tel. 714/835–5100; FAX. 714/835–5567; Stephanie Quinn, Administrator

Glendale Eye Surgery Center, 607 North Central, Suite 103, Glendale, CA 91203; tel. 818/956–1010; FAX. 818/543–6083; Stephen S. Chang, M.D.

Glenwood Surgical Center, L.P., 8945 Magnolia Avenue, Suite 200, Riverside, CA 92503; tel. 909/688–7270; Calvin Nash

Golden Triangle Surgicenter, 25405 Hancock Avenue, Suite 103, Murrieta, CA 92562; tel. 909/698–4670; FAX. 909/698–4675; Ella Stockstill, Administrator

Greater Long Beach Endoscopy Center, 2880 Atlantic Avenue, Suite 180, Long Beach, CA 90806; tel. 562/426–2606; FAX. 562/426–5866; Andrea Campbell, Business Office Manager

Greater Sacramento Surgery Center, 2288 Auburn Boulevard, Suite 201, Sacramento, CA 95821; tel. 916/929–7229; FAX. 916/929–2590; Susan Brunone, MHS, Administrator

Grossmont Plaza Surgery Center, 5525 Grossmont Center Drive, La Mesa, CA 91942; tel. 619/644–4561; Chris Ekern, Manager

Halcyon Laser and Surgery Center, Inc., 303 South Halcyon Road, Arroyo Grande, CA 93420; tel. 805/489–8254; FAX. 805/474–1997; Lura Wilson, Administrator Michael B. Limberg,M.D.,Medical Director

Harbor-UCLA Medical Foundation, Inc., Ambulatory Surgery Center, 21840 South Normandie Avenue, Suite 700, Torrance, CA 90502; tel. 310/222–5189; Lee Scher, RN, Administrator

HealthSouth, 8929 University Center Lane, Suite 103, San Diego, CA 92122; tel. 858/554–0220; FAX. 858/554–0458; Biu Tussy Administrator

HealthSouth Arcadia Outpatient Surgery, Inc., 614 West Duarte Road, Arcadia, CA 91007; tel. 626/445–4714; FAX. 626/445–1701; Sara Lamm, Administrator

HealthSouth Forest Surgery Center, 2110 Forest Avenue, San Jose, CA 95128; tel. 408/297–3432; FAX. 408/298–3338; Camille Magamon RN

HealthSouth Grossmont Surgery Center, 8881 Fletcher Parkway, Suite 100, La Mesa, CA 91942; tel. 619/698–0930; FAX. 619/698–3093; Administrator

HealthSouth North Coast Surgery Center, 3903 Waring Road, Oceanside, CA 92056; tel. 760/940–0997; FAX. 760/940–0407; Donna Danley, Administrator

HealthSouth Surgery Center of Auburn, 3123 Professional Drive, Suite 100, Auburn, CA 95603; tel. 530/888–8899; FAX. 530/888–1464; Fran Thompson, Administrator

HealthSouth Surgery Center of San Luis Obispo, 1304-C Ella Street, San Luis Obis, CA 93401; tel. 805/544–7874; FAX. 805/544–6057; Marilyn Kirkland, RN, Administrator

HealthSouth Surgery Center-Alhambra, 1201 Alhambra Boulevard, Sacramento, CA 95816; tel. 916/733–8222; FAX. 916/733–8224; Rita Brown, Administrator

HealthSouth Surgery Center-J Street, 3810 J Street, Sacramento, CA 95816; tel. 916/929–9431; FAX. 916/929–0132; Marci Watson, Administrator

HealthSouth Surgery Center-Scripps, 75 Scripps Drive, Sacramento, CA 95825; tel. 916/929–9431; FAX. 916/929–0132; Charlene Nakayama, Administrator

HealthSouth Surgery Center-Solano, 991 Nut Tree Road, Suite 100, Vacaville, CA 95687; tel. 707/447–5400; FAX. 707/447–2356; Debra Winslow, Administrator

HealthSouth Surgery, Center of Ventura, 3525 Loma Vista Road, Ventura, CA 93003; tel. 805/641–6434; FAX. 805/641–6437; Chris Behm, Administrator

HealthSouth Tri-Valley Surgery Center, 4487 Stoneridge Drive, Pleasanton, CA 94588; tel. 510/484–3100; FAX. 510/484–3113; Karen Stevens, RN, CNOR, Administrator

Heart Institute of the Desert an The Heart Hospital, 39-600 Bob Hope Drive, Rancho Mirage, CA 92270; tel. 760/324–3278; FAX. 760/346–1867; Jack J. Sternlieb, Administrator

Hemet Endoscopy Center, 1003 East Florida Avenue, Suite 104, Hemet, CA 92543; tel. 951/652–2252; FAX. 951/925–9252; Milan S. Chakrabarty, M.D.

Hemet Healthcare Surgicenter, 301 North San Jacinto Avenue, Hemet, CA 92543; tel. 909/765–1717; FAX. 909/765–1716; Josh Hoffner, Business Office Manager

Hesperia Podiatry Surgery Center, 14661 Main Street, Hesperia, CA 92345; tel. 760/244–0222; FAX. 760/244–1242; William S. Beal

Hi-Desert Surgery Center, 18002 Outer Highway 18, Apple Valley, CA 92307; tel. 619/242–5505; FAX. 619/242–3502; Venkat R. Vangala, M.D.

High Desert Endoscopy, 18523 Corwin Road, Suite H2, Apple Valley, CA 92307; tel. 760/242–3000; FAX. 760/242–1802; Raman S. Poola, M.D., Administrator

Hope Square Surgical Center, 39700 Bob Hope Drive, Suite 301, Rancho Mirage, CA 92270; tel. 760/346–7696; FAX. 760/776–1069; Marilee Kyler, Administrator

Huntington Outpatient Surgery Center, 797 South Fair Oaks Avenue, Pasadena, CA 91105; tel. 626/535–2434; FAX. 626/535–2430; Sandra Bidlack, Administrator

Imperial Valley Surgery Center, 608 G Street, Brawley, CA 92227; tel. 619/344–1101; FAX. 619/344–4985; Vida C. Baron, M.D., Administrator

Inland Endoscopy Center, Inc., d/b/a Mountain View Surgery Center, 10408 Industrial Circle, Redlands, CA 92374; tel. 909/796–7803; FAX. 909/796–0614; Khushal Stanisai

Inland Surgery Center, 1620 Laurel Avenue, Redlands, CA 92373; tel. 909/793–4701; FAX. 909/792–6397; Debra Eisner, Facility Administrator

Inland Surgery Center, 361 North San Jacinto, Hemet, CA 92543; tel. 909/652–4343; FAX. 909/765–6036; Barratt Phillips MD.

Irvine Multi-Specialty Surgical Care, 4900 Barranca Parkway, Suite 104, Irvine, CA 92604-8603; tel. 714/726–0677; FAX. 714/726–0678; Lauren Parrott, B.S, Administrator

Kaiser Ambulatory Surgical Center, 2025 Morse Avenue, Sacramento, CA 95825; tel. 916/973–7675; FAX. 916/973–7786; Richard R. Stading, RN, MSHA., A.S.C. Manager

Kaiser Ambulatory Surgical Center, 10725 International Drive, Rancho Cordov, CA 95670; tel. 916/631–2000; FAX. 916/631–2013; Steven Metzger, RN, Manager

Kaiser Permanente Medical Facility-Stockton, 7373 West Lane, Stockton, CA 95210; tel. 209/476–3300; Jose R. Rivera, Administrator

La Jolla Gastroenterology Medical Group, Inc., Endoscopy Center, 9850 Genesee Avenue, Suite 980, La Jolla, CA 92037; tel. 858/453–5200; FAX. 858/453–5753; Robert H. Goldklang MD Medical Director

La Veta Surgical Center, an Office of Healthsouth, 725 West La Veta, Suite 270, Orange, CA 92868; tel. 714/744–0900; FAX. 714/744–0283; Joyce Hall, Administrator

Laser and Skin Surgery Center of La Jolla, 9850 Genesee Avenue, Suite 490, La Jolla, CA 92037; tel. 858/558–2424; FAX. 858/558–5782; Lupe Rolon, Clinical Manager

Laser Surgery Center, LTD., 2021 Ygnacio Valley Road, Building H-102, Walnut Creek, CA 94598; tel. 925/944–9400; FAX. 925/947–2160; Michele McKinley, Administrator

Lassen Surgery Center, 103 Fair Drive, P.O. Box 1150, Susanville, CA 96130; tel. 530/257–7772; FAX. 530/257–2939; Tina Kennemore, Medical Staff Coordinator

Lodi Outpatient Surgical Center, 521 South Ham Lane, Suite F, Lodi, CA 95242; tel. 209/333–0905; FAX. 209/333–0219; Marklin E. Brown, Administrator, CFO

Loma Linda Foot and Ankle Center, Ambulatory Surgical Center, Podiatry Corp, 11332 Mountain View Avenue, Suite A, Loma Linda, CA 92354; tel. 909/796–3707; FAX. 909/796–3709; Mariam Amiri, D.P.M., Administrator

Los Altos Surgery Center, 795 Altos Oaks Drive, Los Altos, CA 94024; tel. 650/941–8888; Harry Mittelman, M.D.

Los Robles Surgicenter, 2190 Lynn Road, Suite 100, Thousand Oaks, CA 91360; tel. 805/497–3737; FAX. 805/373–8878; Le Anne Schai, Administrative Director

M/S Surgery Center, 3510 Martin Luther King Boulevard, Lynwood, CA 90262; tel. 310/635-7550; FAX. 310/603-8749; John H. Shammas, M.D., Medical Director

Madera Ambulatory Endoscopy Center, 1015 West Yosemite Avenue, Suite 101, Madera, CA 93637; tel. 559/673-4000; FAX. 209/673-1430; Naeem M. Akhtar, M.D.

Madison Park Surgery and Laser Center, 3445 Pacific Coast Highway, Suite 250, Torrance, CA 90505; tel. 310/530-2900; FAX. 310/891-0367; John Abrams

Magnolia Plastic Surgery Center, 10694 Magnolia Avenue, Riverside, CA 92505; tel. 909/358-1445; FAX. 909/688-2803; Alexander Carli

Marin Ophthalmic Surgery Center, 901 E Street, Suite 270, San Rafael, CA 94901; tel. 415/454-2112; FAX. 415/454-6542; Vicki Wininger, RN Clinical Director

Martel Eye Surgical Center, 11216 Trinity River, Rancho Cordov, CA 95670; tel. 916/635-6161; FAX. 916/635-5145; Joseph Martel, M.D.

McHenry Surgery Center, 1524 McHenry Street, Suite 240, Modesto, CA 95350; tel. 209/576-2900; FAX. 209/575-5815; Coleen DeLeon, RNFA,Director

Medical Arts Ambulatory Surgery Center, 205 South West Street, Suite B, Visalia, CA 93291; tel. 209/625-9601; FAX. 209/625-3124; Thomas F. Mitts, M.D., Administrator

Medical Plaza Orthopedic Surgery Center, 1301 20th Street, Suite 140, Santa Monica, CA 90404; tel. 310/315-0333; FAX. 310/315-0341; Trish Fowler, Director Surgical Services

Merced Ambulatory Endoscopy Center, 750 West Olive Avenue, Suite 107A, Merced, CA 95348; tel. 209/384-3116; FAX. 209/384-0878; Gabina Villanavueva, Administrator

Mercy Surgical and Diagnostic Center, 3303 North M Street, Merced, CA 95348; tel. 209/384-3533; FAX. 209/383-5047; Lynda Pitts, Administrator

Mission Ambulatory Surgicenter, 26730 Crown Valley Parkway, First Floor, Mission Viejo, CA 92691; tel. 949/364-2201; FAX. 949/364-5372; Mary Parker, Administrator

Mission Valley Surgery Center, 39263 Mission Boulevard, Fremont, CA 94539; tel. 510/796-4500; FAX. 510/796-4573; Sarb S. Hundal, M.D.

Modesto Surgery Center, Inc., 400 East Orangeburg Avenue, Suite One, Modesto, CA 95350; tel. 209/526-3000; FAX. 209/526-3133; Dr. Greg Tesluk, Administrator

Monterey Bay Endoscopy Center, 833 Cass Street, Suite B, Monterey, CA 93940; tel. 831/375-3577; FAX. 831/375-1478; Daniel G Luba, M.D., Medical Director

Monterey Peninsula Surgery Center, LLC., 966 Cass Street, Suite 210, Monterey, CA 93940; tel. 831/372-2169; FAX. 408/372-6323; David J. Ogimachi, Administrator

Napa Surgery Center, 3444 Valle Verde Drive, Napa, CA 94558; tel. 707/252-9669; FAX. 707/257-3328; Eric Grigsby, M.D., Managing Partner

Newport Beach Orange Coast Endoscopy Center, 1525 Superior Avenue, Suite 114, Newport Beach, CA 92663; tel. 949/646-6999; FAX. 949/646-9699; Donald Abraham

Newport Beach Surgery Center, 361 Hospital Road, Suite 124, Newport Beach, CA 92663; tel. 714/631-0988; FAX. 714/631-2036; Eric Reints, Administrator

Newport Surgery Institute, 360 San Miguel Drive, Suite 406, Newport Beach, CA 92660; tel. 949/759-0995; Suzanne Tavenner, Office Manager

North Anaheim Surgicenter, 1154 North Euclid, Anaheim, CA 92801; tel. 714/635-6272; FAX. 714/635-0943; Jeanette Rasmussen, Administrator

North County Outpatient Surgery Center, 1101 Las Tablas Road #G, P.O. Box 147, Templeton, CA 93465; tel. 805/434-l333; FAX. 805/434-3171; Becky McGraw, B/O Manager

Northern California Kidney Stone Center, 15195 National Avenue, Suite 204, Los Gatos, CA 95032; tel. 408/358-7144; FAX. 408/356-2359; John Kersten Kraft, Medical Director

Northridge Maxillofacial Surgery Center, 18546 Roscoe Boulevard, Suite 125, Northridge, CA 91324; tel. 818/349-8890; FAX. 818/349-1532; Estar Acosta, Practice Manager

Optima Ophthalmic Medical Associates, Inc., 1237 B Street, Hayward, CA 94541-2977; tel. 510/886-3937; FAX. 510/886-6304; Kelly Best, Office Manager

Orange County Institute of Gastroenterology and Endoscopy, 26732 Crown Valley Parkway, Suite 241, Mission Viejo, CA 92691; tel. 949/364-2611; FAX. 949/364-0226; Dina Moatazedi, Office Manager

Orange County Litho Center, Inc., 12555 Garden Grove Boulevard, Suite 200, Garden Grove, CA 92843; tel. 714/530-6000; FAX. 714/534-7061; Guy A. Biagiotti, M.D.

Out-Patient Surgery Center, 17752 Beach Boulevard, Huntington Beach, CA 92647; tel. 714/842-1426; FAX. 714/847-1503; Madelyn Tinkler, Administrator

Outpatient Care Surgery Center South, 5225 Kearny Villa Way, Suite 110, San Diego, CA 92123; tel. 619/278-1611; FAX. 619/278-5853; Ronald Gertsch, M.D.

Pacific Eye Institute, 555 North 13th Avenue, Upland, CA 91786; tel. 909/982-8846; FAX. 909/982-4007; Robert Fabricant, M.D., FACS, Medical Director

Pacific Hills Surgery Center, Inc., 24022 Calle De La Plata, Suite 180, Laguna Hills, CA 92653; tel. 714/951-9470; FAX. 714/951-9478; Norman D. Peterson, M.D., Medical Director

Pacific Surgicenter, Inc., 1301 20th Street, Suite 470, Santa Monica, CA 90404; tel. 310/315-0222; FAX. 310/828-8852; Randi Ogilvie- Manager

Palm Desert Ambulatory Surgery Center, 73-345 Highway 111, Palm Desert, CA 92260; tel. 619/346-4780; FAX. 619/340-4650; S. C. Shah, M.D., Administrator

Paul L. Archambeau, M.D., Inc., Ambulatory Surgery Center, 380 Tesconi Court, Santa Rosa, CA 95401; tel. 707/544-3375; FAX. 707/544-0808; Paul L. Archambeau, M.D., Administrator

Petaluma Surgicenter, 1400 Professional Drive, Suite 102, Petaluma, CA 94954; tel. 707/763-9325; FAX. 707/769-0751; Ronald M. La Vigna, D.P.M. Manager

Physician's Surgery Center, 901 Campus Drive, Suite 102, Daly City, CA 94015; tel. 650/991-2000; FAX. 650/755-8638; Stuart Katz, FACHE, Administrator

Physicians Plaza Surgical Center, 6000 Physicians Boulevard, Bakersfield, CA 93301; tel. 661/322-4744; FAX. 661/322-2938; Terri Waller, Administrator

Plastic and Reconstructive Surgery Center, 1387 Santa Rita Road, Pleasanton, CA 94566; tel. 510/462-3700; FAX. 510/462-4681; Ronald Iverson, Administrator

Plaza Surgical Center, Inc., 168 North Brent Street, Suite 403B, Ventura, CA 93003; tel. 805/643-5438; FAX. 805/643-1625; Dale P. Armstrong, M.D.

Podiatric Surgery Center, 255 North Gilbert, Suite B, Hemet, CA 92543; tel. 909/925-2186; FAX. 909/925-4947; Robert Drake, D.P.M., Administrator

Porterville Surgical Center, 577 West Putnam Avenue, Porterville, CA 93257; tel. 559/788-6400; FAX. 559/788-6401; Alicia Meja, RN, Administrator

Premiere Surgery Center, Inc., 700 West El Norte Parkway, Escondido, CA 92026; tel. 760/738-7830; FAX. 760/738-7834; R. K. Massengill, M.D., Medical Director

Providence Ambulatory Surgical Center, 1310 West Stewart Drive, Suite 310, Orange, CA 92668; tel. 714/771-6363; FAX. 714/771-0754; Harrell E. Robinson, M.D., President

Providence Holy Cross Surgery Center, 11550 Indian Hills Road, Suite 160, Mission Hills, CA 91345; tel. 818/256-2100; FAX. 818/256-2156; Dale Bowman, Administrator

Pueblo Nuevo Aesthetic and Reconstructive Surgery, 1334 Nelson Avenue, Modesto, CA 95350; tel. 209/524-9904; FAX. 209/524-4101; Diane Payne, Administrator

Redlands Dental Surgery Center, 1180 Nevada Street, Suite 100, Redlands, CA 92374; tel. 909/335-0474; Russell O. Seheult, D.D.S.

Richburg Valley Eye Institute Ambulatory Surgical Center, 1680 East Herndon Avenue, Fresno, CA 93720; tel. 209/432-4200; FAX. 209/432-0147; Frederick Richburg, M.D., Administrator

Riverside Community Surgi-Center, 3980 14th Street, Riverside, CA 92501; tel. 909/787-0580; FAX. 909/787-8201; Pat Finley, Administrator

Riverside Eye, Ear, Nose and Throat Institute Surgery Center, 4500 Brockton Avenue, Suite 105, Riverside, CA 92501; tel. 714/788-2788; FAX. 909/788-4374; B. G. Smith, M.D., Medical Director

Riverside Medical Clinic Surgery Center, 7160 Brockton Avenue, Riverside, CA 92506; tel. 909/782-3801; FAX. 909/782-3861; Diego A. Galvez-Ramirez, MBA, Service Area Director

Rose Eye Laser Center, Rose Eye Cataract Surgery Center, 3325 North Broadway, Los Angeles, CA 90031; tel. 323/221-6121; FAX. 323/221-6120; Michael R. Rose, Administrator

Sacramento Eye Surgicenter, 3150 J Street, Sacramento, CA 95816; tel. 916/444-7052; FAX. 916/446-1145; Kim Russell, ASC Director

Sacramento Midtown Endoscopy Center, 3941 J Street, Suite 460, Sacramento, CA 95819; tel. 916/733-6940; FAX. 916/733-6934; Tommy Poirier, M.D.

Saddleback Eye Center, 23161 Moulton Parkway, Laguna Hills, CA 92653; tel. 949/951-4641; FAX. 949/951-4601; Linda Riley, Administrator

Saddleback Valley Outpatient Surgery, 24302 Paseo De Valencia, Laguna Hills, CA 92653; tel. 949/472-0244; FAX. 949/472-0380; Brian FitzGerald, Administrator

Salinas Surgery Center, 955-A Blanco Circle, Salinas, CA 93901; tel. 831/753-5800; FAX. 831/753-5808; Christine Gallagher, Executive Director

San Diego Endoscopy Center, A Partnership, 4033 Third Avenue, Suite 106, San Diego, CA 92103; tel. 619/291-6064; FAX. 619/291-3078; John D. Goodman, M.D.

San Diego Outpatient Surgical Center, 770 Washington Street, Suite 101, San Diego, CA 92103; tel. 619/299-9530; FAX. 619/296-5386; Carla G. Ramirez, Administrator

San Francisco Surgi Center, 1635 Divisidero Street, Suite 200, San Francisco, CA 94115; tel. 415/346-1218; FAX. 415/346-2930; Judith Mulligan, Administrator

San Gabriel Valley Surgical Center, 1250 South Sunset Avenue, Suite 100, West Covina, CA 91790; tel. 626/960-6623; FAX. 626/962-4341; Susan Raub, Administrator

San Jacquin Laser Surgery Center, 1805 North California Street, Stockton, CA 95204; tel. 209/948-3241; FAX. 209/948-9321; Susan Ford, Administrator

San Jose Eye Ambulatory Surgicenter, Inc., 4585 Stevens Creek Boulevard, Suite 500, Santa Clara, CA 95051; tel. 408/247-2706; FAX. 408/296-2020; Lolita Ancheta, Manager

San Leandro Surgery Center, 15035 East 14th Street, San Leandro, CA 94578; tel. 510/276-2800; FAX. 510/276-2890; Sheila L. Cook, Executive Director

Sani Eye Surgery Center, 1315 Las Tablas Road, Templeton, CA 93465; tel. 805/434-2533; FAX. 805/434-3037; Javad N. Sani, M.D., Director

Santa Cruz Surgery Center, 3003 Paul Sweet Road, Santa Cruz, CA 95065; tel. 408/462-5512; FAX. 408/462-2451; Mary Ann Dunlap, RN

Santa Monica Surgery and Laser Center, 2001 Santa Monica Boulevard, Suite 1288W, Santa Monica, CA 90404; tel. 310/829-2005; FAX. 310/453-9201; Cindy Schlaak, RN, Administrator

Sebastopol Ambulatory Surgery Center, 6880 Palm Avenue, Sebastopol, CA 95472; tel. 707/823-7628; FAX. 707/823-1521; Edward J. Boland, Administrator

Sequoia Endoscopy Center, 2900 Whipple Avenue, Suite 100, Redwood City, CA 94062; tel. 650/363-5200; FAX. 650/369-4609; James Torosis M.D., Medical Director

Shepard Eye Center Medical Group, 1414 East Main Street, Santa Maria, CA 93454-4806; tel. 805/925-2637; FAX. 805/928-2067; Dennis D. Shepard, M.D.

Sierra Plastic Surgery Center, 6153 North Thesta, Fresno, CA 93710; tel. 559/432-5156; FAX. 559/432-2247; Terry A. Gillian, M.D., Medical Director

Sierra Vista Medical Pavilion Ambulatory Surgery, 77 Casa Street, Suite 203, San Luis Obis, CA 93405; tel. 805/544-6471; FAX. 805/544-4913; James W. Thornton, M.D., Administrator

Solis Surgical Arts Center, 4940 Van Nuys Boulevard, Suite 105, Sherman Oaks, CA 91403; tel. 818/787-1144; Dr. H. William Gottschalk, Administrator

Sonora Eye Surgery Center, 940 Sylva Lane, Suite G, Sonora, CA 95370; tel. 209/532-2020; FAX. 209/532-1687; Christy Clogg, RN, Surgery Administrator

South Bay Endoscopy Center, 256 Landis Avenue, Suite 100, Chula Vista, CA 91910; tel. 619/420-6864; FAX. 619/420-0477; Sylvia Casey, Administrator

Section C

South Coast Laser Center, 3420 Bristol Street, Suite 701, Costa Mesa, CA 92626; tel. 714/957-0272; FAX. 714/641-2020; Michael R. Rose, M.D., Medical Director

Southern California Surgery Center, 7305 Pacific Boulevard, Huntington Pa, CA 90255; tel. 213/584-8222; Amgad A. Awad, Administrator

Southland Endoscopy Center, 949 East Calhoun Place, Suite B, Hemet, CA 92543; tel. 909/929-1177; FAX. 909/765-9111; Sreenivasa R. Nakka, M.D., F.A.C.P.

Southwest Surgical Center, Health South, 201 New Stine Road, Suite 130, Bakersfield, CA 93309; tel. 661/396-8900; FAX. 661/397-2929; Linda Bloomquist, Administrator

St. Joseph Surgery and Laser Center, Inc., d/b/a St. Mary And Joseph Surgery And Laser Center, Inc., 436 South Glassell Street, Orange, CA 92866; tel. 714/633-9566; FAX. 714/633-5193; Kathleen Ruper, Administrator

Starpoint Health, 19000 Macarthur Blvd., #450, Irvine, CA 92612; tel. 949/705-5100; FAX. 949/985-0055; Eric D. Friedlander, CEO

Stockton Eye Surgery Center, 36 West Yokuts Avenue, Suite 3, Stockton, CA 95207; tel. 209/473-2940; FAX. 209/474-1168; Kathy Barton, Administrator

Surgecenter of Palo Alto, 795 El Camino Real, Palo Alto, CA 94301; tel. 415/324-1832; FAX. 650/330-4520; Margo Mynderse - Isola, Chief Executive Officer

Surgery Center, 1111 Sonoma Avenue, Lower Level, Santa Rosa, CA 95405; tel. 707/578-4100; FAX. 707/578-7997; Ken Alban, Administrator

Surgery Center of Santa Monica, 2121 Wilshire Boulevard, Santa Monica, CA 90403; tel. 310/264-7300; Ruth F. Andrews

Surgical Eye Care Center, 655 Laguna Drive, Carlsbad, CA 92008; tel. 760/729-7101; FAX. 760/729-7106; Lisa Barron, Administrator

Surgitek Outpatient Center, Inc., 460 North Greenfield Avenue, Suite Eight, Hanford, CA 93230; tel. 209/582-0238; Wiley Elick, Owner, Administrator

Sutter North Procedure Center, 550 B Street, Yuba City, CA 95991; tel. 530/749-3653; FAX. 530/749-3493; Deborah Smith, Ancillary Services Director

The Beverly Hills Center for Special Surgery, 1125 South Beverly Drive, Suite 505, Los Angeles, CA 90035; tel. 310/277-6780; Alina Pnini, Administrator

The Center for Endoscopy, 3921 Waring Road, Suite B, Oceanside, CA 92056; tel. 760/940-6300; FAX. 760/940-8074; Barbara Bockover, RN, Administrator

The Centre for Plastic Surgery, 401 East Highland Avenue, Suite 352, San Bernardino, CA 92404; tel. 909/883-8686; FAX. 909/881-6537; Dennis K. Anderson, Administrator

The Darr Eye Clinic Surgical Medical Group, Inc., 44119 Monterey Avenue, Suite A, Palm Desert, CA 92260; tel. 619/773-3099; FAX. 619/341-6863; Joseph L. Darr, M.D., Administrator

The Endoscopy Center, 870 Shasta Street, Suite 100, Yuba City, CA 95991; tel. 530/671-3636; FAX. 530/671-4099; Floyd V. Burton, M.D.

The Endoscopy Center of the South Bay, 23560 Madison Street, Suite 109, Torrance, CA 90505; tel. 310/325-6331; FAX. 310/325-6335; Jerome Cohen M.D., Medical Director

The Eye Surgery Center (Colton), 1900 East Washington Street, Colton, CA 92324; tel. 909/825-8002; FAX. 909/422-8905; Melissa Goins, RN, Director

The Eye Surgery Center of Northern California, 5959 Greenback Lane Suite 310, Citrus Height, CA 95621; tel. 916/723-7400; FAX. 916/723-4449; Terre Lamb, Manager

The Montebello Surgery Center, 229 East Beverly Boulevard, Montebello, CA 90640; tel. 213/728-7998; Millie Kelly, Administrator

The Palos Verdes Ambulatory Surgery Medical Center, 3400 West Lomita Boulevard, Suite 307A, Torrance, CA 90505; tel. 310/517-8689; FAX. 310/517-9916; Christine Petti, M.D., Medical Director

The Plastic Surgery Center Medical Group, Inc., 95 Scripps Drive, Sacramento, CA 95825; tel. 916/929-1833; FAX. 916/929-6730; John Murphy, Administrator

The Specialists Surgery Center, 2450 Martin Road, Fairfield, CA 94533; tel. 707/427-6233; FAX. 707/427-6255; Ann Karg, Executive Director

The Surgery Center Of Riverside, INC, 8990 Garfield, Suite One, Riverside, CA 92503; tel. 909/785-5421; FAX. 909/785-0130

The Surgery Center, A HealthSouth Surgery Center, 3875 Telegraph Avenue, Oakland, CA 94609; tel. 510/547-2244; FAX. 510/547-6637; Ann Banchero, Administrator

The Valley Endoscopy Center, 18425 Burbank Boulevard, Suite 525, Tarzana, CA 91356; tel. 818/708-6050; FAX. 818/708-6009; Betty Asato, RN, Clinical Director

Third Street Surgery Center, 420 East Third Street, Suite 110, Los Angeles, CA 90013; tel. 213/617-9194; FAX. 213/617-0605; Yukiko Hattori, Director of Nursing

Thousand Oaks Endoscopy Center, 227 West Janss Road, Suite 240, Thousand Oaks, CA 91360; tel. 805/371-0455; FAX. 805/371-0459; Hector Caballero, M.D., Administrator

Time Surgical Facility, 720 North Tustin Avenue, Suite 202, Santa Ana, CA 92705; tel. 714/972-1811; Denise Reale, Administrator

Torrance Surgicenter, 22410 Hawthorne Boulevard, Suite Three, Torrance, CA 90505; tel. 310/373-2238; FAX. 310/373-8238; Lindon KenKawahara, M.D., Medical Director

Truxtun Surgery Center, Inc., 4260 Truxtun Avenue, Suite 120, Bakersfield, CA 93309; tel. 661/327-3636; Mary Moesler, AOM

Twin Cities Surgicenter, Inc., 812 Fourth Street, Suite A, Marysville, CA 95901; tel. 916/741-3937; FAX. 916/743-0427; Karen M. Wasilenko, CASC Administrator

Upland Outpatient Surgical Center, Inc., 1330 San Bernardino Road #F, Upland, CA 91786; tel. 909/981-8755; FAX. 909/981-9462; Brian Olson, Administrator

Valencia Outpatient Surgical Center Partners, L.P., d/b/a Valencia Surgical Center, 24355 Lyons Avenue, Suite 120, Santa Clarita, CA 91321; tel. 661/255-6644; FAX. 661/255-7653; Nina Turner, Administrative Director

Valley Surgical Center, 5555 West Las Positas Boulevard, Pleasanton, CA 94566; tel. 510/734-3360; FAX. 510/734-3358; Beth Combs, RN, Director, Nursing

Ventura Out-Patient Surgery, Inc., 3555 Loma Vista Road, Suite 204, Ventura, CA 93003; tel. 805/653-5460; FAX. 805/653-1470; Brian D. Brantner, M.D.

Victorville Ambulatory Surgery Center, 15030 Seventh Street, Victorville, CA 92392; tel. 760/241-2273; FAX. 760/245-6798; John D. Amar, M.D., Medical Director

Wardlow Surgery Center, 200 West Wardlow Road, Long Beach, CA 90806; tel. 310/424-3574; FAX. 310/490-0329; Marisol Magana, Administrator

Washington Outpatient Surgery Center, 2299 Mowry Avenue, First Floor, Fremont, CA 94538; tel. 510/791-5374; FAX. 510/790-8916; Dr. Jeffery Stuart Medical Director

West Valley Surgery Center, 3803 South Bascom Avenue, Suite 106, Campbell, CA 95008; tel. 408/559-4886; FAX. 408/559-4908; Annette Wunderlich, RN, Administrator

Westlake Eye Surgery Center, 2900 Townsgate Road, Suite 201, Westlake Village, CA 91361; tel. 805/496-6789; FAX. 805/494-8392; John Darin, M.D., Medical Director

Women's Health Care and Cosmetic Surgical Center, 15306 Devonshire Street, Mission Hills, CA 91311; tel. 818/892-0274; FAX. 818/895-0663; Martha P. Nazemi, Administrator

Woodland Surgery Center, 1321 Cottonwood Street, Woodland, CA 95695; tel. 530/304-2257; FAX. 530/668-5783; Jack Donaldson, Manager

Woodward Park Surgicenter, 7055 North Fresno Street, Suite 100, Fresno, CA 93720; tel. 559/449-9977; FAX. 559/449-9350; Dee Patrick, RN, BHA, Administrator

COLORADO

St. Anthony Health-Summit Surgery Center, Highway Nine at School Road, P.O. Box 4460, Frisco, CO 80443; tel. 303/668-2852; FAX. 970/668-1703; Paul Chodlawski, Administrator

Aurora Surgery Center LTD, 13701 E. Mississippi, #200, Aurora, CO 80012; tel. 303/363-8646; FAX. 303/363-8689; Rosalie Warrington, Administrator

Avista Surgery Center, 2525 Fourth Street, Lower Level, Boulder, CO 80304; tel. 303/443-3672; John Sackett, Administrator

Boulder Medical Center, P C, 2750 Broadway, Boulder, CO 80304; tel. 303/440-3000; Mr. Bradford McKane, Administrator

Centennial Medical Plaza, a Division of HCA-Health one, 14200 East Arapahoe Road, Englewood, CO 80112; tel. 303/699-3000; FAX. 303/699-3152; Julie Taylor

Center for Reproductive Surgery, 799 East Hampden Avenue, Suite 300, Englewood, CO 80110; tel. 303/788-8300; FAX. 303/788-8310; Dr. William Schoolcraft, Administrator

Centrum Surgical Center, 8200 East Belleview, Suite 300, East Tower, Greenwood Village, CO 80111; tel. 303/290-0600; FAX. 303/290-6359; David Parrott, Administrator

Cherry Creek Eye Surgery Center, (Rose Medical Center), 4999 East Kentucky Avenue, Denver, CO 80222; tel. 303/692-0903; Jeffrey Dorsey, Administrator

Colorado Outpatient Eye Surgical Center, 2480 South Downing, Suite G-20, Denver, CO 80210; tel. 303/7777303; FAX. 303/282-0266; Susan Larkin, Administrator

Colorado Springs Eye Surgery Center, 2920 North Cascade Avenue, Colorado Springs, CO 80907; tel. 719/636-5054; FAX. 719/520-3576; Dr. Robert Foerster, Medical Director

Colorado Springs Health Partners Ambulatory Surgery Unit, 209 South Nevada Avenue, Colorado Springs, CO 80903; tel. 719/475-7700; FAX. 719/538-2999; Ms. Joan Compton, VP Operations

Denver Eye Surgery Center, Inc., 13772 Denver West Parkway, Building 55, Suite 120, Golden, CO 80401; tel. 303/273-8770; Larry W. Kreider, M.D., Chief of Surgery

Denver Midtown Surgery Center, 1919 East 18th Avenue, Denver, CO 80206; tel. 303/322-3993; FAX. 303/322-7329; Lisa Cross, Administrator

Durango Surgicenter, 316 Sawyer Drive, Durango, CO 81303; tel. 970/259-3818; FAX. 970/259-9553; D.J. Winder, M.D., Administrator

Eye Center of Northern Colorado Surgery Center, 1725 E. Prospect Ave., Fort Collins, CO 80525; tel. 970/221-2222; FAX. 970/221-2223; Carol Wittmer, Administrator

Eye Surgery Center of Colorado, P.C., 8403 Bryant Street, Westminster, CO 80031; tel. 303/426-4810; FAX. 303/426-8708; William G. Self, Jr., M.D., Administrator

Foot Surgery Center of Northern Colorado, 1355 Riverside Ave., #B, Fort Collins, CO 80524; tel. 970/484-4620; FAX. 970/407-1194; Connie Nelson, RN, Nurse Administrator

HealthSouth Aurora Surgery Center, Ltd., 13701 Mississippi Avenue, Suite 200, Aurora, CO 80012; tel. 303/363-8646; FAX. 303/363-8689; Rosalie Warrington, RN, Administrator

HealthSouth Denver West Surgery Center, 13952 Denver West Parkway, Building 53, Suite 100, Golden, CO 80401; tel. 303/271-1112; FAX. 303/271-1117; Ms. Lisa Austin, Administrator

HealthSouth Pueblo Surgery Center, 25 Montebello Road, Pueblo, CO 81001; tel. 719/544-1600; FAX. 719/544-2599; Jennifer Arellano, Administrator

HealthSouth Surgery Center of Colorado Springs, 1615 Medical Center Point, Colorado Springs, CO 80907; tel. 719/635-7740; FAX. 719/635-7750; David Lewis, Administrator

Kaiser Permanente Ambulatory Surgery Center, 2045 Franklin Street, Denver, CO 80205; tel. 303/764-4444; Rosemarie Polemi, Director

Lakewood Surgical Center, 2201 Wadsworth Boulevard, Lakewood, CO 80215; tel. 303/234-0445; FAX. 303/232-7182; Connie Holtz, Administrator

Laser Institute of the Rockies, 8400 East Prentice Avenue, Suite 1200, Greenwood Village, CO 80111; tel. 303/793-3000; Jon Dishler, M.D., President

Littleton Day Surgery Center, 8381 South Park Lane, Littleton, CO 80120; tel. 303/795-2244; FAX. 303/795-5965; Judy Rich, Administrator

Mountain View Surgery Center, 1850 N. Boise Ave., Loveland, CO 80538; tel. 970/622-1999; Mary Glass, Administrator

North Denver Endoscopy Center, 10001 North Washington, Thornton, CO 80229; tel. 303/252-0083; FAX. 303/252-9095; Craig J. Bakken, Administrator

Orthopedic Center of the Rockies Ambulatory Surgery Center, 2500 East Prospect Road, Fort Collins, CO 80525; tel. 970/493-4010; FAX. 970/419-7151; Yvonne Bochmer, RN, BSN, Director of Surgical Services

Pain Treatment Centers, LLC, 1625 Medical Center Point, #240, Colorado Spire, CO 80907; tel. 719/577-9063; FAX. 719/577-9124; John W. Nelson, M.D., Medical Director

Park Meadows Outpatient Surgery, 7430 Park Meadows Drive #300, Lonetree, CO 80124; tel. 303/706-1100; FAX. 303/790-7322; Charlene A. Sherwood, Practice Administrator

Pikes Peak Endoscopy & Surgery Center, 1699 Medical Center Pt., Colorado Springs, CO 80907; tel. 719/632-7101; FAX. 719/632-4468; Rebecca Gooding, CEO

South Denver Endoscopy Center, Inc., 499 East Hampden Avenue, Suite 430, Englewood, CO 80110; tel. 303/788-8888; Dr. Pete Baker, Administrator

Spring Creek Surgery Center, Spring Creek Medical Park, 2001 South Shields Street, Building H, Su, Fort Collins, CO 80526; tel. 970/221-9363; FAX. 970/221-9636; Natalie Coubrough, Facility Administrator

Surgery Center of Fort Collins, 1100 East Prospect Road, Fort Collins, CO 80525; tel. 970/494-4800; FAX. 970/493-2380; Ross Alexander, Administrator

Surgicenter of the San Luis Valley Medical, P.C., 2115 Stuart, Alamosa, CO 81101; tel. 719/589-8010; FAX. 719/589-8112; Lori Ann Snow, RN., Supervisor

Western Rockies Surgery Center, Inc., 1000 Wellington Avenue, Grand Junction, CO 81501; tel. 970/243-9000; FAX. 970/245-4936; Carol Ann Campbell, RN, CNOR Surgery Center Administrator

CONNECTICUT

Bridgeport Surgical Center, 4920 Main Street, Bridgeport, CT 06606; tel. 203/374-1515; FAX. 203/374-4702; Anthony German, Administrative Director

Connecticut Foot Surgery Center, 318 New Haven Avenue, Milford, CT 06460; tel. 203/882-0065; FAX. 203/882-0248; Martin Pressman, D.P.M., Administrator

Connecticut Surgical Center, 81 Gillett Street, Hartford, CT 06105; tel. 203/247-5555; FAX. 203/249-5860; Margaret Rubino, President

Danbury Surgical Center, 73 Sandpit Road, Suite 101, Danbury, CT 06810; tel. 203/743-2400; Bernard A. Kershner, President

HealthSouth Surgery Center of Hartford, 100 Retreat Avenue, Hartford, CT 06106; tel. 860/549-7970; FAX. 860/247-4121; Theresa Klimczyk, Administrative Director

Johnson Surgery Center, 148 Hazard Avenue, P.O. Box 1151, Enfield, CT 06083; tel. 860/763-7650; FAX. 860/763-7675; Anthony T. Valente, Vice President

Middlesex Surgical Center, 530 Saybrook Road, Middletown, CT 06457; tel. 203/343-0400; FAX. 203/343-0396; Louise DeChesser, RN, CNOR, M.S.

Naugatuck Valley Surgical Center, Ltd., 160 Robbins Street, Waterbury, CT 06708; tel. 203/755-6663; FAX. 203/756-9645; Bernard A. Kershner, President

Stamford Surgical Center, 32 Strawberry Hill Court, Stamford, CT 06902; tel. 203/276-6196; FAX. 213/359-6341; Steven P. Oster, Executive Director Ambulatory Services

Waterbury Outpatient Surgical Center, 87 Grandview Avenue, Waterbury, CT 06708; tel. 203/574-2020; Nancy Noll, Administrator

Woman's Surgical Center, 40 Temple Street, New Haven, CT 06510; tel. 203/624-3080; Bruce I. Fisher, Administrator

Yale-New Haven Ambulatory Services Corporation, d/b/a Temple Surgical Center, 60 Temple Street, New Haven, CT 06510; tel. 203/624-6008; Alvin D. Greenberg, M.D., Administrator

DELAWARE

Bayview Endoscopy Center, Inc., 1539 Savannah Road, Lewes, DE 19958; tel. 302/644-0455; FAX. 302/645-5214; Harry J. Anagnostakos, D.O., President

Central Delaware Endoscopy Unit, 644 South Queen Street, Suite 105, Dover, DE 19904; tel. 302/677-1617; FAX. 302/677-1669; William M. Kaplan, M.D., Medical Director

Central Delaware Surgery Center, 100 Scull Terrace, Dover, DE 19901; tel. 302/735-8290; Paul Francisco, Administrator

Endoscopy Center of Delaware, Inc., 1090 Old Churchman's Road, Newark, DE 19713; tel. 302/892-2710; FAX. 302/892-2715; Jean-Marie M. Taylor, Administrator

Eye Care of Delaware Cataract and Laser Center, 4102 Ogletown/Stanton Road, Suite 1, Newark, DE 19713; tel. 302/454-8802; FAX. 302/454-8801; Jane Baker, Officer Manager

Glasgow Medical Center, L.L.C., 2600 Glasgow Avenue, Suite 204, Newark, DE 19702-4777; tel. 302/836-8350; FAX. 302/836-1906; Arthur C. Kretz, C.O.O.

Limestone Medical Center, Inc., 1941 Limestone Road, Suite 113, Wilmington, DE 19808; tel. 302/633-9873; FAX. 302/992-0563; Thomas E. Mulhern, Executive Director

DISTRICT OF COLUMBIA

Hillcrest Northwest, 7603 Georgia Avenue, N.W., Washington, DC 20012; tel. 202/829-5620; FAX. 202/882-8387; Alice Harper, Administrator

Hillcrest Women's Surgi-Center, 3233 Pennsylvania Avenue, S.E., Washington, DC 20020; tel. 202/584-6500; Ms. Caridad V. Wright, Administrator

Medlantic Center for Ambulatory Surgery, Inc., 1145 19th Street, N.W., Suite 850, Washington, DC 20036; tel. 202/223-9040; FAX. 202/223-9047; William Heron, M.D., Medical Director

Planned Parenthood of Metropolitan Washington, D.C., Schumacher Center, 1108 16th Street, N.W., Washington, DC 20036; tel. 202/347-8512; FAX. 202/347-0281; Carin Johnson, Center Manager

Premier Surgery Center of D.C., 6323 Georgia Avenue, N.W., Suite 200, Washington, DC 20011; tel. 202/291-0126; FAX. 202/291-0126; Lenora Hollaway, RN, Administrative Director

The Endoscopy Center of Washington, DC, L.P., 2021 K Street, N.W., Suite T-115, Washington, DC 20006; tel. 202/775-8692; FAX. 202/463-1165; Debra Jay RN, Center Director

Washington Surgi-Clinic, 1018 22nd Street, N.W., Washington, DC 20037; tel. 202/659-9403; FAX. 202/467-0056; Maria Barrera, Administrator

FLORIDA

Brandon Surgery Center, 711 South Parsons, Brandon, FL 33511; tel. 813/654-7771; FAX. 813/654-3347; Charlene Harrell, RN, Administrator

Aesthetic Cosmetic Surgery Center, Inc, 598 Sterthaus Avenue, Ormond Beach, FL 32174; tel. 904/673-2262; FAX. 904/677-3808; Bonnie Dantoni, RN, D.D.N.

Aker-Kasten Vision & Laser Center, 1445 Northwest Boca Raton Boulevard, Boca Raton, FL 33432; tel. 561/338-7722; FAX. 561/338-7785; Kim Harrington, Administrator

All Saints Surgery Center, 11377 Cortez Boulevard, Brooksville, FL 34613; tel. 352/597-3060; FAX. 352/597-3077; Teresa Wiley-Director Of Nursing

Alpha Ambulatory Surgery, Inc., 2160 Capital Circle, N.E., Tallahassee, FL 32308; tel. 904/385-0033; FAX. 904/422-0201; Gloria Jeter, Office Manager

Ambulatory Ankle and Foot Center of Florida, 1509 South Orange Avenue, P.O. Box 536951, Orlando, FL 32853; tel. 407/839-6155; FAX. 407/839-1221; Gregory J. Renton, Administrator

Ambulatory Surgery Center, 4500 East Fletcher Avenue, Tampa, FL 33613; tel. 813/977-8550; FAX. 813/977-7941; Carole Cornell, Administrator

Ambulatory Surgery Center of Brevard, 719 East New Haven Avenue, Melbourne, FL 32901; tel. 321/726-4106; FAX. 321/728-3001; Norm Gagnon, General Manager

Ambulatory Surgery Center/Bradenton, 5817 21st Avenue, W., Bradenton, FL 34209; tel. 813/794-0379; J. Leikensohn, M.D., Medical Director

Ambulatory Surgical Care, 1045 North Courtenay Parkway, Merritt Island, FL 32953; tel. 321/452-4448; FAX. 321/452-4533; Patricia Holley, Office Manager

Ambulatory Surgical Center of Central Florida, Inc., 801 North Stone Street, Deland, FL 32720; tel. 904/734-4431; FAX. 904/738-1045; Albert C. Neumann, M.D., Medical Director

Ambulatory Surgical Center of Lake County, Inc., 803 East Dixie Avenue, Leesburg, FL 34748; tel. 352/787-6666; FAX. 352/787-9008; Patricia R. Hux, RN, Business Manager, Administrator

Ambulatory Surgical Facility of South Florida, LTD-East, 4470 Sheridan Street, Hollywood, FL 33021; tel. 305/962-3210; FAX. 305/962-3466; Carl T. Waskiewicz, Executive Director and Administrator

ASC- North, 590 Dundas Drive, Jacksonville, FL 32218; tel. 904/751-5556; FAX. 904/751-5909; Teresa Heatwole, RN, Director Surgical Services

Atlantic Surgery Center, 541 Health Boulevard, Daytona Beach, FL 32114; tel. 386/239-0021; Linda Boyum, Director

Atlantic Surgery Center, A HealthSouth Facility, 1707 South 25th Street, Fort Pierce, FL 34947; tel. 772/464-8900; FAX. 561/464-1104; Michele Weinberg, Business Office Manager

Atlantic Surgical Center, 150 Southwest 12th Avenue, Suite 450, Pompano Beach, FL 33069; tel. 305/941-3369; Ruben Paradela, Chief Executive Officer

Ayers Surgery Center, 720 Southwest Second Avenue, Suite 101, Gainesville, FL 32601; tel. 904/338-7100; FAX. 904/338-7102; Barbara Hyder, RN, Nurse Manager

Barkley Surgicenter, 63 Barkley Circle, Suite 104, Fort Myers, FL 33907; tel. 941/275-8452; FAX. 941/275-1969; Kerri Gantt LHRM, CMM, Administrative Director

Bayfront Same Day Surgery Center, LLC, 603 Seventh Street South, St. Petersburg, FL 33701; tel. 813/553-7907; FAX. 813/553-7880; Jatin Motiwal, Director

Beraja Healthcare Corp., 2550 Douglas Road, Coral Gables, FL 33134; tel. 305/357-1711; FAX. 305/357-1701; Margarita Caffe, R.N., D.O.N.

Bethesda Outpatient Surgery Center, LLC, 10301 Hagen Ranch Road, Suite 520, Boynton Beach, FL 33437; tel. 561/374-5550; FAX. 561/374-9977; Maddie Linder, Rn, Director of Surgical Services

Boca Raton Outpatient Surgery and Laser Center, 501 Glades Road, Boca Raton, FL 33432; tel. 561/362-4400; FAX. 561/362-4440; Karen Raiano, Administrator

Bon Secours-Venice HealthPark Surgery Center, 1283 Jacaranda Boulevard, Venice, FL 34292; tel. 941/497-5660; FAX. 941/492-3942; Kermit Knight,CASC Administrator

Brevard Surgery Center, 665 Apollo Boulevard, Melbourne, FL 32901; tel. 321/984-0300; FAX. 321/984-0032; Narda Cotman, Surgical Director

Cape Surgery Center, 1941 Waldemere Street, Sarasota, FL 34239-3555; tel. 941/917-1900; FAX. 941/917-2356; Sharon Tolhurst, RN, MBA, Executive

Center for Digestive Health and Pain Management, 12700 Creekside Lane, Suite 202, P.O. Box 33906, Fort Myers, FL 33919; tel. 941/489-4454; FAX. 941/489-2114; Vivian DiCarlo, RN, Nursing Director

Center for Special Surgery, 4650 Fourth Street, N., St. Petersburg, FL 33703; tel. 727/527-1919; FAX. 727/527-0714; Patti Holston, CMPE, Administrator

Central Florida Eye Institute, 3133 Southwest 32nd Avenue, Ocala, FL 34474; tel. 352/237-8400; FAX. 352/237-7190; Thomas L. Croley, M.D.

Clearwater Endoscopy Center, 401 Corbett Street, Suite 220, Clearwater, FL 33756; tel. 727/443-0100; FAX. 727/461-4893; Lori Parrinello, RN Clinical Director

Cleveland Clinic Florida, 3000 West Cypress Creek Road, Fort Lauderdale, FL 33309

Collier Surgery Center, 800 Goodlette Road, N., Suite 120, Naples, FL 34104; tel. 941/262-5757; FAX. 941/262-6073; David W. Douglas, Administrator

Columbia Belair Surgery Center, 1130 Ponce de Leon Boulevard, Clearwater, FL 34616; tel. 813/581-4800; FAX. 813/585-0319; Margie Maddock, Administrator

Columbia Florida Surgery Center, 180 Boston Avenue, Altamonte Springs, FL 32701; tel. 407/830-0573; FAX. 407/830-4373; Anne Hutcheson, Administrator

Columbia Surgery Center, 3901 University Boulevard #111, Jacksonville, FL 32216; tel. 904/448-1948; Debbie Overton-Raines, Administrator

Coral View Surgery Center, 8390 West Flager, Suite 216, Miami, FL 33144; tel. 305/226-5574; Victor Suarez, M.D., President

Cordova Ambulatory Surgical Center, 545 Brent Lane, Pensacola, FL 32503; tel. 904/477-5437; Cynthia Blake, Assistant Administrator

Cortez Foot Surgery Center, PA, 1800 Cortez Road, W., Suite B, Bradenton, FL 34207; tel. 941/758-4608; FAX. 941/758-4438; Margaret Provencher, Administrator

Countryside Surgery Center, 3291 North McMullen Booth Road, Clearwater, FL 33761; tel. 727/725-5800; FAX. 727/797-4002; Karen Nelson, Administrator

Day Surgery, Inc., 1715 Southeast Tiffany Avenue, Port St. Luci, FL 34952; tel. 407/335-7005; Mary Holobaugh, RN, Administrator

DeLand Surgery Center, 651 West Plymouth Avenue, Deland, FL 32720; tel. 386/738-6811; FAX. 386/822-4316; Lynette Knight, Administrator

Section C

Dermatologic and Cosmetic Surgery Center, L.C., 2668 Swamp Cabbage Court, Fort Myers, FL 33901; tel. 813/275-7546; FAX. 813/275-5074; Charles Eby, M.D.

Doctors Surgery Center, 921 North Main Street, Kissimmee, FL 34744; tel. 407/933-7800; FAX. 407/933-0564; Roschelle Cutte, Administrator

Endoscopy Associates of Citrus, 6412 West Gulf to Lake Highway, Crystal River, FL 34429

Endoscopy Center of Ocala, Inc., 1160 Southeast 18th Place, Ocala, FL 34471; tel. 352/732-8905; FAX. 352/732-2661; Fay McCrocklin, RN, Nurse Manager

Endoscopy Center of Sarasota, 1435 Osprey Avenue, Suite 100, Sarasota, FL 34239; tel. 941/366-4475; FAX. 941/366-4390; Susan M. Brongel, RN, Administrator

Eye Care and Surgery Center of Ft. Lauderdale, 2540 Northeast Ninth Street, Ft. Lauderdale, FL 33304; tel. 954/561-3533; FAX. 954/565-9706; Jane M. Beatly, Administrator

Eye Surgery and Laser Center, 4120 Del Prado Boulevard, Cape Coral, FL 33904; tel. 239/542-4068; FAX. 239/542-0704; Deborah Hughes, RN, BSN, CNOR, Risk Manager Designee

Eye Surgery and Laser Center, LLC, 409 Avenue K, S.E., Winter Haven, FL 33880; tel. 863/299-8574; FAX. 863/294-8305; Patricia R. Kent, RN, MBA, CNOR, Center Director

Eye Surgicenter, 2521 Northwest 41st Street, Gainesville, FL 32606; tel. 352/377-7733; FAX. 352/377-9577; William A. Newsome, M.D.

Faculty Clinic, Inc., 653 West Eighth Street, Jacksonville, FL 32209; tel. 904/350-6708

Florida Eye Clinic Ambulatory Surgical Center, 160 Boston Avenue, Altamonte Springs, FL 32701; tel. 407/834-7776; FAX. 407/831-8607; Genevieve Parm, Chief Executive Officer

Florida Eye Institute Surgicenter, L.L.C, 2750 Indian River Boulevard, Vero Beach, FL 32960; tel. 772/569-9500; FAX. 772/569-9507; Mary Lynne MacDonald, Administrator

Florida Medical Clinic Special Procedures Center, 38135 Market Square, Zephyrhills, FL 33540; tel. 813/780-8266; FAX. 813/715-4150; Lou Boyette, RN Supervisor

Forest Oaks Ambulatory Surgical Center, Inc., 7320 Forest Oaks Boulevard, Spring Hill, FL 34606; tel. 352/683-5666; Thomas D. Stelnicki, D.P.M.

Foundation for Advanced Eye Care, 3737 Pine Island Road, Sunrise, FL 33351; tel. 305/572-5888; Wayne Bizer, D.O. Medical Director

Gaskins Eye Care and Surgery Center, 2335 Ninth Street, N., Suite 304, Naples, FL 34103; tel. 239/263-7750; Cindy Gaskins, RN, M.S.N., R.M.

Gulf Coast Endoscopy Center, Inc., 665 Del Prado Boulevard, Cape Coral, FL 33990; tel. 239/772-8892; FAX. 239/574-6262; Sharon Fries, Center Director

Gulf Coast Surgery Center, 411 Second Street, E., Bradenton, FL 34208; tel. 941/746-1121; FAX. 941/746-7816; Carlene Bailey, RN, Administrator

Gulfcoast Surgery Center, 12132 Cortez Boulevard, Brooksville, FL 34613; tel. 352/596-0744; Fawzi Soliman, M.D.

Gulfshore Endoscopy Center, 1064 Goodletter Road, Naples, FL 33940

Harborside Surgery Center, 610 East Olympia Avenue, Punta Gorda, FL 33950; tel. 941/637-0065; FAX. 941/637-0437; Charlene Gorrill - Director of Nurses

HealthSouth Citrus Surgery Center, 110 North Lecanto Highway, Lecanto, FL 34461; tel. 352/527-1825; FAX. 352/527-1827; Douglas Vybiral, Facility Administrator

HealthSouth Emerald Coast Surgery Center, 995 Northwest Mar Walt Drive, Fort Walton Beach, FL 32547; tel. 850/863-7887; FAX. 850/863-4955; Jimmy Bailey, Administrator

HealthSouth Indian River Surgery Center, 1200 37th Street, Vero Beach, FL 32960; tel. 407/770-5600; FAX. 407/770-1793; Regina Ludicke, Clinical Administrator

HealthSouth Medical Partners Surgery Center, 4545 Emerson Expressway, Jacksonville, FL 32207; tel. 904/399-2600; Debbie Loeffler, Administrator

HealthSouth Melbourne Surgery Center, 1340 Medical Park Drive, Suite 101, Melbourne, FL 32901; tel. 407/729-9493; FAX. 407/768-6043; Lee Rocque, Administrator/CEO

HealthSouth Orlando Center for Outpatient Surgery, 1405 South Orange Avenue, Suite 400, Orlando, FL 32806; tel. 407/426-8331; FAX. 407/425-9582

HealthSouth St. Petersburg Surgery Center, 539 Pasadena Avenue, S., St. Petersburg, FL 33707; tel. 727/345-8337; FAX. 727/347-4675; Patsy Conyer, Administrator

Hialeah Ambulatory Care Center, 445 East 25th Street, Hialeah, FL 33176; tel. 305/691-4450; FAX. 305/693-0823; Jose Kone, Administrative Director

Holiday Surgery Center, 1109 U.S. Highway 19, Suite B, Holiday, FL 34691; tel. 727/934-5705; FAX. 727/937-3756; David Wall, Practice Administrator

Jacksonville Surgery Center, 4253 Salisbury Road, Jacksonville, FL 32216; tel. 904/281-0021; FAX. 904/281-0988; Katherine Anderson, RN, B.S.N., Center Director

Kissimmee Surgery Center, 2275 North Central Avenue, Kissimmee, FL 34741; tel. 407/870-0573; FAX. 407/870-1859; Lou Warmijak, Administrator

Lake Surgery and Endoscopy Center, 8100 CR 44 LEG A, Leesburg, FL 34788; tel. 352/323-1995; FAX. 352/323-1691; Marie Free, RN, BSN, Nurse Administrator

Laser & Surgical Center of FL., L.C., Boynton Beach ASC. LLC, 1717-1799 Woolbright Road, Boynton Beach, FL 33426; tel. 516/737-8031; FAX. 561/737-7055; Lily Lee, Administrator

Lee County Center for Foot and Ankle Surgery, Inc., 12734 Kenwood Lane, Suite 44, Fort Myers, FL 33907; tel. 941/936-2454; FAX. 941/936-1974; Sandra Desai, D.P.M.

Leesburg Regional Day Surgery Center, 601 East Dixie Avenue, Plaza 501, Leesburg, FL 34748; tel. 904/365-0700; FAX. 904/365-0758; Renae Vaughn, RN, B.S.N., CNOR, Clinical Director

Manatee Endoscopy Center, Inc., 6010 Pointe West Boulevard, Bradenton, FL 34209; tel. 813/792-4239

Martin Memorial SurgiCenter, 509 Riverside Drive, Suite 100, Stuart, FL 34994; tel. 772/223-5920; FAX. 772/288-5820

Martin Memorial Surgicenter at St. Lucie West, 1095 Northwest St. Lucie West Boulevard, Port St. Lucie, FL 34986; tel. 561/223-5945; FAX. 561/223-6862; Charles S. Immordino, RN, Director, Clinical Operation

Mayo Clinic Jacksonville Ambulatory Surgery Center for G.I., 4500 San Pablo Road, Jacksonville, FL 32224; tel. 904/223-2000; Evelyn Leddy, ASC for GI Coordinator

Mease Countryside Surgery Care Center, 1880 Mease Drive, Safety Harbor, FL 34695; tel. 727/725-6373; FAX. 727/725-6417; Celia Larimore, Administrator

Medical Development Corporation of Pasco County, 7315 Hudson Avenue, Hudson, FL 34667; tel. 727/868-9563; FAX. 727/869-9563; Dawn M. Ernst, Director, Nursing

Medivision of Northern Palm Beach County, 2889 10th Avenue, N., Suite 201, Lake Worth, FL 33461; tel. 407/969-0139; FAX. 407/642-1167; Denise Brower, Administrator

Merritt Island Surgery Center, 220 North Sykes Creek Parkway, Suite 101, Merritt Island, FL 32953; tel. 321/459-0015; FAX. 321/459-2291; Cynthia Johnson, Administrator

Miami Eye Center, 619 Northwest 12th Avenue, Miami, FL 33136; tel. 305/326-0260; FAX. 305/326-1907; Edward C. Gelber, M.D., F.A.C.S.

Mid Florida Surgery Center, 17564 West Highway 441, Mt. Dora, FL 32757; tel. 352/735-4100; FAX. 352/735-2444; Patsy Lentz, RN, Administrative Director

Montgomery Eye Center, 700 Neapolitan Way, Naples, FL 34103; tel. 239/261-8383; FAX. 239/261-8443; Jay E. Montgomery, Administrator

Mullis Eye Institute, Inc., 1600 Jenks Avenue, Panama City, FL 32405; tel. 904/763-6666; FAX. 904/763-6665; Colette Smith, RN, Director

Naples Day Surgery North, 11161 Health Park Boulevard, Naples, FL 34110; tel. 813/598-3111; FAX. 813/598-1707; Thomas C. Buckley, Executive Director

Naples Day Surgery, LLC, 11161 Health Park Blvd., Naples, FL 34110; tel. 941/598-3111; FAX. 941/598-1707; Thomas C. Buckley, Executive Director

New Port Richey Surgery Center, 5415 Gulf Drive, New Port Rich, FL 34652; tel. 727/848-0446; FAX. 727/842-3166; Sandra McFarland, RN, Administrator

New Smyrna Beach Ambulatory Care Center, Inc., 612 Palmetto Street, New Smyrna Beach, FL 32168; tel. 904/423-5500

Newgate Surgery Center, Inc., 5200 Tamiami Trail, Suite 202, Naples, FL 34103; tel. 239/263-6766; FAX. 239/263-3320; Dr. R. Crane

North County Surgicenter, 4000 Burns Road, Palm Beach, FL 33410; tel. 561/626-6446; FAX. 561/626-7244; Victoria Giraldo, Business Manager

North Florida Surgery Center, 4600 North Davis, Pensacola, FL 32503; tel. 904/494-0048; FAX. 904/494-0065; D. M. Whitehead, Administrator and CEO

North Florida Surgery Center, 256 Professional Glen, Lake City, FL 32025; tel. 386/758-8937; Angela Kohlhepp, Administrator

North Florida Surgical Pavilion, 6705 Northwest 10th Place, Gainesville, FL 32605; tel. 352/333-4555; FAX. 352/333-4569; Susan Roland, Administrative Director

Northwest Florida Gastroenterology Center, Inc., 202 Doctors Drive, Panama City, FL 32405; tel. 904/769-7599; FAX. 904/769-7389

Northwest Florida Surgery Center, 767 Airport Road, Panama City, FL 32405; tel. 850/747-0400; FAX. 850/913-9744; Ron Samuelian, Chief Executive Officer

Oakwater Surgical Center, Inc., 3885 Oakwater Circle, Suite B, Orlando, FL 32806; tel. 407/438-9533; FAX. 407/438-9542; Karen Keith, RN, BSN, Administrator

Orange Park Surgery Center, 2050 Professional Center Drive, Orange Park, FL 32073; tel. 904/272-2550; FAX. 904/272-7911; Michele K. Cook, RN, Administrator

Orlando Surgery Center, LTD., 2000 North Orange Avenue, Orlando, FL 32804; tel. 407/894-5808; FAX. 407/894-7802; Rodney C. Hollis, Administrator

Outpatient Surgical Services, Ltd., 301 Northwest 82nd Avenue, Plantation, FL 33324; tel. 954693-8600; FAX. 954/424-1966; Katherine S. Wilson, Administrator

Pal-Med Same Day Surgery, 6950 West 20th Avenue, Hialeah, FL 33016; tel. 305/821-0079; FAX. 305/558-7494; Mario Machado, RN, Director

Palm Beach Eye Clinic, 130 Butler Street, West Palm Beach, FL 33407; tel. 561/832-6113; FAX. 561/833-3003; Andre J. Golino, M.D.

Palm Beach Lakes Surgery Center, 2047 Palm Beach Lakes Boulevard, West Palm Beach, FL 33409; tel. 561/684-1375; FAX. 561/683-0332; Gary Carroll, Manager

Parkside Surgery Center, 2731 Park Street, Jacksonville, FL 32205; tel. 904/389-1077; FAX. 904/389-9959; David Manning, Administrator

Pasco Surgery Center, 5923 Seventh Street, Zephyrhills, FL 33539; tel. 813/782-2143; FAX. 813/788-6011; Mary LePiere, Center Director

Physician's Surgical Care Center, 2056 Aloma Avenue, Winter Park, FL 32792; tel. 407/647-5100; FAX. 407/647-1966

Physicians Ambulatory Surgery Center, 300 Clyde Morris Boulevard, Suite B, Ormond Beach, FL 32174; tel. 386/672-1080; FAX. 386/672-8628; Joel M. Wilder, RN, Administrator

Physicians Surgery Center, Ltd., DBA Lee Island Coast Surgery Center, 4035 Evans Avenue, Fort Myers, FL 33901; tel. 941/939-7375; FAX. 941/275-5248; Michael Pankey, RN, Administrator

Presidential Surgicenter, Inc., 1501 Presidential Way, Suite Nine, West Palm Beach, FL 33401; tel. 407/689-7255; FAX. 407/683-7342; Steve S. Spector, M.D.

Rand Surgical Pavilion Corp., Five West Sample Road, Pompano Beach, FL 33064; tel. 800/782-1711; FAX. 954/782-7490; Deborah Rand, Administrator

Reed Centre for Ambulatory Urological Surgery, 1111 Kane Concourse, Suite 311, Bay Harbor, FL 33154; tel. 305/865-2000

Riverside Park Surgicenter, 2001 College Street, Jacksonville, FL 32204; tel. 904/355-9800; Janice Carter, RN, Director, Nursing

Same-Day Surgicenter of Orlando, 88 West Kaley Street, Orlando, FL 32806; tel. 407/423-0573; FAX. 407/841-7317; Rob Bashone, Administrator

Samuel Wells Surgicenter, Inc., 3599 University Boulevard, S., Suite 604, Jacksonville, FL 32216; tel. 904/399-0905; FAX. 904/346-0757; Faye T. Evans, Administrator

Santa Lucia Surgical Center Inc., 2441 Southwest 37th Avenue, Miami, FL 33145; tel. 305/442-0066; FAX. 305/445-6896

Sarasota Surgery Center, 983 South Beneva Road, Sarasota, FL 34232; tel. 941/365-5355; FAX. 941/953-7080; Administrator

Seven Springs Surgery Center, Inc., 2024 Seven Springs Boulevard, New Port Richey, FL 34655; tel. 727/376-7000; FAX. 727/375-8944; Kathleen M. Geiger, RN, Surgery Director

Southwest Florida Endoscopy Center, 5050 Mason Corbin Court, Ft. Myers, FL 33907; tel. 813/275-6678; FAX. 813/275-1785; Connie Byrd, Administrator

Southwest Florida Institute of Ambulatory Surgery, 3700 Central Avenue, Suite Two, Ft. Myers, FL 33901; tel. 239/275-0665; FAX. 239/275-0503; Susan Hanzevack, Executive Director

Specialty Surgery Of Ocala, LLC, 3201 Southwest 34th Street, Ocala, FL 34474; tel. 352/237-3387; FAX. 352/861-4208; Raymond J. Mencal, Administrator

St. Augustine Endoscopy Center, 212 South Park Circle, E., St. Augustine, FL 32086; tel. 904/824-6108; FAX. 904/823-9613; Santiago A. Rosado, M.D., President

St. John's Surgery Center, Inc., 8901 Conference Drive, Fort Myers, FL 33919; tel. 941/481-8833; FAX. 941/481-7898; Linda Pavletich, RN, Administrator

St. Joseph's Same Day Surgery Center, 3003 West Martin Luther King Boulevard, Tampa, FL 33607; tel. 813/870-4711; FAX. 813/870-4907; Paula McGuiness, Executive Director

St. Lucy's Outpatient Surgery Center, 21275 Olean Boulevard, Port Charlotte, FL 33952; tel. 941/625-1325; FAX. 941/625-6482; E.Q. Skip Fahel, Administrator

St. Luke's Outpatient Surgery Center - Satellite, 4500 San Pablo Road, Jacksonville, FL 32224; tel. 904/953-0100; FAX. 904/953-0019; Debbie Thornblom, Manager

St. Luke's Surgical Center, 43309 U.S. Highway 19, N., P.O. Box 5000, Tarpon Spring, FL 34688-5000; tel. 813/938-2020; FAX. 813/938-5606; Glenn S. Wolfson, M.D., Medical Director

Suncoast Eye Center, Eye Surgery Institute, 14003 Lakeshore Boulevard, Hudson, FL 34667; tel. 727/868-9442; FAX. 727/862-6210; Lawrence A. Seigel, M.D., P.A., Medical Director

Suncoast Medical Clinic,LLC, 601 Seventh Street, S., St. Petersburg, FL 33701; tel. 727/894-1818; FAX. 727/824-7177; Cheryl Macurdy, Director of Clinical Service

Suncoast Skin Surgery Clinic, 4519 U.S. Highway 19, New Port Richey, FL 34652; tel. 813/849-8922; FAX. 813/841-7553; Bethany Carvallo, Administrator

Suncoast Surgery Center of Hernando, Inc., 5060 Commercial Way, Spring Hill, FL 34606; tel. 904/596-3696; FAX. 904/596-2707; Bethany Carvallo, Administrator

Sunrise Surgical Center, 110 Yorktowne Drive, Daytona Beach, FL 32119; tel. 904/788-6696; FAX. 904/788-2219; Carolyn Teal

Surgery Center at Coral Springs, 967 University Drive, Coral Springs, FL 33071; tel. 954341-5553; FAX. 954/344-7054

Surgery Center at St. Andrews, Inc., 1350 East Venice Avenue, Venice, FL 34285; tel. 941/488-2030; FAX. 941/484-2010; Laura Hendershott, Business Office Supervisor

Surgery Center of Jupiter, Inc., 102 Coastal Way, Jupiter, FL 33477; tel. 561/747-1111; FAX. 560/747-4151; Monroe N. Benaim, M.D., Medical Director

Surgery Center of North Florida, Inc., 6520 Northwest Ninth Boulevard, Gainsville, FL 32615; tel. 352/331-7987; FAX. 352/331-2787; Joy Ingram, Administrator

Surgery Center of Stuart, 2096 Southeast Ocean Boulevard, Stuart, FL 34996; tel. 561/223-0174; FAX. 561/223-0946; Charles Immordino, RN, Administrator

Surgical Center of Central Florida, 3601 South Highlands Avenue, Sebring, FL 33870; tel. 863/382-7500; FAX. 863/385-7332; Sharon Keiber, RN, Administrator

Surgical Licensed Ward, 110 West Underwood Street, Suite B, Orlando, FL 32806; tel. 407/648-9151; FAX. 407/426-7017; Cheryl Modica, RN, LHRM, Administrator

Surgical Park Center, Ltd., 9100 Southwest 87th Avenue, Miami, FL 33176; tel. 305/271-9100; FAX. 305/270-8527; Mike Casanova, Administrator

Surgicare Center, Inc., 4101 Evans Avenue, Ft. Myers, FL 33901; tel. 239/939-3456; FAX. 239/939-1164; Paula M. Dobberstein, RN, HCRM, Director of Nursing

Tallahassee Endoscopy Center, 2400 Miccosukee Road, Tallahassee, FL 32308; tel. 850/877-2105; FAX. 850/942-1761; Noel Withers, Administrator

Tallahassee Outpatient Surgery Center, Inc., 3334 Capital Medical Boulevard, Suite 500, Tallahassee, FL 32308; tel. 904/877-4688; FAX. 904/877-0368; Judi Cleckner RN, Administrator

Tallahassee Single Day Surgery, 1661 Phillips Road, Tallahassee, FL 32308; tel. 850/878-5165; FAX. 850/942-5545; Elizabeth Trikardos, Director of Nursing

Tampa Bay Surgery Center, Inc., 11811 North Dale Mabry, Tampa, FL 33618; tel. 813/961-8500; FAX. 813/265-2564; Jay L. Rosen, M.D., Executive Director

Tampa Eye Surgery Center, 4302 North Gomez, Tampa, FL 33607; tel. 813/870-6330; FAX. 813/871-3956; Beverly Martin, Administrator

Tampa Outpatient Surgical Facility, 5013 North Armenia Avenue, Tampa, FL 33603; tel. 813/875-0562; FAX. 813/871-5236; Maureen F. Martin RN, CASC

The Aesthetic Plastic Surgery Center, 135 San Marco Drive, Venice, FL 34285; tel. 941/484-6836; FAX. 941/484-9690; Linda Martin, Administrative Director

The Endoscopy Center, 4810 North Davis Highway, Pensacola, FL 32503; tel. 850/474-8988; FAX. 850/478-9903; Alice Cartee, Administrator

The Endoscopy Center of Naples, 150 Tamiami Trail, N., Suite One, Naples, FL 34102; tel. 941/262-8306; FAX. 941/262-3179; Marjorie Venditti, Billing Office Manager

The Endoscopy Center, Inc., 5101 Southwest Eighth Street, Miami, FL 33134; Regina Dhanani, Center Director

The Eye Associates Surgery Center, 6002 Pointe West Boulevard, Bradenton, FL 34209; tel. 941/792-2020; FAX. 941/792-2832; Linda Colson, RN, Director

The Gastrointestinal Center of Hialeah, 135 West 49th Street, Hialeah, FL 33012; tel. 305/825-1487; FAX. 305/826-6910; Annette Aivardo, RN

The Ocala Eye Surgery Center, 3330 Southwest 33rd Road, Ocala, FL 34474; tel. 352/873-9311; FAX. 352/873-9652; Carol Hiatt, RN, Nurse Administrator

The Sarasota Ophthalmology, ASC, LLC, dba Center for Advanced Eye Surgery, 3920 Bee Ridge Road Building F, Suite C, Sarasota, FL 34233; tel. 941/925-0000; FAX. 941/927-2726; Darice Downs, RN, LHRM,Center Director

The Sheridan Surgery Center, 95 Bulldog Boulevard, Melbourne, FL 32901; tel. 321/952-9800; FAX. 321/952-7889; Anne Latorra, Director

The Surgery Center of Coral Gables, LLC., 1097 S.W. Le Jeune Road, Miami, FL 33134; tel. 305/461-1300; Laura Lilburn, RN, CNOR, Center Director

The Treasure Coast Cosmetic Surgery Center, 1901 Port St. Lucie Boulevard, Port St. Lucie, FL 34952; tel. 561/335-3954; Donato A. Viggiano, M.D.

Total Surgery Center, 130 Tamiami Trail, Suite 210, Naples, FL 34102; tel. 239/434-4118; FAX. 239/434-6343; Mary Ploski, Administrator

Treasure Coast Center for Surgery, 1411 East Ocean Boulevard, Stuart, FL 34996; tel. 772/286-8028; FAX. 772/283-6628; Andrea Day, Business Office Manager

Trinity Outpatient Center, 2102 Trinity Oaks Boulevard, New Port Richey, FL 34655; tel. 727/372-4000; FAX. 727/372-4065; Nancy Burden, Director

University Surgical Center, 7251 University Boulevard, Suite 100, Winter Park, FL 32792; tel. 407/677-0066; FAX. 407/677-4199; Laura Hofma, MBA, RHIA, CASC, Administrator

Urological Ambulatory Surgery Center, Inc., 1812 North Mills Avenue, Orlando, FL 32803; tel. 407/992-2640; FAX. 407/897-2290; Susan A. Wuerz, Administrator

Urology Health Center, 5652 Meadow Lane, New Port Rich, FL 34652; tel. 813/842-9561; FAX. 813/848-7270; Greg Toney, Administrator

Venture Ambulatory Surgery Center, 16853 Northeast Second Avenue, Suite 400, North Miami Beach, FL 33162; tel. 305/652-2999; FAX. 305/652-8156; Lali Perez, RN, B.S.N., Center Director

Vero Eye Center, 70 Royal Palm Pointe, Vero Beach, FL 32960; tel. 772/569-6600; FAX. 772/569-5341; E.S. Branigan, III, M.D.

Volusia Endoscopy & Surgery Center, Inc., 550 Memorial Circle, Suite G, Ormond Beach, FL 32174; tel. 386/672-0017; FAX. 386/672-6732; Susan K. Amon, RN, DON LHCRM

Waterside Ambulatory Surgical Center, Inc., 2001 North Flagler Drive, West Palm Beach, FL 33407; tel. 561/659-6543; FAX. 561/659-3533; Lisa Bolognini, Admin. Director

Winter Park Ambulatory Surgical Center, 1000 South Orlando Avenue, Winter Park, FL 32789; tel. 407/629-1500; FAX. 407/629-1741; Shirley Mead, Administrative Nurse Manager

GEORGIA

Advanced Aesthetics Plastic Surgery Center, 499 Arrowhead Boulevard, Jonesboro, GA 30236; tel. 770/603-6000; FAX. 770/603-7064; Paul D. Feldman, President

Advanced Surgery Center of Georgia, 220 Hospital Road, Canton, GA 30114; tel. 770/479-2202; FAX. 770/479-6666; Judith Grady, Administrator

Aesthetic Laser & Surgery Facility, 416 Gordon Ave., Thomasville, GA 31792-6644; tel. 229/228-7200; FAX. 229/228-5193; G. Courtney Houston, M.D., Medical Director

Aestheticare Surgicenter, P.C., 975 Johnson Ferry Road, Suite 160, Atlanta, GA 30342; tel. 404/303-7542; FAX. 404/531-0649; Sharon A. Pesselato, Director

Affinity Outpatient Services, 2224 US Highway 41 North, Tifton, GA 31794; tel. 912/391-4299; FAX. 912/391-4291; Barry L. Cutts, Administrator

Albany Surgery Center, LLP, 531 Seventh Avenue, Albany, GA 31701; tel. 912/883-3535; FAX. 912/888-1079; Stephen M. Wilder, D.P.M., Medical Director

Ambulatory Foot and Leg Surgical Center, 1650 Mulkey Road, Austell, GA 30001; tel. 770/941-3633; Alan Shaw, D.P.M., Chief Executive Officer

Ambulatory Laser and Surgery Center, 425 Forest Parkway, Suite 103, Forest Park, GA 30297-2135; tel. 404/363-1087; FAX. 404/363-9951; Dr. Paul A. Colon, Medical Director

Athens Plastic Surgery Center, 2325 Prince Avenue, Athens, GA 30606; tel. 706/546-0280; FAX. 404/548-0258; Stephen B. Lober, M.D., Administrator

Atlanta Aesthetic Surgery Center, Inc., 4200 Northside Parkway, Building Eight, Atlanta, GA 30327; tel. 404/233-3833; Debbie Clotfelter, Administrator

Atlanta Endoscopy Center, LTD, 2665 North Decatur Road, Suite 545, Decatur, GA 30033; tel. 404/297-5000; FAX. 404/296-9890; Kevin Mussareb RN Clinical Coordinator

Atlanta Eye Surgery Center, P.C., 3200 Downwood Circle, NW, Suite 200, Atlanta, GA 30327; tel. 404/355-8721; Walter G. Elliott, Administrator

Atlanta Outpatient Peachtree Dunwoody Center, 5505 Peachtree-Dunwoody Road, Suite 150, Atlanta, GA 30342; tel. 404/847-0893; FAX. 404/843-8664; Janie Ellison, Administrator

Atlanta Outpatient Surgery Center, 993 Johnson Ferry Road, Suite 300, Atlanta, GA 30342; tel. 404/252-3074; FAX. 404/843-2089; Marjane Ellison, Administrator

Atlanta Surgi-Center, Inc., 1113 Spring Street, Atlanta, GA 30309; tel. 404/892-8608; FAX. 404/892-8143; Toni P. Hawkins, Administrator

Atlanta Women's Medical Center, Inc., 235 West Wieuca Road, Atlanta, GA 30342; tel. 404/257-0057; FAX. 404/257-1245; Golda Melnik, Administrator

Augusta Plastic Surgery Center, Inc., 1348 Walton Way, Suite 6300, Augusta, GA 30901-2772; tel. 706/724-5611; FAX. 706/724-5435; Sandy Woodward, Administrator

Augusta Surgical Center, 915 Russell Street, Augusta, GA 30904-4115; tel. 706/738-4925; FAX. 706/738-7224; Jeff Simless, Administrator

Brunswick Endoscopy Center, 3217 4th Street, Brunswick, GA 31520-3759; tel. 912/267-1802; FAX. 912/267-0061; Rita Warren, Administrator

Center for Plastic Surgery, 365 East Paces Ferry Road, Atlanta, GA 30305; tel. 404/814-1100; FAX. 404/814-0015; Dr. Vincent Zubowicz, Medical Director

Center for Reconstructive Surgery, 5335 Old National Highway, College Park, GA 30349; tel. 404/768-3668; FAX. 404/763-2929; Gregory Alvarez, D.P.M.

Clayton Outpatient Surgical Center, Inc., 6911 Tara Boulevard, Jonesboro, GA 30236; tel. 770/477-9535; FAX. 770/471-7826; Rhonda Aydlotte Osborne, R.N.

Section C

Cobb Foot and Leg Surgery Center, 792 Church Street, Suite 102, Marietta, GA 30060; tel. 770/422–9864; FAX. 770/984–0303; Glyn Lewis, Administrator

Coliseum Same Day Surgery, 340 Hospital Drive, P.O. Box 6154, Macon, GA 31208; tel. 912/742–1403; FAX. 912/742–1671; Lenore Sell, Administrator

Columbia Augusta Surgical Center, 915 Russell Street, Augusta, GA 30904; tel. 706/738–4925; FAX. 706/738–7224; Beryl Barrett, RN, Administrator

Columbus Women's Health Organization, Inc., 3850 Rosemont Drive, Columbus, GA 31901; tel. 706/323–8363

Decatur Urological Clinic-Ambulatory Surgery Center, Inc., 428 Winn Court, Decatur, GA 30030; tel. 404/298–0217; FAX. 404/299–5178; Sabrina Jones, Office Manager

DeKalb Endoscopy Center, 2675 North Decatur Road, Suite 506, Decatur, GA 30033; tel. 404/299–1679; FAX. 404/501–7558; Peter Leff, M.D.

Dennis Surgery Center, Inc., 3193 Howell Mill Road, Suite 215, Atlanta, GA 30327; tel. 404/355–1312; Valerie Garrett, Administrator

Doctors Hospital Surgery Center, 635 Ronald Reagan Drive, Evans, GA 30809; tel. 706/868–3110; FAX. 706/868–3156; Sharon Gelinas, Administrator

Dunwoody Outpatient Surgicenter, Inc., 4553 North Shallowford Road, Suite 60C, Atlanta, GA 30338; tel. 770/455–1983; FAX. 770/457–2823; Janet Davies, Administrator

Endoscopy Center of Columbus, Inc, 1041 Talbotton Road, Columbus, GA 31904-8745; tel. 706/327–0700; Jean Patterson, RN, Administrator

Endoscopy Center of Southeast Georgia, Inc., 200 Maple Drive, P.O. Box 1367, Vidalia, GA 30475; tel. 912/537–9851; Dixie Calhoun, RN, Administrator

Feminist Women's Health Center, 1924 Cliff Valley Way, Atlanta, GA 30329; tel. 404/874–7551; FAX. 404/874–3028; Jan Lockridge, Administrator

G.I. Endoscopy Center, 6555 Professional Place, Suite B, Riverdale, GA 30274; tel. 404/996–5959; FAX. 404/991–1596; Aruna Jaya Prakash, Administrator

Gainesville Surgery Center, 1945 Beverly Road, Gainesville, GA 30501-2034; tel. 770/287–1500; Karen Fankhauser, Administrator

Gastrointestinal Endoscopy of Gwinnett, 600 Professional Drive, Suite 130, Lawrenceville, GA 30045; tel. 770/995–7989; FAX. 770/339–8646; Betsy Roberts, Practice Manager

Georgia Lithotripsy Center, 120 Trinity Place, Athens, GA 30607; tel. 404/543–2718; David C. Allen, M.D., Administrator

Georgia Surgical Centers - South, 541 Forest Parkway, Suite 14, Forest Park, GA 30297-6110; tel. 404/366–5652; Trudy Hunley, Administrator

Golden Isles Surgical Center, Inc., 2916 Glynn Avenue, Brunswick, GA 31530; tel. 912/265–3210; FAX. 912/265–1481; J. Brooker, Office Manager

Gwinnet Endoscopy Center, 758 Old Norcross Road, Suite 250, Lawrenceville, GA 30045; tel. 770682–7220; FAX. 770/338–0510; Kerry H. King, M.D., Medical Director

HealthSouth Surgery Center of Atlanta, 1140 Hammond Drive, Building F, Suite 6100, Atlanta, GA 30328; tel. 770/551–9944; FAX. 770/551–8826; Mary Hardwick, Administrator

HealthSouth Surgery Center of Gwinnett, 2131 Fountain Drive, Snellville, GA 30078; tel. 770/979–8200; FAX. 770/979–1327; Holly Kouts, Administrator

Marietta Surgical Center, Ambulatory Surgery Division, HCA, The Health Company, 780 Canton Road, Suite 100, Marietta, GA 30060; tel. 770/422–1579; FAX. 770/428–4861; Faith Wheeler, Rn CNDR QA/Risk Manager

Medical Eye Associates, Inc., 1429 Oglethorpe Street, Macon, GA 31201; tel. 478/743–7061; FAX. 478/743–6296; Diane Vaughn, Practice Manager

Midtown Urology Surgical Center, 128 North Avenue, N.E., Suite 100, Atlanta, GA 30308; tel. 404/881–0966; FAX. 404/881–6398; Jenelle E. Foote, M.D., Medical Director

North Atlanta Endoscopy Center, 5555 Peachtree-Dunwoody Road, Suite G70, Atlanta, GA 30342-1703; tel. 404/843–0500; Phyllis Pritchett, Administrator

North Atlanta Head and Neck Surgery Center, Inc., 980 Johnson Ferry Road, Northside Doctors Centre, Atlanta, GA 30342; tel. 404/256–5428; FAX. 404/250–1881; Pradeep K. Snha, M.D.,PhD

North Fulton Diagnostic Gastrointestinal, 2500 Hospital Boulevard, Suite 480, Roswell, GA 30076; tel. 770/475–3085; David A. Atefi, M.D.

North Georgia Endoscopy Center, Inc., 320 Hospital Road, Canton, GA 30114; tel. 770/479–5535; FAX. 770/479–8821; Kevin W. Kellogg, Administrator

North Georgia Outpatient Surgery Center, 795 Red Bud Road, Calhoun, GA 30701; tel. 706/629–1852; FAX. 706/629–8004; Herbert E. Kosmahl, President

North Oak Ambulatory Surgical Center, 2718 North Oak Street, Valdosta, GA 31602; tel. 229/242–3668; FAX. 229/253–8666; T.E. Pitts, D.P.M.

Northeast Georgia Plastic Surgery Center, 1296 Sims Street, Gainesville, GA 30501; tel. 770/534–1856; FAX. 770/531–0355; Sam Richwine, Medical Director

Northlake Ambulatory Surgical Center, 2193 Northlake Parkway, Building 12, Suite 114, Tucker, GA 30084-4113; tel. 770/938–4860; Winfield Butlin, Administrator

Northlake Endoscopy Center, 1459 Montreal Road, Suite 204, Tucker, GA 30084; tel. 770/939–4721; FAX. 770/939–1187; Gayle Carter, Administrator

Northside Foot and Ankle Outpatient Surgical Center, 3415 Holcomb Bridge Road, Norcross, GA 30092; tel. 770/449–1122; FAX. 770/242–8709; Steven T. Arminio, DPM, Administrator

Northside Hospital Outpatient Surgical Center, 3400-A State Bridge Road, Suite 240, Alpharetta, GA 30202; tel. 404/667–4060; Sidney Kirscher, Administrator

Northside Women's Clinic, Inc., 3543 Chamblee-Dunwoody Road, Atlanta, GA 30341; tel. 770/455–4210; FAX. 770/451–9529; James W. Gay, M.D., Administrator

Novamed Surgery Center Of Columbus, GA, 7351 Old Moon Road, Columbus, GA 31909; tel. 706/221–2721; FAX. 706/221–2754; Nancy Beth Pedersen, RN ASC Director

Outpatient Center for Foot Surgery, Inc., 730 South Eighth Street, Suite B, Griffin, GA 30224; tel. 770/228–6644; FAX. 770/228–5769; Allison Sliger, Administrator

Paces Plastic Surgery Center, Inc., 3200 Downwood Circle, Suite 640, Atlanta, GA 30327; tel. 404/351–0051; FAX. 404/351–0632; Cathy Wood, Administrator

Parkwood Ambulatory Surgical Center, 2605 Parkwood Drive, Brunswick, GA 31520; tel. 912/265–4766; FAX. 912/267–9857; Louise Shaw, RN

Piedmont Surgery Center, 4660 Riverside Park Boulevard, Macon, GA 31210; tel. 912/471–6300; Mikell Peed, Administrator

Planned Parenthood of Reproductive Health Services, 1289 Broad Street, Augusta, GA 30911; tel. 706/724–5557; FAX. 706/724–5293; Vanetta D. King, Center Manager

Podiatric Surgi Center, 215 Clairemont Avenue, Decatur, GA 30030; tel. 404/373–2529; FAX. 404/373–1655; Jerald N. Kramer, President

Pulliam Ambulatory Surgical Center, 4167 Hospital Drive, Covington, GA 30015, P.O. Box 469, Covington, GA 30015; tel. 404/786–1234; M.M. Pulliam, P.C., Medical Director

Resurgens Surgical Center, 5671 Peachtree Dunwoody Road, Suite 800, Atlanta, GA 30342; tel. 404/531–8532; Leslie Mattson, RN Administrator

Roswell Ambulatory Surgery Center, 1250 Upper Hembree Road, Ste. A, Roswell, GA 30076; tel. 770/663–8011; FAX. 770/754–9820; Dr. Glyn Lewis, Administrator

Savannah Medical Clinic, 120 East 34th Street, Savannah, GA 31401; tel. 912/236–1603; FAX. 912/236–1605; William Knorr, M.D., Administrator

Savannah Outpatient Foot And Ankle Surgery Center, 310 Eisenhower Drive, Suite Seven B, Savannah, GA 31406; tel. 912/356–8440; FAX. 912/356–8439; Susan Brown, RN Administrator

Savannah Plastic Surgicenter, 7208 Hodgson Memorial, Suite 505, Savannah, GA 31406; tel. 912/351–5050; FAX. 912/351–5051; Scott W. Vann MD

Statesboro Ambulatory Surgery Center, 95 Bel-Air Drive, Statesboro, GA 30461-6879; tel. 912/489–6519; FAX. 912/764–1882; Luane L. Jordan, RN

Surgery Center At Mount Zion, 4000 Corporate Center Drive, Suite 100, Morrow, GA 30260-1407; tel. 770/960–2701; FAX. 770/960–2702; Linda Simmons, Administrator

The Cosmetic and Plastic Surgicenter of South Atlanta, 6524 Professional Place, Riverdale, GA 30274; tel. 770/991–1733; FAX. 770/997–7204; Nabil Elsahy, M.D.

The Emory Clinic Ambulatory Surgery Center, 1365 Clifton Road, N.E., Atlanta, GA 30322; tel. 404/778–5000; W. Mike Mason, Administrator

The Foot Surgery Center, 2520 Windy Hill Road, Suite 105, Marietta, GA 30067; tel. 770/952–0868; L. Susan Rothstein, Administrator

The Rome Surgery Center, 16 John Maddox Drive, Rome, GA 30165; tel. 706/802–3727; FAX. 706/802–3883; Neal Jochimsen, Administrator

Tifton Endoscopy Center, Inc., 1111 E. 20th Street, Tifton, GA 31794-3668; tel. 229/382–9338; FAX. 229/382–4282; Linda Ingram, RN, Nursing Administrator

HAWAII

Aloha Surgical Center, 239 Hoohana Street, Kahului, HI 96732; tel. 808/877–3984; FAX. 808/871–6498; Russell T. Stodd, M.D., Medical Director

Cataract and Vision Center of Hawaii, 1712 Liliha Street, Suite 400, Honolulu, HI 96817; tel. 808/524–1010; FAX. 808/531–1030; Worldster Lee, Administrator

Hawaiian Eye Surgicenter, 606 Kilani Avenue, Wahiawa, HI 96786; tel. 808/622–2645; FAX. 808/621–3151; Christopher M. Tortora, M.D., Surgeon, Director

HealthSouth Surgicare of Hawaii, Inc., 550 South Beretania Street, Suite 700, Honolulu, HI 96813; tel. 808/528–2511; FAX. 808/526–0651; Administrator

Kaiser Honolulu Clinic, 1010 Pensacola Street, Honolulu, HI 96814; tel. 808/545–2950; FAX. 808/597–2249; Jonathan Ganz, Administrator

Kaiser Wailuku Clinic, 80 Mahalani Street, Wailuku, HI 96793; tel. 808/243–6112; FAX. 808/243–6609; Martha Turner, Director

The Endoscopy Center, 134 Pu'uhou Way, Hilo, HI 96720; tel. 808/935–1956; FAX. 808/935–7657; Jody Montell, Administrator

The Surgical Suites, LLC, 1100 Ward Avenue, Suite 1001, Honolulu, HI 96814; tel. 808/531–0127; FAX. 808/531–0455; Carlos Omphroy, M.D., President

IDAHO

Addison Surgery Center, 191 Addison Avenue, Twin Falls, ID 83301; tel. 208/734–5993; FAX. 208/734–8441; David A. Blackmer, D.P.M., President

Boise Center for Foot Surgery, 1400 West Bannock, Boise, ID 83702; tel. 208/381–0262; FAX. 208/429–8575; Christine Graviet, Administrator

Boise Gastroenterology Associates, P.A., Idaho Endoscopy Center, 6259 W. Emerald Street, Boise, ID 83704; tel. 208/489–1900; FAX. 208/375–5286; Robb F. Gibson, M.D., President

Coeur D'Alene Foot and Ankle Surgery Center, 101 Ironwood Drive, Suite 131, Coeur D'Alene, ID 83814; tel. 208/666–0814; Stephen A. Isham, D.P.M., Chairman, Board of Directors

Coeur D'Alene Surgery Center, 2121 Ironwood Center Drive, Coeur D'Alene, ID 83814; tel. 208/765–9059; FAX. 208/664–9998; Peter C. Jones, M.D., President

Emerald Surgical Center, 811 North Liberty, Boise, ID 83704; tel. 208/323–4522; FAX. 208/321–9585; William Evans, Administrator

Idaho Ambucare Center, Inc., 4400 Flamingo Ave., Nampa, ID 83686; tel. 208/288–4750; FAX. 208/288–4765; Gary Botimer, Administrator

Idaho Eye Surgicenter, 2025 East 17th Street, Idaho Falls, ID 83404; tel. 208/524–2025; FAX. 208/529–1924; Bradley P. Garnder, M.D.

Idaho Falls Surgical Center, 1945 East 17th Street, Idaho Falls, ID 83404; tel. 208/529–1945; FAX. 208/529–1961; Steven V. Klippert, M.D., CEO

Idaho Foot Surgery Center, 782 South Woodruff, Idaho Falls, ID 83401; tel. 208/529–8393; FAX. 208/529–8078; Bruce G. Tolman, D.P.M., Facility Director

Jefferson Day Surgery Center, 220 West Jefferson, Boise, ID 83702; tel. 208/343–3802; FAX. 208/343–9161; William Stano, President

North Idaho Cataract and Laser Center, Inc., 1814 Lincoln Way, Coeur D'Alene, ID 83814; tel. 208/667–2531; FAX. 208/765–9385; Karen Sines, Administrator

Pacific Cataract and Laser Institute, 250 Bobwhite Court, Suite 100, Boise, ID 83706-3983; tel. 208/385-7576; FAX. 208/385-0050; Sherri Mellville, Site Coordinator

Rock Creek Endoscopy Center, 284 Martin Street, Suite Two, Twin Falls, ID 83301; tel. 208/732-3030; FAX. 208/733-8970; Tammy Pehrson, Nurse Manager

Surgicare Center of Idaho,L. L.C., 360 East Mallard Drive, Suite 125, Boise, ID 83706; tel. 208/336-8700; FAX. 208/426-0902; Mark Hollingshead, Medical Director

The Surgery Center, 115 Falls Avenue, W., P.O. Box 1864, Twin Falls, ID 83303-1864; tel. 208/733-1662; FAX. 208/734-3632; Larry Maxwell, M.D., Administrator

ILLINOIS

25 East Same Day Surgery, 25 East Washington, Suite 300, Chicago, IL 60602; tel. 312/726-3329; FAX. 312/726-3823; Patricia Wamsley, Administrator

A.C.T. Medical Center, 5714 West Division Street, Chicago, IL 60651; tel. 312/921-4300; Anthony Centrachio, Administrator

A.C.U. Health Center, LTD., 736 York Road, Hinsdale, IL 60521; tel. 630/794-0645; FAX. 630/794-0169; Lisa Shyne, Administrator

Able Health Center, Ltd., 1640 Arlington Heights Road, Suite 110, Arlington Heights, IL 60004; tel. 847/255-7400; FAX. 847/398-4585

Access Health Center, Ltd., 1700 75th Street, Downers Grove, IL 60516; tel. 630/964-0000; FAX. 630/964-0047; Lisa Shyne, Director

Advantage Health Care, LTD., 203 E. Irving Park Road, Wood Dale, IL 60191; tel. 630/595-1515; FAX. 630/595-9097; Lynn Henricks, Administrator

Albany Medical Surgical Center, 5086 North Elston, Chicago, IL 60630; tel. 312/725-0200; FAX. 312/725-6152; Diana Lammon, Administrator

Ambulatory Surgicenter of Downers Grove, Ltd., 4333 Main Street, Downers Grove, IL 60515; tel. 630/332-9451; Inga Ferdkoff, M.D., Administrator

American Women's Medical Center, 2744 North Western, Chicago, IL 60647; tel. 773/772-7726; FAX. 773/772-3696; Jan Barton, M.D., Administrator

AmSurg/Columbia HCA, 330 North Madison Street, Joliet, IL 60435; tel. 815/744-3000; FAX. 815/744-7916; Anne M. Cole, Administrator

Apple Tree Health Care, Ltd, dba Chang's Medical Arts Surgicenter, 2809 North Center Street, Maryville, IL 62062; tel. 618/288-1882; FAX. 618/288-3575; Patty Roeder

Arlington Health Center, Ltd., 1640 Arlington Heights Road, Suite 210, Arlington Heights, IL 60004; tel. 847/255-7474

Bel-Clair Ambulatory Surgical Treatment Center, 325 West Lincoln, Belleville, IL 62220; tel. 618/235-2299; FAX. 618/235-2556; David Horace, Administrator

Carbondale Clinic Ambulatory Surgical Treatment Center, 2601 West Main Street, Carbondale, IL 62901; tel. 618/549-5361; FAX. 618/549-5128; Susan Hankins, RN

Carle Surgicenter, 1702 South Mattis Avenue, Champaign, IL 61821; tel. 217/326-2030; Julie Root, RN, Administrator

Center for Reconstructive Surgery, 6311 West 95th Street, Oak Lawn, IL 60453; tel. 708/499-3355; FAX. 708/425-5654; Carmen Hollimon, Administrator

Children's Pediatric Specialty Services In Westchester, 2301 Enterprise Drive, Westchester, IL 60154; tel. 708/836-4800; FAX. 708/836-4805; Grace Doherty, Director, Satellite Services

CMP Surgicenter, Ltd, 3412 West Fullerton Avenue, Chicago, IL 60647; tel. 773/235-8000; FAX. 773/235-7018; Carlos G. Baldoceda, M.D., Medical Director

Columbia Surgicare-North Michigan Avenue, L.P., 60 East Delaware, 15th Floor, Chicago, IL 60611; tel. 312/440-5100; FAX. 312/440-5114; Barbara Villa, Administrator

Columbia-Northwest Surgicare, 1100 West Central Road, Arlington Heights, IL 60005; tel. 847/259-3080; FAX. 847/259-3190; Barbara Cerwin, RN, Administrator

Community Health and Emergency Services, 13245 Kessler Road, P.O. Box 233, Cairo, IL 62914; tel. 618/734-4400; FAX. 618/734-9406; Frederick L. Bernstein, Chief Executive Officer

Concord Medical Center, 17 West Grand, Chicago, IL 60610; tel. 312/467-6555; FAX. 312/467-9683; Ali Nilli, Administrator

Dimensions Medical Center, Ltd., 1455 East Golf Road, Suite 108, Des Plaines, IL 60016; tel. 847/390-9300; FAX. 847/390-0035; Vera Schmidt, Administrator

Dreyer Ambulatory Surgery Center, 1221 North Highland Avenue, Aurora, IL 60506; tel. 630/264-8400; FAX. 630/264-8402; Josie Nash, RN, BSN, Administrator

Eastland Medical Plaza SurgiCenter, LLC, 1505 Eastland Drive, Suite 180, Bloomington, IL 61701; tel. 309/662-2500; FAX. 309/662-7143; Brenda Cyrulik, Manager

Edwardsville Ambulatory Surgical Center, LLC, 12, Ginger Creek Parkway, Glen Carbon, IL 62034; tel. 618/656-8200; FAX. 618/656-8204; Brian Burnside, Administrator

Effingham Ambulatory Surgical Treatment Center, LTD., 904 West Temple Street, Effingham, IL 62401; tel. 217/342-1234; FAX. 217/342-1230; Leanne Fish, RN, CNOR, Administrator

Elmwood Park Same Day Surgery Center, 1614 North Harlem Avenue, Elmwood Park, IL 60607; tel. 708/452-5000; FAX. 708/452-5588; K. Rainone, Administrator

Foot and Ankle Surgical Center, Ltd., 1455 Golf Road, Suite 131, Des Plaines, IL 60016; tel. 847/390-7666; Lowell S. Weil, DPM, FACFS,Medical Director

Golf Surgical Center, 8901 Golf Road, Des Plaines, IL 60016; tel. 847/299-2273; FAX. 847/299-2297; John B. Kinzer, M.D., Executive Director

HealthSouth Popular Creek Surgical Center, 1800 McDonough Road, Hoffman Estates, IL 60192; tel. 847/742-7272; FAX. 847/697-3210; Randy Patton, Administrator

HealthSouth Surgery Center of Belleville, 28 North 64th Street, Belleville, IL 62223; tel. 618/398-5705; FAX. 618/398-5764; Diane Joiner, RN, Administrator

HealthSouth Surgery Center of Hawthorn, 1900 Hollister Drive, Suite 100, Libertyville, IL 60048; tel. 847/367-8100; FAX. 847/367-8335; Dr. Gary Rippberger, Administrator

HealthSouth Surgery Center of Southern Illinois, P.O. Box 1729, 806 N. Treas, Marion, IL 62959; tel. 618/993-2113; FAX. 618/993-2041; Linda Bickers, RN, Administrator

Hinsdale Surgical Center, LLC, 908 North Elm Street, Suite 401, Hinsdale, IL 60521; tel. 630/325-5035; FAX. 630/325-5134; Shirley E. Zemansky, RN, Executive Director

Hope Clinic for Women, Ltd., 1602 21st Street, Granite City, IL 62040; tel. 800/844-3130; FAX. 615/451-9092; Sally Burgess, MBA, Executive Director

Illinois Eye Surgeons Cataract Surgery, 3990 North Illinois Street, Belleville, IL 62221; tel. 618/235-3100; Cathy Vieluf, Administrator

Ingalls Same Day Surgery, 6701 West 159th Street, Tinley Park, IL 60477; tel. 708/429-0222; FAX. 708/429-0293; John Czech, Administrator

Loyola Ambulatory Surgery Center at Oakbrook, One South 224 Summit Avenue, Suite 201, Oakbrook Terr, IL 60181; tel. 630/916-7088; Geoff Abbott, Administrator

LP Central Community Halth Centre, 355 East Fifth Ave., P.O. Box 68, Clifton, IL 60927; tel. 815/694-2392; Steve Wilder, Administrator

Midwest Center for Day Surgery, 3811 Highland Avenue, Downers Grove, IL 60515; tel. 630/852-9300; FAX. 630/852-7773; Ronald P. Ladniak, Administrator

Midwest Eye Center, S.C., 1700 East West Road, Calumet City, IL 60409; tel. 708/891-3330; FAX. 708/891-0904; Afzal Ahmad, M.D., Administrator

Naperville Surgical Centre, 1263 Rickert Drive, Naperville, IL 60540; tel. 630/305-3300; FAX. 630/305-3301; Ronald P. Ladniak

North Shore Endoscopy Center, 101 South Waukegan Road, Suite 980, Lake Bluff, IL 60044; tel. 847/604-8700; FAX. 847/604-8711; Everett P. Kirch, M.D., Administrator

North Shore Same Day Surgicenter, 815 Howard Street, Evanston, IL 60202; tel. 847/869-8500; FAX. 847/869-0028; Edward Atkins, M.D., Medical Director

Northern Illinois Women's Center, Ltd., 1400 Broadway Street, Suite 201, Rockford, IL 61104; tel. 815/963-4101; FAX. 815/963-6122; Deborah D. Demars, Administrator

Northwest Community Day Surgery Center, 675 West Kirchoff Road, Arlington Heights, IL 60005; tel. 874/618-7075; FAX. 874/618-7069; Meaghan Reshoft, Director

Nova Med Eye Surgery Center of Maryville, L.L.C., 12 Maryville Professional Park Drive, Maryville, IL 62062; tel. 618/288-7483; Adrienne Forsythe, Administrator

NovaMed Eye Surgery Center River Forest, 7427 Lake Street, River Forest, IL 60305; tel. 708/771-3334; FAX. 708/771-0841; Karen Hyman, Administrator

Oak Brook Surgical Centre, Inc., 2425 West 22nd Street, Suite 101, Oak Brook, IL 60523; tel. 630/990-2212; FAX. 630/990-3130; George H. Olsen, Administrator

Oak Park Eye Center, S.C., 7055-61 West North Avenue, Oak Park, IL 60302; tel. 708/848-1182; FAX. 708/848-5033; James L. McCarthy, M.D., Administrator

Orthopedic and Sports Medicine Clinic, P.C., 4411 Alby, Alton, IL 62002; tel. 618/474-8052; FAX. 618/474-8054; Bruce T. Vest, Jr., M.D., Director, Surgery

Orthopedic Institute of Illinois Ambulatory Surgery Center, 303 North Kumpf Boulevard, Peoria, IL 61605; tel. 309/676-5559; FAX. 309/676-5045; Donna Adair, Administrator

Palos Surgicenter, 7340 West College Drive, Palos Heights, IL 60463; tel. 708/361-3233; FAX. 708/361-4876; Paul P. Skowron

Peoria Ambulatory Surgery Center, 4909 North Glen Park Place, Peoria, IL 61614; tel. 309/691-9069; FAX. 309/691-9286; Cynthia J. Leisinger, MBA,CASC, Director of Surgical Services

Peoria Day Surgery Center, 7309 North Knoxville, Peoria, IL 61614; tel. 309/692-9210; FAX. 309/693-6472; Wanda Spacht, RN, Nursing Administrator

Physicians' Surgical Center, Ltd., 311 West Lincoln, Suite 300, Belleville, IL 62220; tel. 618/233-7077; FAX. 618/233-2814; Debra Stoneclifer, RN, Supervisor

Planned Parenthood of East Central Illinois, 302 East Stoughton Street, Champaign, IL 61820; tel. 217/359-8022; FAX. 217/359-2683; Robin Beach, Director of Client Services

Quad City Ambulatory Surgery Center, 520 Valley View Drive, Suite 300, Moline, IL 61265; tel. 309/762-1952; FAX. 309/762-3642; Gloria Catlett, RN, Administrative Manager

Quad City Endoscopy, LLC, 2525 24th Street, Suite 104, Rock Island, IL 61201; tel. 309/788-5624; FAX. 309/788-5668

Regional Surgicenter, Ltd., 545 Valley View Drive, Moline, IL 61265; tel. 309/762-5560; FAX. 309/762-7351; Kay Wynn, Administrator

Resurrection Health Care Surgery Center, 3101 North Harlem Avenue, Chicago, IL 60634; tel. 773/889-2000; FAX. 773/745-5522; Sandra Ankebrant, Executive Director

River North Same Day Surgery, One East Erie, Suite 300, Chicago, IL 60611; tel. 312/649-3939; FAX. 312/649-5747; Lori Hoffer, Administrator

Rockford Ambulatory Surgery Center, 1016 Featherstone Drive, Rockford, IL 61107; tel. 815/226-3300; FAX. 815/226-9990; Dr. Steven Gunderson, CEO/Medical Director

Rockford Endoscopy Center, 401 Roxbury Road, Rockford, IL 61107; tel. 815/397-7340; FAX. 815/397-7388; Nancy Garry, Administrator

Rogers Park One Day Surgery Center, 7616 North Paulina, Chicago, IL 60626; tel. 773/761-0500; FAX. 773/761-0500; Jerry Ruffino, RN Nurse Administrator

South Shore Surgicenter, Inc., 8300 South Brandon Avenue, Chicago, IL 60617; tel. 773/721-9861; FAX. 773/721-6000; Lucy Morales, RN, Administrator

Southwestern Medical Center, LLC, dba Magna Surgical Center, 9831 South Western Avenue, Chicago, IL 60643; tel. 312/445-9696; FAX. 312/445-9590; Gelyn Lipscomb

Spiritus Dei Eye Surgery Center, 7600 West College Drive, Palos Heights, IL 60463; tel. 708/361-0010; Audrey Schmidt-Annerino, Administrator

Springfield Clinic Ambulatory Surgery and Endoscopy Center, 1025 South Seventh Street, Springfield, IL 62794-9248; tel. 217/528-7541; FAX. 217/527-8956; Ginny Timke

SureVision Surgery & Laser Center-Northshore, 3034 West Peterson Avenue, Chicago, IL 60659; tel. 773/973-7432; FAX. 773/973-1119; MaryAnn Lassiter, Administrator

Surgicare Center, Inc., 333 Dixie Highway, Chicago Heights, IL 60411; tel. 708/754-4890; FAX. 708/709-6242; Dolores Stam, RN - Supervisor

Surgicore, Inc., 10547 South Ewing Avenue, Chicago, IL 60617; tel. 773/221–1690; William Wood, DPM, Medical Director

The Center for Orthopedic Medicine, LLC, d/ba/ The Center For Outpatient Medicine, 2502-B East Empire, Bloomington, IL 61704; tel. 309/662–6120; FAX. 309/661–0060; Sarah Gardner, Business Director

The Center for Surgery, 475 East Diehl Road, Naperville, IL 60563-1253; tel. 630/505–7733; FAX. 630/505–0656; Eric Myers, Administrator

The Surgery Center of Centrailia, 1045 Martin Luther King Jr. Drive, Centralia, IL 62801; tel. 618/532–3110; FAX. 618/532–7226; Ghulam Merchant, M.D., Medical Director

Valley Ambulatory Surgery Center and Valley Medical Inn, 2210 Dean Street, St. Charles, IL 60175; tel. 630/584–9800; FAX. 630/584–9805; Mark Mayo, Administrator

Women's Aid Clinic, 4751 West Touhy Avenue, Lincolnwood, IL 60712-2212; tel. 847/676–2428; Iris Schneider

INDIANA

Aesthetic Surgery Center, 13590 N. Meridian, Carmel, IN 46032; tel. 317/846–0846; FAX. 317/846–0722; William H. Beeson, M.D., Medical Director

Akin Medical Center/Surgical Division, ENT Head and Neck Allergy Specialists, 2019 State Street, New Albany, IN 47150-4963; tel. 812/945–3557; FAX. 812/949–3599; Carolyn S. Newlin, R.N., B.S., MSM, Administrator

Calumet Surgery Center, 7847 Calumet Avenue, Munster, IN 46321-1296; tel. 219/836–5102; FAX. 219/836–4496; Denise Cheek, RN Administrator

Central Indiana Surgery Center, 9002 North Meridian, Lower Level, Indianapolis, IN 46260; tel. 317/846–9906; FAX. 317/846–9949; William E. Whitson, M.D., Medical Director

Columbus Surgery Center, 940 North Marr Road, Suite B, Columbus, IN 47201; tel. 812/372–1370; FAX. 812/373–9526; Marcy Ross, R.N.

Digestive Health Center, 1120 AAA Way, Suite A, Carmel, IN 46032-3210; tel. 317/848–5494; FAX. 317/575–0392; Daniel J. Stout, M.D., President

Dupont Ambulatory Surgery Center, 2510 East Dupont Road, Suite 130, Fort Wayne, IN 46825; tel. 219/489–8785; FAX. 219/489–2148; Rick C. Trego, Administrator

Evansville Surgery Center, 1212 Lincoln Ave., Evansville, IN 47714-1076; tel. 812/428–0810; FAX. 812/421–6070; Cathy Head, RN, Facility Manager

Foot and Ankle Surgery Center, Inc., 1950 West 86th Street, Suite 105, Indianapolis, IN 46260; tel. 317/334–0232; FAX. 317/334–0268; Anthony E. Miller, D.P.M., Administrator

Fort Wayne Cardiology Outpatient Catheterization Laboratory, 1819 Carew Street, Fort Wayne, IN 46805; tel. 260/481–4896; FAX. 260/481–4814; Douglas W. Martin, RN, MBA, Director of Clinical Operations

Fort Wayne Ophthalmic Surgical Center, 321 East Wayne Street, Ft. Wayne, IN 46802-2713; tel. 260/422–5976; FAX. 260/969–1041; J. Rex Parent, M.D., Chief Executive Officer

Fort Wayne Orthopaedics LLC, 7601 West Jefferson Boulevard, Fort Wayne, IN 46804-4133; tel. 260/436–8383; FAX. 260/436–8477; Richard E. Rhoad, CEO

Gastrointestinal Endoscopy Center, 801 St. Mary's Drive, Suite 110 West, Evansville, IN 47714; tel. 812/477–6103; FAX. 812/477–4897; Butch Moors, CPA, Administrator

Grand Park Surgical Center, 1479 East 84th Place, Merrillville, IN 46410; tel. 219/738–2828; FAX. 219/756–3349; Chris Macarthy, Administrator

Grossnickle Eye Surgery Center, Inc., 2251 DuBois Drive, Warsaw, IN 46580-3292; tel. 574/269–3777; FAX. 574/269–9828; Diana Ostrom, R.N., Clinical Administrator

Illiana Surgery & Medical Center, 701 Superior Avenue, Munster, IN 46321; tel. 219/924–1300; FAX. 219/922–4810; Virgil Villaflor, Executive Director

Illiana Surgery Center Of Merrillville, 315 W. 89th Ave., Merrillville, IN 46410-2904; tel. 219/757–5275; FAX. 219/757–5290; Mike Baker, COO

IMA Endoscopy Surgicenter, P.C., 8895 Broadway, Merrillville, IN 46410; tel. 219/736–4660; FAX. 219/736–4663; Dawn Bailey, Administrator

Indiana Eye Clinic, 30 North Emerson Avenue, Greenwood, IN 46143-9760; tel. 317/881–3937; FAX. 317/887–4008; Charles O. McCormick, M.D., Administrator

Indiana Surgery Center, 1550 East County Line Road, Suite 100, Indianapolis, IN 46227; tel. 317/621–7600; FAX. 317/621–7606; Peggy Davidson, Administrator

Indiana Surgery Center - North, 8040 Clearvista Parkway, Indianapolis, IN 46256; tel. 317/621–2000; FAX. 317/621–2005; Amy D. Glover, RN, B.S.N., CNOR, Administrator

Indianapolis Endoscopy Center, 7353 East 21st Street, Indianapolis, IN 46219; tel. 317/353–2232; FAX. 317/353–2522; Kathy Anderson

Lafayette Ambulatory Surgery Center, 3733 Rome Drive, Box 6477, Lafayette, IN 47903; tel. 765/449–5272; FAX. 765/447–1276; Dawn Hughes, RN, DON

Meridian Endoscopy Center, 1801 North Senate, Suite 400, Indianapolis, IN 46202; tel. 317/962–5660; FAX. 317/962–2346; Robert J. Whitmore, Executive Director

Meridian Plastic Surgery Center, 170 West 106th Street, Indianapolis, IN 46290-1004; tel. 317/575–0336; FAX. 317/571–8667; Joann Jones,RN, Director

MHC Surgical Center Associates, Inc., d/b/a Broadwest Surgical Center, 315 West 89th Avenue, Merrillville, IN 46410-2904; tel. 219/757–5275; FAX. 219/757–5290; Melvin Lichtenfeld, P.D., Administrator

Michiana Endoscopy Center, LLC, 53830 Generation Drive, South Bend, IN 46635; tel. 219/271–0893; FAX. 219/271–1285; David Mark, M.D., CEO

Midwest Surgery Centers, Inc., 650 Surgery Center Drive, Terre Haute, IN 47802; tel. 812/232–8325; FAX. 812/234–8385; Brenda R. Stallop, Corporate Manager

Muncie Ambulatory Surgicenter, LLC, 200 North Tillotson Avenue, Muncie, IN 47304-3988; tel. 765/286–8888; FAX. 765/747–7962; Jeffrey S. Rapkin, M.D., Medical Director

Munster Same Day Surgery Center, 761 Forty Fifth Avenue, Suite 116, Munster, IN 46321; tel. 219/924–3090; FAX. 219/924–2161

Nasser Smith and Pinkerton Cardiac Cath Lab, 8333 Naab Road, Suite 400, Indianapolis, IN 46260; tel. 317/338–6094; FAX. 317/338–6066; Stephen A. McAdams, M.D., CEO

North Meridian Surgery Center, 10601 North Meridian Street, Suite 100, Indianapolis, IN 46290; tel. 317/574–5400; FAX. 317/575–0173; Julie Berzins, Director/CEO

Northeast Indiana Endoscopy Center, 7900 West Jefferson Boulevard, Suite 200, Fort Wayne, IN 46804; tel. 206/969–7181; FAX. 260/969–7182; Jerry Steele, Administrator

Northside Cardiac Cath Lab, 8333 Naab Road, Suite 180, Indianapolis, IN 46260; tel. 317/338–9001; FAX. 317/338–9045; Beth Higgins, RN, MSN, Clinical Director

NovaMed Eyecare Management, L.L.C., 8514 Broadway, Merrillville, IN 46410; tel. 219/756–5010; FAX. 219/736–2222; Joan Klug, Administrator

NovaMed Eyecare Management, L.L.C., d/b/a NovaMed Eye Surgery Center-Hammond, 6836 Hohman Avenue, Hammond, IN 46324; tel. 219/937–5063; FAX. 219/937–5068; Renee Peters, Administrator

Oakview Surgical Center, Inc., 120 E. 18th St., Rochester, IN 46975; tel. 574/224–7500; FAX. 574/223–3057; Laurence C. Rogers, D.P.M., Administrator

Outpatient Surgery Center of Indiana, LLP, 711 Gardner Drive, Marion, IN 46952; tel. 317/664–2000; FAX. 317/668–6797; Dixie Hewitt, RN, Director

Premier Surgery Center, 1333 Maycrest Drive, Fort Wayne, IN 46805-5478; tel. 260/423–3339; FAX. 260/423–6344; Becky Trimbur, Executive Director

Richmond Surgery Center, 1900 Chester Boulevard, Richmond, IN 47374; tel. 765/966–1776; FAX. 765/962–1191; Lynn Greene, RN, Nurse Manager

Riverpointe Surgery Center, 500 Arcade Avenue, Suite 100, Elkhart, IN 46514-2459; tel. 574/522–9505; FAX. 574/296–6484; John Cloyd, PhD, Executive Director

Sagamore Surgical Services, Inc., 2320 Concord Road, Suite B, Lafayette, IN 47909; tel. 317/474–7838; Carol Blanar, Administrator

South Bend Clinic Surgicenter, 211 North Eddy Street, P.O. Box 1755, South Bend, IN 46634-4061; tel. 574/237–9366; FAX. 574/237–9363; Paul J. Meyer, Executive Director

Southern Indiana Surgery Center, 2800 Rex Grossman Boulevard, Bloomington, IN 47403; tel. 812/333–8969; FAX. 812/335–2309; Miriam Malone, RN, B.S.N., Executive Director

Surgery Center of Eye Specialists, 1901 North Meridian Street, Indianapolis, IN 46202; tel. 317/925–2200; FAX. 317/921–6614; Dan Bradford, Administrator

Surgery Center of Southeastern Indiana, Inc., 999 N. Michigan Ave., Greensburg, IN 47240; tel. 812/663–3222; FAX. 812/663–3622; Deanna Borgman, RN, DON

Surgery Center Plus, 7430 North Shadeland Avenue, Suite 100, Indianapolis, IN 46250-2025; tel. 317/841–8005; FAX. 317/577–7538; James Hansen, Administrator

Surgery ONE, 5052 North Clinton, Fort Wayne, IN 46825-5822; tel. 219/482–5194; FAX. 219/482–5686; Debra McCarter, Director

Surgical Care Center, Inc., 8103 Clearvista Parkway, Indianapolis, IN 46256-4600; tel. 317/842–5173; FAX. 317/570–7429; Janelle Gray, RN, Director

Surgical Center of New Albany, 2201 Green Valley Road, New Albany, IN 47150-4648; tel. 812/949–1223; FAX. 812/945–4765; Tamara E. Jones, B.S.N., Administrator

Surgicare, 2907 McIntire Drive, Suite C, Bloomington, IN 47403; tel. 812/339–8000; FAX. 812/339–2524; Rhonda Jacobs, RN, Administrator

Surgicare of Jeffersonville, 1305 Wall Street, Suite 101, Jeffersonville, IN 47130-3898; tel. 812/288–9674; FAX. 812/283–6955; Marsha Parker, Administrator

The Ambulatory Care Center, LLC d/b/a, Surgicare-Outpatient Surgical Center, 1125 Professional Boulevard, Evansville, IN 47714; tel. 812/475–1000; FAX. 812/475–1001; Diana McDaniel, Facility Administrator

The Endoscopy Center, 8051 South Emerson, Suite 150, Indianapolis, IN 46237; tel. 317/865–2950; FAX. 317/865–2952; Robert Intress, Ph.D., Administrator

The Heart Group Outpatient Cath Lab, 415 West Columbia Street, Evansville, IN 47710; tel. 812/464–0542; Sue Krieg, RN, Clinical Manager

The Indiana Hand Center, 8501 Harcourt Road, P.O. Box 80434, Indianapolis, IN 46260-0434; tel. 317/875–9105; FAX. 317/471–4382; Valeria M. Wareham, Chief Operating Officer

Unity Surgery Center, 1011 West Second Street, Bloomington, IN 47403-2216; tel. 812/334–1213; FAX. 812/333–5039; Michael D. Bishop, M.D., CEO

Valley Cataract and Laser Institute, Inc., dba Valley Surgery Center, 220 East Virginia, Evansville, IN 47711; tel. 812/435–1600; FAX. 812/435–1603; Lisa J. Gossman-Werner, Facility Administrator

Valparaiso Physician and Surgery Center, 1700 Pointe Drive, Valparaiso, IN 46383; tel. 219/531–5000; FAX. 219/531–5010; Lilly Veljovic, RN, Manager

Welborn Clinic Surgery Center, 421 Chestnut Street, Evansville, IN 47713; tel. 812/426–9412; Claudia R. Earnest, Administrator

IOWA

Iowa Endoscopy Center, 2600 Grand Avenue, Suite 418, Des Moines, IA 50312; tel. 515/288–6097; FAX. 515/288–0384; Loraine Hansen, B.S.N., Administrator

Iowa Eye Institute, P.C., 1721 West 18th Street, P.O. Box 420, Spencer, IA 51301; tel. 712/262–8878; FAX. 712/262–8807; Dennis D. Gordy, M.D., Administrator

Jones Eye Clinic, 4405 Hamilton Boulevard, Sioux City, IA 51104-1140; tel. 712/239–3937; FAX. 712/239–4946; Charles E. Jones, M.D., Medical Director

Mississippi Valley Surgery Center, L.C., 3400 Dexter Court, Suite 200, Davenport, IA 52807; tel. 563/344–6600; FAX. 563/344–6699; John B. Dooley, Administrator

Spring Park Surgery Center, LLC, 3319 Spring Street, Suite 202-A, Davenport, IA 52807; tel. 319/355–6236; FAX. 319/359–6347; David Rohlf, Medical Director

Surgery Center of Des Moines, 1301 Penn Avenue, Suite 100, Des Moines, IA 50312; tel. 515/266–3140; FAX. 515/266–3073; Kathleen Supplee, RN, Administrator

KANSAS

Cotton-O'Neil Clinic Endoscopy Center, 823 Southwest Mulvane Street, Suite 375, Topeka, KS 66606-1679; tel. 785/354–0538; FAX. 785/368–0735; Irene Hasenbank, RN,Director

Emporia Ambulatory Surgery Center, 2528 West 15th Avenue, Emporia, KS 66801-6102; tel. 602/343-2233; J. E. Bosiljevac, M.D., Administrator

Endoscopic Services, P.A., 1431 South Bluffview Street, Suite 215, Wichita, KS 67218-3000; tel. 316/687-0234; FAX. 316/687-0360; Jace Hyder, M.D.

Endoscopy and Surgery Center of Topeka, L.P., 2200 Southwest Sixth Avenue, Suite 103, Topeka, KS 66606-1707; tel. 913/354-1254; FAX. 913/354-1255; Ashraf M. Sufi, M.D., Medical Director

EyeSurg of Kansas City, 5520 College Boulevard, Overland Park, KS 66211-1600; tel. 913/491-3757; FAX. 913/469-6686; Phillip Hoopes, M.D., Medical Administrator

Hutchinson Clinic Ambulatory Surgery Center, 2101 North Waldron, Hutchinson, KS 67502; tel. 620/728-2700; Karen Hammersmith, Director

Laser Center, 1518A East Iron Avenue, Salina, KS 67401-3236; tel. 913/825-6016; Brian E. Conner, M.D., Administrator

Newton Surgery Centre, 215 South Pine Street, Newton, KS 67114-3761; tel. 316/283-4400; FAX. 316/283-6606; Tom Moses, Administrator

Ochsner Eye Medical/Associated Eye Surgical Center, 1100 North Topeka Street, Wichita, KS 67214-2810; tel. 316/263-6273; FAX. 316/263-5568; Bruce B. Ochsner, Medical Director

South Pointe Surgery Center, 151 West 151st Street, Suite 200, Olathe, KS 66061-5351; tel. 913/764-2471; FAX. 913/764-3826; Katherine Thon, RN, Administrator

Surgery Center of Kansas, Inc., 1507 West 21st Street, Wichita, KS 67203-2449; tel. 316/838-8388; FAX. 316/838-2999; Karen Gabbert, RN, B.S.N., Administrator

Surgicare of Wichita, Inc., 810 North Lorraine, Wichita, KS 67214-4841; tel. 316/685-2207; FAX. 316/685-2861; Carolyn J. Exley, Administrator

Surgicenter of Johnson County, 8800 Ballentine Street, Overland Park, KS 66214-1985; tel. 913/894-4050; FAX. 913/894-0384; Rose Weintraub, Administrator

Team Vision Surgery Center East, 6100 East Central Street, Suite Six, Wichita, KS 67208-4237; tel. 316/681-2020; FAX. 316/684-4939; Judy Brown, Administrative Director

Team Vision Surgery Center West, 834 North Socora, Suite One, Wichita, KS 67212-3238; tel. 316/681-2020; FAX. 316/684-4939; Judy Brown, Administrative Director

The Center for Same Day Surgery, 818 North Emporia Street, Suite 108, Wichita, KS 67214-3725; tel. 316/262-7263; FAX. 316/262-6253; Judy Noetze, RN, MSN, CNOr, Administrator

The Headache and Pain Center, 11111 Nall Avenue, Suite 222, Leawood, KS 66211-1625; tel. 913/491-3999; FAX. 913/491-6453; Steven D. Waldman, Administrator

Topeka Single Day Surgery, 823 Southwest Mulvane Street, Suite 101, Topeka, KS 66606-1679; tel. 913/354-8737; FAX. 913/354-1440; Linda Daniel, Executive Director

Wichita Clinic DaySurgery, 3311 East Murdock Street, Wichita, KS 67208-3054; tel. 316/689-9596; Janelle Oliver, RN, Manager

KENTUCKY

Ambulatory Surgery Center, 2831 Lone Oak Road, Paducah, KY 42003; tel. 270/554-8373; FAX. 502/554-8987; Laxmaiah Manchikanti, M.D.

Caritas Surgical Center, 4414 Churchman Avenue, Louisville, KY 40215; tel. 502/366-9525; Danny Cain

Center For Surgical Care, 7575 U.S. 42, Florence, KY 41042; tel. 606/283-6050; FAX. 606/283-6046; Jenny Brallier, RN Nurse Manager

Downing -McPeak Surgery Center, 1507 Bravo Boulevard, Glasgow, KY 42141; tel. 270/651-2181; FAX. 270/651-2183; Sheila Dishman, Administrator

Dupont Surgery Center, 4004 Dupont Circle, Louisville, KY 40207; tel. 502/896-6428; FAX. 502/893-5270; Sherry Oeswein, Administrator

E.M.W. Women's Surgical Center, 138 West Market Street, Louisville, KY 40202; tel. 502/589-2124; FAX. 502/589-1588; Dona F. Wells, Administrator

HealthSouth Surgery Center of Louisville, 4005 DuPont Circle, Paducah, KY 40207; tel. 502/897-7401; FAX. 502/897-5652; Sheila S. Boros, Administrator

HealthSouth Surgical Center of Elizabethtown, 708 Westport Road, Elizabethtown, KY 42701; tel. 270/737-5200; FAX. 270/765-5362

Louisville Surgery Center, 614 East Chestnut Street, Louisville, KY 40202; tel. 502/589-9488; FAX. 502/589-9928; Vanessa McDermott, Administrator

Medical Heights Surgery Center, 2374 Professional Heights Drive, Lexington, KY 40503; tel. 859/278-1460; FAX. 859/278-0115; Kelvin Hanger, Administrator

Somerset Surgery Center, 353 Bogle Street, Suite 101, Somerset, KY 42501; tel. 606/679-9322; FAX. 606/678-2666; Kathy Turner, Administrator

The Eye Surgery Center of Paducah, 100 Medical Center Drive, P.O. Box 8269, Paducah, KY 42002-8269; tel. 502/442-1024; FAX. 502/442-1001; Kelly Harris, RN, Administrator

The Pain Treatment Center Inc. d/b/a Stone Road Surgery Center, 280 Pasadena Drive, Lexington, KY 40503; tel. 606/278-1316; FAX. 606/276-3847; Heather Loy, CEO

Tri-State Digestive Disorder Center Ambulatory Surgery Center, 196 Barnwood Drive, Edgewood, KY 41017; tel. 859/341-3575; FAX. 859/341-5701; Ross McHenry, M.D.

LOUISIANA

Acadiana Endoscopy Center, 113 St. Louis Street, Lafayette, LA 70506; tel. 318/269-1126; FAX. 318/269-0553; Stephen M. Person, M.D., Administrator

Acadiana Surgery Center, Inc., 2309 East Main Street, Suite 102, New Iberia, LA 70560; tel. 337/364-9680; FAX. 337/364-9689; Lori Theriot, RN. Director of Nurses

Alexandria Laser and Surgery Center, 4100 Parliament Drive, Alexandria, LA 71303; tel. 318/487-8342; FAX. 318/487-9942; Martina Anders, RN., Center Director

Ambulatory Eye Surgery Center of Louisiana, 3900 Veterans Boulevard, Suite 100, Metairie, LA 70002; tel. 504/455-1550; FAX. 504/455-2011; Judy Dufrechou RN, Director

Broussard Surgery Institute, 1250 Pecanland Road, Suite E-1, Monroe, LA 71203; tel. 318/387-2015; FAX. 318/387-2097; Gerald Broussard, M.D., Administrator

Central Louisiana Ambulatory Surgical Center, 720 Madison Street, P.O. Box 8646, Alexandria, LA 71301; tel. 318/443-3511; FAX. 318/443-5628; Louise Barker, RN, Administrator

Colonnade Surgery, 555 South Ryan Street, Lake Charles, LA 70601; tel. 337/439-6226; FAX. 337/436-6223; Nellie Rideaux, Administrative Assistant

Columbia Greater New Orleans Surgery Center, 3434 Houma Boulevard, Suite 300, Metairie, LA 70006; tel. 504/454-2017; FAX. 530/869-5348; Penny A. Nichols, Administrator

Eye Care and Surgery Center, 10423 Old Hammond Highway, Baton Rouge, LA 70816; tel. 504/923-0960; FAX. 504/923-2419; M. Brian Roper

Foot Surgery Center of Shreveport, 9308 Mansfield Road, Suite 300, Shreveport, LA 71118; tel. 318/686-9622; Richard Havens, D.P.M., Administrator

Gamble Ambulatory Surgery Center, 2601 Line Avenue, Suite B, Shreveport, LA 71104; tel. 318/424-3291; Michael Drews, D.P.M., Administrator

Green Clinic Surgery Center, 1200 South Farmerville Street, Ruston, LA 71270; tel. 318/255-3690; FAX. 318/251-6116; Glenn Scott, Executive Director

HealthSouth Brass Surgery Center, 5328 Didesse Drive, Baton Rouge, LA 70808; tel. 225/766-1718; FAX. 225/767-0161; Derald W. Smith, Administrator

HealthSouth Surgi-Center of Baton Rouge, 5222 Brittany Drive, Baton Rouge, LA 70808; tel. 225/767-5636; FAX. 225/215-3477; Denise T. Fortenberry, Administrator

Hedgewood Surgical Center, 2427 St. Charles Avenue, New Orleans, LA 70130; tel. 504/895-7642; FAX. 504/895-0728; Sally Carpenter, RN

Houma Outpatient Surgery Center, Ltd., 3717 Houma Boulevard, Suite 300, Metairie, LA 70006; tel. 504/456-1515; FAX. 504/454-3810; Melany Pierson, Manager

Houma Surgi Center, Inc., 1020 School Street, Houma, LA 70360; tel. 985/868-4320; FAX. 985/868-3617; Pat Hitt, RN Assistant Administrator

LaHaye Eye and Ambulatory Surgical Center, 4313 I-49 S. Service Rd., Opelousas, LA 70570; tel. 337/942-2024; FAX. 337/948-8869; Douglas C. Mankin, Administrator

LaHaye Total Eye Care, 201 Rue Iberville, Suite 800, Lafayette, LA 70508; tel. 337/235-2149; Bridget Ray

Lake Forest Surgical Center, 10545 Lake Forest Boulevard, New Orleans, LA 70127; tel. 504/244-3000; FAX. 504/246-2600; Karan Prieto, Facility Manager

Laser and Surgery Center of Acadiana, 514 St. Landry Street, Lafayette, LA 70506; tel. 318/234-2020; FAX. 318/234-8230; Barbara L. Azar, Administrator

Laser and Surgery Center of the South, 1101 Audubon Avenue, Suite S-Four, Thibodaux, LA 70301; tel. 504/447-7258; FAX. 504/446-7614; Nate Graff, Administrator

Louisiana Endoscopy Center, Inc., 8150 Jefferson Highway, Baton Rouge, LA 70809; tel. 225/927-0970; FAX. 225/927-0989; Albert Hart, IV, Administrator

LSU Eye Surgery Center, 2020 Gravier Street, Suite B, New Orleans, LA 70112; tel. 504/412-1590; FAX. 504/472-1268; W. L. Blackwell, Chief Executive Officer

Magnolia Surgical Facility, 3939 Houma Boulevard, Suite 216, Metairie, LA 70006; tel. 504/455-7771; FAX. 504/885-5063; Melissa Johnson, Administrator, Medical Director

MGA GI Diagnostic and Therapeutic Center, 1111 Medical Center Boulevard, Suite 310, Marrero, LA 70072; tel. 504/349-6401; FAX. 504/349-6444; Thomas D. McCaffery, Jr., President

MGA GI Diagnostic and Therapeutic Center, 2633 Napolean Avenue, Suite 707, New Orleans, LA 70115; tel. 504/896-8680; FAX. 504/896-8699; Thomas D. McCaffery, Jr., Administrator

Northeast Louisiana Surgery Center, 3101 Kilpatrick Boulevard, Monroe, LA 71201; tel. 318/322-5916; FAX. 318/322-5916; David G. Gardner, President

Ochsner Clinic-Center for Cosmetic Surgery, 1514 Jefferson Highway, Fifth Floor, New Orleans, LA 70121; tel. 504/842-3950; FAX. 504/842-5003; Rachel Franz, RN, B.S.N., Manager

Omega Hospital, LLC, 2525 Severn Avenue, Metairie, LA 70001; tel. 504/832-4200; FAX. 504/832-4209; Deborah Scnenck, Administrator

Outpatient Eye Surgery Center, 4324 Veterans Boulevard, Metairie, LA 70006; tel. 504/455-4046; FAX. 504/455-9890; Cheryl Crouse, RN, Administrator

Outpatient Surgery Center for Sight, 550 Connell's Park Lane, Baton Rouge, LA 70809; tel. 504/924-2020; Alan DeCorte, Administrator

P & S Surgical Hospital, 312 Grammont Street, Suite 101, P.O. Box 3187, Monroe, LA 71201-3187; tel. 318/388-4040; FAX. 318/388-4099; Terri Hicks, Operations Director/CFO

Physicians Surgery Center, 218 Corporate Drive, Houma, LA 70360; tel. 504/853-1390; FAX. 504/853-1470; Connie K. Martin, Administrator

Prytania Surgery, Inc., 3525 Prytania Street, New Orleans, LA 70115; tel. 504/897-8880; Jay Weil III, Administrator

Saints Streets ASC Endoscopy Center, Inc., 201 St. Patrick Street, Suite 202, Lafayette, LA 70506; tel. 337/269-6062; FAX. 337/269-6062; Stephen G. Abshire, M.D., Administrator

Shreveport Endoscopy Center, A.M.C., 3217 Mabel Street, P.O. Box 37045, Shreveport, LA 71133-7045; tel. 318/631-0072; FAX. 318/631-9688; Linda Ray, Administrator

Shreveport Surgery Center, 745 Olive Street, Suite 100, Shreveport, LA 71104; tel. 318/227-1163; FAX. 318/227-0413; Mary Jones, Administrator

Surgery Center, Inc., 1101 South College Road, Suite 100, Lafayette, LA 70503; tel. 337/233-8603; FAX. 337/234-0341; Russell J. Arceneaux, Administrator

Surginet Outpatient Surgery, LLC, 101 La Rue France, Suite 400, Lafayette, LA 70508; tel. 318/269-9828; FAX. 318/269-9823; Millissa R. Coco, Administrator

Surgiunit, Inc., 4204 Teuton Street, Metairie, LA 70006; tel. 504/888-3836; Gustavo A. Colon, M.D., Administrator

The Endoscopy Center of Monroe, 316 South Sixth Street, Monroe, LA 71201; tel. 318/325-2649; FAX. 318/325-0717; Andy W. Waldo, Administrator

The Endoscopy Clinic of Lake Charles Medical and Surgical Clinic, 501 South Ryan, Lake Charles, LA 70601; tel. 337/433-8400; Patsy Bellard, Administrator of Endoscopy

The Outpatient Surgery Center for Sight, 7732 Goodwood Blvd., Ste D., Baton Rouge, LA 70806; tel. 225/925-2031; FAX. 225/924-2809; Connie Commons

Section C

The Plastic Surgery Center, Inc., 4224 Houma Boulevard, Suite 430, Metairie, LA 70006; tel. 504/456-5150; FAX. 504/456-5055; James B. Johnson, M.D., Administrator

The Surgery Suite, 103 Medical Center Drive, Slidell, LA 70461; tel. 504/646-4466; FAX. 504/646-4485; Allison F. Maestro, RN, Administrator

Urology Specialty and Surgery Center, 234 South Ryan Street, Lake Charles, LA 70601; tel. 318/433-5282; FAX. 318/433-1159; Charles Enright, Administrator

West Monroe Endoscopy Center, 102 Thomas Road, Suite 506, West Monroe, LA 71291; tel. 318/388-8878; FAX. 318/388-8870; C.B. Dunn, Jr. M.D.

Westbank Medical Clinic Surgical Facility, Inc., 4700 Wichers Drive, Suite 200, Marrero, LA 70072; tel. 504/347-2297; FAX. 504/347-2299; Robert L. Sudderth, Administrator

Young Eye Surgery Center, Inc., 204 North Magdalen Square, Abbeville, LA 70510; tel. 318/893-4452; FAX. 318/893-7870; Virginia Y. Hebert, Administrator

MAINE

Acadia Medical Arts Ambulatory Surgical Suite, 404 State Street, Bangor, ME 04401; tel. 207/990-0928; Jordan J. Shubert, M.D., President

Eyecare Medical Group, 53 Sewall Street, Portland, ME 04102; tel. 207/773-6336; FAX. 207/773-7034; William S. Holt, M.D., President

Maine Cataract and Eye Center, 386 Bridgeton Road, Route 302, Westbrook, ME 04092; tel. 207/797-9214; FAX. 207/797-8236; Elliot Schweid, D.O., Director

Maine Eye Center, P.A., 15 Lowell Street, Portland, ME 04102; tel. 207/774-8277; FAX. 207/871-1415; Frank Read, M.D., Director

Northern Maine Ambulatory Endoscopy Center, 11 Martin Street, P.O. Box 748, Presque Isle, ME 04769-0151; tel. 207/764-2482; FAX. 207/764-1569; Shelley Silber, RN, Administrator

Orthopedic Surgery Center, 33 Sewall Street, Portland, ME 04102; tel. 207/828-2130; FAX. 207/828-2190; Linda M. Ruterbories, Medical Director

Vision Care Of Maine-Ardostook,LLC, 173 Academy Street, Presque Isle, ME 04769; tel. 207/764-0376; FAX. 207/764-7612; Craig W. Young, M.D., Director

Western Avenue Day Surgery Center, a/k/a Plastic and Hand Surgical Associates, P.A., 244 Western Avenue, South Portland, ME 04106; tel. 207/775-3446; FAX. 207/879-1646; Jean J. Labelle, M.D., President

MARYLAND

Albert Shoumer, D.P.M., Dundalk Professional Center, 40 South Dundalk Avenue, Dundalk, MD 21222; tel. 410/282-6434; FAX. 410/284-4636; Darleen Grupp, Office Manager

Albert Shoumer, D.P.M., 1645 Liberty Road, Eldersburg, MD 21784; tel. 310/795-2889

Amber Ridge Operating Room Center, 1475 Taney Avenue, Suite 101, Frederick, MD 21702; tel. 301/694-5656; FAX. 301/846-4117; Lorin F. Busselberg, M.D., Director

Ambulatory Endoscopy Center of Maryland, Inc., 7350 Van Dusen Road, Suite 230, Laurel, MD 20707; tel. 301/498-5500; FAX. 301/604-5956; Kim Wilson, RN Nurse Manager

Ambulatory Foot Surgery Center of Burtonsville, Inc., 15300 Spencerville Court, Suite 101, Burtonsville, MD 20866; tel. 301/421-4286; Dr. Kressin, President

Ambulatory Plastic Surgery Center Associates, CHTD, 9715 Medical Center Drive, Suite 315, Rockville, MD 20850; tel. 301/738-9137; FAX. 301/738-7920; Mary Vincent, Office Manager

American Podiatric Surgery, 10236 River Road, Potomac, MD 20854; tel. 301/983-9873; FAX. 301/299-3985; Amy Meehan, Administrator

Annapolis Plastic Surgery Center, 1300 Ritchie Highway, Arnold, MD 21012; tel. 410/544-0707; FAX. 410/544-0724; Jack Frost, M.D., President

Anne Arundel Gastroenterology Associates, 703 Giddings Avenue, Suite M, Annapolis, MD 21401; tel. 410/224-2116; Gary M. Evans, Administrator

Baltimore Ambulatory Center for Endoscopy, 19 Fontana Lane, Suite 104, Baltimore, MD 21237; tel. 410/574-7776; FAX. 410/574-9038; Dr.J. Khan, Medical Director

Baltimore Podiatry Group, 5205 East Drive, Suite I, Arbutus, MD 21227; tel. 410/247-5333; Neil Scheffler, D.P.M., President

Baltimore Washington Eye Center, 200 Hospital Drive, Suite 600, Glen Burnie, MD 21061; tel. 410/766-3937; FAX. 410/761-4386; Denise Adams, ASC Coordinator

Bayside Surgical Center, Inc., 8023 Ritchie Highway, Pasadena, MD 21122; tel. 410/761-4190; FAX. 410/761-0265; Sheila Freeze, Office Manager

Beitler, Samuel D., D.P.M. Ambulatory Surgery Center, Glen Burnie Podiatric Surgery Center, 795 Aquahart Road, Suite 125, Glen Burnie, MD 21061; tel. 410/768-0702; FAX. 410/768-0649; Samuel D. Beitler, D.P.M.

Bel Air Ambulatory Surgical Center, LLC, 2007 Rock Spring Road, Lower Level, Forest Hill, MD 21050; tel. 410/879-2474; FAX. 410/879-8194; Karen Aske, RN, Nurse Manager

Belcrest Surgery Center, 6505 Belcrest Road, Suite One, Hyattsville, MD 20782; tel. 301/699-5900; FAX. 301/699-9297; Mark H. Sugar, D.P.M., Director

Bethesda Ambulatory Surgical Center, 5620 Shields Dr., Bethesda, MD 20817; tel. 301/530-4181; FAX. 301/530-4373; John Lydon, D.P.M., Administrator

Carroll Medicine, d/b/a Steven Shaffer, M.D., 211 Hanover Pike, Hampstead, MD 21074; tel. 410/239-7073

Center for Oral & Maxillofacial Surgery, 1212 York Road, Suite A201, Lutherville, MD 21093; tel. 410/337-7755; FAX. 410/337-7922; Laurie Kolmer, Office Manager

Center for Plastic Surgery, 5550 Friendship Boulevard, Suite 130, Chevy Chase, MD 20815; tel. 301/652-7700; Jean, Administrator

Chesapeake Ambulatory Surgery Center, LLC, 8028 Governor Ritchie Highway, Suite 100, Pasadena, MD 21122; tel. 410/768-5800; FAX. 410/768-5806; Ira J. Gottlieb, D.P.M., Owner, Administrator

Chesapeake Surgery Center, 145 East Carroll Street, Salisbury, MD 21801; tel. 410/548-1108; FAX. 410/548-2607; Joseph G. Walters, PA-C Administrative Director

Clinical Associates, 515 Fairmont Avenue, Suite 500, Towson, MD 21286; tel. 410/494-1335

Cumberland Valley Surgical Center, LLC, 1110 Professional Court, Hagerstown, MD 21740; tel. 301/739-7900

De Leonibus and Palmer, L.L.C., A.S.C., MedSurg Foot Center, 2086 Generals Highway, Suite 101, Annapolis, MD 21401; tel. 410/266-7666; FAX. 410/266-7703; Courtney Palmer, DPM

Digestive Disease Consultant of Frederick, 915 Toll House Avenue, Suite 201, Frederick, MD 21701; tel. 301/662-7822; James A. Frizzell, M.D.

Dimensions Surgery Center, 14999 Health Center Drive, Bowie, MD 20716; tel. 301/262-5511; FAX. 301/464-3572; Ricardo Pallia, Vice President

Dr. Michael K. Schwartz, D.D.S., P.A., 723 South Charles Street, Baltimore, MD 21230; tel. 410/727-4886

Drs. Smith and Schwartz, D.D.S., P.A., 10 Warren Road, Suite 330, Cockeysville, MD 21030; tel. 410/666-5225; FAX. 410/666-7220; Mary Thompson, Office Manager

Dulaney Eye Institute, 901 Dulaney Valley Road, Towson, MD 21204; tel. 410/583-1000; Andrea Hyatt, Administrator

Dundalk Ambulatory Surgery Center, 1123 Merritt Boulevard, Baltimore, MD 21222; tel. 410/282-2666; FAX. 410/282-0357; Pam Green, Office Manager

Easton Foot Center, 8579 Commerce Drive, Suite 100A, Easton, MD 21061; tel. 410/822-0645

Eye Surgery Center of Ophthalmology Associates, L.L.C., 10755 Falls Road, Suite 110B, Lutherville, MD 21093; tel. 410/583-2808; FAX. 410/583-2814; Amina C. Barnes, Operating Manager

Eye Surgical Center Associates of Baltimore, 1122 Kenilworth Drive, Suite 18, Towson, MD 21204; tel. 410/321-4000; FAX. 410/321-4909; Cynthia Hamill, Nurse Manager

Facial Plastic Surgicenter, Ltd., 1838 Greene Tree Road, Baltimore, MD 21208; tel. 410/486-3400; FAX. 410/486-0092; Ira D. Papel, M.D., President

Flaum, Martin/Rockville Ambulatory Surgical Center, LLC, 50 West Edmonston Drive, Suite 306, Rockville, MD 20852; tel. 301/340-8666; FAX. 301/340-7448; Martin C. Flaum, Owner

Foot and Ankle Surgical Center, Kensington Surgery Center, 10901 Connecticut Avenue, Suite 200, Kensington, MD 20895; tel. 301/949-2000; Dr. Gene Mirkin

Foot Care Associates Ambulatory Care Center at Joppa Foot Care, 2316 East Joppa Road, Baltimore, MD 21234; tel. 410/882-5100

Footer, Ronald, D.P.M., P.A., 16220 Frederick Avenue, Suite 200, Gaithersburg, MD 20877; tel. 301/948-2995; FAX. 301/948-6056; Maryrose Hanks, Office Manager

Four Corners Ambulatory Surgical Center, LLC, Dr. Gary A. Lieberman, PA, 10101 Lorain Avenue, Silver Spring, MD 20901; tel. 301/681-8400; FAX. 301/681-3339; Gayle Rickert, Administrator

Frederick Surgical Center, 915 Toll House Avenue, Suite 103, Frederick, MD 21701; tel. 301/694-3400; FAX. 301/694-3620; Barbara Smith, Administrator

Gastrointestinal Diagnostic Center, 4660 Wilkens Avenue, Suite 302, Baltimore, MD 21229; tel. 410/242-3636; FAX. 410/242-4404; Mary C . Harrison, Business Manager

Gehris, Heroy and Associates of Lutherville, 1212 York Road, Suite 201B, Lutherville, MD 21093; tel. 410/821-6130; James H. Heroy III, Administrator

Giardina and Glubo, P.A., 4660 Wilkens Avenue, Baltimore, MD 21229; tel. 410/242-7066; FAX. 410/242-4126; Eileen Giardina, RN

Gynemed Surgi-Center, 17 Fontana Lane, Suite 201, Baltimore, MD 21237; tel. 410/686-8220; FAX. 410/391-0943; David O'Neil, M.D.

Hamilton Foot Care Associates ASC, 5508 Harford Road, Baltimore, MD 21214; tel. 410/426-5508

Harford County Ambulatory Surgery Center, 1952-A Pulaski Highway, Edgewood, MD 21040; tel. 410/538-7000; FAX. 410/679-4291; Ms. Linda A. Terzigni, RN, BSN, CNOR, Administrator

Harford Endoscopy Center, LLC, Two North Avenue, Suite 102, Belair, MD 21014; tel. 410/838-6345; FAX. 410/838-1595; Sherry Adkins, Center Director

HealthSouth St. Agnes Surgery Center of Ellicott City, 2850 North Ridge Road, Ellicott City, MD 21043; tel. 410/461-1600; FAX. 410/750-7615; Melaine Medura Faculty Administrator

Johns Hopkins Plastic Surgery Associates, JHOC 8, 601 North Caroline Street, Baltimore, MD 21287; tel. 410/955-6897; FAX. 410/614-1296

Kaiser-Permanente-Kensington, 10810 Connecticut Avenue, Kensington, MD 20895; tel. 301/929-7275; FAX. 301/929-7577; Wanda McCulley, RN, Administrator

Kenneth Margolis, M.D., P.A., Ambulatory Endoscopy Surgical Center, 9101 Franklin Square Drive, Suite 213, Baltimore, MD 21237; tel. 410/687-0202; FAX. 410/687-0985; Jo Ann Smith, Office Manager

Lake Forest Ambulatory Surgical Center, 702 Russell Avenue, Gaithersburg, MD 20877; tel. 301/948-3668; FAX. 301/926-7787

Laser Surgery Center, Inc., 484A Ritchie Highway, Severna Park, MD 21146; tel. 410/544-4600; FAX. 410/544-0997; Dottie Scholes, Office Manager

Laurel Foot and Ankle Surgery Center Inc., 14440 Cherry Lane Court, Suite 104, Laurel, MD 20707; tel. 301/953-3668; Dr. Frank Smith, Administrator

Maclean, Kishel, Applestein, M.D., A.S.C., 11085 Little Patuxent Parkway, Columbia, MD 21044; tel. 410/997-1930

Maple Springs Ambulatory Surgery Center, 10810 Darnstown Road, Suite 101, Gaithersburg, MD 20878; tel. 301/762-3338; FAX. 301/762-1585; Dr. Stuart Snyder, PA, President

Maryland Endoscopy Center, L.L.C., 100 West Road, Suite 115, Towson, MD 21204; tel. 410/494-0144; FAX. 410/494-0147; Irma Haak, R.N., Nurse Manage

Maryland Kidney Stone Center/AKSM, 6115 Falls Road,LL-a, Baltimore, MD 21209; tel. 410/377-2622; FAX. 410/377-4410; Walter Weinstein, Regional Manager

Maryland Outpatient Foot Surgery Center, Dennis M. Weber D.P.M., 4701 Randolph Road, Suite 115, Rockville, MD 20852; tel. 301/770-5741; FAX. 301/468-1093; Dennis M. Weber, D.P.M., Director

Maryland Urology Surgicenters, LLC, 6830 Hospital Drive, Suite 204, Baltimore, MD 21209; tel. 410/391-6131; FAX. 410/391-6144; Robert F. Hoofnagle, M.D., President & CEO

McCone, Jonathan, Jr., M.D., 6196 Oxon Hill Road, Suite 640, Oxon Hill, MD 20745; tel. 301/567-2400

Metropolitan Ambulatory Urologic Institute LLC, 7759 Belle Point Drive, Greenbelt, MD 20770; tel. 301/474-5583; FAX. 301/474-5742; Sharu Verma, RN

Michetti, Michael, Dr. of District Heights, 6400 Marlboro Pike, District Heights., MD 20747; tel. 301/736-6900

Mid Shore Surgical Eye & Laser Center, 8420 Ocean Gateway, Suite One, Easton, MD 21601; tel. 410/822-0424; FAX. 410/822-2283; Adrienne Welch, RN

Montgomery Endoscopy Center P.A., Montgomery Gastroenterology P.A., 12012 Veirs Mill Road, Wheaton, MD 20906; tel. 301/942-3550; FAX. 301/933-3621; Howard Goldberg, M.D., A.S.C Director

Montgomery Surgical Center, 46 West Gude Drive, Rockville, MD 20850; tel. 301/424-6901; FAX. 301/294-7847; Patti Hartsfield, Administrator

Moulsdale, Murphy, Siegelbaum and Lerner, 7505 Osler Drive, Suite 508, Towson, MD 21204; tel. 410/296-0166; FAX. 410/828-7275

Neil J. Napora, D.P.M., 7809 Wise Avenue, Baltimore, MD 21222; tel. 410/285-0310; FAX. 410/288-1569; Neil J. Napora, D.P.M.

North Arundel Plastic Surgery Specialists, 203 Hospital Drive, Suite 308, Glen Burnie, MD 21061; tel. 410/841-5355; FAX. 410/841-6589; Ajia S. Layman, Administrator

Parris-Castoro Eye & Laser Center, 620 Boulton Street, Bel Air, MD 21014; tel. 410/836-7010; FAX. 410/399-8427; Michael Grasham, ASC Administrator

Peninsula Obstetrics and Gynecology, 314 West Carroll Street, Salisbury, MD 21801; tel. 410/546-3125; FAX. 410/546-3128; J. Cutchin, M.D., Director

Plastic Surgery Specialists, 2448 Holly Avenue, Suite 400, Annapolis, MD 21401; tel. 410/841-5355; FAX. 410/841-6589; Ajia S. Layman, Administrator

Plaza Ambulatory Surgical Center, 6506 Reisterstown Road, Suite 501, Baltimore, MD 21215; tel. 410/764-7044; Dr. Brian Kashan, Administrator

Podiatry Associates of Hagerstown, A.S.C, Long Meadow Ambulatory SurgiCenter, 12821 Oak Hill Avenue, Hagerstown, MD 21742; tel. 301/739-1575; FAX. 301/739-1578; Crystal Shankle, Office Manager

Podiatry Associates, P.A., 9712 Bel Air Road, Baltimore, MD 21236; tel. 410/574-6060; FAX. 410/256-2727; Stanley Book

Podiatry Associates, P.A., One North Main Street, Bel Air, MD 21014; tel. 410/879-1212; FAX. 410/893-1081

Podiatry Associates, P.A., 6569 North Charles Street, Suite 702, Towson, MD 21204; tel. 410/828-5420; FAX. 410/828-1663; Stan Book, Billing Manager

Podiatry Associates, P.A., Charter Professional Center, 10700 Charter Drive, Suite 300, Columbia, MD 21044; tel. 410/730-0970; FAX. 410/730-0161; Dr. Boyd, Capello, Ritter, Podiatrist

Podiatry Group, P.A. of Annapolis, 139 Old Solomons Island Road, Suite C, Annapolis, MD 21401; tel. 410/224-4448; FAX. 410/841-5200; Kate Pearson, Administrator

Podiatry Group, P.A. of Laurel, Ambulatory Surgery Center, 14333 Laurel-Bowie Road, Suite 205, Laurel, MD 20708; tel. 301/725-5650; FAX. 301/953-0365; Lance Caffiero, Administrator

Prince George's Ambulatory Care Center/ Endoscopy Suites, Inc., 6001 Landover Road, Suite One, Cheverly, MD 20785; tel. 301/773-3900; FAX. 301/773-7869; Jeannette Figueroa, Administrator

Prince George's Multi-Specialty Surgery Centre, Inc., 8700 Central Avenue, Suite 106, Landover, MD 20785; tel. 301/808-9298; FAX. 301/499-1266; Douglas Hallgren, Administrator

Professional Village Surgical Center, 356 Mill Street, Hagerstown, MD 21740; tel. 301/791-1800

Queen Anne Plastic, L.L.C., 2110 Red Apple Plaza, Chester, MD 2161; tel. 410/643-7207; FAX. 410/643-6945

Queen Anne Surgery Center, 2108 DiDonato Drive, Chester, MD 21619; tel. 410/643-7207; FAX. 410/643-9274; Lisa Parks, Administrator

River Reach Outpatient Surgery Center, 790 Governor Ritchie Highway, Suite E-35, Severna Park, MD 21146; tel. 410/544-2487; FAX. 410/544-1872; Pat Hofmeier, Administrator

Riverside Ambulatory Surgery Center, 560 Riverside Drive, Suite A-101, Salisbury, MD 21801; tel. 410/749-0121; FAX. 410/749-6807; Patricia Timmons, PMAC, Administrator

Rivertowne Surgery Center, 6196 Oxon Hill Road, Suite 650, Oxon Hill, MD 20745; tel. 301/839-7499; FAX. 301/839-8726; Deborah Arminio, Administrator

Robinwood Surgery Center, LLC, 11110 Medical Campus Road, Suite 200, Hagerstown, MD 21742; tel. 301/714-4300; FAX. 301/714-4324; Lana Gladhill,Director

Roger J. Oldham, M.D., Ambulatory Surgery Center, LLC, Bethesda Surgery Center, 10215 Fernwood Road, Suite 412, Bethesda, MD 20817; tel. 301/530-6100; Lauren Cole

Rotunda Ambulatory Surgery Center, 711 West 40th Street, Suite 410, Baltimore, MD 21211; tel. 410/889-4885; FAX. 410/889-2497; Theresa Steele, Administrator

Saint Mary's Multispecialty Surgery Center, Inc., Route 235 and Chancellors Run Road, Suite 15, P.O. Box 1310, California, MD 20619; tel. 301/862-3984; FAX. 301/862-3335; Douglas H. Hallgren, Administrator

Silver Spring Ambulatory Surgical Center, Inc., 1104 Spring Street, Suite T110, Silver Spring, MD 20910; tel. 301/589-7664; FAX. 301/589-3410; Todd A. Nitkin, D.P.M., President

Spector, Adam, D.P.M., Ambulatory Surgery Center, 1111 Spring Street, Silver Spring, MD 20910; tel. 301/589-8886; FAX. 301/589-8889; Adam Spector, D.P.M., Administrator

Suburban Endoscopy Center, L.L.C., 10215 Fernwood Road, Suite 206, Bethesda, MD 20817; tel. 301/530-2800

Suhayl Kalash, Ambulatory Surgery Center, 3455 Wilkens Avenue, Suite 203, Baltimore, MD 21229; tel. 410/646-0330; Bridget Vracar, Accounts Coordinator

Summit Ambulatory Surgery Center, Ambulatory Surgery Center, 1001 Pine Heights Avenue, Suite 104, Baltimore, MD 21229; tel. 410/644-0929; Narang Ashok, Administrator

SurgiCenter of Baltimore, LLP, 23 Crossroads Drive, Suite 100, Owings Mills, MD 21117; tel. 410/356-0300; FAX. 410/356-7507; Jerry W. Henderson, Executive Director

The Ambulatory Urosurgical Center, 401 East Jefferson Street, Suite 105, Rockville, MD 20850; tel. 301/309-8219; FAX. 301/309-9370; Jacqueline Hillman, RN, B.S.N. M.S., Director of Nursing

The Endoscopy Center, 7402 York Road, Suite 101, Towson, MD 21204; tel. 410/494-0156; FAX. 410/828-1706; Barry Gendason, General Manager

The Friendship Ambulatory Surgery Center, P.C., 5550 Friendship Boulevard, Suite 270, Chevy Chase, MD 20815; tel. 301/215-7347; FAX. 301/215-7345; Anthony Ruffin, Administrator/Dr. Mary Craddock, Medical Director

Total Foot Care Surgery Center, Inc., 7525 Greenway Center Drive, Suite 112, Greenbelt, MD 20770; tel. 301/345-4087; FAX. 301/345-0482; Dale Scoville, Office Manager

W.G.. Armiger, P.A., d/b/a Chesapeake Plastic Surgery Associates, 1421 South Caton Avenue, Suite 203, Baltimore, MD 21227; tel. 410/646-3226; FAX. 410/644-2134; William G. Armiger, M.D., Director

Waldorf Endoscopy Center, 11340 Pembroke Square, Suite 202, Waldorf, MD 20603; tel. 310/638-5354; FAX. 301/843-5184; Denise Moran Center Director

Washington Surgi Center, 6228 Oxon Hill Road, Oxon Hill, MD 20745; tel. 301/839-0770; FAX. 301/839-1350; Dr. Othman A. Baban

Western Maryland Eye Surgical Center, 1003 West Seventh Street, Suite 400, Frederick, MD 21701; tel. 301/662-3721; FAX. 301/698-8164

MASSACHUSETTS

Andover Surgery Center, LP, 138 Haverhill Street, Andover, MA 01810; tel. 508/475-2880; FAX. 508/475-9562; Carl J. Coder, Executive Director

Boston Center for Ambulatory Surgery, Inc., 170 Commonwealth Avenue, Boston, MA 02116; tel. 617/267-0710; FAX. 617/236-8704; Philip J. Gaven, MBA, Administrator

Boston Eye Surgery & Laser Center, P.C., 50 Stanford Street, Boston, MA 02114; tel. 617/723-2015; FAX. 617/723-7787; Sheila M. Harney, Business Manager

Boston University Eye Assoc., Inc., 90 New State Highway, Raynham, MA 02767; tel. 508/822-8839; FAX. 508/880-3616; Jeanne H. Tierney Chief Operating Officers

Cataract and Laser Center West, LLC., 171 Interstate Drive, West Springfield, MA 01089; tel. 413/737-5500; FAX. 413/732-3514; Robert E. Dempsey, Jr, Administrator

Cataract and Laser Center, Inc., 333 Elm Street, Dedham, MA 02026; tel. 781/326-3800; FAX. 728/326-2120; John Dunne, Administrator

Cosmetic Surgery Center, 68 Camp Street, Hyannis, MA 02601; tel. 508/775-7026; FAX. 508/771-0499; Laura Norkatis, Office Manager

Eye Institute of the Merrimack Valley, 280 Haverhill Street, Lawrence, MA 01840; tel. 508/685-5366

HealthSouth Maple Surgery Center, 298 Carew Street, Springfield, MA 01104; tel. 413/739-9668; FAX. 413/781-3652; Kathleen S. Loomis, RN, Facility Administrator

McGowan Eye Care Center, 297 Union Avenue, Framingham, MA 01702; tel. 508/872-4590; FAX. 508/872-0038; Bernard L. McGowan, M.D., Director

New England Eye Surgery Center, 696 Main Street, Weymouth, MA 02190; tel. 617/331-3820; FAX. 617/331-1076; Kenneth Camerota

New England Surgicare, One Brookline Place, Suite 201, Brookline, MA 02146; tel. 617/730-9650; Gratia S. Chase, RN, Administrator

Northeast Ambulatory Center, Three Woodland Road, Suite 321, Stoneham, MA 02180; tel. 781/665-5233; FAX. 781/662-4878; Anil Kumar M.D., Medical Director

Plymouth Laser and Surgical Center, 40 Industrial Park Road, Plymouth, MA 02360; tel. 508/746-8600; FAX. 508/747-0824; Kathleen Murphy, Administrator

Same Day SurgiClinic, 272 Stanley Street, Fall River, MA 02720; tel. 508/672-2290; FAX. 508/679-3766; Cynthia Hines, M.D., Chief Executive Officer

Surgery Center of Waltham, 40 Second Avenue, Suite 200, Waltham, MA 02451; tel. 781/437-6400; FAX. 781/437-6401; Alan S. Penzias, Director of Surgery

Worcester Surgical Center, Inc., 300 Grove Street, Worcester, MA 01650; tel. 508/754-0700; FAX. 508/831-9989; Andy H. Poritz, M.D., Professional Services Director

MICHIGAN

Balian Eye Center, 432 West University Drive, Rochester, MI 48307; tel. 313/651-6122; John V. Balian, M.D.

Birth Control Center, Inc., 2783 Fourteen Mile Road, Sterling Heights, MI 48310; tel. 810/939-4000; Armen Vartanian, Administrator

Borgess at Woodbridge Hills Outpatient Surgery, 7901 Angling Road, Portage, MI 49024; tel. 269/324-8406; FAX. 269/324-8476; Renee Langeland,M.S.N., RN, Administrator

Castleman Surgery Center, 14050 Dix-Toledo Road, Southgate, MI 48195; tel. 734/283-0500; FAX. 734/283-2720; Linda Phillips, RN, Administrator

Center for Specialty Care Clinics, 19900 Haggerty Road, Livonia, MI 48152; tel. 313/462-1888; FAX. 313/462-1944; Pamela Cittan, Administrator

Centre for Plastic Surgery, 426 Michigan Street, N.E., Suite 300, Grand Rapids, MI 49503; tel. 616/454-1256; FAX. 616/454-0308; Daniel Reeder, Administrator

Community Surgical Center, 30671 Stephenson Highway, Madison Height, MI 48071; tel. 810/588-8000; FAX. 810/588-9140; C. J. Yanos, Administrator

Detroit Medical Center Surgery Center, 27207 Lahser Road, Suite 100, Southfield, MI 48034; tel. 810/357-0880; FAX. 810/357-1738; Patrick Voight, Administrative Manager

East Michigan Surgery Center, 701 South Ballenger, Flint, MI 48532; tel. 810/238-3603; FAX. 810/767-5194; Bridget Charlesworth, Administrator

Eastside Endoscopy Center, 28963 Little Mack, Suite 103, St. Clair Shores, MI 48081; tel. 586/447-5115; FAX. 586/774-6091; Beth Miller, Administrator

Feminine Health Care Clinic of Flint, 2032 South Saginaw Street, Flint, MI 48503; tel. 800/323-6205; FAX. 313/232-8071; Dawn LoRec, Director

Glascco Ambulatory Surgery Center, 1707 West Lake Lansing Road, Lansing, MI 48912; tel. 517/267-0033; FAX. 517/267-0430; Michael Falatko, CEO

Health Midwest Surgery Center, 125 West Walnut, Kalamazoo, MI 49007; tel. 616/343-1381; Gregor W. Blix, M.D., Medical Director

Hemorrhoid Clinics of America, 22000 Greenfield Road, Oak Park, MI 48237; tel. 248/967-4140; FAX. 248/967-0745; Max Ali, M.D., President

Henry Ford Hospital Fairlane Center, 19401 Hubbard Drive, Dearborn, MI 48126; tel. 313/593-8100; Jay Zerwekh, Administrator

Henry Ford Medical Center, 6777 West Maple Road, West Bloomfield, MI 48322; tel. 248/661–4100; FAX. 248/661–6494; Sally Bertonia, Administrative Manager

Henry Ford Medical Center-Lakeside Ambulatory Surgery, 14500 Hall Road, Sterling Heights, MI 48313; tel. 810/247–2680; FAX. 810/247–2682; Mary Vidaurri, Ph.D., Regional Administrator

Holland Eye Clinic, 999 South Washington, Holland, MI 49423; tel. 616/396–2316; FAX. 616/396–0085; Kristine Curtis, Assistant Administrator

Hutzel Health Center, 4050 East 12 Mile Road, Warren, MI 48092; tel. 586/751–6473; Marie Wisniewski, ADM. SEC.

John Michael Garrett, M.D., 1301 Carpenter Avenue, Iron Mountain, MI 49801; tel. 906/774–1404; FAX. 906/774–8132; Susan Brunnette, RN, ASC Supervisor

M.D. Surgicenter, 375 Barclay Circle, Rochester Hill, MI 48307; tel. 810/852–3636; FAX. 810/852–3631; Robert Swartz, Administrator

Metropolitan Eye Center, 21711 Greater Mack Avenue, St. Clair Shores, MI 48080; tel. 586/774–0343; FAX. 586/777–2214; James W. Klein, M.D., Director

Michigan Center for Outpatient Ocular Surgery, 33080 Utica Road, P.O. Box 26010, Fraser, MI 48026; tel. 810/296–7250; FAX. 810/296–0276; Norbert P. Czajkowski, M.D., Director

Midwest Health Center, 5050 Schaefer Avenue, Dearborn, MI 48126; tel. 313/581–5500; FAX. 313/581–6013; Mark B. Saffer, M.D., President and CEO

Oakland Surgi Center, Inc., 2820 Crooks Road, Suite 200, Rochester Hill, MI 48309; tel. 248/852–7484; FAX. 248/852–4279; Beverly Huffman, CMM, Administrator

Oakwood Healthcare Center-Dearborn, 10151 Michigan Avenue, Dearborn, MI 48126; tel. 313/624–0855; FAX. 313/624–0857; Patricia Glosser, Nursing Supervisor

Park Eye and Surgicenter, 5014 Villa Linde Parkway, Flint, MI 48532

Planned Parenthood League, Inc., 25932 Dequindre, Warren, MI 48091; tel. 810/758–2100; FAX. 810/758–2104; Carrie Haneckow, Administrator

Planned Parenthood of Mid-Michigan Alliance, 3100 Professional Drive, P.O. Box 3673, Ann Arbor, MI 48106-3673; tel. 734/973–0710; FAX. 734/973–0595; Danielle Terry

Planned Parenthood of South Central Michigan, 4201 West Michigan Avenue, Kalamazoo, MI 49006-5803; tel. 269/372–1205; FAX. 269/372–1279; Rev. Mark Pawlowski,CEO

Providence Hospital Ambulatory Surgery Center, 47601 Grand River, Novi, MI 48374; tel. 810/380–4170; Brian Connolly, Administrator

Providence Surgical Center, 29877 Telegraph Road, Suite 200, Southfield, MI 48034

Sinai Surgery Center, 28500 Orchard Lake Road, Farmington Hi, MI 48334; tel. 810/851–9215; FAX. 810/851–2077; Michael K. Rosenberg, M.D., Medical Director

Somerset Surgery Center, P.C., 1565 West Big Beaver Road, Building F, Troy, MI 48084; tel. 248/649–7343; FAX. 248/643–0999; Frank A. Nesi, M.D., Medical Director

Spectrum Health Surgical Center, 1000 East Paris S.E., Suite 100, Grand Rapids, MI 49546; tel. 616/285–1822; FAX. 616/285–1850; Deb Williams, Senior Manager

St. John Surgery Center, 21000 12 Mile Road, St. Clair Shores, MI 48081; tel. 810/447–5015; FAX. 810/447–5012; Cheri Dendy, Administrator

St. Mary's Ambulatory Care Center, 4599 Towne Centre, Saginaw, MI 48604; tel. 517/797–3000; FAX. 517/797–3010; Lori Jurgens, Director

Superior Endoscopy Center/U P Digestive Disease Associates, P.C., 1414 West Fair Avenue, Suite 135, Marquette, MI 49855; tel. 906/226–6025; FAX. 906/226–5366; Kristine Gorsalitz, RN, Director of Nursing

Surgery Center of Michigan, 44650 Delco Boulevard, Sterling Heights, MI 48313; tel. 586/254–3391; FAX. 586/254–3344; Jay Novetsky, M.D., Medical Director

Surgical Care Center of Michigan, 750 East Beltline, N.E., Grand Rapids, MI 49525; tel. 616/940–3600; FAX. 616/954–0216; Kris Kilgore, RN, B.S.N, Administrative Director

Upper Peninsula Surgery Center, 1414 West Fair Avenue, Suite 232, Marquette, MI 49855; tel. 906/225–7547; FAX. 906/225–7548; Sally J. Achatz, RN, Administrator

Waterford Ambulatory Surgi-Center, 1305 North Oakland Boulevard, Waterford, MI 48327; tel. 248/666–5546; FAX. 248/666–5508; Sandra Parrott, Administrator & Cynthia Ford, Manager

MINNESOTA

Centennial Lakes Same Day Surgery Center, 7373 France Avenue, S., Suite 404, Edina, MN 55435; tel. 612/921–0100; FAX. 612/921–0999; Kathleen L. Whatley, Administrator

Children's West, 6050 Clearwater Drive, Minnetonka, MN 55343; tel. 612/930–8600; FAX. 612/930–8650; Lynn Goodenough, Director

Columbia St. Cloud Surgical Center, 1526 Northway Drive, St. Cloud, MN 56303; tel. 320/251–8385; FAX. 320/251–1267; Jeanette I. Stack, Administrator

Dakota Clinic, Ltd., 125 East Frazee Street, Detroit Lakes, MN 56501; tel. 218/844–2300; FAX. 218/844–2445; Linda L. Walz, Division Manager

First Eye Care Center, Inc., 9117 Lyndale Avenue, S., Bloomington, MN 55420; tel. 612/884–7568; FAX. 612/884–2656; Barbara McGovern, Administrator

Landmark Surgery Center, 17 West Exchange Street, Suite 310, St. Paul, MN 55102; tel. 651/842–5468; FAX. 651/842–5491; Jayne Baker, RN Clinical Nurse Manager

Maplewood Surgery Center, 1655 Beam Ave., Maplewood, MN 55109; tel. 612/232–7780; Sandra Todd, Administrator

Midwest Surgery Centers, 2080 Woodwinds Drive, Woodbury, MN 55125; tel. 651/642–1106; FAX. 651/642–9837; H. Joseph Drannen, Administrator

WestHealth, Inc., 2855 Campus Drive, Plymouth, MN 55441; tel. 763/577–7120; FAX. 763/577–7130; Paula Green, Chief Executive Officer

Willmar Surgery Center, 1320 South First Street, Willmar, MN 56201; tel. 320/235–6506; FAX. 320/235–7069; Harley Pakola, Medical Director

MISSISSIPPI

Ambu-Care Outpatient Surgery Center, 6204 North State Street, Jackson, MS 39213; tel. 601/956–3251; FAX. 601/957–8456; Frank McCune, M.D., Administrator

Better Living Clinic Endoscopy Center, 3000 Halls Ferry Road, Vicksburg, MS 39180; tel. 601/638–9800; FAX. 601/638–9808; Barbara Neal, Office Manager

ENT and Facial Plastic Surgery, P.A., DBA Head & Neck Surgery Center, LLC., 107 Millsaps Drive, P.O. Box 17829, Hattiesburg, MS 39402; tel. 601/268–5131; FAX. 601/268–5138; Sandy Mikell, Office Manager

Gulf South Outpatient Center, 1206 31st Avenue, P.O. Box 1778, Gulfport, MS 39501; tel. 228/864–0008; FAX. 228/863–1747; Jason V. Smith, M.D., President

Gulfport Outpatient Surgical Center, 1240 Broad Avenue, Gulfport, MS 39501; tel. 228/868–1120; FAX. 228/864–0265; William Peaks, Administrator

Lowery A. Woodall Outpatient Surgery Facility, 105 South 28th Avenue, Hattiesburg, MS 39401; tel. 601/288–1072; FAX. 601/288–3132; Marshall H. Tucker, FACHE, Administrator

Mississippi Surgical Center, 1421 North State Street, Jackson, MS 39202; tel. 601/353–8000; Judy Gray, Administrator

North Mississippi Surgery Center, LLC, 589 Garfield, Tupelo, MS 38801; tel. 662/377–4700; FAX. 662/377–3101; Beth Taylor, RN, Clinical Manager

Southern Eye Center of Excellence, 1420 South 28th Avenue, Hattiesburg, MS 39402; tel. 601/264–3937; FAX. 601/264–5930; Lynn McMahan, M.D., Medical Director

Southwest Mississippi Ambulatory Surgery Center, 215 Marion Avenue, McComb, MS 39648; tel. 601/249–1477; FAX. 601/249–1375; Gary M. Heim, Administrator/ASC

MISSOURI

Auburn Surgery Center, Inc., 300 South Mount Auburn Road, Suite 200, Cape Girardeau, MO 63703; tel. 573/332–7881; FAX. 573/332–7176; Beth Carter, Administrator

Cape Girardeau Outpatient Surgery Center, 1429 Mount Auburn Road, Cape Girardeau, MO 63701; tel. 573/335–9175; FAX. 573/335–2392; Mary S. Vickery, RN, Administrator

Cataract and Glaucoma Outpatient Surgicenter, 7220 Watson Road, St. Louis, MO 63119; tel. 314/352–5515; Stanley C. Becker, M.D.

Cataract Surgery Center of Young Eye Clinic, Inc., 3201 Ashland Avenue, St. Joseph, MO 64506; tel. 816/279–0079; FAX. 816/364–1100; Judy Watowa, RN, B.S.N, Administrator

CMMP Surgical Center, 1705 Christy Drive, Suite 100, Jefferson City, MO 65101; tel. 573/635–7022; FAX. 573/635–7029; Angela R. Erosenko, Administrator

Creekwood Surgery Center, 211 Northeast 54th Street, Suite 100, Kansas City, MO 64118; tel. 816/455–4214; FAX. 816/455–4216; Diana Carr, Administrator

Creve Coeur Surgery Center, LLC, 633 Emerson-Suite B, Creve Coeur, MO 63141; tel. 314/872–7100; FAX. 314/872–9176; Carolyn Hollowood, Administrator, RN,BSN,CASC

Doctors' Park Surgery, Inc., 30 Doctors' Park, Cape Girardeau, MO 63703; tel. 573/334–9606; FAX. 573/334–9608; Ronald G. Wittmer, President

ENT/Urology Surgical Care, Inc., 5301 Faraon Street, St. Joseph, MO 64506; tel. 816/364–2772; Sidney G. Christiansen, M.D.

Eye Surgery Center-The Cliffs, 4801 Cliff Avenue, Suite 101, Independence, MO 64055; tel. 816/478–4400; FAX. 816/478–8240; Jacki Wyrick, RN, B.S.N., Direct of Nursing

G.I. Diagnostics, Inc., 4321 Washington, Suite 5700, Kansas City, MO 64111; tel. 816/561–2000; FAX. 816/931–7559; Craig B. Reeves, Administrator

HealthSouth Surgery Center of Kirkwood, 1028 South Kirkwood Road, Kirkwood, MO 63122; tel. 314/984–0080; FAX. 314/984–9037; Judy Mai-Lombardo, Administrator

HealthSouth Surgery Center of West County, 1130 Town and Country Commons, Chesterfield, MO 63017; tel. 314/394–0698; FAX. 314/394–7493; Sandi Baber RN, Administrator

HealthSouth Tri County Surgery Center, 1111 East Sixth Street, Washington, MO 63090; tel. 636/239–I766; FAX. 636/239–2964; Ellen Kluesner, Administrator

North County Surgery Center, 637 Dunn Road, Suite 101, Hazelwood, MO 63042; tel. 314/895–4001; FAX. 314/895–1791; Christine Frederick, Administrator

NovaMed Eye Surgery Center (Plaza) L.L.C., 4321 Washington, Suite 6001, Kansas City, MO 64111; tel. 816/753–6511; FAX. 816/753–6513; Ann Israel, ASC Director

NovaMed Eye Surgery Center of North county, d/b/a Cataract Surgery Center, 900 North Highway 67 (Lindbergh), Florissant, MO 63031; tel. 314/838–0321; FAX. 314/838–6532; Leigh Ann Schmidt, RN, Nurse Manager

Outpatient Surgery Center, 450 North New Ballas Road, Suite 103, St. Louis, MO 63141; tel. 314/991–0776; FAX. 314/991–3076; Raymond Mangrich, Administrator

Regional Surgery Center, P.C., 1531 West 32nd Street, Suite 107, Joplin, MO 64804; tel. 417/781–9595; FAX. 417/781–9814; Cynthia Shofner, Administrator

South County Outpatient Surgery Center, 13303 Tesson Ferry Road, St. Louis, MO 63128; tel. 314/842–3200; Terri Seidel, Administrator

St. Charles County Surgery Center, Inc., 4203 South Cloverleaf Drive, St. Peters, MO 63376; tel. 314/928–0087; FAX. 314/928–1242; Sandi Baber, Administrator

Surgery Center of Springfield, L.P., 1350 East Woodhurst Drive, Springfield, MO 65804; tel. 417/887–5243; FAX. 417/887–6507; Joyce Gillespie, Administrator

Surgicenter of Kansas City, LLC, 1800 East Meyer Boulevard, Kansas City, MO 64132; tel. 816/523–0100; FAX. 816/995–3190; Cynthia Clark, RN, MBA, CNOR, Administrator

The Ambulatory Head and Neck Surgical Center, 1965 South Fremont, Suite 1940, Springfield, MO 65804; tel. 417/887–5750; FAX. 417/887–6612; Shawn K. Shanklin, Administrator

The Endoscopy Center, 3800 South Whitney, Independence, MO 64055; tel. 816/478–4887; FAX. 816/478–7140; Jean Thomposn, FACMPE Administrator

The Endoscopy Center II, 5330 North Oak Trafficway, Suite 100, Kansas City, MO 64118; tel. 816/478–4887; FAX. 816/478–7140; Jean Thompson, Administrator

The Tobin Eye Institute, 3902 Sherman Avenue, St. Joseph, MO 64506; tel. 816/279–1363; FAX. 816/233–8936; Andy Patrick, C.O.O.

MONTANA

Billings Cataract and Laser Surgicenter, 1221 North 26th Street, Billings, MT 59101; tel. 406/252–5681; FAX. 406/252–5025; Brenda Emerick, Business Manager

HealthSouth Surgery Center of Billings, 940 North 30th Street, Billings, MT 59101; tel. 406/248–7186; FAX. 406/248–6889; Karen Fillner, Administrator

Montana Surgical Center, Inc., 840 South Montana, Butte, MT 59701; tel. 406/782–2391; Charles Harris, Manager

Rocky Mountain Eye Surgery Center, 700 West Kent, Missoula, MT 59801; tel. 406/543–8179; Darlene Timmerhoff, Administrator

Same Day Surgery Center, Inc., 300 North Wilson, Suite 600F, Bozeman, MT 59715; tel. 406/586–1956; Ann Guenther, Supervisor

The Eye Surgicenter, 2475 Village Lane, Billings, MT 59102; tel. 406/252–6608; FAX. 406/252–6600; Sara Coleman, Supervisor

NEBRASKA

Aesthetic Surgical Images, P.C., 8900 West Dodge Road, Omaha, NE 68114; tel. 402/390–0100; FAX. 402/390–2711; Rita Petersen, Administrator

Anis Eye Institute, P.C., 1500 South 48th Street, Suite 610, Lincoln, NE 68506; tel. 402/483–4448; FAX. 402/483–4750; Dr. Aziz Y. Anis

Bergan Mercy Surgical Center, 11704 West Center Road, Omaha, NE 68124; tel. 402/333–3111; Richard A. Hachten III

Clarkson West Medical Center, 2727 S. 144th Street, Omaha, NE 68144; tel. 402/778–5300; FAX. 402/778–5310; Connie Mimick

Jones Eye Clinic, 825 North 90th Street, Omaha, NE 68114; tel. 402/397–1180; Shelly J. Junck, Director of Operations

Lincoln Surgical Center, 1710 South 70th, Suite 200, Lincoln, NE 68506; tel. 402/484–9090; FAX. 402/483–0476; Robin Linnafelter, Administrator

Omaha Surgical Center, 8051 West Center Road, Omaha, NE 68124; tel. 402/391–3333; James Quinn, M.D., Administrator

Omega Surgery Centers, LLC, 11606 Nicholas Street, Suite 200, Omaha, NE 68154; tel. 402/493–2020; FAX. 402/493–8987; Dr. Robert S. Vandervort, Administrator

The Nebraska Eye Surgical Center, 1500 S. 48th Street, Suite 612, Lincoln, NE 68506; tel. 402/483–4448; FAX. 402/483–4750; Aziz Anis, M.D., Administrator

The Urology Center, P.C., 111 1/2 South 90th Street, Omaha, NE 68114; tel. 402/397–9800; Laura Forehead, Administrator

Tobin Eye Institute, 4151 E Street, Omaha, NE 68107; tel. 402/731–1363; FAX. 402/731–3292; Amy Anderson, RN

NEVADA

Ambulatory Surgery Center of Nevada, 4631 E. Charleston Blvd., Las Vegas, NV 89104; tel. 702/438–8417; Neal A. Marek, Administrator

American Surgery Center of Las Vegas, 2575 Lindell Road, Las Vegas, NV 89102; tel. 702/367–7874; FAX. 702/227–6055; Fay dela Cruz, Center Director

Carson Endoscopy Center, 707 North Minnesota, Carson City, NV 89703; tel. 775/884–8818; FAX. 775/884–4569; Jay M. Coller, Executive Director

Carson Valley Ambulatory Surgery Center, 1107 Highway 395, Gardnerville, NV 89410; tel. 775/782–1595; FAX. 775/782–1592; Laura D. Strong, Director

Center for Outpatient Surgery, 343 Elm Street, Suite 100, Reno, NV 89503; tel. 775/770–6500; FAX. 775/770–6535; Linda Cundiff, Exec. Dir

Columbia Sunrise Flamingo Surgery Center, 2565 East Flamingo Road, Las Vegas, NV 89121; tel. 702/697–7900; FAX. 702/697–5383; Mia Alfonso, Business Manager

Columbia Sunrise Surgical Center-Sahara, 2401 Paseo Del Prado, Las Vegas, NV 89102; tel. 702/362–7874; FAX. 702/362–3567; Stephanie Finkelstein, Administrator

Digestive Disease Center, 2136 East Desert Inn Road, Suite B, Las Vegas, NV 89109; tel. 702/734–0075; FAX. 702/734–3912; Osama Haikal, M.D., Administrator

Digestive Health Center, 5250 Kietzke Lane, Reno, NV 89511; tel. 775/829–8855; FAX. 775/829–3752; Theresa Brandt, Center Director

Endoscopic Institute of Nevada, 3777 Pecos-McLeod, Suite 102, Las Vegas, NV 89121; tel. 702/433–5686; Rebecca Duty, Administrator

Endoscopy Center of Southern Nevada, LLC, 700 Shadow Lane, Suite 165B, Las Vegas, NV 89106; tel. 702/382–8101; FAX. 702/382–4641; Dipak K. Desai, Administrator

Eye Surgery Center of Nevada, 3839 North Carson Street, Carson City, NV 89706; tel. 702/882–3950; FAX. 708/882–1726; Michael J. Fischer, M.D., Administrator

Foot Surgery Center of Northern Nevada, 1300 East Plumb Lane, Suite A, Reno, NV 89502; tel. 702/829–8066; FAX. 702/829–8069; Dr. Frank M. Davis, Jr., Administrator

Ford Center for Foot Surgery, 2321 Pyramid Way, Sparks, NV 89431; tel. 702/331–1919; FAX. 702/331–2008; Dr. L. Bruce Ford, Administrator

Gastrointestinal Diagnostic Clinic, 3196 South Maryland Parkway, Suite 207, Las Vegas, NV 89109; tel. 702/369–3400; Nourollah Gharhreman, MD, Administrator

Goldring Surgical Center, 2020 Goldring, Suite 300, Las Vegas, NV 89106; tel. 702/477–7000; Texas Gustavson, Administrator

HealthSouth Reno Medical Plaza, 2005 Silverada Boulevard, Suite 100, Reno, NV 89512; tel. 775/359–0212; FAX. 775/359–0645; Maggie Summerfelt, Administrator

La Tourette Surgical Center, 2300 South Rancho Drive, Suite 216, Las Vegas, NV 89102; tel. 702/386–6979; FAX. 702/386–8700; Gary J. La Tourette, Administrator

Las Vegas Surgicare, Ltd., 870 South Rancho Drive, Las Vegas, NV 89106; tel. 702/870–2090; FAX. 702/870–5468; Kathy King, Administrator

Shepherd Eye Surgicenter, 3575 Pecos McLeod, Las Vegas, NV 89121; tel. 702/731–2088; FAX. 702/734–7836; Christina Kennelley, Administrator

Sierra Center for Foot Surgery, 1801 North Carson, Suite B, Carson City, NV 89701; tel. 702/882–1441; FAX. 702/882–6844; H. Kim Bean, D.P.M., Administrator

Sierra Surgery And Imaging, 1400 Medical Parkway, Carson City, NV 89703; tel. 775/883–1700; FAX. 775/883–8905; Joan P. Lapham, MBA, Executive Director

SMA Surgery Center, 2450 West Charleston, Las Vegas, NV 89102; tel. 702/877–8660; FAX. 702/877–5180; Steve Evans, M.D., Medical Director

Valley View Surgery Center, 1330 Valley View Boulevard, Las Vegas, NV 89102; tel. 702/870–7101; FAX. 702/870–7118; Shelia Donnell, Administrator

NEW HAMPSHIRE

Ambulatory Surgery Center, 100 Hitchcock Way, Manchester, NH 03104; tel. 603/695–1800; FAX. 603/629–1730; Jach Anderson, Supervisor-ASC

Bedford Ambulatory Surgical Center, 11 Washington Place, Bedford, NH 03110; tel. 603/622–3670; FAX. 603/626–9750; Laurie T. Roderiques, CRNFA, Nurse Director

Clinic Surgery Center (The), 253 Pleasant Street, Concord, NH 03301; tel. 603/226–2200; Kevin Appleton, Administrator

Dr. O'Connell's Pain Care Centers, Inc., Pinewood Medical Center, 255 Route 108, Somersworth, NH 03878; tel. 603/692–3166; FAX. 603/692–3168; Michael J. O'Connell, M.D., M.H.A., CEO

Dunning Street Ambulatory Care Center, Seven Dunning Street, Claremont, NH 03743; tel. 603/543–3501; Jyl Bradley, Administrator

Elliot One Day Surgery Center, One Elliot Way, Manchester, NH 03103; tel. 603/627–4889; FAX. 603/663–5900; MaryBeth Jenkins, RN,MS, Director

Nashua Eye Surgery Center, Inc., Five Coliseum Avenue, Nashua, NH 03063; tel. 603/882–9800; FAX. 603/882–0556; Paul O'Leary, Administrator

Orthopeadic Surgery Center, 264 Pleasant Street, Concord, NH 03301; tel. 603/228–7211; FAX. 603/228–7192; Donna Quinn, Administrator

Salem Surgery Center, 32 Stiles Road, Salem, NH 03079; tel. 603/898–3610; FAX. 603/890–3313; Cynthia C. Fortune, Director

NEW JERSEY

A Center for Advanced Surgery, Three Winslow Place, Paramus, NJ 07652; tel. 201/843–9390; FAX. 201/843–0591; Marc L. Reichman, Director of Administration

Affiliated Ambulatory Surgery PA, 182 South Street, Suite One, Morristown, NJ 07960; tel. 973/267–0300; FAX. 973/984–2670; Sylvia Wexler, Administrator

Arthur W. Perry, M.D., FACS Plastic Surgery Center, 3055 Route 27, Franklin Park, NJ 08823; tel. 908/422–9600; FAX. 908/422–9606; Arthur W. Perry, M.D., Director

Associated Surgeon of Northern New Jersey, 25 Rockwood Place, Englewood, NJ 07631; tel. 201/567–3999; FAX. 201/567–9288

Atlantic Surgery Center, LLC, 279 Third Avenue,, Suite 105, Long Branch, NJ 07740; tel. 732/222–7373; FAX. 732/571–9212; Daniel B. Goldberg, M.D., President

Atrium Surgery Center, Inc., 195 Route 46, Suite 202, Mine Hill, NJ 07803; tel. 201/989–5185; FAX. 201/328–4097; Jennifer Rand, RN, CNOR, President

Bergen Gastroenterology, 466 Old Hook Road, Suite One, Emerson, NJ 07630; tel. 201/967–8221; FAX. 201/967–0340; Robert Ein, M.D., President

Berkeley Heights Eye Groups, Summit Eye Group, 369 Springfield Avenue, Berkeley Heights, NJ 07922; tel. 908/464–4600; FAX. 908/464–4737; Susan Smith, RN, Administrator

Burlington County Internal Medicine, 651 John F Kennedy Way, Willingboro, NJ 08046; tel. 609/871–7070; FAX. 609/835–4510; Toni McNeil, Administrator

Campus Eye Group, 1700 Whitehorse Hamilton Square Road, Suite A, Hamilton Square, NJ 08690; tel. 609/587–2020; FAX. 609/588–9545; Denise Agness, O.D., Office Manager

Cataract and Laser Institute, PA, 101 Prospect Street, Suite 102, Lakewood, NJ 08701; tel. 908/367–0699; FAX. 908/367–0937

Cataract Surgery and Laser Center, Inc., 1921 Fair Lawn Avenue, Fair Lawn, NJ 07410; tel. 201/794–8444; FAX. 201/794–1615

Center for Special Surgery, 104 Lincoln Avenue, Hawthorne, NJ 07506; tel. 973/427–6800; FAX. 973/427–9602; John Tauber, Business Administrator

Clifton Surgery Center, 1117 Route 46 East Suite 303, Clifton, NJ 07013; tel. 973/779–7210; FAX. 973/779–7387; Ramon Silen, M.D., President and Medical Director

Drs. Scherl, Chessler, Zingler, Spinnell, PA, 1555 Center Avenue, Fort Lee, NJ 07024; tel. 201/945–6564; FAX. 201/461–9038; Lynn A. Sculley, Practice Administrator

Endo-Surgi Center, 1201 Morris Avenue, Union, NJ 07083; tel. 908/686–0066; FAX. 908/686–5388; Sharon DeMato, Executive Director

Endo/Surgical Center of New Jersey, 925 Clifton Avenue, Clifton, NJ 07013; tel. 201/777–3938; FAX. 201/777–6738; Pauline Perrino, RN, CGRN, Director of Nursing

Englewood Endoscopic Associates, 420 Grand Avenue, Englewood, NJ 07631; tel. 201/569–7044; FAX. 201/569–1999; Carmen Rivera, Office Manager

Essex Eye Surgery and Laser Center, 1460 Broad Street, Bloomfield, NJ 07003; tel. 201/338–5566; FAX. 201/338–0753; Ellen Lee, Director Patient Accounts

Essex Surgical, LLC, 776 Northfield Ave., West Orange, NJ 07052; tel. 973/324–2300; FAX. 973/324–1421; George C. Peck, Jr., M.D.

Eye Institute of Essex Surgeye Center, 50 Newark Avenue, Belleville, NJ 07109; tel. 201/751–6060; FAX. 201/450–1464; Eileen Beltramba, Administrator

Eye Physician of Sussex County Surgical Center, 183 High Street, Newton, NJ 07860; tel. 973/383–6345; FAX. 973/383–0032; Patricia Fowler, RN

Eye Surgery Princeton, 419 North Harrison Street, Princeton, NJ 08540; tel. 609/921–9437; FAX. 609/921–0277; Richard H. Wong, M.D., Medical Director

Freehold Ent, d/b/a Face to Face, Patriots Park, 222 Schanck Road, Freehold, NJ 07728; tel. 908/431–1666; FAX. 908/431–1665

Garden State Ambulatory Surgical Center, One Plaza Drive, Suite 20-21, Toms River, NJ 08757; tel. 732/341–7010; FAX. 732/341–5066; Moshe Rothkopf, M.D., FACS

Gastroenterology Diagnosis Northern New Jersey, 205 Browertown Road, Suite 102, West Paterson, NJ 07424; tel. 973/890–4780; FAX. 973/890–1097; Kathy Shadiack, Administrative Director

Hand Surgery and Rehabilitation Center of New Jersey, P.A., 5000 Sagemore Drive, Suite 103, Marlton, NJ 08053; tel. 856/983–4263; FAX. 856/983–9362; Tina Hunt, Administrator

HealthSouth Surgical Center of South Jersey, 130 Gaither Drive, Suite 160, Mount Laurel, NJ 08054; tel. 856/722–7000; FAX. 856/722–8962; Eleanor O. Peschko, Administrator

Horizon Laser and Eye Surgery Center, 9701 Ventnor Avenue, Suite 301, Margate City, NJ 08402; tel. 609/822–7171; FAX. 609/822–3211; Suzanne D. Bruno, Administrator

Hunterdon Center for Surgery, LLC T/A Surgery Today, 121 Highway 31, Suite 1300, Flemington, NJ 08822; tel. 908/806–7017; FAX. 908/806–2838; Saleha Faruqi, M.D., Medical Director

---

Health Organizations, Agencies, and Providers **C59**

James Street Surgical Suite, 261 James Street, Morristown, NJ 07960; tel. 973/267–7181; Sherylynn Barta, RN

Mediplex Surgery Center, 98 James Street, Suite 108, Edison, NJ 08820-3998; tel. 732/632–1600; FAX. 732/632–1678; Ruth Mosher, Administrator

Metropolitan Surgical Association, 40 Eagle Street, Englewood, NJ 07631

Mid Atlantic Eye Center, 70 East Front Street, Red Bank, NJ 07701; tel. 732/741–0858; FAX. 732/219–0180; Walter J. Kahn, M.D.

Newark Mini-Surgi Site, Inc., 145 Roseville Avenue, Newark, NJ 07107; tel. 201/485–3300; FAX. 201/485–2404; Monica Chomsky

North Jersey Center for Surgery, 39 Newton Sparta Road, Newton, NJ 07860; tel. 973/383–0153; FAX. 973/300–9002; Bruno J. Casatelli, D.P.M., Administrator

Northern New Jersey Eye Institute, 71 Second Street, South Orange, NJ 07079; tel. 973/763–2203; FAX. 973/763–5207; Shirley Vitale, Practice Administrator

Northwest Jersey Ambulatory Surgery Center, 350 Sparta Avenue, Building A, Sparta, NJ 07871; tel. 973/729–8580; FAX. 973/729–2344; L.LeRose, RN, Executive Director

Ocean County Eye Associates, P.C., 18 Mule Road, Toms River, NJ 08755

Ocean Surgical Pavilion, Inc., 1907 Highway 35, Suite Nine, Oakhurst, NJ 07755; tel. 732/517–8885; FAX. 732/517–0304; Dona M. Stein, RNBSN Center Director

Ophthalmic Physicians of Monmouth, 733 North Beers Street, Holmdel, NJ 07733; tel. 908/739–0707; FAX. 908/739–6722; Renee Sharkey, RN, Surgical Coordinator

Pavonia Surgery Center, Inc., 600 Pavonia Avenue, Fourth Floor, Jersey City, NJ 07306; tel. 201/216–1700; FAX. 201/216–1800; William H. Constad, M.D., President

Princeton Orthopaedic Associates, P.A., 727 State Road, Princeton, NJ 08540; tel. 609/924–8131; FAX. 609/924–8532; William G. Hyncik, Jr., Executive Director

Princeton Surgical Center, Inc., 281 Witherspoon Street, Third Floor, Princeton, NJ 08542; tel. 609/497–4380; FAX. 609/497–4986; James Demetriades, Administrative Director

Retina Consultants Surgery Center, 39 Sycamore Avenue, Little Silver, NJ 07739; tel. 732/530–7730; FAX. 732/530–3837

Ridgedale Surgery Center, 14 Ridgedale Avenue, Suite 120, Cedar Knolls, NJ 07927; tel. 973/605–5151; FAX. 973/605–1208; Rosalind Silber,Office Administrator

Ridgewood Ambulatory Surgery Center, 1200 Ridgewood Avenue, Ridgewood, NJ 07450; tel. 201/444–4499; FAX. 201/612–8114

Robert Wood Johnson Surgery Center, 561 Cranbury Road, East Brunswick, NJ 08816; tel. 908/390–4300; FAX. 908/390–4405; Evelyn Tornquist, Office Manager

Roseland Surgery Center, 556 Eagle Rock Avenue, Roseland, NJ 07068; tel. 201/226–1717; FAX. 201/403–9034; Joseph Brandspiegel, Executive Director

Saddle Brook Surgicenter, Inc., 289 Market Street, Saddle Brook, NJ 07663; tel. 201/843–4444; FAX. 201/368–2817; Dr. Ronald Sollitto, President and CEO

Seashore Ambulatory Surgery Center, 1907 New Road, Northfield, NJ 08225; tel. 609/646–2323; FAX. 609/645–9780; Richard Vernouski, Administrator

Somerset Eye Institute, P.C., 562 Easton Avenue, Somerset, NJ 08873; tel. 732/828–5900; FAX. 732/828–3327; Suzanne Eileen SoSardo, Business Manager

Somerset Surgical Center, P.A., 1081 Route 22 West, Suite 201, Bridgewater, NJ 08807; tel. 908/575–0020; FAX. 908/575–1515; Ileana Pustai, Administrator and Colleen Relay, Business Manager

South Jersey Endoscopy Center, 17 West Red Bank Avenue, Suite 302, Woodbury, NJ 08096; tel. 856/848–4464; FAX. 856/848–8706; Sue Lampman, Billing Manager

South Jersey Surgicenter, 2835 South Delsea Drive, Vineland, NJ 08360; tel. 856/696–0020; FAX. 856/205–1721; Julie Rivera-Office Manager

Surgery Center of Cherry Hill, 408 Route 70 East, Cherry Hill, NJ 08034; tel. 856/354–1600; FAX. 856/429–7555; Gina Marone RN, MSN

Surgicare of Central Jersey, Inc., 40 Stirling Road, Watchung, NJ 07060; tel. 908/769–8000; FAX. 908/668–3139; Marion Jenkins, Executive Director

Surgicare Surgical Associates, PC, 15 01 Broadway, Route 4 West, Suite One and Three, Fairlawn, NJ 07410; tel. 201/791–6585; John H. Haffar, M.D., Medical Director

Teaneck Gastroenterology and Endoscopy Center, 1086 Teaneck Road, Suite Three B, Teaneck, NJ 07666; tel. 201/837–9636; FAX. 201/837–9544; Mia D. Oliver, Manager

The Endoscopy Center of Red Bank, 365 Broad Street, Red Bank, NJ 07701; tel. 732/842–4294; FAX. 732/842–3854; Elizabeth Boyle, Provider Relations or Joan Halvey, Office Manager

The Endoscopy Center of South Jersey, 2791 South Delsea Drive, South Vinelan, NJ 08360; tel. 609/691–1400; FAX. 609/691–7117; Richard Wagar, Assistant Director

The Eye Care Center, 500 West Main Street, Freehold, NJ 07728; tel. 908/462–8707; FAX. 908/462–1296; Dale A. Ingram, Administrator

The Hernia Center, 222 Schanck Road, Suite 100, Freehold, NJ 07728; tel. 908/462–2999; FAX. 908/462–7760; Jackie Porter, RN

The New Jersey Eye Center, 1 North Washington Avenue, Bergenfield, NJ 07621; tel. 201/384–7333; FAX. 201/384–2564; James Dello Russo

The Surgical Center at South Jersey Eye Physicians, P.A., 509 South Lenola Road,Suite 11B, Moorestown, NJ 08057; tel. 856/234–0258; FAX. 609/727–0064; Elizabeth Hanley, RN

Trocki Plastic Surgery Center, PA, 635 Tilton Road, Northfield, NJ 08225

Virtua Summit Surgical Center, 110 Carnie Boulevard, Voorhees, NJ 08043; tel. 856/325–5813; FAX. 856/325–5858; Dee Brennan, Administrator Director

NEW MEXICO

Alamogordo Eye Clinic and Surgical Center, 1124 10th Street, Alamogordo, NM 88310; tel. 505/434–1200; FAX. 505/437–3947; Cindy Buttram, RN

Eye Care Surgery, 105 North Coronado Avenue, Espanola, NM 87532; tel. 505/753–7391; FAX. 505/753–2749; Dr. Gary Puro

HealthSouth Albuquerque Surgery Center, 1720 Wyoming Boulevard, N.E., Albuquerque, NM 87112; tel. 505/292–9200; FAX. 505/292–1398; Terry Sanchez, Administrator

Lazaro Eye Surgical Center, 1131 Mall Drive, Las Cruces, NM 88011; tel. 505/522–7676; Corine B. Lazaro, M.D., Administrator

Northside Presbyterian, P.O. Box 26666, 5901 Harper Drive, NE, Albuquerque, NM 87125; tel. 505/291–2114; FAX. 505/291–2983; Karin Vantiunen

The Endoscopy Center of Santa Fe, 1650 Hospital Drive, Suite 900, Santa Fe, NM 87505; tel. 505/988–3373; FAX. 505/984–1858; Jim Howlett, Administrator

NEW YORK

Ambulatory Surgery Center of Brooklyn, 313 43rd Street, Brooklyn, NY 11232; tel. 718/369–1900; FAX. 718/965–4157; Michael M. Levi, M.D., Ph.D., Governing Authority

Ambulatory Surgery Center of Greater New York, Inc., 1101 Pelham Parkway, N., Bronx, NY 10469; tel. 718/515–3500; FAX. 718/655–1795; Joanne McLaughlin, Administrator

Brook Plaza Ambulatory Surgical Center, 1901 Utica Avenue, Brooklyn, NY 11234; tel. 718/629–5590; FAX. 718/629–2833; David Doretsky, Administrator

Brooklyn Eye Surgery Center, LLC, 1301 Avenue J, Brooklyn, NY 11230; tel. 718/688–3937; FAX. 718/692–4456; Yafa L. Shevlin, Administrator

Buffalo Ambulatory Surgery Center, 3095 Harlem Road, Cheektowaga, NY 14225; tel. 716/896–3815; FAX. 716/896–3015; Dorothy L. Zimdahl, RN, B.S., CNOR, Administrator

Central New York Eye Center, 22 Green Street, Poughkeepsie, NY 12601; tel. 845/471–3720; Kim M. Quickr, R.N., CRNO

Day-Op Center of Long Island, Inc., 110 Willis Avenue, Mineola, NY 11501; tel. 516/294–0030; FAX. 516/294–0228; Juliette LaRegina, Administrator

Fifth Avenue Surgery Center, 1049 Fifth Avenue, New York, NY 10028; tel. 212/772–6667; FAX. 212/988–8018; Charles J. Raab, CEO

Harrison Center Outpatient Surgery, 5700 Genesee Street, Suite 11, Camillus, NY 13031; tel. 315/701–9378; FAX. 315/701–0871; Margaret M. Alteri, Administrator/CEO

Harrison Center Outpatient Surgery, Inc., 550 Harrison Street, Suite 230, Syracuse, NY 13202; tel. 315/472–4424; FAX. 315/475–8056; Margaret M. Alteri, Administrator and CEO

Hurley Avenue Surgical Center, Inc., 40 Hurley Avenue, Kingston, NY 12401; tel. 914/338–4777; FAX. 914/339–7339; Steven L. Kelley, CHE, Administrator and CEO

Lattimore Community Surgicenter, 125 Lattimore Road, Rochester, NY 14620; tel. 585/473–9000; FAX. 585/473–9018; Peter G. Varlan, Administrator

Long Island Eye Surgery Center, 601 Suffolk Avenue, Brentwood, NY 11717; tel. 631/231–4455; FAX. 631/434–1728; Sally Rienzo, RN, Compliance Officer

Long Island Surgi-Center, 1895 Walt Whitman Road, Melville, NY 11747; tel. 516/293–9700; FAX. 516/293–1018; Ronald Perrone M.D.

Millard Fillmore Ambulatory Surgery Center, 215 Klein Road, Williamsville, NY 14221; tel. 716/568–6100; FAX. 716/568–6166; Joel C. Farwell, Business Manager

Nassau Center for Ambulatory Surgery, Inc., dba Garden City SurgiCenter, 400 Endo Boulevard, NY 11530; tel. 516/832–8504; FAX. 516/228–9429; Carol Stahl, Administrator

New York Institute for Same Day Surgery, Inc., 99 Dutch Hill Plaza, Orangeburg, NY 10962; tel. 845/359–9000; FAX. 845/359–1495; Lisa A. Bloise, COA Operations Director

North Shore Surgi Center, Inc., 989 West Jericho Turnpike, Smithtown, NY 11787; tel. 631/864–7100; FAX. 631/864–7129; George Seaman, CEO

Our Lady of Victory Surgery Center, 6300 Powers Road, Orchard Park, NY 14127; tel. 716/667–3222; FAX. 716/667–3120; Dana M. Mata, Administrative Director

Queens Surgi-Center, 83-40 Woodhaven Boulevard, Glendale, NY 11385; tel. 718/849–8700; FAX. 718/849–6523; Ayman Soliman, Administrator

Queens Surgical Community Center, 46-04 31st Avenue, Long Island C, NY 11103; tel. 718/545–5050; FAX. 718/721–8709; Mr. Misk, Partner

Same Day Surgery of Latham, Inc., Seven Century Hill Drive, Latham, NY 12110; tel. 518/785–5741; FAX. 518/785–8134; Jennifer L. Allen, RN, BSN, OR, Coordinator

The Mackool Eye Institute, 31-27 41st Street, Astoria, NY 11103; tel. 718/728–3400; FAX. 718/721–7562

Westfall Surgery Center, LLP, 1065 Senator Keating Boulevard, Rochester, NY 14618; tel. 585/256–1330; FAX. 585/256–3823; Gary J. Scott, Administrative Director

NORTH CAROLINA

Asheboro Endoscopy Center, 700 Sunset Avenue, P.O. Box 4830, Asheboro, NC 27203; tel. 336/625–0305; FAX. 336/625–9941; Vickie Whitaker, RN, Clinical Director

Blue Ridge Day Surgery Center, 2308 Wesvill Court, Raleigh, NC 27607; tel. 919/781–4311; FAX. 919/781–0625; Susan S. Swift, Facility Manager

Caromont Specialty Surgery, 2511 Court Drive, Gastonia, NC 28054; tel. 704/671–5600; FAX. 704/671–5650; Elizabeth Kohli, Director

Carteret Surgery Center, 3714 Guardian Avenue, Morehead City, NC 28557; tel. 252/247–0314; FAX. 252/247–2031; Kim Blaine, Business Manager

Chapel Hill Surgical Center, 109 Conner Drive, Suite 1201, Chapel Hill, NC 27514; tel. 919/968–0611; FAX. 919/967–8637; Gary S. Berger, M.D., President

Cleveland Ambulatory Services, 1100 North Lafayette Street, Shelby, NC 28150; tel. 704/482–1331; FAX. 704/482–4833; Thomas D. Bailey, M.D., Medical Director

Craven Surgery Center, 630 McCarthy Blvd, P.O. Box 12446, New Bern, NC 28561; tel. 252/633–2000; FAX. 252/633–9045; Joseph Hageman, RN, Executive Director

Eye Surgery and Laser Clinic, 500 Lake Concord Road, N.E., Concord, NC 28025; tel. 704/782–1127; FAX. 704/782–1207; Clayton Bonnett, Administrator

Eye Surgery Center of Shelby, 1622 East Marion Street, Shelby, NC 28150; tel. 704/482–2020; FAX. 704/482–7707; Frank T. Hannah, M.D., Medical Director

Fayetteville Ambulatory Surgery Center, 1781 Metromedical Drive, Fayetteville, NC 28304; tel. 910/323–1647; FAX. 910/323–4142; John T. Henley, Jr., M.D., Medical Director

FemCare, 62 Orange Street, Asheville, NC 28801; tel. 828/255–8400; Lorraine M. Cummings M.D., Medical Director

Goldsboro Endoscopy Center, Inc., 2705 Medical Office Place, Goldsboro, NC 27534; tel. 919/580–9111; FAX. 919/580–0988; Venkata C. Motaparthy, M.D., Chief Executive Officer

Hawthorne Surgical Center, 1999 South Hawthorne Road, Winston-Salem, NC 27103; tel. 910/718–6800; FAX. 910/718–6847; Teresa L. Carter, Facility Director

HealthSouth Greensboro Specialty Surgical Center, 522 North Elam Avenue, Greensboro, NC 27403; tel. 336/294–1833; FAX. 336/294–8831; Cathy Bryant, Administrator

HealthSouth Surgecenter of Wilson, 1709 Medical Park Drive, Wilson, NC 27893; tel. 919/237–5649; Phyllis S. Renfrow, Administrator

HealthSouth Surgery Center of Charlotte, 2825 Randolph Road, Charlotte, NC 28211; tel. 704/377–1647; FAX. 704/358–8267; Connie M. Wilson, Administrator

HealthSouth Surgery Center of Charlotte, 2825 Randolph Rd., Charlotte, NC 28211; tel. 704/377–1647; Connie M. Wilson, Administrator

HealthSouth Surgery Center of Hickory, L.P., 27 13th Avenue, N.E., Hickory, NC 28601; tel. 704/328–1493; FAX. 704/322–6097; Kevin Deal, RN, Administrator

High Point Surgery Center, 600 Lindsay Street, P.O. Box 2476, High Point, NC 27261; tel. 336/878–6068; FAX. 336/878–6111; Joan D. White, Administrative Director

Iredell Head, Neck and Ear Ambulatory Surgery Center, Inc., 707 Bryant Street, Statesville, NC 28677; tel. 704/873–5224; FAX. 704/873–5984; Angie Kerr, Office Manager

Iredell Surgical Center, 1720 Davie Avenue, Statesville, NC 28677; tel. 704/871–0081; FAX. 704/871–0086; Debra C. Hartman, Administrator

James E. Davis Ambulatory Surgical Center, 120 E. Carver Street, P.O. Box 15727, Durham, NC 27704; tel. 919/470–1000; FAX. 919/470–1055; Hope Mangum, Director

Medivision, Inc., 2170 Midland Road, P.O. Box 1938, Southern Pine, NC 28387; tel. 910/295–1221; FAX. 910/295–0512; Kathy Stout, RN, Administrator

Piedmont Gastroenterology Center, Inc., 1901 South Hawthorne Road, Suite 308, Winston-Salem, NC 27103; tel. 910/760–4340; FAX. 919/765–2869; Charles H. Hauser, Administrator

Plastic Surgery Center of North Carolina, Inc., 2901 Maplewood Avenue, Winston-Salem, NC 27103; tel. 336/768–6210; FAX. 336/768–6236; Melba Edwards, Administrator

Raleigh Plastic Surgery Center, Inc., 1112 Dresser Court, Raleigh, NC 27609; tel. 919/872–2616; FAX. 919/872–2771; Nancy Nicoll O'Neil, Administrator

Raleigh Women's Health Organization, Inc., 3613 Haworth Drive, Raleigh, NC 27609; tel. 919/783–0444; FAX. 919/781–8432; Susan Hill, President

Regional Medical Services Surgery Center, 5200 North Croatan Highway, Kitty Hawk, NC 27949; tel. 252/261–9000; FAX. 919/261–4329; Yvonne Burdick, Executive Director

Southern Eye Associates, P.A., Ophthalmic Surgery Center, 2801 Blue Ridge Road, Suite 200, Raleigh, NC 27607; tel. 919/571–0081; Kathryn Levari, Director of Clinical Services

Surgery Center of Morganton Eye Physicians, P.A., 335 East Parker Road, Morganton, NC 28655; tel. 704/433–6225; L. A. Raynor, M.D., Medical Director

Surgical Eye Center, 3312 Battleground Avenue, Greensboro, NC 27410; tel. 336/282–8330; FAX. 336/282–2625; Trudy Wester, Center Director

SurgiCare of Jacksonville, 166 Memorial Court, Jacksonville, NC 28546; tel. 910/353–9565; FAX. 919/353–5497; Takey Crist, Medical Director

SurgiCenter of Wilson, 209 Richards Street, Wilson, NC 27893; tel. 919/237–5649; FAX. 919/237–4977; Phyllis Renfrow, President

Surgicenter Services of Pitt, Inc., 102 Bethesda Drive, Greenville, NC 27834; tel. 919/847–7700; FAX. 919/847–7784; Anna M. Weaver, President

The Endoscopy Center, 191 Biltmore Avenue, Asheville, NC 28801; tel. 704/254–0881; Michael Grier, M.D.

WHA Medical Clinic, PLLC, 1202 Medical Center Drive, Wilmington, NC 28401; tel. 910/341–3433; Diane A. Atkinson, Executive Director

Wilmington SurgCare, 1801 South 17th Street, Wilmington, NC 28401; tel. 910/763–4555; FAX. 910/763–9044; David Gross, Facility Administrator

Wilson OB-GYN, 2500 Horton Boulevard, Zip 27893, P.O. Box 7639, Wilson, NC 27895; tel. 919/206–1000; FAX. 919/237–0704; Daniel P. Michalak, M.D., Administrator

Woman Care and Carolina Birth Center, 712 North Elm Street, High Point, NC 27262; tel. 910/889–3646; Robert C. Crawford, M.D., Chief Executive Officer

NORTH DAKOTA

Altru Health System, 1000 South Columbia Road, Grand Forks, ND 58201; tel. 701/780–6000; Wayne K. Larson, Associate Administrator

Bismarck Surgical Associates, 600 N. 9th Street, Bismarck, ND 58501; tel. 701/221–2299; FAX. 701/221–3239; Dr. Atlas Boutrous, Administrator

Centennial Medical Center, 1500 24th Avenue, S.W., Minot, ND 58702; tel. 701/852–0777; Dr. Manuel Neto, Administrator

Dakota Clinic Ltd Endoscopy, 1702 S. University Drive, Fargo, ND 58108; tel. 701/280–8900; Curt Noyes-Chief Operating Officer

Dakota Surgery & Laser Center, 430 E. Sweet Avenue, Bismarck, ND 58504; tel. 701/222–4900; Charles R. Volk, Administrator

Day Surgery-Wahpeton, 275 South 11th Street, Wahpeton, ND 58075; tel. 701/642–2000; FAX. 701/671–4106; Jeffery A. Cook, Administrator

Great Plains Clinic Surgery Center, 33 Ninth Street, W., Dickinson, ND 58601; tel. 701/483–6017; FAX. 701/483–5018; Mark Grove, Administrator

Institute for Special Surgery, 2301 25th Street, Fargo, ND 58103; tel. 702/271–1045; FAX. 702/271–1044; Timothy Haugen, Administrator

Medical Arts, ASC, Inc., 400 East Burdick Expressway, Minot, ND 58702; tel. 701/857–7000; Doug Eberhard, Exec. Director

North Dakota Surgery Center, 3035 Demers Ave., Grand Forks, ND 58201; tel. 701/775–3151; FAX. 701/775–3153; Ross J. Gonitzke, Administrator

St. Alexius Same Day Surgery Center, 810 East Rosser, Bismarck, ND 58501; tel. 701/530–5000; Sandy Gerving, Director

TMC Western Dakota Medical Group, 1102 Main, Williston, ND 58801; tel. 701/572–7711; Mary Banta, Administrator

Trinity Community Clinic-Western Dakota, 1102 Main, Williston, ND 58801; tel. 701/572–7711; FAX. 701/572–2283; Mary E. Banta, Administrator

OHIO

Advanced Cosmetic and Laser Surgery Center, Inc., 2200 Philadelphia Drive, Suite 651, Dayton, OH 45406; tel. 937/278–0809; FAX. 937/278–3590

Akron Endoscopy Center, 1037 North Main Street, Suite B, Akron, OH 44310; tel. 330/940–3000; FAX. 330/940–3675; Nicole King, RN, Center Director

Amend Center for Eye Surgery, 5939 Colerain Avenue, Cincinnati, OH 45239; tel. 513/923–3900; FAX. 513/923–3012

Austintown Surgery, 45 North Canfield-Niles Road, Youngstown, OH 44515; tel. 330/792–2722; FAX. 330/793–2830; JoAnn Sulenski, Administrator

Bloomberg Eye Center, 1651 West Main Street, Newark, OH 43055; tel. 614/522–3937; FAX. 614/522–0063; Judy Mackey, Director of Corp. Services

Cincinnati Eye Institute and Outpatient Eye Surgery Center, 10494 Montgomery Road, Cincinnati, OH 45242; tel. 513/984–5133; FAX. 513/984–4240; Doris Holton, Administrator

Cincinnati Foot Clinic, Inc., 9600 Colerain Avenue, Suite 400, Cincinnati, OH 45239; tel. 513/385–6946; Robert Hayman, M.D., President

Columbia The Surgery Center, 19250 East Bagley Road, Middleburg Heights, OH 44130; tel. 440/826–3240; FAX. 440/826–3250

Columbus Eye Surgery Center, 5965 East Broad Street, Suite 460, Columbus, OH 43213; tel. 614/751–4080; FAX. 614/751–4092; Toni Van Horn, Executive Director

Consultants in Gastroenterology, Inc., 29001 Cedar Road, Suite 110, Lyndhurst, OH 44124; tel. 216/461–2550; FAX. 216/461–5319; Karen Wahl, Manager

Crystal Clinic Surgery Center, 3975 Embassy Parkway, Suite 202, Akron, OH 44313; tel. 330/668–4085; FAX. 330/668–2624; Katherine L. McNeal, RN, Administrator

Dayton Ear, Nose and Throat Surgeons, Inc., 7076 Corporate Way, Centerville, OH 45459; tel. 937/434–0555; FAX. 937/434–7413; Jana White, Administrator

Digestivecare Endoscopy Unit, 75 Sylvania Drive, Beavercreek, OH 45440; tel. 937/320–5050; FAX. 937/320–5060; Susan Lewis, Craig Penno, Endoscopy Administrator Manager

Endoscopy Center of Dayton LTD, 4200 Indian Ripple Road, Beavercreek, OH 45440; tel. 937/427–1680; FAX. 937/427–9081; Tamme Hafer, Practice Administrator

Eye Care Center of Cincinnati, 5300 Cornell Road, Cincinnati, OH 45242; tel. 513/489–6161; FAX. 513/489–6442; Amy D. Riegler, Coordinator

Eye Institute of Northwestern Ohio, 5555 Airport Highway, Suite 110, Toledo, OH 43615; tel. 419/865–3866; FAX. 419/865–3451; Carol R. Kollarits, M.D., President

Eye Surgery Center of Wooster, 3519 Friendsville Road, Wooster, OH 44691; tel. 330/345–6371; FAX. 330/345–8029; Michelle Morrison, Director

Facial Surgery Center, 1130 Congress Avenue, Glendale, OH 45246; tel. 513/772–2442; FAX. 513/772–2844; Joseph J. Moravec, M.D., Medical Director

Fairview Hospital Surgery Center, 850 Columbia Road, Westlake, OH 44145; tel. 216/808–4000; FAX. 216/808–4010; Michelle Padden, RN, Administrator

Firas Atassi, M.D. Outpatient Surgery Center, 34500 Center Ridge Road, North Ridgeville, OH 33039; tel. 216/327–2414

Gastroenterology Associates of Cleveland, 6801 Mayfield Road, Suite 142, Mayfield Heights, OH 44124; tel. 440/461–8800; FAX. 440/646–8594; James Andrassy, Administrator

Gastroenterology Associates, Inc., 4665 Belpar Street, NW, P.O. Box 36329, Canton, OH 44735; tel. 330/493–1480; FAX. 330/493–6805; Linda Snyder, Practice Administrator

Gastroenterology Specialists, Inc., 2726 Fulton Drive, N.W., Canton, OH 44718; tel. 330/455–5011; FAX. 330/588–7127; Diane S. Milenbachs, RN

HealthSouth Endoscopy Center West, 3654 Werk Road, Cincinnati, OH 45248; tel. 513/451–6001; FAX. 513/451–7310; Linda Ballhaus, Administrator

HealthSouth Endoscopy West, 1930 State Route 59, Kent, OH 44240; tel. 216/677–3292; FAX. 330/677–3624; Laurie Simon, Office Manager

Heritage Surgical Associates of Cincinnati, d/b/a Healthsouth Surgery Center of Cincinnati, 2925 Vernon Place, Suite 101, Cincinnati, OH 45219; tel. 513/872–4541; FAX. 513/872–4558; Patti Murphy, RN, Director

Kunesh Eye Surgery Center, 2601 Far Hills Avenue, Dayton, OH 45419-1665; tel. 937/298–1093; FAX. 937/298–6344; Lucy Helmers, Administrator

Mid-Ohio Outpatient Surgery Center, 245 Taylor Station Road, Columbus, OH 43213; tel. 614/861–0448; FAX. 614/861–7717; Dr. Grace Z. Kim, Director

Midwest Eye Center, 119 West Kemper Road, Cincinnati, OH 45246; tel. 513/671–6112; FAX. 513/671–6386; Lorrie Walters, Business Office Supervisor

Midwest Eye Surgery Center, 4452 Eastgate Boulevard, Suite 305, Cincinnati, OH 45245; tel. 513/752–5700; FAX. 513/752–5716; Holly Schwab, RN, Surgery Manager

North Coast Endoscopy, Inc., 9500 Mentor Avenue, Suite 380, Mentor, OH 44060; tel. 440/352–9400; FAX. 440/352–9407; Ahmad Ascha, M.D.

North Shore Endoscopy Center, 850 Columbia Road, Suite 201, Westlake, OH 44145; tel. 440/808–1212; FAX. 440/808–0321; Christine St.George, RN, BSN, Operations Manager

Ohio Eye Associates, Eye Surgery & Laser Center, 466 South Trimble Road, Mansfield, OH 44906; tel. 419/756–8000; FAX. 419/756–7100; John L. Marquardt, M.D.

Ohio Gastroenterology Group, Inc., Endoscopy Center, 777 West State Street, Suite 402, Columbus, OH 43222; tel. 614/221–7431; FAX. 614/341–2401; Jean Yarletts, RN, B.S.N.

Optivue Vision, 2740 Navarre Avenue, Oregon, OH 43616; tel. 419/697–3616; FAX. 419/697–3637; Karen R. Hess, RN, LMt, O.R. Manager

Parkway Surgery Center, Ltd., 3500 Executive Parkway, Toledo, OH 43606; tel. 419/531–8349; FAX. 419/531–6833; Richard I. Tapper, Md, Medical Executive Director

Ross Park Surgical Services, One Ross Park, Steubenville, OH 43952; tel. 614/282–4790; Kathy Lemasters, RN, Manager

Sandusky Surgeons, Inc., 1221 Hayes Avenue, Sandusky, OH 44870; tel. 419/625–1374; William A. Schuchardt, MD. President

Sidney Foot and Ankle Center, 1000 Michigan, Sidney, OH 45365; tel. 937/492-1211; FAX. 937/492-6557; Norma Polasky, Administrative Director

South Dayton Urological Associates, Inc., 10 Southmoor Circle, N.W., Kettering, OH 45429; tel. 937/294-1489; Donald Bailey, Practice Administrator

Stoneridge Endoscopy Center, 3900 Stoneridge Lane, Dublin, OH 43017; tel. 614/889-5001; FAX. 614/889-5913; Cheryl Miller, Clinic Manager

Surgery Alliance Ltd., 975 Sawburg Avenue, Alliance, OH 44601; tel. 330/821-7997; FAX. 330/821-7295; Hazel Thomas, Administrator

Taylor Station Surgery Center, 275 Taylor Station Road, Columbus, OH 43213; tel. 614/751-4466; FAX. 614/751-4474; Julie Bernard, Director

The Endoscopy Center, 3439 Granite Circle, Toledo, OH 43617; tel. 419/843-7993; FAX. 419/841-7789; Alice Horner, R.N. Nurse Manager

The LCA Center for Surgery, 7840 Montgomery Road, Cincinnati, OH 45236; tel. 513/792-9099; FAX. 513/792-5634; Rene Fischer, President and CEO

The Surgery Center At Southwoods, 7525 California Avenue, Youngstown, OH 44512; tel. 330/758-1954; FAX. 330/758-3254

The Surgical Center of East Liverpool, 16480 St. Clair Avenue, P.O. Box 2640, East Liverpool, OH 43920; tel. 330/386-9000; FAX. 330/386-1255; Joseph P. Sitarik D.O., Medical Director

Tippecanoe Endoscopy, Inc., 1210 Boardman Canfield Road, Youngstown, OH 44512; tel. 330/726-0132; FAX. 330/726-2571; Mary Amorn, RN, Administrator

Toledo Clinic, Inc., 4235 Secor Road, Toledo, OH 43623; tel. 419/473-3561; FAX. 419/472-0838; Roberta Reichle, Administrator

Toledo Community Lithotripter Center, 3158 West Central Avenue, Toledo, OH 43606; tel. 419/531-3538; FAX. 419/531-2807; Richard Kranz, Director

Tri-State Centers, For Sight Surgery Center, 8044 Montgomery Road, Suite 155, Cincinnati, OH 45236; tel. 513/791-3937; FAX. 513/791-1473

Wright Surgery Center, 1611 South Green Road, Suite 124, South Euclid, OH 44121; tel. 216/382-1868; FAX. 216/382-0584; Sheryl Ontell-Silverman, MD, PhD, Medical Director

Zeeba Ambulatory Surgery Center, 29017 Cedar Road, Lyndhurst, OH 44124; tel. 440/460-8000; FAX. 440/460-4225; Franklin Keathley, Administrator

OKLAHOMA

Ambulatory Surgery Associates, 6160 South Yale Avenue, Tulsa, OK 74136; tel. 918/495-2625; FAX. 918/497-3259; Kathy Helberg, RN, Director

Central Oklahoma Ambulatory Surgical Center, Inc., 3301 Northwest 63rd Street, Oklahoma City, OK 73116; tel. 405/842-9732; FAX. 405/842-9771; Paul Silverstein, M.D., Administrator

Columbia Surgicare of Tulsa, 4415 South Harvard Avenue, Suite 100, Tulsa, OK 74135; tel. 918/742-2502; FAX. 918/745-9750; Dirk Foxworthy, Administrator

Eastern Oklahoma Surgery Center, L. L. C., 5020 East 68th Street, Tulsa, OK 74136; tel. 918/492-1539; FAX. 918/494-8683; Linda Taylor, RN Supervisor

Great Plains Ambulatory Surgery Center, 5404 West Lee Boulevard, Suite 100, Lawton, OK 73505; tel. 580/536-7533; FAX. 580/536-7535; Donald Garrett, M.D., Medical Director

Heritage Eye Surgicenter of Oklahoma, 6922 South Western, Oklahoma City, OK 73139; tel. 405/636-1508; FAX. 405/636-1239; Edward D. Glinski, D.O., MBA, Administrator

Medical Plaza Endoscopy Unit, 1125 North Porter, Suite 304, Norman, OK 73071; tel. 405/360-2799; FAX. 405/447-0321; Philip C. Bird, M.D.

Midtown Surgicare, 1000 North Lincoln, Suite 150, Oklahoma City, OK 73104; tel. 405/232-8696; FAX. 405/235-4023; June R. Ricards, RN, Administrator

Oklahoma Ambulatory Surgery Center, 6908-B East Reno, Midwest City, OK 73110; tel. 405/737-6900; FAX. 405/732-0885; A.C. Vyas, M.D., Administrator

Oklahoma Surgicare, 4317 W. Memorial Road, Oklahoma City, OK 73134; tel. 405/755-6240; FAX. 405/752-1819; Lindie Slater, Administrator

Orthopedic Associates Ambulatory Surgery Center, Inc., 3301 Northwest 50th Street, Oklahoma City, OK 73112; tel. 405/947-5610; FAX. 405/948-5166; Carolyn Moles, RN, Director

Outpatient Surgical Center of Ponca City, 400 Fairview, Ponca City, OK 74601; tel. 405/762-0695; FAX. 405/765-9406; Peggy Maples, RN, Executive Director

Physicians Surgical Center, 805 East Robinson, Norman, OK 73071-6610; tel. 405/364-9789; FAX. 405/366-8081; Sandra Vaughn, RN, Administrator

Southern Oklahoma Surgical Center, Inc., 2412 North Commerce, Ardmore, OK 73401; tel. 580/226-5000; Ann Willis, RN, Administrator

Southern Plains Ambulatory Surgery Center, 2222 Iowa Avenue, P.O. Box 1069, Chickasha, OK 73023; tel. 405/224-8111; FAX. 405/222-9557; Gary Gaspaid, Executive Director

Southwest Ambulatory Surgery Center, LLC, 8125 South Walker Avenue, Oklahoma City, OK 73139; tel. 405/631-1014; FAX. 405/619-4404; Anthony L. Cruse, D.O., Medical Director

Surgery Center of Edmond, 1700 South State Street, Edmond, OK 73013; tel. 405/330-1003; FAX. 405/330-1087; Carol Weddle, RN, Administrator

Surgery Center of Midwest City, 8121 National Avenue, Suite 108, Midwest City, OK 73110; tel. 405/732-7905; FAX. 405/732-3561; Steve Powell, Administrator

Surgery Center of South Oklahoma City, 100 Southeast 59th Street, Oklahoma City, OK 73109; tel. 405/634-9300; FAX. 405/634-8300; Larry Smith, Administrator

The Cataract Center of Lawton, 4214 Southwest Lee Boulevard, Lawton, OK 73505; tel. 405/353-5860; Stephen W. Gilkeson, Executive Administrator

Three Rivers Surgery Center, 3800 West Okmulgee, Muskogee, OK 74401; tel. 918/682-9899; FAX. 918/687-0786; Doug Blessen, Chief Executive Officer

Tower Day Surgery, 1044 Southwest 44th Street, Suite 100, Oklahoma City, OK 73109; tel. 405/636-1701; FAX. 405/636-4314; Marie Smith, RN, Director

Triad Eye Medical Clinic and Cataract Institute, 6140 South Memorial, Tulsa, OK 74133; tel. 918/252-2020; FAX. 918/252-7466; Marc L. Abel, D.O., Medical Director

OREGON

Aesthetic Breast and Cosmetic Surgery Center, 10201 Southeast Main, Suite 20, Portland, OR 97216; tel. 503/253-3458; FAX. 503/253-0856; Ronald V. DeMars, M.D., Administrator

Center for Cosmetic and Plastic Surgery, 1353 East McAndrews Road, Medford, OR 97504; tel. 541/770-6776; FAX. 541/770-5791; Robert M. Jensen, M.D., Administrator

Eye Surgery Center, 2925 Siskiyou Boulevard, Medford, OR 97504; tel. 541/779-2020; FAX. 541/770-6838; Loren R. Barrus, M.D., Administrator

Eye Surgery Institute, The, 813 S.W. Highland Ave., Redmond, OR 97756; tel. 541/548-7170; FAX. 541/548-3842; Kathleen Peterson, RN, Administrator

Futures Outpatient Surgical Center, Inc., 1849 Northwest Kearney, Suite 302, Portland, OR 97209; tel. 503/224-0723; FAX. 503/224-0722; Bryce E. Potter, M.D.

GI Endoscopy Center, 2560 N.W. Medical Park Drive, Roseburg, OR 97470; tel. 541/673-2046; FAX. 541/673-0454; Ruth E. Harpole, RN, Administrator

Lawrence W. O'Dell, d/b/a Northwest Eye Center, 9975 Southwest Nimbus Avenue, Beaverton, OR 97005; tel. 503/646-7644; Jim Heath, Administrator

Lovejoy Surgicenter, Inc., 933 Northwest 25th Avenue, Portland, OR 97210; tel. 503/221-1870; FAX. 503/221-1488; Kayla Reich, Administrator

McKenzie Surgery Center, 940 Country Club Road, Eugene, OR 97401; tel. 541/344-2600; FAX. 541/344-3317; Lynn M. Staples, RN, Administrator

North Bend Medical Center, Inc., 1900 Woodland Drive, Coos Bay, OR 97420; tel. 541/267-5151; FAX. 541/266-4501; J. Peter Johnson, CEO

Northbank Surgical Center, 700 Bellevue Street, S., Suite 300, Salem, OR 97301; tel. 503/364-3704; Peggy Seidler, Administrator

Ontario Surgery Center, 251 S.W. 19th Street, Ontario, OR 97914; tel. 541/889-3198; FAX. 541/881-9106; Jeffrey C. Pitts, M.D., Administrator

Oregon Cataract and Laser Institute, 2700 Southeast 14th Avenue, Albany, OR 97321; tel. 503/928-1666; Darrell Genstler, M.D., Administrator

Oregon Eye Surgery Center, Inc., 1550 Oak Street, Eugene, OR 97401; tel. 541/683-8771; FAX. 541/484-4993; Virginia Pecora, RN, Administrator

Oregon Surgery Center, 2801 NW Mercy Drive, Suite 200, Roseburg, OR 97470; tel. 541/677-2800; FAX. 541/677-2820; Vanessa Vu, M.D., C.O.O.

The Gastroenterology Endoscopy Center, Inc., 6464 Southwest Borland Road, Suite D-4, Tualatin, OR 97062; tel. 503/692-4537; FAX. 503/691-2324; Gale R. Dupell, MBA, Administrator

The Oregon Clinic Gastroenterology Division Gresham Office, 24900 Southeast Stark, Suite 205, Gresham, OR 97030; tel. 503/661-2000; FAX. 503/661-2001; Jeffrey S. Albaugh, M.D., Administrator

The Portland Clinic Surgical Center, 800 Southwest 13th Avenue, Portland, OR 97205; tel. 503/221-0161; FAX. 503/221-4451; J. Michael Schwab, CEO

Tigard Surgery Center, 13240 Southwest Pacific Highway, Suite 200, Tigard, OR 97223; tel. 503/639-6571; FAX. 503/624-6037; Ivan L. Bakos, M.D., Administrator

Willamette Valley Eye SurgiCenter, 2001 Commercial Street, S.E., Salem, OR 97302; tel. 503/363-1500; FAX. 503/588-2028; Gordon Miller, M.D., Administrator

PENNSYLVANIA

Abington Surgical Center, 2701 Blair Mill Road, Suite 35, Willow Grove, PA 19090; tel. 215/443-8505; FAX. 215/957-0565; Stanley E. Grissinger, MBA, CHE, Executive Director

Aestique Ambulatory Surgical Center, One Aesthetic Way, Greensburg, PA 15601; tel. 724/832-7555; FAX. 724/832-7568; Theodore A. Lazzaro, M.D., Medical Director

Apple Hill Surgical Center, 25 Monument Road, Suite 270, York, PA 17403; tel. 717/741-8250; FAX. 717/741-8254; Gwendolyn J. Grothouse, RN, Administrative Director

Delaware Valley Laser Surgery Institute, Two Bala Plaza, Pl 33, Bala Cynwd, PA 19004; tel. 215/668-2847; FAX. 215/668-1509; Herbert J. Nevyas, M.D., Medical Director

Dermatologic SurgiCenter, 1200 Locust Street, Philadelphia, PA 19107; tel. 215/546-3666; FAX. 215/546-6060; Anthony V. Benedetto, D.O., FACP, Medical Director

Dermatologic SurgiCenter, 2221 Garrett Road, Drexel Hill, PA 19026; tel. 610/623-5885; FAX. 610/623-7276; Anthony V. Benedetto, D.O. Medical Director

Digestive Disease Institute, 899 Poplar Church Road, Camp Hill, PA 17011; tel. 717/763-1239; FAX. 717/763-9854; Iris Garman, Administrator

Eye Clinic Ambulatory Surgical Center, Inc., 601 Wyoming Avenue, Kingston, PA 18704; tel. 717/288-7405; Mark Kelly, Administrator

Fairgrounds Surgical Center, 400 North 17th Street, Suite 300, Allentown, PA 18104; tel. 610/821-2020; FAX. 610/821-2016; Darlene G. Hinkle/ Debi Baker, Co-Administrative Directors

Fort Washington Surgery Center, 467 Pennsylvania Avenue, Fort Washington, PA 19034; tel. 215/628-4300; FAX. 215/628-4253; Charles Pappas, M. D.

Grandview Surgery & Laser Center, 205 Grandview Avenue, Camp Hill, PA 17011; tel. 717/731-5444; FAX. 717/731-0415; Larry Rodabaugh, Administrator

Hanover SurgiCenter, 3130 Grandview Road, Building B, Hanover, PA 17331; tel. 717/633-1600; FAX. 717/633-6556; Charlene D. Baker, Administrator

HealthSouth Mt. Pleasant Surgery Center, 200 Bessemer Road, Mt. Pleasant, PA 15666; tel. 724/547-5432; FAX. 724/547-2435; Dan Greene, Administrative Director

HealthSouth Scranton Surgery and Laser Center, 425 Adams Street, Scranton, PA 18510; tel. 717/348-1114; FAX. 717/347-4351; Marion Smith, Administrative Director

HealthSouth Surgery Center of Lancaster, 217 Harrisburg Avenue, Suite 103, Lancaster, PA 17603; tel. 717/295-2500; FAX. 717/295-4898; Joanne Hettel, Administrator

Jefferson Surgery Center, Coal Valley Road, P.O. Box 18420, Pittsburgh, PA 15236; tel. 412/469-6060; FAX. 412/469-7322; Sheran Sullivan, Manager

Section C

John A. Zitelli, M.D., P.C., Ambulatory Surgery Facility, 5200 Centre Avenue, Suite 303, Pittsburgh, PA 15232; tel. 412/681-9400; FAX. 412/681-5240; John A. Zitelli, M.D.

Kremer Laser Eye Center, 200 Mall Boulevard, King of Prussia, PA 19406; tel. 610/337-1580; FAX. 610/337-1153; Tara Hopewell, RN

Lebanon Outpatient Surgical Center, L.P., 830 Tuck Street, Lebanon, PA 17042; tel. 717/228-1620; FAX. 717/228-1642; Anita Gingrich Fuhrman, RN, B.S., CASC, Director

Lowry SurgiCenter, 1115 Lowry Avenue, Jeannette, PA 15644; tel. 412/527-2885; FAX. 412/527-6885; K. Diddle, M.D., Medical Director

Mary Ann Lebas RN, 204 Mifflin Avenue, Scranton, PA 18503; tel. 717/342-3145; FAX. 717/342-3136

Mt. Lebanon Surgical Center, Professional Office Building, 1050 Bower Hill Road, Suite 102, Pittsburgh, PA 15243; tel. 412/563-6808; FAX. 412/563-6857; Patricia Strosnider, Director, Nursing

North Shore Surgi-Center, Two Allegheny Center, Suite 530, Pittsburgh, PA 15212-5493; tel. 412/231-0200; FAX. 412/231-0613; Jack Demos, M.D., FACS

Northwood Surgery Center, 3729 Easton-Nazareth Highway, Easton, PA 18045; tel. 610/559-7110; FAX. 610/559-7317; Chitu Patel, Administrator

Ophthalmology Laser and Surgery Center, Inc., 92 Tuscarora Street, Harrisburg, PA 17104; tel. 717/233-2020; FAX. 717/233-0825

Paoli Surgery Center, One Industrial Boulevard, Paoli, PA 19301; tel. 610/408-0822; FAX. 610/408-9933; Karla A. German, Facility Manager

Pennsylvania Eye Surgery Center, 4100 Linglestown Road, Harrisburg, PA 17112; tel. 717/657-2020; FAX. 717/657-2071; Jill Stileler, RN, Director, Surgical Services

Pocono Ambulatory Surgery Center, One Veterans Place, Stroudsburg, PA 18360; tel. 570/421-4978; Mary P. Hayden RN, B.S.CASC, Administrative Director

Ridgeway Esper Medical Center Ambulatory Surgical Center, 5050 West Ridge Road, Erie, PA 16506-1298; tel. 814/833-8800; FAX. 814/833-2079; Deborah Hartmann, RN, Director, Nursing

Shadyside Surgi-Center, Inc., 5727 Centre Avenue, Pittsburgh, PA 15206; tel. 412/363-6626; FAX. 412/363-7008; Susan M. Katch, RN, Director

Southwestern Ambulatory Surgery Center, 500 Lewis Run Road, Suite 202, Pittsburgh, PA 15122; tel. 412/469-6964; FAX. 412/469-6948; Pamela Wrobleski, CRNA, M.P.M., Director

Southwestern Pennsylvania Eye Surgery Center, 750 East Beau Street, Washington, PA 15301; tel. 412/228-7477; FAX. 412/228-6271; Mary Roth, RN, Clinical Director

Surgical Center of York, 1750 Fifth Avenue, P.O. Box 290, York, PA 17405; tel. 717/843-7613; FAX. 717/849-5662; James Van Etten, Administrative Director

Surgical Eye Institute of Western Pennsylvania, 618 Monongahela Avenue, Glassport, PA 15045; tel. 412/664-7874; FAX. 412/673-5720; Shirley A. Smith, RN

The Surgery Center of Chester County, Suite 100, 460 Creamery Way, Oaklands Corporate Center, Exton, PA 19341-2500; tel. 610/594-8900; FAX. 610/594-8907; Lorraine Gamber, Manager

The SurgiCenter at Ligonier, 221 West Main Street, Ligonier, PA 15658; tel. 724/238-9573; FAX. 724/238-4709; Kim Kenney-Ciarimboli, Ambulatory Services Director

UPMC Monroeville Surgery Center, 125 Daugherty Drive, Monroeville, PA 15146-2749; tel. 412/374-9385; FAX. 412/374-9490; Carol Fiske Boumbouras, CMSC, Administrative Assistant, Medical Staff Mgr.

Valley Surgery Center, 1130 Highway 315, Wilkes-Barre, PA 18702; tel. 570/821-2830; FAX. 570/823-7921; Patricia Williams, Administrator

West Shore Endoscopy Center, 423 North 21st Street, Camp Hill, PA 17011; tel. 717/975-2430; FAX. 717/730-2158; Marilee Ball, RN, MHA, Administrator

Wills Surgery Center of Bucks County, 401 North York Road, Warminster, PA 18974; tel. 215/443-3022; FAX. 215/443-5859; JoAnn Quinn, Director, Nursing

RHODE ISLAND

Bayside Endoscopy Center, 33 Staniford Street, Providence, RI 02905; tel. 401/274-1810; FAX. 401/273-9689; Nicholas Califano, M.D., Administrator

Koch Eye Surgi Center, Inc., 566 Tollgate Road, Warwick, RI 02886; tel. 401/738-4800; FAX. 401/738-8153; Paul S. Koch, M.D., Administrator

Ocean State Endoscopy, 100 Highland Avenue, Providence, RI 02906; tel. 401/421-6306; Joel Spellun, M.D.

Wayland Square Surgicare, 17 Seekonk Street, Providence, RI 02906; tel. 401/453-3311; FAX. 401/351-1280; Ann Dugan, Administrator

Women's Medical Center, 1725 Broad Street, Cranston, RI 02905; tel. 401/467-9111; FAX. 401/461-1390; Nancy Ganem, Administrator

SOUTH CAROLINA

Ambulatory Eye Surgery and Laser Center, Inc., 9297 Medical Plaza Drive, Charleston, SC 29406; tel. 803/572-2888; Margaret A. Thompson

Bay Microsurgical Unit, Inc., 1200 Highmarket St., Georgetown, SC 29440; tel. 843/546-8421; FAX. 843/546-1173; Janet Spring, Director of Nursing

Bearwood Ambulatory Surgery Center, 3031 Highway 81, N., Anderson, SC 29621; tel. 864/226-0837; FAX. 864/226-8367; Kathy D. Gibson, R.N., Administrator

Carolina Surgical Center, 198 South Herlong Avenue, Rock Hill, SC 29732; tel. 803/327-4664; Gary Fillers, Administrator

Charleston Plastic Surgery Center, Inc., 261 Calhoun St., Ste. 200, Charleston, SC 29401; tel. 843/722-1985; FAX. 843/722-4840; Linda Crosby, Office Manager

Columbia Gastrointestinal Endoscopy Center, 2739 Laurel Street, Suite One-B, Columbia, SC 29240; tel. 803/254-9588; FAX. 803/931-8085; Cindy Sease, R.N., Administrator

Columbia Surgery Center, Inc., 338 Harbison Boulevard, Columbia, SC 29212; tel. 803/732-6180; FAX. 803/732-6563; Vickie H. Ott, Administrator

Cross Creek Surgery Center of Greenville Hospital System, Nine Doctors Drive, Crosscreek Medical Park, Greenville, SC 29605; tel. 803/455-8400; Barbara Callahan, Administrator

Greenville Endoscopy Center, Inc., 317 St. Francis Drive, Suite 150, Greenville, SC 29601; tel. 864/232-7338; FAX. 864/240-8140; Rebecca K. Swoyer, Administrator

HealthSouth Surgery Center of Charleston, 2690 Lake Park Drive, North Charles, SC 29406; tel. 803/764-0992; FAX. 803/764-3187; Rosina Feagin, RN, M.S.N., Administrator

HealthSouth Surgery Center of Greenville, Five Memorial Medical Court, Greenville, SC 29605; tel. 864/295-3067; FAX. 864/295-3096; Joyce Tollison, Facility Manager

Medicus Surgery Center, Inc., 107 Professional Court, P.O. Box 1886, Anderson, SC 29622-1886; tel. 864/225-1933; FAX. 864/716-7965; Ann Geier, RN, M.S., CNOR, Administrator

Outpatient Surgery Center of Lexington Medical Center in Irmo, 7035 Saint Andrews Road, Columbia, SC 29212; tel. 803/749-0924; Barbara Williams, Administrator

Patewood Surgery Center, LLC, 10 Enterprise Boulevard, Suite 104, Greenville, SC 29615; tel. 803/458-7141; FAX. 803/676-9116; Mary Jane Knottek, RN, B.S.N., CNOR, Clinical Nurse

Pee Dee Ambulatory Surgery Center, 602 Cheves, P.O. Box F-17, Florence, SC 29501; tel. 803/669-3822; Joseph J. McEvoy, Administrator

Roper West Ashley Surgery Center, 18 Farmfield Avenue, Charleston, SC 29407; tel. 843/763-3763; FAX. 843/763-3721; Maria I. Sample, Administrator

Spartanburg Urology Surgicenter, Inc., 391 Serpentine Drive, Suite 330, Spartanburg, SC 29303; tel. 864/585-2002; FAX. 864/585-3300; Rick Sizemore, RN, OR Director

The Greenwood Endoscopy Center, 103 Liner Drive, Greenwood, SC 29646; tel. 803/227-3838; FAX. 803/227-6116; A. A. Ramage, M.D., Administrator

Trident Surgery Center, 9313 Medical Plaza Drive, Suite 102, Charleston, SC 29406; tel. 803/797-8992; FAX. 803/797-4094; Leah J. Dawson, Administrator

SOUTH DAKOTA

Aberdeen Surgical Center, 1200 South Main, Box 1150, Aberdeen, SD 57401-1150; tel. 605/225-2466; Scott H. Berry, M.D., Administrator

Black Hills Regional Eye Surgery Center, 2800 Third Street, Rapid City, SD 57701-7394; tel. 605/341-2000; FAX. 605/341-0278; Richard B. Hanafin, Executive Director

Jones Eye Clinic, 3801 South Elmwood Avenue, Sioux Falls, SD 57105-6565; tel. 605/336-3142; FAX. 605/334-0737; Charles E. Jones, M.D.

Mallard Pointe Surgical Center, 1201 Mickelson Drive, Watertown, SD 57201-7100; tel. 605/882-4743; FAX. 605/882-6064; Mary Petersen, Administrative Director

Medical Associates Clinic Surgery Center, 772 East Dakota, Pierre, SD 57501-3399; tel. 605/945-5210; FAX. 605/224-2217; Michael Pfeifer, Administrator

Sioux Falls Surgical Center, 910 East 20th Street, Sioux Falls, SD 57105-1012; tel. 605/334-6730; FAX. 605/334-8096; Donald A. Schellpfeffer, M.D., Ph.D., Medical Director

Spearfish Surgery Center, LLC, 1316 10th Street, Spearfish, SD 57783-1530; tel. 605/642-3113; FAX. 605/642-3117; Jan Fett, Director of Nursing

Women's Health Services, Ltd., 909 South Miller, Mitchell, SD 57301; tel. 605/995-8040; FAX. 605/995-8043; Sheri Trudeau, CNP, Clinic Director

TENNESSEE

Appalachian Ambulatory Surgical Center, Medical Arts Building, 106 Rogosin Drive, Elizabethton, TN 37643; tel. 615/543-5888

Atrium Memorial Surgical Center, 1949 Gunbarrel Road, Suite 290, Chattanooga, TN 37421; tel. 615/495-3550; FAX. 615/495-3580; Sandy Proctor, Administrator

Bristol Surgery Center, 350 Blountville Highway, Suite 108, Bristol, TN 37620; tel. 423/844-6120; FAX. 423/844-6119; Karen Williams,GCHC,MPH,NHA,CHES Administrator

Cataract Surgery Center, 5406 Knight Arnold Road, Memphis, TN 38115; tel. 901/360-8081; FAX. 901/368-3822

Centennial Surgery Center, 340 23rd Avenue, N., Nashville, TN 37203; tel. 615/327-1123; FAX. 615/327-0261; Cynthia S. Duvall, RN, B.S., Administrator

Chattanooga Surgery Center, 400 North Holtzclaw Avenue, Chattanooga, TN 37404; tel. 423/698-6871; FAX. 423/622-8993; K.D. Ratchford,Administrator

Clarksville Endoscopy Center, 132 Hillcrest Drive, Clarksville, TN 37043; tel. 931/552-0180; FAX. 931/572-0915

Columbia Endoscopy Center, Inc., 1510 1/2 Hatcher Lane, Columbia, TN 38401; tel. 615/381-7818; FAX. 615/381-5625; Dianne Roberts, RN, Head Nurse

Columbia Outpatient Surgery, Inc., 1405 Hatcher Lane, Columbia, TN 38401; tel. 615/381-3700; Judy Griffin, Administrator

Columbia Sullins Surgery Center, 2761 Sullins Street, Knoxville, TN 37919; tel. 423/522-2949; FAX. 423/637-3259; Tina Shelby-Kahl, Assistant Administrator

D D C Surgery Center, Nine Physicians Drive, Jackson, TN 38305; tel. 731/661-0086; FAX. 731/661-9783; Vicki Hale, Clinical Director

East Memphis Surgery Center, 80 Humphreys Center Drive, Suite 101, Memphis, TN 38120; tel. 901/747-3233; FAX. 901/747-3230; Cathy Gilland, RN, Facility Administrator

Endoscopy Center of Kingsport, d/b/a Sullivan Digestive Center, 2204 Pavilion Drive, Kingsport, TN 37660; tel. 423/392-6100; FAX. 423/392-6159; Penny Lloyd, Administrator

Endoscopy Center of Northeast Tennessee, 310 State of Franklin Road, Suite 202, Johnson City, TN 37604; tel. 615/929-7111

Eye Surgery Center of East Tennessee, 1124 Weisgarber Road, Suite 110, Knoxville, TN 37909; tel. 423/588-1037; FAX. 423/909-9104; Pat Pullen, RN

Eye Surgery Center of Middle Tennessee, Parkview Tower, Suite 900, 210 25th Avenue, N., Nashville, TN 37203; tel. 615/327-2244; FAX. 615/327-9254; Amanda Elam Executive Administrator

Fort Sanders West Outpatient Surgery Center, Ltd., 210 Fort Sanders West Boulevard, Knoxville, TN 37922; tel. 865/531-5200; FAX. 865/531-5729; Leslie Irwin, Vice President

Franklin Surgery Center at MedCore, 2105 Edward Curd Lane, Franklin, TN 37067; tel. 615/794-7320

G. Baker Hubbard Ambulatory Surgery Center, 616 West Forest Avenue, Jackson, TN 38301; tel. 731/422-0330; FAX. 731/422-0478

Germantown Ambulatory Surgical Center, Inc., 7499 Poplar Pike, Germantown, TN 38138; tel. 901/756-5474; FAX. 901/756-5292

HealthSouth Nashville Surgery Center, 1717 Patterson Street, Nashville, TN 37203; tel. 615/329-1888; FAX. 615/329-0179; Lori Seymore, Administrator

Section C

HealthSouth Surgery Center of Clarksville, 121 Hillcrest Drive, Clarksville, TN 37043; tel. 931/552–9992; Jennifer Hines, Administrator

Kingsport Bronchoscopy Center, Inc., 135 West Ravine Road, Suite Eight-A, Kingsport, TN 37660; tel. 615/247–5197; FAX. 615/247–5254; Shirley Hawkins, Administrator

Knoxville Center for Reproductive Health, 1547 West Clinch Avenue, Knoxville, TN 37916; tel. 423/637–3861; FAX. 865/637–0222; Kim Denison, Director

Knoxville Surgery Center, 9300 Park West Boulevard, Knoxville, TN 37923; tel. 615/691–2725; FAX. 615/691–3090; Ranae Thompson, RN, Facility Administrator

Lebanon HMA Surgical Center, 1414 Baddour Parkway, Lebanon, TN 37088; tel. 615/444–8944; FAX. 615/444–8994; Sylvia Black, Clinical Director

LeBonheur East Surgery Center, L.P., 786 Estate Place, Memphis, TN 38120; tel. 901/681–4100; FAX. 901/681–4140; Sarah Wainscott, Administrative Director, Carol Langston, Asst. Director

Lisa Ross Birth & Women's Center, Inc, Maternity Center of East Tennessee (formerly), 1925-B Ailor Avenue, Knoxville, TN 37921; tel. 865/524–4422; FAX. 865/523–3687; Cliff Honicker, CAO or Linda Cole, CNM Exec. Dir.

Mays & Schnapp Pain Clinic and Rehabilitation Center, 55 Humphreys Center Drive, Suite 200, Memphis, TN 38120; tel. 901/747–0040; FAX. 901/747–0042; Lori Parris, RN, Administrator

Medical Center Endoscopy Group, 930 Madison, Suite 870, Memphis, TN 38103; tel. 901/578–2538; FAX. 901/578–2572; John W. Flowers, Administrator

Memphis Area Medical Center for Women, 29 South Bellevue Boulevard, Memphis, TN 38104; tel. 901/722–8050

Memphis Center for Reproductive Health, 1462 Poplar Avenue, Memphis, TN 38104; tel. 901/274–3550; FAX. 901/274–3551

Memphis Eye and Cataract Ambulatory Surgery Center, 6485 Poplar Avenue, Memphis, TN 38119; tel. 901/767–3937

Memphis Gastroenterology Endoscopy Center, 80 Humphrey's Center, Suite 220, Memphis, TN 38120; tel. 901/747–3630; FAX. 901/747–0039; Sylvia Hawkins, RN, Compliance Manager

Memphis Regional Gamma Knife Center, 1265 Union Avenue, Memphis, TN 38104; tel. 901/726–6444; FAX. 901/726–6145

Memphis Regional Planned Parenthood, Inc., 1407 Union Avenue, Third Floor, Memphis, TN 38104; tel. 901/725–1717; Ellen Ruby - Markie, Chief Executive Officer

Memphis Surgery Center, 1044 Cresthaven Road, Memphis, TN 38119; tel. 901/682–1516; FAX. 901/682–1545; Jane Almon RN, CNOR, Facility Administrator

Mid-State Endoscopy Center, 2010 Church Street, Suite 420, Nashville, TN 37203; tel. 615/329–2141; FAX. 615/321–0522; Allan H. Bailey, M.D., Medical Director

Nashville Endoscopy Center, 300 20th N., Eighth Floor, Nashville, TN 37203; tel. 615/284–1335; FAX. 615/284–1316; Margaret Sullivan, RN

Nashville Gastrointestinal Endoscopy Center, 4230 Harding Road, Suite 309, Nashville, TN 37205; tel. 615/383–0165; FAX. 615/292–4657; Ron E. Pruitt, M.D.

Northridge Surgery Center, 647 Myatt Drive, Madison, TN 37115; tel. 615/868–8942; FAX. 615/860–3820; Melba Willis, Administrator

Ophthalmic Ambulatory Surgery Center, P.C., 342 22nd Street, Nashville, TN 37203; tel. 615/327–2001; FAX. 615/327–2069; Alec Dryden, Administrator

Oral Facial Surgery Center, 322 22nd Avenue, N., Nashville, TN 37203; tel. 615/321–6160; FAX. 615/327–9612; Shea Love, Administrator

Physicians Pavilion Surgery Center, 360 Wallace Road, Nashville, TN 37211; tel. 615/781–9020; FAX. 615/781–9944; Jason Beam, Administrator

Ridge Lake Ambulatory Surgery Center, 825 Ridge Lake Boulevard, Memphis, TN 38119; tel. 901/685–0777

Shea Ear Clinic, 6133 Poplar Pike, Memphis, TN 38119; tel. 901/761–9720; FAX. 901/763–4400; John J. Shea Jr., MD, President

Southern Endoscopy Center, 397 Wallace Road, Suite 407, Nashville, TN 37211; tel. 615/832–5530; FAX. 615/832–5713; Robert W. Herring, Jr., M.D., Medical Director

St. Thomas Medical Group Endoscopy Center, 4230 Harding Road, Suite 400, Nashville, TN 37205; tel. 615/297–2700; Jeff May RN, Center Director

Surgical Services, P.C., 604 South Main Street, Sweetwater, TN 37874; tel. 423/337–4508; FAX. 423/337–4588

Surgicenter Of Murfreesboro Medical Clinic, P.A., 1004 North Highland Avenue, Murfreesboro, TN 37130; tel. 615/893–4480; FAX. 615/876–7876; Jenny Bloebaum, Coordinator

Tennessee Endoscopy Center, 1706 East Lamar Alexander Parkway, Maryville, TN 37804; tel. 615/983–0073; FAX. 615/984–1731; Craig Jarvis, M.D., Administrator

The Cookeville Surgery Center, 100 West Fourth Street, Suite 100, Cookeville, TN 38501; tel. 931/526–8115; FAX. 931/526–7619; Sherry Harder,RN Administrator

The Endoscopy Center, 801 Weisgarber Road, Suite 100, Knoxville, TN 37909, Knoxville, TN 37950-9002; tel. 615/588–5121; Gayle Mahan, Office Manager

The Endoscopy Center of Centennial, L.P., 2400 Patterson Street, Suite 515, Nashville, TN 37203; tel. 615/327–2111; FAX. 615/327–9292; Donna Crumley, RN, B.S., MBA, Endoscopy Administrator

The Eye Surgery Center Oak Ridge, 90 Vermont Avenue, Oak Ridge, TN 37830; tel. 423/482–8894; FAX. 865/481–8349; Sally Jones, Administrator

Urology Surgery Center, L.P., 2801 Charlotte Avenue, Nashville, TN 37209; tel. 615/250–9200; FAX. 615/250–9251; Mark Flora, M.D., Chairman

Van Dyke Ambulatory Surgery Center, 1024 Kelley Drive, Paris, TN 38242; tel. 901/642–5003; FAX. 901/642–8756; John T. VanDyck III, M.D., Owner

Volunteer Women's Medical Clinic, 313 Concord Street, Knoxville, TN 37919; tel. 865/522–5173; FAX. 865/522–9907; Elizabeth Fraley-Dumas, Clinical Director

Wesberry Surgery Center, 2900 South Perkins Road, Memphis, TN 38118-3237; tel. 901/362–3100; FAX. 901/362–3372; Jesse Wesberry, Jr., M.D., President

Wesley Ophthalmic Plastic Surgery Center, 250 25th Avenue North, Suite 213, Nashville, TN 37203; tel. 615/329–3624; Janie Stucker, RN, Director

TEXAS

Las Colinas Surgery Center, 4255 North Macarthur Boulevard, Irving, TX 75038; tel. 214/257–0144; FAX. 214/258–0436; Michael Scott, Administrator

Abilene Cataract and Refractive Surgery Center, 2120 Antilley Road, Abilene, TX 79606; tel. 325/695–2020; FAX. 325/695–2326; Paul B. Thomas M.D. Medical Director

Abilene Endoscopy Center, 1249 Ambler Avenue, Abilene, TX 79601; tel. 325/677–2626; FAX. 325/677–6835; Gary Roark, M.D., Medical Director

Amarillo Cataract and Eye Surgery Center, Inc., 7310 Fleming Avenue, Amarillo, TX 79106; tel. 806/354–8891; FAX. 806/354–2591; Carol A. Pearson, Director

Ambulatory Urological Surgery Center, Inc., 1149 Ambler, Abilene, TX 79601; tel. 915/676–3557; FAX. 915/673–2143; Angela X. Young, RN, Manager

American Surgery Centers of South Texas, LTD, 7810 Louis Pasteur, Suite 100, San Antonio, TX 78229; tel. 210/692–0218; FAX. 210/692–7980; Letty Herrera, Administrator

Bailey Square Surgical Center, Ltd., 1111 West 34th Street, Austin, TX 78705; tel. 512/454–6753; FAX. 512/454–4314; Donna Hutto, RN, CNOR, Director of Nursing Services Operation

Bay Area Endoscopy Center, 444 FM 1959, Houston, TX 77034; tel. 281/481–9400; FAX. 281/481–9490; N.S. Bala, Medical Director

Bay Area Surgery, 7101 South Padre Island Drive, Corpus Christ, TX 78412; tel. 361/761–3500; FAX. 361/761–3754; Gene Hybner, Administrator

Bay Area Surgicare Center, 502 Medical Center Boulevard, Webster, TX 77598; tel. 281/332–2433; FAX. 281/332–0619; Carol Simons, Administrator

Baylor SurgiCare, 3920 Worth Street, Dallas, TX 75246; tel. 214/820–2581; FAX. 214/820–7484; Robin Shaw, Administrative Director

Bellaire Surgicare, Inc., 6699 Chimney Rock, Suite 200, Houston, TX 77081; tel. 713/665–1406; FAX. 713/665–8262; Sheila M. Liccketto, Administrator

Brazosport Eye Institute, 103 Parking Way, P.O. Box 369, Lake Jackson, TX 77566; tel. 979/297–2961; FAX. 979/297–2395; Frank J. Grady, M.D., Ph.D., FACS, Director

Brownsville Surgicare, 1024 Los Ebanos Boulevard, Brownsville, TX 78520; tel. 210/548–0101; FAX. 210/541–3752; Karen Solis, CMM, CEO

Central Texas Day Surgery Center, L.P., 1817 Southwest Dodgen, Loop, Temple, TX 76502; tel. 817/773–7785; FAX. 817/773–9333; Debby Meyer, Director

Coastal Bend Ambulatory Surgical Center, 900 Morgan, Corpus Christ, TX 78404; tel. 512/888–4288; FAX. 512/888–4786; Barbara VandenBout

Columbia Physicians DaySurgery Center, 3930 Crutcher Street, Dallas, TX 75246; tel. 214/827–0760; FAX. 214/827–0944; Robin Shaw, RN, Administrator

Columbia Surgical Center, 2800 East 29th Street, P.O. Box 2700, Bryan, TX 77805; tel. 409/776–4300; FAX. 409/774–7149; Bob Lemay RN, Director

Conroe Surgery Center, 1501 River Pointe Dr., Suite 200, Conroe, TX 77304; tel. 409/760–3443; FAX. 409/760–1322; Kathy Schutz, RN, B.S.N., Facility Administrator

Covenant Surgicenter, Ltd., 2301 Quaker Avenue, Lubbock, TX 79410; tel. 806/725–8801; FAX. 806/725–8820; David S. Weil, Executive Director

Crystal Outpatient Surgery Center, Inc., 215 Oak Drive, S., Suite J, Lake Jackson, TX 77566; tel. 409/299–6118; FAX. 409/299–1007; R. Scott Yarish, M.D., Administrator

Cy-Fair Surgery Center, 11250 Fallbrook Drive, Houston, TX 77065; tel. 713/955–7194; FAX. 713/890–0895; Sonja Christmas, Administrator

Dallas DaySurgery of Texas LTD., 411 North Washington, Suite 5400, Dallas, TX 75246; tel. 214/821–8613; Henry S. Byrd, President

Dallas Ophthalmology Center, Inc., 4633 North Central Expressway, Suite 310, Dallas, TX 75205; tel. 214/520–7600; FAX. 214/528–6522; Jean Vining, RN, Administrator

DeHaven Surgical Center, 1424 East Front Street, Tyler, TX 75702; tel. 903/595–4144; FAX. 903/595–6821; Terri McDougal, RN, Administrator

Doctors' Surgery Center, Inc., 5300 North Street, Nacogdoches, TX 75965; tel. 936/569–8278; FAX. 936/569–0275; Robert P. Lehmann, M.D., Director

East El Paso Surgery Center, 7835 Corral Drive, El Paso, TX 79915; tel. 915/595–3353; FAX. 915/595–6796; Laura Ice, Administrator

East Side Surgery Center, Inc., 10918 East Freeway, Houston, TX 77029; tel. 713/451–4299; FAX. 713/451–4383; Vicky Mizell, Administor

East Texas Eye Associates Surgery Center, 1306 Frank Avenue, Lufkin, TX 75904; tel. 409/634–8381; Jo Ann O'Neill, C.O.T., Administrator

El Paso Institute of Eye Surgery, Inc., 1717 North Brown Street, Building #3, El Paso, TX 79902; tel. 915/544–0526; FAX. 915/544–2877; Esther A. Calderon, Administrator

Elm Place Ambulatory Surgical Center, 2217 South Danville Drive, Abilene, TX 79605; tel. 325/695–0600; FAX. 325/695–3908; Susan King, RN, Director

Endoscopy Center of Dallas, Ambulatory Endoscopy Clinic of Dallas, 6390 LBJ Freeway, Suite 200, Dallas, TX 75240; tel. 972/934–3691; FAX. 972/934–3694; Jeane Suggs, Administrator

Facial Plastic and Cosmetic Surgical Center, 6300 Humana Plaza, Suite 475, Abilene, TX 79606; tel. 915/695–3630; FAX. 915/695–3633; Howard A. Tobin, M.D., FACS, Medical Director

Forest Park Surgery Pavilion, 5920 Forest Park Road, Suite 700, Dallas, TX 75235; tel. 214/350–2400; FAX. 214/352–4862; Tom Clark, Administrator

Fort Worth Endoscopy Center, 1201 Summit Avenue, Suite 400, Fort Worth, TX 76102; tel. 817/332–6500; Donna Drerup, RN, M.S.N., Administrator

Forth Worth Surgery Center, 2001 West Rosedale, Fort Worth, TX 76104; tel. 817/877–4777; David Yodge, Administrator

Foundation Surgery Center of Dickinson, 3810 Hughes Court, Dickinson, TX 77539; tel. 713/337–7001; FAX. 713/337–7091; Sara Bledsoe, Administrator

Garland Surgery Center L.P., 777 Walter Reed Boulevard, Suite 105, Garland, TX 75042; tel. 214/494–2400; FAX. 214/494–3873; Dan Nicholson, President

Gastroenterology Consultants Outpatient Surgical Center, 8214 Wurzbach, San Antonio, TX 78229; tel. 210/614-1234; FAX. 210/614-7749; Bonnie Draude, B.S.N., RN, C.G.RN, Clinical Manager

Gastrointestinal Endoscopy Center Number Two, LTD, 1600 Coit Road, Suite 401A, Plano, TX 75075; tel. 214/867-0019; Brian Cooley, M.D., Administrator

Gonzaba Surgical Center, 720 Pleasanton Road, San Antonio, TX 78214; tel. 210/921-3826; FAX. 210/921-3825; William Gonzaba, M.D., Chief Executive Officer

Gramercy Outpatient Surgery Center, LTD, 2727 Gramercy, Houston, TX 77025; tel. 713/660-6900; FAX. 713/660-0704; Anita Gill, RN, Clinical Director

HealthSouth Arlington Day Surgery, 918 North Davis Street, Arlington, TX 76012; tel. 817/860-9933; FAX. 817/860-2314; Diane Wood, RN, Administrator

HealthSouth Northeast Surgery Center, 18929 Highway 59, Humble, TX 77338; tel. 713/446-4053; Holly Reems, R.N.

HealthSouth Outpatient Surgery Center, 7515 South Main Street, Suite 800, Houston, TX 77030; tel. 713/796-9666; FAX. 713/796-9660; Joan M. Culberson, RN, Administrator

HealthSouth Surgery Center of Beaumont, 3050 Liberty, Beaumont, TX 77702; tel. 409/835-3535; FAX. 409/835-6005; Tammie Clodfelter, Administrator

HealthSouth Surgery Center of Dallas, 7150 Greenville Avenue, Suite 200, Dallas, TX 75231; tel. 214/891-0466; FAX. 214/739-4702; Vicki V. Schultz, RN, Administrator

HealthSouth Surgery Center or Dunkanville, 1018 East Wheatland Road, Duncanville, TX 75116; tel. 972/296-6912; FAX. 972/296-6912; David Gross, Administrator

HealthSouth Waco Surgery Center, 2911 Herring, Waco, TX 76708; tel. 817/755-4430; FAX. 817/755-4590; Connie Allen, RN, Administrator

Heart of Texas Outpatient Cataract Center, 100 South Park Drive, Brownwood, TX 76801; tel. 325/643-3561; Larry Smith, CRNA, Administrator

Heritage Surgery Center, 1501 Redbud, McKinney, TX 75069; tel. 972/548-0771; FAX. 972/562-2300; Rudolf Churner, M.D., Administrator

Howerton Eye and Laser Surgical Center, 2610 I.H. 35 South, Austin, TX 78704-5703; tel. 512/443-9715; FAX. 512/443-9845; Ernest E. Howerton, M.D., Administrator

Key Whitman Surgery Center, 2801 Lemmon Avenue, Suite 400, Dallas, TX 75204; tel. 214/754-0000; FAX. 214/754-0079; Jeffrey Whitman, M.D.

Longview Ambulatory Surgical Center, 703 East Marshall Avenue, Suite 2000, Longview, TX 75601-5563; tel. 903/236-2111; FAX. 903/236-2479; Jerry D. Adair, President and CEO

Lufkin Endoscopy Center, 317 Gaslight Boulevard, Lufkin, TX 75901; tel. 409/634-3713; FAX. 409/634-8136; Bhagvan R. Malladi, M.D., Administrator

Mann Cataract Surgery Center, 18850 South Memorial Boulevard, Humble, TX 77338; tel. 713/446-9164; Elpidio Fahel, Administrator

Medical City Dallas Ambulatory Surgery Center, 7777 Forest Lane, Suite C-150, Dallas, TX 75230; tel. 972/566-6170; FAX. 972/566-6181; Jennifer Bertaut, RN, Director

Medical Mall Surgery Center, Inc., 1665 Antilley Road, Suite 170, Abilene, TX 79606; tel. 325/692-6694; FAX. 325/691-1568; Daniel Brewer, RN

Methodist Ambulatory Surgery Center-Central San Antonio, 1008 Brooklyn Avenue, San Antonio, TX 78215-1600; tel. 210/225-0496; FAX. 210/225-8462; Carl J. Collazo, Administrator

Metroplex Ambulatory Surgical Center, 2717 Osler Drive, Suite 102, Grand Prairie, TX 75051; tel. 972/647-6272; FAX. 972/660-1822; Glenda Daniels, RN, Director

Metroplex Surgicare, 1600 Central Drive, Suite 180, Bedford, TX 76022; tel. 817/571-1999; FAX. 817/571-1220; Susan McKeever, Administrator

Mid-Town Surgical Center, LLP, 2105 Jackson Street, Suite 200, Houston, TX 77003; tel. 713/571-8141; FAX. 713/571-8184; Louis Varela, M.D.

North Carrier Surgicenter, 517 North Carrier Parkway, Suite A, Grand Prairie, TX 75050-5494; tel. 972/264-0533; FAX. 972/262-5974; Abraham F. Syrquin, M.D., Medical Director

North Dallas Surgicare, 375 Municipal Drive, Suite 214, Richardson, TX 75080; tel. 214/918-9400; FAX. 214/918-9749; Mike Kelley, Administrator

North Texas Surgi-Center, 917 Midwestern Parkway, E., Wichita Falls, TX 76302; tel. 940/767-7273; FAX. 940/723-9059; Barbara Dawson, Administrator

Northeast Texas Surgical Center, 1801 Galleria Oaks Drive, Texarkana, TX 75503; tel. 903/792-2108; FAX. 903/792-0606; Ruby Bearden, Business Manager

Park Central Surgical Center, 12200 Park Central Drive, Third Floor, Dallas, TX 75251; tel. 972/661-0505; FAX. 972/661-5511; Molly Paulose, Administrator

Plano Ambulatory Surgery Associates, L.P., d/b/a Surgery Center of Plano, 1620 Coit Road, Plano, TX 75075-7799; tel. 972/519-1100; DeWayne Hodges, Administrator

Plaza Day Surgery, 909 Ninth Avenue, Fort Worth, TX 76104-3986; tel. 817/336-6060; FAX. 817/339-2329; Deborah Pelton RN,Administrator

Port Arthur Day Surgery Center, 3449 Gates Boulevard, Port Arthur, TX 77642; tel. 409/983-6144; Vicki Clark, Administrative Director

Premier Ambulatory Surgery of Austin, dba South Austin Surgery Center, 4207 James Casey, Suite 203, Austin, TX 78745; tel. 512/440-7894; FAX. 512/440-1932; Patricia Philbin, Executive Director

Q Plus Outpatient Surgery Center, 2507 Medical Row, Suite 101, Grand Prairie, TX 75051; tel. 972/647-8520; FAX. 972/336-0488; James L. Grace Administrator

Rio Grande Surgery Center, 1809 South Cynthia, McAllen, TX 78503; tel. 956/618-4402; FAX. 956/618-4174; Janet R. West, Administrator

San Antonio Digestive Disease Endoscopy Center, 1804 Northeast Loop 410, Suite 101, San Antonio, TX 78217; tel. 210/828-8400; FAX. 210/828-8648

San Antonio Eye Surgicenter, 800 McCullough, San Antonio, TX 78215; tel. 210/226-6169; FAX. 210/226-6383; Carol Harris, Administrator

San Antonio Gastroenterology Endoscopy Center, 520 Euclid Avenue, San Antonio, TX 78212; tel. 210/271-0606; FAX. 210/271-0180; Ernesto Guerra, M.D.

San Antonio Surgery Center, Inc., 5290 Medical Drive, San Antonio, TX 78229; tel. 210/614-0187; FAX. 210/692-7757; Kevin Jones, Administrator

South Plains Endoscopy Center, 3610 24th Street, Lubbock, TX 79410; tel. 806/797-1015; Pat S. Wheeler, Administrator

South Texas Eye Surgicenter, Inc., 4406 North Laurent, Victoria, TX 77901; tel. 800/352-5928; Robert T. McMahon, M.D., Chief Executive Officer

South West Surgery Center, 1717 Precinct Line Road, Suite 101, Hurst, TX 76054; tel. 817/788-1881; FAX. 817/656-1490; Caressa Holland, Administrator

Southwest Endoscopy Center, 11803 South Freeway, Suite 115, Fort Worth, TX 76115; tel. 817/293-9292; FAX. 817/551-0616; Esther Cruz, MA/Office Manager

Surgery Center of Texas, 155 East Loop 338, Suite 500, Odessa, TX 79762; tel. 432/367-3906; FAX. 432/367-3895; Libby Palma, Administrator

SurgEyeCare, Inc., 5421 La Sierra Drive, Dallas, TX 75231; tel. 214/361-1443; FAX. 214/691-3299; Sandra J. Yankee, Administrator

Surgi-Care Center of Midland, Inc., 3001 West Illinois, Suite 5-A, Midland, TX 79701; tel. 915/697-1067; FAX. 915/697-8802; Michelle Coleman, RN, Director

Surgical and Diagnostic Center, Inc., 729 Bedford Euless Road West 100, Hurst, TX 76053; tel. 817/282-6905; FAX. 817/285-8114; Robert T. Myles, D.O., Medical Director

Surgical Center of El Paso, 1815 North Stanton, El Paso, TX 79902; tel. 915/533-8412; FAX. 915/542-0367; Raymond Sainz, Administrator

Surgicare of Travis Centre, Inc., 6655 Travis, Suite 200, Houston, TX 77030; tel. 713/526-5100; FAX. 713/520-1782; Sherri Bronikowski, Administrator

Surgicare, Ltd., 3534 Vista, Pasadena, TX 77504; tel. 713/947-0330; Evelyn Grimes, Administrator

Surgicenter of San Antonio, L.P., 5290 Medical Drive, San Antonio, TX 78229; tel. 210/614-0187; FAX. 210/692-7757; Ann Mueller, Executive Director

Texarkana Surgery Center, 5404 Summerhill Road, Texarkana, TX 75503; tel. 903/793-4872; FAX. 903/794-6300; Kimble Hatridge, Administrator

Texas Institute of Surgery, 12700 North Featherwood Drive, Suite 100, Houston, TX 77034; tel. 713/481-9303; FAX. 713/481-4263; Glenn Rodriguez, Administrator

Texoma Outpatient Surgery Center, Inc., 1712 Eleventh Street, Wichita Falls, TX 76301; tel. 940/723-2499; FAX. 940/923-2497; Tracy Youngblood, Administrator

The Cataract Center of East Texas, 802 Turtle Creek Drive, Tyler, TX 75701; tel. 903/595-4333; FAX. 903/535-9845; Nancy M. Grimes, Administrator

The Center for Sight, P.A., 2 Medical Center Boulevard, Lufkin, TX 75904-3175; tel. 936/634-8434; FAX. 936/639-2581; Richard J. Ruckman, M.D.

The Endoscopy Center of Southeast Texas, 950 North 11th Street,#200, Beaumont, TX 77702; tel. 409/833-5555; FAX. 409/833-9911; Jackie Sullivan, RN Center Director

The Eye Surgery Center of the Rio Grande Valley, 1402 East Sixth Street, Weslaco, TX 78596; tel. 210/968-6155; FAX. 210/968-8291; Linda Funston, Administrator

The Ocular Surgery Center, Inc., 1100 North Main Avenue, San Antonio, TX 78212; tel. 210/222-2154; FAX. 512/222-0706; Jane Wilson, Administrator

The Surgery Center of Mesquite, 2690 North Galloway Avenue, Mesquite, TX 75150; tel. 972/279-8100; FAX. 972/279-3300; Chris Fremme, Administrator

The Surgery Center of the Woodlands, 1441 Woodstead Court, Suite 100, The Woodlands, TX 77380; tel. 281/363-0058; FAX. 281/363-0450; Kathleen Budd, Administrator

Thorstenson Eye Clinic Surgery Center, 3302 Northeast Stallings Drive, Nacogdoches, TX 75963-2020; tel. 936/564-2411; FAX. 936/564-1280; Lyle S. Thorstenson, M.D., FACS, Administrator

Urological Surgery Center of Fort Worth, 418 South Henderson, Fort Worth, TX 76104; tel. 817/338-4637; Charles Bamberger, M.D.

Valley Endoscopy Center, LLP, 3101 South 77 Sunshine Strip, Suite B, Harlingen, TX 78550; tel. 956/421-2324; FAX. 956/421-5791; Oral James MD/ Lou Valenwela RN Center Director

Valley Eye Surgery Center, 1515 North Ed Carey Drive, Harlingen, TX 78550; tel. 210/423-2773; FAX. 210/423-5618; Michael D. Laney, Administrator

Valley View Surgery Center, 5744 LBJ Freeway, Suite 200, Dallas, TX 75240; tel. 972/490-4333; FAX. 972/490-2494; Ronald W. Disney, Chief Executive Officer

Vista Healthcare, Inc., 4301 Vista, Pasadena, TX 77504; tel. 713/947-0891; FAX. 713/947-1377; Chiu M. Chan, Administrator

Vista Surgical Center West, 2500 Fondren, Suite 350, Houston, TX 77063; tel. 713/782-8279; FAX. 713/782-3139; Diana Hastings, RN, CNOR - Clinical Director

West Houston Surgicare, 970 Campbell Road, Houston, TX 77024-2804; tel. 713/461-3547; FAX. 713/722-8921; Charles Mattea, Administrator

WestPark Surgery Center, 130 South Central Expressway, McKinney, TX 75070; tel. 214/542-9382; FAX. 214/548-5303; Debbie Taylor

Wilson Surgicenter, 4315 28th Street, Lubbock, TX 79410; tel. 806/792-2104; Bill W. Wilson, M.D., Chief Executive Officer

UTAH

Central Utah Surgical Center, 1067 North 500 West, Provo, UT 84604; tel. 801/374-0354; FAX. 801/374-3210; Jill Andrews, RN, BSN, CNOR, Administrator

HealthSouth Provo Surgical Center, 585 North 500 West, Provo, UT 84601; tel. 801/375-0983; Francis Gibson, Administrator

Institute of Facial and Cosmetic Surgery, 5929 Fashion Boulevard, Salt Lake City, UT 84107; tel. 801/261-3637; FAX. 801/261-4096; Dr. Brent D. Kennedy, Administrator

Intermountain Surgical Center, 359 Eighth Avenue, Salt Lake City, UT 84103; tel. 801/321-3200; FAX. 801/321-3035; Joan W. Lelis, Administrative Director

Salt Lake Endoscopy Center, 24 South 1100 East, Salt Lake City, UT 84102; tel. 801/355-2987; FAX. 801/531-9704; Cher Struck, Office Manager

Salt Lake Surgical Center, 617 East 3900 South, Salt Lake City, UT 84107; tel. 801/261-3141; FAX. 801/268-2599; Jay T. Lighthall, Administrator

St. George Surgical Center, 676 South Bluff Street, St. George, UT 84770; tel. 435/673-8080; FAX. 435/673-0096; Terrill Dick, Administrator

St. Mark's Outpatient Surgery Center, 1250 East 3900 South, Suite 100, Salt Lake City, UT 84124; tel. 801/262-0358; FAX. 801/262-0901; Marjorie Kimes, Administrator

The SurgiCare Center of Utah, 755 East 3900 South, Salt Lake City, UT 84107; tel. 801/266-2283; FAX. 801/268-6151; Edward Barber, Administrator

Wasatch Endoscopy, 1220 East 3900 South, Suite 1B, Salt Lake City, UT 84124; tel. 801/281-3657; Marjorie Kimes, RN, Administrator

Wasatch Surgery Center, 555 South Foothill Boulevard, Salt Lake City, UT 84112; tel. 801/581-7782; FAX. 801/581-8962; Karen Ipson, Administrator, Manager

VERMONT

David S. Chase, M.D., Ambulatory Surgical Center, 183 St. Paul Street, Burlington, VT 05401; tel. 802/864-0381; FAX. 802/864-5338; David S. Chase, M.D., Administrator

VIRGINIA

Ambulatory Surgery Center, 844 Kempsville Road, Norfolk, VA 23502; tel. 757/466-6900; FAX. 757/466-6313; Darleen S. Anderson, Site Administrator

Columbia Fairfax Surgical Center, 10730 Main Street, Fairfax, VA 22030; tel. 703/691-0670; Sharon B. Johnson, Chief Executive Officer

CountrySide Ambulatory Surgery Center, Four Pidgeon Hill Drive, Sterling, VA 20165; tel. 703/444-6060; FAX. 703/444-2278; Deborah F. Arminio, RN, Director

Fredericksburg Ambulatory Surgery Center, 1201 Sam Perry Blvd., Suite 101, Fredericksburg, VA 22401; tel. 540/741-7000; FAX. 540/899-6893; Jeane Bullock, Administrator

Hanover Outpatient Center, 7016 Lee Park Road, Mechanicsville, VA 23111; tel. 804/730-9000; FAX. 804/730-1460; Valene S. Rice, RN, Director

Kaiser Permanente Falls Church Medical Center Ambulatory Surge, 201 North Washington Street, Falls Church, VA 22046; tel. 703/536-1325; FAX. 703/536-1400; Donna-Rae Barnett, Administrator ASC

Lakeview Medical Center, Inc., 2000 Meade Parkway, Suffolk, VA 23424; tel. 757/934-9452; FAX. 757/934-9497; Michael B. Stout, Executive Director

Lewis-Gale Clinic, Same Day Surgery,LLC, 1802 Braeburn Drive, Salem, VA 24153; tel. 540/772-3601; FAX. 540/725-4543; Kay Walke, Administrator

Novamed Surgery Center of Richmond, LLC, 2010 Bremo Road, Suite 132, Richmond, VA 23226; tel. 804/285-0680; FAX. 804/285-3441; Patricia Lampman, Director

Piedmont Day Surgery Center, Inc., 1040 Main Street, P.O. Box 1360, Danville, VA 24543-1360; tel. 804/792-1433; FAX. 804/797-1398; Aaron Lieberman, Chief Operating Officer

Riverside Surgery Center-Warwick, 12420 Warwick Boulevard, Building 3, Newport News, VA 23606; tel. 804/594-2796; FAX. 804/594-3911; M. Caroline Martin, Executive Vice President

Surgi Center of Central Virginia, Inc., 12 White Oak Road, Fredericksburg, VA 22405; tel. 703/371-5349; FAX. 703/373-1745; Janet P. O'Keefe, Facility Administrator

Surgi-Center of Winchester, Inc., 1860 Amherst Street, P.O. Box 2660, Winchester, VA 22604; tel. 540/536-8934; FAX. 540/536-8936; Nelson N. Isenhower, M.D., Medical Director

Tuckahoe Surgery Center, Inc., 8919 Three Chopt Road, Richmond, VA 23229; tel. 804/285-4763; FAX. 804/288-8946; Sandra W. Pearson, Administrator

Urosurgical Center of Richmond, 9105 Stony Point Dr, Richmond, VA 23235; tel. 804/330-9105; FAX. 804/560-0914; Terry W. Coffey, Administrator

Urosurgical Center of Richmond-North, 8228 Meadowbridge Road, Mechanicsville, VA 23111; tel. 804/730-5023; FAX. 804/746-4015; Terry W. Coffey, Administrator

Virginia Ambulatory Surgery,Inc., 337-15th Street, S.W., Charlottesville, VA 22903; tel. 434/951-4000; FAX. 434/817-8465; Gerry Dobrasz, Administrator

Virginia Beach Ambulatory Surgery Center, 1700 Will-o-Wisp Drive, Virginia Beach, VA 23454; tel. 757/496-6400; FAX. 757/496-3137; Renee Woodford, M.D.

Virginia Eye Institute/Eye Surgeons of Richmond, Inc., 400 Westhampton Station, Richmond, VA 23226; tel. 804/287-4200; FAX. 804/287-4210; Michelle Tobin, Marketing Director

Virginia Heart Institute, LTD., 205 North Hamilton Street, Richmond, VA 23221; tel. 804/359-9265; Charles L. Baird, Jr., M.D., Director

Woodburn Surgery Center, 3289 Woodburn Road, Suite 100, Annandale, VA 22003; tel. 703/207-7520; Jolene Tornabeni, Senior Vice President, Administrator

WASHINGTON

Aesteem Outpatient Surgery Center, 1200 North Northgate Way, Seattle, WA 98133-8916; tel. 206/522-0200; FAX. 206/522-7019; Peter R. N. Chatard, Jr., M.D., Facility Director

Aesthetic Eye Associates, P.S., 625 4th Avenue, Suite 302, Kirkland, WA 98033; tel. 425/216-7200; FAX. 425/216-7272; Janet Jordan, Administrator

Auburn Outpatient Surgery Center, 101 Second Street, N.E., Auburn, WA 98002; tel. 253/833-6241; FAX. 253/833-4113; Christine Puig MD, Medical Director

Bel-Red Ambulatory Surgical Facility, 1370 116th Avenue, N.E., Suite 209, Bellevue, WA 98004-3825; tel. 425/455-7225; FAX. 425/455-0045; Jan Zemplenyi, M.D., Director

Bellingham Surgery Center, 2980 Squalicum Parkway, Bellingham, WA 98225; tel. 206/671-6933; Richard Brumenschenkel, Managing Agent

Cascade Valley Arlington Surgery Center, 875 Wesley Street, Suite 160, Arlington, WA 98223; tel. 360/435-6969; FAX. 360/435-1068

Central Washington Cataract Surgery, 1450 North 16th Avenue, Building J, Yakima, WA 98902; tel. 509/457-5000; FAX. 509/457-6498

Central Washington Surgicare, 307 South 12th Avenue, Suite Nine, Yakima, WA 98902; tel. 509/248-4900; FAX. 509/248-0609

Covington Day Surgery Center, 17700 Southeast 272nd Street, Kent, WA 98042; tel. 206/639-8302; FAX. 206/639-8301; Victoria Fitzpatrick, B.S.N., Director

Eastside Podiatry Ambulatory Surgery Center, 15617 Bel-Red Road, Bellevue, WA 98008; tel. 425/881-5592; G. Curda, D.P.M.

Edmonds Surgery Center, 21229 84th Avenue W., Edmonds, WA 98026; tel. 206/775-1505; FAX. 206/775-9078; Mark A. Kuzel, D.P.M., F.A.C.F.S

Evergreen Endoscopy Center, 13030 121st Way, N.E., Suite 100, Kirkland, WA 98034; tel. 425/899-4500; FAX. 425/899-4510; James Hudson Practice Manager

Evergreen Eye Surgery Center, 34719 Sixth Avenue South, Federal Way, WA 98003; tel. 253/874-3969; FAX. 253/661-7383; Richard A. Boudreau, Administrator

First Hill Surgery Center, 515 Minor Avenue, Suite 130, Seattle, WA 98104; tel. 206/682-6103; FAX. 206/682-3511; Debbie Perdue, Director

Good Samaritan Surgery Center, 1322 Third Street S.E., Suite 100, Puyallup, WA 98372; tel. 206/840-2200; FAX. 206/840-2352; William Rinker, MD, Medical Director

HealthSouth, Green River Surgical Center, 126 Auburn Avenue, Suite 200, Auburn, WA 98002; tel. 253/735-0500; FAX. 253/939-8526; Donna Hansen, Administrator

Inland Eye Center Outpatient Surgery, South 842 Cowley, Spokane, WA 99202; tel. 509/624-5300; FAX. 509/747-1348; Michael H. Cunningham, M.D., Administrator

Kruger Clinic Day Surgery, 21600 Highway 99, Suite 150, Edmonds, WA 98026; tel. 425/774-2636; FAX. 425/774-2688; Marilyn Degan, Director

Lomas Surgery Center, 17800 Talbot Road, S., Renton, WA 98055; tel. 425/255-0986; FAX. 425/271-5703; Marilyn Kritzer - Administrator

Madrona Medical Group, ASC, 4545 Cordata Parkway, Bellingham, WA 98226; tel. 360/738-2200; FAX. 360/752-5677; Sandy Mellott, Clinical Services Director

Minor & James Medical, PLLC, 515 Minor Avenue, Suite 200, Seattle, WA 98104; tel. 206/386-9500; FAX. 206/386-9605; Naomi States, RN, ASC Coordinator

Monroe Foot Care Associates Ambulatory Surgery Center, 14692 179th Avenue, S.E., Suite 300, Monroe, WA 98272; tel. 206/794-1266; Dr. Brunsman, Medical Director

Moses Lake Surgery Center, 840 East Hill Avenue, Moses Lake, WA 98837; tel. 509/764-6400; FAX. 509/764-6464; Larry Poff, RN, BSN, Mgr ASC

North Cascade ENT and Facial Plastic Surgery, 111 South 13th Street, Mount Vernon, WA 98273; tel. 360/336-2178; Alex O'Dell, Business Administrator

North Cascade ENT Facial Plastic Surgery, 111 South 13th Street, Mt. Vernon, WA 98274; tel. 360/336-2178; FAX. 360/336-2642; Alex O'Dell

North Kitsap Ambulatory Surgical Center Pacific Surgery Center, DBA Pacific Surgery Center, 20669 Bond Road, N.E., Poulsbo, WA 98370; tel. 360/779-6527; FAX. 360/697-2743; Susan Simons, RN, Director of Surgical Services

Northwest Center for Plastic and Reconstructive Surgery, 16259 Sylvester Road, S.W., Suite 302, Seattle, WA 98166; tel. 206/241-5400; FAX. 206/241-8591; Sindi Miller, Office Manager

Northwest Eye Surgery, P.C., 1120 N. Pines Road, Spokane, WA 99206; tel. 509/927-0700

Northwest Gastroenterology, d/b/a Northwest Endoscopy, 3149 Ellis, Suite 301, Bellingham, WA 98225; tel. 360/734-1420; FAX. 360/734-8748; Kathy Burns, Manager

Northwest Nasal Sinus Center, 10330 Meridan Avenue, N., Suite 240, Seattle, WA 98133; tel. 206/525-2525; FAX. 206/525-0346; Rick Fischer, Business Adminstrator

Northwest Surgery Center, 1920 100th Street, S.E., Everett, WA 98208; tel. 425/316-3700; FAX. 425/316-6881; Chris Vance, President

Northwest Surgery Center, Inc., West 123 Francis, Spokane, WA 99205; tel. 509/483-9363; FAX. 509/483-0355; Douglas P. Romney

NW Center for Corrective Jaw Surgery, 550 16th Avenue, Suite 303, Seattle, WA 98122; tel. 206/324-6570; FAX. 206/324-9936; Dotti Miller, Practice Manager

Olympia Outpatient Surgery Center, 205 Lilly Road, NE, Suite D, Olympia, WA 98506; tel. 360/412-1281; FAX. 360/491-7902; Robert Kugel, M.D., Director

Olympic Ambulatory Surgery Center, Inc., 2613 Wheaton Way, Bremerton, WA 98310; tel. 206/479-5990; FAX. 360/377-5731; Judy Hughes, RN

Olympic Plastic Surgery Suite, 2600 Cherry Avenue, Suite 201, Bremerton, WA 98310; tel. 360/415-0762; Suzanne Fletcher, Administrator

Pacific Cataract and Laser Institute, 2517 Northeast Kresky, Chehalis, WA 98532; tel. 206/748-8632; Debbie Eldredge, Vice President and COO

Pacific Cataract and Laser Institute, 10500 Northeast Eighth Street, Suite 1650, Bellevue, WA 98004-4332; tel. 425/462-7664; FAX. 425/462-6429; Maynard Pohl, O.D., Clinical Director

Pacific Cataract and Laser Institute, 8200 West Grandridge, Kennewick, WA 99336; FAX. 360/748-4007; Debbie Eldredge, Vice President and COO

Pacific NW Facial Plastic Ambulatory Surgery Center, 600 Broadway, Suite 280, Seattle, WA 98122; tel. 206/386-3550; FAX. 206/386-3553; Sherry Gizewski, Practice Manager

Parkway Surgical Center, 2940 Squalicum Parkway, Suite 204, Bellingham, WA 98225; tel. 206/676-8350; FAX. 206/676-8351; Orville Vandergriend, M.D., Administrator

Physicians Eye Surgical Center, 3930 Hoyt Avenue, Everett, WA 98201; tel. 206/259-2020; Carol Schoenfelder, Administrator

Plastic Surgery Center, 1017 South 40th Avenue, Yakima, WA 98908; tel. 509/966-6000; FAX. 509/966-6565; Christine Eakin, RNFA

Plastic Surgicenter of Olympia, 400 Lilly Road, N.E., Building Four, Olympia, WA 98506; tel. 360/456-4400; FAX. 360/491-7619; Wayne L. Dickason, M.D.

Redmond Foot Care Associates, ASC, 16146 Cleveland Street, Redmond, WA 98052; tel. 206/885-7004

Rockwood Clinic, d/b/a Gastrointestinal Endoscopy Unit, Sacred Heart Building, West 105 Eighth Avenue, Spokane, WA 99204; tel. 509/838-2531; FAX. 509/455-8828; Stephen Burgert, M.D., Administrator

Rockwood Clinic, PS, East 400 Fifth Avenue, Spokane, WA 99202; tel. 509/838-2531; FAX. 509/455-5315; Kevin D. Sweeney, M.D., CEO/President

Seattle Endoscopy Center, 11027 Meridian Avenue, N., Suite 100, Seattle, WA 98133; tel. 206/365-4492; FAX. 206/368-3456; Mary Beth Philips, BSN,RN, CGRN, Manager

Seattle Hand Surgery Group, P.C., 600 Broadway, Suite 440, Seattle, WA 98122; tel. 206/292-6252; FAX. 206/292-7893; Tamiko Gandy, Administrator

Seattle Microsurgical Eyecare Center, 5300 17th Avenue, N.W., Seattle, WA 98107; tel. 206/783-3929; Jack C. Bunn, M.D., Medical Director

Seattle Plastic Surgery Center, 600 Broadway, Suite 320, Seattle, WA 98122; tel. 206/324-1120; FAX. 206/720-0800; Doris Sevedge, Manager

Seattle Surgery Center, Columbus Pavilion, 900 Terry Avenue, Third Floor, Seattle, WA 98104-1240; tel. 206/382-1021; FAX. 206/332-9369; Jim Sapienza, FACHE, CEO

Sequim Same Day Surgery, 777 North Fifth Avenue, Sequim, WA 98382; tel. 360/582-2632; FAX. 360/582-2631; Tammy Paolini, Surgical Technician

South Hill Ambulatory Surgical Center, South 3028 Grand Boulevard, Spokane, WA 99203; tel. 509/747-0279; FAX. 509/747-3220; Borys Markewych

Southwest Washington Ambulatory Surgery Center, 102 West Fourth Plain Boulevard, Suite B, Vancouver, WA 98660; tel. 360/696-4400; FAX. 360/696-4287; Joseph H. Leas, DPM, Owner, President

Spokane Digestive Disease Center, 105 West Eighth Avenue, Suite 6010, Spokane, WA 99204-2318; tel. 509/838-5950; FAX. 509/838-5961; Margie Troske-Johnson, RN, B.S.N., Director

Spokane Eye Surgery Center, West 208 Fifth Street, Spokane, WA 99204; tel. 509/456-8150; FAX. 509/455-9887; Donald Ellingson, M.D.

Spokane Surgery Center, North 1120 Pines Road, Spokane, WA 99206; tel. 509/928-1990; FAX. 509/928-2933; Stewart P. Brim, D.P.M.

St. Mark's Micro Surgical Center, Inc., 502 South M Street, Tacoma, WA 98405; tel. 206/627-8266; Roy Baker, Chief Executive Officer

Stanley M. Jackson, M.D. and Phillip C. Klerney, M.D., Cosmetic and Plastic Surgery, 105 27th Avenue, S.E., Puyallup, WA 98374; tel. 253/848-8110; FAX. 253/845-3561; Jane Hafer, LDN, Clinical Manager

Surgery Center Of Spokane, 9405 East Sprague Avenue, Spokane, WA 99206; tel. 509/922-3199; Dr. Jacqueline Borbol

Sutcliffe Facial And Laser Center, 1229 Madison Street, Suite 1190, Seattle, WA 98104; tel. 206/621-0800; FAX. 206/621-7023; R. Toby Sutcliffe, M.D.

Tacoma Ambulatory Surgery Center, 1112 Sixth Avenue, Suite 100, Tacoma, WA 98405; tel. 253/272-3916; FAX. 253/627-1713; Liza Down, Administrator

Tacoma Endoscopy Center, 1112 Sixth Avenue, Suite 200, Tacoma, WA 98405; tel. 253/272-8664; FAX. 253/627-7880; Richard Baerg, M.D., Medical Director

Tacoma Specialty ASU, 209 Martin Luther King Jr. Way, Tacoma, WA 98405; tel. 253/596-3590; Linda Shirley, Manager

The Eastside Endoscopy Center, P.L.L.C., A Physicians Endoscopy Partnered Facility, 1135 116th Ave NE Suite 570, Bellevue, WA 98004-3049; tel. 425/451-7335; FAX. 425/451-1226; Michelle Steele, CGRN, Clinical Nurse Manager

The Plastic SurgiCentre, Inc., 535 South Pine Street, Spokane, WA 99202; tel. 509/623-2160; FAX. 509/623-1135; Pamala Silvers, RN, Manager

The Polyclinic, Inc., 1145 Broadway, Seattle, WA 98122; tel. 206/329-1760; Word, Cho-pagme Manager

Valley Outpatient Surgery Center, North 1414 Houk Road, Suite 204, Spokane, WA 99216; tel. 509/922-0362; FAX. 509/927-8316; Joel San Nicholas, Administrator

Virginia Mason Federal Way, 33501 First Way South, Federal Way, WA 98003; tel. 253/874-1635; FAX. 253/874-1732; Steven Alley

Virginia Mason-Issaquah, 100 Northeast Gilman Boulevard, Issaquah, WA 98027; tel. 425/557-8000; Bobbie Eatmon, Diredtor Ambulatory Services

Washington Centre for Reproductive Medicine, ASC, 1370 116th Avenue, N.E., Suite 202, Bellevue, WA 98004; tel. 425/462-6100; FAX. 425/635-0742; Dr. James Kustin,Medical Director

Washington Orthopedic Center, Inc., PS, 1900 Cooks Hill Road, Centralia, WA 98531; tel. 360/736-2889; Dondi Sahlinger, OR Manager

Wenatchee Valley Clinic/Cascade Surgery Center, 820 North Chelan, Wenatchee, WA 98801; tel. 509/663-8711; FAX. 509/665-2309; Dr. Don Paugh, Chief, Cascade Surgery Center

Whidbey SurgiCare, 31775-SR 20, Suite A Two, Oak Harbor, WA 98277-2334; tel. 360/679-3117; FAX. 360/679-3118; Stephen T. Miller, DPM, Medical Director

WEST VIRGINIA

Anwar Eye Center, 1500 Lafayette Avenue, Moundsville, WV 26041; tel. 304/845-0908; M. F. Anwar, M.D.

Cabell Huntington Surgery Center, 1201 Hal Greer Boulevard, Huntington, WV 25701; tel. 304/523-1885; FAX. 304/523-8942; Deborah Sparks, Administrator

Cook Eye Surgery Center, 1300 Third Avenue, Huntington, WV 25701; tel. 304/522-1802; FAX. 304/529-6752; David W. Cook, M.D., President

Jerry N. Black, M.D., Surgical Suite, 10 Amalia Drive, Suite 3C, Buckhannon, WV 26201; tel. 304/472-2100; FAX. 304/472-2118; Jerry N. Black, M.D., Medical Director

Kanawha Valley Surgi-Center, 4803 MacCorkle Avenue, S.E., Charleston, WV 25304; tel. 304/925-6390; FAX. 304/925-7931; Gorli Harish, M.D., Medical Director

Lee's Surgi-Center, 415 Morris Street, Suite 200, Charleston, WV 25301; tel. 304/342-1113; FAX. 304/346-2271; Hans Lee, M.D., President

WISCONSIN

Aurora Health Center, 10400 75th Street, Kenosha, WI 53142; tel. 414/697-6907; FAX. 414/697-3022; Thomas M. Warsocki, Administrator

Bay Lake Surgery Outpatient Surgery Center, Inc., 1843 Michigan Street, P.O. Box 678, Sturgeon Bay, WI 54235; tel. 414/746-1070; FAX. 414/746-1072; Michael Herlache, Administrator

BayCare Surgery Center, 2253 West Mason, P.O. Box 33227, Green Bay, WI 54303-0102; tel. 920/592-9100; FAX. 920/497-8056; Tammy Kruegger, Executive Director

Davis Duehr Day Surgery, 1025 Regent Street, Madison, WI 53715; tel. 608/282-2050; Rodney Sturm, M.D.

Green Bay Surgical Center, Ltd., 704 South Webster Avenue, Green Bay, WI 54301; tel. 920/432-7433; FAX. 920/432-6003; Herbert F. Sandmire, M.D., Medical Director, Administrator

HealthSouth Surgery Center of Wausau, 2809 Westhill Drive, Wausau, WI 54401; tel. 715/842-4490; FAX. 715/842-4645; Sharon Schwartz, RN, Facility Administrator

LaSalle Surgery Center, 1550 Midway Place, Menasha, WI 54952; tel. 920/727-8200; FAX. 920/727-8203; Laura Ruys, Manager

Marshfield Clinic Ambulatory Surgery Center, 1000 North Oak Avenue, Marshfield, WI 54449; tel. 715/387-5218; FAX. 715/389-3414; Reed E. Hall, Executive Director

Menomonee Falls Ambulatory Surgery Center, W180 N8045 Town Hall Road, Menomonee Falls, WI 53051; tel. 262/250-0950; FAX. 262/250-0955; Dianne Wallace, Executive Director

North Shore Surgical Center, 7007 North Range Line Road, Milwaukee, WI 53209; tel. 414/352-3341; FAX. 414/352-3218; Helen Kowalski, Executive Director

Northlake Surgery Center, 2110 Medical Drive, Box 636, Menomonee, WI 54751; tel. 715/235-8884; Douglas Carson

Northwest Surgery Center, 2300 North Mayfair Road, Wauwatosa, WI 53226; tel. 414/257-3322; Nancy Jones, Administrator

Riverview Surgery Center, 616 North Washington Street, Janesville, WI 53545; tel. 608/758-7300; FAX. 608/758-1050; Lynn Jenkins, Director

St. Mary's Dean Ventures Surgery Centers, 800 South Brooks Street, Madison, WI 53715; tel. 608/259-3510; FAX. 608/255-1272; Lynn Jenkins, Director

Surgery Center of Wisconsin, 10401 West Lincoln Avenue, Suite 201, West Allis, WI 53227; tel. 414/321-7850; FAX. 414/328-5899; Daniel R. Hellman, M.D., Facility Administrator

Surgicenter of Greater Milwaukee, 3223 South 103rd Street, Milwaukee, WI 53227; tel. 414/328-5800; FAX. 414/328-5805; Denise Augustin, President

Surgicenter of Racine, Ltd., 5802 Washington Avenue, Racine, WI 53406; tel. 262/886-9100; FAX. 262/886-9130; Dennis J. Kontra, Administrator

Wauwatosa Surgery Center, d/b/a HealthSouth Surgery Center of Wauwatosa, 10900 West Potter Road, Wauwatosa, WI 53226-3424; tel. 414/774-9227; FAX. 414/774-0957; Pamela Peters, RN., Director Of Nursing

WYOMING

Gem City Bone and Joint Surgery Center, 1909 Vista Drive, Laramie, WY 82070; tel. 307/745-8851; FAX. 307/742-8851; Trent Kaufman, Admin. Director

Wyoming Outpatient Services, 5050 Powderhouse Road, Cheyenne, WY 82009; tel. 307/634-1311; FAX. 307/638-6820; Robin Brown, Administrator

Yellowstone Surgery Center, LLC., 5201 Yellowstone Road, Cheyenne, WY 82009; tel. 307/635-7070; FAX. 307/632-9920; Deborah Wright, Office Administrator

U.S. Associated Areas

PUERTO RICO

ASC Espanola Clinic, Box 490, La Quinta, Mayaguez, PR 00681; tel. 787/832-2094

Cirugia Ambulatoria y Centro de Diagnostico y Tratamiento de S, Box 486, San Sebastian, PR 00755; tel. 809/896-1850

Clinica de Cirugia Ambulatoria de Puerto Rico, Box 3748, Marina Station, Mayaguez, PR 00681; tel. 787/833-4400; FAX. 787/265-6621; Roberto Ruiz Asencio, Administrator

Clinica del Turabo, P.O. Box 1900, Caguas, PR 00726; tel. 787/746-8899; FAX. 787/258-1776; Francisco J. Olivera, Esq.

Instituto Cirugia Plastica Del Oeste, Plastica Del Oeste, 165 Este Mendez Virgo Street, Mayaguez, PR 00680; tel. 787/833-3248; FAX. 787/831-4400; Oscar Vargas, M.D., Medical Director

Instituto de Ojos y Piel, Carr Three, KM 12.3, Carolina, PR 00985; tel. 809/769-2477

Instituto Quirurgico De Un Dia - Dr. Pila, P.O. Box 1910, Ponce, PR 00733; tel. 809/844-5600

OJOS, Inc., Calle Hipodromo, Esquina Las Palmas, Santurce, PR 00908; tel. 787/721-8330; FAX. 787/722-3222; Maria Delos A. Tirado, Administrator

San Juan Medical Plaza, 150 De Diego Avenue, Baldorioty Corner, San Juan, PR 00907; tel. 787/977-7575; FAX. 787/977-7587; Modesto Ramos, MHSA Administrator

Southern SurgiCenter, Edificio Parra Office 201, Ponce, PR 00717-1320; tel. 787/841-0303; FAX. 787/841-0387; Mr. Roberto Rentas, MHSA

Section C

State Government Agencies for Freestanding Hospices

Information for the following list was obtained directly from the agencies. For a complete list of hospital based hospice programs please refer to Section A of AHA Guide. In Section A hospice program are identified by Facility Code F36.

United States

ALABAMA
Alabama Department of Public Health, Division of Licensure and Certification, 434 Monroe Street, Montgomery, AL 36130-1701; tel. 334/240-3503; FAX. 334/240-3147; Rick Harris, Director

ALASKA
Division of Public Health, Certification and Licensing, 619 E. Ship Creek Ave, Suite 232, Anchorage, AK 99501; tel. 907/334-2483; FAX. 907/561-3011; Myra Flores, Manager

ARIZONA
Arizona Department of Health Services, Health Care Facilities, 1647 East Morten, Phoenix, AZ 85020; tel. 602/542-1100; FAX. 602/861-0645; Mary Wiley, Assistant Director

ARKANSAS
Department of Health, Division of Health Facility Services, 5800 West 10th, Suite 400, Little Rock, AR 72204-9916; tel. 501/661-2201; FAX. 501/661-2165; Renee Mallory, Director

CALIFORNIA
Department of Health Services, Licensing and Certification Program, 1800 Third Street, Suite 210, P.O. Box 942732, Sacramento, CA 94234-7320; tel. 916/324-8628; FAX. 916/445-6979; Brenda Klutz, Deputy Director

COLORADO
Colorado Department of Public Health, Health Facilities Division, 4300 Cherry Creek Drive., Denver, CO 80222-1530; tel. 303/692-2800; FAX. 303/782-4883; Priscilla Ezell, RN, Program Administrator

CONNECTICUT
Department of Public Health Division of Health Systems Regulation, 410 Capital Avenue, Hartford, CT 06134-0308; tel. 860/509-7400; FAX. 860/509-7538; Cynthia Denne, RN, MPA., Bureau Chief Regulatory Services

DELAWARE
Department of Health and Social Services, Office of Health Facilities Licensing and Certification, 2055 Limestone Road, Suite 200, Wilmington, DE 19808; tel. 302/995-8529; FAX. 302/577-8524; Mary Peterson, Director

DISTRICT OF COLUMBIA
Department of Health, Health Care Regulatory Licensing Admin, 825 North Capital, NE, Washington, DC 20002; tel. 202/442-5888; FAX. 202/442-9430; Denise Pope, Administrator

FLORIDA
Agency for HealthCare Administration, Division of Health Quality Assurance, Home Care Unit, Fort Knox Executive Center, Building 1, 2727 Mahan Drive, Tallahassee, FL 32308-5407; tel. 850/414-6010; FAX. 850/487-6240; Noel Cronin Lawrence, Senior Management Analyst II

GEORGIA
Health Care Section - Georgia Dept. of Human Resources, Office of Regulatory Services, Two Peachtree Street, N.W., Room 33-250, Atlanta, GA 30303-3142; tel. 404/657-5550; FAX. 404/657-8934

HAWAII
Department of Health, Licensing and Certification, Office Health Care Assurance, P.O. Box 3378, Honolulu, HI 96801; tel. 808/586-4080; FAX. 808/586-4444; Dianne M. Okumura, BSN, MPH, Chief, OHCA

IDAHO
Bureau of Facility Standards, Department of Health and Welfare, P.O. Box 83720, Boise, ID 83720-0036; tel. 208/334-6626; FAX. 208/364-1888; Sylvia Cresell, Supervisor - Non Long Term Care

ILLINOIS
Department of Public Health, Office of Health Care Regulation, Bureau of Hospitals and Ambulatory Services, 525 West Jefferson Street, Fourth Floor, Springfield, IL 62761; tel. 217/782-7412; FAX. 217/782-0382; Williams A. Bell, Assistant Deputy Director

INDIANA
Indiana State Department of Health, Division of Acute Care, Two North Meridian Street, Indianapolis, IN 46204; tel. 317/233-7474; FAX. 317/233-7157; Mary Azbill, Director

KANSAS
Department of Health and Environment, Bureau of Child Care and Health Facilities, 1000 Southwest Jackson, Suite 200, Topeka, KS 66612-1365; tel. 785/296-1240; FAX. 785/291-3419; Charles Moore, Director of Medical Facilities

KENTUCKY
Cabinet for Health and Family Services, Division of Health Care Facilities and Services, 275 East Main Street, Fifth Floor East, Frankfort, KY 40621; tel. 502/564-2800; FAX. 502/564-6546; Jennifer Mitchell, Director

LOUISIANA
Department of Health and Hospitals, Bureau of Health Services , Health Standards Section Licensing Unit, P.O. Box 3767, Baton Rouge, LA 70821; tel. 225/342-0138; FAX. 225/342-5292; Lisa Deaton, RN, Manager

MAINE
Division of Licensing and Certification, Department of Human Services, State House, Station 11, Augusta, ME 04333; tel. 207/287-9300; FAX. 207/287-9304; Louis Dorogi, Assistant Director

MARYLAND
Department of Health and Mental Hygiene, Licensing and Certification Administration, 55 Wade Avenue, Cantonville, MD 21228; tel. 410/764-4980; FAX. 410/402-8211; Carol Benner, Director

MASSACHUSETTS
Massachusetts Department of Public Health, Division of Health Care Quality, 10 West Street, 5th Floor, Boston, MA 02111; tel. 617/753-8000; Dr. Howard Kyongju Koh, Commissioner

MICHIGAN
Michigan Department of Community Health, Division of Licensing and Certification, 611 W. Ottawa Street, Lansing, MI 48933; tel. 517/241-3829; Darryl Horton, Director

MINNESOTA
Department of Health, Division of Compliance Monitoring, Licensing and Certification Program, 85 East Seventh Place, Suite 300, St. Paul, MN 55164-0900; tel. 651/215-8719; FAX. 651/215-8709; Carol Hirschfeld, Supervisor, Program Assurance Unit

MISSISSIPPI
Department of Health, Division of Health Facilities, Licensure and Certification, P.O. Box 1700, Jackson, MS 39215; tel. 601/576-7300; FAX. 601/576-7230; Vanessa Phipps, Director

MISSOURI
Department of Health of Senior Services, Unit of Home Care and Rehabilitative Standards, P.O. Box 570, Jefferson City, MO 65102; tel. 573/751-6336; FAX. 573/751-6315; Lisa Coots, RN, Administrator

MONTANA
Department of Public Health and Human Services, Quality Assurance Division, Licensure Bureau, P.O. Box 202953, 2401 Colonial Drive, Helena, MT 59620-2953; tel. 406/444-2676; FAX. 406/444-1742; Roy P. Kemp, Bureau Chief

NEBRASKA
Nebraska Department of Health and Human Services Regulation and Licensure, Credentialing Division, 301 Centennial Mall, South, 3rd Floor., P.O. Box 94986, Lincoln, NE 68509-4986; tel. 402/471-2946; FAX. 402/471-0555; Helen L. Meeks, Administrator

NEVADA
Nevada State Health Division, Bureau of Licensure and Certification, 1550 East College Parkway, Suite 158, Carson City, NV 89706-7921; tel. 775/687-4475; FAX. 775/687-6588; Pamela Graham, Chief

NEW JERSEY
New Jersey Department of Health and Senior Services, Division , Certificate of Need and Acute Care Licensure, John Fitchway, Market and Warren Streets, Trenton, NJ 08625-0360; tel. 609/292-8773; FAX. 609/292-3780; John Calabria, Director

NEW MEXICO
Department of Health, Health Facility Licensing and Certification Bureau, 525 Camino de los Marquez, Suite Two, Santa Fe, NM 87501; tel. 505/827-4200; FAX. 505/827-4222; Wilma Hammer, Bureau Chief

NEW YORK
Division of Surveillance and Quality Assurance for Nursing Homes and ICFs/MR, 161 Delaware Avenue, Delmar, NY 12054; tel. 518/408-1267; FAX. 518/408-1271; Keith W. Servis, Director

NORTH CAROLINA
Department of Human Resources, Division of Facility Services, 805 Biggs Drive, Raleigh, NC 27626-0530; tel. 919/733-7461; FAX. 919/733-8274; Steve White, Chief, Licensure and Certification

NORTH DAKOTA
Department of Health, Health Resources Section, 600 East Boulevard Avenue, Bismarck, ND 58505; tel. 701/328-2352; FAX. 701/328-1890; Darleen Bartz Chief

OHIO
Division of Quality Assurance, Ohio Department of Health, 246 North High Street, Columbus, OH 43266-0588; tel. 614/466-7857; FAX. 614/644-0208; Rebecca Maust, Division Chief

OKLAHOMA
Department of Health, Special Health Services, 1000 Northeast 10th Street, Oklahoma City, OK 73117; tel. 405/271-6576; FAX. 405/271-1308; Gary Glover, Chief, Medical Facilities

OREGON
Health Care Licensing and Certification, Department of Human Services, 800 Northeast Oregon Street, # 21, Suite 640, P.O. Box 14450, Portland, OR 97293-0450; tel. 503/731-4013; FAX. 503/731-4080; Kathleen Smail, Manager

PENNSYLVANIA
Department of Health, Division of Home Health, 132 Kline Plaza, Suite A, Harrisburg, PA 17104; tel. 717/783-1379; FAX. 717/787-3188; Janet Staloski, Director

RHODE ISLAND
Rhode Island Department of Health, Division of Facilities Regulation, Three Capitol Hill, Providence, RI 02908-5097; tel. 401/222-2566; FAX. 401/222-3999; Wayne I. Farrington, Chief

SOUTH CAROLINA
Department of Health and Environmental Control, Division of Certification, 2600 Bull Street, Columbia, SC 29201; tel. 803/545-4205; FAX. 803/545-4292; Arthur I. Starnes, Division Director

SOUTH DAKOTA
   Department of Health, Office of Licensure and Certification, 615 East 4th Street, Pierre, SD 57501-1700; tel. 605/773–3356; FAX. 605/773–6667; Kevin Forsch, Division Director

TENNESSEE
   Department of Health, Division of Health Care Facilities, Cordell Hull Building, 425 5th Ave. North, 1st Floor, Nashville, TN 37247-0508; tel. 615/741–7603; FAX. 615/741–7051; Eddie Stewart

TEXAS
   Texas Department of Health, Health Facility Compliance Division, 1100 West 49th Street, Austin, TX 78756; tel. 512/834–6650; FAX. 512/834–6653; Nance Stearman, RN, M.S.N., Director

UTAH
   Utah Department of Health, Bureau of Health Facility Licensure, P.O. Box 142003, Salt Lake City, UT 84114-2003; tel. 801/538–6152; FAX. 801/538–6325; Debra Wynkoop, Director

VERMONT
   Hospice and Palliative Care, Council of Vermont, 10 Maine Street, Montpelier, VT 05602; tel. 802/229–0579; FAX. 802/223–6218; Virginia L. Fry, Director

VIRGINIA
   Virginia Department of Health, Center for Quality Health Care Services and Consumer Protection, 3600 Centre, Suite 216, Richmond, VA 23230; tel. 804/367–2102; FAX. 804/367–2149; Nancy R. Hofheimer, Director

WEST VIRGINIA
   Office of Health Facility Licensure and Certification, West Virginia Division of Health, 1 Davis Square, Suite 101, Charleston, WV 25301-3718; tel. 304/558–0050; FAX. 304/558–2515; Anita Barnhouse, DO Program Manager

WISCONSIN
   Bureau of Quality Assurance, Division of Supportive Living, P.O. Box 2969, Madison, WI 53701-2969; tel. 608/267–7185; FAX. 608/267–0352; Susan Schroder, Director, Bureau of Quality Assurance

WYOMING
   Department of Health, Office of Health Quality, 2020 Carey Avenue, 8th Floor, Cheyenne, WY 82002; tel. 307/777–7123; FAX. 307/777–7127; Gerald E. Bronnenberg, Administrator

U.S. Associated Areas

PUERTO RICO
   Puerto Rico Department of Health, PO Box 70184, San Juan, PR 00936-8184; tel. 787/274–7601; FAX. 787/250–6547; Carmen Feliciano de Melecio, M.D., Secretary of Health

Section C

JCAHO Accredited Freestanding Long-Term Care Organizations

The accredited freestanding long-term care organizations listed have been accredited as of April, 2005 by the Joint Commission on Accreditation of Healthcare Organizations by decision of the Accreditation Committee of the Board of Commissioners.

The organizations listed here have been found to be in compliance with the Joint Commission standards for long-term care organizations, as found in the Comprehensive Accreditation Manual for the Long-Term Care Organizations.

Please refer to section A of the AHA Guide for information on hospitals with Long-Term Care services. These hospitals are identified by Facility Code 92. In section A, those hospitals identified by Approval Code 1 are JCAHO accredited.

We present this list simply as a convenient directory. Inclusion or omission of any organization's name indicates neither approval nor disapproval by Health Forum LLC, an American Hospital Association company.

United States

ARIZONA

Citadel Care Center, 5121 East Broadway Road, Mesa, AZ 85206; tel. 480/832–5555; Mrs. Michelle L Donahue

Desert Cove Nursing Center, 1750 West Frye Road, Chandler, AZ 85224; tel. 480/899–0641; Ms. Melanie S Seamans

Las Fuentes Care Center, 1045 Scott Drive, Prescott, AZ 86301; tel. 928/778–9603; Ms. Gail Brannan

Life Care Center at South Mountain, 8008 South Jesse Owens Parkway, Phoenix, AZ 85040; tel. 602/243–2780; Ms. MaryAnn Stanford

Life Care Center of North Glendale, 13620 North 55th Avenue, Glendale, AZ 85304; tel. 602/843–8433; Mr. Gary Davis

Life Care Center of Paradise Valley, 4065 East Bell Road, Phoenix, AZ 85032; tel. 602/867–0212; Mr. David W Derushia

Life Care Center of Scottsdale, 9494 East Becker Lane, Scottsdale, AZ 85260; tel. 480/860–6396; Ms. Barbara Brown

Life Care Center of Sierra Vista, 2305 East Wilcox Drive, Sierra Vista, AZ 85635; tel. 520/458–1050; Mrs. Rebecca Main

Life Care Center of Tucson, 6211 North LaCholla Boulevard, Tucson, AZ 85741; tel. 520/575–0900; Ms. Jennifer Gibbon

Life Care Center of Yuma, 2450 South 19th Avenue, Yuma, AZ 85364; tel. 928/344–0425; Mr. Lawrence P Rugar

Life Care Centers of America, Inc., 7970 North LaCanada Dr., Tucson, AZ 85704; tel. 520/797–1191; Mr. Forrest L Preston

Mi Casa Nursing Center, 330 S. Pinnule Circle, Mesa, AZ 85206; tel. 480/981–0687; Ms. Rosemary Anderson

Mountain View Care Center, 1313 West Magee Road, Tucson, AZ 85704; tel. 520/797–2600; Mr. Forrest Preston

Payson Care Center, 107 East Lone Pine Drive, Payson, AZ 85541; tel. 928/474–6896; Mr. James R Gann, Jr.

Sun Grove Village Care Center, 20625 N. Lake Pleasant Road, Peoria, AZ 85382; tel. 623/566–0642; Mrs. Susan Bender

CALIFORNIA

Auburn Gardens Care Center, 260 Racetrack Street, Auburn, CA 95603; tel. 530/885–7051; Mr. Arden Bennett

Bel Tooren Villa Convalescent Hospital, 16910 Woodruff Avenue, Bellflower, CA 90706; tel. 562/867–1761; Mr. Ed Cayetano

California Special Care Center, Inc., 8787 Center Drive, La Mesa, CA 91941; tel. 619/460–4444; Mr. John Jimenez

CareMeridian, 11500 Center Avenue, Gilroy, CA 95020; tel. 949/263–6639; Ms. Sherri L Medina

CareMeridian - Ventura County - Oxnard, 18-A Journey, Suite 200, Aliso Viejo, CA 92656; tel. 949/263–6639; Ms. Sherri L Medina

El Camino Hospital, 2500 Grant Road, Mountain View, CA 94040; tel. 650/940–7000; Mr. Lee Domanico

Hollenbeck Home, 573 South Boyle Avenue, Los Angeles, CA 90033; tel. 323/263–6195; Mr. Morris Shockley

Imperial Convalescent Center, 11926 S La Mirada Boulevard, La Mirada, CA 90638; tel. 562/943–7156; Mr. Chris Stottlemyer

La Habra Convalescent Hospital, 1233 West La Habra Boulevard, La Habra, CA 90631; tel. 562/691–0781; Mr. Daniel Husband

La Sierra Care Center, 2424 M Street, Merced, CA 95340; tel. 209/723–4224; Mr. Arden Bennett

Lake Forest Nursing Center, 25652 Old Trabuco Road, Lake Forest, CA 92630; tel. 949/380–9380; Mr. William K Schifferli

Life Care Center Corona, 2600 South Main Street, Corona, CA 92882; tel. 909/736–4700; Ms. Kerry Pitcher

Life Care Center of Escondido, 1980 Felicita Road, Escondido, CA 92025; tel. 760/741–6109; Mr. Rodger Groves

Life Care Center of San Gabriel, 909 W. Santa Anita Street, San Gabriel, CA 91776; tel. 626/289–5365; Mrs. Eunice R Fletcher

Life Care Center of Vista, 304 North Melrose Drive, Vista, CA 92083; tel. 760/724–8222; Mr. William V Adams

Madera Rehabilitation and Convalescent Center, 517 South A Street, Madera, CA 93638; tel. 559/673–9228; Mr. Arden Bennett

Magnolia Special Care Center, 635 South Magnolia, El Cajon, CA 92020; tel. 619/442–8826; Ms. Harriet Haugen

Marlora Post Acute Rehabilitation Hospital, 3801 East Anaheim Street, Long Beach, CA 90804; tel. 562/494–3311; Ms. Marilyn A Hauser

Merced Living Care Center, 510 West 26th Street, Merced, CA 95340; tel. 209/723–2911; Mr. Arden Bennett

Mirada Hills Rehabilitation and Convalescent Hospital, 12200 LaMirada Boulevard, La Mirada, CA 90638; tel. 562/947–8691; Mr. John Ryan

North Walk Villa Convalescent Hospital, 12350 Rosecrans Avenue, Norwalk, CA 90650; tel. 562/921–6624; Mr. Michael Kremer

Orangegrove Rehabilitation Hospital, 12332 Garden Grove Boulevard, Garden Grove, CA 92843; tel. 714/534–1041; Mrs. Nelia d Yonzon

Pacifica Nursing and Rehabilitation Center, 385 Esplanade Avenue, Pacifica, CA 94044; tel. 650/993–5576; Mr. Brian Ramos

Reche Canyon Rehabilitation and Health Care Center, 1350 Reche Canyon Road, Colton, CA 92324; tel. 909/370–4411; Mr. Fred Frank

Rimrock Villa Convalescent Hospital, 27555 Rimrock Rd, Barstow, CA 92311; tel. 760/252–2515; Mrs. Sharron L Clark

Sequoia Health Services, 170 Alameda de las Pulgas, Redwood City, CA 94062-2799; tel. 650/369–5811; Ms. Glenna Vaskelis

Sub-Acute Saratoga Hospital, 13425 Sousa Lane, Saratoga, CA 95070; tel. 408/378–8875; Mr. Michael Zarcone

Sun City Convalescent Center, 27600 Encanto Drive, Sun City, CA 92586; tel. 909/679–6858; Mr. Steve Browne

The Cloisters of La Jolla, 7160 Fay Avenue, La Jolla, CA 92037; tel. 858/459–4361; Ms. Cheryl Thompson

The Cloisters of Mission Hills, 3680 Reynard Way, San Diego, CA 92103; tel. 619/297–4484; Ms. Katherine Oh

Totally Kids Specialty Healthcare, 1720 Mountain View Avenue, Loma Linda, CA 92354; tel. 909/796–6915; Mr. Doug Padgett

COLORADO

Berkley Manor Care Center, 735 South Locust Street, Denver, CO 80224; tel. 303/320–4377; Ms. Jayne B Keller

Briarwood Health Care Center, 1440 Vine St., Denver, CO 80206; tel. 303/399–0350; Mr. Gerry Lafont

Canon Lodge Care Center, 905 Harding Avenue, Canon City, CO 81212; tel. 719/275–4106; Mr. Dan Skillman

Columbine Manor Care Center, 530 W 16th st., Salida, CO 81201; tel. 719/539–6112; Ms. Lisa A Forsyth

Evergreen Nursing Home, 1991 Carroll Avenue, Alamosa, CO 81101; tel. 719/589–4951; Mrs. Barbara Fransen

Garden Terrace Alzheimer's Center of Excellence, 1600 South Potomac Street, Aurora, CO 80012; tel. 303/750–8418; Mr. Anthony J Jensen

Hallmark Nursing Center, 3701 West Radcliff Avenue, Denver, CO 80236; tel. 303/794–6484; Mr. Lenny Ow

Heritage Park Care Center, 1200 Village Road, Carbondale, CO 81623; tel. 970/963–1500; Mr. Patrick Raab

Life Care Center of Aurora, 14101 East Evans Avenue, Aurora, CO 80014; tel. 303/751–2000; Ms. Ann Kokish

Life Care Center of Colorado Springs, 2490 International Circle, Colorado Springs, CO 80910; tel. 719/630–8888; Mr. David Strain

Life Care Center of Evergreen, 2987 Bergen Peak Drive, Evergreen, CO 80439; tel. 303/674–4500; Mr. Treg Warnsholz

Life Care Center of Greeley, 4800 25th Street, Greeley, CO 80634; tel. 970/330–6400; Mr. Dan Gauger

Life Care Center of Littleton, 1500 West Mineral Avenue, Littleton, CO 80120; tel. – –; Mrs. Erin E Cook

Life Care Center of Longmont, 2451 Pratt Street, Longmont, CO 80501; tel. 303/776–5000; Ms. Kathryn M Evans

Life Care Center of Pueblo, 2118 Chatalet Lane, Pueblo, CO 81005; tel. 719/564–2000; Mr. Stanley J Murdoch

Life Care Center of Westminster, 7751 Zenobia Court, Westminster, CO 80030; tel. 303/412–9121; Ms. Anne Deines

Sage Lakewood, LLC, 5301 West 1st Avenue, Lakewood, CO 80226; tel. 303/238–8333; Ms. Joan M Dugan

San Luis Care Center, 240 Craft Drive, Alamosa, CO 81101; tel. 719/589–9081; Ms. Carol Riggenbach

University Park Care Center, 945 Desert Flower Boulevard, Pueblo, CO 81001; tel. 719/545–5321; Ms. Barbara Strombeck

Vista Grande Rehabilitation and Care Center, 1221 North Mildred Road, Cortez, CO 81321; tel. 970/564–2600; Adm. Marsha K Rasek

CONNECTICUT

Aaron Manor Nursing & Rehabilitation Center, 3 South Wig Hill Road, Chester, CT 06412; tel. 860/526–5316; Dr. Robert Sbriglio

Alexandria Manor, 55 Tunxis Avenue, Bloomfield, CT 06002; tel. 860/242–0703; Mr. Clifton P Mix

Arbors of Hop Brook Limited Partnership, 385 West Center Street, Manchester, CT 06040; tel. 860/646–0129; Ms. Mary Ellen Gaudette

Ashlar of Newtown, Toddy Hill Road, Newtown, CT 06470; tel. 203/426–5847; Mr. Thomas M Gutner

Astoria Park, 725 Park Avenue, Bridgeport, CT 06604; tel. 203/366–3653; Mr. Donald L Franco

Avery Heights, 705 New Britain Avenue, Hartford, CT 06106; tel. 860/527–9126; Dr. Miriam E Parker

Bayview Health Care Center, 301 Rope Ferry Road, Waterford, CT 06385; tel. 860/444–1175; Mr. Darryl LeCours

Beechwood Rehabilitation and Nursing Center, 31 Vauxhall Street, New London, CT 06320; tel. 860/442–4363; Mr. William G White

Bel-Air Manor Nursing and Rehabilitation Center, 256 New Britain Avenue, Newington, CT 06111; tel. 860/666-5689; Mr. Martin Sbriglio

Bethel Health and Rehabilitation Center, LLC, 13 Parklawn Drive, Bethel, CT 06801; tel. 203/830-4180; Mrs. Grace L Flight

Bickford Health Care Center, Fourteen Main Street, Windsor Locks, CT 06096; tel. 860/623-4351; Ms. Michele Carney

Bidwell Healthcare Center, 333 Bidwell Street, Manchester, CT 06040; tel. 860/647-9191; Mr. David M Sones

Bishop Wicke Health and Rehabilitation Center, Inc, 584 Long Hill Avenue, Shelton, CT 06484; tel. 203/929-5321; Mr. Robert L Clapp

Blair Manor, 612 Hazard Avenue, Enfield, CT 06082; tel. 860/749-8388; Ms. Judy Johnson

Bloomfield Health Care Center, 355 Park Avenue, Bloomfield, CT 06002; tel. 860/242-8595; Mrs. Audrey Cushing

Branford Hills Health Care Center, 189 Alps Road, Branford, CT 06405; tel. 203/481-6221; Mr. Stephen J Shelton

Bridgeport Health Care Center, Inc., 600 Bond Street, Bridgeport, CT 06610; tel. 203/384-6400; Mr. Christopher A Massaro, Sr.

Brightview of Avon, 220 Scoville Road, Avon, CT 06001; tel. 860/673-3265; Mrs. Marvette E Lowrie-Morris

Brittany Farms Health Center, 400 Brittany Farms Road, New Britain, CT 06053; tel. 860/224-3111; Mr. David Crandall

Brook Hollow Health Care Center, LLC, 55 Kondracki Lane, Wallingford, CT 06492; tel. 203/265-6771; Mr. Stuart Lindeman

Cambridge Manor, 2428 Easton Turnpike, Fairfield, CT 06825; tel. 203/372-0313; Mr. William H Thompson

Carolton Chronic and Convalescent Hospital, 400 Mill Plain Road, Fairfield, CT 06430; tel. 203/255-3573; Ms. Carmen Tortora, Jr.

Cedar Lane Rehabilitation and Health Care Center, 128 Cedar Avenue, Waterbury, CT 06705; tel. 203/757-9271; Mrs. Tamlyn S Campanelli

Cherry Brook Health Care Center, 102 Dyer Avenue, Canton, CT 06019; tel. 860/693-7777; Mr. Clifton P Mix

Cheshire House Nursing and Rehabilitation Center, 3396 East Main Street, Waterbury, CT 06705; tel. 203/754-2161; Mr. Martin Sbriglio

Coccomo Memorial Health Care Center, 33 Cone Avenue, Meriden, CT 06450; tel. 203/238-1606; Ms. Jessica Flood

Countryside Manor, 1660 Stafford Avenue, Bristol, CT 06010; tel. 860/583-8483; Mr. Charles Hallgren

Crescent Manor, 1243 West Main Street, Waterbury, CT 06708; tel. 203/757-0561; Mr. George Giblin

Douglas Manor, 103 North Road, Windham, CT 06280; tel. 860/423-4636; Mr. James Lopez

Ellis Manor, 210 George Street, Hartford, CT 06114; tel. 860/296-9166; Mr. Eric M Dana

Elm Hill Nursing Center, 45 Elm Street, Rocky Hill, CT 06067; tel. 860/529-8661; Mr. Brian J Foley

Evergreen Health Care Center, PO Box 549, Stafford Springs, CT 06076; tel. 860/684-6341; Ms. Pamela B Klapproth

Farmington Care Center, LLC, 20 Scott Swamp Road, Farmington, CT 06032; tel. 860/677-7707; Mr. Michael A Landi

Filosa Convalescent Home, Inc., & Hancock Hall, 31 Staples Street, Danbury, CT 06811; tel. 203/794-9466; Dr. Frank D Malone

Fowler Nursing Center, Inc., 10 Boston Post Road, Guilford, CT 06437; tel. 203/453-3725; Ms. Janet Woxland

Gladeview Health Care Center, 60 Boston Post Road, Old Saybrook, CT 06475; tel. 860/388-6696; Mr. James M Pettey

Golden Hill Health Care Center, 2028 Bridgeport Avenue, Milford, CT 06460; tel. 203/877-0371; Mr. Kevin Breslin

Greentree Manor Nursing and Rehabilitation Center, 4 Greentree Drive, Waterford, CT 06385; tel. 860/442-0647; Mr. Kenneth S Kopchik

Harbor Hill Care Center, Inc., 111 Church Street, Middletown, CT 06457; tel. 860/347-7286; Mr. Larry J Condon

Harbor View Manor, 308 Savin Avenue, West Haven, CT 06516; tel. 203/932-6411; Ms. Betsy A Rosenblum

Harborside Healthcare - Glen Hill, 1 Glen Hill Road, Danbury, CT 06811; tel. 203/744-2840; Miss Marnie Tetreault

Harborside Healthcare - The Reservoir, One Emily Way, West Hartford, CT 06107; tel. 860/561-7022; Ms. Marian Chuga

Harborside Healthcare -- Arden House, 850 Mix Avenue, Hamden, CT 06514; tel. 203/281-3500; Mrs. Joanne Scafati

Haven Health Center of Norwich, LLC, 60 Crouch Avenue, Norwich, CT 06360; tel. 860/889-2631; Mr. Raymond Termini

Hebrew Health Care, Inc., One Abrahms Boulevard, West Hartford, CT 06117-1525; tel. 860/523-3800; Ms. Bonnie B Gauthier

High View Health Care Center, 600 Highland Avenue, Middletown, CT 06457; tel. 860/347-3315; Mr. Frank Fiore

Hilltop Health Center, 126 Ford Street, Ansonia, CT 06401; tel. 203/736-1100; Ms. Sandra Podany

Honey Hill Care Center, 34 Midrocks Drive, Norwalk, CT 06851; tel. 203/847-9686; Ms. Betty A Karkut

Jerome Home, 975 Corbin Avenue, New Britain, CT 06052; tel. 860/229-3707; Mr. John A Kelly

Jewish Home for the Aged, Inc., 169 Davenport Avenue, New Haven, CT 06519; tel. 203/789-1650; Mrs. Beth Goldstein

Jewish Home for the Elderly of Fairfield County, Inc., 175 Jefferson Street, Fairfield, CT 06432; tel. 203/365-6400; Mr. Andrew H Banoff

Kettle Brook Care Center, LLC, 96 Prospect Hill Road, East Windsor, CT 06088; tel. 860/623-9846; Mr. Chris Wright

Kimberly Hall South, One Emerson Drive, Windsor, CT 06095; tel. 860/688-6443; Mr. Barry Slotnick

Laurel Woods, Inc., 451 North High Street, East Haven, CT 06512; tel. 203/466-6850; Mr. Robert M Mislow

Lord Chamberlain Nursing and Rehabilitation Center, 7003 Main Street, Stratford, CT 06614; tel. 203/375-5894; Mr. Martin Sbriglio

Mansfield Center for Nursing and Rehabilitation, 100 Warren Circle, Mansfield, CT 06268; tel. 860/487-2300; Mr. Alan Green

Masonic Healthcare Center, PO Box 70, Wallingford, CT 06492; tel. 203/679-5900; Mr. Arthur E Santilli

McLean Health Center, 75 Great Pond Road, Simsbury, CT 06070; tel. 860/658-3918; Mrs. David J Bordonaro

MercyKnoll, Inc., 243 Steele Road, West Hartford, CT 06117; tel. 860/236-3503; Mrs. Kristin L Butler

Meriden Center, 845 Paddock Avenue, Meriden, CT 06450; tel. 203/238-2645; Ms. Linda P Garcia

Meridian Manor Corporation, 1132 Meriden Road, Waterbury, CT 06705; tel. 203/757-1228; Ms. Sheila L Smith

Montowese Health and Rehabilitation Center, Inc., 163 Quinnipiac Avenue, North Haven, CT 06473; tel. 203/624-3303; Mr. Farooq H Khan

Noble Horizons, 17 Cobble Road, Salisbury, CT 06068; tel. 860/435-9851; Ms. Eileen M Mulligan

Odd Fellows Home of Connecticut, 235 Lestertown Road, Groton, CT 06340; tel. 860/445-7478; Mr. James K Malloy

Plainville Health Care Center, Inc., 269 Farmington Avenue, Plainville, CT 06062; tel. 860/747-1637; Ms. Terri Golec

Ridgeview Health Care Center, 156 Berlin Road, Cromwell, CT 06416; tel. 860/635-1010; Mr. Jarrett L McClurg

Roncalli Health Center - Jewett City, 97 Preston Road, Griswold, CT 06351-2516; tel. 860/376-4438; Mr. Robert A Haswell

Rose Haven, Ltd., PO Box 157, Litchfield, CT 06759; tel. 860/567-9475; Ms. Linda D Klauber

Saint Joseph's Living Center, Inc., 14 Club Road, Windham, CT 06280; tel. 860/456-1107; Ms. Maureen Kolaczenko

Saint Mary Home, Incorporated, 2021 Albany Avenue, West Hartford, CT 06117; tel. 860/570-8200; Ms. Patty Morse

Salmon Brook Center, 72 Salmon Brook Drive, Glastonbury, CT 06033; tel. 860/633-5244; Mr. Trevor Kinney

Seabury Retirement Community, 200 Seabury Drive, Bloomfield, CT 06002; tel. 860/286-0243; Mr. John S Mobley

Sharon Health Care Center, PO Box 1268, Sharon, CT 06069; tel. 860/364-1002; Mr. Robert L Clapp

Shelton Lakes Residence and Health Care Center, Inc., 5 Lake Road, Shelton, CT 06484; tel. 203/924-2635; Ms. Diana Carrano

Sister Anne Virginie Grimes Health Care, 1354 Chapel Street, New Haven, CT 06511; tel. 203/867-8300; Sister Ann Casagrande

Skyview Center, 35 Marc Drive, Wallingford, CT 06492; tel. 203/265-0981; Mr. Edward Varjabedian

Southington Care Center, 45 Meriden Avenue, Southington, CT 06489; tel. 860/621-9559; Ms. Lisa Connolly

Subacute Center of Bristol, 23 Fair Street, Forestville, CT 06010; tel. 860/589-2923; Mrs. Linda Bradigo

The Elim Park Baptist Home, Inc., 140 Cook Hill Road, Cheshire, CT 06410; tel. 203/272-3547; Mr. Ronald Dischinger

The Flora and Mary Hewitt Memorial Hospital, Inc., 45 Maltby Street, Shelton, CT 06484; tel. 203/924-4671; Ms. Beatrice Coulombe

The Glendale Center, 4 Hazel Avenue, Naugatuck, CT 06770; tel. 203/723-1456; Mrs. Giovanna A Griffin

The Kent, 46 Maple Street, Kent, CT 06757; tel. 860/927-5368; Mr. Brian J Foley

The Mary Wade Home, Incorporated, 118 Clinton Avenue, New Haven, CT 06513; tel. 203/562-7222; Mr. David V Hunter

The William and Sally Tandet Center for Continuing Care, 146 West Broad Street, Stamford, CT 06902; tel. 203/964-8500; Mr. Daniel T Katz

Vernon Manor Health Care Center, 180 Regan Road, Vernon Rockville, CT 06066; tel. 860/871-0385; Mr. William H Nelson

Walnut Hill Care Center, 55 Grand Street, New Britain, CT 06052; tel. 860/223-3617; Mr. David Bond

Watrous Nursing Center, 9 Neck Road, Madison, CT 06443; tel. 203/245-9483; Ms. Sharon G Craft

Waveny Care Center, 3 Farm Road, New Canaan, CT 06840; tel. 203/594-5200; Mr. Jeremy M Vickers

Wintonbury Care Center, LLC, 140 Park Avenue, Bloomfield, CT 06002; tel. 860/243-9591; Mr. Richard A DeMio

Wolcott Hall Nursing Center, Inc., 215 Forest Street, Torrington, CT 06790; tel. 860/482-8554; Mr. Gregory J Hamley

Wolcott View Manor, Inc., PO Box 6192, Wolcott, CT 06716; tel. 203/879-8066; Mr. James E Cleary, Jr.

Woodlake at Tolland (ECHN Eldercare Services), 26 Shenipsit Lake Road, Tolland, CT 06084; tel. 860/872-2999; Mr. Marc H Lory

DELAWARE

Evergreen Alzheimer Adult Day Care Center, 3000 Newport Gap Pike Building F, Wilmington, DE 19808; tel. 302/995-8448; Ms. Michele Campbell

Kentmere Nursing Care Center, 1900 Lovering Avenue, Wilmington, DE 19806; tel. 302/652-3311; Ms. Eileen Mahler

DISTRICT OF COLUMBIA

Armed Forces Retirement Home-WASHINGTON, 3700 North Capitol Street, NW, Washington, DC 20011-8400; tel. 202/730-3323; Dr. Linda Rader

Center For Aging's Health Care Institute, 1380 Southern Avenue, Southeast, Washington, DC 20032; tel. 202/279-5825; Mr. Paul E Porter

FLORIDA

Bay Tree Rehabilitation and Nursing Center, 2600 Highlands Boulevard North, Palm Harbor, FL 34684; tel. 727/785-5671; Mr. Alan Cooper

Bon Secours Maria Manor Nursing & Rehabilitation Center, 10300 4th Street North, Saint Petersburg, FL 33716; tel. 727/576-1025; Mr. Michael Ward

Darcy Hall of Life Care, 2170 Palm Beach Lakes Blvd., West Palm Beach, FL 33409; tel. 561/683-3333; Ms. Karin Dipiero

Halifax Convalescent Center, 820 North Clyde Morris Blvd, Daytona Beach, FL 32114; tel. 904/274-4575; William Jenkins

Heritage Park Retirement Communities, LLC, 5861 Heritage Park Way, Delray Beach, FL 33484; tel. 561/496-4440; Mr. Robert Schemel

Huntington Place Rehab and Nursing Center, 1775 Huntington Lane, Rockledge, FL 32955; tel. 321/632-7341; Ms. Stacy G Thomas

Jackson Plaza Nursing and Rehabilitation Center, 1861 Northwest 8th Avenue, Miami, FL 33136; tel. 305/347-3380; Ms. Terry G Escobar

Lakeside Pavilion Rehab and Nursing Center, 2900 12th Street, North, Naples, FL 34103; tel. 941/261-2554; Mr. Bill Maggard

Life Care Center of Citrus County, 3325 Jerwayne Lane, Lecanto, FL 34461; tel. 352/746-4434; Ms. Janet E Sorel

Life Care Center of Hilliard, 3756 W. 3rd Street, Hilliard, FL 32046; tel. 904/845-3988; Ms. Brenda Williams

Life Care Center of Melbourne, 606 East Sheridan Road, Melbourne, FL 32901; tel. 321/727-0984; Mr. Brian Lynch

Section C

Life Care Center of Ocala, 2800 Southwest 41st Street, Ocala, FL 34474; tel. 352/873–7570; Mr. Victor Piperata

Life Care Center of Punta Gorda, 450 Shreve Street, Punta Gorda, FL 33950; tel. 941/639–8771; Mr. Michael Kirsch

Life Care Center of Sarasota, 8104 Tuttle Avenue, Sarasota, FL 34243; tel. 941/360–6411; Mrs. Nina K Willingham

Life Care Center of Winter Haven, 1510 Cypress Gardens Boulevard, Winter Haven, FL 33884; tel. 863/318–8646; Mr. Ralph M Jacobs

Miami Jewish Home & Hospital for the Aged, 5200 Northeast 2nd Avenue, Miami, FL 33137; tel. 305/751–8626; Mr. Fred Stock

Oakhurst Rehabilitation and Nursing Center, 1501 Southeast 24th Road, Ocala, FL 34471; tel. 352/629–8900; Mr. Brad Evans

Orchard Ridge Rehabilitation and Nursing Center, 4927 Voorhees Road, New Port Richey, FL 34653; tel. 727/848–3578; Ms. Dawn Jones DeBrunner

Pinebrook Rehabilitation and Nursing Center, 1240 Pinebrook Road, Venice, FL 34285; tel. 941/488–6733; Ms. Marguerite Kraska

Springwood Rehab and Nursing Center, 4602 Northgate Court, Sarasota, FL 34234; tel. 941/355–2913; Mr. Brad J Lee

St. Anne's Nursing Center, 11855 Quail Roost Drive, Miami, FL 33177; tel. 305/252–4000; Mr. Tim Reardon

Sunrise Health and Rehabilitation Center, 4800 Nob Hill Road, Sunrise, FL 33351; tel. 954/577–3600; Mr. Morris S Funk

Sunset Point Rehab and Nursing Center, 1980 Sunset Point Road, Clearwater, FL 33765; tel. 727/443–1588; Mr. Chris Riggs

Tandem Health Care of St. Petersburg, 9393 Park Boulevard, Seminole, FL 33772; tel. 727/391–2200; Mr. Paul Jeannotte

Tandem Health Care of Bayonet Point, 8132 Hudson Avenue, Hudson, FL 34667; tel. 727/863–3100; Mr. Delbert G Downing

Tandem Healthcare of Melbourne, 3033 Sarno Road, Melbourne, FL 32934; tel. 321/255–9200; Ms. Debra A Wallace

The Gardens Court, 3803 PGA Boulevard, Palm Beach Gardens, FL 33410; tel. 561/626–1125; Ms. Patricia Allard

Water's Edge Extended Care, 1500 Southwest Capri, Palm City, FL 34990; tel. 772/223–5863; Mr. Jon P Tagatz

West Bay Rehab and Nursing Center, 3865 Tampa Road, Oldsmar, FL 34677; tel. 813/855–4661; Ms. Kendra L Rogers

GEORGIA

Camellia Gardens of Life Care, 804 South Broad Street, Thomasville, GA 31792; tel. 229/226–0076; Mrs. Vicki Cooper

Dogwood Health and Rehabilitation, 7560 Butner Road, Fairburn, GA 30213-1914; tel. 770/306–7878; Mr. Neil L Pruitt, Jr.

Family Life Enrichment Center, Inc., PO Box 10, High Shoals, GA 30645; tel. 706/769–7738; Ms. Magda D Bennett

Georgia War Veterans Home, 2249 Vinson Highway, Milledgeville, GA 31061; tel. 478/445–4516; Mr. Melvin Moses

Georgia War Veterans Nursing Home, 1101 15th Street, Augusta, GA 30901; tel. 706/721–2531; Mr. Charles Esposito

Life Care Center of Gwinnett, 3850 Safehaven Drive, Lawrenceville, GA 30044; tel. 770/923–0005; Ms. Carol Brown

Quinton Memorial Health Care and Rehabilitation Center, 1114 Burleyson Road, Dalton, GA 30720; tel. 706/226–4642; Ms. Jo Reynolds

Regency Park Health Care Center, 1212 Broadrick Drive, Dalton, GA 30720; tel. 706/270–8008; Mr. Steve Fromm

Ridgewood Manor Nursing Home, 1110 Burleyson Road, Dalton, GA 30720; tel. 706/226–1021; Mr. Scott Edens

Sadie G. Mays Health and Rehabilitation Center, 1821 Anderson Avenue, NW, Atlanta, GA 30314; tel. 404/794–2477; Mr. Charles Robinson, Jr.

Southland Nursing Home, Inc., 151 Wisdom Road, Peachtree City, GA 30269; tel. 770/631–9000; Mr. Gary Massengale

Traditions Health and Rehabilitation, PO Box 855, Lithonia, GA 30058; tel. 770/482–2961; Ms. Delores G Scroggs

Wood Dale Health Care Center, 1102 Burleyson Road, Dalton, GA 30720; tel. 706/226–1285; Ms. Natalie McNeal

HAWAII

Hale Anuenue Restorative Care Center, 1333 Waianuenue Avenue, Hilo, HI 96720; tel. 808/961–6644; Mr. Ivan S Yamamoto

Life Care Center of Hilo, 944 West Kawailani Street, Hilo, HI 96720; tel. 808/959–9151; Mr. Fred Horwitz

IDAHO

Life Care Center of Boise, 808 North Curtis Road, Boise, ID 83706; tel. 208/376–5273; Mr. Randal Barnes

Life Care Center of Lewiston, 325 Warner Drive, Lewiston, ID 83501; tel. 208/798–8500; Mr. Dan Knapp

Life Care Center of Sandpoint, 1125 North Division Street, Sandpoint, ID 83864; tel. 208/265–9299; Mr. Brian V Sawyer

Life Care Center of Treasure Valley, 502 North Kimball Place, Boise, ID 83704; tel. 208/377–1900; Mr. Joe Rudd

Valley View Retirement Community, 1130 N Allumbaugh Street, Boise, ID 83704; tel. 208/322–0311; Mr. Cole Clarke

ILLINOIS

Alden - Des Plaines Skilled Nursing and Rehabilitation, 1221 East Golf Road, Des Plaines, IL 60016; tel. 847/768–1300; Mr. Floyd A Schlossberg

Alden - Princeton Nursing and Rehabilitation Center, 255 West 69th Street, Chicago, IL 60621; tel. 773/224–5900; Mr. Floyd A Schlossberg

Alden Estates of Evanston, 2520 Gross Point Road, Evanston, IL 60201; tel. 847/328–6000; Mr. Floyd A Schlossberg

Alden North Shore Rehabilitation Health Care Ctr, 5050 West Touhy Avenue, Skokie, IL 60077; tel. 847/679–6100; Mr. Floyd A Schlossberg

Alden Northmoor Rehabilitation Health Care Center, 5831 North Northwest Highway, Chicago, IL 60631; tel. 773/775–8080; Mr. Floyd A Schlossberg

Alden Poplar Creek Rehabilitation & Hlth Care Ctr, 1545 Barrington Road, Hoffman Est, IL 60194; tel. 847/884–0011; Mr. Bob Molitor

Alden Rehabilitation and Health Care Center/ Orland Park, 16450 South 97th Avenue, Orland Park, IL 60462; tel. 708/403–6500; Mr. Floyd A Schlossberg

Alden Waterford, LLC, 2021 Randi Drive, Aurora, IL 60504; tel. 630/851–7266; Mr. Floyd A Schlossberg

Alden-Lakeland Rehabilitation and Health Care Center, 820 West Lawrence Avenue, Chicago, IL 60640; tel. 773/769–2570; Mr. Floyd A Schlossberg

Anchorage of Beecher, 1201 Dixie Highway, Beecher, IL 60401; tel. 708/946–2600; Mrs. Marcia Quale

Asta Care Center, 300 West Lowell Street, Pontiac, IL 61764; tel. 815/842–1181; Mr. Michael Gillman

ASTA Care Center of Bloomington, 1509 North Calhoun Street, Bloomington, IL 61701; tel. 309/827–6046; Ms. Patricia A Grady

ASTA Care Center of Elgin, 134 North McLean Boulevard, Elgin, IL 60123; tel. 847/742–8822; Dr. Michael Gillman

ASTA Care Center of Rockford, 707 West Riverside Boulevard, Rockford, IL 61103; tel. 815/877–5752; Mrs. Judith L Zbinden

ASTA Care Center of Toluca, 101 East Via Ghigleiri, Toluca, IL 61369; tel. 815/452–2367; Mr. Michael Gillman

Burgess Square Healthcare Centre, 5801 South Cass Avenue, Westmont, IL 60559; tel. 630/971–2645; Ms. Jacqueline L Mason

Continental Care Center, 5336 North Western Avenue, Chicago, IL 60625; tel. 773/271–5600; Ms. Carol Considine

Dolton Health Care and Rehabilitation Centre, 14325 South Blackstone Avenue, Dolton, IL 60419; tel. 708/849–5000; Mr. Safet Keljalic

DuPage Convalescent Center, 400 North County Farm Road, Wheaton, IL 60187; tel. 630/665–6400; Ms. Beth Welch

ElmBrook Healthcare and Rehabilitation Center, 127 West Diversey Avenue, Elmhurst, IL 60126; tel. 630/530–5225; Mrs. Connie L Sherman

Elmhurst Extended Care Center, Inc., 200 East Lake Street, Elmhurst, IL 60126; tel. 630/834–4337; Mr. John W Massard

Evergreen Healthcare Center, 10124 South Kedzie Avenue, Evergreen Park, IL 60805; tel. 708/636–9200; Ms. Judy Dabertin

Fairmont Care Centre, 5061 North Pulaski Road, Chicago, IL 60630; tel. 773/604–8112; Mr. William Pfeiffer

Forest Villa Nursing and Rehabilitation Center, LLC, 6840 West Touhy Avenue, Niles, IL 60714; tel. 847/647–6400; Mr. Barry Carr

Glen Elston Nursing and Rehabilitation Centre, 4340 North Keystone Avenue, Chicago, IL 60641; tel. 773/545–8700; Mr. Steven Schayer

Glen Oaks Nursing and Rehabilitation Centre, Ltd, 270 Skokie Boulevard, Northbrook, IL 60062; tel. 847/498–9320; Mr. Sidney Glenner

GlenBridge Nursing and Rehabilitation Centre, Ltd, 8333 West Golf Road, Niles, IL 60714; tel. 847/966–9190; Mr. Joseph Agnello

Glencrest Nursing and Rehabilitation Centre, 2451 West Touhy Avenue, Chicago, IL 60645; tel. 773/338–6800; Mr. Joshua Ray

GlenShire Nursing and Rehabilitation Centre, Ltd., 22660 South Cicero Avenue, Richton Park, IL 60471; tel. 708/747–6120; Mr. Sidney Glenner

Glenview Terrace Nursing Center, 1511 Greenwood Road, Glenview, IL 60026; tel. 847/729–9090; Mr. Mark Hollander

Halsted Terrace Nursing Center, 10935 South Halsted, Chicago, IL 60628; tel. 773/928–2000; Ms. Bonnie Williams

Harmony Nursing and Rehabilitation Center, 3919 West Foster Avenue, Chicago, IL 60625; tel. 773/588–9500; Mr. Mark Hollander

King-Bruwaert House, 6101 South County Line Road, Burr Ridge, IL 60527; tel. 630/323–2250; Mr. Carl Baker

Lake Shore HealthCare and Rehabilitation Centre, 7200 North Sheridan Road, Chicago, IL 60626; tel. 773/973–7200; Mr. James R Farlee

Manor Care Health Services, 4660 Old Orchard Rd, Skokie, IL 60076; tel. 847/676–4800; Mr. Robert Mabley

Manor Care Health Services - Naperville, 200 Martin Avenue, Naperville, IL 60540; tel. 630/355–4111; Mr. John Hurley

ManorCare Health Services, 512 East Ogden Avenue, Westmont, IL 60559; tel. 630/323–4400; Ms. Jennifer Miller

ManorCare Health Services - Arlington Heights, 715 West Central Road, Arlington Heights, IL 60005; tel. 847/392–2020; Ms. Theresa Smelser

ManorCare Health Services - Elk Grove Village, 1920 Nerge Road, Elk Grove Village, IL 60007; tel. 847/301–0550; Mr. Brian Gross

ManorCare Health Services - Hinsdale, 600 West Ogden Avenue, Hinsdale, IL 60521; tel. 630/325–9630; Mr. John F Vrba

ManorCare Health Services-Oak Lawn East, 9401 South Kostner Avenue, Oak Lawn, IL 60453; tel. 708/423–7882; Ms. Vicki Tomer

Norridge Healthcare and Rehabilitation Centre, 7001 West Cullom Avenue, Norridge, IL 60706; tel. 708/457–0700; Ms. Sandra Bernett

Oak Brook Healthcare Centre, 2013 Midwest Road, Oak Brook, IL 60523; tel. 630/495–0220; Ms. Joanne Bedrosian

Oakton Pavilion Health Care Facility, 1660 Oakton Place, Des Plaines, IL 60018; tel. 847/299–5588; Mr. Jay Lewkowitz

Pine Acres Care Center, 1212 South Second Street, Dekalb, IL 60115; tel. 815/758–8151; Mr. James Formal

Regency Healthcare and Rehabilitation Centre, 6631 North Milwaukee Avenue, Niles, IL 60714; tel. 847/647–7444; Mr. Benjamin Rogow

Rest Haven Illiana Christian Convalescent Home, 13259 South Central Avenue, Palos Heights, IL 60463; tel. 708/597–1000; Ms. Laura Witt

Rest Haven South, 16300 South Wausau Avenue, South Holland, IL 60473; tel. 708/596–5500; Ms. Nancy Van Drunen

Rest Haven West, 3450 Saratoga Avenue, Downers Grove, IL 60515; tel. 630/969–2900; Ms. Caterine A DeVries

Rosewood Care Center Inc. of Northbrook, 4101 Lake Cook Road, Northbrook, IL 60062; tel. 847/562–1770; Mr. Larry Vander Maten

Sheridan Health Care Center, 2534 Elim Avenue, Zion, IL 60099; tel. 847/746–8435; Ms. Marla Benson

Sherman West Court, 1950 Larkin Avenue, Elgin, IL 60123; tel. 847/742–7070; Ms. Anne S Huang

The Abington of Glenview, 3901 Glenview Road, Glenview, IL 60025; tel. 847/729–0000; Ms. Barbara Lyons

The Carlton at the Lake, Inc., 725 West Montrose Avenue, Chicago, IL 60613; tel. 773/929–1700; Mrs. Rose Marie Betz

The Claremont Rehab and Living Center, 150 North Weiland Road, Buffalo Grove, IL 60089; tel. 847/465–0200; Mr. Larry Putz

THI at Governors Park, 1420 South Barrington Road, Barrington, IL 60010; tel. 847/382–6664; Mr. Robert Molitor

Wauconda Health Care and Rehabilitation Centre, 176 Thomas Court, Wauconda, IL 60084; tel. 847/526–5551; Mr. James Farlee

Whitehall North, 300 Waukegan Road, Deerfield, IL 60015-4988; tel. 847/945–4600; Ms. Wendy Heiden

Willows on Main, 1920 N. Main St, Rockford, IL 61114; tel. – –; Marianne Miragia

INDIANA

Gibson General Hospital, Inc., 1808 Sherman Drive, Princeton, IN 47670; tel. 812/385–9221; Mr. Michael J Budnick

Hammond Whiting Care Center, 1000 114th Street, Whiting, IN 46394; tel. 219/659–2770; Ms. Caryn G Moore

Harborside Healthcare - Terre Haute, 1001 E. Springhill Drive, Terre Haute, IN 47802; tel. 812/238–2441; Mr. Stephen L Guillard

Lafayette Medical Investors, 3401 Soldiers Home Road, West Lafayette, IN 47906; tel. 765/463–1541; Ms. Raelene Wing

Life Care Center of LaGrange, 0770 N 075 E, Lagrange, IN 46761; tel. 260/463–7445; Ms. Karen Sandberg

Life Care Center of Michigan City, 802 US Highway 20 East, Michigan City, IN 46360; tel. 219/872–7251; Mr. Pete Seghy

Life Care Center of Valparaiso, 3405 Campbell Road, Valparaiso, IN 46385; tel. 219/462–1023; Ms. Amber Janeczko

Northlake Nursing and Rehabilitation Center, LLC, 601 West 61st Avenue, Merrillville, IN 46410; tel. 219/980–5950; Mark Steinberg

Northwest Manor Health Care Center, 6440 West 34th Street, Indianapolis, IN 46224; tel. 317/293–4930; Mr. Steven J Moser

Parkview Care Center, 2819 North St. Joseph Avenue, Evansville, IN 47712; tel. 812/424–2941; Ms. Connie Kirwer

Rensselaer Care Center, 1309 East Grace Street, Rensselaer, IN 47978; tel. 219/866–4181; Mrs. Roxanne S Bagozzi

The Lane House, 1000 Lane Avenue, Crawfordsville, IN 47933; tel. 765/362–0007; Ms. Sheri Harmon

Vermillion Convalescent Center, 1705 South Main Street, Clinton, IN 47842; tel. 765/832–3573; Mr. Parke Swaim

IOWA

Iowa Veterans Home, 1301 Summit Street, Marshalltown, IA 50158; tel. 515/752–1501; Mr. Daniel Steen

KANSAS

Andover Health Care Center, 621 West 21st Street, Andover, KS 67002; tel. 316/733–1349; Ms. Rhody Burnett

Garden Terrace at Overland Park, 7541 Switzer Rd., Overland, KS 66214; tel. 913/631–2273; Ms. Debra L Biehl

Life Care Center of Wichita, 622 North Edgemoor, Wichita, KS 67208; tel. 316/686–5100; Mrs. Stacy Allen

KENTUCKY

Highlands of Ft. Thomas, 960 Highland Avenue, Fort Thomas, KY 41075; tel. 859/572–0660; Mr. Barry N Bortz

J. J. Jordan Geriatric Center, 270 East Clayton Lane, Louisa, KY 41230; tel. 606/638–4586; Mr. David McKenzie

Parkview Nursing and Rehabilitation Center, 544 Lone Oak Road, Paducah, KY 42003; tel. 502/443–6543; Mr. William B Boyd

VillaSpring Healthcare Center, 630 Viox Drive, Erlanger, KY 41018; tel. 859/727–6700; Mr. Barry Bortz

LOUISIANA

Lafon Nursing Facility of the Holy Family, 6900 Chef Menteur Highway, New Orleans, LA 70126; tel. 504/246–1100; Sister Augustine McDaniel

Martin de Porres Nursing Home, Inc., PO Box 1294, Lake Charles, LA 70602; tel. 337/439–5761; Mr. Robert Leonards

National Hansen's Disease Programs, 1770 Physicians Park Drive, Baton Rouge, LA 70816; tel. 225/756–3700; Cpt. Charles D Stanley

Trinity Neurologic Rehabilitation Center, LLC, 1400 Lindberg Drive, Slidell, LA 70458; tel. 985/641–4985; Mr. Patrick Foret

MAINE

Ross Manor, 758 Broadway, Bangor, ME 04401; tel. 207/941–8400; Ms. Valerie E Coleman

Seaside Rehabilitation and Health Care Center, 850 Baxter Boulevard, Portland, ME 04103; tel. 207/774–7878; Mr. Kenneth Bowden

Windward Gardens, 105 Mechanic Street, Camden, ME 04843; tel. 207/236–4197; Mr. Carl Chadwick

MARYLAND

Bradford Oaks Nursing and Rehabilitation Center, 7520 Surratts Road, Clinton, MD 20735; tel. 301/856–1660; Ms. Lori Lusby-Hamilton

Charles Street Healthcare, LLC, 2700 North Charles Street, Baltimore, MD 21218; tel. 410/554–6300; Ms. Elissa Heck

Fox Chase Rehabilitation and Nursing Center, 2015 East West Highway, Silver Spring, MD 20910; tel. 301/587–2400; Ms. Jean A Raiche

Franklin Woods Center - Genesis Eldercare Network, 9200 Franklin Square Drive, Baltimore, MD 21237; tel. 410/391–2600; Mr. J B Pabst

FutureCare Old Court, 5412 Old Court Road, Randallstown, MD 21133-5196; tel. 410/922–3200; Mr. Brian Abramson

FutureCare Sandtown Winchester Nursing Center, 1000 North Gilmor Street, Baltimore, MD 21217; tel. 410/669–2750; Mr. Leslie D Goldschmidt

FutureCare-Chesapeake, 305 College Parkway, Arnold, MD 21012; tel. 410/647–0015; Ms. Gwen Katner

Hebrew Home of Greater Washington, 6121 Montrose Road, Rockville, MD 20852; tel. 301/770–8468; Mr. Warren R Slavin

Jewish Convalescent and Nursing Home, 7920 Scotts Level Road, Baltimore, MD 21208; tel. 410/521–3600; Ms. Kathy L Gelzhiser

Keswick Multi-Care Center, 700 West 40th Street, Baltimore, MD 21211; tel. 410/662–4200; Ms. Elizabeth Bowerman

Levindale Hebrew Geriatric Center and Hospital, 2434 West Belvedere Avenue, Baltimore, MD 21215; tel. 410/466–8700; Mr. Ronald Rothstein

Potomac Valley Nursing Facilities Inc., 1235 Potomac Valley Road, Rockville, MD 20850; tel. 301/762–0700; Mrs. Leah T Bowden

Shady Grove Adventist Nursing and Rehabilitation Center, 9701 Medical Center Drive, Rockville, MD 20850; tel. 301/315–1900; Ms. Michelle Mahn

St. Elizabeth Rehabilitation and Nursing Center, 3320 Benson Avenue, Baltimore, MD 21227; tel. 410/644–7100; Ms. Christine L Mour

St. Thomas More Nursing and Rehabilitation Center, 4922 LaSalle Road, Hyattsville, MD 20782; tel. 301/864–2333; Mr. Matt Neiswanger

MASSACHUSETTS

Abbott House, 28 Essex Street, Lynn, MA 01902; tel. 781/595–5500; Ms. Michele Desmarais

Aberjona Nursing Center, Inc., 184 Swanton Street, Winchester, MA 01890; tel. 781/729–9370; Mr. Robert F Salter

Alden Court Nursing Care and Rehabilitation Center, 389 Alden Road, Fairhaven, MA 02719; tel. 508/991–8600; Mr. Brad Truini

Anchorage Nursing Home, 904 Mohawk Trail, Shelburne Falls, MA 01370; tel. 413/625–2305; Mr. Francis B Caldwell

Apple Valley Nursing and Rehabilitation Center, 400 Groton Road, Ayer, MA 01432; tel. 978/772–1704; Ms. Joanne McCarron

Autumn Village, LLC, 25 Oriol Drive, Worcester, MA 01605; tel. 508/852–3330; Mrs. Alicia Nordin

Avery Manor, 100 West Street, Needham Heights, MA 02494; tel. 781/433–0202; Mr. Jerry E Shaffer

Bay Path Rehabilitation & Nursing Center, 308 Kingstown Way, Duxbury, MA 02332; tel. 781/585–5561; Mrs. Marianne Welch-Martinez

Baypointe Rehabilitation and Skilled Care Center, 50 Christy Place, Brockton, MA 02301; tel. 508/580–6800; Mr. Robert Grady

Bear Hill Nursing Center at Wakefield, 11 North Street, Stoneham, MA 02180; tel. 781/438–8515; Mr. William E Ring, Jr.

Beaumont Rehabilitation & Skilled Nursing Center, 3 Vision Drive, Natick, MA 01760; tel. 508/655–3344; Mr. William McGinley

Beaumont Rehabilitation and Nursing Center at Northborough, 238 West Main Street, Northborough, MA 01532; tel. 508/393–2368; Mr. Phil LaCasse

Beaumont Rehabilitation and Skilled Nursing Center, PO Box 935, Northbridge, MA 01534-0935; tel. 508/234–9771; Mr. Matthew Salmon

Beaumont Rehabilitation and Skilled Nursing Facility, One Lyman Street, Westborough, MA 01581; tel. 508/366–9933; Mr. Paul O'Connell

Beverly Healthcare Birchwood Care Center, 1199 John Fitch Highway, Fitchburg, MA 01420; tel. 978/345–0146; Ms. Fran Herr

Beverly Manor, 19 Obery Street, Plymouth, MA 02360; tel. 508/747–4790; Mr. Robert Eisenstein

Blaire House of Milford, 20 Claflin Street, Milford, MA 01757; tel. 508/473–1272; Ms. Deborah Klock

Blaire House of Tewksbury, 10 Erlin Terrace, Tewksbury, MA 01876; tel. 978/851–3121; Ms. Frances Herr

Blueberry Hill Healthcare, 75 Brimbal Avenue, Beverly, MA 01915; tel. 978/927–2020; Mr. Michael Takesian

Bolton Manor Nursing and Rehabilitation Center, 400 Bolton Street, Marlborough, MA 01752; tel. 508/481–6123; Mr. Scott A Bullock

Bostonian Nursing Care and Rehabilitation Center, 337 Neponset Ave, Dorchester, MA 02122; tel. 617/265–2350; Mr. Richard J SciaccaJr.

Bourne Manor Extended Care Facility, 146 MacArthur Boulevard, Bourne, MA 02532; tel. 508/759–8880; Mr. William C Jones

Braemoor Rehabilitation and Nursing Center, Inc., 34 North Pearl Street, Brockton, MA 02301; tel. 508/586–3696; Mr. Michael J Roland

Braintree Landing Skilled Nursing & Rehabilitation Center, 95 Commerical Street, Braintree, MA 02184; tel. 781/848–3678; Ms. Pamela Pattavina

Braintree Manor Rehabilitation and Nursing Center, 1102 Washington Street, Braintree, MA 02184; tel. 781/848–3100; Mr. David Noble

Brookline Health Care Center, 99 Park Street, Brookline, MA 02446; tel. 617/731–1050; Mr. Wayne Pultman

Buckley HealthCare Center, 95 Laurel Street, Greenfield, MA 01301; tel. 413/774–3143; Mr. Brad T Rector

Caldwell Skilled Nursing & Rehabilitation Center, Inc., 16 Green Street, Ipswich, MA 01938; tel. 978/356–2526; Mr. Philip S Sher

Calvin Coolidge Nursing & Rehabilitation Center, 548 Elm Street, Northampton, MA 01060; tel. 413/586–3150; Mr. Eric Fritz

Cape Heritage Nursing and Rehabilitation Center, 37 Route 6A, Sandwich, MA 02563; tel. 508/888–8222; Mr. Emmanuel Freddura

Cape Regency Rehabilitation and Nursing Center, 120 South Main Street, Centerville, MA 02632; tel. 508/778–1835; Mr. Thomas C Lavallee

Catholic Memorial Home, Inc., 2446 Highland Avenue, Fall River, MA 02720-4599; tel. 508/679–0011; Rev. Edmund J Fitzgerald

Charlene Manor, 130 Colrain Road, Greenfield, MA 01301; tel. 413/774–3724; Mr. William C Jones, Jr.

Charlwell House, 305 Walpole Street, Norwood, MA 02062; tel. 781/762–7700; Mr. Donald C Baker

Chestnut Hill Rehabilitation and Nursing Center, 32 Chestnut Street, East Longmeadow, MA 01028; tel. 413/525–1893; Ms. Dolores Schermer

Christopher House of Worcester, Inc., 10 Mary Scano Drive, Worcester, MA 01605; tel. 508/754–3800; Mr. Walter V Ohanian

Clark House at Fox Hill Village, 30 Longwood Drive, Westwood, MA 02090; tel. 781/326–5652; Mr. Chris Wasel

Clifton Rehabilitative Nursing Center, 500 Wilbur Avenue, Somerset, MA 02725; tel. 508/675–7589; Ms. Andrea Greenwood-Syron

Cohasset Knoll Skilled Nursing and Rehabilitation Facility, 1 Chief Justice Cushing Hwy., Cohasset, MA 02025; tel. 781/383–9060; Mr. William Floyd

Colonial Rehabilitation and Nursing Center, 125 Broad Street, Weymouth, MA 02188; tel. 781/337–3121; Mr. Steven Kelly

Concord Health Care Center, 57 Old Road to Nine Acre Corner, Concord, MA 01742; tel. 978/371–3400; Mr. Kenneth Kelley

Coolidge House Nursing Care Center - Genesis ElderCare, 30 Webster Street, Brookline, MA 02446; tel. 617/734–2300; Mr. Mark R LaRoche

Copley at Stoughton Nursing Care Center, 380 Sumner Street, Stoughton, MA 02072; tel. 781/341–2300; Mr. Mark Presutti

Country Estates Nursing and Rehabilitation Center, 1200 Suffield Street, Agawam, MA 01001; tel. 413/789–2200; Mr. Daniel Larouche

Country Rehabilitation and Nursing Center, 180 Low Street, Newburyport, MA 01950; tel. 978/465–5361; Ms. Shari LaRoche

Courtyard Nursing Care Center, 200 Governors Avenue, Medford, MA 02155; tel. 781/391–5400; Mr. Andrew Salmon

Crawford Skilled Nursing and Rehabilitation Center, 273 Oak Grove Avenue, Fall River, MA 02723; tel. 508/679–4866; Mr. Jeffrey Govoni

Crestview Healthcare Facility, Inc., 86 Greenleaf Street, Quincy, MA 02169; tel. 617/479–2978; Mr. Joel K Logan

Section C

D'Youville Senior Care, Inc., 981 Varnum Avenue, Lowell, MA 01854; tel. 978/569–1000; Ms. Naomi M Prendergast

Den Mar Rehabilitation and Nursing Center, 44 South Street, Rockport, MA 01966; tel. 978/546–6311; Ms. Kate Hawk

Deutsches Altenheim Inc. German Centre for Extended Care, 2222 Centre Street, West Roxbury, MA 02132; tel. 617/325–1230; Mr. W. Bruce Glass

Devereux House Nursing Home, 39 Lafayette Street, Marblehead, MA 01945-1997; tel. 781/631–6120; Mrs. Erin Mondello

Don Orione Nursing Home, 111 Orient Avenue, East Boston, MA 02128; tel. 617/569–2100; Ms. Nancy J Walsh

Eagle Pond Rehabilitation and Living Center, PO Box 208, South Dennis, MA 02660; tel. 508/385–6034; Mr. Michael J Gallagher

East Longmeadow Skilled Nursing Center, 305 Maple Street, East Longmeadow, MA 01028; tel. 413/525–6361; Mr. William C Jones, Jr.

East Village Rehabilitation and Nursing Center, 840 Emerson Gardens Road, Lexington, MA 02420; tel. 781/861–8630; Mr. Clyde L Tyler, Jr.

Easton Lincoln Rehabilitation and Nursing Center, 184 Lincoln Street, North Easton, MA 02356; tel. 508/238–7053; Mr. Jeffrey Aframe

Eastpointe Rehabilitation and Skilled Care Center, 255 Central Avenue, Chelsea, MA 02150; tel. 617/884–5700; Mr. Joseph Veno

Edgar P. Benjamin Healthcare Center, 120 Fisher Avenue, Boston, MA 02120; tel. 617/738–1500; Ms. Myrna E Wynn

Emerald Court Health and Rehabilitation Center, 460 Washington Street, Norwood, MA 02062; tel. 781/769–2200; Mr. David A Johnson

Emerson Rehabilitation and Nursing Center, 59 Coolidge Hill Road, Watertown, MA 02472-2884; tel. 617/924–1130; Mr. Steven P Duffy

EPOCH Senior Healthcare of Brewster, 873 Harwich Road, Brewster, MA 02631; tel. 508/896–7046; Ms. Maureen Kalivas

EPOCH Senior Healthcare of Chestnut Hill, 615 Heath Street, Chestnut Hill, MA 02467; tel. 617/243–9990; Dr. Ellen Alperen

EPOCH Senior Healthcare of Harwich, 111 Headwaters Drive, Harwich, MA 02645-1726; tel. 508/430–1717; Mr. David Maloney

EPOCH Senior Healthcare of Melrose, 15 Green Street, Melrose, MA 02176; tel. 781/665–3950; Ms. Bonnie Jean McLean

EPOCH Senior Healthcare of Norton, 184 Mansfield Avenue, Norton, MA 02766; tel. 508/285–7745; Mr. Laurence Gerber

EPOCH Senior Healthcare of Sharon, 259 Norwood Street, Sharon, MA 02067; tel. 781/784–6781; Mr. Adam Goldman

EPOCH Senior Healthcare of Weston, 75 Norumbega Road, Weston, MA 02493; tel. 781/891–6100; Mr. Gerry Labourene

Fairhaven Nursing Home, Inc., 476 Varnum Avenue, Lowell, MA 01854; tel. 978/458–3388; Ms. Sherrie Palmieri

Fairlawn Nursing Home, 370 West Street, Leominster, MA 01453; tel. 978/537–0771; Mr. Jeffrey J Martin

Fairview Commons Nursing & Rehabilitation Center, 151 Christian Hill Road, Great Barrington, MA 01230; tel. 413/528–4560; Mr. William Jones

Fall River Nursing LLC, 1748 Highland Avenue, Fall River, MA 02720; tel. 508/730–1070; Mr. Peter Callagy

Farren Care Center, Inc., 340 Montague City Road, Turners Falls, MA 01376; tel. 413/774–3111; Mr. Christopher J McLaughlin

Forestview Nursing Home of Wareham, Inc., 50 Indian Neck Road, Wareham, MA 02571; tel. 508/295–6264; Ms. Marcia Mac Innis

Geriatric Authority of Milford Nursing and Rehabilitation Ct, 1 Countryside Drive, Milford, MA 01757; tel. 508/473–0435; Mr. Barry Chiler

GF Pilgrim, Inc., 888 North Main Street, Brockton, MA 02301; tel. 508/587–6556; Ms. Jennifer Conley

Glen Ridge Nursing Care Center, Hospital Road, Malden, MA 02148; tel. 781/391–0800; Mr. Robert Hayes

Goddard House, 201 S. Huntington Avenue, Jamaica Plain, MA 02130; tel. 617/522–3080; Ms. Christine Battisti

Governor's Center, 66 Broad Street, Westfield, MA 01085; tel. 413/562–5464; Mr. Jeffrey J Graham

Greycliff at Cape Ann, 272 Washington Street, Gloucester, MA 01930; tel. 978/281–0333; Ms. Joanne Carbone

Grosvenor Park Nursing Center, Inc., 7 Loring Hills Avenue, Salem, MA 01970; tel. 978/741–5700; Ms. Nancy Escalada

Hancock Park Rehabilitation and Nursing Center, 164 Parkingway, Quincy, MA 02169; tel. 617/773–4222; Mr. Richard Coughlin

Hannah Duston Healthcare Center, 126 Monument Street, Haverhill, MA 01832; tel. 978/373–1747; Mrs. Beth Skafas

Harbor House Rehabilitation and Nursing Center, 11 Condito Road, Hingham, MA 02043; tel. 781/749–4774; Ms. Susan Jessup

Harborlights Rehabilitation and Nursing Center, 804 East 7th Street, South Boston, MA 02127; tel. 617/268–8968; Mrs. Tara L Gibney

Harborside Healthcare Danvers Twin Oaks, 63 Locust Street, Danvers, MA 01923; tel. 978/777–0011; Ms. Carolyn Fenn

Harborside Healthcare Falmouth Rehabilitation and Nursing, 359 Jones Road, Falmouth, MA 02540; tel. 508/457–9000; Mr. John L Bonfardeci

Harborside Healthcare Wakefield, One Bathol Street, Wakefield, MA 01880; tel. 781/245–7600; Mr. Charles M Crush

Harborside Healthcare-Mashpee, 161 Falmouth Road, Mashpee, MA 02649; tel. 508/477–2490; Mr. Robert D Theroux

Harrington House Nursing and Rehabilitation Center, 160 Main Street, Walpole, MA 02081; tel. 508/660–3080; Mr. Anthony D Lacke

Hathaway Manor, ECF, 863 Hathaway Road, New Bedford, MA 02740; tel. 508/996–6763; Mr. Paul Marois

Haven Health Center of Chelsea, 932 Broadway, Chelsea, MA 02150; tel. 617/889–2250; Mr. Paul Knutsen

Heathwood Nursing and Rehabilitation Center, 188 Florence Street, Chestnut Hill, MA 02467; tel. 617/332–4730; Ms. Diane Dickerman

Heritage Hall East Center, 464 Main Street, Agawam, MA 01001; tel. 413/821–0753; Mr. Ira M Schoenberger

Heritage Hall North, 55 Cooper Street, Agawam, MA 01001; tel. 413/821–0751; Mrs. Regina A Bossig

Heritage Hall West - Genesis Eldercare, 61 Cooper Street, Agawam, MA 01001; tel. 413/786–8000; Mr. George A Mercier

Heritage Manor - Genesis ElderCare, 841 Merrimack Street, Lowell, MA 01854; tel. 978/459–0546; Ms. Elizabeth Rozzi

Highgate Manor, 10 CareMatrix Drive, Dedham, MA 02026; tel. 781/461–9663; Mr. James Morris

Hillcrest Extended Care, 169 Valentine Road, Pittsfield, MA 01201; tel. 413/445–2300; Mr. William Kittler

Holy Trinity Nursing and Rehabilitation Center, 300 Barber Avenue, Worcester, MA 01606; tel. 508/852–1000; Ms. Karen Laganelli

Holyoke Rehabilitation Center, 260 Easthampton Road, Holyoke, MA 01040; tel. 413/538–9733; Mr. Kevin Breslin

Hunt Nursing and Retirement Home, 90 Lindall Street, Danvers, MA 01923; tel. 978/777–3740; Mr. Marc Neustadt

Hyannis Skilled Care Center, 89 Lewis Bay Road, Hyannis, MA 02601; tel. 508/775–7601; Ms. Pat Green

Jewish Healthcare Center, Inc., 629 Salisbury Street, Worcester, MA 01609; tel. 508/798–8653; Mr. Steven Willens

Jewish Rehabilitation Center for Aged of the North Shore, 330 Paradise Road, Swampscott, MA 01907; tel. 781/598–5310; Mr. Matt Weinstock

JML Care Center, Inc., 184 Ter Heun Drive, Falmouth, MA 02540-2503; tel. 508/457–4621; Mr. Charles Peterman

John Scott House Rehabilitation and Nursing Center, 233 Middle Street, Braintree, MA 02184; tel. 781/843–1860; Mr. Thomas D Nolan

Kathleen Daniel Nursing and Rehabilitation Center, 485 Franklin Street, Framingham, MA 01702; tel. 508/872–8801; Mr. Ray Diuto

Knollwood Nursing Center, 87 Briarwood Circle, Worcester, MA 01606; tel. 508/853–6910; Mr. Paul Bowler

Laurel Lake Center for Health and Rehabilitation, 620 Laurel Street, Lee, MA 01238; tel. 413/243–2010; Ms. Debbie Richardson

Ledgewood Rehabilitation and Skilled Nursing Center, 87 Herrick Street, Beverly, MA 01915; tel. 978/921–1392; Ms. Judy H Manchester

Leo P. LaChance Center for Rehabilitation and Nursing, 59 Eastwood Circle, Gardner, MA 01440; tel. 978/632–8776; Mr. Dennis P Lopata

Lexington Health Care Center, 178 Lowell St., Lexington, MA 02420; tel. 781/862–7400; Mr. Steven Davis

Liberty Commons of Chatham, 390 Orleans Rd., North Chatham, MA 02650; tel. 508/945–4611; Mr. William A Dobson

Life Care Center of Acton, One Great Road, Acton, MA 01720; tel. 978/263–9101; Mr. Joseph J Deveau

Life Care Center of Auburn, 14 Masonic Circle, Auburn, MA 01501; tel. 508/832–4800; Mr. James A Nugent

Life Care Center of Merrimack Valley, 80 Boston Road, North Billerica, MA 01862; tel. 978/667–2166; Ms. Colleen Lovering

Life Care Center of Nashoba Valley, 191 Foster Street, Littleton, MA 01460; tel. 978/486–3512; Ms. Ellen Levinson

Life Care Center of Plymouth, 94 Obery Street, Plymouth, MA 02360; tel. 508/747–9800; Ms. Mary M Schroeder

Life Care Center of Raynham, 546 South Street East, Raynham, MA 02767; tel. 508/821–5700; Ms. Deborah Ready

Life Care Center of Stoneham, 25 Woodland Road, Stoneham, MA 02180; tel. 781/662–2545; Mr. Carl H Anderson

Life Care Center of the North Shore, 111 Birch Street, Lynn, MA 01902; tel. 781/592–9667; Mr. Tony Traino

Life Care Center of the South Shore, PO Box 830, Scituate, MA 02066; tel. 781/545–1370; Mr. Kevin Morris

Life Care Center of West Bridgewater, 765 West Center Street, West Bridgewater, MA 02379; tel. 508/580–4400; Mr. Alan J Richman

Life Care Center of Wilbraham, 2399 Boston Road, Wilbraham, MA 01095; tel. 413/596–3111; Mr. Ronald L Cherubin

LifeCare Center of Attleboro, 969 Park Street, Attleboro, MA 02703; tel. 508/222–4182; Mr. Patrick O'Connor

Lighthouse Nursing Care Center, 204 Proctor Avenue, Revere, MA 02151; tel. 781/286–3100; Mr. Roger Marks

Linda Manor Extended Care Facility, 349 Haydenville Road, Leeds, MA 01053; tel. 413/586–7700; Ms. Robin J Longo

Logan Nursing & Rehabilitation Center, 175 Grove Street, Braintree, MA 02184; tel. 781/848–2050; Ms. Mary Kilcommons

Lowell Health Care Center, 19 Varnum Street, Lowell, MA 01850; tel. 978/454–5644; Mr. Mark O'Flaherty

Madonna Manor, Inc., 85 North Washington Street, North Attleboro, MA 02760; tel. 508/699–2740; Rev. Edmund J Fitzgerald

Marian Manor, Inc., 33 Summer Street, Taunton, MA 02780; tel. 508/822–4885; Rev. Edmund J Fitzgerald

Marina Bay Skilled Nursing and Rehabilitation Center, 2 Seaport Drive, Quincy, MA 02171; tel. 617/745–5100; Ms. Rosemary McLaughlin

Maristhill Nursing & Rehabilitation Center, 66 Newton Street, Waltham, MA 02453; tel. 781/893–0240; Ms. Janet C Murphy

Mary Ann Morse Nursing and Rehabilitation Center, 45 Union Street, Natick, MA 01760; tel. 508/650–9003; Ms. Joan Thompson

Mary Lyon Nursing & Rehabilitation Center, 34 Main Street, Hampden, MA 01036; tel. 413/566–5511; Adm. MARYANNE Stout

Masconomet Healthcare Center, 123 High Street, Topsfield, MA 01983-1926; tel. 978/887–7002; Mr. David Lewis

Masonic Home, Inc., PO Box 1000, Charlton, MA 01507-1000; tel. 508/248–7344; Mr. David C Turner

Mayflower Nursing and Rehabilitation Center, 123 South Street, Plymouth, MA 02360; tel. 508/746–4343; Mr. Matt Muratore

Mayflower Place Nursing and Rehabilitation Center, 579 Buck Island Road, W Yarmouth, MA 02673; tel. 508/957–7007; Ms. Cathy S Sawyer

Meadow Green Nursing and Rehabilitation Center, 45 Woburn Street, Waltham, MA 02452; tel. 781/899–8600; Mr. David L Bell

Medway Country Manor Skilled Nursing and Rehabilitation, 115 Holliston Street, Medway, MA 02053; tel. 508/533–6634; Mr. John PetersIII

Mercy Care Center of Springfield, 370 Pine Street, Springfield, MA 01105; tel. 413/731–5318; Mr. Vincent McCorkle

Mercy Senior Care Network, Inc., 35 Holy Family Road, Holyoke, MA 01040; tel. 413/532–3246; Ms. Eriko K Umana

Middleboro Skilled Care Center, 23 Isaac Street, Middleboro, MA 02346; tel. 508/947-9295; Ms. Marcia MacInnis

Millbury Health Care Center, 312 Millbury Avenue, Millbury, MA 01527; tel. 508/793-0088; Ms. Joanne Bruell

Milton Health Care, 1200 Brush Hill Road, Milton, MA 02186; tel. 617/333-0600; Mr. Michael Lincoln

Montserrat Nursing and Rehabilitation Center of Beverly, 265 Essex Street, Beverly, MA 01915; tel. 978/927-3260; Mr. Gregory Karr

Mt. Greylock Extended Care Facility, 1000 North Street, Pittsfield, MA 01201; tel. 413/499-7186; Mrs. Maria T Craft

New Bedford Health Care Center, 221 Fitzgerald Drive, New Bedford, MA 02745; tel. 508/996-4600; Mr. Albert E Crabtree, Jr.

New Bedford Jewish Convalescent Home, Inc., 200 Hawthorn Street, New Bedford, MA 02740; tel. 508/997-9314; Mrs. Carol A Trudeau

New England Pediatric Care, 78 Boston Road, North Billerica, MA 01862; tel. 978/667-5123; Ms. Ellen J O'Gorman

Newton Health Care Center, 2101 Washington Street, Newton Lower Falls, MA 02462; tel. 617/969-4660; Mr. Stewart R Goff

North Adams Commons, 175 Franklin Street, North Adams, MA 01247; tel. 413/664-4041; Ms. Sandra Cunningham

North Shore Health Care Center, 70 Granite Street, Lynn, MA 01904; tel. 781/581-2400; Mr. Mike Corbett

Northwood Rehabilitation and Nursing Center, 1010 Varnum Avenue, Lowell, MA 01854; tel. 978/458-8773; Mr. Scott Stone

Oak Knoll Healthcare Center, 9 Arbetter Drive, Framingham, MA 01701; tel. 508/877-3300; Mr. Edmund Taglieri

Oakwood Rehabilitation and Nursing Center, 11 Pontiac Avenue, Webster, MA 01570; tel. 508/943-3889; Mr. Paul Diaz

Our Lady's Haven of Fairhaven, Inc., 71 Center Street, Fairhaven, MA 02719; tel. 508/999-4561; Rev. Edmund J Fitzgerald

Palm Manor Nursing Center, 40 Parkhurst Road, Chelmsford, MA 01824; tel. 978/256-3151; Ms. Andrea Rathbone

Park Avenue Nursing and Rehabilitation Center, 146 Park Avenue, Arlington, MA 02476; tel. 781/648-9530; Mr. John J Alessandroni

Pavilion Nursing and Rehabilitation Center, 876 Falmouth Road, Hyannis, MA 02601; tel. 508/775-6663; Adm. Mary E Benoit

Peabody Glen Health Care Center, 199 Andover Street, Peabody, MA 01960; tel. 978/531-0772; Mr. David J Madigan

Pilgrim Rehabilitation and Skilled Nursing Center, 96 Forest Street, Peabody, MA 01960-3907; tel. 978/532-0303; Ms. Allison S Bottomley

Poets Seat's Nursing Home, 359 High Street, Greenfield, MA 01301; tel. 413/774-6318; Ms. Michele Carney

Port Healthcare Center, 113 Low Street, Newburyport, MA 01950; tel. 978/462-7373; Mr. Jeff Gangi

Prescott House Nursing Home, 140 Prescott Street, North Andover, MA 01845; tel. 978/685-8086; Mr. Chris Sintros

Presentation Nursing and Rehabilitation Center, 10 Bellamy Street, Brighton, MA 02135; tel. 617/782-8113; Mr. Mark W Jessup

Providence Care Center of Lenox, 320 Pittsfield Road, Lenox, MA 01240; tel. 413/637-2660; Mr. Vincent McCorkle

Quabbin Valley Healthcare, 821 Daniel Shays Highway, Athol, MA 01331; tel. 978/249-3717; Mr. Mark Ailinger

Queen Anne Nursing Home, Inc., 50 Recreation Park Drive, Hingham, MA 02043; tel. 781/749-4982; Mr. Peter H Starr

Quincy Rehabilitation and Nursing Center, 11 McGrath Highway, Quincy, MA 02169-5311; tel. 617/479-2820; Ms. Karen Wadlow

Radius Healthcare Center at Beverly, 40 Heather Street, Beverly, MA 01915; tel. 978/927-6220; Ms. Joyce Sears-Whitbeck

Radius HealthCare Center at Millbury, 29 Main Street, Millbury, MA 01527; tel. 508/865-6106; Ms. Dolores Schermer

Radius HealthCare Center at Worcester, 119 Providence Street, Worcester, MA 01604; tel. 508/860-5000; Mr. Daniel Mitchell

Radius-Ring Operating, LLC, 215 Bicentennial Highway, Springfield, MA 01118; tel. 413/796-7511; Mrs. Diane Goncalves

Randolph Healthcare Center, 49 Thomas Patten Drive, Randolph, MA 02368; tel. 781/961-1160; Mr. Kenneth Kelley

Renaissance Manor of Westfield, 37 Feeding Hills Road, Westfield, MA 01085; tel. 413/568-2341; Ms. Mary O'Connor

Riverdale Gardens Rehabilitation and Nursing Center, 42 Prospect Avenue, West Springfield, MA 01089; tel. 413/733-3151; Mr. Robert Engell

Rosewood Nursing and Rehabilitation Center, 22 Johnson Street, Peabody, MA 01960; tel. 978/535-8700; Mr. Paul B Mahony, Jr.

Royal Nursing Center, 545 Main Street, Falmouth, MA 02540; tel. 508/548-3800; Mr. James Mamary

Sacred Heart Home, Inc., 359 Summer Street, New Bedford, MA 02740; tel. 508/996-6751; Rev. Edmund J Fitzgerald

Sancta Maria Nursing Facility, 799 Concord Avenue, Cambridge, MA 02138; tel. 617/868-2200; Sister Mary Mark Pizzotti

Sarah S. Brayton Nursing Care Center, 4901 North Main Street, Fall River, MA 02720; tel. 508/675-1001; Adm. Jeffrey A Govoni

Seacoast Nursing and Rehabilitation Center, 292 Washington Street, Gloucester, MA 01930; tel. 978/283-0300; Ms. Cynthia Cafasso Donaldson

Senior Residential Care/ South Hadley, LLC, 573 Granby Road, South Hadley, MA 01075; tel. 413/532-2200; Ms. Kara Yereance

Sherrill House, Inc., 135 South Huntington Avenue, Boston, MA 02130; tel. 617/731-2400; Mr. Patrick Stapleton

Sippican Healthcare Center, 15 Mill Street, Marion, MA 02738; tel. 508/748-3830; Dr. Alfred L Arcidi

Southpointe Rehabilitation and Skilled Care Center, 100 Amity Street, Fall River, MA 02721; tel. 508/675-2500; Mr. Barry Freid

Southwood at Norwell Nursing Center, 501 Cordwainer Drive, Norwell, MA 02061; tel. 781/982-7450; Mr. Richard H Starr

St. Camillus Health Center, 447 Hill Street, Whitinsville, MA 01588; tel. 508/234-7306; Mr. William Graves

Sterling Healthcare Center, 18 Dana Hill Road, Sterling, MA 01564; tel. 978/422-5111; Mr. Robert Taber

Sudbury Pines Extended Care Facility, 642 Boston Post Road, Sudbury, MA 01776; tel. 978/443-9000; Ms. Roberta C Henderson

SunBridge Care & Rehabilitation for North Reading, 134 North Street, North Reading, MA 01864; tel. 978/276-2000; Mrs. Linda E Santamaria

SunBridge Care and Rehabilitation for Milford, 10 Veterans Memorial Drive, Milford, MA 01757; tel. 508/473-6414; Mr. Dennis Diglioria

SunBridge Care and Rehabilitation for Weymouth, 64 Performance Drive, Weymouth, MA 02189; tel. 781/340-9800; Mr. Dennis Diglioria

SunBridge Healthcare Corporation, 20 North Maple Street, Hadley, MA 01035; tel. 413/584-5057; Ms. Karen Crafa

Sunny Acres Nursing Home, Inc., 254 Billerica Road, Chelmsford, MA 01824; tel. 978/256-1616; Ms. Shirley Freitas

Sweet Brook Transitional Care and Living Centers, 1561 Cold Spring Road, Williamstown, MA 01267; tel. 413/458-8127; Mr. David M Laplante

The Boston Center For Rehabilitative & Subacute Care, 1245 Centre Street, Roslindale, MA 02131; tel. 617/325-5400; Ms. Christine Reilly

The Ellis Nursing and Rehabilitation Center, 135 Ellis Avenue, Norwood, MA 02062; tel. 781/762-6880; Mr. Anthony A Franchi, Sr.

The Goddard Center, 909 Sumner Street, Stoughton, MA 02072; tel. 781/297-8200; Mr. James Keane

The Hermitage - A Beverly Healthcare Facility, 383 Mill Street, Worcester, MA 01602; tel. 508/791-8131; Mr. Robert Petroff

The Highlands, 335 Nichols Road, Fitchburg, MA 01420; tel. 978/343-4411; Ms. JoAnn Piedrafite

The Kimball Farms Nursing Care Center, 40 Sunset Avenue, Lenox, MA 01240; tel. 413/637-5011; Mr. William C Jones, Jr.

The Lafayette Convalescent Home, 25 Lafayette Street, Marblehead, MA 01945; tel. 781/631-4535; Mr. William Mantzoukas

The Meadows Skilled Nursing and Rehabilitation Center, 111 Huntoon Memorial Highway, Rochdale, MA 01542; tel. 508/892-4858; Mr. Jeffrey A Diminico

The Nevins Nursing and Rehabilitation Centre, Ten Ingalls Court, Methuen, MA 01844; tel. 978/682-7611; Mr. Felix F Albano, Jr.

The Oaks Nursing Center, 4525 Acushnet Avenue, New Bedford, MA 02745; tel. 508/998-7807; Mr. Robert G Noonan

The Oxford, 689 Main Street, Haverhill, MA 01830; tel. 978/373-1131; Mr. John Holt

The Skilled Care Center at Silver Lake, 17 Chipman Way, Kingston, MA 02364; tel. 781/585-4100; Ms. Joan P Chamberlain

Tower Hill Center for Health and Rehabilitation, One Meadowbrook Way, Canton, MA 02021; tel. 781/961-5600; Mrs. Valerie Gingras

Town & Country Nursing Center, 259 Baldwin Avenue, Lowell, MA 01851; tel. 978/454-5438; Mr. Norman Michaud

University Commons Nursing Care Center, 378 Plantation Street, Worcester, MA 01605; tel. 508/755-7300; Mr. James V Divver

Wachusett Extended Care Facility, 56 Boyden Road, Holden, MA 01520; tel. 508/829-5555; Mr. James M Oliver

Walden Rehabilitation and Nursing Center, 785 Main Street, Concord, MA 01742; tel. 978/369-6889; Ms. Joanne Shaw

Webster Manor, 745 School Street, Webster, MA 01570; tel. 508/949-0644; Mr. Richard Kravetz

West Acres Nursing Home and Rehabilitation Center, 804 Pleasant Street, Brockton, MA 02301-3099; tel. 508/583-6000; Mr. John G Soule

Westborough Health Care Center, 5 Colonial Drive, Westborough, MA 01581; tel. 508/366-9131; Mr. Michael E Isabella

Westford House, 3 Park Drive, Westford, MA 01886; tel. 978/392-1144; Ms. Donna Beck

Willimansett Center West, 546 Chicopee Street, Chicopee, MA 01013; tel. 413/536-2540; Mr. Michael Stroetzel

Willow Manor Genesis ElderCare, 30 Princeton Boulevard, Lowell, MA 01851; tel. 978/454-8086; Ms. Katie Pudil

Willowood of Williamstown, 25 Adams Road, Williamstown, MA 01267; tel. 413/458-2111; Mr. William C Jones

Winchester Nursing Center, Inc, 223 Swanton Street, Winchester, MA 01890; tel. 781/729-9595; Mr. Richard H Salter

Windsor Skilled Nursing and Rehabilitation Center, 265 North Main Street, South Yarmouth, MA 02664; tel. 508/394-3514; Mr. Arthur C Taylor

Wingate at Andover, 80 Andover Street, Andover, MA 01810; tel. 978/470-3434; Ms. Anne L Brennan

Wingate at Brighton, Inc., 100 North Beacon Street, Boston, MA 02134; tel. 617/787-2300; Mr. Andrew Gillis

Wingate at Needham, 589 Highland Avenue, Needham, MA 02492; tel. 781/455-9090; Ms. Denise Riley-Okun

Wingate at Reading, 1364 Main Street, Reading, MA 01867; tel. 781/942-1210; Ms. Anne L Pelrine

Wingate at Sudbury, Inc., 136 Boston Post Road, Sudbury, MA 01776; tel. 617/787-2300; Mr. Andrew Gillis

Wingate at Wilbraham, 9 Maple Street, Wilbraham, MA 01095; tel. 413/596-2411; Ms. Lisa McLaughlin

Winthrop House Senior Care, LLC, 300 Winthrop Street, Medford, MA 02155; tel. 781/396-4400; Mr. David J Friedler

Woburn Nursing Center, 18 Frances Street, Woburn, MA 01801; tel. 781/933-8175; Mrs. Cheryl Evangelista

Woodbriar of Wilmington Rehab and Skilled Nursing Center, 90 West Street, Wilmington, MA 01887; tel. 978/658-2700; Mr. Dennis S Sargent

Worcester Skilled Care Center, 59 Acton Street, Worcester, MA 01604; tel. 508/791-3147; Mr. Joel R Stevens

MICHIGAN

Calhoun County Medical Care Facility, 1150 East Michigan Avenue, Battle Creek, MI 49014; tel. 269/962-5458; Mrs. Donna J Mahoney

Father Murray Nursing Center, 8444 Engleman, Center Line, MI 48015; tel. 586/755-2400; Mr. Michael C Richards

Genesys Convalescent Center - Grand Blanc, Inc., 8481 Holly Road, Grand Blanc, MI 48439; tel. 810/694-1711; Mr. Robert K Stevens

Marlette Community Hospital, PO Box 307, Marlette, MI 48453-0307; tel. 989/635-4000; Mr. David S McEwen

Marwood Nursing and Rehab, 1300 Beard Street, Port Huron, MI 48060; tel. 810/982-8591; Mr. Brian Oberly

Metron of Greenville, 828 East Washington Street, Greenville, MI 48838; tel. 616/754-7186; Mrs. B. J. Hockenberry

Section C

Rivergate Health Care Center, 14041 Pennsylvania Road, Riverview, MI 48192; tel. 734/284–7200; Ms. Elizabeth Edenstrom

Rivergate Terrace, 14141 Pennsylvania Road, Riverview, MI 48192; tel. 734/284–8000; Mr. John Polturanus

Special Tree NeuroCare Center, 39000 Chase Road, Romulus, MI 48174; tel. 734/941–1142; Ms. Cathy A Blevins

St. John Senior Community, 18300 East Warren Avenue, Detroit, MI 48224; tel. 313/343–8000; Ms. Susan M Pierce

MISSISSIPPI

Armed Forces Retirement Home-Gulfport, 1800 Beach Drive, Gulfport, MS 39507-1597; tel. 228/897–4003; Capt Jerald L Ulmer, Sr.

MISSOURI

Bethesda Health Group, Inc, 1630 Des Peres Road, Saint Louis, MO 63131; tel. 314/800–1983; Mr. John W Rowe

Life Care Center of Grandview, 6301 East 125th Street, Grandview, MO 64030; tel. 816/765–7714; Mr. Frank Trimboli

Life Care Center of Saint Louis, 3520 Chouteau Avenue, Saint Louis, MO 63129; tel. 314/771–2100; Mr. Bret Hoffman

ManorCare Health Services, 1200 Graham Road, Florissant, MO 63031; tel. 314/838–6555; Ms. Anita Martinez

St. Sophia Health and Rehabilitation Center, 936 Charbonier Road, Florissant, MO 63031; tel. 314/831–4800; Mr. Dennis G Menos

Village North Health Center, 11160 Village North Drive, Saint Louis, MO 63136; tel. 314/355–8010; Ms. Dianne M Strutynski

Village North Manor, 6768 North Highway 67, Florissant, MO 63034; tel. 314/741–9101; Ms. Tracy Allison

NEBRASKA

Good Samaritan Village, PO Box 2149, Hastings, NE 68902-2149; tel. 402/463–3181; Ms. Kimberly Johansen

Life Care Center of Elkhorn, 315 Hopper Street, Elkhorn, NE 68022; tel. 402/289–2572; Ms. Judy M Sealer

Life Care Center of Omaha, 6032 Ville De Sante Drive, Omaha, NE 68104; tel. 402/571–6770; Ms. Michelle Yosick

NEVADA

Life Care Center of Las Vegas, 6151 Vegas Drive, Las Vegas, NV 89108; tel. 702/648–4900; Mr. Mark C Krueger

Life Care Center of Paradise Valley, 2325 East Harmon Ave, Las Vegas, NV 89119; tel. 702/798–7999; Ms. Jeni Terwilliger

Life Care Center of Reno, 445 West Holcomb Lane, Reno, NV 89511; tel. 775/851–0123; Mr. Daniel A Barber

NEW HAMPSHIRE

Good Shepherd Healthcare Center, 20 Plantation Drive, Jaffrey, NH 03452; tel. 603/532–8762; Mrs. Ann E Nunn

Mount Carmel Healthcare Center, 235 Myrtle Street, Manchester, NH 03104; tel. 603/627–3811; Mr. Ted J Purdy

Saint Ann Healthcare Center, 195 Dover Point Road, Dover, NH 03820; tel. 603/742–2612; Mrs. Karyn J Partin

Saint Teresa Healthcare Center, 519 Bridge Street, Manchester, NH 03104; tel. 603/668–2373; Ms. Monique Dosogne

Saint Vincent de Paul Healthcare Center, 29 Providence Avenue, Berlin, NH 03570; tel. 603/752–1820; Mrs. Louise L Marquis

St. Francis Healthcare Center, 406 Court Street, Laconia, NH 03246; tel. 603/524–0466; Ms. Julieann R Fay

NEW JERSEY

Absecon Manor Nursing and Rehabilitation Center, 1020 Pitney Road, Absecon, NJ 08201; tel. 609/646–5400; Miss Tara Mullineaux

Arnold Walter Nursing Home, 622 S. Laurel Avenue, Hazlet, NJ 07730; tel. 732/787–6300; Mr. Benezion Schachter

Bartley Healthcare Nursing and Rehabilitation, 175 Bartley Road, Jackson, NJ 08527; tel. 732/370–4700; Mr. Philip Scalo

Berkeley Heights Nursing and Rehabilitation Center, 35 Cottage Street, Berkeley Heights, NJ 07922; tel. 908/464–0048; Ms. Joanna T Gorczyca

Bey Lea Village Care Center, 1351 Old Freehold Road, Toms River, NJ 08753-2795; tel. 732/240–0090; Mrs. Brenda Bacon

Brakeley Park Center - Genesis ElderCare Network, 290 Red School Lane, Phillipsburg, NJ 08865; tel. 908/859–2800; Ms. Kathleen M Madden

Cedar Oaks Care Center, 1311 Durham Avenue, South Plainfield, NJ 07080; tel. 732/287–9555; Mr. Morris Wiesel

Chestnut Hill Convalescent and Rehabilitation Center, 360 Chestnut Street, Passaic, NJ 07055; tel. 973/777–7800; Mr. Michael G Mazzola

Clara Maass Continuing Care Center at Belleville, 1 Clara Maass Drive, Belleville, NJ 07109; tel. 973/450–2911; Mr. Carmen Alecci

Clara Maass Continuing Care Center at Kearny, 195 Belgrove Drive, Kearny, NJ 07032; tel. 201/844–4804; Mr. Carmen Alecci

Daughters of Miriam Center, 155 Hazel Street, Clifton, NJ 07015; tel. 973/772–3700; Mr. Frank DaSilva

Delaire Nursing and Convalescent Center, 400 West Stimpson Avenue, Linden, NJ 07036; tel. 908/862–3399; Ms. Barbara F Andrews

Forest Hill Healthcare Center, Inc., 497 Mount Prospect Ave., Newark, NJ 07104; tel. 973/482–5000; Dr. Richard G Stefanacci

Franklin Care Center, 433 Hackensack Avenue, 8th Floor, Hackensack, NJ 07601; tel. 732/489–7400; Adm. Diane B Delaney

Gateway Care Center, LLC, 139 Grant Avenue, Eatontown, NJ 07724; tel. 732/542–4700; Mr. Jonathan Rosenberg

Green Acres Manor, 1931 Lakewood Road, Route 9, Toms River, NJ 08755; tel. 732/286–2323; Mr. Robert Michael Lapid

Hamilton Plaza Nursing and Rehabilitation Center, 56 Hamilton Avenue, Passaic, NJ 07055; tel. 973/773–7070; Mr. Robert Arnold

Healthcare Centers of Wayne, 493 Black Oak Ridge Road, Wayne, NJ 07470; tel. 973/692–9500; Ms. Marta Santiago

Inglemoor Care Center of Livingston, 311 South Livingston Avenue, Livingston, NJ 07039; tel. 973/994–0221; Mr. Steve Izzo

Innova Health and Rehab, 3718 Church Road, Mount Laurel, NJ 08054; tel. 856/235–7100; Ms. Susan Goldberg

Integrated Health Services of New Jersey at Somerset Valley, 1621 Route 22 West, Bound Brook, NJ 08805; tel. 732/469–2000; Ms. Carolyn Allen

JFK Hartwyck at Cedar Brook, 1340 Park Avenue, Plainfield, NJ 07060; tel. 908/754–3100; Ms. Aimee Allen

JFK Hartwyck at Edison Estates, 10 Brunswick Avenue, Edison, NJ 08817; tel. 732/985–1500; Ms. Renee Lake

JFK Hartwyck at Oak Tree Nrsg, Convalescent, & Rehab Center, 2048 Oak Tree Road, Edison, NJ 08820; tel. 732/906–2100; Ms. Dawn A Giakas

Lakeview Subacute Care Center, Inc., 130 Terhune Drive, Wayne, NJ 07470; tel. 973/616–5815; Mr. Richard F Grosso, Jr.

Laurelton Village, 475 Jack Martin Boulevard, Brick, NJ 08724; tel. 732/458–6600; Ms. Diane Dwulet

Lincoln Park Renaissance Rehab and Nursing Center, 521 Pine Brook Road, Lincoln Park, NJ 07035; tel. 973/696–3300; Mrs. Mimi Feliciano

Linwood Care Center, New Road and Central Avenue, Linwood, NJ 08221; tel. 609/927–6131; Mr. Robert K Schneider

Mainland Manor Nursing and Rehabilitation Center, PO Box 1309, Pleasantville, NJ 08232; tel. 609/646–6900; Ms. Linda M Gatier

McCarrick Care Center, 15 Dellwood Lane, Somerset, NJ 08873; tel. 732/545–4200; Mr. James F Caron

Medford Care Center, 185 Tuckerton Road, Medford, NJ 08055; tel. 856/983–8500; Ms. Sandy Lowden

Medicenter/Neptune City, 2050 Sixth Avenue, Neptune, NJ 07753-6197; tel. 732/774–8300; Mrs. Mary Lou Browning

Meridian Nursing and Rehabilitation at Brick, 415 Jack Martin Boulevard, Brick, NJ 08724; tel. 732/206–8001; Mr. Anthony P Adinolfi

Meridian Nursing and Rehabilitation at Red Bank, 55 West Front Street, Red Bank, NJ 07701; tel. 732/842–3800; Ms. Linda B Stevens

Neptune Rehabilitation and Care Center, 101 Walnut Street, Neptune, NJ 07753; tel. 732/774–3550; Mr. Ray Medina

Parkway Manor Health Center, 480 Parkway Drive, East Orange, NJ 07017; tel. 973/674–2700; Mr. Steven Cicchino

Regent Care Center, 50 Polifly Road, Hackensack, NJ 07601; tel. 201/646–1166; Mr. Bruce London

Seacrest Village Nursing and Rehabilitation Center, PO Box 1480, Little Egg Harbor Twp, NJ 08087; tel. 609/296–9292; Mr. Brian T Holloway

South Mountain Healthcare and Rehabilitation Center, 2385 Springfield Avenue, Vauxhall, NJ 07088-1046; tel. 908/688–3400; Mr. Jacob Frommer

The Manor, 689 West Main Street, Freehold, NJ 07728; tel. 732/431–5200; Mr. John Gribbin

The Pope John Paul II Pavilion at Saint Mary's Life Center, 135 South Center Street, Orange, NJ 07050; tel. 973/266–3202; Mr. Jason Hutchens

Twin Bridges at Whiting, 23 Schoolhouse Road, Whiting, NJ 08759; tel. 732/849–4300; Mr. Nochum Feder

Voorhees Pediatric Facility, 1304 Laurel Oak Road, Voorhees, NJ 08043; tel. 856/346–3300; Mr. Scott L Goldberg

Wayne View Care Center, 2020 Route 23 North, Wayne, NJ 07470; tel. 973/305–8400; Mr. Vincent Tufariello

West Caldwell Care Center, 165 Fairfield Avenue, West Caldwell, NJ 07006; tel. 973/226–1100; Mr. Michael P Duffy

Whiting Healthcare Center, 3000 Hilltop Road, Whiting, NJ 08759; tel. 732/849–4400; Mr. Gary Pizzichillo

Willow Creek Rehabilitation and Care Center, 1165 Easton Avenue, Somerset, NJ 08873; tel. 732/246–4100; Ms. Allyson Brown

NEW MEXICO

Life Care Center of Farmington, 1101 West Murray Drive, Farmington, NM 87401; tel. – –; Mr. John Snyder

New Mexico State Veteran's Home, 992 South Broadway, Truth Or Consequences, NM 87901; tel. 505/894–4200; Adm. Lori Montgomery

NEW YORK

Bainbridge Nursing and Rehabilitation Center, 3518 Bainbridge Avenue, Bronx, NY 10467; tel. 718/655–1991; Mr. James K Ryan

Beth Abraham Health Services, 612 Allerton Avenue, Bronx, NY 10467; tel. 718/519–4180; Mr. Michael Fassler

Brooklyn Queens Nursing Home, Inc., 2749 Linden Boulevard, Brooklyn, NY 11208; tel. 718/277–5100; Dr. Anthony A Summers

Carillon Nursing and Rehabilitation Center, 830 Park Avenue, Huntington, NY 11743; tel. 631/271–5800; Mr. Joseph Carillo, Jr.

Casa Promesa, Residential Health Care Facility, Inc., 308 East 175th Street, Bronx, NY 10457; tel. 718/960–7600; Mr. Ruben Medina

Center for Nursing and Rehabilitation, 520 Prospect Place, Brooklyn, NY 11238; tel. 718/636–1000; Ms. Mary Blanchett

Concourse Rehabilitation and Nursing Center, Inc., 1072 Grand Concourse, Bronx, NY 10456; tel. 718/681–4000; Ms. Helen Neiman

Crown Nursing & Rehabilitation Center, 3457 Nostrand Avenue, Brooklyn, NY 11229; tel. 718/615–1100; Mr. David Fielding

Daughters of Jacob Nursing Home, 1160 Teller Avenue, Bronx, NY 10456; tel. 718/293–1500; Mr. Gilbert Preira

DeWitt Rehabilitation and Nursing Center, 211 East 79th Street, New York, NY 10021; tel. 212/879–1600; Mr. Saunders Ted Preiss

Dr. Susan Smith McKinney Nursing/Rehabilitation Center, 594 Albany Avenue, Brooklyn, NY 11203; tel. 718/245–7170; Ms. Ruth R Ogieste

Dumont Masonic Home, 676 Pelham Road, New Rochelle, NY 10805; tel. 914/632–9600; Ms. Patricia Walsh

East Haven Nursing and Rehab Center, 2323 Eastchester Road, Bronx, NY 10469; tel. 718/655–2848; Mr. Joseph Brachfeld

Fort Tryon Center for Rehabilitation & Nursing, 801 West 190th Street, New York, NY 10040; tel. 212/544–6400; Mr. Benjamin Philipson

Four Seasons Nursing and Rehabilitation Center, 1555 Rockaway Parkway, Brooklyn, NY 11236; tel. 718/927–6300; Mr. Barry Friedman

Franklin Center for Rehabilitation and Nursing, 142-27 Franklin Avenue, Flushing, NY 11355; tel. 718/670–3416; Mr. Israel Sherman

Golden Gate Rehabilitation and Health Care Center, LLC., 191 Bradley Avenue, Staten Island, NY 10314; tel. 718/698–8800; Mr. Philip Buchsbaum

Gouverneur Nursing Facility, 227 Madison Street, New York, NY 10002; tel. 212/238–7800; Mr. Mendel Hagler, Esq.

Grace Plaza Nursing and Rehabilitation Center, 15 St. Paul's Place, Great Neck, NY 11021; tel. 516/466–3001; Ms. Martha Sweet

Grandell Rehabilitation and Nursing Center, Inc., 645 West Broadway, Long Beach, NY 11561-2902; tel. 516/889–1100; Mr. Marty H Dicker

Greater Harlem Nursing Home, 30 West 138th Street, New York, NY 10037; tel. 212/690–7400; Ms. Reita Fuller

Gurwin Jewish Geriatric Center, 68 Hauppauge Road, Commack, NY 11725; tel. 631/715–2600; Mr. Herbert H Friedman

Helen and Michael Schaffer Extended Care Center, 16 Guion Place, New Rochelle, NY 10802; tel. 914/632–5000; Mr. John R Spicer

Holliswood Care Center, 195-44 Woodhull Avenue, Hollis, NY 11423; tel. 718/740–3500; Mrs. Veena Ahuja

Isabella Geriatric Center, 515 Audubon Avenue, New York, NY 10040; tel. 212/342–9300; Mr. Mark Kator

Kateri Residence, 150 Riverside Drive, New York, NY 10024; tel. 646/505–3500; Mr. Lascelles L Bond

Laconia Nursing Home, Inc., 1050 East 230th Street, Bronx, NY 10466; tel. 718/654–5875; Mr. Barry Braunstein

M.J.G. Nursing Home Company, Inc., 4915 Tenth Avenue, Brooklyn, NY 11219; tel. 718/851–3700; Mr. Eli S Feldman

Manhattanville Health Care Center, LLC, 311 West 231st Street, Bronx, NY 10463; tel. 914/601–8400; Mr. Leonard J Wiener

Maplewood Nursing Home, Inc., 100 Daniel Drive, Webster, NY 14580; tel. 716/872–1800; Mr. Gregory J Chambery

Margaret Tietz Nursing and Rehabilitation Center, 164-11 Chapin Parkway, Jamaica, NY 11432; tel. 718/298–7800; Mr. Kenneth M Brown

Marquis Care Center, 2 Medical Plaza, Glen Cove, NY 11542; tel. 516/671–0858; Ms. Helen M Lantry

Menorah Home and Hospital for the Aged and Infirm, Inc., 1516 Oriental Boulevard, Brooklyn, NY 11235; tel. 718/646–4441; Ms. Jane Rosenthal

Morningside House Nursing Home Company, Inc., 1000 Pelham Parkway South, Bronx, NY 10461; tel. 718/409–8200; Dr. William T Smith

Morris Park Nursing Home, 1235 Pelham Parkway North, Bronx, NY 10469; tel. 718/231–4300; Mr. Morris Berkowitz

Mosholu Parkway Nursing and Rehabilitation Center, 3356 Perry Avenue, Bronx, NY 10467; tel. 718/655–3568; Mr. Isaac Shapiro

Nassau Extended Care Center, 377 Oak Street, Garden City, NY 11530; tel. 516/565–4800; Mr. Kurt Mohr

No Shore Univ Hosp Center for Extended Care & Rehabilitation, 330 Community Drive, Manhasset, NY 11030; tel. 516/562–8070; Mr. Michael Dowling

Northern Manhattan Rehabilitation & Nursing Cntr, 116 East 125th Street, New York, NY 10035; tel. 212/426–1284; Ms. Verna Fitzpatrick

Northwoods Rehabilitation and Extended Care Facility, PO Box 5510, Cortland, NY 13045-5510; tel. 607/753–9631; Mrs. Dorothy C Zegarelli

Northwoods Rehabilitation and Extended Care Facility, 284 Troy Road, Rensselaer, NY 12144-9474; tel. 518/286–1621; Ms. Nancy Emerick

Northwoods Rehabilitation and Extended Care Facility at Troy, 100 New Turnpike Road, Troy, NY 12182; tel. 518/235–1410; Mr. Raymond Klocek

Northwoods Rehabilitation and Extended Care Facility-Hilltop, 1805 Providence Avenue, Niskayuna, NY 12309; tel. 518/374–2212; Mr. Jeff Ruso

Oceanview Nursing Home, 315 Beach 9th Street, Far Rockaway, NY 11691; tel. 718/471–6000; Mr. Louis Wolcowitz

Orzac Center for Extended Care and Rehabilitation, 900 Franklin Ave, Valley Stream, NY 11580; tel. 516/256–6502; Mr. Eric Yalowitz

Our Lady of Consolation Nursing & Rehabilitative Care Center, 111 Beach Drive, West Islip, NY 11795; tel. 631/587–1600; Mr. Dennis J Verzi

Parker Jewish Institute for Health Care and Rehabilitation, 271-11 76th Avenue, New Hyde Park, NY 11040-1433; tel. 718/289–2108; Mr. Michael N Rosenblut

Providence Rest, 3304 Waterbury Avenue, Bronx, NY 10465; tel. 718/931–3000; Sister Seline Mary Flores

Queens Boulevard Extended Care Facility, 61-11 Queens Boulevard, Woodside, NY 11377; tel. 718/205–0288; Mr. Michael Tartaglia

Ramapo Manor Nursing Center, Inc., PO Box 248, Suffern, NY 10901-0248; tel. 845/357–1230; Ms. Marsha Z Squires

Rego Park Health Care Facility, 111-26 Corona Avenue, Flushing, NY 11368; tel. 718/592–6400; Mr. Nelson Tuchman

Rehab Institute of NY at Florence Nightingale Health Center, 1760 3rd Avenue, New York, NY 10029; tel. 212/410–8760; Mr. William Pascocello

Riverdale Nursing Home, Inc., 641 West 230th Street, Bronx, NY 10463; tel. 718/796–4800; Mr. Eric Paneth

Ross Health Care Center, 839 Suffolk Avenue, Brentwood, NY 11717; tel. 631/273–4700; Ms. Suzy Douyon

Sands Point Center for Health and Rehabilitation, 1440 Port Washington Boulevard, Port Washington, NY 11050; tel. 516/719–9400; Mr. David Moskowitz

Sarah Neuman Center for Healthcare and Rehabilitation, 845 Palmer Avenue, Mamaroneck, NY 10543; tel. 914/777–6100; Ms. Rita Morgan

Schnurmacher Center for Rehabilitation and Nursing, 12 Tibbits Avenue, White Plains, NY 10606; tel. 914/287–7200; Mr. Michael Fassler

Sea View Hospital Rehabilitation Center and Home, 460 Brielle Avenue, Staten Island, NY 10314; tel. 718/317–3000; Mr. Thomas W Matteo

Shore View Nursing Home, 2865 Brighton 3rd Street, Brooklyn, NY 11235; tel. 718/891–4400; Mr. Howard M Small

Shorefront Jewish Geriatric Center, 3015 West 29th Street, Brooklyn, NY 11224; tel. 718/266–5700; Mr. Eli S Feldman

St. Ann's Community, 1500 Portland Avenue, Rochester, NY 14621; tel. 585/697–6457; Ms. Elizabeth (Betty) Mullin-Diprosa

St. James Healthcare Center, 275 Moriches Road, St James, NY 11780; tel. 631/862–8000; Mr. William J St. George

St. Johnland Nursing Center, Inc., 395 Sunken Meadow Road, Kings Park, NY 11754; tel. 631/269–5800; Ms. Mary Jean Weber

The Guild Home for Aged Blind, 75 Stratton Street South, Yonkers, NY 10701; tel. 914/220–8504; Dr. Alan R Morse

The Jewish Home and Hospital - Bronx Division, 100 West Kingsbridge Road, Bronx, NY 10468; tel. 718/410–1500; Mr. Kenneth J Sherman

The Jewish Home and Hospital Lifecare System, 120 West 106 Street, New York, NY 10025; tel. 212/870–4901; Ms. Audrey Weiner

The Silvercrest Center for Nursing and Rehabilitation, 144-45 87th Avenue, Briarwood, NY 11435; tel. 718/480–4026; Mr. Cosmo J LaCosta

The Wayne Center for Nursing & Rehabilitation, 3530 Wayne Avenue, Bronx, NY 10467; tel. 718/655–1700; Mr. Jospeh Brachfeld

United Hebrew Geriatric Center, 60 Willow Drive, New Rochelle, NY 10805; tel. 914/632–2804; Ms. Rita C Mabli

Waterview Nursing Care Center, 119-15 27th Avenue, Flushing, NY 11354; tel. 718/461–5000; Mr. Larry I Slatky

Wingate at Dutchess, Inc., 3 Summit Court, Fishkill, NY 12524; tel. 845/896–1500; Mr. Clayton Harbby

Wingate at Saint Francis, L.L.C., 10 Hastings Drive, Beacon, NY 12508; tel. 845/440–1600; Mr. Joseph Murabito

Wingate at Ulster, One Wingate Way, Highland, NY 12528; tel. 845/691–6800; Mr. Steven Tyer

NORTH CAROLINA

Beverly Enterprises-North Carolina,Inc, 1000 Western Blvd., Tarboro, NC 27886; tel. 252/823–0401; Mrs. Effie E Webb

Cleveland Pines Nursing Center, 1404 North LaFayette Street, Shelby, NC 28150; tel. 704/480–0128; Ms. Angela Orsky

Life Care Center of Hendersonville, 400 Thompson Street, Hendersonville, NC 28792; tel. – –; Mr. Ray Kelley

Mariner Health of Wilmington, 820 Wellington Avenue, Wilmington, NC 28401; tel. 910/343–0425; Mr. John W Strawcutter

North Carolina Special Care Center, 4761 Ward Boulevard, Wilson, NC 27893-4359; tel. 252/399–2112; Mr. William R Benton, Jr.

Priva-Trends of North Carolina, Inc., 214 Cochran Avenue, Fayetteville, NC 28301; tel. 910/482–4131; Mr. Neil L Pruitt, Jr.

OHIO

Altercare of Alliance, 11750 Klinger Avenue Northeast, Alliance, OH 44601; tel. 330/823–8263; Mr. David Burnham

Altercare of Navarre Center for Rehabilitation & Nursing Care, 517 Park Street, Navarre, OH 44662; tel. 330/879–2765; Ms. Sue Doherty

Arbors at Dayton, 320 Albany Street, Dayton, OH 45408; tel. 937/496–6200; Ms. Sophia Gordon

Arbors at Hilliard, 5471 Scioto Darby Road, Hilliard, OH 43026; tel. 614/876–7356; Mrs. Lura B Sandy

Arbors at Milford, 5900 Meadowcreek Drive, Milford, OH 45150; tel. 513/248–1655; Miss Jennifer D Fehn

Arbors at Oregon, 904 Isaac Streets Drive, Oregon, OH 43616; tel. 419/691–2483; Mel Rhinelander

Arbors East Skilled and Rehabilitation Center, 5500 East Broad Street, Columbus, OH 43213; tel. 614/575–9003; Mr. Jim Wilson

Arlington Court Nursing and Rehabilitation Center, 1605 NW Professional Plaza, Columbus, OH 43220; tel. 614/451–5677; Mr. Doug Speelman

Aurora Manor Special Care Centre, 101 Bissell Road, Aurora, OH 44202; tel. 330/562–5000; Ms. Christa L Mayes

AustinWoods Nursing Center, Inc., 4780 Kirk Road, Austintown, OH 44515; tel. 330/792–7681; Ms. Sally Demidovich

Bellbrook Rehab & Healthcare Center, 1957 North Lakeman Drive, Bellbrook, OH 45305; tel. 937/848–7800; Ms. Melissa S Bennett

Broadview Health Care Center, Inc., 5151 North Hamilton Road, Columbus, OH 43230; tel. 614/337–1066; Ms. Kelly Whitehead

Broadview Multi-Care Center, 5520 Broadview Road, Parma, OH 44134; tel. 216/749–4010; Mr. Harold Shachter

Carriage Inn of Steubenville, 3102 St. Charles Drive, Steubenville, OH 43952; tel. 740/264–7161; Mr. Bradley J Conto

Chapel Hill Community, 12200 Strausser Road, Canal Fulton, OH 44614; tel. 330/854–4177; Ms. Dianna Krumpak

Christel Manor of Miamisburg, 1120 South Dunaway, Miamisburg, OH 45342; tel. 937/866–9089; Mr. Richard Porter

Columbus Rehabilitation and Subacute Institute, 44 Souder Avenue, Columbus, OH 43222; tel. 614/228–5900; Mr. Blu Johnson

Community Healthcare Center, 175 Community Drive, Marion, OH 43302; tel. 740/387–7537; Ms. Kelly A Welsh

Copley Health Center, 155 Heritage Woods Drive, Akron, OH 44321-1398; tel. 330/666–0980; Mrs. Alicia T Holland

Crestview Health Care Center, 68637 Bannock Road, St Clairsville, OH 43950; tel. 740/695–2500; Mr. Stacey Howell

Cuyahoga Falls Country Place, 2728 Bailey Road, Cuyahoga Falls, OH 44221; tel. 330/929–4231; Mr. Scott Bower

DaySpring Health Care Center and Rehabilitation, 8001 Dayton-Springfield Road, Fairborn, OH 45324; tel. 937/864–5800; Mr. Barry N Bortz

Deupree Health Center, 3939 Erie Avenue, Cincinnati, OH 45208; tel. 513/561–6363; Mr. R. Douglas Spitler

Eastgate Health Care Center and Rehabilitation, 4400 Gleneste Withamsville Rd, Cincinnati, OH 45245; tel. 513/947–3710; Mr. Barry N Bortz

Extendicare Health Services Inc., 375 West Main Street, West Jefferson, OH 43162; tel. 614/879–7661; Mr. Scott E Van De Water

Fairhaven Community, 850 Marseilles Street, Upper Sandusky, OH 43351; tel. 419/294–4973; Mr. Dan Miller

Franklin Plaza, 3600 Franklin Blvd, Cleveland, OH 44113; tel. 216/651–1600; Mr. Bruce Daskal

Friendship Village of Columbus, 5800 Forest Hills Boulvard, Columbus, OH 43231; tel. 614/890–8287; Ms. Gretchen L Vakiener

Harborside Healthcare - Broadview Heights, 2801 East Royalton Road, Broadview Heights, OH 44147; tel. 440/526–4770; Mr. Joe A Garrett

Harborside Healthcare - Defiance, 395 Harding Street, Defiance, OH 43512; tel. 419/784–1450; Ms. Tara L Sibert

Harborside Healthcare - Northwestern Ohio, 1104 Wesley Avenue, Bryan, OH 43506; tel. 419/636–5071; Ms. Katherine Hitchcock

Harborside Healthcare - Perrysburg, 28546 Starbright Boulevard, Perrysburg, OH 43551; tel. 419/666–0935; Ms. Kandace Potts

Harborside Healthcare - Swanton, 401 West Airport Highway, Swanton, OH 43558; tel. 419/825–1111; Ms. Mary McConnell

Heartland of Beavercreek, 1974 North Fairfield Road, Dayton, OH 45432; tel. 937/429–1106; Mr. Troy Hutchison

Heartland of Centerburg, PO Box 720, Centerburg, OH 43011; tel. 740/625–5774; Ms. Amber Downey

Heartland of Centerville, 1001 East Alexander Bell Road, Centerville, OH 45459; tel. 937/436–9700; Mr. Jon Rarick

Heartland of Kettering, 3313 Wilmington Pike, Kettering, OH 45429; tel. 937/298–8084; Mrs. Jennifer Woodward

Heartland of Marysville, 755 South Plum Street, Marysville, OH 43040; tel. 937/644–8836; Mr. Charles T George

Heartland of Miamisburg, 450 Oak Ridge Boulevard, Miamisburg, OH 45342; tel. 937/866–8885; Mr. Lee Elliott

Heartland of Piqua, 275 Kienle Drive, Piqua, OH 45356; tel. 937/773–9346; Mr. Darrell Woods

Heartland of Springfield, 2615 Derr Road, Springfield, OH 45503; tel. 937/390–0005; Mr. Mike Lacey

Hickory Creek of Athens, 51 East 4th Street, The Plains, OH 45780; tel. 740/797–4561; Ms. Caroline Z Gibson

Hospitality Homes, 1301 North Monroe Drive, Xenia, OH 45385; tel. 937/372–8081; Adm. John P Flanagan

IHS of West Carrollton at Elm Creek, 115 Elmwood Circle, West Carrollton, OH 45449; tel. 937/866–3814; Ms. Patricia A Walter

Indian Hills Health and Rehabilitation Center, 1500 East 191st Street, Euclid, OH 44117; tel. 216/486–8880; Ms. Yuvette M Bozman

Integrated Health Services of Huber Heights at Spring Creek, 5440 Charlesgate Road, Huber, OH 45424; tel. 937/236–6707; Ms. Karma L Winburn

Kethley House at Benjamin Rose Place, 11900 Fairhill Road, Cleveland, OH 44120; tel. 216/795–5450; Dr. Alice J Kethley

Kingston of Ashland, Post Office Box 347, Ashland, OH 44805; tel. 419/289–3859; Mr. Timothy K Callahan

Kingston of Vermilion, 4210 Telegraph Lane, Vermilion, OH 44089; tel. 440/967–1800; Mrs. Heather Shirley

Life Care Center of Elyria, 1212 South Abbe Road, Elyria, OH 44035; tel. 440/365–5200; Mr. Douglas R McDermott

Life Care Center of Medina, 2400 Columbia Road, Medina, OH 44256; tel. 330/483–3131; Mr. James Eberly

Lincoln Park Manor, 694 Isaac Prugh Way, Kettering, OH 45429; tel. 937/297–4300; Mr. Russell M Holtz

Lutheran Social Services of Mid-America, 6451 Far Hills Avenue, Dayton, OH 45459; tel. 937/433–2110; Mr. Willis O Serrll

Madeira Health Care, Inc., 6940 Steigler Lane, Cincinnati, OH 45243; tel. 513/561–6400; Ms. Carol Bottonari

Magnolia Care and Rehabilitation Center, 365 Johnson Road, Wadsworth, OH 44281; tel. 330/335–1558; Mr. Rick Mitchell

Manor Care Health Services-North Olmsted, 23225 Lorain Road, North Olmsted, OH 44070; tel. 440/779–6900; Mr. Stephen J Wolf

ManorCare Health Services - Willoughby, 37603 Euclid Avenue, Willoughby, OH 44094; tel. 440/951–5551; Mrs. Marie Thur

ManorCare Health Services of Akron, 1211 West Market Street, Akron, OH 44313; tel. 330/867–8530; Ms. Carla D'Antonio

Marjorie P. Lee Care Center, 3550 Shaw Avenue, Cincinnati, OH 45208; tel. 513/871–2090; Mr. R. Douglas Spitler

Mayfair Village Nursing Care Center, 3000 Bethel Road, Columbus, OH 43220; tel. 614/889–6320; Ms. Julie M Klein

Menorah Park Center for Senior Living, 27100 Cedar Road, Beachwood, OH 44122; tel. 216/831–6500; Mr. Steven Raichilson

Newark Healthcare Centre, 75 McMillen Drive, Newark, OH 43055; tel. 740/344–0357; Mr. Brian E Newman

Ohio Valley Manor Nursing and Rehabilitation Center, 5280 Routes 62 and 68, Ripley, OH 45167; tel. 937/392–4318; Mr. George W Balz

Olmsted Manor Nursing Center, 27500 Mill Road, North Olmsted, OH 44070; tel. 440/777–8444; Mr. James M Eberly

Parkvue Health Care Center, 3800 Boardwalk Boulevard, Sandusky, OH 44870; tel. 419/621–1900; Mr. Kenneth Keller

Pleasant Lake Villa, 7260 Ridge Road, Parma, OH 44129; tel. 440/842–2273; Ms. Sherrie Klein

Ridgewood Manor, 3231 Manley Road, Maumee, OH 43537; tel. 419/865–1248; Mr. Martin Jan

Riverview Community, 5999 Bender Road, Cincinnati, OH 45233; tel. 513/922–1440; Mrs. Leigh Deaton

SEM Haven Health and Residential Care Center, 225 Cleveland Avenue, Milford, OH 45150; tel. 513/248–1270; Ms. Barbara Wolf

Southern Hills Health and Rehabilitation Center, 19530 Bagley Road, Middleburg Heights, OH 44130; tel. 216/816–7500; Ms. Rosalyn Semelsberger

St. Augustine Manor, Inc., 7801 Detroit Avenue, Cleveland, OH 44102-2895; tel. 216/634–7400; Mr. K. Patrick Gareau

St. Leonard, 8100 Clyo Road, Centerville, OH 45458; tel. 937/439–7119; Mr. Timothy C Dressman

Sunrise Pointe Care and Rehabilitation Center, 19900 Clare Avenue, Maple Heights, OH 44137; tel. 216/662–3343; Mr. Motti Schonfeld

Sycamore Glen Health Center, 2175 Leiter Road, Miamisburg, OH 45342; tel. 937/384–4300; Mr. Ken Crawford

The Gables at Green Pastures, 390 Gables Drive, Marysville, OH 43040; tel. 937/642–3893; Adm. Shannon M Kellogg

The Maria-Joseph Center, 4830 Salem Avenue, Dayton, OH 45416-1798; tel. 937/278–2692; Ms. Bonnie G Langdon

The Oakridge Home, 26520 Center Ridge Road, Westlake, OH 44145; tel. 440/871–3030; Ms. Maryann Dubyoski

The Village of Westerville Nursing Center, 1060 Eastwind Drive, Westerville, OH 43081; tel. 614/895–1038; Ms. Tara Guggenbiller

Three Rivers Nursing and Rehabilitation, 7800 Jandaracres Drive, Cincinnati, OH 45248; tel. 513/941–0787; Carol Bottonari

Toledo Health Investors, 2005 Ashland Avenue, Toledo, OH 43620; tel. 419/255–3040; Mrs. Kim Dunlap

Trinity Community of Beavercreek, 3218 Indian Ripple Road, Dayton, OH 45440; tel. 937/426–8481; Ms. Laura M Farrell

Villa Angela Care Center, 5700 Karl Road, Columbus, OH 43229; tel. 614/846–5420; Mr. James A Griffiths

Wickliffe Country Place, 1919 Bishop Road, Wickliffe, OH 44092; tel. 440/944–9400; Mr. Mark Yantek

OKLAHOMA

Saint Simeon's Episcopal Home, Inc., 3701 North Cincinnati Ave., Tulsa, OK 74106-1599; tel. 918/425–3583; Mrs. Marian P Matthews

PENNSYLVANIA

Attleboro Nursing and Rehabilitation Center, 300 East Winchester Avenue, Langhorne, PA 19047; tel. 215/752–3739; Ms. Terry L Hogan

Baldwin Health Center, 1717 Skyline Drive, Pittsburgh, PA 15227; tel. 412/885–8400; Ms. Peggy Means

Barclay Friends, 700 North Franklin Street, West Chester, PA 19380; tel. 610/696–5211; Ms. J Carol Hanson

Broomall Presbyterian Village, 146 Marple Road, Broomall, PA 19008-2099; tel. 610/356–0100; Ms. Rosemary Kuhlman

Broomall Rehabilitation & Nursing Center, 50 North Malin Road, Broomall, PA 19008; tel. 610/356–0800; Ms. Susan Eccles

Ephrata Manor, 99 Bethany Road, Ephrata, PA 17522; tel. 717/738–4940; Mr. John F Esbenshade

Evangelical Manor, 8401 Roosevelt Boulevard, Philadelphia, PA 19152; tel. 215/624–5800; Mr. Allen Holsopple

Fellowship Community, 3000 Fellowship Drive, Whitehall, PA 18052; tel. 610/799–3000; Mr. Robert Zentz

Fox Subacute at Clara Burke, 251 Stenton Avenue, Plymouth Meeting, PA 19462; tel. 610/828–2272; Mr. James M Foulke

Fox Subacute Center, 2644 Bristol Road, Warrington, PA 18976; tel. 215/343–2700; Mr. James Foulke

Good Samaritan Nursing Care Center, 1017 Franklin Street, Johnstown, PA 15905; tel. 814/533–1934; Mr. Patrick J McFeeley, Sr.

Greenery Specialty Care Center of Canonsburg, 2200 Hill Church-Houston Road, Canonsburg, PA 15317; tel. 724/745–8000; Adm. Robert P Bagdon

HCR - ManorCare at Mercy Fitzgerald, 600 South Wycombe Avenue, Yeadon, PA 19050; tel. 610/626–8065; Ms. Annette Vecchiarille

Hickory House Nursing Home, 3120 Horseshoe Pike, Honey Brook, PA 19344; tel. 610/273–2915; Ms. Mary E Magner

Holland-Glen, 412 South York Road, Hatboro, PA 19040; tel. 215/441–1178; Mr. William Schlacter

Jefferson Manor Health Center, Route 28 RR5 Box42, Brookville, PA 15825; tel. 814/849–0601; Ms. Karen Wilshire

LifeQuest Nursing Center, 2450 John Fries Highway, Quakertown, PA 18951; tel. 215/536–0770; Mr. Roger B Hiser

Normandie Ridge, 1700 Normandie Drive, York, PA 17404; tel. 717/764–6262; Ms. Carol McKinley

Pembrooke Health and Rehabilitation Residence, 1130 West Chester Pike, West Chester, PA 19382; tel. 610/692–3636; Ms. Margaret Brockett

Philadelphia Nursing Home, 2100 W. Girard Avenue, Philadelphia, PA 19130; tel. 215/685–0800; Mrs. Mary K Hess

Philadelphia Protestant Home, 6500 Tabor Road, Philadelphia, PA 19111; tel. 215/697–8006; Mr. Anthony Manzo

Presbyterian Medical Center of Oakmont, Inc., 1215 Hulton Road, Oakmont, PA 15139; tel. 412/828–5600; Mr. Paul M Winkler

Quarryville Presbyterian Retirement Community, 625 Robert Fulton Highway, Quarryville, PA 17566; tel. 717/786–7321; Mr. Bruce Hartshorne

River's Edge Nursing and Rehabilitation Center, 9501 State Road, Philadelphia, PA 19114; tel. 215/632–5700; Ms. Roseann Marsicano

Rockhill Mennonite Community, 3250 State Road, Sellersville, PA 18960; tel. 215/257–2751; Mr. Ron Sawatsky

Saint John Neumann Nursing Home, 10400 Roosevelt Boulevard, Philadelphia, PA 19116; tel. 215/698–5600; Ms. Michelle Bieszczad

Saint Martha Manor, 470 Manor Avenue, Downingtown, PA 19335; tel. 610/873–8490; Ms. Maureen Reisinger

Saint Mary Manor, 701 Lansdale Avenue, Lansdale, PA 19446-2994; tel. 215/368–0900; Mr. John T Chapman

Sarah A. Todd Memorial Home, 1000 West South Street, Carlisle, PA 17013; tel. 717/245–2187; Ms. Mary Jane Walker

South Mountain Restoration Center, 10058 South Mountain Road, South Mountain, PA 17261-0999; tel. 717/749–3121; Mr. Thomas J White

St. Paul Homes, 339 East Jamestown Road, Greenville, PA 16125; tel. 724/588–7610; Mr. G. Bryan Oros

Statesman Health and Rehabilitation Center, 2629 Trenton Road, Levittown, PA 19056; tel. 215/943–7777; Ms. Patricia Keyes

Sterling Healthcare and Rehabilitation Center, 318 South Orange Street, Media, PA 19063; tel. 610/566–1400; Mr. Geoffrey Henry

Suburban Woods Health and Rehabilitation Center, 2751 DeKalb Pike, Norristown, PA 19401; tel. 610/278–2700; Mrs. Diane Orzechowski

The Commons At Squirrel Hill, 2025 Wightman Street, Pittsburgh, PA 15217; tel. 412/421–8443; Mr. Bernard E Erb

The United Church of Christ Homes, 550 East Main Street, Annville, PA 17003; tel. 717/867–4467; Mr. Steven Horvath

Thornwald Home, 442 Walnut Bottom Road, Carlisle, PA 17013-3799; tel. 717/249–4118; Ms. Gail K Potter

RHODE ISLAND

Briarcliffe Manor Nursing Home, 49 Old Pocasset Road, Johnston, RI 02919; tel. 401/944–2450; Mr. Ray Tetreault

Cedar Crest Sub Acute & Rehabilitation Centre, 125 Scituate Avenue, Cranston, RI 02921; tel. 401/944–8500; Ms. Susan K Whipple

Cherry Hill Manor, 2 Cherry Hill Road, Johnston, RI 02919; tel. 401/231–3102; Mr. Steven Haase

Elmhurst Extended Care Facility, 50 Maude Street, Providence, RI 02908; tel. 401/456–2600; Mr. Richard E Gamache

EPOCH SL 1, Inc/EPOCH Senior Healthcare on Blackstone Blvd, 353 Blackstone Boulevard, Providence, RI 02906; tel. 401/273–6565; Mr. Gerry Paulhus

Evergreen House Health Center, One Evergreen Drive, East Providence, RI 02914; tel. 401/438–3250; Ms. Deborah Ready

Forest Farm Health Care Centre, 193 Forest Avenue, Middletown, RI 02842; tel. 401/847–2777; Mr. Karl H LyonJr.

Golden Crest Nursing Centre, 100 Smithfield Road, North Providence, RI 02904; tel. 401/353–1710; Mr. Paul Pezzelli

Heatherwood Nursing and Subacute Center, Inc, 398 Bellevue Ave, Newport, RI 02840; tel. 401/849–6600; Mr. Travis J Blaser

Kent Regency Genesis Elder Care, 660 Commonwealth Avenue, Warwick, RI 02886; tel. 401/739–4241; Mr. Mark A Wozniak

Oakland Grove Health Care Center, 560 Cumberland Hill Road, Woonsocket, RI 02895; tel. 401/769–0800; Mr. Antonio C Sousa

Ryan Health Center, Inc., 80 Morgan Avenue, Johnston, RI 02919; tel. 401/944–7800; Mr. David Ryan

South County Nursing and Subacute Center, 740 Oak Hill Road, North Kingstown, RI 02852; tel. 401/294–4545; Mr. Donald E Woods

The Clipper Home, Inc., 161 Post Road, Westerly, RI 02891; tel. 401/322–8081; Mr. Brian J Foley

Westerly Health Center, 280 High Street, Westerly, RI 02891; tel. 401/348–0020; Mrs. Melissa M Prevey

Woonsocket Health and Rehabilitation Center, 262 Poplar Street, Woonsocket, RI 02895; tel. 401/765–2100; Ms. Norma M Pezzelli

SOUTH CAROLINA

C. M. Tucker, Jr. Nursing Care Center, 2200 Harden Street, Columbia, SC 29203; tel. 803/737–5301; Ms. Laura W Hughes

Life Care Center of Charleston, 2600 Elms Plantation Boulevard, N Charleston, SC 29406; tel. 843/764–3500; Ms. Beth A Cliett

Life Care Center of Columbia, 2514 Faraway Drive, Columbia, SC 29223; tel. 803/865–1999; Ms. Carol D Cordan

TENNESSEE

Allen Morgan Health Center, 177 North Highland, Memphis, TN 38111; tel. 901/325–4003; Mr. John Webb

Colonial Hills Nursing Center, 2034 Cochran Road, Maryville, TN 37803; tel. 865/982–6161; Ms. Mary Pfeifer

Life Care Center of Chattanooga, 455 N. Highland Park Ave, Chattanooga, TN 37404; tel. 423/698–5494; Mrs. Lauren T McCann

Life Care Center of Elizabethton, 1641 Hwy 19E Bypass, Elizabethton, TN 37643; tel. 423/542–4133; Mr. Chuck Arnold

Life Care Center of Athens, PO Box 786, Athens, TN 37371-0786; tel. 423/754–8181; Ms. Amy McCowan

Life Care Center of Bruceton, PO Box 137, Bruceton, TN 38317; tel. 731/586–2061; Mr. Walter E Weingarten

Life Care Center of Centerville, 112 Old Dickson Road, Centerville, TN 37033; tel. 931/729–4236; Mr. Chris Matchim

Life Care Center of Collegedale, PO Box 658, Collegedale, TN 37315; tel. 423/396–2182; Ms. Carla K Trotter

Life Care Center of Columbia, 841 W. James Campbell Blvd., Columbia, TN 38401; tel. 931/388–5035; Mr. Michael W Cunningham

Life Care Center of Copper Basin, PO Box 518, Ducktown, TN 37326-0518; tel. 423/496–3245; Mr. Doyle Love

Life Care Center of East Ridge, 1500 Fincher Avenue, East Ridge, TN 37412; tel. 423/894–1254; Mr. Trevor S Matchim

Life Care Center of Jefferson City, 336 W Old Andrew Johnson Hwy, Jefferson City, TN 37760; tel. 865/475–6097; Mrs. Laurah M Branam

Life Care Center of Missionary Ridge, 708 Dwight Ave, Chattanooga, TN 37406; tel. 423/622–4301; Ms. Tommie S Birchett

Life Care Center of Morgan County, 419 South Kingston Street, Wartburg, TN 37887; tel. 423/346–6691; Mr. Jeffery Beaty

Life Care Center of Morristown, PO Box 1899, Morristown, TN 37814; tel. 423/581–5435; Mr. Marvin Frey

Life Care Center of Red Bank, 1020 Runyan Drive, Chattanooga, TN 37405; tel. 423/473–5553; Mr. Guy Crosson

Life Care Center of Sparta, 508 Mose Drive, Sparta, TN 38583; tel. 931/738–9430; Mrs. Suzanne M Brown

Life Care Center of Tullahoma, 1715 No. Jackson Street, Tullahoma, TN 37388; tel. 931/455–8557; Ms. Dawn R Rowe

Lynchburg Nursing Center, 40 Nursing Home Road, Lynchburg, TN 37352; tel. 931/759–6000; Ms. Jane Roberts

McKendree Village, Inc., 4343-47 Lebanon Road, Hermitage, TN 37076; tel. 615/871–8232; Ms. Mary Anna Womeldorf

Ridgeview Terrace of Life Care, PO Box 26, Rutledge, TN 37861; tel. 865/828–5295; Ms. Karen L Bourgeois

The Heritage Center, 1026 McFarland Street, Morristown, TN 37814; tel. 423/581–5100; Ms. Wilda T Scates

TEXAS

Alameda Oaks Nursing Center, 1101 South Alameda, Corpus Christi, TX 78404; tel. 361/882–2711; Mr. James Hardee

Bivins Memorial, 1001 Wallace Boulevard, Amarillo, TX 79106-1736; tel. 806/355–7453; Mr. Tyler S Kendall

Elizabeth Jane Bivins Home for the Aged, 3115 Tee Anchor Boulevard, Amarillo, TX 79104; tel. 806/373–7671; Mr. Steven M Schmidt

Fort Worth Nursing and Rehabilitation Center, 1000 6th Avenue, Fort Worth, TX 76104; tel. 817/336–2586; Mr. Mack Baldridge

Garden Terrace Alzheimer's Center of Excellence, 7500 Oakmont Boulevard, Fort Worth, TX 76132; tel. 817/346–8080; Mr. David McClure

Garden Terrace Alzheimer's Center of Excellence, 7887 Cambridge Street, Houston, TX 77054; tel. 713/796–2777; Ms. Carol C Pritchett

Life Care Center of Plano, 3800 West Park Boulevard, Plano, TX 75075; tel. 972/612–1700; Ms. Becky Stocker

Mariner Health of Fort Worth, 4825 Wellesley Avenue, Fort Worth, TX 76107; tel. 817/732–6608; Mr. Joseph Vernon

Memorial Medical Nursing Center, 307 West Cypress, San Antonio, TX 78212; tel. 210/223–5521; Mr. James Knight

North Texas VA Health Care System, 4500 South Lancaster Road, Dallas, TX 75216; tel. 202/273–8334; Ms. Betty B Brown

Renaissance Park Multi-Care Center, 4252 Bryant Irvin Road, Fort Worth, TX 76109; tel. 817/738–2975; Mr. Tim O'Sullivan

Silver Creek Manor, 9014 Timber Path, San Antonio, TX 78250; tel. 210/523–2455; Adm. Jeanine Medley

The Vosswood Nursing Center, 815 South Voss Road, Houston, TX 77057; tel. 713/827–0883; Mr. John Julius

Ware Memorial Care Center, 400 West 14th, Amarillo, TX 79101; tel. 806/337–4000; Mr. T.H. Holloway

UTAH

Garden Terrace Alzheimer's Center of Excellence, 1201 East 4500 South, Salt Lake City, UT 84117; tel. 801/261–3664; Mr. Shawn Matheson

Sunshine Terrace Foundation, Inc., 225 North 200 West, Logan, UT 84321-3805; tel. 435/752–0411; Ms. Sara V Sinclair

VERMONT

SVHC Centers for Living and Rehabilitation, 160 Hospital Drive, Bennington, VT 05201; tel. 802/447–1547; Ms. Susan Kane

VIRGINIA

Beth Sholom Home of Eastern Virginia, 6401 Auburn Drive, Virginia Beach, VA 23464; tel. 757/420–2512; Mr. Bryan R Mesh

Beth Sholom Home of Virginia, 1600 John Rolfe Parkway, Richmond, VA 23233; tel. 804/750–2183; Mr. Mark W Finkle

Friendship Manor, Inc., 327 Hershberger Road, NW, Roanoke, VA 24012; tel. 540/265–2100; Mrs. Tamera Q Kelly

Health Care Center at Lucy Corr Village, PO Drawer 170, Chesterfield, VA 23832; tel. 804/748–1511; Mr. Jacob W Mast, Jr.

Iliff Nursing and Rehabilitation Center, 8000 Iliff Drive, Dunn Loring, VA 22027; tel. 703/560–1000; Mr. Denny G Dennis

Inova Cameron Glen Care Center, 1800 Cameron Glen Drive, Reston, VA 20190; tel. 703/834–5891; Ms. Elissa Clark

Inova Commonwealth Care Center, 4315 Chain Bridge Road, Fairfax, VA 22030; tel. 703/934–5000; Ms. Carla Shipley

James River Convalescent Center, 540 Aberthaw Avenue, Newport News, VA 23601; tel. 757/595–2273; Mr. Jeffrey L Mendelsohn

Manor Care Skilled Nursing & Rehabilitation, 550 South Carlin Springs Road, Arlington, VA 22204; tel. 703/379–7200; Ms. Marcia Jarrell

Patrick Henry Hospital , Inc., 1000 Old Denbigh Boulevard, Newport News, VA 23602; tel. 757/875–2000; Mrs. Lynda C Burton

Woodbine Rehabilitation and Healthcare Center, 2729 King Street, Alexandria, VA 22302; tel. 703/836–8838; Mr. Richard B Heimendinger

WASHINGTON

Hallmark Manor, 32300 1st Ave. South, Federal Way, WA 98003; tel. 253/874–3580; Mr. Roger Joice

Lake Vue Gardens Convalescent Center, 10101 Northeast 120th Street, Kirkland, WA 98034; tel. 425/823–2323; Ms. Nancy Butner

LCCA Federal Way, 1045 S. 308th Street, Federal Way, WA 98003; tel. 253/946–2273; Mr. Bryan K Tapia

Life Care Center of Mount Vernon, 2120 East Division Street, Mount Vernon, WA 98274; tel. 360/424–4258; Ms. Patricia Schumacher

Life Care Center of Bothell, 707 228th Street Southwest, Bothell, WA 98021; tel. 425/481–8500; Ms. Erin Doss

Life Care Center of Burien, 1031 Southwest 130th Street, Burien, WA 98146; tel. 206/242–3213; Ms. Kathleen Lowery-Chugg

Life Care Center of Kennewick, 1508 W. Seventh Avenue, Kennewick, WA 99336; tel. 509/586–9185; Mr. Don Werner

Life Care Center of Richland, 44 Goethals Drive, Richland, WA 99352; tel. 509/943–1117; Mr. Michael Littman

Life Care Center of Skagit Valley, 1462 West SR 20, Sedro Woolley, WA 98284; tel. 360/856–6867; Ms. Teri Lindgren

Life Care Center of West Seattle, 4700 SW Admiral Way, Seattle, WA 98116; tel. 206/935–2480; Mrs. LYNDA K BALDWIN

Marysville Care Center, 1821 Grove Street, Marysville, WA 98270; tel. 360/659–3926; Ms. Sandra P Reuble

Port Orchard Care Center, 2301 Pottery Avenue, Port Orchard, WA 98367; tel. 360/876–8035; Mr. Larry Oden

WISCONSIN

Clement Manor, Inc, 3939 South 92nd Street, Greenfield, WI 53228; tel. 414/321–1800; Mr. Richard Rau

Eastview Medical and Rehab Center, 729 Park Street, Antigo, WI 54409-2798; tel. 715/623–2356; Ms. Wanda J Hose

WYOMING

Life Care Center of Casper, 4041 South Poplar Street, Casper, WY 82601; tel. 307/266–0000; Ms. Patricia Miller

Life Care Center of Cheyenne, 1330 Prairie Avenue, Cheyenne, WY 82009; tel. 307/778–8997; Mr. Derek Schmidt

Section C

The accredited freestanding mental health care organizations listed have been accredited as of April, 2005 by the Joint Commission on Accreditation of Healthcare Organizations by decision of the Accreditation Committee of the Board of Commissioners.

The organizations listed here have been found to be in compliance with the Joint Commissions standards for Accreditation Manual for Mental Health, Chemical Dependency, and Mental Retardation/Development Disabilities Services.

Please refer to section A of the AHA Guide for information on hospitals with inpatient and/or outpatient services. These hospitals are identified by Facility Codes F72, F73, F74, F75, F76, and F77. In section A, those hospitals identified by Approval Code 1 are JCAHO accredited.

We present this list simply as a convenient directory. Inclusion or omission of any organization's name indicates neither approval nor disapproval by Health Forum LLC, an American Hospital Association company.

United States

ALABAMA
Bradford Health Services - Huntsville Lodge, 1600 Browns Ferry Road, Madison, AL 35758; tel. 256/461–7272; Mr. Robert S Hinds
Bradford Health Services - Warrior Lodge, PO Box 129, Warrior, AL 35180; tel. 205/647–1945; Mr. Roy M Ramsey
Greater Mobile-Washington County MH-MR Board, Inc., 5750-A Southland Drive, Mobile, AL 36693; tel. 251/450–5901; Mr. J. T Schlesinger
Mobile Mental Health Center, Inc., 2400 Gordon Smith Drive, Mobile, AL 36617; tel. 251/450–5901; Mr. Tuerk Schlesinger

ALASKA
Juneau Recovery Hospital - OTP, 3250 Hospital Drive, Juneau, AK 99801; tel. 907/796–8900; Mr. Robert Valliant

ARIZONA
Arizona's Children Association, PO Box 7277, Tucson, AZ 85725-7277; tel. 520/622–7611; Mr. Fred J Chaffee
Banner Behavioral Health, 5555 Thunderbird Road, Glendale, AZ 85306; tel. 602/588–5904; Ms. Colleen Hallberg
Banner Behavioral Health, 2225 West Southern Avenue, Mesa, AZ 85202; tel. 480/464–4055; Mr. Peter S Fine
Chandler Valley Hope, PO Box 1839, Chandler, AZ 85244-1839; tel. 602/899–3335; Dr. Kenneth C Gregoire
Community Behavioral Health Services, PO Box 790, Page, AZ 86040; tel. 928/645–5133; Mr. Thomas J Wright
Community Counseling Centers, Inc., 105 North Fifth Avenue, Holbrook, AZ 86025; tel. 928/524–6701; Dr. Robert Wilderman
Cottonwood de Tucson, 4110 West Sweetwater Drive, Tucson, AZ 85745; tel. 520/743–0411; Mr. Ronald B Welch
Desert Visions Youth Wellness Center, PO Box 458, Sacaton, AZ 85247; tel. 888/431–4096; Dr. Richard L Zephier
Helping Associates, Inc., 1901 North Trekell Road, Ste A, Casa Grande, AZ 85222; tel. 520/836–1029; Dr. Joan McGillicuddy
Horizon Human Services, Inc., 210 East Cottonwood Lane, Casa Grande, AZ 85222; tel. 520/836–1688; Mr. Norman E Mudd
Little Colorado Behavioral Health Centers, PO Box 579, St Johns, AZ 85936; tel. 928/337–4301; Mr. Michael T Downs
Mohave Mental Health Clinic, Inc., 1743 Sycamore Avenue, Kingman, AZ 86401; tel. 928/757–8111; Mr. B.W. Brown
New Hope Behavioral Health Center, Inc, 6550 East Broadway, Suite 101, Mesa, AZ 85206; tel. 480/981–1022; Mr. David Campbell
Pinal Hispanic Council, 712 North Main Street, Eloy, AZ 85231; tel. 520/466–7765; Mr. Ralph Varela
Sierra Tucson,LLC, 39580 S. Lago del Oro Parkway, Tucson, AZ 85739; tel. 520/624–4000; Dr. David E Anderson
Southeastern Arizona Behavioral Health Services, Inc., PO Box 2161, Benson, AZ 85602; tel. 520/586–0800; Mrs. Dana Johnson
Southern Arizona VA Health Care, 3601 S 6th Avenue, Building 2, Tucson, AZ 85723; tel. 520/629–1821; Dr. David Emelity

St. Luke's Behavioral Hospital L.P., 1800 East Van Buren, Phoenix, AZ 85006; tel. 602/251–8808; Mr. David White
Superstition Mountain Mental Health Center, Inc., PO Box 3160, Apache Junction, AZ 85217-3160; tel. 480/983–0065; Mr. Robert Rundio
the EXCEL group, 2573 Arizona Avenue, Suite I, Yuma, AZ 85364; tel. 928/329–8995; Mr. Michael Coleman
The Guidance Center, Inc., 2187 North Vickey Street, Flagstaff, AZ 86004; tel. 928/527–1899; Ms. Linda Cowan
The Haven, 1107 East Adelaide Drive, Tucson, AZ 85719; tel. 520/623–4590; Ms. Sharon A Lashinger
The Meadows of Wickenburg, L.P., 1655 North Tegner, Wickenburg, AZ 85390; tel. 928/684–3926; Mr. Robert Fulton
Verde Valley Guidance Clinic, Inc., 8 East Cottonwood Street, Cottonwood, AZ 86326; tel. 928/634–2236; Mr. Robert D Cartia
West Yavapai Guidance Clinic, 505 South Cortez Street, Prescott, AZ 86303; tel. 520/445–5211; Mr. Don Ostendorf

ARKANSAS
Ozark Counseling Services, Inc, PO Box 1776, Mountain Home, AR 72654-1776; tel. 870/425–6901; Mr. John C Greer
Ozark Guidance Center, Inc., PO Box 6430, Springdale, AR 72762-6430; tel. 479/750–2020; Dr. David L Williams
University of Arkansas for Medical Sciences, 4301 West Markham Street, Mail Slot 554, Little Rock, AR 72205; tel. 501/686–5483; Dr. G. Richard Smith
University of Arkansas for Substance Abuse Treatment Clinic, 3924 West Markham Street Slot # 611-1, Little Rock, AR 72205-4096; tel. 501/686–9630; Dr. G R Smith

CALIFORNIA
Action Family Counseling, Inc., 26893 Bouquet Canyon Road, Suite C-134, Saugus, CA 91350; tel. 661/297–9716; Mr. Cary Quashen
AltaMed Health Services Corporation, 500 Citadel Drive Suite 490, Los Angeles, CA 90040; tel. 323/889–7307; Mr. John C Grace
Berkeley Addiction Treatment Services, Inc., 2975 Sacramento Street, Berkeley, CA 94702; tel. 510/644–0200; Ms. Matonia Williams
Betty Ford Center, 39000 Bob Hope Drive, Rancho Mirage, CA 92270; tel. 760/773–4100; Mr. John T Schwarzlose
Bi-Valley Medical Clinic, Inc. (Carmichael), 310 Harris Ave, Ste A, Sacramento, CA 95838; tel. 916/649–6793; Mr. Garrett Stenson
Bi-Valley Medical Clinic, Inc. - (Norwood), 310 Harris Avenue, Suite B, Sacramento, CA 95838; tel. 916/649–6793; Mr. Garrett Stenson
California Institution for Women, P.O. Box 6000, Corona, CA 92878-6000; tel. 909/606–4925; Dr. Jacqueline Long
Community Human Services - Methadone Clinic, PO Box 3076, Monterey, CA 93942; tel. 831/424–4828; Ms. Robin McCrae
Cornerstone of Southern California, 13682 Yorba Street, Tustin, CA 92780; tel. 714/730–5399; Ms. Lynda Klinger
Eastside Health Services, 5200 San Gabriel Place, Pico Rivera, CA 90660; tel. 562/948–3306; Ms. Pauline Bahat
eGetgoing, Inc., 105 N. Bascom Avenue, Second Floor, San Jose, CA 95128-1811; tel. 408/998–3040; Dr. Barry Karlin

Fort Help Methadone Program, 915 Bryant Street, San Francisco, CA 94103; tel. 415/777–9953; Dr. Norbert Bohmer
HAART- Oakland, 10850 MacArthur Boulevard, Suite 200, Oakland, CA 94605; tel. 510/875–2300; Mr. Walter E Rosenthal
HAART-Hayward, 10850 MacArthur Boulevard, Oakland, CA 94605; tel. 510/727–9755; Ms. Anne Bolla
Impact Drug and Alcohol Treatment Center, PO Box 93607, Pasadena, CA 91103; tel. 626/798–0884; Mr. James M Stillwell
L. A. Treatment Service, 6965 El Camino Real, Ste. 105- #281, Carlsbad, CA 92009; tel. 760/471–3860; Mr. Philip S Brailsford
Los Angeles Center for Alcohol and Drug Abuse, PO Box 3205 11015 Bloomfield Avenue, Santa Fe Springs, CA 90670; tel. 562/906–2676; Ms. Brenda Wiewel
Mendocino County Department of Public Health (AODP), 333 Laws Avenue, Ukiah, CA 95482; tel. 707/472–4511; Ms. Linnea Ritter-Hunter
Mental Health Program Dept of Veterans Affairs, 2505 West 14th Street, Oakland Army Base, Oakland, CA 94607; tel. 510/587–3434; Dr. Matthew Moore
OTP Los Angeles Ambulatory Care Center, 351 East Temple Street, Los Angeles, CA 90012; tel. 310/268–3132; Mr. David M Riley
R House, Inc., 533 Carr Avenue, Santa Rosa, CA 95404; tel. 707/571–2215; Ms. Mimi G Donohue
San Mateo Medical Center Methadone Treatment Program, 795 Willow Road, Building #332, Menlo Park, CA 94025; tel. 650/578–7190; Ms. Nancy Steiger
Sepulveda CA VAH Opioid Treatment Program, 16111 Plummer Street, Bldg 62, Sepulveda, CA 91343; tel. 310/268–3132; Mr. David M Riley
Sharp Vista Pacifica, 7989 Linda Vista Road, San Diego, CA 92111; tel. 858/637–6920; Mr. Daniel L Gross
Spencer Recovery Centers, Inc., PO Box 118, Monrovia, CA 91017; tel. 949/376–3705; Mr. Christopher C Spencer
Tarzana Treatment Centers, Inc., 18646 Oxnard Street, Tarzana, CA 91356; tel. 818/996–1051; Mr. Scott Taylor, Esq.
The 14th Street Clinic, 1124 International Boulevard, Oakland, CA 94606; tel. 510/533–0800; Dr. Joan E Zweben
Twin Town Treatment Centers, 5122 E Katella Avenue, Suite 102, Los Alamitos, CA 90720; tel. 562/594–8844; Mr. David Lisonbee
Valley Health Associates, 338 Monterey Street, Salinas, CA 93901; tel. 831/424–6655; Ms. Cecile E Rohde
VAMC-San Francisco Substance Abuse Treatment Clinic, 4150 Clement Street, Bldg 1, San Francisco, CA 94121; tel. 415/750–2050; Dr. Peter Banys
West Los Angeles Drug Treatment Services, 11301 Wilshire Blvd, Bldg 257C, Los Angeles, CA 90073; tel. 310/268–3132; Mr. David M Riley
West Oakland Health Council, Inc, 700 Adeline Street, Oakland, CA 94607; tel. 510/433–1500; Dr. Robert Cooper
Westside Community Mental Health, Inc., 1301 Pierce Street, San Francisco, CA 94115; tel. 415/563–8200; Mr. Abner Boles

COLORADO
Denver Health and Hospital Authority, 777 Bannock Street, Unit 9, Denver, CO 80204; tel. 303/436–5690; Mrs. Patricia Gabow

Parker Valley Hope, PO Box 670, Parker, CO 80134; tel. 303/841–7857; Dr. Kenneth C Gregoire

Pikes Peak Mental Health, 220 Ruskin Drive, Colorado Springs, CO 80910; tel. 719/572–6100; Mr. Morris Roth

CONNECTICUT

Alcohol & Drug Recovery Centers, Inc.- Detoxification Center, 500 Blue Hills Avenue, Hartford, CT 06112; tel. 860/714–3701; Mr. Kenneth J Talge

Alcohol and Drug Recovery Centers, Inc., 500 Blue Hills Avenue, 6th Floor Administration, Hartford, CT 06112; tel. 860/714–3701; Mr. Kenneth J Talge

Alliance Treatment Center, Inc., PO Box 1357, Avon, CT 06001-1357; tel. 860/673–6115; Dr. Mark Muradian

Blue Hills Substance Abuse Services, 500 Vine Street, Hartford, CT 06112-1639; tel. 860/293–6401; Ms. Susan Graham

Community Mental Health Affiliates, Inc., 29 Russell Street, New Britain, CT 06052; tel. 860/826–1358; Dr. Mark Muradian

Connecticut Counseling Centers Norwalk Methadone Maintenance, 984 Southford Road, Middlebury, CT 06762; tel. 203/577–5320; Mr. Roger Lambert

Connecticut Counseling Centers Norwalk Opiate Detoxification, 984 Southford Road, Middlebury, CT 06762; tel. 203/577–5320; Mr. Robert Lambert

Connecticut Counseling Centers Waterbury Methadone Maintenance, 984 Southford Road, Middlebury, CT 06762; tel. 203/577–5320; Mr. Michael Freeman

Connecticut Counseling Centers Waterbury Opiate Detoxification, 984 Southford Road, Middlebury, CT 06762; tel. 203/577–5320; Mr. Michael Freeman

Connecticut Valley Hospital- Addiction Services Div-Merritt, PO Box 351, Middletown, CT 06457-7023; tel. 860/262–5887; Mr. Garrell S Mullaney

New Era Rehabilitation Center, 3851 Main Street, Bridgeport, CT 06606; tel. 203/372–3333; Dr. Ebenezer A Kolade

Opiate Treatment Program, VA Connecticut Healthcare System, 950 Campbell Avenue, Bldg 36, West Haven, CT 06516; tel. 203/932–5711; Dr. Kishorchandra Gonsai

Perception Programs, Inc., PO Box 407, Willimantic, CT 06226; tel. 860/450–7122; Ms. Linda Mastrianni

Rushford Center, Inc., 1250 Silver Street, Middletown, CT 06457; tel. 203/235–1792; Mr. Jeffrey L Walter

Saint Francis Hospital & Medical Center - 8 West Unit, 500 Blue Hills Avenue, Hartford, CT 06112; tel. 860/714–2333; Mr. Christopher M Dadlez

Silver Hill Hospital, 208 Valley Road, New Canaan, CT 06840; tel. 203/801–2297; Dr. Sigurd H Ackerman

South Central Rehabilitation Center, 232 Cedar Street, New Haven, CT 06519; tel. 203/503–3356; Mr. Cornell Scott

Southwest Connecticut Mental Health System, 97 Middle Street, Bridgeport, CT 06604; tel. 203/579–7368; Mr. James M Pisciotta

State of CT DMHAS - Southeastern Mental Health Authority, 401 West Thames Street, Bldg. 301, Norwich, CT 06360; tel. 860/859–4674; Mr. John H Simsarian

Stonington Institute, 75 Swantown Hill Road, North Stonington, CT 06359; tel. 860/439–6000; Mr. William A Aniskovich

The Children's Center of Hamden, Inc., 1400 Whitney Avenue, Hamden, CT 06517; tel. 203/248–2116; Mr. Anthony DelMastro

The Danbury Hopsital - OTP, 24 Hospital Ave., Danbury, CT 06810; tel. 203/797–7000; Mr. Frank J Kelly

The Wheeler Clinic, 91 Northwest Drive, Plainville, CT 06062; tel. 860/793–3500; Dr. David J Berkowitz

United Services, Inc., Post Office Box 839, Dayville, CT 06241; tel. 860/774–2020; Ms. Diane L Manning

DELAWARE

Brandywine Counseling, Inc, Lancaster, 2713 Lancaster Avenue, Wilmington, DE 19805; tel. 302/656–2348; Ms. Sara T Allshouse

Brandywine Counseling, Inc., 2814 West Second Street, Wilmington, DE 19805; tel. 302/472–0381; Ms. Sara T Allshouse

Brandywine Counseling, Inc., Riverfront, 350 South Madison Street, Wilmington, DE 19801; tel. 302/661–6200; Ms. Sara T Allshouse

Brandywine Counseling, Inc., South Chapel, 24 Brookhill Drive, Newark, DE 19702; tel. 302/454–3020; Ms. Sara T Allshouse

Connections Community Support Programs, Inc., 500 West 10th Street, Wilmington, DE 19801; tel. 302/984–3380; Ms. Catherine Devaney McKay

SODAT - Delaware, Inc., 625 North Orange Street, Wilmington, DE 19801; tel. 302/656–4044; Mr. Kenneth R Collins

DISTRICT OF COLUMBIA

Department of Veterans Affairs, Substance Abuse Rehab Program, 50 Irving Street, Northwest, Washington, DC 20002; tel. 202/745–8313; Dr. Stephen Deutsch

Psychiatric Institute of Washington, 4228 Wisconsin Avenue, NW, Washington, DC 20016; tel. 202/885–5600; Mr. Ken Courage

FLORIDA

Act Corporation, 1220 Willis Avenue #25, Daytona Beach, FL 32114; tel. 386/947–3600; Mr. J W Dreggors

Alternatives In Treatment, Inc., 7601 North Federal Highway, Suite 100B, Boca Raton, FL 33487; tel. 561/998–0866; Mr. Jacob Frydman

American Therapeutic Corp., 1881 NE 2nd Avenue, Miami, FL 33132; tel. 305/371–5777; Ms. Marianella Valera

Apalachee Center, Inc., 2634-J Capital Circle NE, Tallahassee, FL 32308; tel. 850/523–3333; Mr. Ronald P Kirkland

Beachcomber Rehab, Inc., 4493 North Ocean Boulevard, Delray Beach, FL 33483; tel. 561/276–6226; Mr. Joseph R Bryan

Behavioral Health of the Palm Beaches, Inc., 5725 Corporate Way, Suite 209, West Palm Beach, FL 33407; tel. 561/615–6664; Mr. Donald Mullaney

Bridgeway Center, Inc., 137 Hospital Drive, Fort Walton Beach, FL 32548; tel. 850/833–7430; Mr. Dan Cobbs

Broward Treatment Center, 1101 South 21st Avenue, Hollywood, FL 33020; tel. 954/922–0522; Mr. Mark Gallagher

Caron Foundation of Florida, I d/b/a Renaissance Institute, 7000 N Federal Hwy, 2nd Floor, Boca Raton, FL 33487; tel. 561/241–7977; Mr. Douglas Tieman

Central Florida Treatment Centers, 7 North Cocoa Boulevard, Cocoa, FL 32922; tel. 321/631–4578; Mr. Carlos A Ball-llovera

Central Florida Treatment Centers - Orlando, 1800 West Colonial Drive, Orlando, FL 32804; tel. 407/843–0041; Mrs. Carol Ball

Central Florida Treatment Centers - Palm Bay, 2198 Harris Avenue, Palm Bay, FL 32905; tel. 321/951–9750; Mrs. Carol Ball

Chautauqua Offices of Psychotherapy and Evaluation, 3686 US Highway 331 South, Defuniak Springs, FL 32435; tel. 850/892–8035; Ms. Rachel R Gillis

Citrus Health Network, Inc, 4175 West 20th Avenue, Hialeah, FL 33012; tel. 305/825–0300; Mr. Mario E Jardon

Coastal Behavioral Healthcare, Inc., 1565 State Street, Sarasota, FL 34236; tel. 941/927–8900; Dr. Christine Cauffield

Comprehensive Psychiatric Center, 9735 East Fern Street, Miami, FL 33157; tel. 305/238–5121; Mr. Roberto Ruiz, Jr.

Comprehensive Psychiatric Center - Miami Beach, 960 41st Street (Arthur Godfrey Rd) Ste 106, Miami Beach, FL 33140; tel. 305/534–5121; Mrs. Patricia Cunningham

Comprehensive Psychiatric Center North, 240 Northwest 183rd Street, Miami, FL 33169; tel. 305/651–2332; Dr. Roberto Ruiz

Comprehensive Psychiatric Center-Central, 1501 N.W. 36th Street, Miami, FL 33142; tel. 305/634–1401; Dr. Roberto Ruiz, Jr.

David Lawrence Center, 6075 Golden Gate Parkway, Naples, FL 34116; tel. 239/354–1440; Mr. David C Schimmel

Fair Oaks Pavilion at Delray Medical Center, 5352 Linton Boulevard, Delray Beach, FL 33484; tel. 561/495–3270; Mr. Mitchell S Feldman

Fairwinds Treatment Center, 1569 S Fort Harrison Avenue, Clearwater, FL 33756; tel. 727/449–0300; Mr. Mazhar K Al-Abed

Florida Center for Recovery, 3451 West Midway Road, Fort Pierce, FL 34950; tel. 772/460–2777; Mr. Jack Hamilton

Focus Healthcare of Florida, 5960 Southwest 106th Avenue, Cooper City, FL 33328; tel. 954/680–2700; Mr. Alan Goodstat

Focus Healthcare of Florida - OTP, 5960 Southwest 106th Avenue, Cooper City, FL 33328; tel. 954/680–2700; Mr. Alan Goodstat

Hanley Center, 5200 East Avenue, West Palm Beach, FL 33407-2374; tel. 561/841–1000; Mr. Terry Allen

Hanley-Hazelden Center at St. Mary's, 5200 East Avenue, West Palm Beach, FL 33407; tel. 561/841–1000; Mr. Terry Allen

HealthCare Connection, 825 West Linebaugh Avenue, Tampa, FL 33612; tel. 813/931–5560; Mr. Jess Loven

Hendry Glades Mental Health Clinic, Inc., 601 West Alverdez Avenue, Clewiston, FL 33440; tel. 863/983–1423; Mr. Joseph F Hosick

Jacksonville Metro Treatment Center, 3609 Emerson Street, Jacksonville, FL 32207; tel. 904/398–7015; Mr. T. Mark Gallagher

Lakeview Health Systems, LLC, 8889 Corporate Square Court, Jacksonville, FL 32216; tel. 904/727–6455; Mr. David Shurgin

LifeStream Behavioral Center, PO Box 491000, Leesburg, FL 34749-1000; tel. 352/315–7500; Mr. Jonathan M Cherry

Manatee Glens Corporation, PO Box 9478, Bradenton, FL 34206-9478; tel. 941/782–4299; Ms. Mary Ruiz

Marion-Citrus Mental Health Centers, Inc., 5664 SW 60th Ave, Ocala, FL 34477-1929; tel. 352/291–5456; Mr. Russell Rasco

Meridian Behavioral Healthcare, Inc., PO Box 141750, Gainesville, FL 32608; tel. 352/374–5600; Dr. Margarita Labarta

Metro Treatment of Florida, LP dba Sunrise Treatment Center, 14050 Town Loop Blvd, Suite 204, Orlando, FL 32837; tel. 407/351–7080; Mr. T. M Gallagher

Operation PAR, Inc., 6655 66th Street North, Pinellas Park, FL 33781; tel. 888/727–6398; Mrs. Nancy L Hamilton

Operation PAR, Inc. (NATC - Bradenton), 6655 66th Street North, Pinellas Park, FL 33781; tel. 888/727–6398; Mrs. Nancy L Hamilton

Operation PAR, Inc. (NATC-Clearwater), 6655 66th Street North, Pinellas Park, FL 33781; tel. 888/727–6398; Mrs. Nancy L Hamilton

Operation PAR, Inc. (NATC-Fort Myers), 6655 66th Street North, Pinellas Park, FL 33781; tel. 888/727–6398; Mrs. Nancy L Hamilton

Operation PAR, Inc. (NATC-Pasco), 6655 66th Street North, Pinellas Park, FL 33781; tel. 888/727–6398; Mrs. Nancy L Hamilton

Orlando Methadone Treatment Center, 14050 Town Loop Blvd., Suite 204, Orlando, FL 32837; tel. 407/275–8939; Mr. T. M Gallagher

Pathways to Recovery,Inc, 13132 Barwick Road, Delray Beach, FL 33445; tel. 561/496–7532; Ms. Carol Parks

PB Institute Partners Limited Partnership, 1017 N. Olive Avenue, West Palm Beach, FL 33401; tel. 800/433–5098; Mr. David McVinney

Personal Enrichment through Mental Health Services, Inc., 11254 58th Street North, Pinellas Park, FL 33782; tel. 727/545–6477; Mr. Thomas C Wedekind

Pompano Treatment Center, 380 Southwest 12th Avenue, Pompano Beach, FL 33069; tel. 954/782–9774; Mr. Mike Ford

Recovery First, Inc., 2701 W. Oakland Park Blvd., Oakland Park, FL 33311; tel. 954/497–0824; Mr. James Davis

Renaissance Behavioral Health Systems, Inc., PO Box 19249, Jacksonville, FL 32245-9249; tel. 904/743–1883; Dr. Robert Sommers

Ruth Cooper Center for Behavioral Health Care, Inc., 2789 Ortiz Avenue, Southeast, Fort Myers, FL 33905; tel. 239/275–3222; Ms. Janet W Eustis

Southwest Miami Treatment Center, 11980 SW 8th Street, Ste 15/16, Miami, FL 33184; tel. 305/553–8807; Mr. Mark Gallagher

Substance Abuse and Health Care Services, 115 S. Andrews Avenue Suite 318, Fort Lauderdale, FL 33301; tel. 954/357–5455; Mr. Paul Jaquith

Tampa Bay Academy, 12012 Boyette Road, Riverview, FL 33569; tel. 813/677–6700; Mr. Edward C Hoefle

Ten Broeck Ocala, 3130 SW 27th Avenue, Ocala, FL 34474; tel. 352/671–3130; Mr. Keith Lewis

The Centre for Women, Inc., 305 South Hyde Park Avenue, Tampa, FL 33606; tel. 813/251–8437; Ms. Beth Ficquette

The Village South, Inc., 3180 Biscayne Boulevard, Miami, FL 33137; tel. 305/573–3784; Mr. Frank Rabbito

The Watershed at Clear Lake, 200 Congress Park Drive, Suite 100, Delray Beach, FL 33445; tel. 561/860–8228; Mr. Chris Crosby

Section C

The Watershed Treatment Programs, 200 Congress Park Drive, #100, Delray Beach, FL 33445; tel. 561/860–8228; Mr. Chris Crosby

The Willough at Naples, 9001 Tamiami Trail East, Naples, FL 34113; tel. 941/775–4500; Mr. James O'Shea

Transitions Recovery Program, 1928 Northeast 154th Street, North Miami, FL 33162; tel. 305/949–9001; Mr. Lee Barchan

Treatment Resources of Margate, Inc., 5100 Coconut Creek Parkway, Margate, FL 33063; tel. 954/917–3334; Ms. Bea Redlich

Turning Point of Tampa, Inc., 6227 Sheldon Road, Tampa, FL 33615; tel. 813/882–3003; Ms. Robin Piper

Twelve Oaks, 2068 Healthcare Avenue, Navarre, FL 32566; tel. 850/939–1200; Ms. Candance Henderson

West Palm Beach Treatment Center, 1497 Forest Hill Blvd., Suite E, Lake Clarke Shores, FL 33406; tel. 561/433–5687; Mr. Mark Gallagher

West Psychiatric Associates, PA/Serenity Addiction Center, 6780 Taft Street, Hollywood, FL 33024; tel. 954/981–7612; Dr. Sayonara Baez

GEORGIA

Albany Area Community Service Board, PO Box 1988, Albany, GA 31702; tel. 229/430–4005; Dr. John C BurnsIll

Behavioral Health Services of South Georgia, 3120 N Oak Street Ext, Suite C, Valdosta, GA 31602-1007; tel. 229/333–7095; Mr. W. David McCracken

Community Mental Health Center of East Central Georgia, 3421 Mike Padgett Highway, Building D, Augusta, GA 30906; tel. 706/771–7800; Dr. Philip A Horton

Community Service Board of Middle Georgia, 2121A Bellevue Road, Dublin, GA 31021-2998; tel. 478/272–1190; Ms. Patsy H Thomas

DeKalb Community Service Board, PO Box 1648, Decatur, GA 30031; tel. 404/294–3834; Mr. Gary S Richey

Dept., of Veterans Affairs - Atlanta VA Medical Center, 1670 Clairmont Road, Decatur, GA 30033; tel. 404/321–6111; Mr. Thomas A Cappello

DM & ADR, Inc., 1720 Commerce Road, Athens, GA 30607; tel. 706/552–0688; Ms. Ali McCorkle

Fulton County Dept of MHDDAD, 115 MLK, Jr., Drive, Suite 277, Atlanta, GA 30303; tel. 404/730–0268; Dr. Barbara J Lattimore

Gateway Community Service Board, 1000 Commisioners Drive, Darien, GA 31305; tel. 912/437–9300; Dr. Frank A Bonati

Georgia Pines Community Service Board, 1102 Smith Avenue Suite K, Thomasville, GA 31799; tel. 229/225–4335; Mr. Robert H Jones, Jr.

Georgia Psychological Services, PO Box 211626, Augusta, GA 30917-1626; tel. 706/210–3066; Mr. David W Proefrock

Grady Health System-Drug Dependence Unit, 48-50 Coca Cola Place, Atlanta, GA 30303-3043; tel. 404/616–3970; Dr. Andrew Agwunobi

McIntosh Trail MH/MR/SA Community Service Board, PO Box 1320, Griffin, GA 30224; tel. 770/358–8250; Ms. Cathy Johnson

Metro Atlanta Recovery Residences, Inc., PO Box 48349, Doraville, GA 30340; tel. 770/457–1222; Mr. Doug Brush

Oconee Center, PO Box 1827, Milledgeville, GA 31061; tel. 478/445–4717; Mr. John W Prather

Ogeechee Behavioral Health Services, PO Box 1259, Swainsboro, GA 30401; tel. 478/289–2522; Mr. J. Frank Brantley

River Edge Behavioral Health Center, 175 Emery Highway, Macon, GA 31217; tel. 478/751–4519; Mr. Jim Riley

Southside Medical Treatment Center, 1039 Ridge Avenue, Southwest, Atlanta, GA 30315; tel. 404/688–1350; Mr. Avon Lauder

Talbott Recovery Campus, 5448 Yorktowne Drive, Atlanta, GA 30349; tel. 770/994–0185; Mr. Benjamin H Underwood

Turning Point Hospital, PO Box 1177, Moultrie, GA 31768; tel. 229/985–4815; Mr. Ben Marion

Willingway Hospital, 311 Jones Mill Road, Statesboro, GA 30458; tel. 912/764–6236; Mr. Jimmy Mooney

ILLINOIS

Advocate Addiction Treatment Program, 1775 Dempster Street, 10 South, Park Ridge, IL 60068; tel. 847/795–3900; Ms. Debra Geihsler

Ben Gordon Center, 12 Health Services Drive, Dekalb, IL 60115; tel. 815/756–4875; Mr. Michael D Flora

CAP of Downers Grove, 4954 South Main Street, Downers Grove, IL 60515; tel. 630/810–0186; Dr. Marc Shinderman

Center for Addictive Problems, 609 North Wells Street, Chicago, IL 60610; tel. 312/266–0404; Dr. Marc Shinderman

Central Illinois Center for the Treatment of Addiction, 228 Northeast Jefferson, Peoria, IL 61654; tel. 309/671–8000; Mr. Michael G Boyle

Chestnut Health Systems, 1003 Martin Luther King Drive, Bloomington, IL 61701; tel. 309/827–6026; Mr. Russell J Hagen

Chicago Lakeshore Hospital, 4840 North Marine Drive, Chicago, IL 60640; tel. 773/878–9700; Mr. C. A Eaks

Community Counseling Centers of Chicago, 4740 North Clark Street, Chicago, IL 60640; tel. 773/769–0205; Dr. Anthony A Kopera

Comprehensive Mental Health Center of St. Clair County, 3911 State Street, East Saint Louis, IL 62205; tel. 618/482–7330; Mrs. Marsha R Johnson

Cornell Interventions - DuPage, 11 S 250 Route 83, Hinsdale, IL 60521; tel. 630/325–5050; Mr. Walter Carlson

Cornell Interventions - Southwood, 901 W. Jackson Boulevard Suite 400, Chicago, IL 60607; tel. 773/737–4600; Mr. Mark K Thompson

Cornell Interventions - Woodridge, 2221 64th Street, Woodridge, IL 60517; tel. 630/968–6477; Mr. Casey Radkiewicz

Cornell Interventions East St. Louis, 302 North 5thStreet, East Saint Louis, IL 62201; tel. 618/271–4542; Mr. Don Otis

Cornell Interventions Life Works, 1611 Jefferson Street, Joliet, IL 60435; tel. 815/730–7521; Ms. Loretta Berry

Cornell Interventions Northside Clinic, 2723 North Clark Street, Chicago, IL 60614; tel. 773/525–3250; Mr. Ron McDearmon

Cornell Interventions Southwood, 5701 South Wood Street, Chicago, IL 60636; tel. 773/737–4600; Mr. David L Johnson

Counseling Center of Lake View, 3225 North Sheffield Avenue, Chicago, IL 60657; tel. 773/549–5886; Mr. Norman J Groetzinger

Edward Hines Jr VA Hospital / Drug Dependency Treatment Ct, PO Box 5000, Hines, IL 60141; tel. 708/202–8387; Dr. Pradipkumar Desai

Family Guidance Center, Inc., 751 Aurora Avenue, Aurora, IL 60505; tel. 312/943–6545; Dr. Larry Kroll

Family Guidance Center, Inc., 484 Lee Street, Des Plaines, IL 60016; tel. 312/943–6545; Dr. Larry Kroll

Family Guidance Centers, Inc., 310 W. Chicago Ave., Chicago, IL 60610; tel. 312/943–6545; Dr. Larry Kroll

Family Service and Community Mental Health Center/McHenry, 5320 West Elm Street, McHenry, IL 60050; tel. 815/385–6400; Mr. Robert M Martens

Garfield Counseling Center, Inc., 4132 West Madison, Chicago, IL 60624; tel. 773/533–0433; Mr. Richard E Shelton, Jr.

Gateway Foundation Inc., 55 East Jackson Blvd, Suite 1500, Chicago, IL 60604; tel. 312/663–1130; Mr. Michael Darcy

Hazelden Foundation - Chicago Office, 867 North Dearborn Street, Chicago, IL 60610; tel. 651/213–4060; Mrs. Ellen Breyer

Heartland Human Services, PO Box 1047, Effingham, IL 62401; tel. 217/347–7179; Ms. Cheryl Compton

Heritage Behavior Health Center, Inc., P.O. Box 710, Decatur, IL 62525; tel. 217/362–6262; Mrs. Diana Knaebe

Human Service Center, PO Box 1346, Peoria, IL 61654-1346; tel. 309/671–8000; Mr. Michael G Boyle

Lake County Health Department, 3004 Grand Avenue, Waukegan, IL 60085; tel. 847/377–8120; Mr. Dale W Galassie

Lake County Health Department / Behavioral Health Services, 3012 Grand Avenue, Waukegan, IL 60085; tel. 847/377–8299; Mr. Dale W Galassie

Leyden Family Service and Mental Health Center, 10001 West Grand Avenue, Franklin Park, IL 60131; tel. 847/451–0330; Mr. Dennis P Vaccaro

McHenry County Youth Service Bureau, 101 South Jefferson Street, Woodstock, IL 60098; tel. 815/338–7360; Ms. Susan H Krause

Michael Reese Hospital - OTP, 2929 South Ellis Avenue, Chicago, IL 60616; tel. 312/791–3545; Dr. Enrique Beckmann

Naperville Psychiatric Venture d/b/a Linden Oaks Hospital, 801 South Washington, Naperville, IL 60566-7060; tel. 630/305–5500; Ms. Mary L Mastro

North Central Behavioral Health Systems, Inc., PO Box 1488, La Salle, IL 61301; tel. 815/223–0160; Mr. Donald P Miskowiec

Northwest Community Hospital Youth Center, 901 Kirchoff Road, Arlington Heights, IL 60005; tel. 847/618–1000; Mr. Bruce K Crowther

Northwestern Memorial Hospital Opioid Treatment Program, 320 Huron Street, Chicago, IL 60611; tel. 312/926–2000; Mr. Dean M Harrison

P.H.A.S.E. Inc., Methadone Treatment Program, 516 Green Street, Rockford, IL 61102; tel. 815/966–1285; Ms. Judy Weiher

PEER Services, Inc., 906 Davis Street, Evanston, IL 60201; tel. 847/492–1778; Ms. Kate Mahoney

Perry County Counseling Center, Inc., 1016 S Madison St, Suite A, Du Quoin, IL 62832; tel. 618/542–4357; Mr. John R Venskus

ProCare Centers, 1820 South 25th Avenue, Broadview, IL 60153; tel. 708/338–3806; Mr. J. Melvin J Smith

Sangamon Menard Alcoholism and Drugs Council, 120 North 11th Street, Springfield, IL 62703-1002; tel. 217/544–9858; Mr. Stephen J Knox

Sinnissippi Centers, Inc., 325 Illinois Route 2, Dixon, IL 61021; tel. 815/284–6611; Mr. James R Sarver

Sojourn House, Inc., 565 North Turner Avenue, Freeport, IL 61032; tel. 815/232–5121; Ms. Brenda J Bombard

South Shore Hospital, 8012 S. Crandon Avenue, Chicago, IL 60617; tel. 773/356–5200; Mr. Jesus M Ong

Southeastern Illinois Counseling Centers, Inc., Drawer M, Olney, IL 62450; tel. 618/395–4306; Mr. Glenn Jackson

Tazwood Mental Health Center, Inc., 1423 Valle Vista Boulevard, Pekin, IL 61554; tel. 309/347–5579; Mr. Michael Polson

The South Suburban Council on Alcoholism and Substance Abuse, 1909 Cheker Square, East Hazel Crest, IL 60429; tel. 708/647–3333; Mr. Allen Sandusky

The Women's Treatment Center, 140 N. Ashland Avenue, Chicago, IL 60607; tel. 312/850–0050; Dr. Jewell Oates

Triangle Center Methadone Clinic, 120 North 11th Street, Springfield, IL 62703; tel. 217/544–9858; Mr. Stephen J Knox

VA Chicago Health Care System (OTP), 820 South Damen Avenue (Independence Hall), Chicago, IL 60612; tel. 312/569–6289; Dr. Robert J Craig

INDIANA

BehaviorCorp, Inc., 697 Pro-Med Lane, Carmel, IN 46032-5323; tel. 317/587–0500; Mr. Larry L Burch

Center for Behavioral Health, 645 South Rogers Street, Bloomington, IN 47403; tel. 812/339–1691; Dr. Dennis P Morrison

Community Mental Health Center, Inc., 285 Bielby Road, Lawrenceburg, IN 47025; tel. 812/537–1302; Mr. Joseph D Stephens

Comprehensive Mental Health Services, Inc., 240 North Tillotson Avenue, Muncie, IN 47304; tel. 765/288–1928; Mr. Hank A Milius

Cummins Behavioral Health Systems, Inc., 6655 East US 36, Avon, IN 46123; tel. 317/272–6361; Ms. Ann Borders

Fairbanks Hospital, Inc., 8102 Clearvista Parkway, Indianapolis, IN 46256-4698; tel. 317/849–8222; Ms. Helene M Cross

Family & Children's Center Counseling and Development Service, 105 East Jefferson Blvd Suite 700, South Bend, IN 46601; tel. 574/232–2255; Dr. James J Reisinger

Four County Comprehensive Mental Health, Inc., 1015 Michigan Avenue, Logansport, IN 46947; tel. 574/722–5151; Mr. Laurence R Ulrich

Grant-Blackford Mental Health, Inc., 505 Wabash Avenue, Marion, IN 46952; tel. 765/662–3971; Mr. Paul G Kuczora

Hamilton Center, Inc, PO Box 4323, Terre Haute, IN 47804-0323; tel. 812/231–8323; Mr. Galen Goode

LifeSpring Mental Health Services, 460 Spring Street, Jeffersonville, IN 47130; tel. 812/280–2080; Dr. Terry L Stawar

Madison Center, Inc., PO Box 80, South Bend, IN 46624; tel. 574/234–0061; Mr. Jack Roberts

Midtown Narcotics Treatment Program, 832 North Meridian Street, Indianapolis, IN 46204; tel. 317/686–5634; Mr/Mrs Margie Payne

Oaklawn, PO Box 809 330 Lakeview Drive, Goshen, IN 46527-0809; tel. 219/533–1234; Mr. Harold C Loewen

Quinco Behavioral Health Systems, 720 N. Marr Rd., Columbus, IN 47201; tel. 812/348-7449; Dr. Robert J Williams

Richard L. Roudebush VA Medical Center, 1481 West 10th Street, Bldg 1, Indianapolis, IN 46202; tel. 317/554-0000; Dr. Sean O'Connor

Southlake Center for Mental Health, 8555 Taft Street, Merrillville, IN 46410-6199; tel. 219/769-4005; Mr. Lee Strawhun

Southwestern Indiana Mental Health Center, Inc., 415 Mulberry Street, Evansville, IN 47713-1298; tel. 812/436-4231; Mr. John K Browning

Tara Treatment Center, Inc., 6231 South US 31, Franklin, IN 46131; tel. 812/526-2611; Ms. Ann Daugherty

The Center for Mental Health, Inc., PO Box 1258, Anderson, IN 46015; tel. 765/649-8161; Mr. C. Richard DeHaven

The Otis R. Bowen Center for Human Services, Inc., PO Box 497, Warsaw, IN 46581-0497; tel. 574/267-7169; Mr. Kurt Carlson

Tri-City Community Mental Health Center, Inc., 3903 Indianapolis Boulevard, East Chicago, IN 46312; tel. 219/392-6010; Mr. Robert Krumwied

Wabash Valley Hospital, Inc., 2900 North River Road, West Lafayette, IN 47906; tel. 765/463-2555; Mr. Rick Crawley

IOWA

Hillcrest Family Services, 2005 Asbury Road, Dubuque, IA 52001; tel. 563/583-7357; Mr. Gary L Gansemer

Orchard Place, 925 Southwest Porter Avenue, Des Moines, IA 50315; tel. 515/285-6781; Mr. Brock Wolff

KANSAS

Atchison Valley Hope, PO Box 312, Atchison, KS 66002; tel. 913/367-1618; Dr. Kenneth C Gregoire

Marillac Center, 8000 W. 127th Street, Overland Park, KS 66213; tel. 816/508-3300; Mr. R. Michael Bowen

Norton Valley Hope, PO Box 510, Norton, KS 67654; tel. 785/877-5101; Dr. Kenneth C Gregoire

The Kansas City Metro Methadone Program, 3901 Rainbow Boulevard, Kansas City, KS 66160-7341; tel. 913/588-6493; Dr. William F Gabrielli, Jr.

The Saint Francis Academy, Incorporated, 509 East Elm Street, Salina, KS 67401; tel. 785/825-0541; Rev. Edward W Fellhauer

KENTUCKY

Adanta Behavioral Health Services, 259 Parkers Mill Road, Somerset, KY 42501; tel. 606/679-4782; Ms. Cathy Epperson

Bluegrass Regional / Narcotics Addiction Program, 1351 Newtown Pike, Lexington, KY 40511; tel. 859/253-1686; Mr. Joseph Toy

Bluegrass Regional Mental Health - Mental Retardation Bd, 1351 Newtown Pike, Lexington, KY 40511; tel. 859/253-1686; Mr. Joseph A Toy

Cumberland River Regional MH/MR Board, Inc., 1203 American Greeting Road, Corbin, KY 40702; tel. 606/528-7010; Mr. Danny Jones

NorthKey Community Care, PO Box 2680, Covington, KY 41012; tel. 859/578-3233; Dr. Edward G Muntel

Seven Counties Services, Inc., 101 W Muhammad Ali Boulevard, Louisville, KY 40202; tel. 502/589-8600; Dr. Howard F Bracco

LOUISIANA

Addiction Recovery Resources of New Orleans, 4836 Wabash Street, Suite 202, Metairie, LA 70001; tel. 504/780-2766; Ms. Darci R Jones

DRD New Orleans Medical Clinic, 417 S. Johnson Street, New Orleans, LA 70112; tel. 816/357-2461; Ms. Janet Hasler

Lifecare Psychiatric Services, 170 Industrial Parkway, Lafayette, LA 70508; tel. 337/262-8672; Mr. Harry CiceroSr.

Opioid Substitution Treatment Program, VA Medical Center, 1601 Perdido Street, New Orleans, LA 70112; tel. 504/568-0811; Dr. Jose Pena

Vermilion Hospital for Psychiatric and Addictive Medicine, 2520 North University Avenue, Lafayette, LA 70507; tel. 337/234-5614; Mr. Russell B Kahn

MAINE

Acadia Hospital - Narcotic Treatment Program, PO Box 422, Bangor, ME 04402-0422; tel. 207/973-6100; Mr. Scott O Farnum

Cap Quality Care, 1 Delta Drive, Suite A, Westbrook, ME 04092; tel. 207/856-7227; Mrs. Susan Sullivan

KidsPeace National Centers of New England, P.O. Box 787, Ellsworth, ME 04605; tel. 207/771-5700; Mr. Ken Olson

Mercy Recovery Center, 40 Park Road, Portland, ME 04102; tel. 207/857-8085; Mrs. Eileen F Skinner

MARYLAND

Addiction Treatment Services of Hopkins Bayview, 5510 Nathan Shock Drive, Suite 1500, Baltimore, MD 21224; tel. 410/550-0028; Mr. Gregory Schaffer

Addiction Treatment Services of Hopkins Bayview, 5200 Eastern Avenue, MFL-6-E, Baltimore, MD 21224; tel. 410/550-0004; Mr. Gregory Schaffer

Ashley, Inc., 800 Tydings Lane, Havre De Grace, MD 21078; tel. 410/273-6600; Mr. Leonard A Dahl

Awakenings, 2 West Aylesbury Road, Timonium, MD 21093; tel. 410/561-9591; Dr. Sheldon D Glass

Baltimore Behavioral Health, Inc., 200 South Arlington Avenue, Baltimore, MD 21223; tel. 410/962-7180; Mr. William K Hathaway

Behavioral Pharmacology Research Unit, 5510 Nathan Shock Drive, Baltimore, MD 21224; tel. 410/550-0048; Mr. Gregory Schaffer

Bon Secours New Hope Treatment Center, 2401 West Baltimore Street, Baltimore, MD 21223; tel. 410/945-7706; Mr. Percy AllenII

Bon Secours' ADAPT Cares, 2000 W Baltimore Street, Baltimore, MD 21223; tel. 410/383-4995; Mr. Percy AllenII

Center for Addiction Medicine, 827 Linden Avenue, Baltimore, MD 21201; tel. 410/225-8240; Dr. Michael Hayes

Daybreak Rehabilitation Center, 2490 Giles Road, Baltimore, MD 21225; tel. 410/396-1646; Dr. Sheldon D Glass

Druid Heights Treatment and Counseling Center, Inc., 2009 Druid Hill Avenue, Baltimore, MD 21217; tel. 410/669-0475; Ms. Barbara Bostick-Hunt

Frederick County Health Dept. / Substance Abuse Services, 300-B Scholl's Lane, Frederick, MD 21701; tel. 301/694-1775; Dr. Barbara Brookmyer

Glass Substance Abuse Program, Inc., 821 North Eutaw Street, Baltimore, MD 21202; tel. 410/225-9185; Dr. Sheldon D Glass

Hope House, PO Box 546, Crownsville, MD 21032; tel. 410/923-6700; Ms. Marilyn Moran

Hudson Health Services, Inc., PO Box 1096, Salisbury, MD 21802-1096; tel. 410/219-9000; Mr. James O Freeman, Jr.

Maryland Treatment Centers, Inc., PO Box 136, Emmitsburg, MD 21727; tel. 301/447-2361; Ms. Mary A Roby

MBA - Cherry Hill, 2490 Giles Road, Baltimore, MD 21225; tel. 410/225-9185; Dr. Sheldon D Glass

Methadone for Business Achievers (MBA), 821 North Eutaw Street, Baltimore, MD 21201; tel. 410/225-9185; Dr. Sheldon D Glass

Methadone for Business Achievers - Timonium, 2 West Aylesbury Road, Timonium, MD 21093; tel. 410/561-9591; Dr. Sheldon D Glass

Mid-Atlantic Treatment Services, Inc., 2100 North Charles Street, Baltimore, MD 21201; tel. 410/752-6505; Ms. Barbara Q McKenna

New Life Addiction Counseling Services, Inc., 2528 Mountain Road, Suite 204, Pasadena, MD 21122; tel. 410/255-4475; Mr. Thomas S Porter

Partners in Recovery, 6525 North Charles Street, Baltimore, MD 21204; tel. 410/296-9747; Ms. Dawn James

Pathways, 2620 Riva Road, Annapolis, MD 21401; tel. 410/573-5400; Mrs. Helen K Reines

Potomac Ridge Behavioral Health Center, 14901 Broschart Road, Rockville, MD 20850; tel. 301/251-4500; Mr. Craig S Juengling

Prince George's County Health Department, 1701 McCormick Drive, Suite 230, Upper Marlboro, MD 20772; tel. 301/883-7903; Dr. Frederick J Corder

Prince George's County Health Dept/Northern Region Treatment, 1701 McCormick Drive, Largo, MD 20774; tel. 301/883-7853; Dr. Frederick Corder

Reflective Treatment Center, 707 Constitution Street, Baltimore, MD 21202; tel. 410/727-7400; Dr. Marie J Washington

Sinai Hospital Addictions Recovery Program, 2401 West Belvedere Avenue, Baltimore, MD 21215; tel. 410/601-5355; Mr. Neil Meltzer

The Johns Hopkins Hospital Drug Abuse Program, 911 Broadway, Baltimore, MD 21205; tel. 410/955-5439; Ms. Mary Elizabeth McCaul

Tuerk House, Inc., PO Box 31419, Baltimore, MD 21216-6119; tel. 410/233-0684; Dr. John E Hickey

VA Maryland Health Care System Opioid Treatment Program, 10 North Greene Street, Baltimore, MD 21201; tel. 410/605-7410; Dr. Joseph Liberto

Wicomico County Health Department, 108 East Main Street, Salisbury, MD 21801; tel. 410/742-3784; Dr. Judith A Sensenbrenner

Worcester County Health Department, PO Box 249, Snow Hill, MD 21863; tel. 410/632-1100; Ms. Deborah Goeller

MASSACHUSETTS

AdCare Hospital of Worcester, Inc., 107 Lincoln Street, Worcester, MA 01605; tel. 508/799-9000; Mr. David Hillis

Baldpate Hospital, 83 Baldpate Road, Georgetown, MA 01833; tel. 978/352-2131; Dr. Subhash C Mukherjee

Bournewood Hospital (Detoxification Program), 300 South Street, Chestnut Hill, MA 02467; tel. 617/469-0300; Dr. Nasir A Khan

Center for Human Services, Inc., 86 R Gifford Street, New Bedford, MA 02744; tel. 508/999-3126; Dr. Warren E Berube

Center for Human Services, Inc., P.O. BOX 2097, New Bedford, MA 02741; tel. 508/675-9281; Dr. Warren E Berube

Dimock Community Foundation, Inc. - OTP, 55 Dimock Street, Roxbury, MA 02119; tel. 617/442-8800; Ms. RuthEllen Fitch

Gosnold, Inc., PO Box 929, Falmouth, MA 02541; tel. 508/540-6550; Mr. Raymond V Tamasi

High Point Treatment Center, Inc., 1233 State Road, Plymouth, MA 02360-5133; tel. 508/224-7701; Ms. Fran Markle

Lowell Community Health Center Addiction Treatment Services, 365 East Street, Tewksbury, MA 01876; tel. 978/858-0533; Ms. Dorcas Griss-Saito

McLean Hospital, 115 Mill Street, Belmont, MA 02478; tel. 617/855-3450; Dr. Bruce M Cohen

Mercy Medical Center - MMTP, 1233 Main Street, Holyoke, MA 01040; tel. 413/539-2942; Mr. Vincent J McCorkle

Mercy Medical Center - MMTP, 227 Mill Street, Springfield, MA 01102; tel. 413/539-2942; Mr. Vincent J McCorkle

SSTAR (Detoxification Program), 386 Stanley Street, Fall River, MA 02720; tel. 508/324-7768; Ms. Nancy E Paull

St. Anne's Hospital Lifeline Program, 795 Middle Street, Fall River, MA 02721; tel. 508/675-0131; Ms. Lisa Garcia

VA Boston Health Care System, 150 South Huntington Avenue, Boston, MA 02130; tel. 617/323-7700; Dr. John Renner

MICHIGAN

ACAC, Inc., 3949 Sparks Drive SE Suite 103, Grand Rapids, MI 49546; tel. 616/957-5850; Mr. Michael R Durco

Access Behavioral Healthcare, LLC, 42189 E. Ann Arbor Road, Plymouth, MI 48170; tel. 734/453-5635; Mr. Donald Warner

Apex Behavioral Health, PLLC, 2001 South Merriman, Suite 500, Westland, MI 48186; tel. 734/727-1111; Mr. Thomas Johnson

Arbor Circle Corporation, 1115 Ball Avenue, Grand Rapids, MI 49505; tel. 616/456-7775; Ms. Mary Alice Williams

Brighton Hospital, 12851 East Grand River, Brighton, MI 48116; tel. 810/227-1211; Mr. Frank P Iacobell

Catholic Services of Macomb, Inc., P.O. Box 380290, Clinton Township, MI 48038; tel. 586/416-2300; Mr. Thomas J Reed

City of Detroit Dept of Human Services/Drug Treatment Division, 5031 Grandy, Detroit, MI 48211; tel. 313/852-5601; Mr. William Warren

Community Care Services, 26184 West Outer Drive, Lincoln Park, MI 48146; tel. 313/389-7525; Mr. William P Walsh

Community Mental Health of Clinton-Eaton-Ingham Counties, 812 East Jolly Road, Lansing, MI 48910; tel. 517/346-8238; Ms. Judith L Cates

Community Mental Health Services of Muskegon County, 376 Apple Avenue, Muskegon, MI 49442; tel. 231/724-1111; Mr. James M Elwell

Deaf Options, 220 Bagley, Suite 600, Detroit, MI 48226-1420; tel. 313/961-8120; Ms. Reichelle Anderson

Department of Human Services - Gratiot Clinic, 3506 Gratiot Clinic, Detroit, MI 48207; tel. 313/852-5609; Mr. Ronald McWhite

Department of Human Services - Northwest Clinic, 14602 Greenfield, Detroit, MI 48202; tel. 313/876-4240; Mr. Kenneth Perry

Department of Human Services, Herman Kiefer Hospital, Bldg 5, 8809 John C. Lodge, Detroit, MI 48202; tel. 313/852–5609; Mr. Calvin Carter

East Side Substance Abuse Clinic, 445 East Sherman Boulevard, Muskegon, MI 49444; tel. 231/739–4359; Mr. Daryl L Smith

Eastern Clinic, 1555 Eastern Southeast, Grand Rapids, MI 49507; tel. 616/243–6262; Mr. Daryl L Smith

Eleonore Hutzel Recovery Center, 301 East Hancock Street, Detroit, MI 48201; tel. 313/745–7411; Dr. Arthur Porter

Gerontology Network, 500 Cherry Street, SE, Grand Rapids, MI 49503; tel. 616/977–3300; Dr. Thomas A Hartwig

Gratiot/McNichols Clinic/Metro East Substance Abuse Treatment, PO Box 13408, Detroit, MI 48205; tel. 313/371–7770; Mr. Leslie B Carroll

Growth Works Incorporated, PO Box 6115, Plymouth, MI 48170-0115; tel. 734/455–4095; Mr. Dale F Yagiela

Harper/Chalmers Clinic & Corp Metro East Substance Abuse, PO Box 13408, Detroit, MI 48213; tel. 313/371–0055; Mr. Leslie B Carroll

Hegira Programs, Inc., 8623 N Wayne Road, Suite 200, Westland, MI 48185; tel. 734/458–4601; Mr. Edward L Forry

Heron Ridge Associates, PLC, 3694 Clarkston Road, Suite D, Clarkston, MI 48348; tel. 248/391–0050; Ms. Debra Scheck

Horizon Treatment Services, LLC, 29444 Joy Road, Livonia, MI 48150; tel. 734/421–8272; Mrs. Kellie Puro

Kairos Healthcare, Inc., 6379 Dixie Hwy., Bridgeport, MI 48722; tel. 989/777–4357; Mr. Frederick E Wigen, Jr.

Lapeer County Health Department, 1800 Imlay City Road, Lapeer, MI 48446; tel. 810/667–0243; Ms. Stephanie Mercer

Latino Family Services, Inc., 3815 West Fort Street, Detroit, MI 48216; tel. 313/841–7380; Ms. Alicia Villarreal

Meridian Professional Psychological Consultants, PC, 5031 Park Lake Road, East Lansing, MI 48823; tel. 517/332–0811; Dr. Thomas S Gunnings

Nardin Park Recovery Center, 9605 Grand River, Detroit, MI 48204; tel. 313/834–5930; Mrs. Annie B Scott

National Council on Alcoholism and Addictions, 3600 S. Dort Highway #46, Flint, MI 48507; tel. 810/767–0350; Ms. Linda Bielskis

NCADD/GDA, 16647 Wyoming, Detroit, MI 48221; tel. 313/861–0666; Mr. Benjamin A Jones

Northeast Guidance Center, 12800 E. Warren, Detroit, MI 48215; tel. 313/824–8000; Ms. Cheryl C Coleman

Oakland Psychological Clinic, P.C., 40950 N Woodward Avenue Suite 110, Bloomfield Hills, MI 48304; tel. 248/594–1200; Dr. Barry H Tigay

ProMed Management, 33200 Dequindre Road Suite200, Sterling Heights, MI 48310; tel. 586/268–4239; Mr. Karl L Senkowski

Quality Behavioral Health, Inc., 751 East Grand Boulevard, Detroit, MI 48207; tel. 313/922–2222; Mr. Naveed Syed

Rainbow Center of Michigan, P.O. Box 14947, Detroit, MI 48214; tel. 313/871–2243; Ms. Winnifred Griffin

Rainbow Center of Michigan Inc, 12501 Hamilton Avenue, Highland Park, MI 48203; tel. 313/865–1580; Ms. Winnifred Griffin

Redford Counseling Center, 25945 West Seven Mile Road, Redford, MI 48240; tel. 313/535–6560; Ms. JoAnn Sadler

River's Bend, P.C., 33975 Dequindre, Suite 5, Troy, MI 48083; tel. 248/585–3239; Mr. James L Keener

Star Center, Inc., 13575 Lesure, Detroit, MI 48227; tel. 313/493–4410; Ms. Lucila S Ryder

STM Clinic - Mental Health and Addiction Services, 501 Lapeer Avenue, Suite 200, Saginaw, MI 48607-1203; tel. 517/755–2532; Ms. Sara Terry-Moton

The Center for Counseling, 32743 23 Mile Road, New Baltimore, MI 48047; tel. 586/716–0980; Ms. Cherie C Whiting

The Guidance Center, 13101 Allen Road, Southgate, MI 48195; tel. 734/785–7000; Mr. Leroy A Lott

Turning Point Programs, 72 Sheldon Boulevard, S.E., Grand Rapids, MI 49503; tel. 616/742–0351; Mr. Robert E Byrd

Tuscola Behavioral Health Systems, PO Box 239, Caro, MI 48723; tel. 989/673–6191; Mr. Robert E Chadwickll

VA Medical Center - John D. Dingell - OTP, 4646 John R. Street, Detroit, MI 48201; tel. 313/576–3725; Dr. John Grabowski

Washington Way Recovery Center of Foote Hospital, 2424 West Washington Avenue, Jackson, MI 49203; tel. 517/788–4800; Ms. Georgia' Fojtasek

Washtenaw County Community Supports and Treatment Services, PO Box 915, Ypsilanti, MI 48197; tel. 734/544–3000; Ms. Donna Sabourin

MINNESOTA

Hazelden Recovery Services, PO Box 11, Center City, MN 55012; tel. 612/257–4000; Ms. Ellen Breyer

Hennepin Faculty Associates Addiction Medicine Program, 914 South Eighth St. (D131), Minneapolis, MN 55404; tel. 612/347–5324; Mr. Larry Fosbury

Miller-Dwan Medical Center, Inc., 502 East Second Street, Duluth, MN 55805; tel. 218/727–8762; Adm. Rocklon B Chapin

New Beginnings at Waverly, LLC, 109 North Shore Drive, Waverly, MN 55390-9743; tel. – –; Mr. Dick Kessler

St. Joseph's Hospital Chemical Dependency Unit, 69 West Exchange Street, Saint Paul, MN 55102; tel. 651/232–3300; Mr. Tim Hansen

Veterans Affairs Medical Cente Outpatient Methadone Program, One Veterans Drive, Minneapolis, MN 55417; tel. 612/725–2228; Dr. Mark Willenbring

Willmar Regional Treatment Center - Bradley Center, 1550 Highway 71 Northeast, Willmar, MN 56201; tel. 320/231–5356; Ms. Sandra J Butturff

MISSISSIPPI

CARES Center, Inc., 402 Wesley Avenue, Jackson, MS 39202; tel. 601/352–7784; Mr. Christopher M Cherney

COPAC, Inc., 3949 Highway 43 North, Brandon, MS 39047; tel. 601/829–2500; Dr. J. Stacy Hughes

Pine Belt Mental Healthcare Resources, PO Drawer 1030, Hattiesburg, MS 39401; tel. 601/544–4641; Mr. Jerry Mayo

MISSOURI

Boonville Valley Hope, PO Box 398, Boonville, MO 65233; tel. 660/882–6547; Dr. Kenneth C Gregoire

Centrec Care, Inc., 1030 Woodcrest Terrace Drive, Saint Louis, MO 63141; tel. 314/205–8068; Dr. Mohammed A Kabir

DRD Columbia Medical Clinic, 1415 Paris Road, Columbia, MO 65201; tel. 573/449–8338; Ms. Janet Hasler

DRD Kansas City Medical Clinic, 723 East 18th Street, Kansas City, MO 64108; tel. 816/357–2461; Ms. Janet Hasler

DRD Springfield Medical Clinic, 404 East Battlefield Street, Springfield, MO 65807; tel. 417/865–8045; Ms. Janet Hasler

Northland Family Counseling Center, Inc., 429 Northeast 69 Highway, Kansas City, MO 64119; tel. 816/452–8777; Mr. Maurice L Cummings

Paseo Comprehensive Rehabilitation Clinic - WMMHC, 2211 Charlotte, Felix Building, Lower Level, Kansas City, MO 64108; tel. 816/512–7143; Mr. David V Fleming

Provident Counseling, Inc., 2650 Olive Street, Saint Louis, MO 63103; tel. 314/371–6500; Ms. Kathleen E Buescher

ReDiscover, 901 NE Independence Avenue, Lees Summit, MO 64086; tel. 816/246–8000; Mr. Alan Flory

St. Louis VA Medical Center - Opioid Treatment Program, 915 North Grand Boulevard, Saint Louis, MO 63106; tel. 314/289–7020; Mr. Glen Struchtemeyer

MONTANA

Rocky Boy Chemical Dependency Center, Rural Route 1, Box 664, Box Elder, MT 59521; tel. 406/395–4818; Mr. James Eastlick

Rocky Mountain Treatment Center, 920 Fourth Avenue North, Great Falls, MT 59401; tel. 406/727–8832; Mrs. Marcie J Dardis

NEBRASKA

Behavioral Health Specialists, Inc., 600 South 13th Street, Norfolk, NE 68701; tel. 402/370–3140; Ms. Connie Barnes

Blue Valley Mental Health Center, Inc., 1121 North 10th Street, Beatrice, NE 68310; tel. 402/228–3386; Dr. Wayne R Price

Hastings Regional Center, PO Box 579, Hastings, NE 68902-0579; tel. 402/462–1971; Mr. William R Gibson

O'Neill Valley Hope, 1421 North 10th Street, O' Neill, NE 68763; tel. 402/336–3747; Dr. Kenneth C Gregoire

University Drug and Alcohol Program, 1941 S. 42nd Street, Suite 210, Omaha, NE 68105; tel. 402/595–1703; Dr. Todd Stull

NEVADA

Las Vegas Recovery Center, 3371 N. Buffalo Drive, Las Vegas, NV 89129; tel. 702/515–1373; Mr. Stuart P Smith

NEW HAMPSHIRE

Southern New Hampshire Medical Center, PO Box 2014, Nashua, NH 03061-2014; tel. 603/577–2000; Dr. Gary Kaufman

NEW JERSEY

AtlantiCare Behavioral Health, 2511 Fire Road, Unit B10 Bellevue Commons, Egg Harbor Township, NJ 08234; tel. 609/645–7600; Mr. Ted Stryker

Bayonne Community Mental Health Center, 601 Broadway, Bayonne, NJ 07002; tel. 201/339–9200; Mr. Joseph M Kadian

Bonnie Brae, 3415 Valley Road, P. O. Box 825, Liberty Corner, NJ 07938-0825; tel. 908/647–0800; Mr. William M Powers

Cape Counseling Services, 217 N. Main Street Suite 202, Cape May Court House, NJ 08210; tel. 609/463–0014; Mr. Gregory Speed

Carrier Clinic, PO Box 147, Belle Mead, NJ 08502-0147; tel. 908/281–1381; Mr. C. R Sarle

Catholic Charities - Diocese of Metuchen, 319 Maple Street, Perth Amboy, NJ 08861; tel. 732/324–8200; Ms. Marianne Majewski

Comprehensive Behavioral Healthcare, Inc., 516 Valley Brook Avenue, Lyndhurst, NJ 07071; tel. 201/935–3322; Mr. Peter Scerbo

CPC Behavioral Healthcare, Inc, Parkway 100, 3535 Route 66, Building 5, Suite D, Neptune, NJ 07753; tel. 732/643–4301; Mr. John Mans

Daytop Village, Inc., 80 W. Main St., Mendham, NJ 07945; tel. 973/543–5656; Mr. Joseph Hennen

Discovery Institute for Addictive Disorders, Inc., PO Box 177, Marlboro, NJ 07746; tel. 732/946–9444; Mr. Robert C Denes

Drug Dependence Treatment Program-VANJHCS-East Orange Campus, 385 Tremont Avenue. Bldg 15, East Orange, NJ 07018; tel. 973/676–1000; Dr. Miklos Losonczy

Family Service of Burlington County, 770 Woodlane Road, Mount Holly, NJ 08060; tel. 609/267–5928; Ms. Mary Wells

High Focus Centers, 47 Maple Street, Suite 404, Summit, NJ 07901; tel. 908/363–1023; Dr. David Nyman

Kennedy Opioid Treatment Program, Kennedy Mem Hospitals, 300 Woodbury-Turnersville Road, Blackwood, NJ 08012; tel. 856/227–5254; Ms. Terry Marini

Khaleidoscope Health Care, Inc., Jones and Associates-111 Wayne Street, Jersey City, NJ 07302; tel. 201/451–5425; Mr. Larry M Ali Blake, Jr.

Mount Carmel Guild Behavioral Healthcare System, 1160 Raymond Boulevard, Newark, NJ 07102; tel. 973/639–6508; Mr. Michael Leitzes

New Hope Foundation, Inc, PO Box 66, Marlboro, NJ 07746; tel. 732/946–3030; Dr. Anthony W Comerford

Ocean Medical Services, Inc, 2001 Route 37 East, Toms River, NJ 08753; tel. 732/288–9322; Ms. Edie Novak

Organization for Recovery, Inc, P.O. Box 827, Plainfield, NJ 07061; tel. 908/769–4700; Ms. Linda Voorhis

Preferred Behavioral Health of New Jersey, Inc., 700 Airport Road, P.O. Box 2036, Lakewood, NJ 08701; tel. 732/364–4590; Mr. William J Sette

Raritan Bay Medical Center - Methadone Program, 595 New Brunswick Avenue, Perth Amboy, NJ 08861; tel. 732/442–3700; Mr. Michael D'Agnes

Recovery Services of New Jersey, Inc., 5034 Atlantic Avenue, Mays Landing, NJ 08330; tel. 609/625–4900; Dr. Kenneth R Sandler

Richard Hall Community Mental Health Center, 500 North Bridge Street, Bridgewater, NJ 08807; tel. 908/253–3136; Mr. Peter O Casey

Saint Barnabas Behavioral Health Center, Inc., 1691 US Highway 9, CN 2025, Toms River, NJ 08754; tel. 732/914–1688; Mr. Joe Hicks

Strathmore Treatment Associates, LLC, PO Box 125, South Amboy, NJ 08879; tel. 732/727–2555; Mr. Anthony Caputo

Suburban Treatment Associates, 43 Progress Street, Union, NJ 07083; tel. 908/687–7188; Ms. Van Macaluso

Sunrise House Foundation, PO Box 600, Lafayette, NJ 07848; tel. 973/383–6300; Dr. Philip N Horowitz

Urban Treatment Associates Inc., 424-32 Market Street, Camden, NJ 08102; tel. 856/338–1811; Mrs. Michelle Norquest

Warren Medical Services, Inc, 590 Marshall Street, Phillipsburg, NJ 08865; tel. 908/387–0003; Mr. Gary D Gavornik

NEW MEXICO

University of New Mexico Health Sciences Center, 2121 Lomas Blvd. N.E., Albuquerque, NM 87106; tel. 505/272–2121; Dr. Philip R Eaton

Youth and Family Centered Services of New Mexico, Inc., 5310 Sequoia Northwest, Albuquerque, NM 87120; tel. 505/836–7330; Ms. Carol Bickelman

NEW YORK

A.R.E.B.A.-Casriel, Inc, 500 West 57th Street, New York, NY 10019; tel. 212/293–3000; Mr. Steven J Yohay

Acute Chemical Dependency Detox Unit - Kings County, 606 Winthrop Street, Brooklyn, NY 11203; tel. 718/245–3901; Ms. Jean Leon

Arms Acres, 75 Seminary Hill Road, Carmel, NY 10512; tel. 845/225–3400; Ms. Patrice Wallace-Moore

Bellevue Hospital Center Chemi Dependency Medically Detox, 462 First Avenue, New York, NY 10016; tel. 212/562–4132; Mr. Carlos Perez

Bellevue Hospital Methadone Treatment Program, 462 First Avenue, New York, NY 10016; tel. 212/562–4132; Mr. Carlos Perez

Beth Israel Medical Center, 201 West 13th Street, New York, NY 10011; tel. 212/420–2015; Mr. Charles Jacknow

Beth Israel Medical Center, 1-9 Nathan Perlman Place, New York, NY 10003; tel. 212/420–4275; Dr. Mathew E Fink

Beth Israel Medical Center MMTP - Gouverneur Clinic, 109 Delaney Street, New York, NY 10002; tel. 212/420–2086; Ms. Marie Marciano

Beth Israel Medical Center MMTP - Harlem 6/7, 103 East 125th Street, 2nd Flr, New York, NY 10035; tel. 212/774–3260; Ms. Marie Marciano

Beth Israel Medical Center MMTP - Marie Nyswander Clinic, 721 Ninth Avenue, New York, NY 10019; tel. 212/247–7180; Ms. Marie Marciano

Beth Israel Medical Center MMTP - Vincent P Dole, 215 Park Avenue South, New York, NY 10003; tel. 718/965–7901; Ms. Marie Marciano

Beth Israel Medical Center MMTP Clinic 1E, First Avenue @ 16 Street, New York, NY 10003; tel. 212/844–1929; Ms. Marie Marciano

Beth Israel Medical Center MMTP Clinic 2C, 435 Second Avenue, 2nd Floor, New York, NY 10010; tel. 212/726–6822; Ms. Marie Marciano

Beth Israel Medical Center MMTP Clinic 2F, 429 Second Avenue, New York, NY 10010; tel. 212/726–6821; Ms. Marie Marciano

Beth Israel Medical Center MMTP Clinic 3C, 215 Park Avenue, New York, NY 10003; tel. 212/726–6824; Ms. Marie Marciano

Beth Israel Medical Center MMTP Clinic 3G, 215 Park Avenue, New York, NY 10003; tel. 212/726–6863; Ms. Marie Marciano

Beth Israel Medical Center MMTP Clinic 8D, 140 West 125th Street, 6th Flr, New York, NY 10027; tel. 212/864–0904; Ms. Marie Marciano

Beth Israel Medical Center MMTP Cumberland Clinic, 100 Flatbush Avenue, Brooklyn, NY 11217; tel. 718/237–9600; Ms. Marie Marciano

Beth Israel Medical Center MMTP Harlem 3, 215 Park Avenue South, New York, NY 10003; tel. 212/774–3230; Ms. Marie Marciano

Beth Israel Medical Center MMTP Harlem Clinic 1, First Avenue @ 16th Street, New York, NY 10003; tel. 212/774–3210; Ms. Marie Marciano

Beth Israel Medical Center MMTP Harlem Clinic 2, 103 East 125th Street, 4th Flr, New York, NY 10035; tel. 212/774–3200; Ms. Marie Marciano

Beth Israel Medical Center MMTP Harlem Clinic 8, 215 Park Avenue South, New York, NY 10003; tel. 212/864–8177; Ms. Marie Marciano

Beth Israel Medical Center MMTP, Avenue A Clinic, 26 Avenue A, New York, NY 10009; tel. 212/420–2078; Ms. Marie Marciano

Bronx-Lebanon Hospital Center, 1650 Grand Concourse, Bronx, NY 10457; tel. 718/590–1800; Mr. Miguel A Fuentes, Jr.

Bronx-Lebanon Hospital Center - MMTP/Keep, 3100 Third Avenue, Bronx, NY 10451; tel. 718/579–2600; Dr. Jeffrey Levine

Cabrini Medical Center, 227 E 19th Street, 13th Floor - Chemical Dependency Unit, New York, NY 10003; tel. 212/995–6000; Mr. Robert S Chaloner

Carnegie Hill Institute, 116 East 92nd Street, New York, NY 10128; tel. 212/289–7166; Dr. Harvey D Karkus

Coney Island Hospital - Acute Care Addictions Program, 2601 Ocean Parkway, Brooklyn, NY 11235; tel. 718/616–4083; Mr. William Walsh

Conifer Park, Inc, 79 Glenridge Road, Glenville, NY 12302; tel. 518/399–6446; Mr. Patrick Carrese

Cornerstone of Medical Arts Center Hospital, 57 West 57th Street, New York, NY 10019; tel. 212/755–0200; Mr. Norman J Sokolow

Cornerstone of Medical Arts Center Hospital, 57 West 57th Street, New York, NY 10019; tel. 212/755–0200; Mr. Thomas C Puzo

Correctional Health Services, Westchester County Health Care, Valhalla Campus, Valhalla, NY 10595; tel. 914/493–8878; Ms. Mary Brown

Crouse Hospital Methadone Maintenance Treatment Program, 410 South Crouse Avenue, Syracuse, NY 13210; tel. 315/470–7829; Dr. Paul Kronenberg

Drug Treatment & Education Cen North Shore Univ Hospital, 400 Community Drive, Manhasset, NY 11030; tel. 516/562–3010; Mr. Dennis Dowling

Elmhurst Hospital Center Methadone Treatment Program, 79-01 Broadway, 2nd Floor, Annex O, Elmhurst, NY 11373; tel. 718/334–1638; Mr. Chris D Constantino

Erie County Medical Center, 462 Grider Street, Buffalo, NY 14215; tel. 716/898–3000; Dr. Roger E Kaiser, Jr.

Flushing Hospital Medical Ctr / Chemical Dependency Unit, 45th Avenue at Parsons Blvd, Flushing, NY 11355; tel. 718/670–5918; Mr. David P Rosen

Good Samaritan Hospital, 255 Lafayette Avenue, Suffern, NY 10901; tel. 845/368–5302; Mr. Michael Schnieders

Gracie Square Hospital - OTP, 420 East 76th Street, New York, NY 10021; tel. 212/434–5322; Mr. Frank Bruno

Harlem Hospital Center Chemica Dependence Detoxification Unit, 506 Lenox Ave, New York, NY 10037; tel. 212/939–1340; Dr. John M Palmer

Harlem Hospital Center MMTP, 264 West 118th Street, New York, NY 10026; tel. 212/939–1340; Dr. John Palmer

Hudson Valley Hospital Center M.M.T.P., 1980 Crompond Road, Cortlandt Manor, NY 10567; tel. 914/737–6117; Mr. John Federspiel

Interfaith Medical Center Substance Abuse Detoxification, 1545 Atlantic Avenue, Brooklyn, NY 11213; tel. 718/613–4001; Mr. Edward Glicksman

Interfaith Medical Center Substance Abuse Detoxification, 1545 Atlantic Avenue, 6th Floor, Brooklyn, NY 11213; tel. 718/613–4001; Mr. Edward J Glicksman

Jacobi Medical Center Chemical Dependence/ Medically Detox, 1400 Pelham Parkway, Bronx, NY 10461; tel. 718/918–5322; Mr. Joseph S Orlando

Long Beach Medical Center M.M.T.P., 455 East Bay Drive, Long Beach, NY 11561; tel. 516/897–1330; Mr. Douglas Melnick

Long Island Center for Recovery Inc., 320 West Montauk Highway, Hampton Bays, NY 11946; tel. 631/728–3100; Mr. Jack Hamilton

Long Island Jewish Medical Center - M.M.T.P., 270-05 76th Avenue, New Hyde Park, NY 11040; tel. 718/470–8940; Mr. Dennis Dowling

Lutheran Medical Center (Acute Care Addiction Program), 150 55th Street, Brooklyn, NY 11220; tel. 718/630–7363; Ms. Wendy Z Goldstein

Mary Immaculate Hospital Clinic I, MMTP, 275 North St, Harrison, NY 10528; tel. 914/925–5301; Dr. Brian Fitzsimmons

Medical Arts Sanitarium, Inc., 500 Milan Hollow Road, Rhinebeck, NY 12572; tel. 845/266–3481; Mr. Norman Sokolow

Medically Managed Inpatient Detoxification, 2 Park Avenue, Yonkers, NY 10703; tel. 914/964–7383; Mr. Jim Foy

Methadone Treatment Program - Kings County / Clinic 3, 600 Albany Avenue, Brooklyn, NY 11203; tel. 718/245–3901; Ms. Jean G Leon

Methadone Treatment Program - Kings County / Clinic I, 600 Albany Avenue, Brooklyn, NY 11203; tel. 718/245–3901; Ms. Jean G Leon

Methadone Treatment Program - Kings County Clinic 2, 600 Albany Avenue, Brooklyn, NY 11203; tel. 718/245–3901; Ms. Jean G Leon

Metropolitan Correctional Center - New York / OTP, 150 Park Row, New York, NY 10007; tel. 646/836–6300; Mr. Marvin D Morrison

Metropolitan Hospital Center Detoxification Unit, 1901 First Avenue, New York, NY 10029; tel. 212/423–7122; Dr. Jose R Sanchez

Metropolitan Hospital Methadone Treatment Program, 1900 Second Avenue, Room 2M29, New York, NY 10029; tel. 212/423–6822; Mr. Louis Martir

Montefiore Medical Center - SATP, 111 East 210th Street, Bronx, NY 10467; tel. 718/920–2001; Mr. Robert B Conaty

Montefiore Medical Center - SATP - OTP - Unit 3, 2005 Jerome Avenue, 1st Floor, Bronx, NY 10467; tel. 718/583–0600; Dr. Spencer Foreman

Montefiore Medical Center - SATP Unit 1, 3550 Jerome Avenue, 1st Floor, Bronx, NY 10467; tel. 718/583–0600; Dr. Spencer Foreman

Narco Freedom Inc. MMTP - Court Street, 250 Grand Concourse, Bronx, NY 10451; tel. 718/292–2240; Mr. Alan Brand

Narco Freedom Inc. MMTP - Willis Avenue, 250 Grand Concourse, Bronx, NY 10455; tel. 718/292–2240; Mr. Alan Brand

Narco Freedom, Inc. MMTP - Redhook, 250 Grand Concourse, Bronx, NY 10451; tel. 718/292–2240; Mr. Alan Brand

Narco Freedom, Inc., Grand Concourse MMTP, 250 Grand Concourse, Bronx, NY 10451; tel. 718/292–2240; Mr. Alan Brand

Narco Freedom, Inc.-Bridge Plaza MMTP, 37-18 34th Street, Long Island City, NY 11101; tel. 718/292–2240; Mr. Alan Brand

Nassau County Department of Drug and Alcohol Addiction, NUMC, 2201 Hempstead Turnpike, East Meadow, NY 11554; tel. 516/572–5906; Dr. John Imhof

New York United Hospital Medical Center, 406 Boston Post Road, Port Chester, NY 10573; tel. 914/934–3000; Mr. Philip Dionne

North General Hospital - MMTP Program, 1879 Madison Avenue, New York, NY 10035; tel. 212/423–4337; Dr. Samuel J Daniel

NYU Downtown (Trinity M.M.T.P.), 74 Trinity Place, 2nd Flr Mezz, New York, NY 10006; tel. 212/312–5000; Dr. Bruce D Logan

Outpatient Methadone Treatment Program at North Shore Univ., 101 St. Andrews Lane, Glen Cove, NY 11542; tel. 516/674–7852; Mr. Dennis Connors

Passages Counseling Center, Inc., 3680 Route 112, Coram, NY 11727; tel. 631/698–9222; Mr. Arnt Monge

Pathways - St. Louise, 209 Niagara Street, Buffalo, NY 14201; tel. 716/856–8411; Mr. Harry Smith

Pathways, Sisters of Charity Hospital, 2157 Main Street, Buffalo, NY 14214; tel. 716/862–1000; Mr. Harry Smith

PROMESA METHADONE TREATMENT PROGRAM, 1776 Clay Ave, Bronx, NY 10457; tel. 718/960–7601; Mr. Ruben A Medina

Quannacut at Eastern Long Island Hospital, 201 Manor Place, Greenport, NY 11944; tel. 631/477–1000; Mr. Paul J ConnorIll

Queens Hospital Center Inpatient Detox Unit, 82-68 164 Street, Jamaica, NY 11434; tel. 718/883–2222; Mr. Antonio D Martin

Restorative Management Corporation, 15 King Street, Middletown, NY 10940; tel. 845/342–5941; Mr. Charles Scharf

Rochester Pathways, Sisters of Charity Hospital, 435 East Henrietta Road, Rochester, NY 14607; tel. 585/424–6580; Mr. Harry Smith

SBH Chemical Dependence Methadone Substance Abuse Treatment, 4535-39 Third Avenue, Bronx, NY 10457; tel. 718/960–6170; Dr. Scott Cooper

Seafield Center, Inc., 7 Seafield Lane, Westhampton Beach, NY 11978; tel. 631/288–1122; Mr. John C Haley

Sound Shore Medical Center, 16 Guion Place, New Rochelle, NY 10802; tel. 914/637–1700; Mr. John R Spicer

South Oaks Hospital, 400 Sunrise Highway, Amityville, NY 11701; tel. 631/264–4000; Mr. Robert Detor

Southside Hospital - Detox Program, 301 East Main Street, Bay Shore, NY 11706; tel. 631/968–3000; Mr. Michael L Nolan

SPAN - Special Prevention Addiction Network, 15 West 136th Steret, New York, NY 10037; tel. 212/939–1340; Dr. John Palmer

St. Catherine of Siena Medical Center - OTP, 50 Route 25A, Smithtown, NY 11787; tel. 631/862–3000; Mr. Vincent DiRubbio

St. John's Episcopal Hospital, 700 Hicksville Road, Bethpage, NY 11714; tel. 718/869–7320; Mr. Luis Hernandez

Section C

St. Johns Riverside Hospital M.M.T.P., 70 Ashburton Avenue, 2nd Floor, Yonkers, NY 10701; tel. 914/964–4000; Mr. Jim Foy

St. Joseph's Hospital - MMTP, 8 Guion Street, 1st Floor, Yonkers, NY 10701; tel. 914/378–7000; Mr. Michael Spicer

St. Joseph's Villa of Rochester, 3300 Dewey Avenue, Rochester, NY 14616; tel. 585/865–1550; Mr. Roger C Battaglia

St. Luke's Cornwall Hospital Unity Center for Recovery, 3 Commercial Place, Newburgh, NY 12550; tel. 845/565–0150; Mr. Allan E Atzrott

St. Lukes-Roosevelt Hospital - Inpatient Rehab Unit, 1000 Tenth Avenue, New York, NY 10019; tel. 212/523–6166; Dr. Jin Suh

St. Lukes-Roosevelt Hospital Center - MMTP, 1000 Tenth Avenue, New York, NY 10019; tel. 212/523–6166; Dr. Jin Suh

St. Vincent's Midtown Hospital MMTP, 415 West 51st Street, New York, NY 10019; tel. 212/459–8402; Mr. Len Walsh

St.Barnabas Hospital-Chemical Dependence-Medically Managed, 183rd Street and Third Avenue, Bronx, NY 10457; tel. 718/960–6170; Dr. Scott Cooper

Staten Island Univ Hospital (Canarsie M.M.T.P. Clinic), 567 East 105th Street, Brooklyn, NY 11236; tel. 718/226–9000; Mr. Anthony Ferreri

Staten Island Univ Hospital (Coney Island M.M.T.P. Clinic), 425 Coney Island Avenue, Brooklyn, NY 11218; tel. 718/226–9000; Mr. Anthony Ferreri

Staten Island Univ Hospital (Princess Bay M.M.T.P. Clinic), 392 Seguine Avenue, Staten Island, NY 10309; tel. 718/226–9000; Mr. Anthony C Ferreri

Staten Island Univ Hospital (Stapleton M.M.T.P. Clinic), 111 Water Street, Staten Island, NY 10305; tel. 718/226–9000; Mr. Anthony C Ferreri

Staten Island Univ Hospital Inpatient Chem Dep Detox Unit, 475 Seaview Avenue, Staten Island, NY 10305; tel. 718/226–9000; Mr. Anthony Ferreri

Strong Memorial Hospital - MMTC - Dept of Psychiatry, 601 Elmwood Avenue, Rochester, NY 14642; tel. 585/275–5489; Mr. Stephen Goldstein

Stuyvesant Square Chemical Dependency Outpatient Detox, 1st Avenue At 16th Street, New York, NY 10003; tel. 212/420–4220; Dr. Mathew E Fink

Suffolk County Department of Health - Babylon MMTP, Building 159 North County Complex, Hauppauge, NY 11788; tel. 631/854–1919; Mr. Thomas McGilvray

Suffolk County Department of Health - East End Clinic, 300 Center Drive, Riverhead, NY 11901; tel. 631/852–2680; Mr. Thomas MacGilvray

Suffolk County Department of Health - Hauppauge Clinic, Building 159 North County Complex, Hauppauge, NY 11788; tel. 631/853–7373; Mr. Thomas O MacGilvray

Suffolk County Department of Health - North County Complex, Veterans Highway, Bldg 159, North County Complex, Hauppauge, NY 11788; tel. 631/853–6410; Mr. Thomas O MacGilvray

Suffolk County Dept. of Health, Huntington Methadone Clinic, Building 159 North County Complex, Hauppauge, NY 11788; tel. 631/854–4400; Mr. Thomas MacGilvary

SVCMC Mary Immaculate Hospital, 275 North St, Harrison, NY 10528; tel. 718/774–8436; Dr. Brian Fitzsimmons

SVCMC St. Mary's Hospital - Prospect Place Clinic, 275 North St., Harrison, NY 10528; tel. 718/774–8436; Dr. Brian Fitzsimmons

SVCMC St. Mary's Hospital of Brooklyn - Alabama Ave, 275 North St, Harrison, NY 10528; tel. 718/774–8436; Dr. Brian Fitzsimmons

SVCMC St. Vincent's Hospital Westchester, MMTP, 275 North St, Harrison, NY 10528; tel. 800/784–8804; Dr. Brian Fitzsimmons

The Adolescent Development Program of the NY Presbyterian Hospital, 411 East 69th Street, New York, NY 10021; tel. 212/746–1277; Dr. Herbert Pardes

The Astor Home for Children, PO Box 5005, Rhinebeck, NY 12572-5005; tel. 845/871–1000; Dr. James McGuirk

The Brooklyn Hospital Center Parkside Drug Detox Program, 121 DeKalb Avenue, Brooklyn, NY 11201; tel. 718/250–8320; Mr. Samuel Lehrfield

The Guidance Center Chemical Dependency Treatment Center, 26 Sickles Avenue, New Rochelle, NY 10801; tel. 914/632–1374; Ms. Marge Klein

The Mount Sinai Hospital Narcotics Rehabilitation Center, 17 East 102nd Street, New York, NY 10029; tel. 212/241–7006; Dr. Kenneth Davis

The Mount Vernon Hospital Methadone Maintenance Program, 3 South 6th Avenue, 3rd Floor, Mount Vernon, NY 10550; tel. 914/664–8000; Mr. John R Spicer

The New York and Presbyterian Hospital, Inc., 525 E 68th Street, F172, New York, NY 10021; tel. 212/746–0421; Dr. Herbert Pardes

The Support Center, Inc., 188 Route 209, Port Jervis, NY 12771; tel. 800/724–9322; Mr. Carmine Mosca

The Turning Point - Detox Unit Saint Francis Hospital, 11 Hastings Drive, Beacon, NY 12508; tel. 845/838–4405; Mr. Robert Savage

Tully Hill Corporation, PO Box 1116, Tully, NY 13159-1116; tel. 315/696–6114; Ms. Cathy L Palm

Ulster County Mental Health Services Methadone Maintenance, 239 Golden Hill Lane, Kingston, NY 12401; tel. 845/340–4100; Mr. Allen Nace

United Health Services Hospitals, 33-57 Harrison Street, Johnson City, NY 13790; tel. 607/763–5300; Mr. Matthew Salanger

VA New York Harbor Healthcare System, 800 Poly Place, Brooklyn, NY 11209; tel. 718/630–3521; Dr. Eric Peselow

VA New York Harbor Healthcare System - OTP, 437 West 16th Street, New York, NY 10011; tel. 212/462–4461; Dr. Paul Casadante

Veritas Villa, Inc., PO Box 610, Kerhonkson, NY 12446-0610; tel. 845/626–3555; Ms. Peggy Healy

West Midtown Medical Group - OTP, 505 Eighth Avenue, 10th Floor, New York, NY 10018; tel. 212/736–5900; Mr. Peter Schorr

White Plains Hospital Center, Davis Avenue at East Post Road, White Plains, NY 10601; tel. 914/681–2800; Mr. Jon B Schandler

Whitney M. Young, Jr. MMTP, 4-10 Dewitt Street, Albany, NY 12207; tel. 518/463–3882; Mr. Jamed D Sinkoff

Woodhull Medical & Mental Health Medically Managed Detoxification, 760 Broadway, Units 8-300 and 9-300, Brooklyn, NY 11206; tel. 718/963–5959; Ms. Lynda D Curtis

NORTH CAROLINA

Brynn Marr Behavioral Healthcare System, 192 Village Drive, Jacksonville, NC 28546; tel. 910/577–1400; Mr. Joey Jacobs

Fellowship Hall, Inc., PO Box 13890, Greensboro, NC 27415; tel. 336/621–3381; Mr. Rodney Battles

Julian F. Keith Alcohol and Drug Abuse Treatment Center, 201 Tabernacle Road, Black Mountain, NC 28711; tel. 828/669–3421; Mr. William A Rafter

R. J. Blackley, MD-Alcohol & Drug Abuse Treatment Center, 1003 12th Street, Butner, NC 27509-1626; tel. 919/575–7928; Ms. Patricia L Christian

Unity Healing Center, PO Box 201, Cherokee, NC 28719; tel. 828/497–3958; Ms. Hillane Lambert

Wilmington Treatment Center Inc, 2520 Troy Drive, Wilmington, NC 28401; tel. 910/762–2727; Mr. Charles Sharp

NORTH DAKOTA

The Dakota Boys and Girls Ranch Association, PO Box 5007, Minot, ND 58703; tel. 701/852–3628; Mr. Gene Kasemen

OHIO

Akron Drug Abuse Clinic - Community Health Center, 725 East Market Street, Akron, OH 44305; tel. 330/434–4141; Mr. Theodore P Ziegler

Akron-Urban Minority Alcoholism Drug Abuse Outreach, 665 W Market Street, Suite 2D, Akron, OH 44303; tel. 330/379–3467; Ms. Janice T Mercier

Behavioral Connections of Wood County, Inc., Post Office Box 29, Bowling Green, OH 43402; tel. 419/352–8254; Dr. Richard M Goldberg

Bellefaire Jewish Children's Bureau, 22001 Fairmount Boulevard, Shaker Heights, OH 44118; tel. 216/932–2800; Dr. Adam G Jacobs

Catholic Charities Services Corporation, 7911 Detroit Ave, Cleveland, OH 44102; tel. 440/843–5582; Mr. Thomas W Woll

Center for Chemical Addictions Treatment, 830 Ezzard Charles Drive, Cincinnati, OH 45214; tel. 513/381–6672; Ms. Sandra L Kuehn

Community Health Center, 725 East Market Street, Akron, OH 44305; tel. 330/434–4141; Mr. Theodore P Ziegler

Comprehensive Addiction Service Systems, Inc., 2465 Collingwood Blvd., Toledo, OH 43620; tel. 419/241–8827; Mr. Ross M Chaban

Connecting Point, 1212 Cherry Street, Toledo, OH 43608; tel. 419/243–6326; Mr. Jeff Deckebach

Crisis Intervention Center of Stark County, Inc., 2421-13th Street, Northwest, Canton, OH 44708; tel. 330/452–9812; Dr. Bernard S Jesiolowski

Department of Veteran Affairs - Dayton Campus, 4100 W Third Street, Bldg 302, Dayton, OH 45428; tel. 937/268–6511; Dr. Alberto Rincon-Belzres

Glenbeigh Hospital & Outpatient Services, PO Box 298, Rock Creek, OH 44084-0298; tel. 440/563–3400; Ms. Pat Weston-Hall

Harbor Behavioral Healthcare, 4334 Secor Road, Toledo, OH 43623-4234; tel. 419/475–4449; Mr. Dale E Shreve

Interval Brotherhood Homes, Inc., 3445 South Main Street, Akron, OH 44319; tel. 330/644–4095; Mr. Samuel R Ciccolini

McKinley Hall, Inc., 1101 East High Street, Springfield, OH 45505; tel. 937/328–5300; Mr. Daniel M Barksdale

Methadone Maintenance Program, Substance Abuse,Mental Health, 10701 East Blvd, Room H127, Cleveland, OH 44106; tel. 440/526–3030; Dr. Mark Bondeson

Neil Kennedy Recovery Clinic, 2151 Rush Boulevard, Youngstown, OH 44507; tel. 330/744–1181; Mr. Gerald V Carter

New Directions, Inc., 30800 Chagrin Boulevard, Cleveland, OH 44124; tel. 216/591–0324; Mr. Michael E Matoney

Nova Behavioral Health, Inc., 832 McKinley Avenue, Northwest, Canton, OH 44703; tel. 330/455–9407; Ms. Carol A Hales

Opiate Substitution Services - SUDEP, CVAMC, 3200 Vine Street, Cincinnati, OH 45220; tel. 513/861–3100; Dr. Show W Lin

PsyCare, Inc., 2980 Belmont Avenue, Youngstown, OH 44505; tel. 330/759–2310; Dr. Douglas C Darnall

Ravenwood Mental Health Center, 12557 Ravenwood Drive, Chardon, OH 44024; tel. 440/285–3568; Mr. David A Boyle

Rescue Mental Health Services, 3350 Collingwood Boulevard, Toledo, OH 43610; tel. 419/255–9585; Mr. Frank A Ayers

Southeast, Inc., 16 West Long Street, Columbus, OH 43215; tel. 614/225–0980; Ms. Sandra Stephenson

Stella Maris, Inc., 1320 Washington Avenue, Cleveland, OH 44113; tel. 216/781–0550; Mrs. Margaret A Roche

Substance Abuse Services, Inc., 1832 Adams Street, Toledo, OH 43624; tel. 419/243–7274; Mr. Ross M Chaban

The Buckeye Ranch, Inc., 5665 Hoover Road, Grove City, OH 43123; tel. 614/875–2371; Mr. Richard E Rieser

The Crossroads Center, 311 Martin Luther King Drive, Cincinnati, OH 45219-3116; tel. 513/475–5300; Mrs. Jacqueline P Butler

The Woods at Parkside, 349 Olde Ridenour Road, Columbus, OH 43230; tel. 614/471–2552; Mrs. Susan J Carmichael

Unison Behavioral Health Group, PO Box 10015, Toledo, OH 43699-0015; tel. 419/242–9577; Mrs. Courtney Weiss

OKLAHOMA

Brookhaven Hospital, 201 South Garnett Road, Tulsa, OK 74128-1800; tel. 918/438–4257; Dr. Rolf B Gainer

Cushing Valley Hope, PO Box 472, Cushing, OK 74023-0472; tel. 918/225–1736; Dr. Kenneth C Gregoire

Northwest Center for Behavioral Health (NCBH), 1222 10th Street, Suite 211, Woodward, OK 73801; tel. 580/256–8615; Mr. Steve Norwood

Oklahoma City VA Medical Center, Substance Abuse Treatment, 921 NE 13th St, Bldg 1, 116C, Oklahoma City, OK 73104; tel. 405/270–5194; Dr. Gita Pujari

OREGON

CODA, Inc., 1027 E. Burnside, Portland, OR 97214; tel. 503/236–2290; Mr. Timothy T Hartnett

Portland VA Medical Center, 3710 SW US Hospital Road, Building 100, Portland, OR 97207; tel. 503/220–8262; Dr. Peter Benson

Serenity Lane, 2133 Centennial Plaza, Eugene, OR 97401; tel. 541/484–2156; Mr. Neil McNaughton

VA Southern Oregon Rehabilitation Center and Clinics, 8495 Crater Lake Highway, White City, OR 97503; tel. 541/830–3515; Dr. Max E McIntosh

PENNSYLVANIA

Addiction Medicine Services - Homewood Outreach Program, 6714 Kelly Street, Pittsburgh, PA 15208; tel. 412/246–6806; Dr. Dennis Daley

Adelphoi Village, Inc., 1003 Village Way, Latrobe, PA 15650; tel. 724/537-7858; Mr. Larry Breitenstein

Bowling Green Brandywine, PO Box 787, Kennett Square, PA 19348; tel. 610/268-3588; Ms. Claire F Beckwith

Child Guidance Resource Centers, 600 North Olive Street, Media, PA 19063-2418; tel. 610/565-6000; Mr. Brad Barry

Clear Brook, Inc., 1003 Wyoming Avenue, Forty Fort, PA 18704; tel. 570/288-6692; Dr. Nicholas F Colangelo

Cornell Abraxas I, PO Box 59, Marienville, PA 16239; tel. 814/927-6615; Mr. James E Newsome

Crozer Chester Medical Center-Community Hospital of Chester, 2600 West Ninth Street, Ground Floor, Community Hosp, Chester, PA 19013; tel. 610/447-2785; Mr. Gerald Miller

Eagleville Hospital, 100 Eagleville Road, Eagleville, PA 19408; tel. 610/539-6000; Ms. Kendria Kurtz McWilliams

Gateway Rehabilitation Center/ Genesis Division, Moffett Run Road, Aliquippa, PA 15001; tel. 412/766-8700; Dr. Kenneth S Ramsey

Gaudenzia Crossroads, 414 West Fifth Street, Erie, PA 16507; tel. 814/459-4775; Mr. Michael Harle

Gaudenzia, Inc. - Common Ground, 2835 North Front Street, Harrisburg, PA 17110; tel. 717/238-4200; Mr. Michael B Harle

Greenbriar Treatment Center, 800 Manor Drive, Washington, PA 15301; tel. 724/225-9700; Ms. Mary G Banaszak

Greenway Center, Inc., P. O. Box 188, Henryville, PA 18332; tel. 570/688-9162; Mr. Peter D'Souza

Holcomb Behavioral Health Systems, 930 E Lancaster Ave, Suite 220, Exton, PA 19341; tel. 610/363-1488; Mr. William DiFabio

Jefferson-Kensington Methadone Treatment Program, 136 West Diamond Street, Philadelphia, PA 19122; tel. 215/426-8100; Ms. Eileen Hause

Kensington Hospital (Non- Hospital Detoxification Unit), 136 West Diamond Street, Philadelphia, PA 19122; tel. 215/426-8100; Ms. Eileen Hause

KidsPeace Corporation, 5300 KidsPeace Drive, Orefield, PA 18069-9101; tel. 610/799-8000; Mr. C T O'Donnellll

Kirkbride Center-A Better Way, 111 North 49th Street, Philadelphia, PA 19139; tel. 215/471-2600; Ms. Rose Diottavio

Livengrin Foundation, Inc., 4833 Hulmeville Road, Bensalem, PA 19020-3099; tel. 215/638-5200; Mr. Richard M Pine

Malvern Institute, 940 King Road, Malvern, PA 19355; tel. 610/647-0330; Mr. Richard Mangano

Marworth, PO Box 36, Waverly, PA 18471; tel. 570/563-1112; Mr. James J Dougherty

Mercy Catholic Medical Center/Mercy Hospital of Philadelphia, 501 South 54th Street, Philadelphia, PA 19143; tel. 215/748-9300; Ms. Bernadette Mangan

Mirmont Treatment Center, 100 Yearsley Mill Road, Media, PA 19063-5593; tel. 610/744-1400; Mr. Thomas F Cain

Montgomery County Emergency Service, Inc., 50 Beech Drive, Norristown, PA 19403-5421; tel. 610/279-6100; Dr. Rocio Nell

Narcotic Addict Rehabilitation Program of Thomas Jefferson Univ., South 21st St. & Washington Av, Philadelphia, PA 19146; tel. 215/735-5979; Dr. Michael J Vergare

NorthEast Treatment Centers - OTP, 499 North 5th Street, Philadelphia, PA 19123; tel. 215/451-7000; Mr. Terence McSherry

Penn Foundation, Inc., 807 Lawn Avenue, Sellersville, PA 18960; tel. 215/257-6551; Mr. John Goshow

Philadelphia VA Medical Center Opioid Treatment Program, University and Woodland Aves, Building 7, Philadelphia, PA 19104; tel. 215/823-5809; Dr. Isabelle Arndt

Progressive Medical Specialists, Inc., 2453 West Pike Road, Houston, PA 15342; tel. 724/873-5655; Ms. Annamarie Roberto

Progressive Medical Specialists, Inc., 2900 Smallman Street, Pittsburgh, PA 15201; tel. 412/391-6384; Ms. Annamaire Roberto

Pyramid Healthcare, Inc., P.O. Box 1153, Altoona, PA 16603; tel. 814/940-0407; Mr. Jonathan Wolf

Renewal Operations, Inc., PO Box 107, Zionhill, PA 18981; tel. 215/536-9070; Mrs. Loretta Anderer Brausen

RHJ Medical Center, Inc., RR 1, Box 224, Hunker, PA 15639; tel. 724/696-9600; Mrs. Kerri A Csikesz

Roxbury Treatment Center, 601 Roxbury Road, Shippensburg, PA 17257; tel. 717/532-4217; Mr. William Niles

Stairways Behavioral Health, 138 East 26th Street, Erie, PA 16504; tel. 814/453-5806; Mr. William F McCarthy

The Bridge, 8400 Pine Road, Philadelphia, PA 19111; tel. 215/342-5000; Mr. Jose A Benitez

The Goldman Clinic, 8th Street and Girard Avenue, Philadelphia, PA 19122; tel. 215/787-2070; Ms. Marlene D-Walsh

The Mitchell Clinic, 555 Harrison Street, Emmaus, PA 18049; tel. 610/965-6418; Dr. John F Mitchell

Thomas Jefferson University - Family Center, 1201 Chestnut Street, Philadelphia, PA 19107; tel. 215/955-1951; Dr. Karol Kaltenbach

TODAY, Inc., PO Box 908, Newtown, PA 18940; tel. 215/968-4713; Dr. John E Howell

Universal Recovery Foundation, 2001 Providence Avenue, Chester, PA 19013; tel. 610/876-9000; Mr. Billy Young

VA Medical Center - (SATU), 1400 Blackhorse Hill Road, Coatesville, PA 19320; tel. 610/384-7711; Ms. Nancy C Elliott-Carter

Valley Forge Medical Center & Hospital/Non-Hospital Service, 1033 West Germantown Pike, Norristown, PA 19403; tel. 610/539-8500; Ms. Marian Colcher

VAPHS - CTAD-OPIOID SUBSTITUTION THERAPY CLINIC, 7180 Highland Drive, Bldg 4-1W, Pittsburgh, PA 15206; tel. 412/365-5010; Dr. Steven D Forman

White Deer Run Detoxification Unit, PO Box 97 - DeVitt Camp Road, Allenwood, PA 17810; tel. 570/538-2567; Mr. Mark G Sarneso

White Deer Run Inc., 360 White Deer Run Road, Allenwood, PA 17810; tel. 800/255-2335; Mr. Mark G Sarneso

RHODE ISLAND

Butler Hospital Alcohol and Drug Treatment Services, 345 Blackstone Boulevard, Providence, RI 02906; tel. 401/455-6220; Dr. Patricia R Recupero

CODAC Behavioral Healthcare, Inc., 1052 Park Avenue,, Cranston, RI 02910; tel. 401/275-5039; Mr. Michael A Rizzi

CODAC East Bay, 1052 Park Avenue, Cranston, RI 02910; tel. 401/275-5039; Mr. Michael Rizzi

CODAC II, 1052 Park Avenue, Cranston, RI 02910; tel. 401/942-1450; Mr. Michael Rizzi

CODAC III-Newport, 1052 Park Avenue, Cranston, RI 02910; tel. 401/846-4150; Mr. Michael Rizzi

Community Counseling Center, 249 Roosevelt Avenue, Pawtucket, RI 02860; tel. 401/724-8400; Mr. Richard H Leclerc

East Bay Mental Health Center, Inc., 2 Old County Road, Barrington, RI 02806; tel. 401/431-9870; Mr. John P Digits, Jr.

Mental Health Services, 249 Roosevelt Avenue, Pawtucket, RI 02860; tel. 401/724-8400; Mr. Richard H Leclerc

Providence VA Medical Center, 830 Chalkstone Avenue, Bldg 1, Providence, RI 02908; tel. 401/273-7100; Mr. Vincent Ng

South Shore Mental Health Center, Inc., P.O. Box 899, Charlestown, RI 02813; tel. 401/364-7705; Mr. Richard C Antonelli

SSTAR of Rhode Island, 1950 Tower Hill Road, North Kingstown, RI 02852; tel. 401/294-6160; Ms. Nancy E Paull

The Providence Center, 951 North Main Street, Providence, RI 02904; tel. 401/528-0123; Mr. Dale K Klatzker

Tri-Hab, Inc., 58 Hamlet Avenue, Woonsocket, RI 02895; tel. 401/765-4040; Mr. David Spencer

SOUTH CAROLINA

Lighthouse Care Center of Conway, 152 Waccamaw Medical Park Dr., Conway, SC 29526; tel. 843/347-8871; Mr. Francis Sauvageau

SOUTH DAKOTA

Keystone Treatment Center, PO Box 159, Canton, SD 57013; tel. 605/987-2751; Ms. Carol Regier

TENNESSEE

Buffalo Valley, Inc., PO Box 879, Hohenwald, TN 38462; tel. 931/796-5427; Mr. Jerry T Risner

Child & Family Tennessee, 901 East Summit Hill Drive, Knoxville, TN 37915; tel. 865/524-7483; Ms. Kathryn R O'Day

Cornerstone of Recovery, Inc., 1214 Topside Road, Louisville, TN 37777; tel. 865/970-7747; Mr. Dan R Caldwell

Council for Alcohol and Drug Abuse Services, Inc., PO Box 4797, Chattanooga, TN 37405; tel. 423/756-7644; Dr. Paul Fuchcar

Cumberland Heights Foundation, Inc., PO Box 90727, Nashville, TN 37209; tel. 615/353-4831; Mr. James B Moore

DRD Knoxville Medical Clinic, 626 Bernard Street, Knoxville, TN 37921; tel. 865/522-0161; Ms. Mary Little

Pathways of Tennessee, Inc., 238 Summar Drive, Jackson, TN 38301; tel. 731/935-8200; Mr. Kelly R Yenawine

Peninsula Behavioral Health, PO Box 2000, Louisville, TN 37777-0789; tel. 865/970-9800; Ms. Barbara Blevins, Jr.

SummaCare Outpatient Services, 4015 Travis Road, 2nd Floor, Nashville, TN 37203; tel. 615/248-4989; Mr. Michael Carell

TEXAS

A.A.M.A., Narcotic Education League (NEL), 434 S. Main, Suite 217, San Antonio, TX 78204; tel. 210/270-8575; Ms. Acenete Flores

Addiction and Psychotherapy Services, 2824 South Congress Avenue, Austin, TX 78704; tel. 512/444-5092; Dr. Heinz Aeschbach

Alternatives Centre for Behavioral Health, 5001 Alabama Street, El Paso, TX 79930; tel. 915/565-4800; Ms. Carol J Amundson

Assn for the Advancement of Mexican-Americans, Inc., 434 South Main, Suite 217, San Antonio, TX 78204; tel. 210/270-8575; Mr. Gilbert Moreno

Austin Travis County MHMR Methadone Mntce Tx Program, 1631 A East 2nd Street, Austin, TX 78702; tel. 512/472-6261; Mr. David Evans

Burke Center, 4101 South Medford Drive, Lufkin, TX 75901; tel. 936/639-1141; Ms. Susan Rushing

Conlan Family Partners, Limited, 1100 McCart Street, Stephenville, TX 76401; tel. 254/968-2907; Ms. Nicole Conlan

DebLin Health Concepts and Associates, Inc., 6813 Northampton Way, Houston, TX 77055; tel. 713/686-9194; Ms. Debra R Jackson

East Texas Clinic, PO Box 9486, Longview, TX 75608; tel. 903/759-4966; Ms. Diane Stalnaker

Grapevine Valley Hope, 2300 William D Tate Avenue, Grapevine, TX 76051; tel. 817/424-1305; Dr. Kenneth C Gregoire

Johnnie M. Hawkins LAMP Clinic, 431 Fulton, Fort Worth, TX 76104; tel. 817/336-3754; Dr. Robert W Greene

La Hacienda Treatment Center, PO Box 1, Hunt, TX 78024; tel. 830/238-4222; Mr. Arthur VanDivier

Meth-Laam, 3204 Ennis Street, Houston, TX 77004; tel. 713/526-2441; Mr. Earnest Gibson, III

Montrose Counseling Center, Inc., 701 Richmond Ave., Houston, TX 77006; tel. 713/529-0037; Dr. Ann J Robison

New Dimensions, 1345 Space Park, Suite C, Houston, TX 77058; tel. 281/333-2284; Mr. George R Brazzel

Pasadena Substance Abuse Clinic, Inc, 1645 Pasadena Boulevard, Pasadena, TX 77502; tel. 713/473-1405; Ms. Nighat Shaheen

River Oaks Academy Day Hospital, 10600 Richmond Avenue, Houston, TX 77042; tel. 713/783-7200; Dr. Sandra E Phares

Serenity Foundation of Texas, 1546 North 2nd Street, Abilene, TX 79601; tel. 325/673-6489; Mr. Richard L Spalding

Shoreline, Inc., PO Box 68, Taft, TX 78390; tel. 361/528-3356; Dr. Sharel Zacharias

Spindletop MHMR Services, PO Box 3846, Beaumont, TX 77704; tel. 409/839-5554; Dr. N. Charles Harris

Starlite Recovery Center, PO Box 317, Center Point, TX 78010-0317; tel. 830/292-0148; Mr. Kirk Kureska

Substance Dependence Treatment Program - VA Medical Center, 2002 Holcombe Blvd, Bldg 100, Houston, TX 77030; tel. 713/794-7900; Dr. Janine Shaw

Sundown Ranch, Inc., 3120 Van Zandt County Road #2318, Canton, TX 75103; tel. 903/479-3933; Mr. Robert H Power

The Huntsville Clinic, Inc., 829 10th Street, Huntsville, TX 77320; tel. 936/291-9172; Ms. Gerri Parish

The Patrician Movement, 222 East Mitchell Street, San Antonio, TX 78210; tel. 210/532-3126; Dr. Patrick M Clancey

VA North TX Health Care System / Opioid Replacement Clinic, 4500 Lancaster Road, Bldg 71C, Dallas, TX 75216; tel. 214/857-0805; Dr. Bryon Adinoff

UTAH

Blue Mountain Family Center / Wilderness Quest, PO Box 12, Monticello, UT 84535; tel. 435/587-2801; Mr. Larry J Wells

Cirque Lodge, RR 3, Box A-10, Sundance, UT 84604; tel. 801/222-9200; Mr. Gary Fisher

Heritage Schools Inc, 5600 N. Heritage School Drive, Provo, UT 84604; tel. 801/226-4600; Mr. Gerald H Spanos

Highland Ridge Hospital, 7309 South 180 West, Midvale, UT 84047; tel. 801/569-2153; Dr. David W Schroeder

Hightop Ranch School, PO Box 440029, Koosharem, UT 84744; tel. 435/638-7411; Mr. Chad Sorenson

Kids Behavioral Health of Utah Inc., 5899 West Rivendell Drive, West Jordan, UT 84088; tel. 801/561-3377; Mr. R M Rowley

Raindancer Youth Services, Inc., P.O. Box 910400, Saint George, UT 84791; tel. 435/673-6474; Mr. Ronald N Hatch, Sr.

Sorenson's Ranch School, Inc., Box 440219, Koosharem, UT 84744; tel. 435/638-7318; Mr. Shane Sorenson

UT-TEX, Inc., PO Box 69, Magna, UT 84044; tel. 801/250-9762; Mr. H. Matthew Dixon, Jr.

VERMONT

Brattleboro Retreat, Anna Marsh Lane, PO BOX 803, Brattleboro, VT 05302; tel. 802/257-7785; Mr. Richard Palmisano

Health Care & Rehabilitation Services of Southeastern VT, One Hospital Court, Bellows Falls, VT 05101; tel. 802/463-3294; Ms. Judith P Hayward

VIRGINIA

Carilion Saint Albans Hospital - Methadone Short Term, PO Box 3608, Radford, VA 24143; tel. 540/731-2000; Mr. Matthew J Perry

Family Counseling Center, 4906 Radford Avenue, Richmond, VA 23230; tel. 804/354-1996; Mr. Charles R Adcock

Inova Comprehensive Addiction Treatment Services (CATS), 3300 Gallows Road, Falls Church, VA 22042; tel. 703/698-1530; Mr. Douglas Cropper

Inova Kellar Center, 10396 Democracy Lane, Fairfax, VA 22030; tel. 703/218-8500; Dr. Richard Leichtweis

Life Center of Galax, Tazewell Opiod Treatment Program, 111 Town Hollow Road, Cedar Bluff, VA 24609; tel. 540/963-3554; Ms. Tina R Bullins

Mount Regis Center, 405 Kimball Avenue, Salem, VA 24153; tel. 540/389-4761; Ms. Gail S Basham

Poplar Springs Hospital, PO Box 3060, Petersburg, VA 23805; tel. 804/733-6874; Mr. John F Gallagher

The Life Center of Galax - Galax Clinic - OTP, PO Box 27, Galax, VA 24333; tel. 276/236-2994; Mrs. Tina Bullins

VA Medical Center - Methadone Maintenance Program, 1201 Broad Rock Boulevard, SATP Inpatient Unit 1F, Richmond, VA 23249; tel. 804/675-5000; Dr. Janakibai Theogaraj

Williamsburg Place, 5477 Mooretown Road, Williamsburg, VA 23188; tel. 757/565-0106; Ms. Stephanie M Loebs

WASHINGTON

Addiction Treatment Center Opi Treatment Program, Tacoma Div, American Lake Drive, Bldg 61, Tacoma, WA 98493; tel. 206/762-1010; Dr. Andrew J Saxon

Central Washington Comprehensive Mental Health, 402 South Fourth Avenue, Yakima, WA 98902; tel. 509/575-4084; Mr. Rick Weaver

VA Puget Sound/Addiction Treatment Center/Opioid, 1660 S Columbian Way, Bldg 24, Seattle, WA 98108; tel. 206/764-2782; Dr. Andrew Saxon

Valley Cities Counseling & Consultation, 2704 I Street NE, Auburn, WA 98002; tel. 253/833-7444; Ms. Marilyn LaCelle

WEST VIRGINIA

Olympic Center - Preston, Inc., PO Box 158, Kingwood, WV 26537; tel. 304/329-2400; Ms. Arlene Glover

WISCONSIN

Aurora Psychiatric Hospital, 1220 Dewey Avenue, Wauwatosa, WI 53213; tel. 414/454-6600; Mr. Peter Carlson

Cadott Medical Center, SC - Methadone Program, PO Box 69, Cadott, WI 54727; tel. 715/289-4221; Dr. Clifford T Bowe

Gundersen Lutheran Medical Center, Inc.-Methadone Maintenance, 1910 South Avenue, La Crosse, WI 54601; tel. 608/782-7300; Dr. Jeffrey Thompson

Libertas Treatment Center, 1701 Dousman Street, Green Bay, WI 54303; tel. 920/498-8600; Mr. David B Fish

Meriter Hospital/New Start Alcohol/Drug Treatment Program, 202 South Park Street, Madison, WI 53715-1599; tel. 608/267-6291; Mr. Terri Potter

WYOMING

Wyoming Recovery, LLC, 231 South Wilson, Casper, WY 82601; tel. 307/265-3791; Ms. Carolyn Toews

---

U.S. Associated Areas

APO/AE

ASAP-IMA-E, 104 Roemerstrasse, Bldg 3734 (Heidelberg), APO, AE 09014; tel. 011-496-2215; Mr. Patrick Teel

PUERTO RICO

Clinica Interdisciplinaria de Psiquiatria Avanzada, 650 Lloveras Cond Centro Plaza Suite 101, San Juan, PR 00909-2113; tel. 787/721-4020; Dr. Carlos A Caban

VIRGIN ISLANDS

Division of Mental Health, Alcoholism & Drug Dependency Services, Barbel Plaza South, Second Floor, St Thomas, VI 00802; tel. 340/773-1992; Dr. Celia Victor

The accredited freestanding substance abuse programs listed have been accredited as of April, 2005 by the Joint Commission on Accreditation of Healthcare Organizations by decision of the Accreditation Committee of the Board of Commissioners.

The organizations listed here have been found to be in compliance with the Joint Commission standards for subtance abuse organizations, as found in the Accreditation Manual for Mental Health, Chemical Dependency, and Mental Retardation/Developmental Disabilities Services.

Please refer to section A of the AHA Guide for information on hospitals with inpatient and/or outpatient alcohol and chemical dependency services. These hospitals are identified by Facility Codes F3 and F4. In section A, those hospitals identified by Approval Code 1 are JCAHO accredited.

We present this list simply as a convenient directory. Inclusion or omission of any organization's name indicates neither approval nor disapproval by Health Forum LLC, an American Hospital Association company.

United States

ALABAMA
Alabama Clinical Schools, P.O. Box 100968, Birmingham, AL 35210; tel. 205/836–9923; Mr. Ed Mehollin
Bradford Health Services - Huntsville Lodge, 1600 Browns Ferry Road, Madison, AL 35758; tel. 256/461–7272; Mr. Robert S Hinds
Bradford Health Services - Warrior Lodge, PO Box 129, Warrior, AL 35180; tel. 205/647–1945; Mr. Roy M Ramsey
Glenwood, Inc., 150 Glenwood Lane, Birmingham, AL 35242; tel. 205/969–2880; Ms. D. Lee Yount
Greater Mobile-Washington County MH-MR Board, Inc., 5750-A Southland Drive, Mobile, AL 36693; tel. 251/450–5901; Mr. J. T Schlesinger
Mobile Mental Health Center, Inc., 2400 Gordon Smith Drive, Mobile, AL 36617; tel. 251/450–5901; Mr. Tuerk Schlesinger
New Perspectives, 1000 Fairfax Park, Tuscaloosa, AL 35406; tel. 205/391–4738; Ms. Martha Hinkle
Pathway, Inc., P.O. Box 311206, Enterprise, AL 36331; tel. 334/894–5591; Mr. Norman G Hemp

ALASKA
Alaska Children's Services Inc., 4600 Abbott Road, Anchorage, AK 99507-4314; tel. 907/348–9272; Mr. James E Maley
Juneau Recovery Hospital - OTP, 3250 Hospital Drive, Juneau, AK 99801; tel. 907/796–8900; Mr. Robert Valliant
Providence Adolescent Residential Treatment Program, 3400 East 20th, Anchorage, AK 99508; tel. 907/272–2148; Ms. Susan Humphrey-Barnett

ARIZONA
ANASAZI Foundation, 1424 S. Stapley Dr., Mesa, AZ 85204; tel. 480/892–7403; Mr. Michael Merchant
Arizona Baptist Children's Services, 6015 West Peoria Avenue, Glendale, AZ 85302; tel. 623/349–2227; Mr. P. David Jakes
Arizona's Children Association, PO Box 7277, Tucson, AZ 85725-7277; tel. 520/622–7611; Mr. Fred J Chaffee
Banner Behavioral Health, 2225 West Southern Avenue, Mesa, AZ 85202; tel. 480/464–4055; Mr. Peter S Fine
Banner Behavioral Health, 5555 Thunderbird Road, Glendale, AZ 85306; tel. 602/588–5904; Ms. Colleen Hallberg
Chandler Valley Hope, PO Box 1839, Chandler, AZ 85244-1839; tel. 602/899–3335; Dr. Kenneth C Gregoire
Childhelp USA Merv Griffin Village of Arizona, 34801 North Highway 89, Wickenburg, AZ 85390; tel. 928/684–6300; Dr. Lonnie E Wederski
Community Behavioral Health Services, PO Box 790, Page, AZ 86040; tel. 928/645–5133; Mr. Thomas J Wright
Community Counseling Centers, Inc., 105 North Fifth Avenue, Holbrook, AZ 86025; tel. 928/524–6701; Dr. Robert Wilderman
Cottonwood de Tucson, 4110 West Sweetwater Drive, Tucson, AZ 85745; tel. 520/743–0411; Mr. Ronald B Welch
Desert Visions Youth Wellness Center, PO Box 458, Sacaton, AZ 85247; tel. 888/431–4096; Dr. Richard L Zephier
Devereux/Arizona - Richard L. Raskin Treatment Network, 11000 N Scottsdale Rd, Ste 260, Scottsdale, AZ 85254; tel. 480/998–2920; Mrs. Lane Martin-Barker

Helping Associates, Inc., 1901 North Trekell Road, Ste A, Casa Grande, AZ 85222; tel. 520/836–1029; Dr. Joan McGillicuddy
Horizon Human Services, Inc., 210 East Cottonwood Lane, Casa Grande, AZ 85222; tel. 520/836–1688; Mr. Norman E Mudd
Little Colorado Behavioral Health Centers, PO Box 579, St Johns, AZ 85936; tel. 928/337–4301; Mr. Michael T Downs
META Services, Inc., 2701 N 16th Street, Suite 316, Phoenix, AZ 85006; tel. 602/650–1212; Mr. Eugene Johnson
Mingus Mountain Estate Residential Center, Inc., PO Box 26485, Prescott Valley, AZ 86312; tel. 602/335–2000; Mr. Chris A Banken
Mohave Mental Health Clinic, Inc., 1743 Sycamore Avenue, Kingman, AZ 86401; tel. 928/757–8111; Mr. B.W. Brown
New Hope Behavioral Health Center, Inc, 6550 East Broadway, Suite 101, Mesa, AZ 85206; tel. 480/981–1022; Mr. David Campbell
Parc Place, 2190 North Grace Boulevard, Chandler, AZ 85225; tel. 480/917–9301; Mr. Gene Cavallo
Pinal Hispanic Council, 712 North Main Street, Eloy, AZ 85231; tel. 520/466–7765; Mr. Ralph Varela
PREHAB of Arizona, Inc., PO Drawer 5860, Mesa, AZ 85211-5860; tel. 480/969–4024; Mr. Michael T Hughes
Remuda Ranch Center for Anorexia and Bulimia, Inc., One East Apache Street, Wickenburg, AZ 85390; tel. 928/684–3913; Mr. Ward E Keller
Rosewood Ranch L.P., 36075 South Rincon Road, Wickenburg, AZ 85390; tel. 520/684–9594; Ms. Michelle Klinedinst
Sierra Tucson,LLC, 39580 S. Lago del Oro Parkway, Tucson, AZ 85739; tel. 520/624–4000; Dr. David E Anderson
Southeastern Arizona Behavioral Health Services, Inc., PO Box 2161, Benson, AZ 85602; tel. 520/586–0800; Mrs. Dana Johnson
Southern Arizona Mental Health Corporation, 2502 North Dodge Boulevard, Suite 190, Tucson, AZ 85716; tel. 520/617–0043; Ms. Carol Little
Southern Arizona VA Health Care, 3601 S 6th Avenue, Building 2, Tucson, AZ 85723; tel. 520/629–1821; Dr. David Emelity
St. Luke's Behavioral Hospital L.P., 1800 East Van Buren, Phoenix, AZ 85006; tel. 602/251–8808; Mr. David White
Superstition Mountain Mental Health Center, Inc., PO Box 3160, Apache Junction, AZ 85217-3160; tel. 480/983–0065; Mr. Robert Rundio
the EXCEL group, 2573 Arizona Avenue, Suite I, Yuma, AZ 85364; tel. 928/329–8995; Mr. Michael Coleman
The Guidance Center, Inc., 2187 North Vickey Street, Flagstaff, AZ 86004; tel. 928/527–1899; Ms. Linda Cowan
The Haven, 1107 East Adelaide Drive, Tucson, AZ 85719; tel. 520/623–4590; Ms. Sharon A Lashinger
The Meadows of Wickenburg, L.P., 1655 North Tegner, Wickenburg, AZ 85390; tel. 928/684–3926; Mr. Robert Fulton
The New Foundation, PO Box 3828, Scottsdale, AZ 85257; tel. 480/945–3302; Mrs. Jewel D Owens
Touchstone Behavioral Health, 6153 West Olive Avenue, Ste 1, Glendale, AZ 85302; tel. 623/930–8705; Mr. Timothy Dunst
Verde Valley Guidance Clinic, Inc., 8 East Cottonwood Street, Cottonwood, AZ 86326; tel. 928/634–2236; Mr. Robert D Cartia

Vista Care Facility RTC, 4120 East Ramsey Road, Hereford, AZ 85615; tel. 520/378–6466; Mr. Kris Heindel
West Yavapai Guidance Clinic, 505 South Cortez Street, Prescott, AZ 86303; tel. 520/445–5211; Mr. Don Ostendorf
Youth Development Institute, 1830 East Roosevelt Street, Phoenix, AZ 85006; tel. 602/254–0884; Mr. David J Cocoros

ARKANSAS
Boeckmann Consulting, Inc., 1803 Lindauer Road, Forrest City, AR 72335; tel. 870/588–6032; Mrs. Jeannie Boeckmann
Centers for Youth and Families, 5905 Forest Place, Little Rock, AR 72207; tel. 501/666–8686; Mr. Doug Stadter
Community Counseling Services, Inc., PO Box 6399, Hot Springs National Park, AR 71902; tel. 501/620–5130; Dr. Donald G Martin
Delta Counseling Associates, Inc., PO Box 820, Monticello, AR 71657; tel. 870/367–9732; Mr. Patrick K Haynie
Families, Inc. of Arkansas, 4508 Stadium Blvd., Jonesboro, AR 72404; tel. 870/933–6886; Ms. Joy Davis
Habilitation Centers, Inc., PO Box 727, Fordyce, AR 71742; tel. 870/352–8203; Mr. Scott Kelly
Life Strategies Counseling, Inc., 1825 E. Nettleton, Jonesboro, AR 72401; tel. 870/972–1268; Mr. William Wolters
Life Strategies of Arkansas,LLC, 203 West Bond Street, West Memphis, AR 72301; tel. 870/732–1878; Mrs. Jeane P Chapman
Maxus, Inc., PO Box 315, Warm Springs, AR 72478; tel. 870/647–2541; Mr. Ted Suhl
Ozark Counseling Services, Inc, PO Box 1776, Mountain Home, AR 72654-1776; tel. 870/425–6901; Mr. John C Greer
Ozark Guidance Center, Inc., PO Box 6430, Springdale, AR 72762-6430; tel. 479/750–2020; Dr. David L Williams
The Lord's Ranch, 1033 Old Burr Road, Warm Springs, AR 72478; tel. 870/647–2541; Mr. Ted E Suhl
Therapeutic Family Services, Inc., PO Box 27, Gurdon, AR 71743; tel. 501/332–4400; Mr. Birkes Williams
Timber Ridge Ranch NeuroRehabilitation Center, PO Box 208, Benton, AR 72018; tel. 501/594–5211; Mr. Rob McDaniel
United Methodist Behavioral Hospital, P.O. Box 13340, Maumelle, AR 72113; tel. 501/803–3388; Dr. Jennifer Lang
United Methodist Children's Home Inc., PO Box 4848, Little Rock, AR 72214-4848; tel. 501/661–0720; Mr. William A Altom
University of Arkansas for Medical Sciences, 4301 West Markham Street, Mail Slot 554, Little Rock, AR 72205; tel. 501/686–5483; Dr. G. Richard Smith
University of Arkansas for Substance Abuse Treatment Clinic, 3924 West Markham Street Slot # 611-1, Little Rock, AR 72205-4096; tel. 501/686–9630; Dr. G R Smith
Youth Home, Inc., 20400 Colonel Glenn Road, Little Rock, AR 72210-5323; tel. 501/821–5500; Ms. Beth Cartwright

CALIFORNIA
Action Family Counseling, Inc., 26893 Bouquet Canyon Road, Suite C-134, Saugus, CA 91350; tel. 661/297–9716; Mr. Cary Quashen

AltaMed Health Services Corporation, 500 Citadel Drive Suite 490, Los Angeles, CA 90040; tel. 323/889-7307; Mr. Castulo de la Rocha

Aspen Achievement Academy, 17777 Center Court Drive, Suite 300, Cerritos, CA 90703; tel. 562/467-5509; Mr. Gilbert Hallows

Berkeley Addiction Treatment Services, Inc., 2975 Sacramento Street, Berkeley, CA 94702; tel. 510/644-0200; Ms. Matonia Williams

Betty Ford Center, 39000 Bob Hope Drive, Rancho Mirage, CA 92270; tel. 760/773-4100; Mr. John T Schwarzlose

BHC Heritage Oaks Hospital, 4250 Auburn Boulevard, Sacramento, CA 95841; tel. 916/489-3336; Mr. Kenneth Meibert

Bi-Valley Medical Clinic, Inc. (Carmichael), 310 Harris Ave, Ste A, Sacramento, CA 95838; tel. 916/649-6793; Mr. Garrett Stenson

Bi-Valley Medical Clinic, Inc. - (Norwood), 310 Harris Avenue, Suite B, Sacramento, CA 95838; tel. 916/649-6793; Mr. Garrett Stenson

BiValley Medical Clinic, Inc., 310 Harris Avenue, Suite B, Sacramento, CA 95816; tel. 916/649-6793; Mr. Garrett L Stenson

Broad Horizons, PO Box 1920, Ramona, CA 92065; tel. 760/789-7060; Mr. John P DeVries

California Institution for Women, P.O. Box 6000, Corona, CA 92878-6000; tel. 909/606-4925; Dr. Jacqueline Long

Community Human Services - Methadone Clinic, PO Box 3076, Monterey, CA 93942; tel. 831/424-4828; Ms. Robin McCrae

Cornerstone of Southern California, 13682 Yorba Street, Tustin, CA 92780; tel. 714/730-5399; Ms. Lynda Klinger

Creative Care, Inc., 18850 Devonshire Street, Northridge, CA 91324; tel. 818/363-5630; Dr. Morteza Khaleghi

Eastside Health Services, 5200 San Gabriel Place, Pico Rivera, CA 90660; tel. 562/948-3306; Ms. Pauline Bahat

eGetgoing, Inc., 105 N. Bascom Avenue, Second Floor, San Jose, CA 95128-1811; tel. 408/998-3040; Dr. Barry Karlin

Fort Help Methadone Program, 915 Bryant Street, San Francisco, CA 94103; tel. 415/777-9953; Dr. Norbert Bohmer

HAART- Oakland, 10850 MacArthur Boulevard, Suite 200, Oakland, CA 94605; tel. 510/875-2300; Mr. Walter E Rosenthal

HAART-Hayward, 10850 MacArthur Boulevard, Oakland, CA 94605; tel. 510/727-9755; Ms. Anne Bolla

Impact Drug and Alcohol Treatment Center, PO Box 93607, Pasadena, CA 91103; tel. 626/798-0884; Mr. James M Stillwell

L. A. Treatment Service, 6965 El Camino Real, Ste. 105- #281, Carlsbad, CA 92009; tel. 760/471-3860; Mr. Philip S Brailsford

Los Angeles Center for Alcohol and Drug Abuse, PO Box 3205 11015 Bloomfield Avenue, Santa Fe Springs, CA 90670; tel. 562/906-2676; Ms. Brenda Wiewel

Mendocino County Department of Public Health (AODP), 333 Laws Avenue, Ukiah, CA 95482; tel. 707/472-4511; Ms. Linnea Ritter-Hunter

Mental Health Program Dept of Veterans Affairs, 2505 West 14th Street, Oakland Army Base, Oakland, CA 94607; tel. 510/587-3434; Dr. Matthew Moore

Merced Manor, 1255 B Street, Merced, CA 95340; tel. 209/723-8814; Mr. Eric G Williams

Oak Grove Institute, 24275 Jefferson Avenue, Murrieta, CA 92562; tel. 951/677-5599; Dr. Thomas C Lester

OTP Los Angeles Ambulatory Care Center, 351 East Temple Street, Los Angeles, CA 90012; tel. 310/268-3132; Mr. David M Riley

Pasadena Children's Training Society, 210 S DeLacey Avenue, Ste 110, Pasadena, CA 91105-2006; tel. 626/395-7100; Mr. William P Martone

R House, Inc., 533 Carr Avenue, Santa Rosa, CA 95404; tel. 707/571-2215; Ms. Mimi G Donohue

River Oak Center for Children, 4330 Auburn Blvd, Suite 2000, Sacramento, CA 95841; tel. 916/609-5100; Dr. Mary Hargrave

San Diego Center for Children, 3002 Armstrong Street, San Diego, CA 92111-5798; tel. 858/277-9550; Mr. Edwin Kofler

San Mateo Medical Center Methadone Treatment Program, 795 Willow Road, Building #332, Menlo Park, CA 94025; tel. 650/578-7190; Ms. Nancy Steiger

Sepulveda CA VAH Opioid Treatment Program, 16111 Plummer Street, Bldg 62, Sepulveda, CA 91343; tel. 310/268-3132; Mr. David M Riley

Sharp Vista Pacifica, 7989 Linda Vista Road, San Diego, CA 92111; tel. 858/637-6920; Mr. Daniel L Gross

Solano Psychiatric Health Facility, PO Box 2866, Fairfield, CA 94533; tel. 707/435-2136; Ms. Stacey Calhoun

Spencer Recovery Centers, Inc., PO Box 118, Monrovia, CA 91017; tel. 949/376-3705; Mr. Christopher C Spencer

Tarzana Treatment Centers (OTP), 18646 Oxnard Street, Tarzana, CA 91356; tel. 818/996-1051; Mr. Scott Taylor, Esq.

The 14th Street Clinic, 1124 International Boulevard, Oakland, CA 94606; tel. 510/533-0800; Dr. Joan E Zweben

The Discovery Adolescent Program, 4136 Ann Arbor Road, Lakewood, CA 90712; tel. 562/425-6918; Dr. Craig M Brown

Twin Town Treatment Centers, 5122 E Katella Avenue, Suite 102, Los Alamitos, CA 90720; tel. 562/594-8844; Mr. David Lisonbee

Valley Health Associates, 338 Monterey Street, Salinas, CA 93901; tel. 831/424-6655; Ms. Cecile E Rohde

VAMC-San Francisco Substance Abuse Treatment Clinic, 4150 Clement Street, Bldg 1, San Francisco, CA 94121; tel. 415/750-2050; Dr. Peter Banys

Vista Del Mar Child and Family Services, 3200 Motor Avenue, Los Angeles, CA 90034; tel. 310/836-1223; Dr. Elias Lefferman

West Los Angeles Drug Treatment Services, 11301 Wilshire Blvd, Bldg 257C, Los Angeles, CA 90073; tel. 310/268-3132; Mr. David M Riley

West Oakland Health Council, Inc, 700 Adeline Street, Oakland, CA 94607; tel. 510/433-1500; Dr. Robert Cooper

Westside Community Mental Health, Inc., 1301 Pierce Street, San Francisco, CA 94115; tel. 415/563-8200; Mr. Abner Boles

COLORADO

Adolescent and Family Institute of Colorado, Inc., 10001 West 32nd Avenue, Wheat Ridge, CO 80033; tel. 303/238-1231; Dr. Alex M Panio, Jr.

Colorado Boys Ranch, PO Box 681, La Junta, CO 81050; tel. 719/384-5981; Mr. Charles M Thompson

Denver Health and Hospital Authority, 777 Bannock Street, Unit 9, Denver, CO 80204; tel. 303/436-5690; Mrs. Patricia Gabow

Devereux Cleo Wallace, 8405 Church Ranch Blvd., Westminster, CO 80021; tel. 303/438-2251; Mr. Bentley Smith

Forest Heights Lodge, PO Box 789, Evergreen, CO 80437-0789; tel. 303/674-6681; Ms. Linda Clefisch

Parker Valley Hope, PO Box 670, Parker, CO 80134; tel. 303/841-7857; Dr. Kenneth C Gregoire

Pikes Peak Mental Health, 220 Ruskin Drive, Colorado Springs, CO 80910; tel. 719/572-6100; Mr. Morris Roth

CONNECTICUT

Alcohol & Drug Recovery Centers, Inc.- Detoxification Center, 500 Blue Hills Avenue, Hartford, CT 06112; tel. 860/714-3701; Mr. Kenneth J Talge

Alcohol and Drug Recovery Centers, Inc., 500 Blue Hills Avenue, 6th Floor Administration, Hartford, CT 06112; tel. 860/714-3701; Mr. Kenneth J Talge

Alliance Treatment Center, Inc., PO Box 1357, Avon, CT 06001-1357; tel. 860/673-6115; Dr. Mark Muradian

Blue Hills Substance Abuse Services, 500 Vine Street, Hartford, CT 06112-1639; tel. 860/293-6401; Ms. Susan Graham

Capitol Region Mental Health Center, 500 Vine Street, Hartford, CT 06112; tel. 860/297-0903; Mr. Luis Perez

Community Mental Health Affiliates, Inc., 29 Russell Street, New Britain, CT 06052; tel. 860/826-1358; Dr. Mark Muradian

Connecticut Counseling Centers Norwalk Methadone Maintenance, 984 Southford Road, Middlebury, CT 06762; tel. 203/577-5320; Mr. Roger Lambert

Connecticut Counseling Centers Norwalk Opiate Detoxification, 984 Southford Road, Middlebury, CT 06762; tel. 203/577-5320; Mr. Robert Lambert

Connecticut Counseling Centers Waterbury Methadone Maintenan, 984 Southford Road, Middlebury, CT 06762; tel. 203/577-5320; Mr. Michael Freeman

Connecticut Counseling Centers Waterbury Opiate Detoxification, 984 Southford Road, Middlebury, CT 06762; tel. 203/577-5320; Mr. Michael Freeman

Connecticut Counseling Centers, Inc., 984 Southford Road, Middlebury, CT 06762-3234; tel. 203/577-5320; Mr. Richard Bilangi

Connecticut Valley Hospital- Addiction Services Div-Merritt, PO Box 351, Middletown, CT 06457-7023; tel. 860/262-5887; Mr. Garrell S Mullaney

Inter-Community Mental Health Group, Inc., 281 Main Street, East Hartford, CT 06118; tel. 860/569-5900; Ms. Kimberly L Beauregard

Klingberg Family Centers, Inc., 370 Linwood Street, New Britain, CT 06052; tel. 860/224-9113; Ms. Rosemarie Burton

Lake Grove at Durham, Inc., 459R Wallingford Road, Durham, CT 06422; tel. 860/349-3467; Mr. Michael Suchopar

New Era Rehabilitation Center, 3851 Main Street, Bridgeport, CT 06606; tel. 203/372-3333; Dr. Ebenezer A Kolade

North Central Counseling Services, Inc., 995 Day Hill Road, Windsor, CT 06095; tel. 860/253-5020; Ms. Heather M Gates

Opiate Treatment Program, VA Connecticut Heathcare System, 950 Campbell Avenue, Bldg 36, West Haven, CT 06516; tel. 203/932-5711; Dr. Kishorchandra Gonsai

Perception Programs, Inc., PO Box 407, Willimantic, CT 06226; tel. 860/450-7122; Ms. Linda Mastriani

River Valley Services, PO Box 351, Middletown, CT 06457; tel. 860/262-5200; Mr. Howard Reid

Rushford Center, Inc., 1250 Silver Street, Middletown, CT 06457; tel. 203/235-1792; Mr. Jeffrey L Walter

Saint Francis Hospital & Medical Center - 8 West Unit, 500 Blue Hills Avenue, Hartford, CT 06112; tel. 860/714-2333; Mr. Christopher M Dadlez

Silver Hill Hospital, 208 Valley Road, New Canaan, CT 06840; tel. 203/801-2297; Dr. Sigurd H Ackerman

South Central Rehabilitation Center, 232 Cedar Street, New Haven, CT 06519; tel. 203/503-3356; Mr. Cornell Scott

Southwest Connecticut Mental Health System, 97 Middle Street, Bridgeport, CT 06604; tel. 203/579-7368; Mr. James M Pisciotta

State of CT DMHAS - Southeastern Mental Health Authority, 401 West Thames Street, Bldg. 301, Norwich, CT 06360; tel. 860/859-4674; Mr. John H Simsarian

Stonington Institute, 75 Swantown Hill Road, North Stonington, CT 06359; tel. 860/439-6000; Mr. William A Aniskovich

The Children's Center of Hamden, Inc., 1400 Whitney Avenue, Hamden, CT 06517; tel. 203/248-2116; Mr. Anthony DelMastro

The Danbury Hopsital - OTP, 24 Hospital Ave., Danbury, CT 06810; tel. 203/797-7000; Mr. Frank J Kelly

The Wellspring Foundation, Inc., 21 Arch Bridge Road, Bethlehem, CT 06751; tel. 203/266-8000; Mr. Herbert L Hall

The Wheeler Clinic, 91 Northwest Drive, Plainville, CT 06062; tel. 860/793-3500; Dr. David J Berkowitz

United Services, Inc., Post Office Box 839, Dayville, CT 06241; tel. 860/774-2020; Ms. Diane L Manning

Western Connecticut Mental Health Network, 55 West Main Street, Suite 410, Waterbury, CT 06702; tel. 203/805-6400; Ms. Karen Evertson

DELAWARE

Brandywine Counseling, Inc, Lancaster, 2713 Lancaster Avenue, Wilmington, DE 19805; tel. 302/656-2348; Ms. Sara T Allshouse

Brandywine Counseling, Inc., 2814 West Second Street, Wilmington, DE 19805; tel. 302/472-0381; Ms. Sara T Allshouse

Brandywine Counseling, Inc., Riverfront, 350 South Madison Street, Wilmington, DE 19801; tel. 302/661-6200; Ms. Sara T Allshouse

Brandywine Counseling, Inc., South Chapel, 24 Brookhill Drive, Newark, DE 19702; tel. 302/454-3020; Ms. Sara T Allshouse

Connections Community Support Programs, Inc., 500 West 10th Street, Wilmington, DE 19801; tel. 302/984-3380; Ms. Catherine Devaney McKay

Delaware Guidance Services for Children and Youth, 1213 Delaware Avenue, Wilmington, DE 19806; tel. 302/652-3948; Mr. Bruce Kelsey

Silver Lake Treatment Consortium, 493 East Main Street, Middletown, DE 19709; tel. 302/378-5238; Dr. Thomas L Olson

SODAT - Delaware, Inc., 625 North Orange Street, Wilmington, DE 19801; tel. 302/656-4044; Mr. Kenneth R Collins

Terry Children's Psychiatric Center, 10 Central Avenue, New Castle, DE 19720; tel. 302/577-4270; Dr. Thomas Olson

DISTRICT OF COLUMBIA

Department of Veterans Affairs, Substance Abuse Rehab Program, 50 Irving Street, Northwest, Washington, DC 20002; tel. 202/745-8313; Dr. Stephen Deutsch

Jos-Arz Academy, 220 Taylor St., NE, Washington, DC 20017; tel. 202/269-6004; Ms. Linda Harllee

McClendon Center, 1313 New York Avenue, NW, Washington, DC 20005; tel. 202/737-6191; Mr. Richard E Davis

Psychiatric Institute of Washington, 4228 Wisconsin Avenue, NW, Washington, DC 20016; tel. 202/885-5600; Mr. Ken Courage

Riverside Hospital, 4460 MacArthur Boulevard, NW, Washington, DC 20007; tel. 202/333-9355; Mr. Michael Goodman

The Episcopal Center for Children, 5901 Utah Avenue, NW, Washington, DC 20015-1616; tel. 202/363-1333; Mr. Alan C Korz

FLORIDA

Act Corporation, 1220 Willis Avenue #25, Daytona Beach, FL 32114; tel. 386/947-3600; Mr. J W Dreggors

Alternate Family Care, Inc., 10001 W Oakland Park Blvd, Suite 302, Sunrise, FL 33351; tel. 954/746-5200; Dr. David Ferguson

Alternatives In Treatment, Inc., 7601 North Federal Highway, Suite 100B, Boca Raton, FL 33487; tel. 561/998-0866; Mr. Jacob Frydman

American Therapeutic Corp., 1801 NE 2nd Avenue, Miami, FL 33132; tel. 305/371-5777; Ms. Marianella Valera

Apalachee Center, Inc., 2634-J Capital Circle NE, Tallahassee, FL 32308; tel. 850/523-3333; Mr. Ronald P Kirkland

Bayview Center for Mental Health, Inc., 12550 Biscayne Blvd, Suite 919, North Miami, FL 33181; tel. 305/892-4772; Mr. Robert S Ward

Beachcomber Rehab, Inc., 4493 North Ocean Boulevard, Delray Beach, FL 33483; tel. 561/276-6226; Mr. Joseph R Bryan

Behavioral Health of the Palm Beaches, Inc., 5725 Corporate Way, Suite 209, West Palm Beach, FL 33407; tel. 561/615-6664; Mr. Donald Mullaney

Bridgeway Center, Inc., 137 Hospital Drive, Fort Walton Beach, FL 32548; tel. 850/833-7430; Mr. Dan Cobbs

Broward County/Human Services Dept/Family Success Adm Div., 115 S Andrews Ave, Ste 303, Fort Lauderdale, FL 33301; tel. 954/357-5444; Mr. Fredrick J Murry

Broward Treatment Center, 1101 South 21st Avenue, Hollywood, FL 33020; tel. 954/922-0522; Mr. Mark Gallagher

Caron Foundation of Florida, I d/b/a Renaissance Institute, 7000 N Federal Hwy, 2nd Floor, Boca Raton, FL 33487; tel. 561/241-7977; Mr. Douglas Tieman

Central Florida Treatment Centers, 7 North Cocoa Boulevard, Cocoa, FL 32922; tel. 321/631-4578; Mr. Carlos A Ball-llovera

Central Florida Treatment Centers - Orlando, 1800 West Colonial Drive, Orlando, FL 32804; tel. 407/843-0041; Mrs. Carol Ball

Central Florida Treatment Centers - Palm Bay, 2198 Harris Avenue, Palm Bay, FL 32905; tel. 321/951-9750; Mrs. Carol Ball

Chautauqua Offices of Psychotherapy and Evaluation, 3686 US Highway 331 South, Defuniak Springs, FL 32435; tel. 850/892-8035; Ms. Rachel R Gillis

Citrus Health Network, Inc, 4175 West 20th Avenue, Hialeah, FL 33012; tel. 305/825-0300; Mr. Mario E Jardon

Coastal Behavioral Healthcare, Inc., 1565 State Street, Sarasota, FL 34236; tel. 941/927-8900; Dr. Christine Cauffield

Comprehensive Psychiatric Center, 9735 East Fern Street, Miami, FL 33157; tel. 305/238-5121; Mr. Roberto Ruiz, Jr.

Comprehensive Psychiatric Center - Miami Beach, 960 41st Street (Arthur Godfrey Rd) Ste 106, Miami Beach, FL 33140; tel. 305/534-5121; Mrs. Patricia Cunningham

Comprehensive Psychiatric Center North, 240 Northwest 183rd Street, Miami, FL 33169; tel. 305/651-2332; Dr. Roberto Ruiz

Comprehensive Psychiatric Center-Central, 1501 N.W. 36th Street, Miami, FL 33142; tel. 305/634-1401; Dr. Roberto Ruiz, Jr.

David Lawrence Center, 6075 Golden Gate Parkway, Naples, FL 34116; tel. 239/354-1440; Mr. David C Schimmel

Fair Oaks Pavilion at Delray Medical Center, 5352 Linton Boulevard, Delray Beach, FL 33484; tel. 561/495-3270; Mr. Mitchell S Feldman

Fairwinds Treatment Center, 1569 S Fort Harrison Avenue, Clearwater, FL 33756; tel. 727/449-0300; Mr. Mazhar K Al-Abed

Florida Center for Recovery, 3451 West Midway Road, Fort Pierce, FL 34950; tel. 772/460-2777; Mr. Jack Hamilton

Florida Institute for Neurologic Rehabilitation, Inc, PO Box 1348, Wauchula, FL 33873; tel. 800/697-5390; Mr. Joseph Brennick

Focus Healthcare of Florida - OTP, 5960 Southwest 106th Avenue, Cooper City, FL 33328; tel. 954/680-2700; Mr. Alan Goodstat

Green Cross Health Systems, Inc., 2645 Douglas Road, Suite 601, Miami, FL 33133; tel. 305/443-9990; Dr. Miguel A Nunez, Jr.

Gulf Coast Treatment Center, 1015 Mar Walt Drive, Fort Walton Beach, FL 32547; tel. 850/863-4160; Mr. Jeffrey M Kaplan

Hanley Center, 5200 East Avenue, West Palm Beach, FL 33407-2374; tel. 561/841-1000; Mr. Terry Allen

Hanley-Hazelden Center at St. Mary's, 5200 East Avenue, West Palm Beach, FL 33407; tel. 561/841-1000; Mr. Terry Allen

HealthCare Connection, Inc., 825 West Linebaugh Avenue, Tampa, FL 33612; tel. 813/931-5560; Mr. Jess Loven

Hendry Glades Mental Health Clinic, Inc., 601 West Alverdez Avenue, Clewiston, FL 33440; tel. 863/983-1423; Mr. Joseph F Hosick

Homestead Behavioral Health Clinic, 447 Northeast 8th Street, Homestead, FL 33030; tel. 305/248-3488; Mrs. Aidelyn Lopez

Hope Horizon Center, Inc., 7821 SW 24th Street, Suite 100, Miami, FL 33155; tel. 305/269-8550; Mr. Ramon Trabazo

Jacksonville Metro Treatment Center, 3609 Emerson Street, Jacksonville, FL 32207; tel. 904/398-7015; Mr. T. Mark Gallagher

La Amistad Behavioral Health Services, 1650 Park Avenue North, Maitland, FL 32751; tel. 407/647-0660; Ms. Vickie Lewis

Lakeside Alternatives, Inc., 434 West Kennedy Boulevard, Orlando, FL 32810; tel. 407/875-3700; Mr. Jerry Kassab

Lakeview Health Systems, LLC, 8889 Corporate Square Court, Jacksonville, FL 32216; tel. 904/727-6455; Mrs. Joanne Telmosse

LifeStream Behavioral Center, PO Box 491000, Leesburg, FL 34749-1000; tel. 352/315-7500; Mr. Jonathan M Cherry

Lighthouse CMHC, 1704 NW 7th Street, Miami, FL 33125; tel. 305/541-2600; Mr. Alex Menendez

Manatee Glens Corporation, PO Box 9478, Bradenton, FL 34206-9478; tel. 941/782-4299; Ms. Mary Ruiz

Marion-Citrus Mental Health Centers, Inc., 5664 SW 60th Ave, Ocala, FL 34477-1929; tel. 352/291-5456; Mr. Russell Rasco

Mental Health Care, Inc., 5707 North 22nd Street, Tampa, FL 33610; tel. 813/272-2244; Mr. Julian I Rice

Meridian Behavioral Healthcare, Inc., PO Box 141750, Gainesville, FL 32608; tel. 352/374-5600; Dr. Margarita Labarta

Metro Treatment of Florida, LP dba Sunrise Treatment Center, 14050 Town Loop Blvd, Suite 204, Orlando, FL 32837; tel. 407/351-7080; Mr. T. M Gallagher

National Deaf Academy, LLC, 19650 US Highway 441, Mount Dora, FL 32757; tel. 352/735-9500; Dr. Alan M Cohen

New Era Health Center, 9600 Southwest 8th Street Suite 1, Miami, FL 33174; tel. 305/559-8838; Mr. Enrique A Garcia

Northside Mental Health Center, 12512 Bruce B. Downs Boulevard, Tampa, FL 33612-9209; tel. 813/977-8700; Ms. Marsha L Brown

Oakwood Center of the Palm Beaches, Inc., 1041 45th Street, West Palm Beach, FL 33407; tel. 561/383-8000; Dr. Linda C DePiano

Operation PAR, Inc., 6655 66th Street North, Pinellas Park, FL 33781; tel. 888/727-6398; Mrs. Nancy L Hamilton

Operation PAR, Inc. (NATC - Bradenton), 6655 66th Street North, Pinellas Park, FL 33781; tel. 888/727-6398; Mrs. Nancy L Hamilton

Operation PAR, Inc. (NATC-Clearwater), 6655 66th Street North, Pinellas Park, FL 33781; tel. 888/727-6398; Mrs. Nancy L Hamilton

Operation PAR, Inc. (NATC-Fort Myers), 6655 66th Street North, Pinellas Park, FL 33781; tel. 888/727-6398; Mrs. Nancy L Hamilton

Operation PAR, Inc. (NATC-Pasco), 6655 66th Street North, Pinellas Park, FL 33781; tel. 888/727-6398; Mrs. Nancy L Hamilton

Orlando Methadone Treatment Center, 14050 Town Loop Blvd., Suite 204, Orlando, FL 32837; tel. 407/275-8939; Mr. T. M Gallagher

Parent's Information and Resource Center, Inc., 2850 N Federal Hwy, 4th Floor, Lighthouse Point, FL 33064; tel. 954/785-8285; Mrs. Janet V Ward

Pathways to Recovery,Inc, 13132 Barwick Road, Delray Beach, FL 33445; tel. 561/496-7532; Ms. Carol Parks

PB Institute Partners Limited Partnership, 1017 N. Olive Avenue, West Palm Beach, FL 33401; tel. 800/433-5098; Mr. David McVinney

Peace River Center for Personal Development, Inc., P.O. Box 1559, Bartow, FL 33831-1559; tel. 863/534-7020; Mrs. Mary Lu Kiley

Personal Enrichment through Mental Health Services, Inc., 11254 58th Street North, Pinellas Park, FL 33782; tel. 727/545-6477; Mr. Thomas C Wedekind

Pompano Treatment Center, 380 Southwest 12th Avenue, Pompano Beach, FL 33069; tel. 954/782-9774; Mr. Mike Ford

Ramsay Youth Services of Florida, Inc., 4480 51st Street West, Bradenton, FL 34210; tel. 941/792-2222; Ms. Linda Kautz

Recovery First, Inc., 2701 W. Oakland Park Blvd., Oakland Park, FL 33311; tel. 954/497-0824; Mr. James Davis

Renaissance Behavioral Health Systems, Inc., PO Box 19249, Jacksonville, FL 32245-9249; tel. 904/743-1883; Dr. Robert Sommers

Ruth Cooper Center for Behavioral Health Care, Inc., 2789 Ortiz Avenue, Southeast, Fort Myers, FL 33905; tel. 239/275-3222; Ms. Janet W Eustis

SandyPines Hospital, 11301 SE Tequesta Terrace, Tequesta, FL 33469; tel. 561/744-0211; Dr. John W Thompson

South County Mental Health Center, Inc., 16158 South Military Trail, Delray Beach, FL 33484; tel. 561/637-1004; Mr. Joseph S Speicher

Southwest Miami Treatment Center, 11980 SW 8th Street, Ste 15/16, Miami, FL 33184; tel. 305/553-8807; Mr. Mark Gallagher

Substance Abuse and Health Care Services, 115 S. Andrews Avenue Suite 318, Fort Lauderdale, FL 33301; tel. 954/357-5455; Mr. Paul Jaquith

Tampa Bay Academy, 12012 Boyette Road, Riverview, FL 33569; tel. 813/677-6700; Mr. Edward C Hoefle

Ten Broeck Ocala, 3130 SW 27th Avenue, Ocala, FL 34474; tel. 352/671-3130; Mr. Keith Lewis

The Centre for Women, Inc., 305 South Hyde Park Avenue, Tampa, FL 33606; tel. 813/251-8437; Ms. Beth Ficquette

The Devereux Foundation, Inc., 5850 T. G. Lee Blvd, Suite 400, Orlando, FL 32822; tel. 407/812-4555; Mr. Michael C Becker

The Renfrew Centers, Inc. (Florida), 7700 Northwest 48th Avenue, Coconut Creek, FL 33073; tel. 954/698-9222; Ms. Diane Buchter

The Village South, Inc., 3180 Biscayne Boulevard, Miami, FL 33137; tel. 305/573-3784; Mr. Frank Rabbito

The Watershed at Clear Lake, 200 Congress Park Drive, Suite 100, Delray Beach, FL 33445; tel. 561/860-8228; Mr. Chris Crosby

The Watershed Treatment Programs, 200 Congress Park Drive, #100, Delray Beach, FL 33445; tel. 561/860-8228; Mr. Chris Crosby

The Willough at Naples, 9001 Tamiami Trail East, Naples, FL 34113; tel. 941/775-4500; Mr. James O'Shea

Transitions Recovery Program, 1928 Northeast 154th Street, North Miami, FL 33162; tel. 305/949-9001; Mr. Lee Barchan

Treatment Resources of Margate, Inc., 5100 Coconut Creek Parkway, Margate, FL 33063; tel. 954/917-3334; Ms. Bea Redlich

Turning Point of Tampa, Inc., 6227 Sheldon Road, Tampa, FL 33615; tel. 813/882-3003; Ms. Robin Piper

Twelve Oaks, 2068 Healthcare Avenue, Navarre, FL 32566; tel. 850/939-1200; Ms. Candance Henderson

University Behavioral Health Center, 2500 Discovery Drive, Orlando, FL 32826; tel. 407/281-7000; Mr. David Beardsley

Volunteers of America of Florida, Inc., 1205 East 8th Avenue, Tampa, FL 33605; tel. 813/282-1525; Ms. Kathryn E Spearman

Section C

Wellness Resource Center, Inc., 7940 North Federal Highway Suite 120, Boca Raton, FL 33487; tel. 561/995–7388; Ms. Michele Michael

West Palm Beach Treatment Center, 1497 Forest Hill Blvd., Suite E, Lake Clarke Shores, FL 33406; tel. 561/433–5687; Mr. Mark Gallagher

West Psychiatric Associates, PA/Serenity Addiction Center, 6780 Taft Street, Hollywood, FL 33024; tel. 954/981–7612; Dr. Sayonara Baez

GEORGIA

Albany Area Community Service Board, PO Box 1988, Albany, GA 31702; tel. 229/430–4005; Dr. John C BurnsIII

AmericanWork, Inc., PO Box 20664, Saint Simons Island, GA 31522; tel. 912/638–0350; Mr. Ken Whiddon

Behavioral Health Services of South Georgia, 3120 N Oak Street Ext, Suite C, Valdosta, GA 31602-1007; tel. 229/333–7095; Mr. W. David McCracken

Central State Hospital, 620 Broad St, Milledgeville, GA 31062; tel. 478/445–4128; Mr. Marvin Bailey

Coastal Harbor Treatment Center, 1150 Cornell Avenue, Savannah, GA 31406; tel. 912/354–3911; Mr. Raymond F Heckerman

Community Mental Health Center of East Central Georgia, 3421 Mike Padgett Highway, Building D, Augusta, GA 30906; tel. 706/771–7800; Dr. Philip A Horton

Community Service Board of Middle Georgia, 2121A Bellevue Road, Dublin, GA 31021-2998; tel. 478/272–1190; Ms. Patsy H Thomas

DeKalb Community Service Board, PO Box 1648, Decatur, GA 30031; tel. 404/294–3834; Mr. Gary S Richey

Dept., of Veterans Affairs - Atlanta VA Medical Center, 1670 Clairmont Road, Decatur, GA 30033; tel. 404/321–6111; Mr. Thomas A Cappello

Devereux Georgia Treatment Network, PO Box 1688, Kennesaw, GA 30144-8688; tel. 770/422–2135; Mr. Mario Bolivar

DM & ADR, Inc., 1720 Commerce Road, Athens, GA 30607; tel. 706/552–0688; Ms. Ali McCorkle

Fulton County Dept of MHDDAD, 115 MLK, Jr., Drive, Suite 277, Atlanta, GA 30303; tel. 404/730–0268; Dr. Barbara J Lattimore

Gateway Community Service Board, 1000 Commisioners Drive, Darien, GA 31305; tel. 912/437–9300; Dr. Frank A Bonati

Georgia Pines Community Service Board, 1102 Smith Avenue Suite K, Thomasville, GA 31799; tel. 229/225–4335; Mr. Robert H Jones, Jr.

Georgia Psychological Services, PO Box 211626, Augusta, GA 30917-1626; tel. 706/210–3066; Mr. David W Proefrock

Grady Health System-Drug Dependence Unit, 48-50 Coca Cola Place, Atlanta, GA 30303-3043; tel. 404/616–3970; Dr. Andrew Agwunobi

Inner Harbour, Ltd., 4685 Dorsett Shoals Road, Douglasville, GA 30135; tel. 770/942–2391; Mr. Ronald Scroggy

LARC, Inc., 1646 East Park Avenue, Valdosta, GA 31602; tel. 912/244–8290; Dr. Harry A Hamm

Laurel Heights Hospital, 934 Briarcliff Road, Northeast, Atlanta, GA 30306; tel. 404/888–7860; Ms. Ruth Coody

McIntosh Trail MH/MR/SA Community Service Board, PO Box 1320, Griffin, GA 30224; tel. 770/358–8250; Ms. Cathy Johnson

Metro Atlanta Recovery Residences, Inc., PO Box 48349, Doraville, GA 30340; tel. 770/457–1222; Mr. Doug Brush

Murphy Harpst Children's Centers, 740 Fletcher Street, Cedartown, GA 30125; tel. 770/748–1500; Ms. Joanne G Simmons

Oconee Center, PO Box 1827, Milledgeville, GA 31061; tel. 478/445–4717; Mr. John W Prather

Ogeechee Behavioral Health Services, PO Box 1259, Swainsboro, GA 30401; tel. 478/289–2522; Mr. J. Frank Brantley

Ridge Creek, Inc., 830 Hidden Lake Road, Dahlonega, GA 30533; tel. 706/867–1720; Ms. Nicole R Fuglsang

River Edge Behavioral Health Center, 175 Emery Highway, Macon, GA 31217; tel. 478/751–4519; Mr. Jim Riley

Skyland Trail, 1903 North Druid Hills Road, Atlanta, GA 30319; tel. 404/315–8333; Mrs. Elizabeth E Finnerty

Southside Medical Treatment Center, 1039 Ridge Avenue, Southwest, Atlanta, GA 30315; tel. 404/688–1350; Mr. Avon Lauder

Talbott Recovery Campus, 5448 Yorktowne Drive, Atlanta, GA 30349; tel. 770/994–0185; Mr. Benjamin H Underwood

Turning Point Hospital, PO Box 1177, Moultrie, GA 31768; tel. 229/985–4815; Mr. Ben Marion

Willingway Hospital, 311 Jones Mill Road, Statesboro, GA 30458; tel. 912/764–6236; Mr. Jimmy Mooney

HAWAII

Benchmark Behavioral Health Systems - Pearl City, P.O Box 1196, Pearl City, HI 96782; tel. 808/454–1411; Mr. John A Holter

IDAHO

Project Patch, 25 Miracle Lane, Garden Valley, ID 83622; tel. 503/653–8086; Mr. Tom Sanford

ILLINOIS

Advocate Addiction Treatment Program, 1775 Dempster Street, 10 South, Park Ridge, IL 60068; tel. 847/795–3900; Ms. Debra Geihsler

Alexian Center for Mental Health, 3350 Salt Creek Lane, #114, Arlington Heights, IL 60005; tel. 847/952–7460; Mr. Denis Ferguson

Allendale Association, PO Box 1088, Lake Villa, IL 60046; tel. 847/356–2351; Ms. Mary Shahbazian

Beacon Therapeutic Diagnostic and Treatment Center, 1912 West 103rd Street, Chicago, IL 60643; tel. 773/298–1243; Ms. Susan Reyna-Guerrero

Ben Gordon Center, 12 Health Services Drive, Dekalb, IL 60115; tel. 815/756–4875; Mr. Michael D Flora

CAP of Downers Grove, 4954 South Main Street, Downers Grove, IL 60515; tel. 630/810–0186; Dr. Marc Shinderman

Center for Addictive Problems, 609 North Wells Street, Chicago, IL 60610; tel. 312/266–0404; Dr. Marc Shinderman

Center on Deafness, 3444 Dundee Road, Northbrook, IL 60062; tel. 847/559–0110; Mr. Robert Van Dyke

Central Illinois Center for the Treatment of Addiction, 228 Northeast Jefferson, Peoria, IL 61654; tel. 309/671–8000; Mr. Michael G Boyle

Chestnut Health Systems, 1003 Martin Luther King Drive, Bloomington, IL 61701; tel. 309/827–6026; Mr. Russell J Hagen

Chicago Lakeshore Hospital, 4840 North Marine Drive, Chicago, IL 60640; tel. 773/878–9700; Mr. C. A Eaks

Coles County Mental Health Association, Inc., PO Box 1307, Mattoon, IL 61938; tel. 217/234–6405; Ms. Kathleen Roberts

Community Counseling Centers of Chicago, 4740 North Clark Street, Chicago, IL 60640; tel. 773/769–0205; Dr. Anthony A Kopera

Comprehensive Mental Health Center of St. Clair County, 3911 State Street, East Saint Louis, IL 62205; tel. 618/482–7330; Mrs. Marsha R Johnson

Cornell Interventions - DuPage, 11 S 250 Route 83, Hinsdale, IL 60521; tel. 630/325–5050; Mr. Walter Carlson

Cornell Interventions - Southwood, 901 W. Jackson Boulevard Suite 400, Chicago, IL 60607; tel. 773/737–4600; Mr. Mark K Thompson

Cornell Interventions - Woodridge, 2221 64th Street, Woodridge, IL 60517; tel. 630/968–6477; Mr. Casey Radkiewicz

Cornell Interventions East St. Louis, 302 North 5thStreet, East Saint Louis, IL 62201; tel. 618/271–4542; Mr. Don Otis

Cornell Interventions Life Works, 1611 Jefferson Street, Joliet, IL 60435; tel. 815/730–7521; Ms. Loretta Berry

Cornell Interventions Northside Clinic, 2723 North Clark Street, Chicago, IL 60614; tel. 773/525–3250; Mr. Ron McDearmon

Cornell Interventions Southwood, 5701 South Wood Street, Chicago, IL 60636; tel. 773/737–4600; Mr. David L Johnson

Counseling Center of Lake View, 3225 North Sheffield Avenue, Chicago, IL 60657; tel. 773/549–5886; Mr. Norman J Groetzinger

DuPage County Health Dept./ Mental Health Services, 111 North County Farm Road, Wheaton, IL 60187; tel. 630/682–7400; Mr. Leland Lewis

Edward Hines Jr VA Hospital / Drug Dependency Treatment Ctr, PO Box 5000, Hines, IL 60141; tel. 708/202–8387; Dr. Pradipkumar Desai

Family Guidance Center, Inc., 751 Aurora Avenue, Aurora, IL 60505; tel. 312/943–6545; Dr. Larry Kroll

Family Guidance Center, Inc., 310 West Chicago Avenue, Chicago, IL 60610; tel. 312/943–6545; Dr. Larry Kroll

Family Guidance Center, Inc., 484 Lee Street, Des Plaines, IL 60016; tel. 312/943–6545; Dr. Larry Kroll

Family Guidance Centers, Inc., 310 W. Chicago Ave., Chicago, IL 60610; tel. 312/943–6545; Dr. Larry Kroll

Family Service and Community Mental Health Center/McHenry, 5320 West Elm Street, McHenry, IL 60050; tel. 815/385–6400; Mr. Robert M Martens

FHN - Jane Addams, Inc., 1133 W Stephenson Street, Freeport, IL 61032; tel. 815/599–7337; Mr. Daniel E Neal

Garfield Counseling Center, Inc., 4132 West Madison, Chicago, IL 60624; tel. 773/533–0433; Mr. Richard E Shelton, Jr.

Gateway Foundation Inc., 55 East Jackson Blvd, Suite 1500, Chicago, IL 60604; tel. 312/663–1130; Mr. Michael Darcy

Hazelden Foundation - Chicago Office, 867 North Dearborn Street, Chicago, IL 60610; tel. 651/213–4060; Mrs. Ellen Breyer

Heartland Human Services, PO Box 1047, Effingham, IL 62401; tel. 217/347–7179; Ms. Cheryl Compton

Heritage Behavioral Health Center, Inc., PO Box 710, Decatur, IL 62524-2820; tel. 217/362–6262; Ms. Diana L Knaebe

Human Service Center, PO Box 1346, Peoria, IL 61654-1346; tel. 309/671–8000; Mr. Michael G Boyle

Janet Wattles Center, Inc., 526 West State Street, Rockford, IL 61101; tel. 815/968–9300; Mr. Frank H Ware

Kenneth Young Center, 1001 Rohlwing Road, Elk Grove Village, IL 60007; tel. 847/524–8800; Mr. Mitchell Bruski

Lake County Health Department, 3004 Grand Avenue, Waukegan, IL 60085; tel. 847/377–8120; Mr. Dale W Galassie

Lake County Health Department / Behavioral Health Services, 3012 Grand Avenue, Waukegan, IL 60085; tel. 847/377–8299; Mr. Dale W Galassie

Leyden Family Service and Mental Health Center, 10001 West Grand Avenue, Franklin Park, IL 60131; tel. 847/451–0330; Mr. Dennis P Vaccaro

Maryville Academy Scott Nolan Center, 555 Wilson Lane, Des Plaines, IL 60016; tel. 847/768–5430; Dr. Joseph Eraci

McHenry County Department of Public Health, 2200 N. Seminary Way, Woodstock, IL 60098; tel. 815/334–4510; Ms. Debbie Currey

McHenry County Youth Service Bureau, 101 South Jefferson Street, Woodstock, IL 60098; tel. 815/338–7360; Ms. Susan H Krause

McLean County Center for Human Services, Inc., 108 West Market Street, Bloomington, IL 61701-3918; tel. 309/827–5351; Mr. Thomas Barr

Mental Health and Deafness Resources, Inc., 614 Anthony Trail, Northbrook, IL 60062; tel. 847/509–8260; Ms. Patricia A Scherer

Mental Health Center of Champaign County, Inc., 1801 Fox Drive, Champaign, IL 61820; tel. 217/398–3777; Ms. Alexandria W Lewis

Michael Reese Hospital - OTP, 2929 South Ellis Avenue, Chicago, IL 60616; tel. 312/791–3545; Dr. Enrique Beckmann

Naperville Psychiatric Venture d/b/a Linden Oaks Hospital, 801 South Washington, Naperville, IL 60566-7060; tel. 630/305–5500; Ms. Mary L Mastro

North Central Behavioral Health Systems, Inc., PO Box 1488, La Salle, IL 61301; tel. 815/223–0160; Mr. Donald P Miskowiec

Northwest Community Hospital Youth Center, 901 Kirchoff Road, Arlington Heights, IL 60005; tel. 847/618–1000; Mr. Bruce K Crowther

Northwestern Memorial Hospital Opioid Treatment Program, 320 Huron Street, Chicago, IL 60611; tel. 312/926–2000; Mr. Dean M Harrison

P.H.A.S.E. Inc., Methadone Treatment Program, 516 Green Street, Rockford, IL 61102; tel. 815/966–1285; Ms. Judy Weiher

PEER Services, Inc., 906 Davis Street, Evanston, IL 60201; tel. 847/492–1778; Ms. Kate Mahoney

Perry County Counseling Center, Inc., 1016 S Madison St, Suite A, Du Quoin, IL 62832; tel. 618/542–4357; Mr. John R Venskus

ProCare Centers, 1820 South 25th Avenue, Broadview, IL 60153; tel. 708/338–3806; Mr. J. Melvin J Smith

Rosecrance, Inc., 3815 Harrison Avenue, Rockford, IL 61108; tel. 815/391–1000; Mr. Philip W Eaton

Sangamon Menard Alcoholism and Drugs Council, 120 North 11th Street, Springfield, IL 62703-1002; tel. 217/544–9858; Mr. Stephen J Knox

Sinnissippi Centers, Inc., 325 Illinois Route 2, Dixon, IL 61021; tel. 815/284–6611; Mr. James R Sarver

Sojourn House, Inc., 565 North Turner Avenue, Freeport, IL 61032; tel. 815/232–5121; Ms. Brenda J Bombard

South Shore Hospital, 8012 South Crandon Avenue, Chicago, IL 60644; tel. 773/768–0810; Mr. Jesus M Ong

Southeastern Illinois Counseling Centers, Inc., Drawer M, Olney, IL 62450; tel. 618/395–4306; Mr. Glenn Jackson

Stepping Stones of Rockford, Inc., 706 North Main Street, Rockford, IL 61103; tel. 815/963–0683; Mr. Stephen E Langley

Tazwood Mental Health Center, Inc., 1423 Valle Vista Boulevard, Pekin, IL 61554; tel. 309/347–5579; Mr. Michael Polson

The Camelot Schools, LLC, 1502 North Northwest Highway, Palatine, IL 60067; tel. 847/359–5600; Mr. Craig Bogacki

The Ecker Center for Mental Health, 1845 Grandstand Place, Elgin, IL 60123; tel. 847/695–0484; Ms. Karen Beyer

The South Suburban Council on Alcoholism and Substance Abuse, 1909 Cheker Square, East Hazel Crest, IL 60429; tel. 708/647–3333; Mr. Allen Sandusky

The Women's Treatment Center, 140 N. Ashland Avenue, Chicago, IL 60607; tel. 312/850–0050; Dr. Jewell Oates

Triangle Center Methadone Clinic, 120 North 11th Street, Springfield, IL 62703; tel. 217/544–9858; Mr. Stephen J Knox

Turning Point, IN, PO Box 723, Woodstock, IL 60098; tel. 815/338–8081; Ms. Elizabeth Trandel

VA Chicago Health Care System (OTP), 820 South Damen Avenue (Independence Hall), Chicago, IL 60612; tel. 312/569–6289; Dr. Robert J Craig

INDIANA

Adult and Child Mental Health Center, Inc., 8320 Madison Avenue, Indianapolis, IN 46227; tel. 317/883–0285; Mr. A Robert Dunbar

BehaviorCorp, Inc., 697 Pro-Med Lane, Carmel, IN 46032-5323; tel. 317/587–0500; Mr. Larry L Burch

Camelot Community Care, 833 W Lincoln Hwy, Suite 410-W, Schererville, IN 46375; tel. 219/864–7988; Ms. Elena Dwyre

Center for Behavioral Health, 645 South Rogers Street, Bloomington, IN 47403; tel. 812/339–1691; Dr. Dennis P Morrison

Columbus Behavioral Center for Children and Adolescents, PO Box 1549, Columbus, IN 47202-1549; tel. 812/376–1711; Mr. Richard Clark

Community Mental Health Center, Inc., 285 Bielby Road, Lawrenceburg, IN 47025; tel. 812/537–1302; Mr. Joseph D Stephens

Comprehensive Mental Health Services, Inc., 240 North Tillotson Avenue, Muncie, IN 47304; tel. 765/288–1928; Mr. Hank A Milius

Cummins Behavioral Health Systems, Inc., 6655 East US 36, Avon, IN 46123; tel. 317/272–6361; Ms. Ann Borders

Evansville Psychiatric Children's Center, 3300 East Morgan Avenue, Evansville, IN 47715; tel. 812/477–6436; Mr. Tom Rich

Fairbanks Hospital, Inc., 8102 Clearvista Parkway, Indianapolis, IN 46256-4698; tel. 317/849–8222; Ms. Helene M Cross

Family & Children's Center Counseling and Development Servic, 105 East Jefferson Blvd Suite 700, South Bend, IN 46601; tel. 574/232–2255; Dr. James J Reisinger

Four County Comprehensive Mental Health, Inc., 1015 Michigan Avenue, Logansport, IN 46947; tel. 574/722–5151; Mr. Laurence R Ulrich

Ft Wayne Children's Home of United Church of Christ, Inc, 2525 Lake Avenue, Fort Wayne, IN 46805-5457; tel. 260/484–4153; Mr. J.C. Dollar

Grant-Blackford Mental Health, Inc., 505 Wabash Avenue, Marion, IN 46952; tel. 765/662–3971; Mr. Paul G Kuczora

Hamilton Center, Inc, PO Box 4323, Terre Haute, IN 47804-0323; tel. 812/231–8323; Mr. Galen Goode

LifeSpring Mental Health Services, 460 Spring Street, Jeffersonville, IN 47130; tel. 812/280–2080; Dr. Terry L Stawar

Madison Center, Inc., PO Box 80, South Bend, IN 46624; tel. 574/234–0061; Mr. Jack Roberts

Michiana Behavioral Health Center, 1800 North Oak Road, Plymouth, IN 46563; tel. 574/936–3784; Mr. Bryan Lett

Midtown Narcotics Treatment Program, 832 North Meridian Street, Indianapolis, IN 46204; tel. 317/686–5634; Mr/Mrs Margie Payne

Oaklawn, PO Box 809 330 Lakeview Drive, Goshen, IN 46527-0809; tel. 219/533–1234; Mr. Harold C Loewen

Options Treatment Center, 5602 Caito Drive, Indianapolis, IN 46226; tel. 317/544–4340; Ms. Roxane Harcourt

Quinco Behavioral Health Systems, 720 N. Marr Rd., Columbus, IN 47201; tel. 812/348–7449; Dr. Robert J Williams

R.T.C. Resource, Inc., 1404 South State, Indianapolis, IN 46203; tel. 317/783–4003; Mr. Jeff Catlett

Resolute, Inc., 320 North Tibbs, Indianapolis, IN 46222; tel. 317/630–5215; Mr. Michael Johnson

Richard L. Roudebush VA Medical Center, 1481 West 10th Street, Bldg 1, Indianapolis, IN 46202; tel. 317/554–0000; Dr. Sean O'Connor

Riverside Hospital, PO Box 60, South Bend, IN 46624; tel. 574/283–1104; Mr. Jack Roberts

Southlake Center for Mental Health, 8555 Taft Street, Merrillville, IN 46410-6199; tel. 219/769–4005; Mr. Lee Strawhun

Southwestern Indiana Mental Health Center, Inc., 415 Mulberry Street, Evansville, IN 47713-1298; tel. 812/436–4231; Mr. John K Browning

Tara Treatment Center, Inc., 6231 South US 31, Franklin, IN 46131; tel. 812/526–2611; Ms. Ann Daugherty

The Center for Mental Health, Inc., PO Box 1258, Anderson, IN 46015; tel. 765/649–8161; Mr. C. Richard DeHaven

The Children's Campus, Inc., 1411 Lincoln Way West, Mishawaka, IN 46544-1690; tel. 574/259–5666; Ms. Patricia L McLemore

The Midwest Center for Youth and Families, PO Box 669, Kouts, IN 46347; tel. 219/766–2999; Mr. Michael Perry

The Otis R. Bowen Center for Human Services, Inc., PO Box 497, Warsaw, IN 46581-0497; tel. 574/267–7169; Mr. Kurt Carlson

Tri-City Community Mental Health Center, Inc., 3903 Indianapolis Boulevard, East Chicago, IN 46312; tel. 219/392–6010; Mr. Robert Krumwied

Universal Behavioral Services Community Mental Health Center, 820 Fort Wayne Avenue, Indianapolis, IN 46204; tel. 317/684–0442; Mr. Therome Buford

Wabash Valley Hospital, Inc., 2900 North River Road, West Lafayette, IN 47906; tel. 765/463–2555; Mr. Rick Crawley

Willowglen Academy - Indiana, Inc., 308 East 21st Avenue, Gary, IN 46407; tel. 219/886–1320; Mr. Leonard F Dziubla

IOWA

Boys and Girls Home and Family Services, Inc., 2101 Court Street, Sioux City, IA 51104; tel. 712/293–4700; Mr. Robert P Sheehan

Hillcrest Family Services, 2005 Asbury Road, Dubuque, IA 52001; tel. 563/583–7357; Mr. Gary L Gansemer

Orchard Place, 925 Southwest Porter Avenue, Des Moines, IA 50315; tel. 515/285–6781; Mr. Brock Wolff

KANSAS

Atchison Valley Hope, PO Box 312, Atchison, KS 66002; tel. 913/367–1618; Dr. Kenneth C Gregoire

Kaw Valley Center, Inc., 21350 W. 153 Street, Olathe, KS 66061; tel. 913/322–4900; Mr. B. Wayne Sims

Liberty Juvenile Services and Treatment, 2050 West 11th Street, Wichita, KS 67202; tel. 316/267–5710; Ms. Renate' C Doss

Marillac Center, 8000 W. 127th Street, Overland Park, KS 66213; tel. 816/508–3300; Mr. R. Michael Bowen

Norton Valley Hope, PO Box 510, Norton, KS 67654; tel. 785/877–5101; Dr. Kenneth C Gregoire

The Kansas City Metro Methadone Program, 3901 Rainbow Boulevard, Kansas City, KS 66160-7341; tel. 913/588–6493; Dr. William F Gabrielli, Jr.

The Saint Francis Academy, Incorporated, 509 East Elm Street, Salina, KS 67401; tel. 785/825–0541; Rev. Edward W Fellhauer

United Methodist Youthville, Inc., PO Box 210, Newton, KS 67114; tel. 316/283–1950; Mr. John R Francis

KENTUCKY

Adanta Behavioral Health Services, 259 Parkers Mill Road, Somerset, KY 42501; tel. 606/679–4782; Ms. Cathy Epperson

Bluegrass Regional / Narcotics Addiction Program, 1351 Newtown Pike, Lexington, KY 40511; tel. 859/253–1686; Mr. Joseph Toy

Bluegrass Regional Mental Health - Mental Retardation Board, 1351 Newtown Pike, Lexington, KY 40511; tel. 859/253–1686; Mr. Joseph A Toy

Central State ICF/MR, 10510 LaGrange Road, Louisville, KY 40223; tel. 502/253–7311; Ms. T. Richelle Jones

Cumberland River Regional MH/MR Board, Inc., 1203 American Greeting Road, Corbin, KY 40702; tel. 606/528–7010; Mr. Danny Jones

Kentucky Baptist Homes for Children, Inc., 10200 Linn Station Rd, Ste 200, Louisville, KY 40223; tel. 502/245–2101; Dr. William K Smithwick

NorthKey Community Care, PO Box 2680, Covington, KY 41012; tel. 859/578–3233; Dr. Edward G Muntel

Seven Counties Services, Inc., 101 W Muhammad Ali Boulevard, Louisville, KY 40202; tel. 502/589–8600; Dr. Howard F Bracco

Spectrum Care Academy, Inc., PO Box 911, Columbia, KY 42728; tel. 270/384–6444; Dr. Ben Arnold

LOUISIANA

Accelerated Health Care, INC, 4120 Jackson Street, Alexandria, LA 71303; tel. 318/473–0035; Mr. Regan Cupples

Addiction Recovery Resources of New Orleans, 4836 Wabash Street, Suite 202, Metairie, LA 70001; tel. 504/780–2766; Ms. Darci R Jones

DRD New Orleans Medical Clinic, 417 S. Johnson Street, New Orleans, LA 70112; tel. 816/357–2461; Ms. Janet Hasler

Jennings Behavioral Health, 619 North Main Street, Jennings, LA 70546; tel. 337/824–4300; Ms. Tehjan Martin

Lifecare Psychiatric Services, 170 Industrial Parkway, Lafayette, LA 70508; tel. 337/262–8672; Mr. Harry Cicero, Sr.

Mamou Health Resources, Inc., 300 South Street, Mamou, LA 70554; tel. 337/468–5959; Mr. J. Jake Fontenot

Opioid Substitution Treatment Program, VA Medical Center, 1601 Perdido Street, New Orleans, LA 70112; tel. 504/568–0811; Dr. Jose Pena

Vermilion Hospital for Psychiatric and Addictive Medicine, 2520 North University Avenue, Lafayette, LA 70507; tel. 337/234–5614; Mr. Russell B Kahn

MAINE

Acadia Hospital - Narcotic Treatment Program, PO Box 422, Bangor, ME 04402-0422; tel. 207/973–6100; Mr. Scott O Farnum

Cap Quality Care, 1 Delta Drive, Suite A, Westbrook, ME 04092; tel. 207/856–7227; Mrs. Susan Sullivan

KidsPeace National Centers of New England, P.O. Box 787, Ellsworth, ME 04605; tel. 207/771–5700; Mr. Ken Olson

Mercy Recovery Center, 40 Park Road, Portland, ME 04102; tel. 207/857–8085; Mrs. Eileen F Skinner

MARYLAND

Addiction Treatment Services of Hopkins Bayview, 5510 Nathan Shock Drive, Suite 1500, Baltimore, MD 21224; tel. 410/550–0028; Mr. Gregory Schaffer

Addiction Treatment Services of Hopkins Bayview, 5200 Eastern Avenue, MFL-6-E, Baltimore, MD 21224; tel. 410/550–0004; Mr. Gregory Schaffer

Ashley, Inc., 800 Tydings Lane, Havre De Grace, MD 21078; tel. 410/273–6600; Mr. Leonard A Dahl

Awakenings, 2 West Aylesbury Road, Timonium, MD 21093; tel. 410/561–9591; Dr. Sheldon D Glass

Baltimore Behavioral Health, Inc., 200 South Arlington Avenue, Baltimore, MD 21223; tel. 410/962–7180; Mr. William K Hathaway

Behavioral Pharmacology Research Unit, 5510 Nathan Shock Drive, Baltimore, MD 21224; tel. 410/550–0048; Mr. Gregory Schaffer

Bon Secours New Hope Treatment Center, 2401 West Baltimore Street, Baltimore, MD 21223; tel. 410/945–7706; Mr. Percy AllenII

Bon Secours' ADAPT Cares, 2000 W Baltimore Street, Baltimore, MD 21223; tel. 410/383–4995; Mr. Percy AllenII

Brook Lane Health Services, PO Box 1945, Hagerstown, MD 21742-1945; tel. 301/733–0330; Mr. R. L Rushing

Center for Addiction Medicine, 827 Linden Avenue, Baltimore, MD 21201; tel. 410/225–8240; Dr. Michael Hayes

Chesapeake Treatment Centers, Inc., 821 Fieldcrest Road, Cambridge, MD 21613; tel. 410/221–0288; Dr. Marc Fishman

Daybreak Rehabilitation Center, 2490 Giles Road, Baltimore, MD 21225; tel. 410/396–1646; Dr. Sheldon D Glass

Druid Heights Treatment and Counseling Center, Inc., 2009 Druid Hill Avenue, Baltimore, MD 21217; tel. 410/669–0475; Ms. Barbara Bostick-Hunt

Frederick County Health Dept. / Substance Abuse Services, 300-B Scholl's Lane, Frederick, MD 21701; tel. 301/694–1775; Dr. Barbara Brookmyer

Glass Substance Abuse Program, Inc., 821 North Eutaw Street, Baltimore, MD 21202; tel. 410/225–9185; Dr. Sheldon D Glass

Hope House, PO Box 546, Crownsville, MD 21032; tel. 410/923–6700; Ms. Marilyn Moran

House of the Good Shepherd of the City of Baltimore, 4100 Maple Avenue, Baltimore, MD 21227; tel. 410/247–2770; Sister Mary Rosaria Baxter

Hudson Health Services, Inc., PO Box 1096, Salisbury, MD 21802-1096; tel. 410/219–9000; Mr. James O Freeman, Jr.

Jewish Family Services, Inc., 5750 Park Heights Avenue, Baltimore, MD 21215; tel. 410/466–9200; Ms. Barbara L Gradet

John L. Gildner Regional Institute for Children& Adolescents, 15000 Broschart Road, Rockville, MD 20850; tel. 301/251–6800; Mr. Thomas E Pukalski

Maple Shade Youth & Family Services, 23704 Ocean Gateway, Mardela Springs, MD 21837; tel. 410/742–7400; Mr. Gary Frye

Maryland Center for Youth & Family Development, Inc., 13400 Edgemeade Road, Upper Marlboro, MD 20772; tel. 301/888–1330; Mr. David Ennis

Maryland Treatment Centers, Inc., PO Box 136, Emmitsburg, MD 21727; tel. 301/447–2361; Ms. Mary A Roby

MBA - Cherry Hill, 2490 Giles Road, Baltimore, MD 21225; tel. 410/225–9185; Dr. Sheldon D Glass

Methadone for Business Achievers (MBA), 821 North Eutaw Street, Baltimore, MD 21201; tel. 410/225–9185; Dr. Sheldon D Glass

Methadone for Business Achievers - Timonium, 2 West Aylesbury Road, Timonium, MD 21093; tel. 410/561–9591; Dr. Sheldon D Glass

Mid-Atlantic Treatment Services, Inc., 2100 North Charles Street, Baltimore, MD 21218; tel. 410/752–6505; Ms. Barbara Q McKenna

New Life Addiction Counseling Services, Inc., 2528 Mountain Road, Suite 204, Pasadena, MD 21122; tel. 410/255–4475; Mr. Thomas S Porter

Partners in Recovery, 6525 North Charles Street, Baltimore, MD 21204; tel. 410/296–9747; Ms. Dawn James

Pathways, 2620 Riva Road, Annapolis, MD 21401; tel. 410/573–5400; Mrs. Helen K Reines

Potomac Ridge Behavioral Health Center, 14901 Broschart Road, Rockville, MD 20850; tel. 301/251–4500; Mr. Craig S Juengling

Prince George's County Health Department, 1701 McCormick Drive, Suite 230, Upper Marlboro, MD 20772; tel. 301/883–7903; Dr. Frederick J Corder

Prince George's County Health Dept/Northern Region Treatment, 1701 McCormick Drive, Largo, MD 20774; tel. 301/883–7853; Dr. Frederick Corder

Reflective Treatment Center, 707 Constitution Street, Baltimore, MD 21202; tel. 410/727–7400; Dr. Marie J Washington

Regional Institute for Children and Adolescents-Baltimore, 605 South Chapel Gate Lane, Baltimore, MD 21229; tel. 410/368–7800; Ms. Penny Makris

RICA - Southern Maryland, 9400 Surratts Road, Cheltenham, MD 20623; tel. 301/372–1800; Ms. Audrey B Chase

Saint Luke Institute, 8901 New Hampshire Avenue, Silver Spring, MD 20903; tel. 301/445–7970; Rev. Stephen J Rossetti

Sinai Hospital Addictions Recovery Program, 2401 West Belvedere Avenue, Baltimore, MD 21215; tel. 410/601–5355; Mr. Neil Meltzer

The Johns Hopkins Hospital Drug Abuse Program, 911 Broadway, Baltimore, MD 21205; tel. 410/955–5439; Ms. Mary Elizabeth McCaul

Tuerk House, Inc., PO Box 31419, Baltimore, MD 21216-6119; tel. 410/233–0684; Dr. John E Hickey

VA Maryland Health Care System Opioid Treatment Program, 10 North Greene Street, Baltimore, MD 21201; tel. 410/605–7410; Dr. Joseph Liberto

Villa Maria Continuum, 2300 Dulaney Valley Road, Timonium, MD 21093; tel. 410/252–4700; Mr. Mark Greenberg

Wicomico County Health Department, 108 East Main Street, Salisbury, MD 21801; tel. 410/742–3784; Dr. Judith A Sensenbrenner

Woodbourne Center, Inc., 1301 Woodbourne Avenue, Baltimore, MD 21239; tel. 410/433–1000; Dr. Stanley E Weinstein

Worcester County Health Department, PO Box 249, Snow Hill, MD 21863; tel. 410/632–1100; Ms. Deborah Goeller

MASSACHUSETTS

AdCare Hospital of Worcester, Inc., 107 Lincoln Street, Worcester, MA 01605-2499; tel. 508/799–9000; Mr. David W Hillis

AdCare Hospital of Worcester, Inc., 107 Lincoln Street, Worcester, MA 01605; tel. 508/799–9000; Mr. David Hillis

Baldpate Hospital, 83 Baldpate Road, Georgetown, MA 01833; tel. 978/352–2131; Dr. Subhash C Mukherjee

Bournewood Hospital (Detoxification Program), 300 South Street, Chestnut Hill, MA 02467; tel. 617/469–0300; Dr. Nasir A Khan

Bridgewater State Hospital, 20 Administration Road, Bridgewater, MA 02324; tel. 508/279–4500; Mr. Kenneth W Nelson

Brockton Multi Service Center, 165 Quincy Street, Brockton, MA 02302; tel. 508/897–2000; Mr. Richard Jobin

Cape Cod and Islands Community Mental Health Center, 830 County Road, Pocasset, MA 02559; tel. 508/564–9600; Mr. Stephen Jochim

Center for Human Services, Inc., 86 R Gifford Street, New Bedford, MA 02744; tel. 508/999–3126; Dr. Warren E Berube

Center for Human Services, Inc., P.O. BOX 2097, New Bedford, MA 02741; tel. 508/675–9281; Dr. Warren E Berube

Centerpoint, PO Box 374, Tewksbury, MA 01876; tel. 978/858–3776; Ms. Carolyn F Ingalls

Chauncy Hall Academy, PO Box 732, Westborough, MA 01581; tel. 508/898–3280; Mr. Steven Hahn

Cohannet Academy, 60 Hodges Avenue - Goss 3, Taunton, MA 02780; tel. 508/977–3730; Mr. Bryan Lary

Dimock Community Foundation, Inc. - OTP, 55 Dimock Street, Roxbury, MA 02119; tel. 617/442–8800; Ms. RuthEllen Fitch

Doctor Franklin Perkins School, 971 Main Street, Lancaster, MA 01523; tel. 978/365–7376; Dr. Charles P Conroy

Dr. John C. Corrigan Mental Health Center, 49 Hillside Street, Fall River, MA 02720; tel. 508/235–7200; Ms. Katherine A Chmiel

Dr. Solomon Carter Fuller Mental Health Center, 85 East Newton Street, Boston, MA 02118-2337; tel. 617/626–8700; Ms. Mary-Louise White

Erich Lindemann Mental Health Center, 25 Staniford Street, Boston, MA 02114; tel. 617/626–8510; Mr. James E Foley

Everett House, 232 Centre Street, Boston, MA 02124-2334; tel. 617/474–7500; Dr. John P Kelty

Gosnold, Inc., PO Box 929, Falmouth, MA 02541; tel. 508/540–6550; Mr. Raymond V Tamasi

Health and Education Services, Inc., 30 General Street, Lawrence, MA 01841; tel. 978/683–3128; Mr. Mark Libon

High Point Treatment Center, Inc., 1233 State Road, Plymouth, MA 02360; tel. 508/997–0475; Mr. Daniel S Mumbauer

Hillcrest Educational Centers, Inc., PO Box 4699, Pittsfield, MA 01202; tel. 413/499–7924; Mr. Gerard E Burke

Lake Grove at Maple Valley, Inc., 6 Farley Road, Wendell, MA 01379; tel. 978/544–6913; Mr. Roland Paulauskas

Laurel Hill Inn, Ltd., PO Box 368, Medford, MA 02155-0004; tel. 781/396–1116; Mr. William H McDonald

Lowell Community Health Center Addiction Treatment Services, 365 East Street, Tewksbury, MA 01876; tel. 978/858–0533; Ms. Dorcas Griss-Saito

McLean Hospital, 115 Mill Street, Belmont, MA 02478; tel. 617/855–3450; Dr. Bruce M Cohen

McLean Hospital Alcohol & Drug Abuse Treatment Program, 115 Mill Street, Belmont, MA 02478; tel. 617/855–3450; Ms. Michele L Gougeon

Mercy Medical Center - MMTP, 227 Mill Street, Springfield, MA 01102; tel. 413/539–2942; Mr. Vincent J McCorkle

Mercy Medical Center - MMTP, 1233 Main Street, Holyoke, MA 01040; tel. 413/539–2942; Mr. Vincent J McCorkle

Mercy Medical Center Inpatient Detox Program, 1233 Main Street, Holyoke, MA 01040; tel. 413/539–2942; Mr. Vincent J McCorkle

Quincy Mental Health Center, 460 Quincy Avenue, Quincy, MA 02169; tel. 617/626–9003; Mr. Jeffrey Burke

SSTAR (Detoxification Program), 386 Stanley Street, Fall River, MA 02720; tel. 508/324–7768; Ms. Nancy E Paull

St. Anne's Hospital Lifeline Program, 795 Middle Street, Fall River, MA 02721; tel. 508/675–0131; Ms. Lisa Garcia

The Three Rivers Treatment Program, 26 Ridgewood Terrace, Springfield, MA 01105; tel. 413/733–4032; Mr. Andrew Pollock

The Whitney Academy, Inc., PO Box 619, East Freetown, MA 02717; tel. 508/763–3737; Mr. George E Harmon

University of Massachusetts Medical School, Transitions IRTP, 305 Belmont Street, 7th Flr C, Worcester, MA 01604; tel. 508/856–1455; Dr. Aaron Lazare

VA Boston Health Care System, 150 South Huntington Avenue, Boston, MA 02130; tel. 617/323–7700; Dr. John Renner

Wild Acre Inns, Inc., 108 Pleasant Street, Arlington, MA 02476; tel. 781/643–0643; Dr. Bernard S Yudowitz

MICHIGAN

ACAC, Inc., 3949 Sparks Drive SE Suite 103, Grand Rapids, MI 49546; tel. 616/957–5850; Mr. Michael R Durco

Access Behavioral Healthcare, LLC, 42189 E. Ann Arbor Road, Plymouth, MI 48170; tel. 734/453–5635; Mr. Donald Warner

Apex Behavioral Health, PLLC, 2001 South Merriman, Suite 500, Westland, MI 48186; tel. 734/727–1111; Mr. Thomas Johnson

Arbor Circle Corporation, 1115 Ball Avenue, Grand Rapids, MI 49505; tel. 616/456–7775; Ms. Mary Alice Williams

Bay-Arenac Behavioral Health, 201 Mulholland, Bay City, MI 48708; tel. 989/895–2300; Dr. William B Cammin

Berrien Mental Health Authority, P.O. Box 547, Benton Harbor, MI 49023; tel. 269/925–0585; Mr. Allen R Edlefson

Brighton Hospital, 12851 East Grand River, Brighton, MI 48116; tel. 810/227–1211; Mr. Frank P Iacobell

Catholic Services of Macomb, Inc., P.O. Box 380290, Clinton Township, MI 48038; tel. 586/416–2300; Mr. Thomas J Reed

Children's Home of Detroit, 900 Cook Road, Grosse Pointe, MI 48236; tel. 313/886–0800; Mr. Michael R Horwitz

City of Detroit Dept of Human Services/Drug Treatment Div, 5031 Grandy, Detroit, MI 48211; tel. 313/852–5601; Mr. William Warren

Community Care Services, 26184 West Outer Drive, Lincoln Park, MI 48146; tel. 313/389–7525; Mr. William P Walsh

Community Mental Health for Central Michigan, 301 South Crapo, Suite 100, Mount Pleasant, MI 48858; tel. 989/772–5938; Mr. George Rouman

Community Mental Health of Clinton-Eaton-Ingham Counties, 812 East Jolly Road, Lansing, MI 48910; tel. 517/346–8238; Ms. Judith L Cates

Community Mental Health of Ottawa County, 12265 James Street, Holland, MI 49424; tel. 616/392–1873; Mr. Gerald Cyranowski

Community Mental Health Services of Muskegon County, 376 Apple Avenue, Muskegon, MI 49442; tel. 231/724–1111; Mr. James M Elwell

Community Mental Health Services of St. Joseph County, 210 South Main Street, Three Rivers, MI 49093; tel. 616/273–5000; Ms. Kristine Kirsch

Comprehensive Counseling Center, PC, 27351 Dequindre, Madison Heights, MI 48071; tel. 248/967–7320; Dr. Sudhir Lingnurkar

Comprehensive Psychiatric Services, PC, 28800 Orchard Lake Rd, Ste 250, Farmington Hills, MI 48334; tel. 248/932–2500; Dr. Toby Hazan

Cruz Clinic, 17177 North Laurel Park Drive, Suite 131, Livonia, MI 48152; tel. 734/462–3210; Dr. Victor M Cruz

Deaf Options, 220 Bagley, Suite 600, Detroit, MI 48226-1420; tel. 313/961–8120; Ms. Reichelle Anderson

DeLano Clinic, 1722 Shaffer Street, Suite 3, Kalamazoo, MI 49048; tel. 269/226–5655; Ms. Denise R Crawford

Delta Family Clinic South, 6201 Miller Road, Suite A, Swartz Creek, MI 48473; tel. 810/630–1152; Dr. Gerard R Williams

Department of Human Services - Gratiot Clinic, 3506 Gratiot Clinic, Detroit, MI 48207; tel. 313/852–5609; Mr. Ronald McWhite

Department of Human Services - Northwest Clinic, 14602 Greenfield, Detroit, MI 48202; tel. 313/876–4240; Mr. Kenneth Perry

Department of Human Services, Herman Kiefer Hospital, Bldg 5, 8809 John C. Lodge, Detroit, MI 48202; tel. 313/852-5609; Mr. Calvin Carter

Desgranges Psychiatric Center, PC, G 8145 South Saginaw Street, Grand Blanc, MI 48439; tel. 810/694-2730; Dr. Louise Desgranges

East Side Substance Abuse Clinic, 445 East Sherman Boulevard, Muskegon, MI 49444; tel. 231/739-4359; Mr. Daryl L Smith

Eastern Clinic, 1555 Eastern Southeast, Grand Rapids, MI 49507; tel. 616/243-6262; Mr. Daryl L Smith

Eleonore Hutzel Recovery Cente, 301 East Hancock Street, Detroit, MI 48201; tel. 313/745-7411; Dr. Arthur Porter

Gerontology Network, 500 Cherry Street, SE, Grand Rapids, MI 49503; tel. 616/977-3300; Dr. Thomas A Hartwig

Gratiot/McNichols Clinic/Metro East Substance Abuse Treatment, PO Box 13408, Detroit, MI 48205; tel. 313/371-7770; Mr. Leslie B Carroll

Growth Works Incorporated, PO Box 6115, Plymouth, MI 48170-0115; tel. 734/455-4095; Mr. Dale F Yagiela

Harper/Chalmers Clinic & Corp Metro East Substance Abuse, PO Box 13408, Detroit, MI 48213; tel. 313/371-0055; Mr. Leslie B Carroll

Hegira Programs, Inc., 8623 N Wayne Road, Suite 200, Westland, MI 48185; tel. 734/458-4601; Mr. Edward L Forry

Heron Ridge Associates, PLC, 3694 Clarkston Road, Suite D, Clarkston, MI 48348; tel. 248/391-0050; Ms. Debra Scheck

Horizon Treatment Services, LLC, 29444 Joy Road, Livonia, MI 48150; tel. 734/421-8272; Mrs. Kellie Puro

Huron Valley Consultation Center, Inc., 15 Research Drive, Ann Arbor, MI 48103; tel. 734/662-6300; Mr. Alex Martinez

Integro, llc, 1200 N West Avenue, Suite 300, Jackson, MI 49202; tel. 517/789-1234; Mrs. Marilyn Meadowcroft

Ionia County Community Mental Health Services, 5827 North Orleans Road, Orleans, MI 48865; tel. 616/761-3151; Mr. Robert Lathers

Journeys of Michigan, PC, 25 Care Drive, Hillsdale, MI 49242; tel. 517/439-9327; Ms. Nancy Lonsberry

Kairos Healthcare, Inc., 6379 Dixie Hwy., Bridgeport, MI 48722; tel. 989/777-4357; Mr. Frederick E Wigen, Jr.

Kalamazoo Community Mental Health Services, PO Box 63, Nazareth, MI 49074-0063; tel. 616/553-8000; Mr. Charles Widener

Karalee & Associates, P.C., 1308 South Main Street, Plymouth, MI 48170; tel. 734/451-3440; Dr. Karen J Maier

Lapeer County Health Department, 1800 Imlay City Road, Lapeer, MI 48446; tel. 810/667-0243; Ms. Stephanie Mercer

Latino Family Services, Inc., 3815 West Fort Street, Detroit, MI 48216; tel. 313/841-7380; Ms. Alicia Villarreal

Lenawee Community Mental Health Authority, 1040 S. Winter St., Ste.#1022, Adrian, MI 49221; tel. 517/263-8905; Mr. Roger Myers

Livingston County Community Mental Health Authority, 2280 East Grand River, Howell, MI 48843; tel. 517/546-4126; Mr. Angus Miller

Meridian Professional Psychological Consultants, PC, 5031 Park Lake Road, East Lansing, MI 48823; tel. 517/332-0811; Dr. Thomas S Gunnings

Metro Emergency Services, Inc., 224 Highland Avenue, Highland Park, MI 48203-3405; tel. 313/867-0111; Mr. Jon P Rutherford

Monroe Community Mental Health Authority, P.O. Box 726, Monroe, MI 48161-0726; tel. 734/243-7340; Ms. Jane S Terwilliger

Nardin Park Recovery Center, 9605 Grand River, Detroit, MI 48204; tel. 313/834-5930; Mrs. Annie B Scott

National Council on Alcoholism and Addictions, 3600 S. Dort Highway #46, Flint, MI 48507; tel. 810/767-0350; Ms. Linda Bielskis

NCADD/GDA, 16647 Wyoming, Detroit, MI 48221; tel. 313/861-0666; Mr. Benjamin A Jones

New Center Community Mental Health Services, 2051 West Grand Boulevard, Detroit, MI 48208; tel. 313/961-3200; Ms. Roberta V Sanders

Newaygo County Mental Health Center, PO Box 867, White Cloud, MI 49349; tel. 231/689-7330; Mr. Greg Snyder

North Country Community Mental Health, One MacDonald Dr., Suite A, Petoskey, MI 49770; tel. 231/347-7890; Ms. Alexis Kaczynski

Northeast Guidance Center, 12800 E. Warren, Detroit, MI 48215; tel. 313/824-8000; Ms. Cheryl C Coleman

Northeast Michigan Community Mental Health Services, 400 Johnson Street, Alpena, MI 49707; tel. 517/356-2161; Mr. Charles A White

Oakland Psychological Clinic, P.C., 40950 N Woodward Avenue Suite 110, Bloomfield Hills, MI 48304; tel. 248/594-1200; Dr. Barry H Tigay

ProMed Management, 33200 Dequindre Road Suite200, Sterling Heights, MI 48310; tel. 586/268-4239; Mr. Karl L Sankowski

Quality Behavioral Health, Inc., 751 East Grand Boulevard, Detroit, MI 48207; tel. 313/922-2222; Mr. Naveed Syed

Rainbow Center of Michigan, P.O. Box 14947, Detroit, MI 48214; tel. 313/871-2243; Ms. Winnifred Griffin

Redford Counseling Center, 25945 West Seven Mile Road, Redford, MI 48240; tel. 313/535-6560; Ms. JoAnn Sadler

River's Bend, P.C., 33975 Dequindre, Suite 5, Troy, MI 48083; tel. 248/585-3239; Mr. James L Keener

Rose Hill Center, Inc., 5130 Rose Hill Boulevard, Holly, MI 48442; tel. 248/634-5530; Mr. Daniel J Kelly

Shiawassee County Community Mental Health Services, PO Box 428, Owosso, MI 48867; tel. 989/723-6791; Mr. Robert L Blackford

Star Center, Inc., 13575 Lesure, Detroit, MI 48227; tel. 313/493-4410; Ms. Lucila S Ryder

STM Clinic - Mental Health and Addiction Services, 501 Lapeer Avenue, Suite 210, Saginaw, MI 48607-1203; tel. 517/755-2532; Ms. Sara Terry-Moton

Summit Pointe, 140 West Michigan Avenue, Battle Creek, MI 49017; tel. 616/966-1460; Mr. Ervin R Brinker

Taylor Psychological Clinic, PC, 1172 Robert T Longway Blvd, Flint, MI 48503; tel. 810/232-8466; Dr. Maxwell F Taylor, II

The Center for Counseling, 32743 23 Mile Road, New Baltimore, MI 48047; tel. 586/716-0980; Ms. Cherie C Whiting

The Guidance Center, 13101 Allen Road, Southgate, MI 48195; tel. 734/785-7000; Mr. Leroy A Lott

The Montcalm Center for Behavioral Health, 611 North State Street, Stanton, MI 48888; tel. 989/831-7520; Mr. Robert Brown

Turning Point Programs, 72 Sheldon Boulevard, S.E., Grand Rapids, MI 49503; tel. 616/742-0351; Mr. Robert E Byrd

Tuscola Behavioral Health Systems, PO Box 239, Caro, MI 48723; tel. 989/673-6191; Mr. Robert E Chadwick, II

United Community Hospital, 2401 20th Street, Detroit, MI 48216; tel. 313/964-1133; Ms. Robin M Barclay

VA Medical Center - John D. Dingell - OTP, 4646 John R. Street, Detroit, MI 48201; tel. 313/576-3725; Dr. John Grabowski

Washington Way Recovery Center of Foote Hospital, 2424 West Washington Avenue, Jackson, MI 49203; tel. 517/788-4800; Ms. Georgia' Fojtasek

Washtenaw County Community Supports and Treatment Services, PO Box 915, Ypsilanti, MI 48197; tel. 734/544-3000; Ms. Donna Sabourin

MINNESOTA

Andrew Residence, 1215 South 9th Street, Minneapolis, MN 55404; tel. 612/333-0111; Ms. Karen Foy

Hazelden Recovery Services, PO Box 11, Center City, MN 55012; tel. 612/257-4000; Ms. Ellen Breyer

Hennepin Faculty Associates Addiction Medicine Program, 914 South Eighth St. (D131), Minneapolis, MN 55404; tel. 612/347-5324; Mr. Larry Fosbury

Miller-Dwan Medical Center, Inc., 502 East Second Street, Duluth, MN 55805; tel. 218/727-8762; Adm. Rocklon B Chapin

Minnesota Security Hospital, 2100 Sheppard Drive, St Peter, MN 56082; tel. 507/931-7115; Mr. Larry TeBrake

New Beginnings at Waverly, LLC, 109 North Shore Drive, Waverly, MN 55390-9743; tel. - -; Mr. Dick Kessler

St. Joseph's Hospital Chemical Dependency Unit, 69 West Exchange Street, Saint Paul, MN 55102; tel. 651/232-3300; Mr. Tim Hansen

Veterans Affairs Medical Cente Outpatient Methadone Program, One Veterans Drive, Minneapolis, MN 55417; tel. 612/725-2228; Dr. Mark Willenbring

Willmar Regional Treatment Center - Bradley Center, 1550 Highway 71 Northeast, Willmar, MN 56201; tel. 320/231-5356; Ms. Sandra J Butturff

MISSISSIPPI

CARES Center, Inc., 402 Wesley Avenue, Jackson, MS 39202; tel. 601/352-7784; Mr. Christopher M Cherney

COPAC, Inc., 3949 Highway 43 North, Brandon, MS 39047; tel. 601/829-2500; Dr. J. Stacy Hughes

Diamond Grove Center for Children and Adolescents, PO Box 848, Louisville, MS 39339; tel. 662/779-0119; Mr. Patrick Swoopes

Millcreek of Pontotoc, PO Box 619, Pontotoc, MS 38863; tel. 662/488-8878; Ms. Margaret Stept

Pine Belt Mental Healthcare Resources, PO Drawer 1030, Hattiesburg, MS 39401; tel. 601/544-4641; Mr. Jerry Mayo

Rehabilitation Centers, Inc., PO Box 1160, Magee, MS 39111; tel. 601/849-4221; Ms. Lisa Hilton

The Saint Francis Academy, Inc. - Picayune, PO Drawer 640, Picayune, MS 39466; tel. 785/825-0541; Rev. Edward W Fellhauer

MISSOURI

Boonville Valley Hope, PO Box 398, Boonville, MO 65233; tel. 660/882-6547; Dr. Kenneth C Gregoire

Boys Town of Missouri, Inc., 13160 County Rd 3610, Saint James, MO 65559; tel. 573/265-3251; Mr. Vincent Hillyer

Centrec Care, Inc., 1030 Woodcrest Terrace Drive, Saint Louis, MO 63141; tel. 314/205-8068; Dr. Mohammed A Kabir

Child Advocacy Services Center Inc., 2 East 59th Street, Kansas City, MO 64113-2116; tel. 816/363-1898; Mr. Alan Murray

Child Center of Our Lady, 7900 Natural Bridge Road, Saint Louis, MO 63121; tel. 314/383-0200; Mr. Edward S Koszykowski

DRD Columbia Medical Clinic, 1415 Paris Road, Columbia, MO 65201; tel. 573/449-8338; Ms. Janet Hasler

DRD Kansas City Medical Clinic, 723 East 18th Street, Kansas City, MO 64108; tel. 816/357-2461; Ms. Janet Hasler

DRD Springfield Medical Clinic, 404 East Battlefield Street, Springfield, MO 65807; tel. 417/865-8045; Ms. Janet Hasler

Epworth Children and Family Services, 110 North Elm Avenue, Saint Louis, MO 63119; tel. 314/961-5718; Mr. Kevin Drollinger

Northland Family Counseling Center, Inc., 429 Northeast 69 Highway, Kansas City, MO 64119; tel. 816/452-8777; Mr. Maurice L Cummings

Paseo Comprehensive Rehabilitation Clinic - WMMHC, 2211 Charlotte, Felix Building, Lower Level, Kansas City, MO 64108; tel. 816/512-7143; Mr. David V Fleming

Piney Ridge Center, Inc., PO Box 4067, Waynesville, MO 65583; tel. 573/774-5353; Mr. Jeffrey W Suis

Provident Counseling, Inc., 2650 Olive Street, Saint Louis, MO 63103; tel. 314/371-6500; Ms. Kathleen E Buescher

ReDiscover, 901 NE Independence Avenue, Lees Summit, MO 64086; tel. 816/246-8000; Mr. Alan Flory

St. Louis VA Medical Center - Opioid Treatment Program, 915 North Grand Boulevard, Saint Louis, MO 63106; tel. 314/289-7020; Mr. Glen Struchtemeyer

MONTANA

Inter-Mountain Deaconess Home for Children, 500 South Lamborn, Helena, MT 59601; tel. 406/442-7920; Mr. Jim FitzGerald

KIDS Behavioral Health of Montana, Inc., 55 Basin Creek Road, Butte, MT 59701; tel. 406/494-4183; Ms. Pam Broughton

Rocky Boy Chemical Dependency Center, Rural Route 1, Box 664, Box Elder, MT 59521; tel. 406/395-4818; Mr. James Eastlick

Rocky Mountain Treatment Center, 920 Fourth Avenue North, Great Falls, MT 59401; tel. 406/727-8832; Mrs. Marcie J Dardis

Shodair Children's Hospital, PO Box 5539, Helena, MT 59604; tel. 406/444-7500; Mr. John P Casey

NEBRASKA

Alpha School, 1615 South 6th Street, Omaha, NE 68108; tel. 402/444-6557; Mr. Ray Christensen

Behavioral Health Specialists, Inc., 600 South 13th Street, Norfolk, NE 68701; tel. 402/370-3140; Ms. Connie Barnes

Blue Valley Mental Health Center, Inc., 1121 North 10th Street, Beatrice, NE 68310; tel. 402/228-3386; Dr. Wayne R Price

Section C

Developmental Services of Nebraska, Inc., 2610 West M Court, Lincoln, NE 68522; tel. 402/435–2800; Mr. Scott Lefevre

Epworth Village, Inc., PO Box 503, York, NE 68467-0503; tel. 402/362–3353; Mr. Thomas G McBride

Father Flanagan's Boys' Home, 13603 Flanagan Boulevard, Boys Town, NE 68010; tel. 402/498–1979; Rev. Father Val J Peter, JCD,STD

Hastings Regional Center, PO Box 579, Hastings, NE 68902-0579; tel. 402/462–1971; Mr. William R Gibson

Lincoln Lancaster County Child Guidance Center, 2444 'O' Street, Lincoln, NE 68510; tel. 402/475–7666; Dr. Carol Crumpacker

O'Neill Valley Hope, 1421 North 10th Street, O'Neill, NE 68763; tel. 402/336–3747; Dr. Kenneth C Gregoire

OMNI Behavioral Health, 7000 West Center Road, Ste 120, Omaha, NE 68106-2717; tel. 402/397–9866; Dr. William E Reay

University Drug and Alcohol Program, 1941 S. 42nd Street, Suite 210, Omaha, NE 68105; tel. 402/595–1703; Dr. Todd Stull

Uta Halee Girls Village, 10625 Calhoun Road, Omaha, NE 68112; tel. 402/453–0803; Mr. Denis D McCarville

NEVADA

Desert Willow Treatment Center, 6171 W Charleston Boulevard, Building #17, Las Vegas, NV 89146; tel. 702/486–8900; Dr. Yangcha P Crabb

Las Vegas Recovery Center, 3371 N. Buffalo Drive, Las Vegas, NV 89129; tel. 702/515–1373; Mr. Stuart P Smith

Spring Mountain Treatment Center, 7000 Spring Mountain Road, Las Vegas, NV 89117; tel. 702/873–2400; Mr. Darryl Dubroca

NEW HAMPSHIRE

Community Council of Nashua, NH, 7 Prospect Street, Nashua, NH 03060; tel. 603/889–6147; Dr. Zlatko M Kuftinec

Lakeview NeuroRehabilitation Center, Inc., 244 Highwatch Road, Center Ossipee, NH 03814; tel. 603/539–7451; Dr. Tina M Trudel

Southern New Hampshire Medical Center, Pregnant Women's Methadone Program, PO Box 2014, Nashua, NH 03061-2014; tel. 603/577–2000; Dr. Gary Kaufman

NEW JERSEY

AAMH Association for Advancement of Mental Health, 819 Alexander Road, Princeton, NJ 08540-6303; tel. 609/452–2088; Mr. Richard McDonnell

Arthur Brisbane Child Treatment Center, PO Box 625, Farmingdale, NJ 07727; tel. 732/938–5061; Ms. Kathy Enerlich

AtlantiCare Behavioral Health, 2511 Fire Road, Unit B10 Bellevue Commons, Egg Harbor Township, NJ 08234; tel. 609/645–7600; Mr. Ted Stryker

Bancroft Rehabilitation Services, Hopkins Lane, P.O. Box 20, Haddonfield, NJ 08033-0018; tel. 856/429–0010; Dr. Robert Martin

Bayonne Community Mental Health Center, 601 Broadway, Bayonne, NJ 07002; tel. 201/339–9200; Mr. Joseph M Kadian

Bonnie Brae, 3415 Valley Road, P. O. Box 825, Liberty Corner, NJ 07938-0825; tel. 908/647–0800; Mr. William M Powers

Cape Counseling Services, 217 N. Main Street Suite 202, Cape May Court House, NJ 08210; tel. 609/463–0014; Mr. Gregory Speed

Care Plus NJ, Inc., 610 Valley Health Plaza, Paramus, NJ 07652; tel. 201/265–8200; Mr. Joseph A Masciandaro

Carrier Clinic, PO Box 147, Belle Mead, NJ 08502-0147; tel. 908/281–1381; Mr. C. R Sarle

Catholic Charities - Diocese of Metuchen, 319 Maple Street, Perth Amboy, NJ 08861; tel. 732/324–8200; Ms. Marianne Majewski

Comprehensive Behavioral Healthcare, Inc., 516 Valley Brook Avenue, Lyndhurst, NJ 07071; tel. 201/935–3322; Mr. Peter Scerbo

CPC Behavioral Healthcare, Inc, Parkway 100, 3535 Route 66, Building 5, Suite D, Neptune, NJ 07753; tel. 732/643–4301; Mr. John Mans

Daytop Village, Inc., 80 W. Main St., Mendham, NJ 07945; tel. 973/543–5656; Mr. Joseph Hennen

Discovery Institute for Addictive Disorders, Inc., PO Box 177, Marlboro, NJ 07746; tel. 732/946–9444; Mr. Robert C Denes

Drug Dependence Treatment Program-VANJHCS-East Orange Campus, 385 Tremont Avenue. Bldg 15, East Orange, NJ 07018; tel. 973/676–1000; Dr. Miklos Losonczy

Ewing Residential Treatment Center, 1610 Stuyvesant Avenue, Trenton, NJ 08618; tel. 609/530–3350; Mr. Robert Clarke

Family Service of Burlington County, 770 Woodlane Road, Mount Holly, NJ 08060; tel. 609/267–5928; Ms. Mary Wells

Kennedy Opioid Treatment Program, Kennedy Mem Hospitals, 300 Woodbury-Turnersville Road, Blackwood, NJ 08012; tel. 856/227–5254; Ms. Terry Marini

Khaleidoscope Health Care, Inc., Jones and Associates-111 Wayne Street, Jersey City, NJ 07302; tel. 201/451–5425; Mr. Larry M Ali Blake, Jr.

Mount Carmel Guild Behavioral Healthcare System, 1160 Raymond Boulevard, Newark, NJ 07102; tel. 973/639–6508; Mr. Michael Leitzes

Mt. Carmel Guild Behavioral Healthcare System, 1160 Raymond Boulevard, Newark, NJ 07102; tel. 973/639–6508; Ms. Anita Holland

New Hope Foundation, Inc, PO Box 66, Marlboro, NJ 07746; tel. 732/946–3030; Dr. Anthony W Comerford

Ocean Medical Services, Inc, 2001 Route 37 East, Toms River, NJ 08753; tel. 732/288–9322; Ms. Edie Novak

Ocean Mental Health Services, Inc., 160 Route 9, Bayville, NJ 08721; tel. 732/349–5550; Dr. Charles J Langan

Organization for Recovery, Inc, P.O. Box 827, Plainfield, NJ 07061; tel. 908/769–4700; Ms. Linda Voorhis

Preferred Behavioral Health of New Jersey, Inc., 700 Airport Road, P.O. Box 2036, Lakewood, NJ 08701; tel. 732/364–4590; Mr. William J Sette

Raritan Bay Medical Center - Methadone Program, 595 New Brunswick Avenue, Perth Amboy, NJ 08861; tel. 732/442–3700; Mr. Michael D'Agnes

Recovery Services of New Jersey, Inc., 5034 Atlantic Avenue, Mays Landing, NJ 08330; tel. 609/625–4900; Dr. Kenneth R Sandler

Richard Hall Community Mental Health Center, 500 North Bridge Street, Bridgewater, NJ 08807; tel. 908/253–3136; Mr. Peter O Casey

Saint Barnabas Behavioral Health Center, Inc., 1691 US Highway 9, CN 2025, Toms River, NJ 08754; tel. 732/914–1688; Mr. Joe Hicks

St. Joseph's Hospital and Medical Center, 703 Main Street, Paterson, NJ 07503; tel. 973/754–2098; Mr. William McDonald

Strathmore Treatment Associates, LLC, PO Box 125, South Amboy, NJ 08879; tel. 732/727–2555; Mr. Anthony Caputo

Suburban Treatment Associates, 43 Progress Street, Union, NJ 07083; tel. 908/687–7188; Ms. Van Macaluso

Sunrise House Foundation, PO Box 600, Lafayette, NJ 07848; tel. 973/383–6300; Dr. Philip N Horowitz

The Lester A. Drenk Behavioral Health Center, Inc., 1289 Route 38 West, Suite 203, Hainesport, NJ 08036; tel. 609/267–5656; Mr. Harry Marmorstein

UCPC Behavioral Health Care, 117-119 Roosevelt Avenue, Plainfield, NJ 07060; tel. 908/756–6870; Ms. Marcyann E Sosnoski

UMDNJ - University Behavioral HealthCare, PO Box 1392, Piscataway, NJ 08855-1392; tel. 732/235–5900; Mr. Christopher Kosseff

Urban Treatment Associates Inc., 424-32 Market Street, Camden, NJ 08102; tel. 856/338–1811; Mrs. Michelle Norquest

Vineland Children's Residential Treatment Center, 2000 Maple Avenue, Vineland, NJ 08361-2990; tel. 856/696–6620; Ms. Sandra Schirick

Warren Medical Services, Inc, 590 Marshall Street, Phillipsburg, NJ 08865; tel. 908/387–0003; Mr. Gary D Gavornik

Willowglen Academy New Jersey, Inc., 4 Gail Court, Suite 1, Sparta, NJ 07871; tel. 973/579–3700; Mr. Leonard F Dziubla

Woodbridge Child Diagnostic and Treatment Center, 15 Paddock Street, Avenel, NJ 07001; tel. 732/499–5050; Mr. Albert Compoly

Youth Consultation Service, 284 Broadway, Newark, NJ 07104; tel. 973/482–8411; Mr. Richard Mingoia

NEW MEXICO

Sequoyah Adolescent Treatment Center, 3405 W Pan American Freeway NE, Albuquerque, NM 87107; tel. 505/344–4673; Dr. W. Henry Gardner

University of New Mexico Health Sciences Center, 2121 Lomas Blvd. N.E., Albuquerque, NM 87106; tel. 505/272–2121; Dr. Philip R Eaton

Youth and Family Centered Services of New Mexico, Inc., 5310 Sequoia Northwest, Albuquerque, NM 87120; tel. 505/836–7330; Ms. Carol Bickelman

NEW YORK

A.R.E.B.A.-Casriel, Inc, 500 West 57th Street, New York, NY 10019; tel. 212/293–3000; Mr. Steven J Yohay

Acute Chemical Dependency Detox Unit - Kings County, 606 Winthrop Street, Brooklyn, NY 11203; tel. 718/245–3901; Ms. Jean Leon

Arms Acres, 75 Seminary Hill Road, Carmel, NY 10512; tel. 845/225–3400; Ms. Patrice Wallace-Moore

August Aichhorn R.T.F., 23 West 106th Street, New York, NY 10025; tel. 212/316–9353; Dr. Michael A Pawel

Baker Victory Services, Inc., 780 Ridge Road, Lackawanna, NY 14218; tel. 716/828–9515; Mr. James J Casion

Bellevue Hospital Center Chemical Dependency Medically Detox, 462 First Avenue, New York, NY 10016; tel. 212/562–4132; Mr. Carlos Perez

Bellevue Hospital Methadone Treatment Program, 462 First Avenue, New York, NY 10016; tel. 212/562–4132; Mr. Carlos Perez

Beth Israel Medical Center, 201 West 13th Street, New York, NY 10011; tel. 212/420–2015; Mr. Charles Jacknow

Beth Israel Medical Center, 1-9 Nathan Perlman Place, New York, NY 10003; tel. 212/420–4275; Dr. Mathew E Fink

Beth Israel Medical Center MMTP - Gouverneur Clinic, 109 Delaney Street, New York, NY 10002; tel. 212/420–2086; Ms. Marie Marciano

Beth Israel Medical Center MMTP - Harlem 6/7, 103 East 125th Street, 2nd Flr, New York, NY 10035; tel. 212/774–3260; Ms. Marie Marciano

Beth Israel Medical Center MMTP - Marie Nyswander Clinic, 721 Ninth Avenue, New York, NY 10019; tel. 212/247–7180; Ms. Marie Marciano

Beth Israel Medical Center MMTP - Vincent P Dole, 215 Park Avenue South, New York, NY 10003; tel. 718/965–7901; Ms. Marie Marciano

Beth Israel Medical Center MMTP Clinic 1E, First Avenue @ 16 Street, New York, NY 10003; tel. 212/844–1929; Ms. Marie Marciano

Beth Israel Medical Center MMTP Clinic 2C, 435 Second Avenue, 2nd Floor, New York, NY 10010; tel. 212/726–6822; Ms. Marie Marciano

Beth Israel Medical Center MMTP Clinic 2F, 429 Second Avenue, New York, NY 10010; tel. 212/726–6821; Ms. Marie Marciano

Beth Israel Medical Center MMTP Clinic 3C, 215 Park Avenue, New York, NY 10003; tel. 212/726–6824; Ms. Marie Marciano

Beth Israel Medical Center MMTP Clinic 3G, 215 Park Avenue, New York, NY 10003; tel. 212/726–6863; Ms. Marie Marciano

Beth Israel Medical Center MMTP Clinic 8D, 140 West 125th Street, 6th Flr, New York, NY 10027; tel. 212/864–0904; Ms. Marie Marciano

Beth Israel Medical Center MMTP Cumberland Clinic, 100 Flatbush Avenue, Brooklyn, NY 11217; tel. 718/237–9600; Ms. Marie Marciano

Beth Israel Medical Center MMTP Harlem 3, 215 Park Avenue South, New York, NY 10003; tel. 212/774–3230; Ms. Marie Marciano

Beth Israel Medical Center MMTP Harlem Clinic 1, First Avenue @ 16th Street, New York, NY 10003; tel. 212/774–3210; Ms. Marie Marciano

Beth Israel Medical Center MMTP Harlem Clinic 2, 103 East 125th Street, 4th Flr, New York, NY 10035; tel. 212/774–3200; Ms. Marie Marciano

Beth Israel Medical Center MMTP Harlem Clinic 8, 215 Park Avenue South, New York, NY 10003; tel. 212/864–8177; Ms. Marie Marciano

Beth Israel Medical Center MMTP, Avenue A Clinic, 26 Avenue A, New York, NY 10009; tel. 212/420–2078; Ms. Marie Marciano

Bronx-Lebanon Hospital Center, 1650 Grand Concourse, Bronx, NY 10457; tel. 718/590–1800; Mr. Miguel A Fuentes, Jr.

Bronx-Lebanon Hospital Center - MMTP/Keep, 3100 Third Avenue, Bronx, NY 10451; tel. 718/579–2600; Dr. Jeffrey Levine

Cabrini Medical Center, 227 E 19th Street, 13th Floor - Chemical Dependency Unit, New York, NY 10003; tel. 212/995–6000; Mr. Robert S Chaloner

Carnegie Hill Institute, 116 East 92nd Street, New York, NY 10128; tel. 212/289–7166; Dr. Harvey D Karkus

Coney Island Hospital - Acute Care Addictions Program, 2601 Ocean Parkway, Brooklyn, NY 11235; tel. 718/616–4083; Mr. William Walsh

Conifer Park, Inc, 79 Glenridge Road, Glenville, NY 12302; tel. 518/399–6446; Mr. Patrick Carrese

Section C

Cornerstone of Medical Arts Center Hospital, 57 West 57th Street, New York, NY 10019; tel. 212/755–0200; Mr. Norman J Sokolow

Cornerstone of Medical Arts Center Hospital, 57 West 57th Street, New York, NY 10019; tel. 212/755–0200; Mr. Thomas C Puzo

Correctional Health Services, Westchester County Health Care, Valhalla Campus, Valhalla, NY 10595; tel. 914/493–8878; Ms. Mary Brown

Crestwood Children's Center, 2075 Scottsville Road, Rochester, NY 14623-2098; tel. 585/429–2700; Ms. Barbara J Conradt

Crossings Recovery Centers, 450 Waverly Avenue, Suite 5, Patchogue, NY 11772; tel. 631/447–0155; Mr. Frank Buononotte

Crouse Hospital Methadone Maintenance Treatment Program, 410 South Crouse Avenue, Syracuse, NY 13210; tel. 315/470–7829; Dr. Paul Kronenberg

Drug Treatment & Education Cen North Shore Univ Hospital, 400 Community Drive, Manhasset, NY 11030; tel. 516/562–3010; Mr. Dennis Dowling

Elmhurst Hospital Center Methadone Treatment Program, 79-01 Broadway, 2nd Floor, Annex O, Elmhurst, NY 11373; tel. 718/334–1638; Mr. Chris D Constantino

Erie County Medical Center, 462 Grider Street, Buffalo, NY 14215; tel. 716/898–3000; Dr. Roger E Kaiser, Jr.

Flushing Hospital Medical Ctr / Chemical Dependency Unit, 45th Avenue at Parsons Blvd, Flushing, NY 11355; tel. 718/670–5918; Mr. David P Rosen

Good Samaritan Hospital, 255 Lafayette Avenue, Suffern, NY 10901; tel. 845/368–5302; Mr. Michael Schnieders

Gracie Square Hospital - OTP, 420 East 76th Street, New York, NY 10021; tel. 212/434–5322; Mr. Frank Bruno

Harlem Hospital Center Chemica Dependence Detoxification Unit, 506 Lenox Ave, New York, NY 10037; tel. 212/939–1340; Dr. John M Palmer

Harlem Hospital Center MMTP, 264 West 118th Street, New York, NY 10026; tel. 212/939–1340; Dr. John Palmer

Hillside Children's Center, 1183 Monroe Avenue, Rochester, NY 14620; tel. 716/256–7500; Ms. Dawn M Rice

Hudson Valley Hospital Center M.M.T.P., 1980 Crompond Road, Cortlandt Manor, NY 10567; tel. 914/737–6117; Mr. John Federspiel

Interfaith Medical Center Substance Abuse Detoxification, 1545 Atlantic Avenue, 6th Floor, Brooklyn, NY 11213; tel. 718/613–4001; Mr. Edward J Glicksman

Jacobi Medical Center Chemical Dependence/ Medically Detox, 1400 Pelham Parkway, Bronx, NY 10461; tel. 718/918–5322; Mr. Joseph S Orlando

Jewish Board of Family and Children's Services, Inc., 120 West 57th Street, New York, NY 10019; tel. 212/582–9100; Dr. Alan B Siskind

Julia Dyckman Andrus Memorial, 1156 North Broadway, Yonkers, NY 10701; tel. 914/965–3700; Ms. Nancy W Ment

Long Beach Medical Center M.M.T.P., 455 East Bay Drive, Long Beach, NY 11561; tel. 516/897–1330; Mr. Douglas Melzer

Long Island Center for Recovery Inc., 320 West Montauk Highway, Hampton Bays, NY 11946; tel. 631/728–3100; Mr. Jack Hamilton

Long Island Jewish Medical Center - M.M.T.P., 270-05 76th Avenue, New Hyde Park, NY 11040; tel. 718/470–8940; Mr. Dennis Dowling

Lutheran Medical Center (Acute Care Addiction Program), 150 55th Street, Brooklyn, NY 11220; tel. 718/630–7363; Ms. Wendy Z Goldstein

Mary Immaculate Hospital Clinic I, MMTP, 275 North St, Harrison, NY 10528; tel. 914/925–5301; Dr. Brian Fitzsimmons

Medical Arts Sanitarium, Inc., 500 Milan Hollow Road, Rhinebeck, NY 12572; tel. 845/266–3481; Mr. Norman J Sokolow

Medically Managed Inpatient Detoxification, 2 Park Avenue, Yonkers, NY 10703; tel. 914/964–7383; Mr. Jim Foy

mercyFirst, 525 Convent Road, Syosset, NY 11791-3864; tel. 516/921–0808; Ms. Liz Giordano

Methadone Treatment Program - Kings County / Clinic 3, 600 Albany Avenue, Brooklyn, NY 11203; tel. 718/245–3901; Ms. Jean G Leon

Methadone Treatment Program - Kings County / Clinic I, 600 Albany Avenue, Brooklyn, NY 11203; tel. 718/245–3901; Ms. Jean G Leon

Methadone Treatment Program - Kings County Clinic 2, 600 Albany Avenue, Brooklyn, NY 11203; tel. 718/245–3901; Ms. Jean G Leon

Metropolitan Correctional Center - New York / OTP, 150 Park Row, New York, NY 10007; tel. 646/836–6300; Mr. Marvin J Morrison

Metropolitan Hospital Center Detoxification Unit, 1901 First Avenue, New York, NY 10029; tel. 212/423–7122; Dr. Jose R Sanchez

Metropolitan Hospital Methadone Treatment Program, 1900 Second Avenue, Room 2M29, New York, NY 10029; tel. 212/423–6822; Mr. Louis Martir

Montefiore Medical Center - SATP, 111 East 210th Street, Bronx, NY 10467; tel. 718/920–2001; Mr. Robert B Conaty

Montefiore Medical Center - SATP - OTP - Unit 3, 2005 Jerome Avenue, 1st Floor, Bronx, NY 10467; tel. 718/583–0600; Dr. Spencer Foreman

Montefiore Medical Center - SATP Unit 1, 3550 Jerome Avenue, 1st Floor, Bronx, NY 10467; tel. 718/583–0600; Dr. Spencer Foreman

Narco Freedom Inc. MMTP - Court Street, 250 Grand Concourse, Bronx, NY 10451; tel. 718/292–2240; Mr. Alan Brand

Narco Freedom Inc. MMTP - Willis Avenue, 250 Grand Concourse, Bronx, NY 10455; tel. 718/292–2240; Mr. Alan Brand

Narco Freedom, Inc. MMTP - Redhook, 250 Grand Concourse, Bronx, NY 10451; tel. 718/292–2240; Mr. Alan Brand

Narco Freedom, Inc., Grand Concourse MMTP, 250 Grand Concourse, Bronx, NY 10451; tel. 718/292–2240; Mr. Alan Brand

Narco Freedom, Inc.-Bridge Plaza MMTP, 37-18 34th Street, Long Island City, NY 11101; tel. 718/292–2240; Mr. Alan Brand

Nassau County Department of Drug and Alcohol Addiction, NUMC, 2201 Hempstead Turnpike, East Meadow, NY 11554; tel. 516/572–5906; Dr. John Imhof

New York United Hospital Medical Center, 406 Boston Post Road, Port Chester, NY 10573; tel. 914/934–3000; Mr. Philip Dionne

North General Hospital - MMTP Program, 1879 Madison Avenue, New York, NY 10035; tel. 212/423–4337; Dr. Samuel J Daniel

NYU Downtown (Trinity M.M.T.P.), 74 Trinity Place, 2nd Flr Mezz, New York, NY 10006; tel. 212/312–5000; Dr. Bruce D Logan

Outpatient Methodone Treatment Program at North Shore Univ., 101 St. Andrews Lane, Glen Cove, NY 11542; tel. 516/674–7852; Mr. Dennis Connors

Passages Counseling Center, Inc., 3680 Route 112, Coram, NY 11727; tel. 631/698–9222; Mr. Arnt Monge

Pathways - St. Louise, 209 Niagara Street, Buffalo, NY 14201; tel. 716/856–8411; Mr. Harry Smith

Pathways, Sisters of Charity Hospital, 2157 Main Street, Buffalo, NY 14214; tel. 716/862–1000; Mr. Harry Smith

PROMESA METHADONE TREATMENT PROGRAM, 1776 Clay Ave, Bronx, NY 10457; tel. 718/960–7601; Mr. Ruben A Medina

Quannacut at Eastern Long Island Hospital, 201 Manor Place, Greenport, NY 11944; tel. 631/477–1000; Mr. Paul J Connor, III

Queens Hospital Center Inpatient Detox Unit, 82-68 164 Street, Jamaica, NY 11434; tel. 718/883–2222; Mr. Antonio D Martin

Restorative Management Corporation, 15 King Street, Middletown, NY 10940; tel. 845/342–5941; Mr. Charles Scharf

Rochester Mental Health Center, 490 East Ridge Road, Rochester, NY 14621; tel. 585/922–2500; Mr. Sam Huston

Rochester Pathways, Sisters of Charity Hospital, 435 East Henrietta Road, Rochester, NY 14607; tel. 585/424–6580; Mr. Harry Smith

SBH Chemical Dependence Methadone Substance Abuse Treatment, 4535-39 Third Avenue, Bronx, NY 10457; tel. 718/960–6170; Dr. Scott Cooper

Seafield Center, Inc., 7 Seafield Lane, Westhampton Beach, NY 11978; tel. 631/288–1122; Mr. John C Haley

Sound Shore Medical Center, 16 Guion Place, New Rochelle, NY 10802; tel. 914/637–1700; Mr. John R Spicer

South Oaks Hospital, 400 Sunrise Highway, Amityville, NY 11701; tel. 631/264–4000; Mr. Robert Detor

Southside Hospital - Detox Program, 301 East Main Street, Bay Shore, NY 11706; tel. 631/968–3000; Mr. Michael L Nolan

SPAN - Special Prevention Addiction Network, 15 West 136th Steret, New York, NY 10037; tel. 212/939–1340; Dr. John Palmer

St. Catherine of Siena Medical Center - OTP, 50 Route 25A, Smithtown, NY 11787; tel. 631/862–3000; Mr. Vincent DiRubbio

St. John's Episcopal Hospital, 700 Hicksville Road, Bethpage, NY 11714; tel. 718/869–7320; Mr. Luis Hernandez

St. Johns Riverside Hospital M.M.T.P., 70 Ashburton Avenue, 2nd Floor, Yonkers, NY 10701; tel. 914/964–4000; Mr. Jim Foy

St. Joseph's Hospital - MMTP, 8 Guion Street, 1st Floor, Yonkers, NY 10701; tel. 914/378–7000; Mr. Michael Spicer

St. Joseph's Villa of Rochester, 3300 Dewey Avenue, Rochester, NY 14616; tel. 585/865–1550; Mr. Roger C Battaglia

St. Luke's Cornwall Hospital Unity Center for Recovery, 3 Commercial Place, Newburgh, NY 12550; tel. 845/565–0150; Mr. Allan E Atzrott

St. Lukes-Roosevelt Hospital - Inpatient Rehab Unit, 1000 Tenth Avenue, New York, NY 10019; tel. 212/523–6166; Dr. Jin Suh

St. Lukes-Roosevelt Hospital Center - MMTP, 1000 Tenth Avenue, New York, NY 10019; tel. 212/523–6166; Dr. Jin Suh

St. Vincent's Midtown Hospital MMTP, 415 West 51st Street, New York, NY 10019; tel. 212/459–8402; Mr. Len Walsh

St.Barnabas Hospital-Chemical Dependence-Medically Managed, 183rd Street and Third Avenue, Bronx, NY 10457; tel. 718/960–6170; Dr. Scott Cooper

Staten Island Univ Hospital (Canarsie M.M.T.P. Clinic), 567 East 105th Street, Brooklyn, NY 11236; tel. 718/226–9000; Mr. Anthony Ferreri

Staten Island Univ Hospital (Coney Island M.M.T.P. Clinic), 425 Coney Island Avenue, Brooklyn, NY 11218; tel. 718/226–9000; Mr. Anthony Ferreri

Staten Island Univ Hospital (Princess Bay M.M.T.P. Clinic), 392 Seguine Avenue, Staten Island, NY 10309; tel. 718/226–9000; Mr. Anthony C Ferreri

Staten Island Univ Hospital (Stapleton M.M.T.P. Clinic), 111 Water Street, Staten Island, NY 10305; tel. 718/226–9000; Mr. Anthony C Ferreri

Staten Island Univ Hospital Inpatient Chem Dep Detox Unit, 475 Seaview Avenue, Staten Island, NY 10305; tel. 718/226–9000; Mr. Anthony Ferreri

Stony Lodge Hospital, Inc., PO Box 1250, Briarcliff Manor, NY 10510; tel. 914/941–7400; Mr. Kevin F Czipo

Strong Memorial Hospital - MMTC - Dept of Psychiatry, 601 Elmwood Avenue, Rochester, NY 14642; tel. 585/275–5489; Mr. Stephen Goldstein

Stuyvesant Square Chemical Dependency Outpatient Detox, 1st Avenue At 16th Street, New York, NY 10003; tel. 212/420–4220; Dr. Mathew E Fink

Suffolk County Department of Health - Babylon MMTP, Building 159 North County Complex, Hauppauge, NY 11788; tel. 631/854–1919; Mr. Thomas McGilvray

Suffolk County Department of Health - East End Clinic, 300 Center Drive, Riverhead, NY 11901; tel. 631/852–2680; Mr. Thomas MacGilvray

Suffolk County Department of Health - Hauppauge Clinic, Building 159 North County Complex, Hauppauge, NY 11788; tel. 631/853–7373; Mr. Thomas O MacGilvray

Suffolk County Department of Health - North County Complex, Veterans Highway, Bldg 159, North County Complex, Hauppauge, NY 11788; tel. 631/853–6410; Mr. Thomas O MacGilvray

Suffolk County Dept. of Health, Huntington Methadone Clinic, Building 159 North County Complex, Hauppauge, NY 11788; tel. 631/854–4400; Mr. Thomas MacGilvary

SVCMC Mary Immaculate Hospital, 275 North St, Harrison, NY 10528; tel. 718/774–8436; Dr. Brian Fitzsimmons

SVCMC St. Mary's Hospital - Prospect Place Clinic, 275 North St., Harrison, NY 10528; tel. 718/774–8436; Dr. Brian Fitzsimmons

SVCMC St. Mary's Hospital of Brooklyn, 275 North St, Harrison, NY 10528; tel. 718/485–6000; Dr. Brian Fitzsimmons

SVCMC St. Mary's Hospital of Brooklyn - Alabama Ave, 275 North St, Harrison, NY 10528; tel. 718/774–8436; Dr. Brian Fitzsimmons

SVCMC St. Vincent's Hospital Westchester, MMTP, 275 North St, Harrison, NY 10528; tel. 800/784–8804; Dr. Brian Fitzsimmons

The Adolescent Development Program of the NY Presbyterian Hospital, 411 East 69th Street, New York, NY 10021; tel. 212/746–1277; Dr. Herbert Pardes

Section C

The Astor Home for Children, PO Box 5005, Rhinebeck, NY 12572-5005; tel. 845/871-1000; Dr. James McGuirk

The Brooklyn Hospital Center Parkside Drug Detox Program, 121 DeKalb Avenue, Brooklyn, NY 11201; tel. 718/250-8320; Mr. Samuel Lehrfield

The Children's Home RTF, Inc., 638 Squirrel Hill Road, Chenango Forks, NY 13746; tel. 607/656-9004; Ms. Karen Wright

The Guidance Center Chemical Dependency Treatment Center, 26 Sickles Avenue, New Rochelle, NY 10801; tel. 914/632-1374; Ms. Marge Klein

The House of the Good Shepherd, 1550 Champlin Avenue, Utica, NY 13502; tel. 315/733-0436; Mr. William F Holicky, Jr.

The Mount Sinai Hospital Narcotics Rehabilitation Center, 17 East 102nd Street, New York, NY 10029; tel. 212/241-7006; Dr. Kenneth Davis

The Mount Vernon Hospital Methadone Maintenance Program, 3 South 6th Avenue, 3rd Floor, Mount Vernon, NY 10550; tel. 914/664-8000; Mr. John R Spicer

The New York and Presbyterian Hospital, Inc., 525 E 68th Street, F172, New York, NY 10021; tel. 212/746-0421; Dr. Herbert Pardes

The Support Center, Inc., 188 Route 209, Port Jervis, NY 12771; tel. 800/724-9322; Mr. Carmine Mosca

The Turning Point - Detox Unit Saint Francis Hospital, 11 Hastings Drive, Beacon, NY 12508; tel. 845/838-4405; Mr. Robert Savage

Tully Hill Corporation, PO Box 1116, Tully, NY 13159-1116; tel. 315/696-6114; Ms. Cathy L Palm

Ulster County Mental Health Services Methadone Maintenance, 239 Golden Hill Lane, Kingston, NY 12401; tel. 845/340-4100; Mr. Allen Nace

United Health Services Hospitals, 33-57 Harrison Street, Johnson City, NY 13790; tel. 607/763-5300; Mr. Matthew Salanger

VA New York Harbor Healthcare System, 800 Poly Place, Brooklyn, NY 11209; tel. 718/630-3521; Dr. Eric Peselow

VA New York Harbor Healthcare System - OTP, 437 West 16th Street, New York, NY 10011; tel. 212/462-4461; Dr. Paul Casadante

Veritas Villa, Inc., PO Box 610, Kerhonkson, NY 12446-0610; tel. 845/626-3555; Ms. Peggy Healy

West Midtown Medical Group, 505 Eighth Avenue, 10th Floor, New York, NY 10018; tel. 212/736-5900; Mr. Peter Schorr

West Midtown Medical Group - OTP, 505 Eighth Avenue, 10th Floor, New York, NY 10018; tel. 212/736-5900; Mr. Peter Schorr

Westchester Jewish Community Services, Inc., 845 North Broadway, Suite 2, White Plains, NY 10603; tel. 914/761-0600; Mr. Alan Trager

White Plains Hospital Center, Davis Avenue at East Post Road, White Plains, NY 10601; tel. 914/681-2800; Mr. Jon B Schandler

Whitney M. Young, Jr. MMTP, 4-10 Dewitt Street, Albany, NY 12207; tel. 518/463-3882; Mr. Jamed D Sinkoff

Woodhull Medical & Mental Health Medically Managed Detoxification, 760 Broadway, Units 8-300 and 9-300, Brooklyn, NY 11206; tel. 718/963-5959; Ms. Lynda D Curtis

NORTH CAROLINA
Alexander Youth Network, PO Box 220632, Charlotte, NC 28222-9979; tel. 704/366-8712; Mr. N.Craig Bass

Alpha Omega Health, Inc., 6036 Six Forks Road, Raleigh, NC 27609; tel. 919/844-1008; Mr. John K Horne, Jr.

Brynn Marr Behavioral Healthcare System, 192 Village Drive, Jacksonville, NC 28546; tel. 910/577-1400; Mr. Joey Jacobs

Fellowship Hall, Inc., PO Box 13890, Greensboro, NC 27415; tel. 336/621-3381; Mr. Rodney Battles

Grandfather Home for Children, PO Box 98, Banner Elk, NC 28604; tel. 828/898-5465; Mr. James Swinkola

Julian F. Keith Alcohol and Drug Abuse Treatment Center, 201 Tabernacle Road, Black Mountain, NC 28711; tel. 828/669-3421; Mr. William A Rafter

Old Vineyard Youth Services, 3637 Old Vineyard Road, Winston Salem, NC 27104-4842; tel. 336/794-3550; Mr. Ted Brewer

R. J. Blackley, MD-Alcohol & Drug Abuse Treatment Center, 1003 12th Street, Butner, NC 27509-1626; tel. 919/575-7928; Ms. Patricia L Christian

The Wilmington Treatment Center, Inc., 2520 Troy Drive, Wilmington, NC 28401; tel. 910/762-2727; Mr. Charles Sharp

Timber Ridge Treatment Center, P O Box 259, Gold Hill, NC 28071; tel. 704/279-1199; Mr. Thomas A. R Hibbert

Unity Healing Center, PO Box 201, Cherokee, NC 28719; tel. 828/497-3958; Ms. Hillane Lambert

Wilmington Treatment Center Inc, 2520 Troy Drive, Wilmington, NC 28401; tel. 910/762-2727; Mr. Charles Sharp

NORTH DAKOTA
The Dakota Boys and Girls Ranch Association, PO Box 5007, Minot, ND 58703; tel. 701/852-3628; Mr. Gene Kasemen

OHIO
Akron Drug Abuse Clinic - Community Health Center, 725 East Market Street, Akron, OH 44305; tel. 330/434-4141; Mr. Theodore P Ziegler

Akron-Urban Minority Alcoholism Drug Abuse Outreach, 665 W Market Street, Suite 2D, Akron, OH 44303; tel. 330/379-3467; Ms. Janice T Mercier

Beech Brook, 3737 Lander Road, Cleveland, OH 44124; tel. 216/831-2255; Ms. Debra Rex

Behavioral Connections of Wood County, Inc., Post Office Box 29, Bowling Green, OH 43402; tel. 419/352-8254; Dr. Richard M Goldberg

Bellefaire Jewish Children's Bureau, 22001 Fairmount Boulevard, Shaker Heights, OH 44118; tel. 216/932-2800; Dr. Adam G Jacobs

Catholic Charities Services Corporation, 7911 Detroit Ave, Cleveland, OH 44102; tel. 440/843-5582; Mr. Thomas W Woll

Center for Chemical Addictions Treatment, 830 Ezzard Charles Drive, Cincinnati, OH 45214; tel. 513/381-6672; Ms. Sandra L Kuehn

Child Guidance & Family Solutions, 312 Locust Street, Akron, OH 44302-1878; tel. 330/762-4559; Mr. Charles M Vehlow, Jr.

Community Behavioral Health Center, 3690 Orange Place, Suite 220, Beachwood, OH 44122; tel. 216/831-1494; Mr. Arun K Chattree

Community Counseling Center of Ashtabula County, 2801 C Court, Ashtabula, OH 44004; tel. 440/998-4210; Mr. Dale Brinker

Community Health Center, 725 East Market Street, Akron, OH 44305; tel. 330/434-4141; Mr. Theodore P Ziegler

Comprehensive Addiction Service Systems, Inc., 2465 Collingwood Blvd., Toledo, OH 43620; tel. 419/241-8827; Mr. Ross M Chaban

Comprehensive Counseling Service, 1659 Breiel Boulevard, Middletown, OH 45044; tel. 513/420-5658; Ms. Becky Moss

Comprehensive Psychiatry Specialists, 955 Windham Court, Suite 2, Boardman, OH 44512; tel. 330/726-9570; Mr. Timothy Schaffner

Connecting Point, 1212 Cherry Street, Toledo, OH 43608; tel. 419/243-6326; Mr. Jeff Deckebach

Crisis Intervention Center of Stark County, Inc., 2421-13th Street, Northwest, Canton, OH 44708; tel. 330/452-9812; Dr. Bernard S Jesiolowski

Department of Veteran Affairs - Dayton Campus, 4100 W Third Street, Bldg 302, Dayton, OH 45428; tel. 937/268-6511; Dr. Alberto Rincon-Belzres

Glenbeigh Hospital & Outpatient Services, PO Box 298, Rock Creek, OH 44084-0298; tel. 440/563-3400; Ms. Pat Weston-Hall

Harbor Behavioral Healthcare, 4334 Secor Road, Toledo, OH 43623-4234; tel. 419/475-4449; Mr. Dale E Shreve

Interval Brotherhood Homes, Inc., 3445 South Main Street, Akron, OH 44319; tel. 330/644-4095; Mr. Samuel R Ciccolini

Mandel Adult Day Center, 27100 Cedar Road, Beachwood, OH 44122; tel. 216/831-6500; Mr. Steven Raichilson

McKinley Hall, Inc., 1101 East High Street, Springfield, OH 45505; tel. 937/328-5300; Mr. Daniel M Barksdale

Methadone Maintenance Program, Substance Abuse,Mental Health, 10701 East Blvd, Room H127, Cleveland, OH 44106; tel. 440/526-3030; Dr. Mark Bondeson

Neil Kennedy Recovery Clinic, 2151 Rush Boulevard, Youngstown, OH 44507; tel. 330/744-1181; Mr. Gerald V Carter

New Directions, Inc., 30800 Chagrin Boulevard, Cleveland, OH 44124; tel. 216/591-0324; Mr. Michael E Matoney

Nova Behavioral Health, Inc., 832 McKinley Avenue, Northwest, Canton, OH 44703; tel. 330/455-9407; Ms. Carol A Hales

Opiate Substitution Services - SUDEP, CVAMC, 3200 Vine Street, Cincinnati, OH 45220; tel. 513/861-3100; Dr. Show W Lin

Portage Path Behavioral Health, 340 South Broadway, Akron, OH 44308; tel. 330/376-6144; Mr. Jerome T Kraker

PsyCare, Inc., 2980 Belmont Avenue, Youngstown, OH 44505; tel. 330/759-2310; Dr. Douglas C Darnall

Ravenwood Mental Health Center, 12557 Ravenwood Drive, Chardon, OH 44024; tel. 440/285-3568; Mr. David A Boyle

Rescue Mental Health Services, 3350 Collingwood Boulevard, Toledo, OH 43610; tel. 419/255-9585; Mr. Frank A Ayers

Southeast, Inc., 16 West Long Street, Columbus, OH 43215; tel. 614/225-0980; Ms. Sandra Stephenson

Specialty Care Counseling Services, Ltd, 2000 East Market Street, Warren, OH 44483; tel. 330/399-1221; Mrs. Nivine Sedra

Stella Maris, Inc., 1320 Washington Avenue, Cleveland, OH 44113; tel. 216/781-0550; Mrs. Margaret A Roche

Substance Abuse Services, Inc., 1832 Adams Street, Toledo, OH 43624; tel. 419/243-7274; Mr. Ross M Chaban

The Buckeye Ranch, Inc., 5665 Hoover Road, Grove City, OH 43123; tel. 614/875-2371; Mr. Richard E Rieser

The Crossroads Center, 311 Martin Luther King Drive, Cincinnati, OH 45219-3116; tel. 513/475-5300; Mrs. Jacqueline P Butler

The Woods at Parkside, 349 Olde Ridenour Road, Columbus, OH 43230; tel. 614/471-2552; Mrs. Susan J Carmichael

Unison Behavioral Health Group, PO Box 10015, Toledo, OH 43699-0015; tel. 419/242-9577; Mrs. Courtney Weiss

Wood County Children's Services Association, PO Box 738, Bowling Green, OH 43402; tel. 419/352-7588; Mr. Charles Powell

Zepf Community Mental Health Center, Inc., 6605 West Central Avenue, Toledo, OH 43617; tel. 419/841-7701; Ms. Kathi Cesen

OKLAHOMA
Brookhaven Hospital, 201 South Garnett Road, Tulsa, OK 74128-1800; tel. 918/438-4257; Dr. Rolf B Gainer

Carl Albert Community Mental Health Center, PO Box 579, McAlester, OK 74502; tel. 918/426-7800; Mr. George R Jones

Choices Institute, 529 N. Grand, Enid, OK 73701; tel. 580/234-8880; Ms. Joyce C Bean

Cushing Valley Hope, PO Box 472, Cushing, OK 74023-0472; tel. 918/225-1736; Dr. Kenneth C Gregoire

Divine Interventions, Inc., P. O. Box 274, Oologah, OK 74053; tel. 918/443-1100; Ms. Chrystal Brassfield

Jim Taliaferro Community Mental Health Center, 602 Southwest 38th Street, Lawton, OK 73505; tel. 580/248-5780; Mr. Jim Regan

Northwest Center for Behavioral Health (NCBH), 1222 10th Street, Suite 211, Woodward, OK 73801; tel. 580/256-8615; Mr. Steve Norwood

Oklahoma City VA Medical Center, Substance Abuse Treatment, 921 NE 13th St, Bldg 1, 116C, Oklahoma City, OK 73104; tel. 405/270-5194; Dr. Gita Pujari

Oklahoma Forensic Center, PO Box 69, Vinita, OK 74301-0069; tel. 918/256-7841; Mr. William T Burkett

Oklahoma Youth Center, 320 12th Avenue Northeast, Norman, OK 73071; tel. 405/573-3821; Mr. Robert E Lee

Parkside, Inc., 1620 East 12th Street, Tulsa, OK 74120; tel. 918/582-2131; Ms. Debra Moore

Restorative Counseling Services, 10007 South Pennsylvania Ave Suite B, Oklahoma City, OK 73159; tel. 405/692-5577; Ms. Gina M Pazzaglia-Filkins

Southwest Foster Care Of Oklahoma, 4801 North Classen Blvd Suite 135, Oklahoma City, OK 73118; tel. 405/848-0011; Mr. Jack Lewis

Tulsa County Juvenile Justice Trust Authority, 4012 East 35th Street, Tulsa, OK 74135; tel. 918/749-6668; Mr. Eric Sachau

Willow Crest Hospital, Inc., 130 A Street SouthWest, Miami, OK 74354; tel. 918/542-3413; Ms. Anne G Anthony

OREGON
Catherine Freer Wilderness Therapy Expeditions, PO Box 1064, Albany, OR 97321; tel. 541/926-7252; Dr. Robert Cooley

Christie School, PO Box 368, Marylhurst, OR 97036; tel. 503/635-3416; Ms. Lynne Saxton

CODA, Inc., 1027 E. Burnside, Portland, OR 97214; tel. 503/236-2290; Mr. Timothy T Hartnett

Eastern Oregon Children's Multi-Treatment Center, Inc., 622 Airport Road, Pendleton, OR 97801; tel. 541/276–0057; Ms. Mary Winter

Kerr Youth and Family Center, 722 Northeast 162nd Avenue, Portland, OR 97230; tel. 503/255–4205; Mr. Christopher J Krenk

Northwest Behavioral Healthcare Services, 1800 Southeast Webster Road, Gladstone, OR 97027; tel. 503/722–4470; Mr. Daniel Mahler

Portland VA Medical Center, 3710 SW US Hospital Road, Building 100, Portland, OR 97207; tel. 503/220–8262; Dr. Peter Benson

RiverBend Youth Center, Inc., 15544 S Clackamas River Drive, Oregon City, OR 97045; tel. 503/656–8005; Mr. George B Rex

Serenity Lane, 2133 Centennial Plaza, Eugene, OR 97401; tel. 541/484–2156; Mr. Neil McNaughton

Southern Oregon Adolescent Study and Treatment Center, 210 Tacoma Street, Grants Pass, OR 97526; tel. 541/956–4943; Mr. Robert E Lieberman

Trillium Family Services, 3415 SE Powell Blvd, Portland, OR 97202; tel. 503/234–9591; Mr. Robert L Roy

VA Southern Oregon Rehabilitation Center and Clinics, 8495 Crater Lake Highway, White City, OR 97503; tel. 541/830–3515; Dr. Max E McIntosh

PENNSYLVANIA

ACS Psychological Associates, Inc. - Community Services, 136 East Fayette Street, Uniontown, PA 15401; tel. 724/438–2342; Mr. Adam C Sedlock, Jr.

Addiction Medicine Services - Homewood Outreach Program, 6714 Kelly Street, Pittsburgh, PA 15208; tel. 412/246–6806; Dr. Dennis Daley

Adelphoi Village, Inc., 1003 Village Way, Latrobe, PA 15650; tel. 724/537–7858; Mr. Larry Breitenstein

Associates in Counseling & Child Guidance, 272 East Connelly Boulevard, Sharon, PA 16146; tel. 724/983–1381; Mr. Shayen A George

Beacon Light Behavioral Health Systems, 800 East Main Street, Bradford, PA 16701; tel. 814/362–5250; Mr. Thomas E Urban

Bethesda Children's Home, 15667 State Highway 86, Meadville, PA 16335; tel. 814/724–7510; Mr. Gene Wisinski

Bowling Green Brandywine, PO Box 787, Kennett Square, PA 19348; tel. 610/268–3588; Ms. Claire F Beckwith

Brighter Horizons Behavioral Health, 23062 Jericho Road, Edinboro, PA 16412; tel. 814/398–1805; Ms. Rachel M Mesmer

Child Guidance Resource Centers, 600 North Olive Street, Media, PA 19063-2418; tel. 610/565–6000; Mr. Brad Barry

Children's Aid Home Programs of Somerset County, Inc., PO Box 1195, Somerset, PA 15501; tel. 814/443–1637; Mr. Robert C Miller, Jr.

Children's Service Center of Wyoming Valley, Inc., 335 South Franklin Street, Wilkes Barre, PA 18702; tel. 570/825–6425; Mr. Joseph DeVizia

Clear Brook, Inc., 1003 Wyoming Avenue, Forty Fort, PA 18704; tel. 570/288–6692; Dr. Nicholas F Colangelo

Cornell Abraxas Group, Inc., One Gateway Center, 5th Floor, Pittsburgh, PA 15222; tel. 412/208–4000; Mr. Jack Godlesky

Cornell Abraxas I, PO Box 59, Marienville, PA 16239; tel. 814/927–6615; Mr. James E Newsome

Crozer Chester Medical Center-Community Hospital of Chester, 2600 West Ninth Street, Ground Floor, Community Hosp, Chester, PA 19013; tel. 610/447–2785; Mr. Gerald Miller

Devereux Beneto Center, 655 Sugartown Road, PO Box 297, Malvern, PA 19355-0297; tel. 484/595–6733; Mr. Walter Grono

Diversified Family Services, 3679 East State Street, Hermitage, PA 16148; tel. 724/346–2123; Ms. Marilyn Klemens

Diversified Treatment Alternatives, Inc., 201 Fairfield Road, Lewisburg, PA 17837; tel. 570/523–3457; Mr. Timothy J Kelleher

Eagleville Hospital, 100 Eagleville Road, PO Box 45, Eagleville, PA 19408-0045; tel. 610/539–6000; Ms. Kendria McWilliams

Friendship House, PO Box 3778, Scranton, PA 18505; tel. 570/342–8305; Mr. Robert H Angeloni

Gateway Rehabilitation Center/ Genesis Division, Moffett Run Road, Aliquippa, PA 15001; tel. 412/766–8700; Dr. Kenneth S Ramsey

Gaudenzia Crossroads, 414 West Fifth Street, Erie, PA 16507; tel. 814/459–4775; Mr. Michael Harle

Gaudenzia, Inc. - Common Ground, 2835 North Front Street, Harrisburg, PA 17110; tel. 717/238–4200; Mr. Michael B Harle

Glade Run Lutheran Services, PO Box 70, Zelienople, PA 16063-0070; tel. 724/452–4453; Dr. Charles T Lockwood

Greenbriar Treatment Center, 800 Manor Drive, Washington, PA 15301; tel. 724/225–9700; Ms. Mary L Banaszak

Greenway Center Inc, P. O. Box 188, Henryville, PA 18332; tel. 570/688–9162; Mr. Peter D'Souza

Hoffman Homes, Inc., PO Box 4777, Gettysburg, PA 17325; tel. 717/359–7148; Mr. George Sepic

Holcomb Behavioral Health Systems, 930 E Lancaster Ave, Suite 220, Exton, PA 19341; tel. 610/363–1488; Mr. William DiFabio

Jefferson-Kensington Methadone Treatment Program, 136 West Diamond Street, Philadelphia, PA 19122; tel. 215/426–8100; Ms. Eileen Hause

Kensington Hospital (Non- Hospital Detoxification Unit), 136 West Diamond Street, Philadelphia, PA 19122; tel. 215/426–8100; Ms. Eileen Hause

KidsPeace Corporation, 5300 KidsPeace Drive, Orefield, PA 18069-9101; tel. 610/799–8000; Mr. C T O'Donnel, III

Kirkbride Center-A Better Way, 111 North 49th Street, Philadelphia, PA 19139; tel. 215/471–2600; Ms. Rose Diottavio

Livengrin Foundation, Inc., 4833 Hulmeville Road, Bensalem, PA 19020-3099; tel. 215/638–5200; Mr. Richard M Pine

Malvern Institute, 940 King Road, Malvern, PA 19355; tel. 610/647–0330; Mr. Richard Mangano

Marworth, PO Box 36, Waverly, PA 18471; tel. 570/563–1112; Mr. James J Dougherty

Mercy Catholic Medical Center/Mercy Hospital of Philadelphia, 501 South 54th Street, Philadelphia, PA 19143; tel. 215/748–9300; Ms. Bernadette Mangan

Mirmont Treatment Center, 100 Yearsley Mill Road, Media, PA 19063-5593; tel. 610/744–1400; Mr. Thomas F Cain

Montgomery County Emergency Service, Inc., 50 Beech Drive, Norristown, PA 19403-5421; tel. 610/279–6100; Dr. Rocio Nell

Narcotic Addict Rehabilitation Program of Thomas Jefferson Univ., South 21st St. & Washington Av, Philadelphia, PA 19146; tel. 215/735–5979; Dr. Michael J Vergare

New Vitae, Inc. Partial Hospital Program & Outpatient Clinic, 50 East Broad Street, Bethlehem, PA 18018; tel. 610/814–2707; Mr. Adam Devlin

NorthEast Treatment Centers (NET), 499 North 5th Street, Suite A, Philadelphia, PA 19123; tel. 215/451–7000; Mr. Terence McSherry

NorthEast Treatment Centers - OTP, 499 North 5th Street, Philadelphia, PA 19123; tel. 215/451–7000; Mr. Terence McSherry

Nulton Diagnostic and Treatment Center, PC, 214 College Park Plaza, Johnstown, PA 15904; tel. 814/262–0025; Dr. Larry J Nulton

Penn Foundation, Inc., 807 Lawn Avenue, Sellersville, PA 18960; tel. 215/257–6551; Mr. John Goshow

Perseus House, Inc., 1511 Peach Street, Erie, PA 16501; tel. 814/480–5900; Mr. A. Mark Amendola

Philadelphia VA Medical Center Opioid Treatment Program, University and Woodland Aves, Building 7, Philadelphia, PA 19104; tel. 215/823–5809; Dr. Isabelle Arndt

Presbyterian Children's Village Services, 452 South Roberts Road, Rosemont, PA 19010; tel. 610/525–5400; Mr. Loren Preheim

Progressive Medical Specialists, Inc., 2900 Smallman Street, Pittsburgh, PA 15201; tel. 412/391–6384; Ms. Annamaire Roberto

Progressive Medical Specialists, Inc., 2453 West Pike Road, Houston, PA 15342; tel. 724/873–5655; Ms. Annamarie Roberto

Psychiatric Care Systems, PC, 110 Hidden Valley Road, McMurray, PA 15317; tel. 724/941–4070; Dr. Oscar Urrea

Pyramid Healthcare, Inc., P.O. Box 1153, Altoona, PA 16603; tel. 814/940–0407; Mr. Jonathan Wolf

Renewal Operations, Inc., PO Box 107, Zionhill, PA 18981; tel. 215/536–9070; Mrs. Loretta Anderer Brausen

RHJ Medical Center, Inc., RR 1, Box 224, Hunker, PA 15639; tel. 724/696–9600; Mrs. Kerri A Csikesz

Roxbury Treatment Center, 601 Roxbury Road, Shippensburg, PA 17257; tel. 717/532–4217; Mr. William Niles

Saint John Vianney Center, 151 Woodbine Road, Downingtown, PA 19335; tel. 610/269–2600; Mr. Thomas F Dugan

Salisbury Behavioral Health, Inc., 614 North Easton Road, Glenside, PA 19038; tel. 215/884–5566; Dr. Paul Volosov

Sarah A. Reed Children's Center, 2445 West 34th Street, Erie, PA 16506; tel. 814/838–1954; Mr. James D Mando

Shawnee Academy, River Road, Minisink Hills, PA 18341; tel. 570/420–8601; Mr. Aldo Cavalli

Silver Springs - Martin Luther School, 512 West Township Line Road, Plymouth Meeting, PA 19462-1099; tel. 610/825–4440; Ms. Ruth W Bartelt

St. Michael's School, Box 370 Hoban Heights, Tunkhannock, PA 18657; tel. 570/388–6155; Mr. Andrew M Varzaly

Stairways Behavioral Health, 138 East 26th Street, Erie, PA 16504; tel. 814/453–5806; Mr. William F McCarthy

SummitQuest Academy, PO Box 729, Ephrata, PA 17522; tel. 717/859–4100; Mr. Chris Grala

The Bradley Center, Inc., 3710 Saxonburg Boulevard, Pittsburgh, PA 15238; tel. 412/767–5306; Mr. Walter Goedeke

The Bridge, 8400 Pine Road, Philadelphia, PA 19111; tel. 215/342–5000; Mr. Jose A Benitez

The Children's Home of Reading, 1010 Centre Avenue, Reading, PA 19601-1498; tel. 610/478–8266; Mr. Vince Lasorsa

The Goldman Clinic, 8th Street and Girard Avenue, Philadelphia, PA 19122; tel. 215/787–2070; Ms. Marlene D-Walsh

The Meadows Psychiatric Center, 132 The Meadows Drive, Centre Hall, PA 16828; tel. 814/364–2161; Ms. Felicia Stehley

The Mitchell Clinic, 555 Harrison Street, Emmaus, PA 18049; tel. 610/965–6418; Dr. John F Mitchell

The Renfrew Centers, Inc., 475 Spring Lane, Philadelphia, PA 19128; tel. 215/482–5353; Mr. Samuel E Menaged

Thomas Jefferson University - Family Center, 1201 Chestnut Street, Philadelphia, PA 19107; tel. 215/955–1951; Dr. Karol Kaltenbach

TODAY, Inc., PO Box 908, Newtown, PA 18940; tel. 215/968–4713; Dr. John E Howell

Universal Recovery Foundation, 2001 Providence Avenue, Chester, PA 19013; tel. 610/876–9000; Mr. Billy Young

VA Medical Center - (SATU), 1400 Blackhorse Hill Road, Coatesville, PA 19320; tel. 610/384–7711; Ms. Nancy C Elliott-Carter

Valley Forge Medical Center & Hospital/Non-Hospital Service, 1033 West Germantown Pike, Norristown, PA 19403; tel. 610/539–8500; Ms. Marian Colcher

VAPHS - CTAD-OPIOID SUBSTITUTION THERAPY CLINIC, 7180 Highland Drive, Bldg 4-1W, Pittsburgh, PA 15206; tel. 412/365–5010; Dr. Steven D Forman

Warwick House, Inc., 1460 Meetinghouse Rd., Warminster, PA 18974; tel. 215/491–7404; Mr. Kenneth W Brownell

White Deer Run Detoxification Unit, PO Box 97 - DeVitt Camp Road, Allenwood, PA 17810; tel. 570/538–2567; Mr. Mark G Sarneso

White Deer Run Inc., 360 White Deer Run Road, Allenwood, PA 17810; tel. 800/255–2335; Mr. Mark G Sarneso

Wordsworth, 7827 Old York Road, Elkins Park, PA 19027; tel. 215/635–6600; Mr. Gerald Schatz

RHODE ISLAND

Alternatives, 350 Duncan Drive, Providence, RI 02906; tel. 401/453–4742; Dr. Yitzhak Bakal

Butler Hospital Alcohol and Drug Treatment Services, 345 Blackstone Boulevard, Providence, RI 02906; tel. 401/455–6220; Dr. Patricia R Recupero

CODAC Behavioral Healthcare, Inc., 1052 Park Avenue,, Cranston, RI 02910; tel. 401/275–5039; Mr. Michael A Rizzi

CODAC East Bay, 1052 Park Avenue, Cranston, RI 02910; tel. 401/275–5039; Mr. Michael Rizzi

CODAC II, 1052 Park Avenue, Cranston, RI 02910; tel. 401/942–1450; Mr. Michael Rizzi

CODAC III-Newport, 1052 Park Avenue, Cranston, RI 02910; tel. 401/846–4150; Mr. Michael Rizzi

Community Counseling Center, 249 Roosevelt Avenue, Pawtucket, RI 02860; tel. 401/724–8400; Mr. Richard H Leclerc

East Bay Mental Health Center, Inc., 2 Old County Road, Barrington, RI 02806; tel. 401/431–9870; Mr. John P Digits, Jr.

Mental Health Services, 249 Roosevelt Avenue, Pawtucket, RI 02860; tel. 401/724–8400; Mr. Richard H Leclerc

Newport County Community Mental Health Center, Inc., 127 Johnnycake Hill Road, Middletown, RI 02842; tel. 401/846–1213; Mr. J Clement Cicilline

Health Organizations, Agencies, and Providers **C99**

Providence VA Medical Center, 830 Chalkstone Avenue, Bldg 1, Providence, RI 02908; tel. 401/273-7100; Mr. Vincent Ng

South Shore Mental Health Center, Inc., P.O. Box 899, Charlestown, RI 02813; tel. 401/364-7705; Mr. Richard C Antonelli

SSTAR of Rhode Island, 1950 Tower Hill Road, North Kingstown, RI 02852; tel. 401/294-6160; Ms. Nancy E Paull

The Providence Center, 951 North Main Street, Providence, RI 02904; tel. 401/528-0123; Mr. Dale K Klatzker

Tri-Hab, Inc., 58 Hamlet Avenue, Woonsocket, RI 02895; tel. 401/765-4040; Mr. David Spencer

SOUTH CAROLINA

Lighthouse Care Center of Conway, 152 Waccamaw Medical Park Dr., Conway, SC 29526; tel. 843/347-8871; Mr. Francis Sauvageau

New Hope Treatment Centers, Inc., 7515 Northside Drive, Suite 200, North Charleston, SC 29420; tel. 843/851-5010; Mr. Jay S Orvin

Palmetto Pee Dee Behavioral Health, LLC, 601 Gregg Avenue, Florence, SC 29502; tel. 843/667-0644; Ms. Cherie D Tolley

SOUTH DAKOTA

Black Hills Children's Home, 24100 South Rockerville Road, Rapid City, SD 55701; tel. 605/334-6004; Mr. Dennis Daugaard

Keystone Treatment Center, PO Box 159, Canton, SD 57013; tel. 605/987-2751; Ms. Carol Regier

Sioux Falls Children's Home, 801 North Sycamore, Sioux Falls, SD 57110-5746; tel. 605/334-6004; Mr. Dennis Daugaard

TENNESSEE

Agency for Youth and Family Development, 5050 Poplar Avenue, Suite 1510, Memphis, TN 38157; tel. 901/524-1488; Dr. Gerald J Jordan

Buffalo Valley, Inc., PO Box 879, Hohenwald, TN 38462; tel. 931/796-5427; Mr. Jerry T Risner

Child & Family Tennessee, 901 East Summit Hill Drive, Knoxville, TN 37915; tel. 865/524-7483; Ms. Kathryn R O'Day

Compass Intervention Center, LLC, 7900 Lowrance Road, Memphis, TN 38125; tel. 901/758-2002; Mr. James T Shaheen, Jr.

Cornerstone of Recovery, Inc., 1214 Topside Road, Louisville, TN 37777; tel. 865/970-7747; Mr. Dan R Caldwell

Council for Alcohol and Drug Abuse Services, Inc., PO Box 4797, Chattanooga, TN 37405; tel. 423/756-7644; Dr. Paul Fuchcar

Cumberland Heights Foundation, Inc., PO Box 90727, Nashville, TN 37209; tel. 615/353-4831; Mr. James B Moore

Daybreak Treatment Center and Specialized School, 2262 Germantown Road South, Germantown, TN 38138; tel. 901/753-4300; Ms. Tina C Mills

DRD Knoxville Medical Clinic, 626 Bernard Street, Knoxville, TN 37921; tel. 865/522-0161; Ms. Mary Little

FHC - Cumberland Hall of Chattanooga, 7351 Standifer Gap Road, Chattanooga, TN 37421; tel. 423/499-9007; Mr. Charles Dickens

Foothills Care, Inc., 661 Emory Valley Road, Suite A, Oak Ridge, TN 37830; tel. 865/483-9111; Ms. Heather Dziewulski

Jackson Academy, LLC, 222 Church Street, Dickson, TN 37055; tel. 615/446-3900; Mr. Ted Gorzny

Pathways of Tennessee, Inc., 238 Summar Drive, Jackson, TN 38301; tel. 731/935-8200; Mr. Kelly R Yenawine

Peninsula Behavioral Health, PO Box 2000, Louisville, TN 37777-0789; tel. 865/970-9800; Ms. Barbara Blevins, Jr.

Reflections Treatment Agency, 6628 Central Avenue Pike, Knoxville, TN 37912; tel. 865/219-9444; Mr. James Slattery

Ridgeview Psychiatric Hospital and Center, Inc., 240 West Tyrone Road, Oak Ridge, TN 37830; tel. 865/482-1076; Mr. Robert J Benning

SummaCare Outpatient Services, 4015 Travis Road, 2nd Floor, Nashville, TN 37203; tel. 615/248-4989; Mr. Michael Carell

The Camelot Schools,LLC, 183 Fiddlers Lane, Kingston, TN 37763; tel. 865/376-2296; Mr. Randy Yeager

The Chad Youth Enhancement Center, 1751 Oak Plains Road, Ashland City, TN 37015; tel. 931/362-4723; Dr. Robert D Glasner

Youth Villages, 2890 Bekemeyer Drive, Arlington, TN 38002; tel. 901/252-7200; Mr. Patrick W Lawler

TEXAS

A.A.M.A., Narcotic Education League (NEL), 434 S. Main, Suite 217, San Antonio, TX 78204; tel. 210/270-8575; Ms. Acenete Flores

Addiction and Psychotherapy Services, 2824 South Congress Avenue, Austin, TX 78704; tel. 512/444-5092; Dr. Heinz Aeschbach

Alternatives Centre for Behavioral Health, 5001 Alabama Street, El Paso, TX 79930; tel. 915/565-4800; Ms. Carol J Anderson

Assn for the Advancement of Mexican-Americans, Inc., 434 South Main, Suite 217, San Antonio, TX 78204; tel. 210/270-8575; Mr. Gilbert Moreno

Austin Child Guidance Center, 810 West 45th Street, Austin, TX 78751; tel. 512/451-2242; Dr. Donald J Zappone

Austin Travis County MHMR Methadone Mntce Tx Program, 1631 A East 2nd Street, Austin, TX 78702; tel. 512/472-6261; Mr. David Evans

Burke Center, 4101 South Medford Drive, Lufkin, TX 75901; tel. 936/639-1141; Ms. Susan Rushing

Canyon Lakes Residential Treatment Center, 2402 Canyon Lake Drive, Lubbock, TX 79415; tel. 806/762-5782; Dr. Ray H Brown

Cedar Crest Hospital & RTC, 3500 South I-H 35, Belton, TX 76513; tel. 254/939-2100; Mr. Steve Rublee

Child Study Center, 1300 West Lancaster, Fort Worth, TX 76102; tel. 817/336-8611; Dr. Joyce E Mauk

Conlan Family Partners, Limited, 1100 McCart Street, Stephenville, TX 76401; tel. 254/968-2907; Ms. Nicole Conlan

CONTINUUM, 3003 South Loop West, Suite 475, Houston, TX 77054-4816; tel. 713/383-0888; Dr. Barbara A Candley

DebLin Health Concepts and Associates, Inc., 6813 Northampton Way, Houston, TX 77055; tel. 713/686-9194; Ms. Debra R Jackson

East Texas Clinic, PO Box 9486, Longview, TX 75608; tel. 903/759-4966; Ms. Diane Stalnaker

Family Services of Greater Houston, 3815 Montrose Boulevard, Suite 200, Houston, TX 77006; tel. 713/868-4466; Ms. Nyla K Woods

Five Oaks Achievement Center, P.O. Box 1249, New Ulm, TX 78950; tel. 979/992-3791; Mr. Charles Rougeau

Grapevine Valley Hope, 2300 William D Tate Avenue, Grapevine, TX 76051; tel. 817/424-1305; Dr. Kenneth C Gregoire

InnerWisdom, Inc., 4445 North Braeswood Boulevard, Houston, TX 77096; tel. 713/592-9292; Ms. JoAnne Mandel

Johnnie M. Hawkins LAMP Clinic, 431 Fulton, Fort Worth, TX 76104; tel. 817/336-3754; Dr. Robert W Greene

La Hacienda Treatment Center, PO Box 1, Hunt, TX 78024; tel. 830/238-4222; Mr. Arthur VanDivier

Meridell Achievement Center, PO Box 87, Liberty Hill, TX 78642; tel. 512/515-2100; Ms. Gail M Oberta

Meth-Laam, 3204 Ennis Street, Houston, TX 77004; tel. 713/526-2441; Mr. Earnest Gibson, III

Montrose Counseling Center, Inc., 701 Richmond Ave., Houston, TX 77006; tel. 713/529-0037; Dr. Ann J Robison

New Dimensions, 1345 Space Park, Suite C, Houston, TX 77058; tel. 281/333-2284; Mr. George R Brazzel

Nueces County MHMR Community Center, 1630 South Brownlee Street, Corpus Christi, TX 78404; tel. 361/886-6900; Mrs. Diane Staley

Pasadena Substance Abuse Clinic, Inc, 1645 Pasadena Boulevard, Pasadena, TX 77502; tel. 713/473-1405; Ms. Nighat Shaheen

River Oaks Academy Day Hospital, 10600 Richmond Avenue, Houston, TX 77042; tel. 713/783-7200; Dr. Sandra E Phares

San Marcos Treatment Center, 120 Bert Brown Road, San Marcos, TX 78666; tel. 512/396-8500; Ms. Cassie Schmidt

Serenity Foundation of Texas, 1546 North 2nd Street, Abilene, TX 79601; tel. 325/673-6489; Mr. Richard L Spalding

Shiloh Treatment Center, Inc., 3926 Bahler Road, Manvel, TX 77578; tel. 281/489-1290; Mr. Clay D Hill

Shoreline, Inc., PO Box 68, Taft, TX 78390; tel. 361/528-3356; Dr. Sharel Zacharias

Spindletop MHMR Services, PO Box 3846, Beaumont, TX 77704; tel. 409/839-5554; Dr. N. Charles Harris

Starlite Recovery Center, PO Box 317, Center Point, TX 78010-0317; tel. 830/292-0148; Mr. Kirk Kureska

Substance Dependence Treatment Program - VA Medical Center, 2002 Holcombe Blvd, Bldg 100, Houston, TX 77030; tel. 713/794-7900; Dr. Janine Shaw

Sundown Ranch, Inc., 3120 Van Zandt County Road #2318, Canton, TX 75103; tel. 903/479-3933; Mr. Robert H Power

The Huntsville Clinic, Inc., 829 10th Street, Huntsville, TX 77320; tel. 936/291-9172; Ms. Gerri Parish

The Oaks Treatment Center, 1407 West Stassney Lane, Austin, TX 78745; tel. 512/464-0400; Dr. Edgar E Prettyman

The Patrician Movement, 222 East Mitchell Street, San Antonio, TX 78210; tel. 210/532-3126; Dr. Patrick M Clancey

VA North TX Health Care System / Opioid Replacement Clinic, 4500 Lancaster Road, Bldg 71C, Dallas, TX 75216; tel. 214/857-0805; Dr. Bryon Adinoff

Waco Center for Youth, 3501 North 19th Street, Waco, TX 76708; tel. 254/756-2171; Mr. Eddie Greenfield

UTAH

Benchmark Behavioral Health Systems, 592 West, 1350 South, Woods Cross, UT 84087; tel. 801/299-5300; Mr. John A Holter

Blue Mountain Family Center / Wilderness Quest, PO Box 12, Monticello, UT 84535; tel. 435/587-2801; Mr. Larry J Wells

Center for Change, Inc., 1790 North State Street, Orem, UT 84057; tel. 801/224-8255; Dr. Michael E Berritt

Cinnamon Hills Youth Crisis Center, 770 East St. George Boulevard, St George, UT 84770; tel. 435/674-0984; Mr. Jim Downey

Cirque Lodge, RR 3, Box A-10, Sundance, UT 84604; tel. 801/222-9200; Mr. Gary Fisher

Heritage Schools Inc, 5600 N. Heritage School Drive, Provo, UT 84604; tel. 801/226-4600; Mr. Gerald H Spanos

Highland Ridge Hospital, 7309 South 180 West, Midvale, UT 84047; tel. 801/569-2153; Dr. David W Schroeder

Hightop Ranch School, PO Box 440029, Koosharem, UT 84744; tel. 435/638-7411; Mr. Chad Sorenson

Island View Residential Treatment Center, 2650 West 2700 South, Syracuse, UT 84075; tel. 801/773-0200; Dr. Jared U Balmer

Kids Behavioral Health of Utah Inc., 5899 West Rivendell Drive, West Jordan, UT 84088; tel. 801/561-3377; Mr. R. M Rowley

New Haven, Post Office Box 50238, Provo, UT 84605; tel. 801/794-1218; Mr. Mark McGregor

Raindancer Youth Services, Inc., P.O. Box 910400, Saint George, UT 84791; tel. 435/673-6474; Mr. Ronald N Hatch, Sr.

Sorenson's Ranch School, Inc., Box 440219, Koosharem, UT 84744; tel. 435/638-7318; Mr. Shane Sorenson

UHS of Provo Canyon, Inc, 1350 E 750 North, Orem, UT 84097; tel. 801/227-2000; Mr. Kreg D Gillman

UT-TEX, Inc., PO Box 69, Magna, UT 84044; tel. 801/250-9762; Mr. H. Matthew Dixon, Jr.

Youth Care of Utah, Inc., PO Box 909, Draper, UT 84020; tel. 801/572-6989; Ms. Barbara Noblet

Youthtrack - Utah, PO Box 887, Brigham City, UT 84302; tel. 435/723-1799; Mr. Scott Stringam

VERMONT

Brattleboro Retreat, Anna Marsh Lane, PO BOX 803, Brattleboro, VT 05302; tel. 802/257-7785; Mr. Richard Palmisano

Health Care & Rehabilitation Services of Southeastern VT, One Hospital Court, Bellows Falls, VT 05101; tel. 802/463-3294; Ms. Judith P Hayward

VIRGINIA

Alice C. Tyler Village of Childhelp East, 23164 Dragoon Road, Lignum, VA 22726; tel. 540/399-1926; Ms. Diane McClure

Carilion Saint Albans Hospital - Methadone Short Term, PO Box 3608, Radford, VA 24143; tel. 540/731-2000; Mr. Matthew J Perry

Commonwealth Center for Children and Adolescents, P.O. Biox 4000, Staunton, VA 24402-4000; tel. 540/332-2100; Mr. William J Tuell

Ed Murphy & Associates, 1410 Dusty Road, Bumpass, VA 23024; tel. 540/872-4545; Mr. Ed J Murphy

Family Counseling Center, 4906 Radford Avenue, Richmond, VA 23230; tel. 804/354-1996; Mr. Charles R Adcock

Graydon Manor, 801 Children's Center Road, SW, Leesburg, VA 20175; tel. 703/777–3485; Mr. Bernard J Haberlein

Hallmark Youthcare - Richmond, 12800 West Creek Parkway, Richmond, VA 23238; tel. 804/784–2200; Ms. Wanda H Sadler

Inova Comprehensive Addiction Treatment Services (CATS), 3300 Gallows Road, Falls Church, VA 22042; tel. 703/698–1530; Mr. Douglas Cropper

Inova Kellar Center, 10396 Democracy Lane, Fairfax, VA 22030; tel. 703/218–8500; Dr. Richard Leichtweis

Keystone Newport News Youth Center, 17579 Warwick Boulevard, Newport News, VA 23603; tel. 757/888–0400; Mr. Robert Lehmann

Life Center of Galax, Tazewell Opiod Treatment Program, 111 Town Hollow Road, Cedar Bluff, VA 24609; tel. 540/963–3554; Ms. Tina R Bullins

Marion Correctional Treatment Center, PO Box 1027, Marion, VA 24354-1027; tel. 276/783–7154; Mr. Kenneth L Osborne

Mount Regis Center, 405 Kimball Avenue, Salem, VA 24153; tel. 540/389–4761; Ms. Gail S Basham

Poplar Springs Hospital, PO Box 3060, Petersburg, VA 23805; tel. 804/733–6874; Mr. John F Gallagher

The Barry Robinson Center, 443 Kempsville Road, Norfolk, VA 23502; tel. 757/455–6100; Mr. Thomas D Pittman

The Life Center of Galax - Galax Clinic - OTP, PO Box 27, Galax, VA 24333; tel. 276/236–2994; Mrs. Tina Bullins

The Pines Residential Treatment Center, 825 Crawford Parkway, Portsmouth, VA 23704; tel. 757/393–0061; Ms. Debra Goldstein

VA Medical Center - Methadone Maintenance Program, 1201 Broad Rock Boulevard, SATP Inpatient Unit 1F, Richmond, VA 23249; tel. 804/675–5000; Dr. Janakibai Theogaraj

Whisper Ridge Behavioral Health System, 2101 Arlington Boulevard, Charlottesville, VA 22903; tel. 434/977–1523; Ms. Cynthia R Young

Whisper Ridge Behavioral Health System at Leesburg, PO Box 2547, Leesburg, VA 20177; tel. 703/777–0800; Ms. Cindy Young

Williamsburg Place, 5477 Mooretown Road, Williamsburg, VA 23188; tel. 757/565–0106; Ms. Stephanie M Loebs

WASHINGTON

Addiction Treatment Center Opi Treatment Program, Tacoma Div., American Lake Drive, Bldg 61, Tacoma, WA 98493; tel. 206/762–1010; Dr. Andrew J Saxon

Central Washington Comprehensive Mental Health, PO Box 959, Yakima, WA 98907; tel. 509/575–4084; Mr. Rick Weaver

Central Washington Comprehensive Mental Health, 402 South Fourth Avenue, Yakima, WA 98902; tel. 509/575–4084; Mr. Rick Weaver

Grant Mental Healthcare, PO Box 1057, Moses Lake, WA 98837; tel. 509/765–9239; Ms. Sharon E Kiehn

Pearl Street Center / Comprehensive Mental Health, 815 South Pearl Street, Tacoma, WA 98465; tel. 253/396–5930; Dr. Michael K Laederich

Seattle Children's Home, Inc., 2142 Tenth Avenue West, Seattle, WA 98119; tel. 206/283–3300; Ms. Bonnie Sandahl

Seattle Mental Health, 1600 East Olive Street, Seattle, WA 98122; tel. 206/302–2200; Mr. David Stone

Tamarack Center, 2901 W Ft. George Wright Drive, Spokane, WA 99224; tel. 509/326–8100; Mr. Tim Davis

VA Puget Sound/Addiction Treatment Center/ Opioid, 1660 S Columbian Way, Bldg 24, Seattle, WA 98108; tel. 206/764–2782; Dr. Andrew Saxon

Valley Cities Counseling & Consultation, 2704 I Street NE, Auburn, WA 98002; tel. 253/833–7444; Ms. Marilyn LaCelle

WEST VIRGINIA

Elkins Mountain Schools, 100 Bell Street, Elkins, WV 26241; tel. 304/637–8000; Ms. Carolyn J Yokum

Olympic Center - Preston, Inc., PO Box 158, Kingwood, WV 26537; tel. 304/329–2400; Ms. Arlene Glover

WISCONSIN

Aurora Psychiatric Hospital, 1220 Dewey Avenue, Wauwatosa, WI 53213; tel. 414/454–6600; Mr. Peter Carlson

Cadott Medical Center, SC - Methadone Program, PO Box 69, Cadott, WI 54727; tel. 715/289–4221; Dr. Clifford T Bowe

Gundersen Lutheran Medical Center, Inc.- Methadone Maintenance, 1910 South Avenue, La Crosse, WI 54601; tel. 608/782–7300; Dr. Jeffrey Thompson

Libertas Treatment Center, 1701 Dousman Street, Green Bay, WI 54303; tel. 920/498–8600; Mr. David B Fish

Meriter Hospital/New Start Alcohol/Drug Treatment Program, 202 South Park Street, Madison, WI 53715-1599; tel. 608/267–6291; Mr. Terri Potter

WYOMING

Cathedral Home for Children, PO Box 520, Laramie, WY 82073; tel. 307/745–8997; Ms. Robin Haas

Normative Services, Inc., 5 Lane Lane, Sheridan, WY 82801; tel. 307/674–6878; Mr. Cal Furnish

St. Joseph's Children's Home, PO Box 1117, Torrington, WY 82240; tel. 307/532–4197; Mr. Robert C Mayor

Wyoming Recovery, LLC, 231 South Wilson, Casper, WY 82601; tel. 307/265–3791; Ms. Carolyn Toews

---

U.S. Associated Areas

APO/AE

ASAP-IMA-E, 104 Roemerstrasse, Bldg 3734 (Heidelberg), APO, AE 09014; tel. 011–496–2215; Mr. Patrick Teel

PUERTO RICO

Clinica Interdisciplinaria de Psiquiatria Avanzada, 650 Lloveras Cond Centro Plaza Suite 101, San Juan, PR 00909-2113; tel. 787/721–4020; Dr. Carlos A Caban

Instituto Latino Americano, Carretera # 2 M239 Villa Caparra, Guaynabo, PR 00966; tel. 787/792–8383; Dr. Rafael Padro-Castro

Instituto Psicoterapeutico de Puerto Rico, PO Box 367221, San Juan, PR 00936-7221; tel. 787/753–9515; Dr. Alberto Varela

VIRGIN ISLANDS

Division of Mental Health, Alcoholism & Drug Dependency Service, Barbel Plaza South, Second Floor, St Thomas, VI 00802; tel. 340/773–1992; Dr. Celia Victor

Section C

Abbreviations Used in the AHA Guide

AB, Army Base
ACSW, Academy of Certified Social Workers
AEC, Atomic Energy Commission
AFB, Air Force Base
AHA, American Hospital Association
AK, Alaska
AL, Alabama
AODA, Alcohol and Other Drug Abuse
APO, Army Post Office
AR, Arkansas
A.R.T., Accredited Record Technician
A.S.C., Ambulatory Surgical Center
A.T.C., Alcoholism Treatment Center
Ave., Avenue
AZ, Arizona

B.A., Bachelor of Arts
B.B.A., Bachelor of Business Administration
B.C., British Columbia
Blvd., Boulevard
B.S., Bachelor of Science
B.S.Ed., Bachelor of Science in Education
B.S.H.S., Bachelor of Science in Health Studies
B.S.N., Bachelor of Science in Nursing
B.S.W., Bachelor of Science and Social Worker
CA, California; Controller of Accounts

C.A.A.D.A.C., Certified Alcohol and Drug Abuse Counselor
CAC, Certified Alcoholism Counselor
CAE, Certified Association Executive
CAP, College of American Pathologists
CAPA, Certified Ambulatory Post Anesthesia
C.A.S., Certificate of Advanced Study
CCDC, Certified Chemical Dependency Counselor
C.D., Commander of the Order of Distinction
CDR, Commander
CDS, Chemical Dependency Specialist
CFACHE, Certified Fellow American College of Healthcare Executives
CFRE, Certified Fund Raising Executive
C.G., Certified Gastroenterology
CHC, Certified Health Consultant
C.L.D., Clinical Laboratory Director
CLU, Certified Life Underwriter, Chartered Life Underwriter
CMA, Certified Medical Assistant
C.M.H.A., Certified Mental Health Administrator
CNHA, Certified Nursing Home Administrator
CNM, Certified Nurse Midwife
CNOR, Certified Operating Room Nurse
C.N.S., Clinical Nurse Specialist
CO, Colorado; Commanding Officer
COA, Certified Ophthalmic Assistant
COMT, Commandant
C.O.M.T., Certified Ophthalmic Medical Technician
Conv., Conventions
Corp., Corporation; Corporate
C.O.T., Certified Ophthalmic Technician
CPA, Certified Public Accountant
C.P.H.Q., Certified Professional in Health Care Quality
CPM, Certified Public Manager
CRNA, Certified Registered Nurse Anesthetist
CRNH, Certified Registered Nurse Hospice
C.S.J.B, Catholic Saint John the Baptist
CSW, Certified Social Worker
CT, Connecticut
CWO, Chief Warrant Officer

D.B.A., Doctor of Business Administration

DC, District of Columbia
D.D., Doctor of Divinity
D.D.S., Doctor of Dental Surgery
DE, Delaware
Diet, Dietitian; Dietary; Dietetics
D.M.D., Doctor of Dental Medicine
D.MIN., Doctor of Ministry
D.O., Doctor of Osteopathic Medicine and Surgery, Doctor of Osteopathy
DPA, Doctorate Public Administration
D.P.M., Doctor of Podiatric Medicine
Dr., Drive
Dr.P.h., Doctor of Public Health
D.Sc., Doctor of Science
D.S.W., Doctor of Social Welfare
D.V.M., Doctor of Veterinary Medicine

E., East
Ed.D., Doctor of Education
Ed.S., Specialist in Education
ENS, Ensign
Esq., Esquire
Expwy., Expressway
ext., extension

FAAN, Fellow of the American Academy of Nursing
FACATA, Fellow of the American College of Addiction Treatment Administrators
FACHE, Fellow of the American College of Healthcare Executives
FACMGA, Fellow of the American College of Medical Group Administrators
FACP, Fellow of the American College of Physicians
FACS, Fellow of the American College of Surgeons
FAX, Facsimile
FL, Florida
FPO, Fleet Post Office
FRCPSC, Fellow of the Royal College of Physicians and Surgeons of Canada
FT, Full-time

GA, Georgia
Govt., Government; Governmental

HHS, Department of Health and Human Services
HI, Hawaii
HM, Helmsman
HMO, Health Maintenance Organization
Hon., Honorable; Honorary
H.S.A., Health System Administrator
Hts., Heights
Hwy., Highway

IA, Iowa
ID, Idaho
IL, Illinois
IN, Indiana
Inc., Incorporated

J.D., Doctor of Law
J.P., Justice of the Peace
Jr., Junior

KS, Kansas
KY, Kentucky

LA, Louisiana
LCDR, Lieutenant Commander
LCSW, Licensed Certified Social Worker
L.H.D., Doctor of Humanities

L.I.S.W., Licensed Independent Social Worker
LL.D., Doctor of Laws
L.L.P., Limited Licensed Practitioner
L.M.H.C., Licensed Master of Health Care
L.M.S.W., Licensed Master of Social Work
L.N.H.A., Licensed Nursing Home Administrator
L.P.C., Licensed Professional Counselor
LPN, Licensed Practical Nurse
L.P.N., Licensed Practical Nurse
L.S.W., Licensed Social Worker
Lt., Lieutenant
LTC, Lieutenant Colonel
Ltd., Limited
LT.GEN., Lieutenant General
LTJG, Lieutenant (junior grade)

MA, Massachusetts
M.A., Master of Arts
Maj., Major
M.B., Bachelor of Medicine
M.B.A., Masters of Business Administration
MC, Medical Corps; Marine Corps
M.C., Member of Congress
MD, Maryland
M.D., Doctor of Medicine
ME, Maine
M.Ed., Master of Education
MFCC, Marriage/Family/Child Counselor
MHA, Mental Health Association
M.H.S., Masters in Health Science; Masters in Human Service
MI, Michigan
MM, Masters of Management
MN, Minnesota
M.N., Master of Nursing
MO, Missouri
M.P.A., Master of Public Administration; Master Public Affairs
M.P.H., Master of Public Health
M.P.S., Master of Professional Studies; Master of Public Science
MS, Mississippi
M.S., Master of Science
MSC, Medical Service Corps
M.S.D., Doctor of Medical Science
MSHSA, Master of Science Health Service Administration
M.S.N., Master of Science in Nursing
M.S.P.H., Master of Science in Public Health
M.S.S.W., Master of Science in Social Work
M.S.W., Master of Social Work
MT, Montana
Mt., Mount

N., North
NC, North Carolina
N.C.A.D.C., National Certification of Alcohol and Drug Counselors
ND, North Dakota
NE, Nebraska
NH, New Hampshire
NHA, National Hearing Association; Nursing Home Administrator
NJ, New Jersey
NM, New Mexico
NPA, National Perinatal Association
NV, Nevada
NY, New York

OCN, Oncology Certified Nurse
O.D., Doctor of Optometry
O.F.M., Order Franciscan Monks, Order of Friars. Minor
OH, Ohio
OK, Oklahoma
OR, Oregon
O.R., Operating Room

O.R.S., Operating Room Supervisor
OSF, Order of St. Francis

PA, Pennsylvania
P.A., Professional Association
P.C., Professional Corporation
Pharm.D., Doctor of Pharmacy
Ph.B., Bachelor of Philosophy
Ph.D., Doctor of Philosophy
PHS, Public Health Service
Pkwy., Parkway
Pl., Place
PR, Puerto Rico
PS, Professional Services
PSRO, Professional Standards Review Organization

RADM, Rear Admiral
RD, Rural Delivery
Rd., Road
R.F.D., Rural Free Delivery
RI, Rhode Island
R.M., Risk Manager
RN, Registered Nurse
RNC, Republican National Committee; Registered Nurse or Board Certified
R.Ph., Registered Pharmacist
RRA, Registered Record Administrator
R.S.M., Religious Sisters of Mercy
Rte., Route

S., South
SC, South Carolina
S.C., Surgery Center
SCAC, Senior Certified Addiction Counselor
Sc.D., Doctor of Science
Sci., Science, Scientific
SD, South Dakota
SHCC, Statewide Health Coordinating Council
Sgt., Sergeant
SNA, Surgical Nursing Assistant
SNF, Skilled Nursing Facility
Sq., Square
Sr., Senior, Sister
St., Saint, Street
Sta., Station
Ste., Saint; Suite

Tel., Telephone
Terr., Terrace
TN, Tennessee
Tpke, Turnpike
Twp., Township
TX, Texas

USA, United States Army
USAF, United States Air Force
USMC, United States Marine Corps
USN, United States Navy
USPHS, United States Public Health Service
UT, Utah

VA, Virginia
VADM, Vice Admiral
VI, Virgin Islands
Vlg., Village
VT, Vermont

W., West
WA, Washington
WI, Wisconsin
WV, West Virginia
WY, Wyoming

Index